The College Blue Book®

34th Edition

Degrees Offered by College and Subject

The College Blue Book®

34th Edition

Degrees Offered by College and Subject

MACMILLAN REFERENCE USA
An imprint of Thomson Gale, a part of The Thomson Corporation

Detroit • New York • San Francisco • New Haven, Conn. • Waterville, Maine • London

THOMSON
GALE

The College Blue Book, 34th Edition
Volume 3

Project Editors
Bohdan Romaniuk, Verne Thompson

Editorial
Jessica Boguslawski, Kim Hunt-Lowrance,
Amanda Sams, Kristy Swartout

Editorial Support Services
Wayne Fong

Imaging and Multimedia
Randy Bassett, Lezlie Light, Mike Logusz, Dan
Newell

Rights and Acquisitions
Dean Dauphinais

Composition and Electronic Prepress
Gary Leach, Evi Seoud

Manufacturing
Rhonda Dover

Product Manager
Jennifer F. Bernardelli

ISBN-13:
978-0-02-866006-6 (set)
978-0-02-866009-7 (vol. 3)

ISBN-10:
0-02-866006-4 (set)
0-02-866009-9 (vol. 3)

ISSN 1082-7048

This book is also available as an e-book
ISBN 13: 978-0-02-866084-4 (set)   ISBN 10: 0-02-866084-6 (set)
Contact your Thomson Gale sales representative for ordering information.

Printed in the United States of America
10 9 8 7 6 5 4 3 2 1

Contents

CONTENTS

The College Blue Book has been a standard, professional reference on higher education since it was first published in 1923. New features have been added during the intervening years to keep pace with the changing needs for information about our educational facilities. The information, especially in the areas of tuition, room and board, enrollment figures, library holdings, is constantly changing. It is difficult to maintain up-to-date figures in these areas, as many schools change tuition and related costs on an ongoing basis. We therefore urge our readers to check directly with the schools for the most current cost information.

Contents of Each Volume

Volume 1: Narrative Descriptions

More than 4,100 colleges in the United States and Canada are fully described. Entrance requirements are detailed and campus facilities and costs are described. A map of each U.S. state and Canadian province is included and each college has a grid index fore easy location. Web sites are also listed.

Volume 2: Tabular Data

Colleges are listed alphabetically by state or province. Information about costs, accreditation, enrollment figures, faculty, and names of the chief administrative officers are given for each school.

Volume 3: Degrees Offered by College and Subject

In Part I, the name of each college is listed alphabetically by state or province, with a list of the subject areas for which degrees are offered. Part II includes an alphabetical listing of subject areas for which degrees are granted by one or more institutions of higher education.

Volume 4: Occupational Education

More than 5,600 schools in the United States that provide occupational or technical training are fully described, offering such information as tuition costs, enrollment figures, and entrance requirements. Two indexes are provided: an

alphabetical listing of schools in the "Index of Occupational Education Schools," in addition to the "Curricula and Areas of Instruction" index.

Volume 5: Scholarships, Fellowships, Grants, and Loans

This volume provides a listing of almost 3,500 different sources of financial aid for students wishing to further their education. Split alphabetically into eight broad subject areas (each containing several more specialized concentrations of study), as well as a general section, each listing provides basic information about a specific award, including eligibility requirements, amount of award, and application deadlines.

Volume 6: Distance Learning Programs

Responding to this rapidly growing trend in postsecondary education, this volume features comprehensive profiles of nearly 900 institutions offering distance learning programs within the United States and Canada, providing both basic information as well as in-depth descriptions of certain institutions.

For More Information

We are always open to suggestions and recommendations for improvement of The College Blue Book from our readers and from the educational professions. Please write or call:

Editor, The College Blue Book

Macmillan Reference USA

27500 Drake Rd.

Farmington Hills, MI 48331-3535

Phone: (248)699-4253

Toll-free: 800-347-GALE

Fax: (248)699-8075

Email: blue.book@thomson.com

Web site: www.gale.com

The decision to continue education beyond high school years, the selection of a collegiate institution, and the area of study to be pursued are some of the essential experiences necessary for students to determine their futures. Alternatives of choice institutions, work selection, job opportunities, professional training, or even discontinuing any further education are all selective decisions open to the students.

Nearly all students today have opportunities to continue education beyond high school. There are more schools accepting wider ranges of student ability and interest than ever before. This means more effort, more planning, and more personal study in making the college choice.

Self Appraisal

The best place to begin is with oneself. An appraisal with objective, honest answers is necessary. What are the personal potentials as a student? Where has the best performance been? What are the probabilities for improvement? What are the reasons for really wanting to go to college; is it for intellectual development, vocational preparation, or simply to satisfy a desire for status? What are the personal ideas of college? What is expected from the college experience? Have career plans been made? Where are the academic abilities? What subjects are preferred? What is the quality of performance in the preferred areas of study? What is the overall grade average? What is the class rank in high school? In what subject areas is there the greatest interest? What is the quality of work in these areas? Are interests and performance generally consistent? Are the expressed and recorded interests truly and accurately reflecting the inward wishes? What was liked best about the high school experience? Has the college preparatory program been followed in high school? What were the social and cultural experiences during high school years that were most meaningful? What was considered, if anything, to be lacking?

Well-thought-out answers to these and similar questions are helpful. Discussions of such topics with counselors, parents, and teachers increases the probability of success in college selection, attendance, and completion.

The counselor today is an extremely valued resource person available to assist the student. When an effective working team of counselor-student-parent actually exists, the probabilities for the student making selective choices that prove to be the "right" ones are unquestionably the greatest. The better the student and the counselor know one another, the more effective the guidance and counseling program will be. For this to occur, the opportunity for face-to-face student-counselor discussion needs to start in the latter elementary school years and continue through high school and college.

College Appraisals

Research is continuing in the areas of college admissions and student success. The identification and understanding of causes of success and failure need professional study. However, one thing is apparent: the more careful the preparations and planning by the student, the better the chances of college admission and success.

Systemized planning should begin early. The more self-understanding and knowledge about available colleges one has, the better one can plan with corresponding success. Certainly, early in the high school career, students should be reviewing detailed information on colleges and universities with the counselor, noting academic requirements such as scholastic performance, course requirements, costs and other particular qualities of individual collegiate institutions. There is no single one-and- only college for the student. Colleges have personalities just as the students do. There are always several colleges with academic and social climates compatible and acceptable to each student.

Entrance requirements, courses available, costs, size of student body, academic pressure, special programs, geographical location, and specialty schools are some of the considerations of every student in appraising available colleges.

The College Blue Book is dedicated to providing detailed information regarding collegiate institutions throughout the United States and Canada. Students and counselors should browse through The College Blue Book and become familiar with the colleges of our country and neighboring Canada. As interest sharpens and narrows, a more selective and in-depth study of institutions should be made.

Where feasible, students should plan visits to college campuses. Campus visiting may begin during the summer between the sophomore and junior years of high school. The best time to be on a college campus, however, is during the regular term with a carefully planned visit in the spring semester of the junior year. Preparatory plans should be made with the high school counselor, reviewing discussions of earlier personal conferences. Advance arrangements should be made with admission officers of the colleges the student expects to visit. The admission officer's name and telephone number will be found in most instances in *The College Blue Book* volume entitled *Tabular Data*. The admissions officer in many cases will want to know whether the student has actually applied for admission and probably the areas the student may plan to major in or other special interests the student has in the particular institution. The student should have prepared a summary of personal data. If possible, high school students should also talk to students of the colleges they wish to attend.

The growth of community colleges has opened up another avenue for students, especially those of limited finances or those who have not decided on their ultimate educational goals. Students will find many of these community colleges offer an excellent opportunity to gain a solid college background. Then one can choose a four-year institution to complete an undergraduate degree.

Any regular high school graduate can find a school that will accept him. Many students need to be encouraged to consider the smaller, private and public colleges of good standing.

Students entering professional training such as engineering or law might consider small schools that have cooperative programs with major universities. A knowledgeable student, through planning and guidance, can avoid unnecessary disappointment. A college career can be quite beneficial to the student who spends three to four years on a small campus and one, two, or three additional years of graduate work on another, larger campus.

Costs

Costs are continuing to rise. Tuition charges as listed herein should be only be used as a guide. It would be wise to check with the institution of interest to be sure of having the most up-to- date information available.

Should the need for financial aid be a factor in selecting a college, a college-bound student should be aware that the best single source of financial assistance and information is the financial aid officer or admission director at the college. It is most important for the student to contact the finance office as early as possible during the student's senior year in high school. A principal source of financial assistance is the major federal undergraduate aid programs. Applications can be obtained from the college. Most colleges and universities also offer financial assistance in several forms including academic and general scholarships, grants-in-aid, student

loans, and part-time work. For more information, see volume 5 of *The College Blue Book*: *Scholarships, Fellowships, Grants, and Loans*.

Two-year Colleges

Two-year colleges, referred to as junior colleges or community colleges, both public and private, offer programs that prepare students for technical and semiprofessional careers in business and technology fields, and for transfer to senior colleges. There are hundreds of two-year colleges providing comprehensive programs meeting the lower division requirements of virtually all four-year colleges and universities.

There are decided advantages for some students to enroll in a two-year college. Some of these are: less cost, home residence, availability of highly specialized programs, opportunity for the student to mature, a smaller student body, and generally a closer relationship to the faculty. The development of two-year colleges across the nation is one of the most vital forces in education today. The two-year college is neither an extension of high school, nor a little senior college. It has its own identity, sphere of service, and contribution to make to American education. The comprehensive community college is considered one of the best means of accommodating the demands of higher education, embracing the increasing variety of abilities of students graduating from high schools, preparing students in the technological and semiprofessional occupations, and all in an economical manner.

One very important caution needs to be heeded by students enrolling in two-year colleges who are planning to continue their work through a bachelor's program. Students expecting to transfer should very carefully study the requirements of the institution they ultimately plan to attend. In conference with the junior college counselor, a careful review of the planned program should be made to be sure the contemplated courses at the junior college will satisfy the requirements of the senior institution. Students who depart from prescribed courses stated by the senior institution or fail in any of these courses may experience difficulty with admission or normal progress toward the bachelor degree.

Liberal Arts Colleges

The liberal arts colleges offer four years of college and award the Bachelor of Arts and the Bachelor of Science degrees. The curriculum for the first two years is usually broad with an emphasis in the humanities, natural sciences, and cultural history of our society. The last two years may provide a concentration of specific programs such as pre-medicine or pre-law leading to graduate professional training.

Students considering professional training at the graduate level should keep this in mind as they plan their work at the liberal arts college. Graduate schools in some cases have strict preparatory requirements. Familiarity with these requirements can greatly assist in making the transfer to graduate level without loss of credit or time.

Specialized Institutions

Four-year institutions of technology are examples of the more specialized schools where concentration in a specialty is intensively pursued throughout the college career. Most of these institutions are quite selective in admission practice and may require more high school mathematics and science than most other schools for entrance. These programs lead to engineering degrees in many fields emphasizing technology and science. Recently there has been a broadening of the program of the first two years, but, in general, such a program is not nearly as comprehensive and varied as the liberal arts college. The demand for engineers and scientists with specially developed skills creates great competition for entrance into schools of technology.

There are other specialized institutions such as conservatories of music, seminaries, medical and law schools, institutions specializing in teacher training, or schools of the fine arts, most of which require specialized preparation for entrance.

Universities

The university is generally composed of a number of degree- granting colleges and schools where both bachelor and graduate degrees are grouped under one administrative head. Bachelor degrees at the university may be earned in liberal arts or one of the professions such as engineering or the physical sciences. The university, to some extent, combines what is available at the liberal arts college with the specialized institution. Complete professional training in such areas as law, medicine, and science is available on the university campus.

As a rule, universities have much larger student bodies than colleges. In order to meet the demand, most state universities have established several campuses. Many state universities are very selective in admitting students. This is particularly true for a student who is applying for admission from out-of-state.

Entrance Examinations

There are more applicants than there is room for students on many campuses. As this demand increases, colleges and universities attempt to identify those applicants who are most likely to succeed on their campuses. A quality scholastic record has more influence on acceptance and admission than any other single factor. High school grades predict with better accuracy than any other single measurement what college grades and success will be. The more selective colleges and universities may choose students who come out highest on quantitative criteria, that is, high school scholastic averages combined with test scores. Some institutions have far more applicants (whose scholastic records

and test scores are of a maximum quality) than they can accept. In such cases, applicants are sometimes screened and accepted on the basis of categories according to residence in the state or region, special talents, minority groups, or relationship to alumni. Such procedures are used in an attempt to influence the makeup of the enrollment.

When investigating several schools, one of the most accurate ways for evaluation of an institution is to consider test scores and the high school rank order of the students actually on campus. In many instances this is more informative than the announced admission policies.

College testing is required by many colleges and universities for entering students; some have developed their own tests and over the years have established norms for such tests. Most institutions requiring tests for entrance, however, now use either the test of the American College Testing Program (ACT) or the examinations of the College Entrance Examination Board. The College Entrance Examination Board offers the Preliminary Scholastic Assessment Test/National Merit Scholarship Qualifying Test (PSAT/ NM-SQT), the Scholastic Assessment Test I: Reasoning Test (Verbal and Math), and the SAT II: Subject Tests.

Coaching, tutoring, drill, and memorization of facts can do little to improve the scores of the standardized examinations. It is recommended that students not invest time and money in cramming in hopes of improving test scores. Students can do their best preparation in general reading, completing their school assignments, and arriving on the proper day of the test rested and refreshed.

American College Testing Assessment (ACT)

The ACT Assessment provided by the American College Testing Program covers four subject areas: English, mathematics, reading, and science reasoning. The ACT test is scored on a range of 1 to 36. The ACT is administered at various test sites in the United States and other countries on specified dates throughout the year. Many colleges and universities recommend that prospective students take the examination early in the senior year.

The tests provide estimates of the students' current level of educational development in knowledge skill areas often required in college work. The ACT college testing program was founded in 1959. It is a nonprofit educational service offering programs in testing and financial need analysis.

Scholastic Assessment Tests (SAT)

The SAT I: Reasoning Test is an examination to measure the verbal and mathematics abilities students have developed both in and out of school. The SAT II: Subject Tests, which some colleges require for admission or placement purposes, consist of 22 separate tests that cover subjects such as literature, history, math, languages, chemistry, biology, and physics. Unlike the SAT I, which measures more general abilities, the SAT II tests measure the students' knowledge of a particular subject and their ability to apply that knowledge. Because of this, students should try to take a SAT II Test as soon as possible after completion of their last course in that subject.

The SAT I and II tests are given on certain dates throughout the year at various test centers in the United States and foreign countries. The combination of the student's academic record and the SAT scores, along with other pertinent secondary information enables admissions officers to estimate how well the student will perform on a particular college campus. The SAT is scored on a scale of 200 minimum to 800 maximum.

Admission Policies

One of the most important considerations in planning is to note when colleges and universities request applications, and to be sure that the applications are complete and forwarded during the appropriate periods. Failure in any way in this procedure will usually automatically disqualify a student from acceptance.

Counselors can provide students with freshman profiles on many of the institutions. Studying *The College Blue Book*, particularly the volume *Tabular Data*, provides a great amount of information on the kind of student bodies found on the campuses of American institutions. There are four general classifications of admission policies. An understanding of these provides valuable guidelines in identifying colleges for consideration.

Most Selective: Many more students apply who meet the announced admission requirements than the college could possibly accept. In addition to requiring outstanding academic records, personal recommendations are required from the high school, and identification of any special qualities of the student should be made known. In this regard, the high school recommendation made to the collegiate institution requires special attention.

Many times, particularly at selective institutions, the high school recommendation actually provides the necessary edge for admission. The recommendation should be on time, carefully providing all information called for, and finally, be precise and detailed in citing personal qualities of the applicant.

All these qualities, however, do not guarantee acceptance. It is strongly recommended that qualified students apply to more than one institution of this type, and that not all applicants should be made to the same type of institution.

Very Selective: Colleges having a very selective procedure in accepting students require ACT scores of 23 or over, or an SAT I score of 600 or more. Students should rank in the top 10 to 12 percent of their high school graduating classes. In addition, strong recommendations stressing particular talents and achievements are necessary. Applications should be made to several institutions of this type.

Selective: An ACT of 20 or over, or an SAT I score of 550 or more is generally necessary. Applications for admission to selective colleges and universities are usually called for in the spring prior to fall entry. In many situations, applications may be submitted in the fall of the senior year with final confirmation to be made after all grades are recorded and confirmed upon graduation from high school.

Least Selective: The fourth classification represents those institutions that will accept students with a C average on their high school work. In certain unusual instances, and under special situations, even the selective institutions may accept students who are in this category, particularly if the scores on the ACT are in the mid-20's or are in excess of 500 on the SAT I. Generally, for acceptance in the less selective schools, students should have an ACT composite score of 17 or a SAT I score of 450.

Entrance examinations may or may not be required. Occasionally, if examinations are required, the results are used for student placement rather than admission. Most high school graduates can meet the requirements for entry and will be accepted. It should be pointed out, however, that in some cases an institution may be liberal in acceptance but carefully screens candidates for graduation. In such an institution, a high attrition rate may occur.

Open Enrollment Policy: This is becoming more common, particularly with the public community colleges. Many students will find this privilege most helpful in continuing their formal education beyond high school. Such a policy enables those students to have a second chance who have failed to perform up to their ability during their high school years. Enrollment and attendance may enable the student to complete a most rewarding vocational program or to later transfer and complete the Bachelor degree, which otherwise might not have been possible because of the deficiency in the high school scholastic record.

A number of colleges and universities, particularly the publicly supported ones, have adopted the open enrollment policy. In response to a feeling of community responsibility, they accept any student who has a diploma (or G.E.D. equivalency certificate) from an accredited high school. This procedure allows students from disadvantaged and minority backgrounds, who might otherwise be denied such an opportunity, to acquire a college education and prepare for a meaningful occupation. These institutions have not lowered their graduation requirements; they have, instead, created opportunities for more students to satisfy these requirements.

Do not assume the erroneous generality that the tougher it is to get into an institution, the better the quality; or the easier to enter, the poorer the school. In fact, there is research evidence available indicating that it may be wise to re-examine some of our traditional notions and attitudes regarding admissions. Not all degree programs on any particular campus are equally outstanding. Every institution has its particular strengths in programs available. Certain institutions are excellent places for some kinds of students in some kinds of programs, but no institution is the one most suited for everyone.

Degrees Offered by College and Subject provides guidance counselors and high school students with a means to identify those institutions most suitable to their curricular needs.

Part I, *Degrees Offered by College,* tabulates degree programs offered by more than 4,100 two-year colleges, colleges, and universities in the United States, Canada and U.S. Territories. These programs are arranged by college in alphabetical order within states and provinces.

The subject areas are arranged alphabetically in Part II, *Degrees Offered by Subject,* and within each subject arranged alphabetically by state and province and within each state and province by college.

In collecting these data, it became evident that the traditional progression of students in their pursuit of a college education is no longer limited to a choice of a four-year college and perhaps the usual steps toward an advanced degree. Alternatives exist everywhere within the scope of postsecondary education. For example, the phenomenal growth of community colleges alone has provided the student with a vast number of options within the framework of a two-year program. One can decide whether one wants a transfer, a parallel, or a terminal program; an Arts Degree, a Science Degree, or a Certificate; a full-time, a part-time, or a cooperative program; whether to pursue a technical, trade, professional, paraprofessional, or liberal arts program.

Similar alternatives can be found in other institutions as well, making it possible for entire educational programs to be constructed on an individual basis for each student.

Structuring a volume such as this presents many problems. To list each course of study within every institution not only makes for an unwieldy collection of facts, but is in itself a distortion since there is no way the user can be provided with criteria by which to discriminate among programs with similar titles. Also, many colleges list the same course in a different manner (e.g. Speech and Drama and then Drama and Speech).

For this reason an attempt was made to establish some sort of standardized curriculum listing. However, rigidity of subject headings can be just as much of a distortion as too much flexibility, and therefore compromises had to be made. These compromises came about from lengthy study of questionnaires and catalogs in an effort to weigh each school's programs and to make a comparative assessment. (It must be emphasized that no value judgments were or even could be made as to the quality of these programs.)

Users of this volume must bear in mind that degrees are listed for junior and/or community colleges only if a valid curriculum was detailed within the school catalog, but it must also be recognized that these colleges, in most cases, provide a satisfactory basic liberal arts program which will enable the student to transfer without difficulty to an upper level college to gain a degree in the major of choice.

Another evaluation that had to be made was in the curriculum headings themselves. Since there is a great deal of varying terminology among schools, the rule of thumb decided upon was to be reasonably general in listing curricula for two- and four-year degrees, and very specific for graduate degrees.

Users of this volume also must be made aware of the very specific and limited use given here of the word "Education." It must be emphasized that it is used only in the sense of teacher training. If a school has indicated to us either in a catalog or questionnaire that they offer, for example, Business Education, and their meaning of the term indicates this is a program for students interested in the business world, then the word "Education" was dropped. Business Education is used only for programs involving students whose eventual goal is to teach business subjects. Similarly, Education, Music; Education, Home Economics; Education, Art are all programs for future teachers of these subjects. An attempt was made to eliminate confusing terminology among schools.

With regard to the degrees themselves, no effort is made to distinguish between the different types of the same degree, such as Bachelor of Arts or Bachelor of Science. First-professional degrees are DC, DMD or DDS, DO, DPM, DVM, JD or LL B, MD, M Div or BD, MHL, OD, and Pharm D. Other refers to post-baccalaureate degrees other than master's, doctoral, and first-professional (e.g., Certificate, Diploma, Engineer, Specialist).

Those postsecondary institutions which grant certificates only, such as many of the vocational/technical schools or nursing schools, are not listed in this volume. Only those which grant Associate degrees and beyond are included. The number of programs offered by most of these schools is just too numerous for consideration here. More information can be found in the companion volume to this one, *Occupational Education,* which was designed to provide the necessary detail.

A	Associate Degree		M	Master's Degree
B	Bachelor Degree		O	Other Advanced Degree
D	Doctorate Degree		P	First Professional Degree

U.S. COLLEGES: ALABAMA

ALABAMA AGRICULTURAL AND MECHANICAL UNIVERSITY

Accounting, B
Agribusiness, M
Agricultural Economics, B
Agricultural Sciences, MD
Agronomy and Soil Sciences, MD
Animal Sciences, BM
Biological and Biomedical Sciences, M
Biology/Biological Sciences, B
Business Administration and Management, B
Business Administration, Management and
    Operations, M
Business Statistics, B
Business/Commerce, B
Business/Managerial Economics, B
Chemistry, B
City/Urban, Community and Regional Planning, B
Civil Engineering, B
Civil Engineering Technology/Technician, B
Communication Disorders, M
Computer and Information Sciences, B
Computer Science, M
Early Childhood Education and Teaching, MO
Economics, BM
Education, MO
Education/Teaching of Individuals with Speech or
    Language Impairments, B
Educational Administration and Supervision, M
Electrical, Electronics and Communications
    Engineering, B
Elementary Education and Teaching, BMO
Engineering and Applied Sciences, M
English Language and Literature, B
Environmental Sciences, M
Family and Consumer Economics and Related
    Services, B
Finance, B
Finance and Banking, M
Food Science, B
Food Science and Technology, MD
Home Economics, M
Industrial Education, M
Kindergarten/PreSchool Education and Teaching, B
Marketing, M
Marketing/Marketing Management, B
Mathematics, B
Mechanical Engineering, B
Mechanical Engineering/Mechanical
    Technology/Technician, B
Music, M
Music Teacher Education, BM
Physical Education Teaching and Coaching, BM
Physics, BMD
Plant Sciences, MD
Political Science and Government, B
Psychology, BMO
Radio and Television Broadcasting
    Technology/Technician, B
Secondary Education and Teaching, BMO
Social Work, BM

Sociology, B
Special Education and Teaching, BM
Urban and Regional Planning, M

ALABAMA SOUTHERN COMMUNITY COLLEGE

Accounting, A
Administrative Assistant and Secretarial Science, A
Art/Art Studies, General, A
Biology/Biological Sciences, A
Biomedical Technology/Technician, A
Business Administration and Management, A
Business Teacher Education, A
Chemistry, A
Clinical/Medical Laboratory Technician, A
Computer Engineering Technology/Technician, A
Computer Programming/Programmer, A
Computer Science, A
Economics, A
Education, A
Elementary Education and Teaching, A
Engineering, A
English Language and Literature, A
Finance, A
Fine/Studio Arts, A
Fire Science/Firefighting, A
Forestry Technology/Technician, A
Health Information/Medical Records
    Administration/Administrator, A
History, A
Insurance, A
Kindergarten/PreSchool Education and Teaching, A
Liberal Arts and Sciences Studies and
    Humanities, A
Mathematics, A
Nursing - Registered Nurse Training, A
Occupational Therapy/Therapist, A
Physical Education Teaching and Coaching, A
Physical Therapy/Therapist, A
Pre-Engineering, A
Psychology, A
Respiratory Care Therapy/Therapist, A
Social Sciences, A

ALABAMA STATE UNIVERSITY

Accounting, BM
Administrative Assistant and Secretarial Science, AB
Allied Health and Medical Assisting Services, M
Art Teacher Education, B
Art/Art Studies, General, B
Biological and Biomedical Sciences, MO
Biological Anthropology, D
Biology/Biological Sciences, B
Business Administration and Management, AB
Business Administration, Management and
    Operations, M
Business Teacher Education, B
Chemistry, B
Child Development, A
Clinical/Medical Laboratory Technician, B
Community Organization and Advocacy, A
Computer Science, B
Counselor Education/School Counseling and
    Guidance Services, MO

Criminal Justice/Law Enforcement Administration, B
Drama and Dramatics/Theatre Arts, B
Early Childhood Education and Teaching, MO
Economics, B
Education, ABMDO
Educational Administration and Supervision, MDO
Educational Leadership and Administration, MDO
Educational Media/Instructional Technology, MO
Elementary Education and Teaching, BMO
English Education, M
English Language and Literature, B
Finance, B
French Language and Literature, B
Health Education, M
Health Information/Medical Records
    Administration/Administrator, B
History, B
Information Science/Studies, B
Journalism, B
Kindergarten/PreSchool Education and Teaching, B
Liberal Arts and Sciences Studies and
    Humanities, AB
Marine Biology and Biological Oceanography, B
Marketing/Marketing Management, B
Mass Communication/Media Studies, B
Mathematics, BMO
Mathematics Teacher Education, MO
Music, BM
Music Teacher Education, BM
Occupational Therapy/Therapist, B
Parks, Recreation, Leisure and Fitness Studies, B
Physical Education Teaching and Coaching, BMO
Physical Therapy/Therapist, M
Political Science and Government, B
Pre-Medicine/Pre-Medical Studies, B
Psychology, B
Public Relations/Image Management, B
Radio and Television, B
Science Teacher Education/General Science
    Teacher Education, BMO
Secondary Education and Teaching, BO
Social Sciences, B
Social Studies Teacher Education, MO
Social Work, B
Sociology, B
Spanish Language and Literature, B
Special Education and Teaching, BM
Speech and Rhetorical Studies, B
Teacher Assistant/Aide, A

AMERICAN COLLEGE OF COMPUTER & INFORMATION SCIENCES

Business Administration and Management, B
Business/Commerce, B
Computer and Information Sciences, B
Computer Science, BM
Information Science/Studies, BM
Information Technology, B
Management, M
System Administration/Administrator, B

ANDREW JACKSON UNIVERSITY

Business Administration, Management and
    Operations, M

Business/Commerce, AB
Communication Studies/Speech Communication
and Rhetoric, AB
Criminal Justice/Safety Studies, AB
Criminology, M
Entrepreneurship/Entrepreneurial Studies, M
Finance and Banking, M
Health Services Administration, M
Hospitality Administration/Management, M
Human Resources Management and Services, M
International Business/Trade/Commerce, M
Logistics and Materials Management, M
Management, M
Marketing, M
Public Administration, M

ATHENS STATE UNIVERSITY

Accounting, B
Art/Art Studies, General, B
Behavioral Sciences, B
Biology/Biological Sciences, B
Business Administration and Management, B
Business, Management, Marketing, and Related
Support Services, B
Chemistry, B
Computer Science, B
Criminal Justice/Law Enforcement Administration, B
Elementary Education and Teaching, B
English Language and Literature, B
History, B
Human Resources Management/Personnel
Administration, B
Humanities/Humanistic Studies, B
Information Science/Studies, B
Kindergarten/PreSchool Education and Teaching, B
Mathematics, B
Physical Education Teaching and Coaching, B
Physics, B
Political Science and Government, B
Psychology, B
Public Health (MPH, DPH), B
Religion/Religious Studies, B
Science Teacher Education/General Science
Teacher Education, B
Science Technologies/Technicians, B
Secondary Education and Teaching, B
Sociology, B
Special Education and Teaching, B
Trade and Industrial Teacher Education, B

AUBURN UNIVERSITY

Accounting, BM
Adult and Continuing Education and Teaching, BMD
Aerospace, Aeronautical and Astronautical
Engineering, BMD
Agricultural Economics, BMD
Agricultural Sciences, MD
Agricultural Teacher Education, B
Agricultural/Biological Engineering and
Bioengineering, B
Agriculture, B
Agronomy and Crop Science, B
Agronomy and Soil Sciences, MD
Airline/Commercial/Professional Pilot and Flight
Crew, B
Animal Sciences, BMD
Anthropology, B
Apparel and Textiles, B
Applied Mathematics, B
Architectural Engineering, B
Architecture, BMO
Audiology/Audiologist and Speech-Language
Pathology/Pathologist, B
Aviation/Airway Management and Operations, B
Biochemistry, B
Biological and Biomedical Sciences, MD
Biology/Biological Sciences, B
Biomedical Sciences, B
Botany/Plant Biology, BMD
Broadcast Journalism, B
Building Science, M
Business Administration and Management, B
Business Administration, Management and
Operations, M
Business Education, MD

Business Teacher Education, B
Business/Managerial Economics, B
Chemical Engineering, BMD
Chemistry, BMD
Child and Family Studies, MD
Child Development, B
Civil Engineering, BMD
Clinical Laboratory Science/Medical
Technology/Technologist, B
Clinical/Medical Laboratory Technician, B
Clothing and Textiles, M
Commercial and Advertising Art, B
Communication and Media Studies, M
Communication Disorders, BM
Communication, Journalism and Related
Programs, B
Community Psychology, MDO
Computer and Information Sciences, B
Computer Engineering, BMD
Computer Hardware Engineering, B
Computer Science, MD
Computer Software Engineering, B
Construction Engineering and Management, MD
Counseling Psychology, MDO
Counselor Education/School Counseling and
Guidance Services, MDO
Criminology, B
Curriculum and Instruction, MDO
Dairy Science, B
Design and Visual Communications, B
Drama and Dramatics/Theatre Arts, B
Early Childhood Education and Teaching, BMDO
Economics, BMD
Education, MDO
Education/Teaching of Individuals with Vision
Impairments, Including Blindness, B
Educational Administration and Supervision, MDO
Educational Media/Instructional Technology, M
Educational Psychology, D
Electrical Engineering, MD
Electrical, Electronics and Communications
Engineering, B
Elementary Education and Teaching, BMDO
Engineering, B
Engineering and Applied Sciences, MD
English, MD
English Language and Literature, B
English/Language Arts Teacher Education, B
Entomology, MD
Environmental Design/Architecture, B
Environmental Engineering
Technology/Environmental Technology, MD
Environmental Sciences, B
Environmental Studies, B
Family and Consumer Sciences/Human Sciences, B
Finance, B
Finance and Banking, M
Fine Arts and Art Studies, MD
Fine/Studio Arts, B
Fish, Game and Wildlife Management, MD
Food Science, B
Food Science and Technology, MD
Foods, Nutrition, and Wellness Studies, B
Foreign Language Teacher Education, M
Foreign Languages and Literatures, B
Forest Sciences and Biology, B
Forestry, MD
French Language and Literature, BM
French Language Teacher Education, B
Geography, BM
Geological/Geophysical Engineering, B
Geology/Earth Science, BM
Geotechnical Engineering, MD
German Language and Literature, B
German Language Teacher Education, B
Graphic Design, B
Health and Medical Laboratory Technologies, B
Health Education, MDO
Health Teacher Education, B
Health/Health Care Administration/Management, B
Higher Education/Higher Education
Administration, MDO
History, BMD
History Teacher Education, B
Horticultural Science, BMD
Hospitality Administration/Management, B

Hotel/Motel Administration/Management, B
Human Development, MD
Human Development and Family Studies, B
Human Resources Management and Services, D
Human Resources Management/Personnel
Administration, B
Hydraulics and Fluid Power Technology, MD
Hydrology and Water Resources Science, MD
Industrial Design, BM
Industrial Engineering, B
Industrial/Management Engineering, MD
Interior Architecture, B
International Business/Trade/Commerce, B
Journalism, BM
Kindergarten/PreSchool Education and Teaching, B
Landscape Architecture, BM
Logistics and Materials Management, B
Management, MD
Management Information Systems and
Services, BMD
Marine Biology and Biological Oceanography, B
Marketing/Marketing Management, B
Mass Communication/Media Studies, BM
Materials Engineering, BMD
Mathematics, BMD
Mathematics Teacher Education, B
Mechanical Engineering, BMD
Medical Microbiology and Bacteriology, B
Microbiology, BMD
Molecular Biology, B
Music, M
Music Teacher Education, BMDO
Nursing - Registered Nurse Training, B
Nutritional Sciences, BMD
Operations Management and Supervision, B
Ornamental Horticulture, B
Parks, Recreation, Leisure and Fitness Studies, B
Pharmaceutical Sciences, MD
Pharmacy, P
Philosophy, B
Physical Education Teaching and Coaching, BMDO
Physics, BMD
Physics Teacher Education, B
Plant Pathology/Phytopathology, BMD
Plant Sciences, B
Political Science and Government, BMDO
Poultry Science, BMD
Pre-Dentistry Studies, B
Pre-Law Studies, B
Pre-Medicine/Pre-Medical Studies, B
Pre-Pharmacy Studies, B
Pre-Veterinary Studies, B
Psychology, BMD
Public Administration, BMDO
Public Relations/Image Management, B
Radio and Television, B
Reading Teacher Education, DO
Rural Sociology, MD
School Psychology, MDO
Science Teacher Education/General Science
Teacher Education, B
Secondary Education and Teaching, BMDO
Secondary School Administration/Principalship, B
Social Work, B
Sociology, BM
Software Engineering, MD
Spanish Language and Literature, BM
Spanish Language Teacher Education, B
Special Education and Teaching, BMDO
Speech and Rhetorical Studies, B
Structural Engineering, MD
Systems Engineering, MD
Teaching English as a Second or Foreign
Language/ESL Language Instructor, B
Textile Sciences and Engineering, BMD
Trade and Industrial Teacher Education, B
Transportation and Highway Engineering, MD
Urban and Regional Planning, MO
Veterinary Medicine, PO
Veterinary Sciences, MD
Wildlife and Wildlands Science and Management, B
Zoology/Animal Biology, BMD

AUBURN UNIVERSITY MONTGOMERY

Accounting, B
Art/Art Studies, General, B

Biology/Biological Sciences, B
Business Administration and Management, B
Business Administration, Management and
    Operations, M
Business/Commerce, B
Business/Managerial Economics, B
Communication Studies/Speech Communication
    and Rhetoric, B
Counselor Education/School Counseling and
    Guidance Services, MO
Criminal Justice/Safety Studies, B
Criminology, M
Early Childhood Education and Teaching, MO
Education, MO
Educational Administration and Supervision, MO
Elementary Education and Teaching, BMO
English Language and Literature, B
Finance, B
Foreign Languages and Literatures, B
History, B
Human Resources Management/Personnel
    Administration, B
Liberal Arts and Sciences Studies and
    Humanities, B
Liberal Studies, M
Management Information Systems and Services, B
Marketing/Marketing Management, B
Mathematics, B
Nursing - Registered Nurse Training, B
Physical Education Teaching and Coaching, MO
Physical Sciences, B
Political Science and Government, BMD
Psychology, BM
Public Administration, MD
Reading Teacher Education, MO
Secondary Education and Teaching, BMO
Sociology, B
Special Education and Teaching, MO

BEVILL STATE COMMUNITY COLLEGE

Administrative Assistant and Secretarial Science, A
Business Administration and Management, A
Clinical/Medical Laboratory Technician, A
Computer and Information Sciences, A
Drafting and Design Technology/Technician, A
Emergency Medical Technology/Technician (EMT
    Paramedic), A
General Studies, A
Heating, Air Conditioning and Refrigeration
    Technology/Technician, A
Liberal Arts and Sciences Studies and
    Humanities, A
Nursing - Registered Nurse Training, A
Tool and Die Technology/Technician, A
Welding Technology/Welder, A

BIRMINGHAM-SOUTHERN COLLEGE

Accounting, B
Art History, Criticism and Conservation, B
Art Teacher Education, B
Art/Art Studies, General, B
Asian Studies/Civilization, B
Biology/Biological Sciences, B
Business Administration and Management, B
Chemistry, B
Computer Science, B
Dance, B
Drama and Dramatics/Theatre Arts, B
Drawing, B
Economics, B
Education, B
Elementary Education and Teaching, B
English Language and Literature, B
Fine/Studio Arts, B
French Language and Literature, B
German Language and Literature, B
History, B
Human Resources Management/Personnel
    Administration, B
Interdisciplinary Studies, B
International Business/Trade/Commerce, B
Management, M
Mathematics, B
Music, B
Music History, Literature, and Theory, B
Music Teacher Education, B

Painting, B
Philosophy, B
Physics, B
Piano and Organ, B
Political Science and Government, B
Pre-Dentistry Studies, B
Pre-Law Studies, B
Pre-Medicine/Pre-Medical Studies, B
Printmaking, B
Psychology, B
Public Administration, M
Religion/Religious Studies, B
Sculpture, B
Secondary Education and Teaching, B
Sociology, B
Spanish Language and Literature, B
Voice and Opera, B

BISHOP STATE COMMUNITY COLLEGE

Accounting Technology/Technician and
    Bookkeeping, A
Administrative Assistant and Secretarial Science, A
Civil Engineering Technology/Technician, A
Computer and Information Sciences, A
Drafting and Design Technology/Technician, A
Education/Teaching of Individuals with Hearing
    Impairments, Including Deafness, A
Electrical, Electronic and Communications
    Engineering Technology/Technician, A
Engineering Technology, A
Funeral Service and Mortuary Science, A
General Studies, A
Graphic and Printing Equipment Operator
    Production, A
Health Information/Medical Records
    Technology/Technician, A
Instrumentation Technology/Technician, A
Liberal Arts and Sciences Studies and
    Humanities, A
Nursing - Registered Nurse Training, A

CALHOUN COMMUNITY COLLEGE

Accounting, A
Aeronautical/Aerospace Engineering
    Technology/Technician, A
Agriculture, A
Biology/Biological Sciences, A
Business Administration and Management, A
Child Care and Support Services Management, A
Computer and Information Sciences, A
Computer Graphics, A
Criminal Justice/Police Science, A
Dental Assisting/Assistant, A
Drafting and Design Technology/Technician, A
Drama and Dramatics/Theatre Arts, A
Education, A
Education/Teaching of Individuals in Early Childhood
    Special Education Programs, A
Electrical and Power Transmission Installers, A
Electrical, Electronic and Communications
    Engineering Technology/Technician, A
Electromechanical and Instrumentation and
    Maintenance Technologies/Technicians, A
Elementary Education and Teaching, A
Emergency Medical Technology/Technician (EMT
    Paramedic), A
English Language and Literature, A
Entrepreneurship/Entrepreneurial Studies, A
Family Resource Management Studies, A
Fire Services Administration, A
General Studies, A
Graphic Design, A
Heating, Air Conditioning and Refrigeration
    Technology/Technician, A
Heating, Air Conditioning, Ventilation and
    Refrigeration Maintenance
    Technology/Technician, A
Industrial Mechanics and Maintenance
    Technology, A
Legal Assistant/Paralegal, A
Liberal Arts and Sciences Studies and
    Humanities, A
Machine Tool Technology/Machinist, A
Mathematics, A
Military Technologies, A
Music, A

Nursing - Registered Nurse Training, A
Office Management and Supervision, A
Photographic and Film/Video Technology/Technician
    and Assistant, A
Pre-Dentistry Studies, A
Pre-Law Studies, A
Pre-Medicine/Pre-Medical Studies, A
Pre-Pharmacy Studies, A
Pre-Veterinary Studies, A
Real Estate, A
Secondary Education and Teaching, A
Transportation/Transportation Management, A

CENTRAL ALABAMA COMMUNITY COLLEGE

Administrative Assistant and Secretarial Science, A
Apparel and Textiles, A
Business Administration and Management, A
Computer Programming/Programmer, A
Computer Science, A
Drafting and Design Technology/Technician, A
Electrical, Electronic and Communications
    Engineering Technology/Technician, A
Environmental Engineering
    Technology/Environmental Technology, A
Information Science/Studies, A
Liberal Arts and Sciences Studies and
    Humanities, A
Nursing - Registered Nurse Training, A

CHATTAHOOCHEE VALLEY COMMUNITY COLLEGE

Administrative Assistant and Secretarial Science, A
Agriculture, A
Biology/Biological Sciences, A
Business Administration and Management, A
Chemistry, A
Clinical Laboratory Science/Medical
    Technology/Technologist, A
Criminal Justice/Law Enforcement Administration, A
Data Processing and Data Processing
    Technology/Technician, A
Drama and Dramatics/Theatre Arts, A
Elementary Education and Teaching, A
Fire Science/Firefighting, A
Forestry, A
Industrial Radiologic Technology/Technician, A
Information Science/Studies, A
Legal Administrative Assistant/Secretary, A
Liberal Arts and Sciences Studies and
    Humanities, A
Licensed Practical/Vocational Nurse Training, A
Mathematics, A
Music, A
Music Teacher Education, A
Nursing - Registered Nurse Training, A
Physical Education Teaching and Coaching, A
Physics, A
Pre-Engineering, A

COLUMBIA SOUTHERN UNIVERSITY

Business Administration and Management, B
Business Administration, Management and
    Operations, M
Criminal Justice/Safety Studies, B
Electronic Commerce, M
Environmental and Occupational Health, M
Environmental Studies, B
Fire Protection and Safety Technology/Technician, B
Fire Services Administration, B
Health Services Administration, M
Health/Health Care Administration/Management, B
Human Resources Management and Services, BM
International Business/Trade/Commerce, BM
Management, M
Management Information Systems and Services, B
Marketing, M
Marketing/Marketing Management, B
Occupational Safety and Health
    Technology/Technician, B

Sport and Fitness Administration/Management, B

COMMUNITY COLLEGE OF THE AIR FORCE

Aeronautics/Aviation/Aerospace Science and Technology, A
Air Traffic Controller, A
Airframe Mechanics and Aircraft Maintenance Technology/Technician, A
Apparel and Textile Marketing Management, A
Atmospheric Sciences and Meteorology, A
Automobile/Automotive Mechanics Technology/Technician, A
Avionics Maintenance Technology/Technician, A
Biomedical Technology/Technician, A
Cardiovascular Technology/Technologist, A
Clinical/Medical Laboratory Technician, A
Commercial and Advertising Art, A
Communications Technology/Technician, A
Construction Engineering Technology/Technician, A
Criminal Justice/Law Enforcement Administration, A
Dental Assisting/Assistant, A
Dental Laboratory Technology/Technician, A
Dietetics/Dieticians, A
Educational Leadership and Administration, A
Educational/Instructional Media Design, A
Electrical, Electronic and Communications Engineering Technology/Technician, A
Environmental Health, A
Environmental Studies, A
Finance, A
Fire Science/Firefighting, A
Health/Health Care Administration/Management, A
Hematology Technology/Technician, A
Hotel/Motel Administration/Management, A
Human Resources Management/Personnel Administration, A
Industrial Technology/Technician, A
Legal Assistant/Paralegal, A
Logistics and Materials Management, A
Management Information Systems and Services, A
Medical Radiologic Technology/Science - Radiation Therapist, A
Mental Health/Rehabilitation, A
Metallurgical Technology/Technician, A
Military Technologies, A
Music Performance, A
Nuclear Medical Technology/Technologist, A
Occupational Safety and Health Technology/Technician, A
Office Management and Supervision, A
Ophthalmic Laboratory Technology/Technician, A
Parks, Recreation, Leisure and Fitness Studies, A
Pharmacy Technician/Assistant, A
Physical Therapist Assistant, A
Physiology, A
Public Relations/Image Management, A
Purchasing, Procurement/Acquisitions and Contracts Management, A
Security and Loss Prevention Services, A
Social Work, A
Surgical Technology/Technologist, A

CONCORDIA COLLEGE

Business Administration and Management, B
Early Childhood Education and Teaching, B
Elementary Education and Teaching, B
General Studies, A

ENTERPRISE-OZARK COMMUNITY COLLEGE

Administrative Assistant and Secretarial Science, A
Agricultural Business and Management, A
Airframe Mechanics and Aircraft Maintenance Technology/Technician, A
Automobile/Automotive Mechanics Technology/Technician, A
Avionics Maintenance Technology/Technician, A
Biological and Physical Sciences, A
Business Administration and Management, A
Child Development, A
Computer Science, A
Consumer Merchandising/Retailing Management, A
Criminal Justice/Law Enforcement Administration, A
Criminal Justice/Police Science, A
Education, A

Finance, A
Health Information/Medical Records Administration/Administrator, A
Insurance, A
Journalism, A
Kindergarten/PreSchool Education and Teaching, A
Legal Administrative Assistant/Secretary, A
Liberal Arts and Sciences Studies and Humanities, A
Marketing/Marketing Management, A
Mass Communication/Media Studies, A
Medical Administrative Assistant/Secretary, A
Parks, Recreation, Leisure and Fitness Studies, A
Pre-Engineering, A
Real Estate, A
Social Sciences, A
Special Products Marketing Operations, A

FAULKNER UNIVERSITY

Accounting, AB
Administrative Assistant and Secretarial Science, A
Athletic Training and Sports Medicine, B
Bible/Biblical Studies, AB
Biology/Biological Sciences, B
Biomedical Technology/Technician, A
Business Administration and Management, AB
Business Teacher Education, A
Clinical Laboratory Science/Medical Technology/Technologist, A
Clinical/Medical Laboratory Technician, A
Computer Typography and Composition Equipment Operator, A
Criminal Justice/Law Enforcement Administration, AB
Criminology, A
Dietetics/Dieticians, A
Divinity/Ministry (BD, MDiv.), AB
Drama and Dramatics/Theatre Arts, B
Education, B
Elementary Education and Teaching, B
Emergency Medical Technology/Technician (EMT Paramedic), A
English Language and Literature, B
Health Information/Medical Records Administration/Administrator, A
History, B
Human Resources Management/Personnel Administration, B
Humanities/Humanistic Studies, AB
Industrial Radiologic Technology/Technician, A
Information Science/Studies, AB
Kindergarten/PreSchool Education and Teaching, B
Law and Legal Studies, P
Legal Assistant/Paralegal, AB
Liberal Arts and Sciences Studies and Humanities, AB
Marketing/Marketing Management, B
Medical/Clinical Assistant, A
Occupational Therapy/Therapist, A
Pastoral Studies/Counseling, B
Physical Education Teaching and Coaching, B
Physical Sciences, A
Physical Therapy/Therapist, A
Political Science and Government, B
Pre-Engineering, A
Pre-Law Studies, B
Psychology, B
Religion/Religious Studies, B
Religious Education, B
Respiratory Care Therapy/Therapist, A
Secondary Education and Teaching, B
Social Sciences, AB
Sport and Fitness Administration/Management, B
Theology/Theological Studies, B

GADSDEN STATE COMMUNITY COLLEGE

Administrative Assistant and Secretarial Science, A
Child Care and Support Services Management, A
Civil Engineering Technology/Technician, A
Clinical/Medical Laboratory Technician, A
Computer and Information Sciences, A
Court Reporting/Court Reporter, A
Criminal Justice/Police Science, A
Emergency Medical Technology/Technician (EMT Paramedic), A

General Studies, A
Heating, Air Conditioning and Refrigeration Technology/Technician, A
Legal Assistant/Paralegal, A
Liberal Arts and Sciences Studies and Humanities, A
Mechanical Engineering/Mechanical Technology/Technician, A
Medical Radiologic Technology/Science - Radiation Therapist, A
Nursing - Registered Nurse Training, A
Physical Education Teaching and Coaching, A
Radio and Television Broadcasting Technology/Technician, A
Substance Abuse/Addiction Counseling, A
Telecommunications Technology/Technician, A
Tool and Die Technology/Technician, A

GADSDEN STATE COMMUNITY COLLEGE-AYERS CAMPUS

Accounting, A
Child Care Provider/Assistant, A
Computer Science, A
Drafting and Design Technology/Technician, A
Electrical, Electronic and Communications Engineering Technology/Technician, A
Electrical/Electronics Equipment Installation and Repair, A
Heating, Air Conditioning, Ventilation and Refrigeration Maintenance Technology/Technician, A
Machine Shop Technology/Assistant, A
Machine Tool Technology/Machinist, A
Office Management and Supervision, A
System Administration/Administrator, A

GEORGE C. WALLACE COMMUNITY COLLEGE

Accounting, A
Administrative Assistant and Secretarial Science, A
Automobile/Automotive Mechanics Technology/Technician, A
Business Administration and Management, A
Carpentry/Carpenter, A
Clinical/Medical Laboratory Technician, A
Commercial and Advertising Art, A
Computer Science, A
Criminal Justice/Police Science, A
Data Processing and Data Processing Technology/Technician, A
Drafting and Design Technology/Technician, A
Electrical, Electronic and Communications Engineering Technology/Technician, A
Emergency Medical Technology/Technician (EMT Paramedic), A
Heating, Air Conditioning, Ventilation and Refrigeration Maintenance Technology/Technician, A
Industrial Mechanics and Maintenance Technology, A
Laser and Optical Technology/Technician, A
Liberal Arts and Sciences Studies and Humanities, A
Licensed Practical/Vocational Nurse Training, A
Machine Tool Technology/Machinist, A
Medical Administrative Assistant/Secretary, A
Medical/Clinical Assistant, A
Nursing - Registered Nurse Training, A
Physical Therapist Assistant, A
Radiologic Technology/Science - Radiographer, A
Respiratory Care Therapy/Therapist, A
Welding Technology/Welder, A

GEORGE CORLEY WALLACE STATE COMMUNITY COLLEGE

Accounting, A
Biomedical Technology/Technician, A
Business Administration and Management, A
Business Teacher Education, A
Clinical/Medical Laboratory Technician, A
Computer Programming/Programmer, A
Computer Science, A
Criminal Justice/Law Enforcement Administration, A
Criminal Justice/Police Science, A
Drafting and Design Technology/Technician, A

Electrical, Electronic and Communications
   Engineering Technology/Technician, A
Fire Science/Firefighting, A
Health Information/Medical Records
   Administration/Administrator, A
Industrial Radiologic Technology/Technician, A
Licensed Practical/Vocational Nurse Training, A
Machine Tool Technology/Machinist, A
Medical/Clinical Assistant, A
Nursing - Registered Nurse Training, A
Occupational Therapy/Therapist, A
Physical Therapy/Therapist, A
Respiratory Care Therapy/Therapist, A
Welding Technology/Welder, A

H. COUNCILL TRENHOLM STATE TECHNICAL COLLEGE

Accounting Technology/Technician and
   Bookkeeping, A
Administrative Assistant and Secretarial Science, A
Apparel and Textiles, A
Automobile/Automotive Mechanics
   Technology/Technician, A
Automotive Engineering Technology/Technician, A
Carpentry/Carpenter, A
Child Care and Support Services Management, A
Computer and Information Sciences, A
Construction Engineering Technology/Technician, A
Cosmetology/Cosmetologist, A
Culinary Arts/Chef Training, A
Dental Assisting/Assistant, A
Dental Laboratory Technology/Technician, A
Drafting and Design Technology/Technician, A
Electrical, Electronic and Communications
   Engineering Technology/Technician, A
Electrician, A
Emergency Medical Technology/Technician (EMT
   Paramedic), A
Graphic and Printing Equipment Operator
   Production, A
Graphic Communications, A
Heating, Air Conditioning, Ventilation and
   Refrigeration Maintenance
   Technology/Technician, A
Heavy Equipment Maintenance
   Technology/Technician, A
Industrial Electronics Technology/Technician, A
Industrial Mechanics and Maintenance
   Technology, A
Information Science/Studies, A
Instrumentation Technology/Technician, A
Machine Tool Technology/Machinist, A
Massage Therapy/Therapeutic Massage, A
Medical/Clinical Assistant, A
Pipefitting/Pipefitter and Sprinkler Fitter, A
Tool and Die Technology/Technician, A

HERITAGE CHRISTIAN UNIVERSITY

Bible/Biblical Studies, AB

HERZING COLLEGE

Administrative Assistant and Secretarial Science, A
Business Machine Repairer, A
Business, Management, Marketing, and Related
   Support Services, B
Computer and Information Sciences, A
Computer Programming/Programmer, A
Computer Science, A
Data Processing and Data Processing
   Technology/Technician, A
Electrical, Electronic and Communications
   Engineering Technology/Technician, AB
Information Science/Studies, AB

HUNTINGDON COLLEGE

Accounting, B
American/United States Studies/Civilization, B
Applied Art, B
Art Teacher Education, B
Art/Art Studies, General, B
Athletic Training and Sports Medicine, B
Biology/Biological Sciences, B
Business Administration and Management, B
Business/Managerial Economics, B
Cell/Cellular Biology and Anatomical Sciences, B

Chemistry, B
Chemistry Teacher Education, B
Computer and Information Sciences, B
Computer Graphics, B
Computer Science, B
Counseling Psychology, B
Creative Writing, B
Drama and Dramatics/Theatre Arts, B
Education, B
English Language and Literature, B
English/Language Arts Teacher Education, B
European Studies/Civilization, B
Experimental Psychology, B
History, B
History Teacher Education, B
Interdisciplinary Studies, B
International Business/Trade/Commerce, B
International Relations and Affairs, B
Kinesiology and Exercise Science, B
Liberal Arts and Sciences Studies and
   Humanities, B
Marketing/Marketing Management, B
Mathematics, B
Mathematics Teacher Education, B
Multi-/Interdisciplinary Studies, B
Music, B
Music Teacher Education, B
Parks, Recreation, Leisure and Fitness Studies, B
Physical Education Teaching and Coaching, B
Physical Therapy/Therapist, B
Piano and Organ, B
Political Science and Government, B
Public Administration, B
Religion/Religious Studies, B
Religious Education, B
Secondary Education and Teaching, B
Spanish Language and Literature, B
Speech and Rhetorical Studies, B
Sport and Fitness Administration/Management, B
Visual and Performing Arts, B
Voice and Opera, B

J. F. DRAKE STATE TECHNICAL COLLEGE

Accounting, A
Administrative Assistant and Secretarial Science, A
Commercial and Advertising Art, A
Drafting and Design Technology/Technician, A
Electrical, Electronic and Communications
   Engineering Technology/Technician, A
Information Science/Studies, A
Machine Tool Technology/Machinist, A

JACKSONVILLE STATE UNIVERSITY

Accounting, B
Animal Genetics, B
Anthropology, B
Apparel and Textiles, B
Army JROTC/ROTC, B
Art/Art Studies, General, B
Biological and Biomedical Sciences, M
Biology/Biological Sciences, B
Business Administration and Management, B
Business Administration, Management and
   Operations, M
Chemistry, B
Communication Studies/Speech Communication
   and Rhetoric, B
Computer and Information Sciences, B
Computer Science, M
Corrections, B
Counselor Education/School Counseling and
   Guidance Services, M
Criminal Justice/Law Enforcement Administration, B
Criminal Justice/Police Science, B
Criminology, M
Dietetics/Dieticians, B
Drama and Dramatics/Theatre Arts, B
Early Childhood Education and Teaching, M
Ecology, B
Economics, B
Education, BMO
Educational Administration and Supervision, MO
Educational Media/Instructional Technology, M
Educational Psychology, B
Educational/Instructional Media Design, B

Electrical, Electronic and Communications
   Engineering Technology/Technician, B
Elementary Education and Teaching, BM
English, M
English Language and Literature, B
Environmental Biology, B
Family and Consumer Sciences/Home Economics
   Teacher Education, B
Family and Consumer Sciences/Human Sciences, B
Finance, B
Foods, Nutrition, and Wellness Studies, B
Forensic Science and Technology, B
French Language and Literature, B
Geography, B
Geology/Earth Science, B
German Language and Literature, B
Health and Physical Education, B
Health Education, M
Health Teacher Education, B
History, BM
Industrial Technology/Technician, B
Junior High/Intermediate/Middle School Education
   and Teaching, B
Kindergarten/PreSchool Education and Teaching, B
Kinesiology and Exercise Science, B
Liberal Studies, M
Marine Biology and Biological Oceanography, B
Marketing/Marketing Management, B
Mathematics, BM
Music, BM
Music Teacher Education, B
Nursing, M
Nursing - Registered Nurse Training, B
Occupational Safety and Health
   Technology/Technician, B
Parks, Recreation, Leisure and Fitness Studies, B
Physical Education Teaching and Coaching, BM
Physics, B
Political Science and Government, B
Psychology, BM
Public Administration, M
Reading Teacher Education, M
Secondary Education and Teaching, BM
Social Work, B
Sociology, B
Software Engineering, M
Spanish Language and Literature, B
Special Education and Teaching, BM

JAMES H. FAULKNER STATE COMMUNITY COLLEGE

Administrative Assistant and Secretarial Science, A
Agricultural Economics, A
Business Administration and Management, A
Commercial and Advertising Art, A
Computer and Information Sciences, A
Criminal Justice/Law Enforcement Administration, A
Dental Assisting/Assistant, A
Environmental Engineering
   Technology/Environmental Technology, A
General Studies, A
Hospitality Administration/Management, A
Landscaping and Groundskeeping, A
Legal Assistant/Paralegal, A
Liberal Arts and Sciences Studies and
   Humanities, A
Licensed Practical/Vocational Nurse Training, A
Mass Communication/Media Studies, A
Nursing - Registered Nurse Training, A
Parks, Recreation and Leisure Facilities
   Management, A
Surgical Technology/Technologist, A

JEFFERSON DAVIS COMMUNITY COLLEGE

Administrative Assistant and Secretarial Science, A
Applied Art, A
Biological and Physical Sciences, A
Biology/Biological Sciences, A
Business Administration and Management, A
Criminal Justice/Police Science, A
Drama and Dramatics/Theatre Arts, A
Education, A
Elementary Education and Teaching, A
Finance, A
History, A

Liberal Arts and Sciences Studies and
  Humanities, A
Marketing/Marketing Management, A
Medical/Clinical Assistant, A
Music, A
Nursing - Registered Nurse Training, A
Parks, Recreation, Leisure and Fitness Studies, A
Physical Education Teaching and Coaching, A
Political Science and Government, A

JEFFERSON STATE COMMUNITY COLLEGE

Accounting Technology/Technician and
  Bookkeeping, A
Administrative Assistant and Secretarial Science, A
Agricultural Business and Management, A
Banking and Financial Support Services, A
Biomedical Technology/Technician, A
Business/Commerce, A
Child Care and Support Services Management, A
Clinical/Medical Laboratory Technician, A
Computer and Information Sciences, A
Construction Engineering Technology/Technician, A
Criminal Justice/Police Science, A
Fire Services Administration, A
Funeral Service and Mortuary Science, A
General Studies, A
Home Furnishings and Equipment Installers, A
Hospitality Administration/Management, A
Liberal Arts and Sciences Studies and
  Humanities, A
Medical Radiologic Technology/Science - Radiation
  Therapist, A
Nursing - Registered Nurse Training, A
Physical Therapist Assistant, A
Radio and Television Broadcasting
  Technology/Technician, A
Robotics Technology/Technician, A
Veterinary/Animal Health Technology/Technician and
  Veterinary Assistant, A

JUDSON COLLEGE

Art/Art Studies, General, B
Biology/Biological Sciences, B
Business/Commerce, B
Chemistry, B
Criminal Justice/Law Enforcement Administration, B
Education, B
Elementary Education and Teaching, B
English Language and Literature, B
English/Language Arts Teacher Education, B
History, B
Interdisciplinary Studies, B
Junior High/Intermediate/Middle School Education
  and Teaching, B
Mathematics, B
Mathematics Teacher Education, B
Modern Languages, B
Multi-/Interdisciplinary Studies, B
Music, B
Music Teacher Education, B
Psychology, B
Religion/Religious Studies, B
Romance Languages, Literatures, and Linguistics, B
Science Teacher Education/General Science
  Teacher Education, B
Social Science Teacher Education, B

LAWSON STATE COMMUNITY COLLEGE

Accounting, A
Administrative Assistant and Secretarial Science, A
Apparel and Textiles, A
Art/Art Studies, General, A
Biology/Biological Sciences, A
Business Administration and Management, A
Business Teacher Education, A
Carpentry/Carpenter, A
Chemistry, A
Clinical Laboratory Science/Medical
  Technology/Technologist, A
Computer and Information Sciences, A
Cosmetology/Cosmetologist, A
Crafts/Craft Design, Folk Art and Artisanry, A
Criminal Justice/Law Enforcement Administration, A
Criminal Justice/Police Science, A

Dietetics/Dieticians, A
Drafting and Design Technology/Technician, A
Education, A
Electrical, Electronic and Communications
  Engineering Technology/Technician, A
English Language and Literature, A
Fire Science/Firefighting, A
Health and Physical Education, A
Heavy Equipment Maintenance
  Technology/Technician, A
History, A
Hydrology and Water Resources Science, A
Information Science/Studies, A
Legal Administrative Assistant/Secretary, A
Liberal Arts and Sciences Studies and
  Humanities, A
Library Science, A
Mathematics, A
Music, A
Nursing - Registered Nurse Training, A
Parks, Recreation, Leisure and Fitness Studies, A
Physical Sciences, A
Physical Therapy/Therapist, A
Political Science and Government, A
Pre-Engineering, A
Pre-Law Studies, A
Psychology, A
Radio and Television, A
Social Sciences, A
Social Work, A
Sociology, A
Urban Studies/Affairs, A

LURLEEN B. WALLACE COMMUNITY COLLEGE

Emergency Medical Technology/Technician (EMT
  Paramedic), A
Forestry Technology/Technician, A
Liberal Arts and Sciences Studies and
  Humanities, A

MARION MILITARY INSTITUTE

Biological and Physical Sciences, A
Engineering, A
Liberal Arts and Sciences Studies and
  Humanities, A

MILES COLLEGE

Accounting and Business/Management, B
African Studies, B
Behavioral Sciences, B
Biology/Biological Sciences, B
Business Administration and Management, B
Chemistry, B
Communication and Media Studies, B
Computer and Information Sciences, B
Criminal Justice/Law Enforcement Administration, B
Early Childhood Education and Teaching, B
Education, B
Elementary Education and Teaching, B
English Language and Literature, B
English/Language Arts Teacher Education, B
Environmental Sciences, B
History, B
Mass Communication/Media Studies, B
Mathematics, B
Mathematics Teacher Education, B
Physics, B
Political Science and Government, B
Religion/Religious Studies, B
Secondary Education and Teaching, B
Social Sciences, B
Social Work, B

NORTHEAST ALABAMA COMMUNITY COLLEGE

Administrative Assistant and Secretarial Science, A
Biological and Physical Sciences, A
Business Administration and Management, A
Computer Graphics, A
Computer Science, A
Computer Typography and Composition Equipment
  Operator, A
Electrical, Electronic and Communications
  Engineering Technology/Technician, A

Emergency Medical Technology/Technician (EMT
  Paramedic), A
Finance, A
Hydrology and Water Resources Science, A
Information Science/Studies, A
Legal Administrative Assistant/Secretary, A
Legal Assistant/Paralegal, A
Liberal Arts and Sciences Studies and
  Humanities, A
Medical Administrative Assistant/Secretary, A
Nursing - Registered Nurse Training, A
Pre-Engineering, A
Real Estate, A

NORTHWEST-SHOALS COMMUNITY COLLEGE

Accounting, A
Administrative Assistant and Secretarial Science, A
Agricultural Teacher Education, A
Art/Art Studies, General, A
Business Administration and Management, A
Child Development, A
Clinical Laboratory Science/Medical
  Technology/Technologist, A
Computer and Information Sciences, A
Computer Engineering Technology/Technician, A
Computer Programming/Programmer, A
Computer Science, A
Computer Typography and Composition Equipment
  Operator, A
Criminal Justice/Law Enforcement Administration, A
Criminal Justice/Police Science, A
Drafting and Design Technology/Technician, A
Education, A
Electrical, Electronic and Communications
  Engineering Technology/Technician, A
Elementary Education and Teaching, A
Environmental Biology, A
Environmental Sciences, A
Fire Science/Firefighting, A
Forestry, A
General Studies, A
Health and Medical Laboratory Technologies, A
Industrial Electronics Technology/Technician, A
Industrial Mechanics and Maintenance
  Technology, A
Information Science/Studies, A
Liberal Arts and Sciences Studies and
  Humanities, A
Licensed Practical/Vocational Nurse Training, A
Multi-/Interdisciplinary Studies, A
Nursing - Registered Nurse Training, A
Pre-Dentistry Studies, A
Pre-Engineering, A
Pre-Law Studies, A
Pre-Nursing Studies, A
Pre-Pharmacy Studies, A
Pre-Veterinary Studies, A
Secondary Education and Teaching, A
Water Quality and Wastewater Treatment
  Management and Recycling
  Technology/Technician, A
Welding Technology/Welder, A

OAKWOOD COLLEGE

Accounting, AB
Administrative Assistant and Secretarial Science, AB
Applied Mathematics, B
Bible/Biblical Studies, A
Biochemistry, B
Biology/Biological Sciences, B
Business Administration and Management, B
Business Teacher Education, B
Chemistry, B
Clinical Laboratory Science/Medical
  Technology/Technologist, B
Commercial and Advertising Art, A
Computer Science, B
Dietetics/Dieticians, AB
Economics, B
Elementary Education and Teaching, B
Engineering, B
English Language and Literature, B
Family and Consumer Sciences/Home Economics
  Teacher Education, B
Family and Consumer Sciences/Human Sciences, B

French Language and Literature, B
History, B
Information Science/Studies, AB
Interdisciplinary Studies, B
Mass Communication/Media Studies, B
Mathematics, B
Music, B
Music Teacher Education, B
Natural Sciences, B
Nursing - Registered Nurse Training, AB
Occupational Therapy/Therapist, A
Pastoral Studies/Counseling, A
Physical Education Teaching and Coaching, B
Physical Therapy/Therapist, A
Psychology, B
Religion/Religious Studies, A
Religious Education, B
Science Teacher Education/General Science
    Teacher Education, B
Social Sciences, B
Social Work, B
Spanish Language and Literature, B
Theology/Theological Studies, B

PRINCE INSTITUTE OF PROFESSIONAL STUDIES

Court Reporting/Court Reporter, A

REID STATE TECHNICAL COLLEGE

Administrative Assistant and Secretarial Science, A
Electrical, Electronic and Communications
    Engineering Technology/Technician, A

REMINGTON COLLEGE-MOBILE CAMPUS

Computer and Information Sciences, A
Computer Engineering Technology/Technician, A
Computer Systems Networking and
    Telecommunications, A
Drafting and Design Technology/Technician, A
Information Science/Studies, A
Operations Management and Supervision, AB
Web/Multimedia Management and Webmaster, A

SAMFORD UNIVERSITY

Accounting, B
Asian Studies/Civilization, B
Athletic Training and Sports Medicine, B
Biochemistry, B
Biology Teacher Education, B
Biology/Biological Sciences, B
Business Administration and Management, B
Business Administration, Management and
    Operations, MO
Cartography, B
Chemistry, B
Classical, Ancient Mediterranean and Near Eastern
    Studies and Archaeology, B
Classics and Classical
    Languages, Literatures, and Linguistics, B
Commercial and Advertising Art, B
Community Organization and Advocacy, AB
Computer Science, B
Counseling Psychology, B
Criminal Justice/Law Enforcement Administration, B
Drama and Dramatics/Theatre Arts, B
Early Childhood Education and Teaching, MO
Education, MDO
Educational Administration and Supervision, MO
Educational Leadership and Administration, D
Elementary Education and Teaching, MO
Engineering, B
Engineering Physics, B
English Language and Literature, B
English/Language Arts Teacher Education, B
Environmental Sciences, B
Environmental Studies, AB
Foreign Languages and Literatures, B
French Language and Literature, B
General Studies, B
Geography, B
German Language and Literature, B
Health and Physical Education, B
History, B
History Teacher Education, B

Human Development and Family Studies, B
Human Nutrition, B
Human Resources Management/Personnel
    Administration, B
Interior Design, B
International Business/Trade/Commerce, B
International Relations and Affairs, B
Journalism, B
Kinesiology and Exercise Science, B
Latin American Studies, B
Latin Language and Literature, B
Law and Legal Studies, MPO
Marine Biology and Biological Oceanography, B
Mathematics, B
Music, M
Music Performance, B
Music Teacher Education, BM
Music Theory and Composition, B
Nursing, MO
Nursing - Registered Nurse Training, B
Pharmacy, P
Philosophy, B
Philosophy and Religious Studies, B
Physical Education Teaching and Coaching, B
Physics, B
Piano and Organ, B
Political Science and Government, B
Pre-Medicine/Pre-Medical Studies, B
Psychology, B
Public Administration, B
Religion/Religious Studies, B
Religious/Sacred Music, B
Sacred Music, M
Science Teacher Education/General Science
    Teacher Education, B
Science, Technology and Society, AB
Social Science Teacher Education, B
Social Sciences, AB
Sociology, B
Spanish Language and Literature, B
Speech and Rhetorical Studies, B
Speech Teacher Education, B
Theology and Religious Vocations, MDPO
Visual and Performing Arts, B
Voice and Opera, B

SHELTON STATE COMMUNITY COLLEGE

Administrative Assistant and Secretarial Science, A
Culinary Arts/Chef Training, A
Diesel Mechanics Technology/Technician, A
Drafting and Design Technology/Technician, A
Electrical, Electronic and Communications
    Engineering Technology/Technician, A
Emergency Medical Technology/Technician (EMT
    Paramedic), A
Heating, Air Conditioning, Ventilation and
    Refrigeration Maintenance
    Technology/Technician, A
Industrial Electronics Technology/Technician, A
Liberal Arts and Sciences Studies and
    Humanities, A
Machine Tool Technology/Machinist, A
Medical Administrative Assistant/Secretary, A
Nursing - Registered Nurse Training, A
Respiratory Care Therapy/Therapist, A
Welding Technology/Welder, A

SNEAD STATE COMMUNITY COLLEGE

Business Administration and Management, A
Child Care and Support Services Management, A
Computer and Information Sciences, A
Data Processing and Data Processing
    Technology/Technician, A
Engineering Technology, A
General Studies, A
Liberal Arts and Sciences Studies and
    Humanities, A

SOUTH UNIVERSITY

Accounting, A
Business Administration and Management, AB
Criminal Justice/Law Enforcement Administration, B
Information Science/Studies, AB
Law and Legal Studies, B
Legal Assistant/Paralegal, A

Medical/Clinical Assistant, A
Physical Therapist Assistant, A
Public Health (MPH, DPH), A

SOUTHEASTERN BIBLE COLLEGE

Bible/Biblical Studies, AB
Education, B
Music, B
Pastoral Studies/Counseling, B
Religion/Religious Studies, B
Religious Education, B
Religious/Sacred Music, B
Theology/Theological Studies, B

SOUTHERN CHRISTIAN UNIVERSITY

Bible/Biblical Studies, B
Business/Corporate Communications, B
Counseling Psychology, MP
Human Resources Management/Personnel
    Administration, B
Liberal Arts and Sciences Studies and
    Humanities, B
Marriage and Family Therapy/Counseling, BMDP
Organizational Behavior Studies, M
Organizational Management, M
Pastoral Studies/Counseling, BMP
Public Administration and Social Service
    Professions, B
Religion/Religious Studies, D
Theology and Religious Vocations, MDP

SOUTHERN UNION STATE COMMUNITY COLLEGE

Administrative Assistant and Secretarial Science, A
Business Administration and Management, A
Finance, A
Information Science/Studies, A
Liberal Arts and Sciences Studies and
    Humanities, A
Nursing - Registered Nurse Training, A

SPRING HILL COLLEGE

Accounting, B
Art Therapy/Therapist, B
Arts Management, B
Biochemistry, B
Biology/Biological Sciences, B
Business Administration and Management, AB
Business Administration, Management and
    Operations, M
Chemistry, B
Communication, Journalism and Related
    Programs, B
Computer and Information Sciences, AB
Drama and Dramatics/Theatre Arts, B
Early Childhood Education and Teaching, BM
Education, AM
Elementary Education and Teaching, BM
Engineering, B
English Language and Literature, B
Finance, B
Fine/Studio Arts, B
General Studies, B
Graphic Design, B
History, B
Humanities/Humanistic Studies, B
International Business/Trade/Commerce, B
International Relations and Affairs, B
Journalism, B
Liberal Studies, M
Marine Biology and Biological Oceanography, B
Marketing/Marketing Management, B
Mathematics, B
Multi-/Interdisciplinary Studies, B
Nursing - Registered Nurse Training, B
Philosophy, B
Political Science and Government, B
Pre-Dentistry Studies, B
Pre-Medicine/Pre-Medical Studies, B
Pre-Veterinary Studies, B
Psychology, B
Radio and Television, B
Secondary Education and Teaching, BM
Spanish Language and Literature, B
Theology and Religious Vocations, M

Theology/Theological Studies, B

STILLMAN COLLEGE

Biology/Biological Sciences, B
Business Administration and Management, B
Chemistry, B
Computer Science, B
Education, B
English Language and Literature, B
History, B
Interdisciplinary Studies, B
International Relations and Affairs, B
Mass Communication/Media Studies, B
Mathematics, B
Music, B
Parks, Recreation and Leisure Facilities
   Management, B
Philosophy, B
Physical Education Teaching and Coaching, B
Physics, B
Religion/Religious Studies, B
Sociology, B

TALLADEGA COLLEGE

Accounting, B
African-American/Black Studies, B
Biology Teacher Education, B
Biology/Biological Sciences, B
Business Administration and Management, B
Chemistry, B
Chemistry Teacher Education, B
Computer Science, B
Economics, B
Education, B
English Language and Literature, B
English/Language Arts Teacher Education, B
Finance, B
Fine/Studio Arts, B
French Language and Literature, B
French Language Teacher Education, B
History, B
History Teacher Education, B
Journalism, B
Marketing/Marketing Management, B
Mass Communication/Media Studies, B
Mathematics, B
Mathematics Teacher Education, B
Music, B
Music Performance, B
Music Teacher Education, B
Physics, B
Pre-Law Studies, B
Psychology, B
Public Administration, B
Science Teacher Education/General Science
   Teacher Education, B
Social Work, B
Sociology, B
Spanish Language and Literature, B
Voice and Opera, B

TROY UNIVERSITY

Accounting, B
Art History, Criticism and Conservation, B
Art Teacher Education, B
Art/Art Studies, General, B
Athletic Training and Sports Medicine, B
Biology/Biological Sciences, B
Broadcast Journalism, B
Business Administration and Management, B
Business Administration, Management and
   Operations, M
Business Teacher Education, B
Business/Commerce, AB
Chemistry, B
Clinical Psychology, M
Communication and Media Studies, M
Computer and Information Sciences, AB
Corrections, B
Counselor Education/School Counseling and
   Guidance Services, MO
Criminology, M
Drama and Dramatics/Theatre Arts, B
Education, BMO
Educational Administration and Supervision, MO
Elementary Education and Teaching, BMO

English Language and Literature, B
Environmental Policy and Resource
   Management, M
Environmental Sciences, B
Finance, B
Finance and Banking, M
Fine Arts and Art Studies, M
Fine/Studio Arts, B
Foundations and Philosophy of Education, M
Health Teacher Education, B
History, B
Human Resources Management and Services, M
Human Resources Management/Personnel
   Administration, B
International Affairs, M
Journalism, B
Kindergarten/PreSchool Education and Teaching, B
Liberal Arts and Sciences Studies and
   Humanities, A
Management, M
Management Information Systems and Services, B
Marine Biology and Biological Oceanography, B
Marketing, B
Mathematics, B
Music, M
Music Teacher Education, B
Nursing, M
Nursing - Registered Nurse Training, AB
Parks, Recreation, Leisure and Fitness Studies, B
Performance, M
Physical Education Teaching and Coaching, B
Physical Sciences, B
Political Science and Government, B
Pre-Dentistry Studies, B
Pre-Medicine/Pre-Medical Studies, B
Pre-Veterinary Studies, B
Psychology, B
Public Administration, BM
Rehabilitation Counseling, O
School Psychology, M
Science Teacher Education/General Science
   Teacher Education, B
Secondary Education and Teaching, BMO
Securities Services Administration/Management, M
Social Sciences, B
Social Work, B
Sociology, B
Special Education and Teaching, B
Speech and Rhetorical Studies, B
Sport and Fitness Administration/Management, BM
Survey Technology/Surveying, B

TUSKEGEE UNIVERSITY

Accounting, B
Aerospace, Aeronautical and Astronautical
   Engineering, B
Agricultural Business and Management, B
Agricultural Economics, M
Agricultural Sciences, M
Agriculture, B
Agronomy and Crop Science, B
Agronomy and Soil Sciences, M
Animal Sciences, BM
Architecture, B
Biological and Biomedical Sciences, M
Biology/Biological Sciences, B
Building/Home/Construction Inspection/Inspector, B
Business Administration and Management, B
Chemical Engineering, B
Chemistry, BM
Clinical Laboratory Science/Medical
   Technology/Technologist, B
Computer Science, B
Construction Engineering Technology/Technician, B
Dietetics/Dieticians, B
Economics, B
Education, M
Electrical Engineering, M
Electrical, Electronics and Communications
   Engineering, B
Elementary Education and Teaching, B
Engineering and Applied Sciences, MD
Engineering Technology, B
English Language and Literature, B
Environmental Sciences, M
Environmental Studies, B

Finance, B
Food Science, B
Food Science and Technology, M
Foods, Nutrition, and Wellness Studies, B
History, B
Hospitality Administration/Management, B
Hospitality and Recreation Marketing Operations, B
Management Science, B
Marketing/Marketing Management, B
Materials Engineering, D
Mathematics, B
Mechanical Engineering, BM
Natural Resources Management/Development and
   Policy, B
Nursing - Registered Nurse Training, B
Nutritional Sciences, M
Occupational Therapy/Therapist, B
Physics, B
Plant Sciences, BM
Political Science and Government, B
Poultry Science, B
Psychology, B
Sales, Distribution and Marketing Operations, B
Social Work, B
Sociology, B
Veterinary Medicine, P
Veterinary Sciences, M

THE UNIVERSITY OF ALABAMA

Accounting, BMD
Advertising, B
Advertising and Public Relations, M
Aerospace, Aeronautical and Astronautical
   Engineering, BMD
American/United States Studies/Civilization, BM
Anthropology, BMD
Apparel and Textiles, B
Applied Mathematics, D
Art History, Criticism and Conservation, BM
Asian Studies/Civilization, B
Athletic Training and Sports Medicine, B
Audiology/Audiologist and Speech-Language
   Pathology/Pathologist, B
Biological and Biomedical Sciences, MD
Biological and Physical Sciences, B
Biology/Biological Sciences, B
Business Administration and Management, B
Business/Managerial Economics, B
Chemical Engineering, BMD
Chemistry, BMD
Child and Family Studies, M
Civil Engineering, BMD
Classics and Classical
   Languages, Literatures, and Linguistics, B
Clinical Psychology, D
Clothing and Textiles, M
Cognitive Sciences, D
Communication and Media Studies, MD
Communication Disorders, M
Communication Studies/Speech Communication
   and Rhetoric, B
Computer and Information Sciences, B
Computer Science, MD
Consumer Economics, BM
Counselor Education/School Counseling and
   Guidance Services, MDO
Criminal Justice/Safety Studies, B
Criminology, M
Curriculum and Instruction, MDO
Dance, B
Drama and Dramatics/Theatre Arts, B
Early Childhood Education and Teaching, B
Economics, MD
Educational Administration and Supervision, MD
Educational Leadership and Administration, MDO
Electrical Engineering, MD
Electrical, Electronics and Communications
   Engineering, B
Elementary Education and Teaching, BMDO
Engineering and Applied Sciences, MD
English, MD
English as a Second Language, M
English Language and Literature, B
Environmental Engineering
   Technology/Environmental Technology, MD
Family and Consumer Sciences/Human Sciences, B

Film, Television, and Video Production, M
Finance, B
Finance and Banking, MD
Fine Arts and Art Studies, M
Fine/Studio Arts, B
Foods, Nutrition, and Wellness Studies, B
French Language and Literature, BMD
French Studies, B
Geography, BM
Geology/Earth Science, BMD
German Language and Literature, BM
German Studies, B
Health Education, MD
Health Professions and Related Clinical Sciences, B
Health Promotion, MD
Higher Education/Higher Education
   Administration, MD
History, BMD
Home Economics, MD
Hospital and Health Care Facilities
   Administration/Management, B
Hospitality Administration/Management, M
Human Development, M
Human Development and Family Studies, B
Industrial Engineering, B
Industrial/Management Engineering, M
Information Science/Studies, MD
Interdisciplinary Studies, B
Interior Design, BM
International Relations and Affairs, B
Journalism, BM
Kindergarten/PreSchool Education and Teaching, B
Kinesiology and Movement Studies, MD
Latin American Studies, BMO
Law and Legal Studies, MPO
Library Science, MD
Management, MD
Management Information Systems and Services, B
Management Science, B
Marine Biology and Biological Oceanography, B
Marketing, MD
Marketing/Marketing Management, B
Materials Engineering, MD
Materials Sciences, D
Mathematics, BMD
Mechanical Engineering, BMD
Mechanics, MD
Media Studies, M
Medical Microbiology and Bacteriology, B
Metallurgical Engineering, BMD
Music, BMD
Music Teacher Education, BMDO
Nursing, M
Nursing - Registered Nurse Training, B
Nutritional Sciences, M
Philosophy, B
Physical Education Teaching and Coaching, B
Physics, BMD
Political Science and Government, BMD
Psychology, BD
Public Administration, M
Public Relations/Image Management, B
Radio and Television, B
Religion/Religious Studies, B
Rhetoric, D
Romance
   Languages, Literatures, and Linguistics, MD
Russian Language and Literature, B
Secondary Education and Teaching, BMDO
Social Work, BMD
Sociology, B
Spanish and Iberian Studies, B
Spanish Language and Literature, BMD
Special Education and Teaching, B
Speech and Interpersonal Communication, M
Speech and Rhetorical Studies, B
Statistics, MD
Taxation, M
Theater, M
Women's Studies, M
Writing, M

THE UNIVERSITY OF ALABAMA AT BIRMINGHAM

Accounting, B
African-American/Black Studies, B

Allied Health and Medical Assisting Services, MDO
Allopathic Medicine, MDPO
Anthropology, BM
Applied Mathematics, D
Art Education, M
Art History, Criticism and Conservation, M
Biochemistry, D
Biological and Biomedical Sciences, MD
Biological and Physical Sciences, B
Biology/Biological Sciences, B
Biomedical Engineering, MD
Biomedical/Medical Engineering, B
Biometry/Biometrics, MD
Biophysics, MD
Biostatistics, MD
Business Administration and Management, B
Business Administration, Management and
   Operations, MD
Business/Managerial Economics, B
Cell Biology and Anatomy, D
Chemistry, BMD
Civil Engineering, BMD
Clinical Laboratory Science/Medical
   Technology/Technologist, B
Clinical Laboratory Sciences, M
Clinical Psychology, D
Communication and Media Studies, M
Communication Studies/Speech Communication
   and Rhetoric, B
Computer and Information Sciences, B
Computer Engineering, MD
Computer Science, MD
Corrections and Criminal Justice, B
Counselor Education/School Counseling and
   Guidance Services, M
Criminology, M
CytoTechnology/Cytotechnologist, B
Dentistry, P
Developmental Psychology, D
Early Childhood Education and Teaching, MD
Education, MDO
Educational Leadership and Administration, MDO
Electrical Engineering, MD
Electrical, Electronics and Communications
   Engineering, B
Elementary Education and Teaching, BM
Engineering and Applied Sciences, MD
English, M
English Language and Literature, B
Environmental and Occupational Health, D
Environmental Engineering
   Technology/Environmental Technology, MD
Epidemiology, D
Finance, B
Fine/Studio Arts, B
Forensic Science and Technology, M
French Language and Literature, B
Genetics, D
Health Education, MD
Health Informatics, M
Health Information/Medical Records
   Administration/Administrator, B
Health Promotion, D
Health Services Administration, MD
Health Teacher Education, B
History, BM
Industrial Hygiene, D
Information Science/Studies, MD
Kindergarten/PreSchool Education and Teaching, B
Management Information Systems and Services, B
Marketing/Marketing Management, B
Marriage and Family Therapy/Counseling, M
Materials Engineering, BMD
Materials Sciences, D
Maternal and Child Health, M
Mathematics, BMD
Mechanical Engineering, BMD
Medical Radiologic Technology/Science - Radiation
   Therapist, B
Microbiology, D
Music, B
Neurobiology and Neurophysiology, D
Neuroscience, D
Nuclear Medical Technology/Technologist, B
Nurse Anesthetist, M
Nursing, MD

Nursing - Registered Nurse Training, B
Nutritional Sciences, MDO
Occupational Therapy/Therapist, M
Optometry, P
Oral and Dental Sciences, M
Pathology/Experimental Pathology, D
Pharmacology, D
Philosophy, B
Physical Education Teaching and Coaching, BM
Physical Therapy/Therapist, D
Physician Assistant, B
Physics, BMD
Physiology, MD
Political Science and Government, B
Psychology, BMD
Public Administration, M
Public Health, MD
Rehabilitation Counseling, M
Rehabilitation Sciences, O
Respiratory Care Therapy/Therapist, B
School Psychology, M
Secondary Education and Teaching, BM
Social Sciences, B
Social Work, B
Sociology, BMD
Spanish Language and Literature, B
Special Education and Teaching, BM
Toxicology, D
Vision Science/Physiological Optics, MD
Visual and Performing Arts, B

THE UNIVERSITY OF ALABAMA IN HUNTSVILLE

Accounting, BMO
Aerospace, Aeronautical and Astronautical
   Engineering, M
Applied Mathematics, D
Art/Art Studies, General, B
Atmospheric Sciences and Meteorology, MD
Biological and Biomedical Sciences, M
Biology/Biological Sciences, B
BioTechnology, D
Business Administration and Management, B
Chemical Engineering, BMD
Chemistry, BM
Civil Engineering, BMD
Computer and Information Sciences, B
Computer Engineering, BMD
Computer Science, MDO
Electrical Engineering, MD
Electrical, Electronics and Communications
   Engineering, B
Elementary Education and Teaching, B
Engineering, B
Engineering and Applied Sciences, MD
English, MO
English as a Second Language, O
English Language and Literature, B
Environmental Engineering
   Technology/Environmental Technology, MD
Environmental Sciences, MD
Finance, B
Foreign Languages and Literatures, B
History, BM
Human Resources Management and Services, O
Industrial Engineering, B
Industrial/Management Engineering, MD
Management, MO
Management Information Systems and
   Services, BM
Marketing/Marketing Management, B
Materials Sciences, MD
Maternal/Child Health and Neonatal
   Nurse/Nursing, O
Mathematics, BMD
Mechanical Engineering, BMD
Music, B
Nursing, MO
Nursing - Registered Nurse Training, B
Operations Research, M
Optics/Optical Sciences, D
Philosophy, B
Physics, BMD
Political Science and Government, B
Psychology, BM
Public Affairs, M

Sociology, B
Software Engineering, MO
Speech and Rhetorical Studies, B
Technical and Business Writing, O
Vision Science/Physiological Optics, D

UNIVERSITY OF MOBILE

Accounting, B
Art/Art Studies, General, B
Athletic Training and Sports Medicine, B
Behavioral Sciences, B
Bible/Biblical Studies, B
Biological and Physical Sciences, B
Biology/Biological Sciences, B
Business Administration and Management, B
Business Administration, Management and
   Operations, M
Computer Science, B
Drama and Dramatics/Theatre Arts, B
Economics, B
Education, M
Elementary Education and Teaching, B
English Language and Literature, B
Environmental Studies, B
General Studies, AB
History, B
Humanities/Humanistic Studies, B
Information Science/Studies, B
Kindergarten/PreSchool Education and Teaching, B
Kinesiology and Exercise Science, B
Marriage and Family Therapy/Counseling, M
Mass Communication/Media Studies, B
Mathematics, B
Music, B
Nursing, M
Nursing - Registered Nurse Training, AB
Political Science and Government, B
Psychology, B
Religion/Religious Studies, BM
Secondary Education and Teaching, B
Social Sciences, B
Sociology, B
Theology and Religious Vocations, M

UNIVERSITY OF MONTEVALLO

Accounting, B
Art Teacher Education, B
Art/Art Studies, General, B
Audiology/Audiologist and Speech-Language
   Pathology/Pathologist, B
Biology/Biological Sciences, B
Broadcast Journalism, B
Business Administration and Management, B
Ceramic Arts and Ceramics, B
Chemistry, B
Commercial and Advertising Art, B
Communication Disorders, M
Consumer Merchandising/Retailing Management, B
Counselor Education/School Counseling and
   Guidance Services, M
Dietetics/Dieticians, B
Drama and Dramatics/Theatre Arts, B
Drawing, B
Early Childhood Education and Teaching, M
Education, MO
Educational Administration and Supervision, MO
Educational Leadership and Administration, O
Elementary Education and Teaching, BM
English, M
English Language and Literature, B
Family and Consumer Economics and Related
   Services, B
Family and Consumer Sciences/Home Economics
   Teacher Education, B
Family and Consumer Sciences/Human Sciences, B
Fashion Merchandising, B
Fine/Studio Arts, B
French Language and Literature, B
Health and Physical Education, B
History, B
Interior Design, B
Kindergarten/PreSchool Education and Teaching, B
Management Information Systems and Services, B
Marketing/Marketing Management, B
Mass Communication/Media Studies, B
Mathematics, B

Music, BM
Music Teacher Education, B
Photography, B
Piano and Organ, B
Political Science and Government, B
Pre-Dentistry Studies, B
Pre-Law Studies, B
Pre-Medicine/Pre-Medical Studies, B
Pre-Veterinary Studies, B
Printmaking, B
Psychology, B
Radio and Television, B
Sculpture, B
Secondary Education and Teaching, M
Social Sciences, B
Social Work, B
Sociology, B
Spanish Language and Literature, B
Speech and Rhetorical Studies, B
Voice and Opera, B

UNIVERSITY OF NORTH ALABAMA

Accounting, B
Biological and Biomedical Sciences, B
Biology/Biological Sciences, B
Business Administration and Management, B
Business Administration, Management and
   Operations, M
Business/Managerial Economics, B
Chemistry, B
Computer and Information Sciences, B
Counseling Psychology, B
Counselor Education/School Counseling and
   Guidance Services, M
Criminal Justice/Law Enforcement Administration, B
Criminology, M
Education, MO
Educational Administration and Supervision, M
Educational Leadership and Administration, O
Elementary Education and Teaching, BMO
English, M
English Language and Literature, B
Family and Consumer Sciences/Human Sciences, B
Finance, B
Fine Arts and Art Studies, B
Fine/Studio Arts, B
Foreign Languages and Literatures, B
General Studies, B
Geography, B
Geology/Earth Science, B
History, B
Kindergarten/PreSchool Education and Teaching, B
Management Information Systems and Services, B
Marine Biology and Biological Oceanography, B
Marketing/Marketing Management, B
Mathematics, B
Music, B
Nursing - Registered Nurse Training, B
Parks, Recreation, Leisure and Fitness Studies, B
Physical Sciences, B
Physics, B
Political Science and Government, B
Psychology, B
Secondary Education and Teaching, BM
Social Work, B
Sociology, B
Special Education and Teaching, BM
Speech and Rhetorical Studies, B
Teacher Education, Multiple Levels, B

UNIVERSITY OF SOUTH ALABAMA

Accounting, BM
Allied Health and Medical Assisting Services, MD
Allopathic Medicine, P
Anthropology, B
Art Education, M
Art/Art Studies, General, B
Atmospheric Sciences and Meteorology, B
Audiology/Audiologist and Speech-Language
   Pathology/Pathologist, B
Biochemistry, D
Biological and Biomedical Sciences, MD
Biology/Biological Sciences, B
Biomedical Sciences, B
Business Administration and Management, B

Business Administration, Management and
   Operations, M
Business Education, M
Business/Commerce, B
Cell Biology and Anatomy, D
Chemical Engineering, BM
Chemistry, B
Civil Engineering, B
Clinical Laboratory Science/Medical
   Technology/Technologist, B
Communication and Media Studies, M
Communication Disorders, MD
Communication Studies/Speech Communication
   and Rhetoric, B
Community Health Nursing, M
Computer and Information Sciences, B
Computer Engineering, B
Computer Science, M
Counselor Education/School Counseling and
   Guidance Services, MO
Criminal Justice/Law Enforcement Administration, B
Drama and Dramatics/Theatre Arts, B
Early Childhood Education and Teaching, BMO
E-Commerce/Electronic Commerce, B
Education, MDO
Education/Teaching of Individuals with Multiple
   Disabilities, M
Education/Teaching of the Gifted and Talented, M
Educational Administration and Supervision, MO
Educational Media/Instructional Technology, MD
Electrical Engineering, M
Electrical, Electronics and Communications
   Engineering, B
Elementary Education and Teaching, BMO
Engineering and Applied Sciences, M
English, M
English Language and Literature, B
Environmental and Occupational Health, M
Exercise and Sports Science, M
Finance, B
Foreign Languages and Literatures, B
Geography, B
Geology/Earth Science, B
Gerontology, O
Health Education, M
Health/Medical Preparatory Programs, B
History, BM
Immunology, D
Information Science/Studies, M
Leisure Studies, B
Liberal Arts and Sciences Studies and
   Humanities, B
Marine Sciences, MD
Marketing/Marketing Management, B
Maternal/Child Health and Neonatal
   Nurse/Nursing, M
Mathematics, M
Mathematics and Statistics, B
Mechanical Engineering, BM
Microbiology, D
Molecular Biology, D
Multi-/Interdisciplinary Studies, B
Music, B
Music Teacher Education, M
Neuroscience, D
Nursing, M
Nursing - Adult, M
Nursing - Registered Nurse Training, B
Occupational Therapy/Therapist, M
Parks, Recreation, Leisure and Fitness Studies, B
Pharmacology, D
Philosophy, B
Physical Education Teaching and Coaching, BMO
Physical Therapy/Therapist, D
Physician Assistant, M
Physics, B
Physiology, D
Political Science and Government, B
Psychology, BM
Public Administration, M
Radiologic Technology/Science - Radiographer, B
Reading Teacher Education, M
Respiratory Care Therapy/Therapist, B
Science Teacher Education/General Science
   Teacher Education, M
Secondary Education and Teaching, BMO

Sociology, BM
Special Education and Teaching, BMO
Therapeutic Recreation, M
Toxicology, M

THE UNIVERSITY OF WEST ALABAMA

Accounting, AB
Adult and Continuing Education and Teaching, M
Athletic Training and Sports Medicine, BM
Biology/Biological Sciences, B
Business Administration and Management, B
Chemistry, B
Counselor Education/School Counseling and
    Guidance Services, M
Early Childhood Education and Teaching, BM
Education, M
Educational Administration and Supervision, M
Educational Media/Instructional Technology, M
Elementary Education and Teaching, BM
Engineering Technology, B
English Education, M
English Language and Literature, B
Foundations and Philosophy of Education, M
History, B
Industrial Technology/Technician, B
Management Information Systems and Services, B
Marine Biology and Biological Oceanography, B
Mathematics, B
Mathematics Teacher Education, M
Nursing - Registered Nurse Training, A
Physical Education Teaching and Coaching, BM
Psychology, B
Science Teacher Education/General Science
    Teacher Education, M
Social Studies Teacher Education, M
Sociology, B
Special Education and Teaching, BM

VIRGINIA COLLEGE AT BIRMINGHAM

Accounting Technology/Technician and
    Bookkeeping, A
Administrative Assistant and Secretarial Science, A
Baking and Pastry Arts/Baker/Pastry Chef, A
Business Administration and Management, B
Business Administration, Management and
    Operations, M
Cooking and Related Culinary Arts, A
Culinary Arts/Chef Training, A
Diagnostic Medical Sonography/Sonographer and
    Ultrasound Technician, A
Drafting and Design Technology/Technician, A
Information Technology, B
Interior Design, AB
Legal Assistant/Paralegal, A
Massage Therapy/Therapeutic Massage, A
Medical Insurance Coding Specialist/Coder, A
Medical Insurance Specialist/Medical Biller, A
Medical Office Assistant/Specialist, A
Medical Office Computer Specialist/Assistant, A
Medical/Clinical Assistant, A
Office Management and Supervision, A
Securities Services Administration/Management, M
Surgical Technology/Technologist, A

VIRGINIA COLLEGE AT HUNTSVILLE

Administrative Assistant and Secretarial Science, A
Commercial and Advertising Art, A
Computer and Information Sciences, A
Computer Systems Networking and
    Telecommunications, A
Interior Design, A
Legal Administrative Assistant/Secretary, A
Medical/Clinical Assistant, A

WALLACE STATE COMMUNITY COLLEGE

Accounting, A
Administrative Assistant and Secretarial Science, A
Agriculture, A
Airline/Commercial/Professional Pilot and Flight
    Crew, A
Art Teacher Education, A
Automobile/Automotive Mechanics
    Technology/Technician, A
Avionics Maintenance Technology/Technician, A

Business Administration and Management, A
Business Teacher Education, A
Carpentry/Carpenter, A
Child Development, A
Clinical/Medical Laboratory Technician, A
Computer Programming/Programmer, A
Computer Science, A
Construction Engineering Technology/Technician, A
Cosmetology/Cosmetologist, A
Criminal Justice/Law Enforcement Administration, A
Criminal Justice/Police Science, A
Dental Assisting/Assistant, A
Dental Hygiene/Hygienist, A
Drafting and Design Technology/Technician, A
Education, A
Electrical, Electronic and Communications
    Engineering Technology/Technician, A
Elementary Education and Teaching, A
Emergency Medical Technology/Technician (EMT
    Paramedic), A
Engineering, A
Farm/Farm and Ranch Management, A
Fashion Merchandising, A
Finance, A
Fire Science/Firefighting, A
Health Information/Medical Records
    Administration/Administrator, A
Heating, Air Conditioning, Ventilation and
    Refrigeration Maintenance
    Technology/Technician, A
Horticultural Science, A
Industrial Radiologic Technology/Technician, A
Interior Design, A
Kindergarten/PreSchool Education and Teaching, A
Labor and Industrial Relations, A
Legal Administrative Assistant/Secretary, A
Legal Assistant/Paralegal, A
Liberal Arts and Sciences Studies and
    Humanities, A
Library Science, A
Licensed Practical/Vocational Nurse Training, A
Machine Tool Technology/Machinist, A
Marketing/Marketing Management, A
Medical Administrative Assistant/Secretary, A
Medical/Clinical Assistant, A
Mental Health/Rehabilitation, A
Music, A
Nursing - Registered Nurse Training, A
Occupational Safety and Health
    Technology/Technician, A
Occupational Therapy/Therapist, A
Physical Therapy/Therapist, A
Poultry Science, A
Real Estate, A
Religion/Religious Studies, A
Respiratory Care Therapy/Therapist, A
Special Products Marketing Operations, A
Welding Technology/Welder, A

Alaska

ALASKA BIBLE COLLEGE

Bible/Biblical Studies, AB

ALASKA PACIFIC UNIVERSITY

Accounting and Business/Management, B
Business Administration and Management, AB
Business Administration, Management and
    Operations, M
Counseling Psychology, M
Education, M
Elementary Education and Teaching, ABM
Environmental Sciences, BM
Finance and Banking, M
Health Services Administration, M
Health/Health Care Administration/Management, B
Human Services, B
Interdisciplinary Studies, M
Junior High/Intermediate/Middle School Education
    and Teaching, B
Liberal Arts and Sciences Studies and
    Humanities, B
Marine Biology and Biological Oceanography, B
Middle School Education, M

Natural Resources Management/Development and
    Policy, B
Parks, Recreation, Leisure and Fitness Studies, B
Psychology, B
Telecommunications Management, M

CHARTER COLLEGE

Accounting, A
Business Administration and Management, A
Computer Science, A
Computer Systems Networking and
    Telecommunications, A
Computer Technology/Computer Systems
    Technology, A
Medical/Clinical Assistant, A

ILISAGVIK COLLEGE

Accounting Technology/Technician and
    Bookkeeping, A
Business/Commerce, A
Construction Trades, A
General Studies, A
Management Information Systems and Services, A

SHELDON JACKSON COLLEGE

Business Administration and Management, AB
Elementary Education and Teaching, B
Environmental Sciences, B
General Studies, B
Human Services, AB
Liberal Arts and Sciences Studies and
    Humanities, B
Multi-/Interdisciplinary Studies, B
Parks, Recreation, Leisure and Fitness Studies, B
Secondary Education and Teaching, B
Teacher Education and Professional
    Development, Specific Levels and Methods, A

UNIVERSITY OF ALASKA ANCHORAGE

Accounting, AB
Adult and Continuing Education and Teaching, M
Air Traffic Controller, A
Airframe Mechanics and Aircraft Maintenance
    Technology/Technician, A
Airline/Commercial/Professional Pilot and Flight
    Crew, A
Anthropology, B
Architectural Engineering Technology/Technician, A
Art/Art Studies, General, A
Automobile/Automotive Mechanics
    Technology/Technician, A
Aviation/Airway Management and Operations, A
Avionics Maintenance Technology/Technician, A
Biological and Biomedical Sciences, M
Biological and Physical Sciences, B
Business Administration and Management, AB
Business Administration, Management and
    Operations, M
Business Machine Repairer, A
Business/Managerial Economics, B
Chemistry, B
Civil Engineering, BM
Clinical Psychology, M
Clinical/Medical Laboratory Technician, A
Computer and Information Sciences, A
Computer Science, B
Counselor Education/School Counseling and
    Guidance Services, M
Criminal Justice/Law Enforcement Administration, B
Culinary Arts/Chef Training, A
Dental Assisting/Assistant, A
Dental Hygiene/Hygienist, A
Diesel Mechanics Technology/Technician, A
Drafting and Design Technology/Technician, A
Drama and Dramatics/Theatre Arts, B
Economics, B
Education, BM
Educational Leadership and Administration, M
Electrical, Electronic and Communications
    Engineering Technology/Technician, A
Elementary Education and Teaching, B
Emergency Medical Technology/Technician (EMT
    Paramedic), A
Engineering and Applied Sciences, M
Engineering Management, M
Engineering Technology, A

English, M
English Language and Literature, B
Environmental Sciences, M
Family and Consumer Sciences/Human Sciences, A
Finance, B
Fire Science/Firefighting, A
Foreign Languages and Literatures, B
Heating, Air Conditioning, Ventilation and
   Refrigeration Maintenance
   Technology/Technician, A
Heavy Equipment Maintenance
   Technology/Technician, A
History, B
Human Services, A
Information Science/Studies, A
Interdisciplinary Studies, BM
Journalism, B
Kindergarten/PreSchool Education and Teaching, B
Legal Assistant/Paralegal, A
Management Information Systems and Services, B
Marketing/Marketing Management, B
Mass Communication/Media Studies, B
Mathematics, B
Medical/Clinical Assistant, A
Music, B
Music Performance, B
Music Teacher Education, B
Natural Sciences, B
Nursing, M
Nursing - Registered Nurse Training, AB
Petroleum Technology/Technician, A
Physical Education Teaching and Coaching, B
Political Science and Government, B
Psychology, BM
Public Administration, M
Public Health (MPH, DPH), B
Science, Technology and Society, B
Secondary Education and Teaching, B
Social Work, BM
Sociology, B
Special Education and Teaching, M
Substance Abuse/Addiction Counseling, O
Survey Technology/Surveying, AB
Vocational and Technical Education, M
Welding Technology/Welder, A
Writing, M

UNIVERSITY OF ALASKA ANCHORAGE, KENAI PENINSULA COLLEGE

Administrative Assistant and Secretarial Science, A
Business Administration and Management, A
Electrical, Electronic and Communications
   Engineering Technology/Technician, A
Instrumentation Technology/Technician, A
Liberal Arts and Sciences Studies and
   Humanities, A
Machine Tool Technology/Machinist, A
Petroleum Technology/Technician, A

UNIVERSITY OF ALASKA ANCHORAGE, KODIAK COLLEGE

Administrative Assistant and Secretarial Science, A
Business Administration and Management, A
Liberal Arts and Sciences Studies and
   Humanities, A

UNIVERSITY OF ALASKA ANCHORAGE, MATANUSKA-SUSITNA COLLEGE

Accounting, A
Administrative Assistant and Secretarial Science, A
Business Administration and Management, A
Electrical, Electronic and Communications
   Engineering Technology/Technician, A
Fire Science/Firefighting, A
Heating, Air Conditioning, Ventilation and
   Refrigeration Maintenance
   Technology/Technician, A
Human Services, A

Liberal Arts and Sciences Studies and
   Humanities, A

UNIVERSITY OF ALASKA FAIRBANKS

Accounting, B
Accounting Technology/Technician and
   Bookkeeping, A
Administrative Assistant and Secretarial Science, A
Airframe Mechanics and Aircraft Maintenance
   Technology/Technician, A
American Indian/Native American Studies, B
Anthropology, BMD
Applied Mathematics, B
Area Studies, B
Art/Art Studies, General, B
Astrophysics, MD
Atmospheric Sciences and Meteorology, MD
Aviation/Airway Management and Operations, A
Biochemistry, MD
Biological and Biomedical Sciences, MD
Biological and Physical Sciences, B
Biology/Biological Sciences, B
Business Administration and Management, AB
Business Administration, Management and
   Operations, M
Chemistry, BMD
Child Care Provider/Assistant, A
Civil Engineering, BMD
Clinical Psychology, D
Communication and Media Studies, M
Communication Studies/Speech Communication
   and Rhetoric, B
Community Organization and Advocacy, B
Community Psychology, D
Computer and Information Sciences, B
Computer Engineering, MD
Computer Science, BM
Corporate and Organizational Communication, M
Corrections and Criminal Justice, B
Counselor Education/School Counseling and
   Guidance Services, M
Criminology, M
Culinary Arts/Chef Training, A
Cultural Studies, M
Curriculum and Instruction, M
Drama and Dramatics/Theatre Arts, B
Economics, BM
Education, BM
Electrical Engineering, MD
Electrical, Electronics and Communications
   Engineering, B
Elementary Education and Teaching, B
Engineering and Applied Sciences, D
Engineering Management, M
English, M
English Education, M
English Language and Literature, B
Environmental Engineering
   Technology/Environmental Technology, MD
Environmental Sciences, M
Ethnomusicology, M
Finance and Banking, M
Fine Arts and Art Studies, M
Fire Science/Firefighting, A
Fish, Game and Wildlife Management, MD
Fishing and Fisheries Sciences and Management, B
Foreign Languages and Literatures, B
Foreign Languages, Literatures, and Linguistics, A
General Office Occupations and Clerical Services, A
Geography, B
Geological Engineering, MO
Geological/Geophysical Engineering, B
Geology/Earth Science, BMD
Geophysics and Seismology, MD
History, B
Human Resources Management/Personnel
   Administration, B
Industrial Engineering, B
Industrial Technology/Technician, A
Interdisciplinary Studies, MD
Japanese Language and Literature, B
Journalism, BM
Kindergarten/PreSchool Education and Teaching, B
Legal Assistant/Paralegal, A
Liberal Arts and Sciences Studies and
   Humanities, A

Limnology, MD
Linguistics, BM
Management, M
Marine Biology and Biological Oceanography, MD
Marine Sciences, MD
Mathematics, BMD
Mechanical Engineering, BMD
Medical/Clinical Assistant, A
Mental and Social Health Services and Allied
   Professions, A
Mineral/Mining Engineering, MO
Mining and Petroleum Technologies/Technicians, B
Multi-/Interdisciplinary Studies, AB
Multilingual and Multicultural Education, M
Music, BM
Music History, Literature, and Theory, M
Music Teacher Education, M
Music Theory and Composition, M
Natural Resources and Conservation, B
Natural Resources Management/Development and
   Policy, AM
Northern Studies, M
Oceanography, Chemical and Physical, MD
Performance, M
Petroleum Engineering, BM
Philosophy, B
Physics, BMD
Political Science and Government, B
Psychology, BD
Public Health (MPH, DPH), A
Rural Planning and Studies, M
Russian Studies, B
Social Work, B
Sociology, B
Software Engineering, M
Speech and Rhetorical Studies, B
Statistics, M
Technical Theatre/Theatre Design and
   Technology, B
Vehicle Maintenance and Repair Technologies, A
Wildlife and Wildlands Science and Management, B
Writing, M

UNIVERSITY OF ALASKA, PRINCE WILLIAM SOUND COMMUNITY COLLEGE

Administrative Assistant and Secretarial Science, A
Broadcast Journalism, A
Business Administration and Management, A
Liberal Arts and Sciences Studies and
   Humanities, A
Mental Health/Rehabilitation, A

UNIVERSITY OF ALASKA SOUTHEAST

Administrative Assistant and Secretarial Science, A
Biology/Biological Sciences, B
Business Administration and Management, AB
Business Administration, Management and
   Operations, M
Construction Trades, A
Consumer Economics, A
Early Childhood Education and Teaching, M
Education, BM
Educational Media/Instructional Technology, M
Elementary Education and Teaching, M
Engineering-Related Technologies, A
English Language and Literature, B
General Studies, AB
Health Professions and Related Clinical Sciences, A
History, B
Humanities/Humanistic Studies, AB
Law and Legal Studies, A
Liberal Arts and Sciences Studies and
   Humanities, AB
Mathematics, B
Natural Resources and Conservation, AB
Public Administration, M
Secondary Education and Teaching, M
Social Sciences, B

UNIVERSITY OF ALASKA SOUTHEAST, KETCHIKAN CAMPUS

Administrative Assistant and Secretarial Science, A
Business Administration and Management, A

Liberal Arts and Sciences Studies and
Humanities, A
Tourism and Travel Services Management, A

UNIVERSITY OF ALASKA SOUTHEAST, SITKA CAMPUS

Business Administration and Management, A
Computer and Information Sciences, A
Computer Engineering Technology/Technician, A
Computer Systems Analysis/Analyst, A
Environmental Engineering
Technology/Environmental Technology, A
Health/Health Care Administration/Management, A
Liberal Arts and Sciences Studies and
Humanities, A
Medical/Clinical Assistant, A
Water Quality and Wastewater Treatment
Management and Recycling
Technology/Technician, A

Arizona

AMERICAN INDIAN COLLEGE OF THE ASSEMBLIES OF GOD, INC.

Business Administration and Management, A
Elementary Education and Teaching, B
Pastoral Studies/Counseling, B

APOLLO COLLEGE-PHOENIX, INC.

Clinical/Medical Laboratory Technician, A
Occupational Therapy/Therapist, A
Radiologic Technology/Science - Radiographer, A
Respiratory Care Therapy/Therapist, A

APOLLO COLLEGE-TRI-CITY, INC.

Respiratory Care Therapy/Therapist, A

APOLLO COLLEGE-TUCSON, INC.

Clinical/Medical Laboratory Technician, A
Occupational Therapist Assistant, A

APOLLO COLLEGE-WESTSIDE, INC.

Hospital and Health Care Facilities
Administration/Management, A
Medical Radiologic Technology/Science - Radiation
Therapist, A
Occupational Therapist Assistant, A
Physical Therapist Assistant, A

ARGOSY UNIVERSITY/PHOENIX

Business Administration, Management and
Operations, MD
Clinical Psychology, MDO
Counseling Psychology, M
Curriculum and Instruction, DO
Education, DO
Educational Leadership and Administration, DO
Forensic Psychology, M
International Business/Trade/Commerce, D
Psychology, BMDO
School Psychology, MD
Sport Psychology, MDO

ARIZONA AUTOMOTIVE INSTITUTE

Automobile/Automotive Mechanics
Technology/Technician, A
Automotive Engineering Technology/Technician, A
Diesel Mechanics Technology/Technician, A

ARIZONA STATE UNIVERSITY

Accounting, BMDO
Aeronautics/Aviation/Aerospace Science and
Technology, A
Aerospace, Aeronautical and Astronautical
Engineering, MD
African-American/Black Studies, B
American Indian/Native American Studies, B
Animal Behavior and Ethology, MD
Anthropology, BMDO
Applied Mathematics, BMD
Architectural History and Criticism, D
Architecture, BMO
Art/Art Studies, General, B
Astronomy, MD

Biochemistry, BMD
Bioengineering, MD
Biological and Biomedical Sciences, BMD
Biology/Biological Sciences, B
Biomedical/Medical Engineering, B
Biostatistics, MD
Botany/Plant Biology, B
Building Science, M
Business Administration and Management, B
Business Administration, Management and
Operations, MDO
Cell Biology and Anatomy, MD
Chemical Engineering, BMD
Chemistry, BMD
Child and Family Studies, D
City/Urban, Community and Regional Planning, B
Civil Engineering, BMD
Clinical Laboratory Science/Medical
Technology/Technologist, B
Clinical Psychology, D
Cognitive Sciences, D
Communication and Media Studies, MD
Communication Disorders, BMD
Communication Studies/Speech Communication
and Rhetoric, B
Computational Biology, M
Computational Sciences, MD
Computer Engineering, B
Computer Science, BMD
Conservation Biology, BMD
Construction Engineering, M
Construction Engineering and Management, M
Counseling Psychology, D
Counselor Education/School Counseling and
Guidance Services, M
Criminal Justice/Safety Studies, B
Curriculum and Instruction, MD
Dance, BM
Demography and Population Studies, MD
Design and Applied Arts, M
Developmental Biology and Embryology, MD
Developmental Psychology, D
Drama and Dramatics/Theatre Arts, B
East Asian
Languages, Literatures, and Linguistics, B
Ecology, MD
Economics, BMDO
Education, MD
Educational Administration and Supervision, MD
Educational Leadership and Administration, D
Educational Media/Instructional Technology, MD
Educational Psychology, MD
Electrical Engineering, MD
Electrical, Electronics and Communications
Engineering, B
Elementary Education and Teaching, B
Engineering and Applied Sciences, MDO
English, MD
English as a Second Language, M
English Language and Literature, B
Environmental Design/Architecture, D
Evolutionary Biology, MD
Exercise and Sports Science, D
Family Resource Management Studies, B
Film/Cinema Studies, B
Finance, B
Finance and Banking, D
Fine Arts and Art Studies, M
Foundations and Philosophy of Education, M
French Language and Literature, BM
Genetics, MD
Geography, BMD
Geological Engineering, MD
Geology/Earth Science, B
Geosciences, MD
German Language and Literature, BM
Graphic Design, B
Health Services Administration, MO
Health Services Research, D
Higher Education/Higher Education
Administration, MD
Hispanic-American, Puerto Rican, and Mexican-
American/Chicano Studies, B
History, BMD
History of Science and Technology, MD
Human Development, MD

Humanities/Humanistic Studies, M
Industrial Design, B
Industrial Engineering, B
Industrial/Management Engineering, MDO
Interdisciplinary Studies, B
Interior Architecture, B
International/Global Studies, B
Italian Language and Literature, B
Journalism, BM
Kindergarten/PreSchool Education and Teaching, B
Kinesiology and Exercise Science, B
Kinesiology and Movement Studies, M
Landscape Architecture, BM
Latin American Studies, MD
Law and Legal Studies, PO
Legal and Justice Studies, MDO
Liberal Arts and Sciences Studies and
Humanities, B
Logistics and Materials Management, D
Management, D
Management Information Systems and
Services, BMDO
Marketing, D
Marketing/Marketing Management, B
Mass Communication/Media Studies, B
Materials Engineering, BMD
Materials Sciences, MD
Mathematics, BMD
Mechanical Engineering, BMD
Medical Microbiology and Bacteriology, B
Microbiology, MD
Molecular Biology, B
Multi-/Interdisciplinary Studies, B
Music, BMD
Music Performance, B
Music Teacher Education, B
Music Theory and Composition, B
Music Therapy/Therapist, B
Neuroscience, MD
Nursing, MO
Nursing - Registered Nurse Training, B
Parks, Recreation, Leisure and Fitness Studies, B
Philosophy, BMD
Physics, BMD
Physiology, MD
Political Science and Government, BMD
Psychology, BD
Public Affairs, MD
Public History, M
Purchasing, Procurement/Acquisitions and
Contracts Management, B
Real Estate, B
Recreation and Park Management, M
Religion/Religious Studies, BMD
Russian Language and Literature, B
Science Teacher Education/General Science
Teacher Education, MD
Secondary Education and Teaching, B
Social Psychology, D
Social Sciences, MDO
Social Work, BMD
Sociology, BMD
Spanish Language and Literature, BMD
Special Education and Teaching, BM
Speech and Interpersonal Communication, M
Statistics, M
Theater, MD
Transportation/Transportation Management, O
Urban and Regional Planning, M
Urban Studies/Affairs, B
Women's Studies, B
Writing, M

ARIZONA STATE UNIVERSITY AT THE POLYTECHNIC CAMPUS

Aeronautics/Aviation/Aerospace Science and
Technology, B
Aerospace, Aeronautical and Astronautical
Engineering, M
Agribusiness, M
Agricultural Business and Management, B
Biological and Biomedical Sciences, M
Biology/Biological Sciences, B
Business Administration and Management, B
Communication, Journalism and Related
Programs, B

Computer Engineering, M
Computer Engineering Technology/Technician, B
Computer Science, M
Computer Systems Analysis/Analyst, B
Electrical Engineering, M
Electrical/Electronics Equipment Installation and
  Repair, B
Elementary Education and Teaching, B
Engineering, B
Engineering and Applied Sciences, M
Environmental Policy and Resource
  Management, M
Environmental/Environmental Health Engineering, B
Exercise and Sports Science, M
Foods, Nutrition, and Wellness Studies, B
General Studies, B
Graphic Communications, B
Health and Physical Education/Fitness, B
Health Professions and Related Clinical Sciences, B
Industrial Technology/Technician, B
Information Science/Studies, M
Interdisciplinary Studies, B
Management Information Systems and Services, M
Manufacturing Engineering, M
Manufacturing Technology/Technician, B
Mechanical Engineering, M
Mechanical Engineering/Mechanical
  Technology/Technician, B
Multi-/Interdisciplinary Studies, B
Nutritional Sciences, M
Psychology, B
Real Estate, B
Science Technologies/Technicians, B
Secondary Education and Teaching, B
Transportation/Transportation Management, M

ARIZONA STATE UNIVERSITY WEST

Accounting, BO
American/United States Studies/Civilization, B
Biology/Biological Sciences, B
Business Administration, Management and
  Operations, M
Communication and Media Studies, MO
Communication Studies/Speech Communication
  and Rhetoric, B
Computer and Information Sciences, B
Criminal Justice/Law Enforcement Administration, B
Criminology, M
Education, MO
Educational Administration and Supervision, M
Elementary Education and Teaching, BMO
English Language and Literature, B
Gerontology, O
History, B
Interdisciplinary Studies, BM
International Business/Trade/Commerce, B
Multi-/Interdisciplinary Studies, B
Parks, Recreation, Leisure and Fitness Studies, B
Political Science and Government, B
Psychology, B
Secondary Education and Teaching, BMO
Social Sciences, B
Social Work, BM
Sociology, B
Spanish Language and Literature, B
Special Education and Teaching, BM
Visual and Performing Arts, B
Women's Studies, B

ARIZONA WESTERN COLLEGE

Administrative Assistant and Secretarial Science, A
Agricultural Business and Management, A
Agriculture, A
Art/Art Studies, General, A
Automobile/Automotive Mechanics
  Technology/Technician, A
Biological and Physical Sciences, A
Biology/Biological Sciences, A
Broadcast Journalism, A
Business Administration and Management, A
Chemistry, A
Computer Science, A
Criminal Justice/Law Enforcement Administration, A
Criminal Justice/Police Science, A
Developmental and Child Psychology, A
Drafting and Design Technology/Technician, A

Drama and Dramatics/Theatre Arts, A
Education, A
Electrical, Electronic and Communications
  Engineering Technology/Technician, A
Engineering Technology, A
English Language and Literature, A
Environmental Studies, A
Family and Consumer Economics and Related
  Services, A
Fire Science/Firefighting, A
Geology/Earth Science, A
Heating, Air Conditioning, Ventilation and
  Refrigeration Maintenance
  Technology/Technician, A
Hospitality Administration/Management, A
Human Services, A
Information Science/Studies, A
Licensed Practical/Vocational Nurse Training, A
Marketing/Marketing Management, A
Massage Therapy/Therapeutic Massage, A
Mathematics, A
Music, A
Nursing - Registered Nurse Training, A
Physical Education Teaching and Coaching, A
Physics, A
Public Health (MPH, DPH), A
Radiologic Technology/Science - Radiographer, A
Social Sciences, A
Spanish Language and Literature, A
Water Quality and Wastewater Treatment
  Management and Recycling
  Technology/Technician, A
Welding Technology/Welder, A

THE ART CENTER DESIGN COLLEGE

Animation, Interactive Technology, Video Graphics
  and Special Effects, B
Commercial and Advertising Art, A
Fine/Studio Arts, B
Graphic Design, B
Illustration, B
Interior Design, AB
Photography, B

THE ART INSTITUTE OF PHOENIX

Advertising, B
Animation, Interactive Technology, Video Graphics
  and Special Effects, B
Culinary Arts/Chef Training, AB
Fashion Merchandising, B
Graphic Design, AB
Interior Design, B
Web Page, Digital/Multimedia and Information
  Resources Design, B

THE BRYMAN SCHOOL

Dental Assisting/Assistant, A
Hospital and Health Care Facilities
  Administration/Management, A
Medical Radiologic Technology/Science - Radiation
  Therapist, A
Medical/Clinical Assistant, A
Surgical Technology/Technologist, A

CENTRAL ARIZONA COLLEGE

Accounting, A
Administrative Assistant and Secretarial Science, A
Agriculture, A
Automobile/Automotive Mechanics
  Technology/Technician, A
Business Administration and Management, A
Child Development, A
Civil Engineering Technology/Technician, A
Computer and Information Sciences, A
Computer Science, A
Corrections, A
Criminal Justice/Law Enforcement Administration, A
Dietetics/Dieticians, A
Emergency Medical Technology/Technician (EMT
  Paramedic), A
Engineering, A
Health Aide, A
Hotel/Motel Administration/Management, A
Industrial Technology/Technician, A
Kindergarten/PreSchool Education and Teaching, A
Legal Administrative Assistant/Secretary, A

Liberal Arts and Sciences Studies and
  Humanities, A
Licensed Practical/Vocational Nurse Training, A
Marketing/Marketing Management, A
Materials Sciences, A
Medical Administrative Assistant/Secretary, A
Medical Transcription/Transcriptionist, A
Nursing - Registered Nurse Training, A

CHANDLER-GILBERT COMMUNITY COLLEGE

Accounting, A
Airframe Mechanics and Aircraft Maintenance
  Technology/Technician, A
Avionics Maintenance Technology/Technician, A
Business Administration and Management, A
Computer Engineering Technology/Technician, A
Liberal Arts and Sciences Studies and
  Humanities, A
Management Information Systems and Services, A

CHAPARRAL COLLEGE

Accounting, AB
Administrative Assistant and Secretarial Science, A
Business Administration and Management, AB
Computer Systems Networking and
  Telecommunications, AB
Criminal Justice/Safety Studies, AB

COCHISE COLLEGE (DOUGLAS)

Administrative Assistant and Secretarial Science, A
Agricultural Business and Management, A
Airframe Mechanics and Aircraft Maintenance
  Technology/Technician, A
Airline/Commercial/Professional Pilot and Flight
  Crew, A
Anthropology, A
Art/Art Studies, General, A
Avionics Maintenance Technology/Technician, A
Biology/Biological Sciences, A
Business Administration and Management, A
Chemistry, A
Communication Studies/Speech Communication
  and Rhetoric, A
Computer and Information Systems Security, A
Computer Programming/Programmer, A
Computer Science, A
Computer Systems Networking and
  Telecommunications, A
Criminal Justice/Police Science, A
Culinary Arts/Chef Training, A
Data Processing and Data Processing
  Technology/Technician, A
Early Childhood Education and Teaching, A
Economics, A
Education, A
Electrical, Electronic and Communications
  Engineering Technology/Technician, A
Emergency Medical Technology/Technician (EMT
  Paramedic), A
English Language and Literature, A
Family Psychology, A
Fire Science/Firefighting, A
Foreign Languages and Literatures, A
General Studies, A
Health and Physical Education, A
Health Services/Allied Health/Health Sciences, A
History, A
Hospitality Administration/Management, A
Human Services, A
Humanities/Humanistic Studies, A
Information Science/Studies, A
Journalism, A
Language Interpretation and Translation, A
Liberal Arts and Sciences Studies and
  Humanities, A
Manufacturing Engineering, A
Mathematics, A
Military Technologies, A
Nursing - Registered Nurse Training, A
Physical Education Teaching and Coaching, A
Political Science and Government, A
Pre-Nursing Studies, A
Psychology, A
Social Work, A
Sociology, A

Welding Technology/Welder, A

COCHISE COLLEGE (SIERRA VISTA)

Administrative Assistant and Secretarial Science, A
Anthropology, A
Art/Art Studies, General, A
Behavioral Sciences, A
Biology/Biological Sciences, A
Business Administration and Management, A
Chemistry, A
Computer Programming/Programmer, A
Computer Science, A
Criminal Justice/Law Enforcement Administration, A
Criminal Justice/Police Science, A
Drafting and Design Technology/Technician, A
Education, A
Electrical, Electronic and Communications
   Engineering Technology/Technician, A
English Language and Literature, A
Film/Cinema Studies, A
Fire Science/Firefighting, A
History, A
Hotel/Motel Administration/Management, A
Information Science/Studies, A
International Relations and Affairs, A
Journalism, A
Legal Administrative Assistant/Secretary, A
Liberal Arts and Sciences Studies and
   Humanities, A
Mass Communication/Media Studies, A
Medical Administrative Assistant/Secretary, A
Nursing - Registered Nurse Training, A
Physical Education Teaching and Coaching, A
Political Science and Government, A
Psychology, A
Social Sciences, A
Social Work, A
Teacher Assistant/Aide, A
Welding Technology/Welder, A

COCONINO COMMUNITY COLLEGE

Accounting, A
Biological and Physical Sciences, A
Business Administration and Management, A
Criminal Justice/Law Enforcement Administration, A
Fire Science/Firefighting, A
Information Science/Studies, A
Liberal Arts and Sciences Studies and
   Humanities, A

COLLINS COLLEGE: A SCHOOL OF DESIGN AND TECHNOLOGY

Cinematography and Film/Video Production, A
Commercial and Advertising Art, A
Computer Technology/Computer Systems
   Technology, A
Design and Visual Communications, AB
Graphic Design, B
Interior Design, B

DEVRY UNIVERSITY (MESA)

Business Administration, Management and
   Operations, M

DEVRY UNIVERSITY (PHOENIX)

Biomedical Technology/Technician, B
Business Administration, Management and
   Operations, BM
Computer and Information Sciences, B
Computer Engineering Technology/Technician, B
Computer Programming, Specific Applications, B
Computer Systems Networking and
   Telecommunications, B
Electrical, Electronic and Communications
   Engineering Technology/Technician, AB
Information Science/Studies, B
Medical Informatics, B
Operations Management and Supervision, B

DINÉ COLLEGE

Administrative Assistant and Secretarial Science, A
American Indian/Native American Studies, A
Art/Art Studies, General, A
Business Administration and Management, A
Computer Science, A

Elementary Education and Teaching, A
Geology/Earth Science, A
Information Science/Studies, A
Kinesiology and Exercise Science, A
Liberal Arts and Sciences Studies and
   Humanities, A
Pre-Engineering, A
Public Health (MPH, DPH), A
Social Sciences, A
Social Work, A

EASTERN ARIZONA COLLEGE

Agribusiness, A
Agriculture, A
Anthropology, A
Art Teacher Education, A
Art/Art Studies, General, A
Automobile/Automotive Mechanics
   Technology/Technician, A
Biology/Biological Sciences, A
Business Administration and Management, A
Business Operations Support and Secretarial
   Services, A
Business Teacher Education, A
Business, Management, Marketing, and Related
   Support Services, A
Chemistry, A
Child Care Provider/Assistant, A
Civil Engineering Technology/Technician, A
Commercial and Advertising Art, A
Corrections, A
Criminal Justice/Law Enforcement Administration, A
Criminal Justice/Police Science, A
Data Entry/Microcomputer Applications, A
Drafting and Design Technology/Technician, A
Drama and Dramatics/Theatre Arts, A
Elementary Education and Teaching, A
Emergency Medical Technology/Technician (EMT
   Paramedic), A
English Language and Literature, A
Entrepreneurship/Entrepreneurial Studies, A
Foreign Languages and Literatures, A
Forestry, A
Geology/Earth Science, A
Health and Physical Education, A
Health/Medical Preparatory Programs, A
History, A
Information Science/Studies, A
Liberal Arts and Sciences Studies and
   Humanities, A
Machine Shop Technology/Assistant, A
Management Information Systems and Services, A
Mathematics, A
Mining Technology/Technician, A
Music, A
Nursing - Registered Nurse Training, A
Physics, A
Political Science and Government, A
Pre-Law Studies, A
Pre-Medicine/Pre-Medical Studies, A
Pre-Pharmacy Studies, A
Psychology, A
Secondary Education and Teaching, A
Sociology, A
Technology Teacher Education/Industrial Arts
   Teacher Education, A
Welding Technology/Welder, A
Wildlife Biology, A

EMBRY-RIDDLE AERONAUTICAL UNIVERSITY

Aeronautics/Aviation/Aerospace Science and
   Technology, B
Aerospace, Aeronautical and Astronautical
   Engineering, B
Airline/Commercial/Professional Pilot and Flight
   Crew, B
Atmospheric Sciences and Meteorology, B
Business Administration, Management and
   Operations, B
Computer Engineering, B
Computer Software Engineering, B
Electrical, Electronics and Communications
   Engineering, B
International Relations and Affairs, B
Physics, B

Safety Engineering, M
Science, Technology and Society, B

ESTRELLA MOUNTAIN COMMUNITY COLLEGE

General Studies, A
Liberal Arts and Sciences Studies and
   Humanities, A

EVEREST COLLEGE

Accounting, A
Business/Commerce, A
Criminal Justice/Police Science, AB
Legal Assistant/Paralegal, A
Medical/Clinical Assistant, A

GATEWAY COMMUNITY COLLEGE

Accounting, A
Aeronautical/Aerospace Engineering
   Technology/Technician, A
Automobile/Automotive Mechanics
   Technology/Technician, A
Business/Commerce, A
Carpentry/Carpenter, A
Computer and Information Sciences, A
Computer Programming, Specific Applications, A
Computer
   Programming, Vendor/Product Certification, A
Construction Engineering Technology/Technician, A
Court Reporting/Court Reporter, A
Diagnostic Medical Sonography/Sonographer and
   Ultrasound Technician, A
Economics, A
Education, A
Electromechanical Technology/Electromechanical
   Engineering Technology, A
Finance, A
General Office Occupations and Clerical Services, A
General Studies, A
Health/Health Care Administration/Management, A
Heating, Air Conditioning and Refrigeration
   Technology/Technician, A
Heating, Air Conditioning, Ventilation and
   Refrigeration Maintenance
   Technology/Technician, A
Industrial Technology/Technician, A
Information Technology, A
International Business/Trade/Commerce, A
Liberal Arts and Sciences Studies and
   Humanities, A
Management Science, A
Materials Sciences, A
Medical Radiologic Technology/Science - Radiation
   Therapist, A
Nuclear Medical Technology/Technologist, A
Nursing - Registered Nurse Training, A
Occupational Safety and Health
   Technology/Technician, A
Physical Therapist Assistant, A
Pipefitting/Pipefitter and Sprinkler Fitter, A
Psychology, A
Real Estate, A
Respiratory Care Therapy/Therapist, A
Social Work, A
Surgical Technology/Technologist, A
System Administration/Administrator, A

GLENDALE COMMUNITY COLLEGE

Accounting Technology/Technician and
   Bookkeeping, A
Administrative Assistant and Secretarial Science, A
Agribusiness, A
Applied Horticulture/Horticultural Operations, A
Architectural Drafting and Architectural
   CAD/CADD, A
Automobile/Automotive Mechanics
   Technology/Technician, A
Business Administration and Management, A
Business/Commerce, A
Cinematography and Film/Video Production, A
Commercial and Advertising Art, A
Computer Systems Networking and
   Telecommunications, A
Consumer Merchandising/Retailing Management, A
Criminal Justice/Law Enforcement Administration, A

Criminal Justice/Police Science, A
Electrical, Electronic and Communications
  Engineering Technology/Technician, A
Emergency Medical Technology/Technician (EMT
  Paramedic), A
Engineering Technology, A
Fire Science/Firefighting, A
Human Services, A
Industrial Technology/Technician, A
Kindergarten/PreSchool Education and Teaching, A
Landscaping and Groundskeeping, A
Liberal Arts and Sciences Studies and
  Humanities, A
Management Information Systems and Services, A
Nurse/Nursing Assistant/Aide and Patient Care
  Assistant, A
Nursing - Registered Nurse Training, A
Public Relations/Image Management, A
Real Estate, A

GRAND CANYON UNIVERSITY

Accounting, B
Art Teacher Education, B
Art/Art Studies, General, B
Athletic Training and Sports Medicine, B
Bible/Biblical Studies, B
Biology/Biological Sciences, B
Business Administration and Management, B
Business Administration, Management and
  Operations, M
Business Teacher Education, B
Business/Managerial Economics, B
Chemistry, B
Commercial and Advertising Art, B
Comparative Literature, B
Criminal Justice/Law Enforcement Administration, B
Divinity/Ministry (BD, MDiv.), B
Drama and Dramatics/Theatre Arts, B
Economics, B
Education, M
Elementary Education and Teaching, BM
English as a Second Language, M
English Language and Literature, B
Environmental Biology, B
Finance, B
Fine/Studio Arts, B
History, B
Human Resources Management/Personnel
  Administration, B
International Business/Trade/Commerce, B
International Relations and Affairs, B
Kinesiology and Exercise Science, B
Liberal Arts and Sciences Studies and
  Humanities, B
Marketing/Marketing Management, B
Mass Communication/Media Studies, B
Mathematics, B
Music, B
Music Management and Merchandising, B
Music Teacher Education, B
Nursing - Registered Nurse Training, B
Physical Education Teaching and Coaching, B
Physical Sciences, B
Piano and Organ, B
Political Science and Government, B
Pre-Dentistry Studies, B
Pre-Law Studies, B
Pre-Medicine/Pre-Medical Studies, B
Pre-Veterinary Studies, B
Psychology, B
Reading Teacher Education, M
Religion/Religious Studies, B
Religious/Sacred Music, B
Science Teacher Education/General Science
  Teacher Education, B
Secondary Education and Teaching, BM
Social Sciences, B
Sociology, B
Special Education and Teaching, B
Speech and Rhetorical Studies, B
Theology/Theological Studies, B
Voice and Opera, B
Wildlife Biology, B

Wind and Percussion Instruments, B

HIGH-TECH INSTITUTE

Computer Engineering Technology/Technician, A
Computer Systems Networking and
  Telecommunications, A
Computer Technology/Computer Systems
  Technology, A
Drafting and Design Technology/Technician, A

INTERNATIONAL BAPTIST COLLEGE

Bible/Biblical Studies, AB
Pastoral Studies/Counseling, MD
Teacher Education, Multiple Levels, B
Theology and Religious Vocations, M

INTERNATIONAL INSTITUTE OF THE
AMERICAS (MESA)

Accounting, A
Business Administration and Management, AB
Criminal Justice/Law Enforcement Administration, A
Health/Health Care Administration/Management, A
Legal Assistant/Paralegal, A

INTERNATIONAL INSTITUTE OF THE
AMERICAS (PHOENIX)

Accounting, A
Business Administration and Management, AB
Health/Health Care Administration/Management, A
Legal Assistant/Paralegal, A
Nursing - Registered Nurse Training, A

INTERNATIONAL INSTITUTE OF THE
AMERICAS (TUCSON)

Accounting, A
Business Administration and Management, AB
Criminal Justice/Law Enforcement Administration, A
Health/Health Care Administration/Management, A
Legal Assistant/Paralegal, A

INTERNATIONAL INSTITUTE OF THE
AMERICAS (WEST VALLEY)

Accounting, A
Business Administration and Management, AB
Criminal Justice/Law Enforcement Administration, A
Health/Health Care Administration/Management, A
Legal Assistant/Paralegal, A

ITT TECHNICAL INSTITUTE (PHOENIX)

Computer and Information Systems Security, B
Computer Programming/Programmer, A
Computer Systems Networking and
  Telecommunications, B
Electrical, Electronic and Communications
  Engineering Technology/Technician, AB
Information Technology, B
System Administration/Administrator, A
Web Page, Digital/Multimedia and Information
  Resources Design, A

ITT TECHNICAL INSTITUTE (TEMPE)

Animation, Interactive Technology, Video Graphics
  and Special Effects, A
Business Administration and Management, B
CAD/CADD Drafting and/or Design
  Technology/Technician, A
Computer and Information Systems Security, A
Computer Programming/Programmer, A
Computer Software Technology/Technician, B
Computer Systems Networking and
  Telecommunications, A
Criminal Justice/Law Enforcement Administration, B
E-Commerce/Electronic Commerce, B
Electrical, Electronic and Communications
  Engineering Technology/Technician, AB
System, Networking, and LAN/WAN
  Management/Manager, A
Web Page, Digital/Multimedia and Information
  Resources Design, A
Web/Multimedia Management and Webmaster, A

ITT TECHNICAL INSTITUTE (TUCSON)

Animation, Interactive Technology, Video Graphics
  and Special Effects, B

Business Administration and Management, B
CAD/CADD Drafting and/or Design
  Technology/Technician, A
Computer Programming/Programmer, A
Computer Software Technology/Technician, B
Computer Systems Networking and
  Telecommunications, B
Criminal Justice/Law Enforcement Administration, B
E-Commerce/Electronic Commerce, B
Electrical, Electronic and Communications
  Engineering Technology/Technician, AB
System, Networking, and LAN/WAN
  Management/Manager, A
Web Page, Digital/Multimedia and Information
  Resources Design, A
Web/Multimedia Management and Webmaster, A

LAMSON COLLEGE

Accounting, A
Administrative Assistant and Secretarial Science, A
Business Administration and Management, A
Information Science/Studies, A
Legal Administrative Assistant/Secretary, A
Legal Assistant/Paralegal, A

MESA COMMUNITY COLLEGE

Accounting, A
Administrative Assistant and Secretarial Science, A
Agricultural Business and Management, A
Agricultural Mechanization, A
Agronomy and Crop Science, A
Art/Art Studies, General, A
Automobile/Automotive Mechanics
  Technology/Technician, A
Biology/Biological Sciences, A
Business Administration and Management, A
Child Development, A
Criminal Justice/Law Enforcement Administration, A
Data Processing and Data Processing
  Technology/Technician, A
Drafting and Design Technology/Technician, A
Electrical, Electronic and Communications
  Engineering Technology/Technician, A
Engineering Technology, A
Family and Consumer Sciences/Human Sciences, A
Fashion Merchandising, A
Finance, A
Fire Science/Firefighting, A
Heavy Equipment Maintenance
  Technology/Technician, A
Horticultural Science, A
Industrial Technology/Technician, A
Insurance, A
Interior Design, A
Liberal Arts and Sciences Studies and
  Humanities, A
Library Science, A
Marketing/Marketing Management, A
Mathematics, A
Medical Administrative Assistant/Secretary, A
Music, A
Nursing - Registered Nurse Training, A
Ornamental Horticulture, A
Pre-Engineering, A
Quality Control Technology/Technician, A
Real Estate, A
Teacher Assistant/Aide, A

MIDWESTERN
UNIVERSITY, GLENDALE CAMPUS

Allied Health and Medical Assisting Services, MPO
Bioethics/Medical Ethics, MO
Biological and Biomedical Sciences, M
Biomedical Sciences, B
Cardiovascular Sciences, M
Health Education, M
Nurse Anesthetist, M
Occupational Therapy/Therapist, M
Osteopathic Medicine, P
Pharmacy, P
Physician Assistant, M

Podiatric Medicine, P

MOHAVE COMMUNITY COLLEGE

Accounting, A
Art/Art Studies, General, A
Automobile/Automotive Mechanics
    Technology/Technician, A
Business Administration and Management, A
Ceramic Arts and Ceramics, A
Computer and Information Sciences, A
Computer Programming, Specific Applications, A
Computer Science, A
Criminal Justice/Police Science, A
English Language and Literature, A
Fire Science/Firefighting, A
History, A
Information Technology, A
Liberal Arts and Sciences Studies and
    Humanities, A
Marketing/Marketing Management, A
Mathematics, A
Metal and Jewelry Arts, A
Music, A
Nursing - Registered Nurse Training, A
Psychology, A
Public Health (MPH, DPH), A
Sociology, A
Word Processing, A

NORTHCENTRAL UNIVERSITY

Business Administration and Management, B
General Studies, B
Psychology, B

NORTHERN ARIZONA UNIVERSITY

Accounting, B
Advertising, B
Allied Health and Medical Assisting Services, MDO
American Government and Politics (United States)
    , B
American Indian/Native American Studies, B
Anthropology, BM
Applied Physics, M
Archeology, M
Art History, Criticism and Conservation, B
Art Teacher Education, B
Art/Art Studies, General, B
Arts Management, B
Astronomy, B
Biochemistry, M
Biological and Biomedical Sciences, MD
Biology Teacher Education, B
Biology/Biological Sciences, B
Botany/Plant Biology, B
Business Administration and Management, B
Business Administration, Management and
    Operations, M
Business/Commerce, B
Business/Managerial Economics, B
Cell/Cellular Biology and Anatomical Sciences, B
Chemistry, BM
Civil Engineering, B
Communication and Media Studies, M
Communication Disorders, M
Communication Studies/Speech Communication
    and Rhetoric, B
Communication, Journalism and Related
    Programs, B
Community College Education, M
Composition, M
Computer and Information Sciences, B
Construction Engineering Technology/Technician, B
Counseling Psychology, D
Counselor Education/School Counseling and
    Guidance Services, BM
Criminal Justice/Law Enforcement Administration, B
Criminology, MO
Curriculum and Instruction, D
Dental Hygiene/Hygienist, B
Drama and Dance Teacher Education, B
Drama and Dramatics/Theatre Arts, B
Early Childhood Education and Teaching, M
Ecology, BO
Economics, B
Education, BMDO

Education/Teaching of Individuals with Speech or
    Language Impairments, B
Educational Administration and Supervision, M
Educational Leadership and Administration, BMD
Educational Media/Instructional Technology, MO
Educational Psychology, D
Electrical, Electronics and Communications
    Engineering, B
Elementary Education and Teaching, BM
Engineering, B
Engineering and Applied Sciences, MDO
Engineering Physics, B
English, M
English as a Second Language, MDO
English Education, M
English Language and Literature, B
English/Language Arts Teacher Education, B
Environmental Policy, MO
Environmental Sciences, MO
Environmental Studies, B
Environmental/Environmental Health Engineering, B
Exercise and Sports Science, M
Finance, B
Foreign Language Teacher Education, M
Forest Sciences and Biology, B
Forestry, MD
French Language and Literature, B
General Studies, B
Geochemistry, B
Geographic Information Systems, MO
Geography, BMO
Geology/Earth Science, BM
Geosciences, M
German Language and Literature, B
Health Education, M
Health Promotion, M
Health Psychology, M
Health Teacher Education, B
History, BMD
History Teacher Education, B
Hotel/Motel Administration/Management, B
Humanities/Humanistic Studies, B
Interior Design, B
International Relations and Affairs, B
Journalism, B
Kinesiology and Exercise Science, B
Liberal Arts and Sciences Studies and
    Humanities, B
Liberal Studies, M
Linguistics, MDO
Management, M
Management Information Systems and
    Services, BM
Marine Biology and Biological Oceanography, B
Marketing/Marketing Management, B
Mathematics, BM
Mathematics Teacher Education, BM
Mechanical Engineering, B
Medical Microbiology and Bacteriology, B
Multilingual and Multicultural Education, MO
Music, BM
Music History, Literature, and Theory, M
Music Performance, B
Music Teacher Education, BM
Music Theory and Composition, M
Nursing, MO
Nursing - Registered Nurse Training, B
Parks, Recreation, Leisure and Fitness Studies, B
Performance, M
Philosophy, B
Photography, B
Physical Education Teaching and Coaching, BM
Physical Sciences, B
Physical Therapy/Therapist, D
Physics, B
Physics Teacher Education, B
Political Science and Government, BMDO
Pre-Law Studies, B
Pre-Medicine/Pre-Medical Studies, B
Pre-Veterinary Studies, B
Psychology, BM
Public Administration, MO
Public Health, M
Public Policy Analysis, BD
Public Relations/Image Management, B
Radio and Television, B

Religion/Religious Studies, B
Rhetoric, M
School Psychology, MD
Science Teacher Education/General Science
    Teacher Education, BM
Science Technologies/Technicians, B
Secondary Education and Teaching, M
Social Science Teacher Education, B
Social Sciences, B
Social Work, B
Sociology, BM
Spanish Language and Literature, B
Spanish Language Teacher Education, B
Special Education and Teaching, BM
Speech and Rhetorical Studies, B
Statistics, M
Teacher Education and Professional
    Development, Specific Subject Areas, B
Teaching English as a Second or Foreign
    Language/ESL Language Instructor, B
Technology Teacher Education/Industrial Arts
    Teacher Education, B
Vocational and Technical Education, M
Wildlife and Wildlands Science and Management, B
Women's Studies, B
Writing, M
Zoology/Animal Biology, B

NORTHLAND PIONEER COLLEGE

Accounting Technology/Technician and
    Bookkeeping, A
Administrative Assistant and Secretarial Science, A
Agriculture, A
Apparel and Textiles, A
Biological and Physical Sciences, A
Building/Property Maintenance and Management, A
Business Administration and Management, A
Business and Personal/Financial Services Marketing
    Operations, A
Business/Commerce, A
Business/Office Automation/Technology/Data
    Entry, A
Carpentry/Carpenter, A
Child Care and Support Services Management, A
Child Care Provider/Assistant, A
Child Development, A
Computer and Information Sciences, A
Computer Graphics, A
Computer Installation and Repair
    Technology/Technician, A
Computer Systems Networking and
    Telecommunications, A
Corrections, A
Cosmetology/Cosmetologist, A
Court Reporting/Court Reporter, A
Data Modeling/Warehousing and Database
    Administration, A
Drafting and Design Technology/Technician, A
Early Childhood Education and Teaching, A
Education/Teaching of Individuals in Early Childhood
    Special Education Programs, A
Electrical, Electronic and Communications
    Engineering Technology/Technician, A
Electrician, A
Elementary Education and Teaching, A
Emergency Medical Technology/Technician (EMT
    Paramedic), A
Entrepreneurial and Small Business Operations, A
Fire Science/Firefighting, A
General Studies, A
Health Information/Medical Records
    Administration/Administrator, A
Industrial Mechanics and Maintenance
    Technology, A
Industrial Technology/Technician, A
Information Science/Studies, A
Kindergarten/PreSchool Education and Teaching, A
Legal Administrative Assistant/Secretary, A
Legal Assistant/Paralegal, A
Legal Professions and Studies, A
Liberal Arts and Sciences Studies and
    Humanities, A
Library Assistant/Technician, A
Licensed Practical/Vocational Nurse Training, A
Management Information Systems and Services, A
Massage Therapy/Therapeutic Massage, A

Medical Transcription/Transcriptionist, A
Museology/Museum Studies, A
Nursing - Registered Nurse Training, A
Parks, Recreation and Leisure Facilities .
  Management, A
Photography, A
Restaurant, Culinary, and Catering
  Management/Manager, A
Small Business Administration/Management, A
Teacher Assistant/Aide, A
Teaching Assistants/Aides, A
Turf and Turfgrass Management, A
Welding Technology/Welder, A

PARADISE VALLEY COMMUNITY COLLEGE

Accounting, A
Administrative Assistant and Secretarial Science, A
Business Administration and Management, A
Computer Typography and Composition Equipment
  Operator, A
International Business/Trade/Commerce, A
Liberal Arts and Sciences Studies and
  Humanities, A
Occupational Safety and Health
  Technology/Technician, A

THE PARALEGAL INSTITUTE, INC.

Criminal Justice/Law Enforcement Administration, A
Legal Assistant/Paralegal, A

PHOENIX COLLEGE

Accounting, A
Administrative Assistant and Secretarial Science, A
Architectural Engineering Technology/Technician, A
Art/Art Studies, General, A
Behavioral Sciences, A
Business Administration and Management, A
Civil Engineering Technology/Technician, A
Clinical Laboratory Science/Medical
  Technology/Technologist, A
Clinical/Medical Laboratory Technician, A
Computer and Information Sciences, A
Computer Graphics, A
Construction Engineering Technology/Technician, A
Corrections, A
Criminal Justice/Police Science, A
Criminal Justice/Safety Studies, A
Data Processing and Data Processing
  Technology/Technician, A
Dental Hygiene/Hygienist, A
Drafting and Design Technology/Technician, A
Drafting/Design Engineering
  Technologies/Technicians, A
Emergency Medical Technology/Technician (EMT
  Paramedic), A
Family and Consumer Sciences/Human Sciences, A
Fashion/Apparel Design, A
Finance, A
Fire Science/Firefighting, A
Health and Medical Laboratory Technologies, A
Health Information/Medical Records
  Administration/Administrator, A
Information Science/Studies, A
Interior Design, A
Legal Administrative Assistant/Secretary, A
Legal Assistant/Paralegal, A
Liberal Arts and Sciences Studies and
  Humanities, A
Management Science, A
Marketing/Marketing Management, A
Mass Communication/Media Studies, A
Medical Administrative Assistant/Secretary, A
Medical/Clinical Assistant, A
Nursing - Registered Nurse Training, A
Real Estate, A
Special Products Marketing Operations, A
Tourism and Travel Services Management, A

PIMA COMMUNITY COLLEGE

Accounting, A
Administrative Assistant and Secretarial Science, A
Aircraft Powerplant Technology/Technician, A
American Indian/Native American Studies, A
Anthropology, A

Architectural Drafting and Architectural
  CAD/CADD, A
Automobile/Automotive Mechanics
  Technology/Technician, A
Building/Construction
  Finishing, Management, and Inspection, A
Building/Property Maintenance and Management, A
Business Administration and Management, A
Child Care and Support Services Management, A
Child Care Provider/Assistant, A
Computer and Information Sciences, A
Computer Engineering Technology/Technician, A
Computer Systems Analysis/Analyst, A
Computer Systems Networking and
  Telecommunications, A
Computer Technology/Computer Systems
  Technology, A
Construction Engineering Technology/Technician, A
Criminal Justice/Police Science, A
Criminal Justice/Safety Studies, A
Dental Hygiene/Hygienist, A
Dental Laboratory Technology/Technician, A
Design and Visual Communications, A
Drama and Dramatics/Theatre Arts, A
Electrical, Electronic and Communications
  Engineering Technology/Technician, A
Elementary Education and Teaching, A
Emergency Medical Technology/Technician (EMT
  Paramedic), A
Environmental Engineering
  Technology/Environmental Technology, A
Fire Science/Firefighting, A
General Studies, A
Hospitality Administration/Management, A
International Business/Trade/Commerce, A
Legal Assistant/Paralegal, A
Liberal Arts and Sciences Studies and
  Humanities, A
Machine Shop Technology/Assistant, A
Medical Radiologic Technology/Science - Radiation
  Therapist, A
Music, A
Nursing - Registered Nurse Training, A
Pharmacy Technician/Assistant, A
Political Science and Government, A
Real Estate, A
Respiratory Care Therapy/Therapist, A
Restaurant, Culinary, and Catering
  Management/Manager, A
Security and Protective Services, A
Sign Language Interpretation and Translation, A
Sociology, A
Veterinary/Animal Health Technology/Technician and
  Veterinary Assistant, A
Welding Technology/Welder, A

PIMA MEDICAL INSTITUTE (MESA)

Radiologic Technology/Science - Radiographer, A
Respiratory Therapy Technician/Assistant, A

PIMA MEDICAL INSTITUTE (TUCSON)

Physical Therapist Assistant, A
Radiologic Technology/Science - Radiographer, A
Respiratory Therapy Technician/Assistant, A

PRESCOTT COLLEGE

Accounting, B
Anthropology, B
Art Therapy/Therapist, B
Art/Art Studies, General, B
Bilingual and Multilingual Education, B
Biology/Biological Sciences, B
Communication Studies/Speech Communication
  and Rhetoric, B
Comparative Literature, B
Computer and Information Sciences, B
Counseling Psychology, M
Criminal Justice/Safety Studies, B
Dance, B
Drama and Dramatics/Theatre Arts, B
Ecology, BM
Education, BM
Elementary Education and Teaching, B
English/Language Arts Teacher Education, B
Environmental Design/Architecture, B
Environmental Education, BM

Environmental Studies, BM
Family and Consumer Sciences/Human Sciences, B
Film/Cinema Studies, B
History, BM
Human Development and Family Studies, B
Humanities/Humanistic Studies, BM
Interdisciplinary Studies, B
Junior High/Intermediate/Middle School Education
  and Teaching, B
Kindergarten/PreSchool Education and Teaching, B
Latin American Studies, B
Leisure Studies, M
Liberal Arts and Sciences Studies and
  Humanities, B
Management Science, B
Marine Science/Merchant Marine Officer, B
Mathematics Teacher Education, B
Mental Health/Rehabilitation, B
Multilingual and Multicultural Education, M
Music Teacher Education, B
Natural Resources and Conservation, B
Natural Resources Management/Development and
  Policy, B
Parks, Recreation, Leisure and Fitness Studies, B
Philosophy, B
Photography, B
Physical Education Teaching and Coaching, B
Political Science and Government, B
Psychology, B
Science Teacher Education/General Science
  Teacher Education, B
Secondary Education and Teaching, B
Social Psychology, M
Social Science Teacher Education, B
Sociology, B
Spanish Language and Literature, B
Special Education and Teaching, B
Sustainable Development, M
Wildlife and Wildlands Science and Management, B

THE REFRIGERATION SCHOOL

Mechanical Engineering/Mechanical
  Technology/Technician, A

RIO SALADO COLLEGE

Business Administration and Management, A
Computer and Information Sciences, A
Computer Programming, A
Computer Science, A
Consumer Services and Advocacy, A
Data Entry/Microcomputer Applications, A
Dental Hygiene/Hygienist, A
Information Science/Studies, A
Information Technology, A
Management Information Systems and Services, A
Public Administration, A
Substance Abuse/Addiction Counseling, A
System Administration/Administrator, A
Web Page, Digital/Multimedia and Information
  Resources Design, A
Web/Multimedia Management and Webmaster, A

SCOTTSDALE COMMUNITY COLLEGE

Accounting, A
Administrative Assistant and Secretarial Science, A
Business Administration and Management, A
Criminal Justice/Law Enforcement Administration, A
Culinary Arts/Chef Training, A
Drama and Dramatics/Theatre Arts, A
Electrical, Electronic and Communications
  Engineering Technology/Technician, A
Emergency Medical Technology/Technician (EMT
  Paramedic), A
Environmental Design/Architecture, A
Equestrian/Equine Studies, A
Fashion Merchandising, A
Finance, A
Fire Science/Firefighting, A
Hospitality Administration/Management, A
Hotel/Motel Administration/Management, A
Information Science/Studies, A
Interior Design, A
Kindergarten/PreSchool Education and Teaching, A
Mathematics, A
Medical Administrative Assistant/Secretary, A
Nursing - Registered Nurse Training, A

Photography, A
Public Administration, A
Real Estate, A
Special Products Marketing Operations, A

SOUTH MOUNTAIN COMMUNITY COLLEGE

Administrative Assistant and Secretarial Science, A
Art/Art Studies, General, A
Biology/Biological Sciences, A
Business Administration and Management, A
Chemistry, A
Computer Typography and Composition Equipment
   Operator, A
Family and Consumer Sciences/Human Sciences, A
History, A
Information Science/Studies, A
Liberal Arts and Sciences Studies and
   Humanities, A
Mass Communication/Media Studies, A
Mathematics, A
Music, A
Physical Education Teaching and Coaching, A
Physics, A
Political Science and Government, A
Pre-Engineering, A
Psychology, A
Sociology, A

SOUTHWESTERN COLLEGE

Bible/Biblical Studies, B
Business Administration and Management, B
Counseling Psychology, B
Elementary Education and Teaching, B
Music Teacher Education, B
Secondary Education and Teaching, B
Youth Ministry, B

UNIVERSITY OF ADVANCING TECHNOLOGY

Cinematography and Film/Video Production, B
Commercial and Advertising Art, B
Computer Graphics, AB
Computer Programming/Programmer, AB
Computer Systems Analysis/Analyst, B
Data Processing and Data Processing
   Technology/Technician, B
Design and Visual Communications, B
Management of Technology, M

THE UNIVERSITY OF ARIZONA

Accounting, BM
Aerospace, Aeronautical and Astronautical
   Engineering, BMD
Agricultural Economics, BM
Agricultural Education, M
Agricultural Engineering, MD
Agricultural Sciences, MD
Agricultural Teacher Education, B
Agricultural/Biological Engineering and
   Bioengineering, B
Agriculture, B
Agronomy and Soil Sciences, MD
Allopathic Medicine, PO
American Indian/Native American Studies, MDO
Anatomy, D
Animal Physiology, B
Animal Sciences, BMD
Anthropology, BMD
Applied Mathematics, MD
Applied Physics, M
Architecture, BM
Art Education, M
Art History, Criticism and Conservation, BMD
Art Teacher Education, B
Astronomy, BMD
Atmospheric Sciences and Meteorology, BMD
Biochemistry, BMD
Biological and Biomedical Sciences, MDO
Biology Teacher Education, B
Biology/Biological Sciences, B
Biosystems Engineering, MD
Business Administration, Management and
   Operations, MDO
Business/Commerce, B

Business/Managerial Economics, B
Cancer Biology/Oncology, D
Cell Biology and Anatomy, MD
Cell/Cellular Biology and Histology, B
Chemical Engineering, BMD
Chemistry, BMD
Chemistry Teacher Education, B
Child and Family Studies, MD
City/Urban, Community and Regional Planning, B
Civil Engineering, BMD
Classics and Classical
   Languages, Literatures, and Linguistics, BM
Clinical Laboratory Science/Medical
   Technology/Technologist, B
Communication and Media Studies, MD
Communication Disorders, BMD
Communication Studies/Speech Communication
   and Rhetoric, B
Comparative Literature, MD
Composition, MD
Computer and Information Sciences, B
Computer Engineering, BMD
Computer Science, MD
Consumer Economics, BMD
Creative Writing, B
Criminal Justice/Law Enforcement Administration, B
Dance, B
Drama and Dance Teacher Education, B
Drama and Dramatics/Theatre Arts, B
East Asian Studies, BMD
Ecology, MD
Economics, BMDO
Education, MDO
Educational Administration and Supervision, D
Educational Psychology, MD
Electrical Engineering, MD
Electrical, Electronics and Communications
   Engineering, B
Elementary Education and Teaching, BMD
Engineering, B
Engineering and Applied Sciences, MD
Engineering Physics, B
Engineering/Industrial Management, B
English, MD
English as a Second Language, MD
English Education, MD
English Language and Literature, B
English/Language Arts Teacher Education, B
Entomology, MD
Entrepreneurship/Entrepreneurial Studies, B
Environmental Engineering
   Technology/Environmental Technology, MD
Environmental Policy and Resource
   Management, M
Environmental Sciences, MD
Environmental Studies, B
Epidemiology, MD
Evolutionary Biology, MD
Family and Consumer Sciences/Home Economics
   Teacher Education, B
Finance, B
Finance and Banking, MD
Fine Arts and Art Studies, M
Fine/Studio Arts, B
Fish, Game and Wildlife Management, MD
Foreign Language Teacher Education, BM
Forestry, MD
French Language and Literature, BMD
French Language Teacher Education, B
Genetics, MD
Geography, BMD
Geological/Geophysical Engineering, B
Geology/Earth Science, B
Geosciences, MD
German Language and Literature, BM
German Language Teacher Education, B
Gerontology, MO
Health Teacher Education, B
Health/Health Care Administration/Management, B
Higher Education/Higher Education
   Administration, MD
Hispanic-American, Puerto Rican, and Mexican-
   American/Chicano Studies, B
History, BMD
History Teacher Education, B
Home Economics, MD

Human Development, MD
Human Development and Family Studies, B
Human Resources Management/Personnel
   Administration, B
Hydrology and Water Resources Science, MD
Immunology, MD
Industrial Engineering, B
Industrial/Management Engineering, MD
Information Science/Studies, MD
Interdisciplinary Studies, MDO
Italian Language and Literature, B
Jewish/Judaic Studies, B
Journalism, BM
Kindergarten/PreSchool Education and Teaching, B
Landscape Architecture, BM
Latin American Studies, BM
Law and Legal Studies, MPO
Liberal Arts and Sciences Studies and
   Humanities, B
Library Science, MD
Linguistics, BMD
Management Information Systems and
   Services, BMD
Management Strategy and Policy, M
Marketing, MD
Marketing/Marketing Management, B
Materials Engineering, MD
Materials Sciences, BMD
Mathematics, BM
Mathematics Teacher Education, B
Mechanical Engineering, BMD
Mechanics, MD
Media Studies, M
Microbiology, MD
Mineral/Mining Engineering, MD
Mining and Mineral Engineering, B
Molecular Biology, MD
Multi-/Interdisciplinary Studies, B
Multilingual and Multicultural Education, MDO
Music, BMD
Music Performance, B
Music Teacher Education, BMD
Music Theory and Composition, MD
Musicology and Ethnomusicology, M
Natural Resources and Conservation, MD
Near and Middle Eastern Studies, BMD
Neuroscience, D
Nuclear Engineering, BMD
Nursing, MD
Nursing - Registered Nurse Training, B
Nutritional Sciences, BMD
Operations Management and Supervision, B
Optics/Optical Sciences, BMD
Pathobiology, MD
Performance, MD
Pharmaceutical Sciences, MD
Pharmacology, MD
Pharmacy, MDP
Philosophy, BMDO
Physical Education Teaching and Coaching, B
Physics, BMD
Physics Teacher Education, B
Physiology, D
Planetary Astronomy and Science, MD
Plant Pathology/Phytopathology, MD
Plant Sciences, BMD
Political Science and Government, BMD
Pre-Veterinary Studies, B
Psychology, BDO
Public Administration, BMD
Public Health, M
Public Policy Analysis, MD
Radio and Television, B
Range Science and Management, MD
Reading Teacher Education, MDO
Rehabilitation Counseling, MDO
Reliability Engineering, M
Religion/Religious Studies, B
Rhetoric, MD
Russian Language and Literature, BM
Science Teacher Education/General Science
   Teacher Education, B
Science Technologies/Technicians, B
Secondary Education and Teaching, BMD
Social Science Teacher Education, B
Social Studies Teacher Education, B

Sociology, BMD
Soil Science and Agronomy, B
Spanish Language and Literature, BMD
Spanish Language Teacher Education, B
Special Education and Teaching, BMDO
Speech Teacher Education, B
Systems Engineering, BMD
Teacher Education and Professional
  Development, Specific Subject Areas, B
Teaching English as a Second or Foreign
  Language/ESL Language Instructor, B
Technical Theatre/Theatre Design and
  Technology, B
Theater, M
Toxicology, D
Urban and Regional Planning, M
Visual and Performing Arts, B
Water Resources, MD
Water Resources Engineering, BM
Wildlife and Wildlands Science and Management, B
Women's Studies, BM
Writing, M

UNIVERSITY OF PHOENIX ONLINE CAMPUS

Accounting, BM
Adult and Continuing Education and Teaching, M
Business Administration and Management, B
Business Administration, Management and
  Operations, MD
Computer Programming/Programmer, B
Corrections and Criminal Justice, B
Curriculum and Instruction, M
Early Childhood Education and Teaching, M
Education, MDO
Educational Administration and Supervision, M
Educational Media/Instructional Technology, M
Electronic Commerce, M
Elementary Education and Teaching, M
Finance, B
General Studies, B
Health Services Administration, MD
Health/Health Care Administration/Management, B
Human Resources Management and Services, M
Management, M
Management Information Systems and Services, M
Management of Technology, M
Management Science, B
Marketing, M
Nursing, M
Organizational Management, MD
Secondary Education and Teaching, M
Special Education and Teaching, MO

UNIVERSITY OF PHOENIX-PHOENIX CAMPUS

Accounting, M
Adult and Continuing Education and Teaching, M
Business Administration and Management, B
Business Administration, Management and
  Operations, M
Community Psychology, M
Computer Science, M
Counselor Education/School Counseling and
  Guidance Services, MO
Criminal Justice/Law Enforcement Administration, B
Curriculum and Instruction, M
Distance Education Development, M
Education, MO
Educational Administration and Supervision, M
Educational Media/Instructional Technology, M
Electronic Commerce, M
Elementary Education and Teaching, M
English as a Second Language, M
General Studies, A
Health Services Administration, M
Health/Health Care Administration/Management, B
Human Resources Management and Services, M
Information Science/Studies, M
Information Technology, B
International Business/Trade/Commerce, M
Management, M
Management Information Systems and
  Services, BM
Management of Technology, M
Management Science, B

Marketing, M
Marketing/Marketing Management, B
Marriage and Family Therapy/Counseling, M
Nursing, MO
Nursing - Advanced Practice, MO
Nursing Administration, M
Nursing Science, B
Organizational Management, M
Public Administration and Social Service
  Professions, B
Secondary Education and Teaching, M
Special Education and Teaching, MO

UNIVERSITY OF PHOENIX-SOUTHERN ARIZONA CAMPUS

Accounting, BM
Business Administration and Management, B
Business Administration, Management and
  Operations, M
Community Psychology, M
Corrections and Criminal Justice, B
Counselor Education/School Counseling and
  Guidance Services, M
Curriculum and Instruction, M
Education, MO
Educational Psychology, M
Electronic Commerce, M
Elementary Education and Teaching, M
Finance, B
Health Services Administration, M
Health/Health Care Administration/Management, B
Information Technology, B
International Business/Trade/Commerce, M
Management, M
Management Information Systems and
  Services, BM
Management of Technology, M
Management Science, B
Marketing/Marketing Management, B
Marriage and Family Therapy/Counseling, M
Nursing, MO
Nursing - Advanced Practice, O
Nursing - Registered Nurse Training, B
Nursing Science, B
Organizational Management, M
Public Administration and Social Service
  Professions, B
Secondary Education and Teaching, M
Special Education and Teaching, O

WESTERN INTERNATIONAL UNIVERSITY

Accounting, B
Behavioral Sciences, B
Business Administration and Management, B
Business Administration, Management and
  Operations, M
Criminal Justice/Law Enforcement Administration, B
Finance, B
Finance and Banking, M
Health/Health Care Administration/Management, B
Information Science/Studies, B
International Business/Trade/Commerce, BM
International Relations and Affairs, B
Liberal Arts and Sciences Studies and
  Humanities, AB
Management Information Systems and Services, M
Marketing, M
Marketing/Marketing Management, B

YAVAPAI COLLEGE

Accounting, A
Administrative Assistant and Secretarial Science, A
Agribusiness, A
Agricultural Business and Management, A
Agriculture, A
Aquaculture, A
Architectural Drafting and Architectural
  CAD/CADD, A
Automobile/Automotive Mechanics
  Technology/Technician, A
Business Administration and Management, A
Commercial and Advertising Art, A
Construction Engineering Technology/Technician, A
Criminal Justice/Police Science, A
Education, A

Equestrian/Equine Studies, A
Film/Cinema Studies, A
Fine Arts and Art Studies, A
Fire Science/Firefighting, A
Graphic Design, A
Gunsmithing/Gunsmith, A
Horse Husbandry/Equine Science and
  Management, A
Information Science/Studies, A
Legal Administrative Assistant/Secretary, A
Legal Assistant/Paralegal, A
Liberal Arts and Sciences Studies and
  Humanities, A
Nursing - Registered Nurse Training, A

Arkansas
ARKANSAS BAPTIST COLLEGE

Adult and Continuing Education and Teaching, B
Business Administration and Management, B
Computer Science, AB
Elementary Education and Teaching, B
Liberal Arts and Sciences Studies and
  Humanities, B
Religion/Religious Studies, B
Secondary Education and Teaching, B
Social Work, B

ARKANSAS NORTHEASTERN COLLEGE

Agriculture, A
Applied Horticulture/Horticultural Operations, A
Business/Commerce, A
Criminal Justice/Police Science, A
General Studies, A
Industrial Mechanics and Maintenance
  Technology, A
Industrial Production Technologies/Technicians, A
Industrial Technology/Technician, A
Junior High/Intermediate/Middle School Education
  and Teaching, A
Marketing/Marketing Management, A
Metallurgical Technology/Technician, A
Nursing - Registered Nurse Training, A

ARKANSAS STATE UNIVERSITY

Accounting, BM
Administrative Assistant and Secretarial Science, A
Agribusiness, B
Agricultural Education, MO
Agricultural Sciences, MO
Agricultural Teacher Education, B
Agriculture, B
Allied Health and Medical Assisting Services, MO
Animal Sciences, B
Art Teacher Education, B
Art/Art Studies, General, B
Athletic Training and Sports Medicine, B
Audiology/Audiologist and Speech-Language
  Pathology/Pathologist, B
Automobile/Automotive Mechanics
  Technology/Technician, A
Biological and Biomedical Sciences, MO
Biology Teacher Education, B
Biology/Biological Sciences, B
Business Administration and Management, B
Business Administration, Management and
  Operations, MO
Business Education, MO
Business Teacher Education, B
Business/Managerial Economics, B
Chemistry, BMO
Chemistry Teacher Education, B
Clinical Laboratory Science/Medical
  Technology/Technologist, AB
Commercial and Advertising Art, B
Communication and Media Studies, MO
Communication Disorders, M
Communication, Journalism and Related
  Programs, B
Computer and Information Sciences, B
Computer Science, BM
Counselor Education/School Counseling and
  Guidance Services, MO
Criminal Justice/Law Enforcement Administration, A

Criminal Justice/Police Science, A
Criminology, B
Curriculum and Instruction, MDO
Data Processing and Data Processing
    Technology/Technician, B
Drama and Dramatics/Theatre Arts, B
Early Childhood Education and Teaching, BM
Economics, B
Education, MDO
Educational Administration and Supervision, MO
Educational Leadership and Administration, MDO
Electrical, Electronic and Communications
    Engineering Technology/Technician, A
Electronic Commerce, M
Elementary Education and Teaching, MO
Emergency Medical Technology/Technician (EMT
    Paramedic), A
Engineering, B
Engineering Technology, AB
English, MO
English Education, MO
English Language and Literature, B
English/Language Arts Teacher Education, B
Environmental Sciences, D
Exercise and Sports Science, M
Finance, B
Fine Arts and Art Studies, M
Forensic Science and Technology, AB
French Language and Literature, B
French Language Teacher Education, B
General Studies, AB
Geography, B
Gerontological Nursing, O
Graphic Communications, B
Health and Physical Education, B
Health Education, O
Health Teacher Education, B
History, BMDO
International Business/Trade/Commerce, B
Journalism, BM
Junior High/Intermediate/Middle School Education
    and Teaching, B
Kinesiology and Exercise Science, B
Management Information Systems and
    Services, AM
Marketing/Marketing Management, B
Mathematics, BM
Mathematics Teacher Education, B
Media Studies, M
Medical Radiologic Technology/Science - Radiation
    Therapist, AB
Music, BMO
Music Performance, B
Music Teacher Education, BMO
Nurse Anesthetist, M
Nursing, MO
Nursing - Registered Nurse Training, AB
Performance, M
Philosophy, B
Physical Education Teaching and Coaching, BMO
Physical Therapist Assistant, A
Physical Therapy/Therapist, M
Physics, B
Physics Teacher Education, B
Plant Sciences, B
Political Science and Government, BMO
Psychology, B
Public Administration, M
Radio and Television, B
Reading Teacher Education, MO
Rehabilitation Counseling, M
School Psychology, M
Science Teacher Education/General Science
    Teacher Education, MO
Social Science Teacher Education, B
Social Studies Teacher Education, M
Social Work, B
Sociology, BMO
Spanish Language and Literature, B
Spanish Language Teacher Education, B
Special Education and Teaching, BMDO
Speech and Interpersonal Communication, MO
Speech and Rhetorical Studies, B
Speech Teacher Education, B
Sport and Fitness Administration/Management, B
Student Personnel Services, M

Technology Teacher Education/Industrial Arts
    Teacher Education, A
Theater, MO
Transportation/Transportation Management, B
Wildlife and Wildlands Science and Management, B

ARKANSAS STATE UNIVERSITY-BEEBE

Agriculture, A
Animal Sciences, A
Business Administration and Management, A
Clinical/Medical Laboratory Technician, A
Computer
    Programming, Vendor/Product Certification, A
Computer Systems Networking and
    Telecommunications, A
Computer Technology/Computer Systems
    Technology, A
Drafting and Design Technology/Technician, A
Electrical, Electronic and Communications
    Engineering Technology/Technician, A
General Studies, A
Health/Medical Preparatory Programs, A
Industrial Mechanics and Maintenance
    Technology, A
Information Technology, A
Liberal Arts and Sciences Studies and
    Humanities, A
Nursing - Registered Nurse Training, A
Quality Control Technology/Technician, A
Vehicle Maintenance and Repair Technologies, A

ARKANSAS STATE UNIVERSITY-MOUNTAIN HOME

Audiology/Audiologist and Hearing Sciences, A
Business/Office Automation/Technology/Data
    Entry, A
Criminal Justice/Law Enforcement Administration, A
Criminal Justice/Safety Studies, A
Emergency Medical Technology/Technician (EMT
    Paramedic), A
Forensic Science and Technology, A
Funeral Service and Mortuary Science, A
Information Science/Studies, A
Junior High/Intermediate/Middle School Education
    and Teaching, A
Liberal Arts and Sciences Studies and
    Humanities, A
Opticianry/Ophthalmic Dispensing Optician, A

ARKANSAS TECH UNIVERSITY

Accounting, B
Administrative Assistant and Secretarial Science, A
Agribusiness, B
Art Teacher Education, B
Art/Art Studies, General, B
Biology Teacher Education, B
Biology/Biological Sciences, B
Business Administration and Management, B
Business Teacher Education, B
Chemistry, B
Chemistry Teacher Education, B
Child Development, A
Clinical Laboratory Science/Medical
    Technology/Technologist, B
Clinical/Medical Social Work, B
Computer and Information Sciences, B
Computer Systems Analysis/Analyst, B
Creative Writing, B
Criminal Justice/Safety Studies, A
Curriculum and Instruction, M
Economics, B
Education, BM
Education/Teaching of the Gifted and Talented, M
Educational Leadership and Administration, M
Elementary Education and Teaching, B
Engineering, B
Engineering Physics, B
English, M
English as a Second Language, M
English Education, M
English Language and Literature, B
English/Language Arts Teacher Education, B
Fish, Game and Wildlife Management, M
Foreign Language Teacher Education, B
Foreign Languages and Literatures, B

General Studies, AB
Geology/Earth Science, B
Health Information/Medical Records
    Administration/Administrator, B
Health Professions and Related Clinical Sciences, B
History, M
Hospitality Administration/Management, B
Humanities/Humanistic Studies, B
Industrial Mechanics and Maintenance
    Technology, A
Information Science/Studies, AM
Journalism, BM
Junior High/Intermediate/Middle School Education
    and Teaching, B
Liberal Studies, M
Mathematics, B
Mathematics Teacher Education, B
Mechanical Engineering, B
Medical/Clinical Assistant, A
Multi-/Interdisciplinary Studies, A
Music, B
Music Teacher Education, B
Nuclear Engineering Technology/Technician, A
Nursing - Registered Nurse Training, B
Parks, Recreation and Leisure Facilities
    Management, B
Physical Education Teaching and Coaching, B
Physical Sciences, B
Psychology, B
Science Teacher Education/General Science
    Teacher Education, B
Secondary Education and Teaching, M
Social Studies Teacher Education, B
Sociology, B
Spanish Language and Literature, M
Student Personnel Services, M
Systems Science and Theory, M

BLACK RIVER TECHNICAL COLLEGE

Avionics Maintenance Technology/Technician, A
Business Administration and Management, A
Data Processing and Data Processing
    Technology/Technician, A
Dietetics/Dieticians, A
Emergency Medical Technology/Technician (EMT
    Paramedic), A
Fire Science/Firefighting, A
Industrial Technology/Technician, A
Information Science/Studies, A
Liberal Arts and Sciences Studies and
    Humanities, A
Nursing - Registered Nurse Training, A

CENTRAL BAPTIST COLLEGE

Bible/Biblical Studies, B
Business Administration and Management, AB
Counseling Psychology, B
Data Processing and Data Processing
    Technology/Technician, B
Education, A
General Studies, A
Human Services, B
Music, AB
Organizational Behavior Studies, B
Religious/Sacred Music, B
Theology and Religious Vocations, B

COSSATOT COMMUNITY COLLEGE OF THE UNIVERSITY OF ARKANSAS

Automobile/Automotive Mechanics
    Technology/Technician, A
Business Administration and Management, A
Carpentry/Carpenter, A
Emergency Medical Technology/Technician (EMT
    Paramedic), A
Environmental Studies, A
Industrial Technology/Technician, A
Liberal Arts and Sciences Studies and
    Humanities, A
Medical/Clinical Assistant, A
Occupational Safety and Health
    Technology/Technician, A
Welding Technology/Welder, A

Wood Science and Wood Products/Pulp and Paper Technology, A

CROWLEY'S RIDGE COLLEGE

Bible/Biblical Studies, A
General Studies, A

EAST ARKANSAS COMMUNITY COLLEGE

Business Administration and Management, A
Computer Engineering Technology/Technician, A
Criminal Justice/Law Enforcement Administration, A
Criminal Justice/Police Science, A
Drafting and Design Technology/Technician, A
Liberal Arts and Sciences Studies and Humanities, A
Licensed Practical/Vocational Nurse Training, A

HARDING UNIVERSITY

Accounting, B
Advertising, B
American/United States Studies/Civilization, B
Art Teacher Education, B
Art Therapy/Therapist, B
Athletic Training and Sports Medicine, B
Biochemistry, B
Biology Teacher Education, B
Biology/Biological Sciences, B
Broadcast Journalism, B
Business Administration and Management, B
Business Administration, Management and Operations, M
Business/Corporate Communications, B
Chemistry, B
Christian Studies, B
Clinical Laboratory Science/Medical Technology/Technologist, B
Communication and Media Studies, B
Communication Disorders, B
Communication Studies/Speech Communication and Rhetoric, B
Computer and Information Sciences, B
Computer Engineering, B
Computer Science, B
Corrections and Criminal Justice, B
Counselor Education/School Counseling and Guidance Services, BM
Criminal Justice/Safety Studies, B
Design and Applied Arts, B
Dietetics/Dieticians, B
Digital Communication and Media/Multimedia, B
Divinity/Ministry (BD, MDiv.), B
Drama and Dramatics/Theatre Arts, B
Early Childhood Education and Teaching, BM
Economics, B
Education, MO
Education/Teaching of Individuals in Early Childhood Special Education Programs, B
Education/Teaching of Individuals with Specific Learning Disabilities, B
Educational Leadership and Administration, BMO
Elementary Education and Teaching, BM
English Language and Literature, B
English/Language Arts Teacher Education, B
Family and Consumer Sciences/Home Economics Teacher Education, B
Family and Consumer Sciences/Human Sciences, B
Fashion Merchandising, B
Fine/Studio Arts, B
French Language and Literature, B
General Studies, B
Graphic Design, B
Health Teacher Education, B
Health/Health Care Administration/Management, B
History, B
Human Development and Family Studies, B
Human Resources Management/Personnel Administration, B
Humanities/Humanistic Studies, B
Information Technology, B
Interior Design, B
International Business/Trade/Commerce, B
International Relations and Affairs, B
International/Global Studies, B
Junior High/Intermediate/Middle School Education and Teaching, B

Kindergarten/PreSchool Education and Teaching, B
Kinesiology and Exercise Science, B
Law and Legal Studies, B
Marketing/Marketing Management, B
Marriage and Family Therapy/Counseling, BM
Mathematics, B
Mathematics Teacher Education, B
Missions/Missionary Studies and Missiology, B
Music, B
Music Teacher Education, B
Nursing - Registered Nurse Training, B
Painting, B
Pastoral Counseling and Specialized Ministries, B
Pastoral Studies/Counseling, BM
Physical Education Teaching and Coaching, B
Physics, B
Political Science and Government, B
Pre-Dentistry Studies, B
Pre-Medicine/Pre-Medical Studies, B
Pre-Veterinary Studies, B
Psychology, B
Public Administration, B
Public Relations/Image Management, B
Reading Teacher Education, BM
Religion/Religious Studies, B
Religious Education, B
Sales, Distribution and Marketing Operations, B
Science Teacher Education/General Science Teacher Education, B
Secondary Education and Teaching, BM
Social Sciences, B
Social Studies Teacher Education, B
Social Work, B
Spanish Language and Literature, B
Special Education and Teaching, BM
Speech Teacher Education, B
Speech-Language Pathology/Pathologist, B
Sport and Fitness Administration/Management, B
Teacher Education, Multiple Levels, B
Theology and Religious Vocations, M
Theology/Theological Studies, B
Youth Ministry, B

HENDERSON STATE UNIVERSITY

Accounting, B
Administrative Assistant and Secretarial Science, A
Aeronautics/Aviation/Aerospace Science and Technology, B
Art Teacher Education, B
Art/Art Studies, General, B
Athletic Training and Sports Medicine, B
Biology/Biological Sciences, B
Business Administration, Management and Operations, M
Business Teacher Education, B
Business/Commerce, B
Chemistry, B
Child Care and Support Services Management, A
Clinical Laboratory Science/Medical Technology/Technologist, B
Community Psychology, M
Computer and Information Sciences, B
Counselor Education/School Counseling and Guidance Services, M
Curriculum and Instruction, M
Drama and Dramatics/Theatre Arts, B
Early Childhood Education and Teaching, BM
Education, MO
Educational Administration and Supervision, M
Educational Leadership and Administration, MO
Elementary Education and Teaching, B
English as a Second Language, M
English Education, M
English Language and Literature, B
Family and Consumer Sciences/Home Economics Teacher Education, B
Family and Consumer Sciences/Human Sciences, B
History, B
Journalism, B
Junior High/Intermediate/Middle School Education and Teaching, B
Liberal Studies, M
Management Information Systems and Services, B
Mathematics, B
Mathematics Teacher Education, M
Middle School Education, M

Music, B
Music Performance, B
Music Teacher Education, B
Nursing - Registered Nurse Training, B
Painting, B
Parks, Recreation and Leisure Facilities Management, B
Physical Education Teaching and Coaching, BM
Physics, B
Political Science and Government, B
Psychology, B
Public Administration, B
Reading Teacher Education, M
Science Teacher Education/General Science Teacher Education, B
Social Studies Teacher Education, M
Social Work, B
Sociology, B
Spanish Language and Literature, B
Special Education and Teaching, MO
Sport and Fitness Administration/Management, BM
Teacher Education and Professional Development, Specific Subject Areas, B

HENDRIX COLLEGE

Accounting, BM
Anthropology, B
Art/Art Studies, General, B
Biology/Biological Sciences, B
Business/Managerial Economics, B
Chemistry, B
Computer Science, B
Drama and Dramatics/Theatre Arts, B
Economics, B
Elementary Education and Teaching, B
English Language and Literature, B
French Language and Literature, B
German Language and Literature, B
History, B
Interdisciplinary Studies, B
International Relations and Affairs, B
Mathematics, B
Music, B
Philosophy, B
Physical Education Teaching and Coaching, B
Physics, B
Political Science and Government, B
Psychology, B
Religion/Religious Studies, B
Sociology, B
Spanish Language and Literature, B

ITT TECHNICAL INSTITUTE

Accounting and Business/Management, B
Animation, Interactive Technology, Video Graphics and Special Effects, B
Business Administration and Management, B
CAD/CADD Drafting and/or Design Technology/Technician, A
Computer and Information Systems Security, B
Computer Programming/Programmer, A
Computer Software Technology/Technician, B
Computer Systems Networking and Telecommunications, B
Criminal Justice/Law Enforcement Administration, B
E-Commerce/Electronic Commerce, B
Electrical, Electronic and Communications Engineering Technology/Technician, A
System, Networking, and LAN/WAN Management/Manager, A
Web Page, Digital/Multimedia and Information Resources Design, A
Web/Multimedia Management and Webmaster, A

JOHN BROWN UNIVERSITY

Accounting, B
Athletic Training and Sports Medicine, B
Bible/Biblical Studies, AB
Biochemistry, B
Biology Teacher Education, B
Biology/Biological Sciences, B
Broadcast Journalism, AB
Building/Construction Finishing, Management, and Inspection, AB
Business Administration and Management, B

Business Administration, Management and
Operations, M
Business Teacher Education, B
Chemistry, B
Chemistry Teacher Education, B
Computer Graphics, B
Construction Engineering, B
Counselor Education/School Counseling and
Guidance Services, M
Divinity/Ministry (BD, MDiv.), B
Education, B
Electrical, Electronics and Communications
Engineering, B
Elementary Education and Teaching, B
Engineering, B
Engineering Technology, A
Engineering/Industrial Management, B
English Language and Literature, B
English/Language Arts Teacher Education, B
Environmental Sciences, B
Environmental Studies, B
Health Teacher Education, B
History, B
Interdisciplinary Studies, B
International Business/Trade/Commerce, B
International Relations and Affairs, B
Journalism, AB
Junior High/Intermediate/Middle School Education
and Teaching, B
Kindergarten/PreSchool Education and Teaching, B
Kinesiology and Exercise Science, B
Liberal Arts and Sciences Studies and
Humanities, A
Marketing/Marketing Management, B
Marriage and Family Therapy/Counseling, M
Mass Communication/Media Studies, B
Mathematics, B
Mechanical Engineering, B
Missions/Missionary Studies and Missiology, B
Music, AB
Music Teacher Education, B
Pastoral Studies/Counseling, BM
Psychology, B
Public Relations, Advertising, and Applied
Communication, AB
Public Relations/Image Management, AB
Radio and Television, B
Radio, Television, and Digital Communication, B
Religion/Religious Studies, B
Religious Education, B
Secondary Education and Teaching, B
Social Sciences, B
Social Studies Teacher Education, B
Spanish Language and Literature, B
Special Education and Teaching, B
Teaching English as a Second or Foreign
Language/ESL Language Instructor, B
Theology/Theological Studies, B

LYON COLLEGE

Accounting, B
Art/Art Studies, General, B
Biology/Biological Sciences, B
Business Administration and Management, B
Chemistry, B
Computer Science, B
Drama and Dramatics/Theatre Arts, B
Early Childhood Education and Teaching, B
Economics, B
English Language and Literature, B
Environmental Studies, B
History, B
Mathematics, B
Music, B
Philosophy and Religious Studies, B
Political Science and Government, B
Psychology, B
Spanish Language and Literature, B

MID-SOUTH COMMUNITY COLLEGE

Computer and Information Sciences, A
Liberal Arts and Sciences Studies and
Humanities, A
Management Information Systems and Services, A
Multi-/Interdisciplinary Studies, A

Web/Multimedia Management and Webmaster, A

NATIONAL PARK COMMUNITY COLLEGE

Accounting, A
Administrative Assistant and Secretarial Science, A
Art/Art Studies, General, A
Business Administration and Management, A
Child Development, A
Clinical Laboratory Science/Medical
Technology/Technologist, A
Clinical/Medical Laboratory Technician, A
Commercial and Advertising Art, A
Computer Graphics, A
Criminal Justice/Law Enforcement Administration, A
Data Processing and Data Processing
Technology/Technician, A
Education, A
Electrical, Electronic and Communications
Engineering Technology/Technician, A
Elementary Education and Teaching, A
Emergency Medical Technology/Technician (EMT
Paramedic), A
Finance, A
Fire Science/Firefighting, A
Health Information/Medical Records
Administration/Administrator, A
Health/Health Care Administration/Management, A
Industrial Radiologic Technology/Technician, A
Information Science/Studies, A
Liberal Arts and Sciences Studies and
Humanities, A
Medical Administrative Assistant/Secretary, A
Nursing - Registered Nurse Training, A
Parks, Recreation and Leisure Facilities
Management, A
Parks, Recreation, Leisure and Fitness Studies, A
Physical Sciences, A
Public Administration, A
Public Health (MPH, DPH), A
Radiologic Technology/Science - Radiographer, A

NORTH ARKANSAS COLLEGE

Administrative Assistant and Secretarial Science, A
Agricultural Business and Management, A
Agriculture, A
Automobile/Automotive Mechanics
Technology/Technician, A
Biomedical Technology/Technician, A
Business/Commerce, A
Clinical/Medical Laboratory Assistant, A
Clinical/Medical Laboratory Technician, A
Computer and Information Sciences, A
Criminal Justice/Law Enforcement Administration, A
Criminal Justice/Police Science, A
Drafting and Design Technology/Technician, A
Electrical, Electronic and Communications
Engineering Technology/Technician, A
Electromechanical and Instrumentation and
Maintenance Technologies/Technicians, A
Electromechanical Technology/Electromechanical
Engineering Technology, A
Emergency Medical Technology/Technician (EMT
Paramedic), A
Forensic Science and Technology, A
Industrial Technology/Technician, A
Institutional Food Workers, A
Junior High/Intermediate/Middle School Education
and Teaching, A
Liberal Arts and Sciences Studies and
Humanities, A
Medical Radiologic Technology/Science - Radiation
Therapist, A
Nursing - Registered Nurse Training, A
Surgical Technology/Technologist, A

NORTHWEST ARKANSAS COMMUNITY COLLEGE

Accounting, A
Administrative Assistant and Secretarial Science, A
Business Administration and Management, A
Computer Programming/Programmer, A
Criminal Justice/Law Enforcement Administration, A
Data Processing and Data Processing
Technology/Technician, A
Drafting and Design Technology/Technician, A

Education, A
Electrical, Electronic and Communications
Engineering Technology/Technician, A
Emergency Medical Technology/Technician (EMT
Paramedic), A
Finance, A
Industrial Radiologic Technology/Technician, A
Liberal Arts and Sciences Studies and
Humanities, A
Nursing - Registered Nurse Training, A
Occupational Safety and Health
Technology/Technician, A
Physical Therapy/Therapist, A
Respiratory Care Therapy/Therapist, A

OUACHITA BAPTIST UNIVERSITY

Accounting, B
Art Teacher Education, B
Athletic Training and Sports Medicine, B
Bible/Biblical Studies, AB
Biology/Biological Sciences, B
Business Administration and Management, B
Chemistry, B
Communication Disorders Sciences and Services, B
Communication Studies/Speech Communication
and Rhetoric, B
Computer Science, B
Dietetics/Dieticians, B
Drama and Dramatics/Theatre Arts, B
Early Childhood Education and Teaching, B
Education, B
English Language and Literature, B
Fine/Studio Arts, B
French Language and Literature, B
Graphic Design, B
History, B
Junior High/Intermediate/Middle School Education
and Teaching, B
Kinesiology and Exercise Science, B
Mass Communication/Media Studies, B
Mathematics, B
Missions/Missionary Studies and Missiology, B
Music, B
Music History, Literature, and Theory, B
Music Performance, B
Music Teacher Education, B
Music Theory and Composition, B
Pastoral Counseling and Specialized Ministries, B
Pastoral Studies/Counseling, B
Philosophy, B
Physical Education Teaching and Coaching, B
Physics, B
Piano and Organ, B
Political Science and Government, B
Pre-Dentistry Studies, B
Pre-Engineering, B
Pre-Law Studies, B
Pre-Medicine/Pre-Medical Studies, B
Pre-Nursing Studies, B
Pre-Pharmacy Studies, B
Pre-Veterinary Studies, B
Psychology, B
Religious/Sacred Music, B
Russian Language and Literature, B
Science Teacher Education/General Science
Teacher Education, B
Secondary Education and Teaching, B
Social Studies Teacher Education, B
Sociology, B
Spanish Language and Literature, B
Theology/Theological Studies, B
Voice and Opera, B
Youth Ministry, B

OUACHITA TECHNICAL COLLEGE

Accounting, A
Administrative Assistant and Secretarial Science, A
Automobile/Automotive Mechanics
Technology/Technician, A
Business Administration and Management, A
Child Care and Support Services Management, A
Computer and Information Sciences, A
Industrial Technology/Technician, A
Legal Administrative Assistant/Secretary, A
Legal Assistant/Paralegal, A

Liberal Arts and Sciences Studies and
Humanities, A
Licensed Practical/Vocational Nurse Training, A
Machine Tool Technology/Machinist, A
Management Information Systems and Services, A
Marketing/Marketing Management, A
Medical Administrative Assistant/Secretary, A

OZARKA COLLEGE

Administrative Assistant and Secretarial Science, A
Automobile/Automotive Mechanics
Technology/Technician, A
Banking and Financial Support Services, A
Business Administration and Management, A
Criminal Justice/Law Enforcement Administration, A
Culinary Arts/Chef Training, A
Health Information/Medical Records
Technology/Technician, A
Information Science/Studies, A
Junior High/Intermediate/Middle School Education
and Teaching, A
Liberal Arts and Sciences Studies and
Humanities, A

PHILANDER SMITH COLLEGE

Biological and Physical Sciences, B
Biology/Biological Sciences, B
Business Administration and Management, B
Chemistry, B
Computer Science, B
Educational Administration and Supervision, B
Elementary and Middle School
Administration/Principalship, B
English Language and Literature, B
Health and Physical Education, B
Hospitality Administration/Management, B
Kindergarten/PreSchool Education and Teaching, B
Mathematics, B
Music, B
Organizational Behavior Studies, B
Political Science and Government, B
Psychology, B
Religion/Religious Studies, B
Social Work, B
Sociology, B

PHILLIPS COMMUNITY COLLEGE OF THE UNIVERSITY OF ARKANSAS

Administrative Assistant and Secretarial Science, A
Agricultural Business and Management, A
Art/Art Studies, General, A
Automobile/Automotive Mechanics
Technology/Technician, A
Biological and Physical Sciences, A
Biology/Biological Sciences, A
Business Administration and Management, A
Business Teacher Education, A
Chemistry, A
Clinical/Medical Laboratory Technician, A
Computer Programming/Programmer, A
Cosmetology/Cosmetologist, A
Data Processing and Data Processing
Technology/Technician, A
Drafting and Design Technology/Technician, A
Drama and Dramatics/Theatre Arts, A
Education, A
English Language and Literature, A
Graphic and Printing Equipment Operator
Production, A
Heating, Air Conditioning, Ventilation and
Refrigeration Maintenance
Technology/Technician, A
Industrial Radiologic Technology/Technician, A
Instrumentation Technology/Technician, A
Liberal Arts and Sciences Studies and
Humanities, A
Licensed Practical/Vocational Nurse Training, A
Mathematics, A
Medical Administrative Assistant/Secretary, A
Music, A
Nursing - Registered Nurse Training, A
Physics, A
Social Sciences, A

Technology Education/Industrial Arts, A

PULASKI TECHNICAL COLLEGE

Administrative Assistant and Secretarial Science, A
Computer Engineering Technology/Technician, A
Drafting and Design Technology/Technician, A
Electromechanical Technology/Electromechanical
Engineering Technology, A
Industrial Technology/Technician, A
Information Science/Studies, A
Occupational Therapist Assistant, A
Respiratory Care Therapy/Therapist, A

RICH MOUNTAIN COMMUNITY COLLEGE

Administrative Assistant and Secretarial Science, A
Liberal Arts and Sciences Studies and
Humanities, A

SOUTH ARKANSAS COMMUNITY COLLEGE

Administrative Assistant and Secretarial Science, A
Business/Commerce, A
Clinical/Medical Laboratory Technician, A
Criminal Justice/Police Science, A
Emergency Medical Technology/Technician (EMT
Paramedic), A
General Studies, A
Industrial Technology/Technician, A
Management Information Systems and Services, A
Medical Radiologic Technology/Science - Radiation
Therapist, A
Physical Therapist Assistant, A

SOUTHEAST ARKANSAS COLLEGE

Automobile/Automotive Mechanics
Technology/Technician, A
Biology Technician/BioTechnology Laboratory
Technician, A
Business Administration and Management, A
Business/Commerce, A
Criminology, A
Drafting and Design Technology/Technician, A
Electrical, Electronic and Communications
Engineering Technology/Technician, A
Emergency Medical Technology/Technician (EMT
Paramedic), A
General Studies, A
Industrial Technology/Technician, A
Legal Assistant/Paralegal, A
Radiologic Technology/Science - Radiographer, A
Science, Technology and Society, A
Surgical Technology/Technologist, A

SOUTHERN ARKANSAS UNIVERSITY-MAGNOLIA

Accounting, B
Administrative Assistant and Secretarial Science, A
Agricultural Business and Management, B
Agricultural Teacher Education, B
Agriculture, B
Art Teacher Education, B
Art/Art Studies, General, B
Biological and Physical Sciences, B
Biology Teacher Education, B
Biology/Biological Sciences, B
Broadcast Journalism, B
Business Teacher Education, B
Business/Commerce, B
Chemistry, B
Chemistry Teacher Education, B
Clinical Laboratory Science/Medical
Technology/Technologist, B
Community Organization and Advocacy, B
Computer and Information Sciences, B
Counselor Education/School Counseling and
Guidance Services, M
Criminal Justice/Safety Studies, B
Drama and Dramatics/Theatre Arts, B
Education, M
Elementary Education and Teaching, B
Engineering Physics, B
English Language and Literature, B
English/Language Arts Teacher Education, B
General Studies, A

History, B
Industrial Technology/Technician, AB
Journalism, B
Kindergarten/PreSchool Education and Teaching, B
Kinesiology and Exercise Science, B
Library Science, M
Mass Communication/Media Studies, B
Mathematics, B
Mathematics Teacher Education, B
Music Teacher Education, B
Nursing - Registered Nurse Training, A
Physical Education Teaching and Coaching, B
Physics Teacher Education, B
Political Science and Government, B
Psychology, B
Science Teacher Education/General Science
Teacher Education, B
Social Studies Teacher Education, B
Social Work, B
Sociology, B
Spanish Language and Literature, B
Spanish Language Teacher Education, B

SOUTHERN ARKANSAS UNIVERSITY TECH

Airframe Mechanics and Aircraft Maintenance
Technology/Technician, A
Business Administration and Management, A
Computer and Information Sciences, A
Computer and Information Sciences and Support
Services, A
Emergency Medical Technology/Technician (EMT
Paramedic), A
Engineering Technologies/Technicians, A
Environmental Engineering
Technology/Environmental Technology, A
Fire Science/Firefighting, A
General Studies, A
Industrial Mechanics and Maintenance
Technology, A
Industrial Technology/Technician, A
Office Management and Supervision, A
Teaching Assistants/Aides, A
Web Page, Digital/Multimedia and Information
Resources Design, A
Web/Multimedia Management and Webmaster, A

UNIVERSITY OF ARKANSAS

Accounting, BM
Adult and Continuing Education and Teaching, MDO
Agribusiness, B
Agricultural Communication/Journalism, B
Agricultural Economics, BM
Agricultural Education, M
Agricultural Sciences, MD
Agricultural Teacher Education, B
Agricultural/Biological Engineering and
Bioengineering, B
Agronomy and Soil Sciences, MD
American/United States Studies/Civilization, B
Animal Sciences, BMD
Anthropology, BM
Apparel and Textiles, B
Applied Physics, M
Architecture, B
Art/Art Studies, General, B
Bioengineering, MD
Biological and Biomedical Sciences, MD
Biology/Biological Sciences, B
Business Administration and Management, B
Business Administration, Management and
Operations, MD
Business/Commerce, B
Business/Managerial Economics, B
Cell Biology and Anatomy, MD
Cell/Cellular Biology and Anatomical Sciences, B
Chemical Engineering, BMD
Chemistry, BMD
Civil Engineering, BMD
Classics and Classical
Languages, Literatures, and Linguistics, B
Communication and Media Studies, M
Communication Disorders, M
Communication Studies/Speech Communication
and Rhetoric, B
Comparative Literature, MD

Computer and Information Sciences, B
Computer Engineering, BMD
Computer Science, MD
Counselor Education/School Counseling and
   Guidance Services, MDO
Criminal Justice/Safety Studies, B
Crop Production, B
Curriculum and Instruction, D
Drama and Dramatics/Theatre Arts, B
Early Childhood Education and Teaching, BM
Economics, BMD
Education, MDO
Educational Administration and Supervision, MDO
Educational Media/Instructional Technology, M
Electrical Engineering, MD
Electrical, Electronics and Communications
   Engineering, B
Electronic Materials, MD
Elementary Education and Teaching, BMO
Engineering and Applied Sciences, MD
English, MD
English Language and Literature, B
Entomology, MD
Environmental Engineering
   Technology/Environmental Technology, M
Environmental Sciences, B
Family and Consumer Sciences/Human
   Sciences, M
Finance, B
Fine Arts and Art Studies, M
Food Science, B
Food Science and Technology, MD
Foods, Nutrition, and Wellness Studies, B
French Language and Literature, BM
Geography, BM
Geological and Earth Sciences/Geosciences, B
Geology/Earth Science, BM
German Language and Literature, BM
Health and Physical Education, B
Health Education, MD
Higher Education/Higher Education
   Administration, MDO
History, BMD
Horticultural Science, BM
Hospitality and Recreation Marketing Operations, B
Human Development and Family Studies, B
Industrial and Manufacturing Management, M
Industrial Engineering, B
Industrial/Management Engineering, MD
Information Technology, B
Interdisciplinary Studies, D
Interior Design, B
International Business/Trade/Commerce, B
International Relations and Affairs, B
Journalism, BM
Junior High/Intermediate/Middle School Education
   and Teaching, B
Kinesiology and Exercise Science, B
Kinesiology and Movement Studies, MD
Landscape Architecture, B
Law and Legal Studies, MP
Logistics and Materials Management, BM
Management Information Systems and Services, M
Management Science, B
Marketing/Marketing Management, B
Mathematics, BMD
Mathematics Teacher Education, M
Mechanical Engineering, BMD
Middle School Education, M
Molecular Biology, MD
Music, BM
Nursing - Registered Nurse Training, B
Operations Research, M
Ornamental Horticulture, B
Philosophy, BMD
Photonics, MD
Physical Education Teaching and Coaching, M
Physics, BMD
Plant Pathology/Phytopathology, M
Plant Sciences, D
Political Science and Government, BM
Poultry Science, BMD
Psychology, BMD
Public Administration, BM
Public Health (MPH, DPH), B
Public Policy Analysis, D

Recreation and Park Management, MD
Rehabilitation Counseling, MD
Secondary Education and Teaching, MO
Social Work, BM
Sociology, BM
Spanish Language and Literature, BM
Special Education and Teaching, M
Statistics, M
Telecommunications, M
Theater, M
Translation and Interpretation, M
Transportation and Highway Engineering, BM
Transportation/Transportation Management, M
Vocational and Technical Education, MDO
Writing, M

UNIVERSITY OF ARKANSAS COMMUNITY COLLEGE AT BATESVILLE

Business/Commerce, A
Computer Systems Networking and
   Telecommunications, A
Criminal Justice/Safety Studies, A
Data Entry/Microcomputer Applications, A
Education, A
Emergency Medical Technology/Technician (EMT
   Paramedic), A
Industrial Technology/Technician, A
Information Technology, A
Kindergarten/PreSchool Education and Teaching, A
Medical Office Management/Administration, A
Nursing - Registered Nurse Training, A
System Administration/Administrator, A
Web Page, Digital/Multimedia and Information
   Resources Design, A

UNIVERSITY OF ARKANSAS COMMUNITY COLLEGE AT HOPE

Business Administration and Management, A
Child Care Provider/Assistant, A
Criminal Justice/Law Enforcement Administration, A
Funeral Service and Mortuary Science, A
Human Services, A
Industrial Mechanics and Maintenance
   Technology, A
Liberal Arts and Sciences Studies and
   Humanities, A
Machine Shop Technology/Assistant, A
Respiratory Care Therapy/Therapist, A
Trade and Industrial Teacher Education, A

UNIVERSITY OF ARKANSAS COMMUNITY COLLEGE AT MORRILTON

Administrative Assistant and Secretarial Science, A
Automobile/Automotive Mechanics
   Technology/Technician, A
Child Development, A
Commercial and Advertising Art, A
Computer Systems Networking and
   Telecommunications, A
Computer Typography and Composition Equipment
   Operator, A
Drafting and Design Technology/Technician, A
Heating, Air Conditioning, Ventilation and
   Refrigeration Maintenance
   Technology/Technician, A
Horticultural Science, A
Information Science/Studies, A
Liberal Arts and Sciences Studies and
   Humanities, A
Licensed Practical/Vocational Nurse Training, A
Machine Tool Technology/Machinist, A
Marketing/Marketing Management, A
Ornamental Horticulture, A
Survey Technology/Surveying, A
Welding Technology/Welder, A

UNIVERSITY OF ARKANSAS AT FORT SMITH

Accounting, B
Administrative Assistant and Secretarial Science, A
Biology Teacher Education, B
Business Administration and Management, AB
Child Development, A

Computer and Information Sciences, B
Computer and Information Sciences and Support
   Services, AB
Criminal Justice/Law Enforcement
   Administration, AB
Dental Hygiene/Hygienist, A
Diagnostic Medical Sonography/Sonographer and
   Ultrasound Technician, B
Drafting and Design Technology/Technician, A
Electrical/Electronics Equipment Installation and
   Repair, A
English/Language Arts Teacher Education, B
Forensic Science and Technology, A
General Studies, A
Graphic Design, AB
History, B
History Teacher Education, B
Junior High/Intermediate/Middle School Education
   and Teaching, AB
Kindergarten/PreSchool Education and Teaching, B
Legal Assistant/Paralegal, A
Liberal Arts and Sciences Studies and
   Humanities, AB
Mathematics, B
Mathematics Teacher Education, B
Multi-/Interdisciplinary Studies, A
Music, B
Music Teacher Education, B
Nursing - Registered Nurse Training, AB
Psychology, B
Radiologic Technology/Science - Radiographer, A
Respiratory Care Therapy/Therapist, A
Surgical Technology/Technologist, A
Technical and Business Writing, B
Visual and Performing Arts, A

UNIVERSITY OF ARKANSAS AT LITTLE ROCK

Accounting, B
Adult and Continuing Education and Teaching, M
Advertising, B
Anthropology, B
Applied Mathematics, M
Applied Science and Technology, MD
Art Education, M
Art History, Criticism and Conservation, BM
Art/Art Studies, General, B
Audiology/Audiologist and Speech-Language
   Pathology/Pathologist, B
Bioinformatics, MD
Biological and Biomedical Sciences, M
Biology/Biological Sciences, B
Business Administration and Management, B
Business Administration, Management and
   Operations, MO
Business/Commerce, B
Chemistry, BM
Computer Engineering Technology/Technician, B
Computer Programming/Programmer, A
Computer Science, BM
Construction Engineering Technology/Technician, B
Corporate and Organizational Communication, M
Counselor Education/School Counseling and
   Guidance Services, M
Criminal Justice/Law Enforcement Administration, B
Criminal Justice/Police Science, A
Criminology, M
Drama and Dramatics/Theatre Arts, B
Early Childhood Education and Teaching, M
Economics, B
Education, BMDO
Education/Teaching of Individuals with Hearing
   Impairments, Including Deafness, B
Education/Teaching of Individuals with Multiple
   Disabilities, M
Education/Teaching of the Gifted and Talented, M
Educational Administration and Supervision, MDO
Educational Media/Instructional Technology, M
Electrical, Electronic and Communications
   Engineering Technology/Technician, AB
Elementary Education and Teaching, B
English Language and Literature, B
Environmental Health, B
Finance, B
Fine Arts and Art Studies, M
French Language and Literature, B

General Studies, A
Geology/Earth Science, B
Gerontology, MO
Health Services Administration, M
Health Teacher Education, B
Higher Education/Higher Education
    Administration, D
History, B
Information Science/Studies, B
International Business/Trade/Commerce, B
International Relations and Affairs, B
Journalism, B
Kindergarten/PreSchool Education and Teaching, B
Landscape Architecture, A
Law and Legal Studies, PO
Liberal Arts and Sciences Studies and
    Humanities, B
Liberal Studies, M
Management Information Systems and Services, M
Marketing/Marketing Management, B
Mass Communication/Media Studies, M
Mathematics, BM
Mechanical Engineering/Mechanical
    Technology/Technician, AB
Middle School Education, M
Music, B
Nursing - Registered Nurse Training, A
Philosophy, B
Physics, B
Political Science and Government, B
Psychology, BM
Public Administration, M
Public Affairs, M
Public Health (MPH, DPH), B
Public History, M
Radio and Television, B
Reading Teacher Education, M
Rhetoric, M
Secondary Education and Teaching, M
Sign Language Interpretation and Translation, AB
Social Work, BM
Sociology, B
Spanish Language and Literature, B
Special Education and Teaching, M
Speech and Interpersonal Communication, M
Speech and Rhetorical Studies, B
Survey Technology/Surveying, B
Technical and Business Writing, BM
Writing, M

UNIVERSITY OF ARKANSAS FOR MEDICAL SCIENCES

Anatomy, MDO
Biochemistry, MDO
Biological and Biomedical Sciences, MDO
Biomedical Technology/Technician, A
Biophysics, MDO
Clinical Laboratory Science/Medical
    Technology/Technologist, B
Communication Disorders, M
CytoTechnology/Cytotechnologist, B
Dental Hygiene/Hygienist, AB
Emergency Medical Technology/Technician (EMT
    Paramedic), A
Environmental and Occupational Health, M
Immunology, MDO
Industrial Radiologic Technology/Technician, AB
Microbiology, MDO
Molecular Biology, MDO
Neurobiology and Neurophysiology, MDO
Nuclear Medical Technology/Technologist, B
Nursing, MD
Nursing - Registered Nurse Training, B
Nutritional Sciences, M
Pathology/Experimental Pathology, M
Pharmaceutical Administration, M
Pharmaceutical Sciences, M
Pharmacology, MDO
Pharmacy, MP
Physiology, MDO
Respiratory Care Therapy/Therapist, A
Surgical Technology/Technologist, A

Toxicology, MDO

UNIVERSITY OF ARKANSAS AT MONTICELLO

Accounting, B
Agricultural Production Operations, A
Agriculture, B
Art/Art Studies, General, B
Biology/Biological Sciences, B
Business Administration and Management, B
Business Teacher Education, B
Chemistry, B
Criminal Justice/Safety Studies, B
Education, BM
Educational Leadership and Administration, M
Elementary Education and Teaching, B
English Language and Literature, B
Forestry, BM
History, B
Liberal Arts and Sciences Studies and
    Humanities, A
Management Information Systems and Services, B
Mathematics, B
Music, B
Music Teacher Education, B
Natural Resources and Conservation, M
Nursing - Registered Nurse Training, B
Physical Education Teaching and Coaching, B
Physical Sciences, B
Political Science and Government, B
Pre-Dentistry Studies, B
Pre-Law Studies, B
Pre-Medicine/Pre-Medical Studies, B
Pre-Veterinary Studies, B
Psychology, B
Social Work, B
Special Education and Teaching, B
Speech and Rhetorical Studies, B
Wildlife and Wildlands Science and Management, B
Wood Science and Wood Products/Pulp and Paper
    Technology, A

UNIVERSITY OF ARKANSAS AT PINE BLUFF

Accounting, B
Agricultural Economics, B
Agricultural Teacher Education, B
Agriculture, B
Agronomy and Crop Science, B
Animal Sciences, B
Apparel and Textiles, B
Art Teacher Education, B
Art/Art Studies, General, B
Automobile/Automotive Mechanics
    Technology/Technician, B
Biology/Biological Sciences, B
Business Administration and Management, B
Business Teacher Education, B
Business/Managerial Economics, B
Chemistry, B
Computer Science, B
Corrections, B
Criminal Justice/Law Enforcement Administration, B
Criminal Justice/Police Science, A
Dietetics/Dieticians, B
Drama and Dramatics/Theatre Arts, B
Economics, B
Education, M
Elementary Education and Teaching, BM
English Language and Literature, B
Environmental Biology, B
Family and Consumer Sciences/Home Economics
    Teacher Education, B
Family and Consumer Sciences/Human Sciences, B
Fashion Merchandising, B
Gerontology, B
History, B
Hotel/Motel Administration/Management, B
Industrial Technology/Technician, AB
Kindergarten/PreSchool Education and
    Teaching, AB
Mathematics, B
Music, B
Music Teacher Education, B
Nursing - Registered Nurse Training, B
Parks, Recreation, Leisure and Fitness Studies, B

Physical Education Teaching and Coaching, B
Physics, B
Political Science and Government, B
Pre-Medicine/Pre-Medical Studies, B
Psychology, B
Secondary Education and Teaching, BM
Social Sciences, B
Social Work, B
Sociology, B
Special Education and Teaching, B
Speech and Rhetorical Studies, B
Technology Education/Industrial Arts, B
Trade and Industrial Teacher Education, B

UNIVERSITY OF CENTRAL ARKANSAS

Accounting, BM
Art/Art Studies, General, B
Athletic Training and Sports Medicine, B
Audiology/Audiologist and Speech-Language
    Pathology/Pathologist, B
Biological and Biomedical Sciences, M
Biological and Physical Sciences, B
Biology/Biological Sciences, B
Business Administration and Management, B
Business Administration, Management and
    Operations, M
Business Teacher Education, B
Business/Commerce, B
Chemistry, B
Child Care and Support Services Management, A
Clinical Laboratory Science/Medical
    Technology/Technologist, B
Communication Disorders, M
Community Psychology, M
Computer and Information Sciences, B
Computer Science, M
Counseling Psychology, M
Counselor Education/School Counseling and
    Guidance Services, M
Early Childhood Education and Teaching, M
Economics, BM
Education, MD
Educational Leadership and Administration, O
Educational Media/Instructional Technology, M
Elementary and Middle School
    Administration/Principalship, B
Elementary Education and Teaching, B
English, M
English Composition, B
English Language and Literature, B
English/Language Arts Teacher Education, B
Environmental Studies, B
Family and Consumer Sciences/Home Economics
    Teacher Education, B
Family and Consumer Sciences/Human Sciences, B
Finance, B
Foreign Language Teacher Education, M
French Language and Literature, B
General Studies, A
Geographic Information Systems, O
Geography, BO
Health Education, M
History, BM
Home Economics, M
Human Development, M
Insurance, B
International Business/Trade/Commerce, M
Journalism, B
Junior High/Intermediate/Middle School Education
    and Teaching, B
Kinesiology and Exercise Science, B
Kinesiology and Movement Studies, M
Library Science, M
Management Information Systems and Services, B
Marketing/Marketing Management, B
Mathematics, BM
Mathematics Teacher Education, B
Medical Physics, M
Medical Radiologic Technology/Science - Radiation
    Therapist, B
Music, BM
Music Performance, B
Music Teacher Education, M
Music Theory and Composition, M
Nuclear Medical Technology/Technologist, B
Nursing, M

Nursing - Advanced Practice, M
Nursing - Registered Nurse Training, B
Occupational Therapy/Therapist, BM
Performance, M
Philosophy, B
Physical Education Teaching and Coaching, B
Physical Sciences, B
Physical Therapist Assistant, A
Physical Therapy/Therapist, ABMD
Physics, B
Political Science and Government, B
Psychology, BMD
Public Administration, B
Reading Teacher Education, BM
Religion/Religious Studies, B
School Psychology, MD
Science Teacher Education/General Science
    Teacher Education, B
Social Studies Teacher Education, B
Sociology, B
Spanish Language and Literature, B
Special Education and Teaching, BM
Speech and Rhetorical Studies, B
Student Personnel Services, M

UNIVERSITY OF THE OZARKS

Accounting, B
Art Teacher Education, B
Art/Art Studies, General, B
Biology Teacher Education, B
Biology/Biological Sciences, B
Business Administration and Management, B
Business Teacher Education, B
Chemistry, B
Communication Studies/Speech Communication
    and Rhetoric, B
Drama and Dramatics/Theatre Arts, B
English Language and Literature, B
English/Language Arts Teacher Education, B
Environmental Studies, B
General Studies, B
History, B
Junior High/Intermediate/Middle School Education
    and Teaching, B
Marketing/Marketing Management, B
Mathematics, B
Mathematics Teacher Education, B
Music, B
Philosophy and Religious Studies, B
Physical Education Teaching and Coaching, B
Political Science and Government, B
Pre-Dentistry Studies, B
Pre-Medicine/Pre-Medical Studies, B
Pre-Veterinary Studies, B
Psychology, B
Religious Education, B
Science Teacher Education/General Science
    Teacher Education, B
Secondary Education and Teaching, B
Social Sciences, B
Social Studies Teacher Education, B
Sociology, B
Special Education and Teaching, B
Teacher Education, Multiple Levels, B

UNIVERSITY OF PHOENIX-LITTLE ROCK CAMPUS

Business Administration and Management, B
Business Administration, Management and
    Operations, M
Criminal Justice/Law Enforcement Administration, B
Information Technology, B

WILLIAMS BAPTIST COLLEGE

Administrative Assistant and Secretarial Science, A
Art Teacher Education, B
Art/Art Studies, General, B
Biology/Biological Sciences, B
Business Administration and Management, AB
Computer and Information Sciences, B
Divinity/Ministry (BD, MDiv.), B
Education, B
Elementary Education and Teaching, B
English Language and Literature, B
Fine/Studio Arts, B
History, B

Kindergarten/PreSchool Education and Teaching, B
Liberal Arts and Sciences Studies and
    Humanities, AB
Music, AB
Music Teacher Education, B
Pastoral Studies/Counseling, B
Physical Education Teaching and Coaching, B
Pre-Dentistry Studies, B
Pre-Law Studies, B
Pre-Medicine/Pre-Medical Studies, B
Psychology, B
Religion/Religious Studies, B
Religious Education, B
Religious/Sacred Music, B
Theology/Theological Studies, AB

California

ACADEMY OF ART UNIVERSITY

Advertising, AB
Advertising and Public Relations, M
Animation, Interactive Technology, Video Graphics
    and Special Effects, AB
Apparel and Textiles, AB
Applied Art, AB
Applied Arts and Design, M
Architecture, M
Cinematography and Film/Video Production, AB
Clothing and Textiles, M
Commercial and Advertising Art, AB
Computer Art and Design, M
Computer Graphics, AB
Digital Communication and Media/Multimedia, AB
Drawing, AB
Fashion Merchandising, AB
Fashion/Apparel Design, AB
Fiber, Textile and Weaving Arts, AB
Film, Television, and Video Production, M
Film/Cinema Studies, AB
Fine Arts and Art Studies, M
Fine/Studio Arts, AB
Graphic Communications, AB
Graphic Design, ABM
Illustration, ABM
Industrial Design, ABM
Interior Design, ABM
Metal and Jewelry Arts, AB
Painting, ABM
Photography, ABM
Printmaking, ABM
Radio and Television, AB
Sculpture, ABM
Textile Design, M
Web/Multimedia Management and Webmaster, AB

ALLAN HANCOCK COLLEGE

Accounting, A
Administrative Assistant and Secretarial Science, A
Aerospace, Aeronautical and Astronautical
    Engineering, A
Agribusiness, A
Applied Art, A
Architectural Engineering Technology/Technician, A
Art/Art Studies, General, A
Automobile/Automotive Mechanics
    Technology/Technician, A
Biology/Biological Sciences, A
Business Administration and Management, A
Chemistry, A
Civil Engineering Technology/Technician, A
Commercial and Advertising Art, A
Computer Engineering Technology/Technician, A
Computer Science, A
Cosmetology/Cosmetologist, A
Criminal Justice/Police Science, A
Dance, A
Dental Assisting/Assistant, A
Dietetics/Dieticians, A
Electrical, Electronic and Communications
    Engineering Technology/Technician, A
Engineering, A
Engineering Technology, A
English Language and Literature, A
Environmental Engineering
    Technology/Environmental Technology, A

Family and Consumer Economics and Related
    Services, A
Fashion/Apparel Design, A
Film/Cinema Studies, A
Fire Science/Firefighting, A
Heavy Equipment Maintenance
    Technology/Technician, A
Human Services, A
Information Science/Studies, A
Interior Design, A
International Relations and Affairs, A
Kindergarten/PreSchool Education and Teaching, A
Legal Administrative Assistant/Secretary, A
Liberal Arts and Sciences Studies and
    Humanities, A
Licensed Practical/Vocational Nurse Training, A
Machine Tool Technology/Machinist, A
Medical/Clinical Assistant, A
Music, A
Nursing - Registered Nurse Training, A
Parks, Recreation, Leisure and Fitness Studies, A
Photography, A
Physical Education Teaching and Coaching, A
Physical Therapy/Therapist, A
Physics, A
Social Sciences, A
Spanish Language and Literature, A
Welding Technology/Welder, A

ALLIANT INTERNATIONAL UNIVERSITY

Business Administration and Management, B
Education, B
Hotel/Motel Administration/Management, B
International Business/Trade/Commerce, B
International Relations and Affairs, B
Journalism, B
Latin American Studies, B
Management Information Systems and Services, B
Psychology, B
Tourism and Travel Services Management, B

AMERICAN ACADEMY OF DRAMATIC ARTS/HOLLYWOOD

Drama and Dramatics/Theatre Arts, A

AMERICAN INTERCONTINENTAL UNIVERSITY

Business Administration and Management, AB
Business Administration, Management and
    Operations, M
Cinematography and Film/Video Production, B
Commercial and Advertising Art, AB
Criminal Justice/Law Enforcement
    Administration, AB
Fashion Merchandising, AB
Fashion/Apparel Design, AB
Interior Design, AB
Management Information Systems and
    Services, BM
Marketing/Marketing Management, B
Photography, B

AMERICAN RIVER COLLEGE

Accounting, A
Administrative Assistant and Secretarial Science, A
Advertising, A
Art/Art Studies, General, A
Automobile/Automotive Mechanics
    Technology/Technician, A
Biological and Physical Sciences, A
Business Administration and Management, A
Carpentry/Carpenter, A
Child Development, A
Computer and Information Sciences, A
Computer and Information Systems Security, A
Computer Engineering Technology/Technician, A
Computer Graphics, A
Computer Programming, A
Computer Programming, Specific Applications, A
Computer
    Programming, Vendor/Product Certification, A
Computer Programming/Programmer, A
Computer Software and Media Applications, A
Computer Systems Networking and
    Telecommunications, A

Construction Engineering Technology/Technician, A
Consumer Merchandising/Retailing Management, A
Culinary Arts/Chef Training, A
Data Entry/Microcomputer Applications, A
Data Processing and Data Processing
    Technology/Technician, A
Drafting and Design Technology/Technician, A
Drama and Dramatics/Theatre Arts, A
Electrical, Electronic and Communications
    Engineering Technology/Technician, A
Engineering Technology, A
Family and Consumer Sciences/Home Economics
    Teacher Education, A
Fashion Merchandising, A
Fashion/Apparel Design, A
Finance, A
Fire Science/Firefighting, A
Forestry Technology/Technician, A
Gerontology, A
Horticultural Science, A
Hospitality and Recreation Marketing Operations, A
Hotel/Motel Administration/Management, A
Human Services, A
Interior Design, A
Journalism, A
Kindergarten/PreSchool Education and Teaching, A
Landscape Architecture, A
Legal Administrative Assistant/Secretary, A
Legal Assistant/Paralegal, A
Liberal Arts and Sciences Studies and
    Humanities, A
Management Information Systems and Services, A
Marketing/Marketing Management, A
Mathematics, A
Medical Administrative Assistant/Secretary, A
Music, A
Music Management and Merchandising, A
Natural Resources Management/Development and
    Policy, A
Nursing - Registered Nurse Training, A
Parks, Recreation, Leisure and Fitness Studies, A
Physical Sciences, A
Pre-Engineering, A
Real Estate, A
Respiratory Care Therapy/Therapist, A
Sign Language Interpretation and Translation, A
Social Sciences, A
Special Products Marketing Operations, A
System Administration/Administrator, A
Technology Education/Industrial Arts, A
Web Page, Digital/Multimedia and Information
    Resources Design, A
Web/Multimedia Management and Webmaster, A
Welding Technology/Welder, A

ANTELOPE VALLEY COLLEGE

Administrative Assistant and Secretarial Science, A
Aircraft Powerplant Technology/Technician, A
Airframe Mechanics and Aircraft Maintenance
    Technology/Technician, A
Apparel and Textiles, A
Autobody/Collision and Repair
    Technology/Technician, A
Automobile/Automotive Mechanics
    Technology/Technician, A
Avionics Maintenance Technology/Technician, A
Biology/Biological Sciences, A
Business Administration and Management, A
Business/Commerce, A
Child Care and Support Services Management, A
Child Development, A
Cinematography and Film/Video Production, A
Computer and Information Sciences, A
Computer Graphics, A
Computer Programming/Programmer, A
Construction Engineering Technology/Technician, A
Corrections, A
Criminal Justice/Law Enforcement Administration, A
Criminal Justice/Police Science, A
Data Processing and Data Processing
    Technology/Technician, A
Drafting and Design Technology/Technician, A
Electrical, Electronic and Communications
    Engineering Technology/Technician, A
Engineering, A
Engineering Technology, A

Family and Consumer Sciences/Home Economics
    Teacher Education, A
Fiber, Textile and Weaving Arts, A
Fire Protection and Safety Technology/Technician, A
Foods, Nutrition, and Wellness Studies, A
Health and Physical Education, A
Heating, Air Conditioning, Ventilation and
    Refrigeration Maintenance
    Technology/Technician, A
Interior Design, A
Liberal Arts and Sciences Studies and
    Humanities, A
Marketing/Marketing Management, A
Mathematics, A
Medical Administrative Assistant/Secretary, A
Music, A
Nursing - Registered Nurse Training, A
Ornamental Horticulture, A
Photography, A
Physical Sciences, A
Real Estate, A
Teacher Assistant/Aide, A
Welding Technology/Welder, A
Work and Family Studies, A

ANTIOCH UNIVERSITY LOS ANGELES

Clinical Psychology, M
Education, M
Human Resources Development, M
Liberal Arts and Sciences Studies and
    Humanities, B
Management, M
Organizational Management, M
Psychology, M
Writing, MO

ANTIOCH UNIVERSITY SANTA BARBARA

Clinical Psychology, MD
Counseling Psychology, M
Education, M
General Studies, B
Organizational Management, M
Psychology, M

ARGOSY UNIVERSITY/ORANGE COUNTY

Business Administration, Management and
    Operations, AMD
Clinical Psychology, MD
Counseling Psychology, MD
Criminal Justice/Law Enforcement Administration, A
Curriculum and Instruction, MD
Education, MD
Educational Leadership and Administration, MD
Finance and Banking, M
Health Services Administration, M
Human Resources Management and Services, M
International Business/Trade/Commerce, D
International Trade, M
Legal Assistant/Paralegal, A
Management, D
Management Information Systems and
    Services, MD
Marketing, MD
Medical/Clinical Assistant, A
Psychology, MD

ARGOSY UNIVERSITY/SAN DIEGO

Business Administration, Management and
    Operations, A
Criminal Justice/Law Enforcement Administration, A
Legal Assistant/Paralegal, A
Medical/Clinical Assistant, A

ARGOSY UNIVERSITY/SAN FRANCISCO BAY AREA

Business Administration, Management and
    Operations, MD
Clinical Psychology, MD
Counseling Psychology, MD
Curriculum and Instruction, MD
Education, MD
Educational Leadership and Administration, MD
Educational Media/Instructional Technology, M

Psychology, MD
Special Education and Teaching, M

ARGOSY UNIVERSITY/SANTA MONICA

Business Administration, Management and
    Operations, A
Criminal Justice/Law Enforcement Administration, A
Legal Assistant/Paralegal, A
Medical/Clinical Assistant, A

ART CENTER COLLEGE OF DESIGN

Advertising, B
Art/Art Studies, General, B
Cinematography and Film/Video Production, B
Commercial and Advertising Art, B
Commercial Photography, B
Computer Art and Design, M
Design and Applied Arts, BM
Environmental Design/Architecture, BM
Film, Television, and Video Production, M
Film/Cinema Studies, B
Film/Video and Photographic Arts, B
Fine Arts and Art Studies, BM
Fine/Studio Arts, B
Graphic Design, B
Illustration, B
Industrial Design, BM
Interior Design, B
Intermedia/Multimedia, B
Painting, B
Photography, B
Visual and Performing Arts, B

THE ART INSTITUTE OF CALIFORNIA-INLAND EMPIRE

Animation, Interactive Technology, Video Graphics
    and Special Effects, B
Graphic Design, AB
Interior Design, B
Web Page, Digital/Multimedia and Information
    Resources Design, B

THE ART INSTITUTE OF CALIFORNIA-LOS ANGELES

Advertising, B
Animation, Interactive Technology, Video Graphics
    and Special Effects, B
Cinematography and Film/Video Production, AB
Cooking and Related Culinary Arts, AB
Graphic Design, AB
Interior Design, B
Web Page, Digital/Multimedia and Information
    Resources Design, AB

THE ART INSTITUTE OF CALIFORNIA-ORANGE COUNTY

Advertising, B
Animation, Interactive Technology, Video Graphics
    and Special Effects, B
Computer Graphics, AB
Cooking and Related Culinary Arts, A
Graphic Design, AB
Industrial Design, B
Interior Design, B
Restaurant, Culinary, and Catering
    Management/Manager, B

THE ART INSTITUTE OF CALIFORNIA-SAN DIEGO

Advertising, AB
Baking and Pastry Arts/Baker/Pastry Chef, AB
Commercial and Advertising Art, AB
Communication, Journalism and Related
    Programs, B
Cooking and Related Culinary Arts, AB
Culinary Arts/Chef Training, A
Design and Applied Arts, B
Digital Communication and Media/Multimedia, B
Graphic Design, AB
Interior Architecture, B
Interior Design, B
Intermedia/Multimedia, B
Restaurant, Culinary, and Catering
    Management/Manager, B

Restaurant/Food Services Management, B

THE ART INSTITUTE OF CALIFORNIA-SAN FRANCISCO

Advertising, B
Animation, Interactive Technology, Video Graphics and Special Effects, B
Business, Management, Marketing, and Related Support Services, AB
Commercial and Advertising Art, AB
Computer Graphics, AB
Computer Programming, Specific Applications, B
Fashion/Apparel Design, AB
Graphic Design, B
Interior Design, B
Web Page, Digital/Multimedia and Information Resources Design, B

AZUSA PACIFIC UNIVERSITY

Accounting, B
Applied Art, B
Athletic Training and Sports Medicine, B
Bible/Biblical Studies, B
Biochemistry, B
Biology/Biological Sciences, B
Business Administration and Management, B
Business Administration, Management and Operations, M
Chemistry, B
Clinical Psychology, MD
Communication Studies/Speech Communication and Rhetoric, B
Community Psychology, M
Computer Science, BMO
Counselor Education/School Counseling and Guidance Services, M
Curriculum and Instruction, M
Divinity/Ministry (BD, MDiv.), B
Education, MD
Educational Administration and Supervision, MD
Educational Leadership and Administration, M
Educational Media/Instructional Technology, M
English as a Second Language, M
English Language and Literature, B
Ethics, M
Ethnic and Cultural Studies, B
Higher Education/Higher Education Administration, M
History, B
Human Resources Development, M
International Business/Trade/Commerce, M
International Relations and Affairs, B
Liberal Arts and Sciences Studies and Humanities, B
Library Science, M
Management Information Systems and Services, B
Management Strategy and Policy, M
Marketing/Marketing Management, B
Marriage and Family Therapy/Counseling, M
Mathematics, B
Multilingual and Multicultural Education, M
Music, BM
Music Teacher Education, M
Natural Sciences, B
Non-Profit/Public/Organizational Management, M
Nursing, M
Nursing - Registered Nurse Training, B
Organizational Management, M
Pastoral Studies/Counseling, MP
Philosophy, B
Physical Education Teaching and Coaching, BM
Physical Therapy/Therapist, D
Physics, B
Political Science and Government, B
Pre-Engineering, B
Pre-Law Studies, B
Psychology, BMD
Public Health (MPH, DPH), B
Religion/Religious Studies, BM
Religious Education, M
School Psychology, M
Social Sciences, B
Social Work, B
Sociology, B
Spanish Language and Literature, B
Special Education and Teaching, M

Student Personnel Services, M
Telecommunications, O
Theology and Religious Vocations, MD
Theology/Theological Studies, B
Web Page, Digital/Multimedia and Information Resources Design, B

BAKERSFIELD COLLEGE

Accounting, A
Administrative Assistant and Secretarial Science, A
Agricultural Business and Management, A
Agriculture, A
Animal Sciences, A
Anthropology, A
Architectural Engineering Technology/Technician, A
Art Teacher Education, A
Art/Art Studies, General, A
Automobile/Automotive Mechanics Technology/Technician, A
Biology/Biological Sciences, A
Broadcast Journalism, A
Business Administration and Management, A
Carpentry/Carpenter, A
Chemistry, A
Child Development, A
Computer Science, A
Corrections, A
Cosmetology/Cosmetologist, A
Criminal Justice/Law Enforcement Administration, A
Criminal Justice/Police Science, A
Culinary Arts/Chef Training, A
Data Processing and Data Processing Technology/Technician, A
Dental Hygiene/Hygienist, A
Developmental and Child Psychology, A
Dietetics/Dieticians, A
Drafting and Design Technology/Technician, A
Drama and Dramatics/Theatre Arts, A
Economics, A
Electrical, Electronic and Communications Engineering Technology/Technician, A
Emergency Medical Technology/Technician (EMT Paramedic), A
Engineering, A
English Language and Literature, A
Environmental Engineering Technology/Environmental Technology, A
Family and Consumer Economics and Related Services, A
Finance, A
Fire Science/Firefighting, A
Foods, Nutrition, and Wellness Studies, A
Forestry, A
French Language and Literature, A
Geography, A
Geology/Earth Science, A
German Language and Literature, A
History, A
Horticultural Science, A
Hotel/Motel Administration/Management, A
Human Services, A
Industrial Radiologic Technology/Technician, A
Industrial Technology/Technician, A
Information Science/Studies, A
Interior Design, A
Journalism, A
Legal Administrative Assistant/Secretary, A
Liberal Arts and Sciences Studies and Humanities, A
Machine Tool Technology/Machinist, A
Marketing/Marketing Management, A
Mathematics, A
Music, A
Nursing - Registered Nurse Training, A
Ornamental Horticulture, A
Parks, Recreation, Leisure and Fitness Studies, A
Petroleum Technology/Technician, A
Philosophy, A
Photography, A
Physical Education Teaching and Coaching, A
Physics, A
Pipefitting/Pipefitter and Sprinkler Fitter, A
Political Science and Government, A
Psychology, A
Real Estate, A
Sociology, A

Spanish Language and Literature, A
Speech and Rhetorical Studies, A
Survey Technology/Surveying, A
Technology Education/Industrial Arts, A
Welding Technology/Welder, A
Wood Science and Wood Products/Pulp and Paper Technology, A

BARSTOW COLLEGE

Accounting, A
Administrative Assistant and Secretarial Science, A
Automobile/Automotive Mechanics Technology/Technician, A
Business Administration and Management, A
Child Development, A
Computer Science, A
Cosmetology/Cosmetologist, A
Drafting and Design Technology/Technician, A
Education, A
Electrical, Electronic and Communications Engineering Technology/Technician, A
Humanities/Humanistic Studies, A
Kindergarten/PreSchool Education and Teaching, A
Liberal Arts and Sciences Studies and Humanities, A
Mathematics, A
Medical/Clinical Assistant, A
Physical Education Teaching and Coaching, A
Social Sciences, A

BERKELEY CITY COLLEGE

Accounting, A
Art/Art Studies, General, A
Biology Technician/BioTechnology Laboratory Technician, A
Business Administration and Management, A
Business/Commerce, A
Computer and Information Sciences, A
Computer and Information Systems Security, A
Computer Graphics, A
Computer Software and Media Applications, A
Creative Writing, A
Data Entry/Microcomputer Applications, A
English Composition, A
English Language and Literature, A
Fine/Studio Arts, A
General Studies, A
Liberal Arts and Sciences Studies and Humanities, A
Medical Administrative Assistant/Secretary, A
Office Management and Supervision, A
Spanish Language and Literature, A
Web Page, Digital/Multimedia and Information Resources Design, A

BETHANY UNIVERSITY

Ancient Near Eastern and Biblical Languages, Literatures, and Linguistics, B
Bible/Biblical Studies, B
Divinity/Ministry (BD, MDiv.), B
Drama and Dramatics/Theatre Arts, B
Education, BM
Educational Leadership and Administration, M
Elementary Education and Teaching, B
English Language and Literature, B
Interdisciplinary Studies, B
International Relations and Affairs, B
Kindergarten/PreSchool Education and Teaching, AB
Liberal Arts and Sciences Studies and Humanities, AB
Music Teacher Education, B
Pastoral Studies/Counseling, B
Psychology, B
Religious/Sacred Music, B
Social Sciences, B
Substance Abuse/Addiction Counseling, B
Theology/Theological Studies, B

BETHESDA CHRISTIAN UNIVERSITY

Bible/Biblical Studies, B
Conducting, B
Design and Visual Communications, B
Divinity/Ministry (BD, MDiv.), B
Early Childhood Education and Teaching, B
Missions/Missionary Studies and Missiology, B

Music Management and Merchandising, B
Music Theory and Composition, B
Pastoral Studies/Counseling, B
Piano and Organ, B
Religion/Religious Studies, M
Religious Education, B
Religious/Sacred Music, B
Theology and Religious Vocations, MP
Violin, Viola, Guitar and Other Stringed
   Instruments, B

BIOLA UNIVERSITY

Adult and Continuing Education and Teaching, B
Anthropology, B
Bible/Biblical Studies, B
Bilingual and Multilingual Education, B
Biochemistry, B
Biology/Biological Sciences, B
Business Administration and Management, B
Business Administration, Management and
   Operations, M
Clinical Psychology, B
Commercial and Advertising Art, B
Communication Disorders, B
Computer and Information Sciences, B
Cultural Studies, MDO
Divinity/Ministry (BD, MDiv.), B
Drawing, B
Education, BM
Elementary Education and Teaching, B
English as a Second Language, MO
English Language and Literature, B
Ethics, M
Fine/Studio Arts, B
History, B
Humanities/Humanistic Studies, B
Kinesiology and Exercise Science, B
Linguistics, M
Mathematics, B
Missions/Missionary Studies and Missiology, BMD
Music, B
Nursing - Registered Nurse Training, B
Organizational Management, M
Pastoral Studies/Counseling, B
Philosophy, B
Physical Education Teaching and Coaching, B
Physical Sciences, B
Pre-Law Studies, B
Psychology, BMD
Radio and Television, B
Religion/Religious Studies, BM
Religious Education, BMD
Secondary Education and Teaching, B
Social Sciences, B
Sociology, B
Spanish Language and Literature, B
Teacher Education, Multiple Levels, B
Theology and Religious Vocations, MDP

BROOKS COLLEGE (LONG BEACH)

Animation, Interactive Technology, Video Graphics
   and Special Effects, A
Apparel and Textiles, A
Commercial and Advertising Art, A
Fashion Merchandising, A
Fashion/Apparel Design, A
Interior Design, A
Telecommunications Technology/Technician, A

BROOKS INSTITUTE OF PHOTOGRAPHY

Cinematography and Film/Video Production, B
Photography, BM

BUTTE COLLEGE

Accounting, A
Administrative Assistant and Secretarial Science, A
Agricultural Business and Management, A
Agricultural Economics, A
Agriculture, A
Agronomy and Crop Science, A
Animal Sciences, A
Applied Art, A
Art/Art Studies, General, A

Automobile/Automotive Mechanics
   Technology/Technician, A
Biology/Biological Sciences, A
Business Teacher Education, A
Civil Engineering Technology/Technician, A
Clinical Laboratory Science/Medical
   Technology/Technologist, A
Commercial and Advertising Art, A
Construction Engineering Technology/Technician, A
Cosmetology/Cosmetologist, A
Court Reporting/Court Reporter, A
Criminal Justice/Law Enforcement Administration, A
Criminal Justice/Police Science, A
Data Processing and Data Processing
   Technology/Technician, A
Drafting and Design Technology/Technician, A
Electrical, Electronic and Communications
   Engineering Technology/Technician, A
Family and Consumer Economics and Related
   Services, A
Family and Consumer Sciences/Human Sciences, A
Fashion Merchandising, A
Fashion/Apparel Design, A
Finance, A
Fire Science/Firefighting, A
Horticultural Science, A
Kindergarten/PreSchool Education and Teaching, A
Landscape Architecture, A
Legal Administrative Assistant/Secretary, A
Liberal Arts and Sciences Studies and
   Humanities, A
Licensed Practical/Vocational Nurse Training, A
Marketing/Marketing Management, A
Mathematics, A
Medical Administrative Assistant/Secretary, A
Music, A
Natural Resources Management/Development and
   Policy, A
Nursing - Registered Nurse Training, A
Ornamental Horticulture, A
Parks, Recreation and Leisure Facilities
   Management, A
Photography, A
Physical Education Teaching and Coaching, A
Physical Sciences, A
Political Science and Government, A
Psychology, A
Public Health (MPH, DPH), A
Real Estate, A
Respiratory Care Therapy/Therapist, A
Social Sciences, A
Telecommunications Technology/Technician, A
Tourism and Travel Services Management, A
Welding Technology/Welder, A

CABRILLO COLLEGE

Accounting, A
Biological and Physical Sciences, A
Building/Construction
   Finishing, Management, and Inspection, A
Business Administration and Management, A
Business Machine Repairer, A
Cartography, A
Ceramic Arts and Ceramics, A
Child Development, A
Computer Programming/Programmer, A
Computer Science, A
Consumer Merchandising/Retailing Management, A
Data Processing and Data Processing
   Technology/Technician, A
Dental Hygiene/Hygienist, A
Drafting and Design Technology/Technician, A
Electrical, Electronic and Communications
   Engineering Technology/Technician, A
Energy Management and Systems
   Technology/Technician, A
Fire Science/Firefighting, A
Food Science, A
Food Technology and Processing, A
Health Information/Medical Records
   Administration/Administrator, A
Horticultural Science, A
Industrial Design, A
Kindergarten/PreSchool Education and Teaching, A
Liberal Arts and Sciences Studies and
   Humanities, A

Medical Administrative Assistant/Secretary, A
Natural Sciences, A
Nursing - Registered Nurse Training, A
Parks, Recreation, Leisure and Fitness Studies, A
Physical Education Teaching and Coaching, A
Pre-Engineering, A
Public Health (MPH, DPH), A
Real Estate, A
Solar Energy Technology/Technician, A
Spanish Language and Literature, A
Special Products Marketing Operations, A
Welding Technology/Welder, A
Wildlife and Wildlands Science and Management, A
Women's Studies, A

CALIFORNIA BAPTIST UNIVERSITY

Accounting, B
Behavioral Sciences, B
Bible/Biblical Studies, B
Biology/Biological Sciences, B
Business Administration and Management, B
Business Administration, Management and
   Operations, M
Christian Studies, B
Communication Studies/Speech Communication
   and Rhetoric, B
Communication, Journalism and Related
   Programs, B
Counseling Psychology, M
Criminal Justice/Law Enforcement Administration, B
Curriculum and Instruction, M
Drama and Dramatics/Theatre Arts, B
Education, M
Educational Leadership and Administration, M
Educational Media/Instructional Technology, M
English, M
English Language and Literature, B
Health and Physical Education/Fitness, B
History, B
Information Science/Studies, B
Interdisciplinary Studies, B
Journalism, B
Kinesiology and Exercise Science, B
Kinesiology and Movement Studies, M
Liberal Arts and Sciences Studies and
   Humanities, B
Marriage and Family Therapy/Counseling, M
Mathematics, B
Multilingual and Multicultural Education, M
Music, BM
Music Performance, B
Music Theory and Composition, B
Philosophy, B
Political Science and Government, B
Pre-Theology/Pre-Ministerial Studies, B
Psychology, B
Reading Teacher Education, M
Social Sciences, B
Sociology, B
Special Education and Teaching, M
Theological and Ministerial Studies, B
Theology/Theological Studies, B
Visual and Performing Arts, B
Vocational and Technical Education, M
Youth Ministry, B

CALIFORNIA CHRISTIAN COLLEGE

Bible/Biblical Studies, AB
Pre-Theology/Pre-Ministerial Studies, B

CALIFORNIA COAST UNIVERSITY

Business Administration and Management, AB
Health/Health Care Administration/Management, B
Psychology, AB

CALIFORNIA COLLEGE OF THE ARTS

Applied Art, B
Architecture, BM
Art/Art Studies, General, B
Ceramic Arts and Ceramics, BM
Commercial and Advertising Art, B
Crafts, M
Design and Applied Arts, M
Drawing, B
Fashion/Apparel Design, B
Fiber, Textile and Weaving Arts, B

Film, Television, and Video Production, M
Film, Television, and Video Theory and Criticism, M
Film/Cinema Studies, B
Fine Arts and Art Studies, M
Fine/Studio Arts, B
Industrial Design, B
Interior Architecture, B
Jewelry/Metalsmithing, M
Metal and Jewelry Arts, B
Museology/Museum Studies, M
Painting, BM
Photography, BM
Printmaking, BM
Sculpture, BM
Textile Design, M
Writing, M

CALIFORNIA CULINARY ACADEMY

Culinary Arts/Chef Training, A
Restaurant, Culinary, and Catering
    Management/Manager, A

CALIFORNIA DESIGN COLLEGE

Apparel and Accessories Marketing Operations, A
Fashion Merchandising, A
Fashion/Apparel Design, A

CALIFORNIA INSTITUTE OF THE ARTS

Acting, B
Applied Arts and Design, MO
Art/Art Studies, General, B
Commercial and Advertising Art, B
Composition, MO
Computer Graphics, B
Dance, BMO
Drama and Dramatics/Theatre Arts, B
Dramatic/Theatre Arts and Stagecraft, B
Film, Television, and Video Production, MO
Film/Cinema Studies, B
Film/Video and Photographic Arts, B
Fine Arts and Art Studies, MO
Fine/Studio Arts, B
Graphic Design, BMO
Jazz/Jazz Studies, B
Music, BMO
Music Performance, B
Music Theory and Composition, B
Performance, MO
Photography, BMO
Piano and Organ, B
Sculpture, B
Technical Theatre/Theatre Design and
    Technology, B
Theater, MO
Theatre/Theatre Arts Management, B
Violin, Viola, Guitar and Other Stringed
    Instruments, B
Voice and Opera, B
Writing, MO

CALIFORNIA INSTITUTE OF INTEGRAL STUDIES

Anthropology, MD
Art Therapy/Therapist, M
Clinical Psychology, D
Counseling Psychology, M
Drama Therapy, M
Health Psychology, M
Humanities/Humanistic Studies, MD
Philosophy, MD
Psychology, BMD
Religion/Religious Studies, MD
Theology and Religious Vocations, M

CALIFORNIA INSTITUTE OF TECHNOLOGY

Aerospace, Aeronautical and Astronautical
    Engineering, BMDO
Applied Mathematics, BMD
Applied Physics, MD
Astronomy, BD
Biochemistry, BD
Bioengineering, MD
Biological and Biomedical Sciences, D
Biology/Biological Sciences, B

Biophysics, D
Business/Managerial Economics, B
Cell Biology and Anatomy, D
Chemical Engineering, BMD
Chemical Physics, B
Chemistry, BMD
Civil Engineering, BMD
Comparative Literature, B
Computational Sciences, MD
Computer Engineering, B
Computer Science, BMD
Developmental Biology and Embryology, D
Economics, BD
Electrical Engineering, MD
Electrical, Electronics and Communications
    Engineering, B
Engineering and Applied Sciences, MDO
Engineering Physics, B
Environmental Engineering
    Technology/Environmental Technology, MD
Environmental/Environmental Health Engineering, B
General Studies, B
Genetics, D
Geochemistry, BMD
Geology/Earth Science, BMD
Geophysics and Seismology, BMD
History, B
Immunology, D
Inorganic Chemistry, B
Materials Sciences, MD
Mathematics, BD
Mechanical Engineering, BMDO
Mechanics, MD
Molecular Biology, D
Molecular Biophysics, D
Neurobiology and Neurophysiology, D
Neuroscience, MD
Organic Chemistry, B
Physical Sciences, B
Physics, BD
Planetary Astronomy and Science, BMD
Political Science and Government, D
Science, Technology and Society, B
Social Sciences, BMD
Systems Engineering, MD

CALIFORNIA LUTHERAN UNIVERSITY

Accounting, B
Art Teacher Education, B
Art/Art Studies, General, B
Athletic Training and Sports Medicine, B
Biochemistry, B
Biology/Biological Sciences, B
Biomedical/Medical Engineering, B
Business Administration and Management, B
Business Administration, Management and
    Operations, M
Chemistry, B
Clinical Psychology, M
Computer and Information Sciences, B
Computer Science, B
Counselor Education/School Counseling and
    Guidance Services, M
Criminal Justice/Law Enforcement Administration, B
Digital Communication and Media/Multimedia, B
Drama and Dramatics/Theatre Arts, B
Economics, B
Education, MO
Educational Administration and Supervision, M
English Language and Literature, B
Entrepreneurship/Entrepreneurial Studies, M
Finance and Banking, M
French Language and Literature, B
French Language Teacher Education, B
Geology/Earth Science, B
German Language and Literature, B
German Language Teacher Education, B
Health Services Administration, M
History, B
Information Science/Studies, B
Interdisciplinary Studies, B
International Business/Trade/Commerce, M
International Relations and Affairs, B
Journalism, B
Kinesiology and Exercise Science, B

Liberal Arts and Sciences Studies and
    Humanities, B
Management Information Systems and Services, M
Marketing, M
Marketing/Marketing Management, B
Marriage and Family Therapy/Counseling, M
Mass Communication/Media Studies, B
Mathematics, B
Mathematics Teacher Education, B
Molecular Biology, B
Multi-/Interdisciplinary Studies, B
Music, B
Music Teacher Education, B
Organizational Behavior Studies, M
Philosophy, B
Physical Education Teaching and Coaching, B
Physics, B
Political Science and Government, B
Psychology, BM
Psychology Teacher Education, B
Public Administration, M
Public Policy Analysis, M
Public Relations, Advertising, and Applied
    Communication, B
Public Relations/Image Management, B
Reading Teacher Education, M
Religion/Religious Studies, B
Science Teacher Education/General Science
    Teacher Education, B
Social Science Teacher Education, B
Social Sciences, B
Sociology, B
Spanish Language and Literature, B
Spanish Language Teacher Education, B
Special Education and Teaching, M

CALIFORNIA MARITIME ACADEMY

Business Administration and Management, B
Engineering Technologies/Technicians, B
Marine Technology, B
Mechanical Engineering, B

CALIFORNIA NATIONAL UNIVERSITY FOR ADVANCED STUDIES

Business Administration and Management, B
Business Administration, Management and
    Operations, M
Computer Science, B
Engineering, B
Engineering and Applied Sciences, M
Quality Control Technology/Technician, B

CALIFORNIA POLYTECHNIC STATE UNIVERSITY, SAN LUIS OBISPO

Aerospace, Aeronautical and Astronautical
    Engineering, BM
Agricultural Business and Management, B
Agricultural Economics, M
Agricultural Sciences, M
Agricultural/Biological Engineering and
    Bioengineering, B
Agriculture, B
Agronomy and Crop Science, B
Animal Sciences, B
Applied Art, B
Architectural Engineering, B
Architecture, BM
Biochemical Engineering, M
Biochemistry, B
Biological and Biomedical Sciences, M
Biology/Biological Sciences, B
Business Administration and Management, B
Business Administration, Management and
    Operations, MO
Chemistry, B
City/Urban, Community and Regional Planning, B
Civil Engineering, BMO
Commercial and Advertising Art, B
Computer Engineering, B
Computer Science, BM
Counselor Education/School Counseling and
    Guidance Services, M
Curriculum and Instruction, M
Dairy Science, B
Developmental and Child Psychology, B
Economics, B

Education, M
Educational Administration and Supervision, M
Electrical Engineering, M
Electrical, Electronics and Communications
  Engineering, B
Engineering and Applied Sciences, MO
Engineering Science, B
English, M
English Language and Literature, B
Environmental Biology, B
Environmental Engineering
  Technology/Environmental Technology, MO
Environmental/Environmental Health Engineering, B
Farm/Farm and Ranch Management, B
Food Science, B
Foods, Nutrition, and Wellness Studies, B
Forestry, BM
Graphic and Printing Equipment Operator
  Production, B
History, B
Horticultural Science, B
Human Resources Management/Personnel
  Administration, B
Industrial and Manufacturing Management, M
Industrial Engineering, B
Industrial Technology/Technician, B
Industrial/Management Engineering, MO
Journalism, B
Kindergarten/PreSchool Education and Teaching, B
Kinesiology and Movement Studies, M
Landscape Architecture, B
Liberal Arts and Sciences Studies and
  Humanities, B
Management Information Systems and Services, B
Management of Technology, M
Manufacturing Engineering, O
Materials Engineering, B
Materials Sciences, M
Mathematics, BM
Mechanical Engineering, B
Mechanical Engineering/Mechanical
  Technology/Technician, B
Medical Microbiology and Bacteriology, B
Music, B
Ornamental Horticulture, B
Parks, Recreation, Leisure and Fitness Studies, B
Philosophy, B
Physical Education Teaching and Coaching, BM
Physical Sciences, B
Physics, B
Political Science and Government, B
Pre-Medicine/Pre-Medical Studies, B
Psychology, BM
Reading Teacher Education, M
Social Sciences, B
Special Education and Teaching, M
Speech and Rhetorical Studies, B
Statistics, B
Trade and Industrial Teacher Education, B
Urban and Regional Planning, MO
Water Resources Engineering, M

CALIFORNIA STATE POLYTECHNIC UNIVERSITY, POMONA

Accounting, B
Aerospace, Aeronautical and Astronautical
  Engineering, B
Agricultural Business and Management, B
Agricultural Sciences, M
Agricultural Teacher Education, B
Agricultural/Biological Engineering and
  Bioengineering, B
Agriculture, B
Agronomy and Crop Science, B
Animal Sciences, BM
Anthropology, B
Applied Mathematics, BM
Architecture, BM
Art/Art Studies, General, B
Behavioral Sciences, B
Bilingual and Multilingual Education, B
Biological and Biomedical Sciences, M
Biology Technician/BioTechnology Laboratory
  Technician, B
Biology/Biological Sciences, B
Botany/Plant Biology, B

Business Administration and Management, B
Business Administration, Management and
  Operations, M
Chemical Engineering, B
Chemistry, BM
City/Urban, Community and Regional Planning, B
Civil Engineering, B
Commercial and Advertising Art, B
Computer and Information Sciences, B
Computer Engineering, B
Computer Science, BM
Construction Engineering Technology/Technician, B
Counselor Education/School Counseling and
  Guidance Services, B
Dietetics/Dieticians, B
Drama and Dramatics/Theatre Arts, B
Economics, BM
Education, M
Electrical Engineering, M
Electrical, Electronic and Communications
  Engineering Technology/Technician, B
Electrical, Electronics and Communications
  Engineering, B
Engineering and Applied Sciences, M
Engineering Technologies/Technicians, B
Engineering Technology, B
English, M
English Language and Literature, B
Environmental Sciences, M
Ethnic and Cultural Studies, B
Ethnic, Cultural Minority, and Gender Studies, B
Family and Consumer Sciences/Human Sciences, B
Farm/Farm and Ranch Management, B
Finance, B
Food Science and Technology, M
Foods, Nutrition, and Wellness Studies, B
Geography, B
Geology/Earth Science, B
History, BM
Horticultural Science, B
Hotel/Motel Administration/Management, B
Human Resources Management/Personnel
  Administration, B
Humanities/Humanistic Studies, B
Industrial Engineering, B
Information Science/Studies, B
Insurance, B
International Business/Trade/Commerce, B
Journalism, B
Kinesiology and Movement Studies, M
Landscape Architecture, BM
Liberal Arts and Sciences Studies and
  Humanities, B
Marketing/Marketing Management, B
Mass Communication/Media Studies, B
Materials Engineering, B
Mathematics, BM
Mechanical Engineering, BM
Mechanical Engineering/Mechanical
  Technology/Technician, B
Medical Microbiology and Bacteriology, B
Music, B
Nutritional Sciences, M
Ornamental Horticulture, B
Petroleum Engineering, B
Philosophy, B
Physical Education Teaching and Coaching, B
Physics, B
Plant Protection and Integrated Pest
  Management, B
Political Science and Government, B
Pre-Law Studies, B
Pre-Medicine/Pre-Medical Studies, B
Pre-Veterinary Studies, B
Psychology, BM
Public Administration, BM
Public Relations/Image Management, B
Radio, Television, and Digital Communication, B
Real Estate, B
Social Sciences, B
Sociology, B
Soil Science and Agronomy, B
Spanish Language and Literature, B
Statistics, B
Structural Engineering, M
Survey Technology/Surveying, B

Telecommunications Technology/Technician, B
Urban and Regional Planning, M
Urban Studies/Affairs, B
Zoology/Animal Biology, B

CALIFORNIA STATE UNIVERSITY, BAKERSFIELD

Anthropology, BM
Art/Art Studies, General, B
Biology/Biological Sciences, B
Business Administration and Management, B
Business Administration, Management and
  Operations, M
Chemistry, B
Computer Science, B
Counseling Psychology, M
Counselor Education/School Counseling and
  Guidance Services, M
Criminal Justice/Law Enforcement Administration, B
Curriculum and Instruction, M
Developmental and Child Psychology, B
Drama and Dramatics/Theatre Arts, B
Economics, B
Education, M
Educational Administration and Supervision, M
English, M
English Language and Literature, B
Finance, B
Geology/Earth Science, BM
Health Services Administration, M
History, BM
Hydrology and Water Resources Science, M
Interdisciplinary Studies, BM
Land Use Planning and
  Management/Development, B
Liberal Arts and Sciences Studies and
  Humanities, B
Marriage and Family Therapy/Counseling, O
Mass Communication/Media Studies, B
Mathematics, B
Mathematics Teacher Education, M
Multilingual and Multicultural Education, M
Music, B
Nursing, M
Nursing - Registered Nurse Training, B
Philosophy, B
Physical Education Teaching and Coaching, B
Physics, B
Political Science and Government, B
Psychology, BMO
Public Administration, BM
Religion/Religious Studies, B
Secondary Education and Teaching, M
Social Work, M
Sociology, BM
Spanish Language and Literature, BM

CALIFORNIA STATE UNIVERSITY CHANNEL ISLANDS

Art/Art Studies, General, B
Biology/Biological Sciences, B
Business Administration and Management, B
Cell/Cellular and Molecular Biology, B
Chemistry, B
Computer Science, B
Economics, B
Education, B
English Language and Literature, B
Environmental Sciences, B
History, B
Information Technology, B
Liberal Arts and Sciences Studies and
  Humanities, B
Mathematics, B
Political Science and Government, B
Psychology, B
Sociology, B
Spanish Language and Literature, B
Visual and Performing Arts, B

CALIFORNIA STATE UNIVERSITY, CHICO

Accounting, BM
Accounting and Computer Science, B
Agricultural Business and Management, B

Agricultural Teacher Education, B
Agronomy and Crop Science, B
American/United States Studies/Civilization, B
Animal Sciences, B
Anthropology, BM
Applied Mathematics, B
Art History, Criticism and Conservation, BM
Art Teacher Education, B
Art/Art Studies, General, B
Asian Studies/Civilization, B
Biochemistry, B
Biological and Biomedical Sciences, M
Biology Teacher Education, B
Biology/Biological Sciences, B
Botany/Plant Biology, M
Business Administration and Management, B
Business Administration, Management and
   Operations, BM
Chemistry, B
Chemistry Teacher Education, B
City/Urban, Community and Regional Planning, B
Civil Engineering, B
Clinical Laboratory Science/Medical
   Technology/Technologist, B
Communication and Media Studies, M
Communication Disorders, BM
Computer and Information Sciences and Support
   Services, B
Computer Engineering, BM
Computer Graphics, B
Computer Science, BM
Construction Engineering Technology/Technician, B
Criminal Justice/Safety Studies, B
Curriculum and Instruction, M
Design and Applied Arts, M
Design and Visual Communications, B
Dietetics/Dieticians, B
Drama and Dramatics/Theatre Arts, B
Dramatic/Theatre Arts and Stagecraft, B
Early Childhood Education and Teaching, B
Ecology, B
Economics, B
Education, M
Educational Administration and Supervision, M
Educational Media/Instructional Technology, M
Educational/Instructional Media Design, B
Electrical Engineering, M
Electrical, Electronics and Communications
   Engineering, B
Engineering, B
Engineering and Applied Sciences, M
English, M
English Language and Literature, B
English/Language Arts Teacher Education, B
Environmental Sciences, M
Ethnic, Cultural Minority, and Gender Studies, B
Finance, B
Fine Arts and Art Studies, M
Fine/Studio Arts, B
Foreign Language Teacher Education, M
French Language and Literature, B
French Language Teacher Education, B
Geography, BM
Geological and Earth Sciences/Geosciences, B
Geology/Earth Science, BM
German Language and Literature, B
German Language Teacher Education, B
Gerontology, B
Graphic Design, B
Health and Physical Education, B
Health Services Administration, M
Health Services/Allied Health/Health Sciences, B
Health Teacher Education, B
History, BM
Human Resources Management/Personnel
   Administration, B
Humanities/Humanistic Studies, B
Hydrology and Water Resources Science, BM
Information Technology, B
Interdisciplinary Studies, M
Interior Design, B
International Economics, B
International Relations and Affairs, B
Jewish/Judaic Studies, B
Journalism, B
Kinesiology and Exercise Science, B

Kinesiology and Movement Studies, M
Latin American Studies, B
Law and Legal Studies, B
Legal Assistant/Paralegal, B
Liberal Arts and Sciences Studies and
   Humanities, B
Linguistics, B
Management, M
Management Information Systems and Services, B
Marketing/Marketing Management, B
Marriage and Family Therapy/Counseling, M
Mathematics, B
Mathematics Teacher Education, B
Mechanical Engineering, B
Microbiology, B
Multi-/Interdisciplinary Studies, B
Multilingual and Multicultural Education, M
Museology/Museum Studies, M
Music, BM
Music Performance, B
Music Teacher Education, B
Music Theory and Composition, B
Natural Resources Management/Development and
   Policy, B
Nursing, M
Nursing - Registered Nurse Training, B
Nutritional Sciences, M
Operations Management and Supervision, B
Organizational Communication, B
Parks, Recreation and Leisure Facilities
   Management, B
Parks, Recreation, Leisure and Fitness Studies, B
Philosophy, B
Physical Education Teaching and Coaching, B
Physics, B
Piano and Organ, B
Political Science and Government, BM
Pre-Dentistry Studies, B
Pre-Medicine/Pre-Medical Studies, B
Pre-Veterinary Studies, B
Psychology, BM
Public Administration, BM
Public Relations/Image Management, B
Radio and Television, B
Range Science and Management, B
Reading Teacher Education, M
Recreation and Park Management, M
Religion/Religious Studies, B
Rural Planning and Studies, B
Science Teacher Education/General Science
   Teacher Education, BM
Social Science Teacher Education, B
Social Sciences, BM
Social Studies Teacher Education, M
Social Work, BM
Sociology, B
Spanish Language and Literature, B
Spanish Language Teacher Education, B
Special Education and Teaching, M
Speech and Rhetorical Studies, B
Statistics, B
Therapeutic Recreation/Recreational Therapy, B
Urban and Regional Planning, M
Women's Studies, B

CALIFORNIA STATE UNIVERSITY, DOMINGUEZ HILLS

Accounting, B
African-American/Black Studies, B
Anthropology, B
Applied Art, B
Art History, Criticism and Conservation, B
Art/Art Studies, General, B
Behavioral Sciences, B
Bilingual and Multilingual Education, B
Biochemistry, B
Bioinformatics, MO
Biological and Biomedical Sciences, MO
Biology/Biological Sciences, B
Business Administration and Management, B
Business Administration, Management and
   Operations, M
Chemistry, B
Child Development, B
Clinical Laboratory Science/Medical
   Technology/Technologist, B

Clinical Laboratory Sciences, MO
Clinical Psychology, M
Clinical/Medical Laboratory Technician, B
Commercial and Advertising Art, B
Comparative Literature, B
Computer Education, MO
Computer Science, B
Conflict Resolution and Mediation/Peace
   Studies, MO
Counselor Education/School Counseling and
   Guidance Services, M
Criminal Justice/Law Enforcement Administration, B
Curriculum and Instruction, M
CytoTechnology/Cytotechnologist, B
Drama and Dramatics/Theatre Arts, B
Economics, B
Education, MO
Educational Administration and Supervision, M
English, MO
English as a Second Language, O
English Language and Literature, B
Finance, B
Fine/Studio Arts, B
French Language and Literature, B
Geography, B
Geology/Earth Science, B
Gerontology, B
Health Education, M
Health/Health Care Administration/Management, B
Hispanic-American, Puerto Rican, and Mexican-
   American/Chicano Studies, B
History, B
Human Resources Management/Personnel
   Administration, B
Human Services, B
Humanities/Humanistic Studies, BM
Information Science/Studies, B
Interdisciplinary Studies, B
International Business/Trade/Commerce, B
Labor and Industrial Relations, B
Liberal Arts and Sciences Studies and
   Humanities, B
Linguistics, B
Management Information Systems and
   Services, BM
Marketing/Marketing Management, B
Marriage and Family Therapy/Counseling, M
Mass Communication/Media Studies, B
Mathematics, B
Mathematics Teacher Education, M
Medical Microbiology and Bacteriology, B
Medical/Clinical Assistant, B
Multilingual and Multicultural Education, M
Music, B
Music Teacher Education, B
Nuclear Medical Technology/Technologist, B
Nursing, M
Nursing - Registered Nurse Training, B
Parks, Recreation, Leisure and Fitness Studies, B
Philosophy, B
Physical Education Teaching and Coaching, BM
Physician Assistant, BM
Physics, B
Political Science and Government, B
Pre-Dentistry Studies, B
Pre-Law Studies, B
Pre-Medicine/Pre-Medical Studies, B
Pre-Veterinary Studies, B
Psychology, BM
Public Administration, BM
Public Health (MPH, DPH), B
Public Relations/Image Management, B
Quality Management, M
Real Estate, B
Religion/Religious Studies, B
Rhetoric, O
School Psychology, O
Sociology, BMO
Spanish Language and Literature, B

CALIFORNIA STATE UNIVERSITY, EAST BAY

Accounting, BM
Advertising, B
African-American/Black Studies, B
American Indian/Native American Studies,

Anthropology, BM
Applied Mathematics, B
Art History, Criticism and Conservation, B
Arts Management, B
Asian-American Studies, B
Athletic Training and Sports Medicine, B
Audiology/Audiologist and Speech-Language
   Pathology/Pathologist, B
Biochemistry, BM
Biological and Biomedical Sciences, M
Biology/Biological Sciences, B
Biomedical Technology/Technician, B
Broadcast Journalism, B
Business Administration and Management, B
Business Administration, Management and
   Operations, M
Business/Managerial Economics, B
Ceramic Arts and Ceramics, B
Chemistry, BM
Child Development, B
Clinical/Medical Laboratory Technician, B
Commercial and Advertising Art, B
Communication and Media Studies, M
Communication Disorders, M
Computer Graphics, B
Computer Science, BM
Computer Systems Networking and
   Telecommunications, B
Corrections, B
Counselor Education/School Counseling and
   Guidance Services, M
Creative Writing, B
Criminal Justice/Law Enforcement Administration, B
Criminal Justice/Police Science, B
Dance, B
Developmental and Child Psychology, B
Drama and Dramatics/Theatre Arts, B
Drawing, B
Ecology, B
Economics, BM
Education, M
Educational Leadership and Administration, M
Electronic Commerce, M
English, M
English Language and Literature, B
Entrepreneurship/Entrepreneurial Studies, M
Environmental Studies, B
Ethnic and Cultural Studies, B
Family and Consumer Sciences/Human Sciences, B
Finance, B
Finance and Banking, M
Fine/Studio Arts, B
French Language and Literature, B
Geography, BM
Geology/Earth Science, BM
Gerontology, B
Hispanic-American, Puerto Rican, and Mexican-
   American/Chicano Studies, B
History, BM
Human Development and Family Studies, B
Human Resources Management and Services, M
Human Resources Management/Personnel
   Administration, B
Industrial and Organizational Psychology, B
Industrial Engineering, B
Information Science/Studies, B
Interdisciplinary Studies, BMO
International Business/Trade/Commerce, M
International Relations and Affairs, B
Journalism, B
Kinesiology and Exercise Science, B
Latin American Studies, B
Liberal Arts and Sciences Studies and
   Humanities, B
Logistics and Materials Management, M
Management, M
Management Information Systems and
   Services, BM
Marine Sciences, M
Marketing, M
Marketing/Marketing Management, B
Mass Communication/Media Studies, B
Mathematics, BM
Music, BM
Nursing - Registered Nurse Training, B
Operations Research, M

Painting, B
Parks, Recreation, Leisure and Fitness Studies, B
Philosophy, B
Photography, B
Physical Education Teaching and Coaching, BM
Physical Sciences, B
Physics, B
Political Science and Government, B
Pre-Dentistry Studies, B
Pre-Medicine/Pre-Medical Studies, B
Pre-Veterinary Studies, B
Printmaking, B
Psychology, B
Public Administration, BM
Public Health (MPH, DPH), B
Public Relations/Image Management, B
Purchasing, Procurement/Acquisitions and
   Contracts Management, B
Quantitative Analysis, M
Real Estate, B
Religion/Religious Studies, B
Sculpture, B
Social Work, BM
Sociology, BM
Spanish Language and Literature, B
Special Education and Teaching, M
Speech and Rhetorical Studies, B
Statistics, BM
Taxation, M
Telecommunications Technology/Technician, B
Therapeutic Recreation/Recreational Therapy, B

CALIFORNIA STATE UNIVERSITY, FRESNO

Accounting, BM
African-American/Black Studies, B
Agricultural Business and Management, B
Agricultural Sciences, M
Agricultural Teacher Education, B
Agronomy and Crop Science, B
Animal Physiology, B
Animal Sciences, BM
Anthropology, B
Art/Art Studies, General, B
Audiology/Audiologist and Speech-Language
   Pathology/Pathologist, B
Biological and Biomedical Sciences, M
Biological and Physical Sciences, B
Biology/Biological Sciences, B
Business Administration and Management, B
Business Administration, Management and
   Operations, M
Cell/Cellular Biology and Histology, B
Chemistry, BM
Child Development, B
Civil Engineering, BM
Commercial and Advertising Art, B
Communication and Media Studies, M
Communication Disorders, BM
Communication Studies/Speech Communication
   and Rhetoric, B
Computer Engineering, B
Computer Science, BM
Construction Engineering Technology/Technician, B
Construction Management, B
Counselor Education/School Counseling and
   Guidance Services, M
Criminology, BM
Curriculum and Instruction, M
Dance, B
Design and Applied Arts, M
Dietetics/Dieticians, B
Drama and Dramatics/Theatre Arts, B
Ecology, BM
Economics, B
Education, MD
Educational Administration and Supervision, M
Educational Leadership and Administration, D
Electrical Engineering, M
Electrical, Electronics and Communications
   Engineering, B
Engineering and Applied Sciences, M
English, M
English Language and Literature, B
Environmental and Occupational Health, M
Environmental Sciences, B

Exercise and Sports Science, M
Family and Consumer Economics and Related
   Services, B
Family and Consumer Sciences/Human
   Sciences, M
Finance, B
Fine Arts and Art Studies, M
Food Science and Technology, M
Foods, Nutrition, and Wellness Studies, B
French Language and Literature, B
Geography, B
Geology/Earth Science, BM
Health Promotion, M
Health Services Administration, M
Hispanic-American, Puerto Rican, and Mexican-
   American/Chicano Studies, B
History, BM
Human Resources Management/Personnel
   Administration, B
Industrial Technology/Technician, B
Industrial/Management Engineering, M
Interior Design, B
International Affairs, M
International Business/Trade/Commerce, B
Journalism, BM
Kinesiology and Movement Studies, M
Liberal Arts and Sciences Studies and
   Humanities, B
Linguistics, BM
Management Information Systems and Services, B
Marine Sciences, M
Marketing/Marketing Management, B
Marriage and Family Therapy/Counseling, M
Mass Communication/Media Studies, BM
Mathematics, BM
Mathematics Teacher Education, M
Mechanical Engineering, BM
Molecular Biology, B
Music, BM
Music History, Literature, and Theory, B
Music Teacher Education, BM
Natural Sciences, B
Nursing, M
Nursing - Registered Nurse Training, B
Occupational Health and Industrial Hygiene, B
Occupational Safety and Health
   Technology/Technician, B
Ornamental Horticulture, B
Parks, Recreation and Leisure Facilities
   Management, B
Parks, Recreation, Leisure and Fitness Studies, B
Performance, M
Philosophy, B
Physical Education Teaching and Coaching, B
Physical Therapy/Therapist, BM
Physics, BM
Plant Sciences, BM
Political Science and Government, B
Pre-Law Studies, B
Psychology, BM
Public Administration, BM
Public Health, M
Public Health (MPH, DPH), B
Public Relations/Image Management, B
Radio and Television, B
Reading Teacher Education, M
Real Estate, B
Rehabilitation Counseling, M
Religion/Religious Studies, B
Social Work, BM
Sociology, B
Spanish Language and Literature, BM
Special Education and Teaching, M
Speech and Rhetorical Studies, B
Sport Psychology, M
Survey Technology/Surveying, B
Technology Education/Industrial Arts, B
Trade and Industrial Teacher Education, B
Women's Studies, B
Writing, M

CALIFORNIA STATE UNIVERSITY, FULLERTON

Accounting, BM
Advertising, B
Advertising and Public Relations, M

African-American/Black Studies, B
American/United States Studies/Civilization, BM
Analytical Chemistry, M
Anthropology, BM
Applied Mathematics, BM
Art History, Criticism and Conservation, BM
Art Teacher Education, B
Art/Art Studies, General, B
Asian-American Studies, B
Audiology/Audiologist and Speech-Language
    Pathology/Pathologist, B
Biochemistry, BM
Biological and Biomedical Sciences, M
Biology/Biological Sciences, B
Botany/Plant Biology, M
Business Administration and Management, B
Business Administration, Management and
    Operations, M
Business/Managerial Economics, B
Ceramic Arts and Ceramics, B
Chemistry, BM
Civil Engineering, BM
Clinical Psychology, BM
Commercial and Advertising Art, B
Communication and Media Studies, M
Communication Disorders, BM
Communication Studies/Speech Communication
    and Rhetoric, B
Community Psychology, M
Comparative Literature, BM
Composition, M
Computer Science, BM
Counselor Education/School Counseling and
    Guidance Services, M
Criminal Justice/Law Enforcement Administration, B
Dance, BM
Design and Applied Arts, M
Drama and Dramatics/Theatre Arts, B
Drawing, B
Early Childhood Education and Teaching, B
Economics, BM
Education, M
Educational Leadership and Administration, M
Educational Media/Instructional Technology, M
Electrical Engineering, M
Electrical, Electronics and Communications
    Engineering, B
Elementary Education and Teaching, M
Engineering, B
Engineering and Applied Sciences, M
Engineering Science, B
English, M
English as a Second Language, M
English Language and Literature, M
Entrepreneurship/Entrepreneurial Studies, B
Environmental Education, M
Environmental Policy and Resource
    Management, M
Environmental Sciences, M
Environmental Studies, M
Ethnic and Cultural Studies, B
Film, Television, and Video Production, M
Finance, B
Finance and Banking, M
Fine Arts and Art Studies, MO
Fine/Studio Arts, B
French Language and Literature, BM
Geochemistry, M
Geography, BM
Geology/Earth Science, BM
German Language and Literature, BM
Gerontology, M
Graphic Design, B
Health and Physical Education, B
Health Professions and Related Clinical Sciences, B
Hispanic-American, Puerto Rican, and Mexican-
    American/Chicano Studies, B
History, BM
Illustration, B
Information Science/Studies, BM
Inorganic Chemistry, M
International Business/Trade/Commerce, M
Japanese Language and Literature, B
Journalism, BM
Latin American Studies, B

Liberal Arts and Sciences Studies and
    Humanities, B
Linguistics, BM
Management, M
Management Information Systems and Services, M
Marketing, M
Marketing/Marketing Management, B
Mathematics, BM
Mathematics Teacher Education, M
Mechanical Engineering, BM
Mechanics, M
Media Studies, M
Microbiology, M
Middle School Education, M
Multilingual and Multicultural Education, M
Museology/Museum Studies, O
Music, BM
Music History, Literature, and Theory, BM
Music Performance, B
Music Teacher Education, BM
Music Theory and Composition, M
Nursing, BM
Nursing - Registered Nurse Training, B
Operations Research, BM
Organic Chemistry, M
Painting, B
Performance, M
Philosophy, B
Photography, B
Physical Chemistry, M
Physical Education Teaching and Coaching, BM
Physics, BM
Piano and Organ, B
Political Science and Government, BM
Printmaking, B
Psychology, BM
Public Administration, BM
Public Health, M
Public Relations/Image Management, B
Radio and Television, B
Reading Teacher Education, M
Religion/Religious Studies, B
Russian Studies, B
Science Teacher Education/General Science
    Teacher Education, M
Sculpture, B
Secondary Education and Teaching, M
Sociology, BM
Software Engineering, M
Spanish Language and Literature, BM
Special Education and Teaching, M
Speech and Interpersonal Communication, M
Speech and Rhetorical Studies, B
Statistics, BM
Systems Engineering, M
Taxation, BM
Theater, M
Violin, Viola, Guitar and Other Stringed
    Instruments, B
Voice and Opera, B
Wind and Percussion Instruments, B
Women's Studies, B

CALIFORNIA STATE UNIVERSITY, LONG BEACH

Accounting, B
Acting, B
Aerospace, Aeronautical and Astronautical
    Engineering, BM
African-American/Black Studies, B
American/United States Studies/Civilization, B
Ancient/Classical Greek Language and Literature, B
Anthropology, BM
Apparel and Textiles, B
Applied Mathematics, BMD
Art Education, M
Art History, Criticism and Conservation, BM
Art Teacher Education, B
Art/Art Studies, General, B
Asian Studies/Civilization, BMO
Asian-American Studies, BMO
Athletic Training and Sports Medicine, B
Audiology/Audiologist and Hearing Sciences, B
Audiology/Audiologist and Speech-Language
    Pathology/Pathologist, B
Biochemistry, BM

Biochemistry, Biophysics and Molecular Biology, B
Biological and Biomedical Sciences, M
Biology Teacher Education, B
Biology/Biological Sciences, B
Biomedical/Medical Engineering, B
Botany/Plant Biology, B
Broadcast Journalism, B
Building/Construction
    Finishing, Management, and Inspection, B
Business Administration and Management, B
Business Administration, Management and
    Operations, B
Business/Managerial Economics, B
Cell/Cellular Biology and Histology, B
Ceramic Arts and Ceramics, B
Chemical Engineering, B
Chemistry, BM
Child Development, B
Chinese Language and Literature, B
Cinematography and Film/Video Production, B
Civil Engineering, BMDO
Classics and Classical
    Languages, Literatures, and Linguistics, B
Commercial and Advertising Art, B
Communication and Media Studies, M
Communication Disorders, BM
Comparative Literature, B
Computer Engineering, BM
Computer Engineering Technology/Technician, B
Computer Science, BM
Construction Engineering, B
Construction Engineering Technology/Technician, B
Counselor Education/School Counseling and
    Guidance Services, MO
Crafts, M
Creative Writing, B
Criminal Justice/Law Enforcement Administration, B
Criminology, M
Dance, BM
Dietetics/Dieticians, B
Directing and Theatrical Production, B
Drama and Dramatics/Theatre Arts, B
Drawing, B
Ecology, B
Economics, BM
Education, MDO
Educational Administration and Supervision, M
Educational Psychology, M
Electrical Engineering, M
Electrical, Electronic and Communications
    Engineering Technology/Technician, B
Electrical, Electronics and Communications
    Engineering, B
Elementary Education and Teaching, M
Emergency Medical Services, M
Engineering, B
Engineering Management, M
Engineering Technology, B
Engineering/Industrial Management, B
English, M
English Language and Literature, B
English/Language Arts Teacher Education, B
Environmental Engineering
    Technology/Environmental Technology, B
Environmental Sciences, B
Epidemiology, M
Family and Consumer Sciences/Human Sciences, B
Fashion Merchandising, B
Fiber, Textile and Weaving Arts, B
Film/Cinema Studies, B
Finance, B
Fine Arts and Art Studies, BM
Fine/Studio Arts, B
Foods, Nutrition, and Related Services, B
Foundations and Philosophy of Education, M
French Language and Literature, BM
Geography, BM
Geology/Earth Science, BM
German Language and Literature, BM
Gerontology, M
Graphic Design, B
Hazardous Materials Management and Waste
    Technology/Technician, O
Health and Physical Education/Fitness, B
Health Education, M
Health Services Administration, MO

Health/Health Care Administration/Management, B
Hispanic-American, Puerto Rican, and Mexican-
    American/Chicano Studies, B
History, BM
Home Economics, M
Hotel/Motel Administration/Management, B
Human Development and Family Studies, B
Human Resources Management/Personnel
    Administration, B
Illustration, BM
Industrial Design, B
Industrial Engineering, B
Industrial Technology/Technician, B
Interdisciplinary Studies, BM
Interior Design, B
International Business/Trade/Commerce, BM
International Relations and Affairs, B
Italian Language and Literature, B
Japanese Language and Literature, B
Journalism, B
Kinesiology and Exercise Science, B
Kinesiology and Movement Studies, M
Kinesiotherapy/Kinesiotherapist, B
Leisure Studies, M
Liberal Arts and Sciences Studies and
    Humanities, B
Linguistics, M
Management Information Systems and Services, B
Manufacturing Technology/Technician, B
Marine Biology and Biological Oceanography, B
Marketing/Marketing Management, B
Mass Communication/Media Studies, B
Materials Engineering, B
Mathematics, BM
Mathematics Teacher Education, B
Mechanical Engineering, BMD
Mechanical Engineering/Mechanical
    Technology/Technician, B
Medical Radiologic Technology/Science - Radiation
    Therapist, B
Medical Technology, M
Metal and Jewelry Arts, B
Metallurgy, M
Microbiology, BM
Multi-/Interdisciplinary Studies, B
Music, BM
Music History, Literature, and Theory, B
Music Performance, B
Music Theory and Composition, B
Nurse Anesthetist, M
Nursing, MO
Nursing - Registered Nurse Training, B
Nutritional Sciences, M
Ocean Engineering, B
Operations Management and Supervision, B
Painting, BM
Parks, Recreation, Leisure and Fitness Studies, B
Philosophy, BM
Photography, B
Physical Education Teaching and Coaching, BM
Physical Therapy/Therapist, M
Physics, BM
Physiology, B
Political Science and Government, BM
Printmaking, B
Psychology, BM
Public Administration, MO
Public Health (MPH, DPH), B
Public Health Education and Promotion, B
Public Policy Analysis, MO
Public Relations/Image Management, B
Quality Control Technology/Technician, B
Radio and Television, B
Recreation and Park Management, M
Religion/Religious Studies, BM
Sculpture, B
Secondary Education and Teaching, M
Social Work, BM
Sociology, B
Spanish Language and Literature, BM
Special Education and Teaching, M
Speech and Rhetorical Studies, B
Statistics, B
Theater, M
Trade and Industrial Teacher Education, B
Vocational and Technical Education, M

Voice and Opera, B
Women's Studies, B
Writing, M
Zoology/Animal Biology, B

CALIFORNIA STATE UNIVERSITY, LOS ANGELES

Accounting, M
African-American/Black Studies, B
Analytical Chemistry, M
Anthropology, BM
Applied Arts and Design, M
Art/Art Studies, General, B
Asian Studies/Civilization, B
Asian-American Studies, B
Aviation/Airway Management and Operations, B
Biochemistry, BM
Biological and Biomedical Sciences, M
Biology/Biological Sciences, B
Business Administration and Management, B
Business Administration, Management and
    Operations, M
Chemistry, BM
Child and Family Studies, M
Child Development, B
Chinese Language and Literature, B
Civil Engineering, BM
Communication and Media Studies, M
Communication Disorders, BM
Communication Studies/Speech Communication
    and Rhetoric, B
Composition, M
Computer and Information Sciences, B
Computer and Information Sciences and Support
    Services, B
Computer Education, M
Computer Science, B
Counselor Education/School Counseling and
    Guidance Services, M
Criminal Justice/Safety Studies, B
Criminology, M
Dance, B
Dietetics/Dieticians, B
Drama and Dramatics/Theatre Arts, B
Early Childhood Education and Teaching, B
Economics, BM
Education, MD
Educational Administration and Supervision, M
Educational Media/Instructional Technology, M
Electrical Engineering, M
Electrical, Electronics and Communications
    Engineering, B
Elementary Education and Teaching, M
Engineering, B
Engineering and Applied Sciences, M
English, M
English as a Second Language, M
English Language and Literature, B
Finance and Banking, M
Fine Arts and Art Studies, M
Fire Services Administration, B
Foods, Nutrition, and Wellness Studies, B
Foundations and Philosophy of Education, M
French Language and Literature, BM
Geography, BM
Geology/Earth Science, BM
Health Education, M
Health Professions and Related Clinical Sciences, B
Health Services Administration, M
Hispanic Studies, M
Hispanic-American, Puerto Rican, and Mexican-
    American/Chicano Studies, B
History, BM
Industrial Technology/Technician, B
Information Technology, B
Inorganic Chemistry, M
Interdisciplinary Studies, B
International Business/Trade/Commerce, M
Japanese Language and Literature, B
Kinesiology and Exercise Science, B
Kinesiology and Movement Studies, M
Latin American Studies, BM
Liberal Arts and Sciences Studies and
    Humanities, B
Management, M
Management Information Systems and Services, M

Marketing, M
Mathematics, BM
Mechanical Engineering, BM
Microbiology, B
Multi-/Interdisciplinary Studies, B
Music, BM
Music Performance, B
Music Teacher Education, M
Musicology and Ethnomusicology, M
Natural Sciences, B
Nursing, M
Nursing - Registered Nurse Training, B
Nutritional Sciences, BM
Organic Chemistry, M
Performance, M
Philosophy, BM
Physical Chemistry, M
Physical Education Teaching and Coaching, M
Physics, BM
Political Science and Government, BM
Psychology, BM
Public Administration, M
Public Health (MPH, DPH), B
Radio and Television, M
Reading Teacher Education, M
Rehabilitation Counseling, M
Rehabilitation Therapy, B
School Psychology, M
Secondary Education and Teaching, M
Social Sciences, B
Social Work, BM
Sociology, BM
Spanish Language and Literature, BM
Speech and Interpersonal Communication, M
Speech and Rhetorical Studies, M
Technology and Public Policy, M
Theater, M

CALIFORNIA STATE UNIVERSITY, MONTEREY BAY

Art/Art Studies, General, B
Behavioral Sciences, B
Business Administration and Management, B
Communication Studies/Speech Communication
    and Rhetoric, B
Drama and Dramatics/Theatre Arts, B
Education, M
Environmental Biology, B
Environmental Studies, B
Foreign Languages and Literatures, B
Geology/Earth Science, B
Human Services, B
Humanities/Humanistic Studies, B
Interdisciplinary Studies, B
International Business/Trade/Commerce, B
International Relations and Affairs, B
Liberal Arts and Sciences Studies and
    Humanities, B
Management Information Systems and Services, M
Marine Sciences, M
Public Policy Analysis, M
Telecommunications Technology/Technician, B

CALIFORNIA STATE UNIVERSITY, NORTHRIDGE

Accounting, B
Aerospace, Aeronautical and Astronautical
    Engineering, M
African-American/Black Studies, B
Anthropology, BM
Art Education, M
Art History, Criticism and Conservation, M
Art/Art Studies, General, B
Asian-American Studies, B
Biochemistry, B
Biological and Biomedical Sciences, M
Biology/Biological Sciences, B
Biomedical Engineering, M
Business Administration and Management, B
Chemistry, BM
Child Development, B
Cinematography and Film/Video Production, B
Civil Engineering, B
Communication and Media Studies, M
Communication Disorders, BM
Composition, M

Computer Engineering, M
Computer Science, BM
Counselor Education/School Counseling and
  Guidance Services, MO
Drama and Dramatics/Theatre Arts, B
Economics, B
Education, MO
Education/Teaching of the Gifted and Talented, M
Educational Administration and Supervision, M
Educational Psychology, MO
Electrical Engineering, M
Elementary Education and Teaching, M
Engineering, B
Engineering and Applied Sciences, M
Engineering Management, M
English, M
English Language and Literature, B
Environmental and Occupational Health, M
Environmental Health, B
Family and Consumer Sciences/Human
  Sciences, BM
Film/Cinema Studies, B
Fine Arts and Art Studies, M
Foundations and Philosophy of Education, M
French Language and Literature, B
Genetic Counseling/Counselor, M
Geography, BM
Geology/Earth Science, BM
German Language and Literature, B
Health Education, M
Health Services Administration, M
Health/Medical Physics, B
Hispanic Studies, M
Hispanic-American, Puerto Rican, and Mexican-
  American/Chicano Studies, B
History, BM
Humanities/Humanistic Studies, B
Industrial/Management Engineering, M
Information Science/Studies, B
Interdisciplinary Studies, M
Journalism, BM
Kinesiology and Exercise Science, B
Kinesiology and Movement Studies, M
Leisure Studies, M
Liberal Arts and Sciences Studies and
  Humanities, B
Linguistics, BM
Management Information Systems and Services, M
Marriage and Family Therapy/Counseling, O
Mass Communication/Media Studies, M
Materials Engineering, M
Mathematics, BM
Mechanical Engineering, M
Mechanics, M
Music, BM
Music Teacher Education, M
Music Theory and Composition, M
Musicology and Ethnomusicology, M
Nursing - Registered Nurse Training, B
Parks, Recreation, Leisure and Fitness Studies, B
Performance, M
Philosophy, B
Physical Therapy/Therapist, M
Physics, BM
Political Science and Government, BM
Psychology, BM
Public Administration, M
Public Health, M
Public Health (MPH, DPH), B
Recreation and Park Management, M
Religion/Religious Studies, B
Secondary Education and Teaching, M
Social Work, M
Sociology, B
Spanish Language and Literature, BM
Special Education and Teaching, M
Speech and Rhetorical Studies, M
Structural Engineering, M
Theater, M
Urban Studies/Affairs, B
Women's Studies, B

CALIFORNIA STATE UNIVERSITY, SACRAMENTO

Accounting, BM
Accounting and Related Services, B

Anthropology, BM
Apparel and Textiles, B
Art/Art Studies, General, B
Asian Studies/Civilization, B
Audiology/Audiologist and Speech-Language
  Pathology/Pathologist, B
Biological and Biomedical Sciences, M
Biology Technician/BioTechnology Laboratory
  Technician, B
Biology/Biological Sciences, B
Business Administration and Management, B
Business Administration, Management and
  Operations, M
Business, Management, Marketing, and Related
  Support Services, B
Chemistry, BM
Civil Engineering, BM
Communication and Media Studies, M
Communication Disorders, M
Communication Studies/Speech Communication
  and Rhetoric, B
Community Health Services/Liaison/Counseling, B
Computer and Information Sciences, B
Computer Engineering, B
Computer Science, M
Conservation Biology, B
Construction Engineering Technology/Technician, B
Counseling Psychology, M
Counselor Education/School Counseling and
  Guidance Services, M
Criminal Justice/Law Enforcement Administration, B
Criminology, M
Curriculum and Instruction, M
Dance, BM
Digital Communication and Media/Multimedia, B
Drama and Dramatics/Theatre Arts, B
Early Childhood Education and Teaching, M
Economics, B
Education, M
Educational Administration and Supervision, M
Electrical Engineering, M
Electrical, Electronics and Communications
  Engineering, B
Engineering and Applied Sciences, M
English, M
English as a Second Language, M
English Language and Literature, B
Environmental Studies, B
Ethnic and Cultural Studies, B
Ethnic, Cultural Minority, and Gender Studies, B
Family and Consumer Economics and Related
  Services, B
Finance, B
Fine Arts and Art Studies, M
French Language and Literature, BM
Geography, B
Geology/Earth Science, B
German Language and Literature, M
Gerontology, B
Graphic Design, B
Health and Physical Education, B
Health and Physical Education/Fitness, B
Health Professions and Related Clinical Sciences, B
Health Services/Allied Health/Health Sciences, B
Health/Health Care Administration/Management, B
History, B
Human Resources Development, M
Human Resources Management and Services, M
Human Resources Management/Personnel
  Administration, B
Human Services, M
Humanities/Humanistic Studies, B
Industrial and Organizational Psychology, B
Insurance, B
Interdisciplinary Studies, M
Interior Design, B
International Affairs, M
International Business/Trade/Commerce, B
Journalism, B
Kinesiology and Exercise Science, B
Liberal Arts and Sciences Studies and
  Humanities, B
Liberal Studies, M
Management Information Systems and
  Services, BM
Marine Sciences, M

Marketing/Marketing Management, B
Mass Communication/Media Studies, B
Mathematics, BM
Mechanical Engineering, BM
Mechanical Engineering/Mechanical
  Technology/Technician, B
Molecular Biology, B
Multilingual and Multicultural Education, M
Music, BM
Music Management and Merchandising, B
Music Pedagogy, B
Music Theory and Composition, B
Natural Resources and Conservation, B
Nursing, M
Nursing - Registered Nurse Training, B
Operations Management and Supervision, B
Organizational Communication, B
Parks, Recreation and Leisure Facilities
  Management, B
Parks, Recreation, Leisure and Fitness Studies, B
Philosophy, B
Philosophy and Religious Studies, B
Photography, B
Physical Education Teaching and Coaching, M
Physical Sciences, B
Physics, B
Piano and Organ, B
Political Science and Government, BM
Psychology, BM
Public Administration, M
Public History, M
Public Policy Analysis, M
Reading Teacher Education, M
Real Estate, BM
Recreation and Park Management, M
School Psychology, M
Social Sciences, B
Social Work, BM
Sociology, BM
Software Engineering, M
Spanish Language and Literature, BM
Special Education and Teaching, M
Statistics, M
Theater, M
Vocational and Technical Education, M
Women's Studies, B
Writing, M

CALIFORNIA STATE UNIVERSITY, SAN BERNARDINO

Accounting, B
American/United States Studies/Civilization, B
Anthropology, B
Art History, Criticism and Conservation, B
Art/Art Studies, General, B
Biochemistry, B
Biological and Biomedical Sciences, M
Biology/Biological Sciences, M
Business Administration and Management, B
Business Administration, Management and
  Operations, M
Business/Managerial Economics, B
Chemistry, B
Clinical Psychology, M
Communication and Media Studies, M
Computer and Information Sciences, B
Computer Science, BM
Counseling Psychology, M
Counselor Education/School Counseling and
  Guidance Services, M
Creative Writing, B
Criminal Justice/Law Enforcement Administration, B
Criminology, M
Curriculum and Instruction, M
Developmental and Child Psychology, B
Developmental Psychology, M
Dietetics/Dieticians, B
Drama and Dramatics/Theatre Arts, B
Economics, B
Education, M
Educational Administration and Supervision, M
Educational Media/Instructional Technology, M
Educational Psychology, M
Elementary Education and Teaching, M
English, M
English as a Second Language, M

English Education, M
English Language and Literature, B
Environmental Education, M
Environmental Studies, B
Experimental Psychology, M
Finance, B
Fine Arts and Art Studies, M
Foods, Nutrition, and Wellness Studies, B
French Language and Literature, B
Geography, B
Geology/Earth Science, B
Health Education, M
Health Services Administration, M
Health Teacher Education, B
Health/Health Care Administration/Management, B
History, B
Human Development and Family Studies, B
Human Services, B
Humanities/Humanistic Studies, B
Industrial and Organizational Psychology, M
Interdisciplinary Studies, BM
Kinesiology and Movement Studies, M
Liberal Arts and Sciences Studies and
    Humanities, B
Management Information Systems and Services, B
Marketing/Marketing Management, B
Mathematics, BM
Military and Defense Studies, M
Multilingual and Multicultural Education, M
Music, B
Natural Sciences, B
Nursing, M
Nursing - Registered Nurse Training, B
Philosophy, B
Physical Education Teaching and Coaching, B
Physics, B
Political Science and Government, B
Psychology, BM
Public Administration, BM
Public Health (MPH, DPH), B
Reading Teacher Education, M
Rehabilitation Counseling, M
Science Teacher Education/General Science
    Teacher Education, M
Secondary Education and Teaching, M
Social Sciences, BM
Social Studies Teacher Education, M
Social Work, BM
Sociology, B
Spanish Language and Literature, BM
Special Education and Teaching, M
Trade and Industrial Teacher Education, B
Vocational and Technical Education, M

CALIFORNIA STATE UNIVERSITY, SAN MARCOS

Accounting, B
Biochemistry, B
Biological and Biomedical Sciences, M
Biology/Biological Sciences, B
Business Administration and Management, B
Business Administration, Management and
    Operations, M
Cell/Cellular Biology and Histology, B
Chemistry, B
Communication Studies/Speech Communication
    and Rhetoric, B
Computer Science, BM
Ecology, B
Economics, B
Education, M
English, M
English Language and Literature, B
History, B
Liberal Arts and Sciences Studies and
    Humanities, B
Management, M
Mathematics, BM
Molecular Biology, B
Political Science and Government, B
Psychology, BM
Science Teacher Education/General Science
    Teacher Education, B
Social Sciences, B
Sociology, BM
Spanish Language and Literature, BM

Visual and Performing Arts, B
Women's Studies, B
Writing, M

CALIFORNIA STATE UNIVERSITY, STANISLAUS

Agriculture, B
Anthropology, B
Art/Art Studies, General, B
Biology/Biological Sciences, B
Business Administration and Management, B
Business Administration, Management and
    Operations, M
Business, Management, Marketing, and Related
    Support Services, B
Chemistry, B
Cognitive Psychology and Psycholinguistics, B
Communication Studies/Speech Communication
    and Rhetoric, B
Computer and Information Sciences, B
Counseling Psychology, M
Counselor Education/School Counseling and
    Guidance Services, M
Criminal Justice/Law Enforcement Administration, B
Criminology, M
Curriculum and Instruction, M
Drama and Dramatics/Theatre Arts, B
Economics, B
Education, M
Educational Administration and Supervision, M
Educational Media/Instructional Technology, M
Elementary Education and Teaching, M
English, M
English Language and Literature, B
Finance and Banking, M
Fine/Studio Arts, B
French Language and Literature, B
Geography, B
Geology/Earth Science, B
History, BM
Information Science/Studies, B
Interdisciplinary Studies, M
Liberal Arts and Sciences Studies and
    Humanities, B
Marine Biology and Biological Oceanography, M
Mathematics, B
Multi-/Interdisciplinary Studies, B
Multilingual and Multicultural Education, M
Music, B
Music Performance, B
Nursing - Registered Nurse Training, B
Philosophy, B
Physical Education Teaching and Coaching, BM
Physical Sciences, B
Physics, B
Political Science and Government, BM
Psychology, BM
Public Administration, M
Reading Teacher Education, M
Secondary Education and Teaching, M
Social Sciences, B
Social Work, M
Sociology, B
Spanish Language and Literature, B
Special Education and Teaching, M

CAÑADA COLLEGE

Accounting, A
Administrative Assistant and Secretarial Science, A
Anatomy, A
Anthropology, A
Art History, Criticism and Conservation, A
Art/Art Studies, General, A
Biological and Physical Sciences, A
Biology/Biological Sciences, A
Business Administration and Management, A
Business Machine Repairer, A
Chemistry, A
Computer Engineering Technology/Technician, A
Computer Programming/Programmer, A
Computer Science, A
Dance, A
Data Processing and Data Processing
    Technology/Technician, A
Drama and Dramatics/Theatre Arts, A
Drawing, A

Economics, A
Engineering, A
English Language and Literature, A
Environmental Studies, A
Fashion/Apparel Design, A
French Language and Literature, A
Geography, A
Geology/Earth Science, A
German Language and Literature, A
Health Teacher Education, A
History, A
Humanities/Humanistic Studies, A
Industrial Radiologic Technology/Technician, A
Information Science/Studies, A
Interior Design, A
Journalism, A
Kindergarten/PreSchool Education and Teaching, A
Kinesiology and Exercise Science, A
Legal Assistant/Paralegal, A
Liberal Arts and Sciences Studies and
    Humanities, A
Mathematics, A
Music, A
Philosophy, A
Physical Education Teaching and Coaching, A
Political Science and Government, A
Psychology, A
Public Health (MPH, DPH), A
Sociology, A
Spanish Language and Literature, A
Speech and Rhetorical Studies, A
Tourism and Travel Services Management, A

CERRITOS COLLEGE

Accounting, A
Administrative Assistant and Secretarial Science, A
Agriculture, A
Anthropology, A
Architectural Engineering Technology/Technician, A
Art/Art Studies, General, A
Automobile/Automotive Mechanics
    Technology/Technician, A
Biology/Biological Sciences, A
Biomedical Technology/Technician, A
Botany/Plant Biology, A
Business Administration and Management, A
Chemistry, A
Computer Programming/Programmer, A
Computer Science, A
Cosmetology/Cosmetologist, A
Court Reporting/Court Reporter, A
Criminal Justice/Police Science, A
Data Processing and Data Processing
    Technology/Technician, A
Dental Hygiene/Hygienist, A
Drafting and Design Technology/Technician, A
Drama and Dramatics/Theatre Arts, A
Economics, A
Electrical, Electronic and Communications
    Engineering Technology/Technician, A
English Language and Literature, A
Family and Consumer Sciences/Human Sciences, A
Fashion/Apparel Design, A
Food Technology and Processing, A
Forestry, A
French Language and Literature, A
Geography, A
Geology/Earth Science, A
German Language and Literature, A
Hispanic-American, Puerto Rican, and Mexican-
    American/Chicano Studies, A
History, A
Industrial Technology/Technician, A
Journalism, A
Kindergarten/PreSchool Education and Teaching, A
Legal Administrative Assistant/Secretary, A
Liberal Arts and Sciences Studies and
    Humanities, A
Machine Tool Technology/Machinist, A
Marketing/Marketing Management, A
Mathematics, A
Medical Administrative Assistant/Secretary, A
Medical/Clinical Assistant, A
Music, A
Nursing - Registered Nurse Training, A
Ornamental Horticulture, A

Parks, Recreation, Leisure and Fitness Studies, A
Pharmacy, A
Philosophy, A
Photography, A
Physical Education Teaching and Coaching, A
Physical Sciences, A
Physical Therapy/Therapist, A
Physics, A
Plastics Engineering Technology/Technician, A
Political Science and Government, A
Pre-Engineering, A
Psychology, A
Real Estate, A
Sociology, A
Spanish Language and Literature, A
Speech and Rhetorical Studies, A
Technology Education/Industrial Arts, A
Welding Technology/Welder, A
Wildlife and Wildlands Science and Management, A
Zoology/Animal Biology, A

CERRO COSO COMMUNITY COLLEGE

Art/Art Studies, General, A
Automobile/Automotive Mechanics
  Technology/Technician, A
Business Administration and Management, A
Child Care and Support Services Management, A
Child Care Provider/Assistant, A
Computer and Information Sciences, A
Computer Engineering Technology/Technician, A
Computer Graphics, A
Computer Software and Media Applications, A
Criminal Justice/Law Enforcement Administration, A
Data Processing and Data Processing
  Technology/Technician, A
Drafting and Design Technology/Technician, A
Early Childhood Education and Teaching, A
Emergency Medical Technology/Technician (EMT
  Paramedic), A
Engineering Technology, A
Fine/Studio Arts, A
Fire Science/Firefighting, A
Health and Physical Education, A
History, A
Humanities/Humanistic Studies, A
Kindergarten/PreSchool Education and Teaching, A
Liberal Arts and Sciences Studies and
  Humanities, A
Licensed Practical/Vocational Nurse Training, A
Machine Tool Technology/Machinist, A
Natural Resources Management/Development and
  Policy, A
Parks, Recreation and Leisure Facilities
  Management, A
Physical Sciences, A
Pre-Engineering, A
Web Page, Digital/Multimedia and Information
  Resources Design, A
Welding Technology/Welder, A

CHABOT COLLEGE

Accounting, A
Administrative Assistant and Secretarial Science, A
Advertising, A
Animal Physiology, A
Applied Mathematics, A
Architectural Engineering Technology/Technician, A
Art/Art Studies, General, A
Automobile/Automotive Mechanics
  Technology/Technician, A
Behavioral Sciences, A
Biological and Physical Sciences, A
Biology/Biological Sciences, A
Broadcast Journalism, A
Business Administration and Management, A
Business Machine Repairer, A
Business Teacher Education, A
Business/Managerial Economics, A
Chemistry, A
Civil Engineering Technology/Technician, A
Commercial and Advertising Art, A
Comparative Literature, A
Computer and Information Sciences, A
Computer Engineering Technology/Technician, A
Computer Programming, Specific Applications, A
Computer Science, A

Computer Typography and Composition Equipment
  Operator, A
Consumer Merchandising/Retailing Management, A
Corrections, A
Criminal Justice/Law Enforcement Administration, A
Criminal Justice/Police Science, A
Data Processing and Data Processing
  Technology/Technician, A
Dental Hygiene/Hygienist, A
Drawing, A
Ecology, A
Economics, A
Education, A
Electrical, Electronic and Communications
  Engineering Technology/Technician, A
Electromechanical Technology/Electromechanical
  Engineering Technology, A
Emergency Medical Technology/Technician (EMT
  Paramedic), A
Engineering, A
Engineering Technology, A
English Language and Literature, A
Fashion Merchandising, A
Fashion/Apparel Design, A
Finance, A
Fine/Studio Arts, A
Fire Science/Firefighting, A
Health Information/Medical Records
  Administration/Administrator, A
Health Teacher Education, A
History, A
Horticultural Science, A
Human Services, A
Humanities/Humanistic Studies, A
Industrial Technology/Technician, A
Information Science/Studies, A
Instrumentation Technology/Technician, A
Interdisciplinary Studies, A
Italian Language and Literature, A
Journalism, A
Kindergarten/PreSchool Education and Teaching, A
Landscaping and Groundskeeping, A
Legal Administrative Assistant/Secretary, A
Liberal Arts and Sciences Studies and
  Humanities, A
Mass Communication/Media Studies, A
Mathematics, A
Medical/Clinical Assistant, A
Music, A
Natural Sciences, A
Nursing - Registered Nurse Training, A
Ornamental Horticulture, A
Parks, Recreation, Leisure and Fitness Studies, A
Photography, A
Physical Education Teaching and Coaching, A
Physics, A
Political Science and Government, A
Pre-Engineering, A
Psychology, A
Radio and Television, A
Real Estate, A
Social Sciences, A
Sociology, A
Solar Energy Technology/Technician, A
Spanish Language and Literature, A
Statistics, A
Survey Technology/Surveying, A
Teacher Assistant/Aide, A
Technology Education/Industrial Arts, A
Tourism and Travel Services Management, A
Welding Technology/Welder, A
Women's Studies, A
Zoology/Animal Biology, A

CHAFFEY COLLEGE

Accounting, A
Administrative Assistant and Secretarial Science, A
Anthropology, A
Art/Art Studies, General, A
Automobile/Automotive Mechanics
  Technology/Technician, A
Biology/Biological Sciences, A
Broadcast Journalism, A
Business Administration and Management, A
Business Teacher Education, A
Ceramic Arts and Ceramics, A

Chemistry, A
Child Development, A
Computer Typography and Composition Equipment
  Operator, A
Corrections, A
Court Reporting/Court Reporter, A
Dance, A
Developmental and Child Psychology, A
Dietetics/Dieticians, A
Drafting and Design Technology/Technician, A
Drama and Dramatics/Theatre Arts, A
Economics, A
Electrical, Electronic and Communications
  Engineering Technology/Technician, A
Engineering, A
English Language and Literature, A
Environmental Engineering
  Technology/Environmental Technology, A
Family and Consumer Sciences/Human Sciences, A
Fashion/Apparel Design, A
French Language and Literature, A
Geology/Earth Science, A
German Language and Literature, A
Gerontology, A
History, A
Hotel/Motel Administration/Management, A
Humanities/Humanistic Studies, A
Industrial Design, A
Information Science/Studies, A
Interior Design, A
Journalism, A
Kindergarten/PreSchool Education and Teaching, A
Legal Administrative Assistant/Secretary, A
Liberal Arts and Sciences Studies and
  Humanities, A
Marketing/Marketing Management, A
Mathematics, A
Medical Administrative Assistant/Secretary, A
Medical Radiologic Technology/Science - Radiation
  Therapist, A
Music, A
Nursing - Registered Nurse Training, A
Philosophy, A
Photography, A
Physical Education Teaching and Coaching, A
Physical Sciences, A
Physics, A
Political Science and Government, A
Psychology, A
Quality Control Technology/Technician, A
Real Estate, A
Religion/Religious Studies, A
Social Sciences, A
Sociology, A
Spanish Language and Literature, A
Special Products Marketing Operations, A
Speech and Rhetorical Studies, A
Telecommunications Technology/Technician, A

CHAPMAN UNIVERSITY

Accounting, B
Advertising, B
American Government and Politics (United States)
  , B
American History (United States), B
Art History, Criticism and Conservation, B
Art/Art Studies, General, B
Athletic Training and Sports Medicine, B
Biochemistry, B
Biology/Biological Sciences, B
Biopsychology, B
Broadcast Journalism, B
Business Administration and Management, B
Business Administration, Management and
  Operations, MO
Business/Managerial Economics, B
Chemistry, B
Cinematography and Film/Video Production, B
Communication Studies/Speech Communication
  and Rhetoric, B
Comparative Literature, B
Computer and Information Sciences, B
Computer Science, B
Counselor Education/School Counseling and
  Guidance Services, M
Creative Writing, B

Curriculum and Instruction, M
Dance, B
Drama and Dramatics/Theatre Arts, B
Education, MO
Educational Administration and Supervision, M
Educational Leadership and Administration, M
Educational Psychology, MO
Elementary Education and Teaching, M
English, M
English Language and Literature, B
European History, B
Exercise Physiology, B
Film, Television, and Video Production, M
Film/Cinema Studies, B
Fine/Studio Arts, B
Food Science and Technology, M
French Language and Literature, B
Graphic Design, B
Human Resources Management and Services, MO
International Business/Trade/Commerce, B
International Relations and Affairs, B
Law and Legal Studies, BMPO
Liberal Arts and Sciences Studies and
  Humanities, B
Marriage and Family Therapy/Counseling, M
Mathematics, B
Molecular Biology, B
Music, B
Music Performance, B
Music Teacher Education, B
Music Theory and Composition, B
Music Therapy/Therapist, B
Nutritional Sciences, BM
Organizational Behavior Studies, B
Peace Studies and Conflict Resolution, B
Philosophy, B
Physical Therapy/Therapist, D
Political Science and Government, B
Psychology, B
Public/Applied History and Archival Administration, B
Reading Teacher Education, M
Religion/Religious Studies, B
School Psychology, MO
Secondary Education and Teaching, M
Social Work, B
Sociology, B
Spanish Language and Literature, B
Special Education and Teaching, M
Taxation, M
Voice and Opera, B
Wind and Percussion Instruments, B
Writing, M

CHARLES R. DREW UNIVERSITY OF MEDICINE AND SCIENCE

Allopathic Medicine, P
Biomedical Sciences, B
Diagnostic Medical Sonography/Sonographer and
  Ultrasound Technician, B
Health Information/Medical Records
  Administration/Administrator, A
Health Information/Medical Records
  Technology/Technician, A
Health/Medical Preparatory Programs, B
Medical Radiologic Technology/Science - Radiation
  Therapist, AB
Nuclear Medical Technology/Technologist, B
Pharmacy Technician/Assistant, A
Physician Assistant, B
Substance Abuse/Addiction Counseling, A

CITRUS COLLEGE

Administrative Assistant and Secretarial Science, A
Art/Art Studies, General, A
Automobile/Automotive Mechanics
  Technology/Technician, A
Behavioral Sciences, A
Biology/Biological Sciences, A
Business Administration and Management, A
Computer and Information Sciences, A
Computer Science, A
Cosmetology/Cosmetologist, A
Criminal Justice/Law Enforcement Administration, A
Criminal Justice/Police Science, A
Dance, A

Data Processing and Data Processing
  Technology/Technician, A
Dental Assisting/Assistant, A
Drafting and Design Technology/Technician, A
Drama and Dramatics/Theatre Arts, A
Electrical, Electronic and Communications
  Engineering Technology/Technician, A
Engineering, A
Engineering Technology, A
English Language and Literature, A
French Language and Literature, A
German Language and Literature, A
Health and Physical Education, A
Hydrology and Water Resources Science, A
Japanese Language and Literature, A
Journalism, A
Liberal Arts and Sciences Studies and
  Humanities, A
Library Assistant/Technician, A
Library Science, A
Licensed Practical/Vocational Nurse Training, A
Mathematics, A
Mechanical Engineering/Mechanical
  Technology/Technician, A
Modern Languages, A
Music, A
Natural Sciences, A
Photography, A
Physical Education Teaching and Coaching, A
Physical Sciences, A
Public Administration, A
Real Estate, A
Social Sciences, A
Spanish Language and Literature, A
Visual and Performing Arts, A

CITY COLLEGE OF SAN FRANCISCO

Accounting, A
African-American/Black Studies, A
Agricultural Business and Management, A
Airframe Mechanics and Aircraft Maintenance
  Technology/Technician, A
Art/Art Studies, General, A
Asian Studies/Civilization, A
Atmospheric Sciences and Meteorology, A
Automobile/Automotive Mechanics
  Technology/Technician, A
Avionics Maintenance Technology/Technician, A
Botany/Plant Biology, A
Broadcast Journalism, A
Building/Construction
  Finishing, Management, and Inspection, A
Business Administration and Management, A
Chemical Engineering, A
Chemistry, A
Cinematography and Film/Video Production, A
Civil Engineering Technology/Technician, A
Computer Programming/Programmer, A
Computer Science, A
Consumer Services and Advocacy, A
Court Reporting/Court Reporter, A
Criminal Justice/Law Enforcement Administration, A
Criminal Justice/Police Science, A
Dental Hygiene/Hygienist, A
Developmental and Child Psychology, A
Dietetics/Dieticians, A
Educational/Instructional Media Design, A
Electrical, Electronic and Communications
  Engineering Technology/Technician, A
English Language and Literature, A
Fashion Merchandising, A
Finance, A
Fire Science/Firefighting, A
Forestry, A
Geology/Earth Science, A
Graphic and Printing Equipment Operator
  Production, A
Health Information/Medical Records
  Administration/Administrator, A
Horticultural Science, A
Hotel/Motel Administration/Management, A
Industrial Radiologic Technology/Technician, A
Industrial Technology/Technician, A
Insurance, A
Interior Design, A
Journalism, A

Labor and Industrial Relations, A
Landscape Architecture, A
Latin American Studies, A
Legal Administrative Assistant/Secretary, A
Library Science, A
Licensed Practical/Vocational Nurse Training, A
Marketing/Marketing Management, A
Mathematics, A
Mechanical Engineering/Mechanical
  Technology/Technician, A
Music, A
Nursing - Registered Nurse Training, A
Ornamental Horticulture, A
Parks, Recreation, Leisure and Fitness Studies, A
Photography, A
Physical Therapy/Therapist, A
Pre-Engineering, A
Psychology, A
Public Administration, A
Public Health (MPH, DPH), A
Real Estate, A
Respiratory Care Therapy/Therapist, A
Social Sciences, A
Social Work, A
Transportation and Materials Moving, A
Wildlife and Wildlands Science and Management, A
Women's Studies, A

CLAREMONT MCKENNA COLLEGE

Accounting, B
African-American/Black Studies, B
American Government and Politics (United States)
  , B
American/United States Studies/Civilization, B
Anthropology, B
Archeology, B
Area Studies, B
Area, Ethnic, Cultural, and Gender Studies, B
Art History, Criticism and Conservation, B
Art/Art Studies, General, B
Asian Studies/Civilization, B
Asian-American Studies, B
Biochemistry, B
Biology/Biological Sciences, B
Biophysics, B
Chemistry, B
Chinese Language and Literature, B
Chinese Studies, B
Classics and Classical
  Languages, Literatures, and Linguistics, B
Comparative Literature, B
Computer and Information Sciences, B
Computer Science, B
Dance, B
Drama and Dramatics/Theatre Arts, B
East Asian
  Languages, Literatures, and Linguistics, B
Economics, B
Engineering, B
Engineering Science, B
Engineering/Industrial Management, B
English Language and Literature, B
Environmental Studies, B
Ethnic, Cultural Minority, and Gender Studies, B
European Studies/Civilization, B
Film/Cinema Studies, B
Fine/Studio Arts, B
French Language and Literature, B
French Studies, B
German Language and Literature, B
German Studies, B
Germanic Languages, Literatures, and Linguistics, B
Hispanic-American, Puerto Rican, and Mexican-
  American/Chicano Studies, B
History, B
International Business/Trade/Commerce, B
International Economics, B
International Relations and Affairs, B
Italian Language and Literature, B
Japanese Language and Literature, B
Japanese Studies, B
Korean Studies, B
Latin American Studies, B
Latin Language and Literature, B
Law and Legal Studies, B
Mathematics, B

Modern Greek Language and Literature, B
Modern Languages, B
Music, B
Near and Middle Eastern Studies, B
Pacific Area/Pacific Rim Studies, B
Philosophy, B
Philosophy and Religious Studies, B
Physics, B
Physiological Psychology/Psychobiology, B
Political Science and Government, B
Pre-Dentistry Studies, B
Pre-Law Studies, B
Pre-Medicine/Pre-Medical Studies, B
Psychology, B
Religion/Religious Studies, B
Russian Language and Literature, B
Russian Studies, B
Sociology, B
South Asian
    Languages, Literatures, and Linguistics, B
Spanish Language and Literature, B
Visual and Performing Arts, B
Western European Studies, B

CLEVELAND CHIROPRACTIC COLLEGE-LOS ANGELES CAMPUS

Biology/Biological Sciences, AB
Chiropractic, P

COASTLINE COMMUNITY COLLEGE

Liberal Arts and Sciences Studies and
    Humanities, A

COGSWELL POLYTECHNICAL COLLEGE

Animation, Interactive Technology, Video Graphics
    and Special Effects, B
Audio Engineering, B
Computer Graphics, B
Digital Communication and Media/Multimedia, B
Electrical, Electronic and Communications
    Engineering Technology/Technician, B
Electrical, Electronics and Communications
    Engineering, B
Fire Science/Firefighting, B

THE COLBURN SCHOOL CONSERVATORY OF MUSIC

Music Performance, B
Piano and Organ, B
Violin, Viola, Guitar and Other Stringed
    Instruments, B

COLEMAN COLLEGE (LA MESA)

Business Administration, Management and
    Operations, AB
Computer and Information Sciences, AB
Computer Graphics, A
Computer Systems Networking and
    Telecommunications, AB
Information Science/Studies, M
Management of Technology, M
System Administration/Administrator, AB

COLLEGE OF ALAMEDA

Accounting, A
Administrative Assistant and Secretarial Science, A
African-American/Black Studies, A
Anthropology, A
Art/Art Studies, General, A
Automobile/Automotive Mechanics
    Technology/Technician, A
Avionics Maintenance Technology/Technician, A
Biological and Physical Sciences, A
Biology/Biological Sciences, A
Business Administration and Management, A
Business Teacher Education, A
Dental Hygiene/Hygienist, A
English Language and Literature, A
Fashion Merchandising, A
Fashion/Apparel Design, A
General Studies, A
Geography, A
Hispanic-American, Puerto Rican, and Mexican-
    American/Chicano Studies, A

History, A
Human Development and Family Studies, A
Humanities/Humanistic Studies, A
Information Science/Studies, A
Liberal Arts and Sciences Studies and
    Humanities, A
Marketing/Marketing Management, A
Mathematics, A
Philosophy, A
Political Science and Government, A
Psychology, A
Social Sciences, A
Sociology, A

COLLEGE OF THE CANYONS

Accounting, A
Administrative Assistant and Secretarial Science, A
Art/Art Studies, General, A
Biological and Physical Sciences, A
Biology/Biological Sciences, A
Business Administration and Management, A
Chemistry, A
Child Development, A
Cinematography and Film/Video Production, A
Computer and Information Sciences, A
Computer Engineering, A
Computer Science, A
Criminal Justice/Law Enforcement Administration, A
Criminal Justice/Police Science, A
Developmental and Child Psychology, A
Drafting and Design Technology/Technician, A
Electrical, Electronic and Communications
    Engineering Technology/Technician, A
English Language and Literature, A
French Language and Literature, A
Geography, A
Geology/Earth Science, A
German Language and Literature, A
History, A
Hotel/Motel Administration/Management, A
Humanities/Humanistic Studies, A
Hydrology and Water Resources Science, A
Information Science/Studies, A
Interior Design, A
Journalism, A
Kindergarten/PreSchool Education and Teaching, A
Liberal Arts and Sciences Studies and
    Humanities, A
Licensed Practical/Vocational Nurse Training, A
Mathematics, A
Natural Sciences, A
Nursing - Registered Nurse Training, A
Physical Education Teaching and Coaching, A
Physical Sciences, A
Political Science and Government, A
Pre-Engineering, A
Psychology, A
Public Health (MPH, DPH), A
Quality Control Technology/Technician, A
Real Estate, A
Social Sciences, A
Spanish Language and Literature, A

COLLEGE OF THE DESERT

Administrative Assistant and Secretarial Science, A
Agricultural Business and Management, A
Anthropology, A
Architectural Engineering Technology/Technician, A
Art/Art Studies, General, A
Automobile/Automotive Mechanics
    Technology/Technician, A
Biology/Biological Sciences, A
Building/Construction
    Finishing, Management, and Inspection, A
Business Administration and Management, A
Business/Managerial Economics, A
Chemistry, A
Computer and Information Sciences, A
Computer Graphics, A
Computer Programming, A
Computer Science, A
Computer Typography and Composition Equipment
    Operator, A
Criminal Justice/Law Enforcement Administration, A
Criminal Justice/Police Science, A
Culinary Arts/Chef Training, A

Drafting and Design Technology/Technician, A
Drama and Dramatics/Theatre Arts, A
Economics, A
Education, A
Engineering Technology, A
English Language and Literature, A
Environmental Studies, A
Fire Science/Firefighting, A
French Language and Literature, A
Geography, A
Geology/Earth Science, A
Heating, Air Conditioning, Ventilation and
    Refrigeration Maintenance
    Technology/Technician, A
History, A
Horticultural Science, A
Interior Design, A
Italian Language and Literature, A
Journalism, A
Kindergarten/PreSchool Education and Teaching, A
Liberal Arts and Sciences Studies and
    Humanities, A
Management Information Systems and Services, A
Marketing/Marketing Management, A
Mass Communication/Media Studies, A
Mathematics, A
Medical/Clinical Assistant, A
Music, A
Natural Resources Management/Development and
    Policy, A
Nursing - Registered Nurse Training, A
Ornamental Horticulture, A
Parks, Recreation and Leisure Facilities
    Management, A
Parks, Recreation, Leisure and Fitness Studies, A
Philosophy, A
Physical Education Teaching and Coaching, A
Physics, A
Political Science and Government, A
Pre-Engineering, A
Psychology, A
Real Estate, A
Respiratory Care Therapy/Therapist, A
Romance Languages, Literatures, and Linguistics, A
Social Sciences, A
Sociology, A
Speech and Rhetorical Studies, A
Teacher Assistant/Aide, A
Welding Technology/Welder, A
Word Processing, A

COLLEGE OF MARIN

Accounting, A
Administrative Assistant and Secretarial Science, A
Applied Art, A
Architectural Engineering Technology/Technician, A
Art/Art Studies, General, A
Automobile/Automotive Mechanics
    Technology/Technician, A
Behavioral Sciences, A
Biology/Biological Sciences, A
Business Administration and Management, A
Chemistry, A
Computer Science, A
Consumer Merchandising/Retailing Management, A
Corrections, A
Court Reporting/Court Reporter, A
Criminal Justice/Police Science, A
Dance, A
Data Processing and Data Processing
    Technology/Technician, A
Dental Hygiene/Hygienist, A
Drama and Dramatics/Theatre Arts, A
Ecology, A
Electrical, Electronic and Communications
    Engineering Technology/Technician, A
Engineering, A
Engineering Technology, A
Ethnic and Cultural Studies, A
Fire Science/Firefighting, A
French Language and Literature, A
Geology/Earth Science, A
German Language and Literature, A
History, A
Humanities/Humanistic Studies, A
Information Science/Studies, A

Interior Design, A
Journalism, A
Kindergarten/PreSchool Education and Teaching, A
Landscape Architecture, A
Landscaping and Groundskeeping, A
Liberal Arts and Sciences Studies and
   Humanities, A
Machine Tool Technology/Machinist, A
Marine Technology, A
Marketing/Marketing Management, A
Mass Communication/Media Studies, A
Mathematics, A
Medical Administrative Assistant/Secretary, A
Medical/Clinical Assistant, A
Music, A
Natural Sciences, A
Nursing - Registered Nurse Training, A
Philosophy, A
Physical Education Teaching and Coaching, A
Physics, A
Political Science and Government, A
Psychology, A
Real Estate, A
Sociology, A
Spanish Language and Literature, A
Speech and Rhetorical Studies, A

COLLEGE OF THE REDWOODS

Administrative Assistant and Secretarial Science, A
Agricultural Business and Management, A
Agronomy and Crop Science, A
Architectural Engineering Technology/Technician, A
Automobile/Automotive Mechanics
   Technology/Technician, A
Business Administration and Management, A
Child Care Provider/Assistant, A
Commercial and Advertising Art, A
Computer and Information Sciences, A
Computer Engineering Technology/Technician, A
Computer Programming/Programmer, A
Computer Typography and Composition Equipment
   Operator, A
Construction Engineering Technology/Technician, A
Criminal Justice/Law Enforcement Administration, A
Dental Assisting/Assistant, A
Diesel Mechanics Technology/Technician, A
Drafting and Design Technology/Technician, A
Electrical, Electronic and Communications
   Engineering Technology/Technician, A
Forestry, A
Kindergarten/PreSchool Education and Teaching, A
Legal Administrative Assistant/Secretary, A
Legal Assistant/Paralegal, A
Machine Tool Technology/Machinist, A
Marine Science/Merchant Marine Officer, A
Medical/Clinical Assistant, A
Nursing - Registered Nurse Training, A
Real Estate, A
Web Page, Digital/Multimedia and Information
   Resources Design, A
Welding Technology/Welder, A

COLLEGE OF SAN MATEO

Accounting, A
Administrative Assistant and Secretarial Science, A
Airframe Mechanics and Aircraft Maintenance
   Technology/Technician, A
Airline/Commercial/Professional Pilot and Flight
   Crew, A
Architectural Engineering Technology/Technician, A
Art/Art Studies, General, A
Avionics Maintenance Technology/Technician, A
Biology Technician/BioTechnology Laboratory
   Technician, A
Biology/Biological Sciences, A
Broadcast Journalism, A
Business Administration and Management, A
Chemistry, A
Cinematography and Film/Video Production, A
Commercial and Advertising Art, A
Computer Science, A
Construction Engineering Technology/Technician, A
Consumer Merchandising/Retailing Management, A
Cosmetology/Cosmetologist, A
Criminal Justice/Police Science, A
Dental Hygiene/Hygienist, A

Drafting and Design Technology/Technician, A
Drawing, A
Electrical, Electronic and Communications
   Engineering Technology/Technician, A
Engineering, A
Engineering Technology, A
English Language and Literature, A
Environmental Studies, A
Ethnic and Cultural Studies, A
Fire Science/Firefighting, A
French Language and Literature, A
Geology/Earth Science, A
German Language and Literature, A
Horticultural Science, A
Humanities/Humanistic Studies, A
Information Science/Studies, A
Journalism, A
Landscape Architecture, A
Landscaping and Groundskeeping, A
Liberal Arts and Sciences Studies and
   Humanities, A
Machine Tool Technology/Machinist, A
Management Information Systems and Services, A
Marketing/Marketing Management, A
Mathematics, A
Medical Administrative Assistant/Secretary, A
Medical/Clinical Assistant, A
Music, A
Nursing - Registered Nurse Training, A
Ornamental Horticulture, A
Photography, A
Physical Sciences, A
Physics, A
Pipefitting/Pipefitter and Sprinkler Fitter, A
Printmaking, A
Radio and Television, A
Real Estate, A
Social Sciences, A
Spanish Language and Literature, A
Speech and Rhetorical Studies, A
Substance Abuse/Addiction Counseling, A
Welding Technology/Welder, A

COLLEGE OF THE SEQUOIAS

Accounting, A
Administrative Assistant and Secretarial Science, A
Agricultural Business and Management, A
Agricultural Mechanization, A
Agricultural Teacher Education, A
Agriculture, A
Animal Sciences, A
Architectural Engineering Technology/Technician, A
Art/Art Studies, General, A
Athletic Training and Sports Medicine, A
Automobile/Automotive Mechanics
   Technology/Technician, A
Biological and Physical Sciences, A
Biology/Biological Sciences, A
Business Administration and Management, A
Carpentry/Carpenter, A
Chemistry, A
Commercial and Advertising Art, A
Community Organization and Advocacy, A
Computer Engineering Technology/Technician, A
Computer Graphics, A
Computer Programming/Programmer, A
Computer Science, A
Computer Software and Media Applications, A
Computer Typography and Composition Equipment
   Operator, A
Construction Engineering Technology/Technician, A
Corrections, A
Cosmetology/Cosmetologist, A
Criminal Justice/Law Enforcement Administration, A
Criminal Justice/Police Science, A
Culinary Arts/Chef Training, A
Dairy Science, A
Data Modeling/Warehousing and Database
   Administration, A
Developmental and Child Psychology, A
Drafting and Design Technology/Technician, A
Drama and Dramatics/Theatre Arts, A
Electrical, Electronic and Communications
   Engineering Technology/Technician, A
Engineering, A
English Language and Literature, A

Ethnic and Cultural Studies, A
Family and Consumer Sciences/Home Economics
   Teacher Education, A
Family and Consumer Sciences/Human Sciences, A
Fashion Merchandising, A
Fashion/Apparel Design, A
Fire Science/Firefighting, A
French Language and Literature, A
Health Teacher Education, A
Heating, Air Conditioning, Ventilation and
   Refrigeration Maintenance
   Technology/Technician, A
History, A
Horticultural Science, A
Humanities/Humanistic Studies, A
Information Science/Studies, A
Interior Design, A
Journalism, A
Kindergarten/PreSchool Education and Teaching, A
Legal Assistant/Paralegal, A
Liberal Arts and Sciences Studies and
   Humanities, A
Marketing/Marketing Management, A
Mass Communication/Media Studies, A
Mathematics, A
Modern Languages, A
Music, A
Nursing - Registered Nurse Training, A
Ornamental Horticulture, A
Physical Education Teaching and Coaching, A
Pre-Engineering, A
Real Estate, A
Sign Language Interpretation and Translation, A
Social Sciences, A
Sociology, A
Spanish Language and Literature, A
Speech and Rhetorical Studies, A
Technology Education/Industrial Arts, A
Web Page, Digital/Multimedia and Information
   Resources Design, A
Welding Technology/Welder, A
Word Processing, A

COLLEGE OF THE SISKIYOUS

Accounting, A
Biology Teacher Education, A
Biology/Biological Sciences, A
Business Administration and Management, A
Chemistry, A
Chemistry Teacher Education, A
Computer Graphics, A
Computer Programming/Programmer, A
Computer Science, A
Criminal Justice/Law Enforcement Administration, A
English Language and Literature, A
English/Language Arts Teacher Education, A
Fire Science/Firefighting, A
Geology/Earth Science, A
History, A
Information Technology, A
Intermedia/Multimedia, A
Kindergarten/PreSchool Education and Teaching, A
Law and Legal Studies, A
Legal Assistant/Paralegal, A
Management Information Systems and Services, A
Mathematics, A
Philosophy, A
Physical Sciences, A
Physics, A
Physics Teacher Education, A
Web Page, Digital/Multimedia and Information
   Resources Design, A
Web/Multimedia Management and Webmaster, A

COLUMBIA COLLEGE

Administrative Assistant and Secretarial Science, A
Anthropology, A
Art/Art Studies, General, A
Automobile/Automotive Mechanics
   Technology/Technician, A
Biology/Biological Sciences, A
Business Administration and Management, A
Chemistry, A
Computer Science, A
Culinary Arts/Chef Training, A
Developmental and Child Psychology, A

Drama and Dramatics/Theatre Arts, A
English Language and Literature, A
Environmental Studies, A
Fire Science/Firefighting, A
Food Technology and Processing, A
Forestry Technology/Technician, A
Geology/Earth Science, A
Health Teacher Education, A
History, A
Hotel/Motel Administration/Management, A
Humanities/Humanistic Studies, A
Liberal Arts and Sciences Studies and
  Humanities, A
Mathematics, A
Music, A
Natural Resources Management/Development and
  Policy, A
Photography, A
Physical Education Teaching and Coaching, A
Physical Sciences, A
Physics, A
Psychology, A
Sociology, A
Special Products Marketing Operations, A

COLUMBIA COLLEGE HOLLYWOOD

Broadcast Journalism, B
Cinematography and Film/Video Production, B
Film/Cinema Studies, B
Radio and Television, B
Telecommunications Technology/Technician, AB

COMPTON COMMUNITY COLLEGE

Accounting, A
Administrative Assistant and Secretarial Science, A
African-American/Black Studies, A
Airline/Commercial/Professional Pilot and Flight
  Crew, A
Art Teacher Education, A
Art/Art Studies, General, A
Automobile/Automotive Mechanics
  Technology/Technician, A
Behavioral Sciences, A
Biological and Physical Sciences, A
Biology/Biological Sciences, A
Business Administration and Management, A
Chemistry, A
Child Development, A
Civil Engineering Technology/Technician, A
Commercial and Advertising Art, A
Comparative Literature, A
Computer Engineering Technology/Technician, A
Computer Programming/Programmer, A
Construction Engineering Technology/Technician, A
Criminal Justice/Law Enforcement Administration, A
Criminal Justice/Police Science, A
Dance, A
Data Processing and Data Processing
  Technology/Technician, A
Developmental and Child Psychology, A
Drafting and Design Technology/Technician, A
Drama and Dramatics/Theatre Arts, A
Economics, A
Electrical, Electronic and Communications
  Engineering Technology/Technician, A
Emergency Medical Technology/Technician (EMT
  Paramedic), A
Engineering, A
English Language and Literature, A
Ethnic and Cultural Studies, A
Family and Consumer Sciences/Human Sciences, A
Fiber, Textile and Weaving Arts, A
Fire Science/Firefighting, A
Foods, Nutrition, and Wellness Studies, A
French Language and Literature, A
German Language and Literature, A
Graphic and Printing Equipment Operator
  Production, A
Hispanic-American, Puerto Rican, and Mexican-
  American/Chicano Studies, A
History, A
Human Services, A
Industrial Radiologic Technology/Technician, A
Information Science/Studies, A
Jazz/Jazz Studies, A
Journalism, A

Kindergarten/PreSchool Education and Teaching, A
Legal Assistant/Paralegal, A
Liberal Arts and Sciences Studies and
  Humanities, A
Machine Tool Technology/Machinist, A
Mathematics, A
Mechanical Engineering/Mechanical
  Technology/Technician, A
Music, A
Nuclear Medical Technology/Technologist, A
Nursing - Registered Nurse Training, A
Parks, Recreation and Leisure Facilities
  Management, A
Parks, Recreation, Leisure and Fitness Studies, A
Philosophy, A
Photography, A
Physical Education Teaching and Coaching, A
Physical Sciences, A
Physics, A
Pre-Engineering, A
Psychology, A
Public Health (MPH, DPH), A
Real Estate, A
Respiratory Care Therapy/Therapist, A
Social Sciences, A
Social Work, A
Sociology, A
Spanish Language and Literature, A
Speech and Rhetorical Studies, A
Teacher Assistant/Aide, A
Telecommunications Technology/Technician, A
Trade and Industrial Teacher Education, A

CONCORDIA UNIVERSITY

Art/Art Studies, General, B
Behavioral Sciences, B
Biology/Biological Sciences, B
Business Administration and Management, B
Business Administration, Management and
  Operations, M
Chemistry, B
Communication Studies/Speech Communication
  and Rhetoric, B
Curriculum and Instruction, M
Divinity/Ministry (BD, MDiv.), B
Drama and Dramatics/Theatre Arts, B
Education, M
English Language and Literature, B
History, B
Humanities/Humanistic Studies, B
Information Technology, B
International Business/Trade/Commerce, B
International/Global Studies, B
Kinesiology and Exercise Science, B
Liberal Arts and Sciences Studies and
  Humanities, B
Mathematics, B
Missions/Missionary Studies and Missiology, M
Music, B
Political Science and Government, B
Psychology, B
Religious Education, B
Social Sciences, B
Theology and Religious Vocations, M
Theology/Theological Studies, B

CONTRA COSTA COLLEGE

Administrative Assistant and Secretarial Science, A
African-American/Black Studies, A
Anthropology, A
Art/Art Studies, General, A
Automobile/Automotive Mechanics
  Technology/Technician, A
Biology Technician/BioTechnology Laboratory
  Technician, A
Biology/Biological Sciences, A
Business Administration and Management, A
Chemistry, A
Computer Programming/Programmer, A
Computer Science, A
Criminal Justice/Law Enforcement Administration, A
Criminal Justice/Police Science, A
Culinary Arts/Chef Training, A
Dental Hygiene/Hygienist, A
Drafting and Design Technology/Technician, A

Electrical, Electronic and Communications
  Engineering Technology/Technician, A
Emergency Medical Technology/Technician (EMT
  Paramedic), A
Engineering, A
English Language and Literature, A
Family and Consumer Sciences/Human Sciences, A
French Language and Literature, A
Geography, A
Geology/Earth Science, A
German Language and Literature, A
Hispanic-American, Puerto Rican, and Mexican-
  American/Chicano Studies, A
History, A
Humanities/Humanistic Studies, A
Italian Language and Literature, A
Journalism, A
Kindergarten/PreSchool Education and Teaching, A
Liberal Arts and Sciences Studies and
  Humanities, A
Licensed Practical/Vocational Nurse Training, A
Materials Sciences, A
Mathematics, A
Music, A
Nursing - Registered Nurse Training, A
Philosophy, A
Physics, A
Political Science and Government, A
Quality Control Technology/Technician, A
Real Estate, A
Sociology, A
Spanish Language and Literature, A
Technology Education/Industrial Arts, A

COSUMNES RIVER COLLEGE
(SACRAMENTO)

Accounting, A
Advertising, A
Agricultural Business and Management, A
Agricultural Mechanization, A
Agronomy and Crop Science, A
American/United States Studies/Civilization, A
Animal Sciences, A
Applied Art, A
Architectural Engineering Technology/Technician, A
Art/Art Studies, General, A
Automobile/Automotive Mechanics
  Technology/Technician, A
Biological and Physical Sciences, A
Biology/Biological Sciences, A
Broadcast Journalism, A
Building/Construction
  Finishing, Management, and Inspection, A
Business Administration and Management, A
Child Development, A
Computer Programming/Programmer, A
Construction Engineering Technology/Technician, A
Criminal Justice/Law Enforcement Administration, A
Drafting and Design Technology/Technician, A
Drama and Dramatics/Theatre Arts, A
Electrical, Electronic and Communications
  Engineering Technology/Technician, A
Emergency Medical Technology/Technician (EMT
  Paramedic), A
Environmental Design/Architecture, A
Environmental Engineering
  Technology/Environmental Technology, A
Environmental Studies, A
Ethnic and Cultural Studies, A
Family and Consumer Economics and Related
  Services, A
Farm/Farm and Ranch Management, A
Finance, A
Fire Science/Firefighting, A
Geology/Earth Science, A
Gerontology, A
Health Information/Medical Records
  Administration/Administrator, A
Horticultural Science, A
Human Services, A
Humanities/Humanistic Studies, A
Information Science/Studies, A
Interior Design, A
Journalism, A
Kindergarten/PreSchool Education and Teaching, A
Landscaping and Groundskeeping, A

Liberal Arts and Sciences Studies and
  Humanities, A
Management Information Systems and Services, A
Marketing/Marketing Management, A
Mass Communication/Media Studies, A
Mathematics, A
Medical Administrative Assistant/Secretary, A
Medical/Clinical Assistant, A
Music, A
Photography, A
Pre-Engineering, A
Public Relations/Image Management, A
Radio and Television, A
Real Estate, A
Social Sciences, A
Special Products Marketing Operations, A
Veterinary/Animal Health Technology/Technician and
  Veterinary Assistant, A
Women's Studies, A

CRAFTON HILLS COLLEGE

Accounting, A
Administrative Assistant and Secretarial Science, A
Anthropology, A
Art/Art Studies, General, A
Astronomy, A
Biological and Physical Sciences, A
Biology/Biological Sciences, A
Business Administration and Management, A
Chemistry, A
Child Care Provider/Assistant, A
Child Development, A
Community Organization and Advocacy, A
Computer Science, A
Criminal Justice/Law Enforcement Administration, A
Drama and Dramatics/Theatre Arts, A
Economics, A
Emergency Medical Technology/Technician (EMT
  Paramedic), A
English Language and Literature, A
Fire Science/Firefighting, A
French Language and Literature, A
Geology/Earth Science, A
History, A
Human Services, A
Humanities/Humanistic Studies, A
Industrial Radiologic Technology/Technician, A
Liberal Arts and Sciences Studies and
  Humanities, A
Marketing/Marketing Management, A
Mathematics, A
Medical Administrative Assistant/Secretary, A
Music, A
Philosophy, A
Physical Education Teaching and Coaching, A
Physics, A
Political Science and Government, A
Pre-Engineering, A
Psychology, A
Religion/Religious Studies, A
Respiratory Care Therapy/Therapist, A
Sociology, A
Spanish Language and Literature, A
Speech and Rhetorical Studies, A
Speech-Language Pathology/Pathologist, A

CUESTA COLLEGE

Administrative Assistant and Secretarial Science, A
Agricultural Mechanization, A
Applied Art, A
Art/Art Studies, General, A
Artificial Intelligence and Robotics, A
Arts Management, A
Automobile/Automotive Mechanics
  Technology/Technician, A
Biology/Biological Sciences, A
Business Administration and Management, A
Chemistry, A
Child Development, A
Computer Engineering Technology/Technician, A
Computer Hardware Engineering, A
Computer Science, A
Computer Systems Networking and
  Telecommunications, A
Construction Engineering Technology/Technician, A

Data Processing and Data Processing
  Technology/Technician, A
Electrical, Electronic and Communications
  Engineering Technology/Technician, A
Engineering, A
Family and Consumer Economics and Related
  Services, A
Fashion Merchandising, A
Foods, Nutrition, and Wellness Studies, A
Geology/Earth Science, A
Human Development and Family Studies, A
Human Services, A
Industrial Technology/Technician, A
Information Technology, A
Interior Design, A
Journalism, A
Kindergarten/PreSchool Education and Teaching, A
Liberal Arts and Sciences Studies and
  Humanities, A
Library Science, A
Management Information Systems and Services, A
Marketing/Marketing Management, A
Mass Communication/Media Studies, A
Mathematics, A
Medical/Clinical Assistant, A
Nursing - Registered Nurse Training, A
Parks, Recreation and Leisure Facilities
  Management, A
Physical Education Teaching and Coaching, A
Physics, A
Pre-Engineering, A
Psychology, A
Radio and Television, A
Real Estate, A
System Administration/Administrator, A
Telecommunications Technology/Technician, A
Therapeutic Recreation/Recreational Therapy, A
Web Page, Digital/Multimedia and Information
  Resources Design, A
Welding Technology/Welder, A

CUYAMACA COLLEGE

Accounting, A
Accounting Technology/Technician and
  Bookkeeping, A
Automobile/Automotive Mechanics
  Technology/Technician, A
Biological and Physical Sciences, A
Business Administration and Management, A
Business/Commerce, A
Chemistry, A
Child Development, A
Commercial and Advertising Art, A
Drafting and Design Technology/Technician, A
Drafting/Design Engineering
  Technologies/Technicians, A
Drawing, A
Elementary Education and Teaching, A
English Language and Literature, A
Entrepreneurship/Entrepreneurial Studies, A
Environmental Engineering
  Technology/Environmental Technology, A
General Studies, A
History, A
Information Science/Studies, A
Landscaping and Groundskeeping, A
Legal Assistant/Paralegal, A
Liberal Arts and Sciences Studies and
  Humanities, A
Occupational Safety and Health
  Technology/Technician, A
Office Management and Supervision, A
Ornamental Horticulture, A
Painting, A
Physics, A
Plant Nursery Operations and Management, A
Real Estate, A
Special Products Marketing Operations, A
Speech and Rhetorical Studies, A
Survey Technology/Surveying, A
Turf and Turfgrass Management, A

CYPRESS COLLEGE

Accounting, A
Administrative Assistant and Secretarial Science, A
Advertising, A

Airline Flight Attendant, A
Airline/Commercial/Professional Pilot and Flight
  Crew, A
Anthropology, A
Applied Art, A
Art/Art Studies, General, A
Autobody/Collision and Repair
  Technology/Technician, A
Automobile/Automotive Mechanics
  Technology/Technician, A
Aviation/Airway Management and Operations, A
Biological and Physical Sciences, A
Biology/Biological Sciences, A
Business Administration and Management, A
Chemistry, A
Computer and Information Sciences, A
Computer Graphics, A
Computer Programming, A
Computer Programming, Specific Applications, A
Computer Science, A
Computer Software and Media Applications, A
Computer Systems Networking and
  Telecommunications, A
Computer/Information Technology Services
  Administration and Management, A
Court Reporting/Court Reporter, A
Culinary Arts/Chef Training, A
Dance, A
Data Entry/Microcomputer Applications, A
Dental Assisting/Assistant, A
Dental Hygiene/Hygienist, A
Drama and Dramatics/Theatre Arts, A
Economics, A
Engineering, A
English Language and Literature, A
Funeral Service and Mortuary Science, A
Geography, A
Geology/Earth Science, A
Health Information/Medical Records
  Administration/Administrator, A
Heating, Air Conditioning, Ventilation and
  Refrigeration Maintenance
  Technology/Technician, A
History, A
Hotel/Motel Administration/Management, A
Human Services, A
Industrial Radiologic Technology/Technician, A
Information Science/Studies, A
Legal Administrative Assistant/Secretary, A
Liberal Arts and Sciences Studies and
  Humanities, A
Marketing/Marketing Management, A
Mathematics, A
Medical Administrative Assistant/Secretary, A
Music, A
Natural Sciences, A
Nursing - Registered Nurse Training, A
Philosophy, A
Photography, A
Physical Education Teaching and Coaching, A
Physics, A
Political Science and Government, A
Psychiatric/Mental Health Services Technician, A
Psychology, A
Public Health (MPH, DPH), A
Social Sciences, A
Sociology, A
Special Products Marketing Operations, A
Speech and Rhetorical Studies, A
System Administration/Administrator, A
Tourism and Travel Services Management, A
Web Page, Digital/Multimedia and Information
  Resources Design, A
Word Processing, A

DE ANZA COLLEGE

Accounting, A
Administrative Assistant and Secretarial Science, A
Art History, Criticism and Conservation, A
Art/Art Studies, General, A
Automobile/Automotive Mechanics
  Technology/Technician, A
Behavioral Sciences, A
Biology/Biological Sciences, A
Business Administration and Management, A
Business Machine Repairer, A

Ceramic Arts and Ceramics, A
Child Development, A
Commercial and Advertising Art, A
Computer Graphics, A
Computer Programming/Programmer, A
Computer Science, A
Construction Engineering Technology/Technician, A
Corrections, A
Criminal Justice/Law Enforcement Administration, A
Criminal Justice/Police Science, A
Developmental and Child Psychology, A
Drafting/Design Engineering
  Technologies/Technicians, A
Drama and Dramatics/Theatre Arts, A
Drawing, A
Economics, A
Engineering, A
Engineering Technology, A
English Language and Literature, A
Environmental Studies, A
Ethnic and Cultural Studies, A
Film/Cinema Studies, A
History, A
Humanities/Humanistic Studies, A
Industrial Technology/Technician, A
Information Science/Studies, A
International Relations and Affairs, A
Journalism, A
Legal Assistant/Paralegal, A
Liberal Arts and Sciences Studies and
  Humanities, A
Licensed Practical/Vocational Nurse Training, A
Machine Tool Technology/Machinist, A
Marketing/Marketing Management, A
Mass Communication/Media Studies, A
Mathematics, A
Medical/Clinical Assistant, A
Music, A
Nursing - Registered Nurse Training, A
Philosophy, A
Photography, A
Physical Education Teaching and Coaching, A
Physical Therapy/Therapist, A
Physics, A
Political Science and Government, A
Pre-Engineering, A
Printmaking, A
Psychology, A
Purchasing, Procurement/Acquisitions and
  Contracts Management, A
Radio and Television, A
Real Estate, A
Sculpture, A
Social Sciences, A
Sociology, A
Spanish Language and Literature, A
Speech and Rhetorical Studies, A
Technical and Business Writing, A

DESIGN INSTITUTE OF SAN DIEGO

Interior Design, B

DEVRY UNIVERSITY (ELK GROVE)

Business Administration, Management and
  Operations, M

DEVRY UNIVERSITY (FREMONT)

Business Administration, Management and
  Operations, BM
Computer Engineering Technology/Technician, B
Computer Programming, Specific Applications, B
Computer Systems Analysis/Analyst, B
Computer Systems Networking and
  Telecommunications, AB
Electrical, Electronic and Communications
  Engineering Technology/Technician, AB
Health Information/Medical Records
  Technology/Technician, A
Information Science/Studies, B
Medical Informatics, B
Operations Management and Supervision, B

System, Networking, and LAN/WAN
  Management/Manager, B

DEVRY UNIVERSITY (IRVINE)

Business Administration, Management and
  Operations, M

DEVRY UNIVERSITY (LONG BEACH)

Business Administration, Management and
  Operations, BM
Computer Engineering Technology/Technician, B
Computer Programming, Specific Applications, B
Computer Systems Analysis/Analyst, B
Computer Systems Networking and
  Telecommunications, AB
Electrical, Electronic and Communications
  Engineering Technology/Technician, AB
Health Information/Medical Records
  Technology/Technician, A
Information Science/Studies, B
Medical Informatics, B
Operations Management and Supervision, B

DEVRY UNIVERSITY (POMONA)

Biomedical Technology/Technician, B
Business Administration, Management and
  Operations, BM
Computer Engineering Technology/Technician, AB
Computer Programming, Specific Applications, B
Computer Systems Analysis/Analyst, B
Computer Systems Networking and
  Telecommunications, AB
Electrical, Electronic and Communications
  Engineering Technology/Technician, AB
Health Information/Medical Records
  Technology/Technician, A
Information Science/Studies, B
Operations Management and Supervision, B

DEVRY UNIVERSITY (SAN DIEGO)

Business Administration, Management and
  Operations, M

DEVRY UNIVERSITY (SAN FRANCISCO)

Business Administration, Management and
  Operations, M

DEVRY UNIVERSITY (WEST HILLS)

Biomedical Technology/Technician, B
Business Administration and Management, B
Business Administration, Management and
  Operations, BM
Computer Engineering Technology/Technician, B
Computer Programming, Specific Applications, B
Computer Systems Analysis/Analyst, B
Computer Systems Networking and
  Telecommunications, AB
Electrical, Electronic and Communications
  Engineering Technology/Technician, AB
Health Information/Medical Records
  Technology/Technician, A
Information Science/Studies, B
Operations Management and Supervision, B

DIABLO VALLEY COLLEGE

Liberal Arts and Sciences Studies and
  Humanities, A

DOMINICAN SCHOOL OF PHILOSOPHY AND THEOLOGY

Philosophy, BMO
Theology and Religious Vocations, MPO

DOMINICAN UNIVERSITY OF CALIFORNIA

Art History, Criticism and Conservation, B
Art/Art Studies, General, B
Biology/Biological Sciences, B
Business Administration and Management, B
Business Administration, Management and
  Operations, M
Communication Studies/Speech Communication
  and Rhetoric, B
Computer Graphics, B

Counseling Psychology, M
Creative Writing, B
Curriculum and instruction, M
E-Commerce/Electronic Commerce, B
Education, BMO
English Language and Literature, B
Environmental Studies, B
Ethnic, Cultural Minority, and Gender Studies, B
Foreign Languages and Literatures, B
History, B
Human Resources Management/Personnel
  Administration, B
Humanities/Humanistic Studies, BM
International Business/Trade/Commerce, BM
International/Global Studies, B
Liberal Arts and Sciences Studies and
  Humanities, B
Management Strategy and Policy, M
Music, B
Music Performance, B
Nursing, M
Nursing - Registered Nurse Training, B
Occupational Therapy/Therapist, BM
Political Science and Government, B
Psychology, B
Religion/Religious Studies, B
Special Education and Teaching, O
Visual and Performing Arts, B
Women's Studies, B

DON BOSCO TECHNICAL INSTITUTE

Automobile/Automotive Mechanics
  Technology/Technician, A
Commercial and Advertising Art, A
Construction Engineering Technology/Technician, A
Drafting and Design Technology/Technician, A
Electrical, Electronic and Communications
  Engineering Technology/Technician, A
Graphic and Printing Equipment Operator
  Production, A
Industrial Technology/Technician, A
Metallurgical Technology/Technician, A

EAST LOS ANGELES COLLEGE

Accounting, A
Administrative Assistant and Secretarial Science, A
Anthropology, A
Architectural Engineering Technology/Technician, A
Art/Art Studies, General, A
Asian Studies/Civilization, A
Automobile/Automotive Mechanics
  Technology/Technician, A
Biology/Biological Sciences, A
Business Administration and Management, A
Chemistry, A
Child Development, A
Civil Engineering Technology/Technician, A
Computer Engineering Technology/Technician, A
Computer Programming/Programmer, A
Counselor Education/School Counseling and
  Guidance Services, A
Criminal Justice/Law Enforcement Administration, A
Criminal Justice/Police Science, A
Data Processing and Data Processing
  Technology/Technician, A
Developmental and Child Psychology, A
Drafting and Design Technology/Technician, A
Drama and Dramatics/Theatre Arts, A
Electrical, Electronic and Communications
  Engineering Technology/Technician, A
Emergency Medical Technology/Technician (EMT
  Paramedic), A
Engineering, A
English Language and Literature, A
Environmental Studies, A
Family and Consumer Sciences/Human Sciences, A
Fashion/Apparel Design, A
Finance, A
Fire Science/Firefighting, A
French Language and Literature, A
Geography, A
Geology/Earth Science, A
Health Information/Medical Records
  Administration/Administrator, A
Hispanic-American, Puerto Rican, and Mexican-
  American/Chicano Studies, A

History, A
Japanese Language and Literature, A
Journalism, A
Legal Administrative Assistant/Secretary, A
Liberal Arts and Sciences Studies and
  Humanities, A
Marketing/Marketing Management, A
Mathematics, A
Medical Administrative Assistant/Secretary, A
Medical/Clinical Assistant, A
Music, A
Nursing - Registered Nurse Training, A
Philosophy, A
Photography, A
Physical Education Teaching and Coaching, A
Political Science and Government, A
Pre-Engineering, A
Psychology, A
Public Administration, A
Real Estate, A
Respiratory Care Therapy/Therapist, A
Social Work, A
Sociology, A
Spanish Language and Literature, A
Speech and Rhetorical Studies, A
Trade and Industrial Teacher Education, A

EL CAMINO COLLEGE

Accounting, A
Administrative Assistant and Secretarial Science, A
Advertising, A
African-American/Black Studies, A
American/United States Studies/Civilization, A
Anthropology, A
Architectural Engineering Technology/Technician, A
Art History, Criticism and Conservation, A
Art/Art Studies, General, A
Asian Studies/Civilization, A
Astronomy, A
Automobile/Automotive Mechanics
  Technology/Technician, A
Biology/Biological Sciences, A
Botany/Plant Biology, A
Business Administration and Management, A
Chemistry, A
Construction Engineering Technology/Technician, A
Cosmetology/Cosmetologist, A
Criminal Justice/Police Science, A
Culinary Arts/Chef Training, A
Data Processing and Data Processing
  Technology/Technician, A
Drafting and Design Technology/Technician, A
Drama and Dramatics/Theatre Arts, A
Economics, A
Electrical, Electronic and Communications
  Engineering Technology/Technician, A
Engineering, A
English Language and Literature, A
Family and Consumer Sciences/Human Sciences, A
Fashion/Apparel Design, A
Finance, A
Fire Science/Firefighting, A
Forestry Technology/Technician, A
Geography, A
Geology/Earth Science, A
German Language and Literature, A
Gerontology, A
Heating, Air Conditioning, Ventilation and
  Refrigeration Maintenance
  Technology/Technician, A
History, A
Horticultural Science, A
Interior Design, A
Italian Language and Literature, A
Japanese Language and Literature, A
Journalism, A
Kindergarten/PreSchool Education and Teaching, A
Labor and Industrial Relations, A
Legal Assistant/Paralegal, A
Liberal Arts and Sciences Studies and
  Humanities, A
Licensed Practical/Vocational Nurse Training, A
Marketing/Marketing Management, A
Mathematics, A
Medical/Clinical Assistant, A
Music, A

Nursing - Registered Nurse Training, A
Ornamental Horticulture, A
Philosophy, A
Photography, A
Physical Education Teaching and Coaching, A
Physical Sciences, A
Physics, A
Political Science and Government, A
Psychology, A
Real Estate, A
Respiratory Care Therapy/Therapist, A
Russian Language and Literature, A
Social Work, A
Sociology, A
Spanish Language and Literature, A
Special Products Marketing Operations, A
Speech and Rhetorical Studies, A
Technical and Business Writing, A
Technology Education/Industrial Arts, A
Welding Technology/Welder, A
Zoology/Animal Biology, A

EMMANUEL BIBLE COLLEGE

Bible/Biblical Studies, AB

EMPIRE COLLEGE

Accounting, A
Administrative Assistant and Secretarial Science, A
Computer and Information Sciences, A
Legal Administrative Assistant/Secretary, A
Medical/Clinical Assistant, A

EVERGREEN VALLEY COLLEGE

Accounting, A
Applied Art, A
Automobile/Automotive Mechanics
  Technology/Technician, A
Biology/Biological Sciences, A
Business Administration and Management, A
Business/Commerce, A
Computer and Information Sciences, A
Computer Graphics, A
Criminal Justice/Law Enforcement Administration, A
Data Processing and Data Processing
  Technology/Technician, A
Drafting and Design Technology/Technician, A
Electrical, Electronic and Communications
  Engineering Technology/Technician, A
Engineering, A
English Language and Literature, A
Family and Consumer Economics and Related
  Services, A
Fashion Merchandising, A
General Studies, A
Industrial Technology/Technician, A
Information Science/Studies, A
Interdisciplinary Studies, A
Legal Assistant/Paralegal, A
Liberal Arts and Sciences Studies and
  Humanities, A
Management Information Systems and Services, A
Mental Health/Rehabilitation, A
Nursing - Registered Nurse Training, A
Pre-Engineering, A
Prepress/Desktop Publishing and Digital Imaging
  Design, A

FASHION CAREERS COLLEGE

Fashion Merchandising, A
Fashion/Apparel Design, A

FEATHER RIVER COLLEGE

Administrative Assistant and Secretarial Science, A
Animal/Livestock Husbandry and Production, A
Biology/Biological Sciences, A
Business/Commerce, A
Child Care and Support Services Management, A
Construction Engineering Technology/Technician, A
Criminal Justice/Law Enforcement Administration, A
English Language and Literature, A
Forestry, A
History, A
Liberal Arts and Sciences Studies and
  Humanities, A
Licensed Practical/Vocational Nurse Training, A

Mathematics, A
Natural Resources Management/Development and
  Policy, A
Parks, Recreation and Leisure Facilities
  Management, A
Parks, Recreation, Leisure and Fitness Studies, A
Physical Sciences, A
Social Sciences, A

FIDM/THE FASHION INSTITUTE OF DESIGN & MERCHANDISING, LOS ANGELES CAMPUS

Apparel and Accessories Marketing Operations, A
Apparel and Textiles, A
Business Administration and Management, B
Commercial and Advertising Art, A
Consumer Merchandising/Retailing Management, A
Design and Visual Communications, A
Fashion Merchandising, A
Fashion/Apparel Design, A
Interior Design, A

FIDM/THE FASHION INSTITUTE OF DESIGN & MERCHANDISING, ORANGE COUNTY CAMPUS

Apparel and Textiles, A
Commercial and Advertising Art, A
Consumer Merchandising/Retailing Management, A
Fashion Merchandising, A
Fashion/Apparel Design, A
Fiber, Textile and Weaving Arts, A
Industrial Technology/Technician, A
Interior Design, A
Marketing/Marketing Management, A

FIDM/THE FASHION INSTITUTE OF DESIGN & MERCHANDISING, SAN DIEGO CAMPUS

Apparel and Accessories Marketing Operations, A
Commercial and Advertising Art, A
Consumer Merchandising/Retailing Management, A
Design and Visual Communications, A
Fashion Merchandising, A
Fashion/Apparel Design, A
Interior Design, A

FIDM/THE FASHION INSTITUTE OF DESIGN & MERCHANDISING, SAN FRANCISCO CAMPUS

Apparel and Accessories Marketing Operations, A
Apparel and Textiles, A
Commercial and Advertising Art, A
Consumer Merchandising/Retailing Management, A
Design and Visual Communications, A
Fashion Merchandising, A
Fashion/Apparel Design, A
Interior Design, A

FOLSOM LAKE COLLEGE

Accounting, A
Art/Art Studies, General, A
Biology/Biological Sciences, A
Business Administration and Management, A
Communication, Journalism and Related
  Programs, A
Computer and Information Sciences, A
Criminal Justice/Law Enforcement Administration, A
Early Childhood Education and Teaching, A
Education, A
English Language and Literature, A
Finance, A
Geology/Earth Science, A
Human Services, A
Interdisciplinary Studies, A
Liberal Arts and Sciences Studies and
  Humanities, A
Marketing/Marketing Management, A
Mathematics, A
Physical Sciences, A
Physics, A

Psychology, A
Real Estate, A
Social Sciences, A

FOOTHILL COLLEGE

Accounting, A
American/United States Studies/Civilization, A
Anthropology, A
Art History, Criticism and Conservation, A
Art/Art Studies, General, A
Athletic Training and Sports Medicine, A
Avionics Maintenance Technology/Technician, A
Biology Technician/BioTechnology Laboratory
    Technician, A
Biology/Biological Sciences, A
Business Administration and Management, A
Chemistry, A
Child Development, A
Classics and Classical
    Languages, Literatures, and Linguistics, A
Comparative Literature, A
Creative Writing, A
Dental Assisting/Assistant, A
Dental Hygiene/Hygienist, A
Diagnostic Medical Sonography/Sonographer and
    Ultrasound Technician, A
Economics, A
Electrical, Electronic and Communications
    Engineering Technology/Technician, A
Emergency Medical Technology/Technician (EMT
    Paramedic), A
English Language and Literature, A
Ethnic and Cultural Studies, A
Fine/Studio Arts, A
History, A
International Business/Trade/Commerce, A
Landscape Architecture, A
Law and Legal Studies, A
Linguistics, A
Mathematics, A
Medical Radiologic Technology/Science - Radiation
    Therapist, A
Music, A
Ornamental Horticulture, A
Philosophy, A
Photography, A
Physical Education Teaching and Coaching, A
Physician Assistant, A
Physics, A
Plant Nursery Operations and Management, A
Political Science and Government, A
Psychology, A
Radio and Television, A
Radiologic Technology/Science - Radiographer, A
Real Estate, A
Respiratory Care Therapy/Therapist, A
Social Sciences, A
Sociology, A
Spanish Language and Literature, A
Speech and Rhetorical Studies, A
Tourism and Travel Services Management, A
Veterinary/Animal Health Technology/Technician and
    Veterinary Assistant, A
Women's Studies, A

FOUNDATION COLLEGE

Computer Engineering Technology/Technician, A
Computer Programming/Programmer, A
Computer Science, A
Computer Systems Networking and
    Telecommunications, A
Computer Technology/Computer Systems
    Technology, A
Data Processing and Data Processing
    Technology/Technician, A

FRESNO CITY COLLEGE

Administrative Assistant and Secretarial Science, A
African-American/Black Studies, A
American Indian/Native American Studies, A
Anthropology, A
Art/Art Studies, General, A
Autobody/Collision and Repair
    Technology/Technician, A
Automobile/Automotive Mechanics
    Technology/Technician, A

Building/Construction
    Finishing, Management, and Inspection, A
Business Administration and Management, A
Carpentry/Carpenter, A
Commercial and Advertising Art, A
Computer Typography and Composition Equipment
    Operator, A
Construction Engineering Technology/Technician, A
Corrections, A
Criminal Justice/Law Enforcement Administration, A
Criminal Justice/Police Science, A
Dental Hygiene/Hygienist, A
Design and Visual Communications, A
Dietetics/Dieticians, A
Drafting and Design Technology/Technician, A
Drama and Dramatics/Theatre Arts, A
Engineering, A
Ethnic and Cultural Studies, A
Family and Consumer Sciences/Human Sciences, A
Fashion Merchandising, A
Fire Science/Firefighting, A
Food Technology and Processing, A
Graphic and Printing Equipment Operator
    Production, A
Health Information/Medical Records
    Administration/Administrator, A
Heating, Air Conditioning, Ventilation and
    Refrigeration Maintenance
    Technology/Technician, A
Hispanic-American, Puerto Rican, and Mexican-
    American/Chicano Studies, A
Human Services, A
Humanities/Humanistic Studies, A
Industrial Radiologic Technology/Technician, A
Industrial Technology/Technician, A
Journalism, A
Legal Administrative Assistant/Secretary, A
Legal Assistant/Paralegal, A
Liberal Arts and Sciences Studies and
    Humanities, A
Library Science, A
Licensed Practical/Vocational Nurse Training, A
Machine Tool Technology/Machinist, A
Mathematics and Computer Science, A
Medical Administrative Assistant/Secretary, A
Medical/Clinical Assistant, A
Music Performance, A
Nursing - Registered Nurse Training, A
Parks, Recreation, Leisure and Fitness Studies, A
Photography, A
Physical Sciences, A
Piano and Organ, A
Real Estate, A
Respiratory Care Therapy/Therapist, A
Social Sciences, A
Spanish Language and Literature, A
Speech and Rhetorical Studies, A
Substance Abuse/Addiction Counseling, A
Teacher Assistant/Aide, A
Technical Theatre/Theatre Design and
    Technology, A
Technology Education/Industrial Arts, A
Voice and Opera, A
Women's Studies, A

FRESNO PACIFIC UNIVERSITY

Accounting, B
Applied Mathematics, B
Athletic Training and Sports Medicine, B
Bible/Biblical Studies, AB
Bilingual and Multilingual Education, B
Biology/Biological Sciences, AB
Business Administration and Management, AB
Business Administration, Management and
    Operations, M
Chemistry, B
Comparative Literature, B
Computer and Information Sciences, B
Conflict Resolution and Mediation/Peace Studies, M
Counselor Education/School Counseling and
    Guidance Services, M
Curriculum and Instruction, M
Developmental and Child Psychology, AB
Divinity/Ministry (BD, MDiv.), B
Education, BM

Education/Teaching of Individuals with Multiple
    Disabilities, M
Educational Administration and Supervision, M
Educational Media/Instructional Technology, M
Elementary Education and Teaching, B
English as a Second Language, M
English Language and Literature, AB
Finance, B
History, AB
Humanities/Humanistic Studies, B
Interdisciplinary Studies, M
International Business/Trade/Commerce, B
Liberal Arts and Sciences Studies and
    Humanities, AB
Marketing/Marketing Management, B
Mass Communication/Media Studies, AB
Mathematics, AB
Mathematics Teacher Education, M
Multilingual and Multicultural Education, M
Music, AB
Music Teacher Education, B
Natural Sciences, AB
Non-Profit/Public/Organizational Management, B
Pastoral Studies/Counseling, B
Physical Education Teaching and Coaching, AB
Political Science and Government, AB
Pre-Law Studies, B
Pre-Medicine/Pre-Medical Studies, B
Psychology, AB
Reading Teacher Education, M
Religion/Religious Studies, B
Religious/Sacred Music, B
School Psychology, M
Science Teacher Education/General Science
    Teacher Education, BM
Secondary Education and Teaching, B
Social Sciences, B
Social Work, B
Sociology, A
Spanish Language and Literature, AB
Special Education and Teaching, M
Sport and Fitness Administration/Management, B
Student Personnel Services, M

FULLERTON COLLEGE

Accounting, A
Agriculture, A
Anthropology, A
Architectural Engineering Technology/Technician, A
Art/Art Studies, General, A
Astronomy, A
Automobile/Automotive Mechanics
    Technology/Technician, A
Biology/Biological Sciences, A
Business Administration and Management, A
Carpentry/Carpenter, A
Chemistry, A
Civil Engineering Technology/Technician, A
Computer Science, A
Construction Engineering Technology/Technician, A
Cosmetology/Cosmetologist, A
Criminal Justice/Police Science, A
Dance, A
Data Processing and Data Processing
    Technology/Technician, A
Developmental and Child Psychology, A
Drafting and Design Technology/Technician, A
Drama and Dramatics/Theatre Arts, A
Economics, A
English Language and Literature, A
Environmental Studies, A
Ethnic and Cultural Studies, A
Family and Consumer Sciences/Human Sciences, A
Fashion Merchandising, A
Fashion/Apparel Design, A
Forestry, A
Geology/Earth Science, A
Graphic and Printing Equipment Operator
    Production, A
History, A
Horticultural Science, A
Industrial Technology/Technician, A
Information Science/Studies, A
Interior Design, A
International Business/Trade/Commerce, A
Journalism, A

Kindergarten/PreSchool Education and Teaching, A
Land Use Planning and Management/Development, A
Latin American Studies, A
Legal Administrative Assistant/Secretary, A
Legal Assistant/Paralegal, A
Liberal Arts and Sciences Studies and Humanities, A
Library Science, A
Marketing/Marketing Management, A
Mass Communication/Media Studies, A
Mathematics, A
Music, A
Oceanography, Chemical and Physical, A
Ornamental Horticulture, A
Parks, Recreation, Leisure and Fitness Studies, A
Philosophy, A
Physical Education Teaching and Coaching, A
Physics, A
Political Science and Government, A
Psychology, A
Purchasing, Procurement/Acquisitions and Contracts Management, A
Radio and Television, A
Real Estate, A
Religion/Religious Studies, A
Sociology, A
Speech and Rhetorical Studies, A
Technology Education/Industrial Arts, A
Tourism and Travel Services Management, A
Wildlife and Wildlands Science and Management, A
Zoology/Animal Biology, A

GAVILAN COLLEGE

Accounting, A
Administrative Assistant and Secretarial Science, A
Art/Art Studies, General, A
Avionics Maintenance Technology/Technician, A
Biological and Physical Sciences, A
Biology/Biological Sciences, A
Business Administration and Management, A
Chemistry, A
Child Development, A
Computer and Information Sciences, A
Computer Graphics, A
Computer Programming/Programmer, A
Computer Science, A
Corrections, A
Cosmetology/Cosmetologist, A
Criminal Justice/Law Enforcement Administration, A
Criminal Justice/Police Science, A
Developmental and Child Psychology, A
Digital Communication and Media/Multimedia, A
Drafting and Design Technology/Technician, A
English Language and Literature, A
History, A
Information Science/Studies, A
Journalism, A
Kindergarten/PreSchool Education and Teaching, A
Liberal Arts and Sciences Studies and Humanities, A
Licensed Practical/Vocational Nurse Training, A
Mathematics, A
Music, A
Natural Sciences, A
Nursing - Registered Nurse Training, A
Physical Education Teaching and Coaching, A
Political Science and Government, A
Pre-Engineering, A
Psychology, A
Social Sciences, A
Sociology, A
Spanish Language and Literature, A

GLENDALE COMMUNITY COLLEGE

Accounting, A
Administrative Assistant and Secretarial Science, A
Airframe Mechanics and Aircraft Maintenance Technology/Technician, A
Airline/Commercial/Professional Pilot and Flight Crew, A
Applied Art, A
Art History, Criticism and Conservation, A
Art/Art Studies, General, A
Aviation/Airway Management and Operations, A
Avionics Maintenance Technology/Technician, A

Biological and Physical Sciences, A
Business Administration and Management, A
Ceramic Arts and Ceramics, A
Child Development, A
Commercial and Advertising Art, A
Computer and Information Sciences, A
Computer Engineering, A
Computer Engineering Technology/Technician, A
Computer Programming, A
Computer Programming, Specific Applications, A
Computer Science, A
Computer Software and Media Applications, A
Cosmetology/Cosmetologist, A
Criminal Justice/Police Science, A
Culinary Arts/Chef Training, A
Dance, A
Data Entry/Microcomputer Applications, A
Data Processing and Data Processing Technology/Technician, A
Drafting and Design Technology/Technician, A
Drama and Dramatics/Theatre Arts, A
Education, A
Electromechanical Technology/Electromechanical Engineering Technology, A
English Language and Literature, A
Fashion/Apparel Design, A
Finance, A
Fire Science/Firefighting, A
Foreign Languages and Literatures, A
Health Information/Medical Records Administration/Administrator, A
Hotel/Motel Administration/Management, A
Humanities/Humanistic Studies, A
Industrial Technology/Technician, A
Journalism, A
Legal Administrative Assistant/Secretary, A
Liberal Arts and Sciences Studies and Humanities, A
Licensed Practical/Vocational Nurse Training, A
Machine Tool Technology/Machinist, A
Management Information Systems and Services, A
Mass Communication/Media Studies, A
Mathematics, A
Medical Administrative Assistant/Secretary, A
Medical/Clinical Assistant, A
Mental Health/Rehabilitation, A
Music, A
Nursing - Registered Nurse Training, A
Parks, Recreation, Leisure and Fitness Studies, A
Photography, A
Prepress/Desktop Publishing and Digital Imaging Design, A
Real Estate, A
Social Sciences, A
Speech and Rhetorical Studies, A
Welding Technology/Welder, A

GOLDEN GATE UNIVERSITY

Accounting, BM
Advertising and Public Relations, MO
Business Administration and Management, B
Business Administration, Management and Operations, MDO
Engineering and Applied Sciences, MO
Finance, B
Finance and Banking, MO
Human Resources Management and Services, MO
Human Resources Management/Personnel Administration, B
Information Technology, B
International Business/Trade/Commerce, BM
Law and Legal Studies, MDPO
Legal and Justice Studies, MD
Management, M
Marketing, MO
Marketing/Marketing Management, B
Operations Management and Supervision, B
Psychology, MO
Taxation, MO

GOLDEN WEST COLLEGE

Accounting, A
Administrative Assistant and Secretarial Science, A
Architectural Engineering Technology/Technician, A
Art/Art Studies, General, A

Automobile/Automotive Mechanics Technology/Technician, A
Biological and Physical Sciences, A
Biology/Biological Sciences, A
Business Administration and Management, A
Commercial and Advertising Art, A
Consumer Merchandising/Retailing Management, A
Cosmetology/Cosmetologist, A
Criminal Justice/Law Enforcement Administration, A
Criminal Justice/Police Science, A
Drafting and Design Technology/Technician, A
Electrical, Electronic and Communications Engineering Technology/Technician, A
Engineering Technology, A
Graphic and Printing Equipment Operator Production, A
Humanities/Humanistic Studies, A
Journalism, A
Legal Administrative Assistant/Secretary, A
Liberal Arts and Sciences Studies and Humanities, A
Marketing/Marketing Management, A
Mathematics, A
Music, A
Natural Sciences, A
Nursing - Registered Nurse Training, A
Ornamental Horticulture, A
Physical Sciences, A
Pre-Engineering, A
Public Relations/Image Management, A
Radio and Television, A
Real Estate, A
Sign Language Interpretation and Translation, A
Technical and Business Writing, A
Telecommunications Technology/Technician, A

GROSSMONT COLLEGE

Accounting, A
Administrative Assistant and Secretarial Science, A
Advertising, A
Art History, Criticism and Conservation, A
Art/Art Studies, General, A
Biology/Biological Sciences, A
Business Administration and Management, A
Ceramic Arts and Ceramics, A
Chemistry, A
Child Development, A
Clinical Laboratory Science/Medical Technology/Technologist, A
Computer Programming/Programmer, A
Computer Science, A
Consumer Merchandising/Retailing Management, A
Corrections, A
Creative Writing, A
Criminal Justice/Law Enforcement Administration, A
Criminal Justice/Police Science, A
Dance, A
Developmental and Child Psychology, A
Dietetics/Dieticians, A
Drama and Dramatics/Theatre Arts, A
Drawing, A
Economics, A
English Language and Literature, A
Ethnic and Cultural Studies, A
Family and Consumer Economics and Related Services, A
French Language and Literature, A
Geography, A
Geology/Earth Science, A
German Language and Literature, A
History, A
Information Science/Studies, A
International Business/Trade/Commerce, A
Legal Administrative Assistant/Secretary, A
Liberal Arts and Sciences Studies and Humanities, A
Marketing/Marketing Management, A
Mathematics, A
Medical Administrative Assistant/Secretary, A
Medical/Clinical Assistant, A
Music, A
Nursing - Registered Nurse Training, A
Occupational Therapy/Therapist, A
Philosophy, A
Photography, A
Physics, A

Political Science and Government, A
Radio and Television, A
Respiratory Care Therapy/Therapist, A
Sculpture, A
Spanish Language and Literature, A
Speech and Rhetorical Studies, A
Telecommunications Technology/Technician, A

HARTNELL COLLEGE

Administrative Assistant and Secretarial Science, A
Agricultural Business and Management, A
Agronomy and Crop Science, A
Animal Sciences, A
Anthropology, A
Architectural Engineering Technology/Technician, A
Art/Art Studies, General, A
Automobile/Automotive Mechanics
  Technology/Technician, A
Behavioral Sciences, A
Business Administration and Management, A
Business Machine Repairer, A
Carpentry/Carpenter, A
Child Development, A
Commercial and Advertising Art, A
Computer Graphics, A
Computer Science, A
Construction Engineering Technology/Technician, A
Corrections, A
Criminal Justice/Law Enforcement Administration, A
Criminology, A
Data Processing and Data Processing
  Technology/Technician, A
Developmental and Child Psychology, A
Drafting and Design Technology/Technician, A
Drafting/Design Engineering
  Technologies/Technicians, A
Economics, A
Electrical, Electronic and Communications
  Engineering Technology/Technician, A
English Language and Literature, A
Family and Consumer Economics and Related
  Services, A
Fire Science/Firefighting, A
Forestry Technology/Technician, A
Health Teacher Education, A
History, A
Horticultural Science, A
Human Services, A
Hydrology and Water Resources Science, A
Industrial Technology/Technician, A
Kindergarten/PreSchool Education and Teaching, A
Liberal Arts and Sciences Studies and
  Humanities, A
Library Science, A
Machine Tool Technology/Machinist, A
Marketing/Marketing Management, A
Mathematics, A
Musical Instrument Fabrication and Repair, A
Nursing - Registered Nurse Training, A
Parks, Recreation, Leisure and Fitness Studies, A
Photography, A
Physical Education Teaching and Coaching, A
Physician Assistant, A
Real Estate, A
Substance Abuse/Addiction Counseling, A
Veterinary/Animal Health Technology/Technician and
  Veterinary Assistant, A
Welding Technology/Welder, A

HARVEY MUDD COLLEGE

Biology/Biological Sciences, B
Chemistry, B
Computer Science, B
Engineering, B
Mathematics, B
Physics, B

HEALD COLLEGE-CONCORD

Computer Engineering Technology/Technician, A
Electrical, Electronic and Communications
  Engineering Technology/Technician, A

HEALD COLLEGE-FRESNO

Accounting, A
Administrative Assistant and Secretarial Science, A
Business Administration and Management, A

Computer Engineering Technology/Technician, A
Electrical, Electronic and Communications
  Engineering Technology/Technician, A
Information Science/Studies, A
Legal Administrative Assistant/Secretary, A
Medical Administrative Assistant/Secretary, A

HEALD COLLEGE-HAYWARD

Accounting, A
Administrative Assistant and Secretarial Science, A
Computer and Information Sciences, A
Computer
  Programming, Vendor/Product Certification, A
Computer Science, A
Computer/Information Technology Services
  Administration and Management, A
Legal Administrative Assistant/Secretary, A
Medical Administrative Assistant/Secretary, A

HEALD COLLEGE-RANCHO CORDOVA

Accounting, A
Administrative Assistant and Secretarial Science, A
Business Administration and Management, A
Legal Administrative Assistant/Secretary, A
Medical Administrative Assistant/Secretary, A

HEALD COLLEGE-ROSEVILLE

Business Administration and Management, A
Computer Engineering Technology/Technician, A
Electrical, Electronic and Communications
  Engineering Technology/Technician, A

HEALD COLLEGE-SALINAS

Accounting, A
Business Administration and Management, A
Hospitality Administration/Management, A
Legal Administrative Assistant/Secretary, A
Medical Administrative Assistant/Secretary, A

HEALD COLLEGE-SAN FRANCISCO

Accounting, A
Administrative Assistant and Secretarial Science, A
Computer Engineering Technology/Technician, A
Computer Systems Networking and
  Telecommunications, A
Electrical, Electronic and Communications
  Engineering Technology/Technician, A
Hospitality Administration/Management, A
Legal Administrative Assistant/Secretary, A
Medical Administrative Assistant/Secretary, A

HEALD COLLEGE-SAN JOSE

Accounting, A
Computer Engineering Technology/Technician, A
Computer Science, A
Electrical, Electronic and Communications
  Engineering Technology/Technician, A
Legal Administrative Assistant/Secretary, A
Telecommunications Technology/Technician, A

HEALD COLLEGE-STOCKTON

Accounting, A
Computer Systems Analysis/Analyst, A
Data Processing and Data Processing
  Technology/Technician, A

HOLY NAMES UNIVERSITY

Biological and Biomedical Sciences, B
Biology/Biological Sciences, B
Business Administration and Management, B
Business/Corporate Communications, B
Community Health Nursing, M
Computer Software and Media Applications, B
Computer/Information Technology Services
  Administration and Management, B
Counseling Psychology, M
Curriculum and Instruction, M
Education, MO
Educational Psychology, M
English as a Second Language, MO
English Language and Literature, B
History, B
Human Resources Management/Personnel
  Administration, B
Human Services, B

Humanities/Humanistic Studies, B
International Relations and Affairs, B
Liberal Arts and Sciences Studies and
  Humanities, B
Management, M
Marketing/Marketing Management, B
Music, BMO
Music Pedagogy, B
Music Performance, B
Music Teacher Education, MO
Nursing, M
Nursing - Advanced Practice, M
Nursing - Registered Nurse Training, B
Nursing Science, B
Pastoral Studies/Counseling, MO
Performance, M
Philosophy, B
Philosophy and Religious Studies, B
Physiological Psychology/Psychobiology, B
Psychology, B
Religion/Religious Studies, BMO
Sociology, B
Spanish Language and Literature, B
Special Education and Teaching, M
Urban Education and Leadership, M

HOPE INTERNATIONAL UNIVERSITY

Athletic Training and Sports Medicine, B
Bible/Biblical Studies, B
Business Administration and Management, B
Child Development, B
Counseling Psychology, M
Education, M
Elementary Education and Teaching, B
English/Language Arts Teacher Education, B
General Studies, A
Human Development and Family Studies, B
Interdisciplinary Studies, B
International Business/Trade/Commerce, M
International Development, M
Kindergarten/PreSchool Education and Teaching, A
Marriage and Family Therapy/Counseling, M
Missions/Missionary Studies and Missiology, AB
Music Teacher Education, B
Non-Profit/Public/Organizational Management, M
Pastoral Studies/Counseling, M
Physical Therapy/Therapist, B
Physiological Psychology/Psychobiology, B
Psychology, BM
Religious/Sacred Music, B
Sacred Music, M
Social Science Teacher Education, B
Social Sciences, B
Social Work, B

HUMBOLDT STATE UNIVERSITY

Accounting, B
American Indian/Native American Studies, B
Anthropology, B
Applied Mathematics, B
Art History, Criticism and Conservation, B
Art Teacher Education, B
Art/Art Studies, General, B
Athletic Training and Sports Medicine, M
Biochemistry, B
Biological and Biomedical Sciences, M
Biology/Biological Sciences, B
Botany/Plant Biology, B
Broadcast Journalism, B
Business Administration and Management, B
Business Administration, Management and
  Operations, M
Cell/Cellular Biology and Histology, B
Chemistry, B
Child Development, B
Clinical Laboratory Science/Medical
  Technology/Technologist, B
Communication Studies/Speech Communication
  and Rhetoric, B
Computer Science, B
Developmental and Child Psychology, B
Drama and Dramatics/Theatre Arts, B
Economics, B
Education, B
Elementary Education and Teaching, B
English, M

English Language and Literature, B
Environmental Biology, B
Environmental Sciences, M
Environmental Studies, B
Environmental/Environmental Health Engineering, B
Exercise and Sports Science, M
Fine/Studio Arts, B
Fishing and Fisheries Sciences and Management, B
Forestry, B
French Language and Literature, B
Geography, B
Geology/Earth Science, B
German Language and Literature, B
History, B
Hydrology and Water Resources Science, B
Information Science/Studies, B
Journalism, B
Kindergarten/PreSchool Education and Teaching, B
Kinesiology and Exercise Science, B
Kinesiology and Movement Studies, M
Liberal Arts and Sciences Studies and
  Humanities, B
Marine Biology and Biological Oceanography, B
Marketing/Marketing Management, B
Mathematics, B
Medical Microbiology and Bacteriology, B
Molecular Biology, B
Music, B
Music Teacher Education, B
Natural Resources and Conservation, BM
Natural Resources Management/Development and
  Policy, B
Natural Sciences, B
Nursing - Registered Nurse Training, B
Oceanography, Chemical and Physical, B
Parks, Recreation and Leisure Facilities
  Management, B
Parks, Recreation, Leisure and Fitness Studies, B
Philosophy, B
Physical Education Teaching and Coaching, BM
Physical Sciences, B
Physical Therapy/Therapist, M
Physics, B
Political Science and Government, B
Pre-Dentistry Studies, B
Pre-Law Studies, B
Pre-Medicine/Pre-Medical Studies, B
Pre-Veterinary Studies, B
Psychology, BM
Range Science and Management, B
Religion/Religious Studies, B
Secondary Education and Teaching, B
Social Sciences, BM
Social Work, B
Sociology, BM
Spanish Language and Literature, B
Speech and Rhetorical Studies, B
Technology Education/Industrial Arts, B
Theater, M
Toxicology, B
Wildlife and Wildlands Science and Management, B
Zoology/Animal Biology, B

HUMPHREYS COLLEGE

Accounting, AB
Administrative Assistant and Secretarial Science, AB
Business Administration and Management, AB
Community Organization and Advocacy, B
Computer Programming/Programmer, AB
Computer Science, AB
Court Reporting/Court Reporter, A
Data Processing and Data Processing
  Technology/Technician, A
Information Science/Studies, AB
Law and Legal Studies, P
Legal Administrative Assistant/Secretary, A
Legal Assistant/Paralegal, B
Liberal Arts and Sciences Studies and
  Humanities, A
Medical Administrative Assistant/Secretary, A

IMPERIAL VALLEY COLLEGE

Accounting, A
Administrative Assistant and Secretarial Science, A
Agricultural Business and Management, A
Agricultural Mechanization, A

Agriculture, A
Anthropology, A
Art/Art Studies, General, A
Automobile/Automotive Mechanics
  Technology/Technician, A
Behavioral Sciences, A
Biological and Physical Sciences, A
Business Administration and Management, A
Criminal Justice/Law Enforcement Administration, A
English Language and Literature, A
Fire Science/Firefighting, A
French Language and Literature, A
Human Development and Family Studies, A
Humanities/Humanistic Studies, A
Hydrology and Water Resources Science, A
Information Science/Studies, A
Journalism, A
Kindergarten/PreSchool Education and Teaching, A
Liberal Arts and Sciences Studies and
  Humanities, A
Licensed Practical/Vocational Nurse Training, A
Marketing/Marketing Management, A
Mathematics, A
Modern Languages, A
Music, A
Nursing - Registered Nurse Training, A
Physical Education Teaching and Coaching, A
Physical Sciences, A
Pre-Engineering, A
Psychology, A
Social Sciences, A
Spanish Language and Literature, A
Welding Technology/Welder, A

INSTITUTE OF COMPUTER TECHNOLOGY

Business Administration and Management, AB
Computer Science, AB

INTERNATIONAL TECHNOLOGICAL UNIVERSITY

Business Administration, Management and
  Operations, M
Computer Engineering, M
Electrical Engineering, M
Software Engineering, M

IRVINE VALLEY COLLEGE

Accounting, A
Administrative Assistant and Secretarial Science, A
Art/Art Studies, General, A
Behavioral Sciences, A
Biological and Physical Sciences, A
Biology/Biological Sciences, A
Business Administration and Management, A
Business Machine Repairer, A
Comparative Literature, A
Computer Engineering Technology/Technician, A
Creative Writing, A
Criminal Justice/Law Enforcement Administration, A
Data Processing and Data Processing
  Technology/Technician, A
Electromechanical Technology/Electromechanical
  Engineering Technology, A
English Language and Literature, A
History, A
Humanities/Humanistic Studies, A
Liberal Arts and Sciences Studies and
  Humanities, A
Mathematics, A
Social Sciences, A
Speech and Rhetorical Studies, A

ITT TECHNICAL INSTITUTE (ANAHEIM)

Animation, Interactive Technology, Video Graphics
  and Special Effects, B
Business Administration and Management, B
CAD/CADD Drafting and/or Design
  Technology/Technician, A
Computer and Information Systems Security, B
Computer Systems Networking and
  Telecommunications, B
Criminal Justice/Law Enforcement Administration, B
E-Commerce/Electronic Commerce, B

Electrical, Electronic and Communications
  Engineering Technology/Technician, AB
System, Networking, and LAN/WAN
  Management/Manager, A
Web Page, Digital/Multimedia and Information
  Resources Design, A

ITT TECHNICAL INSTITUTE (LATHROP)

Animation, Interactive Technology, Video Graphics
  and Special Effects, B
Business Administration and Management, B
CAD/CADD Drafting and/or Design
  Technology/Technician, A
Computer and Information Systems Security, B
Computer Programming/Programmer, A
Computer Software Technology/Technician, A
Computer Systems Networking and
  Telecommunications, B
Criminal Justice/Law Enforcement Administration, B
E-Commerce/Electronic Commerce, B
Electrical, Electronic and Communications
  Engineering Technology/Technician, AB
System, Networking, and LAN/WAN
  Management/Manager, A
Web Page, Digital/Multimedia and Information
  Resources Design, A

ITT TECHNICAL INSTITUTE (OXNARD)

Animation, Interactive Technology, Video Graphics
  and Special Effects, B
Business Administration and Management, B
CAD/CADD Drafting and/or Design
  Technology/Technician, A
Computer and Information Systems Security, B
Criminal Justice/Law Enforcement Administration, B
E-Commerce/Electronic Commerce, B
Electrical, Electronic and Communications
  Engineering Technology/Technician, AB
System, Networking, and LAN/WAN
  Management/Manager, A
Web Page, Digital/Multimedia and Information
  Resources Design, A

ITT TECHNICAL INSTITUTE (RANCHO CORDOVA)

Animation, Interactive Technology, Video Graphics
  and Special Effects, B
Business Administration and Management, B
CAD/CADD Drafting and/or Design
  Technology/Technician, A
Computer and Information Systems Security, B
Computer Programming/Programmer, A
Computer Systems Networking and
  Telecommunications, B
Criminal Justice/Law Enforcement Administration, B
E-Commerce/Electronic Commerce, B
Electrical, Electronic and Communications
  Engineering Technology/Technician, AB
System, Networking, and LAN/WAN
  Management/Manager, A
Web Page, Digital/Multimedia and Information
  Resources Design, A
Web/Multimedia Management and Webmaster, A

ITT TECHNICAL INSTITUTE (SAN BERNARDINO)

Animation, Interactive Technology, Video Graphics
  and Special Effects, B
Business Administration and Management, B
CAD/CADD Drafting and/or Design
  Technology/Technician, A
Computer and Information Systems Security, B
Computer Programming/Programmer, A
Criminal Justice/Law Enforcement Administration, B
E-Commerce/Electronic Commerce, B
Electrical, Electronic and Communications
  Engineering Technology/Technician, AB
System, Networking, and LAN/WAN
  Management/Manager, A

Web Page, Digital/Multimedia and Information
   Resources Design, A

ITT TECHNICAL INSTITUTE (SAN DIEGO)

Animation, Interactive Technology, Video Graphics
   and Special Effects, B
Business Administration and Management, B
CAD/CADD Drafting and/or Design
   Technology/Technician, A
Computer and Information Systems Security, B
Computer Programming/Programmer, A
Criminal Justice/Law Enforcement Administration, B
E-Commerce/Electronic Commerce, B
Electrical, Electronic and Communications
   Engineering Technology/Technician, AB
System, Networking, and LAN/WAN
   Management/Manager, A
Web Page, Digital/Multimedia and Information
   Resources Design, A

ITT TECHNICAL INSTITUTE (SYLMAR)

Animation, Interactive Technology, Video Graphics
   and Special Effects, B
Business Administration and Management, B
CAD/CADD Drafting and/or Design
   Technology/Technician, A
Computer and Information Systems Security, B
Computer Programming/Programmer, A
Computer Systems Networking and
   Telecommunications, B
Criminal Justice/Law Enforcement Administration, B
E-Commerce/Electronic Commerce, B
Electrical, Electronic and Communications
   Engineering Technology/Technician, AB
System, Networking, and LAN/WAN
   Management/Manager, A
Web Page, Digital/Multimedia and Information
   Resources Design, A

ITT TECHNICAL INSTITUTE (TORRANCE)

Animation, Interactive Technology, Video Graphics
   and Special Effects, B
Business Administration and Management, B
CAD/CADD Drafting and/or Design
   Technology/Technician, A
Computer and Information Systems Security, B
Computer Software Technology/Technician, A
Computer Systems Networking and
   Telecommunications, B
Criminal Justice/Law Enforcement Administration, B
E-Commerce/Electronic Commerce, B
Electrical, Electronic and Communications
   Engineering Technology/Technician, AB
System, Networking, and LAN/WAN
   Management/Manager, A
Web Page, Digital/Multimedia and Information
   Resources Design, A

ITT TECHNICAL INSTITUTE (WEST COVINA)

Animation, Interactive Technology, Video Graphics
   and Special Effects, B
Business Administration and Management, B
CAD/CADD Drafting and/or Design
   Technology/Technician, A
Computer and Information Systems Security, B
Criminal Justice/Law Enforcement Administration, B
E-Commerce/Electronic Commerce, B
Electrical, Electronic and Communications
   Engineering Technology/Technician, AB
Robotics Technology/Technician, B
System, Networking, and LAN/WAN
   Management/Manager, A
Web Page, Digital/Multimedia and Information
   Resources Design, A

JOHN F. KENNEDY UNIVERSITY

Accounting, B
Business Administration and Management, B
Business Administration, Management and
   Operations, MO
Comparative and Interdisciplinary Arts, M
Conflict Resolution and Mediation/Peace Studies, O

Consumer Merchandising/Retailing Management, B
Counseling Psychology, M
Education, M
Fine Arts and Art Studies, M
Health Education, M
Human Resources Development, MO
Humanities/Humanistic Studies, B
Industrial and Organizational Psychology, MO
Interdisciplinary Studies, M
Law and Legal Studies, P
Liberal Arts and Sciences Studies and
   Humanities, B
Museology/Museum Studies, MO
Organizational Management, O
Psychology, BMDO
Sport Psychology, M

LA SIERRA UNIVERSITY

Accounting, B
Art/Art Studies, General, B
Biochemistry, B
Biophysics, B
Business Administration and Management, B
Business Administration, Management and
   Operations, MO
Chemistry, B
Communication Studies/Speech Communication
   and Rhetoric, B
Computer Science, B
Counselor Education/School Counseling and
   Guidance Services, MO
Curriculum and Instruction, MDO
Education, MDO
Educational Administration and Supervision, MDO
Educational Psychology, MO
Elementary Education and Teaching, B
English, M
English Language and Literature, B
Experimental Psychology, B
Fine/Studio Arts, B
Health and Physical Education, B
History, B
Information Science/Studies, B
Kinesiology and Exercise Science, B
Liberal Arts and Sciences Studies and
   Humanities, B
Mathematics, B
Music, B
Music Teacher Education, B
Physical Sciences, B
Physiological Psychology/Psychobiology, B
Political Science and Government, B
Pre-Dentistry Studies, B
Pre-Law Studies, B
Pre-Medicine/Pre-Medical Studies, B
Psychology, B
Religion/Religious Studies, BM
Religious Education, M
School Psychology, O
Secondary Education and Teaching, B
Social Work, B
Sociology, B
Spanish Language and Literature, B
Special Education and Teaching, BM

LAGUNA COLLEGE OF ART & DESIGN

Art/Art Studies, General, B
Commercial and Advertising Art, B
Design and Applied Arts, B
Design and Visual Communications, B
Drawing, B
Fine/Studio Arts, B
Graphic Design, B
Illustration, B
Intermedia/Multimedia, B
Painting, B
Printmaking, B
Sculpture, B

LAKE TAHOE COMMUNITY COLLEGE

Accounting, A
Administrative Assistant and Secretarial Science, A
Art/Art Studies, General, A
Biological and Physical Sciences, A
Business Administration and Management, A
Computer Science, A

Criminal Justice/Law Enforcement Administration, A
Criminal Justice/Police Science, A
Dance, A
Drama and Dramatics/Theatre Arts, A
Finance, A
Fire Science/Firefighting, A
Hotel/Motel Administration/Management, A
Humanities/Humanistic Studies, A
Kindergarten/PreSchool Education and Teaching, A
Liberal Arts and Sciences Studies and
   Humanities, A
Marketing/Marketing Management, A
Mathematics, A
Medical Administrative Assistant/Secretary, A
Medical/Clinical Assistant, A
Music, A
Natural Sciences, A
Physical Education Teaching and Coaching, A
Psychology, A
Real Estate, A
Social Sciences, A
Spanish Language and Literature, A

LANEY COLLEGE

Accounting, A
Administrative Assistant and Secretarial Science, A
African-American/Black Studies, A
Architectural Engineering Technology/Technician, A
Art/Art Studies, General, A
Asian Studies/Civilization, A
Biological and Physical Sciences, A
Broadcast Journalism, A
Building/Construction
   Finishing, Management, and Inspection, A
Business Administration and Management, A
Carpentry/Carpenter, A
Ceramic Arts and Ceramics, A
Commercial and Advertising Art, A
Computer Programming/Programmer, A
Computer Typography and Composition Equipment
   Operator, A
Cosmetology/Cosmetologist, A
Culinary Arts/Chef Training, A
Dance, A
Drama and Dramatics/Theatre Arts, A
Engineering, A
Engineering Technology, A
Ethnic and Cultural Studies, A
Finance, A
Graphic and Printing Equipment Operator
   Production, A
Heating, Air Conditioning, Ventilation and
   Refrigeration Maintenance
   Technology/Technician, A
Hispanic-American, Puerto Rican, and Mexican-
   American/Chicano Studies, A
Humanities/Humanistic Studies, A
Information Science/Studies, A
Journalism, A
Labor and Industrial Relations, A
Liberal Arts and Sciences Studies and
   Humanities, A
Machine Tool Technology/Machinist, A
Management Information Systems and Services, A
Marketing/Marketing Management, A
Mathematics, A
Music, A
Photography, A
Radio and Television, A
Reading Teacher Education, A
Social Sciences, A
Welding Technology/Welder, A
Wood Science and Wood Products/Pulp and Paper
   Technology, A

LAS POSITAS COLLEGE

Accounting, A
Administrative Assistant and Secretarial Science, A
Automobile/Automotive Mechanics
   Technology/Technician, A
Business Administration and Management, A
Computer Science, A
Criminal Justice/Police Science, A
Drafting and Design Technology/Technician, A
Education, A

Electrical, Electronic and Communications
   Engineering Technology/Technician, A
Environmental Studies, A
Fashion Merchandising, A
Fire Science/Firefighting, A
Horticultural Science, A
Industrial Design, A
Industrial Radiologic Technology/Technician, A
Information Science/Studies, A
Interior Design, A
Kindergarten/PreSchool Education and Teaching, A
Liberal Arts and Sciences Studies and
   Humanities, A
Marketing/Marketing Management, A
Occupational Safety and Health
   Technology/Technician, A
Real Estate, A
Welding Technology/Welder, A

LASSEN COMMUNITY COLLEGE DISTRICT

Accounting, A
Administrative Assistant and Secretarial Science, A
Agricultural Business and Management, A
Agricultural Economics, A
Agricultural Mechanization, A
Agriculture, A
Agronomy and Crop Science, A
Applied Art, A
Art/Art Studies, General, A
Automobile/Automotive Mechanics
   Technology/Technician, A
Biological and Physical Sciences, A
Biology/Biological Sciences, A
Botany/Plant Biology, A
Business Administration and Management, A
Business Machine Repairer, A
Carpentry/Carpenter, A
Ceramic Arts and Ceramics, A
Chemistry, A
Commercial and Advertising Art, A
Communications Technology/Technician, A
Computer Science, A
Construction Engineering Technology/Technician, A
Cosmetology/Cosmetologist, A
Criminal Justice/Police Science, A
Drafting and Design Technology/Technician, A
Drawing, A
Energy Management and Systems
   Technology/Technician, A
Farm/Farm and Ranch Management, A
History, A
Humanities/Humanistic Studies, A
Journalism, A
Kindergarten/PreSchool Education and Teaching, A
Legal Administrative Assistant/Secretary, A
Liberal Arts and Sciences Studies and
   Humanities, A
Licensed Practical/Vocational Nurse Training, A
Mass Communication/Media Studies, A
Mathematics, A
Medical Administrative Assistant/Secretary, A
Natural Sciences, A
Nursing - Registered Nurse Training, A
Photography, A
Physical Education Teaching and Coaching, A
Pre-Engineering, A
Psychology, A
Radio and Television, A
Social Sciences, A
Welding Technology/Welder, A

LIFE PACIFIC COLLEGE

Bible/Biblical Studies, AB
Pastoral Studies/Counseling, B
Theology/Theological Studies, B

LINCOLN UNIVERSITY

Accounting, B
Business Administration and Management, B
Business Administration, Management and
   Operations, M
Computer Science, B
Economics, B
International Business/Trade/Commerce, B

Management Information Systems and Services, B

LOMA LINDA UNIVERSITY

Allied Health and Medical Assisting Services, MD
Allopathic Medicine, MDPO
Anatomy, MD
Audiology/Audiologist and Speech-Language
   Pathology/Pathologist, B
Biochemistry, MD
Bioethics/Medical Ethics, M
Biological and Biomedical Sciences, MDO
Biostatistics, M
Child and Family Studies, MO
Clinical Laboratory Science/Medical
   Technology/Technologist, B
Clinical Psychology, D
Communication Disorders, M
CytoTechnology/Cytotechnologist, B
Dental and Oral Surgery, MO
Dental Hygiene/Hygienist, B
Dentistry, MPO
Dietetics/Dieticians, AB
Emergency Medical Technology/Technician (EMT
   Paramedic), B
Environmental and Occupational Health, M
Epidemiology, MD
Geology/Earth Science, M
Gerontological Nursing, M
Health Education, MD
Health Informatics, M
Health Information/Medical Records
   Administration/Administrator, B
Health Promotion, MD
Health Services Administration, M
International Public Health/International Health, M
Marriage and Family Therapy/Counseling, MD
Medical Radiologic Technology/Science - Radiation
   Therapist, AB
Microbiology, MD
Molecular Genetics, MD
Nursing, MO
Nursing - Registered Nurse Training, AB
Nursing Administration, MO
Nutritional Sciences, MD
Occupational Therapist Assistant, A
Occupational Therapy/Therapist, B
Oral and Dental Sciences, MO
Orthodontics, MO
Pastoral Studies/Counseling, MO
Pediatric Nurse/Nursing, M
Periodontics, M
Pharmaceutical Sciences, MD
Physical Therapist Assistant, A
Physical Therapy/Therapist, MD
Physician Assistant, M
Physiology, MD
Public Health, MD
Religion/Religious Studies, M
Respiratory Care Therapy/Therapist, AB
Social Work, MD
Surgical Technology/Technologist, A

LONG BEACH CITY COLLEGE

Accounting, A
Administrative Assistant and Secretarial Science, A
Advertising, A
Airline/Commercial/Professional Pilot and Flight
   Crew, A
Architectural Engineering Technology/Technician, A
Art/Art Studies, General, A
Automobile/Automotive Mechanics
   Technology/Technician, A
Aviation/Airway Management and Operations, A
Avionics Maintenance Technology/Technician, A
Biology/Biological Sciences, A
Business Administration and Management, A
Carpentry/Carpenter, A
Computer Programming/Programmer, A
Computer Typography and Composition Equipment
   Operator, A
Consumer Merchandising/Retailing Management, A
Criminal Justice/Law Enforcement Administration, A
Culinary Arts/Chef Training, A
Dance, A
Data Processing and Data Processing
   Technology/Technician, A

Developmental and Child Psychology, A
Dietetics/Dieticians, A
Drafting and Design Technology/Technician, A
Drama and Dramatics/Theatre Arts, A
Electrical, Electronic and Communications
   Engineering Technology/Technician, A
Engineering, A
English Language and Literature, A
Family and Consumer Economics and Related
   Services, A
Family and Consumer Sciences/Human Sciences, A
Fashion Merchandising, A
Fashion/Apparel Design, A
Film/Cinema Studies, A
Fire Science/Firefighting, A
Food Technology and Processing, A
French Language and Literature, A
German Language and Literature, A
Heating, Air Conditioning, Ventilation and
   Refrigeration Maintenance
   Technology/Technician, A
Heavy Equipment Maintenance
   Technology/Technician, A
Horticultural Science, A
Hotel/Motel Administration/Management, A
Human Services, A
Industrial Radiologic Technology/Technician, A
Industrial Technology/Technician, A
Interior Design, A
International Business/Trade/Commerce, A
Journalism, A
Kindergarten/PreSchool Education and Teaching, A
Legal Administrative Assistant/Secretary, A
Liberal Arts and Sciences Studies and
   Humanities, A
Machine Tool Technology/Machinist, A
Marketing/Marketing Management, A
Mathematics, A
Medical Administrative Assistant/Secretary, A
Medical/Clinical Assistant, A
Music, A
Nursing - Registered Nurse Training, A
Ornamental Horticulture, A
Photography, A
Physical Education Teaching and Coaching, A
Physical Sciences, A
Pre-Engineering, A
Radio and Television, A
Real Estate, A
Social Sciences, A
Spanish Language and Literature, A
Special Products Marketing Operations, A
Speech and Rhetorical Studies, A
Technology Education/Industrial Arts, A
Tourism and Travel Services Management, A
Welding Technology/Welder, A

LOS ANGELES CITY COLLEGE

Accounting, A
Administrative Assistant and Secretarial Science, A
Advertising, A
African-American/Black Studies, A
American/United States Studies/Civilization, A
Apparel and Textiles, A
Architectural Engineering Technology/Technician, A
Art/Art Studies, General, A
Biological and Physical Sciences, A
Biology/Biological Sciences, A
Broadcast Journalism, A
Business Administration and Management, A
Ceramic Arts and Ceramics, A
Chemistry, A
Child Development, A
Computer and Information Sciences, A
Computer and Information Systems Security, A
Computer Engineering Technology/Technician, A
Computer Programming, A
Computer Programming, Specific Applications, A
Computer
   Programming, Vendor/Product Certification, A
Computer Programming/Programmer, A
Computer Software and Media Applications, A
Computer Systems Networking and
   Telecommunications, A

Computer/Information Technology Services
Administration and Management, A
Consumer Merchandising/Retailing Management, A
Corrections, A
Criminal Justice/Law Enforcement Administration, A
Criminal Justice/Police Science, A
Data Entry/Microcomputer Applications, A
Data Processing and Data Processing
Technology/Technician, A
Dental Hygiene/Hygienist, A
Developmental and Child Psychology, A
Dietetics/Dieticians, A
Drafting and Design Technology/Technician, A
Drama and Dramatics/Theatre Arts, A
Electrical, Electronic and Communications
Engineering Technology/Technician, A
Engineering, A
English Language and Literature, A
Family and Consumer Economics and Related
Services, A
Family and Consumer Sciences/Human Sciences, A
Finance, A
Food Science, A
Food Technology and Processing, A
French Language and Literature, A
German Language and Literature, A
Hispanic-American, Puerto Rican, and Mexican-
American/Chicano Studies, A
History, A
Human Services, A
Industrial Radiologic Technology/Technician, A
Information Technology, A
Journalism, A
Legal Administrative Assistant/Secretary, A
Liberal Arts and Sciences Studies and
Humanities, A
Management Information Systems and Services, A
Marketing/Marketing Management, A
Mass Communication/Media Studies, A
Mathematics, A
Medical Administrative Assistant/Secretary, A
Mental Health/Rehabilitation, A
Music, A
Nuclear Medical Technology/Technologist, A
Ophthalmic Laboratory Technology/Technician, A
Photography, A
Physics, A
Psychology, A
Public Administration, A
Public Relations/Image Management, A
Radio and Television, A
Radiologic Technology/Science - Radiographer, A
Real Estate, A
Sociology, A
Spanish Language and Literature, A
Special Products Marketing Operations, A
Speech and Rhetorical Studies, A
System Administration/Administrator, A
Teacher Assistant/Aide, A
Telecommunications Technology/Technician, A
Tourism and Travel Services Management, A
Web Page, Digital/Multimedia and Information
Resources Design, A
Web/Multimedia Management and Webmaster, A
Word Processing, A

LOS ANGELES HARBOR COLLEGE

Accounting, A
Administrative Assistant and Secretarial Science, A
Architectural Engineering Technology/Technician, A
Automobile/Automotive Mechanics
Technology/Technician, A
Biology/Biological Sciences, A
Business Administration and Management, A
Computer Engineering Technology/Technician, A
Criminal Justice/Police Science, A
Data Processing and Data Processing
Technology/Technician, A
Developmental and Child Psychology, A
Drafting and Design Technology/Technician, A
Electrical, Electronic and Communications
Engineering Technology/Technician, A
Electromechanical Technology/Electromechanical
Engineering Technology, A
Engineering Technology, A
Fire Science/Firefighting, A

Information Science/Studies, A
Legal Administrative Assistant/Secretary, A
Liberal Arts and Sciences Studies and
Humanities, A
Medical Administrative Assistant/Secretary, A
Nursing - Registered Nurse Training, A
Physics, A
Pre-Engineering, A
Real Estate, A

LOS ANGELES MISSION COLLEGE

Accounting, A
Administrative Assistant and Secretarial Science, A
Art Teacher Education, A
Avionics Maintenance Technology/Technician, A
Biology/Biological Sciences, A
Business Administration and Management, A
Chemistry, A
Computer Programming/Programmer, A
Consumer Services and Advocacy, A
Criminal Justice/Police Science, A
Culinary Arts/Chef Training, A
Developmental and Child Psychology, A
Drama and Dramatics/Theatre Arts, A
Economics, A
English Language and Literature, A
Family and Consumer Economics and Related
Services, A
Family and Consumer Sciences/Home Economics
Teacher Education, A
Finance, A
French Language and Literature, A
Geography, A
Health Teacher Education, A
History, A
Humanities/Humanistic Studies, A
Italian Language and Literature, A
Journalism, A
Liberal Arts and Sciences Studies and
Humanities, A
Mathematics, A
Music, A
Philosophy, A
Physical Education Teaching and Coaching, A
Physical Sciences, A
Psychology, A
Real Estate, A
Social Sciences, A
Sociology, A
Spanish Language and Literature, A
Speech and Rhetorical Studies, A
Teacher Assistant/Aide, A

LOS ANGELES PIERCE COLLEGE

Accounting, A
Agriculture, A
Animal Sciences, A
Architectural Engineering Technology/Technician, A
Art/Art Studies, General, A
Automobile/Automotive Mechanics
Technology/Technician, A
Computer Engineering Technology/Technician, A
Computer Programming/Programmer, A
Computer Science, A
Construction Engineering Technology/Technician, A
Data Processing and Data Processing
Technology/Technician, A
Drafting and Design Technology/Technician, A
Drama and Dramatics/Theatre Arts, A
Electrical, Electronic and Communications
Engineering Technology/Technician, A
Equestrian/Equine Studies, A
Horticultural Science, A
Industrial Technology/Technician, A
Journalism, A
Landscape Architecture, A
Landscaping and Groundskeeping, A
Liberal Arts and Sciences Studies and
Humanities, A
Machine Tool Technology/Machinist, A
Music, A
Nursing - Registered Nurse Training, A
Ornamental Horticulture, A
Photography, A
Plant Protection and Integrated Pest
Management, A

Pre-Engineering, A
Quality Control Technology/Technician, A
Real Estate, A
Sign Language Interpretation and Translation, A
Technology Education/Industrial Arts, A
Veterinary/Animal Health Technology/Technician and
Veterinary Assistant, A
Welding Technology/Welder, A

LOS ANGELES SOUTHWEST COLLEGE

Accounting, A
Administrative Assistant and Secretarial Science, A
African Studies, A
Anthropology, A
Behavioral Sciences, A
Biology/Biological Sciences, A
Business Administration and Management, A
Child Development, A
Computer Science, A
Criminal Justice/Law Enforcement Administration, A
Criminal Justice/Police Science, A
Data Processing and Data Processing
Technology/Technician, A
Developmental and Child Psychology, A
Drafting and Design Technology/Technician, A
Drama and Dramatics/Theatre Arts, A
Economics, A
Education, A
Electrical, Electronic and Communications
Engineering Technology/Technician, A
Engineering, A
English Language and Literature, A
Family and Consumer Economics and Related
Services, A
Finance, A
Humanities/Humanistic Studies, A
Kindergarten/PreSchool Education and Teaching, A
Marketing/Marketing Management, A
Music, A
Nursing - Registered Nurse Training, A
Quality Control Technology/Technician, A
Radio and Television, A
Real Estate, A
Sign Language Interpretation and Translation, A
Social Sciences, A
Spanish Language and Literature, A
Teacher Assistant/Aide, A

LOS ANGELES TRADE-TECHNICAL COLLEGE

Accounting, A
Architectural Engineering Technology/Technician, A
Automobile/Automotive Mechanics
Technology/Technician, A
Business Administration and Management, A
Carpentry/Carpenter, A
Chemical Engineering, A
Commercial and Advertising Art, A
Computer Engineering Technology/Technician, A
Computer Programming/Programmer, A
Construction Engineering Technology/Technician, A
Cosmetology/Cosmetologist, A
Culinary Arts/Chef Training, A
Data Processing and Data Processing
Technology/Technician, A
Drafting and Design Technology/Technician, A
Electrical, Electronic and Communications
Engineering Technology/Technician, A
Engineering, A
Fashion Merchandising, A
Fashion/Apparel Design, A
Graphic and Printing Equipment Operator
Production, A
Heating, Air Conditioning, Ventilation and
Refrigeration Maintenance
Technology/Technician, A
Heavy Equipment Maintenance
Technology/Technician, A
Hydrology and Water Resources Science, A
Industrial Technology/Technician, A
Information Science/Studies, A
Journalism, A
Labor and Industrial Relations, A
Liberal Arts and Sciences Studies and
Humanities, A

Mechanical Engineering/Mechanical
Technology/Technician, A
Nursing - Registered Nurse Training, A
Photography, A
Pipefitting/Pipefitter and Sprinkler Fitter, A
Real Estate, A
Transportation and Materials Moving, A
Welding Technology/Welder, A

LOS ANGELES VALLEY COLLEGE

Accounting, A
Administrative Assistant and Secretarial Science, A
Advertising, A
African-American/Black Studies, A
Art/Art Studies, General, A
Biology/Biological Sciences, A
Broadcast Journalism, A
Business Administration and Management, A
Business Machine Repairer, A
Ceramic Arts and Ceramics, A
Child Development, A
Civil Engineering Technology/Technician, A
Commercial and Advertising Art, A
Computer and Information Sciences, A
Computer Programming/Programmer, A
Consumer Merchandising/Retailing Management, A
Criminal Justice/Law Enforcement Administration, A
Criminal Justice/Police Science, A
Data Processing and Data Processing
Technology/Technician, A
Developmental and Child Psychology, A
Drafting and Design Technology/Technician, A
Drafting/Design Engineering
Technologies/Technicians, A
Drama and Dramatics/Theatre Arts, A
Economics, A
Electrical, Electronic and Communications
Engineering Technology/Technician, A
Engineering, A
Family and Consumer Economics and Related
Services, A
Family and Consumer Sciences/Human Sciences, A
Film/Cinema Studies, A
Fire Science/Firefighting, A
French Language and Literature, A
Geography, A
Geology/Earth Science, A
Hebrew Language and Literature, A
History, A
Hotel/Motel Administration/Management, A
Information Science/Studies, A
Interior Design, A
Italian Language and Literature, A
Journalism, A
Kindergarten/PreSchool Education and Teaching, A
Liberal Arts and Sciences Studies and
Humanities, A
Library Science, A
Licensed Practical/Vocational Nurse Training, A
Machine Tool Technology/Machinist, A
Marketing/Marketing Management, A
Mass Communication/Media Studies, A
Mathematics, A
Mechanical Engineering/Mechanical
Technology/Technician, A
Music, A
Nursing - Registered Nurse Training, A
Photography, A
Physical Education Teaching and Coaching, A
Pre-Engineering, A
Psychology, A
Radio and Television, A
Real Estate, A
Respiratory Care Therapy/Therapist, A
Sociology, A
Spanish Language and Literature, A
Speech and Rhetorical Studies, A
Word Processing, A

LOS MEDANOS COLLEGE

Accounting, A
Administrative Assistant and Secretarial Science, A
Anthropology, A
Art/Art Studies, General, A
Automobile/Automotive Mechanics
Technology/Technician, A

Behavioral Sciences, A
Biology/Biological Sciences, A
Business Administration and Management, A
Business/Managerial Economics, A
Chemistry, A
Commercial and Advertising Art, A
Developmental and Child Psychology, A
Drafting and Design Technology/Technician, A
Electrical, Electronic and Communications
Engineering Technology/Technician, A
Emergency Medical Technology/Technician (EMT
Paramedic), A
Fire Science/Firefighting, A
Heating, Air Conditioning, Ventilation and
Refrigeration Maintenance
Technology/Technician, A
Journalism, A
Liberal Arts and Sciences Studies and
Humanities, A
Mathematics, A
Music, A
Music Management and Merchandising, A
Nursing - Registered Nurse Training, A
Psychology, A
Real Estate, A
Small Engine Mechanics and Repair
Technology/Technician, A
Sociology, A
Tourism and Travel Services Management, A
Welding Technology/Welder, A

LOYOLA MARYMOUNT UNIVERSITY

Accounting, B
African-American/Black Studies, B
Art History, Criticism and Conservation, B
Asian-American Studies, B
Biochemistry, B
Bioethics/Medical Ethics, M
Biology/Biological Sciences, B
Business Administration and Management, B
Business Administration, Management and
Operations, MO
Chemistry, B
Cinematography and Film/Video Production, B
Civil Engineering, BM
Classics and Classical
Languages, Literatures, and Linguistics, B
Communication and Media Studies, M
Computer Engineering, B
Computer Science, BM
Conducting, B
Counselor Education/School Counseling and
Guidance Services, M
Dance, B
Drama and Dramatics/Theatre Arts, B
Economics, B
Education, MD
Educational Administration and Supervision, M
Educational Leadership and Administration, D
Educational Psychology, M
Electrical Engineering, M
Electrical, Electronics and Communications
Engineering, B
Elementary Education and Teaching, M
Engineering and Applied Sciences, MO
Engineering Management, MO
Engineering Physics, B
English, M
English Language and Literature, B
Environmental Sciences, M
European Studies/Civilization, B
Film, Television, and Video Production, M
Fine/Studio Arts, B
French Language and Literature, B
Hispanic-American, Puerto Rican, and Mexican-
American/Chicano Studies, B
History, B
Humanities/Humanistic Studies, B
Industrial/Management Engineering, M
International Economics, B
Latin Language and Literature, B
Law and Legal Studies, MPO
Liberal Arts and Sciences Studies and
Humanities, B
Logistics and Materials Management, M
Marriage and Family Therapy/Counseling, M

Mass Communication/Media Studies, B
Mathematics, B
Mathematics Teacher Education, M
Mechanical Engineering, BM
Modern Greek Language and Literature, B
Multilingual and Multicultural Education, M
Music, B
Music History, Literature, and Theory, B
Music Theory and Composition, B
Musicology and Ethnomusicology, B
Natural Sciences, B
Pastoral Studies/Counseling, M
Philosophy, BM
Physics, B
Playwriting and Screenwriting, B
Political Science and Government, B
Psychology, B
Reading Teacher Education, M
Religious Education, M
School Psychology, M
Secondary Education and Teaching, M
Sociology, B
Spanish Language and Literature, B
Special Education and Teaching, M
Systems Engineering, MO
Taxation, M
Theology and Religious Vocations, M
Theology/Theological Studies, B
Urban Studies/Affairs, B
Voice and Opera, B
Writing, M

MARIC COLLEGE (SAN DIEGO)

Nursing - Registered Nurse Training, A

MARYMOUNT COLLEGE, PALOS VERDES, CALIFORNIA

Liberal Arts and Sciences Studies and
Humanities, A

THE MASTER'S COLLEGE AND SEMINARY

Accounting, B
Actuarial Science, B
American Government and Politics (United States)
, B
Ancient Near Eastern and Biblical
Languages, Literatures, and Linguistics, B
Applied Mathematics, B
Bible/Biblical Studies, B
Biological and Physical Sciences, B
Biology/Biological Sciences, B
Business Administration and Management, B
Computer and Information Sciences, B
Divinity/Ministry (BD, MDiv.), B
Education, B
Elementary Education and Teaching, B
English Language and Literature, B
Environmental Biology, B
Family and Consumer Sciences/Human Sciences, B
Finance, B
Foods, Nutrition, and Wellness Studies, B
Health and Physical Education, B
History, B
Junior High/Intermediate/Middle School Education
and Teaching, B
Kinesiology and Exercise Science, B
Liberal Arts and Sciences Studies and
Humanities, B
Management Information Systems and Services, B
Mass Communication/Media Studies, B
Mathematics, B
Music, B
Music Management and Merchandising, B
Music Teacher Education, B
Natural Sciences, B
Pastoral Studies/Counseling, BMD
Physical Education Teaching and Coaching, B
Physical Sciences, B
Piano and Organ, B
Political Science and Government, B
Pre-Law Studies, B
Pre-Medicine/Pre-Medical Studies, B
Public Relations/Image Management, B
Radio and Television, B
Religion/Religious Studies, B

Religious Education, B
Religious/Sacred Music, B
Science Teacher Education/General Science
   Teacher Education, B
Secondary Education and Teaching, B
Speech and Rhetorical Studies, B
Theology and Religious Vocations, MDP
Theology/Theological Studies, B
Voice and Opera, B

MENDOCINO COLLEGE

Accounting, A
Administrative Assistant and Secretarial Science, A
Agriculture, A
Animal Sciences, A
Art/Art Studies, General, A
Automobile/Automotive Mechanics
   Technology/Technician, A
Biology/Biological Sciences, A
Business Administration and Management, A
Chemistry, A
Child Development, A
Criminal Justice/Law Enforcement Administration, A
Criminal Justice/Police Science, A
Data Processing and Data Processing
   Technology/Technician, A
Developmental and Child Psychology, A
Drama and Dramatics/Theatre Arts, A
Electrical, Electronic and Communications
   Engineering Technology/Technician, A
English Language and Literature, A
Ethnic and Cultural Studies, A
Fiber, Textile and Weaving Arts, A
Finance, A
French Language and Literature, A
Human Services, A
Information Science/Studies, A
Kindergarten/PreSchool Education and Teaching, A
Liberal Arts and Sciences Studies and
   Humanities, A
Mathematics, A
Music, A
Ornamental Horticulture, A
Physical Education Teaching and Coaching, A
Physical Sciences, A
Psychology, A
Public Health (MPH, DPH), A
Real Estate, A
Social Sciences, A
Spanish Language and Literature, A
Speech and Rhetorical Studies, A
Substance Abuse/Addiction Counseling, A
Welding Technology/Welder, A

MENLO COLLEGE

Business Administration and Management, B
Liberal Arts and Sciences Studies and
   Humanities, B
Mass Communication/Media Studies, B

MERCED COLLEGE

Accounting, A
Administrative Assistant and Secretarial Science, A
Agricultural Business and Management, A
Agriculture, A
Agronomy and Crop Science, A
Airframe Mechanics and Aircraft Maintenance
   Technology/Technician, A
Animal Sciences, A
Applied Art, A
Art/Art Studies, General, A
Automobile/Automotive Mechanics
   Technology/Technician, A
Biological and Physical Sciences, A
Business Administration and Management, A
Carpentry/Carpenter, A
Computer Engineering Technology/Technician, A
Computer Science, A
Construction Engineering Technology/Technician, A
Consumer Merchandising/Retailing Management, A
Criminal Justice/Police Science, A
Data Processing and Data Processing
   Technology/Technician, A
Dental Hygiene/Hygienist, A
Developmental and Child Psychology, A
Dietetics/Dieticians, A

Drama and Dramatics/Theatre Arts, A
Electrical, Electronic and Communications
   Engineering Technology/Technician, A
Environmental Engineering
   Technology/Environmental Technology, A
Family and Consumer Sciences/Human Sciences, A
Fashion Merchandising, A
Fashion/Apparel Design, A
Finance, A
Fire Science/Firefighting, A
Human Services, A
Humanities/Humanistic Studies, A
Industrial Radiologic Technology/Technician, A
Insurance, A
Kindergarten/PreSchool Education and Teaching, A
Landscape Architecture, A
Legal Administrative Assistant/Secretary, A
Liberal Arts and Sciences Studies and
   Humanities, A
Library Science, A
Licensed Practical/Vocational Nurse Training, A
Management Information Systems and Services, A
Marketing/Marketing Management, A
Mathematics, A
Medical Administrative Assistant/Secretary, A
Medical/Clinical Assistant, A
Music, A
Natural Sciences, A
Nursing - Registered Nurse Training, A
Ornamental Horticulture, A
Physical Education Teaching and Coaching, A
Physical Sciences, A
Political Science and Government, A
Pre-Engineering, A
Real Estate, A
Social Sciences, A
Special Products Marketing Operations, A
Teacher Assistant/Aide, A
Technology Education/Industrial Arts, A

MERRITT COLLEGE

Accounting, A
Administrative Assistant and Secretarial Science, A
African-American/Black Studies, A
Biological and Physical Sciences, A
Business Administration and Management, A
Business Teacher Education, A
Child Development, A
Community Organization and Advocacy, A
Computer Engineering Technology/Technician, A
Computer Programming/Programmer, A
Computer Typography and Composition Equipment
   Operator, A
Economics, A
French Language and Literature, A
General Studies, A
Horticultural Science, A
Humanities/Humanistic Studies, A
Industrial Radiologic Technology/Technician, A
Information Science/Studies, A
Kindergarten/PreSchool Education and Teaching, A
Land Use Planning and
   Management/Development, A
Landscape Architecture, A
Landscaping and Groundskeeping, A
Legal Assistant/Paralegal, A
Liberal Arts and Sciences Studies and
   Humanities, A
Licensed Practical/Vocational Nurse Training, A
Mathematics, A
Nursing - Registered Nurse Training, A
Parks, Recreation, Leisure and Fitness Studies, A
Public Health (MPH, DPH), A
Reading Teacher Education, A
Real Estate, A
Social Sciences, A
Spanish Language and Literature, A

MILLS COLLEGE

American/United States Studies/Civilization, B
Anthropology, B
Art History, Criticism and Conservation, B
Art/Art Studies, General, B
Biochemistry, B
Biological and Biomedical Sciences, O
Biology/Biological Sciences, B

Business/Managerial Economics, B
Ceramic Arts and Ceramics, M
Chemistry, B
Comparative Literature, B
Computer Science, BMO
Creative Writing, B
Dance, BM
Developmental and Child Psychology, B
Early Childhood Education and Teaching, M
Economics, B
Education, MD
Educational Administration and Supervision, D
Engineering, B
English, M
English Language and Literature, B
Environmental Sciences, B
Environmental Studies, B
Ethnic and Cultural Studies, B
Fine Arts and Art Studies, M
Fine/Studio Arts, B
French Language and Literature, B
French Studies, B
Health Education, M
Hispanic-American, Puerto Rican, and Mexican-
   American/Chicano Studies, B
History, B
Interdisciplinary Studies, B
Intermedia/Multimedia, B
International Relations and Affairs, B
Liberal Arts and Sciences Studies and
   Humanities, B
Management, M
Mathematics, B
Music, BM
Painting, M
Philosophy, B
Photography, M
Physiological Psychology/Psychobiology, B
Political Science and Government, B
Psychology, B
Public Policy Analysis, B
Sculpture, M
Sociology, B
Spanish Language and Literature, B
Women's Studies, B
Writing, M

MIRACOSTA COLLEGE

Accounting, A
Administrative Assistant and Secretarial Science, A
African Studies, A
Architectural Engineering Technology/Technician, A
Art/Art Studies, General, A
Automobile/Automotive Mechanics
   Technology/Technician, A
Behavioral Sciences, A
Biology/Biological Sciences, A
Business Administration and Management, A
Chemistry, A
Child Care and Support Services Management, A
Computer Engineering Technology/Technician, A
Cosmetology/Cosmetologist, A
Criminal Justice/Law Enforcement Administration, A
Criminal Justice/Police Science, A
Dance, A
Developmental and Child Psychology, A
Drafting and Design Technology/Technician, A
Drama and Dramatics/Theatre Arts, A
Economics, A
English Language and Literature, A
Family and Consumer Sciences/Home Economics
   Teacher Education, A
French Language and Literature, A
General Studies, A
History, A
Horticultural Science, A
Hotel/Motel Administration/Management, A
Humanities/Humanistic Studies, A
Industrial Technology/Technician, A
Information Science/Studies, A
Institutional Food Workers, A
Japanese Language and Literature, A
Journalism, A
Kindergarten/PreSchool Education and Teaching, A
Landscaping and Groundskeeping, A

Liberal Arts and Sciences Studies and
    Humanities, A
Licensed Practical/Vocational Nurse Training, A
Machine Tool Technology/Machinist, A
Marketing/Marketing Management, A
Mathematics, A
Music, A
Ornamental Horticulture, A
Philosophy, A
Physical Sciences, A
Physics, A
Political Science and Government, A
Psychology, A
Real Estate, A
Social Sciences, A
Sociology, A
Spanish Language and Literature, A
Speech and Rhetorical Studies, A
Teacher Assistant/Aide, A
Tourism and Travel Services Management, A

MISSION COLLEGE

Accounting, A
Administrative Assistant and Secretarial Science, A
Art/Art Studies, General, A
Business Administration and Management, A
Commercial and Advertising Art, A
Computer Engineering Technology/Technician, A
Computer Programming/Programmer, A
Data Processing and Data Processing
    Technology/Technician, A
Drafting and Design Technology/Technician, A
Electrical, Electronic and Communications
    Engineering Technology/Technician, A
Electrical/Electronics Drafting and
    Electrical/Electronics CAD/CADD, A
Fire Science/Firefighting, A
Food Technology and Processing, A
Graphic and Printing Equipment Operator
    Production, A
Information Science/Studies, A
Liberal Arts and Sciences Studies and
    Humanities, A
Licensed Practical/Vocational Nurse Training, A
Marketing/Marketing Management, A
Mathematics, A
Pre-Engineering, A
Public Health (MPH, DPH), A
Real Estate, A
Social Sciences, A
Special Products Marketing Operations, A

MODESTO JUNIOR COLLEGE

Accounting, A
Administrative Assistant and Secretarial Science, A
Agricultural Business and Management, A
Agricultural Mechanization, A
Agricultural Production Operations, A
Agriculture, A
Agronomy and Crop Science, A
Animal Sciences, A
Apparel and Textiles, A
Architectural Engineering Technology/Technician, A
Art/Art Studies, General, A
Autobody/Collision and Repair
    Technology/Technician, A
Automobile/Automotive Mechanics
    Technology/Technician, A
Banking and Financial Support Services, A
Behavioral Sciences, A
Biology/Biological Sciences, A
Building/Construction
    Finishing, Management, and Inspection, A
Building/Home/Construction Inspection/Inspector, A
Business Administration and Management, A
Child Care and Support Services Management, A
Child Care Provider/Assistant, A
Child Development, A
Commercial and Advertising Art, A
Communications Systems Installation and Repair
    Technology, A
Computer Graphics, A
Computer Installation and Repair
    Technology/Technician, A
Computer Science, A

Computer/Information Technology Services
    Administration and Management, A
Corrections, A
Criminal Justice/Law Enforcement Administration, A
Criminal Justice/Police Science, A
Dairy Science, A
Data Entry/Microcomputer Applications, A
Dental Assisting/Assistant, A
Drafting and Design Technology/Technician, A
Drama and Dramatics/Theatre Arts, A
Electrical, Electronic and Communications
    Engineering Technology/Technician, A
Electrical/Electronics Equipment Installation and
    Repair, A
Emergency Medical Technology/Technician (EMT
    Paramedic), A
Engineering, A
English Language and Literature, A
Family and Consumer Economics and Related
    Services, A
Fashion Merchandising, A
Finance, A
Fire Science/Firefighting, A
Food Science, A
Food Technology and Processing, A
Foreign Languages and Literatures, A
Forestry, A
Forestry Technology/Technician, A
General Office Occupations and Clerical Services, A
General Studies, A
Graphic and Printing Equipment Operator
    Production, A
Heating, Air Conditioning, Ventilation and
    Refrigeration Maintenance
    Technology/Technician, A
Housing and Human Environments, A
Human Services, A
Humanities/Humanistic Studies, A
Industrial Electronics Technology/Technician, A
Interior Design, A
Kindergarten/PreSchool Education and Teaching, A
Landscape Architecture, A
Machine Shop Technology/Assistant, A
Machine Tool Technology/Machinist, A
Management Information Systems and Services, A
Marketing/Marketing Management, A
Mass Communication/Media Studies, A
Mathematics, A
Medical/Clinical Assistant, A
Music, A
Nurse/Nursing Assistant/Aide and Patient Care
    Assistant, A
Nursing - Registered Nurse Training, A
Office Management and Supervision, A
Ornamental Horticulture, A
Parks, Recreation and Leisure Facilities
    Management, A
Photography, A
Physical Education Teaching and Coaching, A
Plant Nursery Operations and Management, A
Poultry Science, A
Radio and Television, A
Real Estate, A
Respiratory Care Therapy/Therapist, A
Social Sciences, A
Special Products Marketing Operations, A
Speech and Rhetorical Studies, A
Technology Education/Industrial Arts, A
Welding Technology/Welder, A
Word Processing, A

MONTEREY PENINSULA COLLEGE

Accounting, A
Administrative Assistant and Secretarial Science, A
Anthropology, A
Apparel and Textiles, A
Art History, Criticism and Conservation, A
Art/Art Studies, General, A
Automobile/Automotive Mechanics
    Technology/Technician, A
Biology/Biological Sciences, A
Business Administration and Management, A
Ceramic Arts and Ceramics, A
Chemistry, A
Child Development, A
Commercial and Advertising Art, A

Computer Engineering Technology/Technician, A
Computer Science, A
Computer Typography and Composition Equipment
    Operator, A
Criminal Justice/Law Enforcement Administration, A
Criminal Justice/Police Science, A
Dance, A
Data Processing and Data Processing
    Technology/Technician, A
Dental Hygiene/Hygienist, A
Drama and Dramatics/Theatre Arts, A
Drawing, A
Economics, A
Engineering, A
English Language and Literature, A
Ethnic and Cultural Studies, A
Family and Consumer Economics and Related
    Services, A
Fashion Merchandising, A
Fiber, Textile and Weaving Arts, A
Fine/Studio Arts, A
Fire Science/Firefighting, A
French Language and Literature, A
Geology/Earth Science, A
German Language and Literature, A
History, A
Hospitality Administration/Management, A
Hotel/Motel Administration/Management, A
Information Science/Studies, A
Interior Design, A
International Business/Trade/Commerce, A
Kindergarten/PreSchool Education and Teaching, A
Kinesiology and Exercise Science, A
Legal Administrative Assistant/Secretary, A
Liberal Arts and Sciences Studies and
    Humanities, A
Marketing/Marketing Management, A
Mass Communication/Media Studies, A
Mathematics, A
Medical Administrative Assistant/Secretary, A
Medical/Clinical Assistant, A
Metal and Jewelry Arts, A
Music, A
Nursing - Registered Nurse Training, A
Occupational Therapy/Therapist, A
Ornamental Horticulture, A
Parks, Recreation and Leisure Facilities
    Management, A
Philosophy, A
Photography, A
Physical Education Teaching and Coaching, A
Physical Therapy/Therapist, A
Physics, A
Political Science and Government, A
Psychology, A
Real Estate, A
Sculpture, A
Sociology, A
Spanish Language and Literature, A
Wildlife and Wildlands Science and Management, A
Women's Studies, A

MOORPARK COLLEGE

Accounting, A
Animal Sciences, A
Anthropology, A
Art/Art Studies, General, A
Behavioral Sciences, A
Biology/Biological Sciences, A
Broadcast Journalism, A
Business Administration and Management, A
Business Machine Repairer, A
Chemistry, A
Commercial and Advertising Art, A
Computer Science, A
Corrections, A
Criminal Justice/Law Enforcement Administration, A
Criminal Justice/Police Science, A
Data Processing and Data Processing
    Technology/Technician, A
Drama and Dramatics/Theatre Arts, A
Electrical, Electronic and Communications
    Engineering Technology/Technician, A
Engineering, A
Engineering Technology, A
Fashion/Apparel Design, A

Film/Cinema Studies, A
Geology/Earth Science, A
Graphic and Printing Equipment Operator
   Production, A
Information Science/Studies, A
Journalism, A
Kindergarten/PreSchool Education and Teaching, A
Laser and Optical Technology/Technician, A
Liberal Arts and Sciences Studies and
   Humanities, A
Marketing/Marketing Management, A
Mathematics, A
Music, A
Natural Sciences, A
Nursing - Registered Nurse Training, A
Photography, A
Teacher Assistant/Aide, A
Telecommunications Technology/Technician, A
Wildlife and Wildlands Science and Management, A

MOUNT ST. MARY'S COLLEGE

Accounting, B
American/United States Studies/Civilization, B
Art Teacher Education, B
Art/Art Studies, General, B
Biochemistry, B
Biology/Biological Sciences, B
Business Administration and Management, AB
Business Teacher Education, B
Chemistry, B
Counseling Psychology, M
Developmental and Child Psychology, B
Education, BM
Educational Administration and Supervision, M
Elementary Education and Teaching, BM
English Language and Literature, B
French Language and Literature, B
Gerontology, B
Health/Health Care Administration/Management, B
History, B
Humanities/Humanistic Studies, M
International Business/Trade/Commerce, B
Kindergarten/PreSchool Education and Teaching, A
Liberal Arts and Sciences Studies and
   Humanities, A
Marketing/Marketing Management, B
Mathematics, B
Music, B
Music Teacher Education, B
Nursing, M
Nursing - Registered Nurse Training, AB
Occupational Therapist Assistant, A
Philosophy, B
Physical Therapist Assistant, A
Physical Therapy/Therapist, D
Political Science and Government, B
Pre-Dentistry Studies, B
Pre-Law Studies, B
Pre-Medicine/Pre-Medical Studies, B
Psychology, B
Religion/Religious Studies, BM
Secondary Education and Teaching, BM
Social Sciences, B
Sociology, B
Spanish Language and Literature, B
Special Education and Teaching, M
Urban Studies/Affairs, A

MT. SAN ANTONIO COLLEGE

Accounting, A
Administrative Assistant and Secretarial Science, A
Advertising, A
Agricultural Business and Management, A
Agricultural Mechanization, A
Agriculture, A
Agronomy and Crop Science, A
Air Traffic Controller, A
Airframe Mechanics and Aircraft Maintenance
   Technology/Technician, A
Airline/Commercial/Professional Pilot and Flight
   Crew, A
Animal Sciences, A
Apparel and Textiles, A
Architectural Engineering Technology/Technician, A
Avionics Maintenance Technology/Technician, A

Building/Construction
   Finishing, Management, and Inspection, A
Business Administration and Management, A
Business Teacher Education, A
Child Development, A
Civil Engineering Technology/Technician, A
Commercial and Advertising Art, A
Computer Engineering Technology/Technician, A
Computer Graphics, A
Computer Science, A
Corrections, A
Criminal Justice/Police Science, A
Dairy Science, A
Data Processing and Data Processing
   Technology/Technician, A
Drafting and Design Technology/Technician, A
Drafting/Design Engineering
   Technologies/Technicians, A
Electrical, Electronic and Communications
   Engineering Technology/Technician, A
Emergency Medical Technology/Technician (EMT
   Paramedic), A
Engineering Technology, A
Family and Consumer Sciences/Human Sciences, A
Fashion Merchandising, A
Finance, A
Fire Science/Firefighting, A
Forestry Technology/Technician, A
Heating, Air Conditioning, Ventilation and
   Refrigeration Maintenance
   Technology/Technician, A
Horticultural Science, A
Hotel/Motel Administration/Management, A
Industrial Design, A
Industrial Radiologic Technology/Technician, A
Interior Design, A
Journalism, A
Kindergarten/PreSchool Education and Teaching, A
Landscape Architecture, A
Legal Administrative Assistant/Secretary, A
Legal Assistant/Paralegal, A
Liberal Arts and Sciences Studies and
   Humanities, A
Machine Tool Technology/Machinist, A
Marketing/Marketing Management, A
Materials Sciences, A
Medical Administrative Assistant/Secretary, A
Mental Health/Rehabilitation, A
Nursing - Registered Nurse Training, A
Occupational Safety and Health
   Technology/Technician, A
Ornamental Horticulture, A
Parks, Recreation and Leisure Facilities
   Management, A
Parks, Recreation, Leisure and Fitness Studies, A
Photography, A
Physical Sciences, A
Pre-Engineering, A
Quality Control Technology/Technician, A
Radio and Television, A
Real Estate, A
Respiratory Care Therapy/Therapist, A
Sign Language Interpretation and Translation, A
Survey Technology/Surveying, A
Technology Education/Industrial Arts, A
Transportation and Materials Moving, A
Welding Technology/Welder, A
Wildlife and Wildlands Science and Management, A

MT. SAN JACINTO COLLEGE

Administrative Assistant and Secretarial Science, A
Art/Art Studies, General, A
Audio Engineering, A
Automobile/Automotive Mechanics
   Technology/Technician, A
Behavioral Sciences, A
Biological and Physical Sciences, A
Business Administration and Management, A
Computer Science, A
Computer Software Engineering, A
Criminal Justice/Police Science, A
Dance, A
Engineering, A
Fire Science/Firefighting, A
Gerontology, A
Home Health Aide/Home Attendant, A

Humanities/Humanistic Studies, A
Interdisciplinary Studies, A
Kindergarten/PreSchool Education and Teaching, A
Legal Assistant/Paralegal, A
Mathematics, A
Music, A
Nursing - Registered Nurse Training, A
Photography, A
Physical Education Teaching and Coaching, A
Public Administration, A
Real Estate, A
Social Sciences, A
Substance Abuse/Addiction Counseling, A
Visual and Performing Arts, A

MT. SIERRA COLLEGE

Business Administration and Management, B
Business/Commerce, B
Commercial and Advertising Art, B
Computer and Information Sciences, B
Computer and Information Sciences and Support
   Services, B
Computer and Information Systems Security, B
Computer Programming/Programmer, B
Computer Science, B
Computer Systems Networking and
   Telecommunications, B
Computer/Information Technology Services
   Administration and Management, B
Design and Applied Arts, B
E-Commerce/Electronic Commerce, B
Graphic Design, B
Illustration, B
Information Science/Studies, B
Intermedia/Multimedia, B
System Administration/Administrator, B
System, Networking, and LAN/WAN
   Management/Manager, B
Web/Multimedia Management and Webmaster, B

MTI COLLEGE OF BUSINESS AND TECHNOLOGY

Accounting, A
Business Administration and Management, A
Computer Technology/Computer Systems
   Technology, A
Legal Administrative Assistant/Secretary, A
Medical Office Management/Administration, A

MUSICIANS INSTITUTE

Music, AB

NAPA VALLEY COLLEGE

Accounting, A
Administrative Assistant and Secretarial Science, A
Agriculture, A
Art/Art Studies, General, A
Behavioral Sciences, A
Biological and Physical Sciences, A
Biomedical Technology/Technician, A
Business Administration and Management, A
Child Development, A
Communications Technology/Technician, A
Computer Science, A
Corrections, A
Cosmetology/Cosmetologist, A
Criminal Justice/Law Enforcement Administration, A
Criminal Justice/Police Science, A
Data Processing and Data Processing
   Technology/Technician, A
Drafting and Design Technology/Technician, A
Electrical, Electronic and Communications
   Engineering Technology/Technician, A
Emergency Medical Technology/Technician (EMT
   Paramedic), A
Engineering, A
Environmental Engineering
   Technology/Environmental Technology, A
Environmental Studies, A
Humanities/Humanistic Studies, A
Kindergarten/PreSchool Education and Teaching, A
Legal Administrative Assistant/Secretary, A
Legal Assistant/Paralegal, A
Machine Tool Technology/Machinist, A
Management Information Systems and Services, A

Marketing/Marketing Management, A
Music, A
Nursing - Registered Nurse Training, A
Photography, A
Radio and Television, A
Real Estate, A
Respiratory Care Therapy/Therapist, A
Telecommunications Technology/Technician, A
Welding Technology/Welder, A

THE NATIONAL HISPANIC UNIVERSITY

Business Administration and Management, AB
Computer Programming/Programmer, AB
Education, AB
Information Science/Studies, AB
Liberal Arts and Sciences Studies and
  Humanities, AB

NATIONAL POLYTECHNIC COLLEGE OF ENGINEERING AND OCEANEERING

Emergency Medical Technology/Technician (EMT
  Paramedic), A
Marine Technology, A
Welding Technology/Welder, A

NATIONAL UNIVERSITY

Accounting, BM
Animation, Interactive Technology, Video Graphics
  and Special Effects, A
Banking and Financial Support Services, B
Behavioral Sciences, B
Biology/Biological Sciences, B
Business Administration and Management, B
Business Administration, Management and
  Operations, M
Child Development, B
Communication and Media Studies, M
Computer Science, BM
Computer Software Engineering, B
Construction Engineering, B
Counseling Psychology, M
Counselor Education/School Counseling and
  Guidance Services, M
Criminal Justice/Law Enforcement Administration, B
Data Modeling/Warehousing and Database
  Administration, B
Drafting/Design Engineering
  Technologies/Technicians, B
E-Commerce/Electronic Commerce, B
Economics, BM
Education, AM
Educational Administration and Supervision, M
Educational Media/Instructional Technology, M
Electronic Commerce, M
Engineering and Applied Sciences, M
Engineering Management, M
English, M
English Language and Literature, B
Entrepreneurship/Entrepreneurial Studies, B
Environmental Engineering
  Technology/Environmental Technology, M
Environmental Sciences, B
Film, Television, and Video Production, M
Finance, B
Finance and Banking, M
Forensic Science and Technology, M
General Studies, B
Geology/Earth Science, B
Health Services Administration, M
Health Services/Allied Health/Health Sciences, B
History, B
Hospitality Administration/Management, B
Human Resources Management/Personnel
  Administration, B
Industrial and Organizational Psychology, M
Information Science/Studies, BM
Information Technology, B
Interdisciplinary Studies, B
Intermedia/Multimedia, B
International/Global Studies, B
Law and Legal Studies, B
Management Information Systems and
  Services, BM
Management of Technology, M
Marketing/Marketing Management, B
Mathematics, B

Multilingual and Multicultural Education, M
Nursing Science, AB
Occupational Safety and Health
  Technology/Technician, B
Operations Management and Supervision, B
Organizational Behavior Studies, B
Organizational Management, M
Pre-Law Studies, B
Psychology, BM
Public Administration, M
Public Health (MPH, DPH), A
Safety Engineering, M
School Psychology, M
Sociology, B
Software Engineering, M
Special Education and Teaching, M
Sport and Fitness Administration/Management, B
Taxation, M
Telecommunications, M
Telecommunications Technology/Technician, B
Writing, M

NEW COLLEGE OF CALIFORNIA

Clinical Psychology, M
Comparative Literature, B
Creative Writing, B
Ecology, B
Education, B
Ethnic and Cultural Studies, B
Humanities/Humanistic Studies, BMO
Interdisciplinary Studies, B
Law and Legal Studies, P
Media Studies, M
Psychology, BM
Social Psychology, M
Social Sciences, B
Sustainable Development, M
Women's Studies, M

NEWSCHOOL OF ARCHITECTURE & DESIGN

Applied Art, A
Architectural Engineering Technology/Technician, A
Architecture, BM
Art/Art Studies, General, A
Commercial and Advertising Art, A
Computer Graphics, AB

NORTHWESTERN POLYTECHNIC UNIVERSITY

Business Administration and Management, B
Business Administration, Management and
  Operations, M
Computer Engineering, BM
Computer Science, BM
Electrical Engineering, M
Electrical, Electronics and Communications
  Engineering, B
Engineering and Applied Sciences, M

NOTRE DAME DE NAMUR UNIVERSITY

Advertising, B
Art Therapy/Therapist, M
Behavioral Sciences, B
Biochemistry, B
Biological and Biomedical Sciences, O
Biology/Biological Sciences, B
Business Administration and Management, B
Business Administration, Management and
  Operations, M
Business/Managerial Economics, B
Commercial and Advertising Art, B
Communication Studies/Speech Communication
  and Rhetoric, B
Communication, Journalism and Related
  Programs, B
Computer Science, B
Computer Software Engineering, B
Counseling Psychology, M
Curriculum and Instruction, M
Drama and Dramatics/Theatre Arts, B
Education, BM
Educational Administration and Supervision, MO
Educational Media/Instructional Technology, MO
Elementary Education and Teaching, B

English, M
English Language and Literature, B
Finance, B
Fine/Studio Arts, B
Gerontology, MO
History, B
Human Services, B
International Business/Trade/Commerce, B
Liberal Arts and Sciences Studies and
  Humanities, B
Management, M
Marketing/Marketing Management, B
Marriage and Family Therapy/Counseling, M
Music, BM
Music Performance, B
Music Teacher Education, M
Performance, M
Philosophy, B
Piano and Organ, B
Political Science and Government, B
Pre-Dentistry Studies, B
Pre-Law Studies, B
Pre-Medicine/Pre-Medical Studies, B
Psychology, BMO
Public Administration, M
Reading Teacher Education, MO
Religion/Religious Studies, B
Secondary Education and Teaching, B
Social Sciences, B
Sociology, B
Special Education and Teaching, MO
Substance Abuse/Addiction Counseling, M
Violin, Viola, Guitar and Other Stringed
  Instruments, B
Voice and Opera, B

OCCIDENTAL COLLEGE

American/United States Studies/Civilization, B
Anthropology, B
Art History, Criticism and Conservation, B
Asian Studies/Civilization, B
Biochemistry, B
Biological and Biomedical Sciences, M
Biology/Biological Sciences, B
Business/Managerial Economics, B
Chemistry, B
Cognitive Psychology and Psycholinguistics, B
Comparative Literature, B
Drama and Dramatics/Theatre Arts, B
Economics, B
Education, M
Elementary Education and Teaching, M
English Education, M
Fine/Studio Arts, B
Foreign Language Teacher Education, M
French Language and Literature, B
Geology/Earth Science, B
Geophysics and Seismology, B
History, B
International Relations and Affairs, B
Kinesiology and Exercise Science, B
Liberal Studies, M
Mathematics, B
Mathematics Teacher Education, M
Music, B
Philosophy, B
Physics, B
Physiological Psychology/Psychobiology, B
Political Science and Government, B
Psychology, B
Public Policy Analysis, B
Religion/Religious Studies, B
Science Teacher Education/General Science
  Teacher Education, M
Secondary Education and Teaching, M
Social Studies Teacher Education, M
Sociology, B
Spanish Language and Literature, B
Women's Studies, B

OHLONE COLLEGE

Accounting, A
Administrative Assistant and Secretarial Science, A
Art/Art Studies, General, A
Biology/Biological Sciences, A
Broadcast Journalism, A

Business Administration and Management, A
Child Development, A
Commercial and Advertising Art, A
Computer Programming/Programmer, A
Computer Science, A
Computer Typography and Composition Equipment
   Operator, A
Consumer Services and Advocacy, A
Criminal Justice/Law Enforcement Administration, A
Criminal Justice/Police Science, A
Drafting and Design Technology/Technician, A
Electrical, Electronic and Communications
   Engineering Technology/Technician, A
Family and Consumer Sciences/Human Sciences, A
Fashion Merchandising, A
Food Science, A
Foods, Nutrition, and Wellness Studies, A
Interior Design, A
Journalism, A
Kindergarten/PreSchool Education and Teaching, A
Liberal Arts and Sciences Studies and
   Humanities, A
Marketing/Marketing Management, A
Mass Communication/Media Studies, A
Medical Administrative Assistant/Secretary, A
Medical/Clinical Assistant, A
Natural Sciences, A
Nursing - Registered Nurse Training, A
Physical Sciences, A
Physical Therapist Assistant, A
Pre-Engineering, A
Public Health (MPH, DPH), A
Radio and Television, A
Real Estate, A
Respiratory Care Therapy/Therapist, A
Sign Language Interpretation and Translation, A
Social Sciences, A

ORANGE COAST COLLEGE

Accounting, A
Administrative Assistant and Secretarial Science, A
Aeronautics/Aviation/Aerospace Science and
   Technology, A
Airline/Commercial/Professional Pilot and Flight
   Crew, A
Anthropology, A
Architectural Engineering Technology/Technician, A
Art/Art Studies, General, A
Athletic Training and Sports Medicine, A
Avionics Maintenance Technology/Technician, A
Behavioral Sciences, A
Biology/Biological Sciences, A
Building/Home/Construction Inspection/Inspector, A
Business Administration and Management, A
Cardiovascular Technology/Technologist, A
Chemistry, A
Child Care and Support Services Management, A
Child Care Provider/Assistant, A
Cinematography and Film/Video Production, A
Clinical Laboratory Science/Medical
   Technology/Technologist, A
Commercial and Advertising Art, A
Communications Technology/Technician, A
Computer Engineering Technology/Technician, A
Computer Graphics, A
Computer Programming, Specific Applications, A
Computer Programming/Programmer, A
Computer Typography and Composition Equipment
   Operator, A
Construction Engineering Technology/Technician, A
Culinary Arts/Chef Training, A
Dance, A
Data Entry/Microcomputer Applications, A
Data Processing and Data Processing
   Technology/Technician, A
Dental Hygiene/Hygienist, A
Dietetics/Dieticians, A
Drafting and Design Technology/Technician, A
Drama and Dramatics/Theatre Arts, A
Economics, A
Electrical and Power Transmission
   Installation/Installer, A
Electrical, Electronic and Communications
   Engineering Technology/Technician, A
Electrical/Electronics Equipment Installation and
   Repair, A

Emergency Medical Technology/Technician (EMT
   Paramedic), A
Engineering, A
English Language and Literature, A
Ethnic and Cultural Studies, A
Family and Consumer Economics and Related
   Services, A
Family and Consumer Sciences/Human Sciences, A
Fashion Merchandising, A
Film/Cinema Studies, A
Food Science, A
Food Technology and Processing, A
Foods, Nutrition, and Wellness Studies, A
French Language and Literature, A
Geography, A
Geology/Earth Science, A
German Language and Literature, A
Heating, Air Conditioning, Ventilation and
   Refrigeration Maintenance
   Technology/Technician, A
History, A
Horticultural Science, A
Hotel/Motel Administration/Management, A
Housing and Human Environments, A
Human Development and Family Studies, A
Humanities/Humanistic Studies, A
Industrial Design, A
Industrial Radiologic Technology/Technician, A
Information Science/Studies, A
Interior Design, A
Journalism, A
Kindergarten/PreSchool Education and Teaching, A
Kinesiology and Exercise Science, A
Legal Administrative Assistant/Secretary, A
Liberal Arts and Sciences Studies and
   Humanities, A
Machine Shop Technology/Assistant, A
Machine Tool Technology/Machinist, A
Marine Technology, A
Marketing/Marketing Management, A
Mass Communication/Media Studies, A
Mathematics, A
Medical Administrative Assistant/Secretary, A
Medical/Clinical Assistant, A
Music, A
Music Management and Merchandising, A
Musical Instrument Fabrication and Repair, A
Natural Sciences, A
Nuclear Medical Technology/Technologist, A
Ornamental Horticulture, A
Philosophy, A
Photography, A
Physical Education Teaching and Coaching, A
Physics, A
Political Science and Government, A
Public Health (MPH, DPH), A
Religion/Religious Studies, A
Respiratory Care Therapy/Therapist, A
Restaurant, Culinary, and Catering
   Management/Manager, A
Retailing and Retail Operations, A
Selling Skills and Sales Operations, A
Social Sciences, A
Sociology, A
Spanish Language and Literature, A
Special Products Marketing Operations, A
Welding Technology/Welder, A
Word Processing, A

OTIS COLLEGE OF ART AND DESIGN

Applied Art, B
Art/Art Studies, General, B
Commercial and Advertising Art, B
Drawing, B
Environmental Design/Architecture, B
Fashion/Apparel Design, B
Fine Arts and Art Studies, M
Fine/Studio Arts, B
Interior Design, B
Painting, M
Photography, BM
Sculpture, BM

Writing, M

OXNARD COLLEGE

Accounting, A
Administrative Assistant and Secretarial Science, A
Agricultural Business and Management, A
Agricultural Mechanization, A
Anthropology, A
Art Teacher Education, A
Automobile/Automotive Mechanics
   Technology/Technician, A
Behavioral Sciences, A
Biology/Biological Sciences, A
Business Administration and Management, A
Child Development, A
Culinary Arts/Chef Training, A
Dental Assisting/Assistant, A
Dental Hygiene/Hygienist, A
Drama and Dramatics/Theatre Arts, A
Economics, A
Electrical, Electronic and Communications
   Engineering Technology/Technician, A
English Language and Literature, A
Family and Community Services, A
Family and Consumer Sciences/Human Sciences, A
Fashion Merchandising, A
Fire Science/Firefighting, A
Heating, Air Conditioning, Ventilation and
   Refrigeration Maintenance
   Technology/Technician, A
History, A
Hotel/Motel Administration/Management, A
Information Science/Studies, A
Journalism, A
Kindergarten/PreSchool Education and Teaching, A
Law and Legal Studies, A
Liberal Arts and Sciences Studies and
   Humanities, A
Library Science, A
Machine Tool Technology/Machinist, A
Marketing/Marketing Management, A
Mathematics, A
Mental Health/Rehabilitation, A
Philosophy, A
Physical Education Teaching and Coaching, A
Radio and Television, A
Real Estate, A
Sociology, A
Spanish Language and Literature, A
Telecommunications Technology/Technician, A
Transportation and Materials Moving, A
Welding Technology/Welder, A

PACIFIC OAKS COLLEGE

Child Development, B
Elementary Education and Teaching, B
Human Development, M
Human Development and Family Studies, B
Human Services, B
Kindergarten/PreSchool Education and Teaching, B
Marriage and Family Therapy/Counseling, M
Special Education and Teaching, B

PACIFIC STATES UNIVERSITY

Business Administration and Management, B
Business Administration, Management and
   Operations, M
Computer Science, BM
Electrical, Electronics and Communications
   Engineering, B
Finance and Banking, M
International Business/Trade/Commerce, M
Management Information Systems and Services, M
Management of Technology, M

PACIFIC UNION COLLEGE

Accounting, B
Applied Mathematics, B
Art History, Criticism and Conservation, B
Art/Art Studies, General, B
Behavioral Sciences, B
Bible/Biblical Studies, A
Biochemistry, B
Biology/Biological Sciences, B
Biophysics, B
Business Administration and Management, B

Business Teacher Education, B
Chemistry, B
Child Care and Support Services Management, B
Child Care Provider/Assistant, A
Clinical Laboratory Science/Medical
 Technology/Technologist, B
Computer and Information Sciences, B
Computer Programming/Programmer, B
Computer Science, B
Data Processing and Data Processing
 Technology/Technician, B
Drafting and Design Technology/Technician, B
Education, BM
Electrical, Electronic and Communications
 Engineering Technology/Technician, B
Elementary Education and Teaching, B
Engineering, B
Engineering Technology, AB
English Language and Literature, B
Finance, B
Fine/Studio Arts, B
History, B
Information Science/Studies, AB
Interdisciplinary Studies, B
International Business/Trade/Commerce, B
Journalism, B
Kindergarten/PreSchool Education and
 Teaching, AB
Kinesiology and Exercise Science, B
Legal Administrative Assistant/Secretary, A
Management Information Systems and Services, B
Marketing/Marketing Management, B
Mass Communication/Media Studies, B
Mathematics, B
Medical Administrative Assistant/Secretary, A
Music, B
Music Teacher Education, B
Nursing - Registered Nurse Training, AB
Parks, Recreation, Leisure and Fitness Studies, B
Pastoral Studies/Counseling, B
Photography, A
Physical Education Teaching and Coaching, B
Physical Sciences, B
Physics, B
Piano and Organ, B
Political Science and Government, B
Pre-Dentistry Studies, B
Pre-Law Studies, B
Pre-Medicine/Pre-Medical Studies, B
Pre-Veterinary Studies, B
Psychology, B
Public Relations/Image Management, B
Religion/Religious Studies, B
Social Sciences, B
Social Work, B
Sociology, B
Spanish Language and Literature, B
Teacher Education, Multiple Levels, B
Theology/Theological Studies, B

PALO VERDE COLLEGE

Accounting, A
Administrative Assistant and Secretarial Science, A
Agriculture, A
Automobile/Automotive Mechanics
 Technology/Technician, A
Behavioral Sciences, A
Biology/Biological Sciences, A
Business Administration and Management, A
Child Development, A
Computer and Information Sciences, A
Construction Trades, A
Criminal Justice/Law Enforcement Administration, A
Criminal Justice/Police Science, A
Developmental and Child Psychology, A
Economics, A
Education, A
English Language and Literature, A
Entrepreneurship/Entrepreneurial Studies, A
Forestry, A
General Studies, A
History, A
Interior Design, A
Kindergarten/PreSchool Education and Teaching, A
Liberal Arts and Sciences Studies and
 Humanities, A

Marketing/Marketing Management, A
Political Science and Government, A
Pre-Engineering, A
Psychology, A
Public Health (MPH, DPH), A
Sociology, A
Transportation and Materials Moving, A

PALOMAR COLLEGE

Accounting, A
Administrative Assistant and Secretarial Science, A
Advertising, A
Anthropology, A
Applied Art, A
Archeology, A
Art Teacher Education, A
Art/Art Studies, General, A
Arts Management, A
Astronomy, A
Automobile/Automotive Mechanics
 Technology/Technician, A
Aviation/Airway Management and Operations, A
Avionics Maintenance Technology/Technician, A
Biology/Biological Sciences, A
Business Administration and Management, A
Business Machine Repairer, A
Business Teacher Education, A
Carpentry/Carpenter, A
Ceramic Arts and Ceramics, A
Chemistry, A
Commercial and Advertising Art, A
Computer Science, A
Construction Engineering Technology/Technician, A
Criminal Justice/Law Enforcement Administration, A
Criminal Justice/Police Science, A
Dance, A
Dental Hygiene/Hygienist, A
Developmental and Child Psychology, A
Drafting and Design Technology/Technician, A
Drama and Dramatics/Theatre Arts, A
Drawing, A
Economics, A
Electrical, Electronic and Communications
 Engineering Technology/Technician, A
Emergency Medical Technology/Technician (EMT
 Paramedic), A
Engineering, A
Family and Consumer Economics and Related
 Services, A
Fashion Merchandising, A
Fashion/Apparel Design, A
Film/Cinema Studies, A
Fire Science/Firefighting, A
Food Technology and Processing, A
Geology/Earth Science, A
Graphic and Printing Equipment Operator
 Production, A
Hydrology and Water Resources Science, A
Information Science/Studies, A
Interior Design, A
International Business/Trade/Commerce, A
Journalism, A
Kindergarten/PreSchool Education and Teaching, A
Legal Administrative Assistant/Secretary, A
Legal Assistant/Paralegal, A
Liberal Arts and Sciences Studies and
 Humanities, A
Library Science, A
Marketing/Marketing Management, A
Mathematics, A
Medical Administrative Assistant/Secretary, A
Medical/Clinical Assistant, A
Metal and Jewelry Arts, A
Music, A
Nursing - Registered Nurse Training, A
Parks, Recreation and Leisure Facilities
 Management, A
Parks, Recreation, Leisure and Fitness Studies, A
Photography, A
Physical Education Teaching and Coaching, A
Pipefitting/Pipefitter and Sprinkler Fitter, A
Public Administration, A
Radio and Television, A
Real Estate, A
Sign Language Interpretation and Translation, A
Special Products Marketing Operations, A

Speech and Rhetorical Studies, A
Survey Technology/Surveying, A
Telecommunications Technology/Technician, A
Tourism and Travel Services Management, A
Welding Technology/Welder, A
Women's Studies, A
Zoology/Animal Biology, A

PASADENA CITY COLLEGE

Accounting, A
Administrative Assistant and Secretarial Science, A
Advertising, A
African Studies, A
African-American/Black Studies, A
Airline/Commercial/Professional Pilot and Flight
 Crew, A
Anthropology, A
Architectural Engineering Technology/Technician, A
Art History, Criticism and Conservation, A
Art/Art Studies, General, A
Astronomy, A
Automobile/Automotive Mechanics
 Technology/Technician, A
Aviation/Airway Management and Operations, A
Avionics Maintenance Technology/Technician, A
Biological and Physical Sciences, A
Biology/Biological Sciences, A
Broadcast Journalism, A
Business Administration and Management, A
Business Teacher Education, A
Carpentry/Carpenter, A
Ceramic Arts and Ceramics, A
Ceramic Sciences and Engineering, A
Chemistry, A
Civil Engineering Technology/Technician, A
Communications Technology/Technician, A
Computer Engineering Technology/Technician, A
Computer Programming/Programmer, A
Computer Science, A
Computer Typography and Composition Equipment
 Operator, A
Construction Engineering Technology/Technician, A
Cosmetology/Cosmetologist, A
Criminal Justice/Law Enforcement Administration, A
Data Processing and Data Processing
 Technology/Technician, A
Dental Hygiene/Hygienist, A
Developmental and Child Psychology, A
Drafting and Design Technology/Technician, A
Drama and Dramatics/Theatre Arts, A
Drawing, A
Economics, A
Electrical, Electronic and Communications
 Engineering Technology/Technician, A
Engineering, A
Engineering Technology, A
English Language and Literature, A
Ethnic and Cultural Studies, A
Fashion Merchandising, A
Fiber, Textile and Weaving Arts, A
Finance, A
Fire Science/Firefighting, A
Forestry Technology/Technician, A
French Language and Literature, A
Geography, A
Geology/Earth Science, A
German Language and Literature, A
Hispanic-American, Puerto Rican, and Mexican-
 American/Chicano Studies, A
History, A
Human Services, A
Industrial Radiologic Technology/Technician, A
Information Science/Studies, A
Interdisciplinary Studies, A
Interior Design, A
Journalism, A
Kindergarten/PreSchool Education and Teaching, A
Landscape Architecture, A
Latin American Studies, A
Law and Legal Studies, A
Legal Administrative Assistant/Secretary, A
Liberal Arts and Sciences Studies and
 Humanities, A
Library Science, A
Licensed Practical/Vocational Nurse Training, A
Machine Tool Technology/Machinist, A

Marketing/Marketing Management, A
Mass Communication/Media Studies, A
Mathematics, A
Mechanical Engineering/Mechanical
  Technology/Technician, A
Medical/Clinical Assistant, A
Metal and Jewelry Arts, A
Modern Languages, A
Music, A
Music Therapy/Therapist, A
Nursing - Registered Nurse Training, A
Occupational Therapy/Therapist, A
Parks, Recreation, Leisure and Fitness Studies, A
Pharmacy, A
Philosophy, A
Photography, A
Physical Education Teaching and Coaching, A
Physical Sciences, A
Physics, A
Political Science and Government, A
Psychology, A
Radio and Television, A
Real Estate, A
Religion/Religious Studies, A
Sign Language Interpretation and Translation, A
Social Sciences, A
Sociology, A
Spanish Language and Literature, A
Speech and Rhetorical Studies, A
Statistics, A
Teacher Assistant/Aide, A
Telecommunications Technology/Technician, A
Tourism and Travel Services Management, A
Welding Technology/Welder, A

PATTEN UNIVERSITY

Bible/Biblical Studies, AB
Business Administration and Management, B
Divinity/Ministry (BD, MDiv.), B
Kindergarten/PreSchool Education and Teaching, B
Liberal Arts and Sciences Studies and
  Humanities, AB
Pastoral Studies/Counseling, B
Religious/Sacred Music, B

PEPPERDINE UNIVERSITY

Accounting, B
Advertising, B
American/United States Studies/Civilization, M
Art/Art Studies, General, B
Athletic Training and Sports Medicine, B
Biology/Biological Sciences, B
Business Administration and Management, B
Business Administration, Management and
  Operations, MO
Chemistry, B
Communication and Media Studies, M
Communication Studies/Speech Communication
  and Rhetoric, B
Computer Science, B
Conflict Resolution and Mediation/Peace Studies, M
Drama and Dramatics/Theatre Arts, B
Economics, B
Education, B
Elementary Education and Teaching, B
English Language and Literature, B
Foods, Nutrition, and Wellness Studies, B
French Language and Literature, B
German Language and Literature, B
History, BM
Humanities/Humanistic Studies, BM
Interdisciplinary Studies, B
International Business/Trade/Commerce, BM
International Relations and Affairs, B
Journalism, B
Law and Legal Studies, PO
Liberal Arts and Sciences Studies and
  Humanities, B
Mathematics, B
Music, B
Music Teacher Education, B
Natural Sciences, B
Philosophy, B
Physical Education Teaching and Coaching, B
Political Science and Government, B
Pre-Dentistry Studies, B

Pre-Law Studies, B
Pre-Medicine/Pre-Medical Studies, B
Psychology, B
Public Policy Analysis, M
Public Relations/Image Management, B
Religion/Religious Studies, BMP
Religious Education, B
Secondary Education and Teaching, B
Sociology, B
Spanish Language and Literature, B
Speech and Rhetorical Studies, B
Telecommunications Technology/Technician, B

PIMA MEDICAL INSTITUTE

Radiologic Technology/Science - Radiographer, A
Respiratory Therapy Technician/Assistant, A

PITZER COLLEGE

African-American/Black Studies, B
American/United States Studies/Civilization, B
Anthropology, B
Art History, Criticism and Conservation, B
Art/Art Studies, General, B
Asian Studies/Civilization, B
Asian-American Studies, B
Biochemistry, B
Biology/Biological Sciences, B
Chemistry, B
Classics and Classical
  Languages, Literatures, and Linguistics, B
Comparative Literature, B
Creative Writing, B
Dance, B
Drama and Dramatics/Theatre Arts, B
Ecology, B
Economics, B
Engineering, B
English Language and Literature, B
Environmental Sciences, B
Environmental Studies, B
European Studies/Civilization, B
Film/Cinema Studies, B
Fine/Studio Arts, B
Foreign Languages and Literatures, B
French Language and Literature, B
German Language and Literature, B
Hispanic-American, Puerto Rican, and Mexican-
  American/Chicano Studies, B
History, B
Interdisciplinary Studies, B
International Relations and Affairs, B
International/Global Studies, B
Latin American Studies, B
Linguistics, B
Mathematics, B
Molecular Biology, B
Music, B
Neuroscience, B
Organizational Behavior Studies, B
Philosophy, B
Physics, B
Political Science and Government, B
Pre-Medicine/Pre-Medical Studies, B
Psychology, B
Regional Studies (U.S., Canadian, Foreign), B
Religion/Religious Studies, B
Romance Languages, Literatures, and Linguistics, B
Russian Language and Literature, B
Science, Technology and Society, B
Sociology, B
Spanish Language and Literature, B
Women's Studies, B

PLATT COLLEGE (CERRITOS)

Commercial and Advertising Art, A
Intermedia/Multimedia, A
Legal Assistant/Paralegal, A

PLATT COLLEGE-LOS ANGELES, INC

Commercial and Advertising Art, A
Computer and Information Sciences, A
Computer Graphics, A
Design and Visual Communications, A
Information Science/Studies, A
Information Technology, A

Legal Assistant/Paralegal, A

PLATT COLLEGE (NEWPORT BEACH)

Commercial and Advertising Art, A
Computer Graphics, AB
Design and Applied Arts, B
Information Science/Studies, A
Information Technology, A
Intermedia/Multimedia, B
Legal Assistant/Paralegal, A

PLATT COLLEGE (ONTARIO)

Commercial and Advertising Art, A
Computer Graphics, A
Computer Systems Networking and
  Telecommunications, A
Information Technology, A
Legal Assistant/Paralegal, A

PLATT COLLEGE SAN DIEGO

Animation, Interactive Technology, Video Graphics
  and Special Effects, AB
Commercial and Advertising Art, A
Computer Graphics, A
Computer Software and Media Applications, A
Digital Communication and Media/Multimedia, A
Graphic Design, A
Intermedia/Multimedia, A
Web Page, Digital/Multimedia and Information
  Resources Design, AB
Web/Multimedia Management and Webmaster, A

POINT LOMA NAZARENE UNIVERSITY

Accounting, B
Art Teacher Education, B
Art/Art Studies, General, B
Athletic Training and Sports Medicine, B
Bible/Biblical Studies, B
Biochemistry, B
Biology/Biological Sciences, B
Broadcast Journalism, B
Business Administration and Management, B
Business Administration, Management and
  Operations, M
Business/Corporate Communications, B
Chemistry, B
Child Development, B
Communication Studies/Speech Communication
  and Rhetoric, B
Computer Science, B
Development Economics and International
  Development, B
Dietetics/Dieticians, B
Drama and Dramatics/Theatre Arts, B
Education, MO
Engineering Physics, B
English Language and Literature, B
Family and Community Services, B
Family and Consumer Sciences/Human Sciences, B
Fine Arts and Art Studies, B
Foods, Nutrition, and Wellness Studies, B
Graphic Communications, B
Graphic Design, B
Health and Physical Education, B
History, B
Industrial and Organizational Psychology, B
International/Global Studies, B
Journalism, B
Kinesiology and Exercise Science, B
Liberal Arts and Sciences Studies and
  Humanities, B
Management Information Systems and Services, B
Mass Communication/Media Studies, B
Mathematics, B
Music, B
Music Performance, B
Music Teacher Education, B
Music Theory and Composition, B
Nursing, M
Nursing - Registered Nurse Training, B
Philosophy, B
Philosophy and Religious Studies, B
Physics, B
Political Science and Government, B
Pre-Theology/Pre-Ministerial Studies, B
Psychology, B

Religion/Religious Studies, BM
Religious/Sacred Music, B
Romance Languages, Literatures, and Linguistics, B
Social Sciences, B
Social Work, B
Sociology, B
Spanish Language and Literature, B
Theological and Ministerial Studies, B
Youth Ministry, B

POMONA COLLEGE

African-American/Black Studies, B
American/United States Studies/Civilization, B
Anthropology, B
Art History, Criticism and Conservation, B
Art/Art Studies, General, B
Asian Studies/Civilization, B
Astronomy, B
Biochemistry, B
Biology/Biological Sciences, B
Cell/Cellular Biology and Histology, B
Chemistry, B
Chinese Language and Literature, B
Classics and Classical
    Languages, Literatures, and Linguistics, B
Computer Science, B
Dance, B
Drama and Dramatics/Theatre Arts, B
East Asian Studies, B
Ecology, B
Economics, B
English Language and Literature, B
Environmental Studies, B
Film/Cinema Studies, B
Fine/Studio Arts, B
French Language and Literature, B
Geochemistry, B
Geology/Earth Science, B
German Language and Literature, B
Hispanic-American, Puerto Rican, and Mexican-
    American/Chicano Studies, B
History, B
Humanities/Humanistic Studies, B
Interdisciplinary Studies, B
International Relations and Affairs, B
Japanese Language and Literature, B
Liberal Arts and Sciences Studies and
    Humanities, B
Linguistics, B
Mathematics, B
Medical Microbiology and Bacteriology, B
Modern Languages, B
Molecular Biology, B
Music, B
Neuroscience, B
Philosophy, B
Physics, B
Political Science and Government, B
Pre-Medicine/Pre-Medical Studies, B
Psychology, B
Public Policy Analysis, B
Religion/Religious Studies, B
Romance Languages, Literatures, and Linguistics, B
Russian Language and Literature, B
Sociology, B
Spanish Language and Literature, B
Women's Studies, B

PORTERVILLE COLLEGE

Administrative Assistant and Secretarial Science, A
Agricultural Business and Management, A
Applied Art, A
Art/Art Studies, General, A
Automobile/Automotive Mechanics
    Technology/Technician, A
Biological and Physical Sciences, A
Biology/Biological Sciences, A
Business Administration and Management, A
Business Teacher Education, A
Carpentry/Carpenter, A
Child Development, A
Commercial and Advertising Art, A
Computer Science, A
Criminal Justice/Law Enforcement Administration, A
Criminal Justice/Police Science, A
Drafting and Design Technology/Technician, A

Education, A
English Language and Literature, A
Finance, A
Fire Science/Firefighting, A
History, A
Human Services, A
Liberal Arts and Sciences Studies and
    Humanities, A
Licensed Practical/Vocational Nurse Training, A
Mathematics, A
Mental Health/Rehabilitation, A
Music, A
Natural Sciences, A
Photography, A
Physical Education Teaching and Coaching, A
Pre-Engineering, A
Social Sciences, A
Technology Education/Industrial Arts, A
Welding Technology/Welder, A

QUEEN OF THE HOLY ROSARY COLLEGE

Religion/Religious Studies, A

REEDLEY COLLEGE

Accounting, A
Administrative Assistant and Secretarial Science, A
Agricultural Business and Management, A
Agricultural Mechanization, A
Agriculture, A
Animal Sciences, A
Art/Art Studies, General, A
Automobile/Automotive Mechanics
    Technology/Technician, A
Avionics Maintenance Technology/Technician, A
Biology/Biological Sciences, A
Business/Commerce, A
Child Care and Support Services Management, A
Commercial and Advertising Art, A
Computer and Information Sciences, A
Corrections and Criminal Justice, A
Criminal Justice/Police Science, A
Dental Assisting/Assistant, A
English Language and Literature, A
Entrepreneurship/Entrepreneurial Studies, A
Fine Arts and Art Studies, A
Foreign Languages and Literatures, A
General Office Occupations and Clerical Services, A
General Studies, A
Health and Physical Education, A
Horticultural Science, A
Hospitality Administration/Management, A
Information Science/Studies, A
Liberal Arts and Sciences Studies and
    Humanities, A
Machine Tool Technology/Machinist, A
Management Science, A
Mathematics, A
Music Performance, A
Natural Resources Management/Development and
    Policy, A
Physical Sciences, A
Plant Sciences, A
Precision Metal Working, A
Social Sciences, A
Voice and Opera, A
Welding Technology/Welder, A

RIO HONDO COLLEGE

Business Teacher Education, A
Criminal Justice/Law Enforcement Administration, A
Liberal Arts and Sciences Studies and
    Humanities, A
Nursing - Registered Nurse Training, A

RIVERSIDE COMMUNITY COLLEGE DISTRICT

Autobody/Collision and Repair
    Technology/Technician, A
Automobile/Automotive Mechanics
    Technology/Technician, A
Business Administration and Management, A
Cinematography and Film/Video Production, A
Computer Programming, A
Computer Programming/Programmer, A

Construction Engineering Technology/Technician, A
Consumer Merchandising/Retailing Management, A
Cosmetology/Cosmetologist, A
Criminal Justice/Law Enforcement Administration, A
Culinary Arts/Chef Training, A
Fire Science/Firefighting, A
Graphic and Printing Equipment Operator
    Production, A
Heating, Air Conditioning and Refrigeration
    Technology/Technician, A
Legal Assistant/Paralegal, A
Liberal Arts and Sciences Studies and
    Humanities, A
Licensed Practical/Vocational Nurse Training, A
Nursing - Registered Nurse Training, A
Office Management and Supervision, A
Photography, A
Sign Language Interpretation and Translation, A
Welding Technology/Welder, A

SACRAMENTO CITY COLLEGE

Accounting, A
Administrative Assistant and Secretarial Science, A
Advertising, A
Airframe Mechanics and Aircraft Maintenance
    Technology/Technician, A
Army JROTC/ROTC, A
Art/Art Studies, General, A
Avionics Maintenance Technology/Technician, A
Biological and Physical Sciences, A
Business Administration and Management, A
Comparative Literature, A
Computer Science, A
Cosmetology/Cosmetologist, A
Criminal Justice/Law Enforcement Administration, A
Data Processing and Data Processing
    Technology/Technician, A
Dental Assisting/Assistant, A
Dental Hygiene/Hygienist, A
Drafting and Design Technology/Technician, A
Drama and Dramatics/Theatre Arts, A
Electrical, Electronic and Communications
    Engineering Technology/Technician, A
Engineering, A
Ethnic and Cultural Studies, A
Family and Consumer Economics and Related
    Services, A
Graphic and Printing Equipment Operator
    Production, A
Human Services, A
Humanities/Humanistic Studies, A
Kindergarten/PreSchool Education and Teaching, A
Legal Administrative Assistant/Secretary, A
Liberal Arts and Sciences Studies and
    Humanities, A
Library Science, A
Licensed Practical/Vocational Nurse Training, A
Mass Communication/Media Studies, A
Mathematics, A
Medical Administrative Assistant/Secretary, A
Music, A
Natural Resources Management/Development and
    Policy, A
Natural Sciences, A
Nursing - Registered Nurse Training, A
Occupational Therapy/Therapist, A
Physical Education Teaching and Coaching, A
Physical Sciences, A
Physical Therapist Assistant, A
Psychology, A
Real Estate, A
Social Sciences, A
Social Work, A
Speech and Rhetorical Studies, A
Survey Technology/Surveying, A
Transportation and Materials Moving, A
Women's Studies, A

SADDLEBACK COLLEGE

Accounting, A
Administrative Assistant and Secretarial Science, A
American/United States Studies/Civilization, A
Anthropology, A
Architectural Engineering Technology/Technician, A
Art/Art Studies, General, A
Astronomy, A

Automobile/Automotive Mechanics Technology/Technician, A
Biology/Biological Sciences, A
Business Administration and Management, A
Carpentry/Carpenter, A
Chemical Engineering, A
Chemistry, A
Child Development, A
Cinematography and Film/Video Production, A
Commercial and Advertising Art, A
Comparative Literature, A
Computer and Information Sciences, A
Computer Programming/Programmer, A
Computer Science, A
Computer Typography and Composition Equipment Operator, A
Construction Engineering Technology/Technician, A
Consumer Merchandising/Retailing Management, A
Consumer Services and Advocacy, A
Cosmetology/Cosmetologist, A
Developmental and Child Psychology, A
Drafting and Design Technology/Technician, A
Drama and Dramatics/Theatre Arts, A
Economics, A
Electrical, Electronic and Communications Engineering Technology/Technician, A
Emergency Medical Technology/Technician (EMT Paramedic), A
Engineering, A
Environmental Studies, A
Family and Community Services, A
Family and Consumer Sciences/Human Sciences, A
Fashion Merchandising, A
Fashion/Apparel Design, A
Food Science, A
Food Technology and Processing, A
Foods, Nutrition, and Wellness Studies, A
Geography, A
Geology/Earth Science, A
Gerontology, A
History, A
Horticultural Science, A
Human Development and Family Studies, A
Human Services, A
Humanities/Humanistic Studies, A
Information Science/Studies, A
Interior Design, A
Journalism, A
Kindergarten/PreSchool Education and Teaching, A
Landscape Architecture, A
Law and Legal Studies, A
Legal Administrative Assistant/Secretary, A
Legal Assistant/Paralegal, A
Liberal Arts and Sciences Studies and Humanities, A
Marine Science/Merchant Marine Officer, A
Marine Technology, A
Mathematics, A
Medical/Clinical Assistant, A
Music, A
Natural Sciences, A
Nursing - Registered Nurse Training, A
Ornamental Horticulture, A
Philosophy, A
Photography, A
Physical Education Teaching and Coaching, A
Physical Sciences, A
Physics, A
Political Science and Government, A
Pre-Engineering, A
Psychology, A
Radio and Television, A
Real Estate, A
Social Sciences, A
Sociology, A
Special Products Marketing Operations, A
Speech and Rhetorical Studies, A
Substance Abuse/Addiction Counseling, A
Teacher Assistant/Aide, A
Technology Education/Industrial Arts, A
Tourism and Travel Services Management, A

Women's Studies, A

SAINT MARY'S COLLEGE OF CALIFORNIA

Accounting, B
Accounting and Related Services, B
American/United States Studies/Civilization, B
Anthropology, B
Archeology, B
Area, Ethnic, Cultural, and Gender Studies, B
Art History, Criticism and Conservation, B
Art/Art Studies, General, B
Biochemistry, B
Biological and Biomedical Sciences, B
Biology/Biological Sciences, B
Business Administration and Management, B
Business Administration, Management and Operations, M
Business/Commerce, B
Chemistry, B
Communication Studies/Speech Communication and Rhetoric, B
Communication, Journalism and Related Programs, B
Comparative Literature, B
Counselor Education/School Counseling and Guidance Services, M
Dance, B
Drama and Dramatics/Theatre Arts, B
Early Childhood Education and Teaching, M
Economics, B
Education, MD
Educational Administration and Supervision, MD
Engineering, B
English Language and Literature, B
European Studies/Civilization, B
Finance and Financial Management Services, B
Foreign Languages, Literatures, and Linguistics, B
French Language and Literature, B
German Language and Literature, B
Health and Physical Education, B
Health and Physical Education/Fitness, B
Health Professions and Related Clinical Sciences, B
Historic Preservation and Conservation, B
History, B
Industrial and Organizational Psychology, B
Interdisciplinary Studies, B
International Business/Trade/Commerce, B
International Relations and Affairs, B
Italian Language and Literature, B
Kinesiology and Exercise Science, B
Kinesiology and Movement Studies, M
Latin American Studies, B
Latin Language and Literature, B
Liberal Arts and Sciences Studies and Humanities, B
Liberal Studies, M
Management, M
Marriage and Family Therapy/Counseling, M
Mathematics, B
Mathematics and Computer Science, B
Mathematics and Statistics, B
Modern Greek Language and Literature, B
Modern Languages, B
Multi-/Interdisciplinary Studies, B
Music, B
Nursing - Registered Nurse Training, B
Philosophy, B
Physics, B
Physiological Psychology/Psychobiology, B
Political Science and Government, B
Psychology, B
Reading Teacher Education, M
Religion/Religious Studies, B
Social Sciences, B
Sociology, B
Spanish Language and Literature, B
Special Education and Teaching, M
Sport and Fitness Administration/Management, B
Theatre Literature, History and Criticism, B
Theology/Theological Studies, B
Visual and Performing Arts, B
Women's Studies, B

Writing, M

THE SALVATION ARMY COLLEGE FOR OFFICER TRAINING AT CRESTMONT

Divinity/Ministry (BD, MDiv.), A

SAMUEL MERRITT COLLEGE

Nurse Anesthetist, MO
Nursing, MO
Nursing - Advanced Practice, MO
Nursing - Registered Nurse Training, B
Nursing Administration, M
Occupational Therapy/Therapist, M
Physical Therapy/Therapist, M
Physician Assistant, M

SAN BERNARDINO VALLEY COLLEGE

Accounting, A
Administrative Assistant and Secretarial Science, A
Aeronautics/Aviation/Aerospace Science and Technology, A
Anthropology, A
Architectural Engineering Technology/Technician, A
Art/Art Studies, General, A
Astronomy, A
Automobile/Automotive Mechanics Technology/Technician, A
Biology/Biological Sciences, A
Botany/Plant Biology, A
Business Administration and Management, A
Chemical Engineering, A
Chemistry, A
Civil Engineering Technology/Technician, A
Clinical/Medical Laboratory Technician, A
Commercial and Advertising Art, A
Computer Engineering Technology/Technician, A
Computer Science, A
Corrections, A
Criminal Justice/Police Science, A
Data Processing and Data Processing Technology/Technician, A
Dental Hygiene/Hygienist, A
Developmental and Child Psychology, A
Drafting and Design Technology/Technician, A
Economics, A
Electrical, Electronic and Communications Engineering Technology/Technician, A
English Language and Literature, A
Environmental Studies, A
Family and Consumer Economics and Related Services, A
Finance, A
French Language and Literature, A
Geography, A
Geology/Earth Science, A
German Language and Literature, A
Heating, Air Conditioning, Ventilation and Refrigeration Maintenance Technology/Technician, A
History, A
Hotel/Motel Administration/Management, A
Human Services, A
Interior Design, A
Journalism, A
Liberal Arts and Sciences Studies and Humanities, A
Machine Tool Technology/Machinist, A
Marketing/Marketing Management, A
Mathematics, A
Mental Health/Rehabilitation, A
Music, A
Nursing - Registered Nurse Training, A
Parks, Recreation, Leisure and Fitness Studies, A
Philosophy, A
Photography, A
Physical Education Teaching and Coaching, A
Physical Sciences, A
Physics, A
Political Science and Government, A
Pre-Engineering, A
Psychology, A
Radio and Television, A
Real Estate, A
Religion/Religious Studies, A
Sociology, A
Spanish Language and Literature, A

Telecommunications Technology/Technician, A
Welding Technology/Welder, A
Zoology/Animal Biology, A

SAN DIEGO CHRISTIAN COLLEGE

Adult and Continuing Education and Teaching, B
Athletic Training and Sports Medicine, B
Bible/Biblical Studies, B
Biology/Biological Sciences, B
Business Administration and Management, B
Communication Studies/Speech Communication
   and Rhetoric, B
Counseling Psychology, B
Divinity/Ministry (BD, MDiv.), B
Education, B
Elementary Education and Teaching, B
English Language and Literature, B
History, B
Human Development and Family Studies, B
Interdisciplinary Studies, B
Kinesiology and Exercise Science, B
Liberal Arts and Sciences Studies and
   Humanities, B
Mathematics, B
Multi-/Interdisciplinary Studies, B
Music, B
Music Teacher Education, B
Pastoral Studies/Counseling, B
Physical Education Teaching and Coaching, B
Psychology, B
Religious/Sacred Music, B
Secondary Education and Teaching, B
Social Sciences, B
Teacher Education, Multiple Levels, B
Theology/Theological Studies, B
Voice and Opera, B

SAN DIEGO CITY COLLEGE

Accounting, A
Administrative Assistant and Secretarial Science, A
African-American/Black Studies, A
Anthropology, A
Art/Art Studies, General, A
Artificial Intelligence and Robotics, A
Automobile/Automotive Mechanics
   Technology/Technician, A
Behavioral Sciences, A
Biology/Biological Sciences, A
Business Administration and Management, A
Carpentry/Carpenter, A
Commercial and Advertising Art, A
Computer Engineering Technology/Technician, A
Consumer Services and Advocacy, A
Cosmetology/Cosmetologist, A
Court Reporting/Court Reporter, A
Data Processing and Data Processing
   Technology/Technician, A
Developmental and Child Psychology, A
Drafting and Design Technology/Technician, A
Drama and Dramatics/Theatre Arts, A
Electrical, Electronic and Communications
   Engineering Technology/Technician, A
Emergency Medical Technology/Technician (EMT
   Paramedic), A
Engineering Technology, A
English Language and Literature, A
Environmental Engineering
   Technology/Environmental Technology, A
Fashion Merchandising, A
Finance, A
Graphic and Printing Equipment Operator
   Production, A
Hispanic-American, Puerto Rican, and Mexican-
   American/Chicano Studies, A
Hospitality Administration/Management, A
Industrial Technology/Technician, A
Insurance, A
Interior Design, A
Journalism, A
Labor and Industrial Relations, A
Latin American Studies, A
Legal Administrative Assistant/Secretary, A
Legal Assistant/Paralegal, A
Liberal Arts and Sciences Studies and
   Humanities, A
Licensed Practical/Vocational Nurse Training, A

Machine Tool Technology/Machinist, A
Marketing/Marketing Management, A
Mathematics, A
Modern Languages, A
Music, A
Nursing - Registered Nurse Training, A
Occupational Safety and Health
   Technology/Technician, A
Parks, Recreation, Leisure and Fitness Studies, A
Photography, A
Physical Education Teaching and Coaching, A
Physical Sciences, A
Political Science and Government, A
Pre-Engineering, A
Psychology, A
Radio and Television, A
Real Estate, A
Social Sciences, A
Social Work, A
Sociology, A
Special Products Marketing Operations, A
Speech and Rhetorical Studies, A
Teacher Assistant/Aide, A
Technology Education/Industrial Arts, A
Telecommunications Technology/Technician, A
Tourism and Travel Services Management, A
Transportation and Materials Moving, A
Welding Technology/Welder, A

SAN DIEGO GOLF ACADEMY

Physical Education Teaching and Coaching, A
Sport and Fitness Administration/Management, A

SAN DIEGO MESA COLLEGE

Accounting, A
Administrative Assistant and Secretarial Science, A
African-American/Black Studies, A
Architectural Engineering Technology/Technician, A
Architecture, A
Art/Art Studies, General, A
Biology/Biological Sciences, A
Business Administration and Management, A
Chemistry, A
Child Care Provider/Assistant, A
Clinical/Medical Laboratory Technician, A
Computer and Information Sciences, A
Computer Programming, A
Computer Programming, Specific Applications, A
Computer Science, A
Computer Software and Media Applications, A
Construction Engineering Technology/Technician, A
Data Entry/Microcomputer Applications, A
Dental Assisting/Assistant, A
Engineering, A
English Language and Literature, A
Fashion Merchandising, A
Fashion/Apparel Design, A
Foods, Nutrition, and Related Services, A
Foods, Nutrition, and Wellness Studies, A
French Language and Literature, A
Geography, A
Health Information/Medical Records
   Administration/Administrator, A
Hispanic-American, Puerto Rican, and Mexican-
   American/Chicano Studies, A
Hospitality and Recreation Marketing Operations, A
Hotel/Motel Administration/Management, A
Industrial Radiologic Technology/Technician, A
Interior Design, A
Intermedia/Multimedia, A
Landscape Architecture, A
Legal Administrative Assistant/Secretary, A
Liberal Arts and Sciences Studies and
   Humanities, A
Marketing Research, A
Marketing/Marketing Management, A
Mathematics, A
Medical/Clinical Assistant, A
Music, A
Physical Education Teaching and Coaching, A
Physical Sciences, A
Physical Therapist Assistant, A
Physics, A
Psychology, A
Real Estate, A
Social Sciences, A

Sociology, A
Spanish Language and Literature, A
Speech and Rhetorical Studies, A
Tourism and Travel Services Management, A
Tourism and Travel Services Marketing
   Operations, A
Veterinary/Animal Health Technology/Technician and
   Veterinary Assistant, A

SAN DIEGO MIRAMAR COLLEGE

Accounting, A
Administrative Assistant and Secretarial Science, A
Airframe Mechanics and Aircraft Maintenance
   Technology/Technician, A
Anthropology, A
Applied Mathematics, A
Art/Art Studies, General, A
Automobile/Automotive Mechanics
   Technology/Technician, A
Avionics Maintenance Technology/Technician, A
Biology/Biological Sciences, A
Business Administration and Management, A
Chemistry, A
Corrections, A
Criminal Justice/Law Enforcement Administration, A
Criminal Justice/Police Science, A
Developmental and Child Psychology, A
Emergency Medical Technology/Technician (EMT
   Paramedic), A
English Language and Literature, A
Fine/Studio Arts, A
Fire Science/Firefighting, A
Geography, A
Humanities/Humanistic Studies, A
Information Science/Studies, A
Legal Assistant/Paralegal, A
Liberal Arts and Sciences Studies and
   Humanities, A
Mathematics, A
Occupational Safety and Health
   Technology/Technician, A
Philosophy, A
Physical Education Teaching and Coaching, A
Physical Sciences, A
Physics, A
Psychology, A
Social Sciences, A
Sociology, A
Spanish Language and Literature, A
Transportation and Materials Moving, A

SAN DIEGO STATE UNIVERSITY

Accounting, BM
Advertising, B
Advertising and Public Relations, M
Aerospace, Aeronautical and Astronautical
   Engineering, BMD
African-American/Black Studies, B
Agricultural Business and Management, B
American/United States Studies/Civilization, B
Anthropology, BM
Applied Arts and Design, M
Applied Mathematics, BM
Art History, Criticism and Conservation, BM
Asian Studies/Civilization, BM
Astronomy, BM
Atomic/Molecular Physics, B
Biological and Biomedical Sciences, MD
Biology/Biological Sciences, B
Biometry/Biometrics, D
Biostatistics, D
Business Administration and Management, B
Business Administration, Management and
   Operations, M
Business/Commerce, B
Cell Biology and Anatomy, D
Central/Middle and Eastern European Studies, B
Chemistry, BMD
Child and Family Studies, M
Child Development, B
Civil Engineering, BM
Classics and Classical
   Languages, Literatures, and Linguistics, B
Clinical Psychology, MD
Communication and Media Studies, M
Communication Disorders, BMD

Communication, Journalism and Related
  Programs, B
Comparative Literature, B
Composition, M
Computational Sciences, MD
Computer Engineering, B
Computer Science, BM
Counselor Education/School Counseling and
  Guidance Services, M
Creative Writing, B
Criminal Justice/Law Enforcement Administration, B
Criminology, M
Curriculum and Instruction, M
Dance, B
Design and Visual Communications, B
Drama and Dramatics/Theatre Arts, B
Early Childhood Education and Teaching, B
Ecology, MD
Economics, BM
Education, MD
Educational Leadership and Administration, M
Educational Media/Instructional Technology, MD
Electrical Engineering, M
Electrical, Electronics and Communications
  Engineering, B
Elementary Education and Teaching, M
Emergency Medical Services, M
Engineering, B
Engineering and Applied Sciences, MD
Engineering Design, M
English, M
English as a Second Language, MO
English Language and Literature, B
Entrepreneurship/Entrepreneurial Studies, M
Environmental and Occupational Health, M
Environmental Studies, B
Epidemiology, MD
Ethnomusicology, M
European Studies/Civilization, B
Exercise and Sports Science, M
Film, Television, and Video Production, M
Finance, B
Finance and Banking, M
Finance and Financial Management Services, B
Fine Arts and Art Studies, M
Fine/Studio Arts, B
French Language and Literature, B
Geography, BMD
Geology/Earth Science, BM
German Language and Literature, B
Gerontology, BM
Graphic Design, B
Health and Physical Education, B
Health Physics/Radiological Health, M
Health Professions and Related Clinical Sciences, B
Health Promotion, M
Health Psychology, D
Health Services Administration, M
Health Services/Allied Health/Health Sciences, B
Higher Education/Higher Education
  Administration, M
Hispanic-American, Puerto Rican, and Mexican-
  American/Chicano Studies, B
History, BM
Hospitality Administration/Management, B
Hotel/Motel Administration/Management, B
Human Resources Management and Services, M
Humanities/Humanistic Studies, B
Industrial and Manufacturing Management, M
Industrial and Organizational Psychology, M
Industrial Hygiene, M
Information Science/Studies, B
Information Technology, B
Interdisciplinary Studies, M
Interior Design, B
International Business/Trade/Commerce, BM
International Relations and Affairs, B
Internet and Interactive Multimedia, M
Japanese Language and Literature, B
Jewish/Judaic Studies, B
Journalism, B
Kindergarten/PreSchool Education and Teaching, B
Latin American Studies, BMO
Liberal Arts and Sciences Studies and
  Humanities, B
Liberal Studies, M

Linguistics, BMO
Management, M
Management Information Systems and Services, M
Marketing, M
Marketing/Marketing Management, B
Mass Communication/Media Studies, B
Mathematics, BM
Mathematics Teacher Education, BD
Mechanical Engineering, BMD
Mechanics, MD
Media Studies, M
Microbiology, BM
Molecular Biology, D
Multi-/Interdisciplinary Studies, B
Multilingual and Multicultural Education, MD
Music, BM
Music Teacher Education, BM
Music Theory and Composition, M
Musicology and Ethnomusicology, M
Nursing, BM
Nursing - Registered Nurse Training, B
Nutritional Sciences, MO
Operations Management and Supervision, B
Parks, Recreation, Leisure and Fitness Studies, B
Performance, M
Pharmaceutical Administration, M
Philosophy, BM
Physical Education Teaching and Coaching, M
Physical Sciences, B
Physics, BM
Political Science and Government, BM
Psychology, BMD
Public Administration, BM
Public Health, MDO
Public Relations/Image Management, B
Radio and Television, B
Reading Teacher Education, M
Real Estate, B
Rehabilitation Counseling, M
Religion/Religious Studies, B
Rhetoric, M
Romance
  Languages, Literatures, and Linguistics, M
Russian Language and Literature, B
Russian Studies, B
School Psychology, M
Science Teacher Education/General Science
  Teacher Education, D
Secondary Education and Teaching, M
Social Sciences, B
Social Work, BMDO
Sociology, BM
Spanish Language and Literature, BM
Special Education and Teaching, M
Speech and Rhetorical Studies, B
Statistics, BM
Telecommunications Management, M
Theater, M
Theoretical and Mathematical Physics, B
Tourism and Travel Services Management, B
Toxicology, M
Trade and Industrial Teacher Education, B
Urban and Regional Planning, M
Urban Studies/Affairs, B
Western European Studies, M
Women's Studies, BM
Writing, M

SAN FRANCISCO ART INSTITUTE

Ceramic Arts and Ceramics, MO
Cinematography and Film/Video Production, B
Design and Visual Communications, B
Film, Television, and Video Production, MO
Multi-/Interdisciplinary Studies, B
Painting, BMO
Photography, BMO
Printmaking, BMO
Sculpture, BMO
Visual and Performing Arts, B

SAN FRANCISCO CONSERVATORY OF MUSIC

Composition, M
Music, BM
Music Performance, B
Music Theory and Composition, B

Performance, M
Piano and Organ, B
Violin, Viola, Guitar and Other Stringed
  Instruments, B
Voice and Opera, B
Wind and Percussion Instruments, B

SAN FRANCISCO STATE UNIVERSITY

Accounting, B
Adult and Continuing Education and Teaching, MO
African-American/Black Studies, B
American/United States Studies/Civilization, B
Animal Physiology, B
Anthropology, BM
Apparel and Textiles, B
Applied Mathematics, B
Art History, Criticism and Conservation, M
Art/Art Studies, General, B
Astronomy, B
Astrophysics, BM
Atmospheric Sciences and Meteorology, B
Audiology/Audiologist and Speech-Language
  Pathology/Pathologist, B
Biochemistry, BM
Biological and Biomedical Sciences, M
Biological and Physical Sciences, B
Biology/Biological Sciences, B
Botany/Plant Biology, B
Business Administration and Management, B
Business Administration, Management and
  Operations, M
Cell Biology and Anatomy, M
Cell/Cellular Biology and Histology, B
Chemistry, BM
Chinese Language and Literature, B
Chinese Studies, M
Civil Engineering, B
Classics and Classical
  Languages, Literatures, and Linguistics, BM
Clinical Laboratory Sciences, M
Communication Disorders, M
Comparative Literature, BM
Composition, M
Computer Science, BM
Conservation Biology, M
Consumer Merchandising/Retailing Management, B
Counseling Psychology, M
Creative Writing, B
Criminal Justice/Law Enforcement Administration, B
Dance, B
Dietetics/Dieticians, B
Drama and Dramatics/Theatre Arts, B
Early Childhood Education and Teaching, M
Ecology, BM
Economics, BM
Education, MDO
Educational Administration and Supervision, MO
Educational Media/Instructional Technology, MO
Electrical, Electronics and Communications
  Engineering, B
Elementary Education and Teaching, M
Engineering and Applied Sciences, M
English, MO
English as a Second Language, M
English Education, MO
English Language and Literature, B
Ethnic and Cultural Studies, M
Family and Consumer Sciences/Human Sciences, B
Film, Television, and Video Production, M
Film, Television, and Video Theory and Criticism, M
Film/Cinema Studies, B
Finance, B
Fine Arts and Art Studies, M
French Language and Literature, BM
Geography, BM
Geology/Earth Science, B
Geosciences, M
German Language and Literature, BM
Gerontology, M
Health Teacher Education, B
Hispanic-American, Puerto Rican, and Mexican-
  American/Chicano Studies, B
History, BM
Home Economics, M
Hospitality Administration/Management, B
Humanities/Humanistic Studies, BM

Industrial Design, BM
Information Science/Studies, B
Interior Design, B
International Affairs, M
International Business/Trade/Commerce, B
International Relations and Affairs, B
Italian Language and Literature, BM
Japanese Language and Literature, B
Japanese Studies, M
Journalism, B
Labor and Industrial Relations, B
Legal and Justice Studies, O
Leisure Studies, M
Liberal Arts and Sciences Studies and
    Humanities, B
Linguistics, M
Marine Biology and Biological Oceanography, BM
Marketing/Marketing Management, B
Marriage and Family Therapy/Counseling, M
Mathematics, BM
Mathematics Teacher Education, M
Mechanical Engineering, B
Media Studies, M
Medical Microbiology and Bacteriology, B
Microbiology, M
Molecular Biology, BM
Museology/Museum Studies, M
Music, BM
Music History, Literature, and Theory, M
Music Teacher Education, M
Non-Profit/Public/Organizational Management, M
Nursing, M
Nursing - Advanced Practice, M
Nursing - Registered Nurse Training, B
Nursing Administration, M
Nursing Education, M
Parks, Recreation, Leisure and Fitness Studies, B
Performance, M
Philosophy, BMO
Physical Education Teaching and Coaching, BM
Physical Sciences, B
Physical Therapy/Therapist, MD
Physics, BM
Physiology, M
Political Science and Government, BM
Psychology, BM
Public Administration, M
Public Health, M
Public Health (MPH, DPH), B
Public Policy Analysis, M
Radio and Television, B
Reading Teacher Education, MO
Real Estate, B
Recreation and Park Management, M
Rehabilitation Counseling, M
Religion/Religious Studies, B
Russian Language and Literature, BM
Secondary Education and Teaching, MO
Social Sciences, BM
Social Work, BM
Sociology, B
Spanish Language and Literature, BM
Special Education and Teaching, MDO
Special Products Marketing Operations, B
Speech and Rhetorical Studies, BM
Statistics, B
Technical and Business Writing, B
Technology Education/Industrial Arts, B
Theater, M
Trade and Industrial Teacher Education, B
Transportation and Materials Moving, B
Urban Studies/Affairs, B
Women's Studies, BM
Writing, M
Zoology/Animal Biology, B

SAN JOAQUIN DELTA COLLEGE

Accounting, A
Agricultural Business and Management, A
Agricultural Mechanization, A
Agriculture, A
Animal Sciences, A
Anthropology, A
Art/Art Studies, General, A
Automobile/Automotive Mechanics
    Technology/Technician, A

Behavioral Sciences, A
Biology/Biological Sciences, A
Botany/Plant Biology, A
Broadcast Journalism, A
Business Administration and Management, A
Business/Managerial Economics, A
Carpentry/Carpenter, A
Chemistry, A
Child Development, A
Civil Engineering Technology/Technician, A
Commercial and Advertising Art, A
Comparative Literature, A
Computer Engineering Technology/Technician, A
Computer Programming/Programmer, A
Computer Science, A
Construction Engineering Technology/Technician, A
Corrections, A
Criminal Justice/Police Science, A
Culinary Arts/Chef Training, A
Dance, A
Developmental and Child Psychology, A
Drafting and Design Technology/Technician, A
Drama and Dramatics/Theatre Arts, A
Drawing, A
Economics, A
Electrical, Electronic and Communications
    Engineering Technology/Technician, A
Emergency Medical Technology/Technician (EMT
    Paramedic), A
Engineering, A
Engineering Technology, A
English Language and Literature, A
Family and Consumer Sciences/Human Sciences, A
Fashion Merchandising, A
Fire Science/Firefighting, A
Food Technology and Processing, A
French Language and Literature, A
Geology/Earth Science, A
German Language and Literature, A
Graphic and Printing Equipment Operator
    Production, A
Heating, Air Conditioning, Ventilation and
    Refrigeration Maintenance
    Technology/Technician, A
History, A
Humanities/Humanistic Studies, A
Industrial Radiologic Technology/Technician, A
Interior Design, A
Italian Language and Literature, A
Japanese Language and Literature, A
Journalism, A
Kindergarten/PreSchool Education and Teaching, A
Liberal Arts and Sciences Studies and
    Humanities, A
Licensed Practical/Vocational Nurse Training, A
Machine Tool Technology/Machinist, A
Marketing/Marketing Management, A
Mathematics, A
Mechanical Engineering/Mechanical
    Technology/Technician, A
Music, A
Natural Resources Management/Development and
    Policy, A
Natural Sciences, A
Nursing - Registered Nurse Training, A
Ornamental Horticulture, A
Philosophy, A
Photography, A
Physical Education Teaching and Coaching, A
Physical Sciences, A
Political Science and Government, A
Psychiatric/Mental Health Services Technician, A
Psychology, A
Public Administration, A
Public Health (MPH, DPH), A
Religion/Religious Studies, A
Social Sciences, A
Sociology, A
Spanish Language and Literature, A
Special Products Marketing Operations, A
Speech and Rhetorical Studies, A

SAN JOAQUIN VALLEY COLLEGE

Aircraft Powerplant Technology/Technician, A
Airframe Mechanics and Aircraft Maintenance
    Technology/Technician, A

Building/Construction
    Finishing, Management, and Inspection, A
Business/Commerce, A
Computer Systems Networking and
    Telecommunications, A
Corrections, A
Dental Assisting/Assistant, A
Dental Hygiene/Hygienist, A
Heating, Air Conditioning, Ventilation and
    Refrigeration Maintenance
    Technology/Technician, A
Industrial Mechanics and Maintenance
    Technology, A
Licensed Practical/Vocational Nurse Training, A
Management Information Systems and Services, A
Medical Administrative Assistant/Secretary, A
Medical Insurance Specialist/Medical Biller, A
Medical Office Management/Administration, A
Medical/Clinical Assistant, A
Nursing - Registered Nurse Training, A
Pharmacy Technician/Assistant, A
Respiratory Care Therapy/Therapist, A
Security and Loss Prevention Services, A
Surgical Technology/Technologist, A
Veterinary/Animal Health Technology/Technician and
    Veterinary Assistant, A

SAN JOSE CITY COLLEGE

Accounting, A
Administrative Assistant and Secretarial Science, A
Business Administration and Management, A
Child Development, A
Computer Engineering Technology/Technician, A
Computer Science, A
Construction Engineering Technology/Technician, A
Cosmetology/Cosmetologist, A
Criminal Justice/Law Enforcement Administration, A
Data Processing and Data Processing
    Technology/Technician, A
Dental Hygiene/Hygienist, A
Drafting and Design Technology/Technician, A
Electrical, Electronic and Communications
    Engineering Technology/Technician, A
Engineering, A
Family and Community Services, A
Heating, Air Conditioning, Ventilation and
    Refrigeration Maintenance
    Technology/Technician, A
History, A
Human Services, A
Kindergarten/PreSchool Education and Teaching, A
Labor and Industrial Relations, A
Liberal Arts and Sciences Studies and
    Humanities, A
Machine Tool Technology/Machinist, A
Marketing/Marketing Management, A
Public Administration, A
Real Estate, A
Solar Energy Technology/Technician, A
Teacher Assistant/Aide, A

SAN JOSE STATE UNIVERSITY

Accounting, BM
Accounting and Computer Science, B
Advertising, B
Aeronautics/Aviation/Aerospace Science and
    Technology, B
Aerospace, Aeronautical and Astronautical
    Engineering, BM
African-American/Black Studies, B
American/United States Studies/Civilization, B
Anthropology, B
Applied Arts and Design, M
Applied Economics, M
Applied Mathematics, B
Art History, Criticism and Conservation, BM
Art/Art Studies, General, B
Atmospheric Sciences and Meteorology, B
Behavioral Sciences, B
Biochemistry, B
Biological and Biomedical Sciences, M
Biology/Biological Sciences, B
Business Administration and Management, B
Business Administration, Management and
    Operations, BM
Chemical Engineering, BM

Chemistry, BM
Child and Family Studies, M
Chinese Language and Literature, B
Civil Engineering, BM
Clinical Psychology, M
Communication and Media Studies, M
Communication Disorders, BM
Comparative Literature, MO
Computer Engineering, BM
Computer Science, BMO
Counseling Psychology, M
Counselor Education/School Counseling and
    Guidance Services, M
Criminal Justice/Safety Studies, B
Criminology, M
Dance, B
Dietetics/Dieticians, B
Drama and Dramatics/Theatre Arts, B
Early Childhood Education and Teaching, B
Economics, BM
Education, MO
Educational Administration and Supervision, MO
Educational Media/Instructional Technology, MO
Electrical Engineering, M
Electrical, Electronics and Communications
    Engineering, B
Elementary Education and Teaching, MO
Engineering, B
Engineering and Applied Sciences, M
English, MO
English as a Second Language, M
English Language and Literature, B
Environmental Engineering
    Technology/Environmental Technology, M
Environmental Studies, BM
Ergonomics and Human Factors, M
Film, Television, and Video Production, M
Finance, B
Finance and Financial Management Services, B
Fine Arts and Art Studies, M
Fine/Studio Arts, B
Food Science, B
French Language and Literature, BM
Geography, BMO
Geological and Earth Sciences/Geosciences, B
Geology/Earth Science, BM
German Language and Literature, B
Gerontological Nursing, M
Gerontology, O
Graphic Design, B
Health and Physical Education, B
Health Services/Allied Health/Health Sciences, B
Health/Health Care Administration/Management, B
Higher Education/Higher Education
    Administration, MO
Hispanic Studies, M
History, BM
Hospitality Administration/Management, B
Human Resources Management/Personnel
    Administration, B
Humanities/Humanistic Studies, B
Industrial and Manufacturing Management, M
Industrial and Organizational Psychology, M
Industrial Design, B
Industrial Engineering, B
Industrial/Management Engineering, M
Information Science/Studies, M
Information Technology, B
Interdisciplinary Studies, M
Interior Design, B
International Business/Trade/Commerce, B
Japanese Language and Literature, B
Journalism, B
Kinesiology and Movement Studies, M
Liberal Arts and Sciences Studies and
    Humanities, B
Library Science, M
Linguistics, BMO
Management Information Systems and Services, M
Marine Biology and Biological Oceanography, B
Marine Sciences, M
Marketing/Marketing Management, B
Mass Communication/Media Studies, M
Materials Engineering, BM
Mathematics, BM
Mathematics Teacher Education, M

Mechanical Engineering, BM
Meteorology, M
Microbiology, M
Molecular Biology, BM
Multi-/Interdisciplinary Studies, B
Music, BM
Music Performance, B
Natural Sciences, B
Nursing, MO
Nursing - Advanced Practice, M
Nursing - Registered Nurse Training, B
Nursing Administration, M
Nursing Education, M
Nutritional Sciences, M
Occupational Therapy/Therapist, BM
Parks, Recreation, Leisure and Fitness Studies, B
Performance, M
Philosophy, BMO
Photography, M
Physics, BM
Physiology, BM
Political Science and Government, B
Psychology, BM
Public Administration, M
Public Health, MO
Public Relations/Image Management, B
Quality Control Technology/Technician, B
Quality Management, M
Radio and Television, B
Recreation and Park Management, M
Religion/Religious Studies, B
Secondary Education and Teaching, M
Social Sciences, BM
Social Work, BMO
Sociology, BM
Spanish Language and Literature, BM
Special Education and Teaching, MO
Speech and Interpersonal Communication, M
Speech and Rhetorical Studies, BM
Student Personnel Services, M
Systems Engineering, M
Taxation, M
Theater, M
Transportation/Transportation Management, M
Urban and Regional Planning, MO
Visual and Performing Arts, B
Writing, M

SANTA ANA COLLEGE

Accounting, A
Administrative Assistant and Secretarial Science, A
African-American/Black Studies, A
Anthropology, A
Art/Art Studies, General, A
Automobile/Automotive Mechanics
    Technology/Technician, A
Biological and Physical Sciences, A
Biology/Biological Sciences, A
Business Administration and Management, A
Chemistry, A
Commercial and Advertising Art, A
Communication Studies/Speech Communication
    and Rhetoric, A
Computer and Information Sciences, A
Computer Programming, A
Computer Science, A
Cosmetology/Cosmetologist, A
Criminal Justice/Law Enforcement Administration, A
Criminal Justice/Police Science, A
Dance, A
Data Entry/Microcomputer Applications, A
Diesel Mechanics Technology/Technician, A
Drafting and Design Technology/Technician, A
Drama and Dramatics/Theatre Arts, A
Economics, A
Electrical, Electronic and Communications
    Engineering Technology/Technician, A
Engineering, A
Engineering Technology, A
English Language and Literature, A
Environmental Studies, A
Ethnic and Cultural Studies, A
Family and Consumer Economics and Related
    Services, A
Fashion Merchandising, A
Fashion/Apparel Design, A

Fire Science/Firefighting, A
Foods, Nutrition, and Wellness Studies, A
Geography, A
Geology/Earth Science, A
Hispanic-American, Puerto Rican, and Mexican-
    American/Chicano Studies, A
History, A
Industrial Technology/Technician, A
Information Science/Studies, A
Information Technology, A
Journalism, A
Kindergarten/PreSchool Education and Teaching, A
Kinesiology and Exercise Science, A
Law and Legal Studies, A
Liberal Arts and Sciences Studies and
    Humanities, A
Library Science, A
Management Science, A
Marketing/Marketing Management, A
Mathematics, A
Medical/Clinical Assistant, A
Modern Languages, A
Music, A
Nursing - Registered Nurse Training, A
Occupational Therapy/Therapist, A
Pharmacy Technician/Assistant, A
Philosophy, A
Photography, A
Physics, A
Political Science and Government, A
Psychology, A
Quality Control Technology/Technician, A
Real Estate, A
Sales, Distribution and Marketing Operations, A
Social Sciences, A
Sociology, A
Telecommunications Technology/Technician, A
Tourism and Travel Services Management, A
Water Resources Engineering, A
Welding Technology/Welder, A
Women's Studies, A
Word Processing, A

SANTA BARBARA CITY COLLEGE

Accounting, A
Acting, A
Administrative Assistant and Secretarial Science, A
African-American/Black Studies, A
American Indian/Native American Studies, A
Anthropology, A
Applied Horticulture/Horticultural Operations, A
Art History, Criticism and Conservation, A
Athletic Training and Sports Medicine, A
Automobile/Automotive Mechanics
    Technology/Technician, A
Biology/Biological Sciences, A
Biomedical Technology/Technician, A
BioTechnology, A
Business Administration and Management, A
Chemistry, A
Child Care and Support Services Management, A
Commercial and Advertising Art, A
Communication Studies/Speech Communication
    and Rhetoric, A
Computer Engineering, A
Computer Science, A
Cosmetology/Cosmetologist, A
Criminal Justice/Law Enforcement Administration, A
Culinary Arts and Related Services, A
Drafting and Design Technology/Technician, A
Drama and Dramatics/Theatre Arts, A
Economics, A
Electrical, Electronic and Communications
    Engineering Technology/Technician, A
Electrical/Electronics Equipment Installation and
    Repair, A
Engineering, A
Engineering Technology, A
English Language and Literature, A
Environmental Studies, A
Environmental/Environmental Health Engineering, A
Ethnic and Cultural Studies, A
Film/Cinema Studies, A
Finance, A
Fine/Studio Arts, A

Foodservice Systems
Administration/Management, A
French Language and Literature, A
Geography, A
Geology/Earth Science, A
Health Information/Medical Records
Technology/Technician, A
Hispanic-American, Puerto Rican, and Mexican-
American/Chicano Studies, A
History, A
Hotel/Motel Administration/Management, A
Industrial Engineering, A
Industrial Technology/Technician, A
Information Science/Studies, A
Information Technology, A
Institutional Food Workers, A
Interior Design, A
International Relations and Affairs, A
Kindergarten/PreSchool Education and Teaching, A
Kinesiology and Exercise Science, A
Landscaping and Groundskeeping, A
Law and Legal Studies, A
Liberal Arts and Sciences Studies and
Humanities, A
Licensed Practical/Vocational Nurse Training, A
Marine Technology, A
Marketing/Marketing Management, A
Mathematics, A
Medical Radiologic Technology/Science - Radiation
Therapist, A
Music, A
Nursing - Registered Nurse Training, A
Ornamental Horticulture, A
Parks, Recreation, Leisure and Fitness Studies, A
Philosophy, A
Physical Education Teaching and Coaching, A
Physics, A
Political Science and Government, A
Psychology, A
Real Estate, A
Sales, Distribution and Marketing Operations, A
Selling Skills and Sales Operations, A
Sociology, A
Spanish Language and Literature, A
System Administration/Administrator, A
Technical Theatre/Theatre Design and
Technology, A
Therapeutic Recreation/Recreational Therapy, A

SANTA CLARA UNIVERSITY

Accounting, B
Ancient Studies/Civilization, B
Ancient/Classical Greek Language and Literature, B
Anthropology, B
Applied Mathematics, M
Art History, Criticism and Conservation, B
Biological and Physical Sciences, B
Biology/Biological Sciences, B
Business Administration, Management and
Operations, MO
Chemistry, B
Civil Engineering, BM
Classics and Classical
Languages, Literatures, and Linguistics, B
Communication Studies/Speech Communication
and Rhetoric, B
Computer Engineering, BMDO
Computer Science, BMDO
Counseling Psychology, MO
Counselor Education/School Counseling and
Guidance Services, M
Drama and Dramatics/Theatre Arts, B
Economics, B
Education, MO
Educational Administration and Supervision, M
Electrical Engineering, MDO
Electrical, Electronics and Communications
Engineering, B
Engineering, B
Engineering and Applied Sciences, MDO
Engineering Design, O
Engineering Management, M
Engineering Physics, B
English Language and Literature, B
Environmental Sciences, B
Finance, B

French Language and Literature, B
French Studies, B
German Studies, B
History, B
Interdisciplinary Studies, B
Italian Language and Literature, B
Italian Studies, B
Latin Language and Literature, B
Law and Legal Studies, MPO
Liberal Arts and Sciences Studies and
Humanities, B
Management Information Systems and
Services, BM
Marketing/Marketing Management, B
Materials Engineering, O
Mathematics, B
Mechanical Engineering, BMDO
Music, B
Pastoral Studies/Counseling, M
Philosophy, B
Physics, B
Political Science and Government, B
Psychology, B
Religion/Religious Studies, BM
Sacred Music, M
Sociology, B
Software Engineering, MO
Spanish and Iberian Studies, B
Spanish Language and Literature, B
Special Education and Teaching, MO
Telecommunications Management, O

SANTA MONICA COLLEGE

Accounting, A
Administrative Assistant and Secretarial Science, A
Anthropology, A
Architectural Engineering Technology/Technician, A
Art/Art Studies, General, A
Astronomy, A
Athletic Training and Sports Medicine, A
Automobile/Automotive Mechanics
Technology/Technician, A
Biology/Biological Sciences, A
Broadcast Journalism, A
Business Administration and Management, A
Chemistry, A
Commercial and Advertising Art, A
Computer and Information Sciences, A
Computer Programming, Specific Applications, A
Computer Programming/Programmer, A
Construction Engineering Technology/Technician, A
Cosmetology/Cosmetologist, A
Criminal Justice/Law Enforcement Administration, A
Criminal Justice/Police Science, A
Dance, A
Data Processing and Data Processing
Technology/Technician, A
Dental Hygiene/Hygienist, A
Developmental and Child Psychology, A
Drafting and Design Technology/Technician, A
Drama and Dramatics/Theatre Arts, A
Economics, A
Electrical, Electronic and Communications
Engineering Technology/Technician, A
English Language and Literature, A
Environmental Studies, A
Ethnic and Cultural Studies, A
Family and Consumer Sciences/Human Sciences, A
Fashion Merchandising, A
Fire Science/Firefighting, A
French Language and Literature, A
Geography, A
Geology/Earth Science, A
German Language and Literature, A
Graphic and Printing Equipment Operator
Production, A
History, A
Information Science/Studies, A
Interior Design, A
Journalism, A
Kindergarten/PreSchool Education and Teaching, A
Liberal Arts and Sciences Studies and
Humanities, A
Mass Communication/Media Studies, A
Mathematics, A
Music, A

Nursing - Registered Nurse Training, A
Parks, Recreation, Leisure and Fitness Studies, A
Philosophy, A
Photography, A
Physical Education Teaching and Coaching, A
Physics, A
Political Science and Government, A
Pre-Engineering, A
Psychology, A
Radio and Television, A
Real Estate, A
Respiratory Care Therapy/Therapist, A
Sociology, A
Technology Education/Industrial Arts, A
Urban Studies/Affairs, A
Welding Technology/Welder, A

SANTA ROSA JUNIOR COLLEGE

Adult Development and Aging, A
Advertising, A
Aeronautical/Aerospace Engineering
Technology/Technician, A
Agricultural Business and Management, A
Agricultural Mechanization, A
Agriculture, A
Animal Health, A
Animal Physiology, A
Animal Sciences, A
Anthropology, A
Art/Art Studies, General, A
Astronomy, A
Athletic Training and Sports Medicine, A
Atmospheric Sciences and Meteorology, A
Behavioral Sciences, A
Biology/Biological Sciences, A
Botany/Plant Biology, A
Building/Construction
Finishing, Management, and Inspection, A
Business Administration and Management, A
Chemistry, A
Child Development, A
Civil Engineering, A
Communication Studies/Speech Communication
and Rhetoric, A
Computer Science, A
Criminal Justice/Law Enforcement Administration, A
Culinary Arts/Chef Training, A
Dance, A
Dental Hygiene/Hygienist, A
Dietetics/Dieticians, A
Drama and Dramatics/Theatre Arts, A
Economics, A
Education, A
Electrical, Electronic and Communications
Engineering Technology/Technician, A
Emergency Medical Technology/Technician (EMT
Paramedic), A
Engineering, A
Engineering Technology, A
English Language and Literature, A
Environmental Studies, A
Ethnic and Cultural Studies, A
Ethnic, Cultural Minority, and Gender Studies, A
Family and Consumer Sciences/Human Sciences, A
Film/Cinema Studies, A
Fire Science/Firefighting, A
Fishing and Fisheries Sciences and Management, A
Floriculture/Floristry Operations and Management, A
Geography, A
Geology/Earth Science, A
Graphic Design, A
Health and Physical Education/Fitness, A
History, A
Horse Husbandry/Equine Science and
Management, A
Hotel/Motel Administration/Management, A
Human Services, A
Industrial Design, A
Interior Design, A
Journalism, A
Landscape Architecture, A
Latin American Studies, A
Liberal Arts and Sciences Studies and
Humanities, A
Mathematics, A
Mechanics and Repairers, A

Music, A
Natural Resources and Conservation, A
Natural Resources Management/Development and
   Policy, A
Nursing - Registered Nurse Training, A
Oceanography, Chemical and Physical, A
Ophthalmic Laboratory Technology/Technician, A
Philosophy, A
Physical Education Teaching and Coaching, A
Physical Sciences, A
Physician Assistant, A
Physics, A
Political Science and Government, A
Precision Production Trades, A
Pre-Pharmacy Studies, A
Psychology, A
Social Sciences, A
Sociology, A
Speech-Language Pathology/Pathologist, A
Surveying Engineering, A
Wildlife and Wildlands Science and Management, A
Women's Studies, A

SANTIAGO CANYON COLLEGE

Accounting, A
Anthropology, A
Art/Art Studies, General, A
Biology/Biological Sciences, A
Business Administration and Management, A
Business Administration, Management and
   Operations, A
Business/Office Automation/Technology/Data
   Entry, A
Carpentry/Carpenter, A
Cartography, A
Chemistry, A
Communication Studies/Speech Communication
   and Rhetoric, A
Computer and Information Sciences, A
Computer Science, A
Cosmetology/Cosmetologist, A
Drama and Dramatics/Theatre Arts, A
Economics, A
Electrician, A
English Language and Literature, A
Ethnic and Cultural Studies, A
Geography, A
Geology/Earth Science, A
History, A
Human Development and Family Studies, A
Kinesiology and Exercise Science, A
Liberal Arts and Sciences Studies and
   Humanities, A
Management Science, A
Marketing/Marketing Management, A
Mathematics, A
Modern Languages, A
Music, A
Natural Sciences, A
Philosophy, A
Physics, A
Political Science and Government, A
Psychology, A
Public Administration, A
Radio, Television, and Digital Communication, A
Real Estate, A
Sheet Metal Technology/Sheetworking, A
Social Sciences, A
Sociology, A
Survey Technology/Surveying, A
Tourism and Travel Services Management, A
Water Quality and Wastewater Treatment
   Management and Recycling
   Technology/Technician, A
Women's Studies, A

SCRIPPS COLLEGE

African-American/Black Studies, B
American/United States Studies/Civilization, B
Anthropology, B
Art History, Criticism and Conservation, B
Art/Art Studies, General, B
Asian Studies/Civilization, B
Asian-American Studies, B
Biochemistry, B
Biology/Biological Sciences, B

Chemistry, B
Chinese Language and Literature, B
Classics and Classical
   Languages, Literatures, and Linguistics, B
Computer Science, B
Dance, B
Drama and Dramatics/Theatre Arts, B
East Asian Studies, B
Economics, B
English Language and Literature, B
Environmental Sciences, B
Environmental Studies, B
European Studies/Civilization, B
Film/Video and Photographic Arts, B
Fine/Studio Arts, B
Foreign Languages and Literatures, B
French Language and Literature, B
Geology/Earth Science, B
German Language and Literature, B
Hispanic-American, Puerto Rican, and Mexican-
   American/Chicano Studies, B
History, B
International Relations and Affairs, B
Italian Language and Literature, B
Japanese Language and Literature, B
Jewish/Judaic Studies, B
Latin American Studies, B
Latin Language and Literature, B
Law and Legal Studies, B
Linguistics, B
Mathematics, B
Modern Languages, B
Molecular Biology, B
Multi-/Interdisciplinary Studies, B
Music, B
Neuroscience, B
Organizational Behavior Studies, B
Philosophy, B
Physics, B
Physiological Psychology/Psychobiology, B
Political Science and Government, B
Pre-Medicine/Pre-Medical Studies, B
Psychology, B
Religion/Religious Studies, B
Russian Language and Literature, B
Science, Technology and Society, B
Sociology, B
Spanish Language and Literature, B
Visual and Performing Arts, B
Women's Studies, B

SHASTA BIBLE COLLEGE

Bible/Biblical Studies, AB
Education, B
Educational Administration and Supervision, M
Educational Leadership and Administration, A
Pastoral Studies/Counseling, M
Religious Education, M

SHASTA COLLEGE

Accounting, A
Administrative Assistant and Secretarial Science, A
Agricultural Business and Management, A
Animal Sciences, A
Art/Art Studies, General, A
Automobile/Automotive Mechanics
   Technology/Technician, A
Avionics Maintenance Technology/Technician, A
Business Administration and Management, A
Civil Engineering Technology/Technician, A
Construction Engineering Technology/Technician, A
Criminal Justice/Law Enforcement Administration, A
Culinary Arts/Chef Training, A
Dental Hygiene/Hygienist, A
Design and Visual Communications, A
Diesel Mechanics Technology/Technician, A
Drafting and Design Technology/Technician, A
Drama and Dramatics/Theatre Arts, A
Electrical, Electronic and Communications
   Engineering Technology/Technician, A
Family and Consumer Sciences/Human Sciences, A
Fire Science/Firefighting, A
Horticultural Science, A
Journalism, A
Kindergarten/PreSchool Education and Teaching, A
Legal Administrative Assistant/Secretary, A

Legal Assistant/Paralegal, A
Management Information Systems and Services, A
Medical Administrative Assistant/Secretary, A
Medical/Clinical Assistant, A
Music, A
Natural Resources Management/Development and
   Policy, A
Nursing - Registered Nurse Training, A
Ornamental Horticulture, A
Real Estate, A
Speech and Rhetorical Studies, A
Welding Technology/Welder, A

SIERRA COLLEGE

Accounting, A
Administrative Assistant and Secretarial Science, A
Agricultural Mechanization, A
Agronomy and Crop Science, A
Animal Sciences, A
Art/Art Studies, General, A
Automobile/Automotive Mechanics
   Technology/Technician, A
Biology/Biological Sciences, A
Building/Construction
   Finishing, Management, and Inspection, A
Business Administration and Management, A
Carpentry/Carpenter, A
Chemistry, A
Computer Engineering Technology/Technician, A
Computer Science, A
Construction Engineering Technology/Technician, A
Corrections, A
Criminal Justice/Law Enforcement Administration, A
Criminal Justice/Police Science, A
Drafting and Design Technology/Technician, A
Electrical, Electronic and Communications
   Engineering Technology/Technician, A
Engineering, A
Equestrian/Equine Studies, A
Family and Consumer Sciences/Human Sciences, A
Fashion Merchandising, A
Fire Science/Firefighting, A
Food Technology and Processing, A
Forestry, A
Forestry Technology/Technician, A
Geology/Earth Science, A
Horticultural Science, A
Industrial Technology/Technician, A
Information Science/Studies, A
Interior Design, A
Journalism, A
Kindergarten/PreSchool Education and Teaching, A
Legal Administrative Assistant/Secretary, A
Liberal Arts and Sciences Studies and
   Humanities, A
Licensed Practical/Vocational Nurse Training, A
Marketing/Marketing Management, A
Mass Communication/Media Studies, A
Medical Administrative Assistant/Secretary, A
Metallurgical Technology/Technician, A
Mining Technology/Technician, A
Nursing - Registered Nurse Training, A
Ornamental Horticulture, A
Photography, A
Real Estate, A
Survey Technology/Surveying, A
Teacher Assistant/Aide, A
Technology Education/Industrial Arts, A
Welding Technology/Welder, A

SIMPSON UNIVERSITY

Bible/Biblical Studies, AB
Business Administration and Management, B
Communication Studies/Speech Communication
   and Rhetoric, B
Education, M
Educational Administration and Supervision, M
Elementary Education and Teaching, B
English Language and Literature, B
English/Language Arts Teacher Education, B
General Studies, A
History, B
Human Resources Management/Personnel
   Administration, B
Liberal Arts and Sciences Studies and
   Humanities, B

Management Information Systems and Services, B
Mathematics, B
Missions/Missionary Studies and Missiology, BM
Music, B
Music Teacher Education, B
Organizational Behavior Studies, B
Pastoral Studies/Counseling, M
Psychology, B
Religious Education, B
Social Science Teacher Education, B
Theology and Religious Vocations, B

SKYLINE COLLEGE

Accounting, A
Administrative Assistant and Secretarial Science, A
Anthropology, A
Applied Art, A
Art History, Criticism and Conservation, A
Art/Art Studies, General, A
Automobile/Automotive Mechanics
   Technology/Technician, A
Biological and Physical Sciences, A
Biology/Biological Sciences, A
Business Administration and Management, A
Chemistry, A
Comparative Literature, A
Computer Programming/Programmer, A
Computer Science, A
Cosmetology/Cosmetologist, A
Criminal Justice/Law Enforcement Administration, A
Criminal Justice/Police Science, A
Data Processing and Data Processing
   Technology/Technician, A
Economics, A
Emergency Medical Technology/Technician (EMT
   Paramedic), A
English Language and Literature, A
Family and Consumer Sciences/Human Sciences, A
Fashion Merchandising, A
Finance, A
Fine/Studio Arts, A
French Language and Literature, A
History, A
Hotel/Motel Administration/Management, A
Journalism, A
Legal Administrative Assistant/Secretary, A
Legal Assistant/Paralegal, A
Liberal Arts and Sciences Studies and
   Humanities, A
Mathematics, A
Music, A
Parks, Recreation, Leisure and Fitness Studies, A
Philosophy, A
Physical Education Teaching and Coaching, A
Physics, A
Political Science and Government, A
Psychology, A
Respiratory Care Therapy/Therapist, A
Social Sciences, A
Sociology, A
Spanish Language and Literature, A
Speech and Rhetorical Studies, A
Surgical Technology/Technologist, A
Telecommunications Technology/Technician, A

SOKA UNIVERSITY OF AMERICA

Liberal Arts and Sciences Studies and
   Humanities, B

SOLANO COMMUNITY COLLEGE

Accounting, A
African Studies, A
African-American/Black Studies, A
Airframe Mechanics and Aircraft Maintenance
   Technology/Technician, A
Art/Art Studies, General, A
Automobile/Automotive Mechanics
   Technology/Technician, A
Avionics Maintenance Technology/Technician, A
Biological and Physical Sciences, A
Biology/Biological Sciences, A
Business Administration and Management, A
Business Machine Repairer, A
Chemistry, A
Commercial and Advertising Art, A
Computer Programming/Programmer, A

Cosmetology/Cosmetologist, A
Criminal Justice/Law Enforcement Administration, A
Drafting and Design Technology/Technician, A
Electrical, Electronic and Communications
   Engineering Technology/Technician, A
English Language and Literature, A
Ethnic and Cultural Studies, A
Family and Consumer Sciences/Human Sciences, A
Fashion Merchandising, A
Finance, A
Fire Science/Firefighting, A
French Language and Literature, A
German Language and Literature, A
Hispanic-American, Puerto Rican, and Mexican-
   American/Chicano Studies, A
History, A
Journalism, A
Kindergarten/PreSchool Education and Teaching, A
Legal Administrative Assistant/Secretary, A
Liberal Arts and Sciences Studies and
   Humanities, A
Machine Tool Technology/Machinist, A
Marketing/Marketing Management, A
Mathematics, A
Music, A
Nursing - Registered Nurse Training, A
Ornamental Horticulture, A
Photography, A
Physical Education Teaching and Coaching, A
Physics, A
Political Science and Government, A
Psychology, A
Public Administration, A
Social Sciences, A
Spanish Language and Literature, A
Telecommunications Technology/Technician, A
Welding Technology/Welder, A

SONOMA COLLEGE (PETALUMA)

Allied Health
   Diagnostic, Intervention, and Treatment
   Professions, A
Occupational Therapist Assistant, A
Physical Therapist Assistant, A

SONOMA STATE UNIVERSITY

African-American/Black Studies, B
American Indian/Native American Studies, B
American/United States Studies/Civilization, B
Animal Physiology, B
Anthropology, B
Applied History, M
Applied Mathematics, B
Art History, Criticism and Conservation, B
Art/Art Studies, General, B
Biological and Biomedical Sciences, M
Biology/Biological Sciences, B
Botany/Plant Biology, B
Business Administration and Management, B
Business Administration, Management and
   Operations, M
Business/Managerial Economics, B
Cell/Cellular Biology and Histology, B
Chemistry, B
Clinical/Medical Laboratory Technician, B
Communication Studies/Speech Communication
   and Rhetoric, B
Comparative Literature, B
Computer Science, B
Counselor Education/School Counseling and
   Guidance Services, M
Criminal Justice/Law Enforcement Administration, B
Curriculum and Instruction, M
Developmental and Child Psychology, B
Drama and Dramatics/Theatre Arts, B
Drawing, B
Ecology, B
Economics, B
Education, M
Educational Administration and Supervision, M
Elementary Education and Teaching, M
Engineering Science, B
English, M
English Language and Literature, B
Environmental Biology, M
Environmental Education, B

Environmental Studies, B
Ethnic and Cultural Studies, B
Fine/Studio Arts, B
French Language and Literature, B
Geography, B
Geology/Earth Science, B
Hispanic-American, Puerto Rican, and Mexican-
   American/Chicano Studies, B
History, BM
Interdisciplinary Studies, BM
International Relations and Affairs, B
Kinesiology and Exercise Science, B
Kinesiology and Movement Studies, M
Liberal Arts and Sciences Studies and
   Humanities, B
Marine Biology and Biological Oceanography, B
Marriage and Family Therapy/Counseling, M
Mass Communication/Media Studies, B
Mathematics, B
Medical Microbiology and Bacteriology, B
Multi-/Interdisciplinary Studies, B
Music, B
Music Teacher Education, B
Nursing - Advanced Practice, M
Nursing - Registered Nurse Training, B
Philosophy, B
Physical Education Teaching and Coaching, B
Physics, B
Political Science and Government, BM
Pre-Dentistry Studies, B
Pre-Law Studies, B
Pre-Medicine/Pre-Medical Studies, B
Pre-Veterinary Studies, B
Printmaking, B
Psychology, B
Public Administration, M
Public Health (MPH, DPH), B
Sculpture, B
Sociology, B
Spanish Language and Literature, B
Special Education and Teaching, M
Statistics, B
Women's Studies, B
Writing, M
Zoology/Animal Biology, B

SOUTHERN CALIFORNIA INSTITUTE OF ARCHITECTURE

Architecture, BM

SOUTHERN CALIFORNIA INSTITUTE OF TECHNOLOGY

Business Administration and Management, A
Computer Science, AB
Electrical, Electronic and Communications
   Engineering Technology/Technician, AB
Electrical, Electronics and Communications
   Engineering, AB

SOUTHERN CALIFORNIA SEMINARY

Counseling Psychology, M
Religion/Religious Studies, M
Theology and Religious Vocations, MP

SOUTHWESTERN COLLEGE

Accounting, A
Administrative Assistant and Secretarial Science, A
African Studies, A
African-American/Black Studies, A
Anthropology, A
Architectural Engineering Technology/Technician, A
Art/Art Studies, General, A
Asian-American Studies, A
Astronomy, A
Automobile/Automotive Mechanics
   Technology/Technician, A
Biological and Physical Sciences, A
Biology/Biological Sciences, A
Business Administration and Management, A
Chemistry, A
Commercial and Advertising Art, A
Comparative Literature, A
Computer and Information Sciences, A
Computer and Information Systems Security, A
Computer Graphics, A

Computer Programming/Programmer, A
Computer Science, A
Construction Engineering Technology/Technician, A
Corrections, A
Criminal Justice/Law Enforcement Administration, A
Dance, A
Dental Hygiene/Hygienist, A
Drama and Dramatics/Theatre Arts, A
Economics, A
Electrical, Electronic and Communications
   Engineering Technology/Technician, A
Elementary Education and Teaching, A
Emergency Medical Technology/Technician (EMT
   Paramedic), A
Engineering, A
English Language and Literature, A
Finance, A
Fire Science/Firefighting, A
French Language and Literature, A
General Studies, A
Geography, A
Geology/Earth Science, A
Hispanic-American, Puerto Rican, and Mexican-
   American/Chicano Studies, A
History, A
Information Science/Studies, A
Information Technology, A
Journalism, A
Kindergarten/PreSchool Education and Teaching, A
Landscape Architecture, A
Landscaping and Groundskeeping, A
Legal Administrative Assistant/Secretary, A
Liberal Arts and Sciences Studies and
   Humanities, A
Marketing/Marketing Management, A
Mathematics, A
Music, A
Nursing - Registered Nurse Training, A
Parks, Recreation and Leisure Facilities
   Management, A
Philosophy, A
Photography, A
Physical Sciences, A
Physics, A
Political Science and Government, A
Pre-Engineering, A
Psychology, A
Public Administration, A
Real Estate, A
Small Engine Mechanics and Repair
   Technology/Technician, A
Social Work, A
Sociology, A
Spanish Language and Literature, A
Surgical Technology/Technologist, A
Telecommunications Technology/Technician, A
Tourism and Travel Services Management, A
Web Page, Digital/Multimedia and Information
   Resources Design, A
Web/Multimedia Management and Webmaster, A
Women's Studies, A

STANFORD UNIVERSITY

Aerospace, Aeronautical and Astronautical
   Engineering, BMDO
African Studies, B
Allopathic Medicine, P
American Indian/Native American Studies, B
American/United States Studies/Civilization, B
Ancient Studies/Civilization, B
Ancient/Classical Greek Language and Literature, B
Anthropology, BMD
Applied Physics, MD
Archeology, B
Art Education, MD
Art History, Criticism and Conservation, B
Art/Art Studies, General, B
Asian Studies/Civilization, BM
Biochemistry, D
Bioengineering, MD
Biological and Biomedical Sciences, MD
Biology/Biological Sciences, B
Biomedical Engineering, M
Biophysics, D
Business Administration, Management and
   Operations, MDO

Cancer Biology/Oncology, D
Chemical Engineering, BMDO
Chemistry, BD
Child and Family Studies, D
Chinese Language and Literature, B
Chinese Studies, MD
Civil Engineering, BMDO
Classics and Classical
   Languages, Literatures, and Linguistics, BMD
Communication and Media Studies, MD
Communication Studies/Speech Communication
   and Rhetoric, B
Communication Theory, D
Comparative Literature, BD
Composition, MD
Computational Sciences, MD
Computer Education, MD
Computer Engineering, B
Computer Science, BMD
Counseling Psychology, D
Curriculum and Instruction, MD
Developmental Biology and Embryology, D
Developmental Psychology, D
Drama and Dramatics/Theatre Arts, B
East Asian Studies, B
East European and Russian Studies, M
Economics, BD
Education, MD
Educational Administration and Supervision, MD
Educational Measurement and Evaluation, M
Educational Psychology, D
Electrical Engineering, MDO
Electrical, Electronics and Communications
   Engineering, B
Engineering, B
Engineering and Applied Sciences, MDO
Engineering Design, M
Engineering Management, MD
English, MD
English Education, MD
English Language and Literature, B
Environmental Engineering
   Technology/Environmental Technology, MDO
Environmental Policy and Resource
   Management, M
Environmental Sciences, MDO
Environmental Studies, D
Environmental/Environmental Health Engineering, B
Epidemiology, MD
Film, Television, and Video Production, M
Film/Cinema Studies, B
Fine Arts and Art Studies, MDO
Fine/Studio Arts, B
Foreign Language Teacher Education, M
Foundations and Philosophy of Education, D
French Language and Literature, BMD
Genetics, D
Geology/Earth Science, B
Geophysics and Seismology, BMD
Geosciences, MDO
German Language and Literature, BMD
German Studies, B
Health Services Research, M
Higher Education/Higher Education
   Administration, D
Hispanic-American, Puerto Rican, and Mexican-
   American/Chicano Studies, B
History, BMD
Humanities/Humanistic Studies, BM
Immunology, D
Industrial Engineering, B
Industrial/Management Engineering, MD
Interdisciplinary Studies, BD
International Affairs, M
International and Comparative Education, MD
International Relations and Affairs, B
Italian Language and Literature, BMD
Japanese Language and Literature, B
Japanese Studies, MD
Journalism, M
Latin Language and Literature, B
Law and Legal Studies, MDPO
Linguistics, BMD
Materials Engineering, BMDO
Materials Sciences, BMDO
Mathematical and Computational Finance, M

Mathematics, BMD
Mathematics and Computer Science, B
Mathematics Teacher Education, MD
Mechanical Engineering, BMDO
Medical Informatics, MD
Microbiology, D
Molecular Pharmacology, D
Music, BMD
Music History, Literature, and Theory, M
Music Theory and Composition, MD
Musicology and Ethnomusicology, D
Neuroscience, D
Petroleum Engineering, BMDO
Philosophy, BMD
Physics, BD
Physiology, D
Political Science and Government, BMD
Portuguese Language and Literature, B
Psychology, BD
Public Policy Analysis, B
Religion/Religious Studies, BMD
Russian Language and Literature, M
Science Teacher Education/General Science
   Teacher Education, MD
Science, Technology and Society, B
Slavic Languages, Literatures, and Linguistics, BMD
Social Studies Teacher Education, MD
Sociology, BD
Spanish Language and Literature, BMD
Statistics, BMD
Structural Biology, D
Systems Science and Theory, B
Theater, D
Urban Studies/Affairs, B
Women's Studies, B

TAFT COLLEGE

Accounting, A
Administrative Assistant and Secretarial Science, A
Art/Art Studies, General, A
Automobile/Automotive Mechanics
   Technology/Technician, A
Biology/Biological Sciences, A
Business Administration and Management, A
Computer Science, A
Criminal Justice/Law Enforcement Administration, A
Data Processing and Data Processing
   Technology/Technician, A
Dental Hygiene/Hygienist, A
Drafting and Design Technology/Technician, A
Electrical, Electronic and Communications
   Engineering Technology/Technician, A
English Language and Literature, A
General Studies, A
Journalism, A
Kindergarten/PreSchool Education and Teaching, A
Liberal Arts and Sciences Studies and
   Humanities, A
Mathematics, A
Parks, Recreation, Leisure and Fitness Studies, A
Physical Education Teaching and Coaching, A
Physical Sciences, A
Pre-Engineering, A
Social Sciences, A
Technology Education/Industrial Arts, A

THOMAS AQUINAS COLLEGE

European Studies/Civilization, B
Interdisciplinary Studies, B
Liberal Arts and Sciences Studies and
   Humanities, B
Multi-/Interdisciplinary Studies, B

TOURO UNIVERSITY INTERNATIONAL

Business Administration, Management and
   Operations, MD
Business/Commerce, B
Clinical Research, M
Conflict Resolution and Mediation/Peace Studies, M
Criminology, M
Education, MDO
Educational Leadership and Administration, MD
Educational Media/Instructional Technology, D
Emergency Medical Services, MO
Finance and Banking, M
Health Education, M

Health Informatics, O
Health Services Administration, MO
Health Teacher Education, B
Health/Health Care Administration/Management, B
Higher Education/Higher Education
    Administration, D
Hospitality Administration/Management, B
Human Resources Management and Services, M
International Business/Trade/Commerce, M
International Public Health/International Health, M
Logistics and Materials Management, M
Management Information Systems and
    Services, BM
Public Administration, M
Public Health, MO
Public Health (MPH, DPH), B
Quality Management, O

UNIVERSITY OF CALIFORNIA, BERKELEY

Accounting, D
African-American/Black Studies, BD
Agricultural Economics, D
American Indian/Native American Studies, B
American/United States Studies/Civilization, B
Ancient/Classical Greek Language and Literature, B
Anthropology, BD
Applied Mathematics, BD
Applied Science and Technology, D
Archeology, MD
Architectural History and Criticism, MD
Architecture, BMDO
Art History, Criticism and Conservation, BD
Art/Art Studies, General, B
Asian Languages, MD
Asian Studies/Civilization, BMDO
Asian-American Studies, B
Astrophysics, BD
Atmospheric Sciences and Meteorology, B
Biochemistry, MD
Bioengineering, D
Biological and Biomedical Sciences, D
Biology/Biological Sciences, B
Biomedical/Medical Engineering, B
Biophysics, D
Biostatistics, MD
Botany/Plant Biology, B
Building Science, D
Business Administration and Management, B
Business Administration, Management and
    Operations, MDO
Cell Biology and Anatomy, D
Cell/Cellular and Molecular Biology, B
Celtic Languages, Literatures, and Linguistics, B
Ceramic Sciences and Engineering, MD
Chemical Engineering, BMD
Chemistry, BMD
Chinese Language and Literature, B
Chinese Studies, MD
Civil Engineering, BMDO
Classical, Ancient Mediterranean and Near Eastern
    Studies and Archaeology, B
Classics and Classical
    Languages, Literatures, and Linguistics, BMD
Cognitive Sciences, B
Comparative Literature, BD
Computer Science, BMD
Dance, B
Demography, MD
Design and Applied Arts, M
Developmental Education, M
Drama and Dramatics/Theatre Arts, B
Dutch/Flemish Language and Literature, B
East Asian Studies, M
Economics, BDO
Education, MDO
Educational Administration and Supervision, MD
Educational Leadership and Administration, D
Educational Measurement and Evaluation, MD
Educational Psychology, D
Electrical Engineering, MD
Electrical, Electronics and Communications
    Engineering, B
Energy Management and Policy, MD
Engineering and Applied Sciences, MDO
Engineering Management, MD

Engineering Physics, B
Engineering Science, B
English, D
English Language and Literature, B
Environmental and Occupational Health, MD
Environmental Design/Architecture, M
Environmental Engineering
    Technology/Environmental Technology, MDO
Environmental Policy and Resource
    Management, MD
Environmental Sciences, BMD
Environmental Studies, B
Environmental/Environmental Health Engineering, B
Epidemiology, MD
Ethnic and Cultural Studies, D
Ethnic, Cultural Minority, and Gender Studies, B
Film/Cinema Studies, B
Finance and Banking, D
Financial Engineering, M
Fine Arts and Art Studies, M
Folklore, M
Foreign Languages, Literatures, and Linguistics, B
Forest Management/Forest Resources
    Management, B
Forestry, BMD
Foundations and Philosophy of Education, MD
French Language and Literature, BD
Genetic Counseling/Counselor, MO
Geography, BD
Geological Engineering, MD
Geological/Geophysical Engineering, B
Geology/Earth Science, BMD
Geophysics and Seismology, MD
Geotechnical Engineering, MD
German Language and Literature, BMD
Health Education, M
Health Services Administration, MDO
Hispanic Studies, MD
Hispanic-American, Puerto Rican, and Mexican-
    American/Chicano Studies, B
History, BMDO
History of Science and Technology, D
Human Development, MD
Immunology, D
Industrial and Labor Relations, D
Industrial/Management Engineering, MD
Infectious Diseases, MD
Information Science/Studies, MD
International Affairs, MO
Italian Language and Literature, BD
Japanese Language and Literature, B
Japanese Studies, MD
Jewish/Judaic Studies, D
Journalism, MO
Landscape Architecture, BMO
Latin American Studies, BMDO
Latin Language and Literature, B
Law and Legal Studies, BMDPO
Legal and Justice Studies, D
Linguistics, BMD
Manufacturing Engineering, B
Marketing, D
Mass Communication/Media Studies, B
Materials Engineering, MD
Materials Sciences, BMD
Maternal and Child Health, M
Mathematics, BMD
Mathematics Teacher Education, MD
Mechanical Engineering, BMD
Mechanics, BMD
Metallurgy, MD
Microbiology, BD
Mineral/Mining Engineering, MD
Molecular Biology, D
Molecular Toxicology, D
Multi-/Interdisciplinary Studies, B
Multilingual and Multicultural Education, MD
Music, BMD
Natural Resources and Conservation, B
Natural Resources Management/Development and
    Policy, BMD
Near and Middle Eastern Studies, BMD
Neuroscience, D
Nuclear Engineering, BMD
Nutritional Sciences, BMD
Ocean Engineering, MD

Operations Research, BMD
Optometry, PO
Organizational Behavior Studies, D
Peace Studies and Conflict Resolution, B
Petroleum Engineering, MD
Philosophy, BD
Physical Sciences, B
Physics, BD
Physiology, MD
Plant Biology, D
Political Science and Government, BD
Psychology, BD
Public Health, BMDO
Public Policy Analysis, MDO
Range Science and Management, M
Reading Teacher Education, MD
Real Estate, D
Religion/Religious Studies, BD
Rhetoric, D
Romance Languages, Literatures, and Linguistics, D
Russian Language and Literature, MD
Scandinavian
    Languages, Literatures, and Linguistics, BMD
School Psychology, D
Science Teacher Education/General Science
    Teacher Education, MD
Slavic Languages, Literatures, and Linguistics, BMD
Social Sciences, B
Social Work, BMDO
Sociology, BD
South and Southeast Asian Studies, M
Southeast Asian Studies, B
Spanish Language and Literature, BMD
Special Education and Teaching, D
Speech and Rhetorical Studies, B
Statistics, BMD
Structural Engineering, MD
Theater, D
Toxicology, B
Transportation and Highway Engineering, MD
Urban and Regional Planning, MDO
Urban Design, MD
Urban Studies/Affairs, B
Vision Science/Physiological Optics, MD
Water Resources Engineering, MD
Women's Studies, B

UNIVERSITY OF CALIFORNIA, DAVIS

Aerospace, Aeronautical and Astronautical
    Engineering, BMDO
African-American/Black Studies, B
Agricultural Business and Management, B
Agricultural Economics, MDO
Agricultural Sciences, M
Agriculture, Agriculture Operations and Related
    Sciences, B
Agronomy and Soil Sciences, MD
Allopathic Medicine, MPO
American Indian/Native American Studies, BMD
American/United States Studies/Civilization, B
Animal Behavior and Ethology, MD
Animal Sciences, BMD
Anthropology, BMD
Apparel and Textiles, B
Applied Mathematics, BMD
Applied Science and Technology, MD
Art History, Criticism and Conservation, BM
Asian-American Studies, B
Atmospheric Sciences and Meteorology, BMD
Biochemistry, MD
Bioengineering, MDO
Biology/Biological Sciences, B
Biomedical Engineering, MD
Biomedical/Medical Engineering, B
Biophysics, MD
Biostatistics, MD
BioTechnology, B
Botany/Plant Biology, B
Business Administration, Management and
    Operations, M
Cell Biology and Anatomy, MD
Cell/Cellular Biology and Histology, B
Chemical Engineering, BMD
Chemistry, BMD
Child and Family Studies, M
Chinese Language and Literature, B

City/Urban, Community and Regional Planning, B
Civil Engineering, BMDO
Classical, Ancient Mediterranean and Near Eastern
  Studies and Archaeology, B
Clothing and Textiles, M
Communication Studies/Speech Communication
  and Rhetoric, B
Comparative Literature, BD
Composition, MD
Computational Mathematics, B
Computer Engineering, MD
Computer Science, MD
Cultural Studies, MD
Curriculum and Instruction, D
Developmental Biology and Embryology, MD
East Asian Studies, B
Ecology, MD
Ecology, Evolution, Systematics and Population
  Biology, B
Economics, BMD
Education, MD
Educational Psychology, D
Electrical Engineering, MD
Electrical, Electronics and Communications
  Engineering, B
Engineering, B
Engineering and Applied Sciences, MDO
English, MD
English Language and Literature, B
Entomology, BMD
Environmental Engineering
  Technology/Environmental Technology, MDO
Environmental Sciences, MD
Environmental Studies, B
Environmental Toxicology, B
Epidemiology, MD
Exercise and Sports Science, M
Exercise Physiology, M
Film/Cinema Studies, B
Fine Arts and Art Studies, M
Fine/Studio Arts, B
Food Science, B
Food Science and Technology, MD
Forensic Science and Technology, M
French Language and Literature, BD
Genetics, BMD
Geography, MD
Geology/Earth Science, BMD
German Language and Literature, BMD
Hispanic-American, Puerto Rican, and Mexican-
  American/Chicano Studies, B
History, BMD
Horticultural Science, M
Human Development, D
Human Development and Family Studies, B
Hydrology and Water Resources Science, BMD
Immunology, MD
International Agriculture, B
International Relations and Affairs, B
Italian Language and Literature, B
Japanese Language and Literature, B
Landscape Architecture, B
Law and Legal Studies, MPO
Linguistics, BM
Materials Engineering, BMD
Materials Sciences, MD
Mathematics, BMD
Mechanical Engineering, BMDO
Medical Informatics, M
Microbiology, BMD
Molecular Biochemistry, B
Molecular Biology, MD
Multi-/Interdisciplinary Studies, B
Music, BMD
Musicology and Ethnomusicology, D
Natural Resources and Conservation, B
Neurobiology and Neurophysiology, B
Neuroscience, D
Nutritional Sciences, BMD
Pathology/Experimental Pathology, MD
Performance, MD
Pharmacology, MD
Philosophy, BMD
Physical Sciences, B
Physics, BMD
Physiology, MD

Plant Biology, MD
Plant Pathology/Phytopathology, MD
Political Science and Government, BMD
Psychology, BD
Religion/Religious Studies, B
Russian Language and Literature, B
Sociobiology, D
Sociology, BMD
Soil Science and Agronomy, B
Spanish Language and Literature, BMD
Statistics, BMD
Textile Design, M
Theater, MD
Toxicology, MD
Transportation and Highway Engineering, MD
Transportation/Transportation Management, MD
Urban and Regional Planning, M
Urban Forestry, B
Veterinary Medicine, PO
Veterinary Sciences, MO
Visual and Performing Arts, B
Women's Studies, B
Writing, M
Zoology/Animal Biology, BM

UNIVERSITY OF CALIFORNIA, IRVINE

Aerospace, Aeronautical and Astronautical
  Engineering, BMD
African-American/Black Studies, B
Allopathic Medicine, PO
Anatomy, MDO
Anthropology, BMD
Area, Ethnic, Cultural, and Gender Studies, B
Art History, Criticism and Conservation, BMD
Art/Art Studies, General, B
Asian Languages, MD
Asian-American Studies, B
Biochemical Engineering, MD
Biochemistry, MDO
Biological and Biomedical Sciences, MDO
Biology/Biological Sciences, B
Biomedical Engineering, MD
Biomedical/Medical Engineering, B
Biophysics, DO
BioTechnology, M
Business Administration, Management and
  Operations, MD
Cell Biology and Anatomy, MD
Chemical Engineering, BMD
Chemistry, BMD
Chinese Language and Literature, B
Chinese Studies, MD
Civil Engineering, BMD
Classical, Ancient Mediterranean and Near Eastern
  Studies and Archaeology, B
Classics and Classical
  Languages, Literatures, and Linguistics, BMD
Comparative Literature, BMD
Computer and Information Sciences, B
Computer and Information Sciences and Support
  Services, B
Computer Engineering, BMD
Computer Science, BMD
Criminology, BMD
Dance, BM
Demography and Population Studies, M
Developmental Biology and Embryology, MD
Drama and Dramatics/Theatre Arts, B
East Asian Studies, B
Ecology, BMD
Economics, BMD
Education, MD
Educational Administration and Supervision, D
Electrical Engineering, MD
Electrical, Electronics and Communications
  Engineering, B
Elementary Education and Teaching, M
Engineering and Applied Sciences, MD
English, MD
English Language and Literature, B
Environmental Design/Architecture, BMD
Environmental Engineering
  Technology/Environmental Technology, MD
Environmental Policy and Resource
  Management, MD
Environmental/Environmental Health Engineering, B

Ethnic and Cultural Studies, B
European Studies/Civilization, B
Evolutionary Biology, MD
Family and Consumer Sciences/Human Sciences, B
Film/Cinema Studies, B
Fine Arts and Art Studies, M
Fine/Studio Arts, B
Foreign Language Teacher Education, M
French Language and Literature, BMD
Genetic Counseling/Counselor, M
Genetics, D
Geology/Earth Science, B
Geosciences, MD
German Language and Literature, BMD
German Studies, B
Hispanic-American, Puerto Rican, and Mexican-
  American/Chicano Studies, B
History, BMD
Humanities/Humanistic Studies, B
Information Science/Studies, MD
International/Global Studies, B
Japanese Language and Literature, B
Japanese Studies, MD
Journalism, B
Linguistics, B
Materials Engineering, BMD
Materials Sciences, MD
Mathematics, BMD
Mechanical Engineering, BMD
Microbiology, BMDO
Molecular Biochemistry, B
Molecular Biology, MDO
Molecular Genetics, MDO
Multi-/Interdisciplinary Studies, B
Music, BM
Music Performance, B
Neurobiology and Neurophysiology, MDO
Neuroscience, B
Pharmacology, MDO
Philosophy, BMD
Physics, BMDO
Physiology, DO
Political Science and Government, BD
Psychology, BD
Russian Language and Literature, B
Secondary Education and Teaching, M
Social Psychology, B
Social Sciences, BMD
Sociology, BMD
Spanish Language and Literature, BMD
Theater, MD
Toxicology, MDO
Transportation and Highway Engineering, MD
Urban and Regional Planning, MD
Urban Studies/Affairs, MD
Women's Studies, B
Writing, M

UNIVERSITY OF CALIFORNIA, LOS ANGELES

Aerospace, Aeronautical and Astronautical
  Engineering, BMD
African Languages, Literatures, and Linguistics, B
African Studies, BMO
African-American/Black Studies, BM
Agricultural/Biological Engineering and
  Bioengineering, B
Allopathic Medicine, PO
American Indian/Native American Studies, BMO
American Literature (United States), B
American/United States Studies/Civilization, B
Anatomy, D
Ancient/Classical Greek Language and Literature, B
Anthropology, BMD
Applied Mathematics, B
Arabic Language and Literature, B
Archeology, BMD
Architecture, BMD
Area Studies, B
Art History, Criticism and Conservation, BMD
Art/Art Studies, General, B
Asian Languages, MD
Asian Studies/Civilization, B
Asian-American Studies, BM
Astronomy, BMD
Astrophysics, BMD

Atmospheric Sciences and Meteorology, BMD
Biochemistry, BMD
Biological and Biomedical Sciences, MDO
Biology/Biological Sciences, B
Biomathematics and Bioinformatics, B
Biomedical Engineering, MD
Biomedical/Medical Engineering, B
Biometry/Biometrics, MD
Biophysics, B
Biostatistics, BMD
BioTechnology, B
Botany/Plant Biology, B
Business Administration and Management, B
Business Administration, Management and
    Operations, MDO
Business/Managerial Economics, B
Cell Biology and Anatomy, MD
Cell/Cellular and Molecular Biology, B
Ceramic Sciences and Engineering, MD
Chemical Engineering, BMD
Chemistry, BMD
Chinese Language and Literature, B
City/Urban, Community and Regional Planning, B
Civil Engineering, BMD
Classical, Ancient Mediterranean and Near Eastern
    Studies and Archaeology, B
Classics and Classical
    Languages, Literatures, and Linguistics, BMD
Clinical Research, M
Cognitive Sciences, B
Communication Studies/Speech Communication
    and Rhetoric, B
Community Health and Preventive Medicine, BMD
Comparative Literature, BMD
Computational Mathematics, B
Computer Engineering, B
Computer Science, BMDO
Dance, BMD
Dentistry, PO
Design and Applied Arts, BM
Development Economics and International
    Development, B
Developmental Biology and Embryology, MD
Drama and Dramatics/Theatre Arts, B
East Asian
    Languages, Literatures, and Linguistics, B
East Asian Studies, BMD
Ecology, B
Economics, BMD
Education, BMDO
Educational Leadership and Administration, B
Electrical Engineering, MD
Electrical, Electronics and Communications
    Engineering, B
Engineering, B
Engineering and Applied Sciences, MDO
English, MD
English as a Second Language, M
English Language and Literature, B
Environmental and Occupational Health, MD
Environmental Engineering
    Technology/Environmental Technology, MD
Environmental Health, B
Environmental Sciences, BD
Epidemiology, BMD
Ethnomusicology, MD
European Studies/Civilization, B
Film, Television, and Video Production, MDO
Film/Cinema Studies, B
Fine Arts and Art Studies, BM
Foreign Languages, Literatures, and Linguistics, B
French Language and Literature, BMD
Geochemistry, BMD
Geography, BMD
Geological and Earth Sciences/Geosciences, B
Geological/Geophysical Engineering, B
Geology/Earth Science, BMD
Geophysics and Seismology, BMD
Geosciences, MD
Geotechnical Engineering, MD
German Language and Literature, BMD
Germanic Languages, Literatures, and Linguistics, B
Health Services Administration, BMD
Hebrew Language and Literature, B
Hispanic Studies, D

Hispanic-American, Puerto Rican, and Mexican-
    American/Chicano Studies, B
History, BMDO
Human Genetics, MD
Human/Medical Genetics, B
Hydrology and Water Resources Science, M
Immunology, MD
Information Science/Studies, BMDO
International Economics, B
Islamic Studies, B
Italian Language and Literature, BMD
Japanese Language and Literature, B
Jewish/Judaic Studies, B
Kinesiology and Exercise Science, B
Korean Language and Literature, B
Latin American Studies, BMO
Latin Language and Literature, B
Law and Legal Studies, MPO
Liberal Arts and Sciences Studies and
    Humanities, B
Library Science, BMDO
Linguistic, Comparative, and Related Language
    Studies and Services, B
Linguistics, BMD
Manufacturing Engineering, BM
Marine Biology and Biological Oceanography, B
Materials Engineering, BMD
Materials Sciences, BMD
Mathematics, BMD
Mechanical Engineering, BMD
Medical Microbiology and Bacteriology, B
Medical Physics, MD
Metallurgy, MD
Microbiological Sciences and Immunology, B
Microbiology, MD
Middle/Near Eastern and Semitic
    Languages, Literatures, and Linguistics, B
Modern Greek Language and Literature, B
Molecular Biochemistry, B
Molecular Biology, BMD
Molecular Genetics, MD
Molecular Pharmacology, B
Molecular Physiology, B
Molecular Toxicology, BD
Multi-/Interdisciplinary Studies, B
Music, BMD
Music History, Literature, and Theory, B
Musicology and Ethnomusicology, BMD
Near and Middle Eastern Languages, MD
Near and Middle Eastern Studies, BMDO
Neurobiology and Neurophysiology, BD
Neuroscience, BD
Nursing, BMDO
Nursing - Registered Nurse Training, B
Operations Research, MD
Oral Biology, MDO
Pathology/Experimental Pathology, BMD
Pharmacology, D
Philosophy, BMD
Physics, BMD
Physiological Psychology/Psychobiology, B
Physiology, BMD
Planetary Astronomy and Science, MD
Plant Molecular Biology, D
Plant Sciences, B
Political Science and Government, BMD
Portuguese Language and Literature, BM
Psychology, BMD
Public Administration, B
Public Health, BMDO
Public Policy Analysis, BM
Religion/Religious Studies, B
Romance
    Languages, Literatures, and Linguistics, MD
Russian Language and Literature, B
Russian Studies, B
Scandinavian
    Languages, Literatures, and Linguistics, BMD
Science Teacher Education/General Science
    Teacher Education, M
Slavic Languages, Literatures, and Linguistics, BMD
Social Work, BMDO
Sociology, BMD
Southeast Asian Studies, B
Spanish Language and Literature, BM
Special Education and Teaching, BD

Statistics, BMD
Structural Engineering, MD
Teaching English as a Second or Foreign
    Language/ESL Language Instructor, B
Theater, MD
Urban Design, MD
Urban Planning, MDO
Visual and Performing Arts, B
Water Resources Engineering, MD
Women's Studies, BMD

UNIVERSITY OF CALIFORNIA, RIVERSIDE

African-American/Black Studies, B
Agronomy and Soil Sciences, MD
American Indian/Native American Studies, B
Anthropology, BMD
Art History, Criticism and Conservation, BM
Asian Studies/Civilization, B
Asian-American Studies, B
Biochemistry, BMD
Biological and Biomedical Sciences, MDO
Biology/Biological Sciences, B
Biomedical Sciences, B
Botany/Plant Biology, BMD
Business Administration and Management, B
Business Administration, Management and
    Operations, M
Business/Managerial Economics, B
Cell Biology and Anatomy, MD
Chemical Engineering, BMD
Chemistry, BMD
Chinese Language and Literature, B
Classics and Classical
    Languages, Literatures, and Linguistics, BMD
Comparative Literature, BMD
Computer Science, BMD
Creative Writing, B
Dance, BMD
Developmental Biology and Embryology, MD
Drama and Dramatics/Theatre Arts, B
Economics, BMD
Education, MD
Electrical Engineering, MD
Electrical, Electronics and Communications
    Engineering, B
English, MD
English Language and Literature, B
Entomology, BMD
Environmental Engineering
    Technology/Environmental Technology, MD
Environmental Sciences, MD
Environmental Studies, B
Environmental/Environmental Health Engineering, B
Ethnic and Cultural Studies, B
Evolutionary Biology, MD
Fine Arts and Art Studies, M
Fine/Studio Arts, B
French Language and Literature, B
Genetics, D
Geology/Earth Science, BMD
Geophysics and Seismology, B
German Language and Literature, B
Hispanic Studies, MD
Hispanic-American, Puerto Rican, and Mexican-
    American/Chicano Studies, B
Historic Preservation and Conservation, M
History, BMD
Human Development and Family Studies, B
Humanities/Humanistic Studies, B
Latin American Studies, B
Liberal Arts and Sciences Studies and
    Humanities, B
Linguistics, B
Mathematics, BMD
Mechanical Engineering, BMD
Microbiology, MD
Molecular Biology, MD
Museology/Museum Studies, M
Music, BM
Neuroscience, BD
Philosophy, BMD
Physics, BMD
Physiological Psychology/Psychobiology, B
Plant Biology, MD
Plant Pathology/Phytopathology, MD

Plant Sciences, MD
Political Science and Government, BMD
Pre-Law Studies, B
Psychology, BMD
Public Administration, B
Religion/Religious Studies, B
Russian Language and Literature, B
Russian Studies, B
Social Sciences, B
Sociology, BMD
Spanish Language and Literature, BMD
Statistics, BMD
Toxicology, MD
Water Resources, MD
Women's Studies, B
Writing, M

UNIVERSITY OF CALIFORNIA, SAN DIEGO

Aerospace, Aeronautical and Astronautical
   Engineering, BMD
Allopathic Medicine, PO
Animal Physiology, B
Anthropology, BD
Applied Mathematics, BM
Applied Physics, MD
Archeology, B
Art History, Criticism and Conservation, B
Art/Art Studies, General, B
Artificial Intelligence and Robotics, MD
Atomic/Molecular Physics, B
Biochemistry, BMD
Bioengineering, MD
Bioinformatics, D
Biological and Biomedical Sciences, MDO
Biology/Biological Sciences, B
Biomedical/Medical Engineering, B
Biophysics, BMD
BioTechnology, B
Business Administration, Management and
   Operations, M
Cancer Biology/Oncology, D
Cardiovascular Sciences, D
Cell Biology and Anatomy, D
Cell/Cellular Biology and Histology, B
Chemical Engineering, BMD
Chemistry, BMD
Chemistry Teacher Education, B
Chinese Language and Literature, B
Classics and Classical
   Languages, Literatures, and Linguistics, B
Clinical Psychology, D
Clinical Research, M
Cognitive Psychology and Psycholinguistics, B
Cognitive Sciences, D
Communication and Media Studies, MD
Communication Disorders, D
Comparative Literature, BMD
Computer Engineering, BMD
Computer Science, BMD
Creative Writing, B
Dance, B
Developmental Biology and Embryology, D
Drama and Dramatics/Theatre Arts, B
Ecology, BD
Econometrics and Quantitative Economics, B
Economics, BD
Education, MD
Electrical Engineering, MD
Electrical, Electronics and Communications
   Engineering, B
Engineering, B
Engineering Physics, BMD
Engineering Science, B
English, M
English Language and Literature, B
Environmental Studies, B
Epidemiology, D
Ethnic and Cultural Studies, BMD
Evolutionary Biology, D
Family and Consumer Sciences/Human Sciences, B
Film/Cinema Studies, B
Fine Arts and Art Studies, MD
Fine/Studio Arts, B
Foreign Languages and Literatures, B
French Language and Literature, BM

Genetics, D
Geology/Earth Science, B
German Language and Literature, BM
Health Services Administration, M
History, BMD
History of Science and Technology, D
Immunology, D
Interdisciplinary Studies, B
Intermedia/Multimedia, B
International Affairs, MD
Italian Language and Literature, B
Japanese Language and Literature, B
Jewish/Judaic Studies, BM
Latin American Studies, BM
Linguistics, BD
Management Science, B
Marine Biology and Biological Oceanography, MD
Marine Geology, MD
Marine Sciences, MD
Mass Communication/Media Studies, B
Materials Sciences, MD
Mathematics, BMD
Mathematics Teacher Education, BD
Mechanical Engineering, BMD
Mechanics, MD
Medical Microbiology and Bacteriology, B
Medicinal and Pharmaceutical Chemistry, B
Microbiology, D
Molecular Biology, BD
Molecular Pathology, D
Music, BMD
Music History, Literature, and Theory, B
Natural Resources Management/Development and
   Policy, B
Neurobiology and Neurophysiology, D
Neuroscience, D
Ocean Engineering, MD
Oceanography, Chemical and Physical, MD
Pharmacology, D
Pharmacy, P
Philosophy, BD
Photonics, MD
Physics, BMD
Physics Teacher Education, B
Physiology, D
Plant Biology, D
Plant Molecular Biology, D
Political Science and Government, BMD
Psychology, BD
Public Health, D
Religion/Religious Studies, B
Russian Language and Literature, B
Russian Studies, B
Science Teacher Education/General Science
   Teacher Education, D
Sociology, BD
Spanish Language and Literature, BM
Statistics, M
Structural Biology, D
Structural Engineering, BMD
Systematic Biology/Biological Systematics, D
Systems Engineering, B
Telecommunications, MD
Theater, MD
Urban Studies/Affairs, B
Virology, D
Women's Studies, B

UNIVERSITY OF CALIFORNIA, SANTA BARBARA

African-American/Black Studies, B
Agricultural Economics, MD
Animal Physiology, B
Anthropology, BMD
Applied Mathematics, M
Aquatic Biology/Limnology, B
Archeology, MD
Art History, Criticism and Conservation, BDO
Art/Art Studies, General, B
Asian Languages, D
Asian Studies/Civilization, B
Asian-American Studies, B
Biochemistry, BMDO
Bioengineering, MD
Biology/Biological Sciences, B
Biophysics, MD

Biopsychology, B
Business/Managerial Economics, B
Cell Biology and Anatomy, MDO
Cell/Cellular Biology and Histology, B
Chemical Engineering, BMD
Chemistry, BMD
Chinese Language and Literature, B
Classics and Classical
   Languages, Literatures, and Linguistics, BMD
Clinical Psychology, D
Communication and Media Studies, DO
Communication Studies/Speech Communication
   and Rhetoric, B
Comparative Literature, BDO
Composition, MD
Computational Sciences, MD
Computer Engineering, BMDO
Computer Science, BD
Counseling Psychology, D
Dance, B
Developmental Biology and Embryology, MDO
Drama and Dramatics/Theatre Arts, B
East Asian Studies, M
Ecology, BMD
Economics, BMD
Education, MD
Educational Leadership and Administration, D
Electrical Engineering, MDO
Electrical, Electronic and Communications
   Engineering Technology/Technician, B
Electrical, Electronics and Communications
   Engineering, B
Engineering and Applied Sciences, MDO
English, DO
English Language and Literature, B
Environmental Policy and Resource
   Management, MD
Environmental Sciences, MD
Environmental Studies, B
Ethnomusicology, MD
Evolutionary Biology, MD
Film, Television, and Video Production, DO
Film/Cinema Studies, B
Fine Arts and Art Studies, M
Fine/Studio Arts, B
French Language and Literature, BMD
Geography, BMD
Geology/Earth Science, BMD
Geophysics and Seismology, BM
German Language and Literature, BMD
Hispanic Studies, DO
Hispanic-American, Puerto Rican, and Mexican-
   American/Chicano Studies, B
History, BMD
Hydrology and Water Resources Science, B
Interdisciplinary Studies, B
Islamic Studies, B
Italian Language and Literature, B
Japanese Language and Literature, B
Latin American Studies, BMD
Linguistics, BDO
Marine Biology and Biological Oceanography, BMD
Marine Sciences, MD
Materials Engineering, MDO
Materials Sciences, MDO
Mathematical and Computational Finance, D
Mathematics, BMD
Mechanical Engineering, BDO
Medical Microbiology and Bacteriology, B
Medieval and Renaissance Studies, B
Microbiology, B
Molecular Biology, BMDO
Multi-/Interdisciplinary Studies, B
Music, BMD
Music Theory and Composition, MD
Musicology and Ethnomusicology, MD
Near and Middle Eastern Studies, B
Performance, MD
Pharmacology, B
Philosophy, BMDO
Physics, BD
Physiology, B
Political Science and Government, BMD
Portuguese Language and Literature, BMD
Pre-Law Studies, B
Psychology, BD

Public/Applied History and Archival Administration, B
Quantitative Analysis, D
Religion/Religious Studies, BMD
Slavic Languages, Literatures, and Linguistics, B
Sociology, BDO
Spanish Language and Literature, BMD
Statistics, BMD
Theater, MDO
Western European Studies, M
Women's Studies, BD
Zoology/Animal Biology, B

UNIVERSITY OF CALIFORNIA, SANTA CRUZ

American/United States Studies/Civilization, B
Ancient/Classical Greek Language and Literature, B
Anthropology, BMD
Applied Economics, M
Applied Mathematics, BMD
Art History, Criticism and Conservation, B
Art/Art Studies, General, B
Asian Studies/Civilization, B
Astronomy, D
Astrophysics, BD
Biochemistry, B
Bioinformatics, MD
Biological and Biomedical Sciences, MD
Biology/Biological Sciences, B
Botany/Plant Biology, B
Business/Managerial Economics, B
Cell Biology and Anatomy, MD
Cell/Cellular Biology and Histology, B
Chemistry, BMD
Chinese Language and Literature, B
Cinematography and Film/Video Production, B
Classics and Classical
   Languages, Literatures, and Linguistics, B
Cognitive Psychology and Psycholinguistics, B
Communication and Media Studies, O
Comparative Literature, BMD
Computer Art and Design, M
Computer Engineering, BMD
Computer Science, BMD
Creative Writing, B
Dance, B
Developmental and Child Psychology, B
Developmental Psychology, D
Drama and Dramatics/Theatre Arts, B
Drawing, B
East Asian Studies, B
Ecology, BMD
Economics, BMD
Education, MO
Electrical Engineering, MD
Electrical, Electronics and Communications
   Engineering, B
Engineering and Applied Sciences, MD
English Language and Literature, B
Environmental Biology, MD
Environmental Studies, BD
European History, B
Evolutionary Biology, MD
Experimental Psychology, D
Family and Community Services, B
Film/Cinema Studies, B
Fine Arts and Art Studies, M
Foreign Languages and Literatures, B
French Language and Literature, B
Geology/Earth Science, B
Geophysics and Seismology, B
Geosciences, MD
German Language and Literature, B
Hispanic-American, Puerto Rican, and Mexican-
   American/Chicano Studies, B
History, BD
Humanities/Humanistic Studies, D
Information Science/Studies, B
International Affairs, MD
International Economics, B
Italian Language and Literature, B
Italian Studies, B
Japanese Language and Literature, B
Latin American Studies, B
Latin Language and Literature, B
Law and Legal Studies, B
Linguistics, BMD

Marine Biology and Biological Oceanography, B
Marine Sciences, MD
Mathematics, BMD
Mathematics Teacher Education, B
Molecular Biology, BMD
Music, BM
Peace Studies and Conflict Resolution, B
Philosophy, BD
Photography, B
Physics, BMD
Physiological Psychology/Psychobiology, B
Plant Sciences, B
Political Science and Government, BD
Printmaking, B
Psychology, BD
Religion/Religious Studies, B
Russian Studies, B
Sculpture, B
Social Psychology, BD
Social Sciences, D
Sociology, BD
South Asian Studies, B
Southeast Asian Studies, B
Spanish Language and Literature, B
Technical Theatre/Theatre Design and
   Technology, B
Theater, O
Toxicology, MD
Women's Studies, B

UNIVERSITY OF JUDAISM

Business Administration, Management and
   Operations, M
Business/Managerial Economics, B
Comparative Literature, B
Education, M
Interdisciplinary Studies, B
Jewish/Judaic Studies, BM
Liberal Arts and Sciences Studies and
   Humanities, B
Non-Profit/Public/Organizational Management, M
Political Science and Government, B
Pre-Medicine/Pre-Medical Studies, B
Psychology, B
Social Work, M
Theology and Religious Vocations, M

UNIVERSITY OF LA VERNE

Accounting, BM
Anthropology, B
Art History, Criticism and Conservation, B
Art/Art Studies, General, B
Behavioral Sciences, B
Biology/Biological Sciences, B
Broadcast Journalism, B
Business Administration and Management, B
Business Administration, Management and
   Operations, M
Chemistry, B
Child and Family Studies, M
Child Development, B
Clinical Psychology, D
Communication Studies/Speech Communication
   and Rhetoric, B
Community Psychology, D
Comparative Literature, B
Computer Engineering, B
Computer Science, B
Counseling Psychology, M
Counselor Education/School Counseling and
   Guidance Services, MO
Criminology, B
Drama and Dramatics/Theatre Arts, B
E-Commerce/Electronic Commerce, B
Economics, B
Education, BMO
Educational Administration and Supervision, MO
Educational Leadership and Administration, D
Elementary Education and Teaching, B
English Language and Literature, B
Environmental Biology, B
Finance and Banking, M
French Language and Literature, B
German Language and Literature, B
Gerontology, M
Health Informatics, M

Health Services Administration, M
Health/Health Care Administration/Management, B
History, B
International Business/Trade/Commerce, BM
International Relations and Affairs, B
Journalism, B
Kinesiology and Exercise Science, B
Law and Legal Studies, P
Legal Assistant/Paralegal, B
Liberal Arts and Sciences Studies and
   Humanities, AB
Management, M
Management Information Systems and Services, M
Marketing, M
Marketing/Marketing Management, B
Marriage and Family Therapy/Counseling, M
Mathematics, B
Multilingual and Multicultural Education, O
Music, B
Natural Resources Management/Development and
   Policy, B
Natural Sciences, B
Organizational Management, MDO
Philosophy, B
Physical Education Teaching and Coaching, B
Physics, B
Political Science and Government, B
Pre-Law Studies, B
Psychology, BMD
Public Administration, BMD
Reading Teacher Education, MO
Religion/Religious Studies, B
Social Sciences, B
Sociology, B
Spanish Language and Literature, B
Special Education and Teaching, M

UNIVERSITY OF THE PACIFIC

Art History, Criticism and Conservation, B
Art/Art Studies, General, B
Audiology/Audiologist and Speech-Language
   Pathology/Pathologist, B
Biochemistry, B
Biological and Biomedical Sciences, M
Biology/Biological Sciences, B
Biomedical/Medical Engineering, B
Business Administration and Management, B
Business Administration, Management and
   Operations, MO
Chemistry, B
Civil Engineering, B
Classics and Classical
   Languages, Literatures, and Linguistics, B
Commercial and Advertising Art, B
Communication and Media Studies, M
Communication Disorders, M
Communication Studies/Speech Communication
   and Rhetoric, B
Computer Engineering, B
Computer Science, B
Curriculum and Instruction, MD
Dental and Oral Surgery, O
Dentistry, MPO
Drama and Dramatics/Theatre Arts, B
Economics, B
Education, BMDO
Educational Administration and Supervision, MD
Educational Psychology, MDO
Electrical, Electronics and Communications
   Engineering, B
Engineering Physics, B
Engineering/Industrial Management, B
English Language and Literature, B
Environmental Studies, B
Exercise and Sports Science, M
Fine/Studio Arts, B
French Language and Literature, B
Geology/Earth Science, B
German Language and Literature, B
History, B
Information Science/Studies, B
Interdisciplinary Studies, B
International Affairs, M
International Relations and Affairs, B
Japanese Language and Literature, B
Kinesiology and Exercise Science, B

Law and Legal Studies, MDPO
Legal and Justice Studies, M
Mathematics, B
Mechanical Engineering, B
Music, BM
Music History, Literature, and Theory, B
Music Management and Merchandising, B
Music Teacher Education, BM
Music Theory and Composition, B
Music Therapy/Therapist, BM
Orthodontics, M
Pharmaceutical Sciences, MD
Pharmacy, BP
Philosophy, B
Physical Sciences, B
Physical Therapy/Therapist, MD
Physics, B
Piano and Organ, B
Political Science and Government, B
Psychology, BM
Public Policy Analysis, M
Religion/Religious Studies, B
School Psychology, MDO
Social Sciences, B
Sociology, B
Spanish Language and Literature, B
Special Education and Teaching, BM
Voice and Opera, B

UNIVERSITY OF PHOENIX-BAY AREA CAMPUS

Accounting, BM
Business Administration and Management, B
Business Administration, Management and
    Operations, M
Corrections and Criminal Justice, B
Curriculum and Instruction, M
Education, M
Electronic Commerce, M
Health/Health Care Administration/Management, B
Human Resources Management and Services, M
Information Technology, B
International Business/Trade/Commerce, M
Management, M
Management Information Systems and
    Services, BM
Management of Technology, M
Management Science, B
Marketing, M
Marketing/Marketing Management, B
Nursing, M
Nursing Administration, M
Nursing Science, B
Organizational Management, M
Public Administration and Social Service
    Professions, B

UNIVERSITY OF PHOENIX-CENTRAL VALLEY CAMPUS

Accounting, B
Business Administration and Management, B
Corrections and Criminal Justice, B
Health/Health Care Administration/Management, B
Management Information Systems and Services, B
Marketing/Marketing Management, B
Nursing Science, B
Public Administration and Social Service
    Professions, B

UNIVERSITY OF PHOENIX-SACRAMENTO VALLEY CAMPUS

Accounting, B
Adult and Continuing Education and Teaching, M
Business Administration and Management, B
Business Administration, Management and
    Operations, M
Corrections and Criminal Justice, B
Curriculum and Instruction, M
Distance Education Development, M
Education, MO
Educational Media/Instructional Technology, M
Electronic Commerce, M
Elementary Education and Teaching, M
Health Services Administration, M

Health/Health Care Administration/Management, B
Human Resources Management and Services, M
Human Services, B
Information Technology, B
International Business/Trade/Commerce, M
Management, M
Management Information Systems and
    Services, BM
Management of Technology, M
Management Science, B
Marketing, M
Marketing/Marketing Management, B
Marriage and Family Therapy/Counseling, M
Nursing, M
Nursing - Advanced Practice, M
Nursing Science, B
Organizational Management, M
Public Administration and Social Service
    Professions, B

UNIVERSITY OF PHOENIX-SAN DIEGO CAMPUS

Accounting, B
Adult and Continuing Education and Teaching, M
Business Administration and Management, B
Business Administration, Management and
    Operations, M
Business/Commerce, B
Corrections and Criminal Justice, B
Curriculum and Instruction, M
Education, M
Educational Media/Instructional Technology, M
Elementary Education and Teaching, M
Health Services Administration, MO
Health/Health Care Administration/Management, B
Information Technology, B
International Business/Trade/Commerce, M
Management, M
Management Information Systems and
    Services, BM
Management of Technology, M
Marketing/Marketing Management, B
Marriage and Family Therapy/Counseling, MO
Nursing, MO
Nursing Science, B
Organizational Management, M
Public Administration and Social Service
    Professions, B
Secondary Education and Teaching, M

UNIVERSITY OF PHOENIX-SOUTHERN CALIFORNIA CAMPUS

Accounting, BM
Business Administration and Management, B
Business Administration, Management and
    Operations, M
Corrections and Criminal Justice, B
Curriculum and Instruction, M
Education, MO
Educational Media/Instructional Technology, M
Electronic Commerce, M
Elementary Education and Teaching, M
Health Services Administration, M
Human Resources Management and Services, M
Information Science/Studies, M
Information Technology, B
International Business/Trade/Commerce, M
Management, M
Management Information Systems and Services, M
Management of Technology, M
Nursing, MO
Nursing - Advanced Practice, MO
Nursing Science, B
Organizational Management, M
Public Administration and Social Service
    Professions, B
Secondary Education and Teaching, M
Special Education and Teaching, M

UNIVERSITY OF REDLANDS

Accounting, B
Anthropology, B
Art History, Criticism and Conservation, B
Asian Studies/Civilization, B
Audiology/Audiologist and Speech-Language
    Pathology/Pathologist, B

Biology/Biological Sciences, B
Business Administration and Management, B
Business Administration, Management and
    Operations, MO
Business/Commerce, B
Chemistry, B
Communication Disorders, BM
Comparative Literature, B
Computer Science, B
Creative Writing, B
Economics, B
Education, BM
Elementary Education and Teaching, B
English Language and Literature, B
Environmental Studies, B
Finance and Banking, O
Fine/Studio Arts, B
French Language and Literature, B
Geographic Information Systems, MO
German Language and Literature, B
History, B
Interdisciplinary Studies, B
International Business/Trade/Commerce, O
International Relations and Affairs, B
Liberal Arts and Sciences Studies and
    Humanities, B
Management, M
Management Information Systems and
    Services, BMO
Mathematics, B
Music, BM
Music History, Literature, and Theory, B
Music Performance, B
Music Teacher Education, B
Music Theory and Composition, B
Philosophy, B
Physics, B
Piano and Organ, B
Political Science and Government, B
Psychology, B
Religion/Religious Studies, B
Secondary Education and Teaching, B
Sociology, B
Spanish Language and Literature, B
Voice and Opera, B

UNIVERSITY OF SAN DIEGO

Accounting, BM
Anthropology, B
Art/Art Studies, General, B
Biology/Biological Sciences, B
Business Administration and Management, B
Business Administration, Management and
    Operations, MO
Business/Managerial Economics, B
Chemistry, B
Computer Science, B
Conflict Resolution and Mediation/Peace Studies, M
Counselor Education/School Counseling and
    Guidance Services, M
Curriculum and Instruction, MD
Drama and Dramatics/Theatre Arts, B
Economics, B
Education, MDO
Educational Leadership and Administration, MDO
Electrical, Electronics and Communications
    Engineering, B
English Language and Literature, B
Environmental Studies, B
Finance and Banking, M
French Language and Literature, B
Geosciences, B
Hispanic-American, Puerto Rican, and Mexican-
    American/Chicano Studies, B
History, BM
Humanities/Humanistic Studies, B
Industrial Engineering, B
International Affairs, MO
International Relations and Affairs, B
Law and Legal Studies, MPO
Legal and Justice Studies, M
Liberal Arts and Sciences Studies and
    Humanities, B
Marine Affairs, M
Marine Science/Merchant Marine Officer, B
Marine Sciences, M

Marriage and Family Therapy/Counseling, M
Mass Communication/Media Studies, B
Mathematics, B
Mechanical Engineering, B
Music, B
Non-Profit/Public/Organizational Management, O
Nursing, MDO
Nursing - Adult, O
Nursing - Advanced Practice, MO
Nursing Administration, M
Pastoral Studies/Counseling, MO
Pediatric Nurse/Nursing, MO
Philosophy, B
Physics, B
Political Science and Government, B
Pre-Medicine/Pre-Medical Studies, B
Psychology, B
Religion/Religious Studies, B
Sociology, B
Spanish Language and Literature, B
Taxation, MO
Theater, M
Theology and Religious Vocations, M
Urban Studies/Affairs, B
Visual and Performing Arts, B

UNIVERSITY OF SAN FRANCISCO

Accounting, B
Adult and Continuing Education and Teaching, B
Applied Economics, B
Architecture, B
Art History, Criticism and Conservation, B
Art/Art Studies, General, B
Arts Management, B
Asian Studies/Civilization, BM
Bilingual and Multilingual Education, B
Biological and Biomedical Sciences, M
Biology/Biological Sciences, B
Business Administration and Management, B
Business Administration, Management and
  Operations, MO
Business/Commerce, B
Chemistry, BM
City/Urban, Community and Regional Planning, B
Communication Studies/Speech Communication
  and Rhetoric, B
Computer and Information Sciences, B
Computer Science, BM
Counseling Psychology, MD
Counselor Education/School Counseling and
  Guidance Services, M
Curriculum and Instruction, MD
Drawing, B
Economics, BM
Education, BMD
Educational Administration and Supervision, MD
Educational Leadership and Administration, B
Educational Media/Instructional Technology, M
Electronic Commerce, M
Elementary Education and Teaching, B
English as a Second Language, M
English Language and Literature, B
Environmental Sciences, B
Environmental Studies, B
Finance, B
Finance and Banking, M
Fine/Studio Arts, B
French Language and Literature, B
Graphic Design, B
Health and Physical Education, B
Health Services Administration, M
History, B
Hotel/Motel Administration/Management, B
Illustration, B
Information Science/Studies, B
Interdisciplinary Studies, B
International and Comparative Education, MD
International Business/Trade/Commerce, BM
Internet and Interactive Multimedia, M
Japanese Studies, B
Latin American Studies, B
Law and Legal Studies, MPO
Liberal Arts and Sciences Studies and
  Humanities, B
Management, M

Management Information Systems and
  Services, BM
Marketing, M
Marketing/Marketing Management, B
Mass Communication/Media Studies, B
Mathematics, B
Multilingual and Multicultural Education, MD
Natural Resources Management/Development and
  Policy, M
Non-Profit/Public/Organizational Management, M
Nursing, MO
Nursing - Advanced Practice, M
Nursing - Registered Nurse Training, B
Nursing Administration, BM
Organizational Behavior Studies, B
Organizational Management, M
Painting, B
Pastoral Studies/Counseling, M
Philosophy, B
Physical Education Teaching and Coaching, B
Physics, B
Political Science and Government, B
Pre-Dentistry Studies, B
Pre-Medicine/Pre-Medical Studies, B
Pre-Veterinary Studies, B
Printmaking, B
Psychology, B
Public Administration, BM
Religion/Religious Studies, B
Religious Education, MD
Restaurant/Food Services Management, B
Secondary Education and Teaching, B
Sociology, B
Spanish Language and Literature, B
Sport and Fitness Administration/Management, M
Telecommunications Management, M
Theology and Religious Vocations, M
Theology/Theological Studies, B
Visual and Performing Arts, B
Writing, M

UNIVERSITY OF SOUTHERN CALIFORNIA

Accounting, BM
Acting, B
Advertising and Public Relations, M
Aerospace, Aeronautical and Astronautical
  Engineering, BMDO
African-American/Black Studies, B
Allied Health and Medical Assisting Services, MD
Allopathic Medicine, PO
American Literature (United States), B
American/United States Studies/Civilization, BD
Anthropology, BMDO
Applied Mathematics, MD
Architecture, BMO
Art History, Criticism and Conservation, BMDO
Art/Art Studies, General, B
Artificial Intelligence and Robotics, M
Arts Management, M
Asian Languages, MDO
Asian-American Studies, B
Astronomy, B
Biochemistry, BMD
Biological and Biomedical Sciences, MDO
Biology/Biological Sciences, B
Biomedical Engineering, MD
Biomedical/Medical Engineering, B
Biometry/Biometrics, M
Biophysics, BMDO
Biostatistics, MD
Broadcast Journalism, B
Building Science, MO
Business Administration and Management, B
Business Administration, Management and
  Operations, BMDO
Business, Management, Marketing, and Related
  Support Services, B
Cell Biology and Anatomy, MD
Chemical Engineering, BMDO
Chemistry, BMD
Cinematography and Film/Video Production, B
City/Urban, Community and Regional Planning, B
Civil Engineering, BMDO
Classics and Classical
  Languages, Literatures, and Linguistics, BMD

Clinical Psychology, D
Communication and Media Studies, MDO
Communication Studies/Speech Communication
  and Rhetoric, B
Communication Theory, D
Comparative Literature, BMD
Composition, MD
Computational Biology, D
Computer and Information Sciences, B
Computer Engineering, BMD
Computer Science, BMD
Construction Engineering, B
Construction Engineering and Management, M
Corporate and Organizational Communication, O
Counseling Psychology, MDO
Creative Writing, B
Curriculum and Instruction, MD
Dental Hygiene/Hygienist, B
Dentistry, PO
Directing and Theatrical Production, B
Drama and Dramatics/Theatre Arts, B
East Asian
  Languages, Literatures, and Linguistics, B
East Asian Studies, BMDO
Economics, BMDO
Education, BMDO
Educational Administration and Supervision, MD
Educational Leadership and Administration, M
Educational Media/Instructional Technology, M
Educational Psychology, D
Electrical Engineering, MDO
Electrical, Electronics and Communications
  Engineering, B
Engineering, B
Engineering and Applied Sciences, MDO
Engineering Management, M
English as a Second Language, M
English Language and Literature, B
English Literature (British and Commonwealth), B
Environmental Engineering
  Technology/Environmental Technology, MD
Environmental Studies, B
Environmental/Environmental Health Engineering, B
Epidemiology, MD
Ethnic and Cultural Studies, B
Film, Television, and Video Production, M
Film, Television, and Video Theory and
  Criticism, MD
Film/Cinema Studies, B
Finance and Banking, M
Fine Arts and Art Studies, M
Fine/Studio Arts, B
French Language and Literature, BMD
General Studies, B
Genetics, D
Geography, BMD
Geology/Earth Science, B
Geosciences, MD
Geotechnical Engineering, M
German Language and Literature, B
Gerontology, BMDO
Health Promotion, M
Health Services Administration, MO
Health Services Research, MD
Hispanic-American, Puerto Rican, and Mexican-
  American/Chicano Studies, B
Historic Preservation and Conservation, O
History, BMD
Immunology, MD
Industrial/Management Engineering, MDO
Interdisciplinary Studies, B
International Affairs, MDO
International and Comparative Education, M
International Business/Trade/Commerce, BM
International Relations and Affairs, B
Internet and Interactive Multimedia, M
Italian Language and Literature, B
Jazz/Jazz Studies, B
Jewish/Judaic Studies, B
Journalism, BM
Kinesiology and Exercise Science, B
Kinesiology and Movement Studies, MD
Landscape Architecture, BMO
Law and Legal Studies, MPO
Linguistics, BMD
Management Information Systems and Services, M

Manufacturing Engineering, M
Marine Biology and Biological Oceanography, D
Marine Sciences, D
Marriage and Family Therapy/Counseling, O
Mass Communication/Media Studies, B
Materials Engineering, M
Materials Sciences, MDO
Mathematics, BMD
Mechanical Engineering, BMDO
Mechanics, M
Media Studies, MO
Microbiology, MD
Molecular Biology, MD
Molecular Pharmacology, MDO
Music, BMD
Music History, Literature, and Theory, M
Music Management and Merchandising, B
Music Performance, B
Music Teacher Education, BMD
Music Theory and Composition, B
Musicology and Ethnomusicology, D
Neurobiology and Neurophysiology, MD
Neuroscience, BD
Nutritional Sciences, M
Occupational Therapy/Therapist, BMD
Ocean Engineering, M
Oceanography, Chemical and Physical, D
Operations Research, M
Oral and Dental Sciences, MD
Pathobiology, D
Pathology/Experimental Pathology, MD
Performance, MD
Petroleum Engineering, BMDO
Pharmaceutical Sciences, MDO
Pharmacy, PO
Philosophy, BMDO
Physical Chemistry, D
Physical Sciences, B
Physical Therapy/Therapist, MD
Physician Assistant, M
Physics, BMD
Physiological Psychology/Psychobiology, B
Physiology, MDO
Playwriting and Screenwriting, B
Political Science and Government, BMD
Polymer/Plastics Engineering, B
Portuguese Language and Literature, B
Psychology, BMD
Public Administration, BMDO
Public Health, M
Public Health (MPH, DPH), B
Public Health Education and Promotion, B
Public Policy Analysis, MD
Public Relations/Image Management, B
Radio and Television, B
Reading Teacher Education, D
Real Estate, MO
Religion/Religious Studies, BMDO
Russian Language and Literature, B
Sacred Music, MD
Slavic Languages, Literatures, and Linguistics, BMD
Social Sciences, B
Social Work, MDO
Sociology, BMD
Software Engineering, M
Spanish Language and Literature, B
Special Education and Teaching, M
Statistics, M
Structural Engineering, BM
Student Personnel Services, M
Systems Engineering, BMDO
Taxation, MO
Technical Theatre/Theatre Design and
    Technology, B
Theater, M
Theatre/Theatre Arts Management, B
Toxicology, MDO
Transportation and Highway Engineering, M
Urban and Regional Planning, MDO
Urban Studies/Affairs, B
Violin, Viola, Guitar and Other Stringed
    Instruments, B
Water Resources Engineering, BM
Wind and Percussion Instruments, B

Writing, M

UNIVERSITY OF THE WEST

Asian History, B
Buddhist Studies, B
Business Administration and Management, B
Business Administration, Management and
    Operations, M
Chinese Studies, B
English Language and Literature, B
Finance and Banking, M
History, B
International Business/Trade/Commerce, M
Management Information Systems and Services, M
Non-Profit/Public/Organizational Management, M
Philosophy, B
Psychology, B
Religion/Religious Studies, BMD

UNIVERSITY OF WEST LOS ANGELES

Law and Legal Studies, BP
Legal Administrative Assistant/Secretary, B
Legal Assistant/Paralegal, B
Pre-Law Studies, B

VANGUARD UNIVERSITY OF SOUTHERN CALIFORNIA

Accounting, B
Anthropology, B
Athletic Training and Sports Medicine, B
Bible/Biblical Studies, B
Biological and Physical Sciences, B
Biology/Biological Sciences, B
Business Administration and Management, B
Business Administration, Management and
    Operations, M
Chemistry, B
Cinematography and Film/Video Production, B
Clinical Psychology, M
Communication Studies/Speech Communication
    and Rhetoric, B
Drama and Dramatics/Theatre Arts, B
Education, BM
English Language and Literature, B
Finance, B
Health and Physical Education, B
History, B
Interdisciplinary Studies, B
International Business/Trade/Commerce, B
Kinesiology and Exercise Science, B
Marketing/Marketing Management, B
Mathematics, B
Missions/Missionary Studies and Missiology, B
Music, B
Organizational Management, M
Pastoral Studies/Counseling, B
Physical Education Teaching and Coaching, B
Physical Therapy/Therapist, B
Political Science and Government, B
Pre-Law Studies, B
Psychology, B
Radio and Television, B
Religion/Religious Studies, BM
Religious Education, B
Secondary Education and Teaching, B
Sociology, B
Spanish Language and Literature, B
Speech and Rhetorical Studies, B
Theology and Religious Vocations, M
Youth Ministry, B

VENTURA COLLEGE

Accounting, A
Agriculture, A
Automobile/Automotive Mechanics
    Technology/Technician, A
Biology/Biological Sciences, A
Business Administration and Management, A
Ceramic Arts and Ceramics, A
Commercial and Advertising Art, A
Computer and Information Sciences, A
Construction Engineering Technology/Technician, A
Criminal Justice/Law Enforcement Administration, A
Drama and Dramatics/Theatre Arts, A
Engineering, A

Fashion/Apparel Design, A
Fine/Studio Arts, A
Hydrology and Water Resources Science, A
Journalism, A
Liberal Arts and Sciences Studies and
    Humanities, A
Machine Tool Technology/Machinist, A
Medical Transcription/Transcriptionist, A
Medical/Clinical Assistant, A
Music, A
Natural Resources Management/Development and
    Policy, A
Nursing - Registered Nurse Training, A
Parks, Recreation, Leisure and Fitness Studies, A
Physical Sciences, A
Plant Sciences, A
Real Estate, A
Tool and Die Technology/Technician, A
Welding Technology/Welder, A

VICTOR VALLEY COLLEGE

Administrative Assistant and Secretarial Science, A
Agricultural Teacher Education, A
Art/Art Studies, General, A
Automobile/Automotive Mechanics
    Technology/Technician, A
Biological and Physical Sciences, A
Biology/Biological Sciences, A
Building/Construction
    Finishing, Management, and Inspection, A
Business Administration and Management, A
Business/Commerce, A
Child Care and Support Services Management, A
Child Development, A
Computer and Information Sciences, A
Computer Programming, Specific Applications, A
Computer Science, A
Construction Engineering Technology/Technician, A
Criminal Justice/Police Science, A
Drama and Dramatics/Theatre Arts, A
Electrical, Electronic and Communications
    Engineering Technology/Technician, A
Fire Protection and Safety Technology/Technician, A
Fire Science/Firefighting, A
Food Technology and Processing, A
Horticultural Science, A
Humanities/Humanistic Studies, A
Information Science/Studies, A
Kindergarten/PreSchool Education and Teaching, A
Liberal Arts and Sciences Studies and
    Humanities, A
Management Information Systems and Services, A
Mathematics, A
Music, A
Natural Sciences, A
Nursing - Registered Nurse Training, A
Ornamental Horticulture, A
Physical Sciences, A
Real Estate, A
Respiratory Care Therapy/Therapist, A
Science Technologies/Technicians, A
Social Sciences, A
Teacher Assistant/Aide, A
Trade and Industrial Teacher Education, A
Vehicle Maintenance and Repair Technologies, A
Welding Technology/Welder, A

WEST HILLS COMMUNITY COLLEGE

Accounting, A
Administrative Assistant and Secretarial Science, A
Agricultural Business and Management, A
Agricultural Mechanization, A
Agronomy and Crop Science, A
Animal Sciences, A
Art/Art Studies, General, A
Automobile/Automotive Mechanics
    Technology/Technician, A
Biology/Biological Sciences, A
Business Administration and Management, A
Chemistry, A
Child Development, A
Criminal Justice/Law Enforcement Administration, A
Equestrian/Equine Studies, A
Geography, A
Geology/Earth Science, A
Humanities/Humanistic Studies, A

Information Science/Studies, A
Kindergarten/PreSchool Education and Teaching, A
Liberal Arts and Sciences Studies and
    Humanities, A
Mathematics, A
Physical Education Teaching and Coaching, A
Physics, A
Pre-Engineering, A
Psychology, A
Public Health (MPH, DPH), A
Social Sciences, A
Transportation and Materials Moving, A
Welding Technology/Welder, A

WEST LOS ANGELES COLLEGE

Accounting, A
Administrative Assistant and Secretarial Science, A
Airframe Mechanics and Aircraft Maintenance
    Technology/Technician, A
Anthropology, A
Art/Art Studies, General, A
Avionics Maintenance Technology/Technician, A
Biology/Biological Sciences, A
Business Administration and Management, A
Chemistry, A
Computer Programming/Programmer, A
Consumer Merchandising/Retailing Management, A
Criminal Justice/Law Enforcement Administration, A
Criminal Justice/Police Science, A
Data Processing and Data Processing
    Technology/Technician, A
Dental Hygiene/Hygienist, A
Developmental and Child Psychology, A
Drafting and Design Technology/Technician, A
Economics, A
Education, A
Electrical, Electronic and Communications
    Engineering Technology/Technician, A
Engineering, A
English Language and Literature, A
Family and Consumer Economics and Related
    Services, A
French Language and Literature, A
Geography, A
Geology/Earth Science, A
History, A
Journalism, A
Legal Administrative Assistant/Secretary, A
Legal Assistant/Paralegal, A
Liberal Arts and Sciences Studies and
    Humanities, A
Marketing/Marketing Management, A
Mathematics, A
Medical Administrative Assistant/Secretary, A
Music, A
Philosophy, A
Physical Education Teaching and Coaching, A
Physics, A
Political Science and Government, A
Psychology, A
Real Estate, A
Sociology, A
Spanish Language and Literature, A
Speech and Rhetorical Studies, A
Tourism and Travel Services Management, A

WEST VALLEY COLLEGE

Accounting, A
Administrative Assistant and Secretarial Science, A
Art/Art Studies, General, A
Biology/Biological Sciences, A
Business Administration and Management, A
Chemistry, A
Court Reporting/Court Reporter, A
Criminal Justice/Law Enforcement Administration, A
Criminal Justice/Police Science, A
Data Processing and Data Processing
    Technology/Technician, A
Drafting and Design Technology/Technician, A
Drama and Dramatics/Theatre Arts, A
Economics, A
English Language and Literature, A
Fashion/Apparel Design, A
French Language and Literature, A
German Language and Literature, A

Health Information/Medical Records
    Administration/Administrator, A
History, A
Information Science/Studies, A
Interior Design, A
Italian Language and Literature, A
Kindergarten/PreSchool Education and Teaching, A
Landscape Architecture, A
Legal Administrative Assistant/Secretary, A
Liberal Arts and Sciences Studies and
    Humanities, A
Marketing/Marketing Management, A
Mathematics, A
Medical Administrative Assistant/Secretary, A
Medical/Clinical Assistant, A
Music, A
Parks, Recreation and Leisure Facilities
    Management, A
Physical Education Teaching and Coaching, A
Physics, A
Psychology, A
Social Sciences, A
Sociology, A
Spanish Language and Literature, A
Speech and Rhetorical Studies, A
Women's Studies, A

WESTERN CAREER COLLEGE (SAN JOSE)

Architectural Drafting and Architectural
    CAD/CADD, A
Computer Graphics, AB
Mechanical Drafting and Mechanical Drafting
    CAD/CADD, A
Medical/Clinical Assistant, A
Pharmacy Technician/Assistant, A
System Administration/Administrator, A

WESTERN CAREER COLLEGE (WALNUT CREEK)

Animation, Interactive Technology, Video Graphics
    and Special Effects, AB
Architectural Drafting and Architectural
    CAD/CADD, A
Architectural Technology/Technician, A
Architecture, A
Architecture and Related Services, A
CAD/CADD Drafting and/or Design
    Technology/Technician, A
Design and Visual Communications, B
Drafting and Design Technology/Technician, A
Graphic and Printing Equipment Operator
    Production, A
Graphic Communications, AB
Health and Medical Administrative Services, A
Information Technology, A
Mechanical Drafting and Mechanical Drafting
    CAD/CADD, A
Medical Administrative Assistant/Secretary, A
Medical Office Assistant/Specialist, A
Pharmacology and Toxicology, A
Pharmacy Technician/Assistant, A
Prepress/Desktop Publishing and Digital Imaging
    Design, AB
System Administration/Administrator, A
System, Networking, and LAN/WAN
    Management/Manager, A

WESTMONT COLLEGE

Anthropology, B
Art Teacher Education, B
Art/Art Studies, General, B
Biology/Biological Sciences, B
Business/Commerce, B
Business/Managerial Economics, B
Chemistry, B
Communication Studies/Speech Communication
    and Rhetoric, B
Computer Science, B
Dance, B
Drama and Dramatics/Theatre Arts, B
Economics, B
Education, B
Elementary Education and Teaching, B
Engineering Physics, B
English Language and Literature, B

English/Language Arts Teacher Education, B
French Language and Literature, B
History, B
Kinesiology and Exercise Science, B
Liberal Arts and Sciences Studies and
    Humanities, B
Mathematics, B
Mathematics Teacher Education, B
Modern Languages, B
Music, B
Neuroscience, B
Philosophy, B
Physical Education Teaching and Coaching, B
Physics, B
Political Science and Government, B
Pre-Dentistry Studies, B
Pre-Law Studies, B
Pre-Medicine/Pre-Medical Studies, B
Pre-Pharmacy Studies, B
Pre-Theology/Pre-Ministerial Studies, B
Pre-Veterinary Studies, B
Psychology, B
Religion/Religious Studies, B
Secondary Education and Teaching, B
Social Science Teacher Education, B
Social Sciences, B
Sociology, B
Spanish Language and Literature, B

WESTWOOD COLLEGE-ANAHEIM

Accounting and Business/Management, B
Animation, Interactive Technology, Video Graphics
    and Special Effects, B
Architectural Drafting and Architectural
    CAD/CADD, A
Computer and Information Systems Security, B
Computer Systems Networking and
    Telecommunications, AB
Corrections and Criminal Justice, B
Design and Applied Arts, B
Design and Visual Communications, B
E-Commerce/Electronic Commerce, B
Graphic Design, A
Interior Design, B
Intermedia/Multimedia, AB
Marketing/Marketing Management, B

WESTWOOD COLLEGE-INLAND EMPIRE

Accounting, B
Accounting and Business/Management, B
Animation, Interactive Technology, Video Graphics
    and Special Effects, B
Architectural Drafting and Architectural
    CAD/CADD, A
Commercial and Advertising Art, A
Computer and Information Systems Security, B
Computer Programming, Specific Applications, B
Computer Programming/Programmer, A
Computer Software and Media Applications, B
Computer Systems Networking and
    Telecommunications, AB
Corrections and Criminal Justice, B
Design and Applied Arts, B
Design and Visual Communications, B
E-Commerce/Electronic Commerce, B
Fashion Merchandising, B
Graphic Design, A
Interior Design, B
Intermedia/Multimedia, AB
Marketing/Marketing Management, B
System, Networking, and LAN/WAN
    Management/Manager, B
Web Page, Digital/Multimedia and Information
    Resources Design, B
Web/Multimedia Management and Webmaster, B

WESTWOOD COLLEGE-LONG BEACH

Architectural Drafting and Architectural
    CAD/CADD, A
Computer and Information Systems Security, B
Computer Systems Networking and
    Telecommunications, AB
Corrections and Criminal Justice, B
Design and Visual Communications, B
Fashion Merchandising, B

Graphic Design, A
Web Page, Digital/Multimedia and Information
    Resources Design, A

WESTWOOD COLLEGE-LOS ANGELES

Accounting and Business/Management, B
Computer Programming/Programmer, A
Computer Systems Networking and
    Telecommunications, AB
Corrections and Criminal Justice, B
Design and Visual Communications, B
E-Commerce/Electronic Commerce, B
Fashion Merchandising, A
Graphic Design, AB
Interior Design, B
Intermedia/Multimedia, A
Marketing/Marketing Management, B
Web/Multimedia Management and Webmaster, B

WHITTIER COLLEGE

Art/Art Studies, General, B
Biochemistry, B
Biology/Biological Sciences, B
Business Administration and Management, B
Chemistry, B
Developmental and Child Psychology, B
Drama and Dramatics/Theatre Arts, B
Economics, B
Education, M
Educational Administration and Supervision, M
Elementary Education and Teaching, M
English Language and Literature, B
French Language and Literature, B
History, B
International Relations and Affairs, B
Kindergarten/PreSchool Education and Teaching, B
Law and Legal Studies, MP
Legal and Justice Studies, M
Liberal Arts and Sciences Studies and
    Humanities, B
Mathematics, B
Music, B
Philosophy, B
Physical Education Teaching and Coaching, B
Physics, B
Political Science and Government, B
Psychology, B
Religion/Religious Studies, B
Secondary Education and Teaching, M
Social Work, B
Sociology, B

WILLIAM JESSUP UNIVERSITY

Business Administration, Management and
    Operations, B
Education, B
Intercultural/Multicultural and Diversity Studies, B
Psychology, B
Theology/Theological Studies, AB
Visual and Performing Arts, B

WOODBURY UNIVERSITY

Accounting, B
Architecture, B
Business Administration and Management, B
Business Administration, Management and
    Operations, BM
Commercial and Advertising Art, B
Communication Studies/Speech Communication
    and Rhetoric, B
Fashion Merchandising, B
Fashion/Apparel Design, B
Film/Video and Photographic Arts, B
History, B
Information Science/Studies, B
Interdisciplinary Studies, B
Interior Architecture, B
Marketing/Marketing Management, B
Organizational Behavior Studies, B
Organizational Management, M
Political Science and Government, B

Psychology, B

WYOTECH (FREMONT)

Automobile/Automotive Mechanics
    Technology/Technician, A
Automotive Engineering Technology/Technician, A
Heating, Air Conditioning, Ventilation and
    Refrigeration Maintenance
    Technology/Technician, A

YESHIVA OHR ELCHONON
CHABAD/WEST COAST TALMUDICAL
SEMINARY

Jewish/Judaic Studies, B
Religion/Religious Studies, B
Theology/Theological Studies, B

YUBA COLLEGE

Accounting, A
Administrative Assistant and Secretarial Science, A
Advertising, A
African-American/Black Studies, A
Agricultural Business and Management, A
Agricultural Mechanization, A
Agriculture, A
Agronomy and Crop Science, A
Animal Sciences, A
Art/Art Studies, General, A
Automobile/Automotive Mechanics
    Technology/Technician, A
Biological and Physical Sciences, A
Biology/Biological Sciences, A
Business Administration and Management, A
Chemistry, A
Child Development, A
Communication Studies/Speech Communication
    and Rhetoric, A
Computer and Information Sciences, A
Computer Science, A
Corrections, A
Cosmetology/Cosmetologist, A
Criminal Justice/Law Enforcement Administration, A
Criminal Justice/Police Science, A
Drama and Dramatics/Theatre Arts, A
Education, A
Electrical, Electronic and Communications
    Engineering Technology/Technician, A
Elementary Education and Teaching, A
English Language and Literature, A
Ethnic and Cultural Studies, A
Family and Consumer Economics and Related
    Services, A
Family and Consumer Sciences/Human Sciences, A
Fire Science/Firefighting, A
Health Teacher Education, A
Hispanic-American, Puerto Rican, and Mexican-
    American/Chicano Studies, A
History, A
Human Services, A
Industrial Radiologic Technology/Technician, A
Industrial Technology/Technician, A
Kindergarten/PreSchool Education and Teaching, A
Licensed Practical/Vocational Nurse Training, A
Machine Tool Technology/Machinist, A
Mass Communication/Media Studies, A
Mathematics, A
Music, A
Nursing - Registered Nurse Training, A
Philosophy, A
Photography, A
Physical Education Teaching and Coaching, A
Pre-Engineering, A
Psychiatric/Mental Health Services Technician, A
Psychology, A
Robotics Technology/Technician, A
Social Sciences, A
Substance Abuse/Addiction Counseling, A
Veterinary/Animal Health Technology/Technician and
    Veterinary Assistant, A
Welding Technology/Welder, A
Women's Studies, A

Word Processing, A

Colorado

ADAMS STATE COLLEGE

Agribusiness, A
Art/Art Studies, General, B
Biological and Physical Sciences, B
Biology/Biological Sciences, B
Business Administration and Management, B
Chemistry, B
Communication Studies/Speech Communication
    and Rhetoric, B
Counselor Education/School Counseling and
    Guidance Services, M
Drama and Dramatics/Theatre Arts, B
Education, M
Elementary Education and Teaching, B
English Language and Literature, B
Fine Arts and Art Studies, M
Geology/Earth Science, B
Health Education, M
History, B
Kinesiology and Exercise Science, B
Liberal Arts and Sciences Studies and
    Humanities, AB
Mathematics, B
Music, B
Music Performance, B
Physical Education Teaching and Coaching, M
Political Science and Government, B
Pre-Dentistry Studies, B
Pre-Engineering, B
Pre-Law Studies, B
Pre-Medicine/Pre-Medical Studies, B
Pre-Nursing Studies, B
Pre-Pharmacy Studies, B
Pre-Veterinary Studies, B
Psychology, B
Secondary Education and Teaching, B
Social Sciences, B
Sociology, B
Spanish Language and Literature, B
Special Education and Teaching, M
Speech and Rhetorical Studies, B

AIMS COMMUNITY COLLEGE

Accounting, A
Administrative Assistant and Secretarial Science, A
Agricultural Mechanization, A
Automobile/Automotive Mechanics
    Technology/Technician, A
Avionics Maintenance Technology/Technician, A
Child Development, A
Commercial and Advertising Art, A
Criminal Justice/Law Enforcement Administration, A
Criminal Justice/Police Science, A
Electrical, Electronic and Communications
    Engineering Technology/Technician, A
Engineering Technology, A
Fire Science/Firefighting, A
Industrial Radiologic Technology/Technician, A
Information Science/Studies, A
Kindergarten/PreSchool Education and Teaching, A
Liberal Arts and Sciences Studies and
    Humanities, A
Marketing/Marketing Management, A
Welding Technology/Welder, A

ARAPAHOE COMMUNITY COLLEGE

Administrative Assistant and Secretarial Science, A
Architectural Engineering Technology/Technician, A
Automobile/Automotive Mechanics
    Technology/Technician, A
Biological and Physical Sciences, A
Building/Construction
    Finishing, Management, and Inspection, A
Building/Home/Construction Inspection/Inspector, A
Business Administration and Management, A
Child Care and Support Services Management, A
Child Care Provider/Assistant, A
Clinical Laboratory Science/Medical
    Technology/Technologist, A
Clinical/Medical Laboratory Technician, A
Commercial and Advertising Art, A

Communications Systems Installation and Repair
Technology, A
Communications Technology/Technician, A
Computer Graphics, A
Computer Programming, A
Computer Programming, Specific Applications, A
Computer Programming/Programmer, A
Computer Science, A
Computer Software and Media Applications, A
Computer Systems Networking and
Telecommunications, A
Computer/Information Technology Services
Administration and Management, A
Consumer Merchandising/Retailing Management, A
Criminal Justice/Law Enforcement Administration, A
Criminal Justice/Police Science, A
Data Modeling/Warehousing and Database
Administration, A
Drafting and Design Technology/Technician, A
Drafting/Design Engineering
Technologies/Technicians, A
Electrical, Electronic and Communications
Engineering Technology/Technician, A
Emergency Medical Technology/Technician (EMT
Paramedic), A
Environmental Engineering
Technology/Environmental Technology, A
Finance, A
Food Technology and Processing, A
Funeral Service and Mortuary Science, A
Health Information/Medical Records
Administration/Administrator, A
Information Science/Studies, A
Legal Administrative Assistant/Secretary, A
Legal Assistant/Paralegal, A
Liberal Arts and Sciences Studies and
Humanities, A
Management Information Systems and Services, A
Marketing/Marketing Management, A
Medical/Clinical Assistant, A
Nursing - Registered Nurse Training, A
Physical Therapy/Therapist, A
Tourism and Travel Services Management, A

ARGOSY UNIVERSITY/DENVER

Business Administration, Management and
Operations, A
Criminal Justice/Law Enforcement Administration, A
Legal Assistant/Paralegal, A
Medical/Clinical Assistant, A

THE ART INSTITUTE OF COLORADO

Advertising, B
Art/Art Studies, General, AB
Cinematography and Film/Video Production, A
Commercial and Advertising Art, AB
Computer Graphics, AB
Culinary Arts/Chef Training, AB
Industrial Design, B
Interior Design, B
Intermedia/Multimedia, A
Photography, A

ASPEN UNIVERSITY

Business Administration, Management and
Operations, MO
Information Science/Studies, M
Management Information Systems and
Services, MO
Project Management, MO

BEL-REA INSTITUTE OF ANIMAL TECHNOLOGY

Veterinary/Animal Health Technology/Technician and
Veterinary Assistant, A

BLAIR COLLEGE

Accounting, A
Administrative Assistant and Secretarial Science, A
Business Administration and Management, A
Computer Programming/Programmer, A
Computer Science, A
Legal Assistant/Paralegal, A
Medical Administrative Assistant/Secretary, A
Medical/Clinical Assistant, A

Tourism and Travel Services Management, A

COLLEGEAMERICA-FORT COLLINS

Accounting, B
Business Administration and Management, AB
Computer and Information Sciences, B
Computer Graphics, A
Computer Installation and Repair
Technology/Technician, A
Computer Programming, Specific Applications, A
Computer Programming/Programmer, A
Computer Systems Networking and
Telecommunications, A
Medical/Clinical Assistant, A
Web Page, Digital/Multimedia and Information
Resources Design, A

COLORADO CHRISTIAN UNIVERSITY

Accounting, B
Art/Art Studies, General, B
Bible/Biblical Studies, B
Biological and Physical Sciences, B
Biology/Biological Sciences, B
Business Administration and Management, B
Business Administration, Management and
Operations, M
Communication Studies/Speech Communication
and Rhetoric, B
Computer and Information Sciences, B
Counseling Psychology, M
Curriculum and Instruction, M
Drama and Dramatics/Theatre Arts, B
Education, M
English Language and Literature, B
Fine/Studio Arts, B
Health and Physical Education, B
History, B
International/Global Studies, B
Liberal Arts and Sciences Studies and
Humanities, AB
Management Information Systems and Services, AB
Management Science, B
Mathematics, B
Music, B
Music Performance, B
Music Teacher Education, B
Political Science and Government, B
Psychology, B
Social Sciences, B
Youth Ministry, B

THE COLORADO COLLEGE

Anthropology, B
Art Education, M
Art History, Criticism and Conservation, B
Asian Studies/Civilization, B
Biochemistry, B
Biology/Biological Sciences, B
Chemistry, B
Classics and Classical
Languages, Literatures, and Linguistics, B
Comparative Literature, B
Creative Writing, B
Dance, B
Drama and Dramatics/Theatre Arts, B
Econometrics and Quantitative Economics, B
Economics, B
Education, M
Elementary Education and Teaching, M
English Education, M
English Language and Literature, B
Environmental Sciences, B
Ethnic, Cultural Minority, and Gender Studies, B
Film/Cinema Studies, B
Fine/Studio Arts, B
Foreign Language Teacher Education, M
French Language and Literature, B
French Studies, B
Geology/Earth Science, B
German Language and Literature, B
Hispanic-American, Puerto Rican, and Mexican-
American/Chicano Studies, B
History, B
International Economics, B
Italian Language and Literature, B

Liberal Arts and Sciences Studies and
Humanities, B
Mathematics, B
Mathematics and Computer Science, B
Mathematics Teacher Education, M
Multi-/Interdisciplinary Studies, B
Music, B
Music Teacher Education, M
Neuroscience, B
Philosophy, B
Physics, B
Political Science and Government, B
Psychology, B
Religion/Religious Studies, B
Romance Languages, Literatures, and Linguistics, B
Russian Language and Literature, B
Russian Studies, B
Science Teacher Education/General Science
Teacher Education, M
Secondary Education and Teaching, M
Social Sciences, B
Social Studies Teacher Education, M
Sociology, B
Spanish Language and Literature, B
Women's Studies, B

COLORADO MOUNTAIN COLLEGE

Accounting, A
Behavioral Sciences, A
Biological and Physical Sciences, A
Biology/Biological Sciences, A
Business Administration and Management, A
Commercial and Advertising Art, A
Computer Engineering Technology/Technician, A
Computer Systems Networking and
Telecommunications, A
Criminal Justice/Law Enforcement Administration, A
Data Entry/Microcomputer Applications, A
Drama and Dramatics/Theatre Arts, A
English Language and Literature, A
Humanities/Humanistic Studies, A
Liberal Arts and Sciences Studies and
Humanities, A
Licensed Practical/Vocational Nurse Training, A
Management Information Systems and Services, A
Mathematics, A
Natural Sciences, A
Nursing - Registered Nurse Training, A
Photography, A
Psychology, A
Social Sciences, A
Therapeutic Recreation/Recreational Therapy, A
Veterinary/Animal Health Technology/Technician and
Veterinary Assistant, A

COLORADO MOUNTAIN COLLEGE, ALPINE CAMPUS

Accounting, A
Behavioral Sciences, A
Biological and Physical Sciences, A
Biology/Biological Sciences, A
Business Administration and Management, A
Computer Engineering Technology/Technician, A
Consumer Merchandising/Retailing Management, A
Data Entry/Microcomputer Applications, A
English Language and Literature, A
Fine/Studio Arts, A
Geology/Earth Science, A
Hospitality Administration/Management, A
Hotel/Motel Administration/Management, A
Humanities/Humanistic Studies, A
Liberal Arts and Sciences Studies and
Humanities, A
Marketing/Marketing Management, A
Mathematics, A
Parks, Recreation and Leisure Facilities
Management, A
Physical Sciences, A
Pre-Engineering, A
Social Sciences, A

COLORADO MOUNTAIN COLLEGE, TIMBERLINE CAMPUS

Accounting, A
Business/Commerce, A
Corrections, A

Criminal Justice/Law Enforcement Administration, A
Early Childhood Education and Teaching, A
Environmental Studies, A
General Studies, A
Historic Preservation and Conservation, A
Land Use Planning and
    Management/Development, A
Liberal Arts and Sciences Studies and
    Humanities, A
Parks, Recreation and Leisure Facilities
    Management, A
Parks, Recreation, Leisure and Fitness Studies, A

COLORADO NORTHWESTERN COMMUNITY COLLEGE

Accounting, A
Aesthetician/Esthetician and Skin Care Specialist, A
Aircraft Powerplant Technology/Technician, A
Airframe Mechanics and Aircraft Maintenance
    Technology/Technician, A
Airline/Commercial/Professional Pilot and Flight
    Crew, A
Art/Art Studies, General, A
Business Administration and Management, A
Child Care and Support Services Management, A
Criminal Justice/Law Enforcement Administration, A
Dental Hygiene/Hygienist, A
Early Childhood Education and Teaching, A
E-Commerce/Electronic Commerce, A
Education, A
Emergency Medical Technology/Technician (EMT
    Paramedic), A
English Language and Literature, A
Entrepreneurship/Entrepreneurial Studies, A
Environmental Sciences, A
Fine Arts and Art Studies, A
Fire Science/Firefighting, A
General Studies, A
Geology/Earth Science, A
Hair Styling/Stylist and Hair Design, A
Health Services/Allied Health/Health Sciences, A
History, A
Human Services, A
Instrumentation Technology/Technician, A
Legal Assistant/Paralegal, A
Liberal Arts and Sciences Studies and
    Humanities, A
Marine Biology and Biological Oceanography, A
Music, A
Nail Technician/Specialist and Manicurist, A
Natural Resources and Conservation, A
Nurse/Nursing Assistant/Aide and Patient Care
    Assistant, A
Nursing - Registered Nurse Training, A
Parks, Recreation, Leisure and Fitness Studies, A
Physical Sciences, A
Political Science and Government, A
Psychology, A
Teacher Assistant/Aide, A
Wildlife Biology, A

COLORADO SCHOOL OF HEALING ARTS

Massage Therapy/Therapeutic Massage, A

COLORADO SCHOOL OF MINES

Applied Physics, D
Chemical Engineering, BMD
Chemistry, BMD
Civil Engineering, B
Computer Science, BMD
Economics, B
Electrical, Electronics and Communications
    Engineering, B
Electronic Materials, M
Engineering, B
Engineering and Applied Sciences, MDO
Engineering Management, M
Engineering Physics, B
Engineering Science, B
Environmental Engineering
    Technology/Environmental Technology, MD
Environmental Sciences, MD
Environmental/Environmental Health Engineering, B
Geochemistry, MD
Geological Engineering, MDO

Geological/Geophysical Engineering, B
Geology/Earth Science, MDO
Geophysics and Seismology, MDO
Geophysics Engineering, MD
Geosciences, O
Hydrology and Water Resources Science, O
Management of Technology, M
Materials Engineering, MD
Materials Sciences, MD
Mathematics, BMD
Mechanical Engineering, B
Metallurgical Engineering, BMD
Mineral Economics, MD
Mineral/Mining Engineering, MD
Mining and Mineral Engineering, B
Petroleum Engineering, BMD
Physics, MD
Systems Engineering, MD

COLORADO SCHOOL OF TRADES

Gunsmithing/Gunsmith, A

COLORADO STATE UNIVERSITY

Accounting, BM
Advertising and Public Relations, M
African Studies, M
Agribusiness, B
Agricultural and Extension Education Services, B
Agricultural and Horticultural Plant Breeding, B
Agricultural Economics, BMD
Agricultural Engineering, MD
Agricultural Sciences, MD
Agricultural Teacher Education, B
Agriculture, B
Agronomy and Crop Science, B
Agronomy and Soil Sciences, MD
American/United States Studies/Civilization, B
Animal Sciences, BMD
Anthropology, BM
Apparel and Textiles, B
Applied Horticulture/Horticultural Operations, B
Applied Mathematics, B
Art History, Criticism and Conservation, B
Art Teacher Education, B
Asian Studies/Civilization, B
Asian-American Studies, B
Athletic Training and Sports Medicine, B
Atmospheric Sciences and Meteorology, MD
Biochemistry, BMD
Bioengineering, MD
Biological and Biomedical Sciences, MD
Biology Teacher Education, B
Biology/Biological Sciences, B
Biomedical Engineering, MD
Botany/Plant Biology, BMD
Building Science, M
Business Administration and Management, B
Business Administration, Management and
    Operations, M
Business Teacher Education, B
Cell Biology and Anatomy, MD
Ceramic Arts and Ceramics, B
Chemical Engineering, BMD
Chemistry, BMD
Chemistry Teacher Education, B
Child and Family Studies, M
Civil Engineering, BMD
Cognitive Sciences, M
Commercial and Advertising Art, B
Communication Studies/Speech Communication
    and Rhetoric, B
Communication Theory, M
Composition, M
Computer and Information Sciences, B
Computer Engineering, BMD
Computer Science, BMD
Construction Engineering and Management, M
Consumer Economics, M
Counseling Psychology, M
Creative Writing, B
Criminal Justice/Safety Studies, B
Crop Production, B
Dance, B
Dietetics/Dieticians, B
Drama and Dramatics/Theatre Arts, B
Drawing, B

Ecology, MD
Economics, MD
Electrical Engineering, MD
Electrical, Electronics and Communications
    Engineering, MD
Engineering and Applied Sciences, MD
Engineering Management, M
Engineering Physics, B
Engineering Science, B
English, M
English Education, M
English Language and Literature, B
English/Language Arts Teacher Education, B
Entomology, BMD
Environmental and Occupational Health, MD
Environmental Engineering
    Technology/Environmental Technology, MD
Environmental Health, B
Environmental Policy, D
Environmental/Environmental Health Engineering, B
Equestrian/Equine Studies, B
Exercise and Sports Science, M
Family and Consumer Sciences/Home Economics
    Teacher Education, B
Family and Consumer Sciences/Human Sciences, B
Farm/Farm and Ranch Management, B
Fiber, Textile and Weaving Arts, B
Finance, B
Fine Arts and Art Studies, M
Fine/Studio Arts, B
Fish, Game and Wildlife Management, MD
Fishing and Fisheries Sciences and Management, B
Food Science and Technology, MD
Foods, Nutrition, and Wellness Studies, B
Foreign Languages and Literatures, B
Forest Sciences and Biology, B
Forestry, MD
French Language and Literature, BM
French Language Teacher Education, B
Genetics, MD
Geology/Earth Science, BM
Geosciences, MD
Geotechnical Engineering, MD
German Language and Literature, BM
German Language Teacher Education, B
Graphic Design, M
Historic Preservation and Conservation, M
History, BM
Horticultural Science, BMD
Hotel/Motel Administration/Management, B
Human Development, M
Human Development and Family Studies, B
Humanities/Humanistic Studies, B
Hydraulics and Fluid Power Technology, MD
Hydrology and Water Resources Science, MD
Immunology, MD
Industrial and Organizational Psychology, M
Industrial/Management Engineering, MD
Information Science/Studies, B
Interior Design, B
Jewelry/Metalsmithing, M
Journalism, B
Kinesiology and Exercise Science, B
Landscape Architecture, BMD
Landscaping and Groundskeeping, B
Latin American Studies, B
Liberal Arts and Sciences Studies and
    Humanities, B
Management Information Systems and Services, M
Manufacturing Engineering, MD
Marketing/Marketing Management, B
Materials Engineering, MD
Mathematics, BMD
Mathematics Teacher Education, B
Mechanical Engineering, BMD
Mechanics, MD
Medical Microbiology and Bacteriology, B
Metal and Jewelry Arts, B
Microbiology, MD
Molecular Biology, MD
Museology/Museum Studies, M
Music, BM
Music Performance, B
Music Teacher Education, BM
Music Therapy/Therapist, BM
Natural Resources and Conservation, D

Natural Resources Management/Development and
Policy, BM
Neuroscience, M
Nutritional Sciences, MD
Occupational Therapy/Therapist, MD
Painting, BM
Parks, Recreation and Leisure Facilities
Management, B
Pathology/Experimental Pathology, MD
Performance, M
Philosophy, BM
Photography, B
Physical Sciences, B
Physics, BMD
Physics Teacher Education, B
Plant Pathology/Phytopathology, MD
Plant Physiology, MD
Plant Sciences, BMD
Political Science and Government, BMD
Pre-Veterinary Studies, B
Printmaking, BM
Psychology, BMD
Public Relations/Image Management, B
Radiation Biology/Radiobiology, MD
Radio and Television, B
Range Science and Management, BMD
Real Estate, B
Recreation and Park Management, MD
Resource Management, MD
Rhetoric, M
Sales and Marketing Operations/Marketing and
Distribution Teacher Education, B
Science Teacher Education/General Science
Teacher Education, B
Sculpture, BM
Social Psychology, M
Social Sciences, B
Social Studies Teacher Education, B
Social Work, BM
Sociology, BMD
Spanish Language and Literature, BM
Spanish Language Teacher Education, B
Speech and Interpersonal Communication, M
Statistics, MD
Structural Engineering, MD
Technical and Business Writing, M
Technical Communication, M
Textile Design, M
Turf and Turfgrass Management, B
Veterinary Medicine, P
Veterinary Sciences, MD
Vocational and Technical Education, MD
Water Resources, MD
Wildlife and Wildlands Science and Management, B
Writing, M
Zoology/Animal Biology, BMD

COLORADO STATE UNIVERSITY-PUEBLO

Accounting, B
Advertising, B
Applied Art, B
Applied Science and Technology, M
Art Teacher Education, B
Art/Art Studies, General, B
Athletic Training and Sports Medicine, B
Automobile/Automotive Mechanics
Technology/Technician, B
Biology/Biological Sciences, B
Biomedical Technology/Technician, B
Broadcast Journalism, B
Business Administration and Management, B
Business Administration, Management and
Operations, M
Chemistry, B
Cinematography and Film/Video Production, B
Civil Engineering Technology/Technician, B
Clinical Psychology, B
Computer and Information Sciences, B
Computer Engineering Technology/Technician, B
Construction Engineering Technology/Technician, B
Corrections, B
Criminology, B
Developmental and Child Psychology, B
Education, B
Elementary Education and Teaching, B

Engineering and Applied Sciences, M
Engineering Technology, B
English Language and Literature, B
Environmental Biology, B
Environmental Health, B
Experimental Psychology, B
Finance, B
History, B
Industrial Engineering, B
Industrial/Management Engineering, M
Instrumentation Technology/Technician, B
Journalism, B
Junior High/Intermediate/Middle School Education
and Teaching, B
Kinesiology and Exercise Science, B
Marketing/Marketing Management, B
Mass Communication/Media Studies, B
Mathematics, B
Mathematics Teacher Education, B
Mechanical Engineering/Mechanical
Technology/Technician, B
Music, B
Music Teacher Education, B
Nursing - Registered Nurse Training, B
Parks, Recreation, Leisure and Fitness Studies, B
Physical Education Teaching and Coaching, B
Physics, B
Political Science and Government, B
Pre-Dentistry Studies, B
Pre-Law Studies, B
Pre-Medicine/Pre-Medical Studies, B
Pre-Pharmacy Studies, B
Pre-Veterinary Studies, B
Psychology, B
Public Relations/Image Management, B
Radio and Television, B
Science Teacher Education/General Science
Teacher Education, B
Secondary Education and Teaching, B
Social Sciences, B
Social Studies Teacher Education, B
Social Work, B
Sociology, B
Spanish Language and Literature, B
Spanish Language Teacher Education, B
Systems Engineering, M
Technology Education/Industrial Arts, B
Telecommunications Technology/Technician, B

COLORADO TECHNICAL UNIVERSITY

Business Administration and Management, B
Business Administration, Management and
Operations, MD
Computer Engineering, BM
Computer Science, BMD
Electrical Engineering, M
Electrical, Electronic and Communications
Engineering Technology/Technician, AB
Electrical, Electronics and Communications
Engineering, B
Human Resources Management and Services, M
Human Resources Management/Personnel
Administration, B
Information Science/Studies, BM
Logistics and Materials Management, M
Management Information Systems and
Services, BM
Organizational Management, M
Project Management, M
Software Engineering, M
Systems Science and Theory, M
Telecommunications Technology/Technician, B

COLORADO TECHNICAL UNIVERSITY DENVER CAMPUS

Business Administration and Management, B
Business Administration, Management and
Operations, M
Computer and Information Sciences, AB
Computer Science, BM
Information Science/Studies, AB
Management Information Systems and Services, M
Project Management, M
Securities Services Administration/Management, M
Software Engineering, M
System Management, M

Systems Science and Theory, M

COMMUNITY COLLEGE OF AURORA

Accounting, A
Biological and Physical Sciences, A
Business Administration and Management, A
Commercial and Advertising Art, A
Criminal Justice/Law Enforcement Administration, A
Emergency Medical Technology/Technician (EMT
Paramedic), A
Finance, A
Fire Services Administration, A
Information Science/Studies, A
Kindergarten/PreSchool Education and Teaching, A
Legal Assistant/Paralegal, A
Liberal Arts and Sciences Studies and
Humanities, A
Marketing/Marketing Management, A
Web Page, Digital/Multimedia and Information
Resources Design, A
Welding Technology/Welder, A

COMMUNITY COLLEGE OF DENVER

Accounting, A
Administrative Assistant and Secretarial Science, A
Business Administration and Management, A
Computer and Information Sciences, A
Dental Hygiene/Hygienist, A
Drafting and Design Technology/Technician, A
Electroneurodiagnostic/Electroencephalographic
Technology/Technologist, A
General Studies, A
Graphic Design, A
Human Services, A
Legal Assistant/Paralegal, A
Licensed Practical/Vocational Nurse Training, A
Nursing - Registered Nurse Training, A
Office Management and Supervision, A
Radiologic Technology/Science - Radiographer, A
Teacher Assistant/Aide, A
Veterinary/Animal Health Technology/Technician and
Veterinary Assistant, A
Welding Technology/Welder, A

DENVER ACADEMY OF COURT REPORTING

Court Reporting/Court Reporter, A
Medical Transcription/Transcriptionist, A

DENVER AUTOMOTIVE AND DIESEL COLLEGE

Automobile/Automotive Mechanics
Technology/Technician, A

DENVER CAREER COLLEGE

Legal and Justice Studies, O

DEVRY UNIVERSITY (COLORADO SPRINGS)

Business Administration and Management, B
Business Administration, Management and
Operations, BM
Computer and Information Sciences, B
Computer Systems Analysis/Analyst, B
Computer Systems Networking and
Telecommunications, AB
Electrical, Electronic and Communications
Engineering Technology/Technician, A
Information Science/Studies, AB

DEVRY UNIVERSITY (WESTMINSTER)

Biomedical Technology/Technician, B
Business Administration and Management, B
Computer and Information Sciences, B
Computer Engineering Technology/Technician, B
Computer Systems Networking and
Telecommunications, AB
Computer Technology/Computer Systems
Technology, AB
Electrical, Electronic and Communications
Engineering Technology/Technician, AB
Health Information/Medical Records
Technology/Technician, A

Medical Informatics, B

FORT LEWIS COLLEGE

Accounting, B
Agricultural Business and Management, B
Agriculture, A
American Indian/Native American Studies, B
Anthropology, B
Art/Art Studies, General, B
Arts Management, B
Asian Studies/Civilization, B
Athletic Training and Sports Medicine, B
Biochemistry, B
Biology Teacher Education, B
Biology/Biological Sciences, B
Business Administration and Management, B
Business/Managerial Economics, B
Cell/Cellular and Molecular Biology, B
Chemistry, B
Chemistry Teacher Education, B
Computer Science, B
Drama and Dramatics/Theatre Arts, B
Early Childhood Education and Teaching, B
Economics, B
Elementary Education and Teaching, B
Engineering Physics, B
Engineering/Industrial Management, B
English Language and Literature, B
English/Language Arts Teacher Education, B
Environmental Biology, B
Ethnic and Cultural Studies, B
European Studies/Civilization, B
Finance, B
Geology/Earth Science, B
History, B
Humanities/Humanistic Studies, B
Information Science/Studies, B
International Business/Trade/Commerce, B
Kinesiology and Exercise Science, B
Latin American Studies, B
Liberal Arts and Sciences Studies and
  Humanities, B
Management Information Systems and Services, B
Marketing/Marketing Management, B
Mathematics, B
Music, B
Music Performance, B
Music Teacher Education, B
Philosophy, B
Physical Education Teaching and Coaching, B
Physics, B
Political Science and Government, B
Psychology, B
Secondary Education and Teaching, B
Sociology, B
Spanish Language and Literature, B
Sport and Fitness Administration/Management, B
Tourism and Travel Services Management, B
Women's Studies, B

FRONT RANGE COMMUNITY COLLEGE

Accounting, A
Architectural Engineering Technology/Technician, A
Automotive Engineering Technology/Technician, A
Business Administration and Management, A
Business/Office Automation/Technology/Data
  Entry, A
Computer and Information Sciences, A
Construction Trades, A
Dietetic Technician (DTR), A
Drafting/Design Engineering
  Technologies/Technicians, A
Early Childhood Education and Teaching, A
Electrical/Electronics Maintenance and Repair
  Technology, A
General Studies, A
Heating, Air Conditioning and Refrigeration
  Technology/Technician, A
Intermedia/Multimedia, A
Landscaping and Groundskeeping, A
Language Interpretation and Translation, A
Legal Assistant/Paralegal, A
Liberal Arts and Sciences Studies and
  Humanities, A
Machine Tool Technology/Machinist, A
Medical Staff Services Technology/Technician, A

Nurse/Nursing Assistant/Aide and Patient Care
  Assistant, A
Nursing - Registered Nurse Training, A
Restaurant/Food Services Management, A
Veterinary/Animal Health Technology/Technician and
  Veterinary Assistant, A
Welding Technology/Welder, A

INSTITUTE OF BUSINESS & MEDICAL CAREERS

Accounting Technology/Technician and
  Bookkeeping, A
Business Administration and Management, A
General Office Occupations and Clerical Services, A
Legal Administrative Assistant/Secretary, A
Legal Assistant/Paralegal, A
Massage Therapy/Therapeutic Massage, A
Medical Administrative Assistant/Secretary, A
Medical/Clinical Assistant, A
Pharmacy Technician/Assistant, A

INTELLITEC COLLEGE (COLORADO SPRINGS)

Drafting and Design Technology/Technician, A
Electrical, Electronic and Communications
  Engineering Technology/Technician, A
Environmental Engineering
  Technology/Environmental Technology, A
Interior Design, A

INTELLITEC COLLEGE (GRAND JUNCTION)

Architectural Drafting and Architectural
  CAD/CADD, A
Clinical/Medical Laboratory Assistant, A
Computer and Information Sciences, A
Computer Systems Networking and
  Telecommunications, A
Data Entry/Microcomputer Applications, A
Electrical, Electronic and Communications
  Engineering Technology/Technician, A
Heating, Air Conditioning, Ventilation and
  Refrigeration Maintenance
  Technology/Technician, A
Massage Therapy/Therapeutic Massage, A
Mechanical Drafting and Mechanical Drafting
  CAD/CADD, A
Medical Administrative Assistant/Secretary, A
System Administration/Administrator, A

INTELLITEC MEDICAL INSTITUTE

Clinical/Medical Laboratory Technician, A
Medical Administrative Assistant/Secretary, A
Medical/Clinical Assistant, A

ITT TECHNICAL INSTITUTE

Animation, Interactive Technology, Video Graphics
  and Special Effects, B
Business Administration and Management, B
CAD/CADD Drafting and/or Design
  Technology/Technician, A
Computer and Information Systems Security, B
Computer Programming/Programmer, A
Criminal Justice/Law Enforcement Administration, B
Electrical, Electronic and Communications
  Engineering Technology/Technician, AB
System, Networking, and LAN/WAN
  Management/Manager, A
Web Page, Digital/Multimedia and Information
  Resources Design, A
Web/Multimedia Management and Webmaster, A

JOHNSON & WALES UNIVERSITY

Accounting, AB
Advertising, A
Baking and Pastry Arts/Baker/Pastry Chef, A
Business Administration and Management, A
Business Teacher Education, B
Criminal Justice/Law Enforcement Administration, A
Culinary Arts/Chef Training, AB
Entrepreneurship/Entrepreneurial Studies, AB
Family and Consumer Sciences/Home Economics
  Teacher Education, B
Fashion Merchandising, A
Finance and Financial Management Services, B

Food Service, Waiter/Waitress, and Dining Room
  Management/Manager, B
Hotel/Motel Administration/Management, B
International Business/Trade/Commerce, B
Marketing/Marketing Management, AB
Parks, Recreation and Leisure Facilities
  Management, B
Public Relations/Image Management, B
Restaurant/Food Services Management, AB

JONES INTERNATIONAL UNIVERSITY

Accounting and Finance, B
Business Administration, Management and
  Operations, M
Business/Corporate Communications, B
Conflict Resolution and Mediation/Peace Studies, M
Corporate and Organizational Communication, M
Curriculum and Instruction, M
Distance Education Development, M
Education, M
Educational Leadership and Administration, M
Educational Media/Instructional Technology, M
Entrepreneurship/Entrepreneurial Studies, M
Finance, B
Finance and Banking, M
Health Services Administration, M
Management of Technology, M
Marketing/Marketing Management, B
Organizational Management, M
Selling Skills and Sales Operations, B

LAMAR COMMUNITY COLLEGE

Accounting, A
Administrative Assistant and Secretarial Science, A
Agricultural Business and Management, A
Agricultural Teacher Education, A
Agriculture, A
Agronomy and Crop Science, A
Animal Sciences, A
Art/Art Studies, General, A
Behavioral Sciences, A
Biological and Physical Sciences, A
Biology/Biological Sciences, A
Business Administration and Management, A
Business Teacher Education, A
Community Organization and Advocacy, A
Comparative Literature, A
Computer Engineering Technology/Technician, A
Computer Programming/Programmer, A
Computer Science, A
Computer Typography and Composition Equipment
  Operator, A
Cosmetology/Cosmetologist, A
Criminal Justice/Safety Studies, A
Data Processing and Data Processing
  Technology/Technician, A
Emergency Medical Technology/Technician (EMT
  Paramedic), A
Engineering, A
English Language and Literature, A
Equestrian/Equine Studies, A
European Studies/Civilization, A
Farm/Farm and Ranch Management, A
History, A
Humanities/Humanistic Studies, A
Information Science/Studies, A
Legal Administrative Assistant/Secretary, A
Liberal Arts and Sciences Studies and
  Humanities, A
Licensed Practical/Vocational Nurse Training, A
Management Information Systems and Services, A
Marketing/Marketing Management, A
Mass Communication/Media Studies, A
Mathematics, A
Medical Administrative Assistant/Secretary, A
Medical Office Management/Administration, A
Nursing - Registered Nurse Training, A
Physical Sciences, A
Physics, A
Pre-Engineering, A
Quality Control Technology/Technician, A
Range Science and Management, A
Social Sciences, A
Social Work, A

Teacher Assistant/Aide, A

MESA STATE COLLEGE

Accounting, B
Administrative Assistant and Secretarial Science, AB
Anthropology, B
Applied Art, B
Applied Mathematics, B
Art/Art Studies, General, AB
Automobile/Automotive Mechanics
   Technology/Technician, A
Behavioral Sciences, B
Biology/Biological Sciences, AB
Broadcast Journalism, B
Business Administration and Management, AB
Business Administration, Management and
   Operations, M
Business/Managerial Economics, B
Chemistry, B
Commercial and Advertising Art, A
Computer Science, AB
Counselor Education/School Counseling and
   Guidance Services, B
Criminal Justice/Law Enforcement Administration, A
Criminology, B
Culinary Arts/Chef Training, A
Drama and Dramatics/Theatre Arts, AB
Education, B
Electrical, Electronic and Communications
   Engineering Technology/Technician, A
Elementary Education and Teaching, B
Engineering, A
English Language and Literature, AB
Environmental Engineering
   Technology/Environmental Technology, A
Finance, B
Geology/Earth Science, AB
Heavy Equipment Maintenance
   Technology/Technician, A
History, B
Hotel/Motel Administration/Management, A
Human Resources Management/Personnel
   Administration, B
Human Services, B
Humanities/Humanistic Studies, AB
Industrial Radiologic Technology/Technician, A
Industrial Technology/Technician, A
Information Science/Studies, B
Junior High/Intermediate/Middle School Education
   and Teaching, B
Kindergarten/PreSchool Education and Teaching, A
Kinesiology and Exercise Science, B
Legal Administrative Assistant/Secretary, A
Liberal Arts and Sciences Studies and
   Humanities, AB
Machine Tool Technology/Machinist, A
Marketing/Marketing Management, B
Mass Communication/Media Studies, B
Mathematics, AB
Medical Administrative Assistant/Secretary, A
Music, AB
Music Teacher Education, B
Nursing - Registered Nurse Training, AB
Physical Education Teaching and Coaching, B
Physical Sciences, B
Physics, AB
Political Science and Government, B
Pre-Engineering, A
Pre-Veterinary Studies, B
Psychology, B
Public Relations/Image Management, B
Radio and Television, B
Radiologic Technology/Science - Radiographer, A
Science Teacher Education/General Science
   Teacher Education, B
Secondary Education and Teaching, B
Social Sciences, AB
Sociology, B
Statistics, B
Tourism and Travel Services Management, A
Welding Technology/Welder, A

METROPOLITAN STATE COLLEGE OF DENVER

Accounting, B
African-American/Black Studies, B

Anthropology, B
Art/Art Studies, General, B
Atmospheric Sciences and Meteorology, B
Aviation/Airway Management and Operations, B
Behavioral Sciences, B
Biology/Biological Sciences, B
Chemistry, B
Civil Engineering Technology/Technician, B
Computer and Information Sciences, B
Computer Science, B
Criminal Justice/Law Enforcement Administration, B
Economics, B
Electrical, Electronic and Communications
   Engineering Technology/Technician, B
English Language and Literature, B
Environmental Studies, B
Finance, B
Foreign Languages and Literatures, B
Health/Health Care Administration/Management, B
Hispanic-American, Puerto Rican, and Mexican-
   American/Chicano Studies, B
History, B
Hospitality Administration/Management, B
Human Services, B
Industrial Design, B
Industrial Technology/Technician, B
Journalism, B
Kinesiology and Exercise Science, B
Land Use Planning and
   Management/Development, B
Management Science, B
Marketing Research, B
Mathematics, B
Mechanical Engineering/Mechanical
   Technology/Technician, B
Music Performance, B
Music Teacher Education, B
Nursing - Registered Nurse Training, B
Parks, Recreation, Leisure and Fitness Studies, B
Philosophy, B
Physics, B
Political Science and Government, B
Psychology, B
Public Relations/Image Management, B
Social Work, B
Sociology, B
Spanish Language and Literature, B
Speech and Rhetorical Studies, B
Survey Technology/Surveying, B
Teacher Education, Multiple Levels, B
Urban Studies/Affairs, B

MORGAN COMMUNITY COLLEGE

Accounting, A
Administrative Assistant and Secretarial Science, A
Automobile/Automotive Mechanics
   Technology/Technician, A
Biological and Physical Sciences, A
Business Administration and Management, A
Business Teacher Education, A
Business/Managerial Economics, A
Liberal Arts and Sciences Studies and
   Humanities, A
Occupational Therapy/Therapist, A
Physical Therapy/Therapist, A

NAROPA UNIVERSITY

Art Therapy/Therapist, M
Asian Languages, M
Counseling Psychology, M
Dance Therapy/Therapist, M
Drama and Dramatics/Theatre Arts, B
Early Childhood Education and Teaching, B
Education, M
English Language and Literature, B
Environmental Policy and Resource
   Management, M
Environmental Studies, B
Fine/Studio Arts, B
Gerontology, M
Health and Physical Education/Fitness, B
Multi-/Interdisciplinary Studies, B
Music Performance, B
Music Therapy/Therapist, M
Psychoanalysis and Psychotherapy, M
Psychology, B

Religion/Religious Studies, BM
Theater, M
Theology and Religious Vocations, MP
Therapeutic Recreation, M
Transpersonal and Humanistic Psychology, M
Visual and Performing Arts, B
Writing, M

NATIONAL AMERICAN UNIVERSITY (COLORADO SPRINGS)

Accounting, AB
Accounting and Business/Management, AB
Allied Health and Medical Assisting Services, A
Business Administration and Management, AB
Health/Health Care Administration/Management, B
Hotel/Motel Administration/Management, A
Information Science/Studies, AB
Medical Office Management/Administration, A
Medical/Clinical Assistant, A
Tourism and Travel Services Management, A

NATIONAL AMERICAN UNIVERSITY (DENVER)

Accounting, AB
Business Administration and Management, AB
Computer and Information Sciences, AB
Computer Programming, AB
Computer Programming, Specific Applications, AB
Computer Programming/Programmer, AB
Computer Systems Networking and
   Telecommunications, AB
Computer/Information Technology Services
   Administration and Management, AB
Data Entry/Microcomputer Applications, AB
Health Services/Allied Health/Health Sciences, A
Health/Health Care Administration/Management, AB
Information Science/Studies, AB
Information Technology, AB
Management Information Systems and Services, B
Medical/Clinical Assistant, A
Medical/Health Management and Clinical
   Assistant/Specialist, A
System Administration/Administrator, AB
System, Networking, and LAN/WAN
   Management/Manager, AB
Web Page, Digital/Multimedia and Information
   Resources Design, AB

NAZARENE BIBLE COLLEGE

Bible/Biblical Studies, AB
Pastoral Studies/Counseling, B
Pre-Theology/Pre-Ministerial Studies, A
Religious Education, AB
Religious/Sacred Music, AB
Women's Studies, A

NORTHEASTERN JUNIOR COLLEGE

Accounting, A
Administrative Assistant and Secretarial Science, A
Agricultural Business and Management, A
Agricultural Economics, A
Agricultural Mechanization, A
Agricultural Teacher Education, A
Agriculture, A
Agronomy and Crop Science, A
Anatomy, A
Animal Sciences, A
Applied Mathematics, A
Art Teacher Education, A
Art/Art Studies, General, A
Automobile/Automotive Mechanics
   Technology/Technician, A
Biological and Physical Sciences, A
Biology/Biological Sciences, A
Business Administration and Management, A
Business Teacher Education, A
Child Development, A
Clinical Laboratory Science/Medical
   Technology/Technologist, A
Computer Engineering Technology/Technician, A
Computer Science, A
Corrections, A
Cosmetology/Cosmetologist, A
Criminal Justice/Police Science, A

Data Processing and Data Processing
    Technology/Technician, A
Drama and Dramatics/Theatre Arts, A
Drawing, A
Economics, A
Education, A
Elementary Education and Teaching, A
Emergency Medical Technology/Technician (EMT
    Paramedic), A
English Language and Literature, A
Equestrian/Equine Studies, A
Family and Consumer Sciences/Human Sciences, A
Farm/Farm and Ranch Management, A
Fashion Merchandising, A
Fine/Studio Arts, A
Forestry, A
History, A
Horticultural Science, A
Humanities/Humanistic Studies, A
Journalism, A
Kindergarten/PreSchool Education and Teaching, A
Landscaping and Groundskeeping, A
Legal Administrative Assistant/Secretary, A
Liberal Arts and Sciences Studies and
    Humanities, A
Licensed Practical/Vocational Nurse Training, A
Marine Technology, A
Marketing/Marketing Management, A
Mathematics, A
Medical Administrative Assistant/Secretary, A
Music, A
Music Teacher Education, A
Natural Sciences, A
Nursing - Registered Nurse Training, A
Physical Education Teaching and Coaching, A
Physical Sciences, A
Pre-Engineering, A
Psychology, A
Public Health (MPH, DPH), A
Radio and Television, A
Social Sciences, A
Social Work, A
Trade and Industrial Teacher Education, A
Zoology/Animal Biology, A

OTERO JUNIOR COLLEGE

Administrative Assistant and Secretarial Science, A
Agricultural Business and Management, A
Automobile/Automotive Mechanics
    Technology/Technician, A
Biological and Physical Sciences, A
Biology/Biological Sciences, A
Business Administration and Management, A
Child Development, A
Comparative Literature, A
Data Processing and Data Processing
    Technology/Technician, A
Drama and Dramatics/Theatre Arts, A
Elementary Education and Teaching, A
History, A
Humanities/Humanistic Studies, A
Kindergarten/PreSchool Education and Teaching, A
Legal Administrative Assistant/Secretary, A
Liberal Arts and Sciences Studies and
    Humanities, A
Mathematics, A
Medical Administrative Assistant/Secretary, A
Modern Languages, A
Nursing - Registered Nurse Training, A
Political Science and Government, A
Pre-Engineering, A
Psychology, A
Social Sciences, A

PARKS COLLEGE (DENVER)

Accounting, A
Administrative Assistant and Secretarial Science, A
Business Administration and Management, A
Computer Programming/Programmer, A
Computer Science, A
Consumer Merchandising/Retailing Management, A
Data Processing and Data Processing
    Technology/Technician, A
Economics, A
English Language and Literature, A
Fashion Merchandising, A

Geography, A
Hospitality Administration/Management, A
Hotel/Motel Administration/Management, A
Medical/Clinical Assistant, A
Psychology, A

PIKES PEAK COMMUNITY COLLEGE

Accounting Technology/Technician and
    Bookkeeping, A
Architectural Engineering Technology/Technician, A
Autobody/Collision and Repair
    Technology/Technician, A
Automobile/Automotive Mechanics
    Technology/Technician, A
Building/Construction
    Finishing, Management, and Inspection, A
Building/Property Maintenance and Management, A
Business Administration and Management, A
Child Development, A
Cooking and Related Culinary Arts, A
Criminal Justice/Law Enforcement Administration, A
Dental Assisting/Assistant, A
Electrical, Electronic and Communications
    Engineering Technology/Technician, A
Emergency Medical Technology/Technician (EMT
    Paramedic), A
Fire Protection and Safety Technology/Technician, A
General Studies, A
Graphic Communications, A
Interior Design, A
Landscaping and Groundskeeping, A
Legal Assistant/Paralegal, A
Liberal Arts and Sciences Studies and
    Humanities, A
Machine Shop Technology/Assistant, A
Management Information Systems and Services, A
Medical Office Management/Administration, A
Natural Resources Management/Development and
    Policy, A
Nursing - Registered Nurse Training, A
Psychiatric/Mental Health Services Technician, A
Robotics Technology/Technician, A
Sign Language Interpretation and Translation, A
System, Networking, and LAN/WAN
    Management/Manager, A
Welding Technology/Welder, A

PIMA MEDICAL INSTITUTE

Ophthalmic Technician/Technologist, A
Physical Therapist Assistant, A
Radiologic Technology/Science - Radiographer, A
Respiratory Therapy Technician/Assistant, A

PLATT COLLEGE

Advertising, B
Commercial and Advertising Art, AB
Computer Graphics, A
Computer/Information Technology Services
    Administration and Management, A
Intermedia/Multimedia, AB
Web Page, Digital/Multimedia and Information
    Resources Design, AB

PUEBLO COMMUNITY COLLEGE

Accounting, A
Administrative Assistant and Secretarial Science, A
Autobody/Collision and Repair
    Technology/Technician, A
Automobile/Automotive Mechanics
    Technology/Technician, A
Business Administration and Management, A
Civil Engineering Technology/Technician, A
Computer Graphics, A
Corrections, A
Criminal Justice/Law Enforcement Administration, A
Criminal Justice/Police Science, A
Culinary Arts/Chef Training, A
Dental Assisting/Assistant, A
Dental Hygiene/Hygienist, A
Design and Visual Communications, A
Electrical, Electronic and Communications
    Engineering Technology/Technician, A
Engineering Technology, A
General Studies, A
Health Information/Medical Records
    Administration/Administrator, A

Heavy Equipment Maintenance
    Technology/Technician, A
Information Science/Studies, A
Kindergarten/PreSchool Education and Teaching, A
Legal Administrative Assistant/Secretary, A
Legal Assistant/Paralegal, A
Liberal Arts and Sciences Studies and
    Humanities, A
Machine Tool Technology/Machinist, A
Management Information Systems and Services, A
Medical Administrative Assistant/Secretary, A
Medical Radiologic Technology/Science - Radiation
    Therapist, A
Metal and Jewelry Arts, A
Nursing - Registered Nurse Training, A
Occupational Therapist Assistant, A
Occupational Therapy/Therapist, A
Ophthalmic Laboratory Technology/Technician, A
Physical Therapist Assistant, A
Physical Therapy/Therapist, A
Psychiatric/Mental Health Services Technician, A
Respiratory Care Therapy/Therapist, A
Special Products Marketing Operations, A
Surgical Technology/Technologist, A
Tourism and Travel Services Management, A
Welding Technology/Welder, A

RED ROCKS COMMUNITY COLLEGE

Accounting, A
Administrative Assistant and Secretarial Science, A
Art/Art Studies, General, A
Biological and Physical Sciences, A
Biology/Biological Sciences, A
Business Administration and Management, A
Carpentry/Carpenter, A
Chemistry, A
Computer Engineering Technology/Technician, A
Computer Programming/Programmer, A
Computer Science, A
Criminal Justice/Law Enforcement Administration, A
Drafting and Design Technology/Technician, A
Economics, A
Electrical, Electronic and Communications
    Engineering Technology/Technician, A
English Language and Literature, A
Fire Science/Firefighting, A
French Language and Literature, A
Geology/Earth Science, A
German Language and Literature, A
Heavy Equipment Maintenance
    Technology/Technician, A
History, A
Humanities/Humanistic Studies, A
Hydrology and Water Resources Science, A
Liberal Arts and Sciences Studies and
    Humanities, A
Marketing/Marketing Management, A
Mass Communication/Media Studies, A
Mathematics, A
Mechanical Engineering/Mechanical
    Technology/Technician, A
Physics, A
Political Science and Government, A
Psychology, A
Public Administration, A
Real Estate, A
Sociology, A
Solar Energy Technology/Technician, A
Spanish Language and Literature, A
Survey Technology/Surveying, A
Welding Technology/Welder, A

REGIS UNIVERSITY

Accounting, BM
Adult and Continuing Education and Teaching, MO
Allied Health and Medical Assisting Services, MD
Biochemistry, B
Biology/Biological Sciences, B
Business Administration and Management, B
Business Administration, Management and
    Operations, MO
Chemistry, B
Communication and Media Studies, MO
Communication Studies/Speech Communication
    and Rhetoric, B
Computer Science, BMO

Conflict Resolution and Mediation/Peace Studies, O
Counseling Psychology, M
Criminal Justice/Law Enforcement Administration, B
Early Childhood Education and Teaching, M
Economics, B
Education, BMO
Educational Media/Instructional Technology, O
Electronic Commerce, MO
Elementary Education and Teaching, BM
English as a Second Language, M
English Language and Literature, B
Environmental Studies, B
Family and Consumer Sciences/Human Sciences, B
Finance and Banking, M
Fine Arts and Art Studies, M
French Language and Literature, B
Health Information/Medical Records
   Administration/Administrator, B
Health Services Administration, M
History, B
Human Resources Management and Services, MO
Humanities/Humanistic Studies, B
Industrial and Manufacturing Management, M
Information Science/Studies, MO
International Business/Trade/Commerce, MO
Legal and Justice Studies, O
Liberal Arts and Sciences Studies and
   Humanities, B
Liberal Studies, MO
Management, MO
Management Information Systems and Services, M
Management of Technology, MO
Marketing, M
Mathematics, B
Neuroscience, B
Non-Profit/Public/Organizational Management, MO
Nursing, M
Nursing - Registered Nurse Training, B
Organizational Management, M
Philosophy, B
Physical Therapy/Therapist, D
Physician Assistant, M
Political Science and Government, B
Pre-Dentistry Studies, B
Pre-Law Studies, B
Pre-Medicine/Pre-Medical Studies, B
Pre-Veterinary Studies, B
Project Management, MO
Psychology, BM
Religion/Religious Studies, B
Secondary Education and Teaching, M
Social Sciences, M
Sociology, B
Spanish Language and Literature, B
Special Education and Teaching, M
Technical and Business Writing, O
Telecommunications Management, M
Visual and Performing Arts, B

REMINGTON COLLEGE-COLORADO SPRINGS CAMPUS

Computer Systems Networking and
   Telecommunications, A
Criminal Justice/Law Enforcement
   Administration, AB
Operations Management and Supervision, B

REMINGTON COLLEGE-DENVER CAMPUS

Business Administration and Management, AB
Criminal Justice/Safety Studies, AB

ROCKY MOUNTAIN COLLEGE OF ART & DESIGN

Art Teacher Education, B
Film/Video and Photographic Arts, B
Graphic Design, B
Illustration, B
Interior Design, B
Painting, B
Sculpture, B

TRINIDAD STATE JUNIOR COLLEGE

Accounting, A
Administrative Assistant and Secretarial Science, A

Aquaculture, A
Art Teacher Education, A
Automobile/Automotive Mechanics
   Technology/Technician, A
Biological and Physical Sciences, A
Biology/Biological Sciences, A
Business Administration and Management, A
Carpentry/Carpenter, A
Chemistry, A
Civil Engineering Technology/Technician, A
Commercial and Advertising Art, A
Computer and Information Sciences, A
Computer Science, A
Computer Systems Networking and
   Telecommunications, A
Construction Engineering Technology/Technician, A
Corrections, A
Cosmetology/Cosmetologist, A
Criminal Justice/Police Science, A
Data Processing and Data Processing
   Technology/Technician, A
Design and Visual Communications, A
Digital Communication and Media/Multimedia, A
Drafting and Design Technology/Technician, A
Drama and Dramatics/Theatre Arts, A
Education, A
Engineering, A
English Language and Literature, A
Farm/Farm and Ranch Management, A
Forestry, A
Gunsmithing/Gunsmith, A
Heavy Equipment Maintenance
   Technology/Technician, A
Industrial Technology/Technician, A
Information Science/Studies, A
Information Technology, A
Kindergarten/PreSchool Education and Teaching, A
Liberal Arts and Sciences Studies and
   Humanities, A
Licensed Practical/Vocational Nurse Training, A
Management Information Systems and Services, A
Music, A
Natural Resources Management/Development and
   Policy, A
Nurse/Nursing Assistant/Aide and Patient Care
   Assistant, A
Nursing - Registered Nurse Training, A
Occupational Safety and Health
   Technology/Technician, A
Physical Education Teaching and Coaching, A
Pre-Engineering, A

UNITED STATES AIR FORCE ACADEMY

Aerospace, Aeronautical and Astronautical
   Engineering, B
Area Studies, B
Atmospheric Sciences and Meteorology, B
Behavioral Sciences, B
Biochemistry, B
Biological and Physical Sciences, B
Biology/Biological Sciences, B
Business Administration and Management, B
Chemistry, B
Civil Engineering, B
Computer Science, B
Economics, B
Electrical, Electronics and Communications
   Engineering, B
Engineering, B
Engineering Mechanics, B
Engineering Science, B
English Language and Literature, B
Environmental/Environmental Health Engineering, B
Geography, B
History, B
Humanities/Humanistic Studies, B
Interdisciplinary Studies, B
Law and Legal Studies, B
Materials Sciences, B
Mathematics, B
Mechanical Engineering, B
Military Studies, B
Operations Research, B
Physics, B

Political Science and Government, B

UNIVERSITY OF COLORADO AT BOULDER

Accounting, BM
Advertising, B
Aerospace, Aeronautical and Astronautical
   Engineering, BMD
Animal Behavior and Ethology, MD
Anthropology, BMD
Applied Mathematics, BMD
Architectural Engineering, BMD
Art History, Criticism and Conservation, M
Asian Studies/Civilization, B
Astronomy, B
Astrophysics, MD
Atmospheric Sciences and Meteorology, MD
Behavioral Genetics, MD
Biochemistry, BMD
Broadcast Journalism, B
Business Administration, Management and
   Operations, MDO
Cell Biology and Anatomy, MD
Cell/Cellular and Molecular Biology, B
Ceramic Arts and Ceramics, M
Chemical Engineering, BMD
Chemistry, BMD
Chinese Language and Literature, B
Chinese Studies, M
Civil Engineering, BMD
Classics and Classical
   Languages, Literatures, and Linguistics, BMD
Communication and Media Studies, MD
Communication Disorders, MD
Communication Studies/Speech Communication
   and Rhetoric, B
Comparative Literature, MD
Composition, MD
Computer Engineering, BMD
Computer Science, BMD
Construction Engineering and Management, MD
Corporate and Organizational Communication, M
Curriculum and Instruction, MD
Dance, BMD
Developmental Biology and Embryology, BMD
Drama and Dramatics/Theatre Arts, B
East Asian Studies, M
Ecology, MD
Ecology, Evolution, Systematics and Population
   Biology, B
Economics, BMD
Education, MD
Educational Measurement and Evaluation, D
Educational Psychology, MD
Electrical Engineering, MD
Electrical, Electronics and Communications
   Engineering, B
Engineering and Applied Sciences, MDO
Engineering Management, M
Engineering Physics, B
English, MD
English Language and Literature, B
Entrepreneurship/Entrepreneurial Studies, M
Environmental Design/Architecture, B
Environmental Engineering
   Technology/Environmental Technology, MD
Environmental Studies, BMD
Environmental/Environmental Health Engineering, B
Ethnic and Cultural Studies, B
Evolutionary Biology, BMD
Film/Cinema Studies, B
Finance, B
Finance and Banking, MD
Fine Arts and Art Studies, M
Fine/Studio Arts, B
French Language and Literature, BMD
Genetics, MD
Geography, BMD
Geology/Earth Science, BMD
Geophysics and Seismology, D
Geotechnical Engineering, MD
German Language and Literature, M
Germanic Languages, Literatures, and Linguistics, B
History, BMD
Humanities/Humanistic Studies, B
Industrial and Manufacturing Management, M

International Affairs, M
International/Global Studies, B
Italian Language and Literature, B
Japanese Language and Literature, B
Japanese Studies, M
Journalism, BMD
Kinesiology and Movement Studies, MD
Law and Legal Studies, PO
Linguistics, BMD
Management of Technology, M
Marine Biology and Biological Oceanography, MD
Marketing, MD
Marketing/Marketing Management, B
Mass Communication/Media Studies, MD
Mathematical Physics, D
Mathematics, BMD
Mechanical Engineering, BMD
Media Studies, D
Medical Physics, D
Microbiology, MD
Molecular Biology, MD
Multilingual and Multicultural Education, MD
Museology/Museum Studies, M
Music, BMD
Music Teacher Education, BMD
Musicology and Ethnomusicology, D
Neurobiology and Neurophysiology, MD
Oceanography, Chemical and Physical, MD
Operations Research, M
Optics/Optical Sciences, D
Organizational Management, MD
Painting, M
Performance, MD
Philosophy, BMD
Photography, M
Physical Chemistry, D
Physical Education Teaching and Coaching, M
Physics, BMD
Physiology, MD
Plant Biology, MD
Plant Physiology, MD
Plasma and High-Temperature Physics, MD
Political Science and Government, BMD
Printmaking, M
Psychology, BMD
Public Policy Analysis, M
Real Estate, M
Religion/Religious Studies, BM
Russian Studies, B
Sacred Music, M
Sculpture, M
Sociology, BMD
Spanish Language and Literature, BMD
Structural Engineering, MD
Taxation, M
Telecommunications, MO
Telecommunications Management, MO
Theater, MD
Water Resources Engineering, MD
Women's Studies, B

UNIVERSITY OF COLORADO AT COLORADO SPRINGS

Accounting, BM
Aerospace, Aeronautical and Astronautical
   Engineering, M
Anthropology, B
Applied Mathematics, BM
Art/Art Studies, General, B
Biology/Biological Sciences, B
Business Administration and Management, B
Business Administration, Management and
   Operations, M
Chemistry, B
Cognitive Sciences, D
Communication and Media Studies, M
Communication Studies/Speech Communication
   and Rhetoric, B
Computer and Information Sciences, B
Computer Engineering, B
Computer Science, BMD
Counselor Education/School Counseling and
   Guidance Services, M
Criminology, M
Curriculum and Instruction, M
Ecology, B

Economics, B
Education, M
Educational Administration and Supervision, M
Educational Leadership and Administration, M
Electrical Engineering, MD
Electrical, Electronics and Communications
   Engineering, B
Engineering and Applied Sciences, MD
Engineering Management, M
English Language and Literature, B
Environmental Sciences, M
Finance, B
Finance and Banking, M
Fine/Studio Arts, B
Geography, BM
Gerontological Nursing, M
Health Services Administration, M
History, BM
Human Services, M
Information Science/Studies, M
International Business/Trade/Commerce, M
Management Information Systems and Services, M
Management of Technology, M
Manufacturing Engineering, M
Marketing, M
Marketing/Marketing Management, B
Maternal/Child Health and Neonatal
   Nurse/Nursing, M
Maternity Nursing, M
Mathematics, B
Mechanical Engineering, BM
Nursing, M
Nursing - Adult, M
Nursing - Advanced Practice, M
Nursing - Registered Nurse Training, B
Nursing Administration, M
Philosophy, B
Physics, B
Political Science and Government, B
Pre-Dentistry Studies, B
Pre-Law Studies, B
Pre-Medicine/Pre-Medical Studies, B
Pre-Veterinary Studies, B
Psychology, BMD
Public Administration, M
Public Affairs, M
Public Health (MPH, DPH), B
Sociology, BM
Software Engineering, M
Spanish Language and Literature, B
Special Education and Teaching, M
Women's Health Nursing, M

UNIVERSITY OF COLORADO AT DENVER AND HEALTH SCIENCES CENTER - DOWNTOWN DENVER CAMPUS

Accounting, M
Anthropology, BM
Applied Mathematics, MD
Applied Science and Technology, M
Architecture, MD
Biological and Biomedical Sciences, M
Biology/Biological Sciences, B
Biomedical Sciences, B
Business Administration, Management and
   Operations, M
Business/Commerce, B
Chemistry, BM
Civil Engineering, BMD
Communication and Media Studies, M
Communication Studies/Speech Communication
   and Rhetoric, B
Computational Sciences, D
Computer and Information Sciences, B
Computer Engineering, M
Computer Science, MD
Counseling Psychology, MO
Counselor Education/School Counseling and
   Guidance Services, MO
Criminology, M
Dental Hygiene/Hygienist, B
Drama and Dramatics/Theatre Arts, B
Early Childhood Education and Teaching, M
Economics, BM
Education, MDO

Educational Administration and Supervision, MO
Educational Leadership and Administration, D
Educational Media/Instructional Technology, M
Educational Psychology, M
Electrical Engineering, M
Electrical, Electronics and Communications
   Engineering, B
Engineering and Applied Sciences, M
English, M
English as a Second Language, M
English Composition, B
English Education, M
English Language and Literature, B
Environmental Sciences, M
Finance and Banking, M
Fine/Studio Arts, B
French Language and Literature, B
Geography, B
Health Education, D
Health Services Administration, M
History, BM
Humanities/Humanistic Studies, M
Information Science/Studies, D
International Business/Trade/Commerce, M
International/Global Studies, B
Landscape Architecture, M
Management, M
Management Information Systems and
   Services, MD
Marketing, M
Mathematics, BM
Mechanical Engineering, BM
Multi-/Interdisciplinary Studies, B
Music, BM
Nursing - Registered Nurse Training, B
Philosophy, B
Physics, B
Political Science and Government, BM
Psychology, BM
Public Administration, M
Public Affairs, D
School Psychology, O
Social Sciences, M
Sociology, BM
Spanish Language and Literature, B
Technical Communication, M
Theater, M
Urban and Regional Planning, M
Urban Design, M

UNIVERSITY OF DENVER

Accounting, BM
Adult and Continuing Education and Teaching, MD
Advertising and Public Relations, M
Animal Sciences, B
Anthropology, BM
Applied Mathematics, M
Art History, Criticism and Conservation, BM
Art Teacher Education, B
Art/Art Studies, General, B
Asian-American Studies, B
Biochemistry, B
Bioinformatics, B
Biological and Biomedical Sciences, MD
Biological and Physical Sciences, B
Biology/Biological Sciences, B
Biopsychology, B
Building/Construction
   Finishing, Management, and Inspection, B
Business Administration and Management, B
Business Administration, Management and
   Operations, M
Business, Management, Marketing, and Related
   Support Services, B
Business/Commerce, B
Business/Managerial Economics, B
Chemistry, BMD
Clinical Psychology, MD
Commercial and Advertising Art, B
Communication and Media Studies, MD
Communication Studies/Speech Communication
   and Rhetoric, B
Composition, M
Computer and Information Sciences, B
Computer Engineering, BM
Computer Science, MD

Computer Systems Analysis/Analyst, B
Construction Engineering and Management, M
Counseling Psychology, MD
Creative Writing, B
Criminology, BM
Curriculum and Instruction, MD
Drama and Dramatics/Theatre Arts, B
Economics, BM
Education, MDO
Educational Administration and Supervision, D
Educational Psychology, MDO
Electrical Engineering, M
Electrical, Electronics and Communications
    Engineering, B
Electronic Commerce, M
Engineering, B
Engineering and Applied Sciences, MD
English, MD
English Language and Literature, B
Environmental Policy and Resource
    Management, M
Environmental Studies, B
Film, Television, and Video Production, M
Finance, B
Finance and Banking, M
Fine Arts and Art Studies, M
Fine/Studio Arts, B
French Language and Literature, BM
Geographic Information Systems, M
Geography, BMD
German Language and Literature, BM
Higher Education/Higher Education
    Administration, MD
History, BM
Hospitality Administration/Management, BM
Hotel/Motel Administration/Management, B
Human Resources Management and Services, M
Information Science/Studies, M
International Affairs, MD
International Business/Trade/Commerce, BM
International Relations and Affairs, B
Italian Language and Literature, B
Jewish/Judaic Studies, M
Journalism, B
Latin American Studies, B
Law and Legal Studies, MP
Legal and Justice Studies, M
Liberal Studies, M
Library Science, M
Management, M
Management Information Systems and
    Services, BM
Management of Technology, M
Marketing, M
Marketing/Marketing Management, B
Mass Communication/Media Studies, M
Materials Sciences, D
Mathematics, BMD
Mechanical Engineering, BM
Media Studies, M
Molecular Biology, B
Multi-/Interdisciplinary Studies, B
Museology/Museum Studies, M
Music, BM
Music History, Literature, and Theory, M
Music Performance, B
Music Teacher Education, M
Music Theory and Composition, M
Musicology and Ethnomusicology, B
Operations Research, B
Organizational Management, M
Performance, M
Philosophy, BM
Physics, BMD
Political Science and Government, B
Psychology, BMD
Public Administration, B
Public Policy Analysis, M
Real Estate, BM
Religion/Religious Studies, BM
Russian Language and Literature, B
Social Sciences, B
Social Work, MD
Sociology, BM
Spanish Language and Literature, BM
Speech and Interpersonal Communication, MD

Statistics, B
Taxation, M
Telecommunications, M
Transportation/Transportation Management, M
Travel and Tourism, M
Women's Studies, B

UNIVERSITY OF NORTHERN COLORADO

Adult Development and Aging, B
African-American/Black Studies, B
Audiology/Audiologist and Hearing Sciences, B
Biological and Biomedical Sciences, MD
Biology/Biological Sciences, B
Business Administration and Management, B
Chemistry, BMD
Communication and Media Studies, M
Communication Disorders, M
Communication Studies/Speech Communication
    and Rhetoric, B
Community Health and Preventive Medicine, M
Counseling Psychology, MD
Counselor Education/School Counseling and
    Guidance Services, MD
Criminal Justice/Safety Studies, B
Dietetics/Dieticians, B
Drama and Dramatics/Theatre Arts, B
Dramatic/Theatre Arts and Stagecraft, B
Early Childhood Education and Teaching, M
Economics, B
Education, MDO
Education/Teaching of the Gifted and Talented, M
Educational Leadership and Administration, MDO
Educational Measurement and Evaluation, MD
Educational Media/Instructional Technology, MD
Educational Psychology, MD
Elementary Education and Teaching, MD
English, M
English Language and Literature, B
Exercise and Sports Science, MD
Fine Arts and Art Studies, M
Fine/Studio Arts, B
Foreign Languages and Literatures, B
French Language and Literature, B
Geography, B
Geology/Earth Science, B
Geosciences, M
German Language and Literature, B
Gerontology, M
Higher Education/Higher Education
    Administration, D
Hispanic-American, Puerto Rican, and Mexican-
    American/Chicano Studies, B
History, BM
Human Services, B
Interdisciplinary Studies, BMDO
Journalism, B
Kinesiology and Exercise Science, B
Mathematics, BMD
Mathematics Teacher Education, MD
Multi-/Interdisciplinary Studies, B
Music, BMD
Music Teacher Education, BMD
Nursing, M
Nursing - Advanced Practice, M
Nursing - Registered Nurse Training, B
Nursing Education, M
Parks, Recreation and Leisure Facilities
    Management, B
Philosophy, B
Physics, B
Political Science and Government, B
Psychology, BM
Public Health, M
Public Health Education and Promotion, B
Reading Teacher Education, MD
Rehabilitation Counseling, MD
School Psychology, DO
Science Teacher Education/General Science
    Teacher Education, MD
Social Sciences, B
Sociology, BM
Spanish Language and Literature, BM
Special Education and Teaching, BMD
Speech-Language Pathology/Pathologist, B
Student Personnel Services, D

Vocational Rehabilitation Counseling/Counselor, B

UNIVERSITY OF PHOENIX-DENVER CAMPUS

Accounting, B
Adult and Continuing Education and Teaching, M
Business Administration and Management, B
Business Administration, Management and
    Operations, M
Community Psychology, M
Counselor Education/School Counseling and
    Guidance Services, M
Criminal Justice/Law Enforcement Administration, B
Curriculum and Instruction, M
Distance Education Development, M
Education, M
Educational Administration and Supervision, M
Educational Media/Instructional Technology, M
Electronic Commerce, M
Elementary Education and Teaching, M
English as a Second Language, M
Information Technology, B
Management, M
Management Information Systems and
    Services, BM
Management of Technology, M
Management Science, M
Nursing, M
Nursing Science, B
Organizational Management, M
Public Administration and Social Service
    Professions, B
School Psychology, M
Secondary Education and Teaching, M

UNIVERSITY OF PHOENIX-SOUTHERN COLORADO CAMPUS

Accounting, B
Business Administration and Management, B
Business Administration, Management and
    Operations, M
Community Psychology, M
Corrections and Criminal Justice, B
Counselor Education/School Counseling and
    Guidance Services, M
Curriculum and Instruction, M
Education, MO
Educational Administration and Supervision, MO
Electronic Commerce, M
Elementary Education and Teaching, M
Health Services Administration, M
Human Resources Management and Services, M
Information Science/Studies, M
Information Technology, B
International Business/Trade/Commerce, M
Management, M
Management Information Systems and
    Services, BM
Management of Technology, M
Management Science, B
Nursing, M
Nursing Science, B
Organizational Management, M
Secondary Education and Teaching, M

WESTERN STATE COLLEGE OF COLORADO

Accounting, B
American/United States Studies/Civilization, B
Anthropology, B
Architecture, B
Art History, Criticism and Conservation, B
Art Teacher Education, B
Art/Art Studies, General, B
Athletic Training and Sports Medicine, B
Biochemistry, B
Biology/Biological Sciences, B
Biopsychology, B
Business Administration and Management, B
Cell/Cellular Biology and Histology, B
Chemistry, B
Clinical Psychology, B
Commercial and Advertising Art, B
Computer Science, B
Counseling Psychology, B

Creative Writing, B
Criminal Justice/Law Enforcement Administration, B
Drama and Dramatics/Theatre Arts, B
Ecology, B
Economics, B
Education, B
Elementary Education and Teaching, B
English Language and Literature, B
Environmental Sciences, B
Environmental Studies, B
Finance, B
Fine/Studio Arts, B
French Language and Literature, B
Geology/Earth Science, B
Graphic Design, B
History, B
Human Resources Management/Personnel
   Administration, B
Interdisciplinary Studies, B
International Business/Trade/Commerce, B
Journalism, B
Kinesiology and Exercise Science, B
Liberal Arts and Sciences Studies and
   Humanities, B
Management Information Systems and Services, B
Marketing/Marketing Management, B
Mass Communication/Media Studies, B
Mathematics, B
Molecular Biology, B
Music, B
Music Management and Merchandising, B
Music Teacher Education, B
Organizational Communication, B
Parks, Recreation and Leisure Facilities
   Management, B
Parks, Recreation, Leisure and Fitness Studies, B
Physical Education Teaching and Coaching, B
Physics, B
Political Science and Government, B
Pre-Dentistry Studies, B
Pre-Law Studies, B
Pre-Medicine/Pre-Medical Studies, B
Pre-Veterinary Studies, B
Psychology, B
Public Policy Analysis, B
Radio and Television, B
Resort Management, B
Sales, Distribution and Marketing Operations, B
School Psychology, B
Science Teacher Education/General Science
   Teacher Education, B
Secondary Education and Teaching, B
Social Science Teacher Education, B
Social Sciences, B
Sociology, B
Spanish Language and Literature, B
Special Education and Teaching, B
Sport and Fitness Administration/Management, B
Technology Education/Industrial Arts, B
Tourism and Travel Services Marketing
   Operations, B
Wildlife Biology, B

WESTWOOD COLLEGE-DENVER NORTH

Accounting and Business/Management, B
Animation, Interactive Technology, Video Graphics
   and Special Effects, B
Architectural Drafting and Architectural
   CAD/CADD, A
Automobile/Automotive Mechanics
   Technology/Technician, A
Business/Commerce, B
Computer and Information Systems Security, B
Computer Engineering Technology/Technician, A
Computer Programming, Specific Applications, B
Computer Software Technology/Technician, A
Computer Systems Networking and
   Telecommunications, AB
Computer/Information Technology Services
   Administration and Management, B
Corrections and Criminal Justice, B
Design and Visual Communications, B
E-Commerce/Electronic Commerce, B
Electrical, Electronic and Communications
   Engineering Technology/Technician, AB

Fashion Merchandising, B
Graphic Design, A
Hotel/Motel Administration/Management, A
Interior Design, B
Marketing/Marketing Management, B
Survey Technology/Surveying, A
Web Page, Digital/Multimedia and Information
   Resources Design, B

WESTWOOD COLLEGE-DENVER SOUTH

Accounting and Business/Management, B
Animation, Interactive Technology, Video Graphics
   and Special Effects, B
Architectural Drafting and Architectural
   CAD/CADD, A
Clinical/Medical Laboratory Assistant, A
Computer and Information Systems Security, B
Computer Programming, Specific Applications, B
Computer Programming/Programmer, A
Computer Systems Networking and
   Telecommunications, AB
Corrections and Criminal Justice, B
Design and Visual Communications, B
E-Commerce/Electronic Commerce, B
Electrical, Electronic and Communications
   Engineering Technology/Technician, B
Fashion Merchandising, B
Graphic Design, A
Interior Design, B
Intermedia/Multimedia, AB
Marketing/Marketing Management, B
System, Networking, and LAN/WAN
   Management/Manager, B
Web/Multimedia Management and Webmaster, B

YESHIVA TORAS CHAIM TALMUDICAL SEMINARY

Jewish/Judaic Studies, B
Rabbinical Studies, B

Connecticut

ALBERTUS MAGNUS COLLEGE

Accounting, B
Accounting and Finance, B
Art History, Criticism and Conservation, B
Art Therapy/Therapist, BM
Art/Art Studies, General, B
Biology/Biological Sciences, B
Business/Managerial Economics, B
Chemistry, B
Child Development, B
Classics and Classical
   Languages, Literatures, and Linguistics, B
Commercial and Advertising Art, B
Criminal Justice/Law Enforcement Administration, B
Curriculum and Instruction, M
Drama and Dramatics/Theatre Arts, B
Economics, B
Education, B
Elementary Education and Teaching, B
English Language and Literature, B
Finance, B
Fine/Studio Arts, B
French Language and Literature, B
General Studies, B
Graphic Design, B
Health/Health Care Administration/Management, B
History, B
Human Resources Management and Services, B
Human Services, B
Humanities/Humanistic Studies, B
Information Science/Studies, AB
Interdisciplinary Studies, B
International Business/Trade/Commerce, B
International Economics, B
Italian Language and Literature, B
Junior High/Intermediate/Middle School Education
   and Teaching, B
Liberal Arts and Sciences Studies and
   Humanities, AB
Liberal Studies, M
Management, M
Management Information Systems and Services, B

Marketing/Marketing Management, B
Mass Communication/Media Studies, B
Mathematics, B
Mathematics Teacher Education, B
Philosophy, B
Photography, B
Political Science and Government, B
Pre-Dentistry Studies, B
Pre-Law Studies, B
Pre-Medicine/Pre-Medical Studies, B
Pre-Veterinary Studies, B
Psychology, B
Religion/Religious Studies, B
Romance Languages, Literatures, and Linguistics, B
Secondary Education and Teaching, B
Social Sciences, B
Social Work, B
Sociology, B
Spanish Language and Literature, B
Urban Studies/Affairs, B

ASNUNTUCK COMMUNITY COLLEGE

Accounting, A
Administrative Assistant and Secretarial Science, A
Banking and Financial Support Services, A
Business Administration and Management, A
Business/Office Automation/Technology/Data
   Entry, A
Communication and Media Studies, A
Computer and Information Sciences, A
Criminal Justice/Safety Studies, A
Engineering Science, A
Fine/Studio Arts, A
General Studies, A
Human Services, A
Industrial Technology/Technician, A
Kindergarten/PreSchool Education and Teaching, A
Legal Administrative Assistant/Secretary, A
Liberal Arts and Sciences Studies and
   Humanities, A
Machine Tool Technology/Machinist, A
Mass Communication/Media Studies, A
Medical Office Assistant/Specialist, A
Radio and Television, A
Special Products Marketing Operations, A

BRIARWOOD COLLEGE

Accounting, A
Administrative Assistant and Secretarial Science, A
BioTechnology, A
Business Administration and Management, A
Child Development, A
Communication Studies/Speech Communication
   and Rhetoric, A
Criminal Justice/Law Enforcement
   Administration, AB
Dental Assisting/Assistant, A
Dietetics/Dieticians, A
Fashion Merchandising, A
Funeral Service and Mortuary Science, AB
General Studies, A
Health Information/Medical Records
   Administration/Administrator, A
Hotel/Motel Administration/Management, A
Legal Administrative Assistant/Secretary, A
Legal Assistant/Paralegal, A
Medical Administrative Assistant/Secretary, A
Medical Office Management/Administration, A
Medical/Clinical Assistant, A
Occupational Therapist Assistant, A
Radio and Television Broadcasting
   Technology/Technician, A
Tourism and Travel Services Management, A

CAPITAL COMMUNITY COLLEGE

Accounting, A
Administrative Assistant and Secretarial Science, A
Business Administration and Management, A
Computer and Information Sciences, A
Computer Engineering Technology/Technician, A
Data Entry/Microcomputer Applications, A
Electrical, Electronic and Communications
   Engineering Technology/Technician, A
Emergency Medical Technology/Technician (EMT
   Paramedic), A
Fire Protection and Safety Technology/Technician, A

Fire Services Administration, A
Information Technology, A
Kindergarten/PreSchool Education and Teaching, A
Liberal Arts and Sciences Studies and
Humanities, A
Medical Radiologic Technology/Science - Radiation
Therapist, A
Medical/Clinical Assistant, A
Nursing - Registered Nurse Training, A
Physical Therapist Assistant, A
Social Work, A
Web Page, Digital/Multimedia and Information
Resources Design, A

CENTRAL CONNECTICUT STATE UNIVERSITY

Accounting, B
Anthropology, B
Art Education, M
Art Teacher Education, B
Art/Art Studies, General, B
Athletic Training and Sports Medicine, B
Biochemistry, B
Biological and Biomedical Sciences, MO
Biology/Biological Sciences, B
Building/Construction
Finishing, Management, and Inspection, B
Business Administration and Management, B
Business Administration, Management and
Operations, M
Business Education, M
Cell Biology and Anatomy, O
Chemistry, BM
Civil Engineering, M
Civil Engineering Technology/Technician, B
Communication and Media Studies, M
Communication Studies/Speech Communication
and Rhetoric, B
Community Psychology, M
Computer and Information Sciences, B
Computer Science, M
Construction Engineering and Management, M
Corporate and Organizational Communication, M
Counselor Education/School Counseling and
Guidance Services, MO
Criminology, BM
Design and Visual Communications, B
Drama and Dramatics/Theatre Arts, B
Early Childhood Education and Teaching, M
Economics, B
Education, MDO
Educational Leadership and Administration, MDO
Educational Media/Instructional Technology, M
Electrical, Electronics and Communications
Engineering, B
Elementary Education and Teaching, BMO
Engineering and Applied Sciences, M
Engineering Technology, B
English, M
English as a Second Language, M
English Language and Literature, B
Exercise and Sports Science, MO
Finance, B
Foreign Language Teacher Education, M
Foundations and Philosophy of Education, M
French Language and Literature, BM
Geography, BM
Geology/Earth Science, B
Geosciences, M
German Language and Literature, B
Health Psychology, M
History, BM
Industrial Production Technologies/Technicians, B
Information Science/Studies, M
Interdisciplinary Studies, B
International Affairs, M
International Business/Trade/Commerce, BM
Italian Language and Literature, B
Management Information Systems and Services, B
Management of Technology, M
Manufacturing Engineering, M
Manufacturing Technology/Technician, B
Marketing/Marketing Management, B
Marriage and Family Therapy/Counseling, M
Mathematics, BM
Mechanical Engineering, M

Mechanical Engineering/Mechanical
Technology/Technician, B
Molecular Biology, BO
Multi-/Interdisciplinary Studies, B
Music, B
Music Teacher Education, BM
Nursing - Registered Nurse Training, B
Philosophy, B
Physical Education Teaching and Coaching, BMO
Physical Sciences, B
Physics, BM
Political Science and Government, B
Psychology, BM
Reading Teacher Education, MO
Rehabilitation Counseling, MO
School Psychology, M
Secondary Education and Teaching, M
Social Sciences, B
Social Work, B
Sociology, B
Spanish Language and Literature, BM
Special Education and Teaching, M
Technology Teacher Education/Industrial Arts
Teacher Education, B
Tourism and Travel Services Marketing
Operations, B
Vocational and Technical Education, MO

CHARTER OAK STATE COLLEGE

Liberal Arts and Sciences Studies and
Humanities, AB

CONNECTICUT COLLEGE

African Studies, B
American/United States Studies/Civilization, B
Anthropology, B
Architecture, B
Art History, Criticism and Conservation, B
Art/Art Studies, General, B
Astrophysics, B
Biochemistry, B
Biology/Biological Sciences, B
Botany/Plant Biology, BM
Cell/Cellular and Molecular Biology, B
Central/Middle and Eastern European Studies, B
Chemistry, B
Chinese Language and Literature, B
Classics and Classical
Languages, Literatures, and Linguistics, BM
Computer and Information Sciences, B
Dance, BM
Drama and Dramatics/Theatre Arts, B
East Asian Studies, B
Economics, B
Education, M
Elementary Education and Teaching, BM
Engineering Physics, B
English, M
English Education, M
English Language and Literature, B
Environmental Studies, B
Ethnic, Cultural Minority, and Gender Studies, B
Family and Consumer Sciences/Human Sciences, B
Film/Cinema Studies, B
Foreign Language Teacher Education, M
French Language and Literature, BM
German Studies, B
Hispanic Studies, M
Hispanic-American, Puerto Rican, and Mexican-
American/Chicano Studies, B
History, B
Interdisciplinary Studies, B
International Relations and Affairs, B
Italian Language and Literature, BM
Italian Studies, B
Japanese Language and Literature, B
Latin American Studies, B
Mathematics, B
Mathematics Teacher Education, M
Medieval and Renaissance Studies, B
Museology/Museum Studies, B
Music, BM
Music Teacher Education, BM
Neuroscience, B
Philosophy, B
Physics Teacher Education, B

Political Science and Government, B
Psychology, BM
Religion/Religious Studies, B
Science Teacher Education/General Science
Teacher Education, M
Secondary Education and Teaching, BM
Slavic Studies, B
Sociology, B
Spanish Language and Literature, B
Teacher Education, Multiple Levels, B
Urban Studies/Affairs, B
Women's Studies, B
Zoology/Animal Biology, M

EASTERN CONNECTICUT STATE UNIVERSITY

Accounting, BM
Art/Art Studies, General, B
Biochemistry, B
Biology/Biological Sciences, B
Business Administration and Management, B
Business/Commerce, B
Communication Studies/Speech Communication
and Rhetoric, B
Computer and Information Sciences, B
Developmental and Child Psychology, B
Early Childhood Education and Teaching, BM
Economics, B
Education, M
Educational Media/Instructional Technology, M
Elementary Education and Teaching, BM
English Language and Literature, B
Environmental Sciences, B
General Studies, AB
History, B
Industrial and Organizational Psychology, B
Kindergarten/PreSchool Education and Teaching, B
Management Information Systems and Services, B
Mathematics, B
Organizational Management, M
Physical Education Teaching and Coaching, B
Political Science and Government, B
Psychology, B
Reading Teacher Education, M
Science Teacher Education/General Science
Teacher Education, M
Secondary Education and Teaching, BM
Social Work, B
Sociology, B
Spanish Language and Literature, B
Sport and Fitness Administration/Management, B
Visual and Performing Arts, B

FAIRFIELD UNIVERSITY

Accounting, BMO
American/United States Studies/Civilization, BM
Art/Art Studies, General, B
Biology/Biological Sciences, B
Business Administration and Management, B
Business Administration, Management and
Operations, MO
Chemistry, B
Clinical Psychology, B
Computer Engineering, M
Computer Science, B
Computer Software Engineering, B
Counselor Education/School Counseling and
Guidance Services, MO
Economics, B
Education, MO
Educational Media/Instructional Technology, MO
Electrical Engineering, M
Electrical, Electronics and Communications
Engineering, AB
Elementary Education and Teaching, M
Engineering, B
Engineering and Applied Sciences, M
English as a Second Language, MO
English Language and Literature, B
Finance, B
Finance and Banking, MO
Foreign Language Teacher Education, MO
Foundations and Philosophy of Education, MO
French Language and Literature, B
German Language and Literature, B
History, B

Human Resources Management and Services, MO
Information Science/Studies, B
International Business/Trade/Commerce, MO
International Relations and Affairs, B
Management, M
Management Information Systems and
  Services, BMO
Management of Technology, M
Marketing, MO
Marketing/Marketing Management, B
Marriage and Family Therapy/Counseling, M
Mass Communication/Media Studies, B
Mathematics, BM
Mechanical Engineering, A
Modern Languages, B
Multilingual and Multicultural Education, MO
Music History, Literature, and Theory, B
Nursing, MO
Nursing - Advanced Practice, MO
Nursing - Registered Nurse Training, B
Philosophy, B
Physics, B
Political Science and Government, B
Psychiatric/Mental Health Nurse/Nursing, MO
Psychology, BM
Religion/Religious Studies, B
School Psychology, MO
Secondary Education and Teaching, B
Sociology, B
Software Engineering, M
Spanish Language and Literature, B
Special Education and Teaching, MO

GATEWAY COMMUNITY COLLEGE

Accounting, A
Automobile/Automotive Mechanics
  Technology/Technician, A
Avionics Maintenance Technology/Technician, A
Biomedical Technology/Technician, A
Business Administration and Management, A
Computer and Information Sciences, A
Computer Engineering, A
Computer Engineering Technology/Technician, A
Computer Graphics, A
Computer Typography and Composition Equipment
  Operator, A
Consumer Merchandising/Retailing Management, A
Data Entry/Microcomputer Applications, A
Data Processing and Data Processing
  Technology/Technician, A
Dietetics/Dieticians, A
Electrical, Electronic and Communications
  Engineering Technology/Technician, A
Engineering Technology, A
Fashion Merchandising, A
Fire Science/Firefighting, A
Gerontology, A
Hotel/Motel Administration/Management, A
Human Services, A
Industrial Radiologic Technology/Technician, A
Industrial Technology/Technician, A
Kindergarten/PreSchool Education and Teaching, A
Legal Administrative Assistant/Secretary, A
Liberal Arts and Sciences Studies and
  Humanities, A
Mechanical Engineering/Mechanical
  Technology/Technician, A
Medical Administrative Assistant/Secretary, A
Mental Health/Rehabilitation, A
Nuclear Medical Technology/Technologist, A
Special Products Marketing Operations, A
Substance Abuse/Addiction Counseling, A
Word Processing, A

GIBBS COLLEGE

Administrative Assistant and Secretarial Science, A
Design and Visual Communications, A
Information Science/Studies, A
Legal Administrative Assistant/Secretary, A
Medical Administrative Assistant/Secretary, A

GOODWIN COLLEGE

Accounting Technology/Technician and
  Bookkeeping, A
Business Administration and Management, A
Business/Commerce, A

Computer and Information Sciences, A
Early Childhood Education and Teaching, A
Emergency Medical Technology/Technician (EMT
  Paramedic), A
Entrepreneurship/Entrepreneurial Studies, A
Histologic Technician, A
Human Services, A
Medical Administrative Assistant/Secretary, A
Medical Insurance Coding Specialist/Coder, A
Medical Insurance Specialist/Medical Biller, A
Medical/Clinical Assistant, A
Nursing - Registered Nurse Training, A
Respiratory Care Therapy/Therapist, A
Security and Protective Services, A
Teacher Assistant/Aide, A

HOLY APOSTLES COLLEGE AND SEMINARY

Bible/Biblical Studies, B
Humanities/Humanistic Studies, B
Philosophy, B
Religion/Religious Studies, AB
Social Sciences, B
Theology and Religious Vocations, MPO
Theology/Theological Studies, B

HOUSATONIC COMMUNITY COLLEGE

Accounting, A
Administrative Assistant and Secretarial Science, A
Art/Art Studies, General, A
Avionics Maintenance Technology/Technician, A
Business Administration and Management, A
Child Development, A
Clinical/Medical Laboratory Technician, A
Commercial and Advertising Art, A
Computer Typography and Composition Equipment
  Operator, A
Criminal Justice/Law Enforcement Administration, A
Data Processing and Data Processing
  Technology/Technician, A
Environmental Studies, A
Human Services, A
Humanities/Humanistic Studies, A
Journalism, A
Liberal Arts and Sciences Studies and
  Humanities, A
Mathematics, A
Mental Health/Rehabilitation, A
Nursing - Registered Nurse Training, A
Physical Therapy/Therapist, A
Pre-Engineering, A
Public Administration, A
Social Sciences, A
Substance Abuse/Addiction Counseling, A

INTERNATIONAL COLLEGE OF HOSPITALITY MANAGEMENT

Culinary Arts/Chef Training, A
Hospitality Administration/Management, A

LYME ACADEMY COLLEGE OF FINE ARTS

Drawing, B
Painting, B
Sculpture, B

MANCHESTER COMMUNITY COLLEGE

Accounting, A
Administrative Assistant and Secretarial Science, A
Business Administration and Management, A
Clinical/Medical Laboratory Technician, A
Commercial and Advertising Art, A
Communication Studies/Speech Communication
  and Rhetoric, A
Criminal Justice/Law Enforcement Administration, A
Drama and Dramatics/Theatre Arts, A
Engineering Science, A
Fine/Studio Arts, A
General Studies, A
Hotel/Motel Administration/Management, A
Human Services, A
Industrial Engineering, A
Industrial Technology/Technician, A
Information Science/Studies, A
Journalism, A

Kindergarten/PreSchool Education and Teaching, A
Legal Administrative Assistant/Secretary, A
Legal Assistant/Paralegal, A
Liberal Arts and Sciences Studies and
  Humanities, A
Management Information Systems and Services, A
Marketing/Marketing Management, A
Medical Administrative Assistant/Secretary, A
Music, A
Occupational Therapist Assistant, A
Physical Therapist Assistant, A
Respiratory Care Therapy/Therapist, A
Social Work, A
Surgical Technology/Technologist, A

MIDDLESEX COMMUNITY COLLEGE

Accounting, A
Administrative Assistant and Secretarial Science, A
Biological and Physical Sciences, A
Biology Technician/BioTechnology Laboratory
  Technician, A
Broadcast Journalism, A
Business Administration and Management, A
Commercial and Advertising Art, A
Computer Programming/Programmer, A
Engineering Science, A
Engineering Technology, A
Environmental Studies, A
Fine/Studio Arts, A
Human Services, A
Industrial Radiologic Technology/Technician, A
Intermedia/Multimedia, A
Legal Administrative Assistant/Secretary, A
Liberal Arts and Sciences Studies and
  Humanities, A
Marketing/Marketing Management, A
Mass Communication/Media Studies, A
Medical Administrative Assistant/Secretary, A
Mental Health/Rehabilitation, A
Ophthalmic Laboratory Technology/Technician, A
Pre-Engineering, A
Radio and Television, A
Substance Abuse/Addiction Counseling, A

MITCHELL COLLEGE

Accounting, A
Athletic Training and Sports Medicine, A
Biological and Physical Sciences, A
Business Administration and Management, AB
Child Development, AB
Commercial and Advertising Art, A
Criminal Justice/Law Enforcement
  Administration, AB
Developmental and Child Psychology, A
Engineering, A
Human Development and Family Studies, AB
Human Services, A
Kindergarten/PreSchool Education and
  Teaching, AB
Liberal Arts and Sciences Studies and
  Humanities, AB
Marine Biology and Biological Oceanography, A
Parks, Recreation, Leisure and Fitness Studies, A
Physical Education Teaching and Coaching, A
Physical Sciences, A
Psychology, A
Sport and Fitness Administration/Management, A
Therapeutic Recreation/Recreational Therapy, A

NAUGATUCK VALLEY COMMUNITY COLLEGE

Accounting, A
Administrative Assistant and Secretarial Science, A
American/United States Studies/Civilization, A
Automobile/Automotive Mechanics
  Technology/Technician, A
Biological and Physical Sciences, A
Business Administration and Management, A
Chemical Engineering, A
Computer Programming, Specific Applications, A
Computer Programming/Programmer, A
Computer/Information Technology Services
  Administration and Management, A
Criminal Justice/Law Enforcement Administration, A
Drafting and Design Technology/Technician, A

Electrical, Electronic and Communications
  Engineering Technology/Technician, A
Engineering Technology, A
Environmental Studies, A
Finance, A
Fire Science/Firefighting, A
Gerontology, A
History, A
Horticultural Science, A
Hospitality Administration/Management, A
Hotel/Motel Administration/Management, A
Human Services, A
Industrial Radiologic Technology/Technician, A
Industrial Technology/Technician, A
Information Science/Studies, A
Information Technology, A
International Relations and Affairs, A
Kindergarten/PreSchool Education and Teaching, A
Kinesiology and Exercise Science, A
Legal Administrative Assistant/Secretary, A
Legal Assistant/Paralegal, A
Liberal Arts and Sciences Studies and
  Humanities, A
Marketing/Marketing Management, A
Mathematics, A
Mechanical Engineering/Mechanical
  Technology/Technician, A
Medical Administrative Assistant/Secretary, A
Mental Health/Rehabilitation, A
Music, A
Natural Sciences, A
Nursing - Registered Nurse Training, A
Physical Sciences, A
Physical Therapist Assistant, A
Pre-Engineering, A
Quality Control Technology/Technician, A
Social Work, A
Special Products Marketing Operations, A
Substance Abuse/Addiction Counseling, A
System Administration/Administrator, A
Word Processing, A

NORTHWESTERN CONNECTICUT COMMUNITY COLLEGE

Accounting, A
Administrative Assistant and Secretarial Science, A
Art/Art Studies, General, A
Behavioral Sciences, A
Biology/Biological Sciences, A
Business Administration and Management, A
Child Development, A
Commercial and Advertising Art, A
Communications Technology/Technician, A
Computer Engineering Technology/Technician, A
Computer Graphics, A
Computer Programming/Programmer, A
Computer Science, A
Criminal Justice/Law Enforcement Administration, A
Criminal Justice/Police Science, A
Electrical, Electronic and Communications
  Engineering Technology/Technician, A
Engineering, A
English Language and Literature, A
Human Services, A
Information Science/Studies, A
Kindergarten/PreSchool Education and Teaching, A
Legal Assistant/Paralegal, A
Liberal Arts and Sciences Studies and
  Humanities, A
Mathematics, A
Medical/Clinical Assistant, A
Parks, Recreation and Leisure Facilities
  Management, A
Parks, Recreation, Leisure and Fitness Studies, A
Physical Sciences, A
Pre-Engineering, A
Public Health (MPH, DPH), A
Sign Language Interpretation and Translation, A
Social Sciences, A
Substance Abuse/Addiction Counseling, A
Therapeutic Recreation/Recreational Therapy, A

Veterinary/Animal Health Technology/Technician and
  Veterinary Assistant, A

NORWALK COMMUNITY COLLEGE

Accounting, A
Administrative Assistant and Secretarial Science, A
Architectural Engineering Technology/Technician, A
Art/Art Studies, General, A
Business Administration and Management, A
Commercial and Advertising Art, A
Computer and Information Sciences, A
Computer Programming, A
Construction Engineering Technology/Technician, A
Criminal Justice/Law Enforcement Administration, A
Data Processing and Data Processing
  Technology/Technician, A
Electrical, Electronic and Communications
  Engineering Technology/Technician, A
Engineering Science, A
Engineering Technology, A
Finance, A
Fine/Studio Arts, A
Fire Science/Firefighting, A
General Studies, A
Hotel/Motel Administration/Management, A
Human Services, A
Information Science/Studies, A
Kindergarten/PreSchool Education and Teaching, A
Legal Assistant/Paralegal, A
Liberal Arts and Sciences Studies and
  Humanities, A
Marketing/Marketing Management, A
Mass Communication/Media Studies, A
Nursing - Registered Nurse Training, A
Parks, Recreation, Leisure and Fitness Studies, A
Respiratory Care Therapy/Therapist, A
Sales, Distribution and Marketing Operations, A
Substance Abuse/Addiction Counseling, A
Therapeutic Recreation/Recreational Therapy, A

PAIER COLLEGE OF ART, INC.

Commercial and Advertising Art, B
Commercial Photography, A
Design and Visual Communications, B
Fine/Studio Arts, B
Interior Design, B
Painting, B

POST UNIVERSITY

Accounting, AB
Biology/Biological Sciences, B
Business Administration and Management, AB
Business Administration, Management and
  Operations, B
Child Care and Support Services Management, A
Criminal Justice/Law Enforcement Administration, B
English Language and Literature, B
Environmental Sciences, B
Environmental Studies, B
Equestrian/Equine Studies, AB
Finance, B
History, B
Human Services, B
International Business/Trade/Commerce, B
Legal Assistant/Paralegal, AB
Liberal Arts and Sciences Studies and
  Humanities, AB
Management Information Systems and Services, B
Marketing/Marketing Management, AB
Psychology, B
Sociology, B

QUINEBAUG VALLEY COMMUNITY COLLEGE

Accounting, A
Administrative Assistant and Secretarial Science, A
Art/Art Studies, General, A
Avionics Maintenance Technology/Technician, A
Business Administration and Management, A
Computer and Information Sciences, A
Computer Graphics, A
Computer Systems Networking and
  Telecommunications, A
Data Entry/Microcomputer Applications, A
Engineering Technology, A

Human Services, A
Liberal Arts and Sciences Studies and
  Humanities, A
Medical/Clinical Assistant, A
Plastics Engineering Technology/Technician, A
Pre-Engineering, A
Substance Abuse/Addiction Counseling, A
System Administration/Administrator, A
Word Processing, A

QUINNIPIAC UNIVERSITY

Accounting, BM
Actuarial Science, B
Advertising, B
Allied Health and Medical Assisting Services, M
Applied Mathematics, B
Athletic Training and Sports Medicine, B
Biochemistry, B
Biological and Biomedical Sciences, M
Biological and Physical Sciences, B
Biology/Biological Sciences, B
Broadcast Journalism, B
Business Administration and Management, B
Business Administration, Management and
  Operations, MO
Business/Managerial Economics, B
Cell Biology and Anatomy, M
Chemistry, B
Child Development, B
Cinematography and Film/Video Production, B
Clinical Laboratory Sciences, M
Communication and Media Studies, M
Communication, Journalism and Related
  Programs, B
Comparative Literature, B
Computer Science, B
Criminal Justice/Safety Studies, B
Developmental and Child Psychology, B
Economics, BM
Education, BM
Elementary Education and Teaching, M
English Education, M
English Language and Literature, B
Film/Cinema Studies, B
Finance, B
Finance and Banking, M
Foreign Language Teacher Education, M
Forensic Nursing, M
Gerontology, B
Health and Medical Laboratory Technologies, B
Health Services Administration, M
History, B
Human Resources Management/Personnel
  Administration, B
Human Services, B
Information Science/Studies, B
International Business/Trade/Commerce, BM
International Relations and Affairs, B
Internet and Interactive Multimedia, M
Journalism, BM
Law and Legal Studies, BPO
Legal Assistant/Paralegal, B
Liberal Arts and Sciences Studies and
  Humanities, B
Management, M
Management Information Systems and Services, M
Marketing, M
Marketing/Marketing Management, B
Mass Communication/Media Studies, B
Mathematics, B
Mathematics Teacher Education, M
Medical Microbiology and Bacteriology, B
Microbiology, M
Middle School Education, M
Molecular Biology, M
Nursing, M
Nursing - Adult, M
Nursing - Advanced Practice, M
Nursing - Registered Nurse Training, B
Occupational Therapy/Therapist, BM
Pathology/Experimental Pathology, M
Physical Therapy/Therapist, BM
Physician Assistant, BM
Physiological Psychology/Psychobiology, B
Political Science and Government, B
Pre-Dentistry Studies, B

Pre-Law Studies, B
Pre-Medicine/Pre-Medical Studies, B
Pre-Veterinary Studies, B
Psychology, B
Public Relations/Image Management, B
Radiologic Technology/Science - Radiographer, B
Sales, Distribution and Marketing Operations, B
Science Teacher Education/General Science
 Teacher Education, M
Secondary Education and Teaching, M
Social Sciences, B
Social Studies Teacher Education, M
Sociology, B
Spanish Language and Literature, B
Veterinary/Animal Health Technology/Technician and
 Veterinary Assistant, B
Web Page, Digital/Multimedia and Information
 Resources Design, B

SACRED HEART UNIVERSITY

Accounting, AB
Athletic Training and Sports Medicine, B
Biochemistry, B
Biological and Physical Sciences, A
Biology Teacher Education, B
Biology/Biological Sciences, AB
Business Administration and Management, AB
Business Administration, Management and
 Operations, MO
Business/Managerial Economics, B
Celtic Languages, Literatures, and Linguistics, A
Chemistry, ABM
Chemistry Teacher Education, B
Cinematography and Film/Video Production, B
Commercial and Advertising Art, AB
Comparative Literature, AB
Computer and Information Sciences, AB
Computer Science, ABMO
Criminal Justice/Law Enforcement Administration, B
Data Processing and Data Processing
 Technology/Technician, A
Drama and Dramatics/Theatre Arts, B
Drawing, AB
Economics, AB
Education, BMO
Educational Administration and Supervision, O
Electronic Commerce, O
Elementary Education and Teaching, BM
English Language and Literature, AB
English/Language Arts Teacher Education, B
Environmental Biology, B
Environmental Sciences, B
European Studies/Civilization, A
Film/Cinema Studies, B
Finance, AB
Gerontology, M
History, AB
History Teacher Education, B
Information Science/Studies, MO
Information Technology, B
International Business/Trade/Commerce, B
International Relations and Affairs, B
Internet and Interactive Multimedia, O
Journalism, B
Junior High/Intermediate/Middle School Education
 and Teaching, B
Kindergarten/PreSchool Education and Teaching, B
Kinesiology and Exercise Science, B
Liberal Arts and Sciences Studies and
 Humanities, A
Liberal Studies, M
Management Information Systems and
 Services, MO
Marketing/Marketing Management, B
Mass Communication/Media Studies, AB
Mathematics, AB
Mathematics and Computer Science, B
Mathematics Teacher Education, B
Modern Languages, A
Molecular Biochemistry, A
Music, A
Nursing, MO
Nursing - Advanced Practice, M
Nursing - Registered Nurse Training, B
Nursing Administration, M
Occupational Therapy/Therapist, BM

Philosophy, AB
Physical Therapy/Therapist, BMD
Political Science and Government, AB
Pre-Dentistry Studies, B
Pre-Medicine/Pre-Medical Studies, B
Pre-Veterinary Studies, B
Psychology, AB
Radio and Television, B
Radio, Television, and Digital Communication, B
Religion/Religious Studies, ABM
Science Teacher Education/General Science
 Teacher Education, B
Secondary Education and Teaching, BM
Social Science Teacher Education, B
Social Work, B
Sociology, AB
Spanish Language and Literature, AB
Sport and Fitness Administration/Management, B

SAINT JOSEPH COLLEGE

American/United States Studies/Civilization, B
Art History, Criticism and Conservation, B
Biochemistry, B
Biological and Biomedical Sciences, M
Biology/Biological Sciences, B
Business Administration and Management, B
Chemistry, BM
Child Development, B
Community Psychology, M
Counselor Education/School Counseling and
 Guidance Services, MO
Dietetics/Dieticians, B
Early Childhood Education and Teaching, M
Economics, B
Education, BM
Elementary Education and Teaching, B
English Language and Literature, B
Environmental Studies, B
Family and Consumer Economics and Related
 Services, B
Family and Consumer Sciences/Home Economics
 Teacher Education, B
Family and Consumer Sciences/Human Sciences, B
Foods, Nutrition, and Wellness Studies, B
Gerontology, O
History, B
Human Development, O
Kindergarten/PreSchool Education and Teaching, B
Liberal Arts and Sciences Studies and
 Humanities, B
Management, M
Marriage and Family Therapy/Counseling, MO
Maternal/Child Health and Neonatal
 Nurse/Nursing, M
Mathematics, B
Natural Sciences, B
Nursing, MO
Nursing - Advanced Practice, M
Nursing - Registered Nurse Training, B
Philosophy, B
Political Science and Government, B
Pre-Law Studies, B
Pre-Medicine/Pre-Medical Studies, B
Psychiatric/Mental Health Nurse/Nursing, M
Psychology, B
Religion/Religious Studies, B
Secondary Education and Teaching, B
Social Work, B
Sociology, B
Spanish Language and Literature, B

ST. VINCENT'S COLLEGE

Health/Health Care Administration/Management, A
Medical Radiologic Technology/Science - Radiation
 Therapist, A
Medical/Clinical Assistant, A
Nursing - Registered Nurse Training, A

SOUTHERN CONNECTICUT STATE UNIVERSITY

Accounting, B
Art Education, M
Art History, Criticism and Conservation, B
Art Teacher Education, B
Biological and Biomedical Sciences, M
Biology/Biological Sciences, B

Business Administration and Management, B
Business Administration, Management and
 Operations, M
Business/Managerial Economics, B
Chemistry, BMO
Communication Disorders, M
Communication Studies/Speech Communication
 and Rhetoric, B
Comparative Literature, B
Computer Science, BM
Counselor Education/School Counseling and
 Guidance Services, MO
Drama and Dramatics/Theatre Arts, B
Economics, B
Education, MDO
Educational Leadership and Administration, DO
Educational Measurement and Evaluation, M
Educational Media/Instructional Technology, M
Elementary Education and Teaching, BMO
English, MO
English as a Second Language, M
English Language and Literature, B
Environmental Education, MO
Exercise and Sports Science, M
Finance, B
Fine/Studio Arts, B
Foundations and Philosophy of Education, O
French Language and Literature, BMO
Geography, B
Geology/Earth Science, B
German Language and Literature, B
Health Education, M
History, BMO
Information Science/Studies, O
Italian Language and Literature, B
Journalism, B
Leisure Studies, M
Liberal Arts and Sciences Studies and
 Humanities, AB
Library Science, BMO
Marriage and Family Therapy/Counseling, M
Mathematics, BM
Multilingual and Multicultural Education, M
Music, B
Nursing, M
Nursing - Registered Nurse Training, B
Nursing Administration, M
Nursing Education, M
Parks, Recreation, Leisure and Fitness Studies, B
Philosophy, B
Physical Education Teaching and Coaching, M
Physics, B
Political Science and Government, BM
Psychology, BM
Public Health, M
Public Health (MPH, DPH), B
Reading Teacher Education, MO
Recreation and Park Management, M
Romance
 Languages, Literatures, and Linguistics, MO
School Psychology, MO
Science Teacher Education/General Science
 Teacher Education, MO
Secondary Education and Teaching, B
Social Work, BMO
Sociology, BM
Spanish Language and Literature, BMO
Special Education and Teaching, BMO
Sport Psychology, M
Urban Studies/Affairs, MO
Women's Studies, M

THREE RIVERS COMMUNITY COLLEGE

Accounting, A
Administrative Assistant and Secretarial Science, A
Architectural Engineering Technology/Technician, A
Avionics Maintenance Technology/Technician, A
Business Administration and Management, A
Civil Engineering Technology/Technician, A
Computer Engineering Technology/Technician, A
Computer Programming/Programmer, A
Computer Typography and Composition Equipment
 Operator, A
Consumer Merchandising/Retailing Management, A
Corrections, A
Criminal Justice/Law Enforcement Administration, A

Data Processing and Data Processing
  Technology/Technician, A
Drafting and Design Technology/Technician, A
Drama and Dramatics/Theatre Arts, A
Electrical, Electronic and Communications
  Engineering Technology/Technician, A
Engineering, A
Engineering Science, A
Engineering Technology, A
Environmental Engineering
  Technology/Environmental Technology, A
Fire Science/Firefighting, A
Hospitality Administration/Management, A
Hotel/Motel Administration/Management, A
Human Services, A
Hydrology and Water Resources Science, A
Industrial Technology/Technician, A
Kindergarten/PreSchool Education and Teaching, A
Laser and Optical Technology/Technician, A
Legal Administrative Assistant/Secretary, A
Liberal Arts and Sciences Studies and
  Humanities, A
Marketing/Marketing Management, A
Mechanical Engineering/Mechanical
  Technology/Technician, A
Medical Administrative Assistant/Secretary, A
Nuclear/Nuclear Power Technology/Technician, A
Nursing - Registered Nurse Training, A
Pre-Engineering, A
Public Administration, A
Special Products Marketing Operations, A
Substance Abuse/Addiction Counseling, A
Technical and Business Writing, A
Tourism and Travel Services Management, A

TRINITY COLLEGE

American/United States Studies/Civilization, BM
Anthropology, B
Art History, Criticism and Conservation, B
Art/Art Studies, General, B
Biochemistry, B
Biology/Biological Sciences, B
Biomedical/Medical Engineering, B
Chemistry, B
Classics and Classical
  Languages, Literatures, and Linguistics, B
Comparative Literature, B
Computer Engineering, B
Computer Science, B
Creative Writing, B
Dance, B
Drama and Dramatics/Theatre Arts, B
Economics, BM
Education, B
Electrical, Electronics and Communications
  Engineering, B
Engineering, B
English, M
English Language and Literature, B
Environmental Sciences, B
Fine/Studio Arts, B
French Language and Literature, B
German Language and Literature, B
History, BM
Interdisciplinary Studies, B
International Relations and Affairs, B
Italian Language and Literature, B
Jewish/Judaic Studies, B
Mathematics, B
Mechanical Engineering, B
Modern Languages, B
Music, B
Neuroscience, B
Philosophy, B
Physics, B
Political Science and Government, B
Psychology, B
Public Policy Analysis, BM
Religion/Religious Studies, B
Russian Language and Literature, B
Sociology, B
Spanish Language and Literature, B

Women's Studies, B

TUNXIS COMMUNITY COLLEGE

Accounting, A
Administrative Assistant and Secretarial Science, A
Applied Art, A
Art/Art Studies, General, A
Business Administration and Management, A
Commercial and Advertising Art, A
Corrections, A
Criminal Justice/Law Enforcement Administration, A
Data Processing and Data Processing
  Technology/Technician, A
Dental Hygiene/Hygienist, A
Engineering, A
Engineering Technology, A
Fashion Merchandising, A
Forensic Science and Technology, A
Human Services, A
Information Science/Studies, A
Kindergarten/PreSchool Education and Teaching, A
Legal Administrative Assistant/Secretary, A
Liberal Arts and Sciences Studies and
  Humanities, A
Marketing/Marketing Management, A
Medical Administrative Assistant/Secretary, A
Physical Therapy/Therapist, A
Substance Abuse/Addiction Counseling, A

UNITED STATES COAST GUARD ACADEMY

Civil Engineering, B
Electrical, Electronics and Communications
  Engineering, B
Management Science, B
Mechanical Engineering, B
Naval Architecture and Marine Engineering, B
Oceanography, Chemical and Physical, B
Operations Research, B
Political Science and Government, B

UNIVERSITY OF BRIDGEPORT

Accounting, B
Acupuncture and Oriental Medicine, M
Biology/Biological Sciences, B
Business Administration and Management, AB
Business Administration, Management and
  Operations, M
Chiropractic, P
Computer Education, MO
Computer Engineering, BM
Computer Science, BM
Dental Hygiene/Hygienist, AB
Early Childhood Education and Teaching, MO
Education, MDO
Educational Administration and Supervision, DO
Electrical Engineering, M
Elementary Education and Teaching, MO
Engineering and Applied Sciences, M
English Language and Literature, B
Fashion Merchandising, AB
Finance, B
Graphic Design, B
Human Resources Development, M
Human Services, BM
Humanities/Humanistic Studies, B
Illustration, B
Industrial Design, B
Information Science/Studies, B
Interdisciplinary Studies, B
Interior Design, B
International and Comparative Education, MO
International Business/Trade/Commerce, B
International Relations and Affairs, B
Journalism, B
Liberal Arts and Sciences Studies and
  Humanities, AB
Management of Technology, M
Marketing/Marketing Management, AB
Mass Communication/Media Studies, B
Mathematics, B
Mechanical Engineering, M
Music, B
Naturopathic Medicine/Naturopathy, D
Nutritional Sciences, M
Pre-Dentistry Studies, B

Pre-Law Studies, B
Pre-Medicine/Pre-Medical Studies, B
Pre-Veterinary Studies, B
Psychology, B
Reading Teacher Education, MO
Religion/Religious Studies, B
Secondary Education and Teaching, MO
Social Sciences, B

UNIVERSITY OF CONNECTICUT

Accounting, BMD
Acting, B
Actuarial Science, BMD
Adult and Continuing Education and Teaching, MD
Aerospace, Aeronautical and Astronautical
  Engineering, MD
African Studies, M
Agricultural Economics, BMD
Agricultural Sciences, MD
Agricultural Teacher Education, B
Agriculture, B
Agronomy and Crop Science, B
Agronomy and Soil Sciences, MD
Allied Health and Medical Assisting Services, M
Allied Health
  Diagnostic, Intervention, and Treatment
  Professions, M
American/United States Studies/Civilization, B
Animal Physiology, B
Animal Sciences, ABMD
Animal/Livestock Husbandry and Production, A
Anthropology, BMD
Applied Horticulture/Horticultural Operations, A
Applied Mathematics, BM
Art History, Criticism and Conservation, BM
Biochemistry, MD
Biological and Biomedical Sciences, MD
Biology/Biological Sciences, B
Biomedical Engineering, MD
Biomedical/Medical Engineering, B
Biophysics, BMD
BioTechnology, MD
Botany/Plant Biology, MD
Business Administration, Management and
  Operations, MDO
Business/Commerce, B
Cell Biology and Anatomy, MD
Cell/Cellular Biology and Anatomical Sciences, B
Chemical Engineering, BMD
Chemistry, BMD
Child and Family Studies, MD
Civil Engineering, BMD
Classics and Classical
  Languages, Literatures, and Linguistics, B
Clinical Laboratory Science/Medical
  Technology/Technologist, B
Clinical Psychology, MD
Cognitive Sciences, BMD
Communication and Media Studies, M
Communication Disorders, MDO
Communication Studies/Speech Communication
  and Rhetoric, B
Comparative Literature, MD
Composition, M
Computer Engineering, B
Computer Science, BMD
Corporate and Organizational Communication, D
Counseling Psychology, MD
Curriculum and Instruction, MD
CytoTechnology/Cytotechnologist, B
Developmental Biology and Embryology, MD
Developmental Psychology, MD
Dietetics/Dieticians, B
Drama and Dramatics/Theatre Arts, B
Dramatic/Theatre Arts and Stagecraft, B
Ecology, BMD
Economics, BMD
Education, MD
Education/Teaching of the Gifted and Talented, MD
Educational Administration and Supervision, MD
Educational Measurement and Evaluation, MD
Educational Media/Instructional Technology, MD
Educational Psychology, MD
Electrical Engineering, MD
Electrical, Electronics and Communications
  Engineering, B

Elementary Education and Teaching, BMD
Engineering, B
Engineering and Applied Sciences, MD
Engineering Physics, B
English, MD
English Education, MD
English Language and Literature, B
Entomology, MD
Environmental and Occupational Health, M
Environmental Engineering
   Technology/Environmental Technology, MD
Environmental Studies, B
Environmental/Environmental Health Engineering, B
Exercise and Sports Science, MD
Experimental Psychology, MD
Finance, B
Finance and Banking, D
Fine Arts and Art Studies, M
Fine/Studio Arts, B
Foreign Language Teacher Education, MD
Foundations and Philosophy of Education, MD
French Language and Literature, BMD
General Studies, B
Genetics, MD
Genomic Sciences, M
Geography, BMD
Geology/Earth Science, BMD
Geophysics Engineering, D
German Language and Literature, BMD
Health Services Administration, M
Health/Health Care Administration/Management, B
Higher Education/Higher Education
   Administration, MD
History, BMD
Horticultural Science, AB
Human Development, MD
Human Development and Family Studies, B
Human Resources Development, M
Human Resources Management and Services, M
Industrial and Organizational Psychology, MD
Industrial Engineering, B
Insurance, B
International Affairs, M
Italian Language and Literature, BMD
Jewish/Judaic Studies, M
Journalism, B
Kinesiology and Movement Studies, MD
Landscape Architecture, B
Latin American Studies, BM
Law and Legal Studies, PO
Leisure Studies, MD
Linguistics, BMD
Management Information Systems and Services, B
Management Science, B
Manufacturing Engineering, B
Marine Biology and Biological Oceanography, B
Marine Sciences, MD
Marketing, MD
Marketing/Marketing Management, B
Materials Engineering, BMD
Materials Sciences, MD
Mathematical and Computational Finance, M
Mathematics, BMD
Mathematics Teacher Education, MD
Mechanical Engineering, BMD
Medicinal and Pharmaceutical Chemistry, MD
Medieval and Renaissance Studies, MD
Metallurgy, MD
Microbiology, MD
Molecular Biology, MD
Multi-/Interdisciplinary Studies, B
Multilingual and Multicultural Education, MD
Music, BMD
Music History, Literature, and Theory, D
Music Teacher Education, BMD
Music Theory and Composition, MD
Musicology and Ethnomusicology, M
Natural Resources and Conservation, BMD
Natural Resources Management/Development and
   Policy, MD
Neurobiology and Neurophysiology, MD
Neuroscience, MD
Nursing, MD
Nursing - Registered Nurse Training, B
Nutritional Sciences, BMD
Oceanography, Chemical and Physical, MD

Oral and Dental Sciences, M
Parks, Recreation and Leisure Facilities
   Management, B
Pathobiology, MD
Pathology/Experimental Pathology, B
Performance, MD
Pharmaceutical Sciences, MD
Pharmacology, MD
Pharmacy, B
Pharmacy, Pharmaceutical Sciences, and
   Administration, B
Philosophy, BMD
Physical Education Teaching and Coaching, B
Physical Therapy/Therapist, BM
Physics, BMD
Physiology, MD
Plant Sciences, MD
Political Science and Government, BMD
Polymer/Plastics Engineering, MD
Pre-Pharmacy Studies, B
Psychology, BMD
Public Health, MO
Public Policy Analysis, MO
Reading Teacher Education, MD
Real Estate, B
School Psychology, MD
Science Teacher Education/General Science
   Teacher Education, MD
Secondary Education and Teaching, MD
Social Psychology, MD
Social Studies Teacher Education, MD
Social Work, MDO
Sociology, BMD
Software Engineering, MD
Spanish Language and Literature, BMD
Special Education and Teaching, BMD
Statistics, BMD
Structural Biology, BMD
Sustainable Development, M
Systems Engineering, MD
Technical Theatre/Theatre Design and
   Technology, B
Theater, M
Theatre Literature, History and Criticism, B
Toxicology, MD
Urban Studies/Affairs, B
Western European Studies, M
Women's Studies, B

UNIVERSITY OF HARTFORD

Accounting, BMO
Architectural Engineering Technology/Technician, B
Architecture, M
Art History, Criticism and Conservation, B
Audio Engineering, B
Biological and Biomedical Sciences, M
Biology/Biological Sciences, B
Biomedical/Medical Engineering, B
Business Administration and Management, B
Business Administration, Management and
   Operations, MO
Business/Managerial Economics, B
Ceramic Arts and Ceramics, B
Chemistry, B
Cinematography and Film/Video Production, B
Civil Engineering, B
Clinical Laboratory Science/Medical
   Technology/Technologist, B
Clinical Psychology, MD
Communication and Media Studies, M
Communication Studies/Speech Communication
   and Rhetoric, B
Community Health Nursing, M
Composition, MDO
Computer and Information Sciences, B
Computer Engineering, B
Computer Engineering Technology/Technician, A
Counselor Education/School Counseling and
   Guidance Services, MO
Criminal Justice/Police Science, B
Dance, B
Drama and Dramatics/Theatre Arts, B
Drawing, B
Early Childhood Education and Teaching, BM
Economics, B
Education, MDO
Educational Leadership and Administration, MDO

Educational Media/Instructional Technology, M
Electrical, Electronic and Communications
   Engineering Technology/Technician, AB
Electrical, Electronics and Communications
   Engineering, B
Elementary Education and Teaching, BM
Engineering, B
Engineering and Applied Sciences, M
Engineering Technologies/Technicians, B
Engineering Technology, B
English Language and Literature, B
Environmental/Environmental Health Engineering, B
Experimental Psychology, M
Film/Cinema Studies, B
Finance, B
Fine Arts and Art Studies, BM
Foreign Languages and Literatures, B
General Studies, A
History, B
Insurance, B
Interdisciplinary Studies, B
Jazz/Jazz Studies, B
Jewish/Judaic Studies, B
Law and Legal Studies, AB
Liberal Arts and Sciences Studies and
   Humanities, A
Management, M
Management Information Systems and Services, B
Mathematics, B
Mathematics and Statistics, B
Mechanical Engineering, B
Mechanical Engineering Related
   Technologies/Technicians, B
Medical Radiologic Technology/Science - Radiation
   Therapist, B
Multi-/Interdisciplinary Studies, B
Music, BMDO
Music History, Literature, and Theory, BM
Music Management and Merchandising, B
Music Performance, B
Music Teacher Education, BMD
Music Theory and Composition, BM
Neuroscience, M
Nursing, M
Nursing - Registered Nurse Training, B
Nursing Education, M
Occupational Therapy/Therapist, B
Organizational Behavior Studies, M
Painting, B
Performance, MDO
Philosophy, B
Photography, B
Physical Therapy/Therapist, BM
Physics, B
Political Science and Government, B
Pre-Dentistry Studies, B
Pre-Medicine/Pre-Medical Studies, B
Pre-Veterinary Studies, B
Psychology, BMD
Public Health (MPH, DPH), AB
Respiratory Care Therapy/Therapist, B
School Psychology, M
Sculpture, B
Secondary Education and Teaching, B
Sociology, B
Special Education and Teaching, B
Taxation, MO
Technical and Business Writing, B

UNIVERSITY OF NEW HAVEN

Accounting, BM
Advertising and Public Relations, M
Applied Mathematics, B
Aviation, M
Biology Technician/BioTechnology Laboratory
   Technician, B
Biology/Biological Sciences, B
Business Administration and Management, B
Business Administration, Management and
   Operations, MO
Business/Managerial Economics, B
Cell Biology and Anatomy, M
Chemical Engineering, AB
Chemistry, B
Civil Engineering, B
Commercial and Advertising Art, AB

Communication Studies/Speech Communication
  and Rhetoric, AB
Community Psychology, MO
Computer and Information Sciences, B
Computer Engineering, B
Computer Science, AM
Corrections, M
Criminal Justice/Law Enforcement Administration, B
Criminal Justice/Police Science, A
Criminology, M
Dental Hygiene/Hygienist, AB
Dietetics/Dieticians, B
Ecology, B
Education, M
Electrical Engineering, M
Electrical, Electronics and Communications
  Engineering, B
Engineering, B
Engineering and Applied Sciences, MO
Engineering Design, O
Engineering Management, M
English Language and Literature, B
Environmental and Occupational Health, M
Environmental Engineering
  Technology/Environmental Technology, MO
Environmental Sciences, M
Finance, B
Finance and Banking, M
Fine/Studio Arts, B
Fire Protection, B
Fire Protection and Safety
  Technology/Technician, AB
Fire Protection Engineering, M
Foodservice Systems
  Administration/Management, A
Forensic Science and Technology, BM
General Studies, A
Health Services Administration, M
History, B
Hospitality Administration/Management, BM
Hotel/Motel Administration/Management, B
Human Resources Management and Services, M
Industrial and Labor Relations, M
Industrial and Organizational Psychology, MO
Industrial Hygiene, M
Industrial/Management Engineering, MO
Information Science/Studies, BM
Interior Architecture, AB
International Business/Trade/Commerce, BM
Law and Legal Studies, AB
Liberal Arts and Sciences Studies and
  Humanities, B
Logistics and Materials Management, O
Management Information Systems and Services, M
Management of Technology, M
Management Strategy and Policy, M
Marine Biology and Biological Oceanography, B
Marketing, M
Marketing/Marketing Management, B
Mathematics, B
Mechanical Engineering, BM
Molecular Biology, M
Music, B
Music Management and Merchandising, B
Nutritional Sciences, M
Occupational Safety and Health
  Technology/Technician, AB
Operations Research, M
Political Science and Government, B
Psychology, B
Public Administration, BMO
Securities Services Administration/Management, M
Software Engineering, M
Sport and Fitness Administration/Management, M
Taxation, M
Travel and Tourism, M
Visual and Performing Arts, B

WESLEYAN UNIVERSITY

African-American/Black Studies, B
American/United States Studies/Civilization, B
Anthropology, B
Archeology, B
Art History, Criticism and Conservation, B
Art/Art Studies, General, B
Astronomy, BM

Biochemistry, BMD
Biological and Biomedical Sciences, D
Biology/Biological Sciences, B
Cell Biology and Anatomy, D
Central/Middle and Eastern European Studies, B
Chemistry, BMD
Classics and Classical
  Languages, Literatures, and Linguistics, B
Computer Science, B
Dance, B
Developmental Biology and Embryology, D
Drama and Dramatics/Theatre Arts, B
East Asian Studies, B
Economics, B
English Language and Literature, B
Environmental Studies, B
Ethnomusicology, D
Film/Cinema Studies, B
Fine/Studio Arts, B
French Language and Literature, B
Genetics, D
Geology/Earth Science, B
Geosciences, M
German Language and Literature, B
Health and Physical Education, B
History, B
Humanities/Humanistic Studies, B
Inorganic Chemistry, MD
Interdisciplinary Studies, B
Italian Language and Literature, B
Latin American Studies, B
Liberal Studies, MO
Mathematics, BMD
Medieval and Renaissance Studies, B
Molecular Biology, BD
Music, BMD
Neurobiology and Neurophysiology, D
Neuroscience, B
Organic Chemistry, MD
Philosophy, B
Physical Chemistry, MD
Physics, BMD
Physiology, D
Political Science and Government, B
Psychology, BM
Religion/Religious Studies, B
Romance Languages, Literatures, and Linguistics, B
Russian Language and Literature, B
Russian Studies, B
Science, Technology and Society, B
Social Sciences, B
Sociobiology, D
Sociology, B
Spanish Language and Literature, B
Theoretical Chemistry, MD
Women's Studies, B

WESTERN CONNECTICUT STATE UNIVERSITY

Accounting, BM
American/United States Studies/Civilization, B
Anthropology, B
Atmospheric Sciences and Meteorology, B
Biological and Biomedical Sciences, M
Biology/Biological Sciences, B
Business Administration and Management, B
Business Administration, Management and
  Operations, M
Chemistry, B
Clinical Laboratory Science/Medical
  Technology/Technologist, B
Commercial and Advertising Art, B
Community Psychology, M
Computer Science, BM
Counselor Education/School Counseling and
  Guidance Services, M
Criminal Justice/Police Science, B
Criminology, M
Curriculum and Instruction, M
Drama and Dramatics/Theatre Arts, B
Economics, B
Education, BM
Educational Leadership and Administration, D
Educational Media/Instructional Technology, M
Elementary Education and Teaching, B
English, M

English Education, M
English Language and Literature, B
Environmental Sciences, M
Environmental Studies, B
Finance, B
Fine Arts and Art Studies, M
Geology/Earth Science, B
Geosciences, M
Health Services Administration, M
Health Teacher Education, B
History, BM
Illustration, M
Liberal Arts and Sciences Studies and
  Humanities, AB
Management Information Systems and Services, B
Marketing/Marketing Management, B
Mass Communication/Media Studies, B
Mathematics, BM
Mathematics Teacher Education, M
Music, B
Music History, Literature, and Theory, B
Music Teacher Education, BM
Nursing, M
Nursing - Adult, M
Nursing - Advanced Practice, M
Nursing - Registered Nurse Training, B
Painting, M
Planetary Astronomy and Science, M
Political Science and Government, B
Pre-Dentistry Studies, B
Pre-Medicine/Pre-Medical Studies, B
Psychology, B
Reading Teacher Education, M
Secondary Education and Teaching, B
Social Sciences, B
Social Work, B
Sociology, B
Spanish Language and Literature, B
Special Education and Teaching, M

YALE UNIVERSITY

Accounting, D
African Studies, BM
African-American/Black Studies, BMD
Allopathic Medicine, P
American/United States Studies/Civilization, BMD
Ancient/Classical Greek Language and Literature, B
Anthropology, BMD
Applied Arts and Design, M
Applied Mathematics, BMD
Applied Physics, MD
Archeology, BM
Architecture, BMO
Art History, Criticism and Conservation, BD
Art/Art Studies, General, B
Asian Languages, D
Astronomy, BMD
Astrophysics, B
Biochemistry, MDO
Bioinformatics, DO
Biological and Biomedical Sciences, DO
Biology/Biological Sciences, B
Biomedical/Medical Engineering, B
Biophysics, MD
Biostatistics, MD
Business Administration, Management and
  Operations, MDO
Cancer Biology/Oncology, DO
Cell Biology and Anatomy, DO
Cell/Cellular Biology and Anatomical Sciences, B
Chemical Engineering, BMD
Chemistry, BD
Chinese Language and Literature, B
Classics and Classical
  Languages, Literatures, and Linguistics, BD
Cognitive Psychology and Psycholinguistics, B
Comparative Literature, BD
Computational Biology, DO
Computer and Information Sciences, B
Computer Science, D
Developmental Biology and Embryology, D
Drama and Dramatics/Theatre Arts, B
East Asian Studies, BM
East European and Russian Studies, M
Ecology, BD
Economics, BMD

Electrical Engineering, MD
Electrical, Electronics and Communications
    Engineering, B
Engineering and Applied Sciences, MD
Engineering Physics, BMD
Engineering Science, B
English, MD
English Language and Literature, B
Environmental and Occupational Health, MD
Environmental Design/Architecture, MO
Environmental Policy and Resource
    Management, MDO
Environmental Sciences, MDO
Environmental Studies, B
Environmental/Environmental Health Engineering, B
Epidemiology, MD
Ethnic and Cultural Studies, B
Ethnic, Cultural Minority, and Gender Studies, B
Evolutionary Biology, BD
Film/Cinema Studies, B
Finance and Banking, D
Fine Arts and Art Studies, M
Foreign Languages, Literatures, and Linguistics, B
Forestry, MDO
French Language and Literature, BMD
Genetics, DO
Genomic Sciences, DO
Geochemistry, D
Geological and Earth Sciences/Geosciences, B
Geology/Earth Science, D
Geophysics and Seismology, D
Geosciences, D
German Language and Literature, BMD
Graphic Design, M
Health Services Administration, MD
History, BMD
History of Medicine, MD
History of Science and Technology, MD
Humanities/Humanistic Studies, B
Immunology, DO
Infectious Diseases, DO
Inorganic Chemistry, D
International Affairs, MO
International Public Health/International Health, M
Italian Language and Literature, BD
Japanese Language and Literature, B
Jewish/Judaic Studies, B
Latin American Studies, B
Latin Language and Literature, B
Law and Legal Studies, MDPO
Linguistics, BD
Marketing, D
Mathematics, BMD
Mathematics and Computer Science, B
Mechanical Engineering, BMD
Mechanics, MD
Medieval and Renaissance Studies, MD
Meteorology, D
Microbiology, DO
Mineralogy, D
Molecular Biology, BDO
Molecular Biophysics, DO
Molecular Medicine, DO
Molecular Pathology, DO
Molecular Physiology, D
Multi-/Interdisciplinary Studies, B
Music, BMDO
Near and Middle Eastern Languages, MD
Neurobiology and Neurophysiology, D
Neuroscience, DO
Nursing, MDO
Oceanography, Chemical and Physical, D
Organic Chemistry, D
Painting, M
Parasitology, D
Pathobiology, DO
Pathology/Experimental Pathology, DO
Pharmacology, DO
Philosophy, BD
Photography, M
Physical Chemistry, D
Physician Assistant, M
Physics, BD
Physiology, DO
Plant Biology, D
Political Science and Government, BD

Portuguese Language and Literature, BMD
Printmaking, M
Psychology, BD
Public Health, MDO
Religion/Religious Studies, BD
Russian Language and Literature, B
Russian Studies, B
Sculpture, M
Slavic Languages, Literatures, and Linguistics, D
Social Sciences, M
Sociology, BD
South Asian
    Languages, Literatures, and Linguistics, B
Spanish Language and Literature, BMD
Statistics, MD
Structural Biology, DO
Systems Science and Theory, B
Theater, MDO
Theology and Religious Vocations, MPO
Virology, DO
Women's Studies, B

Delaware

DELAWARE COLLEGE OF ART AND DESIGN

Animation, Interactive Technology, Video Graphics
    and Special Effects, A
Fine/Studio Arts, A
Graphic Design, A
Illustration, A
Interior Design, A
Photography, A

DELAWARE STATE UNIVERSITY

Accounting, B
Agricultural and Horticultural Plant Breeding, B
Agricultural Business and Management, B
Agriculture, B
Agronomy and Crop Science, B
Airline/Commercial/Professional Pilot and Flight
    Crew, B
Animal Sciences, B
Apparel and Textiles, B
Art Teacher Education, B
Art/Art Studies, General, B
Arts Management, B
Aviation/Airway Management and Operations, B
Banking and Financial Support Services, B
Biological and Biomedical Sciences, M
Biology Teacher Education, B
Biology/Biological Sciences, B
BioTechnology, B
Broadcast Journalism, B
Business Administration and Management, B
Business Administration, Management and
    Operations, M
Business Teacher Education, B
Business/Managerial Economics, B
Chemistry, BM
Chemistry Teacher Education, B
Civil Engineering, B
Community Health Services/Liaison/Counseling, B
Computer and Information Sciences, B
Computer Science, B
Criminal Justice/Law Enforcement Administration, B
Curriculum and Instruction, M
Dietetics/Dieticians, B
Early Childhood Education and Teaching, B
E-Commerce/Electronic Commerce, B
Education, M
Education/Teaching of Individuals in Early Childhood
    Special Education Programs, B
Electrical, Electronic and Communications
    Engineering Technology/Technician, B
Elementary Education and Teaching, B
Engineering Physics, B
English Language and Literature, B
English/Language Arts Teacher Education, B
Environmental Sciences, B
Family and Consumer Sciences/Human Sciences, B
Fashion Merchandising, B
Finance, B
Foods, Nutrition, and Wellness Studies, B
Forestry, B

French Language and Literature, B
French Language Teacher Education, B
History, B
Hospitality Administration/Management, B
Human Resources Management/Personnel
    Administration, B
Information Science/Studies, B
Journalism, B
Junior High/Intermediate/Middle School Education
    and Teaching, B
Kindergarten/PreSchool Education and Teaching, B
Marketing/Marketing Management, B
Mathematics, BM
Mathematics Teacher Education, B
Mechanical Engineering, B
Mechanical Engineering/Mechanical
    Technology/Technician, B
Music, B
Music Teacher Education, B
Musical Instrument Fabrication and Repair, B
Nursing - Registered Nurse Training, B
Parks, Recreation and Leisure Facilities
    Management, B
Physical Education Teaching and Coaching, B
Physics, BM
Physics Teacher Education, B
Political Science and Government, B
Poultry Science, B
Pre-Engineering, B
Pre-Veterinary Studies, B
Psychology, B
Public Relations/Image Management, B
Radio and Television, B
Science Teacher Education/General Science
    Teacher Education, BM
Secondary Education and Teaching, B
Social Work, BM
Sociology, B
Spanish Language and Literature, B
Spanish Language Teacher Education, B
Special Education and Teaching, BM
Sport and Fitness Administration/Management, B
Systems Engineering, B
Tourism and Travel Services Management, B
Trade and Industrial Teacher Education, B
Voice and Opera, B
Wildlife and Wildlands Science and Management, B

DELAWARE TECHNICAL & COMMUNITY COLLEGE, JACK F. OWENS CAMPUS

Accounting, A
Administrative Assistant and Secretarial Science, A
Agricultural Business and Management, A
Architectural Engineering Technology/Technician, A
Automobile/Automotive Mechanics
    Technology/Technician, A
Building/Construction
    Finishing, Management, and Inspection, A
Business Administration and Management, A
Carpentry/Carpenter, A
Chemical Engineering, A
Child Development, A
Civil Engineering Technology/Technician, A
Clinical/Medical Laboratory Technician, A
Computer Programming/Programmer, A
Consumer Merchandising/Retailing Management, A
Criminal Justice/Law Enforcement Administration, A
Data Processing and Data Processing
    Technology/Technician, A
Drafting and Design Technology/Technician, A
Electrical, Electronic and Communications
    Engineering Technology/Technician, A
Emergency Medical Technology/Technician (EMT
    Paramedic), A
Engineering, A
Engineering Technology, A
Environmental Engineering
    Technology/Environmental Technology, A
Health and Medical Laboratory Technologies, A
Heavy Equipment Maintenance
    Technology/Technician, A
Hospitality Administration/Management, A
Hotel/Motel Administration/Management, A
Human Services, A
Journalism, A

Legal Administrative Assistant/Secretary, A
Licensed Practical/Vocational Nurse Training, A
Marketing/Marketing Management, A
Medical Administrative Assistant/Secretary, A
Medical/Clinical Assistant, A
Nursing - Registered Nurse Training, A
Veterinary/Animal Health Technology/Technician and
  Veterinary Assistant, A
Welding Technology/Welder, A

DELAWARE TECHNICAL & COMMUNITY COLLEGE, STANTON/WILMINGTON CAMPUS

Accounting, A
Administrative Assistant and Secretarial Science, A
Architectural Engineering Technology/Technician, A
Banking and Financial Support Services, A
Biomedical Technology/Technician, A
Business Administration and Management, A
Chemical Engineering, A
Civil Engineering Technology/Technician, A
Corrections, A
Criminal Justice/Law Enforcement Administration, A
Criminal Justice/Police Science, A
Culinary Arts/Chef Training, A
Data Processing and Data Processing
  Technology/Technician, A
Dental Hygiene/Hygienist, A
Diagnostic Medical Sonography/Sonographer and
  Ultrasound Technician, A
Drafting and Design Technology/Technician, A
Electrical, Electronic and Communications
  Engineering Technology/Technician, A
Emergency Medical Technology/Technician (EMT
  Paramedic), A
Engineering, A
Fire Science/Firefighting, A
Food Technology and Processing, A
Gerontology, A
Hotel/Motel Administration/Management, A
Human Services, A
Industrial Radiologic Technology/Technician, A
Industrial Technology/Technician, A
Information Science/Studies, A
Instrumentation Technology/Technician, A
Kindergarten/PreSchool Education and Teaching, A
Kinesiology and Exercise Science, A
Management Information Systems and Services, A
Marketing/Marketing Management, A
Mechanical Engineering/Mechanical
  Technology/Technician, A
Medical Administrative Assistant/Secretary, A
Nuclear Medical Technology/Technologist, A
Nursing - Registered Nurse Training, A
Occupational Safety and Health
  Technology/Technician, A
Occupational Therapist Assistant, A
Physical Therapist Assistant, A
Respiratory Care Therapy/Therapist, A
Sign Language Interpretation and Translation, A
Substance Abuse/Addiction Counseling, A
Transportation and Materials Moving, A

DELAWARE TECHNICAL & COMMUNITY COLLEGE, TERRY CAMPUS

Accounting, A
Administrative Assistant and Secretarial Science, A
Aeronautics/Aviation/Aerospace Science and
  Technology, A
Architectural Engineering Technology/Technician, A
Aviation/Airway Management and Operations, A
Avionics Maintenance Technology/Technician, A
Building/Construction
  Finishing, Management, and Inspection, A
Business Administration and Management, A
Civil Engineering Technology/Technician, A
Computer Engineering Technology/Technician, A
Computer Programming/Programmer, A
Construction Engineering Technology/Technician, A
Corrections, A
Criminal Justice/Law Enforcement Administration, A
Data Processing and Data Processing
  Technology/Technician, A
Drafting and Design Technology/Technician, A

Electrical, Electronic and Communications
  Engineering Technology/Technician, A
Electromechanical Technology/Electromechanical
  Engineering Technology, A
Engineering Technology, A
Human Services, A
Industrial Technology/Technician, A
Kindergarten/PreSchool Education and Teaching, A
Licensed Practical/Vocational Nurse Training, A
Nursing - Registered Nurse Training, A
Survey Technology/Surveying, A

GOLDEY-BEACOM COLLEGE

Accounting, AB
Business Administration and Management, AB
Business Administration, Management and
  Operations, M
Finance, B
Finance and Banking, M
Human Resources Management and Services, M
Information Science/Studies, AB
International Business/Trade/Commerce, B
Management, M
Management Information Systems and
  Services, BM
Marketing, M
Marketing/Marketing Management, B

UNIVERSITY OF DELAWARE

Accounting, BM
African-American/Black Studies, B
Agribusiness, B
Agricultural Business and Management, B
Agricultural Economics, BM
Agricultural Sciences, MD
Agricultural Teacher Education, B
Agricultural/Biological Engineering and
  Bioengineering, B
Agriculture, AB
Agronomy and Crop Science, B
Agronomy and Soil Sciences, MD
American/United States Studies/Civilization, M
Animal Sciences, BMD
Anthropology, B
Applied Art, B
Applied Mathematics, MD
Art History, Criticism and Conservation, BMD
Art/Art Studies, General, B
Astronomy, BMD
Astrophysics, B
Athletic Training and Sports Medicine, B
Atmospheric Sciences and Meteorology, D
Bilingual and Multilingual Education, B
Biochemistry, BMD
Biological and Biomedical Sciences, MD
Biology Teacher Education, B
Biology Technician/BioTechnology Laboratory
  Technician, B
Biology/Biological Sciences, B
BioTechnology, BMD
Botany/Plant Biology, B
Business Administration and Management, B
Business Administration, Management and
  Operations, MO
Business Education, M
Business/Managerial Economics, B
Cell Biology and Anatomy, MD
Chemical Engineering, BMD
Chemistry, BMD
Chemistry Teacher Education, B
Child and Family Studies, MD
Child Development, B
Civil Engineering, BMD
Classics and Classical
  Languages, Literatures, and Linguistics, B
Clinical Laboratory Science/Medical
  Technology/Technologist, B
Clinical Psychology, D
Cognitive Sciences, D
Commercial and Advertising Art, B
Communication and Media Studies, M
Communication Studies/Speech Communication
  and Rhetoric, B
Community Organization and Advocacy, B
Comparative Literature, B
Composition, M

Computer and Information Sciences, B
Computer Engineering, B
Computer Science, BMD
Consumer Economics, B
Counselor Education/School Counseling and
  Guidance Services, M
Criminal Justice/Law Enforcement Administration, B
Criminology, MD
Curriculum and Instruction, M
Design and Applied Arts, M
Developmental and Child Psychology, B
Dietetics/Dieticians, B
East Asian Studies, B
Ecology, BMD
Economics, BMDO
Education, BMD
Educational Leadership and Administration, MD
Electrical Engineering, MD
Electrical, Electronics and Communications
  Engineering, B
Elementary Education and Teaching, B
Engineering, B
Engineering and Applied Sciences, MD
English, MDO
English as a Second Language, M
English Language and Literature, B
English/Language Arts Teacher Education, B
Entomology, BMD
Entrepreneurship/Entrepreneurial Studies, M
Environmental Engineering
  Technology/Environmental Technology, BMD
Environmental Policy, M
Environmental Policy and Resource
  Management, MD
Environmental Studies, B
Environmental/Environmental Health Engineering, B
Evolutionary Biology, MD
Exercise and Sports Science, M
Family and Community Services, B
Family and Consumer Economics and Related
  Services, B
Fashion Merchandising, B
Fashion/Apparel Design, B
Film/Cinema Studies, B
Finance, B
Fine Arts and Art Studies, M
Food Science, B
Food Science and Technology, MD
Foods, Nutrition, and Wellness Studies, B
Foreign Language Teacher Education, BM
Foreign Languages and Literatures, B
French Language and Literature, B
Genetics, MD
Geography, BMD
Geology/Earth Science, BMD
Geophysics and Seismology, B
Geotechnical Engineering, MD
German Language and Literature, B
Gerontological Nursing, MO
Health and Physical Education, B
Health Promotion, M
Health Teacher Education, B
Higher Education/Higher Education
  Administration, M
Historic Preservation and Conservation, BM
History, BMD
History Teacher Education, B
HIV/AIDS Nursing, MO
Horticultural Science, BM
Hospitality Administration/Management, M
Hospitality and Recreation Marketing Operations, B
Hotel/Motel Administration/Management, B
Human Development, MD
Human Development and Family Studies, B
Information Science/Studies, MD
International Affairs, MD
International Relations and Affairs, B
Italian Language and Literature, B
Journalism, B
Junior High/Intermediate/Middle School Education
  and Teaching, B
Kindergarten/PreSchool Education and Teaching, B
Kinesiology and Exercise Science, B
Kinesiology and Movement Studies, MD
Latin American Studies, B
Latin Language and Literature, B

Liberal Arts and Sciences Studies and
Humanities, AB
Liberal Studies, M
Linguistics, BMD
Management Information Systems and Services, M
Management of Technology, M
Marine Affairs, MD
Marine Sciences, MD
Marketing/Marketing Management, B
Mass Communication/Media Studies, B
Materials Engineering, MD
Materials Sciences, MD
Maternal/Child Health and Neonatal
Nurse/Nursing, MO
Mathematics, BMD
Mathematics Teacher Education, B
Mechanical Engineering, BMD
Microbiology, MD
Molecular Biology, MD
Multilingual and Multicultural Education, M
Museology/Museum Studies, O
Music, BM
Music Teacher Education, BM
Music Theory and Composition, B
Natural Resources Management/Development and
Policy, B
Neuroscience, BD
Non-Profit/Public/Organizational Management, M
Nursing, MO
Nursing - Adult, MO
Nursing - Advanced Practice, MO
Nursing - Registered Nurse Training, B
Nursing Administration, MO
Nursing Science, B
Nutritional Sciences, BM
Ocean Engineering, MD
Oceanography, Chemical and Physical, MD
Oncology Nursing, MO
Operations Management and Supervision, B
Operations Research, MD
Ornamental Horticulture, B
Paleontology, B
Parks, Recreation and Leisure Facilities
Management, B
Pediatric Nurse/Nursing, MO
Performance, M
Philosophy, B
Physical Education Teaching and Coaching, B
Physical Therapy/Therapist, D
Physics, BMD
Physics Teacher Education, B
Physiology, MD
Piano and Organ, B
Plant Protection and Integrated Pest
Management, B
Plant Sciences, MD
Political Science and Government, BMD
Pre-Veterinary Studies, B
Psychiatric/Mental Health Nurse/Nursing, MO
Psychology, BD
Public Administration, M
Public Policy Analysis, MD
Public Relations/Image Management, B
Russian Language and Literature, B
School Psychology, M
Science Teacher Education/General Science
Teacher Education, B
Secondary Education and Teaching, B
Social Psychology, D
Sociology, BMD
Soil Science and Agronomy, B
Spanish Language and Literature, B
Special Education and Teaching, BM
Sport and Fitness Administration/Management, B
Statistics, M
Structural Engineering, MD
Teaching English as a Second or Foreign
Language/ESL Language Instructor, B
Technical and Business Writing, B
Technical Theatre/Theatre Design and
Technology, B
Theater, M
Transportation and Highway Engineering, MD
Urban Studies/Affairs, MD
Voice and Opera, B
Water Resources Engineering, MD

Wildlife and Wildlands Science and Management, B
Women's Health Nursing, MO

WESLEY COLLEGE

Accounting, B
American/United States Studies/Civilization, B
Biology/Biological Sciences, B
Business Administration and Management, B
Business Administration, Management and
Operations, M
Clinical Laboratory Science/Medical
Technology/Technologist, B
Education, BM
English Language and Literature, B
Environmental Studies, BM
History, B
Legal Assistant/Paralegal, B
Liberal Arts and Sciences Studies and
Humanities, B
Marketing/Marketing Management, B
Mass Communication/Media Studies, B
Nursing, M
Nursing - Registered Nurse Training, B
Parks, Recreation, Leisure and Fitness Studies, B
Physical Education Teaching and Coaching, B
Political Science and Government, B
Psychology, B

WILMINGTON COLLEGE

Accounting, B
Airframe Mechanics and Aircraft Maintenance
Technology/Technician, B
Aviation/Airway Management and Operations, B
Avionics Maintenance Technology/Technician, B
Behavioral Sciences, B
Business Administration and Management, B
Business Administration, Management and
Operations, M
Communication and Media Studies, B
Community Psychology, M
Counselor Education/School Counseling and
Guidance Services, M
Criminal Justice/Law Enforcement Administration, B
Criminology, M
Design and Visual Communications, AB
Early Childhood Education and Teaching, AB
Education, M
Education/Teaching of the Gifted and Talented, M
Educational Administration and Supervision, M
Educational Leadership and Administration, MD
Educational Media/Instructional Technology, M
Elementary Education and Teaching, BM
Finance, B
General Studies, AB
Gerontology, M
Health Services Administration, M
Human Resources Management and Services, M
Human Resources Management/Personnel
Administration, B
Information Technology, B
Junior High/Intermediate/Middle School Education
and Teaching, B
Kindergarten/PreSchool Education and Teaching, A
Law and Legal Studies, B
Logistics and Materials Management, M
Management, M
Management Information Systems and Services, M
Marketing/Marketing Management, B
Nursing, M
Nursing - Advanced Practice, M
Nursing - Registered Nurse Training, B
Psychology, BM
Public Administration, M
Reading Teacher Education, M
School Psychology, M
Science Teacher Education/General Science
Teacher Education, B
Special Education and Teaching, M
Sport and Fitness Administration/Management, B

Vocational and Technical Education, M

District of Columbia

AMERICAN UNIVERSITY

Accounting, M
American/United States Studies/Civilization, BO
Anthropology, BMDO
Applied Economics, O
Applied Mathematics, B
Applied Science and Technology, M
Art History, Criticism and Conservation, BM
Art/Art Studies, General, B
Arts Management, MO
Audio Engineering, B
Biochemistry, B
Biological and Biomedical Sciences, M
Biology/Biological Sciences, B
Biopsychology, M
Business Administration and Management, B
Business Administration, Management and
Operations, MO
Chemistry, BM
Cinematography and Film/Video Production, B
Clinical Psychology, D
Communication and Media Studies, M
Comparative Literature, BM
Computer Science, BMO
Conflict Resolution and Mediation/Peace Studies, M
Criminology, MDO
Dance, MO
Design and Visual Communications, B
Drama and Dramatics/Theatre Arts, B
Economics, BMDO
Education, MDO
Educational Administration and Supervision, D
Educational Leadership and Administration, M
Educational Media/Instructional Technology, M
Electronic Commerce, M
Elementary Education and Teaching, BMO
English as a Second Language, MO
Entrepreneurship/Entrepreneurial Studies, M
Environmental Policy, M
Environmental Policy and Resource
Management, M
Environmental Sciences, M
Environmental Studies, B
Ethics, M
European Studies/Civilization, B
Exercise and Sports Science, M
Experimental Psychology, M
Film, Television, and Video Production, M
Finance and Banking, MO
Fine/Studio Arts, B
Foreign Languages and Literatures, B
French Language and Literature, BO
German Language and Literature, B
Graphic Design, B
History, BMD
Human Resources Management and Services, M
Interdisciplinary Studies, BM
Intermedia/Multimedia, B
International Affairs, MDO
International and Comparative Education, M
International Business/Trade/Commerce, M
International Development, MO
International Relations and Affairs, B
Internet and Interactive Multimedia, M
Jewish/Judaic Studies, B
Journalism, BM
Latin American Studies, BMO
Law and Legal Studies, BMPO
Legal and Justice Studies, MDO
Liberal Arts and Sciences Studies and
Humanities, B
Management Information Systems and
Services, MO
Marine Biology and Biological Oceanography, B
Marine Science/Merchant Marine Officer, B
Marketing, M
Mass Communication/Media Studies, BM
Mathematics, BM
Media Studies, M
Music, B
Neuroscience, D
Organizational Management, MO

Painting, M
Peace Studies and Conflict Resolution, B
Philosophy, BM
Physics, BM
Political Science and Government, BMDO
Printmaking, M
Psychology, BMD
Public Administration, MDO
Public Affairs, M
Public Health (MPH, DPH), B
Public Health Education and Promotion, B
Public Policy Analysis, M
Public Relations/Image Management, B
Real Estate, M
Russian Language and Literature, BO
Russian Studies, B
Sculpture, M
Secondary Education and Teaching, BMO
Social Psychology, M
Sociology, BMO
Spanish Language and Literature, BMO
Special Education and Teaching, M
Statistics, BMO
Taxation, M
Toxicology, MO
Translation and Interpretation, O
Women's Studies, B
Writing, M

THE CATHOLIC UNIVERSITY OF AMERICA

Accounting, BM
Acoustics, MD
Anthropology, BMD
Architecture, BM
Art History, Criticism and Conservation, B
Art Teacher Education, B
Art/Art Studies, General, B
Artificial Intelligence and Robotics, MD
Atomic/Molecular Physics, B
Biochemistry, B
Biological and Biomedical Sciences, MDO
Biology Teacher Education, B
Biology/Biological Sciences, B
Biomedical Engineering, MD
Biomedical/Medical Engineering, B
Business Administration and Management, B
Business Administration, Management and
   Operations, MO
Business/Commerce, B
Cell Biology and Anatomy, MD
Chemistry, BM
Chemistry Teacher Education, B
Civil Engineering, BMD
Classics and Classical
   Languages, Literatures, and Linguistics, BMDO
Clinical Laboratory Science/Medical
   Technology/Technologist, B
Clinical Laboratory Sciences, MD
Clinical Psychology, D
Communication Studies/Speech Communication
   and Rhetoric, B
Comparative Literature, MD
Composition, MD
Computer Engineering, B
Computer Science, BMD
Construction Engineering and Management, MD
Counselor Education/School Counseling and
   Guidance Services, M
Curriculum and Instruction, M
Drama and Dance Teacher Education, B
Drama and Dramatics/Theatre Arts, B
Economics, BM
Education, BMD
Educational Administration and Supervision, MD
Educational Leadership and Administration, M
Educational Psychology, BD
Electrical Engineering, MD
Electrical, Electronics and Communications
   Engineering, B
Elementary Education and Teaching, B
Engineering, B
Engineering and Applied Sciences, MD
Engineering Design, D
Engineering Management, M
English, MDO

English as a Second Language, M
English Language and Literature, B
English/Language Arts Teacher Education, B
Environmental Engineering
   Technology/Environmental Technology, MD
Ergonomics and Human Factors, M
Experimental Psychology, MD
Finance, B
Finance and Banking, M
Fine Arts and Art Studies, B
Fine/Studio Arts, B
Foreign Language Teacher Education, B
French Language and Literature, BMD
French Language Teacher Education, B
General Studies, B
Geotechnical Engineering, M
German Language and Literature, B
German Language Teacher Education, B
History, BMDO
History Teacher Education, B
Human Development, D
Human Resources Management and Services, M
Human Resources Management/Personnel
   Administration, B
Information Science/Studies, MO
Interdisciplinary Studies, B
International Affairs, M
International Economics, B
International Finance, B
International Relations and Affairs, B
Italian Language and Literature, M
Kindergarten/PreSchool Education and Teaching, B
Latin Language and Literature, B
Law and Legal Studies, PO
Legal and Justice Studies, DO
Library Science, MO
Mathematics, B
Mathematics Teacher Education, B
Mechanical Engineering, BMD
Mechanics, MD
Medieval and Renaissance Studies, BMDO
Microbiology, MD
Modern Greek Language and Literature, B
Music, BMD
Music History, Literature, and Theory, B
Music Performance, B
Music Teacher Education, BMD
Music Theory and Composition, B
Musicology and Ethnomusicology, MDO
Near and Middle Eastern Languages, MD
Nursing, MD
Nursing - Advanced Practice, M
Nursing - Registered Nurse Training, B
Painting, B
Performance, MD
Philosophy, BMDO
Physics, BMD
Piano and Organ, B
Political Science and Government, BMDO
Psychology, BMDO
Religion/Religious Studies, BMDO
Religious Education, BMD
Rhetoric, MD
Romance
   Languages, Literatures, and Linguistics, BMD
Sacred Music, MD
Sculpture, B
Secondary Education and Teaching, B
Social Work, BMDO
Sociology, BMD
Spanish Language and Literature, BMD
Spanish Language Teacher Education, B
Structural Engineering, M
Theater, M
Theology and Religious Vocations, MDPO
Urban and Regional Planning, M
Voice and Opera, B
Western European Studies, M

CORCORAN COLLEGE OF ART AND DESIGN

Art/Art Studies, General, B
Ceramic Arts and Ceramics, B
Digital Communication and Media/Multimedia, AB
Drawing, B
Fine/Studio Arts, AB

Graphic Design, AB
Photography, AB
Photojournalism, B
Printmaking, B
Sculpture, B

GALLAUDET UNIVERSITY

Accounting, B
American Government and Politics (United States)
   , B
Apparel and Textiles, B
Art History, Criticism and Conservation, B
Art Teacher Education, B
Art/Art Studies, General, B
Biology/Biological Sciences, B
Business Administration and Management, B
Chemical Engineering, B
Chemistry, B
Child Development, B
Civil Engineering, B
Clinical Psychology, D
Commercial and Advertising Art, B
Communication Disorders, MD
Communication Studies/Speech Communication
   and Rhetoric, B
Computer and Information Sciences, B
Computer Engineering, B
Computer Science, B
Counseling Psychology, M
Counselor Education/School Counseling and
   Guidance Services, M
Criminology, B
Developmental Psychology, M
Drama and Dramatics/Theatre Arts, B
Early Childhood Education and Teaching, MO
Economics, B
Education, BMDO
Education/Teaching of Individuals with Multiple
   Disabilities, MO
Educational Administration and Supervision, MDO
Educational Leadership and Administration, M
Educational Measurement and Evaluation, O
Educational Media/Instructional Technology, O
Electrical, Electronics and Communications
   Engineering, B
Elementary Education and Teaching, BMO
Engineering, B
Engineering Science, B
Engineering Technology, B
English Composition, B
English Language and Literature, B
English/Language Arts Teacher Education, B
Family Systems, B
Fine/Studio Arts, B
Foods, Nutrition, and Wellness Studies, B
French Language and Literature, B
History, B
Information Science/Studies, B
International Relations and Affairs, B
Kindergarten/PreSchool Education and Teaching, B
Leisure Studies, M
Linguistics, M
Mass Communication/Media Studies, B
Mathematics, B
Mechanical Engineering, B
Philosophy, B
Photography, B
Physical Education Teaching and Coaching, B
Physics, B
Psychology, BMDO
Radio and Television, B
School Psychology, MO
Secondary Education and Teaching, BMO
Sign Language Interpretation and Translation, B
Social Work, BM
Sociology, B
Spanish Language and Literature, B
Special Education and Teaching, MDO
Therapeutic Recreation/Recreational Therapy, B
Translation and Interpretation, M

THE GEORGE WASHINGTON UNIVERSITY

Accounting, BMD
Aerospace, Aeronautical and Astronautical
   Engineering, MDO

Allopathic Medicine, PO
American/United States Studies/Civilization, BMD
Analytical Chemistry, MD
Anthropology, BMD
Applied Mathematics, BM
Archeology, B
Art History, Criticism and Conservation, BMD
Art Therapy/Therapist, MO
Art/Art Studies, General, B
Asian Studies/Civilization, BMO
Audiology/Audiologist and Speech-Language
   Pathology/Pathologist, B
Biochemistry, MD
Bioinformatics, M
Biological and Biomedical Sciences, MD
Biological Anthropology, MD
Biology/Biological Sciences, B
Biostatistics, MD
Business Administration and Management, B
Business/Managerial Economics, B
Cancer Biology/Oncology, D
Ceramic Arts and Ceramics, M
Chemistry, BMD
Chinese Language and Literature, B
Civil Engineering, BMDO
Classics and Classical
   Languages, Literatures, and Linguistics, B
Clinical Laboratory Science/Medical
   Technology/Technologist, B
Clinical Psychology, D
Clinical/Medical Laboratory Technician, A
Cognitive Sciences, D
Communication Disorders, M
Community Health and Preventive Medicine, MO
Computer and Information Sciences, B
Computer Engineering, BMDO
Computer Science, BMDO
Counselor Education/School Counseling and
   Guidance Services, MDO
Criminal Justice/Law Enforcement Administration, B
Criminology, M
Curriculum and Instruction, MDO
Dance, B
Design and Applied Arts, M
Drama and Dramatics/Theatre Arts, B
Early Childhood Education and Teaching, M
East Asian Studies, BMO
East European and Russian Studies, MO
Economics, BMD
Education, MDO
Educational Administration and Supervision, MDO
Educational Leadership and Administration, MO
Educational Media/Instructional Technology, M
Electrical Engineering, MDO
Electrical, Electronics and Communications
   Engineering, B
Elementary Education and Teaching, M
Emergency Medical Services, O
Emergency Medical Technology/Technician (EMT
   Paramedic), B
Engineering, B
Engineering and Applied Sciences, MDO
Engineering Management, MDO
English, MD
English Language and Literature, B
Environmental and Occupational Health, MD
Environmental Engineering
   Technology/Environmental Technology, MDO
Environmental Policy and Resource
   Management, M
Environmental Studies, BMD
Environmental/Environmental Health Engineering, B
Epidemiology, MD
European Studies/Civilization, B
Exercise and Sports Science, M
Finance, B
Finance and Banking, MD
Fine/Studio Arts, B
Folklore, M
Forensic Science and Technology, MO
French Language and Literature, B
Genetics, MD
Genomic Sciences, M
Geography, BM
Geology/Earth Science, BMD
Geosciences, MD

German Language and Literature, B
Health and Medical Laboratory Technologies, B
Health Informatics, M
Health Promotion, M
Health Psychology, D
Health Services Administration, MDO
Higher Education/Higher Education
   Administration, MDO
Historic Preservation and Conservation, M
History, BMD
Hospitality Administration/Management, M
Human Development, MD
Human Resources Development, MDO
Human Resources Management and Services, M
Human Resources Management/Personnel
   Administration, B
Human Services, B
Humanities/Humanistic Studies, B
Immunology, D
Industrial and Manufacturing Management, M
Industrial and Organizational Psychology, D
Industrial Radiologic Technology/Technician, A
Infectious Diseases, M
Inorganic Chemistry, MD
Interdisciplinary Studies, B
Interior Design, M
International Affairs, MO
International and Comparative Education, M
International Business/Trade/Commerce, BMDO
International Development, MO
International Public Health/International Health, M
International Relations and Affairs, B
International Trade, MO
Investment Management, M
Jewish/Judaic Studies, B
Journalism, B
Kinesiology and Exercise Science, B
Latin American Studies, BMO
Law and Legal Studies, MDPO
Liberal Arts and Sciences Studies and
   Humanities, B
Logistics and Materials Management, M
Management, MD
Management Information Systems and Services, M
Management of Technology, M
Management Strategy and Policy, MD
Marketing, MD
Marketing/Marketing Management, B
Mass Communication/Media Studies, BM
Materials Sciences, MD
Maternal and Child Health, M
Mathematics, BMD
Mechanical Engineering, BMDO
Microbiology, M
Military and Defense Studies, MO
Molecular Biology, MD
Museology/Museum Studies, MO
Museum Education, M
Music, B
Near and Middle Eastern Studies, B
Neuroscience, D
Non-Profit/Public/Organizational Management, M
Nuclear Medical Technology/Technologist, A
Nursing - Adult, O
Nursing - Advanced Practice, O
Oral Biology, M
Organic Chemistry, MD
Organizational Behavior Studies, M
Organizational Management, MO
Painting, M
Pharmacology, D
Philosophy, BM
Photography, M
Physical Chemistry, MD
Physical Therapy/Therapist, M
Physician Assistant, BMO
Physics, BMD
Political Science and Government, BMDO
Pre-Dentistry Studies, B
Pre-Law Studies, B
Pre-Medicine/Pre-Medical Studies, B
Printmaking, M
Project Management, M
Psychology, BD
Public Administration, MD
Public Health, MDO

Public Policy Analysis, BMD
Radio and Television, B
Radiologic Technology/Science - Radiographer, B
Real Estate, M
Rehabilitation Counseling, M
Religion/Religious Studies, BM
Russian Language and Literature, B
Russian Studies, B
Sculpture, M
Secondary Education and Teaching, M
Securities Services Administration/Management, MO
Social Psychology, D
Sociology, BM
Spanish Language and Literature, B
Special Education and Teaching, MDO
Speech and Rhetorical Studies, B
Sport and Fitness Administration/Management, M
Statistics, BMD
Systems Engineering, BMDO
Technology and Public Policy, MO
Theater, M
Travel and Tourism, MO
Western European Studies, MO
Women's Studies, MO

GEORGETOWN UNIVERSITY

Accounting, B
Allopathic Medicine, PO
American/United States Studies/Civilization, B
Analytical Chemistry, MD
Anthropology, B
Arabic Language and Literature, BMD
Art History, Criticism and Conservation, B
Biochemistry, BMDO
Biological and Biomedical Sciences, MDO
Biology/Biological Sciences, B
Biophysics, MDO
Biostatistics, M
Business Administration and Management, B
Business Administration, Management and
   Operations, MO
Cell Biology and Anatomy, DO
Chemistry, BMD
Chinese Language and Literature, B
Classics and Classical
   Languages, Literatures, and Linguistics, B
Communication and Media Studies, M
Comparative Literature, B
Computer Science, B
Demography, M
East European and Russian Studies, MO
Economics, BDO
English, M
English as a Second Language, MO
English Language and Literature, B
Epidemiology, M
Finance, B
Fine/Studio Arts, B
French Language and Literature, B
German Language and Literature, BMDO
Health Physics/Radiological Health, M
Health Promotion, M
History, BMDO
Immunology, MD
Infectious Diseases, M
Inorganic Chemistry, MD
Interdisciplinary Studies, B
International Affairs, MDO
International Business/Trade/Commerce, B
International Economics, B
International Relations and Affairs, B
Internet and Interactive Multimedia, M
Italian Language and Literature, B
Japanese Language and Literature, B
Latin American Studies, MO
Law and Legal Studies, MDPO
Liberal Arts and Sciences Studies and
   Humanities, B
Liberal Studies, M
Linguistics, BMDO
Marketing/Marketing Management, B
Mathematics, B
Medieval and Renaissance Studies, B
Microbiology, MD
Military and Defense Studies, MO
Molecular Biology, DO

Multi-/Interdisciplinary Studies, B
Multilingual and Multicultural Education, MO
Near and Middle Eastern Studies, MO
Neuroscience, DO
Nursing, M
Nursing - Registered Nurse Training, B
Organic Chemistry, MD
Pathology/Experimental Pathology, MDO
Pharmacology, DO
Philosophy, BMDO
Physical Chemistry, MD
Physics, B
Physiology, MDO
Political Science and Government, BMDO
Portuguese Language and Literature, B
Psychology, BD
Public Health, M
Public Health (MPH, DPH), B
Public Policy Analysis, MO
Radiation Biology/Radiobiology, M
Russian Language and Literature, B
Science, Technology and Society, B
Social Sciences, B
Sociology, B
Spanish Language and Literature, BMDO
Taxation, M
Theology/Theological Studies, B
Theoretical Chemistry, MD
Western European Studies, MO
Women's Studies, B

HOWARD UNIVERSITY

Accounting, BM
African Studies, MD
African-American/Black Studies, B
Allopathic Medicine, DPO
Analytical Chemistry, MD
Anatomy, BMD
Anthropology, B
Applied Art, B
Applied Mathematics, MD
Architecture, B
Art History, Criticism and Conservation, M
Art Therapy/Therapist, B
Art/Art Studies, General, B
Atmospheric Sciences and Meteorology, MD
Biochemistry, MD
Biological and Biomedical Sciences, MD
Biology/Biological Sciences, B
Biophysics, D
Biopsychology, D
BioTechnology, M
Broadcast Journalism, B
Business Administration and Management, B
Business Administration, Management and
   Operations, MO
Ceramic Arts and Ceramics, BM
Chemical Engineering, BM
Chemistry, BMD
Civil Engineering, BM
Classics and Classical
   Languages, Literatures, and Linguistics, B
Clinical Laboratory Science/Medical
   Technology/Technologist, B
Clinical Psychology, D
Communication and Media Studies, MD
Communication Disorders, MD
Computer Science, M
Corporate and Organizational Communication, MD
Counseling Psychology, MDO
Counselor Education/School Counseling and
   Guidance Services, BMO
Criminal Justice/Police Science, B
Dental and Oral Surgery, O
Dental Hygiene/Hygienist, B
Dentistry, PO
Design and Applied Arts, M
Developmental Psychology, D
Drama and Dramatics/Theatre Arts, B
Drama Therapy, B
Early Childhood Education and Teaching, MO
Economics, BMD
Education, BMDO
Educational Administration and Supervision, MDO
Educational Psychology, MDO
Electrical Engineering, MD

Electrical, Electronics and Communications
   Engineering, B
Elementary Education and Teaching, M
Engineering and Applied Sciences, MD
English, MD
English Language and Literature, B
Environmental Sciences, MD
Exercise and Sports Science, M
Experimental Psychology, D
Family and Consumer Economics and Related
   Services, B
Fashion/Apparel Design, B
Film, Television, and Video Production, M
Film/Cinema Studies, B
Finance, B
Finance and Banking, M
Fine Arts and Art Studies, M
Foods, Nutrition, and Wellness Studies, B
French Language and Literature, BM
Genetics, MD
German Language and Literature, B
Health Education, M
History, BMD
Hotel/Motel Administration/Management, B
Human Development, M
Human Genetics, MD
Industrial Radiologic Technology/Technician, B
Information Science/Studies, B
Inorganic Chemistry, MD
Insurance, B
Interior Design, B
International Business/Trade/Commerce, BM
International Economics, B
Journalism, B
Kindergarten/PreSchool Education and Teaching, B
Law and Legal Studies, MPO
Leisure Studies, M
Management, M
Management Information Systems and Services, M
Marketing, M
Marketing/Marketing Management, B
Mass Communication/Media Studies, BMD
Mathematics, BMD
Mechanical Engineering, BMD
Media Studies, MD
Microbiology, D
Molecular Biology, MD
Multilingual and Multicultural Education, MD
Music, BM
Music Teacher Education, M
Nursing, MO
Nursing - Advanced Practice, O
Nursing - Registered Nurse Training, B
Nutritional Sciences, MD
Occupational Therapy/Therapist, B
Organic Chemistry, MD
Orthodontics, O
Painting, M
Pedodontics, O
Pharmacology, MDO
Pharmacy, BP
Philosophy, BM
Photography, M
Physical Chemistry, MD
Physical Education Teaching and Coaching, B
Physical Therapy/Therapist, B
Physician Assistant, B
Physics, BMD
Physiology, D
Political Science and Government, BMD
Printmaking, M
Psychology, BMD
Public Administration, M
Public Affairs, M
Radio and Television, B
Reading Teacher Education, MO
Recreation and Park Management, M
Russian Language and Literature, B
School Psychology, MDO
Sculpture, M
Secondary Education and Teaching, MO
Social Psychology, D
Social Work, BMD
Sociology, BMD
Spanish Language and Literature, BM
Special Education and Teaching, MO

Theology and Religious Vocations, MDP

POTOMAC COLLEGE

Accounting, AB
Business Administration and Management, B
International Business/Trade/Commerce, AB
Management Information Systems and Services, A
Purchasing, Procurement/Acquisitions and
   Contracts Management, B
Security and Loss Prevention Services, A

SOUTHEASTERN UNIVERSITY

Accounting, M
Banking and Financial Support Services, B
Business Administration and Management, AB
Business Administration, Management and
   Operations, M
Computer Science, ABM
Finance and Banking, M
Health Services Administration, M
Health/Health Care Administration/Management, AB
Information Science/Studies, AB
International Business/Trade/Commerce, M
Law and Legal Studies, AB
Management Information Systems and
   Services, ABM
Marketing, M
Marketing/Marketing Management, AB
Public Administration, M

STRAYER UNIVERSITY

Accounting, ABM
Business Administration and Management, AB
Business Administration, Management and
   Operations, M
Computer and Information Sciences and Support
   Services, AB
Computer Systems Networking and
   Telecommunications, AB
Economics, AB
Information Science/Studies, ABM
International Business/Trade/Commerce, B
Liberal Arts and Sciences Studies and
   Humanities, A
Management Information Systems and Services, M
Marketing/Marketing Management, A
Purchasing, Procurement/Acquisitions and
   Contracts Management, A
Web Page, Digital/Multimedia and Information
   Resources Design, AB

TRINITY (WASHINGTON) UNIVERSITY

Art History, Criticism and Conservation, B
Biochemistry, B
Biology/Biological Sciences, B
Biomedical/Medical Engineering, B
Business Administration and Management, B
Business Administration, Management and
   Operations, M
Chemistry, B
Communication and Media Studies, M
Counselor Education/School Counseling and
   Guidance Services, M
Early Childhood Education and Teaching, M
Economics, B
Education, BM
Educational Administration and Supervision, M
Elementary Education and Teaching, BM
English as a Second Language, M
English Language and Literature, B
Environmental Studies, B
French Language and Literature, B
History, B
Human Development and Family Studies, B
Interdisciplinary Studies, B
International Relations and Affairs, B
Kindergarten/PreSchool Education and Teaching, B
Liberal Arts and Sciences Studies and
   Humanities, B
Mass Communication/Media Studies, B
Mathematics, B
Organizational Management, M
Political Science and Government, B
Pre-Law Studies, B
Pre-Medicine/Pre-Medical Studies, B
Psychology, B

Reading Teacher Education, M
Secondary Education and Teaching, BM
Spanish Language and Literature, B
Special Education and Teaching, BM

UNIVERSITY OF THE DISTRICT OF COLUMBIA

Accounting, AB
Administrative Assistant and Secretarial Science, A
Advertising, A
Aeronautics/Aviation/Aerospace Science and Technology, B
Anthropology, B
Apparel and Textiles, B
Architectural Engineering Technology/Technician, A
Architecture, B
Art Teacher Education, B
Art/Art Studies, General, B
Audiology/Audiologist and Speech-Language Pathology/Pathologist, B
Aviation/Airway Management and Operations, A
Avionics Maintenance Technology/Technician, A
Biology Technician/BioTechnology Laboratory Technician, A
Biology/Biological Sciences, B
Building/Construction Finishing, Management, and Inspection, B
Business Administration and Management, B
Business Administration, Management and Operations, M
Business Teacher Education, AB
Ceramic Arts and Ceramics, B
Chemical Engineering, A
Chemistry, B
Child Development, A
City/Urban, Community and Regional Planning, AB
Civil Engineering, B
Civil Engineering Technology/Technician, A
Clinical Laboratory Science/Medical Technology/Technologist, B
Clinical Psychology, M
Clinical/Medical Laboratory Technician, A
Commercial and Advertising Art, A
Communication Disorders, M
Computer Engineering Technology/Technician, A
Computer Science, B
Corrections, A
Counseling Psychology, M
Counselor Education/School Counseling and Guidance Services, M
Criminal Justice/Law Enforcement Administration, AB
Criminal Justice/Police Science, A
Criminology, A
Developmental and Child Psychology, B
Drama and Dramatics/Theatre Arts, B
Early Childhood Education and Teaching, M
Economics, B
Education, M
Electrical, Electronic and Communications Engineering Technology/Technician, A
Electrical, Electronics and Communications Engineering, B
Electromechanical Technology/Electromechanical Engineering Technology, AB
Elementary Education and Teaching, B
Emergency Medical Technology/Technician (EMT Paramedic), AB
Engineering Technology, AB
English, M
English Language and Literature, AB
Entrepreneurship/Entrepreneurial Studies, A
Environmental Engineering Technology/Environmental Technology, A
Environmental Studies, B
Family and Consumer Sciences/Home Economics Teacher Education, B
Family and Consumer Sciences/Human Sciences, B
Fashion Merchandising, A
Finance, B
Fine/Studio Arts, B
Fire Science/Firefighting, AB
Food Science, B
Food Technology and Processing, A
Forestry, B
French Language and Literature, B

Funeral Service and Mortuary Science, B
Geography, B
Graphic and Printing Equipment Operator Production, AB
Graphic Communications, B
Health Teacher Education, B
History, AB
Hospitality Administration/Management, AB
Human Resources Management and Services, B
Hydrology and Water Resources Science, A
Industrial Radiologic Technology/Technician, A
Information Science/Studies, B
Kindergarten/PreSchool Education and Teaching, B
Law and Legal Studies, P
Legal Administrative Assistant/Secretary, A
Library Science, AB
Licensed Practical/Vocational Nurse Training, A
Marine Science/Merchant Marine Officer, A
Marketing/Marketing Management, AB
Mass Communication/Media Studies, B
Mathematics, BM
Mechanical Engineering, B
Mechanical Engineering/Mechanical Technology/Technician, A
Music, AB
Music Teacher Education, B
Nursing - Registered Nurse Training, AB
Nutritional Sciences, B
Ornamental Horticulture, B
Parks, Recreation, Leisure and Fitness Studies, AB
Philosophy, AB
Physical Education Teaching and Coaching, B
Physical Sciences, A
Physics, B
Political Science and Government, B
Psychology, B
Public Administration, ABM
Purchasing, Procurement/Acquisitions and Contracts Management, B
Respiratory Care Therapy/Therapist, A
Social Work, B
Sociology, B
Spanish Language and Literature, B
Special Education and Teaching, BM
Technology Education/Industrial Arts, B
Trade and Industrial Teacher Education, B
Urban Studies/Affairs, AB
Water Quality and Wastewater Treatment Management and Recycling Technology/Technician, A

Florida

AMERICAN INTERCONTINENTAL UNIVERSITY

Business/Commerce, B
Design and Visual Communications, B
Educational Media/Instructional Technology, M
Fashion/Apparel Design, B
Information Science/Studies, M
Information Technology, B
Interior Design, B
International Business/Trade/Commerce, M
Photography, B

ARGOSY UNIVERSITY/SARASOTA

Accounting, MD
Business Administration and Management, B
Business Administration, Management and Operations, BMD
Business, Management, Marketing, and Related Support Services, B
Clinical Psychology, D
Counseling Psychology, D
Counselor Education/School Counseling and Guidance Services, M
Curriculum and Instruction, MDO
E-Commerce/Electronic Commerce, B
Education, MDO
Educational Leadership and Administration, MDO
Finance and Banking, M
Health Services Administration, M
Human Resources Management and Services, M
International Business/Trade/Commerce, MD
Management, MD

Management Information Systems and Services, BMD
Marketing, MD
Pastoral Studies/Counseling, D
Psychology, BMDO
Public Administration, M
School Psychology, O

ARGOSY UNIVERSITY/TAMPA

Business Administration and Management, B
Business Administration, Management and Operations, M
Clinical Psychology, MD
Curriculum and Instruction, MDO
E-Commerce/Electronic Commerce, B
Education, MDO
Educational Leadership and Administration, MDO
Finance and Banking, M
Health Services Administration, M
Human Resources Development, M
International Trade, M
Marketing, M
Psychology, BMD

THE ART INSTITUTE OF FORT LAUDERDALE

Apparel and Textiles, A
Applied Art, A
Cinematography and Film/Video Production, A
Commercial and Advertising Art, A
Computer Graphics, B
Culinary Arts/Chef Training, A
Fashion/Apparel Design, A
Industrial Design, B
Interior Design, B
Photography, A
Radio and Television, A

THE ART INSTITUTE OF TAMPA

Advertising, B
Animation, Interactive Technology, Video Graphics and Special Effects, AB
Culinary Arts/Chef Training, A
Graphic Design, AB
Interior Design, B

ATI CAREER TRAINING CENTER (FORT LAUDERDALE)

Drafting and Design Technology/Technician, A
Electrical, Electronic and Communications Engineering Technology/Technician, A
Medical Administrative Assistant/Secretary, A

ATI HEALTH EDUCATION CENTER

Diagnostic Medical Sonography/Sonographer and Ultrasound Technician, A
Medical/Clinical Assistant, A
Respiratory Care Therapy/Therapist, A

AVE MARIA UNIVERSITY

American History (United States), B
American Literature (United States), B
Biology/Biological Sciences, B
Classics and Classical Languages, Literatures, and Linguistics, B
English Language and Literature, B
European History, B
Latin Language and Literature, B
Mathematics, B
Pastoral Studies/Counseling, M
Philosophy, B
Pre-Theology/Pre-Ministerial Studies, B
Theology and Religious Vocations, MD
Theology/Theological Studies, B

THE BAPTIST COLLEGE OF FLORIDA

Bible/Biblical Studies, B
Child Care and Support Services Management, A
Education, B
Elementary Education and Teaching, B
Music Teacher Education, B
Pastoral Studies/Counseling, B
Religious Education, AB
Religious/Sacred Music, AB

Theology/Theological Studies, AB

BARRY UNIVERSITY

Accounting, B
Acting, B
Advertising, B
Athletic Training and Sports Medicine, M
Biological and Biomedical Sciences, M
Biology/Biological Sciences, B
Broadcast Journalism, B
Business Administration and Management, B
Business Administration, Management and
   Operations, MO
Chemistry, B
Clinical Laboratory Science/Medical
   Technology/Technologist, B
Clinical Psychology, M
Clinical/Medical Laboratory Technician, B
Communication and Media Studies, MO
Communication Studies/Speech Communication
   and Rhetoric, B
Comparative Literature, B
Computer Science, B
Corporate and Organizational Communication, M
Counselor Education/School Counseling and
   Guidance Services, MDO
Criminology, B
CytoTechnology/Cytotechnologist, B
Drama and Dramatics/Theatre Arts, B
Early Childhood Education and Teaching, M
Ecology, B
Economics, B
Education, BMDO
Education/Teaching of the Gifted and
   Talented, MDO
Educational Administration and Supervision, MD
Educational Leadership and Administration, MDO
Educational Media/Instructional Technology, MDO
Elementary Education and Teaching, BMO
Engineering, B
English Language and Literature, B
English/Language Arts Teacher Education, B
Exercise and Sports Science, M
Finance, B
Fine Arts and Art Studies, MO
French Language and Literature, B
Health Services Administration, M
Higher Education/Higher Education
   Administration, MD
History, B
Human Resources Development, MD
Information Science/Studies, BM
International Business/Trade/Commerce, B
International Relations and Affairs, B
Journalism, B
Kindergarten/PreSchool Education and Teaching, B
Kinesiology and Exercise Science, B
Kinesiology and Movement Studies, M
Law and Legal Studies, P
Liberal Arts and Sciences Studies and
   Humanities, B
Management Information Systems and
   Services, BO
Marine Biology and Biological Oceanography, B
Marketing/Marketing Management, B
Marriage and Family Therapy/Counseling, MO
Mass Communication/Media Studies, B
Mathematics, B
Nuclear Medical Technology/Technologist, B
Nurse Anesthetist, M
Nursing, MDO
Nursing - Advanced Practice, M
Nursing - Registered Nurse Training, B
Nursing Administration, MDO
Nursing Education, M
Occupational Therapy/Therapist, M
Pastoral Studies/Counseling, M
Philosophy, B
Photography, BMO
Physical Education Teaching and Coaching, B
Physician Assistant, M
Piano and Organ, B
Podiatric Medicine, PO
Political Science and Government, B
Pre-Dentistry Studies, B
Pre-Law Studies, B

Pre-Medicine/Pre-Medical Studies, B
Pre-Pharmacy Studies, B
Pre-Veterinary Studies, B
Psychology, BMO
Public Relations/Image Management, B
Radio and Television, B
Reading Teacher Education, MO
Rehabilitation Counseling, MO
School Psychology, MO
Social Work, MD
Sociology, B
Spanish Language and Literature, B
Special Education and Teaching, BMDO
Sport and Fitness
   Administration/Management, BMO
Theology and Religious Vocations, MD
Theology/Theological Studies, B
Voice and Opera, B

BEACON COLLEGE

Human Services, AB
Information Science/Studies, AB
Liberal Arts and Sciences Studies and
   Humanities, AB

BETHUNE-COOKMAN COLLEGE

Accounting, B
Biology Teacher Education, B
Biology/Biological Sciences, B
Business Administration and Management, B
Business Teacher Education, B
Chemistry, B
Chemistry Teacher Education, B
Clinical Laboratory Science/Medical
   Technology/Technologist, B
Computer and Information Sciences, B
Computer Engineering, B
Computer Science, B
Corrections and Criminal Justice, B
Education/Teaching of Individuals with Specific
   Learning Disabilities, B
Elementary Education and Teaching, B
English Language and Literature, B
English/Language Arts Teacher Education, B
Gerontology, B
History, B
Hotel/Motel Administration/Management, B
Information Science/Studies, B
International Business/Trade/Commerce, B
International Relations and Affairs, B
Liberal Arts and Sciences Studies and
   Humanities, B
Mass Communication/Media Studies, B
Mathematics, B
Music Performance, B
Music Teacher Education, B
Nursing - Registered Nurse Training, B
Philosophy and Religious Studies, B
Physical Education Teaching and Coaching, B
Physics, B
Physics Teacher Education, B
Political Science and Government, B
Psychology, B
Social Studies Teacher Education, B
Sociology, B
Speech and Rhetorical Studies, B

BREVARD COMMUNITY COLLEGE

Accounting, A
Business Administration and Management, A
Chemical Engineering, A
Clinical/Medical Laboratory Technician, A
Computer Engineering Technology/Technician, A
Computer Programming, Specific Applications, A
Computer Programming/Programmer, A
Computer Software and Media Applications, A
Computer Systems Analysis/Analyst, A
Computer Systems Networking and
   Telecommunications, A
Computer/Information Technology Services
   Administration and Management, A
Corrections, A
Criminal Justice/Law Enforcement Administration, A
Criminal Justice/Police Science, A
Culinary Arts/Chef Training, A
Dental Hygiene/Hygienist, A

Digital Communication and Media/Multimedia, A
Drafting and Design Technology/Technician, A
Early Childhood Education and Teaching, A
Electrical, Electronic and Communications
   Engineering Technology/Technician, A
Electrical/Electronics Drafting and
   Electrical/Electronics CAD/CADD, A
Emergency Medical Technology/Technician (EMT
   Paramedic), A
Fire Science/Firefighting, A
International Business/Trade/Commerce, A
Legal Assistant/Paralegal, A
Liberal Arts and Sciences Studies and
   Humanities, A
Manufacturing Technology/Technician, A
Medical Administrative Assistant/Secretary, A
Medical/Clinical Assistant, A
Nursing - Registered Nurse Training, A
Radio and Television, A
Radiologic Technology/Science - Radiographer, A
Surgical Technology/Technologist, A
System Administration/Administrator, A
System, Networking, and LAN/WAN
   Management/Manager, A
Veterinary/Animal Health Technology/Technician and
   Veterinary Assistant, A
Web Page, Digital/Multimedia and Information
   Resources Design, A

BROWARD COMMUNITY COLLEGE

Accounting, A
Administrative Assistant and Secretarial Science, A
Airline/Commercial/Professional Pilot and Flight
   Crew, A
Architectural Engineering Technology/Technician, A
Automobile/Automotive Mechanics
   Technology/Technician, A
Aviation/Airway Management and Operations, A
Avionics Maintenance Technology/Technician, A
Building/Construction
   Finishing, Management, and Inspection, A
Business Administration and Management, A
Child Development, A
Civil Engineering Technology/Technician, A
Clinical Laboratory Science/Medical
   Technology/Technologist, A
Clinical/Medical Laboratory Technician, A
Computer Engineering Technology/Technician, A
Computer Programming/Programmer, A
Computer Science, A
Corrections, A
Criminal Justice/Law Enforcement Administration, A
Criminal Justice/Police Science, A
Data Processing and Data Processing
   Technology/Technician, A
Dental Hygiene/Hygienist, A
Electrical, Electronic and Communications
   Engineering Technology/Technician, A
Elementary Education and Teaching, A
Emergency Medical Technology/Technician (EMT
   Paramedic), A
Engineering Science, A
Environmental Engineering
   Technology/Environmental Technology, A
Finance, A
Fire Science/Firefighting, A
Hotel/Motel Administration/Management, A
Industrial Radiologic Technology/Technician, A
Information Science/Studies, A
Insurance, A
Interior Design, A
Kindergarten/PreSchool Education and Teaching, A
Legal Administrative Assistant/Secretary, A
Legal Assistant/Paralegal, A
Liberal Arts and Sciences Studies and
   Humanities, A
Marketing/Marketing Management, A
Mechanical Engineering/Mechanical
   Technology/Technician, A
Medical Administrative Assistant/Secretary, A
Medical/Clinical Assistant, A
Nuclear Medical Technology/Technologist, A
Nursing - Registered Nurse Training, A
Physical Therapy/Therapist, A
Pre-Engineering, A
Respiratory Care Therapy/Therapist, A

Special Products Marketing Operations, A
Tourism and Travel Services Management, A

BROWN MACKIE COLLEGE-MIAMI

Accounting Technology/Technician and
    Bookkeeping, A
Business Administration and Management, A
Computer Software Technology/Technician, A
Criminal Justice/Safety Studies, A
Legal Assistant/Paralegal, A
Medical/Clinical Assistant, A

CARLOS ALBIZU
UNIVERSITY, MIAMI CAMPUS

Business Administration and Management, B
Business Administration, Management and
    Operations, BMD
Clinical Psychology, D
Counseling Psychology, M
Education/Teaching of the Gifted and Talented, M
Elementary Education and Teaching, B
Entrepreneurship/Entrepreneurial Studies, M
Industrial and Organizational Psychology, M
Marriage and Family Therapy/Counseling, M
Non-Profit/Public/Organizational Management, M
Organizational Management, M
Psychology, BMD
School Psychology, M
Special Education and Teaching, M

CENTRAL FLORIDA COMMUNITY
COLLEGE

Accounting Technology/Technician and
    Bookkeeping, A
Automobile/Automotive Mechanics
    Technology/Technician, A
Business/Commerce, A
Drafting and Design Technology/Technician, A
Early Childhood Education and Teaching, A
Emergency Medical Technology/Technician (EMT
    Paramedic), A
Fire Science/Firefighting, A
Health Information/Medical Records
    Technology/Technician, A
Human Services, A
Information Technology, A
Landscaping and Groundskeeping, A
Liberal Arts and Sciences Studies and
    Humanities, A
Marketing/Marketing Management, A
Nursing - Registered Nurse Training, A
Office Management and Supervision, A
Parks, Recreation, Leisure and Fitness Studies, A
Physical Therapist Assistant, A
Restaurant, Culinary, and Catering
    Management/Manager, A
Veterinary/Animal Health Technology/Technician and
    Veterinary Assistant, A

CHIPOLA COLLEGE

Accounting, A
Agriculture, A
Agronomy and Crop Science, A
Art/Art Studies, General, A
Biological and Physical Sciences, A
Business Administration and Management, A
Clinical Laboratory Science/Medical
    Technology/Technologist, A
Computer and Information Sciences, A
Computer Science, A
Education, A
Finance, A
Liberal Arts and Sciences Studies and
    Humanities, A
Mass Communication/Media Studies, A
Mathematics Teacher Education, B
Nursing - Registered Nurse Training, A
Pre-Engineering, A
Science Teacher Education/General Science
    Teacher Education, B
Secondary Education and Teaching, B

Social Work, A

CLEARWATER CHRISTIAN COLLEGE

Accounting, B
Administrative Assistant and Secretarial Science, AB
Bible/Biblical Studies, B
Biology Teacher Education, B
Biology/Biological Sciences, B
Business Administration and Management, B
Communication Studies/Speech Communication
    and Rhetoric, B
Elementary Education and Teaching, B
English Language and Literature, B
English/Language Arts Teacher Education, B
General Studies, AB
History, B
Humanities/Humanistic Studies, B
Kinesiology and Exercise Science, B
Mathematics, B
Mathematics Teacher Education, B
Music, B
Music Teacher Education, B
Pastoral Studies/Counseling, B
Physical Education Teaching and Coaching, B
Pre-Law Studies, B
Pre-Medicine/Pre-Medical Studies, B
Psychology, B
Religious/Sacred Music, B
Social Studies Teacher Education, B

COLLEGE OF BUSINESS AND
TECHNOLOGY

Accounting, A
Business Administration and Management, A
Computer Graphics, A
Computer Systems Networking and
    Telecommunications, A
Heating, Air Conditioning, Ventilation and
    Refrigeration Maintenance
    Technology/Technician, A
Medical/Clinical Assistant, A
System, Networking, and LAN/WAN
    Management/Manager, A

DAYTONA BEACH COMMUNITY
COLLEGE

Accounting, A
Administrative Assistant and Secretarial Science, A
Advertising, A
Agriculture, A
Anthropology, A
Architectural Engineering Technology/Technician, A
Art/Art Studies, General, A
Astronomy, A
Atmospheric Sciences and Meteorology, A
Automobile/Automotive Mechanics
    Technology/Technician, A
Behavioral Sciences, A
Biological and Physical Sciences, A
Biology/Biological Sciences, A
Business Administration and Management, A
Chemistry, A
Child Development, A
Cinematography and Film/Video Production, A
Civil Engineering Technology/Technician, A
Commercial and Advertising Art, A
Computer and Information Sciences, A
Computer Engineering, A
Computer Graphics, A
Computer Programming, Specific Applications, A
Computer Programming/Programmer, A
Computer Science, A
Computer Systems Networking and
    Telecommunications, A
Computer Typography and Composition Equipment
    Operator, A
Computer/Information Technology Services
    Administration and Management, A
Construction Engineering Technology/Technician, A
Corrections, A
Cosmetology/Cosmetologist, A
Court Reporting/Court Reporter, A
Criminal Justice/Law Enforcement Administration, A
Criminal Justice/Police Science, A
Criminology, A
Culinary Arts/Chef Training, A

Dance, A
Drafting and Design Technology/Technician, A
Drama and Dramatics/Theatre Arts, A
Economics, A
Education, A
Electrical, Electronic and Communications
    Engineering Technology/Technician, A
Emergency Medical Technology/Technician (EMT
    Paramedic), A
Engineering, A
English Language and Literature, A
Fashion/Apparel Design, A
Finance, A
Fire Science/Firefighting, A
Foods, Nutrition, and Wellness Studies, A
Forestry, A
Geology/Earth Science, A
Health Information/Medical Records
    Administration/Administrator, A
Health Teacher Education, A
Heating, Air Conditioning, Ventilation and
    Refrigeration Maintenance
    Technology/Technician, A
History, A
Hospitality Administration/Management, A
Hotel/Motel Administration/Management, A
Human Services, A
Humanities/Humanistic Studies, A
Industrial Radiologic Technology/Technician, A
Information Science/Studies, A
Information Technology, A
Insurance, A
Interior Design, A
Journalism, A
Kindergarten/PreSchool Education and Teaching, A
Legal Administrative Assistant/Secretary, A
Legal Assistant/Paralegal, A
Liberal Arts and Sciences Studies and
    Humanities, A
Licensed Practical/Vocational Nurse Training, A
Marine Biology and Biological Oceanography, A
Marketing/Marketing Management, A
Mass Communication/Media Studies, A
Mathematics, A
Medical Administrative Assistant/Secretary, A
Music, A
Nursing - Registered Nurse Training, A
Occupational Therapy/Therapist, A
Philosophy, A
Photography, A
Physical Education Teaching and Coaching, A
Physical Therapy/Therapist, A
Physics, A
Psychology, A
Public Health (MPH, DPH), A
Radio and Television, A
Respiratory Care Therapy/Therapist, A
Social Sciences, A
Sociology, A
Special Products Marketing Operations, A
Statistics, A
Telecommunications Technology/Technician, A
Tourism and Travel Services Management, A
Zoology/Animal Biology, A

DEVRY UNIVERSITY (MIAMI)

Business Administration, Management and
    Operations, M

DEVRY UNIVERSITY (MIRAMAR)

Biomedical Technology/Technician, B
Business Administration and Management, B
Business Administration, Management and
    Operations, BM
Computer and Information Sciences, B
Computer Engineering Technology/Technician, B
Computer Systems Networking and
    Telecommunications, AB
Electrical, Electronic and Communications
    Engineering Technology/Technician, AB
Health Information/Medical Records
    Technology/Technician, A

Medical Informatics, B

DEVRY UNIVERSITY (ORLANDO)

Biomedical Technology/Technician, B
Business Administration, Management and
    Operations, BM
Computer and Information Sciences, B
Computer Engineering Technology/Technician, B
Computer Programming, Specific Applications, B
Computer Systems Analysis/Analyst, B
Computer Systems Networking and
    Telecommunications, AB
Electrical, Electronic and Communications
    Engineering Technology/Technician, AB
Health Information/Medical Records
    Technology/Technician, A
Information Science/Studies, B
Medical Informatics, B

DEVRY UNIVERSITY (TAMPA)

Business Administration, Management and
    Operations, M

ECKERD COLLEGE

American/United States Studies/Civilization, B
Anthropology, B
Biology/Biological Sciences, B
Business Administration and Management, B
Chemistry, B
Communication Studies/Speech Communication
    and Rhetoric, B
Comparative Literature, B
Computer Science, B
Creative Writing, B
Drama and Dramatics/Theatre Arts, B
East Asian
    Languages, Literatures, and Linguistics, B
Economics, B
Environmental Studies, B
Foreign Languages and Literatures, B
French Language and Literature, B
German Language and Literature, B
History, B
Human Development and Family Studies, B
Human Resources Management/Personnel
    Administration, B
Humanities/Humanistic Studies, B
Interdisciplinary Studies, B
International Business/Trade/Commerce, B
International Relations and Affairs, B
Marine Biology and Biological Oceanography, B
Mathematics, B
Modern Languages, B
Music, B
Philosophy, B
Physics, B
Political Science and Government, B
Psychology, B
Religion/Religious Studies, B
Sociology, B
Spanish Language and Literature, B
Visual and Performing Arts, B
Women's Studies, B

EDISON COLLEGE

Accounting, A
Applied Art, A
Art/Art Studies, General, A
Business Administration and Management, A
Clinical Laboratory Science/Medical
    Technology/Technologist, A
Computer Programming, Specific Applications, A
Computer Programming/Programmer, A
Computer Science, A
Criminal Justice/Law Enforcement Administration, A
Dental Hygiene/Hygienist, A
Drafting and Design Technology/Technician, A
Electrical, Electronic and Communications
    Engineering Technology/Technician, A
Emergency Medical Technology/Technician (EMT
    Paramedic), A
Engineering, A
Engineering Technology, A
Finance, A
Fire Science/Firefighting, A
Horticultural Science, A

Hospitality Administration/Management, A
Human Services, A
Information Technology, A
Law and Legal Studies, A
Liberal Arts and Sciences Studies and
    Humanities, A
Music, A
Nursing - Registered Nurse Training, A
Radiologic Technology/Science - Radiographer, A
Respiratory Care Therapy/Therapist, A
Social Sciences, A
System Administration/Administrator, A

EDWARD WATERS COLLEGE

Biology/Biological Sciences, B
Business Administration and Management, B
Chemistry, B
Criminal Justice/Law Enforcement Administration, B
Education, B
Elementary Education and Teaching, B
English Language and Literature, B
History, B
Information Science/Studies, B
Journalism, B
Kindergarten/PreSchool Education and Teaching, B
Mathematics, B
Physical Education Teaching and Coaching, B
Psychology, B
Public Administration, B
Secondary Education and Teaching, B
Social Sciences, B
Social Work, B
Sociology, B

EMBRY-RIDDLE AERONAUTICAL
UNIVERSITY

Aeronautics/Aviation/Aerospace Science and
    Technology, B
Aerospace, Aeronautical and Astronautical
    Engineering, BM
Air Traffic Controller, B
Aircraft Powerplant Technology/Technician, B
Airline/Commercial/Professional Pilot and Flight
    Crew, B
Atmospheric Sciences and Meteorology, B
Aviation/Airway Management and Operations, BM
Business Administration, Management and
    Operations, BM
Civil Engineering, B
Communication Studies/Speech Communication
    and Rhetoric, B
Computer Engineering, B
Computer Software Engineering, B
Electrical and Electronic Engineering
    Technologies/Technicians, B
Electrical, Electronics and Communications
    Engineering, B
Engineering Physics, B
Environmental Psychology, B
Ergonomics and Human Factors, M
Mechanical Engineering, B
Occupational Safety and Health
    Technology/Technician, B
Physics, B
Planetary Astronomy and Science, M
Software Engineering, M
Systems Engineering, M

EMBRY-RIDDLE AERONAUTICAL
UNIVERSITY, EXTENDED CAMPUS

Aeronautics/Aviation/Aerospace Science and
    Technology, AB
Aerospace, Aeronautical and Astronautical
    Engineering, M
Aircraft Powerplant Technology/Technician, A
Aviation/Airway Management and Operations, BM
Business Administration, Management and
    Operations, AB
Management of Technology, M

EVERGLADES UNIVERSITY (BOCA
RATON)

Airline/Commercial/Professional Pilot and Flight
    Crew, B
Aviation, M

Aviation/Airway Management and Operations, B
Business Administration and Management, B
Business Administration, Management and
    Operations, M
Construction Management, B
Information Science/Studies, M
Information Technology, B
Management Science, B

EVERGLADES UNIVERSITY
(SARASOTA)

Alternative and Complementary Medicine and
    Medical Systems, B
Aviation/Airway Management and Operations, B
Business/Commerce, B
Construction Management, B
Information Technology, B

FLAGLER COLLEGE

Accounting, B
Art Teacher Education, B
Business Administration and Management, B
Communication, Journalism and Related
    Programs, B
Drama and Dramatics/Theatre Arts, B
Education/Teaching of Individuals with Hearing
    Impairments, Including Deafness, B
Education/Teaching of Individuals with Specific
    Learning Disabilities, B
Education/Teaching of the Gifted and Talented, B
Elementary Education and Teaching, B
English Language and Literature, B
Fine/Studio Arts, B
Graphic Design, B
History, B
Latin American Studies, B
Liberal Arts and Sciences Studies and
    Humanities, B
Philosophy, B
Political Science and Government, B
Psychology, B
Public Administration, B
Secondary Education and Teaching, B
Sociology, B
Spanish Language and Literature, B
Sport and Fitness Administration/Management, B

FLORIDA AGRICULTURAL AND
MECHANICAL UNIVERSITY

Accounting, BM
Accounting and Business/Management, B
Actuarial Science, B
Administrative Assistant and Secretarial Science, B
Adult and Continuing Education and Teaching, M
African-American/Black Studies, BM
Agribusiness, M
Agricultural Business and Management, B
Agricultural Education, M
Agriculture, B
Allied Health and Medical Assisting Services, M
Animal Sciences, BM
Architectural Engineering Technology/Technician, B
Architecture, BM
Art Teacher Education, B
Art/Art Studies, General, B
Biological and Biomedical Sciences, M
Biology/Biological Sciences, B
Biomedical Engineering, MD
Business Administration and Management, B
Business Administration, Management and
    Operations, M
Business Education, M
Business Teacher Education, B
Chemical Engineering, BMD
Chemistry, BM
Civil Engineering, BMD
Civil Engineering Technology/Technician, B
Commercial and Advertising Art, B
Community Psychology, M
Computer and Information Sciences, B
Computer Engineering, B
Construction Engineering Technology/Technician, B
Counselor Education/School Counseling and
    Guidance Services, M
Criminal Justice/Law Enforcement Administration, B
Criminology, M

Drama and Dramatics/Theatre Arts, B
Early Childhood Education and Teaching, M
Economics, BM
Education, BMD
Educational Administration and Supervision, MD
Educational Leadership and Administration, D
Electrical Engineering, MD
Electrical, Electronic and Communications
   Engineering Technology/Technician, B
Electrical, Electronics and Communications
   Engineering, B
Elementary Education and Teaching, BM
Engineering and Applied Sciences, MD
English Education, M
English Language and Literature, B
Entomology, M
Environmental Engineering
   Technology/Environmental Technology, MD
Environmental Sciences, BMD
Finance, B
Finance and Banking, M
Finance and Financial Management Services, B
Food Science and Technology, M
French Language and Literature, B
Geography, B
Graphic and Printing Equipment Operator
   Production, B
Health and Physical Education, B
Health Education, M
Health Information/Medical Records
   Administration/Administrator, B
Health Teacher Education, B
Health/Health Care Administration/Management, B
History, BM
Horticultural Science, B
Industrial Education, M
Industrial Engineering, B
Industrial/Management Engineering, MD
Information Science/Studies, B
International Affairs, M
Jazz/Jazz Studies, B
Journalism, BM
Kindergarten/PreSchool Education and Teaching, B
Landscape Architecture, BM
Law and Legal Studies, P
Liberal Arts and Sciences Studies and
   Humanities, A
Management Information Systems and
   Services, BM
Marketing, M
Mass Communication/Media Studies, B
Mathematics, B
Mathematics Teacher Education, M
Mechanical Engineering, BMD
Medical Illustration and Informatics, B
Medicinal and Pharmaceutical Chemistry, MD
Molecular Biology, B
Music, B
Music Performance, B
Music Teacher Education, B
Nursing, M
Nursing - Registered Nurse Training, B
Nursing Administration, M
Occupational Therapy/Therapist, B
Ornamental Horticulture, B
Parks, Recreation and Leisure Facilities
   Management, B
Pharmaceutical Administration, M
Pharmaceutical Sciences, MD
Pharmacology, MD
Pharmacy, BDP
Philosophy, B
Physical Education Teaching and Coaching, BM
Physical Therapy/Therapist, BM
Physics, BMD
Plant Protection and Integrated Pest
   Management, B
Plant Sciences, M
Political Science and Government, BM
Pre-Dentistry Studies, B
Psychology, BM
Public Administration, BM
Public Health, M
Public Relations/Image Management, B
Recreation and Park Management, M
Religion/Religious Studies, B

Respiratory Care Therapy/Therapist, B
School Psychology, M
Science Teacher Education/General Science
   Teacher Education, M
Secondary Education and Teaching, M
Social Sciences, BM
Social Studies Teacher Education, M
Social Work, BM
Sociology, BM
Software Engineering, M
Spanish Language and Literature, B
Technology Education/Industrial Arts, B
Toxicology, MD
Trade and Industrial Teacher Education, B
Vocational and Technical Education, M

FLORIDA ATLANTIC UNIVERSITY

Accounting, BM
Adult and Continuing Education and Teaching, MDO
Anthropology, BM
Applied Arts and Design, M
Applied Mathematics, M
Architecture, B
Art Education, M
Art/Art Studies, General, B
Biochemistry, MD
Biological and Biomedical Sciences, MD
Biology/Biological Sciences, B
Business Administration and Management, B
Business Administration, Management and
   Operations, MD
Ceramic Arts and Ceramics, M
Chemistry, BMD
City/Urban, Community and Regional Planning, B
Civil Engineering, BM
Clinical Laboratory Science/Medical
   Technology/Technologist, B
Communication and Media Studies, M
Communication Disorders, M
Comparative and Interdisciplinary Arts, D
Comparative Literature, M
Computer and Information Sciences, B
Computer Engineering, BMD
Computer Science, MD
Counseling Psychology, MO
Counselor Education/School Counseling and
   Guidance Services, MO
Criminal Justice/Safety Studies, B
Criminology, M
Curriculum and Instruction, MDO
Digital Communication and Media/Multimedia, B
Drama and Dramatics/Theatre Arts, B
Economics, BM
Education, MDO
Educational Administration and Supervision, D
Educational Leadership and Administration, MDO
Educational Media/Instructional Technology, M
Educational Psychology, M
Electrical Engineering, MD
Electrical, Electronics and Communications
   Engineering, B
Electronic Commerce, M
Elementary Education and Teaching, BM
Engineering and Applied Sciences, MD
English, M
English Language and Literature, B
English/Language Arts Teacher Education, B
Entrepreneurship/Entrepreneurial Studies, M
Environmental Sciences, M
Exercise and Sports Science, M
Finance, B
Finance and Banking, M
Foreign Language Teacher Education, M
Forensic Science and Technology, M
Foundations and Philosophy of Education, M
French Language and Literature, BM
Geography, BM
Geology/Earth Science, BM
German Language and Literature, BM
Health Services/Allied Health/Health Sciences, B
Health/Health Care Administration/Management, B
Higher Education/Higher Education
   Administration, MD
History, BM
Hospitality Administration/Management, B

Human Resources Management/Personnel
   Administration, B
International Business/Trade/Commerce, BM
Jewish/Judaic Studies, B
Kinesiology and Exercise Science, B
Liberal Arts and Sciences Studies and
   Humanities, AB
Liberal Studies, M
Linguistics, B
Management Information Systems and Services, B
Marketing, M
Marketing/Marketing Management, B
Marriage and Family Therapy/Counseling, O
Mathematics, BMD
Mathematics Teacher Education, B
Mechanical Engineering, BMD
Multilingual and Multicultural Education, M
Music, BM
Music Teacher Education, B
Neuroscience, D
Non-Profit/Public/Organizational Management, M
Nursing, MDO
Nursing - Registered Nurse Training, B
Nursing Administration, M
Ocean Engineering, BMD
Painting, M
Philosophy, B
Physics, BMD
Physiological Psychology/Psychobiology, B
Political Science and Government, BM
Psychology, BMD
Public Administration, BMD
Public Health (MPH, DPH), B
Reading Teacher Education, M
Real Estate, M
Rehabilitation Counseling, M
Science Teacher Education/General Science
   Teacher Education, B
Social Psychology, B
Social Science Teacher Education, B
Social Sciences, B
Social Work, BM
Sociology, BM
Spanish Language and Literature, BM
Special Education and Teaching, BMD
Speech and Rhetorical Studies, B
Sport and Fitness Administration/Management, M
Taxation, M
Theater, M
Urban and Regional Planning, M
Women's Studies, MO

FLORIDA CAREER COLLEGE

Computer Engineering, A
Computer Programming, Specific Applications, A
Computer Programming/Programmer, A
Computer Science, A
Web/Multimedia Management and Webmaster, A

FLORIDA CHRISTIAN COLLEGE

Bible/Biblical Studies, AB
Divinity/Ministry (BD, MDiv.), AB
Theology/Theological Studies, B

FLORIDA COLLEGE

Bible/Biblical Studies, B
Elementary Education and Teaching, B
Liberal Arts and Sciences Studies and
   Humanities, AB

FLORIDA COMMUNITY COLLEGE AT JACKSONVILLE

Accounting, A
Administrative Assistant and Secretarial Science, A
Aircraft Powerplant Technology/Technician, A
Airframe Mechanics and Aircraft Maintenance
   Technology/Technician, A
Airline/Commercial/Professional Pilot and Flight
   Crew, A
Architectural Drafting and Architectural
   CAD/CADD, A
Architectural Engineering Technology/Technician, A
Autobody/Collision and Repair
   Technology/Technician, A

Automobile/Automotive Mechanics Technology/Technician, A
Aviation/Airway Management and Operations, A
Banking and Financial Support Services, A
Biomedical Technology/Technician, A
Business Administration and Management, A
Child Care and Support Services Management, A
Child Care Provider/Assistant, A
Civil Engineering Technology/Technician, A
Commercial and Advertising Art, A
Computer and Information Sciences, A
Computer and Information Systems Security, A
Computer Engineering Technology/Technician, A
Computer Graphics, A
Computer Hardware Engineering, A
Computer Programming, A
Computer Programming, Specific Applications, A
Computer Programming, Vendor/Product Certification, A
Computer Programming/Programmer, A
Computer Software and Media Applications, A
Computer Software Engineering, A
Computer Systems Analysis/Analyst, A
Computer Systems Networking and Telecommunications, A
Computer/Information Technology Services Administration and Management, A
Construction Engineering Technology/Technician, A
Criminal Justice/Law Enforcement Administration, A
Criminal Justice/Police Science, A
Culinary Arts/Chef Training, A
Data Entry/Microcomputer Applications, A
Data Modeling/Warehousing and Database Administration, A
Dental Hygiene/Hygienist, A
Design and Visual Communications, A
Diagnostic Medical Sonography/Sonographer and Ultrasound Technician, A
Dietetics/Dieticians, A
Dietician Assistant, A
Drafting and Design Technology/Technician, A
Electrical, Electronic and Communications Engineering Technology/Technician, A
Emergency Medical Technology/Technician (EMT Paramedic), A
Engineering Technology, A
Fashion Merchandising, A
Fire Protection and Safety Technology/Technician, A
Fire Science/Firefighting, A
Foodservice Systems Administration/Management, A
General Office Occupations and Clerical Services, A
Health and Medical Laboratory Technologies, A
Health Information/Medical Records Administration/Administrator, A
Hospitality Administration/Management, A
Hospitality and Recreation Marketing Operations, A
Hotel/Motel Administration/Management, A
Human Services, A
Information Science/Studies, A
Information Technology, A
Instrumentation Technology/Technician, A
Insurance, A
Interior Design, A
Legal Assistant/Paralegal, A
Liberal Arts and Sciences Studies and Humanities, A
Machine Shop Technology/Assistant, A
Management Information Systems and Services, A
Marketing/Marketing Management, A
Mason/Masonry, A
Medical Office Management/Administration, A
Medical Radiologic Technology/Science - Radiation Therapist, A
Nuclear/Nuclear Power Technology/Technician, A
Nursing - Registered Nurse Training, A
Office Management and Supervision, A
Physical Therapist Assistant, A
Printmaking, A
Real Estate, A
Respiratory Care Therapy/Therapist, A
Retailing and Retail Operations, A
Sign Language Interpretation and Translation, A
Substance Abuse/Addiction Counseling, A
System Administration/Administrator, A

Technical Theatre/Theatre Design and Technology, A
Tourism and Travel Services Marketing Operations, A
Visual and Performing Arts, A
Water Quality and Wastewater Treatment Management and Recycling Technology/Technician, A
Web Page, Digital/Multimedia and Information Resources Design, A
Web/Multimedia Management and Webmaster, A
Word Processing, A

FLORIDA CULINARY INSTITUTE

Baking and Pastry Arts/Baker/Pastry Chef, A
Culinary Arts/Chef Training, A
Restaurant, Culinary, and Catering Management/Manager, A

FLORIDA GULF COAST UNIVERSITY

Accounting, BM
Allied Health and Medical Assisting Services, M
Athletic Training and Sports Medicine, B
BioTechnology, B
Business Administration and Management, B
Business Administration, Management and Operations, M
Computer and Information Sciences, B
Computer Science, M
Counselor Education/School Counseling and Guidance Services, M
Criminal Justice/Safety Studies, B
Criminology, M
Curriculum and Instruction, M
Early Childhood Education and Teaching, B
Education, M
Educational Leadership and Administration, M
Educational Media/Instructional Technology, M
Elementary Education and Teaching, BM
English Education, M
Environmental Policy, M
Environmental Sciences, BM
Finance, B
General Studies, B
Health Services/Allied Health/Health Sciences, B
Human Services, B
Information Science/Studies, M
Kinesiology and Exercise Science, B
Legal Assistant/Paralegal, B
Liberal Arts and Sciences Studies and Humanities, B
Management Information Systems and Services, B
Marketing/Marketing Management, B
Mathematics Teacher Education, M
Mental Health Counseling/Counselor, B
Nursing, M
Nursing - Registered Nurse Training, B
Occupational Therapy/Therapist, B
Physical Therapy/Therapist, M
Political Science and Government, B
Public Administration, M
Reading Teacher Education, M
Resort Management, B
Science Teacher Education/General Science Teacher Education, M
Secondary Education and Teaching, M
Social Studies Teacher Education, M
Social Work, BM
Special Education and Teaching, BM

FLORIDA HOSPITAL COLLEGE OF HEALTH SCIENCES

Diagnostic Medical Sonography/Sonographer and Ultrasound Technician, A
General Studies, AB
Nuclear Medical Technology/Technologist, A
Nursing - Registered Nurse Training, AB
Occupational Therapist Assistant, A
Radiologic Technology/Science - Radiographer, AB

FLORIDA INSTITUTE OF TECHNOLOGY

Accounting, B
Aerospace, Aeronautical and Astronautical Engineering, BMD
Air Transportation, B

Analytical Chemistry, B
Applied Mathematics, BMD
Aquatic Biology/Limnology, B
Astrophysics, B
Aviation/Airway Management and Operations, B
Biochemistry, B
Biological and Biomedical Sciences, MD
Biological and Physical Sciences, B
Biology Teacher Education, B
Biology/Biological Sciences, B
Biomedical Sciences, B
BioTechnology, M
Business Administration and Management, B
Business Administration, Management and Operations, BM
Cell Biology and Anatomy, D
Chemical Engineering, BMD
Chemistry, BMD
Chemistry Teacher Education, B
Civil Engineering, BMD
Clinical Psychology, D
Communication and Media Studies, M
Communication Studies/Speech Communication and Rhetoric, B
Computer Education, M
Computer Engineering, BMD
Computer Science, BMD
Computer Software Engineering, B
Computer Teacher Education, B
Ecology, BM
Electrical Engineering, MD
Electrical, Electronics and Communications Engineering, B
Electronic Commerce, M
Engineering and Applied Sciences, MD
Engineering Management, M
Environmental Education, M
Environmental Policy and Resource Management, M
Environmental Sciences, BMD
Ergonomics and Human Factors, M
Forensic Psychology, B
Human Resources Management and Services, M
Humanities/Humanistic Studies, B
Hydrology and Water Resources Science, B
Industrial and Organizational Psychology, MD
Information Science/Studies, BM
Interdisciplinary Studies, B
Logistics and Materials Management, M
Management, M
Management Information Systems and Services, BM
Marine Affairs, M
Marine Biology and Biological Oceanography, BM
Marine Sciences, M
Mathematics Teacher Education, BMDO
Mechanical Engineering, BMD
Meteorology, BM
Molecular Biology, BD
Multi-/Interdisciplinary Studies, B
Ocean Engineering, BMD
Oceanography, Chemical and Physical, BMD
Operations Research, MD
Physics, BMD
Physics Teacher Education, B
Planetary Astronomy and Science, MD
Psychology, BMD
Public Administration, M
Science Teacher Education/General Science Teacher Education, BMDO
Software Engineering, M
System Management, M
Systems Engineering, M
Systems Science and Theory, M
Transportation/Transportation Management, M

FLORIDA INTERNATIONAL UNIVERSITY

Accounting, BM
Adult and Continuing Education and Teaching, MD
African Studies, M
Applied Mathematics, B
Architecture, M
Architecture and Related Services, B
Art Education, MD
Art History, Criticism and Conservation, B

Art Teacher Education, B
Asian Studies/Civilization, B
Biological and Biomedical Sciences, MD
Biology/Biological Sciences, B
Biomedical Engineering, M
Biomedical/Medical Engineering, B
Broadcast Journalism, B
Business Administration and Management, B
Business Administration, Management and
  Operations, MD
Chemical Engineering, B
Chemistry, BMD
Civil Engineering, BMD
Communication Disorders, M
Communication Studies/Speech Communication
  and Rhetoric, B
Computer and Information Sciences, B
Computer Engineering, BM
Computer Science, BMD
Construction Engineering and Management, M
Construction Engineering Technology/Technician, B
Counselor Education/School Counseling and
  Guidance Services, M
Criminal Justice/Safety Studies, B
Criminology, M
Curriculum and Instruction, MDO
Dance, B
Developmental Psychology, D
Dietetics/Dieticians, B
Drama and Dramatics/Theatre Arts, B
Early Childhood Education and Teaching, M
Economics, BMD
Education, MDO
Education/Teaching of Individuals with Emotional
  Disturbances, B
Education/Teaching of Individuals with Mental
  Retardation, B
Education/Teaching of Individuals with Specific
  Learning Disabilities, B
Educational Administration and Supervision, MD
Educational Leadership and Administration, MO
Electrical Engineering, MD
Electrical, Electronics and Communications
  Engineering, B
Elementary Education and Teaching, BM
Engineering and Applied Sciences, MD
English, M
English as a Second Language, M
English Education, MD
English Language and Literature, B
English/Language Arts Teacher Education, B
Environmental Control Technologies/Technicians, B
Environmental Design/Architecture, B
Environmental Engineering
  Technology/Environmental Technology, M
Environmental Sciences, M
Environmental Studies, BM
Family and Consumer Sciences/Home Economics
  Teacher Education, B
Finance, B
Finance and Banking, M
Fine Arts and Art Studies, M
Fine/Studio Arts, B
Foreign Language Teacher Education, BMD
Forensic Science and Technology, M
French Language and Literature, B
Geography, B
Geology/Earth Science, B
Geosciences, MD
German Language and Literature, B
Health Education, M
Health Information/Medical Records
  Administration/Administrator, B
Health Services Administration, M
Health Services/Allied Health/Health Sciences, B
Health Teacher Education, B
Health/Health Care Administration/Management, B
Higher Education/Higher Education
  Administration, D
History, BMD
Home Economics Education, M
Hospitality Administration/Management, BM
Human Resources Development, M
Human Resources Management/Personnel
  Administration, B
Humanities/Humanistic Studies, B

Industrial/Management Engineering, M
Information Technology, B
Insurance, B
Interior Design, B
International Affairs, MD
International and Comparative Education, MDO
International Business/Trade/Commerce, BM
International Relations and Affairs, B
Italian Language and Literature, B
Kinesiology and Exercise Science, B
Landscape Architecture, M
Latin American Studies, M
Law and Legal Studies, P
Liberal Arts and Sciences Studies and
  Humanities, B
Linguistics, M
Logistics and Materials Management, B
Management Information Systems and Services, BD
Marine Biology and Biological Oceanography, B
Marketing/Marketing Management, B
Mass Communication/Media Studies, M
Mathematics, BM
Mathematics Teacher Education, BM
Mechanical Engineering, BMD
Music, BM
Music Teacher Education, BM
Nursing, MD
Nursing - Registered Nurse Training, B
Nutritional Sciences, MD
Occupational Therapy/Therapist, BM
Orthotist/Prosthetist, B
Parks, Recreation and Leisure Facilities
  Management, B
Philosophy, B
Physical Education Teaching and Coaching, BM
Physical Therapy/Therapist, M
Physics, BMD
Political Science and Government, BMD
Portuguese Language and Literature, B
Psychology, BMD
Public Administration, BMD
Public Health, M
Public Health (MPH, DPH), B
Reading Teacher Education, M
Real Estate, B
Recreation and Park Management, M
Religion/Religious Studies, BM
School Psychology, O
Science Teacher Education/General Science
  Teacher Education, BMD
Social Science Teacher Education, B
Social Studies Teacher Education, M
Social Work, BMD
Sociology, BMD
Spanish Language and Literature, BMD
Special Education and Teaching, MD
Statistics, BM
Systems Engineering, B
Taxation, M
Telecommunications, M
Tourism and Travel Services Management, B
Trade and Industrial Teacher Education, B
Urban Education and Leadership, M
Urban Studies/Affairs, B
Vocational and Technical Education, M
Women's Studies, B
Writing, M

FLORIDA KEYS COMMUNITY COLLEGE

Business Administration and Management, A
Commercial and Advertising Art, A
Computer Programming/Programmer, A
Liberal Arts and Sciences Studies and
  Humanities, A
Marine Biology and Biological Oceanography, A
Marine Technology, A
Nursing - Registered Nurse Training, A
Parks, Recreation, Leisure and Fitness Studies, A

FLORIDA MEMORIAL COLLEGE

Accounting, B
Air Traffic Controller, B
Aviation/Airway Management and Operations, B
Biology/Biological Sciences, B
Business Administration and Management, B

Clinical Laboratory Science/Medical
  Technology/Technologist, B
Computer Science, B
Criminal Justice/Law Enforcement Administration, B
Data Processing and Data Processing
  Technology/Technician, B
Elementary Education and Teaching, B
English Language and Literature, B
Mathematics, B
Modern Languages, B
Music Teacher Education, B
Physical Education Teaching and Coaching, B
Political Science and Government, B
Psychology, B
Public Administration, B
Religion/Religious Studies, B
Secondary Education and Teaching, B
Sociology, B
Urban Studies/Affairs, B

FLORIDA METROPOLITAN UNIVERSITY-BRANDON CAMPUS

Accounting, AB
Business Administration and Management, AB
Business Administration, Management and
  Operations, M
Computer and Information Sciences, AB
Computer and Information Sciences and Support
  Services, A
Criminal Justice/Safety Studies, AB
Criminology, M
Legal Assistant/Paralegal, AB
Marketing/Marketing Management, AB
Medical/Clinical Assistant, A
Pharmacy Technician/Assistant, A
Surgical Technology/Technologist, A

FLORIDA METROPOLITAN UNIVERSITY-JACKSONVILLE CAMPUS

Accounting, AB
Business Administration and Management, AB
Computer Science, AB
Criminal Justice/Safety Studies, AB
Medical/Clinical Assistant, AB

FLORIDA METROPOLITAN UNIVERSITY-LAKELAND CAMPUS

Accounting, AB
Business Administration and Management, AB
Computer Programming/Programmer, AB
Computer Science, AB
Criminal Justice/Safety Studies, AB
Data Processing and Data Processing
  Technology/Technician, A
Legal Assistant/Paralegal, A
Marketing/Marketing Management, A

FLORIDA METROPOLITAN UNIVERSITY-MELBOURNE CAMPUS

Accounting, AB
Business Administration and Management, AB
Business Administration, Management and
  Operations, M
Cinematography and Film/Video Production, A
Criminal Justice/Law Enforcement
  Administration, AB
Information Science/Studies, AB
Medical/Clinical Assistant, A
Tourism and Travel Services Management, A

FLORIDA METROPOLITAN UNIVERSITY-NORTH ORLANDO CAMPUS

Accounting, AB
Business Administration and Management, AB
Business Administration, Management and
  Operations, M
Cinematography and Film/Video Production, A
Commercial and Advertising Art, A
Computer and Information Sciences, B
Computer Programming/Programmer, AB
Criminal Justice/Safety Studies, AB
Data Processing and Data Processing
  Technology/Technician, AB

Health/Health Care Administration/Management, B
Legal Assistant/Paralegal, AB
Marketing/Marketing Management, AB
Medical/Clinical Assistant, A
Web Page, Digital/Multimedia and Information
  Resources Design, B

FLORIDA METROPOLITAN UNIVERSITY-PINELLAS CAMPUS

Accounting, AB
Business Administration, Management and
  Operations, M
Business/Commerce, AB
Computer and Information Sciences, AB
Criminal Justice/Safety Studies, AB
Criminology, M
Legal Assistant/Paralegal, A
Marketing/Marketing Management, AB

FLORIDA METROPOLITAN UNIVERSITY-POMPANO BEACH CAMPUS

Accounting, AB
Business Administration and Management, AB
Business Administration, Management and
  Operations, M
Computer Programming/Programmer, AB
Criminal Justice/Police Science, B
Hotel/Motel Administration/Management, AB
International Business/Trade/Commerce, AB
Legal Assistant/Paralegal, A
Management Information Systems and Services, AB
Marketing/Marketing Management, AB

FLORIDA METROPOLITAN UNIVERSITY-SOUTH ORLANDO CAMPUS

Accounting, ABM
Business Administration and Management, AB
Business Administration, Management and
  Operations, M
Computer and Information Sciences, AB
Criminal Justice/Safety Studies, AB
Health/Health Care Administration/Management, B
Human Resources Management and Services, M
International Business/Trade/Commerce, M
Legal Assistant/Paralegal, AB
Management, M
Medical/Clinical Assistant, A

FLORIDA METROPOLITAN UNIVERSITY-TAMPA CAMPUS

Accounting, ABM
Business Administration and Management, AB
Business Administration, Management and
  Operations, M
Commercial and Advertising Art, A
Computer Programming/Programmer, AB
Computer Science, AB
Criminal Justice/Law Enforcement
  Administration, AB
Data Processing and Data Processing
  Technology/Technician, AB
Human Resources Management and Services, M
International Business/Trade/Commerce, M
Legal Assistant/Paralegal, A
Marketing/Marketing Management, AB
Medical/Clinical Assistant, A

FLORIDA NATIONAL COLLEGE

Accounting, A
Administrative Assistant and Secretarial Science, A
Allied Health and Medical Assisting Services, A
Business Administration and Management, A
Computer and Information Systems Security, A
Computer Graphics, A
Computer Programming, A
Computer Programming, Specific Applications, A
Computer Programming/Programmer, A
Computer Science, A
Computer Systems Networking and
  Telecommunications, A
Data Entry/Microcomputer Applications, A

Data Processing and Data Processing
  Technology/Technician, A
Dental Hygiene/Hygienist, A
Diagnostic Medical Sonography/Sonographer and
  Ultrasound Technician, A
Education, A
Health Services/Allied Health/Health Sciences, A
Hospitality Administration/Management, A
Law and Legal Studies, A
Legal Administrative Assistant/Secretary, A
Legal Assistant/Paralegal, A
Legal Professions and Studies, A
Liberal Arts and Sciences Studies and
  Humanities, A
Management Information Systems and Services, A
Medical Administrative Assistant/Secretary, A
Medical/Clinical Assistant, A
Radiologic Technology/Science - Radiographer, A
System Administration/Administrator, A
Technical and Business Writing, A
Tourism and Travel Services Management, A
Tourism Promotion Operations, A
Web Page, Digital/Multimedia and Information
  Resources Design, A
Word Processing, A

THE FLORIDA SCHOOL OF MIDWIFERY

Direct Entry Midwifery (LM, CPM), A
Nurse Midwife/Nursing Midwifery, A

FLORIDA SOUTHERN COLLEGE

Accounting, BM
Advertising, B
Agricultural Business and Management, B
Art Teacher Education, B
Art/Art Studies, General, B
Athletic Training and Sports Medicine, B
Biology/Biological Sciences, B
Broadcast Journalism, B
Business Administration and Management, B
Business Administration, Management and
  Operations, M
Business/Commerce, B
Chemistry, B
Commercial and Advertising Art, B
Communication Studies/Speech Communication
  and Rhetoric, B
Computer Science, B
Criminal Justice/Safety Studies, B
Drama and Dramatics/Theatre Arts, B
Economics, B
Education, BM
Education/Teaching of Individuals with Specific
  Learning Disabilities, B
Elementary Education and Teaching, B
English Composition, B
English Language and Literature, B
Environmental Studies, B
Finance, B
Fine/Studio Arts, B
History, B
Horticultural Science, B
Hotel/Motel Administration/Management, B
Human Resources Management/Personnel
  Administration, B
Humanities/Humanistic Studies, B
International Business/Trade/Commerce, BM
Journalism, B
Kindergarten/PreSchool Education and Teaching, B
Management Information Systems and Services, B
Marketing/Marketing Management, B
Mathematics, B
Music, B
Music Management and Merchandising, B
Music Teacher Education, B
Natural Sciences, B
Nursing, M
Nursing - Registered Nurse Training, B
Operations Management and Supervision, B
Ornamental Horticulture, B
Physical Education Teaching and Coaching, B
Political Science and Government, B
Pre-Dentistry Studies, B
Pre-Medicine/Pre-Medical Studies, B
Pre-Veterinary Studies, B

Psychology, B
Public Relations/Image Management, B
Religion/Religious Studies, B
Religious Education, B
Religious/Sacred Music, B
Secondary Education and Teaching, B
Social Sciences, B
Sociology, B
Spanish Language and Literature, B

FLORIDA STATE UNIVERSITY

Accounting, BM
Acting, B
Adult and Continuing Education and Teaching, MDO
Advertising, B
Allopathic Medicine, DP
American/United States Studies/Civilization, BMO
Analytical Chemistry, MD
Anthropology, BMD
Apparel and Textile Marketing Management, B
Apparel and Textiles, B
Applied Economics, B
Applied Mathematics, BMD
Archeology, M
Art Education, MDO
Art History, Criticism and Conservation, BMDO
Art Teacher Education, B
Arts Management, M
Asian Studies/Civilization, BM
Athletic Training and Sports Medicine, B
Atmospheric Sciences and Meteorology, B
Bilingual and Multilingual Education, B
Bilingual, Multilingual, and Multicultural Education, B
Biochemistry, BMD
Biological and Biomedical Sciences, MD
Biology/Biological Sciences, B
Biomathematics and Bioinformatics, B
Biomedical Engineering, MD
Biomedical/Medical Engineering, B
Biostatistics, M
Business Administration and Management, B
Business Administration, Management and
  Operations, MDO
Business/Commerce, B
Caribbean Studies, B
Cell Biology and Anatomy, MD
Cell/Cellular and Molecular Biology, B
Central/Middle and Eastern European Studies, B
Chemical Engineering, BMD
Chemistry, BMD
Child and Family Studies, MD
Child Development, B
Cinematography and Film/Video Production, B
Civil Engineering, BMD
Classics and Classical
  Languages, Literatures, and Linguistics, BMD
Clinical Psychology, D
Clothing and Textiles, MD
Cognitive Sciences, D
Commercial and Advertising Art, B
Communication and Media Studies, BMD
Communication Disorders, MD
Communication Studies/Speech Communication
  and Rhetoric, B
Community Health Services/Liaison/Counseling, B
Comparative Literature, B
Composition, MD
Computational Biology, D
Computer Engineering, BMD
Computer Programming/Programmer, B
Computer Science, BMD
Computer Software and Media Applications, B
Computer Software Engineering, B
Consumer Economics, MD
Corporate and Organizational Communication, M
Counseling Psychology, D
Counselor Education/School Counseling and
  Guidance Services, MO
Creative Writing, B
Criminal Justice/Safety Studies, B
Criminology, BMDO
Dance, BM
Demography and Population Studies, MO
Design and Applied Arts, M
Developmental Biology and Embryology, MD
Developmental Psychology, D

Dietetics/Dieticians, B
Distance Education Development, M
Drama and Dramatics/Theatre Arts, B
Early Childhood Education and Teaching, BMDO
East European and Russian Studies, M
Ecology, BMD
Economics, BMDO
Education, MDO
Education/Teaching of Individuals with Emotional
  Disturbances, B
Education/Teaching of Individuals with Mental
  Retardation, B
Education/Teaching of Individuals with Specific
  Learning Disabilities, B
Education/Teaching of Individuals with Vision
  Impairments, Including Blindness, B
Educational Administration and Supervision, MDO
Educational Measurement and Evaluation, MD
Educational Media/Instructional Technology, MDO
Educational Psychology, MD
Electrical Engineering, MD
Electrical, Electronics and Communications
  Engineering, B
Elementary Education and Teaching, BMDO
Engineering and Applied Sciences, MD
English, MD
English Education, MDO
English Language and Literature, B
English/Language Arts Teacher Education, B
Entrepreneurial and Small Business Operations, B
Environmental Biology, B
Environmental Engineering
  Technology/Environmental Technology, MD
Environmental Studies, B
Environmental/Environmental Health Engineering, B
Ethnomusicology, M
Evolutionary Biology, BMD
Exercise and Sports Science, MD
Family and Consumer Economics and Related
  Services, B
Family and Consumer Sciences/Home Economics
  Teacher Education, B
Family and Consumer Sciences/Human
  Sciences, BMD
Fashion Merchandising, B
Fashion/Apparel Design, B
Film, Television, and Video Production, M
Film/Cinema Studies, B
Finance, B
Fine Arts and Art Studies, M
Fine/Studio Arts, B
Food Science and Technology, MD
Foods, Nutrition, and Wellness Studies, B
Foreign Language Teacher Education, B
Foundations and Philosophy of Education, MDO
French Language and Literature, BMD
Genetics, MD
Geographic Information Systems, M
Geography, BMD
Geology/Earth Science, BMD
Geophysics and Seismology, D
German Language and Literature, BM
Gerontology, M
Graphic Design, B
Health Education, M
Health Services Research, MO
Health Teacher Education, B
Higher Education/Higher Education
  Administration, MDO
History, BMD
Hospitality Administration/Management, B
Housing and Human Environments, B
Human Development and Family Studies, B
Human Resources Development, MDO
Human Resources Management/Personnel
  Administration, B
Humanities/Humanistic Studies, BMD
Immunology, MD
Industrial Engineering, B
Industrial/Management Engineering, MD
Information Science/Studies, BMDO
Inorganic Chemistry, MD
Insurance, M
Interior Design, BM
International Affairs, MO
International and Comparative Education, MDO

International Business/Trade/Commerce, B
International Relations and Affairs, B
Internet and Interactive Multimedia, M
Italian Language and Literature, BM
Jazz/Jazz Studies, B
Junior High/Intermediate/Middle School Education
  and Teaching, B
Kindergarten/PreSchool Education and Teaching, B
Kinesiology and Exercise Science, B
Kinesiology and Movement Studies, M
Latin American Studies, B
Latin Language and Literature, B
Law and Legal Studies, PO
Liberal Arts and Sciences Studies and
  Humanities, A
Library Science, MDO
Management Information Systems and Services, M
Manufacturing Engineering, MD
Marine Biology and Biological Oceanography, BMD
Marketing, M
Marriage and Family Therapy/Counseling, D
Mass Communication/Media Studies, BMD
Materials Engineering, B
Mathematical and Computational Finance, MD
Mathematics, BMD
Mathematics Teacher Education, BMDO
Mechanical Engineering, BMD
Media Studies, M
Meteorology, BMD
Microbiology, MD
Military and Defense Studies, D
Modern Greek Language and Literature, B
Molecular Biology, MD
Molecular Biophysics, D
Multilingual and Multicultural Education, BMDO
Museology/Museum Studies, O
Music, BMD
Music History, Literature, and Theory, B
Music Pedagogy, B
Music Performance, B
Music Teacher Education, BMD
Music Theory and Composition, BMD
Music Therapy/Therapist, BM
Musicology and Ethnomusicology, MD
Neurobiology and Neurophysiology, B
Neuroscience, D
Nursing, MO
Nursing - Advanced Practice, MO
Nursing - Registered Nurse Training, B
Nursing Education, MO
Nutritional Sciences, BMD
Oceanography, Chemical and Physical, MD
Organic Chemistry, MD
Parks, Recreation and Leisure Facilities
  Management, B
Performance, MD
Philosophy, BMD
Physical Chemistry, MD
Physical Education Teaching and Coaching, BMDO
Physical Sciences, B
Physics, BMD
Piano and Organ, B
Plant Biology, MD
Plant Physiology, B
Political Science and Government, BMD
Pre-Dentistry Studies, B
Pre-Law Studies, B
Pre-Medicine/Pre-Medical Studies, B
Pre-Pharmacy Studies, B
Pre-Veterinary Studies, B
Psychology, BMD
Public Administration, MDO
Public Health, MO
Public History, M
Public Policy Analysis, MDO
Public Relations/Image Management, B
Radio and Television, B
Radio, Television, and Digital Communication, B
Reading Teacher Education, MDO
Recreation and Park Management, MDO
Religion/Religious Studies, BMD
Russian Language and Literature, B
Russian Studies, B
School Psychology, MO
Science Teacher Education/General Science
  Teacher Education, BMDO

Secondary Education and Teaching, B
Slavic Languages, Literatures, and Linguistics, M
Social Psychology, D
Social Science Teacher Education, B
Social Sciences, BM
Social Studies Teacher Education, MDO
Social Work, BMDO
Sociology, BMD
Software Engineering, M
Spanish Language and Literature, BMD
Speech and Rhetorical Studies, D
Sport and Fitness
  Administration/Management, BMDO
Sport Psychology, MD
Statistics, BMD
Structural Biology, D
Technical Theatre/Theatre Design and
  Technology, B
Textile Design, MD
Textile Science, B
Theater, MD
Urban and Regional Planning, MDO
Violin, Viola, Guitar and Other Stringed
  Instruments, B
Vocational Rehabilitation Counseling/Counselor, B
Voice and Opera, B
Wind and Percussion Instruments, B
Women's Studies, B
Writing, MD
Zoology/Animal Biology, B

FLORIDA TECHNICAL COLLEGE (DELAND)

CAD/CADD Drafting and/or Design
  Technology/Technician, A
Computer Science, A
Criminal Justice/Safety Studies, A
Legal Assistant/Paralegal, A
Medical Administrative Assistant/Secretary, A
Medical/Clinical Assistant, A
Web Page, Digital/Multimedia and Information
  Resources Design, A

FLORIDA TECHNICAL COLLEGE (JACKSONVILLE)

Computer Programming/Programmer, A
Electrical, Electronic and Communications
  Engineering Technology/Technician, A

FLORIDA TECHNICAL COLLEGE (ORLANDO)

Architectural Drafting and Architectural
  CAD/CADD, A
Civil Drafting and Civil Engineering CAD/CADD, A
Computer Programming/Programmer, A
Computer Systems Networking and
  Telecommunications, A
Electrical, Electronic and Communications
  Engineering Technology/Technician, A
Electrical/Electronics Drafting and
  Electrical/Electronics CAD/CADD, A
Legal Assistant/Paralegal, A
Management Information Systems and Services, A
Mechanical Drafting and Mechanical Drafting
  CAD/CADD, A
Medical Administrative Assistant/Secretary, A

FULL SAIL REAL WORLD EDUCATION

Animation, Interactive Technology, Video Graphics
  and Special Effects, B
Business, Management, Marketing, and Related
  Support Services, B
Computer Graphics, B
Design and Applied Arts, B
Dramatic/Theatre Arts and Stagecraft, A
Film/Video and Photographic Arts, B
Recording Arts Technology/Technician, A

GULF COAST COLLEGE

Computer Science, A
Computer Systems Analysis/Analyst, A
Information Technology, A
Licensed Practical/Vocational Nurse Training, A
Medical/Clinical Assistant, A

System Administration/Administrator, A

GULF COAST COMMUNITY COLLEGE

Accounting, A
Administrative Assistant and Secretarial Science, A
Anthropology, A
Art/Art Studies, General, A
Biology/Biological Sciences, A
Business Administration and Management, A
Child Care Provider/Assistant, A
Child Development, A
Civil Engineering Technology/Technician, A
Computer Engineering Technology/Technician, A
Computer Programming, Specific Applications, A
Computer Programming/Programmer, A
Construction Engineering Technology/Technician, A
Criminal Justice/Law Enforcement Administration, A
Culinary Arts/Chef Training, A
Dental Hygiene/Hygienist, A
Drafting and Design Technology/Technician, A
Economics, A
Electrical, Electronic and Communications
    Engineering Technology/Technician, A
Electromechanical and Instrumentation and
    Maintenance Technologies/Technicians, A
Elementary Education and Teaching, A
Emergency Medical Technology/Technician (EMT
    Paramedic), A
Engineering Technology, A
English Language and Literature, A
Fire Science/Firefighting, A
Foreign Languages and Literatures, A
History, A
Hospitality Administration/Management, A
Human Services, A
Industrial Radiologic Technology/Technician, A
Legal Assistant/Paralegal, A
Liberal Arts and Sciences Studies and
    Humanities, A
Mathematics, A
Music, A
Nursing - Registered Nurse Training, A
Physical Therapist Assistant, A
Political Science and Government, A
Pre-Law Studies, A
Psychology, A
Radio and Television, A
Respiratory Care Therapy/Therapist, A
Secondary Education and Teaching, A
Sociology, A
Theatre/Theatre Arts Management, A

HERZING COLLEGE

Business Administration and Management, A
Computer and Information Sciences, A

HILLSBOROUGH COMMUNITY COLLEGE

Accounting, A
Administrative Assistant and Secretarial Science, A
Agricultural Production Operations, A
Aquaculture, A
Architectural Engineering Technology/Technician, A
Art/Art Studies, General, A
Biomedical Technology/Technician, A
Business Administration and Management, A
Business Operations Support and Secretarial
    Services, A
Child Development, A
Commercial and Advertising Art, A
Computer Engineering Technology/Technician, A
Computer Programming/Programmer, A
Computer Systems Networking and
    Telecommunications, A
Construction Engineering Technology/Technician, A
Corrections, A
Criminal Justice/Law Enforcement Administration, A
Criminal Justice/Police Science, A
Culinary Arts and Related Services, A
Culinary Arts/Chef Training, A
Dance, A
Dental Hygiene/Hygienist, A
Diagnostic Medical Sonography/Sonographer and
    Ultrasound Technician, A
Digital Communication and Media/Multimedia, A
Drama and Dramatics/Theatre Arts, A

Education, A
Electrical, Electronic and Communications
    Engineering Technology/Technician, A
Elementary Education and Teaching, A
Emergency Medical Technology/Technician (EMT
    Paramedic), A
Engineering, A
Environmental Studies, A
Finance, A
Fire Science/Firefighting, A
General Office Occupations and Clerical Services, A
Hospitality Administration/Management, A
Hotel/Motel Administration/Management, A
Human Services, A
Industrial Radiologic Technology/Technician, A
Information Science/Studies, A
Interior Design, A
Intermedia/Multimedia, A
Law and Legal Studies, A
Legal Administrative Assistant/Secretary, A
Liberal Arts and Sciences Studies and
    Humanities, A
Marketing/Marketing Management, A
Mass Communication/Media Studies, A
Medical Administrative Assistant/Secretary, A
Music, A
Nuclear Medical Technology/Technologist, A
Nursing - Registered Nurse Training, A
Occupational Therapy/Therapist, A
Ophthalmic Laboratory Technology/Technician, A
Ornamental Horticulture, A
Pharmacy Technician/Assistant, A
Physical Education Teaching and Coaching, A
Physical Therapy/Therapist, A
Radio and Television, A
Radio and Television Broadcasting
    Technology/Technician, A
Radio, Television, and Digital Communication, A
Radiologic Technology/Science - Radiographer, A
Respiratory Care Therapy/Therapist, A
Restaurant, Culinary, and Catering
    Management/Manager, A
Sign Language Interpretation and Translation, A

HOBE SOUND BIBLE COLLEGE

Administrative Assistant and Secretarial Science, A
Bible/Biblical Studies, AB
Elementary Education and Teaching, B
Missions/Missionary Studies and Missiology, AB
Music Teacher Education, B
Secondary Education and Teaching, B
Teaching English as a Second or Foreign
    Language/ESL Language Instructor, B
Theology/Theological Studies, B

INDIAN RIVER COMMUNITY COLLEGE

Accounting, A
Administrative Assistant and Secretarial Science, A
Agricultural Business and Management, A
Airline/Commercial/Professional Pilot and Flight
    Crew, A
Anthropology, A
Apparel and Textiles, A
Architectural Drafting and Architectural
    CAD/CADD, A
Art Teacher Education, A
Automobile/Automotive Mechanics
    Technology/Technician, A
Banking and Financial Support Services, A
Biology/Biological Sciences, A
Business Administration and Management, A
Carpentry/Carpenter, A
Chemistry, A
Child Development, A
Civil Engineering Technology/Technician, A
Clinical/Medical Laboratory Technician, A
Computer Engineering Technology/Technician, A
Computer Programming/Programmer, A
Computer Science, A
Computer Typography and Composition Equipment
    Operator, A
Consumer Merchandising/Retailing Management, A
Corrections, A
Cosmetology/Cosmetologist, A
Criminal Justice/Law Enforcement Administration, A
Criminal Justice/Police Science, A

Culinary Arts/Chef Training, A
Dental Hygiene/Hygienist, A
Drafting and Design Technology/Technician, A
Drama and Dramatics/Theatre Arts, A
Economics, A
Education, A
Electrical, Electronic and Communications
    Engineering Technology/Technician, A
Emergency Medical Technology/Technician (EMT
    Paramedic), A
Engineering, A
Engineering Technology, A
English Language and Literature, A
Family and Consumer Sciences/Human Sciences, A
Fashion Merchandising, A
Finance, A
Fire Science/Firefighting, A
Foods, Nutrition, and Wellness Studies, A
Forestry, A
French Language and Literature, A
Health Information/Medical Records
    Administration/Administrator, A
Heating, Air Conditioning, Ventilation and
    Refrigeration Maintenance
    Technology/Technician, A
History, A
Hotel/Motel Administration/Management, A
Human Services, A
Humanities/Humanistic Studies, A
Hydrology and Water Resources Science, A
Industrial Radiologic Technology/Technician, A
Information Science/Studies, A
Interior Design, A
Journalism, A
Kindergarten/PreSchool Education and Teaching, A
Language Interpretation and Translation, A
Legal Assistant/Paralegal, A
Liberal Arts and Sciences Studies and
    Humanities, A
Library Science, A
Licensed Practical/Vocational Nurse Training, A
Marine Science/Merchant Marine Officer, A
Marketing/Marketing Management, A
Mathematics, A
Medical Administrative Assistant/Secretary, A
Music, A
Nursing - Registered Nurse Training, A
Pharmacy, A
Philosophy, A
Physical Education Teaching and Coaching, A
Physical Therapist Assistant, A
Physical Therapy/Therapist, A
Physics, A
Political Science and Government, A
Pre-Engineering, A
Psychology, A
Respiratory Care Therapy/Therapist, A
Social Sciences, A
Social Work, A
Sociology, A
Spanish Language and Literature, A
Special Products Marketing Operations, A
Speech and Rhetorical Studies, A
Survey Technology/Surveying, A
Teacher Assistant/Aide, A

INTERNATIONAL ACADEMY OF DESIGN & TECHNOLOGY

Commercial and Advertising Art, AB
Computer Graphics, A
Design and Visual Communications, AB
Fashion/Apparel Design, AB
Interior Design, AB
Intermedia/Multimedia, A

INTERNATIONAL COLLEGE

Accounting, AB
Business Administration and Management, AB
Business Administration, Management and
    Operations, B
Computer/Information Technology Services
    Administration and Management, B
Criminal Justice/Safety Studies, AB
Health Information/Medical Records
    Technology/Technician, A
Health/Health Care Administration/Management, B

Health/Medical Preparatory Programs, B
Information Technology, AB
Legal Assistant/Paralegal, A
Legal Professions and Studies, B
Medical/Clinical Assistant, A
Multi-/Interdisciplinary Studies, AB

ITT TECHNICAL INSTITUTE (FORT LAUDERDALE)

Animation, Interactive Technology, Video Graphics
   and Special Effects, B
Business Administration and Management, B
CAD/CADD Drafting and/or Design
   Technology/Technician, A
Computer and Information Systems Security, B
Computer Programming/Programmer, A
Criminal Justice/Law Enforcement
   Administration, AB
Electrical, Electronic and Communications
   Engineering Technology/Technician, AB
System, Networking, and LAN/WAN
   Management/Manager, A
Web Page, Digital/Multimedia and Information
   Resources Design, A
Web/Multimedia Management and Webmaster, A

ITT TECHNICAL INSTITUTE (JACKSONVILLE)

Animation, Interactive Technology, Video Graphics
   and Special Effects, B
Business Administration and Management, B
CAD/CADD Drafting and/or Design
   Technology/Technician, A
Computer and Information Systems Security, B
Computer Programming/Programmer, A
Criminal Justice/Law Enforcement
   Administration, AB
E-Commerce/Electronic Commerce, B
Electrical, Electronic and Communications
   Engineering Technology/Technician, AB
System, Networking, and LAN/WAN
   Management/Manager, A
Web Page, Digital/Multimedia and Information
   Resources Design, A
Web/Multimedia Management and Webmaster, A

ITT TECHNICAL INSTITUTE (LAKE MARY)

Animation, Interactive Technology, Video Graphics
   and Special Effects, B
Business Administration and Management, B
CAD/CADD Drafting and/or Design
   Technology/Technician, A
Computer and Information Systems Security, B
Computer Programming/Programmer, A
Computer Systems Networking and
   Telecommunications, B
Criminal Justice/Law Enforcement
   Administration, AB
Electrical, Electronic and Communications
   Engineering Technology/Technician, AB
System, Networking, and LAN/WAN
   Management/Manager, A
Web Page, Digital/Multimedia and Information
   Resources Design, A
Web/Multimedia Management and Webmaster, A

ITT TECHNICAL INSTITUTE (MIAMI)

Accounting and Business/Management, B
Animation, Interactive Technology, Video Graphics
   and Special Effects, B
Business Administration and Management, B
Computer and Information Systems Security, B
Computer Programming/Programmer, A
Computer Systems Networking and
   Telecommunications, B
Criminal Justice/Law Enforcement Administration, B
Electrical, Electronic and Communications
   Engineering Technology/Technician, AB
System, Networking, and LAN/WAN
   Management/Manager, A
Web Page, Digital/Multimedia and Information
   Resources Design, A

Web/Multimedia Management and Webmaster, A

ITT TECHNICAL INSTITUTE (TAMPA)

Animation, Interactive Technology, Video Graphics
   and Special Effects, B
Business Administration and Management, B
CAD/CADD Drafting and/or Design
   Technology/Technician, A
Computer and Information Systems Security, B
Computer Programming/Programmer, A
Criminal Justice/Law Enforcement Administration, A
E-Commerce/Electronic Commerce, B
Electrical, Electronic and Communications
   Engineering Technology/Technician, AB
System, Networking, and LAN/WAN
   Management/Manager, A
Web Page, Digital/Multimedia and Information
   Resources Design, A
Web/Multimedia Management and Webmaster, A

JACKSONVILLE UNIVERSITY

Accounting, B
Airline/Commercial/Professional Pilot and Flight
   Crew, B
Art History, Criticism and Conservation, B
Art/Art Studies, General, B
Aviation/Airway Management and Operations, B
Biology/Biological Sciences, B
Business Administration and Management, B
Business Administration, Management and
   Operations, M
Business/Commerce, B
Chemistry, B
Communication Studies/Speech Communication
   and Rhetoric, B
Computer and Information Sciences, B
Computer Education, M
Dance, B
Design and Visual Communications, B
Drama and Dance Teacher Education, B
Drama and Dramatics/Theatre Arts, B
Early Childhood Education and Teaching, O
Economics, B
Education, MO
Educational Media/Instructional Technology, M
Electrical, Electronics and Communications
   Engineering, B
Elementary Education and Teaching, BM
Engineering Physics, B
English Language and Literature, B
Environmental Studies, B
Finance, B
Fine/Studio Arts, B
French Language and Literature, B
Geography, B
History, B
Humanities/Humanistic Studies, B
Interdisciplinary Studies, B
International Business/Trade/Commerce, B
International Relations and Affairs, B
Kinesiology and Exercise Science, B
Liberal Arts and Sciences Studies and
   Humanities, B
Management Information Systems and Services, B
Marine Science/Merchant Marine Officer, B
Marketing/Marketing Management, B
Mathematics, B
Mathematics Teacher Education, M
Mechanical Engineering, B
Music, B
Music Management and Merchandising, B
Music Performance, B
Music Teacher Education, BM
Music Theory and Composition, B
Nursing, M
Nursing - Registered Nurse Training, B
Orthodontics, O
Philosophy, B
Physical Education Teaching and Coaching, B
Physics, B
Political Science and Government, B
Pre-Dentistry Studies, B
Pre-Law Studies, B
Pre-Medicine/Pre-Medical Studies, B
Pre-Veterinary Studies, B
Psychology, B

Reading Teacher Education, M
Secondary Education and Teaching, B
Sociology, B
Spanish Language and Literature, B
Special Education and Teaching, B
Visual and Performing Arts, B
Voice and Opera, B

JOHNSON & WALES UNIVERSITY

Accounting, AB
Advertising, A
Baking and Pastry Arts/Baker/Pastry Chef, A
Business Administration and Management, AB
Criminal Justice/Law Enforcement
   Administration, AB
Culinary Arts/Chef Training, AB
Fashion Merchandising, A
Food Service, Waiter/Waitress, and Dining Room
   Management/Manager, AB
Hospitality Administration/Management, AB
Hotel/Motel Administration/Management, AB
Marketing/Marketing Management, AB
Parks, Recreation and Leisure Facilities
   Management, B
Public Relations/Image Management, B
Restaurant, Culinary, and Catering
   Management/Manager, A
Special Products Marketing Operations, A

JONES COLLEGE (JACKSONVILLE)

Accounting, AB
Administrative Assistant and Secretarial Science, AB
Business Administration and Management, AB
Information Science/Studies, AB
Interdisciplinary Studies, B
Legal Assistant/Paralegal, AB
Medical/Clinical Assistant, AB

JONES COLLEGE (MIAMI)

Business Administration and Management, AB
Clinical/Medical Laboratory Assistant, A
Computer and Information Sciences, AB
Health Services/Allied Health/Health Sciences, B
Interdisciplinary Studies, B
Legal Assistant/Paralegal, AB

KEISER COLLEGE (DAYTONA BEACH)

Accounting, A
Business Administration and Management, A
Cinematography and Film/Video Production, A
Computer Graphics, A
Computer Programming/Programmer, A
Health/Health Care Administration/Management, A
Legal Assistant/Paralegal, A
Management Information Systems and Services, A
Medical/Clinical Assistant, A

KEISER COLLEGE (FORT LAUDERDALE)

Accounting, A
Business Administration and Management, AB
Clinical/Medical Laboratory Technician, A
Computer Engineering Technology/Technician, A
Computer Graphics, A
Computer Programming/Programmer, A
Corrections and Criminal Justice, A
Culinary Arts/Chef Training, A
Emergency Medical Technology/Technician (EMT
   Paramedic), A
Engineering Technology, A
Fire Science/Firefighting, A
Health/Health Care Administration/Management, A
Hospitality Administration/Management, A
Industrial Radiologic Technology/Technician, A
Legal Assistant/Paralegal, A
Management Information Systems and Services, B
Medical Radiologic Technology/Science - Radiation
   Therapist, A
Medical/Clinical Assistant, A
Occupational Therapy/Therapist, A
Physical Therapist Assistant, A
Public Administration, A

System Administration/Administrator, A

KEISER COLLEGE (MELBOURNE)

Business Administration and Management, A
Computer Graphics, A
Computer Programming/Programmer, A
Culinary Arts/Chef Training, A
Diagnostic Medical Sonography/Sonographer and
   Ultrasound Technician, A
Drafting and Design Technology/Technician, A
Health/Health Care Administration/Management, A
Hospitality Administration/Management, A
Legal Assistant/Paralegal, A
Medical/Clinical Assistant, A

KEISER COLLEGE (MIAMI)

Business Administration and Management, A
Computer Systems Networking and
   Telecommunications, A
Criminal Justice/Law Enforcement Administration, A
Health and Medical Administrative Services, A
Health Services/Allied Health/Health Sciences, A
Legal Assistant/Paralegal, A
Medical Office Assistant/Specialist, A
Nursing - Registered Nurse Training, A
Radiologic Technology/Science - Radiographer, A

KEISER COLLEGE (SARASOTA)

Accounting, A
Business Administration and Management, A
Computer Graphics, A
Computer Programming/Programmer, A
Information Science/Studies, A
Legal Assistant/Paralegal, A
Medical/Clinical Assistant, A

KEISER COLLEGE (TALLAHASSEE)

Accounting, A
Business Administration and Management, A
Computer Graphics, A
Computer Programming/Programmer, A
Computer Systems Analysis/Analyst, A
Culinary Arts/Chef Training, A
Health/Health Care Administration/Management, A
Legal Assistant/Paralegal, A
Medical/Clinical Assistant, A

KEY COLLEGE

Computer Programming, A
Court Reporting/Court Reporter, A
Legal Assistant/Paralegal, A
Medical Office Management/Administration, A
Medical Transcription/Transcriptionist, A

LAKE CITY COMMUNITY COLLEGE

Administrative Assistant and Secretarial Science, A
Business Administration and Management, A
Clinical/Medical Laboratory Technician, A
Computer Hardware Engineering, A
Computer Programming, Specific Applications, A
Computer
   Programming, Vendor/Product Certification, A
Computer Programming/Programmer, A
Computer Software Engineering, A
Criminal Justice/Law Enforcement Administration, A
Electrical, Electronic and Communications
   Engineering Technology/Technician, A
Emergency Medical Technology/Technician (EMT
   Paramedic), A
Forest Management/Forest Resources
   Management, A
Forestry Technology/Technician, A
Landscaping and Groundskeeping, A
Liberal Arts and Sciences Studies and
   Humanities, A
Nursing - Registered Nurse Training, A
Physical Therapist Assistant, A
Turf and Turfgrass Management, A
Web Page, Digital/Multimedia and Information
   Resources Design, A

LAKE-SUMTER COMMUNITY COLLEGE

Business Administration and Management, A
Commercial and Advertising Art, A
Computer and Information Sciences, A

Computer Science, A
Criminal Justice/Law Enforcement Administration, A
Emergency Medical Technology/Technician (EMT
   Paramedic), A
Fire Science/Firefighting, A
Health Information/Medical Records
   Administration/Administrator, A
Legal Assistant/Paralegal, A
Liberal Arts and Sciences Studies and
   Humanities, A
Nursing - Registered Nurse Training, A
Office Management and Supervision, A
Sport and Fitness Administration/Management, A
Technical Theatre/Theatre Design and
   Technology, A

LYNN UNIVERSITY

Accounting, B
Adult and Continuing Education and Teaching, B
Airline/Commercial/Professional Pilot and Flight
   Crew, B
Aviation/Airway Management and Operations, BM
Business Administration and Management, B
Business Administration, Management and
   Operations, MD
Commercial and Advertising Art, B
Criminology, M
Drafting and Design Technology/Technician, B
Education, B
Education/Teaching of the Gifted and Talented, M
Educational Leadership and Administration, MD
Electronic Commerce, M
Elementary Education and Teaching, B
Emergency Medical Services, MO
English Language and Literature, B
Environmental Studies, B
Fashion Merchandising, AB
Fashion/Apparel Design, B
Funeral Service and Mortuary Science, A
Gerontology, B
Health Services Administration, M
Health/Health Care Administration/Management, B
History, B
Hospitality Administration/Management, M
Hotel/Motel Administration/Management, B
Humanities/Humanistic Studies, B
International and Comparative Education, D
International Business/Trade/Commerce, BM
Junior High/Intermediate/Middle School Education
   and Teaching, B
Kindergarten/PreSchool Education and
   Teaching, AB
Liberal Arts and Sciences Studies and
   Humanities, B
Marketing, M
Marketing/Marketing Management, B
Mass Communication/Media Studies, BM
Media Studies, M
Music, B
Natural Sciences, B
Nursing - Registered Nurse Training, B
Parks, Recreation and Leisure Facilities
   Management, B
Performance, O
Physical Therapy/Therapist, A
Political Science and Government, B
Pre-Law Studies, B
Pre-Medicine/Pre-Medical Studies, B
Psychology, B
Secondary Education and Teaching, B
Securities Services Administration/Management, M
Social Sciences, B
Special Education and Teaching, M
Special Products Marketing Operations, B
Sport and Fitness Administration/Management, BM
Tourism and Travel Services Management, B

MANATEE COMMUNITY COLLEGE

Accounting, A
Administrative Assistant and Secretarial Science, A
Advertising, A
African-American/Black Studies, A
American Government and Politics (United States)
   , A
American/United States Studies/Civilization, A
Art History, Criticism and Conservation, A

Art/Art Studies, General, A
Asian Studies/Civilization, A
Astronomy, A
Biology Teacher Education, A
Biology/Biological Sciences, A
Business Administration and Management, A
Business/Commerce, A
Business/Managerial Economics, A
Central/Middle and Eastern European Studies, A
Chemistry, A
Chemistry Teacher Education, A
Child Development, A
Civil Engineering Technology/Technician, A
Commercial and Advertising Art, A
Community Health Services/Liaison/Counseling, A
Computer and Information Sciences, A
Computer Engineering Technology/Technician, A
Computer Graphics, A
Computer Programming, A
Computer Programming/Programmer, A
Construction Engineering Technology/Technician, A
Criminal Justice/Safety Studies, A
Dietetics/Dieticians, A
Drafting and Design Technology/Technician, A
Drama and Dramatics/Theatre Arts, A
Economics, A
Electrical, Electronic and Communications
   Engineering Technology/Technician, A
Engineering, A
English Language and Literature, A
English/Language Arts Teacher Education, A
Family and Consumer Sciences/Home Economics
   Teacher Education, A
Finance, A
Fine/Studio Arts, A
Fire Science/Firefighting, A
Foreign Language Teacher Education, A
French Language and Literature, A
German Language and Literature, A
Health Teacher Education, A
Health/Health Care Administration/Management, A
History, A
Hospital and Health Care Facilities
   Administration/Management, A
Humanities/Humanistic Studies, A
Information Science/Studies, A
Jazz/Jazz Studies, A
Jewish/Judaic Studies, A
Journalism, A
Kindergarten/PreSchool Education and Teaching, A
Latin American Studies, A
Legal Assistant/Paralegal, A
Liberal Arts and Sciences Studies and
   Humanities, A
Mass Communication/Media Studies, A
Mathematics Teacher Education, A
Medical Radiologic Technology/Science - Radiation
   Therapist, A
Music, A
Music Performance, A
Music Teacher Education, A
Music Theory and Composition, A
Nursing - Registered Nurse Training, A
Occupational Therapist Assistant, A
Occupational Therapy/Therapist, A
Philosophy, A
Physical Education Teaching and Coaching, A
Physical Therapist Assistant, A
Physical Therapy/Therapist, A
Physician Assistant, A
Physics, A
Physics Teacher Education, A
Pre-Pharmacy Studies, A
Psychology, A
Public Administration, A
Radio and Television, A
Radio and Television Broadcasting
   Technology/Technician, A
Radiologic Technology/Science - Radiographer, A
Religion/Religious Studies, A
Respiratory Care Therapy/Therapist, A
Russian Studies, A
Science Teacher Education/General Science
   Teacher Education, A
Social Psychology, A
Social Sciences, A

Social Studies Teacher Education, A
Social Work, A
Spanish Language and Literature, A
Speech and Rhetorical Studies, A
Statistics, A
Technology Teacher Education/Industrial Arts
Teacher Education, A
Trade and Industrial Teacher Education, A
Vocational Rehabilitation Counseling/Counselor, A
Women's Studies, A

MIAMI DADE COLLEGE

Accounting Technology/Technician and
Bookkeeping, A
Administrative Assistant and Secretarial Science, A
Aeronautics/Aviation/Aerospace Science and
Technology, A
Agriculture, A
Air Traffic Controller, A
Airline/Commercial/Professional Pilot and Flight
Crew, A
American/United States Studies/Civilization, A
Anthropology, A
Architectural Drafting and Architectural
CAD/CADD, A
Architectural Engineering Technology/Technician, A
Art/Art Studies, General, A
Asian Studies/Civilization, A
Audiology/Audiologist and Speech-Language
Pathology/Pathologist, A
Aviation/Airway Management and Operations, A
Behavioral Sciences, A
Biology Teacher Education, B
Biology/Biological Sciences, A
Biomedical Technology/Technician, A
Business Administration and Management, A
Chemistry, A
Chemistry Teacher Education, B
Child Development, A
Cinematography and Film/Video Production, A
Civil Engineering Technology/Technician, A
Clinical/Medical Laboratory Technician, A
Commercial and Advertising Art, A
Comparative Literature, A
Computer Engineering Technology/Technician, A
Computer Graphics, A
Computer Programming/Programmer, A
Computer Science, A
Computer Software Technology/Technician, A
Computer Technology/Computer Systems
Technology, A
Construction Engineering Technology/Technician, A
Court Reporting/Court Reporter, A
Criminal Justice/Law Enforcement Administration, A
Criminal Justice/Police Science, A
Dance, A
Data Processing and Data Processing
Technology/Technician, A
Dental Hygiene/Hygienist, A
Diagnostic Medical Sonography/Sonographer and
Ultrasound Technician, A
Dietetic Technician (DTR), A
Dietetics/Dieticians, A
Drafting and Design Technology/Technician, A
Drama and Dramatics/Theatre Arts, A
Economics, A
Education, A
Electrical and Electronic Engineering
Technologies/Technicians, A
Electrical, Electronic and Communications
Engineering Technology/Technician, A
Elementary Education and Teaching, A
Emergency Medical Technology/Technician (EMT
Paramedic), A
Engineering, A
Engineering Technology, A
English Language and Literature, A
Environmental Engineering
Technology/Environmental Technology, A
Finance, A
Fire Science/Firefighting, A
Food Science, A
Forestry, A
French Language and Literature, A
Funeral Service and Mortuary Science, A
General Studies, A

Geology/Earth Science, A
German Language and Literature, A
Health Information/Medical Records
Administration/Administrator, A
Health Professions and Related Clinical Sciences, A
Health/Medical Preparatory Programs, A
Heating, Air Conditioning and Refrigeration
Technology/Technician, A
Heating, Air Conditioning, Ventilation and
Refrigeration Maintenance
Technology/Technician, A
Histologic Technician, A
History, A
Horticultural Science, A
Hospitality Administration/Management, A
Human Services, A
Humanities/Humanistic Studies, A
Industrial Technology/Technician, A
Information Science/Studies, A
Interior Design, A
International Relations and Affairs, A
Italian Language and Literature, A
Journalism, A
Junior High/Intermediate/Middle School Education
and Teaching, A
Kindergarten/PreSchool Education and Teaching, A
Landscaping and Groundskeeping, A
Latin American Studies, A
Legal Administrative Assistant/Secretary, A
Legal Assistant/Paralegal, A
Management Information Systems and Services, A
Marketing/Marketing Management, A
Mass Communication/Media Studies, A
Mathematics, A
Mathematics Teacher Education, B
Medical/Clinical Assistant, A
Music, A
Music Performance, A
Music Teacher Education, A
Natural Sciences, A
Non-Profit/Public/Organizational Management, A
Nuclear Medical Technology/Technologist, A
Nursing - Registered Nurse Training, A
Ophthalmic Technician/Technologist, A
Ornamental Horticulture, A
Parks, Recreation, Leisure and Fitness Studies, A
Philosophy, A
Photographic and Film/Video Technology/Technician
and Assistant, A
Photography, A
Physical Education Teaching and Coaching, A
Physical Sciences, A
Physical Therapist Assistant, A
Physics, A
Physics Teacher Education, B
Plant Nursery Operations and Management, A
Political Science and Government, A
Portuguese Language and Literature, A
Pre-Engineering, A
Psychology, A
Public Administration, A
Radio and Television, A
Radio and Television Broadcasting
Technology/Technician, A
Radiologic Technology/Science - Radiographer, A
Recording Arts Technology/Technician, A
Respiratory Care Therapy/Therapist, A
Respiratory Therapy Technician/Assistant, A
Science Teacher Education/General Science
Teacher Education, A
Sign Language Interpretation and Translation, A
Social Sciences, A
Social Work, A
Sociology, A
Spanish Language and Literature, A
Special Education and Teaching, B
Substance Abuse/Addiction Counseling, A
Teacher Assistant/Aide, A
Teacher Education and Professional
Development, Specific Subject Areas, B
Telecommunications Technology/Technician, A

Tourism and Travel Services Management, A

MIAMI INTERNATIONAL UNIVERSITY OF ART & DESIGN

Advertising, B
Animation, Interactive Technology, Video Graphics
and Special Effects, B
Art/Art Studies, General, A
Cinematography and Film/Video Production, B
Commercial and Advertising Art, A
Computer Art and Design, M
Computer Graphics, A
Fashion Merchandising, AB
Fashion/Apparel Design, A
Film, Television, and Video Production, M
Fine Arts and Art Studies, M
Graphic Design, M
Interior Design, ABM
Metal and Jewelry Arts, A
Visual and Performing Arts, AB

NATIONAL SCHOOL OF TECHNOLOGY, INC. (NORTH MIAMI BEACH)

Massage Therapy/Therapeutic Massage, A
Medical Insurance Coding Specialist/Coder, A
Medical/Clinical Assistant, A
Surgical Technology/Technologist, A

NEW COLLEGE OF FLORIDA

Anthropology, B
Art History, Criticism and Conservation, B
Biology/Biological Sciences, B
Chemistry, B
Classics and Classical
Languages, Literatures, and Linguistics, B
Comparative Literature, B
Economics, B
English Language and Literature, B
Environmental Studies, B
Fine/Studio Arts, B
Foreign Languages and Literatures, B
French Language and Literature, B
French Studies, B
General Studies, B
German Language and Literature, B
Germanic Languages, Literatures, and Linguistics, B
History, B
Humanities/Humanistic Studies, B
International/Global Studies, B
Liberal Arts and Sciences Studies and
Humanities, B
Marine Biology and Biological Oceanography, B
Mathematics, B
Medieval and Renaissance Studies, B
Music, B
Music History, Literature, and Theory, B
Natural Sciences, B
Neurobiology and Neurophysiology, B
Philosophy, B
Physics, B
Political Science and Government, B
Psychology, B
Public Policy Analysis, B
Religion/Religious Studies, B
Russian Language and Literature, B
Social Sciences, B
Sociology, B
Spanish Language and Literature, B
Urban Studies/Affairs, B

NEW ENGLAND INSTITUTE OF TECHNOLOGY AT PALM BEACH

Architectural Drafting and Architectural
CAD/CADD, A
Automobile/Automotive Mechanics
Technology/Technician, A
Computer Systems Networking and
Telecommunications, A
Dental Assisting/Assistant, A
Drafting and Design Technology/Technician, A
Electrical, Electronic and Communications
Engineering Technology/Technician, A

Heating, Air Conditioning, Ventilation and
  Refrigeration Maintenance
  Technology/Technician, A
Medical/Clinical Assistant, A
Office Management and Supervision, A

NEW WORLD SCHOOL OF THE ARTS

Acting, AB
Applied Art, AB
Dance, AB
Drama and Dramatics/Theatre Arts, AB
Drawing, AB
Graphic Design, AB
Intermedia/Multimedia, AB
Music Performance, AB
Music Theory and Composition, AB
Painting, AB
Photography, AB
Piano and Organ, AB
Printmaking, AB
Sculpture, AB
Violin, Viola, Guitar and Other Stringed
  Instruments, AB
Voice and Opera, AB
Wind and Percussion Instruments, AB

NORTH FLORIDA COMMUNITY COLLEGE

Accounting Technology/Technician and
  Bookkeeping, A
Architectural Drafting and Architectural
  CAD/CADD, A
Business Administration and Management, A
Business and Personal/Financial Services Marketing
  Operations, A
Criminal Justice/Safety Studies, A
Education/Teaching of Individuals with Hearing
  Impairments, Including Deafness, A
Industrial Technology/Technician, A
Liberal Arts and Sciences Studies and
  Humanities, A
Mechanical Drafting and Mechanical Drafting
  CAD/CADD, A

NORTHWOOD UNIVERSITY, FLORIDA CAMPUS

Accounting, AB
Advertising, AB
Banking and Financial Support Services, AB
Business Administration and Management, AB
Computer and Information Sciences, B
Hotel/Motel Administration/Management, AB
International Business/Trade/Commerce, AB
Management Information Systems and Services, B
Marketing/Marketing Management, B
Sport and Fitness Administration/Management, AB
Vehicle and Vehicle Parts and Accessories
  Marketing Operations, AB

NOVA SOUTHEASTERN UNIVERSITY

Accounting, BM
Adult and Continuing Education and Teaching, D
Allied Health and Medical Assisting Services, MD
American/United States Studies/Civilization, B
Athletic Training and Sports Medicine, B
Biological and Biomedical Sciences, M
Biology/Biological Sciences, B
Business Administration and Management, B
Business Administration, Management and
  Operations, MDO
Child and Family Studies, MD
Clinical Psychology, DO
Communication Disorders, MD
Computer and Information Sciences, B
Computer Education, MD
Computer Science, BMDO
Conflict Resolution and Mediation/Peace
  Studies, MDO
Counseling Psychology, M
Criminology, M
Dentistry, MP
Distance Education Development, MD
Drama and Dramatics/Theatre Arts, B
Early Childhood Education and Teaching, MO
Education, MDO

Education/Teaching of the Gifted and Talented, M
Educational Administration and Supervision, M
Educational Leadership and Administration, MDO
Educational Media/Instructional Technology, MDO
Elementary Education and Teaching, BMO
English as a Second Language, MO
English Education, MO
English Language and Literature, B
Environmental Sciences, BM
Environmental Studies, B
Finance, B
Health Education, D
Health Services Administration, M
Health Services/Allied Health/Health Sciences, B
Higher Education/Higher Education
  Administration, D
History, B
Human Resources Management and Services, M
Humanities/Humanistic Studies, B
Information Science/Studies, MDO
Interdisciplinary Studies, BM
International Business/Trade/Commerce, MD
Kindergarten/PreSchool Education and
  Teaching, AB
Law and Legal Studies, MPO
Legal and Justice Studies, M
Legal Assistant/Paralegal, B
Liberal Arts and Sciences Studies and
  Humanities, B
Management Information Systems and
  Services, MD
Management Science, B
Marine Affairs, M
Marine Biology and Biological Oceanography, BMD
Marine Sciences, M
Marketing/Marketing Management, B
Marriage and Family Therapy/Counseling, MDO
Mathematics Teacher Education, MO
Multi-/Interdisciplinary Studies, B
Nursing, M
Nursing - Registered Nurse Training, B
Occupational Therapy/Therapist, MD
Oceanography, Chemical and Physical, MD
Optometry, MP
Oral Biology, M
Organizational Management, D
Osteopathic Medicine, MP
Pharmacology, M
Pharmacy, P
Physical Therapy/Therapist, D
Physician Assistant, BM
Pre-Dentistry Studies, B
Pre-Law Studies, B
Pre-Medicine/Pre-Medical Studies, B
Psychology, BMDO
Public Administration, MD
Public Health, M
Reading Teacher Education, MO
Religious Education, O
School Psychology, MDO
Science Teacher Education/General Science
  Teacher Education, MO
Social Studies Teacher Education, MO
Spanish Language and Literature, M
Special Education and Teaching, B
Sport and Fitness Administration/Management, B
Student Personnel Services, M
Taxation, M
Vision Science/Physiological Optics, M
Vocational and Technical Education, D

OKALOOSA-WALTON COLLEGE

Accounting, A
Administrative Assistant and Secretarial Science, A
Art/Art Studies, General, A
Atmospheric Sciences and Meteorology, A
Automobile/Automotive Mechanics
  Technology/Technician, A
Avionics Maintenance Technology/Technician, A
Biological and Physical Sciences, A
Biology/Biological Sciences, A
Business Administration and Management, A
Chemistry, A
Child Development, A
Clinical Laboratory Science/Medical
  Technology/Technologist, A

Commercial and Advertising Art, A
Computer Engineering, A
Computer Programming, Specific Applications, A
Computer Programming/Programmer, A
Computer Science, A
Computer Systems Networking and
  Telecommunications, A
Construction Engineering Technology/Technician, A
Criminal Justice/Law Enforcement Administration, A
Criminal Justice/Police Science, A
Data Entry/Microcomputer Applications, A
Dietetics/Dieticians, A
Divinity/Ministry (BD, MDiv.), A
Drafting and Design Technology/Technician, A
Education, A
Electrical, Electronic and Communications
  Engineering Technology/Technician, A
Elementary Education and Teaching, A
Engineering, A
Family and Consumer Sciences/Home Economics
  Teacher Education, A
Fashion Merchandising, A
Finance, A
Foods, Nutrition, and Wellness Studies, A
Heating, Air Conditioning, Ventilation and
  Refrigeration Maintenance
  Technology/Technician, A
Hotel/Motel Administration/Management, A
Human Resources Management/Personnel
  Administration, A
Humanities/Humanistic Studies, A
Information Technology, A
Interior Design, A
Kindergarten/PreSchool Education and Teaching, A
Law and Legal Studies, A
Legal Assistant/Paralegal, A
Liberal Arts and Sciences Studies and
  Humanities, A
Mathematics, A
Modern Languages, A
Music, A
Nursing - Registered Nurse Training, AB
Physical Education Teaching and Coaching, A
Physics, A
Purchasing, Procurement/Acquisitions and
  Contracts Management, B
Real Estate, A
Social Sciences, A
Social Work, A
Welding Technology/Welder, A
Word Processing, A

PALM BEACH ATLANTIC UNIVERSITY

Accounting and Finance, B
Acting, B
Art Teacher Education, B
Bible/Biblical Studies, B
Biology/Biological Sciences, B
Broadcast Journalism, B
Business Administration and Management, B
Business Administration, Management and
  Operations, BM
Communication Studies/Speech Communication
  and Rhetoric, B
Computer and Information Sciences, B
Counseling Psychology, M
Dance, B
Drama and Dramatics/Theatre Arts, B
Education, BM
Elementary Education and Teaching, BM
Engineering, A
English Language and Literature, B
Entrepreneurship/Entrepreneurial Studies, B
Fine/Studio Arts, B
General Studies, AB
Graphic Design, B
History, B
Human Resources Development, M
Human Resources Management/Personnel
  Administration, B
International Business/Trade/Commerce, B
Journalism, B
Marketing/Marketing Management, B
Mathematics, B
Music, B
Music Performance, B

Music Teacher Education, B
Music Theory and Composition, B
Nursing - Registered Nurse Training, B
Organizational Communication, B
Organizational Management, M
Pharmacy, P
Philosophy, B
Physical Education Teaching and Coaching, B
Piano and Organ, B
Playwriting and Screenwriting, B
Political Science and Government, B
Pre-Law Studies, B
Psychology, B
Radio and Television, B
Religion/Religious Studies, B
Religious/Sacred Music, B
Secondary Education and Teaching, B
Theological and Ministerial Studies, B
Theology and Religious Vocations, M
Voice and Opera, B
Wind and Percussion Instruments, B

PALM BEACH COMMUNITY COLLEGE

Accounting, A
Administrative Assistant and Secretarial Science, A
Airline/Commercial/Professional Pilot and Flight
    Crew, A
Apparel and Textiles, A
Art History, Criticism and Conservation, A
Art/Art Studies, General, A
Biology/Biological Sciences, A
Botany/Plant Biology, A
Building/Construction
    Finishing, Management, and Inspection, A
Business Administration and Management, A
Ceramic Arts and Ceramics, A
Chemistry, A
Commercial and Advertising Art, A
Comparative Literature, A
Computer Programming, Specific Applications, A
Computer Programming/Programmer, A
Computer Science, A
Criminal Justice/Law Enforcement Administration, A
Criminal Justice/Police Science, A
Data Processing and Data Processing
    Technology/Technician, A
Dental Hygiene/Hygienist, A
Drafting and Design Technology/Technician, A
Drama and Dramatics/Theatre Arts, A
Economics, A
Education, A
Electrical, Electronic and Communications
    Engineering Technology/Technician, A
Elementary Education and Teaching, A
English Language and Literature, A
Family and Consumer Sciences/Human Sciences, A
Fashion Merchandising, A
Fashion/Apparel Design, A
Finance, A
Fire Science/Firefighting, A
Foods, Nutrition, and Wellness Studies, A
Health Teacher Education, A
History, A
Hotel/Motel Administration/Management, A
Industrial Radiologic Technology/Technician, A
Interior Design, A
Journalism, A
Kindergarten/PreSchool Education and Teaching, A
Legal Administrative Assistant/Secretary, A
Liberal Arts and Sciences Studies and
    Humanities, A
Management Information Systems and Services, A
Marketing/Marketing Management, A
Mass Communication/Media Studies, A
Mathematics, A
Music, A
Nursing - Registered Nurse Training, A
Occupational Therapy/Therapist, A
Philosophy, A
Photography, A
Physical Education Teaching and Coaching, A
Physical Sciences, A
Physical Therapy/Therapist, A
Political Science and Government, A
Pre-Engineering, A
Psychology, A

Religion/Religious Studies, A
Social Sciences, A
Social Work, A
Special Products Marketing Operations, A
Survey Technology/Surveying, A
System Administration/Administrator, A
Web Page, Digital/Multimedia and Information
    Resources Design, A
Word Processing, A
Zoology/Animal Biology, A

PASCO-HERNANDO COMMUNITY COLLEGE

Business Administration and Management, A
Computer Programming, A
Computer Programming, Specific Applications, A
Computer Systems Networking and
    Telecommunications, A
Computer Technology/Computer Systems
    Technology, A
Criminal Justice/Law Enforcement Administration, A
Dental Hygiene/Hygienist, A
Drafting and Design Technology/Technician, A
E-Commerce/Electronic Commerce, A
Emergency Medical Technology/Technician (EMT
    Paramedic), A
Human Services, A
Information Technology, A
Legal Assistant/Paralegal, A
Liberal Arts and Sciences Studies and
    Humanities, A
Marketing/Marketing Management, A
Nursing - Registered Nurse Training, A
Physical Therapist Assistant, A
Radiologic Technology/Science - Radiographer, A
Web Page, Digital/Multimedia and Information
    Resources Design, A

PENSACOLA JUNIOR COLLEGE

Accounting, A
Administrative Assistant and Secretarial Science, A
Agriculture, A
Art Teacher Education, A
Art/Art Studies, General, A
Automobile/Automotive Mechanics
    Technology/Technician, A
Biology/Biological Sciences, A
Business Administration and Management, A
Business/Commerce, A
Chemical Technology/Technician, A
Chemistry, A
Child Development, A
Civil Engineering Technology/Technician, A
Clinical Laboratory Science/Medical
    Technology/Technologist, A
Commercial and Advertising Art, A
Computer Science, A
Construction Engineering Technology/Technician, A
Court Reporting/Court Reporter, A
Criminal Justice/Safety Studies, A
Criminology, A
Culinary Arts/Chef Training, A
Dental Hygiene/Hygienist, A
Design and Visual Communications, A
Dietetics/Dieticians, A
Drafting and Design Technology/Technician, A
Drama and Dramatics/Theatre Arts, A
Education, A
Electrical, Electronic and Communications
    Engineering Technology/Technician, A
Emergency Medical Technology/Technician (EMT
    Paramedic), A
Environmental Studies, A
Fire Science/Firefighting, A
Forestry Technology/Technician, A
General Studies, A
Geology/Earth Science, A
Health and Physical Education, A
Health Information/Medical Records
    Administration/Administrator, A
Health/Health Care Administration/Management, A
History, A
Horticultural Science, A
Hotel/Motel Administration/Management, A
Industrial Technology/Technician, A
Information Science/Studies, A

Journalism, A
Kindergarten/PreSchool Education and Teaching, A
Landscaping and Groundskeeping, A
Legal Assistant/Paralegal, A
Liberal Arts and Sciences Studies and
    Humanities, A
Mathematics, A
Medical Administrative Assistant/Secretary, A
Music, A
Music Teacher Education, A
Natural Resources and Conservation, A
Nursing - Registered Nurse Training, A
Ornamental Horticulture, A
Philosophy, A
Physical Therapist Assistant, A
Physical Therapy/Therapist, A
Physics, A
Pre-Engineering, A
Psychology, A
Radiologic Technology/Science - Radiographer, A
Religion/Religious Studies, A
Respiratory Care Therapy/Therapist, A
Zoology/Animal Biology, A

POLK COMMUNITY COLLEGE

Accounting Technology/Technician and
    Bookkeeping, A
Business Administration and Management, A
Child Development, A
Corrections, A
Criminal Justice/Law Enforcement Administration, A
Data Processing and Data Processing
    Technology/Technician, A
Emergency Medical Technology/Technician (EMT
    Paramedic), A
Finance, A
Fire Science/Firefighting, A
Health Information/Medical Records
    Administration/Administrator, A
Information Science/Studies, A
Legal Administrative Assistant/Secretary, A
Liberal Arts and Sciences Studies and
    Humanities, A
Marketing/Marketing Management, A
Medical Administrative Assistant/Secretary, A
Nursing - Registered Nurse Training, A
Occupational Therapist Assistant, A
Physical Therapist Assistant, A
Pre-Engineering, A
Radiologic Technology/Science - Radiographer, A
Respiratory Care Therapy/Therapist, A

REMINGTON COLLEGE-PINELLAS CAMPUS

Artificial Intelligence and Robotics, A
Business Administration and Management, B
Computer and Information Sciences, A
Corrections and Criminal Justice, A

REMINGTON COLLEGE-TAMPA CAMPUS

Business Administration and Management, A
Computer Technology/Computer Systems
    Technology, A
Criminal Justice/Safety Studies, A
Electrical, Electronic and Communications
    Engineering Technology/Technician, A
Information Science/Studies, A
Operations Management and Supervision, B

RINGLING SCHOOL OF ART AND DESIGN

Design and Applied Arts, B
Fine/Studio Arts, B
Graphic Design, B
Illustration, B
Interior Design, B
Photography, B

ROLLINS COLLEGE

Anthropology, B
Art History, Criticism and Conservation, B
Biochemistry, B
Biology/Biological Sciences, B

Business Administration, Management and
  Operations, M
Chemistry, B
Classics and Classical
  Languages, Literatures, and Linguistics, B
Computer Science, B
Corporate and Organizational Communication, M
Counselor Education/School Counseling and
  Guidance Services, M
Drama and Dramatics/Theatre Arts, B
Economics, B
Education, BM
Elementary Education and Teaching, M
English Language and Literature, B
Environmental Studies, B
European Studies/Civilization, B
Fine/Studio Arts, B
French Language and Literature, B
History, B
Human Resources Development, M
Human Resources Management and Services, M
International Business/Trade/Commerce, B
International Relations and Affairs, B
Latin American Studies, B
Liberal Studies, M
Mathematics, B
Music, B
Philosophy, B
Physics, B
Political Science and Government, B
Pre-Dentistry Studies, B
Pre-Law Studies, B
Pre-Medicine/Pre-Medical Studies, B
Psychology, B
Religion/Religious Studies, B
Secondary Education and Teaching, M
Sociology, B
Spanish Language and Literature, B

ST. JOHN VIANNEY COLLEGE SEMINARY

Philosophy, B
Theology/Theological Studies, B

ST. JOHNS RIVER COMMUNITY COLLEGE

Accounting Technology/Technician and
  Bookkeeping, A
Administrative Assistant and Secretarial Science, A
Applied Art, A
Art/Art Studies, General, A
Business Administration and Management, A
Chemical Technology/Technician, A
Commercial and Advertising Art, A
Computer and Information Sciences, A
Computer Engineering Technology/Technician, A
Computer Programming/Programmer, A
Computer Typography and Composition Equipment
  Operator, A
Criminal Justice/Law Enforcement Administration, A
Dance, A
Drama and Dramatics/Theatre Arts, A
Electrical, Electronic and Communications
  Engineering Technology/Technician, A
Emergency Medical Technology/Technician (EMT
  Paramedic), A
Fire Science/Firefighting, A
Health Information/Medical Records
  Administration/Administrator, A
Liberal Arts and Sciences Studies and
  Humanities, A
Marketing/Marketing Management, A
Nursing - Registered Nurse Training, A

SAINT LEO UNIVERSITY

Accounting, BM
Biology/Biological Sciences, B
Business Administration and Management, B
Business Administration, Management and
  Operations, M
Clinical Laboratory Science/Medical
  Technology/Technologist, B
Community Organization and Advocacy, B
Counseling Psychology, M
Criminal Justice/Safety Studies, B
Criminology, M

Curriculum and Instruction, M
Education, M
Education/Teaching of the Gifted and Talented, M
Educational Leadership and Administration, M
Elementary Education and Teaching, B
English Language and Literature, B
History, B
Hospital and Health Care Facilities
  Administration/Management, B
Hospitality Administration/Management, B
Human Resources Management/Personnel
  Administration, B
Human Services, B
International Relations and Affairs, B
Junior High/Intermediate/Middle School Education
  and Teaching, B
Liberal Arts and Sciences Studies and
  Humanities, A
Management Information Systems and Services, B
Mass Communication/Media Studies, B
Mathematics, B
Pastoral Studies/Counseling, M
Political Science and Government, B
Psychology, B
Social Work, B
Sociology, B
Sport and Fitness Administration/Management, B
Theology/Theological Studies, B

ST. PETERSBURG COLLEGE

Accounting Technology/Technician and
  Bookkeeping, A
Architectural Engineering Technology/Technician, A
Aviation/Airway Management and Operations, A
Biology Teacher Education, B
Business Administration and Management, A
Business Teacher Education, B
Clinical/Medical Laboratory Technician, A
Commercial and Advertising Art, A
Computer Engineering Technology/Technician, A
Computer Systems Networking and
  Telecommunications, A
Computer/Information Technology Services
  Administration and Management, A
Construction Engineering Technology/Technician, A
Corrections, A
Corrections Administration, A
Criminal Justice/Law Enforcement Administration, A
Criminal Justice/Police Science, A
Criminalistics and Criminal Science, A
Data Modeling/Warehousing and Database
  Administration, A
Dental Hygiene/Hygienist, A
Drafting and Design Technology/Technician, A
Early Childhood Education and Teaching, A
Education, B
Electrical, Electronic and Communications
  Engineering Technology/Technician, A
Electromechanical and Instrumentation and
  Maintenance Technologies/Technicians, A
Elementary Education and Teaching, B
Emergency Medical Technology/Technician (EMT
  Paramedic), A
Engineering/Industrial Management, A
Fire Protection and Safety
  Technology/Technician, AB
Fire Science/Firefighting, A
Funeral Service and Mortuary Science, A
Graphic Design, A
Health Information/Medical Records
  Administration/Administrator, A
Health/Health Care Administration/Management, A
Hospitality Administration/Management, A
Human Services, A
Hydrology and Water Resources Science, A
Industrial Radiologic Technology/Technician, A
Industrial Technology/Technician, A
Information Technology, A
International Business/Trade/Commerce, B
Kindergarten/PreSchool Education and Teaching, A
Legal Administrative Assistant/Secretary, A
Legal Assistant/Paralegal, A
Liberal Arts and Sciences Studies and
  Humanities, A
Manufacturing Technology/Technician, A
Marketing/Marketing Management, A

Mathematics Teacher Education, B
Nursing - Registered Nurse Training, A
Orthotist/Prosthetist, B
Physical Therapist Assistant, A
Plastics Engineering Technology/Technician, A
Quality Control Technology/Technician, A
Radiologic Technology/Science - Radiographer, A
Respiratory Care Therapy/Therapist, A
Security and Loss Prevention Services, A
Security and Protective Services, AB
Sign Language Interpretation and Translation, A
Special Education and Teaching, B
Substance Abuse/Addiction Counseling, A
Technology Teacher Education/Industrial Arts
  Teacher Education, B
Telecommunications Technology/Technician, A
Tourism and Travel Services Management, A
Veterinary/Animal Health Technology/Technician and
  Veterinary Assistant, AB
Web Page, Digital/Multimedia and Information
  Resources Design, A
Web/Multimedia Management and Webmaster, A

ST. THOMAS UNIVERSITY

Accounting, BMO
Biology/Biological Sciences, B
Business Administration and Management, B
Business Administration, Management and
  Operations, MO
Chemistry, B
Communication and Media Studies, MO
Computer Science, B
Counseling Psychology, M
Counselor Education/School Counseling and
  Guidance Services, MO
Criminal Justice/Law Enforcement Administration, B
Criminology, MO
Education, MDO
Educational Administration and Supervision, MO
Educational Leadership and Administration, D
Elementary Education and Teaching, BM
English Language and Literature, B
Finance, B
Health Services Administration, MO
Hispanic Studies, MO
History, B
Hotel/Motel Administration/Management, B
Human Resources Management and Services, MO
Information Science/Studies, B
International Business/Trade/Commerce, BMO
Law and Legal Studies, MPO
Liberal Arts and Sciences Studies and
  Humanities, B
Management, MO
Marketing/Marketing Management, B
Marriage and Family Therapy/Counseling, MO
Mass Communication/Media Studies, B
Pastoral Studies/Counseling, BMDO
Political Science and Government, B
Pre-Dentistry Studies, B
Pre-Law Studies, B
Pre-Medicine/Pre-Medical Studies, B
Psychology, B
Public Administration, BMO
Reading Teacher Education, M
Religion/Religious Studies, B
Secondary Education and Teaching, B
Sociology, B
Special Education and Teaching, M
Sport and Fitness Administration/Management, B
Taxation, M
Theology and Religious Vocations, D

SANTA FE COMMUNITY COLLEGE

Accounting, A
Automobile/Automotive Mechanics
  Technology/Technician, A
Biomedical Technology/Technician, A
Business Administration and Management, A
Child Development, A
Commercial and Advertising Art, A
Communications Technology/Technician, A
Computer Engineering Technology/Technician, A
Computer Programming/Programmer, A
Construction Engineering Technology/Technician, A
Corrections, A

Criminal Justice/Law Enforcement Administration, A
Criminal Justice/Police Science, A
Data Processing and Data Processing
  Technology/Technician, A
Dental Hygiene/Hygienist, A
Drafting and Design Technology/Technician, A
Education, A
Electrical, Electronic and Communications
  Engineering Technology/Technician, A
Emergency Medical Technology/Technician (EMT
  Paramedic), A
Engineering, A
Environmental Studies, A
Fashion Merchandising, A
Finance, A
Fire Science/Firefighting, A
Health Information/Medical Records
  Administration/Administrator, A
Industrial Radiologic Technology/Technician, A
Information Science/Studies, A
Kindergarten/PreSchool Education and Teaching, A
Law and Legal Studies, A
Legal Administrative Assistant/Secretary, A
Liberal Arts and Sciences Studies and
  Humanities, A
Marketing/Marketing Management, A
Medical Administrative Assistant/Secretary, A
Nuclear Medical Technology/Technologist, A
Nursing - Registered Nurse Training, A
Ornamental Horticulture, A
Parks, Recreation and Leisure Facilities
  Management, A
Respiratory Care Therapy/Therapist, A

SCHILLER INTERNATIONAL UNIVERSITY

Business Administration, Management and
  Operations, M
Hospitality Administration/Management, M
Hotel/Motel Administration/Management, B
Interdisciplinary Studies, B
International Business/Trade/Commerce, ABM
International Relations and Affairs, B
Liberal Arts and Sciences Studies and
  Humanities, A
Management Information Systems and Services, M
Marketing/Marketing Management, B
Tourism and Travel Services Management, AB
Travel and Tourism, M

SEMINOLE COMMUNITY COLLEGE

Accounting, A
Administrative Assistant and Secretarial Science, A
Architectural Engineering Technology/Technician, A
Automobile/Automotive Mechanics
  Technology/Technician, A
Banking and Financial Support Services, A
Building/Construction
  Finishing, Management, and Inspection, A
Business Administration and Management, A
Child Development, A
Civil Engineering Technology/Technician, A
Computer and Information Sciences, A
Computer and Information Systems Security, A
Computer Engineering, A
Computer Engineering Technology/Technician, A
Computer Graphics, A
Computer Hardware Engineering, A
Computer Programming, A
Computer Programming, Specific Applications, A
Computer
  Programming, Vendor/Product Certification, A
Computer Programming/Programmer, A
Computer Software and Media Applications, A
Computer Software Engineering, A
Computer Systems Networking and
  Telecommunications, A
Computer/Information Technology Services
  Administration and Management, A
Construction Engineering Technology/Technician, A
Criminal Justice/Law Enforcement Administration, A
Data Entry/Microcomputer Applications, A
Data Modeling/Warehousing and Database
  Administration, A
Data Processing and Data Processing
  Technology/Technician, A

Drafting and Design Technology/Technician, A
Electrical, Electronic and Communications
  Engineering Technology/Technician, A
Emergency Medical Technology/Technician (EMT
  Paramedic), A
Finance, A
Fire Science/Firefighting, A
Industrial Technology/Technician, A
Information Science/Studies, A
Information Technology, A
Interior Design, A
Legal Assistant/Paralegal, A
Liberal Arts and Sciences Studies and
  Humanities, A
Management Information Systems and Services, A
Marketing/Marketing Management, A
Nursing - Registered Nurse Training, A
Physical Therapy/Therapist, A
Respiratory Care Therapy/Therapist, A
System Administration/Administrator, A
Telecommunications Technology/Technician, A
Web Page, Digital/Multimedia and Information
  Resources Design, A
Web/Multimedia Management and Webmaster, A
Word Processing, A

SOUTH FLORIDA COMMUNITY COLLEGE

Accounting, A
Administrative Assistant and Secretarial Science, A
Agricultural Business and Management, A
Agricultural Mechanization, A
Business Administration and Management, A
Business/Commerce, A
Child Development, A
Computer Programming/Programmer, A
Construction Engineering Technology/Technician, A
Criminal Justice/Law Enforcement Administration, A
Drafting and Design Technology/Technician, A
Education, A
Electrical, Electronic and Communications
  Engineering Technology/Technician, A
Finance, A
Hospitality Administration/Management, A
Liberal Arts and Sciences Studies and
  Humanities, A
Marketing/Marketing Management, A
Medical Administrative Assistant/Secretary, A
Nursing - Registered Nurse Training, A
Ornamental Horticulture, A

SOUTH UNIVERSITY (TAMPA)

Public Health (MPH, DPH), B

SOUTH UNIVERSITY (WEST PALM BEACH)

Accounting, A
Administrative Assistant and Secretarial Science, A
Business Administration and Management, AB
Health Services/Allied Health/Health Sciences, A
Health/Health Care Administration/Management, B
Information Science/Studies, A
Information Technology, AB
Law and Legal Studies, B
Legal Administrative Assistant/Secretary, B
Legal Assistant/Paralegal, A
Medical/Clinical Assistant, A
Nursing - Registered Nurse Training, B
Physical Therapist Assistant, A
Pre-Nursing Studies, A

SOUTHEASTERN UNIVERSITY

Accounting, B
Bible/Biblical Studies, B
Biology/Biological Sciences, B
Business, Management, Marketing, and Related
  Support Services, B
Communication Studies/Speech Communication
  and Rhetoric, B
Drama and Dramatics/Theatre Arts, B
Elementary Education and Teaching, B
English Language and Literature, B
English/Language Arts Teacher Education, B
Interdisciplinary Studies, B
Marketing/Marketing Management, B

Mathematics Teacher Education, B
Missions/Missionary Studies and Missiology, B
Music Performance, B
Music Teacher Education, B
Pastoral Studies/Counseling, B
Pre-Medicine/Pre-Medical Studies, B
Psychology, B
Religious/Sacred Music, B
Science Teacher Education/General Science
  Teacher Education, B
Social Studies Teacher Education, B
Social Work, B
Theological and Ministerial Studies, B

SOUTHWEST FLORIDA COLLEGE (FORT MYERS)

Accounting, A
Administrative Assistant and Secretarial Science, A
Business Administration and Management, A
Court Reporting/Court Reporter, A
Information Science/Studies, A
Legal Assistant/Paralegal, A
Medical/Clinical Assistant, A

STETSON UNIVERSITY

Accounting, BM
American/United States Studies/Civilization, B
Aquatic Biology/Limnology, B
Art/Art Studies, General, B
Biochemistry, B
Biology/Biological Sciences, B
Business Administration and Management, B
Business Administration, Management and
  Operations, MO
Business/Managerial Economics, B
Chemistry, B
Clinical Laboratory Science/Medical
  Technology/Technologist, B
Communication Studies/Speech Communication
  and Rhetoric, B
Computer Science, B
Counselor Education/School Counseling and
  Guidance Services, M
Curriculum and Instruction, O
Drama and Dramatics/Theatre Arts, B
E-Commerce/Electronic Commerce, B
Economics, B
Education, BMO
Educational Leadership and Administration, MO
Elementary Education and Teaching, B
English, M
English Language and Literature, B
Entrepreneurial and Small Business Operations, B
Environmental Studies, B
Finance, B
French Language and Literature, B
Geography, B
German Language and Literature, B
Health Services/Allied Health/Health Sciences, B
History, B
Humanities/Humanistic Studies, B
International Business/Trade/Commerce, B
International Relations and Affairs, B
Kinesiology and Exercise Science, B
Latin American Studies, B
Law and Legal Studies, MPO
Management Science, B
Marketing/Marketing Management, B
Marriage and Family Therapy/Counseling, M
Mathematics, B
Molecular Biology, B
Music, B
Music Performance, B
Music Teacher Education, B
Music Theory and Composition, B
Philosophy, B
Physics, B
Piano and Organ, B
Political Science and Government, B
Pre-Dentistry Studies, B
Pre-Law Studies, B
Pre-Medicine/Pre-Medical Studies, B
Pre-Veterinary Studies, B
Psychology, B
Reading Teacher Education, M
Religion/Religious Studies, B

Russian Studies, B
Secondary Education and Teaching, B
Social Science Teacher Education, B
Social Sciences, B
Sociology, B
Spanish Language and Literature, B
Special Education and Teaching, M
Sport and Fitness Administration/Management, B
Violin, Viola, Guitar and Other Stringed
  Instruments, B
Visual and Performing Arts, B
Voice and Opera, B
Web Page, Digital/Multimedia and Information
  Resources Design, B

TALLAHASSEE COMMUNITY COLLEGE

Accounting Technology/Technician and
  Bookkeeping, A
Administrative Assistant and Secretarial Science, A
Business Administration and Management, A
Civil Engineering Technology/Technician, A
Computer and Information Sciences, A
Computer Graphics, A
Computer Programming, Specific Applications, A
Computer Programming/Programmer, A
Computer Systems Networking and
  Telecommunications, A
Construction Engineering Technology/Technician, A
Criminal Justice/Law Enforcement Administration, A
Data Processing and Data Processing
  Technology/Technician, A
Dental Hygiene/Hygienist, A
Emergency Medical Technology/Technician (EMT
  Paramedic), A
Engineering, A
Film/Cinema Studies, A
Finance, A
Health Information/Medical Records
  Technology/Technician, A
Kindergarten/PreSchool Education and Teaching, A
Legal Administrative Assistant/Secretary, A
Legal Assistant/Paralegal, A
Liberal Arts and Sciences Studies and
  Humanities, A
Management Information Systems and Services, A
Marketing/Marketing Management, A
Nursing - Registered Nurse Training, A
Parks, Recreation, Leisure and Fitness Studies, A
Public Administration, A
Respiratory Care Therapy/Therapist, A
System Administration/Administrator, A
Word Processing, A

TALMUDIC COLLEGE OF FLORIDA

Bible/Biblical Studies, B
Jewish/Judaic Studies, B
Rabbinical Studies, B
Religious Education, B
Talmudic Studies, B
Theology and Religious Vocations, MD

TRINITY BAPTIST COLLEGE

Administrative Assistant and Secretarial Science, A
Bible/Biblical Studies, B
Elementary Education and Teaching, B
Missions/Missionary Studies and Missiology, B
Pastoral Studies/Counseling, B
Secondary Education and Teaching, B

TRINITY COLLEGE OF FLORIDA

Bible/Biblical Studies, AB
Business/Commerce, B
Counseling Psychology, B
Elementary Education and Teaching, B
Missions/Missionary Studies and Missiology, B
Pastoral Studies/Counseling, B
Theological and Ministerial Studies, B
Youth Ministry, B

UNIVERSITY OF CENTRAL FLORIDA

Accounting, BM
Actuarial Science, BMO
Advertising, B
Aerospace, Aeronautical and Astronautical
  Engineering, BM

Anthropology, B
Applied Mathematics, O
Art Education, M
Art Teacher Education, B
Art/Art Studies, General, B
Audiology/Audiologist and Speech-Language
  Pathology/Pathologist, B
Biological and Biomedical Sciences, MDO
Biology/Biological Sciences, B
Business Administration and Management, B
Business Administration, Management and
  Operations, MD
Business Teacher Education, B
Business/Commerce, B
Business/Managerial Economics, B
Chemistry, BMD
Cinematography and Film/Video Production, B
Civil Engineering, BMDO
Clinical Laboratory Science/Medical
  Technology/Technologist, B
Clinical Psychology, MD
Communication and Media Studies, M
Communication Disorders, M
Community College Education, O
Computer and Information Sciences, B
Computer Art and Design, MD
Computer Engineering, BMD
Computer Science, MD
Computer Technology/Computer Systems
  Technology, B
Conservation Biology, DO
Construction Engineering and Management, O
Counselor Education/School Counseling and
  Guidance Services, MD
Criminal Justice/Safety Studies, B
Criminology, MO
Curriculum and Instruction, DO
Drama and Dramatics/Theatre Arts, B
Early Childhood Education and Teaching, BM
Economics, BM
Education, MDO
Educational Leadership and Administration, MDO
Educational Media/Instructional Technology, MDO
Electrical Engineering, MDO
Electrical, Electronic and Communications
  Engineering Technology/Technician, B
Electrical, Electronics and Communications
  Engineering, B
Elementary Education and Teaching, BMD
Engineering and Applied Sciences, MDO
Engineering Design, O
Engineering Management, M
Engineering Technology, B
English, MDO
English as a Second Language, MO
English Education, M
English Language and Literature, B
English/Language Arts Teacher Education, B
Environmental Engineering
  Technology/Environmental Technology, MDO
Environmental/Environmental Health Engineering, B
Ergonomics and Human Factors, O
Exercise and Sports Science, MD
Experimental Psychology, D
Film, Television, and Video Production, M
Finance, B
Finance and Banking, D
Fine Arts and Art Studies, M
Fine/Studio Arts, B
Foreign Language Teacher Education, BO
Foreign Languages and Literatures, B
Forensic Science and Technology, BO
French Language and Literature, B
Gender Studies, O
Gerontology, O
Hazardous Materials Management and Waste
  Technology/Technician, O
Health Informatics, O
Health Information/Medical Records
  Administration/Administrator, B
Health Promotion, O
Health Services Administration, MO
Health Services/Allied Health/Health Sciences, B
Health/Health Care Administration/Management, B
History, BM
Hospitality Administration/Management, BM

Humanities/Humanistic Studies, B
Industrial and Organizational Psychology, MD
Industrial Engineering, B
Industrial/Management Engineering, MDO
Information Technology, B
Intermedia/Multimedia, B
Internet and Interactive Multimedia, M
Journalism, B
Latin American Studies, O
Legal Assistant/Paralegal, B
Liberal Arts and Sciences Studies and
  Humanities, AB
Liberal Studies, M
Management, M
Management Information Systems and
  Services, BM
Manufacturing Engineering, M
Marketing/Marketing Management, B
Mass Communication/Media Studies, B
Materials Engineering, MD
Materials Sciences, MD
Mathematics, BMDO
Mathematics Teacher Education, BMD
Mechanical Engineering, BMDO
Mechanical Engineering Related
  Technologies/Technicians, B
Medical Microbiology and Bacteriology, B
Medical Radiologic Technology/Science - Radiation
  Therapist, B
Microbiology, M
Molecular Biology, MD
Music Performance, B
Music Teacher Education, BM
Non-Profit/Public/Organizational Management, O
Nursing, MDO
Nursing - Adult, O
Nursing - Registered Nurse Training, B
Nursing Education, O
Operations Research, MO
Optical Technologies, MDO
Optics/Optical Sciences, MDO
Pediatric Nurse/Nursing, O
Philosophy, B
Photography, B
Photonics, MDO
Physical Education Teaching and Coaching, BM
Physical Therapy/Therapist, M
Physics, BMD
Political Science and Government, BM
Psychology, BMD
Public Administration, BMO
Public Affairs, D
Public Health (MPH, DPH), B
Quality Management, O
Radio and Television, O
Reading Teacher Education, M
Respiratory Care Therapy/Therapist, B
School Psychology, O
Science Teacher Education/General Science
  Teacher Education, BM
Social Science Teacher Education, B
Social Sciences, B
Social Studies Teacher Education, M
Social Work, BMO
Sociology, BMDO
Spanish Language and Literature, BM
Special Education and Teaching, BMD
Speech and Rhetorical Studies, B
Sport and Fitness Administration/Management, M
Statistics, BMO
Structural Engineering, O
Systems Engineering, O
Taxation, M
Technical and Business Writing, M
Theater, M
Trade and Industrial Teacher Education, B
Transportation and Highway Engineering, O
Travel and Tourism, M
Vocational and Technical Education, M
Water Resources Engineering, O
Writing, MO

UNIVERSITY OF FLORIDA

Accounting, BMDO
Advertising, B
Advertising and Public Relations, MD

Aerospace, Aeronautical and Astronautical
  Engineering, BMDO
African Studies, O
Agribusiness, M
Agricultural and Food Products Processing, B
Agricultural Economics, BMD
Agricultural Education, MD
Agricultural Engineering, MDO
Agricultural Sciences, MDO
Agricultural Teacher Education, B
Agricultural/Biological Engineering and
  Bioengineering, B
Agronomy and Crop Science, B
Agronomy and Soil Sciences, MD
Allied Health and Medical Assisting Services, MD
Allopathic Medicine, PO
American/United States Studies/Civilization, B
Anatomy, D
Animal Sciences, BMD
Anthropology, BMDO
Aquaculture, MD
Architecture, BMD
Art Education, M
Art History, Criticism and Conservation, BMD
Art Teacher Education, B
Asian Studies/Civilization, B
Astronomy, BMD
Athletic Training and Sports Medicine, MD
Audiology/Audiologist and Speech-Language
  Pathology/Pathologist, B
Biochemistry, MD
Bioengineering, MDO
Biological and Biomedical Sciences, DO
Biomedical Engineering, MDO
Biostatistics, M
Botany/Plant Biology, BMD
Building Science, MD
Business Administration and Management, B
Business Administration, Management and
  Operations, MO
Cell Biology and Anatomy, MD
Chemical Engineering, BMD
Chemistry, BMD
Civil Engineering, BMDO
Classics and Classical
  Languages, Literatures, and Linguistics, BMD
Clinical Psychology, D
Clinical Research, M
Communication and Media Studies, MDO
Communication Disorders, M
Community Health and Preventive Medicine, M
Community Health Services/Liaison/Counseling, B
Computer and Information Sciences, B
Computer Art and Design, M
Computer Engineering, BMDO
Computer Science, MDO
Construction Engineering and Management, MD
Construction Engineering Technology/Technician, B
Consumer Economics, M
Counselor Education/School Counseling and
  Guidance Services, MDO
Criminology, BMDO
Curriculum and Instruction, MDO
Dairy Science, B
Dance, B
Dentistry, PO
Drama and Dramatics/Theatre Arts, B
Early Childhood Education and Teaching, D
East Asian
  Languages, Literatures, and Linguistics, B
Ecology, MD
Economics, BMD
Education, MDO
Educational Administration and Supervision, MDO
Educational Measurement and Evaluation, MDO
Educational Media/Instructional Technology, MD
Educational Psychology, MDO
Electrical Engineering, MD
Electrical, Electronics and Communications
  Engineering, B
Elementary Education and Teaching, BM
Engineering and Applied Sciences, MDO
Engineering Science, B
English, MD
English as a Second Language, MDO
English Education, MD

English Language and Literature, B
Entomology, BMD
Environmental and Occupational Health, M
Environmental Engineering
  Technology/Environmental Technology, MDO
Environmental Sciences, B
Environmental/Environmental Health Engineering, B
Epidemiology, M
Exercise and Sports Science, MD
Family and Community Services, B
Family and Consumer Sciences/Human
  Sciences, M
Finance, B
Finance and Banking, MDO
Fine Arts and Art Studies, MD
Fine/Studio Arts, B
Fire Science/Firefighting, B
Fish, Game and Wildlife Management, MD
Food Science, B
Food Science and Technology, MD
Foreign Language Teacher Education, M
Forestry, BMDO
French Language and Literature, BMD
Gender Studies, MDO
Genetics, D
Genomic Sciences, D
Geography, BMD
Geology/Earth Science, BMD
Geosciences, MD
German Language and Literature, BMD
Graphic Design, B
Health Education, MD
Health Promotion, M
Health Psychology, D
Health Services Administration, MD
Health Services Research, D
Health Services/Allied Health/Health Sciences, B
Health Teacher Education, M
Higher Education/Higher Education
  Administration, DO
History, BMDO
Horticultural Science, BMD
Immunology, D
Industrial Engineering, B
Industrial/Management Engineering, MDO
Information Science/Studies, MDO
Insurance, B
Interior Design, BMD
Intermedia/Multimedia, B
International Affairs, MD
International Business/Trade/Commerce, M
International Development, MO
Jewish/Judaic Studies, B
Journalism, BMD
Junior High/Intermediate/Middle School Education
  and Teaching, B
Kinesiology and Exercise Science, B
Kinesiology and Movement Studies, MD
Landscape Architecture, BMD
Latin American Studies, MO
Law and Legal Studies, MDPO
Limnology, MD
Linguistics, BMDO
Management, MD
Management Information Systems and
  Services, MDO
Management Science, B
Marine Sciences, MD
Marketing, MD
Marketing/Marketing Management, B
Marriage and Family Therapy/Counseling, MDO
Mass Communication/Media Studies, MD
Materials Engineering, BMDO
Materials Sciences, MDO
Mathematics, BMD
Mathematics Teacher Education, MD
Mechanical Engineering, BMDO
Media Studies, MD
Medical Microbiology and Bacteriology, B
Medicinal and Pharmaceutical Chemistry, MDP
Microbiology, MD
Molecular Biology, MD
Molecular Genetics, MD
Multi-/Interdisciplinary Studies, B
Museology/Museum Studies, M
Music, BMD

Music Teacher Education, BMD
Natural Resources and Conservation, MDO
Neuroscience, MD
Nuclear Engineering, BMDO
Nursing, MD
Nursing - Registered Nurse Training, B
Nutritional Sciences, MD
Occupational Therapy/Therapist, M
Ocean Engineering, MDO
Oral and Dental Sciences, MO
Oral Biology, D
Orthodontics, MO
Parks, Recreation and Leisure Facilities
  Management, B
Pathology/Experimental Pathology, D
Periodontics, MO
Pharmaceutical Administration, MD
Pharmaceutical Sciences, D
Pharmacology, MDO
Pharmacy, PO
Philosophy, BMD
Physical Education Teaching and Coaching, M
Physical Therapy/Therapist, M
Physician Assistant, M
Physics, BMD
Physiology, MD
Plant Biology, MD
Plant Molecular Biology, MD
Plant Pathology/Phytopathology, BMD
Plant Sciences, BD
Political Science and Government, BMDO
Portuguese Language and Literature, B
Poultry Science, B
Psychology, BMDO
Public Affairs, M
Public Health, M
Public Relations/Image Management, B
Radio and Television, B
Reading Teacher Education, MD
Real Estate, BMDO
Recreation and Park Management, MD
Rehabilitation Counseling, M
Rehabilitation Sciences, D
Religion/Religious Studies, BMD
Russian Language and Literature, B
School Psychology, MDO
Science Teacher Education/General Science
  Teacher Education, MD
Social Sciences, M
Social Studies Teacher Education, MD
Sociology, BMDO
Soil Science and Agronomy, B
Spanish Language and Literature, BMD
Special Education and Teaching, BMDO
Sport Psychology, MD
Sports Medicine, MD
Statistics, BMD
Student Personnel Services, M
Survey Technology/Surveying, B
Systems Engineering, BMDO
Taxation, MD
Theater, M
Toxicology, O
Urban and Regional Planning, MDO
Veterinary Medicine, P
Veterinary Sciences, MDO
Water Resources, MD
Women's Studies, MDO
Writing, M
Zoology/Animal Biology, BMD

UNIVERSITY OF MIAMI

Accounting, BM
Advertising, B
Advertising and Public Relations, M
Aerospace, Aeronautical and Astronautical
  Engineering, B
African-American/Black Studies, B
Allopathic Medicine, PO
American/United States Studies/Civilization, B
Anthropology, B
Architectural Engineering, BMD
Architecture, BM
Art History, Criticism and Conservation, BM
Art/Art Studies, General, B
Athletic Training and Sports Medicine, B

Atmospheric Sciences and Meteorology, BMD
Biochemistry, BDO
Biological and Biomedical Sciences, MDO
Biology/Biological Sciences, B
Biomedical Engineering, MD
Biomedical/Medical Engineering, B
Biophysics, BDO
Broadcast Journalism, B
Business Administration and Management, B
Business Administration, Management and
  Operations, BMO
Business/Managerial Economics, B
Caribbean Studies, B
Cell Biology and Anatomy, DO
Ceramic Arts and Ceramics, BM
Chemistry, BMD
Cinematography and Film/Video Production, B
Civil Engineering, BMD
Clinical Psychology, D
Commercial and Advertising Art, B
Communication and Media Studies, MD
Communication Studies/Speech Communication
  and Rhetoric, B
Communication, Journalism and Related
  Programs, B
Community Health and Preventive Medicine, M
Composition, MD
Computer and Information Sciences, B
Computer Engineering, BMD
Computer Science, BM
Computer Systems Analysis/Analyst, B
Conducting, B
Counseling Psychology, D
Counselor Education/School Counseling and
  Guidance Services, MO
Creative Writing, B
Criminology, B
Dance, B
Developmental Biology and Embryology, DO
Developmental Psychology, D
Drama and Dramatics/Theatre Arts, B
Early Childhood Education and Teaching, MO
Ecology, BMD
Economics, BMD
Education, BMDO
Educational Administration and Supervision, M
Educational Measurement and Evaluation, MD
Electrical Engineering, MD
Electrical, Electronics and Communications
  Engineering, B
Elementary Education and Teaching, BMO
Engineering and Applied Sciences, MDO
Engineering Science, B
English, MD
English as a Second Language, MDO
English Language and Literature, B
English Literature (British and Commonwealth), B
Entrepreneurial and Small Business Operations, B
Entrepreneurship/Entrepreneurial Studies, B
Environmental and Occupational Health, M
Environmental Policy and Resource Management, D
Environmental Studies, B
Environmental/Environmental Health Engineering, B
Epidemiology, D
Ergonomics and Human Factors, D
Evolutionary Biology, MD
Exercise and Sports Science, MD
Family and Community Services, B
Film, Television, and Video Production, M
Film, Television, and Video Theory and Criticism, M
Film/Cinema Studies, B
Finance, B
Finance and Banking, M
Fine Arts and Art Studies, M
Fine/Studio Arts, B
Fish, Game and Wildlife Management, MD
French Language and Literature, BD
General Studies, B
Genetics, MD
Geography, B
Geological and Earth Sciences/Geosciences, B
Geology/Earth Science, B
Geophysics and Seismology, MD
German Language and Literature, B
Graphic Design, BM
Health and Medical Administrative Services, B

Health Professions and Related Clinical Sciences, B
Health/Medical Preparatory Programs, B
Higher Education/Higher Education
  Administration, M
History, BMD
Human Resources Management/Personnel
  Administration, B
Illustration, B
Immunology, DO
Industrial Engineering, B
Industrial/Management Engineering, MDO
Information Science/Studies, B
Inorganic Chemistry, D
International Affairs, MD
International Business/Trade/Commerce, BM
International Relations and Affairs, B
Internet and Interactive Multimedia, M
Italian Language and Literature, B
Jewish/Judaic Studies, B
Journalism, BM
Kinesiology and Exercise Science, B
Latin American Studies, B
Law and Legal Studies, BMPO
Liberal Arts and Sciences Studies and
  Humanities, B
Liberal Studies, M
Management, MD
Management Information Systems and Services, M
Management of Technology, M
Marine Affairs, MO
Marine Biology and Biological Oceanography, BMD
Marine Geology, MD
Marine Sciences, MD
Marketing, M
Marketing/Marketing Management, B
Marriage and Family Therapy/Counseling, M
Mass Communication/Media Studies, B
Mathematics, BMD
Mathematics and Statistics, B
Mathematics Teacher Education, MDO
Mechanical Engineering, BMD
Medical Informatics, B
Medical Microbiology and Bacteriology, B
Meteorology, BMD
Microbiology, BDO
Molecular Biology, DO
Music, BM
Music Management and Merchandising, B
Music Performance, B
Music Teacher Education, BMDO
Music Theory and Composition, BMD
Music Therapy/Therapist, BMDO
Musicology and Ethnomusicology, BM
Natural Resources and Conservation, B
Natural Resources Management/Development and
  Policy, B
Neurobiology and Neurophysiology, B
Neuroscience, BDO
Nursing, MD
Nursing - Registered Nurse Training, B
Ocean Engineering, M
Oceanography, Chemical and Physical, BMD
Organic Chemistry, D
Painting, BM
Parks, Recreation and Leisure Facilities
  Management, B
Performance, MD
Pharmacology, DO
Philosophy, BMD
Photography, BM
Physical Chemistry, D
Physical Therapy/Therapist, D
Physics, BMD
Physiological Psychology/Psychobiology, B
Physiology, DO
Piano and Organ, B
Political Science and Government, BMO
Pre-Pharmacy Studies, B
Printmaking, BM
Psychology, BMD
Public Health, MO
Public Relations/Image Management, B
Radio and Television, B
Reading Teacher Education, MDO
Religion/Religious Studies, B

Science Teacher Education/General Science
  Teacher Education, MDO
Sculpture, BM
Sociology, BMD
Spanish Language and Literature, BMD
Special Education and Teaching, BMDO
Sport and Fitness Administration/Management, M
Sports Medicine, M
Taxation, M
Urban Design, M
Visual and Performing Arts, B
Voice and Opera, B
Wildlife and Wildlands Science and Management, B
Women's Studies, B

UNIVERSITY OF NORTH FLORIDA

Accounting, BM
Allied Health and Medical Assisting Services, MO
Anthropology, B
Art Teacher Education, B
Art/Art Studies, General, B
Athletic Training and Sports Medicine, M
Banking and Financial Support Services, B
Biological and Biomedical Sciences, M
Biological and Physical Sciences, B
Biology/Biological Sciences, B
Business Administration and Management, B
Business Administration, Management and
  Operations, M
Business/Managerial Economics, B
Chemistry, B
Civil Engineering, B
Communication Studies/Speech Communication
  and Rhetoric, B
Community Health and Preventive Medicine, M
Computer and Information Sciences, B
Computer Science, M
Construction Engineering Technology/Technician, B
Counseling Psychology, M
Counselor Education/School Counseling and
  Guidance Services, M
Criminal Justice/Safety Studies, B
Criminology, M
Economics, B
Education, MD
Educational Administration and Supervision, M
Educational Leadership and Administration, MD
Electrical, Electronics and Communications
  Engineering, B
Elementary Education and Teaching, BM
English, M
English Language and Literature, B
Ethics, M
Finance, B
Fine/Studio Arts, B
General Studies, A
Gerontology, MO
Health Services Administration, M
Health Services/Allied Health/Health Sciences, B
History, BM
Information Science/Studies, M
International Business/Trade/Commerce, B
International Relations and Affairs, B
Jazz/Jazz Studies, B
Junior High/Intermediate/Middle School Education
  and Teaching, B
Liberal Arts and Sciences Studies and
  Humanities, B
Marketing/Marketing Management, B
Mathematics, BM
Mathematics Teacher Education, B
Mechanical Engineering, B
Music, B
Music Performance, B
Music Teacher Education, B
Nursing, MO
Nursing - Advanced Practice, MO
Nursing - Registered Nurse Training, B
Nutritional Sciences, M
Philosophy, BM
Physical Education Teaching and Coaching, B
Physical Therapy/Therapist, M
Physics, B
Political Science and Government, B
Psychology, BM
Public Administration, M

Public Health, MO
Rehabilitation Counseling, M
Science Teacher Education/General Science
   Teacher Education, B
Secondary Education and Teaching, BM
Sociology, BM
Spanish Language and Literature, B
Special Education and Teaching, BM
Statistics, BM
Trade and Industrial Teacher Education, B
Transportation/Transportation Management, B
Writing, M

UNIVERSITY OF PHOENIX-CENTRAL FLORIDA CAMPUS

Accounting, BM
Business Administration and Management, B
Business Administration, Management and
   Operations, M
Corrections and Criminal Justice, B
Curriculum and Instruction, M
E-Commerce/Electronic Commerce, B
Education, M
Educational Media/Instructional Technology, M
Health Services Administration, M
Information Science/Studies, M
Information Technology, B
International Business/Trade/Commerce, M
Management, M
Management Information Systems and
   Services, BM
Management of Technology, M
Management Science, B
Marketing, M
Marketing/Marketing Management, B
Nursing, M
Nursing Science, B
Organizational Management, M

UNIVERSITY OF PHOENIX-NORTH FLORIDA CAMPUS

Accounting, BM
Business Administration and Management, B
Business Administration, Management and
   Operations, M
Curriculum and Instruction, M
E-Commerce/Electronic Commerce, B
Education, M
Electronic Commerce, M
Elementary Education and Teaching, M
Entrepreneurship/Entrepreneurial Studies, B
Health Services Administration, M
Health/Health Care Administration/Management, B
Information Science/Studies, B
Management Information Systems and
   Services, BM
Management of Technology, M
Management Science, B
Marketing, M
Marketing/Marketing Management, B
Nursing, M
Nursing Science, B
Organizational Management, M

UNIVERSITY OF PHOENIX-SOUTH FLORIDA CAMPUS

Accounting, BM
Business Administration and Management, B
Business Administration, Management and
   Operations, M
Curriculum and Instruction, M
Education, M
Educational Media/Instructional Technology, M
Health Services Administration, M
Health/Health Care Administration/Management, B
Human Resources Management and Services, M
Information Technology, B
International Business/Trade/Commerce, M
Management, M
Management Information Systems and Services, M
Management Science, B
Marketing, M
Marketing/Marketing Management, B
Nursing, MO
Nursing Science, B

Organizational Management, M

UNIVERSITY OF PHOENIX-WEST FLORIDA CAMPUS

Accounting, B
Business Administration and Management, B
Business Administration, Management and
   Operations, M
Computer and Information Sciences, B
Corrections and Criminal Justice, B
Curriculum and Instruction, M
Education, M
Educational Media/Instructional Technology, M
Health Services Administration, M
Health/Health Care Administration/Management, B
Management, M
Management Information Systems and
   Services, BM
Management of Technology, M
Management Science, B
Marketing/Marketing Management, B
Nursing, M
Nursing - Registered Nurse Training, B
Organizational Management, M
Public Administration and Social Service
   Professions, B

UNIVERSITY OF SOUTH FLORIDA

Accounting, BM
Adult and Continuing Education and Teaching, MDO
African Studies, M
African-American/Black Studies, B
Allopathic Medicine, P
American/United States Studies/Civilization, BM
Analytical Chemistry, MD
Anatomy, D
Anthropology, BMD
Applied Mathematics, D
Applied Physics, D
Architecture, M
Art History, Criticism and Conservation, M
Art Teacher Education, B
Art/Art Studies, General, B
Athletic Training and Sports Medicine, B
Audiology/Audiologist and Speech-Language
   Pathology/Pathologist, B
Biochemistry, MD
Biological and Biomedical Sciences, MD
Biological and Physical Sciences, B
Biology/Biological Sciences, B
Biomedical Engineering, MD
Biophysics, D
Biostatistics, MD
Botany/Plant Biology, M
Business Administration and Management, B
Business Administration, Management and
   Operations, MD
Business Teacher Education, B
Business/Commerce, B
Business/Managerial Economics, B
Cancer Biology/Oncology, D
Chemical Engineering, BMD
Chemistry, BMD
Civil Engineering, BMD
Classics and Classical
   Languages, Literatures, and Linguistics, B
Clinical Laboratory Science/Medical
   Technology/Technologist, B
Clinical Psychology, D
Communication and Media Studies, MD
Communication Disorders, D
Communication Studies/Speech Communication
   and Rhetoric, B
Community College Education, MDO
Community Health and Preventive Medicine, MD
Composition, M
Computer and Information Sciences, B
Computer Engineering, BMD
Computer Science, MD
Computer/Information Technology Services
   Administration and Management, B
Counselor Education/School Counseling and
   Guidance Services, M
Criminal Justice/Safety Studies, B
Criminology, MD
Dance, B

Drama and Dance Teacher Education, B
Drama and Dramatics/Theatre Arts, B
Early Childhood Education and Teaching, MDO
Ecology, D
Economics, BMD
Education, BMDO
Education/Teaching of Individuals with Emotional
   Disturbances, B
Education/Teaching of Individuals with Mental
   Retardation, B
Education/Teaching of Individuals with Specific
   Learning Disabilities, B
Education/Teaching of the Gifted and Talented, M
Educational Leadership and Administration, MDO
Educational Measurement and Evaluation, MDO
Educational Media/Instructional Technology, MD
Electrical Engineering, MD
Electrical, Electronics and Communications
   Engineering, D
Elementary Education and Teaching, BMDO
Engineering, B
Engineering and Applied Sciences, MD
Engineering Management, MD
English, MD
English Education, MD
English Language and Literature, B
English/Language Arts Teacher Education, B
Environmental and Occupational Health, MD
Environmental Engineering
   Technology/Environmental Technology, MD
Environmental Policy and Resource
   Management, M
Environmental Sciences, M
Environmental Studies, B
Epidemiology, MD
Experimental Psychology, D
Finance, B
Fine Arts and Art Studies, M
Foreign Language Teacher Education, BM
French Language and Literature, BM
General Studies, B
Geography, BM
Geology/Earth Science, BMD
German Language and Literature, B
Gerontology, BMD
Health Services Administration, MD
Higher Education/Higher Education
   Administration, MDO
History, BM
Hospitality Administration/Management, B
Humanities/Humanistic Studies, B
Immunology, D
Industrial and Organizational Psychology, D
Industrial Education, M
Industrial Engineering, B
Industrial/Management Engineering, MD
Information Science/Studies, BM
Inorganic Chemistry, MD
International Affairs, M
International Business/Trade/Commerce, B
International Public Health/International Health, MD
International Relations and Affairs, B
Italian Language and Literature, B
Kindergarten/PreSchool Education and Teaching, B
Liberal Arts and Sciences Studies and
   Humanities, AB
Liberal Studies, M
Library Science, M
Linguistics, M
Management, M
Management Information Systems and
   Services, BM
Management Science, B
Marine Sciences, MD
Marketing/Marketing Management, B
Mass Communication/Media Studies, M
Mathematics, BMD
Mathematics Teacher Education, BMDO
Mechanical Engineering, BMD
Medical Microbiology and Bacteriology, BD
Microbiology, M
Middle School Education, M
Modern Languages, B
Molecular Biology, MD
Music, M
Music Performance, B

Music Teacher Education, BMD
Music Theory and Composition, M
Nursing, MD
Nursing - Registered Nurse Training, B
Oceanography, Chemical and Physical, MD
Organic Chemistry, MD
Pathology/Experimental Pathology, D
Performance, M
Pharmacology, D
Philosophy, BMD
Physical Chemistry, MD
Physical Education Teaching and Coaching, BM
Physical Therapy/Therapist, M
Physics, BMD
Physiology, D
Political Science and Government, BM
Psychology, BMD
Public Administration, M
Public Health, MD
Reading Teacher Education, MDO
Rehabilitation Counseling, M
Religion/Religious Studies, BM
Russian Language and Literature, B
School Psychology, DO
Science Teacher Education/General Science
   Teacher Education, BMDO
Secondary Education and Teaching, D
Social Science Teacher Education, B
Social Sciences, B
Social Studies Teacher Education, M
Social Work, BM
Sociology, BM
Spanish Language and Literature, BM
Special Education and Teaching, BM
Speech and Rhetorical Studies, B
Student Personnel Services, M
Trade and Industrial Teacher Education, B
Vocational and Technical Education, MDO
Women's Studies, BM
Zoology/Animal Biology, M

THE UNIVERSITY OF TAMPA

Accounting, BM
Art/Art Studies, General, B
Biochemistry, B
Biology/Biological Sciences, AB
Business Administration and Management, B
Business Administration, Management and
   Operations, M
Chemistry, AB
Computer Graphics, B
Computer Programming/Programmer, B
Creative Writing, AB
Criminology, B
Drama and Dramatics/Theatre Arts, B
Economics, AB
Elementary Education and Teaching, B
English Language and Literature, AB
Entrepreneurship/Entrepreneurial Studies, M
Environmental Biology, B
Environmental Studies, B
Finance, B
Geography, A
History, AB
Information Science/Studies, AB
International Business/Trade/Commerce, BM
International Relations and Affairs, B
Kinesiology and Exercise Science, B
Liberal Arts and Sciences Studies and
   Humanities, B
Management Information Systems and Services, M
Management of Technology, M
Marine Science/Merchant Marine Officer, B
Marketing, M
Marketing/Marketing Management, B
Mass Communication/Media Studies, B
Mathematics, AB
Music, AB
Nursing, MO
Nursing - Adult, M
Nursing - Advanced Practice, M
Nursing - Registered Nurse Training, B
Nursing Administration, M
Nursing Education, M
Philosophy, A
Physical Education Teaching and Coaching, B

Political Science and Government, AB
Pre-Dentistry Studies, B
Pre-Law Studies, B
Pre-Medicine/Pre-Medical Studies, B
Pre-Veterinary Studies, B
Psychology, AB
Secondary Education and Teaching, B
Social Sciences, B
Sociology, AB
Spanish Language and Literature, AB
Teacher Education, Multiple Levels, B
Urban Studies/Affairs, B
Visual and Performing Arts, B

UNIVERSITY OF WEST FLORIDA

Accounting, BM
Anthropology, BM
Art/Art Studies, General, B
Biological and Biomedical Sciences, M
Biological and Physical Sciences, B
Biology/Biological Sciences, B
Business Administration and Management, B
Business Administration, Management and
   Operations, M
Business/Managerial Economics, B
Chemistry, B
Clinical Laboratory Science/Medical
   Technology/Technologist, B
Communication and Media Studies, M
Communication Studies/Speech Communication
   and Rhetoric, B
Community Health Services/Liaison/Counseling, B
Computer and Information Sciences, B
Computer Engineering, B
Computer Science, M
Counselor Education/School Counseling and
   Guidance Services, M
Criminal Justice/Safety Studies, B
Curriculum and Instruction, MDO
Drama and Dramatics/Theatre Arts, B
Early Childhood Education and Teaching, BM
Economics, B
Education/Teaching of Individuals with Mental
   Retardation, B
Educational Leadership and Administration, MO
Educational Media/Instructional Technology, M
Electrical, Electronics and Communications
   Engineering, B
Elementary Education and Teaching, BM
Engineering Technology, B
English, M
English Language and Literature, B
English/Language Arts Teacher Education, B
Environmental Sciences, M
Environmental Studies, B
Exercise and Sports Science, M
Finance, B
Fine/Studio Arts, B
Foreign Language Teacher Education, B
Health and Physical Education, B
Health Education, M
History, BM
Hospitality Administration/Management, B
Humanities/Humanistic Studies, BM
International Relations and Affairs, B
Junior High/Intermediate/Middle School Education
   and Teaching, B
Leisure Studies, M
Liberal Arts and Sciences Studies and
   Humanities, A
Management Information Systems and Services, B
Marine Affairs, M
Marine Biology and Biological Oceanography, B
Marketing/Marketing Management, B
Mathematics, BM
Mathematics Teacher Education, BM
Middle School Education, M
Music Performance, B
Music Teacher Education, B
Nursing - Registered Nurse Training, B
Philosophy, B
Physical Education Teaching and Coaching, M
Physics, B
Political Science and Government, BM
Psychology, BM
Public Administration, M

Reading Teacher Education, M
Religion/Religious Studies, B
Science Teacher Education/General Science
   Teacher Education, BM
Secondary Education and Teaching, M
Social Science Teacher Education, B
Social Sciences, B
Social Work, B
Sociology, B
Special Education and Teaching, BM
Statistics, M
Systems Engineering, M
Trade and Industrial Teacher Education, B

VALENCIA COMMUNITY COLLEGE

Accounting, A
Administrative Assistant and Secretarial Science, A
Business Administration and Management, A
Cardiovascular Technology/Technologist, A
Cinematography and Film/Video Production, A
Civil Engineering Technology/Technician, A
Commercial and Advertising Art, A
Computer Programming, A
Computer Programming, Specific Applications, A
Computer Programming/Programmer, A
Construction Engineering Technology/Technician, A
Criminal Justice/Law Enforcement Administration, A
Culinary Arts/Chef Training, A
Data Entry/Microcomputer Applications, A
Dental Hygiene/Hygienist, A
Diagnostic Medical Sonography/Sonographer and
   Ultrasound Technician, A
Drafting and Design Technology/Technician, A
Drama and Dramatics/Theatre Arts, A
Electrical, Electronic and Communications
   Engineering Technology/Technician, A
Emergency Medical Technology/Technician (EMT
   Paramedic), A
Environmental Engineering
   Technology/Environmental Technology, A
Fire Science/Firefighting, A
Hospitality Administration/Management, A
Human Resources Management/Personnel
   Administration, A
Industrial Technology/Technician, A
Information Technology, A
Legal Administrative Assistant/Secretary, A
Legal Assistant/Paralegal, A
Liberal Arts and Sciences Studies and
   Humanities, A
Marketing/Marketing Management, A
Medical Administrative Assistant/Secretary, A
Medical Radiologic Technology/Science - Radiation
   Therapist, A
Nursing - Registered Nurse Training, A
Office Management and Supervision, A
Ornamental Horticulture, A
Physical Education Teaching and Coaching, A
Pre-Engineering, A
Respiratory Care Therapy/Therapist, A
Survey Technology/Surveying, A
Tourism and Travel Services Management, A
Word Processing, A

WARNER SOUTHERN COLLEGE

Bible/Biblical Studies, B
Biology/Biological Sciences, B
Business Administration and Management, B
Business Administration, Management and
   Operations, M
Business/Commerce, B
Communication Studies/Speech Communication
   and Rhetoric, B
Comparative Literature, B
Divinity/Ministry (BD, MDiv.), AB
Education/Teaching of the Gifted and Talented, B
Elementary Education and Teaching, B
English Language and Literature, B
General Studies, A
History, B
Human Resources Management/Personnel
   Administration, B
Kinesiology and Exercise Science, B
Music Teacher Education, B
Physical Education Teaching and Coaching, B
Psychology, B

Religious/Sacred Music, B
Science Teacher Education/General Science
   Teacher Education, B
Secondary Education and Teaching, B
Social Science Teacher Education, B
Social Work, B
Special Education and Teaching, B
Technical and Business Writing, B

WEBBER INTERNATIONAL UNIVERSITY

Accounting, ABM
Business Administration and Management, AB
Business Administration, Management and
   Operations, M
Business/Commerce, AB
Computer and Information Sciences, B
Finance, AB
Hotel/Motel Administration/Management, AB
International Business/Trade/Commerce, AB
Management, M
Marketing/Marketing Management, AB
Pre-Law Studies, B
Sport and Fitness Administration/Management, ABM
Tourism and Travel Services Management, AB

WEBSTER COLLEGE (HOLIDAY)

Accounting, A
Business Administration and Management, A
Computer Science, A
Law and Legal Studies, A
Medical/Clinical Assistant, A
Tourism and Travel Services Management, A

WEBSTER COLLEGE (OCALA)

Accounting, A
Administrative Assistant and Secretarial Science, A
Business Administration and Management, A
Data Processing and Data Processing
   Technology/Technician, A
Legal Administrative Assistant/Secretary, A
Medical Administrative Assistant/Secretary, A
Medical/Clinical Assistant, A

Georgia

ABRAHAM BALDWIN AGRICULTURAL COLLEGE

Accounting, A
Administrative Assistant and Secretarial Science, A
Agricultural Business and Management, A
Agricultural Economics, A
Agricultural Mechanization, A
Agriculture, A
Animal Sciences, A
Art/Art Studies, General, A
Biological and Physical Sciences, A
Biology/Biological Sciences, A
Business Administration and Management, A
Chemistry, A
Child Development, A
Computer Engineering Technology/Technician, A
Computer Programming/Programmer, A
Computer Science, A
Computer Typography and Composition Equipment
   Operator, A
Criminal Justice/Law Enforcement Administration, A
Criminal Justice/Police Science, A
Data Processing and Data Processing
   Technology/Technician, A
Ecology, A
Education, A
Elementary Education and Teaching, A
English Language and Literature, A
Environmental Design/Architecture, A
Family and Consumer Sciences/Human Sciences, A
Farm/Farm and Ranch Management, A
Fashion Merchandising, A
Forestry, A
Forestry Technology/Technician, A
History, A
Horticultural Science, A
Hospitality Administration/Management, A
Humanities/Humanistic Studies, A
Journalism, A

Kindergarten/PreSchool Education and Teaching, A
Landscaping and Groundskeeping, A
Liberal Arts and Sciences Studies and
   Humanities, A
Marketing/Marketing Management, A
Mathematics, A
Music, A
Nursing - Registered Nurse Training, A
Ornamental Horticulture, A
Parks, Recreation and Leisure Facilities
   Management, A
Pharmacy Technician/Assistant, A
Physical Education Teaching and Coaching, A
Physical Sciences, A
Political Science and Government, A
Poultry Science, A
Pre-Engineering, A
Psychology, A
Social Sciences, A
Social Work, A
Sociology, A
Speech and Rhetorical Studies, A
Wildlife and Wildlands Science and Management, A

AGNES SCOTT COLLEGE

Anthropology, B
Art/Art Studies, General, B
Astrophysics, B
Biochemistry, B
Biology/Biological Sciences, B
Chemistry, B
Classics and Classical
   Languages, Literatures, and Linguistics, B
Comparative Literature, B
Creative Writing, B
Drama and Dramatics/Theatre Arts, B
Economics, B
English Education, M
English Language and Literature, B
French Language and Literature, B
German Language and Literature, B
History, B
Interdisciplinary Studies, B
International Relations and Affairs, B
Mathematics, B
Music, B
Philosophy, B
Physics, B
Political Science and Government, B
Psychology, B
Religion/Religious Studies, B
Sociology, B
Spanish Language and Literature, B
Women's Studies, B

ALBANY STATE UNIVERSITY

Accounting, B
Administrative Assistant and Secretarial Science, B
Art/Art Studies, General, B
Biology/Biological Sciences, B
Business Administration and Management, B
Business Administration, Management and
   Operations, M
Business Education, M
Business Teacher Education, B
Chemistry, B
Computer and Information Sciences, B
Counselor Education/School Counseling and
   Guidance Services, M
Criminal Justice/Safety Studies, B
Criminology, M
Early Childhood Education and Teaching, M
Economics, M
Education, BMO
Educational Administration and Supervision, MO
English Education, M
English Language and Literature, B
French Language and Literature, B
Health Education, M
Health Professions and Related Clinical Sciences, B
Health Services Administration, M
History, B
Human Resources Management and Services, M
Junior High/Intermediate/Middle School Education
   and Teaching, B
Kindergarten/PreSchool Education and Teaching, B

Marketing/Marketing Management, B
Mathematics, B
Mathematics Teacher Education, M
Middle School Education, M
Music, B
Music Teacher Education, M
Nursing, M
Nursing - Registered Nurse Training, B
Physical Education Teaching and Coaching, BM
Political Science and Government, B
Psychology, B
Public Administration, M
Public Policy Analysis, M
Reading Teacher Education, M
Science Teacher Education/General Science
   Teacher Education, BM
Social Studies Teacher Education, M
Social Work, B
Sociology, B
Spanish Language and Literature, B
Special Education and Teaching, BM
Speech and Rhetorical Studies, B
Water Resources, M

ALBANY TECHNICAL COLLEGE

Accounting, A
Adult Development and Aging, A
Child Development, A
Computer and Information Sciences, A
Corrections and Criminal Justice, A
Culinary Arts/Chef Training, A
Drafting and Design Technology/Technician, A
Electrical and Electronic Engineering
   Technologies/Technicians, A
Forestry Technology/Technician, A
Hotel/Motel Administration/Management, A
Human Development and Family Studies, A
Industrial Technology/Technician, A
Manufacturing Technology/Technician, A
Marketing/Marketing Management, A
Medical Radiologic Technology/Science - Radiation
   Therapist, A
Pharmacy Technician/Assistant, A
Tourism and Travel Services Management, A

ALTAMAHA TECHNICAL COLLEGE

Administrative Assistant and Secretarial Science, A
Child Development, A
Computer Programming/Programmer, A
Computer Systems Networking and
   Telecommunications, A
Criminal Justice/Safety Studies, A
Information Science/Studies, A
Machine Tool Technology/Machinist, A
Manufacturing Technology/Technician, A
Marketing/Marketing Management, A

AMERICAN INTERCONTINENTAL UNIVERSITY (ATLANTA)

Business Administration, Management and
   Operations, M
Cinematography and Film/Video Production, AB
Design and Visual Communications, B
Fashion Merchandising, AB
Fashion/Apparel Design, AB
Interior Design, AB
International Business/Trade/Commerce, B
Marketing, M
Marketing/Marketing Management, B

AMERICAN INTERCONTINENTAL UNIVERSITY (DUNWOODY CAMPUS)

Design and Visual Communications, AB
Information Science/Studies, M
Information Technology, B
International Business/Trade/Commerce, BM
Management Information Systems and Services, M
Marketing/Marketing Management, AB

ANDREW COLLEGE

Agriculture, A
Athletic Training and Sports Medicine, A
Biological and Physical Sciences, A
Biology/Biological Sciences, A
Business Administration and Management, A

Clinical Laboratory Science/Medical
Technology/Technologist, A
Comparative Literature, A
Computer and Information Sciences, A
Criminal Justice/Safety Studies, A
Dental Hygiene/Hygienist, A
Education, A
English Language and Literature, A
Environmental Sciences, A
Health and Physical Education, A
Health Information/Medical Records
Technology/Technician, A
History, A
Humanities/Humanistic Studies, A
International/Global Studies, A
Kinesiology and Exercise Science, A
Mass Communication/Media Studies, A
Mathematics, A
Music, A
Occupational Therapy/Therapist, A
Parks, Recreation and Leisure Facilities
Management, A
Physical Therapy/Therapist, A
Physician Assistant, A
Pre-Dentistry Studies, A
Pre-Engineering, A
Pre-Law Studies, A
Pre-Medicine/Pre-Medical Studies, A
Pre-Nursing Studies, A
Pre-Pharmacy Studies, A
Pre-Theology/Pre-Ministerial Studies, A
Pre-Veterinary Studies, A
Psychology, A
Radiologic Technology/Science - Radiographer, A
Social Sciences, A
Social Work, A
Sociology, A
Sport and Fitness Administration/Management, A
Visual and Performing Arts, A

APPALACHIAN TECHNICAL COLLEGE

Accounting, A
Administrative Assistant and Secretarial Science, A
Business Administration and Management, A
Child Development, A
Computer Systems Networking and
Telecommunications, A
Criminal Justice/Safety Studies, A
Forensic Science and Technology, A
Information Science/Studies, A
Legal Assistant/Paralegal, A

ARGOSY UNIVERSITY/ATLANTA

Business Administration, Management and
Operations, M
Clinical Psychology, MD
Counseling Psychology, M
Curriculum and Instruction, MD
Education, MD
Educational Leadership and Administration, D
Psychology, MD

ARMSTRONG ATLANTIC STATE UNIVERSITY

Adult and Continuing Education and Teaching, M
Art Teacher Education, B
Art/Art Studies, General, B
Biology/Biological Sciences, B
Business Teacher Education, B
Chemistry, B
Clinical Laboratory Science/Medical
Technology/Technologist, B
Computer Science, BM
Criminal Justice/Police Science, A
Criminology, M
Dental Hygiene/Hygienist, AB
Drama and Dramatics/Theatre Arts, B
Early Childhood Education and Teaching, M
Economics, B
Education, M
Elementary Education and Teaching, M
English Language and Literature, B
Exercise and Sports Science, M
Health Professions and Related Clinical Sciences, B
Health Services Administration, M
Health Teacher Education, B

History, BM
Information Science/Studies, B
Information Technology, B
Junior High/Intermediate/Middle School Education
and Teaching, B
Kindergarten/PreSchool Education and Teaching, B
Liberal Arts and Sciences Studies and
Humanities, AB
Liberal Studies, M
Mathematics, B
Middle School Education, M
Music, B
Music Teacher Education, B
Nursing, M
Nursing - Registered Nurse Training, B
Physical Education Teaching and Coaching, B
Physical Therapy/Therapist, BM
Physics, B
Political Science and Government, B
Psychology, B
Public Health, M
Public Health (MPH, DPH), B
Respiratory Care Therapy/Therapist, B
Secondary Education and Teaching, M
Spanish Language and Literature, B
Special Education and Teaching, BM
Sports Medicine, M
Visual and Performing Arts, B

THE ART INSTITUTE OF ATLANTA

Advertising, B
Animation, Interactive Technology, Video Graphics
and Special Effects, B
Cinematography and Film/Video Production, AB
Commercial and Advertising Art, AB
Commercial Photography, AB
Culinary Arts/Chef Training, A
Interior Design, B
Intermedia/Multimedia, A
Restaurant, Culinary, and Catering
Management/Manager, B
Web Page, Digital/Multimedia and Information
Resources Design, AB

ATHENS TECHNICAL COLLEGE

Accounting, A
Administrative Assistant and Secretarial Science, A
Biology Technician/BioTechnology Laboratory
Technician, A
Child Development, A
Clinical Laboratory Science/Medical
Technology/Technologist, A
Communications Technology/Technician, A
Computer Programming/Programmer, A
Computer Systems Networking and
Telecommunications, A
Criminal Justice/Law Enforcement Administration, A
Dental Assisting/Assistant, A
Dental Hygiene/Hygienist, A
Diagnostic Medical Sonography/Sonographer and
Ultrasound Technician, A
Electrical, Electronic and Communications
Engineering Technology/Technician, A
Emergency Medical Technology/Technician (EMT
Paramedic), A
Health and Medical Laboratory Technologies, A
Hotel/Motel Administration/Management, A
Information Science/Studies, A
Legal Assistant/Paralegal, A
Licensed Practical/Vocational Nurse Training, A
Logistics and Materials Management, A
Marketing/Marketing Management, A
Medical Radiologic Technology/Science - Radiation
Therapist, A
Nursing - Registered Nurse Training, A
Physical Therapy/Therapist, A
Respiratory Care Therapy/Therapist, A
Surgical Technology/Technologist, A
Tourism and Travel Services Management, A
Veterinary/Animal Health Technology/Technician and
Veterinary Assistant, A

ATLANTA CHRISTIAN COLLEGE

Bible/Biblical Studies, B
Business Administration and Management, B
Business/Commerce, A

Counseling Psychology, B
Humanities/Humanistic Studies, B
Kindergarten/PreSchool Education and Teaching, B
Music, B
Pre-Theology/Pre-Ministerial Studies, B
Theology/Theological Studies, B

ATLANTA METROPOLITAN COLLEGE

African-American/Black Studies, A
Art/Art Studies, General, A
Biology/Biological Sciences, A
Business Administration and Management, A
Chemistry, A
Child Development, A
Communication Studies/Speech Communication
and Rhetoric, A
Computer and Information Sciences, A
Computer Science, A
Computer/Information Technology Services
Administration and Management, A
Criminal Justice/Law Enforcement Administration, A
Engineering Technology, A
English Language and Literature, A
Foreign Languages and Literatures, A
General Studies, A
Health and Physical Education, A
Health Services/Allied Health/Health Sciences, A
History, A
Human Services, A
Information Science/Studies, A
Information Technology, A
Licensed Practical/Vocational Nurse Training, A
Mathematics, A
Music, A
Operations Management and Supervision, A
Physics, A
Political Science and Government, A
Psychology, A
Social Work, A
Speech and Rhetorical Studies, A

ATLANTA TECHNICAL COLLEGE

Accounting, A
Child Development, A
Computer Programming/Programmer, A
Culinary Arts/Chef Training, A
Dental Hygiene/Hygienist, A
Health Information/Medical Records
Technology/Technician, A
Hotel/Motel Administration/Management, A
Information Technology, A
Legal Assistant/Paralegal, A
Marketing/Marketing Management, A
Tourism and Travel Services Management, A

AUGUSTA STATE UNIVERSITY

Accounting, B
Biology/Biological Sciences, B
Business Administration and Management, B
Business Administration, Management and
Operations, M
Chemistry, B
Clinical Laboratory Science/Medical
Technology/Technologist, B
Communication Studies/Speech Communication
and Rhetoric, B
Computer and Information Sciences, B
Counselor Education/School Counseling and
Guidance Services, MO
Criminal Justice/Safety Studies, AB
Early Childhood Education and Teaching, MO
Education, MO
Education/Teaching of Individuals with Mental
Retardation, B
Educational Leadership and Administration, MO
Elementary Education and Teaching, B
English Language and Literature, B
Finance, B
French Language and Literature, B
History, B
Intermedia/Multimedia, B
Junior High/Intermediate/Middle School Education
and Teaching, B
Kindergarten/PreSchool Education and Teaching, B
Liberal Arts and Sciences Studies and
Humanities, A

Marketing/Marketing Management, B
Mathematics, B
Middle School Education, MO
Music, B
Music Performance, B
Music Teacher Education, B
Nursing - Registered Nurse Training, A
Physical Education Teaching and Coaching, B
Physical Sciences, B
Physics, B
Political Science and Government, BM
Psychology, BM
Secondary Education and Teaching, MO
Social Work, B
Sociology, B
Spanish Language and Literature, B
Special Education and Teaching, BMO

AUGUSTA TECHNICAL COLLEGE

Accounting, A
Administrative Assistant and Secretarial Science, A
BioTechnology, A
Business Administration and Management, A
Cardiovascular Technology/Technologist, A
Child Development, A
Computer Programming/Programmer, A
Computer Systems Networking and
   Telecommunications, A
Criminal Justice/Safety Studies, A
Culinary Arts/Chef Training, A
E-Commerce/Electronic Commerce, A
Electrical, Electronic and Communications
   Engineering Technology/Technician, A
Emergency Medical Technology/Technician (EMT
   Paramedic), A
Fire Science/Firefighting, A
Information Science/Studies, A
Marketing/Marketing Management, A
Mechanical Engineering/Mechanical
   Technology/Technician, A
Medical Radiologic Technology/Science - Radiation
   Therapist, A
Occupational Therapist Assistant, A
Parks, Recreation and Leisure Facilities
   Management, A
Pharmacy Technician/Assistant, A
Respiratory Care Therapy/Therapist, A
Respiratory Therapy Technician/Assistant, A
Surgical Technology/Technologist, A

BAINBRIDGE COLLEGE

Accounting, A
Administrative Assistant and Secretarial Science, A
Agriculture, A
Art/Art Studies, General, A
Automobile/Automotive Mechanics
   Technology/Technician, A
Biology/Biological Sciences, A
Business Administration and Management, A
Business Teacher Education, A
Chemistry, A
Criminal Justice/Law Enforcement Administration, A
Data Processing and Data Processing
   Technology/Technician, A
Drafting and Design Technology/Technician, A
Drama and Dramatics/Theatre Arts, A
Education, A
Electrical, Electronic and Communications
   Engineering Technology/Technician, A
Elementary Education and Teaching, A
English Language and Literature, A
Family and Consumer Sciences/Human Sciences, A
Forestry, A
Health Teacher Education, A
History, A
Information Science/Studies, A
Journalism, A
Kindergarten/PreSchool Education and Teaching, A
Liberal Arts and Sciences Studies and
   Humanities, A
Licensed Practical/Vocational Nurse Training, A
Marketing/Marketing Management, A
Mathematics, A
Nursing - Registered Nurse Training, A
Political Science and Government, A
Psychology, A

Sociology, A
Speech and Rhetorical Studies, A
Welding Technology/Welder, A

BAUDER COLLEGE

Business Administration and Management, A
Fashion Merchandising, A
Fashion/Apparel Design, A
Information Technology, A
Interior Design, A

BEACON UNIVERSITY

Bible/Biblical Studies, AB
Business Administration and Management, B
Psychology, B

BERRY COLLEGE

Accounting, B
Animal Sciences, B
Anthropology, B
Art/Art Studies, General, B
Biochemistry, B
Biology/Biological Sciences, B
Business Administration and Management, B
Business Administration, Management and
   Operations, M
Chemistry, B
Communication, Journalism and Related
   Programs, B
Computer Science, B
Curriculum and Instruction, O
Early Childhood Education and Teaching, BM
Economics, B
Education, MO
Engineering Technology, B
English Language and Literature, B
Environmental Sciences, B
Finance, B
French Language and Literature, B
German Language and Literature, B
History, B
International Relations and Affairs, B
Junior High/Intermediate/Middle School Education
   and Teaching, B
Marketing/Marketing Management, B
Mathematics, B
Mathematics Teacher Education, B
Middle School Education, M
Multi-/Interdisciplinary Studies, B
Music, B
Music Management and Merchandising, B
Music Performance, B
Music Teacher Education, B
Nursing - Registered Nurse Training, B
Philosophy and Religious Studies, B
Physical Education Teaching and Coaching, B
Physics, B
Political Science and Government, B
Psychology, B
Reading Teacher Education, M
Secondary Education and Teaching, M
Social Sciences, B
Sociology, B
Spanish Language and Literature, B
Theatre/Theatre Arts Management, B

BEULAH HEIGHTS BIBLE COLLEGE

Bible/Biblical Studies, AB
Urban Studies/Affairs, AB

BRENAU UNIVERSITY

Accounting, BM
Art Teacher Education, B
Arts Management, B
Biology/Biological Sciences, B
Business Administration and Management, B
Business Administration, Management and
   Operations, M
Business/Corporate Communications, B
Commercial and Advertising Art, B
Conflict Resolution and Mediation/Peace Studies, O
Dance, B
Drama and Dance Teacher Education, B
Drama and Dramatics/Theatre Arts, B
Early Childhood Education and Teaching, MO

Education, BMO
English Language and Literature, B
Environmental Studies, B
Fashion Merchandising, B
Fine/Studio Arts, B
General Studies, B
Health Services Administration, M
History, B
Interior Design, B
International Relations and Affairs, B
Junior High/Intermediate/Middle School Education
   and Teaching, B
Kindergarten/PreSchool Education and Teaching, B
Legal Professions and Studies, B
Management, M
Management Strategy and Policy, M
Marketing/Marketing Management, B
Mass Communication/Media Studies, B
Middle School Education, MO
Music, B
Music Teacher Education, B
Nursing - Advanced Practice, M
Nursing - Registered Nurse Training, B
Occupational Therapy/Therapist, BM
Organizational Management, M
Piano and Organ, B
Political Science and Government, B
Pre-Law Studies, B
Psychology, BM
Special Education and Teaching, BM
Voice and Opera, B

BREWTON-PARKER COLLEGE

Accounting, B
Biology Teacher Education, B
Biology/Biological Sciences, AB
Business Administration and Management, B
Communication Studies/Speech Communication
   and Rhetoric, B
Computer and Information Sciences, B
Early Childhood Education and Teaching, B
Education, B
English Language and Literature, B
English/Language Arts Teacher Education, B
General Studies, AB
Health and Physical Education/Fitness, B
History, B
History Teacher Education, B
Information Science/Studies, B
Junior High/Intermediate/Middle School Education
   and Teaching, B
Mathematics, B
Mathematics Teacher Education, B
Music, B
Music Performance, B
Music Teacher Education, B
Physical Education Teaching and Coaching, B
Political Science and Government, B
Pre-Law Studies, B
Psychology, B
Religion/Religious Studies, AB
Science Teacher Education/General Science
   Teacher Education, B
Secondary Education and Teaching, B
Social Sciences, B
Sociology, B

BROWN MACKIE COLLEGE-ATLANTA

Accounting Technology/Technician and
   Bookkeeping, A
Business Administration and Management, A
Computer Software Technology/Technician, A
Criminal Justice/Safety Studies, A
Legal Assistant/Paralegal, A

CENTRAL GEORGIA TECHNICAL COLLEGE

Accounting, A
Administrative Assistant and Secretarial Science, A
Adult Development and Aging, A
Banking and Financial Support Services, A
Business Administration and Management, A
Cabinetmaking and Millwork/Millwright, A
Cardiovascular Technology/Technologist, A
Carpentry/Carpenter, A
Child Care and Support Services Management, A

Child Development, A
Clinical/Medical Laboratory Technician, A
Computer Programming/Programmer, A
Computer Systems Networking and
  Telecommunications, A
Criminal Justice/Safety Studies, A
Dental Hygiene/Hygienist, A
Drafting and Design Technology/Technician, A
E-Commerce/Electronic Commerce, A
Electrical, Electronic and Communications
  Engineering Technology/Technician, A
Health and Medical Laboratory Technologies, A
Hotel/Motel Administration/Management, A
Industrial Technology/Technician, A
Information Science/Studies, A
Legal Assistant/Paralegal, A
Marketing/Marketing Management, A
Medical Radiologic Technology/Science - Radiation
  Therapist, A
Tourism and Travel Services Management, A
Veterinary/Animal Health Technology/Technician and
  Veterinary Assistant, A
Web Page, Digital/Multimedia and Information
  Resources Design, A

CHATTAHOOCHEE TECHNICAL COLLEGE

Accounting, A
Administrative Assistant and Secretarial Science, A
Automobile/Automotive Mechanics
  Technology/Technician, A
Biomedical Technology/Technician, A
Business Administration and Management, A
Child Development, A
Civil Engineering Technology/Technician, A
Computer and Information Systems Security, A
Computer Programming/Programmer, A
Computer Systems Networking and
  Telecommunications, A
Criminal Justice/Safety Studies, A
Culinary Arts/Chef Training, A
Drafting and Design Technology/Technician, A
Electrical, Electronic and Communications
  Engineering Technology/Technician, A
Fire Science/Firefighting, A
Health and Medical Laboratory Technologies, A
Horticultural Science, A
Information Science/Studies, A
Logistics and Materials Management, A
Marketing/Marketing Management, A
Medical Radiologic Technology/Science - Radiation
  Therapist, A
Parks, Recreation and Leisure Facilities
  Management, A
Web Page, Digital/Multimedia and Information
  Resources Design, A

CLARK ATLANTA UNIVERSITY

Accounting, B
African-American/Black Studies, MD
Applied Mathematics, M
Art Teacher Education, B
Art/Art Studies, General, B
Biological and Biomedical Sciences, MD
Biology/Biological Sciences, B
Business Administration and Management, B
Business Administration, Management and
  Operations, M
Business Teacher Education, B
Chemistry, BMD
Computer and Information Sciences, B
Computer Science, BM
Counselor Education/School Counseling and
  Guidance Services, MD
Criminal Justice/Law Enforcement Administration, B
Criminology, M
Curriculum and Instruction, MO
Developmental and Child Psychology, B
Drama and Dramatics/Theatre Arts, B
Early Childhood Education and Teaching, B
Economics, BM
Education, BMDO
Education/Teaching of the Gifted and Talented, MO
Educational Leadership and Administration, MDO
Educational Psychology, MD
Elementary Education and Teaching, B

Engineering, B
English, M
English Language and Literature, B
Fashion/Apparel Design, B
Finance and Banking, M
French Language and Literature, B
Health Information/Medical Records
  Administration/Administrator, B
Health Teacher Education, B
History, BM
History Teacher Education, B
Humanities/Humanistic Studies, D
Information Science/Studies, BMO
Inorganic Chemistry, MD
Interdisciplinary Studies, B
International Affairs, MD
International Business/Trade/Commerce, M
International Development, MD
Junior High/Intermediate/Middle School Education
  and Teaching, B
Kindergarten/PreSchool Education and Teaching, B
Library Science, MO
Marketing, BM
Mass Communication/Media Studies, B
Mathematics, B
Medical Illustration/Medical Illustrator, B
Music, B
Music Teacher Education, B
Organic Chemistry, MD
Philosophy, B
Physical Chemistry, MD
Physical Education Teaching and Coaching, B
Physics, BM
Political Science and Government, BMD
Psychology, B
Public Administration, M
Quantitative Analysis, M
Religion/Religious Studies, B
Romance
  Languages, Literatures, and Linguistics, M
Science Teacher Education/General Science
  Teacher Education, BD
Secondary Education and Teaching, B
Social Sciences, B
Social Work, BMD
Sociology, BM
Spanish Language and Literature, B
Speech and Rhetorical Studies, B
Women's Studies, MD

CLAYTON STATE UNIVERSITY

Accounting, AB
Administrative Assistant and Secretarial Science, A
Agricultural Business and Management, A
Agricultural Mechanization, A
Agriculture, A
Airframe Mechanics and Aircraft Maintenance
  Technology/Technician, A
Apparel and Accessories Marketing Operations, A
Architectural Engineering Technology/Technician, A
Art Teacher Education, A
Art/Art Studies, General, A
Artificial Intelligence and Robotics, A
Aviation/Airway Management and Operations, A
Avionics Maintenance Technology/Technician, A
Biological and Physical Sciences, A
Biology/Biological Sciences, B
Business Administration and Management, AB
Business Teacher Education, A
Chemistry, A
Clinical Laboratory Science/Medical
  Technology/Technologist, A
Clinical/Medical Laboratory Technician, A
Communication and Media Studies, B
Computer Engineering Technology/Technician, A
Computer Science, A
Computer/Information Technology Services
  Administration and Management, B
Criminal Justice/Law Enforcement Administration, A
Data Processing and Data Processing
  Technology/Technician, A
Dental Hygiene/Hygienist, AB
Drafting and Design Technology/Technician, A
Drafting/Design Engineering
  Technologies/Technicians, A
Drama and Dramatics/Theatre Arts, A

Economics, A
Education, A
Electrical, Electronic and Communications
  Engineering Technology/Technician, A
Electromechanical Technology/Electromechanical
  Engineering Technology, A
Elementary Education and Teaching, A
Emergency Medical Technology/Technician (EMT
  Paramedic), A
Engineering, A
Engineering Technology, A
English Language and Literature, A
Family and Consumer Sciences/Human Sciences, A
Fashion Merchandising, A
Finance, A
Forestry, A
French Language and Literature, A
General Merchandising, Sales, and Related
  Marketing Operations, A
Geology/Earth Science, A
Health Information/Medical Records
  Administration/Administrator, A
Health Teacher Education, A
Health/Health Care Administration/Management, B
History, B
Human Services, B
Information Science/Studies, AB
Instrumentation Technology/Technician, A
Journalism, A
Junior High/Intermediate/Middle School Education
  and Teaching, B
Kindergarten/PreSchool Education and Teaching, A
Law and Legal Studies, A
Legal Administrative Assistant/Secretary, A
Legal Assistant/Paralegal, A
Management Information Systems and Services, B
Marketing, B
Marketing/Marketing Management, A
Mass Communication/Media Studies, A
Mathematics, A
Medical Illustration/Medical Illustrator, A
Medical/Clinical Assistant, A
Merchandising and Buying Operations, A
Multi-/Interdisciplinary Studies, B
Music, AB
Music Performance, B
Music Theory and Composition, B
Nursing - Registered Nurse Training, B
Occupational Therapy/Therapist, A
Parks, Recreation, Leisure and Fitness Studies, A
Pharmacy, A
Philosophy, A
Physical Education Teaching and Coaching, A
Physical Therapy/Therapist, A
Physics, A
Political Science and Government, A
Pre-Engineering, A
Psychology, B
Public/Applied History and Archival Administration, B
Radiologic Technology/Science - Radiographer, A
Social Sciences, A
Sociology, A
Spanish Language and Literature, A
Specialized Merchandising, Sales, and Marketing
  Operations, A
Speech and Rhetorical Studies, A
Telecommunications Technology/Technician, A

COASTAL GEORGIA COMMUNITY COLLEGE

Agricultural Business and Management, A
Art/Art Studies, General, A
Biology/Biological Sciences, A
Business Administration and Management, A
Chemistry, A
Clinical/Medical Laboratory Technician, A
Computer Science, A
Criminal Justice/Law Enforcement Administration, A
Dental Hygiene/Hygienist, A
English Language and Literature, A
Foreign Languages and Literatures, A
Forestry, A
Geology/Earth Science, A
Health and Physical Education, A
History, A

Liberal Arts and Sciences Studies and
Humanities, A
Mathematics, A
Medical Radiologic Technology/Science - Radiation
Therapist, A
Nursing - Registered Nurse Training, A
Occupational Therapy/Therapist, A
Parks, Recreation and Leisure Facilities
Management, A
Philosophy, A
Physical Therapy/Therapist, A
Physician Assistant, A
Physics, A
Political Science and Government, A
Pre-Dentistry Studies, A
Pre-Engineering, A
Pre-Medicine/Pre-Medical Studies, A
Pre-Pharmacy Studies, A
Pre-Veterinary Studies, A
Psychology, A
Respiratory Care Therapy/Therapist, A
Sociology, A
Teacher Education, Multiple Levels, A

COLUMBUS STATE UNIVERSITY

Accounting, B
Applied Mathematics, B
Art Education, M
Art Teacher Education, B
Art/Art Studies, General, B
Athletic Training and Sports Medicine, B
Biology Teacher Education, B
Biology/Biological Sciences, B
Business Administration and Management, B
Business Administration, Management and
Operations, M
Business/Commerce, B
Business/Managerial Economics, B
Chemistry, B
Chemistry Teacher Education, B
Comparative Literature, B
Computer Science, ABM
Counseling Psychology, M
Counselor Education/School Counseling and
Guidance Services, MO
Creative Writing, B
Criminal Justice/Law Enforcement
Administration, AB
Drama and Dance Teacher Education, B
Drama and Dramatics/Theatre Arts, B
Early Childhood Education and Teaching, BMO
Education, MO
Educational Leadership and Administration, MO
Engineering, A
English Language and Literature, B
English/Language Arts Teacher Education, B
Environmental Sciences, M
Finance, B
Forest Engineering, A
Forestry, A
French Language Teacher Education, B
Geology/Earth Science, B
Health Services/Allied Health/Health Sciences, B
Health Teacher Education, B
History, B
History Teacher Education, B
Information Science/Studies, B
Junior High/Intermediate/Middle School Education
and Teaching, B
Kinesiology and Exercise Science, B
Liberal Arts and Sciences Studies and
Humanities, A
Marketing/Marketing Management, B
Mass Communication/Media Studies, B
Mathematics, B
Mathematics Teacher Education, B
Medical Radiologic Technology/Science - Radiation
Therapist, B
Middle School Education, MO
Music, B
Music Pedagogy, B
Music Teacher Education, BM
Nursing - Registered Nurse Training, B
Physical Education Teaching and Coaching, BM
Piano and Organ, B
Political Science and Government, B

Pre-Dentistry Studies, B
Pre-Engineering, A
Pre-Law Studies, B
Pre-Medicine/Pre-Medical Studies, B
Pre-Pharmacy Studies, B
Pre-Veterinary Studies, B
Psychology, B
Public Administration, M
Public Health (MPH, DPH), B
Public Relations/Image Management, B
Science Teacher Education/General Science
Teacher Education, B
Secondary Education and Teaching, BMO
Social Science Teacher Education, B
Sociology, B
Spanish Language Teacher Education, B
Special Education and Teaching, BO
Speech Teacher Education, B
Teacher Education, Multiple Levels, B
Violin, Viola, Guitar and Other Stringed
Instruments, B
Voice and Opera, B

COLUMBUS TECHNICAL COLLEGE

Accounting, A
Administrative Assistant and Secretarial Science, A
Automobile/Automotive Mechanics
Technology/Technician, A
Child Development, A
Computer Engineering, A
Computer Systems Networking and
Telecommunications, A
Dental Hygiene/Hygienist, A
Diagnostic Medical Sonography/Sonographer and
Ultrasound Technician, A
Drafting and Design Technology/Technician, A
Electrical, Electronic and Communications
Engineering Technology/Technician, A
Emergency Medical Technology/Technician (EMT
Paramedic), A
Health Information/Medical Records
Technology/Technician, A
Horticultural Science, A
Industrial Technology/Technician, A
Information Science/Studies, A
Machine Tool Technology/Machinist, A
Mechanical Engineering/Mechanical
Technology/Technician, A
Medical Office Management/Administration, A
Medical Radiologic Technology/Science - Radiation
Therapist, A
Nursing - Registered Nurse Training, A
Pharmacy Technician/Assistant, A
Respiratory Therapy Technician/Assistant, A
Surgical Technology/Technologist, A
Web Page, Digital/Multimedia and Information
Resources Design, A

COOSA VALLEY TECHNICAL COLLEGE

Accounting, A
Child Development, A
Computer Programming/Programmer, A
Criminal Justice/Safety Studies, A
Environmental Engineering
Technology/Environmental Technology, A
Fire Science/Firefighting, A
Information Science/Studies, A
Legal Assistant/Paralegal, A
Marketing/Marketing Management, A
Medical Office Management/Administration, A
Respiratory Therapy Technician/Assistant, A
Surgical Technology/Technologist, A
Web Page, Digital/Multimedia and Information
Resources Design, A

COVENANT COLLEGE

Art/Art Studies, General, B
Bible/Biblical Studies, AB
Biology/Biological Sciences, B
Business Administration and Management, AB
Chemistry, B
Computer Science, B
Economics, B
Education, M
Elementary Education and Teaching, B
English Language and Literature, B

Foreign Languages and Literatures, B
History, B
Interdisciplinary Studies, B
Junior High/Intermediate/Middle School Education
and Teaching, B
Mathematics, B
Music, B
Natural Sciences, B
Nursing - Registered Nurse Training, AB
Philosophy, B
Physics, B
Pre-Engineering, A
Pre-Law Studies, B
Pre-Medicine/Pre-Medical Studies, B
Pre-Nursing Studies, B
Psychology, B
Public Health (MPH, DPH), A
Sociology, B

DALTON STATE COLLEGE

Agriculture, A
Biological and Physical Sciences, A
Biology/Biological Sciences, A
Business Administration and Management, A
Business/Commerce, A
Chemistry, A
Clinical Laboratory Science/Medical
Technology/Technologist, A
Clinical/Medical Laboratory Technician, A
Computer and Information Sciences, A
Computer Engineering Technology/Technician, A
Computer Installation and Repair
Technology/Technician, A
Computer Science, A
Computer Technology/Computer Systems
Technology, A
Computer/Information Technology Services
Administration and Management, A
Criminal Justice/Law Enforcement Administration, A
Criminal Justice/Police Science, A
Criminology, A
Dental Hygiene/Hygienist, A
Drafting and Design Technology/Technician, A
Economics, A
Education, A
Electrical, Electronic and Communications
Engineering Technology/Technician, A
Elementary Education and Teaching, A
English Language and Literature, A
Family and Consumer Economics and Related
Services, A
Foreign Languages and Literatures, A
Forestry, A
General Studies, A
Geography, A
Geology/Earth Science, A
Health Information/Medical Records
Administration/Administrator, A
History, A
Industrial Electronics Technology/Technician, A
Industrial Mechanics and Maintenance
Technology, A
Industrial Technology/Technician, A
Information Science/Studies, A
Journalism, A
Junior High/Intermediate/Middle School Education
and Teaching, A
Machine Shop Technology/Assistant, A
Management Information Systems and Services, B
Marketing/Marketing Management, AB
Mathematics, A
Medical Office Management/Administration, A
Medical Transcription/Transcriptionist, A
Nuclear Medical Technology/Technologist, A
Nursing - Registered Nurse Training, A
Occupational Therapy/Therapist, A
Office Management and Supervision, A
Operations Management and Supervision, B
Philosophy, A
Physical Therapy/Therapist, A
Physician Assistant, A
Physics, A
Political Science and Government, A
Pre-Pharmacy Studies, A
Psychology, A
Radiologic Technology/Science - Radiographer, A

Respiratory Care Therapy/Therapist, A
Sales, Distribution and Marketing Operations, AB
Secondary Education and Teaching, A
Social Work, AB
Sociology, A
Speech and Rhetorical Studies, A
Technology Education/Industrial Arts, A

DARTON COLLEGE

Accounting, A
Administrative Assistant and Secretarial Science, A
Agriculture, A
Anthropology, A
Art/Art Studies, General, A
Biology/Biological Sciences, A
Business Administration and Management, A
Business Teacher Education, A
Cardiovascular Technology/Technologist, A
Chemistry, A
Clinical Laboratory Science/Medical
  Technology/Technologist, A
Computer and Information Sciences, A
Computer Programming/Programmer, A
Computer Science, A
Criminal Justice/Law Enforcement Administration, A
Diagnostic Medical Sonography/Sonographer and
  Ultrasound Technician, A
Drama and Dramatics/Theatre Arts, A
Economics, A
Education, A
Engineering Technology, A
English Language and Literature, A
Environmental Studies, A
Foreign Languages and Literatures, A
Forensic Science and Technology, A
Forestry, A
General Office Occupations and Clerical Services, A
General Studies, A
Geography, A
Health and Physical Education, A
Health Information/Medical Records
  Administration/Administrator, A
Health Information/Medical Records
  Technology/Technician, A
Histologic Technician, A
History, A
Journalism, A
Licensed Practical/Vocational Nurse Training, A
Mathematics, A
Music, A
Nuclear Medical Technology/Technologist, A
Nursing - Registered Nurse Training, A
Occupational Therapist Assistant, A
Optometric Technician/Assistant, A
Pharmacy Technician/Assistant, A
Philosophy, A
Physical Therapist Assistant, A
Physician Assistant, A
Physics, A
Political Science and Government, A
Pre-Dentistry Studies, A
Pre-Engineering, A
Pre-Law Studies, A
Pre-Medicine/Pre-Medical Studies, A
Pre-Pharmacy Studies, A
Pre-Veterinary Studies, A
Psychiatric/Mental Health Services Technician, A
Psychology, A
Respiratory Care Therapy/Therapist, A
Social Work, A
Sociology, A
Speech and Rhetorical Studies, A

DEKALB TECHNICAL COLLEGE

Accounting, A
Administrative Assistant and Secretarial Science, A
Automobile/Automotive Mechanics
  Technology/Technician, A
Business/Commerce, A
Clinical/Medical Laboratory Technician, A
Computer Engineering Technology/Technician, A
Computer Programming/Programmer, A
Computer Systems Networking and
  Telecommunications, A
Criminal Justice/Safety Studies, A
Drafting and Design Technology/Technician, A

Electrical, Electronic and Communications
  Engineering Technology/Technician, A
Electromechanical Technology/Electromechanical
  Engineering Technology, A
Engineering Technology, A
Health and Medical Laboratory Technologies, A
Heating, Air Conditioning and Refrigeration
  Technology/Technician, A
Industrial Technology/Technician, A
Information Science/Studies, A
Instrumentation Technology/Technician, A
Legal Administrative Assistant/Secretary, A
Legal Assistant/Paralegal, A
Machine Tool Technology/Machinist, A
Marketing/Marketing Management, A
Medical/Clinical Assistant, A
Operations Management and Supervision, A
Ophthalmic Laboratory Technology/Technician, A
Opticianry/Ophthalmic Dispensing Optician, A
Surgical Technology/Technologist, A
Telecommunications Technology/Technician, A

DEVRY UNIVERSITY (ALPHARETTA)

Business Administration, Management and
  Operations, BM
Computer Engineering Technology/Technician, B
Computer Programming, Specific Applications, B
Computer Systems Analysis/Analyst, B
Computer Systems Networking and
  Telecommunications, AB
Electrical, Electronic and Communications
  Engineering Technology/Technician, AB
Health Information/Medical Records
  Technology/Technician, A
Information Science/Studies, B
Medical Informatics, B
Operations Management and Supervision, B

DEVRY UNIVERSITY (ATLANTA)

Business Administration, Management and
  Operations, M

DEVRY UNIVERSITY (DECATUR)

Biomedical/Medical Engineering, B
Business Administration, Management and
  Operations, BM
Computer and Information Sciences, B
Computer Engineering Technology/Technician, B
Computer Programming, Specific Applications, B
Computer Systems Analysis/Analyst, B
Computer Systems Networking and
  Telecommunications, AB
Electrical, Electronic and Communications
  Engineering Technology/Technician, AB
Health Information/Medical Records
  Technology/Technician, A
Information Science/Studies, B
Medical Informatics, B
Operations Management and Supervision, B

DEVRY UNIVERSITY (DULUTH)

Business Administration, Management and
  Operations, M

EAST CENTRAL TECHNICAL COLLEGE

Administrative Assistant and Secretarial Science, A
Child Development, A
Computer Systems Networking and
  Telecommunications, A
Criminal Justice/Safety Studies, A
Information Science/Studies, A

EAST GEORGIA COLLEGE

Agriculture, A
Anthropology, A
Art/Art Studies, General, A
Biology/Biological Sciences, A
Business Administration and Management, A
Business Teacher Education, A
Chemistry, A
Criminal Justice/Law Enforcement Administration, A
Education, A
Elementary Education and Teaching, A
English Language and Literature, A

Family and Consumer Sciences/Home Economics
  Teacher Education, A
Geology/Earth Science, A
Health Teacher Education, A
History, A
Liberal Arts and Sciences Studies and
  Humanities, A
Mathematics, A
Nursing - Registered Nurse Training, A
Parks, Recreation, Leisure and Fitness Studies, A
Physical Education Teaching and Coaching, A
Political Science and Government, A
Psychology, A
Sociology, A

EMMANUEL COLLEGE

Biology/Biological Sciences, B
Business Administration and Management, AB
Business Teacher Education, B
Computer and Information Sciences, B
Elementary Education and Teaching, B
English Language and Literature, B
English/Language Arts Teacher Education, B
Health/Medical Preparatory Programs, AB
Junior High/Intermediate/Middle School Education
  and Teaching, B
Kinesiology and Exercise Science, B
Liberal Arts and Sciences Studies and
  Humanities, A
Mass Communication/Media Studies, B
Mathematics, B
Mathematics Teacher Education, B
Music, B
Music Teacher Education, B
Office Management and Supervision, A
Organizational Communication, B
Pastoral Studies/Counseling, B
Pre-Law Studies, A
Pre-Pharmacy Studies, A
Psychology, B
Religious/Sacred Music, B
Social Science Teacher Education, B
Sport and Fitness Administration/Management, B
Youth Ministry, B

EMORY UNIVERSITY

Accounting, BD
African Studies, B
African-American/Black Studies, B
Allied Health and Medical Assisting Services, MD
Allopathic Medicine, PO
American/United States Studies/Civilization, B
Anthropology, BD
Art History, Criticism and Conservation, BD
Asian Studies/Civilization, B
Asian-American Studies, B
Banking and Financial Support Services, B
Biochemistry, D
Biological and Biomedical Sciences, D
Biology/Biological Sciences, B
Biomedical Sciences, B
Biopsychology, D
Biostatistics, MD
Business Administration and Management, B
Business Administration, Management and
  Operations, MDO
Business/Managerial Economics, B
Cell Biology and Anatomy, D
Chemistry, BD
Chinese Language and Literature, B
Classics and Classical
  Languages, Literatures, and Linguistics, B
Clinical Psychology, D
Clinical Research, M
Cognitive Sciences, D
Community Health and Preventive Medicine, MD
Comparative Literature, BDO
Computer Science, BMD
Creative Writing, B
Dance, B
Developmental Biology and Embryology, D
Developmental Psychology, D
Drama and Dramatics/Theatre Arts, B
Ecology, D
Economics, BD
Education, BMDO

English, DO
English Language and Literature, B
Environmental and Occupational Health, M
Epidemiology, MD
Evolutionary Biology, D
Film, Television, and Video Theory and
  Criticism, MO
Film/Cinema Studies, B
Finance, B
Finance and Banking, D
Fine/Studio Arts, B
French Language and Literature, BDO
Genetics, D
German Language and Literature, B
Health Informatics, M
Health Promotion, M
Health Services Administration, MD
Health Services Research, D
History, BD
Immunology, D
Interdisciplinary Studies, BD
International Public Health/International Health, MD
International Relations and Affairs, B
Italian Language and Literature, B
Japanese Language and Literature, B
Jewish/Judaic Studies, BM
Journalism, B
Latin American Studies, B
Latin Language and Literature, B
Law and Legal Studies, MPO
Liberal Arts and Sciences Studies and
  Humanities, AB
Management Information Systems and Services, D
Marketing, D
Marketing/Marketing Management, B
Maternal and Child Health, M
Mathematics, BMD
Medical Informatics, M
Medical Technology, M
Medieval and Renaissance Studies, B
Microbiology, D
Middle School Education, M
Modern Greek Language and Literature, B
Molecular Biology, D
Molecular Genetics, D
Music, BM
Neuroscience, BD
Nurse Anesthetist, M
Nurse Midwife/Nursing Midwifery, M
Nursing, MDO
Nursing - Adult, M
Nursing - Advanced Practice, M
Nursing - Registered Nurse Training, B
Nursing Administration, M
Nutritional Sciences, MD
Organizational Management, D
Pediatric Nurse/Nursing, M
Pharmacology, D
Philosophy, BD
Physical Therapy/Therapist, D
Physician Assistant, M
Physics, BD
Political Science and Government, BD
Portuguese Language and Literature, DO
Psychology, BD
Public Health, MDO
Religion/Religious Studies, BD
Russian Language and Literature, B
Secondary Education and Teaching, M
Sociology, BMD
Spanish Language and Literature, BDO
Theology and Religious Vocations, MDPO
Vision Science/Physiological Optics, M
Women's Health Nursing, M
Women's Studies, BDO

EMORY
UNIVERSITY, OXFORD COLLEGE

Liberal Arts and Sciences Studies and
  Humanities, A

FLINT RIVER TECHNICAL COLLEGE

Accounting, A
Administrative Assistant and Secretarial Science, A
Child Development, A
Computer and Information Systems Security, A

Computer Systems Networking and
  Telecommunications, A
Criminal Justice/Safety Studies, A
Electrical, Electronic and Communications
  Engineering Technology/Technician, A
Health and Medical Laboratory Technologies, A
Information Science/Studies, A
Manufacturing Technology/Technician, A
Web Page, Digital/Multimedia and Information
  Resources Design, A

FORT VALLEY STATE UNIVERSITY

Accounting, B
Administrative Assistant and Secretarial Science, AB
African Studies, B
Agricultural Economics, B
Agricultural/Biological Engineering and
  Bioengineering, B
Agronomy and Crop Science, B
Animal Sciences, BM
Biology/Biological Sciences, B
Botany/Plant Biology, B
Business Administration and Management, B
Chemistry, B
Computer Science, B
Counseling Psychology, M
Counselor Education/School Counseling and
  Guidance Services, MO
Criminal Justice/Law Enforcement
  Administration, AB
Developmental and Child Psychology, B
Early Childhood Education and Teaching, M
Economics, B
Electrical, Electronic and Communications
  Engineering Technology/Technician, AB
Environmental and Occupational Health, M
Family and Consumer Sciences/Home Economics
  Teacher Education, B
Foods, Nutrition, and Wellness Studies, B
French Language and Literature, B
Health Teacher Education, B
Kindergarten/PreSchool Education and Teaching, B
Liberal Arts and Sciences Studies and
  Humanities, B
Marketing/Marketing Management, B
Mass Communication/Media Studies, B
Mathematics, B
Middle School Education, M
Ornamental Horticulture, B
Physical Education Teaching and Coaching, B
Political Science and Government, B
Pre-Engineering, A
Psychology, B
Public Health, M
Rehabilitation Counseling, M
Social Sciences, B
Social Work, B
Sociology, B
Veterinary/Animal Health Technology/Technician and
  Veterinary Assistant, A
Zoology/Animal Biology, B

GAINESVILLE COLLEGE

Anthropology, A
Biology/Biological Sciences, A
Business Administration and Management, A
Chemistry, A
Computer Science, A
Criminal Justice/Law Enforcement Administration, A
Drama and Dramatics/Theatre Arts, A
Early Childhood Education and Teaching, AB
Elementary Education and Teaching, A
Engineering Technology, A
English Language and Literature, A
Environmental Design/Architecture, B
Foreign Languages and Literatures, A
Forestry, A
General Studies, A
Geography, A
Geology/Earth Science, A
History, A
Information Technology, B
Journalism, A
Junior High/Intermediate/Middle School Education
  and Teaching, A
Kinesiology and Exercise Science, A

Mass Communication/Media Studies, A
Mathematics, A
Music, A
Physics, A
Political Science and Government, A
Pre-Medicine/Pre-Medical Studies, A
Pre-Nursing Studies, A
Pre-Pharmacy Studies, A
Psychology, A
Secondary Education and Teaching, A
Social Work, A
Sociology, A
Sport and Fitness Administration/Management, A

GEORGIA AVIATION & TECHNICAL COLLEGE

Air Traffic Controller, A
Airline/Commercial/Professional Pilot and Flight
  Crew, A
Aviation/Airway Management and Operations, A

GEORGIA COLLEGE & STATE UNIVERSITY

Accounting, BM
Art/Art Studies, General, B
Biological and Biomedical Sciences, M
Biology/Biological Sciences, B
Business Administration and Management, B
Business Administration, Management and
  Operations, M
Business/Managerial Economics, B
Chemistry, B
Computer and Information Sciences, B
Creative Writing, B
Criminal Justice/Law Enforcement Administration, B
Criminology, M
Drama and Dramatics/Theatre Arts, B
Early Childhood Education and Teaching, BMO
Education, MO
Educational Administration and Supervision, MO
Educational Media/Instructional Technology, M
English, M
English Education, M
English Language and Literature, B
Environmental Studies, B
French Language and Literature, B
Health Education, MO
Health Teacher Education, B
History, BM
International Business/Trade/Commerce, B
Journalism, B
Junior High/Intermediate/Middle School Education
  and Teaching, B
Logistics and Materials Management, M
Management Information Systems and Services, M
Marketing/Marketing Management, B
Mathematics, B
Mathematics Teacher Education, M
Middle School Education, MO
Music, B
Music Teacher Education, B
Music Therapy/Therapist, BM
Nursing, MO
Nursing - Registered Nurse Training, B
Office Management and Supervision, B
Parks, Recreation, Leisure and Fitness Studies, B
Physical Education Teaching and Coaching, BMO
Political Science and Government, B
Psychology, B
Public Administration, M
Public Affairs, M
Science Teacher Education/General Science
  Teacher Education, MO
Secondary Education and Teaching, MO
Social Studies Teacher Education, MO
Sociology, B
Spanish Language and Literature, B
Special Education and Teaching, BM
Speech and Rhetorical Studies, B
Writing, M

GEORGIA HIGHLANDS COLLEGE

Accounting, A
Agriculture, A
Art/Art Studies, General, A

Automobile/Automotive Mechanics Technology/Technician, A
Biological and Physical Sciences, A
Business Administration and Management, A
Clinical Laboratory Science/Medical Technology/Technologist, A
Computer Programming/Programmer, A
Criminal Justice/Police Science, A
Criminal Justice/Safety Studies, A
Dental Hygiene/Hygienist, A
Economics, A
Electrical, Electronic and Communications Engineering Technology/Technician, A
Emergency Medical Technology/Technician (EMT Paramedic), A
English Language and Literature, A
Foreign Languages and Literatures, A
Forestry, A
Geology/Earth Science, A
History, A
Horticultural Science, A
Hotel/Motel Administration/Management, A
Human Services, A
Information Science/Studies, A
Journalism, A
Kindergarten/PreSchool Education and Teaching, A
Legal Assistant/Paralegal, A
Liberal Arts and Sciences Studies and Humanities, A
Marketing/Marketing Management, A
Nursing - Registered Nurse Training, A
Occupational Therapy/Therapist, A
Philosophy, A
Physical Therapist Assistant, A
Physical Therapy/Therapist, A
Physician Assistant, A
Political Science and Government, A
Psychology, A
Radiologic Technology/Science - Radiographer, A
Respiratory Care Therapy/Therapist, A
Secondary Education and Teaching, A
Sociology, A

GEORGIA INSTITUTE OF TECHNOLOGY

Accounting, MD
Aerospace, Aeronautical and Astronautical Engineering, BMD
Applied Mathematics, BM
Architecture, BMDO
Architecture and Related Services, B
Atmospheric Sciences and Meteorology, MD
Biochemistry, MD
Bioengineering, MDO
Bioinformatics, MD
Biological and Biomedical Sciences, MD
Biology/Biological Sciences, B
Biomedical Engineering, MDO
Biomedical/Medical Engineering, B
Building Science, MD
Business Administration and Management, B
Business Administration, Management and Operations, MO
Business/Managerial Economics, B
Chemical Engineering, BMD
Chemistry, BMD
Civil Engineering, BMDO
Computer and Information Sciences, B
Computer Engineering, BMD
Computer Science, B
Construction Engineering and Management, MD
Digital Communication and Media/Multimedia, B
Economics, M
Electrical Engineering, MD
Electrical, Electronics and Communications Engineering, B
Electronic Commerce, O
Engineering and Applied Sciences, MDO
Entrepreneurship/Entrepreneurial Studies, MO
Environmental Engineering Technology/Environmental Technology, MD
Environmental Policy, M
Environmental Sciences, MD
Finance and Banking, MD
Geochemistry, MD
Geographic Information Systems, M

Geological and Earth Sciences/Geosciences, B
Geophysics and Seismology, MD
Geosciences, MD
Health Physics/Radiological Health, MD
Health Services Administration, M
History and Philosophy of Science and Technology, B
History of Science and Technology, MD
Human-Computer Interaction, M
Hydrology and Water Resources Science, MD
Industrial and Organizational Psychology, B
Industrial Design, B
Industrial Engineering, B
Industrial/Management Engineering, MD
International Affairs, M
International Business/Trade/Commerce, MO
International Relations and Affairs, B
International/Global Studies, B
Internet and Interactive Multimedia, M
Management, MD
Management Information Systems and Services, MD
Management of Technology, MO
Management Strategy and Policy, MD
Marketing, MD
Materials Engineering, BMD
Mathematical and Computational Finance, M
Mathematics, B
Mechanical Engineering, BMD
Mechanics, MD
Medical Physics, M
Modern Languages, B
Multi-/Interdisciplinary Studies, B
Natural Resources and Conservation, MD
Nuclear Engineering, BMD
Ocean Engineering, MD
Operations Management and Supervision, B
Operations Research, M
Organizational Behavior Studies, MD
Physics, BMD
Physiology, M
Polymer Chemistry, B
Polymer/Plastics Engineering, MD
Psychology, MD
Public Policy Analysis, BMD
Science, Technology and Society, B
Statistics, M
Systems Engineering, MD
Textile Sciences and Engineering, BMD
Urban and Regional Planning, MDO
Urban Design, M

GEORGIA MEDICAL INSTITUTE-DEKALB

Massage Therapy/Therapeutic Massage, A
Medical Administrative Assistant/Secretary, A
Medical Insurance Specialist/Medical Biller, A
Renal/Dialysis Technologist/Technician, A
Respiratory Therapy Technician/Assistant, A

GEORGIA MILITARY COLLEGE

Army JROTC/ROTC, A
Biological and Physical Sciences, A
Business Administration and Management, A
Criminal Justice/Law Enforcement Administration, A
Engineering, A
Fire Science/Firefighting, A
Liberal Arts and Sciences Studies and Humanities, A
Mass Communication/Media Studies, A
Nuclear/Nuclear Power Technology/Technician, A
Pre-Engineering, A

GEORGIA PERIMETER COLLEGE

Anthropology, A
Art/Art Studies, General, A
Biological and Physical Sciences, A
Biology/Biological Sciences, A
Business Administration and Management, A
Chemistry, A
Computer Science, A
Computer/Information Technology Services Administration and Management, A
Dental Hygiene/Hygienist, A
Drama and Dramatics/Theatre Arts, A
Education, A

Elementary Education and Teaching, A
English Language and Literature, A
Fire Science/Firefighting, A
Foreign Languages and Literatures, A
Foreign Languages, Literatures, and Linguistics, A
General Studies, A
Geology/Earth Science, A
Health and Physical Education, A
History, A
Journalism, A
Marketing/Marketing Management, A
Mathematics, A
Music, A
Nursing - Registered Nurse Training, A
Philosophy, A
Physical Education Teaching and Coaching, A
Physics, A
Political Science and Government, A
Pre-Dentistry Studies, A
Pre-Engineering, A
Pre-Medicine/Pre-Medical Studies, A
Pre-Pharmacy Studies, A
Psychology, A
Sign Language Interpretation and Translation, A
Sociology, A
Teacher Education, Multiple Levels, A

GEORGIA SOUTHERN UNIVERSITY

Accounting, BM
Allied Health and Medical Assisting Services, MO
Anthropology, B
Apparel and Textiles, B
Art Education, MO
Art Teacher Education, B
Art/Art Studies, General, B
Athletic Training and Sports Medicine, B
Biological and Biomedical Sciences, M
Biology Teacher Education, B
Biology/Biological Sciences, B
Business Administration and Management, B
Business Administration, Management and Operations, M
Business Education, M
Business Teacher Education, B
Business/Managerial Economics, B
Chemistry, B
Chemistry Teacher Education, B
Civil Engineering Technology/Technician, B
Clinical Laboratory Science/Medical Technology/Technologist, B
Communication Studies/Speech Communication and Rhetoric, B
Community Health Nursing, MO
Computer and Information Sciences, B
Construction Engineering Technology/Technician, B
Counselor Education/School Counseling and Guidance Services, MO
Criminal Justice/Safety Studies, B
Curriculum and Instruction, D
Development Economics and International Development, B
Drama and Dramatics/Theatre Arts, B
Early Childhood Education and Teaching, M
Economics, B
Education, BMDO
Educational Administration and Supervision, D
Educational Leadership and Administration, MO
Educational Media/Instructional Technology, MO
Electrical, Electronic and Communications Engineering Technology/Technician, B
Engineering and Applied Sciences, M
English, M
English Education, M
English Language and Literature, B
English/Language Arts Teacher Education, B
Family and Consumer Sciences/Home Economics Teacher Education, B
Finance, B
Fine Arts and Art Studies, M
Foods, Nutrition, and Wellness Studies, B
Foreign Language Teacher Education, M
French Language and Literature, B
French Language Teacher Education, B
General Studies, B
Geography, B
Geology/Earth Science, B

German Language and Literature, B
German Language Teacher Education, B
Graphic and Printing Equipment Operator
    Production, B
Health and Physical Education, B
Health Education, M
Health Services Administration, M
Higher Education/Higher Education
    Administration, M
History, BM
History Teacher Education, B
Hotel/Motel Administration/Management, B
Human Development and Family Studies, B
Industrial Production Technologies/Technicians, B
Industrial Technology/Technician, B
Interior Design, B
International Business/Trade/Commerce, B
International Relations and Affairs, B
Journalism, B
Junior High/Intermediate/Middle School Education
    and Teaching, B
Kindergarten/PreSchool Education and Teaching, B
Kinesiology and Exercise Science, B
Kinesiology and Movement Studies, M
Logistics and Materials Management, B
Management Information Systems and Services, B
Marketing/Marketing Management, B
Mathematics, BM
Mathematics Teacher Education, BM
Mechanical Engineering/Mechanical
    Technology/Technician, B
Middle School Education, M
Music, BM
Music Performance, B
Music Teacher Education, BM
Music Theory and Composition, B
Nursing, MO
Nursing - Advanced Practice, MO
Nursing - Registered Nurse Training, B
Parks, Recreation, Leisure and Fitness Studies, B
Philosophy, B
Physical Education Teaching and Coaching, BM
Physics, B
Physics Teacher Education, B
Political Science and Government, B
Psychology, BM
Public Administration, M
Public Health, M
Public Health Education and Promotion, B
Public Relations/Image Management, B
Radio and Television, B
Reading Teacher Education, M
Recreation and Park Management, M
School Psychology, MO
Science Teacher Education/General Science
    Teacher Education, M
Social Studies Teacher Education, M
Sociology, BM
Spanish Language and Literature, B
Spanish Language Teacher Education, B
Special Education and Teaching, BM
Speech and Rhetorical Studies, B
Sport and Fitness Administration/Management, BM
Technology Teacher Education/Industrial Arts
    Teacher Education, B
Vocational and Technical Education, M
Women's Health Nursing, MO

GEORGIA SOUTHWESTERN STATE UNIVERSITY

Accounting, B
Accounting Technology/Technician and
    Bookkeeping, A
Administrative Assistant and Secretarial Science, A
Aircraft Powerplant Technology/Technician, A
Airframe Mechanics and Aircraft Maintenance
    Technology/Technician, A
Applied Horticulture/Horticultural Operations, A
Art/Art Studies, General, B
Autobody/Collision and Repair
    Technology/Technician, A
Automobile/Automotive Mechanics
    Technology/Technician, A
Avionics Maintenance Technology/Technician, A
Biology/Biological Sciences, B
Business Administration and Management, B

Business Administration, Management and
    Operations, M
Chemistry, B
Child Care and Support Services Management, A
Computer and Information Sciences, B
Computer Engineering Technology/Technician, B
Computer Programming, Specific Applications, AB
Computer Science, BM
Cosmetology/Cosmetologist, A
Criminal Justice/Law Enforcement Administration, A
Criminal Justice/Safety Studies, A
Culinary Arts/Chef Training, A
Dental Assisting/Assistant, A
Diesel Mechanics Technology/Technician, A
Drafting and Design Technology/Technician, A
Drama and Dramatics/Theatre Arts, B
Early Childhood Education and Teaching, MO
Education, BMO
Electrical/Electronics Equipment Installation and
    Repair, A
Electrician, A
Electromechanical and Instrumentation and
    Maintenance Technologies/Technicians, A
Elementary Education and Teaching, B
English Language and Literature, B
Forestry Technology/Technician, A
General Office Occupations and Clerical Services, A
Geology/Earth Science, B
Graphic and Printing Equipment Operator
    Production, A
Health Education, M
Heavy Equipment Maintenance
    Technology/Technician, A
History, B
Hotel/Motel Administration/Management, A
Human Resources Development, A
Human Resources Management/Personnel
    Administration, B
Information Science/Studies, M
Junior High/Intermediate/Middle School Education
    and Teaching, B
Licensed Practical/Vocational Nurse Training, A
Machine Shop Technology/Assistant, A
Machine Tool Technology/Machinist, A
Management Information Systems and Services, AB
Marketing/Marketing Management, AB
Mathematics, B
Medical Radiologic Technology/Science - Radiation
    Therapist, A
Medical/Clinical Assistant, A
Middle School Education, MO
Music, B
Nursing - Registered Nurse Training, B
Parks, Recreation and Leisure Facilities
    Management, B
Physical Education Teaching and Coaching, BM
Physical Sciences, B
Political Science and Government, B
Pre-Dentistry Studies, B
Pre-Medicine/Pre-Medical Studies, B
Pre-Veterinary Studies, B
Psychology, B
Reading Teacher Education, M
Secondary Education and Teaching, M
Sociology, B
Special Education and Teaching, BM
Surgical Technology/Technologist, A
Welding Technology/Welder, A

GEORGIA STATE UNIVERSITY

Accounting, BMDO
Actuarial Science, BM
African-American/Black Studies, B
Allied Health and Medical Assisting Services, MDO
Anthropology, BM
Art Education, MO
Art History, Criticism and Conservation, M
Art Teacher Education, B
Art/Art Studies, General, B
Astronomy, D
Biochemistry, MD
Biological and Biomedical Sciences, MD
Biological Anthropology, MDO
Biology/Biological Sciences, B
Business Administration and Management, B

Business Administration, Management and
    Operations, M
Business/Managerial Economics, B
Cell Biology and Anatomy, MD
Chemistry, BMD
Communication and Media Studies, MD
Communication Disorders, M
Computer and Information Sciences, B
Computer Science, MD
Counseling Psychology, MDO
Counselor Education/School Counseling and
    Guidance Services, MDO
Criminal Justice/Safety Studies, B
Criminology, M
Early Childhood Education and Teaching, BMDO
Economics, BMD
Education, MDO
Education/Teaching of Individuals with Multiple
    Disabilities, M
Educational Administration and Supervision, MDO
Educational Measurement and Evaluation, MD
Educational Media/Instructional Technology, MDO
Educational Psychology, MD
Elementary Education and Teaching, B
English, MD
English as a Second Language, MD
English Education, MDO
English Language and Literature, B
Entrepreneurship/Entrepreneurial Studies, M
Environmental Biology, MD
Exercise and Sports Science, MD
Facilities Planning and Management, B
Film/Cinema Studies, B
Finance, B
Finance and Banking, MD
Fine Arts and Art Studies, M
Fine/Studio Arts, B
Foods, Nutrition, and Wellness Studies, B
Foreign Language Teacher Education, O
Foundations and Philosophy of Education, MD
French Language and Literature, BM
Geography, BM
Geology/Earth Science, BM
German Language and Literature, BM
Health Promotion, D
Health Services Administration, M
Higher Education/Higher Education
    Administration, D
Historic Preservation and Conservation, M
History, BMD
Human Resources Development, B
Human Resources Management and Services, MD
Human Services, M
Industrial and Labor Relations, MD
Industrial and Manufacturing Management, D
Insurance, BMD
International Business/Trade/Commerce, MO
Internet and Interactive Multimedia, MD
Journalism, B
Law and Legal Studies, PO
Linguistics, MD
Management, MD
Management Information Systems and
    Services, MD
Marketing, MD
Marketing/Marketing Management, B
Mathematics, BM
Mathematics Teacher Education, MDO
Microbiology, MD
Middle School Education, MDO
Molecular Genetics, MD
Multi-/Interdisciplinary Studies, B
Music, M
Music Management and Merchandising, B
Music Performance, B
Music Teacher Education, O
Neurobiology and Neurophysiology, MD
Nursing, MDO
Nursing - Adult, M
Nursing - Advanced Practice, M
Nursing - Registered Nurse Training, B
Nutritional Sciences, M
Operations Research, M
Pediatric Nurse/Nursing, M
Philosophy, BMO
Physical Education Teaching and Coaching, M

Physical Therapy/Therapist, M
Physics, BMD
Physiology, MD
Political Science and Government, BMD
Psychiatric/Mental Health Nurse/Nursing, M
Psychology, BMD
Public Administration, MO
Public Health, M
Public Policy Analysis, D
Reading Teacher Education, MO
Real Estate, BMDO
Rehabilitation Counseling, MO
Religion/Religious Studies, B
Respiratory Care Therapy/Therapist, B
Rhetoric, MD
School Psychology, MDO
Science Teacher Education/General Science
   Teacher Education, MDO
Social Studies Teacher Education, MDO
Social Work, BM
Sociology, BMD
Spanish Language and Literature, BM
Special Education and Teaching, MDO
Speech and Rhetorical Studies, B
Sport and Fitness Administration/Management, M
Sports Medicine, M
Taxation, M
Technical and Business Writing, MD
Translation and Interpretation, O
Urban Education and Leadership, M
Urban Studies/Affairs, BM
Vocational and Technical Education, M
Women's Health Nursing, M
Women's Studies, BM
Writing, MD

GORDON COLLEGE

Administrative Assistant and Secretarial Science, A
Agriculture, A
Art/Art Studies, General, A
Behavioral Sciences, A
Biological and Physical Sciences, A
Biology/Biological Sciences, A
Business Administration and Management, A
Computer and Information Sciences, A
Computer Science, A
Drama and Dramatics/Theatre Arts, A
Education, A
English Language and Literature, A
General Studies, A
History, A
Information Technology, A
Journalism, A
Licensed Practical/Vocational Nurse Training, A
Mathematics, A
Nursing - Registered Nurse Training, A
Parks, Recreation, Leisure and Fitness Studies, A
Physical Sciences, A
Political Science and Government, A
Psychology, A
Sociology, A
Spanish Language and Literature, A

GRIFFIN TECHNICAL COLLEGE

Accounting, A
Administrative Assistant and Secretarial Science, A
Automobile/Automotive Mechanics
   Technology/Technician, A
Business Administration and Management, A
Child Development, A
Computer and Information Systems Security, A
Computer Programming/Programmer, A
Computer Systems Networking and
   Telecommunications, A
Criminal Justice/Safety Studies, A
Drafting and Design Technology/Technician, A
Electrical, Electronic and Communications
   Engineering Technology/Technician, A
Emergency Medical Technology/Technician (EMT
   Paramedic), A
Heating, Air Conditioning and Refrigeration
   Technology/Technician, A
Horticultural Science, A
Industrial Technology/Technician, A
Legal Assistant/Paralegal, A
Manufacturing Technology/Technician, A

Marketing/Marketing Management, A
Medical Radiologic Technology/Science - Radiation
   Therapist, A
Pharmacy Technician/Assistant, A
Respiratory Therapy Technician/Assistant, A
Surgical Technology/Technologist, A
Web Page, Digital/Multimedia and Information
   Resources Design, A

GUPTON-JONES COLLEGE OF FUNERAL SERVICE

Funeral Service and Mortuary Science, A

GWINNETT TECHNICAL COLLEGE

Accounting, A
Administrative Assistant and Secretarial Science, A
Automobile/Automotive Mechanics
   Technology/Technician, A
Building/Construction
   Finishing, Management, and Inspection, A
Business Administration and Management, A
Computer Programming/Programmer, A
Computer Science, A
Computer Systems Networking and
   Telecommunications, A
Drafting and Design Technology/Technician, A
Electrical, Electronic and Communications
   Engineering Technology/Technician, A
Emergency Medical Technology/Technician (EMT
   Paramedic), A
Horticultural Science, A
Hotel/Motel Administration/Management, A
Information Science/Studies, A
Interior Design, A
Machine Tool Technology/Machinist, A
Management Information Systems and Services, A
Marketing/Marketing Management, A
Medical Radiologic Technology/Science - Radiation
   Therapist, A
Medical/Clinical Assistant, A
Ornamental Horticulture, A
Photography, A
Physical Therapist Assistant, A
Physical Therapy/Therapist, A
Respiratory Care Therapy/Therapist, A
Tourism and Travel Services Management, A
Veterinary/Animal Health Technology/Technician and
   Veterinary Assistant, A

HEART OF GEORGIA TECHNICAL COLLEGE

Business, Management, Marketing, and Related
   Support Services, A
Child Development, A
Criminal Justice/Safety Studies, A
Electrical, Electronic and Communications
   Engineering Technology/Technician, A
Health Information/Medical Records
   Technology/Technician, A
Machine Tool Technology/Machinist, A
Marketing/Marketing Management, A
Medical Radiologic Technology/Science - Radiation
   Therapist, A
Respiratory Therapy Technician/Assistant, A

HERZING COLLEGE

Business Administration and Management, AB
Computer and Information Sciences, AB
Electrical, Electronic and Communications
   Engineering Technology/Technician, AB
Information Science/Studies, AB
Securities Services Administration/Management, AB
System, Networking, and LAN/WAN
   Management/Manager, AB

ITT TECHNICAL INSTITUTE (DULUTH)

Animation, Interactive Technology, Video Graphics
   and Special Effects, B
Business Administration and Management, B
CAD/CADD Drafting and/or Design
   Technology/Technician, A
Computer and Information Systems Security, B
Criminal Justice/Law Enforcement Administration, B
E-Commerce/Electronic Commerce, B

Electrical, Electronic and Communications
   Engineering Technology/Technician, AB
System, Networking, and LAN/WAN
   Management/Manager, A
Web Page, Digital/Multimedia and Information
   Resources Design, A

ITT TECHNICAL INSTITUTE (KENNESAW)

Business Administration and Management, B
CAD/CADD Drafting and/or Design
   Technology/Technician, A
Criminal Justice/Law Enforcement Administration, B
Electrical, Electronic and Communications
   Engineering Technology/Technician, A
System, Networking, and LAN/WAN
   Management/Manager, A
Web Page, Digital/Multimedia and Information
   Resources Design, A

KENNESAW STATE UNIVERSITY

Accounting, B
African Studies, B
Art Teacher Education, B
Art/Art Studies, General, B
Biochemistry, B
Biology Teacher Education, B
Biology/Biological Sciences, B
BioTechnology, B
Business Administration and Management, B
Business Administration, Management and
   Operations, M
Cartography, B
Chemistry, B
Chemistry Teacher Education, B
Communication Studies/Speech Communication
   and Rhetoric, B
Computer and Information Sciences, B
Computer Science, BM
Conflict Resolution and Mediation/Peace Studies, M
Criminal Justice/Safety Studies, B
Drama and Dramatics/Theatre Arts, B
Early Childhood Education and Teaching, BM
Economics, B
Education, M
Educational Leadership and Administration, M
Elementary Education and Teaching, B
English Language and Literature, B
English/Language Arts Teacher Education, B
Family and Consumer Sciences/Human Sciences, B
Finance, B
French Language and Literature, B
History, B
Information Science/Studies, M
International Relations and Affairs, B
Junior High/Intermediate/Middle School Education
   and Teaching, B
Kinesiology and Exercise Science, B
Marketing/Marketing Management, B
Mathematics, B
Mathematics Teacher Education, B
Middle School Education, M
Modern Languages, B
Music, B
Music Teacher Education, B
Nursing, M
Nursing - Advanced Practice, M
Nursing - Registered Nurse Training, B
Physical Education Teaching and Coaching, B
Political Science and Government, B
Psychology, B
Public Administration, M
Social Science Teacher Education, B
Social Work, B
Sociology, B
Spanish Language and Literature, B
Special Education and Teaching, M
Sport and Fitness Administration/Management, B
Writing, M

LAGRANGE COLLEGE

Accounting, B
Art Education, M
Biochemistry, B
Biology/Biological Sciences, B
Business Administration and Management, B

Business/Commerce, B
Chemistry, B
Computer and Information Sciences, B
Computer Science, B
Curriculum and Instruction, M
Drama and Dramatics/Theatre Arts, B
Early Childhood Education and Teaching, B
Economics, B
Education, BM
Elementary Education and Teaching, B
English Language and Literature, B
History, B
Human Services, B
Junior High/Intermediate/Middle School Education
   and Teaching, B
Liberal Arts and Sciences Studies and
   Humanities, A
Mathematics, B
Music, B
Music Teacher Education, M
Nursing - Registered Nurse Training, B
Political Science and Government, B
Pre-Dentistry Studies, B
Pre-Engineering, A
Pre-Law Studies, B
Pre-Medicine/Pre-Medical Studies, B
Pre-Veterinary Studies, B
Psychology, B
Religion/Religious Studies, B
Religious Education, B
Secondary Education and Teaching, M
Social Work, B
Spanish Language and Literature, B
Visual and Performing Arts, B

LANIER TECHNICAL COLLEGE

Accounting, A
Administrative Assistant and Secretarial Science, A
Banking and Financial Support Services, A
Child Development, A
Computer and Information Systems Security, A
Computer Programming/Programmer, A
Computer Science, A
Computer Systems Networking and
   Telecommunications, A
Criminal Justice/Safety Studies, A
Drafting and Design Technology/Technician, A
Electrical, Electronic and Communications
   Engineering Technology/Technician, A
Fire Science/Firefighting, A
Health and Medical Laboratory Technologies, A
Health Professions and Related Clinical Sciences, A
Industrial Technology/Technician, A
Information Science/Studies, A
Interior Design, A
Marketing/Marketing Management, A
Medical Radiologic Technology/Science - Radiation
   Therapist, A
Occupational Safety and Health
   Technology/Technician, A
Surgical Technology/Technologist, A
Web Page, Digital/Multimedia and Information
   Resources Design, A

LIFE UNIVERSITY

Biology/Biological Sciences, B
Business Administration and Management, B
Chiropractic, P
Dietetics/Dieticians, B
Exercise and Sports Science, M
Human Nutrition, B

LUTHER RICE UNIVERSITY

Bible/Biblical Studies, B
Missions/Missionary Studies and Missiology, MP
Pastoral Studies/Counseling, BDP
Religious Education, P
Theology and Religious Vocations, MDP

MACON STATE COLLEGE

Accounting, A
Administrative Assistant and Secretarial Science, A
Agriculture, A
Art/Art Studies, General, A
Biology/Biological Sciences, A
Business Administration and Management, AB

Business Teacher Education, A
Business/Commerce, AB
Chemistry, A
Civil Engineering, A
Clinical/Medical Laboratory Technician, A
Communication and Media Studies, B
Computer Programming, Specific Applications, A
Computer Programming/Programmer, A
Computer Science, A
Corrections, A
Criminal Justice/Law Enforcement Administration, A
Criminal Justice/Police Science, A
Data Processing and Data Processing
   Technology/Technician, A
Drama and Dramatics/Theatre Arts, A
Economics, A
Education, A
Electrical, Electronics and Communications
   Engineering, A
Elementary Education and Teaching, A
Engineering, A
Engineering Technology, A
English Language and Literature, A
Environmental Studies, A
Food Science, A
General Studies, A
Health Information/Medical Records
   Administration/Administrator, B
Health Information/Medical Records
   Technology/Technician, A
Health/Health Care Administration/Management, B
History, A
Humanities/Humanistic Studies, A
Information Science/Studies, AB
Journalism, A
Liberal Arts and Sciences Studies and
   Humanities, A
Marketing, B
Mass Communication/Media Studies, A
Mathematics, A
Mechanical Engineering, A
Modern Languages, A
Music, A
Nursing - Registered Nurse Training, AB
Physical Education Teaching and Coaching, A
Physical Therapy/Therapist, A
Physics, A
Political Science and Government, A
Pre-Engineering, A
Pre-Pharmacy Studies, A
Psychology, A
Public Administration, A
Public Health (MPH, DPH), A
Respiratory Care Therapy/Therapist, A
Sociology, A
Speech and Rhetorical Studies, A

MEDICAL COLLEGE OF GEORGIA

Allied Health and Medical Assisting Services, MD
Allopathic Medicine, PO
Anatomy, D
Biochemistry, D
Biological and Biomedical Sciences, MD
Cardiovascular Sciences, MD
Cell Biology and Anatomy, D
Clinical Laboratory Science/Medical
   Technology/Technologist, B
Community Health Nursing, M
Dental Hygiene/Hygienist, BM
Dentistry, PO
Diagnostic Medical Sonography/Sonographer and
   Ultrasound Technician, B
Health Informatics, M
Health Information/Medical Records
   Administration/Administrator, B
Health Physics/Radiological Health, M
Maternal/Child Health and Neonatal
   Nurse/Nursing, M
Medical Illustration and Informatics, M
Medical Technology, M
Molecular Biology, D
Molecular Medicine, D
Nuclear Medical Technology/Technologist, B
Nurse Anesthetist, M
Nursing, MD
Nursing - Adult, M

Nursing - Advanced Practice, M
Nursing - Registered Nurse Training, B
Occupational Therapy/Therapist, BM
Oral Biology, MD
Pharmacology, D
Physical Therapy/Therapist, MD
Physician Assistant, BM
Physiology, D
Psychiatric/Mental Health Nurse/Nursing, M
Radiologic Technology/Science - Radiographer, B
Respiratory Care Therapy/Therapist, B
Toxicology, D

MERCER UNIVERSITY

African-American/Black Studies, B
Allopathic Medicine, MP
Art/Art Studies, General, B
Biochemistry, B
Biology/Biological Sciences, B
Biomedical Engineering, M
Business Administration, Management and
   Operations, BMO
Business/Commerce, B
Chemistry, B
Christian Studies, B
Classics and Classical
   Languages, Literatures, and Linguistics, B
Communication, Journalism and Related
   Programs, B
Community Organization and Advocacy, B
Computer Engineering, M
Computer Science, B
Criminal Justice/Safety Studies, B
Drama and Dramatics/Theatre Arts, B
Early Childhood Education and Teaching, MO
Economics, B
Education, BMO
Educational Leadership and Administration, M
Electrical Engineering, M
Elementary Education and Teaching, B
Engineering, B
Engineering and Applied Sciences, M
Engineering Management, M
English Language and Literature, B
Environmental Sciences, B
Environmental Studies, B
French Language and Literature, B
German Language and Literature, B
Health/Medical Preparatory Programs, B
History, B
Human Services, B
Information Science/Studies, B
International Relations and Affairs, B
Journalism, B
Junior High/Intermediate/Middle School Education
   and Teaching, B
Latin Language and Literature, B
Law and Legal Studies, PO
Liberal Arts and Sciences Studies and
   Humanities, B
Management of Technology, M
Mass Communication/Media Studies, B
Mathematics, B
Mechanical Engineering, M
Middle School Education, MO
Multi-/Interdisciplinary Studies, B
Music, B
Music Performance, B
Music Teacher Education, B
Nursing, M
Nursing - Registered Nurse Training, B
Pharmaceutical Sciences, DPO
Pharmacy, DPO
Philosophy, B
Physics, B
Political Science and Government, B
Pre-Dentistry Studies, B
Pre-Medicine/Pre-Medical Studies, B
Psychology, B
Reading Teacher Education, M
Regional Studies (U.S., Canadian, Foreign), B
Secondary Education and Teaching, M
Sociology, B
Software Engineering, M
Spanish Language and Literature, B

Theology and Religious Vocations, DP

MIDDLE GEORGIA COLLEGE

Business Administration and Management, A
Computer and Information Sciences, A
Computer Engineering, A
Computer Science, A
Computer/Information Technology Services
    Administration and Management, A
Criminal Justice/Police Science, A
Data Processing and Data Processing
    Technology/Technician, A
Fashion Merchandising, A
Information Science/Studies, A
Liberal Arts and Sciences Studies and
    .Humanities, A
Nursing - Registered Nurse Training, A
Occupational Therapist Assistant, A
Physical Therapist Assistant, A
Public Administration, A
Survey Technology/Surveying, A

MIDDLE GEORGIA TECHNICAL
COLLEGE

Accounting, A
Administrative Assistant and Secretarial Science, A
Airframe Mechanics and Aircraft Maintenance
    Technology/Technician, A
Child Development, A
Computer Systems Networking and
    Telecommunications, A
Dental Hygiene/Hygienist, A
Drafting and Design Technology/Technician, A
Information Science/Studies, A
Marketing/Marketing Management, A
Medical Radiologic Technology/Science - Radiation
    Therapist, A
Web Page, Digital/Multimedia and Information
    Resources Design, A

MOREHOUSE COLLEGE

Accounting, B
Adult and Continuing Education and Teaching, B
African-American/Black Studies, B
Art/Art Studies, General, B
Biology/Biological Sciences, B
Business Administration and Management, B
Chemistry, B
Computer and Information Sciences, B
Drama and Dramatics/Theatre Arts, B
Economics, B
Elementary Education and Teaching, B
Engineering, B
English Language and Literature, B
Finance, B
French Language and Literature, B
German Language and Literature, B
History, B
Interdisciplinary Studies, B
International Relations and Affairs, B
Junior High/Intermediate/Middle School Education
    and Teaching, B
Marketing/Marketing Management, B
Mathematics, B
Music, B
Philosophy, B
Physical Education Teaching and Coaching, B
Physics, B
Political Science and Government, B
Psychology, B
Religion/Religious Studies, B
Secondary Education and Teaching, B
Sociology, B
Spanish Language and Literature, B
Urban Studies/Affairs, B

MOULTRIE TECHNICAL COLLEGE

Accounting, A
Administrative Assistant and Secretarial Science, A
Child Development, A
Civil Engineering Technology/Technician, A
Computer Systems Networking and
    Telecommunications, A
Criminal Justice/Safety Studies, A

Electrical, Electronic and Communications
    Engineering Technology/Technician, A
Information Science/Studies, A
Marketing/Marketing Management, A
Web Page, Digital/Multimedia and Information
    Resources Design, A

NORTH GEORGIA COLLEGE & STATE
UNIVERSITY

Accounting, B
Art Teacher Education, B
Art/Art Studies, General, B
Biology/Biological Sciences, B
Business Administration and Management, B
Business/Managerial Economics, B
Chemistry, B
Community Psychology, M
Computer and Information Sciences, B
Computer Science, B
Crafts/Craft Design, Folk Art and Artisanry, B
Criminal Justice/Law Enforcement Administration, B
Criminal Justice/Safety Studies, B
Drawing, B
Early Childhood Education and Teaching, M
Education, BMO
Educational Administration and Supervision, O
Educational Leadership and Administration, B
Elementary Education and Teaching, B
English Language and Literature, B
English/Language Arts Teacher Education, B
Family Practice Nurse/Nurse Practitioner, B
Finance, B
French Language and Literature, B
History, B
Information Science/Studies, B
Junior High/Intermediate/Middle School Education
    and Teaching, B
Kindergarten/PreSchool Education and Teaching, B
Marketing/Marketing Management, B
Mathematics, B
Mathematics Teacher Education, B
Middle School Education, M
Music, B
Music Teacher Education, B
Nursing, M
Nursing - Advanced Practice, M
Nursing - Registered Nurse Training, AB
Physical Education Teaching and Coaching, B
Physical Therapy/Therapist, M
Physics, B
Political Science and Government, B
Pre-Dentistry Studies, B
Pre-Medicine/Pre-Medical Studies, B
Pre-Veterinary Studies, B
Psychology, B
Public Administration, BM
Purchasing, Procurement/Acquisitions and
    Contracts Management, B
Reading Teacher Education, B
Science Teacher Education/General Science
    Teacher Education, B
Secondary Education and Teaching, BM
Social Science Teacher Education, B
Social Sciences, B
Sociology, B
Spanish Language and Literature, B
Special Education and Teaching, BM

NORTH GEORGIA TECHNICAL
COLLEGE

Administrative Assistant and Secretarial Science, A
Computer Systems Networking and
    Telecommunications, A
Criminal Justice/Safety Studies, A
Culinary Arts/Chef Training, A
Health and Medical Laboratory Technologies, A
Heating, Air Conditioning and Refrigeration
    Technology/Technician, A
Horticultural Science, A
Industrial Technology/Technician, A
Parks, Recreation and Leisure Facilities
    Management, A
Turf and Turfgrass Management, A

Web Page, Digital/Multimedia and Information
    Resources Design, A

NORTH METRO TECHNICAL COLLEGE

Accounting, A
Administrative Assistant and Secretarial Science, A
Child Development, A
Computer Systems Networking and
    Telecommunications, A
Design and Visual Communications, A
Electrical, Electronic and Communications
    Engineering Technology/Technician, A
Horticultural Science, A
Marketing/Marketing Management, A
Medical Radiologic Technology/Science - Radiation
    Therapist, A
Web Page, Digital/Multimedia and Information
    Resources Design, A

NORTHWESTERN TECHNICAL
COLLEGE

Accounting, A
Administrative Assistant and Secretarial Science, A
Automobile/Automotive Mechanics
    Technology/Technician, A
Cardiovascular Technology/Technologist, A
Child Development, A
Computer Systems Networking and
    Telecommunications, A
Criminal Justice/Safety Studies, A
Drafting and Design Technology/Technician, A
Electrical, Electronic and Communications
    Engineering Technology/Technician, A
Health Information/Medical Records
    Technology/Technician, A
Information Science/Studies, A
Nursing - Registered Nurse Training, A
Occupational Therapist Assistant, A
Pharmacy Technician/Assistant, A
Social Work, A
Surgical Technology/Technologist, A
Web Page, Digital/Multimedia and Information
    Resources Design, A

OGEECHEE TECHNICAL COLLEGE

Accounting, A
Administrative Assistant and Secretarial Science, A
Agribusiness, A
Automobile/Automotive Mechanics
    Technology/Technician, A
Banking and Financial Support Services, A
Child Development, A
Computer Systems Networking and
    Telecommunications, A
Construction Trades, A
Culinary Arts/Chef Training, A
Dental Hygiene/Hygienist, A
Forestry Technology/Technician, A
Funeral Service and Mortuary Science, A
Health Information/Medical Records
    Technology/Technician, A
Hotel/Motel Administration/Management, A
Information Science/Studies, A
Interior Design, A
Legal Assistant/Paralegal, A
Marketing/Marketing Management, A
Opticianry/Ophthalmic Dispensing Optician, A
Tourism and Travel Services Management, A
Veterinary/Animal Health Technology/Technician and
    Veterinary Assistant, A
Water Quality and Wastewater Treatment
    Management and Recycling
    Technology/Technician, A
Wildlife and Wildlands Science and Management, A
Wood Science and Wood Products/Pulp and Paper
    Technology, A

OGLETHORPE UNIVERSITY

Accounting, B
American/United States Studies/Civilization, B
Art History, Criticism and Conservation, B
Art/Art Studies, General, B
Biology/Biological Sciences, B
Business Administration and Management, B

Business Administration, Management and
Operations, M
Business/Managerial Economics, B
Chemistry, B
Communication Studies/Speech Communication
and Rhetoric, B
Computer Science, B
Early Childhood Education and Teaching, M
Economics, B
Education, M
English Language and Literature, B
French Language and Literature, B
History, B
Interdisciplinary Studies, B
International Relations and Affairs, B
Junior High/Intermediate/Middle School Education
and Teaching, B
Kindergarten/PreSchool Education and Teaching, B
Mass Communication/Media Studies, B
Mathematics, B
Philosophy, B
Physics, B
Political Science and Government, B
Pre-Dentistry Studies, B
Pre-Law Studies, B
Pre-Medicine/Pre-Medical Studies, B
Pre-Veterinary Studies, B
Psychology, B
Social Work, B
Sociology, B
Spanish Language and Literature, B
Theatre/Theatre Arts Management, B
Urban Studies/Affairs, B

OKEFENOKEE TECHNICAL COLLEGE

Administrative Assistant and Secretarial Science, A
Child Development, A
Clinical/Medical Laboratory Technician, A
Computer Systems Networking and
Telecommunications, A
Computer Technology/Computer Systems
Technology, A
Criminal Justice/Police Science, A
Forestry Technology/Technician, A
Information Science/Studies, A
Occupational Safety and Health
Technology/Technician, A
Respiratory Therapy Technician/Assistant, A
Surgical Technology/Technologist, A

PAINE COLLEGE

Accounting, B
Biology Teacher Education, B
Biology/Biological Sciences, B
Broadcast Journalism, B
Business Administration and Management, B
Chemistry, B
Counseling Psychology, B
Criminology, B
Drama and Dramatics/Theatre Arts, B
Elementary Education and Teaching, B
English Language and Literature, B
English/Language Arts Teacher Education, B
Environmental Sciences, B
Experimental Psychology, B
History, B
History Teacher Education, B
International Business/Trade/Commerce, B
Journalism, B
Management Information Systems and Services, B
Mathematics, B
Mathematics and Computer Science, B
Mathematics Teacher Education, B
Philosophy, B
Psychology, B
Public Relations/Image Management, B
Religion/Religious Studies, B
Social Psychology, B
Sociology, B

PIEDMONT COLLEGE

Art/Art Studies, General, B
Biology/Biological Sciences, B
Business Administration and Management, B
Business Administration, Management and
Operations, M

Chemistry, B
Computer Science, B
Criminal Justice/Law Enforcement Administration, B
Curriculum and Instruction, O
Drama and Dramatics/Theatre Arts, B
Early Childhood Education and Teaching, M
Education, MO
Elementary and Middle School
Administration/Principalship, B
English Language and Literature, B
Environmental Sciences, B
Environmental Studies, B
Fine/Studio Arts, B
Geology/Earth Science, B
History, B
Interdisciplinary Studies, B
Junior High/Intermediate/Middle School Education
and Teaching, B
Kindergarten/PreSchool Education and Teaching, B
Mass Communication/Media Studies, B
Mathematics, B
Mathematics and Computer Science, B
Music, B
Music Performance, B
Nursing - Registered Nurse Training, B
Philosophy, B
Physics, B
Political Science and Government, B
Psychology, B
Religion/Religious Studies, B
Secondary Education and Teaching, M
Social Sciences, B
Sociology, B
Spanish Language and Literature, B
Special Education and Teaching, B

REINHARDT COLLEGE

Accounting, B
Art/Art Studies, General, B
Biology/Biological Sciences, B
Business Administration and Management, AB
Business/Commerce, B
Education, B
English Language and Literature, B
Entrepreneurship/Entrepreneurial Studies, B
Health and Physical Education/Fitness, B
History, B
Information Science/Studies, B
Junior High/Intermediate/Middle School Education
and Teaching, B
Kindergarten/PreSchool Education and Teaching, B
Liberal Arts and Sciences Studies and
Humanities, AB
Mass Communication/Media Studies, B
Music, B
Nursing - Registered Nurse Training, A
Physical Education Teaching and Coaching, B
Psychology, B
Religion/Religious Studies, B
Sociology, B
Sport and Fitness Administration/Management, B

SANDERSVILLE TECHNICAL COLLEGE

Accounting, A
Administrative Assistant and Secretarial Science, A
Child Development, A
Computer Systems Networking and
Telecommunications, A
Information Science/Studies, A

SAVANNAH COLLEGE OF ART AND DESIGN

Advertising and Public Relations, M
Animation, Interactive Technology, Video Graphics
and Special Effects, B
Applied Arts and Design, M
Architectural History and Criticism, BM
Architecture, BM
Art History, Criticism and Conservation, BM
Cinematography and Film/Video Production, B
Computer Art and Design, M
Computer Graphics, B
Design and Applied Arts, B
Design and Visual Communications, B
Digital Communication and Media/Multimedia, B
Drama and Dramatics/Theatre Arts, B

Fashion/Apparel Design, B
Fiber, Textile and Weaving Arts, B
Film, Television, and Video Production, M
Fine Arts and Art Studies, M
Graphic Design, BM
Historic Preservation and Conservation, BM
Illustration, BM
Industrial Design, BM
Interior Design, BM
Internet and Interactive Multimedia, M
Media Studies, M
Metal and Jewelry Arts, B
Music, M
Painting, BM
Photography, BM
Recording Arts Technology/Technician, B
Textile Design, M

SAVANNAH STATE UNIVERSITY

Accounting, B
African-American/Black Studies, B
Biology/Biological Sciences, B
Business Administration and Management, B
Chemical Engineering, B
Chemistry, B
Civil Engineering, B
Civil Engineering Technology/Technician, B
Computer Engineering, B
Computer Engineering Technology/Technician, B
Criminal Justice/Law Enforcement Administration, B
Electrical, Electronic and Communications
Engineering Technology/Technician, B
English Language and Literature, B
Environmental Studies, B
History, B
International Business/Trade/Commerce, B
Management Information Systems and Services, B
Marine Biology and Biological Oceanography, B
Marine Sciences, M
Marketing/Marketing Management, B
Mass Communication/Media Studies, B
Mathematics, B
Mechanical Engineering/Mechanical
Technology/Technician, B
Music, B
Parks, Recreation and Leisure Facilities
Management, B
Political Science and Government, B
Public Administration, M
Social Work, BM
Sociology, B
Urban Studies/Affairs, M

SAVANNAH TECHNICAL COLLEGE

Accounting, A
Administrative Assistant and Secretarial Science, A
Automobile/Automotive Mechanics
Technology/Technician, A
Child Development, A
Computer Systems Networking and
Telecommunications, A
Criminal Justice/Safety Studies, A
Culinary Arts/Chef Training, A
Electrical, Electronic and Communications
Engineering Technology/Technician, A
Fire Science/Firefighting, A
Heating, Air Conditioning and Refrigeration
Technology/Technician, A
Hotel/Motel Administration/Management, A
Industrial Technology/Technician, A
Information Technology, A
Marketing/Marketing Management, A
Surgical Technology/Technologist, A

SHORTER COLLEGE

Accounting, B
Art Teacher Education, B
Art/Art Studies, General, B
Biology/Biological Sciences, B
Business Administration and Management, B
Business Administration, Management and
Operations, M
Business/Managerial Economics, B
Chemistry, B
Computer and Information Sciences, B
Divinity/Ministry (BD, MDiv.), B

Drama and Dramatics/Theatre Arts, B
Economics, B
Elementary Education and Teaching, B
English Language and Literature, B
Environmental Studies, B
Fine/Studio Arts, B
French Language and Literature, B
General Studies, B
History, B
Junior High/Intermediate/Middle School Education
and Teaching, B
Liberal Arts and Sciences Studies and
Humanities, B
Mathematics, B
Mathematics Teacher Education, B
Music, B
Music Teacher Education, B
Natural Sciences, B
Organizational Communication, B
Parks, Recreation, Leisure and Fitness Studies, B
Piano and Organ, B
Pre-Theology/Pre-Ministerial Studies, B
Psychology, B
Public Relations, Advertising, and Applied
Communication, B
Religion/Religious Studies, B
Religious/Sacred Music, B
Social Sciences, B
Sociology, B
Spanish Language and Literature, B
Therapeutic Recreation/Recreational Therapy, B
Voice and Opera, B

SOUTH GEORGIA COLLEGE

Accounting, A
Administrative Assistant and Secretarial Science, A
Agricultural Business and Management, A
Agricultural Teacher Education, A
Agriculture, A
Animal Sciences, A
Applied Mathematics, A
Biological and Physical Sciences, A
Biology/Biological Sciences, A
Business Administration and Management, A
Business Teacher Education, A
Business/Managerial Economics, A
Chemistry, A
Computer and Information Sciences, A
Computer Programming/Programmer, A
Computer Science, A
Creative Writing, A
Criminal Justice/Law Enforcement Administration, A
Criminology, A
Drama and Dramatics/Theatre Arts, A
Economics, A
Education, A
Elementary Education and Teaching, A
English Language and Literature, A
Finance, A
French Language and Literature, A
German Language and Literature, A
Health Teacher Education, A
History, A
Humanities/Humanistic Studies, A
Information Science/Studies, A
Journalism, A
Junior High/Intermediate/Middle School Education
and Teaching, A
Kindergarten/PreSchool Education and Teaching, A
Kinesiology and Exercise Science, A
Liberal Arts and Sciences Studies and
Humanities, A
Mass Communication/Media Studies, A
Mathematics, A
Nursing - Registered Nurse Training, A
Parks, Recreation and Leisure Facilities
Management, A
Parks, Recreation, Leisure and Fitness Studies, A
Philosophy, A
Physical Education Teaching and Coaching, A
Physical Sciences, A
Physics, A
Political Science and Government, A
Pre-Engineering, A
Psychology, A

Science Teacher Education/General Science
Teacher Education, A
Sociology, A
Spanish Language and Literature, A
Speech and Rhetorical Studies, A
Sport and Fitness Administration/Management, A

SOUTH GEORGIA TECHNICAL COLLEGE

Accounting, A
Administrative Assistant and Secretarial Science, A
Child Development, A
Computer Systems Networking and
Telecommunications, A
Criminal Justice/Safety Studies, A
Culinary Arts/Chef Training, A
Drafting and Design Technology/Technician, A
Electrical, Electronic and Communications
Engineering Technology/Technician, A
Heating, Air Conditioning and Refrigeration
Technology/Technician, A
Horticultural Science, A
Industrial Technology/Technician, A
Information Science/Studies, A
Legal Assistant/Paralegal, A
Manufacturing Technology/Technician, A
Marketing/Marketing Management, A

SOUTH UNIVERSITY

Accounting, A
Business Administration and Management, AB
Criminal Justice/Law Enforcement Administration, B
Health/Health Care Administration/Management, B
Information Technology, AB
Law and Legal Studies, B
Legal Assistant/Paralegal, A
Medical/Clinical Assistant, A
Pharmacy, P
Physical Therapist Assistant, A
Physician Assistant, BM

SOUTHEASTERN TECHNICAL COLLEGE

Accounting, A
Administrative Assistant and Secretarial Science, A
Child Development, A
Computer Systems Networking and
Telecommunications, A
Criminal Justice/Safety Studies, A
Dental Hygiene/Hygienist, A
Design and Visual Communications, A
Electrical, Electronic and Communications
Engineering Technology/Technician, A
Health and Medical Laboratory Technologies, A
Information Science/Studies, A
Marketing/Marketing Management, A
Medical Radiologic Technology/Science - Radiation
Therapist, A
Respiratory Therapy Technician/Assistant, A
Web Page, Digital/Multimedia and Information
Resources Design, A

SOUTHERN POLYTECHNIC STATE UNIVERSITY

Architectural Engineering Technology/Technician, B
Architecture, B
Biology/Biological Sciences, B
Business Administration, Management and
Operations, M
Civil Engineering Technology/Technician, B
Computer and Information Sciences, B
Computer and Information Sciences and Support
Services, B
Computer Engineering, M
Computer Engineering Technology/Technician, B
Computer Science, M
Construction Engineering and Management, M
Construction Engineering Technology/Technician, B
Electrical and Electronic Engineering
Technologies/Technicians, B
Electrical Engineering, M
Electrical, Electronic and Communications
Engineering Technology/Technician, B
Engineering and Applied Sciences, M
Entrepreneurship/Entrepreneurial Studies, B

Industrial Production Technologies/Technicians, B
Industrial Technology/Technician, B
Industrial/Management Engineering, M
Information Science/Studies, BM
International Relations and Affairs, M
Internet and Interactive Multimedia, M
Liberal Arts and Sciences Studies and
Humanities, A
Mathematics, B
Mechanical Engineering/Mechanical
Technology/Technician, B
Organizational Behavior Studies, B
Physics, B
Quality Management, M
Software Engineering, M
Survey Technology/Surveying, B
Systems Engineering, M
Technical and Business Writing, B
Technical Communication, M
Telecommunications Technology/Technician, B

SOUTHWEST GEORGIA TECHNICAL COLLEGE

Accounting, A
Administrative Assistant and Secretarial Science, A
Agricultural Mechanization, A
Child Development, A
Computer Systems Networking and
Telecommunications, A
Criminal Justice/Safety Studies, A
Health and Medical Laboratory Technologies, A
Information Science/Studies, A
Medical Radiologic Technology/Science - Radiation
Therapist, A
Nursing - Registered Nurse Training, A
Respiratory Care Therapy/Therapist, A
Surgical Technology/Technologist, A

SPELMAN COLLEGE

Anthropology, B
Art/Art Studies, General, B
Biochemistry, B
Biology/Biological Sciences, B
Chemistry, B
Computer Science, B
Developmental and Child Psychology, B
Drama and Dramatics/Theatre Arts, B
Economics, B
Engineering, B
English Language and Literature, B
Environmental Studies, B
French Language and Literature, B
History, B
Mathematics, B
Music, B
Natural Sciences, B
Philosophy, B
Physics, B
Political Science and Government, B
Psychology, B
Religion/Religious Studies, B
Sociology, B
Spanish Language and Literature, B
Women's Studies, B

SWAINSBORO TECHNICAL COLLEGE

Accounting, A
Administrative Assistant and Secretarial Science, A
Child Development, A
Computer Systems Networking and
Telecommunications, A
Criminal Justice/Safety Studies, A
Drafting and Design Technology/Technician, A
Electrical, Electronic and Communications
Engineering Technology/Technician, A
Forestry Technology/Technician, A
Information Science/Studies, A

THOMAS UNIVERSITY

Accounting, B
Biology/Biological Sciences, B
Business Administration and Management, B
Business Administration, Management and
Operations, M
Business/Commerce, A

Communication Studies/Speech Communication
   and Rhetoric, B
Criminal Justice/Law Enforcement
   Administration, AB
Criminology, B
Early Childhood Education and Teaching, B
English Language and Literature, B
Humanities/Humanistic Studies, B
Junior High/Intermediate/Middle School Education
   and Teaching, B
Kindergarten/PreSchool Education and Teaching, B
Liberal Arts and Sciences Studies and
   Humanities, AB
Mathematics, A
Nursing - Registered Nurse Training, AB
Parks, Recreation and Leisure Facilities
   Management, B
Political Science and Government, B
Psychology, B
Rehabilitation Counseling, M
Rehabilitation Therapy, B
Secondary Education and Teaching, B
Social Sciences, B
Social Work, B
Sociology, B

TOCCOA FALLS COLLEGE

Bible/Biblical Studies, B
Biology/Biological Sciences, B
Business Administration and Management, B
Counseling Psychology, B
Early Childhood Education and Teaching, B
English Language and Literature, B
English/Language Arts Teacher Education, B
General Studies, A
History Teacher Education, B
Junior High/Intermediate/Middle School Education
   and Teaching, B
Mass Communication/Media Studies, B
Missions/Missionary Studies and Missiology, B
Music, B
Music Performance, B
Music Teacher Education, B
Organizational Communication, B
Philosophy, B
Pre-Law Studies, B
Religion/Religious Studies, B
Religious Education, B
Religious/Sacred Music, B
Youth Ministry, B

TRUETT-MCCONNELL COLLEGE

Business/Commerce, AB
Christian Studies, AB
Education, A
General Studies, A
Humanities/Humanistic Studies, B
Liberal Arts and Sciences Studies and
   Humanities, A
Music, AB

UNIVERSITY OF GEORGIA

Accounting, BMO
Adult and Continuing Education and Teaching, MDO
Advertising, B
African-American/Black Studies, B
Agricultural Business and Management, B
Agricultural Communication/Journalism, B
Agricultural Economics, BMD
Agricultural Education, M
Agricultural Engineering, MDO
Agricultural Sciences, MD
Agricultural Teacher Education, B
Agricultural/Biological Engineering and
   Bioengineering, B
Agriculture, B
Agriculture, Agriculture Operations and Related
   Sciences, B
Agronomy and Soil Sciences, MD
Analytical Chemistry, MD
Anatomy, M
Ancient/Classical Greek Language and Literature, B
Animal Health, B
Animal Sciences, BMD
Anthropology, BMD
Apparel and Textiles, B

Applied Economics, MD
Applied Horticulture/Horticultural Operations, B
Applied Mathematics, M
Art Education, MDO
Art History, Criticism and Conservation, BM
Art Teacher Education, B
Art/Art Studies, General, B
Artificial Intelligence and Robotics, M
Astronomy, MD
Athletic Training and Sports Medicine, B
Biochemistry, BMD
Bioengineering, MD
Biological and Physical Sciences, B
Biology/Biological Sciences, B
Botany/Plant Biology, B
Broadcast Journalism, B
Business Administration, Management and
   Operations, MDO
Business, Management, Marketing, and Related
   Support Services, B
Cell Biology and Anatomy, MD
Cell/Cellular Biology and Histology, B
Ceramic Sciences and Engineering, B
Chemistry, BMD
Child and Family Studies, MD
Child Development, B
Classics and Classical
   Languages, Literatures, and Linguistics, BM
Clothing and Textiles, MD
Cognitive Psychology and Psycholinguistics, B
Communication and Media Studies, MD
Communication Disorders, BMDO
Comparative Literature, BMD
Computer and Information Sciences, B
Computer Science, MD
Consumer Economics, BMD
Counseling Psychology, D
Counselor Education/School Counseling and
   Guidance Services, MD
Criminal Justice/Safety Studies, B
Dairy Science, BM
Dance, B
Dietetics/Dieticians, B
Digital Communication and Media/Multimedia, B
Drama and Dance Teacher Education, B
Drama and Dramatics/Theatre Arts, B
Drawing, B
Early Childhood Education and Teaching, BMDO
Ecology, BMD
Economics, BMD
Education, MDO
Education/Teaching of the Gifted and Talented, D
Educational Administration and Supervision, MO
Educational Media/Instructional Technology, MDO
Educational Psychology, MDO
Elementary Education and Teaching, MDO
English, MD
English Education, MO
English Language and Literature, B
English/Language Arts Teacher Education, B
Entomology, BMD
Environmental and Occupational Health, MD
Environmental Health, B
Environmental Studies, B
Exercise and Sports Science, MDO
Family and Consumer Sciences/Home Economics
   Teacher Education, B
Family and Consumer Sciences/Human
   Sciences, MD
Fashion and Fabric Consultant, B
Fashion Merchandising, B
Film/Cinema Studies, B
Finance, B
Fine Arts and Art Studies, MD
Fishing and Fisheries Sciences and Management, B
Food Science, B
Food Science and Technology, MD
Foreign Language Teacher Education, BMDO
Foreign Languages and Literatures, B
Forest Sciences and Biology, B
Forestry, BMD
Foundations and Philosophy of Education, D
French Language and Literature, BM
Genetics, BMD
Geography, BMD
Geology/Earth Science, BMD

German Language and Literature, BM
Germanic Languages, Literatures, and Linguistics, B
Graphic Design, B
Health and Physical Education, B
Health and Physical Education/Fitness, B
Health Education, MDO
Health Occupations Teacher Education, B
Health Promotion, MDO
Health Teacher Education, B
Higher Education/Higher Education
   Administration, D
Historic Preservation and Conservation, M
History, BMD
Horticultural Science, BMD
Housing and Human Environments, B
Human Development and Family Studies, B
Human Resources Development, M
Infectious Diseases, MD
Inorganic Chemistry, MD
Insurance, B
Interdisciplinary Studies, B
Interior Design, BMD
International Business/Trade/Commerce, B
International Relations and Affairs, B
Italian Language and Literature, B
Japanese Language and Literature, B
Journalism, BMD
Junior High/Intermediate/Middle School Education
   and Teaching, B
Landscape Architecture, BM
Landscaping and Groundskeeping, B
Latin Language and Literature, B
Law and Legal Studies, MP
Leisure Studies, MD
Linguistics, BMD
Management Information Systems and Services, B
Marine Sciences, MD
Marketing Research, M
Marketing/Marketing Management, B
Mass Communication/Media Studies, BMD
Mathematics, BMD
Mathematics Teacher Education, BMDO
Medical Microbiology and Bacteriology, B
Medicinal and Pharmaceutical Chemistry, MD
Metal and Jewelry Arts, B
Microbiology, BMD
Middle School Education, MDO
Modern Greek Language and Literature, B
Molecular Biology, MD
Music, BMD
Music Performance, B
Music Teacher Education, BMDO
Music Theory and Composition, B
Music Therapy/Therapist, B
Natural Resources and Conservation, MD
Non-Profit/Public/Organizational Management, M
Nutritional Sciences, BMD
Oceanography, Chemical and Physical, MD
Organic Chemistry, MD
Painting, B
Parasitology, MD
Pathology/Experimental Pathology, MD
Pharmaceutical Administration, MD
Pharmaceutical Sciences, MD
Pharmacology, MD
Pharmacy, P
Philosophy, BMD
Physical Chemistry, MD
Physical Education Teaching and Coaching, BMDO
Physics, BMD
Physiology, MD
Plant Biology, MD
Plant Pathology/Phytopathology, MD
Plant Protection and Integrated Pest
   Management, B
Plant Sciences, B
Political Science and Government, BMD
Poultry Science, BMD
Pre-Engineering, B
Pre-Medicine/Pre-Medical Studies, B
Pre-Veterinary Studies, B
Printmaking, B
Psychology, BMD
Public Administration, MD
Public Relations/Image Management, B
Reading Teacher Education, BMDO

Real Estate, B
Recreation and Park Management, MD
Religion/Religious Studies, BM
Romance
    Languages, Literatures, and Linguistics, BMD
Russian Language and Literature, B
Sales and Marketing Operations/Marketing and
    Distribution Teacher Education, B
Sales, Distribution and Marketing Operations, B
School Psychology, O
Science Teacher Education/General Science
    Teacher Education, BMDO
Sculpture, B
Secondary Education and Teaching, MDO
Slavic Languages, Literatures, and Linguistics, B
Social Science Teacher Education, B
Social Studies Teacher Education, MD
Social Work, BMD
Sociology, BMD
Spanish Language and Literature, BM
Special Education and Teaching, MDO
Speech and Interpersonal Communication, MD
Speech and Rhetorical Studies, B
Sport and Fitness Administration/Management, B
Statistics, BMD
Student Personnel Services, MD
Sustainable Development, M
Technology Teacher Education/Industrial Arts
    Teacher Education, B
Telecommunications Technology/Technician, B
Theater, MD
Toxicology, MD
Turf and Turfgrass Management, B
Veterinary Medicine, P
Veterinary Sciences, MD
Vocational and Technical Education, MDO
Water, Wetlands, and Marine Resources
    Management, B
Wildlife and Wildlands Science and Management, B
Women's Studies, B

UNIVERSITY OF PHOENIX-ATLANTA CAMPUS

Accounting, B
Business Administration and Management, B
Business Administration, Management and
    Operations, M
Information Technology, B
Management Information Systems and
    Services, BM
Management of Technology, M
Management Science, B
Nursing Science, B
Organizational Management, M

UNIVERSITY OF PHOENIX-COLUMBUS GEORGIA CAMPUS

Accounting, B
Business Administration and Management, B
Business Administration, Management and
    Operations, M
Computer and Information Sciences, B
Health/Health Care Administration/Management, B
Human Resources Management and Services, M
International Business/Trade/Commerce, M
Management of Technology, M
Marketing, M
Marketing/Marketing Management, B
Nursing Science, B
Public Administration, B

UNIVERSITY OF WEST GEORGIA

Accounting, M
Anthropology, B
Art Education, M
Art/Art Studies, General, B
Biological and Biomedical Sciences, M
Biology Teacher Education, B
Biology/Biological Sciences, B
Business Administration and Management, B
Business Administration, Management and
    Operations, M
Business Education, MO
Business Teacher Education, B
Business/Managerial Economics, B
Chemistry, B

Chemistry Teacher Education, B
Communication Disorders, M
Computer and Information Sciences, B
Computer Science, M
Counselor Education/School Counseling and
    Guidance Services, MO
Drama and Dramatics/Theatre Arts, B
Early Childhood Education and Teaching, MO
Economics, B
Education, MDO
Education/Teaching of Individuals with Mental
    Retardation, B
Educational Administration and Supervision, MO
Educational Leadership and Administration, MO
Educational Measurement and Evaluation, D
Educational Media/Instructional Technology, MO
Elementary Education and Teaching, B
English, M
English Education, MO
English Language and Literature, B
Environmental Sciences, B
Environmental Studies, B
Finance, B
Foreign Language Teacher Education, M
French Language and Literature, B
Geography, B
Geological and Earth Sciences/Geosciences, B
Geology/Earth Science, B
German Language and Literature, B
Gerontology, M
History, BM
International Economics, B
International Relations and Affairs, B
Journalism, B
Junior High/Intermediate/Middle School Education
    and Teaching, B
Management Information Systems and Services, B
Marketing/Marketing Management, B
Mathematics, B
Mathematics Teacher Education, MO
Middle School Education, MO
Music Performance, B
Music Teacher Education, BM
Music Theory and Composition, B
Nursing, M
Nursing - Registered Nurse Training, B
Parks, Recreation and Leisure Facilities
    Management, B
Performance, M
Philosophy, B
Physical Education Teaching and Coaching, BMO
Physics, B
Physics Teacher Education, B
Political Science and Government, B
Pre-Law Studies, B
Pre-Medicine/Pre-Medical Studies, B
Pre-Veterinary Studies, B
Psychology, BM
Public Administration, M
Reading Teacher Education, MO
Real Estate, B
Rural Planning and Studies, M
Science Teacher Education/General Science
    Teacher Education, MO
Secondary Education and Teaching, BMO
Social Studies Teacher Education, MO
Sociology, BM
Spanish Language and Literature, B
Special Education and Teaching, MO
Speech-Language Pathology/Pathologist, B

VALDOSTA STATE UNIVERSITY

Accounting, B
Administrative Assistant and Secretarial Science, B
Adult and Continuing Education and Teaching, D
Applied Mathematics, B
Art Teacher Education, B
Art/Art Studies, General, B
Astronomy, B
Athletic Training and Sports Medicine, B
Biology/Biological Sciences, B
Business Administration and Management, B
Business Administration, Management and
    Operations, M
Business Education, MDO
Business Teacher Education, B

Business/Managerial Economics, B
Chemistry, B
Clinical Psychology, M
Communication Disorders, M
Communication Studies/Speech Communication
    and Rhetoric, B
Community Health Nursing, M
Computer and Information Sciences, B
Computer Science, B
Counseling Psychology, M
Counselor Education/School Counseling and
    Guidance Services, MO
Criminal Justice/Safety Studies, B
Criminology, M
Drama and Dramatics/Theatre Arts, B
Early Childhood Education and Teaching, BMO
Education, MDO
Educational Leadership and Administration, MDO
English, M
English Language and Literature, B
Finance, B
French Language and Literature, B
General Studies, B
Health Education, M
History, BM
Human Resources Management and Services, M
Industrial and Organizational Psychology, M
Information Science/Studies, BM
Interior Design, B
Junior High/Intermediate/Middle School Education
    and Teaching, B
Kinesiology and Exercise Science, B
Legal Assistant/Paralegal, B
Liberal Arts and Sciences Studies and
    Humanities, A
Library Science, M
Marketing/Marketing Management, B
Marriage and Family Therapy/Counseling, M
Mass Communication/Media Studies, B
Mathematics, B
Middle School Education, MO
Music, B
Music Performance, B
Music Teacher Education, BM
Nursing, M
Nursing - Registered Nurse Training, B
Nursing Administration, M
Philosophy, B
Physical Education Teaching and Coaching, BM
Physics, B
Political Science and Government, B
Psychology, BMO
Public Administration, M
Reading Teacher Education, MO
School Psychology, BMO
Secondary Education and Teaching, BMO
Social Work, M
Sociology, BM
Spanish Language and Literature, B
Special Education and Teaching, BMO
Speech-Language Pathology/Pathologist, B
Trade and Industrial Teacher Education, B
Urban and Regional Planning, M
Visual and Performing Arts, B
Vocational and Technical Education, MDO

VALDOSTA TECHNICAL COLLEGE

Accounting, A
Administrative Assistant and Secretarial Science, A
Banking and Financial Support Services, A
Child Development, A
Computer and Information Systems Security, A
Computer Programming/Programmer, A
Computer Systems Networking and
    Telecommunications, A
Criminal Justice/Safety Studies, A
Drafting and Design Technology/Technician, A
E-Commerce/Electronic Commerce, A
Fire Science/Firefighting, A
Health and Medical Laboratory Technologies, A
Machine Tool Technology/Machinist, A
Marketing/Marketing Management, A

Medical Radiologic Technology/Science - Radiation
Therapist, A

WAYCROSS COLLEGE

Accounting, A
Administrative Assistant and Secretarial Science, A
Agriculture, A
Automobile/Automotive Mechanics
Technology/Technician, A
Biology/Biological Sciences, A
Business Administration and Management, A
Business Teacher Education, A
Chemistry, A
Clinical Laboratory Science/Medical
Technology/Technologist, A
Clinical/Medical Laboratory Technician, A
Computer and Information Sciences, A
Computer Science, A
Cosmetology/Cosmetologist, A
Criminal Justice/Law Enforcement Administration, A
Developmental and Child Psychology, A
Drafting and Design Technology/Technician, A
Education, A
Electrical, Electronic and Communications
Engineering Technology/Technician, A
Elementary Education and Teaching, A
Emergency Medical Technology/Technician (EMT
Paramedic), A
Engineering Technology, A
English Language and Literature, A
Forestry, A
Forestry Technology/Technician, A
Health Teacher Education, A
Heavy Equipment Maintenance
Technology/Technician, A
History, A
Liberal Arts and Sciences Studies and
Humanities, A
Machine Tool Technology/Machinist, A
Mathematics, A
Medical Radiologic Technology/Science - Radiation
Therapist, A
Nursing - Registered Nurse Training, A
Physical Education Teaching and Coaching, A
Physical Therapy/Therapist, A
Political Science and Government, A
Psychology, A
Radiologic Technology/Science - Radiographer, A
Respiratory Care Therapy/Therapist, A
Sociology, A
Surgical Technology/Technologist, A
Welding Technology/Welder, A

WESLEYAN COLLEGE

Advertising, B
American/United States Studies/Civilization, B
Art History, Criticism and Conservation, B
Biology/Biological Sciences, B
Business Administration and Management, B
Business Administration, Management and
Operations, M
Chemistry, B
Communication Studies/Speech Communication
and Rhetoric, B
Computer and Information Sciences, B
Early Childhood Education and Teaching, BM
Economics, B
Education, BM
English Language and Literature, B
Environmental Sciences, B
Fine/Studio Arts, B
French Language and Literature, B
History, B
Humanities/Humanistic Studies, B
Interdisciplinary Studies, B
International Business/Trade/Commerce, B
International Relations and Affairs, B
Junior High/Intermediate/Middle School Education
and Teaching, B
Mathematics, B
Mathematics Teacher Education, M
Middle School Education, M
Music, B
Philosophy, B
Physical Sciences, B
Physics, B

Political Science and Government, B
Psychology, B
Religion/Religious Studies, B
Science Teacher Education/General Science
Teacher Education, M
Social Sciences, B
Spanish Language and Literature, B

WEST CENTRAL TECHNICAL COLLEGE

Accounting, A
Administrative Assistant and Secretarial Science, A
Business Administration and Management, A
Child Development, A
Computer and Information Sciences, A
Computer Programming, Specific Applications, A
Computer Systems Networking and
Telecommunications, A
Criminal Justice/Safety Studies, A
Data Entry/Microcomputer Applications, A
Dental Hygiene/Hygienist, A
Electrical, Electronic and Communications
Engineering Technology/Technician, A
Health and Medical Laboratory Technologies, A
Heavy Equipment Maintenance
Technology/Technician, A
Industrial Radiologic Technology/Technician, A
Information Science/Studies, A
Manufacturing Technology/Technician, A
Marketing/Marketing Management, A
Medical Radiologic Technology/Science - Radiation
Therapist, A
Nursing - Registered Nurse Training, A
Web Page, Digital/Multimedia and Information
Resources Design, A
Word Processing, A

WEST GEORGIA TECHNICAL COLLEGE

Accounting, A
Administrative Assistant and Secretarial Science, A
Automobile/Automotive Mechanics
Technology/Technician, A
Child Development, A
Computer Systems Networking and
Telecommunications, A
Criminal Justice/Safety Studies, A
Electrical, Electronic and Communications
Engineering Technology/Technician, A
Fire Science/Firefighting, A
Health Information/Medical Records
Technology/Technician, A
Industrial Technology/Technician, A
Information Science/Studies, A
Marketing/Marketing Management, A
Medical Radiologic Technology/Science - Radiation
Therapist, A
Pharmacy Technician/Assistant, A
Plastics Engineering Technology/Technician, A
Social Work, A
Web Page, Digital/Multimedia and Information
Resources Design, A

WESTWOOD COLLEGE-ATLANTA MIDTOWN

Animation, Interactive Technology, Video Graphics
and Special Effects, B
Architectural Drafting and Architectural
CAD/CADD, A
Computer Systems Networking and
Telecommunications, AB
Design and Visual Communications, B
E-Commerce/Electronic Commerce, B
Graphic Design, A
Interior Design, B
Web/Multimedia Management and Webmaster, B

WESTWOOD COLLEGE-ATLANTA NORTHLAKE

Animation, Interactive Technology, Video Graphics
and Special Effects, B
Architectural Drafting and Architectural
CAD/CADD, A
Computer Systems Networking and
Telecommunications, AB
Design and Visual Communications, B

E-Commerce/Electronic Commerce, B
Graphic Design, A
Interior Design, B

YOUNG HARRIS COLLEGE

Agriculture, A
Art Teacher Education, A
Art/Art Studies, General, A
Biological and Physical Sciences, A
Biology/Biological Sciences, A
Business Administration and Management, A
Chemistry, A
Clinical Laboratory Science/Medical
Technology/Technologist, A
Computer Science, A
Criminal Justice/Law Enforcement Administration, A
Drama and Dramatics/Theatre Arts, A
Education, A
English Language and Literature, A
French Language and Literature, A
Geology/Earth Science, A
Health Teacher Education, A
History, A
Hospitality Administration/Management, A
International Business/Trade/Commerce, A
Journalism, A
Liberal Arts and Sciences Studies and
Humanities, A
Mathematics, A
Music, A
Music Teacher Education, A
Natural Sciences, A
Nursing - Registered Nurse Training, A
Parks, Recreation, Leisure and Fitness Studies, A
Physical Therapy/Therapist, A
Physics, A
Political Science and Government, A
Pre-Engineering, A
Psychology, A
Religion/Religious Studies, A
Sociology, A
Spanish Language and Literature, A

Guam

GUAM COMMUNITY COLLEGE

Accounting, A
Administrative Assistant and Secretarial Science, A
Architectural Engineering Technology/Technician, A
Automobile/Automotive Mechanics
Technology/Technician, A
Business Administration and Management, A
Child Development, A
Civil Engineering Technology/Technician, A
Computer
Programming, Vendor/Product Certification, A
Computer Science, A
Corrections, A
Criminal Justice/Law Enforcement Administration, A
Criminal Justice/Police Science, A
Education, A
Electrical, Electronic and Communications
Engineering Technology/Technician, A
Fire Science/Firefighting, A
Hospitality Administration/Management, A
Hospitality and Recreation Marketing Operations, A
Hotel/Motel Administration/Management, A
Kindergarten/PreSchool Education and Teaching, A
Marketing Research, A
Marketing/Marketing Management, A
Medical/Clinical Assistant, A
Operations Management and Supervision, A
Sign Language Interpretation and Translation, A
Tourism and Travel Services Management, A
Tourism and Travel Services Marketing
Operations, A
Tourism Promotion Operations, A

Vehicle and Vehicle Parts and Accessories
Marketing Operations, A

PACIFIC ISLANDS BIBLE COLLEGE

Religion/Religious Studies, AB

UNIVERSITY OF GUAM

Accounting, B
Agriculture, B
Anthropology, B
Art Teacher Education, B
Art/Art Studies, General, B
Biological and Biomedical Sciences, M
Biological and Physical Sciences, B
Biology/Biological Sciences, B
Business Administration and Management, B
Business Administration, Management and
Operations, M
Ceramic Arts and Ceramics, M
Chemistry, B
Computer Science, B
Counselor Education/School Counseling and
Guidance Services, M
Criminal Justice/Law Enforcement Administration, B
Criminal Justice/Police Science, B
East Asian Studies, B
Economics, B
Education, BM
Educational Administration and Supervision, M
Educational Leadership and Administration, M
Elementary Education and Teaching, B
English as a Second Language, M
English Language and Literature, B
Environmental Sciences, M
Family and Consumer Sciences/Home Economics
Teacher Education, B
Finance, B
Fine Arts and Art Studies, M
Graphic Design, M
History, B
International Business/Trade/Commerce, B
Kindergarten/PreSchool Education and Teaching, B
Marine Biology and Biological Oceanography, M
Marketing/Marketing Management, B
Mass Communication/Media Studies, B
Mathematics, B
Music Teacher Education, B
Nursing - Registered Nurse Training, B
Painting, M
Physical Education Teaching and Coaching, B
Physical Sciences, B
Political Science and Government, B
Psychology, B
Public Administration, BM
Reading Teacher Education, M
Secondary Education and Teaching, BM
Social Work, B
Sociology, B
Special Education and Teaching, BM

Hawaii

ARGOSY UNIVERSITY/HAWAII

Business Administration, Management and
Operations, M
Clinical Psychology, MD
Curriculum and Instruction, MD
Education, MD
Educational Leadership and Administration, MD
Human Development, MD
International Business/Trade/Commerce, M
Marriage and Family Therapy/Counseling, M
Pharmacology, O
Psychology, MDO
School Psychology, MD

BRIGHAM YOUNG UNIVERSITY-HAWAII

Accounting, AB
Anthropology, B
Area, Ethnic, Cultural, and Gender Studies, B
Art Teacher Education, B
Art/Art Studies, General, B
Biochemistry, B
Biology Teacher Education, B
Biology/Biological Sciences, B

Business Administration and Management, B
Business Teacher Education, B
Chemistry, B
Chemistry Teacher Education, B
Communication Studies/Speech Communication
and Rhetoric, A
Communication, Journalism and Related
Programs, B
Computer Programming/Programmer, B
Computer Science, B
Drama and Dramatics/Theatre Arts, A
Education, B
Elementary Education and Teaching, B
English Language and Literature, B
English/Language Arts Teacher Education, B
Ethnic and Cultural Studies, B
Health and Physical Education, B
History, B
Hotel/Motel Administration/Management, B
Humanities/Humanistic Studies, B
Information Science/Studies, B
Interdisciplinary Studies, B
International Business/Trade/Commerce, B
Kinesiology and Exercise Science, B
Mathematics, B
Mathematics Teacher Education, B
Multi-/Interdisciplinary Studies, B
Music, AB
Music Performance, B
Music Teacher Education, B
Pacific Area/Pacific Rim Studies, B
Physical Education Teaching and Coaching, B
Physical Sciences, B
Physics Teacher Education, B
Piano and Organ, B
Political Science and Government, B
Psychology, B
Science Teacher Education/General Science
Teacher Education, B
Secondary Education and Teaching, B
Social Science Teacher Education, B
Social Work, B
Special Education and Teaching, B
Teaching English as a Second or Foreign
Language/ESL Language Instructor, B
Tourism and Travel Services Management, AB
Voice and Opera, B

CHAMINADE UNIVERSITY OF HONOLULU

Accounting, B
Behavioral Sciences, B
Biology/Biological Sciences, B
Business Administration and Management, AB
Business Administration, Management and
Operations, M
Computer and Information Sciences, AB
Computer Science, B
Conflict Resolution and Mediation/Peace Studies, M
Counseling Psychology, M
Criminology, ABM
Early Childhood Education and Teaching, B
Education, M
Elementary Education and Teaching, B
English Language and Literature, B
Environmental Studies, B
Forensic Science and Technology, B
General Studies, A
History, B
Humanities/Humanistic Studies, B
Interior Design, AB
International Relations and Affairs, B
Marketing/Marketing Management, B
Mass Communication/Media Studies, B
Pastoral Studies/Counseling, M
Psychology, B
Religion/Religious Studies, B
Social Sciences, B
Social Studies Teacher Education, M
Theology and Religious Vocations, M

HAWAII BUSINESS COLLEGE

Accounting, A
Business Administration and Management, A
Computer Science, A
Health and Medical Administrative Services, A

Tourism and Travel Services Management, A
Web Page, Digital/Multimedia and Information
Resources Design, A

HAWAII COMMUNITY COLLEGE

Accounting, A
Administrative Assistant and Secretarial Science, A
Agriculture, A
Automobile/Automotive Mechanics
Technology/Technician, A
Carpentry/Carpenter, A
Criminal Justice/Law Enforcement Administration, A
Drafting and Design Technology/Technician, A
Electrical, Electronic and Communications
Engineering Technology/Technician, A
Fire Science/Firefighting, A
Food Technology and Processing, A
Hotel/Motel Administration/Management, A
Kindergarten/PreSchool Education and Teaching, A
Liberal Arts and Sciences Studies and
Humanities, A
Licensed Practical/Vocational Nurse Training, A
Mechanical Engineering/Mechanical
Technology/Technician, A
Nursing - Registered Nurse Training, A
Welding Technology/Welder, A

HAWAII PACIFIC UNIVERSITY

Accounting, ABM
Advertising, B
Anthropology, B
Applied Mathematics, AB
Area Studies, B
Behavioral Sciences, B
Biology/Biological Sciences, B
Business Administration and Management, AB
Business Administration, Management and
Operations, M
Business/Corporate Communications, B
Business/Managerial Economics, AB
Communication and Media Studies, M
Communication Studies/Speech Communication
and Rhetoric, B
Communication, Journalism and Related
Programs, B
Community Health Nursing, M
Comparative Literature, B
Computer and Information Sciences, B
Computer Science, B
Criminal Justice/Law Enforcement Administration, B
Data Processing and Data Processing
Technology/Technician, A
Economics, BM
Electronic Commerce, M
Engineering, B
English as a Second Language, M
English Language and Literature, B
Entrepreneurship/Entrepreneurial Studies, B
Environmental Sciences, B
Environmental Studies, B
Finance, AB
Finance and Banking, M
History, B
Human Development and Family Studies, B
Human Resources Management and Services, M
Human Resources Management/Personnel
Administration, B
Human Services, B
Humanities/Humanistic Studies, B
Information Science/Studies, B
Interdisciplinary Studies, B
International Business/Trade/Commerce, BM
International Relations and Affairs, B
Journalism, B
Liberal Arts and Sciences Studies and
Humanities, B
Management, M
Management Information Systems and
Services, BM
Marine Biology and Biological Oceanography, B
Marketing, M
Marketing/Marketing Management, AB
Mass Communication/Media Studies, B
Military and Defense Studies, M
Military Studies, AB
Multi-/Interdisciplinary Studies, B

Nursing, M
Nursing - Advanced Practice, M
Nursing - Registered Nurse Training, B
Oceanography, Chemical and Physical, B
Organizational Management, M
Political Science and Government, BM
Pre-Medicine/Pre-Medical Studies, B
Psychology, B
Public Administration, B
Public Relations/Image Management, B
Social Sciences, B
Social Work, B
Sociology, B
Teaching English as a Second or Foreign
  Language/ESL Language Instructor, B
Tourism and Travel Services Management, B

HAWAII THEOLOGICAL SEMINARY

Religion/Religious Studies, M
Theology and Religious Vocations, MP
Theology/Theological Studies, B

HAWAII TOKAI INTERNATIONAL COLLEGE

Japanese Language and Literature, A
Japanese Studies, A

HEALD COLLEGE-HONOLULU

Accounting, A
Administrative Assistant and Secretarial Science, A
Business Administration and Management, A
Electrical, Electronic and Communications
  Engineering Technology/Technician, A
Information Science/Studies, A
Legal Administrative Assistant/Secretary, A
Medical Administrative Assistant/Secretary, A
Tourism and Travel Services Management, A

HONOLULU COMMUNITY COLLEGE

Architectural Engineering Technology/Technician, A
Automobile/Automotive Mechanics
  Technology/Technician, A
Avionics Maintenance Technology/Technician, A
Carpentry/Carpenter, A
Commercial and Advertising Art, A
Community Organization and Advocacy, A
Cosmetology/Cosmetologist, A
Criminal Justice/Police Science, A
Drafting and Design Technology/Technician, A
Electrical, Electronic and Communications
  Engineering Technology/Technician, A
Engineering Technology, A
Fashion/Apparel Design, A
Fire Science/Firefighting, A
Food Technology and Processing, A
Heating, Air Conditioning, Ventilation and
  Refrigeration Maintenance
  Technology/Technician, A
Human Services, A
Kindergarten/PreSchool Education and Teaching, A
Liberal Arts and Sciences Studies and
  Humanities, A
Marine Technology, A
Occupational Safety and Health
  Technology/Technician, A
Technology Education/Industrial Arts, A
Welding Technology/Welder, A

KAPIOLANI COMMUNITY COLLEGE

Accounting, A
Clinical/Medical Laboratory Technician, A
Culinary Arts/Chef Training, A
Data Processing and Data Processing
  Technology/Technician, A
Hotel/Motel Administration/Management, A
Industrial Radiologic Technology/Technician, A
Legal Administrative Assistant/Secretary, A
Legal Assistant/Paralegal, A
Liberal Arts and Sciences Studies and
  Humanities, A
Marketing/Marketing Management, A
Medical/Clinical Assistant, A
Nursing - Registered Nurse Training, A
Occupational Therapy/Therapist, A
Physical Therapy/Therapist, A

Respiratory Care Therapy/Therapist, A
Special Products Marketing Operations, A
Tourism and Travel Services Management, A

KAUAI COMMUNITY COLLEGE

Accounting, A
Administrative Assistant and Secretarial Science, A
Autobody/Collision and Repair
  Technology/Technician, A
Automobile/Automotive Mechanics
  Technology/Technician, A
Carpentry/Carpenter, A
Culinary Arts/Chef Training, A
Electrical, Electronic and Communications
  Engineering Technology/Technician, A
Hospitality Administration/Management, A
Kindergarten/PreSchool Education and Teaching, A
Liberal Arts and Sciences Studies and
  Humanities, AD
Nursing - Registered Nurse Training, A

LEEWARD COMMUNITY COLLEGE

Accounting, A
Administrative Assistant and Secretarial Science, A
Automobile/Automotive Mechanics
  Technology/Technician, A
Business Administration and Management, A
Commercial and Advertising Art, A
Computer Science, A
Consumer Merchandising/Retailing Management, A
Drafting and Design Technology/Technician, A
Food Technology and Processing, A
Human Services, A
Liberal Arts and Sciences Studies and
  Humanities, A
Parks, Recreation, Leisure and Fitness Studies, A

MAUI COMMUNITY COLLEGE

Accounting, A
Administrative Assistant and Secretarial Science, A
Agricultural Mechanization, A
Automobile/Automotive Mechanics
  Technology/Technician, A
Carpentry/Carpenter, A
Construction Engineering Technology/Technician, A
Criminal Justice/Law Enforcement Administration, A
Fashion/Apparel Design, A
Fire Science/Firefighting, A
Food Technology and Processing, A
Horticultural Science, A
Hotel/Motel Administration/Management, A
Human Services, A
Liberal Arts and Sciences Studies and
  Humanities, A
Marketing/Marketing Management, A
Nursing - Registered Nurse Training, A
Welding Technology/Welder, A

TRANSPACIFIC HAWAII COLLEGE

Liberal Arts and Sciences Studies and
  Humanities, A

UNIVERSITY OF HAWAII AT HILO

Agricultural Business and Management, B
Agriculture, B
Animal Sciences, B
Anthropology, B
Art/Art Studies, General, B
Biology/Biological Sciences, B
Business Administration and Management, B
Chemistry, B
Computer Science, B
Economics, B
Elementary Education and Teaching, B
English Language and Literature, B
Geography, B
Geology/Earth Science, B
History, B
Horticultural Science, B
Interdisciplinary Studies, B
Japanese Language and Literature, B
Linguistics, B
Mathematics, B
Music, B
Natural Sciences, B

Nursing - Registered Nurse Training, B
Philosophy, B
Physics, B
Political Science and Government, B
Psychology, B
Secondary Education and Teaching, B
Sociology, B

UNIVERSITY OF HAWAII AT MANOA

Accounting, BMD
Agricultural Economics, B
Agricultural Production Operations, B
Agricultural Sciences, MD
Allopathic Medicine, P
American/United States Studies/Civilization, BMD
Anatomy, MD
Animal Sciences, BM
Anthropology, BMD
Architecture, BD
Art History, Criticism and Conservation, M
Art/Art Studies, General, B
Asian Languages, MD
Asian Studies/Civilization, BMO
Astronomy, MD
Bioengineering, MD
Biological and Biomedical Sciences, MD
Biological Anthropology, D
Biology/Biological Sciences, B
Botany/Plant Biology, BMD
Business Administration, Management and
  Operations, M
Business/Commerce, B
Business/Managerial Economics, B
Cell Biology and Anatomy, MD
Chemistry, BMD
Chinese Language and Literature, B
Civil Engineering, BMD
Classics and Classical
  Languages, Literatures, and Linguistics, BM
Clinical Psychology, D
Communication and Media Studies, M
Communication Disorders, M
Communication Studies/Speech Communication
  and Rhetoric, B
Computer and Information Sciences, B
Computer Science, BMDO
Conservation Biology, MD
Counselor Education/School Counseling and
  Guidance Services, BM
Curriculum and Instruction, MD
Dance, BMD
Dental Hygiene/Hygienist, B
Dietetics/Dieticians, B
Drama and Dramatics/Theatre Arts, B
Early Childhood Education and Teaching, M
Ecology, MD
Economics, BMD
Education, BMD
Educational Administration and Supervision, MD
Educational Media/Instructional Technology, M
Educational Psychology, MD
Electrical Engineering, MD
Electrical, Electronics and Communications
  Engineering, B
Elementary Education and Teaching, B
Engineering and Applied Sciences, MD
English, MD
English as a Second Language, MD
English Language and Literature, B
Entomology, BMD
Entrepreneurship/Entrepreneurial Studies, M
Environmental Engineering
  Technology/Environmental Technology, MD
Environmental Policy and Resource
  Management, MD
Environmental Sciences, B
Environmental Studies, B
Epidemiology, MD
Ethnic, Cultural Minority, and Gender Studies, B
Evolutionary Biology, MD
Family and Consumer Sciences/Human Sciences, B
Fashion/Apparel Design, B
Filipino/Tagalog Language and Literature, B
Finance, B
Finance and Banking, MD
Fine Arts and Art Studies, M

Food Science and Technology, M
Foreign Language Teacher Education, D
Foundations and Philosophy of Education, MD
French Language and Literature, BM
Genetics, MD
Geochemistry, MD
Geography, BMD
Geology/Earth Science, BMD
Geophysics and Seismology, MD
German Language and Literature, BM
Health and Physical Education, B
History, BMD
Horticultural Science, MD
Human Development and Family Studies, B
Human Resources Management and Services, M
Human Resources Management/Personnel
   Administration, B
Hydrology and Water Resources Science, MD
Information Science/Studies, MDO
Interdisciplinary Studies, B
International Business/Trade/Commerce, BMD
Japanese Language and Literature, B
Journalism, B
Kinesiology and Exercise Science, B
Kinesiology and Movement Studies, M
Korean Language and Literature, B
Landscape Architecture, B
Law and Legal Studies, PO
Leisure Studies, M
Library Science, MDO
Linguistics, BMD
Management Information Systems and
   Services, BMD
Marine Biology and Biological Oceanography, BMD
Marine Geology, MD
Marketing, MD
Marketing/Marketing Management, B
Mathematics, BMD
Mechanical Engineering, BMD
Medical Microbiology and Bacteriology, MD
Meteorology, BMD
Microbiology, BMD
Molecular Biology, MD
Music, BMD
Natural Resources and Conservation, MD
Natural Resources Management/Development and
   Policy, B
Neuroscience, MD
Nursing, MDO
Nursing - Advanced Practice, M
Nursing - Registered Nurse Training, B
Nursing Administration, M
Nutritional Sciences, M
Ocean Engineering, MD
Oceanography, Chemical and Physical, MD
Organizational Behavior Studies, M
Organizational Management, MD
Pacific Area/Pacific Rim Studies, B
Parks, Recreation, Leisure and Fitness Studies, B
Peace Studies and Conflict Resolution, B
Philosophy, BMD
Physical Education Teaching and Coaching, B
Physics, BMD
Planetary Astronomy and Science, MD
Plant Biology, MD
Plant Pathology/Phytopathology, MD
Plant Protection and Integrated Pest
   Management, B
Plant Sciences, MD
Political Science and Government, BMD
Psychology, BMD
Public Administration, MO
Public Health, MD
Real Estate, M
Religion/Religious Studies, BM
Reproductive Biology, MD
Russian Language and Literature, B
Sanskrit and Classical Indian
   Languages, Literatures, and Linguistics, B
Secondary Education and Teaching, B
Social Work, BMD
Sociology, BMD
South Asian
   Languages, Literatures, and Linguistics, B
Spanish Language and Literature, BM
Special Education and Teaching, BMD

Speech and Rhetorical Studies, BM
Taxation, M
Teaching English as a Second or Foreign
   Language/ESL Language Instructor, B
Theater, MD
Tourism and Travel Services Management, B
Travel and Tourism, MO
Urban and Regional Planning, MO
Women's Studies, B
Zoology/Animal Biology, BMD

UNIVERSITY OF HAWAII-WEST OAHU

Anthropology, B
Business Administration and Management, B
Criminal Justice/Law Enforcement Administration, B
Economics, B
English Language and Literature, B
History, B
Humanities/Humanistic Studies, B
Philosophy, B
Political Science and Government, B
Psychology, B
Public Administration, B
Social Sciences, B
Sociology, B

UNIVERSITY OF PHOENIX-HAWAII CAMPUS

Accounting, B
Business Administration, Management and
   Operations, M
Counselor Education/School Counseling and
   Guidance Services, M
Curriculum and Instruction, M
Early Childhood Education and Teaching, M
E-Commerce/Electronic Commerce, B
Education, MO
Educational Administration and Supervision, M
Educational Media/Instructional Technology, M
Electronic Commerce, M
Elementary Education and Teaching, MO
English as a Second Language, M
Finance, M
General Studies, A
Health Services Administration, M
Health/Health Care Administration/Management, B
Information Technology, B
International Business/Trade/Commerce, M
Management, M
Management Information Systems and
   Services, BM
Management of Technology, M
Management Science, B
Marketing, M
Marketing/Marketing Management, B
Marriage and Family Therapy/Counseling, M
Nursing, M
Nursing - Advanced Practice, M
Nursing - Registered Nurse Training, B
Nursing Science, B
Organizational Management, M
Public Administration and Social Service
   Professions, B
Secondary Education and Teaching, O
Special Education and Teaching, MO

WINDWARD COMMUNITY COLLEGE

Liberal Arts and Sciences Studies and
   Humanities, A
Professional Studies, A

Idaho

ALBERTSON COLLEGE OF IDAHO

Accounting, B
Anthropology, B
Art/Art Studies, General, B
Biology/Biological Sciences, B
Business Administration and Management, B
Chemistry, B
Creative Writing, B
Drama and Dramatics/Theatre Arts, B
Economics, B
Education, B
English Language and Literature, B

History, B
International Business/Trade/Commerce, B
International Economics, B
Kinesiology and Exercise Science, B
Mathematics, B
Music, B
Philosophy, B
Physical Education Teaching and Coaching, B
Physics, B
Political Science and Government, B
Pre-Medicine/Pre-Medical Studies, B
Psychology, B
Religion/Religious Studies, B
Sociology, B
Spanish Language and Literature, B
Sport and Fitness Administration/Management, B

APOLLO COLLEGE

Dental Hygiene/Hygienist, A
Medical Office Management/Administration, A
Occupational Therapist Assistant, A

BOISE BIBLE COLLEGE

Bible/Biblical Studies, AB
Divinity/Ministry (BD, MDiv.), AB
Modern Greek Language and Literature, B
Pastoral Studies/Counseling, AB
Religion/Religious Studies, AB
Religious Education, AB
Religious/Sacred Music, AB

BOISE STATE UNIVERSITY

Accounting, BM
Advertising, B
Anthropology, B
Art Education, M
Art History, Criticism and Conservation, B
Art Teacher Education, B
Art/Art Studies, General, B
Athletic Training and Sports Medicine, B
Automobile/Automotive Mechanics
   Technology/Technician, A
Bilingual and Multilingual Education, B
Biological and Biomedical Sciences, M
Biology/Biological Sciences, B
Building/Construction
   Finishing, Management, and Inspection, B
Business Administration and Management, B
Business Administration, Management and
   Operations, M
Business Machine Repairer, A
Business Teacher Education, B
Business/Managerial Economics, B
Chemistry, B
Child Development, A
Civil Engineering, BM
Clinical Laboratory Science/Medical
   Technology/Technologist, B
Commercial and Advertising Art, B
Communication and Media Studies, M
Comparative Literature, B
Computer and Information Sciences, B
Computer Engineering, M
Computer Science, BM
Computer Systems Networking and
   Telecommunications, B
Counselor Education/School Counseling and
   Guidance Services, M
Criminal Justice/Law Enforcement
   Administration, AB
Criminology, M
Culinary Arts/Chef Training, A
Curriculum and Instruction, MD
Drafting and Design Technology/Technician, A
Drama and Dramatics/Theatre Arts, B
Drawing, B
Early Childhood Education and Teaching, M
Economics, B
Education, BMD
Educational Media/Instructional Technology, M
Electrical and Electronic Engineering
   Technologies/Technicians, A
Electrical Engineering, M
Electrical, Electronic and Communications
   Engineering Technology/Technician, A

Electrical, Electronics and Communications
Engineering, B
Elementary Education and Teaching, B
English, M
English Language and Literature, B
Environmental Health, B
Environmental Policy and Resource
Management, M
Environmental Studies, B
Ethnic and Cultural Studies, B
Exercise and Sports Science, M
Finance, B
Fine Arts and Art Studies, M
French Language and Literature, B
Geology/Earth Science, BM
Geophysics and Seismology, BMD
Geosciences, M
German Language and Literature, B
Health Information/Medical Records
Administration/Administrator, A
Heating, Air Conditioning, Ventilation and
Refrigeration Maintenance
Technology/Technician, A
History, BM
Horticultural Science, A
Human Resources Management/Personnel
Administration, B
Industrial Radiologic Technology/Technician, AB
Industrial Technology/Technician, B
Information Science/Studies, B
Interdisciplinary Studies, BM
International Business/Trade/Commerce, B
Kindergarten/PreSchool Education and Teaching, B
Kinesiology and Exercise Science, B
Legal Assistant/Paralegal, A
Liberal Arts and Sciences Studies and
Humanities, B
Machine Tool Technology/Machinist, A
Management Information Systems and Services, M
Marketing/Marketing Management, AB
Mass Communication/Media Studies, B
Materials Engineering, M
Mathematics, B
Mathematics Teacher Education, M
Mechanical Engineering, M
Mechanical Engineering/Mechanical
Technology/Technician, B
Medical Administrative Assistant/Secretary, A
Music, BM
Music Management and Merchandising, B
Music Teacher Education, BM
Nursing - Registered Nurse Training, AB
Operations Management and Supervision, B
Perfusion Technology/Perfusionist, A
Philosophy, B
Physical Education Teaching and Coaching, B
Physician Assistant, B
Physics, B
Political Science and Government, B
Pre-Dentistry Studies, B
Pre-Engineering, A
Pre-Medicine/Pre-Medical Studies, B
Pre-Veterinary Studies, B
Psychology, B
Public Administration, BM
Public Health, M
Public Health (MPH, DPH), B
Public Policy Analysis, M
Radiologic Technology/Science - Radiographer, AB
Reading Teacher Education, BM
Respiratory Care Therapy/Therapist, B
Science Teacher Education/General Science
Teacher Education, BM
Secondary Education and Teaching, B
Social Sciences, B
Social Work, BM
Sociology, B
Spanish Language and Literature, B
Special Education and Teaching, BM
Sport and Fitness Administration/Management, M
Surgical Technology/Technologist, A
Teacher Assistant/Aide, A
Technical and Business Writing, B
Technical Communication, M

Welding Technology/Welder, A

BRIGHAM YOUNG UNIVERSITY -IDAHO

Accounting, A
Administrative Assistant and Secretarial Science, A
Advertising, A
Agricultural Business and Management, A
Agricultural Economics, A
Agriculture, A
Agronomy and Crop Science, A
Animal Sciences, A
Apparel and Textiles, A
Architectural Engineering Technology/Technician, A
Army JROTC/ROTC, A
Art/Art Studies, General, A
Athletic Training and Sports Medicine, A
Automobile/Automotive Mechanics
Technology/Technician, A
Biology/Biological Sciences, A
Botany/Plant Biology, A
Broadcast Journalism, A
Business Administration and Management, A
Business Teacher Education, A
Carpentry/Carpenter, A
Chemical Engineering, A
Chemistry, A
Child Development, A
Chinese Language and Literature, A
Civil Engineering Technology/Technician, A
Clinical/Medical Laboratory Technician, A
Commercial and Advertising Art, A
Communication Disorders, A
Computer Programming/Programmer, A
Computer Science, A
Construction Engineering Technology/Technician, A
Criminal Justice/Law Enforcement Administration, A
Criminal Justice/Police Science, A
Dairy Science, A
Dance, A
Data Processing and Data Processing
Technology/Technician, A
Dental Hygiene/Hygienist, A
Dietetics/Dieticians, A
Drafting and Design Technology/Technician, A
Drafting/Design Engineering
Technologies/Technicians, A
Drama and Dramatics/Theatre Arts, A
Ecology, A
Economics, A
Education, A
Electrical, Electronic and Communications
Engineering Technology/Technician, A
Elementary Education and Teaching, A
Emergency Medical Technology/Technician (EMT
Paramedic), A
Engineering, A
Engineering Technology, A
English Language and Literature, A
Family and Community Services, A
Family and Consumer Sciences/Home Economics
Teacher Education, A
Family and Consumer Sciences/Human Sciences, A
Farm/Farm and Ranch Management, A
Fashion Merchandising, A
Fashion/Apparel Design, A
Finance, A
Foods, Nutrition, and Wellness Studies, A
Forestry, A
French Language and Literature, A
Geography, A
Geology/Earth Science, A
German Language and Literature, A
History, A
Horticultural Science, A
Humanities/Humanistic Studies, A
Industrial Design, A
Industrial Technology/Technician, A
Information Science/Studies, A
Interior Design, A
Journalism, A
Kindergarten/PreSchool Education and Teaching, A
Landscape Architecture, A
Liberal Arts and Sciences Studies and
Humanities, A
Machine Tool Technology/Machinist, A
Marine Biology and Biological Oceanography, A

Marketing/Marketing Management, A
Mass Communication/Media Studies, A
Mathematics, A
Mechanical Engineering/Mechanical
Technology/Technician, A
Metallurgical Technology/Technician, A
Music, A
Music Teacher Education, A
Nursing - Registered Nurse Training, A
Occupational Therapy/Therapist, A
Ornamental Horticulture, A
Parks, Recreation, Leisure and Fitness Studies, A
Photography, A
Physical Education Teaching and Coaching, A
Physical Sciences, A
Physical Therapy/Therapist, A
Physics, A
Piano and Organ, A
Plastics Engineering Technology/Technician, A
Political Science and Government, A
Pre-Engineering, A
Psychology, A
Public Health (MPH, DPH), A
Radio and Television, A
Radiologic Technology/Science - Radiographer, A
Range Science and Management, A
Russian Language and Literature, A
Social Work, A
Sociology, A
Spanish Language and Literature, A
Special Products Marketing Operations, A
Technology Education/Industrial Arts, A
Trade and Industrial Teacher Education, A
Welding Technology/Welder, A
Wildlife and Wildlands Science and Management, A
Zoology/Animal Biology, A

COLLEGE OF SOUTHERN IDAHO

Accounting, A
Agricultural Business and Management, A
Agriculture, A
Anthropology, A
Art/Art Studies, General, A
Autobody/Collision and Repair
Technology/Technician, A
Automobile/Automotive Mechanics
Technology/Technician, A
Biology/Biological Sciences, A
Botany/Plant Biology, A
Business Administration and Management, A
Business/Commerce, A
Cabinetmaking and Millwork/Millwright, A
Chemistry, A
Child Development, A
Clinical Laboratory Science/Medical
Technology/Technologist, A
Commercial and Advertising Art, A
Communication Studies/Speech Communication
and Rhetoric, A
Computer Science, A
Criminal Justice/Law Enforcement Administration, A
Criminal Justice/Police Science, A
Culinary Arts/Chef Training, A
Dental Assisting/Assistant, A
Dental Hygiene/Hygienist, A
Diesel Mechanics Technology/Technician, A
Dietetics/Dieticians, A
Drafting and Design Technology/Technician, A
Drama and Dramatics/Theatre Arts, A
Education, A
Electrical, Electronic and Communications
Engineering Technology/Technician, A
Elementary Education and Teaching, A
Engineering, A
English Language and Literature, A
Environmental Studies, A
Equestrian/Equine Studies, A
Finance, A
Foreign Languages and Literatures, A
Forestry, A
Geography, A
Geology/Earth Science, A
Health/Health Care Administration/Management, A
Heating, Air Conditioning, Ventilation and
Refrigeration Maintenance
Technology/Technician, A

History, A
Hotel/Motel Administration/Management, A
Human Services, A
Hydrology and Water Resources Science, A
Liberal Arts and Sciences Studies and
   Humanities, A
Library Science, A
Marketing/Marketing Management, A
Mathematics, A
Medical Radiologic Technology/Science - Radiation
   Therapist, A
Music, A
Natural Sciences, A
Nursing - Registered Nurse Training, A
Occupational Therapy/Therapist, A
Photography, A
Physical Education Teaching and Coaching, A
Physical Therapy/Therapist, A
Physician Assistant, A
Physics, A
Political Science and Government, A
Pre-Pharmacy Studies, A
Psychology, A
Public Health Education and Promotion, A
Range Science and Management, A
Real Estate, A
Respiratory Care Therapy/Therapist, A
Sociology, A
Surgical Technology/Technologist, A
Veterinary/Animal Health Technology/Technician and
   Veterinary Assistant, A
Welding Technology/Welder, A
Woodworking, A
Zoology/Animal Biology, A

EASTERN IDAHO TECHNICAL COLLEGE

Accounting, A
Administrative Assistant and Secretarial Science, A
Automobile/Automotive Mechanics
   Technology/Technician, A
Computer Systems Networking and
   Telecommunications, A
Diesel Mechanics Technology/Technician, A
Electrical, Electronic and Communications
   Engineering Technology/Technician, A
Legal Assistant/Paralegal, A
Marketing/Marketing Management, A
Medical/Clinical Assistant, A
Prepress/Desktop Publishing and Digital Imaging
   Design, A
Surgical Technology/Technologist, A
Welding Technology/Welder, A

IDAHO STATE UNIVERSITY

Accounting, B
Administrative Assistant and Secretarial Science, A
Aircraft Powerplant Technology/Technician, A
Allied Health and Medical Assisting Services, MDO
American Indian/Native American
   Languages, Literatures, and Linguistics, A
American Sign Language (ASL), A
American/United States Studies/Civilization, B
Anthropology, BM
Art/Art Studies, General, AB
Audiology/Audiologist and Speech-Language
   Pathology/Pathologist, A
Autobody/Collision and Repair
   Technology/Technician, A
Automobile/Automotive Mechanics
   Technology/Technician, A
Biochemistry, B
Biological and Biomedical Sciences, MD
Biology/Biological Sciences, AB
Botany/Plant Biology, B
Business Administration and Management, B
Business Administration, Management and
   Operations, MO
Business Machine Repairer, A
Business/Commerce, AB
Carpentry/Carpenter, A
Chemistry, ABM
Child Care and Support Services Management, A
Civil Engineering, BM
Civil Engineering Technology/Technician, A

Clinical Laboratory Science/Medical
   Technology/Technologist, B
Clinical Microbiology, M
Clinical Psychology, D
Communication Disorders, MD
Communication Studies/Speech Communication
   and Rhetoric, AB
Communications Systems Installation and Repair
   Technology, A
Community Health and Preventive Medicine, O
Computer and Information Sciences, B
Computer Programming, Specific Applications, A
Counseling Psychology, O
Counselor Education/School Counseling and
   Guidance Services, MDO
Criminal Justice/Police Science, A
Criminal Justice/Safety Studies, A
Culinary Arts/Chef Training, A
Curriculum and Instruction, M
Dance, M
Dental Hygiene/Hygienist, BM
Dental Laboratory Technology/Technician, A
Dentistry, O
Diesel Mechanics Technology/Technician, A
Dietetics/Dieticians, B
Drafting and Design Technology/Technician, A
Drafting/Design Engineering
   Technologies/Technicians, A
Drama and Dramatics/Theatre Arts, B
Ecology, B
Economics, B
Education, MDO
Educational Administration and Supervision, MO
Educational Leadership and Administration, DO
Educational Media/Instructional Technology, M
Electrical, Electronic and Communications
   Engineering Technology/Technician, A
Electrical, Electronics and Communications
   Engineering, B
Electrical/Electronics Equipment Installation and
   Repair, A
Electromechanical Technology/Electromechanical
   Engineering Technology, A
Elementary Education and Teaching, B
Emergency Medical Technology/Technician (EMT
   Paramedic), A
Engineering, B
Engineering and Applied Sciences, MDO
English, MD
English Language and Literature, AB
Environmental Engineering
   Technology/Environmental Technology, M
Environmental Sciences, M
Family and Consumer Sciences/Human Sciences, B
Farm/Farm and Ranch Management, AB
Finance, B
Fine Arts and Art Studies, M
Fire Science/Firefighting, A
Foods, Nutrition, and Wellness Studies, B
French Language and Literature, AB
General Studies, AB
Geographic Information Systems, M
Geology/Earth Science, ABMO
Geophysics and Seismology, M
Geosciences, MO
German Language and Literature, AB
Graphic and Printing Equipment Operator
   Production, A
Hazardous Materials Management and Waste
   Technology/Technician, M
Health Education, M
Health Information/Medical Records
   Technology/Technician, A
Health Services/Allied Health/Health Sciences, B
Health Teacher Education, B
Health/Health Care Administration/Management, B
History, AB
Human Resources Management/Personnel
   Administration, B
Hydrology and Water Resources Science, M
Industrial Education, M
Information Science/Studies, B
Instrumentation Technology/Technician, A
Interdisciplinary Studies, M
Laser and Optical Technology/Technician, A
Latin Language and Literature, A

Machine Tool Technology/Machinist, A
Management Information Systems and
   Services, MO
Management of Technology, M
Marketing/Marketing Management, AB
Mass Communication/Media Studies, B
Mathematics, ABMD
Mechanical Engineering, BM
Mechanics, M
Mechanics and Repairers, A
Medical Microbiology and Bacteriology, B
Medical Radiologic Technology/Science - Radiation
   Therapist, AB
Medical/Clinical Assistant, A
Medicinal and Pharmaceutical Chemistry, M
Microbiology, BM
Multi-/Interdisciplinary Studies, B
Music, B
Music Performance, B
Music Teacher Education, B
Nuclear Engineering, MDO
Nursing, MO
Nursing - Registered Nurse Training, B
Nutritional Sciences, O
Occupational Therapist Assistant, A
Occupational Therapy/Therapist, M
Operations Research, M
Oral and Dental Sciences, MO
Pharmaceutical Administration, MDP
Pharmaceutical Sciences, MD
Pharmacognosy, M
Pharmacology, MD
Pharmacy, MDP
Pharmacy Technician/Assistant, A
Philosophy, B
Physical Education Teaching and Coaching, BM
Physical Therapist Assistant, A
Physical Therapy/Therapist, D
Physician Assistant, M
Physics, ABM
Political Science and Government, ABMD
Psychology, BMD
Public Administration, M
Public Health, M
Reading Teacher Education, M
School Psychology, O
Secondary Education and Teaching, B
Sign Language Interpretation and Translation, B
Social Work, B
Sociology, BM
Spanish Language and Literature, AB
Special Education and Teaching, BMO
Speech and Interpersonal Communication, M
Survey Technology/Surveying, B
Theater, M
Vocational and Technical Education, M
Welding Technology/Welder, A
Zoology/Animal Biology, B

ITT TECHNICAL INSTITUTE

Animation, Interactive Technology, Video Graphics
   and Special Effects, B
Business Administration and Management, B
CAD/CADD Drafting and/or Design
   Technology/Technician, A
Computer and Information Systems Security, B
Computer Programming/Programmer, A
Computer Software Technology/Technician, B
Computer Systems Networking and
   Telecommunications, B
Criminal Justice/Law Enforcement Administration, B
E-Commerce/Electronic Commerce, B
Electrical, Electronic and Communications
   Engineering Technology/Technician, AB
System, Networking, and LAN/WAN
   Management/Manager, A
Web Page, Digital/Multimedia and Information
   Resources Design, A
Web/Multimedia Management and Webmaster, A

LEWIS-CLARK STATE COLLEGE

Accounting Technology/Technician and
   Bookkeeping, AB
Administrative Assistant and Secretarial Science, AB
Autobody/Collision and Repair
   Technology/Technician, AB

Automobile/Automotive Mechanics
Technology/Technician, AB
Behavioral Sciences, A
Biology/Biological Sciences, B
Business Administration and Management, B
Chemistry, B
Child Development, AB
Communication Studies/Speech Communication
and Rhetoric, B
Computer and Information Sciences, AB
Computer Science, B
Corrections, B
Creative Writing, B
Diesel Mechanics Technology/Technician, AB
Drafting and Design Technology/Technician, AB
Electrical/Electronics Equipment Installation and
Repair, AB
Elementary Education and Teaching, B
English Language and Literature, B
English/Language Arts Teacher Education, B
Fire Science/Firefighting, AB
Graphic and Printing Equipment Operator
Production, AB
Heating, Air Conditioning, Ventilation and
Refrigeration Maintenance
Technology/Technician, AB
Hospitality Administration/Management, AB
Industrial Electronics Technology/Technician, AB
Interdisciplinary Studies, B
Kinesiology and Exercise Science, B
Legal Administrative Assistant/Secretary, AB
Legal Assistant/Paralegal, AB
Liberal Arts and Sciences Studies and
Humanities, A
Licensed Practical/Vocational Nurse Training, A
Manufacturing Technology/Technician, AB
Mathematics, B
Mathematics Teacher Education, B
Mechanics and Repairers, AB
Medical Office Assistant/Specialist, AB
Medical/Health Management and Clinical
Assistant/Specialist, AB
Multi-/Interdisciplinary Studies, B
Natural Sciences, B
Nursing - Registered Nurse Training, B
Physical Education Teaching and Coaching, B
Psychology, B
Radiologic Technology/Science - Radiographer, A
Science Teacher Education/General Science
Teacher Education, B
Small Business Administration/Management, AB
Social Science Teacher Education, B
Social Sciences, B
Social Work, B
Web/Multimedia Management and Webmaster, AB
Welding Technology/Welder, AB

NORTH IDAHO COLLEGE

Administrative Assistant and Secretarial Science, A
Agriculture, A
American Indian/Native American Studies, A
Anthropology, A
Art/Art Studies, General, A
Astronomy, A
Athletic Training and Sports Medicine, A
Automobile/Automotive Mechanics
Technology/Technician, A
Biological and Physical Sciences, A
Biology/Biological Sciences, A
Botany/Plant Biology, A
Business Administration and Management, A
Business Teacher Education, A
Carpentry/Carpenter, A
Chemistry, A
Clinical Laboratory Science/Medical
Technology/Technologist, A
Commercial and Advertising Art, A
Computer and Information Sciences, A
Computer Programming/Programmer, A
Computer Science, A
Criminal Justice/Law Enforcement Administration, A
Criminal Justice/Police Science, A
Culinary Arts/Chef Training, A
Developmental and Child Psychology, A
Drafting and Design Technology/Technician, A
Drama and Dramatics/Theatre Arts, A

Education, A
Electrical, Electronic and Communications
Engineering Technology/Technician, A
Elementary Education and Teaching, A
Engineering, A
English Language and Literature, A
Environmental Health, A
Forestry, A
French Language and Literature, A
Geology/Earth Science, A
German Language and Literature, A
Health/Health Care Administration/Management, A
Heating, Air Conditioning, Ventilation and
Refrigeration Maintenance
Technology/Technician, A
Heavy Equipment Maintenance
Technology/Technician, A
History, A
Hospitality Administration/Management, A
Human Services, A
Journalism, A
Legal Administrative Assistant/Secretary, A
Legal Assistant/Paralegal, A
Liberal Arts and Sciences Studies and
Humanities, A
Licensed Practical/Vocational Nurse Training, A
Machine Tool Technology/Machinist, A
Management Information Systems and Services, A
Marine Technology, A
Mass Communication/Media Studies, A
Mathematics, A
Medical Administrative Assistant/Secretary, A
Music, A
Music Teacher Education, A
Nursing - Registered Nurse Training, A
Physical Sciences, A
Physics, A
Political Science and Government, A
Psychology, A
Social Sciences, A
Sociology, A
Spanish Language and Literature, A
Welding Technology/Welder, A
Wildlife and Wildlands Science and Management, A
Wildlife Biology, A
Zoology/Animal Biology, A

NORTHWEST NAZARENE UNIVERSITY

Accounting, B
Ancient Near Eastern and Biblical
Languages, Literatures, and Linguistics, B
Art Teacher Education, B
Art/Art Studies, General, B
Athletic Training and Sports Medicine, B
Biochemistry, B
Biology Teacher Education, B
Biology/Biological Sciences, B
Business Administration and Management, B
Business Administration, Management and
Operations, M
Ceramic Arts and Ceramics, B
Chemistry, B
Chemistry Teacher Education, B
Commercial and Advertising Art, B
Communication Studies/Speech Communication
and Rhetoric, B
Computer Science, B
Counselor Education/School Counseling and
Guidance Services, M
Curriculum and Instruction, M
Divinity/Ministry (BD, MDiv.), B
Education, M
Educational Leadership and Administration, M
Elementary Education and Teaching, B
Engineering Physics, B
English Language and Literature, B
English/Language Arts Teacher Education, B
Finance, B
Forensic Science and Technology, B
Graphic Design, B
Health and Physical Education, B
History, B
History Teacher Education, B
International Business/Trade/Commerce, B
International Relations and Affairs, B
Kinesiology and Exercise Science, B

Liberal Arts and Sciences Studies and
Humanities, B
Marketing/Marketing Management, B
Mass Communication/Media Studies, B
Mathematics, B
Mathematics Teacher Education, B
Missions/Missionary Studies and Missiology, B
Music, B
Music Performance, B
Music Teacher Education, B
Music Theory and Composition, B
Nursing - Registered Nurse Training, B
Painting, B
Parks, Recreation, Leisure and Fitness Studies, B
Pastoral Studies/Counseling, B
Philosophy, B
Physical Education Teaching and Coaching, B
Physical Therapy/Therapist, B
Physics, B
Political Science and Government, B
Pre-Law Studies, B
Pre-Medicine/Pre-Medical Studies, B
Psychology, B
Public Relations/Image Management, B
Radio and Television Broadcasting
Technology/Technician, B
Reading Teacher Education, M
Religion/Religious Studies, BM
Religious Education, B
Religious/Sacred Music, B
Sculpture, B
Secondary Education and Teaching, B
Social Science Teacher Education, B
Social Sciences, B
Social Work, BM
Spanish Language and Literature, B
Spanish Language Teacher Education, B
Special Education and Teaching, M
Theology/Theological Studies, B

UNIVERSITY OF IDAHO

Accounting, BM
Administrative Assistant and Secretarial Science, B
Adult and Continuing Education and Teaching, MDO
Agricultural Business and Management, B
Agricultural Economics, BM
Agricultural Education, M
Agricultural Engineering, MD
Agricultural Mechanization, B
Agricultural Sciences, M
Agricultural Teacher Education, B
Agricultural/Biological Engineering and
Bioengineering, B
Agriculture, B
Agronomy and Soil Sciences, MD
American/United States Studies/Civilization, B
Animal Sciences, BMD
Anthropology, BM
Apparel and Textiles, B
Applied Mathematics, B
Architecture, BM
Art Education, M
Art Teacher Education, B
Art/Art Studies, General, B
Athletic Training and Sports Medicine, B
Biochemistry, MD
Bioinformatics, MD
Biological and Biomedical Sciences, MD
Biology/Biological Sciences, B
Biomedical/Medical Engineering, B
Botany/Plant Biology, B
Business Administration, Management and
Operations, M
Business Education, MD
Business Teacher Education, B
Cartography, B
Chemical Engineering, BMD
Chemistry, BMD
Child Development, B
Civil Engineering, BMD
Classics and Classical
Languages, Literatures, and Linguistics, B
Clinical Laboratory Science/Medical
Technology/Technologist, B
Communication and Media Studies, M

Communication Studies/Speech Communication and Rhetoric, B
Computational Biology, MD
Computer Engineering, BM
Computer Science, BMD
Counselor Education/School Counseling and Guidance Services, MDO
Criminal Justice/Safety Studies, B
Dance, B
Design and Applied Arts, M
Drama and Dramatics/Theatre Arts, B
Economics, B
Education, MDO
Educational Administration and Supervision, MDO
Electrical Engineering, MD
Electrical, Electronics and Communications Engineering, B
Elementary Education and Teaching, BM
Engineering, B
Engineering and Applied Sciences, MDO
English, M
English as a Second Language, M
English Education, M
English Language and Literature, B
Entomology, BMD
Environmental Engineering Technology/Environmental Technology, MDO
Environmental Sciences, M
Environmental Studies, B
Family and Consumer Sciences/Home Economics Teacher Education, B
Film, Television, and Video Production, M
Finance, B
Fine Arts and Art Studies, M
Fine/Studio Arts, B
Fish, Game and Wildlife Management, MD
Food Science, B
Food Science and Technology, M
Foods, Nutrition, and Wellness Studies, B
Foreign Language Teacher Education, M
Foreign Languages and Literatures, B
Forestry, BMD
French Language and Literature, BM
General Studies, B
Geography, BMD
Geological Engineering, M
Geological/Geophysical Engineering, B
Geology/Earth Science, BMD
Geophysics and Seismology, M
German Language and Literature, B
Hazardous Materials Management and Waste Technology/Technician, M
History, BMD
Home Economics, M
Horticultural Science, BMD
Human Resources Management/Personnel Administration, B
Hydrology and Water Resources Science, M
Industrial Education, MD
Industrial Engineering, B
Industrial Technology/Technician, B
Interdisciplinary Studies, M
Interior Architecture, B
Interior Design, B
International Relations and Affairs, B
Journalism, B
Landscape Architecture, BM
Latin American Studies, B
Latin Language and Literature, B
Law and Legal Studies, P
Liberal Arts and Sciences Studies and Humanities, B
Management Information Systems and Services, B
Marketing/Marketing Management, B
Materials Engineering, MD
Materials Sciences, MD
Mathematics, BMD
Mathematics Teacher Education, M
Mechanical Engineering, BMD
Medical Microbiology and Bacteriology, B
Metallurgical Engineering, BMD
Metallurgy, MD
Microbiology, MD
Military Technologies, B
Mineral/Mining Engineering, MD
Mining and Mineral Engineering, B

Molecular Biology, BMD
Multi-/Interdisciplinary Studies, B
Music, M
Music History, Literature, and Theory, B
Music Management and Merchandising, B
Music Performance, B
Music Teacher Education, B
Music Theory and Composition, B
Natural Resources Management/Development and Policy, BMD
Nuclear Engineering, MD
Operations Management and Supervision, B
Parks, Recreation, Leisure and Fitness Studies, B
Philosophy, B
Photography, B
Physical Education Teaching and Coaching, BMD
Physics, BMD
Plant Sciences, BMD
Political Science and Government, BMD
Pre-Medicine/Pre-Medical Studies, B
Psychology, BM
Public Administration, M
Public Affairs, MD
Public Relations/Image Management, B
Radio and Television, B
Range Science and Management, BMD
Recreation and Park Management, MD
Rural Sociology, M
School Psychology, DO
Science Teacher Education/General Science Teacher Education, M
Secondary Education and Teaching, BM
Social Sciences, MD
Social Studies Teacher Education, M
Sociology, B
Soil Science and Agronomy, B
Spanish Language and Literature, BM
Special Education and Teaching, BM
Statistics, M
Systems Engineering, M
Technical Teacher Education, B
Technology Teacher Education/Industrial Arts Teacher Education, B
Theater, M
Trade and Industrial Teacher Education, B
Veterinary Sciences, MD
Vocational and Technical Education, MDO
Voice and Opera, B
Wildlife and Wildlands Science and Management, B
Wood Science and Wood Products/Pulp and Paper Technology, B
Writing, M
Zoology/Animal Biology, B

UNIVERSITY OF PHOENIX-IDAHO CAMPUS

Accounting, BM
Business Administration, Management and Operations, BM
Computer and Information Sciences, B
E-Commerce/Electronic Commerce, B
Health/Health Care Administration/Management, B
Human Resources Management and Services, M
Management of Technology, M
Marketing/Marketing Management, B

Illinois

AMERICAN ACADEMY OF ART

Advertising, B
Applied Art, B
Art/Art Studies, General, B
Commercial and Advertising Art, B
Computer Art and Design, M
Computer Graphics, B
Design and Visual Communications, B
Drawing, B
Fine/Studio Arts, B
Internet and Interactive Multimedia, M
Painting, BM

Visual and Performing Arts, B

AMERICAN INTERCONTINENTAL UNIVERSITY ONLINE

Accounting, M
Accounting and Finance, B
Business Administration, Management and Operations, ABM
Computer Programming/Programmer, B
Corrections and Criminal Justice, B
Curriculum and Instruction, M
Data Processing and Data Processing Technology/Technician, A
Design and Visual Communications, B
Educational Media/Instructional Technology, M
Finance and Banking, M
Health Services Administration, M
Health/Health Care Administration/Management, B
Human Resources Management and Services, M
Human Resources Management/Personnel Administration, B
Industrial and Manufacturing Management, M
Industrial and Organizational Psychology, M
Information Science/Studies, M
Information Technology, B
Management, M
Marketing, M
Marketing/Marketing Management, B
Project Management, M
System, Networking, and LAN/WAN Management/Manager, B
Systems Science and Theory, M

ARGOSY UNIVERSITY/CHICAGO

Business Administration and Management, B
Business Administration, Management and Operations, MD
Clinical Psychology, MD
Counseling Psychology, MD
Education, MDO
Forensic Psychology, D
Health Psychology, D
Human Development, D
Marriage and Family Therapy/Counseling, D
Psychoanalysis and Psychotherapy, D
Psychology, BMDO

ARGOSY UNIVERSITY/SCHAUMBURG

Accounting, D
Business Administration, Management and Operations, MD
Business/Commerce, B
Clinical Psychology, MD
Counseling Psychology, MD
Curriculum and Instruction, MDO
Education, MDO
Educational Leadership and Administration, MDO
Finance and Banking, M
Health Services Administration, M
Human Resources Management and Services, M
International Business/Trade/Commerce, D
International Trade, M
Management, D
Management Information Systems and Services, D
Marketing, MD
Psychology, BMD

AUGUSTANA COLLEGE

Accounting, B
Anthropology, B
Art History, Criticism and Conservation, B
Art Teacher Education, B
Art/Art Studies, General, B
Asian Studies/Civilization, B
Biology/Biological Sciences, B
Business Administration and Management, B
Chemistry, B
Chinese Language and Literature, B
Classics and Classical Languages, Literatures, and Linguistics, B
Communication Disorders, B
Comparative Literature, B
Computer Science, B
Creative Writing, B
Drama and Dramatics/Theatre Arts, B

Economics, B
Education, B
Elementary Education and Teaching, B
Engineering, B
Engineering Physics, B
English Language and Literature, B
Environmental Studies, B
Finance, B
Fine/Studio Arts, B
French Language and Literature, B
Geography, B
Geology/Earth Science, B
German Language and Literature, B
History, B
Japanese Language and Literature, B
Jazz/Jazz Studies, B
Latin Language and Literature, B
Liberal Arts and Sciences Studies and
    Humanities, B
Marketing/Marketing Management, B
Mass Communication/Media Studies, B
Mathematics, B
Mathematics and Computer Science, B
Music, B
Music Performance, B
Music Teacher Education, B
Occupational Therapy/Therapist, B
Philosophy, B
Physical Education Teaching and Coaching, B
Physics, B
Piano and Organ, B
Political Science and Government, B
Pre-Dentistry Studies, B
Pre-Law Studies, B
Pre-Medicine/Pre-Medical Studies, B
Pre-Veterinary Studies, B
Psychology, B
Public Administration, B
Religion/Religious Studies, B
Religious/Sacred Music, B
Scandinavian
    Languages, Literatures, and Linguistics, B
Science Teacher Education/General Science
    Teacher Education, B
Secondary Education and Teaching, B
Sociology, B
Spanish Language and Literature, B
Speech and Rhetorical Studies, B
Speech-Language Pathology/Pathologist, B
Swedish Language and Literature, B
Violin, Viola, Guitar and Other Stringed
    Instruments, B
Voice and Opera, B
Wind and Percussion Instruments, B
Women's Studies, B

AURORA UNIVERSITY

Accounting, B
Biology/Biological Sciences, B
Business Administration, Management and
    Operations, M
Business/Commerce, B
Business/Managerial Economics, B
Chemistry, B
Clinical Laboratory Science/Medical
    Technology/Technologist, B
Communication Studies/Speech Communication
    and Rhetoric, B
Computer and Information Sciences, B
Computer Systems Networking and
    Telecommunications, B
Criminal Justice/Law Enforcement Administration, B
Criminal Justice/Safety Studies, B
Curriculum and Instruction, D
Economics, B
Education, MD
Educational Administration and Supervision, D
Educational Leadership and Administration, M
Elementary Education and Teaching, B
Engineering Physics, B
English Composition, B
English Language and Literature, B
Environmental Studies, B
Finance, B
Health/Medical Preparatory Programs, B
History, B

Humanities/Humanistic Studies, B
Leisure Studies, M
Management Information Systems and Services, B
Marketing/Marketing Management, B
Mathematics, B
Nursing - Registered Nurse Training, B
Operations Management and Supervision, B
Philosophy, B
Physical Education Teaching and Coaching, B
Political Science and Government, B
Psychology, B
Social Work, BM
Sociology, B
Therapeutic Recreation, M

BENEDICTINE UNIVERSITY

Accounting, B
Arts Management, B
Biochemistry, B
Biology/Biological Sciences, B
Business Administration and Management, A
Business Administration, Management and
    Operations, MO
Business, Management, Marketing, and Related
    Support Services, B
Business/Commerce, B
Business/Managerial Economics, B
Chemistry, B
Clinical Laboratory Science/Medical
    Technology/Technologist, B
Clinical Psychology, M
Communication Studies/Speech Communication
    and Rhetoric, B
Comparative Literature, B
Computer Science, B
Curriculum and Instruction, M
Economics, B
Education, BM
Educational Administration and Supervision, M
Educational Leadership and Administration, M
Elementary Education and Teaching, BM
Engineering Science, B
English Language and Literature, B
Environmental Studies, B
Exercise and Sports Science, M
Finance, B
Fine/Studio Arts, B
Health Promotion, M
Health/Health Care Administration/Management, B
History, B
Information Science/Studies, B
International Business/Trade/Commerce, B
International Relations and Affairs, B
Management, MO
Management Information Systems and
    Services, MO
Marketing/Marketing Management, B
Mathematics, B
Molecular Biology, B
Music, B
Music Teacher Education, B
Nuclear Medical Technology/Technologist, B
Nursing Science, B
Nutritional Sciences, BM
Organizational Behavior Studies, BMO
Organizational Management, D
Philosophy, B
Physics, B
Political Science and Government, B
Pre-Dentistry Studies, B
Pre-Law Studies, B
Pre-Medicine/Pre-Medical Studies, B
Pre-Veterinary Studies, B
Psychology, B
Public Health, MO
Public Health (MPH, DPH), B
Publishing, B
Reading Teacher Education, M
Science Teacher Education/General Science
    Teacher Education, B
Secondary Education and Teaching, BM
Social Sciences, B
Sociology, B
Spanish Language and Literature, B

Special Education and Teaching, BM

BLACK HAWK COLLEGE

Accounting, A
Administrative Assistant and Secretarial Science, A
Agribusiness, A
Agricultural Mechanics and Equipment/Machine
    Technology, A
Agricultural Mechanization, A
Agricultural Production Operations, A
Animal Sciences, A
Animal/Livestock Husbandry and Production, A
Autobody/Collision and Repair
    Technology/Technician, A
Banking and Financial Support Services, A
Business Administration and Management, A
CAD/CADD Drafting and/or Design
    Technology/Technician, A
Carpentry/Carpenter, A
Child Development, A
Civil Engineering Technology/Technician, A
Communications Technology/Technician, A
Computer Installation and Repair
    Technology/Technician, A
Computer Programming/Programmer, A
Computer Systems Networking and
    Telecommunications, A
Computer/Information Technology Services
    Administration and Management, A
Criminal Justice/Law Enforcement Administration, A
Culinary Arts/Chef Training, A
Data Processing and Data Processing
    Technology/Technician, A
Dental Assisting/Assistant, A
Design and Visual Communications, A
Diesel Mechanics Technology/Technician, A
Electrical, Electronics and Communications
    Engineering, A
Electrician, A
Electromechanical Technology/Electromechanical
    Engineering Technology, A
Electroneurodiagnostic/Electroencephalographic
    Technology/Technologist, A
Engine Machinist, A
Environmental Control Technologies/Technicians, A
Environmental Health, A
Equestrian/Equine Studies, A
Finance, A
Finance and Financial Management Services, A
Fire Services Administration, A
Health Information/Medical Records
    Administration/Administrator, A
Heating, Air Conditioning, Ventilation and
    Refrigeration Maintenance
    Technology/Technician, A
Horse Husbandry/Equine Science and
    Management, A
Horticultural Science, A
Information Technology, A
Interior Design, A
International Business/Trade/Commerce, A
Legal Administrative Assistant/Secretary, A
Legal Assistant/Paralegal, A
Library Assistant/Technician, A
Licensed Practical/Vocational Nurse Training, A
Machine Tool Technology/Machinist, A
Management Information Systems and Services, A
Management Science, A
Manufacturing Technology/Technician, A
Marketing, A
Mechanics and Repairers, A
Medical Transcription/Transcriptionist, A
Nursing - Registered Nurse Training, A
Physical Therapist Assistant, A
Radio and Television Broadcasting
    Technology/Technician, A
Radiologic Technology/Science - Radiographer, A
Retailing and Retail Operations, A
Security and Protective Services, A
Sheet Metal Technology/Sheetworking, A
Sign Language Interpretation and Translation, A
Small Business Administration/Management, A
Teacher Assistant/Aide, A
Tool and Die Technology/Technician, A
Truck and Bus Driver/Commercial Vehicle
    Operation, A

Vehicle Maintenance and Repair Technologies, A
Web/Multimedia Management and Webmaster, A
Welding Technology/Welder, A

BLACKBURN COLLEGE

Accounting, B
Art History, Criticism and Conservation, B
Art/Art Studies, General, B
Biology/Biological Sciences, B
Business Administration and Management, B
Chemistry, B
Clinical Laboratory Science/Medical
    Technology/Technologist, B
Clinical Psychology, B
Communication Studies/Speech Communication
    and Rhetoric, B
Comparative Literature, B
Computer Science, B
Criminal Justice/Law Enforcement Administration, B
Elementary Education and Teaching, B
English Language and Literature, B
Environmental Sciences, B
Experimental Psychology, B
History, B
Interdisciplinary Studies, B
Liberal Arts and Sciences Studies and
    Humanities, B
Marketing/Marketing Management, B
Mathematics, B
Molecular Biology, B
Music, B
Physical Education Teaching and Coaching, B
Political Science and Government, B
Pre-Dentistry Studies, B
Pre-Law Studies, B
Pre-Medicine/Pre-Medical Studies, B
Pre-Veterinary Studies, B
Psychology, B
Public Administration, B
Secondary Education and Teaching, B
Spanish Language and Literature, B
Speech and Rhetorical Studies, B

BLESSING-RIEMAN COLLEGE OF NURSING

Nursing - Registered Nurse Training, B

BRADLEY UNIVERSITY

Accounting, BM
Actuarial Science, B
Advertising, B
Art History, Criticism and Conservation, B
Art/Art Studies, General, B
Biochemistry, B
Biological and Biomedical Sciences, M
Biology/Biological Sciences, B
Broadcast Journalism, B
Business Administration and Management, B
Business Administration, Management and
    Operations, M
Business/Managerial Economics, B
Ceramic Arts and Ceramics, M
Chemistry, BM
Civil Engineering, BM
Clinical Laboratory Science/Medical
    Technology/Technologist, B
Communication Studies/Speech Communication
    and Rhetoric, B
Communication, Journalism and Related
    Programs, B
Comparative and Interdisciplinary Arts, M
Computer and Information Sciences, B
Computer Science, M
Construction Engineering, B
Construction Engineering and Management, M
Criminal Justice/Law Enforcement Administration, B
Curriculum and Instruction, M
Design and Applied Arts, M
Drama and Dramatics/Theatre Arts, B
Ecology, B
Economics, B
Education, MD
Education/Teaching of Individuals with Emotional
    Disturbances, B
Education/Teaching of Individuals with Mental
    Retardation, B

Education/Teaching of Individuals with Specific
    Learning Disabilities, B
Educational Leadership and Administration, M
Electrical Engineering, M
Electrical, Electronic and Communications
    Engineering Technology/Technician, B
Electrical, Electronics and Communications
    Engineering, B
Elementary Education and Teaching, B
Engineering and Applied Sciences, M
Engineering Physics, B
English, B
English Language and Literature, B
Entrepreneurship/Entrepreneurial Studies, B
Environmental/Environmental Health Engineering, B
Family Resource Management Studies, B
Finance, B
Fine Arts and Art Studies, M
Fine/Studio Arts, B
French Language and Literature, B
Geology/Earth Science, B
German Language and Literature, B
Health Professions and Related Clinical Sciences, B
History, B
Human Development, M
Illustration, M
Industrial Engineering, B
Industrial Technology/Technician, B
Industrial/Management Engineering, M
Information Science/Studies, BM
Insurance, B
International Business/Trade/Commerce, B
International Relations and Affairs, B
Journalism, B
Kindergarten/PreSchool Education and Teaching, B
Liberal Arts and Sciences Studies and
    Humanities, B
Liberal Studies, M
Management Information Systems and Services, B
Manufacturing Engineering, M
Marketing/Marketing Management, B
Mathematics, B
Mathematics and Statistics, B
Mechanical Engineering, BM
Molecular Biology, B
Music, B
Music Performance, B
Music Teacher Education, B
Music Theory and Composition, B
Nurse Anesthetist, M
Nursing, M
Nursing - Registered Nurse Training, B
Nursing Administration, M
Painting, M
Philosophy, B
Photography, M
Physical Therapy/Therapist, BD
Physics, B
Political Science and Government, B
Printmaking, M
Psychology, B
Public Health (MPH, DPH), B
Public Relations/Image Management, B
Radio and Television, B
Religion/Religious Studies, B
Sculpture, M
Social Work, B
Sociology, B
Spanish Language and Literature, B
Speech and Rhetorical Studies, B
Teacher Education and Professional
    Development, Specific Subject Areas, B

CAREER COLLEGES OF CHICAGO

Computer Science, A
Court Reporting/Court Reporter, A
Legal Administrative Assistant/Secretary, A
Medical Administrative Assistant/Secretary, A

CARL SANDBURG COLLEGE

Accounting, A
Administrative Assistant and Secretarial Science, A
Agricultural Business and Management, A
Agricultural Mechanization, A
Automobile/Automotive Mechanics
    Technology/Technician, A

Business Administration and Management, A
Cosmetology/Cosmetologist, A
Criminal Justice/Law Enforcement Administration, A
Criminal Justice/Police Science, A
Data Processing and Data Processing
    Technology/Technician, A
Developmental and Child Psychology, A
Drafting and Design Technology/Technician, A
Electrical, Electronic and Communications
    Engineering Technology/Technician, A
Fashion Merchandising, A
Funeral Service and Mortuary Science, A
Industrial Radiologic Technology/Technician, A
Liberal Arts and Sciences Studies and
    Humanities, A
Licensed Practical/Vocational Nurse Training, A
Marketing/Marketing Management, A
Nursing - Registered Nurse Training, A
Real Estate, A

CHICAGO STATE UNIVERSITY

Accounting, B
African-American/Black Studies, B
Applied Art, B
Art Teacher Education, B
Bilingual and Multilingual Education, B
Biochemistry, B
Biological and Biomedical Sciences, M
Biology Teacher Education, B
Biology/Biological Sciences, B
Business Administration and Management, B
Business Teacher Education, B
Chemistry, B
Comparative Literature, B
Computer Science, BM
Counselor Education/School Counseling and
    Guidance Services, M
Criminal Justice/Law Enforcement Administration, B
Criminal Justice/Police Science, B
Criminology, M
Early Childhood Education and Teaching, BM
Economics, B
Education, BM
Educational Administration and Supervision, M
Educational Media/Instructional Technology, M
Elementary Education and Teaching, BM
English, M
English Language and Literature, B
English/Language Arts Teacher Education, B
Environmental Biology, B
Finance, B
Fine/Studio Arts, B
General Studies, B
Geography, BM
Geography Teacher Education, B
Health Information/Medical Records
    Administration/Administrator, B
Health Teacher Education, B
History, BM
Information Science/Studies, B
Junior High/Intermediate/Middle School Education
    and Teaching, B
Kindergarten/PreSchool Education and Teaching, B
Liberal Arts and Sciences Studies and
    Humanities, B
Library Science, M
Management Information Systems and Services, B
Marketing/Marketing Management, B
Mathematics, BM
Mathematics Teacher Education, B
Molecular Biology, B
Multilingual and Multicultural Education, M
Music, B
Music Teacher Education, B
Nursing - Registered Nurse Training, B
Parks, Recreation, Leisure and Fitness Studies, B
Physical Education Teaching and Coaching, BM
Physics, B
Physics Teacher Education, B
Political Science and Government, B
Pre-Dentistry Studies, B
Pre-Law Studies, B
Pre-Medicine/Pre-Medical Studies, B
Pre-Veterinary Studies, B
Psychology, B
Public Health (MPH, DPH), B

Reading Teacher Education, M
Science Teacher Education/General Science
   Teacher Education, B
Secondary Education and Teaching, BM
Social Work, M
Sociology, B
Spanish Language and Literature, B
Spanish Language Teacher Education, B
Special Education and Teaching, BM
Speech and Rhetorical Studies, B
Technical and Business Writing, B
Technology Education/Industrial Arts, B
Technology Teacher Education/Industrial Arts
   Teacher Education, B
Vocational and Technical Education, M

CITY COLLEGES OF CHICAGO, HAROLD WASHINGTON COLLEGE

Accounting, A
Administrative Assistant and Secretarial Science, A
Architectural Engineering Technology/Technician, A
Art/Art Studies, General, A
Biology/Biological Sciences, A
Business Administration and Management, A
Chemistry, A
Child Development, A
Commercial and Advertising Art, A
Corrections, A
Criminal Justice/Law Enforcement Administration, A
Criminal Justice/Police Science, A
Data Processing and Data Processing
   Technology/Technician, A
Developmental and Child Psychology, A
Drama and Dramatics/Theatre Arts, A
Elementary Education and Teaching, A
Emergency Medical Technology/Technician (EMT
   Paramedic), A
Engineering, A
Engineering Technology, A
English Language and Literature, A
Finance, A
Fire Science/Firefighting, A
French Language and Literature, A
German Language and Literature, A
Hospitality Administration/Management, A
Hotel/Motel Administration/Management, A
Humanities/Humanistic Studies, A
Information Science/Studies, A
International Business/Trade/Commerce, A
Italian Language and Literature, A
Japanese Language and Literature, A
Journalism, A
Kindergarten/PreSchool Education and Teaching, A
Law and Legal Studies, A
Liberal Arts and Sciences Studies and
   Humanities, A
Marketing/Marketing Management, A
Mathematics, A
Mental Health/Rehabilitation, A
Music, A
Philosophy, A
Physical Sciences, A
Physics, A
Pre-Engineering, A
Social Sciences, A
Social Work, A
Spanish Language and Literature, A
Speech and Rhetorical Studies, A
Substance Abuse/Addiction Counseling, A
Teacher Assistant/Aide, A
Tourism and Travel Services Management, A

CITY COLLEGES OF CHICAGO, HARRY S. TRUMAN COLLEGE

Accounting, A
Art/Art Studies, General, A
Business Administration and Management, A
Chemical Engineering, A
Clinical Laboratory Science/Medical
   Technology/Technologist, A
Criminal Justice/Police Science, A
Developmental and Child Psychology, A
Drafting and Design Technology/Technician, A

Education, A
Elementary Education and Teaching, A
Health Information/Medical Records
   Administration/Administrator, A
Information Science/Studies, A
Journalism, A
Law and Legal Studies, A
Liberal Arts and Sciences Studies and
   Humanities, A
Marketing/Marketing Management, A
Medical Administrative Assistant/Secretary, A
Modern Languages, A
Nursing - Registered Nurse Training, A
Physical Education Teaching and Coaching, A
Pre-Engineering, A
Speech and Rhetorical Studies, A
Teacher Assistant/Aide, A

CITY COLLEGES OF CHICAGO, KENNEDY-KING COLLEGE

Accounting, A
Administrative Assistant and Secretarial Science, A
Architectural Engineering Technology/Technician, A
Automobile/Automotive Mechanics
   Technology/Technician, A
Biology/Biological Sciences, A
Broadcast Journalism, A
Business Administration and Management, A
Chemistry, A
Child Development, A
Clinical Laboratory Science/Medical
   Technology/Technologist, A
Commercial and Advertising Art, A
Data Processing and Data Processing
   Technology/Technician, A
Education, A
Engineering, A
Family and Consumer Sciences/Human Sciences, A
Graphic and Printing Equipment Operator
   Production, A
Heating, Air Conditioning, Ventilation and
   Refrigeration Maintenance
   Technology/Technician, A
Kindergarten/PreSchool Education and Teaching, A
Law and Legal Studies, A
Liberal Arts and Sciences Studies and
   Humanities, A
Marketing/Marketing Management, A
Mathematics, A
Mental Health/Rehabilitation, A
Nursing - Registered Nurse Training, A
Parks, Recreation, Leisure and Fitness Studies, A
Pharmacy, A
Physics, A
Pre-Engineering, A
Public Health (MPH, DPH), A
Radio and Television, A
Social Work, A
Special Products Marketing Operations, A
Teacher Assistant/Aide, A

CITY COLLEGES OF CHICAGO, MALCOLM X COLLEGE

Accounting, A
Administrative Assistant and Secretarial Science, A
Art/Art Studies, General, A
Child Care Provider/Assistant, A
Clinical/Medical Laboratory Technician, A
Computer Programming, Specific Applications, A
Dietician Assistant, A
Elementary Education and Teaching, A
Emergency Medical Technology/Technician (EMT
   Paramedic), A
Funeral Service and Mortuary Science, A
General Studies, A
Hospital and Health Care Facilities
   Administration/Management, A
Liberal Arts and Sciences Studies and
   Humanities, A
Medical Radiologic Technology/Science - Radiation
   Therapist, A
Medical/Clinical Assistant, A
Music, A
Nursing - Registered Nurse Training, A
Physical Education Teaching and Coaching, A
Physician Assistant, A

Pre-Medicine/Pre-Medical Studies, A
Pre-Pharmacy Studies, A
Respiratory Care Therapy/Therapist, A
Restaurant, Culinary, and Catering
   Management/Manager, A
Secondary Education and Teaching, A
Surgical Technology/Technologist, A
Teacher Assistant/Aide, A

CITY COLLEGES OF CHICAGO, OLIVE-HARVEY COLLEGE

Accounting, A
African-American/Black Studies, A
Art/Art Studies, General, A
Biology/Biological Sciences, A
Business Administration and Management, A
Chemistry, A
Computer Engineering Technology/Technician, A
Developmental and Child Psychology, A
Electrical, Electronic and Communications
   Engineering Technology/Technician, A
Engineering, A
Geology/Earth Science, A
Kindergarten/PreSchool Education and Teaching, A
Liberal Arts and Sciences Studies and
   Humanities, A
Marketing/Marketing Management, A
Mathematics, A
Music, A
Nursing - Registered Nurse Training, A
Philosophy, A
Photography, A
Physics, A
Respiratory Therapy Technician/Assistant, A
Social Sciences, A

CITY COLLEGES OF CHICAGO, RICHARD J. DALEY COLLEGE

Accounting, A
Administrative Assistant and Secretarial Science, A
Architectural Engineering Technology/Technician, A
Art/Art Studies, General, A
Avionics Maintenance Technology/Technician, A
Business Administration and Management, A
Child Development, A
Clinical Laboratory Science/Medical
   Technology/Technologist, A
Criminal Justice/Police Science, A
Data Processing and Data Processing
   Technology/Technician, A
Dental Hygiene/Hygienist, A
Developmental and Child Psychology, A
Drafting and Design Technology/Technician, A
Drama and Dramatics/Theatre Arts, A
Education, A
Electrical, Electronic and Communications
   Engineering Technology/Technician, A
Elementary Education and Teaching, A
Fire Science/Firefighting, A
Horticultural Science, A
Humanities/Humanistic Studies, A
Journalism, A
Law and Legal Studies, A
Liberal Arts and Sciences Studies and
   Humanities, A
Machine Tool Technology/Machinist, A
Marketing/Marketing Management, A
Mass Communication/Media Studies, A
Medical Administrative Assistant/Secretary, A
Modern Languages, A
Music, A
Nursing - Registered Nurse Training, A
Pharmacy, A
Photography, A
Pre-Engineering, A
Social Work, A
Speech and Rhetorical Studies, A
Teacher Assistant/Aide, A
Telecommunications Technology/Technician, A

Transportation and Materials Moving, A

CITY COLLEGES OF CHICAGO, WILBUR WRIGHT COLLEGE

Accounting, A
Architectural Engineering Technology/Technician, A
Architectural Technology/Technician, A
Art/Art Studies, General, A
Biological and Physical Sciences, A
Business Administration and Management, A
Computer and Information Sciences, A
Computer and Information Systems Security, A
Criminal Justice/Police Science, A
Data Processing and Data Processing Technology/Technician, A
Elementary Education and Teaching, A
Engineering, A
English Language and Literature, A
Environmental Engineering Technology/Environmental Technology, A
Environmental Sciences, A
General Studies, A
Gerontology, A
Hispanic-American, Puerto Rican, and Mexican-American/Chicano Studies, A
Journalism, A
Liberal Arts and Sciences Studies and Humanities, A
Library Science, A
Machine Tool Technology/Machinist, A
Marketing/Marketing Management, A
Medical Radiologic Technology/Science - Radiation Therapist, A
Modern Languages, A
Music, A
Occupational Therapy/Therapist, A
Physical Sciences, A
Pre-Engineering, A
Speech and Rhetorical Studies, A

COLLEGE OF DUPAGE

Accounting, A
Administrative Assistant and Secretarial Science, A
Automobile/Automotive Mechanics Technology/Technician, A
Baking and Pastry Arts/Baker/Pastry Chef, A
Biological and Physical Sciences, A
Building/Property Maintenance and Management, A
Business Administration and Management, A
Child Care and Support Services Management, A
Child Care Provider/Assistant, A
Child Development, A
Cinematography and Film/Video Production, A
Commercial and Advertising Art, A
Communications Systems Installation and Repair Technology, A
Communications Technology/Technician, A
Computer Installation and Repair Technology/Technician, A
Computer Programming, Specific Applications, A
Computer Typography and Composition Equipment Operator, A
Corrections, A
Criminal Justice/Law Enforcement Administration, A
Criminal Justice/Police Science, A
Culinary Arts/Chef Training, A
Data Entry/Microcomputer Applications, A
Dental Hygiene/Hygienist, A
Design and Visual Communications, A
Drafting and Design Technology/Technician, A
Drafting/Design Engineering Technologies/Technicians, A
Electrical, Electronic and Communications Engineering Technology/Technician, A
Electrical/Electronics Equipment Installation and Repair, A
Electromechanical Technology/Electromechanical Engineering Technology, A
Emergency Medical Technology/Technician (EMT Paramedic), A
Engineering, A
Fashion and Fabric Consultant, A
Fashion Merchandising, A
Fashion/Apparel Design, A
Fire Science/Firefighting, A

Graphic and Printing Equipment Operator Production, A
Health Information/Medical Records Administration/Administrator, A
Health Information/Medical Records Technology/Technician, A
Health/Health Care Administration/Management, A
Heating, Air Conditioning, Ventilation and Refrigeration Maintenance Technology/Technician, A
Hospital and Health Care Facilities Administration/Management, A
Hospitality Administration/Management, A
Hotel/Motel Administration/Management, A
Human Services, A
Industrial Electronics Technology/Technician, A
Industrial Technology/Technician, A
Interior Design, A
Landscaping and Groundskeeping, A
Legal Administrative Assistant/Secretary, A
Liberal Arts and Sciences Studies and Humanities, A
Library Assistant/Technician, A
Library Science, A
Machine Tool Technology/Machinist, A
Manufacturing Technology/Technician, A
Marketing/Marketing Management, A
Massage Therapy/Therapeutic Massage, A
Medical Radiologic Technology/Science - Radiation Therapist, A
Merchandising and Buying Operations, A
Nuclear Medical Technology/Technologist, A
Nursing - Registered Nurse Training, A
Occupational Therapist Assistant, A
Occupational Therapy/Therapist, A
Office Management and Supervision, A
Ornamental Horticulture, A
Photography, A
Physical Therapist Assistant, A
Plastics Engineering Technology/Technician, A
Precision Production Trades, A
Prepress/Desktop Publishing and Digital Imaging Design, A
Real Estate, A
Respiratory Care Therapy/Therapist, A
Restaurant, Culinary, and Catering Management/Manager, A
Retailing and Retail Operations, A
Robotics Technology/Technician, A
Sales, Distribution and Marketing Operations, A
Selling Skills and Sales Operations, A
Speech-Language Pathology/Pathologist, A
Substance Abuse/Addiction Counseling, A
Surgical Technology/Technologist, A
Tourism and Travel Services Management, A
Tourism and Travel Services Marketing Operations, A
Tourism Promotion Operations, A
Transportation and Materials Moving, A
Welding Technology/Welder, A

COLLEGE OF LAKE COUNTY

Accounting Technology/Technician and Bookkeeping, A
Administrative Assistant and Secretarial Science, A
Architectural Drafting and Architectural CAD/CADD, A
Art/Art Studies, General, A
Automobile/Automotive Mechanics Technology/Technician, A
Biological and Physical Sciences, A
Business Administration and Management, A
Business/Office Automation/Technology/Data Entry, A
Chemical Technology/Technician, A
Child Care Provider/Assistant, A
Civil Engineering Technology/Technician, A
Computer Installation and Repair Technology/Technician, A
Computer Programming, Specific Applications, A
Computer Systems Networking and Telecommunications, A
Construction Engineering Technology/Technician, A
Criminal Justice/Police Science, A
Dental Hygiene/Hygienist, A

Electrical, Electronic and Communications Engineering Technology/Technician, A
Electrician, A
Engineering, A
Fire Protection and Safety Technology/Technician, A
Heating, Air Conditioning, Ventilation and Refrigeration Maintenance Technology/Technician, A
Industrial Mechanics and Maintenance Technology, A
Landscaping and Groundskeeping, A
Liberal Arts and Sciences Studies and Humanities, A
Machine Shop Technology/Assistant, A
Mechanical Engineering/Mechanical Technology/Technician, A
Medical Office Management/Administration, A
Medical Radiologic Technology/Science - Radiation Therapist, A
Music, A
Music Teacher Education, A
Natural Resources Management/Development and Policy, A
Nursing - Registered Nurse Training, A
Ornamental Horticulture, A
Restaurant, Culinary, and Catering Management/Manager, A
Selling Skills and Sales Operations, A
Social Work, A
Substance Abuse/Addiction Counseling, A
Technical and Business Writing, A
Turf and Turfgrass Management, A

COLUMBIA COLLEGE CHICAGO

Acting, B
Advertising, B
Architecture, M
Area, Ethnic, Cultural, and Gender Studies, B
Art/Art Studies, General, B
Arts Management, BM
Broadcast Journalism, B
Business Administration and Management, B
Cinematography and Film/Video Production, B
Commercial and Advertising Art, B
Comparative and Interdisciplinary Arts, M
Computer and Information Sciences and Support Services, B
Creative Writing, B
Dance, B
Dance Therapy/Therapist, BMO
Design and Visual Communications, B
Drama and Dramatics/Theatre Arts, B
Early Childhood Education and Teaching, B
Education, M
Elementary Education and Teaching, M
English Education, M
Fashion/Apparel Design, B
Film, Television, and Video Production, M
Film/Cinema Studies, B
Fine/Studio Arts, B
Industrial Design, B
Interdisciplinary Studies, B
Interior Design, BM
Intermedia/Multimedia, B
Journalism, BM
Kindergarten/PreSchool Education and Teaching, B
Liberal Arts and Sciences Studies and Humanities, B
Marketing/Marketing Management, B
Multi-/Interdisciplinary Studies, B
Multilingual and Multicultural Education, M
Music, B
Music Management and Merchandising, B
Music Performance, B
Photography, BM
Playwriting and Screenwriting, B
Public Relations/Image Management, B
Radio and Television, B
Recording Arts Technology/Technician, B
Sign Language Interpretation and Translation, B
Teacher Education and Professional Development, Specific Levels and Methods, B
Teacher Education and Professional Development, Specific Subject Areas, B
Technical Theatre/Theatre Design and Technology, B

Urban Education and Leadership, M
Web Page, Digital/Multimedia and Information
   Resources Design, B
Writing, MO

CONCORDIA UNIVERSITY

Accounting, B
Ancient Near Eastern and Biblical
   Languages, Literatures, and Linguistics, B
Art Teacher Education, B
Art/Art Studies, General, B
Biological and Physical Sciences, B
Biology Teacher Education, B
Biology/Biological Sciences, B
Business Administration and Management, B
Chemistry, B
Commercial and Advertising Art, B
Communication Studies/Speech Communication
   and Rhetoric, B
Computer Science, B
Computer Teacher Education, B
Counseling Psychology, M
Counselor Education/School Counseling and
   Guidance Services, MO
Curriculum and Instruction, M
Drama and Dramatics/Theatre Arts, B
Early Childhood Education and Teaching, MD
Education, BM
Educational Administration and Supervision, MO
Educational Leadership and Administration, D
Elementary Education and Teaching, B
English Language and Literature, B
English/Language Arts Teacher Education, B
Environmental Studies, B
Geography, B
Gerontology, M
History, B
History Teacher Education, B
Human Services, M
Information Science/Studies, B
Kindergarten/PreSchool Education and Teaching, B
Kinesiology and Exercise Science, B
Law and Legal Studies, B
Liberal Studies, M
Mathematics, B
Mathematics Teacher Education, B
Music, BM
Music Teacher Education, B
Natural Sciences, B
Nursing - Registered Nurse Training, B
Pastoral Studies/Counseling, B
Philosophy, B
Physical Education Teaching and Coaching, B
Physical Sciences, B
Piano and Organ, B
Political Science and Government, B
Pre-Dentistry Studies, B
Pre-Law Studies, B
Pre-Medicine/Pre-Medical Studies, B
Pre-Theology/Pre-Ministerial Studies, B
Psychology, BM
Reading Teacher Education, M
Religion/Religious Studies, M
Religious Education, BM
Religious/Sacred Music, B
Sacred Music, M
Science Teacher Education/General Science
   Teacher Education, B
Secondary Education and Teaching, B
Social Science Teacher Education, B
Social Work, B
Sociology, B
Speech Teacher Education, B
Theology/Theological Studies, B
Urban Education and Leadership, M
Voice and Opera, B

Wind and Percussion Instruments, B

THE COOKING AND HOSPITALITY INSTITUTE OF CHICAGO

Baking and Pastry Arts/Baker/Pastry Chef, A
Culinary Arts/Chef Training, A

DANVILLE AREA COMMUNITY COLLEGE

Accounting, A
Agricultural Business and Management, A
Agriculture, A
Art/Art Studies, General, A
Automobile/Automotive Mechanics
   Technology/Technician, A
Biological and Physical Sciences, A
Biology/Biological Sciences, A
Business Administration and Management, A
Child Development, A
Computer Programming/Programmer, A
Criminal Justice/Law Enforcement Administration, A
Criminal Justice/Police Science, A
Data Processing and Data Processing
   Technology/Technician, A
Drafting and Design Technology/Technician, A
Education, A
Electrical, Electronic and Communications
   Engineering Technology/Technician, A
Elementary Education and Teaching, A
Engineering, A
English Language and Literature, A
History, A
Horticultural Science, A
Human Services, A
Humanities/Humanistic Studies, A
Industrial Radiologic Technology/Technician, A
Industrial Technology/Technician, A
Information Science/Studies, A
Journalism, A
Kindergarten/PreSchool Education and Teaching, A
Landscaping and Groundskeeping, A
Legal Administrative Assistant/Secretary, A
Liberal Arts and Sciences Studies and
   Humanities, A
Licensed Practical/Vocational Nurse Training, A
Marketing/Marketing Management, A
Mathematics, A
Mechanical Engineering/Mechanical
   Technology/Technician, A
Medical Administrative Assistant/Secretary, A
Nursing - Registered Nurse Training, A
Occupational Therapy/Therapist, A
Ornamental Horticulture, A
Philosophy, A
Physical Education Teaching and Coaching, A
Physical Therapy/Therapist, A
Pre-Engineering, A
Psychology, A
Real Estate, A
Respiratory Care Therapy/Therapist, A
Social Sciences, A
Social Work, A
Substance Abuse/Addiction Counseling, A
Teacher Assistant/Aide, A
Tourism and Travel Services Management, A
Welding Technology/Welder, A

DEPAUL UNIVERSITY

Accounting, BM
Acting, B
Adult and Continuing Education and Teaching, B
Advertising, B
African Studies, B
African-American/Black Studies, B
American/United States Studies/Civilization, B
Anthropology, B
Applied Art, B
Applied Mathematics, B
Applied Physics, M
Art History, Criticism and Conservation, B
Art/Art Studies, General, B
Arts Management, B
Biochemistry, BM
Biological and Biomedical Sciences, M
Biology/Biological Sciences, B
Business Administration and Management, B

Business Administration, Management and
   Operations, BMO
Business/Commerce, B
Business/Managerial Economics, B
Chemistry, BM
City/Urban, Community and Regional Planning, B
Clinical Laboratory Science/Medical
   Technology/Technologist, B
Clinical Psychology, MD
Clinical/Medical Laboratory Technician, B
Commercial and Advertising Art, B
Communication and Media Studies, M
Communication Studies/Speech Communication
   and Rhetoric, B
Community Psychology, MDO
Comparative Literature, B
Composition, M
Computer and Information Sciences, B
Computer Art and Design, M
Computer Graphics, B
Computer Programming, Specific Applications, B
Computer Programming/Programmer, B
Computer Science, BMD
Computer Systems Networking and
   Telecommunications, B
Corporate and Organizational Communication, M
Counselor Education/School Counseling and
   Guidance Services, BM
Creative Writing, B
Curriculum and Instruction, MD
Drama and Dramatics/Theatre Arts, B
Dramatic/Theatre Arts and Stagecraft, B
Drawing, B
East Asian Studies, B
Economics, BM
Education, BM
Educational Administration and Supervision, M
Educational Leadership and Administration, MD
Educational Media/Instructional Technology, MD
Electronic Commerce, M
Elementary Education and Teaching, BM
English, M
English Language and Literature, B
Entrepreneurship/Entrepreneurial Studies, M
Environmental Studies, B
Experimental Psychology, MD
Finance, B
Finance and Banking, MO
Fine/Studio Arts, B
Foundations and Philosophy of Education, M
French Language and Literature, B
General Studies, B
Geography, B
German Language and Literature, B
Health Services Administration, M
Health Teacher Education, B
Higher Education/Higher Education
   Administration, M
History, BM
Human Resources Management and Services, M
Human Resources Management/Personnel
   Administration, B
Human Services, M
Human-Computer Interaction, M
Industrial and Manufacturing Management, M
Industrial and Organizational Psychology, MD
Information Science/Studies, BM
Interdisciplinary Studies, BM
International Affairs, MO
International Business/Trade/Commerce, BM
International Relations and Affairs, B
Internet and Interactive Multimedia, M
Italian Language and Literature, B
Japanese Language and Literature, B
Jazz/Jazz Studies, B
Jewish/Judaic Studies, B
Kindergarten/PreSchool Education and Teaching, B
Latin American Studies, B
Law and Legal Studies, MPO
Legal and Justice Studies, M
Liberal Studies, M
Management, M
Management Information Systems and
   Services, BM
Management Strategy and Policy, M
Marketing, M

Marketing Research, M
Marketing/Marketing Management, B
Mass Communication/Media Studies, B
Mathematics, BM
Mathematics Teacher Education, M
Modern Languages, B
Multilingual and Multicultural Education, M
Music, BM
Music Management and Merchandising, B
Music Performance, B
Music Teacher Education, BM
Music Theory and Composition, B
Non-Profit/Public/Organizational Management, MO
Nurse Anesthetist, M
Nursing, M
Nursing - Advanced Practice, M
Nursing - Registered Nurse Training, B
Operations Research, B
Performance, MO
Philosophy, BMD
Physical Education Teaching and Coaching, BM
Physics, BM
Piano and Organ, B
Playwriting and Screenwriting, B
Political Science and Government, B
Polymer/Plastics Engineering, M
Pre-Law Studies, B
Psychology, BMDO
Public Administration, MO
Public Affairs, O
Public Policy Analysis, B
Reading Teacher Education, M
Religion/Religious Studies, B
Russian Language and Literature, M
Sculpture, B
Secondary Education and Teaching, BM
Social Sciences, B
Sociology, BM
Software Engineering, M
Spanish Language and Literature, B
Special Education and Teaching, M
Statistics, BM
Taxation, M
Technical Theatre/Theatre Design and
    Technology, B
Telecommunications, M
Theater, MO
Theatre Literature, History and Criticism, B
Urban and Regional Planning, O
Urban Education and Leadership, M
Urban Studies/Affairs, B
Violin, Viola, Guitar and Other Stringed
    Instruments, B
Voice and Opera, B
Web Page, Digital/Multimedia and Information
    Resources Design, B
Wind and Percussion Instruments, B
Women's Studies, BO
Writing, M

DEVRY UNIVERSITY (ADDISON)

Business Administration, Management and
    Operations, B
Computer Engineering Technology/Technician, B
Computer Systems Analysis/Analyst, B
Computer Systems Networking and
    Telecommunications, AB
Electrical, Electronic and Communications
    Engineering Technology/Technician, AB
Information Science/Studies, B
Medical Informatics, B
Operations Management and Supervision, B

DEVRY UNIVERSITY (CHICAGO)

Business Administration and Management, B
Business Administration, Management and
    Operations, B
Computer and Information Sciences, B
Computer Engineering Technology/Technician, B
Computer Systems Analysis/Analyst, B
Computer Systems Networking and
    Telecommunications, AB
Electrical, Electronic and Communications
    Engineering Technology/Technician, AB
Health Information/Medical Records
    Technology/Technician, A

Information Science/Studies, B
Medical Informatics, B
Operations Management and Supervision, B

DEVRY UNIVERSITY (ELGIN)

Business Administration, Management and
    Operations, M

DEVRY UNIVERSITY (GURNEE)

Business Administration, Management and
    Operations, M

DEVRY UNIVERSITY (NAPERVILLE)

Business Administration, Management and
    Operations, M

DEVRY UNIVERSITY (OAKBROOK TERRACE)

Accounting, M
Business Administration, Management and
    Operations, M
Communication and Media Studies, M
Finance and Banking, M
Human Resources Management and Services, M
Management Information Systems and Services, M
Project Management, M
Public Administration, M
Telecommunications Management, M

DEVRY UNIVERSITY (TINLEY PARK)

Business Administration, Management and
    Operations, BM
Computer and Information Sciences, B
Computer Engineering Technology/Technician, B
Computer Programming, Specific Applications, B
Computer Systems Analysis/Analyst, B
Computer Systems Networking and
    Telecommunications, AB
Electrical, Electronic and Communications
    Engineering Technology/Technician, AB
Information Science/Studies, B
Operations Management and Supervision, B

DOMINICAN UNIVERSITY

Accounting, BM
American/United States Studies/Civilization, B
Art History, Criticism and Conservation, B
Biochemistry, B
Biology/Biological Sciences, B
Business Administration and Management, B
Business Administration, Management and
    Operations, MO
Chemistry, B
Clinical Laboratory Science/Medical
    Technology/Technologist, B
Commercial and Advertising Art, B
Computer Engineering, B
Computer Science, B
Criminology, B
Curriculum and Instruction, M
Dietetics/Dieticians, B
Drama and Dramatics/Theatre Arts, B
Early Childhood Education and Teaching, M
Economics, B
Education, M
Educational Administration and Supervision, M
Electrical, Electronics and Communications
    Engineering, B
Elementary Education and Teaching, B
English Language and Literature, B
Environmental Studies, B
Fashion Merchandising, B
Fashion/Apparel Design, B
Food Science, B
Foods, Nutrition, and Wellness Studies, B
Foodservice Systems
    Administration/Management, B
French Language and Literature, B
Gerontology, B
History, B
Information Science/Studies, BMO
International Business/Trade/Commerce, B
Italian Language and Literature, B
Library Science, MO
Management Information Systems and Services, M

Mass Communication/Media Studies, B
Mathematics, B
Organizational Management, M
Philosophy, B
Photography, B
Political Science and Government, B
Pre-Dentistry Studies, B
Pre-Law Studies, B
Pre-Medicine/Pre-Medical Studies, B
Pre-Veterinary Studies, B
Psychology, B
Religion/Religious Studies, B
Social Sciences, B
Social Work, M
Sociology, B
Spanish Language and Literature, B
Special Education and Teaching, M
Special Products Marketing Operations, B
Teacher Education, Multiple Levels, B

EAST-WEST UNIVERSITY

Accounting, B
Administrative Assistant and Secretarial Science, B
Behavioral Sciences, B
Biology/Biological Sciences, B
Business Administration and Management, AB
Computer Engineering Technology/Technician, B
Computer Programming/Programmer, B
Computer Science, AB
Electrical, Electronic and Communications
    Engineering Technology/Technician, B
Electrical, Electronics and Communications
    Engineering, B
English Language and Literature, B
Finance, B
Islamic Studies, B
Liberal Arts and Sciences Studies and
    Humanities, A
Mathematics, B
Social Sciences, B
Sociology, B

EASTERN ILLINOIS UNIVERSITY

Accounting, BO
African-American/Black Studies, B
Art Education, M
Art/Art Studies, General, B
Biological and Biomedical Sciences, M
Biology/Biological Sciences, B
Business Administration and Management, B
Business Administration, Management and
    Operations, MO
Chemistry, BM
Clinical Laboratory Science/Medical
    Technology/Technologist, B
Clinical Psychology, M
Communication Disorders, BM
Community Psychology, M
Computer and Information Sciences, B
Computer Science, MO
Computer/Information Technology Services
    Administration and Management, B
Consumer Economics, M
Counselor Education/School Counseling and
    Guidance Services, M
Drama and Dramatics/Theatre Arts, B
Early Childhood Education and Teaching, M
Economics, BM
Education, MO
Educational Administration and Supervision, MO
Elementary Education and Teaching, BM
Engineering, B
Engineering and Applied Sciences, MO
English, M
English Language and Literature, B
Family and Consumer Sciences/Human Sciences, B
Finance, B
Fine Arts and Art Studies, M
Foreign Languages and Literatures, B
Geography, B
Geology/Earth Science, B
Gerontology, M
Health Teacher Education, B
History, BM
Home Economics, M
Industrial Technology/Technician, B

Journalism, B
Junior High/Intermediate/Middle School Education
   and Teaching, B
Kindergarten/PreSchool Education and Teaching, B
Liberal Arts and Sciences Studies and
   Humanities, B
Management, M
Marketing/Marketing Management, B
Mathematics, BM
Mathematics and Computer Science, B
Mathematics Teacher Education, M
Middle School Education, M
Multi-/Interdisciplinary Studies, B
Music, BM
Nutritional Sciences, M
Parks, Recreation and Leisure Facilities
   Management, B
Philosophy, B
Physical Education Teaching and Coaching, BM
Physics, B
Political Science and Government, BM
Psychology, BMO
Public History, M
School Psychology, O
Social Science Teacher Education, B
Sociology, B
Special Education and Teaching, BM
Speech and Interpersonal Communication, M
Student Personnel Services, M
Systems Science and Theory, O
Technical Teacher Education, B

ELGIN COMMUNITY COLLEGE

Accounting, A
Accounting Technology/Technician and
   Bookkeeping, A
Administrative Assistant and Secretarial Science, A
Art/Art Studies, General, A
Automobile/Automotive Mechanics
   Technology/Technician, A
Biological and Physical Sciences, A
Business Administration and Management, A
Clinical/Medical Laboratory Technician, A
Commercial and Advertising Art, A
Computer Graphics, A
Computer Programming, Specific Applications, A
Computer Typography and Composition Equipment
   Operator, A
Consumer Merchandising/Retailing Management, A
Corrections, A
Criminal Justice/Law Enforcement Administration, A
Criminal Justice/Police Science, A
Culinary Arts/Chef Training, A
Design and Visual Communications, A
Drafting and Design Technology/Technician, A
Electrical, Electronic and Communications
   Engineering Technology/Technician, A
Emergency Medical Technology/Technician (EMT
   Paramedic), A
Executive Assistant/Executive Secretary, A
Fire Protection and Safety Technology/Technician, A
Fire Science/Firefighting, A
Gerontology, A
Health Information/Medical Records
   Administration/Administrator, A
Heating, Air Conditioning, Ventilation and
   Refrigeration Maintenance
   Technology/Technician, A
Hotel/Motel Administration/Management, A
Human Services, A
Industrial Technology/Technician, A
Information Science/Studies, A
Kindergarten/PreSchool Education and Teaching, A
Legal Administrative Assistant/Secretary, A
Legal Assistant/Paralegal, A
Liberal Arts and Sciences Studies and
   Humanities, A
Licensed Practical/Vocational Nurse Training, A
Machine Tool Technology/Machinist, A
Marketing/Marketing Management, A
Medical Administrative Assistant/Secretary, A
Medical Transcription/Transcriptionist, A
Mental Health/Rehabilitation, A
Metallurgical Technology/Technician, A
Nursing - Registered Nurse Training, A
Pre-Engineering, A

Social Work, A
Substance Abuse/Addiction Counseling, A
Tourism and Travel Services Management, A
Welding Technology/Welder, A

ELMHURST COLLEGE

Accounting, BM
Actuarial Science, B
American/United States Studies/Civilization, B
Art Teacher Education, B
Art/Art Studies, General, B
Audiology/Audiologist and Speech-Language
   Pathology/Pathologist, B
Biology Teacher Education, B
Biology/Biological Sciences, B
Business Administration and Management, B
Business Administration, Management and
   Operations, M
Chemistry, B
Chemistry Teacher Education, B
Clinical Laboratory Science/Medical
   Technology/Technologist, B
Communication Studies/Speech Communication
   and Rhetoric, B
Computer Science, BM
CytoTechnology/Cytotechnologist, B
Drama and Dramatics/Theatre Arts, B
Economics, B
Education, B
Educational Leadership and Administration, M
Elementary Education and Teaching, B
English, M
English Language and Literature, B
English/Language Arts Teacher Education, B
Environmental Studies, B
Finance, B
French Language and Literature, B
French Language Teacher Education, B
Geography, B
German Language and Literature, B
German Language Teacher Education, B
Health and Physical Education, B
History, B
History Teacher Education, B
Industrial and Organizational Psychology, M
Interdisciplinary Studies, B
International Business/Trade/Commerce, B
Kindergarten/PreSchool Education and Teaching, B
Kinesiology and Exercise Science, B
Logistics and Materials Management, BM
Management Information Systems and Services, B
Marketing/Marketing Management, B
Mathematics, B
Mathematics Teacher Education, B
Music, B
Music Management and Merchandising, B
Music Teacher Education, B
Nursing, M
Nursing - Registered Nurse Training, B
Nutritional Sciences, B
Occupational Therapy/Therapist, B
Philosophy, B
Physical Education Teaching and Coaching, B
Physical Therapy/Therapist, B
Physician Assistant, B
Physics, B
Physics Teacher Education, B
Political Science and Government, B
Pre-Dentistry Studies, B
Pre-Law Studies, B
Pre-Medicine/Pre-Medical Studies, B
Pre-Pharmacy Studies, B
Pre-Veterinary Studies, B
Psychology, B
Secondary Education and Teaching, B
Sociology, B
Spanish Language and Literature, B
Spanish Language Teacher Education, B
Special Education and Teaching, BM
Sport and Fitness Administration/Management, B
Theology/Theological Studies, B
Urban Studies/Affairs, B

EUREKA COLLEGE

Accounting, B
Art/Art Studies, General, B

Athletic Training and Sports Medicine, B
Biological and Physical Sciences, B
Biology/Biological Sciences, B
Business Administration and Management, B
Chemistry, B
Clinical Laboratory Science/Medical
   Technology/Technologist, B
Comparative Literature, B
Computer Science, B
Drama and Dramatics/Theatre Arts, B
Economics, B
Education, B
Educational Leadership and Administration, B
Elementary Education and Teaching, B
English Language and Literature, B
Finance, B
History, B
Kinesiology and Exercise Science, B
Liberal Arts and Sciences Studies and
   Humanities, B
Management Information Systems and Services, B
Mass Communication/Media Studies, B
Mathematics, B
Music, B
Music Teacher Education, B
Natural Sciences, B
Nursing - Registered Nurse Training, B
Philosophy, B
Physical Education Teaching and Coaching, B
Physical Sciences, B
Political Science and Government, B
Pre-Dentistry Studies, B
Pre-Law Studies, B
Pre-Medicine/Pre-Medical Studies, B
Pre-Veterinary Studies, B
Psychology, B
Religion/Religious Studies, B
Science Teacher Education/General Science
   Teacher Education, B
Secondary Education and Teaching, B
Social Sciences, B
Sociology, B
Voice and Opera, B

GEM CITY COLLEGE

Accounting, A
Administrative Assistant and Secretarial Science, A
Business Administration and Management, A
Computer Science, A
Cosmetology/Cosmetologist, A
Information Science/Studies, A
Legal Administrative Assistant/Secretary, A
Legal Assistant/Paralegal, A
Medical Administrative Assistant/Secretary, A
Medical/Clinical Assistant, A
Metal and Jewelry Arts, A

GOVERNORS STATE UNIVERSITY

Accounting, BM
Analytical Chemistry, M
Art History, Criticism and Conservation, B
Art/Art Studies, General, B
Audiology/Audiologist and Speech-Language
   Pathology/Pathologist, B
Biology/Biological Sciences, B
Business Administration and Management, B
Business Administration, Management and
   Operations, M
Chemistry, B
Communication and Media Studies, M
Communication Disorders, M
Communication Studies/Speech Communication
   and Rhetoric, M
Computer Science, BM
Consumer Merchandising/Retailing Management, B
Counseling Psychology, M
Criminal Justice/Law Enforcement Administration, B
Drawing, B
Early Childhood Education and Teaching, BM
Educational Administration and Supervision, M
Educational Media/Instructional Technology, M
Elementary Education and Teaching, B
English, M
English Language and Literature, B
Environmental Biology, M
Finance, B

Fine Arts and Art Studies, M
Fine/Studio Arts, B
Health Services Administration, M
Health/Health Care Administration/Management, B
Human Resources Management/Personnel
    Administration, B
Junior High/Intermediate/Middle School Education
    and Teaching, B
Kindergarten/PreSchool Education and Teaching, B
Labor and Industrial Relations, B
Legal and Justice Studies, M
Liberal Arts and Sciences Studies and
    Humanities, B
Management Information Systems and
    Services, BM
Marketing/Marketing Management, B
Mass Communication/Media Studies, B
Media Studies, M
Mental Health/Rehabilitation, B
Nursing, M
Nursing - Registered Nurse Training, B
Occupational Therapy/Therapist, M
Photography, B
Physical Therapy/Therapist, M
Political Science and Government, M
Psychology, BM
Public Administration, BM
Reading Teacher Education, M
Science Teacher Education/General Science
    Teacher Education, B
Social Sciences, B
Social Work, BM
Special Education and Teaching, M
Speech and Rhetorical Studies, B
Substance Abuse/Addiction Counseling, M

GREENVILLE COLLEGE

Accounting, B
Art/Art Studies, General, B
Audiovisual Communications
    Technologies/Technicians, B
Biology Teacher Education, B
Biology/Biological Sciences, B
Business Administration and Management, B
Chemistry, B
Chemistry Teacher Education, B
Communication and Media Studies, B
Computer Science, B
Criminal Justice/Law Enforcement Administration, B
Drama and Dramatics/Theatre Arts, B
Early Childhood Education and Teaching, B
Education, M
Elementary Education and Teaching, BM
English Language and Literature, B
English/Language Arts Teacher Education, B
Environmental Biology, B
History Teacher Education, B
Kinesiology and Exercise Science, B
Liberal Arts and Sciences Studies and
    Humanities, B
Management Information Systems and Services, B
Marketing/Marketing Management, B
Mass Communication/Media Studies, B
Mathematics, B
Mathematics Teacher Education, B
Modern Languages, B
Multi-/Interdisciplinary Studies, B
Music, B
Music Management and Merchandising, B
Music Teacher Education, B
Organizational Behavior Studies, B
Parks, Recreation, Leisure and Fitness Studies, B
Pastoral Counseling and Specialized Ministries, B
Pastoral Studies/Counseling, BM
Philosophy, B
Physical Education Teaching and Coaching, B
Physics, B
Physics Teacher Education, B
Psychology, B
Public Relations/Image Management, B
Religion/Religious Studies, B
Secondary Education and Teaching, M
Social Sciences, B
Social Work, B
Sociology, B
Spanish Language and Literature, B

Spanish Language Teacher Education, B
Special Education and Teaching, B
Speech and Rhetorical Studies, B
Sport and Fitness Administration/Management, B
Youth Ministry, B

HARRINGTON COLLEGE OF DESIGN

Commercial Photography, A
Interior Design, AB

HEARTLAND COMMUNITY COLLEGE

Administrative Assistant and Secretarial Science, A
Biological and Physical Sciences, A
Business Administration and Management, A
Business and Personal/Financial Services Marketing
    Operations, A
Child Care Provider/Assistant, A
Child Development, A
Computer and Information Sciences, A
Computer Engineering Technology/Technician, A
Computer Programming, Specific Applications, A
Computer
    Programming, Vendor/Product Certification, A
Computer Programming/Programmer, A
Computer Science, A
Computer Systems Networking and
    Telecommunications, A
Corrections, A
Data Entry/Microcomputer Applications, A
Drafting and Design Technology/Technician, A
Drafting/Design Engineering
    Technologies/Technicians, A
Electrical, Electronic and Communications
    Engineering Technology/Technician, A
Engineering, A
Heating, Air Conditioning, Ventilation and
    Refrigeration Maintenance
    Technology/Technician, A
Industrial Mechanics and Maintenance
    Technology, A
Industrial Technology/Technician, A
Information Science/Studies, A
Information Technology, A
Kindergarten/PreSchool Education and Teaching, A
Liberal Arts and Sciences Studies and
    Humanities, A
Licensed Practical/Vocational Nurse Training, A
Machine Tool Technology/Machinist, A
Management Information Systems and Services, A
Nursing - Registered Nurse Training, A
Quality Control Technology/Technician, A
System Administration/Administrator, A
Web Page, Digital/Multimedia and Information
    Resources Design, A
Welding Technology/Welder, A

HEBREW THEOLOGICAL COLLEGE

Hebrew Language and Literature, B
Jewish/Judaic Studies, B
Pastoral Studies/Counseling, B
Religion/Religious Studies, B
Theology and Religious Vocations, O
Theology/Theological Studies, B

HIGHLAND COMMUNITY COLLEGE

Accounting, A
Administrative Assistant and Secretarial Science, A
Agricultural Business and Management, A
Agricultural Mechanization, A
Art/Art Studies, General, A
Automobile/Automotive Mechanics
    Technology/Technician, A
Biological and Physical Sciences, A
Business Administration and Management, A
Chemistry, A
Child Care and Support Services Management, A
Child Care Provider/Assistant, A
Child Development, A
Commercial and Advertising Art, A
Computer and Information Sciences, A
Computer Programming, Specific Applications, A
Computer Science, A
Data Processing and Data Processing
    Technology/Technician, A
Drafting and Design Technology/Technician, A
Drama and Dramatics/Theatre Arts, A

Education, A
Electrical, Electronic and Communications
    Engineering Technology/Technician, A
Engineering, A
Engineering Science, A
Engineering Technology, A
Geology/Earth Science, A
History, A
Human Services, A
Kindergarten/PreSchool Education and Teaching, A
Liberal Arts and Sciences Studies and
    Humanities, A
Management Information Systems and Services, A
Marketing/Marketing Management, A
Mathematics, A
Mechanical Engineering/Mechanical
    Technology/Technician, A
Music Teacher Education, A
Nursing - Registered Nurse Training, A
Physical Sciences, A
Physics, A
Political Science and Government, A
Pre-Engineering, A
Psychology, A
Sociology, A
Speech Teacher Education, A
Web Page, Digital/Multimedia and Information
    Resources Design, A

ILLINOIS CENTRAL COLLEGE

Accounting, A
Administrative Assistant and Secretarial Science, A
Agricultural Business and Management, A
Agricultural Mechanization, A
Architectural Engineering Technology/Technician, A
Artificial Intelligence and Robotics, A
Automobile/Automotive Mechanics
    Technology/Technician, A
Biological and Physical Sciences, A
Business Administration and Management, A
Clinical/Medical Laboratory Technician, A
Commercial and Advertising Art, A
Court Reporting/Court Reporter, A
Criminal Justice/Police Science, A
Data Processing and Data Processing
    Technology/Technician, A
Dental Hygiene/Hygienist, A
Developmental and Child Psychology, A
Drafting/Design Engineering
    Technologies/Technicians, A
Electrical, Electronic and Communications
    Engineering Technology/Technician, A
Engineering Technology, A
Finance, A
Fire Science/Firefighting, A
Health Information/Medical Records
    Administration/Administrator, A
Health/Health Care Administration/Management, A
Horticultural Science, A
Industrial Radiologic Technology/Technician, A
Industrial Technology/Technician, A
Interior Design, A
Legal Assistant/Paralegal, A
Liberal Arts and Sciences Studies and
    Humanities, A
Library Science, A
Marketing/Marketing Management, A
Nursing - Registered Nurse Training, A
Occupational Therapy/Therapist, A
Physical Therapy/Therapist, A
Real Estate, A
Respiratory Care Therapy/Therapist, A
Welding Technology/Welder, A

ILLINOIS COLLEGE

Accounting, B
Art/Art Studies, General, B
Biology/Biological Sciences, B
Business Administration and Management, B
Business/Managerial Economics, B
Chemistry, B
Clinical Laboratory Science/Medical
    Technology/Technologist, B
Computer Science, B
CytoTechnology/Cytotechnologist, B
Drama and Dramatics/Theatre Arts, B

Early Childhood Education and Teaching, B
Economics, B
Education, B
Elementary Education and Teaching, B
English Language and Literature, B
Environmental Studies, B
Finance, B
French Language and Literature, B
German Language and Literature, B
History, B
Information Science/Studies, B
Interdisciplinary Studies, B
International Relations and Affairs, B
Liberal Arts and Sciences Studies and
    Humanities, B
Management Information Systems and Services, B
Mass Communication/Media Studies, B
Mathematics, B
Music, B
Occupational Therapy/Therapist, B
Philosophy, B
Physical Education Teaching and Coaching, B
Physics, B
Political Science and Government, B
Pre-Dentistry Studies, B
Pre-Law Studies, B
Pre-Medicine/Pre-Medical Studies, B
Pre-Veterinary Studies, B
Psychology, B
Religion/Religious Studies, B
Secondary Education and Teaching, B
Sociology, B
Spanish Language and Literature, B
Speech and Rhetorical Studies, B
Teacher Education, Multiple Levels, B

ILLINOIS EASTERN COMMUNITY COLLEGES, FRONTIER COMMUNITY COLLEGE

Administrative Assistant and Secretarial Science, A
Biological and Physical Sciences, A
Business/Office Automation/Technology/Data
    Entry, A
Corrections, A
General Studies, A
Liberal Arts and Sciences Studies and
    Humanities, A
Nursing - Registered Nurse Training, A
Quality Control Technology/Technician, A

ILLINOIS EASTERN COMMUNITY COLLEGES, LINCOLN TRAIL COLLEGE

Biological and Physical Sciences, A
Building/Property Maintenance and Management, A
Business/Office Automation/Technology/Data
    Entry, A
Corrections, A
Culinary Arts/Chef Training, A
General Studies, A
Heating, Air Conditioning, Ventilation and
    Refrigeration Maintenance
    Technology/Technician, A
Liberal Arts and Sciences Studies and
    Humanities, A
Mechanical Engineering/Mechanical
    Technology/Technician, A
Music, A
Music Teacher Education, A
Quality Control Technology/Technician, A
Teacher Assistant/Aide, A
Telecommunications Technology/Technician, A

ILLINOIS EASTERN COMMUNITY COLLEGES, OLNEY CENTRAL COLLEGE

Accounting, A
Administrative Assistant and Secretarial Science, A
Autobody/Collision and Repair
    Technology/Technician, A
Automobile/Automotive Mechanics
    Technology/Technician, A
Biological and Physical Sciences, A
Business/Office Automation/Technology/Data
    Entry, A
Cabinetmaking and Millwork/Millwright, A

Corrections, A
Criminal Justice/Police Science, A
General Studies, A
Heavy Equipment Maintenance
    Technology/Technician, A
Industrial Mechanics and Maintenance
    Technology, A
Liberal Arts and Sciences Studies and
    Humanities, A
Licensed Practical/Vocational Nurse Training, A
Medical Administrative Assistant/Secretary, A
Medical Radiologic Technology/Science - Radiation
    Therapist, A
Music, A
Music Teacher Education, A
Nursing - Registered Nurse Training, A

ILLINOIS EASTERN COMMUNITY COLLEGES, WABASH VALLEY COLLEGE

Administrative Assistant and Secretarial Science, A
Agricultural Business and Management, A
Agricultural Production Operations, A
Biological and Physical Sciences, A
Business Administration and Management, A
Business/Office Automation/Technology/Data
    Entry, A
Child Development, A
Corrections, A
Court Reporting/Court Reporter, A
Diesel Mechanics Technology/Technician, A
Electrical, Electronic and Communications
    Engineering Technology/Technician, A
General Studies, A
Industrial Technology/Technician, A
Liberal Arts and Sciences Studies and
    Humanities, A
Machine Shop Technology/Assistant, A
Manufacturing Technology/Technician, A
Mining Technology/Technician, A
Radio and Television, A
Social Work, A

THE ILLINOIS INSTITUTE OF ART-CHICAGO

Animation, Interactive Technology, Video Graphics
    and Special Effects, AB
Apparel and Accessories Marketing Operations, B
Apparel and Textiles, A
Cinematography and Film/Video Production, B
Commercial and Advertising Art, AB
Computer Graphics, B
Culinary Arts/Chef Training, A
Design and Applied Arts, B
Design and Visual Communications, B
Fashion Merchandising, B
Fashion/Apparel Design, B
Film/Video and Photographic Arts, B
Interior Design, AB
Web Page, Digital/Multimedia and Information
    Resources Design, B

THE ILLINOIS INSTITUTE OF ART-SCHAUMBURG

Advertising, B
Animation, Interactive Technology, Video Graphics
    and Special Effects, B
Design and Visual Communications, B
Digital Communication and Media/Multimedia, B
Interior Design, B
Web Page, Digital/Multimedia and Information
    Resources Design, B

ILLINOIS INSTITUTE OF TECHNOLOGY

Aerospace, Aeronautical and Astronautical
    Engineering, BMD
Analytical Chemistry, MD
Applied Arts and Design, MD
Applied Mathematics, BMD
Architectural Engineering, BMD
Architecture, BMD
Biochemistry, M
Biochemistry, Biophysics and Molecular Biology, B
Biological and Biomedical Sciences, MD
Biology/Biological Sciences, B

Biomedical Engineering, D
Biomedical/Medical Engineering, B
Biophysics, B
BioTechnology, M
Business Administration, Management and
    Operations, MO
Business/Commerce, B
Cell Biology and Anatomy, M
Chemical Engineering, BMD
Chemistry, BMD
Civil Engineering, BMD
Clinical Psychology, D
Communication and Media Studies, MD
Communication, Journalism and Related
    Programs, B
Computer Engineering, BMD
Computer Science, BMDO
Construction Engineering and Management, M
Corporate and Organizational Communication, M
Design and Visual Communications, B
Electrical Engineering, MD
Electrical, Electronics and Communications
    Engineering, B
Electronic Commerce, M
Engineering and Applied Sciences, MDO
Engineering/Industrial Management, M
Entrepreneurship/Entrepreneurial Studies, M
Environmental Engineering
    Technology/Environmental Technology, MD
Environmental Policy and Resource
    Management, MO
Environmental/Environmental Health Engineering, B
Finance and Banking, MO
Food Engineering, M
Food Science and Technology, M
Geotechnical Engineering, M
Graphic Design, MD
Health Physics/Radiological Health, M
Human Resources Development, M
Industrial and Manufacturing Management, M
Industrial and Organizational Psychology, D
Industrial Design, MD
Industrial Technology/Technician, B
Information Science/Studies, B
Information Technology, B
Inorganic Chemistry, MD
International Business/Trade/Commerce, M
Law and Legal Studies, MPO
Management, MD
Management Information Systems and
    Services, MD
Management Strategy and Policy, M
Manufacturing Engineering, M
Manufacturing Technology/Technician, B
Marketing, M
Materials Engineering, BMD
Materials Sciences, MD
Mathematics Teacher Education, MD
Mechanical Engineering, BMD
Metallurgical Engineering, B
Microbiology, M
Molecular Biology, MD
Molecular Biophysics, MD
Multi-/Interdisciplinary Studies, B
Organic Chemistry, MD
Physical Chemistry, MD
Physics, BMD
Political Science and Government, B
Psychology, BMD
Public Administration, MO
Rehabilitation Counseling, M
Science Teacher Education/General Science
    Teacher Education, MD
Software Engineering, M
Structural Engineering, M
Sustainable Development, M
Taxation, M
Technical and Business Writing, BMD
Telecommunications, M
Transportation and Highway Engineering, M

ILLINOIS STATE UNIVERSITY

Accounting, BM
Accounting and Business/Management, B
Agribusiness, BM
Agricultural Sciences, M

Agriculture, B
Anthropology, B
Archeology, M
Art History, Criticism and Conservation, M
Art/Art Studies, General, B
Athletic Training and Sports Medicine, B
Audiology/Audiologist and Speech-Language
    Pathology/Pathologist, B
Biochemistry, B
Biological and Biomedical Sciences, MD
Biological Anthropology, D
Biology/Biological Sciences, B
BioTechnology, M
Botany/Plant Biology, D
Business Administration and Management, B
Business Administration, Management and
    Operations, M
Business Teacher Education, B
Ceramic Arts and Ceramics, M
Chemistry, BM
Clinical Laboratory Science/Medical
    Technology/Technologist, B
Communication and Media Studies, M
Communication Disorders, M
Counselor Education/School Counseling and
    Guidance Services, M
Criminal Justice/Safety Studies, B
Criminology, M
Curriculum and Instruction, MD
Drama and Dramatics/Theatre Arts, B
Early Childhood Education and Teaching, B
Ecology, D
Economics, BM
Education, MD
Educational Administration and Supervision, MD
Elementary Education and Teaching, B
English, MD
English Language and Literature, B
Environmental and Occupational Health, M
Environmental Health, B
Family and Consumer Sciences/Human
    Sciences, BM
Finance, B
Fine Arts and Art Studies, M
Fine/Studio Arts, B
French Language and Literature, BM
Genetics, D
Geography, B
Geology/Earth Science, B
German Language and Literature, BM
Graphic Design, M
Health Education, M
Health Information/Medical Records
    Administration/Administrator, B
Health Teacher Education, B
Higher Education/Higher Education
    Administration, D
History, BM
Hydrology and Water Resources Science, M
Industrial Technology/Technician, B
Industrial/Management Engineering, M
Information Science/Studies, B
Information Technology, B
Insurance, B
Interdisciplinary Studies, B
International Business/Trade/Commerce, B
Jewelry/Metalsmithing, M
Journalism, B
Kinesiology and Exercise Science, B
Management Information Systems and Services, M
Management of Technology, M
Marketing/Marketing Management, B
Mass Communication/Media Studies, B
Mathematics, BM
Mathematics Teacher Education, D
Microbiology, D
Music, BM
Music Performance, B
Music Teacher Education, B
Nurse Midwife/Nursing Midwifery, O
Nursing, MO
Nursing - Registered Nurse Training, B
Painting, M
Parks, Recreation and Leisure Facilities
    Management, B
Philosophy, B

Photography, M
Physical Education Teaching and Coaching, BM
Physics, B
Physiology, D
Political Science and Government, BM
Printmaking, M
Psychology, BMDO
Public Relations/Image Management, B
Reading Teacher Education, M
School Psychology, DO
Sculpture, M
Social Studies Teacher Education, B
Social Work, BM
Sociology, BM
Spanish Language and Literature, BM
Special Education and Teaching, BMD
Speech and Rhetorical Studies, B
Technology Teacher Education/Industrial Arts
    Teacher Education, B
Textile Design, M
Theater, M
Visual and Performing Arts, B
Writing, M
Zoology/Animal Biology, D

ILLINOIS VALLEY COMMUNITY COLLEGE

Accounting, A
Administrative Assistant and Secretarial Science, A
Agricultural Business and Management, A
Agriculture, A
Automobile/Automotive Mechanics
    Technology/Technician, A
Business Administration and Management, A
Carpentry/Carpenter, A
Child Development, A
Computer Programming/Programmer, A
Computer Systems Networking and
    Telecommunications, A
Criminal Justice/Law Enforcement Administration, A
Criminal Justice/Police Science, A
Data Processing and Data Processing
    Technology/Technician, A
Drafting and Design Technology/Technician, A
Drafting/Design Engineering
    Technologies/Technicians, A
Education, A
Electrical, Electronic and Communications
    Engineering Technology/Technician, A
Elementary Education and Teaching, A
English Language and Literature, A
Industrial Technology/Technician, A
Journalism, A
Liberal Arts and Sciences Studies and
    Humanities, A
Marketing/Marketing Management, A
Mechanical Engineering/Mechanical
    Technology/Technician, A
Nursing - Registered Nurse Training, A
Pre-Engineering, A

ILLINOIS WESLEYAN UNIVERSITY

Accounting, B
African Studies, B
American/United States Studies/Civilization, B
Area Studies, B
Art/Art Studies, General, B
Asian Studies/Civilization, B
Biology Teacher Education, B
Biology/Biological Sciences, B
Business Administration and Management, B
Chemistry, B
Chemistry Teacher Education, B
Classics and Classical
    Languages, Literatures, and Linguistics, B
Computer Science, B
Drama and Dramatics/Theatre Arts, B
Economics, B
Education, B
Elementary Education and Teaching, B
English Language and Literature, B
English/Language Arts Teacher Education, B
Environmental Studies, B
French Language and Literature, B
French Language Teacher Education, B
German Language and Literature, B

History, B
History Teacher Education, B
Insurance, B
Interdisciplinary Studies, B
International Business/Trade/Commerce, B
International/Global Studies, B
Latin American Studies, B
Mathematics, B
Mathematics Teacher Education, B
Music, B
Music Teacher Education, B
Nursing - Registered Nurse Training, B
Philosophy, B
Physics, B
Physics Teacher Education, B
Piano and Organ, B
Political Science and Government, B
Psychology, B
Religion/Religious Studies, B
Secondary Education and Teaching, B
Sociology, B
Spanish Language and Literature, B
Spanish Language Teacher Education, B
Violin, Viola, Guitar and Other Stringed
    Instruments, B
Visual and Performing Arts, B
Voice and Opera, B
Western European Studies, B
Wind and Percussion Instruments, B
Women's Studies, B

INTERNATIONAL ACADEMY OF DESIGN & TECHNOLOGY

Commercial and Advertising Art, AB
Computer and Information Sciences and Support
    Services, B
Computer Graphics, A
Design and Visual Communications, B
Fashion Merchandising, AB
Fashion/Apparel Design, AB
Information Technology, A
Interior Design, AB
Intermedia/Multimedia, A

ITT TECHNICAL INSTITUTE (BURR RIDGE)

Computer and Information Systems Security, B
Computer Programming/Programmer, A
E-Commerce/Electronic Commerce, B
Electrical, Electronic and Communications
    Engineering Technology/Technician, A
System, Networking, and LAN/WAN
    Management/Manager, A
Web Page, Digital/Multimedia and Information
    Resources Design, A
Web/Multimedia Management and Webmaster, A

ITT TECHNICAL INSTITUTE (MATTESON)

CAD/CADD Drafting and/or Design
    Technology/Technician, A
Computer Programming/Programmer, A
E-Commerce/Electronic Commerce, B
Electrical, Electronic and Communications
    Engineering Technology/Technician, A
System, Networking, and LAN/WAN
    Management/Manager, A
Web Page, Digital/Multimedia and Information
    Resources Design, A
Web/Multimedia Management and Webmaster, A

ITT TECHNICAL INSTITUTE (MOUNT PROSPECT)

CAD/CADD Drafting and/or Design
    Technology/Technician, A
Computer and Information Systems Security, B
Computer Programming/Programmer, A
E-Commerce/Electronic Commerce, B
Electrical, Electronic and Communications
    Engineering Technology/Technician, AB
System, Networking, and LAN/WAN
    Management/Manager, A

Web Page, Digital/Multimedia and Information
Resources Design, A

JOHN A. LOGAN COLLEGE

Accounting, A
Agriculture, A
Art Teacher Education, A
Art/Art Studies, General, A
Automobile/Automotive Mechanics
Technology/Technician, A
Biology/Biological Sciences, A
Business Administration and Management, A
Business Teacher Education, A
Chemistry, A
Clinical/Medical Laboratory Technician, A
Computer Science, A
Consumer Merchandising/Retailing Management, A
Cosmetology/Cosmetologist, A
Criminal Justice/Law Enforcement Administration, A
Data Processing and Data Processing
Technology/Technician, A
Dental Hygiene/Hygienist, A
Drafting and Design Technology/Technician, A
Education, A
Electrical, Electronic and Communications
Engineering Technology/Technician, A
Elementary Education and Teaching, A
Emergency Medical Technology/Technician (EMT
Paramedic), A
English Language and Literature, A
Fashion Merchandising, A
Finance, A
Health Information/Medical Records
Administration/Administrator, A
Heating, Air Conditioning, Ventilation and
Refrigeration Maintenance
Technology/Technician, A
History, A
Humanities/Humanistic Studies, A
Information Science/Studies, A
Journalism, A
Kindergarten/PreSchool Education and Teaching, A
Legal Administrative Assistant/Secretary, A
Liberal Arts and Sciences Studies and
Humanities, A
Licensed Practical/Vocational Nurse Training, A
Machine Tool Technology/Machinist, A
Marketing/Marketing Management, A
Mathematics, A
Nursing - Registered Nurse Training, A
Occupational Therapy/Therapist, A
Physical Education Teaching and Coaching, A
Physics, A
Political Science and Government, A
Pre-Engineering, A
Psychology, A
Sign Language Interpretation and Translation, A
Social Work, A
Teacher Assistant/Aide, A
Tourism and Travel Services Management, A
Welding Technology/Welder, A

JOHN WOOD COMMUNITY COLLEGE

Accounting, A
Accounting Technology/Technician and
Bookkeeping, A
Administrative Assistant and Secretarial Science, A
Agricultural Business and Management, A
Agricultural Production Operations, A
Animal/Livestock Husbandry and Production, A
Applied Horticulture/Horticultural Operations, A
Biological and Physical Sciences, A
Business Administration and Management, A
Business/Commerce, A
Child Development, A
Clinical/Medical Laboratory Technician, A
Computer Programming, Specific Applications, A
Criminal Justice/Police Science, A
Early Childhood Education and Teaching, A
Electrical, Electronic and Communications
Engineering Technology/Technician, A
Electrician, A
Emergency Medical Technology/Technician (EMT
Paramedic), A
Executive Assistant/Executive Secretary, A
Fire Protection and Safety Technology/Technician, A

General Studies, A
Health and Physical Education, A
Hotel/Motel Administration/Management, A
Industrial Electronics Technology/Technician, A
Industrial Mechanics and Maintenance
Technology, A
Legal Administrative Assistant/Secretary, A
Liberal Arts and Sciences Studies and
Humanities, A
Mechanical Drafting and Mechanical Drafting
CAD/CADD, A
Medical Administrative Assistant/Secretary, A
Medical Radiologic Technology/Science - Radiation
Therapist, A
Nursing - Registered Nurse Training, A
Psychology, A
Restaurant, Culinary, and Catering
Management/Manager, A
Sales, Distribution and Marketing Operations, A
Sociology, A

JOLIET JUNIOR COLLEGE

Accounting, A
Administrative Assistant and Secretarial Science, A
Agricultural Business and Management, A
Animal Physiology, A
Art/Art Studies, General, A
Automobile/Automotive Mechanics
Technology/Technician, A
Biology/Biological Sciences, A
Business Administration and Management, A
Business/Managerial Economics, A
Business/Office Automation/Technology/Data
Entry, A
Chemistry, A
Clinical Laboratory Science/Medical
Technology/Technologist, A
Computer and Information Sciences, A
Computer Programming, Specific Applications, A
Computer Programming/Programmer, A
Computer Systems Networking and
Telecommunications, A
Construction Engineering Technology/Technician, A
Corrections, A
Criminal Justice/Law Enforcement Administration, A
Criminal Justice/Police Science, A
Culinary Arts/Chef Training, A
Drafting/Design Engineering
Technologies/Technicians, A
Ecology, A
Education, A
Electrical, Electronic and Communications
Engineering Technology/Technician, A
Electrical/Electronics Drafting and
Electrical/Electronics CAD/CADD, A
Emergency Medical Technology/Technician (EMT
Paramedic), A
Fashion Merchandising, A
Fire Science/Firefighting, A
Geography, A
Greenhouse Operations and Management, A
Horticultural Science, A
Hospitality Administration/Management, A
Industrial Technology/Technician, A
Interior Design, A
Landscaping and Groundskeeping, A
Management Information Systems and Services, A
Marketing/Marketing Management, A
Massage Therapy/Therapeutic Massage, A
Mathematics, A
Medical Administrative Assistant/Secretary, A
Nuclear/Nuclear Power Technology/Technician, A
Nursing - Registered Nurse Training, A
Plant Nursery Operations and Management, A
Real Estate, A
Special Products Marketing Operations, A
Teacher Assistant/Aide, A
Turf and Turfgrass Management, A
Veterinary/Animal Health Technology/Technician and
Veterinary Assistant, A
Web Page, Digital/Multimedia and Information
Resources Design, A

Welding Technology/Welder, A

JUDSON COLLEGE

Accounting, B
Anthropology, B
Architecture, B
Art/Art Studies, General, B
Bible/Biblical Studies, B
Biological and Physical Sciences, B
Biology/Biological Sciences, B
Business Administration and Management, B
Chemistry, B
Commercial and Advertising Art, B
Comparative Literature, B
Computer Graphics, B
Computer Science, B
Criminal Justice/Safety Studies, B
Drama and Dramatics/Theatre Arts, B
Drawing, B
Education, B
Elementary Education and Teaching, B
English Language and Literature, B
Fine/Studio Arts, B
History, B
Human Resources Management/Personnel
Administration, B
Human Services, B
Information Science/Studies, B
International Business/Trade/Commerce, B
Journalism, B
Kindergarten/PreSchool Education and Teaching, B
Linguistics, B
Management Information Systems and Services, B
Mass Communication/Media Studies, B
Mathematics, B
Music, B
Music Teacher Education, B
Nursing - Registered Nurse Training, B
Philosophy, B
Physical Education Teaching and Coaching, B
Physical Sciences, B
Pre-Law Studies, B
Pre-Medicine/Pre-Medical Studies, B
Psychology, B
Religion/Religious Studies, B
Science Teacher Education/General Science
Teacher Education, B
Secondary Education and Teaching, B
Social Sciences, B
Sociology, B
Speech and Rhetorical Studies, B
Sport and Fitness Administration/Management, B
Voice and Opera, B

KANKAKEE COMMUNITY COLLEGE

Accounting, A
Administrative Assistant and Secretarial Science, A
Automobile/Automotive Mechanics
Technology/Technician, A
Avionics Maintenance Technology/Technician, A
Biological and Physical Sciences, A
Business/Commerce, A
Child Development, A
Clinical/Medical Laboratory Technician, A
Criminal Justice/Law Enforcement Administration, A
Criminal Justice/Police Science, A
Drafting and Design Technology/Technician, A
Electrical, Electronic and Communications
Engineering Technology/Technician, A
Elementary Education and Teaching, A
Emergency Medical Technology/Technician (EMT
Paramedic), A
Engineering, A
Fine/Studio Arts, A
Heating, Air Conditioning, Ventilation and
Refrigeration Maintenance
Technology/Technician, A
Industrial Radiologic Technology/Technician, A
Information Science/Studies, A
Liberal Arts and Sciences Studies and
Humanities, A
Machine Tool Technology/Machinist, A
Marketing/Marketing Management, A
Nursing - Registered Nurse Training, A
Physical Therapist Assistant, A
Psychology, A

Real Estate, A
Respiratory Care Therapy/Therapist, A
Welding Technology/Welder, A

KASKASKIA COLLEGE

Agricultural Business and Management, A
Applied Horticulture/Horticultural Operations, A
Architectural Drafting and Architectural
  CAD/CADD, A
Autobody/Collision and Repair
  Technology/Technician, A
Automobile/Automotive Mechanics
  Technology/Technician, A
Biological and Physical Sciences, A
Business Administration and Management, A
Business/Office Automation/Technology/Data
  Entry, A
Carpentry/Carpenter, A
Computer Programming, Specific Applications, A
Criminal Justice/Police Science, A
Culinary Arts/Chef Training, A
Electrical, Electronic and Communications
  Engineering Technology/Technician, A
Executive Assistant/Executive Secretary, A
General Studies, A
Industrial Mechanics and Maintenance
  Technology, A
Liberal Arts and Sciences Studies and
  Humanities, A
Medical Radiologic Technology/Science - Radiation
  Therapist, A
Nursing - Registered Nurse Training, A
Physical Therapist Assistant, A
Respiratory Care Therapy/Therapist, A

KENDALL COLLEGE

Baking and Pastry Arts/Baker/Pastry Chef, A
Business Administration and Management, B
Cooking and Related Culinary Arts, AB
Culinary Arts/Chef Training, AB
Early Childhood Education and Teaching, B
Education, B
Educational Administration and Supervision, B
Educational Leadership and Administration, B
Elementary Education and Teaching, B
Entrepreneurial and Small Business Operations, B
Entrepreneurship/Entrepreneurial Studies, B
Hospitality Administration/Management, AB
Hospitality and Recreation Marketing Operations, B
Hotel/Motel Administration/Management, AB
Human Services, AB
Institutional Food Workers, AB
Kindergarten/PreSchool Education and
  Teaching, AB
Marketing/Marketing Management, B
Restaurant, Culinary, and Catering
  Management/Manager, B
Restaurant/Food Services Management, B
Small Business Administration/Management, B
Teacher Education and Professional
  Development, Specific Levels and Methods, B

KISHWAUKEE COLLEGE

Administrative Assistant and Secretarial Science, A
Agricultural Business and Management, A
Agricultural Mechanization, A
Agricultural Production Operations, A
Applied Horticulture/Horticultural Operations, A
Art Teacher Education, A
Art/Art Studies, General, A
Autobody/Collision and Repair
  Technology/Technician, A
Automobile/Automotive Mechanics
  Technology/Technician, A
Business Administration and Management, A
Child Care and Support Services Management, A
Computer and Information Sciences, A
Computer Programming, A
Computer Programming, Specific Applications, A
Criminal Justice/Police Science, A
Emergency Medical Technology/Technician (EMT
  Paramedic), A
Engineering, A
Greenhouse Operations and Management, A
Industrial Design, A
Landscaping and Groundskeeping, A

Liberal Arts and Sciences Studies and
  Humanities, A
Medical Radiologic Technology/Science - Radiation
  Therapist, A
Nursing - Registered Nurse Training, A
Operations Management and Supervision, A
Ornamental Horticulture, A
Quality Control Technology/Technician, A
Tool and Die Technology/Technician, A
Turf and Turfgrass Management, A
Word Processing, A

KNOX COLLEGE

African-American/Black Studies, B
American/United States Studies/Civilization, B
Anthropology, B
Art History, Criticism and Conservation, B
Art/Art Studies, General, B
Biochemistry, B
Biology/Biological Sciences, B
Chemistry, B
Classics and Classical
  Languages, Literatures, and Linguistics, B
Computer and Information Sciences, B
Creative Writing, B
Drama and Dramatics/Theatre Arts, B
Economics, B
Education, B
English Language and Literature, B
Environmental Studies, B
Foreign Languages and Literatures, B
French Language and Literature, B
German Language and Literature, B
History, B
International Relations and Affairs, B
Mathematics, B
Multi-/Interdisciplinary Studies, B
Music, B
Philosophy, B
Physics, B
Political Science and Government, B
Psychology, B
Russian Language and Literature, B
Russian Studies, B
Sociology, B
Spanish Language and Literature, B
Women's Studies, B

LAKE FOREST COLLEGE

American/United States Studies/Civilization, B
Anthropology, B
Art History, Criticism and Conservation, B
Asian Studies/Civilization, B
Biology/Biological Sciences, B
Business/Managerial Economics, B
Chemistry, B
Communication Studies/Speech Communication
  and Rhetoric, B
Computer Science, B
Economics, B
Education, B
Elementary Education and Teaching, B
English Language and Literature, B
Environmental Studies, B
Fine/Studio Arts, B
French Language and Literature, B
History, B
International Relations and Affairs, B
Latin American Studies, B
Liberal Studies, M
Mathematics, B
Music, B
Philosophy, B
Physics, B
Political Science and Government, B
Pre-Dentistry Studies, B
Pre-Law Studies, B
Pre-Medicine/Pre-Medical Studies, B
Pre-Veterinary Studies, B
Psychology, B
Secondary Education and Teaching, B
Sociology, B

Spanish Language and Literature, B

LAKE LAND COLLEGE

Accounting Technology/Technician and
  Bookkeeping, A
Administrative Assistant and Secretarial Science, A
Agricultural Business and Management, A
Agricultural Mechanization, A
Agricultural Production Operations, A
Architectural Engineering Technology/Technician, A
Automobile/Automotive Mechanics
  Technology/Technician, A
Biological and Physical Sciences, A
Business Administration and Management, A
Child Care and Support Services Management, A
Civil Engineering Technology/Technician, A
Computer Programming, Specific Applications, A
Computer Systems Networking and
  Telecommunications, A
Corrections, A
Criminal Justice/Police Science, A
Dental Hygiene/Hygienist, A
Drafting and Design Technology/Technician, A
Electrical, Electronic and Communications
  Engineering Technology/Technician, A
Electromechanical Technology/Electromechanical
  Engineering Technology, A
Executive Assistant/Executive Secretary, A
General Studies, A
Graphic and Printing Equipment Operator
  Production, A
Human Services, A
Industrial Technology/Technician, A
Information Technology, A
Legal Administrative Assistant/Secretary, A
Liberal Arts and Sciences Studies and
  Humanities, A
Marketing/Marketing Management, A
Medical Administrative Assistant/Secretary, A
Nursing - Registered Nurse Training, A
Office Management and Supervision, A
Physical Therapist Assistant, A
Prepress/Desktop Publishing and Digital Imaging
  Design, A
Printing Press Operator, A
Radio and Television, A
Social Work, A
Telecommunications Technology/Technician, A

LAKEVIEW COLLEGE OF NURSING

Nursing - Registered Nurse Training, B

LEWIS AND CLARK COMMUNITY
COLLEGE

Accounting, A
Administrative Assistant and Secretarial Science, A
Art/Art Studies, General, A
Automobile/Automotive Mechanics
  Technology/Technician, A
Biological and Physical Sciences, A
Biology/Biological Sciences, A
Business Administration and Management, A
Child Development, A
Computer Programming/Programmer, A
Criminal Justice/Law Enforcement Administration, A
Data Processing and Data Processing
  Technology/Technician, A
Dental Hygiene/Hygienist, A
Drafting and Design Technology/Technician, A
Fire Science/Firefighting, A
Kindergarten/PreSchool Education and Teaching, A
Legal Administrative Assistant/Secretary, A
Liberal Arts and Sciences Studies and
  Humanities, A
Machine Tool Technology/Machinist, A
Medical Administrative Assistant/Secretary, A
Music, A
Nursing - Registered Nurse Training, A
Occupational Therapist Assistant, A
Pre-Engineering, A
Radio and Television, A

Teacher Assistant/Aide, A

LEWIS UNIVERSITY

Accounting, B
Airframe Mechanics and Aircraft Maintenance
    Technology/Technician, AB
Airline/Commercial/Professional Pilot and Flight
    Crew, B
American/United States Studies/Civilization, B
Area Studies, B
Art Teacher Education, B
Art/Art Studies, General, B
Aviation/Airway Management and Operations, B
Avionics Maintenance Technology/Technician, AB
Biochemistry, B
Biology/Biological Sciences, B
Broadcast Journalism, B
Business Administration and Management, B
Business Administration, Management and
    Operations, M
Business/Managerial Economics, B
Chemistry, B
Clinical Laboratory Science/Medical
    Technology/Technologist, B
Commercial and Advertising Art, B
Computer Science, B
Counseling Psychology, M
Counselor Education/School Counseling and
    Guidance Services, M
Criminal Justice/Law Enforcement Administration, B
Criminology, M
Curriculum and Instruction, M
Drama and Dramatics/Theatre Arts, B
Drawing, B
Economics, B
Education, BMO
Educational Administration and Supervision, M
Educational Leadership and Administration, M
Elementary Education and Teaching, B
English Language and Literature, B
Environmental Studies, B
Finance, B
Fine/Studio Arts, B
Health/Health Care Administration/Management, B
History, B
Human Resources Management/Personnel
    Administration, B
Intermedia/Multimedia, B
International Business/Trade/Commerce, B
International/Global Studies, B
Journalism, B
Liberal Arts and Sciences Studies and
    Humanities, B
Management Information Systems and Services, B
Marketing/Marketing Management, B
Mass Communication/Media Studies, B
Mathematics, B
Music, B
Music Management and Merchandising, B
Nursing, MO
Nursing - Registered Nurse Training, B
Nursing Administration, M
Nursing Education, M
Organizational Management, M
Painting, B
Pastoral Studies/Counseling, M
Philosophy, B
Physical Education Teaching and Coaching, B
Physics, B
Political Science and Government, B
Pre-Dentistry Studies, B
Pre-Law Studies, B
Pre-Medicine/Pre-Medical Studies, B
Pre-Veterinary Studies, B
Psychology, B
Public Administration, B
Public Policy Analysis, M
Public Relations/Image Management, B
Radio and Television Broadcasting
    Technology/Technician, B
Religion/Religious Studies, B
Secondary Education and Teaching, B
Security and Protective Services, B
Social Work, B
Sociology, B
Special Education and Teaching, BM

Speech and Rhetorical Studies, B
Speech Teacher Education, B
Student Personnel Services, M
Teacher Education, Multiple Levels, B

LEXINGTON COLLEGE

Cooking and Related Culinary Arts, AB
Culinary Arts and Related Services, AB
Culinary Arts/Chef Training, AB
Food Preparation/Professional Cooking/Kitchen
    Assistant, AB
Food Service, Waiter/Waitress, and Dining Room
    Management/Manager, AB
Hospitality Administration/Management, AB
Hotel/Motel Administration/Management, AB
Institutional Food Workers, AB
Personal and Culinary Services, AB
Restaurant, Culinary, and Catering
    Management/Manager, AB
Restaurant/Food Services Management, AB

LINCOLN CHRISTIAN COLLEGE

Administrative Assistant and Secretarial Science, AB
Bible/Biblical Studies, AB
Business Administration and Management, B
Child Development, B
Divinity/Ministry (BD, MDiv.), B
Elementary Education and Teaching, B
Kindergarten/PreSchool Education and Teaching, B
Piano and Organ, B
Religious Education, B
Religious/Sacred Music, B
Secondary Education and Teaching, B
Theology/Theological Studies, B
Voice and Opera, B

LINCOLN COLLEGE

Accounting, A
Applied Art, A
Applied Mathematics, A
Art History, Criticism and Conservation, A
Art Teacher Education, A
Behavioral Sciences, A
Biological and Physical Sciences, A
Biology/Biological Sciences, A
Botany/Plant Biology, A
Broadcast Journalism, A
Business Administration and Management, A
Business Teacher Education, A
Business/Managerial Economics, A
Ceramic Arts and Ceramics, A
Chemistry, A
Commercial and Advertising Art, A
Computer Programming/Programmer, A
Computer Science, A
Computer Typography and Composition Equipment
    Operator, A
Corrections, A
Cosmetology/Cosmetologist, A
Creative Writing, A
Criminal Justice/Law Enforcement Administration, A
Criminal Justice/Police Science, A
Criminology, A
Dance, A
Data Processing and Data Processing
    Technology/Technician, A
Developmental and Child Psychology, A
Drama and Dramatics/Theatre Arts, A
Drawing, A
Economics, A
Education, A
Elementary Education and Teaching, A
English Language and Literature, A
European Studies/Civilization, A
Fine/Studio Arts, A
Foods, Nutrition, and Wellness Studies, A
Geography, A
Geology/Earth Science, A
History, A
Human Development and Family Studies, A
Humanities/Humanistic Studies, A
Jazz/Jazz Studies, A
Journalism, A
Junior High/Intermediate/Middle School Education
    and Teaching, A
Kindergarten/PreSchool Education and Teaching, A

Liberal Arts and Sciences Studies and
    Humanities, A
Licensed Practical/Vocational Nurse Training, A
Marine Biology and Biological Oceanography, A
Marketing/Marketing Management, A
Mass Communication/Media Studies, A
Mathematics, A
Music, A
Music History, Literature, and Theory, A
Music Management and Merchandising, A
Nursing - Registered Nurse Training, A
Painting, A
Philosophy, A
Photography, A
Physical Education Teaching and Coaching, A
Physical Sciences, A
Piano and Organ, A
Political Science and Government, A
Psychology, A
Radio and Television, A
Religious Education, A
Sociology, A
Spanish Language and Literature, A
Statistics, A
Tourism and Travel Services Management, A
Voice and Opera, A
Zoology/Animal Biology, A

LINCOLN COLLEGE-NORMAL

Accounting, A
Applied Art, A
Art Teacher Education, A
Behavioral Sciences, A
Business Administration and Management, AB
Business Teacher Education, A
Commercial and Advertising Art, A
Computer Graphics, A
Computer Programming/Programmer, A
Computer Science, A
Computer Typography and Composition Equipment
    Operator, A
Corrections, A
Data Processing and Data Processing
    Technology/Technician, A
Drawing, A
Economics, A
Education, A
Humanities/Humanistic Studies, A
Information Science/Studies, A
Legal Administrative Assistant/Secretary, A
Legal Assistant/Paralegal, A
Liberal Arts and Sciences Studies and
    Humanities, AB
Licensed Practical/Vocational Nurse Training, A
Marketing/Marketing Management, A
Medical Administrative Assistant/Secretary, A
Nursing - Registered Nurse Training, A
Philosophy, A
Physical Education Teaching and Coaching, A
Psychology, A
Social Sciences, A
Tourism and Travel Services Management, A

LINCOLN LAND COMMUNITY
COLLEGE

Administrative Assistant and Secretarial Science, A
Agricultural Production Operations, A
Architectural Drafting and Architectural
    CAD/CADD, A
Art/Art Studies, General, A
Automobile/Automotive Mechanics
    Technology/Technician, A
Biological and Physical Sciences, A
Business Administration and Management, A
Business/Office Automation/Technology/Data
    Entry, A
Child Care Provider/Assistant, A
Child Development, A
Comparative Literature, A
Computer Programming, Specific Applications, A
Computer Systems Networking and
    Telecommunications, A
Criminal Justice/Police Science, A
Electrical, Electronic and Communications
    Engineering Technology/Technician, A
Fire Protection and Safety Technology/Technician, A

General Studies, A
Hotel/Motel Administration/Management, A
Landscaping and Groundskeeping, A
Legal Administrative Assistant/Secretary, A
Liberal Arts and Sciences Studies and
    Humanities, A
Medical Radiologic Technology/Science - Radiation
    Therapist, A
Music, A
Nursing - Registered Nurse Training, A
Occupational Therapist Assistant, A
Physical Therapist Assistant, A
Pre-Engineering, A
Respiratory Care Therapy/Therapist, A
Selling Skills and Sales Operations, A

LOYOLA UNIVERSITY CHICAGO

Accounting, BM
Allopathic Medicine, MDPO
Anatomy, MDO
Ancient/Classical Greek Language and Literature, B
Anthropology, B
Biochemistry, BMDO
Biological and Biomedical Sciences, M
Biological Anthropology, MD
Biology/Biological Sciences, B
Business Administration and Management, B
Business Administration, Management and
    Operations, MO
Business/Managerial Economics, B
Cell Biology and Anatomy, MDO
Chemistry, BMD
Classics and Classical
    Languages, Literatures, and Linguistics, B
Clinical Psychology, MD
Communication Studies/Speech Communication
    and Rhetoric, B
Communication, Journalism and Related
    Programs, B
Computer Science, BM
Corporate and Organizational Communication, M
Counseling Psychology, D
Counselor Education/School Counseling and
    Guidance Services, M
Criminal Justice/Safety Studies, B
Criminology, M
Curriculum and Instruction, MD
Developmental Psychology, D
Drama and Dramatics/Theatre Arts, B
Economics, B
Education, MDO
Educational Administration and Supervision, MD
Educational Leadership and Administration, M
Educational Measurement and Evaluation, MD
Educational Psychology, MD
Elementary Education and Teaching, B
English, MD
English Language and Literature, B
Environmental and Occupational Health, M
Environmental Studies, B
Finance, B
Fine Arts and Art Studies, B
Foods, Nutrition, and Wellness Studies, B
Foundations and Philosophy of Education, MD
French Language and Literature, B
General Studies, B
German Language and Literature, B
Health Services Administration, MO
Higher Education/Higher Education
    Administration, MD
History, BMD
Human Resources Management and Services, MO
Human Resources Management/Personnel
    Administration, B
Immunology, MDO
Industrial and Labor Relations, MO
Infectious Diseases, M
Information Science/Studies, M
International Affairs, MD
International and Comparative Education, MD
International Relations and Affairs, B
Italian Language and Literature, B
Journalism, B
Latin Language and Literature, B
Law and Legal Studies, MDPO

Management Information Systems and
    Services, BM
Marketing, M
Marketing/Marketing Management, B
Mathematics, BM
Mathematics and Computer Science, B
Microbiology, MDO
Molecular Biology, DO
Molecular Physiology, MD
Music, B
Neurobiology and Neurophysiology, MDO
Neuroscience, MDO
Nursing, MDO
Nursing - Adult, M
Nursing - Advanced Practice, M
Nursing - Registered Nurse Training, B
Nursing Administration, MO
Oncology Nursing, M
Operations Management and Supervision, B
Organizational Behavior Studies, B
Pastoral Studies/Counseling, MO
Pharmacology, MDO
Philosophy, BMD
Physics, B
Political Science and Government, BMDO
Pre-Theology/Pre-Ministerial Studies, B
Psychology, BMD
Public History, M
Religion/Religious Studies, M
Religious Education, MO
School Psychology, MDO
Social Psychology, MD
Social Work, BMDO
Sociology, BMD
Software Engineering, M
Spanish Language and Literature, BM
Special Education and Teaching, BM
Statistics, B
Theology and Religious Vocations, MDPO
Theology/Theological Studies, B
Virology, MD
Women's Health Nursing, M
Women's Studies, B

MACCORMAC COLLEGE

Accounting, A
Administrative Assistant and Secretarial Science, A
Business Administration and Management, A
Computer and Information Sciences, A
Computer Typography and Composition Equipment
    Operator, A
Consumer Merchandising/Retailing Management, A
Court Reporting/Court Reporter, A
Hotel/Motel Administration/Management, A
International Business/Trade/Commerce, A
Law and Legal Studies, A
Legal Administrative Assistant/Secretary, A
Legal Assistant/Paralegal, A
Marketing/Marketing Management, A
Medical Administrative Assistant/Secretary, A
Tourism and Travel Services Management, A

MACMURRAY COLLEGE

Accounting, B
Art History, Criticism and Conservation, B
Art/Art Studies, General, B
Biology/Biological Sciences, B
Business Administration and Management, AB
Chemistry, B
Criminal Justice/Law Enforcement
    Administration, AB
Criminal Justice/Police Science, AB
Drama and Dramatics/Theatre Arts, B
Education/Teaching of Individuals with Hearing
    Impairments, Including Deafness, B
Elementary Education and Teaching, B
English Language and Literature, B
Finance, B
Fine/Studio Arts, B
History, B
Information Science/Studies, B
Liberal Arts and Sciences Studies and
    Humanities, B
Management Information Systems and Services, B
Marketing/Marketing Management, B
Mathematics, B

Music, B
Music Teacher Education, B
Nursing - Registered Nurse Training, B
Philosophy, B
Physical Education Teaching and Coaching, B
Physics, B
Political Science and Government, B
Pre-Dentistry Studies, B
Pre-Law Studies, B
Pre-Medicine/Pre-Medical Studies, B
Pre-Veterinary Studies, B
Psychology, B
Religion/Religious Studies, B
Secondary Education and Teaching, B
Sign Language Interpretation and Translation, B
Social Work, B
Spanish Language and Literature, B
Special Education and Teaching, B
Sport and Fitness Administration/Management, B

MCHENRY COUNTY COLLEGE

Accounting Technology/Technician and
    Bookkeeping, A
Administrative Assistant and Secretarial Science, A
Applied Horticulture/Horticultural Operations, A
Art/Art Studies, General, A
Automobile/Automotive Mechanics
    Technology/Technician, A
Biological and Physical Sciences, A
Building/Home/Construction Inspection/Inspector, A
Business Administration and Management, A
Child Care and Support Services Management, A
Child Care Provider/Assistant, A
Computer Programming, Specific Applications, A
Criminal Justice/Police Science, A
Electrical, Electronic and Communications
    Engineering Technology/Technician, A
Emergency Medical Technology/Technician (EMT
    Paramedic), A
Engineering, A
Fire Science/Firefighting, A
General Studies, A
Liberal Arts and Sciences Studies and
    Humanities, A
Mechanical Engineering/Mechanical
    Technology/Technician, A
Music, A
Operations Management and Supervision, A
Real Estate, A
Selling Skills and Sales Operations, A

MCKENDREE COLLEGE

Accounting, B
Art Teacher Education, B
Art/Art Studies, General, B
Athletic Training and Sports Medicine, B
Biology Teacher Education, B
Biology/Biological Sciences, B
Business Administration and Management, B
Business Teacher Education, B
Chemistry, B
Clinical Laboratory Science/Medical
    Technology/Technologist, B
Computer Science, B
Criminal Justice/Law Enforcement Administration, B
Economics, B
Elementary Education and Teaching, B
English Language and Literature, B
English/Language Arts Teacher Education, B
Finance, B
History, B
History Teacher Education, B
Information Science/Studies, B
International Relations and Affairs, B
Junior High/Intermediate/Middle School Education
    and Teaching, B
Marketing/Marketing Management, B
Mass Communication/Media Studies, B
Mathematics, B
Mathematics Teacher Education, B
Music, B
Music Teacher Education, B
Nursing - Registered Nurse Training, B
Occupational Therapy/Therapist, B
Organizational Communication, B
Philosophy, B

Physical Education Teaching and Coaching, B
Political Science and Government, B
Pre-Dentistry Studies, B
Pre-Law Studies, B
Pre-Medicine/Pre-Medical Studies, B
Pre-Veterinary Studies, B
Psychology, B
Public Relations/Image Management, B
Religion/Religious Studies, B
Sales, Distribution and Marketing Operations, B
Secondary Education and Teaching, B
Social Science Teacher Education, B
Social Sciences, B
Social Work, B
Sociology, B
Speech and Rhetorical Studies, B
Speech Teacher Education, B
Teacher Education, Multiple Levels, B

MIDSTATE COLLEGE

Accounting, A
Administrative Assistant and Secretarial Science, A
Business Administration and Management, AB
Computer and Information Sciences, A
Court Reporting/Court Reporter, A
Hospitality Administration/Management, A
Information Science/Studies, A
Legal Administrative Assistant/Secretary, A
Legal Assistant/Paralegal, A
Marketing/Marketing Management, A
Medical Administrative Assistant/Secretary, A
Medical/Clinical Assistant, A
Tourism and Travel Services Management, A

MILLIKIN UNIVERSITY

Accounting, B
Applied Mathematics, B
Art Teacher Education, B
Art Therapy/Therapist, B
Arts Management, B
Athletic Training and Sports Medicine, B
Biology/Biological Sciences, B
Business Administration, Management and
　Operations, M
Chemistry, B
Chemistry Teacher Education, B
Commercial and Advertising Art, B
Communication Studies/Speech Communication
　and Rhetoric, B
Computer and Information Sciences, B
Creative Writing, B
Drama and Dramatics/Theatre Arts, B
Elementary Education and Teaching, B
English Language and Literature, B
Entrepreneurship/Entrepreneurial Studies, B
Finance, B
Fine/Studio Arts, B
Foreign Languages and Literatures, B
French Language and Literature, B
German Language and Literature, B
History, B
Human Resources Management/Personnel
　Administration, B
Interdisciplinary Studies, B
International Business/Trade/Commerce, B
International Relations and Affairs, B
Kindergarten/PreSchool Education and Teaching, B
Management Information Systems and Services, B
Marketing/Marketing Management, B
Mathematics, B
Music, B
Music Management and Merchandising, B
Music Performance, B
Music Teacher Education, B
Nursing - Registered Nurse Training, B
Philosophy, B
Physical Education Teaching and Coaching, B
Physics, B
Piano and Organ, B
Political Science and Government, B
Pre-Dentistry Studies, B
Pre-Law Studies, B
Pre-Medicine/Pre-Medical Studies, B
Pre-Veterinary Studies, B
Psychology, B
Religious/Sacred Music, B

Social Science Teacher Education, B
Sociology, B
Spanish Language and Literature, B
Voice and Opera, B

MONMOUTH COLLEGE

Accounting, B
Art/Art Studies, General, B
Biochemistry, B
Biochemistry, Biophysics and Molecular Biology, B
Biological and Biomedical Sciences, B
Biology/Biological Sciences, B
Business Administration and Management, B
Chemistry, B
Classics and Classical
　Languages, Literatures, and Linguistics, B
Computer Science, B
Drama and Dramatics/Theatre Arts, B
Economics, B
Education, B
Elementary Education and Teaching, B
English Language and Literature, B
Environmental Sciences, B
French Language and Literature, B
History, B
Humanities/Humanistic Studies, B
Latin Language and Literature, B
Liberal Arts and Sciences Studies and
　Humanities, B
Mathematics, B
Modern Greek Language and Literature, B
Modern Languages, B
Music, B
Natural Sciences, B
Philosophy, B
Physical Education Teaching and Coaching, B
Physics, B
Political Science and Government, B
Psychology, B
Public Relations/Image Management, B
Religion/Religious Studies, B
Secondary Education and Teaching, B
Sociology, B
Spanish Language and Literature, B
Speech and Rhetorical Studies, B

MOODY BIBLE INSTITUTE

Avionics Maintenance Technology/Technician, B
Bible/Biblical Studies, B
Communication Studies/Speech Communication
　and Rhetoric, B
English as a Second Language, O
Linguistics, B
Missions/Missionary Studies and Missiology, B
Pre-Theology/Pre-Ministerial Studies, B
Religious Education, B
Religious/Sacred Music, B
Teaching English as a Second or Foreign
　Language/ESL Language Instructor, B
Theology and Religious Vocations, MPO

MORAINE VALLEY COMMUNITY COLLEGE

Administrative Assistant and Secretarial Science, A
Automobile/Automotive Mechanics
　Technology/Technician, A
Biological and Physical Sciences, A
Business Administration and Management, A
Business/Commerce, A
Child Care Provider/Assistant, A
Computer Programming, Specific Applications, A
Computer Systems Networking and
　Telecommunications, A
Corrections, A
Criminal Justice/Police Science, A
Design and Visual Communications, A
Entrepreneurship/Entrepreneurial Studies, A
Fire Protection and Safety Technology/Technician, A
Health Information/Medical Records
　Technology/Technician, A
Human Resources Management/Personnel
　Administration, A
Instrumentation Technology/Technician, A
Liberal Arts and Sciences Studies and
　Humanities, A

Mechanical Engineering/Mechanical
　Technology/Technician, A
Medical Radiologic Technology/Science - Radiation
　Therapist, A
Nursing - Registered Nurse Training, A
Parks, Recreation and Leisure Facilities
　Management, A
Respiratory Care Therapy/Therapist, A
Restaurant, Culinary, and Catering
　Management/Manager, A
Retailing and Retail Operations, A
Selling Skills and Sales Operations, A
Therapeutic Recreation/Recreational Therapy, A
Tourism and Travel Services Marketing
　Operations, A
Visual and Performing Arts, A

MORRISON INSTITUTE OF TECHNOLOGY

CAD/CADD Drafting and/or Design
　Technology/Technician, A
Construction Engineering Technology/Technician, A
Drafting and Design Technology/Technician, A
Engineering Technology, A
Mechanical Drafting and Mechanical Drafting
　CAD/CADD, A
Survey Technology/Surveying, A

MORTON COLLEGE

Accounting, A
Administrative Assistant and Secretarial Science, A
Art/Art Studies, General, A
Automobile/Automotive Mechanics
　Technology/Technician, A
Biological and Physical Sciences, A
Business Administration and Management, A
Criminal Justice/Police Science, A
Data Processing and Data Processing
　Technology/Technician, A
Drafting and Design Technology/Technician, A
Finance, A
Fine/Studio Arts, A
Heating, Air Conditioning, Ventilation and
　Refrigeration Maintenance
　Technology/Technician, A
Legal Administrative Assistant/Secretary, A
Liberal Arts and Sciences Studies and
　Humanities, A
Marketing/Marketing Management, A
Medical Administrative Assistant/Secretary, A
Music, A
Nursing - Registered Nurse Training, A
Physical Therapy/Therapist, A
Real Estate, A

NATIONAL-LOUIS UNIVERSITY

Accounting, B
Adult and Continuing Education and Teaching, MDO
Anthropology, B
Art/Art Studies, General, B
Behavioral Sciences, B
Biological and Physical Sciences, B
Biology/Biological Sciences, B
Business Administration and Management, B
Business Administration, Management and
　Operations, M
Clinical Laboratory Science/Medical
　Technology/Technologist, B
Curriculum and Instruction, MDO
Developmental Education, MO
Drama and Dramatics/Theatre Arts, B
Early Childhood Education and Teaching, MO
Education, MDO
Educational Administration and Supervision, MO
Educational Leadership and Administration, MD
Educational Media/Instructional Technology, MO
Educational Psychology, MDO
Elementary Education and Teaching, BM
English Education, MO
English Language and Literature, B
Gerontology, BMO
Health Psychology, M
Health/Health Care Administration/Management, B
Human Development, MDO
Human Development and Family Studies, B
Human Resources Development, M

Human Resources Management and Services, M
Human Services, BMO
Industrial and Organizational Psychology, M
Industrial Radiologic Technology/Technician, B
Information Science/Studies, B
International Business/Trade/Commerce, B
Kindergarten/PreSchool Education and Teaching, B
Liberal Arts and Sciences Studies and
    Humanities, B
Management, M
Mathematics, B
Mathematics Teacher Education, MO
Psychology, BMO
Reading Teacher Education, MDO
Respiratory Care Therapy/Therapist, B
School Psychology, MDO
Science Teacher Education/General Science
    Teacher Education, MO
Secondary Education and Teaching, M
Social Sciences, B
Special Education and Teaching, MO
Substance Abuse/Addiction Counseling, BMO
Writing, M

NORTH CENTRAL COLLEGE

Accounting, B
Actuarial Science, B
Animation, Interactive Technology, Video Graphics
    and Special Effects, B
Anthropology, B
Applied Mathematics, B
Art Teacher Education, B
Art/Art Studies, General, B
Athletic Training and Sports Medicine, B
Biochemistry, B
Biological and Physical Sciences, B
Biology/Biological Sciences, B
Business Administration and Management, B
Business Administration, Management and
    Operations, M
Chemistry, B
Classics and Classical
    Languages, Literatures, and Linguistics, B
Computer Science, BM
Creative Writing, B
Drama and Dramatics/Theatre Arts, B
East Asian Studies, B
Economics, B
Education, BM
Educational Leadership and Administration, M
Elementary Education and Teaching, B
English Language and Literature, B
Finance, B
French Language and Literature, B
German Language and Literature, B
Graphic Design, B
History, B
Human Resources Management/Personnel
    Administration, B
Humanities/Humanistic Studies, B
International Business/Trade/Commerce, B
International Relations and Affairs, B
Japanese Language and Literature, B
Jazz/Jazz Studies, B
Journalism, B
Kinesiology and Exercise Science, B
Liberal Arts and Sciences Studies and
    Humanities, B
Liberal Studies, M
Management, M
Management Information Systems and
    Services, BM
Marketing/Marketing Management, B
Mathematics, B
Medical Radiologic Technology/Science - Radiation
    Therapist, B
Multi-/Interdisciplinary Studies, B
Music, B
Music Teacher Education, B
Non-Profit/Public/Organizational Management, M
Nuclear Medical Technology/Technologist, B
Organizational Communication, B
Philosophy, B
Physical Education Teaching and Coaching, B
Physics, B
Political Sciences and Government, B

Pre-Dentistry Studies, B
Pre-Law Studies, B
Pre-Medicine/Pre-Medical Studies, B
Pre-Veterinary Studies, B
Psychology, B
Radio and Television, B
Religion/Religious Studies, B
Secondary Education and Teaching, B
Small Business Administration/Management, B
Social Sciences, B
Sociology, B
Spanish Language and Literature, B
Speech and Rhetorical Studies, B
Sport and Fitness Administration/Management, B

NORTH PARK UNIVERSITY

Accounting, B
Anthropology, B
Art Teacher Education, B
Art/Art Studies, General, B
Athletic Training and Sports Medicine, B
Bible/Biblical Studies, B
Biological and Physical Sciences, B
Biology/Biological Sciences, B
Business Administration and Management, B
Business Administration, Management and
    Operations, MO
Chemistry, B
Clinical Laboratory Science/Medical
    Technology/Technologist, B
Community Organization and Advocacy, B
Comparative Literature, B
Divinity/Ministry (BD, MDiv.), B
Drama and Dramatics/Theatre Arts, B
Economics, B
Education, BM
Elementary Education and Teaching, B
English Language and Literature, B
Finance, B
Fine/Studio Arts, B
French Language and Literature, B
History, B
International Business/Trade/Commerce, B
International Relations and Affairs, B
Kindergarten/PreSchool Education and Teaching, B
Kinesiology and Exercise Science, B
Marketing/Marketing Management, B
Mass Communication/Media Studies, B
Mathematics, B
Modern Languages, B
Music, B
Music Management and Merchandising, B
Music Teacher Education, B
Natural Sciences, B
Nursing, MO
Nursing - Registered Nurse Training, B
Philosophy, B
Physical Education Teaching and Coaching, B
Physics, B
Political Science and Government, B
Pre-Dentistry Studies, B
Pre-Law Studies, B
Pre-Medicine/Pre-Medical Studies, B
Pre-Veterinary Studies, B
Psychology, B
Religion/Religious Studies, B
Religious/Sacred Music, B
Scandinavian
    Languages, Literatures, and Linguistics, B
Secondary Education and Teaching, B
Social Sciences, B
Sociology, B
Spanish Language and Literature, B
Speech and Rhetorical Studies, B
Theology/Theological Studies, B
Urban and Regional Planning, M
Urban Studies/Affairs, B
Voice and Opera, B

NORTHEASTERN ILLINOIS UNIVERSITY

Accounting, BM
Anthropology, B
Art/Art Studies, General, B
Bilingual and Multilingual Education, B
Biological and Biomedical Sciences, M

Biology/Biological Sciences, B
Business Administration and Management, B
Business Administration, Management and
    Operations, M
Business/Commerce, B
Chemistry, BM
Community Health Services/Liaison/Counseling, B
Computer and Information Sciences, B
Computer Science, BM
Counselor Education/School Counseling and
    Guidance Services, M
Criminal Justice/Safety Studies, B
Early Childhood Education and Teaching, B
Economics, B
Education, M
Education/Teaching of the Gifted and Talented, M
Educational Administration and Supervision, M
Educational Leadership and Administration, M
Elementary Education and Teaching, B
English, M
English Education, M
English Language and Literature, B
Environmental Studies, BM
Finance, B
Finance and Banking, M
French Language and Literature, B
Geography, B
Geology/Earth Science, B
Geosciences, M
Gerontology, M
History, BM
Human Resources Development, M
Human Resources Management/Personnel
    Administration, B
Kindergarten/PreSchool Education and Teaching, B
Liberal Arts and Sciences Studies and
    Humanities, B
Linguistics, BM
Management, M
Marketing, M
Marketing/Marketing Management, B
Mathematics, BM
Mathematics Teacher Education, M
Multilingual and Multicultural Education, M
Music, BM
Philosophy, B
Physical Education Teaching and Coaching, B
Physics, B
Political Science and Government, BM
Psychology, BM
Public Administration and Social Service
    Professions, B
Reading Teacher Education, M
Social Work, B
Sociology, B
Spanish Language and Literature, B
Special Education and Teaching, BM
Speech and Rhetorical Studies, BM
Urban Education and Leadership, M
Urban Studies/Affairs, B
Women's Studies, B
Writing, M

NORTHERN ILLINOIS UNIVERSITY

Accounting, BM
Adult and Continuing Education and Teaching, MD
Anthropology, BM
Apparel and Textiles, B
Applied Mathematics, B
Art History, Criticism and Conservation, B
Art Teacher Education, B
Art/Art Studies, General, B
Atmospheric Sciences and Meteorology, B
Biochemistry, MD
Biological and Biomedical Sciences, MD
Biology/Biological Sciences, B
Business Administration and Management, B
Business Administration, Management and
    Operations, M
Business/Commerce, B
Chemistry, BMD
Child and Family Studies, M
Clinical Laboratory Science/Medical
    Technology/Technologist, B
Communication and Media Studies, M
Communication Disorders, BMD

Communication Studies/Speech Communication and Rhetoric, B
Computational Mathematics, B
Computer Science, BM
Counselor Education/School Counseling and Guidance Services, MD
Curriculum and Instruction, MD
Dance, M
Drama and Dramatics/Theatre Arts, B
Early Childhood Education and Teaching, M
Economics, BMD
Education, BMDO
Educational Administration and Supervision, MDO
Educational Media/Instructional Technology, MD
Educational Psychology, MDO
Electrical Engineering, M
Electrical, Electronics and Communications Engineering, B
Elementary Education and Teaching, BM
Engineering and Applied Sciences, M
Engineering Technology, B
English, MD
English Language and Literature, B
Family and Consumer Sciences/Home Economics Teacher Education, B
Finance, B
Fine Arts and Art Studies, M
Fine/Studio Arts, B
Foods, Nutrition, and Wellness Studies, B
Foundations and Philosophy of Education, M
French Language and Literature, BM
Geography, BM
Geology/Earth Science, BMD
German Language and Literature, B
Health Teacher Education, B
Higher Education/Higher Education Administration, MD
History, BMD
Human Development and Family Studies, B
Industrial and Manufacturing Management, M
Industrial Engineering, B
Industrial Technology/Technician, B
Industrial/Management Engineering, M
Journalism, B
Kindergarten/PreSchool Education and Teaching, B
Law and Legal Studies, P
Liberal Arts and Sciences Studies and Humanities, B
Management Information Systems and Services, BM
Marketing/Marketing Management, B
Mathematical Statistics and Probability, B
Mathematics, BMD
Mechanical Engineering, BM
Music, BMO
Music Teacher Education, B
Nursing, M
Nursing - Registered Nurse Training, B
Nutritional Sciences, M
Operations Management and Supervision, B
Philosophy, BM
Physical Education Teaching and Coaching, BM
Physical Therapy/Therapist, BM
Physics, BMD
Political Science and Government, BMD
Psychology, BMD
Public Administration, M
Public Health, M
Public Health (MPH, DPH), B
Public Health/Community Nurse/Nursing, B
Reading Teacher Education, MD
Romance Languages, Literatures, and Linguistics, M
Russian Language and Literature, B
Sociology, BM
Spanish Language and Literature, BM
Special Education and Teaching, BM
Sport and Fitness Administration/Management, M
Statistics, M
Taxation, M
Theater, M

NORTHWESTERN BUSINESS COLLEGE

Accounting, A
Administrative Assistant and Secretarial Science, A

Animation, Interactive Technology, Video Graphics and Special Effects, A
Business Administration and Management, A
Computer and Information Systems Security, A
Computer Programming/Programmer, A
Computer Science, A
Criminal Justice/Law Enforcement Administration, A
Health Information/Medical Records Technology/Technician, A
Hospitality Administration/Management, A
Legal Assistant/Paralegal, A
Management Information Systems and Services, A
Massage Therapy/Therapeutic Massage, A
Medical/Clinical Assistant, A
Real Estate, A

NORTHWESTERN UNIVERSITY

Accounting, D
Advertising and Public Relations, M
African Studies, BO
African-American/Black Studies, B
Allopathic Medicine, PO
American/United States Studies/Civilization, B
Anthropology, BDO
Applied Mathematics, BMD
Area Studies, B
Art History, Criticism and Conservation, BD
Art/Art Studies, General, B
Asian Studies/Civilization, B
Astronomy, BMD
Astrophysics, D
Audiology/Audiologist and Hearing Sciences, B
Audiology/Audiologist and Speech-Language Pathology/Pathologist, B
Biochemistry, BD
Bioinformatics, M
Biological and Biomedical Sciences, DO
Biological and Physical Sciences, B
Biology/Biological Sciences, B
Biomedical Engineering, MD
Biomedical/Medical Engineering, B
Biophysics, D
Biopsychology, D
BioTechnology, D
Business Administration, Management and Operations, MO
Cancer Biology/Oncology, D
Caribbean Studies, B
Cell Biology and Anatomy, D
Cell/Cellular Biology and Histology, B
Chemical Engineering, BMD
Chemistry, BD
Civil Engineering, BMD
Classics and Classical Languages, Literatures, and Linguistics, B
Clinical Psychology, D
Clinical Research, MO
Cognitive Psychology and Psycholinguistics, B
Cognitive Sciences, D
Communication and Media Studies, BMD
Communication Disorders, BMD
Communication Studies/Speech Communication and Rhetoric, B
Community Organization and Advocacy, B
Community Psychology, B
Comparative Literature, BMD
Composition, MD
Computational Biology, M
Computational Sciences, M
Computer and Information Sciences, B
Computer Engineering, BMDO
Computer Science, BMD
Corporate and Organizational Communication, M
Counseling Psychology, BM
Dance, B
Developmental Biology and Embryology, D
Drama and Dramatics/Theatre Arts, B
East Asian Languages, Literatures, and Linguistics, B
Ecology, B
Economics, BMDO
Education, BMD
Education/Teaching of Individuals with Specific Learning Disabilities, B
Educational Media/Instructional Technology, MD
Electrical Engineering, MDO

Electrical, Electronics and Communications Engineering, B
Electronic Commerce, M
Electronic Materials, MDO
Elementary Education and Teaching, M
Engineering, B
Engineering and Applied Sciences, MDO
Engineering Management, MD
Engineering Science, B
English, MD
English Language and Literature, B
Environmental Engineering Technology/Environmental Technology, MD
Environmental Sciences, B
Environmental Studies, B
Environmental/Environmental Health Engineering, B
Evolutionary Biology, D
Film, Television, and Video Production, MD
Film/Cinema Studies, B
Finance and Banking, D
Fine Arts and Art Studies, M
French Language and Literature, BDO
Gender Studies, O
General Studies, B
Genetic Counseling/Counselor, M
Genetics, D
Geography, B
Geology/Earth Science, BMD
Geosciences, MD
Geotechnical Engineering, MD
German Language and Literature, BD
Higher Education/Higher Education Administration, M
History, BDO
Human Development, D
Humanities/Humanistic Studies, B
Immunology, D
Industrial Engineering, B
Industrial/Management Engineering, MD
Information Science/Studies, BM
Interdisciplinary Studies, B
International Affairs, O
International Relations and Affairs, B
Italian Language and Literature, BDO
Jazz/Jazz Studies, B
Journalism, BM
Law and Legal Studies, BMPO
Liberal Arts and Sciences Studies and Humanities, B
Liberal Studies, M
Linguistics, BMDO
Management Information Systems and Services, M
Management Strategy and Policy, D
Manufacturing Engineering, BM
Marketing, MD
Marriage and Family Therapy/Counseling, M
Materials Engineering, BMDO
Materials Sciences, BMDO
Mathematics, BD
Mathematics Teacher Education, B
Mechanical Engineering, BMD
Media Studies, MD
Microbiology, D
Molecular Biology, BD
Multi-/Interdisciplinary Studies, B
Music, BMD
Music History, Literature, and Theory, B
Music Performance, B
Music Teacher Education, BMD
Music Theory and Composition, BMD
Musicology and Ethnomusicology, BMD
Neurobiology and Neurophysiology, MD
Neuroscience, BD
Operations Research, MD
Organizational Behavior Studies, BMD
Organizational Management, MD
Performance, MDO
Pharmacology, D
Philosophy, BD
Physical Therapy/Therapist, D
Physics, BMD
Physiology, M
Piano and Organ, B
Political Science and Government, BMDO
Pre-Medicine/Pre-Medical Studies, B
Project Management, M

Psychology, BDO
Public Health, MO
Public Policy Analysis, BD
Publishing, M
Radio and Television, B
Religion/Religious Studies, B
Reproductive Biology, D
Science, Technology and Society, B
Secondary Education and Teaching, BM
Slavic Languages, Literatures, and Linguistics, BD
Slavic Studies, B
Social and Philosophical Foundations of
    Education, B
Social Psychology, D
Social Sciences, BMO
Sociology, BDO
South Asian
    Languages, Literatures, and Linguistics, B
Spanish Language and Literature, B
Special Education and Teaching, MD
Speech and Interpersonal Communication, MD
Speech and Rhetorical Studies, B
Speech-Language Pathology/Pathologist, B
Statistics, BMD
Structural Biology, D
Structural Engineering, MD
Theater, MD
Theatre Literature, History and Criticism, B
Toxicology, D
Transportation and Highway Engineering, MD
Urban Studies/Affairs, B
Violin, Viola, Guitar and Other Stringed
    Instruments, B
Visual and Performing Arts, B
Voice and Opera, B
Wind and Percussion Instruments, B
Women's Studies, B
Writing, M

OAKTON COMMUNITY COLLEGE

Accounting, A
Administrative Assistant and Secretarial Science, A
Architectural Engineering Technology/Technician, A
Art/Art Studies, General, A
Automobile/Automotive Mechanics
    Technology/Technician, A
Biological and Physical Sciences, A
Building/Construction
    Finishing, Management, and Inspection, A
Business Administration and Management, A
CAD/CADD Drafting and/or Design
    Technology/Technician, A
Clinical/Medical Laboratory Technician, A
Computer and Information Sciences, A
Computer Graphics, A
Computer Programming, Specific Applications, A
Computer Programming/Programmer, A
Computer Science, A
Criminal Justice/Police Science, A
Drafting/Design Engineering
    Technologies/Technicians, A
Early Childhood Education and Teaching, A
Electrical, Electronic and Communications
    Engineering Technology/Technician, A
Engineering, A
Finance, A
Fire Science/Firefighting, A
Health Information/Medical Records
    Administration/Administrator, A
Heating, Air Conditioning and Refrigeration
    Technology/Technician, A
Information Science/Studies, A
International Business/Trade/Commerce, A
Kindergarten/PreSchool Education and Teaching, A
Liberal Arts and Sciences Studies and
    Humanities, A
Licensed Practical/Vocational Nurse Training, A
Machine Tool Technology/Machinist, A
Management Information Systems and Services, A
Management Science, A
Marketing/Marketing Management, A
Mathematics, A
Mechanical Drafting and Mechanical Drafting
    CAD/CADD, A
Music, A
Nursing - Registered Nurse Training, A

Physical Therapist Assistant, A
Physical Therapy/Therapist, A
Pre-Engineering, A
Real Estate, A
Special Products Marketing Operations, A

OLIVET NAZARENE UNIVERSITY

Accounting, B
Apparel and Textiles, B
Art Teacher Education, B
Art/Art Studies, General, B
Athletic Training and Sports Medicine, B
Bible/Biblical Studies, B
Biochemistry, B
Biological and Physical Sciences, B
Biology/Biological Sciences, B
Broadcast Journalism, B
Business Administration and Management, B
Business Administration, Management and
    Operations, M
Business/Managerial Economics, B
Chemistry, B
Child Development, B
Clinical Laboratory Science/Medical
    Technology/Technologist, B
Commercial and Advertising Art, B
Comparative Literature, B
Computer Science, B
Criminal Justice/Law Enforcement Administration, B
Curriculum and Instruction, M
Developmental and Child Psychology, B
Dietetics/Dieticians, B
Economics, B
Education, BM
Elementary Education and Teaching, BM
Engineering, B
English Language and Literature, B
Environmental Studies, B
Family and Community Services, B
Family and Consumer Sciences/Home Economics
    Teacher Education, B
Family and Consumer Sciences/Human Sciences, B
Fashion Merchandising, B
Film/Cinema Studies, B
Finance, B
Food Science, B
Geology/Earth Science, B
History, B
Human Resources Management/Personnel
    Administration, B
Information Science/Studies, B
Interdisciplinary Studies, B
Journalism, B
Kindergarten/PreSchool Education and Teaching, B
Kinesiology and Exercise Science, B
Liberal Arts and Sciences Studies and
    Humanities, B
Marketing/Marketing Management, B
Mass Communication/Media Studies, B
Mathematics, B
Modern Languages, B
Music, B
Music Teacher Education, B
Natural Sciences, B
Nursing - Registered Nurse Training, B
Pastoral Studies/Counseling, BM
Philosophy, B
Physical Education Teaching and Coaching, B
Physical Sciences, B
Piano and Organ, B
Pre-Dentistry Studies, B
Pre-Law Studies, B
Pre-Medicine/Pre-Medical Studies, B
Pre-Veterinary Studies, B
Psychology, B
Radio and Television, B
Religion/Religious Studies, BM
Religious Education, B
Religious/Sacred Music, B
Romance Languages, Literatures, and Linguistics, B
Science Teacher Education/General Science
    Teacher Education, B
Secondary Education and Teaching, BM
Social Sciences, B
Spanish Language and Literature, B
Speech and Rhetorical Studies, B

Sport and Fitness Administration/Management, B
Theology and Religious Vocations, M
Theology/Theological Studies, B
Violin, Viola, Guitar and Other Stringed
    Instruments, B
Voice and Opera, B
Wind and Percussion Instruments, B
Zoology/Animal Biology, B

PARKLAND COLLEGE

Accounting Technology/Technician and
    Bookkeeping, A
Administrative Assistant and Secretarial Science, A
Advertising, A
Agricultural Business and Management, A
Agricultural Mechanization, A
Art Teacher Education, A
Art/Art Studies, General, A
Autobody/Collision and Repair
    Technology/Technician, A
Automobile/Automotive Mechanics
    Technology/Technician, A
Biological and Physical Sciences, A
Biomedical Technology/Technician, A
Building/Construction
    Finishing, Management, and Inspection, A
Business Administration and Management, A
Business/Office Automation/Technology/Data
    Entry, A
Child Care Provider/Assistant, A
Computer and Information Sciences, A
Computer Graphics, A
Computer Programming, Specific Applications, A
Computer
    Programming, Vendor/Product Certification, A
Computer Programming/Programmer, A
Computer Science, A
Computer Software and Media Applications, A
Computer Systems Networking and
    Telecommunications, A
Computer/Information Technology Services
    Administration and Management, A
Consumer Merchandising/Retailing Management, A
Criminal Justice/Safety Studies, A
Data Entry/Microcomputer Applications, A
Dental Hygiene/Hygienist, A
Design and Visual Communications, A
Electroneurodiagnostic/Electroencephalographic
    Technology/Technologist, A
Elementary Education and Teaching, A
Engineering Science, A
English Language and Literature, A
General Studies, A
Graphic Design, A
History, A
Human Services, A
Industrial Technology/Technician, A
Information Science/Studies, A
Kindergarten/PreSchool Education and Teaching, A
Landscaping and Groundskeeping, A
Liberal Arts and Sciences Studies and
    Humanities, A
Management Information Systems and Services, A
Mass Communication/Media Studies, A
Medical Radiologic Technology/Science - Radiation
    Therapist, A
Music Performance, A
Music Teacher Education, A
Nursing - Registered Nurse Training, A
Occupational Therapist Assistant, A
Radio and Television, A
Radio and Television Broadcasting
    Technology/Technician, A
Respiratory Care Therapy/Therapist, A
Sales and Marketing Operations/Marketing and
    Distribution Teacher Education, A
Secondary Education and Teaching, A
Speech-Language Pathology/Pathologist, A
Surgical Technology/Technologist, A
System Administration/Administrator, A
Theatre/Theatre Arts Management, A
Veterinary/Animal Health Technology/Technician and
    Veterinary Assistant, A

Web Page, Digital/Multimedia and Information
Resources Design, A

PRAIRIE STATE COLLEGE

Autobody/Collision and Repair
Technology/Technician, A
Automobile/Automotive Mechanics
Technology/Technician, A
Child Development, A
Computer and Information Sciences, A
Computer Graphics, A
Criminal Justice/Law Enforcement Administration, A
Dental Hygiene/Hygienist, A
Drafting/Design Engineering
Technologies/Technicians, A
Electrical, Electronic and Communications
Engineering Technology/Technician, A
Executive Assistant/Executive Secretary, A
Finance, A
Fire Science/Firefighting, A
Human Resources Management/Personnel
Administration, A
Industrial Technology/Technician, A
Interior Design, A
Liberal Arts and Sciences Studies and
Humanities, A
Logistics and Materials Management, A
Management Science, A
Mental Health/Rehabilitation, A
Nursing - Registered Nurse Training, A
Photography, A
Substance Abuse/Addiction Counseling, A
Teacher Assistant/Aide, A
Tool and Die Technology/Technician, A

PRINCIPIA COLLEGE

Anthropology, B
Art History, Criticism and Conservation, B
Biology/Biological Sciences, B
Business Administration and Management, B
Chemistry, B
Computer and Information Sciences, B
Drama and Dramatics/Theatre Arts, B
Economics, B
Elementary Education and Teaching, B
Engineering, B
English Language and Literature, B
Environmental Studies, B
Fine/Studio Arts, B
Foreign Languages and Literatures, B
French Language and Literature, B
German Language and Literature, B
History, B
Humanities/Humanistic Studies, B
Mass Communication/Media Studies, B
Mathematics, B
Music, B
Philosophy, B
Physics, B
Political Science and Government, B
Religion/Religious Studies, B
Sociology, B
Spanish Language and Literature, B
Sport and Fitness Administration/Management, B

QUINCY UNIVERSITY

Accounting, B
Airline/Commercial/Professional Pilot and Flight
Crew, B
Arts Management, B
Aviation/Airway Management and Operations, B
Biology/Biological Sciences, B
Business Administration and Management, B
Business Administration, Management and
Operations, M
Chemistry, B
Clinical Laboratory Science/Medical
Technology/Technologist, B
Communication Studies/Speech Communication
and Rhetoric, B
Computer and Information Sciences, B
Computer Science, B
Criminal Justice/Safety Studies, B
Education, M
Elementary Education and Teaching, B
English Language and Literature, B

Finance, B
Graphic Design, B
History, B
Humanities/Humanistic Studies, B
Information Science/Studies, B
Journalism, B
Marketing/Marketing Management, B
Music, B
Music Teacher Education, B
Nursing - Registered Nurse Training, B
Philosophy, B
Physical Education Teaching and Coaching, B
Political Science and Government, B
Pre-Dentistry Studies, B
Pre-Medicine/Pre-Medical Studies, B
Pre-Veterinary Studies, B
Psychology, B
Public Administration and Social Service
Professions, B
Public Relations/Image Management, B
Radio and Television, B
Social Work, B
Special Education and Teaching, B
Sport and Fitness Administration/Management, B
Theological and Ministerial Studies, B
Theology/Theological Studies, B
Visual and Performing Arts, B

REND LAKE COLLEGE

Administrative Assistant and Secretarial Science, A
Agricultural Business and Management, A
Agricultural Mechanization, A
Agricultural Production Operations, A
Agriculture, A
Applied Horticulture/Horticultural Operations, A
Architectural Technology/Technician, A
Art/Art Studies, General, A
Automobile/Automotive Mechanics
Technology/Technician, A
Automotive Engineering Technology/Technician, A
Biological and Physical Sciences, A
Business Administration and Management, A
Chemistry, A
Child Development, A
Clinical/Medical Laboratory Technician, A
Commercial and Advertising Art, A
Computer and Information Sciences, A
Computer Engineering Technology/Technician, A
Computer Programming, Specific Applications, A
Computer Science, A
Corrections, A
Criminal Justice/Police Science, A
Culinary Arts/Chef Training, A
Diesel Mechanics Technology/Technician, A
Early Childhood Education and Teaching, A
Electrician, A
Elementary Education and Teaching, A
Emergency Medical Technology/Technician (EMT
Paramedic), A
Engineering, A
Engineering Physics, A
Engineering Science, A
Engineering Technology, A
English Language and Literature, A
Health Information/Medical Records
Technology/Technician, A
Health Services/Allied Health/Health Sciences, A
Heavy Equipment Maintenance
Technology/Technician, A
History, A
Hospitality Administration/Management, A
Industrial Electronics Technology/Technician, A
Industrial Mechanics and Maintenance
Technology, A
Industrial Technology/Technician, A
Manufacturing Technology/Technician, A
Mathematics, A
Medical Administrative Assistant/Secretary, A
Nursing - Registered Nurse Training, A
Occupational Therapist Assistant, A
Parks, Recreation, Leisure and Fitness Studies, A
Plant Sciences, A
Political Science and Government, A
Pre-Dentistry Studies, A
Pre-Law Studies, A
Pre-Medicine/Pre-Medical Studies, A

Pre-Pharmacy Studies, A
Pre-Veterinary Studies, A
Psychology, A
Secondary Education and Teaching, A
Social Work, A
Sociology, A
Special Education and Teaching, A
Speech and Rhetorical Studies, A
Survey Technology/Surveying, A
Welding Technology/Welder, A

RICHLAND COMMUNITY COLLEGE

Accounting, A
Administrative Assistant and Secretarial Science, A
Agricultural Business and Management, A
Automobile/Automotive Mechanics
Technology/Technician, A
Biological and Physical Sciences, A
Business Administration and Management, A
Child Development, A
Computer and Information Sciences, A
Computer Graphics, A
Computer Programming, Specific Applications, A
Construction Engineering Technology/Technician, A
Criminal Justice/Police Science, A
Data Entry/Microcomputer Applications, A
Drafting and Design Technology/Technician, A
Electrical, Electronic and Communications
Engineering Technology/Technician, A
Fire Science/Firefighting, A
Food Technology and Processing, A
Industrial Technology/Technician, A
Information Science/Studies, A
Insurance, A
Legal Administrative Assistant/Secretary, A
Liberal Arts and Sciences Studies and
Humanities, A
Medical Administrative Assistant/Secretary, A
Nursing - Registered Nurse Training, A
Pre-Engineering, A
Word Processing, A

ROBERT MORRIS COLLEGE

Accounting Technology/Technician and
Bookkeeping, A
Administrative Assistant and Secretarial Science, A
Business Administration and Management, AB
Commercial and Advertising Art, A
Computer Programming, Specific Applications, A
Computer Systems Networking and
Telecommunications, A
Culinary Arts/Chef Training, A
Dental Assisting/Assistant, A
Design and Applied Arts, B
Drafting and Design Technology/Technician, A
Executive Assistant/Executive Secretary, A
Graphic Communications, A
Health and Physical Education, A
Health Information/Medical Records
Technology/Technician, A
Information Technology, B
Interior Design, A
Intermedia/Multimedia, A
Legal Administrative Assistant/Secretary, A
Legal Assistant/Paralegal, A
Management Information Systems and Services, A
Medical/Clinical Assistant, A
Surgical Technology/Technologist, A
Tourism and Travel Services Management, A
Web Page, Digital/Multimedia and Information
Resources Design, A

ROCK VALLEY COLLEGE

Accounting, A
Automobile/Automotive Mechanics
Technology/Technician, A
Avionics Maintenance Technology/Technician, A
Business Administration and Management, A
Child Development, A
Computer Engineering Technology/Technician, A
Computer Science, A
Construction Engineering Technology/Technician, A
Criminal Justice/Law Enforcement Administration, A
Drafting/Design Engineering
Technologies/Technicians, A

Electrical, Electronic and Communications
 Engineering Technology/Technician, A
Fire Science/Firefighting, A
Human Services, A
Industrial Design, A
Industrial Technology/Technician, A
Liberal Arts and Sciences Studies and
 Humanities, A
Marketing/Marketing Management, A
Nursing - Registered Nurse Training, A
Pre-Engineering, A
Quality Control Technology/Technician, A
Respiratory Care Therapy/Therapist, A
Welding Technology/Welder, A

ROCKFORD BUSINESS COLLEGE

Accounting, A
Business Administration and Management, A
Computer and Information Sciences, A
Executive Assistant/Executive Secretary, A
Legal Administrative Assistant/Secretary, A
Legal Assistant/Paralegal, A
Marketing/Marketing Management, A
Medical Transcription/Transcriptionist, A
Medical/Clinical Assistant, A

ROCKFORD COLLEGE

Accounting, B
Ancient Studies/Civilization, B
Ancient/Classical Greek Language and Literature, B
Anthropology, B
Art Education, M
Art History, Criticism and Conservation, B
Biochemistry, B
Biological and Physical Sciences, B
Biology/Biological Sciences, B
Business Administration and Management, B
Business Administration, Management and
 Operations, M
Chemistry, B
Classics and Classical
 Languages, Literatures, and Linguistics, B
Comparative Literature, B
Computer Science, B
Drama and Dramatics/Theatre Arts, B
Economics, B
Education, BM
Elementary Education and Teaching, BM
English Education, M
English Language and Literature, B
Finance, B
French Language and Literature, B
History, B
Humanities/Humanistic Studies, B
International Economics, B
International/Global Studies, B
Latin Language and Literature, B
Management Information Systems and Services, B
Marketing/Marketing Management, B
Mathematics, B
Music, B
Music Performance, B
Nursing - Registered Nurse Training, B
Philosophy, B
Physical Education Teaching and Coaching, B
Political Science and Government, B
Pre-Dentistry Studies, B
Pre-Law Studies, B
Pre-Medicine/Pre-Medical Studies, B
Pre-Veterinary Studies, B
Psychology, B
Reading Teacher Education, M
Romance Languages, Literatures, and Linguistics, B
Secondary Education and Teaching, BM
Social Sciences, B
Social Studies Teacher Education, M
Social Work, B
Sociology, B
Spanish Language and Literature, B
Special Education and Teaching, BM

ROOSEVELT UNIVERSITY

Accounting, BM
Actuarial Science, B
African-American/Black Studies, B
Applied Economics, M

Art History, Criticism and Conservation, B
Art/Art Studies, General, B
Biology/Biological Sciences, B
BioTechnology, BM
Business Administration and Management, B
Business Administration, Management and
 Operations, M
Business/Commerce, B
Business/Managerial Economics, B
Chemistry, BM
Clinical Laboratory Science/Medical
 Technology/Technologist, B
Clinical Psychology, MD
Clinical/Medical Laboratory Science and Allied
 Professions, B
Communication and Media Studies, M
Communication Studies/Speech Communication
 and Rhetoric, B
Community Organization and Advocacy, B
Comparative Literature, B
Computer Science, BM
Computer Systems Networking and
 Telecommunications, B
Corporate and Organizational Communication, M
Counselor Education/School Counseling and
 Guidance Services, M
Drama and Dramatics/Theatre Arts, B
Early Childhood Education and Teaching, M
Economics, BM
Education, BMD
Educational Leadership and Administration, MD
Electrical, Electronic and Communications
 Engineering Technology/Technician, B
Elementary Education and Teaching, BM
English, M
English Language and Literature, B
Finance, B
Foreign Languages and Literatures, B
Gender Studies, M
Geography, B
Gerontology, BM
Health and Medical Laboratory Technologies, B
Health/Health Care Administration/Management, B
Health/Medical Preparatory Programs, B
History, BM
Hospitality Administration/Management, BM
Human Resources Management and Services, M
Human Resources Management/Personnel
 Administration, B
Human Services, B
Industrial and Organizational Psychology, M
Insurance, B
International Business/Trade/Commerce, BM
International Relations and Affairs, B
Jazz/Jazz Studies, B
Journalism, BM
Kindergarten/PreSchool Education and Teaching, B
Labor and Industrial Relations, B
Law and Legal Studies, B
Legal Assistant/Paralegal, B
Liberal Arts and Sciences Studies and
 Humanities, B
Management Information Systems and Services, M
Management Science, B
Marketing/Marketing Management, B
Mathematics, BM
Medical Radiologic Technology/Science - Radiation
 Therapist, B
Music, BMO
Music History, Literature, and Theory, B
Music Pedagogy, M
Music Performance, B
Music Teacher Education, BO
Music Theory and Composition, B
Nuclear Medical Technology/Technologist, B
Organizational Management, MD
Philosophy, B
Piano and Organ, B
Political Science and Government, BM
Pre-Dentistry Studies, B
Pre-Law Studies, B
Pre-Medicine/Pre-Medical Studies, B
Pre-Pharmacy Studies, B
Psychology, B
Public Administration, BM

Public Administration and Social Service
 Professions, B
Public Health (MPH, DPH), B
Public Relations/Image Management, B
Radio and Television, B
Reading Teacher Education, M
Secondary Education and Teaching, BM
Social Sciences, B
Sociology, BM
Spanish Language and Literature, BM
Special Education and Teaching, BM
Statistics, B
Telecommunications, M
Telecommunications Technology/Technician, B
Theater, M
Urban Studies/Affairs, B
Violin, Viola, Guitar and Other Stringed
 Instruments, B
Voice and Opera, B
Wind and Percussion Instruments, B
Women's Studies, BM
Writing, M

RUSH UNIVERSITY

Allopathic Medicine, PO
Anatomy, MDO
Biochemistry, DO
Bioethics/Medical Ethics, M
Cell Biology and Anatomy, MDO
Clinical Laboratory Science/Medical
 Technology/Technologist, B
Clinical Laboratory Sciences, M
Communication Disorders, MD
Community Health Nursing, MD
Gerontological Nursing, MDO
Health Services Administration, MD
Immunology, MD
Maternal/Child Health and Neonatal
 Nurse/Nursing, MDO
Medical Physics, MD
Medical Technology, M
Medical/Surgical Nursing, MDO
Microbiology, D
Neuroscience, MD
Nurse Anesthetist, M
Nursing, MDO
Nursing - Advanced Practice, MDO
Nursing - Registered Nurse Training, B
Nutritional Sciences, M
Occupational Therapy/Therapist, M
Pediatric Nurse/Nursing, MDO
Perfusion Technology/Perfusionist, B
Pharmaceutical Sciences, M
Pharmacology, MDO
Physiology, DO
Psychiatric/Mental Health Nurse/Nursing, MDO

SAINT ANTHONY COLLEGE OF NURSING

Nursing - Registered Nurse Training, B

ST. AUGUSTINE COLLEGE

Accounting Technology/Technician and
 Bookkeeping, A
Administrative Assistant and Secretarial Science, A
Business Administration and Management, A
Business Administration, Management and
 Operations, A
Child Care and Support Services Management, A
Computer and Information Sciences, A
Culinary Arts/Chef Training, A
Early Childhood Education and Teaching, A
General Studies, A
Liberal Arts and Sciences Studies and
 Humanities, A
Management Information Systems and Services, A
Mental Health/Rehabilitation, A
Respiratory Care Therapy/Therapist, A
Social Work, B
Special Education and Teaching, A

SAINT FRANCIS MEDICAL CENTER COLLEGE OF NURSING

Medical/Surgical Nursing, MO
Nursing - Registered Nurse Training, B

Nursing Education, MO

ST. JOHN'S COLLEGE

Nursing --Registered Nurse Training, B

SAINT XAVIER UNIVERSITY

Accounting, B
Art Teacher Education, B
Art/Art Studies, General, B
Biological and Physical Sciences, B
Biology Teacher Education, B
Biology/Biological Sciences, B
Botany/Plant Biology, B
Business Administration, Management and
    Operations, MO
Business/Commerce, B
Chemistry, B
Communication Disorders, M
Communication Studies/Speech Communication
    and Rhetoric, B
Community Health Nursing, M
Computer and Information Sciences, B
Computer Science, BMO
Counseling Psychology, BMO
Counselor Education/School Counseling and
    Guidance Services, M
Criminal Justice/Safety Studies, B
Curriculum and Instruction, M
Early Childhood Education and Teaching, M
Education, MO
Educational Administration and Supervision, M
Electronic Commerce, M
Elementary Education and Teaching, BM
English, MO
English Language and Literature, B
English/Language Arts Teacher Education, B
Finance and Banking, MO
Health Services Administration, MO
History, B
History Teacher Education, B
Industrial and Organizational Psychology, B
Information Science/Studies, M
International Business/Trade/Commerce, B
International Relations and Affairs, B
Kindergarten/PreSchool Education and Teaching, B
Liberal Arts and Sciences Studies and
    Humanities, B
Management, M
Marketing, M
Mathematics, BM
Mathematics Teacher Education, B
Music, B
Music Performance, B
Music Teacher Education, B
Non-Profit/Public/Organizational Management, M
Nursing, MO
Nursing - Adult, M
Nursing - Advanced Practice, MO
Nursing - Registered Nurse Training, B
Nursing Administration, M
Philosophy, B
Political Science and Government, B
Psychiatric/Mental Health Nurse/Nursing, MO
Psychology, BMO
Public Health, M
Reading Teacher Education, M
Religion/Religious Studies, B
Secondary Education and Teaching, M
Social Sciences, B
Sociology, B
Spanish Language and Literature, B
Spanish Language Teacher Education, B
Special Education and Teaching, M
Speech-Language Pathology/Pathologist, B
Travel and Tourism, M
Writing, MO

SAUK VALLEY COMMUNITY COLLEGE

Accounting, A
Administrative Assistant and Secretarial Science, A
Architecture, A
Art/Art Studies, General, A
Athletic Training and Sports Medicine, A
Biology/Biological Sciences, A
Business Administration and Management, A
Chemistry, A

Chiropractic, A
Communication Studies/Speech Communication
    and Rhetoric, A
Computer and Information Sciences, A
Corrections, A
Criminal Justice/Law Enforcement Administration, A
Criminal Justice/Police Science, A
Drama and Dramatics/Theatre Arts, A
Early Childhood Education and Teaching, A
Economics, A
Education, A
Electrical, Electronic and Communications
    Engineering Technology/Technician, A
Elementary Education and Teaching, A
English Language and Literature, A
French Language and Literature, A
Heating, Air Conditioning, Ventilation and
    Refrigeration Maintenance
    Technology/Technician, A
History, A
Human Services, A
Industrial Radiologic Technology/Technician, A
Legal Administrative Assistant/Secretary, A
Liberal Arts and Sciences Studies and
    Humanities, A
Marketing/Marketing Management, A
Mathematics, A
Mechanical Engineering/Mechanical
    Technology/Technician, A
Medical Office Assistant/Specialist, A
Music, A
Nursing - Registered Nurse Training, A
Occupational Therapy/Therapist, A
Optometric Technician/Assistant, A
Physical Education Teaching and Coaching, A
Physical Therapy/Therapist, A
Physics, A
Political Science and Government, A
Pre-Dentistry Studies, A
Pre-Medicine/Pre-Medical Studies, A
Pre-Pharmacy Studies, A
Pre-Veterinary Studies, A
Psychology, A
Public Administration and Social Service
    Professions, A
Secondary Education and Teaching, A
Social Work, A
Sociology, A
Spanish Language and Literature, A
Special Education and Teaching, A
Speech and Rhetorical Studies, A

SCHOOL OF THE ART INSTITUTE OF CHICAGO

Animation, Interactive Technology, Video Graphics
    and Special Effects, B
Architecture and Related Services, B
Art Education, MO
Art History, Criticism and Conservation, BMO
Art Teacher Education, B
Art Therapy/Therapist, M
Art/Art Studies, General, B
Arts Management, M
Ceramic Arts and Ceramics, BM
Cinematography and Film/Video Production, B
Commercial and Advertising Art, B
Computer Graphics, B
Crafts/Craft Design, Folk Art and Artisanry, B
Creative Writing, B
Design and Applied Arts, B
Design and Visual Communications, B
Digital Communication and Media/Multimedia, B
Drawing, B
Fashion/Apparel Design, B
Fiber, Textile and Weaving Arts, B
Film, Television, and Video Production, M
Film/Cinema Studies, B
Film/Video and Photographic Arts, B
Fine Arts and Art Studies, BM
Fine/Studio Arts, B
Graphic Communications, B
Graphic Design, BM
Historic Preservation and Conservation, M
Illustration, B
Interior Architecture, B
Interior Design, BM

Intermedia/Multimedia, B
Metal and Jewelry Arts, B
Music, B
Painting, BM
Photography, BM
Printmaking, BM
Sculpture, BM
Visual and Performing Arts, B
Web Page, Digital/Multimedia and Information
    Resources Design, B
Writing, M

SHAWNEE COMMUNITY COLLEGE

Accounting, A
Administrative Assistant and Secretarial Science, A
Agricultural Business and Management, A
Agriculture, A
Agronomy and Crop Science, A
Animal Sciences, A
Automobile/Automotive Mechanics
    Technology/Technician, A
Biological and Physical Sciences, A
Business Administration and Management, A
Child Development, A
Cosmetology/Cosmetologist, A
Criminal Justice/Police Science, A
Electrical, Electronic and Communications
    Engineering Technology/Technician, A
Food Technology and Processing, A
Horticultural Science, A
Human Services, A
Information Science/Studies, A
Legal Administrative Assistant/Secretary, A
Liberal Arts and Sciences Studies and
    Humanities, A
Machine Tool Technology/Machinist, A
Medical Administrative Assistant/Secretary, A
Nursing - Registered Nurse Training, A
Social Work, A
Welding Technology/Welder, A
Wildlife and Wildlands Science and Management, A

SHIMER COLLEGE

Comparative Literature, B
General Studies, B
Humanities/Humanistic Studies, B
Liberal Arts and Sciences Studies and
    Humanities, B
Natural Sciences, B
Social Sciences, B

SOUTH SUBURBAN COLLEGE

Accounting, A
Administrative Assistant and Secretarial Science, A
Advertising, A
Architectural Engineering Technology/Technician, A
Biomedical Technology/Technician, A
Chemistry, A
Child Development, A
Commercial and Advertising Art, A
Construction Engineering Technology/Technician, A
Consumer Merchandising/Retailing Management, A
Court Reporting/Court Reporter, A
Criminal Justice/Law Enforcement Administration, A
Criminal Justice/Police Science, A
Data Processing and Data Processing
    Technology/Technician, A
Drafting and Design Technology/Technician, A
Drafting/Design Engineering
    Technologies/Technicians, A
Electrical, Electronic and Communications
    Engineering Technology/Technician, A
Elementary Education and Teaching, A
Fashion Merchandising, A
Finance, A
Fine/Studio Arts, A
Fire Science/Firefighting, A
Graphic and Printing Equipment Operator
    Production, A
Human Services, A
Industrial Radiologic Technology/Technician, A
Industrial Technology/Technician, A
Information Science/Studies, A
Kindergarten/PreSchool Education and Teaching, A
Legal Assistant/Paralegal, A

Liberal Arts and Sciences Studies and
Humanities, A
Machine Tool Technology/Machinist, A
Management Information Systems and Services, A
Marketing/Marketing Management, A
Mathematics, A
Mental Health/Rehabilitation, A
Nursing - Registered Nurse Training, A
Occupational Therapist Assistant, A
Pre-Engineering, A
Sales, Distribution and Marketing Operations, A
Teacher Assistant/Aide, A

SOUTHEASTERN ILLINOIS COLLEGE

Accounting, A
Administrative Assistant and Secretarial Science, A
Agricultural Mechanization, A
Automobile/Automotive Mechanics
Technology/Technician, A
Business Administration and Management, A
Child Development, A
Clinical/Medical Laboratory Technician, A
Corrections, A
Criminal Justice/Police Science, A
Electrical, Electronic and Communications
Engineering Technology/Technician, A
Emergency Medical Technology/Technician (EMT
Paramedic), A
Fire Science/Firefighting, A
Forestry Technology/Technician, A
Health Information/Medical Records
Administration/Administrator, A
Human Services, A
Hydrology and Water Resources Science, A
Information Science/Studies, A
Licensed Practical/Vocational Nurse Training, A
Mining Technology/Technician, A
Nursing - Registered Nurse Training, A
Occupational Therapy/Therapist, A
Real Estate, A
Surgical Technology/Technologist, A
Welding Technology/Welder, A
Wildlife and Wildlands Science and Management, A

SOUTHERN ILLINOIS UNIVERSITY CARBONDALE

Accounting, BMDO
Agricultural Economics, BMO
Agricultural Sciences, MO
Agriculture, B
Agronomy and Soil Sciences, M
Airline/Commercial/Professional Pilot and Flight
Crew, A
Allopathic Medicine, PO
Animal Sciences, BM
Anthropology, BMD
Apparel and Textiles, B
Applied Arts and Design, M
Applied Physics, MD
Architecture, B
Art/Art Studies, General, B
Automotive Engineering Technology/Technician, B
Aviation/Airway Management and Operations, B
Avionics Maintenance Technology/Technician, B
Biochemistry, MD
Biological and Biomedical Sciences, MD
Biology/Biological Sciences, B
Botany/Plant Biology, B
Business Administration and Management, B
Business Administration, Management and
Operations, MDO
Business/Managerial Economics, B
Ceramic Arts and Ceramics, M
Chemistry, BMD
Cinematography and Film/Video Production, B
Civil Engineering, BM
Classics and Classical
Languages, Literatures, and Linguistics, B
Clinical Psychology, MD
Communication and Media Studies, MDO
Communication Disorders, BM
Composition, M
Computer Engineering, B
Computer Science, BM
Construction Engineering Technology/Technician, B
Counseling Psychology, MD

Counselor Education/School Counseling and
Guidance Services, MD
Crafts, M
Criminal Justice/Law Enforcement Administration, B
Criminology, M
Cultural Studies, M
Curriculum and Instruction, MD
Dental Hygiene/Hygienist, B
Dental Laboratory Technology/Technician, A
Design and Visual Communications, B
Drama and Dramatics/Theatre Arts, B
Early Childhood Education and Teaching, B
Economics, BMD
Education, MDO
Educational Administration and Supervision, MD
Educational Measurement and Evaluation, D
Educational Psychology, MD
Electrical and Electronic Engineering
Technologies/Technicians, B
Electrical Engineering, MD
Electrical, Electronics and Communications
Engineering, B
Elementary Education and Teaching, B
Energy and Power Engineering, D
Engineering and Applied Sciences, MD
Engineering Technology, B
English, MD
English as a Second Language, M
English Language and Literature, B
Environmental Sciences, D
Experimental Psychology, MD
Finance, B
Fine Arts and Art Studies, M
Fine/Studio Arts, B
Fire Services Administration, B
Foods, Nutrition, and Wellness Studies, B
Foreign Languages, Literatures, and Linguistics, B
Forestry, BM
French Language and Literature, B
Funeral Service and Mortuary Science, B
Geography, BMD
Geology/Earth Science, BMD
German Language and Literature, B
Health Education, MD
Health Teacher Education, B
Health/Health Care Administration/Management, B
Higher Education/Higher Education
Administration, M
History, BMD
Horticultural Science, M
Human Development, M
Industrial Technology/Technician, B
Information Science/Studies, B
Interior Design, B
Jewelry/Metalsmithing, M
Journalism, B
Law and Legal Studies, PO
Legal Assistant/Paralegal, B
Liberal Arts and Sciences Studies and
Humanities, B
Linguistics, BM
Management Science, B
Manufacturing Engineering, M
Marketing/Marketing Management, B
Mathematics, BMD
Mechanical Engineering, BM
Mechanics, MD
Medical Radiologic Technology/Science - Radiation
Therapist, A
Microbiology, BMD
Mineral/Mining Engineering, M
Mining and Mineral Engineering, B
Molecular Biology, MD
Multi-/Interdisciplinary Studies, B
Music, BM
Music History, Literature, and Theory, M
Music Teacher Education, M
Music Theory and Composition, M
Nutritional Sciences, M
Painting, M
Parks, Recreation, Leisure and Fitness Studies, B
Performance, M
Pharmacology, MD
Philosophy, BMD
Physical Education Teaching and Coaching, BM
Physical Therapist Assistant, A

Physician Assistant, B
Physics, BMD
Physiology, BMD
Plant Biology, MD
Plant Sciences, BM
Political Science and Government, BMDO
Printmaking, M
Psychology, BMD
Public Administration, MO
Radio and Television, B
Recreation and Park Management, M
Rehabilitation and Therapeutic Professions, B
Rehabilitation Counseling, MD
Respiratory Care Therapy/Therapist, A
Rhetoric, MD
Russian Language and Literature, B
Sculpture, M
Social Sciences, B
Social Work, BMO
Sociology, BMD
Spanish Language and Literature, B
Special Education and Teaching, MD
Speech and Interpersonal Communication, MD
Speech and Rhetorical Studies, B
Statistics, M
Theater, MD
Trade and Industrial Teacher Education, B
Vocational and Technical Education, MD
Writing, M
Zoology/Animal Biology, BMD

SOUTHERN ILLINOIS UNIVERSITY EDWARDSVILLE

Accounting, BM
Anthropology, B
Art Education, M
Art Therapy/Therapist, MO
Art/Art Studies, General, B
Audiology/Audiologist and Speech-Language
Pathology/Pathologist, B
Biological and Biomedical Sciences, M
Biology/Biological Sciences, B
BioTechnology, M
Business Administration and Management, B
Business Administration, Management and
Operations, M
Business/Managerial Economics, B
Chemistry, BM
Civil Engineering, BM
Communication Disorders, M
Community Health Nursing, MO
Computer Engineering, B
Computer Science, BM
Construction Engineering Technology/Technician, B
Corporate and Organizational Communication, O
Criminal Justice/Safety Studies, B
Dentistry, P
Drama and Dramatics/Theatre Arts, B
Early Childhood Education and Teaching, B
Economics, BM
Education, MO
Educational Administration and Supervision, MO
Educational Media/Instructional Technology, M
Electrical Engineering, M
Electrical, Electronics and Communications
Engineering, B
Elementary Education and Teaching, BM
Engineering and Applied Sciences, M
English, MO
English as a Second Language, MO
English Education, MO
English Language and Literature, B
Environmental Policy and Resource
Management, M
Environmental Sciences, M
Finance and Banking, M
Fine Arts and Art Studies, M
Fine/Studio Arts, B
Foreign Language Teacher Education, M
Foreign Languages and Literatures, B
Geography, BM
Health and Physical Education, B
Health Education, MO
Health Teacher Education, B
History, BM
Industrial Engineering, B

Kinesiology and Movement Studies, MO
Liberal Arts and Sciences Studies and
  Humanities, B
Management Information Systems and
  Services, BM
Manufacturing Engineering, B
Marketing Research, M
Mass Communication/Media Studies, BMO
Mathematics, BM
Mathematics Teacher Education, M
Mechanical Engineering, BM
Media Studies, O
Medical/Surgical Nursing, MO
Museology/Museum Studies, O
Music, BM
Music Teacher Education, M
Nurse Anesthetist, MO
Nursing, MO
Nursing - Advanced Practice, MO
Nursing - Registered Nurse Training, B
Nursing Administration, MO
Nursing Education, MO
Pharmacy, P
Philosophy, B
Physics, BM
Political Science and Government, B
Psychiatric/Mental Health Nurse/Nursing, MO
Psychology, BMO
Public Administration, M
Reading Teacher Education, M
School Psychology, O
Science Teacher Education/General Science
  Teacher Education, BM
Secondary Education and Teaching, M
Social Studies Teacher Education, M
Social Work, BM
Sociology, BM
Special Education and Teaching, BM
Speech and Interpersonal Communication, M
Speech and Rhetorical Studies, BMO
Writing, M

SOUTHWESTERN ILLINOIS COLLEGE

Accounting, A
Administrative Assistant and Secretarial Science, A
Airframe Mechanics and Aircraft Maintenance
  Technology/Technician, A
Autobody/Collision and Repair
  Technology/Technician, A
Avionics Maintenance Technology/Technician, A
Banking and Financial Support Services, A
Building/Construction
  Finishing, Management, and Inspection, A
Business Administration and Management, A
Carpentry/Carpenter, A
Child Development, A
Clinical/Medical Laboratory Technician, A
Construction Engineering Technology/Technician, A
Criminal Justice/Law Enforcement Administration, A
Data Processing and Data Processing
  Technology/Technician, A
Drafting and Design Technology/Technician, A
Electrical, Electronic and Communications
  Engineering Technology/Technician, A
Elementary Education and Teaching, A
Engineering Technology, A
Fine/Studio Arts, A
Fire Science/Firefighting, A
Health Information/Medical Records
  Administration/Administrator, A
Heating, Air Conditioning, Ventilation and
  Refrigeration Maintenance
  Technology/Technician, A
Horticultural Science, A
Hospitality Administration/Management, A
Industrial Radiologic Technology/Technician, A
Information Science/Studies, A
Instrumentation Technology/Technician, A
Legal Administrative Assistant/Secretary, A
Legal Assistant/Paralegal, A
Liberal Arts and Sciences Studies and
  Humanities, A
Machine Tool Technology/Machinist, A
Marketing/Marketing Management, A
Medical Administrative Assistant/Secretary, A
Medical/Clinical Assistant, A

Metallurgical Technology/Technician, A
Nursing - Registered Nurse Training, A
Physical Education Teaching and Coaching, A
Physical Therapist Assistant, A
Pre-Pharmacy Studies, A
Prepress/Desktop Publishing and Digital Imaging
  Design, A
Real Estate, A
Sign Language Interpretation and Translation, A
Welding Technology/Welder, A

SPOON RIVER COLLEGE

Accounting, A
Administrative Assistant and Secretarial Science, A
Agricultural Mechanization, A
Agricultural Teacher Education, A
Art/Art Studies, General, A
Automobile/Automotive Mechanics
  Technology/Technician, A
Biological and Physical Sciences, A
Biology/Biological Sciences, A
Botany/Plant Biology, A
Business Administration and Management, A
Business Teacher Education, A
Chemistry, A
Child Development, A
Criminal Justice/Law Enforcement Administration, A
Criminal Justice/Police Science, A
Drama and Dramatics/Theatre Arts, A
Education, A
Electrical, Electronic and Communications
  Engineering Technology/Technician, A
English Language and Literature, A
Finance, A
History, A
Industrial Technology/Technician, A
Information Science/Studies, A
Kindergarten/PreSchool Education and Teaching, A
Legal Administrative Assistant/Secretary, A
Liberal Arts and Sciences Studies and
  Humanities, A
Mass Communication/Media Studies, A
Mathematics, A
Medical Administrative Assistant/Secretary, A
Nursing - Registered Nurse Training, A
Physical Education Teaching and Coaching, A
Physical Sciences, A
Physics, A
Political Science and Government, A
Pre-Engineering, A
Psychology, A
Public Health (MPH, DPH), A
Social Sciences, A
Sociology, A
Speech and Rhetorical Studies, A
Zoology/Animal Biology, A

SPRINGFIELD COLLEGE IN ILLINOIS

Art/Art Studies, General, A
Business Administration and Management, A
Computer Science, A
Education, A
Forensic Science and Technology, A
General Studies, A
Liberal Arts and Sciences Studies and
  Humanities, A
Mass Communication/Media Studies, A
Mathematics, A
Pre-Dentistry Studies, A
Pre-Law Studies, A
Pre-Medicine/Pre-Medical Studies, A
Pre-Nursing Studies, A
Pre-Pharmacy Studies, A
Pre-Veterinary Studies, A

TELSHE YESHIVA-CHICAGO

Rabbinical Studies, B

TRINITY CHRISTIAN COLLEGE

Accounting, B
Art Teacher Education, B
Art/Art Studies, General, B
Biology Teacher Education, B
Biology/Biological Sciences, B
Business Administration and Management, B

Business Administration, Management and
  Operations, B
Business Teacher Education, B
Business/Commerce, B
Ceramic Arts and Ceramics, B
Chemistry, B
Chemistry Teacher Education, B
Commercial and Advertising Art, B
Communication Studies/Speech Communication
  and Rhetoric, B
Computer Science, B
Drawing, B
Education, B
Education/Teaching of Individuals with Emotional
  Disturbances, B
Education/Teaching of Individuals with Mental
  Retardation, B
Education/Teaching of Individuals with Specific
  Learning Disabilities, B
Elementary Education and Teaching, B
English Language and Literature, B
English/Language Arts Teacher Education, B
Financial Planning and Services, B
History, B
History Teacher Education, B
Human Resources Management/Personnel
  Administration, B
Information Science/Studies, B
Junior High/Intermediate/Middle School Education
  and Teaching, B
Management Information Systems and Services, B
Marketing/Marketing Management, B
Mathematics, B
Mathematics Teacher Education, B
Music, B
Music Performance, B
Music Teacher Education, B
Nursing - Registered Nurse Training, B
Painting, B
Philosophy, B
Photography, B
Physical Education Teaching and Coaching, B
Piano and Organ, B
Pre-Dentistry Studies, B
Pre-Medicine/Pre-Medical Studies, B
Pre-Theology/Pre-Ministerial Studies, B
Pre-Veterinary Studies, B
Printmaking, B
Psychology, B
Public Relations/Image Management, B
Religion/Religious Studies, B
Religious Education, B
Sales, Distribution and Marketing Operations, B
Science Teacher Education/General Science
  Teacher Education, B
Sculpture, B
Secondary Education and Teaching, B
Social Work, B
Sociology, B
Spanish Language and Literature, B
Special Education and Teaching, B
Theology/Theological Studies, B

TRINITY COLLEGE OF NURSING AND HEALTH SCIENCES

Emergency Care Attendant (EMT Ambulance), A
Medical Radiologic Technology/Science - Radiation
  Therapist, A
Nursing - Registered Nurse Training, AB
Nursing Science, AB
Surgical Technology/Technologist, A

TRINITY INTERNATIONAL UNIVERSITY

Accounting, B
Athletic Training and Sports Medicine, B
Bible/Biblical Studies, B
Bioethics/Medical Ethics, MD
Biology/Biological Sciences, B
Business Administration and Management, B
Chemistry, B
Communication and Media Studies, BM
Computer Science, B
Counseling Psychology, M
Education, BM
Educational Leadership and Administration, M
Elementary Education and Teaching, B

English Language and Literature, B
History, B
Human Resources Development, B
Human Resources Management/Personnel
    Administration, B
Humanities/Humanistic Studies, B
International Business/Trade/Commerce, B
Law and Legal Studies, P
Liberal Arts and Sciences Studies and
    Humanities, B
Management, D
Management Science, B
Marketing/Marketing Management, B
Mathematics, B
Missions/Missionary Studies and Missiology, MD
Music, B
Music History, Literature, and Theory, B
Music Pedagogy, B
Music Teacher Education, B
Music Theory and Composition, B
Non-Profit/Public/Organizational Management, B
Pastoral Counseling and Specialized Ministries, B
Pastoral Studies/Counseling, MDP
Philosophy, B
Physical Education Teaching and Coaching, B
Pre-Medicine/Pre-Medical Studies, B
Pre-Nursing Studies, A
Pre-Theology/Pre-Ministerial Studies, B
Psychology, B
Religion/Religious Studies, M
Religious Education, MD
Religious/Sacred Music, B
Secondary Education and Teaching, B
Social Sciences, B
Teacher Education, Multiple Levels, B
Theology and Religious Vocations, MDPO
Youth Ministry, B

TRITON COLLEGE

Accounting, A
Administrative Assistant and Secretarial Science, A
Architectural Engineering Technology/Technician, A
Art/Art Studies, General, A
Automobile/Automotive Mechanics
    Technology/Technician, A
Baking and Pastry Arts/Baker/Pastry Chef, A
Building/Construction
    Finishing, Management, and Inspection, A
Business Administration and Management, A
Child Care Provider/Assistant, A
Commercial and Advertising Art, A
Computer and Information Systems Security, A
Computer Engineering Technology/Technician, A
Computer Graphics, A
Computer Programming, A
Computer Science, A
Computer Software and Media Applications, A
Computer Systems Networking and
    Telecommunications, A
Computer Typography and Composition Equipment
    Operator, A
Construction Engineering Technology/Technician, A
Consumer Merchandising/Retailing Management, A
Court Reporting/Court Reporter, A
Criminal Justice/Law Enforcement Administration, A
Criminal Justice/Police Science, A
Culinary Arts/Chef Training, A
Data Processing and Data Processing
    Technology/Technician, A
Drafting and Design Technology/Technician, A
Drama and Dramatics/Theatre Arts, A
Electrical, Electronic and Communications
    Engineering Technology/Technician, A
Engineering Technology, A
Fashion Merchandising, A
Fire Science/Firefighting, A
Graphic and Printing Equipment Operator
    Production, A
Heating, Air Conditioning, Ventilation and
    Refrigeration Maintenance
    Technology/Technician, A
Hospitality Administration/Management, A
Hotel/Motel Administration/Management, A
Industrial Technology/Technician, A
Information Science/Studies, A
Interdisciplinary Studies, A

Interior Design, A
International Business/Trade/Commerce, A
Kindergarten/PreSchool Education and Teaching, A
Landscape Architecture, A
Landscaping and Groundskeeping, A
Legal Administrative Assistant/Secretary, A
Liberal Arts and Sciences Studies and
    Humanities, A
Licensed Practical/Vocational Nurse Training, A
Machine Tool Technology/Machinist, A
Management Information Systems and Services, A
Marketing/Marketing Management, A
Music, A
Nuclear Medical Technology/Technologist, A
Nursing - Registered Nurse Training, A
Ophthalmic Laboratory Technology/Technician, A
Ophthalmic Technician/Technologist, A
Opticianry/Ophthalmic Dispensing Optician, A
Ornamental Horticulture, A
Radiologic Technology/Science - Radiographer, A
Real Estate, A
Respiratory Care Therapy/Therapist, A
Substance Abuse/Addiction Counseling, A
System Administration/Administrator, A
Transportation and Materials Moving, A
Web Page, Digital/Multimedia and Information
    Resources Design, A
Web/Multimedia Management and Webmaster, A
Welding Technology/Welder, A

UNIVERSITY OF CHICAGO

African Studies, B
African-American/Black Studies, B
Allopathic Medicine, PO
American/United States Studies/Civilization, B
Anatomy, D
Ancient Near Eastern and Biblical
    Languages, Literatures, and Linguistics, B
Ancient/Classical Greek Language and Literature, B
Anthropology, BD
Applied Mathematics, BMD
Arabic Language and Literature, B
Archeology, MD
Area, Ethnic, Cultural, and Gender Studies, B
Art History, Criticism and Conservation, BMD
Art/Art Studies, General, B
Asian Languages, MD
Asian Studies/Civilization, B
Astronomy, MD
Astrophysics, MD
Atmospheric Sciences and Meteorology, MD
Behavioral Sciences, B
Bengali Language and Literature, B
Biochemistry, BDO
Biological and Biomedical Sciences, MDPO
Biology/Biological Sciences, B
Business Administration, Management and
    Operations, MD
Cancer Biology/Oncology, D
Cell Biology and Anatomy, D
Central/Middle and Eastern European Studies, B
Chemistry, BD
Chinese Language and Literature, B
Classics and Classical
    Languages, Literatures, and Linguistics, BMD
Comparative Literature, BMD
Computer Science, BM
Creative Writing, B
Cultural Studies, MD
Developmental Biology and Embryology, D
East Asian Studies, BMD
Ecology, D
Economics, BD
English, MD
English Language and Literature, B
Environmental Policy and Resource
    Management, M
Environmental Sciences, M
Environmental Studies, B
Evolutionary Biology, D
Film, Television, and Video Theory and
    Criticism, MD
Film/Cinema Studies, B
Fine Arts and Art Studies, MD
Fine/Studio Arts, B
French Language and Literature, BMD

Genetics, D
Geography, B
Geophysics and Seismology, BMD
Geosciences, MD
German Language and Literature, BMD
Health Promotion, M
Hindi Language and Literature, B
History, BMD
History of Science and Technology, MD
Human Development, D
Human Development and Family Studies, B
Human Genetics, D
Humanities/Humanistic Studies, BM
Immunology, D
Interdisciplinary Studies, B
International Affairs, MO
International Business/Trade/Commerce, M
International/Global Studies, B
Italian Language and Literature, BMD
Japanese Language and Literature, B
Jewish/Judaic Studies, BMD
Latin American Studies, BMO
Latin Language and Literature, B
Law and Legal Studies, MDPO
Liberal Arts and Sciences Studies and
    Humanities, B
Linguistics, BMD
Mathematical and Computational Finance, M
Mathematics, BMD
Media Studies, MD
Medical Physics, D
Medieval and Renaissance Studies, B
Microbiology, D
Modern Languages, B
Molecular Biology, DO
Molecular Genetics, D
Molecular Physiology, D
Music, BMD
Music History, Literature, and Theory, B
Near and Middle Eastern Languages, MD
Near and Middle Eastern Studies, BMDO
Neurobiology and Neurophysiology, D
Nutritional Sciences, D
Paleontology, D
Pathology/Experimental Pathology, D
Pharmacology, D
Philosophy, BMD
Physics, BMD
Physiology, D
Planetary Astronomy and Science, MD
Political Science and Government, BD
Psychology, BD
Public Policy Analysis, BMDO
Religion/Religious Studies, BMDPO
Romance
    Languages, Literatures, and Linguistics, BMD
Russian Language and Literature, B
Russian Studies, B
Sanskrit and Classical Indian
    Languages, Literatures, and Linguistics, B
Slavic Languages, Literatures, and Linguistics, BMD
Social Sciences, BMD
Social Work, MDO
Sociology, BD
South and Southeast Asian Studies, MD
South Asian
    Languages, Literatures, and Linguistics, B
South Asian Studies, B
Southeast Asian Studies, B
Spanish Language and Literature, BMD
Statistics, BMD
Tamil Language and Literature, B
Theology and Religious Vocations, MDPO
Tibetan Language and Literature, B
Turkish Language and Literature, B
Urdu Language and Literature, B
Vision Science/Physiological Optics, D
Zoology/Animal Biology, D

UNIVERSITY OF ILLINOIS AT CHICAGO

Accounting, BMO
African-American/Black Studies, B
Allied Health and Medical Assisting Services, MD
Allopathic Medicine, PO
Anatomy, MDO
Anthropology, BMD

Applied Mathematics, MD
Architecture, BM
Art History, Criticism and Conservation, BMD
Art Teacher Education, B
Biochemistry, BMD
Bioengineering, MDO
Biological and Biomedical Sciences, MDO
Biological Anthropology, D
Biology Teacher Education, B
Biology/Biological Sciences, B
Biomedical/Medical Engineering, B
Biophysics, MD
Biostatistics, MD
BioTechnology, MD
Business Administration and Management, B
Business Administration, Management and
  Operations, MDO
Cell Biology and Anatomy, MDO
Chemical Engineering, BMD
Chemistry, BMD
Chemistry Teacher Education, B
Cinematography and Film/Video Production, B
Civil Engineering, BMD
Classics and Classical
  Languages, Literatures, and Linguistics, B
Commercial and Advertising Art, B
Communication and Media Studies, M
Community Health and Preventive Medicine, MD
Community Health Nursing, M
Computer and Information Sciences, B
Computer Engineering, BMD
Computer Science, MD
Criminal Justice/Safety Studies, B
Criminology, M
Curriculum and Instruction, MD
Dentistry, PO
Developmental Biology and Embryology, D
Dietetics/Dieticians, B
Disability Studies, MD
Drama and Dramatics/Theatre Arts, B
East European and Russian Studies, MD
Ecology, MD
Economics, BMDO
Education, MD
Educational Administration and Supervision, MD
Educational Psychology, D
Electrical Engineering, MD
Electrical, Electronics and Communications
  Engineering, B
Elementary Education and Teaching, B
Engineering and Applied Sciences, MDO
Engineering Physics, B
Engineering/Industrial Management, B
English, MD
English as a Second Language, M
English Language and Literature, B
English/Language Arts Teacher Education, B
Entrepreneurship/Entrepreneurial Studies, B
Environmental and Occupational Health, MD
Epidemiology, MD
Evolutionary Biology, MD
Finance, B
Fine Arts and Art Studies, M
Fine/Studio Arts, B
Foreign Language Teacher Education, B
Forensic Science and Technology, M
French Language and Literature, BM
French Language Teacher Education, B
Genetics, D
Geochemistry, MD
Geography, M
Geology/Earth Science, BMD
Geophysics and Seismology, MD
Geosciences, MD
Geotechnical Engineering, D
German Language and Literature, BMD
German Language Teacher Education, B
Graphic Design, BM
Health Education, M
Health Information/Medical Records
  Administration/Administrator, B
Health Services Administration, MD
Hispanic Studies, MD
History, BMD
History Teacher Education, B
Human Development, MD

Hydrology and Water Resources Science, MD
Immunology, DO
Industrial Design, BM
Industrial Engineering, B
Industrial/Management Engineering, MD
Italian Language and Literature, B
Kinesiology and Exercise Science, B
Kinesiology and Movement Studies, M
Latin American Studies, B
Linguistics, M
Management Information Systems and
  Services, BMD
Marketing/Marketing Management, B
Mass Communication/Media Studies, M
Materials Engineering, MD
Maternal/Child Health and Neonatal
  Nurse/Nursing, M
Maternity Nursing, M
Mathematics, BMD
Mathematics and Computer Science, B
Mathematics Teacher Education, BM
Mechanical Engineering, BMD
Medical Illustration and Informatics, M
Microbiology, DO
Mineralogy, MD
Molecular Biology, MD
Molecular Genetics, D
Music, B
Neurobiology and Neurophysiology, MDO
Nurse Midwife/Nursing Midwifery, M
Nursing, MDO
Nursing - Registered Nurse Training, B
Nursing Administration, M
Nutritional Sciences, MD
Occupational Therapy/Therapist, M
Operations Research, D
Oral and Dental Sciences, M
Paleontology, MD
Pediatric Nurse/Nursing, M
Pharmaceutical Administration, MD
Pharmaceutical Sciences, MD
Pharmacognosy, MD
Pharmacology, DO
Pharmacy, MDP
Philosophy, BMD
Photography, BM
Physical Therapy/Therapist, M
Physics, BMD
Physics Teacher Education, B
Physiology, MD
Plant Biology, MD
Polish Language and Literature, B
Political Science and Government, BMD
Pre-Dentistry Studies, B
Pre-Law Studies, B
Psychiatric/Mental Health Nurse/Nursing, M
Psychology, BD
Public Administration, MD
Public Health, MDO
Public Policy Analysis, D
Rhetoric, D
Russian Language and Literature, B
Science Teacher Education/General Science
  Teacher Education, B
Secondary Education and Teaching, B
Slavic Languages, Literatures, and Linguistics, BMD
Social Science Teacher Education, B
Social Work, BMD
Sociology, BMD
Spanish Language and Literature, B
Spanish Language Teacher Education, B
Special Education and Teaching, MD
Speech and Rhetorical Studies, B
Statistics, BMD
Surgical Nursing, M
Urban and Regional Planning, MD
Urban Education and Leadership, D
Water Resources, MD
Writing, D

UNIVERSITY OF ILLINOIS AT SPRINGFIELD

Accounting, BM
Anthropology, B
Biological and Biomedical Sciences, M
Biology/Biological Sciences, B

Business Administration and Management, B
Business Administration, Management and
  Operations, BM
Chemistry, B
Child and Family Studies, M
Communication and Media Studies, BM
Computer Science, BM
Economics, B
Educational Administration and Supervision, M
English, M
English Language and Literature, B
Environmental Sciences, M
Environmental Studies, M
Gerontology, M
History, B
Human Development, M
Human Services, M
Interdisciplinary Studies, M
Journalism, M
Law and Legal Studies, B
Legal and Justice Studies, M
Liberal Arts and Sciences Studies and
  Humanities, B
Management Information Systems and Services, M
Mathematics, B
Philosophy, B
Political Science and Government, BM
Psychology, B
Public Administration, MD
Public Health, M
Public History, M
Social Sciences, M
Social Work, B
Sociology, B
Substance Abuse/Addiction Counseling, M

UNIVERSITY OF ILLINOIS AT URBANA-CHAMPAIGN

Accounting, BMD
Actuarial Science, B
Advertising, B
Advertising and Public Relations, M
Aerospace, Aeronautical and Astronautical
  Engineering, BMD
African Studies, M
Agribusiness, B
Agricultural Communication/Journalism, B
Agricultural Economics, BMD
Agricultural Education, M
Agricultural Engineering, MD
Agricultural Mechanization, B
Agricultural Sciences, MDO
Agricultural Teacher Education, B
Agricultural/Biological Engineering and
  Bioengineering, B
Agriculture, B
Agronomy and Crop Science, B
Agronomy and Soil Sciences, MD
Airline/Commercial/Professional Pilot and Flight
  Crew, B
Allopathic Medicine, O
Animal Sciences, BMD
Anthropology, BMD
Apparel and Textiles, B
Applied Arts and Design, MD
Applied Mathematics, M
Architecture, MO
Architecture and Related Services, B
Area Studies, B
Art Education, MD
Art History, Criticism and Conservation, BMD
Art Teacher Education, B
Asian Languages, MD
Astronomy, BMD
Athletic Training and Sports Medicine, B
Atmospheric Sciences and Meteorology, MD
Audiology/Audiologist and Speech-Language
  Pathology/Pathologist, B
Aviation/Airway Management and Operations, B
Banking and Financial Support Services, B
Biochemistry, BMD
Bioengineering, D
Biological and Biomedical Sciences, BMD
Biological Anthropology, MDO
Biology/Biological Sciences, B
Biomedical/Medical Engineering, B

Biophysics, BD
Biopsychology, MD
BioTechnology, B
Botany/Plant Biology, B
Broadcast Journalism, B
Business Administration and Management, B
Business Administration, Management and
   Operations, MDO
Business Teacher Education, B
Business/Commerce, B
Cell Biology and Anatomy, D
Cell/Cellular and Molecular Biology, B
Cell/Cellular Biology and Histology, B
Chemical Engineering, BMD
Chemistry, BMD
Chemistry Teacher Education, B
Child Development, B
City/Urban, Community and Regional Planning, B
Civil Engineering, BMDO
Classics and Classical
   Languages, Literatures, and Linguistics, BMD
Clinical Psychology, MD
Cognitive Sciences, MD
Communication and Media Studies, D
Communication Disorders, MD
Communication, Journalism and Related
   Programs, B
Community Health and Preventive Medicine, BMD
Comparative Literature, BMD
Computational Biology, D
Computer Engineering, BMD
Computer Science, BMD
Consumer Economics, MD
Counselor Education/School Counseling and
   Guidance Services, MDO
Crafts/Craft Design, Folk Art and Artisanry, B
Curriculum and Instruction, MDO
Dance, BM
Demography, MD
Developmental Psychology, MD
Dietetics/Dieticians, B
Drama and Dramatics/Theatre Arts, B
East Asian Studies, BMD
East European and Russian Studies, M
Ecology, BD
Economics, BMD
Education, MDO
Education/Teaching of Individuals with Multiple
   Disabilities, MDO
Educational Administration and Supervision, MDO
Educational Psychology, MDO
Electrical Engineering, MD
Electrical, Electronics and Communications
   Engineering, B
Elementary Education and Teaching, B
Engineering, B
Engineering and Applied Sciences, MDO
Engineering Design, MO
Engineering Mechanics, B
Engineering Physics, B
English, MD
English as a Second Language, M
English Composition, B
English Language and Literature, B
English/Language Arts Teacher Education, B
Entomology, BMD
Environmental Engineering
   Technology/Environmental Technology, MDO
Environmental Sciences, BMD
Evolutionary Biology, D
Fashion Merchandising, B
Finance, B
Finance and Banking, MD
Food Science, B
Food Science and Technology, MDO
Foreign Language Teacher Education, BM
Forest Sciences and Biology, B
Forestry, B
French Language and Literature, BMD
French Language Teacher Education, B
General Studies, B
Geochemistry, MD
Geography, BMD
Geological and Earth Sciences/Geosciences, B
Geology/Earth Science, BMD
Geophysics and Seismology, MD

Geosciences, MD
German Language and Literature, BMD
German Language Teacher Education, B
Graphic Design, BM
Health Physics/Radiological Health, MD
Hebrew Language and Literature, B
Higher Education/Higher Education
   Administration, MDO
History, BMD
Horticultural Science, B
Hospitality Administration/Management, B
Human Development, MD
Human Development and Family Studies, B
Human Resources Development, MDO
Human Resources Management and Services, MD
Human Resources Management/Personnel
   Administration, B
Humanities/Humanistic Studies, B
Industrial and Labor Relations, MD
Industrial and Organizational Psychology, BMD
Industrial Design, BM
Industrial Engineering, B
Industrial/Management Engineering, MD
Information Science/Studies, MDO
Italian Language and Literature, BMD
Journalism, BM
Kindergarten/PreSchool Education and Teaching, B
Kinesiology and Exercise Science, B
Kinesiology and Movement Studies, MD
Landscape Architecture, BM
Latin American Studies, BM
Latin Teacher Education, B
Law and Legal Studies, MDPO
Leisure Studies, MD
Liberal Arts and Sciences Studies and
   Humanities, B
Library Science, MDO
Linguistics, BMD
Management of Technology, M
Marketing, B
Mass Communication/Media Studies, B
Materials Engineering, MD
Materials Sciences, BMD
Mathematics, BMD
Mathematics and Computer Science, B
Mathematics Teacher Education, M
Mechanical Engineering, BMD
Mechanics, MD
Microbiology, BMDO
Music, BMD
Music History, Literature, and Theory, B
Music Performance, B
Music Teacher Education, B
Music Theory and Composition, B
Natural Resources and Conservation, BMD
Natural Resources Conservation and Research, B
Neuroscience, DO
Nuclear Engineering, BMD
Nutritional Sciences, MDO
Operations Management and Supervision, B
Organizational Behavior Studies, B
Ornamental Horticulture, B
Painting, B
Parks, Recreation, Leisure and Fitness Studies, B
Pathobiology, MD
Philosophy, BMD
Photography, B
Physics, BMD
Physiology, BMD
Plant Biology, MD
Political Science and Government, BMD
Portuguese Language and Literature, B
Pre-Law Studies, B
Pre-Veterinary Studies, B
Psychology, BMD
Public Health, B
Real Estate, B
Rehabilitation Counseling, M
Rehabilitation Sciences, M
Religion/Religious Studies, B
Restaurant, Culinary, and Catering
   Management/Manager, B
Russian Language and Literature, BMD
Russian Studies, B
Sales, Distribution and Marketing Operations, B

Science Teacher Education/General Science
   Teacher Education, B
Sculpture, B
Secondary Education and Teaching, B
Slavic Languages, Literatures, and Linguistics, MD
Social Psychology, MD
Social Studies Teacher Education, B
Social Work, MD
Sociology, BMD
Spanish Language and Literature, BMD
Spanish Language Teacher Education, B
Special Education and Teaching, BMDO
Speech and Rhetorical Studies, BMD
Statistics, BMD
Structural Biology, D
Structural Engineering, D
Systems Engineering, MO
Theater, MD
Urban and Regional Planning, MDO
Veterinary Medicine, P
Veterinary Sciences, MD
Vocational and Technical Education, MDO
Vocational Rehabilitation Counseling/Counselor, B
Voice and Opera, B
Wildlife and Wildlands Science and Management, B
Women's Studies, B
Zoology/Animal Biology, D

UNIVERSITY OF PHOENIX-CHICAGO CAMPUS

Accounting, B
Business Administration and Management, B
Business Administration, Management and
   Operations, M
Criminal Justice/Law Enforcement Administration, B
E-Commerce/Electronic Commerce, B
Electronic Commerce, M
Human Resources Management and Services, M
International Business/Trade/Commerce, M
Management Information Systems and
   Services, BM
Management of Technology, M
Management Science, B
Marketing/Marketing Management, B
Organizational Management, M

UNIVERSITY OF ST. FRANCIS

Accounting, B
Adult and Continuing Education and Teaching, M
Allied Health and Medical Assisting Services, M
Biology/Biological Sciences, B
Business Administration and Management, B
Business Administration, Management and
   Operations, M
Clinical Laboratory Science/Medical
   Technology/Technologist, B
Computer Science, B
Curriculum and Instruction, M
Education, M
Educational Leadership and Administration, M
Elementary Education and Teaching, BM
English Language and Literature, B
English/Language Arts Teacher Education, B
Environmental Sciences, B
Finance, B
Health Services Administration, M
Health/Health Care Administration/Management, B
History, B
Human Resources Management/Personnel
   Administration, B
Information Technology, B
Liberal Arts and Sciences Studies and
   Humanities, B
Management, M
Marketing/Marketing Management, B
Mass Communication/Media Studies, B
Mathematics, B
Mathematics and Computer Science, B
Mathematics Teacher Education, B
Medical Radiologic Technology/Science - Radiation
   Therapist, B
Multi-/Interdisciplinary Studies, B
Music, B
Music Performance, B
Music Teacher Education, B
Nuclear Medical Technology/Technologist, B

Nursing, M
Nursing - Registered Nurse Training, B
Organizational Behavior Studies, B
Parks, Recreation and Leisure Facilities
    Management, B
Physician Assistant, M
Political Science and Government, B
Pre-Dentistry Studies, B
Pre-Medicine/Pre-Medical Studies, B
Pre-Veterinary Studies, B
Psychology, B
Radiologic Technology/Science - Radiographer, B
Science Teacher Education/General Science
    Teacher Education, B
Secondary Education and Teaching, M
Social Studies Teacher Education, B
Social Work, B
Special Education and Teaching, BM
System Administration/Administrator, B
Theology/Theological Studies, B
Visual and Performing Arts, B
Web/Multimedia Management and Webmaster, B

VANDERCOOK COLLEGE OF MUSIC

Music Teacher Education, BM

WAUBONSEE COMMUNITY COLLEGE

Accounting Technology/Technician and
    Bookkeeping, A
Administrative Assistant and Secretarial Science, A
Art Teacher Education, A
Art/Art Studies, General, A
Autobody/Collision and Repair
    Technology/Technician, A
Automobile/Automotive Mechanics
    Technology/Technician, A
Banking and Financial Support Services, A
Biological and Physical Sciences, A
Business Administration and Management, A
Business/Office Automation/Technology/Data
    Entry, A
CAD/CADD Drafting and/or Design
    Technology/Technician, A
Child Care Provider/Assistant, A
Communication Studies/Speech Communication
    and Rhetoric, A
Computer and Information Sciences, A
Computer Programming, Specific Applications, A
Criminal Justice/Police Science, A
Design and Visual Communications, A
Electrical, Electronic and Communications
    Engineering Technology/Technician, A
Engineering, A
Entrepreneurship/Entrepreneurial Studies, A
Executive Assistant/Executive Secretary, A
Fire Protection and Safety Technology/Technician, A
General Studies, A
Graphic Design, A
Heating, Air Conditioning, Ventilation and
    Refrigeration Maintenance
    Technology/Technician, A
Industrial Mechanics and Maintenance
    Technology, A
Industrial Technology/Technician, A
Kindergarten/PreSchool Education and Teaching, A
Liberal Arts and Sciences Studies and
    Humanities, A
Logistics and Materials Management, A
Machine Tool Technology/Machinist, A
Mass Communication/Media Studies, A
Massage Therapy/Therapeutic Massage, A
Medical/Clinical Assistant, A
Music, A
Music Teacher Education, A
Nurse/Nursing Assistant/Aide and Patient Care
    Assistant, A
Nursing - Registered Nurse Training, A
Operations Management and Supervision, A
Quality Control Technology/Technician, A
Retailing and Retail Operations, A
Robotics Technology/Technician, A
Sign Language Interpretation and Translation, A
Social Work, A

Tourism and Travel Services Marketing
    Operations, A

WEST SUBURBAN COLLEGE OF NURSING

Nursing - Registered Nurse Training, B

WESTERN ILLINOIS UNIVERSITY

Accounting, BM
African-American/Black Studies, B
Agriculture, B
Art/Art Studies, General, B
Bilingual and Multilingual Education, B
Biological and Biomedical Sciences, MO
Biology/Biological Sciences, B
Business Administration and Management, B
Business Administration, Management and
    Operations, M
Business/Managerial Economics, B
Chemistry, BM
Clinical Laboratory Science/Medical
    Technology/Technologist, B
Clinical Psychology, M
Communication and Media Studies, M
Communication Disorders, BM
Communication Studies/Speech Communication
    and Rhetoric, B
Community Psychology, M
Computer and Information Sciences, B
Computer Science, M
Counselor Education/School Counseling and
    Guidance Services, M
Criminal Justice/Law Enforcement Administration, B
Curriculum and Instruction, M
Distance Education Development, O
Drama and Dramatics/Theatre Arts, B
Economics, BM
Education, MO
Educational Leadership and Administration, MO
Educational Media/Instructional Technology, MO
Educational/Instructional Media Design, B
Elementary Education and Teaching, BM
English, M
English Language and Literature, B
Family and Consumer Sciences/Human Sciences, B
Finance, B
Fine/Studio Arts, B
Foundations and Philosophy of Education, M
French Language and Literature, B
Geography, BMO
Geology/Earth Science, B
Graphic and Printing Equipment Operator
    Production, B
Graphic Design, O
Health Education, MO
Health Services Administration, O
Health Teacher Education, B
Health/Health Care Administration/Management, B
History, BM
Human Resources Management/Personnel
    Administration, B
Industrial Technology/Technician, B
Internet and Interactive Multimedia, O
Journalism, B
Kinesiology and Movement Studies, M
Law Enforcement, M
Liberal Arts and Sciences Studies and
    Humanities, B
Management Information Systems and Services, B
Manufacturing Technology/Technician, B
Marine Biology and Biological Oceanography, O
Marketing/Marketing Management, B
Mathematics, BM
Meteorology, B
Music, BM
Parks, Recreation and Leisure Facilities
    Management, B
Philosophy, B
Physical Education Teaching and Coaching, BM
Physics, BM
Political Science and Government, BM
Psychology, BMO
Radio and Television, B
Reading Teacher Education, M
Recreation and Park Management, M
School Psychology, O

Secondary Education and Teaching, M
Social Work, B
Sociology, BM
Spanish Language and Literature, B
Special Education and Teaching, BM
Sport and Fitness Administration/Management, M
Student Personnel Services, M
Sustainable Development, O
Technology and Public Policy, M
Telecommunications, MO
Theater, M
Trade and Industrial Teacher Education, B
Travel and Tourism, M
Women's Studies, B
Writing, M
Zoology/Animal Biology, O

WESTWOOD COLLEGE-CHICAGO DU PAGE

Accounting, B
Accounting and Business/Management, B
Architectural Drafting and Architectural
    CAD/CADD, A
Commercial and Advertising Art, AB
Computer and Information Systems Security, B
Computer Programming, Specific Applications, B
Computer Programming/Programmer, A
Computer Software Engineering, A
Computer Systems Networking and
    Telecommunications, AB
Corrections and Criminal Justice, B
Design and Applied Arts, B
Design and Visual Communications, AB
E-Commerce/Electronic Commerce, B
Graphic Design, A
Interior Design, B
Intermedia/Multimedia, AB
Marketing/Marketing Management, B
System, Networking, and LAN/WAN
    Management/Manager, B
Web/Multimedia Management and Webmaster, B

WESTWOOD COLLEGE-CHICAGO LOOP CAMPUS

Accounting and Business/Management, AB
Architectural Drafting and Architectural
    CAD/CADD, A
Computer and Information Systems Security, B
Computer Programming, Specific Applications, B
Computer Programming/Programmer, A
Computer Software and Media Applications, B
Computer Systems Networking and
    Telecommunications, AB
Design and Visual Communications, B
Graphic Design, AB
Interior Design, B
Intermedia/Multimedia, AB
Marketing/Marketing Management, B
Web Page, Digital/Multimedia and Information
    Resources Design, B
Web/Multimedia Management and Webmaster, B

WESTWOOD COLLEGE-CHICAGO O'HARE AIRPORT

Accounting, B
Accounting and Business/Management, B
Architectural Drafting and Architectural
    CAD/CADD, A
Commercial and Advertising Art, AB
Computer and Information Systems Security, B
Computer Programming/Programmer, A
Computer Software Engineering, A
Computer Systems Networking and
    Telecommunications, AB
Corrections and Criminal Justice, B
Design and Applied Arts, B
Design and Visual Communications, AB
E-Commerce/Electronic Commerce, B
Graphic Design, A
Interior Design, B
Intermedia/Multimedia, AB
Marketing/Marketing Management, B
System, Networking, and LAN/WAN
    Management/Manager, B

Web/Multimedia Management and Webmaster, B

WESTWOOD COLLEGE-CHICAGO RIVER OAKS

Accounting and Business/Management, B
Architectural Drafting and Architectural
   CAD/CADD, A
Computer and Information Systems Security, B
Computer Programming, Specific Applications, B
Computer Programming/Programmer, A
Computer Systems Networking and
   Telecommunications, AB
Corrections and Criminal Justice, B
Design and Visual Communications, B
E-Commerce/Electronic Commerce, B
Graphic Design, A
Interior Design, B
Intermedia/Multimedia, AB
Marketing/Marketing Management, B
System, Networking, and LAN/WAN
   Management/Manager, B
Web/Multimedia Management and Webmaster, B

WHEATON COLLEGE

American/United States Studies/Civilization, M
Anthropology, B
Archeology, BM
Art/Art Studies, General, B
Bible/Biblical Studies, B
Biology/Biological Sciences, B
Business/Managerial Economics, B
Chemistry, B
Clinical Psychology, MD
Communication Studies/Speech Communication
   and Rhetoric, B
Computer Science, B
Cultural Studies, MO
Economics, B
Education, M
Elementary Education and Teaching, B
Engineering, B
English as a Second Language, MO
English Language and Literature, B
Environmental Studies, B
French Language and Literature, B
Geology/Earth Science, B
German Language and Literature, B
Health/Medical Preparatory Programs, B
History, B
Interdisciplinary Studies, M
International Relations and Affairs, B
Mathematics, B
Missions/Missionary Studies and Missiology, MO
Multi-/Interdisciplinary Studies, B
Music, B
Music History, Literature, and Theory, B
Music Performance, B
Music Teacher Education, B
Music Theory and Composition, B
Philosophy, B
Physics, B
Political Science and Government, B
Psychology, BMD
Religion/Religious Studies, BM
Religious Education, BM
Science Teacher Education/General Science
   Teacher Education, B
Secondary Education and Teaching, M
Social Studies Teacher Education, B
Sociology, B
Spanish Language and Literature, B

WILLIAM RAINEY HARPER COLLEGE

Accounting, A
Administrative Assistant and Secretarial Science, A
Architectural Engineering Technology/Technician, A
Art/Art Studies, General, A
Biological and Physical Sciences, A
Biology/Biological Sciences, A
Botany/Plant Biology, A
Business Administration and Management, A
Child Development, A
Computer and Information Sciences, A
Computer Engineering Technology/Technician, A
Computer Programming/Programmer, A
Computer Science, A

Computer Typography and Composition Equipment
   Operator, A
Criminal Justice/Law Enforcement Administration, A
Criminal Justice/Police Science, A
Culinary Arts/Chef Training, A
Data Processing and Data Processing
   Technology/Technician, A
Dental Hygiene/Hygienist, A
Dietetics/Dieticians, A
Drafting and Design Technology/Technician, A
Drafting/Design Engineering
   Technologies/Technicians, A
Electrical, Electronic and Communications
   Engineering Technology/Technician, A
Engineering, A
Fashion Merchandising, A
Fashion/Apparel Design, A
Finance, A
Fire Science/Firefighting, A
Health Teacher Education, A
Heating, Air Conditioning, Ventilation and
   Refrigeration Maintenance
   Technology/Technician, A
Horticultural Science, A
Hospitality Administration/Management, A
Hotel/Motel Administration/Management, A
Human Resources Management/Personnel
   Administration, A
Humanities/Humanistic Studies, A
Industrial Technology/Technician, A
Information Science/Studies, A
Insurance, A
Interior Design, A
International Business/Trade/Commerce, A
Journalism, A
Kindergarten/PreSchool Education and Teaching, A
Kinesiology and Exercise Science, A
Landscape Architecture, A
Landscaping and Groundskeeping, A
Legal Administrative Assistant/Secretary, A
Legal Assistant/Paralegal, A
Liberal Arts and Sciences Studies and
   Humanities, A
Licensed Practical/Vocational Nurse Training, A
Machine Tool Technology/Machinist, A
Management Information Systems and Services, A
Marketing/Marketing Management, A
Materials Sciences, A
Mathematics, A
Mechanical Engineering/Mechanical
   Technology/Technician, A
Medical Administrative Assistant/Secretary, A
Medical/Clinical Assistant, A
Music, A
Nursing - Registered Nurse Training, A
Parks, Recreation and Leisure Facilities
   Management, A
Physical Education Teaching and Coaching, A
Physical Sciences, A
Pre-Engineering, A
Purchasing, Procurement/Acquisitions and
   Contracts Management, A
Quality Control Technology/Technician, A
Real Estate, A
Rehabilitation Therapy, A
Sign Language Interpretation and Translation, A
Social Sciences, A

WORSHAM COLLEGE OF MORTUARY SCIENCE

Funeral Service and Mortuary Science, A

Indiana

ANCILLA COLLEGE

Art Teacher Education, A
Art/Art Studies, General, A
Behavioral Sciences, A
Biological and Physical Sciences, A
Biology Teacher Education, A
Biology/Biological Sciences, A
Business Administration and Management, A
Business Operations Support and Secretarial
   Services, A
Business/Commerce, A

Chemistry, A
Chemistry Teacher Education, A
Computer Programming/Programmer, A
Computer Software and Media Applications, A
Computer Systems Networking and
   Telecommunications, A
Criminal Justice/Law Enforcement Administration, A
Criminal Justice/Safety Studies, A
Early Childhood Education and Teaching, A
Elementary Education and Teaching, A
English Language and Literature, A
English/Language Arts Teacher Education, A
Fine Arts and Art Studies, A
Fine/Studio Arts, A
Graphic Design, A
Health Services/Allied Health/Health Sciences, A
Health/Medical Preparatory Programs, A
History, A
History Teacher Education, A
Humanities/Humanistic Studies, A
Liberal Arts and Sciences Studies and
   Humanities, A
Mathematics, A
Mathematics Teacher Education, A
Nursing - Registered Nurse Training, A
Piano and Organ, A
Social Sciences, A

ANDERSON UNIVERSITY

Accounting, BM
Art Teacher Education, B
Athletic Training and Sports Medicine, B
Bible/Biblical Studies, B
Biology/Biological Sciences, B
Business Administration and Management, B
Business Administration, Management and
   Operations, MD
Business/Commerce, A
Business/Managerial Economics, B
Chemistry, B
Clinical Laboratory Science/Medical
   Technology/Technologist, B
Commercial and Advertising Art, B
Computer Science, B
Criminal Justice/Law Enforcement
   Administration, AB
Drama and Dramatics/Theatre Arts, B
Education, B
Elementary Education and Teaching, B
English Language and Literature, B
English/Language Arts Teacher Education, B
Family Systems, B
Finance, B
Fine/Studio Arts, B
French Language and Literature, B
French Language Teacher Education, B
General Studies, A
Health and Physical Education, B
History, B
Information Science/Studies, B
Marketing/Marketing Management, B
Mass Communication/Media Studies, B
Mathematics, B
Mathematics and Computer Science, B
Mathematics and Statistics, B
Mathematics Teacher Education, B
Missions/Missionary Studies and Missiology, M
Music Management and Merchandising, B
Music Performance, B
Music Teacher Education, B
Nursing - Registered Nurse Training, B
Organizational Behavior Studies, B
Philosophy, B
Physical Education Teaching and Coaching, B
Physics, B
Political Science and Government, B
Pre-Dentistry Studies, B
Pre-Engineering, A
Pre-Law Studies, B
Pre-Medicine/Pre-Medical Studies, B
Pre-Veterinary Studies, B
Psychology, B
Religion/Religious Studies, B
Religious/Sacred Music, B
Science Teacher Education/General Science
   Teacher Education, B

Social Studies Teacher Education, B
Social Work, B
Sociology, B
Spanish Language and Literature, B
Spanish Language Teacher Education, B
Speech Teacher Education, B
Theology and Religious Vocations, MDP

BALL STATE UNIVERSITY

Accounting, BM
Actuarial Science, BM
Administrative Assistant and Secretarial Science, A
Adult and Continuing Education and Teaching, MD
Advertising, B
Advertising and Public Relations, M
Animal Genetics, B
Anthropology, BM
Architecture, BM
Art Education, M
Art Teacher Education, B
Art/Art Studies, General, B
Athletic Training and Sports Medicine, B
Audiology/Audiologist and Speech-Language
   Pathology/Pathologist, B
Biological and Biomedical Sciences, MD
Biology/Biological Sciences, B
Botany/Plant Biology, B
Business Administration and Management, AB
Business Administration, Management and
   Operations, M
Business Education, M
Business Teacher Education, B
Business/Managerial Economics, B
Cartography, B
Cell/Cellular Biology and Histology, B
Ceramic Arts and Ceramics, B
Chemical Engineering, A
Chemistry, BM
City/Urban, Community and Regional Planning, B
Classics and Classical
   Languages, Literatures, and Linguistics, B
Clinical Laboratory Science/Medical
   Technology/Technologist, B
Clinical Psychology, M
Cognitive Sciences, M
Commercial and Advertising Art, B
Communication and Media Studies, M
Communication Disorders, MD
Computer Science, BM
Counseling Psychology, MD
Criminal Justice/Law Enforcement
   Administration, AB
Criminology, AB
Curriculum and Instruction, MO
Dance, B
Dietetics/Dieticians, AB
Drama and Dramatics/Theatre Arts, B
Drawing, B
Ecology, B
Economics, B
Education, BMDO
Educational Administration and Supervision, MDO
Educational Psychology, MDO
Educational/Instructional Media Design, B
Elementary Education and Teaching, BMD
Emergency Medical Technology/Technician (EMT
   Paramedic), A
English, MD
English as a Second Language, M
English Language and Literature, B
Environmental Design/Architecture, B
Environmental Studies, B
Exercise and Sports Science, D
Family and Consumer Economics and Related
   Services, B
Family and Consumer Sciences/Home Economics
   Teacher Education, B
Family and Consumer Sciences/Human
   Sciences, BM
Fashion Merchandising, B
Finance, B
Fine Arts and Art Studies, M
Fine/Studio Arts, B
French Language and Literature, B
Geography, B
Geology/Earth Science, BM

Geosciences, M
German Language and Literature, B
Gerontology, M
Graphic and Printing Equipment Operator
   Production, A
Health Education, M
Health Promotion, M
Health Teacher Education, B
Higher Education/Higher Education
   Administration, MD
Historic Preservation and Conservation, M
History, BM
Human Resources Management/Personnel
   Administration, B
Industrial Radiologic Technology/Technician, A
Industrial Technology/Technician, AB
Information Science/Studies, ABM
Insurance, B
Japanese Language and Literature, B
Journalism, ABM
Kindergarten/PreSchool Education and Teaching, B
Kinesiology and Exercise Science, B
Landscape Architecture, BM
Latin American Studies, B
Latin Language and Literature, B
Legal Administrative Assistant/Secretary, AB
Legal Assistant/Paralegal, AB
Liberal Arts and Sciences Studies and
   Humanities, AB
Linguistics, MD
Management Information Systems and Services, B
Marine Biology and Biological Oceanography, B
Marketing/Marketing Management, AB
Mathematics, BM
Mathematics Teacher Education, M
Medical Microbiology and Bacteriology, B
Middle School Education, M
Modern Greek Language and Literature, B
Modern Languages, B
Molecular Biology, B
Music, B
Music Teacher Education, BMD
Musical Instrument Fabrication and Repair, B
Natural Resources and Conservation, M
Natural Resources Management/Development and
   Policy, B
Nuclear Medical Technology/Technologist, A
Nursing, M
Nursing - Registered Nurse Training, AB
Occupational Safety and Health
   Technology/Technician, A
Parks, Recreation and Leisure Facilities
   Management, B
Philosophy, B
Photography, B
Physical Education Teaching and Coaching, BMD
Physics, BM
Physiology, M
Piano and Organ, B
Plastics Engineering Technology/Technician, B
Political Science and Government, BM
Polymer/Plastics Engineering, B
Pre-Dentistry Studies, B
Pre-Law Studies, B
Pre-Medicine/Pre-Medical Studies, B
Printmaking, B
Psychology, BM
Public Administration, M
Public Health (MPH, DPH), B
Public Relations/Image Management, B
Real Estate, B
Religion/Religious Studies, B
Respiratory Care Therapy/Therapist, A
Rhetoric, M
School Psychology, MDO
Science Teacher Education/General Science
   Teacher Education, BMD
Sculpture, B
Secondary Education and Teaching, BM
Social Psychology, M
Social Sciences, BM
Social Work, B
Sociology, BM
Soil Science and Agronomy, B
Spanish Language and Literature, B
Special Education and Teaching, BMDO

Special Products Marketing Operations, AB
Speech and Interpersonal Communication, M
Speech and Rhetorical Studies, B
Sport and Fitness Administration/Management, B
Statistics, M
Technology Education/Industrial Arts, B
Telecommunications, M
Telecommunications Technology/Technician, B
Tourism and Travel Services Management, B
Trade and Industrial Teacher Education, B
Urban Planning, M
Violin, Viola, Guitar and Other Stringed
   Instruments, B
Vocational and Technical Education, M
Voice and Opera, B
Wildlife Biology, B
Wind and Percussion Instruments, B
Zoology/Animal Biology, B

BETHEL COLLEGE

Accounting, B
American Sign Language (ASL), AB
Art/Art Studies, General, B
Bible/Biblical Studies, AB
Biology/Biological Sciences, B
Business Administration and Management, AB
Business Administration, Management and
   Operations, M
Business Teacher Education, B
Chemical Engineering, B
Chemistry, AB
Christian Studies, B
Communication Studies/Speech Communication
   and Rhetoric, B
Computer and Information Sciences, B
Computer Science, AB
Counseling Psychology, M
Creative Writing, A
Criminal Justice/Safety Studies, AB
Design and Visual Communications, B
Divinity/Ministry (BD, MDiv.), B
Drama and Dramatics/Theatre Arts, B
Early Childhood Education and Teaching, A
Education, B
Elementary Education and Teaching, B
Engineering, B
English Language and Literature, B
English/Language Arts Teacher Education, B
Environmental Biology, B
Health and Physical Education, AB
History, B
Human Services, B
International Business/Trade/Commerce, B
Journalism, A
Junior High/Intermediate/Middle School Education
   and Teaching, B
Kinesiology and Exercise Science, B
Liberal Arts and Sciences Studies and
   Humanities, AB
Marriage and Family Therapy/Counseling, M
Mathematics, B
Mathematics and Computer Science, B
Mathematics Teacher Education, B
Missions/Missionary Studies and Missiology, B
Music, AB
Music Performance, B
Music Teacher Education, B
Nursing, M
Nursing - Registered Nurse Training, AB
Pastoral Studies/Counseling, BM
Philosophy, B
Physical Education Teaching and Coaching, B
Physics, B
Piano and Organ, B
Pre-Law Studies, B
Pre-Medicine/Pre-Medical Studies, B
Psychology, B
Religious/Sacred Music, B
Science Teacher Education/General Science
   Teacher Education, B
Secondary Education and Teaching, B
Sign Language Interpretation and Translation, AB
Social Sciences, B
Social Studies Teacher Education, B
Sociology, B
Sport and Fitness Administration/Management, B

Theology and Religious Vocations, M
Voice and Opera, B
Youth Ministry, B

BROWN MACKIE COLLEGE-FORT WAYNE

Accounting Technology/Technician and
   Bookkeeping, A
Business Administration and Management, A
Computer Software Technology/Technician, A
Criminal Justice/Police Science, A
Legal Assistant/Paralegal, A
Medical/Clinical Assistant, A
Occupational Therapist Assistant, A

BROWN MACKIE COLLEGE-MERRILLVILLE

Accounting Technology/Technician and
   Bookkeeping, A
Business Administration and Management, A
Computer Software Technology/Technician, A
Criminal Justice/Safety Studies, A
Gerontology, A
Legal Assistant/Paralegal, A
Medical Office Management/Administration, A
Medical/Clinical Assistant, A
Surgical Technology/Technologist, A

BROWN MACKIE COLLEGE-MICHIGAN CITY

Accounting Technology/Technician and
   Bookkeeping, A
Business Administration and Management, A
Computer Software Technology/Technician, A
Criminal Justice/Safety Studies, A
Legal Administrative Assistant/Secretary, A
Medical Administrative Assistant/Secretary, A
Medical/Clinical Assistant, A

BROWN MACKIE COLLEGE-SOUTH BEND

Business Administration and Management, A
Legal Assistant/Paralegal, A
Medical/Clinical Assistant, A
Occupational Therapist Assistant, A
Physical Therapist Assistant, A

BUTLER UNIVERSITY

Accounting, B
Actuarial Science, B
Anthropology, B
Arts Management, B
Audiology/Audiologist and Speech-Language
   Pathology/Pathologist, B
Biology/Biological Sciences, B
Business Administration and Management, B
Business Administration, Management and
   Operations, M
Business/Managerial Economics, B
Chemistry, B
Composition, M
Computer Science, B
Counselor Education/School Counseling and
   Guidance Services, M
Criminal Justice/Safety Studies, B
Dance, B
Drama and Dramatics/Theatre Arts, B
Economics, B
Education, M
Educational Administration and Supervision, M
Elementary Education and Teaching, BM
English, M
English Language and Literature, B
Finance, B
French Language and Literature, B
German Language and Literature, B
History, BM
Information Science/Studies, B
International Business/Trade/Commerce, B
International Relations and Affairs, B
Journalism, B
Latin Language and Literature, B
Liberal Arts and Sciences Studies and
   Humanities, A
Marketing/Marketing Management, B

Mathematics, B
Medicinal and Pharmaceutical Chemistry, B
Modern Greek Language and Literature, B
Music, BM
Music History, Literature, and Theory, BM
Music Management and Merchandising, B
Music Teacher Education, BM
Performance, M
Pharmaceutical Sciences, MP
Pharmacy, BMP
Philosophy, B
Physician Assistant, B
Physics, B
Piano and Organ, B
Political Science and Government, B
Psychology, B
Public Relations/Image Management, B
Reading Teacher Education, M
Religion/Religious Studies, B
Science, Technology and Society, B
Secondary Education and Teaching, BM
Sociology, B
Spanish Language and Literature, B
Special Education and Teaching, M
Speech and Rhetorical Studies, B
Telecommunications Technology/Technician, B
Violin, Viola, Guitar and Other Stringed
   Instruments, B
Voice and Opera, B
Wind and Percussion Instruments, B

CALUMET COLLEGE OF SAINT JOSEPH

Accounting, AB
Art Teacher Education, B
Business Administration and Management, AB
Business Teacher Education, B
Communication and Media Studies, B
Communication Studies/Speech Communication
   and Rhetoric, B
Computer Science, AB
Computer Typography and Composition Equipment
   Operator, A
Criminal Justice/Law Enforcement
   Administration, AB
Elementary Education and Teaching, B
English Language and Literature, AB
English/Language Arts Teacher Education, B
General Studies, AB
Health/Health Care Administration/Management, B
Human Services, B
Information Science/Studies, AB
Intermedia/Multimedia, B
Legal Assistant/Paralegal, B
Liberal Arts and Sciences Studies and
   Humanities, AB
Political Science and Government, B
Pre-Law Studies, AB
Psychology, B
Religion/Religious Studies, AB
Science Teacher Education/General Science
   Teacher Education, B
Secondary Education and Teaching, B
Social Studies Teacher Education, B
Substance Abuse/Addiction Counseling, B
Theology/Theological Studies, B

COLLEGE OF COURT REPORTING

Court Reporting/Court Reporter, A

CROSSROADS BIBLE COLLEGE

Bible/Biblical Studies, B
Elementary Education and Teaching, B
Missions/Missionary Studies and Missiology, B
Pastoral Counseling and Specialized Ministries, B
Pre-Theology/Pre-Ministerial Studies, B
Religious Education, B
Urban Studies/Affairs, B
Youth Ministry, B

DEPAUW UNIVERSITY

African-American/Black Studies, B
Ancient/Classical Greek Language and Literature, B
Anthropology, B
Art History, Criticism and Conservation, B

Athletic Training and Sports Medicine, B
Biochemistry, B
Biology/Biological Sciences, B
Chemistry, B
Classics and Classical
   Languages, Literatures, and Linguistics, B
Computer Science, B
Drama and Dramatics/Theatre Arts, B
East Asian Studies, B
Economics, B
Elementary Education and Teaching, B
English Composition, B
English Language and Literature, B
Environmental Studies, B
Fine/Studio Arts, B
French Language and Literature, B
Geology/Earth Science, B
German Language and Literature, B
History, B
Interdisciplinary Studies, B
Kinesiology and Exercise Science, B
Latin Language and Literature, B
Mass Communication/Media Studies, B
Mathematics, B
Multi-/Interdisciplinary Studies, B
Music, B
Music Management and Merchandising, B
Music Performance, B
Music Teacher Education, B
Music Theory and Composition, B
Peace Studies and Conflict Resolution, B
Philosophy, B
Physical Education Teaching and Coaching, B
Physics, B
Political Science and Government, B
Psychology, B
Religion/Religious Studies, B
Romance Languages, Literatures, and Linguistics, B
Russian Studies, B
Sociology, B
Spanish Language and Literature, B
Women's Studies, B

DEVRY UNIVERSITY (INDIANAPOLIS)

Business Administration and Management, B
Business Administration, Management and
   Operations, BM
Computer and Information Sciences, B
Electrical, Electronic and Communications
   Engineering Technology/Technician, A

DEVRY UNIVERSITY (MERRILLVILLE)

Business Administration, Management and
   Operations, M

EARLHAM COLLEGE

African-American/Black Studies, B
Art/Art Studies, General, B
Biology/Biological Sciences, B
Business Administration and Management, B
Chemistry, B
Classics and Classical
   Languages, Literatures, and Linguistics, B
Computer Science, B
Drama and Dramatics/Theatre Arts, B
Economics, B
English Language and Literature, B
Environmental Studies, B
French Language and Literature, B
Geology/Earth Science, B
German Language and Literature, B
History, B
Interdisciplinary Studies, B
International Relations and Affairs, B
Japanese Studies, B
Latin American Studies, B
Mathematics, B
Music, B
Peace Studies and Conflict Resolution, B
Philosophy, B
Physics, B
Political Science and Government, B
Pre-Law Studies, B
Pre-Medicine/Pre-Medical Studies, B
Psychology, B
Religion/Religious Studies, B

Sociology, B
Spanish Language and Literature, B
Women's Studies, B

FRANKLIN COLLEGE

Accounting, B
American/United States Studies/Civilization, B
Athletic Training and Sports Medicine, B
Biology Teacher Education, B
Biology/Biological Sciences, B
Business/Commerce, B
Canadian Studies, B
Chemistry, B
Chemistry Teacher Education, B
Computer and Information Sciences, B
Computer Science, B
Drama and Dramatics/Theatre Arts, B
Economics, B
Elementary Education and Teaching, B
English Language and Literature, B
English/Language Arts Teacher Education, B
French Language and Literature, B
French Language Teacher Education, B
History, B
Journalism, B
Mathematics, B
Mathematics Teacher Education, B
Parks, Recreation, Leisure and Fitness Studies, B
Philosophy, B
Physical Education Teaching and Coaching, B
Political Science and Government, B
Psychology, B
Religion/Religious Studies, B
Social Studies Teacher Education, B
Sociology, B
Spanish Language and Literature, B
Spanish Language Teacher Education, B

GOSHEN COLLEGE

Accounting, B
Art Teacher Education, B
Art Therapy/Therapist, B
Art/Art Studies, General, B
Bible/Biblical Studies, B
Bilingual and Multilingual Education, B
Biology/Biological Sciences, B
Broadcast Journalism, B
Business Administration and Management, B
Business Teacher Education, B
Chemistry, B
Child Development, B
Computer Science, B
Drama and Dramatics/Theatre Arts, B
Economics, B
Education, B
Elementary Education and Teaching, B
English Language and Literature, B
Environmental Studies, B
Family and Community Services, B
History, B
Information Science/Studies, B
Journalism, B
Kindergarten/PreSchool Education and Teaching, B
Liberal Arts and Sciences Studies and
  Humanities, B
Mass Communication/Media Studies, B
Mathematics, B
Music, B
Music Teacher Education, B
Natural Sciences, B
Nursing - Registered Nurse Training, B
Peace Studies and Conflict Resolution, B
Physical Education Teaching and Coaching, B
Physical Sciences, B
Physics, B
Pre-Dentistry Studies, B
Pre-Law Studies, B
Pre-Medicine/Pre-Medical Studies, B
Pre-Veterinary Studies, B
Psychology, B
Religion/Religious Studies, B
Science Teacher Education/General Science
  Teacher Education, B
Secondary Education and Teaching, B
Sign Language Interpretation and Translation, B
Social Work, B

Sociology, B
Spanish Language and Literature, B
Teaching English as a Second or Foreign
  Language/ESL Language Instructor, B

GRACE COLLEGE

Accounting, B
Administrative Assistant and Secretarial Science, A
Art Teacher Education, B
Art/Art Studies, General, B
Bible/Biblical Studies, AB
Biology/Biological Sciences, B
Business Administration and Management, B
Business/Commerce, B
Commercial and Advertising Art, B
Counseling Psychology, BM
Criminal Justice/Law Enforcement Administration, B
Divinity/Ministry (BD, MDiv.), B
Drawing, B
Elementary Education and Teaching, B
English Language and Literature, B
English/Language Arts Teacher Education, B
French Language and Literature, B
French Language Teacher Education, B
German Language and Literature, B
German Language Teacher Education, B
International Business/Trade/Commerce, B
Journalism, B
Management Information Systems and Services, B
Mass Communication/Media Studies, B
Mathematics, B
Mathematics Teacher Education, B
Music Teacher Education, B
Painting, B
Pastoral Studies/Counseling, B
Physical Education Teaching and Coaching, B
Piano and Organ, B
Psychology, B
Science Teacher Education/General Science
  Teacher Education, B
Social Work, B
Sociology, B
Spanish Language and Literature, B
Spanish Language Teacher Education, B
Special Education and Teaching, B

HANOVER COLLEGE

Anthropology, B
Art History, Criticism and Conservation, B
Art/Art Studies, General, B
Biology/Biological Sciences, B
Business Administration and Management, B
Chemistry, B
Classics and Classical
  Languages, Literatures, and Linguistics, B
Computer Science, B
Drama and Dramatics/Theatre Arts, B
Economics, B
English Language and Literature, B
French Language and Literature, B
Geology/Earth Science, B
German Language and Literature, B
History, B
International/Global Studies, B
Latin American Studies, B
Mass Communication/Media Studies, B
Mathematics, B
Medieval and Renaissance Studies, B
Music, B
Philosophy, B
Physical Education Teaching and Coaching, B
Physics, B
Political Science and Government, B
Psychology, B
Sociology, B
Spanish Language and Literature, B
Theology/Theological Studies, B

HOLY CROSS COLLEGE

Liberal Arts and Sciences Studies and
  Humanities, AB

HUNTINGTON UNIVERSITY

Accounting, B
Art Teacher Education, B
Art/Art Studies, General, B

Bible/Biblical Studies, B
Biological and Physical Sciences, B
Biology/Biological Sciences, B
Broadcast Journalism, B
Business Administration and Management, B
Business Teacher Education, B
Business/Managerial Economics, B
Chemistry, B
Commercial and Advertising Art, B
Communication Studies/Speech Communication
  and Rhetoric, B
Computer Science, B
Digital Communication and Media/Multimedia, B
Divinity/Ministry (BD, MDiv.), B
Drama and Dance Teacher Education, B
Drama and Dramatics/Theatre Arts, B
Economics, B
Education, B
Elementary Education and Teaching, B
English Language and Literature, B
Film/Cinema Studies, B
Graphic Design, B
History, B
Journalism, B
Junior High/Intermediate/Middle School Education
  and Teaching, B
Kinesiology and Exercise Science, B
Mass Communication/Media Studies, B
Mathematics, B
Missions/Missionary Studies and Missiology, B
Music, B
Music Management and Merchandising, B
Music Teacher Education, B
Music Theory and Composition, B
Natural Resources Management/Development and
  Policy, B
Parks, Recreation, Leisure and Fitness Studies, B
Pastoral Studies/Counseling, M
Philosophy, B
Physical Education Teaching and Coaching, B
Piano and Organ, B
Political Science and Government, B
Pre-Dentistry Studies, B
Pre-Law Studies, B
Pre-Medicine/Pre-Medical Studies, B
Pre-Veterinary Studies, B
Psychology, B
Public Relations/Image Management, B
Religion/Religious Studies, B
Religious/Sacred Music, B
Science Teacher Education/General Science
  Teacher Education, B
Secondary Education and Teaching, B
Social Work, B
Sociology, B
Special Education and Teaching, B
Technical Theatre/Theatre Design and
  Technology, B
Theological and Ministerial Studies, B
Theology/Theological Studies, B
Voice and Opera, B

INDIANA BUSINESS COLLEGE (ANDERSON)

Accounting, A
Administrative Assistant and Secretarial Science, A
Business Administration and Management, A
Business Administration, Management and
  Operations, A
Criminal Justice/Safety Studies, A
Health Information/Medical Records
  Technology/Technician, A
Human Resources Management/Personnel
  Administration, A
Medical Insurance Specialist/Medical Biller, A
Medical/Clinical Assistant, A

INDIANA BUSINESS COLLEGE (COLUMBUS)

Accounting, A
Administrative Assistant and Secretarial Science, A
Business Administration and Management, A
Business Administration, Management and
  Operations, A
Criminal Justice/Safety Studies, A

Human Resources Management/Personnel
  Administration, A
Medical Insurance Specialist/Medical Biller, A
Medical/Clinical Assistant, A

INDIANA BUSINESS COLLEGE (EVANSVILLE)

Accounting, A
Administrative Assistant and Secretarial Science, A
Business Administration and Management, A
Information Technology, A
Medical Insurance Coding Specialist/Coder, A
Medical Insurance Specialist/Medical Biller, A
Medical/Clinical Assistant, A

INDIANA BUSINESS COLLEGE (FORT WAYNE)

Accounting, A
Administrative Assistant and Secretarial Science, A
Business Administration and Management, A
Medical Insurance Specialist/Medical Biller, A
Medical/Clinical Assistant, A
Surgical Technology/Technologist, A

INDIANA BUSINESS COLLEGE (INDIANAPOLIS)

Accounting, A
Administrative Assistant and Secretarial Science, A
Business Administration and Management, A
Medical Insurance Coding Specialist/Coder, A
Medical Insurance Specialist/Medical Biller, A
Medical/Clinical Assistant, A
Surgical Technology/Technologist, A

INDIANA BUSINESS COLLEGE (INDIANAPOLIS)

Accounting, A
Administrative Assistant and Secretarial Science, A
Business Administration and Management, A
Business Administration, Management and
  Operations, A
Computer and Information Sciences, A
Computer and Information Sciences and Support
  Services, A
Computer Programming, Specific Applications, A
Computer Programming/Programmer, A
Fashion Merchandising, A
Human Resources Management/Personnel
  Administration, A
Information Technology, A
Legal Administrative Assistant/Secretary, A
Management Information Systems and Services, A
Medical/Clinical Assistant, A

INDIANA BUSINESS COLLEGE (INDIANAPOLIS-NORTHWEST CAMPUS)

Health and Medical Laboratory Technologies, A
Massage Therapy/Therapeutic Massage, A
Medical Insurance Coding Specialist/Coder, A
Medical Insurance Specialist/Medical Biller, A
Medical/Clinical Assistant, A
Surgical Technology/Technologist, A

INDIANA BUSINESS COLLEGE (LAFAYETTE)

Accounting, A
Administrative Assistant and Secretarial Science, A
Business Administration and Management, A
Business Administration, Management and
  Operations, A
Computer and Information Sciences and Support
  Services, A
Information Technology, A
Medical Insurance Coding Specialist/Coder, A
Medical Insurance Specialist/Medical Biller, A
Medical/Clinical Assistant, A

INDIANA BUSINESS COLLEGE (MARION)

Accounting, A
Administrative Assistant and Secretarial Science, A
Business Administration and Management, A
Medical Insurance Coding Specialist/Coder, A

Medical/Clinical Assistant, A

INDIANA BUSINESS COLLEGE-MEDICAL

Clinical/Medical Laboratory Technician, A
Massage Therapy/Therapeutic Massage, A
Medical Insurance Coding Specialist/Coder, A
Medical Insurance Specialist/Medical Biller, A
Medical/Clinical Assistant, A
Surgical Technology/Technologist, A

INDIANA BUSINESS COLLEGE (MUNCIE)

Accounting, A
Administrative Assistant and Secretarial Science, A
Business Administration and Management, A
Business Administration, Management and
  Operations, A
Computer and Information Sciences and Support
  Services, A
Computer Programming, Specific Applications, A
Criminal Justice/Safety Studies, A
Health Information/Medical Records
  Technology/Technician, A
Information Technology, A
Management Information Systems and Services, A
Medical Office Assistant/Specialist, A

INDIANA BUSINESS COLLEGE (TERRE HAUTE)

Accounting, A
Administrative Assistant and Secretarial Science, A
Business Administration and Management, A
Business Administration, Management and
  Operations, A
Criminal Justice/Safety Studies, A
Human Resources Management/Personnel
  Administration, A
Medical Insurance Specialist/Medical Biller, A
Medical/Clinical Assistant, A

INDIANA STATE UNIVERSITY

Accounting, B
Aeronautics/Aviation/Aerospace Science and
  Technology, A
African-American/Black Studies, B
Airline/Commercial/Professional Pilot and Flight
  Crew, B
Anthropology, B
Apparel and Textiles, B
Architectural Drafting and Architectural
  CAD/CADD, A
Architectural Engineering Technology/Technician, B
Art Teacher Education, B
Art/Art Studies, General, B
Athletic Training and Sports Medicine, BM
Audiology/Audiologist and Speech-Language
  Pathology/Pathologist, B
Automotive Engineering Technology/Technician, B
Aviation/Airway Management and Operations, B
Biological and Biomedical Sciences, MD
Biology/Biological Sciences, B
Business Administration and Management, B
Business Administration, Management and
  Operations, M
Business Teacher Education, B
Ceramic Arts and Ceramics, M
Chemistry, B
Child and Family Studies, M
Clinical Laboratory Science/Medical
  Technology/Technologist, B
Clinical Psychology, D
Clothing and Textiles, M
Communication and Media Studies, M
Communication Disorders, M
Communication Studies/Speech Communication
  and Rhetoric, B
Communication, Journalism and Related
  Programs, B
Community Health and Preventive Medicine, M
Community Health Services/Liaison/Counseling, B
Computer and Information Sciences, B
Computer Engineering, M
Computer Engineering Technology/Technician, B
Computer Science, M

Consumer Economics, M
Counseling Psychology, MD
Counselor Education/School Counseling and
  Guidance Services, MD
Criminology, ABM
Curriculum and Instruction, MD
Drama and Dramatics/Theatre Arts, B
Early Childhood Education and Teaching, BM
Ecology, D
Economics, B
Education, MDO
Educational Administration and Supervision, MDO
Educational Media/Instructional Technology, MD
Educational Psychology, MDO
Educational/Instructional Media Design, B
Electrical, Electronic and Communications
  Engineering Technology/Technician, AB
Elementary Education and Teaching, BM
Engineering and Applied Sciences, MD
English, M
English as a Second Language, MO
English Language and Literature, B
Environmental and Occupational Health, M
Environmental Health, B
Exercise and Sports Science, M
Family and Consumer Sciences/Human Sciences, B
Finance, B
Fine Arts and Art Studies, BM
Foods, Nutrition, and Wellness Studies, B
Foreign Languages and Literatures, B
French Language and Literature, BM
Geography, BMD
Geology/Earth Science, B
Geosciences, M
German Language and Literature, B
Graphic Design, M
Health Education, M
Health Promotion, M
Health Teacher Education, B
History, BM
Home Economics, M
Home Economics Education, M
Human Development and Family Studies, B
Human Resources Development, M
Human Resources Management/Personnel
  Administration, B
Industrial Education, M
Industrial Technology/Technician, B
Industrial/Management Engineering, M
Insurance, B
Interior Architecture, B
Journalism, B
Liberal Arts and Sciences Studies and
  Humanities, AB
Linguistics, M
Management Information Systems and Services, B
Management of Technology, D
Management Sciences and Quantitative Methods, B
Marketing/Marketing Management, B
Marriage and Family Therapy/Counseling, M
Mathematics, BM
Mechanical Engineering Related
  Technologies/Technicians, B
Media Studies, M
Microbiology, D
Multilingual and Multicultural Education, O
Music, BM
Nursing, M
Nursing - Registered Nurse Training, B
Nutritional Sciences, M
Occupational Safety and Health
  Technology/Technician, B
Office Management and Supervision, B
Painting, M
Parks, Recreation and Leisure Facilities
  Management, B
Philosophy, B
Photography, M
Physical Education Teaching and Coaching, BM
Physics, B
Physiology, D
Political Science and Government, BM
Printmaking, M
Psychology, BMD
Public Administration, M
Radio and Television, B

Reading Teacher Education, M
Robotics Technology/Technician, B
School Psychology, MDO
Science Teacher Education/General Science
Teacher Education, BM
Sculpture, M
Social Studies Teacher Education, B
Social Work, B
Sociology, B
Spanish Language and Literature, BM
Special Education and Teaching, B
Sport and Fitness Administration/Management, M
Sports Medicine, D
Theater, M
Trade and Industrial Teacher Education, AB
Vocational and Technical Education, M

INDIANA TECH

Accounting, AB
Business Administration and Management, AB
Business Administration, Management and
Operations, M
Computer Engineering, B
Computer Science, B
Criminal Justice/Law Enforcement
Administration, AB
Electrical, Electronics and Communications
Engineering, B
Electronic Commerce, M
Entrepreneurship/Entrepreneurial Studies, M
Graphic Communications, A
Human Resources Development, M
Human Resources Management and Services, M
Human Resources Management/Personnel
Administration, B
Human Services, B
Industrial Engineering, B
Information Science/Studies, AB
Information Technology, A
Management, M
Marketing, M
Marketing/Marketing Management, B
Mechanical Engineering, B
Parks, Recreation and Leisure Facilities
Management, AB
Psychology, B
Therapeutic Recreation/Recreational Therapy, AB
Web Page, Digital/Multimedia and Information
Resources Design, A

INDIANA UNIVERSITY BLOOMINGTON

Accounting, BMD
African Studies, B
African-American/Black Studies, BM
Analytical Chemistry, D
Anatomy, MD
Ancient/Classical Greek Language and Literature, B
Anthropology, BMD
Apparel and Textiles, B
Applied Art, B
Applied Arts and Design, M
Applied Mathematics, MD
Art Education, M
Art History, Criticism and Conservation, BMDO
Art Teacher Education, B
Art/Art Studies, General, B
Arts Management, M
Asian Languages, MDO
Asian Studies/Civilization, BMD
Astronomy, BMD
Astrophysics, BD
Athletic Training and Sports Medicine, BM
Audiology/Audiologist and Hearing Sciences, B
Audiology/Audiologist and Speech-Language
Pathology/Pathologist, B
Bilingual and Multilingual Education, B
Biochemistry, BMD
Bioinformatics, M
Biological and Biomedical Sciences, MDO
Biological Anthropology, MDO
Biology Teacher Education, B
Biology/Biological Sciences, B
Broadcast Journalism, B
Business Administration and Management, B
Business Administration, Management and
Operations, MDO

Business/Commerce, B
Business/Managerial Economics, B
Cell Biology and Anatomy, MD
Central/Middle and Eastern European Studies, B
Ceramic Arts and Ceramics, BM
Chemistry, BMD
Chemistry Teacher Education, B
Child Development, B
Chinese Language and Literature, B
Chinese Studies, MD
City/Urban, Community and Regional Planning, B
Classics and Classical
Languages, Literatures, and Linguistics, BMD
Clothing and Textiles, M
Cognitive Psychology and Psycholinguistics, B
Cognitive Sciences, D
Commercial and Advertising Art, B
Communication and Media Studies, MD
Communication Disorders, BMD
Communication Studies/Speech Communication
and Rhetoric, B
Comparative Literature, BMDO
Computer and Information Sciences, B
Computer Art and Design, M
Computer Science, MD
Consumer Merchandising/Retailing Management, B
Counselor Education/School Counseling and
Guidance Services, MD
Criminal Justice/Safety Studies, B
Criminology, MD
Curriculum and Instruction, MDO
Dance, B
Developmental Biology and Embryology, D
Developmental Psychology, D
Dietetics/Dieticians, B
Drama and Dramatics/Theatre Arts, AB
Drawing, B
East Asian Studies, BMDO
East European and Russian Studies, MO
Ecology, MD
Economics, BMD
Education, BMDO
Educational Administration and Supervision, MDO
Educational Leadership and Administration, D
Educational Media/Instructional Technology, MDO
Educational Psychology, MD
Elementary Education and Teaching, BMO
English, M
English as a Second Language, MDO
English Education, M
English Language and Literature, B
English/Language Arts Teacher Education, B
Entrepreneurship/Entrepreneurial Studies, M
Environmental Education, D
Environmental Sciences, MDO
Environmental Studies, B
Ethnic, Cultural Minority, and Gender Studies, B
Ethnomusicology, MD
Evolutionary Biology, MD
Exercise and Sports Science, MD
Family and Consumer Economics and Related
Services, B
Fashion Merchandising, B
Fashion/Apparel Design, AB
Finance, B
Finance and Banking, MD
Fine Arts and Art Studies, M
Fine/Studio Arts, B
Folklore, MD
Foods, Nutrition, and Wellness Studies, B
Foreign Language Teacher Education, M
Forensic Science and Technology, B
Foundations and Philosophy of Education, MD
French Language and Literature, BMD
French Language Teacher Education, B
General Studies, AB
Genetics, D
Geochemistry, MD
Geography, BMD
Geology/Earth Science, BMDO
Geophysics and Seismology, MD
Geosciences, MDO
German Language and Literature, BMD
German Language Teacher Education, B
Graphic Design, M

Higher Education/Higher Education
Administration, MD
History, BMDO
History of Science and Technology, MDO
Human Development and Family Studies, B
Human Resources Development, M
Human Resources Management and Services, M
Human-Computer Interaction, M
Information Science/Studies, MDO
Inorganic Chemistry, D
Interior Design, M
International and Comparative Education, M
International Business/Trade/Commerce, M
Italian Language and Literature, BMD
Japanese Language and Literature, B
Japanese Studies, MD
Jazz/Jazz Studies, B
Jewelry/Metalsmithing, M
Jewish/Judaic Studies, B
Journalism, BMDO
Kindergarten/PreSchool Education and Teaching, B
Kinesiology and Movement Studies, MDO
Labor and Industrial Relations, AB
Laser and Optical Technology/Technician, A
Latin American Studies, BMO
Latin Language and Literature, B
Law and Legal Studies, MDPO
Legal and Justice Studies, P
Leisure Studies, D
Library Science, MDO
Linguistics, BMDO
Management, MD
Management Information Systems and
Services, BMD
Marketing, MD
Marketing/Marketing Management, B
Mass Communication/Media Studies, BD
Mathematics, BMD
Mathematics Teacher Education, BM
Medical Microbiology and Bacteriology, B
Medieval and Renaissance Studies, D
Metal and Jewelry Arts, B
Microbiology, MD
Mineralogy, MD
Molecular Biology, MD
Music, BMD
Music History, Literature, and Theory, B
Music Teacher Education, BMD
Musical Instrument Fabrication and Repair, A
Near and Middle Eastern Languages, MD
Near and Middle Eastern Studies, B
Neuroscience, D
Occupational Safety and Health
Technology/Technician, A
Ophthalmic Laboratory Technology/Technician, A
Ophthalmic/Optometric Services, B
Optics/Optical Sciences, MD
Optometric Technician/Assistant, A
Optometry, P
Organizational Behavior Studies, D
Painting, M
Parks, Recreation and Leisure Facilities
Management, B
Parks, Recreation, Leisure and Fitness Studies, B
Pharmacology, MD
Philosophy, BMD
Photography, BM
Physical Chemistry, D
Physical Education Teaching and Coaching, BMDO
Physics, BMD
Physics Teacher Education, B
Physiology, MD
Piano and Organ, B
Plant Biology, MD
Political Science and Government, BMD
Portuguese Language and Literature, BMD
Pre-Dentistry Studies, B
Pre-Law Studies, B
Pre-Medicine/Pre-Medical Studies, B
Printmaking, M
Psychology, BD
Public Administration, AB
Public Affairs, MDO
Public Health, MDO
Public Health (MPH, DPH), B
Public Policy Analysis, AB

Radio and Television, B
Reading Teacher Education, MDO
Real Estate, B
Recreation and Park Management, MDO
Religion/Religious Studies, BMD
Russian Language and Literature, B
Russian Studies, B
School Psychology, O
Science Teacher Education/General Science
   Teacher Education, BMD
Sculpture, BM
Secondary Education and Teaching, BMO
Slavic Languages, Literatures, and Linguistics, BMD
Social Psychology, D
Social Sciences, D
Social Studies Teacher Education, BM
Social Work, B
Sociology, BMD
Spanish Language and Literature, BMD
Spanish Language Teacher Education, B
Special Education and Teaching, BMDO
Speech and Interpersonal Communication, MD
Speech and Rhetorical Studies, B
Speech Teacher Education, B
Sport and Fitness Administration/Management, BM
Statistics, MD
Systems Science and Theory, B
Technical Theatre/Theatre Design and
   Technology, A
Telecommunications Technology/Technician, B
Textile Design, M
Theater, MD
Therapeutic Recreation, M
Therapeutic Recreation/Recreational Therapy, B
Urban Studies/Affairs, B
Vision Science/Physiological Optics, MD
Voice and Opera, B
Western European Studies, MDO
Wind and Percussion Instruments, B
Women's Studies, B
Writing, M
Zoology/Animal Biology, MD

INDIANA UNIVERSITY EAST

Biological and Physical Sciences, A
Biology/Biological Sciences, B
Business/Commerce, AB
Clinical Laboratory Science/Medical
   Technology/Technologist, AB
Communication Studies/Speech Communication
   and Rhetoric, B
Computer Programming/Programmer, A
Criminal Justice/Safety Studies, A
Education, B
Elementary Education and Teaching, B
English Language and Literature, B
General Studies, AB
Geology/Earth Science, A
History, A
Human Services, A
Mathematics, A
Nursing - Registered Nurse Training, AB
Psychology, B
Secondary Education and Teaching, B
Social Work, AB
Sociology, B
Visual and Performing Arts, A

INDIANA UNIVERSITY KOKOMO

Accounting, O
Behavioral Sciences, B
Biological and Physical Sciences, B
Biology/Biological Sciences, B
Business Administration, Management and
   Operations, MO
Business/Commerce, AB
Clinical Laboratory Science/Medical
   Technology/Technologist, B
Communication Studies/Speech Communication
   and Rhetoric, B
Criminal Justice/Safety Studies, AB
Data Processing and Data Processing
   Technology/Technician, B
Education, M
Elementary Education and Teaching, BM
English Language and Literature, B

General Studies, AB
Humanities/Humanistic Studies, B
Labor and Industrial Relations, AB
Liberal Studies, M
Mathematics, B
Nursing - Registered Nurse Training, AB
Psychology, B
Public Administration, O
Secondary Education and Teaching, M
Sociology, B

INDIANA UNIVERSITY NORTHWEST

Accounting, BMO
Actuarial Science, B
African-American/Black Studies, B
Art/Art Studies, General, B
Biology Teacher Education, B
Biology/Biological Sciences, B
Business Administration and Management, AB
Business Administration, Management and
   Operations, MO
Chemistry, B
Chemistry Teacher Education, B
Clinical/Medical Laboratory Technician, A
Criminal Justice/Law Enforcement
   Administration, AB
Criminology, M
Data Processing and Data Processing
   Technology/Technician, B
Dental Hygiene/Hygienist, A
Drama and Dramatics/Theatre Arts, B
Economics, B
Education, BM
Elementary Education and Teaching, BM
English Language and Literature, B
English/Language Arts Teacher Education, B
French Language and Literature, B
French Language Teacher Education, B
General Studies, AB
Geology/Earth Science, B
Health Information/Medical Records
   Administration/Administrator, AB
Health Services Administration, M
Health/Health Care Administration/Management, B
History, B
Human Services, M
Labor and Industrial Relations, AB
Mass Communication/Media Studies, B
Mathematics, B
Mathematics Teacher Education, B
Medical Radiologic Technology/Science - Radiation
   Therapist, AB
Non-Profit/Public/Organizational Management, O
Nursing - Registered Nurse Training, AB
Philosophy, B
Political Science and Government, B
Psychology, B
Public Administration, ABM
Public Affairs, MO
Public Relations/Image Management, B
Radiologic Technology/Science - Radiographer, AB
Respiratory Care Therapy/Therapist, A
Secondary Education and Teaching, BM
Social Studies Teacher Education, B
Social Work, M
Sociology, B
Spanish Language and Literature, B
Spanish Language Teacher Education, B

INDIANA UNIVERSITY-PURDUE UNIVERSITY FORT WAYNE

Accounting, B
Anthropology, B
Applied Mathematics, M
Architectural Engineering Technology/Technician, A
Art Teacher Education, B
Audiology/Audiologist and Hearing Sciences, B
Biological and Biomedical Sciences, M
Biology Teacher Education, B
Biology/Biological Sciences, AB
Business Administration and Management, AB
Business Administration, Management and
   Operations, M
Business/Managerial Economics, B
Chemical Technology/Technician, A
Chemistry, B

Chemistry Teacher Education, B
Civil Engineering Technology/Technician, A
Clinical Laboratory Science/Medical
   Technology/Technologist, B
Commercial and Advertising Art, AB
Communication and Media Studies, BM
Community Health Services/Liaison/Counseling, B
Computational Mathematics, B
Computer Engineering, B
Computer Engineering Technology/Technician, B
Computer Science, ABM
Computer Software and Media Applications, AB
Construction Engineering Technology/Technician, B
Counselor Education/School Counseling and
   Guidance Services, M
Crafts/Craft Design, Folk Art and Artisanry, B
Creative Writing, B
Criminal Justice/Safety Studies, AB
Dental Hygiene/Hygienist, A
Dental Laboratory Technology/Technician, A
Drama and Dance Teacher Education, B
Drama and Dramatics/Theatre Arts, B
Drawing, B
Early Childhood Education and Teaching, A
Economics, B
Education, BM
Educational Administration and Supervision, M
Electrical, Electronic and Communications
   Engineering Technology/Technician, AB
Electrical, Electronics and Communications
   Engineering, B
Elementary Education and Teaching, BM
Engineering and Applied Sciences, M
English, M
English Education, M
English Language and Literature, AB
English Literature (British and Commonwealth), B
English/Language Arts Teacher Education, B
Finance, B
Fine/Studio Arts, B
French Language and Literature, AB
French Language Teacher Education, B
General Studies, AB
Geology/Earth Science, B
German Language and Literature, AB
German Language Teacher Education, B
Graphic Design, B
Health Services Administration, B
History, AB
Hospitality Administration/Management, AB
Human Services, AB
Industrial Technology/Technician, AB
Interior Design, A
Labor Studies, AB
Law and Legal Studies, B
Liberal Studies, M
Marketing/Marketing Management, B
Mathematics, ABM
Mathematics Teacher Education, B
Mechanical Engineering, B
Mechanical Engineering/Mechanical
   Technology/Technician, AB
Music, B
Music Teacher Education, B
Music Therapy/Therapist, B
Nursing, M
Nursing - Registered Nurse Training, AB
Nursing Administration, M
Operations Management and Supervision, AB
Operations Research, M
Organizational Communication, B
Painting, B
Philosophy, B
Photography, B
Physics, B
Physics Teacher Education, B
Piano and Organ, B
Political Science and Government, AB
Pre-Dentistry Studies, B
Pre-Medicine/Pre-Medical Studies, B
Printmaking, B
Psychology, AB
Public Administration, AB
Public Administration and Social Service
   Professions, A
Public Affairs, MO

Public Policy Analysis, B
Radiologic Technology/Science - Radiographer, A
Science Teacher Education/General Science
   Teacher Education, B
Sculpture, B
Secondary Education and Teaching, BM
Social Studies Teacher Education, B
Sociology, BM
Spanish Language and Literature, AB
Spanish Language Teacher Education, B
Speech Teacher Education, B
Statistics, B
Substance Abuse/Addiction Counseling, B
Therapeutic Recreation/Recreational Therapy, B
Voice and Opera, B
Women's Studies, AB
Youth Services/Administration, B

INDIANA UNIVERSITY-PURDUE UNIVERSITY INDIANAPOLIS

Allopathic Medicine, PO
Anatomy, MDO
Anthropology, B
Applied Mathematics, MD
Architectural Drafting and Architectural
   CAD/CADD, A
Architectural Engineering Technology/Technician, B
Art Education, M
Art History, Criticism and Conservation, B
Art Teacher Education, B
Biochemistry, MDO
Biological and Biomedical Sciences, MD
Biology/Biological Sciences, B
Biomedical Engineering, MD
Biomedical Technology/Technician, A
Biomedical/Medical Engineering, B
Biophysics, MDO
Biopsychology, D
Business Administration, Management and
   Operations, MO
Business/Commerce, B
Cell Biology and Anatomy, MDO
Chemistry, BMDO
Civil Engineering Technology/Technician, A
Clinical Laboratory Science/Medical
   Technology/Technologist, B
Clinical Psychology, MD
Communication Studies/Speech Communication
   and Rhetoric, B
Computer and Information Sciences, B
Computer Engineering, BMD
Computer Science, M
Criminal Justice/Safety Studies, AB
CytoTechnology/Cytotechnologist, AB
Dental Hygiene/Hygienist, AB
Dentistry, MDP
Economics, BMO
Education, BM
Electrical Engineering, MD
Electrical, Electronic and Communications
   Engineering Technology/Technician, AB
Electrical, Electronics and Communications
   Engineering, B
Elementary Education and Teaching, B
Emergency Medical Technology/Technician (EMT
   Paramedic), A
Engineering, B
English, M
English Education, M
English Language and Literature, B
English/Language Arts Teacher Education, B
Fine/Studio Arts, B
French Language and Literature, B
French Language Teacher Education, B
General Studies, AB
Geography, B
Geology/Earth Science, BM
German Language and Literature, B
German Language Teacher Education, B
Health Education, M
Health Information/Medical Records
   Administration/Administrator, B
Health Services Administration, MO
Health Services Research, M
Health Teacher Education, B
Health/Health Care Administration/Management, B

History, BM
Hospitality Administration/Management, B
Hotel/Motel Administration/Management, A
Immunology, MDO
Industrial and Organizational Psychology, M
Information Science/Studies, MO
Interior Design, B
Internet and Interactive Multimedia, M
Journalism, B
Kindergarten/PreSchool Education and Teaching, A
Labor and Industrial Relations, AB
Library Science, MO
Maternal/Child Health and Neonatal
   Nurse/Nursing, M
Mathematics, BMD
Mechanical Drafting and Mechanical Drafting
   CAD/CADD, A
Mechanical Engineering, BM
Mechanical Engineering/Mechanical
   Technology/Technician, AB
Medical Radiologic Technology/Science - Radiation
   Therapist, AB
Microbiology, MDO
Molecular Biology, MDO
Molecular Genetics, MDO
Music, M
Neurobiology and Neurophysiology, MDO
Non-Profit/Public/Organizational Management, M
Nuclear Medical Technology/Technologist, B
Nursing, MDO
Nursing - Adult, M
Nursing - Advanced Practice, M
Nursing - Registered Nurse Training, AB
Nutritional Sciences, M
Occupational Therapy/Therapist, B
Operations Management and Supervision, AB
Pathology/Experimental Pathology, MDO
Pediatric Nurse/Nursing, M
Pharmacology, MDO
Philanthropic Studies, MO
Philosophy, B
Physical Education Teaching and Coaching, B
Physical Therapy/Therapist, BM
Physics, BMD
Physiology, MDO
Political Science and Government, B
Pre-Dentistry Studies, B
Pre-Law Studies, B
Pre-Medicine/Pre-Medical Studies, B
Pre-Veterinary Studies, B
Psychology, BMD
Public Administration, ABMO
Public Health (MPH, DPH), B
Public History, M
Rehabilitation Counseling, MD
Rehabilitation Sciences, M
Religion/Religious Studies, B
Respiratory Care Therapy/Therapist, AB
Robotics Technology/Technician, AB
Secondary Education and Teaching, B
Sign Language Interpretation and Translation, B
Social Studies Teacher Education, B
Social Work, BMD
Sociology, B
Spanish Language and Literature, B
Spanish Language Teacher Education, B
Speech Teacher Education, B
Statistics, M
Toxicology, MDO
Urban and Regional Planning, MO
Women's Health Nursing, M

INDIANA UNIVERSITY SOUTH BEND

Accounting, M
Applied Mathematics, BM
Art/Art Studies, General, B
Biology Teacher Education, B
Biology/Biological Sciences, AB
Business Administration, Management and
   Operations, M
Business/Commerce, AB
Chemistry, AB
Chemistry Teacher Education, B
Computer Science, ABM
Counselor Education/School Counseling and
   Guidance Services, M

Criminal Justice/Law Enforcement
   Administration, AB
Dental Hygiene/Hygienist, A
Drama and Dramatics/Theatre Arts, B
Economics, B
Education, BM
Educational Administration and Supervision, M
Elementary Education and Teaching, BM
English Language and Literature, B
English/Language Arts Teacher Education, B
Film/Cinema Studies, A
Finance, A
Fine/Studio Arts, B
French Language and Literature, B
French Language Teacher Education, B
General Studies, AB
German Language and Literature, B
German Language Teacher Education, B
Health Services Administration, MO
Health/Health Care Administration/Management, B
History, B
Jazz/Jazz Studies, A
Kindergarten/PreSchool Education and Teaching, A
Labor and Industrial Relations, AB
Legal Assistant/Paralegal, A
Management Information Systems and Services, M
Marketing/Marketing Management, B
Mass Communication/Media Studies, B
Mathematics, B
Mathematics Teacher Education, B
Medical Radiologic Technology/Science - Radiation
   Therapist, A
Music, M
Music Performance, B
Music Teacher Education, B
Non-Profit/Public/Organizational Management, O
Nursing - Registered Nurse Training, AB
Philosophy, B
Physics, B
Physics Teacher Education, B
Political Science and Government, B
Psychology, BM
Public Administration, ABO
Public Affairs, MO
Science Teacher Education/General Science
   Teacher Education, B
Secondary Education and Teaching, BM
Social Studies Teacher Education, B
Social Work, M
Sociology, B
Spanish Language and Literature, B
Spanish Language Teacher Education, B
Special Education and Teaching, BM
Speech and Rhetorical Studies, B
Women's Studies, B

INDIANA UNIVERSITY SOUTHEAST

Accounting, O
Art/Art Studies, General, B
Biology Teacher Education, B
Biology/Biological Sciences, B
Business Administration, Management and
   Operations, MO
Business/Commerce, AB
Business/Managerial Economics, B
Chemistry, B
Clinical Laboratory Science/Medical
   Technology/Technologist, B
Communication Studies/Speech Communication
   and Rhetoric, B
Computer Science, AB
Counselor Education/School Counseling and
   Guidance Services, M
CytoTechnology/Cytotechnologist, AB
Economics, BO
Education, BM
Elementary Education and Teaching, BM
English Language and Literature, B
English/Language Arts Teacher Education, B
Finance and Banking, MO
Fine/Studio Arts, B
French Language and Literature, B
General Studies, AB
Geography, B
German Language and Literature, B
History, B

Industrial and Manufacturing Management, O
Journalism, A
Labor and Industrial Relations, AB
Liberal Studies, M
Management Information Systems and Services, O
Marketing, O
Mathematics, B
Mathematics Teacher Education, B
Music, B
Nursing - Registered Nurse Training, B
Parks, Recreation and Leisure Facilities
   Management, B
Philosophy, B
Political Science and Government, B
Psychology, B
Science Teacher Education/General Science
   Teacher Education, B
Secondary Education and Teaching, BM
Social Studies Teacher Education, B
Sociology, B
Spanish Language and Literature, B
Special Education and Teaching, B

INDIANA WESLEYAN UNIVERSITY

Accounting, AB
Ancient Near Eastern and Biblical
   Languages, Literatures, and Linguistics, AB
Art Teacher Education, B
Art/Art Studies, General, AB
Athletic Training and Sports Medicine, B
Bible/Biblical Studies, B
Biology/Biological Sciences, AB
Business Administration and Management, AB
Business Administration, Management and
   Operations, M
Ceramic Arts and Ceramics, B
Chemistry, AB
Clinical Laboratory Science/Medical
   Technology/Technologist, B
Communication Studies/Speech Communication
   and Rhetoric, AB
Community Health Nursing, M
Community Psychology, M
Computer and Information Sciences, AB
Computer Graphics, B
Counseling Psychology, M
Counselor Education/School Counseling and
   Guidance Services, M
Creative Writing, B
Criminal Justice/Safety Studies, AB
Curriculum and Instruction, M
Economics, B
Education, BM
Elementary Education and Teaching, B
English Language and Literature, AB
English/Language Arts Teacher Education, B
Ethnic and Cultural Studies, AB
Finance, AB
General Studies, AB
History, AB
Junior High/Intermediate/Middle School Education
   and Teaching, B
Kinesiology and Exercise Science, B
Management, M
Marketing/Marketing Management, B
Marriage and Family Therapy/Counseling, M
Mathematics, AB
Mathematics Teacher Education, B
Music, AB
Music Teacher Education, B
Music Theory and Composition, B
Nursing, MO
Nursing - Registered Nurse Training, B
Organizational Management, D
Painting, B
Parks, Recreation and Leisure Facilities
   Management, B
Pastoral Studies/Counseling, AB
Philosophy, B
Photography, B
Physical Education Teaching and Coaching, B
Political Science and Government, AB
Pre-Dentistry Studies, B
Pre-Law Studies, B
Pre-Medicine/Pre-Medical Studies, B
Pre-Veterinary Studies, B

Printmaking, B
Psychology, B
Religious Education, AB
Religious/Sacred Music, AB
Science Teacher Education/General Science
   Teacher Education, B
Secondary Education and Teaching, B
Social Sciences, AB
Social Studies Teacher Education, B
Social Work, B
Sociology, B
Spanish Language and Literature, B
Special Education and Teaching, B
Sport and Fitness Administration/Management, B
Substance Abuse/Addiction Counseling, AB
Teacher Education, Multiple Levels, B
Theology and Religious Vocations, M
Theology/Theological Studies, B

INTERNATIONAL BUSINESS COLLEGE (FORT WAYNE)

Accounting, AB
Administrative Assistant and Secretarial Science, AB
Business Administration and Management, AB
Commercial and Advertising Art, AB
Computer Engineering Technology/Technician, AB
Computer Programming/Programmer, AB
Consumer Merchandising/Retailing
   Management, AB
Engineering/Industrial Management, AB
Finance, AB
Hospitality Administration/Management, AB
Legal Administrative Assistant/Secretary, AB
Legal Assistant/Paralegal, AB
Medical/Clinical Assistant, AB
Tourism and Travel Services Management, AB

INTERNATIONAL BUSINESS COLLEGE (INDIANAPOLIS)

Accounting Technology/Technician and
   Bookkeeping, A
Administrative Assistant and Secretarial Science, A
Computer Programming/Programmer, A
Graphic Design, A
Legal Administrative Assistant/Secretary, A
Legal Assistant/Paralegal, A
Management Information Systems and Services, A
Medical/Clinical Assistant, A
System, Networking, and LAN/WAN
   Management/Manager, A
Tourism and Travel Services Marketing
   Operations, A

ITT TECHNICAL INSTITUTE (FORT WAYNE)

Accounting and Business/Management, B
Animation, Interactive Technology, Video Graphics
   and Special Effects, B
Business Administration and Management, B
CAD/CADD Drafting and/or Design
   Technology/Technician, A
Computer and Information Systems Security, B
Computer Programming/Programmer, A
Computer Systems Networking and
   Telecommunications, B
Criminal Justice/Law Enforcement Administration, B
E-Commerce/Electronic Commerce, B
Electrical, Electronic and Communications
   Engineering Technology/Technician, AB
Robotics Technology/Technician, B
System, Networking, and LAN/WAN
   Management/Manager, A
Web Page, Digital/Multimedia and Information
   Resources Design, A

ITT TECHNICAL INSTITUTE (INDIANAPOLIS)

Accounting and Business/Management, B
Animation, Interactive Technology, Video Graphics
   and Special Effects, B
Business Administration and Management, B
Business Administration, Management and
   Operations, M
CAD/CADD Drafting and/or Design
   Technology/Technician, A

Computer and Information Systems Security, B
Computer Programming/Programmer, A
Computer Software Technology/Technician, B
Computer Systems Networking and
   Telecommunications, A
Criminal Justice/Law Enforcement Administration, B
E-Commerce/Electronic Commerce, B
Electrical, Electronic and Communications
   Engineering Technology/Technician, AB
Information Technology, B
Robotics Technology/Technician, B
System, Networking, and LAN/WAN
   Management/Manager, A
Web Page, Digital/Multimedia and Information
   Resources Design, A
Web/Multimedia Management and Webmaster, A

ITT TECHNICAL INSTITUTE (NEWBURGH)

Animation, Interactive Technology, Video Graphics
   and Special Effects, B
Business Administration and Management, B
CAD/CADD Drafting and/or Design
   Technology/Technician, A
Computer and Information Systems Security, B
Computer Programming/Programmer, A
Computer Software Technology/Technician, B
Computer Systems Networking and
   Telecommunications, B
Criminal Justice/Law Enforcement Administration, B
E-Commerce/Electronic Commerce, B
Electrical, Electronic and Communications
   Engineering Technology/Technician, AB
Robotics Technology/Technician, B
System, Networking, and LAN/WAN
   Management/Manager, A
Web Page, Digital/Multimedia and Information
   Resources Design, A
Web/Multimedia Management and Webmaster, A

IVY TECH COMMUNITY COLLEGE-BLOOMINGTON

Accounting Technology/Technician and
   Bookkeeping, A
Building/Property Maintenance and Management, A
Business Administration and Management, A
Cabinetmaking and Millwork/Millwright, A
Child Care and Support Services Management, A
Computer and Information Sciences, A
Criminal Justice/Safety Studies, A
Electrical, Electronic and Communications
   Engineering Technology/Technician, A
Electrician, A
Emergency Medical Technology/Technician (EMT
   Paramedic), A
Executive Assistant/Executive Secretary, A
Heating, Air Conditioning, Ventilation and
   Refrigeration Maintenance
   Technology/Technician, A
Industrial Technology/Technician, A
Legal Assistant/Paralegal, A
Liberal Arts and Sciences Studies and
   Humanities, A
Library Assistant/Technician, A
Machine Tool Technology/Machinist, A
Mechanic and Repair Technologies/Technicians, A
Mechanics and Repairers, A
Nursing - Registered Nurse Training, A
Pipefitting/Pipefitter and Sprinkler Fitter, A
Psychiatric/Mental Health Services Technician, A
Tool and Die Technology/Technician, A

IVY TECH COMMUNITY COLLEGE-CENTRAL INDIANA

Accounting Technology/Technician and
   Bookkeeping, A
Automobile/Automotive Mechanics
   Technology/Technician, A
BioTechnology, A
Building/Property Maintenance and Management, A
Business Administration and Management, A
Cabinetmaking and Millwork/Millwright, A
Carpentry/Carpenter, A
Child Care and Support Services Management, A
Child Development, A

Computer and Information Sciences, A
Criminal Justice/Safety Studies, A
Design and Visual Communications, A
Drafting and Design Technology/Technician, A
Electrical, Electronic and Communications
  Engineering Technology/Technician, A
Electrician, A
Executive Assistant/Executive Secretary, A
Heating, Air Conditioning, Ventilation and
  Refrigeration Maintenance
  Technology/Technician, A
Hospitality Administration/Management, A
Industrial Production Technologies/Technicians, A
Industrial Technology/Technician, A
Legal Assistant/Paralegal, A
Liberal Arts and Sciences Studies and
  Humanities, A
Machine Shop Technology/Assistant, A
Machine Tool Technology/Machinist, A
Mason/Masonry, A
Mechanics and Repairers, A
Medical Radiologic Technology/Science - Radiation
  Therapist, A
Medical/Clinical Assistant, A
Nursing - Registered Nurse Training, A
Occupational Safety and Health
  Technology/Technician, A
Occupational Therapist Assistant, A
Painting/Painter and Wall Coverer, A
Pipefitting/Pipefitter and Sprinkler Fitter, A
Psychiatric/Mental Health Services Technician, A
Respiratory Care Therapy/Therapist, A
Sheet Metal Technology/Sheetworking, A
Surgical Technology/Technologist, A
Tool and Die Technology/Technician, A

IVY TECH COMMUNITY COLLEGE-COLUMBUS

Accounting Technology/Technician and
  Bookkeeping, A
Automobile/Automotive Mechanics
  Technology/Technician, A
Building/Property Maintenance and Management, A
Business Administration and Management, A
Cabinetmaking and Millwork/Millwright, A
Child Care and Support Services Management, A
Computer and Information Sciences, A
Design and Visual Communications, A
Drafting and Design Technology/Technician, A
Electrical and Power Transmission
  Installation/Installer, A
Electrical, Electronic and Communications
  Engineering Technology/Technician, A
Executive Assistant/Executive Secretary, A
Heating, Air Conditioning, Ventilation and
  Refrigeration Maintenance
  Technology/Technician, A
Industrial Technology/Technician, A
Legal Assistant/Paralegal, A
Liberal Arts and Sciences Studies and
  Humanities, A
Library Assistant/Technician, A
Machine Tool Technology/Machinist, A
Mason/Masonry, A
Mechanic and Repair Technologies/Technicians, A
Mechanics and Repairers, A
Medical Radiologic Technology/Science - Radiation
  Therapist, A
Medical/Clinical Assistant, A
Pipefitting/Pipefitter and Sprinkler Fitter, A
Psychiatric/Mental Health Services Technician, A
Robotics Technology/Technician, A
Surgical Technology/Technologist, A
Tool and Die Technology/Technician, A

IVY TECH COMMUNITY COLLEGE-EAST CENTRAL

Accounting Technology/Technician and
  Bookkeeping, A
Automobile/Automotive Mechanics
  Technology/Technician, A
Building/Property Maintenance and Management, A
Business Administration and Management, A
Business/Office Automation/Technology/Data
  Entry, A
Cabinetmaking and Millwork/Millwright, A

Carpentry/Carpenter, A
Child Care and Support Services Management, A
Computer and Information Sciences, A
Construction Trades, A
Criminal Justice/Safety Studies, A
Early Childhood Education and Teaching, A
Electrical, Electronic and Communications
  Engineering Technology/Technician, A
Electrician, A
Executive Assistant/Executive Secretary, A
General Studies, A
Heating, Air Conditioning, Ventilation and
  Refrigeration Maintenance
  Technology/Technician, A
Hospitality Administration/Management, A
Human Services, A
Industrial Mechanics and Maintenance
  Technology, A
Industrial Production Technologies/Technicians, A
Industrial Technology/Technician, A
Legal Assistant/Paralegal, A
Liberal Arts and Sciences Studies and
  Humanities, A
Library Assistant/Technician, A
Machine Tool Technology/Machinist, A
Mason/Masonry, A
Medical Radiologic Technology/Science - Radiation
  Therapist, A
Medical/Clinical Assistant, A
Nursing - Registered Nurse Training, A
Painting/Painter and Wall Coverer, A
Physical Therapist Assistant, A
Pipefitting/Pipefitter and Sprinkler Fitter, A
Psychiatric/Mental Health Services Technician, A
Surgical Technology/Technologist, A
Tool and Die Technology/Technician, A

IVY TECH COMMUNITY COLLEGE-KOKOMO

Accounting Technology/Technician and
  Bookkeeping, A
Automobile/Automotive Mechanics
  Technology/Technician, A
Building/Property Maintenance and Management, A
Business Administration and Management, A
Business/Office Automation/Technology/Data
  Entry, A
Cabinetmaking and Millwork/Millwright, A
Child Care and Support Services Management, A
Computer and Information Sciences, A
Construction Trades, A
Criminal Justice/Safety Studies, A
Drafting and Design Technology/Technician, A
Early Childhood Education and Teaching, A
Electrical, Electronic and Communications
  Engineering Technology/Technician, A
Electrician, A
Emergency Medical Technology/Technician (EMT
  Paramedic), A
Executive Assistant/Executive Secretary, A
General Studies, A
Heating, Air Conditioning, Ventilation and
  Refrigeration Maintenance
  Technology/Technician, A
Human Services, A
Industrial Technology/Technician, A
Legal Assistant/Paralegal, A
Liberal Arts and Sciences Studies and
  Humanities, A
Library Assistant/Technician, A
Machine Tool Technology/Machinist, A
Mechanic and Repair Technologies/Technicians, A
Mechanics and Repairers, A
Medical/Clinical Assistant, A
Pipefitting/Pipefitter and Sprinkler Fitter, A
Psychiatric/Mental Health Services Technician, A
Surgical Technology/Technologist, A

IVY TECH COMMUNITY COLLEGE-LAFAYETTE

Accounting, A
Accounting Technology/Technician and
  Bookkeeping, A
Automobile/Automotive Mechanics
  Technology/Technician, A
BioTechnology, A

Building/Property Maintenance and Management, A
Business Administration and Management, A
Cabinetmaking and Millwork/Millwright, A
Carpentry/Carpenter, A
Child Care and Support Services Management, A
Computer and Information Sciences, A
Drafting and Design Technology/Technician, A
Electrical, Electronic and Communications
  Engineering Technology/Technician, A
Electrician, A
Executive Assistant/Executive Secretary, A
Heating, Air Conditioning, Ventilation and
  Refrigeration Maintenance
  Technology/Technician, A
Industrial Production Technologies/Technicians, A
Industrial Technology/Technician, A
Ironworking/Ironworker, A
Legal Assistant/Paralegal, A
Liberal Arts and Sciences Studies and
  Humanities, A
Lineworker, A
Machine Tool Technology/Machinist, A
Mason/Masonry, A
Mechanic and Repair Technologies/Technicians, A
Mechanics and Repairers, A
Medical/Clinical Assistant, A
Nursing - Registered Nurse Training, A
Painting/Painter and Wall Coverer, A
Pipefitting/Pipefitter and Sprinkler Fitter, A
Psychiatric/Mental Health Services Technician, A
Quality Control and Safety
  Technologies/Technicians, A
Quality Control Technology/Technician, A
Respiratory Care Therapy/Therapist, A
Robotics Technology/Technician, A
Sheet Metal Technology/Sheetworking, A
Surgical Technology/Technologist, A
Tool and Die Technology/Technician, A

IVY TECH COMMUNITY COLLEGE-NORTH CENTRAL

Accounting Technology/Technician and
  Bookkeeping, A
Automobile/Automotive Mechanics
  Technology/Technician, A
BioTechnology, A
Building/Property Maintenance and Management, A
Business Administration and Management, A
Business/Office Automation/Technology/Data
  Entry, A
Cabinetmaking and Millwork/Millwright, A
Carpentry/Carpenter, A
Child Care and Support Services Management, A
Clinical/Medical Laboratory Technician, A
Computer and Information Sciences, A
Criminal Justice/Safety Studies, A
Design and Visual Communications, A
Early Childhood Education and Teaching, A
Educational/Instructional Media Design, A
Electrical, Electronic and Communications
  Engineering Technology/Technician, A
Electrician, A
Emergency Medical Technology/Technician (EMT
  Paramedic), A
Executive Assistant/Executive Secretary, A
General Studies, A
Heating, Air Conditioning, Ventilation and
  Refrigeration Maintenance
  Technology/Technician, A
Hospitality Administration/Management, A
Human Services, A
Industrial Production Technologies/Technicians, A
Industrial Technology/Technician, A
Interior Design, A
Ironworking/Ironworker, A
Legal Assistant/Paralegal, A
Liberal Arts and Sciences Studies and
  Humanities, A
Library Assistant/Technician, A
Machine Tool Technology/Machinist, A
Mason/Masonry, A
Mechanic and Repair Technologies/Technicians, A
Mechanics and Repairers, A
Medical/Clinical Assistant, A
Nursing - Registered Nurse Training, A
Painting/Painter and Wall Coverer, A

Pipefitting/Pipefitter and Sprinkler Fitter, A
Robotics Technology/Technician, A
Sheet Metal Technology/Sheetworking, A
Telecommunications Technology/Technician, A
Tool and Die Technology/Technician, A

IVY TECH COMMUNITY COLLEGE-NORTHEAST

Accounting Technology/Technician and
   Bookkeeping, A
Automobile/Automotive Mechanics
   Technology/Technician, A
Building/Property Maintenance and Management, A
Business Administration and Management, A
Business/Office Automation/Technology/Data
   Entry, A
Cabinetmaking and Millwork/Millwright, A
Child Care and Support Services Management, A
Computer and Information Sciences, A
Construction Trades, A
Drafting and Design Technology/Technician, A
Early Childhood Education and Teaching, A
Electrical, Electronic and Communications
   Engineering Technology/Technician, A
Electrician, A
Executive Assistant/Executive Secretary, A
General Studies, A
Heating, Air Conditioning, Ventilation and
   Refrigeration Maintenance
   Technology/Technician, A
Hospitality Administration/Management, A
Human Services, A
Industrial Production Technologies/Technicians, A
Industrial Technology/Technician, A
Ironworking/Ironworker, A
Legal Assistant/Paralegal, A
Liberal Arts and Sciences Studies and
   Humanities, A
Library Assistant/Technician, A
Machine Tool Technology/Machinist, A
Mason/Masonry, A
Massage Therapy/Therapeutic Massage, A
Mechanics and Repairers, A
Medical/Clinical Assistant, A
Occupational Safety and Health
   Technology/Technician, A
Painting/Painter and Wall Coverer, A
Pipefitting/Pipefitter and Sprinkler Fitter, A
Psychiatric/Mental Health Services Technician, A
Respiratory Care Therapy/Therapist, A
Robotics Technology/Technician, A
Sheet Metal Technology/Sheetworking, A
Tool and Die Technology/Technician, A

IVY TECH COMMUNITY COLLEGE-NORTHWEST

Accounting Technology/Technician and
   Bookkeeping, A
Automobile/Automotive Mechanics
   Technology/Technician, A
Building/Construction
   Finishing, Management, and Inspection, A
Building/Property Maintenance and Management, A
Business Administration and Management, A
Cabinetmaking and Millwork/Millwright, A
Carpentry/Carpenter, A
Child Care and Support Services Management, A
Computer and Information Sciences, A
Construction Trades, A
Criminal Justice/Safety Studies, A
Drafting and Design Technology/Technician, A
Early Childhood Education and Teaching, B
Electrical, Electronic and Communications
   Engineering Technology/Technician, A
Electrician, A
Executive Assistant/Executive Secretary, A
Funeral Service and Mortuary Science, A
General Studies, A
Heating, Air Conditioning, Ventilation and
   Refrigeration Maintenance
   Technology/Technician, A
Hospitality Administration/Management, A
Industrial Technology/Technician, A
Ironworking/Ironworker, A
Legal Assistant/Paralegal, A

Liberal Arts and Sciences Studies and
   Humanities, A
Library Assistant/Technician, A
Machine Tool Technology/Machinist, A
Mason/Masonry, A
Mechanic and Repair Technologies/Technicians, A
Mechanics and Repairers, A
Medical/Clinical Assistant, A
Nursing - Registered Nurse Training, A
Occupational Safety and Health
   Technology/Technician, A
Painting/Painter and Wall Coverer, A
Pipefitting/Pipefitter and Sprinkler Fitter, A
Psychiatric/Mental Health Services Technician, A
Respiratory Care Therapy/Therapist, A
Sheet Metal Technology/Sheetworking, A
Surgical Technology/Technologist, A
Telecommunications Technology/Technician, A
Tool and Die Technology/Technician, A

IVY TECH COMMUNITY COLLEGE-SOUTHEAST

Accounting Technology/Technician and
   Bookkeeping, A
Business Administration and Management, A
Child Care and Support Services Management, A
Computer and Information Sciences, A
Electrical, Electronic and Communications
   Engineering Technology/Technician, A
Executive Assistant/Executive Secretary, A
Industrial Technology/Technician, A
Legal Assistant/Paralegal, A
Liberal Arts and Sciences Studies and
   Humanities, A
Library Assistant/Technician, A
Licensed Practical/Vocational Nurse Training, A
Medical/Clinical Assistant, A
Nursing - Registered Nurse Training, A
Psychiatric/Mental Health Services Technician, A

IVY TECH COMMUNITY COLLEGE-SOUTHERN INDIANA

Accounting Technology/Technician and
   Bookkeeping, A
Automobile/Automotive Mechanics
   Technology/Technician, A
Building/Property Maintenance and Management, A
Business Administration and Management, A
Business/Office Automation/Technology/Data
   Entry, A
Cabinetmaking and Millwork/Millwright, A
Carpentry/Carpenter, A
Child Care and Support Services Management, A
Computer and Information Sciences, A
Design and Visual Communications, A
Electrical, Electronic and Communications
   Engineering Technology/Technician, A
Electrician, A
Executive Assistant/Executive Secretary, A
Heating, Air Conditioning, Ventilation and
   Refrigeration Maintenance
   Technology/Technician, A
Industrial Technology/Technician, A
Legal Assistant/Paralegal, A
Liberal Arts and Sciences Studies and
   Humanities, A
Library Assistant/Technician, A
Machine Tool Technology/Machinist, A
Mason/Masonry, A
Mechanics and Repairers, A
Medical/Clinical Assistant, A
Nursing - Registered Nurse Training, A
Pipefitting/Pipefitter and Sprinkler Fitter, A
Psychiatric/Mental Health Services Technician, A
Respiratory Care Therapy/Therapist, A
Sheet Metal Technology/Sheetworking, A
Tool and Die Technology/Technician, A

IVY TECH COMMUNITY COLLEGE-SOUTHWEST

Accounting Technology/Technician and
   Bookkeeping, A
Automobile/Automotive Mechanics
   Technology/Technician, A
Boilermaking/Boilermaker, A

Building/Property Maintenance and Management, A
Business Administration and Management, A
Cabinetmaking and Millwork/Millwright, A
Carpentry/Carpenter, A
Child Care and Support Services Management, A
Computer and Information Sciences, A
Construction/Heavy Equipment/Earthmoving
   Equipment Operation, A
Criminal Justice/Safety Studies, A
Design and Visual Communications, A
Electrical, Electronic and Communications
   Engineering Technology/Technician, A
Electrician, A
Emergency Medical Technology/Technician (EMT
   Paramedic), A
Executive Assistant/Executive Secretary, A
Graphic Design, A
Heating, Air Conditioning, Ventilation and
   Refrigeration Maintenance
   Technology/Technician, A
Industrial Production Technologies/Technicians, A
Industrial Technology/Technician, A
Interior Design, A
Ironworking/Ironworker, A
Legal Assistant/Paralegal, A
Liberal Arts and Sciences Studies and
   Humanities, A
Library Assistant/Technician, A
Machine Tool Technology/Machinist, A
Mason/Masonry, A
Mechanic and Repair Technologies/Technicians, A
Mechanics and Repairers, A
Medical/Clinical Assistant, A
Nursing - Registered Nurse Training, A
Painting/Painter and Wall Coverer, A
Pipefitting/Pipefitter and Sprinkler Fitter, A
Psychiatric/Mental Health Services Technician, A
Robotics Technology/Technician, A
Sheet Metal Technology/Sheetworking, A
Surgical Technology/Technologist, A
Tool and Die Technology/Technician, A

IVY TECH COMMUNITY COLLEGE-WABASH VALLEY

Accounting Technology/Technician and
   Bookkeeping, A
Airframe Mechanics and Aircraft Maintenance
   Technology/Technician, A
Allied Health
   Diagnostic, Intervention, and Treatment
   Professions, A
Automobile/Automotive Mechanics
   Technology/Technician, A
Building/Property Maintenance and Management, A
Business Administration and Management, A
Cabinetmaking and Millwork/Millwright, A
Carpentry/Carpenter, A
Child Care and Support Services Management, A
Clinical/Medical Laboratory Technician, A
Computer and Information Sciences, A
Construction/Heavy Equipment/Earthmoving
   Equipment Operation, A
Criminal Justice/Safety Studies, A
Design and Visual Communications, A
Electrical, Electronic and Communications
   Engineering Technology/Technician, A
Electrician, A
Emergency Medical Technology/Technician (EMT
   Paramedic), A
Executive Assistant/Executive Secretary, A
Heating, Air Conditioning, Ventilation and
   Refrigeration Maintenance
   Technology/Technician, A
Industrial Production Technologies/Technicians, A
Industrial Technology/Technician, A
Ironworking/Ironworker, A
Legal Assistant/Paralegal, A
Liberal Arts and Sciences Studies and
   Humanities, A
Library Assistant/Technician, A
Machine Tool Technology/Machinist, A
Mason/Masonry, A
Mechanics and Repairers, A
Medical Radiologic Technology/Science - Radiation
   Therapist, A
Medical/Clinical Assistant, A

Nursing - Registered Nurse Training, A
Occupational Safety and Health
    Technology/Technician, A
Painting/Painter and Wall Coverer, A
Pipefitting/Pipefitter and Sprinkler Fitter, A
Psychiatric/Mental Health Services Technician, A
Quality Control and Safety
    Technologies/Technicians, A
Robotics Technology/Technician, A
Sheet Metal Technology/Sheetworking, A
Surgical Technology/Technologist, A
Tool and Die Technology/Technician, A

IVY TECH COMMUNITY COLLEGE-WHITEWATER

Accounting Technology/Technician and
    Bookkeeping, A
Automobile/Automotive Mechanics
    Technology/Technician, A
Building/Property Maintenance and Management, A
Business Administration and Management, A
Cabinetmaking and Millwork/Millwright, A
Child Care and Support Services Management, A
Computer and Information Sciences, A
Construction Trades, A
Electrical, Electronic and Communications
    Engineering Technology/Technician, A
Electrician, A
Executive Assistant/Executive Secretary, A
Heating, Air Conditioning, Ventilation and
    Refrigeration Maintenance
    Technology/Technician, A
Industrial Production Technologies/Technicians, A
Industrial Technology/Technician, A
Legal Assistant/Paralegal, A
Liberal Arts and Sciences Studies and
    Humanities, A
Library Assistant/Technician, A
Machine Tool Technology/Machinist, A
Mechanics and Repairers, A
Medical/Clinical Assistant, A
Nursing - Registered Nurse Training, A
Pipefitting/Pipefitter and Sprinkler Fitter, A
Psychiatric/Mental Health Services Technician, A
Robotics Technology/Technician, A
Tool and Die Technology/Technician, A

LINCOLN TECHNICAL INSTITUTE

Automobile/Automotive Mechanics
    Technology/Technician, A
Diesel Mechanics Technology/Technician, A
Drafting and Design Technology/Technician, A

MANCHESTER COLLEGE

Accounting, ABM
Art Teacher Education, B
Art/Art Studies, General, AB
Athletic Training and Sports Medicine, B
Biology/Biological Sciences, B
Broadcast Journalism, A
Business Administration and Management, AB
Business/Commerce, B
Chemistry, B
Clinical Laboratory Science/Medical
    Technology/Technologist, B
Comparative Literature, A
Computer Science, AB
Creative Writing, A
Criminal Justice/Safety Studies, A
Drama and Dramatics/Theatre Arts, B
Ecology, B
Economics, B
Education, B
Elementary Education and Teaching, B
Engineering Science, B
English Language and Literature, AB
Environmental Studies, B
Finance, B
Fine/Studio Arts, AB
French Language and Literature, B
German Language and Literature, B
Gerontology, B
Health Teacher Education, B
History, B
Interdisciplinary Studies, BM
Journalism, A

Kindergarten/PreSchool Education and Teaching, A
Kinesiology and Exercise Science, A
Marketing/Marketing Management, B
Mass Communication/Media Studies, B
Mathematics, B
Music, B
Music Teacher Education, B
Non-Profit/Public/Organizational Management, B
Peace Studies and Conflict Resolution, B
Philosophy, B
Physical Education Teaching and Coaching, B
Physics, B
Political Science and Government, B
Pre-Dentistry Studies, B
Pre-Law Studies, B
Pre-Medicine/Pre-Medical Studies, B
Pre-Theology/Pre-Ministerial Studies, A
Pre-Veterinary Studies, B
Psychology, B
Public Health (MPH, DPH), B
Religion/Religious Studies, AB
Science Teacher Education/General Science
    Teacher Education, B
Secondary Education and Teaching, B
Social Work, B
Sociology, B
Spanish Language and Literature, B
Special Education and Teaching, B
Speech and Rhetorical Studies, B

MARIAN COLLEGE

Accounting, AB
Art History, Criticism and Conservation, B
Art Teacher Education, B
Art/Art Studies, General, AB
Biology/Biological Sciences, B
Business Administration and Management, AB
Chemistry, B
Education, BM
Elementary Education and Teaching, B
English Language and Literature, B
Finance, AB
Fine/Studio Arts, B
French Language and Literature, B
History, AB
Interior Design, A
Kindergarten/PreSchool Education and
    Teaching, AB
Liberal Arts and Sciences Studies and
    Humanities, A
Mass Communication/Media Studies, B
Mathematics, B
Music, AB
Music Teacher Education, B
Nursing - Registered Nurse Training, B
Philosophy, B
Physical Education Teaching and Coaching, B
Pre-Dentistry Studies, B
Pre-Engineering, A
Pre-Law Studies, B
Pre-Medicine/Pre-Medical Studies, B
Pre-Veterinary Studies, B
Psychology, AB
Religious Education, B
Secondary Education and Teaching, B
Sociology, B
Spanish Language and Literature, B
Special Education and Teaching, B
Theology/Theological Studies, AB

MARTIN UNIVERSITY

Accounting, B
Adult and Continuing Education and Teaching, B
African-American/Black Studies, B
Biology/Biological Sciences, B
Business Administration and Management, B
Chemistry, B
Communication Studies/Speech Communication
    and Rhetoric, B
Community Psychology, M
Computer Engineering Technology/Technician, B
Counselor Education/School Counseling and
    Guidance Services, B
Criminal Justice/Law Enforcement Administration, B
Education, B
Elementary Education and Teaching, B

English Language and Literature, B
Fine/Studio Arts, B
History, B
Human Resources Management/Personnel
    Administration, B
Humanities/Humanistic Studies, B
Insurance, B
Kindergarten/PreSchool Education and Teaching, B
Marketing/Marketing Management, B
Mathematics, B
Music, B
Pastoral Studies/Counseling, M
Political Science and Government, B
Psychology, BM
Religion/Religious Studies, B
Secondary Education and Teaching, B
Sociology, B
Substance Abuse/Addiction Counseling, B

MID-AMERICA COLLEGE OF FUNERAL SERVICE

Funeral Service and Mortuary Science, A

OAKLAND CITY UNIVERSITY

Accounting, AB
Administrative Assistant and Secretarial Science, A
Applied Art, B
Applied Horticulture/Horticultural Operations, A
Applied Mathematics, B
Art Teacher Education, B
Art/Art Studies, General, B
Automobile/Automotive Mechanics
    Technology/Technician, A
Bible/Biblical Studies, B
Biological and Physical Sciences, B
Biology Teacher Education, B
Biology/Biological Sciences, B
Business Administration and Management, AB
Business Administration, Management and
    Operations, B
Business Teacher Education, B
Chemistry, B
Computer Engineering Technology/Technician, A
Computer Graphics, B
Computer Programming/Programmer, A
Computer Science, A
Criminal Justice/Law Enforcement Administration, B
Culinary Arts/Chef Training, A
Divinity/Ministry (BD, MDiv.), B
Early Childhood Education and Teaching, A
Education, BMD
Education/Teaching of Individuals with Mental
    Retardation, B
Educational Leadership and Administration, D
Elementary Education and Teaching, B
English Language and Literature, B
English/Language Arts Teacher Education, B
General Studies, AB
Heating, Air Conditioning and Refrigeration
    Technology/Technician, A
Heating, Air Conditioning, Ventilation and
    Refrigeration Maintenance
    Technology/Technician, A
Human Resources Management/Personnel
    Administration, B
Humanities/Humanistic Studies, B
Industrial Design, A
Information Science/Studies, AB
Interdisciplinary Studies, B
Junior High/Intermediate/Middle School Education
    and Teaching, B
Liberal Arts and Sciences Studies and
    Humanities, A
Management, M
Management Science, B
Mathematics, B
Mathematics Teacher Education, B
Music, B
Music Performance, B
Music Teacher Education, B
Organizational Behavior Studies, B
Physical Education Teaching and Coaching, B
Pre-Law Studies, B
Pre-Medicine/Pre-Medical Studies, B
Pre-Veterinary Studies, B
Religion/Religious Studies, B

Religious Education, B
Science Teacher Education/General Science
 Teacher Education, B
Secondary Education and Teaching, B
Social Science Teacher Education, B
Social Sciences, B
Social Studies Teacher Education, B
Theology and Religious Vocations, DP
Theology/Theological Studies, B
Welding Technology/Welder, A

PROFESSIONAL CAREERS INSTITUTE

Computer Programming, Specific Applications, A
Computer Software and Media Applications, A

PURDUE UNIVERSITY

Accounting, BMD
Aeronautical/Aerospace Engineering
 Technology/Technician, A
Aeronautics/Aviation/Aerospace Science and
 Technology, AB
Aerospace, Aeronautical and Astronautical
 Engineering, BMD
African-American/Black Studies, B
Agricultural Economics, BMD
Agricultural Education, MDO
Agricultural Engineering, MD
Agricultural Mechanization, B
Agricultural Sciences, MD
Agricultural Teacher Education, B
Agricultural/Biological Engineering and
 Bioengineering, B
Agriculture, AB
Agronomy and Crop Science, B
Agronomy and Soil Sciences, MD
American/United States Studies/Civilization, MD
Analytical Chemistry, MD
Anatomy, MD
Animal Sciences, BMD
Anthropology, MD
Apparel and Textiles, B
Aquaculture, MD
Architectural Engineering Technology/Technician, AB
Art Education, D
Art/Art Studies, General, B
Atmospheric Sciences and Meteorology, MD
Audiology/Audiologist and Speech-Language
 Pathology/Pathologist, B
Biochemistry, BMD
Bioengineering, MD
Biological and Biomedical Sciences, MD
Biological and Physical Sciences, B
Biology/Biological Sciences, B
Biomedical Engineering, MD
Biophysics, D
Botany/Plant Biology, BMD
Business Administration and Management, B
Business Administration, Management and
 Operations, MD
Cell Biology and Anatomy, D
Chemical Engineering, BMD
Chemistry, BMD
Child and Family Studies, MD
Civil Engineering, BMD
Clinical Laboratory Science/Medical
 Technology/Technologist, B
Clothing and Textiles, MD
Communication and Media Studies, MD
Communication Disorders, MD
Communication Studies/Speech Communication
 and Rhetoric, B
Comparative Literature, MD
Computer and Information Sciences, B
Computer and Information Sciences and Support
 Services, B
Computer Engineering, BMD
Computer Science, MD
Construction Engineering, B
Consumer Economics, MD
Counselor Education/School Counseling and
 Guidance Services, MD
Curriculum and Instruction, MDO
Design and Applied Arts, M
Design and Visual Communications, B
Developmental Biology and Embryology, D
Drama and Dramatics/Theatre Arts, B

Early Childhood Education and Teaching, B
Ecology, MD
Economics, BD
Education, BMDO
Education/Teaching of the Gifted and Talented, M
Educational Administration and Supervision, MDO
Educational Media/Instructional Technology, MDO
Educational Psychology, MD
Electrical Engineering, MD
Electrical, Electronic and Communications
 Engineering Technology/Technician, AB
Electrical, Electronics and Communications
 Engineering, B
Elementary Education and Teaching, BM
Engineering, B
Engineering and Applied Sciences, MD
English, MD
English Education, MDO
English Language and Literature, B
Entomology, BMD
Environmental and Occupational Health, MD
Environmental Policy and Resource
 Management, MD
Epidemiology, MD
Ergonomics and Human Factors, MD
Evolutionary Biology, MD
Exercise and Sports Science, MD
Family and Consumer Sciences/Human Sciences, B
Finance and Banking, MD
Fine Arts and Art Studies, M
Fish, Game and Wildlife Management, MD
Food Science, B
Food Science and Technology, MD
Foods, Nutrition, and Wellness Studies, B
Foreign Language Teacher Education, MDO
Foreign Languages and Literatures, B
Forestry, BMD
Foundations and Philosophy of Education, MD
French Language and Literature, MD
Genetics, MD
Geology/Earth Science, B
Geosciences, MD
German Language and Literature, MD
Health Physics/Radiological Health, MDO
Health Professions and Related Clinical Sciences, B
Health Promotion, MD
Higher Education/Higher Education
 Administration, MD
History, BMD
Home Economics, MD
Home Economics Education, MDO
Horticultural Science, BMD
Hospitality Administration/Management, AMD
Hotel/Motel Administration/Management, B
Human Development, MD
Human Development and Family Studies, B
Human Resources Management and Services, MD
Humanities/Humanistic Studies, B
Immunology, MD
Industrial and Manufacturing Management, MD
Industrial Education, M
Industrial Engineering, B
Industrial Hygiene, MD
Industrial/Management Engineering, MD
Infectious Diseases, MD
Inorganic Chemistry, MD
Interdisciplinary Studies, B
Kindergarten/PreSchool Education and Teaching, B
Landscape Architecture, B
Linguistics, MD
Management Information Systems and
 Services, ABMD
Management Strategy and Policy, MD
Manufacturing Engineering, MD
Marketing, MD
Marriage and Family Therapy/Counseling, MD
Materials Engineering, BMD
Mathematical and Computational Finance, M
Mathematics, BMD
Mathematics Teacher Education, MDO
Mechanical Drafting and Mechanical Drafting
 CAD/CADD, AB
Mechanical Engineering, BMD
Mechanical Engineering Related
 Technologies/Technicians, AB
Medical Physics, MD

Medicinal and Pharmaceutical Chemistry, MDO
Microbiology, MD
Molecular Biology, MD
Molecular Pharmacology, MDO
Multi-/Interdisciplinary Studies, B
Natural Resources and Conservation, BMD
Neurobiology and Neurophysiology, MD
Neuroscience, D
Nuclear Engineering, BMD
Nursing - Registered Nurse Training, B
Nutritional Sciences, MD
Operations Management and Supervision, AB
Operations Research, MD
Organic Chemistry, MD
Organizational Behavior Studies, MD
Parasitology, MD
Pathobiology, MD
Pathology/Experimental Pathology, MD
Pharmaceutical Sciences, MD
Pharmacognosy, D
Pharmacology, MD
Pharmacy, BP
Philosophy, BMD
Physical Chemistry, MD
Physical Education Teaching and Coaching, BMD
Physics, BMD
Physiology, MD
Plant Biology, D
Plant Pathology/Phytopathology, MD
Plant Physiology, D
Political Science and Government, BMD
Psychology, BD
Public Health, MD
Quantitative Analysis, MD
Reading Teacher Education, MDO
Resource Management, MD
Robotics Technology/Technician, AB
Science Teacher Education/General Science
 Teacher Education, MDO
Social Sciences, B
Social Studies Teacher Education, MDO
Sociology, BMD
Spanish Language and Literature, MD
Special Education and Teaching, MD
Sport Psychology, D
Statistics, BMD
Survey Technology/Surveying, B
Systems Engineering, MD
Technology Teacher Education/Industrial Arts
 Teacher Education, B
Theater, M
Toxicology, MD
Trade and Industrial Teacher Education, A
Travel and Tourism, MD
Veterinary Medicine, PO
Veterinary Sciences, MD
Veterinary/Animal Health Technology/Technician and
 Veterinary Assistant, AB
Virology, MD
Vocational and Technical Education, MDO
Wildlife and Wildlands Science and Management, B
Writing, M

PURDUE UNIVERSITY CALUMET

Accounting, BM
Architectural Engineering Technology/Technician, A
Behavioral Sciences, B
Biological and Biomedical Sciences, M
Biological and Physical Sciences, B
Biology Technician/BioTechnology Laboratory
 Technician, B
Biology/Biological Sciences, B
BioTechnology, M
Business Administration and Management, B
Business Administration, Management and
 Operations, M
Chemistry, B
Child Development, A
Civil Engineering Technology/Technician, A
Clinical Laboratory Science/Medical
 Technology/Technologist, B
Clinical/Medical Laboratory Technician, B
Communication and Media Studies, M
Comparative Literature, B
Computer and Information Sciences, B
Computer Engineering, B

Computer Engineering Technology/Technician, AB
Computer Programming/Programmer, A
Computer Science, B
Construction Engineering Technology/Technician, AB
Counselor Education/School Counseling and
   Guidance Services, M
Criminal Justice/Law Enforcement Administration, B
Criminal Justice/Police Science, B
Culinary Arts/Chef Training, A
Curriculum and Instruction, M
Economics, B
Education, BM
Educational Administration and Supervision, M
Educational Media/Instructional Technology, M
Electrical, Electronic and Communications
   Engineering Technology/Technician, AB
Electrical, Electronics and Communications
   Engineering, B
Elementary Education and Teaching, BM
Engineering, B
Engineering and Applied Sciences, M
Engineering Technology, B
English, M
English Language and Literature, B
Food Technology and Processing, A
French Language and Literature, B
German Language and Literature, B
History, BM
Hotel/Motel Administration/Management, AB
Human Resources Management/Personnel
   Administration, B
Industrial Technology/Technician, AB
Information Science/Studies, B
Journalism, B
Kindergarten/PreSchool Education and Teaching, A
Management, M
Marketing/Marketing Management, B
Marriage and Family Therapy/Counseling, M
Mass Communication/Media Studies, B
Mathematics, BM
Mathematics Teacher Education, M
Mechanical Engineering, B
Mechanical Engineering/Mechanical
   Technology/Technician, AB
Metallurgical Technology/Technician, A
Nursing, M
Nursing - Registered Nurse Training, AB
Philosophy, BM
Physics, B
Political Science and Government, BM
Pre-Dentistry Studies, B
Pre-Law Studies, B
Pre-Medicine/Pre-Medical Studies, B
Pre-Veterinary Studies, B
Psychology, B
Public Relations/Image Management, B
Radio and Television, B
Science Teacher Education/General Science
   Teacher Education, BM
Secondary Education and Teaching, BM
Sociology, B
Spanish Language and Literature, B

PURDUE UNIVERSITY NORTH CENTRAL

Accounting, A
Architectural Engineering Technology/Technician, A
Biology/Biological Sciences, B
Business Administration and Management, AB
Chemistry, B
Civil Engineering Technology/Technician, A
Computer Engineering Technology/Technician, AB
Computer Programming/Programmer, A
Construction Engineering Technology/Technician, A
Education, M
Electrical, Electronic and Communications
   Engineering Technology/Technician, A
Elementary Education and Teaching, BM
English Language and Literature, B
Industrial Technology/Technician, A
Information Science/Studies, A
Liberal Arts and Sciences Studies and
   Humanities, A
Marketing/Marketing Management, A
Mathematics, B

Mechanical Engineering/Mechanical
   Technology/Technician, AB
Nursing - Registered Nurse Training, AB
Physics, B
Pre-Engineering, A
Sales, Distribution and Marketing Operations, AB
Statistics, B

ROSE-HULMAN INSTITUTE OF TECHNOLOGY

Biology/Biological Sciences, B
Biomedical Engineering, MO
Biomedical/Medical Engineering, B
Chemical Engineering, BM
Chemistry, B
Civil Engineering, B
Computer Engineering, B
Computer Science, B
Computer Software Engineering, B
Economics, B
Electrical Engineering, M
Electrical, Electronics and Communications
   Engineering, B
Engineering, B
Engineering and Applied Sciences, MO
Engineering Management, M
Engineering Physics, B
Environmental Engineering
   Technology/Environmental Technology, M
Mathematics, B
Mechanical Engineering, BM
Optics/Optical Sciences, M
Physics, B
Systems Engineering, B

SAINT JOSEPH'S COLLEGE

Accounting, B
Art Teacher Education, B
Biochemistry, AB
Biology/Biological Sciences, B
Business/Commerce, B
Chemistry, B
Clinical Laboratory Science/Medical
   Technology/Technologist, B
Computer and Information Sciences, B
Creative Writing, B
Criminal Justice/Safety Studies, B
Drama and Dramatics/Theatre Arts, B
Economics, B
Elementary Education and Teaching, B
English Language and Literature, B
Fine/Studio Arts, B
History, B
International Relations and Affairs, B
Management Information Systems and Services, AB
Mass Communication/Media Studies, B
Mathematics, B
Mathematics and Computer Science, B
Music History, Literature, and Theory, B
Music Management and Merchandising, B
Nursing - Registered Nurse Training, B
Pastoral Studies/Counseling, B
Philosophy, B
Philosophy and Religious Studies, B
Physical Education Teaching and Coaching, B
Political Science and Government, B
Psychology, B
Sacred Music, MO
Secondary Education and Teaching, B
Social Work, B
Sociology, B

SAINT MARY-OF-THE-WOODS COLLEGE

Accounting, B
Accounting and Related Services, B
Adult Development and Aging, AB
Animal/Livestock Husbandry and Production, AB
Art Teacher Education, B
Art Therapy/Therapist, MO
Art/Art Studies, General, B
Biological and Physical Sciences, B
Biology/Biological Sciences, B
Business Administration and Management, B
Business Administration, Management and
   Operations, B

Child Care and Support Services Management, B
Child Care Provider/Assistant, A
Clinical Laboratory Science/Medical
   Technology/Technologist, B
Communications Technologies/Technicians and
   Support Services, B
Communications Technology/Technician, B
Computer and Information Sciences, B
Design and Visual Communications, B
Drama and Dramatics/Theatre Arts, B
Education, B
Elementary Education and Teaching, B
English Language and Literature, B
Environmental Studies, M
Equestrian/Equine Studies, AB
Ethnic and Cultural Studies, B
Fine/Studio Arts, B
French Language and Literature, B
Gerontology, B
History, B
Human Resources Management/Personnel
   Administration, B
Human Services, B
Humanities/Humanistic Studies, B
Information Science/Studies, B
Journalism, B
Kindergarten/PreSchool Education and Teaching, B
Legal Assistant/Paralegal, AB
Liberal Arts and Sciences Studies and
   Humanities, AB
Marketing/Marketing Management, B
Mass Communication/Media Studies, B
Mathematics, B
Music, B
Music Performance, B
Music Teacher Education, B
Music Therapy/Therapist, BM
Non-Profit/Public/Organizational Management, B
Pastoral Studies/Counseling, B
Photography, B
Pre-Dentistry Studies, B
Pre-Law Studies, B
Pre-Medicine/Pre-Medical Studies, B
Pre-Pharmacy Studies, B
Pre-Veterinary Studies, B
Professional Studies, B
Psychology, B
Public Relations/Image Management, B
Religion/Religious Studies, B
Secondary Education and Teaching, B
Social Sciences, B
Spanish Language and Literature, B
Special Education and Teaching, B
Teacher Education, Multiple Levels, B
Theology and Religious Vocations, M
Theology/Theological Studies, B

SAINT MARY'S COLLEGE

Applied Mathematics, B
Art Teacher Education, B
Art/Art Studies, General, B
Biology/Biological Sciences, B
Business Administration and Management, B
Business Teacher Education, B
Chemistry, B
Clinical Laboratory Science/Medical
   Technology/Technologist, B
Communication Studies/Speech Communication
   and Rhetoric, B
Creative Writing, B
CytoTechnology/Cytotechnologist, B
Drama and Dramatics/Theatre Arts, B
Economics, B
Education, B
Elementary Education and Teaching, B
English Literature (British and Commonwealth), B
Finance, B
French Language and Literature, B
History, B
Humanities/Humanistic Studies, B
Interdisciplinary Studies, B
International Business/Trade/Commerce, B
Management Information Systems and Services, B
Marketing/Marketing Management, B
Mathematics, B
Mathematics and Computer Science, B

Music, B
Music Teacher Education, B
Nursing - Registered Nurse Training, B
Philosophy, B
Political Science and Government, B
Psychology, B
Religion/Religious Studies, B
Social Work, B
Sociology, B
Spanish Language and Literature, B

SAWYER COLLEGE (HAMMOND)

Accounting and Business/Management, A
Computer Programming/Programmer, A
Legal Assistant/Paralegal, A
Massage Therapy/Therapeutic Massage, A
Medical Office Assistant/Specialist, A
System, Networking, and LAN/WAN
    Management/Manager, A
Web/Multimedia Management and Webmaster, A

TAYLOR UNIVERSITY

Accounting, B
Ancient Near Eastern and Biblical
    Languages, Literatures, and Linguistics, B
Art Teacher Education, B
Art/Art Studies, General, B
Athletic Training and Sports Medicine, B
Bible/Biblical Studies, B
Biology Teacher Education, B
Biology/Biological Sciences, B
Business Administration and Management, AB
Chemistry, B
Chemistry Teacher Education, B
Clinical Laboratory Science/Medical
    Technology/Technologist, B
Commercial and Advertising Art, B
Communication Studies/Speech Communication
    and Rhetoric, B
Comparative Literature, B
Computer Engineering, B
Computer Graphics, B
Computer Programming/Programmer, B
Computer Science, B
Creative Writing, B
Drama and Dramatics/Theatre Arts, B
Economics, B
Education, B
Elementary Education and Teaching, B
Engineering Physics, B
English Language and Literature, B
Environmental Biology, B
Environmental Sciences, M
Environmental Studies, B
Finance, B
French Language and Literature, B
History, B
History Teacher Education, B
Human Resources Management/Personnel
    Administration, B
Information Science/Studies, B
International Business/Trade/Commerce, B
International Economics, B
International Relations and Affairs, B
Junior High/Intermediate/Middle School Education
    and Teaching, B
Kindergarten/PreSchool Education and
    Teaching, AB
Management Information Systems and Services, A
Marketing/Marketing Management, B
Mass Communication/Media Studies, B
Mathematics, B
Music, B
Music Management and Merchandising, B
Music Performance, B
Music Teacher Education, B
Natural Sciences, B
Philosophy, B
Physical Education Teaching and Coaching, B
Physical Sciences, B
Physics, B
Piano and Organ, B
Political Science and Government, B
Pre-Dentistry Studies, B
Pre-Law Studies, B
Pre-Medicine/Pre-Medical Studies, B

Pre-Veterinary Studies, B
Psychology, B
Religion/Religious Studies, B
Religious Education, B
Religious/Sacred Music, B
Science Teacher Education/General Science
    Teacher Education, B
Secondary Education and Teaching, B
Social Science Teacher Education, B
Social Sciences, B
Social Work, B
Sociology, B
Spanish Language and Literature, B
Spanish Language Teacher Education, B
Speech Teacher Education, B
Sport and Fitness Administration/Management, B
Theology/Theological Studies, B
Voice and Opera, B

TAYLOR UNIVERSITY FORT WAYNE

Business Administration, Management and
    Operations, M
Business, Management, Marketing, and Related
    Support Services, AB
Communication, Journalism and Related
    Programs, B
Counseling Psychology, B
Criminal Justice/Law Enforcement Administration, B
Early Childhood Education and Teaching, A
Education, B
English Language and Literature, B
General Studies, A
Humanities/Humanistic Studies, A
Intercultural/Multicultural and Diversity Studies, B
Liberal Arts and Sciences Studies and
    Humanities, A
Pre-Law Studies, B
Public Administration and Social Service
    Professions, B
Security and Protective Services, B
Social Work, B
Theology and Religious Vocations, B

TRI-STATE UNIVERSITY

Accounting, AB
Biological and Physical Sciences, A
Biology/Biological Sciences, B
Business Administration and Management, AB
Chemical Engineering, B
Chemistry, B
Civil Engineering, B
Communication Studies/Speech Communication
    and Rhetoric, AB
Computer and Information Sciences, A
Computer Engineering, B
Computer Science, B
Criminal Justice/Law Enforcement
    Administration, AB
Drafting and Design Technology/Technician, AB
Education, B
Electrical, Electronics and Communications
    Engineering, B
Elementary Education and Teaching, B
Engineering Technology, A
Engineering/Industrial Management, B
English Language and Literature, B
English/Language Arts Teacher Education, B
Environmental Studies, B
Forensic Science and Technology, B
Industrial Technology/Technician, A
Liberal Arts and Sciences Studies and
    Humanities, A
Management Information Systems and Services, B
Marketing/Marketing Management, B
Mathematics, AB
Mathematics Teacher Education, B
Mechanical Engineering, B
Operations Management and Supervision, B
Parks, Recreation and Leisure Facilities
    Management, B
Physical Education Teaching and Coaching, B
Physical Sciences, B
Pre-Law Studies, B
Pre-Medicine/Pre-Medical Studies, B
Pre-Veterinary Studies, B

Psychology, B
Science Teacher Education/General Science
    Teacher Education, B
Secondary Education and Teaching, B
Social Sciences, AB
Social Studies Teacher Education, B
Sport and Fitness Administration/Management, B

UNIVERSITY OF EVANSVILLE

Accounting, B
Archeology, B
Art History, Criticism and Conservation, B
Art Teacher Education, B
Art/Art Studies, General, B
Athletic Training and Sports Medicine, B
Bible/Biblical Studies, B
Biochemistry, B
Biology Teacher Education, B
Biology/Biological Sciences, B
Business Administration and Management, B
Business/Commerce, B
Business/Managerial Economics, B
Chemistry, B
Chemistry Teacher Education, B
Civil Engineering, B
Classics and Classical
    Languages, Literatures, and Linguistics, B
Cognitive Sciences, B
Communication Studies/Speech Communication
    and Rhetoric, B
Computer and Information Sciences, B
Computer and Information Sciences and Support
    Services, B
Computer Engineering, B
Computer Science, M
Creative Writing, B
Design and Visual Communications, B
Drama and Dance Teacher Education, B
Drama and Dramatics/Theatre Arts, B
Economics, B
Education, BM
Electrical Engineering, M
Electrical, Electronics and Communications
    Engineering, B
Elementary Education and Teaching, B
Engineering and Applied Sciences, M
Engineering/Industrial Management, B
English Composition, B
English Language and Literature, B
English/Language Arts Teacher Education, B
Environmental Sciences, B
Environmental Studies, B
Finance, B
French Language and Literature, B
French Language Teacher Education, B
Geography Teacher Education, B
German Language and Literature, B
German Language Teacher Education, B
Graphic Design, B
Health and Physical Education, B
Health Services Administration, M
Health/Health Care Administration/Management, B
Health/Medical Preparatory Programs, B
History, B
International Business/Trade/Commerce, B
International Relations and Affairs, B
Kinesiology and Exercise Science, B
Legal Professions and Studies, B
Liberal Arts and Sciences Studies and
    Humanities, B
Marketing/Marketing Management, B
Mass Communication/Media Studies, B
Mathematics, B
Mathematics Teacher Education, B
Mechanical Engineering, B
Multi-/Interdisciplinary Studies, B
Music, B
Music Management and Merchandising, B
Music Performance, B
Music Teacher Education, B
Music Therapy/Therapist, B
Nursing, M
Nursing - Registered Nurse Training, B
Philosophy, B
Physical Education Teaching and Coaching, B
Physical Therapist Assistant, A

Physics, B
Physics Teacher Education, B
Physiological Psychology/Psychobiology, B
Political Science and Government, B
Pre-Dentistry Studies, B
Pre-Medicine/Pre-Medical Studies, B
Pre-Pharmacy Studies, B
Pre-Veterinary Studies, B
Psychology, B
Psychology Teacher Education, B
Public Administration, M
Religion/Religious Studies, B
Science Teacher Education/General Science
  Teacher Education, B
Social Science Teacher Education, B
Social Studies Teacher Education, B
Sociology, B
Spanish Language and Literature, B
Spanish Language Teacher Education, B
Special Education and Teaching, B
Theatre/Theatre Arts Management, B

UNIVERSITY OF INDIANAPOLIS

Accounting, BM
Anthropology, B
Archeology, B
Art Education, M
Art Teacher Education, B
Art Therapy/Therapist, B
Art/Art Studies, General, B
Athletic Training and Sports Medicine, B
Banking and Financial Support Services, AB
Biological and Biomedical Sciences, M
Biology/Biological Sciences, B
Business Administration and Management, AB
Business Administration, Management and
  Operations, M
Business Teacher Education, B
Business/Managerial Economics, B
Chemistry, AB
Clinical Laboratory Science/Medical
  Technology/Technologist, B
Commercial and Advertising Art, B
Communication Studies/Speech Communication
  and Rhetoric, B
Computer Engineering, B
Computer Science, B
Corrections, AB
Criminal Justice/Law Enforcement
  Administration, AB
Drama and Dramatics/Theatre Arts, B
Education, BM
Elementary Education and Teaching, BM
English, M
English Education, M
English Language and Literature, B
English/Language Arts Teacher Education, B
Entrepreneurship/Entrepreneurial Studies, B
Environmental Studies, B
Fine Arts and Art Studies, M
Fine/Studio Arts, B
Foreign Language Teacher Education, M
French Language and Literature, B
French Language Teacher Education, B
Geology/Earth Science, B
German Language and Literature, B
Gerontology, M
History, BM
International Business/Trade/Commerce, B
International Relations and Affairs, B
Kinesiology and Exercise Science, B
Liberal Arts and Sciences Studies and
  Humanities, AB
Marketing/Marketing Management, B
Mathematics, B
Mathematics Teacher Education, BM
Mechanical Engineering, B
Music, B
Music Performance, B
Music Teacher Education, B
Nurse Midwife/Nursing Midwifery, M
Nursing, M
Nursing - Registered Nurse Training, AB
Occupational Therapy/Therapist, MD
Operations Management and Supervision, B
Philosophy, B

Physical Education Teaching and Coaching, BM
Physical Therapist Assistant, A
Physical Therapy/Therapist, MD
Physics, B
Political Science and Government, B
Pre-Dentistry Studies, B
Pre-Law Studies, B
Pre-Medicine/Pre-Medical Studies, B
Pre-Theology/Pre-Ministerial Studies, B
Pre-Veterinary Studies, B
Psychology, BMD
Religion/Religious Studies, B
Respiratory Care Therapy/Therapist, B
Science Teacher Education/General Science
  Teacher Education, BM
Secondary Education and Teaching, BM
Social Studies Teacher Education, BM
Social Work, B
Sociology, BM
Spanish Language and Literature, B
Spanish Language Teacher Education, B
Speech Teacher Education, B
Sport and Fitness Administration/Management, B
Youth Ministry, B

UNIVERSITY OF NOTRE DAME

Accounting, BM
Aerospace, Aeronautical and Astronautical
  Engineering, BMD
American/United States Studies/Civilization, B
Ancient/Classical Greek Language and Literature, B
Anthropology, B
Applied Mathematics, M
Arabic Language and Literature, B
Architecture, BM
Art History, Criticism and Conservation, BM
Biochemistry, BMD
Bioengineering, M
Biological and Biomedical Sciences, MD
Biology/Biological Sciences, B
Business Administration, Management and
  Operations, BMO
Business/Commerce, B
Cell Biology and Anatomy, MD
Chemical Engineering, BMD
Chemistry, BMD
Chinese Language and Literature, B
Civil Engineering, BMD
Classics and Classical
  Languages, Literatures, and Linguistics, B
Cognitive Sciences, D
Comparative Literature, D
Computer and Information Sciences, B
Computer and Information Sciences and Support
  Services, B
Computer Engineering, BMD
Computer Science, MD
Conflict Resolution and Mediation/Peace Studies, M
Counseling Psychology, D
Design and Applied Arts, M
Design and Visual Communications, B
Developmental Psychology, D
Drama and Dramatics/Theatre Arts, B
Ecology, MD
Economics, B
Education, M
Electrical Engineering, MD
Electrical, Electronics and Communications
  Engineering, B
Engineering and Applied Sciences, MD
English, MD
English Language and Literature, B
Environmental Engineering
  Technology/Environmental Technology, M
Environmental/Environmental Health Engineering, B
Evolutionary Biology, MD
Finance, B
Fine Arts and Art Studies, M
Fine/Studio Arts, B
French Language and Literature, BM
Genetics, MD
Geology/Earth Science, B
Geosciences, MD
German Language and Literature, BM
History, BMD
History of Science and Technology, MD

Inorganic Chemistry, MD
Italian Language and Literature, BM
Japanese Language and Literature, B
Latin American Studies, M
Latin Language and Literature, B
Law and Legal Studies, MDP
Liberal Arts and Sciences Studies and
  Humanities, B
Management Information Systems and Services, B
Marketing/Marketing Management, B
Mathematics, BMD
Mechanical Engineering, BMD
Medieval and Renaissance Studies, BMD
Molecular Biology, MD
Music, BM
Organic Chemistry, MD
Parasitology, MD
Philosophy, BD
Philosophy and Religious Studies, B
Physical Chemistry, MD
Physics, BD
Physiology, MD
Political Science and Government, BD
Pre-Medicine/Pre-Medical Studies, B
Psychology, BD
Religion/Religious Studies, M
Romance
  Languages, Literatures, and Linguistics, M
Russian Language and Literature, B
Science Teacher Education/General Science
  Teacher Education, B
Sociology, BD
Spanish Language and Literature, BM
Theology and Religious Vocations, MDP
Theology/Theological Studies, B
Writing, M

UNIVERSITY OF
PHOENIX-INDIANAPOLIS CAMPUS

Business Administration and Management, B
Business Administration, Management and
  Operations, M
Computer/Information Technology Services
  Administration and Management, B
Health/Health Care Administration/Management, B
Information Technology, B
Nursing Administration, B
Operations Management and Supervision, B

UNIVERSITY OF SAINT FRANCIS

Accounting, B
Allied Health and Medical Assisting Services, M
Art Teacher Education, B
Art/Art Studies, General, B
Biological and Physical Sciences, B
Biology Teacher Education, B
Biology/Biological Sciences, B
Business Administration and Management, AB
Business Administration, Management and
  Operations, M
Business Teacher Education, B
Chemistry, B
Chemistry Teacher Education, B
Clinical Laboratory Science/Medical
  Technology/Technologist, B
Commercial and Advertising Art, AB
Communication Studies/Speech Communication
  and Rhetoric, B
Counseling Psychology, M
Counselor Education/School Counseling and
  Guidance Services, M
Design and Applied Arts, B
Education, BM
Elementary Education and Teaching, B
Emergency Medical Technology/Technician (EMT
  Paramedic), A
English Language and Literature, B
English/Language Arts Teacher Education, B
Environmental Studies, B
Fine Arts and Art Studies, BM
Health Professions and Related Clinical Sciences, B
Health Teacher Education, B
History, B
Human Resources Management/Personnel
  Administration, AB
Human Services, A

Liberal Arts and Sciences Studies and
Humanities, AB
Marketing/Marketing Management, B
Mass Communication/Media Studies, B
Mathematics, B
Medical Radiologic Technology/Science - Radiation
Therapist, A
Nursing, BM
Nursing - Registered Nurse Training, AB
Occupational Therapist Assistant, A
Physical Therapist Assistant, A
Physician Assistant, BM
Pre-Dentistry Studies, B
Pre-Law Studies, B
Pre-Medicine/Pre-Medical Studies, B
Pre-Pharmacy Studies, B
Pre-Veterinary Studies, B
Psychology, BM
Public Administration and Social Service
Professions, AB
Public Health (MPH, DPH), B
Religion/Religious Studies, B
Science Teacher Education/General Science
Teacher Education, B
Secondary Education and Teaching, B
Social Studies Teacher Education, B
Social Work, B
Special Education and Teaching, BM
Surgical Technology/Technologist, A
Theological and Ministerial Studies, AB

UNIVERSITY OF SOUTHERN INDIANA

Accounting, BM
Advertising, B
Art/Art Studies, General, B
Biological and Physical Sciences, B
Biology/Biological Sciences, B
Biophysics, B
Business Administration and Management, B
Business Administration, Management and
Operations, M
Business Teacher Education, B
Business, Management, Marketing, and Related
Support Services, A
Business/Commerce, B
Chemistry, B
Communication Studies/Speech Communication
and Rhetoric, B
Computer and Information Sciences, B
Data Processing and Data Processing
Technology/Technician, B
Dental Assisting/Assistant, A
Dental Hygiene/Hygienist, AB
Drama and Dramatics/Theatre Arts, B
E-Commerce/Electronic Commerce, B
Economics, B
Education, AM
Elementary Education and Teaching, BM
Engineering, B
Engineering and Applied Sciences, M
Engineering Technologies/Technicians, B
English Language and Literature, B
Entrepreneurship/Entrepreneurial Studies, B
Finance, B
French Language and Literature, B
Geology/Earth Science, B
German Language and Literature, B
Health Professions and Related Clinical Sciences, B
Health Services Administration, M
History, B
Industrial and Manufacturing Management, M
International Relations and Affairs, B
Journalism, B
Kinesiology and Exercise Science, B
Liberal Arts and Sciences Studies and
Humanities, B
Liberal Studies, M
Management Information Systems and Services, A
Marketing/Marketing Management, B
Mathematics, B
Medical Radiologic Technology/Science - Radiation
Therapist, A
Nursing, M
Nursing - Registered Nurse Training, AB
Occupational Therapist Assistant, A
Occupational Therapy/Therapist, BM

Office Management and Supervision, B
Philosophy, B
Physical Education Teaching and Coaching, B
Political Science and Government, B
Psychology, B
Public Administration, M
Public Relations/Image Management, B
Radio and Television, B
Respiratory Care Therapy/Therapist, A
Secondary Education and Teaching, M
Social Sciences, AB
Social Work, BM
Sociology, B
Spanish Language and Literature, B
Special Education and Teaching, B

VALPARAISO UNIVERSITY

Accounting, B
Actuarial Science, B
American/United States Studies/Civilization, B
Art Teacher Education, B
Art/Art Studies, General, B
Astronomy, B
Atmospheric Sciences and Meteorology, B
Biochemistry, B
Biological and Physical Sciences, A
Biology Teacher Education, B
Biology/Biological Sciences, B
Business Administration, Management and
Operations, MO
Chemistry, B
Chemistry Teacher Education, B
Civil Engineering, B
Classics and Classical
Languages, Literatures, and Linguistics, B
Clinical Psychology, M
Communication, Journalism and Related
Programs, B
Computer Engineering, B
Computer Science, B
Counseling Psychology, M
Criminology, B
Cultural Studies, M
Curriculum and Instruction, M
Drama and Dance Teacher Education, B
Drama and Dramatics/Theatre Arts, B
East Asian Studies, B
Economics, B
Education, MO
Electrical, Electronics and Communications
Engineering, B
Elementary Education and Teaching, B
English, MO
English Language and Literature, B
English/Language Arts Teacher Education, B
Environmental Sciences, B
Ethics, MO
Finance, B
Fine/Studio Arts, B
Foreign Language Teacher Education, B
French Language and Literature, B
French Language Teacher Education, B
Geography, B
Geography Teacher Education, B
Geology/Earth Science, B
German Language and Literature, B
German Language Teacher Education, B
Gerontology, MO
Health and Physical Education, B
History, BMO
History Teacher Education, B
Humanities/Humanistic Studies, B
International Business/Trade/Commerce, BM
International Economics, B
International Relations and Affairs, B
Journalism, B
Junior High/Intermediate/Middle School Education
and Teaching, B
Kinesiology and Exercise Science, B
Law and Legal Studies, MPO
Liberal Studies, MO
Management Science, B
Management Sciences and Quantitative Methods, B
Marketing/Marketing Management, B
Mass Communication/Media Studies, B
Mathematics, B

Mathematics Teacher Education, B
Mechanical Engineering, B
Multi-/Interdisciplinary Studies, B
Music, B
Music Management and Merchandising, B
Music Performance, B
Music Teacher Education, B
Music Theory and Composition, B
Nursing, MO
Nursing - Registered Nurse Training, B
Organizational Communication, B
Philosophy, B
Physical Education Teaching and Coaching, B
Physics, B
Physics Teacher Education, B
Piano and Organ, B
Political Science and Government, B
Psychology, BMO
Psychology Teacher Education, B
Public Relations/Image Management, B
Radio and Television, B
Religious/Sacred Music, B
School Psychology, O
Science Teacher Education/General Science
Teacher Education, B
Secondary Education and Teaching, B
Social Science Teacher Education, B
Social Sciences, A
Social Work, B
Sociology, B
Spanish Language and Literature, B
Spanish Language Teacher Education, B
Special Education and Teaching, M
Sport and Fitness Administration/Management, BM
Theology and Religious Vocations, MO
Theology/Theological Studies, B
Voice and Opera, B

VINCENNES UNIVERSITY

Accounting, A
Administrative Assistant and Secretarial Science, A
Advertising, A
Agricultural and Extension Education Services, A
Agricultural Business and Management, A
Agricultural Mechanization, A
Airframe Mechanics and Aircraft Maintenance
Technology/Technician, A
Airline/Commercial/Professional Pilot and Flight
Crew, A
Anthropology, A
Architectural Engineering Technology/Technician, A
Art Teacher Education, A
Art/Art Studies, General, A
Artificial Intelligence and Robotics, A
Athletic Training and Sports Medicine, A
Automobile/Automotive Mechanics
Technology/Technician, A
Avionics Maintenance Technology/Technician, A
Baking and Pastry Arts/Baker/Pastry Chef, A
Behavioral Sciences, A
Biology/Biological Sciences, A
Broadcast Journalism, A
Building/Home/Construction Inspection/Inspector, A
Business Administration and Management, A
Business Teacher Education, A
Chemistry, A
Child Care and Support Services Management, A
Child Care Provider/Assistant, A
Child Development, A
Civil Engineering Technology/Technician, A
Clinical Laboratory Science/Medical
Technology/Technologist, A
Clinical/Medical Laboratory Technician, A
Commercial and Advertising Art, A
Communication Studies/Speech Communication
and Rhetoric, A
Communications Technology/Technician, A
Computer and Information Sciences, A
Computer Engineering, A
Computer Engineering Technology/Technician, A
Computer Graphics, A
Computer Hardware Engineering, A
Computer Programming, A
Computer Programming, Specific Applications, A
Computer
Programming, Vendor/Product Certification, A

Computer Programming/Programmer, A
Computer Science, A
Computer Software and Media Applications, A
Computer Software Engineering, A
Computer Systems Networking and
 Telecommunications, A
Computer/Information Technology Services
 Administration and Management, A
Construction Engineering Technology/Technician, A
Corrections, A
Cosmetology/Cosmetologist, A
Criminal Justice/Law Enforcement Administration, A
Criminal Justice/Police Science, A
Culinary Arts/Chef Training, A
Data Entry/Microcomputer Applications, A
Dental Hygiene/Hygienist, A
Dietetics/Dieticians, A
Drafting and Design Technology/Technician, A
Drama and Dramatics/Theatre Arts, A
Education, A
Electrical, Electronic and Communications
 Engineering Technology/Technician, A
Elementary Education and Teaching, A
Engineering, A
Engineering Technology, A
English Language and Literature, A
Environmental Health, A
Environmental Studies, A
Family and Consumer Economics and Related
 Services, A
Family and Consumer Sciences/Human Sciences, A
Family and Consumer Sciences/Human Sciences
 Communication, A
Fashion Merchandising, A
Fashion/Apparel Design, A
Fire Science/Firefighting, A
Food Science, A
Forestry, A
French Language and Literature, A
Funeral Service and Mortuary Science, A
Geography, A
Geology/Earth Science, A
German Language and Literature, A
Graphic and Printing Equipment Operator
 Production, A
Health and Medical Laboratory Technologies, A
Health Information/Medical Records
 Administration/Administrator, A
Heavy Equipment Maintenance
 Technology/Technician, A
History, A
Horticultural Science, A
Hospitality and Recreation Marketing Operations, A
Hotel/Motel Administration/Management, A
Housing and Human Environments, A
Industrial Design, A
Industrial Electronics Technology/Technician, A
Industrial Mechanics and Maintenance
 Technology, A
Information Science/Studies, A
Information Technology, A
Interior Design, A
International Business/Trade/Commerce, A
Journalism, A
Junior High/Intermediate/Middle School Education
 and Teaching, A
Kindergarten/PreSchool Education and Teaching, A
Kinesiology and Exercise Science, A
Landscape Architecture, A
Laser and Optical Technology/Technician, A
Legal Administrative Assistant/Secretary, A
Legal Assistant/Paralegal, A
Liberal Arts and Sciences Studies and
 Humanities, A
Licensed Practical/Vocational Nurse Training, A
Machine Shop Technology/Assistant, A
Machine Tool Technology/Machinist, A
Management Information Systems and Services, A
Marketing/Marketing Management, A
Mass Communication/Media Studies, A
Mathematics, A
Mechanical Engineering/Mechanical
 Technology/Technician, A
Medical Administrative Assistant/Secretary, A
Medical/Clinical Assistant, A
Music, A

Music Teacher Education, A
Natural Resources and Conservation, A
Natural Resources Management/Development and
 Policy, A
Nuclear Medical Technology/Technologist, A
Nursing - Registered Nurse Training, A
Occupational Therapy/Therapist, A
Parks, Recreation, Leisure and Fitness Studies, A
Pharmacy, A
Physical Education Teaching and Coaching, A
Physical Therapy/Therapist, A
Physics, A
Political Science and Government, A
Pre-Engineering, A
Psychology, A
Public Administration, A
Public Relations/Image Management, A
Radio and Television, A
Respiratory Care Therapy/Therapist, A
Restaurant, Culinary, and Catering
 Management/Manager, A
Sales, Distribution and Marketing Operations, A
Science Teacher Education/General Science
 Teacher Education, A
Sign Language Interpretation and Translation, A
Social Sciences, A
Social Work, A
Sociology, A
Spanish Language and Literature, A
Speech Teacher Education, A
Sport and Fitness Administration/Management, A
Substance Abuse/Addiction Counseling, A
Survey Technology/Surveying, A
System Administration/Administrator, A
Teacher Education, Multiple Levels, A
Therapeutic Recreation/Recreational Therapy, A
Web Page, Digital/Multimedia and Information
 Resources Design, A
Web/Multimedia Management and Webmaster, A
Welding Technology/Welder, A
Word Processing, A

VINCENNES UNIVERSITY JASPER CAMPUS

Accounting, A
Administrative Assistant and Secretarial Science, A
Behavioral Sciences, A
Business Administration and Management, A
Business Teacher Education, A
Computer Programming, A
Computer Programming/Programmer, A
Computer Systems Networking and
 Telecommunications, A
Criminal Justice/Police Science, A
Drafting and Design Technology/Technician, A
Education, A
Elementary Education and Teaching, A
Finance, A
Furniture Design and Manufacturing, A
Industrial Technology/Technician, A
Legal Administrative Assistant/Secretary, A
Liberal Arts and Sciences Studies and
 Humanities, A
Management Information Systems and Services, A
Medical Administrative Assistant/Secretary, A
Psychology, A
Social Sciences, A
Social Work, A
Sociology, A
Teacher Education, Multiple Levels, A
Word Processing, A

WABASH COLLEGE

Art/Art Studies, General, B
Biology/Biological Sciences, B
Chemistry, B
Classics and Classical
 Languages, Literatures, and Linguistics, B
Drama and Dramatics/Theatre Arts, B
Economics, B
English Language and Literature, B
French Language and Literature, B
German Language and Literature, B
History, B
Latin Language and Literature, B
Mathematics, B

Modern Greek Language and Literature, B
Music, B
Philosophy, B
Physics, B
Political Science and Government, B
Pre-Law Studies, B
Pre-Medicine/Pre-Medical Studies, B
Pre-Veterinary Studies, B
Psychology, B
Religion/Religious Studies, B
Spanish Language and Literature, B
Speech and Rhetorical Studies, B

Iowa

AIB COLLEGE OF BUSINESS

Accounting, A
Administrative Assistant and Secretarial Science, A
Business Administration and Management, A
Computer Programming, Specific Applications, A
Computer Software and Media Applications, A
Computer Systems Networking and
 Telecommunications, A
Court Reporting/Court Reporter, A
Data Entry/Microcomputer Applications, A
Finance, A
Hospitality and Recreation Marketing Operations, A
Legal Administrative Assistant/Secretary, A
Marketing/Marketing Management, A
Medical Administrative Assistant/Secretary, A
System Administration/Administrator, A
Tourism and Travel Services Management, A
Tourism and Travel Services Marketing
 Operations, A
Tourism Promotion Operations, A

ALLEN COLLEGE

Health Education, M
Nursing, M
Nursing - Advanced Practice, M
Nursing - Registered Nurse Training, B
Nursing Administration, M
Radiologic Technology/Science - Radiographer, A

ASHFORD UNIVERSITY

Accounting, B
Athletic Training and Sports Medicine, B
Biology/Biological Sciences, B
Business Administration and Management, B
Business Teacher Education, B
Communication, Journalism and Related
 Programs, B
Computer and Information Sciences, B
Criminal Justice/Safety Studies, B
CytoTechnology/Cytotechnologist, B
Education, B
Elementary Education and Teaching, B
English Language and Literature, B
General Studies, B
Health/Health Care Administration/Management, B
History, B
Human Services, B
Humanities/Humanistic Studies, B
Journalism, B
Junior High/Intermediate/Middle School Education
 and Teaching, B
Kindergarten/PreSchool Education and Teaching, B
Liberal Arts and Sciences Studies and
 Humanities, AB
Multi-/Interdisciplinary Studies, B
Music, B
Music Teacher Education, B
Pre-Law Studies, B
Pre-Medicine/Pre-Medical Studies, B
Psychology, B
Religion/Religious Studies, B
Science Teacher Education/General Science
 Teacher Education, B
Secondary Education and Teaching, B
Social Sciences, B
Visual and Performing Arts, B

BRIAR CLIFF UNIVERSITY

Accounting, B
Art/Art Studies, General, B

Biology/Biological Sciences, B
Business Administration and Management, B
Chemistry, B
Creative Writing, B
Criminal Justice/Law Enforcement Administration, B
Drama and Dramatics/Theatre Arts, B
Education, BM
Elementary Education and Teaching, B
English Language and Literature, B
Environmental Sciences, B
Graphic Design, B
History, B
Human Resources Management and Services, M
Human Resources Management/Personnel
　Administration, M
Industrial Radiologic Technology/Technician, B
Liberal Arts and Sciences Studies and
　Humanities, A
Management Information Systems and Services, B
Mass Communication/Media Studies, B
Mathematics, B
Music, B
Nursing, M
Nursing - Registered Nurse Training, B
Physical Education Teaching and Coaching, B
Political Science and Government, B
Professional Studies, B
Psychology, B
Secondary Education and Teaching, B
Social Work, B
Spanish Language and Literature, B
Theology/Theological Studies, AB

BUENA VISTA UNIVERSITY

Accounting, B
Art Teacher Education, B
Art/Art Studies, General, B
Arts Management, B
Athletic Training and Sports Medicine, B
Banking and Financial Support Services, B
Biological and Physical Sciences, B
Biology Teacher Education, B
Biology/Biological Sciences, B
Business Teacher Education, B
Business/Managerial Economics, B
Chemistry, B
Chemistry Teacher Education, B
Commercial and Advertising Art, B
Communication Studies/Speech Communication
　and Rhetoric, B
Computer Science, B
Computer Teacher Education, B
Counselor Education/School Counseling and
　Guidance Services, BM
Criminal Justice/Safety Studies, B
Education, M
Elementary Education and Teaching, B
English Language and Literature, B
English/Language Arts Teacher Education, B
Entrepreneurship/Entrepreneurial Studies, B
History, B
History Teacher Education, B
Human Resources Management/Personnel
　Administration, B
International Business/Trade/Commerce, B
Management Information Systems and Services, B
Marketing/Marketing Management, B
Mass Communication/Media Studies, B
Mathematics, B
Mathematics Teacher Education, B
Multi-/Interdisciplinary Studies, B
Music Performance, B
Music Teacher Education, B
Organizational Communication, B
Philosophy and Religious Studies, B
Physical Education Teaching and Coaching, B
Physics, B
Physics Teacher Education, B
Political Science and Government, B
Psychology, B
Public Administration, B
Public Relations, Advertising, and Applied
　Communication, B
Science Teacher Education/General Science
　Teacher Education, B
Social Science Teacher Education, B

Social Sciences, B
Social Work, B
Sociology, B
Spanish Language and Literature, B
Spanish Language Teacher Education, B
Special Education and Teaching, B
Speech Teacher Education, B
Sport and Fitness Administration/Management, B
Theatre Literature, History and Criticism, B

CENTRAL COLLEGE

Accounting, B
Art/Art Studies, General, B
Biology/Biological Sciences, B
Business Administration and Management, B
Chemistry, B
Communication Studies/Speech Communication
　and Rhetoric, B
Computer Science, B
Drama and Dramatics/Theatre Arts, B
Economics, B
Elementary Education and Teaching, B
English Language and Literature, B
Environmental Studies, B
French Language and Literature, B
General Studies, B
German Studies, B
History, B
Information Science/Studies, B
Interdisciplinary Studies, B
International Business/Trade/Commerce, B
International/Global Studies, B
Kinesiology and Exercise Science, B
Linguistics, B
Mathematics, B
Mathematics and Computer Science, B
Music, B
Music Teacher Education, B
Natural Sciences, B
Philosophy, B
Physics, B
Political Science and Government, B
Psychology, B
Religion/Religious Studies, B
Social Sciences, B
Sociology, B
Spanish Language and Literature, B

CLARKE COLLEGE

Accounting, B
Advertising, B
Art History, Criticism and Conservation, B
Art Teacher Education, B
Art/Art Studies, General, B
Athletic Training and Sports Medicine, B
Biology/Biological Sciences, B
Business Administration and Management, B
Chemistry, B
Computer Science, B
Drama and Dramatics/Theatre Arts, B
Early Childhood Education and Teaching, M
Economics, B
Education, BM
Educational Administration and Supervision, M
Educational Media/Instructional Technology, M
Elementary Education and Teaching, B
English Language and Literature, B
Fine/Studio Arts, B
French Language and Literature, B
History, B
Information Science/Studies, B
International Business/Trade/Commerce, B
Junior High/Intermediate/Middle School Education
　and Teaching, B
Kindergarten/PreSchool Education and Teaching, B
Liberal Arts and Sciences Studies and
　Humanities, A
Management, M
Management Information Systems and Services, B
Marketing/Marketing Management, B
Mass Communication/Media Studies, B
Mathematics, B
Music, B
Music Teacher Education, B
Nursing, MO
Nursing - Advanced Practice, MO

Nursing Administration, M
Nursing Education, M
Nursing Science, B
Philosophy, B
Physical Education Teaching and Coaching, B
Physical Therapy/Therapist, BM
Psychology, B
Public Relations/Image Management, B
Reading Teacher Education, M
Religion/Religious Studies, B
Secondary Education and Teaching, B
Social Work, B
Sociology, B
Spanish Language and Literature, B
Special Education and Teaching, BM
Voice and Opera, B

CLINTON COMMUNITY COLLEGE

Administrative Assistant and Secretarial Science, A
Architectural Drafting and Architectural
　CAD/CADD, A
Business Administration and Management, A
Computer/Information Technology Services
　Administration and Management, A
Electrical, Electronic and Communications
　Engineering Technology/Technician, A
Emergency Medical Technology/Technician (EMT
　Paramedic), A
Environmental Engineering
　Technology/Environmental Technology, A
Graphic and Printing Equipment Operator
　Production, A
Liberal Arts and Sciences Studies and
　Humanities, A
Licensed Practical/Vocational Nurse Training, A
Machine Tool Technology/Machinist, A
Nursing - Registered Nurse Training, A
Occupational Safety and Health
　Technology/Technician, A
Pharmacy Technician/Assistant, A

COE COLLEGE

Accounting, B
Acting, B
African-American/Black Studies, B
American/United States Studies/Civilization, B
Architecture, B
Area, Ethnic, Cultural, and Gender Studies, B
Art Teacher Education, B
Art/Art Studies, General, B
Asian Studies/Civilization, B
Athletic Training and Sports Medicine, B
Biochemistry, B
Biological and Physical Sciences, B
Biology/Biological Sciences, B
Business Administration and Management, B
Ceramic Arts and Ceramics, B
Chemistry, B
Classics and Classical
　Languages, Literatures, and Linguistics, B
Comparative Literature, B
Computer Science, B
Creative Writing, B
Directing and Theatrical Production, B
Drama and Dramatics/Theatre Arts, B
Economics, B
Education, BM
Elementary Education and Teaching, B
English Language and Literature, B
Environmental Studies, B
Fine/Studio Arts, B
French Language and Literature, B
French Studies, B
German Language and Literature, B
German Studies, B
Health and Physical Education/Fitness, B
History, B
Interdisciplinary Studies, B
Liberal Arts and Sciences Studies and
　Humanities, B
Mathematics, B
Molecular Biology, B
Music, B
Music Performance, B
Music Teacher Education, B
Music Theory and Composition, B

Nursing - Registered Nurse Training, B
Painting, B
Philosophy, B
Photography, B
Physical Education Teaching and Coaching, B
Physical Sciences, B
Physics, B
Political Science and Government, B
Pre-Dentistry Studies, B
Pre-Law Studies, B
Pre-Medicine/Pre-Medical Studies, B
Pre-Veterinary Studies, B
Psychology, B
Public Relations/Image Management, B
Religion/Religious Studies, B
Science Teacher Education/General Science
   Teacher Education, B
Secondary Education and Teaching, B
Sociology, B
Spanish and Iberian Studies, B
Spanish Language and Literature, B
Speech and Rhetorical Studies, B
Technical Theatre/Theatre Design and
   Technology, B

CORNELL COLLEGE

Anthropology, B
Architecture, B
Art History, Criticism and Conservation, B
Art/Art Studies, General, B
Biochemistry, B
Biology/Biological Sciences, B
Chemistry, B
Classics and Classical
   Languages, Literatures, and Linguistics, B
Computer Science, B
Drama and Dramatics/Theatre Arts, B
Economics, B
Elementary Education and Teaching, B
English Language and Literature, B
Environmental Studies, B
Ethnic and Cultural Studies, B
Ethnic, Cultural Minority, and Gender Studies, B
French Language and Literature, B
Geology/Earth Science, B
German Language and Literature, B
Health and Physical Education/Fitness, B
History, B
Interdisciplinary Studies, B
International Business/Trade/Commerce, B
International Relations and Affairs, B
Latin American Studies, B
Latin Language and Literature, B
Liberal Arts and Sciences Studies and
   Humanities, B
Mathematics, B
Medieval and Renaissance Studies, B
Modern Greek Language and Literature, B
Modern Languages, B
Multi-/Interdisciplinary Studies, B
Music, B
Music Teacher Education, B
Philosophy, B
Physical Education Teaching and Coaching, B
Physics, B
Political Science and Government, B
Psychology, B
Religion/Religious Studies, B
Russian Language and Literature, B
Secondary Education and Teaching, B
Sociology, B
Spanish Language and Literature, B
Speech and Rhetorical Studies, B

DES MOINES AREA COMMUNITY COLLEGE

Accounting, A
Administrative Assistant and Secretarial Science, A
Agricultural Business and Management, A
Artificial Intelligence and Robotics, A
Automobile/Automotive Mechanics
   Technology/Technician, A
Biology Technician/BioTechnology Laboratory
   Technician, A
Business Administration and Management, A
Carpentry/Carpenter, A

Child Development, A
Civil Engineering Technology/Technician, A
Clinical/Medical Laboratory Technician, A
Commercial and Advertising Art, A
Computer Engineering Technology/Technician, A
Computer Programming, Specific Applications, A
Computer Programming/Programmer, A
Consumer Merchandising/Retailing Management, A
Corrections, A
Criminal Justice/Law Enforcement Administration, A
Criminal Justice/Police Science, A
Culinary Arts/Chef Training, A
Data Processing and Data Processing
   Technology/Technician, A
Dental Hygiene/Hygienist, A
Drafting and Design Technology/Technician, A
Education, A
Electrical, Electronic and Communications
   Engineering Technology/Technician, A
Fashion Merchandising, A
Fire Science/Firefighting, A
Graphic and Printing Equipment Operator
   Production, A
Health/Health Care Administration/Management, A
Heating, Air Conditioning, Ventilation and
   Refrigeration Maintenance
   Technology/Technician, A
Heavy Equipment Maintenance
   Technology/Technician, A
Horticultural Science, A
Hospitality Administration/Management, A
Hotel/Motel Administration/Management, A
Human Services, A
Legal Administrative Assistant/Secretary, A
Legal Assistant/Paralegal, A
Liberal Arts and Sciences Studies and
   Humanities, A
Licensed Practical/Vocational Nurse Training, A
Machine Tool Technology/Machinist, A
Marketing/Marketing Management, A
Medical Administrative Assistant/Secretary, A
Medical/Clinical Assistant, A
Nursing - Registered Nurse Training, A
Quality Control Technology/Technician, A
Respiratory Care Therapy/Therapist, A
Social Work, A
Special Products Marketing Operations, A
Teacher Assistant/Aide, A
Telecommunications Technology/Technician, A
Welding Technology/Welder, A

DIVINE WORD COLLEGE

Philosophy, B
Social Sciences, AB

DORDT COLLEGE

Accounting, B
Administrative Assistant and Secretarial Science, A
Agricultural Business and Management, AB
Agricultural Teacher Education, B
Agricultural/Biological Engineering and
   Bioengineering, B
Agriculture, B
Animal Sciences, B
Animal/Livestock Husbandry and Production, B
Biology Teacher Education, B
Biology/Biological Sciences, B
Business Administration and Management, B
Business Teacher Education, B
Chemistry, B
Chemistry Teacher Education, B
Civil Engineering, B
Clinical Laboratory Science/Medical
   Technology/Technologist, B
Commercial and Advertising Art, B
Computer Engineering, B
Computer Programming/Programmer, B
Computer Science, B
Computer Teacher Education, B
Computer/Information Technology Services
   Administration and Management, B
Criminal Justice/Law Enforcement Administration, B
Data Processing and Data Processing
   Technology/Technician, A
Drama and Dance Teacher Education, B
Drama and Dramatics/Theatre Arts, B

Education, BM
Electrical, Electronics and Communications
   Engineering, B
Elementary Education and Teaching, B
Engineering, B
Engineering Mechanics, B
Engineering Technology, B
English Language and Literature, B
Environmental Studies, B
General Studies, B
German Language and Literature, B
Graphic Design, B
Health and Physical Education, B
History, B
History Teacher Education, B
Journalism, B
Kinesiology and Exercise Science, B
Legal Administrative Assistant/Secretary, A
Management Information Systems and Services, B
Mass Communication/Media Studies, B
Mathematics, B
Mechanical Engineering, B
Missions/Missionary Studies and Missiology, B
Music, B
Music Performance, B
Music Teacher Education, B
Natural Sciences, B
Nursing - Registered Nurse Training, B
Parks, Recreation, Leisure and Fitness Studies, B
Pastoral Studies/Counseling, B
Philosophy, B
Physical Education Teaching and Coaching, B
Physics, B
Piano and Organ, B
Political Science and Government, B
Pre-Dentistry Studies, B
Pre-Law Studies, B
Pre-Medicine/Pre-Medical Studies, B
Pre-Nursing Studies, B
Pre-Pharmacy Studies, B
Pre-Veterinary Studies, B
Psychology, B
Reading Teacher Education, B
Religion/Religious Studies, B
Science Teacher Education/General Science
   Teacher Education, B
Secondary Education and Teaching, B
Social Science Teacher Education, B
Social Sciences, B
Social Studies Teacher Education, B
Social Work, B
Sociology, B
Spanish Language and Literature, B
Spanish Language Teacher Education, B
Speech Teacher Education, B
Superintendency and Educational System
   Administration, B
System Administration/Administrator, B
Teacher Assistant/Aide, A
Teacher Education, Multiple Levels, B
Theology/Theological Studies, B
Voice and Opera, B
Youth Ministry, B

DRAKE UNIVERSITY

Accounting, B
Accounting and Finance, B
Acting, B
Actuarial Science, B
Adult and Continuing Education and Teaching, M
Advertising, B
American/United States Studies/Civilization, M
Anthropology, B
Art History, Criticism and Conservation, B
Art/Art Studies, General, B
Astronomy, B
Biochemistry, B
Biology/Biological Sciences, B
Broadcast Journalism, B
Business Administration and Management, B
Business Administration, Management and
   Operations, MO
Business Education, M
Business/Commerce, B
Chemistry, B
Commercial and Advertising Art, B

Computer Science, B
Counselor Education/School Counseling and
   Guidance Services, M
Directing and Theatrical Production, B
Drama and Dramatics/Theatre Arts, B
Dramatic/Theatre Arts and Stagecraft, B
Drawing, B
Education, MDO
Educational Leadership and Administration, MDO
Elementary Education and Teaching, BM
English Education, M
English Language and Literature, B
Environmental Sciences, B
Environmental Studies, B
Ethics, B
Finance, B
Fine Arts and Art Studies, M
Fine/Studio Arts, B
Graphic Design, B
History, BM
Industrial Education, M
International Business/Trade/Commerce, B
International Relations and Affairs, B
Jazz/Jazz Studies, B
Journalism, BM
Law and Legal Studies, PO
Marketing/Marketing Management, B
Mass Communication/Media Studies, B
Mathematics, B
Mathematics Teacher Education, M
Music, B
Music Management and Merchandising, B
Music Performance, B
Music Teacher Education, B
Neuroscience, B
Painting, B
Pharmacy, BPO
Pharmacy Administration and Pharmacy Policy and
   Regulatory Affairs, B
Philosophy, B
Physics, B
Piano and Organ, B
Political Science and Government, B
Pre-Dentistry Studies, B
Pre-Engineering, B
Pre-Law Studies, B
Pre-Medicine/Pre-Medical Studies, B
Pre-Veterinary Studies, B
Printmaking, B
Psychology, B
Public Administration, MO
Public Relations/Image Management, B
Radio and Television, B
Radio, Television, and Digital Communication, B
Rehabilitation Counseling, M
Religion/Religious Studies, B
Religious/Sacred Music, B
Science Teacher Education/General Science
   Teacher Education, M
Sculpture, B
Secondary Education and Teaching, BM
Social Studies Teacher Education, M
Sociology, BM
Special Education and Teaching, M
Speech and Interpersonal Communication, M
Speech and Rhetorical Studies, BM
Theater, M
Vocational and Technical Education, M
Voice and Opera, B

ELLSWORTH COMMUNITY COLLEGE

Accounting, A
Administrative Assistant and Secretarial Science, A
Agricultural Business and Management, A
Art Teacher Education, A
Art/Art Studies, General, A
Biological and Physical Sciences, A
Biology Technician/BioTechnology Laboratory
   Technician, A
Biology/Biological Sciences, A
Business Administration and Management, A
Child Development, A
Clinical Laboratory Science/Medical
   Technology/Technologist, A
Computer and Information Sciences, A

Computer Systems Networking and
   Telecommunications, A
Consumer Merchandising/Retailing Management, A
Corrections, A
Criminal Justice/Law Enforcement Administration, A
Data Entry/Microcomputer Applications, A
Data Processing and Data Processing
   Technology/Technician, A
Developmental and Child Psychology, A
Economics, A
Education, A
Environmental Engineering
   Technology/Environmental Technology, A
Equestrian/Equine Studies, A
Fashion Merchandising, A
Health and Medical Laboratory Technologies, A
History, A
Human Services, A
Interior Design, A
Kindergarten/PreSchool Education and Teaching, A
Legal Administrative Assistant/Secretary, A
Liberal Arts and Sciences Studies and
   Humanities, A
Marketing/Marketing Management, A
Mathematics, A
Medical Administrative Assistant/Secretary, A
Natural Resources and Conservation, A
Nursing - Registered Nurse Training, A
Physical Education Teaching and Coaching, A
Physical Sciences, A
Political Science and Government, A
Pre-Engineering, A
Psychology, A
Retailing and Retail Operations, A
Social Work, A
Sociology, A
Teacher Assistant/Aide, A
Trade and Industrial Teacher Education, A
Wildlife Biology, A

EMMAUS BIBLE COLLEGE

Bible/Biblical Studies, AB
Computer and Information Sciences, B
Elementary Education and Teaching, B
Missions/Missionary Studies and Missiology, B
Pre-Theology/Pre-Ministerial Studies, B

FAITH BAPTIST BIBLE COLLEGE AND THEOLOGICAL SEMINARY

Administrative Assistant and Secretarial Science, A
Bible/Biblical Studies, AB
Divinity/Ministry (BD, MDiv.), AB
Elementary Education and Teaching, B
English/Language Arts Teacher Education, B
Missions/Missionary Studies and Missiology, AB
Music Teacher Education, B
Pastoral Studies/Counseling, BMP
Religion/Religious Studies, M
Religious Education, B
Religious/Sacred Music, B
Theology and Religious Vocations, MP

GRACELAND UNIVERSITY

Accounting, B
Art Teacher Education, B
Art/Art Studies, General, B
Athletic Training and Sports Medicine, B
Biology/Biological Sciences, B
Business Administration and Management, B
Chemistry, B
Clinical Laboratory Science/Medical
   Technology/Technologist, B
Commercial and Advertising Art, B
Comparative Literature, B
Computer Science, B
Criminal Justice/Law Enforcement Administration, B
Drama and Dramatics/Theatre Arts, B
Economics, B
Education, BM
Elementary Education and Teaching, B
English Composition, B
English Language and Literature, B
Fine/Studio Arts, B
Foreign Languages and Literatures, B
German Language and Literature, B
Health Teacher Education, B

History, B
Human Services, B
International Business/Trade/Commerce, B
International Relations and Affairs, B
Liberal Arts and Sciences Studies and
   Humanities, B
Management Information Systems and Services, B
Mathematics, B
Music, B
Music Teacher Education, B
Nursing, MO
Nursing - Advanced Practice, MO
Nursing - Registered Nurse Training, B
Nursing Administration, MO
Nursing Education, M
Parks, Recreation, Leisure and Fitness Studies, B
Pastoral Studies/Counseling, M
Philosophy and Religious Studies, B
Physical Education Teaching and Coaching, B
Physical Sciences, B
Pre-Dentistry Studies, B
Pre-Law Studies, B
Pre-Medicine/Pre-Medical Studies, B
Psychology, B
Public Health (MPH, DPH), B
Publishing, B
Religion/Religious Studies, BM
Science Teacher Education/General Science
   Teacher Education, B
Secondary Education and Teaching, B
Social Sciences, B
Social Work, B
Sociology, B
Spanish Language and Literature, B
Speech and Rhetorical Studies, B
Speech Teacher Education, B
Sport and Fitness Administration/Management, B
Substance Abuse/Addiction Counseling, B
Teacher Education, Multiple Levels, B

GRAND VIEW COLLEGE

Accounting, B
Applied Mathematics, B
Art/Art Studies, General, B
Biology/Biological Sciences, B
Business Administration and Management, B
Computer Science, B
Criminal Justice/Law Enforcement Administration, B
Drama and Dramatics/Theatre Arts, B
Elementary Education and Teaching, B
English Language and Literature, B
Fine/Studio Arts, B
Graphic Communications, B
Graphic Design, B
History, B
Human Services, B
Information Science/Studies, B
Journalism, B
Liberal Arts and Sciences Studies and
   Humanities, AB
Management Information Systems and Services, B
Mass Communication/Media Studies, B
Music, B
Nursing - Registered Nurse Training, B
Physical Sciences, B
Political Science and Government, B
Pre-Law Studies, B
Psychology, B
Radio and Television, B
Religion/Religious Studies, B
Sociology, A

GRINNELL COLLEGE

Anthropology, B
Art/Art Studies, General, B
Biochemistry, B
Biology/Biological Sciences, B
Chemistry, B
Chinese Language and Literature, B
Classics and Classical
   Languages, Literatures, and Linguistics, B
Computer Science, B
Drama and Dramatics/Theatre Arts, B
English Language and Literature, B
French Language and Literature, B
German Language and Literature, B

History, B
Interdisciplinary Studies, B
Mathematics, B
Music, B
Philosophy, B
Physics, B
Political Science and Government, B
Psychology, B
Religion/Religious Studies, B
Russian Language and Literature, B
Sociology, B
Spanish Language and Literature, B

HAMILTON COLLEGE (CEDAR FALLS)

Accounting, AB
Business, Management, Marketing, and Related
   Support Services, AB
Computer Programming/Programmer, A
Computer Systems Networking and
   Telecommunications, A
Criminal Justice/Safety Studies, AB
Executive Assistant/Executive Secretary, A
Legal Assistant/Paralegal, A
Management Information Systems and Services, B
Medical/Clinical Assistant, A
Multi-/Interdisciplinary Studies, A
Tourism and Travel Services Marketing
   Operations, A

HAMILTON COLLEGE (CEDAR RAPIDS)

Accounting, AB
Administrative Assistant and Secretarial Science, A
Business Administration and Management, AB
Criminal Justice/Law Enforcement Administration, A
General Studies, A
Management Information Systems and Services, AB
Medical/Clinical Assistant, A
Tourism and Travel Services Management, A

HAMILTON TECHNICAL COLLEGE

Drafting and Design Technology/Technician, A
Electrical, Electronic and Communications
   Engineering Technology/Technician, AB

HAWKEYE COMMUNITY COLLEGE

Accounting, A
Administrative Assistant and Secretarial Science, A
Agricultural Business and Management, A
Agricultural Mechanization, A
Agronomy and Crop Science, A
Animal Sciences, A
Architectural Engineering Technology/Technician, A
Autobody/Collision and Repair
   Technology/Technician, A
Automobile/Automotive Mechanics
   Technology/Technician, A
Avionics Maintenance Technology/Technician, A
Biology/Biological Sciences, A
Business Administration and Management, A
Business/Commerce, A
Child Development, A
Civil Engineering Technology/Technician, A
Clinical/Medical Laboratory Technician, A
Commercial and Advertising Art, A
Computer Engineering Technology/Technician, A
Computer Systems Networking and
   Telecommunications, A
Computer/Information Technology Services
   Administration and Management, A
Corrections, A
Criminal Justice/Law Enforcement Administration, A
Criminal Justice/Police Science, A
Data Entry/Microcomputer Applications, A
Dental Hygiene/Hygienist, A
Drafting and Design Technology/Technician, A
Drafting/Design Engineering
   Technologies/Technicians, A
Education, A
Engineering Technology, A
Farm/Farm and Ranch Management, A
Fire Science/Firefighting, A
Food Science, A
Heavy Equipment Maintenance
   Technology/Technician, A
Horticultural Science, A
Information Technology, A

Interdisciplinary Studies, A
Interior Design, A
Liberal Arts and Sciences Studies and
   Humanities, A
Machine Tool Technology/Machinist, A
Management Information Systems and Services, A
Marketing/Marketing Management, A
Mechanical Engineering/Mechanical
   Technology/Technician, A
Medical Administrative Assistant/Secretary, A
Natural Resources Management/Development and
   Policy, A
Nursing - Registered Nurse Training, A
Ornamental Horticulture, A
Parks, Recreation and Leisure Facilities
   Management, A
Photography, A
Respiratory Care Therapy/Therapist, A
Survey Technology/Surveying, A
System Administration/Administrator, A
Tool and Die Technology/Technician, A
Web Page, Digital/Multimedia and Information
   Resources Design, A
Web/Multimedia Management and Webmaster, A
Word Processing, A

INDIAN HILLS COMMUNITY COLLEGE

Agricultural Mechanization, A
Airline/Commercial/Professional Pilot and Flight
   Crew, A
Artificial Intelligence and Robotics, A
Automobile/Automotive Mechanics
   Technology/Technician, A
Avionics Maintenance Technology/Technician, A
Biology Technician/BioTechnology Laboratory
   Technician, A
Business Administration and Management, A
Child Development, A
Computer Engineering Technology/Technician, A
Computer Programming/Programmer, A
Criminal Justice/Law Enforcement Administration, A
Drafting and Design Technology/Technician, A
Electrical, Electronic and Communications
   Engineering Technology/Technician, A
Food Technology and Processing, A
Health Information/Medical Records
   Administration/Administrator, A
Health/Health Care Administration/Management, A
Heavy Equipment Maintenance
   Technology/Technician, A
Horticultural Science, A
Industrial Radiologic Technology/Technician, A
Laser and Optical Technology/Technician, A
Liberal Arts and Sciences Studies and
   Humanities, A
Licensed Practical/Vocational Nurse Training, A
Machine Tool Technology/Machinist, A
Nursing - Registered Nurse Training, A
Physical Therapy/Therapist, A

IOWA CENTRAL COMMUNITY COLLEGE

Accounting, A
Administrative Assistant and Secretarial Science, A
Airline/Commercial/Professional Pilot and Flight
   Crew, A
Automobile/Automotive Mechanics
   Technology/Technician, A
Aviation/Airway Management and Operations, A
Biological and Physical Sciences, A
Broadcast Journalism, A
Business Administration and Management, A
Business Teacher Education, A
Carpentry/Carpenter, A
Clinical/Medical Laboratory Technician, A
Community Organization and Advocacy, A
Computer Engineering Technology/Technician, A
Criminal Justice/Police Science, A
Data Processing and Data Processing
   Technology/Technician, A
Drafting and Design Technology/Technician, A
Education, A
Electrical, Electronic and Communications
   Engineering Technology/Technician, A
Hospitality and Recreation Marketing Operations, A
Industrial Radiologic Technology/Technician, A

Journalism, A
Liberal Arts and Sciences Studies and
   Humanities, A
Licensed Practical/Vocational Nurse Training, A
Machine Tool Technology/Machinist, A
Mass Communication/Media Studies, A
Medical/Clinical Assistant, A
Nursing - Registered Nurse Training, A
Occupational Therapy/Therapist, A
Physical Therapy/Therapist, A
Radio and Television, A
Science Teacher Education/General Science
   Teacher Education, A
Social Work, A
Sociology, A
Telecommunications Technology/Technician, A
Welding Technology/Welder, A

IOWA LAKES COMMUNITY COLLEGE

Accounting, A
Accounting Technology/Technician and
   Bookkeeping, A
Administrative Assistant and Secretarial Science, A
Agribusiness, A
Agricultural Business and Management, A
Agricultural Business Technology, A
Agricultural Economics, A
Agricultural Mechanics and Equipment/Machine
   Technology, A
Agricultural Mechanization, A
Agricultural Power Machinery Operation, A
Agricultural Production Operations, A
Agricultural Teacher Education, A
Agricultural/Farm Supplies Retailing and
   Wholesaling, A
Agriculture, A
Agronomy and Crop Science, A
Airline/Commercial/Professional Pilot and Flight
   Crew, A
Animal Sciences, A
Animal/Livestock Husbandry and Production, A
Applied Art, A
Art History, Criticism and Conservation, A
Art Teacher Education, A
Art/Art Studies, General, A
Astronomy, A
Athletic Training and Sports Medicine, A
Autobody/Collision and Repair
   Technology/Technician, A
Automobile/Automotive Mechanics
   Technology/Technician, A
Aviation/Airway Management and Operations, A
Behavioral Sciences, A
Biological and Physical Sciences, A
Biology/Biological Sciences, A
Botany/Plant Biology, A
Broadcast Journalism, A
Business Administration and Management, A
Business Machine Repairer, A
Business Teacher Education, A
Business/Office Automation/Technology/Data
   Entry, A
Carpentry/Carpenter, A
Ceramic Arts and Ceramics, A
Chemistry, A
Child Care Provider/Assistant, A
Child Development, A
Chiropractic, A
Commercial and Advertising Art, A
Communication, Journalism and Related
   Programs, A
Comparative Literature, A
Computer and Information Sciences, A
Computer Graphics, A
Computer Programming/Programmer, A
Computer Science, A
Computer Software Technology/Technician, A
Computer Systems Networking and
   Telecommunications, A
Computer/Information Technology Services
   Administration and Management, A
Construction Engineering Technology/Technician, A
Construction Management, A
Construction Trades, A
Consumer Merchandising/Retailing Management, A
Cooking and Related Culinary Arts, A

Corrections, A
Criminal Justice/Law Enforcement Administration, A
Criminal Justice/Police Science, A
Crop Production, A
Culinary Arts and Related Services, A
Data Entry/Microcomputer Applications, A
Data Processing and Data Processing
   Technology/Technician, A
Developmental and Child Psychology, A
Drafting and Design Technology/Technician, A
Drawing, A
Early Childhood Education and Teaching, A
Ecology, A
Economics, A
Education, A
Elementary Education and Teaching, A
Emergency Care Attendant (EMT Ambulance), A
Emergency Medical Technology/Technician (EMT
   Paramedic), A
Energy Management and Systems
   Technology/Technician, A
Engineering, A
English Language and Literature, A
Environmental Design/Architecture, A
Environmental Education, A
Environmental Engineering
   Technology/Environmental Technology, A
Environmental Studies, A
Family and Consumer Sciences/Human Sciences, A
Farm/Farm and Ranch Management, A
Fashion Merchandising, A
Finance, A
Fine/Studio Arts, A
Fishing and Fisheries Sciences and Management, A
Flight Instructor, A
Food Preparation/Professional Cooking/Kitchen
   Assistant, A
Food Service, Waiter/Waitress, and Dining Room
   Management/Manager, A
Foods, Nutrition, and Related Services, A
Foreign Languages and Literatures, A
Forestry, A
General Merchandising, Sales, and Related
   Marketing Operations, A
General Office Occupations and Clerical Services, A
General Studies, A
Geology/Earth Science, A
Graphic and Printing Equipment Operator
   Production, A
Graphic Communications, A
Graphic Design, A
Health and Medical Laboratory Technologies, A
Health and Physical Education, A
Health/Health Care Administration/Management, A
History, A
Hospitality Administration/Management, A
Hotel/Motel Administration/Management, A
Human Resources Management and Services, A
Humanities/Humanistic Studies, A
Hydrology and Water Resources Science, A
Information Technology, A
Institutional Food Workers, A
Jazz/Jazz Studies, A
Journalism, A
Kindergarten/PreSchool Education and Teaching, A
Landscaping and Groundskeeping, A
Law and Legal Studies, A
Legal Administrative Assistant/Secretary, A
Legal Assistant/Paralegal, A
Liberal Arts and Sciences Studies and
   Humanities, A
Marine Maintenance/Fitter and Ship Repair
   Technology/Technician, A
Marketing/Marketing Management, A
Mass Communication/Media Studies, A
Massage Therapy/Therapeutic Massage, A
Mathematics, A
Medical Administrative Assistant/Secretary, A
Medical Office Assistant/Specialist, A
Medical Office Computer Specialist/Assistant, A
Medical Reception/Receptionist, A
Medical Transcription/Transcriptionist, A
Medical/Clinical Assistant, A
Motorcycle Maintenance and Repair
   Technology/Technician, A
Music, A

Music Teacher Education, A
Natural Resources and Conservation, A
Natural Sciences, A
Nursing - Registered Nurse Training, A
Office Management and Supervision, A
Parks, Recreation, Leisure and Fitness Studies, A
Pharmacy, A
Philosophy, A
Photography, A
Physical Education Teaching and Coaching, A
Physical Sciences, A
Piano and Organ, A
Political Science and Government, A
Pre-Dentistry Studies, A
Pre-Engineering, A
Pre-Law Studies, A
Pre-Medicine/Pre-Medical Studies, A
Pre-Nursing Studies, A
Pre-Pharmacy Studies, A
Prepress/Desktop Publishing and Digital Imaging
   Design, A
Pre-Veterinary Studies, A
Printing Press Operator, A
Psychology, A
Radio and Television, A
Radio and Television Broadcasting
   Technology/Technician, A
Real Estate, A
Receptionist, A
Rehabilitation Therapy, A
Restaurant, Culinary, and Catering
   Management/Manager, A
Restaurant/Food Services Management, A
Retailing and Retail Operations, A
Sales, Distribution and Marketing Operations, A
Science Teacher Education/General Science
   Teacher Education, A
Selling Skills and Sales Operations, A
Small Business Administration/Management, A
Small Engine Mechanics and Repair
   Technology/Technician, A
Social Sciences, A
Social Work, A
Sociology, A
Soil Science and Agronomy, A
Spanish Language and Literature, A
Speech and Rhetorical Studies, A
Sport and Fitness Administration/Management, A
Surgical Technology/Technologist, A
System Administration/Administrator, A
System, Networking, and LAN/WAN
   Management/Manager, A
Technology Teacher Education/Industrial Arts
   Teacher Education, A
Tourism and Travel Services Management, A
Tourism and Travel Services Marketing
   Operations, A
Tourism Promotion Operations, A
Trade and Industrial Teacher Education, A
Turf and Turfgrass Management, A
Voice and Opera, A
Water, Wetlands, and Marine Resources
   Management, A
Welding Technology/Welder, A
Wildlife and Wildlands Science and Management, A
Wildlife Biology, A
Wind and Percussion Instruments, A
Word Processing, A

IOWA STATE UNIVERSITY OF SCIENCE AND TECHNOLOGY

Accounting, BM
Advertising, B
Aerospace, Aeronautical and Astronautical
   Engineering, BMD
Agricultural Business and Management, B
Agricultural Economics, MD
Agricultural Education, MD
Agricultural Engineering, MD
Agricultural Mechanization, B
Agricultural Sciences, MD
Agricultural Teacher Education, B
Agricultural/Biological Engineering and
   Bioengineering, B
Agriculture, B
Agronomy and Crop Science, B

Agronomy and Soil Sciences, MD
Animal Sciences, BMD
Anthropology, BM
Apparel and Textiles, B
Applied Arts and Design, M
Applied Horticulture/Horticultural Operations, B
Applied Mathematics, MD
Applied Physics, MD
Architecture, BMO
Art Education, M
Art/Art Studies, General, B
Astronomy, MD
Astrophysics, MD
Atmospheric Sciences and Meteorology, B
Biochemistry, BMD
Bioinformatics, MD
Biological and Biomedical Sciences, MD
Biology/Biological Sciences, B
Biophysics, BMD
Biostatistics, MD
Biosystems Engineering, MD
Botany/Plant Biology, B
Business Administration and Management, B
Business Administration, Management and
   Operations, MO
Business, Management, Marketing, and Related
   Support Services, B
Cell Biology and Anatomy, MD
Chemical Engineering, BMD
Chemistry, BMD
Child and Family Studies, MD
City/Urban, Community and Regional Planning, B
Civil Engineering, BMD
Clothing and Textiles, MD
Cognitive Sciences, D
Commercial and Advertising Art, B
Computational Biology, MD
Computer and Information Sciences, B
Computer Engineering, BMD
Computer Science, MD
Condensed Matter Physics, MD
Consumer Economics, MD
Corporate and Organizational Communication, D
Counseling Psychology, D
Counselor Education/School Counseling and
   Guidance Services, M
Curriculum and Instruction, MD
Dairy Science, B
Design and Visual Communications, B
Developmental Biology and Embryology, MD
Dietetics/Dieticians, B
Drama and Dramatics/Theatre Arts, B
Early Childhood Education and Teaching, B
Ecology, BMD
Economics, BMDO
Education, BMD
Educational Administration and Supervision, M
Educational Leadership and Administration, MD
Educational Measurement and Evaluation, M
Educational Media/Instructional Technology, MD
Electrical Engineering, MD
Electrical, Electronics and Communications
   Engineering, B
Elementary Education and Teaching, BM
Engineering, B
Engineering and Applied Sciences, MD
Engineering Science, B
English, MD
English Language and Literature, B
Entomology, BMD
Entrepreneurship/Entrepreneurial Studies, B
Environmental Sciences, MD
Environmental Studies, B
Evolutionary Biology, MD
Exercise and Sports Science, M
Family and Community Services, B
Family and Consumer Economics and Related
   Services, B
Family and Consumer Sciences/Home Economics
   Teacher Education, B
Family and Consumer Sciences/Human
   Sciences, BM
Family Resource Management Studies, B
Farm/Farm and Ranch Management, B
Fashion/Apparel Design, B
Finance, B

Food Science and Technology, MD
Food Technology and Processing, B
Foods, Nutrition, and Wellness Studies, B
Forestry, BMD
Foundations and Philosophy of Education, M
French Language and Literature, B
Genetics, BMD
Geology/Earth Science, BMD
Geosciences, MD
German Language and Literature, B
Graphic Design, BM
Health and Physical Education, B
Health Education, MD
Health Teacher Education, B
Higher Education/Higher Education
    Administration, M
History, BMD
History of Science and Technology, MD
Home Economics, MD
Home Economics Education, MD
Horticultural Science, BMD
Hospitality Administration/Management, MD
Hotel/Motel Administration/Management, B
Human Development, MD
Human Resources Development, M
Human-Computer Interaction, MD
Immunology, MD
Industrial Engineering, B
Industrial/Management Engineering, MD
Information Science/Studies, M
Interdisciplinary Studies, BM
Interior Design, BM
International Agriculture, B
International Business/Trade/Commerce, B
International Relations and Affairs, B
Journalism, BM
Landscape Architecture, BMO
Liberal Arts and Sciences Studies and
    Humanities, B
Linguistics, B
Logistics and Materials Management, B
Management Information Systems and
    Services, BM
Marketing/Marketing Management, B
Marriage and Family Therapy/Counseling, D
Mass Communication/Media Studies, BM
Materials Engineering, BMD
Materials Sciences, MD
Mathematics, BMD
Mathematics Teacher Education, M
Mechanical Engineering, BMD
Mechanics, MD
Medical Illustration/Medical Illustrator, B
Meteorology, MD
Microbiology, BMD
Molecular Biology, MD
Multi-/Interdisciplinary Studies, B
Music, B
Music Teacher Education, B
Natural Resources and Conservation, MD
Natural Resources Management/Development and
    Policy, BMD
Neuroscience, MD
Nutritional Sciences, MD
Operations Management and Supervision, B
Operations Research, M
Ornamental Horticulture, B
Pathology/Experimental Pathology, MD
Philosophy, B
Physical Education Teaching and Coaching, MD
Physics, BMD
Plant Pathology/Phytopathology, MD
Plant Physiology, MD
Plant Protection and Integrated Pest
    Management, B
Political Science and Government, BMO
Pre-Dentistry Studies, B
Pre-Law Studies, B
Pre-Medicine/Pre-Medical Studies, B
Pre-Veterinary Studies, B
Psychology, BMD
Public Administration, BM
Religion/Religious Studies, B
Rhetoric, D
Rural Planning and Studies, D
Rural Sociology, MD

Russian Studies, B
Secondary Education and Teaching, B
Social Psychology, D
Sociology, BMD
Spanish Language and Literature, B
Special Education and Teaching, M
Special Products Marketing Operations, B
Speech and Rhetorical Studies, B
Statistics, BMDO
Structural Biology, MD
Systems Engineering, M
Technical and Business Writing, B
Toxicology, MD
Trade and Industrial Teacher Education, B
Transportation/Transportation Management, M
Urban and Regional Planning, MO
Veterinary Medicine, MP
Veterinary Sciences, MD
Visual and Performing Arts, B
Vocational and Technical Education, MD
Water Resources, MD
Women's Studies, B

IOWA WESLEYAN COLLEGE

Accounting, B
Adult and Continuing Education and Teaching, B
Art Teacher Education, B
Art/Art Studies, General, B
Biological and Physical Sciences, B
Biology/Biological Sciences, B
Business Administration and Management, B
Chemistry, B
Computer Programming/Programmer, B
Computer Science, B
Criminal Justice/Law Enforcement Administration, B
Education, B
Elementary Education and Teaching, B
English Language and Literature, B
Environmental Biology, B
Environmental Health, B
Fine/Studio Arts, B
Graphic Design, B
History, B
Information Science/Studies, B
Kindergarten/PreSchool Education and Teaching, B
Kinesiology and Exercise Science, B
Liberal Arts and Sciences Studies and
    Humanities, B
Mass Communication/Media Studies, B
Mathematics, B
Music, B
Music Teacher Education, B
Natural Sciences, B
Nursing - Registered Nurse Training, B
Philosophy and Religious Studies, B
Physical Education Teaching and Coaching, B
Pre-Dentistry Studies, B
Pre-Law Studies, B
Pre-Medicine/Pre-Medical Studies, B
Pre-Pharmacy Studies, B
Pre-Veterinary Studies, B
Psychology, B
Secondary Education and Teaching, B
Special Education and Teaching, B
Sport and Fitness Administration/Management, B

IOWA WESTERN COMMUNITY COLLEGE

Accounting, A
Administrative Assistant and Secretarial Science, A
Agricultural Business and Management, A
Animal/Livestock Husbandry and Production, A
Architectural Engineering Technology/Technician, A
Automobile/Automotive Mechanics
    Technology/Technician, A
Avionics Maintenance Technology/Technician, A
Building/Home/Construction Inspection/Inspector, A
Business Administration and Management, A
Child Care and Support Services Management, A
Child Care Provider/Assistant, A
Child Development, A
Civil Engineering Technology/Technician, A
Commercial and Advertising Art, A
Computer Programming, A
Computer Programming, Specific Applications, A
Computer Programming/Programmer, A

Consumer Merchandising/Retailing Management, A
Criminal Justice/Law Enforcement Administration, A
Criminal Justice/Police Science, A
Culinary Arts/Chef Training, A
Data Entry/Microcomputer Applications, A
Dental Hygiene/Hygienist, A
Drafting/Design Engineering
    Technologies/Technicians, A
Electrical, Electronic and Communications
    Engineering Technology/Technician, A
Electrical/Electronics Equipment Installation and
    Repair, A
Engineering Technology, A
Farm/Farm and Ranch Management, A
Fashion Merchandising, A
Fire Science/Firefighting, A
Food Technology and Processing, A
Hospitality and Recreation Marketing Operations, A
Hotel/Motel Administration/Management, A
Human Services, A
Industrial Design, A
International Business/Trade/Commerce, A
Journalism, A
Legal Administrative Assistant/Secretary, A
Legal Assistant/Paralegal, A
Liberal Arts and Sciences Studies and
    Humanities, A
Licensed Practical/Vocational Nurse Training, A
Machine Tool Technology/Machinist, A
Management Information Systems and Services, A
Marketing/Marketing Management, A
Mechanical Engineering/Mechanical
    Technology/Technician, A
Medical Administrative Assistant/Secretary, A
Medical/Clinical Assistant, A
Nursing - Registered Nurse Training, A
Sales, Distribution and Marketing Operations, A
Selling Skills and Sales Operations, A
Sign Language Interpretation and Translation, A
Special Products Marketing Operations, A
Speech Teacher Education, A
Substance Abuse/Addiction Counseling, A
Word Processing, A

KAPLAN UNIVERSITY

Accounting, A
Business Administration and Management, AB
Business/Commerce, B
Computer and Information Sciences, AB
Court Reporting/Court Reporter, A
Criminal Justice/Safety Studies, AB
Information Technology, AB
Legal Assistant/Paralegal, AB
Management Information Systems and Services, B
Medical Transcription/Transcriptionist, A
Medical/Clinical Assistant, A
Multi-/Interdisciplinary Studies, A
Tourism and Travel Services Management, A

KIRKWOOD COMMUNITY COLLEGE

Accounting, A
Administrative Assistant and Secretarial Science, A
Agricultural Business and Management, A
Agricultural Teacher Education, A
Agriculture, A
Agronomy and Crop Science, A
Animal Sciences, A
Applied Art, A
Art Teacher Education, A
Art/Art Studies, General, A
Artificial Intelligence and Robotics, A
Automobile/Automotive Mechanics
    Technology/Technician, A
Biological and Physical Sciences, A
Biology Technician/BioTechnology Laboratory
    Technician, A
Biology/Biological Sciences, A
Broadcast Journalism, A
Business Administration and Management, A
Business Teacher Education, A
Ceramic Arts and Ceramics, A
Child Development, A
Communications Technology/Technician, A
Computer Programming/Programmer, A
Computer Science, A
Construction Engineering Technology/Technician, A

Consumer Merchandising/Retailing Management, A
Corrections, A
Criminal Justice/Law Enforcement Administration, A
Criminal Justice/Police Science, A
Culinary Arts/Chef Training, A
Data Processing and Data Processing
 Technology/Technician, A
Developmental and Child Psychology, A
Drafting and Design Technology/Technician, A
Drafting/Design Engineering
 Technologies/Technicians, A
Drama and Dramatics/Theatre Arts, A
Education, A
Electrical, Electronic and Communications
 Engineering Technology/Technician, A
Electromechanical Technology/Electromechanical
 Engineering Technology, A
Elementary Education and Teaching, A
Engineering, A
English Language and Literature, A
Equestrian/Equine Studies, A
Farm/Farm and Ranch Management, A
Fashion Merchandising, A
Fashion/Apparel Design, A
Finance, A
Fire Science/Firefighting, A
Food Technology and Processing, A
Forestry, A
French Language and Literature, A
Graphic and Printing Equipment Operator
 Production, A
Health Information/Medical Records
 Administration/Administrator, A
Heating, Air Conditioning, Ventilation and
 Refrigeration Maintenance
 Technology/Technician, A
History, A
Horticultural Science, A
Hospitality and Recreation Marketing Operations, A
Hotel/Motel Administration/Management, A
Human Services, A
Humanities/Humanistic Studies, A
Hydrology and Water Resources Science, A
Industrial Technology/Technician, A
Interior Design, A
International Business/Trade/Commerce, A
Jazz/Jazz Studies, A
Journalism, A
Kindergarten/PreSchool Education and Teaching, A
Landscape Architecture, A
Law and Legal Studies, A
Legal Administrative Assistant/Secretary, A
Legal Assistant/Paralegal, A
Liberal Arts and Sciences Studies and
 Humanities, A
Licensed Practical/Vocational Nurse Training, A
Management Information Systems and Services, A
Marketing/Marketing Management, A
Mass Communication/Media Studies, A
Mathematics, A
Mechanical Engineering/Mechanical
 Technology/Technician, A
Medical Administrative Assistant/Secretary, A
Medical/Clinical Assistant, A
Music, A
Natural Resources and Conservation, A
Nursing - Registered Nurse Training, A
Occupational Therapy/Therapist, A
Ornamental Horticulture, A
Parks, Recreation and Leisure Facilities
 Management, A
Parks, Recreation, Leisure and Fitness Studies, A
Physical Education Teaching and Coaching, A
Political Science and Government, A
Pre-Engineering, A
Psychology, A
Public Relations/Image Management, A
Radio and Television, A
Respiratory Care Therapy/Therapist, A
Social Sciences, A
Social Work, A
Sociology, A
Spanish Language and Literature, A
Special Products Marketing Operations, A
Teacher Assistant/Aide, A
Telecommunications Technology/Technician, A

Veterinary/Animal Health Technology/Technician and
 Veterinary Assistant, A
Voice and Opera, A
Welding Technology/Welder, A
Wildlife and Wildlands Science and Management, A
Wildlife Biology, A
Wind and Percussion Instruments, A

LORAS COLLEGE

Accounting, B
Art Teacher Education, B
Athletic Training and Sports Medicine, B
Biochemistry, B
Biology/Biological Sciences, B
Business Administration and Management, B
Business/Commerce, B
Chemistry, B
Clinical Laboratory Science/Medical
 Technology/Technologist, B
Clinical Psychology, M
Computer Science, B
Creative Writing, B
Criminal Justice/Safety Studies, B
Economics, B
Education, B
Education/Teaching of Individuals with Emotional
 Disturbances, B
Education/Teaching of Individuals with Mental
 Retardation, B
Educational Administration and Supervision, M
Elementary Education and Teaching, B
Engineering, B
Engineering Physics, B
English Language and Literature, B
Finance, B
Fine/Studio Arts, B
French Language and Literature, B
Health and Physical Education, B
History, B
Human Resources Management/Personnel
 Administration, B
International Business/Trade/Commerce, B
International Relations and Affairs, B
Journalism, B
Kindergarten/PreSchool Education and Teaching, B
Kinesiology and Exercise Science, B
Liberal Arts and Sciences Studies and
 Humanities, AB
Management Information Systems and Services, B
Marketing/Marketing Management, B
Mass Communication/Media Studies, B
Mathematics, B
Music, B
Nuclear Medical Technology/Technologist, B
Pastoral Studies/Counseling, M
Philosophy, B
Physical Education Teaching and Coaching, B
Physical Sciences, B
Physics, B
Political Science and Government, B
Pre-Theology/Pre-Ministerial Studies, B
Psychology, BM
Public Relations/Image Management, B
Religion/Religious Studies, BM
Secondary Education and Teaching, B
Social Work, B
Sociology, B
Spanish Language and Literature, B
Special Education and Teaching, M
Sport and Fitness Administration/Management, B
Theology and Religious Vocations, M
Visual and Performing Arts, B

LUTHER COLLEGE

Accounting, B
African-American/Black Studies, B
Anthropology, B
Art/Art Studies, General, B
Arts Management, B
Athletic Training and Sports Medicine, B
Biology/Biological Sciences, B
Business Administration and Management, B
Chemistry, B
Classics and Classical
 Languages, Literatures, and Linguistics, B

Communication, Journalism and Related
 Programs, B
Computer Science, B
Dance, B
Drama and Dramatics/Theatre Arts, B
Economics, B
Elementary Education and Teaching, B
English Language and Literature, B
French Language and Literature, B
German Language and Literature, B
Health and Physical Education, B
History, B
Interdisciplinary Studies, B
International Relations and Affairs, B
Latin Language and Literature, B
Management Information Systems and Services, B
Mathematics, B
Music, B
Nursing - Registered Nurse Training, B
Philosophy, B
Physical Education Teaching and Coaching, B
Physics, B
Political Science and Government, B
Psychology, B
Religion/Religious Studies, B
Scandinavian Studies, B
Social Work, B
Sociology, B
Spanish Language and Literature, B
Sport and Fitness Administration/Management, B
Statistics, B

MAHARISHI UNIVERSITY OF MANAGEMENT

Asian Studies/Civilization, MD
Ayurvedic Medicine/Ayurveda, B
Business Administration and Management, B
Business Administration, Management and
 Operations, MD
Cinematography and Film/Video Production, B
Computer Science, BM
Education, M
Elementary Education and Teaching, BM
English Language and Literature, B
Environmental Studies, B
Fine/Studio Arts, B
Mathematics, B
Physiology, MD
Secondary Education and Teaching, BM

MARSHALLTOWN COMMUNITY COLLEGE

Accounting, A
Administrative Assistant and Secretarial Science, A
Biological and Physical Sciences, A
Business Administration and Management, A
Child Development, A
Community Organization and Advocacy, A
Computer Science, A
Dental Assisting/Assistant, A
Drafting and Design Technology/Technician, A
Economics, A
Electrical, Electronic and Communications
 Engineering Technology/Technician, A
Heavy Equipment Maintenance
 Technology/Technician, A
Industrial Radiologic Technology/Technician, A
Liberal Arts and Sciences Studies and
 Humanities, A
Licensed Practical/Vocational Nurse Training, A
Machine Tool Technology/Machinist, A
Marketing/Marketing Management, A
Mental Health/Rehabilitation, A
Nursing - Registered Nurse Training, A
Political Science and Government, A
Pre-Engineering, A

MERCY COLLEGE OF HEALTH SCIENCES

Health/Health Care Administration/Management, B
Medical Office Assistant/Specialist, A
Medical Radiologic Technology/Science - Radiation
 Therapist, A
Nursing - Registered Nurse Training, A
Nursing Science, B

Surgical Technology/Technologist, A

MORNINGSIDE COLLEGE

Accounting, B
Art Teacher Education, B
Art/Art Studies, General, B
Biology/Biological Sciences, B
Biopsychology, B
Business Administration and Management, B
Business Teacher Education, B
Business/Corporate Communications, B
Chemistry, B
Clinical Laboratory Science/Medical
    Technology/Technologist, B
Commercial and Advertising Art, B
Comparative Literature, B
Computer Education, M
Computer Science, B
Counseling Psychology, B
Drama and Dramatics/Theatre Arts, B
Education, BM
Elementary Education and Teaching, BM
Engineering Physics, B
English Language and Literature, B
Fine/Studio Arts, B
History, B
Interdisciplinary Studies, B
Management Information Systems and Services, B
Marketing/Marketing Management, B
Mass Communication/Media Studies, B
Mathematics, B
Music, B
Music Teacher Education, B
Nursing - Registered Nurse Training, B
Philosophy, B
Photography, B
Physics, B
Political Science and Government, B
Pre-Dentistry Studies, B
Pre-Law Studies, B
Pre-Medicine/Pre-Medical Studies, B
Pre-Veterinary Studies, B
Psychology, B
Reading Teacher Education, M
Religion/Religious Studies, B
Science Teacher Education/General Science
    Teacher Education, B
Secondary Education and Teaching, B
Spanish Language and Literature, B
Special Education and Teaching, BM

MOUNT MERCY COLLEGE

Accounting, B
Art Teacher Education, B
Art/Art Studies, General, B
Biology/Biological Sciences, B
Business Administration and Management, B
Clinical Laboratory Science/Medical
    Technology/Technologist, B
Communication Studies/Speech Communication
    and Rhetoric, B
Computer and Information Sciences, B
Computer Science, B
Drama and Dramatics/Theatre Arts, B
Education, B
Elementary Education and Teaching, B
English Language and Literature, B
History, B
International Relations and Affairs, B
Junior High/Intermediate/Middle School Education
    and Teaching, B
Marketing/Marketing Management, B
Mathematics, B
Music, B
Music Teacher Education, B
Nursing - Registered Nurse Training, B
Political Science and Government, B
Pre-Dentistry Studies, B
Pre-Law Studies, B
Pre-Medicine/Pre-Medical Studies, B
Pre-Veterinary Studies, B
Psychology, B
Religion/Religious Studies, B
Science Teacher Education/General Science
    Teacher Education, B
Secondary Education and Teaching, B

Social Work, B
Sociology, B
Speech and Rhetorical Studies, B
Urban Studies/Affairs, B
Voice and Opera, B

MUSCATINE COMMUNITY COLLEGE

Accounting, A
Administrative Assistant and Secretarial Science, A
Agricultural Production Operations, A
Agricultural/Farm Supplies Retailing and
    Wholesaling, A
Business Administration and Management, A
Child Care and Support Services Management, A
Computer/Information Technology Services
    Administration and Management, A
Emergency Medical Technology/Technician (EMT
    Paramedic), A
Environmental Engineering
    Technology/Environmental Technology, A
Liberal Arts and Sciences Studies and
    Humanities, A
Licensed Practical/Vocational Nurse Training, A
Machine Tool Technology/Machinist, A
Natural Resources and Conservation, A
Occupational Safety and Health
    Technology/Technician, A
Pharmacy Technician/Assistant, A

NORTH IOWA AREA COMMUNITY COLLEGE

Accounting, A
Accounting Technology/Technician and
    Bookkeeping, A
Administrative Assistant and Secretarial Science, A
Agricultural Business Technology, A
Agricultural Economics, A
Agricultural Production Operations, A
Automobile/Automotive Mechanics
    Technology/Technician, A
Business Administration and Management, A
Carpentry/Carpenter, A
Clinical/Medical Laboratory Technician, A
Computer and Information Sciences, A
Criminal Justice/Police Science, A
Electrical, Electronic and Communications
    Engineering Technology/Technician, A
Emergency Medical Technology/Technician (EMT
    Paramedic), A
Entrepreneurship/Entrepreneurial Studies, A
Fire Services Administration, A
Heating, Air Conditioning, Ventilation and
    Refrigeration Maintenance
    Technology/Technician, A
Industrial Electronics Technology/Technician, A
Liberal Arts and Sciences Studies and
    Humanities, A
Licensed Practical/Vocational Nurse Training, A
Machine Shop Technology/Assistant, A
Machine Tool Technology/Machinist, A
Medical/Clinical Assistant, A
Nurse/Nursing Assistant/Aide and Patient Care
    Assistant, A
Nursing - Registered Nurse Training, A
Physical Therapist Assistant, A
Sport and Fitness Administration/Management, A
Tool and Die Technology/Technician, A
Welding Technology/Welder, A

NORTHEAST IOWA COMMUNITY COLLEGE

Accounting, A
Agricultural Business and Management, A
Clinical/Medical Laboratory Technician, A
Computer Engineering Technology/Technician, A
Construction Engineering Technology/Technician, A
Dairy Science, A
Drafting/Design Engineering
    Technologies/Technicians, A
Electrical, Electronic and Communications
    Engineering Technology/Technician, A
Health Information/Medical Records
    Administration/Administrator, A
Liberal Arts and Sciences Studies and
    Humanities, A
Marketing/Marketing Management, A

Nursing - Registered Nurse Training, A
Trade and Industrial Teacher Education, A

NORTHWEST IOWA COMMUNITY COLLEGE

Accounting, A
Administrative Assistant and Secretarial Science, A
Autobody/Collision and Repair
    Technology/Technician, A
Automobile/Automotive Mechanics
    Technology/Technician, A
Business Administration and Management, A
Computer Programming, A
Computer Programming/Programmer, A
Computer Systems Networking and
    Telecommunications, A
Construction/Heavy Equipment/Earthmoving
    Equipment Operation, A
Diesel Mechanics Technology/Technician, A
Drafting/Design Engineering
    Technologies/Technicians, A
Electrical, Electronic and Communications
    Engineering Technology/Technician, A
Emergency Medical Technology/Technician (EMT
    Paramedic), A
Health Information/Medical Records
    Technology/Technician, A
Industrial Electronics Technology/Technician, A
Liberal Arts and Sciences Studies and
    Humanities, A
Licensed Practical/Vocational Nurse Training, A
Lineworker, A
Machine Shop Technology/Assistant, A
Nursing - Registered Nurse Training, A
Tool and Die Technology/Technician, A
Welding Technology/Welder, A

NORTHWESTERN COLLEGE

Accounting, B
Actuarial Science, B
Agribusiness, B
Art Teacher Education, B
Art/Art Studies, General, B
Athletic Training and Sports Medicine, B
Biology Teacher Education, B
Biology/Biological Sciences, B
Business Administration and Management, B
Business Teacher Education, B
Chemistry, B
Clinical Laboratory Science/Medical
    Technology/Technologist, B
Computer Science, B
Drama and Dramatics/Theatre Arts, B
Economics, B
Elementary Education and Teaching, B
English Language and Literature, B
Environmental Sciences, B
History, B
Humanities/Humanistic Studies, B
Kinesiology and Exercise Science, B
Mass Communication/Media Studies, B
Mathematics, B
Music, B
Music Teacher Education, B
Philosophy, B
Physical Education Teaching and Coaching, B
Political Science and Government, B
Psychology, B
Religion/Religious Studies, B
Religious Education, B
Secondary Education and Teaching, B
Social Work, B
Sociology, B
Spanish Language and Literature, B
Speech and Rhetorical Studies, B
Speech Teacher Education, B
Teacher Education, Multiple Levels, B

PALMER COLLEGE OF CHIROPRACTIC

Anatomy, M
Biological and Physical Sciences, B
Chiropractic, P
Clinical Research, M

Medical/Clinical Assistant, A

ST. AMBROSE UNIVERSITY

Accounting, BM
Advertising, B
Art Teacher Education, B
Art/Art Studies, General, B
Biology Teacher Education, B
Biology/Biological Sciences, B
Business Administration and Management, B
Business Administration, Management and
    Operations, MD
Business Teacher Education, B
Business/Commerce, B
Chemistry, B
Chemistry Teacher Education, B
Computer Science, B
Computer Systems Analysis/Analyst, B
Computer Systems Networking and
    Telecommunications, B
Criminal Justice/Safety Studies, B
Criminology, M
Design and Visual Communications, B
Drama and Dramatics/Theatre Arts, B
Early Childhood Education and Teaching, B
Economics, B
Education, B
Elementary Education and Teaching, B
Engineering Physics, B
English Language and Literature, B
English/Language Arts Teacher Education, B
Finance, B
Fine/Studio Arts, B
Forensic Psychology, B
French Language and Literature, B
French Language Teacher Education, B
German Language and Literature, B
German Language Teacher Education, B
Graphic Design, B
Health and Physical Education, B
Health Services Administration, M
Health Teacher Education, B
History, B
History Teacher Education, B
Industrial Engineering, B
Information Science/Studies, B
International Business/Trade/Commerce, B
Journalism, B
Management, M
Management of Technology, M
Management Science, B
Marketing/Marketing Management, B
Mass Communication/Media Studies, B
Mathematics, B
Mathematics Teacher Education, B
Multi-/Interdisciplinary Studies, B
Music, B
Music Teacher Education, B
Nursing - Registered Nurse Training, B
Occupational Therapy/Therapist, M
Organizational Behavior Studies, B
Organizational Management, M
Pastoral Studies/Counseling, M
Philosophy, B
Physical Education Teaching and Coaching, B
Physical Therapy/Therapist, D
Physics, B
Physics Teacher Education, B
Political Science and Government, B
Psychology, B
Psychology Teacher Education, B
Public Administration, B
Public Relations/Image Management, B
Radio and Television, B
Science Teacher Education/General Science
    Teacher Education, B
Secondary Education and Teaching, B
Security and Protective Services, B
Social Science Teacher Education, B
Social Work, M
Sociology, B
Spanish Language and Literature, B
Spanish Language Teacher Education, B
Special Education and Teaching, M
Speech Teacher Education, B
Sport and Fitness Administration/Management, B

Teacher Education, Multiple Levels, B
Theology/Theological Studies, B

ST. LUKE'S COLLEGE

Nursing - Registered Nurse Training, A
Radiologic Technology/Science - Radiographer, A
Respiratory Care Therapy/Therapist, A

SCOTT COMMUNITY COLLEGE

Accounting, A
Administrative Assistant and Secretarial Science, A
Airline/Commercial/Professional Pilot and Flight
    Crew, A
Autobody/Collision and Repair
    Technology/Technician, A
Automobile/Automotive Mechanics
    Technology/Technician, A
Business Administration and Management, A
Child Care and Support Services Management, A
Clinical/Medical Laboratory Technician, A
Computer and Information Sciences, A
Criminal Justice/Police Science, A
Culinary Arts/Chef Training, A
Diesel Mechanics Technology/Technician, A
Electroneurodiagnostic/Electroencephalographic
    Technology/Technologist, A
Emergency Medical Technology/Technician (EMT
    Paramedic), A
Environmental Engineering
    Technology/Environmental Technology, A
Equestrian/Equine Studies, A
Heating, Air Conditioning, Ventilation and
    Refrigeration Maintenance
    Technology/Technician, A
Interior Design, A
Liberal Arts and Sciences Studies and
    Humanities, A
Licensed Practical/Vocational Nurse Training, A
Machine Tool Technology/Machinist, A
Medical Radiologic Technology/Science - Radiation
    Therapist, A
Nursing - Registered Nurse Training, A
Occupational Safety and Health
    Technology/Technician, A
Occupational Therapist Assistant, A
Pharmacy Technician/Assistant, A
Physical Therapy/Therapist, A
Radio and Television Broadcasting
    Technology/Technician, A
Respiratory Care Therapy/Therapist, A
Sign Language Interpretation and Translation, A

SIMPSON COLLEGE

Accounting, B
Advertising, B
Art Teacher Education, B
Art/Art Studies, General, B
Athletic Training and Sports Medicine, B
Biochemistry, B
Biological and Physical Sciences, B
Biology/Biological Sciences, B
Business Administration and Management, B
Business/Corporate Communications, B
Chemistry, B
Clinical Laboratory Science/Medical
    Technology/Technologist, B
Commercial and Advertising Art, B
Computer Science, B
Criminal Justice/Law Enforcement Administration, B
Drama and Dramatics/Theatre Arts, B
Economics, B
Education, B
Elementary Education and Teaching, B
English Language and Literature, B
Environmental Biology, B
French Language and Literature, B
German Language and Literature, B
History, B
Information Science/Studies, B
International Business/Trade/Commerce, B
International Relations and Affairs, B
Kindergarten/PreSchool Education and Teaching, B
Mass Communication/Media Studies, B
Mathematics, B
Music, B
Music Performance, B

Music Teacher Education, B
Philosophy, B
Physical Education Teaching and Coaching, B
Physical Therapy/Therapist, B
Political Science and Government, B
Pre-Dentistry Studies, B
Pre-Law Studies, B
Pre-Medicine/Pre-Medical Studies, B
Pre-Veterinary Studies, B
Psychology, B
Religion/Religious Studies, B
Secondary Education and Teaching, B
Social Sciences, B
Sociology, B
Spanish Language and Literature, B
Speech and Rhetorical Studies, B
Sport and Fitness Administration/Management, B

SOUTHEASTERN COMMUNITY COLLEGE, NORTH CAMPUS

Accounting, A
Administrative Assistant and Secretarial Science, A
Agricultural Business and Management, A
Agronomy and Crop Science, A
Artificial Intelligence and Robotics, A
Automobile/Automotive Mechanics
    Technology/Technician, A
Biomedical Technology/Technician, A
Business Administration and Management, A
Child Development, A
Computer Programming/Programmer, A
Construction Engineering Technology/Technician, A
Cosmetology/Cosmetologist, A
Criminal Justice/Law Enforcement Administration, A
Drafting and Design Technology/Technician, A
Electrical, Electronic and Communications
    Engineering Technology/Technician, A
Emergency Medical Technology/Technician (EMT
    Paramedic), A
Engineering, A
Industrial Radiologic Technology/Technician, A
Information Science/Studies, A
Liberal Arts and Sciences Studies and
    Humanities, A
Licensed Practical/Vocational Nurse Training, A
Machine Tool Technology/Machinist, A
Mechanical Engineering/Mechanical
    Technology/Technician, A
Medical/Clinical Assistant, A
Nursing - Registered Nurse Training, A
Respiratory Care Therapy/Therapist, A
Substance Abuse/Addiction Counseling, A
Trade and Industrial Teacher Education, A
Welding Technology/Welder, A

SOUTHEASTERN COMMUNITY COLLEGE, SOUTH CAMPUS

Administrative Assistant and Secretarial Science, A
Business Administration and Management, A
Cosmetology/Cosmetologist, A
Criminal Justice/Safety Studies, A
Emergency Medical Technology/Technician (EMT
    Paramedic), A
Information Science/Studies, A
Liberal Arts and Sciences Studies and
    Humanities, A
Licensed Practical/Vocational Nurse Training, A
Medical Administrative Assistant/Secretary, A
Nursing - Registered Nurse Training, A
Substance Abuse/Addiction Counseling, A

SOUTHWESTERN COMMUNITY COLLEGE

Accounting, A
Administrative Assistant and Secretarial Science, A
Agricultural Business and Management, A
Autobody/Collision and Repair
    Technology/Technician, A
Automobile/Automotive Mechanics
    Technology/Technician, A
Business Administration and Management, A
Carpentry/Carpenter, A
Computer Programming/Programmer, A
Consumer Merchandising/Retailing Management, A
Drafting and Design Technology/Technician, A

Electromechanical Technology/Electromechanical
  Engineering Technology, A
Liberal Arts and Sciences Studies and
  Humanities, A
Licensed Practical/Vocational Nurse Training, A
Marketing/Marketing Management, A
Music, A

UNIVERSITY OF DUBUQUE

Accounting, AB
Airline/Commercial/Professional Pilot and Flight
  Crew, AB
Animation, Interactive Technology, Video Graphics
  and Special Effects, B
Aviation/Airway Management and Operations, AB
Biological and Physical Sciences, B
Biology Teacher Education, B
Biology/Biological Sciences, AB
Business Administration and Management, AB
Business Administration, Management and
  Operations, M
Communication and Media Studies, M
Computer and Information Sciences, B
Computer Graphics, B
Computer Science, AB
Criminal Justice/Law Enforcement Administration, B
Elementary Education and Teaching, B
English Language and Literature, AB
English/Language Arts Teacher Education, B
Environmental Biology, B
Environmental Sciences, B
Environmental Studies, AB
Mass Communication/Media Studies, AB
Nursing - Registered Nurse Training, B
Parks, Recreation, Leisure and Fitness Studies, B
Philosophy, B
Physical Education Teaching and Coaching, B
Professional Studies, B
Psychology, B
Religion/Religious Studies, B
Secondary Education and Teaching, B
Sociology, AB
Speech and Rhetorical Studies, B
Theology and Religious Vocations, MDP
Theology/Theological Studies, B
Web Page, Digital/Multimedia and Information
  Resources Design, B
Web/Multimedia Management and Webmaster, B

THE UNIVERSITY OF IOWA

Accounting, BMDO
Actuarial Science, BMD
African Studies, B
African-American/Black Studies, BM
Air Force JROTC/ROTC, B
Allopathic Medicine, PO
American Indian/Native American Studies, B
American Sign Language, B
American/United States Studies/Civilization, BMD
Anatomy, D
Ancient Studies/Civilization, B
Ancient/Classical Greek Language and Literature, B
Anthropology, BMD
Applied Mathematics, BD
Army JROTC/ROTC, B
Art Education, MD
Art History, Criticism and Conservation, BMD
Art Teacher Education, B
Art/Art Studies, General, B
Arts Management, B
Asian Studies/Civilization, BM
Astronomy, BM
Athletic Training and Sports Medicine, B
Audiology/Audiologist and Hearing Sciences, B
Audiology/Audiologist and Speech-Language
  Pathology/Pathologist, B
Bacteriology, MD
Biochemical Engineering, MD
Biochemistry, BMDO
Biological and Biomedical Sciences, MDO
Biological Anthropology, MDO
Biology Teacher Education, B
Biology/Biological Sciences, B
Biomedical Engineering, MD
Biomedical/Medical Engineering, B
Biophysics, MD

Biostatistics, MD
Business Administration and Management, B
Business Administration, Management and
  Operations, MDO
Business/Managerial Economics, B
Cell Biology and Anatomy, D
Ceramic Arts and Ceramics, B
Chemical Engineering, BMD
Chemistry, BMDO
Chemistry Teacher Education, B
Chinese Language and Literature, B
Cinematography and Film/Video Production, B
Civil Engineering, BMD
Classics and Classical
  Languages, Literatures, and Linguistics, BMD
Clinical Laboratory Science/Medical
  Technology/Technologist, B
Clinical Laboratory Sciences, MD
Clinical Research, O
Communication and Media Studies, MD
Communication Disorders, MD
Communication Studies/Speech Communication
  and Rhetoric, B
Communication Theory, MD
Community Health and Preventive Medicine, MD
Comparative Literature, BMD
Computational Sciences, D
Computer and Information Sciences, B
Computer Engineering, MD
Computer Science, BMD
Counseling Psychology, D
Counselor Education/School Counseling and
  Guidance Services, MD
Curriculum and Instruction, MD
Dance, BM
Dental and Oral Surgery, MO
Dentistry, MDPO
Developmental Education, M
Drama and Dance Teacher Education, B
Drama and Dramatics/Theatre Arts, B
Drawing, B
Early Childhood Education and Teaching, MD
Economics, BD
Education, MDO
Educational Administration and Supervision, MDO
Educational Measurement and Evaluation, MD
Educational Psychology, MD
Electrical Engineering, MD
Electrical, Electronics and Communications
  Engineering, B
Elementary Education and Teaching, BMD
Engineering, B
Engineering and Applied Sciences, MD
English, MDO
English Education, MD
English Language and Literature, B
Entrepreneurship/Entrepreneurial Studies, BM
Environmental and Occupational Health, MDO
Environmental Engineering
  Technology/Environmental Technology, MD
Environmental Sciences, B
Environmental Studies, B
Epidemiology, MDO
Ergonomics and Human Factors, MD
Exercise and Sports Science, MD
Film, Television, and Video Production, M
Film, Television, and Video Theory and
  Criticism, MD
Film/Cinema Studies, B
Film/Video and Photographic Arts, B
Finance, B
Finance and Banking, MD
Fine Arts and Art Studies, M
Fine/Studio Arts, B
Foreign Language Teacher Education, MD
Foundations and Philosophy of Education, MDO
French Language and Literature, BMD
French Language Teacher Education, B
Genetics, MDO
Geography, BMD
Geography Teacher Education, B
Geology/Earth Science, B
Geosciences, MD
German Language and Literature, BMD
German Language Teacher Education, B
Health Services Administration, MDO

Higher Education/Higher Education
  Administration, MDO
History, BMD
History Teacher Education, B
Human Resources Management/Personnel
  Administration, B
Immunology, MDO
Industrial and Manufacturing Management, M
Industrial Engineering, B
Industrial/Management Engineering, MD
Information Science/Studies, MO
Interdisciplinary Studies, B
International Development, M
International/Global Studies, B
Investment Management, M
Italian Language and Literature, B
Japanese Language and Literature, B
Jazz/Jazz Studies, B
Journalism, BMO
Kinesiology and Exercise Science, B
Labor and Industrial Relations, B
Latin American Studies, B
Latin Language and Literature, B
Latin Teacher Education, B
Law and Legal Studies, MPO
Leisure Studies, M
Liberal Arts and Sciences Studies and
  Humanities, B
Library Science, MO
Linguistics, BMD
Management, D
Management Information Systems and
  Services, BM
Management Science, B
Management Sciences and Quantitative Methods, B
Management Strategy and Policy, M
Manufacturing Engineering, MD
Marketing, BMD
Marketing/Marketing Management, B
Mass Communication/Media Studies, BMDO
Mathematics, BMD
Mathematics Teacher Education, BMD
Mechanical Engineering, BMD
Medieval and Renaissance Studies, B
Metal and Jewelry Arts, B
Microbiology, BMD
Modern Greek Language and Literature, B
Molecular Biology, DO
Museology/Museum Studies, B
Music, BMD
Music Management and Merchandising, B
Music Teacher Education, BMD
Music Theory and Composition, B
Music Therapy/Therapist, B
Neurobiology and Neurophysiology, D
Neuroscience, DO
Non-Profit/Public/Organizational Management, M
Nuclear Medical Technology/Technologist, B
Nursing, MDO
Nursing - Registered Nurse Training, B
Operations Research, MD
Oral and Dental Sciences, MDO
Organizational Management, M
Orthodontics, MO
Painting, B
Parks, Recreation, Leisure and Fitness Studies, B
Pathology/Experimental Pathology, M
Pedodontics, O
Periodontics, MO
Pharmacology, MD
Pharmacy, BMDO
Philosophy, BMD
Photography, B
Physical Education Teaching and Coaching, MD
Physical Therapy/Therapist, MD
Physician Assistant, M
Physics, BMD
Physics Teacher Education, B
Physiology, MD
Piano and Organ, B
Political Science and Government, BMDO
Portuguese Language and Literature, B
Pre-Dentistry Studies, B
Pre-Law Studies, B
Pre-Medicine/Pre-Medical Studies, B
Pre-Pharmacy Studies, B

Pre-Veterinary Studies, B
Printmaking, B
Psychology, BMDO
Public Health, MDO
Radiation Biology/Radiobiology, MD
Radiologic Technology/Science - Radiographer, B
Rehabilitation Counseling, MD
Rehabilitation Sciences, MD
Religion/Religious Studies, BMDO
Rhetoric, MD
Russian Language and Literature, B
Russian Studies, B
School Psychology, DO
Science Teacher Education/General Science
    Teacher Education, BMD
Sculpture, B
Secondary Education and Teaching, BMD
Social Studies Teacher Education, BMD
Social Work, BMDO
Sociology, BMDO
Spanish Language and Literature, BMDO
Spanish Language Teacher Education, B
Special Education and Teaching, MD
Speech and Rhetorical Studies, B
Speech Teacher Education, B
Sport and Fitness Administration/Management, BM
Sport Psychology, MD
Statistics, BMD
Student Personnel Services, D
Teaching English as a Second or Foreign
    Language/ESL Language Instructor, B
Theater, M
Theatre/Theatre Arts Management, B
Therapeutic Recreation, M
Therapeutic Recreation/Recreational Therapy, B
Translation and Interpretation, M
Urban and Regional Planning, MO
Violin, Viola, Guitar and Other Stringed
    Instruments, B
Virology, MD
Voice and Opera, B
Wind and Percussion Instruments, B
Women's Studies, BD
Writing, M

UNIVERSITY OF NORTHERN IOWA

Accounting, BM
Acting, B
Actuarial Science, B
American/United States Studies/Civilization, B
Anthropology, B
Apparel and Textiles, B
Applied Economics, B
Applied Mathematics, B
Art Education, M
Art History, Criticism and Conservation, B
Art Teacher Education, B
Art/Art Studies, General, B
Asian Studies/Civilization, B
Athletic Training and Sports Medicine, B
Biochemistry, B
Bioinformatics, B
Biological and Biomedical Sciences, M
Biological and Physical Sciences, B
Biology/Biological Sciences, B
BioTechnology, B
Broadcast Journalism, B
Business Administration and Management, B
Business Administration, Management and
    Operations, M
Business Teacher Education, B
Chemistry, BM
Communication and Media Studies, M
Communication Disorders, M
Communication Studies/Speech Communication
    and Rhetoric, B
Community Health Services/Liaison/Counseling, B
Composition, M
Computer and Information Sciences, B
Computer and Information Sciences and Support
    Services, B
Computer Science, BM
Construction Management, B
Counselor Education/School Counseling and
    Guidance Services, MD
Criminology, B

Curriculum and Instruction, MD
Digital Communication and Media/Multimedia, B
Drama and Dramatics/Theatre Arts, B
Driver and Safety Teacher Education, B
Early Childhood Education and Teaching, M
Ecology, B
Economics, B
Education, MDO
Education/Teaching of Individuals in Early Childhood
    Special Education Programs, B
Education/Teaching of Individuals with Mental
    Retardation, B
Education/Teaching of Individuals with Multiple
    Disabilities, B
Educational Administration and Supervision, MD
Educational Media/Instructional Technology, M
Educational Psychology, MO
Electromechanical Technology/Electromechanical
    Engineering Technology, B
Elementary Education and Teaching, BM
Engineering Physics, B
English, M
English as a Second Language, M
English Language and Literature, B
Environmental Sciences, BM
European Studies/Civilization, B
Family and Community Services, B
Family and Consumer Economics and Related
    Services, B
Finance, B
Fine Arts and Art Studies, M
Fine/Studio Arts, B
Foods, Nutrition, and Wellness Studies, B
Foreign Language Teacher Education, B
Foreign Languages and Literatures, B
Foreign Languages, Literatures, and Linguistics, B
French Language and Literature, BM
Geography, BM
Geological and Earth Sciences/Geosciences, B
Geology/Earth Science, B
German Language and Literature, BM
Gerontology, B
Graphic Communications, B
Health and Physical Education, B
Health Education, M
Health Professions and Related Clinical Sciences, B
Health Teacher Education, B
Higher Education/Higher Education
    Administration, M
History, BM
Housing and Human Environments, B
Humanities/Humanistic Studies, B
Industrial Education, MD
Industrial Technology/Technician, B
Interior Design, B
Junior High/Intermediate/Middle School Education
    and Teaching, B
Kindergarten/PreSchool Education and Teaching, B
Latin American Studies, B
Leisure Studies, MD
Liberal Arts and Sciences Studies and
    Humanities, B
Management Information Systems and Services, B
Manufacturing Technology/Technician, B
Marketing/Marketing Management, B
Mathematics, BM
Mathematics Teacher Education, BM
Microbiology, B
Middle School Education, M
Music, BM
Music History, Literature, and Theory, M
Music Performance, B
Music Teacher Education, BM
Music Theory and Composition, B
Organizational Communication, B
Parks, Recreation, Leisure and Fitness Studies, B
Performance, M
Philosophy, B
Physical Education Teaching and Coaching, BM
Physics, B
Political Science and Government, B
Psychology, BM
Public Administration, B
Public Policy Analysis, M
Public Relations/Image Management, B
Radio and Television, B

Reading Teacher Education, BM
Real Estate, B
Religion/Religious Studies, B
Russian Language and Literature, B
Russian Studies, B
School Psychology, O
Science Teacher Education/General Science
    Teacher Education, BMO
Social Science Teacher Education, B
Social Studies Teacher Education, B
Social Work, BM
Sociology, BM
Spanish Language and Literature, BM
Special Education and Teaching, BMD
Speech and Rhetorical Studies, B
Speech Teacher Education, B
Speech-Language Pathology/Pathologist, B
Sport and Fitness Administration/Management, M
Student Personnel Services, M
System, Networking, and LAN/WAN
    Management/Manager, B
Teaching English as a Second or Foreign
    Language/ESL Language Instructor, B
Technical Theatre/Theatre Design and
    Technology, B
Technology Teacher Education/Industrial Arts
    Teacher Education, B
Theatre Literature, History and Criticism, B
Women's Studies, M

UPPER IOWA UNIVERSITY

Accounting, BM
Agricultural Business and Management, B
Art Teacher Education, B
Art/Art Studies, General, B
Arts Management, B
Athletic Training and Sports Medicine, B
Biological and Physical Sciences, B
Biology/Biological Sciences, B
Business Administration and Management, AB
Business Administration, Management and
    Operations, M
Business Teacher Education, B
Chemistry, B
Commercial and Advertising Art, B
Criminology, BM
Education, B
Elementary Education and Teaching, B
English Language and Literature, B
Environmental Sciences, B
Finance and Banking, M
Health/Health Care Administration/Management, B
Human Resources Management and Services, M
Human Services, BM
International Business/Trade/Commerce, M
Kinesiology and Exercise Science, B
Liberal Arts and Sciences Studies and
    Humanities, A
Management Information Systems and Services, B
Marketing/Marketing Management, B
Mass Communication/Media Studies, B
Mathematics, B
Natural Resources and Conservation, B
Organizational Management, M
Parks, Recreation, Leisure and Fitness Studies, B
Physical Education Teaching and Coaching, B
Pre-Dentistry Studies, B
Pre-Medicine/Pre-Medical Studies, B
Pre-Veterinary Studies, B
Psychology, B
Public Administration, BM
Quality Management, M
Reading Teacher Education, B
Science Teacher Education/General Science
    Teacher Education, B
Social Science Teacher Education, B
Social Sciences, B
Sociology, B
Trade and Industrial Teacher Education, B

VATTEROTT COLLEGE

CAD/CADD Drafting and/or Design
    Technology/Technician, A
Computer Technology/Computer Systems
    Technology, AB
Dental Assisting/Assistant, A

Medical Office Management/Administration, A
Medical/Clinical Assistant, A

VENNARD COLLEGE

Bible/Biblical Studies, B
Business Administration and Management, B
Christian Studies, AB
Communications Technology/Technician, A
Computer/Information Technology Services
  Administration and Management, A
Elementary Education and Teaching, AB
General Studies, A
Missions/Missionary Studies and Missiology, B
Multi-/Interdisciplinary Studies, B
Pastoral Counseling and Specialized Ministries, B
Pastoral Studies/Counseling, B
Psychology, B
Religion/Religious Studies, AB
Religious Education, B
Religious/Sacred Music, A
Secondary Education and Teaching, AB
Theology/Theological Studies, B
Youth Ministry, B

WALDORF COLLEGE

Art Teacher Education, B
Broadcast Journalism, B
Business Administration and Management, B
Chemical Engineering, B
Cinematography and Film/Video Production, B
Creative Writing, B
Drama and Dance Teacher Education, B
Drama and Dramatics/Theatre Arts, B
Early Childhood Education and Teaching, B
Education, B
Elementary Education and Teaching, B
English Language and Literature, B
English/Language Arts Teacher Education, B
Finance, B
Health Teacher Education, B
History, B
Humanities/Humanistic Studies, B
Information Science/Studies, B
Journalism, B
Junior High/Intermediate/Middle School Education
  and Teaching, B
Kindergarten/PreSchool Education and Teaching, B
Marketing/Marketing Management, B
Mass Communication/Media Studies, B
Music Management and Merchandising, B
Music Performance, B
Music Teacher Education, B
Physical Education Teaching and Coaching, B
Psychology, B
Public Health (MPH, DPH), B
Social Studies Teacher Education, B

WARTBURG COLLEGE

Accounting, B
Art Teacher Education, B
Art/Art Studies, General, B
Arts Management, B
Biochemistry, B
Biology/Biological Sciences, B
Broadcast Journalism, B
Business Administration and Management, B
Chemistry, B
Clinical Laboratory Science/Medical
  Technology/Technologist, B
Commercial and Advertising Art, B
Computer Science, B
Economics, B
Elementary Education and Teaching, B
Engineering, B
English Composition, B
English Language and Literature, B
Finance, B
French Language and Literature, B
German Language and Literature, B
History, B
History Teacher Education, B
Information Science/Studies, B
International Business/Trade/Commerce, B
International Relations and Affairs, B
Journalism, B
Kindergarten/PreSchool Education and Teaching, B

Marketing/Marketing Management, B
Mass Communication/Media Studies, B
Mathematics, B
Mathematics Teacher Education, B
Music, B
Music Performance, B
Music Teacher Education, B
Music Theory and Composition, B
Music Therapy/Therapist, B
Occupational Therapy/Therapist, B
Philosophy, B
Physical Education Teaching and Coaching, B
Physics, B
Political Science and Government, B
Psychology, B
Public Relations/Image Management, B
Religion/Religious Studies, B
Religious/Sacred Music, B
Secondary Education and Teaching, B
Social Science Teacher Education, B
Social Work, B
Sociology, B
Spanish Language and Literature, B
Speech Teacher Education, B
Sport and Fitness Administration/Management, B

WESTERN IOWA TECH COMMUNITY COLLEGE

Agricultural/Farm Supplies Retailing and
  Wholesaling, A
Architectural Engineering Technology/Technician, A
Autobody/Collision and Repair
  Technology/Technician, A
Automobile/Automotive Mechanics
  Technology/Technician, A
Biomedical Technology/Technician, A
Business Administration and Management, A
Child Care and Support Services Management, A
Clinical/Medical Laboratory Technician, A
Computer Programming, Specific Applications, A
Computer Typography and Composition Equipment
  Operator, A
Criminal Justice/Law Enforcement Administration, A
Diesel Mechanics Technology/Technician, A
Electrical, Electronic and Communications
  Engineering Technology/Technician, A
Emergency Medical Technology/Technician (EMT
  Paramedic), A
Executive Assistant/Executive Secretary, A
Heating, Air Conditioning, Ventilation and
  Refrigeration Maintenance
  Technology/Technician, A
Legal Administrative Assistant/Secretary, A
Liberal Arts and Sciences Studies and
  Humanities, A
Machine Tool Technology/Machinist, A
Medical Administrative Assistant/Secretary, A
Nurse/Nursing Assistant/Aide and Patient Care
  Assistant, A
Nursing - Registered Nurse Training, A
Occupational Therapist Assistant, A
Physical Therapist Assistant, A
Tool and Die Technology/Technician, A
Turf and Turfgrass Management, A

WILLIAM PENN UNIVERSITY

Accounting, B
Biology/Biological Sciences, B
Business Administration and Management, B
Business Teacher Education, B
Communication Studies/Speech Communication
  and Rhetoric, B
Computer Science, B
Criminology, B
Driver and Safety Teacher Education, B
Education, B
Elementary Education and Teaching, B
Engineering Technology, B
English/Language Arts Teacher Education, B
Environmental Biology, B
Health and Physical Education, B
Health Teacher Education, B
History, B
Human Services, B
Industrial Technology/Technician, B
Journalism, B

Mass Communication/Media Studies, B
Mathematics Teacher Education, B
Mechanical Engineering, B
Parks, Recreation, Leisure and Fitness Studies, B
Physical Education Teaching and Coaching, B
Political Science and Government, B
Pre-Dentistry Studies, B
Pre-Law Studies, B
Pre-Medicine/Pre-Medical Studies, B
Psychology, B
Public Relations/Image Management, B
Reading Teacher Education, B
Science Teacher Education/General Science
  Teacher Education, B
Secondary Education and Teaching, B
Social Science Teacher Education, B
Sociology, B
Special Education and Teaching, B
Sport and Fitness Administration/Management, B
Teaching English as a Second or Foreign
  Language/ESL Language Instructor, B
Technology Education/Industrial Arts, B

Kansas

ALLEN COUNTY COMMUNITY COLLEGE

Accounting, A
Administrative Assistant and Secretarial Science, A
Agricultural Production Operations, A
Architecture, A
Art/Art Studies, General, A
Athletic Training and Sports Medicine, A
Banking and Financial Support Services, A
Biology/Biological Sciences, A
Business Administration and Management, A
Business Teacher Education, A
Business/Commerce, A
Chemistry, A
Child Development, A
Computer Science, A
Computer Systems Networking and
  Telecommunications, A
Criminal Justice/Law Enforcement Administration, A
Data Processing and Data Processing
  Technology/Technician, A
Drafting and Design Technology/Technician, A
Drama and Dramatics/Theatre Arts, A
Economics, A
Electrical, Electronic and Communications
  Engineering Technology/Technician, A
Electrical, Electronics and Communications
  Engineering, A
Elementary Education and Teaching, A
Emergency Medical Technology/Technician (EMT
  Paramedic), A
Engineering, A
Engineering Technology, A
English Composition, A
Equestrian/Equine Studies, A
Family and Consumer Sciences/Human Sciences, A
Farm/Farm and Ranch Management, A
Forestry, A
Funeral Service and Mortuary Science, A
General Studies, A
Geography, A
Health Aide, A
Health and Physical Education, A
History, A
Home Health Aide/Home Attendant, A
Hospital and Health Care Facilities
  Administration/Management, A
Humanities/Humanistic Studies, A
Industrial Technology/Technician, A
Information Science/Studies, A
Journalism, A
Language Interpretation and Translation, A
Library Science, A
Mathematics, A
Music, A
Nuclear/Nuclear Power Technology/Technician, A
Nurse/Nursing Assistant/Aide and Patient Care
  Assistant, A
Parks, Recreation and Leisure Facilities
  Management, A

Philosophy, A
Physical Therapy/Therapist, A
Physics, A
Political Science and Government, A
Pre-Dentistry Studies, A
Pre-Law Studies, A
Pre-Medicine/Pre-Medical Studies, A
Pre-Pharmacy Studies, A
Pre-Veterinary Studies, A
Psychology, A
Religion/Religious Studies, A
Secondary Education and Teaching, A
Social Work, A
Sociology, A
Speech and Rhetorical Studies, A
Technology Education/Industrial Arts, A
Technology Teacher Education/Industrial Arts
   Teacher Education, A
Wood Science and Wood Products/Pulp and Paper
   Technology, A

BAKER UNIVERSITY

Accounting, B
Art History, Criticism and Conservation, B
Art Teacher Education, B
Biology/Biological Sciences, B
Business Administration, Management and
   Operations, M
Business/Commerce, B
Chemistry, B
Communication Studies/Speech Communication
   and Rhetoric, B
Computer Science, B
Drama and Dramatics/Theatre Arts, B
Economics, B
Education, M
Elementary Education and Teaching, B
English Language and Literature, B
Fine/Studio Arts, B
French Language and Literature, B
German Language and Literature, B
Health and Physical Education, B
History, B
Information Science/Studies, B
International Business/Trade/Commerce, B
International/Global Studies, B
Kinesiology and Exercise Science, B
Liberal Studies, M
Mass Communication/Media Studies, B
Mathematics, B
Molecular Biology, B
Music, B
Music Teacher Education, B
Nursing - Registered Nurse Training, B
Philosophy, B
Physics, B
Political Science and Government, B
Psychology, B
Religion/Religious Studies, B
Secondary Education and Teaching, B
Sociology, B
Spanish Language and Literature, B
Teacher Education and Professional
   Development, Specific Subject Areas, B
Wildlife Biology, B

BARCLAY COLLEGE

Bible/Biblical Studies, AB
Business Administration and Management, B
Divinity/Ministry (BD, MDiv.), B
Elementary Education and Teaching, B
General Studies, A
Pastoral Studies/Counseling, B
Psychology, B
Religious Education, B
Religious/Sacred Music, B

BARTON COUNTY COMMUNITY COLLEGE

Accounting, A
Administrative Assistant and Secretarial Science, A
Agricultural Business and Management, A
Agriculture, A
Anthropology, A
Architecture, A
Art/Art Studies, General, A

Athletic Training and Sports Medicine, A
Automobile/Automotive Mechanics
   Technology/Technician, A
Banking and Financial Support Services, A
Biology/Biological Sciences, A
Business Administration and Management, A
Chemistry, A
Child Care and Support Services Management, A
Chiropractic, A
Clinical/Medical Laboratory Technician, A
Communication Studies/Speech Communication
   and Rhetoric, A
Computer Programming, Specific Applications, A
Computer Science, A
Computer Systems Networking and
   Telecommunications, A
Computer/Information Technology Services
   Administration and Management, A
Criminal Justice/Police Science, A
Crop Production, A
CytoTechnology/Cytotechnologist, A
Dance, A
Dental Hygiene/Hygienist, A
Dietician Assistant, A
Drama and Dramatics/Theatre Arts, A
Early Childhood Education and Teaching, A
Economics, A
Elementary Education and Teaching, A
Emergency Medical Technology/Technician (EMT
   Paramedic), A
Engineering Technology, A
English Language and Literature, A
Fire Science/Firefighting, A
Forestry, A
Funeral Service and Mortuary Science, A
General Studies, A
Geology/Earth Science, A
Graphic Design, A
Hazardous Materials Management and Waste
   Technology/Technician, A
Health Information/Medical Records
   Administration/Administrator, A
History, A
Home Health Aide/Home Attendant, A
Human Resources Management and Services, A
Information Science/Studies, A
Journalism, A
Kinesiology and Exercise Science, A
Liberal Arts and Sciences Studies and
   Humanities, A
Livestock Management, A
Marketing/Marketing Management, A
Mathematics, A
Medical Administrative Assistant/Secretary, A
Medical/Clinical Assistant, A
Military Studies, A
Modern Languages, A
Music, A
Nursing - Registered Nurse Training, A
Occupational Therapy/Therapist, A
Optometric Technician/Assistant, A
Pharmacy, A
Philosophy, A
Physical Education Teaching and Coaching, A
Physical Sciences, A
Physical Therapist Assistant, A
Physical Therapy/Therapist, A
Physician Assistant, A
Physics, A
Political Science and Government, A
Pre-Dentistry Studies, A
Pre-Engineering, A
Pre-Law Studies, A
Pre-Medicine/Pre-Medical Studies, A
Pre-Veterinary Studies, A
Psychology, A
Public Administration, A
Radiologic Technology/Science - Radiographer, A
Religion/Religious Studies, A
Respiratory Care Therapy/Therapist, A
Secondary Education and Teaching, A
Social Work, A
Sociology, A
Sport and Fitness Administration/Management, A

Wildlife and Wildlands Science and Management, A

BENEDICTINE COLLEGE

Accounting, B
Art/Art Studies, General, B
Arts Management, B
Astronomy, B
Athletic Training and Sports Medicine, B
Biochemistry, B
Biology/Biological Sciences, B
Business Administration and Management, B
Business Administration, Management and
   Operations, M
Chemistry, B
Computer Science, B
Drama and Dramatics/Theatre Arts, B
Economics, B
Educational Administration and Supervision, M
Elementary Education and Teaching, B
English Language and Literature, B
French Language and Literature, B
History, B
Liberal Arts and Sciences Studies and
   Humanities, B
Mass Communication/Media Studies, B
Mathematics, B
Music, B
Music Teacher Education, B
Natural Sciences, B
Philosophy, B
Physical Education Teaching and Coaching, B
Physics, B
Political Science and Government, B
Psychology, B
Religion/Religious Studies, B
Secondary Education and Teaching, B
Social Sciences, B
Sociology, B
Spanish Language and Literature, B
Special Education and Teaching, B
Youth Ministry, B

BETHANY COLLEGE

Accounting, B
Art Teacher Education, B
Art/Art Studies, General, B
Arts Management, B
Athletic Training and Sports Medicine, B
Biology Teacher Education, B
Biology/Biological Sciences, B
Business Administration and Management, B
Business Teacher Education, B
Business/Managerial Economics, B
Ceramic Arts and Ceramics, B
Chemistry, B
Chemistry Teacher Education, B
Christian Studies, B
Communication Studies/Speech Communication
   and Rhetoric, B
Criminal Justice/Safety Studies, B
Drawing, B
Education, B
Elementary Education and Teaching, B
English Language and Literature, B
English/Language Arts Teacher Education, B
Financial Planning and Services, B
History, B
International Business/Trade/Commerce, B
Legal Professions and Studies, B
Mathematics, B
Mathematics Teacher Education, B
Music, B
Music Teacher Education, B
Painting, B
Parks, Recreation, Leisure and Fitness Studies, B
Philosophy, B
Physical Education Teaching and Coaching, B
Political Science and Government, B
Psychology, B
Religion/Religious Studies, B
Sculpture, B
Social Studies Teacher Education, B
Social Work, B
Sociology, B

Sport and Fitness Administration/Management, B

BETHEL COLLEGE

Athletic Training and Sports Medicine, B
Biology/Biological Sciences, B
Business/Commerce, B
Chemistry, B
Computer Science, B
Criminology, B
Drama and Dramatics/Theatre Arts, B
Elementary Education and Teaching, B
English Language and Literature, B
Fine/Studio Arts, B
Germanic Languages, Literatures, and Linguistics, B
Health and Physical Education, B
History, B
Management Information Systems and Services, B
Mass Communication/Media Studies, B
Mathematics, B
Music, B
Natural Sciences, B
Nursing - Registered Nurse Training, B
Peace Studies and Conflict Resolution, B
Physics, B
Psychology, B
Religion/Religious Studies, B
Social Sciences, B
Social Work, B
Spanish Language and Literature, B
Visual and Performing Arts, B

BROWN MACKIE COLLEGE-KANSAS CITY

Accounting, A
Business Administration and Management, A
Computer Programming, A
Computer Typography and Composition Equipment Operator, A
Data Entry/Microcomputer Applications, A
Dental Hygiene/Hygienist, A
Health Information/Medical Records Administration/Administrator, A
Health Unit Coordinator/Ward Clerk, A
Health Unit Manager/Ward Supervisor, A
Information Technology, A
Legal Assistant/Paralegal, A
Management Information Systems and Services, A
Medical Administrative Assistant/Secretary, A
Medical/Clinical Assistant, A
System Administration/Administrator, A

BROWN MACKIE COLLEGE-SALINA

Accounting, A
Business Administration and Management, A
Computer and Information Sciences, A
Criminal Justice/Law Enforcement Administration, A
Legal Assistant/Paralegal, A
Medical Office Management/Administration, A
Medical Transcription/Transcriptionist, A

BUTLER COMMUNITY COLLEGE

Accounting, A
Administrative Assistant and Secretarial Science, A
Agricultural Business and Management, A
Art/Art Studies, General, A
Automobile/Automotive Mechanics Technology/Technician, A
Biology/Biological Sciences, A
Business Administration and Management, A
Chemistry, A
Child Development, A
Computer and Information Sciences, A
Computer Science, A
Criminal Justice/Police Science, A
Data Processing and Data Processing Technology/Technician, A
Drafting and Design Technology/Technician, A
Drama and Dramatics/Theatre Arts, A
Electrical, Electronic and Communications Engineering Technology/Technician, A
English Language and Literature, A
Farm/Farm and Ranch Management, A
Fire Science/Firefighting, A
Health Information/Medical Records Administration/Administrator, A

History, A
Hotel/Motel Administration/Management, A
Journalism, A
Kindergarten/PreSchool Education and Teaching, A
Liberal Arts and Sciences Studies and Humanities, A
Marketing/Marketing Management, A
Mass Communication/Media Studies, A
Mathematics, A
Medical Administrative Assistant/Secretary, A
Music, A
Music Performance, A
Nursing - Registered Nurse Training, A
Physical Education Teaching and Coaching, A
Physical Therapy/Therapist, A
Physics, A
Political Science and Government, A
Pre-Engineering, A
Psychology, A
Sociology, A
Substance Abuse/Addiction Counseling, A
Welding Technology/Welder, A

CENTRAL CHRISTIAN COLLEGE OF KANSAS

Accounting, B
Accounting and Business/Management, AB
Acting, A
Agricultural Business and Management, A
Airline/Commercial/Professional Pilot and Flight Crew, A
Architecture, A
Art Teacher Education, A
Art/Art Studies, General, A
Athletic Training and Sports Medicine, A
Bible/Biblical Studies, B
Biological and Physical Sciences, A
Biology Teacher Education, A
Business Administration and Management, AB
Business Teacher Education, A
Business/Commerce, B
Business/Corporate Communications, A
Business/Managerial Economics, A
Business/Office Automation/Technology/Data Entry, A
Chemistry Teacher Education, A
Communication Studies/Speech Communication and Rhetoric, AB
Computer Science, A
Computer Teacher Education, A
Criminal Justice/Law Enforcement Administration, A
Criminal Justice/Safety Studies, A
Divinity/Ministry (BD, MDiv.), B
Drama and Dance Teacher Education, A
Economics, A
Elementary Education and Teaching, A
Engineering, A
Environmental Studies, A
Family and Community Services, A
Finance, A
Health and Physical Education, A
Health Teacher Education, A
History, A
History Teacher Education, A
Human Resources Management/Personnel Administration, A
Kindergarten/PreSchool Education and Teaching, A
Kinesiology and Exercise Science, B
Law and Legal Studies, A
Liberal Arts and Sciences Studies and Humanities, B
Licensed Practical/Vocational Nurse Training, A
Marketing/Marketing Management, A
Mathematics, A
Mathematics Teacher Education, A
Missions/Missionary Studies and Missiology, AB
Music, B
Music History, Literature, and Theory, A
Music Performance, A
Music Teacher Education, A
Natural Sciences, B
Nurse/Nursing Assistant/Aide and Patient Care Assistant, A
Nursing - Registered Nurse Training, A
Parks, Recreation, Leisure and Fitness Studies, AB
Pastoral Studies/Counseling, B

Photography, A
Physical Education Teaching and Coaching, A
Physician Assistant, A
Pre-Dentistry Studies, B
Pre-Law Studies, B
Pre-Medicine/Pre-Medical Studies, B
Pre-Pharmacy Studies, B
Pre-Theology/Pre-Ministerial Studies, B
Pre-Veterinary Studies, B
Psychology, B
Psychology Teacher Education, A
Religion/Religious Studies, AB
Sales and Marketing Operations/Marketing and Distribution Teacher Education, A
Science Teacher Education/General Science Teacher Education, A
Secondary Education and Teaching, A
Small Business Administration/Management, AB
Social Psychology, A
Social Science Teacher Education, A
Social Sciences, B
Social Studies Teacher Education, A
Social Work, A
Sociology, A
Speech Teacher Education, A
Sport and Fitness Administration/Management, B
Theology/Theological Studies, A
Wildlife Biology, A
Youth Ministry, B
Zoology/Animal Biology, A

CLOUD COUNTY COMMUNITY COLLEGE

Administrative Assistant and Secretarial Science, A
Agricultural Business and Management, A
Art/Art Studies, General, A
Avionics Maintenance Technology/Technician, A
Behavioral Sciences, A
Biological and Physical Sciences, A
Biology/Biological Sciences, A
Broadcast Journalism, A
Business Administration and Management, A
Child Development, A
Criminal Justice/Law Enforcement Administration, A
Drafting and Design Technology/Technician, A
Education, A
Elementary Education and Teaching, A
Family and Consumer Sciences/Home Economics Teacher Education, A
Family and Consumer Sciences/Human Sciences, A
Farm/Farm and Ranch Management, A
Fashion/Apparel Design, A
History, A
Humanities/Humanistic Studies, A
Journalism, A
Liberal Arts and Sciences Studies and Humanities, A
Music, A
Nursing - Registered Nurse Training, A
Physical Education Teaching and Coaching, A
Physical Sciences, A
Pre-Engineering, A
Social Sciences, A
Tourism and Travel Services Management, A

COFFEYVILLE COMMUNITY COLLEGE

Accounting, A
Administrative Assistant and Secretarial Science, A
Agricultural Business and Management, A
Agricultural Economics, A
Agricultural Mechanization, A
Agricultural Teacher Education, A
Agriculture, A
Animal Sciences, A
Applied Art, A
Art/Art Studies, General, A
Athletic Training and Sports Medicine, A
Automobile/Automotive Mechanics Technology/Technician, A
Behavioral Sciences, A
Biological and Physical Sciences, A
Biology/Biological Sciences, A
Botany/Plant Biology, A
Broadcast Journalism, A
Business Administration and Management, A
Business Machine Repairer, A

Business Teacher Education, A
Carpentry/Carpenter, A
Chemistry, A
Communications Technology/Technician, A
Computer and Information Sciences, A
Computer Programming/Programmer, A
Computer Science, A
Construction Engineering Technology/Technician, A
Consumer Merchandising/Retailing Management, A
Drafting and Design Technology/Technician, A
Drama and Dramatics/Theatre Arts, A
Drawing, A
Economics, A
Education, A
Elementary Education and Teaching, A
Emergency Medical Technology/Technician (EMT
    Paramedic), A
Engineering, A
English Language and Literature, A
Family and Consumer Sciences/Human Sciences, A
History, A
Horticultural Science, A
Humanities/Humanistic Studies, A
Industrial Technology/Technician, A
Information Science/Studies, A
Journalism, A
Legal Administrative Assistant/Secretary, A
Liberal Arts and Sciences Studies and
    Humanities, A
Licensed Practical/Vocational Nurse Training, A
Machine Tool Technology/Machinist, A
Marketing/Marketing Management, A
Mass Communication/Media Studies, A
Mathematics, A
Mechanical Engineering/Mechanical
    Technology/Technician, A
Medical Administrative Assistant/Secretary, A
Music, A
Music Teacher Education, A
Nursing - Registered Nurse Training, A
Occupational Therapy/Therapist, A
Physical Education Teaching and Coaching, A
Political Science and Government, A
Pre-Engineering, A
Psychology, A
Radio and Television, A
Social Sciences, A
Social Work, A
Sociology, A
Telecommunications Technology/Technician, A
Voice and Opera, A
Welding Technology/Welder, A
Wind and Percussion Instruments, A

COLBY COMMUNITY COLLEGE

Accounting, A
Agricultural Business and Management, A
Agricultural Economics, A
Agricultural Teacher Education, A
Agriculture, A
Agronomy and Crop Science, A
Animal Sciences, A
Behavioral Sciences, A
Biological and Physical Sciences, A
Biology/Biological Sciences, A
Broadcast Journalism, A
Business Administration and Management, A
Business Teacher Education, A
Business/Managerial Economics, A
Chemistry, A
Child Development, A
Commercial and Advertising Art, A
Computer and Information Sciences, A
Computer Science, A
Criminal Justice/Law Enforcement Administration, A
Dental Hygiene/Hygienist, A
Drama and Dramatics/Theatre Arts, A
Education, A
English Language and Literature, A
Family and Consumer Sciences/Human Sciences, A
Farm/Farm and Ranch Management, A
Foods, Nutrition, and Wellness Studies, A
Forestry, A
Geology/Earth Science, A
History, A
Humanities/Humanistic Studies, A

Journalism, A
Kindergarten/PreSchool Education and Teaching, A
Liberal Arts and Sciences Studies and
    Humanities, A
Library Science, A
Licensed Practical/Vocational Nurse Training, A
Marketing/Marketing Management, A
Mass Communication/Media Studies, A
Mathematics, A
Music, A
Music Teacher Education, A
Nursing - Registered Nurse Training, A
Pharmacy, A
Physical Education Teaching and Coaching, A
Physical Therapist Assistant, A
Physical Therapy/Therapist, A
Political Science and Government, A
Pre-Engineering, A
Psychology, A
Radio and Television, A
Range Science and Management, A
Science Teacher Education/General Science
    Teacher Education, A
Social Work, A
Sociology, A
Veterinary/Animal Health Technology/Technician and
    Veterinary Assistant, A
Wildlife Biology, A
Zoology/Animal Biology, A

COWLEY COUNTY COMMUNITY COLLEGE AND AREA VOCATIONAL-TECHNICAL SCHOOL

Accounting, A
Administrative Assistant and Secretarial Science, A
Agricultural Mechanization, A
Agriculture, A
Agronomy and Crop Science, A
Airframe Mechanics and Aircraft Maintenance
    Technology/Technician, A
Art/Art Studies, General, A
Automobile/Automotive Mechanics
    Technology/Technician, A
Business Administration and Management, A
Chemistry, A
Child Development, A
Computer Graphics, A
Consumer Merchandising/Retailing Management, A
Corrections, A
Cosmetology/Cosmetologist, A
Criminal Justice/Law Enforcement Administration, A
Criminal Justice/Police Science, A
Drafting and Design Technology/Technician, A
Drama and Dramatics/Theatre Arts, A
Education, A
Elementary Education and Teaching, A
Emergency Medical Technology/Technician (EMT
    Paramedic), A
Engineering Technology, A
Family and Consumer Economics and Related
    Services, A
Farm/Farm and Ranch Management, A
Hotel/Motel Administration/Management, A
Industrial Radiologic Technology/Technician, A
Journalism, A
Liberal Arts and Sciences Studies and
    Humanities, A
Machine Tool Technology/Machinist, A
Marketing/Marketing Management, A
Music, A
Parks, Recreation, Leisure and Fitness Studies, A
Physical Education Teaching and Coaching, A
Physical Therapy/Therapist, A
Pre-Engineering, A
Religion/Religious Studies, A
Sign Language Interpretation and Translation, A
Social Work, A
Technology Education/Industrial Arts, A
Technology Teacher Education/Industrial Arts
    Teacher Education, A
Welding Technology/Welder, A

DODGE CITY COMMUNITY COLLEGE

Accounting, A
Administrative Assistant and Secretarial Science, A
Agricultural Business and Management, A

Agricultural Economics, A
Agricultural Mechanization, A
Agronomy and Crop Science, A
Animal Sciences, A
Art/Art Studies, General, A
Athletic Training and Sports Medicine, A
Automobile/Automotive Mechanics
    Technology/Technician, A
Behavioral Sciences, A
Biological and Physical Sciences, A
Biology/Biological Sciences, A
Broadcast Journalism, A
Business Administration and Management, A
Chemistry, A
Child Development, A
Clinical Laboratory Science/Medical
    Technology/Technologist, A
Communications Technology/Technician, A
Computer Programming/Programmer, A
Computer Science, A
Construction Engineering Technology/Technician, A
Cosmetology/Cosmetologist, A
Criminal Justice/Law Enforcement Administration, A
Data Processing and Data Processing
    Technology/Technician, A
Drama and Dramatics/Theatre Arts, A
Education, A
Electrical, Electronic and Communications
    Engineering Technology/Technician, A
Elementary Education and Teaching, A
Engineering, A
Engineering Technology, A
English Language and Literature, A
Equestrian/Equine Studies, A
Farm/Farm and Ranch Management, A
Finance, A
Fire Science/Firefighting, A
Forestry, A
Health Information/Medical Records
    Administration/Administrator, A
History, A
Humanities/Humanistic Studies, A
Hydrology and Water Resources Science, A
Industrial Technology/Technician, A
Information Science/Studies, A
Journalism, A
Legal Administrative Assistant/Secretary, A
Liberal Arts and Sciences Studies and
    Humanities, A
Licensed Practical/Vocational Nurse Training, A
Marketing/Marketing Management, A
Mass Communication/Media Studies, A
Mathematics, A
Medical Administrative Assistant/Secretary, A
Music, A
Music Teacher Education, A
Nursing - Registered Nurse Training, A
Physical Education Teaching and Coaching, A
Physical Sciences, A
Physical Therapy/Therapist, A
Physics, A
Political Science and Government, A
Pre-Engineering, A
Pre-Pharmacy Studies, A
Psychology, A
Radio and Television, A
Real Estate, A
Respiratory Care Therapy/Therapist, A
Social Sciences, A
Social Work, A
Speech and Rhetorical Studies, A
Technology Education/Industrial Arts, A
Welding Technology/Welder, A
Wildlife Biology, A

DONNELLY COLLEGE

Accounting, A
Biological and Physical Sciences, A
Business Administration and Management, A
Computer and Information Sciences, A
Computer Programming, A
Computer Science, A
Data Entry/Microcomputer Applications, A
Data Processing and Data Processing
    Technology/Technician, A
Drafting and Design Technology/Technician, A

Education, A
Engineering, A
English Language and Literature, A
Health Teacher Education, A
History, A
Kindergarten/PreSchool Education and Teaching, A
Liberal Arts and Sciences Studies and
   Humanities, A
Mathematics, A
Nursing - Registered Nurse Training, A
Philosophy, A
Physical Therapy/Therapist, A
Political Science and Government, A
Psychology, A

EMPORIA STATE UNIVERSITY

Accounting, B
Art Therapy/Therapist, M
Art/Art Studies, General, B
Athletic Training and Sports Medicine, B
Biological and Biomedical Sciences, M
Biology/Biological Sciences, B
Botany/Plant Biology, M
Business Administration and Management, B
Business Administration, Management and
   Operations, M
Business Education, M
Cell Biology and Anatomy, M
Chemistry, BM
Clinical Psychology, M
Communication Studies/Speech Communication
   and Rhetoric, B
Computer and Information Sciences, B
Computer Science, M
Counselor Education/School Counseling and
   Guidance Services, M
Curriculum and Instruction, M
Drama and Dramatics/Theatre Arts, B
Early Childhood Education and Teaching, M
Economics, B
Education, MO
Education/Teaching of the Gifted and Talented, M
Educational Administration and Supervision, M
Educational Media/Instructional Technology, M
Elementary Education and Teaching, BM
English, M
English Language and Literature, B
Environmental Biology, M
Foreign Languages and Literatures, B
General Studies, B
Geology/Earth Science, B
Geosciences, M
Health Psychology, M
History, BM
Industrial and Organizational Psychology, M
Information Science/Studies, BMD
Library Science, MD
Marketing/Marketing Management, B
Mathematics, BM
Microbiology, M
Multi-/Interdisciplinary Studies, B
Music, BM
Music Teacher Education, BM
Nursing - Registered Nurse Training, B
Parks, Recreation, Leisure and Fitness Studies, B
Performance, M
Physical Education Teaching and Coaching, M
Physical Sciences, B
Physics, BM
Political Science and Government, B
Psychology, BM
Rehabilitation Counseling, M
School Psychology, MO
Secondary Education and Teaching, B
Social Science Teacher Education, B
Social Sciences, B
Social Studies Teacher Education, M
Sociology, B
Special Education and Teaching, M
Student Personnel Services, M
Vocational Rehabilitation Counseling/Counselor, B
Zoology/Animal Biology, M

FORT HAYS STATE UNIVERSITY

Accounting, BM
Administrative Assistant and Secretarial Science, AB

Agricultural Business and Management, B
Agriculture, B
Agronomy and Crop Science, B
Animal Sciences, B
Art Teacher Education, B
Art/Art Studies, General, B
Audiology/Audiologist and Speech-Language
   Pathology/Pathologist, B
Biological and Biomedical Sciences, M
Biological and Physical Sciences, B
Biology/Biological Sciences, B
Business Administration and Management, B
Business Administration, Management and
   Operations, M
Business Teacher Education, B
Business/Managerial Economics, B
Chemistry, B
Clinical Laboratory Science/Medical
   Technology/Technologist, B
Commercial and Advertising Art, B
Communication and Media Studies, M
Communication Disorders, M
Counselor Education/School Counseling and
   Guidance Services, M
Criminal Justice/Safety Studies, B
Economics, B
Education, MO
Educational Administration and Supervision, MO
Educational Media/Instructional Technology, M
Elementary Education and Teaching, BM
English, M
English Language and Literature, B
Finance, B
Fine Arts and Art Studies, M
French Language and Literature, B
Geology/Earth Science, BM
German Language and Literature, B
Health Education, M
History, BM
Industrial Radiologic Technology/Technician, A
Information Science/Studies, B
Journalism, B
Kindergarten/PreSchool Education and Teaching, B
Liberal Arts and Sciences Studies and
   Humanities, B
Liberal Studies, M
Marketing/Marketing Management, B
Mass Communication/Media Studies, B
Mathematics, B
Middle School Education, M
Music, B
Music Teacher Education, B
Natural Resources Management/Development and
   Policy, B
Nursing, M
Nursing - Registered Nurse Training, B
Philosophy, B
Physical Education Teaching and Coaching, BM
Physical Sciences, B
Physics, B
Political Science and Government, B
Pre-Law Studies, B
Psychology, BMO
Public Relations/Image Management, B
Radio and Television, B
Range Science and Management, B
School Psychology, BO
Science Teacher Education/General Science
   Teacher Education, B
Secondary Education and Teaching, M
Social Work, B
Sociology, B
Spanish Language and Literature, B
Special Education and Teaching, M
Technology Education/Industrial Arts, B
Wildlife and Wildlands Science and Management, B

FORT SCOTT COMMUNITY COLLEGE

Accounting, A
Administrative Assistant and Secretarial Science, A
Agricultural Business and Management, A
Agricultural Economics, A
Agricultural Mechanization, A
Agricultural Teacher Education, A
Agriculture, A
Agronomy and Crop Science, A

Animal Sciences, A
Architectural Engineering Technology/Technician, A
Athletic Training and Sports Medicine, A
Business Administration and Management, A
Clinical Laboratory Science/Medical
   Technology/Technologist, A
Commercial and Advertising Art, A
Computer Science, A
Consumer Merchandising/Retailing Management, A
Cosmetology/Cosmetologist, A
Criminal Justice/Law Enforcement Administration, A
Drafting and Design Technology/Technician, A
Education, A
Electrical, Electronic and Communications
   Engineering Technology/Technician, A
Emergency Medical Technology/Technician (EMT
   Paramedic), A
Hydrology and Water Resources Science, A
Legal Administrative Assistant/Secretary, A
Liberal Arts and Sciences Studies and
   Humanities, A
Medical Administrative Assistant/Secretary, A
Music, A
Nursing - Registered Nurse Training, A
Photography, A
Physical Sciences, A
Public Policy Analysis, A
Quality Control Technology/Technician, A
Teacher Assistant/Aide, A
Technology Education/Industrial Arts, A
Transportation and Materials Moving, A
Welding Technology/Welder, A

FRIENDS UNIVERSITY

Accounting, AB
Applied Art, AB
Art Teacher Education, B
Art/Art Studies, General, AB
Bible/Biblical Studies, B
Biology/Biological Sciences, B
Business Administration and Management, AB
Business Administration, Management and
   Operations, M
Business Teacher Education, B
Ceramic Arts and Ceramics, AB
Chemistry, B
Child Development, AB
Clinical/Medical Laboratory Technician, A
Commercial and Advertising Art, A
Communication Studies/Speech Communication
   and Rhetoric, B
Comparative Literature, AB
Computer and Information Sciences, B
Computer Programming/Programmer, A
Computer Science, AB
Dance, B
Divinity/Ministry (BD, MDiv.), B
Ecology, B
Education, ABM
Educational Leadership and Administration, M
Elementary Education and Teaching, BM
English Language and Literature, B
Environmental Studies, M
Health Teacher Education, B
Health/Health Care Administration/Management, B
History, B
Human Resources Development, M
Human Resources Management/Personnel
   Administration, B
Human Services, B
Industrial and Manufacturing Management, M
Industrial Radiologic Technology/Technician, B
Interdisciplinary Studies, AB
International Business/Trade/Commerce, B
Kindergarten/PreSchool Education and
   Teaching, AB
Law and Legal Studies, M
Liberal Arts and Sciences Studies and
   Humanities, B
Management, M
Management Information Systems and Services, M
Marriage and Family Therapy/Counseling, BM
Mathematics, B
Music, B
Music Management and Merchandising, AB
Music Teacher Education, B

Philosophy, B
Physical Education Teaching and Coaching, B
Piano and Organ, B
Political Science and Government, B
Pre-Dentistry Studies, B
Pre-Engineering, A
Pre-Medicine/Pre-Medical Studies, B
Pre-Veterinary Studies, B
Psychology, B
Religion/Religious Studies, B
Religious/Sacred Music, B
Science Teacher Education/General Science
   Teacher Education, B
Secondary Education and Teaching, BM
Social Sciences, B
Sociology, AB
Spanish Language and Literature, AB
Speech and Rhetorical Studies, B
Theology and Religious Vocations, M
Theology/Theological Studies, B
Violin, Viola, Guitar and Other Stringed
   Instruments, B
Voice and Opera, B

GARDEN CITY COMMUNITY COLLEGE

Accounting, A
Administrative Assistant and Secretarial Science, A
Agricultural Business and Management, A
Agricultural Economics, A
Agricultural Mechanization, A
Agriculture, A
Athletic Training and Sports Medicine, A
Automobile/Automotive Mechanics
   Technology/Technician, A
Biological and Physical Sciences, A
Business Administration and Management, A
Ceramic Arts and Ceramics, A
Child Development, A
Commercial and Advertising Art, A
Computer Engineering Technology/Technician, A
Computer Graphics, A
Computer Programming/Programmer, A
Computer Science, A
Computer Systems Networking and
   Telecommunications, A
Consumer Merchandising/Retailing Management, A
Cosmetology/Cosmetologist, A
Criminal Justice/Law Enforcement Administration, A
Criminal Justice/Police Science, A
Developmental and Child Psychology, A
Drafting and Design Technology/Technician, A
Drafting/Design Engineering
   Technologies/Technicians, A
Drama and Dramatics/Theatre Arts, A
Education, A
Electrical, Electronic and Communications
   Engineering Technology/Technician, A
Elementary Education and Teaching, A
Emergency Medical Technology/Technician (EMT
   Paramedic), A
Engineering, A
Engineering Technology, A
English Language and Literature, A
Family and Community Services, A
Family and Consumer Sciences/Human Sciences, A
Farm/Farm and Ranch Management, A
Fashion Merchandising, A
Fashion/Apparel Design, A
Fine/Studio Arts, A
Health and Physical Education/Fitness, A
Humanities/Humanistic Studies, A
Industrial Technology/Technician, A
Information Science/Studies, A
Interior Design, A
Journalism, A
Legal Administrative Assistant/Secretary, A
Liberal Arts and Sciences Studies and
   Humanities, A
Marketing/Marketing Management, A
Mathematics, A
Mechanical Engineering/Mechanical
   Technology/Technician, A
Metal and Jewelry Arts, A
Music, A
Nursing - Registered Nurse Training, A
Physical Education Teaching and Coaching, A

Pre-Engineering, A
Retailing and Retail Operations, A
Social Sciences, A
Sociology, A
Speech and Rhetorical Studies, A
Teacher Assistant/Aide, A
Technology Education/Industrial Arts, A
Trade and Industrial Teacher Education, A
Welding Technology/Welder, A

HASKELL INDIAN NATIONS UNIVERSITY

American Indian/Native American Studies, B
American Literature (United States), A
Business Administration and Management, AB
Computer and Information Sciences, AB
Creative Writing, A
Elementary Education and Teaching, B
Entrepreneurial and Small Business Operations, A
Environmental Sciences, B
Film/Video and Photographic Arts, A
Health and Physical Education, A
Liberal Arts and Sciences Studies and
   Humanities, A
Natural Sciences, A
Social Work, A
Theatre/Theatre Arts Management, A

HESSTON COLLEGE

Aeronautics/Aviation/Aerospace Science and
   Technology, A
Bible/Biblical Studies, A
Business Administration and Management, A
Computer/Information Technology Services
   Administration and Management, A
Kindergarten/PreSchool Education and Teaching, A
Liberal Arts and Sciences Studies and
   Humanities, A
Nursing - Registered Nurse Training, A
Pastoral Studies/Counseling, A

HIGHLAND COMMUNITY COLLEGE

Accounting, A
Administrative Assistant and Secretarial Science, A
Advertising, A
Agricultural Business and Management, A
Agricultural Economics, A
Agricultural Teacher Education, A
Agriculture, A
Agronomy and Crop Science, A
Animal Sciences, A
Art/Art Studies, General, A
Athletic Training and Sports Medicine, A
Automobile/Automotive Mechanics
   Technology/Technician, A
Biology/Biological Sciences, A
Business Administration and Management, A
Business Teacher Education, A
Carpentry/Carpenter, A
Chemistry, A
Clinical Laboratory Science/Medical
   Technology/Technologist, A
Commercial and Advertising Art, A
Computer Science, A
Construction Engineering Technology/Technician, A
Criminal Justice/Law Enforcement Administration, A
Criminal Justice/Police Science, A
CytoTechnology/Cytotechnologist, A
Dairy Science, A
Data Processing and Data Processing
   Technology/Technician, A
Dental Hygiene/Hygienist, A
Drafting and Design Technology/Technician, A
Drama and Dramatics/Theatre Arts, A
Education, A
Emergency Medical Technology/Technician (EMT
   Paramedic), A
English Language and Literature, A
Family and Consumer Sciences/Human Sciences, A
Farm/Farm and Ranch Management, A
Fashion/Apparel Design, A
Fiber, Textile and Weaving Arts, A
Food Science, A
Forestry, A
Funeral Service and Mortuary Science, A
Geology/Earth Science, A

Health Information/Medical Records
   Administration/Administrator, A
Health Teacher Education, A
History, A
Industrial Radiologic Technology/Technician, A
Information Science/Studies, A
Journalism, A
Legal Administrative Assistant/Secretary, A
Liberal Arts and Sciences Studies and
   Humanities, A
Library Science, A
Mathematics, A
Medical Administrative Assistant/Secretary, A
Music, A
Natural Resources and Conservation, A
Nursing - Registered Nurse Training, A
Occupational Therapy/Therapist, A
Pharmacy, A
Physical Education Teaching and Coaching, A
Physical Sciences, A
Physical Therapy/Therapist, A
Political Science and Government, A
Pre-Engineering, A
Psychology, A
Respiratory Care Therapy/Therapist, A
Social Work, A
Sociology, A
Technology Education/Industrial Arts, A
Telecommunications Technology/Technician, A
Theology/Theological Studies, A

HUTCHINSON COMMUNITY COLLEGE AND AREA VOCATIONAL SCHOOL

Administrative Assistant and Secretarial Science, A
Agricultural Mechanization, A
Agriculture, A
Autobody/Collision and Repair
   Technology/Technician, A
Automobile/Automotive Mechanics
   Technology/Technician, A
Biology/Biological Sciences, A
Business and Personal/Financial Services Marketing
   Operations, A
Business/Commerce, A
Carpentry/Carpenter, A
Child Care and Support Services Management, A
Communication Studies/Speech Communication
   and Rhetoric, A
Communications Technology/Technician, A
Computer and Information Sciences, A
Criminal Justice/Police Science, A
Drafting and Design Technology/Technician, A
Education, A
Educational/Instructional Media Design, A
Electrical/Electronics Equipment Installation and
   Repair, A
Emergency Medical Technology/Technician (EMT
   Paramedic), A
Engineering, A
English Language and Literature, A
Family and Consumer Sciences/Human Sciences, A
Farm/Farm and Ranch Management, A
Fire Science/Firefighting, A
Foreign Languages and Literatures, A
Health Information/Medical Records
   Technology/Technician, A
Legal Assistant/Paralegal, A
Liberal Arts and Sciences Studies and
   Humanities, A
Machine Tool Technology/Machinist, A
Management Information Systems and Services, A
Manufacturing Technology/Technician, A
Mathematics, A
Medical Radiologic Technology/Science - Radiation
   Therapist, A
Nursing - Registered Nurse Training, A
Physical Sciences, A
Psychology, A
Retailing and Retail Operations, A
Social Sciences, A
Visual and Performing Arts, A

Welding Technology/Welder, A

INDEPENDENCE COMMUNITY COLLEGE

Accounting, A
Administrative Assistant and Secretarial Science, A
Art Teacher Education, A
Athletic Training and Sports Medicine, A
Biological and Physical Sciences, A
Biology/Biological Sciences, A
Business Administration and Management, A
Business Teacher Education, A
Chemistry, A
Child Development, A
Civil Engineering Technology/Technician, A
Cosmetology/Cosmetologist, A
Data Processing and Data Processing
    Technology/Technician, A
Drafting and Design Technology/Technician, A
Electrical, Electronic and Communications
    Engineering Technology/Technician, A
Elementary Education and Teaching, A
Emergency Medical Technology/Technician (EMT
    Paramedic), A
Engineering, A
Engineering Technology, A
English Language and Literature, A
Finance, A
French Language and Literature, A
History, A
Humanities/Humanistic Studies, A
Kindergarten/PreSchool Education and Teaching, A
Liberal Arts and Sciences Studies and
    Humanities, A
Mathematics, A
Modern Languages, A
Music, A
Music Management and Merchandising, A
Music Teacher Education, A
Natural Sciences, A
Physical Education Teaching and Coaching, A
Physical Sciences, A
Political Science and Government, A
Pre-Engineering, A
Psychology, A
Science Teacher Education/General Science
    Teacher Education, A
Sociology, A
Spanish Language and Literature, A

JOHNSON COUNTY COMMUNITY COLLEGE

Accounting Technology/Technician and
    Bookkeeping, A
Administrative Assistant and Secretarial Science, A
Airframe Mechanics and Aircraft Maintenance
    Technology/Technician, A
Automobile/Automotive Mechanics
    Technology/Technician, A
Business Administration and Management, A
Chemical Technology/Technician, A
Civil Engineering Technology/Technician, A
Commercial and Advertising Art, A
Computer Programming, Specific Applications, A
Computer Systems Networking and
    Telecommunications, A
Cosmetology/Cosmetologist, A
Criminal Justice/Police Science, A
Dental Hygiene/Hygienist, A
Drafting and Design Technology/Technician, A
Education, A
Electrical and Power Transmission
    Installation/Installer, A
Emergency Medical Technology/Technician (EMT
    Paramedic), A
Fire Services Administration, A
Health Information/Medical Records
    Technology/Technician, A
Heating, Air Conditioning and Refrigeration
    Technology/Technician, A
Hospitality Administration/Management, A
Hotel/Motel Administration/Management, A
Legal Assistant/Paralegal, A
Liberal Arts and Sciences Studies and
    Humanities, A
Licensed Practical/Vocational Nurse Training, A

Machine Tool Technology/Machinist, A
Nurse/Nursing Assistant/Aide and Patient Care
    Assistant, A
Nursing - Registered Nurse Training, A
Occupational Therapist Assistant, A
Physical Therapist Assistant, A
Respiratory Care Therapy/Therapist, A
Retailing and Retail Operations, A
Sales, Distribution and Marketing Operations, A
Sign Language Interpretation and Translation, A
Tourism and Travel Services Management, A
Veterinary/Animal Health Technology/Technician and
    Veterinary Assistant, A

KANSAS CITY KANSAS COMMUNITY COLLEGE

Administrative Assistant and Secretarial Science, A
Business Administration and Management, A
Child Care and Support Services Management, A
Computer Engineering Technology/Technician, A
Criminal Justice/Police Science, A
Data Processing and Data Processing
    Technology/Technician, A
Drafting and Design Technology/Technician, A
Emergency Medical Technology/Technician (EMT
    Paramedic), A
Fire Science/Firefighting, A
Funeral Service and Mortuary Science, A
Hazardous Materials Management and Waste
    Technology/Technician, A
International Business/Trade/Commerce, A
Legal Assistant/Paralegal, A
Liberal Arts and Sciences Studies and
    Humanities, A
Nursing - Registered Nurse Training, A
Physical Therapist Assistant, A
Recording Arts Technology/Technician, A
Respiratory Care Therapy/Therapist, A
Respiratory Therapy Technician/Assistant, A
Substance Abuse/Addiction Counseling, A
Web Page, Digital/Multimedia and Information
    Resources Design, A

KANSAS STATE UNIVERSITY

Accounting, BM
Adult and Continuing Education and Teaching, MD
Aeronautics/Aviation/Aerospace Science and
    Technology, B
Agricultural and Food Products Processing, B
Agricultural Business and Management, B
Agricultural Economics, BMD
Agricultural Engineering, MD
Agricultural Mechanization, B
Agricultural Sciences, MD
Agricultural/Biological Engineering and
    Bioengineering, B
Agronomy and Crop Science, B
Agronomy and Soil Sciences, MD
Airframe Mechanics and Aircraft Maintenance
    Technology/Technician, A
Airline/Commercial/Professional Pilot and Flight
    Crew, AB
Analytical Chemistry, M
Anatomy, MD
Animal Sciences, BMD
Anthropology, B
Apparel and Textiles, B
Architectural Engineering, BM
Architecture, BM
Art/Art Studies, General, B
Athletic Training and Sports Medicine, B
Biochemistry, BMD
Bioengineering, MD
Biological and Biomedical Sciences, MD
Biology/Biological Sciences, B
Business Administration and Management, B
Business Administration, Management and
    Operations, M
Cancer Biology/Oncology, MD
Cell Biology and Anatomy, MD
Chemical Engineering, BMD
Chemistry, BMD
Child and Family Studies, MD
Child Development, B
Civil Engineering, BMD

Clinical Laboratory Science/Medical
    Technology/Technologist, B
Clothing and Textiles, MD
Communication Disorders, B
Communication Studies/Speech Communication
    and Rhetoric, B
Composition, M
Computer and Information Sciences, B
Computer Engineering, BMD
Computer Science, MD
Counselor Education/School Counseling and
    Guidance Services, MD
Curriculum and Instruction, MD
Developmental Biology and Embryology, MD
Dietetics/Dieticians, B
Drama and Dramatics/Theatre Arts, B
Ecology, MD
Economics, BMD
Education, MD
Educational Administration and Supervision, MD
Educational Psychology, MD
Electrical Engineering, MD
Electrical, Electronics and Communications
    Engineering, B
Elementary Education and Teaching, BMD
Engineering and Applied Sciences, MD
Engineering Management, M
English, M
English Language and Literature, B
Entomology, MD
Environmental Policy and Resource
    Management, M
Family and Consumer Sciences/Human
    Sciences, BMD
Finance, B
Fine Arts and Art Studies, M
Food Engineering, MD
Food Science, B
Food Science and Technology, MD
Foods, Nutrition, and Wellness Studies, B
Foreign Languages and Literatures, B
French Language and Literature, M
Genetics, MD
Geography, BMD
Geology/Earth Science, BM
German Language and Literature, M
History, BMD
Horticultural Science, BMD
Hospitality Administration/Management, MD
Hotel/Motel Administration/Management, B
Human Development, D
Human Development and Family Studies, B
Human Services, M
Humanities/Humanistic Studies, B
Immunology, MD
Industrial Engineering, B
Industrial/Management Engineering, MD
Information Science/Studies, BMD
Inorganic Chemistry, M
Interdisciplinary Studies, A
Interior Architecture, B
Interior Design, B
International Affairs, M
Journalism, B
Kinesiology and Exercise Science, B
Kinesiology and Movement Studies, M
Landscape Architecture, BM
Manufacturing Engineering, MD
Marketing/Marketing Management, B
Marriage and Family Therapy/Counseling, D
Mass Communication/Media Studies, M
Mathematics, BMD
Mechanical Engineering, BMD
Microbiology, MD
Molecular Biology, MD
Music, BM
Music History, Literature, and Theory, M
Music Teacher Education, BM
Music Theory and Composition, M
Nuclear Engineering, BM
Nutritional Sciences, MD
Operations Research, M
Organic Chemistry, M
Parks, Recreation and Leisure Facilities
    Management, B
Pathobiology, MD

Performance, M
Philosophy, B
Physical Chemistry, M
Physical Sciences, B
Physics, BMD
Physiology, MD
Plant Pathology/Phytopathology, MD
Political Science and Government, BM
Pre-Dentistry Studies, B
Pre-Medicine/Pre-Medical Studies, B
Pre-Veterinary Studies, B
Psychology, BMD
Public Administration, M
Public Health, M
Public Health (MPH, DPH), B
Range Science and Management, MD
Secondary Education and Teaching, BMD
Social Sciences, B
Social Work, B
Sociology, BMD
Software Engineering, M
Spanish Language and Literature, M
Special Education and Teaching, MD
Speech and Rhetorical Studies, M
Statistics, BMD
Student Personnel Services, MD
Urban and Regional Planning, M
Veterinary Medicine, P
Veterinary Sciences, M
Virology, MD
Wildlife Biology, B
Women's Studies, B

KANSAS WESLEYAN UNIVERSITY

Accounting, B
Art Teacher Education, B
Art/Art Studies, General, B
Arts Management, B
Biology/Biological Sciences, B
Business Administration and Management, AB
Business Administration, Management and
　　Operations, M
Chemistry, B
Comparative Literature, B
Computer Science, AB
Criminal Justice/Law Enforcement
　　Administration, AB
Drama and Dramatics/Theatre Arts, B
Education, B
Elementary Education and Teaching, B
Engineering, B
English Language and Literature, B
Health Teacher Education, B
History, B
Information Science/Studies, B
Kindergarten/PreSchool Education and Teaching, A
Liberal Arts and Sciences Studies and
　　Humanities, B
Mass Communication/Media Studies, B
Mathematics, B
Mental Health/Rehabilitation, B
Nursing - Registered Nurse Training, AB
Physical Education Teaching and Coaching, B
Physics, B
Pre-Dentistry Studies, B
Pre-Law Studies, B
Pre-Medicine/Pre-Medical Studies, B
Pre-Veterinary Studies, B
Psychology, B
Religion/Religious Studies, B
Religious Education, B
Social Sciences, B
Sociology, B
Spanish Language and Literature, B
Special Education and Teaching, B
Speech and Rhetorical Studies, B
Substance Abuse/Addiction Counseling, B

LABETTE COMMUNITY COLLEGE

Accounting, A
Administrative Assistant and Secretarial Science, A
Art/Art Studies, General, A
Behavioral Sciences, A
Biology/Biological Sciences, A
Business Administration and Management, A
Chemistry, A

Child Development, A
Commercial and Advertising Art, A
Computer Science, A
Criminal Justice/Law Enforcement Administration, A
Criminal Justice/Police Science, A
Data Processing and Data Processing
　　Technology/Technician, A
Drafting and Design Technology/Technician, A
Education, A
Elementary Education and Teaching, A
English Language and Literature, A
Fire Science/Firefighting, A
Heating, Air Conditioning, Ventilation and
　　Refrigeration Maintenance
　　Technology/Technician, A
History, A
Industrial Radiologic Technology/Technician, A
Industrial Technology/Technician, A
Kindergarten/PreSchool Education and Teaching, A
Legal Administrative Assistant/Secretary, A
Liberal Arts and Sciences Studies and
　　Humanities, A
Mathematics, A
Medical Administrative Assistant/Secretary, A
Music, A
Nursing - Registered Nurse Training, A
Physical Education Teaching and Coaching, A
Pre-Engineering, A
Respiratory Care Therapy/Therapist, A
Social Sciences, A

MANHATTAN AREA TECHNICAL COLLEGE

Autobody/Collision and Repair
　　Technology/Technician, A
Automobile/Automotive Mechanics
　　Technology/Technician, A
Building/Construction
　　Finishing, Management, and Inspection, A
Computer Systems Networking and
　　Telecommunications, A
Computer Technology/Computer Systems
　　Technology, A
Drafting and Design Technology/Technician, A
Electrical and Power Transmission Installers, A
Heating, Air Conditioning and Refrigeration
　　Technology/Technician, A
Licensed Practical/Vocational Nurse Training, A
Management Information Systems and Services, A
Nursing - Registered Nurse Training, A
Welding Technology/Welder, A

MANHATTAN CHRISTIAN COLLEGE

Bible/Biblical Studies, AB
Business Administration and Management, B
Divinity/Ministry (BD, MDiv.), B
Missions/Missionary Studies and Missiology, AB
Pastoral Studies/Counseling, B
Religion/Religious Studies, B
Religious Education, AB
Religious/Sacred Music, AB
Theology/Theological Studies, B

MCPHERSON COLLEGE

Accounting, B
Agricultural Business and Management, B
Agricultural Economics, B
Art Teacher Education, B
Art/Art Studies, General, B
Automobile/Automotive Mechanics
　　Technology/Technician, A
Behavioral Sciences, B
Biology/Biological Sciences, B
Business Administration and Management, B
Business Teacher Education, B
Chemistry, B
Computer Programming/Programmer, B
Computer Science, B
Drama and Dramatics/Theatre Arts, B
Education, B
Elementary Education and Teaching, B
English Language and Literature, B
Environmental Studies, B
Finance, B
History, B
Interdisciplinary Studies, B

International Business/Trade/Commerce, B
Kindergarten/PreSchool Education and Teaching, B
Mathematics, B
Music, B
Music Teacher Education, B
Philosophy, B
Physical Education Teaching and Coaching, B
Physical Sciences, B
Pre-Dentistry Studies, B
Pre-Engineering, B
Pre-Medicine/Pre-Medical Studies, B
Pre-Pharmacy Studies, B
Pre-Veterinary Studies, B
Psychology, B
Religion/Religious Studies, B
Secondary Education and Teaching, B
Social Sciences, B
Sociology, B
Spanish Language and Literature, B
Special Education and Teaching, B
Speech Teacher Education, B
Teacher Education, Multiple Levels, B
Technology Education/Industrial Arts, B

MIDAMERICA NAZARENE UNIVERSITY

Accounting, B
Athletic Training and Sports Medicine, B
Biology/Biological Sciences, B
Business Administration and Management, AB
Business Administration, Management and
　　Operations, M
Business Teacher Education, B
Chemistry, B
Computer Science, B
Counseling Psychology, M
Criminal Justice/Law Enforcement Administration, B
Curriculum and Instruction, M
Education, M
Educational Media/Instructional Technology, M
Elementary Education and Teaching, B
English Language and Literature, B
English/Language Arts Teacher Education, B
Graphic Design, B
History, B
Human Resources Management/Personnel
　　Administration, B
International Business/Trade/Commerce, B
Junior High/Intermediate/Middle School Education
　　and Teaching, B
Kinesiology and Exercise Science, B
Liberal Arts and Sciences Studies and
　　Humanities, A
Marketing/Marketing Management, B
Mass Communication/Media Studies, B
Mathematics, B
Mathematics Teacher Education, B
Missions/Missionary Studies and Missiology, B
Music Teacher Education, B
Nursing - Registered Nurse Training, B
Physical Education Teaching and Coaching, B
Psychology, B
Public Relations/Image Management, B
Religion/Religious Studies, B
Religious Education, B
Religious/Sacred Music, AB
Secondary Education and Teaching, B
Social Studies Teacher Education, B
Sociology, B
Spanish Language and Literature, B
Spanish Language Teacher Education, B
Special Education and Teaching, M
Sport and Fitness Administration/Management, B
Theology/Theological Studies, B
Urban Studies/Affairs, B

NEOSHO COUNTY COMMUNITY COLLEGE

Accounting, A
Administrative Assistant and Secretarial Science, A
Athletic Training and Sports Medicine, A
Biological and Physical Sciences, A
Business Administration and Management, A
Business Machine Repairer, A
Carpentry/Carpenter, A
Computer Science, A
Construction Engineering Technology/Technician, A

Criminal Justice/Law Enforcement Administration, A
Criminal Justice/Police Science, A
Electrical, Electronic and Communications
    Engineering Technology/Technician, A
Finance, A
Information Science/Studies, A
Liberal Arts and Sciences Studies and
    Humanities, A
Licensed Practical/Vocational Nurse Training, A
Marketing/Marketing Management, A
Materials Sciences, A
Nursing - Registered Nurse Training, A
Physical Sciences, A
Pre-Engineering, A
Teacher Assistant/Aide, A
Trade and Industrial Teacher Education, A
Welding Technology/Welder, A

NEWMAN UNIVERSITY

Accounting, B
Art/Art Studies, General, B
Biology/Biological Sciences, B
Business Administration and Management, AB
Business Administration, Management and
    Operations, M
Chemistry, B
Counseling Psychology, B
Criminal Justice/Law Enforcement Administration, B
Curriculum and Instruction, M
Education, BM
Educational Leadership and Administration, M
Elementary Education and Teaching, BM
English as a Second Language, M
English Language and Literature, B
Entrepreneurship/Entrepreneurial Studies, M
Finance, B
History, B
Information Science/Studies, AB
International Business/Trade/Commerce, M
Legal Assistant/Paralegal, A
Liberal Arts and Sciences Studies and
    Humanities, AB
Management, M
Management Information Systems and
    Services, BM
Marketing/Marketing Management, B
Mass Communication/Media Studies, B
Mathematics, B
Mental Health/Rehabilitation, B
Middle School Education, M
Nurse Anesthetist, M
Nursing - Registered Nurse Training, B
Organizational Management, M
Pastoral Studies/Counseling, B
Pre-Dentistry Studies, B
Pre-Engineering, AB
Pre-Law Studies, B
Pre-Medicine/Pre-Medical Studies, B
Pre-Veterinary Studies, B
Psychology, B
Public Health (MPH, DPH), AB
Radiologic Technology/Science - Radiographer, A
Respiratory Care Therapy/Therapist, A
Sales, Distribution and Marketing Operations, B
Secondary Education and Teaching, B
Social Work, M
Sociology, B
Substance Abuse/Addiction Counseling, AB
Theology/Theological Studies, B

OTTAWA UNIVERSITY

Art Teacher Education, B
Art/Art Studies, General, B
Biology/Biological Sciences, B
Business Administration and Management, B
Business Administration, Management and
    Operations, M
Counseling Psychology, M
Drama and Dramatics/Theatre Arts, B
Education, M
Elementary Education and Teaching, B
English Language and Literature, B
History, B
Human Resources Development, M
Human Resources Management and Services, M
Human Services, B

Information Science/Studies, B
Mass Communication/Media Studies, B
Mathematics, B
Music, B
Music Teacher Education, B
Physical Education Teaching and Coaching, B
Political Science and Government, B
Psychology, B
Religion/Religious Studies, B
Sociology, B

PITTSBURG STATE UNIVERSITY

Accounting, BM
Applied Physics, M
Art Education, M
Art Teacher Education, B
Art/Art Studies, General, B
Automobile/Automotive Mechanics
    Technology/Technician, AB
Banking and Financial Support Services, B
Biological and Biomedical Sciences, M
Biology Teacher Education, B
Biology/Biological Sciences, B
Building/Construction
    Finishing, Management, and Inspection, B
Business Administration and Management, B
Business Administration, Management and
    Operations, M
Chemistry, BM
Chemistry Teacher Education, B
Child Development, B
Clinical/Medical Laboratory Technician, B
Communication and Media Studies, M
Communication Studies/Speech Communication
    and Rhetoric, B
Community College Education, O
Computer Science, B
Construction Engineering Technology/Technician, B
Counselor Education/School Counseling and
    Guidance Services, M
Early Childhood Education and Teaching, M
Economics, B
Education, MO
Educational Leadership and Administration, M
Educational Media/Instructional Technology, M
Electrical, Electronic and Communications
    Engineering Technology/Technician, AB
Elementary Education and Teaching, BM
Engineering and Applied Sciences, M
Engineering Technology, B
English, M
English Language and Literature, B
English/Language Arts Teacher Education, B
Environmental Studies, B
Family and Consumer Sciences/Home Economics
    Teacher Education, B
Family and Consumer Sciences/Human Sciences, B
Finance, B
Fine Arts and Art Studies, M
Forestry Technology/Technician, A
French Language and Literature, B
French Language Teacher Education, B
General Studies, B
Geography, B
Graphic and Printing Equipment Operator
    Production, B
Graphic Communications, B
Graphic Design, M
Health and Physical Education, B
Health Teacher Education, B
Higher Education/Higher Education
    Administration, O
History, BM
History Teacher Education, B
Human Resources Development, MO
Industrial Technology/Technician, B
International Business/Trade/Commerce, B
International/Global Studies, B
Law and Legal Studies, B
Marketing/Marketing Management, B
Mathematics, BM
Mathematics Teacher Education, B
Mechanical Engineering/Mechanical
    Technology/Technician, B
Music, BM
Music History, Literature, and Theory, M

Music Teacher Education, BM
Music Theory and Composition, M
Nursing, M
Nursing - Registered Nurse Training, B
Operations Management and Supervision, B
Performance, M
Physical Education Teaching and Coaching, BM
Physics, BM
Physics Teacher Education, B
Plastics Engineering Technology/Technician, B
Political Science and Government, B
Psychology, BM
Psychology Teacher Education, B
Reading Teacher Education, M
School Psychology, O
Secondary Education and Teaching, M
Social Sciences, M
Social Studies Teacher Education, B
Social Work, B
Sociology, B
Spanish Language and Literature, B
Spanish Language Teacher Education, B
Special Education and Teaching, M
Speech Teacher Education, B
Technology Education/Industrial Arts, B
Technology Teacher Education/Industrial Arts
    Teacher Education, B
Theater, M
Trade and Industrial Teacher Education, B
Vocational and Technical Education, MO

PRATT COMMUNITY COLLEGE

Accounting, A
Administrative Assistant and Secretarial Science, A
Agricultural Business and Management, A
Agricultural Economics, A
Agricultural Mechanization, A
Agricultural Teacher Education, A
Agriculture, A
Animal Sciences, A
Animal/Livestock Husbandry and Production, A
Applied Art, A
Art Teacher Education, A
Art/Art Studies, General, A
Athletic Training and Sports Medicine, A
Automobile/Automotive Mechanics
    Technology/Technician, A
Biological and Physical Sciences, A
Biology/Biological Sciences, A
Broadcast Journalism, A
Business Administration and Management, A
Business Teacher Education, A
Chemistry, A
Child Development, A
Commercial and Advertising Art, A
Comparative Literature, A
Computer Systems Networking and
    Telecommunications, A
Computer Typography and Composition Equipment
    Operator, A
Counselor Education/School Counseling and
    Guidance Services, A
Data Entry/Microcomputer Applications, A
Elementary Education and Teaching, A
Energy Management and Systems
    Technology/Technician, A
English Language and Literature, A
Family and Consumer Sciences/Human Sciences, A
Farm/Farm and Ranch Management, A
Fine/Studio Arts, A
Health Teacher Education, A
History, A
Human Services, A
Humanities/Humanistic Studies, A
Kindergarten/PreSchool Education and Teaching, A
Liberal Arts and Sciences Studies and
    Humanities, A
Management Information Systems and Services, A
Marketing/Marketing Management, A
Mass Communication/Media Studies, A
Mathematics, A
Music, A
Nursing - Registered Nurse Training, A
Physical Education Teaching and Coaching, A
Pre-Engineering, A
Professional Studies, A

Psychology, A
Social Sciences, A
Social Work, A
Sociology, A
Speech and Rhetorical Studies, A
Speech Teacher Education, A
Teacher Education, Multiple Levels, A
Technology Education/Industrial Arts, A
Trade and Industrial Teacher Education, A
Welding Technology/Welder, A
Wildlife and Wildlands Science and Management, A
Wildlife Biology, A

SEWARD COUNTY COMMUNITY COLLEGE

Accounting, A
Administrative Assistant and Secretarial Science, A
Agriculture, A
Art/Art Studies, General, A
Athletic Training and Sports Medicine, A
Biological and Physical Sciences, A
Biology/Biological Sciences, A
Business Administration and Management, A
Chemistry, A
Child Development, A
Clinical/Medical Laboratory Technician, A
Comparative Literature, A
Computer Programming/Programmer, A
Computer Science, A
Criminal Justice/Police Science, A
Data Processing and Data Processing
    Technology/Technician, A
Drama and Dramatics/Theatre Arts, A
Drawing, A
Economics, A
Education, A
Elementary Education and Teaching, A
English Language and Literature, A
Farm/Farm and Ranch Management, A
Finance, A
History, A
Journalism, A
Liberal Arts and Sciences Studies and
    Humanities, A
Licensed Practical/Vocational Nurse Training, A
Marketing/Marketing Management, A
Mass Communication/Media Studies, A
Mathematics, A
Music, A
Natural Sciences, A
Nursing - Registered Nurse Training, A
Physical Education Teaching and Coaching, A
Physical Sciences, A
Pre-Engineering, A
Psychology, A
Respiratory Care Therapy/Therapist, A
Social Work, A
Sociology, A
Speech and Rhetorical Studies, A
Surgical Technology/Technologist, A
Wildlife and Wildlands Science and Management, A

SOUTHWESTERN COLLEGE

Athletic Training and Sports Medicine, B
Biochemistry, B
Biology/Biological Sciences, B
Business Administration and Management, B
Business/Corporate Communications, B
Chemistry, B
Communication and Media Studies, B
Computer Programming/Programmer, B
Computer Science, B
Computer Technology/Computer Systems
    Technology, B
Criminal Justice/Law Enforcement Administration, B
Early Childhood Education and Teaching, B
Education, M
Elementary Education and Teaching, B
Engineering Physics, B
English Language and Literature, B
General Studies, B
Health and Physical Education, B
History, B
Human Resources Management/Personnel
    Administration, B
Industrial Production Technologies/Technicians, B

Liberal Arts and Sciences Studies and
    Humanities, B
Management Information Systems and Services, B
Management Science, B
Manufacturing Technology/Technician, B
Marine Biology and Biological Oceanography, B
Mathematics, B
Music, B
Music Teacher Education, B
Nursing - Registered Nurse Training, B
Pastoral Studies/Counseling, B
Philosophy and Religious Studies, B
Physics, B
Psychology, B
Purchasing, Procurement/Acquisitions and
    Contracts Management, B
Securities Services Administration/Management, B
Special Education and Teaching, M
Sport and Fitness Administration/Management, B

STERLING COLLEGE

Art/Art Studies, General, B
Athletic Training and Sports Medicine, B
Behavioral Sciences, B
Biology/Biological Sciences, B
Business Administration and Management, B
Communication, Journalism and Related
    Programs, B
Computer and Information Sciences, B
Drama and Dramatics/Theatre Arts, B
Elementary Education and Teaching, B
English Language and Literature, B
Health and Physical Education, B
History, B
Interdisciplinary Studies, B
Mathematics, B
Music, B
Music Teacher Education, B
Philosophy and Religious Studies, B
Physical Education Teaching and Coaching, B
Religious Education, B

TABOR COLLEGE

Accounting, B
Actuarial Science, B
Administrative Assistant and Secretarial Science, AB
Adult and Continuing Education and Teaching, B
Agricultural Business and Management, B
Art Teacher Education, B
Athletic Training and Sports Medicine, B
Bible/Biblical Studies, AB
Biological and Physical Sciences, B
Biology/Biological Sciences, B
Business Administration and Management, B
Business Teacher Education, B
Chemistry, B
Clinical Laboratory Science/Medical
    Technology/Technologist, B
Communication Studies/Speech Communication
    and Rhetoric, B
Computer Science, AB
Divinity/Ministry (BD, MDiv.), B
Education, B
Elementary Education and Teaching, B
English Language and Literature, B
Environmental Biology, B
Health Teacher Education, B
History, B
Humanities/Humanistic Studies, B
Interdisciplinary Studies, AB
International Relations and Affairs, B
Journalism, B
Kindergarten/PreSchool Education and Teaching, B
Legal Administrative Assistant/Secretary, B
Marketing/Marketing Management, B
Mass Communication/Media Studies, B
Mathematics, B
Medical Administrative Assistant/Secretary, B
Music, B
Music Management and Merchandising, B
Music Teacher Education, B
Natural Sciences, B
Pastoral Studies/Counseling, B
Philosophy, B
Physical Education Teaching and Coaching, B
Piano and Organ, B

Pre-Dentistry Studies, B
Pre-Medicine/Pre-Medical Studies, B
Psychology, B
Public Relations/Image Management, B
Religion/Religious Studies, AB
Science Teacher Education/General Science
    Teacher Education, B
Secondary Education and Teaching, B
Social Sciences, B
Sociology, B
Special Education and Teaching, B
Teacher Education, Multiple Levels, B
Voice and Opera, B

UNIVERSITY OF KANSAS

Accounting, BMD
Aerospace, Aeronautical and Astronautical
    Engineering, BMD
African Studies, B
African-American/Black Studies, B
Allied Health and Medical Assisting Services, MDO
Allopathic Medicine, PO
American Indian/Native American Studies, M
American/United States Studies/Civilization, BMDO
Anatomy, MDO
Ancient Studies/Civilization, B
Anthropology, BMD
Applied Mathematics, MD
Architectural Engineering, BMD
Architectural History and Criticism, B
Architecture, BMO
Art Education, M
Art History, Criticism and Conservation, BMD
Art Teacher Education, B
Asian Languages, M
Astronomy, BMD
Atmospheric Sciences and Meteorology, B
Behavioral Sciences, B
Biochemistry, MDO
Biochemistry, Biophysics and Molecular Biology, B
Biological and Biomedical Sciences, BMDO
Biological Anthropology, D
Biology/Biological Sciences, B
Biophysics, MD
Botany/Plant Biology, MD
Business Administration, Management and
    Operations, MDO
Business/Commerce, B
Cell Biology and Anatomy, MDO
Ceramic Arts and Ceramics, B
Chemical Engineering, BMD
Chemistry, BMD
Chinese Studies, M
Civil Engineering, BMD
Classics and Classical
    Languages, Literatures, and Linguistics, BM
Clinical Laboratory Science/Medical
    Technology/Technologist, B
Clinical Psychology, MD
Cognitive Psychology and Psycholinguistics, B
Communication and Media Studies, MD
Communication Disorders, BMD
Community Health Services/Liaison/Counseling, B
Composition, MD
Computer and Information Sciences, B
Computer Engineering, BM
Computer Science, MD
Construction Engineering and Management, M
Counseling Psychology, MD
Curriculum and Instruction, MD
CytoTechnology/Cytotechnologist, B
Dance, B
Design and Applied Arts, M
Design and Visual Communications, B
Developmental Biology and Embryology, MD
Developmental Psychology, MD
Drama and Dramatics/Theatre Arts, B
East Asian
    Languages, Literatures, and Linguistics, B
East Asian Studies, M
East European and Russian Studies, MO
Ecology, MD
Economics, BMDO
Education, MDO
Educational Administration and Supervision, MD
Educational Leadership and Administration, D

Educational Measurement and Evaluation, MD
Educational Psychology, MD
Electrical Engineering, MD
Electrical, Electronics and Communications
   Engineering, B
Elementary Education and Teaching, B
Engineering and Applied Sciences, MD
Engineering Management, M
Engineering Physics, B
English, MD
English Language and Literature, B
Entomology, MD
Environmental Engineering
   Technology/Environmental Technology, MD
Environmental Sciences, MD
Environmental Studies, B
European Studies/Civilization, B
Evolutionary Biology, MD
Fiber, Textile and Weaving Arts, B
Film, Television, and Video Theory and
   Criticism, MD
Finance, B
Fine Arts and Art Studies, M
Fine/Studio Arts, B
Foundations and Philosophy of Education, D
French Language and Literature, BMD
Geography, BMD
Geology/Earth Science, BMD
German Language and Literature, MD
Germanic Languages, Literatures, and Linguistics, B
Gerontology, MD
Graphic Design, B
Health and Physical Education, B
Health Information/Medical Records
   Administration/Administrator, B
Health Services Administration, MO
Higher Education/Higher Education
   Administration, MD
History, BMD
Human Development, M
Humanities/Humanistic Studies, B
Illustration, B
Immunology, DO
Industrial Design, B
Interdisciplinary Studies, MDO
Interior Design, B
International Affairs, M
International Relations and Affairs, B
Japanese Studies, M
Journalism, BM
Junior High/Intermediate/Middle School Education
   and Teaching, B
Latin American Studies, BMO
Law and Legal Studies, PO
Liberal Arts and Sciences Studies and
   Humanities, B
Linguistics, BMD
Management Information Systems and
   Services, MD
Mathematics, BMD
Mechanical Engineering, BMD
Medicinal and Pharmaceutical Chemistry, MD
Metal and Jewelry Arts, B
Microbiology, BMDO
Molecular Biology, BMDO
Molecular Genetics, DO
Museology/Museum Studies, M
Music, BMD
Music Performance, B
Music Teacher Education, BMD
Music Theory and Composition, BMD
Music Therapy/Therapist, BM
Musicology and Ethnomusicology, BMD
Near and Middle Eastern Studies, MO
Neuroscience, MD
Nurse Anesthetist, M
Nurse Midwife/Nursing Midwifery, O
Nursing, MDO
Nursing Education, O
Nursing Science, B
Nutritional Sciences, MO
Occupational Therapy/Therapist, BMD
Painting, B
Pathology/Experimental Pathology, MDO
Performance, MD
Petroleum Engineering, BMD

Pharmaceutical Sciences, M
Pharmacology, MDO
Pharmacy, B
Philosophy, BMDO
Physical Education Teaching and Coaching, BMD
Physical Therapy/Therapist, MD
Physics, BMD
Physiology, MDO
Piano and Organ, B
Political Science and Government, BMD
Printmaking, B
Psychiatric/Mental Health Nurse/Nursing, O
Psychology, BMD
Public Administration, BMDO
Public Health, MO
Rehabilitation Sciences, D
Religion/Religious Studies, BM
Respiratory Care Therapy/Therapist, B
Russian Studies, B
Sacred Music, MD
School Psychology, DO
Sculpture, B
Secondary Education and Teaching, B
Slavic Languages, Literatures, and Linguistics, BMD
Social Sciences, MD
Social Work, B
Sociology, BMD
Spanish Language and Literature, BMD
Special Education and Teaching, MD
Speech and Rhetorical Studies, B
Statistics, MD
Technical Theatre/Theatre Design and
   Technology, B
Theater, MD
Toxicology, MDO
Urban and Regional Planning, MO
Violin, Viola, Guitar and Other Stringed
   Instruments, B
Voice and Opera, B
Water Resources, M
Wind and Percussion Instruments, B
Women's Studies, B

UNIVERSITY OF PHOENIX-WICHITA CAMPUS

Business Administration and Management, B
Business Administration, Management and
   Operations, M
Information Technology, B
Management of Technology, M

UNIVERSITY OF SAINT MARY

Accounting, B
Art/Art Studies, General, B
Biology/Biological Sciences, B
Business Administration and Management, B
Business Administration, Management and
   Operations, M
Chemistry, B
Child Development, B
Community Organization and Advocacy, B
Community Psychology, B
Computer and Information Sciences, B
Curriculum and Instruction, BM
Drama and Dramatics/Theatre Arts, B
Education, BM
Elementary Education and Teaching, B
English Language and Literature, B
History, B
Information Science/Studies, B
Interdisciplinary Studies, B
Liberal Arts and Sciences Studies and
   Humanities, AB
Management, M
Mass Communication/Media Studies, B
Mathematics, B
Multi-/Interdisciplinary Studies, B
Pastoral Studies/Counseling, B
Political Science and Government, B
Psychology, BM
Sociology, B
Special Education and Teaching, M
Sport and Fitness Administration/Management, B

Theology/Theological Studies, B

WASHBURN UNIVERSITY

Accounting, B
Administrative Assistant and Secretarial Science, A
Allied Health and Medical Assisting Services, AB
Anthropology, B
Art History, Criticism and Conservation, B
Art/Art Studies, General, B
Athletic Training and Sports Medicine, B
Banking and Financial Support Services, A
Biology/Biological Sciences, B
Biomedical Technology/Technician, B
Business Administration and Management, B
Business Administration, Management and
   Operations, M
Business Teacher Education, B
Chemistry, B
Clinical Psychology, M
Communication Studies/Speech Communication
   and Rhetoric, B
Computer and Information Sciences, AB
Corrections, AB
Criminal Justice/Law Enforcement
   Administration, AB
Criminal Justice/Police Science, AB
Criminology, M
Curriculum and Instruction, BM
Drafting and Design Technology/Technician, A
Drama and Dramatics/Theatre Arts, B
Early Childhood Education and Teaching, AB
Economics, B
Education, BM
Educational Administration and Supervision, M
Elementary Education and Teaching, B
English Language and Literature, B
Finance, B
Food Technology and Processing, A
Forensic Science and Technology, B
French Language and Literature, B
German Language and Literature, B
Gerontology, AB
Health Information/Medical Records
   Technology/Technician, A
Health Services Administration, B
History, B
Human Services, AB
Humanities/Humanistic Studies, A
Industrial Technology/Technician, A
Law and Legal Studies, BP
Legal Administrative Assistant/Secretary, A
Liberal Arts and Sciences Studies and
   Humanities, AB
Liberal Studies, M
Marketing/Marketing Management, B
Mass Communication/Media Studies, B
Mathematics, B
Medical Radiologic Technology/Science - Radiation
   Therapist, B
Mental Health Counseling/Counselor, AB
Music, B
Music Teacher Education, B
Natural Sciences, A
Non-Profit/Public/Organizational Management, B
Nursing - Registered Nurse Training, B
Office Management and Supervision, A
Philosophy, B
Physical Education Teaching and Coaching, B
Physical Therapist Assistant, A
Physics, B
Political Science and Government, B
Pre-Dentistry Studies, B
Pre-Law Studies, B
Pre-Medicine/Pre-Medical Studies, B
Pre-Pharmacy Studies, B
Pre-Theology/Pre-Ministerial Studies, B
Pre-Veterinary Studies, B
Psychology, BM
Public Administration, B
Purchasing, Procurement/Acquisitions and
   Contracts Management, A
Radio and Television, B
Radiologic Technology/Science - Radiographer, A
Reading Teacher Education, M
Religion/Religious Studies, B
Respiratory Care Therapy/Therapist, A

Secondary Education and Teaching, B
Security and Protective Services, B
Social Work, BM
Sociology, B
Spanish Language and Literature, B
Special Education and Teaching, M
Substance Abuse/Addiction Counseling, AB

WICHITA AREA TECHNICAL COLLEGE

Automobile/Automotive Mechanics
 Technology/Technician, A
Clinical/Medical Laboratory Technician, A
Interior Design, A
Mechanical Engineering/Mechanical
 Technology/Technician, A

WICHITA STATE UNIVERSITY

Accounting, BM
Aerospace, Aeronautical and Astronautical
 Engineering, BMD
Allied Health and Medical Assisting Services, MO
Anthropology, BM
Applied Mathematics, D
Art Education, M
Art History, Criticism and Conservation, B
Art Teacher Education, B
Art/Art Studies, General, B
Audiology/Audiologist and Speech-Language
 Pathology/Pathologist, B
Biological and Biomedical Sciences, M
Biology/Biological Sciences, B
Business Administration and Management, B
Business Administration, Management and
 Operations, MO
Chemistry, BMD
Clinical Laboratory Science/Medical
 Technology/Technologist, B
Clinical Psychology, D
Commercial and Advertising Art, B
Communication and Media Studies, M
Communication Disorders, MD
Communication Studies/Speech Communication
 and Rhetoric, B
Community Psychology, D
Computer and Information Sciences, B
Computer Engineering, B
Computer Science, M
Counselor Education/School Counseling and
 Guidance Services, M
Criminal Justice/Safety Studies, B
Criminology, M
Curriculum and Instruction, M
Dental Hygiene/Hygienist, AB
Drama and Dramatics/Theatre Arts, B
Economics, BM
Education, MDO
Educational Administration and Supervision, MDO
Educational Psychology, M
Electrical Engineering, MD
Electrical, Electronics and Communications
 Engineering, B
Elementary Education and Teaching, B
Engineering and Applied Sciences, MD
English, M
English Language and Literature, B
Entrepreneurship/Entrepreneurial Studies, B
Environmental Sciences, M
Exercise and Sports Science, M
Finance, B
Fine Arts and Art Studies, M
French Language and Literature, B
Geology/Earth Science, BM
Gerontology, BM
Health/Health Care Administration/Management, B
History, BM
Human Resources Management/Personnel
 Administration, B
Human Services, M
Industrial Engineering, B
Industrial/Management Engineering, MD
International Business/Trade/Commerce, B
Latin Language and Literature, B
Liberal Arts and Sciences Studies and
 Humanities, AB
Liberal Studies, M
Management Information Systems and Services, B

Manufacturing Engineering, BMD
Marketing/Marketing Management, B
Mathematics, BMD
Mechanical Engineering, BMD
Music, BM
Music Teacher Education, BM
Nursing, MO
Nursing Administration, M
Nursing Education, M
Nursing Science, B
Philosophy, B
Physical Education Teaching and Coaching, BM
Physical Therapy/Therapist, M
Physician Assistant, B
Physics, BM
Political Science and Government, BM
Psychology, BMD
Public Administration, M
Public Health, M
Sales, Distribution and Marketing Operations, B
School Psychology, O
Science Teacher Education/General Science
 Teacher Education, B
Secondary Education and Teaching, B
Social Work, BM
Sociology, BM
Spanish Language and Literature, BM
Special Education and Teaching, M
Sport and Fitness Administration/Management, M
Statistics, MD
Visual and Performing Arts, B
Women's Studies, B
Writing, M

Kentucky

ALICE LLOYD COLLEGE

Biological and Physical Sciences, B
Biology/Biological Sciences, B
Business Administration and Management, B
Elementary Education and Teaching, B
English Language and Literature, B
History, B
Interdisciplinary Studies, B
Physical Education Teaching and Coaching, B
Pre-Dentistry Studies, B
Pre-Law Studies, B
Pre-Medicine/Pre-Medical Studies, B
Pre-Veterinary Studies, B
Science Teacher Education/General Science
 Teacher Education, B
Secondary Education and Teaching, B

ASBURY COLLEGE

Accounting, B
Ancient/Classical Greek Language and Literature, B
Applied Mathematics, B
Art Teacher Education, B
Bible/Biblical Studies, B
Biochemistry, B
Biology/Biological Sciences, B
Business/Commerce, B
Chemistry, B
Classics and Classical
 Languages, Literatures, and Linguistics, B
Elementary Education and Teaching, B
English as a Second Language, M
English Language and Literature, B
Fine/Studio Arts, B
French Language and Literature, B
Health and Physical Education, B
Health/Medical Preparatory Programs, B
History, B
Journalism, B
Junior High/Intermediate/Middle School Education
 and Teaching, B
Latin Language and Literature, B
Mathematics, B
Mathematics Teacher Education, M
Missions/Missionary Studies and Missiology, B
Music, B
Music Teacher Education, B
Parks, Recreation and Leisure Facilities
 Management, B
Philosophy, B

Physical Education Teaching and Coaching, B
Physical Sciences, B
Psychology, B
Radio and Television Broadcasting
 Technology/Technician, B
Religious Education, B
Science Teacher Education/General Science
 Teacher Education, M
Social Sciences, B
Social Work, B
Sociology, B
Spanish Language and Literature, B
Special Education and Teaching, M
Speech and Rhetorical Studies, B
Sport and Fitness Administration/Management, B

ASHLAND COMMUNITY AND TECHNICAL COLLEGE

Accounting, A
Administrative Assistant and Secretarial Science, A
Business Administration and Management, A
Criminal Justice/Police Science, A
Engineering Technology, A
Information Science/Studies, A
Liberal Arts and Sciences Studies and
 Humanities, A
Management Information Systems and Services, A
Nursing - Registered Nurse Training, A
Physical Therapist Assistant, A
Real Estate, A
Respiratory Care Therapy/Therapist, A

BECKFIELD COLLEGE

Business Administration and Management, AB
Legal Assistant/Paralegal, AB
Medical Office Management/Administration, A
Nursing - Registered Nurse Training, B

BELLARMINE UNIVERSITY

Accounting, B
Actuarial Science, B
Art/Art Studies, General, B
Arts Management, B
Biology/Biological Sciences, B
Business Administration and Management, B
Business Administration, Management and
 Operations, M
Business/Managerial Economics, B
Cardiopulmonary Technology/Technologist, B
Chemistry, B
Clinical Laboratory Science/Medical
 Technology/Technologist, B
Clinical/Medical Laboratory Science and Allied
 Professions, B
Communication Studies/Speech Communication
 and Rhetoric, B
Community Health Nursing, M
Community Organization and Advocacy, B
Computer and Information Sciences, B
Computer Engineering, B
Computer Science, B
Criminal Justice/Safety Studies, B
CytoTechnology/Cytotechnologist, B
Early Childhood Education and Teaching, M
Economics, B
Education, BM
Elementary Education and Teaching, BM
English Language and Literature, B
French Language and Literature, B
German Language and Literature, B
Health Services/Allied Health/Health Sciences, B
History, B
Human Resources Management/Personnel
 Administration, B
International Business/Trade/Commerce, B
International Relations and Affairs, B
Junior High/Intermediate/Middle School Education
 and Teaching, B
Liberal Arts and Sciences Studies and
 Humanities, B
Mathematics, B
Middle School Education, M
Music, B
Music Management and Merchandising, B
Musical Instrument Fabrication and Repair, B
Nursing, M

Nursing - Registered Nurse Training, B
Nursing Administration, M
Nursing Education, M
Painting, B
Pastoral Studies/Counseling, B
Philosophy, B
Political Science and Government, B
Pre-Dentistry Studies, B
Pre-Law Studies, B
Pre-Medicine/Pre-Medical Studies, B
Pre-Pharmacy Studies, B
Pre-Veterinary Studies, B
Psychology, B
Respiratory Care Therapy/Therapist, B
Sculpture, B
Secondary Education and Teaching, BM
Sociology, B
Spanish Language and Literature, B
Special Education and Teaching, BM
Theology/Theological Studies, B

BEREA COLLEGE

Agricultural Business and Management, B
Agriculture, B
Art History, Criticism and Conservation, B
Art Teacher Education, B
Art/Art Studies, General, B
Biology Teacher Education, B
Biology/Biological Sciences, B
Business Administration and Management, B
Chemistry, B
Child Development, B
Classics and Classical
   Languages, Literatures, and Linguistics, B
Developmental and Child Psychology, B
Dietetics/Dieticians, B
Drama and Dramatics/Theatre Arts, B
Economics, B
Education, B
Elementary Education and Teaching, B
English Language and Literature, B
English/Language Arts Teacher Education, B
Family and Consumer Economics and Related
   Services, B
Family and Consumer Sciences/Home Economics
   Teacher Education, B
Fine/Studio Arts, B
Foreign Language Teacher Education, B
French Language and Literature, B
French Language Teacher Education, B
German Language and Literature, B
German Language Teacher Education, B
History, B
Industrial Technology/Technician, B
Junior High/Intermediate/Middle School Education
   and Teaching, B
Kindergarten/PreSchool Education and Teaching, B
Mass Communication/Media Studies, B
Mathematics, B
Mathematics Teacher Education, B
Music, B
Music Teacher Education, B
Nursing - Registered Nurse Training, B
Philosophy, B
Physical Education Teaching and Coaching, B
Physics, B
Political Science and Government, B
Pre-Dentistry Studies, B
Pre-Medicine/Pre-Medical Studies, B
Pre-Veterinary Studies, B
Psychology, B
Religion/Religious Studies, B
Secondary Education and Teaching, B
Sociology, B
Spanish Language and Literature, B
Spanish Language Teacher Education, B
Technology Education/Industrial Arts, B
Women's Studies, B

BIG SANDY COMMUNITY AND TECHNICAL COLLEGE

Accounting, A
Business Administration and Management, A
Criminal Justice/Law Enforcement Administration, A
Dental Hygiene/Hygienist, A
General Office Occupations and Clerical Services, A

Human Services, A
Information Technology, A
Liberal Arts and Sciences Studies and
   Humanities, A
Management Information Systems and Services, A
Nursing, A
Nursing - Registered Nurse Training, A
Real Estate, A

BRESCIA UNIVERSITY

Accounting, B
Applied Mathematics, B
Art Teacher Education, B
Art Therapy/Therapist, B
Art/Art Studies, General, B
Audiology/Audiologist and Speech-Language
   Pathology/Pathologist, B
Biological and Physical Sciences, B
Biology/Biological Sciences, B
Business/Commerce, AB
Chemistry, B
Clinical Laboratory Science/Medical
   Technology/Technologist, B
Commercial and Advertising Art, B
Curriculum and Instruction, M
Education, B
Elementary Education and Teaching, B
Engineering, A
English Language and Literature, B
Finance, B
History, B
Human Resources Management/Personnel
   Administration, B
Junior High/Intermediate/Middle School Education
   and Teaching, B
Liberal Arts and Sciences Studies and
   Humanities, AB
Management, M
Marketing/Marketing Management, B
Mathematics and Computer Science, B
Pre-Engineering, A
Psychology, B
Religion/Religious Studies, AB
Secondary Education and Teaching, B
Social Sciences, B
Social Studies Teacher Education, B
Social Work, B
Spanish Language and Literature, B
Special Education and Teaching, B
Theological and Ministerial Studies, AB

BROWN MACKIE COLLEGE-HOPKINSVILLE

Accounting Technology/Technician and
   Bookkeeping, A
Business Administration and Management, A
Computer Programming, Specific Applications, A
Computer Programming/Programmer, A
Computer Software Technology/Technician, A
Criminal Justice/Safety Studies, A
Legal Assistant/Paralegal, A
Medical/Clinical Assistant, A

BROWN MACKIE COLLEGE-LOUISVILLE

Accounting Technology/Technician and
   Bookkeeping, A
Business Administration and Management, A
Computer Systems Networking and
   Telecommunications, A
Criminal Justice/Safety Studies, A
Gerontology, A
Graphic Design, A
Health/Health Care Administration/Management, A
Industrial Electronics Technology/Technician, A
Legal Assistant/Paralegal, A
Medical/Clinical Assistant, A
Pharmacy Technician/Assistant, A

BROWN MACKIE COLLEGE-NORTHERN KENTUCKY

Accounting Technology/Technician and
   Bookkeeping, A
Business Administration and Management, A

CAD/CADD Drafting and/or Design
   Technology/Technician, A
Computer Programming, Specific Applications, A
Computer Software Technology/Technician, A
Criminal Justice/Law Enforcement Administration, A
Legal Assistant/Paralegal, A
Medical/Clinical Assistant, A
Pharmacy Technician/Assistant, A
System, Networking, and LAN/WAN
   Management/Manager, A

CAMPBELLSVILLE UNIVERSITY

Accounting, B
Administrative Assistant and Secretarial Science, AB
Art Teacher Education, B
Art/Art Studies, General, B
Athletic Training and Sports Medicine, B
Bible/Biblical Studies, B
Biology Teacher Education, B
Biology/Biological Sciences, B
Business Administration and Management, AB
Business Administration, Management and
   Operations, M
Business Teacher Education, B
Business/Managerial Economics, B
Chemistry, B
Chemistry Teacher Education, B
Clinical Laboratory Science/Medical
   Technology/Technologist, B
Criminal Justice/Law Enforcement
   Administration, AB
Curriculum and Instruction, M
Data Processing and Data Processing
   Technology/Technician, A
Divinity/Ministry (BD, MDiv.), B
Economics, B
Education, M
Elementary Education and Teaching, B
English Language and Literature, B
English/Language Arts Teacher Education, B
Health Teacher Education, B
History, B
History Teacher Education, B
Information Science/Studies, AB
Journalism, B
Marketing/Marketing Management, B
Mass Communication/Media Studies, B
Mathematics, B
Mathematics Teacher Education, B
Music, BM
Music Teacher Education, BM
Parks, Recreation, Leisure and Fitness Studies, B
Pastoral Studies/Counseling, B
Physical Education Teaching and Coaching, B
Piano and Organ, B
Political Science and Government, B
Pre-Dentistry Studies, B
Pre-Law Studies, B
Pre-Medicine/Pre-Medical Studies, B
Pre-Veterinary Studies, B
Psychology, B
Psychology Teacher Education, B
Religion/Religious Studies, B
Religious Education, B
Religious/Sacred Music, B
Sacred Music, M
Science Teacher Education/General Science
   Teacher Education, B
Secondary Education and Teaching, B
Social Science Teacher Education, B
Social Sciences, ABM
Social Studies Teacher Education, B
Social Work, B
Sociology, B
Special Education and Teaching, M
Theology and Religious Vocations, M
Voice and Opera, B

CENTRE COLLEGE

Anthropology, B
Art History, Criticism and Conservation, B
Art/Art Studies, General, B
Biochemistry, B
Biology/Biological Sciences, B
Chemistry, B

Classics and Classical
  Languages, Literatures, and Linguistics, B
Computer Science, B
Drama and Dramatics/Theatre Arts, B
Economics, B
Elementary Education and Teaching, B
English Language and Literature, B
French Language and Literature, B
German Language and Literature, B
History, B
International Relations and Affairs, B
Mathematics, B
Molecular Biology, B
Music, B
Philosophy, B
Physics, B
Physiological Psychology/Psychobiology, B
Political Science and Government, B
Psychology, B
Religion/Religious Studies, B
Secondary Education and Teaching, B
Sociology, B
Spanish Language and Literature, B

CLEAR CREEK BAPTIST BIBLE COLLEGE

Bible/Biblical Studies, AB
Divinity/Ministry (BD, MDiv.), AB

DAYMAR COLLEGE (LOUISVILLE)

Computer Installation and Repair
  Technology/Technician, A
Computer Programming/Programmer, A
Computer Systems Networking and
  Telecommunications, A
Legal Assistant/Paralegal, A
Medical Office Assistant/Specialist, A

DAYMAR COLLEGE (OWENSBORO)

Administrative Assistant and Secretarial Science, A
Business Administration and Management, A
Communications Systems Installation and Repair
  Technology, A
Computer and Information Systems Security, A
Computer Engineering, A
Computer Graphics, A
Computer Hardware Engineering, A
Computer Installation and Repair
  Technology/Technician, A
Computer Programming, A
Computer Programming, Specific Applications, A
Computer
  Programming, Vendor/Product Certification, A
Computer Science, A
Computer Software and Media Applications, A
Computer Software Engineering, A
Computer Systems Networking and
  Telecommunications, A
Computer/Information Technology Services
  Administration and Management, A
Data Entry/Microcomputer Applications, A
Data Modeling/Warehousing and Database
  Administration, A
Legal Assistant/Paralegal, A
Management Information Systems and Services, A
Medical Office Management/Administration, A
System Administration/Administrator, A
Web Page, Digital/Multimedia and Information
  Resources Design, A
Web/Multimedia Management and Webmaster, A
Word Processing, A

DRAUGHONS JUNIOR COLLEGE

Accounting, A
Administrative Assistant and Secretarial Science, A
Business Administration and Management, A
Health Information/Medical Records
  Administration/Administrator, A
Information Science/Studies, A
Information Technology, A
Legal Administrative Assistant/Secretary, A

Medical/Clinical Assistant, A

EASTERN KENTUCKY UNIVERSITY

Accounting, B
Administrative Assistant and Secretarial Science, AB
Agricultural Business and Management, B
Agricultural Education, M
Agricultural Production Operations, B
Agriculture, B
Agriculture, Agriculture Operations and Related
  Sciences, A
Airline/Commercial/Professional Pilot and Flight
  Crew, B
Allied Health and Medical Assisting Services, M
Anthropology, B
Applied Mathematics, B
Architectural Engineering Technology/Technician, B
Art Education, M
Art Teacher Education, B
Art/Art Studies, General, B
Audiology/Audiologist and Speech-Language
  Pathology/Pathologist, B
Biological and Biomedical Sciences, M
Biology/Biological Sciences, B
Broadcast Journalism, B
Business Administration and Management, B
Business Administration, Management and
  Operations, M
Business Education, M
Business Teacher Education, B
Business/Commerce, B
Business/Managerial Economics, B
Chemistry, BM
Child Care and Support Services Management, A
Child Care Provider/Assistant, A
Child Development, AB
Clinical Laboratory Science/Medical
  Technology/Technologist, B
Clinical Psychology, M
Clinical/Medical Laboratory Technician, A
Commercial and Advertising Art, B
Communication Disorders, BM
Community Health and Preventive Medicine, M
Community Health Services/Liaison/Counseling, B
Composition, M
Computer and Information Sciences, B
Computer Engineering Technology/Technician, A
Computer Science, B
Computer Technology/Computer Systems
  Technology, A
Construction Engineering Technology/Technician, B
Consumer Merchandising/Retailing Management, B
Corrections, ABM
Counselor Education/School Counseling and
  Guidance Services, M
Criminal Justice/Law Enforcement
  Administration, AB
Criminal Justice/Police Science, AB
Criminology, M
Curriculum and Instruction, M
Dietetics/Dieticians, B
Dietician Assistant, A
Drafting and Design Technology/Technician, A
Drama and Dramatics/Theatre Arts, B
Ecology, BM
Economics, B
Education, BM
Education/Teaching of Individuals with Hearing
  Impairments, Including Deafness, B
Education/Teaching of Individuals with Speech or
  Language Impairments, B
Educational Administration and Supervision, M
Educational Leadership and Administration, M
Electrical, Electronic and Communications
  Engineering Technology/Technician, A
Elementary Education and Teaching, BM
Emergency Medical Technology/Technician (EMT
  Paramedic), AB
Engineering, A
English, M
English Education, M
English Language and Literature, B
Environmental and Occupational Health, M
Environmental Engineering
  Technology/Environmental Technology, B
Environmental Health, B

Environmental Studies, B
Family and Community Services, B
Family and Consumer Sciences/Home Economics
  Teacher Education, B
Family and Consumer Sciences/Human Sciences, B
Farm/Farm and Ranch Management, B
Fashion Merchandising, B
Finance, B
Fine/Studio Arts, B
Fire Protection and Safety
  Technology/Technician, AB
Foods, Nutrition, and Wellness Studies, A
Forensic Science and Technology, B
French Language and Literature, B
General Studies, B
Geography, B
Geology/Earth Science, BMD
Graphic and Printing Equipment Operator
  Production, AB
Health Education, M
Health Information/Medical Records
  Administration/Administrator, AB
Health Information/Medical Records
  Technology/Technician, A
Health Services Administration, M
Health Teacher Education, B
Health/Health Care Administration/Management, B
Higher Education/Higher Education
  Administration, M
History, BM
Home Economics Education, M
Home Furnishings and Equipment Installers, A
Horticultural Science, B
Housing and Human Environments, B
Human Development and Family Studies, B
Industrial and Organizational Psychology, M
Industrial Education, M
Industrial Technology/Technician, AB
Industrial/Management Engineering, M
Information Science/Studies, B
Insurance, B
Interior Design, AB
Journalism, B
Junior High/Intermediate/Middle School Education
  and Teaching, B
Kindergarten/PreSchool Education and Teaching, B
Landscape Architecture, AB
Law Enforcement, M
Legal Assistant/Paralegal, AB
Management Information Systems and Services, B
Manufacturing Engineering, M
Marketing/Marketing Management, B
Mass Communication/Media Studies, B
Mathematics, BM
Mathematics Teacher Education, M
Medical Microbiology and Bacteriology, B
Medical Office Management/Administration, B
Medical/Clinical Assistant, A
Music, BM
Music Teacher Education, BM
Music Theory and Composition, M
Natural Sciences, B
Nursing, BM
Nursing - Advanced Practice, M
Nursing - Registered Nurse Training, AB
Nutritional Sciences, M
Occupational Therapy/Therapist, BM
Office Management and Supervision, B
Parks, Recreation and Leisure Facilities
  Management, AB
Performance, M
Philosophy, B
Physical Education Teaching and Coaching, BM
Physical Sciences, B
Physics, B
Political Science and Government, BM
Pre-Engineering, A
Psychology, BMO
Public Administration, M
Public Relations, Advertising, and Applied
  Communication, B
Public Relations/Image Management, B
Quality Control Technology/Technician, A
Radio and Television, B
Reading Teacher Education, M
Real Estate, B

Recreation and Park Management, M
School Psychology, O
Science Teacher Education/General Science
    Teacher Education, BM
Secondary Education and Teaching, BM
Securities Services Administration/Management, M
Security and Loss Prevention Services, B
Sign Language Interpretation and Translation, B
Social Studies Teacher Education, M
Social Work, B
Sociology, B
Spanish Language and Literature, B
Special Education and Teaching, BM
Speech and Rhetorical Studies, B
Sport and Fitness Administration/Management, M
Statistics, B
Substance Abuse/Addiction Counseling, M
Teacher Education and Professional
    Development, Specific Subject Areas, B
Technical Teacher Education, AB
Technology Education/Industrial Arts, AB
Technology Teacher Education/Industrial Arts
    Teacher Education, B
Theater, M
Trade and Industrial Teacher Education, B
Transportation and Materials Moving, B
Urban and Regional Planning, M
Wildlife and Wildlands Science and Management, B
Writing, M

ELIZABETHTOWN COMMUNITY AND TECHNICAL COLLEGE

Administrative Assistant and Secretarial Science, A
Biological and Physical Sciences, A
Business Administration and Management, A
Child Development, A
Criminal Justice/Police Science, A
Dental Hygiene/Hygienist, A
Finance, A
Information Science/Studies, A
Liberal Arts and Sciences Studies and
    Humanities, A
Nursing - Registered Nurse Training, A
Quality Control Technology/Technician, A
Real Estate, A

GEORGETOWN COLLEGE

Accounting, B
American/United States Studies/Civilization, B
Athletic Training and Sports Medicine, B
Biology/Biological Sciences, B
Business Administration and Management, B
Chemistry, B
Computer and Information Sciences, B
Drama and Dramatics/Theatre Arts, B
Ecology, B
Economics, B
Education, M
Elementary Education and Teaching, B
English Language and Literature, B
European Studies/Civilization, B
Fine/Studio Arts, B
French Language and Literature, B
German Language and Literature, B
History, B
Junior High/Intermediate/Middle School Education
    and Teaching, B
Kinesiology and Exercise Science, B
Liberal Arts and Sciences Studies and
    Humanities, B
Mass Communication/Media Studies, B
Mathematics, B
Multi-/Interdisciplinary Studies, B
Music, B
Music Teacher Education, B
Philosophy, B
Physics, B
Political Science and Government, B
Psychology, B
Religion/Religious Studies, B
Sociology, B

Spanish Language and Literature, B

HAZARD COMMUNITY AND TECHNICAL COLLEGE

Administrative Assistant and Secretarial Science, A
Business Administration and Management, A
Clinical/Medical Laboratory Technician, A
Computer Typography and Composition Equipment
    Operator, A
Data Processing and Data Processing
    Technology/Technician, A
Forestry Technology/Technician, A
Information Science/Studies, A
Kindergarten/PreSchool Education and Teaching, A
Liberal Arts and Sciences Studies and
    Humanities, A
Management Science, A
Medical Radiologic Technology/Science - Radiation
    Therapist, A
Nursing - Registered Nurse Training, A
Physical Therapist Assistant, A

HENDERSON COMMUNITY COLLEGE

Administrative Assistant and Secretarial Science, A
Business Administration and Management, A
Clinical Laboratory Science/Medical
    Technology/Technologist, A
Computer and Information Sciences, A
Computer Programming, A
Computer Programming, Specific Applications, A
Computer
    Programming, Vendor/Product Certification, A
Computer Systems Networking and
    Telecommunications, A
Computer/Information Technology Services
    Administration and Management, A
Data Entry/Microcomputer Applications, A
Data Processing and Data Processing
    Technology/Technician, A
Electrical, Electronic and Communications
    Engineering Technology/Technician, A
Engineering Technology, A
Human Services, A
Information Technology, A
Mass Communication/Media Studies, A
Nursing - Registered Nurse Training, A
Word Processing, A

HOPKINSVILLE COMMUNITY COLLEGE

Administrative Assistant and Secretarial Science, A
Animal/Livestock Husbandry and Production, A
Business Administration and Management, A
Child Care and Support Services Management, A
Criminal Justice/Police Science, A
Early Childhood Education and Teaching, A
Electrical, Electronic and Communications
    Engineering Technology/Technician, A
Finance, A
Human Services, A
Industrial Technology/Technician, A
Kindergarten/PreSchool Education and Teaching, A
Liberal Arts and Sciences Studies and
    Humanities, A
Licensed Practical/Vocational Nurse Training, A
Management Information Systems and Services, A
Manufacturing Technology/Technician, A
Mental Health/Rehabilitation, A
Nursing - Registered Nurse Training, A

ITT TECHNICAL INSTITUTE (LEXINGTON)

Business Administration and Management, B
CAD/CADD Drafting and/or Design
    Technology/Technician, A
Computer and Information Systems Security, B
Criminal Justice/Law Enforcement Administration, B
Electrical, Electronic and Communications
    Engineering Technology/Technician, AB
System, Networking, and LAN/WAN
    Management/Manager, A

Web Page, Digital/Multimedia and Information
    Resources Design, A

ITT TECHNICAL INSTITUTE (LOUISVILLE)

Animation, Interactive Technology, Video Graphics
    and Special Effects, B
Business Administration and Management, B
CAD/CADD Drafting and/or Design
    Technology/Technician, A
Computer and Information Systems Security, B
Computer Programming/Programmer, A
Criminal Justice/Law Enforcement Administration, B
E-Commerce/Electronic Commerce, B
Electrical, Electronic and Communications
    Engineering Technology/Technician, A
System, Networking, and LAN/WAN
    Management/Manager, A
Web Page, Digital/Multimedia and Information
    Resources Design, A
Web/Multimedia Management and Webmaster, B

JEFFERSON COMMUNITY AND TECHNICAL COLLEGE

Accounting, A
Business Administration and Management, A
Child Development, A
Commercial and Advertising Art, A
Culinary Arts/Chef Training, A
Data Processing and Data Processing
    Technology/Technician, A
Electrical, Electronic and Communications
    Engineering Technology/Technician, A
Health Information/Medical Records
    Technology/Technician, A
Liberal Arts and Sciences Studies and
    Humanities, A
Mechanical Engineering/Mechanical
    Technology/Technician, A
Medical Radiologic Technology/Science - Radiation
    Therapist, A
Nuclear Medical Technology/Technologist, A
Nursing - Registered Nurse Training, A
Physical Therapy/Therapist, A
Real Estate, A
Respiratory Care Therapy/Therapist, A
Social Work, A
Welding Technology/Welder, A

KENTUCKY CHRISTIAN UNIVERSITY

Administrative Assistant and Secretarial Science, A
Business Administration and Management, B
Elementary Education and Teaching, B
History, B
Interdisciplinary Studies, B
Junior High/Intermediate/Middle School Education
    and Teaching, B
Music, B
Music Teacher Education, B
Nursing - Registered Nurse Training, B
Pastoral Studies/Counseling, B
Psychology, B
Religion/Religious Studies, M
Religious Education, B
Social Work, B
Theology and Religious Vocations, M

KENTUCKY MOUNTAIN BIBLE COLLEGE

Mass Communication/Media Studies, B
Missions/Missionary Studies and Missiology, B
Pre-Theology/Pre-Ministerial Studies, B
Religion/Religious Studies, AB
Religious Education, B

KENTUCKY STATE UNIVERSITY

Apparel and Textiles, B
Applied Mathematics, B
Aquaculture, M
Art Teacher Education, B
Biology/Biological Sciences, B
Business Administration and Management, B
Chemistry, B
Clinical Laboratory Science/Medical
    Technology/Technologist, B

Computer and Information Sciences, AB
Computer Science, M
Criminal Justice/Safety Studies, B
Drafting and Design Technology/Technician, A
Electrical, Electronic and Communications
  Engineering Technology/Technician, A
Elementary Education and Teaching, B
English Language and Literature, B
Executive Assistant/Executive Secretary, A
Fine/Studio Arts, B
Health and Physical Education, B
History, B
Human Development and Family Studies, B
Liberal Arts and Sciences Studies and
  Humanities, AB
Mathematics, B
Music Performance, B
Music Teacher Education, B
Nursing - Registered Nurse Training, AB
Physical Education Teaching and Coaching, B
Political Science and Government, B
Psychology, B
Public Administration, BM
Secondary Education and Teaching, B
Social Studies Teacher Education, B
Social Work, B
Sociology, B

KENTUCKY WESLEYAN COLLEGE

Accounting, B
Art Teacher Education, B
Biology Teacher Education, B
Biology/Biological Sciences, B
Business Administration and Management, B
Chemistry, B
Chemistry Teacher Education, B
Clinical Laboratory Science/Medical
  Technology/Technologist, B
Communication Studies/Speech Communication
  and Rhetoric, B
Computer and Information Sciences, B
Computer Science, B
Criminal Justice/Safety Studies, B
Elementary Education and Teaching, B
Engineering, B
English Language and Literature, B
English/Language Arts Teacher Education, B
Environmental Studies, B
Fine Arts and Art Studies, B
History, B
Human Services, B
Interdisciplinary Studies, B
Junior High/Intermediate/Middle School Education
  and Teaching, B
Mathematics, B
Mathematics Teacher Education, B
Multi-/Interdisciplinary Studies, B
Philosophy, B
Physical Education Teaching and Coaching, B
Physics, B
Political Science and Government, B
Pre-Dentistry Studies, B
Pre-Law Studies, B
Pre-Medicine/Pre-Medical Studies, B
Pre-Veterinary Studies, B
Psychology, B
Public Administration and Social Service
  Professions, B
Secondary Education and Teaching, B
Social Studies Teacher Education, B
Sociology, B
Spanish Language and Literature, B
Spanish Language Teacher Education, B
Sport and Fitness Administration/Management, B

LEXINGTON COMMUNITY COLLEGE

Accounting, A
Architectural Drafting and Architectural
  CAD/CADD, A
Architectural Engineering Technology/Technician, A
Business Administration and Management, A
Civil Engineering Technology/Technician, A
Computer Systems Networking and
  Telecommunications, A
Dental Hygiene/Hygienist, A
Dental Laboratory Technology/Technician, A

Electrical, Electronic and Communications
  Engineering Technology/Technician, A
Information Science/Studies, A
Liberal Arts and Sciences Studies and
  Humanities, A
Medical Radiologic Technology/Science - Radiation
  Therapist, A
Nuclear Medical Technology/Technologist, A
Nursing - Registered Nurse Training, A
Respiratory Care Therapy/Therapist, A

LINDSEY WILSON COLLEGE

American/United States Studies/Civilization, B
Art Teacher Education, B
Art/Art Studies, General, AB
Biology Teacher Education, B
Biology/Biological Sciences, B
Business Administration and Management, AB
Chemistry, A
Computer and Information Sciences, A
Computer Programming/Programmer, A
Criminal Justice/Law Enforcement Administration, B
Early Childhood Education and Teaching, A
Education, B
Educational Psychology, M
Elementary Education and Teaching, B
English Language and Literature, B
Health Services/Allied Health/Health Sciences, A
History, AB
Human Development, M
Human Services, BM
Humanities/Humanistic Studies, B
Journalism, B
Junior High/Intermediate/Middle School Education
  and Teaching, B
Management Information Systems and Services, A
Mass Communication/Media Studies, B
Mathematics, AB
Mathematics Teacher Education, B
Parks, Recreation, Leisure and Fitness Studies, B
Physical Education Teaching and Coaching, B
Pre-Dentistry Studies, B
Pre-Law Studies, B
Pre-Medicine/Pre-Medical Studies, B
Pre-Pharmacy Studies, B
Pre-Veterinary Studies, B
Psychology, B
Religion/Religious Studies, AB
Secondary Education and Teaching, B
Social Science Teacher Education, B
Social Sciences, AB

LOUISVILLE TECHNICAL INSTITUTE

Animation, Interactive Technology, Video Graphics
  and Special Effects, A
Architectural Drafting and Architectural
  CAD/CADD, A
Architectural Engineering Technology/Technician, A
Architecture and Related Services, A
Artificial Intelligence and Robotics, A
CAD/CADD Drafting and/or Design
  Technology/Technician, A
Computer and Information Sciences, A
Computer and Information Sciences and Support
  Services, A
Computer and Information Systems Security, A
Computer Engineering Technology/Technician, A
Computer Graphics, A
Computer Hardware Engineering, A
Computer Hardware Technology/Technician, A
Computer Installation and Repair
  Technology/Technician, A
Computer
  Programming, Vendor/Product Certification, A
Computer Systems Networking and
  Telecommunications, A
Computer Technology/Computer Systems
  Technology, A
Digital Communication and Media/Multimedia, A
Drafting and Design Technology/Technician, A
Drafting/Design Engineering
  Technologies/Technicians, A
Electrical and Electronic Engineering
  Technologies/Technicians, A
Electrical, Electronic and Communications
  Engineering Technology/Technician, A

Electrical/Electronics Equipment Installation and
  Repair, A
Electrical/Electronics Maintenance and Repair
  Technology, A
Electromechanical and Instrumentation and
  Maintenance Technologies/Technicians, A
Engineering Technologies/Technicians, A
Engineering Technology, A
Graphic and Printing Equipment Operator
  Production, A
Graphic Communications, A
Graphic Design, A
Housing and Human Environments, A
Industrial Electronics Technology/Technician, A
Industrial Mechanics and Maintenance
  Technology, A
Information Technology, A
Interior Design, A
Management Information Systems and Services, A
Marine Technology, A
Mechanical Drafting and Mechanical Drafting
  CAD/CADD, A
Mechanical Engineering/Mechanical
  Technology/Technician, A
Prepress/Desktop Publishing and Digital Imaging
  Design, A
Robotics Technology/Technician, A
Small Engine Mechanics and Repair
  Technology/Technician, A
System Administration/Administrator, A
Web Page, Digital/Multimedia and Information
  Resources Design, A

MADISONVILLE COMMUNITY COLLEGE

Accounting, A
Accounting Technology/Technician and
  Bookkeeping, A
Administrative Assistant and Secretarial Science, A
Banking and Financial Support Services, A
Biomedical Technology/Technician, A
Business Administration and Management, A
Computer Technology/Computer Systems
  Technology, A
Consumer Merchandising/Retailing Management, A
Criminal Justice/Police Science, A
Electrical, Electronic and Communications
  Engineering Technology/Technician, A
Information Science/Studies, A
Mechanical Engineering/Mechanical
  Technology/Technician, A
Nursing - Registered Nurse Training, A
Occupational Therapist Assistant, A
Physical Therapist Assistant, A
Radiologic Technology/Science - Radiographer, A
Real Estate, A
Respiratory Care Therapy/Therapist, A

MAYSVILLE COMMUNITY AND TECHNICAL COLLEGE

Accounting, A
Administrative Assistant and Secretarial Science, A
Business Administration and Management, A
Electrical, Electronic and Communications
  Engineering Technology/Technician, A
Electromechanical Technology/Electromechanical
  Engineering Technology, A
Liberal Arts and Sciences Studies and
  Humanities, A
Marketing/Marketing Management, A
Nursing - Registered Nurse Training, A
Respiratory Care Therapy/Therapist, A

MID-CONTINENT UNIVERSITY

Ancient Near Eastern and Biblical
  Languages, Literatures, and Linguistics, B
Bible/Biblical Studies, B
Business Administration and Management, B
Counseling Psychology, B
Elementary Education and Teaching, B
English Language and Literature, B
General Studies, B
Missions/Missionary Studies and Missiology, B
Multi-/Interdisciplinary Studies, B
Organizational Behavior Studies, B
Psychology, B

Religious Education, B
Social Sciences, B

MIDWAY COLLEGE

Biology/Biological Sciences, B
Business Administration and Management, AB
Chemistry, B
Computer and Information Sciences, AB
Education, B
Elementary Education and Teaching, B
English Language and Literature, B
Environmental Biology, B
Equestrian/Equine Studies, AB
Health/Health Care Administration/Management, B
Horse Husbandry/Equine Science and
    Management, B
Human Resources Management/Personnel
    Administration, B
Junior High/Intermediate/Middle School Education
    and Teaching, B
Liberal Arts and Sciences Studies and
    Humanities, B
Mathematics, B
Nursing - Registered Nurse Training, AB
Psychology, B
Secondary Education and Teaching, B
Special Education and Teaching, B
Sport and Fitness Administration/Management, B

MOREHEAD STATE UNIVERSITY

Accounting, B
Adult and Continuing Education and Teaching, MO
Advertising and Public Relations, M
Agribusiness, A
Agriculture, B
Art Education, M
Biological and Biomedical Sciences, M
Biology/Biological Sciences, B
Business Administration and Management, B
Business Administration, Management and
    Operations, M
Business Teacher Education, B
Business/Managerial Economics, B
Chemistry, B
Clinical Psychology, M
Communication and Media Studies, M
Communication Studies/Speech Communication
    and Rhetoric, B
Computer and Information Sciences, B
Counseling Psychology, M
Counselor Education/School Counseling and
    Guidance Services, MO
Criminology, M
Curriculum and Instruction, O
Drama and Dramatics/Theatre Arts, B
Ecology, B
Education, MO
Educational Administration and Supervision, MO
Electronic Commerce, M
Elementary Education and Teaching, BM
English, M
English Language and Literature, B
Exercise and Sports Science, M
Experimental Psychology, M
Family and Consumer Sciences/Human
    Sciences, AB
Finance, B
Fine Arts and Art Studies, M
Fine/Studio Arts, B
French Language and Literature, B
General Studies, AB
Geography, B
Geology/Earth Science, B
Gerontology, M
Health Education, M
Health Teacher Education, B
Higher Education/Higher Education
    Administration, MO
History, B
Industrial Technology/Technician, AB
International and Comparative Education, M
Journalism, M
Junior High/Intermediate/Middle School Education
    and Teaching, B
Kindergarten/PreSchool Education and Teaching, B
Kinesiology and Exercise Science, B

Legal Assistant/Paralegal, B
Management Information Systems and Services, AB
Marketing/Marketing Management, B
Mathematics, B
Medical Radiologic Technology/Science - Radiation
    Therapist, AB
Middle School Education, M
Music, B
Music Teacher Education, M
Nursing - Registered Nurse Training, AB
Performance, M
Philosophy, B
Physical Education Teaching and Coaching, BM
Physics, B
Political Science and Government, B
Psychology, BM
Reading Teacher Education, M
Real Estate, B
Recreation and Park Management, M
Respiratory Care Therapy/Therapist, A
Secondary Education and Teaching, M
Social Sciences, B
Social Work, B
Sociology, BM
Spanish Language and Literature, B
Special Education and Teaching, BM
Speech and Rhetorical Studies, BM
Sport and Fitness Administration/Management, BM
Theater, M
Veterinary/Animal Health Technology/Technician and
    Veterinary Assistant, A
Vocational and Technical Education, M

MURRAY STATE UNIVERSITY

Accounting, BM
Administrative Assistant and Secretarial Science, A
Agricultural Business and Management, B
Agricultural Sciences, M
Agricultural Teacher Education, B
Agriculture, AB
Apparel and Textiles, B
Art Teacher Education, B
Audiology/Audiologist and Speech-Language
    Pathology/Pathologist, B
Biological and Biomedical Sciences, MD
Biology Teacher Education, B
Biology/Biological Sciences, B
Business Administration and Management, B
Business Administration, Management and
    Operations, M
Business Teacher Education, B
Business/Commerce, B
Chemical Engineering, B
Chemical Technology/Technician, B
Chemistry, BM
Chemistry Teacher Education, B
Child Care Provider/Assistant, A
Civil Engineering Technology/Technician, AB
Clinical Laboratory Science/Medical
    Technology/Technologist, B
Clinical Psychology, M
Communication Disorders, BM
Computer and Information Sciences, B
Computer Engineering Technology/Technician, B
Corporate and Organizational Communication, M
Counselor Education/School Counseling and
    Guidance Services, MO
Criminal Justice/Safety Studies, AB
Drafting and Design Technology/Technician, A
Drama and Dramatics/Theatre Arts, B
Early Childhood Education and Teaching, BM
Economics, BM
Education, MDO
Educational Administration and Supervision, MO
Electromechanical Technology/Electromechanical
    Engineering Technology, B
Elementary Education and Teaching, BMO
Engineering Physics, B
Engineering Technology, B
English, M
English as a Second Language, M
English Language and Literature, B
English/Language Arts Teacher Education, B
Environmental and Occupational Health, M
Environmental Engineering
    Technology/Environmental Technology, B

Executive Assistant/Executive Secretary, A
Family and Consumer Economics and Related
    Services, B
Family and Consumer Sciences/Home Economics
    Teacher Education, B
Finance, B
Fine/Studio Arts, B
Fishing and Fisheries Sciences and Management, B
Foods, Nutrition, and Wellness Studies, B
Foodservice Systems
    Administration/Management, A
Foreign Language Teacher Education, B
French Language and Literature, B
French Language Teacher Education, B
General Studies, B
Geography, B
Geology/Earth Science, B
Geosciences, M
German Language and Literature, B
German Language Teacher Education, B
Graphic and Printing Equipment Operator
    Production, B
Health Teacher Education, B
History, BM
History Teacher Education, B
Human Development and Family Studies, B
Human Services, M
Industrial Technology/Technician, AB
Information Science/Studies, AB
International Business/Trade/Commerce, B
International Relations and Affairs, B
Journalism, B
Junior High/Intermediate/Middle School Education
    and Teaching, B
Kinesiology and Exercise Science, B
Leisure Studies, M
Liberal Arts and Sciences Studies and
    Humanities, AB
Library Science, B
Management Information Systems and Services, B
Management of Technology, M
Manufacturing Technology/Technician, B
Marine Biology and Biological Oceanography, M
Marine Sciences, M
Marketing/Marketing Management, B
Mass Communication/Media Studies, BM
Mathematics, BM
Mathematics Teacher Education, B
Mechanical Drafting and Mechanical Drafting
    CAD/CADD, B
Mechanical Engineering, B
Mechanical Engineering/Mechanical
    Technology/Technician, A
Middle School Education, MO
Military Technologies, A
Music, BM
Music Teacher Education, BM
Nursing, M
Nursing - Registered Nurse Training, B
Occupational Safety and Health
    Technology/Technician, B
Office Management and Supervision, B
Parks, Recreation and Leisure Facilities
    Management, B
Perioperative/Operating Room and Surgical
    Nurse/Nursing, B
Philosophy, B
Physical Education Teaching and Coaching, BM
Physics, B
Physics Teacher Education, B
Political Science and Government, B
Psychology, BM
Public Administration, B
Public Affairs, M
Public Relations, Advertising, and Applied
    Communication, B
Public Relations/Image Management, B
Radio and Television, B
Reading Teacher Education, BM
Recreation and Park Management, M
Safety Engineering, M
Science Teacher Education/General Science
    Teacher Education, B
Secondary Education and Teaching, BMO
Social Science Teacher Education, B
Social Studies Teacher Education, B

Social Work, B
Sociology, B
Spanish Language and Literature, B
Spanish Language Teacher Education, B
Special Education and Teaching, BM
Speech and Rhetorical Studies, B
Speech Teacher Education, B
Teaching English as a Second or Foreign
   Language/ESL Language Instructor, B
Technical and Business Writing, A
Technology Teacher Education/Industrial Arts
   Teacher Education, B
Telecommunications Management, M
Telecommunications Technology/Technician, B
Trade and Industrial Teacher Education, AB
Veterinary/Animal Health Technology/Technician and
   Veterinary Assistant, B
Vocational and Technical Education, M
Water Quality and Wastewater Treatment
   Management and Recycling
   Technology/Technician, AB

NATIONAL COLLEGE OF BUSINESS & TECHNOLOGY (DANVILLE)

Accounting, A
Administrative Assistant and Secretarial Science, A
Business Administration and Management, A
Computer and Information Sciences, A
Medical/Clinical Assistant, A

NATIONAL COLLEGE OF BUSINESS & TECHNOLOGY (FLORENCE)

Accounting, A
Administrative Assistant and Secretarial Science, A
Business Administration and Management, A
Computer and Information Sciences, A
Medical/Clinical Assistant, A

NATIONAL COLLEGE OF BUSINESS & TECHNOLOGY (LEXINGTON)

Accounting, A
Administrative Assistant and Secretarial Science, A
Business Administration and Management, A
Computer and Information Sciences, A
Radio and Television, A

NATIONAL COLLEGE OF BUSINESS & TECHNOLOGY (LOUISVILLE)

Accounting, A
Administrative Assistant and Secretarial Science, A
Business Administration and Management, A
Computer and Information Sciences, A
Health/Health Care Administration/Management, A
Medical/Clinical Assistant, A

NATIONAL COLLEGE OF BUSINESS & TECHNOLOGY (PIKEVILLE)

Accounting, A
Administrative Assistant and Secretarial Science, A
Business Administration and Management, A
Computer and Information Sciences, A
Medical/Clinical Assistant, A

NATIONAL COLLEGE OF BUSINESS & TECHNOLOGY (RICHMOND)

Accounting, A
Administrative Assistant and Secretarial Science, A
Business Administration and Management, A
Computer and Information Sciences, A
Medical/Clinical Assistant, A

NORTHERN KENTUCKY UNIVERSITY

Accounting, BM
Adult Health Nurse/Nursing, B
Anthropology, B
Architectural Engineering Technology/Technician, A
Art/Art Studies, General, B
Aviation/Airway Management and Operations, A
Biology/Biological Sciences, B
Business Administration and Management, AB
Business Administration, Management and
   Operations, MO
Business Teacher Education, B
Business/Commerce, A

Chemistry, B
Commercial and Advertising Art, B
Computer and Information Sciences, B
Computer Science, BM
Criminal Justice/Law Enforcement Administration, B
Criminal Justice/Police Science, A
Criminal Justice/Safety Studies, B
Drama and Dramatics/Theatre Arts, B
Economics, B
Education, BMO
Educational Leadership and Administration, M
Electrical, Electronic and Communications
   Engineering Technology/Technician, B
Elementary Education and Teaching, B
English Language and Literature, B
Environmental Studies, B
Finance, B
Fine/Studio Arts, B
French Language and Literature, B
Geography, B
Geology/Earth Science, B
History, B
Human Services, AB
Industrial and Organizational Psychology, M
Industrial Engineering, B
Industrial Radiologic Technology/Technician, A
Industrial Technology/Technician, B
Information Science/Studies, BM
Information Technology, B
International Relations and Affairs, B
Journalism, B
Junior High/Intermediate/Middle School Education
   and Teaching, B
Kindergarten/PreSchool Education and Teaching, B
Kinesiology and Exercise Science, B
Labor and Industrial Relations, B
Law and Legal Studies, PO
Liberal Studies, M
Management Information Systems and Services, B
Management of Technology, M
Marketing/Marketing Management, B
Mathematics, B
Mathematics Teacher Education, B
Medical Radiologic Technology/Science - Radiation
   Therapist, A
Mental Health/Rehabilitation, B
Middle School Education, M
Music, B
Nursing, MO
Nursing - Registered Nurse Training, AB
Operations Management and Supervision, A
Organizational Behavior Studies, B
Philosophy, B
Physical Education Teaching and Coaching, B
Physics, B
Political Science and Government, B
Pre-Dentistry Studies, B
Pre-Law Studies, B
Pre-Medicine/Pre-Medical Studies, B
Pre-Veterinary Studies, B
Psychiatric/Mental Health Services Technician, A
Psychology, B
Public Administration, BMO
Radio and Television, B
Respiratory Care Therapy/Therapist, A
Science Teacher Education/General Science
   Teacher Education, B
Secondary Education and Teaching, M
Social Sciences, B
Social Work, B
Sociology, B
Spanish Language and Literature, B
Special Education and Teaching, BO
Speech and Rhetorical Studies, B
Systems Science and Theory, M
Technical Teacher Education, A
Trade and Industrial Teacher Education, B

OWENSBORO COMMUNITY AND TECHNICAL COLLEGE

Agriculture, A
Business Administration and Management, A
Computer and Information Sciences, A
Computer/Information Technology Services
   Administration and Management, A
Criminal Justice/Police Science, A

Data Entry/Microcomputer Applications, A
Electrical, Electronic and Communications
   Engineering Technology/Technician, A
Executive Assistant/Executive Secretary, A
Human Services, A
Information Technology, A
Kindergarten/PreSchool Education and Teaching, A
Liberal Arts and Sciences Studies and
   Humanities, A
Medical Radiologic Technology/Science - Radiation
   Therapist, A
Nursing - Registered Nurse Training, A
Social Work, A
System Administration/Administrator, A
Word Processing, A

PADUCAH TECHNICAL COLLEGE

Communications Technology/Technician, A
Computer Engineering Technology/Technician, A
Electrical, Electronic and Communications
   Engineering Technology/Technician, A
Industrial Technology/Technician, A

PIKEVILLE COLLEGE

Art/Art Studies, General, B
Biology Teacher Education, B
Biology/Biological Sciences, B
Business Administration and Management, AB
Chemistry, B
Chemistry Teacher Education, B
Communication Studies/Speech Communication
   and Rhetoric, B
Community Psychology, B
Computer and Information Sciences, B
Criminal Justice/Safety Studies, AB
Elementary Education and Teaching, B
English Language and Literature, B
English/Language Arts Teacher Education, B
History, B
Junior High/Intermediate/Middle School Education
   and Teaching, B
Mathematics, B
Mathematics Teacher Education, B
Nursing - Registered Nurse Training, A
Osteopathic Medicine, P
Political Science and Government, B
Psychology, B
Religion/Religious Studies, B
Social Sciences, B
Social Studies Teacher Education, B
Sociology, B
Teacher Education, Multiple Levels, B

ST. CATHARINE COLLEGE

Accounting, A
Administrative Assistant and Secretarial Science, A
Agricultural Business and Management, A
Agriculture, A
Animal Sciences, A
Art History, Criticism and Conservation, A
Art Teacher Education, A
Art/Art Studies, General, A
Bible/Biblical Studies, A
Biological and Physical Sciences, A
Biology/Biological Sciences, A
Business Administration and Management, A
Business Machine Repairer, A
Business Teacher Education, A
Business/Managerial Economics, A
Ceramic Arts and Ceramics, A
Chemistry, A
Computer Engineering Technology/Technician, A
Criminal Justice/Law Enforcement Administration, A
Dance, A
Education, A
Elementary Education and Teaching, A
Environmental Studies, A
Farm/Farm and Ranch Management, A
Health Teacher Education, A
History, A
Horticultural Science, A
Humanities/Humanistic Studies, A
Information Science/Studies, A
Insurance, A
Japanese Language and Literature, A
Journalism, A

Kindergarten/PreSchool Education and Teaching, A
Land Use Planning and
Management/Development, A
Landscape Architecture, A
Landscaping and Groundskeeping, A
Legal Administrative Assistant/Secretary, A
Liberal Arts and Sciences Studies and
Humanities, A
Mathematics, A
Medical Administrative Assistant/Secretary, A
Music, A
Nursing - Registered Nurse Training, A
Physical Education Teaching and Coaching, A
Piano and Organ, A
Range Science and Management, A
Social Sciences, A
Social Work, A
Sociology, A
Spanish Language and Literature, A

SOMERSET COMMUNITY COLLEGE

Autobody/Collision and Repair
Technology/Technician, A
Automobile/Automotive Mechanics
Technology/Technician, A
Avionics Maintenance Technology/Technician, A
Business/Commerce, A
CAD/CADD Drafting and/or Design
Technology/Technician, A
Carpentry/Carpenter, A
Clinical/Medical Laboratory Assistant, A
Communication and Media Studies, A
Cosmetology/Cosmetologist, A
Criminal Justice/Police Science, A
Diesel Mechanics Technology/Technician, A
Early Childhood Education and Teaching, A
Electrical, Electronic and Communications
Engineering Technology/Technician, A
Heating, Air Conditioning, Ventilation and
Refrigeration Maintenance
Technology/Technician, A
Industrial Technology/Technician, A
Information Technology, A
Machine Tool Technology/Machinist, A
Mason/Masonry, A
Medical/Clinical Assistant, A
Nail Technician/Specialist and Manicurist, A
Nursing, A
Nursing - Registered Nurse Training, A
Physical Therapy/Therapist, A
Radiologic Technology/Science - Radiographer, A
Respiratory Care Therapy/Therapist, A
Surgical Technology/Technologist, A
Welding Technology/Welder, A

SOUTHEAST KENTUCKY COMMUNITY AND TECHNICAL COLLEGE

Administrative Assistant and Secretarial Science, A
Business Administration and Management, A
Clinical/Medical Laboratory Technician, A
Computer Engineering Technology/Technician, A
Computer/Information Technology Services
Administration and Management, A
Criminal Justice/Police Science, A
Data Processing and Data Processing
Technology/Technician, A
Information Technology, A
Liberal Arts and Sciences Studies and
Humanities, A
Management Information Systems and Services, A
Medical Radiologic Technology/Science - Radiation
Therapist, A
Nursing - Registered Nurse Training, A
Physical Therapist Assistant, A
Respiratory Care Therapy/Therapist, A

SOUTHERN BAPTIST THEOLOGICAL SEMINARY

Missions/Missionary Studies and Missiology, MDP
Pastoral Studies/Counseling, D
Religious Education, MDP
Sacred Music, MDP

Theology and Religious Vocations, MDP

SOUTHWESTERN COLLEGE OF BUSINESS

Accounting, A
Business Administration and Management, A
Computer Science, A
Medical Administrative Assistant/Secretary, A

SPALDING UNIVERSITY

Accounting, B
Business Administration and Management, AB
Business Administration, Management and
Operations, M
Business/Commerce, AB
Clinical Psychology, MD
Communication and Media Studies, M
Corporate and Organizational Communication, M
Education, BMD
Educational Administration and Supervision, M
Educational Leadership and Administration, D
Elementary Education and Teaching, BM
Emergency Medical Technology/Technician (EMT
Paramedic), A
English Language and Literature, B
History, B
Humanities/Humanistic Studies, B
Junior High/Intermediate/Middle School Education
and Teaching, B
Kindergarten/PreSchool Education and Teaching, B
Liberal Arts and Sciences Studies and
Humanities, B
Mass Communication/Media Studies, B
Middle School Education, M
Natural Sciences, B
Nursing, M
Nursing - Adult, M
Nursing - Advanced Practice, M
Nursing - Registered Nurse Training, B
Nursing Administration, M
Occupational Therapy/Therapist, BM
Pediatric Nurse/Nursing, M
Philosophy, B
Psychology, BMD
Public Health (MPH, DPH), B
Religion/Religious Studies, B
Secondary Education and Teaching, M
Social Sciences, B
Social Work, BM
Special Education and Teaching, BM
Writing, M

SPENCERIAN COLLEGE

Accounting, A
Business Administration and Management, A
Medical Office Management/Administration, A

SPENCERIAN COLLEGE-LEXINGTON

Architectural Drafting and Architectural
CAD/CADD, A
Computer Graphics, A
Electrical, Electronic and Communications
Engineering Technology/Technician, A
Mechanical Drafting and Mechanical Drafting
CAD/CADD, A

SULLIVAN UNIVERSITY

Accounting, AB
Administrative Assistant and Secretarial Science, A
Business Administration and Management, AB
Business Administration, Management and
Operations, M
Computer Science, AB
Conflict Resolution and Mediation/Peace Studies, M
Consumer Merchandising/Retailing Management, A
Criminal Justice/Safety Studies, A
Culinary Arts/Chef Training, AB
Hotel/Motel Administration/Management, AB
Legal Administrative Assistant/Secretary, A
Legal Assistant/Paralegal, AB
Management of Technology, M
Marketing/Marketing Management, AB

Medical Administrative Assistant/Secretary, A

THOMAS MORE COLLEGE

Accounting, AB
Art History, Criticism and Conservation, A
Art Teacher Education, B
Biology/Biological Sciences, AB
Business Administration, Management and
Operations, M
Business Teacher Education, B
Business/Commerce, AB
Chemistry, AB
Clinical Laboratory Science/Medical
Technology/Technologist, B
Communication Studies/Speech Communication
and Rhetoric, AB
Computer and Information Sciences, AB
Criminal Justice/Law Enforcement
Administration, AB
Data Processing and Data Processing
Technology/Technician, A
Drama and Dramatics/Theatre Arts, AB
Economics, AB
Elementary Education and Teaching, B
English Language and Literature, AB
Fine/Studio Arts, A
Forensic Science and Technology, B
Gerontology, A
History, AB
Humanities/Humanistic Studies, AB
International Relations and Affairs, AB
Junior High/Intermediate/Middle School Education
and Teaching, B
Kinesiology and Exercise Science, A
Liberal Arts and Sciences Studies and
Humanities, AB
Mathematics, AB
Music, A
Nursing, B
Nursing - Registered Nurse Training, B
Philosophy, AB
Physics, AB
Political Science and Government, A
Pre-Law Studies, A
Psychology, AB
Religion/Religious Studies, AB
Social Studies Teacher Education, B
Sociology, AB
Spanish Language and Literature, A
Speech and Rhetorical Studies, B
Teacher Education and Professional
Development, Specific Subject Areas, B
Visual and Performing Arts, A
Web Page, Digital/Multimedia and Information
Resources Design, A

TRANSYLVANIA UNIVERSITY

Accounting, B
Anthropology, B
Art History, Criticism and Conservation, B
Art Teacher Education, B
Art/Art Studies, General, B
Biology/Biological Sciences, B
Business Administration and Management, B
Chemistry, B
Computer Science, B
Drama and Dramatics/Theatre Arts, B
Economics, B
Elementary Education and Teaching, B
English Language and Literature, B
Fine/Studio Arts, B
French Language and Literature, B
History, B
Junior High/Intermediate/Middle School Education
and Teaching, B
Kinesiology and Exercise Science, B
Mathematics, B
Music, B
Music Performance, B
Music Teacher Education, B
Philosophy, B
Physical Education Teaching and Coaching, B
Physics, B
Political Science and Government, B
Psychology, B
Religion/Religious Studies, B

Social Sciences, B
Sociology, B

UNION COLLEGE

Accounting, B
Biology/Biological Sciences, B
Business Administration and Management, B
Business Teacher Education, B
Chemistry, B
Communication Studies/Speech Communication
and Rhetoric, B
Criminal Justice/Law Enforcement Administration, B
Education, BM
Educational Administration and Supervision, M
Educational Leadership and Administration, O
Elementary Education and Teaching, BM
Health Education, M
Health Teacher Education, B
History, B
Junior High/Intermediate/Middle School Education
and Teaching, B
Mathematics, B
Middle School Education, M
Music Teacher Education, M
Parks, Recreation and Leisure Facilities
Management, B
Physical Education Teaching and Coaching, BM
Psychology, B
Reading Teacher Education, M
Religion/Religious Studies, B
Secondary Education and Teaching, BM
Social Sciences, B
Special Education and Teaching, BM
Sport and Fitness Administration/Management, B

UNIVERSITY OF THE CUMBERLANDS

Accounting, B
Art Teacher Education, B
Biology/Biological Sciences, B
Business Teacher Education, B
Business/Commerce, B
Chemistry, B
Clinical Laboratory Science/Medical
Technology/Technologist, B
Communication Studies/Speech Communication
and Rhetoric, B
Community Health Services/Liaison/Counseling, B
Computer and Information Sciences, B
Drama and Dramatics/Theatre Arts, B
Early Childhood Education and Teaching, M
Education, MO
Educational Administration and Supervision, O
Elementary Education and Teaching, BMO
English Language and Literature, B
Executive Assistant/Executive Secretary, B
Fine/Studio Arts, B
General Studies, B
Health and Physical Education, B
Health Teacher Education, B
History, B
Junior High/Intermediate/Middle School Education
and Teaching, B
Mathematics, B
Middle School Education, M
Music, B
Music Teacher Education, B
Organizational Behavior Studies, B
Philosophy and Religious Studies, B
Physical Education Teaching and Coaching, B
Physics, B
Political Science and Government, B
Psychology, B
Reading Teacher Education, M
Religious Education, B
Secondary Education and Teaching, MO
Social Studies Teacher Education, B
Social Work, B
Special Education and Teaching, BM
Speech and Rhetorical Studies, B

UNIVERSITY OF KENTUCKY

Accounting, BM
Advertising, B
Agricultural Economics, BMD
Agricultural Engineering, MD
Agricultural Sciences, MD

Agricultural/Biological Engineering and
Bioengineering, B
Agriculture, Agriculture Operations and Related
Sciences, B
Agronomy and Crop Science, B
Agronomy and Soil Sciences, MD
Allied Health and Medical Assisting Services, MD
Allopathic Medicine, PO
Anatomy, D
Animal Sciences, BMD
Anthropology, BMD
Apparel and Textiles, B
Architecture, BM
Art Education, M
Art History, Criticism and Conservation, BM
Art Teacher Education, B
Arts Management, B
Astronomy, MD
Audiology/Audiologist and Speech-Language
Pathology/Pathologist, B
Biochemistry, DO
Biological and Biomedical Sciences, MDO
Biological Anthropology, MD
Biology/Biological Sciences, B
Biomedical Engineering, MD
Business Administration, Management and
Operations, MD
Business/Commerce, B
Business/Managerial Economics, B
Cell/Cellular Biology and Anatomical Sciences, B
Chemical Engineering, BMD
Chemistry, BMD
Child and Family Studies, MD
Civil Engineering, BMD
Classics and Classical
Languages, Literatures, and Linguistics, BM
Clinical Laboratory Science/Medical
Technology/Technologist, B
Clinical Laboratory Sciences, MD
Clothing and Textiles, M
Communication and Media Studies, MD
Communication Disorders, M
Communication Studies/Speech Communication
and Rhetoric, B
Computer and Information Sciences, B
Computer Science, MD
Counseling Psychology, MDO
Curriculum and Instruction, MD
Dentistry, MP
Design and Applied Arts, M
Drama and Dramatics/Theatre Arts, B
Economics, BMD
Education, MDO
Educational Administration and Supervision, MDO
Educational Measurement and Evaluation, MD
Educational Psychology, MDO
Electrical Engineering, MD
Electrical, Electronics and Communications
Engineering, B
Elementary Education and Teaching, B
Engineering and Applied Sciences, MD
English, MD
English Language and Literature, B
Entomology, MD
Exercise and Sports Science, D
Family and Consumer Sciences/Human
Sciences, BMD
Finance, B
Fine Arts and Art Studies, M
Fine/Studio Arts, B
Food Science, B
Foods, Nutrition, and Wellness Studies, B
Forest Sciences and Biology, B
Forestry, M
French Language and Literature, BM
Geography, BMD
Geology/Earth Science, BMD
German Language and Literature, BM
Gerontology, D
Health Physics/Radiological Health, M
Health Promotion, MD
Health Services Administration, M
Health Teacher Education, B
Health/Health Care Administration/Management, B
Higher Education/Higher Education
Administration, M

Historic Preservation and Conservation, M
History, BMD
Hospitality Administration/Management, BM
Immunology, D
Interdisciplinary Studies, B
Interior Design, BM
International Affairs, M
International Business/Trade/Commerce, M
Journalism, B
Junior High/Intermediate/Middle School Education
and Teaching, B
Kindergarten/PreSchool Education and Teaching, B
Kinesiology and Movement Studies, MD
Landscape Architecture, B
Latin American Studies, B
Law and Legal Studies, PO
Library Science, M
Linguistics, B
Management Science, B
Manufacturing Engineering, M
Marketing/Marketing Management, B
Materials Engineering, B
Materials Sciences, MD
Mathematics, BMD
Mechanical Engineering, BMD
Medical Physics, M
Microbiology, D
Mineral/Mining Engineering, MD
Mining and Mineral Engineering, B
Multi-/Interdisciplinary Studies, B
Music, MD
Music History, Literature, and Theory, B
Music Performance, B
Music Teacher Education, B
Natural Resources and Conservation, B
Neurobiology and Neurophysiology, D
Nursing, BMD
Nursing - Registered Nurse Training, B
Nutritional Sciences, MD
Oral and Dental Sciences, M
Pharmaceutical Sciences, D
Pharmacology, DO
Pharmacy, P
Philosophy, BMD
Physical Education Teaching and Coaching, B
Physical Therapy/Therapist, BM
Physician Assistant, M
Physics, BMD
Physiology, D
Plant Pathology/Phytopathology, MD
Plant Physiology, D
Plant Sciences, M
Political Science and Government, BMD
Psychology, BMD
Public Administration, MDO
Public Health, MD
Radio and Television, B
Rehabilitation Counseling, M
Rehabilitation Sciences, D
Russian Language and Literature, B
Science Teacher Education/General Science
Teacher Education, B
Social Sciences, B
Social Work, BMD
Sociology, BMD
Spanish Language and Literature, BMD
Special Education and Teaching, BMDO
Statistics, MD
Teacher Education and Professional
Development, Specific Subject Areas, B
Theater, M
Toxicology, MD
Veterinary Sciences, MD
Vocational and Technical Education, MDO

UNIVERSITY OF LOUISVILLE

Accounting, BM
African Studies, M
African-American/Black Studies, B
Allopathic Medicine, PO
Analytical Chemistry, MD
Anatomy, MD
Anthropology, B
Applied Mathematics, D
Art Education, M
Art History, Criticism and Conservation, BMD

Art Therapy/Therapist, M
Biochemistry, MDO
Biological and Biomedical Sciences, M
Biology/Biological Sciences, B
Biophysics, MD
Biostatistics, MD
Business Administration and Management, B
Business Administration, Management and
  Operations, BM
Business/Managerial Economics, B
Chemical Engineering, BMD
Chemistry, BMD
Civil Engineering, BMD
Clinical Psychology, D
Clinical Research, O
Communication and Media Studies, M
Communication Disorders, MD
Communication Studies/Speech Communication
  and Rhetoric, B
Composition, M
Computer Engineering, BMD
Computer Science, MD
Counseling Psychology, MD
Counselor Education/School Counseling and
  Guidance Services, MD
Criminal Justice/Law Enforcement Administration, B
Criminology, M
Curriculum and Instruction, D
Dental Hygiene/Hygienist, AB
Dentistry, P
Drama and Dramatics/Theatre Arts, B
Early Childhood Education and Teaching, M
Economics, B
Education, MDO
Educational Administration and Supervision, MDO
Educational Leadership and Administration, D
Educational Measurement and Evaluation, M
Educational Media/Instructional Technology, M
Educational Psychology, MD
Electrical Engineering, M
Electrical, Electronics and Communications
  Engineering, B
Elementary Education and Teaching, BM
Engineering, B
Engineering and Applied Sciences, MDO
Engineering Management, M
English, MD
English Language and Literature, B
Entrepreneurship/Entrepreneurial Studies, D
Environmental Biology, D
Environmental Engineering
  Technology/Environmental Technology, MD
Epidemiology, MD
Exercise and Sports Science, M
Experimental Psychology, D
Finance, B
Fine Arts and Art Studies, M
Fine/Studio Arts, B
Foreign Language Teacher Education, M
French Language and Literature, BM
Geography, B
Health and Physical Education, B
Health/Medical Preparatory Programs, B
Higher Education/Higher Education
  Administration, MO
History, BM
Human Resources Development, M
Humanities/Humanistic Studies, MD
Immunology, MD
Industrial and Labor Relations, M
Industrial Education, M
Industrial Engineering, B
Industrial/Management Engineering, MD
Inorganic Chemistry, MD
Interdisciplinary Studies, M
Law and Legal Studies, PO
Legal Assistant/Paralegal, AB
Liberal Arts and Sciences Studies and
  Humanities, B
Management Information Systems and Services, B
Marketing/Marketing Management, B
Mathematics, BMD
Mechanical Engineering, BM
Microbiology, MD
Middle School Education, M
Molecular Biology, MDO

Music, B
Music History, Literature, and Theory, MD
Music Teacher Education, BM
Music Theory and Composition, M
Music Therapy/Therapist, B
Musicology and Ethnomusicology, D
Neurobiology and Neurophysiology, MD
Nursing, M
Nursing - Registered Nurse Training, B
Oral Biology, M
Organic Chemistry, MD
Performance, M
Pharmacology, MD
Philosophy, BM
Physical Chemistry, MD
Physical Education Teaching and Coaching, M
Physics, BMD
Physiology, MD
Political Science and Government, BM
Psychology, BMD
Public Administration, MD
Public Affairs, D
Public Policy Analysis, M
Reading Teacher Education, M
Rhetoric, D
Secondary Education and Teaching, M
Sign Language Interpretation and Translation, AB
Social Work, MD
Sociology, BM
Spanish Language and Literature, BM
Special Education and Teaching, MD
Sport and Fitness Administration/Management, BM
Student Personnel Services, M
Theater, M
Toxicology, MD
Trade and Industrial Teacher Education, B
Urban and Regional Planning, M
Urban Planning, M
Urban Studies/Affairs, D
Women's Studies, BMO

WEST KENTUCKY COMMUNITY AND TECHNICAL COLLEGE

Accounting, A
Administrative Assistant and Secretarial Science, A
Business Administration and Management, A
Consumer Merchandising/Retailing Management, A
Electrical, Electronic and Communications
  Engineering Technology/Technician, A
Industrial Radiologic Technology/Technician, A
Information Science/Studies, A
Mass Communication/Media Studies, A
Nursing - Registered Nurse Training, A
Physical Therapy/Therapist, A

WESTERN KENTUCKY UNIVERSITY

Accounting, B
Advertising, B
Agricultural Production Operations, A
Agricultural Sciences, M
Agriculture, B
Anthropology, B
Apparel and Textiles, B
Architectural Drafting and Architectural
  CAD/CADD, A
Art Education, M
Art Teacher Education, B
Biochemistry, B
Biological and Biomedical Sciences, M
Biology/Biological Sciences, B
Business Administration and Management, AB
Business Administration, Management and
  Operations, M
Business Education, M
Business Teacher Education, B
Business/Managerial Economics, B
Chemistry, BM
Civil Engineering, B
Clinical Laboratory Science/Medical
  Technology/Technologist, B
Commercial and Advertising Art, B
Communication and Media Studies, M
Communication Disorders, M
Communication Studies/Speech Communication
  and Rhetoric, B

Communication, Journalism and Related
  Programs, B
Community Health Services/Liaison/Counseling, B
Comparative Literature, M
Computer and Information Sciences, B
Computer Science, M
Counselor Education/School Counseling and
  Guidance Services, MO
Data Processing and Data Processing
  Technology/Technician, A
Dental Hygiene/Hygienist, AB
Drama and Dramatics/Theatre Arts, B
Early Childhood Education and Teaching, M
Economics, B
Education, MO
Education/Teaching of Individuals with Speech or
  Language Impairments, B
Educational Administration and Supervision, MO
Educational Media/Instructional Technology, M
Electrical, Electronics and Communications
  Engineering, B
Elementary Education and Teaching, BMO
Emergency Medical Technology/Technician (EMT
  Paramedic), A
Engineering Technologies/Technicians, A
English, M
English as a Second Language, M
English Education, M
English Language and Literature, B
Environmental and Occupational Health, M
Environmental Technology/Environmental Technology, B
Executive Assistant/Executive Secretary, A
Family and Consumer Sciences/Home Economics
  Teacher Education, B
Finance, B
Fine/Studio Arts, B
Folklore, M
Foods, Nutrition, and Wellness Studies, B
French Language and Literature, B
General Studies, AB
Geography, BM
Geology/Earth Science, BM
German Language and Literature, B
Gerontology, M
Health Information/Medical Records
  Technology/Technician, A
Health Services Administration, M
Health/Health Care Administration/Management, B
Historic Preservation and Conservation, M
History, BM
Hotel/Motel Administration/Management, B
Housing and Human Environments, B
Industrial Production Technologies/Technicians, B
Industrial Technology/Technician, B
Journalism, B
Junior High/Intermediate/Middle School Education
  and Teaching, B
Kindergarten/PreSchool Education and
  Teaching, AB
Legal Assistant/Paralegal, A
Management Information Systems and Services, B
Marketing/Marketing Management, B
Mathematics, BM
Mechanical Engineering, B
Middle School Education, M
Multi-/Interdisciplinary Studies, B
Music, B
Music Teacher Education, BM
Nursing, BM
Nursing - Registered Nurse Training, AB
Parks, Recreation and Leisure Facilities
  Management, B
Philosophy, B
Physical Education Teaching and Coaching, BM
Physical Science Technologies/Technicians, A
Physics, B
Political Science and Government, B
Psychology, BMO
Public Affairs, M
Public Health, M
Public Relations/Image Management, B
Radio and Television, B
Reading Teacher Education, M
Recreation and Park Management, M
Religion/Religious Studies, B

Respiratory Care Therapy/Therapist, A
School Psychology, O
Science Teacher Education/General Science
   Teacher Education, BM
Secondary Education and Teaching, MO
Social Sciences, B
Social Work, B
Sociology, BM
Spanish Language and Literature, B
Special Education and Teaching, BM
Speech and Rhetorical Studies, B
Technical Teacher Education, A
Trade and Industrial Teacher Education, B
Visual and Performing Arts, B
Writing, M

Louisiana

BOSSIER PARISH COMMUNITY COLLEGE

Business Administration and Management, A
Corrections, A
Criminal Justice/Police Science, A
Drafting and Design Technology/Technician, A
Electrical, Electronic and Communications
   Engineering Technology/Technician, A
Emergency Medical Technology/Technician (EMT
   Paramedic), A
Information Science/Studies, A
Liberal Arts and Sciences Studies and
   Humanities, A
Medical/Clinical Assistant, A
Physical Therapy/Therapist, A
Respiratory Care Therapy/Therapist, A
Telecommunications Technology/Technician, A

CENTENARY COLLEGE OF LOUISIANA

Accounting, B
Art Teacher Education, B
Art/Art Studies, General, B
Biology Teacher Education, B
Biology/Biological Sciences, B
Biophysics, B
Business Administration and Management, B
Business Administration, Management and
   Operations, M
Business Teacher Education, B
Business/Managerial Economics, B
Chemistry, B
Chemistry Teacher Education, B
Communication and Media Studies, B
Communication, Journalism and Related
   Programs, B
Curriculum and Instruction, M
Dance, B
Drama and Dance Teacher Education, B
Drama and Dramatics/Theatre Arts, B
Economics, B
Education, BM
Educational Administration and Supervision, M
Elementary Education and Teaching, BM
English Language and Literature, B
English/Language Arts Teacher Education, B
Environmental Studies, B
Film/Cinema Studies, B
Finance, B
Fine/Studio Arts, B
Foreign Languages and Literatures, B
French Language and Literature, B
French Language Teacher Education, B
Geology/Earth Science, B
German Language and Literature, B
German Language Teacher Education, B
History, B
Interdisciplinary Studies, B
Kinesiology and Exercise Science, B
Latin Language and Literature, B
Latin Teacher Education, B
Liberal Arts and Sciences Studies and
   Humanities, B
Mathematics, B
Mathematics Teacher Education, B
Museology/Museum Studies, B
Music, B
Music Performance, B

Music Teacher Education, B
Music Theory and Composition, B
Neuroscience, B
Philosophy, B
Physical Education Teaching and Coaching, B
Physics, B
Physics Teacher Education, B
Piano and Organ, B
Political Science and Government, B
Pre-Dentistry Studies, B
Pre-Law Studies, B
Pre-Medicine/Pre-Medical Studies, B
Pre-Veterinary Studies, B
Psychology, B
Religion/Religious Studies, B
Religious/Sacred Music, B
Secondary Education and Teaching, BM
Social Studies Teacher Education, B
Sociology, B
Spanish Language and Literature, B
Spanish Language Teacher Education, B
Teacher Education, Multiple Levels, B
Visual and Performing Arts, B
Voice and Opera, B

DELGADO COMMUNITY COLLEGE

Accounting, A
Administrative Assistant and Secretarial Science, A
Applied Horticulture/Horticultural Operations, A
Architectural Engineering Technology/Technician, A
Automobile/Automotive Mechanics
   Technology/Technician, A
Biological and Physical Sciences, A
Biomedical Technology/Technician, A
Building/Construction
   Finishing, Management, and Inspection, A
Building/Property Maintenance and Management, A
Business Administration and Management, A
Civil Engineering Technology/Technician, A
Clinical/Medical Laboratory Technician, A
Commercial and Advertising Art, A
Communication, Journalism and Related
   Programs, A
Computer Engineering Technology/Technician, A
Computer Installation and Repair
   Technology/Technician, A
Criminal Justice/Police Science, A
Data Processing and Data Processing
   Technology/Technician, A
Dental Hygiene/Hygienist, A
Dental Laboratory Technology/Technician, A
Dietetics/Dieticians, A
Drafting and Design Technology/Technician, A
Electrical, Electronic and Communications
   Engineering Technology/Technician, A
Electrical/Electronics Equipment Installation and
   Repair, A
Emergency Medical Technology/Technician (EMT
   Paramedic), A
Fine/Studio Arts, A
Fire Protection and Safety Technology/Technician, A
Funeral Service and Mortuary Science, A
General Studies, A
Health Information/Medical Records
   Technology/Technician, A
Hospitality Administration/Management, A
Institutional Food Workers, A
Interior Architecture, A
Kindergarten/PreSchool Education and Teaching, A
Machine Shop Technology/Assistant, A
Machine Tool Technology/Machinist, A
Medical Radiologic Technology/Science - Radiation
   Therapist, A
Music, A
Nursing - Registered Nurse Training, A
Occupational Safety and Health
   Technology/Technician, A
Occupational Therapist Assistant, A
Physical Therapist Assistant, A
Respiratory Care Therapy/Therapist, A

Sign Language Interpretation and Translation, A

DELTA COLLEGE OF ARTS AND TECHNOLOGY

Commercial and Advertising Art, A
Licensed Practical/Vocational Nurse Training, A

DILLARD UNIVERSITY

Accounting, B
Art Teacher Education, B
Art/Art Studies, General, B
Biology Teacher Education, B
Biology/Biological Sciences, B
Business Administration and Management, B
Chemistry, B
Computer Science, B
Drama and Dramatics/Theatre Arts, B
Economics, B
Education, B
Elementary Education and Teaching, B
English Composition, B
English Language and Literature, B
French Language and Literature, B
German Language and Literature, B
Health Teacher Education, B
Health/Health Care Administration/Management, B
History, B
Information Science/Studies, B
International Business/Trade/Commerce, B
Japanese Language and Literature, B
Kindergarten/PreSchool Education and Teaching, B
Mass Communication/Media Studies, B
Mathematics, B
Modern Languages, B
Music, B
Music Performance, B
Music Teacher Education, B
Music Therapy/Therapist, B
Nursing - Registered Nurse Training, B
Physical Education Teaching and Coaching, B
Physics, B
Piano and Organ, B
Political Science and Government, B
Pre-Dentistry Studies, B
Pre-Law Studies, B
Pre-Medicine/Pre-Medical Studies, B
Pre-Veterinary Studies, B
Psychology, B
Public Health (MPH, DPH), B
Public Health Education and Promotion, B
Religion/Religious Studies, B
Science Teacher Education/General Science
   Teacher Education, B
Secondary Education and Teaching, B
Social Work, B
Sociology, B
Spanish Language and Literature, B
Special Education and Teaching, B
Speech and Rhetorical Studies, B
Urban Studies/Affairs, B

ELAINE P. NUNEZ COMMUNITY COLLEGE

Accounting, A
Administrative Assistant and Secretarial Science, A
Computer and Information Sciences, A
Computer Engineering Technology/Technician, A
Computer Science, A
Computer/Information Technology Services
   Administration and Management, A
Drafting and Design Technology/Technician, A
Electrical, Electronic and Communications
   Engineering Technology/Technician, A
Emergency Medical Technology/Technician (EMT
   Paramedic), A
Environmental Engineering
   Technology/Environmental Technology, A
Health Information/Medical Records
   Administration/Administrator, A
Heating, Air Conditioning, Ventilation and
   Refrigeration Maintenance
   Technology/Technician, A
Information Science/Studies, A
Institutional Food Workers, A
Kindergarten/PreSchool Education and Teaching, A
Laser and Optical Technology/Technician, A

Legal Assistant/Paralegal, A
Liberal Arts and Sciences Studies and
   Humanities, A
Licensed Practical/Vocational Nurse Training, A
Management Information Systems and Services, A
Plastics Engineering Technology/Technician, A

GRAMBLING STATE UNIVERSITY

Accounting, B
Architectural Engineering Technology/Technician, B
Art Teacher Education, B
Art/Art Studies, General, B
Biology/Biological Sciences, B
Business Administration and Management, B
Business Teacher Education, B
Business/Managerial Economics, B
Chemistry, B
Child Development, A
Computer Science, B
Criminal Justice/Law Enforcement
   Administration, AB
Criminal Justice/Police Science, B
Criminology, M
Curriculum and Instruction, D
Developmental Education, MD
Drafting and Design Technology/Technician, B
Drama and Dramatics/Theatre Arts, B
Early Childhood Education and Teaching, M
Education, MD
Educational Leadership and Administration, D
Electrical, Electronic and Communications
   Engineering Technology/Technician, B
Elementary Education and Teaching, BM
English Language and Literature, B
English/Language Arts Teacher Education, B
Family and Consumer Sciences/Home Economics
   Teacher Education, B
French Language and Literature, B
French Language Teacher Education, B
History, B
Hotel/Motel Administration/Management, B
Humanities/Humanistic Studies, M
Industrial Technology/Technician, B
Information Science/Studies, B
Institutional Food Workers, B
Kindergarten/PreSchool Education and Teaching, B
Legal Assistant/Paralegal, A
Marketing/Marketing Management, B
Mass Communication/Media Studies, BM
Mathematics, B
Music Performance, B
Music Teacher Education, B
Nursing, M
Nursing - Advanced Practice, M
Nursing - Registered Nurse Training, B
Physical Education Teaching and Coaching, B
Physics, B
Political Science and Government, B
Pre-Law Studies, B
Psychology, B
Public Administration, BM
Science Teacher Education/General Science
   Teacher Education, BM
Secondary Education and Teaching, B
Social Science Teacher Education, B
Social Studies Teacher Education, M
Social Work, BM
Sociology, B
Spanish Language and Literature, B
Special Education and Teaching, B
Speech Teacher Education, B
Speech-Language Pathology/Pathologist, B
Sport and Fitness Administration/Management, M
Technology Teacher Education/Industrial Arts
   Teacher Education, B

ITI TECHNICAL COLLEGE

Computer Technology/Computer Systems
   Technology, A
Drafting and Design Technology/Technician, A
Electrical, Electronic and Communications
   Engineering Technology/Technician, A
General Office Occupations and Clerical Services, A
Information Technology, A

Instrumentation Technology/Technician, A

ITT TECHNICAL INSTITUTE

Accounting and Business/Management, B
Animation, Interactive Technology, Video Graphics
   and Special Effects, B
Business Administration and Management, B
CAD/CADD Drafting and/or Design
   Technology/Technician, A
Computer and Information Systems Security, B
Computer Programming/Programmer, A
Criminal Justice/Law Enforcement Administration, B
Electrical, Electronic and Communications
   Engineering Technology/Technician, AB
System, Networking, and LAN/WAN
   Management/Manager, B
Web Page, Digital/Multimedia and Information
   Resources Design, A
Web/Multimedia Management and Webmaster, A

LOUISIANA COLLEGE

Accounting, B
Adult and Continuing Education and Teaching, B
Advertising, B
Art Teacher Education, B
Art/Art Studies, General, B
Athletic Training and Sports Medicine, B
Biology/Biological Sciences, B
Broadcast Journalism, B
Business Administration and Management, B
Business Teacher Education, B
Chemistry, B
Clinical Laboratory Science/Medical
   Technology/Technologist, B
Commercial and Advertising Art, B
Criminal Justice/Law Enforcement
   Administration, AB
Criminal Justice/Police Science, B
Drama and Dramatics/Theatre Arts, B
Economics, B
Elementary Education and Teaching, B
English Language and Literature, B
Family and Consumer Economics and Related
   Services, B
Finance, B
Fine/Studio Arts, B
French Language and Literature, B
Health Teacher Education, B
History, B
Interdisciplinary Studies, B
Journalism, B
Kindergarten/PreSchool Education and Teaching, B
Kinesiology and Exercise Science, B
Liberal Arts and Sciences Studies and
   Humanities, B
Marketing/Marketing Management, B
Mass Communication/Media Studies, B
Mathematics, B
Modern Languages, B
Music, B
Music Teacher Education, B
Nursing - Registered Nurse Training, B
Philosophy, B
Physical Education Teaching and Coaching, B
Physics, B
Piano and Organ, B
Pre-Law Studies, B
Psychology, B
Public Administration, B
Religion/Religious Studies, B
Religious Education, B
Religious/Sacred Music, B
Science Teacher Education/General Science
   Teacher Education, B
Secondary Education and Teaching, B
Social Work, B
Sociology, B
Spanish Language and Literature, B
Special Education and Teaching, B
Speech and Rhetorical Studies, B
Theology/Theological Studies, B

Voice and Opera, B

LOUISIANA STATE UNIVERSITY AND AGRICULTURAL AND MECHANICAL COLLEGE

Accounting, BMD
Agricultural Business and Management, B
Agricultural Economics, MD
Agricultural Education, MD
Agricultural Engineering, MD
Agricultural Sciences, MD
Agronomy and Soil Sciences, MD
Animal Sciences, BMD
Anthropology, BMD
Applied Science and Technology, M
Architecture, BM
Art History, Criticism and Conservation, M
Astronomy, MD
Astrophysics, D
Audiology/Audiologist and Speech-Language
   Pathology/Pathologist, B
Biochemistry, BMD
Bioengineering, MD
Biological and Biomedical Sciences, MD
Biology/Biological Sciences, B
Biomedical/Medical Engineering, B
Biopsychology, MD
BioTechnology, B
Business Administration and Management, B
Business Administration, Management and
   Operations, MD
Business Education, M
Business/Managerial Economics, B
Ceramic Arts and Ceramics, M
Chemical Engineering, BMD
Chemistry, BMD
Civil Engineering, BMD
Clinical Psychology, MD
Cognitive Sciences, MD
Communication and Media Studies, MD
Communication Disorders, MD
Comparative Literature, MD
Computer Engineering, BMD
Computer Science, BMD
Construction Management, B
Counselor Education/School Counseling and
   Guidance Services, MDO
Curriculum and Instruction, MDO
Dairy Science, MD
Design and Applied Arts, M
Developmental Psychology, MD
Drama and Dramatics/Theatre Arts, B
Early Childhood Education and Teaching, B
Economics, BMD
Education, MDO
Educational Administration and Supervision, MDO
Educational Leadership and Administration, MDO
Educational Measurement and Evaluation, D
Educational Media/Instructional Technology, M
Electrical Engineering, MD
Electrical, Electronics and Communications
   Engineering, B
Elementary Education and Teaching, BM
Engineering and Applied Sciences, MD
English, MD
English Language and Literature, B
Entomology, MD
Environmental Engineering
   Technology/Environmental Technology, MD
Environmental Policy and Resource
   Management, M
Environmental Sciences, BD
Environmental Studies, M
Environmental/Environmental Health Engineering, B
Family and Consumer Sciences/Human
   Sciences, BMD
Fashion Merchandising, B
Finance, B
Finance and Banking, MD
Fine Arts and Art Studies, M
Fine/Studio Arts, B
Fish, Game and Wildlife Management, MD
Food Science, B
Food Science and Technology, MD
Forest Management/Forest Resources
   Management, B

Forestry, MD
French Language and Literature, BMD
General Studies, B
Geography, BMD
Geology/Earth Science, BMD
Geophysics and Seismology, MD
Geotechnical Engineering, MD
German Language and Literature, B
Graphic Design, M
Higher Education/Higher Education
  Administration, D
History, BMD
Home Economics Education, M
Horticultural Science, MD
Industrial and Organizational Psychology, MD
Industrial Education, M
Industrial Engineering, B
Industrial/Management Engineering, MD
Information Science/Studies, MO
Interior Architecture, B
International and Comparative Education, MD
International Business/Trade/Commerce, B
International/Global Studies, B
Kinesiology and Movement Studies, MD
Landscape Architecture, BM
Latin Language and Literature, B
Law and Legal Studies, MPO
Liberal Arts and Sciences Studies and
  Humanities, B
Liberal Studies, M
Library Science, MO
Linguistics, MD
Management, D
Management Information Systems and
  Services, MD
Management Science, B
Marine Affairs, MD
Marketing, MD
Marketing/Marketing Management, B
Mass Communication/Media Studies, BMD
Mathematics, BMD
Mechanical Engineering, BMD
Mechanics, MD
Media Studies, MD
Microbiology, B
Music, BMD
Music Performance, B
Music Teacher Education, BD
Natural Resources and Conservation, MD
Natural Resources Management/Development and
  Policy, B
Nutritional Sciences, B
Oceanography, Chemical and Physical, MD
Painting, M
Petroleum Engineering, BMD
Philosophy, BM
Photography, M
Physical Education Teaching and Coaching, B
Physics, BMD
Plant Pathology/Phytopathology, MD
Plant Sciences, B
Political Science and Government, BMD
Printmaking, M
Psychology, BMD
Public Administration, MDO
School Psychology, MD
Sculpture, M
Secondary Education and Teaching, BM
Social Work, MD
Sociology, BMD
Spanish Language and Literature, BM
Speech and Rhetorical Studies, B
Statistics, M
Structural Engineering, MD
Systems Science and Theory, M
Teacher Education and Professional
  Development, Specific Subject Areas, B
Theater, MD
Toxicology, M
Transportation and Highway Engineering, MD
Veterinary Medicine, P
Veterinary Sciences, MD
Vocational and Technical Education, MD
Water Resources Engineering, MD
Women's Studies, B

Writing, M

LOUISIANA STATE UNIVERSITY AT ALEXANDRIA

Behavioral Sciences, A
Biology/Biological Sciences, AB
Business Administration and Management, AB
Clinical Laboratory Science/Medical
  Technology/Technologist, A
Communication Studies/Speech Communication
  and Rhetoric, B
Criminal Justice/Police Science, A
Early Childhood Education and Teaching, A
Elementary Education and Teaching, B
English Language and Literature, B
General Studies, B
Health Services/Allied Health/Health Sciences, A
History, B
Information Technology, A
Liberal Arts and Sciences Studies and
  Humanities, AB
Mathematics, AB
Medical Radiologic Technology/Science - Radiation
  Therapist, A
Nursing - Registered Nurse Training, A
Psychology, B
Radiologic Technology/Science - Radiographer, A
Theatre/Theatre Arts Management, B

LOUISIANA STATE UNIVERSITY AT EUNICE

Administrative Assistant and Secretarial Science, A
Business Administration and Management, A
Computer Programming/Programmer, A
Criminal Justice/Police Science, A
Criminal Justice/Safety Studies, A
Fire Science/Firefighting, A
General Studies, A
Legal Assistant/Paralegal, A
Nursing - Registered Nurse Training, A
Radiologic Technology/Science - Radiographer, A
Respiratory Care Therapy/Therapist, A

LOUISIANA STATE UNIVERSITY HEALTH SCIENCES CENTER

Allied Health and Medical Assisting Services, M
Allopathic Medicine, MPO
Anatomy, MDO
Biochemistry, MD
Biological and Biomedical Sciences, MDO
Biometry/Biometrics, M
Cardiovascular Technology/Technologist, B
Cell Biology and Anatomy, MDO
Clinical Laboratory Science/Medical
  Technology/Technologist, B
Communication Disorders, M
Community Health Nursing, MD
CytoTechnology/Cytotechnologist, B
Dental Assisting/Assistant, AB
Dental Hygiene/Hygienist, AB
Dental Laboratory Technology/Technician, AB
Dentistry, P
Electroneurodiagnostic/Electroencephalographic
  Technology/Technologist, B
Human Genetics, MDO
Immunology, MD
Microbiology, MD
Molecular Biology, MD
Neuroscience, DO
Nursing, MD
Nursing - Adult, MD
Nursing - Advanced Practice, M
Nursing - Registered Nurse Training, B
Nursing Administration, MD
Ophthalmic Technician/Technologist, B
Parasitology, MD
Pathology/Experimental Pathology, MDO
Pediatric Nurse/Nursing, M
Pharmacology, MDO
Physical Therapy/Therapist, M
Physiology, MDO
Psychiatric/Mental Health Nurse/Nursing, MD
Public Health, M
Rehabilitation Counseling, M

Respiratory Care Therapy/Therapist, B

LOUISIANA STATE UNIVERSITY IN SHREVEPORT

Accounting, B
Art Teacher Education, B
Art/Art Studies, General, B
Audiology/Audiologist and Speech-Language
  Pathology/Pathologist, B
Biological and Biomedical Sciences, B
Biological and Physical Sciences, B
Biology Teacher Education, B
Biology/Biological Sciences, B
Business Administration and Management, B
Business Administration, Management and
  Operations, M
Business/Managerial Economics, B
Chemistry, B
Chemistry Teacher Education, B
Computer Science, B
Counseling Psychology, M
Criminal Justice/Safety Studies, B
Education, MO
Elementary Education and Teaching, B
English Language and Literature, B
English/Language Arts Teacher Education, B
Environmental Studies, B
Finance, B
French Language and Literature, B
French Language Teacher Education, B
General Studies, B
Geography, B
Health Services Administration, M
History, B
Human Services, M
Information Science/Studies, B
Liberal Studies, M
Marketing/Marketing Management, B
Mass Communication/Media Studies, B
Mathematics, B
Mathematics Teacher Education, B
Physical Education Teaching and Coaching, B
Physics, B
Physics Teacher Education, B
Political Science and Government, B
Psychology, B
Public Health Education and Promotion, B
School Psychology, MO
Social Studies Teacher Education, B
Sociology, B
Spanish Language and Literature, B
Special Education and Teaching, B
Speech and Rhetorical Studies, B
Systems Engineering, M
Systems Science and Theory, M

LOUISIANA TECH UNIVERSITY

Accounting, BMD
Aeronautics/Aviation/Aerospace Science and
  Technology, B
Agricultural Business and Management, B
Agricultural Teacher Education, B
Animal Sciences, B
Applied Arts and Design, M
Architecture, B
Art Teacher Education, B
Art/Art Studies, General, B
Audiology/Audiologist and Speech-Language
  Pathology/Pathologist, B
Aviation/Airway Management and Operations, B
Biological and Biomedical Sciences, M
Biology Teacher Education, B
Biology/Biological Sciences, B
Biomedical Engineering, MD
Biomedical/Medical Engineering, B
Business Administration and Management, B
Business Administration, Management and
  Operations, MD
Business Teacher Education, B
Business/Managerial Economics, B
Chemical Engineering, BMD
Chemistry, BM
Chemistry Teacher Education, B
Child Development, B
Civil Engineering, BMD

Clinical Laboratory Science/Medical
  Technology/Technologist, B
Commercial and Advertising Art, B
Communication Disorders, M
Computational Sciences, D
Computer Science, BM
Construction Engineering Technology/Technician, B
Consumer Economics, B
Counseling Psychology, D
Counselor Education/School Counseling and
  Guidance Services, M
Curriculum and Instruction, MD
Dietetics/Dieticians, B
Early Childhood Education and Teaching, B
Economics, MD
Education, MD
Education/Teaching of Individuals with Speech or
  Language Impairments, B
Educational Leadership and Administration, D
Electrical Engineering, MD
Electrical, Electronic and Communications
  Engineering Technology/Technician, B
Electrical, Electronics and Communications
  Engineering, B
Elementary Education and Teaching, B
Engineering and Applied Sciences, MD
English, M
English Language and Literature, B
English/Language Arts Teacher Education, B
Environmental Studies, B
Exercise and Sports Science, M
Family and Consumer Sciences/Home Economics
  Teacher Education, B
Family and Consumer Sciences/Human
  Sciences, M
Finance, B
Finance and Banking, MD
Fine Arts and Art Studies, M
Forestry, B
French Language and Literature, B
French Language Teacher Education, B
General Studies, AB
Geography, B
Geology/Earth Science, B
Graphic Design, M
Health and Physical Education, B
Health Education, M
Health Information/Medical Records
  Administration/Administrator, B
Health Information/Medical Records
  Technology/Technician, A
History, BM
Human Resources Management/Personnel
  Administration, B
Industrial and Organizational Psychology, M
Industrial Engineering, B
Industrial/Management Engineering, MD
Interior Architecture, B
Interior Design, M
Journalism, B
Junior High/Intermediate/Middle School Education
  and Teaching, B
Kindergarten/PreSchool Education and Teaching, B
Management Information Systems and Services, B
Management Science, B
Manufacturing Engineering, M
Marketing, MD
Marketing/Marketing Management, B
Mathematics, BM
Mathematics Teacher Education, B
Mechanical Engineering, BMD
Music, B
Music Performance, B
Music Teacher Education, B
Natural Resources and Conservation, B
Nursing - Registered Nurse Training, A
Nutritional Sciences, M
Operations Management and Supervision, B
Operations Research, M
Photography, BM
Physical Education Teaching and Coaching, B
Physics, BMD
Physics Teacher Education, B
Plant Sciences, B
Political Science and Government, B
Psychology, BMD

Secondary Education and Teaching, M
Social Studies Teacher Education, B
Sociology, B
Spanish Language and Literature, B
Special Education and Teaching, BM
Speech and Rhetorical Studies, BM
Speech Teacher Education, B
Statistics, M
Teacher Education and Professional
  Development, Specific Subject Areas, B

LOUISIANA TECHNICAL COLLEGE

Accounting Technology/Technician and
  Bookkeeping, A
Administrative Assistant and Secretarial Science, A
Aircraft Powerplant Technology/Technician, A
Automobile/Automotive Mechanics
  Technology/Technician, A
Child Care Provider/Assistant, A
Clinical/Medical Laboratory Assistant, A
Communications Systems Installation and Repair
  Technology, A
Computer Installation and Repair
  Technology/Technician, A
Computer Programming, Specific Applications, A
Computer Systems Analysis/Analyst, A
Computer Systems Networking and
  Telecommunications, A
Criminal Justice/Safety Studies, A
Culinary Arts/Chef Training, A
Data Processing and Data Processing
  Technology/Technician, A
Drafting and Design Technology/Technician, A
Forestry Technology/Technician, A
Hotel/Motel Administration/Management, A
Industrial Electronics Technology/Technician, A
Industrial Production Technologies/Technicians, A
Instrumentation Technology/Technician, A
Precision Systems Maintenance and Repair
  Technologies, A
Prepress/Desktop Publishing and Digital Imaging
  Design, A
Printing Press Operator, A
Respiratory Therapy Technician/Assistant, A
Surgical Technology/Technologist, A
Survey Technology/Surveying, A
System Administration/Administrator, A
Technical Teacher Education, A

LOYOLA UNIVERSITY NEW ORLEANS

Accounting, B
Art/Art Studies, General, B
Behavioral Sciences, B
Biology/Biological Sciences, B
Business Administration and Management, B
Business Administration, Management and
  Operations, MO
Business/Managerial Economics, B
Chemistry, B
Classics and Classical
  Languages, Literatures, and Linguistics, B
Commercial and Advertising Art, B
Communication and Media Studies, MO
Communication Studies/Speech Communication
  and Rhetoric, B
Computer and Information Sciences, B
Counselor Education/School Counseling and
  Guidance Services, M
Creative Writing, B
Criminal Justice/Safety Studies, B
Criminology, M
Drama and Dramatics/Theatre Arts, B
Economics, B
Education, BM
Elementary Education and Teaching, BM
English Language and Literature, B
Finance, B
Forensic Science and Technology, B
French Language and Literature, B
General Studies, B
German Language and Literature, B
Health Services Administration, M
History, B
Humanities/Humanistic Studies, B
Information Science/Studies, B
International Business/Trade/Commerce, B

Jazz/Jazz Studies, B
Law and Legal Studies, PO
Marketing/Marketing Management, B
Mass Communication/Media Studies, M
Mathematics, B
Music, BM
Music Management and Merchandising, B
Music Performance, B
Music Teacher Education, B
Music Theory and Composition, B
Nursing, M
Nursing - Advanced Practice, M
Nursing - Registered Nurse Training, B
Philosophy, B
Physics, B
Piano and Organ, B
Political Science and Government, B
Psychology, B
Reading Teacher Education, M
Religion/Religious Studies, BMO
Religious Education, B
Religious/Sacred Music, B
Russian Language and Literature, B
Secondary Education and Teaching, M
Social Sciences, B
Sociology, B
Spanish Language and Literature, B
Theology and Religious Vocations, MO

MCNEESE STATE UNIVERSITY

Accounting, B
Agricultural Teacher Education, B
Agriculture, B
Applied Art, B
Art Teacher Education, B
Art/Art Studies, General, B
Biological and Biomedical Sciences, M
Biology Teacher Education, B
Biology/Biological Sciences, B
Business Administration and Management, B
Business Administration, Management and
  Operations, M
Business Teacher Education, B
Ceramic Arts and Ceramics, B
Chemical Engineering, M
Chemistry, BM
Chemistry Teacher Education, B
Civil Engineering, M
Clinical Laboratory Science/Medical
  Technology/Technologist, B
Computer Science, M
Computer Typography and Composition Equipment
  Operator, A
Counselor Education/School Counseling and
  Guidance Services, M
Criminal Justice/Safety Studies, B
Drama and Dramatics/Theatre Arts, B
Drawing, B
Early Childhood Education and Teaching, BM
Education, BM
Educational Administration and Supervision, MO
Educational Leadership and Administration, B
Educational Media/Instructional Technology, M
Electrical Engineering, M
Electrical, Electronic and Communications
  Engineering Technology/Technician, AB
Elementary Education and Teaching, BM
Engineering, B
Engineering and Applied Sciences, M
Engineering Management, M
Engineering Technologies/Technicians, A
Engineering Technology, AB
English, M
English Language and Literature, B
English/Language Arts Teacher Education, B
Environmental Sciences, BM
Family and Consumer Sciences/Home Economics
  Teacher Education, B
Family and Consumer Sciences/Human Sciences, B
Finance, B
Foods, Nutrition, and Wellness Studies, B
Foreign Language Teacher Education, B
French Language and Literature, B
General Studies, AB
Geology/Earth Science, B
Health Education, M

History, B
Information Technology, A
Instrumentation Technology/Technician, A
Kindergarten/PreSchool Education and
  Teaching, AB
Kinesiology and Exercise Science, B
Legal Assistant/Paralegal, A
Liberal Arts and Sciences Studies and
  Humanities, B
Marketing/Marketing Management, B
Mass Communication/Media Studies, B
Mathematics, BM
Mathematics Teacher Education, B
Mechanical Engineering, M
Medical Radiologic Technology/Science - Radiation
  Therapist, B
Multilingual and Multicultural Education, M
Music, B
Music Performance, B
Music Teacher Education, BM
Nursing, M
Nursing - Registered Nurse Training, AB
Petroleum Technology/Technician, A
Photography, B
Physical Education Teaching and Coaching, BM
Physics, B
Political Science and Government, B
Printmaking, B
Psychology, BM
School Psychology, M
Secondary Education and Teaching, BM
Social Studies Teacher Education, BM
Sociology, B
Spanish Language and Literature, B
Special Education and Teaching, B
Speech and Rhetorical Studies, B
Speech Teacher Education, B
Statistics, M
Wildlife and Wildlands Science and Management, B
Writing, M

MEDVANCE INSTITUTE

Clinical/Medical Laboratory Technician, A
Radiologic Technology/Science - Radiographer, A

NEW ORLEANS BAPTIST
THEOLOGICAL SEMINARY

Pastoral Studies/Counseling, MDP
Religion/Religious Studies, AB
Religious Education, MDP
Sacred Music, MD
Theology and Religious Vocations, DP

NICHOLLS STATE UNIVERSITY

Accounting, B
Agricultural Business and Management, B
Applied Mathematics, M
Art Teacher Education, B
Art/Art Studies, General, B
Biology/Biological Sciences, B
Business Administration and Management, B
Business Administration, Management and
  Operations, M
Business Teacher Education, B
Business/Commerce, A
Cardiopulmonary Technology/Technologist, A
Chemical Technology/Technician, A
Chemistry, B
Child Care and Support Services Management, A
Computer Science, B
Counseling Psychology, M
Counselor Education/School Counseling and
  Guidance Services, M
Criminal Justice/Police Science, A
Culinary Arts/Chef Training, AB
Curriculum and Instruction, M
Dietetics/Dieticians, B
Early Childhood Education and Teaching, B
Education, BM
Educational Administration and Supervision, M
Elementary Education and Teaching, B
Emergency Medical Technology/Technician (EMT
  Paramedic), A
English Language and Literature, B
Environmental Biology, BM
Family and Consumer Sciences/Human Sciences, B

Finance, B
French Language and Literature, B
General Studies, AB
Health Services/Allied Health/Health Sciences, B
Health Teacher Education, B
History, B
Junior High/Intermediate/Middle School Education
  and Teaching, B
Kindergarten/PreSchool Education and Teaching, B
Legal Assistant/Paralegal, A
Liberal Arts and Sciences Studies and
  Humanities, A
Management Information Systems and Services, B
Marine Biology and Biological Oceanography, BM
Marketing/Marketing Management, B
Mass Communication/Media Studies, B
Mathematics, BM
Mechanical Engineering/Mechanical
  Technology/Technician, B
Music, B
Music Teacher Education, B
Nursing - Registered Nurse Training, AB
Petroleum Technology/Technician, AB
Physical Education Teaching and Coaching, B
Pre-Dentistry Studies, B
Pre-Medicine/Pre-Medical Studies, B
Psychology, B
School Psychology, MO
Science Teacher Education/General Science
  Teacher Education, B
Secondary Education and Teaching, B
Sociology, B
Special Education and Teaching, B
Survey Technology/Surveying, B

NORTHWESTERN STATE UNIVERSITY
OF LOUISIANA

Accounting, B
Administrative Assistant and Secretarial Science, A
Adult and Continuing Education and Teaching, M
Anthropology, B
Art/Art Studies, General, B
Biology Teacher Education, B
Biology/Biological Sciences, B
Business Administration and Management, AB
Business Education, M
Business Teacher Education, B
Chemistry, B
Chemistry Teacher Education, B
Clinical Laboratory Science/Medical
  Technology/Technologist, B
Clinical Psychology, M
Counselor Education/School Counseling and
  Guidance Services, MO
Criminal Justice/Police Science, A
Criminal Justice/Safety Studies, B
Cultural Resource Management and Policy
  Analysis, B
Drama and Dramatics/Theatre Arts, B
Early Childhood Education and Teaching, BM
Education, MO
Educational Administration and Supervision, MO
Educational Media/Instructional Technology, MO
Electrical, Electronic and Communications
  Engineering Technology/Technician, AB
Elementary Education and Teaching, BMO
English, M
English Language and Literature, B
English/Language Arts Teacher Education, B
Family and Consumer Sciences/Home Economics
  Teacher Education, B
Family and Consumer Sciences/Human Sciences, B
Fine Arts and Art Studies, M
Fine/Studio Arts, B
General Studies, AB
Health Education, M
Health Promotion, M
History, B
Home Economics Education, M
Hospitality Administration/Management, B
Industrial Technology/Technician, B
Information Science/Studies, B
Journalism, B
Junior High/Intermediate/Middle School Education
  and Teaching, B

Liberal Arts and Sciences Studies and
  Humanities, B
Mathematics, B
Mathematics Teacher Education, BM
Medical Radiologic Technology/Science - Radiation
  Therapist, B
Music, M
Music Performance, B
Music Teacher Education, B
Nursing, M
Nursing - Registered Nurse Training, AB
Physical Education Teaching and Coaching, BM
Physics, B
Physics Teacher Education, B
Political Science and Government, B
Psychology, BM
Radiologic Technology/Science - Radiographer, B
Reading Teacher Education, MO
Science Teacher Education/General Science
  Teacher Education, M
Secondary Education and Teaching, BMO
Social Sciences, B
Social Studies Teacher Education, BM
Social Work, B
Sociology, B
Special Education and Teaching, BMO
Speech Teacher Education, B
Sport and Fitness Administration/Management, M
Student Personnel Services, M
Substance Abuse/Addiction Counseling, B
Veterinary/Animal Health Technology/Technician and
  Veterinary Assistant, A

OUR LADY OF HOLY CROSS
COLLEGE

Accounting, B
Behavioral Sciences, B
Biology/Biological Sciences, B
Business Administration and Management, B
Business Teacher Education, B
Clinical Laboratory Science/Medical
  Technology/Technologist, B
Counselor Education/School Counseling and
  Guidance Services, AM
Curriculum and Instruction, M
Education, BM
Educational Administration and Supervision, M
Elementary Education and Teaching, B
English Language and Literature, B
General Studies, B
History, B
Marriage and Family Therapy/Counseling, M
Mathematics, B
Nursing - Registered Nurse Training, B
Public Health (MPH, DPH), B
Reading Teacher Education, B
Respiratory Care Therapy/Therapist, AB
Sales, Distribution and Marketing Operations, B
Science Teacher Education/General Science
  Teacher Education, B
Secondary Education and Teaching, B
Social Sciences, B
Teacher Assistant/Aide, A
Teacher Education, Multiple Levels, B
Tourism and Travel Services Management, B
Tourism Promotion Operations, B

OUR LADY OF THE LAKE COLLEGE

Biological and Biomedical Sciences, B
Biology/Biological Sciences, B
Biomedical Sciences, B
Clinical Laboratory Science/Medical
  Technology/Technologist, B
Clinical/Medical Laboratory Technician, AB
Emergency Medical Technology/Technician (EMT
  Paramedic), A
Forensic Science and Technology, B
General Studies, B
Health/Health Care Administration/Management, B
Humanities/Humanistic Studies, B
Industrial Radiologic Technology/Technician, A
Nursing - Registered Nurse Training, AB
Physical Therapist Assistant, A

Surgical Technology/Technologist, A

REMINGTON COLLEGE-LAFAYETTE CAMPUS

Business Administration and Management, A
Computer Programming, A
Computer Programming/Programmer, A
Computer Systems Analysis/Analyst, A
Computer Systems Networking and
  Telecommunications, A
Data Entry/Microcomputer Applications, A
Electrical, Electronic and Communications
  Engineering Technology/Technician, A
Legal Assistant/Paralegal, A
Management Information Systems and Services, A
Medical/Clinical Assistant, A
Web Page, Digital/Multimedia and Information
  Resources Design, A

REMINGTON COLLEGE-NEW ORLEANS CAMPUS

Computer and Information Sciences, A
Computer Graphics, A
Computer Hardware Engineering, A
Computer Programming, A
Computer Systems Networking and
  Telecommunications, A
Data Entry/Microcomputer Applications, A
Engineering Technology, A
System Administration/Administrator, A

RIVER PARISHES COMMUNITY COLLEGE

Chemical Technology/Technician, A
Liberal Arts and Sciences Studies and
  Humanities, A
Physical Sciences, A

SAINT JOSEPH SEMINARY COLLEGE

Liberal Arts and Sciences Studies and
  Humanities, B

SOUTHEASTERN LOUISIANA UNIVERSITY

Accounting, B
Administrative Assistant and Secretarial Science, A
Applied Science and Technology, M
Art Teacher Education, B
Art/Art Studies, General, B
Arts Management, B
Athletic Training and Sports Medicine, B
Biological and Biomedical Sciences, M
Biology/Biological Sciences, B
Business Administration and Management, B
Business Administration, Management and
  Operations, M
Chemistry, B
Communication and Media Studies, M
Communication Disorders, M
Communication Studies/Speech Communication
  and Rhetoric, B
Computer Science, B
Counselor Education/School Counseling and
  Guidance Services, M
Criminal Justice/Police Science, A
Criminal Justice/Safety Studies, B
Curriculum and Instruction, M
Education, M
Education/Teaching of Individuals with Speech or
  Language Impairments, B
Educational Administration and Supervision, M
Elementary Education and Teaching, BM
English, M
English Language and Literature, B
English/Language Arts Teacher Education, B
Family and Consumer Sciences/Human Sciences, B
Finance, B
French Language and Literature, B
French Language Teacher Education, B
General Studies, AB
Health Education, M
History, BM
Horticultural Science, B
Industrial Technology/Technician, AB

Junior High/Intermediate/Middle School Education
  and Teaching, B
Kindergarten/PreSchool Education and Teaching, B
Kinesiology and Movement Studies, M
Liberal Arts and Sciences Studies and
  Humanities, B
Marketing/Marketing Management, B
Mathematics, B
Mathematics Teacher Education, B
Music, M
Music Performance, B
Music Teacher Education, B
Nursing, M
Nursing - Registered Nurse Training, B
Occupational Therapist Assistant, B
Physical Education Teaching and Coaching, B
Physics, B
Political Science and Government, B
Psychology, BM
Public Health Education and Promotion, B
Science Teacher Education/General Science
  Teacher Education, B
Secondary Education and Teaching, M
Social Studies Teacher Education, B
Social Work, B
Sociology, BM
Spanish Language and Literature, B
Spanish Language Teacher Education, B
Special Education and Teaching, BM
Speech Teacher Education, B

SOUTHERN UNIVERSITY AND AGRICULTURAL AND MECHANICAL COLLEGE

Accounting, BM
Agricultural Economics, B
Agricultural Sciences, M
Agricultural Teacher Education, B
Analytical Chemistry, M
Animal Sciences, B
Architecture, B
Art/Art Studies, General, B
Audiology/Audiologist and Speech-Language
  Pathology/Pathologist, B
Biochemistry, M
Biological and Biomedical Sciences, M
Biology Teacher Education, B
Biology/Biological Sciences, B
Business Administration and Management, B
Business Administration, Management and
  Operations, BM
Business/Managerial Economics, B
Chemistry, BM
Chemistry Teacher Education, B
Civil Engineering, B
Communication Studies/Speech Communication
  and Rhetoric, B
Computer Science, BM
Computer Teacher Education, B
Counselor Education/School Counseling and
  Guidance Services, M
Criminal Justice/Police Science, A
Criminal Justice/Safety Studies, B
Drama and Dramatics/Theatre Arts, B
Early Childhood Education and Teaching, B
E-Commerce/Electronic Commerce, B
Education, M
Educational Administration and Supervision, M
Educational Media/Instructional Technology, M
Electrical, Electronic and Communications
  Engineering Technology/Technician, B
Electrical, Electronics and Communications
  Engineering, B
Elementary Education and Teaching, BM
English Language and Literature, B
English/Language Arts Teacher Education, B
Environmental Sciences, M
Family and Consumer Sciences/Human Sciences, B
Finance, B
Fine/Studio Arts, B
Forestry, M
French Language and Literature, B
French Language Teacher Education, B
History, BM
Human Development and Family Studies, B
Inorganic Chemistry, M

Jazz/Jazz Studies, A
Junior High/Intermediate/Middle School Education
  and Teaching, B
Kindergarten/PreSchool Education and Teaching, B
Law and Legal Studies, P
Marketing/Marketing Management, B
Mass Communication/Media Studies, BM
Mathematics, BM
Mathematics Teacher Education, BD
Mechanical Engineering, B
Music Performance, B
Music Teacher Education, B
Nursing, MDO
Nursing - Advanced Practice, DO
Nursing - Registered Nurse Training, B
Nursing Administration, D
Nursing Education, D
Organic Chemistry, M
Physical Chemistry, M
Physical Education Teaching and Coaching, B
Physics, BM
Physics Teacher Education, B
Political Science and Government, BM
Psychology, BM
Public Administration, MD
Rehabilitation and Therapeutic Professions, B
Rehabilitation Counseling, M
Rehabilitation Therapy, B
Science Teacher Education/General Science
  Teacher Education, BD
Secondary Education and Teaching, BM
Social Studies Teacher Education, B
Social Work, B
Sociology, BM
Spanish Language and Literature, B
Spanish Language Teacher Education, B
Special Education and Teaching, BMD
Speech and Rhetorical Studies, B
Therapeutic Recreation, M
Therapeutic Recreation/Recreational Therapy, B
Urban Forestry, B

SOUTHERN UNIVERSITY AT NEW ORLEANS

Accounting, B
Administrative Assistant and Secretarial Science, AB
Art/Art Studies, General, B
Audiology/Audiologist and Speech-Language
  Pathology/Pathologist, B
Biology/Biological Sciences, B
Business Administration and Management, B
Computer Science, A
Criminal Justice/Law Enforcement Administration, B
Elementary Education and Teaching, B
English Language and Literature, B
French Language and Literature, B
History, B
Mathematics, B
Physical Education Teaching and Coaching, B
Physics, B
Real Estate, A
Secondary Education and Teaching, B
Social Work, ABM
Sociology, B
Spanish Language and Literature, B

SOUTHERN UNIVERSITY AT SHREVEPORT

Accounting, A
Avionics Maintenance Technology/Technician, A
Banking and Financial Support Services, A
Biology/Biological Sciences, A
Business Administration and Management, A
Cardiovascular Technology/Technologist, A
Chemistry, A
Clinical/Medical Laboratory Technician, A
Computer Science, A
Criminal Justice/Law Enforcement Administration, A
Dental Hygiene/Hygienist, A
Electrical, Electronic and Communications
  Engineering Technology/Technician, A
General Studies, A
Health Information/Medical Records
  Administration/Administrator, A
Hospitality Administration/Management, A
Hotel/Motel Administration/Management, A

Human Services, A
Kindergarten/PreSchool Education and Teaching, A
Legal Assistant/Paralegal, A
Mathematics, A
Mechanical Engineering/Mechanical
  Technology/Technician, A
Medical Radiologic Technology/Science - Radiation
  Therapist, A
Mental Health/Rehabilitation, A
Physical Therapist Assistant, A
Public Administration, A
Respiratory Care Therapy/Therapist, A
Robotics Technology/Technician, A
Sociology, A
Substance Abuse/Addiction Counseling, A
Surgical Technology/Technologist, A
Teacher Assistant/Aide, A
Tourism and Travel Services Management, A

TULANE UNIVERSITY

Accounting, B
African Studies, B
Allopathic Medicine, PO
American/United States Studies/Civilization, B
Anatomy, B
Anthropology, BMD
Applied Mathematics, M
Architecture, BM
Art History, Criticism and Conservation, BM
Art/Art Studies, General, B
Asian Studies/Civilization, B
Biochemistry, BMDO
Biological and Biomedical Sciences, MDO
Biology/Biological Sciences, B
Biomedical Engineering, MD
Biomedical/Medical Engineering, B
Biostatistics, BMD
Business Administration and Management, AB
Business Administration, Management and
  Operations, MDO
Business/Commerce, A
Cell Biology and Anatomy, MDO
Cell/Cellular Biology and Anatomical Sciences, B
Cell/Cellular Biology and Histology, B
Chemical Engineering, BMD
Chemistry, BMD
Civil Engineering, BMD
Classics and Classical
  Languages, Literatures, and Linguistics, BM
Cognitive Psychology and Psycholinguistics, B
Communication Studies/Speech Communication
  and Rhetoric, A
Communication, Journalism and Related
  Programs, A
Computer and Information Sciences, AB
Computer Engineering, B
Computer Science, BMD
Corrections, B
Criminal Justice/Safety Studies, B
Dance, M
Drama and Dramatics/Theatre Arts, B
Ecology, B
Economics, BMD
Electrical Engineering, MD
Electrical, Electronics and Communications
  Engineering, B
Engineering Science, B
English, MD
English Language and Literature, B
Environmental and Occupational Health, MDO
Environmental Biology, B
Environmental Engineering
  Technology/Environmental Technology, MD
Environmental Studies, B
Environmental/Environmental Health Engineering, B
Epidemiology, MD
Evolutionary Biology, B
Finance, B
Fine Arts and Art Studies, M
Fine/Studio Arts, B
Foreign Languages and Literatures, B
French Language and Literature, BMD
Geology/Earth Science, BMD
German Language and Literature, B
Health Education, M
Health Services Administration, MDO

Hispanic-American, Puerto Rican, and Mexican-
  American/Chicano Studies, B
History, BMD
Human Genetics, MDO
Immunology, MDO
Information Science/Studies, AB
International Development, MD
International Public Health/International
  Health, MDO
International Relations and Affairs, B
Italian Language and Literature, B
Jewish/Judaic Studies, B
Kinesiology and Exercise Science, B
Latin American Studies, BMDO
Latin Language and Literature, B
Law and Legal Studies, MDPO
Legal Assistant/Paralegal, A
Legal Professions and Studies, B
Liberal Arts and Sciences Studies and
  Humanities, B
Liberal Studies, M
Linguistics, B
Marketing/Marketing Management, AB
Mass Communication/Media Studies, B
Maternal and Child Health, MDO
Mathematics, BMD
Mathematics and Statistics, B
Mechanical Engineering, BMD
Medieval and Renaissance Studies, B
Microbiology, MDO
Modern Greek Language and Literature, B
Molecular Biology, BMDO
Multi-/Interdisciplinary Studies, B
Music, BM
Neuroscience, BMDO
Nutritional Sciences, BM
Paleontology, D
Parasitology, MDO
Pharmacology, MDO
Philosophy, BMD
Physics, BMD
Physiology, MDO
Political Science and Government, BMDO
Portuguese Language and Literature, BMD
Psychology, BMD
Public Administration, M
Public Health, MDO
Religion/Religious Studies, B
Russian Language and Literature, B
Russian Studies, B
Social Work, MDO
Sociology, BMD
Spanish Language and Literature, BMD
Sport and Fitness Administration/Management, B
Statistics, BM
Structural Biology, MDO
Theater, M
Women's Studies, B

UNIVERSITY OF LOUISIANA AT LAFAYETTE

Accounting, B
Agribusiness, B
Agriculture, B
American/United States Studies/Civilization, D
Animal Sciences, B
Anthropology, B
Apparel and Textiles, B
Architectural Engineering, M
Architecture, B
Architecture and Related Services, B
Art/Art Studies, General, B
Athletic Training and Sports Medicine, B
Audiology/Audiologist and Speech-Language
  Pathology/Pathologist, B
Biological and Biomedical Sciences, MD
Biology Teacher Education, B
Biology/Biological Sciences, B
Business Administration and Management, B
Business Administration, Management and
  Operations, M
Business/Commerce, B
Business/Managerial Economics, B
Chemical Engineering, BM
Chemistry, B
Chemistry Teacher Education, B

Civil Engineering, BM
Cognitive Sciences, D
Communication and Media Studies, M
Communication Disorders, MD
Communication Studies/Speech Communication
  and Rhetoric, B
Computer and Information Sciences, B
Computer Engineering, BMD
Computer Science, BMD
Computer Systems Analysis/Analyst, B
Counselor Education/School Counseling and
  Guidance Services, M
Criminal Justice/Safety Studies, B
Curriculum and Instruction, M
Dental Hygiene/Hygienist, B
Dietetics/Dieticians, B
Drama and Dramatics/Theatre Arts, B
Education, BM
Education/Teaching of the Gifted and Talented, M
Educational Administration and Supervision, M
Electrical, Electronics and Communications
  Engineering, B
Elementary Education and Teaching, B
Engineering, B
Engineering Management, M
English, MD
English Language and Literature, B
Environmental Biology, D
Evolutionary Biology, D
Family and Consumer Sciences/Human
  Sciences, M
Fashion Merchandising, B
Fashion/Apparel Design, B
Finance, B
French Language and Literature, BMD
French Language Teacher Education, B
General Studies, B
Geology/Earth Science, BM
German Language Teacher Education, B
Health Information/Medical Records
  Administration/Administrator, B
Health Professions and Related Clinical Sciences, B
Health Services Administration, M
History, BM
Horticultural Science, B
Hospitality Administration/Management, B
Human Development and Family Studies, B
Industrial Design, B
Industrial Technology/Technician, B
Insurance, B
Interior Architecture, B
Jazz/Jazz Studies, B
Marketing/Marketing Management, B
Mass Communication/Media Studies, BM
Mathematics, BMD
Mechanical Engineering, BM
Medical Microbiology and Bacteriology, B
Modern Languages, B
Music, BM
Music Pedagogy, B
Music Performance, B
Music Teacher Education, BM
Music Theory and Composition, B
Natural Resources and Conservation, B
Nursing, M
Nursing - Registered Nurse Training, B
Performance, M
Petroleum Engineering, BM
Philosophy, B
Physical Education Teaching and Coaching, B
Physics, BM
Physics Teacher Education, B
Plant Sciences, B
Political Science and Government, B
Pre-Law Studies, B
Psychology, BM
Public Relations/Image Management, B
Rehabilitation Counseling, M
Rhetoric, D
Science Teacher Education/General Science
  Teacher Education, B
Secondary Education and Teaching, B
Social Studies Teacher Education, B
Sociology, B
Spanish Language and Literature, B
Spanish Language Teacher Education, B

Special Education and Teaching, B
Speech Teacher Education, B
Teacher Education and Professional
   Development, Specific Subject Areas, B
Telecommunications, M
Visual and Performing Arts, B
Writing, D

UNIVERSITY OF LOUISIANA AT MONROE

Accounting, B
Aeronautics/Aviation/Aerospace Science and
   Technology, B
Agricultural Business and Management, B
Art/Art Studies, General, B
Atmospheric Sciences and Meteorology, B
Audiology/Audiologist and Speech-Language
   Pathology/Pathologist, B
Biological and Biomedical Sciences, M
Biology Teacher Education, B
Biology/Biological Sciences, B
Business Administration and Management, B
Business Administration, Management and
   Operations, M
Business/Managerial Economics, B
Chemistry, B
Chemistry Teacher Education, B
Child Care and Support Services Management, A
Clinical Laboratory Science/Medical
   Technology/Technologist, B
Communication and Media Studies, M
Communication Disorders, M
Computer Science, B
Computer Systems Analysis/Analyst, B
Construction Engineering Technology/Technician, B
Counselor Education/School Counseling and
   Guidance Services, M
Criminal Justice/Police Science, A
Criminal Justice/Safety Studies, B
Criminology, M
Curriculum and Instruction, DO
Dental Hygiene/Hygienist, B
Education, MDO
Educational Administration and Supervision, M
Educational Leadership and Administration, D
Elementary Education and Teaching, BM
English, M
English Language and Literature, B
English/Language Arts Teacher Education, B
Exercise and Sports Science, M
Family and Consumer Sciences/Home Economics
   Teacher Education, B
Family and Consumer Sciences/Human Sciences, B
Finance, B
French Language and Literature, B
French Language Teacher Education, B
General Studies, AB
Geosciences, M
Gerontology, MO
Health/Medical Preparatory Programs, B
History, BM
Insurance, B
Marketing/Marketing Management, B
Marriage and Family Therapy/Counseling, MD
Mass Communication/Media Studies, B
Mathematics, B
Mathematics Teacher Education, B
Medical Radiologic Technology/Science - Radiation
   Therapist, B
Music, M
Music Performance, B
Music Teacher Education, B
Nursing - Registered Nurse Training, B
Occupational Therapist Assistant, A
Occupational Therapy/Therapist, B
Pharmaceutical Sciences, M
Pharmacy, BDP
Physical Education Teaching and Coaching, B
Physics Teacher Education, B
Political Science and Government, B
Psychology, BMO
Reading Teacher Education, M
School Psychology, O
Secondary Education and Teaching, M
Social Studies Teacher Education, B
Social Work, B

Sociology, B
Spanish Language and Literature, B
Spanish Language Teacher Education, B
Special Education and Teaching, BM
Speech and Rhetorical Studies, B
Speech Teacher Education, B
Substance Abuse/Addiction Counseling, M
Teacher Education and Professional
   Development, Specific Subject Areas, B
Toxicology, B

UNIVERSITY OF NEW ORLEANS

Accounting, BM
Anthropology, B
Art History, Criticism and Conservation, B
Arts Management, M
Biological and Biomedical Sciences, MD
Biology/Biological Sciences, B
Business Administration and Management, B
Business Administration, Management and
   Operations, M
Business/Managerial Economics, B
Chemistry, BMD
Civil Engineering, B
Clinical Laboratory Science/Medical
   Technology/Technologist, B
Communication Studies/Speech Communication
   and Rhetoric, B
Community Health and Preventive Medicine, O
Computer Science, BM
Counselor Education/School Counseling and
   Guidance Services, MDO
Curriculum and Instruction, MDO
Early Childhood Education and Teaching, B
Economics, BD
Education, MDO
Educational Leadership and Administration, MDO
Electrical, Electronics and Communications
   Engineering, B
Elementary Education and Teaching, B
Engineering and Applied Sciences, MDO
Engineering Management, MO
Engineering Science, B
English, M
English Language and Literature, B
English/Language Arts Teacher Education, B
Environmental Studies, B
Exercise and Sports Science, M
Film, Television, and Video Production, M
Finance, B
Fine Arts and Art Studies, M
Fine/Studio Arts, B
Foreign Language Teacher Education, B
Foundations and Philosophy of Education, MDO
French Language and Literature, B
General Studies, B
Geography, BM
Geology/Earth Science, BM
Geophysics and Seismology, BM
Gerontology, O
Health Education, MO
Health Services Administration, M
History, BM
Hospitality Administration/Management, BM
International/Global Studies, B
Junior High/Intermediate/Middle School Education
   and Teaching, B
Management Information Systems and Services, B
Marketing/Marketing Management, B
Mathematics, BM
Mathematics Teacher Education, B
Mechanical Engineering, BM
Music, BM
Music Teacher Education, B
Naval Architecture and Marine Engineering, B
Philosophy, B
Physical Education Teaching and Coaching, BMO
Physics, BMD
Political Science and Government, BMD
Psychology, BMD
Public Administration, M
Public Policy Analysis, M
Romance
   Languages, Literatures, and Linguistics, M
Science Teacher Education/General Science
   Teacher Education, BM

Social Studies Teacher Education, B
Sociology, BM
Spanish Language and Literature, B
Special Education and Teaching, MDO
Sport and Fitness Administration/Management, M
Taxation, M
Theater, M
Travel and Tourism, M
Urban and Regional Planning, M
Urban Studies/Affairs, BMD
Women's Studies, B

UNIVERSITY OF PHOENIX-LOUISIANA CAMPUS

Accounting, BM
Business Administration and Management, B
Business Administration, Management and
   Operations, B
Computer and Information Sciences, B
Electronic Commerce, M
Entrepreneurship/Entrepreneurial Studies, B
General Studies, A
Health Services Administration, M
Human Resources Management and Services, M
Management, M
Management Information Systems and Services, M
Management of Technology, M
Nursing, MO
Nursing Science, M
Organizational Management, M

XAVIER UNIVERSITY OF LOUISIANA

Accounting, B
Art Teacher Education, B
Art/Art Studies, General, B
Biochemistry, B
Biology Teacher Education, B
Biology/Biological Sciences, B
Business Administration and Management, B
Chemistry, B
Chemistry Teacher Education, B
Communication Disorders, B
Computer and Information Sciences, B
Computer Engineering, B
Computer Science, B
Counselor Education/School Counseling and
   Guidance Services, M
Curriculum and Instruction, M
Early Childhood Education and Teaching, B
Education, BM
Educational Administration and Supervision, M
Elementary Education and Teaching, BM
English Language and Literature, B
Environmental Studies, B
French Language and Literature, B
French Language Teacher Education, B
Health Teacher Education, B
History, B
History Teacher Education, B
Junior High/Intermediate/Middle School Education
   and Teaching, B
Marketing/Marketing Management, B
Mass Communication/Media Studies, B
Mathematics, B
Medical Microbiology and Bacteriology, B
Music, B
Music Performance, B
Music Teacher Education, B
Pastoral Studies/Counseling, M
Pharmacy, P
Philosophy, B
Physical Education Teaching and Coaching, B
Physics, B
Piano and Organ, B
Political Science and Government, B
Pre-Dentistry Studies, B
Pre-Law Studies, B
Pre-Medicine/Pre-Medical Studies, B
Pre-Veterinary Studies, B
Psychology, B
Science Teacher Education/General Science
   Teacher Education, B
Secondary Education and Teaching, BM
Social Studies Teacher Education, B
Sociology, B
Spanish Language and Literature, B

Spanish Language Teacher Education, B
Special Education and Teaching, BM
Speech-Language Pathology/Pathologist, B
Statistics, B
Theology and Religious Vocations, M
Theology/Theological Studies, B
Violin, Viola, Guitar and Other Stringed
  Instruments, B
Wind and Percussion Instruments, B

Maine

ANDOVER COLLEGE

Accounting, A
Administrative Assistant and Secretarial Science, A
Business Administration and Management, A
Computer Programming/Programmer, A
Computer Science, A
Computer/Information Technology Services
  Administration and Management, A
Criminal Justice/Law Enforcement Administration, A
Health Information/Medical Records
  Administration/Administrator, A
Kindergarten/PreSchool Education and Teaching, A
Legal Administrative Assistant/Secretary, A
Legal Assistant/Paralegal, A
Medical Administrative Assistant/Secretary, A
Medical/Clinical Assistant, A
System Administration/Administrator, A
Web/Multimedia Management and Webmaster, A

BATES COLLEGE

African-American/Black Studies, B
American/United States Studies/Civilization, B
Anthropology, B
Archeology, B
Art/Art Studies, General, B
Biochemistry, B
Biology/Biological Sciences, B
Chemistry, B
Chinese Language and Literature, B
Classical, Ancient Mediterranean and Near Eastern
  Studies and Archaeology, B
Drama and Dramatics/Theatre Arts, B
East Asian Studies, B
Economics, B
Engineering, B
English Language and Literature, B
Environmental Studies, B
French Language and Literature, B
Geology/Earth Science, B
German Language and Literature, B
History, B
Japanese Language and Literature, B
Mathematics, B
Multi-/Interdisciplinary Studies, B
Music, B
Near and Middle Eastern Studies, B
Neuroscience, B
Philosophy, B
Physics, B
Political Science and Government, B
Psychology, B
Religion/Religious Studies, B
Russian Language and Literature, B
Sociology, B
Spanish Language and Literature, B
Speech and Rhetorical Studies, B
Women's Studies, B

BEAL COLLEGE

Accounting, A
Administrative Assistant and Secretarial Science, A
Business Administration and Management, A
Computer and Information Sciences, A
Criminal Justice/Law Enforcement Administration, A
Early Childhood Education and Teaching, A
Legal Administrative Assistant/Secretary, A
Medical Administrative Assistant/Secretary, A
Medical/Clinical Assistant, A
Tourism and Travel Services Management, A

BOWDOIN COLLEGE

African Studies, B
African-American/Black Studies, B

Anthropology, B
Archeology, B
Art History, Criticism and Conservation, B
Art/Art Studies, General, B
Asian Studies/Civilization, B
Biochemistry, B
Biology/Biological Sciences, B
Central/Middle and Eastern European Studies, B
Chemical Physics, B
Chemistry, B
Classics and Classical
  Languages, Literatures, and Linguistics, B
Computer Science, B
Dramatic/Theatre Arts and Stagecraft, B
Economics, B
English Language and Literature, B
Environmental Studies, B
Fine/Studio Arts, B
French Language and Literature, B
Geochemistry, B
Geology/Earth Science, B
Geophysics and Seismology, B
German Language and Literature, B
History, B
Interdisciplinary Studies, B
Latin American Studies, B
Mathematics, B
Mathematics and Computer Science, B
Music, B
Neuroscience, B
Philosophy, B
Physics, B
Political Science and Government, B
Pre-Medicine/Pre-Medical Studies, B
Psychology, B
Religion/Religious Studies, B
Romance Languages, Literatures, and Linguistics, B
Russian Language and Literature, B
Sociology, B
Spanish Language and Literature, B
Women's Studies, B

CENTRAL MAINE COMMUNITY COLLEGE

Accounting, A
Administrative Assistant and Secretarial Science, A
Architecture, A
Automobile/Automotive Mechanics
  Technology/Technician, A
Business Administration and Management, A
Civil Engineering Technology/Technician, A
Clinical/Medical Laboratory Technician, A
Commercial and Advertising Art, A
Computer Science, A
Construction Engineering Technology/Technician, A
Drafting/Design Engineering
  Technologies/Technicians, A
Electromechanical Technology/Electromechanical
  Engineering Technology, A
General Studies, A
Graphic and Printing Equipment Operator
  Production, A
Health and Medical Laboratory Technologies, A
Hospitality Administration/Management, A
Industrial Radiologic Technology/Technician, A
Kindergarten/PreSchool Education and Teaching, A
Machine Tool Technology/Machinist, A
Medical Administrative Assistant/Secretary, A
Nursing - Registered Nurse Training, A
Occupational Safety and Health
  Technology/Technician, A
Telecommunications Technology/Technician, A

CENTRAL MAINE MEDICAL CENTER SCHOOL OF NURSING

Nursing - Registered Nurse Training, A

COLBY COLLEGE

African-American/Black Studies, B
American/United States Studies/Civilization, B
Anthropology, B
Area Studies, B
Art History, Criticism and Conservation, B
Art/Art Studies, General, B
Biochemistry, B
Biology/Biological Sciences, B

Cell/Cellular Biology and Histology, B
Chemistry, B
Classics and Classical
  Languages, Literatures, and Linguistics, B
Computer Science, B
Creative Writing, B
Drama and Dramatics/Theatre Arts, B
East Asian Studies, B
Economics, B
English Language and Literature, B
Environmental Sciences, B
Environmental Studies, B
Fine/Studio Arts, B
French Language and Literature, B
Geology/Earth Science, B
German Language and Literature, B
History, B
International Relations and Affairs, B
Latin American Studies, B
Mathematics, B
Molecular Biology, B
Multi-/Interdisciplinary Studies, B
Music, B
Neuroscience, B
Philosophy, B
Physics, B
Political Science and Government, B
Psychology, B
Religion/Religious Studies, B
Russian Studies, B
Science, Technology and Society, B
Sociology, B
Spanish Language and Literature, B
Women's Studies, B

COLLEGE OF THE ATLANTIC

Art/Art Studies, General, B
Biological and Physical Sciences, B
Biology/Biological Sciences, B
Botany/Plant Biology, B
Ceramic Arts and Ceramics, B
Comparative Literature, B
Computer Graphics, B
Drawing, B
Economics, B
Education, B
Elementary Education and Teaching, B
English Language and Literature, B
Environmental Biology, B
Environmental Design/Architecture, B
Environmental Education, B
Environmental Studies, BM
Evolutionary Biology, B
Family and Consumer Sciences/Human Sciences, B
Interdisciplinary Studies, B
Junior High/Intermediate/Middle School Education
  and Teaching, B
Landscape Architecture, B
Law and Legal Studies, B
Liberal Arts and Sciences Studies and
  Humanities, B
Marine Biology and Biological Oceanography, B
Maritime Science, B
Museology/Museum Studies, B
Music, B
Natural Sciences, B
Oceanography, Chemical and Physical, B
Philosophy, B
Pre-Veterinary Studies, B
Psychology, B
Public Policy Analysis, B
Science Teacher Education/General Science
  Teacher Education, B
Secondary Education and Teaching, B
Wildlife Biology, B
Zoology/Animal Biology, B

EASTERN MAINE COMMUNITY COLLEGE

Administrative Assistant and Secretarial Science, A
Automobile/Automotive Mechanics
  Technology/Technician, A
Banking and Financial Support Services, A
Business Administration and Management, A
Carpentry/Carpenter, A

Computer Technology/Computer Systems
Technology, A
Construction Engineering Technology/Technician, A
Culinary Arts/Chef Training, A
Drafting and Design Technology/Technician, A
Electrical, Electronic and Communications
Engineering Technology/Technician, A
Heating, Air Conditioning, Ventilation and
Refrigeration Maintenance
Technology/Technician, A
Heavy Equipment Maintenance
Technology/Technician, A
Kindergarten/PreSchool Education and Teaching, A
Liberal Arts and Sciences Studies and
Humanities, A
Licensed Practical/Vocational Nurse Training, A
Machine Tool Technology/Machinist, A
Nursing - Registered Nurse Training, A
Radiologic Technology/Science - Radiographer, A
Welding Technology/Welder, A

HUSSON COLLEGE

Accounting, AB
Accounting and Computer Science, B
Banking and Financial Support Services, B
Biology Teacher Education, B
Biology/Biological Sciences, B
Business Administration and Management, AB
Business Administration, Management and
Operations, M
Clinical Psychology, B
Computer Programming, Specific Applications, B
Computer Programming/Programmer, B
Criminal Justice/Police Science, AB
Criminal Justice/Safety Studies, AB
Criminology, B
Elementary Education and Teaching, B
Finance, B
Hospitality Administration/Management, B
Information Science/Studies, AB
International Business/Trade/Commerce, B
Legal Assistant/Paralegal, AB
Liberal Arts and Sciences Studies and
Humanities, B
Management Information Systems and Services, AB
Marketing/Marketing Management, B
Nursing, M
Nursing - Advanced Practice, M
Nursing - Registered Nurse Training, B
Occupational Therapy/Therapist, B
Physical Education Teaching and Coaching, B
Physical Therapy/Therapist, BM
Psychiatric/Mental Health Nurse/Nursing, M
Sales, Distribution and Marketing Operations, B
Small Business Administration/Management, B
Sport and Fitness Administration/Management, B

KENNEBEC VALLEY COMMUNITY COLLEGE

Accounting, A
Administrative Assistant and Secretarial Science, A
Biology/Biological Sciences, A
Business Administration and Management, A
Child Care and Support Services Management, A
Child Care Provider/Assistant, A
Communications Systems Installation and Repair
Technology, A
Computer Installation and Repair
Technology/Technician, A
Computer Programming, A
Computer Software and Media Applications, A
Computer Systems Networking and
Telecommunications, A
Computer/Information Technology Services
Administration and Management, A
Data Modeling/Warehousing and Database
Administration, A
Drafting and Design Technology/Technician, A
Education, A
Electrical/Electronics Equipment Installation and
Repair, A
Emergency Medical Technology/Technician (EMT
Paramedic), A
Executive Assistant/Executive Secretary, A
General Studies, A

Health Information/Medical Records
Administration/Administrator, A
Industrial Electronics Technology/Technician, A
Industrial Mechanics and Maintenance
Technology, A
Legal Administrative Assistant/Secretary, A
Liberal Arts and Sciences Studies and
Humanities, A
Machine Tool Technology/Machinist, A
Marketing/Marketing Management, A
Medical/Clinical Assistant, A
Nursing - Registered Nurse Training, A
Occupational Therapist Assistant, A
Physical Therapist Assistant, A
Respiratory Care Therapy/Therapist, A
Sales, Distribution and Marketing Operations, A
Web Page, Digital/Multimedia and Information
Resources Design, A
Web/Multimedia Management and Webmaster, A
Wood Science and Wood Products/Pulp and Paper
Technology, A

MAINE COLLEGE OF ART

Ceramic Arts and Ceramics, B
Fine Arts and Art Studies, M
Graphic Design, B
Intermedia/Multimedia, B
Metal and Jewelry Arts, B
Painting, B
Photography, B
Printmaking, B
Sculpture, B
Visual and Performing Arts, B

MAINE MARITIME ACADEMY

Business Administration and Management, B
Engineering, B
Engineering Technology, B
International Business/Trade/Commerce, BMO
Logistics and Materials Management, BMO
Management, MO
Marine Biology and Biological Oceanography, B
Marine Science/Merchant Marine Officer, B
Naval Architecture and Marine Engineering, AB
Oceanography, Chemical and Physical, B
Systems Engineering, B
Transportation and Materials Moving, AB
Transportation/Transportation Management, MO

NEW ENGLAND SCHOOL OF COMMUNICATIONS

Advertising, AB
Animation, Interactive Technology, Video Graphics
and Special Effects, AB
Audio Engineering, AB
Broadcast Journalism, AB
Cinematography and Film/Video Production, AB
Communication, Journalism and Related
Programs, AB
Communications Technologies/Technicians and
Support Services, AB
Computer Graphics, AB
Computer Software and Media Applications, AB
Film/Video and Photographic Arts, AB
Graphic Communications, AB
Intermedia/Multimedia, AB
Marketing/Marketing Management, AB
Photographic and Film/Video Technology/Technician
and Assistant, AB
Public Relations/Image Management, AB
Radio and Television, AB
Radio and Television Broadcasting
Technology/Technician, AB
Recording Arts Technology/Technician, AB
Web Page, Digital/Multimedia and Information
Resources Design, AB
Web/Multimedia Management and Webmaster, AB

NORTHERN MAINE COMMUNITY COLLEGE

Accounting, A
Administrative Assistant and Secretarial Science, A
Automobile/Automotive Mechanics
Technology/Technician, A
Business Administration and Management, A

Carpentry/Carpenter, A
Computer Engineering Technology/Technician, A
Computer Programming/Programmer, A
Data Processing and Data Processing
Technology/Technician, A
Drafting and Design Technology/Technician, A
Electrical, Electronic and Communications
Engineering Technology/Technician, A
Emergency Medical Technology/Technician (EMT
Paramedic), A
Heating, Air Conditioning, Ventilation and
Refrigeration Maintenance
Technology/Technician, A
Heavy Equipment Maintenance
Technology/Technician, A
Instrumentation Technology/Technician, A
Kindergarten/PreSchool Education and Teaching, A
Legal Administrative Assistant/Secretary, A
Medical Administrative Assistant/Secretary, A
Nursing - Registered Nurse Training, A
Pipefitting/Pipefitter and Sprinkler Fitter, A
Technology Education/Industrial Arts, A

SAINT JOSEPH'S COLLEGE OF MAINE

Accounting, B
Advertising, B
Banking and Financial Support Services, B
Biology Teacher Education, B
Biology/Biological Sciences, B
Business Administration and Management, B
Business Administration, Management and
Operations, M
Chemistry, B
Chemistry Teacher Education, B
Classics and Classical
Languages, Literatures, and Linguistics, B
Computer and Information Sciences, B
Criminal Justice/Safety Studies, B
Digital Communication and Media/Multimedia, B
Education, BM
Elementary Education and Teaching, B
English Language and Literature, B
English/Language Arts Teacher Education, B
Environmental Sciences, B
Environmental Studies, B
Finance, B
Health Services Administration, M
History, B
History Teacher Education, B
Human Development and Family Studies, B
International Business/Trade/Commerce, B
Journalism, B
Kinesiology and Exercise Science, B
Liberal Arts and Sciences Studies and
Humanities, B
Marine Biology and Biological Oceanography, B
Marketing/Marketing Management, B
Mathematics, B
Mathematics Teacher Education, B
Nursing, MO
Nursing - Registered Nurse Training, B
Nursing Administration, O
Nursing Education, O
Philosophy, B
Physical Education Teaching and Coaching, B
Psychology, B
Public Relations/Image Management, B
Quality Management, M
Religion/Religious Studies, B
Social Work, B
Sociology, B
Sport and Fitness Administration/Management, B

SOUTHERN MAINE COMMUNITY COLLEGE

Agronomy and Crop Science, A
Architectural Engineering Technology/Technician, A
Automobile/Automotive Mechanics
Technology/Technician, A
Botany/Plant Biology, A
Business Administration and Management, A
Business Machine Repairer, A
Cardiovascular Technology/Technologist, A
Carpentry/Carpenter, A
Child Development, A
Cinematography and Film/Video Production, A

Communications Technology/Technician, A
Computer Engineering Technology/Technician, A
Construction Engineering Technology/Technician, A
Criminal Justice/Law Enforcement Administration, A
Criminal Justice/Police Science, A
Culinary Arts/Chef Training, A
Dietetics/Dieticians, A
Drafting and Design Technology/Technician, A
Electrical, Electronic and Communications
   Engineering Technology/Technician, A
Engineering, A
Environmental Engineering
   Technology/Environmental Technology, A
Fire Science/Firefighting, A
Food Technology and Processing, A
General Studies, A
Heating, Air Conditioning, Ventilation and
   Refrigeration Maintenance
   Technology/Technician, A
Horticultural Science, A
Hospitality Administration/Management, A
Hotel/Motel Administration/Management, A
Industrial Radiologic Technology/Technician, A
Information Science/Studies, A
Kindergarten/PreSchool Education and Teaching, A
Landscaping and Groundskeeping, A
Liberal Arts and Sciences Studies and
   Humanities, A
Licensed Practical/Vocational Nurse Training, A
Machine Tool Technology/Machinist, A
Management Information Systems and Services, A
Marine Biology and Biological Oceanography, A
Medical/Clinical Assistant, A
Nursing - Registered Nurse Training, A
Oceanography, Chemical and Physical, A
Pipefitting/Pipefitter and Sprinkler Fitter, A
Radiologic Technology/Science - Radiographer, A
Respiratory Care Therapy/Therapist, A
Special Products Marketing Operations, A
Surgical Technology/Technologist, A

THOMAS COLLEGE

Accounting, AB
Business Administration and Management, AB
Business Administration, Management and
   Operations, M
Computer and Information Sciences, AB
Computer Education, M
Computer Science, B
Criminal Justice/Law Enforcement Administration, B
Elementary Education and Teaching, B
Finance, B
Hotel/Motel Administration/Management, B
Human Resources Management and Services, M
Human Resources Management/Personnel
   Administration, B
International Business/Trade/Commerce, B
Liberal Arts and Sciences Studies and
   Humanities, A
Management Information Systems and Services, B
Marketing/Marketing Management, B
Psychology, B
Sport and Fitness Administration/Management, B

UNITY COLLEGE

Ecology, B
Environmental Biology, B
Environmental Education, B
Environmental Engineering
   Technology/Environmental Technology, B
Environmental Studies, B
Fishing and Fisheries Sciences and Management, B
Forestry, B
Interdisciplinary Studies, AB
Marine Biology and Biological Oceanography, B
Natural Resources and Conservation, B
Natural Resources Management/Development and
   Policy, B
Parks, Recreation and Leisure Facilities
   Management, B
Wildlife Biology, B

UNIVERSITY OF MAINE

Accounting, M
Agribusiness, B
Agricultural Economics, BM

Agricultural Sciences, MD
Agricultural/Biological Engineering and
   Bioengineering, B
Agronomy and Soil Sciences, MD
Animal Sciences, BM
Anthropology, B
Art History, Criticism and Conservation, B
Art Teacher Education, B
Art/Art Studies, General, B
Biochemistry, BMD
Bioengineering, M
Biological and Biomedical Sciences, D
Biology Teacher Education, B
Biology/Biological Sciences, B
Biomedical Sciences, B
Botany/Plant Biology, BM
Business Administration and Management, B
Business Administration, Management and
   Operations, M
Business/Commerce, B
Cell/Cellular Biology and Histology, B
Chemical Engineering, BMD
Chemistry, BMD
Chemistry Teacher Education, B
Child Development, B
Civil Engineering, BMD
Classics and Classical
   Languages, Literatures, and Linguistics, B
Clinical Laboratory Science/Medical
   Technology/Technologist, B
Clinical Psychology, D
Communication and Media Studies, M
Communication Disorders, BM
Communication Studies/Speech Communication
   and Rhetoric, B
Computer Engineering, BMD
Computer Science, BMD
Construction Engineering Technology/Technician, B
Counselor Education/School Counseling and
   Guidance Services, MDO
Developmental Psychology, M
Drama and Dramatics/Theatre Arts, B
Ecology, BMD
Economics, BM
Education, BMDO
Educational Leadership and Administration, MDO
Educational Media/Instructional Technology, M
Educational/Instructional Media Design, B
Electrical Engineering, MD
Electrical, Electronic and Communications
   Engineering Technology/Technician, B
Electrical, Electronics and Communications
   Engineering, B
Elementary Education and Teaching, BMO
Engineering and Applied Sciences, MD
Engineering Physics, BM
Engineering Technology, B
English, M
English Language and Literature, B
English/Language Arts Teacher Education, B
Entomology, M
Environmental Sciences, BMD
Experimental Psychology, MD
Finance, B
Fine/Studio Arts, B
Fish, Game and Wildlife Management, MD
Food Science, B
Food Science and Technology, MD
Foods, Nutrition, and Wellness Studies, B
Foreign Language Teacher Education, BM
Foreign Languages and Literatures, B
Forest Engineering, B
Forestry, BMD
French Language and Literature, BM
French Language Teacher Education, B
Geology/Earth Science, BMD
Geosciences, MD
German Language and Literature, B
Health Teacher Education, B
Higher Education/Higher Education
   Administration, MDO
History, BMD
History Teacher Education, B
Horticultural Science, M
Human Development, M
Human Development and Family Studies, B

Interdisciplinary Studies, D
International Relations and Affairs, B
Journalism, B
Kinesiology and Movement Studies, M
Labor and Industrial Relations, B
Landscaping and Groundskeeping, B
Latin Language and Literature, B
Liberal Arts and Sciences Studies and
   Humanities, B
Liberal Studies, M
Management Information Systems and
   Services, BM
Marine Affairs, M
Marine Biology and Biological Oceanography, BMD
Marine Sciences, MD
Mass Communication/Media Studies, B
Mathematics, BM
Mathematics Teacher Education, B
Mechanical Engineering, BMD
Mechanical Engineering/Mechanical
   Technology/Technician, B
Medical Microbiology and Bacteriology, B
Microbiology, MD
Modern Languages, B
Molecular Biology, BMD
Music, BM
Music Teacher Education, B
Natural Resources and Conservation, D
Natural Resources Management/Development and
   Policy, BM
Natural Sciences, B
Nursing, MO
Nursing - Registered Nurse Training, B
Nutritional Sciences, MD
Oceanography, Chemical and Physical, MD
Ornamental Horticulture, B
Parks, Recreation and Leisure Facilities
   Management, B
Philosophy, B
Physical Education Teaching and Coaching, BM
Physics, BMD
Plant Biology, D
Plant Pathology/Phytopathology, M
Plant Sciences, BMD
Political Science and Government, B
Pre-Medicine/Pre-Medical Studies, B
Pre-Veterinary Studies, B
Psychology, BMD
Public Administration, BMD
Reading Teacher Education, MDO
Romance Languages, Literatures, and Linguistics, B
Science Teacher Education/General Science
   Teacher Education, BMO
Secondary Education and Teaching, BMO
Social Psychology, M
Social Studies Teacher Education, BMO
Social Work, BM
Sociology, B
Soil Science and Agronomy, B
Spanish Language and Literature, B
Spanish Language Teacher Education, B
Special Education and Teaching, MO
Survey Technology/Surveying, B
Surveying Engineering, B
Systems Engineering, B
Wildlife and Wildlands Science and Management, B
Women's Studies, B
Wood Science and Wood Products/Pulp and Paper
   Technology, B
Zoology/Animal Biology, BMD

THE UNIVERSITY OF MAINE AT AUGUSTA

Accounting, B
Applied Horticulture/Horticultural Operations, A
Architectural Technology/Technician, A
Biology/Biological Sciences, A
Business Administration and Management, AB
Clinical/Medical Laboratory Assistant, A
Computer and Information Sciences, AB
Criminal Justice/Law Enforcement Administration, B
Criminal Justice/Safety Studies, A
Dental Assisting/Assistant, A
Dental Hygiene/Hygienist, AB
English Language and Literature, B
Financial Planning and Services, AB

Fine/Studio Arts, AB
General Studies, B
Human Services, A
Liberal Arts and Sciences Studies and
 Humanities, A
Library Assistant/Technician, A
Library Science, B
Mental and Social Health Services and Allied
 Professions, AB
Music, AB
Nursing - Registered Nurse Training, A
Photography, A
Public Administration, AB
Social Sciences, A
Veterinary/Animal Health Technology/Technician and
 Veterinary Assistant, A

UNIVERSITY OF MAINE AT FARMINGTON

Anthropology, B
Art/Art Studies, General, B
Biology Teacher Education, B
Biology/Biological Sciences, B
Business/Managerial Economics, B
Computer Science, B
Creative Writing, B
Drama and Dramatics/Theatre Arts, B
Education/Teaching of Individuals with Emotional
 Disturbances, B
Education/Teaching of Individuals with Mental
 Retardation, B
Education/Teaching of Individuals with Specific
 Learning Disabilities, B
Elementary Education and Teaching, B
English Language and Literature, B
English/Language Arts Teacher Education, B
Environmental Studies, B
General Studies, B
Geography, B
Geology/Earth Science, B
Health Occupations Teacher Education, B
Health Teacher Education, B
History, B
Interdisciplinary Studies, B
International Relations and Affairs, B
Kindergarten/PreSchool Education and Teaching, B
Liberal Arts and Sciences Studies and
 Humanities, B
Mathematics, B
Mathematics Teacher Education, B
Mental Health/Rehabilitation, B
Music, B
Philosophy, B
Political Science and Government, B
Psychology, B
Rehabilitation Therapy, B
Religion/Religious Studies, B
Science Teacher Education/General Science
 Teacher Education, B
Secondary Education and Teaching, B
Social Science Teacher Education, B
Sociology, B
Special Education and Teaching, B
Women's Studies, B

UNIVERSITY OF MAINE AT FORT KENT

Behavioral Sciences, B
Bilingual and Multilingual Education, B
Biology/Biological Sciences, B
Business Administration and Management, AB
Business Teacher Education, B
Computer Science, AB
Criminal Justice/Law Enforcement Administration, A
Education, B
Elementary Education and Teaching, B
English Language and Literature, B
English/Language Arts Teacher Education, B
Environmental Studies, B
Forestry, A
Forestry Technology/Technician, A
French Language and Literature, B
French Language Teacher Education, B
General Studies, A
Human Services, A
Liberal Arts and Sciences Studies and
 Humanities, AB

Mathematics Teacher Education, B
Nursing - Registered Nurse Training, B
Public Administration, B
Social Science Teacher Education, B
Social Sciences, B
Teacher Education, Multiple Levels, B

UNIVERSITY OF MAINE AT MACHIAS

Accounting, B
Art/Art Studies, General, B
Behavioral Sciences, B
Biology Teacher Education, B
Biology/Biological Sciences, B
Business Administration and Management, B
Business Teacher Education, B
Conservation Biology, B
Creative Writing, B
Drama and Dramatics/Theatre Arts, B
Ecology, B
Education, B
Elementary Education and Teaching, B
English Language and Literature, B
English/Language Arts Teacher Education, B
Entrepreneurship/Entrepreneurial Studies, B
Environmental Education, B
Environmental Studies, B
Family and Community Services, B
General Studies, B
History, B
History Teacher Education, B
Hotel/Motel Administration/Management, B
Human Services, B
Marine Biology and Biological Oceanography, B
Marketing/Marketing Management, B
Mathematics Teacher Education, B
Music, B
Parks, Recreation and Leisure Facilities
 Management, B
Parks, Recreation, Leisure and Fitness Studies, B
Pre-Medicine/Pre-Medical Studies, B
Psychology, B
Public Administration, B
Science Teacher Education/General Science
 Teacher Education, B
Social Science Teacher Education, B
Tourism and Travel Services Management, B
Visual and Performing Arts, B

UNIVERSITY OF MAINE AT PRESQUE ISLE

Accounting, B
Applied Art, A
Art Teacher Education, B
Art/Art Studies, General, B
Athletic Training and Sports Medicine, B
Behavioral Sciences, B
Biology/Biological Sciences, B
Business Administration and Management, B
Clinical/Medical Laboratory Technician, A
Creative Writing, A
Criminal Justice/Law Enforcement
 Administration, AB
Education, B
Elementary Education and Teaching, B
English Language and Literature, B
Environmental Studies, B
Fine/Studio Arts, B
Foods, Nutrition, and Wellness Studies, A
Geology/Earth Science, B
Health Teacher Education, B
International Relations and Affairs, B
Liberal Arts and Sciences Studies and
 Humanities, AB
Parks, Recreation, Leisure and Fitness Studies, AB
Physical Education Teaching and Coaching, B
Political Science and Government, B
Science Teacher Education/General Science
 Teacher Education, B
Secondary Education and Teaching, B
Social Work, B
Sociology, B

UNIVERSITY OF NEW ENGLAND

American/United States Studies/Civilization, B
Aquaculture, B
Athletic Training and Sports Medicine, B

Biochemistry, B
Biology/Biological Sciences, B
Biomedical Sciences, B
Business Administration and Management, B
Chemistry, B
Clinical Laboratory Science/Medical
 Technology/Technologist, B
Dental Hygiene/Hygienist, AB
Education, M
Educational Leadership and Administration, O
Elementary Education and Teaching, B
English Language and Literature, B
Environmental Sciences, B
Environmental Studies, B
Gerontology, O
Health and Medical Laboratory Technologies, B
Health and Physical Education/Fitness, B
Health Professions and Related Clinical Sciences, B
Health/Health Care Administration/Management, B
History, B
Kinesiology and Exercise Science, B
Liberal Arts and Sciences Studies and
 Humanities, B
Marine Biology and Biological Oceanography, B
Mathematics, B
Nurse Anesthetist, M
Nursing - Registered Nurse Training, AB
Occupational Therapy/Therapist, BM
Osteopathic Medicine, P
Physical Therapy/Therapist, BD
Physician Assistant, BM
Physiological Psychology/Psychobiology, B
Political Science and Government, B
Pre-Dentistry Studies, B
Pre-Medicine/Pre-Medical Studies, B
Psychology, B
Public Health, MO
Public Health (MPH, DPH), B
Social Psychology, B
Social Sciences, B
Social Work, MO
Sociology, B
Sport and Fitness Administration/Management, B
Substance Abuse/Addiction Counseling, O

UNIVERSITY OF SOUTHERN MAINE

Accounting, BMO
Adult and Continuing Education and Teaching, MO
American/United States Studies/Civilization, M
Anthropology, B
Art Teacher Education, B
Art/Art Studies, General, B
Athletic Training and Sports Medicine, B
Biological and Biomedical Sciences, M
Biology/Biological Sciences, B
BioTechnology, B
Business Administration and Management, B
Business Administration, Management and
 Operations, MO
Chemistry, B
Classics and Classical
 Languages, Literatures, and Linguistics, B
Communication Studies/Speech Communication
 and Rhetoric, B
Computer Science, BM
Counselor Education/School Counseling and
 Guidance Services, MO
Criminology, B
Drama and Dramatics/Theatre Arts, B
Economics, B
Education, MDO
Educational Administration and Supervision, O
Educational Leadership and Administration, MO
Electrical, Electronics and Communications
 Engineering, B
English as a Second Language, MO
English Language and Literature, B
Environmental Health, B
Environmental Studies, B
French Language and Literature, B
Geography, B
Geology/Earth Science, B
Health Services Administration, MO
Hispanic-American, Puerto Rican, and Mexican-
 American/Chicano Studies, B
History, B

Immunology, M
Industrial Education, M
International Relations and Affairs, B
Law and Legal Studies, PO
Linguistics, B
Manufacturing Engineering, M
Mass Communication/Media Studies, B
Mathematics, B
Medical/Surgical Nursing, M
Middle School Education, O
Modern Languages, B
Molecular Biology, M
Music, B
Music Performance, B
Music Teacher Education, B
Non-Profit/Public/Organizational Management, O
Nursing, MO
Nursing - Adult, MO
Nursing - Advanced Practice, M
Nursing - Registered Nurse Training, B
Occupational Therapy/Therapist, M
Philosophy, B
Physics, B
Political Science and Government, B
Psychiatric/Mental Health Nurse/Nursing, MO
Psychology, B
Public Health (MPH, DPH), B
Public Policy Analysis, MDO
Reading Teacher Education, MO
Russian Studies, B
School Psychology, MD
Social Sciences, B
Social Work, BM
Sociology, B
Special Education and Teaching, M
Sport and Fitness Administration/Management, O
Statistics, M
Technology Education/Industrial Arts, B
Therapeutic Recreation/Recreational Therapy, AB
Trade and Industrial Teacher Education, B
Urban and Regional Planning, MO
Women's Studies, B
Writing, M

WASHINGTON COUNTY COMMUNITY COLLEGE

Automobile/Automotive Mechanics
    Technology/Technician, A
Construction Engineering Technology/Technician, A
Engineering Technology, A
Marine Technology, A

YORK COUNTY COMMUNITY COLLEGE

Accounting, A
Business Administration and Management, A
Computer Engineering Technology/Technician, A
Computer Systems Networking and
    Telecommunications, A
Computer/Information Technology Services
    Administration and Management, A
Culinary Arts/Chef Training, A
Drafting and Design Technology/Technician, A
General Studies, A
Hotel/Motel Administration/Management, A
Kindergarten/PreSchool Education and Teaching, A
Web Page, Digital/Multimedia and Information
    Resources Design, A

Maryland

ALLEGANY COLLEGE OF MARYLAND

Accounting Technology/Technician and
    Bookkeeping, A
Administrative Assistant and Secretarial Science, A
Automobile/Automotive Mechanics
    Technology/Technician, A
Business Administration and Management, A
Clinical/Medical Laboratory Assistant, A
Clinical/Medical Laboratory Technician, A
Communications Technology/Technician, A
Computer Engineering Technology/Technician, A
Cosmetology and Related Personal Grooming
    Arts, A
Criminal Justice/Police Science, A
Culinary Arts/Chef Training, A

Dental Hygiene/Hygienist, A
Forest Management/Forest Resources
    Management, A
Health Professions and Related Clinical Sciences, A
Hospitality Administration/Management, A
Legal Assistant/Paralegal, A
Liberal Arts and Sciences Studies and
    Humanities, A
Management Information Systems and Services, A
Marketing/Marketing Management, A
Medical Radiologic Technology/Science - Radiation
    Therapist, A
Nursing - Registered Nurse Training, A
Occupational Therapist Assistant, A
Occupational Therapy/Therapist, A
Physical Therapist Assistant, A
Psychiatric/Mental Health Services Technician, A
Respiratory Care Therapy/Therapist, A

ANNE ARUNDEL COMMUNITY COLLEGE

Accounting, A
Administrative Assistant and Secretarial Science, A
American/United States Studies/Civilization, A
Applied Art, A
Architectural Engineering Technology/Technician, A
Art/Art Studies, General, A
Astronomy, A
Behavioral Sciences, A
Biological and Physical Sciences, A
Biology/Biological Sciences, A
Botany/Plant Biology, A
Broadcast Journalism, A
Business Administration and Management, A
Business/Managerial Economics, A
Chemistry, A
Cinematography and Film/Video Production, A
Clinical Laboratory Science/Medical
    Technology/Technologist, A
Communications Technology/Technician, A
Computer and Information Sciences, A
Computer Engineering Technology/Technician, A
Computer Programming/Programmer, A
Computer Science, A
Consumer Merchandising/Retailing Management, A
Corrections, A
Criminal Justice/Law Enforcement Administration, A
Criminal Justice/Police Science, A
Data Entry/Microcomputer Applications, A
Data Processing and Data Processing
    Technology/Technician, A
Economics, A
Education, A
Electrical, Electronic and Communications
    Engineering Technology/Technician, A
Elementary Education and Teaching, A
Emergency Medical Technology/Technician (EMT
    Paramedic), A
Engineering Technology, A
English Language and Literature, A
Environmental Studies, A
European Studies/Civilization, A
Food Technology and Processing, A
Health Teacher Education, A
Horticultural Science, A
Hotel/Motel Administration/Management, A
Human Services, A
Humanities/Humanistic Studies, A
Industrial Radiologic Technology/Technician, A
Industrial Technology/Technician, A
Information Science/Studies, A
Kindergarten/PreSchool Education and Teaching, A
Landscape Architecture, A
Legal Assistant/Paralegal, A
Liberal Arts and Sciences Studies and
    Humanities, A
Management Information Systems and Services, A
Marine Science/Merchant Marine Officer, A
Marketing/Marketing Management, A
Mass Communication/Media Studies, A
Mathematics, A
Mechanical Engineering/Mechanical
    Technology/Technician, A
Medical/Clinical Assistant, A
Mental Health/Rehabilitation, A
Music, A

Nursing - Registered Nurse Training, A
Photography, A
Physical Education Teaching and Coaching, A
Public Administration, A
Public Policy Analysis, A
Real Estate, A
Social Sciences, A
System Administration/Administrator, A
Telecommunications Technology/Technician, A

BALTIMORE CITY COMMUNITY COLLEGE

Accounting, A
Administrative Assistant and Secretarial Science, A
Biological and Physical Sciences, A
Business Administration and Management, A
Commercial and Advertising Art, A
Computer Graphics, A
Computer Science, A
Corrections, A
Criminal Justice/Police Science, A
Data Processing and Data Processing
    Technology/Technician, A
Dental Hygiene/Hygienist, A
Dietetics/Dieticians, A
Drafting and Design Technology/Technician, A
Electrical, Electronic and Communications
    Engineering Technology/Technician, A
Emergency Medical Technology/Technician (EMT
    Paramedic), A
Engineering, A
Fashion Merchandising, A
Fashion/Apparel Design, A
Gerontology, A
Health Information/Medical Records
    Administration/Administrator, A
Hospitality Administration/Management, A
Human Services, A
Information Science/Studies, A
Kindergarten/PreSchool Education and Teaching, A
Legal Administrative Assistant/Secretary, A
Legal Assistant/Paralegal, A
Liberal Arts and Sciences Studies and
    Humanities, A
Management Information Systems and Services, A
Marketing/Marketing Management, A
Medical Administrative Assistant/Secretary, A
Nursing - Registered Nurse Training, A
Physical Therapy/Therapist, A
Respiratory Care Therapy/Therapist, A
Surgical Technology/Technologist, A
Word Processing, A

BALTIMORE HEBREW UNIVERSITY

Ancient Near Eastern and Biblical
    Languages, Literatures, and Linguistics, AB
Archeology, AB
Bible/Biblical Studies, AB
Central/Middle and Eastern European Studies, AB
Computer Typography and Composition Equipment
    Operator, AB
Education, AB
Ethnic and Cultural Studies, AB
Hebrew Language and Literature, AB
Hebrew Studies, MD
Jewish/Judaic Studies, AB
Near and Middle Eastern Studies, AB
Philosophy, AB
Rabbinical Studies, AB
Religion/Religious Studies, AB
Religious Education, AB

BALTIMORE INTERNATIONAL COLLEGE

Baking and Pastry Arts/Baker/Pastry Chef, A
Culinary Arts/Chef Training, A
Hospitality Administration/Management, AB
Restaurant, Culinary, and Catering
    Management/Manager, B

BOWIE STATE UNIVERSITY

Accounting, B
Applied Mathematics, B
Art/Art Studies, General, B
Biology/Biological Sciences, B

Broadcast Journalism, B
Business Administration and Management, B
Business Administration, Management and
   Operations, M
Computer and Information Sciences, B
Computer Graphics, B
Computer Science, M
Corporate and Organizational Communication, MO
Counseling Psychology, M
Counselor Education/School Counseling and
   Guidance Services, M
Creative Writing, B
Criminal Justice/Law Enforcement Administration, B
Economics, B
Education, BM
Educational Administration and Supervision, M
Educational Leadership and Administration, D
Elementary Education and Teaching, BM
English Language and Literature, B
History, B
Human Resources Development, M
Kindergarten/PreSchool Education and Teaching, B
Management Information Systems and
   Services, MO
Marketing/Marketing Management, B
Mass Communication/Media Studies, B
Mathematics, B
Mathematics Teacher Education, B
Nursing, M
Nursing - Advanced Practice, M
Nursing - Registered Nurse Training, B
Nursing Administration, M
Nursing Education, M
Political Science and Government, B
Psychology, B
Public Administration, M
Public Relations/Image Management, B
Reading Teacher Education, M
Science Teacher Education/General Science
   Teacher Education, B
Secondary Education and Teaching, BM
Social Work, B
Sociology, B
Special Education and Teaching, BM

CAPITOL COLLEGE

Business Administration, Management and
   Operations, M
Computer Engineering, B
Computer Engineering Technology/Technician, AB
Computer Science, M
Electrical Engineering, M
Electrical, Electronic and Communications
   Engineering Technology/Technician, AB
Electrical, Electronics and Communications
   Engineering, B
Information Science/Studies, M
Laser and Optical Technology/Technician, A
Management Information Systems and
   Services, BM
Telecommunications Management, M
Telecommunications Technology/Technician, AB

CARROLL COMMUNITY COLLEGE

Accounting, A
Business Administration and Management, A
Computer and Information Sciences, A
Computer Graphics, A
Data Processing and Data Processing
   Technology/Technician, A
Drafting/Design Engineering
   Technologies/Technicians, A
General Studies, A
Human Services, A
Kindergarten/PreSchool Education and Teaching, A
Liberal Arts and Sciences Studies and
   Humanities, A
Music, A
Nursing - Registered Nurse Training, A
Physical Therapist Assistant, A
Public Health (MPH, DPH), A
Teacher Education, Multiple Levels, A

CECIL COMMUNITY COLLEGE

Accounting, A
Administrative Assistant and Secretarial Science, A

Air Traffic Controller, A
Art/Art Studies, General, A
Artificial Intelligence and Robotics, A
Biology/Biological Sciences, A
Business Administration and Management, A
Carpentry/Carpenter, A
Computer Engineering Technology/Technician, A
Computer Graphics, A
Computer Programming/Programmer, A
Construction Engineering Technology/Technician, A
Criminal Justice/Law Enforcement Administration, A
Data Processing and Data Processing
   Technology/Technician, A
Education, A
Electrical, Electronic and Communications
   Engineering Technology/Technician, A
Elementary Education and Teaching, A
General Studies, A
Health and Medical Laboratory Technologies, A
Hydrology and Water Resources Science, A
Information Science/Studies, A
Information Technology, A
Kindergarten/PreSchool Education and Teaching, A
Liberal Arts and Sciences Studies and
   Humanities, A
Marketing/Marketing Management, A
Mathematics, A
Nursing - Registered Nurse Training, A
Photography, A
Physical Sciences, A
Physics, A
Pipefitting/Pipefitter and Sprinkler Fitter, A
Teacher Education, Multiple Levels, A
Transportation and Materials Moving, A
Welding Technology/Welder, A

CHESAPEAKE COLLEGE

Accounting, A
Administrative Assistant and Secretarial Science, A
Architectural Engineering Technology/Technician, A
Art/Art Studies, General, A
Biological and Physical Sciences, A
Business Administration and Management, A
Computer Engineering Technology/Technician, A
Computer Programming/Programmer, A
Computer Science, A
Corrections, A
Criminal Justice/Law Enforcement Administration, A
Data Processing and Data Processing
   Technology/Technician, A
Electrical, Electronic and Communications
   Engineering Technology/Technician, A
Elementary Education and Teaching, A
Health Teacher Education, A
Human Services, A
Humanities/Humanistic Studies, A
Kindergarten/PreSchool Education and Teaching, A
Legal Administrative Assistant/Secretary, A
Liberal Arts and Sciences Studies and
   Humanities, A
Mathematics, A
Medical Administrative Assistant/Secretary, A
Medical Radiologic Technology/Science - Radiation
   Therapist, A
Music, A
Parks, Recreation, Leisure and Fitness Studies, A
Physical Education Teaching and Coaching, A
Physical Sciences, A
Social Sciences, A
Sociology, A

COLLEGE OF NOTRE DAME OF MARYLAND

Art/Art Studies, General, B
Biology/Biological Sciences, B
Business Administration and Management, B
Chemistry, B
Classics and Classical
   Languages, Literatures, and Linguistics, B
Communication and Media Studies, M
Computer Science, B
Economics, B
Education, BM
Educational Leadership and Administration, M
Elementary Education and Teaching, B
Engineering Science, B

English as a Second Language, M
English Language and Literature, B
Gerontology, M
History, B
Human Services, B
Information Science/Studies, B
Interdisciplinary Studies, B
International Business/Trade/Commerce, B
International Relations and Affairs, B
Kindergarten/PreSchool Education and Teaching, B
Liberal Arts and Sciences Studies and
   Humanities, B
Liberal Studies, M
Management, M
Mass Communication/Media Studies, B
Mathematics, B
Modern Languages, B
Music, B
Non-Profit/Public/Organizational Management, M
Nursing - Registered Nurse Training, B
Physics, B
Physiological Psychology/Psychobiology, B
Political Science and Government, B
Pre-Law Studies, B
Pre-Medicine/Pre-Medical Studies, B
Pre-Veterinary Studies, B
Psychology, B
Religion/Religious Studies, B
Special Education and Teaching, B

COLLEGE OF SOUTHERN MARYLAND

Accounting, A
Agribusiness, A
Art/Art Studies, General, A
Biology/Biological Sciences, A
BioTechnology, A
Business Administration and Management, A
Communication Studies/Speech Communication
   and Rhetoric, A
Computer Programming/Programmer, A
Drama and Dramatics/Theatre Arts, A
Education, A
Electrical, Electronic and Communications
   Engineering Technology/Technician, A
Elementary Education and Teaching, A
Emergency Medical Technology/Technician (EMT
   Paramedic), A
English Language and Literature, A
Fire Protection and Safety Technology/Technician, A
History, A
Human Services, A
Information Science/Studies, A
Journalism, A
Kindergarten/PreSchool Education and Teaching, A
Legal Assistant/Paralegal, A
Liberal Arts and Sciences Studies and
   Humanities, A
Licensed Practical/Vocational Nurse Training, A
Massage Therapy/Therapeutic Massage, A
Music, A
Nursing - Registered Nurse Training, A
Physical Therapist Assistant, A
Social Sciences, A

COLUMBIA UNION COLLEGE

Accounting, AB
Biochemistry, B
Biology/Biological Sciences, B
Broadcast Journalism, B
Business Administration and Management, B
Chemistry, B
Computer Science, AB
Counseling Psychology, B
Early Childhood Education and Teaching, A
Elementary Education and Teaching, B
Engineering, A
English Language and Literature, B
English/Language Arts Teacher Education, B
General Studies, AB
Health and Physical Education, B
Health/Health Care Administration/Management, B
History, B
Information Science/Studies, B
Journalism, B
Liberal Arts and Sciences Studies and
   Humanities, B

Mass Communication/Media Studies, B
Mathematics, B
Mathematics Teacher Education, B
Music, B
Music Performance, B
Music Teacher Education, B
Nursing - Registered Nurse Training, B
Political Science and Government, B
Pre-Dentistry Studies, B
Pre-Law Studies, B
Pre-Medicine/Pre-Medical Studies, B
Pre-Veterinary Studies, B
Psychology, B
Religious Education, B
Respiratory Care Therapy/Therapist, AB
Special Education and Teaching, B
Theology/Theological Studies, B

COPPIN STATE UNIVERSITY

Adult and Continuing Education and Teaching, M
Biology/Biological Sciences, B
Business Administration and Management, B
Chemistry, B
Computer Science, B
Criminal Justice/Law Enforcement Administration, B
Criminology, M
Curriculum and Instruction, M
Education, BM
Elementary Education and Teaching, B
English Language and Literature, B
History, B
Human Services, M
Kindergarten/PreSchool Education and Teaching, B
Liberal Arts and Sciences Studies and
  Humanities, B
Mathematics, B
Natural Sciences, B
Nursing, MO
Nursing - Advanced Practice, O
Nursing - Registered Nurse Training, B
Philosophy, B
Physical Education Teaching and Coaching, B
Physical Therapy/Therapist, B
Pre-Dentistry Studies, B
Pre-Law Studies, B
Pre-Medicine/Pre-Medical Studies, B
Psychology, B
Reading Teacher Education, M
Rehabilitation Counseling, M
Science Teacher Education/General Science
  Teacher Education, B
Secondary Education and Teaching, B
Social Sciences, B
Social Work, B
Special Education and Teaching, BM
Substance Abuse/Addiction Counseling, M

DEVRY UNIVERSITY

Business Administration and Management, B
Business Administration, Management and
  Operations, BM
Computer and Information Sciences, B

FREDERICK COMMUNITY COLLEGE

Accounting, A
Art/Art Studies, General, A
Biology/Biological Sciences, A
Building/Construction
  Finishing, Management, and Inspection, A
Business Administration and Management, A
Chemistry, A
Child Development, A
Computer Engineering Technology/Technician, A
Computer Science, A
Criminal Justice/Law Enforcement Administration, A
Data Processing and Data Processing
  Technology/Technician, A
Drafting and Design Technology/Technician, A
Education, A
Electrical, Electronic and Communications
  Engineering Technology/Technician, A
Elementary Education and Teaching, A
Emergency Medical Technology/Technician (EMT
  Paramedic), A
Engineering, A
English Language and Literature, A

Finance, A
Fire Science/Firefighting, A
General Studies, A
Health and Medical Laboratory Technologies, A
Human Services, A
Information Technology, A
International Business/Trade/Commerce, A
Kindergarten/PreSchool Education and Teaching, A
Legal Administrative Assistant/Secretary, A
Legal Assistant/Paralegal, A
Liberal Arts and Sciences Studies and
  Humanities, A
Marketing/Marketing Management, A
Mass Communication/Media Studies, A
Mathematics, A
Mathematics Teacher Education, A
Medical Administrative Assistant/Secretary, A
Music Teacher Education, A
Nuclear Medical Technology/Technologist, A
Nursing - Registered Nurse Training, A
Physical Education Teaching and Coaching, A
Physical Sciences, A
Political Science and Government, A
Psychology, A
Respiratory Care Therapy/Therapist, A
Spanish Language Teacher Education, A
Surgical Technology/Technologist, A

FROSTBURG STATE UNIVERSITY

Accounting, B
Biological and Biomedical Sciences, M
Biology/Biological Sciences, B
Business Administration and Management, B
Business Administration, Management and
  Operations, M
Chemistry, B
City/Urban, Community and Regional Planning, B
Communication Studies/Speech Communication
  and Rhetoric, B
Computer and Information Sciences, B
Computer Science, M
Conservation Biology, M
Counseling Psychology, M
Counselor Education/School Counseling and
  Guidance Services, M
Criminal Justice/Law Enforcement Administration, B
Criminal Justice/Police Science, B
Curriculum and Instruction, M
Dance, B
Drama and Dramatics/Theatre Arts, B
Ecology, M
Economics, B
Education, M
Educational Administration and Supervision, M
Educational Media/Instructional Technology, M
Electrical, Electronics and Communications
  Engineering, B
Elementary Education and Teaching, BM
English Language and Literature, B
Environmental Studies, B
Fish, Game and Wildlife Management, M
Foreign Languages and Literatures, B
Geography, B
History, B
Information Science/Studies, B
Interdisciplinary Studies, M
International Relations and Affairs, B
Kindergarten/PreSchool Education and Teaching, B
Kinesiology and Exercise Science, B
Liberal Arts and Sciences Studies and
  Humanities, B
Mass Communication/Media Studies, B
Mathematics, B
Mechanical Engineering, B
Multi-/Interdisciplinary Studies, B
Music, B
Natural Resources and Conservation, B
Parks, Recreation, Leisure and Fitness Studies, B
Philosophy, B
Physical Education Teaching and Coaching, BM
Physical Sciences, B
Physics, B
Political Science and Government, B
Psychology, BM
Reading Teacher Education, M
Recreation and Park Management, M

Secondary Education and Teaching, BM
Social Sciences, B
Social Work, B
Sociology, B
Special Education and Teaching, M
Speech and Rhetorical Studies, B
Sport and Fitness Administration/Management, B
Visual and Performing Arts, B

GARRETT COLLEGE

Administrative Assistant and Secretarial Science, A
Agricultural Mechanization, A
Art/Art Studies, General, A
Behavioral Sciences, A
Biology/Biological Sciences, A
Business Administration and Management, A
Criminal Justice/Safety Studies, A
Education, A
Elementary Education and Teaching, A
General Studies, A
Hotel/Motel Administration/Management, A
Liberal Arts and Sciences Studies and
  Humanities, A
Mathematics, A
Music, A
Natural Resources Management/Development and
  Policy, A
Parks, Recreation and Leisure Facilities
  Management, A
Parks, Recreation, Leisure and Fitness Studies, A
Physical Education Teaching and Coaching, A
Psychology, A
Social Sciences, A
Sociology, A
Wildlife and Wildlands Science and Management, A
Wildlife Biology, A

GOUCHER COLLEGE

American/United States Studies/Civilization, B
Art/Art Studies, General, B
Arts Management, M
Biological and Biomedical Sciences, O
Biology/Biological Sciences, B
Business Administration and Management, B
Chemistry, B
Computer Science, B
Dance, B
Drama and Dramatics/Theatre Arts, B
Economics, B
Education, BM
Elementary Education and Teaching, B
English Language and Literature, B
French Language and Literature, B
Historic Preservation and Conservation, BM
History, B
Interdisciplinary Studies, B
International Relations and Affairs, B
Mass Communication/Media Studies, B
Mathematics, B
Music, B
Peace Studies and Conflict Resolution, B
Philosophy, B
Physics, B
Political Science and Government, B
Psychology, B
Religion/Religious Studies, B
Russian Language and Literature, B
Sociology, B
Spanish Language and Literature, B
Special Education and Teaching, B
Women's Studies, B
Writing, M

GRIGGS UNIVERSITY

Business Administration and Management, B
Religion/Religious Studies, AB
Religious Education, B
Theology/Theological Studies, AB

HAGERSTOWN BUSINESS COLLEGE

Accounting, A
Administrative Assistant and Secretarial Science, A
Business Administration and Management, A
Computer and Information Systems Security, A
Criminal Justice/Law Enforcement Administration, A

Data Processing and Data Processing
Technology/Technician, A
Health Information/Medical Records
Administration/Administrator, A
Information Science/Studies, A
Legal Administrative Assistant/Secretary, A
Legal Assistant/Paralegal, A
Marketing/Marketing Management, A
Medical Administrative Assistant/Secretary, A
Medical/Clinical Assistant, A

HAGERSTOWN COMMUNITY COLLEGE

Accounting Technology/Technician and
Bookkeeping, A
Animation, Interactive Technology, Video Graphics
and Special Effects, A
Business Administration and Management, A
Business/Commerce, A
Child Care and Support Services Management, A
Commercial and Advertising Art, A
Computer and Information Sciences, A
Criminal Justice/Police Science, A
Early Childhood Education and Teaching, A
Education, A
Electromechanical Technology/Electromechanical
Engineering Technology, A
Elementary Education and Teaching, A
Emergency Medical Technology/Technician (EMT
Paramedic), A
Engineering, A
Health Information/Medical Records
Administration/Administrator, A
Industrial Technology/Technician, A
Liberal Arts and Sciences Studies and
Humanities, A
Management Information Systems and Services, A
Mechanical Engineering/Mechanical
Technology/Technician, A
Medical Radiologic Technology/Science - Radiation
Therapist, A
Nursing - Registered Nurse Training, A
Psychiatric/Mental Health Services Technician, A
Web Page, Digital/Multimedia and Information
Resources Design, A

HARFORD COMMUNITY COLLEGE

Accounting Technology/Technician and
Bookkeeping, A
Administrative Assistant and Secretarial Science, A
Audio Engineering, A
Business Administration and Management, A
Business/Commerce, A
Child Care and Support Services Management, A
Commercial and Advertising Art, A
Communications Technologies/Technicians and
Support Services, A
Computer and Information Sciences, A
Education, A
Electroneurodiagnostic/Electroencephalographic
Technology/Technologist, A
Elementary Education and Teaching, A
Engineering, A
Engineering Technologies/Technicians, A
Environmental Engineering
Technology/Environmental Technology, A
Health and Medical Laboratory Technologies, A
Interior Design, A
Legal Assistant/Paralegal, A
Liberal Arts and Sciences Studies and
Humanities, A
Management Information Systems and Services, A
Mechanical Engineering/Mechanical
Technology/Technician, A
Multi-/Interdisciplinary Studies, A
Nursing - Registered Nurse Training, A
Philosophy, A
Political Science and Government, A
Psychology, A
Science Technologies/Technicians, A
Security and Loss Prevention Services, A

HOOD COLLEGE

Art/Art Studies, General, B
Biochemistry, B
Biological and Biomedical Sciences, MO
Biology/Biological Sciences, B

Business Administration and Management, B
Business Administration, Management and
Operations, M
Ceramic Arts and Ceramics, O
Chemistry, B
Communication and Media Studies, B
Computer and Information Sciences, B
Computer Science, M
Curriculum and Instruction, M
Economics, B
Education, MO
Educational Leadership and Administration, M
Engineering, B
English Language and Literature, B
Environmental Biology, M
Environmental Studies, B
Foreign Language Teacher Education, O
French Language and Literature, B
German Language and Literature, B
History, B
Human Development, M
Humanities/Humanistic Studies, M
Information Science/Studies, M
Latin American Studies, B
Law and Legal Studies, B
Mathematics, B
Mathematics Teacher Education, O
Multi-/Interdisciplinary Studies, B
Music, B
Philosophy, B
Political Science and Government, B
Psychology, BMO
Reading Teacher Education, O
Religion/Religious Studies, B
Romance Languages, Literatures, and Linguistics, B
Social Work, B
Sociology, B
Spanish Language and Literature, B
Systems Science and Theory, M
Thanatology, MO

HOWARD COMMUNITY COLLEGE

Accounting, A
Administrative Assistant and Secretarial Science, A
Applied Art, A
Architecture, A
Art/Art Studies, General, A
Biological and Physical Sciences, A
Biomedical Technology/Technician, A
BioTechnology, A
Business Administration and Management, A
Cardiovascular Technology/Technologist, A
Child Development, A
Clinical Laboratory Science/Medical
Technology/Technologist, A
Computer and Information Sciences, A
Computer Graphics, A
Computer Science, A
Computer Systems Networking and
Telecommunications, A
Computer/Information Technology Services
Administration and Management, A
Consumer Merchandising/Retailing Management, A
Criminal Justice/Law Enforcement Administration, A
Data Entry/Microcomputer Applications, A
Drama and Dramatics/Theatre Arts, A
Electrical, Electronic and Communications
Engineering Technology/Technician, A
Elementary Education and Teaching, A
Emergency Medical Technology/Technician (EMT
Paramedic), A
Engineering, A
Environmental Studies, A
Fashion Merchandising, A
Financial Planning and Services, A
General Studies, A
Health Teacher Education, A
Information Science/Studies, A
Information Technology, A
Kindergarten/PreSchool Education and Teaching, A
Legal Administrative Assistant/Secretary, A
Liberal Arts and Sciences Studies and
Humanities, A
Licensed Practical/Vocational Nurse Training, A
Medical Administrative Assistant/Secretary, A
Music, A

Nuclear Medical Technology/Technologist, A
Nursing - Registered Nurse Training, A
Office Management and Supervision, A
Ophthalmic/Optometric Services, A
Photography, A
Physical Sciences, A
Pre-Dentistry Studies, A
Pre-Medicine/Pre-Medical Studies, A
Pre-Pharmacy Studies, A
Pre-Veterinary Studies, A
Psychology, A
Secondary Education and Teaching, A
Social Sciences, A
Sport and Fitness Administration/Management, A
Substance Abuse/Addiction Counseling, A
Technical Theatre/Theatre Design and
Technology, A
Telecommunications Technology/Technician, A

ITT TECHNICAL INSTITUTE

CAD/CADD Drafting and/or Design
Technology/Technician, A
Computer and Information Systems Security, B
Computer Programming/Programmer, A
Computer Systems Networking and
Telecommunications, B
E-Commerce/Electronic Commerce, B
Electrical, Electronic and Communications
Engineering Technology/Technician, AB
System, Networking, and LAN/WAN
Management/Manager, A
Web Page, Digital/Multimedia and Information
Resources Design, A
Web/Multimedia Management and Webmaster, A

THE JOHNS HOPKINS UNIVERSITY

Allopathic Medicine, PO
Anatomy, D
Anthropology, BD
Applied Economics, M
Applied Mathematics, BMD
Applied Physics, M
Art History, Criticism and Conservation, BMD
Astronomy, D
Behavioral Sciences, B
Biochemistry, MD
Bioengineering, MD
Bioinformatics, M
Biological and Biomedical Sciences, MDO
Biological and Physical Sciences, B
Biology/Biological Sciences, B
Biomedical Engineering, MD
Biomedical/Medical Engineering, B
Biophysics, BMD
Biostatistics, MD
BioTechnology, M
Business Administration, Management and
Operations, MO
Business/Commerce, B
Cell Biology and Anatomy, D
Chemical Engineering, BMD
Chemistry, BMD
Civil Engineering, BMD
Classics and Classical
Languages, Literatures, and Linguistics, BMD
Clinical Research, MD
Cognitive Psychology and Psycholinguistics, B
Cognitive Sciences, D
Communication and Media Studies, M
Community Health Nursing, MO
Comparative Literature, BD
Computer and Information Sciences, B
Computer Engineering, BMD
Computer Science, MD
Counselor Education/School Counseling and
Guidance Services, MDO
Creative Writing, B
Curriculum and Instruction, M
Developmental Biology and Embryology, D
Disability Studies, O
East Asian Studies, B
Economics, BD
Education, MDO
Education/Teaching of the Gifted and Talented, O
Educational Administration and Supervision, MO
Educational Leadership and Administration, MDO

Educational Media/Instructional Technology, MO
Electrical Engineering, MD
Electrical, Electronics and Communications
    Engineering, B
Electroneurodiagnostic/Electroencephalographic
    Technology/Technologist, B
Electronic Commerce, O
Elementary Education and Teaching, M
Engineering, B
Engineering and Applied Sciences, MD
Engineering Mechanics, B
English, D
English Language and Literature, B
Environmental and Occupational Health, D
Environmental Engineering
    Technology/Environmental Technology, MD
Environmental Policy, M
Environmental Sciences, M
Environmental Studies, B
Environmental/Environmental Health Engineering, B
Epidemiology, MD
Evolutionary Biology, D
Experimental Psychology, D
Film/Cinema Studies, B
Finance and Banking, M
French Language and Literature, BD
Genetic Counseling/Counselor, M
Genetics, MD
Geochemistry, MD
Geography, BMD
Geology/Earth Science, BMD
Geophysics and Seismology, MD
German Language and Literature, BD
Health Services Administration, MDO
Health Services Research, M
History, BD
History and Philosophy of Science and
    Technology, B
History of Science and Technology, D
Human Genetics, DO
Human Resources Development, M
Immunology, MD
Industrial Engineering, B
Infectious Diseases, MD
Information Science/Studies, M
Interdisciplinary Studies, B
International Affairs, MDO
International Business/Trade/Commerce, O
International Public Health/International Health, MD
International Relations and Affairs, B
Investment Management, O
Italian Language and Literature, BD
Latin American Studies, B
Law Enforcement, M
Liberal Arts and Sciences Studies and
    Humanities, B
Liberal Studies, M
Management, M
Management Information Systems and
    Services, MO
Management of Technology, M
Marketing, M
Materials Engineering, BMD
Materials Sciences, BMD
Mathematics, BD
Mechanical Engineering, BMD
Medical Illustration and Informatics, M
Microbiology, MD
Molecular Biology, MDO
Molecular Medicine, D
Music, BMDO
Natural Sciences, B
Near and Middle Eastern Studies, BD
Neuroscience, BD
Nursing, MDO
Nursing - Advanced Practice, MO
Nursing - Registered Nurse Training, B
Nursing Administration, M
Nutritional Sciences, MD
Oceanography, Chemical and Physical, MD
Operations Research, MD
Pastoral Studies/Counseling, O
Pathobiology, D
Pathology/Experimental Pathology, D
Pharmacology, D
Philosophy, BMD

Physics, BD
Physiological Psychology/Psychobiology, B
Physiology, D
Planetary Astronomy and Science, MD
Political Science and Government, BMD
Psychology, BD
Public Health, MDO
Public Health (MPH, DPH), B
Public Policy Analysis, M
Reading Teacher Education, MO
Real Estate, M
Reproductive Biology, MD
Romance Languages, Literatures, and Linguistics, D
Science Teacher Education/General Science
    Teacher Education, O
Secondary Education and Teaching, M
Social Sciences, BMD
Sociology, BD
Spanish Language and Literature, BD
Special Education and Teaching, MDO
Statistics, MD
Substance Abuse/Addiction Counseling, O
Systems Engineering, M
Technical and Business Writing, M
Toxicology, D
Water Resources, MD
Writing, M

LOYOLA COLLEGE IN MARYLAND

Accounting, B
Applied Mathematics, B
Art/Art Studies, General, B
Biology/Biological Sciences, B
Business Administration, Management and
    Operations, M
Business/Commerce, B
Chemistry, B
Classics and Classical
    Languages, Literatures, and Linguistics, B
Clinical Psychology, MDO
Communication Disorders, MO
Communication Studies/Speech Communication
    and Rhetoric, B
Computer and Information Sciences, B
Counseling Psychology, MO
Counselor Education/School Counseling and
    Guidance Services, MO
Creative Writing, B
Curriculum and Instruction, MO
Early Childhood Education and Teaching, MO
Economics, BM
Education, BMO
Educational Administration and Supervision, MO
Educational Media/Instructional Technology, M
Electrical, Electronics and Communications
    Engineering, B
Elementary Education and Teaching, B
Engineering, B
Engineering and Applied Sciences, M
English Language and Literature, B
Finance, B
Finance and Banking, M
Foundations and Philosophy of Education, MO
French Language and Literature, B
German Language and Literature, B
History, B
Interdisciplinary Studies, BM
International Business/Trade/Commerce, BM
Management, M
Marketing, M
Mathematics, B
Pastoral Studies/Counseling, MDO
Philosophy, B
Physics, B
Political Science and Government, B
Psychology, BMDO
Quantitative Analysis, M
Reading Teacher Education, MO
Religion/Religious Studies, B
Sociology, B
Spanish Language and Literature, B
Special Education and Teaching, BMO
Speech-Language Pathology/Pathologist, B

Substance Abuse/Addiction Counseling, O

MAPLE SPRINGS BAPTIST BIBLE COLLEGE AND SEMINARY

Bible/Biblical Studies, AB
Computer Education, M
Pastoral Studies/Counseling, M
Theology and Religious Vocations, MDPO

MARYLAND INSTITUTE COLLEGE OF ART

Art Education, M
Art History, Criticism and Conservation, B
Art Teacher Education, B
Art/Art Studies, General, B
Ceramic Arts and Ceramics, B
Computer Art and Design, M
Drawing, B
Fiber, Textile and Weaving Arts, B
Film/Video and Photographic Arts, B
Fine Arts and Art Studies, MO
Fine/Studio Arts, B
Graphic Design, BM
Illustration, B
Interior Design, B
Intermedia/Multimedia, B
Painting, BM
Photography, BM
Printmaking, B
Sculpture, BM
Visual and Performing Arts, B

MCDANIEL COLLEGE

Art History, Criticism and Conservation, B
Art/Art Studies, General, B
Biochemistry, B
Biology/Biological Sciences, B
Business Administration and Management, B
Chemistry, B
Communication Studies/Speech Communication
    and Rhetoric, B
Computer and Information Sciences, B
Counselor Education/School Counseling and
    Guidance Services, M
Curriculum and Instruction, M
Drama and Dramatics/Theatre Arts, B
Economics, B
Educational Administration and Supervision, M
Educational Media/Instructional Technology, M
Elementary Education and Teaching, M
English Language and Literature, B
Environmental Sciences, B
French Language and Literature, B
German Language and Literature, B
History, B
Human Resources Development, M
Human Services, B
Kinesiology and Exercise Science, B
Liberal Studies, M
Library Science, M
Mathematics, B
Multi-/Interdisciplinary Studies, B
Music, B
Philosophy, B
Physical Education Teaching and Coaching, BM
Physics, B
Political Science and Government, B
Psychology, B
Reading Teacher Education, M
Religion/Religious Studies, B
Secondary Education and Teaching, M
Social Work, B
Sociology, B
Spanish Language and Literature, B
Special Education and Teaching, M

MONTGOMERY COLLEGE

Accounting Technology/Technician and
    Bookkeeping, A
Applied Horticulture/Horticultural Operations, A
Architectural Drafting and Architectural
    CAD/CADD, A
Automobile/Automotive Mechanics
    Technology/Technician, A

Building/Construction
    Finishing, Management, and Inspection, A
Business Administration and Management, A
Business/Commerce, A
Child Care and Support Services Management, A
Civil Engineering Technology/Technician, A
Commercial and Advertising Art, A
Commercial Photography, A
Computer and Information Sciences, A
Computer Technology/Computer Systems
    Technology, A
Criminal Justice/Police Science, A
Diagnostic Medical Sonography/Sonographer and
    Ultrasound Technician, A
Education, A
Electrical, Electronic and Communications
    Engineering Technology/Technician, A
Electromechanical Technology/Electromechanical
    Engineering Technology, A
Engineering, A
Fire Protection and Safety Technology/Technician, A
General Studies, A
Graphic and Printing Equipment Operator
    Production, A
Health Information/Medical Records
    Technology/Technician, A
Hotel/Motel Administration/Management, A
Legal Assistant/Paralegal, A
Liberal Arts and Sciences Studies and
    Humanities, A
Management Information Systems and Services, A
Medical Radiologic Technology/Science - Radiation
    Therapist, A
Nursing - Registered Nurse Training, A
Physical Therapist Assistant, A

MORGAN STATE UNIVERSITY

Accounting, B
African Studies, B
African-American/Black Studies, BM
Architecture, M
Art History, Criticism and Conservation, B
Art/Art Studies, General, B
Behavioral Sciences, B
Bioinformatics, M
Biology/Biological Sciences, B
Business Administration and Management, B
Business Administration, Management and
    Operations, MD
Business Teacher Education, B
Business/Managerial Economics, B
Chemistry, B
Civil Engineering, BMD
Clinical Laboratory Science/Medical
    Technology/Technologist, B
Clinical/Medical Laboratory Technician, B
Community College Education, D
Computer Science, B
Dietetics/Dieticians, B
Drama and Dramatics/Theatre Arts, B
Economics, BM
Education, BMD
Educational Administration and Supervision, MD
Educational Leadership and Administration, D
Electrical Engineering, MD
Electrical, Electronics and Communications
    Engineering, B
Elementary Education and Teaching, BM
Engineering, B
Engineering and Applied Sciences, MD
Engineering Physics, B
English, MD
English Language and Literature, B
Environmental Biology, D
Family and Consumer Sciences/Human Sciences, B
Finance, B
Foods, Nutrition, and Wellness Studies, B
Health Teacher Education, B
Higher Education/Higher Education
    Administration, D
History, BMD
Hospitality Administration/Management, B
Hotel/Motel Administration/Management, B
Industrial Engineering, B
Industrial/Management Engineering, MD
Information Science/Studies, B

International Affairs, M
Landscape Architecture, M
Management Information Systems and Services, B
Marketing/Marketing Management, B
Mass Communication/Media Studies, B
Mathematics, BM
Mathematics Teacher Education, MD
Mental Health/Rehabilitation, B
Middle School Education, M
Music, BM
Parks, Recreation, Leisure and Fitness Studies, B
Philosophy, B
Physical Education Teaching and Coaching, B
Physics, B
Political Science and Government, B
Pre-Dentistry Studies, B
Pre-Law Studies, B
Pre-Medicine/Pre-Medical Studies, B
Psychology, B
Public Health, MD
Religion/Religious Studies, B
Science Teacher Education/General Science
    Teacher Education, MD
Secondary Education and Teaching, BM
Social Work, BM
Sociology, BM
Speech and Rhetorical Studies, B
Sport and Fitness Administration/Management, B
Telecommunications Management, M
Telecommunications Technology/Technician, B
Transportation and Highway Engineering, M
Transportation/Transportation Management, M
Urban and Regional Planning, M

MOUNT ST. MARY'S UNIVERSITY

Accounting, B
Art/Art Studies, General, B
Biochemistry, B
Biology/Biological Sciences, B
Business Administration, Management and
    Operations, M
Business/Commerce, B
Chemistry, B
Communication Studies/Speech Communication
    and Rhetoric, B
Computer and Information Sciences, B
Criminal Justice/Safety Studies, B
Economics, B
Education, M
Elementary Education and Teaching, B
English Language and Literature, B
French Language and Literature, B
German Language and Literature, B
History, B
Information Resources Management/CIO Training, B
International Relations and Affairs, B
Mathematics, B
Multi-/Interdisciplinary Studies, B
Philosophy, B
Political Science and Government, B
Psychology, B
Secondary Education and Teaching, B
Social Sciences, B
Sociology, B
Spanish Language and Literature, B
Sport and Fitness Administration/Management, B
Theology and Religious Vocations, MP

NER ISRAEL RABBINICAL COLLEGE

Bible/Biblical Studies, B
Jewish/Judaic Studies, B
Rabbinical Studies, B
Religious Education, B
Theology and Religious Vocations, MD

PEABODY CONSERVATORY OF MUSIC OF THE JOHNS HOPKINS UNIVERSITY

Audio Engineering, B
Jazz/Jazz Studies, B
Music, B
Music Teacher Education, B
Piano and Organ, B
Violin, Viola, Guitar and Other Stringed
    Instruments, B
Voice and Opera, B

Wind and Percussion Instruments, B

PRINCE GEORGE'S COMMUNITY COLLEGE

Accounting, A
Aerospace, Aeronautical and Astronautical
    Engineering, A
Business Administration and Management, A
Business Teacher Education, A
Computer Engineering Technology/Technician, A
Computer Programming/Programmer, A
Computer Science, A
Computer Typography and Composition Equipment
    Operator, A
Criminal Justice/Law Enforcement Administration, A
Drafting and Design Technology/Technician, A
Education, A
Electrical, Electronic and Communications
    Engineering Technology/Technician, A
Elementary Education and Teaching, A
Emergency Medical Technology/Technician (EMT
    Paramedic), A
Engineering, A
Forensic Science and Technology, A
Health Information/Medical Records
    Administration/Administrator, A
Health Teacher Education, A
Information Science/Studies, A
Kindergarten/PreSchool Education and Teaching, A
Legal Assistant/Paralegal, A
Liberal Arts and Sciences Studies and
    Humanities, A
Marketing/Marketing Management, A
Medical Office Management/Administration, A
Nuclear Medical Technology/Technologist, A
Nursing - Registered Nurse Training, A
Physical Education Teaching and Coaching, A
Radiologic Technology/Science - Radiographer, A
Respiratory Care Therapy/Therapist, A

ST. JOHN'S COLLEGE

European Studies/Civilization, B
Interdisciplinary Studies, B
Liberal Arts and Sciences Studies and
    Humanities, B
Liberal Studies, M

ST. MARY'S COLLEGE OF MARYLAND

Anthropology, B
Art/Art Studies, General, B
Biochemistry, B
Biological and Physical Sciences, B
Biology/Biological Sciences, B
Chemistry, B
Computer and Information Sciences, B
Drama and Dramatics/Theatre Arts, B
Economics, B
English Language and Literature, B
Foreign Languages and Literatures, B
History, B
Mathematics, B
Multi-/Interdisciplinary Studies, B
Music, B
Philosophy, B
Physics, B
Political Science and Government, B
Psychology, B
Public Policy Analysis, B
Religion/Religious Studies, B
Sociology, B

SALISBURY UNIVERSITY

Accounting, B
Art Education, M
Art/Art Studies, General, B
Athletic Training and Sports Medicine, B
Biology/Biological Sciences, B
Business Administration and Management, B
Business Administration, Management and
    Operations, M
Business Education, M
Chemistry, B
Clinical Laboratory Science/Medical
    Technology/Technologist, B

Communication Studies/Speech Communication and Rhetoric, B
Computer and Information Sciences, B
Drama and Dramatics/Theatre Arts, B
Early Childhood Education and Teaching, M
Economics, B
Education, BM
Educational Administration and Supervision, M
Educational Media/Instructional Technology, M
Elementary Education and Teaching, BM
English, M
English as a Second Language, M
English Education, M
English Language and Literature, B
Environmental Health, B
Finance, B
Fine Arts and Art Studies, B
Foreign Language Teacher Education, M
French Language and Literature, B
Geography, B
Health and Physical Education, B
Health Teacher Education, B
Health/Medical Preparatory Programs, B
History, BM
Liberal Arts and Sciences Studies and Humanities, B
Management Information Systems and Services, B
Management Science, B
Marketing/Marketing Management, B
Mathematics, B
Mathematics Teacher Education, M
Music, B
Music Performance, B
Music Teacher Education, M
Nursing, M
Nursing - Registered Nurse Training, B
Peace Studies and Conflict Resolution, B
Philosophy, B
Physical Education Teaching and Coaching, B
Physics, B
Physiology, M
Political Science and Government, B
Psychology, B
Reading Teacher Education, M
Respiratory Care Therapy/Therapist, B
Science Teacher Education/General Science Teacher Education, M
Secondary Education and Teaching, BM
Social Studies Teacher Education, M
Social Work, BM
Sociology, B
Spanish Language and Literature, B
Writing, M

SOJOURNER-DOUGLASS COLLEGE

Accounting, B
Behavioral Sciences, B
Business Administration and Management, B
City/Urban, Community and Regional Planning, B
Criminal Justice/Law Enforcement Administration, B
Economics, B
Gerontology, B
Health/Health Care Administration/Management, B
Hospitality Administration/Management, B
Human Development and Family Studies, B
Human Resources Management/Personnel Administration, B
Human Services, B
Kindergarten/PreSchool Education and Teaching, B
Psychology, B
Public Administration, B
Social Work, B
Sociology, B
Urban Studies/Affairs, B

TESST COLLEGE OF TECHNOLOGY (TOWSON)

CAD/CADD Drafting and/or Design Technology/Technician, A
Computer Systems Networking and Telecommunications, A
Computer Technology/Computer Systems Technology, A
Criminal Justice/Safety Studies, A
Data Entry/Microcomputer Applications, A
Electrician, A

Graphic Design, A
Heating, Air Conditioning and Refrigeration Technology/Technician, A
Medical/Clinical Assistant, A
Pharmacy Technician/Assistant, A
Telecommunications Technology/Technician, A

TOWSON UNIVERSITY

Accounting, BM
Advertising and Public Relations, O
Allied Health and Medical Assisting Services, M
Applied Mathematics, M
Art Education, M
Art Teacher Education, B
Art/Art Studies, General, B
Athletic Training and Sports Medicine, B
Biological and Biomedical Sciences, M
Biology/Biological Sciences, B
Business Administration and Management, B
Business Administration, Management and Operations, BM
Chemistry, B
Clinical Psychology, M
Communication and Media Studies, MO
Communication Disorders, MD
Communication Studies/Speech Communication and Rhetoric, B
Composition, M
Computer Science, M
Corporate and Organizational Communication, M
Dance, B
Drama and Dramatics/Theatre Arts, B
Early Childhood Education and Teaching, BM
Economics, B
Education, BM
Educational Leadership and Administration, O
Educational Media/Instructional Technology, MD
Elementary Education and Teaching, BM
English Language and Literature, B
Environmental and Occupational Health, D
Environmental Sciences, MO
Environmental Studies, M
Experimental Psychology, M
Family Systems, B
Fine Arts and Art Studies, M
Forensic Science and Technology, B
French Language and Literature, B
Geography, BM
Geology/Earth Science, B
German Language and Literature, B
Gerontology, BMO
Health and Physical Education/Fitness, B
Health Professions and Related Clinical Sciences, B
Health Services Administration, O
Health/Health Care Administration/Management, B
History, B
Human Resources Development, MO
Humanities/Humanistic Studies, M
Information Science/Studies, BO
Interdisciplinary Studies, B
International Relations and Affairs, B
Internet and Interactive Multimedia, O
Kinesiology and Exercise Science, B
Liberal Studies, M
Management Information Systems and Services, MDO
Mass Communication/Media Studies, B
Mathematics, B
Mathematics Teacher Education, M
Music, B
Music Teacher Education, BMO
Nursing, MO
Nursing - Registered Nurse Training, B
Occupational Therapy/Therapist, BM
Organizational Behavior Studies, O
Performance, M
Philosophy, B
Physical Education Teaching and Coaching, B
Physician Assistant, M
Physics, B
Political Science and Government, B
Psychology, B
Reading Teacher Education, MO
Religion/Religious Studies, B
School Psychology, MO

Science Teacher Education/General Science Teacher Education, M
Secondary Education and Teaching, M
Social Sciences, BM
Software Engineering, O
Spanish Language and Literature, B
Special Education and Teaching, BM
Speech-Language Pathology/Pathologist, B
Sport and Fitness Administration/Management, B
Theater, M
Women's Studies, BM
Writing, M

UNITED STATES NAVAL ACADEMY

Aerospace, Aeronautical and Astronautical Engineering, B
Chemistry, B
Computer and Information Sciences, B
Computer Science, B
Econometrics and Quantitative Economics, B
Economics, B
Electrical, Electronics and Communications Engineering, B
Engineering, B
English Language and Literature, B
History, B
Mathematics, B
Mechanical Engineering, B
Naval Architecture and Marine Engineering, B
Ocean Engineering, B
Oceanography, Chemical and Physical, B
Physical Sciences, B
Physics, B
Political Science and Government, B
Systems Engineering, B

UNIVERSITY OF BALTIMORE

Accounting, BM
Business Administration and Management, B
Business Administration, Management and Operations, MO
Communication and Media Studies, MD
Community Organization and Advocacy, B
Comparative Literature, B
Computer and Information Sciences, B
Computer Art and Design, M
Conflict Resolution and Mediation/Peace Studies, M
Criminal Justice/Law Enforcement Administration, B
Criminology, MO
Digital Communication and Media/Multimedia, B
Economics, B
English Language and Literature, B
Ethics, M
Finance, B
Finance and Banking, M
Forensic Science and Technology, B
Graphic Design, M
Health and Medical Administrative Services, B
Health Services Administration, M
History, B
Human Resources Management/Personnel Administration, B
Human Services, BM
Human-Computer Interaction, M
Information Science/Studies, BMD
Interdisciplinary Studies, B
International Business/Trade/Commerce, B
Journalism, B
Law and Legal Studies, BMPO
Legal and Justice Studies, M
Liberal Arts and Sciences Studies and Humanities, B
Management Information Systems and Services, BM
Marketing, M
Marketing/Marketing Management, B
Mass Communication/Media Studies, B
Non-Profit/Public/Organizational Management, B
Political Science and Government, B
Psychology, BM
Public Affairs, MDO
Publishing, M
Sales, Distribution and Marketing Operations, B
Taxation, M
Technical and Business Writing, B

Writing, M

UNIVERSITY OF MARYLAND, BALTIMORE COUNTY

African Studies, B
African-American/Black Studies, B
American/United States Studies/Civilization, B
Ancient Studies/Civilization, B
Anthropology, B
Applied Mathematics, BMD
Applied Physics, MD
Area, Ethnic, Cultural, and Gender Studies, B
Art History, Criticism and Conservation, B
Art/Art Studies, General, B
Atmospheric Sciences and Meteorology, MD
Biochemical Engineering, MDO
Biochemistry, D
Biochemistry, Biophysics and Molecular Biology, B
Bioinformatics, B
Biological and Biomedical Sciences, MD
Biology/Biological Sciences, B
Business Administration and Management, B
Cell Biology and Anatomy, D
Chemical Engineering, BMDO
Chemistry, BMD
Civil Engineering, MD
Classics and Classical
  Languages, Literatures, and Linguistics, B
Cognitive Sciences, D
Communication and Media Studies, M
Computer Education, O
Computer Engineering, BMD
Computer Science, BMD
Dance, B
Developmental Psychology, D
Distance Education Development, O
Drama and Dramatics/Theatre Arts, B
Early Childhood Education and Teaching, M
Economics, BM
Education, MO
Educational Media/Instructional Technology, MO
Electrical Engineering, MD
Elementary Education and Teaching, M
Emergency Medical Technology/Technician (EMT
  Paramedic), B
Engineering and Applied Sciences, MDO
Engineering Management, M
Engineering Science, B
English Language and Literature, B
Environmental Engineering
  Technology/Environmental Technology, MD
Environmental Sciences, BMD
Environmental Studies, B
Epidemiology, M
Film/Cinema Studies, B
Fine Arts and Art Studies, M
French Language and Literature, BM
Geography, B
German Language and Literature, BM
Gerontology, MD
Health Education, M
Health Services Administration, M
Health/Health Care Administration/Management, B
History, BM
Human Services, MD
Information Science/Studies, BMDO
Interdisciplinary Studies, B
Linguistics, BM
Management Information Systems and
  Services, MD
Marine Sciences, MD
Mathematics, B
Mechanical Engineering, BMDO
Modern Languages, B
Molecular Biology, BMD
Multilingual and Multicultural Education, MD
Music, BO
Neuroscience, D
Non-Profit/Public/Organizational Management, O
Optics/Optical Sciences, MD
Philosophy, B
Photography, B
Physics, BMD
Political Science and Government, B
Pre-Dentistry Studies, B
Pre-Law Studies, B

Pre-Medicine/Pre-Medical Studies, B
Pre-Veterinary Studies, B
Psychology, BMD
Public Health (MPH, DPH), B
Public Policy Analysis, MD
Russian Language and Literature, BM
Secondary Education and Teaching, M
Social Work, B
Sociology, BMO
Spanish Language and Literature, BM
Statistics, BMD
Systems Engineering, O
Visual and Performing Arts, B
Women's Studies, O

UNIVERSITY OF MARYLAND, COLLEGE PARK

Accounting, B
Aerospace, Aeronautical and Astronautical
  Engineering, BMD
African-American/Black Studies, B
Agricultural Economics, BMD
Agricultural Engineering, MD
Agricultural Sciences, MDP
Agricultural/Biological Engineering and
  Bioengineering, B
Agriculture, B
Agriculture, Agriculture Operations and Related
  Sciences, B
Agronomy and Crop Science, B
Agronomy and Soil Sciences, MD
American/United States Studies/Civilization, BMD
Analytical Chemistry, MD
Animal Sciences, BMD
Anthropology, BM
Applied Mathematics, MD
Architecture, BMO
Art History, Criticism and Conservation, BMD
Art Teacher Education, B
Astronomy, BMD
Biochemistry, BMD
Bioengineering, MD
Biological and Biomedical Sciences, MD
Biology/Biological Sciences, B
Biophysics, D
Business Administration and Management, B
Business Administration, Management and
  Operations, MO
Business, Management, Marketing, and Related
  Support Services, B
Business/Commerce, B
Cell Biology and Anatomy, MD
Chemical Engineering, BMD
Chemistry, BMD
Child and Family Studies, MD
Chinese Language and Literature, B
Civil Engineering, BMD
Classics and Classical
  Languages, Literatures, and Linguistics, BM
Clinical Psychology, D
Cognitive Sciences, D
Communication and Media Studies, MD
Communication Disorders, MD
Communication Studies/Speech Communication
  and Rhetoric, B
Comparative Literature, MD
Computer and Information Sciences, B
Computer Engineering, BMD
Computer Science, MD
Conservation Biology, M
Counseling Psychology, D
Counselor Education/School Counseling and
  Guidance Services, MDO
Criminology, BMDO
Curriculum and Instruction, MDO
Dance, BM
Developmental Psychology, D
Dietetics/Dieticians, B
Drama and Dramatics/Theatre Arts, B
Early Childhood Education and Teaching, MD
Ecology, BMD
Economics, MD
Education, BMDO
Educational Administration and Supervision, MD
Educational Leadership and Administration, MDO
Educational Measurement and Evaluation, MD

Educational Media/Instructional Technology, MD
Educational Psychology, MD
Electrical Engineering, MD
Electrical, Electronics and Communications
  Engineering, B
Elementary Education and Teaching, B
Engineering, B
Engineering and Applied Sciences, MDO
English, MD
English as a Second Language, M
English Language and Literature, B
English/Language Arts Teacher Education, B
Entomology, MD
Environmental Engineering
  Technology/Environmental Technology, MD
Environmental Sciences, MD
Ethnomusicology, M
Evolutionary Biology, MD
Experimental Psychology, D
Family and Community Services, B
Finance, B
Fine Arts and Art Studies, M
Fire Protection Engineering, M
Food Science, B
Food Science and Technology, MD
Foods, Nutrition, and Wellness Studies, B
Foreign Language Teacher Education, BM
Foreign Languages and Literatures, B
Foundations and Philosophy of Education, MDO
French Language and Literature, BMD
Geography, BMDO
Geology/Earth Science, BMD
German Language and Literature, BMD
Health Education, MD
Health Teacher Education, B
Historic Preservation and Conservation, MO
History, BMDO
Horticultural Science, BD
Human Development, MD
Human Resources Management/Personnel
  Administration, B
Industrial and Organizational Psychology, MD
Information Science/Studies, BMDO
Inorganic Chemistry, MD
Interdisciplinary Studies, DO
Italian Language and Literature, B
Japanese Language and Literature, B
Jewish/Judaic Studies, B
Journalism, BMD
Kindergarten/PreSchool Education and Teaching, B
Kinesiology and Movement Studies, MD
Landscape Architecture, B
Latin Language and Literature, B
Law and Legal Studies, O
Library Science, O
Linguistics, BMD
Management, MD
Management Science, B
Manufacturing Engineering, MD
Marine Sciences, MD
Marketing/Marketing Management, B
Marriage and Family Therapy/Counseling, M
Mass Communication/Media Studies, D
Materials Engineering, BMD
Materials Sciences, MD
Mathematics, BMD
Mathematics Teacher Education, B
Mechanical Engineering, BMD
Mechanics, MD
Media Studies, D
Medical Microbiology and Bacteriology, B
Meteorology, MD
Microbiology, MD
Molecular Biology, D
Molecular Genetics, MD
Music, BMD
Music Performance, B
Music Teacher Education, BMD
Natural Resources and Conservation, BMD
Neuroscience, D
Nuclear Engineering, MD
Nutritional Sciences, MD
Organic Chemistry, MD
Philosophy, BMD
Physical Chemistry, MD
Physical Education Teaching and Coaching, B

Physical Sciences, B
Physics, BMD
Plant Biology, MD
Plant Sciences, B
Political Science and Government, BD
Poultry Science, MD
Psychology, BMD
Public Administration, MO
Public Health, MD
Public Policy Analysis, MDO
Reading Teacher Education, MDO
Rehabilitation Counseling, M
Reliability Engineering, MD
Russian Language and Literature, BM
Russian Studies, B
School Psychology, MD
Science Teacher Education/General Science
   Teacher Education, B
Secondary Education and Teaching, BMDO
Social Psychology, D
Social Studies Teacher Education, B
Sociology, BMD
Software Engineering, M
Spanish Language and Literature, BMD
Special Education and Teaching, BMDO
Speech and Interpersonal Communication, MD
Speech-Language Pathology/Pathologist, B
Statistics, MD
Student Personnel Services, MDO
Survey Methodology, MD
Sustainable Development, M
Systems Engineering, M
Telecommunications, M
Theater, MD
Toxicology, MD
Urban and Regional Planning, MDO
Veterinary Medicine, P
Veterinary Sciences, MD
Visual and Performing Arts, B
Water Resources Engineering, MD
Women's Studies, BMD
Writing, MD

UNIVERSITY OF MARYLAND EASTERN SHORE

Accounting, B
Agricultural Business and Management, B
Agricultural Sciences, MD
Agricultural Teacher Education, B
Agriculture, B
Air Traffic Controller, B
Art Teacher Education, B
Biology/Biological Sciences, B
Building/Construction
   Finishing, Management, and Inspection, B
Business Administration and Management, B
Business Teacher Education, B
Chemistry, B
Child Development, B
Clinical Laboratory Science/Medical
   Technology/Technologist, B
Clinical/Medical Laboratory Technician, B
Computer Science, BM
Construction Engineering Technology/Technician, B
Counselor Education/School Counseling and
   Guidance Services, M
Criminal Justice/Law Enforcement Administration, B
Criminology, M
Dietetics/Dieticians, B
Ecology, B
Education, BM
Educational Leadership and Administration, D
Electrical, Electronic and Communications
   Engineering Technology/Technician, B
Elementary Education and Teaching, B
Engineering Technology, B
English Language and Literature, B
Environmental Sciences, MD
Environmental Studies, B
Family and Consumer Economics and Related
   Services, B
Family and Consumer Sciences/Home Economics
   Teacher Education, B
Family and Consumer Sciences/Human Sciences, B
Fashion Merchandising, B
Fashion/Apparel Design, B

Food Science and Technology, MD
History, B
Hotel/Motel Administration/Management, B
Industrial Radiologic Technology/Technician, B
Kindergarten/PreSchool Education and Teaching, B
Liberal Arts and Sciences Studies and
   Humanities, B
Marine Biology and Biological Oceanography, B
Marine Sciences, MD
Mass Communication/Media Studies, B
Mathematics, B
Music Teacher Education, B
Organizational Management, D
Physical Education Teaching and Coaching, B
Physical Therapy/Therapist, BD
Poultry Science, B
Pre-Dentistry Studies, B
Pre-Law Studies, B
Pre-Medicine/Pre-Medical Studies, B
Rehabilitation Counseling, M
Rehabilitation Sciences, M
Rehabilitation Therapy, B
Social Sciences, B
Social Work, B
Sociology, B
Special Education and Teaching, BM
Special Products Marketing Operations, B
Technology Education/Industrial Arts, B
Toxicology, MD
Vocational and Technical Education, M

UNIVERSITY OF MARYLAND UNIVERSITY COLLEGE

Accounting, BMO
BioTechnology, MO
Business Administration and Management, B
Business Administration, Management and
   Operations, M
Communication Studies/Speech Communication
   and Rhetoric, B
Computer and Information Sciences, B
Computer Science, B
Criminal Justice/Law Enforcement Administration, B
Distance Education Development, MO
Education, M
Electronic Commerce, MO
English Language and Literature, B
Environmental Policy and Resource
   Management, MO
Environmental Studies, B
Finance and Banking, MO
Fire Science/Firefighting, B
Health Services Administration, MO
History, B
Human Resources Management/Personnel
   Administration, B
Humanities/Humanistic Studies, B
Information Science/Studies, BMO
International Business/Trade/Commerce, MO
Legal Assistant/Paralegal, B
Management, MDO
Management Information Systems and
   Services, MO
Management of Technology, MO
Management Science, B
Marketing/Marketing Management, B
Multi-/Interdisciplinary Studies, B
Psychology, B
Social Sciences, B
Software Engineering, MO
Telecommunications Management, MO

UNIVERSITY OF PHOENIX-MARYLAND CAMPUS

Accounting, B
Business Administration and Management, B
Business Administration, Management and
   Operations, M
Business, Management, Marketing, and Related
   Support Services, B
Computer and Information Sciences, B
Electronic Commerce, M
Information Science/Studies, M
International Business/Trade/Commerce, M
Management, M
Management Information Systems and Services, M

Management of Technology, M
Organizational Management, M

VILLA JULIE COLLEGE

Accounting, AB
Applied Art, A
Art/Art Studies, General; A
Biological and Physical Sciences, AB
Biology Technician/BioTechnology Laboratory
   Technician, AB
Biology/Biological Sciences, AB
Business Administration and Management, AB
Chemistry, AB
Child Development, A
Clinical Laboratory Science/Medical
   Technology/Technologist, A
Clinical/Medical Laboratory Technician, A
Commercial and Advertising Art, A
Computer and Information Sciences, AB
Computer Graphics, A
Computer Programming/Programmer, A
Court Reporting/Court Reporter, A
Design and Visual Communications, B
Developmental and Child Psychology, AB
Drama and Dramatics/Theatre Arts, A
Early Childhood Education and Teaching, B
Electronic Commerce, M
Elementary Education and Teaching, AB
English Language and Literature, B
Environmental Studies, B
Family and Community Services, B
Film/Video and Photographic Arts, B
Health and Medical Laboratory Technologies, A
History, A
Humanities/Humanistic Studies, B
Information Science/Studies, ABM
Interdisciplinary Studies, AB
Journalism, A
Junior High/Intermediate/Middle School Education
   and Teaching, B
Kindergarten/PreSchool Education and Teaching, A
Law and Legal Studies, B
Legal Assistant/Paralegal, AB
Liberal Arts and Sciences Studies and
   Humanities, AB
Management Information Systems and
   Services, BM
Management of Technology, M
Mass Communication/Media Studies, A
Nursing - Registered Nurse Training, B
Photography, A
Physical Sciences, A
Political Science and Government, A
Pre-Dentistry Studies, B
Pre-Law Studies, B
Pre-Medicine/Pre-Medical Studies, B
Pre-Veterinary Studies, B
Psychology, AB
Public/Applied History and Archival Administration, B
Social Sciences, A
Sociology, A

WASHINGTON BIBLE COLLEGE

Bible/Biblical Studies, AB
Elementary Education and Teaching, B
Kindergarten/PreSchool Education and Teaching, B
Music, B
Music Teacher Education, B
Religion/Religious Studies, AB
Religious Education, AB
Theology/Theological Studies, AB

WASHINGTON COLLEGE

American/United States Studies/Civilization, B
Anthropology, B
Art/Art Studies, General, B
Biology/Biological Sciences, B
Business Administration and Management, B
Chemistry, B
Computer Science, B
Drama and Dramatics/Theatre Arts, B
Ecology, B
Economics, B
English, M
English Language and Literature, B
Environmental Studies, B

Foreign Languages and Literatures, B
French Language and Literature, B
German Language and Literature, B
History, BM
Humanities/Humanistic Studies, B
International Relations and Affairs, B
Latin American Studies, B
Liberal Arts and Sciences Studies and
    Humanities, B
Mathematics, B
Multi-/Interdisciplinary Studies, B
Music, B
Philosophy, B
Physics, B
Physiological Psychology/Psychobiology, B
Political Science and Government, B
Pre-Dentistry Studies, B
Pre-Law Studies, B
Pre-Medicine/Pre-Medical Studies, B
Pre-Veterinary Studies, B
Psychology, BM
Sociology, B
Spanish Language and Literature, B

WOR-WIC COMMUNITY COLLEGE

Accounting Technology/Technician and
    Bookkeeping, A
Administrative Assistant and Secretarial Science, A
Business Administration and Management, A
Business/Commerce, A
Child Care and Support Services Management, A
Computer and Information Sciences, A
Computer Systems Analysis/Analyst, A
Criminal Justice/Police Science, A
Electrical, Electronic and Communications
    Engineering Technology/Technician, A
Elementary Education and Teaching, A
Emergency Medical Technology/Technician (EMT
    Paramedic), A
Engineering Technologies/Technicians, A
Hospitality Administration/Management, A
Liberal Arts and Sciences Studies and
    Humanities, A
Medical Radiologic Technology/Science - Radiation
    Therapist, A
Nursing - Registered Nurse Training, A
Substance Abuse/Addiction Counseling, A

Massachusetts

AMERICAN INTERNATIONAL COLLEGE

Accounting, B
Adult and Continuing Education and Teaching, B
Biochemistry, B
Biology/Biological Sciences, B
Business Administration and Management, AB
Business Administration, Management and
    Operations, M
Business Teacher Education, B
Business/Managerial Economics, B
Chemistry, B
Clinical Laboratory Science/Medical
    Technology/Technologist, B
Clinical Psychology, M
Criminal Justice/Law Enforcement Administration, B
Criminal Justice/Police Science, B
Criminology, M
Economics, B
Education, BMDO
Educational Administration and Supervision, MO
Educational Psychology, MD
Elementary Education and Teaching, BMO
English Language and Literature, B
Finance, B
Forensic Psychology, M
History, B
Human Resources Development, MO
Human Resources Management/Personnel
    Administration, B
Human Services, B
Information Science/Studies, B
International Business/Trade/Commerce, B
International Relations and Affairs, B
Junior High/Intermediate/Middle School Education
    and Teaching, B

Kindergarten/PreSchool Education and Teaching, B
Liberal Arts and Sciences Studies and
    Humanities, AB
Management Information Systems and Services, B
Marketing/Marketing Management, B
Mass Communication/Media Studies, B
Mathematics, B
Nursing, M
Nursing - Registered Nurse Training, B
Occupational Therapy/Therapist, BM
Organizational Management, M
Philosophy, B
Physical Therapy/Therapist, BM
Political Science and Government, B
Pre-Dentistry Studies, B
Pre-Law Studies, B
Pre-Medicine/Pre-Medical Studies, B
Pre-Veterinary Studies, B
Psychology, BMD
Public Administration, BM
Reading Teacher Education, MO
Secondary Education and Teaching, BMO
Social Sciences, B
Sociology, B
Spanish Language and Literature, B
Special Education and Teaching, BMO

AMHERST COLLEGE

African-American/Black Studies, B
American/United States Studies/Civilization, B
Ancient/Classical Greek Language and Literature, B
Anthropology, B
Art/Art Studies, General, B
Asian Studies/Civilization, B
Astronomy, B
Biology/Biological Sciences, B
Chemistry, B
Classics and Classical
    Languages, Literatures, and Linguistics, B
Computer Science, B
Dance, B
Drama and Dramatics/Theatre Arts, B
Economics, B
English Language and Literature, B
European Studies/Civilization, B
Fine/Studio Arts, B
French Language and Literature, B
Geology/Earth Science, B
German Language and Literature, B
History, B
Interdisciplinary Studies, B
Latin Language and Literature, B
Law and Legal Studies, B
Mathematics, B
Music, B
Neuroscience, B
Philosophy, B
Physics, B
Political Science and Government, B
Psychology, B
Religion/Religious Studies, B
Russian Language and Literature, B
Sociology, B
Spanish Language and Literature, B
Women's Studies, B

ANNA MARIA COLLEGE

Art Teacher Education, B
Art Therapy/Therapist, B
Art/Art Studies, General, B
Behavioral Sciences, B
Biology/Biological Sciences, B
Business Administration and Management, AB
Business Administration, Management and
    Operations, MO
Computer and Information Sciences and Support
    Services, B
Counseling Psychology, M
Criminal Justice/Law Enforcement Administration, B
Criminology, M
Early Childhood Education and Teaching, M
Education, MO
Elementary Education and Teaching, BM
English Language and Literature, B
Environmental and Occupational Health, M
Fine Arts and Art Studies, M

Fine/Studio Arts, B
Fire Protection Engineering, M
Fire Science/Firefighting, B
History, B
Human Services, M
Interdisciplinary Studies, B
Kindergarten/PreSchool Education and Teaching, B
Legal Assistant/Paralegal, AB
Music, B
Music Teacher Education, B
Music Therapy/Therapist, B
Nursing - Registered Nurse Training, B
Pastoral Studies/Counseling, M
Philosophy, B
Piano and Organ, B
Political Science and Government, B
Psychology, BM
Public Policy Analysis, MO
Reading Teacher Education, M
Religion/Religious Studies, B
Social Sciences, B
Social Work, B
Voice and Opera, B

THE ART INSTITUTE OF BOSTON AT LESLEY UNIVERSITY

Fine Arts and Art Studies, M
Fine/Studio Arts, B
Graphic Design, B
Illustration, B
Photography, B

ASSUMPTION COLLEGE

Accounting, B
Biology/Biological Sciences, B
BioTechnology, B
Business Administration and Management, B
Business Administration, Management and
    Operations, MO
Chemistry, B
Classics and Classical
    Languages, Literatures, and Linguistics, B
Computer Science, B
Counseling Psychology, MO
Economics, B
Elementary Education and Teaching, B
English Language and Literature, B
Environmental Sciences, B
Foreign Languages and Literatures, B
French Language and Literature, B
History, B
International Business/Trade/Commerce, B
International/Global Studies, B
Latin American Studies, B
Marketing/Marketing Management, B
Mathematics, B
Molecular Biology, B
Organizational Communication, B
Philosophy, B
Political Science and Government, B
Psychology, B
Rehabilitation and Therapeutic Professions, B
Rehabilitation Counseling, MO
School Psychology, M
Secondary Education and Teaching, B
Sociology, B
Spanish Language and Literature, B
Special Education and Teaching, M
Theology/Theological Studies, B
Visual and Performing Arts, B

ATLANTIC UNION COLLEGE

Accounting, B
Administrative Assistant and Secretarial Science, A
Adult and Continuing Education and Teaching, B
Art Teacher Education, B
Art/Art Studies, General, B
Biochemistry, B
Biological and Physical Sciences, B
Biology/Biological Sciences, B
Business Administration and Management, B
Business Teacher Education, B
Chemistry, B
Clinical Laboratory Science/Medical
    Technology/Technologist, B
Computer Programming/Programmer, A

Computer Science, B
Divinity/Ministry (BD, MDiv.), AB
Education, BM
Elementary Education and Teaching, B
English Language and Literature, B
French Language and Literature, B
History, B
Information Science/Studies, B
Interior Design, B
Kindergarten/PreSchool Education and
  Teaching, AB
Kinesiology and Exercise Science, A
Legal Assistant/Paralegal, A
Mathematics, B
Modern Languages, B
Music, B
Music Teacher Education, B
Natural Sciences, B
Nursing - Registered Nurse Training, AB
Physical Education Teaching and Coaching, B
Pre-Dentistry Studies, B
Pre-Engineering, A
Pre-Law Studies, B
Pre-Medicine/Pre-Medical Studies, B
Pre-Veterinary Studies, B
Psychology, B
Religion/Religious Studies, AB
Religious/Sacred Music, B
Secondary Education and Teaching, B
Social Work, B
Sociology, B
Spanish Language and Literature, B
Theology/Theological Studies, B

BABSON COLLEGE

Accounting, B
Accounting and Business/Management, B
Accounting and Finance, B
Auditing, B
Business Administration and Management, B
Business Administration, Management and
  Operations, BM
Business/Corporate Communications, B
Economics, B
Entrepreneurial and Small Business Operations, B
Entrepreneurship/Entrepreneurial Studies, B
Finance, B
Finance and Financial Management Services, B
International Business/Trade/Commerce, BM
International Finance, B
Investments and Securities, B
Management Information Systems and Services, B
Marketing, B
Marketing/Marketing Management, B
Office Management and Supervision, B
Operations Management and Supervision, B
Operations Research, B
Pre-Law Studies, B
Sales, Distribution and Marketing Operations, B
Small Business Administration/Management, B

BAY PATH COLLEGE

Biology/Biological Sciences, B
BioTechnology, B
Business/Commerce, B
Criminal Justice/Law Enforcement Administration, B
Elementary Education and Teaching, B
Entrepreneurship/Entrepreneurial Studies, M
International Business/Trade/Commerce, B
Kindergarten/PreSchool Education and Teaching, B
Law and Legal Studies, B
Liberal Arts and Sciences Studies and
  Humanities, B
Management Information Systems and Services, M
Occupational Therapy/Therapist, BM
Pre-Law Studies, B
Psychology, B

BAY STATE COLLEGE

Accounting, A
Administrative Assistant and Secretarial Science, A
Business Administration and Management, AB
Consumer Merchandising/Retailing Management, A
Criminal Justice/Law Enforcement Administration, A
Early Childhood Education and Teaching, A
Fashion Merchandising, AB

Fashion/Apparel Design, A
General Studies, A
Hospitality Administration/Management, A
Legal Administrative Assistant/Secretary, A
Liberal Arts and Sciences Studies and
  Humanities, A
Marketing/Marketing Management, B
Medical Administrative Assistant/Secretary, A
Medical/Clinical Assistant, A
Physical Therapy/Therapist, A
Recording Arts Technology/Technician, A
Tourism and Travel Services Management, A

BECKER COLLEGE

Accounting, AB
Animal Sciences, A
Animal Training, A
Business Administration and Management, AB
Business Administration, Management and
  Operations, B
Commercial and Advertising Art, AB
Computer and Information Sciences and Support
  Services, AB
Criminal Justice/Law Enforcement
  Administration, AB
Criminal Justice/Police Science, AB
Dog/Pet/Animal Grooming, A
Early Childhood Education and Teaching, B
Education, B
Elementary Education and Teaching, B
Graphic Design, AB
Horse Husbandry/Equine Science and
  Management, B
Hospitality Administration/Management, B
Hotel/Motel Administration/Management, B
Human Resources Management and Services, AB
Kinesiology and Exercise Science, B
Legal Assistant/Paralegal, A
Liberal Arts and Sciences Studies and
  Humanities, AB
Marketing/Marketing Management, B
Nursing - Registered Nurse Training, A
Physical Therapist Assistant, A
Pre-Veterinary Studies, B
Psychology, B
Sport and Fitness Administration/Management, B
Tourism and Travel Services Management, B
Veterinary/Animal Health Technology/Technician and
  Veterinary Assistant, A

BENJAMIN FRANKLIN INSTITUTE OF TECHNOLOGY

Architectural Engineering Technology/Technician, A
Automobile/Automotive Mechanics
  Technology/Technician, AB
Automotive Engineering Technology/Technician, AB
Computer Engineering Technology/Technician, A
Computer Science, A
Drafting and Design Technology/Technician, A
Electrical and Power Transmission
  Installation/Installer, A
Electrical, Electronic and Communications
  Engineering Technology/Technician, A
Engineering Technology, A
Heating, Air Conditioning and Refrigeration
  Technology/Technician, A
Mechanical Engineering/Mechanical
  Technology/Technician, A

BENTLEY COLLEGE

Accounting, BMO
Business Administration and Management, AB
Business Administration, Management and
  Operations, MO
Business/Corporate Communications, B
Business/Managerial Economics, B
Computer and Information Sciences, B
English Language and Literature, B
Ergonomics and Human Factors, M
Finance, B
Finance and Banking, MO
History, B
Information Science/Studies, M
Interdisciplinary Studies, B
Liberal Arts and Sciences Studies and
  Humanities, B

Marketing, MO
Marketing/Marketing Management, B
Mathematics, B
Philosophy, B
Public Policy Analysis, B
Taxation, MO

BERKLEE COLLEGE OF MUSIC

Audio Engineering, B
Jazz/Jazz Studies, B
Music, B
Music Management and Merchandising, B
Music Performance, B
Music Teacher Education, B
Music Theory and Composition, B
Music Therapy/Therapist, B
Piano and Organ, B
Violin, Viola, Guitar and Other Stringed
  Instruments, B
Voice and Opera, B
Wind and Percussion Instruments, B

BERKSHIRE COMMUNITY COLLEGE

Banking and Financial Support Services, A
Biology/Biological Sciences, A
Business Administration and Management, A
Business/Commerce, A
Business/Office Automation/Technology/Data
  Entry, A
Computer and Information Sciences, A
Criminal Justice/Safety Studies, A
Drama and Dramatics/Theatre Arts, A
Early Childhood Education and Teaching, A
Electrical, Electronic and Communications
  Engineering Technology/Technician, A
Engineering, A
Engineering Technology, A
Environmental Studies, A
Fire Science/Firefighting, A
Health Professions and Related Clinical Sciences, A
Hospitality Administration/Management, A
Human Services, A
International/Global Studies, A
Liberal Arts and Sciences Studies and
  Humanities, A
Music, A
Nursing - Registered Nurse Training, A
Peace Studies and Conflict Resolution, A
Physical Therapist Assistant, A
Respiratory Care Therapy/Therapist, A
Social Work, A
Surgical Technology/Technologist, A
System, Networking, and LAN/WAN
  Management/Manager, A
Visual and Performing Arts, A

BOSTON ARCHITECTURAL COLLEGE

Architecture, BM
Interior Design, BM

BOSTON BAPTIST COLLEGE

Bible/Biblical Studies, AB

BOSTON COLLEGE

Accounting, BM
Art History, Criticism and Conservation, B
Biochemistry, BMDO
Biological and Biomedical Sciences, MDO
Biology/Biological Sciences, B
Business Administration and Management, B
Business Administration, Management and
  Operations, MO
Chemistry, BMD
Classics and Classical
  Languages, Literatures, and Linguistics, BM
Community Health Nursing, M
Computer Science, B
Counseling Psychology, MDO
Curriculum and Instruction, MDO
Developmental Psychology, MD
Drama and Dramatics/Theatre Arts, B
Early Childhood Education and Teaching, M
East European and Russian Studies, MO
Economics, BD
Education, MDO

Education/Teaching of Individuals with Multiple
  Disabilities, M
Educational Administration and Supervision, MDO
Educational Measurement and Evaluation, MD
Educational Psychology, MD
Elementary Education and Teaching, BM
English, MD
English Education, M
English Language and Literature, B
Environmental Studies, B
Finance, B
Finance and Banking, MDO
Fine/Studio Arts, B
Foreign Language Teacher Education, M
French Language and Literature, BMD
Geology/Earth Science, BMO
Geophysics and Seismology, BMO
German Language and Literature, B
Gerontological Nursing, M
Higher Education/Higher Education
  Administration, MDO
Hispanic-American, Puerto Rican, and Mexican-
  American/Chicano Studies, B
History, BMD
Human Development and Family Studies, B
Human Resources Management/Personnel
  Administration, B
Inorganic Chemistry, D
Interdisciplinary Studies, B
Italian Language and Literature, BM
Kindergarten/PreSchool Education and Teaching, B
Law and Legal Studies, PO
Linguistics, MO
Management Information Systems and Services, B
Marketing/Marketing Management, B
Mass Communication/Media Studies, B
Maternal/Child Health and Neonatal
  Nurse/Nursing, M
Mathematics, BMO
Mathematics Teacher Education, M
Music, B
Nurse Anesthetist, M
Nursing, MDO
Nursing - Registered Nurse Training, B
Operations Research, B
Organic Chemistry, D
Organizational Behavior Studies, D
Organizational Management, D
Pastoral Studies/Counseling, MDO
Philosophy, BMD
Physical Chemistry, D
Physics, BMD
Political Science and Government, BMD
Pre-Medicine/Pre-Medical Studies, B
Psychiatric/Mental Health Nurse/Nursing, M
Psychology, BMD
Reading Teacher Education, MO
Religious Education, MDO
Russian Language and Literature, BMO
Russian Studies, B
Science Teacher Education/General Science
  Teacher Education, M
Secondary Education and Teaching, BM
Slavic Languages, Literatures, and Linguistics, BMO
Social Studies Teacher Education, M
Social Work, MDO
Sociology, BMDO
Spanish Language and Literature, MD
Special Education and Teaching, BMO
Theology and Religious Vocations, MD
Theology/Theological Studies, B
Western European Studies, M

THE BOSTON CONSERVATORY

Composition, M
Dance, B
Drama and Dramatics/Theatre Arts, B
Music, BMO
Music Teacher Education, BM
Music Theory and Composition, B
Performance, MO
Piano and Organ, B
Theater, M
Violin, Viola, Guitar and Other Stringed
  Instruments, B
Voice and Opera, B

Wind and Percussion Instruments, B

BOSTON UNIVERSITY

Accounting, BDO
Acting, B
Actuarial Science, M
Advertising and Public Relations, MO
Aerospace, Aeronautical and Astronautical
  Engineering, BMD
African Studies, O
African-American/Black Studies, M
Allied Health and Medical Assisting Services, MD
Allopathic Medicine, PO
American/United States Studies/Civilization, BD
Anatomy, MDO
Ancient/Classical Greek Language and Literature, B
Animal Physiology, B
Anthropology, BMD
Archeology, BMD
Area Studies, B
Art Education, M
Art History, Criticism and Conservation, BMDO
Art Teacher Education, B
Arts Management, M
Astronomy, BMD
Astrophysics, B
Athletic Training and Sports Medicine, B
Bilingual and Multilingual Education, B
Biochemistry, BMDO
Bioethics/Medical Ethics, M
Bioinformatics, MD
Biological and Biomedical Sciences, BMDO
Biology/Biological Sciences, B
Biomedical Engineering, MDO
Biomedical/Medical Engineering, B
Biophysics, B
Biopsychology, M
Biostatistics, MD
Business Administration and Management, B
Business Administration, Management and
  Operations, M
Cell Biology and Anatomy, MDO
Chemistry, BMD
Chemistry Teacher Education, B
Cinematography and Film/Video Production, B
Classics and Classical
  Languages, Literatures, and Linguistics, BMDO
Clinical Laboratory Science/Medical
  Technology/Technologist, B
Clinical Research, M
Cognitive Sciences, MD
Commercial and Advertising Art, B
Communication and Media Studies, MO
Communication Disorders, BMDO
Communication Studies/Speech Communication
  and Rhetoric, B
Composition, MD
Computer Engineering, BMD
Computer Science, BMD
Counseling Psychology, MD
Counselor Education/School Counseling and
  Guidance Services, MO
Criminology, M
Curriculum and Instruction, MDO
Dental and Oral Surgery, MDO
Dental Hygiene/Hygienist, M
Dental Laboratory Technology/Technician, B
Dentistry, O
Drama and Dance Teacher Education, B
Drawing, B
Early Childhood Education and Teaching, MDO
East Asian Studies, B
Ecology, B
Economics, BMDO
Education, BMDO
Education/Teaching of Individuals with Hearing
  Impairments, Including Deafness, B
Educational Administration and Supervision, MO
Educational Media/Instructional Technology, MDO
Electrical Engineering, MD
Electrical, Electronics and Communications
  Engineering, B
Electronic Commerce, M
Elementary Education and Teaching, BM
Energy Management and Policy, M
Engineering, B

Engineering and Applied Sciences, MDO
English, MD
English as a Second Language, MO
English Education, MDO
English Language and Literature, B
English/Language Arts Teacher Education, B
Environmental and Occupational Health, MD
Environmental Policy and Resource
  Management, M
Environmental Studies, B
Epidemiology, MD
Ethnic, Cultural Minority, and Gender Studies, B
Film, Television, and Video Production, MO
Film, Television, and Video Theory and Criticism, M
Finance, B
Finance and Banking, M
Fine Arts and Art Studies, M
Foreign Language Teacher Education, BM
Foreign Languages and Literatures, B
French Language and Literature, BMD
Genetic Counseling/Counselor, M
Geographic Information Systems, M
Geography, BMD
Geology/Earth Science, B
Geosciences, MD
German Language and Literature, B
Graphic Design, M
Health Education, MO
Health Promotion, MD
Health Services Administration, MDO
Historic Preservation and Conservation, MO
History, BMD
Hospitality Administration/Management, B
Hotel/Motel Administration/Management, B
Human Development, MDO
Human Resources Management and Services, MO
Immunology, DO
Industrial and Manufacturing Management, D
Industrial Engineering, B
Information Science/Studies, B
Interdisciplinary Studies, BMD
International Affairs, MO
International and Comparative Education, M
International Business/Trade/Commerce, BM
International Finance, B
International Public Health/International
  Health, MDO
International Relations and Affairs, B
Investment Management, M
Italian Language and Literature, B
Journalism, BM
Kindergarten/PreSchool Education and Teaching, B
Kinesiology and Exercise Science, B
Latin American Studies, B
Latin Language and Literature, B
Law and Legal Studies, MPO
Legal and Justice Studies, M
Legal Assistant/Paralegal, B
Leisure Studies, M
Liberal Studies, M
Linguistics, BMD
Management, M
Management Information Systems and Services, BD
Management of Technology, M
Manufacturing Engineering, MDO
Marine Biology and Biological Oceanography, B
Marketing, D
Marketing Research, B
Marketing/Marketing Management, B
Mass Communication/Media Studies, BMO
Maternal and Child Health, MO
Mathematical and Computational Finance, M
Mathematics, BMD
Mathematics and Computer Science, B
Mathematics Teacher Education, BMDO
Mechanical Engineering, BMD
Media Studies, MO
Microbiology, MDO
Modern Greek Language and Literature, B
Molecular Biology, BMDO
Molecular Medicine, DO
Multilingual and Multicultural Education, MO
Museology/Museum Studies, O
Music, MDO
Music History, Literature, and Theory, BMD
Music Performance, B

Music Teacher Education, BMD
Music Theory and Composition, BMD
Neurobiology and Neurophysiology, MDO
Neuroscience, BMDO
Non-Profit/Public/Organizational Management, M
Nurse Midwife/Nursing Midwifery, O
Nutritional Sciences, BMD
Occupational Therapy/Therapist, BMD
Operations Management and Supervision, B
Oral and Dental Sciences, MDPO
Oral Biology, MD
Organizational Behavior Studies, BD
Orthodontics, MDO
Painting, BM
Parks, Recreation, Leisure and Fitness Studies, B
Pathology/Experimental Pathology, DO
Pedodontics, MDO
Performance, MDO
Periodontics, MDO
Pharmaceutical Sciences, MDO
Pharmacology, MDO
Philosophy, BMDO
Photonics, M
Physical Education Teaching and Coaching, BMDO
Physical Therapy/Therapist, BMD
Physics, BMD
Physiology, MDO
Piano and Organ, B
Political Science and Government, BMD
Pre-Dentistry Studies, B
Psychology, BMD
Public Administration, M
Public Health, MDO
Public Health (MPH, DPH), B
Public Relations/Image Management, B
Radio and Television, B
Reading Teacher Education, MDO
Rehabilitation Counseling, MDO
Rehabilitation Sciences, MD
Rehabilitation Therapy, B
Religion/Religious Studies, BMD
Romance
    Languages, Literatures, and Linguistics, MD
Russian Language and Literature, B
Russian Studies, B
Science Teacher Education/General Science
    Teacher Education, BMDO
Sculpture, BM
Social Sciences, B
Social Studies Teacher Education, BMDO
Social Work, MDO
Sociology, BMD
Spanish Language and Literature, BMD
Special Education and Teaching, BMDO
Speech Teacher Education, B
Systems Engineering, MD
Taxation, M
Teacher Education and Professional
    Development, Specific Levels and Methods, B
Technical Theatre/Theatre Design and
    Technology, B
Telecommunications, M
Theater, MO
Theatre Literature, History and Criticism, B
Theology and Religious Vocations, MDPO
Travel and Tourism, M
Urban and Regional Planning, M
Urban Studies/Affairs, BM
Voice and Opera, B
Writing, MD

BRANDEIS UNIVERSITY

African Studies, B
African-American/Black Studies, B
American/United States Studies/Civilization, BMD
Ancient/Classical Greek Language and Literature, B
Anthropology, BMD
Arabic Language and Literature, B
Area, Ethnic, Cultural, and Gender Studies, B
Art/Art Studies, General, B
Biochemistry, BMD
Biological and Biomedical Sciences, BMDO
Biology/Biological Sciences, B
Biophysics, BMD
Business Administration, Management and
    Operations, MO

Cell Biology and Anatomy, MD
Cell/Cellular Biology and Anatomical Sciences, B
Chemistry, BMD
Child and Family Studies, M
Classics and Classical
    Languages, Literatures, and Linguistics, B
Cognitive Sciences, D
Comparative Literature, B
Composition, MD
Computer Science, BMDO
Conflict Resolution and Mediation/Peace Studies, M
Developmental Psychology, D
Drama and Dramatics/Theatre Arts, B
East Asian Studies, B
Economics, BMD
Elementary Education and Teaching, M
Engineering Physics, B
English, MD
English Language and Literature, B
European Studies/Civilization, B
Finance and Banking, MD
Fine Arts and Art Studies, O
Fine/Studio Arts, B
French Language and Literature, B
Genetic Counseling/Counselor, M
Genetics, D
German Language and Literature, B
Health Services Administration, M
Hebrew Language and Literature, M
History, BMD
Human Services, M
Inorganic Chemistry, MD
International Affairs, MD
International Business/Trade/Commerce, MD
International Development, M
International Public Health/International Health, M
Islamic Studies, B
Jewish/Judaic Studies, BMDO
Latin American Studies, B
Latin Language and Literature, B
Linguistics, B
Mathematics, BMD
Microbiology, D
Molecular Biology, MD
Multi-/Interdisciplinary Studies, B
Music, BMD
Music Theory and Composition, MD
Musicology and Ethnomusicology, MD
Near and Middle Eastern Studies, BMDO
Neurobiology and Neurophysiology, D
Neuroscience, BMD
Organic Chemistry, MD
Philosophy, B
Physical Chemistry, MD
Physics, BMD
Political Science and Government, BMD
Psychology, BMD
Public Administration, M
Public Policy Analysis, D
Religious Education, M
Russian Language and Literature, B
Russian Studies, B
Social Psychology, D
Sociology, BMD
Spanish Language and Literature, B
Structural Biology, MD
Sustainable Development, M
Theater, M
Women's Studies, BM

BRIDGEWATER STATE COLLEGE

Accounting, BM
Airline/Commercial/Professional Pilot and Flight
    Crew, B
American Government and Politics (United States)
    , B
Anthropology, B
Archeology, B
Area Studies, B
Art Education, M
Art History, Criticism and Conservation, B
Art Teacher Education, B
Athletic Training and Sports Medicine, B
Aviation/Airway Management and Operations, B
Biochemistry, B
Biology Teacher Education, B

Biology/Biological Sciences, B
Biomedical Sciences, B
Business Administration and Management, B
Business, Management, Marketing, and Related
    Support Services, B
Cell/Cellular and Molecular Biology, B
Chemistry, B
City/Urban, Community and Regional Planning, B
Communication Disorders, B
Communication Studies/Speech Communication
    and Rhetoric, B
Computer Science, BM
Counselor Education/School Counseling and
    Guidance Services, MO
Crafts/Craft Design, Folk Art and Artisanry, B
Creative Writing, B
Criminal Justice/Safety Studies, B
Criminology, M
Developmental and Child Psychology, B
Drama and Dance Teacher Education, B
Drama and Dramatics/Theatre Arts, B
Early Childhood Education and Teaching, BM
Economics, B
Education, MO
Educational Administration and Supervision, MO
Educational Media/Instructional Technology, M
Elementary Education and Teaching, BM
English, M
English Language and Literature, B
English/Language Arts Teacher Education, B
Environmental Biology, B
Ethics, B
Finance, B
Finance and Banking, M
Fine/Studio Arts, B
Geochemistry, B
Geography, B
Geological and Earth Sciences/Geosciences, B
Geology/Earth Science, B
Graphic Design, B
Health and Physical Education/Fitness, B
Health Promotion, M
Health Teacher Education, B
Health/Medical Psychology, B
History, B
Industrial and Organizational Psychology, B
International Business/Trade/Commerce, B
International Relations and Affairs, B
Kinesiology and Exercise Science, B
Kinesiotherapy/Kinesiotherapist, B
Law and Legal Studies, B
Management, M
Management Information Systems and Services, B
Marketing/Marketing Management, B
Mathematics, B
Mathematics Teacher Education, M
Music, B
Music Teacher Education, B
Parks, Recreation, Leisure and Fitness Studies, B
Philosophy, B
Photography, B
Physical Education Teaching and Coaching, BM
Physics, B
Political Science and Government, B
Psychology, BM
Public Administration, M
Reading Teacher Education, MO
Science Teacher Education/General Science
    Teacher Education, M
Science Technologies/Technicians, B
Secondary Education and Teaching, M
Social Studies Teacher Education, M
Social Work, BM
Sociology, B
Spanish Language and Literature, B
Special Education and Teaching, BM
Sport and Fitness Administration/Management, B
Transportation/Transportation Management, B

BRISTOL COMMUNITY COLLEGE

Accounting, A
Administrative Assistant and Secretarial Science, A
Audiology/Audiologist and Hearing Sciences, A
Business Administration and Management, A
Business/Office Automation/Technology/Data
    Entry, A

Child Care and Support Services Management, A
Civil Engineering, A
Civil Engineering Technology/Technician, A
Clinical/Medical Laboratory Technician, A
Communication Studies/Speech Communication
    and Rhetoric, A
Computer and Information Sciences, A
Computer Programming/Programmer, A
Computer Science, A
Consumer Merchandising/Retailing Management, A
Criminal Justice/Safety Studies, A
Culinary Arts/Chef Training, A
Data Processing and Data Processing
    Technology/Technician, A
Dental Hygiene/Hygienist, A
Dramatic/Theatre Arts and Stagecraft, A
Early Childhood Education and Teaching, A
Electrical, Electronic and Communications
    Engineering Technology/Technician, A
Elementary Education and Teaching, A
Engineering, A
Engineering Science, A
Engineering Technologies/Technicians, A
Environmental Engineering
    Technology/Environmental Technology, A
Environmental Sciences, A
Environmental/Environmental Health Engineering, A
Finance and Financial Management Services, A
Fine/Studio Arts, A
Fire Science/Firefighting, A
General Studies, A
Graphic Design, A
Health Information/Medical Records
    Technology/Technician, A
Human Services, A
Humanities/Humanistic Studies, A
Information Science/Studies, A
Information Technology, A
Legal Administrative Assistant/Secretary, A
Liberal Arts and Sciences Studies and
    Humanities, A
Management Information Systems and Services, A
Marketing/Marketing Management, A
Medical Administrative Assistant/Secretary, A
Nursing - Registered Nurse Training, A
Occupational Therapist Assistant, A
Pre-Engineering, A
Web/Multimedia Management and Webmaster, A

BUNKER HILL COMMUNITY COLLEGE

Accounting, A
Art/Art Studies, General, A
Business Administration and Management, A
Cardiovascular Technology/Technologist, A
Chemistry, A
Communication Studies/Speech Communication
    and Rhetoric, A
Computer and Information Sciences and Support
    Services, A
Computer Programming, Specific Applications, A
Computer Programming/Programmer, A
Computer Science, A
Computer Systems Networking and
    Telecommunications, A
Criminal Justice/Law Enforcement Administration, A
Culinary Arts/Chef Training, A
Data Entry/Microcomputer Applications, A
Design and Visual Communications, A
Drama and Dramatics/Theatre Arts, A
Early Childhood Education and Teaching, A
Education, A
Electrical/Electronics Maintenance and Repair
    Technology, A
English Language and Literature, A
Finance, A
Fire Protection and Safety Technology/Technician, A
General Studies, A
Health Information/Medical Records
    Administration/Administrator, A
History, A
Hospitality Administration/Management, A
Hotel/Motel Administration/Management, A
Human Services, A
International Business/Trade/Commerce, A
Mass Communication/Media Studies, A
Mathematics, A

Medical Radiologic Technology/Science - Radiation
    Therapist, A
Nursing - Registered Nurse Training, A
Operations Management and Supervision, A
Physics, A
Psychology, A
Sociology, A
Tourism and Travel Services Management, A
Web Page, Digital/Multimedia and Information
    Resources Design, A

CAMBRIDGE COLLEGE

Counseling Psychology, M
Education, M
Electronic Commerce, M
Human Services, B
Management, M
Management Science, B
Multi-/Interdisciplinary Studies, B
Psychology, B

CAPE COD COMMUNITY COLLEGE

Accounting, A
Administrative Assistant and Secretarial Science, A
Art/Art Studies, General, A
Biological and Physical Sciences, A
Business Administration and Management, A
Computer and Information Sciences, A
Computer Graphics, A
Computer Science, A
Computer Systems Networking and
    Telecommunications, A
Criminal Justice/Law Enforcement Administration, A
Dental Hygiene/Hygienist, A
Drama and Dramatics/Theatre Arts, A
Education, A
Environmental Engineering
    Technology/Environmental Technology, A
Environmental Studies, A
Executive Assistant/Executive Secretary, A
Fire Science/Firefighting, A
History, A
Hotel/Motel Administration/Management, A
Information Science/Studies, A
Information Technology, A
Kindergarten/PreSchool Education and Teaching, A
Legal Administrative Assistant/Secretary, A
Legal Assistant/Paralegal, A
Liberal Arts and Sciences Studies and
    Humanities, A
Management Science, A
Mass Communication/Media Studies, A
Mathematics, A
Medical Administrative Assistant/Secretary, A
Modern Languages, A
Music, A
Nursing - Registered Nurse Training, A
Parks, Recreation, Leisure and Fitness Studies, A
Philosophy, A
Physical Education Teaching and Coaching, A
Physical Therapist Assistant, A
Pre-Engineering, A
Psychology, A
System Administration/Administrator, A
Web Page, Digital/Multimedia and Information
    Resources Design, A
Web/Multimedia Management and Webmaster, A

CLARK UNIVERSITY

Accounting, M
Art History, Criticism and Conservation, B
Asian Studies/Civilization, B
Biochemistry, B
Biological and Biomedical Sciences, MD
Biology/Biological Sciences, B
Business Administration and Management, B
Business Administration, Management and
    Operations, M
Chemistry, BMD
Classics and Classical
    Languages, Literatures, and Linguistics, B
Clinical Psychology, D
Commercial and Advertising Art, B
Communication and Media Studies, M
Comparative Literature, B
Computer Science, B

Development Economics and International
    Development, B
Developmental Psychology, D
Drama and Dramatics/Theatre Arts, B
Ecology, B
Economics, BD
Education, BM
Elementary Education and Teaching, B
Engineering, B
English, M
English Language and Literature, B
Environmental Policy and Resource
    Management, M
Environmental Studies, M
Ethnic and Cultural Studies, B
Film/Cinema Studies, B
Finance and Banking, M
Fine/Studio Arts, B
French Language and Literature, B
Geographic Information Systems, M
Geography, BD
Geology/Earth Science, B
Health Services Administration, M
History, BMDO
Holocaust Studies, D
Information Science/Studies, M
Interdisciplinary Studies, B
International Business/Trade/Commerce, M
International Development, M
International Relations and Affairs, B
Jewish/Judaic Studies, B
Junior High/Intermediate/Middle School Education
    and Teaching, B
Liberal Studies, M
Management, M
Management Information Systems and Services, M
Marketing, M
Mass Communication/Media Studies, B
Mathematics, B
Modern Languages, B
Molecular Biology, B
Music, B
Natural Resources Management/Development and
    Policy, B
Neuroscience, B
Peace Studies and Conflict Resolution, B
Philosophy, B
Physics, BMD
Political Science and Government, B
Pre-Dentistry Studies, B
Pre-Law Studies, B
Pre-Medicine/Pre-Medical Studies, B
Pre-Veterinary Studies, B
Psychology, BD
Public Administration, MO
Secondary Education and Teaching, B
Social Psychology, D
Sociology, B
Spanish Language and Literature, B
Sustainable Development, M
Urban and Regional Planning, M
Women's Studies, BD

COLLEGE OF THE HOLY CROSS

Accounting, B
Anthropology, B
Art History, Criticism and Conservation, B
Asian Studies/Civilization, B
Biology/Biological Sciences, B
Chemistry, B
Classics and Classical
    Languages, Literatures, and Linguistics, B
Comparative Literature, B
Computer Science, B
Drama and Dramatics/Theatre Arts, B
Economics, B
English Language and Literature, B
Environmental Studies, B
Fine/Studio Arts, B
French Language and Literature, B
German Language and Literature, B
German Studies, B
History, B
Italian Language and Literature, B
Mathematics, B
Medieval and Renaissance Studies, B

Music, B
Philosophy, B
Physics, B
Political Science and Government, B
Pre-Medicine/Pre-Medical Studies, B
Psychology, B
Religion/Religious Studies, B
Russian Language and Literature, B
Russian Studies, B
Sociology, B
Spanish Language and Literature, B

CURRY COLLEGE

Adult and Continuing Education and Teaching, MO
Biology/Biological Sciences, B
Business Administration and Management, B
Commercial and Advertising Art, B
Criminal Justice/Law Enforcement Administration, B
Education, BMO
Elementary Education and Teaching, B
English Language and Literature, B
Environmental Studies, B
Family and Community Services, B
Film/Cinema Studies, B
Health Teacher Education, B
History, B
Information Technology, B
Journalism, B
Kindergarten/PreSchool Education and Teaching, B
Mass Communication/Media Studies, B
Nursing - Registered Nurse Training, B
Philosophy, B
Physics, B
Political Science and Government, B
Pre-Law Studies, B
Psychology, B
Public Relations/Image Management, B
Radio and Television, B
Reading Teacher Education, MO
Sociology, B
Special Education and Teaching, BMO
Women's Studies, B

DEAN COLLEGE

Athletic Training and Sports Medicine, A
Business Administration and Management, A
Communication Studies/Speech Communication
    and Rhetoric, A
Criminal Justice/Law Enforcement Administration, A
Criminal Justice/Police Science, A
Dance, AB
Drama and Dramatics/Theatre Arts, A
Early Childhood Education and Teaching, A
Liberal Arts and Sciences Studies and
    Humanities, A
Mathematics and Computer Science, A
Physical Education Teaching and Coaching, A
Sport and Fitness Administration/Management, A

EASTERN NAZARENE COLLEGE

Advertising, B
Aerospace, Aeronautical and Astronautical
    Engineering, B
Biological and Physical Sciences, B
Biology/Biological Sciences, B
Biomedical/Medical Engineering, B
Business Administration and Management, B
Business/Commerce, A
Chemistry, B
Clinical Psychology, B
Computer Engineering, B
Computer Science, B
Counseling Psychology, M
Drama and Dramatics/Theatre Arts, B
Early Childhood Education and Teaching, MO
Education, BMO
Educational Administration and Supervision, MO
Electrical, Electronics and Communications
    Engineering, B
Elementary Education and Teaching, BMO
Engineering Physics, B
English as a Second Language, MO
English Language and Literature, B
General Studies, A
History, B
Industrial Engineering, B

Journalism, B
Junior High/Intermediate/Middle School Education
    and Teaching, B
Kindergarten/PreSchool Education and
    Teaching, AB
Liberal Arts and Sciences Studies and
    Humanities, B
Marriage and Family Therapy/Counseling, M
Mass Communication/Media Studies, B
Mathematics, B
Mechanical Engineering, B
Middle School Education, MO
Music, B
Music Performance, B
Music Teacher Education, B
Pharmacy, B
Physical Education Teaching and Coaching, B
Physical Therapy/Therapist, B
Physics, B
Pre-Law Studies, B
Pre-Medicine/Pre-Medical Studies, B
Psychology, B
Public Health (MPH, DPH), B
Radio and Television, B
Reading Teacher Education, MO
Religion/Religious Studies, B
Religious Education, AB
Religious/Sacred Music, B
Secondary Education and Teaching, BMO
Social Work, B
Sociology, B
Special Education and Teaching, BMO
Systems Engineering, B

ELMS COLLEGE

Accounting, B
Applied Art, B
Art/Art Studies, General, B
Audiology/Audiologist and Speech-Language
    Pathology/Pathologist, B
Bilingual and Multilingual Education, B
Biology/Biological Sciences, B
Business Administration and Management, B
Chemistry, B
Communication Disorders, BO
Computer Science, B
Early Childhood Education and Teaching, M
Education, BMO
Elementary Education and Teaching, BM
English as a Second Language, M
English Language and Literature, B
English/Language Arts Teacher Education, B
French Language and Literature, B
History, B
Interdisciplinary Studies, B
International Relations and Affairs, B
Kindergarten/PreSchool Education and Teaching, B
Law and Legal Studies, B
Legal Assistant/Paralegal, AB
Liberal Arts and Sciences Studies and
    Humanities, B
Liberal Studies, M
Marketing/Marketing Management, B
Mathematics, B
Mathematics Teacher Education, B
Molecular Biology, B
Natural Sciences, B
Nursing - Registered Nurse Training, B
Pre-Dentistry Studies, B
Pre-Law Studies, B
Pre-Medicine/Pre-Medical Studies, B
Pre-Veterinary Studies, B
Psychology, B
Reading Teacher Education, M
Religion/Religious Studies, BM
Science Teacher Education/General Science
    Teacher Education, B
Secondary Education and Teaching, BM
Social Work, B
Sociology, B
Spanish Language and Literature, B
Special Education and Teaching, BM

Speech-Language Pathology/Pathologist, A

EMERSON COLLEGE

Acting, B
Advertising, B
Advertising and Public Relations, M
Audiology/Audiologist and Speech-Language
    Pathology/Pathologist, B
Broadcast Journalism, B
Cinematography and Film/Video Production, B
Communication and Media Studies, M
Communication Disorders, BM
Communication Studies/Speech Communication
    and Rhetoric, B
Corporate and Organizational Communication, M
Creative Writing, B
Drama and Dance Teacher Education, B
Drama and Dramatics/Theatre Arts, B
Education/Teaching of Individuals with Speech or
    Language Impairments, B
Film, Television, and Video Production, M
Film/Cinema Studies, B
Health Promotion, M
Interdisciplinary Studies, B
Intermedia/Multimedia, B
International Business/Trade/Commerce, M
Journalism, BM
Marketing, M
Marketing/Marketing Management, B
Mass Communication/Media Studies, B
Media Studies, M
Playwriting and Screenwriting, B
Political Communication, B
Public Health, M
Public Relations/Image Management, B
Publishing, BM
Radio and Television, B
Radio and Television Broadcasting
    Technology/Technician, B
Radio, Television, and Digital Communication, B
Speech and Rhetorical Studies, B
Speech-Language Pathology/Pathologist, B
Technical Theatre/Theatre Design and
    Technology, B
Theater, M
Visual and Performing Arts, B
Writing, M

EMMANUEL COLLEGE

American/United States Studies/Civilization, B
Area, Ethnic, Cultural, and Gender Studies, B
Art Therapy/Therapist, B
Art/Art Studies, General, B
Biochemistry, B
Biology/Biological Sciences, B
Biostatistics, B
Business Administration and Management, B
Business/Managerial Economics, B
Chemistry, B
Commercial and Advertising Art, B
Communication Studies/Speech Communication
    and Rhetoric, B
Developmental and Child Psychology, B
Economics, B
Education, BMO
Educational Administration and Supervision, M
Educational Leadership and Administration, O
Elementary Education and Teaching, BM
English Language and Literature, B
Environmental Studies, B
Fine/Studio Arts, B
Graphic Design, B
Health Services/Allied Health/Health Sciences, B
History, B
Human Resources Management and Services, MO
Interdisciplinary Studies, B
Liberal Arts and Sciences Studies and
    Humanities, B
Management, M
Mass Communication/Media Studies, B
Mathematics, B
Multi-/Interdisciplinary Studies, B
Nursing Administration, B
Political Science and Government, B
Psychology, B
Religion/Religious Studies, B

Secondary Education and Teaching, BM
Sociology, B
Spanish Language and Literature, B

ENDICOTT COLLEGE

Art Education, M
Art Therapy/Therapist, B
Athletic Training and Sports Medicine, B
Business Administration and Management, B
Business Administration, Management and
  Operations, M
Criminal Justice/Safety Studies, B
Design and Visual Communications, B
Early Childhood Education and Teaching, B
Education, M
Elementary Education and Teaching, BM
English Language and Literature, B
Environmental Studies, B
Fine/Studio Arts, B
Hospitality Administration/Management, BM
Human Services, B
Information Technology, B
International and Comparative Education, M
International/Global Studies, B
Liberal Arts and Sciences Studies and
  Humanities, AB
Mass Communication/Media Studies, B
Multi-/Interdisciplinary Studies, B
Nursing - Registered Nurse Training, B
Organizational Management, M
Physical Education Teaching and Coaching, B
Psychology, B
Reading Teacher Education, M
Spanish Language and Literature, B
Special Education and Teaching, M
Sport and Fitness Administration/Management, B

FISHER COLLEGE

Accounting, A
Business Administration and Management, AB
Fashion Merchandising, A
Fashion/Apparel Design, A
Hospitality Administration/Management, A
Humanities/Humanistic Studies, A
Kindergarten/PreSchool Education and Teaching, A
Liberal Arts and Sciences Studies and
  Humanities, A
Psychology, A
Public Health (MPH, DPH), A
Tourism and Travel Services Management, A

FITCHBURG STATE COLLEGE

Accounting, BM
Architectural Engineering Technology/Technician, B
Art Education, MO
Biology Teacher Education, B
Biology/Biological Sciences, B
BioTechnology, B
Business Administration and Management, B
Business Administration, Management and
  Operations, M
Child and Family Studies, O
Cinematography and Film/Video Production, B
Communication and Media Studies, BMO
Comparative Literature, B
Computer Science, BM
Construction Engineering Technology/Technician, B
Counseling Psychology, MO
Counselor Education/School Counseling and
  Guidance Services, MO
Criminal Justice/Law Enforcement Administration, B
Criminology, M
Development Economics and International
  Development, B
Developmental and Child Psychology, B
Drama and Dramatics/Theatre Arts, B
Early Childhood Education and Teaching, BM
Economics, B
Education, B
Educational Administration and Supervision, MO
Electrical and Electronic Engineering
  Technologies/Technicians, B
Elementary Education and Teaching, BM
Energy Management and Systems
  Technology/Technician, B
English Education, M

English Language and Literature, B
English/Language Arts Teacher Education, B
Environmental Sciences, B
Forensic Nursing, MO
General Studies, BM
Geography, B
Geography Teacher Education, B
Geology/Earth Science, B
Graphic Design, B
History, B
History Teacher Education, B
Human Resources Management and Services, M
Human Services, B
Humanities/Humanistic Studies, B
Industrial and Organizational Psychology, B
Industrial Technology/Technician, B
Information Science/Studies, B
Interdisciplinary Studies, O
Intermedia/Multimedia, B
Journalism, B
Junior High/Intermediate/Middle School Education
  and Teaching, B
Kinesiology and Exercise Science, B
Liberal Arts and Sciences Studies and
  Humanities, B
Management Science, B
Manufacturing Technology/Technician, B
Marketing/Marketing Management, B
Marriage and Family Therapy/Counseling, MO
Mathematics, B
Mathematics Teacher Education, B
Middle School Education, M
Nursing - Registered Nurse Training, B
Photography, B
Political Science and Government, B
Psychology, B
Science Teacher Education/General Science
  Teacher Education, M
Secondary Education and Teaching, BM
Social Studies Teacher Education, M
Sociology, B
Special Education and Teaching, BM
Sport and Fitness Administration/Management, B
Substance Abuse/Addiction Counseling, O
Technical and Business Writing, BM
Technical Theatre/Theatre Design and
  Technology, B
Technology Education/Industrial Arts, B
Technology Teacher Education/Industrial Arts
  Teacher Education, B
Vocational and Technical Education, M

FRAMINGHAM STATE COLLEGE

Accounting, B
Acting, B
American Government and Politics (United States)
  , B
American History (United States), B
Anthropology, B
Apparel and Textiles, B
Art History, Criticism and Conservation, B
Art Teacher Education, B
Art/Art Studies, General, B
Biology Teacher Education, B
Biology/Biological Sciences, B
Biomedical Sciences, B
BioTechnology, B
Business Administration and Management, B
Business Administration, Management and
  Operations, M
Business/Corporate Communications, B
Business/Managerial Economics, B
Chemistry, B
Chemistry Teacher Education, B
City/Urban, Community and Regional Planning, B
Clinical Nutrition/Nutritionist, B
Communication and Media Studies, B
Communication Studies/Speech Communication
  and Rhetoric, B
Communication, Journalism and Related
  Programs, B
Computer Programming/Programmer, B
Computer Science, B
Counseling Psychology, M
Creative Writing, B
Curriculum and Instruction, M

Design and Visual Communications, B
Developmental and Child Psychology, B
Dietetics/Dieticians, B
Early Childhood Education and Teaching, B
Economics, B
Education, B
Educational Leadership and Administration, M
Educational Media/Instructional Technology, M
Elementary Education and Teaching, B
English as a Second Language, M
English Education, M
English Language and Literature, B
English/Language Arts Teacher Education, B
Environmental Biology, B
Environmental Sciences, B
Environmental Studies, B
European History, B
Family and Consumer Economics and Related
  Services, B
Family and Consumer Sciences/Home Economics
  Teacher Education, B
Family and Consumer Sciences/Human Sciences, B
Family and Consumer Sciences/Human Sciences
  Communication, B
Fashion Merchandising, B
Fashion/Apparel Design, B
Film/Cinema Studies, B
Finance, B
Fine Arts and Art Studies, M
Fine/Studio Arts, B
Food Science, B
Food Science and Technology, BM
Foods, Nutrition, and Related Services, B
Foods, Nutrition, and Wellness Studies, B
Foreign Language Teacher Education, BM
Foreign Languages and Literatures, B
French Language and Literature, B
Geography, B
Geography Teacher Education, B
Geology/Earth Science, B
Graphic Design, B
Health Services Administration, M
Health Teacher Education, B
History, B
History Teacher Education, B
Human Nutrition, B
Human Resources Management and Services, M
Human Services, B
Humanities/Humanistic Studies, B
Information Technology, B
International Business/Trade/Commerce, B
International/Global Studies, B
Journalism, B
Liberal Arts and Sciences Studies and
  Humanities, B
Marketing/Marketing Management, B
Mathematics, B
Mathematics Teacher Education, BM
Nursing - Registered Nurse Training, B
Nutritional Sciences, M
Painting, B
Physical Sciences, B
Political Science and Government, B
Printmaking, B
Psychology, BM
Public Administration, M
Reading Teacher Education, M
Sculpture, B
Secondary Education and Teaching, B
Social Sciences, B
Social Studies Teacher Education, M
Sociology, B
Spanish Language and Literature, BM
Special Education and Teaching, M
Wildlife and Wildlands Science and Management, B
Wildlife Biology, B

GIBBS COLLEGE

Administrative Assistant and Secretarial Science, A
Business Administration and Management, A
Hospitality Administration/Management, A
Legal Administrative Assistant/Secretary, A

Medical Administrative Assistant/Secretary, A

GORDON COLLEGE

Accounting, B
Art/Art Studies, General, B
Biology/Biological Sciences, B
Business Administration and Management, B
Chemistry, B
Christian Studies, B
Communication Studies/Speech Communication
    and Rhetoric, B
Computer Science, B
Economics, B
Education, M
Elementary Education and Teaching, B
English Language and Literature, B
Foreign Languages and Literatures, B
French Language and Literature, B
German Language and Literature, B
History, B
International Relations and Affairs, B
Junior High/Intermediate/Middle School Education
    and Teaching, B
Kinesiology and Exercise Science, B
Mathematics, B
Music, B
Music Performance, B
Music Teacher Education, BM
Parks, Recreation, Leisure and Fitness Studies, B
Philosophy, B
Physics, B
Political Science and Government, B
Psychology, B
Social Work, B
Sociology, B
Spanish Language and Literature, B
Special Education and Teaching, B
Youth Ministry, B

GREENFIELD COMMUNITY COLLEGE

Accounting, A
Administrative Assistant and Secretarial Science, A
American/United States Studies/Civilization, A
Art/Art Studies, General, A
Behavioral Sciences, A
Biological and Physical Sciences, A
Business Administration and Management, A
Commercial and Advertising Art, A
Computer Programming/Programmer, A
Criminal Justice/Law Enforcement Administration, A
Education, A
Engineering Science, A
Family and Consumer Sciences/Human Sciences, A
Fire Science/Firefighting, A
Food Science, A
Human Services, A
Humanities/Humanistic Studies, A
Industrial Technology/Technician, A
Information Science/Studies, A
Kindergarten/PreSchool Education and Teaching, A
Liberal Arts and Sciences Studies and
    Humanities, A
Marketing/Marketing Management, A
Mass Communication/Media Studies, A
Mathematics, A
Natural Resources Management/Development and
    Policy, A
Nursing - Registered Nurse Training, A
Parks, Recreation, Leisure and Fitness Studies, A
Photography, A
Pre-Engineering, A

HAMPSHIRE COLLEGE

African-American/Black Studies, B
Agriculture, B
American/United States Studies/Civilization, B
Anthropology, B
Applied Art, B
Asian Studies/Civilization, B
Asian-American Studies, B
Biology/Biological Sciences, B
Chemistry, B
Cognitive Sciences, B
Comparative Literature, B
Computer Graphics, B
Computer Science, B

Dance, B
Demography and Population Studies, B
Drama and Dramatics/Theatre Arts, B
Economics, B
Education, B
English Language and Literature, B
Environmental Design/Architecture, B
Environmental Studies, B
Film/Video and Photographic Arts, B
Fine/Studio Arts, B
Geology/Earth Science, B
Hispanic-American, Puerto Rican, and Mexican-
    American/Chicano Studies, B
History, B
International/Global Studies, B
Jewish/Judaic Studies, B
Latin American Studies, B
Law and Legal Studies, B
Linguistics, B
Mass Communication/Media Studies, B
Mathematics, B
Music, B
Nutritional Sciences, B
Peace Studies and Conflict Resolution, B
Philosophy, B
Physics, B
Playwriting and Screenwriting, B
Political Science and Government, B
Psychology, B
Public Health (MPH, DPH), B
Religion/Religious Studies, B
Sociology, B
Urban Studies/Affairs, B

HARVARD UNIVERSITY

African Languages, Literatures, and Linguistics, B
African Studies, B
African-American/Black Studies, B
Allopathic Medicine, PO
American/United States Studies/Civilization, BD
Ancient Near Eastern and Biblical
    Languages, Literatures, and Linguistics, B
Animal Genetics, B
Anthropology, BMD
Applied Mathematics, BMD
Applied Physics, MD
Applied Science and Technology, O
Arabic Language and Literature, BMD
Archeology, BMD
Architectural Engineering, B
Architecture, MD
Art Education, M
Art History, Criticism and Conservation, BD
Art/Art Studies, General, B
Artificial Intelligence and Robotics, B
Asian Languages, MD
Asian Studies/Civilization, BMD
Astronomy, BMD
Astrophysics, BMD
Atmospheric Sciences and Meteorology, B
Behavioral Sciences, B
Bible/Biblical Studies, B
Biochemistry, BMD
Biological and Biomedical Sciences, MDO
Biological and Physical Sciences, B
Biological Anthropology, MD
Biology Technician/BioTechnology Laboratory
    Technician, B
Biology/Biological Sciences, B
Biomedical Engineering, MD
Biomedical Sciences, B
Biomedical/Medical Engineering, B
Biometry/Biometrics, B
Biophysics, BD
Biostatistics, MD
BioTechnology, M
Business Administration, Management and
    Operations, MDO
Cancer Biology/Oncology, D
Cell Biology and Anatomy, D
Cell/Cellular Biology and Histology, B
Celtic Languages, Literatures, and Linguistics, MD
Central/Middle and Eastern European Studies, B
Chemical Engineering, B
Chemistry, BMD
Chinese Language and Literature, B

Chinese Studies, MD
City/Urban, Community and Regional Planning, B
Civil Engineering, B
Classics and Classical
    Languages, Literatures, and Linguistics, BMD
Cognitive Psychology and Psycholinguistics, B
Cognitive Sciences, BM
Communication and Media Studies, O
Communication Disorders, D
Community Health and Preventive Medicine, M
Comparative Literature, BD
Composition, MD
Computer and Information Sciences, B
Computer Engineering, B
Computer Engineering Technology/Technician, B
Computer Graphics, B
Computer Programming/Programmer, B
Computer Science, BMD
Creative Writing, B
Curriculum and Instruction, M
Dental and Oral Surgery, O
Dentistry, PO
Drama and Dramatics/Theatre Arts, B
East Asian Studies, BM
East European and Russian Studies, M
Ecology, B
Economics, BMD
Education, MD
Educational Leadership and Administration, MD
Educational Media/Instructional Technology, M
Educational Psychology, M
Electrical, Electronics and Communications
    Engineering, B
Engineering, B
Engineering and Applied Sciences, MD
Engineering Physics, B
Engineering Science, B
English, MDO
English Language and Literature, B
Entomology, B
Environmental and Occupational Health, MD
Environmental Biology, B
Environmental Design/Architecture, B
Environmental Engineering
    Technology/Environmental Technology, MD
Environmental Policy and Resource
    Management, MO
Environmental Sciences, MD
Environmental Studies, B
Environmental/Environmental Health Engineering, B
Epidemiology, MD
Ethnic and Cultural Studies, B
Ethnic, Cultural Minority, and Gender Studies, B
Ethnomusicology, MD
European Studies/Civilization, B
Evolutionary Biology, BD
Film/Cinema Studies, B
Fine/Studio Arts, B
Fluid and Thermal Sciences, B
Forestry, M
Foundations and Philosophy of Education, O
French Language and Literature, BMD
Genetics, D
Genomic Sciences, D
Geochemistry, B
Geological/Geophysical Engineering, B
Geology/Earth Science, B
Geophysics and Seismology, B
Geosciences, MD
German Language and Literature, BMD
Health Promotion, MD
Health Services Administration, MD
Hebrew Language and Literature, BMD
Hispanic-American, Puerto Rican, and Mexican-
    American/Chicano Studies, B
History, BD
History and Philosophy of Science and
    Technology, B
History of Science and Technology, MD
Human Development, MD
Human Development and Family Studies, B
Humanities/Humanistic Studies, B
Immunology, D
Infectious Diseases, D
Information Science/Studies, BM
Inorganic Chemistry, MD

Interdisciplinary Studies, B
International and Comparative Education, M
International Development, M
International Economics, B
International Public Health/International Health, MD
International Relations and Affairs, B
Islamic Studies, B
Italian Language and Literature, BMD
Japanese Language and Literature, B
Japanese Studies, MD
Jewish/Judaic Studies, BMD
Landscape Architecture, MD
Latin American Studies, B
Latin Language and Literature, B
Law and Legal Studies, MDPO
Liberal Arts and Sciences Studies and
    Humanities, B
Liberal Studies, M
Linguistics, BMD
Management Information Systems and Services, D
Marine Biology and Biological Oceanography, B
Materials Engineering, B
Materials Sciences, B
Maternal and Child Health, MD
Mathematics, BMD
Mathematics and Computer Science, B
Mathematics Teacher Education, M
Mechanical Engineering, B
Medical Informatics, M
Medical Microbiology and Bacteriology, B
Medical Physics, D
Medieval and Renaissance Studies, BMD
Metallurgical Engineering, B
Microbiology, D
Modern Greek Language and Literature, B
Modern Languages, B
Molecular Biology, BD
Molecular Genetics, D
Molecular Pharmacology, D
Multilingual and Multicultural Education, D
Museology/Museum Studies, M
Music, BMD
Music History, Literature, and Theory, B
Music Theory and Composition, MD
Musicology and Ethnomusicology, MD
Natural Resources and Conservation, B
Near and Middle Eastern Languages, MD
Near and Middle Eastern Studies, BMDO
Neurobiology and Neurophysiology, D
Neuroscience, BD
Nuclear Physics, B
Nutritional Sciences, D
Oral and Dental Sciences, MDO
Organic Chemistry, MD
Organizational Behavior Studies, D
Orthodontics, O
Pathology/Experimental Pathology, D
Periodontics, O
Philosophy, BMD
Physical Chemistry, MD
Physical Sciences, B
Physics, BMD
Physiological Psychology/Psychobiology, B
Physiology, D
Planetary Astronomy and Science, MD
Political Science and Government, BMDO
Polymer Chemistry, B
Population Studies, MD
Portuguese Language and Literature, BMD
Pre-Dentistry Studies, B
Pre-Law Studies, B
Pre-Medicine/Pre-Medical Studies, B
Pre-Veterinary Studies, B
Psychology, BMD
Public Administration, M
Public Health, MDO
Public Policy Analysis, BMDO
Reading Teacher Education, M
Religion/Religious Studies, BMD
Romance Languages, Literatures, and Linguistics, B
Russian Language and Literature, BMD
Russian Studies, B
Scandinavian
    Languages, Literatures, and Linguistics, BMD
Science Teacher Education/General Science
    Teacher Education, M

Slavic Languages, Literatures, and Linguistics, BMD
Social Psychology, MD
Social Sciences, B
Sociology, BMD
South and Southeast Asian Studies, M
South Asian Studies, B
Southeast Asian Studies, B
Spanish Language and Literature, BMD
Statistics, BMD
Structural Biology, D
Systematic Biology/Biological Systematics, D
Systems Engineering, B
Technical Communication, M
Theology and Religious Vocations, MDP
Theoretical Physics, MD
Urban and Regional Planning, M
Urban Design, M
Urban Education and Leadership, D
Urban Planning, MD
Urban Studies/Affairs, B
Virology, D
Women's Studies, B

HEBREW COLLEGE

Early Childhood Education and Teaching, O
Education, BMO
Jewish/Judaic Studies, BMO
Middle School Education, O
Music, BO
Non-Profit/Public/Organizational Management, O
Religious Education, BMO
Religious/Sacred Music, B
Sacred Music, O
Social Work, O
Special Education and Teaching, O

HELLENIC COLLEGE

Business Administration and Management, B
Classics and Classical
    Languages, Literatures, and Linguistics, B
Elementary Education and Teaching, B
Human Development and Family Studies, B
Religion/Religious Studies, B
Theology/Theological Studies, B

HOLYOKE COMMUNITY COLLEGE

Accounting, A
Administrative Assistant and Secretarial Science, A
American/United States Studies/Civilization, A
Biology/Biological Sciences, A
Business Administration and Management, A
Business Teacher Education, A
Chemistry, A
Cinematography and Film/Video Production, A
Clinical Laboratory Science/Medical
    Technology/Technologist, A
Commercial and Advertising Art, A
Computer Typography and Composition Equipment
    Operator, A
Consumer Merchandising/Retailing Management, A
Criminal Justice/Police Science, A
Drama and Dramatics/Theatre Arts, A
Elementary Education and Teaching, A
Engineering Science, A
Environmental Studies, A
Family and Consumer Sciences/Human Sciences, A
Fine/Studio Arts, A
Foods, Nutrition, and Wellness Studies, A
Health Information/Medical Records
    Administration/Administrator, A
Hospitality Administration/Management, A
Hotel/Motel Administration/Management, A
Human Services, A
Information Science/Studies, A
Kindergarten/PreSchool Education and Teaching, A
Legal Administrative Assistant/Secretary, A
Liberal Arts and Sciences Studies and
    Humanities, A
Mass Communication/Media Studies, A
Music, A
Nursing - Registered Nurse Training, A
Photography, A
Physics, A
Pre-Engineering, A
Radiologic Technology/Science - Radiographer, A
Sport and Fitness Administration/Management, A

Tourism and Travel Services Management, A
Veterinary/Animal Health Technology/Technician and
    Veterinary Assistant, A
Visual and Performing Arts, A

ITT TECHNICAL INSTITUTE (NORWOOD)

CAD/CADD Drafting and/or Design
    Technology/Technician, A
Computer Programming/Programmer, A
Electrical, Electronic and Communications
    Engineering Technology/Technician, A
System, Networking, and LAN/WAN
    Management/Manager, A
Web Page, Digital/Multimedia and Information
    Resources Design, A
Web/Multimedia Management and Webmaster, A

ITT TECHNICAL INSTITUTE (WOBURN)

CAD/CADD Drafting and/or Design
    Technology/Technician, A
Computer Programming/Programmer, A
Electrical, Electronic and Communications
    Engineering Technology/Technician, A
System, Networking, and LAN/WAN
    Management/Manager, A
Web Page, Digital/Multimedia and Information
    Resources Design, A
Web/Multimedia Management and Webmaster, A

LABOURÉ COLLEGE

Clinical Laboratory Science/Medical
    Technology/Technologist, A
Dietetics/Dieticians, A
Health Information/Medical Records
    Administration/Administrator, A
Industrial Radiologic Technology/Technician, A
Nursing - Registered Nurse Training, A

LASELL COLLEGE

Accounting, B
Business Administration and Management, B
Business Administration, Management and
    Operations, M
Child Development, B
Commercial and Advertising Art, B
Communication Studies/Speech Communication
    and Rhetoric, B
Consumer Merchandising/Retailing Management, B
Criminal Justice/Safety Studies, B
Education, B
Elementary Education and Teaching, B
Fashion Merchandising, B
Fashion/Apparel Design, B
Finance, B
Graphic Design, B
History, B
Hotel/Motel Administration/Management, B
Human Services, B
Information Science/Studies, B
Interdisciplinary Studies, B
International Business/Trade/Commerce, B
Kindergarten/PreSchool Education and Teaching, B
Kinesiology and Exercise Science, B
Law and Legal Studies, B
Liberal Arts and Sciences Studies and
    Humanities, B
Management, M
Marketing, M
Marketing/Marketing Management, B
Pre-Law Studies, B
Psychology, B
Sociology, B

LESLEY UNIVERSITY

American/United States Studies/Civilization, B
Art Education, MO
Art Therapy/Therapist, BMD
Art/Art Studies, General, B
Business Administration and Management, B
Child Development, B
Clinical Psychology, M
Communications Technologies/Technicians and
    Support Services, B
Computer Education, MO

Conflict Resolution and Mediation/Peace Studies, M
Counseling Psychology, BMO
Curriculum and Instruction, MO
Early Childhood Education and Teaching, M
Ecology, M
Education, BMDO
Educational Administration and Supervision, MO
Elementary Education and Teaching, BM
English Language and Literature, B
Environmental Education, M
Environmental Studies, B
Fine Arts and Art Studies, M
Health Education, M
Human Development and Family Studies, B
Human Resources Management and Services, M
Human Services, BM
Humanities/Humanistic Studies, B
Interdisciplinary Studies, AM
International Affairs, MO
International and Comparative Education, M
Junior High/Intermediate/Middle School Education
    and Teaching, B
Kindergarten/PreSchool Education and Teaching, B
Liberal Arts and Sciences Studies and
    Humanities, B
Media Studies, M
Middle School Education, M
Multilingual and Multicultural Education, M
Natural Sciences, B
Project Management, M
Psychology, MDO
Reading Teacher Education, MO
School Psychology, M
Science Teacher Education/General Science
    Teacher Education, M
Secondary Education and Teaching, B
Social Sciences, B
Special Education and Teaching, BMO
Therapies--Dance, Drama, and Music, MD

MARIAN COURT COLLEGE

Accounting, A
Administrative Assistant and Secretarial Science, A
Business Administration and Management, A
Clinical Laboratory Science/Medical
    Technology/Technologist, A
Criminal Justice/Safety Studies, A
Data Processing and Data Processing
    Technology/Technician, A
Hospitality Administration/Management, A
Human Resources Management/Personnel
    Administration, A
Legal Administrative Assistant/Secretary, A
Liberal Arts and Sciences Studies and
    Humanities, A
Medical Administrative Assistant/Secretary, A
Tourism and Travel Services Management, A

MASSACHUSETTS BAY COMMUNITY COLLEGE

Accounting, A
Automotive Engineering Technology/Technician, A
Biological and Physical Sciences, A
Biology Technician/BioTechnology Laboratory
    Technician, A
Business Administration and Management, A
Business/Commerce, A
Chemical Technology/Technician, A
Child Care and Support Services Management, A
Communication Studies/Speech Communication
    and Rhetoric, A
Computer and Information Sciences, A
Computer Engineering Technology/Technician, A
Computer Science, A
Criminal Justice/Law Enforcement Administration, A
Drafting and Design Technology/Technician, A
Engineering Technology, A
Environmental Engineering
    Technology/Environmental Technology, A
Forensic Science and Technology, A
General Studies, A
Hospitality Administration/Management, A
Human Services, A
Information Science/Studies, A
International Relations and Affairs, A
Legal Assistant/Paralegal, A

Liberal Arts and Sciences Studies and
    Humanities, A
Mechanical Engineering/Mechanical
    Technology/Technician, A
Medical Radiologic Technology/Science - Radiation
    Therapist, A
Nursing - Registered Nurse Training, A
Physical Therapist Assistant, A
Respiratory Care Therapy/Therapist, A
Social Sciences, A

MASSACHUSETTS COLLEGE OF ART

Animation, Interactive Technology, Video Graphics
    and Special Effects, B
Applied Arts and Design, M
Architecture, B
Art Education, M
Art History, Criticism and Conservation, B
Art Teacher Education, B
Ceramic Arts and Ceramics, BM
Cinematography and Film/Video Production, B
Commercial and Advertising Art, B
Design and Applied Arts, M
Fashion/Apparel Design, B
Fiber, Textile and Weaving Arts, B
Film, Television, and Video Production, M
Fine Arts and Art Studies, M
Fine/Studio Arts, B
Industrial Design, B
Intermedia/Multimedia, B
Jewelry/Metalsmithing, M
Metal and Jewelry Arts, B
Painting, BM
Photography, BM
Printmaking, BM
Sculpture, BM
Textile Design, M
Theater, M

MASSACHUSETTS COLLEGE OF LIBERAL ARTS

Accounting, B
Adult and Continuing Education and Teaching, B
Anthropology, B
Art/Art Studies, General, B
Athletic Training and Sports Medicine, B
Biological and Physical Sciences, B
Biology/Biological Sciences, B
Broadcast Journalism, B
Business Administration and Management, B
Chemistry, B
Clinical Laboratory Science/Medical
    Technology/Technologist, B
Clinical/Medical Laboratory Technician, B
Comparative Literature, B
Computer and Information Sciences, B
Computer Science, B
Creative Writing, B
Curriculum and Instruction, M
Drama and Dramatics/Theatre Arts, B
Economics, B
Education, BM
Educational Administration and Supervision, M
Elementary Education and Teaching, B
English Language and Literature, B
Environmental Studies, B
Finance, B
History, B
Interdisciplinary Studies, B
Journalism, B
Junior High/Intermediate/Middle School Education
    and Teaching, B
Kindergarten/PreSchool Education and Teaching, B
Marketing/Marketing Management, B
Mass Communication/Media Studies, B
Mathematics, B
Multi-/Interdisciplinary Studies, B
Music, B
Philosophy, B
Physics, B
Pre-Law Studies, B
Psychology, B
Reading Teacher Education, M
Secondary Education and Teaching, B
Social Work, B
Sociology, B

Special Education and Teaching, M
Visual and Performing Arts, B

MASSACHUSETTS COLLEGE OF PHARMACY AND HEALTH SCIENCES

Chemistry, BMD
Dental Hygiene/Hygienist, B
Health Professions and Related Clinical Sciences, B
Health Services Administration, M
Health/Medical Psychology, B
Medical Radiologic Technology/Science - Radiation
    Therapist, B
Nuclear Medical Technology/Technologist, B
Pharmaceutical Administration, M
Pharmaceutical Sciences, MD
Pharmacology, MD
Pharmacy, B
Pharmacy, Pharmaceutical Sciences, and Administration, B
Pre-Medicine/Pre-Medical Studies, B
Radiologic Technology/Science - Radiographer, B

MASSACHUSETTS INSTITUTE OF TECHNOLOGY

Aerospace, Aeronautical and Astronautical
    Engineering, BMDO
Anthropology, B
Architecture, BMD
Atmospheric Sciences and Meteorology, MD
Biochemistry, D
Bioengineering, MD
Biological and Biomedical Sciences, MDPO
Biology/Biological Sciences, B
Biomedical Engineering, MD
Biophysics, D
Business/Commerce, B
Cell Biology and Anatomy, D
Ceramic Arts and Ceramics, D
Chemical Engineering, BMDO
Chemistry, BD
City/Urban, Community and Regional Planning, B
Civil Engineering, BMDO
Cognitive Psychology and Psycholinguistics, B
Cognitive Sciences, D
Communication Disorders, D
Computational Biology, D
Computational Sciences, M
Computer Engineering, D
Computer Science, BMDO
Construction Engineering and Management, D
Creative Writing, B
Developmental Biology and Embryology, D
Economics, BMD
Electrical Engineering, MDO
Electrical, Electronics and Communications
    Engineering, B
Electronic Materials, D
Engineering and Applied Sciences, MDO
Engineering Management, M
English Language and Literature, B
Environmental Biology, D
Environmental Engineering
    Technology/Environmental Technology, MDO
Environmental Sciences, D
Environmental/Environmental Health Engineering, B
Foreign Languages and Literatures, B
Genetics, D
Geochemistry, D
Geology/Earth Science, BD
Geophysics and Seismology, MD
Geosciences, MD
Geotechnical Engineering, D
History, B
History of Science and Technology, D
Humanities/Humanistic Studies, M
Hydraulics and Fluid Power Technology, D
Hydrology and Water Resources Science, D
Immunology, D
Information Science/Studies, D
Inorganic Chemistry, D
Liberal Arts and Sciences Studies and
    Humanities, B
Linguistics, BMD
Logistics and Materials Management, M
Management, MDO
Marine Geology, M
Mass Communication/Media Studies, B

Materials Engineering, BMDO
Materials Sciences, MDO
Mathematics, BD
Mathematics and Computer Science, B
Mechanical Engineering, BMDO
Mechanics, D
Media Studies, MD
Medical Informatics, M
Medical Physics, D
Metallurgical Engineering, O
Microbiology, D
Molecular Biology, D
Molecular Pathology, D
Molecular Pharmacology, D
Molecular Toxicology, D
Music, B
Neurobiology and Neurophysiology, D
Neuroscience, D
Nuclear Engineering, BMDO
Ocean Engineering, BMDO
Oceanography, Chemical and Physical, MD
Operations Research, MD
Organic Chemistry, D
Philosophy, BD
Physical Chemistry, D
Physics, BMD
Planetary Astronomy and Science, D
Plasma and High-Temperature Physics, D
Political Science and Government, BMD
Polymer/Plastics Engineering, D
Real Estate, M
Science, Technology and Society, B
Social Sciences, D
Structural Engineering, D
Systematic Biology/Biological Systematics, D
Systems Engineering, MDO
Technical and Business Writing, M
Technology and Public Policy, MDO
Toxicology, MD
Transportation and Highway Engineering, D
Urban and Regional Planning, MD
Urban Studies/Affairs, MD
Writing, M

MASSACHUSETTS MARITIME ACADEMY

Engineering, B
Engineering Technology, B
Environmental Studies, B
Environmental/Environmental Health Engineering, B
International Business/Trade/Commerce, B
Marine Science/Merchant Marine Officer, B
Maritime Science, B
Naval Architecture and Marine Engineering, B

MASSASOIT COMMUNITY COLLEGE

Accounting, A
Administrative Assistant and Secretarial Science, A
Architectural Engineering Technology/Technician, A
Business Administration and Management, A
Business Administration, Management and Operations, A
Child Care and Support Services Management, A
Child Care Provider/Assistant, A
Computer and Information Sciences, A
Computer and Information Sciences and Support Services, A
Computer Programming/Programmer, A
Criminal Justice/Police Science, A
Culinary Arts/Chef Training, A
Dental Assisting/Assistant, A
Diesel Mechanics Technology/Technician, A
Drama and Dramatics/Theatre Arts, A
Electrical and Electronic Engineering Technologies/Technicians, A
Electrical, Electronic and Communications Engineering Technology/Technician, A
Engineering Technologies/Technicians, A
Fine/Studio Arts, A
Fire Science/Firefighting, A
Graphic Design, A
Heating, Air Conditioning and Refrigeration Technology/Technician, A
Hotel/Motel Administration/Management, A
Human Services, A

Liberal Arts and Sciences Studies and Humanities, A
Management Information Systems and Services, A
Marketing/Marketing Management, A
Medical/Clinical Assistant, A
Nursing - Registered Nurse Training, A
Operations Management and Supervision, A
Radiologic Technology/Science - Radiographer, A
Respiratory Care Therapy/Therapist, A
Respiratory Therapy Technician/Assistant, A
Restaurant/Food Services Management, A
Tourism and Travel Services Management, A
Vehicle Maintenance and Repair Technologies, A

MERRIMACK COLLEGE

Biochemistry, B
Biology/Biological Sciences, B
Business Administration and Management, AB
Business/Managerial Economics, B
Chemistry, B
Civil Engineering, B
Communication Studies/Speech Communication and Rhetoric, B
Computer Engineering, B
Computer Science, AB
Economics, B
Education, M
Electrical, Electronic and Communications Engineering Technology/Technician, A
Electrical, Electronics and Communications Engineering, B
Elementary Education and Teaching, B
Engineering Physics, B
Engineering Science, A
English Language and Literature, B
Environmental Studies, B
Finance, B
Fine/Studio Arts, B
French Language and Literature, B
History, B
Human Services, AB
Interdisciplinary Studies, B
International Business/Trade/Commerce, B
Junior High/Intermediate/Middle School Education and Teaching, B
Legal Assistant/Paralegal, A
Liberal Arts and Sciences Studies and Humanities, A
Marketing/Marketing Management, B
Mathematics, B
Philosophy, B
Physical Therapy/Therapist, B
Political Science and Government, B
Pre-Dentistry Studies, B
Pre-Law Studies, B
Pre-Medicine/Pre-Medical Studies, B
Psychology, B
Public Health (MPH, DPH), B
Religion/Religious Studies, B
Secondary Education and Teaching, B
Sociology, B
Spanish Language and Literature, B

MIDDLESEX COMMUNITY COLLEGE

Accounting, A
Art/Art Studies, General, A
Automobile/Automotive Mechanics Technology/Technician, A
Biomedical Technology/Technician, A
Business Administration and Management, A
Business/Corporate Communications, A
Commercial and Advertising Art, A
Computer Engineering Technology/Technician, A
Computer Science, A
Computer Software Technology/Technician, A
Consumer Merchandising/Retailing Management, A
Criminal Justice/Law Enforcement Administration, A
Culinary Arts/Chef Training, A
Data Modeling/Warehousing and Database Administration, A
Dental Assisting/Assistant, A
Dental Hygiene/Hygienist, A
Dental Laboratory Technology/Technician, A
Diagnostic Medical Sonography/Sonographer and Ultrasound Technician, A
Drafting and Design Technology/Technician, A

Drama and Dramatics/Theatre Arts, A
Electrical, Electronic and Communications Engineering Technology/Technician, A
Elementary Education and Teaching, A
Fashion Merchandising, A
Fire Science/Firefighting, A
General Studies, A
Hospitality and Recreation Marketing Operations, A
Hotel/Motel Administration/Management, A
Human Services, A
Kindergarten/PreSchool Education and Teaching, A
Legal Assistant/Paralegal, A
Liberal Arts and Sciences Studies and Humanities, A
Marketing/Marketing Management, A
Mass Communication/Media Studies, A
Medical/Clinical Assistant, A
Nursing - Registered Nurse Training, A
Office Management and Supervision, A
Pre-Engineering, A
Radiologic Technology/Science - Radiographer, A
Telecommunications Technology/Technician, A

MONTSERRAT COLLEGE OF ART

Art Teacher Education, B
Drawing, B
Fine Arts and Art Studies, B
Fine/Studio Arts, B
Graphic Design, B
Illustration, B
Painting, B
Photography, B
Printmaking, B
Sculpture, B

MOUNT HOLYOKE COLLEGE

African-American/Black Studies, B
American/United States Studies/Civilization, B
Ancient Studies/Civilization, B
Anthropology, B
Architectural History and Criticism, B
Art History, Criticism and Conservation, B
Asian Studies/Civilization, B
Astronomy, B
Biochemistry, B
Biology/Biological Sciences, B
Chemistry, B
Classics and Classical Languages, Literatures, and Linguistics, B
Computer Science, B
Dance, B
Drama and Dramatics/Theatre Arts, B
Economics, B
Education, B
English Language and Literature, B
Environmental Studies, B
European Studies/Civilization, B
Film/Cinema Studies, B
Fine/Studio Arts, B
French Language and Literature, B
Geography, B
Geology/Earth Science, B
German Language and Literature, B
History, B
Interdisciplinary Studies, B
International Relations and Affairs, B
Italian Language and Literature, B
Jewish/Judaic Studies, B
Latin American Studies, B
Mathematics, B
Medieval and Renaissance Studies, B
Modern Greek Language and Literature, B
Music, B
Philosophy, B
Physics, B
Political Science and Government, B
Psychology, B
Religion/Religious Studies, B
Romance Languages, Literatures, and Linguistics, B
Russian Studies, B
Sociology, B
Spanish Language and Literature, B
Statistics, B

Women's Studies, B

MOUNT IDA COLLEGE

American/United States Studies/Civilization, B
Animal Sciences, B
Business Administration and Management, AB
Child Development, B
Commercial and Advertising Art, AB
Consumer Merchandising/Retailing
  Management, AB
Criminal Justice/Law Enforcement
  Administration, AB
Dental Hygiene/Hygienist, A
Developmental and Child Psychology, B
Equestrian/Equine Studies, B
Fashion Merchandising, AB
Fashion/Apparel Design, AB
Funeral Service and Mortuary Science, AB
Horse Husbandry/Equine Science and
  Management, B
Hotel/Motel Administration/Management, AB
Human Services, B
Interior Design, B
Kindergarten/PreSchool Education and
  Teaching, AB
Liberal Arts and Sciences Studies and
  Humanities, B
Marketing/Marketing Management, B
Psychology, B
Social Work, B
Teacher Assistant/Aide, A
Veterinary/Animal Health Technology/Technician and
  Veterinary Assistant, AB

MOUNT WACHUSETT COMMUNITY COLLEGE

Accounting, A
Art/Art Studies, General, A
Automobile/Automotive Mechanics
  Technology/Technician, A
Business Administration and Management, A
Child Development, A
Communication Disorders, A
Computer Graphics, A
Computer Technology/Computer Systems
  Technology, A
Criminal Justice/Law Enforcement Administration, A
Dental Hygiene/Hygienist, A
Electrical, Electronic and Communications
  Engineering Technology/Technician, A
Environmental Studies, A
Fine/Studio Arts, A
Fire Science/Firefighting, A
General Studies, A
Human Services, A
Industrial Engineering, A
Industrial Technology/Technician, A
Information Science/Studies, A
Kinesiology and Exercise Science, A
Legal Assistant/Paralegal, A
Liberal Arts and Sciences Studies and
  Humanities, A
Licensed Practical/Vocational Nurse Training, A
Management Information Systems and Services, A
Manufacturing Technology/Technician, A
Massage Therapy/Therapeutic Massage, A
Medical/Clinical Assistant, A
Nursing - Registered Nurse Training, A
Physical Therapy/Therapist, A
Plastics Engineering Technology/Technician, A
Radio and Television Broadcasting
  Technology/Technician, A
Sales, Distribution and Marketing Operations, A
Sign Language Interpretation and Translation, A
Telecommunications Technology/Technician, A
Web Page, Digital/Multimedia and Information
  Resources Design, A

NEW ENGLAND COLLEGE OF FINANCE

Accounting, A
Business Administration and Management, A
Computer Science, A
Finance, A
Management Information Systems and Services, A

Marketing/Marketing Management, A

NEW ENGLAND CONSERVATORY OF MUSIC

Jazz/Jazz Studies, B
Music, MDO
Music History, Literature, and Theory, B
Music Performance, B
Music Theory and Composition, B
Piano and Organ, B
Violin, Viola, Guitar and Other Stringed
  Instruments, B
Voice and Opera, B
Wind and Percussion Instruments, B

THE NEW ENGLAND INSTITUTE OF ART

Animation, Interactive Technology, Video Graphics
  and Special Effects, B
Commercial and Advertising Art, B
Communication Studies/Speech Communication
  and Rhetoric, A
Computer Graphics, B
Design and Applied Arts, B
Digital Communication and Media/Multimedia, B
Graphic Design, B
Interior Design, B
Intermedia/Multimedia, B
Music Management and Merchandising, A
Radio and Television Broadcasting
  Technology/Technician, A
Web Page, Digital/Multimedia and Information
  Resources Design, B
Web/Multimedia Management and Webmaster, B

NEWBURY COLLEGE

Accounting, AB
Business Administration and Management, AB
Commercial and Advertising Art, A
Computer Programming/Programmer, AB
Computer Science, AB
Consumer Merchandising/Retailing Management, A
Criminal Justice/Law Enforcement
  Administration, AB
Culinary Arts and Related Services, B
Culinary Arts/Chef Training, A
Fashion Merchandising, A
Finance, AB
Health/Health Care Administration/Management, B
Hotel/Motel Administration/Management, AB
Human Resources Management/Personnel
  Administration, B
Humanities/Humanistic Studies, A
Interior Design, AB
International Business/Trade/Commerce, B
Law and Legal Studies, B
Legal Assistant/Paralegal, A
Marketing Research, B
Marketing/Marketing Management, AB
Mass Communication/Media Studies, AB
Pre-Law Studies, B
Psychology, AB
Radio and Television, A
Social Sciences, A
Sociology, A
Special Products Marketing Operations, A
Tourism and Travel Services Management, A

NICHOLS COLLEGE

Accounting, BM
Business Administration and Management, AB
Business Administration, Management and
  Operations, M
Business/Commerce, B
Economics, B
English Language and Literature, B
Finance, B
Finance and Banking, M
History, B
Human Resources Management/Personnel
  Administration, B
International Business/Trade/Commerce, M
Management, M
Management Information Systems and Services, B
Marketing, M

Marketing/Marketing Management, B
Mathematics, B
Psychology, B
Secondary Education and Teaching, B
Sport and Fitness Administration/Management, B

NORTH SHORE COMMUNITY COLLEGE

Accounting, A
Administrative Assistant and Secretarial Science, A
Airline/Commercial/Professional Pilot and Flight
  Crew, A
Applied Horticulture/Horticultural Operations, A
Biology Technician/BioTechnology Laboratory
  Technician, A
Business Administration and Management, A
Child Development, A
Computer and Information Sciences, A
Computer Engineering Technology/Technician, A
Computer Graphics, A
Computer Programming, Specific Applications, A
Computer Programming/Programmer, A
Computer Science, A
Criminal Justice/Law Enforcement Administration, A
Culinary Arts/Chef Training, A
Data Entry/Microcomputer Applications, A
Engineering Science, A
Fire Science/Firefighting, A
Foods, Nutrition, and Wellness Studies, A
Forestry, A
Gerontology, A
Hospitality Administration/Management, A
Information Science/Studies, A
Interdisciplinary Studies, A
Kindergarten/PreSchool Education and Teaching, A
Landscaping and Groundskeeping, A
Legal Administrative Assistant/Secretary, A
Legal Assistant/Paralegal, A
Liberal Arts and Sciences Studies and
  Humanities, A
Marketing/Marketing Management, A
Medical Administrative Assistant/Secretary, A
Medical Radiologic Technology/Science - Radiation
  Therapist, A
Mental Health/Rehabilitation, A
Nursing - Registered Nurse Training, A
Occupational Therapy/Therapist, A
Physical Therapist Assistant, A
Pre-Engineering, A
Public Health (MPH, DPH), A
Respiratory Care Therapy/Therapist, A
Substance Abuse/Addiction Counseling, A
Tourism and Travel Services Management, A
Veterinary/Animal Health Technology/Technician and
  Veterinary Assistant, A

NORTHEASTERN UNIVERSITY

Accounting, BMO
Aeronautical/Aerospace Engineering
  Technology/Technician, B
African-American/Black Studies, B
Allied Health and Medical Assisting Services, MDPO
Analytical Chemistry, D
Anthropology, B
Applied Economics, MD
Architecture, BM
Art/Art Studies, General, B
Athletic Training and Sports Medicine, B
Audiology/Audiologist and Speech-Language
  Pathology/Pathologist, B
Behavioral Sciences, B
Biochemistry, BMD
Bioinformatics, M
Biological and Biomedical Sciences, MD
Biology Technician/BioTechnology Laboratory
  Technician, B
Biology/Biological Sciences, B
BioTechnology, M
Business Administration and Management, B
Business Administration, Management and
  Operations, MO
Business/Commerce, B
Cardiovascular Sciences, M
Chemical Engineering, BMD
Chemistry, BMD
Civil Engineering, BMD
Clinical/Medical Laboratory Technician, B

Commercial and Advertising Art, B
Communication Disorders, MD
Communication Studies/Speech Communication
  and Rhetoric, B
Community Health Nursing, MO
Computer Engineering, BMD
Computer Engineering Technology/Technician, B
Computer Science, BMD
Corrections, B
Counseling Psychology, MDO
Counselor Education/School Counseling and
  Guidance Services, M
Criminal Justice/Police Science, B
Criminal Justice/Safety Studies, B
Criminology, M
Dental Hygiene/Hygienist, B
Drama and Dramatics/Theatre Arts, B
Economics, BMD
Education, BM
Educational Psychology, M
Electrical Engineering, MD
Electrical, Electronics and Communications
  Engineering, B
Elementary Education and Teaching, BM
Engineering, B
Engineering and Applied Sciences, MD
Engineering Management, M
English, MDO
English Language and Literature, B
Entrepreneurship/Entrepreneurial Studies, B
Environmental Engineering
  Technology/Environmental Technology, MD
Environmental Studies, B
Exercise and Sports Science, M
Experimental Psychology, MD
Finance, B
Finance and Banking, M
French Language and Literature, B
Geology/Earth Science, B
German Language and Literature, B
Health Services Administration, M
Health/Health Care Administration/Management, B
History, BMD
Human Resources Management/Personnel
  Administration, B
Human Services, B
Industrial Engineering, B
Industrial/Management Engineering, MD
Information Science/Studies, BM
Inorganic Chemistry, D
International Affairs, M
International Business/Trade/Commerce, B
International Relations and Affairs, B
Italian Language and Literature, B
Journalism, BM
Kindergarten/PreSchool Education and Teaching, B
Law and Legal Studies, PO
Legal and Justice Studies, MDO
Liberal Arts and Sciences Studies and
  Humanities, B
Linguistics, B
Logistics and Materials Management, B
Management Information Systems and Services, B
Management Science, B
Manufacturing Engineering, MD
Marine Biology and Biological Oceanography, B
Marketing/Marketing Management, B
Mass Communication/Media Studies, B
Mathematics, BMD
Mechanical Engineering, BMD
Mechanical Engineering/Mechanical
  Technology/Technician, B
Medical Technology, M
Modern Languages, B
Music, B
Music History, Literature, and Theory, B
Music Management and Merchandising, B
Nurse Anesthetist, M
Nursing, BMO
Nursing - Advanced Practice, MO
Nursing Administration, MO
Operations Research, M
Organic Chemistry, D
Pediatric Nurse/Nursing, MO
Pharmaceutical Sciences, P
Pharmacology, M

Pharmacy, B
Philosophy, B
Physical Chemistry, D
Physical Therapy/Therapist, B
Physician Assistant, M
Physics, BMD
Political Science and Government, BMD
Psychiatric/Mental Health Nurse/Nursing, MO
Psychology, BMDO
Public Administration, BM
Public Health (MPH, DPH), B
Public History, M
Public Policy Analysis, MDO
Radio and Television, B
Rehabilitation Counseling, M
Rehabilitation Therapy, B
Russian Language and Literature, B
School Psychology, MDO
Secondary Education and Teaching, M
Sign Language Interpretation and Translation, B
Sociology, BMD
Spanish Language and Literature, B
Special Education and Teaching, M
Speech and Interpersonal Communication, D
Student Personnel Services, M
Systems Engineering, M
Taxation, MO
Telecommunications Management, M
Therapeutic Recreation/Recreational Therapy, B
Toxicology, M
Women's Studies, B
Writing, M

NORTHERN ESSEX COMMUNITY COLLEGE

Accounting, A
Administrative Assistant and Secretarial Science, A
Biological and Physical Sciences, A
Business Administration and Management, A
Business Teacher Education, A
Civil Engineering Technology/Technician, A
Commercial and Advertising Art, A
Computer and Information Sciences, A
Computer Engineering Technology/Technician, A
Computer Graphics, A
Computer Programming, A
Computer Programming, Specific Applications, A
Computer Programming/Programmer, A
Computer Science, A
Computer Systems Networking and
  Telecommunications, A
Computer Typography and Composition Equipment
  Operator, A
Criminal Justice/Law Enforcement Administration, A
Dance, A
Data Processing and Data Processing
  Technology/Technician, A
Dental Assisting/Assistant, A
Drama and Dramatics/Theatre Arts, A
Education, A
Electrical, Electronic and Communications
  Engineering Technology/Technician, A
Elementary Education and Teaching, A
Engineering Science, A
Finance, A
General Studies, A
Health Information/Medical Records
  Administration/Administrator, A
History, A
Hotel/Motel Administration/Management, A
Human Services, A
Industrial Radiologic Technology/Technician, A
International Relations and Affairs, A
Journalism, A
Kindergarten/PreSchool Education and Teaching, A
Legal Assistant/Paralegal, A
Liberal Arts and Sciences Studies and
  Humanities, A
Machine Tool Technology/Machinist, A
Marketing/Marketing Management, A
Materials Sciences, A
Medical Administrative Assistant/Secretary, A
Medical Transcription/Transcriptionist, A
Mental Health/Rehabilitation, A
Music, A
Nursing - Registered Nurse Training, A

Parks, Recreation, Leisure and Fitness Studies, A
Physical Education Teaching and Coaching, A
Political Science and Government, A
Radiologic Technology/Science - Radiographer, A
Real Estate, A
Respiratory Care Therapy/Therapist, A
Respiratory Therapy Technician/Assistant, A
Sign Language Interpretation and Translation, A
Telecommunications Technology/Technician, A
Tourism and Travel Services Management, A
Web Page, Digital/Multimedia and Information
  Resources Design, A
Web/Multimedia Management and Webmaster, A
Women's Studies, A
Word Processing, A

PINE MANOR COLLEGE

American/United States Studies/Civilization, B
Art History, Criticism and Conservation, B
Biology/Biological Sciences, AB
Business Administration and Management, AB
Communication Studies/Speech Communication
  and Rhetoric, B
Creative Writing, B
Elementary Education and Teaching, B
English Language and Literature, AB
Fine/Studio Arts, AB
History, AB
Kindergarten/PreSchool Education and Teaching, B
Liberal Arts and Sciences Studies and
  Humanities, A
Mass Communication/Media Studies, B
Political Science and Government, B
Psychology, B

QUINCY COLLEGE

Accounting, A
American Government and Politics (United States)
  , A
Behavioral Sciences, A
Business Administration and Management, A
Criminal Justice/Law Enforcement Administration, A
Criminal Justice/Police Science, A
Drama and Dramatics/Theatre Arts, A
Early Childhood Education and Teaching, A
Elementary Education and Teaching, A
Emergency Medical Technology/Technician (EMT
  Paramedic), A
English Language and Literature, A
Fire Science/Firefighting, A
General Studies, A
History, A
Human Services, A
Humanities/Humanistic Studies, A
Law and Legal Studies, A
Liberal Arts and Sciences Studies and
  Humanities, A
Management Information Systems and Services, A
Mathematics, A
Music, A
Natural Sciences, A
Nursing - Registered Nurse Training, A
Political Science and Government, A
Psychology, A
Social Sciences, A
Social Work, A
Sociology, A
Visual and Performing Arts, A

QUINSIGAMOND COMMUNITY COLLEGE

Accounting, A
Administrative Assistant and Secretarial Science, A
Art/Art Studies, General, A
Automobile/Automotive Mechanics
  Technology/Technician, A
Business Administration and Management, A
Commercial and Advertising Art, A
Computer Programming/Programmer, A
Computer Technology/Computer Systems
  Technology, A
Consumer Merchandising/Retailing Management, A
Criminal Justice/Law Enforcement Administration, A
Data Processing and Data Processing
  Technology/Technician, A
Dental Hygiene/Hygienist, A

Electrical, Electronic and Communications
  Engineering Technology/Technician, A
Emergency Medical Technology/Technician (EMT
  Paramedic), A
Fire Science/Firefighting, A
General Studies, A
Hotel/Motel Administration/Management, A
Human Services, A
Information Science/Studies, A
Kindergarten/PreSchool Education and Teaching, A
Liberal Arts and Sciences Studies and
  Humanities, A
Medical Radiologic Technology/Science - Radiation
  Therapist, A
Nursing - Registered Nurse Training, A
Occupational Therapist Assistant, A
Occupational Therapy/Therapist, A
Respiratory Care Therapy/Therapist, A
Tourism and Travel Services Management, A

REGIS COLLEGE

Biochemistry, B
Biology/Biological Sciences, B
Business Administration, Management and
  Operations, M
Business/Commerce, B
Communication Studies/Speech Communication
  and Rhetoric, B
Computer and Information Sciences, B
Corporate and Organizational Communication, M
Drama and Dramatics/Theatre Arts, B
Education, M
English Language and Literature, B
Graphic Design, B
History, B
International Relations and Affairs, B
Law and Legal Studies, B
Liberal Arts and Sciences Studies and
  Humanities, B
Mathematics, B
Mathematics Teacher Education, B
Multi-/Interdisciplinary Studies, B
Museology/Museum Studies, B
Nursing, MO
Nursing - Registered Nurse Training, AB
Organizational Management, M
Political Science and Government, B
Psychology, B
Public Health, M
Public Relations, Advertising, and Applied
  Communication, B
Social Work, B
Sociology, B
Spanish Language and Literature, B

ROXBURY COMMUNITY COLLEGE

Accounting, A
Administrative Assistant and Secretarial Science, A
Biology/Biological Sciences, A
Business Administration and Management, A
Criminal Justice/Law Enforcement Administration, A
Data Entry/Microcomputer Applications, A
English Language and Literature, A
Environmental Engineering
  Technology/Environmental Technology, A
General Studies, A
Humanities/Humanistic Studies, A
Information Science/Studies, A
International Business/Trade/Commerce, A
Kindergarten/PreSchool Education and Teaching, A
Legal Administrative Assistant/Secretary, A
Mathematics, A
Medical Administrative Assistant/Secretary, A
Music, A
Nursing - Registered Nurse Training, A
Physical Sciences, A
Pre-Engineering, A
Social Sciences, A
Visual and Performing Arts, A

SALEM STATE COLLEGE

Accounting, B
Administrative Assistant and Secretarial Science, B
Applied Mathematics, B
Art Teacher Education, B
Art/Art Studies, General, B

Aviation/Airway Management and Operations, B
Biology/Biological Sciences, B
Business Administration and Management, B
Business Administration, Management and
  Operations, MO
Business Teacher Education, B
Business/Managerial Economics, B
Cartography, B
Central/Middle and Eastern European Studies, B
Chemistry, B
City/Urban, Community and Regional Planning, B
Clinical Laboratory Science/Medical
  Technology/Technologist, B
Commercial and Advertising Art, B
Comparative Literature, B
Computer Science, B
Consumer Merchandising/Retailing Management, B
Counselor Education/School Counseling and
  Guidance Services, M
Criminal Justice/Law Enforcement Administration, B
Drama and Dramatics/Theatre Arts, B
Drawing, B
Early Childhood Education and Teaching, M
Economics, B
Education, BMO
Educational Administration and Supervision, M
Educational Media/Instructional Technology, M
Elementary Education and Teaching, BM
English, M
English as a Second Language, M
English Education, M
English Language and Literature, B
European Studies/Civilization, B
Finance, B
Geography, BM
Geology/Earth Science, B
Health Teacher Education, B
History, BM
Journalism, B
Kindergarten/PreSchool Education and Teaching, B
Kinesiology and Exercise Science, B
Liberal Arts and Sciences Studies and
  Humanities, B
Management Information Systems and Services, B
Marine Biology and Biological Oceanography, B
Marine Science/Merchant Marine Officer, B
Marketing/Marketing Management, B
Mass Communication/Media Studies, B
Mathematics, BM
Mathematics Teacher Education, M
Middle School Education, M
Multilingual and Multicultural Education, M
Nuclear Medical Technology/Technologist, B
Nursing, MO
Nursing - Registered Nurse Training, B
Parks, Recreation, Leisure and Fitness Studies, B
Photography, B
Physical Education Teaching and Coaching, B
Political Science and Government, B
Pre-Dentistry Studies, B
Pre-Law Studies, B
Pre-Medicine/Pre-Medical Studies, B
Pre-Veterinary Studies, B
Psychology, BM
Public Relations/Image Management, B
Reading Teacher Education, M
Science Teacher Education/General Science
  Teacher Education, M
Secondary Education and Teaching, M
Social Sciences, B
Social Studies Teacher Education, M
Social Work, BM
Sociology, B
Special Education and Teaching, M
Sport and Fitness Administration/Management, B

SCHOOL OF THE MUSEUM OF FINE ARTS, BOSTON

Applied Art, B
Art Teacher Education, B
Art/Art Studies, General, B
Ceramic Arts and Ceramics, B
Cinematography and Film/Video Production, B
Computer Graphics, B
Drawing, B
Film/Cinema Studies, B

Film/Video and Photographic Arts, B
Fine Arts and Art Studies, BM
Fine/Studio Arts, B
Graphic Design, B
Illustration, B
Intermedia/Multimedia, B
Metal and Jewelry Arts, B
Painting, B
Photography, B
Printmaking, B
Sculpture, B
Visual and Performing Arts, B

SIMMONS COLLEGE

Accounting, B
Advertising, B
African-American/Black Studies, B
Art/Art Studies, General, B
Arts Management, B
Biochemistry, B
Biology/Biological Sciences, B
Business Administration and Management, B
Business Administration, Management and
  Operations, M
Chemistry, B
Commercial and Advertising Art, B
Comparative Literature, B
Computer Science, B
Consumer Merchandising/Retailing Management, B
Corporate and Organizational Communication, M
Cultural Studies, M
Dietetics/Dieticians, B
East Asian Studies, B
Economics, B
Education, BMO
Educational Leadership and Administration, MO
Educational Media/Instructional Technology, MO
Elementary Education and Teaching, BMO
English, MO
English as a Second Language, M
English Language and Literature, B
Environmental Studies, B
Finance, B
Foods, Nutrition, and Wellness Studies, B
French Language and Literature, B
Gender Studies, M
Health Promotion, MO
Health Services Administration, MO
History, B
Human Services, B
Information Science/Studies, MDO
Information Technology, B
International Relations and Affairs, B
Kindergarten/PreSchool Education and Teaching, B
Library Science, MDO
Management Information Systems and Services, B
Marketing/Marketing Management, B
Mass Communication/Media Studies, B
Mathematics, B
Music, B
Music History, Literature, and Theory, B
Nursing, MO
Nursing - Advanced Practice, MO
Nursing - Registered Nurse Training, B
Nutritional Sciences, MO
Pharmacy, B
Philosophy, B
Physical Therapy/Therapist, BD
Physiological Psychology/Psychobiology, B
Political Science and Government, B
Pre-Dentistry Studies, B
Pre-Law Studies, B
Pre-Medicine/Pre-Medical Studies, B
Psychology, B
Public History, MO
Public Policy Analysis, B
Public Relations/Image Management, B
Secondary Education and Teaching, BMO
Social Work, MDO
Sociology, B
Spanish Language and Literature, BMO
Special Education and Teaching, BMO
Teaching English as a Second or Foreign
  Language/ESL Language Instructor, B
Urban Education and Leadership, MO

Women's Studies, B

SIMON'S ROCK COLLEGE OF BARD

Acting, B
African-American/Black Studies, B
Agricultural Business and Management, B
American Literature (United States), B
American/United States Studies/Civilization, B
Anthropology, B
Applied Mathematics, B
Art History, Criticism and Conservation, B
Asian Studies/Civilization, B
Biology/Biological Sciences, B
Ceramic Arts and Ceramics, B
Chemistry, B
Chinese Language and Literature, B
Chinese Studies, B
Cognitive Psychology and Psycholinguistics, B
Comparative Literature, B
Computer and Information Sciences, B
Computer Graphics, B
Computer Science, B
Creative Writing, B
Dance, B
Developmental and Child Psychology, B
Drama and Dramatics/Theatre Arts, B
Drawing, B
Ecology, B
Economics, B
English Composition, B
Environmental Studies, B
Ethnic and Cultural Studies, B
Ethnic, Cultural Minority, and Gender Studies, B
European Studies/Civilization, B
Fine/Studio Arts, B
Foreign Languages and Literatures, B
French Language and Literature, B
French Studies, B
Geography, B
Geology/Earth Science, B
German Language and Literature, B
German Studies, B
Indian/Native American Education, B
Interdisciplinary Studies, B
Jazz/Jazz Studies, B
Latin American Studies, B
Latin Language and Literature, B
Liberal Arts and Sciences Studies and
    Humanities, A
Mathematics, B
Metal and Jewelry Arts, B
Music, B
Music Theory and Composition, B
Natural Sciences, B
Painting, B
Philosophy, B
Photography, B
Physics, B
Playwriting and Screenwriting, B
Political Science and Government, B
Pre-Law Studies, B
Pre-Medicine/Pre-Medical Studies, B
Printmaking, B
Psychology, B
Religion/Religious Studies, B
Sculpture, B
Sociology, B
Spanish and Iberian Studies, B
Spanish Language and Literature, B
Technical Theatre/Theatre Design and
    Technology, B
Theatre Literature, History and Criticism, B
Ukraine Studies, B
Visual and Performing Arts, B
Women's Studies, B

SMITH COLLEGE

African-American/Black Studies, B
American/United States Studies/Civilization, B
Ancient/Classical Greek Language and Literature, B
Anthropology, B
Architecture, B
Art History, Criticism and Conservation, B
Art/Art Studies, General, B
Astronomy, B
Biochemistry, B

Biological and Biomedical Sciences, MD
Biology/Biological Sciences, B
Chemistry, BM
Classics and Classical
    Languages, Literatures, and Linguistics, B
Comparative Literature, B
Computer Science, B
Dance, BM
Drama and Dramatics/Theatre Arts, B
East Asian
    Languages, Literatures, and Linguistics, B
East Asian Studies, B
Economics, B
Education, BM
Elementary Education and Teaching, M
Engineering Science, B
English Education, M
English Language and Literature, B
Exercise and Sports Science, M
Fine/Studio Arts, B
Foreign Language Teacher Education, M
French Language and Literature, BM
French Studies, B
Geology/Earth Science, B
German Language and Literature, B
German Studies, B
History, BM
Interdisciplinary Studies, B
Italian Language and Literature, BM
Latin American Studies, B
Latin Language and Literature, B
Mathematics, B
Mathematics Teacher Education, M
Medieval and Renaissance Studies, B
Middle School Education, M
Music, BM
Near and Middle Eastern Studies, B
Neuroscience, B
Philosophy, B
Physics, B
Political Science and Government, B
Portuguese Language and Literature, B
Pre-Law Studies, B
Pre-Medicine/Pre-Medical Studies, B
Psychology, B
Religion/Religious Studies, BM
Russian Language and Literature, B
Russian Studies, B
Science Teacher Education/General Science
    Teacher Education, M
Secondary Education and Teaching, M
Social Studies Teacher Education, M
Social Work, MD
Sociology, B
Spanish Language and Literature, B
Special Education and Teaching, M
Theater, M
Women's Studies, B

SPRINGFIELD COLLEGE

Applied Art, B
Art Therapy/Therapist, BMO
Athletic Training and Sports Medicine, B
Biology/Biological Sciences, B
Business Administration and Management, B
Child and Family Studies, O
Communication Disorders, B
Communication, Journalism and Related
    Programs, B
Computer Graphics, B
Computer Science, B
Counseling Psychology, MO
Counselor Education/School Counseling and
    Guidance Services, MO
Education, BM
Elementary Education and Teaching, B
Emergency Medical Technology/Technician (EMT
    Paramedic), B
English Language and Literature, B
Exercise and Sports Science, MD
General Studies, B
Health Education, M
Health Services Administration, M
Health Teacher Education, B
Health/Health Care Administration/Management, B
History, B

Human Services, M
Industrial and Organizational Psychology, MO
Junior High/Intermediate/Middle School Education
    and Teaching, B
Kindergarten/PreSchool Education and Teaching, B
Kinesiology and Exercise Science, B
Kinesiology and Movement Studies, M
Management Information Systems and Services, B
Marriage and Family Therapy/Counseling, MO
Mathematics, B
Mental Health/Rehabilitation, B
Occupational Therapy/Therapist, BMO
Parks, Recreation and Leisure Facilities
    Management, B
Parks, Recreation, Leisure and Fitness Studies, B
Physical Education Teaching and Coaching, BMDO
Physical Therapy/Therapist, BM
Physician Assistant, BM
Pre-Dentistry Studies, B
Pre-Law Studies, B
Pre-Medicine/Pre-Medical Studies, B
Psychology, B
Public Health (MPH, DPH), B
Recreation and Park Management, M
Rehabilitation Counseling, MO
Rehabilitation Therapy, B
Science Teacher Education/General Science
    Teacher Education, B
Secondary Education and Teaching, BM
Social Work, MO
Sociology, B
Sport and Fitness Administration/Management, BM
Sport Psychology, MDO
Student Personnel Services, MO
Substance Abuse/Addiction Counseling, MO
Therapeutic Recreation, M
Therapeutic Recreation/Recreational Therapy, B

SPRINGFIELD TECHNICAL
COMMUNITY COLLEGE

Accounting, A
Administrative Assistant and Secretarial Science, A
Architectural Engineering Technology/Technician, A
Automotive Engineering Technology/Technician, A
Biology/Biological Sciences, A
BioTechnology, A
Business Administration and Management, A
Business/Commerce, A
CAD/CADD Drafting and/or Design
    Technology/Technician, A
Chemistry, A
Civil Engineering Technology/Technician, A
Clinical/Medical Laboratory Technician, A
Commercial and Advertising Art, A
Communications Technologies/Technicians and
    Support Services, A
Computer and Information Sciences and Support
    Services, A
Computer Engineering Technology/Technician, A
Computer Science, A
Cosmetology/Cosmetologist, A
Criminal Justice/Police Science, A
Dental Hygiene/Hygienist, A
Diagnostic Medical Sonography/Sonographer and
    Ultrasound Technician, A
Electrical and Electronic Engineering
    Technologies/Technicians, A
Electrical, Electronic and Communications
    Engineering Technology/Technician, A
Electromechanical Technology/Electromechanical
    Engineering Technology, A
Elementary Education and Teaching, A
Engineering, A
Entrepreneurship/Entrepreneurial Studies, A
Finance, A
Fine/Studio Arts, A
Fire Science/Firefighting, A
General Studies, A
Graphic Design, A
Health Aide, A
Heating, Air Conditioning and Refrigeration
    Technology/Technician, A
Kindergarten/PreSchool Education and Teaching, A
Landscaping and Groundskeeping, A
Laser and Optical Technology/Technician, A

Liberal Arts and Sciences Studies and
  Humanities, A
Logistics and Materials Management, A
Marketing/Marketing Management, A
Massage Therapy/Therapeutic Massage, A
Mathematics, A
Mechanical Engineering/Mechanical
  Technology/Technician, A
Medical Administrative Assistant/Secretary, A
Medical Insurance Coding Specialist/Coder, A
Medical Radiologic Technology/Science - Radiation
  Therapist, A
Medical/Clinical Assistant, A
Nuclear Medical Technology/Technologist, A
Nursing - Registered Nurse Training, A
Occupational Therapist Assistant, A
Physical Therapist Assistant, A
Prepress/Desktop Publishing and Digital Imaging
  Design, A
Quality Control Technology/Technician, A
Rehabilitation and Therapeutic Professions, A
Respiratory Care Therapy/Therapist, A
Surgical Technology/Technologist, A
Web/Multimedia Management and Webmaster, A

STONEHILL COLLEGE

Accounting, BM
American/United States Studies/Civilization, B
Biochemistry, B
Biology/Biological Sciences, B
Business Administration and Management, B
Chemistry, B
Communication Studies/Speech Communication
  and Rhetoric, B
Computer Engineering, B
Computer Science, B
Criminal Justice/Safety Studies, B
Criminology, B
Economics, B
Elementary Education and Teaching, B
English Language and Literature, B
Ethnic, Cultural Minority, and Gender Studies, B
Finance, B
Fine/Studio Arts, B
Foreign Languages and Literatures, B
Health/Health Care Administration/Management, B
History, B
International Relations and Affairs, B
Kindergarten/PreSchool Education and Teaching, B
Marketing/Marketing Management, B
Mathematics, B
Multi-/Interdisciplinary Studies, B
Philosophy, B
Political Science and Government, B
Psychology, B
Public Administration, B
Religion/Religious Studies, B
Sociology, B
Speech and Rhetorical Studies, B

SUFFOLK UNIVERSITY

Accounting, BMO
Adult and Continuing Education and Teaching, MO
African-American/Black Studies, B
Applied Arts and Design, M
Art/Art Studies, General, A
Biochemistry, B
Biology Technician/BioTechnology Laboratory
  Technician, B
Biology/Biological Sciences, B
Biomedical Sciences, B
Biomedical Technology/Technician, B
Biophysics, B
Broadcast Journalism, B
Business Administration and Management, B
Business Administration, Management and
  Operations, MO
Business Teacher Education, B
Chemistry, B
Clinical Laboratory Science/Medical
  Technology/Technologist, B
Clinical Psychology, D
Commercial and Advertising Art, AB
Communication and Media Studies, M
Computer and Information Sciences, B
Computer Science, BM

Counselor Education/School Counseling and
  Guidance Services, MO
Criminal Justice/Law Enforcement
  Administration, AB
Criminology, O
Curriculum and Instruction, O
Developmental and Child Psychology, B
Developmental Psychology, D
Disability Studies, M
Drama and Dramatics/Theatre Arts, B
Economics, BMDO
Education, BMO
Educational Administration and Supervision, MO
Educational Leadership and Administration, O
Electrical, Electronics and Communications
  Engineering, B
Elementary Education and Teaching, B
English Language and Literature, B
Environmental Biology, B
Environmental Studies, B
Finance, B
Finance and Banking, MO
Foundations and Philosophy of Education, MO
French Language and Literature, B
Health Services Administration, M
History, B
Human Resources Development, MO
Human Resources Management and Services, M
Human Services, B
Humanities/Humanistic Studies, B
Information Science/Studies, B
Interdisciplinary Studies, AB
Interior Design, BM
International Business/Trade/Commerce, MDO
International Economics, B
Journalism, B
Law and Legal Studies, BPO
Legal Assistant/Paralegal, AB
Liberal Arts and Sciences Studies and
  Humanities, B
Management Information Systems and Services, B
Marine Biology and Biological Oceanography, B
Marketing/Marketing Management, B
Mass Communication/Media Studies, B
Mathematics, B
Modern Languages, B
Non-Profit/Public/Organizational Management, M
Philosophy, B
Physics, B
Political Science and Government, BM
Pre-Law Studies, B
Psychology, BD
Public Administration, BMO
Public Policy Analysis, B
Public Relations/Image Management, B
Radiologic Technology/Science - Radiographer, B
Secondary Education and Teaching, BM
Social Sciences, B
Social Work, AB
Sociology, B
Spanish Language and Literature, B
Taxation, M
Women's Studies, B

TUFTS UNIVERSITY

African-American/Black Studies, B
Allopathic Medicine, PO
American/United States Studies/Civilization, B
Analytical Chemistry, MD
Anthropology, B
Archeology, BM
Architectural Engineering, B
Art History, Criticism and Conservation, BM
Asian Studies/Civilization, B
Astronomy, B
Behavioral Sciences, B
Biochemistry, D
Bioengineering, O
Biological and Biomedical Sciences, MDO
Biology/Biological Sciences, B
Biomedical Engineering, MD
Biostatistics, MD
BioTechnology, O
Cell Biology and Anatomy, D
Chemical Engineering, BMD
Chemistry, BMD

Child and Family Studies, MDO
Child Development, B
Chinese Language and Literature, B
Civil Engineering, BMD
Classics and Classical
  Languages, Literatures, and Linguistics, BM
Clinical Research, MD
Community Health and Preventive Medicine, B
Composition, M
Computer Engineering, B
Computer Science, BMDO
Conflict Resolution and Mediation/Peace
  Studies, MDO
Dance, MD
Dentistry, PO
Developmental and Child Psychology, B
Developmental Biology and Embryology, D
Developmental Psychology, D
Drama and Dramatics/Theatre Arts, B
Early Childhood Education and Teaching, M
Ecology, B
Economics, BM
Education, MO
Electrical Engineering, MDO
Electrical, Electronics and Communications
  Engineering, B
Elementary Education and Teaching, BM
Engineering, B
Engineering and Applied Sciences, MD
Engineering Management, M
Engineering Physics, B
Engineering Science, B
English, MD
English Language and Literature, B
Environmental Engineering
  Technology/Environmental Technology, MD
Environmental Policy and Resource
  Management, MO
Environmental Studies, BO
Environmental/Environmental Health Engineering, B
Epidemiology, MDO
Ergonomics and Human Factors, M
Ethnomusicology, M
Experimental Psychology, B
Fine Arts and Art Studies, MO
French Language and Literature, BM
Genetics, D
Geological/Geophysical Engineering, B
Geology/Earth Science, B
German Language and Literature, BM
History, BMD
Human-Computer Interaction, O
Immunology, D
Industrial Engineering, B
Inorganic Chemistry, MD
International Affairs, MDO
International and Comparative Education, MDO
International Business/Trade/Commerce, MDO
International Development, MDO
International Public Health/International
  Health, MDO
International Relations and Affairs, B
Jewish/Judaic Studies, B
Kindergarten/PreSchool Education and Teaching, B
Latin Language and Literature, B
Management Strategy and Policy, O
Manufacturing Engineering, O
Mathematics, BMD
Mechanical Engineering, BMD
Mental Health/Rehabilitation, B
Microbiology, D
Middle School Education, M
Modern Greek Language and Literature, B
Molecular Biology, D
Molecular Physiology, D
Museology/Museum Studies, O
Music, BM
Music History, Literature, and Theory, M
Music Theory and Composition, M
Neuroscience, D
Non-Profit/Public/Organizational Management, O
Nutritional Sciences, MD
Occupational Therapy/Therapist, MDO
Oral and Dental Sciences, MO
Organic Chemistry, MD
Pharmacology, D

Philosophy, BM
Physical Chemistry, MD
Physics, BMD
Political Science and Government, B
Psychology, BMD
Public Administration, O
Public Health, M
Public Health (MPH, DPH), B
Public Policy Analysis, MO
Romance Languages, Literatures, and Linguistics, B
Russian Language and Literature, B
Russian Studies, B
School Psychology, MO
Secondary Education and Teaching, BM
Sociology, B
Southeast Asian Studies, B
Spanish Language and Literature, B
Special Education and Teaching, B
Theater, MD
Urban and Regional Planning, M
Urban Studies/Affairs, BMO
Veterinary Medicine, PO
Veterinary Sciences, MDO
Women's Studies, B

UNIVERSITY OF MASSACHUSETTS AMHERST

Accounting, BM
African-American/Black Studies, BMD
Agricultural Economics, MD
Agronomy and Soil Sciences, MD
Animal Sciences, BMD
Anthropology, BMD
Applied Horticulture/Horticultural Business
    Services, A
Applied Mathematics, M
Art Education, M
Art History, Criticism and Conservation, BM
Astronomy, BMD
Biochemistry, MD
Biochemistry, Biophysics and Molecular Biology, B
Biological and Biomedical Sciences, MD
Biological and Physical Sciences, B
Biology/Biological Sciences, B
BioTechnology, MD
Business Administration and Management, B
Business Administration, Management and
    Operations, M
Cell Biology and Anatomy, D
Chemical Engineering, BMD
Chemistry, BMD
Chinese Language and Literature, B
Chinese Studies, M
Civil Engineering, BMD
Classics and Classical
    Languages, Literatures, and Linguistics, BM
Clinical Psychology, MD
Communication and Media Studies, MD
Communication Disorders, B
Communication Studies/Speech Communication
    and Rhetoric, B
Comparative Literature, BMD
Computer Engineering, BMD
Computer Science, BMD
Counselor Education/School Counseling and
    Guidance Services, MDO
Crop Production, A
Curriculum and Instruction, MDO
Dance, B
Developmental Biology and Embryology, D
Drama and Dramatics/Theatre Arts, B
Early Childhood Education and Teaching, MDO
Economics, BMD
Education, MDO
Educational Administration and Supervision, MDO
Educational Measurement and Evaluation, MDO
Educational Media/Instructional Technology, MDO
Electrical Engineering, MD
Electrical, Electronics and Communications
    Engineering, B
Elementary Education and Teaching, MDO
Engineering, B
Engineering and Applied Sciences, MD
Engineering Management, M
English, MD
English Language and Literature, B

Entomology, MD
Environmental Biology, MD
Environmental Design/Architecture, B
Environmental Engineering
    Technology/Environmental Technology, M
Environmental Sciences, B
Equestrian/Equine Studies, A
Evolutionary Biology, MD
Exercise and Sports Science, MD
Finance, B
Fine Arts and Art Studies, M
Fine/Studio Arts, B
Fish, Game and Wildlife Management, MD
Food Science, B
Food Science and Technology, MD
Foreign Language Teacher Education, M
Forestry, BMD
French Language and Literature, BM
General Studies, B
Geography, BM
Geology/Earth Science, B
Geosciences, MD
German Language and Literature, BMD
Higher Education/Higher Education
    Administration, MDO
History, BMD
History of Science and Technology, M
Hospitality Administration/Management, BM
Human Nutrition, B
Humanities/Humanistic Studies, B
Industrial and Labor Relations, M
Industrial Engineering, B
Industrial/Management Engineering, MD
Interior Design, BM
International and Comparative Education, MDO
Italian Language and Literature, BM
Japanese Language and Literature, B
Japanese Studies, M
Jewish/Judaic Studies, B
Journalism, B
Kinesiology and Exercise Science, B
Landscape Architecture, BMO
Landscaping and Groundskeeping, A
Law and Legal Studies, B
Liberal Arts and Sciences Studies and
    Humanities, B
Linguistics, BMD
Management, MD
Manufacturing Engineering, M
Marine Sciences, M
Marketing/Marketing Management, B
Mathematics, BMD
Mechanical Engineering, BMD
Microbiology, BMD
Molecular Biology, D
Multi-/Interdisciplinary Studies, B
Multilingual and Multicultural Education, MDO
Music, BMD
Music Performance, B
Natural Resources Management/Development and
    Policy, B
Near and Middle Eastern Studies, B
Neuroscience, MD
Nursing, MDO
Nursing - Registered Nurse Training, B
Nutritional Sciences, M
Operations Research, MD
Ornamental Horticulture, A
Philosophy, BMD
Physical Education Teaching and Coaching, MDO
Physics, BMD
Plant Biology, MD
Plant Molecular Biology, MD
Plant Physiology, MD
Plant Sciences, BMD
Political Science and Government, BMD
Polymer/Plastics Engineering, MD
Portuguese Language and Literature, B
Pre-Dentistry Studies, B
Pre-Medicine/Pre-Medical Studies, B
Pre-Veterinary Studies, B
Psychology, BMD
Public Administration, M
Public Health, MD
Public History, M
Public Policy Analysis, M

Reading Teacher Education, MDO
Russian Studies, B
School Psychology, D
Science Teacher Education/General Science
    Teacher Education, D
Secondary Education and Teaching, MDO
Social Sciences, B
Sociology, BMD
Spanish Language and Literature, BMD
Special Education and Teaching, MDO
Sport and Fitness Administration/Management, BMD
Statistics, MD
Theater, M
Travel and Tourism, M
Turf and Turfgrass Management, A
Urban and Regional Planning, MDO
Wildlife and Wildlands Science and Management, B
Women's Studies, B
Wood Science and Wood Products/Pulp and Paper
    Technology, B
Writing, M

UNIVERSITY OF MASSACHUSETTS BOSTON

African-American/Black Studies, B
American/United States Studies/Civilization, BM
Anthropology, B
Applied Physics, M
Archeology, M
Art/Art Studies, General, B
Biochemistry, B
Biological and Biomedical Sciences, M
Biology/Biological Sciences, B
BioTechnology, M
Business Administration and Management, B
Business Administration, Management and
    Operations, MO
Cell Biology and Anatomy, D
Chemistry, BM
Classics and Classical
    Languages, Literatures, and Linguistics, B
Clinical Laboratory Science/Medical
    Technology/Technologist, B
Clinical Psychology, D
Community Organization and Advocacy, B
Computer Science, BMD
Conflict Resolution and Mediation/Peace
    Studies, MO
Counseling Psychology, MO
Counselor Education/School Counseling and
    Guidance Services, MO
Criminal Justice/Safety Studies, B
Curriculum and Instruction, M
Drama and Dramatics/Theatre Arts, B
Economics, B
Education, MDO
Educational Administration and Supervision, MDO
Educational Leadership and Administration, D
Elementary Education and Teaching, M
Engineering Physics, B
English, M
English as a Second Language, M
English Language and Literature, B
Environmental Biology, D
Environmental Sciences, MD
Foreign Language Teacher Education, M
Forensic Psychology, MO
French Language and Literature, B
Geography, B
Geology/Earth Science, B
German Language and Literature, B
Gerontology, BMDO
Health Services Administration, M
Higher Education/Higher Education
    Administration, D
History, BM
Human Services, BM
Interdisciplinary Studies, B
Italian Language and Literature, B
Labor and Industrial Relations, B
Law and Legal Studies, B
Linguistics, M
Marine Sciences, D
Marriage and Family Therapy/Counseling, MO
Mathematics, B
Molecular Biology, D

Multilingual and Multicultural Education, M
Music, B
Nursing, MDO
Nursing - Registered Nurse Training, B
Philosophy, B
Physical Education Teaching and Coaching, B
Physics, B
Political Science and Government, BO
Psychology, B
Public Affairs, MDO
Public History, M
Public Policy Analysis, BMDO
Rehabilitation Counseling, MO
Russian Language and Literature, B
School Psychology, MO
Secondary Education and Teaching, M
Sociology, BM
Spanish Language and Literature, B
Special Education and Teaching, M
Urban Education and Leadership, D
Women's Studies, BO

UNIVERSITY OF MASSACHUSETTS DARTMOUTH

Accounting, BO
Art Education, M
Art History, Criticism and Conservation, B
Art Teacher Education, B
Biochemical Engineering, D
Biological and Biomedical Sciences, M
Biology/Biological Sciences, B
BioTechnology, D
Business Administration and Management, B
Business Administration, Management and
   Operations, MO
Ceramic Arts and Ceramics, B
Chemistry, BM
Civil Engineering, BM
Clinical Laboratory Science/Medical
   Technology/Technologist, B
Clinical Psychology, M
Commercial and Advertising Art, B
Community Health Nursing, MO
Computer and Information Sciences, B
Computer Engineering, BMDO
Computer Science, MO
Design and Applied Arts, BM
Design and Visual Communications, B
Economics, B
Education, MO
Electrical Engineering, MDO
Electrical, Electronic and Communications
   Engineering Technology/Technician, B
Electrical, Electronics and Communications
   Engineering, B
Engineering and Applied Sciences, MDO
English Language and Literature, B
Fiber, Textile and Weaving Arts, B
Finance, B
Fine Arts and Art Studies, BMO
French Language and Literature, B
History, B
Interdisciplinary Studies, B
Intermedia/Multimedia, B
Liberal Arts and Sciences Studies and
   Humanities, B
Management, O
Management Information Systems and Services, B
Marine Biology and Biological Oceanography, M
Marine Sciences, MD
Marketing/Marketing Management, B
Mathematics, B
Mechanical Engineering, BM
Mechanical Engineering/Mechanical
   Technology/Technician, B
Metal and Jewelry Arts, B
Music, B
Nursing, B
Nursing - Registered Nurse Training, B
Painting, B
Philosophy, B
Photography, B
Physics, BM
Political Science and Government, B
Portuguese Language and Literature, BM
Printmaking, B

Psychology, BM
Sculpture, B
Sociology, B
Spanish Language and Literature, B
Textile Sciences and Engineering, BM
Writing, M

UNIVERSITY OF MASSACHUSETTS LOWELL

Allied Health and Medical Assisting Services, MD
American/United States Studies/Civilization, B
Applied Mathematics, BM
Applied Physics, MD
Biochemistry, D
Biological and Biomedical Sciences, MD
Biology/Biological Sciences, B
BioTechnology, M
Business Administration and Management, B
Business Administration, Management and
   Operations, M
Chemical Engineering, BM
Chemistry, BMD
Civil Engineering, BM
Civil Engineering Technology/Technician, AB
Clinical Laboratory Science/Medical
   Technology/Technologist, B
Clinical Laboratory Sciences, M
Community Health and Preventive Medicine, B
Community Health Nursing, M
Computational Sciences, D
Computer Engineering, BM
Computer Science, BMD
Criminal Justice/Law Enforcement Administration, B
Criminology, M
Curriculum and Instruction, MO
Economics, BM
Education, MDO
Educational Administration and Supervision, MO
Educational Leadership and Administration, D
Electrical Engineering, MD
Electrical, Electronic and Communications
   Engineering Technology/Technician, AB
Electrical, Electronics and Communications
   Engineering, B
Energy and Power Engineering, MD
Engineering and Applied Sciences, MDO
Engineering/Industrial Management, B
English Language and Literature, B
Environmental Engineering
   Technology/Environmental Technology, M
Environmental Policy, MD
Environmental Sciences, BMD
Environmental Studies, O
Epidemiology, MD
Ergonomics and Human Factors, MDO
Fine/Studio Arts, B
Foreign Languages and Literatures, B
Gerontological Nursing, M
Health Physics/Radiological Health, MD
Health Promotion, D
Health Services Administration, M
History, B
Industrial and Manufacturing Management, M
Industrial Hygiene, MD
Industrial Technology/Technician, B
Industrial/Management Engineering, MDO
Information Technology, AB
Kinesiology and Exercise Science, B
Liberal Arts and Sciences Studies and
   Humanities, B
Manufacturing Engineering, O
Mathematics, BMD
Mathematics Teacher Education, D
Mechanical Engineering, BMD
Mechanical Engineering/Mechanical
   Technology/Technician, AB
Mechanics, D
Music, BM
Music Performance, B
Music Teacher Education, M
Nursing, MD
Nursing - Registered Nurse Training, B
Nursing Administration, D
Occupational Health Nursing, M
Philosophy, B
Physical Therapy/Therapist, M

Physics, BMD
Political Science and Government, B
Polymer/Plastics Engineering, BMD
Psychiatric/Mental Health Nurse/Nursing, M
Psychology, BM
Reading Teacher Education, MDO
Science Teacher Education/General Science
   Teacher Education, D
Social Psychology, M
Sociology, BM

UNIVERSITY OF PHOENIX-BOSTON CAMPUS

Accounting, M
Business Administration and Management, B
Business Administration, Management and
   Operations, M
International Business/Trade/Commerce, M
Management Information Systems and
   Services, BM
Management of Technology, M
System Management, M

UNIVERSITY OF PHOENIX-CENTRAL MASSACHUSETTS CAMPUS

Business Administration and Management, B
Business Administration, Management and
   Operations, M
E-Commerce/Electronic Commerce, B
Information Technology, B
Management, M
Management of Technology, M
Organizational Management, M

URBAN COLLEGE OF BOSTON

Human Services, A
Kindergarten/PreSchool Education and Teaching, A
Liberal Arts and Sciences Studies and
   Humanities, A

WELLESLEY COLLEGE

African Studies, B
African-American/Black Studies, B
American/United States Studies/Civilization, B
Ancient/Classical Greek Language and Literature, B
Anthropology, B
Archeology, B
Architecture, B
Art History, Criticism and Conservation, B
Astronomy, B
Astrophysics, B
Biochemistry, B
Biology/Biological Sciences, B
Chemistry, B
Chinese Language and Literature, B
Classics and Classical
   Languages, Literatures, and Linguistics, B
Cognitive Psychology and Psycholinguistics, B
Comparative Literature, B
Computer Science, B
Drama and Dramatics/Theatre Arts, B
East Asian Studies, B
Economics, B
English Language and Literature, B
Environmental Studies, B
Ethnic, Cultural Minority, and Gender Studies, B
Film/Cinema Studies, B
Fine/Studio Arts, B
French Language and Literature, B
Geology/Earth Science, B
German Language and Literature, B
History, B
International Relations and Affairs, B
Islamic Studies, B
Italian Language and Literature, B
Italian Studies, B
Japanese Language and Literature, B
Jewish/Judaic Studies, B
Latin American Studies, B
Latin Language and Literature, B
Linguistics, B
Mathematics, B
Medieval and Renaissance Studies, B
Music, B
Neuroscience, B

Peace Studies and Conflict Resolution, B
Philosophy, B
Physics, B
Political Science and Government, B
Psychology, B
Religion/Religious Studies, B
Russian Language and Literature, B
Russian Studies, B
Sociology, B
Spanish Language and Literature, B
Women's Studies, B

WENTWORTH INSTITUTE OF TECHNOLOGY

Airframe Mechanics and Aircraft Maintenance
   Technology/Technician, A
Architectural Engineering Technology/Technician, AB
Architecture, B
Avionics Maintenance Technology/Technician, A
Biomedical Technology/Technician, A
Building/Construction
   Finishing, Management, and Inspection, AB
Business Administration and Management, AB
Civil Engineering Technology/Technician, AB
Computer Engineering Technology/Technician, AB
Computer Science, AB
Construction Engineering Technology/Technician, AB
Electrical, Electronic and Communications
   Engineering Technology/Technician, AB
Electrical, Electronics and Communications
   Engineering, B
Engineering Mechanics, B
Engineering Technology, AB
Environmental Engineering
   Technology/Environmental Technology, A
Environmental/Environmental Health Engineering, B
Industrial Design, AB
Industrial Technology/Technician, A
Interior Design, AB
Mechanical Engineering/Mechanical
   Technology/Technician, AB

WESTERN NEW ENGLAND COLLEGE

Accounting, BM
Advertising, B
Applied Economics, B
Biology/Biological Sciences, B
Biomedical/Medical Engineering, B
Business Administration and Management, B
Business Administration, Management and
   Operations, M
Business/Commerce, B
Chemistry, B
Communication Studies/Speech Communication
   and Rhetoric, B
Computer Engineering, M
Computer Science, B
Creative Writing, B
Criminal Justice/Law Enforcement Administration, B
Criminology, M
Economics, B
Electrical Engineering, M
Electrical, Electronics and Communications
   Engineering, B
Elementary Education and Teaching, BM
Engineering and Applied Sciences, M
English Education, M
English Language and Literature, B
Finance, B
History, B
Industrial Engineering, B
Industrial/Management Engineering, M
International Relations and Affairs, B
Law and Legal Studies, MP
Liberal Arts and Sciences Studies and
   Humanities, AB
Management Information Systems and
   Services, BM
Manufacturing Engineering, M
Marketing, B
Marketing/Marketing Management, B
Mass Communication/Media Studies, B
Mathematics, B
Mathematics Teacher Education, M
Mechanical Engineering, BM
Molecular Biology, B

Philosophy, B
Political Science and Government, B
Psychology, B
Secondary Education and Teaching, B
Social Work, B
Sociology, B
Sport and Fitness Administration/Management, B

WESTFIELD STATE COLLEGE

Accounting, B
Art Teacher Education, B
Art/Art Studies, General, B
Biology/Biological Sciences, B
Business Administration and Management, B
Business Teacher Education, B
City/Urban, Community and Regional Planning, B
Clinical Laboratory Science/Medical
   Technology/Technologist, B
Clinical Psychology, M
Commercial and Advertising Art, B
Comparative Literature, B
Computer Science, B
Corrections, B
Counseling Psychology, M
Counselor Education/School Counseling and
   Guidance Services, B
Criminal Justice/Law Enforcement Administration, B
Criminology, M
Early Childhood Education and Teaching, M
Economics, B
Education, BMO
Educational Administration and Supervision, MO
Educational Media/Instructional Technology, M
Elementary Education and Teaching, BM
English, M
English Language and Literature, B
Environmental Biology, B
Finance, B
Geography, B
History, BM
Information Science/Studies, B
Jazz/Jazz Studies, B
Kindergarten/PreSchool Education and Teaching, B
Liberal Arts and Sciences Studies and
   Humanities, B
Management Information Systems and Services, B
Marketing/Marketing Management, B
Mass Communication/Media Studies, B
Mathematics, B
Middle School Education, M
Music, B
Music History, Literature, and Theory, B
Music Management and Merchandising, B
Music Teacher Education, B
Parks, Recreation, Leisure and Fitness Studies, B
Physical Education Teaching and Coaching, BM
Physical Sciences, B
Political Science and Government, B
Pre-Law Studies, B
Pre-Medicine/Pre-Medical Studies, B
Psychology, B
Radio and Television, B
Reading Teacher Education, BM
Science Teacher Education/General Science
   Teacher Education, B
Secondary Education and Teaching, BM
Social Sciences, B
Sociology, B
Special Education and Teaching, BM
Vocational and Technical Education, M
Voice and Opera, B

WHEATON COLLEGE

American/United States Studies/Civilization, B
Ancient Studies/Civilization, B
Anthropology, B
Art History, Criticism and Conservation, B
Asian Studies/Civilization, B
Astronomy, B
Biochemistry, B
Biology/Biological Sciences, B
Chemistry, B
Classics and Classical
   Languages, Literatures, and Linguistics, B
Comparative Literature, B
Computer Science, B

Drama and Dramatics/Theatre Arts, B
Economics, B
English Language and Literature, B
Environmental Studies, B
Fine/Studio Arts, B
French Language and Literature, B
German Language and Literature, B
German Studies, B
Hispanic-American, Puerto Rican, and Mexican-
   American/Chicano Studies, B
History, B
Interdisciplinary Studies, B
International Relations and Affairs, B
Mathematics, B
Music, B
Philosophy, B
Physics, B
Physiological Psychology/Psychobiology, B
Political Science and Government, B
Pre-Medicine/Pre-Medical Studies, B
Psychology, B
Religion/Religious Studies, B
Russian Language and Literature, B
Russian Studies, B
Sociology, B
Women's Studies, B

WHEELOCK COLLEGE

Child and Family Studies, M
Child Development, B
Early Childhood Education and Teaching, AM
Education, BM
Educational Leadership and Administration, M
Elementary Education and Teaching, BM
Human Development, M
Human Development and Family Studies, B
Kindergarten/PreSchool Education and Teaching, B
Reading Teacher Education, M
Social Work, BM
Special Education and Teaching, BM

WILLIAMS COLLEGE

American/United States Studies/Civilization, B
Anthropology, B
Art History, Criticism and Conservation, BM
Asian Studies/Civilization, B
Astronomy, B
Astrophysics, B
Biology/Biological Sciences, B
Chemistry, B
Chinese Language and Literature, B
Classics and Classical
   Languages, Literatures, and Linguistics, B
Comparative Literature, B
Computer Science, B
Drama and Dramatics/Theatre Arts, B
Economics, B
English Language and Literature, B
Ethnic, Cultural Minority, and Gender Studies, B
Fine/Studio Arts, B
French Language and Literature, B
Geology/Earth Science, B
German Language and Literature, B
History, B
Japanese Language and Literature, B
Mathematics, B
Music, B
Philosophy, B
Physics, B
Political Science and Government, B
Psychology, B
Religion/Religious Studies, B
Russian Language and Literature, B
Sociology, B
Spanish Language and Literature, B
Women's Studies, B

WORCESTER POLYTECHNIC INSTITUTE

Actuarial Science, B
Aerospace, Aeronautical and Astronautical
   Engineering, B
Animal Genetics, B
Applied Mathematics, BM
Biochemistry, BMD
Biological and Biomedical Sciences, MDO

Biology Technician/BioTechnology Laboratory Technician, B
Biology/Biological Sciences, B
Biomedical Engineering, MDO
Biomedical Sciences, B
Biomedical/Medical Engineering, B
BioTechnology, MDO
Business Administration and Management, B
Business Administration, Management and Operations, MO
Cell/Cellular Biology and Histology, B
Chemical Engineering, BMD
Chemistry, BMD
Civil Engineering, BMDO
Computer and Information Sciences, B
Computer Engineering, BMDO
Computer Science, BMDO
Economics, B
Electrical Engineering, MDO
Electrical, Electronics and Communications Engineering, B
Engineering, B
Engineering and Applied Sciences, MDO
Engineering Mechanics, B
Engineering Physics, B
Engineering/Industrial Management, B
Environmental Engineering Technology/Environmental Technology, MDO
Environmental Studies, B
Environmental/Environmental Health Engineering, B
Fire Protection Engineering, MDO
Fluid and Thermal Sciences, B
History, B
History and Philosophy of Science and Technology, B
Humanities/Humanistic Studies, B
Industrial Engineering, B
Information Science/Studies, B
Interdisciplinary Studies, BMD
Management, MO
Management Information Systems and Services, BM
Manufacturing Engineering, MDO
Marketing, M
Materials Engineering, BMDO
Materials Sciences, BMDO
Mathematics, BMDO
Mechanical Engineering, BMDO
Medical Microbiology and Bacteriology, B
Medicinal and Pharmaceutical Chemistry, B
Molecular Biology, B
Music, B
Nuclear Engineering, B
Organizational Management, M
Philosophy, B
Physical Sciences, B
Physics, BMD
Science, Technology and Society, B
Social Sciences, B
Statistics, M

WORCESTER STATE COLLEGE

Accounting, M
Biological and Physical Sciences, B
Biology/Biological Sciences, B
BioTechnology, BM
Business Administration and Management, B
Chemistry, B
Communication Disorders, BM
Community Health Nursing, M
Computer and Information Sciences, B
Criminal Justice/Safety Studies, B
Economics, B
Education, M
Educational Administration and Supervision, M
Elementary Education and Teaching, BM
English Education, M
English Language and Literature, B
Foreign Language Teacher Education, M
Geography, B
Health Education, M
Health Professions and Related Clinical Sciences, B
Health Services Administration, M
History, B
Kindergarten/PreSchool Education and Teaching, B
Management, M

Mass Communication/Media Studies, B
Mathematics, B
Middle School Education, M
Non-Profit/Public/Organizational Management, M
Nursing - Registered Nurse Training, B
Occupational Therapy/Therapist, BM
Organizational Management, M
Psychology, B
Reading Teacher Education, M
Secondary Education and Teaching, M
Social Studies Teacher Education, M
Sociology, B
Spanish Language and Literature, B
Special Education and Teaching, M
Urban Studies/Affairs, B

Michigan

ADRIAN COLLEGE

Accounting, B
Art Teacher Education, B
Art/Art Studies, General, AB
Arts Management, B
Bilingual and Multilingual Education, B
Biology/Biological Sciences, AB
Broadcast Journalism, B
Business Administration and Management, AB
Business Teacher Education, B
Chemistry, AB
Criminal Justice/Law Enforcement Administration, AB
Drama and Dramatics/Theatre Arts, AB
Economics, AB
Education, B
Elementary Education and Teaching, B
English Language and Literature, AB
Environmental Studies, B
French Language and Literature, AB
Geology/Earth Science, AB
German Language and Literature, AB
History, AB
Human Services, AB
Interior Design, B
International Business/Trade/Commerce, B
International Relations and Affairs, B
Kinesiology and Exercise Science, B
Mass Communication/Media Studies, AB
Mathematics, B
Music, B
Music Teacher Education, B
Physical Education Teaching and Coaching, AB
Physics, AB
Political Science and Government, AB
Pre-Medicine/Pre-Medical Studies, B
Pre-Veterinary Studies, B
Psychology, AB
Religion/Religious Studies, AB
Science Teacher Education/General Science Teacher Education, B
Secondary Education and Teaching, B
Social Sciences, AB
Social Work, B
Sociology, AB
Spanish Language and Literature, AB
Teacher Education, Multiple Levels, B

ALBION COLLEGE

American/United States Studies/Civilization, B
Anthropology, B
Art/Art Studies, General, B
Biology/Biological Sciences, B
Business Administration and Management, B
Chemistry, B
Computer Science, B
Drama and Dramatics/Theatre Arts, B
Economics, B
Education, B
Elementary Education and Teaching, B
English Language and Literature, B
Environmental Studies, B
French Language and Literature, B
Geology/Earth Science, B
German Language and Literature, B
History, B
Human Services, B

International Relations and Affairs, B
Mass Communication/Media Studies, B
Mathematics, B
Modern Languages, B
Music, B
Philosophy, B
Physical Education Teaching and Coaching, B
Physics, B
Political Science and Government, B
Pre-Law Studies, B
Pre-Medicine/Pre-Medical Studies, B
Pre-Veterinary Studies, B
Psychology, B
Public Policy Analysis, B
Religion/Religious Studies, B
Secondary Education and Teaching, B
Sociology, B
Spanish Language and Literature, B
Women's Studies, B

ALMA COLLEGE

Accounting, B
Anthropology, B
Art Teacher Education, B
Art/Art Studies, General, B
Biochemistry, B
Biological and Physical Sciences, B
Biology Teacher Education, B
Biology/Biological Sciences, B
Business Administration and Management, B
Chemistry, B
Chemistry Teacher Education, B
Communication and Media Studies, B
Computer Science, B
Computer Teacher Education, B
Dance, B
Design and Visual Communications, B
Drama and Dramatics/Theatre Arts, B
Early Childhood Education and Teaching, B
Economics, B
Education, B
Elementary Education and Teaching, B
English Language and Literature, B
English/Language Arts Teacher Education, B
Fine/Studio Arts, B
French Language and Literature, B
French Language Teacher Education, B
German Language and Literature, B
German Language Teacher Education, B
Gerontology, B
Graphic Design, B
Health Teacher Education, B
History, B
History Teacher Education, B
Humanities/Humanistic Studies, B
International Business/Trade/Commerce, B
Kindergarten/PreSchool Education and Teaching, B
Kinesiology and Exercise Science, B
Liberal Arts and Sciences Studies and Humanities, B
Marketing/Marketing Management, B
Mathematics, B
Mathematics Teacher Education, B
Medical Illustration/Medical Illustrator, B
Modern Languages, B
Music, B
Music Performance, B
Music Teacher Education, B
Philosophy, B
Physical Education Teaching and Coaching, B
Physics, B
Physics Teacher Education, B
Political Science and Government, B
Pre-Dentistry Studies, B
Pre-Law Studies, B
Pre-Medicine/Pre-Medical Studies, B
Pre-Theology/Pre-Ministerial Studies, B
Pre-Veterinary Studies, B
Psychology, B
Psychology Teacher Education, B
Public Health (MPH, DPH), B
Religion/Religious Studies, B
Science Teacher Education/General Science Teacher Education, B
Secondary Education and Teaching, B
Social Science Teacher Education, B

Social Sciences, B
Social Studies Teacher Education, B
Sociology, B
Spanish Language and Literature, B
Spanish Language Teacher Education, B

ALPENA COMMUNITY COLLEGE

Accounting, A
Administrative Assistant and Secretarial Science, A
Automobile/Automotive Mechanics
   Technology/Technician, A
Biology/Biological Sciences, A
Business Administration and Management, A
Business/Office Automation/Technology/Data
   Entry, A
Chemical Engineering, A
Chemistry, A
Computer and Information Sciences, A
Computer Systems Networking and
   Telecommunications, A
Computer/Information Technology Services
   Administration and Management, A
Corrections, A
Criminal Justice/Police Science, A
Data Processing and Data Processing
   Technology/Technician, A
Drafting and Design Technology/Technician, A
Elementary Education and Teaching, A
English Language and Literature, A
General Studies, A
Information Science/Studies, A
Liberal Arts and Sciences Studies and
   Humanities, A
Licensed Practical/Vocational Nurse Training, A
Manufacturing Technology/Technician, A
Mathematics, A
Medical Office Assistant/Specialist, A
Nursing - Registered Nurse Training, A
Office Management and Supervision, A
Operations Management and Supervision, A
Pre-Engineering, A
Secondary Education and Teaching, A

ANDREWS UNIVERSITY

Accounting, BM
Agribusiness, B
Agricultural Business and Management, AB
Agricultural Mechanization, AB
Agricultural Teacher Education, B
Agriculture, AB
Agronomy and Crop Science, AB
Airline/Commercial/Professional Pilot and Flight
   Crew, AB
Allied Health and Medical Assisting Services, M
Anatomy, B
Architectural Engineering, B
Architecture, BM
Art History, Criticism and Conservation, B
Art Teacher Education, B
Art/Art Studies, General, B
Audiology/Audiologist and Speech-Language
   Pathology/Pathologist, B
Avionics Maintenance Technology/Technician, AB
Behavioral Sciences, B
Bible/Biblical Studies, B
Biochemistry, B
Biological and Biomedical Sciences, M
Biology/Biological Sciences, B
Biomedical Technology/Technician, B
Biophysics, B
Botany/Plant Biology, B
Business Administration and Management, AB
Business/Managerial Economics, B
Chemistry, B
Clinical Laboratory Science/Medical
   Technology/Technologist, B
Commercial and Advertising Art, AB
Communication and Media Studies, M
Community Psychology, M
Computer and Information Sciences, B
Computer Engineering Technology/Technician, AB
Computer Programming/Programmer, B
Computer Science, B
Construction Engineering, B
Counseling Psychology, D
Curriculum and Instruction, MDO

Developmental Psychology, MD
Dietetics/Dieticians, B
Economics, BM
Education, BMDO
Educational Administration and Supervision, MDO
Educational Leadership and Administration, MDO
Educational Psychology, MD
Electrical, Electronic and Communications
   Engineering Technology/Technician, AB
Elementary Education and Teaching, BM
Engineering and Applied Sciences, M
Engineering Technology, AB
English, M
English Education, M
English Language and Literature, B
Family and Community Services, B
Family and Consumer Economics and Related
   Services, B
Finance and Banking, M
Foods, Nutrition, and Wellness Studies, B
Foreign Language Teacher Education, M
French Language and Literature, B
History, BM
Horticultural Science, A
Human Services, M
Information Science/Studies, B
International Development, M
Journalism, B
Landscaping and Groundskeeping, B
Liberal Arts and Sciences Studies and
   Humanities, AB
Management, M
Marketing, M
Marketing/Marketing Management, B
Mass Communication/Media Studies, B
Mathematics, BM
Mechanical Engineering, B
Mechanical Engineering/Mechanical
   Technology/Technician, AB
Music, BM
Music Teacher Education, B
Neurobiology and Neurophysiology, B
Nursing, M
Nursing - Registered Nurse Training, B
Nutritional Sciences, M
Pastoral Studies/Counseling, MDP
Photography, AB
Physical Therapy/Therapist, BD
Physics, B
Piano and Organ, B
Political Science and Government, B
Pre-Law Studies, B
Pre-Medicine/Pre-Medical Studies, B
Pre-Veterinary Studies, B
Psychology, BMDO
Public Relations/Image Management, B
Reading Teacher Education, M
Religion/Religious Studies, B
Religious Education, BMDO
School Psychology, MO
Science Teacher Education/General Science
   Teacher Education, BM
Secondary Education and Teaching, BM
Social Sciences, B
Social Studies Teacher Education, M
Social Work, BM
Sociology, B
Software Engineering, M
Spanish Language and Literature, B
Special Education and Teaching, M
Technology Education/Industrial Arts, B
Theology and Religious Vocations, MDPO
Theology/Theological Studies, B
Voice and Opera, B
Youth Ministry, B
Zoology/Animal Biology, B

AQUINAS COLLEGE

Accounting, B
Art History, Criticism and Conservation, B
Art Teacher Education, B
Art/Art Studies, General, B
Arts Management, B
Athletic Training and Sports Medicine, B
Biology/Biological Sciences, B
Business Administration and Management, B

Business/Corporate Communications, B
Ceramic Arts and Ceramics, B
Chemistry, B
Clinical Laboratory Science/Medical
   Technology/Technologist, B
Communication Studies/Speech Communication
   and Rhetoric, B
Computer and Information Sciences, B
Computer Science, B
Drama and Dramatics/Theatre Arts, B
Drawing, B
Economics, B
Education, BM
Education/Teaching of Individuals with Specific
   Learning Disabilities, B
Elementary Education and Teaching, B
English Language and Literature, B
English/Language Arts Teacher Education, B
Environmental Sciences, B
Environmental Studies, B
Fine/Studio Arts, B
French Language and Literature, B
General Studies, B
Geography, B
German Language and Literature, B
Health Teacher Education, B
History, B
International Business/Trade/Commerce, B
International Relations and Affairs, B
Japanese Language and Literature, B
Liberal Arts and Sciences Studies and
   Humanities, B
Management, M
Mathematics, B
Music, B
Music Performance, B
Music Teacher Education, B
Organizational Communication, B
Painting, B
Philosophy, B
Photography, B
Physical Education Teaching and Coaching, B
Physics, B
Political Science and Government, B
Pre-Law Studies, B
Printmaking, B
Psychology, B
Reading Teacher Education, B
Religion/Religious Studies, B
Religious Education, B
Religious/Sacred Music, AB
Science Teacher Education/General Science
   Teacher Education, B
Sculpture, B
Secondary Education and Teaching, B
Social Sciences, B
Social Studies Teacher Education, B
Sociology, B
Spanish Language and Literature, B
Teaching English as a Second or Foreign
   Language/ESL Language Instructor, B
Urban Studies/Affairs, B

AVE MARIA COLLEGE

Classics and Classical
   Languages, Literatures, and Linguistics, B
Comparative Literature, B
Economics, B
History, B
Mathematics, B
Philosophy, B
Political Science and Government, B
Theology/Theological Studies, B

BAKER COLLEGE OF ALLEN PARK

Accounting, A
Business Administration and Management, A
Computer and Information Sciences, A
Computer Science, A
Computer Systems Networking and
   Telecommunications, A
Data Entry/Microcomputer Applications, A
Early Childhood Education and Teaching, A
Executive Assistant/Executive Secretary, A
Interior Design, A
Marketing/Marketing Management, A

Medical Insurance Coding Specialist/Coder, A
Medical Insurance Specialist/Medical Biller, A
Medical Office Computer Specialist/Assistant, A
Medical/Clinical Assistant, A
Receptionist, A
Web Page, Digital/Multimedia and Information
  Resources Design, A
Word Processing, A

BAKER COLLEGE OF AUBURN HILLS

Accounting, AB
Administrative Assistant and Secretarial Science, A
Business Administration and Management, AB
Commercial and Advertising Art, A
Computer Typography and Composition Equipment
  Operator, A
Data Processing and Data Processing
  Technology/Technician, A
Diagnostic Medical Sonography/Sonographer and
  Ultrasound Technician, A
Drafting and Design Technology/Technician, A
Education, A
Health Information/Medical Records
  Administration/Administrator, AB
Health/Health Care Administration/Management, AB
Interior Design, A
Legal Administrative Assistant/Secretary, A
Marketing/Marketing Management, AB
Medical Administrative Assistant/Secretary, AB
Medical/Clinical Assistant, A
System, Networking, and LAN/WAN
  Management/Manager, A

BAKER COLLEGE OF CADILLAC

Accounting, AB
Administrative Assistant and Secretarial Science, A
Architectural Engineering Technology/Technician, A
Business Administration and Management, AB
Computer Graphics, A
Computer Typography and Composition Equipment
  Operator, A
Data Processing and Data Processing
  Technology/Technician, A
Drafting and Design Technology/Technician, A
Education, A
Electrical, Electronic and Communications
  Engineering Technology/Technician, A
Emergency Medical Technology/Technician (EMT
  Paramedic), A
Health Information/Medical Records
  Administration/Administrator, A
Information Science/Studies, AB
Marketing/Marketing Management, A
Medical Administrative Assistant/Secretary, A
Medical/Clinical Assistant, A
Quality Control Technology/Technician, A
Veterinary/Animal Health Technology/Technician and
  Veterinary Assistant, A

BAKER COLLEGE OF CLINTON TOWNSHIP

Accounting, A
Administrative Assistant and Secretarial Science, A
Architectural Engineering Technology/Technician, A
Business Administration and Management, AB
Business/Office Automation/Technology/Data
  Entry, A
Commercial and Advertising Art, A
Computer Typography and Composition Equipment
  Operator, A
Data Processing and Data Processing
  Technology/Technician, A
Drafting and Design Technology/Technician, A
Emergency Medical Technology/Technician (EMT
  Paramedic), A
Health Information/Medical Records
  Administration/Administrator, A
Human Services, A
Information Science/Studies, A
Interior Design, A
Kindergarten/PreSchool Education and Teaching, A
Legal Administrative Assistant/Secretary, A
Marketing/Marketing Management, A
Medical Administrative Assistant/Secretary, A
Medical/Clinical Assistant, A
Nursing - Registered Nurse Training, A

Radiologic Technology/Science - Radiographer, A
Surgical Technology/Technologist, A

BAKER COLLEGE OF FLINT

Accounting, AB
Accounting Technology/Technician and
  Bookkeeping, A
Administrative Assistant and Secretarial Science, AB
Airline/Commercial/Professional Pilot and Flight
  Crew, A
Architectural Drafting and Architectural
  CAD/CADD, A
Automobile/Automotive Mechanics
  Technology/Technician, A
Avionics Maintenance Technology/Technician, A
Biomedical Technology/Technician, A
Building/Construction
  Finishing, Management, and Inspection, A
Business Administration and Management, AB
Business/Commerce, A
Commercial and Advertising Art, AB
Computer Graphics, B
Computer Programming/Programmer, AB
Computer Systems Analysis/Analyst, AB
Computer Systems Networking and
  Telecommunications, A
Computer Teacher Education, A
Computer Typography and Composition Equipment
  Operator, A
Data Processing and Data Processing
  Technology/Technician, AB
Drafting and Design Technology/Technician, AB
Energy Management and Systems
  Technology/Technician, A
Entrepreneurship/Entrepreneurial Studies, A
Environmental Engineering
  Technology/Environmental Technology, A
Executive Assistant/Executive Secretary, A
Family and Community Services, A
Health Information/Medical Records
  Administration/Administrator, AB
Health Information/Medical Records
  Technology/Technician, A
Health/Health Care Administration/Management, AB
Hospitality Administration/Management, A
Human Services, A
Industrial Technology/Technician, B
Information Science/Studies, AB
Interior Design, AB
Legal Administrative Assistant/Secretary, A
Management Information Systems and Services, B
Marketing/Marketing Management, AB
Mechanical Drafting and Mechanical Drafting
  CAD/CADD, A
Mechanical Engineering, B
Mechanical Engineering/Mechanical
  Technology/Technician, A
Medical Administrative Assistant/Secretary, A
Medical Transcription/Transcriptionist, A
Medical/Clinical Assistant, A
Nursing - Registered Nurse Training, A
Occupational Therapy/Therapist, B
Office Management and Supervision, AB
Operations Management and Supervision, AB
Orthotist/Prosthetist, A
Pharmacy Technician/Assistant, A
Physical Therapist Assistant, A
Quality Control Technology/Technician, A
Sales, Distribution and Marketing Operations, A
Surgical Technology/Technologist, A
Tourism and Travel Services Management, A
Transportation and Materials Moving, A

BAKER COLLEGE OF JACKSON

Accounting, AB
Administrative Assistant and Secretarial Science, A
Business Administration and Management, AB
Business/Commerce, B
Communication Studies/Speech Communication
  and Rhetoric, A
Computer Typography and Composition Equipment
  Operator, A
Data Processing and Data Processing
  Technology/Technician, A
Early Childhood Education and Teaching, A

Health Information/Medical Records
  Administration/Administrator, A
Health Information/Medical Records
  Technology/Technician, A
Information Science/Studies, AB
Legal Administrative Assistant/Secretary, A
Marketing Research, B
Marketing/Marketing Management, AB
Medical Administrative Assistant/Secretary, A
Medical Transcription/Transcriptionist, A
Medical/Clinical Assistant, A
Office Management and Supervision, A
Pharmacy Technician/Assistant, A
Sales, Distribution and Marketing Operations, A
Surgical Technology/Technologist, A
Veterinary/Animal Health Technology/Technician and
  Veterinary Assistant, A

BAKER COLLEGE OF MUSKEGON

Accounting, AB
Administrative Assistant and Secretarial Science, AB
Airline/Commercial/Professional Pilot and Flight
  Crew, A
Architectural Drafting and Architectural
  CAD/CADD, A
Aviation/Airway Management and Operations, B
Business Administration and Management, AB
Commercial and Advertising Art, A
Computer and Information Sciences, B
Computer Programming/Programmer, A
Computer Science, B
Corrections, A
Culinary Arts/Chef Training, A
Data Processing and Data Processing
  Technology/Technician, A
Drafting and Design Technology/Technician, A
Electrical, Electronic and Communications
  Engineering Technology/Technician, AB
Emergency Medical Technology/Technician (EMT
  Paramedic), A
Health/Health Care Administration/Management, AB
Hotel/Motel Administration/Management, A
Human Services, A
Industrial Technology/Technician, A
Information Science/Studies, AB
Interior Design, A
Kindergarten/PreSchool Education and Teaching, A
Legal Administrative Assistant/Secretary, A
Marketing/Marketing Management, AB
Medical Administrative Assistant/Secretary, A
Medical/Clinical Assistant, A
Nursing - Registered Nurse Training, A
Occupational Therapist Assistant, A
Pharmacy Technician/Assistant, A
Physical Therapist Assistant, A
Quality Control Technology/Technician, A
Radiologic Technology/Science - Radiographer, A
Rehabilitation Therapy, B
Speech-Language Pathology/Pathologist, A
Surgical Technology/Technologist, A
Tourism and Travel Services Management, A
Veterinary/Animal Health Technology/Technician and
  Veterinary Assistant, A

BAKER COLLEGE OF OWOSSO

Accounting, AB
Administrative Assistant and Secretarial Science, AB
Architectural Engineering Technology/Technician, A
Business Administration and Management, AB
Clinical/Medical Laboratory Technician, A
Commercial and Advertising Art, AB
Computer Engineering Technology/Technician, A
Computer Programming/Programmer, AB
Computer Science, AB
Construction Engineering Technology/Technician, A
Consumer Merchandising/Retailing Management, A
Data Processing and Data Processing
  Technology/Technician, A
Diagnostic Medical Sonography/Sonographer and
  Ultrasound Technician, A
Drafting and Design Technology/Technician, AB
Electrical, Electronic and Communications
  Engineering Technology/Technician, AB
Environmental Engineering
  Technology/Environmental Technology, A
Health/Health Care Administration/Management, B

Hospitality Administration/Management, A
Hotel/Motel Administration/Management, A
Human Resources Management/Personnel
   Administration, AB
Industrial Radiologic Technology/Technician, AB
Information Science/Studies, AB
Interior Design, A
Kindergarten/PreSchool Education and Teaching, A
Legal Administrative Assistant/Secretary, A
Marketing/Marketing Management, AB
Medical Administrative Assistant/Secretary, A
Medical/Clinical Assistant, A
Nursing - Registered Nurse Training, A

BAKER COLLEGE OF PORT HURON

Accounting, AB
Administrative Assistant and Secretarial Science, AB
Architectural Engineering Technology/Technician, A
Business Administration and Management, AB
Commercial and Advertising Art, A
Computer Programming/Programmer, A
Data Processing and Data Processing
   Technology/Technician, A
Dental Hygiene/Hygienist, A
Diagnostic Medical Sonography/Sonographer and
   Ultrasound Technician, A
Drafting and Design Technology/Technician, A
Environmental Engineering
   Technology/Environmental Technology, A
Health Information/Medical Records
   Administration/Administrator, A
Health/Health Care Administration/Management, B
Hotel/Motel Administration/Management, A
Information Science/Studies, AB
Interior Design, A
Legal Administrative Assistant/Secretary, A
Marketing/Marketing Management, AB
Medical Administrative Assistant/Secretary, A
Medical/Clinical Assistant, A

BAY MILLS COMMUNITY COLLEGE

Administrative Assistant and Secretarial Science, A
Business Administration and Management, A
Ethnic and Cultural Studies, A
Hotel/Motel Administration/Management, A
Human Services, A
Information Science/Studies, A
Liberal Arts and Sciences Studies and
   Humanities, A
Modern Languages, A
Public Administration, A
Public Health (MPH, DPH), A
Reading Teacher Education, A
Social Sciences, A

BAY DE NOC COMMUNITY COLLEGE

Accounting, A
Accounting Technology/Technician and
   Bookkeeping, A
Administrative Assistant and Secretarial Science, A
Automobile/Automotive Mechanics
   Technology/Technician, A
Business Administration and Management, A
Business/Commerce, A
Child Care and Support Services Management, A
Community Health Services/Liaison/Counseling, A
Criminal Justice/Law Enforcement Administration, A
Criminal Justice/Police Science, A
Drafting and Design Technology/Technician, A
Electrical, Electronic and Communications
   Engineering Technology/Technician, A
Environmental Engineering
   Technology/Environmental Technology, A
Human Services, A
Hydrology and Water Resources Science, A
Information Science/Studies, A
Liberal Arts and Sciences Studies and
   Humanities, A
Licensed Practical/Vocational Nurse Training, A
Machine Tool Technology/Machinist, A
Marketing/Marketing Management, A
Medical Administrative Assistant/Secretary, A
Nursing - Registered Nurse Training, A
Pre-Engineering, A
Social Work, A

Water Quality and Wastewater Treatment
   Management and Recycling
   Technology/Technician, A
Wood Science and Wood Products/Pulp and Paper
   Technology, A

CALVIN COLLEGE

Accounting, B
Art History, Criticism and Conservation, B
Art Teacher Education, B
Art/Art Studies, General, B
Asian Studies/Civilization, B
Audiology/Audiologist and Speech-Language
   Pathology/Pathologist, B
Bible/Biblical Studies, B
Bilingual and Multilingual Education, B
Biochemistry, B
Biological and Physical Sciences, B
Biology/Biological Sciences, B
BioTechnology, B
Business Administration and Management, B
Business/Corporate Communications, B
Chemical Engineering, B
Chemistry, B
Civil Engineering, B
Classics and Classical
   Languages, Literatures, and Linguistics, B
Communication Studies/Speech Communication
   and Rhetoric, B
Computer Science, B
Conducting, B
Curriculum and Instruction, M
Development Economics and International
   Development, B
Digital Communication and Media/Multimedia, B
Drama and Dramatics/Theatre Arts, B
Economics, B
Education, M
Electrical, Electronics and Communications
   Engineering, B
Elementary Education and Teaching, B
Engineering, B
English Language and Literature, B
Environmental Studies, B
Film/Cinema Studies, B
Fine/Studio Arts, B
French Language and Literature, B
Geography, B
Geology/Earth Science, B
German Language and Literature, B
Germanic Languages, Literatures, and Linguistics, B
History, B
Interdisciplinary Studies, B
International Relations and Affairs, B
Kinesiology and Exercise Science, B
Latin Language and Literature, B
Management Information Systems and Services, B
Mass Communication/Media Studies, B
Mathematics, B
Mechanical Engineering, B
Modern Greek Language and Literature, B
Music, B
Music History, Literature, and Theory, B
Music Performance, B
Music Teacher Education, B
Music Theory and Composition, B
Natural Sciences, B
Nursing - Registered Nurse Training, B
Occupational Therapy/Therapist, B
Parks, Recreation, Leisure and Fitness Studies, B
Philosophy, B
Physical Education Teaching and Coaching, B
Physical Sciences, B
Physics, B
Piano and Organ, B
Political Science and Government, B
Pre-Dentistry Studies, B
Pre-Law Studies, B
Pre-Medicine/Pre-Medical Studies, B
Pre-Veterinary Studies, B
Psychology, B
Public Administration, B
Religion/Religious Studies, B
Religious/Sacred Music, B
Science Teacher Education/General Science
   Teacher Education, B

Secondary Education and Teaching, B
Social Sciences, B
Social Work, B
Sociology, B
Spanish Language and Literature, B
Special Education and Teaching, BM
Speech and Rhetorical Studies, B
Sport and Fitness Administration/Management, B
Teaching English as a Second or Foreign
   Language/ESL Language Instructor, B
Theology/Theological Studies, B
Therapeutic Recreation/Recreational Therapy, B
Voice and Opera, B

CENTRAL MICHIGAN UNIVERSITY

Accounting, BM
Accounting and Related Services, B
Actuarial Science, B
Advertising, B
Anthropology, B
Art Teacher Education, B
Art/Art Studies, General, B
Astronomy, B
Athletic Training and Sports Medicine, B
Audiology/Audiologist and Speech-Language
   Pathology/Pathologist, B
Automotive Engineering
   Technology/Technician, BMO
Banking and Financial Support Services, B
Biological and Biomedical Sciences, M
Biology Teacher Education, B
Biology/Biological Sciences, B
Business Administration and Management, B
Business Administration, Management and
   Operations, BM
Business Education, M
Business Teacher Education, B
Business, Management, Marketing, and Related
   Support Services, B
Business/Commerce, B
Chemistry, BM
Chemistry Teacher Education, B
Child and Family Studies, M
Child Care and Support Services Management, B
Clinical Laboratory Science/Medical
   Technology/Technologist, B
Clinical Psychology, D
Commercial and Advertising Art, B
Communication and Media Studies, M
Communication Disorders, MD
Community Organization and Advocacy, B
Computer and Information Sciences, B
Computer Engineering Technology/Technician, B
Computer Science, M
Computer Teacher Education, B
Conservation Biology, M
Construction Engineering Technology/Technician, B
Corporate and Organizational Communication, M
Counselor Education/School Counseling and
   Guidance Services, M
Creative Writing, B
Criminology, BM
Dietetics/Dieticians, B
Drama and Dramatics/Theatre Arts, B
Economics, BM
Education, MDO
Education/Teaching of Individuals with Emotional
   Disturbances, B
Education/Teaching of Individuals with Mental
   Retardation, B
Educational Administration and Supervision, MDO
Educational Leadership and Administration, D
Educational Media/Instructional Technology, M
Electrical, Electronic and Communications
   Engineering Technology/Technician, B
Elementary Education and Teaching, BM
English, M
English as a Second Language, M
English Language and Literature, B
English/Language Arts Teacher Education, B
Environmental Studies, B
European Studies/Civilization, B
Exercise and Sports Science, M
Experimental Psychology, MD
Family Systems, B
Fashion Merchandising, B

Film, Television, and Video Production, M
Finance, B
Finance and Banking, M
Financial Planning and Services, B
Fine Arts and Art Studies, M
Foodservice Systems
  Administration/Management, B
French Language and Literature, B
French Language Teacher Education, B
Geography, B
Geology/Earth Science, B
German Language and Literature, B
German Language Teacher Education, B
Health Promotion, M
Health Services Administration, MDO
Health Teacher Education, B
History, BMD
History Teacher Education, B
Home Economics, M
Hospital and Health Care Facilities
  Administration/Management, B
Hospitality Administration/Management, BMO
Human Development, M
Human Resources Management and Services, MO
Human Resources Management/Personnel
  Administration, B
Humanities/Humanistic Studies, M
Industrial and Manufacturing Management, M
Industrial and Organizational Psychology, MD
Industrial Education, M
Industrial Engineering, B
Industrial Production Technologies/Technicians, B
Interior Architecture, B
International Affairs, MO
International Business/Trade/Commerce, BM
International Relations and Affairs, B
Journalism, B
Leisure Studies, M
Logistics and Materials Management, B
Management, M
Management Information Systems and
  Services, BMO
Marketing, BM
Marketing/Marketing Management, B
Mass Communication/Media Studies, M
Mathematics, BMD
Mathematics Teacher Education, B
Mechanical Engineering/Mechanical
  Technology/Technician, B
Media Studies, M
Medical Microbiology and Bacteriology, B
Middle School Education, M
Music, BM
Music History, Literature, and Theory, B
Music Teacher Education, BM
Music Theory and Composition, B
Natural Resources and Conservation, B
Neuroscience, B
Nutritional Sciences, M
Oceanography, Chemical and Physical, B
Office Management and Supervision, M
Operations Management and Supervision, B
Parks, Recreation and Leisure Facilities
  Management, B
Parks, Recreation, Leisure and Fitness Studies, B
Philosophy, B
Physical Education Teaching and Coaching, BM
Physical Sciences, B
Physical Therapy/Therapist, D
Physician Assistant, M
Physics, BM
Physics Teacher Education, B
Political Science and Government, BM
Psychology, BMDO
Public Administration, MO
Public Health (MPH, DPH), B
Public Relations/Image Management, B
Radio and Television, B
Reading Teacher Education, M
Recreation and Park Management, M
Rehabilitation and Therapeutic Professions, B
Rehabilitation Sciences, MD
Religion/Religious Studies, B
Sales and Marketing Operations/Marketing and
  Distribution Teacher Education, B
Sales, Distribution and Marketing Operations, B

School Psychology, DO
Science Teacher Education/General Science
  Teacher Education, BM
Secondary Education and Teaching, M
Social Science Teacher Education, B
Social Sciences, B
Social Studies Teacher Education, B
Social Work, B
Sociology, BM
Software Engineering, MO
Spanish Language and Literature, BM
Spanish Language Teacher Education, B
Special Education and Teaching, M
Speech and Interpersonal Communication, M
Speech and Rhetorical Studies, BM
Speech Teacher Education, B
Sport and Fitness Administration/Management, BM
Statistics, B
Teacher Education and Professional
  Development, Specific Subject Areas, B
Technology Teacher Education/Industrial Arts
  Teacher Education, B
Theater, M
Therapeutic Recreation/Recreational Therapy, B
Travel and Tourism, MO
Women's Studies, B
Writing, M

CLEARY UNIVERSITY

Accounting, BM
Accounting Technology/Technician and
  Bookkeeping, A
Business Administration and Management, AB
Business Administration, Management and
  Operations, M
Computer and Information Sciences and Support
  Services, A
Finance, B
Financial Planning and Services, B
Human Resources Management/Personnel
  Administration, B
Information Science/Studies, B
Management, M
Management Information Systems and Services, B
Marketing/Marketing Management, B

CONCORDIA UNIVERSITY

Ancient Near Eastern and Biblical
  Languages, Literatures, and Linguistics, B
Art Teacher Education, B
Art/Art Studies, General, B
Biological and Physical Sciences, B
Biology Teacher Education, B
Biology/Biological Sciences, B
Business Administration and Management, B
Communication Studies/Speech Communication
  and Rhetoric, B
Computer and Information Sciences, B
Criminal Justice/Law Enforcement Administration, B
Drama and Dramatics/Theatre Arts, B
Elementary Education and Teaching, B
English Language and Literature, B
English/Language Arts Teacher Education, B
Fire Services Administration, B
General Studies, A
Health and Physical Education, B
History, B
History Teacher Education, B
Hospitality Administration/Management, B
Human Development and Family Studies, B
Journalism, B
Kindergarten/PreSchool Education and Teaching, B
Mathematics, B
Mathematics Teacher Education, B
Modern Greek Language and Literature, B
Music, B
Music Teacher Education, B
Philosophy, B
Physical Education Teaching and Coaching, B
Physics, B
Pre-Law Studies, B
Pre-Medicine/Pre-Medical Studies, B
Pre-Theology/Pre-Ministerial Studies, B
Psychology, B
Religion/Religious Studies, B
Religious Education, B

Religious/Sacred Music, B
Science Teacher Education/General Science
  Teacher Education, B
Secondary Education and Teaching, B
Social Sciences, B
Social Studies Teacher Education, B
Sociology, B
Spanish Language and Literature, B
Speech Teacher Education, B

CORNERSTONE UNIVERSITY

Accounting, B
Airline/Commercial/Professional Pilot and Flight
  Crew, B
Ancient Near Eastern and Biblical
  Languages, Literatures, and Linguistics, B
Bible/Biblical Studies, B
Biology Teacher Education, B
Biology/Biological Sciences, B
Broadcast Journalism, A
Business Administration and Management, B
Business Administration, Management and
  Operations, B
Creative Writing, B
Cultural Studies, P
Early Childhood Education and Teaching, B
Education, B
Elementary Education and Teaching, B
English Language and Literature, B
English/Language Arts Teacher Education, B
Environmental Biology, B
History, B
History Teacher Education, B
Information Science/Studies, B
Interdisciplinary Studies, BM
Kinesiology and Exercise Science, B
Management Information Systems and Services, B
Marketing/Marketing Management, B
Mass Communication/Media Studies, AB
Mathematics, B
Mathematics Teacher Education, B
Multi-/Interdisciplinary Studies, B
Music, B
Music Performance, B
Music Teacher Education, B
Music Theory and Composition, B
Pastoral Studies/Counseling, BMP
Philosophy, B
Physical Education Teaching and Coaching, B
Political Science and Government, B
Pre-Dentistry Studies, B
Pre-Law Studies, B
Pre-Medicine/Pre-Medical Studies, B
Pre-Theology/Pre-Ministerial Studies, B
Pre-Veterinary Studies, B
Psychology, B
Religion/Religious Studies, B
Religious Education, ABMP
Science Teacher Education/General Science
  Teacher Education, B
Secondary Education and Teaching, B
Social Science Teacher Education, B
Social Studies Teacher Education, B
Social Work, B
Sociology, B
Spanish Language and Literature, B
Speech and Rhetorical Studies, B
Sport and Fitness Administration/Management, B
Theology and Religious Vocations, MP

DAVENPORT UNIVERSITY
(DEARBORN)

Accounting, ABM
Administrative Assistant and Secretarial Science, A
Business Administration and Management, AB
Business Administration, Management and
  Operations, M
Business/Commerce, B
Computer and Information Sciences, AB
Computer and Information Systems Security, B
Computer
  Programming, Vendor/Product Certification, B
Computer Systems Analysis/Analyst, AB
Data Modeling/Warehousing and Database
  Administration, B
E-Commerce/Electronic Commerce, B

Electrical, Electronic and Communications
Engineering Technology/Technician, A
Electronic Commerce, M
Entrepreneurship/Entrepreneurial Studies, AB
Finance, AB
Finance and Banking, M
Health Information/Medical Records
Technology/Technician, A
Health Services Administration, M
Health/Health Care Administration/Management, B
Human Resources Management and Services, M
Information Technology, AB
International Business/Trade/Commerce, BM
Legal Assistant/Paralegal, AB
Management, M
Management Information Systems and Services, AB
Marketing, M
Marketing/Marketing Management, AB
Medical/Clinical Assistant, A
Nursing - Registered Nurse Training, AB
Nursing Science, A
Prepress/Desktop Publishing and Digital Imaging
Design, A
System, Networking, and LAN/WAN
Management/Manager, B

DAVENPORT UNIVERSITY (MIDLAND)

Accounting, A
Accounting Technology/Technician and
Bookkeeping, A
Administrative Assistant and Secretarial Science, A
Business Administration and Management, A
Business/Office Automation/Technology/Data
Entry, A
Carpentry/Carpenter, A
Computer Engineering Technology/Technician, A
Computer Programming/Programmer, A
Computer Typography and Composition Equipment
Operator, A
Data Processing and Data Processing
Technology/Technician, A
Electrical, Electronic and Communications
Engineering Technology/Technician, A
Emergency Medical Technology/Technician (EMT
Paramedic), A
Finance, A
Hospitality Administration/Management, A
Legal Assistant/Paralegal, A
Medical Administrative Assistant/Secretary, A
Medical/Clinical Assistant, A
Nursing - Registered Nurse Training, A

DELTA COLLEGE

Accounting, A
Administrative Assistant and Secretarial Science, A
Apparel and Textile Marketing Management, A
Architectural Engineering Technology/Technician, A
Art/Art Studies, General, A
Automobile/Automotive Mechanics
Technology/Technician, A
Avionics Maintenance Technology/Technician, A
Building/Construction
Finishing, Management, and Inspection, A
Business Administration and Management, A
Carpentry/Carpenter, A
Chemical Engineering, A
Child Development, A
Computer and Information Systems Security, A
Computer Science, A
Construction Engineering Technology/Technician, A
Construction Trades, A
Consumer Merchandising/Retailing Management, A
Corrections, A
Cosmetology/Cosmetologist, A
Criminal Justice/Law Enforcement Administration, A
Criminal Justice/Police Science, A
Dental Assisting/Assistant, A
Dental Hygiene/Hygienist, A
Diagnostic Medical Sonography/Sonographer and
Ultrasound Technician, A
Drafting and Design Technology/Technician, A
Drafting/Design Engineering
Technologies/Technicians, A
Electrician, A
Emergency Medical Technology/Technician (EMT
Paramedic), A

Engineering Technology, A
Entrepreneurship/Entrepreneurial Studies, A
Environmental Engineering
Technology/Environmental Technology, A
Executive Assistant/Executive Secretary, A
Family and Consumer Sciences/Human Sciences, A
Fire Science/Firefighting, A
General Office Occupations and Clerical Services, A
Heating, Air Conditioning and Refrigeration
Technology/Technician, A
Heating, Air Conditioning, Ventilation and
Refrigeration Maintenance
Technology/Technician, A
Industrial Radiologic Technology/Technician, A
Information Technology, A
Interior Design, A
Legal Administrative Assistant/Secretary, A
Legal Assistant/Paralegal, A
Liberal Arts and Sciences Studies and
Humanities, A
Licensed Practical/Vocational Nurse Training, A
Machine Tool Technology/Machinist, A
Marketing/Marketing Management, A
Mechanic and Repair Technologies/Technicians, A
Mechanical Engineering/Mechanical
Technology/Technician, A
Medical Administrative Assistant/Secretary, A
Medical/Clinical Assistant, A
Merchandising and Buying Operations, A
Nursing - Registered Nurse Training, A
Office Management and Supervision, A
Physical Therapist Assistant, A
Physician Assistant, A
Pipefitting/Pipefitter and Sprinkler Fitter, A
Psychology, A
Public Health Education and Promotion, A
Radio and Television Broadcasting
Technology/Technician, A
Radiologic Technology/Science - Radiographer, A
Respiratory Care Therapy/Therapist, A
Security and Loss Prevention Services, A
Surgical Technology/Technologist, A
Technology Education/Industrial Arts, A
Tool and Die Technology/Technician, A
Water Quality and Wastewater Treatment
Management and Recycling
Technology/Technician, A
Web Page, Digital/Multimedia and Information
Resources Design, A
Web/Multimedia Management and Webmaster, A
Welding Technology/Welder, A

EASTERN MICHIGAN UNIVERSITY

Accounting, BM
Actuarial Science, B
African-American/Black Studies, B
Airline/Commercial/Professional Pilot and Flight
Crew, B
American/United States Studies/Civilization, M
Anthropology, B
Applied Economics, M
Architecture, B
Art Education, M
Art History, Criticism and Conservation, B
Art Teacher Education, B
Art/Art Studies, General, B
Arts Management, BM
Athletic Training and Sports Medicine, B
Aviation/Airway Management and Operations, B
Biochemistry, B
Biological and Biomedical Sciences, M
Biological and Physical Sciences, B
Biology Teacher Education, B
Biology/Biological Sciences, B
Business Administration and Management, B
Business Administration, Management and
Operations, M
Business Teacher Education, B
Business/Commerce, B
Business/Managerial Economics, B
CAD/CADD Drafting and/or Design
Technology/Technician, B
Chemistry, BMO
Chemistry Teacher Education, B
City/Urban, Community and Regional Planning, B

Clinical Laboratory Science/Medical
Technology/Technologist, B
Clinical Psychology, MD
Communication and Media Studies, M
Communication Disorders, M
Communications Technology/Technician, B
Community Organization and Advocacy, B
Computer and Information Sciences, M
Computer Engineering Technology/Technician, B
Computer Science, BM
Computer Teacher Education, B
Construction Engineering Technology/Technician, B
Construction Management, B
Counselor Education/School Counseling and
Guidance Services, MO
Creative Writing, B
Criminology, BM
Curriculum and Instruction, M
Dance, B
Dietetics/Dieticians, B
Drama and Dramatics/Theatre Arts, B
Early Childhood Education and Teaching, M
Economics, BM
Education, MDO
Education/Teaching of Individuals with Emotional
Disturbances, B
Education/Teaching of Individuals with Hearing
Impairments, Including Deafness, B
Education/Teaching of Individuals with Mental
Retardation, B
Education/Teaching of Individuals with Orthopedic
and Other Physical Health Impairments, B
Education/Teaching of Individuals with Specific
Learning Disabilities, B
Education/Teaching of Individuals with Speech or
Language Impairments, B
Education/Teaching of Individuals with Vision
Impairments, Including Blindness, B
Educational Leadership and Administration, MDO
Educational Psychology, M
Electrical, Electronic and Communications
Engineering Technology/Technician, B
Electronic Commerce, M
Elementary Education and Teaching, BM
Engineering Technology, B
English, M
English as a Second Language, MO
English Composition, B
English Language and Literature, B
English/Language Arts Teacher Education, B
Entrepreneurship/Entrepreneurial Studies, B
Exercise and Sports Science, M
Facilities Planning and Management, B
Fashion Merchandising, B
Film/Cinema Studies, B
Finance, B
Fine Arts and Art Studies, M
Foreign Language Teacher Education, B
Foundations and Philosophy of Education, M
French Language and Literature, BM
French Language Teacher Education, B
General Merchandising, Sales, and Related
Marketing Operations, B
Geography, BM
Geology/Earth Science, B
Geophysics and Seismology, B
German Language and Literature, BMO
German Language Teacher Education, B
Germanic Languages, Literatures, and Linguistics, B
Gerontology, O
Health and Physical Education, B
Health Promotion, M
Health/Health Care Administration/Management, B
Hispanic Studies, O
Historic Preservation and Conservation, M
History, BM
History Teacher Education, B
Hospitality Administration/Management, B
Human Resources Management and Services, M
Industrial and Manufacturing Management, M
Industrial Technology/Technician, B
Information Science/Studies, B
Interior Design, B
International Business/Trade/Commerce, BM
International Economics, B
International Trade, M

Japanese Language and Literature, B
Journalism, B
Labor Studies, B
Legal Assistant/Paralegal, B
Linguistics, BM
Logistics and Materials Management, M
Management, M
Management Information Systems and
   Services, BMO
Manufacturing Technology/Technician, B
Marketing, M
Marketing/Marketing Management, B
Mathematics, BM
Mathematics Teacher Education, BM
Mechanical Drafting and Mechanical Drafting
   CAD/CADD, B
Mechanical Engineering/Mechanical
   Technology/Technician, B
Middle School Education, M
Multilingual and Multicultural Education, M
Music, BM
Music Performance, B
Music Teacher Education, B
Music Therapy/Therapist, B
Nursing - Adult, M
Nursing - Registered Nurse Training, B
Nursing Education, MO
Occupational Therapy/Therapist, BM
Office Management and Supervision, B
Organizational Management, M
Parks, Recreation and Leisure Facilities
   Management, B
Philosophy, B
Physical Education Teaching and Coaching, B
Physical Sciences, B
Physics, BM
Physics Teacher Education, B
Plastics Engineering Technology/Technician, B
Political Science and Government, B
Polymer/Plastics Engineering, M
Psychology, BMD
Public Administration, BM
Public Administration and Social Service
   Professions, B
Public Relations/Image Management, B
Quality Management, M
Radio and Television Broadcasting
   Technology/Technician, B
Reading Teacher Education, BM
Sales and Marketing Operations/Marketing and
   Distribution Teacher Education, B
Science Teacher Education/General Science
   Teacher Education, BM
Secondary Education and Teaching, M
Security and Protective Services, B
Social Science Teacher Education, B
Social Sciences, BM
Social Studies Teacher Education, B
Social Work, BMO
Sociology, BM
Spanish Language and Literature, BM
Spanish Language Teacher Education, B
Special Education and Teaching, BMO
Specialized Merchandising, Sales, and Marketing
   Operations, B
Speech and Rhetorical Studies, M
Speech-Language Pathology/Pathologist, B
Statistics, BM
Technical and Business Writing, B
Technology and Public Policy, M
Technology Teacher Education/Industrial Arts
   Teacher Education, B
Theater, M
Theatre/Theatre Arts Management, B
Therapeutic Recreation/Recreational Therapy, B
Toxicology, B
Women's Studies, BM
Writing, M

FERRIS STATE UNIVERSITY

Accounting, AB
Actuarial Science, B
Advertising, B
Allied Health and Medical Assisting Services, M
Applied Mathematics, B
Architectural Engineering Technology/Technician, A

Automobile/Automotive Mechanics
   Technology/Technician, AB
Biology Technician/BioTechnology Laboratory
   Technician, A
Biology/Biological Sciences, B
Building/Construction
   Finishing, Management, and Inspection, B
Business Administration and Management, B
Business Administration, Management and
   Operations, M
Business Teacher Education, B
Business/Managerial Economics, B
Chemical Engineering, A
Chemistry, B
Civil Engineering Technology/Technician, A
Clinical Laboratory Science/Medical
   Technology/Technologist, B
Clinical/Medical Laboratory Technician, AB
Commercial and Advertising Art, A
Communications Technology/Technician, A
Computer Programming/Programmer, B
Computer Science, M
Construction Engineering Technology/Technician, A
Consumer Merchandising/Retailing Management, B
Criminal Justice/Police Science, B
Criminology, M
Curriculum and Instruction, M
Dental Hygiene/Hygienist, A
Design and Applied Arts, M
Developmental Education, M
Diagnostic Medical Sonography/Sonographer and
   Ultrasound Technician, A
Drafting and Design Technology/Technician, A
Drafting/Design Engineering
   Technologies/Technicians, A
Education, M
Educational Administration and Supervision, M
Educational Leadership and Administration, M
Educational Media/Instructional Technology, M
Electrical, Electronic and Communications
   Engineering Technology/Technician, B
Electronic Commerce, M
Elementary Education and Teaching, B
Environmental Health, B
Family and Consumer Sciences/Home Economics
   Teacher Education, B
Finance, B
Fine Arts and Art Studies, M
Fine/Studio Arts, B
Furniture Design and Manufacturing, B
Health Information/Medical Records
   Administration/Administrator, AB
Health/Health Care Administration/Management, B
Heating, Air Conditioning, Ventilation and
   Refrigeration Maintenance
   Technology/Technician, AB
Heavy Equipment Maintenance
   Technology/Technician, AB
Hospitality Administration/Management, B
Human Services, M
Industrial Design, A
Industrial Engineering, B
Industrial Production Technologies/Technicians, A
Industrial Radiologic Technology/Technician, A
Industrial Technology/Technician, AB
Information Science/Studies, B
Insurance, B
Interior Design, B
International Business/Trade/Commerce, B
Labor and Industrial Relations, B
Legal Administrative Assistant/Secretary, A
Legal Assistant/Paralegal, A
Liberal Arts and Sciences Studies and
   Humanities, A
Machine Tool Technology/Machinist, A
Management Information Systems and
   Services, BM
Marketing/Marketing Management, B
Mass Communication/Media Studies, B
Mathematics, B
Mathematics and Statistics, B
Mathematics Teacher Education, B
Mechanical Engineering/Mechanical
   Technology/Technician, A
Metal and Jewelry Arts, B
Mortuary Science and Embalming/Embalmer, A

Music Management and Merchandising, B
Nuclear Medical Technology/Technologist, AB
Nursing, M
Nursing - Registered Nurse Training, AB
Nursing Administration, M
Nursing Education, M
Occupational Safety and Health
   Technology/Technician, AB
Opticianry/Ophthalmic Dispensing Optician, A
Optometry, P
Ornamental Horticulture, A
Parks, Recreation, Leisure and Fitness Studies, B
Pharmacy, P
Pharmacy, Pharmaceutical Sciences, and Administration, B
Plastics Engineering Technology/Technician, AB
Polymer/Plastics Engineering, B
Pre-Engineering, A
Pre-Law Studies, A
Pre-Pharmacy Studies, A
Prepress/Desktop Publishing and Digital Imaging
   Design, B
Public Administration, B
Public Relations/Image Management, B
Quality Control Technology/Technician, B
Quality Management, M
Real Estate, A
Respiratory Care Therapy/Therapist, A
Restaurant, Culinary, and Catering
   Management/Manager, A
Restaurant/Food Services Management, A
Science Teacher Education/General Science
   Teacher Education, B
Secondary Education and Teaching, B
Social Work, B
Special Products Marketing Operations, A
Speech and Rhetorical Studies, A
Statistics, B
Survey Technology/Surveying, AB
Technical and Business Writing, AB
Welding Technology/Welder, AB

FINLANDIA UNIVERSITY

Art/Art Studies, General, B
Business Administration and Management, B
Ceramic Arts and Ceramics, B
Criminal Justice/Law Enforcement Administration, A
Education, B
Fiber, Textile and Weaving Arts, B
Fine/Studio Arts, B
General Studies, A
Human Services, B
Industrial Design, B
International Business/Trade/Commerce, B
Liberal Arts and Sciences Studies and
   Humanities, B
Nursing - Registered Nurse Training, B
Physical Therapist Assistant, A
Teacher Education, Multiple Levels, B

GLEN OAKS COMMUNITY COLLEGE

Automobile/Automotive Mechanics
   Technology/Technician, A
Biological and Physical Sciences, A
Business Administration and Management, A
Liberal Arts and Sciences Studies and
   Humanities, A
Nursing - Registered Nurse Training, A

GOGEBIC COMMUNITY COLLEGE

Accounting, A
Administrative Assistant and Secretarial Science, A
Automobile/Automotive Mechanics
   Technology/Technician, A
Biology/Biological Sciences, A
Building/Construction
   Finishing, Management, and Inspection, A
Business Administration and Management, A
Business/Office Automation/Technology/Data
   Entry, A
Carpentry/Carpenter, A
Child Care and Support Services Management, A
Child Development, A
Commercial and Advertising Art, A
Computer Engineering Technology/Technician, A
Computer Graphics, A
Computer Programming, Specific Applications, A

Computer Science, A
Computer Typography and Composition Equipment
    Operator, A
Computer/Information Technology Services
    Administration and Management, A
Construction Engineering Technology/Technician, A
Corrections, A
Criminal Justice/Law Enforcement Administration, A
Data Processing and Data Processing
    Technology/Technician, A
Drafting and Design Technology/Technician, A
Education, A
Engineering, A
Forest Sciences and Biology, A
Graphic and Printing Equipment Operator
    Production, A
Health Information/Medical Records
    Administration/Administrator, A
Humanities/Humanistic Studies, A
Information Technology, A
Kindergarten/PreSchool Education and Teaching, A
Legal Administrative Assistant/Secretary, A
Liberal Arts and Sciences Studies and
    Humanities, A
Licensed Practical/Vocational Nurse Training, A
Mathematics, A
Medical Administrative Assistant/Secretary, A
Nursing - Registered Nurse Training, A
Office Management and Supervision, A
Psychology, A
Social Sciences, A
Social Work, A
Sociology, A
System Administration/Administrator, A
Word Processing, A

GRACE BIBLE COLLEGE

Accounting, B
Bible/Biblical Studies, B
Business Administration and Management, AB
Computer and Information Sciences, B
Digital Communication and Media/Multimedia, B
Early Childhood Education and Teaching, B
Elementary Education and Teaching, B
Finance and Financial Management Services, B
Human Services, B
Liberal Arts and Sciences Studies and
    Humanities, A
Management Science, B
Marketing/Marketing Management, B
Missions/Missionary Studies and Missiology, B
Multi-/Interdisciplinary Studies, B
Music, B
Music Teacher Education, B
Pastoral Studies/Counseling, B
Religion/Religious Studies, A
Secondary Education and Teaching, B
Theology/Theological Studies, B
Youth Ministry, B

GRAND RAPIDS COMMUNITY COLLEGE

Administrative Assistant and Secretarial Science, A
Architectural Engineering Technology/Technician, A
Art/Art Studies, General, A
Automobile/Automotive Mechanics
    Technology/Technician, A
Business Administration and Management, A
Computer Engineering Technology/Technician, A
Computer Programming/Programmer, A
Computer Science, A
Corrections, A
Criminal Justice/Law Enforcement Administration, A
Criminal Justice/Police Science, A
Culinary Arts/Chef Training, A
Dental Hygiene/Hygienist, A
Drafting and Design Technology/Technician, A
Electrical, Electronic and Communications
    Engineering Technology/Technician, A
Fashion Merchandising, A
Forestry, A
Geology/Earth Science, A
Heating, Air Conditioning, Ventilation and
    Refrigeration Maintenance
    Technology/Technician, A
Industrial Technology/Technician, A

Legal Administrative Assistant/Secretary, A
Liberal Arts and Sciences Studies and
    Humanities, A
Licensed Practical/Vocational Nurse Training, A
Mass Communication/Media Studies, A
Medical Administrative Assistant/Secretary, A
Music, A
Nursing - Registered Nurse Training, A
Plastics Engineering Technology/Technician, A
Quality Control Technology/Technician, A
Welding Technology/Welder, A

GRAND VALLEY STATE UNIVERSITY

Accounting, BM
Adult and Continuing Education and Teaching, M
Advertising, B
Allied Health and Medical Assisting Services, MD
Anthropology, B
Applied Mathematics, B
Art History, Criticism and Conservation, B
Art Teacher Education, B
Art/Art Studies, General, B
Athletic Training and Sports Medicine, B
Behavioral Sciences, B
Biochemistry, B
Biological and Biomedical Sciences, M
Biological and Physical Sciences, B
Biology/Biological Sciences, B
Biomedical Sciences, B
Broadcast Journalism, B
Business Administration and Management, B
Business Administration, Management and
    Operations, MO
Cell/Cellular and Molecular Biology, B
Ceramic Arts and Ceramics, B
Chemistry, B
Cinematography and Film/Video Production, B
Classics and Classical
    Languages, Literatures, and Linguistics, B
Clinical Laboratory Science/Medical
    Technology/Technologist, B
Commercial and Advertising Art, B
Communication and Media Studies, M
Comparative Literature, B
Computer and Information Sciences, B
Computer Engineering, BM
Computer Programming/Programmer, B
Computer Science, B
Creative Writing, B
Criminal Justice/Law Enforcement Administration, B
Criminal Justice/Police Science, B
Criminology, MO
Drama and Dramatics/Theatre Arts, B
Drawing, B
Early Childhood Education and Teaching, M
Economics, B
Education, BM
Education/Teaching of the Gifted and Talented, M
Educational Administration and Supervision, M
Educational Leadership and Administration, M
Educational Media/Instructional Technology, M
Electrical Engineering, M
Electrical, Electronics and Communications
    Engineering, B
Elementary Education and Teaching, BM
Engineering, B
Engineering and Applied Sciences, M
Engineering/Industrial Management, B
English, M
English as a Second Language, M
English Language and Literature, B
European Studies/Civilization, B
Film/Cinema Studies, B
Finance, B
Fine/Studio Arts, B
French Language and Literature, B
Geology/Earth Science, B
German Language and Literature, B
Health Services Administration, M
Higher Education/Higher Education
    Administration, M
History, B
Hotel/Motel Administration/Management, B
Human Resources Management/Personnel
    Administration, B
Humanities/Humanistic Studies, B

Hydrology and Water Resources Science, B
Industrial Engineering, B
Information Science/Studies, BM
Interdisciplinary Studies, B
International Business/Trade/Commerce, B
International Relations and Affairs, B
Journalism, B
Labor and Industrial Relations, B
Land Use Planning and
    Management/Development, B
Law and Legal Studies, B
Legal Assistant/Paralegal, B
Liberal Arts and Sciences Studies and
    Humanities, B
Management Information Systems and Services, B
Manufacturing Engineering, M
Marketing/Marketing Management, B
Mass Communication/Media Studies, B
Mathematics, B
Mechanical Engineering, BM
Metal and Jewelry Arts, B
Middle School Education, M
Music, B
Music Teacher Education, B
Natural Resources Management/Development and
    Policy, B
Natural Sciences, B
Nursing, MO
Nursing - Advanced Practice, M
Nursing - Registered Nurse Training, B
Nursing Administration, M
Nursing Education, M
Occupational Safety and Health
    Technology/Technician, B
Occupational Therapist Assistant, B
Occupational Therapy/Therapist, M
Parks, Recreation and Leisure Facilities
    Management, B
Philosophy, B
Photography, B
Physical Education Teaching and Coaching, B
Physical Sciences, B
Physical Therapy/Therapist, BMD
Physician Assistant, BM
Physics, B
Physiological Psychology/Psychobiology, B
Piano and Organ, B
Political Science and Government, B
Pre-Dentistry Studies, B
Pre-Law Studies, B
Pre-Medicine/Pre-Medical Studies, B
Pre-Veterinary Studies, B
Printmaking, B
Psychology, B
Public Administration, BM
Public Health (MPH, DPH), B
Public Policy Analysis, B
Public Relations/Image Management, B
Radiation Biology/Radiobiology, B
Radio and Television, B
Reading Teacher Education, BM
Russian Studies, B
School Psychology, M
Science Teacher Education/General Science
    Teacher Education, B
Sculpture, B
Secondary Education and Teaching, B
Social Sciences, B
Social Studies Teacher Education, B
Social Work, BM
Sociology, B
Software Engineering, M
Spanish Language and Literature, B
Special Education and Teaching, BM
Statistics, B
Taxation, M
Technical and Business Writing, B
Telecommunications Technology/Technician, B
Therapeutic Recreation/Recreational Therapy, B
Tourism and Travel Services Management, B
Violin, Viola, Guitar and Other Stringed
    Instruments, B
Voice and Opera, B
Wildlife and Wildlands Science and Management, B
Wildlife Biology, B
Wind and Percussion Instruments, B

Women's Studies, B

GREAT LAKES CHRISTIAN COLLEGE

Bible/Biblical Studies, B
Divinity/Ministry (BD, MDiv.), B
Education, B
Music, B
Religious Education, A
Theology/Theological Studies, B

HENRY FORD COMMUNITY COLLEGE

Accounting, A
Administrative Assistant and Secretarial Science, A
Applied Art, A
Art/Art Studies, General, A
Artificial Intelligence and Robotics, A
Automobile/Automotive Mechanics
  Technology/Technician, A
Business Administration and Management, A
Business Machine Repairer, A
Ceramic Arts and Ceramics, A
Commercial and Advertising Art, A
Computer and Information Sciences, A
Computer Science, A
Construction Engineering Technology/Technician, A
Corrections, A
Criminal Justice/Law Enforcement Administration, A
Criminal Justice/Police Science, A
Culinary Arts/Chef Training, A
Dance, A
Data Processing and Data Processing
  Technology/Technician, A
Drafting and Design Technology/Technician, A
Drama and Dramatics/Theatre Arts, A
Drawing, A
Electrical, Electronic and Communications
  Engineering Technology/Technician, A
Emergency Medical Technology/Technician (EMT
  Paramedic), A
Energy Management and Systems
  Technology/Technician, A
Fire Science/Firefighting, A
Food Technology and Processing, A
Health Information/Medical Records
  Administration/Administrator, A
Heating, Air Conditioning, Ventilation and
  Refrigeration Maintenance
  Technology/Technician, A
Hospitality Administration/Management, A
Hotel/Motel Administration/Management, A
Industrial Radiologic Technology/Technician, A
Industrial Technology/Technician, A
Information Science/Studies, A
Instrumentation Technology/Technician, A
Interior Design, A
Kinesiology and Exercise Science, A
Legal Administrative Assistant/Secretary, A
Legal Assistant/Paralegal, A
Liberal Arts and Sciences Studies and
  Humanities, A
Marketing/Marketing Management, A
Mass Communication/Media Studies, A
Materials Sciences, A
Medical Administrative Assistant/Secretary, A
Medical/Clinical Assistant, A
Nursing - Registered Nurse Training, A
Pre-Engineering, A
Quality Control Technology/Technician, A
Radiologic Technology/Science - Radiographer, A
Real Estate, A
Respiratory Care Therapy/Therapist, A
Special Products Marketing Operations, A
Transportation and Materials Moving, A

HILLSDALE COLLEGE

Accounting, B
American/United States Studies/Civilization, B
Art/Art Studies, General, B
Biology/Biological Sciences, B
Business Administration and Management, B
Chemistry, B
Christian Studies, B
Classics and Classical
  Languages, Literatures, and Linguistics, B
Comparative Literature, B
Computer Science, B

Drafting and Design Technology/Technician, B
Drama and Dramatics/Theatre Arts, B
Early Childhood Education and Teaching, B
Economics, B
Education, B
Elementary Education and Teaching, B
English Language and Literature, B
European Studies/Civilization, B
Finance, B
French Language and Literature, B
German Language and Literature, B
History, B
Interdisciplinary Studies, B
International Relations and Affairs, B
Kindergarten/PreSchool Education and Teaching, B
Marketing/Marketing Management, B
Mathematics, B
Music, B
Philosophy, B
Physical Education Teaching and Coaching, B
Physics, B
Political Science and Government, B
Pre-Dentistry Studies, B
Pre-Medicine/Pre-Medical Studies, B
Pre-Veterinary Studies, B
Psychology, B
Religion/Religious Studies, B
Secondary Education and Teaching, B
Sociology, B
Spanish Language and Literature, B
Speech and Rhetorical Studies, B
Teacher Education, Multiple Levels, B

HOPE COLLEGE

Accounting, B
Ancient Near Eastern and Biblical
  Languages, Literatures, and Linguistics, B
Architecture, B
Area Studies, B
Art History, Criticism and Conservation, B
Art Teacher Education, B
Athletic Training and Sports Medicine, B
Biology Teacher Education, B
Biology/Biological Sciences, B
Business Administration and Management, B
Business/Managerial Economics, B
Chemistry, B
Chemistry Teacher Education, B
Classics and Classical
  Languages, Literatures, and Linguistics, B
Communication Studies/Speech Communication
  and Rhetoric, B
Computer Science, B
Construction Trades, B
Dance, B
Drama and Dance Teacher Education, B
Drama and Dramatics/Theatre Arts, B
Economics, B
Education/Teaching of Individuals with Emotional
  Disturbances, B
Education/Teaching of Individuals with Specific
  Learning Disabilities, B
Elementary Education and Teaching, B
Engineering, B
Engineering Physics, B
English Language and Literature, B
English/Language Arts Teacher Education, B
Environmental Studies, B
Family and Consumer Sciences/Human Sciences, B
Fine/Studio Arts, B
French Language and Literature, B
French Language Teacher Education, B
General Studies, B
Geology/Earth Science, B
Geophysics and Seismology, B
German Language and Literature, B
German Language Teacher Education, B
History, B
History Teacher Education, B
Humanities/Humanistic Studies, B
Interdisciplinary Studies, B
International/Global Studies, B
Japanese Language and Literature, B
Jazz/Jazz Studies, B
Kinesiology and Exercise Science, B
Latin Language and Literature, B

Latin Teacher Education, B
Law and Legal Studies, B
Liberal Arts and Sciences Studies and
  Humanities, B
Library Science, B
Mathematics, B
Mathematics Teacher Education, B
Mechanic and Repair Technologies/Technicians, B
Multi-/Interdisciplinary Studies, B
Music, B
Music Performance, B
Music Teacher Education, B
Music Theory and Composition, B
Nursing - Registered Nurse Training, B
Philosophy, B
Physical Education Teaching and Coaching, B
Physics, B
Physics Teacher Education, B
Piano and Organ, B
Political Science and Government, B
Precision Production Trades, B
Psychology, B
Religion/Religious Studies, B
Science Teacher Education/General Science
  Teacher Education, B
Science Technologies/Technicians, B
Secondary Education and Teaching, B
Social Sciences, B
Social Studies Teacher Education, B
Social Work, B
Sociology, B
Spanish Language and Literature, B
Spanish Language Teacher Education, B
Teacher Education and Professional
  Development, Specific Subject Areas, B
Theology and Religious Vocations, B
Transportation and Materials Moving, B
Violin, Viola, Guitar and Other Stringed
  Instruments, B
Voice and Opera, B

ITT TECHNICAL INSTITUTE (CANTON)

Business Administration and Management, A
CAD/CADD Drafting and/or Design
  Technology/Technician, A
Computer Programming/Programmer, A
Criminal Justice/Law Enforcement Administration, A
Electrical, Electronic and Communications
  Engineering Technology/Technician, A
System, Networking, and LAN/WAN
  Management/Manager, A
Web Page, Digital/Multimedia and Information
  Resources Design, A
Web/Multimedia Management and Webmaster, A

ITT TECHNICAL INSTITUTE (GRAND RAPIDS)

Business Administration and Management, A
CAD/CADD Drafting and/or Design
  Technology/Technician, A
Computer Programming/Programmer, A
Criminal Justice/Law Enforcement Administration, A
Electrical, Electronic and Communications
  Engineering Technology/Technician, A
System, Networking, and LAN/WAN
  Management/Manager, A
Web Page, Digital/Multimedia and Information
  Resources Design, A
Web/Multimedia Management and Webmaster, A

ITT TECHNICAL INSTITUTE (TROY)

Business Administration and Management, A
CAD/CADD Drafting and/or Design
  Technology/Technician, A
Computer Programming/Programmer, A
Criminal Justice/Law Enforcement Administration, A
Electrical, Electronic and Communications
  Engineering Technology/Technician, A
System, Networking, and LAN/WAN
  Management/Manager, A
Web Page, Digital/Multimedia and Information
  Resources Design, A

Web/Multimedia Management and Webmaster, A

JACKSON COMMUNITY COLLEGE

Accounting and Finance, A
Administrative Assistant and Secretarial Science, A
Airline/Commercial/Professional Pilot and Flight
   Crew, A
Automobile/Automotive Mechanics
   Technology/Technician, A
Business Administration and Management, A
Computer and Information Sciences and Support
   Services, A
Construction Trades, A
Corrections, A
Criminal Justice/Law Enforcement Administration, A
Data Processing and Data Processing
   Technology/Technician, A
Diagnostic Medical Sonography/Sonographer and
   Ultrasound Technician, A
Early Childhood Education and Teaching, A
Electrical, Electronic and Communications
   Engineering Technology/Technician, A
Emergency Medical Technology/Technician (EMT
   Paramedic), A
Executive Assistant/Executive Secretary, A
General Studies, A
Graphic Design, A
Heating, Air Conditioning and Refrigeration
   Technology/Technician, A
Liberal Arts and Sciences Studies and
   Humanities, A
Licensed Practical/Vocational Nurse Training, A
Marketing/Marketing Management, A
Medical Insurance Specialist/Medical Biller, A
Medical Radiologic Technology/Science - Radiation
   Therapist, A
Medical Transcription/Transcriptionist, A
Medical/Clinical Assistant, A
Nursing - Registered Nurse Training, A

KALAMAZOO COLLEGE

Anthropology, B
Art History, Criticism and Conservation, B
Art/Art Studies, General, B
Biology/Biological Sciences, B
Business/Managerial Economics, B
Chemistry, B
Classics and Classical
   Languages, Literatures, and Linguistics, B
Computer Science, B
Drama and Dramatics/Theatre Arts, B
English Language and Literature, B
French Language and Literature, B
German Language and Literature, B
History, B
Interdisciplinary Studies, B
Mathematics, B
Music, B
Philosophy, B
Physics, B
Political Science and Government, B
Psychology, B
Public Health (MPH, DPH), B
Religion/Religious Studies, B
Sociology, B
Spanish Language and Literature, B

KALAMAZOO VALLEY COMMUNITY COLLEGE

Accounting Technology/Technician and
   Bookkeeping, A
Automobile/Automotive Mechanics
   Technology/Technician, A
Business Administration and Management, A
Chemical Technology/Technician, A
Commercial and Advertising Art, A
Computer Programming/Programmer, A
Criminal Justice/Police Science, A
Dental Hygiene/Hygienist, A
Drafting and Design Technology/Technician, A
Electrical, Electronic and Communications
   Engineering Technology/Technician, A
Elementary Education and Teaching, A
Emergency Medical Technology/Technician (EMT
   Paramedic), A
Executive Assistant/Executive Secretary, A

Fire Science/Firefighting, A
Heating, Air Conditioning and Refrigeration
   Technology/Technician, A
Legal Administrative Assistant/Secretary, A
Liberal Arts and Sciences Studies and
   Humanities, A
Machine Tool Technology/Machinist, A
Management Information Systems and Services, A
Marketing/Marketing Management, A
Mechanical Engineering/Mechanical
   Technology/Technician, A
Medical Administrative Assistant/Secretary, A
Medical/Clinical Assistant, A
Nursing - Registered Nurse Training, A
Plastics Engineering Technology/Technician, A
Pre-Engineering, A
Public Health (MPH, DPH), A
Respiratory Care Therapy/Therapist, A
Welding Technology/Welder, A

KELLOGG COMMUNITY COLLEGE

Accounting, A
Accounting Technology/Technician and
   Bookkeeping, A
Administrative Assistant and Secretarial Science, A
Anthropology, A
Art Teacher Education, A
Art/Art Studies, General, A
Biology/Biological Sciences, A
Business Administration and Management, A
Chemical Technology/Technician, A
Chemistry, A
Clinical/Medical Laboratory Technician, A
Commercial and Advertising Art, A
Communication Studies/Speech Communication
   and Rhetoric, A
Computer Engineering Technology/Technician, A
Computer Graphics, A
Computer Programming, Specific Applications, A
Computer Programming/Programmer, A
Computer Software and Media Applications, A
Corrections, A
Criminal Justice/Police Science, A
Criminal Justice/Safety Studies, A
Data Entry/Microcomputer Applications, A
Dental Hygiene/Hygienist, A
Drafting and Design Technology/Technician, A
Drama and Dramatics/Theatre Arts, A
Elementary Education and Teaching, A
Emergency Medical Technology/Technician (EMT
   Paramedic), A
Engineering, A
English Language and Literature, A
Executive Assistant/Executive Secretary, A
Fire Protection and Safety Technology/Technician, A
General Studies, A
Heating, Air Conditioning, Ventilation and
   Refrigeration Maintenance
   Technology/Technician, A
History, A
Human Services, A
Industrial Technology/Technician, A
International Relations and Affairs, A
Journalism, A
Kindergarten/PreSchool Education and Teaching, A
Legal Administrative Assistant/Secretary, A
Legal Assistant/Paralegal, A
Liberal Arts and Sciences Studies and
   Humanities, A
Licensed Practical/Vocational Nurse Training, A
Machine Tool Technology/Machinist, A
Mathematics, A
Medical Administrative Assistant/Secretary, A
Medical Radiologic Technology/Science - Radiation
   Therapist, A
Music, A
Nursing - Registered Nurse Training, A
Philosophy, A
Physical Education Teaching and Coaching, A
Physical Therapist Assistant, A
Physics, A
Pipefitting/Pipefitter and Sprinkler Fitter, A
Plastics Engineering Technology/Technician, A
Political Science and Government, A
Pre-Law Studies, A
Pre-Medicine/Pre-Medical Studies, A

Pre-Pharmacy Studies, A
Pre-Theology/Pre-Ministerial Studies, A
Pre-Veterinary Studies, A
Psychology, A
Public Relations/Image Management, A
Radio and Television Broadcasting
   Technology/Technician, A
Robotics Technology/Technician, A
Secondary Education and Teaching, A
Sheet Metal Technology/Sheetworking, A
Social Work, A
Sociology, A
Special Education and Teaching, A
Technology Teacher Education/Industrial Arts
   Teacher Education, A
Welding Technology/Welder, A
Word Processing, A

KETTERING UNIVERSITY

Accounting, B
Accounting and Finance, B
Applied Mathematics, B
Automotive Engineering Technology/Technician, M
Biochemistry, B
Biomedical/Medical Engineering, B
Business Administration and Management, B
Chemistry, B
Computer Engineering, B
Computer Science, B
Computer/Information Technology Services
   Administration and Management, B
Electrical, Electronics and Communications
   Engineering, B
Engineering and Applied Sciences, M
Engineering Design, M
Engineering Management, M
Engineering/Industrial Management, B
Finance, B
Industrial Engineering, B
Information Science/Studies, BM
Management Information Systems and Services, B
Manufacturing Engineering, M
Marketing/Marketing Management, B
Mechanical Engineering, BM
Operations Management and Supervision, B
Operations Research, M
Physics, B
Polymer/Plastics Engineering, B
Statistics, B

KIRTLAND COMMUNITY COLLEGE

Accounting, A
Administrative Assistant and Secretarial Science, A
Art/Art Studies, General, A
Automobile/Automotive Mechanics
   Technology/Technician, A
Biological and Physical Sciences, A
Business Administration and Management, A
Corrections, A
Cosmetology/Cosmetologist, A
Creative Writing, A
Criminal Justice/Law Enforcement Administration, A
Drafting and Design Technology/Technician, A
Industrial Technology/Technician, A
Information Science/Studies, A
Legal Administrative Assistant/Secretary, A
Liberal Arts and Sciences Studies and
   Humanities, A
Licensed Practical/Vocational Nurse Training, A
Marketing/Marketing Management, A
Medical Administrative Assistant/Secretary, A
Nursing - Registered Nurse Training, A
Welding Technology/Welder, A

KUYPER COLLEGE

Accounting, B
Administrative Assistant and Secretarial Science, A
Bible/Biblical Studies, AB
Broadcast Journalism, B
Business Administration and Management, B
Child Development, AB
Communication Studies/Speech Communication
   and Rhetoric, B
Computer and Information Sciences, B
Divinity/Ministry (BD, MDiv.), B
Elementary Education and Teaching, B

Liberal Arts and Sciences Studies and
   Humanities, A
Missions/Missionary Studies and Missiology, B
Nursing - Registered Nurse Training, B
Pastoral Studies/Counseling, B
Pre-Theology/Pre-Ministerial Studies, B
Religious Education, AB
Religious/Sacred Music, B
Secondary Education and Teaching, B
Social Work, B
Theology/Theological Studies, B
Youth Ministry, B

LAKE MICHIGAN COLLEGE

Accounting Technology/Technician and
   Bookkeeping, A
Administrative Assistant and Secretarial Science, A
Business Administration and Management, A
Computer and Information Sciences, A
Criminal Justice/Police Science, A
Data Processing and Data Processing
   Technology/Technician, A
Dental Assisting/Assistant, A
Drafting and Design Technology/Technician, A
Early Childhood Education and Teaching, A
Electrical, Electronic and Communications
   Engineering Technology/Technician, A
Electromechanical Technology/Electromechanical
   Engineering Technology, A
Graphic Design, A
Hospitality Administration/Management, A
Industrial Technology/Technician, A
Legal Administrative Assistant/Secretary, A
Liberal Arts and Sciences Studies and
   Humanities, A
Machine Tool Technology/Machinist, A
Marketing/Marketing Management, A
Medical Administrative Assistant/Secretary, A
Medical Office Assistant/Specialist, A
Medical Radiologic Technology/Science - Radiation
   Therapist, A
Nuclear/Nuclear Power Technology/Technician, A
Nursing - Registered Nurse Training, A
Plastics Engineering Technology/Technician, A
Precision Production Trades, A

LAKE SUPERIOR STATE UNIVERSITY

Accounting, AB
Athletic Training and Sports Medicine, B
Business Administration and Management, AB
Business/Managerial Economics, B
Chemistry, A
Clinical Laboratory Science/Medical
   Technology/Technologist, B
Comparative Literature, B
Computer Engineering Technology/Technician, AB
Computer Science, B
Construction Engineering Technology/Technician, A
Corrections, AB
Criminal Justice/Law Enforcement
   Administration, AB
Criminal Justice/Police Science, AB
Early Childhood Education and Teaching, AB
Education, B
Electrical, Electronic and Communications
   Engineering Technology/Technician, AB
Electrical, Electronics and Communications
   Engineering, B
Elementary Education and Teaching, B
Engineering, A
Engineering Technology, A
Engineering/Industrial Management, B
English Language and Literature, B
Environmental Engineering
   Technology/Environmental Technology, B
Environmental Studies, B
Finance, B
Fire Science/Firefighting, AB
French Studies, B
Geology/Earth Science, B
History, B
Human Services, B
Hydrology and Water Resources Science, A
Industrial Technology/Technician, B
Interdisciplinary Studies, B

Junior High/Intermediate/Middle School Education
   and Teaching, B
Kinesiology and Exercise Science, B
Law and Legal Studies, AB
Legal Assistant/Paralegal, AB
Liberal Arts and Sciences Studies and
   Humanities, A
Management Information Systems and Services, A
Mathematics, B
Mathematics and Computer Science, B
Mechanical Engineering, B
Mechanical Engineering/Mechanical
   Technology/Technician, AB
Mental Health/Rehabilitation, A
Natural Resources Management/Development and
   Policy, A
Nursing - Registered Nurse Training, B
Office Management and Supervision, A
Parks, Recreation and Leisure Facilities
   Management, B
Parks, Recreation, Leisure and Fitness Studies, B
Political Science and Government, B
Pre-Dentistry Studies, B
Pre-Law Studies, B
Psychiatric/Mental Health Services Technician, A
Psychology, B
Robotics Technology/Technician, B
Secondary Education and Teaching, B
Social Sciences, B
Sociology, B
Sport and Fitness Administration/Management, A
Teacher Education, Multiple Levels, B
Water Quality and Wastewater Treatment
   Management and Recycling
   Technology/Technician, A
Wildlife and Wildlands Science and Management, B

LANSING COMMUNITY COLLEGE

Accounting, A
Administrative Assistant and Secretarial Science, A
Airline/Commercial/Professional Pilot and Flight
   Crew, A
Architectural Engineering Technology/Technician, A
Art/Art Studies, General, A
Automobile/Automotive Mechanics
   Technology/Technician, A
Avionics Maintenance Technology/Technician, A
Biological and Physical Sciences, A
Biology Technician/BioTechnology Laboratory
   Technician, A
Biology/Biological Sciences, A
Broadcast Journalism, A
Business Administration and Management, A
Carpentry/Carpenter, A
Chemical Engineering, A
Chemistry, A
Child Development, A
Cinematography and Film/Video Production, A
Civil Engineering Technology/Technician, A
Clinical Laboratory Science/Medical
   Technology/Technologist, A
Commercial and Advertising Art, A
Computer Engineering Technology/Technician, A
Computer Graphics, A
Computer Programming/Programmer, A
Computer Typography and Composition Equipment
   Operator, A
Construction Engineering Technology/Technician, A
Consumer Merchandising/Retailing Management, A
Corrections, A
Court Reporting/Court Reporter, A
Criminal Justice/Law Enforcement Administration, A
Criminal Justice/Police Science, A
Dance, A
Dental Hygiene/Hygienist, A
Developmental and Child Psychology, A
Diagnostic Medical Sonography/Sonographer and
   Ultrasound Technician, A
Drafting and Design Technology/Technician, A
Drafting/Design Engineering
   Technologies/Technicians, A
Drama and Dramatics/Theatre Arts, A
Education, A
Electrical, Electronic and Communications
   Engineering Technology/Technician, A

Electromechanical Technology/Electromechanical
   Engineering Technology, A
Elementary Education and Teaching, A
Emergency Medical Technology/Technician (EMT
   Paramedic), A
Engineering, A
Engineering Technology, A
English Language and Literature, A
Film/Cinema Studies, A
Finance, A
Fine/Studio Arts, A
Fire Science/Firefighting, A
Geography, A
Geology/Earth Science, A
Gerontology, A
Heating, Air Conditioning, Ventilation and
   Refrigeration Maintenance
   Technology/Technician, A
Heavy Equipment Maintenance
   Technology/Technician, A
Horticultural Science, A
Hospitality Administration/Management, A
Hotel/Motel Administration/Management, A
Human Resources Management/Personnel
   Administration, A
Human Services, A
Industrial Technology/Technician, A
Information Science/Studies, A
International Business/Trade/Commerce, A
Journalism, A
Kindergarten/PreSchool Education and Teaching, A
Labor and Industrial Relations, A
Landscape Architecture, A
Legal Administrative Assistant/Secretary, A
Legal Assistant/Paralegal, A
Liberal Arts and Sciences Studies and
   Humanities, A
Licensed Practical/Vocational Nurse Training, A
Machine Tool Technology/Machinist, A
Management Information Systems and Services, A
Marketing/Marketing Management, A
Mass Communication/Media Studies, A
Mathematics, A
Mechanical Engineering/Mechanical
   Technology/Technician, A
Medical Radiologic Technology/Science - Radiation
   Therapist, A
Medical/Clinical Assistant, A
Music, A
Nursing - Registered Nurse Training, A
Philosophy, A
Photography, A
Physical Education Teaching and Coaching, A
Pre-Engineering, A
Public Administration, A
Public Relations/Image Management, A
Quality Control Technology/Technician, A
Radio and Television, A
Real Estate, A
Religion/Religious Studies, A
Respiratory Care Therapy/Therapist, A
Sign Language Interpretation and Translation, A
Social Work, A
Special Products Marketing Operations, A
Speech and Rhetorical Studies, A
Surgical Technology/Technologist, A
Survey Technology/Surveying, A
Teacher Assistant/Aide, A
Telecommunications Technology/Technician, A
Tourism and Travel Services Management, A
Veterinary/Animal Health Technology/Technician and
   Veterinary Assistant, A
Voice and Opera, A
Welding Technology/Welder, A

LAWRENCE TECHNOLOGICAL
UNIVERSITY

Architecture, BM
Automotive Engineering Technology/Technician, M
Biochemistry, B
Biomedical/Medical Engineering, B
Business Administration and Management, B
Business Administration, Management and
   Operations, MD
Chemical Technology/Technician, A
Chemistry, B

Civil Engineering, BM
Communications Technology/Technician, B
Computer Engineering, BM
Computer Science, BM
Construction Engineering and Management, M
Construction Engineering Technology/Technician, A
Construction Management, B
Education, M
Electrical and Electronic Engineering
   Technologies/Technicians, A
Electrical Engineering, M
Electrical, Electronic and Communications
   Engineering Technology/Technician, A
Electrical, Electronics and Communications
   Engineering, B
Engineering and Applied Sciences, MD
Engineering Management, M
Engineering Technology, B
Engineering/Industrial Management, B
Environmental Design/Architecture, B
General Studies, A
Humanities/Humanistic Studies, B
Illustration, B
Industrial and Manufacturing Management, M
Industrial Technology/Technician, B
Information Technology, B
Interior Architecture, B
Interior Design, M
Management Information Systems and Services, M
Management of Technology, D
Manufacturing Engineering, MD
Manufacturing Technology/Technician, A
Mathematics, B
Mathematics and Computer Science, B
Mechanical Engineering, BM
Mechanical Engineering/Mechanical
   Technology/Technician, A
Physics, B
Psychology, B
Radio and Television, A
Science Teacher Education/General Science
   Teacher Education, M

LEWIS COLLEGE OF BUSINESS

Accounting, A
Administrative Assistant and Secretarial Science, A
Business Administration and Management, A
Computer Programming/Programmer, A
Computer Science, A
Data Processing and Data Processing
   Technology/Technician, A
Information Science/Studies, A
Legal Administrative Assistant/Secretary, A
Liberal Arts and Sciences Studies and
   Humanities, A
Medical Administrative Assistant/Secretary, A

MACOMB COMMUNITY COLLEGE

Accounting, A
Administrative Assistant and Secretarial Science, A
Agriculture, A
Architectural Drafting and Architectural
   CAD/CADD, A
Automobile/Automotive Mechanics
   Technology/Technician, A
Automotive Engineering Technology/Technician, A
Biology/Biological Sciences, A
Business Administration and Management, A
Business/Commerce, A
Business/Office Automation/Technology/Data
   Entry, A
Cabinetmaking and Millwork/Millwright, A
Chemistry, A
Child Care and Support Services Management, A
Civil Engineering Technology/Technician, A
Commercial and Advertising Art, A
Communication Studies/Speech Communication
   and Rhetoric, A
Computer Programming, Specific Applications, A
Computer Programming/Programmer, A
Construction Engineering Technology/Technician, A
Criminal Justice/Law Enforcement Administration, A
Criminal Justice/Police Science, A
Culinary Arts/Chef Training, A
Drafting and Design Technology/Technician, A

Drafting/Design Engineering
   Technologies/Technicians, A
Electrical, Electronic and Communications
   Engineering Technology/Technician, A
Electrical/Electronics Equipment Installation and
   Repair, A
Electromechanical Technology/Electromechanical
   Engineering Technology, A
Emergency Medical Technology/Technician (EMT
   Paramedic), A
Energy Management and Systems
   Technology/Technician, A
Engineering, A
Finance, A
Fire Protection and Safety Technology/Technician, A
Forensic Science and Technology, A
General Studies, A
Graphic and Printing Equipment Operator
   Production, A
Heating, Air Conditioning and Refrigeration
   Technology/Technician, A
Heating, Air Conditioning, Ventilation and
   Refrigeration Maintenance
   Technology/Technician, A
Industrial Mechanics and Maintenance
   Technology, A
Industrial Technology/Technician, A
International/Global Studies, A
Law and Legal Studies, A
Legal Assistant/Paralegal, A
Liberal Arts and Sciences Studies and
   Humanities, A
Machine Tool Technology/Machinist, A
Manufacturing Technology/Technician, A
Marketing/Marketing Management, A
Mathematics, A
Mechanic and Repair Technologies/Technicians, A
Mechanical Drafting and Mechanical Drafting
   CAD/CADD, A
Mechanical Engineering/Mechanical
   Technology/Technician, A
Medical/Clinical Assistant, A
Mental Health/Rehabilitation, A
Metallurgical Technology/Technician, A
Music Performance, A
Nursing - Registered Nurse Training, A
Occupational Therapist Assistant, A
Operations Management and Supervision, A
Physical Therapist Assistant, A
Plastics Engineering Technology/Technician, A
Plumbing Technology/Plumber, A
Pre-Engineering, A
Quality Control Technology/Technician, A
Respiratory Care Therapy/Therapist, A
Robotics Technology/Technician, A
Sheet Metal Technology/Sheetworking, A
Social Psychology, A
Surgical Technology/Technologist, A
Survey Technology/Surveying, A
Tool and Die Technology/Technician, A
Veterinary/Animal Health Technology/Technician and
   Veterinary Assistant, A
Welding Technology/Welder, A

MADONNA UNIVERSITY

Accounting, B
Adult Development and Aging, AB
American Sign Language (ASL), AB
Art Teacher Education, B
Art/Art Studies, General, AB
Biochemistry, B
Biological and Physical Sciences, AB
Biology/Biological Sciences, B
Business Administration and Management, AB
Business Administration, Management and
   Operations, M
Chemistry, AB
Child Development, AB
Clinical Laboratory Science/Medical
   Technology/Technologist, B
Clinical Psychology, M
Clinical/Medical Laboratory Technician, AB
Computer and Information Sciences, AB
Computer Engineering Technology/Technician, A
Computer Science, AB

Consumer Merchandising/Retailing
   Management, AB
Criminal Justice/Safety Studies, AB
Criminology, M
Dietetics and Clinical Nutrition Services, B
Education, BM
Educational Leadership and Administration, M
Elementary Education and Teaching, B
Engineering, B
English as a Second Language, M
English Language and Literature, AB
Family and Consumer Sciences/Home Economics
   Teacher Education, B
Family and Consumer Sciences/Human Sciences, B
Fine Arts and Art Studies, B
Fire Science/Firefighting, AB
Food Technology and Processing, B
Foods, Nutrition, and Wellness Studies, AB
French Language and Literature, B
General Studies, B
Gerontology, AB
Health Services Administration, M
Health/Health Care Administration/Management, AB
Health/Medical Preparatory Programs, B
History, B
Hospice Nursing, M
Hospitality Administration/Management, B
Human Resources Management/Personnel
   Administration, B
Industrial and Organizational Psychology, B
Industrial Radiologic Technology/Technician, B
Information Science/Studies, B
International Business/Trade/Commerce, BM
Journalism, AB
Legal Assistant/Paralegal, AB
Liberal Studies, M
Management Information Systems and Services, B
Management Science, B
Marketing/Marketing Management, B
Mass Communication/Media Studies, AB
Mathematics, B
Mathematics Teacher Education, B
Music, B
Music Management and Merchandising, B
Music Teacher Education, B
Natural Sciences, AB
Nursing, ABMO
Nursing - Adult, M
Nursing - Advanced Practice, M
Nursing - Registered Nurse Training, B
Nursing Administration, M
Parks, Recreation, Leisure and Fitness Studies, B
Pastoral Studies/Counseling, BM
Philosophy, B
Polish Language and Literature, B
Pre-Dentistry Studies, B
Pre-Law Studies, B
Pre-Medicine/Pre-Medical Studies, B
Pre-Pharmacy Studies, B
Pre-Veterinary Studies, B
Psychology, BM
Public Relations, Advertising, and Applied
   Communication, AB
Public Relations/Image Management, AB
Quality Control and Safety
   Technologies/Technicians, AB
Quality Management, M
Radio, Television, and Digital Communication, B
Reading Teacher Education, M
Religion/Religious Studies, AB
Science Teacher Education/General Science
   Teacher Education, B
Science Technologies/Technicians, AB
Secondary Education and Teaching, B
Social Studies Teacher Education, B
Social Work, B
Sociology, B
Spanish Language and Literature, B
Special Education and Teaching, BM
Special Products Marketing Operations, B
Speech and Rhetorical Studies, AB
Teacher Education and Professional
   Development, Specific Subject Areas, B
Technical and Business Writing, B
Theology and Religious Vocations, M

Trade and Industrial Teacher Education, B

MARYGROVE COLLEGE

Accounting, A
Adult and Continuing Education and Teaching, M
Applied Art, B
Art Therapy/Therapist, B
Art/Art Studies, General, B
Biological and Physical Sciences, B
Biology/Biological Sciences, B
Business Administration and Management, B
Business/Commerce, AB
Chemistry, B
Computer and Information Sciences, B
Corrections, A
Dance, B
Education, BM
Education/Teaching of Individuals with Emotional
    Disturbances, B
Educational Leadership and Administration, M
Elementary Education and Teaching, M
English Language and Literature, B
Environmental Biology, B
Environmental Studies, B
Fine/Studio Arts, B
General Studies, B
History, B
Human Resources Management and Services, M
International Business/Trade/Commerce, B
Kindergarten/PreSchool Education and
    Teaching, AB
Legal and Justice Studies, M
Liberal Arts and Sciences Studies and
    Humanities, A
Marketing/Marketing Management, B
Mathematics, B
Music, B
Music Performance, B
Pastoral Studies/Counseling, M
Political Science and Government, B
Psychology, B
Reading Teacher Education, M
Religion/Religious Studies, B
Secondary Education and Teaching, M
Social Sciences, B
Social Work, B
Translation and Interpretation, M
Urban Education and Leadership, M

MICHIGAN STATE UNIVERSITY

Accounting, BMD
Adult and Continuing Education and Teaching, MD
Advertising, B
Advertising and Public Relations, M
African Studies, MD
African-American/Black Studies, MD
Agricultural Business and Management, B
Agricultural Communication/Journalism, B
Agricultural Economics, BMD
Agricultural Engineering, MD
Agricultural Sciences, MD
Agricultural/Biological Engineering and
    Bioengineering, B
Agriculture, Agriculture Operations and Related
    Sciences, B
Agronomy and Soil Sciences, MD
Allopathic Medicine, P
American/United States Studies/Civilization, BMD
Ancient Studies/Civilization, B
Animal Sciences, BMD
Anthropology, BMD
Apparel and Textiles, B
Applied Economics, B
Applied Mathematics, BMD
Art History, Criticism and Conservation, B
Art Teacher Education, B
Art/Art Studies, General, B
Astronomy, MD
Astrophysics, BM
Audiology/Audiologist and Speech-Language
    Pathology/Pathologist, B
Biochemistry, BMD
Biochemistry, Biophysics and Molecular Biology, B
Bioethics/Medical Ethics, M
Biological and Biomedical Sciences, MD
Biological and Physical Sciences, B

Biological Anthropology, D
Biology/Biological Sciences, B
Biomedical/Medical Engineering, B
Biosystems Engineering, MD
Botany/Plant Biology, B
Business Administration and Management, B
Business Administration, Management and
    Operations, MD
Cell Biology and Anatomy, MD
Chemical Engineering, BMD
Chemical Physics, B
Chemistry, BMD
Chemistry Teacher Education, B
Child and Family Studies, MD
Child Development, B
City/Urban, Community and Regional Planning, B
Civil Engineering, BMD
Clinical Laboratory Science/Medical
    Technology/Technologist, B
Clinical Laboratory Sciences, M
Communication and Media Studies, MD
Communication Disorders, M
Communication Studies/Speech Communication
    and Rhetoric, B
Composition, MD
Computational Mathematics, B
Computer and Information Sciences, B
Computer Engineering, B
Computer Science, MD
Construction Engineering and Management, MD
Construction Management, B
Counselor Education/School Counseling and
    Guidance Services, M
Criminal Justice/Law Enforcement Administration, B
Criminal Justice/Safety Studies, B
Criminology, MD
Curriculum and Instruction, MDO
Dietetics/Dieticians, B
Drama and Dramatics/Theatre Arts, B
East Asian
    Languages, Literatures, and Linguistics, B
Economics, BMD
Education, BMDO
Education/Teaching of Individuals with Hearing
    Impairments, Including Deafness, B
Education/Teaching of Individuals with Specific
    Learning Disabilities, B
Educational Administration and Supervision, MDO
Educational Measurement and Evaluation, D
Educational Media/Instructional Technology, MD
Electrical Engineering, MD
Electrical, Electronics and Communications
    Engineering, B
Elementary Education and Teaching, B
Engineering, B
Engineering and Applied Sciences, MD
Engineering Management, M
English, MD
English as a Second Language, M
English Language and Literature, B
Entomology, BMD
Environmental Biology, B
Environmental Design/Architecture, M
Environmental Engineering
    Technology/Environmental Technology, MD
Environmental Sciences, BMD
Environmental Studies, B
Epidemiology, MD
Family and Community Services, B
Family and Consumer Sciences/Home Economics
    Teacher Education, B
Family and Consumer Sciences/Human Sciences, B
Fashion/Apparel Design, B
Finance, B
Finance and Banking, MD
Fine Arts and Art Studies, M
Fish, Game and Wildlife Management, MD
Food Science, B
Food Science and Technology, MD
Food Services Management, M
Forensic Science and Technology, M
Forestry, BMD
French Language and Literature, BMD
Genetics, MD
Geography, BMD
Geology/Earth Science, BMD

Geophysics and Seismology, B
Geosciences, MD
German Language and Literature, BM
Higher Education/Higher Education
    Administration, MD
Hispanic Studies, MD
History, BMD
Home Economics, D
Horticultural Science, BMD
Hospitality Administration/Management, BM
Hotel/Motel Administration/Management, B
Human Resources Management and Services, MD
Human Resources Management/Personnel
    Administration, B
Humanities/Humanistic Studies, BM
Industrial and Labor Relations, MD
Interior Design, BM
International Affairs, M
International Relations and Affairs, B
International/Global Studies, B
Jazz/Jazz Studies, B
Journalism, BM
Kinesiology and Exercise Science, B
Kinesiology and Movement Studies, MD
Landscape Architecture, B
Linguistics, MD
Logistics and Materials Management, BM
Management Information Systems and
    Services, MD
Manufacturing Engineering, MD
Marketing, MD
Marketing/Marketing Management, B
Marriage and Family Therapy/Counseling, M
Mass Communication/Media Studies, B
Materials Engineering, MD
Materials Sciences, BMD
Mathematics, BMD
Mathematics Teacher Education, MD
Mechanical Engineering, BMD
Mechanics, MD
Media Studies, MD
Merchandising and Buying Operations, B
Microbiology, BMD
Molecular Biology, MD
Molecular Genetics, D
Music, BMD
Music Pedagogy, B
Music Performance, B
Music Teacher Education, BM
Music Theory and Composition, BM
Music Therapy/Therapist, BM
Musicology and Ethnomusicology, M
Natural Resource Economics, B
Natural Resources Management/Development and
    Policy, MD
Neuroscience, MD
Nursing, MD
Nursing - Registered Nurse Training, B
Nutritional Sciences, BMD
Operations Management and Supervision, B
Organizational Management, MD
Osteopathic Medicine, P
Parks, Recreation and Leisure Facilities
    Management, B
Pathobiology, MD
Pathology/Experimental Pathology, MD
Performance, MD
Pharmacology, MD
Philosophy, BMD
Physical and Theoretical Chemistry, B
Physical Chemistry, D
Physical Education Teaching and Coaching, B
Physical Sciences, B
Physics, BMD
Physiology, BMD
Plant Biology, MD
Plant Pathology/Phytopathology, BMD
Plant Sciences, MD
Political Science and Government, BMD
Portuguese Language and Literature, MD
Pre-Law Studies, B
Pre-Medicine/Pre-Medical Studies, B
Pre-Veterinary Studies, B
Psychology, BMD
Public Administration, B
Public Health, M

Radio and Television, B
Reading Teacher Education, M
Recreation and Park Management, MD
Rehabilitation Counseling, MD
Religion/Religious Studies, B
Rhetoric, MD
Romance
  Languages, Literatures, and Linguistics, MD
Russian Language and Literature, B
School Psychology, MDO
Science Teacher Education/General Science
  Teacher Education, M
Science, Technology and Society, B
Social Science Teacher Education, B
Social Sciences, BM
Social Studies Teacher Education, M
Social Work, BMD
Sociology, BMD
Soil Science and Agronomy, B
Spanish Language and Literature, BMD
Special Education and Teaching, BMD
Statistics, BMD
Technical and Business Writing, B
Telecommunications, M
Telecommunications Technology/Technician, B
Theater, M
Toxicology, MD
Urban and Regional Planning, M
Veterinary Medicine, P
Veterinary Sciences, MD
Veterinary/Animal Health Technology/Technician and
  Veterinary Assistant, B
Writing, MD
Zoology/Animal Biology, BMD

MICHIGAN TECHNOLOGICAL UNIVERSITY

Accounting, B
Actuarial Science, B
Applied Mathematics, B
Archeology, MD
Audio Engineering, B
Biochemistry, B
Bioinformatics, B
Biological and Biomedical Sciences, MD
Biology Teacher Education, B
Biology Technician/BioTechnology Laboratory
  Technician, B
Biology/Biological Sciences, B
Biomedical Engineering, D
Biomedical/Medical Engineering, B
Business Administration and Management, B
Business Administration, Management and
  Operations, M
Business Teacher Education, B
Business/Managerial Economics, B
Chemical Engineering, BMD
Chemical Physics, B
Chemistry, BMD
Civil Engineering, BMD
Civil Engineering Technology/Technician, A
Clinical Laboratory Science/Medical
  Technology/Technologist, B
Communication Studies/Speech Communication
  and Rhetoric, B
Computational Mathematics, B
Computational Sciences, D
Computer Engineering, BD
Computer Programming/Programmer, B
Computer Science, B
Computer Software Engineering, B
Computer Systems Networking and
  Telecommunications, B
Computer Teacher Education, B
Construction Engineering, B
CytoTechnology/Cytotechnologist, B
Digital Communication and Media/Multimedia, B
Ecology, BM
Economics, B
Electrical Engineering, MD
Electrical, Electronic and Communications
  Engineering Technology/Technician, AB
Electrical, Electronics and Communications
  Engineering, B
Electromechanical Technology/Electromechanical
  Engineering Technology, A

Engineering, B
Engineering and Applied Sciences, MD
Engineering Mechanics, B
Engineering Physics, BD
Engineering Technology, A
English Language and Literature, B
English/Language Arts Teacher Education, B
Environmental Engineering
  Technology/Environmental Technology, MD
Environmental Policy, M
Environmental Sciences, B
Environmental/Environmental Health Engineering, B
Finance, B
Forestry, BMD
Forestry Technology/Technician, A
General Studies, B
Geological Engineering, MD
Geological/Geophysical Engineering, B
Geology/Earth Science, BMD
Geophysics and Seismology, BM
Histologic Technology/Histotechnologist, B
Historic Preservation and Conservation, D
History, B
Humanities/Humanistic Studies, A
Industrial Engineering, B
Information Science/Studies, B
Liberal Arts and Sciences Studies and
  Humanities, B
Management Information Systems and Services, B
Marine Biology and Biological Oceanography, B
Marketing/Marketing Management, B
Materials Engineering, BMD
Mathematics, BMD
Mathematics Teacher Education, B
Mechanical Engineering, BMD
Mechanical Engineering/Mechanical
  Technology/Technician, AB
Mechanics, M
Medical Microbiology and Bacteriology, B
Medicinal and Pharmaceutical Chemistry, B
Metallurgical Engineering, BMD
Microbiology, B
Mineral Economics, M
Mineral/Mining Engineering, MD
Molecular Biochemistry, B
Operations Management and Supervision, B
Physical Sciences, B
Physics, BMD
Plant Molecular Biology, MD
Pre-Dentistry Studies, B
Pre-Law Studies, B
Pre-Medicine/Pre-Medical Studies, B
Pre-Pharmacy Studies, B
Pre-Veterinary Studies, B
Psychology, B
Rhetoric, MD
Science Teacher Education/General Science
  Teacher Education, BM
Secondary Education and Teaching, B
Social Sciences, B
Statistics, B
Survey Technology/Surveying, B
System Administration/Administrator, B
Technical and Business Writing, B
Technical Communication, MD
Technical Theatre/Theatre Design and
  Technology, B
Technology Teacher Education/Industrial Arts
  Teacher Education, B
Wildlife and Wildlands Science and Management, B

MID MICHIGAN COMMUNITY COLLEGE

Accounting, A
Administrative Assistant and Secretarial Science, A
Art/Art Studies, General, A
Automobile/Automotive Mechanics
  Technology/Technician, A
Biological and Physical Sciences, A
Biology Technician/BioTechnology Laboratory
  Technician, A
Biology/Biological Sciences, A
Business Administration and Management, A
Chemical Technology/Technician, A
Chemistry, A
Child Care Provider/Assistant, A
Child Development, A

Commercial and Advertising Art, A
Computer Graphics, A
Computer Science, A
Corrections, A
Criminal Justice/Law Enforcement Administration, A
Drafting and Design Technology/Technician, A
Drama and Dramatics/Theatre Arts, A
Elementary Education and Teaching, A
Emergency Medical Technology/Technician (EMT
  Paramedic), A
Engineering Technologies/Technicians, A
Engineering Technology, A
Environmental Studies, A
Fire Science/Firefighting, A
General Studies, A
Heating, Air Conditioning, Ventilation and
  Refrigeration Maintenance
  Technology/Technician, A
Hospitality Administration/Management, A
Hospitality and Recreation Marketing Operations, A
Industrial Radiologic Technology/Technician, A
Information Science/Studies, A
Legal Administrative Assistant/Secretary, A
Liberal Arts and Sciences Studies and
  Humanities, A
Licensed Practical/Vocational Nurse Training, A
Machine Tool Technology/Machinist, A
Marketing/Marketing Management, A
Mathematics, A
Medical Administrative Assistant/Secretary, A
Medical Transcription/Transcriptionist, A
Medical/Clinical Assistant, A
Nursing - Registered Nurse Training, A
Ophthalmic and Optometric Support Services and
  Allied Professions, A
Pharmacy, A
Physical Therapy/Therapist, A
Pre-Engineering, A
Psychology, A
Secondary Education and Teaching, A
Sociology, A
Speech and Rhetorical Studies, A
Speech Teacher Education, A
Teacher Education, Multiple Levels, A

MONROE COUNTY COMMUNITY COLLEGE

Accounting, A
Administrative Assistant and Secretarial Science, A
Architectural Engineering Technology/Technician, A
Art/Art Studies, General, A
Biology/Biological Sciences, A
Business Administration and Management, A
Child Development, A
Clinical Laboratory Science/Medical
  Technology/Technologist, A
Computer and Information Sciences, A
Computer Engineering Technology/Technician, A
Computer Graphics, A
Computer Programming, Specific Applications, A
Criminal Justice/Police Science, A
Criminal Justice/Safety Studies, A
Culinary Arts/Chef Training, A
Data Processing and Data Processing
  Technology/Technician, A
Drafting and Design Technology/Technician, A
Electrical, Electronic and Communications
  Engineering Technology/Technician, A
Elementary Education and Teaching, A
English Language and Literature, A
Finance, A
Funeral Service and Mortuary Science, A
Industrial Technology/Technician, A
Information Technology, A
Journalism, A
Legal Administrative Assistant/Secretary, A
Liberal Arts and Sciences Studies and
  Humanities, A
Marketing/Marketing Management, A
Mass Communication/Media Studies, A
Mathematics, A
Medical Administrative Assistant/Secretary, A
Nursing - Registered Nurse Training, A
Physical Therapy/Therapist, A
Pre-Engineering, A
Psychology, A

Respiratory Care Therapy/Therapist, A
Social Work, A
Speech and Rhetorical Studies, A
Web Page, Digital/Multimedia and Information
   Resources Design, A
Web/Multimedia Management and Webmaster, A
Welding Technology/Welder, A
Word Processing, A

MONTCALM COMMUNITY COLLEGE

Accounting, A
Administrative Assistant and Secretarial Science, A
Business Administration and Management, A
Child Care and Support Services Management, A
Child Care Provider/Assistant, A
Computer Installation and Repair
   Technology/Technician, A
Corrections, A
Cosmetology/Cosmetologist, A
Criminal Justice/Law Enforcement Administration, A
Data Processing and Data Processing
   Technology/Technician, A
Drafting and Design Technology/Technician, A
Electrical, Electronic and Communications
   Engineering Technology/Technician, A
Emergency Medical Technology/Technician (EMT
   Paramedic), A
Entrepreneurship/Entrepreneurial Studies, A
Executive Assistant/Executive Secretary, A
Industrial Radiologic Technology/Technician, A
Industrial Technology/Technician, A
Liberal Arts and Sciences Studies and
   Humanities, A
Management Information Systems and Services, A
Medical Administrative Assistant/Secretary, A
Medical Radiologic Technology/Science - Radiation
   Therapist, A
Nursing - Registered Nurse Training, A

MOTT COMMUNITY COLLEGE

Accounting Technology/Technician and
   Bookkeeping, A
Administrative Assistant and Secretarial Science, A
Architectural Engineering Technology/Technician, A
Autobody/Collision and Repair
   Technology/Technician, A
Automobile/Automotive Mechanics
   Technology/Technician, A
Business Administration and Management, A
Business/Commerce, A
Communications Technology/Technician, A
Community Health Services/Liaison/Counseling, A
Computer and Information Sciences and Support
   Services, A
Computer Systems Networking and
   Telecommunications, A
Criminal Justice/Police Science, A
Culinary Arts/Chef Training, A
Dental Assisting/Assistant, A
Dental Hygiene/Hygienist, A
Drafting and Design Technology/Technician, A
Early Childhood Education and Teaching, A
Electrical, Electronic and Communications
   Engineering Technology/Technician, A
Emergency Medical Technology/Technician (EMT
   Paramedic), A
Engineering Technologies/Technicians, A
Entrepreneurship/Entrepreneurial Studies, A
Fire Protection and Safety Technology/Technician, A
Foodservice Systems
   Administration/Management, A
General Studies, A
Graphic Design, A
Heating, Air Conditioning and Refrigeration
   Technology/Technician, A
Histologic Technician, A
Information Resources Management/CIO Training, A
International Business/Trade/Commerce, A
Legal Administrative Assistant/Secretary, A
Liberal Arts and Sciences Studies and
   Humanities, A
Management Information Systems and Services, A
Manufacturing Technology/Technician, A
Marketing/Marketing Management, A
Mechanical Drafting and Mechanical Drafting
   CAD/CADD, A

Mechanical Engineering/Mechanical
   Technology/Technician, A
Medical Administrative Assistant/Secretary, A
Medical Radiologic Technology/Science - Radiation
   Therapist, A
Nursing - Registered Nurse Training, A
Occupational Therapist Assistant, A
Office Management and Supervision, A
Photography, A
Physical Therapist Assistant, A
Precision Production, A
Quality Control Technology/Technician, A
Respiratory Care Therapy/Therapist, A
Salon/Beauty Salon Management/Manager, A
Sign Language Interpretation and Translation, A
Survey Technology/Surveying, A
Teacher Assistant/Aide, A

MUSKEGON COMMUNITY COLLEGE

Accounting, A
Administrative Assistant and Secretarial Science, A
Advertising, A
Anthropology, A
Applied Art, A
Applied Mathematics, A
Art History, Criticism and Conservation, A
Art Teacher Education, A
Art/Art Studies, General, A
Automobile/Automotive Mechanics
   Technology/Technician, A
Biology Technician/BioTechnology Laboratory
   Technician, A
Biomedical Technology/Technician, A
Business Administration and Management, A
Business Machine Repairer, A
Chemical Engineering, A
Child Development, A
Commercial and Advertising Art, A
Criminal Justice/Law Enforcement Administration, A
Data Processing and Data Processing
   Technology/Technician, A
Developmental and Child Psychology, A
Drafting and Design Technology/Technician, A
Economics, A
Education, A
Electrical, Electronic and Communications
   Engineering Technology/Technician, A
Electromechanical Technology/Electromechanical
   Engineering Technology, A
Elementary Education and Teaching, A
Emergency Medical Technology/Technician (EMT
   Paramedic), A
Engineering Technology, A
Finance, A
Hospitality Administration/Management, A
Hospitality and Recreation Marketing Operations, A
Hotel/Motel Administration/Management, A
Industrial Technology/Technician, A
Information Science/Studies, A
Legal Administrative Assistant/Secretary, A
Liberal Arts and Sciences Studies and
   Humanities, A
Machine Tool Technology/Machinist, A
Marketing/Marketing Management, A
Medical Administrative Assistant/Secretary, A
Nursing - Registered Nurse Training, A
Parks, Recreation, Leisure and Fitness Studies, A
Special Products Marketing Operations, A
Technology Education/Industrial Arts, A
Transportation and Materials Moving, A
Welding Technology/Welder, A

NORTH CENTRAL MICHIGAN COLLEGE

Accounting, A
Administrative Assistant and Secretarial Science, A
Business Administration and Management, A
Child Development, A
Computer and Information Sciences, A
Computer Programming/Programmer, A
Computer Systems Networking and
   Telecommunications, A
Criminal Justice/Law Enforcement Administration, A
Criminal Justice/Police Science, A
Data Processing and Data Processing
   Technology/Technician, A

Drafting and Design Technology/Technician, A
Emergency Medical Technology/Technician (EMT
   Paramedic), A
Engineering Technology, A
Finance, A
Information Technology, A
Legal Administrative Assistant/Secretary, A
Legal Assistant/Paralegal, A
Liberal Arts and Sciences Studies and
   Humanities, A
Marketing/Marketing Management, A
Nursing - Registered Nurse Training, A
Pre-Engineering, A

NORTHERN MICHIGAN UNIVERSITY

Accounting, B
Art Teacher Education, B
Art/Art Studies, General, B
Athletic Training and Sports Medicine, B
Audiology/Audiologist and Speech-Language
   Pathology/Pathologist, B
Automobile/Automotive Mechanics
   Technology/Technician, A
Avionics Maintenance Technology/Technician, A
Behavioral Sciences, B
Biochemistry, BM
Biological and Biomedical Sciences, M
Biology/Biological Sciences, B
Botany/Plant Biology, B
Broadcast Journalism, B
Business Administration and Management, AB
Business Teacher Education, B
Business/Commerce, A
Chemistry, BM
Child Development, AB
Clinical/Medical Laboratory Assistant, A
Clinical/Medical Laboratory Technician, B
Commercial and Advertising Art, AB
Communication Disorders, M
Communication Studies/Speech Communication
   and Rhetoric, B
Computer and Information Sciences, B
Computer Science, B
Computer Systems Networking and
   Telecommunications, B
Construction Management, B
Construction Trades, A
Corrections, A
Creative Writing, B
Criminal Justice/Law Enforcement
   Administration, AB
Criminal Justice/Police Science, AB
Criminology, M
CytoTechnology/Cytotechnologist, B
Developmental and Child Psychology, B
Drafting and Design Technology/Technician, AB
Drama and Dramatics/Theatre Arts, B
Early Childhood Education and Teaching, B
Ecology, B
Economics, B
Education, BMO
Education/Teaching of Individuals with Mental
   Retardation, B
Educational Administration and Supervision, MO
Electrical, Electronic and Communications
   Engineering Technology/Technician, AB
Electromechanical Technology/Electromechanical
   Engineering Technology, A
Elementary Education and Teaching, BM
English, M
English Language and Literature, B
English/Language Arts Teacher Education, B
Entrepreneurship/Entrepreneurial Studies, B
Environmental Studies, B
Exercise and Sports Science, M
Film/Cinema Studies, B
Finance, B
Financial Planning and Services, B
Forensic Science and Technology, B
French Language and Literature, B
French Language Teacher Education, B
General Studies, A
Geography, B
Geography Teacher Education, B
Geology/Earth Science, B

Health Information/Medical Records
  Administration/Administrator, A
Health Teacher Education, B
Heating, Air Conditioning, Ventilation and
  Refrigeration Maintenance
  Technology/Technician, A
Histologic Technology/Histotechnologist, B
History, B
History Teacher Education, B
Hospitality Administration/Management, B
Hospitality and Recreation Marketing Operations, B
Human/Medical Genetics, B
Hydrology and Water Resources Science, B
Information Science/Studies, B
Intermedia/Multimedia, B
International/Global Studies, B
Liberal Arts and Sciences Studies and
  Humanities, A
Management Information Systems and Services, AB
Manufacturing Technology/Technician, B
Marketing/Marketing Management, B
Mass Communication/Media Studies, B
Mathematics, B
Mathematics Teacher Education, BM
Mechanical Engineering/Mechanical
  Technology/Technician, B
Medical Microbiology and Bacteriology, B
Microbiology, B
Music, B
Music Teacher Education, B
Natural Resources and Conservation, B
Nursing, M
Nursing - Registered Nurse Training, B
Parks, Recreation and Leisure Facilities
  Management, B
Philosophy, B
Physical Education Teaching and Coaching, B
Political Science and Government, B
Pre-Dentistry Studies, B
Pre-Law Studies, B
Pre-Medicine/Pre-Medical Studies, B
Pre-Veterinary Studies, B
Psychology, BM
Public Administration, BM
Public Relations/Image Management, B
Science Teacher Education/General Science
  Teacher Education, BM
Secondary Education and Teaching, BM
Small Business Administration/Management, B
Social Science Teacher Education, B
Social Sciences, B
Social Work, B
Sociology, B
Spanish Language and Literature, B
Spanish Language Teacher Education, B
Special Education and Teaching, BM
Speech and Rhetorical Studies, B
Speech-Language Pathology/Pathologist, B
Sport and Fitness Administration/Management, B
Technical and Business Writing, B
Technology Teacher Education/Industrial Arts
  Teacher Education, B
Writing, M
Zoology/Animal Biology, B

NORTHWESTERN MICHIGAN COLLEGE

Accounting Technology/Technician and
  Bookkeeping, A
Agricultural Production Operations, A
Airline/Commercial/Professional Pilot and Flight
  Crew, A
Art/Art Studies, General, A
Automobile/Automotive Mechanics
  Technology/Technician, A
Biology/Biological Sciences, A
Business Administration and Management, A
Business and Personal/Financial Services Marketing
  Operations, A
Business, Management, Marketing, and Related
  Support Services, A
Business/Office Automation/Technology/Data
  Entry, A
Child Care and Support Services Management, A
Commercial and Advertising Art, A
Communication Studies/Speech Communication
  and Rhetoric, A

Corrections and Criminal Justice, A
Crop Production, A
Culinary Arts/Chef Training, A
Dental Assisting/Assistant, A
Drafting and Design Technology/Technician, A
Drama and Dramatics/Theatre Arts, A
Education, A
Electrical, Electronic and Communications
  Engineering Technology/Technician, A
Electromechanical and Instrumentation and
  Maintenance Technologies/Technicians, A
Engineering, A
English Language and Literature, A
Executive Assistant/Executive Secretary, A
Forest Management/Forest Resources
  Management, A
Health Professions and Related Clinical Sciences, A
Industrial Technology/Technician, A
Landscaping and Groundskeeping, A
Legal Administrative Assistant/Secretary, A
Liberal Arts and Sciences Studies and
  Humanities, A
Machine Shop Technology/Assistant, A
Management Information Systems and Services, A
Marine Science/Merchant Marine Officer, A
Marine Transportation, A
Maritime Science, A
Marketing/Marketing Management, A
Mathematics, A
Medical/Clinical Assistant, A
Music, A
Nursing - Registered Nurse Training, A
Physical Sciences, A
Social Sciences, A
Turf and Turfgrass Management, A

NORTHWOOD UNIVERSITY

Accounting, AB
Advertising, AB
Banking and Financial Support Services, AB
Business Administration and Management, AB
Business Administration, Management and
  Operations, M
Business/Managerial Economics, AB
Computer and Information Sciences, B
Entrepreneurship/Entrepreneurial Studies, AB
Fashion Merchandising, AB
Hotel/Motel Administration/Management, AB
International Business/Trade/Commerce, AB
Management Information Systems and Services, AB
Marketing/Marketing Management, B
Sport and Fitness Administration/Management, AB
Vehicle and Vehicle Parts and Accessories
  Marketing Operations, AB

OAKLAND COMMUNITY COLLEGE

Accounting, A
Allied Health
  Diagnostic, Intervention, and Treatment
  Professions, A
Applied Horticulture/Horticultural Operations, A
Architectural Engineering Technology/Technician, A
Architecture, A
Automobile/Automotive Mechanics
  Technology/Technician, A
Aviation/Airway Management and Operations, A
Business Administration and Management, A
Business/Office Automation/Technology/Data
  Entry, A
Cabinetmaking and Millwork/Millwright, A
Carpentry/Carpenter, A
Ceramic Arts and Ceramics, A
Child Care and Support Services Management, A
Clinical/Medical Laboratory Science and Allied
  Professions, A
Computer and Information Sciences, A
Computer Programming/Programmer, A
Computer Technology/Computer Systems
  Technology, A
Construction Management, A
Consumer Merchandising/Retailing Management, A
Corrections and Criminal Justice, A
Cosmetology/Cosmetologist, A
Court Reporting/Court Reporter, A
Criminal Justice/Law Enforcement Administration, A
Criminal Justice/Police Science, A

Culinary Arts/Chef Training, A
Dental Hygiene/Hygienist, A
Diagnostic Medical Sonography/Sonographer and
  Ultrasound Technician, A
Electrical, Electronic and Communications
  Engineering Technology/Technician, A
Electromechanical Technology/Electromechanical
  Engineering Technology, A
Electroneurodiagnostic/Electroencephalographic
  Technology/Technologist, A
Emergency Medical Technology/Technician (EMT
  Paramedic), A
Engineering, A
Entrepreneurship/Entrepreneurial Studies, A
Environmental Control Technologies/Technicians, A
Fashion Merchandising, A
Fine Arts and Art Studies, A
Fire Science/Firefighting, A
Foodservice Systems
  Administration/Management, A
Forensic Science and Technology, A
General Studies, A
Gerontology, A
Graphic Design, A
Health and Physical Education/Fitness, A
Health Professions and Related Clinical Sciences, A
Health/Health Care Administration/Management, A
Heating, Air Conditioning and Refrigeration
  Technology/Technician, A
Histologic Technician, A
Hotel/Motel Administration/Management, A
Industrial Electronics Technology/Technician, A
Industrial Technology/Technician, A
Interior Design, A
International Business/Trade/Commerce, A
Kinesiology and Exercise Science, A
Landscape Architecture, A
Landscaping and Groundskeeping, A
Legal Assistant/Paralegal, A
Liberal Arts and Sciences Studies and
  Humanities, A
Library Assistant/Technician, A
Licensed Practical/Vocational Nurse Training, A
Machine Tool Technology/Machinist, A
Management Information Systems and Services, A
Management Science, A
Manufacturing Technology/Technician, A
Marketing, A
Massage Therapy/Therapeutic Massage, A
Mechanical Drafting and Mechanical Drafting
  CAD/CADD, A
Medical Radiologic Technology/Science - Radiation
  Therapist, A
Medical Transcription/Transcriptionist, A
Medical/Clinical Assistant, A
Mental and Social Health Services and Allied
  Professions, A
Nuclear Medical Technology/Technologist, A
Nursing - Registered Nurse Training, A
Office Management and Supervision, A
Operations Management and Supervision, A
Ornamental Horticulture, A
Pharmacy Technician/Assistant, A
Photography, A
Precision Metal Working, A
Pre-Engineering, A
Radio and Television Broadcasting
  Technology/Technician, A
Respiratory Care Therapy/Therapist, A
Restaurant/Food Services Management, A
Robotics Technology/Technician, A
Salon/Beauty Salon Management/Manager, A
Sport and Fitness Administration/Management, A
Surgical Technology/Technologist, A
Tool and Die Technology/Technician, A
Welding Technology/Welder, A
Woodworking, A

OAKLAND UNIVERSITY

Accounting, BMO
Allied Health and Medical Assisting Services, MDO
American/United States Studies/Civilization, B
Anthropology, B
Applied Mathematics, MD
Art History, Criticism and Conservation, B
Biochemistry, B

Biological and Biomedical Sciences, M
Biology/Biological Sciences, B
Business Administration, Management and
  Operations, MO
Cell Biology and Anatomy, M
Chemistry, BMD
Communication Studies/Speech Communication
  and Rhetoric, B
Comparative Literature, B
Computer Engineering, BM
Computer Science, BM
Counselor Education/School Counseling and
  Guidance Services, MDO
Dance, B
Directing and Theatrical Production, B
Early Childhood Education and Teaching, MDO
East Asian Studies, B
Economics, BO
Education, MDO
Educational Administration and Supervision, O
Educational Leadership and Administration, MDO
Educational Media/Instructional Technology, O
Electrical Engineering, M
Electrical, Electronics and Communications
  Engineering, B
Elementary Education and Teaching, B
Engineering, B
Engineering and Applied Sciences, MD
Engineering Management, M
English, M
English Language and Literature, B
Environmental Health, B
Environmental Sciences, D
Exercise and Sports Science, MO
Finance, B
Finance and Banking, O
Foundations and Philosophy of Education, M
French Language and Literature, B
German Language and Literature, B
Gerontological Nursing, M
Health and Medical Laboratory Technologies, B
Higher Education/Higher Education
  Administration, O
History, BM
Human Resources Development, M
Human Resources Management and Services, O
Human Resources Management/Personnel
  Administration, B
Industrial and Manufacturing Management, O
International Business/Trade/Commerce, O
Italian Language and Literature, B
Journalism, B
Latin American Studies, B
Liberal Studies, M
Linguistics, BMO
Management Information Systems and
  Services, BMO
Marketing, O
Marketing/Marketing Management, B
Maternal and Child Health, O
Mathematics, BM
Mathematics Teacher Education, BO
Mechanical Engineering, BMD
Medical Physics, D
Music, BM
Music Performance, B
Music Teacher Education, B
Music Theory and Composition, B
Nurse Anesthetist, MO
Nursing, MO
Nursing - Adult, M
Nursing - Advanced Practice, MO
Nursing - Registered Nurse Training, B
Nursing Education, M
Occupational Safety and Health
  Technology/Technician, B
Philosophy, B
Physical Therapy/Therapist, MDO
Physics, BMD
Political Science and Government, B
Psychology, B
Public Administration, BM
Public Health (MPH, DPH), B
Public Health Education and Promotion, B
Reading Teacher Education, BMDO

Science Teacher Education/General Science
  Teacher Education, B
Secondary Education and Teaching, M
Slavic Studies, B
Sociology, B
Software Engineering, M
South Asian
  Languages, Literatures, and Linguistics, B
Spanish Language and Literature, B
Special Education and Teaching, BMO
Statistics, BMO
Systems Engineering, BMD
Systems Science and Theory, M
Women's Studies, B

OLIVET COLLEGE

Accounting, B
Applied Art, B
Art Teacher Education, B
Art/Art Studies, General, B
Biochemistry, B
Biology/Biological Sciences, B
Business Administration and Management, B
Chemistry, B
Commercial and Advertising Art, B
Computer and Information Sciences, B
Computer Science, B
Criminal Justice/Safety Studies, B
Economics, B
Education, BM
Elementary Education and Teaching, B
English Language and Literature, B
Environmental Studies, B
Finance, B
Fine/Studio Arts, B
Health and Physical Education, B
History, B
Insurance, B
Journalism, B
Liberal Arts and Sciences Studies and
  Humanities, B
Marketing/Marketing Management, B
Mass Communication/Media Studies, B
Mathematics, B
Medical Illustration/Medical Illustrator, B
Physical Education Teaching and Coaching, B
Pre-Dentistry Studies, B
Pre-Law Studies, B
Pre-Medicine/Pre-Medical Studies, B
Pre-Veterinary Studies, B
Psychology, B
Secondary Education and Teaching, B
Social Sciences, B
Sociology, B
Sport and Fitness Administration/Management, B

ROCHESTER COLLEGE

Accounting, B
Behavioral Sciences, B
Bible/Biblical Studies, B
Biological and Physical Sciences, B
Biology Teacher Education, B
Business Administration and Management, B
Business/Corporate Communications, B
Communication Studies/Speech Communication
  and Rhetoric, B
Comparative Literature, B
Counseling Psychology, B
Early Childhood Education and Teaching, B
Elementary Education and Teaching, B
English Language and Literature, B
English/Language Arts Teacher Education, B
History, B
History Teacher Education, B
Interdisciplinary Studies, B
Liberal Arts and Sciences Studies and
  Humanities, A
Marketing/Marketing Management, B
Mass Communication/Media Studies, B
Mathematics Teacher Education, B
Missions/Missionary Studies and Missiology, B
Multi-/Interdisciplinary Studies, B
Music, B
Psychology, B
Science Teacher Education/General Science
  Teacher Education, B

Secondary Education and Teaching, B
Social Studies Teacher Education, B
Sport and Fitness Administration/Management, B
Youth Ministry, B

SACRED HEART MAJOR SEMINARY

Liberal Arts and Sciences Studies and
  Humanities, B
Pastoral Studies/Counseling, M
Philosophy, B
Theology and Religious Vocations, MP
Theology/Theological Studies, A

SAGINAW CHIPPEWA TRIBAL COLLEGE

American Indian/Native American Studies, A
Business/Commerce, A
Liberal Arts and Sciences Studies and
  Humanities, A

SAGINAW VALLEY STATE UNIVERSITY

Accounting, B
Art Teacher Education, B
Art/Art Studies, General, B
Athletic Training and Sports Medicine, B
Biochemistry, B
Biology/Biological Sciences, B
Business Administration and Management, B
Business Administration, Management and
  Operations, M
Business/Managerial Economics, B
Chemical Physics, B
Chemistry, B
Clinical Laboratory Science/Medical
  Technology/Technologist, B
Communication and Media Studies, M
Communication Studies/Speech Communication
  and Rhetoric, B
Computer and Information Sciences, B
Criminal Justice/Safety Studies, B
Design and Visual Communications, B
Drama and Dramatics/Theatre Arts, B
Early Childhood Education and Teaching, M
Economics, B
Education, MO
Educational Administration and Supervision, M
Educational Leadership and Administration, MO
Educational Media/Instructional Technology, M
Electrical, Electronics and Communications
  Engineering, B
Elementary Education and Teaching, BM
Engineering and Applied Sciences, M
Engineering/Industrial Management, B
English Language and Literature, B
English/Language Arts Teacher Education, B
Finance, B
Fine/Studio Arts, B
French Language and Literature, B
General Studies, B
History, B
International Business/Trade/Commerce, B
International Relations and Affairs, B
Kinesiology and Exercise Science, B
Management of Technology, M
Marketing Research, B
Mathematics, B
Mechanical Engineering, B
Media Studies, M
Middle School Education, M
Music, B
Music Teacher Education, B
Nursing, M
Nursing - Advanced Practice, M
Nursing - Registered Nurse Training, B
Nursing Administration, M
Operations Management and Supervision, B
Optics/Optical Sciences, B
Physical Education Teaching and Coaching, B
Physics, B
Political Science and Government, B
Psychology, B
Public Administration, BM
Reading Teacher Education, M
Science Teacher Education/General Science
  Teacher Education, BM
Secondary Education and Teaching, M

Social Work, B
Sociology, B
Spanish Language and Literature, B
Special Education and Teaching, BM
Speech Teacher Education, B

ST. CLAIR COUNTY COMMUNITY COLLEGE

Accounting, A
Administrative Assistant and Secretarial Science, A
Advertising, A
Agricultural Business and Management, A
Agricultural Mechanization, A
Agriculture, A
Architectural Engineering Technology/Technician, A
Art/Art Studies, General, A
Artificial Intelligence and Robotics, A
Biological and Physical Sciences, A
Broadcast Journalism, A
Business Administration and Management, A
Child Development, A
Commercial and Advertising Art, A
Computer Typography and Composition Equipment
    Operator, A
Corrections, A
Criminal Justice/Law Enforcement Administration, A
Drafting and Design Technology/Technician, A
Electrical, Electronic and Communications
    Engineering Technology/Technician, A
Fire Science/Firefighting, A
Horticultural Science, A
Industrial Technology/Technician, A
Information Science/Studies, A
Journalism, A
Legal Administrative Assistant/Secretary, A
Liberal Arts and Sciences Studies and
    Humanities, A
Machine Tool Technology/Machinist, A
Marketing/Marketing Management, A
Mass Communication/Media Studies, A
Medical Administrative Assistant/Secretary, A
Mental Health/Rehabilitation, A
Nursing - Registered Nurse Training, A
Pharmacy, A
Plastics Engineering Technology/Technician, A
Quality Control Technology/Technician, A
Welding Technology/Welder, A

SCHOOLCRAFT COLLEGE

Accounting, A
Administrative Assistant and Secretarial Science, A
Biomedical Technology/Technician, A
Business Administration and Management, A
Child Care and Support Services Management, A
Commercial and Advertising Art, A
Computer Programming/Programmer, A
Computer Technology/Computer Systems
    Technology, A
Corrections, A
Criminal Justice/Police Science, A
Culinary Arts/Chef Training, A
Data Processing and Data Processing
    Technology/Technician, A
Drafting and Design Technology/Technician, A
Education, A
Electrical, Electronic and Communications
    Engineering Technology/Technician, A
Electromechanical Technology/Electromechanical
    Engineering Technology, A
Emergency Medical Technology/Technician (EMT
    Paramedic), A
Engineering, A
Entrepreneurship/Entrepreneurial Studies, A
Environmental Engineering
    Technology/Environmental Technology, A
Fire Science/Firefighting, A
Health and Medical Laboratory Technologies, A
Health Information/Medical Records
    Technology/Technician, A
Industrial Technology/Technician, A
Laser and Optical Technology/Technician, A
Liberal Arts and Sciences Studies and
    Humanities, A
Marketing/Marketing Management, A
Mechanical Engineering/Mechanical
    Technology/Technician, A

Metallurgical Technology/Technician, A
Music Teacher Education, A
Nursing - Registered Nurse Training, A
Occupational Therapist Assistant, A
Physical Sciences, A
Radio and Television Broadcasting
    Technology/Technician, A
Robotics Technology/Technician, A
Welding Technology/Welder, A

SIENA HEIGHTS UNIVERSITY

Accounting, AB
Art Teacher Education, B
Art/Art Studies, General, AB
Biology/Biological Sciences, B
Business Administration and Management, AB
Business Teacher Education, B
Chemistry, AB
Child Development, AB
Community Organization and Advocacy, B
Counselor Education/School Counseling and
    Guidance Services, MO
Criminal Justice/Law Enforcement
    Administration, AB
Curriculum and Instruction, M
Drama and Dramatics/Theatre Arts, B
Early Childhood Education and Teaching, M
Education, M
Elementary Education and Teaching, BM
English Language and Literature, AB
General Studies, AB
Gerontology, A
History, B
Hospitality Administration/Management, AB
Human Resources Development, M
Human Services, B
Humanities/Humanistic Studies, B
Information Science/Studies, AB
Kindergarten/PreSchool Education and Teaching, B
Marketing/Marketing Management, AB
Mathematics, B
Middle School Education, M
Music, B
Music Teacher Education, B
Natural Sciences, B
Philosophy, B
Pre-Engineering, A
Pre-Law Studies, B
Psychology, AB
Public Administration, B
Reading Teacher Education, M
Religion/Religious Studies, B
Secondary Education and Teaching, BM
Social Sciences, B
Social Work, AB
Spanish Language and Literature, B

SOUTHWESTERN MICHIGAN COLLEGE

Accounting Technology/Technician and
    Bookkeeping, A
Administrative Assistant and Secretarial Science, A
Airframe Mechanics and Aircraft Maintenance
    Technology/Technician, A
Automobile/Automotive Mechanics
    Technology/Technician, A
Business Administration and Management, A
Business, Management, Marketing, and Related
    Support Services, A
Child Care and Support Services Management, A
Computer and Information Sciences, A
Computer Programming/Programmer, A
Data Entry/Microcomputer Applications, A
Drafting and Design Technology/Technician, A
Electrical and Electronic Engineering
    Technologies/Technicians, A
Engineering Technology, A
General Merchandising, Sales, and Related
    Marketing Operations, A
General Studies, A
Graphic and Printing Equipment Operator
    Production, A
Health Professions and Related Clinical Sciences, A
Heavy/Industrial Equipment Maintenance
    Technologies, A
Industrial Mechanics and Maintenance
    Technology, A

Legal Assistant/Paralegal, A
Liberal Arts and Sciences Studies and
    Humanities, A
Machine Shop Technology/Assistant, A
Nursing - Registered Nurse Training, A
Precision Production, A
Precision Systems Maintenance and Repair
    Technologies, A
Welding Technology/Welder, A

SPRING ARBOR UNIVERSITY

Accounting, B
Art/Art Studies, General, B
Biochemistry, B
Biology/Biological Sciences, B
Business Administration and Management, B
Chemistry, B
Child and Family Studies, M
Communication and Media Studies, M
Communication Studies/Speech Communication
    and Rhetoric, B
Computer Science, B
Counseling Psychology, M
Education, M
Elementary Education and Teaching, B
English Language and Literature, B
Family Systems, M
Health/Health Care Administration/Management, B
History, B
Human Resources Management/Personnel
    Administration, B
Kinesiology and Exercise Science, B
Liberal Arts and Sciences Studies and
    Humanities, A
Management, M
Management Information Systems and Services, B
Mathematics, B
Music, B
Music Teacher Education, B
Organizational Management, M
Philosophy, B
Physical Education Teaching and Coaching, B
Piano and Organ, B
Psychology, B
Religion/Religious Studies, BP
Secondary Education and Teaching, B
Social Sciences, B
Social Work, B
Sociology, B
Spanish Language and Literature, B
Sport and Fitness Administration/Management, B
Youth Ministry, B

UNIVERSITY OF DETROIT MERCY

Accounting, B
Allied Health and Medical Assisting Services, MO
Architectural Engineering, M
Architecture, B
Automotive Engineering Technology/Technician, D
Behavioral Sciences, B
Biochemistry, BM
Biology/Biological Sciences, B
Broadcast Journalism, B
Business Administration and Management, B
Business Administration, Management and
    Operations, MO
Chemical Engineering, MD
Chemistry, BM
Civil Engineering, BM
Clinical Psychology, MD
Computer and Information Sciences, B
Computer Engineering, B
Computer Programming/Programmer, B
Computer Science, BM
Counselor Education/School Counseling and
    Guidance Services, M
Criminal Justice/Law Enforcement Administration, B
Criminology, M
Curriculum and Instruction, M
Dental Hygiene/Hygienist, B
Dentistry, P
Developmental and Child Psychology, B
Drama and Dramatics/Theatre Arts, B
Early Childhood Education and Teaching, M
Economics, B
Education, BM

Education/Teaching of Individuals with Emotional
  Disturbances, B
Education/Teaching of Individuals with Multiple
  Disabilities, B
Education/Teaching of Individuals with Specific
  Learning Disabilities, B
Educational Administration and Supervision, M
Electrical Engineering, MD
Electrical, Electronics and Communications
  Engineering, B
Elementary Education and Teaching, B
Engineering, B
Engineering and Applied Sciences, MD
Engineering Management, M
English Language and Literature, B
Environmental Engineering
  Technology/Environmental Technology, M
Finance, B
Health Services Administration, M
Health/Health Care Administration/Management, B
History, B
Human Resources Management/Personnel
  Administration, B
Human Services, B
Humanities/Humanistic Studies, B
Industrial and Organizational Psychology, M
Information Science/Studies, B
International Business/Trade/Commerce, B
Journalism, B
Kindergarten/PreSchool Education and Teaching, B
Labor and Industrial Relations, B
Law and Legal Studies, ABPO
Legal Administrative Assistant/Secretary, AB
Liberal Studies, M
Management Information Systems and Services, M
Manufacturing Engineering, BD
Marketing/Marketing Management, B
Mass Communication/Media Studies, B
Mathematics, BM
Mathematics Teacher Education, M
Mechanical Engineering, BMD
Nurse Anesthetist, M
Nursing - Advanced Practice, MO
Nursing - Registered Nurse Training, B
Oral and Dental Sciences, MO
Orthodontics, MO
Philosophy, B
Physician Assistant, M
Political Science and Government, B
Polymer/Plastics Engineering, M
Pre-Dentistry Studies, B
Pre-Law Studies, B
Pre-Medicine/Pre-Medical Studies, B
Psychology, BMDO
Public Relations/Image Management, B
Radio and Television, B
Reading Teacher Education, B
Religion/Religious Studies, BM
School Psychology, O
Science Teacher Education/General Science
  Teacher Education, B
Secondary Education and Teaching, B
Securities Services Administration/Management, M
Social Science Teacher Education, B
Social Studies Teacher Education, B
Social Work, B
Sociology, B
Special Education and Teaching, BM
Substance Abuse/Addiction Counseling, BMO
Systems Engineering, B

UNIVERSITY OF MICHIGAN

Aerospace, Aeronautical and Astronautical
  Engineering, BMD
African-American/Black Studies, B
Allopathic Medicine, PO
American/United States Studies/Civilization, BMD
Analytical Chemistry, D
Anthropology, BD
Applied Economics, M
Applied Mathematics, B
Applied Physics, D
Arabic Language and Literature, BMD
Archeology, D
Architecture, BMDO
Art History, Criticism and Conservation, BD

Art Teacher Education, B
Asian Languages, MD
Asian Studies/Civilization, BMDO
Astronomy, BMD
Athletic Training and Sports Medicine, B
Atmospheric Sciences and Meteorology, BMD
Automotive Engineering Technology/Technician, M
Biochemistry, BD
Bioinformatics, MD
Biological and Biomedical Sciences, MDO
Biology/Biological Sciences, B
Biomedical Engineering, MD
Biomedical Sciences, B
Biophysics, BD
Biopsychology, D
Biostatistics, MD
Botany/Plant Biology, B
Business Administration and Management, B
Business Administration, Management and
  Operations, MD
Cell Biology and Anatomy, MD
Cell/Cellular Biology and Histology, B
Ceramic Arts and Ceramics, B
Chemical Engineering, BMDO
Chemistry, BD
Chinese Language and Literature, B
Civil Engineering, BMDO
Classics and Classical
  Languages, Literatures, and Linguistics, BMDO
Clinical Laboratory Science/Medical
  Technology/Technologist, B
Clinical Psychology, D
Clinical Research, M
Commercial and Advertising Art, B
Communication and Media Studies, D
Community Health Nursing, M
Comparative Literature, BD
Computer Education, M
Computer Engineering, BMD
Computer Science, BMD
Construction Engineering and Management, M
Creative Writing, B
Curriculum and Instruction, M
Dance, BM
Dental Hygiene/Hygienist, B
Dentistry, P
Design and Applied Arts, M
Design and Visual Communications, B
Developmental Biology and Embryology, MD
Developmental Psychology, D
Drama and Dramatics/Theatre Arts, B
Drawing, B
Early Childhood Education and Teaching, MD
East Asian Studies, MO
East European and Russian Studies, MO
Ecology, MD
Economics, BMDO
Education, BMDO
Educational Administration and Supervision, MDO
Educational Measurement and Evaluation, D
Educational Media/Instructional Technology, D
Electrical Engineering, MD
Electrical, Electronics and Communications
  Engineering, B
Elementary Education and Teaching, BO
Engineering, B
Engineering and Applied Sciences, MDO
Engineering Physics, B
Engineering Science, B
English, MD
English Education, MD
English Language and Literature, B
Environmental and Occupational Health, MD
Environmental Engineering
  Technology/Environmental Technology, MDO
Environmental Policy and Resource
  Management, MDO
Environmental Studies, B
Environmental/Environmental Health Engineering, B
Epidemiology, MD
European Studies/Civilization, B
Evolutionary Biology, MD
Experimental Psychology, D
Fiber, Textile and Weaving Arts, B
Film, Television, and Video Production, O
Film/Cinema Studies, B

Financial Engineering, M
Fine Arts and Art Studies, M
Foreign Language Teacher Education, M
Forestry, MDO
Foundations and Philosophy of Education, D
French Language and Literature, BD
General Studies, B
Geochemistry, MD
Geology/Earth Science, BMD
German Language and Literature, BMD
Gerontological Nursing, M
Health Physics/Radiological Health, MD
Health Promotion, MDO
Health Services Administration, MDO
Hebrew Language and Literature, BMD
Higher Education/Higher Education
  Administration, M
History, BDO
Human Genetics, MD
Human-Computer Interaction, M
Humanities/Humanistic Studies, B
Immunology, D
Industrial and Organizational Psychology, D
Industrial Design, B
Industrial Engineering, B
Industrial Hygiene, MD
Industrial/Management Engineering, MDO
Information Science/Studies, MD
Inorganic Chemistry, D
Interdisciplinary Studies, B
Intermedia/Multimedia, B
International Public Health/International Health, M
International Relations and Affairs, B
Islamic Studies, B
Italian Language and Literature, B
Japanese Language and Literature, B
Jazz/Jazz Studies, B
Jewish/Judaic Studies, B
Kinesiology and Exercise Science, B
Kinesiology and Movement Studies, MD
Landscape Architecture, BMDO
Latin American Studies, B
Latin Language and Literature, B
Law and Legal Studies, MDPO
Library Science, MD
Linguistics, BMD
Manufacturing Engineering, MDO
Marine Engineering, MDO
Mass Communication/Media Studies, D
Materials Engineering, BMD
Materials Sciences, BMD
Mathematics, BMD
Mathematics Teacher Education, MD
Mechanical Engineering, BMD
Media Studies, M
Medical Illustration and Informatics, M
Medicinal and Pharmaceutical Chemistry, D
Medieval and Renaissance Studies, B
Metal and Jewelry Arts, B
Metallurgical Engineering, B
Microbiology, D
Mineralogy, MD
Modern Greek Language and Literature, B
Molecular Biology, BMD
Multilingual and Multicultural Education, M
Music, BMDO
Music History, Literature, and Theory, B
Music Teacher Education, BMDO
Music Theory and Composition, B
Natural Resources and Conservation, MDO
Natural Resources Management/Development and
  Policy, B
Naval Architecture and Marine Engineering, B
Near and Middle Eastern Languages, MD
Near and Middle Eastern Studies, BMDO
Neuroscience, D
Nuclear Engineering, BMDO
Nurse Midwife/Nursing Midwifery, M
Nursing, MDO
Nursing - Adult, M
Nursing - Advanced Practice, M
Nursing - Registered Nurse Training, B
Nursing Administration, MO
Nutritional Sciences, M
Occupational Health Nursing, M
Ocean Engineering, MDO

Oceanography, Chemical and Physical, BMD
Operations Research, MDO
Oral and Dental Sciences, MDO
Organic Chemistry, D
Painting, B
Pathology/Experimental Pathology, D
Pediatric Nurse/Nursing, M
Pharmaceutical Administration, D
Pharmaceutical Engineering, M
Pharmaceutical Sciences, D
Pharmacology, D
Pharmacy, BPO
Philosophy, BMD
Photography, B
Physical Chemistry, D
Physical Education Teaching and Coaching, B
Physics, MD
Physiology, D
Piano and Organ, B
Planetary Astronomy and Science, MD
Political Science and Government, BMDO
Printmaking, B
Psychiatric/Mental Health Nurse/Nursing, M
Psychology, BD
Public Health, MDO
Public Policy Analysis, MDO
Radiologic Technology/Science - Radiographer, B
Reading Teacher Education, D
Real Estate, O
Religion/Religious Studies, B
Romance
   Languages, Literatures, and Linguistics, BD
Russian Language and Literature, BMD
Russian Studies, B
Scandinavian Studies, B
Science Teacher Education/General Science
   Teacher Education, MD
Sculpture, B
Secondary Education and Teaching, BO
Slavic Languages, Literatures, and Linguistics, MD
Social Psychology, D
Social Sciences, BD
Social Studies Teacher Education, M
Social Work, MDO
Sociology, BD
South and Southeast Asian Studies, MO
South Asian Studies, B
Southeast Asian Studies, B
Spanish Language and Literature, BD
Special Education and Teaching, D
Speech and Rhetorical Studies, B
Sport and Fitness Administration/Management, BM
Statistics, BMD
Surgical Nursing, M
Survey Methodology, MDO
Systems Engineering, MD
Technical Theatre/Theatre Design and
   Technology, B
Theater, MD
Toxicology, MD
Urban and Regional Planning, MDO
Urban Design, M
Violin, Viola, Guitar and Other Stringed
   Instruments, B
Visual and Performing Arts, B
Voice and Opera, B
Wildlife Biology, B
Wind and Percussion Instruments, B
Women's Health Nursing, O
Women's Studies, BDO
Writing, M
Zoology/Animal Biology, B

UNIVERSITY OF MICHIGAN-DEARBORN

Accounting, BM
American/United States Studies/Civilization, B
Anthropology, B
Applied Mathematics, M
Area Studies, B
Art History, Criticism and Conservation, B
Automotive Engineering Technology/Technician, M
Biochemistry, B
Biology/Biological Sciences, B
Business Administration and Management, B

Business Administration, Management and
   Operations, BMO
Chemistry, B
Chemistry Teacher Education, B
Communication Studies/Speech Communication
   and Rhetoric, B
Computational Sciences, M
Computer and Information Sciences, B
Computer Engineering, M
Computer Programming/Programmer, B
Computer Science, M
Criminal Justice/Safety Studies, B
Curriculum and Instruction, MO
Early Childhood Education and Teaching, B
Economics, B
Education, BM
Educational Administration and Supervision, O
Electrical Engineering, M
Electrical, Electronics and Communications
   Engineering, B
Elementary Education and Teaching, B
Engineering, B
Engineering and Applied Sciences, MDO
Engineering Management, M
English Language and Literature, B
Environmental Sciences, BM
Environmental Studies, B
Finance, B
Finance and Banking, M
French Language and Literature, B
General Studies, B
Geology/Earth Science, B
Health Psychology, M
Health/Health Care Administration/Management, B
History, B
Human Resources Management/Personnel
   Administration, B
Humanities/Humanistic Studies, B
Industrial Engineering, B
Industrial/Management Engineering, MO
Information Science/Studies, M
Liberal Arts and Sciences Studies and
   Humanities, B
Liberal Studies, M
Management Information Systems and Services, B
Manufacturing Engineering, BMD
Marketing/Marketing Management, B
Mathematics, B
Mathematics Teacher Education, B
Mechanical Engineering, BM
Microbiology, B
Multi-/Interdisciplinary Studies, B
Non-Profit/Public/Organizational Management, O
Philosophy, B
Physics, B
Political Science and Government, B
Psychology, B
Public Administration, MO
Public Policy Analysis, M
Science Teacher Education/General Science
   Teacher Education, B
Secondary Education and Teaching, B
Social Sciences, B
Social Studies Teacher Education, B
Sociology, B
Software Engineering, M
Spanish Language and Literature, B
Special Education and Teaching, M
Systems Engineering, MO
Systems Science and Theory, M
Women's Studies, B

UNIVERSITY OF MICHIGAN-FLINT

Accounting, B
Actuarial Science, B
African-American/Black Studies, B
American/United States Studies/Civilization, M
Anthropology, B
Art Teacher Education, B
Biological and Biomedical Sciences, M
Biology Teacher Education, B
Biology/Biological Sciences, B
Business Administration and Management, B
Business Administration, Management and
   Operations, M
Ceramic Arts and Ceramics, B

Chemistry, B
Chemistry Teacher Education, B
Clinical Laboratory Science/Medical
   Technology/Technologist, B
Clinical Psychology, B
Communication Studies/Speech Communication
   and Rhetoric, B
Computer Science, BM
Corrections and Criminal Justice, B
Drama and Dramatics/Theatre Arts, B
Early Childhood Education and Teaching, BM
Ecology, B
Economics, B
Education, BM
Elementary Education and Teaching, BM
Engineering Science, B
English Composition, B
English Language and Literature, B
Environmental Health, B
Ethics, B
Finance, B
Fine/Studio Arts, B
Foreign Languages, Literatures, and Linguistics, B
French Language and Literature, B
French Language Teacher Education, B
Graphic Design, B
Health and Medical Administrative Services, B
Health Education, M
Health/Health Care Administration/Management, B
History, B
History Teacher Education, B
Human Resources Management/Personnel
   Administration, B
Information Science/Studies, B
Information Technology, B
Kindergarten/PreSchool Education and Teaching, B
Liberal Arts and Sciences Studies and
   Humanities, B
Marketing/Marketing Management, B
Mass Communication/Media Studies, B
Mathematics, B
Medical Radiologic Technology/Science - Radiation
   Therapist, B
Multilingual and Multicultural Education, M
Music, B
Music Teacher Education, B
Natural Resources and Conservation, B
Nurse Anesthetist, M
Nursing, M
Nursing - Registered Nurse Training, B
Operations Management and Supervision, B
Organizational Behavior Studies, B
Organizational Communication, B
Painting, B
Philosophy, B
Photography, B
Physical Therapy/Therapist, D
Physics, B
Physics Teacher Education, B
Political Science and Government, B
Printmaking, B
Psychology, B
Psychology Teacher Education, B
Public Administration, BM
Public Health Education and Promotion, B
Reading Teacher Education, M
Sculpture, B
Social Sciences, B
Social Work, B
Sociology, B
Spanish Language and Literature, B
Spanish Language Teacher Education, B
Speech Teacher Education, B
Teacher Education and Professional
   Development, Specific Subject Areas, B
Technical and Business Writing, B
Urban Education and Leadership, M
Visual and Performing Arts, B
Wildlife Biology, B

UNIVERSITY OF PHOENIX-METRO DETROIT CAMPUS

Accounting, B
Adult and Continuing Education and Teaching, M
Business Administration and Management, B

Business Administration, Management and
  Operations, M
Curriculum and Instruction, M
Distance Education Development, M
Education, M
Educational Administration and Supervision, M
Elementary Education and Teaching, M
Entrepreneurship/Entrepreneurial Studies, B
Health Services Administration, M
Human Resources Management and Services, M
Information Technology, B
International Business/Trade/Commerce, M
Management Information Systems and
  Services, BM
Management of Technology, M
Management Science, B
Marketing, M
Marketing/Marketing Management, B
Nursing, MO
Nursing Administration, O
Nursing Science, B
Organizational Management, M
Special Education and Teaching, M

UNIVERSITY OF PHOENIX-WEST MICHIGAN CAMPUS

Accounting, B
Business Administration and Management, B
Business Administration, Management and
  Operations, M
Corrections and Criminal Justice, B
Curriculum and Instruction, M
Education, M
Educational Administration and Supervision, M
Electronic Commerce, M
Health Services Administration, M
Health/Health Care Administration/Management, B
Human Resources Management and Services, M
Information Technology, B
International Business/Trade/Commerce, M
Management Information Systems and
  Services, BM
Management of Technology, M
Management Science, B
Nursing, M
Nursing - Registered Nurse Training, B
Organizational Management, M
Public Administration and Social Service
  Professions, B

WALSH COLLEGE OF ACCOUNTANCY AND BUSINESS ADMINISTRATION

Accounting, BM
Business Administration and Management, B
Business Administration, Management and
  Operations, M
Computer and Information Sciences, B
Economics, M
Finance, B
Finance and Banking, M
Management, M
Management Information Systems and Services, M
Marketing/Marketing Management, B
Taxation, M

WASHTENAW COMMUNITY COLLEGE

Accounting, A
Administrative Assistant and Secretarial Science, A
Applied Art, A
Architectural Engineering Technology/Technician, A
Artificial Intelligence and Robotics, A
Automobile/Automotive Mechanics
  Technology/Technician, A
Biology/Biological Sciences, A
Building/Construction
  Finishing, Management, and Inspection, A
Business Administration and Management, A
Business Machine Repairer, A
Child Development, A
Commercial and Advertising Art, A
Computer Engineering Technology/Technician, A
Computer Graphics, A
Computer
  Programming, Vendor/Product Certification, A
Computer Programming/Programmer, A
Computer Science, A

Computer Typography and Composition Equipment
  Operator, A
Corrections, A
Criminal Justice/Law Enforcement Administration, A
Criminal Justice/Police Science, A
Culinary Arts/Chef Training, A
Data Processing and Data Processing
  Technology/Technician, A
Dental Assisting/Assistant, A
Drafting and Design Technology/Technician, A
Electrical, Electronic and Communications
  Engineering Technology/Technician, A
Electromechanical Technology/Electromechanical
  Engineering Technology, A
Engineering Technology, A
Food Technology and Processing, A
Graphic and Printing Equipment Operator
  Production, A
Heating, Air Conditioning, Ventilation and
  Refrigeration Maintenance
  Technology/Technician, A
Hotel/Motel Administration/Management, A
Industrial Design, A
Industrial Technology/Technician, A
Information Science/Studies, A
Kindergarten/PreSchool Education and Teaching, A
Liberal Arts and Sciences Studies and
  Humanities, A
Machine Tool Technology/Machinist, A
Management Information Systems and Services, A
Marketing/Marketing Management, A
Mechanical Engineering/Mechanical
  Technology/Technician, A
Medical Administrative Assistant/Secretary, A
Nursing - Registered Nurse Training, A
Pharmacy Technician/Assistant, A
Photography, A
Pre-Engineering, A
Quality Control Technology/Technician, A
Radiologic Technology/Science - Radiographer, A
Respiratory Care Therapy/Therapist, A
Substance Abuse/Addiction Counseling, A
Surgical Technology/Technologist, A
System Administration/Administrator, A
Technical and Business Writing, A
Technology Education/Industrial Arts, A
Web Page, Digital/Multimedia and Information
  Resources Design, A
Web/Multimedia Management and Webmaster, A
Welding Technology/Welder, A
Word Processing, A

WAYNE COUNTY COMMUNITY COLLEGE DISTRICT

Accounting, A
Administrative Assistant and Secretarial Science, A
Automobile/Automotive Mechanics
  Technology/Technician, A
Avionics Maintenance Technology/Technician, A
Business Administration and Management, A
Child Development, A
Clinical/Medical Laboratory Technician, A
Computer Science, A
Court Reporting/Court Reporter, A
Criminal Justice/Law Enforcement Administration, A
Criminal Justice/Police Science, A
Culinary Arts/Chef Training, A
Data Processing and Data Processing
  Technology/Technician, A
Dental Hygiene/Hygienist, A
Dietetics/Dieticians, A
Drafting and Design Technology/Technician, A
Education, A
Electrical, Electronic and Communications
  Engineering Technology/Technician, A
Emergency Medical Technology/Technician (EMT
  Paramedic), A
Engineering Technology, A
Environmental Engineering
  Technology/Environmental Technology, A
Finance, A
Industrial Technology/Technician, A
Labor and Industrial Relations, A
Legal Administrative Assistant/Secretary, A
Liberal Arts and Sciences Studies and
  Humanities, A

Marketing/Marketing Management, A
Medical Administrative Assistant/Secretary, A
Natural Resources Management/Development and
  Policy, A
Near and Middle Eastern Studies, A
Nursing - Registered Nurse Training, A
Occupational Therapy/Therapist, A
Veterinary/Animal Health Technology/Technician and
  Veterinary Assistant, A
Welding Technology/Welder, A

WAYNE STATE UNIVERSITY

Accounting, BM
Adult and Continuing Education and Teaching, M
Advertising and Public Relations, M
African-American/Black Studies, B
Allopathic Medicine, PO
American/United States Studies/Civilization, B
Anatomy, MD
Anthropology, BMD
Apparel and Textile Marketing Management, B
Applied Mathematics, MD
Art Education, M
Art History, Criticism and Conservation, BM
Art Teacher Education, B
Art/Art Studies, General, B
Asian Studies/Civilization, B
Biochemistry, MD
Biological and Biomedical Sciences, MD
Biological Anthropology, D
Biology/Biological Sciences, B
Biomedical Engineering, MD
Biopsychology, M
Business Administration, Management and
  Operations, MDO
Business Education, M
Cancer Biology/Oncology, MD
Chemical Engineering, BMD
Chemistry, BMD
Child and Family Studies, O
Cinematography and Film/Video Production, B
Civil Engineering, BMD
Classics and Classical
  Languages, Literatures, and Linguistics, BM
Clinical Laboratory Science/Medical
  Technology/Technologist, B
Clinical Laboratory Sciences, MO
Clinical Psychology, DO
Cognitive Sciences, D
Communication and Media Studies, MD
Communication Disorders, MD
Communication Studies/Speech Communication
  and Rhetoric, B
Community Health and Preventive Medicine, MO
Community Health Nursing, M
Comparative Literature, M
Composition, M
Computer and Information Sciences, B
Computer Engineering, MD
Computer Science, MDO
Computer Technology/Computer Systems
  Technology, B
Conflict Resolution and Mediation/Peace
  Studies, MO
Corporate and Organizational Communication, M
Counselor Education/School Counseling and
  Guidance Services, MDO
Criminal Justice/Safety Studies, B
Criminology, M
Curriculum and Instruction, MDO
Dance, B
Design and Applied Arts, M
Developmental Psychology, D
Dietetics/Dieticians, B
Drama and Dramatics/Theatre Arts, B
Early Childhood Education and Teaching, M
East Asian Studies, B
Economics, BMDO
Education, MDO
Education/Teaching of Individuals with Speech or
  Language Impairments, B
Educational Administration and Supervision, MDO
Educational Leadership and Administration, MDO
Educational Measurement and Evaluation, MD
Educational Media/Instructional Technology, MDO
Educational Psychology, MDO

Electrical Engineering, MD
Electrical, Electronic and Communications
  Engineering Technology/Technician, B
Electrical, Electronics and Communications
  Engineering, B
Electromechanical Technology/Electromechanical
  Engineering Technology, B
Elementary Education and Teaching, BMDO
·Engineering, B
Engineering and Applied Sciences, MDO
Engineering Management, M
English, MD
English Education, MO
English Language and Literature, B
English/Language Arts Teacher Education, B
Environmental and Occupational Health, MO
Environmental Sciences, B
Film/Cinema Studies, B
Finance, B
Fine Arts and Art Studies, M
Food Science and Technology, MD
Foods, Nutrition, and Wellness Studies, B
Foreign Language Teacher Education, MD
Foreign Languages and Literatures, B
Foundations and Philosophy of Education, MDO
French Language and Literature, M
Funeral Service and Mortuary Science, B
Genetics, MD
Geography, BM
Geology/Earth Science, BM
German Language and Literature, BMD
Gerontology, O
Hazardous Materials Management and Waste
  Technology/Technician, MO
Health Education, M
Health Physics/Radiological Health, MD
Health Teacher Education, B
Higher Education/Higher Education
  Administration, DO
History, BMDO
Human Development, M
Human Development and Family Studies, B
Human Services, O
Immunology, MDO
Industrial and Labor Relations, M
Industrial and Organizational Psychology, D
Industrial Education, M
Industrial Engineering, B
Industrial Production Technologies/Technicians, B
Industrial Technology/Technician, B
Industrial/Management Engineering, MD
Information Science/Studies, BMO
Interdisciplinary Studies, BMD
Italian Language and Literature, M
Journalism, B
Kinesiology and Movement Studies, M
Labor Studies, B
Law and Legal Studies, MDPO
Library Science, MO
Linguistics, BM
Logistics and Materials Management, B
Management Information Systems and Services, B
Manufacturing Engineering, M
Marketing/Marketing Management, B
Materials Engineering, MDO
Materials Sciences, MDO
Maternal/Child Health and Neonatal
  Nurse/Nursing, MO
Mathematics, BMD
Mathematics Teacher Education, BMO
Mechanical Engineering, BMD
Mechanical Engineering/Mechanical
  Technology/Technician, B
Media Studies, MD
Medical Physics, D
Medical Technology, O
Medicinal and Pharmaceutical Chemistry, MD
Metallurgical Engineering, MD
Microbiology, MDO
Middle/Near Eastern and Semitic
  Languages, Literatures, and Linguistics, B
Molecular Biology, MD
Multilingual and Multicultural Education, M
Museology/Museum Studies, O
Music, BMO
Music Teacher Education, M

Music Theory and Composition, M
Near and Middle Eastern Studies, BM
Neurobiology and Neurophysiology, D
Nurse Anesthetist, MO
Nursing, D
Nursing - Advanced Practice, M
Nursing - Registered Nurse Training, B
Nursing Education, MO
Nutritional Sciences, MD
Occupational Therapy/Therapist, BM
Operations Research, MD
Organizational Behavior Studies, B
Pathology/Experimental Pathology, MD
Pathology/Pathologist Assistant, B
Pediatric Nurse/Nursing, MO
Performance, M
Pharmaceutical Administration, MD
Pharmaceutical Sciences, MDPO
Pharmacology, MD
Pharmacy, MDPO
Philosophy, BMD
Physical Education Teaching and Coaching, BM
Physical Therapy/Therapist, M
Physician Assistant, M
Physics, BMD
Physiology, MDO
Political Science and Government, BMDO
Polymer/Plastics Engineering, O
Psychiatric/Mental Health Nurse/Nursing, MO
Psychology, BMD
Public Administration, BM
Public Health, MO
Public Health (MPH, DPH), B
Public Relations/Image Management, B
Radio and Television, B
Reading Teacher Education, MDO
Recreation and Park Management, M
Rehabilitation Counseling, MO
Rehabilitation Sciences, MO
Romance
  Languages, Literatures, and Linguistics, MD
Russian Language and Literature, M
School Psychology, MO
Science Teacher Education/General Science
  Teacher Education, BMO
Secondary Education and Teaching, MO
Slavic Languages, Literatures, and Linguistics, B
Social Studies Teacher Education, BMDO
Social Work, BMDO
Sociology, BMD
Spanish Language and Literature, M
Special Education and Teaching, BMDO
Speech and Interpersonal Communication, MD
Sport and Fitness Administration/Management, M
Statistics, MD
Substance Abuse/Addiction Counseling, O
Surgical Nursing, M
Taxation, M
Technical Teacher Education, B
Theater, MD
Toxicology, MDO
Urban and Regional Planning, M
Vocational and Technical Education, MDO
Writing, MD

WEST SHORE COMMUNITY COLLEGE

Accounting, A
Corrections, A
Criminal Justice/Police Science, A
Data Entry/Microcomputer Applications, A
Data Processing and Data Processing
  Technology/Technician, A
Electrical, Electronic and Communications
  Engineering Technology/Technician, A
Emergency Medical Technology/Technician (EMT
  Paramedic), A
Information Technology, A
Liberal Arts and Sciences Studies and
  Humanities, A
Licensed Practical/Vocational Nurse Training, A
Machine Tool Technology/Machinist, A
Marketing/Marketing Management, A
Nursing - Registered Nurse Training, A

Welding Technology/Welder, A

WESTERN MICHIGAN UNIVERSITY

Accounting, BM
Acting, B
Aerospace, Aeronautical and Astronautical
  Engineering, B
African Studies, B
Airline/Commercial/Professional Pilot and Flight
  Crew, B
American/United States Studies/Civilization, B
Anthropology, BM
Apparel and Textiles, B
Applied Arts and Design, M
Applied Economics, D
Applied Mathematics, BM
Architecture, B
Art History, Criticism and Conservation, B
Art Teacher Education, B
Art/Art Studies, General, B
Asian Studies/Civilization, B
Athletic Training and Sports Medicine, BM
Audiology/Audiologist and Speech-Language
  Pathology/Pathologist, B
Aviation/Airway Management and Operations, B
Avionics Maintenance Technology/Technician, B
Biochemistry, B
Biological and Biomedical Sciences, MD
Biology/Biological Sciences, B
Biomedical Sciences, B
Biostatistics, M
Building/Construction
  Finishing, Management, and Inspection, B
Business Administration and Management, B
Business Administration, Management and
  Operations, M
Business Statistics, B
Business Teacher Education, B
Business/Commerce, B
Business/Managerial Economics, B
Chemical Engineering, BMD
Chemistry, BMD
Chemistry Teacher Education, B
Child Development, B
Civil Engineering, B
Clinical Psychology, MD
Commercial and Advertising Art, B
Communication and Media Studies, BM
Communication Disorders, M
Communication Studies/Speech Communication
  and Rhetoric, B
Computational Sciences, M
Computer and Information Sciences, B
Computer Engineering, BMD
Computer Science, BMD
Construction Engineering, B
Construction Engineering and Management, M
Construction Engineering Technology/Technician, B
Corporate and Organizational Communication, M
Counseling Psychology, MD
Counselor Education/School Counseling and
  Guidance Services, MD
Creative Writing, B
Criminal Justice/Safety Studies, B
Criminology, B
Dance, B
Dietetics/Dieticians, B
Directing and Theatrical Production, B
Drama and Dramatics/Theatre Arts, B
Early Childhood Education and Teaching, M
E-Commerce/Electronic Commerce, B
Economics, BMD
Education, MDO
Education/Teaching of Individuals with Mental
  Retardation, B
Education/Teaching of Individuals with Vision
  Impairments, Including Blindness, B
Educational Leadership and Administration, MDO
Educational Measurement and Evaluation, MD
Electrical Engineering, MD
Electrical, Electronics and Communications
  Engineering, M
Elementary Education and Teaching, BM
Engineering, B
Engineering and Applied Sciences, MD
Engineering Management, M

Engineering Technologies/Technicians, B
Engineering/Industrial Management, B
English, MD
English Composition, B
English Education, MD
English Language and Literature, B
English/Language Arts Teacher Education, B
Environmental Sciences, B
Environmental Studies, B
Exercise and Sports Science, M
Experimental Psychology, MD
Family and Consumer Sciences/Home Economics
   Teacher Education, B
Family and Consumer Sciences/Human
   Sciences, M
Family Systems, B
Finance, B
Financial Planning and Services, B
Foodservice Systems
   Administration/Management, B
Foreign Language Teacher Education, B
French Language and Literature, B
French Language Teacher Education, B
General Studies, B
Geochemistry, B
Geography, BM
Geography Teacher Education, B
Geological and Earth Sciences/Geosciences, B
Geology/Earth Science, BMD
Geophysics and Seismology, B
Geosciences, M
German Language and Literature, B
German Language Teacher Education, B
Graphic Design, M
Health Teacher Education, B
Health/Health Care Administration/Management, B
History, BMD
History Teacher Education, B
Human Resources Development, M
Human Resources Management/Personnel
   Administration, B
Hydrology and Water Resources Science, B
Industrial and Organizational Psychology, M
Industrial Design, B
Industrial Engineering, B
Industrial/Management Engineering, M
Interior Design, B
International/Global Studies, B
Journalism, B
Kinesiology and Exercise Science, B
Latin Language and Literature, B
Latin Teacher Education, B
Logistics and Materials Management, B
Manufacturing Engineering, BM
Marketing, B
Marketing/Marketing Management, B
Marriage and Family Therapy/Counseling, M
Materials Engineering, M
Materials Sciences, M
Mathematics, BMD
Mathematics Teacher Education, BMD
Mechanical Engineering, BMD
Mechanical Engineering/Mechanical
   Technology/Technician, B
Medieval and Renaissance Studies, M
Middle School Education, M
Music, BM
Music History, Literature, and Theory, B
Music Performance, B
Music Teacher Education, B
Music Theory and Composition, B
Music Therapy/Therapist, B
Nursing - Registered Nurse Training, B
Occupational Therapy/Therapist, BM
Operations Research, M
Organizational Communication, B
Paper and Pulp Engineering, MD
Parks, Recreation, Leisure and Fitness Studies, B
Performance, M
Philosophy, BM
Physical Education Teaching and Coaching, BM
Physician Assistant, M
Physics, BMD
Physics Teacher Education, B
Plastics Engineering Technology/Technician, B
Platemaker/Imager, B

Political Science and Government, BMD
Pre-Dentistry Studies, B
Pre-Law Studies, B
Pre-Medicine/Pre-Medical Studies, B
Professional Studies, B
Psychology, BMDO
Public Administration, BMD
Public Affairs, MD
Public Relations, Advertising, and Applied
   Communication, B
Radio and Television, B
Reading Teacher Education, M
Rehabilitation Counseling, M
Religion/Religious Studies, BMD
Russian Studies, B
School Psychology, DO
Science Teacher Education/General Science
   Teacher Education, BD
Sculpture, B
Secondary Education and Teaching, B
Social Science Teacher Education, B
Social Sciences, B
Social Work, BM
Sociology, BMD
Spanish Language and Literature, BM
Spanish Language Teacher Education, B
Special Education and Teaching, MD
Sport and Fitness Administration/Management, M
Statistics, BMD
Structural Engineering, B
Teaching English or French as a Second or Foreign
   Language, B
Teaching French as a Second or Foreign
   Language, B
Technical Theatre/Theatre Design and
   Technology, B
Technology Teacher Education/Industrial Arts
   Teacher Education, B
Telecommunications Technology/Technician, B
Textile Design, M
Theatre/Theatre Arts Management, B
Tourism and Travel Services Management, B
Tourism and Travel Services Marketing
   Operations, B
Vocational and Technical Education, M
Women's Studies, B
Wood Science and Wood Products/Pulp and Paper
   Technology, B
Writing, M

Minnesota
ACADEMY COLLEGE

Accounting, A
Airline/Commercial/Professional Pilot and Flight
   Crew, A
Aviation/Airway Management and Operations, A
Business Administration and Management, AB
Business/Commerce, A
Commercial and Advertising Art, A
Computer and Information Sciences, A
Computer and Information Sciences and Support
   Services, A
Computer and Information Systems Security, A
Computer Graphics, A
Computer Programming/Programmer, A
Computer Science, B
Computer Systems Networking and
   Telecommunications, A
Data Processing and Data Processing
   Technology/Technician, A
Design and Visual Communications, A
Finance, A
Graphic Design, A
Intermedia/Multimedia, A
Management Information Systems and Services, A
Office Management and Supervision, A
Sales, Distribution and Marketing Operations, A
System Administration/Administrator, A
System, Networking, and LAN/WAN
   Management/Manager, A
Web Page, Digital/Multimedia and Information
   Resources Design, A

Web/Multimedia Management and Webmaster, A

ALEXANDRIA TECHNICAL COLLEGE

Accounting, A
Administrative Assistant and Secretarial Science, A
Banking and Financial Support Services, A
Business Administration and Management, A
CAD/CADD Drafting and/or Design
   Technology/Technician, A
Carpentry/Carpenter, A
Cartography, A
Child Care and Support Services Management, A
Child Care Provider/Assistant, A
Clinical/Medical Laboratory Technician, A
Commercial and Advertising Art, A
Computer and Information Sciences, A
Computer Programming, Specific Applications, A
Computer Systems Networking and
   Telecommunications, A
Computer Technology/Computer Systems
   Technology, A
Criminal Justice/Police Science, A
Diesel Mechanics Technology/Technician, A
Farm/Farm and Ranch Management, A
Fashion Merchandising, A
General Office Occupations and Clerical Services, A
Health and Physical Education, A
Hospitality Administration/Management, A
Hotel/Motel Administration/Management, A
Human Services, A
Hydraulics and Fluid Power Technology, A
Industrial Technology/Technician, A
Interior Design, A
Legal Administrative Assistant/Secretary, A
Legal Assistant/Paralegal, A
Licensed Practical/Vocational Nurse Training, A
Machine Tool Technology/Machinist, A
Marine Maintenance/Fitter and Ship Repair
   Technology/Technician, A
Marketing/Marketing Management, A
Mason/Masonry, A
Mechanical Drafting and Mechanical Drafting
   CAD/CADD, A
Medical Administrative Assistant/Secretary, A
Medical Insurance Coding Specialist/Coder, A
Medical Reception/Receptionist, A
Medical Transcription/Transcriptionist, A
Nurse/Nursing Assistant/Aide and Patient Care
   Assistant, A
Office Management and Supervision, A
Operations Management and Supervision, A
Phlebotomy/Phlebotomist, A
Receptionist, A
Selling Skills and Sales Operations, A
Small Business Administration/Management, A
Small Engine Mechanics and Repair
   Technology/Technician, A
Truck and Bus Driver/Commercial Vehicle
   Operation, A
Web Page, Digital/Multimedia and Information
   Resources Design, A
Welding Technology/Welder, A

ANOKA-RAMSEY COMMUNITY COLLEGE

Accounting, A
Administrative Assistant and Secretarial Science, A
Art/Art Studies, General, A
Biomedical Sciences, A
Business Administration and Management, A
Cartography, A
Clinical Laboratory Science/Medical
   Technology/Technologist, A
Computer Science, A
Computer Systems Networking and
   Telecommunications, A
Liberal Arts and Sciences Studies and
   Humanities, A
Management Information Systems and Services, A
Marketing/Marketing Management, A
Music, A
Nursing - Registered Nurse Training, A

Physical Therapist Assistant, A

ANOKA-RAMSEY COMMUNITY COLLEGE, CAMBRIDGE CAMPUS

Accounting, A
Administrative Assistant and Secretarial Science, A
Art/Art Studies, General, A
Biomedical Sciences, A
Business Administration and Management, A
Cartography, A
Computer Science, A
Computer Systems Networking and
 Telecommunications, A
Liberal Arts and Sciences Studies and
 Humanities, A
Marketing/Marketing Management, A
Music, A
Nursing - Registered Nurse Training, A
Pre-Engineering, A

ANOKA TECHNICAL COLLEGE

Accounting, A
Administrative Assistant and Secretarial Science, A
Air Traffic Controller, A
Applied Horticulture/Horticultural Operations, A
Architectural Drafting and Architectural
 CAD/CADD, A
Automobile/Automotive Mechanics
 Technology/Technician, A
Aviation/Airway Management and Operations, A
Business Administration and Management, A
Child Care and Support Services Management, A
Communications Systems Installation and Repair
 Technology, A
Computer Technology/Computer Systems
 Technology, A
Court Reporting/Court Reporter, A
Electrical, Electronic and Communications
 Engineering Technology/Technician, A
Electrical/Electronics Drafting and
 Electrical/Electronics CAD/CADD, A
Health Information/Medical Records
 Technology/Technician, A
Human Services, A
Landscaping and Groundskeeping, A
Legal Administrative Assistant/Secretary, A
Mechanical Drafting and Mechanical Drafting
 CAD/CADD, A
Medical Administrative Assistant/Secretary, A
Medical/Clinical Assistant, A
Occupational Therapist Assistant, A
Turf and Turfgrass Management, A
Welding Technology/Welder, A

THE ART INSTITUTES INTERNATIONAL MINNESOTA

Animation, Interactive Technology, Video Graphics
 and Special Effects, B
Commercial and Advertising Art, AB
Computer Graphics, B
Culinary Arts/Chef Training, AB
Digital Communication and Media/Multimedia, AB
Graphic Communications, AB
Graphic Design, AB
Interior Design, AB
Intermedia/Multimedia, AB
Restaurant, Culinary, and Catering
 Management/Manager, B
Web Page, Digital/Multimedia and Information
 Resources Design, AB

AUGSBURG COLLEGE

Accounting, B
Aeronautics/Aviation/Aerospace Science and
 Technology, B
Art History, Criticism and Conservation, B
Art Teacher Education, B
Art/Art Studies, General, B
Astrophysics, B
Athletic Training and Sports Medicine, B
Behavioral Sciences, B
Biological and Physical Sciences, B
Biology/Biological Sciences, B
Business Administration and Management, B

Business Administration, Management and
 Operations, M
Business/Managerial Economics, B
Chemistry, B
Community Health Nursing, M
Computer Science, B
Criminal Justice/Safety Studies, B
Drama and Dramatics/Theatre Arts, B
East Asian Studies, B
Economics, B
Education, BM
Education/Teaching of Individuals with Emotional
 Disturbances, B
Elementary Education and Teaching, B
English Language and Literature, B
Finance, B
Fine/Studio Arts, B
French Language and Literature, B
German Language and Literature, B
Health Teacher Education, B
History, B
Humanities/Humanistic Studies, B
Interdisciplinary Studies, B
International Business/Trade/Commerce, B
International Relations and Affairs, B
Kindergarten/PreSchool Education and Teaching, B
Liberal Arts and Sciences Studies and
 Humanities, B
Management Information Systems and Services, B
Marketing/Marketing Management, B
Mass Communication/Media Studies, B
Mathematics, B
Music, B
Music Teacher Education, B
Music Therapy/Therapist, B
Natural Sciences, B
Nursing, M
Nursing - Registered Nurse Training, B
Organizational Management, M
Philosophy, B
Physical Education Teaching and Coaching, B
Physician Assistant, BM
Physics, B
Political Science and Government, B
Pre-Dentistry Studies, B
Pre-Law Studies, B
Pre-Medicine/Pre-Medical Studies, B
Pre-Veterinary Studies, B
Psychology, B
Religion/Religious Studies, B
Scandinavian
 Languages, Literatures, and Linguistics, B
Secondary Education and Teaching, B
Social Sciences, B
Social Work, BM
Sociology, B
Spanish Language and Literature, B
Speech and Rhetorical Studies, B
Theology/Theological Studies, B
Transcultural Nursing, M
Urban Studies/Affairs, B
Women's Studies, B

BEMIDJI STATE UNIVERSITY

Accounting, B
American Indian/Native American
 Languages, Literatures, and Linguistics, B
American Indian/Native American Studies, B
Applied Art, B
Art Teacher Education, B
Art/Art Studies, General, B
Behavioral Sciences, B
Biological and Biomedical Sciences, M
Biological and Physical Sciences, B
Biology/Biological Sciences, B
Broadcast Journalism, B
Business Administration and Management, B
Chemistry, B
Clinical Laboratory Science/Medical
 Technology/Technologist, B
Commercial and Advertising Art, B
Community Organization and Advocacy, B
Computer Science, B
Construction Engineering Technology/Technician, B
Criminal Justice/Law Enforcement
 Administration, AB

Criminal Justice/Police Science, B
Data Processing and Data Processing
 Technology/Technician, B
Drama and Dramatics/Theatre Arts, B
Ecology, B
Economics, B
Education, BM
Elementary Education and Teaching, B
Engineering Physics, B
English, M
English Language and Literature, B
Environmental Studies, BM
Fine/Studio Arts, B
Geography, B
Geology/Earth Science, B
German Language and Literature, B
Health Teacher Education, B
History, B
Humanities/Humanistic Studies, B
Industrial Education, M
Industrial Technology/Technician, B
Information Science/Studies, B
Journalism, B
Liberal Arts and Sciences Studies and
 Humanities, AB
Marine Biology and Biological Oceanography, B
Mass Communication/Media Studies, B
Mathematics, B
Mathematics Teacher Education, M
Modern Languages, B
Music, B
Music Teacher Education, B
Natural Sciences, B
Nursing - Registered Nurse Training, B
Parks, Recreation, Leisure and Fitness Studies, B
Philosophy, B
Physical Education Teaching and Coaching, BM
Physical Sciences, B
Physics, B
Political Science and Government, B
Pre-Law Studies, B
Pre-Medicine/Pre-Medical Studies, B
Pre-Veterinary Studies, B
Professional Studies, B
Psychology, B
Radio and Television, B
Religion/Religious Studies, B
Science Teacher Education/General Science
 Teacher Education, BM
Secondary Education and Teaching, B
Social Sciences, B
Social Work, B
Sociology, B
Spanish Language and Literature, B
Special Education and Teaching, M
Speech and Rhetorical Studies, B
Speech Teacher Education, B
Sport and Fitness Administration/Management, B
Technology Education/Industrial Arts, B
Technology Teacher Education/Industrial Arts
 Teacher Education, B
Trade and Industrial Teacher Education, B

BETHANY LUTHERAN COLLEGE

Art/Art Studies, General, B
Biology/Biological Sciences, B
Business Administration and Management, B
Chemistry, B
Communication Studies/Speech Communication
 and Rhetoric, B
Drama and Dramatics/Theatre Arts, B
Elementary Education and Teaching, B
Engineering, B
English Language and Literature, B
History, B
Liberal Arts and Sciences Studies and
 Humanities, AB
Music, B
Psychology, B
Religious/Sacred Music, B
Social Sciences, B

BETHEL UNIVERSITY

Area, Ethnic, Cultural, and Gender Studies, B
Art Teacher Education, B
Art/Art Studies, General, B

Athletic Training and Sports Medicine, B
Bible/Biblical Studies, B
Biochemical Engineering, M
Biology Teacher Education, B
Biology/Biological Sciences, B
Business Administration and Management, B
Business Administration, Management and
   Operations, M
Chemistry, B
Chemistry Teacher Education, B
Communication and Media Studies, MO
Communication Studies/Speech Communication
   and Rhetoric, B
Community Health Services/Liaison/Counseling, B
Computer and Information Sciences, B
Counseling Psychology, MO
Drama and Dramatics/Theatre Arts, B
Early Childhood Education and Teaching, B
Economics, B
Education, MDO
Educational Administration and Supervision, D
Elementary Education and Teaching, B
Engineering Science, B
English Composition, B
English Language and Literature, B
English/Language Arts Teacher Education, B
Environmental Sciences, B
French Language and Literature, B
French Language Teacher Education, B
Gerontology, M
Health and Physical Education, B
Health Teacher Education, B
Higher Education/Higher Education
   Administration, O
History, B
International Relations and Affairs, B
Kinesiology and Exercise Science, B
Liberal Arts and Sciences Studies and
   Humanities, A
Library Science, B
Mass Communication/Media Studies, B
Mathematics, B
Mathematics Teacher Education, B
Molecular Biology, B
Multi-/Interdisciplinary Studies, B
Music, BMO
Music Performance, B
Music Teacher Education, B
Nursing, MO
Nursing - Registered Nurse Training, B
Nursing Education, MO
Organizational Management, M
Philosophy, B
Physical Education Teaching and Coaching, B
Physics, B
Physics Teacher Education, B
Political Science and Government, B
Psychology, B
Reading Teacher Education, MO
Religious/Sacred Music, B
School Nursing, O
Science Teacher Education/General Science
   Teacher Education, B
Secondary Education and Teaching, M
Social Sciences, B
Social Studies Teacher Education, B
Social Work, B
Spanish Language and Literature, B
Spanish Language Teacher Education, B
Teaching English as a Second or Foreign
   Language/ESL Language Instructor, B
Youth Ministry, B

BROWN COLLEGE

Animation, Interactive Technology, Video Graphics
   and Special Effects, B
Business Administration and Management, B
Cinematography and Film/Video Production, A
Communication and Media Studies, B
Computer Software Technology/Technician, A
Computer Systems Networking and
   Telecommunications, A
Criminal Justice/Law Enforcement
   Administration, AB
Design and Visual Communications, AB

Electrical, Electronic and Communications
   Engineering Technology/Technician, A
Information Science/Studies, A
Information Technology, B
Interior Design, B
Photography, B
Radio and Television Broadcasting
   Technology/Technician, A

CAPELLA UNIVERSITY

Applied Science and Technology, M
Business Administration, Management and
   Operations, MD
Business/Commerce, B
Computer Graphics, B
Computer Systems Networking and
   Telecommunications, B
Computer/Information Technology Services
   Administration and Management, B
Education, MD
Human Resources Management and Services, B
Human Services, MD
Information Science/Studies, M
Information Technology, B
Management Science, B
Marketing, B
Organizational Management, MD
Psychology, MD

CARLETON COLLEGE

African Studies, B
American/United States Studies/Civilization, B
Ancient/Classical Greek Language and Literature, B
Anthropology, B
Art History, Criticism and Conservation, B
Asian Studies/Civilization, B
Biology/Biological Sciences, B
Chemistry, B
Classics and Classical
   Languages, Literatures, and Linguistics, B
Computer Science, B
Economics, B
English Language and Literature, B
Fine/Studio Arts, B
French Language and Literature, B
French Studies, B
Geology/Earth Science, B
German Language and Literature, B
History, B
Interdisciplinary Studies, B
International Relations and Affairs, B
Latin American Studies, B
Latin Language and Literature, B
Mathematics, B
Music, B
Philosophy, B
Physics, B
Political Science and Government, B
Psychology, B
Religion/Religious Studies, B
Romance Languages, Literatures, and Linguistics, B
Russian Language and Literature, B
Russian Studies, B
Sociology, B
Spanish Language and Literature, B
Women's Studies, B

CENTRAL LAKES COLLEGE

Accounting, A
Administrative Assistant and Secretarial Science, A
Business Administration and Management, A
Developmental and Child Psychology, A
Horticultural Science, A
Legal Administrative Assistant/Secretary, A
Liberal Arts and Sciences Studies and
   Humanities, A
Marketing/Marketing Management, A
Medical Administrative Assistant/Secretary, A
Nursing - Registered Nurse Training, A

CENTURY COLLEGE

Accounting, A
Administrative Assistant and Secretarial Science, A
Autobody/Collision and Repair
   Technology/Technician, A

Automobile/Automotive Mechanics
   Technology/Technician, A
Business Administration and Management, A
Computer Engineering Technology/Technician, A
Cosmetology/Cosmetologist, A
Criminal Justice/Police Science, A
Dental Assisting/Assistant, A
Dental Hygiene/Hygienist, A
Dental Laboratory Technology/Technician, A
Diesel Mechanics Technology/Technician, A
Educational/Instructional Media Design, A
Emergency Medical Technology/Technician (EMT
   Paramedic), A
Environmental Studies, A
Fashion Merchandising, A
Heating, Air Conditioning, Ventilation and
   Refrigeration Maintenance
   Technology/Technician, A
Industrial Technology/Technician, A
Interior Design, A
Legal Administrative Assistant/Secretary, A
Liberal Arts and Sciences Studies and
   Humanities, A
Machine Tool Technology/Machinist, A
Management Information Systems and Services, A
Medical Administrative Assistant/Secretary, A
Medical Radiologic Technology/Science - Radiation
   Therapist, A
Medical/Clinical Assistant, A
Music Management and Merchandising, A
Nursing - Registered Nurse Training, A
Orthotist/Prosthetist, A
Pharmacy Technician/Assistant, A
Quality Control Technology/Technician, A
Selling Skills and Sales Operations, A
Small Engine Mechanics and Repair
   Technology/Technician, A
Social Work, A
Substance Abuse/Addiction Counseling, A

COLLEGE OF SAINT BENEDICT

Accounting, B
Art/Art Studies, General, B
Biochemistry, B
Biological and Physical Sciences, B
Biology/Biological Sciences, B
Business Administration and Management, B
Chemistry, B
Classics and Classical
   Languages, Literatures, and Linguistics, B
Computer Science, B
Dietetics/Dieticians, B
Drama and Dramatics/Theatre Arts, B
Economics, B
Education, B
Elementary Education and Teaching, B
English Language and Literature, B
Environmental Studies, B
Fine/Studio Arts, B
Foods, Nutrition, and Wellness Studies, B
Forestry, B
French Language and Literature, B
German Language and Literature, B
History, B
Humanities/Humanistic Studies, B
Liberal Arts and Sciences Studies and
   Humanities, B
Mathematics, B
Music, B
Natural Sciences, B
Nursing - Registered Nurse Training, B
Occupational Therapy/Therapist, B
Peace Studies and Conflict Resolution, B
Philosophy, B
Physical Therapy/Therapist, B
Physics, B
Political Science and Government, B
Pre-Dentistry Studies, B
Pre-Law Studies, B
Pre-Medicine/Pre-Medical Studies, B
Pre-Pharmacy Studies, B
Pre-Theology/Pre-Ministerial Studies, B
Pre-Veterinary Studies, B
Psychology, B
Religious Education, B
Secondary Education and Teaching, B

Social Sciences, B
Social Work, B
Sociology, B
Spanish Language and Literature, B
Speech and Rhetorical Studies, B
Theology/Theological Studies, B

COLLEGE OF ST. CATHERINE

Accounting, B
Art History, Criticism and Conservation, B
Art Teacher Education, B
Art/Art Studies, General, B
Biochemistry, B
Biology Teacher Education, B
Biology/Biological Sciences, B
Business Administration and Management, B
Chemistry, B
Chemistry Teacher Education, B
Clinical Laboratory Science/Medical
   Technology/Technologist, B
Comparative Literature, B
Computer and Information Sciences, B
Creative Writing, B
Diagnostic Medical Sonography/Sonographer and
   Ultrasound Technician, A
Dietetics/Dieticians, B
Drama and Dance Teacher Education, B
Drama and Dramatics/Theatre Arts, B
Economics, B
Education, BM
Elementary Education and Teaching, B
English Language and Literature, B
English/Language Arts Teacher Education, B
Family and Consumer Sciences/Home Economics
   Teacher Education, B
Family and Consumer Sciences/Human Sciences, B
Fashion Merchandising, B
Fashion/Apparel Design, B
Fine/Studio Arts, B
Foods, Nutrition, and Wellness Studies, B
French Language and Literature, B
French Language Teacher Education, B
Health and Physical Education, B
Health Information/Medical Records
   Technology/Technician, A
History, B
Information Science/Studies, M
Intercultural/Multicultural and Diversity Studies, B
International Business/Trade/Commerce, B
International Economics, B
International Relations and Affairs, B
Journalism, B
Kindergarten/PreSchool Education and Teaching, B
Liberal Arts and Sciences Studies and
   Humanities, A
Library Science, M
Management Information Systems and Services, B
Marketing/Marketing Management, B
Mass Communication/Media Studies, B
Mathematics, B
Mathematics Teacher Education, B
Medical Radiologic Technology/Science - Radiation
   Therapist, A
Music, B
Music Teacher Education, B
Nursing, M
Nursing - Registered Nurse Training, B
Occupational Therapist Assistant, A
Occupational Therapy/Therapist, BM
Organizational Management, M
Philosophy, B
Physical Education Teaching and Coaching, B
Physical Therapist Assistant, A
Physical Therapy/Therapist, MD
Physics, B
Political Science and Government, B
Pre-Dentistry Studies, B
Pre-Law Studies, B
Pre-Medicine/Pre-Medical Studies, B
Pre-Veterinary Studies, B
Psychology, B
Public Health, M
Respiratory Care Therapy/Therapist, B
Secondary Education and Teaching, B
Sign Language Interpretation and Translation, A
Social Sciences, B

Social Studies Teacher Education, B
Social Work, BM
Sociology, B
Spanish Language and Literature, B
Spanish Language Teacher Education, B
Speech and Rhetorical Studies, B
Speech Teacher Education, B
Substance Abuse/Addiction Counseling, B
Theology and Religious Vocations, M
Theology/Theological Studies, B
Women's Studies, B

COLLEGE OF ST. CATHERINE-MINNEAPOLIS

Clinical Laboratory Science/Medical
   Technology/Technologist, A
Diagnostic Medical Sonography/Sonographer and
   Ultrasound Technician, A
Health Information/Medical Records
   Administration/Administrator, A
Liberal Arts and Sciences Studies and
   Humanities, A
Medical Radiologic Technology/Science - Radiation
   Therapist, A
Nursing - Registered Nurse Training, A
Occupational Therapist Assistant, A
Physical Therapist Assistant, A

THE COLLEGE OF ST. SCHOLASTICA

Accounting, B
Applied Economics, B
Biochemistry, B
Biology/Biological Sciences, B
Business Administration and Management, B
Chemistry, B
Communication Studies/Speech Communication
   and Rhetoric, B
Computer and Information Sciences, B
Curriculum and Instruction, M
Education, M
Educational Media/Instructional Technology, M
Elementary Education and Teaching, B
English Language and Literature, B
Exercise and Sports Science, M
Exercise Physiology, M
Health Informatics, M
Health Information/Medical Records
   Administration/Administrator, M
Health Services/Allied Health/Health Sciences, B
History, B
Humanities/Humanistic Studies, B
Indian/Native American Education, B
International Business/Trade/Commerce, B
International/Global Studies, B
Liberal Arts and Sciences Studies and
   Humanities, B
Management, M
Management Information Systems and Services, M
Marketing/Marketing Management, B
Mathematics, B
Music Performance, B
Natural Sciences, B
Nursing, M
Nursing - Registered Nurse Training, B
Occupational Therapy/Therapist, M
Organizational Behavior Studies, B
Physical Sciences, B
Physical Therapy/Therapist, D
Psychology, B
Public Relations, Advertising, and Applied
   Communication, B
Religion/Religious Studies, B
School Librarian/School Library Media Specialist, B
Social Sciences, B
Social Work, B
Teacher Education, Multiple Levels, B

COLLEGE OF VISUAL ARTS

Drawing, B
Fine/Studio Arts, B
Graphic Design, B
Photography, B
Printmaking, B
Sculpture, B

Visual and Performing Arts, B

CONCORDIA COLLEGE

Accounting, B
Advertising, B
Art History, Criticism and Conservation, B
Art Teacher Education, B
Art/Art Studies, General, B
Biology Teacher Education, B
Biology/Biological Sciences, B
Broadcast Journalism, B
Business Administration and Management, B
Business Teacher Education, B
Business/Commerce, B
Chemistry, B
Chemistry Teacher Education, B
Child Development, B
Classics and Classical
   Languages, Literatures, and Linguistics, B
Clinical Laboratory Science/Medical
   Technology/Technologist, B
Communication Studies/Speech Communication
   and Rhetoric, B
Computer Science, B
Creative Writing, B
Dietetics/Dieticians, B
Drama and Dramatics/Theatre Arts, B
Economics, B
Education, B
Elementary Education and Teaching, B
English Language and Literature, B
English/Language Arts Teacher Education, B
Environmental Studies, B
Fine/Studio Arts, B
Foods, Nutrition, and Wellness Studies, B
French Language and Literature, B
French Language Teacher Education, B
German Language and Literature, B
German Language Teacher Education, B
Health and Physical Education, B
Health Teacher Education, B
Health/Health Care Administration/Management, B
History, B
Humanities/Humanistic Studies, B
International Business/Trade/Commerce, B
International/Global Studies, B
Journalism, B
Kindergarten/PreSchool Education and Teaching, B
Kinesiology and Exercise Science, B
Latin Language and Literature, B
Mass Communication/Media Studies, B
Mathematics, B
Mathematics Teacher Education, B
Music, B
Music Performance, B
Music Teacher Education, B
Music Theory and Composition, B
Nursing - Registered Nurse Training, B
Occupational Therapy/Therapist, B
Ophthalmic and Optometric Support Services and
   Allied Professions, B
Philosophy, B
Physical Education Teaching and Coaching, B
Physical Therapy/Therapist, B
Physics, B
Physics Teacher Education, B
Piano and Organ, B
Political Science and Government, B
Pre-Dentistry Studies, B
Pre-Law Studies, B
Pre-Medicine/Pre-Medical Studies, B
Pre-Theology/Pre-Ministerial Studies, B
Pre-Veterinary Studies, B
Psychology, B
Public Relations/Image Management, B
Radio and Television, B
Religion/Religious Studies, B
Russian Studies, B
Scandinavian
   Languages, Literatures, and Linguistics, B
Science Teacher Education/General Science
   Teacher Education, B
Secondary Education and Teaching, B
Social Studies Teacher Education, B
Social Work, B
Sociology, B

Spanish Language and Literature, B
Spanish Language Teacher Education, B
Speech and Rhetorical Studies, B
Voice and Opera, B

CONCORDIA UNIVERSITY, ST. PAUL

Accounting, B
Biological and Physical Sciences, B
Biology Teacher Education, B
Biology/Biological Sciences, B
Business Administration and Management, B
Chemistry Teacher Education, B
Child and Family Studies, M
Child Care and Support Services Management, B
Criminal Justice/Safety Studies, B
Criminology, M
Drama and Dramatics/Theatre Arts, B
Early Childhood Education and Teaching, BM
Education, BM
Elementary Education and Teaching, B
English Language and Literature, B
Environmental Sciences, B
Finance, B
Fine/Studio Arts, B
General Studies, AB
Health Teacher Education, B
History, B
Human Resources Management and Services, M
Human Services, B
Junior High/Intermediate/Middle School Education and Teaching, B
Kindergarten/PreSchool Education and Teaching, B
Kinesiology and Exercise Science, B
Management Information Systems and Services, B
Mass Communication/Media Studies, B
Mathematics, B
Mathematics Teacher Education, B
Missions/Missionary Studies and Missiology, B
Music, B
Music Teacher Education, B
Natural Sciences, B
Organizational Behavior Studies, B
Organizational Management, M
Pastoral Studies/Counseling, M
Physical Education Teaching and Coaching, B
Psychology, B
Religious Education, B
Religious/Sacred Music, B
Science Teacher Education/General Science Teacher Education, B
Secondary Education and Teaching, B
Social Studies Teacher Education, B
Sociology, B
Teaching English as a Second or Foreign Language/ESL Language Instructor, B
Theology and Religious Vocations, M
Theology/Theological Studies, B

CROSSROADS COLLEGE

Bible/Biblical Studies, B
Counseling Psychology, B
Liberal Arts and Sciences Studies and Humanities, AB
Missions/Missionary Studies and Missiology, B
Religious Education, B
Religious/Sacred Music, B
Theology and Religious Vocations, B
Theology/Theological Studies, B
Youth Ministry, B

CROWN COLLEGE

Bible/Biblical Studies, AB
Biological and Physical Sciences, A
Biology/Biological Sciences, AB
Business Administration and Management, AB
Business/Commerce, A
Christian Studies, B
Communication and Media Studies, B
Early Childhood Education and Teaching, AB
Elementary Education and Teaching, B
English Language and Literature, B
English/Language Arts Teacher Education, B
General Studies, AB
History, B
History Teacher Education, B

Kindergarten/PreSchool Education and Teaching, AB
Liberal Arts and Sciences Studies and Humanities, AB
Linguistics, B
Missions/Missionary Studies and Missiology, B
Music, AB
Music Teacher Education, B
Nursing - Registered Nurse Training, B
Pastoral Studies/Counseling, B
Physical Education Teaching and Coaching, B
Pre-Law Studies, B
Psychology, AB
Religious Education, B
Social Sciences, A
Social Studies Teacher Education, B
Sport and Fitness Administration/Management, B
Theology and Religious Vocations, M

DAKOTA COUNTY TECHNICAL COLLEGE

Accounting, A
Accounting Technology/Technician and Bookkeeping, A
Administrative Assistant and Secretarial Science, A
Applied Horticulture/Horticultural Business Services, A
Architectural Drafting and Architectural CAD/CADD, A
Architectural Technology/Technician, A
Autobody/Collision and Repair Technology/Technician, A
Automobile/Automotive Mechanics Technology/Technician, A
Biomedical Technology/Technician, A
Child Care and Support Services Management, A
Child Care Provider/Assistant, A
Commercial and Advertising Art, A
Commercial Photography, A
Communications Systems Installation and Repair Technology, A
Computer and Information Systems Security, A
Computer Graphics, A
Computer Programming, A
Computer Programming, Specific Applications, A
Computer Programming, Vendor/Product Certification, A
Computer Software and Media Applications, A
Computer Systems Networking and Telecommunications, A
Concrete Finishing/Concrete Finisher, A
Data Entry/Microcomputer Applications, A
Data Modeling/Warehousing and Database Administration, A
Diesel Mechanics Technology/Technician, A
Drafting and Design Technology/Technician, A
Electrical/Electronics Equipment Installation and Repair, A
Electrician, A
Engineering Technology, A
Entrepreneurial and Small Business Operations, A
Entrepreneurship/Entrepreneurial Studies, A
Executive Assistant/Executive Secretary, A
Furniture Design and Manufacturing, A
Graphic Design, A
Housing and Human Environments, A
Industrial Mechanics and Maintenance Technology, A
Interior Design, A
Landscaping and Groundskeeping, A
Licensed Practical/Vocational Nurse Training, A
Lineworker, A
Marketing/Marketing Management, A
Mason/Masonry, A
Medical Insurance Coding Specialist/Coder, A
Medical Transcription/Transcriptionist, A
Medium/Heavy Vehicle and Truck Technology/Technician, A
Photographic and Film/Video Technology/Technician and Assistant, A
Photography, A
Plant Nursery Operations and Management, A
Prepress/Desktop Publishing and Digital Imaging Design, A
Sales, Distribution and Marketing Operations, A
System Administration/Administrator, A

Tourism and Travel Services Management, A
Tourism and Travel Services Marketing Operations, A
Truck and Bus Driver/Commercial Vehicle Operation, A
Vehicle and Vehicle Parts and Accessories Marketing Operations, A
Web Page, Digital/Multimedia and Information Resources Design, A
Web/Multimedia Management and Webmaster, A
Word Processing, A

DEVRY UNIVERSITY

Business Administration and Management, B
Information Science/Studies, B
System, Networking, and LAN/WAN Management/Manager, A

DULUTH BUSINESS UNIVERSITY

Accounting, A
Administrative Assistant and Secretarial Science, A
Business Administration and Management, A
Computer Systems Networking and Telecommunications, A
Dental Assisting/Assistant, A
Design and Visual Communications, A
Medical/Clinical Assistant, A
Veterinary/Animal Health Technology/Technician and Veterinary Assistant, A
Web Page, Digital/Multimedia and Information Resources Design, A

DUNWOODY COLLEGE OF TECHNOLOGY

Appliance Installation and Repair Technology/Technician, A
Architectural Drafting and Architectural CAD/CADD, A
Autobody/Collision and Repair Technology/Technician, A
Automobile/Automotive Mechanics Technology/Technician, A
Computer and Information Sciences, A
Computer Programming, Specific Applications, A
Electrical and Power Transmission Installation/Installer, A
Electrical, Electronic and Communications Engineering Technology/Technician, A
Engineering, A
Graphic and Printing Equipment Operator Production, A
Heating, Air Conditioning and Refrigeration Technology/Technician, A
Heating, Air Conditioning, Ventilation and Refrigeration Maintenance Technology/Technician, A
Industrial Technology/Technician, A
Tool and Die Technology/Technician, A
Welding Technology/Welder, A

FOND DU LAC TRIBAL AND COMMUNITY COLLEGE

American Indian/Native American Studies, A
Business/Commerce, A
Corrections, A
Criminal Justice/Police Science, A
Environmental Studies, A
Finance, A
Human Services, A
Insurance, A
Liberal Arts and Sciences Studies and Humanities, A
Real Estate, A

GLOBE COLLEGE

Accounting, AB
Animation, Interactive Technology, Video Graphics and Special Effects, A
Business Administration and Management, AB
Clinical Laboratory Science/Medical Technology/Technologist, A
Commercial and Advertising Art, A
Computer Graphics, A
Computer Systems Networking and Telecommunications, A

Digital Communication and Media/Multimedia, A
Information Technology, A
Kinesiology and Exercise Science, A
Legal Assistant/Paralegal, AB
Massage Therapy/Therapeutic Massage, A
Medical Administrative Assistant/Secretary, A
Medical/Clinical Assistant, A
Music, A
Nursing - Registered Nurse Training, B
Taxation, A
Veterinary/Animal Health Technology/Technician and
    Veterinary Assistant, A

GUSTAVUS ADOLPHUS COLLEGE

Accounting, B
Anthropology, B
Art History, Criticism and Conservation, B
Art Teacher Education, B
Art/Art Studies, General, B
Athletic Training and Sports Medicine, B
Biochemistry, B
Biology Teacher Education, B
Biology/Biological Sciences, B
Business Administration and Management, B
Business/Managerial Economics, B
Chemistry, B
Chemistry Teacher Education, B
Classics and Classical
    Languages, Literatures, and Linguistics, B
Computer Science, B
Criminal Justice/Law Enforcement Administration, B
Dance, B
Drama and Dramatics/Theatre Arts, B
Economics, B
Education, B
Elementary Education and Teaching, B
English Language and Literature, B
Environmental Studies, B
French Language and Literature, B
Geography, B
Geology/Earth Science, B
German Language and Literature, B
Health and Physical Education/Fitness, B
Health Teacher Education, B
History, B
Interdisciplinary Studies, B
International Business/Trade/Commerce, B
Japanese Language and Literature, B
Japanese Studies, B
Latin American Studies, B
Mass Communication/Media Studies, B
Mathematics, B
Mathematics Teacher Education, B
Music, B
Music Teacher Education, B
Nursing - Registered Nurse Training, B
Philosophy, B
Physical Education Teaching and Coaching, B
Physical Therapy/Therapist, B
Physics, B
Physics Teacher Education, B
Political Science and Government, B
Pre-Dentistry Studies, B
Pre-Law Studies, B
Pre-Medicine/Pre-Medical Studies, B
Pre-Veterinary Studies, B
Psychology, B
Religion/Religious Studies, B
Religious/Sacred Music, B
Russian Language and Literature, B
Russian Studies, B
Scandinavian
    Languages, Literatures, and Linguistics, B
Scandinavian Studies, B
Secondary Education and Teaching, B
Social Sciences, B
Social Studies Teacher Education, B
Sociology, B
Spanish Language and Literature, B
Speech and Rhetorical Studies, B

HAMLINE UNIVERSITY

Anthropology, B
Art History, Criticism and Conservation, B
Art/Art Studies, General, B
Asian Studies/Civilization, B

Athletic Training and Sports Medicine, B
Biochemistry, B
Biology/Biological Sciences, B
Business Administration and Management, B
Central/Middle and Eastern European Studies, B
Chemistry, B
Criminal Justice/Law Enforcement Administration, B
Drama and Dramatics/Theatre Arts, B
East Asian Studies, B
Economics, B
Education, BMD
Elementary Education and Teaching, B
English Language and Literature, B
Environmental Studies, B
European Studies/Civilization, B
Fine/Studio Arts, B
French Language and Literature, B
German Language and Literature, B
Health and Physical Education, B
Health Teacher Education, B
History, B
International Business/Trade/Commerce, B
International Economics, B
International Relations and Affairs, B
Jewish/Judaic Studies, B
Kinesiology and Exercise Science, B
Latin American Studies, B
Law and Legal Studies, BMPO
Legal Assistant/Paralegal, B
Liberal Studies, MO
Management, MO
Mass Communication/Media Studies, B
Mathematics, B
Music, B
Music Teacher Education, B
Non-Profit/Public/Organizational Management, M
Occupational Therapy/Therapist, B
Peace Studies and Conflict Resolution, B
Philosophy, B
Physical Education Teaching and Coaching, B
Physical Therapy/Therapist, B
Physics, B
Political Science and Government, B
Pre-Dentistry Studies, B
Pre-Law Studies, B
Pre-Medicine/Pre-Medical Studies, B
Pre-Veterinary Studies, B
Psychology, B
Public Administration, BM
Religion/Religious Studies, B
Russian Studies, B
Science Teacher Education/General Science
    Teacher Education, B
Secondary Education and Teaching, B
Social Sciences, B
Sociology, B
Spanish Language and Literature, B
Speech Teacher Education, B
Teacher Education, Multiple Levels, B
Urban Studies/Affairs, B
Women's Studies, B

HENNEPIN TECHNICAL COLLEGE

Architectural Drafting and Architectural
    CAD/CADD, A
Automobile/Automotive Mechanics
    Technology/Technician, A
Carpentry/Carpenter, A
Child Development, A
Computer Programming/Programmer, A
Computer Systems Networking and
    Telecommunications, A
Dental Assisting/Assistant, A
Drafting/Design Engineering
    Technologies/Technicians, A
Electrical, Electronic and Communications
    Engineering Technology/Technician, A
Fire Science/Firefighting, A
Hydraulics and Fluid Power Technology, A
Legal Administrative Assistant/Secretary, A
Machine Tool Technology/Machinist, A
Medical Administrative Assistant/Secretary, A
Photography, A
Plastics Engineering Technology/Technician, A
Prepress/Desktop Publishing and Digital Imaging
    Design, A

Publishing, A

HERZING COLLEGE

Computer and Information Sciences, A
Computer Systems Networking and
    Telecommunications, A
Dental Assisting/Assistant, A
Dental Hygiene/Hygienist, A
Management Information Systems and Services, B
Massage Therapy/Therapeutic Massage, A
Medical Insurance Coding Specialist/Coder, A
Medical/Clinical Assistant, A

HIBBING COMMUNITY COLLEGE

Administrative Assistant and Secretarial Science, A
Business Administration and Management, A
Clinical/Medical Laboratory Technician, A
Computer and Information Sciences, A
Computer Installation and Repair
    Technology/Technician, A
Computer Systems Networking and
    Telecommunications, A
Criminal Justice/Police Science, A
Culinary Arts/Chef Training, A
Dental Assisting/Assistant, A
Drafting and Design Technology/Technician, A
Educational/Instructional Media Design, A
Foodservice Systems
    Administration/Management, A
Legal Administrative Assistant/Secretary, A
Liberal Arts and Sciences Studies and
    Humanities, A
Medical Administrative Assistant/Secretary, A
Nursing - Registered Nurse Training, A
Pre-Engineering, A
Selling Skills and Sales Operations, A
Web Page, Digital/Multimedia and Information
    Resources Design, A

INVER HILLS COMMUNITY COLLEGE

Accounting, A
Administrative Assistant and Secretarial Science, A
Air Traffic Controller, A
Airline/Commercial/Professional Pilot and Flight
    Crew, A
Aviation/Airway Management and Operations, A
Building/Construction
    Finishing, Management, and Inspection, A
Business Administration and Management, A
Computer Programming, Specific Applications, A
Computer
    Programming, Vendor/Product Certification, A
Construction Engineering Technology/Technician, A
Criminal Justice/Police Science, A
Criminal Justice/Safety Studies, A
Emergency Medical Technology/Technician (EMT
    Paramedic), A
Health/Health Care Administration/Management, A
Human Services, A
Legal Administrative Assistant/Secretary, A
Legal Assistant/Paralegal, A
Liberal Arts and Sciences Studies and
    Humanities, A
Management Information Systems and Services, A
Marketing/Marketing Management, A
Medical Administrative Assistant/Secretary, A
Nursing - Registered Nurse Training, A
System Administration/Administrator, A

ITASCA COMMUNITY COLLEGE

Accounting, A
American Indian/Native American Studies, A
Business Administration and Management, A
Chemical Engineering, A
Civil Engineering, A
Computer Engineering, A
Education, A
Education/Teaching of Individuals in Early Childhood
    Special Education Programs, A
Engineering, A
Engineering Science, A
Engineering Technology, A
Environmental Studies, A
Forestry, A
Forestry Technology/Technician, A
General Studies, A

Geography, A
Human Services, A
Liberal Arts and Sciences Studies and
   Humanities, A
Licensed Practical/Vocational Nurse Training, A
Mechanical Engineering, A
Natural Resources and Conservation, A
Natural Resources Management/Development and
   Policy, A
Nuclear Engineering, A
Pre-Engineering, A
Psychology, A
Teacher Education, Multiple Levels, A
Wildlife and Wildlands Science and Management, A

ITT TECHNICAL INSTITUTE

Animation, Interactive Technology, Video Graphics
   and Special Effects, B
CAD/CADD Drafting and/or Design
   Technology/Technician, A
Computer and Information Systems Security, B
Computer Programming/Programmer, A
Computer Software Technology/Technician, B
Electrical, Electronic and Communications
   Engineering Technology/Technician, AB
System, Networking, and LAN/WAN
   Management/Manager, A
Web Page, Digital/Multimedia and Information
   Resources Design, A

LAKE SUPERIOR COLLEGE

Accounting, A
Airline/Commercial/Professional Pilot and Flight
   Crew, A
Architectural Drafting and Architectural
   CAD/CADD, A
Automobile/Automotive Mechanics
   Technology/Technician, A
Business Administration and Management, A
Carpentry/Carpenter, A
Civil Engineering Technology/Technician, A
Clinical/Medical Laboratory Technician, A
Computer Programming, Specific Applications, A
Computer Technology/Computer Systems
   Technology, A
Dental Hygiene/Hygienist, A
Electrical, Electronic and Communications
   Engineering Technology/Technician, A
Electrician, A
Emergency Medical Technology/Technician (EMT
   Paramedic), A
Executive Assistant/Executive Secretary, A
Fire Services Administration, A
Human Resources Management and Services, A
Legal Administrative Assistant/Secretary, A
Legal Assistant/Paralegal, A
Liberal Arts and Sciences Studies and
   Humanities, A
Machine Tool Technology/Machinist, A
Management Information Systems and Services, A
Mechanical Drafting and Mechanical Drafting
   CAD/CADD, A
Medical Administrative Assistant/Secretary, A
Medical Radiologic Technology/Science - Radiation
   Therapist, A
Nursing - Registered Nurse Training, A
Occupational Therapist Assistant, A
Physical Therapist Assistant, A
Respiratory Care Therapy/Therapist, A
Selling Skills and Sales Operations, A

MACALESTER COLLEGE

Anthropology, B
Art History, Criticism and Conservation, B
Asian Studies/Civilization, B
Biology/Biological Sciences, B
Chemistry, B
Classics and Classical
   Languages, Literatures, and Linguistics, B
Communication Studies/Speech Communication
   and Rhetoric, B
Computer Science, B
Drama and Dramatics/Theatre Arts, B
Economics, B
English Language and Literature, B
Environmental Studies, B

Fine/Studio Arts, B
French Language and Literature, B
Geography, B
Geology/Earth Science, B
History, B
Humanities/Humanistic Studies, B
Interdisciplinary Studies, B
International Relations and Affairs, B
Latin American Studies, B
Latin Language and Literature, B
Linguistics, B
Mathematics, B
Modern Greek Language and Literature, B
Music, B
Neuroscience, B
Philosophy, B
Physics, B
Political Science and Government, B
Psychology, B
Religion/Religious Studies, B
Russian Language and Literature, B
Russian Studies, B
Sociology, B
Spanish Language and Literature, B
Urban Studies/Affairs, B
Women's Studies, B

MARTIN LUTHER COLLEGE

Elementary Education and Teaching, B
Interdisciplinary Studies, B
Kindergarten/PreSchool Education and Teaching, B
Pre-Theology/Pre-Ministerial Studies, B
Teacher Education, Multiple Levels, B
Theology/Theological Studies, B

MCNALLY SMITH COLLEGE OF MUSIC

Engineering Technologies/Technicians, A
Music, A
Music Management and Merchandising, AB
Music Performance, AB

MESABI RANGE COMMUNITY AND TECHNICAL COLLEGE

Administrative Assistant and Secretarial Science, A
Business/Commerce, A
Computer Graphics, A
Computer Programming, A
Computer Programming, Specific Applications, A
Computer Software and Media Applications, A
Computer Systems Networking and
   Telecommunications, A
Computer/Information Technology Services
   Administration and Management, A
Electrical/Electronics Equipment Installation and
   Repair, A
Human Services, A
Information Technology, A
Instrumentation Technology/Technician, A
Liberal Arts and Sciences Studies and
   Humanities, A
Pre-Engineering, A
Substance Abuse/Addiction Counseling, A

METROPOLITAN STATE UNIVERSITY

Accounting, B
Advertising, B
Applied Mathematics, B
Biology/Biological Sciences, B
Business Administration and Management, B
Business Administration, Management and
   Operations, M
Communication Studies/Speech Communication
   and Rhetoric, B
Computer Science, B
Computer Systems Analysis/Analyst, B
Criminal Justice/Law Enforcement Administration, B
Criminal Justice/Police Science, B
Criminal Justice/Safety Studies, B
Culinary Arts/Chef Training, B
Developmental and Child Psychology, B
Drama and Dramatics/Theatre Arts, B
Economics, B
English Composition, B
English Language and Literature, B
Ethnic, Cultural Minority, and Gender Studies, B

Finance, B
Finance and Banking, M
General Studies, B
History, B
Hospitality Administration/Management, B
Human Resources Management and Services, M
Human Resources Management/Personnel
   Administration, B
Human Services, B
Information Science/Studies, BM
International Business/Trade/Commerce, BM
Kindergarten/PreSchool Education and Teaching, B
Law Enforcement, M
Liberal Arts and Sciences Studies and
   Humanities, B
Management, M
Management Information Systems and
   Services, BM
Marketing, M
Marketing/Marketing Management, B
Non-Profit/Public/Organizational Management, M
Nursing, M
Nursing - Registered Nurse Training, B
Office Management and Supervision, B
Operations Management and Supervision, B
Organizational Management, M
Philosophy, B
Playwriting and Screenwriting, B
Psychology, B
Public Administration, BM
Sales, Distribution and Marketing Operations, B
Social Sciences, B
Social Work, B
Substance Abuse/Addiction Counseling, B
System Management, M
Technical and Business Writing, BM
Women's Studies, B

MINNEAPOLIS BUSINESS COLLEGE

Accounting, A
Administrative Assistant and Secretarial Science, A
Allied Health and Medical Assisting Services, A
Computer Programming/Programmer, A
Prepress/Desktop Publishing and Digital Imaging
   Design, A
System, Networking, and LAN/WAN
   Management/Manager, A
Tourism and Travel Services Management, A

MINNEAPOLIS COLLEGE OF ART AND DESIGN

Advertising, B
Applied Arts and Design, M
Cinematography and Film/Video Production, B
Commercial and Advertising Art, B
Computer Art and Design, O
Drawing, B
Film, Television, and Video Production, M
Fine Arts and Art Studies, MO
Fine/Studio Arts, B
Graphic Design, M
Illustration, M
Interdisciplinary Studies, B
Intermedia/Multimedia, B
Painting, BM
Photography, BM
Printmaking, BM
Sculpture, BM

MINNEAPOLIS COMMUNITY AND TECHNICAL COLLEGE

Accounting Technology/Technician and
   Bookkeeping, A
Administrative Assistant and Secretarial Science, A
Aircraft Powerplant Technology/Technician, A
Airframe Mechanics and Aircraft Maintenance
   Technology/Technician, A
Automobile/Automotive Mechanics
   Technology/Technician, A
Avionics Maintenance Technology/Technician, A
Business Administration and Management, A
Business/Commerce, A
Child Development, A
Cinematography and Film/Video Production, A
Commercial and Advertising Art, A
Computer and Information Sciences, A

Computer Programming/Programmer, A
Criminal Justice/Police Science, A
Criminal Justice/Safety Studies, A
Culinary Arts/Chef Training, A
Human Services, A
Information Science/Studies, A
Legal Administrative Assistant/Secretary, A
Liberal Arts and Sciences Studies and
  Humanities, A
Nursing - Registered Nurse Training, A
Parks, Recreation, Leisure and Fitness Studies, A
Substance Abuse/Addiction Counseling, A
Web Page, Digital/Multimedia and Information
  Resources Design, A
Web/Multimedia Management and Webmaster, A

MINNESOTA SCHOOL OF BUSINESS

Accounting, AB
Administrative Assistant and Secretarial Science, A
Business Administration and Management, AB
Computer Systems Networking and
  Telecommunications, A
Information Technology, AB
Intermedia/Multimedia, A
Legal Administrative Assistant/Secretary, A
Legal Assistant/Paralegal, AB
Massage Therapy/Therapeutic Massage, A
Medical Administrative Assistant/Secretary, A
Music, A
Nursing - Registered Nurse Training, B
Physician Assistant, A
Taxation, A
Veterinary/Animal Health Technology/Technician and
  Veterinary Assistant, A

MINNESOTA SCHOOL OF
BUSINESS-BROOKLYN CENTER

Accounting, AB
Administrative Assistant and Secretarial Science, A
Business Administration and Management, AB
Computer Systems Networking and
  Telecommunications, A
Information Technology, AB
Intermedia/Multimedia, A
Legal Administrative Assistant/Secretary, A
Legal Assistant/Paralegal, AB
Massage Therapy/Therapeutic Massage, A
Medical Administrative Assistant/Secretary, A
Music, A
Nursing Science, B
Physician Assistant, A
Taxation, A
Veterinary/Animal Health Technology/Technician and
  Veterinary Assistant, A

MINNESOTA SCHOOL OF
BUSINESS-PLYMOUTH

Accounting, AB
Administrative Assistant and Secretarial Science, A
Business Administration and Management, AB
Computer Systems Networking and
  Telecommunications, A
Information Technology, AB
Intermedia/Multimedia, A
Legal Assistant/Paralegal, AB
Massage Therapy/Therapeutic Massage, A
Medical Administrative Assistant/Secretary, A
Music, A
Nursing Science, B
Physician Assistant, A
Taxation, A
Veterinary/Animal Health Technology/Technician and
  Veterinary Assistant, A
Web Page, Digital/Multimedia and Information
  Resources Design, A

MINNESOTA SCHOOL OF
BUSINESS-RICHFIELD

Accounting, AB
Administrative Assistant and Secretarial Science, A
Business Administration and Management, AB
Computer Systems Networking and
  Telecommunications, A
Information Technology, AB
Intermedia/Multimedia, A

Legal Assistant/Paralegal, AB
Massage Therapy/Therapeutic Massage, A
Medical Office Management/Administration, A
Medical/Clinical Assistant, A
Music, A
Nursing Science, B
Taxation, A
Veterinary/Animal Health Technology/Technician and
  Veterinary Assistant, A
Web Page, Digital/Multimedia and Information
  Resources Design, A

MINNESOTA SCHOOL OF BUSINESS-
ST. CLOUD

Accounting, AB
Administrative Assistant and Secretarial Science, A
Business Administration and Management, AB
Computer Systems Networking and
  Telecommunications, A
Information Technology, AB
Intermedia/Multimedia, A
Legal Assistant/Paralegal, AB
Massage Therapy/Therapeutic Massage, A
Medical Administrative Assistant/Secretary, A
Music, A
Nursing Science, B
Physician Assistant, A
Taxation, A
Veterinary/Animal Health Technology/Technician and
  Veterinary Assistant, A
Web Page, Digital/Multimedia and Information
  Resources Design, A

MINNESOTA SCHOOL OF
BUSINESS-SHAKOPEE

Accounting, AB
Business Administration and Management, AB
Computer Systems Networking and
  Telecommunications, A
Information Technology, AB
Intermedia/Multimedia, A
Legal Assistant/Paralegal, AB
Massage Therapy/Therapeutic Massage, A
Music, A
Nursing Science, B
Physician Assistant, A
Veterinary/Animal Health Technology/Technician and
  Veterinary Assistant, A
Web Page, Digital/Multimedia and Information
  Resources Design, A

MINNESOTA STATE
COLLEGE-SOUTHEAST TECHNICAL

Accounting, A
Administrative Assistant and Secretarial Science, A
Automobile/Automotive Mechanics
  Technology/Technician, A
Avionics Maintenance Technology/Technician, A
Business Machine Repairer, A
Carpentry/Carpenter, A
Child Development, A
Computer Engineering Technology/Technician, A
Computer Programming/Programmer, A
Computer Typography and Composition Equipment
  Operator, A
Consumer Merchandising/Retailing Management, A
Cosmetology/Cosmetologist, A
Drafting and Design Technology/Technician, A
Drafting/Design Engineering
  Technologies/Technicians, A
Electrical, Electronic and Communications
  Engineering Technology/Technician, A
Emergency Medical Technology/Technician (EMT
  Paramedic), A
Heating, Air Conditioning, Ventilation and
  Refrigeration Maintenance
  Technology/Technician, A
Industrial Technology/Technician, A
Kindergarten/PreSchool Education and Teaching, A
Legal Administrative Assistant/Secretary, A
Licensed Practical/Vocational Nurse Training, A
Machine Tool Technology/Machinist, A
Marketing/Marketing Management, A
Medical Administrative Assistant/Secretary, A
Musical Instrument Fabrication and Repair, A

Nursing - Registered Nurse Training, A
Violin, Viola, Guitar and Other Stringed
  Instruments, A
Welding Technology/Welder, A

MINNESOTA STATE COMMUNITY AND
TECHNICAL COLLEGE-FERGUS FALLS

Accounting, A
Administrative Assistant and Secretarial Science, A
Architectural Engineering Technology/Technician, A
Automotive Engineering Technology/Technician, A
Biological and Physical Sciences, A
Business Administration and Management, A
Clinical/Medical Laboratory Assistant, A
Clinical/Medical Laboratory Technician, A
Computer and Information Systems Security, A
Computer Programming/Programmer, A
Computer Systems Networking and
  Telecommunications, A
Corrections, A
Cosmetology/Cosmetologist, A
Criminal Justice/Police Science, A
Dental Hygiene/Hygienist, A
Electrical and Electronic Engineering
  Technologies/Technicians, A
Electrical, Electronic and Communications
  Engineering Technology/Technician, A
Financial Planning and Services, A
Fire Services Administration, A
Forensic Science and Technology, A
General Merchandising, Sales, and Related
  Marketing Operations, A
Health and Medical Laboratory Technologies, A
Heating, Air Conditioning and Refrigeration
  Technology/Technician, A
Human Resources Management/Personnel
  Administration, A
Industrial Technology/Technician, A
Kindergarten/PreSchool Education and Teaching, A
Legal Administrative Assistant/Secretary, A
Liberal Arts and Sciences Studies and
  Humanities, A
Licensed Practical/Vocational Nurse Training, A
Manufacturing Technology/Technician, A
Marketing/Marketing Management, A
Mechanical Engineering/Mechanical
  Technology/Technician, A
Medical Administrative Assistant/Secretary, A
Nursing - Registered Nurse Training, A
Pharmacy Technician/Assistant, A
Pre-Engineering, A
Radiologic Technology/Science - Radiographer, A
Telecommunications Technology/Technician, A
Web Page, Digital/Multimedia and Information
  Resources Design, A

MINNESOTA STATE UNIVERSITY
MANKATO

Accounting, B
Allied Health and Medical Assisting Services, MO
Anatomy, B
Animal Physiology, B
Anthropology, BM
Apparel and Textiles, B
Applied Art, B
Army JROTC/ROTC, B
Art Education, M
Art History, Criticism and Conservation, B
Art Teacher Education, B
Art/Art Studies, General, B
Astronomy, BM
Athletic Training and Sports Medicine, B
Audiology/Audiologist and Speech-Language
  Pathology/Pathologist, B
Automotive Engineering Technology/Technician, BM
Aviation/Airway Management and Operations, B
Behavioral Sciences, B
Biochemistry, B
Biological and Biomedical Sciences, M
Biological and Physical Sciences, B
Biology Technician/BioTechnology Laboratory
  Technician, B
Biology/Biological Sciences, B
Botany/Plant Biology, B
Building/Construction
  Finishing, Management, and Inspection, B

Business Administration and Management, B
Ceramic Arts and Ceramics, B
Chemistry, BM
Child Development, B
City/Urban, Community and Regional Planning, B
Civil Engineering, B
Clinical Laboratory Science/Medical
   Technology/Technologist, B
Clinical Psychology, M
Commercial and Advertising Art, B
Communication Disorders, BM
Community Health and Preventive Medicine, M
Comparative Literature, B
Computer Engineering, B
Computer Engineering Technology/Technician, B
Computer Programming/Programmer, B
Computer Science, BM
Consumer Economics, M
Corrections, B
Counselor Education/School Counseling and
   Guidance Services, M
Creative Writing, B
Criminal Justice/Police Science, B
Data Processing and Data Processing
   Technology/Technician, B
Dental Hygiene/Hygienist, AB
Developmental and Child Psychology, B
Dietetics/Dieticians, B
Drama and Dramatics/Theatre Arts, B
Drawing, B
Early Childhood Education and Teaching, M
Ecology, BM
Economics, B
Education, BMO
Education/Teaching of Individuals with Multiple
   Disabilities, M
Education/Teaching of the Gifted and Talented, M
Educational Administration and Supervision, MO
Educational Leadership and Administration, MO
Educational Media/Instructional Technology, MO
Electrical Engineering, M
Electrical, Electronic and Communications
   Engineering Technology/Technician, B
Electrical, Electronics and Communications
   Engineering, B
Elementary Education and Teaching, BM
English, M
English Education, M
English Language and Literature, B
Environmental Biology, B
Environmental Sciences, M
Environmental Studies, B
Ethnic and Cultural Studies, B
Family and Consumer Economics and Related
   Services, M
Family and Consumer Sciences/Home Economics
   Teacher Education, B
Family and Consumer Sciences/Human Sciences, B
Fashion/Apparel Design, B
Finance, B
Fine Arts and Art Studies, M
Fine/Studio Arts, B
Foods, Nutrition, and Wellness Studies, B
French Language and Literature, BM
Geography, BM
Geology/Earth Science, B
German Language and Literature, BM
Gerontology, M
Health Education, M
Health Teacher Education, B
Higher Education/Higher Education
   Administration, M
History, BM
Humanities/Humanistic Studies, B
Industrial and Organizational Psychology, M
Industrial Technology/Technician, B
Information Science/Studies, B
Insurance, B
Interdisciplinary Studies, M
Interior Design, B
International Business/Trade/Commerce, B
International Relations and Affairs, B
Journalism, B
Kindergarten/PreSchool Education and Teaching, B
Liberal Arts and Sciences Studies and
   Humanities, AB

Management Science, B
Manufacturing Engineering, M
Marketing/Marketing Management, B
Mass Communication/Media Studies, B
Mathematics, BM
Mathematics Teacher Education, M
Mechanical Engineering, B
Medical Microbiology and Bacteriology, B
Modern Languages, B
Music, BM
Music Management and Merchandising, B
Music Teacher Education, B
Natural Sciences, B
Nursing, M
Nursing - Registered Nurse Training, B
Parks, Recreation and Leisure Facilities
   Management, B
Parks, Recreation, Leisure and Fitness Studies, B
Philosophy, B
Physical Education Teaching and Coaching, BMO
Physical Sciences, B
Physics, BM
Piano and Organ, B
Political Science and Government, BM
Pre-Dentistry Studies, B
Pre-Engineering, A
Pre-Law Studies, B
Pre-Medicine/Pre-Medical Studies, B
Pre-Theology/Pre-Ministerial Studies, B
Pre-Veterinary Studies, B
Psychology, BM
Public Administration, BMO
Public Health (MPH, DPH), B
Public Relations/Image Management, B
Real Estate, B
Rehabilitation Counseling, M
Science Teacher Education/General Science
   Teacher Education, B
Sculpture, B
Secondary Education and Teaching, B
Social Sciences, B
Social Studies Teacher Education, BM
Social Work, B
Sociology, BM
Spanish Language and Literature, BM
Special Education and Teaching, M
Speech and Rhetorical Studies, BM
Sport and Fitness Administration/Management, B
Statistics, M
Student Personnel Services, M
Technology Education/Industrial Arts, B
Theater, M
Therapeutic Recreation/Recreational Therapy, B
Toxicology, B
Urban Studies/Affairs, BMO
Voice and Opera, B
Wind and Percussion Instruments, B
Women's Studies, BM
Writing, M

MINNESOTA STATE UNIVERSITY MOORHEAD

Accounting, B
Advertising, B
American/United States Studies/Civilization, B
Anthropology, B
Applied Art, B
Archeology, B
Art History, Criticism and Conservation, B
Art Teacher Education, B
Art/Art Studies, General, B
Audiology/Audiologist and Speech-Language
   Pathology/Pathologist, B
Biology Teacher Education, B
Biology/Biological Sciences, B
Broadcast Journalism, B
Business Administration and Management, B
Ceramic Arts and Ceramics, B
Chemistry, B
Chemistry Teacher Education, B
Clinical Laboratory Science/Medical
   Technology/Technologist, B
Commercial and Advertising Art, B
Commercial Photography, B
Communication Disorders, M
Community Health Services/Liaison/Counseling, B

Computer and Information Sciences, B
Computer Science, B
Construction Engineering Technology/Technician, B
Counselor Education/School Counseling and
   Guidance Services, M
Criminal Justice/Safety Studies, B
Curriculum and Instruction, M
CytoTechnology/Cytotechnologist, B
Drama and Dance Teacher Education, B
Drama and Dramatics/Theatre Arts, B
East Asian Studies, B
Economics, B
Education, MO
Education/Teaching of Individuals with Emotional
   Disturbances, B
Education/Teaching of Individuals with Mental
   Retardation, B
Education/Teaching of Individuals with Specific
   Learning Disabilities, B
Educational Administration and Supervision, O
Educational Leadership and Administration, MO
Elementary Education and Teaching, B
English/Language Arts Teacher Education, B
Finance, B
Fine/Studio Arts, B
Foreign Languages and Literatures, B
Gerontology, B
Graphic Communications, B
Health and Physical Education, B
Health Teacher Education, B
Health/Health Care Administration/Management, B
History, B
Human Services, MO
Industrial Technology/Technician, B
Interdisciplinary Studies, B
International Business/Trade/Commerce, B
International/Global Studies, B
Journalism, B
Junior High/Intermediate/Middle School Education
   and Teaching, B
Kindergarten/PreSchool Education and Teaching, B
Kinesiology and Exercise Science, B
Law and Legal Studies, B
Legal Assistant/Paralegal, B
Liberal Arts and Sciences Studies and
   Humanities, A
Liberal Studies, M
Marketing/Marketing Management, B
Mass Communication/Media Studies, B
Mathematics, B
Mathematics Teacher Education, B
Music, BM
Music Management and Merchandising, B
Music Teacher Education, BM
Music Theory and Composition, B
Nursing, M
Nursing - Registered Nurse Training, B
Nursing Education, M
Painting, B
Philosophy, B
Physical Education Teaching and Coaching, B
Physics, B
Physics Teacher Education, B
Piano and Organ, B
Political Science and Government, B
Pre-Dentistry Studies, B
Pre-Law Studies, B
Pre-Medicine/Pre-Medical Studies, B
Pre-Veterinary Studies, B
Printmaking, B
Psychology, B
Public Administration, M
Public Relations/Image Management, B
Reading Teacher Education, M
School Psychology, MO
Science Teacher Education/General Science
   Teacher Education, B
Sculpture, B
Secondary Education and Teaching, B
Social Studies Teacher Education, B
Social Work, B
Sociology, B
Spanish Language and Literature, B
Spanish Language Teacher Education, B
Special Education and Teaching, BM

Speech and Rhetorical Studies, B
Speech Teacher Education, B
Sport and Fitness Administration/Management, B
Voice and Opera, B
Wind and Percussion Instruments, B
Writing, M

MINNESOTA WEST COMMUNITY AND TECHNICAL COLLEGE

Accounting, A
Administrative Assistant and Secretarial Science, A
Clinical/Medical Laboratory Technician, A
Heating, Air Conditioning, Ventilation and
    Refrigeration Maintenance
    Technology/Technician, A
Liberal Arts and Sciences Studies and
    Humanities, A
Medical Administrative Assistant/Secretary, A
Medical/Clinical Assistant, A
Plumbing Technology/Plumber, A

NATIONAL AMERICAN UNIVERSITY (ROSEVILLE)

Accounting, B
Business Administration and Management, AB
Hospitality Administration/Management, B
Information Science/Studies, AB
Management Information Systems and Services, AB

NORMANDALE COMMUNITY COLLEGE

Accounting, A
Architectural Drafting and Architectural
    CAD/CADD, A
Automobile/Automotive Mechanics
    Technology/Technician, A
Business Administration and Management, A
Business/Office Automation/Technology/Data
    Entry, A
Child Care and Support Services Management, A
Commercial Photography, A
Computer and Information Sciences, A
Computer Science, A
Computer Systems Networking and
    Telecommunications, A
Criminal Justice/Police Science, A
Criminal Justice/Safety Studies, A
Dental Assisting/Assistant, A
Dental Hygiene/Hygienist, A
Dietetics/Dieticians, A
Electrical, Electronic and Communications
    Engineering Technology/Technician, A
Hospitality Administration/Management, A
Hydraulics and Fluid Power Technology, A
Legal Administrative Assistant/Secretary, A
Liberal Arts and Sciences Studies and
    Humanities, A
Management Information Systems and Services, A
Marketing/Marketing Management, A
Mechanical Drafting and Mechanical Drafting
    CAD/CADD, A
Mechanical Engineering/Mechanical
    Technology/Technician, A
Medical Administrative Assistant/Secretary, A
Medical Radiologic Technology/Science - Radiation
    Therapist, A
Nursing - Registered Nurse Training, A

NORTH CENTRAL UNIVERSITY

Administrative Assistant and Secretarial Science, A
American Sign Language (ASL), AB
Ancient Near Eastern and Biblical
    Languages, Literatures, and Linguistics, A
Bible/Biblical Studies, AB
Broadcast Journalism, AB
Business Administration and Management, AB
Comparative Literature, A
Divinity/Ministry (BD, MDiv.), AB
Drama and Dramatics/Theatre Arts, AB
Elementary Education and Teaching, B
English Language and Literature, B
Hebrew Language and Literature, A
History, A
Interdisciplinary Studies, AB
Journalism, AB

Liberal Arts and Sciences Studies and
    Humanities, A
Mass Communication/Media Studies, AB
Missions/Missionary Studies and Missiology, AB
Modern Greek Language and Literature, A
Modern Languages, A
Music, AB
Music Performance, B
Music Theory and Composition, AB
Nursing - Registered Nurse Training, A
Pastoral Studies/Counseling, AB
Psychology, AB
Religion/Religious Studies, B
Religious/Sacred Music, AB
Secondary Education and Teaching, B
Sign Language Interpretation and Translation, AB

NORTH HENNEPIN COMMUNITY COLLEGE

Accounting, A
Biology/Biological Sciences, A
Chemistry, A
Computer Science, A
Construction Management, A
Criminal Justice/Law Enforcement Administration, A
Criminal Justice/Safety Studies, A
Finance, A
Fine/Studio Arts, A
Graphic Design, A
Health and Medical Laboratory Technologies, A
Histologic Technology/Histotechnologist, A
Legal Assistant/Paralegal, A
Marketing/Marketing Management, A
Nursing - Registered Nurse Training, A

NORTHLAND COMMUNITY AND TECHNICAL COLLEGE-THIEF RIVER FALLS

Accounting, A
Administrative Assistant and Secretarial Science, A
Aeronautics/Aviation/Aerospace Science and
    Technology, A
Architectural Engineering Technology/Technician, A
Athletic Training and Sports Medicine, A
Automobile/Automotive Mechanics
    Technology/Technician, A
Aviation/Airway Management and Operations, A
Avionics Maintenance Technology/Technician, A
Broadcast Journalism, A
Business Administration and Management, A
Child Care Provider/Assistant, A
Child Development, A
Computer and Information Sciences, A
Computer Graphics, A
Computer Science, A
Computer Software and Media Applications, A
Computer Systems Networking and
    Telecommunications, A
Consumer Merchandising/Retailing Management, A
Cosmetology/Cosmetologist, A
Criminal Justice/Law Enforcement Administration, A
Criminal Justice/Police Science, A
Criminology, A
Data Entry/Microcomputer Applications, A
Data Modeling/Warehousing and Database
    Administration, A
Drafting and Design Technology/Technician, A
Electrical, Electronic and Communications
    Engineering Technology/Technician, A
Farm/Farm and Ranch Management, A
Industrial Electronics Technology/Technician, A
Information Technology, A
International Business/Trade/Commerce, A
Law and Legal Studies, A
Legal Administrative Assistant/Secretary, A
Legal Assistant/Paralegal, A
Liberal Arts and Sciences Studies and
    Humanities, A
Licensed Practical/Vocational Nurse Training, A
Management Information Systems and Services, A
Marketing/Marketing Management, A
Mass Communication/Media Studies, A
Nursing - Registered Nurse Training, A
Radio and Television, A
System Administration/Administrator, A

Web Page, Digital/Multimedia and Information
    Resources Design, A
Web/Multimedia Management and Webmaster, A
Welding Technology/Welder, A
Word Processing, A

NORTHWEST TECHNICAL COLLEGE

Accounting, A
Administrative Assistant and Secretarial Science, A
Architectural Engineering Technology/Technician, A
Autobody/Collision and Repair
    Technology/Technician, A
Automobile/Automotive Mechanics
    Technology/Technician, A
Banking and Financial Support Services, A
Biomedical Technology/Technician, A
Building/Construction
    Finishing, Management, and Inspection, A
Cardiovascular Technology/Technologist, A
Carpentry/Carpenter, A
Child Care and Support Services Management, A
Civil Engineering Technology/Technician, A
Clinical/Medical Laboratory Technician, A
Commercial and Advertising Art, A
Communications Technology/Technician, A
Computer Programming/Programmer, A
Computer Systems Networking and
    Telecommunications, A
Dental Hygiene/Hygienist, A
Diesel Mechanics Technology/Technician, A
Drafting/Design Engineering
    Technologies/Technicians, A
Electrical, Electronic and Communications
    Engineering Technology/Technician, A
Emergency Medical Technology/Technician (EMT
    Paramedic), A
Fashion Merchandising, A
Health Information/Medical Records
    Technology/Technician, A
Heating, Air Conditioning and Refrigeration
    Technology/Technician, A
Human Resources Management/Personnel
    Administration, A
Industrial Technology/Technician, A
Legal Administrative Assistant/Secretary, A
Library Science, A
Licensed Practical/Vocational Nurse Training, A
Marine Technology, A
Marketing/Marketing Management, A
Medical Administrative Assistant/Secretary, A
Medical/Clinical Assistant, A
Occupational Therapist Assistant, A
Pharmacy Technician/Assistant, A
Physical Therapist Assistant, A
Radiologic Technology/Science - Radiographer, A
Respiratory Care Therapy/Therapist, A
Surgical Technology/Technologist, A
Telecommunications Technology/Technician, A

NORTHWEST TECHNICAL INSTITUTE

Architectural Drafting and Architectural
    CAD/CADD, A
Mechanical Drafting and Mechanical Drafting
    CAD/CADD, A

NORTHWESTERN COLLEGE

Accounting, B
Art Teacher Education, B
Bible/Biblical Studies, B
Biology/Biological Sciences, B
Business Administration and Management, B
Communication Studies/Speech Communication
    and Rhetoric, B
Creative Writing, B
Criminal Justice/Safety Studies, B
Digital Communication and Media/Multimedia, B
Drama and Dramatics/Theatre Arts, B
Early Childhood Education and Teaching, B
Elementary Education and Teaching, B
English Language and Literature, B
English/Language Arts Teacher Education, B
Finance, B
Fine/Studio Arts, B
Graphic Design, B
Health and Physical Education, B
History, B

International Business/Trade/Commerce, B
Journalism, B
Kinesiology and Exercise Science, B
Liberal Arts and Sciences Studies and
　Humanities, B
Management Information Systems and Services, B
Marketing/Marketing Management, B
Mathematics, B
Mathematics Teacher Education, B
Missions/Missionary Studies and Missiology, B
Music, B
Music Performance, AB
Music Teacher Education, B
Music Theory and Composition, B
Physical Education Teaching and Coaching, B
Piano and Organ, B
Pre-Theology/Pre-Ministerial Studies, B
Psychology, B
Public Relations/Image Management, B
Radio and Television, AB
Religious Education, B
Social Sciences, B
Social Studies Teacher Education, B
Teaching English as a Second or Foreign
　Language/ESL Language Instructor, B
Technical and Business Writing, B
Voice and Opera, B
Youth Ministry, B

OAK HILLS CHRISTIAN COLLEGE

Bible/Biblical Studies, AB
Counseling Psychology, B
Divinity/Ministry (BD, MDiv.), B
General Studies, A
Pastoral Counseling and Specialized Ministries, B
Pastoral Studies/Counseling, B
Religious Education, B
Youth Ministry, B

PILLSBURY BAPTIST BIBLE COLLEGE

Administrative Assistant and Secretarial Science, AB
Bible/Biblical Studies, B
Business Administration and Management, B
Business Teacher Education, B
Computer Teacher Education, B
Education, B
Elementary Education and Teaching, B
English/Language Arts Teacher Education, B
Mathematics Teacher Education, B
Music, B
Music Teacher Education, B
Pastoral Studies/Counseling, B
Photography, A
Physical Education Teaching and Coaching, B
Religious Education, B
Religious/Sacred Music, B
Science Teacher Education/General Science
　Teacher Education, B
Secondary Education and Teaching, B
Social Studies Teacher Education, B
Speech Teacher Education, B
Theological and Ministerial Studies, A
Youth Ministry, B

PINE TECHNICAL COLLEGE

Administrative Assistant and Secretarial Science, A
Automobile/Automotive Mechanics
　Technology/Technician, A
Business Teacher Education, A
Human Services, A
Machine Tool Technology/Machinist, A

RAINY RIVER COMMUNITY COLLEGE

Administrative Assistant and Secretarial Science, A
Biological and Physical Sciences, A
Business Administration and Management, A
Liberal Arts and Sciences Studies and
　Humanities, A
Pre-Engineering, A
Real Estate, A

RASMUSSEN COLLEGE EAGAN

Accounting, A
Business Administration and Management, A

Child Development, A
Computer Typography and Composition Equipment
　Operator, A
Court Reporting/Court Reporter, A
Health Information/Medical Records
　Administration/Administrator, A
Hotel/Motel Administration/Management, A
Medical Administrative Assistant/Secretary, A
Tourism and Travel Services Management, A

RASMUSSEN COLLEGE EDEN PRAIRIE

Accounting, A
Administrative Assistant and Secretarial Science, A
Business Administration and Management, A
Child Development, A
Court Reporting/Court Reporter, A
Legal Administrative Assistant/Secretary, A
Marketing/Marketing Management, A
Medical Administrative Assistant/Secretary, A

RASMUSSEN COLLEGE MANKATO

Accounting, A
Administrative Assistant and Secretarial Science, A
Business Administration and Management, A
Child Care and Support Services Management, A
Child Care Provider/Assistant, A
Child Development, A
Computer Graphics, A
Computer Software and Media Applications, A
Computer Systems Networking and
　Telecommunications, A
Computer Typography and Composition Equipment
　Operator, A
Data Entry/Microcomputer Applications, A
Data Processing and Data Processing
　Technology/Technician, A
Health Information/Medical Records
　Administration/Administrator, A
Health Unit Coordinator/Ward Clerk, A
Hospitality Administration/Management, A
Hospitality and Recreation Marketing Operations, A
Hotel/Motel Administration/Management, A
Law and Legal Studies, A
Legal Administrative Assistant/Secretary, A
Legal Assistant/Paralegal, A
Management Information Systems and Services, A
Marketing/Marketing Management, A
Medical Administrative Assistant/Secretary, A
Medical/Clinical Assistant, A
Restaurant, Culinary, and Catering
　Management/Manager, A
System Administration/Administrator, A
Tourism and Travel Services Management, A
Tourism and Travel Services Marketing
　Operations, A
Tourism Promotion Operations, A
Web Page, Digital/Multimedia and Information
　Resources Design, A

RASMUSSEN COLLEGE ST. CLOUD

Accounting, A
Administrative Assistant and Secretarial Science, A
Business Administration and Management, A
Court Reporting/Court Reporter, A
Health Information/Medical Records
　Administration/Administrator, A
Legal Administrative Assistant/Secretary, A
Marketing/Marketing Management, A
Medical Administrative Assistant/Secretary, A
Tourism and Travel Services Management, A

RIDGEWATER COLLEGE

Accounting, A
Administrative Assistant and Secretarial Science, A
Agricultural Business and Management, A
Agricultural Mechanization, A
Animal/Livestock Husbandry and Production, A
Applied Art, A
Art/Art Studies, General, A
Audio Engineering, A
Biological and Physical Sciences, A
Broadcast Journalism, A
Business Administration and Management, A
Child Development, A
Community Organization and Advocacy, A
Computer and Information Sciences, A

Computer Engineering Technology/Technician, A
Computer Graphics, A
Computer Installation and Repair
　Technology/Technician, A
Computer Programming, Specific Applications, A
Computer Systems Networking and
　Telecommunications, A
Computer/Information Technology Services
　Administration and Management, A
Consumer Merchandising/Retailing Management, A
Criminal Justice/Law Enforcement Administration, A
Criminal Justice/Police Science, A
Data Processing and Data Processing
　Technology/Technician, A
Developmental and Child Psychology, A
Drafting and Design Technology/Technician, A
Drama and Dramatics/Theatre Arts, A
Electrical, Electronic and Communications
　Engineering Technology/Technician, A
Electrical/Electronics Equipment Installation and
　Repair, A
Engineering, A
Family and Community Services, A
Farm/Farm and Ranch Management, A
Gerontology, A
Health Information/Medical Records
　Administration/Administrator, A
Health Unit Manager/Ward Supervisor, A
History, A
Human Services, A
Humanities/Humanistic Studies, A
Industrial Radiologic Technology/Technician, A
Information Science/Studies, A
Instrumentation Technology/Technician, A
Interdisciplinary Studies, A
Journalism, A
Legal Administrative Assistant/Secretary, A
Liberal Arts and Sciences Studies and
　Humanities, A
Licensed Practical/Vocational Nurse Training, A
Machine Shop Technology/Assistant, A
Mass Communication/Media Studies, A
Mathematics, A
Medical Administrative Assistant/Secretary, A
Mental Health/Rehabilitation, A
Metallurgical Technology/Technician, A
Music, A
Nursing - Registered Nurse Training, A
Photography, A
Physical Education Teaching and Coaching, A
Physical Sciences, A
Pre-Engineering, A
Psychology, A
Quality Control Technology/Technician, A
Real Estate, A
Sales, Distribution and Marketing Operations, A
Social Work, A
Sociology, A
Speech and Rhetorical Studies, A
Substance Abuse/Addiction Counseling, A
System Administration/Administrator, A
Teacher Assistant/Aide, A
Tourism and Travel Services Management, A
Veterinary/Animal Health Technology/Technician and
　Veterinary Assistant, A
Web Page, Digital/Multimedia and Information
　Resources Design, A
Web/Multimedia Management and Webmaster, A

RIVERLAND COMMUNITY COLLEGE

Administrative Assistant and Secretarial Science, A
Autobody/Collision and Repair
　Technology/Technician, A
Business Administration and Management, A
Computer and Information Systems Security, A
Computer Installation and Repair
　Technology/Technician, A
Computer Programming, Specific Applications, A
Computer
　Programming, Vendor/Product Certification, A
Computer Software and Media Applications, A
Computer Systems Networking and
　Telecommunications, A
Corrections, A
Criminal Justice/Police Science, A
Data Entry/Microcomputer Applications, A

Diesel Mechanics Technology/Technician, A
Electrical/Electronics Equipment Installation and
   Repair, A
Health Unit Coordinator/Ward Clerk, A
Human Services, A
Industrial Mechanics and Maintenance
   Technology, A
Legal Administrative Assistant/Secretary, A
Liberal Arts and Sciences Studies and
   Humanities, A
Machine Shop Technology/Assistant, A
Management Information Systems and Services, A
Medical Administrative Assistant/Secretary, A
Medical Radiologic Technology/Science - Radiation
   Therapist, A
Nursing - Registered Nurse Training, A
Web Page, Digital/Multimedia and Information
   Resources Design, A
Web/Multimedia Management and Webmaster, A
Word Processing, A

ROCHESTER COMMUNITY AND TECHNICAL COLLEGE

Administrative Assistant and Secretarial Science, A
Business Administration and Management, A
Child Development, A
Civil Engineering Technology/Technician, A
Clinical/Medical Laboratory Technician, A
Computer Science, A
Criminal Justice/Police Science, A
Dental Hygiene/Hygienist, A
Developmental and Child Psychology, A
Electrical, Electronic and Communications
   Engineering Technology/Technician, A
Fashion Merchandising, A
General Studies, A
Greenhouse Operations and Management, A
Human Services, A
Landscaping and Groundskeeping, A
Legal Administrative Assistant/Secretary, A
Liberal Arts and Sciences Studies and
   Humanities, A
Mechanical Engineering/Mechanical
   Technology/Technician, A
Medical Administrative Assistant/Secretary, A
Natural Resources and Conservation, A
Nursing - Registered Nurse Training, A
Pre-Engineering, A
Respiratory Care Therapy/Therapist, A
Surgical Technology/Technologist, A
Turf and Turfgrass Management, A

ST. CLOUD STATE UNIVERSITY

Accounting, B
Acting, B
Advertising, B
Air Traffic Controller, B
Airline/Commercial/Professional Pilot and Flight
   Crew, B
American/United States Studies/Civilization, B
Anthropology, B
Applied Art, B
Applied Economics, M
Art History, Criticism and Conservation, B
Art Teacher Education, B
Art/Art Studies, General, B
Atmospheric Sciences and Meteorology, B
Audiology/Audiologist and Speech-Language
   Pathology/Pathologist, B
Aviation/Airway Management and Operations, B
Behavioral Sciences, B
Biological and Biomedical Sciences, M
Biology Technician/BioTechnology Laboratory
   Technician, B
Biology/Biological Sciences, B
Biomedical Sciences, B
Botany/Plant Biology, B
Broadcast Journalism, B
Business Administration and Management, B
Business Administration, Management and
   Operations, M
Ceramic Arts and Ceramics, B
Chemistry, B
Child and Family Studies, M
Child Development, B
City/Urban, Community and Regional Planning, B

Clinical Laboratory Science/Medical
   Technology/Technologist, B
Communication Disorders, BM
Communication Disorders Sciences and Services, B
Community Psychology, M
Comparative Literature, B
Computer Engineering, B
Computer Science, BM
Counselor Education/School Counseling and
   Guidance Services, BM
Creative Writing, B
Criminal Justice/Law Enforcement Administration, B
Criminology, BM
Curriculum and Instruction, M
Design and Applied Arts, B
Drama and Dramatics/Theatre Arts, B
Dramatic/Theatre Arts and Stagecraft, B
Drawing, B
Ecology, B
Economics, BM
Education, BMO
Educational Administration and Supervision, M
Educational Leadership and Administration, B
Educational Media/Instructional Technology, M
Educational/Instructional Media Design, B
Electrical Engineering, M
Electrical, Electronic and Communications
   Engineering Technology/Technician, B
Electrical, Electronics and Communications
   Engineering, B
Elementary Education and Teaching, B
Engineering, B
Engineering and Applied Sciences, M
Engineering Management, M
Engineering Technologies/Technicians, B
Engineering Technology, B
English, M
English as a Second Language, M
English Language and Literature, B
Environmental Biology, B
Environmental Studies, M
Exercise and Sports Science, M
Film/Cinema Studies, B
Finance, B
Finance and Banking, M
Fine Arts and Art Studies, M
Fine/Studio Arts, B
French Language and Literature, B
Geography, BM
Geology/Earth Science, B
German Language and Literature, B
Gerontology, BM
Health Services/Allied Health/Health Sciences, B
Health Teacher Education, B
Health/Medical Preparatory Programs, B
History, BM
Human Resources Management/Personnel
   Administration, B
Industrial and Organizational Psychology, M
Industrial Engineering, B
Information Science/Studies, B
Insurance, B
Interdisciplinary Studies, B
International Business/Trade/Commerce, B
International Relations and Affairs, B
Jazz/Jazz Studies, B
Journalism, B
Junior High/Intermediate/Middle School Education
   and Teaching, B
Kindergarten/PreSchool Education and Teaching, B
Kinesiology and Exercise Science, B
Latin American Studies, B
Liberal Arts and Sciences Studies and
   Humanities, AB
Library Science, B
Linguistics, B
Marketing, M
Marketing/Marketing Management, B
Marriage and Family Therapy/Counseling, M
Mass Communication/Media Studies, BM
Mathematics, BM
Mechanical Engineering, BM
Medical Microbiology and Bacteriology, B
Mental Health/Rehabilitation, B
Multi-/Interdisciplinary Studies, B
Music, BM

Music History, Literature, and Theory, B
Music Pedagogy, B
Music Performance, B
Music Teacher Education, BM
Music Theory and Composition, B
Natural Sciences, B
Non-Profit/Public/Organizational Management, M
Nuclear Medical Technology/Technologist, B
Nursing - Registered Nurse Training, B
Painting, B
Philosophy, B
Physical Education Teaching and Coaching, BM
Physical Sciences, B
Physical Therapy/Therapist, B
Physics, B
Piano and Organ, B
Political Science and Government, B
Pre-Dentistry Studies, B
Pre-Law Studies, B
Pre-Medicine/Pre-Medical Studies, B
Pre-Pharmacy Studies, B
Pre-Veterinary Studies, B
Printmaking, B
Psychology, BM
Public Administration, B
Public Policy Analysis, B
Public Relations/Image Management, B
Radio and Television, B
Reading Teacher Education, B
Real Estate, B
Rehabilitation Counseling, M
Science Teacher Education/General Science
   Teacher Education, B
Sculpture, B
Secondary Education and Teaching, B
Social Sciences, B
Social Work, B
Sociology, B
Spanish Language and Literature, B
Special Education and Teaching, BM
Speech and Rhetorical Studies, B
Speech-Language Pathology/Pathologist, B
Sport and Fitness Administration/Management, M
Statistics, BM
Substance Abuse/Addiction Counseling, B
Teacher Education and Professional
   Development, Specific Levels and Methods, B
Technology and Public Policy, M
Technology Education/Industrial Arts, B
Technology Teacher Education/Industrial Arts
   Teacher Education, B
Theatre/Theatre Arts Management, B
Therapeutic Recreation/Recreational Therapy, B
Tourism and Travel Services Management, B
Urban Studies/Affairs, B
Violin, Viola, Guitar and Other Stringed
   Instruments, B
Visual and Performing Arts, B
Voice and Opera, B
Wildlife Biology, B

ST. CLOUD TECHNICAL COLLEGE

Accounting, A
Accounting Technology/Technician and
   Bookkeeping, A
Administrative Assistant and Secretarial Science, A
Advertising, A
Architectural Drafting and Architectural
   CAD/CADD, A
Architectural Engineering Technology/Technician, A
Autobody/Collision and Repair
   Technology/Technician, A
Automobile/Automotive Mechanics
   Technology/Technician, A
Banking and Financial Support Services, A
Business Administration and Management, A
Cardiovascular Technology/Technologist, A
Carpentry/Carpenter, A
Child Care and Support Services Management, A
Child Development, A
Civil Engineering Technology/Technician, A
Computer Programming, A
Computer Programming, Specific Applications, A
Computer Programming/Programmer, A
Computer Systems Networking and
   Telecommunications, A

Computer/Information Technology Services
    Administration and Management, A
Construction Engineering Technology/Technician, A
Consumer Merchandising/Retailing Management, A
Dental Assisting/Assistant, A
Dental Hygiene/Hygienist, A
Diagnostic Medical Sonography/Sonographer and
    Ultrasound Technician, A
Diesel Mechanics Technology/Technician, A
Drafting/Design Engineering
    Technologies/Technicians, A
Electrical and Power Transmission
    Installation/Installer, A
Electrical, Electronic and Communications
    Engineering Technology/Technician, A
Electrocardiograph Technology/Technician, A
Emergency Medical Technology/Technician (EMT
    Paramedic), A
Finance, A
Heating, Air Conditioning and Refrigeration
    Technology/Technician, A
Heating, Air Conditioning, Ventilation and
    Refrigeration Maintenance
    Technology/Technician, A
Information Technology, A
Instrumentation Technology/Technician, A
Kindergarten/PreSchool Education and Teaching, A
Legal Administrative Assistant/Secretary, A
Licensed Practical/Vocational Nurse Training, A
Machine Tool Technology/Machinist, A
Management Information Systems and Services, A
Marketing/Marketing Management, A
Mechanical Drafting and Mechanical Drafting
    CAD/CADD, A
Medical Administrative Assistant/Secretary, A
Medical Office Management/Administration, A
Office Management and Supervision, A
Pipefitting/Pipefitter and Sprinkler Fitter, A
Surgical Technology/Technologist, A
Teacher Assistant/Aide, A
Water Quality and Wastewater Treatment
    Management and Recycling
    Technology/Technician, A
Welding Technology/Welder, A

SAINT JOHN'S UNIVERSITY

Accounting, B
Art/Art Studies, General, B
Biochemistry, B
Biology/Biological Sciences, B
Business Administration and Management, B
Chemistry, B
Classics and Classical
    Languages, Literatures, and Linguistics, B
Computer Science, B
Dietetics/Dieticians, B
Drama and Dramatics/Theatre Arts, B
Economics, B
Education, B
Elementary Education and Teaching, B
English Language and Literature, B
Environmental Studies, B
Fine/Studio Arts, B
Foods, Nutrition, and Wellness Studies, B
Forestry, B
French Language and Literature, B
German Language and Literature, B
History, B
Humanities/Humanistic Studies, B
Mathematics, B
Mathematics and Computer Science, B
Music, B
Natural Sciences, B
Nursing - Registered Nurse Training, B
Occupational Therapy/Therapist, B
Pastoral Studies/Counseling, M
Peace Studies and Conflict Resolution, B
Philosophy, B
Physical Therapy/Therapist, B
Physics, B
Political Science and Government, B
Pre-Dentistry Studies, B
Pre-Law Studies, B
Pre-Medicine/Pre-Medical Studies, B
Pre-Pharmacy Studies, B
Pre-Theology/Pre-Ministerial Studies, B

Pre-Veterinary Studies, B
Psychology, B
Religious Education, B
Sacred Music, M
Secondary Education and Teaching, B
Social Sciences, B
Social Work, B
Sociology, B
Spanish Language and Literature, B
Speech and Rhetorical Studies, B
Theology and Religious Vocations, MPO
Theology/Theological Studies, B

SAINT MARY'S UNIVERSITY OF MINNESOTA

Accounting, B
Arts Management, M
Biochemistry, B
Biology Teacher Education, B
Biology/Biological Sciences, B
Biophysics, B
Business Administration and Management, B
Business Administration, Management and
    Operations, M
Business/Commerce, B
Chemistry, B
Chemistry Teacher Education, B
Clinical Laboratory Science/Medical
    Technology/Technologist, B
Computer Engineering, B
Computer Science, B
Computer/Information Technology Services
    Administration and Management, B
Corrections, B
Counseling Psychology, MO
Criminal Justice/Law Enforcement Administration, B
Criminal Justice/Police Science, B
Criminology, M
Curriculum and Instruction, MO
Cytogenetics/Genetics/Clinical Genetics
    Technology/Technologist, B
CytoTechnology/Cytotechnologist, B
Drama and Dramatics/Theatre Arts, B
Education, M
Educational Administration and Supervision, MO
Educational Leadership and Administration, D
Elementary Education and Teaching, B
Engineering Physics, B
English Language and Literature, B
English/Language Arts Teacher Education, B
Environmental Biology, B
Environmental Policy and Resource
    Management, M
Fine/Studio Arts, B
French Language and Literature, B
French Language Teacher Education, B
Geographic Information Systems, MO
Graphic Design, B
Health Services Administration, M
History, B
Human Development, M
Human Resources Management and Services, M
Human Resources Management/Personnel
    Administration, B
Human Services, B
Industrial Technology/Technician, B
Information Science/Studies, B
International Business/Trade/Commerce, BM
International/Global Studies, B
Management, M
Marketing/Marketing Management, B
Marriage and Family Therapy/Counseling, O
Mathematics, B
Mathematics and Computer Science, B
Mathematics Teacher Education, B
Music, B
Music Management and Merchandising, B
Music Performance, B
Music Teacher Education, B
Nuclear Medical Technology/Technologist, B
Nurse Anesthetist, M
Pastoral Studies/Counseling, MO
Philanthropic Studies, M
Philosophy, B
Physical Therapy/Therapist, B
Physics Teacher Education, B

Political Science and Government, B
Project Management, M
Psychology, B
Public Administration, MO
Public Relations, Advertising, and Applied
    Communication, B
Publishing, B
Religious Education, B
Sales, Distribution and Marketing Operations, B
Social Science Teacher Education, B
Social Sciences, B
Spanish Language and Literature, B
Spanish Language Teacher Education, B
Special Education and Teaching, M
Telecommunications, MO
Theology/Theological Studies, B
Youth Ministry, B

ST. OLAF COLLEGE

American/United States Studies/Civilization, B
Ancient Studies/Civilization, B
Ancient/Classical Greek Language and Literature, B
Art History, Criticism and Conservation, B
Art/Art Studies, General, B
Asian Studies/Civilization, B
Biology/Biological Sciences, B
Chemistry, B
Classics and Classical
    Languages, Literatures, and Linguistics, B
Computer Science, B
Dance, B
Drama and Dramatics/Theatre Arts, B
Economics, B
English Language and Literature, B
Environmental Studies, B
Ethnic and Cultural Studies, B
Ethnic, Cultural Minority, and Gender Studies, B
Family and Community Services, B
French Language and Literature, B
German Language and Literature, B
Hispanic-American, Puerto Rican, and Mexican-
    American/Chicano Studies, B
History, B
Human Development and Family Studies, B
Intercultural/Multicultural and Diversity Studies, B
Kinesiology and Exercise Science, B
Latin American Studies, B
Latin Language and Literature, B
Liberal Arts and Sciences Studies and
    Humanities, B
Mathematics, B
Multi-/Interdisciplinary Studies, B
Music, B
Music Performance, B
Music Teacher Education, B
Music Theory and Composition, B
Nursing - Registered Nurse Training, B
Philosophy, B
Physics, B
Political Science and Government, B
Psychology, B
Religion/Religious Studies, B
Russian Language and Literature, B
Russian Studies, B
Scandinavian
    Languages, Literatures, and Linguistics, B
Social Studies Teacher Education, B
Social Work, B
Sociology, B
Spanish Language and Literature, B
Visual and Performing Arts, B
Women's Studies, B

SAINT PAUL COLLEGE-A COMMUNITY & TECHNICAL COLLEGE

Accounting, A
Administrative Assistant and Secretarial Science, A
Child Development, A
Civil Engineering Technology/Technician, A
Clinical/Medical Laboratory Technician, A
Computer Programming/Programmer, A
Electrical, Electronic and Communications
    Engineering Technology/Technician, A
Human Resources Management/Personnel
    Administration, A
Industrial Technology/Technician, A

International Business/Trade/Commerce, A
Medical Administrative Assistant/Secretary, A
Respiratory Care Therapy/Therapist, A
Sign Language Interpretation and Translation, A

SOUTH CENTRAL TECHNICAL COLLEGE

Accounting, A
Administrative Assistant and Secretarial Science, A
Agribusiness, A
Agricultural Mechanization, A
Agricultural Production Operations, A
Architectural Drafting and Architectural CAD/CADD, A
Autobody/Collision and Repair Technology/Technician, A
Automobile/Automotive Mechanics Technology/Technician, A
Business Administration and Management, A
Computer Programming/Programmer, A
Culinary Arts/Chef Training, A
Dental Assisting/Assistant, A
Emergency Medical Technology/Technician (EMT Paramedic), A
Heating, Air Conditioning, Ventilation and Refrigeration Maintenance Technology/Technician, A
Machine Tool Technology/Machinist, A
Mechanical Drafting and Mechanical Drafting CAD/CADD, A
Nursing - Registered Nurse Training, A

SOUTHWEST MINNESOTA STATE UNIVERSITY

Accounting, AB
Agricultural Business and Management, AB
Agronomy and Crop Science, B
Art Teacher Education, B
Art/Art Studies, General, B
Biology Teacher Education, B
Biology/Biological Sciences, B
Business Administration and Management, AB
Business Administration, Management and Operations, M
Chemistry, B
Chemistry Teacher Education, B
Communication Studies/Speech Communication and Rhetoric, B
Comparative Literature, B
Computer Science, B
Creative Writing, B
Criminal Justice/Safety Studies, B
Drama and Dance Teacher Education, B
Drama and Dramatics/Theatre Arts, B
Education, BM
Educational Leadership and Administration, M
Elementary Education and Teaching, B
English Language and Literature, B
English/Language Arts Teacher Education, B
Environmental Studies, B
Fine/Studio Arts, B
Health and Physical Education, B
Health Teacher Education, B
History, B
Interdisciplinary Studies, B
Kindergarten/PreSchool Education and Teaching, B
Management, M
Marketing/Marketing Management, AB
Mathematics, B
Mathematics Teacher Education, B
Music, B
Music Teacher Education, B
Philosophy, B
Physical Education Teaching and Coaching, B
Physical Sciences, B
Political Science and Government, B
Pre-Dentistry Studies, B
Pre-Law Studies, B
Pre-Medicine/Pre-Medical Studies, B
Pre-Veterinary Studies, B
Psychology, B
Public Administration, B
Radio and Television, B
Secondary Education and Teaching, B
Social Work, B
Sociology, B

Spanish Language and Literature, B
Special Education and Teaching, M
Speech Teacher Education, B

UNIVERSITY OF MINNESOTA, CROOKSTON

Accounting, AB
Agricultural Business and Management, AB
Agricultural Power Machinery Operation, B
Agricultural Teacher Education, B
Agriculture, AB
Agronomy and Crop Science, AB
Animal Sciences, AB
Aviation/Airway Management and Operations, AB
Avionics Maintenance Technology/Technician, A
Business Administration and Management, AB
Dietetics/Dieticians, A
Early Childhood Education and Teaching, B
Environmental Studies, B
Equestrian/Equine Studies, AB
Farm/Farm and Ranch Management, B
Health Services/Allied Health/Health Sciences, B
Health/Health Care Administration/Management, B
Horticultural Science, AB
Hospitality Administration/Management, A
Hotel/Motel Administration/Management, AB
Information Science/Studies, AB
Interdisciplinary Studies, B
Natural Resources and Conservation, B
Natural Resources Management/Development and Policy, AB
Soil Science and Agronomy, A
Special Products Marketing Operations, A
Sport and Fitness Administration/Management, B
System Administration/Administrator, B
System, Networking, and LAN/WAN Management/Manager, B
Turf and Turfgrass Management, B
Water, Wetlands, and Marine Resources Management, B
Wildlife and Wildlands Science and Management, AB

UNIVERSITY OF MINNESOTA, DULUTH

Accounting, B
Actuarial Science, B
Allopathic Medicine, P
American Indian/Native American Studies, B
Anatomy, MD
Anthropology, BM
Applied Mathematics, M
Art History, Criticism and Conservation, B
Art Teacher Education, B
Art/Art Studies, General, B
Audiology/Audiologist and Speech-Language Pathology/Pathologist, B
Biochemistry, BMD
Biological and Biomedical Sciences, M
Biology/Biological Sciences, B
Business Administration and Management, B
Business Administration, Management and Operations, M
Cell Biology and Anatomy, MD
Cell/Cellular Biology and Histology, B
Chemical Engineering, B
Chemistry, BM
Commercial and Advertising Art, B
Communication Disorders, M
Computational Sciences, M
Computer Engineering, BM
Computer Science, BM
Criminology, BM
Drama and Dramatics/Theatre Arts, B
Economics, B
Education, B
Electrical Engineering, M
Electrical, Electronics and Communications Engineering, B
Elementary Education and Teaching, B
Engineering Management, M
English, M
English Language and Literature, B
Environmental Studies, B
Finance, B
Fine Arts and Art Studies, M
Fine/Studio Arts, B

French Language Teacher Education, B
Geography, B
Geology/Earth Science, BMD
German Language Teacher Education, B
Graphic Design, M
Health Teacher Education, B
History, B
Human Resources Management/Personnel Administration, B
Immunology, MD
Industrial Engineering, B
Interdisciplinary Studies, B
International Relations and Affairs, B
Jazz/Jazz Studies, B
Junior High/Intermediate/Middle School Education and Teaching, B
Kindergarten/PreSchool Education and Teaching, B
Kinesiology and Exercise Science, B
Liberal Studies, M
Marketing/Marketing Management, B
Mathematics, B
Mathematics Teacher Education, B
Medical Microbiology and Bacteriology, MD
Molecular Biology, BMD
Music, BM
Music Teacher Education, BM
Parks, Recreation, Leisure and Fitness Studies, B
Performance, M
Pharmacology, MD
Philosophy, B
Physical Education Teaching and Coaching, B
Physics, BM
Physiology, MD
Piano and Organ, B
Political Science and Government, B
Pre-Dentistry Studies, B
Pre-Law Studies, B
Pre-Medicine/Pre-Medical Studies, B
Pre-Pharmacy Studies, B
Pre-Veterinary Studies, B
Psychology, B
Safety Engineering, M
Science Teacher Education/General Science Teacher Education, B
Social Studies Teacher Education, B
Social Work, M
Sociology, BM
Spanish Language and Literature, B
Spanish Language Teacher Education, B
Special Education and Teaching, B
Statistics, B
Toxicology, MD
Urban Studies/Affairs, B
Women's Studies, B

UNIVERSITY OF MINNESOTA, MORRIS

Anthropology, B
Art History, Criticism and Conservation, B
Biology/Biological Sciences, B
Business Administration and Management, B
Chemistry, B
Computer Science, B
Drama and Dramatics/Theatre Arts, B
Economics, B
Education, B
Elementary Education and Teaching, B
English Language and Literature, B
European Studies/Civilization, B
Fine/Studio Arts, B
French Language and Literature, B
Geology/Earth Science, B
German Language and Literature, B
History, B
Human Services, B
Latin American Studies, B
Liberal Arts and Sciences Studies and Humanities, B
Management Science, B
Mathematics, B
Music, B
Philosophy, B
Physical Therapy/Therapist, B
Physics, B
Political Science and Government, B
Pre-Dentistry Studies, B
Pre-Law Studies, B

Pre-Medicine/Pre-Medical Studies, B
Pre-Pharmacy Studies, B
Pre-Veterinary Studies, B
Psychology, B
Secondary Education and Teaching, B
Social Sciences, B
Sociology, B
Spanish Language and Literature, B
Speech and Rhetorical Studies, B
Speech Teacher Education, B
Statistics, B
Teacher Education, Multiple Levels, B
Women's Studies, B

UNIVERSITY OF MINNESOTA, TWIN CITIES CAMPUS

Accounting, BMD
Actuarial Science, B
Adult and Continuing Education and Teaching, MDO
Aerospace, Aeronautical and Astronautical
　Engineering, BMD
African Studies, B
African-American/Black Studies, B
Agricultural Business and Management, B
Agricultural Economics, MD
Agricultural Education, MD
Agricultural Engineering, MD
Agricultural Sciences, MD
Agricultural Teacher Education, B
Agricultural/Biological Engineering and
　Bioengineering, B
Agriculture, B
Agronomy and Crop Science, B
Agronomy and Soil Sciences, MD
Allopathic Medicine, PO
American Indian/Native American Studies, B
American/United States Studies/Civilization, BD
Animal Behavior and Ethology, MD
Animal Genetics, B
Animal Physiology, B
Animal Sciences, BMD
Anthropology, BMD
Apparel and Textiles, B
Applied Economics, MD
Archeology, MD
Architecture, BM
Art Education, MD
Art History, Criticism and Conservation, BMD
Art Teacher Education, B
Art/Art Studies, General, B
Astronomy, BMD
Astrophysics, BMD
Audiology/Audiologist and Speech-Language
　Pathology/Pathologist, B
Biochemistry, BD
Biological and Biomedical Sciences, MD
Biological Anthropology, MDO
Biology/Biological Sciences, B
Biomedical Engineering, MDO
Biophysics, MD
Biopsychology, D
Biostatistics, MD
BioTechnology, M
Botany/Plant Biology, B
Building/Construction
　Finishing, Management, and Inspection, B
Business Administration, Management and
　Operations, MDO
Business Education, MD
Business Teacher Education, B
Cell Biology and Anatomy, MD
Cell/Cellular Biology and Histology, B
Chemical Engineering, BMD
Chemistry, BMD
Child and Family Studies, MD
Chinese Language and Literature, B
Civil Engineering, BMD
Classics and Classical
　Languages, Literatures, and Linguistics, MD
Clinical Laboratory Science/Medical
　Technology/Technologist, B
Clinical Laboratory Sciences, M
Clinical Psychology, D
Clinical Research, M
Clothing and Textiles, MD
Cognitive Sciences, D

Commercial and Advertising Art, B
Communication and Media Studies, MD
Communication Disorders, MD
Community Health and Preventive Medicine, M
Community Health Nursing, M
Comparative Literature, BD
Computational Sciences, MD
Computer Engineering, MD
Computer Science, BMD
Conservation Biology, MD
Counseling Psychology, D
Counselor Education/School Counseling and
　Guidance Services, MDO
Cultural Studies, D
Curriculum and Instruction, MDO
Dance, BMD
Dental Hygiene/Hygienist, B
Dentistry, P
Design and Applied Arts, MDO
Developmental and Child Psychology, B
Developmental Biology and Embryology, MD
Drama and Dramatics/Theatre Arts, B
Early Childhood Education and Teaching, MD
East Asian Studies, B
East European and Russian Studies, M
Ecology, BMD
Economics, BD
Education, BMDO
Education/Teaching of the Gifted and Talented, O
Educational Administration and Supervision, MD
Educational Leadership and Administration, M
Educational Measurement and Evaluation, MDO
Educational Media/Instructional Technology, MDO
Educational Psychology, MDO
Electrical Engineering, MD
Electrical, Electronics and Communications
　Engineering, B
Elementary Education and Teaching, BMD
Emergency Medical Technology/Technician (EMT
　Paramedic), B
Engineering and Applied Sciences, MDO
English, MD
English as a Second Language, M
English Education, MD
English Language and Literature, B
English/Language Arts Teacher Education, B
Entomology, MD
Entrepreneurship/Entrepreneurial Studies, M
Environmental and Occupational Health, MDO
Environmental Education, M
Environmental Policy and Resource
　Management, MO
Environmental Studies, B
Epidemiology, MD
European Studies/Civilization, B
Evolutionary Biology, MD
Exercise and Sports Science, MD
Family and Community Services, B
Family and Consumer Sciences/Home Economics
　Teacher Education, B
Family and Consumer Sciences/Human Sciences, D
Film/Cinema Studies, B
Finance, B
Finance and Banking, MD
Fine Arts and Art Studies, M
Fish, Game and Wildlife Management, MD
Food Science and Technology, MD
Foods, Nutrition, and Wellness Studies, B
Foreign Language Teacher Education, BM
Forest Management/Forest Resources
　Management, B
Forestry, BMD
Foundations and Philosophy of Education, MDO
French Language and Literature, BMD
Funeral Service and Mortuary Science, B
Genetic Counseling/Counselor, M
Genetics, MD
Geographic Information Systems, M
Geography, BMD
Geological Engineering, MD
Geological/Geophysical Engineering, B
Geology/Earth Science, BMD
Geophysics and Seismology, BMD
German Language and Literature, BMD
Gerontological Nursing, M
Health and Physical Education/Fitness, B

Health Informatics, MDO
Health Services Administration, MDO
Health Services Research, MDO
Hebrew Language and Literature, B
Higher Education/Higher Education
　Administration, MD
Hispanic-American, Puerto Rican, and Mexican-
　American/Chicano Studies, B
History, BMD
History of Medicine, MD
History of Science and Technology, MD
Human Resources Development, MDO
Human Resources Management and Services, MD
Industrial and Labor Relations, MD
Industrial and Manufacturing Management, MD
Industrial and Organizational Psychology, D
Industrial Engineering, B
Industrial Hygiene, MD
Industrial/Management Engineering, MD
Infectious Diseases, MD
Information Science/Studies, MD
Insurance, B
Interdisciplinary Studies, D
Interior Design, BMDO
International and Comparative Education, MD
International Business/Trade/Commerce, BM
International Relations and Affairs, B
Italian Language and Literature, B
Japanese Language and Literature, B
Jewish/Judaic Studies, B
Journalism, B
Kindergarten/PreSchool Education and Teaching, B
Kinesiology and Movement Studies, MD
Landscape Architecture, BM
Latin American Studies, B
Latin Language and Literature, B
Law and Legal Studies, MPO
Leisure Studies, MD
Linguistics, BMD
Logistics and Materials Management, MD
Management Information Systems and
　Services, BMD
Management of Technology, M
Management Strategy and Policy, MD
Marketing, MD
Marketing/Marketing Management, B
Marriage and Family Therapy/Counseling, D
Mass Communication/Media Studies, BMD
Materials Engineering, BMD
Materials Sciences, BMD
Maternal and Child Health, M
Mathematics, BMD
Mathematics Teacher Education, BMD
Mechanical Engineering, BMD
Mechanics, MD
Medical Microbiology and Bacteriology, B
Medical Physics, MD
Medicinal and Pharmaceutical Chemistry, MD
Medieval and Renaissance Studies, MD
Microbiology, D
Modern Greek Language and Literature, B
Molecular Biology, MD
Multilingual and Multicultural Education, MD
Music, BMD
Music Teacher Education, B
Music Therapy/Therapist, B
Natural Resources and Conservation, B
Natural Resources Management/Development and
　Policy, BMD
Near and Middle Eastern Studies, B
Neuroscience, BMD
Nurse Anesthetist, M
Nurse Midwife/Nursing Midwifery, M
Nursing, MD
Nursing - Adult, M
Nursing - Advanced Practice, M
Nursing - Registered Nurse Training, B
Nursing Administration, M
Nursing Education, M
Nutritional Sciences, MD
Occupational Health Nursing, MDO
Occupational Therapy/Therapist, B
Oral and Dental Sciences, MO
Oral Biology, MD
Orthodontics, M

Parks, Recreation and Leisure Facilities
    Management, B
Pediatric Nurse/Nursing, M
Periodontics, M
Pharmaceutical Administration, MD
Pharmaceutical Sciences, MD
Pharmacology, MD
Pharmacy, P
Philosophy, BMD
Physical Education Teaching and Coaching, BMD
Physical Therapy/Therapist, BMD
Physics, BMD
Physiology, MD
Plant Biology, MD
Plant Pathology/Phytopathology, MD
Plant Sciences, BMD
Political Science and Government, BMD
Portuguese Language and Literature, BMD
Pre-Dentistry Studies, B
Pre-Law Studies, B
Pre-Medicine/Pre-Medical Studies, B
Pre-Veterinary Studies, B
Psychiatric/Mental Health Nurse/Nursing, M
Psychology, BMD
Public Affairs, M
Public Health, MDO
Public Health (MPH, DPH), B
Public Policy Analysis, MO
Reading Teacher Education, MD
Recreation and Park Management, MD
Rehabilitation Sciences, D
Religion/Religious Studies, BM
Rhetoric, MD
Russian Language and Literature, B
Russian Studies, B
Scandinavian
    Languages, Literatures, and Linguistics, BMD
School Psychology, MDO
Science Teacher Education/General Science
    Teacher Education, BMD
Social Psychology, D
Social Science Teacher Education, B
Social Studies Teacher Education, MD
Social Work, MDO
Sociology, BMD
Software Engineering, M
Soil Science and Agronomy, B
South Asian Studies, B
Spanish Language and Literature, BMD
Special Education and Teaching, MDO
Sport and Fitness Administration/Management, MD
Statistics, MD
Student Personnel Services, MDO
Systems Engineering, M
Taxation, M
Technical Communication, MD
Technology and Public Policy, MO
Textile Design, MDO
Theater, MD
Therapeutic Recreation, MD
Toxicology, MD
Urban and Regional Planning, MO
Urban Studies/Affairs, B
Veterinary Medicine, PO
Veterinary Sciences, MDO
Vocational and Technical Education, MO
Water Resources, MD
Women's Health Nursing, M
Women's Studies, B
Wood Science and Wood Products/Pulp and Paper
    Technology, B

UNIVERSITY OF ST. THOMAS

Accounting, BM
Actuarial Science, B
Ancient/Classical Greek Language and Literature, B
Art History, Criticism and Conservation, BM
Biochemistry, B
Biology Teacher Education, B
Biology/Biological Sciences, B
Broadcast Journalism, B
Business Administration and Management, B
Business Administration, Management and
    Operations, BM
Business/Corporate Communications, B
Chemistry, B

Chemistry Teacher Education, B
Classics and Classical
    Languages, Literatures, and Linguistics, B
Clinical/Medical Social Work, B
Communication Studies/Speech Communication
    and Rhetoric, B
Computer and Information Sciences, B
Corporate and Organizational Communication, M
Counseling Psychology, MD
Creative Writing, B
Criminology, B
Curriculum and Instruction, MDO
Drama and Dance Teacher Education, B
Drama and Dramatics/Theatre Arts, B
East Asian Studies, B
Econometrics and Quantitative Economics, B
Economics, B
Education, M
Educational Administration and Supervision, MDO
Electrical, Electronics and Communications
    Engineering, B
Elementary Education and Teaching, B
Engineering and Applied Sciences, MO
Engineering Management, MO
English, M
English Language and Literature, B
English/Language Arts Teacher Education, B
Entrepreneurship/Entrepreneurial Studies, B
Environmental Policy and Resource
    Management, M
Finance, B
Finance and Banking, M
Foreign Language Teacher Education, B
Foreign Languages, Literatures, and Linguistics, B
French Language and Literature, B
Geography, B
Geology/Earth Science, B
German Language and Literature, B
Health and Physical Education, B
Health Services Administration, M
Health Teacher Education, B
History, B
Human Development, MDO
Human Resources Management and Services, M
Human Resources Management/Personnel
    Administration, B
Industrial and Manufacturing Management, M
Insurance, M
Interdisciplinary Studies, B
International Business/Trade/Commerce, B
International Economics, B
International Relations and Affairs, B
Japanese Language and Literature, B
Journalism, B
Junior High/Intermediate/Middle School Education
    and Teaching, B
Latin Language and Literature, B
Law and Legal Studies, PO
Management, M
Management Information Systems and
    Services, MO
Management of Technology, MO
Manufacturing Engineering, M
Marketing, M
Marketing/Marketing Management, B
Marriage and Family Therapy/Counseling, O
Mathematics, B
Mathematics Teacher Education, B
Mechanical Engineering, B
Multi-/Interdisciplinary Studies, B
Music, B
Music Teacher Education, BM
Non-Profit/Public/Organizational Management, M
Operations Management and Supervision, B
Organizational Management, MDO
Pastoral Studies/Counseling, M
Peace Studies and Conflict Resolution, B
Philosophy, B
Physical Education Teaching and Coaching, B
Physics, B
Physics Teacher Education, B
Political Science and Government, B
Psychology, BMDO
Public Administration, M
Public Health (MPH, DPH), B
Public Health Education and Promotion, B

Reading Teacher Education, O
Real Estate, BM
Religion/Religious Studies, BM
Religious Education, M
Russian Language and Literature, B
Russian Studies, B
Science Teacher Education/General Science
    Teacher Education, B
Social Sciences, B
Social Studies Teacher Education, B
Social Work, BM
Sociology, B
Software Engineering, MO
Spanish Language and Literature, B
Special Education and Teaching, MO
Speech Teacher Education, B
Sport and Fitness Administration/Management, M
Systems Engineering, M
Teacher Education and Professional
    Development, Specific Subject Areas, B
Teacher Education, Multiple Levels, B
Theology and Religious Vocations, MP
Women's Studies, B

VERMILION COMMUNITY COLLEGE

Accounting, A
Aeronautics/Aviation/Aerospace Science and
    Technology, A
Agricultural Business and Management, A
Agricultural Economics, A
Agricultural Teacher Education, A
Agronomy and Crop Science, A
Airline/Commercial/Professional Pilot and Flight
    Crew, A
Architectural Engineering Technology/Technician, A
Art History, Criticism and Conservation, A
Art Teacher Education, A
Art/Art Studies, General, A
Aviation/Airway Management and Operations, A
Biological and Physical Sciences, A
Biology/Biological Sciences, A
Business Administration and Management, A
Business/Managerial Economics, A
Chemistry, A
Computer Engineering Technology/Technician, A
Computer Science, A
Criminal Justice/Law Enforcement Administration, A
Criminal Justice/Police Science, A
Criminal Justice/Safety Studies, A
Data Processing and Data Processing
    Technology/Technician, A
Drama and Dramatics/Theatre Arts, A
Drawing, A
Ecology, A
Economics, A
Education, A
Elementary Education and Teaching, A
Engineering, A
Environmental Education, A
Environmental Engineering
    Technology/Environmental Technology, A
Environmental Studies, A
Family and Consumer Sciences/Human Sciences, A
Finance, A
Forest Management/Forest Resources
    Management, A
Forest Sciences and Biology, A
Forestry, A
Forestry Technology/Technician, A
Geography, A
Geology/Earth Science, A
Health Information/Medical Records
    Administration/Administrator, A
Health Teacher Education, A
History, A
Hydrology and Water Resources Science, A
Industrial Technology/Technician, A
Interdisciplinary Studies, A
Kindergarten/PreSchool Education and Teaching, A
Land Use Planning and
    Management/Development, A
Liberal Arts and Sciences Studies and
    Humanities, A
Mass Communication/Media Studies, A
Mathematics, A
Medical Administrative Assistant/Secretary, A

Music, A
Natural Resources and Conservation, A
Natural Resources Management/Development and
  Policy, A
Parks, Recreation and Leisure Facilities
  Management, A
Parks, Recreation, Leisure and Fitness Studies, A
Physical Education Teaching and Coaching, A
Physical Sciences, A
Physics, A
Political Science and Government, A
Pre-Engineering, A
Psychology, A
Range Science and Management, A
Science Teacher Education/General Science
  Teacher Education, A
Sociology, A
Soil Science and Agronomy, A
Special Products Marketing Operations, A
Speech and Rhetorical Studies, A
Technology Education/Industrial Arts, A
Water Quality and Wastewater Treatment
  Management and Recycling
  Technology/Technician, A
Wildlife and Wildlands Science and Management, A
Wildlife Biology, A

WALDEN UNIVERSITY

Chemical Engineering, M
Computer Engineering, M
Computer Science, M
Education, MD
Electrical Engineering, M
Engineering and Applied Sciences, M
Engineering Management, M
Environmental Policy and Resource
  Management, M
Health Services Administration, D
Human Services, D
International Business/Trade/Commerce, M
Management, MD
Manufacturing Engineering, M
Materials Engineering, M
Materials Sciences, M
Mechanical Engineering, M
Psychology, MDO
Public Administration, MD
Public Health, MD
Software Engineering, M
Systems Engineering, M

WINONA STATE UNIVERSITY

Accounting, B
Advertising, B
Applied Art, B
Applied Mathematics, B
Art Teacher Education, B
Art/Art Studies, General, B
Athletic Training and Sports Medicine, B
Aviation/Airway Management and Operations, B
Biological and Physical Sciences, B
Biology/Biological Sciences, B
Broadcast Journalism, B
Business Administration and Management, B
Business Teacher Education, B
Business/Managerial Economics, B
Chemical Engineering, B
Chemistry, B
Clinical Laboratory Science/Medical
  Technology/Technologist, B
Clinical/Medical Laboratory Technician, B
Commercial and Advertising Art, B
Computer and Information Sciences, B
Computer Programming/Programmer, B
Computer Science, B
Consumer Merchandising/Retailing Management, B
Corrections, B
Counselor Education/School Counseling and
  Guidance Services, M
Criminal Justice/Law Enforcement Administration, B
Criminal Justice/Police Science, B
CytoTechnology/Cytotechnologist, B
Drama and Dramatics/Theatre Arts, B
Drawing, B
Ecology, B
Economics, B

Education, BM
Educational Administration and Supervision, M
Educational Leadership and Administration, MO
Elementary Education and Teaching, B
Engineering, B
English, M
English Language and Literature, B
Environmental Biology, B
Finance, B
Fine/Studio Arts, B
French Language and Literature, B
Geology/Earth Science, B
German Language and Literature, B
Health Teacher Education, B
Health/Health Care Administration/Management, B
History, B
Human Resources Management/Personnel
  Administration, B
Information Science/Studies, B
International Relations and Affairs, B
Journalism, B
Junior High/Intermediate/Middle School Education
  and Teaching, B
Kindergarten/PreSchool Education and Teaching, B
Kinesiology and Exercise Science, B
Labor and Industrial Relations, B
Law and Legal Studies, B
Legal Assistant/Paralegal, B
Liberal Arts and Sciences Studies and
  Humanities, B
Management Information Systems and Services, B
Marketing/Marketing Management, B
Mass Communication/Media Studies, B
Materials Engineering, B
Mathematics, B
Mechanical Engineering, B
Music, B
Music Management and Merchandising, B
Music Teacher Education, B
Natural Resources and Conservation, B
Natural Sciences, B
Nursing, M
Nursing - Adult, M
Nursing - Advanced Practice, M
Nursing - Registered Nurse Training, B
Nursing Administration, M
Nursing Education, M
Parks, Recreation and Leisure Facilities
  Management, B
Parks, Recreation, Leisure and Fitness Studies, B
Physical Education Teaching and Coaching, B
Physical Sciences, B
Physical Therapy/Therapist, B
Physics, B
Political Science and Government, B
Polymer Chemistry, B
Polymer/Plastics Engineering, B
Pre-Dentistry Studies, B
Pre-Law Studies, B
Pre-Medicine/Pre-Medical Studies, B
Pre-Veterinary Studies, B
Psychology, B
Public Administration, B
Public Health (MPH, DPH), B
Public Relations/Image Management, B
Quality Control Technology/Technician, B
Radio and Television, B
Reading Teacher Education, B
Science Teacher Education/General Science
  Teacher Education, B
Secondary Education and Teaching, B
Social Sciences, B
Social Work, B
Sociology, B
Spanish Language and Literature, B
Special Education and Teaching, BM
Speech and Rhetorical Studies, B
Sport and Fitness Administration/Management, B
Statistics, B
Telecommunications Technology/Technician, B
Therapeutic Recreation/Recreational Therapy, B
Voice and Opera, B
Wildlife and Wildlands Science and
  Management, AB
Wildlife Biology, B

Zoology/Animal Biology, B

Mississippi
ALCORN STATE UNIVERSITY

Accounting, B
Administrative Assistant and Secretarial Science, B
Agricultural Business and Management, B
Agricultural Economics, BM
Agricultural Education, M
Agricultural Sciences, M
Agriculture, B
Agronomy and Crop Science, B
Agronomy and Soil Sciences, M
Animal Sciences, BM
Biological and Biomedical Sciences, M
Biology/Biological Sciences, B
Business Administration and Management, B
Business Administration, Management and
  Operations, M
Chemistry, B
Child Development, B
Clinical Laboratory Science/Medical
  Technology/Technologist, B
Computer and Information Sciences, B
Computer Science, M
Counselor Education/School Counseling and
  Guidance Services, M
Criminal Justice/Safety Studies, B
Economics, B
Education, MO
Educational Psychology, B
Elementary Education and Teaching, BMO
English Language and Literature, B
Family and Consumer Sciences/Human Sciences, B
Foods, Nutrition, and Wellness Studies, B
Health Professions and Related Clinical Sciences, B
History, B
Industrial Education, M
Industrial Technology/Technician, B
Information Science/Studies, B
Liberal Arts and Sciences Studies and
  Humanities, B
Mass Communication/Media Studies, B
Mathematics, B
Music Performance, B
Music Teacher Education, B
Nursing, M
Nursing - Registered Nurse Training, AB
Parks, Recreation, Leisure and Fitness Studies, B
Physical Education Teaching and Coaching, B
Physical Therapy/Therapist, B
Political Science and Government, B
Secondary Education and Teaching, BM
Sociology, B
Special Education and Teaching, BM
Technology Teacher Education/Industrial Arts
  Teacher Education, B

BELHAVEN COLLEGE

Accounting, B
Art/Art Studies, General, B
Athletic Training and Sports Medicine, B
Bible/Biblical Studies, B
Biology/Biological Sciences, B
Business Administration and Management, B
Business Administration, Management and
  Operations, M
Chemistry, B
Communication Studies/Speech Communication
  and Rhetoric, B
Computer Science, B
Creative Writing, B
Dance, B
Drama and Dramatics/Theatre Arts, B
Education, M
Elementary Education and Teaching, BM
English Language and Literature, B
Health/Health Care Administration/Management, B
History, B
Humanities/Humanistic Studies, B
Information Science/Studies, B
International/Global Studies, B
Management Information Systems and Services, B
Mathematics, B

Multilingual and Multicultural Education, M
Music, B
Philosophy, B
Psychology, B
Secondary Education and Teaching, M
Social Work, B
Sport and Fitness Administration/Management, B

BLUE MOUNTAIN COLLEGE

Bible/Biblical Studies, B
Biology Teacher Education, B
Biology/Biological Sciences, B
Business Administration and Management, B
Chemistry, B
Chemistry Teacher Education, B
Clinical Laboratory Science/Medical
    Technology/Technologist, B
Elementary Education and Teaching, B
English Language and Literature, B
English/Language Arts Teacher Education, B
History, B
Mathematics, B
Mathematics Teacher Education, B
Music, B
Music Teacher Education, B
Natural Sciences, B
Pre-Dentistry Studies, B
Pre-Law Studies, B
Pre-Medicine/Pre-Medical Studies, B
Pre-Pharmacy Studies, B
Pre-Theology/Pre-Ministerial Studies, B
Pre-Veterinary Studies, B
Psychology, B
Science Teacher Education/General Science
    Teacher Education, B
Social Science Teacher Education, B
Social Sciences, B
Spanish Language and Literature, B
Spanish Language Teacher Education, B

COAHOMA COMMUNITY COLLEGE

Accounting, A
Administrative Assistant and Secretarial Science, A
Art/Art Studies, General, A
Autobody/Collision and Repair
    Technology/Technician, A
Barbering/Barber, A
Biology/Biological Sciences, A
Business Administration and Management, A
Business Machine Repairer, A
Carpentry/Carpenter, A
Chemistry, A
Clinical Laboratory Science/Medical
    Technology/Technologist, A
Computer Installation and Repair
    Technology/Technician, A
Computer Science, A
Cosmetology/Cosmetologist, A
Criminal Justice/Law Enforcement Administration, A
Elementary Education and Teaching, A
English Language and Literature, A
Health Teacher Education, A
Industrial Mechanics and Maintenance
    Technology, A
Kindergarten/PreSchool Education and Teaching, A
Liberal Arts and Sciences Studies and
    Humanities, A
Licensed Practical/Vocational Nurse Training, A
Radio and Television, A
Respiratory Therapy Technician/Assistant, A
Restaurant, Culinary, and Catering
    Management/Manager, A
Social Work, A
Sport and Fitness Administration/Management, A
Welding Technology/Welder, A

COPIAH-LINCOLN COMMUNITY COLLEGE

Accounting, A
Agribusiness, A
Agricultural Business and Management, A
Agricultural Business Technology, A
Agricultural Economics, A
Agricultural/Farm Supplies Retailing and
    Wholesaling, A
Agriculture, A

Architecture, A
Art Teacher Education, A
Biological and Physical Sciences, A
Biology/Biological Sciences, A
Business Administration and Management, A
Chemistry, A
Child Development, A
Civil Engineering Technology/Technician, A
Clinical/Medical Laboratory Technician, A
Computer Programming/Programmer, A
Cosmetology/Cosmetologist, A
Criminal Justice/Police Science, A
Data Processing and Data Processing
    Technology/Technician, A
Drafting and Design Technology/Technician, A
Economics, A
Education, A
Electrical, Electronic and Communications
    Engineering Technology/Technician, A
Elementary Education and Teaching, A
Engineering, A
English Language and Literature, A
Family and Consumer Sciences/Home Economics
    Teacher Education, A
Farm/Farm and Ranch Management, A
Food Technology and Processing, A
Forestry, A
French Language and Literature, A
Health Teacher Education, A
History, A
Industrial Radiologic Technology/Technician, A
Journalism, A
Liberal Arts and Sciences Studies and
    Humanities, A
Library Science, A
Music Teacher Education, A
Nursing - Registered Nurse Training, A
Physical Education Teaching and Coaching, A
Special Products Marketing Operations, A
Trade and Industrial Teacher Education, A
Wood Science and Wood Products/Pulp and Paper
    Technology, A

COPIAH-LINCOLN COMMUNITY COLLEGE-NATCHEZ CAMPUS

Administrative Assistant and Secretarial Science, A
Elementary Education and Teaching, A
Family and Consumer Sciences/Human Sciences, A
Forestry, A
General Studies, A
Hotel/Motel Administration/Management, A
Instrumentation Technology/Technician, A
Liberal Arts and Sciences Studies and
    Humanities, A
Marketing/Marketing Management, A
Political Science and Government, A
Respiratory Care Therapy/Therapist, A

DELTA STATE UNIVERSITY

Accounting, B
Aeronautics/Aviation/Aerospace Science and
    Technology, B
Airline/Commercial/Professional Pilot and Flight
    Crew, B
Art Teacher Education, B
Audiology/Audiologist and Speech-Language
    Pathology/Pathologist, B
Aviation/Airway Management and Operations, M
Biological and Biomedical Sciences, M
Biological and Physical Sciences, B
Biology Teacher Education, B
Biology/Biological Sciences, B
Business Administration and Management, B
Business Administration, Management and
    Operations, M
Business Teacher Education, B
Business/Commerce, B
Chemistry, B
Chemistry Teacher Education, B
Clinical Laboratory Science/Medical
    Technology/Technologist, B
Counselor Education/School Counseling and
    Guidance Services, M
Criminal Justice/Safety Studies, B
Criminology, M
Curriculum and Instruction, D

Education, BMDO
Educational Administration and Supervision, MDO
Elementary Education and Teaching, BMO
English Education, M
English Language and Literature, B
English/Language Arts Teacher Education, B
Family and Consumer Sciences/Home Economics
    Teacher Education, B
Family and Consumer Sciences/Human Sciences, B
Fashion Merchandising, B
Finance, B
Foreign Language Teacher Education, B
Foreign Languages and Literatures, B
History, B
Hospitality Administration/Management, B
Insurance, B
Journalism, B
Kindergarten/PreSchool Education and Teaching, B
Management Information Systems and Services, B
Marketing, M
Marketing/Marketing Management, B
Mathematics, B
Mathematics Teacher Education, BM
Music, B
Music Teacher Education, BM
Nursing, M
Nursing - Registered Nurse Training, B
Office Management and Supervision, B
Physical Education Teaching and Coaching, BM
Political Science and Government, B
Psychology, B
Recreation and Park Management, M
Science Teacher Education/General Science
    Teacher Education, B
Secondary Education and Teaching, B
Social Science Teacher Education, B
Social Sciences, B
Social Studies Teacher Education, M
Social Work, BM
Special Education and Teaching, BM
Urban and Regional Planning, M

EAST CENTRAL COMMUNITY COLLEGE

Accounting, A
Art Teacher Education, A
Art/Art Studies, General, A
Behavioral Sciences, A
Biological and Physical Sciences, A
Biology/Biological Sciences, A
Business Administration and Management, A
Carpentry/Carpenter, A
Chemistry, A
Comparative Literature, A
Computer Science, A
Cosmetology/Cosmetologist, A
Data Processing and Data Processing
    Technology/Technician, A
Drafting and Design Technology/Technician, A
Drawing, A
Economics, A
Education, A
Electrical, Electronic and Communications
    Engineering Technology/Technician, A
Elementary Education and Teaching, A
Engineering, A
English Language and Literature, A
Health Information/Medical Records
    Administration/Administrator, A
Health Teacher Education, A
History, A
Journalism, A
Kindergarten/PreSchool Education and Teaching, A
Liberal Arts and Sciences Studies and
    Humanities, A
Library Science, A
Mathematics, A
Music, A
Music Teacher Education, A
Nursing - Registered Nurse Training, A
Occupational Therapy/Therapist, A
Pharmacy, A
Physical Sciences, A
Physical Therapy/Therapist, A
Political Science and Government, A
Pre-Engineering, A

Psychology, A
Science Teacher Education/General Science
  Teacher Education, A
Social Sciences, A

EAST MISSISSIPPI COMMUNITY COLLEGE

Accounting, A
Administrative Assistant and Secretarial Science, A
Art/Art Studies, General, A
Automobile/Automotive Mechanics
  Technology/Technician, A
Banking and Financial Support Services, A
Biological and Physical Sciences, A
Business Administration and Management, A
Business Teacher Education, A
Computer Programming/Programmer, A
Computer Science, A
Cosmetology/Cosmetologist, A
Criminal Justice/Law Enforcement Administration, A
Drafting and Design Technology/Technician, A
Economics, A
Education, A
Electrical, Electronic and Communications
  Engineering Technology/Technician, A
Elementary Education and Teaching, A
English Language and Literature, A
Fire Science/Firefighting, A
Forestry Technology/Technician, A
Funeral Service and Mortuary Science, A
General Office Occupations and Clerical Services, A
Health Teacher Education, A
History, A
Hotel/Motel Administration/Management, A
Instrumentation Technology/Technician, A
Liberal Arts and Sciences Studies and
  Humanities, A
Mathematics, A
Music, A
Ophthalmic Laboratory Technology/Technician, A
Pre-Engineering, A
Psychology, A
Reading Teacher Education, A
Real Estate, A
Social Sciences, A
Sociology, A

HINDS COMMUNITY COLLEGE

Accounting, A
Administrative Assistant and Secretarial Science, A
Agricultural Business and Management, A
Agricultural Economics, A
Agricultural Mechanization, A
Agricultural Teacher Education, A
Agronomy and Crop Science, A
Apparel and Textiles, A
Art/Art Studies, General, A
Avionics Maintenance Technology/Technician, A
Biology/Biological Sciences, A
Business Administration and Management, A
Carpentry/Carpenter, A
Child Development, A
Civil Engineering Technology/Technician, A
Clinical/Medical Laboratory Technician, A
Commercial and Advertising Art, A
Computer and Information Sciences, A
Computer Graphics, A
Computer Programming, A
Computer Programming/Programmer, A
Computer Science, A
Criminal Justice/Law Enforcement Administration, A
Criminal Justice/Police Science, A
Data Entry/Microcomputer Applications, A
Data Processing and Data Processing
  Technology/Technician, A
Dental Hygiene/Hygienist, A
Developmental and Child Psychology, A
Dietetics/Dieticians, A
Drafting and Design Technology/Technician, A
Drama and Dramatics/Theatre Arts, A
Economics, A
Electrical, Electronic and Communications
  Engineering Technology/Technician, A
Emergency Medical Technology/Technician (EMT
  Paramedic), A
English Language and Literature, A

Family and Consumer Sciences/Human Sciences, A
Fashion/Apparel Design, A
Finance, A
Food Technology and Processing, A
Graphic and Printing Equipment Operator
  Production, A
Health Information/Medical Records
  Administration/Administrator, A
Hotel/Motel Administration/Management, A
Humanities/Humanistic Studies, A
Industrial Radiologic Technology/Technician, A
Information Technology, A
Journalism, A
Landscaping and Groundskeeping, A
Legal Assistant/Paralegal, A
Liberal Arts and Sciences Studies and
  Humanities, A
Licensed Practical/Vocational Nurse Training, A
Machine Tool Technology/Machinist, A
Management Information Systems and Services, A
Marketing/Marketing Management, A
Mass Communication/Media Studies, A
Mathematics, A
Music, A
Nursing - Registered Nurse Training, A
Political Science and Government, A
Pre-Engineering, A
Psychology, A
Public Administration, A
Real Estate, A
Respiratory Care Therapy/Therapist, A
Social Sciences, A
Sociology, A
Special Products Marketing Operations, A
Surgical Technology/Technologist, A
System Administration/Administrator, A
Technology Education/Industrial Arts, A
Telecommunications Technology/Technician, A
Veterinary/Animal Health Technology/Technician and
  Veterinary Assistant, A
Welding Technology/Welder, A

HOLMES COMMUNITY COLLEGE

Administrative Assistant and Secretarial Science, A
Agriculture, A
Biology/Biological Sciences, A
Business Administration and Management, A
Business Teacher Education, A
Child Development, A
Clinical Laboratory Science/Medical
  Technology/Technologist, A
Computer and Information Sciences, A
Computer Science, A
Data Processing and Data Processing
  Technology/Technician, A
Drafting and Design Technology/Technician, A
Elementary Education and Teaching, A
Engineering, A
Finance, A
Forestry, A
Health Information/Medical Records
  Administration/Administrator, A
Liberal Arts and Sciences Studies and
  Humanities, A
Management Information Systems and Services, A
Music Teacher Education, A
Nursing - Registered Nurse Training, A
Pharmacy, A
Physical Therapy/Therapist, A
Radio and Television, A
Respiratory Care Therapy/Therapist, A
Science Teacher Education/General Science
  Teacher Education, A
Social Work, A
System Administration/Administrator, A
Wildlife Biology, A

ITAWAMBA COMMUNITY COLLEGE

Accounting, A
Administrative Assistant and Secretarial Science, A
Agricultural Business and Management, A
Art Teacher Education, A
Art/Art Studies, General, A
Biological and Physical Sciences, A
Biology/Biological Sciences, A
Business Administration and Management, A

Chemistry, A
Civil Engineering Technology/Technician, A
Computer and Information Sciences, A
Computer Science, A
Construction Engineering Technology/Technician, A
Criminal Justice/Police Science, A
Data Processing and Data Processing
  Technology/Technician, A
Developmental and Child Psychology, A
Drafting and Design Technology/Technician, A
Economics, A
Education, A
Electrical, Electronic and Communications
  Engineering Technology/Technician, A
Elementary Education and Teaching, A
English Language and Literature, A
Family and Consumer Sciences/Home Economics
  Teacher Education, A
Family and Consumer Sciences/Human Sciences, A
Fashion/Apparel Design, A
Forestry Technology/Technician, A
Health Information/Medical Records
  Administration/Administrator, A
History, A
Human Services, A
Journalism, A
Kindergarten/PreSchool Education and Teaching, A
Liberal Arts and Sciences Studies and
  Humanities, A
Library Science, A
Marketing/Marketing Management, A
Mathematics, A
Medical Radiologic Technology/Science - Radiation
  Therapist, A
Modern Languages, A
Music, A
Music Teacher Education, A
Nursing - Registered Nurse Training, A
Physical Education Teaching and Coaching, A
Piano and Organ, A
Political Science and Government, A
Pre-Engineering, A
Psychology, A
Public Administration, A
Respiratory Care Therapy/Therapist, A
Science Teacher Education/General Science
  Teacher Education, A
Social Sciences, A
Social Work, A
Sociology, A
Speech and Rhetorical Studies, A
Technology Education/Industrial Arts, A
Trade and Industrial Teacher Education, A
Wind and Percussion Instruments, A

JACKSON STATE UNIVERSITY

Accounting, BM
Administrative Assistant and Secretarial Science, B
Allied Health and Medical Assisting Services, M
Art/Art Studies, General, B
Atmospheric Sciences and Meteorology, B
Audiology/Audiologist and Speech-Language
  Pathology/Pathologist, B
Biological and Biomedical Sciences, MD
Biology/Biological Sciences, B
Business Administration and Management, B
Business Administration, Management and
  Operations, MD
Business Education, M
Business Teacher Education, B
Business/Managerial Economics, B
Chemistry, BMD
Child Development, B
Civil Engineering, B
Clinical Laboratory Science/Medical
  Technology/Technologist, B
Clinical Psychology, D
Communication Disorders, M
Computer and Information Sciences, B
Computer Engineering, B
Computer Science, M
Counselor Education/School Counseling and
  Guidance Services, MO
Criminal Justice/Safety Studies, B
Criminology, M
Early Childhood Education and Teaching, MDO

Economics, B
Education, BMDO
Educational Administration and Supervision, MDO
Educational/Instructional Media Design, B
Electrical, Electronics and Communications
  Engineering, B
Elementary Education and Teaching, BMDO
Engineering Technology, B
English, M
English Education, M
English Language and Literature, B
Environmental Sciences, MD
Finance, B
Fire Science/Firefighting, B
Foreign Languages and Literatures, B
Health Education, M
Health Information/Medical Records
  Administration/Administrator, B
Health Teacher Education, B
Health/Health Care Administration/Management, B
History, BM
Industrial Education, M
Industrial Technology/Technician, B
Journalism, B
Kindergarten/PreSchool Education and Teaching, B
Marketing/Marketing Management, B
Mass Communication/Media Studies, BM
Materials Sciences, M
Mathematics, BM
Mathematics Teacher Education, BM
Music Performance, B
Music Teacher Education, BM
Office Management and Supervision, B
Physical Education Teaching and Coaching, BM
Physics, B
Piano and Organ, B
Political Science and Government, BM
Pre-Dentistry Studies, B
Pre-Law Studies, B
Pre-Medicine/Pre-Medical Studies, B
Pre-Veterinary Studies, B
Psychology, BD
Public Administration, MD
Public Policy Analysis, MD
Rehabilitation Counseling, M
Science Teacher Education/General Science
  Teacher Education, M
Secondary Education and Teaching, BMO
Social Science Teacher Education, B
Social Sciences, B
Social Work, BMD
Sociology, BM
Special Education and Teaching, BMO
Speech and Rhetorical Studies, B
System Management, M
Technology Education/Industrial Arts, B
Technology Teacher Education/Industrial Arts
  Teacher Education, B
Therapeutic Recreation/Recreational Therapy, B
Urban and Regional Planning, M
Urban Studies/Affairs, B
Visual and Performing Arts, B

JONES COUNTY JUNIOR COLLEGE

Accounting, A
Agriculture, A
Applied Art, A
Art Teacher Education, A
Biological and Physical Sciences, A
Biology/Biological Sciences, A
Business Administration and Management, A
Chemistry, A
Child Development, A
Criminal Justice/Police Science, A
Data Processing and Data Processing
  Technology/Technician, A
Drafting and Design Technology/Technician, A
Economics, A
Education, A
Electrical, Electronic and Communications
  Engineering Technology/Technician, A
Emergency Medical Technology/Technician (EMT
  Paramedic), A
Engineering Science, A
English Language and Literature, A

Family and Consumer Sciences/Home Economics
  Teacher Education, A
Family and Consumer Sciences/Human Sciences, A
Forestry Technology/Technician, A
Horticultural Science, A
Licensed Practical/Vocational Nurse Training, A
Mathematics, A
Music, A
Music Teacher Education, A
Nursing - Registered Nurse Training, A
Physical Education Teaching and Coaching, A
Physical Sciences, A
Science Teacher Education/General Science
  Teacher Education, A

MAGNOLIA BIBLE COLLEGE

Bible/Biblical Studies, B

MERIDIAN COMMUNITY COLLEGE

Administrative Assistant and Secretarial Science, A
Athletic Training and Sports Medicine, A
Broadcast Journalism, A
Clinical/Medical Laboratory Technician, A
Computer Engineering Technology/Technician, A
Computer Graphics, A
Dental Hygiene/Hygienist, A
Drafting and Design Technology/Technician, A
Electrical, Electronic and Communications
  Engineering Technology/Technician, A
Emergency Medical Technology/Technician (EMT
  Paramedic), A
Fire Science/Firefighting, A
Health Information/Medical Records
  Administration/Administrator, A
Horticultural Science, A
Hotel/Motel Administration/Management, A
Machine Tool Technology/Machinist, A
Marketing/Marketing Management, A
Medical Radiologic Technology/Science - Radiation
  Therapist, A
Nursing - Registered Nurse Training, A
Physical Therapy/Therapist, A
Respiratory Care Therapy/Therapist, A
Telecommunications Technology/Technician, A

MILLSAPS COLLEGE

Accounting, BM
Anthropology, B
Art/Art Studies, General, B
Biology/Biological Sciences, B
Business Administration and Management, B
Business Administration, Management and
  Operations, M
Chemistry, B
Classics and Classical
  Languages, Literatures, and Linguistics, B
Computer Science, B
Drama and Dramatics/Theatre Arts, B
Economics, B
Education, B
English Language and Literature, B
European Studies/Civilization, B
French Language and Literature, B
Geology/Earth Science, B
German Language and Literature, B
History, B
Mathematics, B
Music, B
Philosophy, B
Philosophy and Religious Studies, B
Physics, B
Political Science and Government, B
Psychology, B
Religion/Religious Studies, B
Sociology, B
Spanish Language and Literature, B

MISSISSIPPI COLLEGE

Accounting, BM
Art Education, M
Art History, Criticism and Conservation, B
Art Teacher Education, B
Art/Art Studies, General, B
Biochemistry, B
Biological and Biomedical Sciences, M
Biology/Biological Sciences, B

Business Administration and Management, B
Business Administration, Management and
  Operations, MO
Business Education, M
Business Teacher Education, B
Chemistry, BM
Christian Studies, B
Communication and Media Studies, M
Communication Studies/Speech Communication
  and Rhetoric, B
Communication, Journalism and Related
  Programs, B
Computer and Information Sciences, B
Computer Education, M
Computer Science, BM
Counseling Psychology, M
Counselor Education/School Counseling and
  Guidance Services, MO
Criminal Justice/Law Enforcement Administration, B
Criminology, M
Education, BMO
Educational Leadership and Administration, M
Educational Measurement and Evaluation, M
Elementary Education and Teaching, BM
English, M
English Language and Literature, B
Fine Arts and Art Studies, M
Foreign Languages and Literatures, B
Foreign Languages, Literatures, and Linguistics, B
French Language and Literature, B
Graphic Design, B
Health and Physical Education, B
Health Services Administration, M
History, BM
Interior Design, B
Kinesiology and Exercise Science, B
Language Interpretation and Translation, B
Law and Legal Studies, PO
Legal Assistant/Paralegal, B
Liberal Arts and Sciences Studies and
  Humanities, B
Liberal Studies, M
Marketing/Marketing Management, B
Mass Communication/Media Studies, B
Mathematics, B
Mathematics Teacher Education, M
Music, BM
Music Performance, B
Music Teacher Education, BM
Music Theory and Composition, BM
Nursing - Registered Nurse Training, B
Performance, M
Physics, B
Piano and Organ, B
Political Science and Government, BM
Pre-Dentistry Studies, B
Pre-Law Studies, B
Pre-Medicine/Pre-Medical Studies, B
Pre-Pharmacy Studies, B
Pre-Veterinary Studies, B
Psychology, BM
Public Relations/Image Management, B
Religious/Sacred Music, B
Science Teacher Education/General Science
  Teacher Education, BM
Secondary Education and Teaching, BM
Social Science Teacher Education, B
Social Sciences, BM
Social Studies Teacher Education, B
Social Work, B
Sociology, BM
Spanish Language and Literature, B
Special Education and Teaching, B
Sport and Fitness Administration/Management, B
Voice and Opera, B

MISSISSIPPI DELTA COMMUNITY COLLEGE

Accounting, A
Administrative Assistant and Secretarial Science, A
Advertising, A
Agricultural Business and Management, A
Agricultural Economics, A
American/United States Studies/Civilization, A
Applied Art, A
Architectural Engineering Technology/Technician, A

Art Teacher Education, A
Behavioral Sciences, A
Biology/Biological Sciences, A
Business Machine Repairer, A
Civil Engineering Technology/Technician, A
Clinical/Medical Laboratory Technician, A
Computer Engineering Technology/Technician, A
Criminal Justice/Law Enforcement Administration, A
Dental Hygiene/Hygienist, A
Developmental and Child Psychology, A
Drama and Dramatics/Theatre Arts, A
Economics, A
Education, A
Electrical, Electronic and Communications
   Engineering Technology/Technician, A
Elementary Education and Teaching, A
English Language and Literature, A
Family and Consumer Sciences/Human Sciences, A
Geography, A
Graphic and Printing Equipment Operator
   Production, A
Health Information/Medical Records
   Administration/Administrator, A
Health Teacher Education, A
History, A
Horticultural Science, A
Liberal Arts and Sciences Studies and
   Humanities, A
Management Information Systems and Services, A
Mason/Masonry, A
Mathematics, A
Medical Office Computer Specialist/Assistant, A
Medical Radiologic Technology/Science - Radiation
   Therapist, A
Music, A
Music Teacher Education, A
Nursing - Registered Nurse Training, A
Physical Education Teaching and Coaching, A
Political Science and Government, A
Science Teacher Education/General Science
   Teacher Education, A
Social Work, A

MISSISSIPPI GULF COAST COMMUNITY COLLEGE

Accounting, A
Administrative Assistant and Secretarial Science, A
Advertising, A
Agricultural Business and Management, A
Art Teacher Education, A
Art/Art Studies, General, A
Automobile/Automotive Mechanics
   Technology/Technician, A
Biological and Physical Sciences, A
Business Administration and Management, A
Business Teacher Education, A
Chemical Engineering, A
Clinical/Medical Laboratory Technician, A
Computer and Information Sciences, A
Computer Engineering Technology/Technician, A
Computer Graphics, A
Computer Programming, A
Computer Science, A
Computer Systems Networking and
   Telecommunications, A
Court Reporting/Court Reporter, A
Criminal Justice/Law Enforcement Administration, A
Criminal Justice/Police Science, A
Data Entry/Microcomputer Applications, A
Drafting and Design Technology/Technician, A
Education, A
Electrical, Electronic and Communications
   Engineering Technology/Technician, A
Elementary Education and Teaching, A
Emergency Medical Technology/Technician (EMT
   Paramedic), A
Fashion Merchandising, A
Finance, A
Horticultural Science, A
Hotel/Motel Administration/Management, A
Human Services, A
Industrial Radiologic Technology/Technician, A
Information Technology, A
Kindergarten/PreSchool Education and Teaching, A
Legal Assistant/Paralegal, A

Liberal Arts and Sciences Studies and
   Humanities, A
Marketing/Marketing Management, A
Nursing - Registered Nurse Training, A
Ornamental Horticulture, A
Pre-Engineering, A
Respiratory Care Therapy/Therapist, A
Welding Technology/Welder, A
Word Processing, A

MISSISSIPPI STATE UNIVERSITY

Accounting, BM
Aerospace, Aeronautical and Astronautical
   Engineering, BM
Agribusiness, B
Agricultural Economics, BMD
Agricultural Education, M
Agricultural Sciences, MD
Agricultural Teacher Education, B
Agricultural/Biological Engineering and
   Bioengineering, B
Agriculture, B
Agronomy and Crop Science, B
Agronomy and Soil Sciences, MD
Animal Sciences, B
Anthropology, BMD
Applied Economics, D
Architecture, BM
Biochemistry, BMD
Bioengineering, MD
Biological and Biomedical Sciences, MD
Biological and Physical Sciences, B
Biology/Biological Sciences, B
Biomedical Engineering, MD
Biomedical/Medical Engineering, B
Building/Construction
   Finishing, Management, and Inspection, B
Business Administration and Management, B
Business Administration, Management and
   Operations, MD
Business Teacher Education, B
Business/Managerial Economics, B
Chemical Engineering, BMD
Chemistry, BMD
Civil Engineering, BMD
Clinical Laboratory Science/Medical
   Technology/Technologist, B
Clinical Psychology, M
Cognitive Sciences, D
Communication Studies/Speech Communication
   and Rhetoric, B
Computer and Information Sciences, B
Computer Art and Design, M
Computer Engineering, BMD
Computer Science, MD
Computer Software Engineering, B
Counselor Education/School Counseling and
   Guidance Services, MDO
Curriculum and Instruction, MDO
Economics, BMD
Education, MDO
Educational Leadership and Administration, M
Educational Media/Instructional Technology, MDO
Educational Psychology, BMDO
Electrical Engineering, MD
Electrical, Electronics and Communications
   Engineering, B
Elementary Education and Teaching, BMDO
Engineering and Applied Sciences, MD
Engineering Physics, D
English, M
English Language and Literature, B
Entomology, MD
Exercise and Sports Science, M
Experimental Psychology, M
Family and Consumer Sciences/Human Sciences, B
Finance, B
Finance and Banking, MD
Fine Arts and Art Studies, M
Fish, Game and Wildlife Management, M
Food Science, B
Food Science and Technology, MD
Foreign Language Teacher Education, M
Foreign Languages and Literatures, B
Forestry, BM
French Language and Literature, M

Geology/Earth Science, B
Geosciences, M
German Language and Literature, M
Health Education, M
History, BMD
Horticultural Science, B
Human Resources Development, MDO
Industrial Engineering, B
Industrial Technology/Technician, B
Industrial/Management Engineering, MD
Insurance, B
Landscape Architecture, BM
Landscaping and Groundskeeping, B
Liberal Arts and Sciences Studies and
   Humanities, B
Management Information Systems and
   Services, BM
Marine Biology and Biological Oceanography, B
Marketing/Marketing Management, B
Mathematics, BMD
Mechanical Engineering, BMD
Mechanics, M
Medical Microbiology and Bacteriology, B
Molecular Biology, MD
Multi-/Interdisciplinary Studies, B
Music Teacher Education, B
Nutritional Sciences, MD
Philosophy, B
Physical Education Teaching and Coaching, BM
Physics, BMD
Plant Pathology/Phytopathology, MD
Plant Protection and Integrated Pest
   Management, B
Plant Sciences, MD
Political Science and Government, BMD
Poultry Science, BM
Project Management, M
Psychology, BMD
Public Administration, MD
Public Policy Analysis, MD
Real Estate, B
Secondary Education and Teaching, BMDO
Social Work, B
Sociology, BMD
Spanish Language and Literature, M
Special Education and Teaching, BMDO
Sport and Fitness Administration/Management, M
Statistics, MD
Taxation, M
Technical Teacher Education, B
Technology Teacher Education/Industrial Arts
   Teacher Education, B
Veterinary Medicine, P
Veterinary Sciences, MD
Visual and Performing Arts, B
Vocational and Technical Education, MDO
Wildlife and Wildlands Science and Management, B

MISSISSIPPI UNIVERSITY FOR WOMEN

Accounting, B
Apparel and Textiles, B
Art Teacher Education, B
Art/Art Studies, General, B
Audiology/Audiologist and Speech-Language
   Pathology/Pathologist, B
Biological and Physical Sciences, B
Biology/Biological Sciences, B
Business Administration and Management, B
Chemistry, B
Communication Disorders, M
Communication Studies/Speech Communication
   and Rhetoric, B
Culinary Arts/Chef Training, B
Drama and Dramatics/Theatre Arts, B
Drawing, B
Education, BM
Education/Teaching of the Gifted and Talented, M
Educational Media/Instructional Technology, M
Elementary Education and Teaching, B
English Language and Literature, B
Health Education, M
History, B
Human Development and Family Studies, B
Information Science/Studies, B
Kinesiology and Exercise Science, B
Legal Assistant/Paralegal, B

Marketing/Marketing Management, B
Mathematics, B
Medical Microbiology and Bacteriology, B
Music Management and Merchandising, B
Music Teacher Education, B
Nursing, MO
Nursing - Registered Nurse Training, AB
Parks, Recreation, Leisure and Fitness Studies, B
Physical Education Teaching and Coaching, B
Physical Sciences, B
Political Science and Government, B
Printmaking, B
Psychology, B
Science Teacher Education/General Science
   Teacher Education, B
Secondary Education and Teaching, B
Social Sciences, B
Spanish Language and Literature, B
Special Education and Teaching, B
Sport and Fitness Administration/Management, B

MISSISSIPPI VALLEY STATE UNIVERSITY

Accounting, B
Art/Art Studies, General, B
Biology/Biological Sciences, B
Business Administration and Management, B
Chemistry, B
Computer Science, B
Criminal Justice/Law Enforcement Administration, B
Criminology, M
Education, BM
Elementary Education and Teaching, BM
English Language and Literature, B
English/Language Arts Teacher Education, B
Environmental and Occupational Health, M
History, B
Industrial Technology/Technician, B
Kindergarten/PreSchool Education and Teaching, B
Mass Communication/Media Studies, B
Mathematics, B
Mathematics Teacher Education, B
Music, B
Music Teacher Education, B
Office Management and Supervision, B
Physical Education Teaching and Coaching, B
Political Science and Government, B
Public Administration, B
Recording Arts Technology/Technician, B
Science Teacher Education/General Science
   Teacher Education, B
Social Science Teacher Education, B
Social Work, B
Sociology, B
Speech and Rhetorical Studies, B
Water Quality and Wastewater Treatment
   Management and Recycling
   Technology/Technician, B

NORTHEAST MISSISSIPPI COMMUNITY COLLEGE

Accounting, A
Administrative Assistant and Secretarial Science, A
Agricultural Teacher Education, A
Agriculture, A
Agronomy and Crop Science, A
Art Teacher Education, A
Art/Art Studies, General, A
Artificial Intelligence and Robotics, A
Bible/Biblical Studies, A
Biological and Physical Sciences, A
Biology/Biological Sciences, A
Broadcast Journalism, A
Business Administration and Management, A
Business Teacher Education, A
Business/Managerial Economics, A
Carpentry/Carpenter, A
Chemistry, A
Child Development, A
Civil Engineering Technology/Technician, A
Clinical Laboratory Science/Medical
   Technology/Technologist, A
Clinical/Medical Laboratory Technician, A
Commercial and Advertising Art, A
Communication Disorders, A
Computer Programming/Programmer, A

Computer Science, A
Criminal Justice/Law Enforcement Administration, A
Criminal Justice/Police Science, A
Dairy Science, A
Data Processing and Data Processing
   Technology/Technician, A
Dental Hygiene/Hygienist, A
Developmental and Child Psychology, A
Drafting and Design Technology/Technician, A
Drama and Dramatics/Theatre Arts, A
Drawing, A
Economics, A
Education, A
Electrical, Electronic and Communications
   Engineering Technology/Technician, A
Elementary Education and Teaching, A
Engineering, A
Engineering Technology, A
English Language and Literature, A
Entomology, A
Family and Consumer Sciences/Home Economics
   Teacher Education, A
Family and Consumer Sciences/Human Sciences, A
Fashion Merchandising, A
Fashion/Apparel Design, A
Food Science, A
Forestry, A
Forestry Technology/Technician, A
Health Teacher Education, A
Heating, Air Conditioning, Ventilation and
   Refrigeration Maintenance
   Technology/Technician, A
History, A
Horticultural Science, A
Hospitality and Recreation Marketing Operations, A
Hotel/Motel Administration/Management, A
Industrial Radiologic Technology/Technician, A
Industrial Technology/Technician, A
Information Science/Studies, A
Insurance, A
Interior Design, A
Journalism, A
Kindergarten/PreSchool Education and Teaching, A
Kinesiology and Exercise Science, A
Landscape Architecture, A
Legal Administrative Assistant/Secretary, A
Legal Assistant/Paralegal, A
Liberal Arts and Sciences Studies and
   Humanities, A
Library Science, A
Mass Communication/Media Studies, A
Mathematics, A
Medical Administrative Assistant/Secretary, A
Medical/Clinical Assistant, A
Music, A
Music Teacher Education, A
Nursing - Registered Nurse Training, A
Occupational Therapy/Therapist, A
Oceanography, Chemical and Physical, A
Parks, Recreation, Leisure and Fitness Studies, A
Pharmacy, A
Photography, A
Physical Education Teaching and Coaching, A
Physical Therapy/Therapist, A
Political Science and Government, A
Pre-Engineering, A
Psychology, A
Public Administration, A
Public Health (MPH, DPH), A
Public Relations/Image Management, A
Radio and Television, A
Religious Education, A
Respiratory Care Therapy/Therapist, A
Science Teacher Education/General Science
   Teacher Education, A
Social Sciences, A
Social Work, A
Special Products Marketing Operations, A
Teacher Assistant/Aide, A
Theology/Theological Studies, A
Trade and Industrial Teacher Education, A
Wildlife and Wildlands Science and Management, A
Wildlife Biology, A

Zoology/Animal Biology, A

NORTHWEST MISSISSIPPI COMMUNITY COLLEGE

Accounting, A
Agricultural Business and Management, A
Agricultural Economics, A
Agricultural Mechanization, A
Agriculture, A
Animal Sciences, A
Art/Art Studies, General, A
Business Administration and Management, A
Civil Engineering Technology/Technician, A
Commercial and Advertising Art, A
Computer and Information Sciences, A
Computer Programming, Specific Applications, A
Computer Programming/Programmer, A
Court Reporting/Court Reporter, A
Dairy Science, A
Data Processing and Data Processing
   Technology/Technician, A
Drafting and Design Technology/Technician, A
Education, A
Electrical, Electronic and Communications
   Engineering Technology/Technician, A
Elementary Education and Teaching, A
Family and Consumer Sciences/Home Economics
   Teacher Education, A
Fashion Merchandising, A
Foods, Nutrition, and Wellness Studies, A
Heating, Air Conditioning and Refrigeration
   Technology/Technician, A
Heating, Air Conditioning, Ventilation and
   Refrigeration Maintenance
   Technology/Technician, A
Hotel/Motel Administration/Management, A
Journalism, A
Legal Assistant/Paralegal, A
Liberal Arts and Sciences Studies and
   Humanities, A
Licensed Practical/Vocational Nurse Training, A
Machine Tool Technology/Machinist, A
Mathematics Teacher Education, A
Medical Administrative Assistant/Secretary, A
Music Teacher Education, A
Nursing - Registered Nurse Training, A
Office Management and Supervision, A
Physical Education Teaching and Coaching, A
Plant Sciences, A
Poultry Science, A
Radio and Television, A
Radio and Television Broadcasting
   Technology/Technician, A
Respiratory Care Therapy/Therapist, A
Sales and Marketing Operations/Marketing and
   Distribution Teacher Education, A
Science Teacher Education/General Science
   Teacher Education, A
Social Science Teacher Education, A
Social Studies Teacher Education, A
Speech Teacher Education, A
Telecommunications Technology/Technician, A

PEARL RIVER COMMUNITY COLLEGE

Administrative Assistant and Secretarial Science, A
Business Administration and Management, A
Drafting and Design Technology/Technician, A
Electrical, Electronic and Communications
   Engineering Technology/Technician, A
Liberal Arts and Sciences Studies and
   Humanities, A
Marketing/Marketing Management, A
Medical Administrative Assistant/Secretary, A
Nursing - Registered Nurse Training, A
Respiratory Care Therapy/Therapist, A

RUST COLLEGE

Biology Teacher Education, B
Biology/Biological Sciences, B
Broadcast Journalism, B
Business Administration and Management, AB
Business Teacher Education, B
Chemistry, B
Computer Science, B
Early Childhood Education and Teaching, A
Elementary Education and Teaching, B

English Composition, B
English/Language Arts Teacher Education, B
Journalism, B
Mathematics, B
Mathematics Teacher Education, B
Music, B
Political Science and Government, B
Social Science Teacher Education, B
Social Work, B
Sociology, B

SOUTHEASTERN BAPTIST COLLEGE

Administrative Assistant and Secretarial Science, A
Bible/Biblical Studies, AB
Business Administration and Management, A
Pastoral Studies/Counseling, B
Religious/Sacred Music, A

SOUTHWEST MISSISSIPPI COMMUNITY COLLEGE

Accounting, A
Administrative Assistant and Secretarial Science, A
Advertising, A
Automobile/Automotive Mechanics
    Technology/Technician, A
Biological and Physical Sciences, A
Biology/Biological Sciences, A
Business Administration and Management, A
Business Teacher Education, A
Carpentry/Carpenter, A
Chemistry, A
Computer Programming, A
Computer Science, A
Construction Engineering Technology/Technician, A
Cosmetology/Cosmetologist, A
Education, A
Electrical, Electronic and Communications
    Engineering Technology/Technician, A
Elementary Education and Teaching, A
Emergency Medical Technology/Technician (EMT
    Paramedic), A
Engineering, A
English Language and Literature, A
Fashion Merchandising, A
Finance, A
History, A
Humanities/Humanistic Studies, A
Information Technology, A
Legal Administrative Assistant/Secretary, A
Liberal Arts and Sciences Studies and
    Humanities, A
Machine Tool Technology/Machinist, A
Marketing/Marketing Management, A
Music, A
Music Teacher Education, A
Nursing - Registered Nurse Training, A
Physical Education Teaching and Coaching, A
Physical Sciences, A
Public Health (MPH, DPH), A
Social Sciences, A
System Administration/Administrator, A
Welding Technology/Welder, A

TOUGALOO COLLEGE

Accounting, B
African-American/Black Studies, B
Art/Art Studies, General, B
Biology/Biological Sciences, B
Business Administration and Management, B
Chemistry, B
Child Development, AB
Computer Science, B
Economics, B
Education, B
Elementary Education and Teaching, B
English Language and Literature, B
History, B
Interdisciplinary Studies, B
Kindergarten/PreSchool Education and
    Teaching, AB
Mathematics, B
Music, B
Physics, B
Political Science and Government, B
Pre-Dentistry Studies, B
Psychology, B

Secondary Education and Teaching, B
Sociology, B

UNIVERSITY OF MISSISSIPPI

Accounting, BMD
Advertising, B
American/United States Studies/Civilization, BM
Anthropology, BM
Applied Science and Technology, MD
Art Education, M
Art History, Criticism and Conservation, BM
Art/Art Studies, General, B
Audiology/Audiologist and Speech-Language
    Pathology/Pathologist, B
Biological and Biomedical Sciences, MD
Biology/Biological Sciences, B
Biomedical Sciences, B
Business Administration and Management, B
Business Administration, Management and
    Operations, MDO
Business/Commerce, B
Business/Managerial Economics, B
Chemical Engineering, B
Chemistry, BMD
Civil Engineering, B
Classics and Classical
    Languages, Literatures, and Linguistics, BM
Clinical Laboratory Science/Medical
    Technology/Technologist, B
Clinical Psychology, D
Communication Disorders, M
Computational Sciences, MD
Computer and Information Sciences, B
Counselor Education/School Counseling and
    Guidance Services, MDO
Court Reporting/Court Reporter, B
Curriculum and Instruction, MDO
Drama and Dramatics/Theatre Arts, B
Economics, BMD
Education, MDO
Educational Leadership and Administration, MDO
Electrical, Electronics and Communications
    Engineering, B
Elementary Education and Teaching, B
Engineering, B
Engineering and Applied Sciences, MD
English, MD
English Language and Literature, B
English/Language Arts Teacher Education, B
Exercise and Sports Science, MD
Experimental Psychology, D
Family and Consumer Sciences/Human Sciences, B
Finance, B
Fine Arts and Art Studies, M
Forensic Science and Technology, B
French Language and Literature, BM
Geological/Geophysical Engineering, B
Geology/Earth Science, B
German Language and Literature, BM
Higher Education/Higher Education
    Administration, M
History, BMD
Insurance, B
International Business/Trade/Commerce, B
International Relations and Affairs, B
Journalism, BM
Kinesiology and Exercise Science, B
Law and Legal Studies, PO
Leisure Studies, MD
Liberal Arts and Sciences Studies and
    Humanities, B
Linguistics, B
Management Information Systems and Services, B
Marketing/Marketing Management, B
Mathematics, BMD
Mathematics Teacher Education, B
Mechanical Engineering, B
Medicinal and Pharmaceutical Chemistry, MD
Music, BMD
Parks, Recreation, Leisure and Fitness Studies, B
Pharmaceutical Administration, MD
Pharmaceutical Sciences, MD
Pharmacognosy, MD
Pharmacology, MD
Pharmacy, BP
Philosophy, BM

Physics, BMD
Political Science and Government, BMD
Psychology, BMD
Public Administration, B
Radio and Television, B
Real Estate, B
Recreation and Park Management, M
Science Teacher Education/General Science
    Teacher Education, B
Secondary Education and Teaching, BM
Social Studies Teacher Education, B
Social Work, B
Sociology, BM
Spanish Language and Literature, BM
Special Education and Teaching, B
Student Personnel Services, M
System Management, M
Taxation, M
Theater, M
Toxicology, D
Writing, M

UNIVERSITY OF MISSISSIPPI MEDICAL CENTER

Allied Health and Medical Assisting Services, M
Allopathic Medicine, PO
Anatomy, MDO
Biochemistry, MDO
Biological and Biomedical Sciences, MDO
Biophysics, MDO
Clinical Laboratory Science/Medical
    Technology/Technologist, B
Clinical Laboratory Sciences, MD
CytoTechnology/Cytotechnologist, B
Dental Hygiene/Hygienist, B
Dentistry, MDP
Health Information/Medical Records
    Administration/Administrator, B
Maternal and Child Health, M
Microbiology, MDO
Nursing, MD
Nursing - Registered Nurse Training, B
Occupational Therapy/Therapist, M
Oral and Dental Sciences, MD
Pathology/Experimental Pathology, MDO
Pharmacology, MDO
Physical Therapy/Therapist, M
Physiology, MDO
Toxicology, MDO

UNIVERSITY OF SOUTHERN MISSISSIPPI

Accounting, BM
Adult and Continuing Education and Teaching, MDO
Advertising, B
Advertising and Public Relations, M
American/United States Studies/Civilization, B
Analytical Chemistry, MD
Anthropology, BM
Apparel and Textiles, B
Architectural Engineering Technology/Technician, B
Art Education, M
Audiology/Audiologist and Speech-Language
    Pathology/Pathologist, B
Biochemistry, MD
Biological and Biomedical Sciences, MD
Biology/Biological Sciences, B
Business Administration and Management, B
Business Administration, Management and
    Operations, M
Business Teacher Education, B
Business/Managerial Economics, B
Chemistry, BMD
Child and Family Studies, M
City/Urban, Community and Regional Planning, B
Clinical Laboratory Science/Medical
    Technology/Technologist, B
Communication Disorders, MD
Communication Studies/Speech Communication
    and Rhetoric, B
Communication, Journalism and Related
    Programs, B
Community Health Nursing, M
Composition, M
Computational Sciences, D
Computer and Information Sciences, B

Computer Engineering Technology/Technician, B
Computer Science, M
Corrections, M
Criminal Justice/Safety Studies, B
Criminology, MD
Curriculum and Instruction, MDO
Dance, B
Data Processing and Data Processing
   Technology/Technician, B
Dietetics/Dieticians, B
Drama and Dramatics/Theatre Arts, B
Early Childhood Education and Teaching, MO
Economics, MD
Education, MDO
Education/Teaching of Individuals with Hearing
   Impairments, Including Deafness, B
Education/Teaching of the Gifted and
   Talented, MDO
Educational Administration and Supervision, MDO
Electrical, Electronic and Communications
   Engineering Technology/Technician, B
Elementary Education and Teaching, BMDO
Engineering and Applied Sciences, M
English, MD
English Language and Literature, B
Environmental and Occupational Health, M
Environmental Biology, MD
Family and Consumer Sciences/Human Sciences, B
Family Systems, B
Finance, B
Finance and Banking, MD
Food Science and Technology, MD
Foreign Language Teacher Education, M
Foreign Languages and Literatures, B
Geography, BM
Geology/Earth Science, BM
Health and Physical Education, B
Health Education, M
Health Services Administration, M
History, BMD
Hotel/Motel Administration/Management, B
Human Resources Development, M
Hydrology and Water Resources Science, M
Industrial Technology/Technician, B
Inorganic Chemistry, MD
Interdisciplinary Studies, B
Interior Architecture, B
International Business/Trade/Commerce, BMD
International Relations and Affairs, B
Journalism, B
Law Enforcement, M
Legal Assistant/Paralegal, B
Library Science, BMO
Management Information Systems and
   Services, BM
Marine Biology and Biological Oceanography, BMD
Marine Sciences, MD
Marketing/Marketing Management, B
Marriage and Family Therapy/Counseling, M
Mass Communication/Media Studies, MD
Maternal/Child Health and Neonatal
   Nurse/Nursing, M
Mathematics, BM
Mathematics Teacher Education, MD
Mechanical Engineering/Mechanical
   Technology/Technician, B
Medical Technology, M
Microbiology, MD
Molecular Biology, MD
Museology/Museum Studies, B
Music, BMD
Music History, Literature, and Theory, M
Music Teacher Education, BMD
Music Theory and Composition, M
Nursing, MD
Nursing - Adult, M
Nursing - Advanced Practice, M
Nursing - Registered Nurse Training, B
Nursing Administration, MD
Nutritional Sciences, MD
Organic Chemistry, MD
Parks, Recreation, Leisure and Fitness Studies, B
Performance, MD
Philosophy, BM
Physical Chemistry, MD
Physical Education Teaching and Coaching, BMD

Physics, BM
Political Science and Government, BM
Polymer/Plastics Engineering, MD
Psychiatric/Mental Health Nurse/Nursing, M
Psychology, BMDO
Public Health, M
Public Health (MPH, DPH), B
Radio and Television, B
Reading Teacher Education, MO
Recreation and Park Management, MD
Sacred Music, M
Science Teacher Education/General Science
   Teacher Education, MD
Secondary Education and Teaching, MDO
Social Studies Teacher Education, O
Social Work, BM
Special Education and Teaching, BMDO
Speech and Interpersonal Communication, MD
Sport and Fitness Administration/Management, M
Technology Teacher Education/Industrial Arts
   Teacher Education, B
Theater, M
Visual and Performing Arts, B
Vocational and Technical Education, M

VIRGINIA COLLEGE AT JACKSON

Accounting and Related Services, A
Administrative Assistant and Secretarial Science, A
Business Operations Support and Secretarial
   Services, A
Computer Systems Networking and
   Telecommunications, A
Educational/Instructional Media Design, A
Health Information/Medical Records
   Administration/Administrator, A
Human Resources Management/Personnel
   Administration, A
Medical Office Management/Administration, A
Medical/Clinical Assistant, A

WESLEY COLLEGE

Bible/Biblical Studies, B
Religious Education, B

WILLIAM CAREY COLLEGE

Art Education, M
Art Teacher Education, B
Art/Art Studies, General, B
Biology Teacher Education, B
Biology/Biological Sciences, B
Business Administration and Management, B
Business Administration, Management and
   Operations, M
Chemistry, B
Communication Studies/Speech Communication
   and Rhetoric, B
Counseling Psychology, M
Drama and Dance Teacher Education, B
Drama and Dramatics/Theatre Arts, B
Education, MO
Elementary Education and Teaching, BO
English Education, M
English Language and Literature, B
English/Language Arts Teacher Education, B
Fine/Studio Arts, B
General Studies, B
Health and Physical Education, B
Health Professions and Related Clinical Sciences, B
History, B
Industrial and Organizational Psychology, M
Journalism, B
Mathematics, B
Mathematics Teacher Education, B
Music, B
Music Performance, B
Music Teacher Education, B
Music Therapy/Therapist, B
Nursing, M
Nursing - Registered Nurse Training, B
Physical Education Teaching and Coaching, B
Psychology, BM
Religion/Religious Studies, B
Religious/Sacred Music, B
Social Sciences, B
Social Studies Teacher Education, B
Special Education and Teaching, M

Speech Teacher Education, B

Missouri

AVIATION INSTITUTE OF MAINTENANCE-KANSAS CITY

Airframe Mechanics and Aircraft Maintenance
   Technology/Technician, A

AVILA UNIVERSITY

Accounting, B
Biological and Physical Sciences, B
Biology/Biological Sciences, B
Business Administration, Management and
   Operations, M
Business/Commerce, B
Chemistry, B
Communication Studies/Speech Communication
   and Rhetoric, B
Computer and Information Sciences, B
Counseling Psychology, M
Drama and Dramatics/Theatre Arts, B
Education, M
Elementary Education and Teaching, B
English Language and Literature, B
Finance, B
General Studies, AB
Health and Physical Education/Fitness, B
Health/Medical Preparatory Programs, B
History, B
Hospital and Health Care Facilities
   Administration/Management, B
International Business/Trade/Commerce, B
Junior High/Intermediate/Middle School Education
   and Teaching, B
Legal Assistant/Paralegal, B
Marketing/Marketing Management, B
Mathematics, B
Medical Radiologic Technology/Science - Radiation
   Therapist, B
Music Performance, B
Natural Sciences, B
Nursing, B
Political Science and Government, B
Psychology, B
Religion/Religious Studies, B
Social Work, B
Sociology, B
Special Education and Teaching, B
Teacher Education and Professional
   Development, Specific Subject Areas, B

BAPTIST BIBLE COLLEGE

Administrative Assistant and Secretarial Science, AB
Business Administration and Management, AB
Cultural Studies, M
Divinity/Ministry (BD, MDiv.), B
Elementary Education and Teaching, B
Music, B
Music Teacher Education, B
Pastoral Studies/Counseling, BM
Religious Education, B
Theology and Religious Vocations, MP

BARNES-JEWISH COLLEGE OF NURSING AND ALLIED HEALTH

Allied Health and Medical Assisting Services, MO
Clinical Laboratory Science/Medical
   Technology/Technologist, B
CytoTechnology/Cytotechnologist, B
Gerontological Nursing, M
Health Promotion, M
Health Services Administration, M
Maternal/Child Health and Neonatal
   Nurse/Nursing, M
Nursing, M
Nursing - Adult, M
Nursing - Advanced Practice, M
Nursing - Registered Nurse Training, AB
Nursing Education, M
Nutritional Sciences, MO

Oncology Nursing, M

BLUE RIVER COMMUNITY COLLEGE

Accounting Technology/Technician and
 Bookkeeping, A
Administrative Assistant and Secretarial Science, A
Business Administration and Management, A
Computer and Information Sciences, A
Computer Science, A
Criminal Justice/Police Science, A
Fire Science/Firefighting, A
Information Science/Studies, A
Liberal Arts and Sciences Studies and
 Humanities, A

CALVARY BIBLE COLLEGE AND THEOLOGICAL SEMINARY

Bible/Biblical Studies, AB
Broadcast Journalism, B
Elementary Education and Teaching, B
Mass Communication/Media Studies, B
Missions/Missionary Studies and Missiology, B
Music, B
Music Teacher Education, B
Organizational Behavior Studies, B
Pastoral Counseling and Specialized Ministries, B
Pastoral Studies/Counseling, BMP
Piano and Organ, B
Religious Education, AB
Religious/Sacred Music, B
Secondary Education and Teaching, B
Theology and Religious Vocations, MP
Urban Studies/Affairs, B
Voice and Opera, B
Youth Ministry, B

CENTRAL BIBLE COLLEGE

Ancient Near Eastern and Biblical
 Languages, Literatures, and Linguistics, B
Bible/Biblical Studies, AB
Pastoral Studies/Counseling, B
Religion/Religious Studies, B
Religious Education, AB
Religious/Sacred Music, AB
Theology/Theological Studies, B

CENTRAL CHRISTIAN COLLEGE OF THE BIBLE

Bible/Biblical Studies, AB
Divinity/Ministry (BD, MDiv.), B
Religion/Religious Studies, B
Religious Education, B
Religious/Sacred Music, B
Social Work, B
Theology/Theological Studies, B

CENTRAL METHODIST UNIVERSITY

Accounting, B
Applied Mathematics, A
Athletic Training and Sports Medicine, B
Biology Teacher Education, B
Biology/Biological Sciences, B
Business Administration and Management, B
Chemistry, AB
Chemistry Teacher Education, B
Communication Studies/Speech Communication
 and Rhetoric, B
Computer Science, AB
Criminal Justice/Safety Studies, B
Drama and Dramatics/Theatre Arts, B
Early Childhood Education and Teaching, B
Economics, B
Education, BM
Elementary Education and Teaching, B
English Language and Literature, AB
Environmental Biology, B
Environmental Sciences, B
Foreign Language Teacher Education, B
Foreign Languages and Literatures, B
French Language and Literature, B
History, B
Interdisciplinary Studies, AB
Junior High/Intermediate/Middle School Education
 and Teaching, B
Kindergarten/PreSchool Education and Teaching, B

Management Science, B
Mathematics, B
Music, B
Music Performance, B
Music Teacher Education, B
Nursing - Registered Nurse Training, B
Nursing Administration, B
Philosophy, B
Physical Education Teaching and Coaching, B
Physics, B
Physics Teacher Education, B
Political Science and Government, B
Psychology, AB
Public Administration, AB
Religion/Religious Studies, B
Science Teacher Education/General Science
 Teacher Education, B
Secondary Education and Teaching, B
Social Science Teacher Education, B
Sociology, M
Spanish Language and Literature, B
Sport and Fitness Administration/Management, B

CENTRAL MISSOURI STATE UNIVERSITY

Accounting, M
Administrative Assistant and Secretarial Science, A
Aeronautical/Aerospace Engineering
 Technology/Technician, B
Agribusiness, B
Agricultural Business and Management, B
Agricultural Economics, B
Apparel and Textiles, B
Applied Mathematics, M
Art Teacher Education, B
Aviation, M
Biological and Biomedical Sciences, M
Biology/Biological Sciences, B
Business Administration and Management, B
Business Administration, Management and
 Operations, M
Business Statistics, B
Business Teacher Education, B
Chemistry, B
Clinical Laboratory Science/Medical
 Technology/Technologist, B
Commercial and Advertising Art, B
Communication and Media Studies, BM
Communication Disorders, M
Computer and Information Sciences, B
Counselor Education/School Counseling and
 Guidance Services, M
Criminal Justice/Law Enforcement Administration, B
Criminology, M
Curriculum and Instruction, MO
Drafting and Design Technology/Technician, AB
Drama and Dramatics/Theatre Arts, B
Economics, BM
Education, BMO
Educational Administration and Supervision, MO
Educational Media/Instructional Technology, M
Electrical, Electronic and Communications
 Engineering Technology/Technician, B
Elementary Education and Teaching, BM
Engineering and Applied Sciences, MO
English, M
English as a Second Language, M
English Language and Literature, B
Environmental and Occupational Health, MO
Exercise and Sports Science, M
Family and Consumer Sciences/Human Sciences, B
Finance, B
Fine/Studio Arts, B
Fire Protection Engineering, M
French Language and Literature, B
Geography, B
Geology/Earth Science, B
German Language and Literature, B
Gerontology, M
History, BM
Hotel/Motel Administration/Management, B
Human Resources Management/Personnel
 Administration, B
Human Services, O
Industrial and Manufacturing Management, M

Industrial Education, MO
Industrial Hygiene, M
Industrial Technology/Technician, AB
Industrial/Management Engineering, M
Information Science/Studies, MO
Interior Architecture, B
Interior Design, B
Journalism, B
Junior High/Intermediate/Middle School Education
 and Teaching, B
Library Science, MO
Management Information Systems and
 Services, BM
Marketing/Marketing Management, B
Mass Communication/Media Studies, M
Mathematics, BM
Music, BM
Music Teacher Education, B
Music Theory and Composition, B
Nursing, M
Nursing - Registered Nurse Training, B
Occupational Safety and Health
 Technology/Technician, B
Office Management and Supervision, B
Parks, Recreation, Leisure and Fitness Studies, B
Photography, B
Physical Education Teaching and Coaching, BM
Physics, B
Physics Teacher Education, B
Political Science and Government, B
Pre-Dentistry Studies, B
Pre-Medicine/Pre-Medical Studies, B
Pre-Pharmacy Studies, B
Pre-Veterinary Studies, B
Printing Management, B
Psychology, BM
Public Relations/Image Management, B
Radio and Television, B
Reading Teacher Education, BM
Secondary Education and Teaching, BM
Securities Services Administration/Management, M
Social Work, B
Sociology, BM
Spanish Language and Literature, B
Special Education and Teaching, BMO
Speech and Rhetorical Studies, BM
Speech-Language Pathology/Pathologist, B
Theater, M
Tourism and Travel Services Marketing
 Operations, B
Transportation/Transportation Management, M

CHAMBERLAIN COLLEGE OF NURSING

Nursing - Registered Nurse Training, AB

CLEVELAND CHIROPRACTIC COLLEGE-KANSAS CITY CAMPUS

Biology/Biological Sciences, AB
Chiropractic, P

COLLEGE OF THE OZARKS

Accounting, B
Acting, B
Agribusiness, B
Agricultural Mechanization, B
Agricultural Teacher Education, B
Agronomy and Crop Science, B
Animal Sciences, B
Apparel and Textiles, B
Applied Horticulture/Horticultural Operations, B
Art Teacher Education, B
Art/Art Studies, General, B
Avionics Maintenance Technology/Technician, B
Biology Teacher Education, B
Biology/Biological Sciences, B
Broadcast Journalism, B
Business Administration and Management, B
Business Teacher Education, B
Business/Managerial Economics, B
Chemistry, B
Chemistry Teacher Education, B
Child Care and Support Services Management, B
Child Development, B
Clinical Laboratory Science/Medical
 Technology/Technologist, B

Communication, Journalism and Related
   Programs, B
Computer and Information Sciences, B
Computer Science, B
Consumer Services and Advocacy, B
Corrections, B
Criminal Justice/Law Enforcement Administration, B
Criminal Justice/Police Science, B
Criminology, B
Dietetics/Dieticians, B
Drama and Dramatics/Theatre Arts, B
Education, B
Elementary Education and Teaching, B
Engineering, B
English Language and Literature, B
English/Language Arts Teacher Education, B
Family and Community Services, B
Family and Consumer Sciences/Home Economics
   Teacher Education, B
Family and Consumer Sciences/Human Sciences, B
Fine/Studio Arts, B
Foods, Nutrition, and Wellness Studies, B
Forensic Science and Technology, B
French Language and Literature, B
French Language Teacher Education, B
German Language and Literature, B
Gerontology, B
Graphic and Printing Equipment Operator
   Production, B
Health and Physical Education, B
Health/Medical Preparatory Programs, B
History, B
History Teacher Education, B
Horticultural Science, B
Hotel/Motel Administration/Management, B
Information Technology, B
Interdisciplinary Studies, B
International Business/Trade/Commerce, B
Journalism, B
Junior High/Intermediate/Middle School Education
   and Teaching, B
Marketing/Marketing Management, B
Mass Communication/Media Studies, B
Mathematics, B
Mathematics Teacher Education, B
Multi-/Interdisciplinary Studies, B
Music, B
Music Management and Merchandising, B
Music Teacher Education, B
Parks, Recreation and Leisure Facilities
   Management, B
Philosophy, B
Philosophy and Religious Studies, B
Physical Education Teaching and Coaching, B
Political Science and Government, B
Pre-Law Studies, B
Pre-Medicine/Pre-Medical Studies, B
Pre-Pharmacy Studies, B
Pre-Veterinary Studies, B
Psychology, B
Public Health (MPH, DPH), B
Public Relations/Image Management, B
Religious/Sacred Music, B
Science Teacher Education/General Science
   Teacher Education, B
Science, Technology and Society, B
Secondary Education and Teaching, B
Social Work, B
Sociology, B
Spanish Language and Literature, B
Speech and Rhetorical Studies, B
Technology Education/Industrial Arts, B
Technology Teacher Education/Industrial Arts
   Teacher Education, B

COLUMBIA COLLEGE

Accounting, B
Art/Art Studies, General, B
Biology/Biological Sciences, B
Business Administration and Management, AB
Business Administration, Management and
   Operations, M
Chemistry, B
Computer and Information Sciences, AB
Computer Science, B

Criminal Justice/Law Enforcement
   Administration, AB
Criminology, M
Drawing, B
Education, BM
English Language and Literature, B
Environmental Studies, B
Finance, B
Forensic Science and Technology, B
Graphic Design, B
History, B
Illustration, B
International Business/Trade/Commerce, B
Liberal Arts and Sciences Studies and
   Humanities, AB
Management Science, B
Marketing/Marketing Management, B
Mathematics, B
Multi-/Interdisciplinary Studies, B
Nursing - Registered Nurse Training, A
Painting, B
Philosophy and Religious Studies, B
Photography, B
Political Science and Government, B
Pre-Dentistry Studies, B
Pre-Engineering, B
Pre-Law Studies, B
Pre-Medicine/Pre-Medical Studies, B
Pre-Veterinary Studies, B
Printmaking, B
Psychology, B
Social Work, B
Sociology, B

CONCEPTION SEMINARY COLLEGE

Liberal Arts and Sciences Studies and
   Humanities, B

COTTEY COLLEGE

Biological and Physical Sciences, A
Liberal Arts and Sciences Studies and
   Humanities, A

COX COLLEGE OF NURSING AND HEALTH SCIENCES

Nursing - Registered Nurse Training, AB

CROWDER COLLEGE

Administrative Assistant and Secretarial Science, A
Agribusiness, A
Agriculture, A
Art/Art Studies, General, A
Biology/Biological Sciences, A
Business Administration and Management, A
Business/Office Automation/Technology/Data
   Entry, A
Computer Systems Networking and
   Telecommunications, A
Construction Engineering Technology/Technician, A
Drafting and Design Technology/Technician, A
Drama and Dramatics/Theatre Arts, A
Education, A
Electrical, Electronic and Communications
   Engineering Technology/Technician, A
Elementary Education and Teaching, A
Environmental Engineering
   Technology/Environmental Technology, A
Environmental Health, A
Executive Assistant/Executive Secretary, A
Farm/Farm and Ranch Management, A
Fire Science/Firefighting, A
General Studies, A
Industrial Technology/Technician, A
Legal Administrative Assistant/Secretary, A
Liberal Arts and Sciences Studies and
   Humanities, A
Mass Communication/Media Studies, A
Mathematics, A
Mathematics and Computer Science, A
Medical Administrative Assistant/Secretary, A
Music, A
Nursing - Registered Nurse Training, A
Physical Education Teaching and Coaching, A
Physical Sciences, A
Poultry Science, A

Pre-Engineering, A
Psychology, A
Public Relations/Image Management, A

CULVER-STOCKTON COLLEGE

Accounting, B
Art Teacher Education, B
Art/Art Studies, General, B
Arts Management, B
Athletic Training and Sports Medicine, B
Biology/Biological Sciences, B
Business Administration and Management, B
Criminal Justice/Law Enforcement Administration, B
Drama and Dramatics/Theatre Arts, B
Elementary Education and Teaching, B
English Language and Literature, B
English/Language Arts Teacher Education, B
Finance, B
History, B
History Teacher Education, B
Information Science/Studies, B
Mass Communication/Media Studies, B
Mathematics, B
Mathematics Teacher Education, B
Music, B
Music Teacher Education, B
Nursing - Registered Nurse Training, B
Parks, Recreation, Leisure and Fitness Studies, B
Physical Education Teaching and Coaching, B
Psychology, B
Religion/Religious Studies, B
Science Teacher Education/General Science
   Teacher Education, B
Special Education and Teaching, B
Speech Teacher Education, B

DEVRY UNIVERSITY (KANSAS CITY)

Business Administration, Management and
   Operations, M

DEVRY UNIVERSITY (KANSAS CITY)

Biomedical Technology/Technician, B
Business Administration, Management and
   Operations, B
Computer Engineering Technology/Technician, B
Computer Systems Analysis/Analyst, B
Computer Systems Networking and
   Telecommunications, B
Electrical, Electronic and Communications
   Engineering Technology/Technician, AB
Information Science/Studies, B
Operations Management and Supervision, B
System, Networking, and LAN/WAN
   Management/Manager, A

DEVRY UNIVERSITY (ST. LOUIS)

Business Administration, Management and
   Operations, M

DRURY UNIVERSITY

Accounting, B
Advertising, B
American Government and Politics (United States)
   , B
Architecture, B
Art History, Criticism and Conservation, B
Art/Art Studies, General, B
Arts Management, B
Biology/Biological Sciences, B
Broadcast Journalism, B
Business Administration and Management, B
Business Administration, Management and
   Operations, MO
Chemistry, B
Communication and Media Studies, M
Communication Studies/Speech Communication
   and Rhetoric, B
Computer and Information Sciences, B
Computer Science, B
Creative Writing, B
Criminology, BM
Design and Visual Communications, B
Drama and Dramatics/Theatre Arts, B
Economics, B
Education, BM

Education/Teaching of the Gifted and Talented, M
Elementary Education and Teaching, BM
Engineering, B
English Language and Literature, B
Environmental Studies, B
Finance, B
Fine/Studio Arts, B
French Language and Literature, B
German Language and Literature, B
Graphic Communications, B
Graphic Design, B
History, B
Human Services, M
International Business/Trade/Commerce, BMO
Journalism, B
Kinesiology and Exercise Science, B
Marketing/Marketing Management, B
Mass Communication/Media Studies, B
Mathematics, B
Middle School Education, M
Music, B
Music Performance, B
Music Teacher Education, B
Music Theory and Composition, B
Occupational Therapy/Therapist, B
Philosophy, B
Physical Education Teaching and Coaching, M
Physics, B
Political Science and Government, B
Pre-Dentistry Studies, B
Pre-Law Studies, B
Pre-Medicine/Pre-Medical Studies, B
Pre-Pharmacy Studies, B
Pre-Veterinary Studies, B
Psychology, B
Public Health (MPH, DPH), B
Public Relations/Image Management, B
Religion/Religious Studies, B
Secondary Education and Teaching, BM
Sociology, B
Spanish Language and Literature, B
Sport and Fitness Administration/Management, B

EAST CENTRAL COLLEGE

Accounting, A
Administrative Assistant and Secretarial Science, A
Automobile/Automotive Mechanics
    Technology/Technician, A
Biology/Biological Sciences, A
Botany/Plant Biology, A
Business Administration and Management, A
Business Operations Support and Secretarial
    Services, A
Chemistry, A
Commercial and Advertising Art, A
Computer Systems Networking and
    Telecommunications, A
Construction Engineering Technology/Technician, A
Construction Trades, A
Criminal Justice/Law Enforcement Administration, A
Criminal Justice/Police Science, A
Culinary Arts/Chef Training, A
Design and Visual Communications, A
Drafting and Design Technology/Technician, A
Ecology, A
Economics, A
Education, A
Electrical, Electronic and Communications
    Engineering Technology/Technician, A
Emergency Medical Technology/Technician (EMT
    Paramedic), A
Engineering, A
English Language and Literature, A
Family and Consumer Sciences/Human Sciences, A
Fire Science/Firefighting, A
Forestry, A
General Studies, A
Geography, A
Geology/Earth Science, A
Heating, Air Conditioning, Ventilation and
    Refrigeration Maintenance
    Technology/Technician, A
History, A
Horticultural Science, A
Hospitality Administration/Management, A
Hotel/Motel Administration/Management, A

Industrial Technology/Technician, A
Interior Design, A
Journalism, A
Kindergarten/PreSchool Education and Teaching, A
Legal Administrative Assistant/Secretary, A
Legal Assistant/Paralegal, A
Library Science, A
Machine Tool Technology/Machinist, A
Management Information Systems and Services, A
Manufacturing Technology/Technician, A
Marketing/Marketing Management, A
Mass Communication/Media Studies, A
Mathematics, A
Medical Administrative Assistant/Secretary, A
Nursing - Registered Nurse Training, A
Parks, Recreation, Leisure and Fitness Studies, A
Philosophy, A
Physical Education Teaching and Coaching, A
Physics, A
Political Science and Government, A
Pre-Engineering, A
Psychology, A
Radiologic Technology/Science - Radiographer, A
Religion/Religious Studies, A
Respiratory Therapy Technician/Assistant, A
Sociology, A
Special Products Marketing Operations, A
Speech and Rhetorical Studies, A
Surgical Technology/Technologist, A
Teacher Assistant/Aide, A
Tourism and Travel Services Management, A
Welding Technology/Welder, A
Wildlife and Wildlands Science and Management, A
Zoology/Animal Biology, A

EVANGEL UNIVERSITY

Accounting, AB
Administrative Assistant and Secretarial Science, AB
Art Teacher Education, B
Art/Art Studies, General, B
Behavioral Sciences, B
Bible/Biblical Studies, B
Biology Teacher Education, B
Biology/Biological Sciences, B
Broadcast Journalism, AB
Business Administration and Management, B
Business Teacher Education, B
Chemistry, B
Chemistry Teacher Education, B
Child Development, A
Clinical Laboratory Science/Medical
    Technology/Technologist, B
Clinical Psychology, M
Computer Science, B
Criminal Justice/Law Enforcement Administration, B
Early Childhood Education and Teaching, B
Education, ABM
Educational Leadership and Administration, M
Elementary Education and Teaching, B
English Language and Literature, B
Health and Medical Laboratory Technologies, B
Health and Physical Education, B
History, B
History Teacher Education, B
Intercultural/Multicultural and Diversity Studies, B
Journalism, AB
Junior High/Intermediate/Middle School Education
    and Teaching, B
Kindergarten/PreSchool Education and Teaching, B
Marketing/Marketing Management, B
Mass Communication/Media Studies, AB
Mathematics, B
Mental Health/Rehabilitation, AB
Music, B
Music Teacher Education, B
Organizational Management, M
Parks, Recreation, Leisure and Fitness Studies, B
Physical Education Teaching and Coaching, B
Political Science and Government, B
Pre-Dentistry Studies, B
Pre-Law Studies, B
Pre-Medicine/Pre-Medical Studies, B
Pre-Veterinary Studies, B
Psychology, BM
Public Administration, B
Radio and Television, B

Reading Teacher Education, M
Religious/Sacred Music, B
School Psychology, M
Science Teacher Education/General Science
    Teacher Education, B
Secondary Education and Teaching, BM
Social Sciences, AB
Social Work, B
Sociology, B
Spanish Language and Literature, B
Spanish Language Teacher Education, B
Special Education and Teaching, B
Speech and Rhetorical Studies, B

FONTBONNE UNIVERSITY

Accounting, B
Advertising, B
Art Teacher Education, B
Art/Art Studies, General, B
Arts Management, B
Audiology/Audiologist and Speech-Language
    Pathology/Pathologist, B
Biology/Biological Sciences, B
Broadcast Journalism, B
Business Administration and Management, B
Business Administration, Management and
    Operations, M
Civil Engineering Technology/Technician, B
Commercial and Advertising Art, B
Communication Disorders, BM
Communication Studies/Speech Communication
    and Rhetoric, B
Computer Education, M
Computer Science, B
Consumer Merchandising/Retailing Management, B
Dietetics/Dieticians, B
Drama and Dramatics/Theatre Arts, B
Education, BM
Elementary Education and Teaching, B
Engineering, B
English Language and Literature, B
Family and Consumer Sciences/Home Economics
    Teacher Education, B
Family and Consumer Sciences/Human
    Sciences, BM
Fashion Merchandising, B
Finance, B
Fine Arts and Art Studies, M
Fine/Studio Arts, B
History, B
Human Services, B
Junior High/Intermediate/Middle School Education
    and Teaching, B
Kindergarten/PreSchool Education and Teaching, B
Liberal Arts and Sciences Studies and
    Humanities, B
Management, M
Management Information Systems and Services, B
Marketing/Marketing Management, B
Mathematics, B
Pre-Law Studies, B
Pre-Medicine/Pre-Medical Studies, B
Psychology, B
Religion/Religious Studies, B
Secondary Education and Teaching, B
Social Sciences, B
Special Education and Teaching, BM
Taxation, M
Theater, M

GLOBAL UNIVERSITY OF THE ASSEMBLIES OF GOD

Bible/Biblical Studies, B
Divinity/Ministry (BD, MDiv.), B
Missions/Missionary Studies and Missiology, B
Pastoral Studies/Counseling, B
Religion/Religious Studies, A
Religious Education, B
Theology and Religious Vocations, MP
Theology/Theological Studies, B

GRANTHAM UNIVERSITY

Business Administration and Management, AB
Business Administration, Management and
    Operations, M
Computer Engineering Technology/Technician, AB

Computer Science, AB
Computer Software Engineering, AB
Criminal Justice/Law Enforcement
  Administration, AB
Criminal Justice/Police Science, AB
Criminal Justice/Safety Studies, AB
Electrical, Electronic and Communications
  Engineering Technology/Technician, AB
Engineering/Industrial Management, AB
General Studies, AB
Information Technology, AB
Interdisciplinary Studies, AB
Management Information Systems and Services, M
Management of Technology, M

HANNIBAL-LAGRANGE COLLEGE

Art Teacher Education, B
Art/Art Studies, General, B
Bible/Biblical Studies, B
Biology/Biological Sciences, B
Business Administration and Management, B
Business Teacher Education, B
Chemistry, A
Communication Studies/Speech Communication
  and Rhetoric, B
Communication, Journalism and Related
  Programs, B
Computer and Information Sciences, B
Criminal Justice/Law Enforcement
  Administration, AB
Drama and Dramatics/Theatre Arts, B
Early Childhood Education and Teaching, B
Education, B
Elementary Education and Teaching, B
Emergency Medical Technology/Technician (EMT
  Paramedic), A
English Language and Literature, AB
English/Language Arts Teacher Education, B
History, B
History Teacher Education, B
Human Services, B
Kindergarten/PreSchool Education and Teaching, B
Liberal Arts and Sciences Studies and
  Humanities, B
Marketing/Marketing Management, B
Mathematics, B
Mathematics Teacher Education, B
Medical Administrative Assistant/Secretary, A
Music, B
Music Teacher Education, B
Nursing - Registered Nurse Training, AB
Parks, Recreation and Leisure Facilities
  Management, B
Physical Education Teaching and Coaching, B
Piano and Organ, B
Pre-Engineering, A
Pre-Law Studies, B
Psychology, B
Religious Education, B
Religious/Sacred Music, B
Science Teacher Education/General Science
  Teacher Education, B
Secondary Education and Teaching, B
Sociology, B
Speech and Rhetorical Studies, B
Voice and Opera, B

HARRIS-STOWE STATE UNIVERSITY

Accounting, B
Business Administration and Management, B
Business/Commerce, B
Criminal Justice/Law Enforcement Administration, B
Early Childhood Education and Teaching, B
Elementary Education and Teaching, B
Health/Health Care Administration/Management, B
Information Science/Studies, B
Interdisciplinary Studies, B
Junior High/Intermediate/Middle School Education
  and Teaching, B
Juvenile Corrections, B
Kindergarten/PreSchool Education and Teaching, B
Marketing/Marketing Management, B
Public Administration, B
Secondary Education and Teaching, B
Urban Education and Leadership, B

Urban Studies/Affairs, B

HICKEY COLLEGE

Accounting, A
Business Administration and Management, B
Computer Programming/Programmer, A
Executive Assistant/Executive Secretary, A
Graphic Design, A
Legal Administrative Assistant/Secretary, A
Legal Assistant/Paralegal, A
Medical Administrative Assistant/Secretary, A
System, Networking, and LAN/WAN
  Management/Manager, A

IHM HEALTH STUDIES CENTER

Emergency Medical Technology/Technician (EMT
  Paramedic), A

ITT TECHNICAL INSTITUTE (ARNOLD)

Accounting and Business/Management, B
Animation, Interactive Technology, Video Graphics
  and Special Effects, B
Business Administration and Management, B
CAD/CADD Drafting and/or Design
  Technology/Technician, A
Computer and Information Systems Security, B
Computer Programming/Programmer, A
Computer Software Technology/Technician, B
Computer Systems Networking and
  Telecommunications, B
Criminal Justice/Law Enforcement Administration, B
E-Commerce/Electronic Commerce, B
Electrical, Electronic and Communications
  Engineering Technology/Technician, AB
System, Networking, and LAN/WAN
  Management/Manager, A
Web Page, Digital/Multimedia and Information
  Resources Design, A
Web/Multimedia Management and Webmaster, A

ITT TECHNICAL INSTITUTE (EARTH CITY)

Accounting and Business/Management, B
Animation, Interactive Technology, Video Graphics
  and Special Effects, B
Business Administration and Management, B
CAD/CADD Drafting and/or Design
  Technology/Technician, A
Computer and Information Systems Security, B
Computer Programming/Programmer, A
Criminal Justice/Law Enforcement Administration, B
E-Commerce/Electronic Commerce, B
Electrical, Electronic and Communications
  Engineering Technology/Technician, AB
System, Networking, and LAN/WAN
  Management/Manager, A
Web Page, Digital/Multimedia and Information
  Resources Design, A
Web/Multimedia Management and Webmaster, A

ITT TECHNICAL INSTITUTE (KANSAS CITY)

Accounting and Business/Management, B
Business Administration and Management, B
Computer and Information Systems Security, B
Criminal Justice/Law Enforcement Administration, B
Electrical, Electronic and Communications
  Engineering Technology/Technician, A
System, Networking, and LAN/WAN
  Management/Manager, A

JEFFERSON COLLEGE

Administrative Assistant and Secretarial Science, A
Art/Art Studies, General, A
Automobile/Automotive Mechanics
  Technology/Technician, A
Biological and Physical Sciences, A
Business Administration and Management, A
Business Teacher Education, A
Business/Commerce, A
CAD/CADD Drafting and/or Design
  Technology/Technician, A
Child Care and Support Services Management, A
Civil Engineering Technology/Technician, A

Computer Systems Networking and
  Telecommunications, A
Consumer Merchandising/Retailing Management, A
Criminal Justice/Law Enforcement Administration, A
Criminal Justice/Police Science, A
Culinary Arts/Chef Training, A
Drafting/Design Engineering
  Technologies/Technicians, A
Drama and Dramatics/Theatre Arts, A
Education, A
Electrical, Electronic and Communications
  Engineering Technology/Technician, A
Elementary Education and Teaching, A
Emergency Medical Technology/Technician (EMT
  Paramedic), A
Engineering, A
English Language and Literature, A
Fire Protection and Safety Technology/Technician, A
Forestry, A
Geography, A
Health Aide, A
Health Unit Coordinator/Ward Clerk, A
Heating, Air Conditioning, Ventilation and
  Refrigeration Maintenance
  Technology/Technician, A
History, A
Hospitality Administration/Management, A
Industrial Mechanics and Maintenance
  Technology, A
Institutional Food Workers, A
Interdisciplinary Studies, A
Journalism, A
Kindergarten/PreSchool Education and Teaching, A
Laser and Optical Technology/Technician, A
Legal Administrative Assistant/Secretary, A
Liberal Arts and Sciences Studies and
  Humanities, A
Licensed Practical/Vocational Nurse Training, A
Machine Tool Technology/Machinist, A
Mathematics, A
Medical Administrative Assistant/Secretary, A
Music, A
Nurse/Nursing Assistant/Aide and Patient Care
  Assistant, A
Nursing - Registered Nurse Training, A
Physical Education Teaching and Coaching, A
Physical Sciences, A
Political Science and Government, A
Precision Metal Working, A
Precision Production, A
Pre-Engineering, A
Psychology, A
Public Administration, A
Robotics Technology/Technician, A
Social Work, A
Sociology, A
Spanish Language and Literature, A
Speech and Rhetorical Studies, A
Telecommunications Technology/Technician, A
Veterinary/Animal Health Technology/Technician and
  Veterinary Assistant, A
Welding Technology/Welder, A

KANSAS CITY ART INSTITUTE

Art History, Criticism and Conservation, B
Ceramic Arts and Ceramics, B
Commercial and Advertising Art, B
Creative Writing, B
Fiber, Textile and Weaving Arts, B
Graphic Design, B
Illustration, B
Intermedia/Multimedia, B
Painting, B
Photography, B
Printmaking, B
Sculpture, B

KANSAS CITY COLLEGE

Court Reporting/Court Reporter, B
Legal Assistant/Paralegal, A

LINCOLN UNIVERSITY

Accounting, BM
Agricultural Business and Management, B
Agriculture, B
Art Teacher Education, B

Biology Teacher Education, B
Biology/Biological Sciences, B
Business Administration and Management, B
Business Administration, Management and
    Operations, M
Business Teacher Education, B
Chemistry, B
Chemistry Teacher Education, B
Civil Engineering, B
Clinical Laboratory Science/Medical
    Technology/Technologist, B
Computer Science, A
Counselor Education/School Counseling and
    Guidance Services, M
Criminal Justice/Law Enforcement
    Administration, AB
Criminology, M
Drafting and Design Technology/Technician, A
Drafting/Design Engineering
    Technologies/Technicians, B
Early Childhood Education and Teaching, AB
Economics, B
Education, MO
Educational Administration and Supervision, M
Educational Leadership and Administration, O
Elementary Education and Teaching, BM
English Language and Literature, B
English/Language Arts Teacher Education, B
Fine/Studio Arts, B
History, BM
Information Science/Studies, B
Journalism, B
Junior High/Intermediate/Middle School Education
    and Teaching, B
Marketing/Marketing Management, B
Mathematics, B
Mathematics Teacher Education, B
Music Teacher Education, B
Nursing - Registered Nurse Training, AB
Physical Education Teaching and Coaching, B
Physics, B
Physics Teacher Education, B
Political Science and Government, B
Pre-Engineering, A
Psychology, B
Public Administration, B
Secondary Education and Teaching, M
Social Sciences, M
Sociology, BM
Spanish Language and Literature, B
Special Education and Teaching, BM

LINDENWOOD UNIVERSITY

Accounting, BM
Agribusiness, B
Applied Art, B
Art History, Criticism and Conservation, B
Art Teacher Education, B
Art/Art Studies, General, B
Athletic Training and Sports Medicine, B
Biology Teacher Education, B
Biology/Biological Sciences, B
Broadcast Journalism, B
Business Administration and Management, B
Business Administration, Management and
    Operations, M
Business Teacher Education, B
Cell/Cellular Biology and Histology, B
Chemistry, B
Chemistry Teacher Education, B
Christian Studies, B
Clinical Laboratory Science/Medical
    Technology/Technologist, B
Computer Science, B
Computer/Information Technology Services
    Administration and Management, B
Consumer Merchandising/Retailing Management, B
Corporate and Organizational Communication, M
Counseling Psychology, M
Criminal Justice/Law Enforcement Administration, B
Criminology, BM
Dance, B
Digital Communication and Media/Multimedia, B
Drama and Dramatics/Theatre Arts, B
Drawing, B
Economics, B

Education, BMO
Educational Administration and Supervision, M
Educational Leadership and Administration, B
Educational Media/Instructional Technology, M
Educational/Instructional Media Design, B
Elementary Education and Teaching, B
English Language and Literature, B
Environmental Sciences, B
Fashion Merchandising, B
Fashion/Apparel Design, B
Finance, B
Finance and Banking, M
Fine/Studio Arts, B
French Language and Literature, B
French Language Teacher Education, B
Funeral Service and Mortuary Science, B
Gerontology, BM
Health and Physical Education, B
Health Services Administration, M
Health/Health Care Administration/Management, B
History, B
History Teacher Education, B
Human Resources Management and Services, M
Human Resources Management/Personnel
    Administration, B
Human Services, BM
International Business/Trade/Commerce, M
International Relations and Affairs, B
Investment Management, M
Journalism, B
Junior High/Intermediate/Middle School Education
    and Teaching, B
Kindergarten/PreSchool Education and Teaching, B
Liberal Arts and Sciences Studies and
    Humanities, B
Management, M
Management Information Systems and
    Services, BM
Marketing, M
Marketing/Marketing Management, B
Mass Communication/Media Studies, BM
Mathematics, B
Mathematics Teacher Education, B
Music, B
Music Teacher Education, B
Organizational Behavior Studies, M
Pastoral Studies/Counseling, B
Physical Education Teaching and Coaching, B
Political Science and Government, B
Pre-Dentistry Studies, B
Pre-Law Studies, B
Pre-Medicine/Pre-Medical Studies, B
Pre-Nursing Studies, B
Pre-Veterinary Studies, B
Psychology, B
Public Administration, BM
Public Relations/Image Management, B
Radio and Television, B
Religion/Religious Studies, B
Restaurant, Culinary, and Catering
    Management/Manager, B
Science Teacher Education/General Science
    Teacher Education, B
Secondary Education and Teaching, B
Social Science Teacher Education, B
Social Work, B
Sociology, B
Spanish Language and Literature, B
Spanish Language Teacher Education, B
Special Education and Teaching, B
Special Products Marketing Operations, B
Sport and Fitness Administration/Management, BM
Teacher Education, Multiple Levels, B
Technology Teacher Education/Industrial Arts
    Teacher Education, B
Theater, M
Voice and Opera, B
Writing, M
Youth Ministry, B

LINN STATE TECHNICAL COLLEGE

Aircraft Powerplant Technology/Technician, A
Autobody/Collision and Repair
    Technology/Technician, A
Automobile/Automotive Mechanics
    Technology/Technician, A

Civil Engineering Technology/Technician, A
Computer Programming/Programmer, A
Computer Systems Analysis/Analyst, A
Drafting and Design Technology/Technician, A
Electrical, Electronic and Communications
    Engineering Technology/Technician, A
Electrician, A
Heating, Air Conditioning, Ventilation and
    Refrigeration Maintenance
    Technology/Technician, A
Heavy Equipment Maintenance
    Technology/Technician, A
Laser and Optical Technology/Technician, A
Lineworker, A
Machine Tool Technology/Machinist, A
Physical Therapist Assistant, A

LOGAN UNIVERSITY-COLLEGE OF CHIROPRACTIC

Biology/Biological Sciences, B
Chiropractic, P

LONGVIEW COMMUNITY COLLEGE

Accounting, A
Administrative Assistant and Secretarial Science, A
Agricultural Mechanization, A
Automobile/Automotive Mechanics
    Technology/Technician, A
Biological and Physical Sciences, A
Biology/Biological Sciences, A
Business Administration and Management, A
Chemistry, A
Computer and Information Sciences, A
Computer Programming/Programmer, A
Computer Science, A
Computer Typography and Composition Equipment
    Operator, A
Corrections, A
Criminal Justice/Law Enforcement Administration, A
Criminal Justice/Police Science, A
Data Processing and Data Processing
    Technology/Technician, A
Engineering, A
Heavy Equipment Maintenance
    Technology/Technician, A
Human Services, A
Legal Administrative Assistant/Secretary, A
Liberal Arts and Sciences Studies and
    Humanities, A
Marketing/Marketing Management, A
Medical Administrative Assistant/Secretary, A
Pre-Engineering, A

MAPLE WOODS COMMUNITY COLLEGE

Accounting, A
Administrative Assistant and Secretarial Science, A
Avionics Maintenance Technology/Technician, A
Biological and Physical Sciences, A
Biology/Biological Sciences, A
Business Administration and Management, A
Chemistry, A
Computer and Information Sciences, A
Computer Programming/Programmer, A
Computer Science, A
Criminal Justice/Law Enforcement Administration, A
Criminal Justice/Police Science, A
Data Processing and Data Processing
    Technology/Technician, A
Legal Administrative Assistant/Secretary, A
Liberal Arts and Sciences Studies and
    Humanities, A
Marketing/Marketing Management, A
Medical Administrative Assistant/Secretary, A
Pre-Engineering, A
Veterinary/Animal Health Technology/Technician and
    Veterinary Assistant, A

MARYVILLE UNIVERSITY OF SAINT LOUIS

Accounting, BMO
Accounting and Related Services, B
Actuarial Science, B
Allied Health and Medical Assisting Services, M
Applied Mathematics, B

Art Education, M
Art Teacher Education, B
Biological and Physical Sciences, B
Biology Teacher Education, B
Biology/Biological Sciences, B
Biomedical Sciences, B
Business Administration and Management, B
Business Administration, Management and
    Operations, MO
Business Education, O
Business/Commerce, B
Chemistry, B
Chemistry Teacher Education, B
Clinical Laboratory Science/Medical
    Technology/Technologist, B
Computer Science, B
Criminology, B
Early Childhood Education and Teaching, M
E-Commerce/Electronic Commerce, B
Education, M
Education/Teaching of the Gifted and Talented, M
Electronic Commerce, MO
Elementary Education and Teaching, BM
English Education, M
English Language and Literature, B
English/Language Arts Teacher Education, B
Environmental Education, M
Environmental Sciences, B
Environmental Studies, B
Fine/Studio Arts, B
Graphic Design, B
Health Services Administration, M
Health/Medical Preparatory Programs, B
History, B
History Teacher Education, B
Industrial and Organizational Psychology, B
Interdisciplinary Studies, B
Interior Design, B
International Business/Trade/Commerce, MO
Junior High/Intermediate/Middle School Education
    and Teaching, B
Kindergarten/PreSchool Education and Teaching, B
Legal Assistant/Paralegal, B
Liberal Arts and Sciences Studies and
    Humanities, B
Management, MO
Management Information Systems and
    Services, BMO
Marketing, MO
Marketing/Marketing Management, B
Mass Communication/Media Studies, B
Mathematics, B
Mathematics Teacher Education, B
Middle School Education, M
Music Therapy/Therapist, BM
Nursing, M
Nursing - Registered Nurse Training, B
Occupational Therapy/Therapist, M
Physical Therapy/Therapist, M
Psychology, B
Public Health (MPH, DPH), B
Reading Teacher Education, M
Rehabilitation Counseling, M
School Psychology, M
Secondary Education and Teaching, BM
Social Psychology, B
Sociology, B
Vocational Rehabilitation Counseling/Counselor, B

MESSENGER COLLEGE

Bible/Biblical Studies, B
Business Administration and Management, B
Divinity/Ministry (BD, MDiv.), B
Education, B
General Studies, A
Missions/Missionary Studies and Missiology, B
Music, B
Pastoral Studies/Counseling, B
Religion/Religious Studies, B
Religious Education, B
Religious/Sacred Music, B
Theological and Ministerial Studies, B

Youth Ministry, B

METRO BUSINESS COLLEGE (CAPE GIRARDEAU)

Business Administration and Management, A
Business/Office Automation/Technology/Data
    Entry, A
Court Reporting/Court Reporter, A
Legal Assistant/Paralegal, A
Medical Administrative Assistant/Secretary, A

METRO BUSINESS COLLEGE (JEFFERSON CITY)

Computer and Information Sciences, A
Medical Administrative Assistant/Secretary, A

METROPOLITAN COMMUNITY COLLEGE-BUSINESS & TECHNOLOGY COLLEGE

Accounting, A
Accounting Technology/Technician and
    Bookkeeping, A
Artificial Intelligence and Robotics, A
Building/Construction Site Management/Manager, A
Business Administration and Management, A
Business/Commerce, A
Carpentry/Carpenter, A
Computer and Information Sciences, A
Computer and Information Sciences and Support
    Services, A
Computer and Information Systems Security, A
Computer Graphics, A
Computer Programming, A
Computer Programming, Specific Applications, A
Computer
    Programming, Vendor/Product Certification, A
Computer Programming/Programmer, A
Computer Science, A
Computer Software and Media Applications, A
Computer Systems Analysis/Analyst, A
Computer Systems Networking and
    Telecommunications, A
Computer/Information Technology Services
    Administration and Management, A
Data Entry/Microcomputer Applications, A
Data Modeling/Warehousing and Database
    Administration, A
Data Processing and Data Processing
    Technology/Technician, A
Drafting and Design Technology/Technician, A
Electrical, Electronic and Communications
    Engineering Technology/Technician, A
Engineering, A
Engineering-Related Technologies, A
Environmental Engineering
    Technology/Environmental Technology, A
Glazier, A
Information Science/Studies, A
Information Technology, A
Liberal Arts and Sciences Studies and
    Humanities, A
Machine Shop Technology/Assistant, A
Management Information Systems and Services, A
Mason/Masonry, A
Quality Control Technology/Technician, A
System Administration/Administrator, A
System, Networking, and LAN/WAN
    Management/Manager, A
Web Page, Digital/Multimedia and Information
    Resources Design, A
Web/Multimedia Management and Webmaster, A
Word Processing, A

MINERAL AREA COLLEGE

Accounting, A
Administrative Assistant and Secretarial Science, A
Agribusiness, A
Applied Horticulture/Horticultural Operations, A
Banking and Financial Support Services, A
Business Administration and Management, A
Child Care Provider/Assistant, A
Clinical Laboratory Science/Medical
    Technology/Technologist, A
Clinical/Medical Laboratory Technician, A
Commercial and Advertising Art, A

Computer Programming/Programmer, A
Construction Engineering Technology/Technician, A
Corrections, A
Criminal Justice/Police Science, A
Drafting and Design Technology/Technician, A
Electrical, Electronic and Communications
    Engineering Technology/Technician, A
Fire Science/Firefighting, A
Health/Health Care Administration/Management, A
Hospitality Administration/Management, A
Industrial Technology/Technician, A
Liberal Arts and Sciences Studies and
    Humanities, A
Licensed Practical/Vocational Nurse Training, A
Marketing/Marketing Management, A
Mass Communication/Media Studies, A
Medical Radiologic Technology/Science - Radiation
    Therapist, A
Nurse/Nursing Assistant/Aide and Patient Care
    Assistant, A
Nursing - Registered Nurse Training, A
Occupational Safety and Health
    Technology/Technician, A
Operations Management and Supervision, A
Parks, Recreation, Leisure and Fitness Studies, A
Radio and Television Broadcasting
    Technology/Technician, A
System Administration/Administrator, A
Tourism and Travel Services Management, A

MISSOURI BAPTIST UNIVERSITY

Accounting, B
Biology/Biological Sciences, B
Business Administration and Management, AB
Business Administration, Management and
    Operations, B
Business Teacher Education, B
Chemistry, B
Child Development, B
Communication Studies/Speech Communication
    and Rhetoric, B
Computer and Information Sciences, B
Criminal Justice/Safety Studies, B
Elementary Education and Teaching, B
English Language and Literature, B
Health Teacher Education, B
History, B
Human Services, B
Junior High/Intermediate/Middle School Education
    and Teaching, B
Kindergarten/PreSchool Education and Teaching, B
Marketing/Marketing Management, B
Mathematics, B
Multi-/Interdisciplinary Studies, B
Music Performance, B
Music Teacher Education, B
Nursing Science, B
Operations Management and Supervision, B
Physical Education Teaching and Coaching, B
Psychology, B
Religion/Religious Studies, AB
Religious Education, B
Religious/Sacred Music, B
Science Teacher Education/General Science
    Teacher Education, B
Social Sciences, B
Sport and Fitness Administration/Management, B
Theology and Religious Vocations, B

MISSOURI COLLEGE

Business/Commerce, A

MISSOURI SOUTHERN STATE UNIVERSITY

Accounting, AB
Animal Genetics, B
Biology/Biological Sciences, B
BioTechnology, B
Chemistry, B
Clinical Laboratory Science/Medical
    Technology/Technologist, B
Commercial and Advertising Art, B
Communication Studies/Speech Communication
    and Rhetoric, B
Computer and Information Sciences, B
Computer Science, AB

Criminal Justice/Law Enforcement Administration, B
Criminal Justice/Police Science, A
Data Processing and Data Processing
  Technology/Technician, A
Dental Hygiene/Hygienist, A
Drafting and Design Technology/Technician, A
Drama and Dramatics/Theatre Arts, B
Ecology, B
Education, B
Elementary Education and Teaching, B
English Language and Literature, B
Environmental Health, B
Finance, B
French Language and Literature, B
German Language and Literature, B
Health Services/Allied Health/Health Sciences, B
History, B
Industrial Technology/Technician, B
Information Science/Studies, AB
International Business/Trade/Commerce, B
International Relations and Affairs, B
Junior High/Intermediate/Middle School Education
  and Teaching, B
Kindergarten/PreSchool Education and Teaching, B
Kinesiology and Exercise Science, B
Machine Tool Technology/Machinist, A
Marine Biology and Biological Oceanography, B
Marketing/Marketing Management, B
Mass Communication/Media Studies, B
Mathematics, B
Medical Microbiology and Bacteriology, B
Medical Radiologic Technology/Science - Radiation
  Therapist, A
Music, B
Nursing - Registered Nurse Training, B
Physics, B
Political Science and Government, B
Pre-Dentistry Studies, B
Pre-Engineering, A
Pre-Medicine/Pre-Medical Studies, B
Pre-Pharmacy Studies, B
Pre-Veterinary Studies, B
Professional Studies, B
Psychology, B
Respiratory Care Therapy/Therapist, A
Secondary Education and Teaching, B
Sociology, B
Spanish Language and Literature, B
Special Education and Teaching, B
Technology Teacher Education/Industrial Arts
  Teacher Education, B

MISSOURI STATE UNIVERSITY

Accounting, BM
Agribusiness, B
Agricultural Sciences, M
Agricultural Teacher Education, B
Agriculture, B
Agronomy and Crop Science, B
Ancient Studies/Civilization, B
Animal Sciences, B
Anthropology, B
Apparel and Textiles, B
Applied Science and Technology, M
Art Education, M
Art Teacher Education, B
Art/Art Studies, General, B
Athletic Training and Sports Medicine, B
Audiology/Audiologist and Speech-Language
  Pathology/Pathologist, B
Biological and Biomedical Sciences, M
Biology Teacher Education, B
Biology/Biological Sciences, B
Business Administration and Management, B
Business Administration, Management and
  Operations, M
Business Teacher Education, B
Business/Commerce, B
Cartography, B
Cell Biology and Anatomy, M
Cell/Cellular and Molecular Biology, B
Chemistry, BM
Chemistry Teacher Education, B
City/Urban, Community and Regional Planning, B
Clinical Laboratory Science/Medical
  Technology/Technologist, B

Communication and Media Studies, M
Communication Disorders, D
Communication Studies/Speech Communication
  and Rhetoric, B
Computer Science, B
Counselor Education/School Counseling and
  Guidance Services, M
Criminal Justice/Safety Studies, B
Curriculum and Instruction, M
Dance, B
Design and Visual Communications, B
Dietetics/Dieticians, B
Drama and Dramatics/Theatre Arts, B
Early Childhood Education and Teaching, BM
Economics, B
Education, M
Educational Administration and Supervision, MO
Educational Media/Instructional Technology, M
Elementary Education and Teaching, BMO
Engineering Physics, B
English, M
English Language and Literature, B
English/Language Arts Teacher Education, B
Environmental Policy and Resource
  Management, M
Family and Consumer Sciences/Home Economics
  Teacher Education, B
Family and Consumer Sciences/Human
  Sciences, M
Finance, B
Fine/Studio Arts, B
Foreign Language Teacher Education, M
French Language and Literature, B
French Language Teacher Education, B
Geography, BM
Geology/Earth Science, BM
Geosciences, M
German Language and Literature, B
German Language Teacher Education, B
Gerontology, B
Health Promotion, M
Health Services Administration, M
History, BM
History Teacher Education, B
Horticultural Science, B
Hospitality Administration/Management, B
Housing and Human Environments, B
Human Development and Family Studies, B
Insurance, B
International Affairs, M
Journalism, B
Junior High/Intermediate/Middle School Education
  and Teaching, B
Latin Language and Literature, B
Management Information Systems and
  Services, BM
Marketing/Marketing Management, B
Mass Communication/Media Studies, B
Materials Sciences, M
Mathematics, BM
Mathematics Teacher Education, B
Medical Radiologic Technology/Science - Radiation
  Therapist, B
Middle School Education, M
Military and Defense Studies, M
Molecular Biology, BM
Music, BM
Music Performance, B
Music Teacher Education, B
Music Theory and Composition, B
Nurse Anesthetist, M
Nursing, M
Nursing - Registered Nurse Training, B
Parks, Recreation, Leisure and Fitness Studies, B
Philosophy, B
Physical Education Teaching and Coaching, BM
Physical Science Technologies/Technicians, B
Physical Therapy/Therapist, M
Physician Assistant, M
Physics, B
Physics Teacher Education, B
Plant Sciences, M
Political Science and Government, BM
Psychology, BM
Public Administration, BM
Public Health, M

Radiologic Technology/Science - Radiographer, B
Reading Teacher Education, M
Religion/Religious Studies, BM
Resource Management, M
Respiratory Care Therapy/Therapist, B
Science Teacher Education/General Science
  Teacher Education, BM
Secondary Education and Teaching, MO
Social Work, BM
Sociology, B
Spanish Language and Literature, B
Spanish Language Teacher Education, B
Special Education and Teaching, BMO
Teacher Education and Professional
  Development, Specific Subject Areas, B
Technical and Business Writing, B
Theater, M
Urban and Regional Planning, M
Visual and Performing Arts, B
Wildlife and Wildlands Science and Management, B

MISSOURI STATE UNIVERSITY-WEST PLAINS

Accounting, A
Agriculture, A
Business Administration and Management, A
Business/Commerce, A
Computer and Information Sciences, A
Computer Graphics, A
Computer Programming, Specific Applications, A
Criminal Justice/Law Enforcement Administration, A
Criminal Justice/Police Science, A
Engineering, A
Entrepreneurship/Entrepreneurial Studies, A
Fire Science/Firefighting, A
General Studies, A
Industrial Technology/Technician, A
Information Technology, A
Legal Assistant/Paralegal, A
Nursing - Registered Nurse Training, A
Respiratory Therapy Technician/Assistant, A

MISSOURI TECH

Computer Engineering, B
Computer Engineering Technology/Technician, A
Electrical, Electronic and Communications
  Engineering Technology/Technician, A
Electrical, Electronics and Communications
  Engineering, AB
Engineering Technology, AB
Engineering/Industrial Management, B
Systems Engineering, AB

MISSOURI VALLEY COLLEGE

Accounting, B
Art/Art Studies, General, B
Athletic Training and Sports Medicine, B
Biology/Biological Sciences, B
Business Administration and Management, AB
Computer Science, B
Criminal Justice/Law Enforcement Administration, B
Drama and Dramatics/Theatre Arts, B
Economics, B
Education, B
Elementary Education and Teaching, B
English Language and Literature, B
Health Teacher Education, B
History, B
Human Services, B
Liberal Arts and Sciences Studies and
  Humanities, AB
Marketing/Marketing Management, B
Mass Communication/Media Studies, B
Mathematics, B
Music, B
Parks, Recreation and Leisure Facilities
  Management, B
Parks, Recreation, Leisure and Fitness Studies, B
Philosophy, B
Physical Education Teaching and Coaching, B
Political Science and Government, B
Pre-Dentistry Studies, B
Pre-Law Studies, B
Pre-Medicine/Pre-Medical Studies, B
Pre-Nursing Studies, B
Pre-Pharmacy Studies, B

Pre-Veterinary Studies, B
Psychology, B
Public Administration, B
Religion/Religious Studies, B
Science Teacher Education/General Science
  Teacher Education, B
Secondary Education and Teaching, B
Sociology, B
Special Education and Teaching, B
Speech and Rhetorical Studies, B
Sport and Fitness Administration/Management, B

MISSOURI WESTERN STATE UNIVERSITY

Accounting, B
Art Teacher Education, B
Art/Art Studies, General, B
Biochemistry, B
Biology/Biological Sciences, B
BioTechnology, B
Business Administration and Management, AB
Chemistry, B
Civil Engineering Technology/Technician, AB
Clinical Laboratory Science/Medical
  Technology/Technologist, B
Computer and Information Sciences, B
Computer Engineering, AB
Criminal Justice/Safety Studies, AB
Economics, B
Electrical, Electronic and Communications
  Engineering Technology/Technician, AB
Elementary Education and Teaching, B
Emergency Medical Technology/Technician (EMT
  Paramedic), A
English Language and Literature, B
English/Language Arts Teacher Education, B
Finance, B
French Language and Literature, B
French Language Teacher Education, B
Graphic Design, B
Health and Physical Education, B
Health Information/Medical Records
  Technology/Technician, A
History, B
Information Science/Studies, B
Legal Assistant/Paralegal, A
Manufacturing Technology/Technician, A
Marketing/Marketing Management, B
Mathematics, B
Multi-/Interdisciplinary Studies, B
Music, B
Music Teacher Education, B
Natural Sciences, B
Nursing - Registered Nurse Training, B
Parks, Recreation and Leisure Facilities
  Management, B
Physical Therapist Assistant, A
Political Science and Government, B
Psychology, B
Social Work, B
Spanish Language and Literature, B
Spanish Language Teacher Education, B
Speech Teacher Education, B

MOBERLY AREA COMMUNITY COLLEGE

Accounting Technology/Technician and
  Bookkeeping, A
Administrative Assistant and Secretarial Science, A
Child Development, A
Clinical/Medical Laboratory Technician, A
Computer and Information Sciences, A
Criminal Justice/Police Science, A
Drafting and Design Technology/Technician, A
Electrical, Electronic and Communications
  Engineering Technology/Technician, A
Graphic and Printing Equipment Operator
  Production, A
Industrial Technology/Technician, A
Liberal Arts and Sciences Studies and
  Humanities, A
Marketing/Marketing Management, A
Nursing - Registered Nurse Training, A
Pre-Engineering, A

Welding Technology/Welder, A

NATIONAL AMERICAN UNIVERSITY

Accounting, AB
Business Administration and Management, AB
Computer Engineering Technology/Technician, B
Education, B
Finance, B
Information Science/Studies, AB
Management Information Systems and Services, B
Management Science, AB

NORTH CENTRAL MISSOURI COLLEGE

Accounting, A
Administrative Assistant and Secretarial Science, A
Agricultural Business and Management, A
Automobile/Automotive Mechanics
  Technology/Technician, A
Business Administration and Management, A
Carpentry/Carpenter, A
Computer Engineering Technology/Technician, A
Construction Engineering Technology/Technician, A
Criminal Justice/Law Enforcement Administration, A
Data Processing and Data Processing
  Technology/Technician, A
Drafting and Design Technology/Technician, A
Early Childhood Education and Teaching, A
E-Commerce/Electronic Commerce, A
Electrical, Electronic and Communications
  Engineering Technology/Technician, A
Emergency Medical Technology/Technician (EMT
  Paramedic), A
Farm/Farm and Ranch Management, A
Human Services, A
Liberal Arts and Sciences Studies and
  Humanities, A
Marketing/Marketing Management, A
Medical/Clinical Assistant, A
Nursing - Registered Nurse Training, A

NORTHWEST MISSOURI STATE UNIVERSITY

Accounting, BM
Administrative Assistant and Secretarial Science, B
Advertising, B
Agricultural Business and Management, B
Agricultural Economics, BM
Agricultural Education, M
Agricultural Mechanization, B
Agricultural Sciences, M
Agricultural Teacher Education, B
Agriculture, B
Agronomy and Crop Science, B
Animal Sciences, B
Apparel and Textiles, B
Army JROTC/ROTC, B
Art Teacher Education, B
Art/Art Studies, General, B
Behavioral Sciences, B
Biological and Biomedical Sciences, M
Biological and Physical Sciences, B
Biology/Biological Sciences, B
Biomedical Technology/Technician, B
Botany/Plant Biology, B
Broadcast Journalism, B
Business Administration and Management, B
Business Administration, Management and
  Operations, M
Business Teacher Education, B
Business/Managerial Economics, B
Chemistry, B
Child Development, B
Clinical Laboratory Science/Medical
  Technology/Technologist, B
Clinical/Medical Laboratory Technician, B
Commercial and Advertising Art, B
Comparative Literature, B
Computer Programming/Programmer, B
Computer Science, BM
Consumer Merchandising/Retailing Management, B
Counseling Psychology, M
Counselor Education/School Counseling and
  Guidance Services, BM
Data Processing and Data Processing
  Technology/Technician, B
Developmental and Child Psychology, B

Dietetics/Dieticians, B
Drama and Dramatics/Theatre Arts, B
Drawing, B
Early Childhood Education and Teaching, M
Ecology, B
Economics, B
Education, BMO
Educational Leadership and Administration, BMO
Educational Media/Instructional Technology, M
Elementary Education and Teaching, BMO
English, M
English Education, M
English Language and Literature, B
Family and Consumer Economics and Related
  Services, B
Family and Consumer Sciences/Home Economics
  Teacher Education, B
Family and Consumer Sciences/Human Sciences, B
Farm/Farm and Ranch Management, B
Fashion Merchandising, B
Fashion/Apparel Design, B
Fiber, Textile and Weaving Arts, B
Finance, B
Fine/Studio Arts, B
Food Science, B
Foods, Nutrition, and Wellness Studies, B
Forestry, B
French Language and Literature, B
Geographic Information Systems, M
Geography, B
Geology/Earth Science, B
Health Education, M
Health Services Administration, M
Health Teacher Education, B
History, BM
Horticultural Science, B
Hospitality and Recreation Marketing Operations, B
Humanities/Humanistic Studies, B
Information Science/Studies, B
Interior Design, B
International Business/Trade/Commerce, B
Journalism, B
Junior High/Intermediate/Middle School Education
  and Teaching, B
Kindergarten/PreSchool Education and Teaching, B
Landscape Architecture, B
Legal Administrative Assistant/Secretary, B
Management Information Systems and
  Services, BM
Marketing/Marketing Management, B
Mass Communication/Media Studies, B
Mathematics, B
Mathematics Teacher Education, M
Metal and Jewelry Arts, B
Middle School Education, M
Music, B
Music Management and Merchandising, B
Music Teacher Education, BM
Natural Resources and Conservation, B
Parks, Recreation, Leisure and Fitness Studies, B
Philosophy, B
Physical Education Teaching and Coaching, BM
Physical Sciences, B
Physics, B
Piano and Organ, B
Political Science and Government, B
Pre-Dentistry Studies, B
Pre-Law Studies, B
Pre-Medicine/Pre-Medical Studies, B
Pre-Veterinary Studies, B
Psychology, BM
Public Administration, B
Public Health (MPH, DPH), B
Public Relations/Image Management, B
Radio and Television, B
Reading Teacher Education, BM
Recreation and Park Management, M
Romance Languages, Literatures, and Linguistics, B
Science Teacher Education/General Science
  Teacher Education, BM
Sculpture, B
Secondary Education and Teaching, BMO
Social Sciences, B
Social Studies Teacher Education, M
Sociology, B
Spanish Language and Literature, B

Special Education and Teaching, BM
Speech and Rhetorical Studies, B
Sport and Fitness Administration/Management, B
Therapeutic Recreation/Recreational Therapy, B
Violin, Viola, Guitar and Other Stringed
  Instruments, B
Voice and Opera, B
Wildlife and Wildlands Science and Management, B
Wildlife Biology, B
Wind and Percussion Instruments, B
Zoology/Animal Biology, B

OZARK CHRISTIAN COLLEGE

Ancient Near Eastern and Biblical
  Languages, Literatures, and Linguistics, B
Bible/Biblical Studies, B
Elementary Education and Teaching, A
Religious Education, B
Religious/Sacred Music, B
Sign Language Interpretation and Translation, B
Theology/Theological Studies, AB

OZARKS TECHNICAL COMMUNITY COLLEGE

Accounting, A
Administrative Assistant and Secretarial Science, A
Autobody/Collision and Repair
  Technology/Technician, A
Automobile/Automotive Mechanics
  Technology/Technician, A
Business Administration and Management, A
Business Machine Repairer, A
Computer Systems Networking and
  Telecommunications, A
Construction Engineering Technology/Technician, A
Culinary Arts/Chef Training, A
Diesel Mechanics Technology/Technician, A
Electrical, Electronic and Communications
  Engineering Technology/Technician, A
Emergency Medical Technology/Technician (EMT
  Paramedic), A
Fire Science/Firefighting, A
Graphic and Printing Equipment Operator
  Production, A
Health Information/Medical Records
  Technology/Technician, A
Heating, Air Conditioning, Ventilation and
  Refrigeration Maintenance
  Technology/Technician, A
Heavy Equipment Maintenance
  Technology/Technician, A
Hotel/Motel Administration/Management, A
Industrial Technology/Technician, A
Information Science/Studies, A
Instrumentation Technology/Technician, A
Kindergarten/PreSchool Education and Teaching, A
Liberal Arts and Sciences Studies and
  Humanities, A
Machine Tool Technology/Machinist, A
Management Information Systems and Services, A
Mechanical Drafting and Mechanical Drafting
  CAD/CADD, A
Occupational Therapist Assistant, A
Occupational Therapy/Therapist, A
Physical Sciences, A
Physical Therapist Assistant, A
Radio and Television Broadcasting
  Technology/Technician, A
Respiratory Care Therapy/Therapist, A
Turf and Turfgrass Management, A
Welding Technology/Welder, A

PARK UNIVERSITY

Accounting, B
Accounting and Related Services, AB
Athletic Training and Sports Medicine, B
Aviation/Airway Management and Operations, AB
Biological and Biomedical Sciences, B
Biology/Biological Sciences, B
Building/Property Maintenance and Management, A
Business Administration and Management, AB
Business Administration, Management and
  Operations, M
Business, Management, Marketing, and Related
  Support Services, B
Business/Managerial Economics, B

Chemistry, B
Communication Studies/Speech Communication
  and Rhetoric, B
Computer and Information Sciences, B
Computer and Information Sciences and Support
  Services, B
Computer Science, AB
Criminal Justice/Law Enforcement
  Administration, AB
Drama and Dramatics/Theatre Arts, B
Early Childhood Education and Teaching, B
Economics, B
Education, BM
Educational Administration and Supervision, M
Elementary Education and Teaching, B
Engineering, B
English Language and Literature, B
Entrepreneurship/Entrepreneurial Studies, M
Finance and Financial Management Services, B
Fine/Studio Arts, B
Geography, B
Graphic Design, B
Health Information/Medical Records
  Administration/Administrator, A
Health Services Administration, M
History, B
Human Development and Family Studies, B
Human Resources Management and Services, B
Human Services, B
Interior Design, B
International Business/Trade/Commerce, M
Law and Legal Studies, BM
Liberal Arts and Sciences Studies and
  Humanities, AB
Logistics and Materials Management, AB
Management Information Systems and
  Services, BM
Marketing/Marketing Management, B
Mathematics, B
Middle School Education, M
Multi-/Interdisciplinary Studies, B
Multilingual and Multicultural Education, M
Music, B
Natural Sciences, B
Non-Profit/Public/Organizational Management, M
Nursing - Registered Nurse Training, A
Office Management and Supervision, A
Political Science and Government, B
Psychology, B
Public Administration, BM
Public Affairs, M
Secondary Education and Teaching, M
Social Psychology, AB
Sociology, B
Spanish Language and Literature, B

PATRICIA STEVENS COLLEGE

Business/Commerce, A
Fashion Merchandising, A
Interior Design, A
Legal Assistant/Paralegal, A
Medical Office Management/Administration, A
Retailing and Retail Operations, A
Tourism and Travel Services Management, A

PENN VALLEY COMMUNITY COLLEGE

Accounting, A
Administrative Assistant and Secretarial Science, A
Biological and Physical Sciences, A
Biology/Biological Sciences, A
Business Administration and Management, A
Chemistry, A
Child Care Provider/Assistant, A
Commercial and Advertising Art, A
Computer and Information Sciences, A
Computer Science, A
Corrections, A
Criminal Justice/Law Enforcement Administration, A
Criminal Justice/Police Science, A
Data Processing and Data Processing
  Technology/Technician, A
Emergency Medical Technology/Technician (EMT
  Paramedic), A
Engineering, A
Family and Consumer Sciences/Human Sciences, A
Fashion Merchandising, A

Fashion/Apparel Design, A
Health Information/Medical Records
  Administration/Administrator, A
Kindergarten/PreSchool Education and Teaching, A
Legal Administrative Assistant/Secretary, A
Legal Assistant/Paralegal, A
Liberal Arts and Sciences Studies and
  Humanities, A
Marketing/Marketing Management, A
Medical Administrative Assistant/Secretary, A
Nursing - Registered Nurse Training, A
Occupational Therapy/Therapist, A
Physical Therapy/Therapist, A
Respiratory Care Therapy/Therapist, A

PINNACLE CAREER INSTITUTE

Computer Programming/Programmer, A
Electrical and Electronic Engineering
  Technologies/Technicians, A

RANKEN TECHNICAL COLLEGE

Architectural Engineering Technology/Technician, AB
Autobody/Collision and Repair
  Technology/Technician, A
Automobile/Automotive Mechanics
  Technology/Technician, A
Carpentry/Carpenter, A
Computer and Information Sciences, A
Computer and Information Sciences and Support
  Services, A
Computer Engineering Technology/Technician, A
Electrical, Electronic and Communications
  Engineering Technology/Technician, A
Heating, Air Conditioning, Ventilation and
  Refrigeration Maintenance
  Technology/Technician, A
Machine Tool Technology/Machinist, A
Pipefitting/Pipefitter and Sprinkler Fitter, A

RESEARCH COLLEGE OF NURSING

Nursing, M
Nursing - Advanced Practice, M
Nursing - Registered Nurse Training, B
Nursing Education, M

ROCKHURST UNIVERSITY

Biochemistry, B
Bioinformatics, B
Biology/Biological Sciences, B
Business Administration and Management, B
Business/Corporate Communications, B
Chemistry, B
Communication Disorders, M
Communication Studies/Speech Communication
  and Rhetoric, B
Community Organization and Advocacy, B
Computer Programming/Programmer, B
Computer Science, B
Creative Writing, B
Economics, B
Education, BM
Elementary Education and Teaching, B
English Language and Literature, B
French Language and Literature, B
Health and Medical Laboratory Technologies, B
History, B
International Relations and Affairs, B
Management, M
Mathematics, B
Nursing - Registered Nurse Training, B
Occupational Therapy/Therapist, M
Philosophy, B
Physical Therapy/Therapist, D
Physics, B
Political Science and Government, B
Psychology, B
Secondary Education and Teaching, B
Social Sciences, B
Sociology, B
Spanish Language and Literature, B
Speech-Language Pathology/Pathologist, B

Theology/Theological Studies, B

SAINT CHARLES COMMUNITY COLLEGE

Accounting, A
Administrative Assistant and Secretarial Science, A
Business Administration and Management, A
Child Development, A
Commercial and Advertising Art, A
Computer Programming, A
Computer Programming, Specific Applications, A
Computer Science, A
Computer Systems Networking and
  Telecommunications, A
Criminal Justice/Law Enforcement Administration, A
Criminal Justice/Police Science, A
Drafting and Design Technology/Technician, A
Health Information/Medical Records
  Administration/Administrator, A
Human Services, A
Liberal Arts and Sciences Studies and
  Humanities, A
Marketing/Marketing Management, A
Medical Transcription/Transcriptionist, A
Nursing - Registered Nurse Training, A
Occupational Therapy/Therapist, A
Office Management and Supervision, A
Pre-Engineering, A
Web/Multimedia Management and Webmaster, A

ST. LOUIS CHRISTIAN COLLEGE

Bible/Biblical Studies, B
Divinity/Ministry (BD, MDiv.), AB
Liberal Arts and Sciences Studies and
  Humanities, A
Religious Education, B
Religious/Sacred Music, B
Theology/Theological Studies, B

ST. LOUIS COLLEGE OF PHARMACY

Pharmaceutical Administration, M
Pharmacy, BP

ST. LOUIS COMMUNITY COLLEGE AT FLORISSANT VALLEY

Accounting, A
Administrative Assistant and Secretarial Science, A
Art/Art Studies, General, A
Broadcast Journalism, A
Business Administration and Management, A
Chemical Engineering, A
Child Development, A
Cinematography and Film/Video Production, A
Civil Engineering Technology/Technician, A
Commercial and Advertising Art, A
Computer Engineering Technology/Technician, A
Computer Programming/Programmer, A
Computer Science, A
Construction Engineering Technology/Technician, A
Corrections, A
Criminal Justice/Law Enforcement Administration, A
Criminal Justice/Police Science, A
Data Processing and Data Processing
  Technology/Technician, A
Dietetics/Dieticians, A
Drama and Dramatics/Theatre Arts, A
Electrical, Electronic and Communications
  Engineering Technology/Technician, A
Elementary Education and Teaching, A
Emergency Medical Technology/Technician (EMT
  Paramedic), A
Engineering, A
Engineering Science, A
Engineering Technology, A
Fashion Merchandising, A
Finance, A
Fire Science/Firefighting, A
Food Science, A
Food Technology and Processing, A
Human Services, A
Information Science/Studies, A
Journalism, A
Law and Legal Studies, A
Liberal Arts and Sciences Studies and
  Humanities, A

Mass Communication/Media Studies, A
Mathematics, A
Mechanical Engineering/Mechanical
  Technology/Technician, A
Music, A
Nursing - Registered Nurse Training, A
Photography, A
Pre-Engineering, A
Radio and Television, A
Real Estate, A
Sign Language Interpretation and Translation, A
Special Products Marketing Operations, A
Telecommunications Technology/Technician, A

ST. LOUIS COMMUNITY COLLEGE AT FOREST PARK

Accounting, A
Administrative Assistant and Secretarial Science, A
African-American/Black Studies, A
Art/Art Studies, General, A
Artificial Intelligence and Robotics, A
Automobile/Automotive Mechanics
  Technology/Technician, A
Biology/Biological Sciences, A
Biomedical Technology/Technician, A
Business Administration and Management, A
Child Development, A
Clinical/Medical Laboratory Technician, A
Commercial and Advertising Art, A
Computer and Information Sciences, A
Computer Programming, A
Computer Programming, Specific Applications, A
Computer
  Programming, Vendor/Product Certification, A
Computer Science, A
Computer Systems Networking and
  Telecommunications, A
Criminal Justice/Law Enforcement Administration, A
Culinary Arts/Chef Training, A
Data Entry/Microcomputer Applications, A
Data Processing and Data Processing
  Technology/Technician, A
Dental Hygiene/Hygienist, A
Developmental and Child Psychology, A
Electrical, Electronic and Communications
  Engineering Technology/Technician, A
Engineering, A
Engineering Science, A
Engineering Technology, A
Finance, A
Fire Science/Firefighting, A
Funeral Service and Mortuary Science, A
Hotel/Motel Administration/Management, A
Human Services, A
Industrial Radiologic Technology/Technician, A
Industrial Technology/Technician, A
Information Technology, A
International Business/Trade/Commerce, A
Liberal Arts and Sciences Studies and
  Humanities, A
Mass Communication/Media Studies, A
Mathematics, A
Mechanical Engineering/Mechanical
  Technology/Technician, A
Music, A
Nursing - Registered Nurse Training, A
Photography, A
Pipefitting/Pipefitter and Sprinkler Fitter, A
Pre-Engineering, A
Respiratory Care Therapy/Therapist, A
Surgical Technology/Technologist, A
Tourism and Travel Services Management, A
Word Processing, A

ST. LOUIS COMMUNITY COLLEGE AT MERAMEC

Accounting, A
Administrative Assistant and Secretarial Science, A
Advertising, A
Architectural Engineering Technology/Technician, A
Art/Art Studies, General, A
Biological and Physical Sciences, A
Broadcast Journalism, A
Business Administration and Management, A
Child Development, A
Cinematography and Film/Video Production, A

Commercial and Advertising Art, A
Comparative Literature, A
Computer Programming/Programmer, A
Computer Science, A
Corrections, A
Court Reporting/Court Reporter, A
Creative Writing, A
Criminal Justice/Law Enforcement Administration, A
Criminal Justice/Police Science, A
Drama and Dramatics/Theatre Arts, A
Education, A
Electrical, Electronic and Communications
  Engineering Technology/Technician, A
Elementary Education and Teaching, A
Emergency Medical Technology/Technician (EMT
  Paramedic), A
Engineering Science, A
Finance, A
Horticultural Science, A
Human Services, A
Information Science/Studies, A
Interior Design, A
Journalism, A
Legal Administrative Assistant/Secretary, A
Legal Assistant/Paralegal, A
Liberal Arts and Sciences Studies and
  Humanities, A
Materials Sciences, A
Mathematics, A
Modern Languages, A
Music, A
Nursing - Registered Nurse Training, A
Occupational Therapy/Therapist, A
Photography, A
Physical Therapy/Therapist, A
Public Relations/Image Management, A
Real Estate, A
Speech and Rhetorical Studies, A

SAINT LOUIS UNIVERSITY

Accounting, M
Aeronautical/Aerospace Engineering
  Technology/Technician, B
Aerospace, Aeronautical and Astronautical
  Engineering, BM
Airline/Commercial/Professional Pilot and Flight
  Crew, B
Allied Health and Medical Assisting Services, MDO
Allopathic Medicine, MDP
American/United States Studies/Civilization, BMD
Anatomy, MD
Art History, Criticism and Conservation, B
Atmospheric Sciences and Meteorology, B
Aviation, M
Aviation/Airway Management and Operations, B
Biochemistry, BD
Bioethics/Medical Ethics, D
Biological and Biomedical Sciences, MD
Biology/Biological Sciences, B
Biomedical Engineering, MD
Biomedical/Medical Engineering, B
Business Administration and Management, B
Business Administration, Management and
  Operations, M
Chemistry, BM
City/Urban, Community and Regional Planning, B
Classics and Classical
  Languages, Literatures, and Linguistics, B
Clinical Laboratory Science/Medical
  Technology/Technologist, B
Clinical Psychology, MD
Clinical/Medical Laboratory Science and Allied
  Professions, B
Communication and Media Studies, M
Communication Disorders, M
Communication Studies/Speech Communication
  and Rhetoric, B
Communication, Journalism and Related
  Programs, B
Community Health and Preventive Medicine, M
Computer and Information Sciences, B
Computer and Information Sciences and Support
  Services, B
Corrections, B
Counselor Education/School Counseling and
  Guidance Services, MDO

Criminal Justice/Law Enforcement Administration, B
Criminal Justice/Police Science, B
Criminology, M
Curriculum and Instruction, MD
Drama and Dramatics/Theatre Arts, B
Economics, BM
Education, BMD
Educational Administration and Supervision, M
Educational Leadership and Administration, MDO
Electrical, Electronics and Communications
    Engineering, B
Engineering/Industrial Management, B
English, MD
English Language and Literature, B
Environmental Sciences, B
Experimental Psychology, MD
Finance and Banking, M
Fine/Studio Arts, B
Foods, Nutrition, and Wellness Studies, B
Foreign Languages and Literatures, B
Foundations and Philosophy of Education, MD
French Language and Literature, BM
Geology/Earth Science, BM
Geophysics and Seismology, BD
Geosciences, MD
German Language and Literature, B
Health Information/Medical Records
    Administration/Administrator, B
Health Services Administration, MD
Health/Health Care Administration/Management, B
Higher Education/Higher Education
    Administration, MDO
History, BMD
Human Development, M
Human Resources Management/Personnel
    Administration, B
Humanities/Humanistic Studies, B
Immunology, D
International Business/Trade/Commerce, BMD
International Relations and Affairs, B
Kinesiology and Exercise Science, B
Latin Language and Literature, B
Law and Legal Studies, MP
Management Information Systems and Services, B
Marketing/Marketing Management, B
Marriage and Family Therapy/Counseling, MDO
Mathematics, BMD
Mechanical Engineering, BM
Meteorology, BMD
Microbiology, D
Modern Greek Language and Literature, B
Molecular Biology, D
Music, B
Nuclear Medical Technology/Technologist, B
Nursing, MDO
Nursing - Registered Nurse Training, B
Nutritional Sciences, M
Occupational Therapy/Therapist, BM
Oral and Dental Sciences, M
Organizational Behavior Studies, B
Pathology/Experimental Pathology, D
Pharmacology, D
Philosophy, BMD
Physical Therapy/Therapist, BMD
Physician Assistant, BM
Physics, B
Physiology, D
Political Science and Government, B
Psychology, BMD
Public Administration, M
Public Health, MD
Public Policy Analysis, MD
Russian Language and Literature, B
Social Sciences, B
Social Work, BM
Sociology, BM
Spanish Language and Literature, BM
Special Education and Teaching, M
Student Personnel Services, M
Teacher Education, Multiple Levels, B
Theology and Religious Vocations, MD
Theology/Theological Studies, B
Urban Studies/Affairs, BM

Women's Studies, B

SAINT LUKE'S COLLEGE

Nursing - Registered Nurse Training, B

SANFORD-BROWN COLLEGE (FENTON)

Accounting, A
Computer Programming, Specific Applications, A
Computer
    Programming, Vendor/Product Certification, A
Computer Science, A
Legal Assistant/Paralegal, A
Radiologic Technology/Science - Radiographer, A
Respiratory Care Therapy/Therapist, A

SANFORD-BROWN COLLEGE (HAZELWOOD)

Accounting, A
Administrative Assistant and Secretarial Science, A
Business Administration and Management, A
Computer Programming/Programmer, A
Health Teacher Education, A
Legal Assistant/Paralegal, A
Physical Therapy/Therapist, A

SANFORD-BROWN COLLEGE (NORTH KANSAS CITY)

Medical/Clinical Assistant, A
Physical Therapy/Therapist, A

SANFORD-BROWN COLLEGE (ST. CHARLES)

Accounting, A
Administrative Assistant and Secretarial Science, A
Business Administration and Management, A
Computer Programming/Programmer, A
Data Processing and Data Processing
    Technology/Technician, A
Legal Assistant/Paralegal, A
Medical/Clinical Assistant, A
Nursing - Registered Nurse Training, A

SOUTHEAST MISSOURI STATE UNIVERSITY

Accounting, BM
Administrative Assistant and Secretarial Science, B
Agribusiness, B
Agriculture, B
American/United States Studies/Civilization, B
Anthropology, B
Art Education, M
Art Teacher Education, B
Art/Art Studies, General, B
Biological and Biomedical Sciences, M
Biology/Biological Sciences, B
Business Administration and Management, B
Business Administration, Management and
    Operations, M
Business Education, M
Business Teacher Education, B
Business/Managerial Economics, B
Chemistry, BM
Child Care and Support Services Management, A
Clinical Laboratory Science/Medical
    Technology/Technologist, A
Communication Disorders, BM
Communication Studies/Speech Communication
    and Rhetoric, B
Community Psychology, M
Computer and Information Sciences, B
Computer Programming/Programmer, B
Computer Technology/Computer Systems
    Technology, A
Construction Engineering Technology/Technician, B
Corrections, B
Counselor Education/School Counseling and
    Guidance Services, MO
Criminology, M
Drama and Dramatics/Theatre Arts, B
Economics, B
Educational Administration and Supervision, MO
Elementary Education and Teaching, BM
Engineering Physics, B

English, M
English as a Second Language, M
English Language and Literature, B
English/Language Arts Teacher Education, B
Environmental Policy and Resource
    Management, M
Environmental Studies, M
Exercise and Sports Science, M
Family and Consumer Sciences/Home Economics
    Teacher Education, B
Family and Consumer Sciences/Human Sciences, B
Finance, B
Finance and Banking, M
Foreign Language Teacher Education, B
Foundations and Philosophy of Education, M
French Language and Literature, B
General Studies, B
Geography, B
Geological and Earth Sciences/Geosciences, B
German Language and Literature, B
Health and Physical Education, B
History, BM
Home Economics, M
Humanities/Humanistic Studies, B
Industrial and Manufacturing Management, M
Industrial Technology/Technician, B
Interdisciplinary Studies, B
International Business/Trade/Commerce, M
Junior High/Intermediate/Middle School Education
    and Teaching, B
Kindergarten/PreSchool Education and Teaching, B
Leisure Studies, M
Marketing/Marketing Management, B
Mathematics, BM
Mathematics Teacher Education, B
Middle School Education, M
Multi-/Interdisciplinary Studies, B
Music, B
Music Teacher Education, BM
Nursing, M
Nursing - Registered Nurse Training, B
Nutritional Sciences, M
Office Management and Supervision, B
Parks, Recreation, Leisure and Fitness Studies, B
Philosophy, B
Physical Education Teaching and Coaching, B
Physics, B
Political Science and Government, B
Psychology, B
Public Administration, M
School Psychology, M
Science Teacher Education/General Science
    Teacher Education, BM
Secondary Education and Teaching, M
Social Studies Teacher Education, BM
Social Work, B
Sociology, B
Spanish Language and Literature, B
Special Education and Teaching, BM
Speech and Rhetorical Studies, B
Speech Teacher Education, B
Sport and Fitness Administration/Management, B
Technology Teacher Education/Industrial Arts
    Teacher Education, B
Visual and Performing Arts, B

SOUTHWEST BAPTIST UNIVERSITY

Accounting, AB
Art Teacher Education, B
Art/Art Studies, General, B
Athletic Training and Sports Medicine, B
Bible/Biblical Studies, B
Biology/Biological Sciences, B
Business Administration, Management and
    Operations, M
Business/Commerce, A
Chemistry, B
Chemistry Teacher Education, B
Clinical Laboratory Science/Medical
    Technology/Technologist, B
Commercial and Advertising Art, B
Communication Studies/Speech Communication
    and Rhetoric, B
Computer Science, AB
Drama and Dramatics/Theatre Arts, B
Education, MO

Educational Administration and Supervision, MO
Elementary Education and Teaching, B
Emergency Medical Technology/Technician (EMT Paramedic), A
English Language and Literature, B
English/Language Arts Teacher Education, B
General Studies, A
Health Services Administration, M
History, B
Human Services, B
Junior High/Intermediate/Middle School Education and Teaching, B
Mathematics, B
Mathematics Teacher Education, B
Music, B
Music Teacher Education, B
Nursing - Registered Nurse Training, A
Occupational Safety and Health Technology/Technician, AB
Parks, Recreation, Leisure and Fitness Studies, B
Pastoral Studies/Counseling, B
Physical Education Teaching and Coaching, B
Physical Therapy/Therapist, MD
Political Science and Government, B
Psychology, B
Religion/Religious Studies, B
Science Teacher Education/General Science Teacher Education, B
Social Science Teacher Education, B
Sociology, B
Spanish Language and Literature, B
Speech Teacher Education, B
Sport and Fitness Administration/Management, B

SPRINGFIELD COLLEGE

Accounting, A
Administrative Assistant and Secretarial Science, A
Business Administration and Management, A
Data Processing and Data Processing Technology/Technician, A
Hospitality Administration/Management, A
Legal Assistant/Paralegal, A
Medical/Clinical Assistant, A

STATE FAIR COMMUNITY COLLEGE

Accounting, A
Administrative Assistant and Secretarial Science, A
Agricultural Business and Management, A
Agricultural Mechanization, A
Agriculture, A
Art/Art Studies, General, A
Automobile/Automotive Mechanics Technology/Technician, A
Business Administration and Management, A
Computer and Information Sciences, A
Computer Engineering Technology/Technician, A
Computer Programming, Specific Applications, A
Computer Systems Networking and Telecommunications, A
Construction Engineering Technology/Technician, A
Court Reporting/Court Reporter, A
Criminal Justice/Law Enforcement Administration, A
Electrical, Electronic and Communications Engineering Technology/Technician, A
Finance, A
Health Information/Medical Records Administration/Administrator, A
Horticultural Science, A
Industrial Technology/Technician, A
Information Science/Studies, A
Legal Administrative Assistant/Secretary, A
Liberal Arts and Sciences Studies and Humanities, A
Licensed Practical/Vocational Nurse Training, A
Machine Tool Technology/Machinist, A
Marketing/Marketing Management, A
Mass Communication/Media Studies, A
Medical Administrative Assistant/Secretary, A
Nursing - Registered Nurse Training, A
Special Products Marketing Operations, A

STEPHENS COLLEGE

Accounting, B
Advertising, B
Biology/Biological Sciences, B
Biomedical Sciences, B

Broadcast Journalism, B
Business Administration and Management, B
Business Administration, Management and Operations, M
Child Development, B
Counselor Education/School Counseling and Guidance Services, M
Creative Writing, B
Dance, B
Drama and Dramatics/Theatre Arts, B
Early Childhood Education and Teaching, B
Elementary Education and Teaching, B
English Language and Literature, B
Environmental Studies, B
Equestrian/Equine Studies, B
Fashion Merchandising, B
Fashion/Apparel Design, B
Health Services Administration, O
Horse Husbandry/Equine Science and Management, B
Interdisciplinary Studies, B
International Relations and Affairs, B
Kindergarten/PreSchool Education and Teaching, B
Liberal Arts and Sciences Studies and Humanities, AB
Marketing/Marketing Management, B
Mass Communication/Media Studies, B
Modern Languages, B
Natural Sciences, B
Occupational Therapy/Therapist, B
Philosophy, B
Political Science and Government, B
Pre-Law Studies, B
Pre-Medicine/Pre-Medical Studies, B
Pre-Veterinary Studies, B
Psychology, B
Public Relations/Image Management, B
Radio and Television, B

THREE RIVERS COMMUNITY COLLEGE

Accounting, A
Administrative Assistant and Secretarial Science, A
Agricultural Business and Management, A
Agricultural Mechanization, A
Business Administration and Management, A
Clinical/Medical Laboratory Technician, A
Computer and Information Sciences, A
Computer Engineering Technology/Technician, A
Construction Engineering Technology/Technician, A
Criminal Justice/Law Enforcement Administration, A
Criminal Justice/Police Science, A
Data Entry/Microcomputer Applications, A
Education, A
Elementary Education and Teaching, A
Engineering Technology, A
Industrial Technology/Technician, A
Information Technology, A
Liberal Arts and Sciences Studies and Humanities, A
Management Information Systems and Services, A
Marketing/Marketing Management, A
Music, A
Nursing - Registered Nurse Training, A
Word Processing, A

TRUMAN STATE UNIVERSITY

Accounting, BM
Agricultural Business and Management, B
Agricultural Economics, B
Agriculture, B
Agronomy and Crop Science, B
Animal Sciences, B
Applied Art, B
Art History, Criticism and Conservation, B
Art/Art Studies, General, B
Biological and Biomedical Sciences, M
Biology/Biological Sciences, B
Business Administration and Management, B
Chemistry, B
Classics and Classical Languages, Literatures, and Linguistics, B
Commercial and Advertising Art, B
Communication Disorders, BM
Communication Studies/Speech Communication and Rhetoric, B
Computer Science, B

Counselor Education/School Counseling and Guidance Services, M
Criminal Justice/Law Enforcement Administration, B
Criminal Justice/Police Science, B
Design and Visual Communications, B
Drama and Dramatics/Theatre Arts, B
Economics, B
Education, M
English, M
English Language and Literature, B
Equestrian/Equine Studies, B
Finance, B
Fine/Studio Arts, B
French Language and Literature, B
German Language and Literature, B
History, B
Horticultural Science, B
Journalism, B
Kinesiology and Exercise Science, B
Mass Communication/Media Studies, B
Mathematics, B
Music, BM
Music Performance, B
Nursing - Registered Nurse Training, B
Philosophy, B
Physics, B
Piano and Organ, B
Political Science and Government, B
Pre-Dentistry Studies, B
Pre-Law Studies, B
Pre-Medicine/Pre-Medical Studies, B
Pre-Pharmacy Studies, B
Pre-Veterinary Studies, B
Psychology, B
Public Health (MPH, DPH), B
Religion/Religious Studies, B
Russian Language and Literature, B
Sociology, B
Spanish Language and Literature, B
Speech and Rhetorical Studies, B
Voice and Opera, B

UNIVERSITY OF MISSOURI-COLUMBIA

Accounting, BMD
Adult and Continuing Education and Teaching, MDO
Advertising, B
Aerospace, Aeronautical and Astronautical Engineering, MD
Agricultural Business and Management, B
Agricultural Communication/Journalism, B
Agricultural Economics, BMD
Agricultural Education, MDO
Agricultural Engineering, MD
Agricultural Mechanization, B
Agricultural Sciences, MDO
Agricultural Teacher Education, B
Agriculture, B
Agronomy and Soil Sciences, MD
Allopathic Medicine, PO
Analytical Chemistry, MD
Animal Sciences, BMD
Anthropology, BMD
Apparel and Textiles, B
Applied Mathematics, M
Archeology, BMD
Architecture, M
Art Education, MDO
Art History, Criticism and Conservation, BMD
Art Teacher Education, B
Art/Art Studies, General, B
Astronomy, MD
Atmospheric Sciences and Meteorology, BMD
Behavioral Sciences, B
Biochemistry, BMD
Bioengineering, MD
Biological and Biomedical Sciences, MDO
Biology Teacher Education, B
Biology/Biological Sciences, B
Biopsychology, MD
Broadcast Journalism, B
Business Administration and Management, B
Business Administration, Management and Operations, MD
Business Education, MDO
Business Teacher Education, B
Business/Managerial Economics, B

Cell Biology and Anatomy, MD
Central/Middle and Eastern European Studies, B
Chemical Engineering, BMD
Chemistry, BMD
Chemistry Teacher Education, B
Child and Family Studies, MD
Civil Engineering, BMD
Classics and Classical
 Languages, Literatures, and Linguistics, BMD
Clothing and Textiles, M
Communication and Media Studies, MD
Communication Disorders, M
Communication Disorders Sciences and Services, B
Communication Studies/Speech Communication
 and Rhetoric, B
Community Health and Preventive Medicine, MO
Comparative Literature, M
Computer and Information Sciences, B
Computer Art and Design, M
Computer Engineering, B
Computer Science, BMD
Conflict Resolution and Mediation/Peace Studies, M
Consumer Economics, M
Counseling Psychology, MDO
Curriculum and Instruction, MDO
Diagnostic Medical Sonography/Sonographer and
 Ultrasound Technician, B
Dietetics/Dieticians, B
Drama and Dramatics/Theatre Arts, B
Early Childhood Education and Teaching, BMDO
East Asian Studies, B
Ecology, MD
Economics, BMDO
Education, BMDO
Education/Teaching of the Gifted and Talented, MD
Educational Administration and Supervision, MDO
Educational Media/Instructional Technology, MDO
Educational Psychology, MDO
Electrical Engineering, MD
Electrical, Electronics and Communications
 Engineering, B
Elementary Education and Teaching, BMDO
Engineering and Applied Sciences, MD
English, MD
English Education, MDO
English Language and Literature, B
Entomology, MD
Environmental Design/Architecture, M
Environmental Engineering
 Technology/Environmental Technology, MD
Environmental Studies, B
European Studies/Civilization, B
Evolutionary Biology, MD
Exercise and Sports Science, MD
Family and Consumer Economics and Related
 Services, B
Finance, B
Fine Arts and Art Studies, M
Fish, Game and Wildlife Management, MD
Fishing and Fisheries Sciences and Management, B
Food Science, B
Food Science and Technology, MD
Foods, Nutrition, and Wellness Studies, B
Foreign Language Teacher Education, MDO
Forestry, BMD
French Language and Literature, BMD
General Studies, B
Genetics, D
Geography, BM
Geology/Earth Science, BMD
Geotechnical Engineering, MD
German Language and Literature, BM
Health Education, MD
Health Informatics, M
Health Physics/Radiological Health, M
Health Services Administration, M
Health/Medical Preparatory Programs, B
Higher Education/Higher Education
 Administration, MDO
History, BMD
Home Economics, MD
Horticultural Science, MD
Hotel/Motel Administration/Management, B
Housing and Human Environments, B
Human Development, MD
Human Development and Family Studies, B

Human Nutrition, B
Immunology, MD
Industrial Engineering, B
Industrial/Management Engineering, MD
Information Science/Studies, MDO
Inorganic Chemistry, MD
Interdisciplinary Studies, B
Interior Architecture, B
International Agriculture, B
International Business/Trade/Commerce, B
International Economics, B
Journalism, BMD
Junior High/Intermediate/Middle School Education
 and Teaching, B
Kindergarten/PreSchool Education and Teaching, B
Latin American Studies, B
Latin Language and Literature, B
Law and Legal Studies, MPO
Library Science, MDO
Linguistics, B
Management Information Systems and Services, B
Manufacturing Engineering, MD
Marketing/Marketing Management, B
Mass Communication/Media Studies, B
Mathematics, BMD
Mathematics Teacher Education, BMDO
Mechanical Engineering, BMD
Medical Radiologic Technology/Science - Radiation
 Therapist, B
Microbiology, BMD
Modern Greek Language and Literature, B
Molecular Biology, MD
Music, BM
Music Teacher Education, BMDO
Natural Resources and Conservation, B
Neurobiology and Neurophysiology, MD
Nuclear Engineering, MD
Nuclear Medical Technology/Technologist, B
Nursing, MD
Nursing - Registered Nurse Training, B
Nutritional Sciences, BMD
Occupational Therapy/Therapist, B
Organic Chemistry, MD
Parks, Recreation, Leisure and Fitness Studies, B
Pathobiology, MD
Peace Studies and Conflict Resolution, B
Pharmacology, MD
Philosophy, BMD
Photojournalism, B
Physical Chemistry, MD
Physical Therapy/Therapist, M
Physics, BMD
Physics Teacher Education, B
Physiology, MD
Plant Biology, MD
Plant Pathology/Phytopathology, MD
Plant Sciences, B
Political Science and Government, BMD
Psychology, BMD
Public Affairs, M
Publishing, B
Radio and Television, B
Radiologic Technology/Science - Radiographer, B
Reading Teacher Education, MDO
Real Estate, B
Recreation and Park Management, M
Religion/Religious Studies, BM
Respiratory Care Therapy/Therapist, B
Restaurant/Food Services Management, B
Romance
 Languages, Literatures, and Linguistics, MD
Rural Sociology, MD
Russian Language and Literature, B
Russian Studies, B
School Psychology, MDO
Science Teacher Education/General Science
 Teacher Education, BMDO
Secondary Education and Teaching, B
Social Studies Teacher Education, BMDO
Social Work, BM
Sociology, BMD
South Asian Studies, B
Spanish Language and Literature, BMD
Special Education and Teaching, BMD
Statistics, BMD
Structural Engineering, MD

Technical Teacher Education, B
Theater, MD
Tourism and Travel Services Marketing
 Operations, B
Transportation and Highway Engineering, M
Veterinary Medicine, P
Veterinary Sciences, MD
Vocational and Technical Education, MDO
Water Resources Engineering, MD

UNIVERSITY OF MISSOURI-KANSAS CITY

Accounting, BM
Allopathic Medicine, PO
American/United States Studies/Civilization, B
Analytical Chemistry, MD
Art History, Criticism and Conservation, BMD
Art/Art Studies, General, B
Biochemistry, D
Biological and Biomedical Sciences, M
Biology/Biological Sciences, B
Biophysics, D
Business Administration and Management, B
Business Administration, Management and
 Operations, MDO
Cell Biology and Anatomy, MD
Chemistry, BMD
Civil Engineering, BM
Clinical/Medical Laboratory Technician, B
Communication Studies/Speech Communication
 and Rhetoric, B
Composition, MD
Computer Engineering, D
Computer Science, BMD
Counseling Psychology, MDO
Criminal Justice/Law Enforcement Administration, B
Criminology, BMD
Curriculum and Instruction, MO
Dance, B
Dental and Oral Surgery, O
Dental Hygiene/Hygienist, BM
Dentistry, MDPO
Drama and Dramatics/Theatre Arts, B
Early Childhood Education and Teaching, B
Economics, BMD
Education, MDO
Educational Administration and Supervision, D
Electrical Engineering, MD
Electrical, Electronics and Communications
 Engineering, B
Elementary Education and Teaching, B
Engineering and Applied Sciences, MD
English, MD
English Language and Literature, B
Fine Arts and Art Studies, MD
Fine/Studio Arts, B
French Language and Literature, B
Geography, B
Geology/Earth Science, BM
Geosciences, MD
German Language and Literature, B
History, BMD
Information Technology, B
Inorganic Chemistry, MD
Interdisciplinary Studies, BD
Junior High/Intermediate/Middle School Education
 and Teaching, B
Law and Legal Studies, MPO
Liberal Arts and Sciences Studies and
 Humanities, B
Mass Communication/Media Studies, B
Maternal/Child Health and Neonatal
 Nurse/Nursing, M
Mathematics, BMD
Mechanical Engineering, BM
Molecular Biology, MD
Music, BMD
Music History, Literature, and Theory, M
Music Performance, B
Music Teacher Education, BMD
Music Theory and Composition, BM
Nursing, MD
Nursing - Adult, M
Nursing - Advanced Practice, M
Nursing - Registered Nurse Training, B
Nursing Administration, M

Nursing Education, M
Oral and Dental Sciences, O
Oral Biology, MD
Organic Chemistry, MD
Orthodontics, O
Pediatric Nurse/Nursing, M
Pedodontics, O
Performance, MD
Periodontics, O
Pharmaceutical Sciences, MD
Pharmacy, BMDP
Philosophy, B
Physical Chemistry, MD
Physics, BMD
Political Science and Government, BMD
Polymer/Plastics Engineering, MD
Psychology, B
Public Administration, MDO
Public Affairs, MD
Reading Teacher Education, MO
Romance
   Languages, Literatures, and Linguistics, M
Secondary Education and Teaching, B
Social Work, M
Sociology, BMD
Spanish Language and Literature, B
Special Education and Teaching, M
Statistics, BMD
Telecommunications, D
Theater, M
Urban Education and Leadership, B
Urban Studies/Affairs, B

UNIVERSITY OF MISSOURI-ROLLA

Aerospace, Aeronautical and Astronautical
   Engineering, BMD
Agricultural/Biological Engineering and
   Bioengineering, B
Applied Mathematics, BM
Architectural Engineering, B
Biological and Biomedical Sciences, M
Biology/Biological Sciences, B
Business Administration and Management, B
Business/Commerce, B
Ceramic Sciences and Engineering, BMD
Chemical Engineering, BMD
Chemistry, BMD
Civil Engineering, BMD
Computer and Information Sciences and Support
   Services, B
Computer Engineering, BMD
Computer Science, BMD
Construction Engineering and Management, MD
Economics, B
Electrical Engineering, MD
Electrical, Electronics and Communications
   Engineering, B
Engineering and Applied Sciences, MD
Engineering Management, MD
Engineering/Industrial Management, B
English Language and Literature, B
Environmental Biology, M
Environmental Engineering
   Technology/Environmental Technology, MD
Environmental/Environmental Health Engineering, B
Geochemistry, MD
Geological Engineering, MD
Geological/Geophysical Engineering, B
Geology/Earth Science, BMD
Geophysics and Seismology, BMD
Geotechnical Engineering, MD
History, B
Hydraulics and Fluid Power Technology, MD
Hydrology and Water Resources Science, MD
Industrial Engineering, B
Information Science/Studies, BM
Manufacturing Engineering, BM
Materials Engineering, B
Mathematics, MD
Mathematics Teacher Education, M
Mechanical Engineering, BMD
Mechanics, MD
Metallurgical Engineering, BMD
Mineral/Mining Engineering, MD
Mining and Mineral Engineering, B
Nuclear Engineering, BMD

Petroleum Engineering, BMD
Philosophy, B
Physics, BMD
Pre-Dentistry Studies, B
Pre-Law Studies, B
Pre-Medicine/Pre-Medical Studies, B
Psychology, B
Science Teacher Education/General Science
   Teacher Education, M
Secondary Education and Teaching, B
Structural Engineering, MD
Systems Engineering, BM
Water Resources, MD

UNIVERSITY OF MISSOURI-ST. LOUIS

Accounting, BMO
Adult and Continuing Education and Teaching, MD
Anthropology, B
Applied Mathematics, BMD
Applied Physics, M
Art History, Criticism and Conservation, B
Astrophysics, M
Biochemistry, MD
Biological and Biomedical Sciences, MDO
Biological Anthropology, D
Biology Teacher Education, B
Biology/Biological Sciences, B
BioTechnology, O
Business Administration and Management, B
Business Administration, Management and
   Operations, MO
Business Teacher Education, B
Business/Commerce, B
Chemistry, BMD
Chemistry Teacher Education, B
Civil Engineering, B
Clinical Laboratory Science/Medical
   Technology/Technologist, B
Clinical Psychology, DO
Communication and Media Studies, M
Communication Studies/Speech Communication
   and Rhetoric, B
Comparative Literature, B
Computer and Information Sciences, B
Computer Science, BMDO
Conflict Resolution and Mediation/Peace Studies, M
Conservation Biology, O
Counselor Education/School Counseling and
   Guidance Services, MD
Criminology, BMD
Curriculum and Instruction, M
Drawing, B
Early Childhood Education and Teaching, B
Economics, BMO
Education, BMDO
Educational Administration and Supervision, MDO
Educational Leadership and Administration, D
Educational Measurement and Evaluation, DO
Educational Psychology, DO
Electrical, Electronics and Communications
   Engineering, B
Electronic Commerce, O
Elementary Education and Teaching, BM
English, M
English Language and Literature, B
English/Language Arts Teacher Education, B
Experimental Psychology, D
Finance, B
Finance and Banking, M
Fine/Studio Arts, B
French Language and Literature, B
French Language Teacher Education, B
General Studies, B
German Language and Literature, B
German Language Teacher Education, B
Gerontology, MO
Graphic Design, B
Health Services Administration, M
Higher Education/Higher Education
   Administration, DO
History, BM
Human Resources Management and Services, MO
Industrial and Organizational Psychology, D
International Business/Trade/Commerce, B
Liberal Arts and Sciences Studies and
   Humanities, B

Linguistics, M
Logistics and Materials Management, O
Management, M
Management Information Systems and
   Services, BMDO
Management Science, B
Marketing, MO
Marketing/Marketing Management, B
Mass Communication/Media Studies, B
Mathematics, BMDO
Mathematics Teacher Education, B
Mechanical Engineering, B
Museology/Museum Studies, MO
Music, B
Music Performance, B
Music Teacher Education, BM
Non-Profit/Public/Organizational Management, MO
Nursing, MD
Nursing - Registered Nurse Training, B
Optometry, P
Painting, B
Philosophy, BM
Photography, B
Physical Education Teaching and Coaching, B
Physics, BMD
Physics Teacher Education, B
Political Science and Government, BMD
Pre-Dentistry Studies, B
Pre-Law Studies, B
Pre-Medicine/Pre-Medical Studies, B
Pre-Pharmacy Studies, B
Pre-Veterinary Studies, B
Printmaking, B
Psychology, BMDO
Psychology Teacher Education, B
Public Administration, BMO
Public Policy Analysis, MO
Quantitative Analysis, M
Reading Teacher Education, M
School Psychology, O
Secondary Education and Teaching, BM
Social Studies Teacher Education, B
Social Work, BMO
Sociology, BM
Spanish Language and Literature, B
Spanish Language Teacher Education, B
Special Education and Teaching, BM
Taxation, MO
Telecommunications Management, O
Vision Science/Physiological Optics, MD
Writing, M

UNIVERSITY OF PHOENIX-KANSAS CITY CAMPUS

Business Administration and Management, B
Business Administration, Management and
   Operations, M
Business, Management, Marketing, and Related
   Support Services, B
Computer and Information Sciences, B
Electronic Commerce, M
Entrepreneurship/Entrepreneurial Studies, B
Health/Health Care Administration/Management, B
Management of Technology, M
Organizational Management, M
Public Administration and Social Service
   Professions, B

UNIVERSITY OF PHOENIX-ST. LOUIS CAMPUS

Business Administration and Management, B
Business Administration, Management and
   Operations, M
Corrections and Criminal Justice, B
Electronic Commerce, M
Health Services Administration, M
Information Technology, B

Organizational Management, M

UNIVERSITY OF PHOENIX-SPRINGFIELD CAMPUS

Business Administration and Management, B
Information Technology, B

VATTEROTT COLLEGE (ST. ANN)

CAD/CADD Drafting and/or Design
    Technology/Technician, A
Computer Engineering, A
Computer Programming/Programmer, A
Electrical and Power Transmission Installers, A
Electrical, Electronic and Communications
    Engineering Technology/Technician, A
Heating, Air Conditioning and Refrigeration
    Technology/Technician, A
Medical Office Assistant/Specialist, A
Plumbing Technology/Plumber, A
Welding Technology/Welder, A

VATTEROTT COLLEGE (ST. JOSEPH)

Administrative Assistant and Secretarial Science, A
Computer Systems Networking and
    Telecommunications, A
Computer Technology/Computer Systems
    Technology, A
Medical/Clinical Assistant, A

VATTEROTT COLLEGE (SPRINGFIELD)

CAD/CADD Drafting and/or Design
    Technology/Technician, A
Computer Programming/Programmer, A
Medical/Clinical Assistant, A
Pharmacy Technician/Assistant, A
System, Networking, and LAN/WAN
    Management/Manager, A

WASHINGTON UNIVERSITY IN ST. LOUIS

Accounting, B
Advertising, B
Aerospace, Aeronautical and Astronautical
    Engineering, B
African Studies, B
African-American/Black Studies, B
Allied Health and Medical Assisting Services, MDO
Allopathic Medicine, PO
American Literature (United States), B
American/United States Studies/Civilization, B
Ancient/Classical Greek Language and Literature, B
Anthropology, BMD
Applied Art, B
Applied Mathematics, B
Arabic Language and Literature, B
Archeology, BMD
Architectural Engineering Technology/Technician, B
Architectural Technology/Technician, B
Architecture, BMO
Architecture and Related Services, B
Area Studies, B
Area, Ethnic, Cultural, and Gender Studies, B
Art History, Criticism and Conservation, BMD
Art Teacher Education, B
Art/Art Studies, General, B
Asian Languages, MDO
Asian Studies/Civilization, BMDO
Biochemistry, BD
Biological and Biomedical Sciences, BDO
Biological and Physical Sciences, B
Biology Teacher Education, B
Biology/Biological Sciences, B
Biomedical Engineering, MDO
Biomedical/Medical Engineering, B
Biophysics, B
Biopsychology, B
Business Administration and Management, B
Business Administration, Management and
    Operations, BMDO
Business/Commerce, B
Business/Managerial Economics, B
Cell Biology and Anatomy, D
Ceramic Arts and Ceramics, BM
Chemical Engineering, BMD
Chemistry, BMD

Chemistry Teacher Education, B
Chinese Language and Literature, B
Chinese Studies, MD
Civil Engineering, BMDO
Civil Engineering Technology/Technician, B
Classics and Classical
    Languages, Literatures, and Linguistics, BM
Clinical Psychology, D
Cognitive Psychology and Psycholinguistics, B
Commercial and Advertising Art, B
Communication Disorders, MD
Communication Studies/Speech Communication
    and Rhetoric, B
Communication, Journalism and Related
    Programs, B
Comparative Literature, BMD
Computational Biology, D
Computer and Information Sciences, B
Computer and Information Sciences and Support
    Services, B
Computer Engineering, BMD
Computer Science, BMD
Computer/Information Technology Services
    Administration and Management, B
Construction Engineering and Management, MO
Creative Writing, B
Dance, B
Design and Visual Communications, B
Developmental Biology and Embryology, D
Drama and Dance Teacher Education, B
Drama and Dramatics/Theatre Arts, B
Drawing, B
East Asian
    Languages, Literatures, and Linguistics, B
East Asian Studies, B
Ecology, D
Economics, BMDO
Education, BMD
Educational Measurement and Evaluation, D
Electrical Engineering, MD
Electrical, Electronics and Communications
    Engineering, B
Elementary Education and Teaching, BM
Engineering, B
Engineering and Applied Sciences, MDO
Engineering Physics, B
Engineering Science, B
English, MD
English Language and Literature, B
English Literature (British and Commonwealth), B
English/Language Arts Teacher Education, B
Entrepreneurship/Entrepreneurial Studies, B
Environmental Biology, D
Environmental Studies, B
Ethnic and Cultural Studies, B
Ethnic, Cultural Minority, and Gender Studies, B
European Studies/Civilization, B
Evolutionary Biology, D
Experimental Psychology, MD
Fashion/Apparel Design, B
Film/Cinema Studies, B
Finance, B
Fine Arts and Art Studies, M
Fine/Studio Arts, B
French Language and Literature, BMD
French Language Teacher Education, B
General Merchandising, Sales, and Related
    Marketing Operations, B
Genetics, MDO
Geochemistry, D
Geology/Earth Science, BMD
Geophysics and Seismology, D
Geosciences, MD
German Language and Literature, BMD
German Language Teacher Education, B
Germanic Languages, Literatures, and Linguistics, B
Graphic Design, B
Health Professions and Related Clinical Sciences, B
Health Services Administration, MO
Hebrew Language and Literature, B
History, BMD
History Teacher Education, B
Human Resources Management/Personnel
    Administration, B
Humanities/Humanistic Studies, B
Illustration, B

Immunology, D
Industrial and Organizational Psychology, B
Information Science/Studies, B
Interdisciplinary Studies, B
International Business/Trade/Commerce, B
International Economics, B
International Finance, B
International Relations and Affairs, B
Islamic Studies, B
Italian Language and Literature, B
Japanese Language and Literature, B
Japanese Studies, MD
Jewish/Judaic Studies, BM
Junior High/Intermediate/Middle School Education
    and Teaching, B
Kinesiology and Movement Studies, D
Latin American Studies, B
Latin Language and Literature, B
Law and Legal Studies, MDPO
Liberal Arts and Sciences Studies and
    Humanities, B
Marketing, B
Marketing/Marketing Management, B
Mathematics, BMD
Mathematics and Computer Science, B
Mathematics Teacher Education, BM
Mechanical Engineering, BMD
Medieval and Renaissance Studies, B
Microbiology, D
Modern Languages, B
Molecular Biology, D
Molecular Biophysics, D
Molecular Genetics, D
Multi-/Interdisciplinary Studies, B
Music, BMD
Music History, Literature, and Theory, B
Music Theory and Composition, B
Natural Resources and Conservation, B
Natural Sciences, B
Near and Middle Eastern Studies, BM
Neuroscience, BD
Occupational Therapy/Therapist, MD
Operations Management and Supervision, B
Painting, BM
Philosophy, BMD
Philosophy and Religious Studies, B
Photography, BM
Physical Therapy/Therapist, DO
Physics, BMD
Physics Teacher Education, B
Planetary Astronomy and Science, MD
Plant Biology, D
Political Science and Government, BMDO
Pre-Dentistry Studies, B
Pre-Medicine/Pre-Medical Studies, B
Pre-Pharmacy Studies, B
Pre-Veterinary Studies, B
Printmaking, BM
Psychology, BMD
Public Policy Analysis, M
Religion/Religious Studies, BM
Romance
    Languages, Literatures, and Linguistics, BMD
Russian Language and Literature, B
Russian Studies, B
Science Teacher Education/General Science
    Teacher Education, B
Science, Technology and Society, B
Sculpture, BM
Secondary Education and Teaching, BM
Social and Philosophical Foundations of
    Education, B
Social Psychology, MD
Social Science Teacher Education, B
Social Sciences, B
Social Studies Teacher Education, B
Social Work, MDO
Spanish Language and Literature, BMD
Spanish Language Teacher Education, B
Special Education and Teaching, M
Speech and Interpersonal Communication, D
Statistics, BMD
Structural Engineering, MD
Systems Engineering, BD
Systems Science and Theory, BMD

Teacher Education and Professional
  Development, Specific Levels and Methods, B
Teacher Education, Multiple Levels, B
Theater, M
Theatre Literature, History and Criticism, B
Transportation and Highway Engineering, D
Urban Design, MO
Urban Studies/Affairs, B
Voice and Opera, B
Women's Studies, B
Writing, M

WEBSTER UNIVERSITY

Accounting, B
Advertising, B
Aerospace, Aeronautical and Astronautical
  Engineering, M
Anthropology, B
Art History, Criticism and Conservation, B
Art Therapy/Therapist, B
Art/Art Studies, General, B
Arts Management, M
Biology/Biological Sciences, B
Broadcast Journalism, B
Business Administration and Management, B
Business Administration, Management and
  Operations, M
Business/Commerce, B
Cinematography and Film/Video Production, B
Communication and Media Studies, M
Communication, Journalism and Related
  Programs, B
Comparative Literature, B
Composition, M
Computer Science, BMO
Counseling Psychology, M
Dance, B
Drama and Dramatics/Theatre Arts, B
Early Childhood Education and Teaching, M
Economics, B
Education, BMO
Educational Leadership and Administration, O
Educational Media/Instructional Technology, M
Elementary Education and Teaching, B
English Language and Literature, B
Environmental Policy and Resource
  Management, M
Environmental Studies, B
Film/Cinema Studies, B
Finance and Banking, M
Fine Arts and Art Studies, M
Fine/Studio Arts, B
French Language and Literature, B
German Language and Literature, B
Gerontology, M
Health Services Administration, M
History, B
Human Resources Development, M
Human Resources Management and Services, M
Human Resources Management/Personnel
  Administration, B
Information Science/Studies, B
Interdisciplinary Studies, B
International Affairs, M
International Business/Trade/Commerce, BM
International Relations and Affairs, B
Journalism, B
Law and Legal Studies, B
Legal and Justice Studies, MO
Liberal Arts and Sciences Studies and
  Humanities, B
Management, MD
Management Information Systems and
  Services, BMO
Marketing, M
Marketing/Marketing Management, B
Mathematics, B
Mathematics Teacher Education, M
Media Studies, M
Music, BM
Music Performance, B
Music Teacher Education, BM
Music Theory and Composition, B
Nurse Anesthetist, BM
Nursing, M
Nursing - Registered Nurse Training, B

Performance, M
Philosophy, B
Photography, B
Political Science and Government, B
Psychology, B
Public Administration, M
Public Relations/Image Management, B
Radio and Television, B
Real Estate, M
Religion/Religious Studies, B
Sacred Music, M
Science Teacher Education/General Science
  Teacher Education, M
Securities Services Administration/Management, M
Social Sciences, B
Social Studies Teacher Education, M
Spanish Language and Literature, B
Special Education and Teaching, M
Technical and Business Writing, B
Technical Theatre/Theatre Design and
  Technology, B
Telecommunications Management, M

WENTWORTH MILITARY ACADEMY AND JUNIOR COLLEGE

Liberal Arts and Sciences Studies and
  Humanities, A

WESTMINSTER COLLEGE

Accounting, B
Anthropology, B
Biology/Biological Sciences, B
Business Administration and Management, B
Chemistry, B
Computer Science, B
Economics, B
Elementary Education and Teaching, B
English Language and Literature, B
Environmental Sciences, B
Environmental Studies, B
French Language and Literature, B
History, B
International Business/Trade/Commerce, B
International Relations and Affairs, B
Junior High/Intermediate/Middle School Education
  and Teaching, B
Management Information Systems and Services, B
Mathematics, B
Philosophy, B
Physical Education Teaching and Coaching, B
Physics, B
Political Science and Government, B
Pre-Law Studies, B
Psychology, B
Religion/Religious Studies, B
Secondary Education and Teaching, B
Sociology, B
Spanish Language and Literature, B

WILLIAM JEWELL COLLEGE

Accounting, B
Art/Art Studies, General, B
Biochemistry, B
Biology/Biological Sciences, B
Business Administration and Management, B
Cell/Cellular Biology and Histology, B
Chemistry, B
Clinical Laboratory Science/Medical
  Technology/Technologist, B
Computer Science, B
Drama and Dance Teacher Education, B
Drama and Dramatics/Theatre Arts, B
Economics, B
Education, B
Elementary Education and Teaching, B
English Language and Literature, B
French Language and Literature, B
History, B
Information Science/Studies, B
Interdisciplinary Studies, B
International Business/Trade/Commerce, B
International Relations and Affairs, B
Mathematics, B
Molecular Biology, B
Music, B
Music Performance, B

Music Teacher Education, B
Music Theory and Composition, B
Nursing - Registered Nurse Training, B
Philosophy, B
Physics, B
Political Science and Government, B
Pre-Dentistry Studies, B
Pre-Law Studies, B
Pre-Medicine/Pre-Medical Studies, B
Pre-Veterinary Studies, B
Psychology, B
Religion/Religious Studies, B
Religious/Sacred Music, B
Secondary Education and Teaching, B
Spanish Language and Literature, B
Speech and Rhetorical Studies, B
Speech Teacher Education, B

WILLIAM WOODS UNIVERSITY

Accounting, BM
Advertising, B
Art Teacher Education, B
Art/Art Studies, General, B
Athletic Training and Sports Medicine, B
Biology/Biological Sciences, B
Broadcast Journalism, B
Business Administration and Management, B
Business Administration, Management and
  Operations, M
Business/Managerial Economics, B
Commercial and Advertising Art, B
Communication Studies/Speech Communication
  and Rhetoric, B
Comparative Literature, B
Computer and Information Sciences, B
Curriculum and Instruction, M
Design and Visual Communications, B
Drama and Dramatics/Theatre Arts, B
Education, BMO
Educational Administration and Supervision, M
Elementary Education and Teaching, B
English Composition, B
English Language and Literature, B
English/Language Arts Teacher Education, B
Equestrian/Equine Studies, B
Fine/Studio Arts, B
French Language Teacher Education, B
Health Services Administration, M
History, B
Human Resources Development, M
Interdisciplinary Studies, B
Interior Design, B
International Business/Trade/Commerce, B
International Relations and Affairs, B
Junior High/Intermediate/Middle School Education
  and Teaching, B
Legal Assistant/Paralegal, AB
Management Information Systems and Services, B
Mathematics, B
Mathematics Teacher Education, B
Physical Education Teaching and Coaching, B
Political Science and Government, B
Psychology, B
Public Relations/Image Management, B
Radio and Television, B
Science Teacher Education/General Science
  Teacher Education, B
Secondary Education and Teaching, B
Sign Language Interpretation and Translation, B
Social Work, B
Spanish Language and Literature, B
Special Education and Teaching, B
Speech Teacher Education, B
Technical Theatre/Theatre Design and
  Technology, B

Montana

BLACKFEET COMMUNITY COLLEGE

Administrative Assistant and Secretarial Science, A
American Indian/Native American Studies, A
Bilingual and Multilingual Education, A
Business Administration and Management, A
Computer and Information Sciences and Support
  Services, A

Construction Engineering Technology/Technician, A
Elementary Education and Teaching, A
Entrepreneurship/Entrepreneurial Studies, A
General Studies, A
Health/Medical Preparatory Programs, A
Hospitality Administration/Management, A
Human Services, A
Kindergarten/PreSchool Education and Teaching, A
Liberal Arts and Sciences Studies and
   Humanities, A
Natural Resources Management/Development and
   Policy, A

CARROLL COLLEGE

Accounting, B
Acting, B
Art/Art Studies, General, A
Biology Teacher Education, B
Biology/Biological Sciences, B
Business Administration and Management, AB
Business/Managerial Economics, B
Chemistry, B
Civil Engineering, B
Clinical Laboratory Science/Medical
   Technology/Technologist, B
Communication Studies/Speech Communication
   and Rhetoric, B
Computer Science, AB
Drama and Dramatics/Theatre Arts, B
Education, B
Elementary Education and Teaching, B
Engineering, B
English Language and Literature, AB
English/Language Arts Teacher Education, B
Environmental Studies, B
Finance, B
French Language and Literature, B
General Studies, B
Health Information/Medical Records
   Administration/Administrator, B
History, B
History Teacher Education, B
International Relations and Affairs, B
Latin Language and Literature, B
Mathematics, B
Mathematics Teacher Education, B
Nursing - Registered Nurse Training, B
Philosophy, B
Physical Education Teaching and Coaching, B
Political Science and Government, B
Pre-Dentistry Studies, B
Pre-Law Studies, B
Pre-Medicine/Pre-Medical Studies, B
Pre-Pharmacy Studies, B
Pre-Veterinary Studies, B
Psychology, B
Public Administration, B
Public Relations/Image Management, B
Religion/Religious Studies, B
Religious Education, B
Secondary Education and Teaching, B
Social Science Teacher Education, B
Social Sciences, B
Social Work, B
Sociology, B
Spanish Language and Literature, B
Spanish Language Teacher Education, B
Sport and Fitness Administration/Management, B
Teaching English as a Second or Foreign
   Language/ESL Language Instructor, B
Technical and Business Writing, B
Technical Theatre/Theatre Design and
   Technology, B
Theology/Theological Studies, B
Visual and Performing Arts, B

CHIEF DULL KNIFE COLLEGE

Administrative Assistant and Secretarial Science, A
Agriculture, A
Business Administration and Management, A
Liberal Arts and Sciences Studies and
   Humanities, A
Mental Health/Rehabilitation, A
Natural Resources Management/Development and
   Policy, A
Office Management and Supervision, A

Public Health (MPH, DPH), A

DAWSON COMMUNITY COLLEGE

Administrative Assistant and Secretarial Science, A
Agricultural Business and Management, A
Automobile/Automotive Mechanics
   Technology/Technician, A
Business/Commerce, A
Child Care and Support Services Management, A
Clinical/Medical Social Work, A
Computer and Information Sciences, A
Criminal Justice/Police Science, A
Liberal Arts and Sciences Studies and
   Humanities, A
Substance Abuse/Addiction Counseling, A

FLATHEAD VALLEY COMMUNITY
COLLEGE

Accounting, A
Administrative Assistant and Secretarial Science, A
Business Administration and Management, A
Computer Engineering Technology/Technician, A
Computer Typography and Composition Equipment
   Operator, A
Computer/Information Technology Services
   Administration and Management, A
Construction Engineering Technology/Technician, A
Criminal Justice/Law Enforcement Administration, A
Data Entry/Microcomputer Applications, A
Developmental and Child Psychology, A
Forestry Technology/Technician, A
Hospitality and Recreation Marketing Operations, A
Hotel/Motel Administration/Management, A
Human Services, A
Liberal Arts and Sciences Studies and
   Humanities, A
Medical Administrative Assistant/Secretary, A
Medical/Clinical Assistant, A
Metal and Jewelry Arts, A
Survey Technology/Surveying, A
Web/Multimedia Management and Webmaster, A
Wildlife and Wildlands Science and Management, A
Word Processing, A

FORT BELKNAP COLLEGE

Administrative Assistant and Secretarial Science, A
American Indian/Native American Studies, A
Business/Commerce, A
Data Processing and Data Processing
   Technology/Technician, A
Elementary Education and Teaching, A
Kindergarten/PreSchool Education and Teaching, A
Liberal Arts and Sciences Studies and
   Humanities, A
Natural Resources Management/Development and
   Policy, A
Pre-Engineering, A

FORT PECK COMMUNITY COLLEGE

Administrative Assistant and Secretarial Science, A
Agricultural Mechanization, A
American Indian/Native American Studies, A
Automobile/Automotive Mechanics
   Technology/Technician, A
Business Administration and Management, A
Computer Science, A
Construction Engineering Technology/Technician, A
Criminal Justice/Law Enforcement Administration, A
Electrical, Electronic and Communications
   Engineering Technology/Technician, A
Human Services, A
Kindergarten/PreSchool Education and Teaching, A
Liberal Arts and Sciences Studies and
   Humanities, A
Mental Health/Rehabilitation, A
Natural Resources Management/Development and
   Policy, A

LITTLE BIG HORN COLLEGE

Biological and Physical Sciences, A
Business Administration and Management, A
Carpentry/Carpenter, A
Computer Science, A
Elementary Education and Teaching, A

Liberal Arts and Sciences Studies and
   Humanities, A
Mathematics, A

MILES COMMUNITY COLLEGE

Administrative Assistant and Secretarial Science, A
Agricultural Mechanization, A
Automobile/Automotive Mechanics
   Technology/Technician, A
Building/Property Maintenance and Management, A
Business Administration and Management, A
Carpentry/Carpenter, A
Commercial and Advertising Art, A
Computer Engineering Technology/Technician, A
Computer Graphics, A
Construction Engineering Technology/Technician, A
Consumer Merchandising/Retailing Management, A
Electrical, Electronic and Communications
   Engineering Technology/Technician, A
Electrical/Electronics Equipment Installation and
   Repair, A
Energy Management and Systems
   Technology/Technician, A
Fire Science/Firefighting, A
Human Services, A
Information Technology, A
Liberal Arts and Sciences Studies and
   Humanities, A
Marketing/Marketing Management, A
Medical Administrative Assistant/Secretary, A
Nursing - Registered Nurse Training, A
Telecommunications Technology/Technician, A

MONTANA STATE UNIVERSITY

Accounting, M
Agricultural Business and Management, B
Agricultural Economics, M
Agricultural Mechanization, A
Agricultural Sciences, MD
Agricultural Teacher Education, B
American Indian/Native American Studies, M
Animal Sciences, BMD
Anthropology, M
Applied Economics, M
Architecture, M
Art/Art Studies, General, B
Biochemistry, MD
Biological and Biomedical Sciences, MD
Biology/Biological Sciences, B
BioTechnology, B
Business/Commerce, B
Cell Biology and Anatomy, B
Chemical Engineering, BMD
Chemistry, BMD
Cinematography and Film/Video Production, B
Civil Engineering, BMD
Computer Engineering, B
Computer Science, BMD
Construction Engineering Technology/Technician, B
Design and Visual Communications, B
Drama and Dramatics/Theatre Arts, B
Ecology, MD
Economics, B
Education, MDO
Electrical Engineering, MD
Electrical, Electronics and Communications
   Engineering, B
Elementary Education and Teaching, B
Engineering and Applied Sciences, MD
English, M
English Language and Literature, B
Entomology, M
Environmental Biology, M
Environmental Design/Architecture, B
Environmental Engineering
   Technology/Environmental Technology, M
Environmental Sciences, BMD
Environmental Studies, B
Family and Consumer Sciences/Human Sciences, B
Film, Television, and Video Production, M
Fine Arts and Art Studies, M
Fine/Studio Arts, B
Fish, Game and Wildlife Management, M
Foreign Languages and Literatures, B
Geology/Earth Science, B
Geosciences, MD

Health and Physical Education, B
Health Education, M
Health/Health Care Administration/Management, B
History, BMD
Horticultural Science, B
Human Development, M
Human Development and Family Studies, B
Industrial Engineering, B
Industrial/Management Engineering, MD
Mathematics, BMD
Mechanical Engineering, BMD
Mechanical Engineering/Mechanical
  Technology/Technician, B
Medical Microbiology and Bacteriology, B
Microbiology, MD
Molecular Biology, MD
Music, B
Music Teacher Education, B
Natural Resources and Conservation, BMD
Natural Resources Management/Development and
  Policy, M
Neuroscience, BMD
Nursing, MO
Nursing - Advanced Practice, O
Nursing - Registered Nurse Training, B
Philosophy, B
Physics, BMD
Plant Pathology/Phytopathology, M
Plant Sciences, BMD
Political Science and Government, B
Psychology, BM
Public Administration, M
Range Science and Management, BMD
Secondary Education and Teaching, B
Sociology, B
Sport and Fitness Administration/Management, B
Statistics, MD
Technology Teacher Education/Industrial Arts
  Teacher Education, B
Veterinary Sciences, MD
Zoology/Animal Biology, D

MONTANA STATE
UNIVERSITY-BILLINGS

Accounting, B
Accounting and Related Services, A
Accounting Technology/Technician and
  Bookkeeping, A
Administrative Assistant and Secretarial Science, A
Advertising and Public Relations, M
Art Teacher Education, B
Art/Art Studies, General, B
Athletic Training and Sports Medicine, M
Autobody/Collision and Repair
  Technology/Technician, A
Automobile/Automotive Mechanics
  Technology/Technician, A
Biology Teacher Education, B
Biology/Biological Sciences, B
Business Administration and Management, AB
Business/Commerce, AB
Business/Managerial Economics, B
Business/Office Automation/Technology/Data
  Entry, A
Chemistry, B
Chemistry Teacher Education, B
Communication and Media Studies, M
Community Psychology, B
Computer and Information Sciences, A
Computer and Information Sciences and Support
  Services, A
Counselor Education/School Counseling and
  Guidance Services, M
Curriculum and Instruction, M
Data Processing and Data Processing
  Technology/Technician, A
Dental Hygiene/Hygienist, A
Diesel Mechanics Technology/Technician, A
Drafting and Design Technology/Technician, A
Drama and Dramatics/Theatre Arts, B
Early Childhood Education and Teaching, M
Education, ABMO
Educational Media/Instructional Technology, M
Elementary Education and Teaching, B
Emergency Medical Technology/Technician (EMT
  Paramedic), A

Engineering, A
English Language and Literature, B
English/Language Arts Teacher Education, B
Environmental Studies, B
Finance, B
Fire Protection and Safety Technology/Technician, A
General Studies, A
Health and Physical Education, B
Health Information/Medical Records
  Administration/Administrator, A
Health Services Administration, M
Health Teacher Education, B
Health/Health Care Administration/Management, B
Heating, Air Conditioning, Ventilation and
  Refrigeration Maintenance
  Technology/Technician, A
History, B
History Teacher Education, B
Human Resources Management/Personnel
  Administration, A
Interdisciplinary Studies, M
Legal Administrative Assistant/Secretary, A
Liberal Arts and Sciences Studies and
  Humanities, AB
Licensed Practical/Vocational Nurse Training, A
Marketing/Marketing Management, B
Mass Communication/Media Studies, B
Mathematics, B
Mathematics Teacher Education, B
Medical Administrative Assistant/Secretary, A
Medical/Clinical Assistant, A
Multi-/Interdisciplinary Studies, B
Music, B
Music Teacher Education, B
Petroleum Technology/Technician, A
Physical Education Teaching and Coaching, B
Pre-Engineering, A
Pre-Law Studies, B
Pre-Medicine/Pre-Medical Studies, B
Pre-Nursing Studies, B
Pre-Pharmacy Studies, B
Psychology, ABM
Public Relations/Image Management, B
Reading Teacher Education, M
Rehabilitation and Therapeutic Professions, B
Rehabilitation Counseling, M
Rehabilitation Therapy, B
Science Teacher Education/General Science
  Teacher Education, B
Secondary Education and Teaching, BM
Sheet Metal Technology/Sheetworking, A
Social Science Teacher Education, B
Sociology, AB
Spanish Language and Literature, B
Spanish Language Teacher Education, B
Special Education and Teaching, ABM
Sport and Fitness Administration/Management, BM
Surgical Technology/Technologist, A

MONTANA STATE UNIVERSITY-GREAT
FALLS COLLEGE OF TECHNOLOGY

Accounting, A
Administrative Assistant and Secretarial Science, A
Autobody/Collision and Repair
  Technology/Technician, A
Biology Technician/BioTechnology Laboratory
  Technician, A
Business/Commerce, A
Computer and Information Sciences, A
Computer Systems Networking and
  Telecommunications, A
Data Entry/Microcomputer Applications, A
Dental Assisting/Assistant, A
Dental Hygiene/Hygienist, A
Drafting and Design Technology/Technician, A
Elementary Education and Teaching, A
Emergency Medical Technology/Technician (EMT
  Paramedic), A
Fire Science/Firefighting, A
General Studies, A
Health Information/Medical Records
  Administration/Administrator, A
Health Information/Medical Records
  Technology/Technician, A
Interior Design, A
Legal Administrative Assistant/Secretary, A

Licensed Practical/Vocational Nurse Training, A
Medical Administrative Assistant/Secretary, A
Medical Transcription/Transcriptionist, A
Medical/Clinical Assistant, A
Physical Therapist Assistant, A
Respiratory Care Therapy/Therapist, A
Web Page, Digital/Multimedia and Information
  Resources Design, A

MONTANA STATE
UNIVERSITY-NORTHERN

Agricultural Business and Management, A
Agricultural Mechanization, A
Automobile/Automotive Mechanics
  Technology/Technician, AB
Biological and Physical Sciences, B
Biology/Biological Sciences, B
Business Administration and Management, AB
Business Teacher Education, B
Civil Engineering Technology/Technician, AB
Commercial and Advertising Art, AB
Community Organization and Advocacy, AB
Counselor Education/School Counseling and
  Guidance Services, M
Drafting and Design Technology/Technician, AB
Education, BM
Electrical, Electronic and Communications
  Engineering Technology/Technician, AB
Elementary Education and Teaching, B
Heavy Equipment Maintenance
  Technology/Technician, A
Humanities/Humanistic Studies, AB
Hydrology and Water Resources Science, AB
Industrial Technology/Technician, AB
Information Science/Studies, AB
Interdisciplinary Studies, AB
Machine Tool Technology/Machinist, A
Mass Communication/Media Studies, B
Metallurgical Technology/Technician, A
Nursing - Registered Nurse Training, AB
Physical Education Teaching and Coaching, B
Science Teacher Education/General Science
  Teacher Education, BM
Secondary Education and Teaching, B
Social Sciences, AB
Welding Technology/Welder, A

MONTANA TECH OF THE UNIVERSITY
OF MONTANA

Accounting, B
Administrative Assistant and Secretarial Science, A
Applied Mathematics, B
Architectural Drafting and Architectural
  CAD/CADD, A
Artificial Intelligence and Robotics, B
Autobody/Collision and Repair
  Technology/Technician, A
Automobile/Automotive Mechanics
  Technology/Technician, A
Biological and Physical Sciences, AB
Biology/Biological Sciences, AB
Business Administration and Management, B
Business/Commerce, B
Business/Office Automation/Technology/Data
  Entry, A
Chemistry, B
Civil Drafting and Civil Engineering CAD/CADD, A
Civil Engineering, B
Communication Studies/Speech Communication
  and Rhetoric, B
Computer and Information Sciences, B
Computer Engineering, B
Computer Programming/Programmer, B
Computer Science, AB
Computer Systems Analysis/Analyst, B
Data Processing and Data Processing
  Technology/Technician, A
Drafting and Design Technology/Technician, A
Engineering, AB
Engineering and Applied Sciences, M
Engineering Science, B
Engineering Technology, A
Environmental Engineering
  Technology/Environmental Technology, M
Environmental/Environmental Health Engineering, B
Executive Assistant/Executive Secretary, A

Finance, B
Geochemistry, M
Geological Engineering, M
Geological/Geophysical Engineering, B
Geology/Earth Science, M
Geophysics Engineering, M
Geosciences, M
Geotechnical Engineering, B
Human Resources Management/Personnel
   Administration, A
Hydrology and Water Resources Science, M
Industrial Hygiene, M
Industrial/Management Engineering, M
Information Science/Studies, B
Legal Administrative Assistant/Secretary, A
Liberal Arts and Sciences Studies and
   Humanities, AB
Materials Engineering, B
Materials Sciences, B
Mathematics, B
Mechanical Drafting and Mechanical Drafting
   CAD/CADD, A
Mechanical Engineering, B
Medical Administrative Assistant/Secretary, A
Metallurgical Engineering, BM
Mineral/Mining Engineering, M
Mining and Mineral Engineering, M
Nurse/Nursing Assistant/Aide and Patient Care
   Assistant, A
Nursing - Registered Nurse Training, A
Occupational Health and Industrial Hygiene, B
Occupational Safety and Health
   Technology/Technician, AB
Petroleum Engineering, BM
Petroleum Technology/Technician, A
Project Management, M
Public Health (MPH, DPH), B
Systems Engineering, B
Technical and Business Writing, B
Technical Communication, M
Welding Technology/Welder, B

ROCKY MOUNTAIN COLLEGE

Accounting, B
Accounting and Related Services, B
Agricultural Business and Management, B
Airline/Commercial/Professional Pilot and Flight
   Crew, B
Art Teacher Education, B
Art/Art Studies, General, B
Athletic Training and Sports Medicine, B
Aviation/Airway Management and Operations, B
Biology Teacher Education, B
Biology/Biological Sciences, B
Business Administration and Management, B
Chemistry, B
Chemistry Teacher Education, B
Communication Studies/Speech Communication
   and Rhetoric, B
Computer Science, B
Drama and Dramatics/Theatre Arts, B
Economics, B
Education, B
Elementary Education and Teaching, B
English Language and Literature, B
English/Language Arts Teacher Education, B
Environmental Sciences, B
Environmental Studies, B
Equestrian/Equine Studies, B
Geology/Earth Science, B
Health and Physical Education/Fitness, B
Health Teacher Education, B
History, B
History Teacher Education, B
Information Technology, B
Interdisciplinary Studies, B
Kinesiology and Exercise Science, B
Liberal Arts and Sciences Studies and
   Humanities, A
Management Information Systems and Services, B
Management Science, B
Mathematics, B
Mathematics Teacher Education, B
Multi-/Interdisciplinary Studies, B
Music Performance, B
Music Teacher Education, B

Philosophy, B
Physical Education Teaching and Coaching, B
Physician Assistant, B
Political Science and Government, B
Psychology, B
Religion/Religious Studies, B
Secondary Education and Teaching, B
Social Studies Teacher Education, B
Sociology, B
Technical Theatre/Theatre Design and
   Technology, B

SALISH KOOTENAI COLLEGE

Administrative Assistant and Secretarial Science, A
American Indian/Native American Studies, A
Carpentry/Carpenter, A
Child Development, A
Computer Science, A
Dental Hygiene/Hygienist, A
Environmental Studies, AB
Forestry, A
Forestry Technology/Technician, A
Human Services, AB
Kindergarten/PreSchool Education and Teaching, A
Liberal Arts and Sciences Studies and
   Humanities, A
Natural Resources Management/Development and
   Policy, A
Natural Sciences, A
Nursing - Registered Nurse Training, A

STONE CHILD COLLEGE

Administrative Assistant and Secretarial Science, A
Business Administration and Management, A
Computer Science, A
Human Services, A
Liberal Arts and Sciences Studies and
   Humanities, A

UNIVERSITY OF GREAT FALLS

Accounting, B
Accounting and Business/Management, B
American Literature (United States), B
Art Teacher Education, B
Art/Art Studies, General, B
Biology Teacher Education, B
Biology/Biological Sciences, B
Botany/Plant Biology, B
Business Administration and Management, B
Chemistry, B
Chemistry Teacher Education, B
Child and Family Studies, M
Computer and Information Sciences, B
Computer and Information Sciences and Support
   Services, B
Computer and Information Systems Security, B
Computer Graphics, B
Computer Programming/Programmer, B
Computer Science, B
Computer Software and Media Applications, B
Computer Systems Analysis/Analyst, B
Computer Systems Networking and
   Telecommunications, B
Computer/Information Technology Services
   Administration and Management, B
Corrections, B
Corrections Administration, B
Corrections and Criminal Justice, B
Counseling Psychology, BM
Counselor Education/School Counseling and
   Guidance Services, M
Creative Writing, B
Criminal Justice/Law Enforcement Administration, B
Criminal Justice/Police Science, B
Criminal Justice/Safety Studies, B
Criminology, M
Curriculum and Instruction, M
Early Childhood Education and Teaching, A
Education, M
Education/Teaching of the Gifted and Talented, B
Educational Administration and Supervision, M
Elementary Education and Teaching, B
English Composition, B
English Language and Literature, B
English/Language Arts Teacher Education, B
Fine/Studio Arts, B

Forensic Science and Technology, B
Health and Physical Education, B
Health Teacher Education, B
Health/Health Care Administration/Management, B
History, B
History Teacher Education, B
Human Services, ABM
Information Science/Studies, BM
Information Technology, B
Junior High/Intermediate/Middle School Education
   and Teaching, B
Kindergarten/PreSchool Education and
   Teaching, AB
Legal Assistant/Paralegal, AB
Library Science, B
Management Science, B
Marketing/Marketing Management, B
Marriage and Family Therapy/Counseling, M
Mathematics, B
Mathematics Teacher Education, B
Physical Education Teaching and Coaching, B
Political Science and Government, B
Psychology, B
Reading Teacher Education, B
Religion/Religious Studies, B
School Librarian/School Library Media Specialist, B
School Psychology, M
Science Teacher Education/General Science
   Teacher Education, B
Secondary Education and Teaching, BM
Social Science Teacher Education, B
Social Sciences, B
Social Studies Teacher Education, B
Sociology, B
Special Education and Teaching, B
Substance Abuse/Addiction Counseling, ABM
System Administration/Administrator, B
System, Networking, and LAN/WAN
   Management/Manager, B
Teacher Education, Multiple Levels, B
Theology/Theological Studies, B
Web Page, Digital/Multimedia and Information
   Resources Design, B
Web/Multimedia Management and Webmaster, B

THE UNIVERSITY OF MONTANA-HELENA COLLEGE OF TECHNOLOGY

Accounting Technology/Technician and
   Bookkeeping, A
Agricultural Mechanization, A
Airframe Mechanics and Aircraft Maintenance
   Technology/Technician, A
Automobile/Automotive Mechanics
   Technology/Technician, A
Business/Office Automation/Technology/Data
   Entry, A
Carpentry/Carpenter, A
Computer Programming/Programmer, A
Diesel Mechanics Technology/Technician, A
Electrical, Electronic and Communications
   Engineering Technology/Technician, A
Executive Assistant/Executive Secretary, A
Fire Science/Firefighting, A
General Office Occupations and Clerical Services, A
General Studies, A
Legal Administrative Assistant/Secretary, A
Licensed Practical/Vocational Nurse Training, A
Machine Tool Technology/Machinist, A
Medical Administrative Assistant/Secretary, A
Welding Technology/Welder, A

THE UNIVERSITY OF MONTANA-MISSOULA

Accounting, BM
Accounting Technology/Technician and
   Bookkeeping, A
Administrative Assistant and Secretarial Science, B
African-American/Black Studies, B
American Government and Politics (United States)
   , B
American Indian/Native American Studies, B
Anthropology, BMD
Apparel and Accessories Marketing Operations, A
Applied Mathematics, B
Area Studies, B

Art History, Criticism and Conservation, B
Art Teacher Education, B
Art/Art Studies, General, B
Asian Studies/Civilization, B
Astronomy, B
Audiology/Audiologist and Speech-Language
 Pathology/Pathologist, B
Biochemistry, BMD
Biological and Biomedical Sciences, MD
Biology/Biological Sciences, B
Botany/Plant Biology, B
Business Administration, Management and
 Operations, MO
Business Teacher Education, B
Business/Commerce, B
Chemistry, BMD
Chinese Language and Literature, B
City/Urban, Community and Regional Planning, B
Classics and Classical
 Languages, Literatures, and Linguistics, B
Clinical Laboratory Science/Medical
 Technology/Technologist, B
Clinical Psychology, D
Clinical/Medical Laboratory Technician, B
Communication and Media Studies, M
Communication Studies/Speech Communication
 and Rhetoric, B
Computer and Information Sciences, B
Computer Science, BM
Counselor Education/School Counseling and
 Guidance Services, MDO
Creative Writing, B
Criminology, M
Culinary Arts/Chef Training, A
Curriculum and Instruction, BMD
Dance, B
Drama and Dramatics/Theatre Arts, B
Drawing, B
East Asian Studies, B
Ecology, MD
Economics, BM
Education, BMDO
Educational Administration and Supervision, MDO
Electrical, Electronic and Communications
 Engineering Technology/Technician, A
Elementary Education and Teaching, B
English, M
English Education, M
English Language and Literature, B
Environmental Education, B
Environmental Sciences, MO
Environmental Studies, BMO
Executive Assistant/Executive Secretary, A
Exercise and Sports Science, M
Experimental Psychology, D
Fashion Merchandising, B
Finance, B
Fine Arts and Art Studies, M
Fish, Game and Wildlife Management, MD
Foreign Languages and Literatures, B
Forest Management/Forest Resources
 Management, B
Forestry, BMD
French Language and Literature, BM
Geography, BM
Geology/Earth Science, BMD
German Language and Literature, BM
Health Education, M
Health Promotion, M
Health Psychology, M
Health Teacher Education, B
Heavy Equipment Maintenance
 Technology/Technician, A
History, BMD
Information Science/Studies, B
Information Technology, B
Interdisciplinary Studies, BMD
International Business/Trade/Commerce, B
Japanese Language and Literature, B
Journalism, BM
Latin Language and Literature, B
Law and Legal Studies, ABPO
Legal Administrative Assistant/Secretary, A
Legal Assistant/Paralegal, A
Liberal Arts and Sciences Studies and
 Humanities, B

Licensed Practical/Vocational Nurse Training, A
Linguistics, BM
Marketing/Marketing Management, B
Mathematics, BMD
Mathematics Teacher Education, B
Medical Administrative Assistant/Secretary, A
Medical Microbiology and Bacteriology, B
Microbiology, MD
Music, BM
Music Performance, B
Music Teacher Education, B
Natural Resources and Conservation, BM
Natural Resources Management/Development and
 Policy, BM
Parks, Recreation, Leisure and Fitness Studies, B
Pharmaceutical Sciences, MD
Pharmaceutics and Drug Design, B
Pharmacology, D
Pharmacy, B
Pharmacy Technician/Assistant, B
Philosophy, BM
Physical Education Teaching and Coaching, BM
Physical Therapy/Therapist, BD
Physics, B
Political Science and Government, M
Pre-Engineering, B
Pre-Law Studies, B
Pre-Medicine/Pre-Medical Studies, B
Pre-Pharmacy Studies, B
Psychology, BMDO
Public Administration, MO
Radio and Television, B
Radiologic Technology/Science - Radiographer, A
Reading Teacher Education, B
Receptionist, A
Recreation and Park Management, M
Respiratory Care Therapy/Therapist, A
Rural Sociology, M
Russian Language and Literature, B
Russian Studies, B
School Psychology, MDO
Science Teacher Education/General Science
 Teacher Education, BM
Secondary Education and Teaching, B
Small Engine Mechanics and Repair
 Technology/Technician, A
Social Science Teacher Education, B
Social Sciences, B
Social Work, B
Sociology, BM
Spanish Language and Literature, BM
Speech and Rhetorical Studies, B
Statistics, M
Surgical Technology/Technologist, A
Teaching English as a Second or Foreign
 Language/ESL Language Instructor, B
Technical and Business Writing, B
Technology Education/Industrial Arts, A
Theater, M
Toxicology, MD
Welding Technology/Welder, A
Wildlife and Wildlands Science and Management, B
Women's Studies, B
Writing, M
Zoology/Animal Biology, BMD

THE UNIVERSITY OF MONTANA-WESTERN

Administrative Assistant and Secretarial Science, A
Applied Art, AB
Art Teacher Education, B
Biology Teacher Education, B
Business Administration and Management, A
Business Teacher Education, B
Business/Commerce, AB
Business/Corporate Communications, B
Business/Office Automation/Technology/Data
 Entry, A
Comparative Literature, B
Computer and Information Sciences, A
Data Processing and Data Processing
 Technology/Technician, A
Drama and Dramatics/Theatre Arts, B
Education, B
Elementary Education and Teaching, B
English Language and Literature, B

English/Language Arts Teacher Education, B
Environmental Studies, B
Equestrian/Equine Studies, A
Health Teacher Education, B
History Teacher Education, B
Human Resources Management/Personnel
 Administration, A
Information Science/Studies, A
Kindergarten/PreSchool Education and Teaching, A
Liberal Arts and Sciences Studies and
 Humanities, B
Mathematics Teacher Education, B
Music Teacher Education, B
Physical Education Teaching and Coaching, B
Pre-Dentistry Studies, B
Pre-Law Studies, B
Pre-Medicine/Pre-Medical Studies, B
Pre-Veterinary Studies, B
Science Teacher Education/General Science
 Teacher Education, B
Secondary Education and Teaching, B
Social Science Teacher Education, B
Social Sciences, B
Teacher Education, Multiple Levels, B
Technology Education/Industrial Arts, B
Technology Teacher Education/Industrial Arts
 Teacher Education, B
Tourism and Travel Services Management, A
Tourism and Travel Services Marketing
 Operations, AB

Nebraska

BELLEVUE UNIVERSITY

Accounting, B
Business Administration and Management, B
Business Administration, Management and
 Operations, M
Communication and Media Studies, BM
Computer and Information Sciences, B
Computer/Information Technology Services
 Administration and Management, B
Criminal Justice/Law Enforcement Administration, B
Health Services Administration, M
Health/Health Care Administration/Management, B
Human Services, M
Information Science/Studies, BM
Information Technology, B
Management, M
Management Information Systems and
 Services, BM
Marketing/Marketing Management, B
Physical Education Teaching and Coaching, B
Securities Services Administration/Management, M
Web Page, Digital/Multimedia and Information
 Resources Design, B

CENTRAL COMMUNITY COLLEGE-COLUMBUS CAMPUS

Accounting, A
Administrative Assistant and Secretarial Science, A
Agricultural Business and Management, A
Automobile/Automotive Mechanics
 Technology/Technician, A
Business Administration and Management, A
Commercial and Advertising Art, A
Computer and Information Sciences, A
Computer Programming, Specific Applications, A
Drafting and Design Technology/Technician, A
Electrical, Electronic and Communications
 Engineering Technology/Technician, A
Electromechanical Technology/Electromechanical
 Engineering Technology, A
Family and Consumer Sciences/Human Sciences, A
Industrial Technology/Technician, A
Information Technology, A
Liberal Arts and Sciences Studies and
 Humanities, A
Licensed Practical/Vocational Nurse Training, A
Machine Tool Technology/Machinist, A
Marketing/Marketing Management, A
Quality Control Technology/Technician, A
System Administration/Administrator, A
Web/Multimedia Management and Webmaster, A

Welding Technology/Welder, A

CENTRAL COMMUNITY COLLEGE-GRAND ISLAND CAMPUS

Accounting, A
Administrative Assistant and Secretarial Science, A
Automobile/Automotive Mechanics
   Technology/Technician, A
Business Administration and Management, A
Child Development, A
Clinical/Medical Social Work, A
Computer and Information Sciences, A
Computer Programming, Specific Applications, A
Criminal Justice/Safety Studies, A
Data Processing and Data Processing
   Technology/Technician, A
Drafting and Design Technology/Technician, A
Electrical, Electronic and Communications
   Engineering Technology/Technician, A
Heating, Air Conditioning, Ventilation and
   Refrigeration Maintenance
   Technology/Technician, A
Industrial Technology/Technician, A
Information Technology, A
Legal Assistant/Paralegal, A
Liberal Arts and Sciences Studies and
   Humanities, A
Licensed Practical/Vocational Nurse Training, A
Nursing - Registered Nurse Training, A
System Administration/Administrator, A
Web/Multimedia Management and Webmaster, A
Welding Technology/Welder, A

CENTRAL COMMUNITY COLLEGE-HASTINGS CAMPUS

Accounting, A
Administrative Assistant and Secretarial Science, A
Agricultural Business and Management, A
Applied Horticulture/Horticultural Operations, A
Autobody/Collision and Repair
   Technology/Technician, A
Automobile/Automotive Mechanics
   Technology/Technician, A
Business Administration and Management, A
Child Development, A
Clinical/Medical Social Work, A
Commercial and Advertising Art, A
Computer and Information Sciences, A
Computer Programming, Specific Applications, A
Construction Engineering Technology/Technician, A
Dental Assisting/Assistant, A
Dental Hygiene/Hygienist, A
Diesel Mechanics Technology/Technician, A
Drafting and Design Technology/Technician, A
Electrical, Electronic and Communications
   Engineering Technology/Technician, A
Graphic and Printing Equipment Operator
   Production, A
Health Information/Medical Records
   Technology/Technician, A
Heating, Air Conditioning, Ventilation and
   Refrigeration Maintenance
   Technology/Technician, A
Hospital and Health Care Facilities
   Administration/Management, A
Hospitality Administration/Management, A
Hotel/Motel Administration/Management, A
Industrial Technology/Technician, A
Information Technology, A
Liberal Arts and Sciences Studies and
   Humanities, A
Machine Tool Technology/Machinist, A
Mass Communication/Media Studies, A
Medical Administrative Assistant/Secretary, A
Medical/Clinical Assistant, A
Radio and Television Broadcasting
   Technology/Technician, A
System Administration/Administrator, A
Web/Multimedia Management and Webmaster, A
Welding Technology/Welder, A

CHADRON STATE COLLEGE

Art Teacher Education, B
Art/Art Studies, General, B
Biology Teacher Education, B
Biology/Biological Sciences, B

Business Administration and Management, B
Business Administration, Management and
   Operations, M
Business Education, M
Business Teacher Education, B
Chemistry, B
Chemistry Teacher Education, B
Corrections and Criminal Justice, B
Counselor Education/School Counseling and
   Guidance Services, M
Drama and Dance Teacher Education, B
Drama and Dramatics/Theatre Arts, B
Education, MO
Educational Administration and Supervision, MO
Elementary Education and Teaching, BM
English Education, M
English Language and Literature, B
English/Language Arts Teacher Education, B
Family and Consumer Economics and Related
   Services, B
Family and Consumer Sciences/Home Economics
   Teacher Education, B
Health/Medical Preparatory Programs, B
History, B
History Teacher Education, B
Industrial Production Technologies/Technicians, B
Information Science/Studies, B
Interdisciplinary Studies, B
Junior High/Intermediate/Middle School Education
   and Teaching, B
Library Science, B
Mathematics, B
Mathematics Teacher Education, B
Music, B
Music Teacher Education, B
Parks, Recreation, Leisure and Fitness Studies, B
Physical Education Teaching and Coaching, B
Physics, B
Physics Teacher Education, B
Psychology, B
Range Science and Management, B
Science Teacher Education/General Science
   Teacher Education, B
Secondary Education and Teaching, BM
Social Science Teacher Education, B
Social Studies Teacher Education, M
Social Work, B
Sociology, B
Spanish Language and Literature, B
Spanish Language Teacher Education, B
Special Education and Teaching, B
Speech and Rhetorical Studies, B
Speech Teacher Education, B
Teacher Education and Professional
   Development, Specific Subject Areas, B
Technology Teacher Education/Industrial Arts
   Teacher Education, B

CLARKSON COLLEGE

Business Administration and Management, B
Nursing, M
Nursing - Advanced Practice, M
Nursing - Registered Nurse Training, B
Nursing Administration, BM
Nursing Education, M
Nursing Science, B
Occupational Therapy/Therapist, A
Physical Therapy/Therapist, A
Radiologic Technology/Science - Radiographer, AB

COLLEGE OF SAINT MARY

Accounting, A
Art/Art Studies, General, B
Biology/Biological Sciences, B
Business Administration and Management, AB
Chemistry, B
Clinical Laboratory Science/Medical
   Technology/Technologist, B
Early Childhood Education and Teaching, AB
Education, B
Elementary Education and Teaching, B
English Language and Literature, B
General Studies, AB
Health Information/Medical Records
   Administration/Administrator, AB
Humanities/Humanistic Studies, B

Legal Assistant/Paralegal, AB
Mathematics, B
Natural Sciences, B
Nursing - Registered Nurse Training, AB
Pre-Dentistry Studies, B
Pre-Law Studies, B
Pre-Medicine/Pre-Medical Studies, B
Pre-Veterinary Studies, B
Psychology, B
Science Teacher Education/General Science
   Teacher Education, B
Secondary Education and Teaching, B
Social Sciences, B
Special Education and Teaching, B
Teacher Education, Multiple Levels, B

CONCORDIA UNIVERSITY

Accounting, B
Art Teacher Education, B
Art/Art Studies, General, B
Behavioral Sciences, B
Biology Teacher Education, B
Biology/Biological Sciences, B
Business Administration and Management, B
Business Teacher Education, B
Business/Commerce, B
Chemistry, B
Chemistry Teacher Education, B
Commercial and Advertising Art, B
Communication Studies/Speech Communication
   and Rhetoric, B
Computer and Information Sciences, B
Computer Science, B
Computer Teacher Education, B
Curriculum and Instruction, M
Drama and Dance Teacher Education, B
Drama and Dramatics/Theatre Arts, B
Early Childhood Education and Teaching, BM
Education, BM
Educational Administration and Supervision, M
Elementary Education and Teaching, B
English Language and Literature, B
English/Language Arts Teacher Education, B
Family and Consumer Sciences/Home Economics
   Teacher Education, B
Fine/Studio Arts, B
Geography, B
Geography Teacher Education, B
Health and Physical Education, B
Health Teacher Education, B
Health/Medical Preparatory Programs, B
History, B
History Teacher Education, B
Junior High/Intermediate/Middle School Education
   and Teaching, B
Kindergarten/PreSchool Education and Teaching, B
Kinesiology and Exercise Science, B
Management Information Systems and Services, B
Mass Communication/Media Studies, B
Mathematics, B
Mathematics Teacher Education, B
Music, B
Music Teacher Education, B
Natural Sciences, B
Pastoral Studies/Counseling, BM
Physical Education Teaching and Coaching, B
Physical Sciences, B
Physics Teacher Education, B
Piano and Organ, B
Pre-Dentistry Studies, B
Pre-Law Studies, B
Pre-Medicine/Pre-Medical Studies, B
Pre-Nursing Studies, B
Pre-Pharmacy Studies, B
Pre-Theology/Pre-Ministerial Studies, B
Pre-Veterinary Studies, B
Psychology, B
Reading Teacher Education, M
Religious Education, BM
Religious/Sacred Music, B
Science Teacher Education/General Science
   Teacher Education, B
Secondary Education and Teaching, B
Social Science Teacher Education, B
Social Sciences, B
Sociology, B

Spanish Language and Literature, B
Spanish Language Teacher Education, B
Special Education and Teaching, B
Speech and Rhetorical Studies, B
Speech Teacher Education, B
Sport and Fitness Administration/Management, B
Teaching English as a Second or Foreign
   Language/ESL Language Instructor, B
Technology Teacher Education/Industrial Arts
   Teacher Education, B
Theology/Theological Studies, B
Trade and Industrial Teacher Education, B

THE CREATIVE CENTER

Computer Graphics, A
Design and Visual Communications, A
Illustration, A

CREIGHTON UNIVERSITY

Accounting, B
Allied Health and Medical Assisting Services, MDPO
Allopathic Medicine, PO
American Indian/Native American Studies, B
American/United States Studies/Civilization, B
Ancient/Classical Greek Language and Literature, B
Applied Mathematics, B
Art/Art Studies, General, B
Athletic Training and Sports Medicine, B
Atmospheric Sciences and Meteorology, BM
Biological and Biomedical Sciences, MDO
Biology/Biological Sciences, B
Business Administration, Management and
   Operations, MO
Chemistry, B
Classical, Ancient Mediterranean and Near Eastern
   Studies and Archaeology, B
Communication Studies/Speech Communication
   and Rhetoric, B
Computer Science, AB
Counselor Education/School Counseling and
   Guidance Services, M
Dentistry, P
Drama and Dramatics/Theatre Arts, B
Economics, B
Education, M
Educational Administration and Supervision, M
Electronic Commerce, M
Elementary Education and Teaching, B
Emergency Medical Technology/Technician (EMT
   Paramedic), AB
English Language and Literature, B
Environmental Studies, B
Finance, B
French Language and Literature, B
German Language and Literature, B
Graphic Design, B
Health/Health Care Administration/Management, B
History, B
Immunology, MD
International Affairs, M
International Business/Trade/Commerce, B
International Relations and Affairs, B
Journalism, B
Kinesiology and Exercise Science, B
Latin Language and Literature, B
Law and Legal Studies, PO
Liberal Studies, M
Management Information Systems and
   Services, BM
Marketing/Marketing Management, B
Mathematics, AB
Medical Microbiology and Bacteriology, MD
Music, B
Nursing, M
Nursing - Registered Nurse Training, B
Occupational Therapy/Therapist, D
Organizational Communication, A
Pharmaceutical Sciences, MO
Pharmacology, MD
Pharmacy, P
Philosophy, B
Physical Therapy/Therapist, D
Physics, BM
Political Science and Government, B
Pre-Law Studies, B
Psychology, B

Social Work, B
Sociology, B
Spanish Language and Literature, B
Speech and Rhetorical Studies, B
Theology and Religious Vocations, M
Theology/Theological Studies, AB

DANA COLLEGE

Accounting, B
Art Teacher Education, B
Art/Art Studies, General, B
Biology/Biological Sciences, B
Business Administration and Management, B
Business Teacher Education, B
Chemistry, B
Communication Studies/Speech Communication
   and Rhetoric, B
Computer Science, B
Criminal Justice/Law Enforcement Administration, B
Drama and Dance Teacher Education, B
Education, B
Elementary Education and Teaching, B
English Language and Literature, B
English/Language Arts Teacher Education, B
Environmental Studies, B
Foreign Language Teacher Education, B
German Language and Literature, B
Health and Physical Education, B
History, B
History Teacher Education, B
Interdisciplinary Studies, B
Management Information Systems and Services, B
Mathematics, B
Mathematics Teacher Education, B
Music, B
Music Teacher Education, B
Organizational Communication, B
Physical Education Teaching and Coaching, B
Psychology, B
Religion/Religious Studies, B
Science Teacher Education/General Science
   Teacher Education, B
Secondary Education and Teaching, B
Social Science Teacher Education, B
Social Work, B
Sociology, B
Spanish Language and Literature, B
Special Education and Teaching, B
Speech Teacher Education, B
Web Page, Digital/Multimedia and Information
   Resources Design, B
Web/Multimedia Management and Webmaster, B

DOANE COLLEGE

Accounting, B
Art/Art Studies, General, B
Biology/Biological Sciences, B
Business Administration and Management, B
Business Administration, Management and
   Operations, M
Business Teacher Education, B
Chemistry, B
Communication Studies/Speech Communication
   and Rhetoric, B
Computer and Information Sciences, B
Computer Science, B
Counselor Education/School Counseling and
   Guidance Services, M
Curriculum and Instruction, M
Drama and Dramatics/Theatre Arts, B
Economics, B
Education, M
Educational Leadership and Administration, M
Elementary Education and Teaching, B
English Language and Literature, B
Environmental Studies, B
French Language and Literature, B
German Language and Literature, B
Health and Physical Education, B
History, B
Human Services, B
International Relations and Affairs, B
Mass Communication/Media Studies, B
Mathematics, B
Music, B
Natural Sciences, B

Philosophy, B
Physical Education Teaching and Coaching, B
Physical Sciences, B
Physics, B
Political Science and Government, B
Psychology, B
Public Administration, B
Public Relations/Image Management, B
Religion/Religious Studies, B
Secondary Education and Teaching, B
Social Sciences, B
Sociology, B
Spanish Language and Literature, B
Special Education and Teaching, B
Speech and Rhetorical Studies, B
Teaching English as a Second or Foreign
   Language/ESL Language Instructor, B

GRACE UNIVERSITY

Accounting, B
Agricultural Business and Management, B
Airline/Commercial/Professional Pilot and Flight
   Crew, B
Avionics Maintenance Technology/Technician, B
Bible/Biblical Studies, AB
Broadcast Journalism, B
Business Administration and Management, B
Business Teacher Education, B
Communication Studies/Speech Communication
   and Rhetoric, B
Computer and Information Sciences, B
Computer Programming/Programmer, B
Computer Science, B
Counseling Psychology, M
Divinity/Ministry (BD, MDiv.), B
Elementary Education and Teaching, B
Human Resources Management/Personnel
   Administration, B
Humanities/Humanistic Studies, B
Junior High/Intermediate/Middle School Education
   and Teaching, B
Liberal Arts and Sciences Studies and
   Humanities, AB
Licensed Practical/Vocational Nurse Training, A
Marriage and Family Therapy/Counseling, B
Mass Communication/Media Studies, B
Missions/Missionary Studies and Missiology, B
Music, AB
Music Teacher Education, B
Music Theory and Composition, B
Nursing - Registered Nurse Training, B
Pastoral Studies/Counseling, BM
Piano and Organ, B
Pre-Theology/Pre-Ministerial Studies, B
Psychology, B
Religious Education, B
Religious/Sacred Music, B
Secondary Education and Teaching, B
Social Science Teacher Education, B
Teacher Education, Multiple Levels, B
Theology and Religious Vocations, M
Voice and Opera, B
Web/Multimedia Management and Webmaster, B
Youth Ministry, B

HAMILTON COLLEGE-LINCOLN

Accounting, A
Administrative Assistant and Secretarial Science, A
Business Administration and Management, A
Computer Programming, A
Computer Programming/Programmer, A
Information Technology, A
Legal Administrative Assistant/Secretary, A
Legal Assistant/Paralegal, A
Medical Administrative Assistant/Secretary, A
Medical/Clinical Assistant, A
Tourism and Travel Services Management, A
Word Processing, A

HAMILTON COLLEGE-OMAHA

Accounting, A
Administrative Assistant and Secretarial Science, A
Business Administration and Management, A
Computer Programming, Specific Applications, A
Computer Programming/Programmer, A
Legal Administrative Assistant/Secretary, A

Legal Assistant/Paralegal, A
Medical Administrative Assistant/Secretary, A
Medical/Clinical Assistant, A

HASTINGS COLLEGE

Accounting, B
Advertising, B
Art History, Criticism and Conservation, B
Art Teacher Education, B
Art/Art Studies, General, B
Biology Teacher Education, B
Biology/Biological Sciences, B
Biopsychology, B
Broadcast Journalism, B
Business Administration and Management, B
Business Teacher Education, B
Chemistry, B
Chemistry Teacher Education, B
Communication Studies/Speech Communication
   and Rhetoric, B
Communications Technology/Technician, B
Comparative Literature, B
Computer and Information Sciences, B
Computer Science, B
Corrections and Criminal Justice, B
Creative Writing, B
Drama and Dance Teacher Education, B
Drama and Dramatics/Theatre Arts, B
Early Childhood Education and Teaching, B
Economics, B
Education, BM
Elementary Education and Teaching, B
English Language and Literature, B
English/Language Arts Teacher Education, B
Foreign Language Teacher Education, B
Foreign Languages and Literatures, B
German Language and Literature, B
German Language Teacher Education, B
Health and Physical Education, B
Health/Health Care Administration/Management, B
History, B
History Teacher Education, B
Human Resources Management/Personnel
   Administration, B
Human Services, B
International Relations and Affairs, B
Journalism, B
Kinesiology and Exercise Science, B
Liberal Arts and Sciences Studies and
   Humanities, B
Marketing/Marketing Management, B
Mass Communication/Media Studies, B
Mathematics, B
Mathematics Teacher Education, B
Music, B
Music History, Literature, and Theory, B
Music Pedagogy, B
Music Performance, B
Music Teacher Education, B
Parks, Recreation and Leisure Facilities
   Management, B
Philosophy, B
Physical Education Teaching and Coaching, B
Physics, B
Physics Teacher Education, B
Piano and Organ, B
Political Science and Government, B
Pre-Dentistry Studies, B
Pre-Law Studies, B
Pre-Medicine/Pre-Medical Studies, B
Pre-Veterinary Studies, B
Psychology, B
Public Administration, B
Public Relations/Image Management, B
Radio and Television, B
Religion/Religious Studies, B
Science Teacher Education/General Science
   Teacher Education, B
Secondary Education and Teaching, B
Social Science Teacher Education, B
Social Studies Teacher Education, B
Sociology, B
Spanish Language and Literature, B
Spanish Language Teacher Education, B
Special Education and Teaching, B
Speech and Rhetorical Studies, B

Speech Teacher Education, B
Sport and Fitness Administration/Management, B
Violin, Viola, Guitar and Other Stringed
   Instruments, B
Voice and Opera, B

ITT TECHNICAL INSTITUTE

Accounting and Business/Management, B
Animation, Interactive Technology, Video Graphics
   and Special Effects, B
Business Administration and Management, B
CAD/CADD Drafting and/or Design
   Technology/Technician, A
Computer and Information Systems Security, B
Computer Programming/Programmer, A
Computer Software Technology/Technician, B
Computer Systems Networking and
   Telecommunications, B
Criminal Justice/Law Enforcement Administration, A
E-Commerce/Electronic Commerce, B
Electrical, Electronic and Communications
   Engineering Technology/Technician, AB
System, Networking, and LAN/WAN
   Management/Manager, A
Web Page, Digital/Multimedia and Information
   Resources Design, A
Web/Multimedia Management and Webmaster, A

METROPOLITAN COMMUNITY COLLEGE

Accounting, A
Administrative Assistant and Secretarial Science, A
Architectural Engineering Technology/Technician, A
Automobile/Automotive Mechanics
   Technology/Technician, A
Business Administration and Management, A
Child Development, A
Civil Engineering Technology/Technician, A
Commercial and Advertising Art, A
Computer Programming/Programmer, A
Construction Engineering Technology/Technician, A
Criminal Justice/Police Science, A
Culinary Arts/Chef Training, A
Drafting and Design Technology/Technician, A
Electrical, Electronic and Communications
   Engineering Technology/Technician, A
Graphic and Printing Equipment Operator
   Production, A
Heating, Air Conditioning, Ventilation and
   Refrigeration Maintenance
   Technology/Technician, A
Heavy Equipment Maintenance
   Technology/Technician, A
Human Services, A
Interior Design, A
Kindergarten/PreSchool Education and Teaching, A
Law and Legal Studies, A
Legal Administrative Assistant/Secretary, A
Legal Assistant/Paralegal, A
Liberal Arts and Sciences Studies and
   Humanities, A
Licensed Practical/Vocational Nurse Training, A
Mental Health/Rehabilitation, A
Nursing - Registered Nurse Training, A
Ornamental Horticulture, A
Photography, A
Pre-Engineering, A
Respiratory Care Therapy/Therapist, A
Surgical Technology/Technologist, A
Welding Technology/Welder, A

MID-PLAINS COMMUNITY COLLEGE

Administrative Assistant and Secretarial Science, A
Autobody/Collision and Repair
   Technology/Technician, A
Automobile/Automotive Mechanics
   Technology/Technician, A
Building/Construction
   Finishing, Management, and Inspection, A
Business Administration and Management, A
Clinical/Medical Laboratory Technician, A
Computer and Information Sciences, A
Construction Engineering Technology/Technician, A
Dental Assisting/Assistant, A
Diesel Mechanics Technology/Technician, A

Electrical, Electronic and Communications
   Engineering Technology/Technician, A
Fire Science/Firefighting, A
Heating, Air Conditioning, Ventilation and
   Refrigeration Maintenance
   Technology/Technician, A
Liberal Arts and Sciences Studies and
   Humanities, A
Licensed Practical/Vocational Nurse Training, A
Nursing - Registered Nurse Training, A
Transportation and Materials Moving, A
Welding Technology/Welder, A

MIDLAND LUTHERAN COLLEGE

Accounting, AB
Administrative Assistant and Secretarial Science, B
Art Teacher Education, B
Art/Art Studies, General, B
Athletic Training and Sports Medicine, B
Behavioral Sciences, B
Biological and Physical Sciences, B
Biology/Biological Sciences, B
Broadcast Journalism, B
Business Administration and Management, B
Business Teacher Education, B
Chemistry, B
Community Organization and Advocacy, A
Computer Programming/Programmer, AB
Computer Science, B
Criminal Justice/Law Enforcement Administration, B
Criminology, B
Drama and Dramatics/Theatre Arts, B
Economics, B
Education, B
Elementary Education and Teaching, B
English Language and Literature, B
Environmental Studies, B
History, B
Human Services, B
Humanities/Humanistic Studies, B
Journalism, B
Junior High/Intermediate/Middle School Education
   and Teaching, B
Kindergarten/PreSchool Education and
   Teaching, AB
Legal Administrative Assistant/Secretary, A
Liberal Arts and Sciences Studies and
   Humanities, B
Management Information Systems and Services, B
Marketing/Marketing Management, B
Mass Communication/Media Studies, B
Mathematics, B
Medical Administrative Assistant/Secretary, A
Music, B
Music Teacher Education, B
Natural Sciences, B
Nursing - Registered Nurse Training, B
Parks, Recreation, Leisure and Fitness Studies, B
Physical Education Teaching and Coaching, B
Physical Sciences, B
Pre-Dentistry Studies, B
Pre-Law Studies, B
Pre-Medicine/Pre-Medical Studies, B
Pre-Veterinary Studies, B
Psychology, B
Religion/Religious Studies, B
Respiratory Care Therapy/Therapist, AB
Science Teacher Education/General Science
   Teacher Education, B
Secondary Education and Teaching, B
Social Sciences, B
Sociology, B
Speech Teacher Education, B
Teacher Education, Multiple Levels, B
Tourism and Travel Services Management, A

NEBRASKA CHRISTIAN COLLEGE

Administrative Assistant and Secretarial Science, A
Divinity/Ministry (BD, MDiv.), AB
Elementary Education and Teaching, B
Pastoral Studies/Counseling, AB
Religion/Religious Studies, B
Religious Education, AB
Religious/Sacred Music, AB
Secondary Education and Teaching, B
Sign Language Interpretation and Translation, A

Theology/Theological Studies, B

NEBRASKA COLLEGE OF TECHNICAL AGRICULTURE

Agricultural Business and Management, A
Agricultural Mechanization, A
Agronomy and Crop Science, A
Animal Sciences, A
Heavy Equipment Maintenance
    Technology/Technician, A
Horticultural Science, A
Natural Resources and Conservation, A
Natural Resources Management/Development and
    Policy, A
Soil Science and Agronomy, A
Veterinary/Animal Health Technology/Technician and
    Veterinary Assistant, A

NEBRASKA INDIAN COMMUNITY COLLEGE

American Indian/Native American Studies, A
Business Administration and Management, A
Carpentry/Carpenter, A
Corrections and Criminal Justice, A
Data Entry/Microcomputer Applications, A
Early Childhood Education and Teaching, A
Human Services, A
Information Technology, A
Liberal Arts and Sciences Studies and
    Humanities, A
Natural Resources and Conservation, A
Social Work, A

NEBRASKA METHODIST COLLEGE

Cardiovascular Technology/Technologist, AB
Diagnostic Medical Sonography/Sonographer and
    Ultrasound Technician, AB
Emergency Medical Technology/Technician (EMT
    Paramedic), AB
Health Promotion, M
Nursing, M
Nursing - Registered Nurse Training, AB
Radiologic Technology/Science - Radiographer, A
Respiratory Care Therapy/Therapist, AB

NEBRASKA WESLEYAN UNIVERSITY

Accounting, B
Art/Art Studies, General, B
Athletic Training and Sports Medicine, B
Biochemistry, B
Biochemistry, Biophysics and Molecular Biology, B
Biology/Biological Sciences, B
Biopsychology, B
Business Administration and Management, B
Business, Management, Marketing, and Related
    Support Services, B
Chemistry, B
Communication Studies/Speech Communication
    and Rhetoric, B
Computer Science, B
Drama and Dramatics/Theatre Arts, B
Dramatic/Theatre Arts and Stagecraft, B
Economics, B
Elementary Education and Teaching, B
English Language and Literature, B
English/Language Arts Teacher Education, B
Forensic Science and Technology, M
French Language and Literature, B
German Language and Literature, B
Health and Physical Education, B
History, B
Industrial and Organizational Psychology, B
Information Science/Studies, B
Interdisciplinary Studies, B
International Business/Trade/Commerce, B
International/Global Studies, B
Junior High/Intermediate/Middle School Education
    and Teaching, B
Kinesiology and Exercise Science, B
Mathematics, B
Music, B
Music Performance, B
Music Teacher Education, B
Nursing, M
Nursing Administration, B

Philosophy, B
Physical Education Teaching and Coaching, B
Physics, B
Political Communication, B
Political Science and Government, B
Psychology, B
Religion/Religious Studies, B
Science Teacher Education/General Science
    Teacher Education, B
Social Science Teacher Education, B
Social Work, B
Sociology, B
Spanish Language and Literature, B
Special Education and Teaching, B
Speech and Rhetorical Studies, B
Sport and Fitness Administration/Management, B
Women's Studies, B

NORTHEAST COMMUNITY COLLEGE

Accounting, A
Administrative Assistant and Secretarial Science, A
Agricultural Business and Management, A
Agricultural Mechanization, A
Agricultural Production Operations, A
Agriculture, A
Agronomy and Crop Science, A
Animal Sciences, A
Applied Horticulture/Horticultural Operations, A
Art Teacher Education, A
Art/Art Studies, General, A
Audio Engineering, A
Autobody/Collision and Repair
    Technology/Technician, A
Automobile/Automotive Mechanics
    Technology/Technician, A
Biological and Physical Sciences, A
Biology/Biological Sciences, A
Broadcast Journalism, A
Business Administration and Management, A
Business Teacher Education, A
Carpentry/Carpenter, A
Chemistry, A
Computer and Information Sciences, A
Computer Programming, Specific Applications, A
Computer Programming/Programmer, A
Computer Science, A
Corrections, A
Criminal Justice/Law Enforcement Administration, A
Criminal Justice/Police Science, A
Crop Production, A
Diesel Mechanics Technology/Technician, A
Drafting and Design Technology/Technician, A
Drama and Dramatics/Theatre Arts, A
Education, A
Electrical, Electronic and Communications
    Engineering Technology/Technician, A
Electrician, A
Electromechanical Technology/Electromechanical
    Engineering Technology, A
Elementary Education and Teaching, A
Emergency Medical Technology/Technician (EMT
    Paramedic), A
Engineering, A
English Language and Literature, A
Entrepreneurship/Entrepreneurial Studies, A
Farm/Farm and Ranch Management, A
General Studies, A
Health and Physical Education, A
Heating, Air Conditioning, Ventilation and
    Refrigeration Maintenance
    Technology/Technician, A
Horticultural Science, A
Journalism, A
Legal Administrative Assistant/Secretary, A
Legal Assistant/Paralegal, A
Liberal Arts and Sciences Studies and
    Humanities, A
Licensed Practical/Vocational Nurse Training, A
Lineworker, A
Livestock Management, A
Marketing, A
Marketing/Marketing Management, A
Mass Communication/Media Studies, A
Mathematics, A
Medical Administrative Assistant/Secretary, A
Music, A

Music Management and Merchandising, A
Music Performance, A
Music Teacher Education, A
Nursing - Registered Nurse Training, A
Physical Education Teaching and Coaching, A
Physical Therapy/Therapist, A
Physics, A
Pre-Law Studies, A
Radio and Television, A
Real Estate, A
Retailing and Retail Operations, A
Social Sciences, A
Social Work, A
Speech and Rhetorical Studies, A
Surgical Technology/Technologist, A
Veterinary/Animal Health Technology/Technician and
    Veterinary Assistant, A

PERU STATE COLLEGE

Accounting, B
Applied Art, B
Art Teacher Education, B
Art/Art Studies, General, B
Biological and Physical Sciences, B
Biology/Biological Sciences, B
Business Administration and Management, B
Chemistry, B
Clinical Laboratory Science/Medical
    Technology/Technologist, B
Commercial and Advertising Art, B
Criminal Justice/Law Enforcement Administration, B
Education, BM
Elementary Education and Teaching, B
English Language and Literature, B
Health Teacher Education, B
History, B
Junior High/Intermediate/Middle School Education
    and Teaching, B
Kindergarten/PreSchool Education and Teaching, B
Management Information Systems and Services, B
Marketing/Marketing Management, B
Mathematics, B
Music, B
Music Management and Merchandising, B
Music Teacher Education, B
Natural Resources and Conservation, B
Natural Sciences, B
Nuclear Medical Technology/Technologist, B
Physical Education Teaching and Coaching, B
Physician Assistant, B
Pre-Dentistry Studies, B
Pre-Law Studies, B
Pre-Medicine/Pre-Medical Studies, B
Pre-Veterinary Studies, B
Psychology, B
Science Teacher Education/General Science
    Teacher Education, B
Secondary Education and Teaching, B
Social Sciences, B
Special Education and Teaching, B
Voice and Opera, B
Wildlife and Wildlands Science and Management, B
Wind and Percussion Instruments, B

SOUTHEAST COMMUNITY COLLEGE, BEATRICE CAMPUS

Accounting, A
Administrative Assistant and Secretarial Science, A
Agricultural Business and Management, A
Agricultural Mechanization, A
Agriculture, A
Agronomy and Crop Science, A
Animal Sciences, A
Art/Art Studies, General, A
Biological and Physical Sciences, A
Biology Technician/BioTechnology Laboratory
    Technician, A
Biology/Biological Sciences, A
Broadcast Journalism, A
Business Administration and Management, A
Computer Science, A
Education, A
Elementary Education and Teaching, A
Finance, A
Journalism, A
Legal Administrative Assistant/Secretary, A

Liberal Arts and Sciences Studies and
   Humanities, A
Licensed Practical/Vocational Nurse Training, A
Medical Administrative Assistant/Secretary, A
Physical Sciences, A
Soil Science and Agronomy, A

SOUTHEAST COMMUNITY COLLEGE, LINCOLN CAMPUS

Administrative Assistant and Secretarial Science, A
Automobile/Automotive Mechanics
   Technology/Technician, A
Business Administration and Management, A
Child Development, A
Clinical/Medical Laboratory Technician, A
Computer and Information Sciences, A
Culinary Arts/Chef Training, A
Dietetics/Dieticians, A
Drafting and Design Technology/Technician, A
Electrical, Electronic and Communications
   Engineering Technology/Technician, A
Environmental Studies, A
Fire Science/Firefighting, A
Food Technology and Processing, A
Human Services, A
Liberal Arts and Sciences Studies and
   Humanities, A
Machine Tool Technology/Machinist, A
Medical Radiologic Technology/Science - Radiation
   Therapist, A
Nursing - Registered Nurse Training, A
Respiratory Care Therapy/Therapist, A
Welding Technology/Welder, A

SOUTHEAST COMMUNITY COLLEGE, MILFORD CAMPUS

Architectural Engineering Technology/Technician, A
Automobile/Automotive Mechanics
   Technology/Technician, A
Carpentry/Carpenter, A
Civil Engineering Technology/Technician, A
Commercial and Advertising Art, A
Computer and Information Sciences, A
Computer Engineering Technology/Technician, A
Computer Programming/Programmer, A
Construction Engineering Technology/Technician, A
Data Processing and Data Processing
   Technology/Technician, A
Drafting and Design Technology/Technician, A
Drafting/Design Engineering
   Technologies/Technicians, A
Electrical, Electronic and Communications
   Engineering Technology/Technician, A
Electromechanical Technology/Electromechanical
   Engineering Technology, A
Heating, Air Conditioning, Ventilation and
   Refrigeration Maintenance
   Technology/Technician, A
Industrial Design, A
Industrial Technology/Technician, A
Machine Tool Technology/Machinist, A
Mechanical Engineering/Mechanical
   Technology/Technician, A
Metallurgical Technology/Technician, A
Physical Sciences, A
Pipefitting/Pipefitter and Sprinkler Fitter, A
Plastics Engineering Technology/Technician, A
Quality Control Technology/Technician, A
Solar Energy Technology/Technician, A
Survey Technology/Surveying, A
Technology Education/Industrial Arts, A
Transportation and Materials Moving, A
Welding Technology/Welder, A

UNION COLLEGE

Accounting, AB
Art Teacher Education, B
Art/Art Studies, General, A
Biochemistry, B
Biology Teacher Education, B
Biology/Biological Sciences, B
Business Administration and Management, AB
Business Teacher Education, B
Chemistry, B
Chemistry Teacher Education, B

Clinical Laboratory Science/Medical
   Technology/Technologist, B
Commercial and Advertising Art, B
Computer Science, B
Computer Teacher Education, B
Education, B
Elementary Education and Teaching, B
Engineering, A
English Language and Literature, B
English/Language Arts Teacher Education, B
Entrepreneurship/Entrepreneurial Studies, B
Fine/Studio Arts, B
French Language and Literature, B
German Language and Literature, B
Graphic Design, AB
Health/Medical Preparatory Programs, A
History, B
History Teacher Education, B
Information Science/Studies, AB
International Relations and Affairs, B
Journalism, B
Kinesiology and Exercise Science, B
Mathematics, B
Mathematics Teacher Education, B
Music, B
Music Performance, B
Music Teacher Education, AB
Nursing - Registered Nurse Training, B
Pastoral Studies/Counseling, B
Physical Education Teaching and Coaching, B
Physician Assistant, B
Physics, B
Physics Teacher Education, B
Psychology, B
Public Health (MPH, DPH), A
Public Relations/Image Management, B
Religion/Religious Studies, B
Religious Education, B
Secondary Education and Teaching, B
Social Science Teacher Education, B
Social Sciences, B
Social Work, B
Spanish Language and Literature, B
Sport and Fitness Administration/Management, B
Theology/Theological Studies, B

UNIVERSITY OF NEBRASKA AT KEARNEY

Agricultural Business and Management, B
Art Education, M
Art/Art Studies, General, B
Aviation/Airway Management and Operations, B
Biological and Biomedical Sciences, M
Biology/Biological Sciences, B
Business Administration and Management, B
Business Administration, Management and
   Operations, M
Business Teacher Education, B
Chemistry, B
Communication Disorders, BM
Computer and Information Sciences, B
Counselor Education/School Counseling and
   Guidance Services, MO
Criminal Justice/Safety Studies, B
Curriculum and Instruction, M
Dietetics/Dieticians, B
Drama and Dramatics/Theatre Arts, B
Economics, B
Education, MO
Educational Administration and Supervision, MO
Educational Media/Instructional Technology, M
Elementary Education and Teaching, B
English, M
English Language and Literature, B
Exercise and Sports Science, M
Family and Consumer Economics and Related
   Services, B
Foreign Language Teacher Education, M
French Language and Literature, B
General Studies, B
Geography, B
German Language and Literature, B
History, BM
International Relations and Affairs, B
Journalism, B
Mass Communication/Media Studies, B

Mathematics, B
Music, B
Music Teacher Education, M
Operations Management and Supervision, B
Parks, Recreation, Leisure and Fitness Studies, B
Physical Education Teaching and Coaching, BM
Physics, B
Political Science and Government, B
Psychology, B
Reading Teacher Education, M
School Psychology, MO
Science Teacher Education/General Science
   Teacher Education, M
Social Work, B
Sociology, B
Spanish Language and Literature, B
Special Education and Teaching, BM
Speech and Rhetorical Studies, B
Sport and Fitness Administration/Management, B
Statistics, B
Technical Teacher Education, B
Therapeutic Recreation/Recreational Therapy, B
Writing, M

UNIVERSITY OF NEBRASKA-LINCOLN

Accounting, BMDO
Actuarial Science, BM
Advertising, B
Agricultural Business and Management, B
Agricultural Communication/Journalism, B
Agricultural Economics, BMD
Agricultural Education, M
Agricultural Engineering, M
Agricultural Mechanization, B
Agricultural Sciences, MD
Agricultural Teacher Education, B
Agricultural/Biological Engineering and
   Bioengineering, B
Agriculture, B
Agronomy and Crop Science, B
Agronomy and Soil Sciences, MD
Analytical Chemistry, D
Ancient/Classical Greek Language and Literature, B
Animal Sciences, BMD
Anthropology, BM
Apparel and Textiles, B
Architectural Engineering, BM
Architecture, BMO
Art History, Criticism and Conservation, BM
Art Teacher Education, B
Astronomy, MD
Athletic Training and Sports Medicine, B
Atmospheric Sciences and Meteorology, B
Biochemistry, BMD
Bioengineering, M
Biological and Biomedical Sciences, MD
Biology Teacher Education, B
Biology/Biological Sciences, B
Biomedical/Medical Engineering, B
Biometry/Biometrics, M
Broadcast Journalism, B
Business Administration and Management, B
Business Administration, Management and
   Operations, MDO
Business Teacher Education, B
Business/Managerial Economics, B
Chemical Engineering, BMD
Chemistry, BMD
Chemistry Teacher Education, B
Child and Family Studies, MD
Civil Engineering, BMDO
Classics and Classical
   Languages, Literatures, and Linguistics, BM
Clothing and Textiles, M
Communication and Media Studies, MD
Communication Disorders, M
Communication Studies/Speech Communication
   and Rhetoric, B
Community Health Services/Liaison/Counseling, B
Computer and Information Sciences, B
Computer Engineering, BMD
Computer Science, MD
Computer Teacher Education, B
Construction Engineering Technology/Technician, B
Consumer Economics, MD
Curriculum and Instruction, MDO

Dance, B
Drama and Dramatics/Theatre Arts, B
Economics, BMDO
Education, MDO
Education/Teaching of Individuals with Hearing
    Impairments, Including Deafness, B
Educational Administration and Supervision, MDO
Educational Psychology, MO
Electrical Engineering, MD
Electrical, Electronic and Communications
    Engineering Technology/Technician, B
Electrical, Electronics and Communications
    Engineering, B
Elementary Education and Teaching, B
Engineering, B
Engineering and Applied Sciences, MDO
English, MD
English Language and Literature, B
English/Language Arts Teacher Education, B
Entomology, MD
Environmental Engineering
    Technology/Environmental Technology, MD
Environmental Studies, B
Family and Consumer Economics and Related
    Services, B
Family and Consumer Sciences/Human
    Sciences, MD
Film/Cinema Studies, B
Finance, B
Finance and Banking, MD
Fine Arts and Art Studies, M
Fine/Studio Arts, B
Fire Protection and Safety Technology/Technician, A
Food Science, B
Food Science and Technology, MD
Foods, Nutrition, and Wellness Studies, B
Foreign Language Teacher Education, B
French Language and Literature, BMD
French Language Teacher Education, B
Geography, BMD
Geology/Earth Science, B
Geosciences, MD
German Language and Literature, BMD
German Language Teacher Education, B
Health Education, M
Health Teacher Education, B
History, BMD
History Teacher Education, B
Horticultural Science, BMD
Housing and Human Environments, B
Industrial Engineering, B
Industrial Production Technologies/Technicians, AB
Industrial Technology/Technician, B
Industrial/Management Engineering, MD
Inorganic Chemistry, D
Interior Architecture, B
International Business/Trade/Commerce, B
International Relations and Affairs, B
Journalism, BM
Junior High/Intermediate/Middle School Education
    and Teaching, B
Kinesiology and Exercise Science, B
Landscaping and Groundskeeping, B
Latin American Studies, B
Latin Language and Literature, B
Law and Legal Studies, MPO
Legal and Justice Studies, M
Legal Professions and Studies, B
Liberal Arts and Sciences Studies and
    Humanities, B
Management, M
Management Science, B
Manufacturing Engineering, MD
Marketing, MD
Marketing/Marketing Management, B
Mass Communication/Media Studies, M
Mathematics, BMD
Mathematics Teacher Education, B
Mechanical Engineering, BMD
Mechanics, MD
Medieval and Renaissance Studies, B
Museology/Museum Studies, M
Music, BMD
Music Teacher Education, B
Natural Resources and Conservation, BMD

Natural Resources Management/Development and
    Policy, B
Nutritional Sciences, MD
Office Management and Supervision, B
Organic Chemistry, D
Philosophy, BMD
Physical Chemistry, D
Physical Education Teaching and Coaching, BM
Physics, BMD
Physics Teacher Education, B
Plant Protection and Integrated Pest
    Management, B
Political Science and Government, BMDO
Pre-Dentistry Studies, B
Pre-Medicine/Pre-Medical Studies, B
Pre-Pharmacy Studies, B
Pre-Veterinary Studies, B
Psychology, BMDO
Range Science and Management, B
Reading Teacher Education, B
Recreation and Park Management, M
Russian Language and Literature, B
Sales and Marketing Operations/Marketing and
    Distribution Teacher Education, B
Science Teacher Education/General Science
    Teacher Education, B
Social Science Teacher Education, B
Sociology, BMD
Soil Science and Agronomy, B
Spanish Language and Literature, BMD
Spanish Language Teacher Education, B
Special Education and Teaching, BM
Speech-Language Pathology/Pathologist, B
Statistics, MD
Survey Methodology, M
System Management, M
Teacher Education and Professional
    Development, Specific Subject Areas, B
Teacher Education, Multiple Levels, B
Teaching English as a Second or Foreign
    Language/ESL Language Instructor, B
Technology Teacher Education/Industrial Arts
    Teacher Education, B
Theater, MD
Toxicology, MD
Trade and Industrial Teacher Education, B
Urban and Regional Planning, MO
Veterinary Sciences, MD
Veterinary/Animal Health Technology/Technician and
    Veterinary Assistant, B
Western European Studies, B
Women's Studies, B

UNIVERSITY OF NEBRASKA MEDICAL CENTER

Allied Health and Medical Assisting Services, MDO
Allopathic Medicine, PO
Anatomy, MD
Biochemistry, MD
Biological and Biomedical Sciences, MD
Cancer Biology/Oncology, MD
Cell Biology and Anatomy, MD
Clinical Laboratory Science/Medical
    Technology/Technologist, B
Clinical Laboratory Sciences, M
Dental Hygiene/Hygienist, B
Dentistry, PO
Diagnostic Medical Sonography/Sonographer and
    Ultrasound Technician, B
Medical Radiologic Technology/Science - Radiation
    Therapist, B
Medical Technology, O
Microbiology, MD
Molecular Biology, MD
Nuclear Medical Technology/Technologist, B
Nursing, MD
Nursing - Registered Nurse Training, B
Nutritional Sciences, O
Pathology/Experimental Pathology, MD
Pharmaceutical Sciences, MD
Pharmacology, MD
Pharmacy, P
Physical Therapy/Therapist, D
Physician Assistant, M
Physiology, MD
Public Health, M

Radiologic Technology/Science - Radiographer, B
Toxicology, MD

UNIVERSITY OF NEBRASKA AT OMAHA

Accounting, BM
Aeronautics/Aviation/Aerospace Science and
    Technology, B
African-American/Black Studies, B
Architectural Engineering, B
Art History, Criticism and Conservation, B
Art/Art Studies, General, B
Banking and Financial Support Services, B
Biological and Biomedical Sciences, M
Biology/Biological Sciences, B
BioTechnology, B
Broadcast Journalism, B
Business Administration and Management, B
Business Administration, Management and
    Operations, M
Business/Commerce, B
Business/Managerial Economics, B
Chemistry, B
Civil Engineering, B
Communication and Media Studies, M
Communication Disorders, M
Communication Studies/Speech Communication
    and Rhetoric, B
Community Health Services/Liaison/Counseling, B
Computer Engineering, B
Computer Science, BM
Construction Engineering Technology/Technician, B
Counselor Education/School Counseling and
    Guidance Services, M
Creative Writing, B
Criminal Justice/Safety Studies, B
Criminology, MD
Developmental Psychology, D
Drama and Dramatics/Theatre Arts, B
Economics, M
Education, MDO
Education/Teaching of Individuals with Speech or
    Language Impairments, A
Educational Administration and Supervision, MDO
Educational Media/Instructional Technology, O
Educational Psychology, M
Electrical, Electronics and Communications
    Engineering, B
Elementary Education and Teaching, BM
Engineering Physics, B
English, MO
English as a Second Language, O
English Language and Literature, B
Environmental Studies, B
Experimental Psychology, D
Family and Consumer Sciences/Human Sciences, B
Family and Consumer Sciences/Human Sciences
    Communication, B
Family Resource Management Studies, B
Finance, B
Fine/Studio Arts, B
French Language and Literature, B
General Studies, B
Geography, BMO
Geology/Earth Science, B
German Language and Literature, B
Gerontology, BMO
Health and Physical Education, B
Health Education, M
History, BM
Human Resources Management/Personnel
    Administration, B
Industrial and Organizational Psychology, MD
Industrial Technology/Technician, B
Information Science/Studies, D
International/Global Studies, B
Journalism, B
Latin American Studies, B
Library Science, B
Management Information Systems and
    Services, BMD
Manufacturing Technology/Technician, B
Marketing/Marketing Management, B
Mathematics, BM
Multi-/Interdisciplinary Studies, B
Music, BM

Music Performance, B
Music Teacher Education, B
Music Theory and Composition, B
Natural Sciences, B
Parks, Recreation, Leisure and Fitness Studies, B
Philosophy, B
Physical Education Teaching and Coaching, BM
Physics, B
Political Science and Government, BM
Psychology, BMDO
Public Administration, MD
Public Health, M
Reading Teacher Education, M
Real Estate, B
Recreation and Park Management, M
Religion/Religious Studies, B
School Psychology, O
Secondary Education and Teaching, BM
Social Work, BM
Sociology, BM
Spanish Language and Literature, B
Special Education and Teaching, M
Speech and Rhetorical Studies, B
Technical Communication, O
Theater, M
Urban Education and Leadership, O
Voice and Opera, B
Women's Studies, B
Writing, O

VATTEROTT COLLEGE (OMAHA)

Commercial and Advertising Art, A
Heating, Air Conditioning, Ventilation and
    Refrigeration Maintenance
    Technology/Technician, A
Medical Administrative Assistant/Secretary, A
Medical/Clinical Assistant, A
Veterinary/Animal Health Technology/Technician and
    Veterinary Assistant, A

WAYNE STATE COLLEGE

Accounting, B
Advertising, B
Agricultural Business and Management, B
Applied Mathematics, B
Art Teacher Education, B
Art/Art Studies, General, B
Athletic Training and Sports Medicine, B
Biology Teacher Education, B
Biology/Biological Sciences, B
Business Administration and Management, B
Business Administration, Management and
    Operations, M
Business Teacher Education, B
Business/Managerial Economics, B
Chemistry, B
Chemistry Teacher Education, B
Child Care Provider/Assistant, B
Clinical Laboratory Science/Medical
    Technology/Technologist, B
Communication and Media Studies, M
Comparative Literature, B
Computer and Information Sciences, B
Counseling Psychology, B
Counselor Education/School Counseling and
    Guidance Services, M
Creative Writing, B
Criminal Justice/Law Enforcement Administration, B
Criminal Justice/Police Science, B
Criminal Justice/Safety Studies, B
Drama and Dance Teacher Education, B
Drama and Dramatics/Theatre Arts, B
Early Childhood Education and Teaching, B
Education, BMO
Educational Administration and Supervision, MO
Educational Media/Instructional Technology, M
Elementary Education and Teaching, BM
English as a Second Language, M
English Education, M
English Language and Literature, B
English/Language Arts Teacher Education, B
Exercise and Sports Science, M
Family and Consumer Sciences/Home Economics
    Teacher Education, B
Family and Consumer Sciences/Human Sciences, B
Fashion Merchandising, B

Finance, B
Foreign Language Teacher Education, B
French Language and Literature, B
Geography, B
Geography Teacher Education, B
German Language and Literature, B
Graphic Design, B
Health Education, M
History, B
History Teacher Education, B
Home Economics Education, M
Industrial Production Technologies/Technicians, B
Information Science/Studies, B
Interdisciplinary Studies, BM
Interior Design, B
Journalism, B
Junior High/Intermediate/Middle School Education
    and Teaching, B
Kinesiology and Exercise Science, B
Mass Communication/Media Studies, B
Mathematics, B
Mathematics Teacher Education, BM
Modern Languages, B
Music, B
Music Teacher Education, BM
Natural Sciences, B
Physical Education Teaching and Coaching, BM
Physical Sciences, B
Political Science and Government, B
Pre-Medicine/Pre-Medical Studies, B
Pre-Veterinary Studies, B
Psychology, B
Psychology Teacher Education, B
Public Administration, B
Science Teacher Education/General Science
    Teacher Education, BM
Social Science Teacher Education, B
Social Sciences, B
Social Studies Teacher Education, M
Sociology, B
Spanish Language and Literature, B
Special Education and Teaching, BM
Special Products Marketing Operations, B
Speech and Rhetorical Studies, B
Speech Teacher Education, B
Sport and Fitness Administration/Management, BM
Trade and Industrial Teacher Education, B
Vocational and Technical Education, M

WESTERN NEBRASKA COMMUNITY COLLEGE

Agriculture, A
Anthropology, A
Art Teacher Education, A
Art/Art Studies, General, A
Biology/Biological Sciences, A
Business Administration and Management, A
Chemistry, A
Clinical Laboratory Science/Medical
    Technology/Technologist, A
Community Psychology, A
Computer and Information Sciences, A
Criminal Justice/Safety Studies, A
Dietetics/Dieticians, A
Drama and Dance Teacher Education, A
Ecology, A
Economics, A
Elementary Education and Teaching, A
English Language and Literature, A
Forest Management/Forest Resources
    Management, A
French Language and Literature, A
General Studies, A
Geography, A
German Language and Literature, A
Health and Physical Education, A
History, A
Information Technology, A
Interdisciplinary Studies, A
Journalism, A
Kindergarten/PreSchool Education and Teaching, A
Liberal Arts and Sciences Studies and
    Humanities, A
Mathematics, A
Music Teacher Education, A
Nursing - Registered Nurse Training, A

Physical Therapist Assistant, A
Physical Therapy/Therapist, A
Physics, A
Political Science and Government, A
Pre-Dentistry Studies, A
Pre-Engineering, A
Pre-Law Studies, A
Pre-Medicine/Pre-Medical Studies, A
Pre-Pharmacy Studies, A
Pre-Veterinary Studies, A
Psychology, A
Radiologic Technology/Science - Radiographer, A
Secondary Education and Teaching, A
Social Work, A
Sociology, A
Spanish Language and Literature, A

YORK COLLEGE

Accounting, B
Ancient Near Eastern and Biblical
    Languages, Literatures, and Linguistics, B
Art Teacher Education, B
Bible/Biblical Studies, B
Biological and Physical Sciences, B
Biology Teacher Education, B
Biology/Biological Sciences, B
Business Administration and Management, B
Business Teacher Education, B
Education, B
Elementary Education and Teaching, B
English Language and Literature, B
English/Language Arts Teacher Education, B
General Studies, B
History, B
History Teacher Education, B
Human Resources Management/Personnel
    Administration, B
Junior High/Intermediate/Middle School Education
    and Teaching, B
Liberal Arts and Sciences Studies and
    Humanities, AB
Mathematics Teacher Education, B
Music, B
Music Teacher Education, B
Natural Sciences, B
Physical Education Teaching and Coaching, B
Physiological Psychology/Psychobiology, B
Psychology, B
Psychology Teacher Education, B
Reading Teacher Education, B
Religion/Religious Studies, B
Religious Education, B
Science Teacher Education/General Science
    Teacher Education, B
Secondary Education and Teaching, B
Social Science Teacher Education, B
Social Studies Teacher Education, B
Special Education and Teaching, B
Speech Teacher Education, B
Teacher Education, Multiple Levels, B

Nevada

THE ART INSTITUTE OF LAS VEGAS

CAD/CADD Drafting and/or Design
    Technology/Technician, A
Interior Design, AB
Restaurant, Culinary, and Catering
    Management/Manager, B

CAREER COLLEGE OF NORTHERN NEVADA

Business Administration and Management, A
Computer and Information Sciences, A
Data Processing and Data Processing
    Technology/Technician, A
Electrical, Electronic and Communications
    Engineering Technology/Technician, A
Management Information Systems and Services, A
Medical/Clinical Assistant, A

COMMUNITY COLLEGE OF SOUTHERN NEVADA

Accounting, A
Administrative Assistant and Secretarial Science, A

Anthropology, A
Art/Art Studies, General, A
Automobile/Automotive Mechanics
    Technology/Technician, A
Behavioral Sciences, A
Biological and Physical Sciences, A
Biology/Biological Sciences, A
Building/Construction
    Finishing, Management, and Inspection, A
Business Administration and Management, A
Chemistry, A
Child Development, A
Clinical Laboratory Science/Medical
    Technology/Technologist, A
Clinical/Medical Laboratory Technician, A
Commercial and Advertising Art, A
Comparative Literature, A
Computer Engineering Technology/Technician, A
Computer Programming/Programmer, A
Computer Science, A
Computer Typography and Composition Equipment
    Operator, A
Construction Engineering Technology/Technician, A
Consumer Merchandising/Retailing Management, A
Corrections, A
Criminal Justice/Law Enforcement Administration, A
Criminal Justice/Police Science, A
Culinary Arts/Chef Training, A
Data Processing and Data Processing
    Technology/Technician, A
Dental Hygiene/Hygienist, A
Drafting and Design Technology/Technician, A
Drafting/Design Engineering
    Technologies/Technicians, A
Drama and Dramatics/Theatre Arts, A
Economics, A
Electrical, Electronic and Communications
    Engineering Technology/Technician, A
Emergency Medical Technology/Technician (EMT
    Paramedic), A
English Language and Literature, A
Environmental Studies, A
Finance, A
Fire Science/Firefighting, A
Food Technology and Processing, A
Graphic and Printing Equipment Operator
    Production, A
Health Information/Medical Records
    Administration/Administrator, A
Heating, Air Conditioning, Ventilation and
    Refrigeration Maintenance
    Technology/Technician, A
Heavy Equipment Maintenance
    Technology/Technician, A
History, A
Horticultural Science, A
Hospitality Administration/Management, A
Hotel/Motel Administration/Management, A
Industrial Radiologic Technology/Technician, A
Information Science/Studies, A
Kindergarten/PreSchool Education and Teaching, A
Landscaping and Groundskeeping, A
Legal Administrative Assistant/Secretary, A
Legal Assistant/Paralegal, A
Liberal Arts and Sciences Studies and
    Humanities, A
Licensed Practical/Vocational Nurse Training, A
Marketing/Marketing Management, A
Mass Communication/Media Studies, A
Mathematics, A
Mechanical Engineering/Mechanical
    Technology/Technician, A
Medical Administrative Assistant/Secretary, A
Medical/Clinical Assistant, A
Music, A
Nursing - Registered Nurse Training, A
Occupational Therapy/Therapist, A
Ornamental Horticulture, A
Parks, Recreation, Leisure and Fitness Studies, A
Pharmacy, A
Photography, A
Radio and Television, A
Radiologic Technology/Science - Radiographer, A
Real Estate, A
Respiratory Care Therapy/Therapist, A

Science Teacher Education/General Science
    Teacher Education, A
Sign Language Interpretation and Translation, A
Social Sciences, A
Sociology, A
Special Products Marketing Operations, A
Survey Technology/Surveying, A
Teacher Assistant/Aide, A
Veterinary/Animal Health Technology/Technician and
    Veterinary Assistant, A
Welding Technology/Welder, A
Wildlife and Wildlands Science and Management, A

DEEP SPRINGS COLLEGE

Liberal Arts and Sciences Studies and
    Humanities, A

DEVRY UNIVERSITY

Business Administration and Management, B
Business Administration, Management and
    Operations, M
Computer Technology/Computer Systems
    Technology, A
Electrical, Electronic and Communications
    Engineering Technology/Technician, A

GREAT BASIN COLLEGE

Anthropology, A
Art/Art Studies, General, A
Business Administration and Management, A
Business/Commerce, A
Chemistry, A
Criminal Justice/Safety Studies, A
Data Processing and Data Processing
    Technology/Technician, A
Diesel Mechanics Technology/Technician, A
Electrical, Electronic and Communications
    Engineering Technology/Technician, A
Elementary Education and Teaching, AB
English Language and Literature, A
Environmental Studies, A
Geology/Earth Science, A
History, A
Industrial Technology/Technician, A
Interdisciplinary Studies, A
Kindergarten/PreSchool Education and Teaching, A
Mathematics, A
Nursing - Registered Nurse Training, AB
Office Management and Supervision, A
Operations Management and Supervision, A
Physics, A
Psychology, A
Secondary Education and Teaching, B
Social Work, B
Sociology, A
Welding Technology/Welder, A

ITT TECHNICAL INSTITUTE

Animation, Interactive Technology, Video Graphics
    and Special Effects, B
Business Administration and Management, B
CAD/CADD Drafting and/or Design
    Technology/Technician, A
Computer and Information Systems Security, B
Computer Programming/Programmer, A
Criminal Justice/Law Enforcement Administration, B
Electrical, Electronic and Communications
    Engineering Technology/Technician, AB
System, Networking, and LAN/WAN
    Management/Manager, A
Web Page, Digital/Multimedia and Information
    Resources Design, A
Web/Multimedia Management and Webmaster, A

LAS VEGAS COLLEGE

Accounting, A
Administrative Assistant and Secretarial Science, A
Business Administration and Management, A
Court Reporting/Court Reporter, A
Legal Assistant/Paralegal, A
Medical/Clinical Assistant, A

MORRISON UNIVERSITY

Accounting, AB
Administrative Assistant and Secretarial Science, A

Business Administration and Management, AB
Business Administration, Management and
    Operations, M
Computer Science, A
Information Science/Studies, A
Legal Administrative Assistant/Secretary, A
Legal Assistant/Paralegal, A
Medical Administrative Assistant/Secretary, A
Tourism and Travel Services Management, A

NEVADA STATE COLLEGE AT HENDERSON

Animation, Interactive Technology, Video Graphics
    and Special Effects, B
Audiovisual Communications
    Technologies/Technicians, B
Bilingual and Multilingual Education, B
Biology Teacher Education, B
Biology/Biological Sciences, B
Business Administration and Management, B
Computer Programming/Programmer, B
Criminal Justice/Law Enforcement Administration, B
Economics, B
Education, B
English Language and Literature, B
English/Language Arts Teacher Education, B
Environmental Sciences, B
History, B
History Teacher Education, B
Liberal Arts and Sciences Studies and
    Humanities, B
Mathematics Teacher Education, B
Multi-/Interdisciplinary Studies, B
Nursing - Registered Nurse Training, B
Pre-Nursing Studies, B
Psychology, B
Public Administration, B
Science Teacher Education/General Science
    Teacher Education, B
Social Science Teacher Education, B
Special Education and Teaching, B
Speech-Language Pathology/Pathologist, B

PIMA MEDICAL INSTITUTE

Radiologic Technology/Science - Radiographer, A
Respiratory Therapy Technician/Assistant, A

SIERRA NEVADA COLLEGE

Art/Art Studies, General, B
Biological and Physical Sciences, B
Business Administration and Management, B
Computer and Information Sciences, B
Ecology, B
Education, O
Elementary Education and Teaching, O
Environmental Studies, B
Fine/Studio Arts, B
Hotel/Motel Administration/Management, B
Humanities/Humanistic Studies, B
Music, B
Sales, Distribution and Marketing Operations, B
Secondary Education and Teaching, O

TRUCKEE MEADOWS COMMUNITY COLLEGE

Accounting, A
Administrative Assistant and Secretarial Science, A
Architectural Engineering Technology/Technician, A
Automobile/Automotive Mechanics
    Technology/Technician, A
Business Administration and Management, A
Carpentry/Carpenter, A
Child Development, A
Commercial and Advertising Art, A
Computer Engineering Technology/Technician, A
Computer Programming, A
Computer Programming/Programmer, A
Construction Engineering Technology/Technician, A
Corrections, A
Criminal Justice/Law Enforcement Administration, A
Criminal Justice/Police Science, A
Culinary Arts/Chef Training, A
Data Processing and Data Processing
    Technology/Technician, A
Dental Assisting/Assistant, A

Dental Hygiene/Hygienist, A
Dietician Assistant, A
Drafting and Design Technology/Technician, A
Electrical, Electronic and Communications
  Engineering Technology/Technician, A
Elementary Education and Teaching, A
Engineering Technology, A
Environmental Biology, A
Environmental Studies, A
Fire Science/Firefighting, A
Heating, Air Conditioning, Ventilation and
  Refrigeration Maintenance
  Technology/Technician, A
Hospitality Administration/Management, A
Industrial Radiologic Technology/Technician, A
Information Science/Studies, A
Kindergarten/PreSchool Education and Teaching, A
Landscape Architecture, A
Legal Administrative Assistant/Secretary, A
Liberal Arts and Sciences Studies and
  Humanities, A
Marketing/Marketing Management, A
Medical Administrative Assistant/Secretary, A
Mental Health/Rehabilitation, A
Military Studies, A
Nursing - Registered Nurse Training, A
Pipefitting/Pipefitter and Sprinkler Fitter, A
Radiologic Technology/Science - Radiographer, A
Real Estate, A
Secondary Education and Teaching, A
Solar Energy Technology/Technician, A
Substance Abuse/Addiction Counseling, A
Teacher Education, Multiple Levels, A
Welding Technology/Welder, A

UNIVERSITY OF NEVADA, LAS VEGAS

Accounting, BM
Adult and Continuing Education and Teaching, B
African-American/Black Studies, B
Anthropology, BMD
Applied Mathematics, BM
Architecture, BM
Art History, Criticism and Conservation, B
Art/Art Studies, General, B
Athletic Training and Sports Medicine, B
Biochemistry, BM
Biological and Biomedical Sciences, MD
Biology/Biological Sciences, B
Business Administration and Management, B
Business Administration, Management and
  Operations, M
Chemistry, BMD
City/Urban, Community and Regional Planning, B
Civil Engineering, BMD
Clinical Laboratory Science/Medical
  Technology/Technologist, B
Clinical Psychology, D
Communication and Media Studies, M
Communication Studies/Speech Communication
  and Rhetoric, B
Comparative Literature, B
Composition, M
Computer Engineering, BMD
Computer Science, BMD
Construction Engineering, B
Construction Engineering and Management, M
Counseling Psychology, M
Criminal Justice/Law Enforcement Administration, B
Criminology, M
Culinary Arts/Chef Training, B
Curriculum and Instruction, MDO
Dance, BM
Drama and Dramatics/Theatre Arts, B
Dramatic/Theatre Arts and Stagecraft, B
Economics, BM
Education, BMDO
Educational Administration and Supervision, MDO
Educational Leadership and Administration, M
Educational Measurement and Evaluation, D
Educational Media/Instructional Technology, M
Educational Psychology, MDO
Electrical Engineering, MD
Electrical, Electronics and Communications
  Engineering, B
Elementary Education and Teaching, BM
Engineering and Applied Sciences, MD

English, MD
English as a Second Language, M
English Education, M
English Language and Literature, B
Environmental Sciences, MD
Environmental Studies, B
Ethics, M
Ethnic and Cultural Studies, B
Exercise and Sports Science, M
Experimental Psychology, D
Film, Television, and Video Production, M
Film/Cinema Studies, B
Finance, B
Fine Arts and Art Studies, M
French Language and Literature, BM
Geological and Earth Sciences/Geosciences, B
Geology/Earth Science, B
Geosciences, MD
German Language and Literature, B
Gerontological Nursing, M
Gerontology, B
Health and Medical Laboratory Technologies, B
Health Physics/Radiological Health, M
Health Promotion, M
Health Teacher Education, B
Health/Health Care Administration/Management, B
Health/Medical Physics, B
Higher Education/Higher Education
  Administration, M
History, BMD
Hospitality Administration/Management, BMD
Human Resources Management/Personnel
  Administration, B
Human Services, B
Interdisciplinary Studies, B
Interior Architecture, B
International Business/Trade/Commerce, B
Jazz/Jazz Studies, B
Kindergarten/PreSchool Education and Teaching, B
Kinesiology and Exercise Science, B
Kinesiology and Movement Studies, M
Landscape Architecture, B
Law and Legal Studies, PO
Leisure Studies, M
Management Information Systems and
  Services, BM
Marketing/Marketing Management, B
Marriage and Family Therapy/Counseling, BM
Mass Communication/Media Studies, M
Mathematics, BM
Mathematics Teacher Education, M
Mechanical Engineering, BMD
Medical Radiologic Technology/Science - Radiation
  Therapist, B
Middle School Education, M
Music, BMD
Music Teacher Education, M
Music Theory and Composition, BM
Nuclear Medical Technology/Technologist, B
Nursing, MD
Nursing - Advanced Practice, M
Nursing - Registered Nurse Training, B
Nutritional Sciences, B
Parks, Recreation, Leisure and Fitness Studies, B
Pediatric Nurse/Nursing, M
Performance, MD
Philosophy, B
Physical Education Teaching and Coaching, BMD
Physical Therapy/Therapist, MD
Physics, BMD
Political Science and Government, BM
Psychology, BMD
Public Administration, MD
Public Affairs, D
Public Health (MPH, DPH), B
Public Policy Analysis, M
Real Estate, B
Rehabilitation Counseling, M
Romance Languages, Literatures, and Linguistics, B
School Psychology, O
Secondary Education and Teaching, BM
Social Sciences, B
Social Work, BM
Sociology, BMD
Spanish Language and Literature, BM
Special Education and Teaching, BMDO

Sport and Fitness Administration/Management, BMD
Statistics, BM
Theater, M
Tourism and Travel Services Management, B
Transportation and Highway Engineering, M
Vocational and Technical Education, M
Water Resources, M
Women's Studies, B
Writing, M

UNIVERSITY OF NEVADA, RENO

Accounting, BM
Advertising, B
Agricultural Animal Breeding, B
Agricultural Economics, BM
Agricultural Sciences, MD
Agricultural Teacher Education, B
Animal Sciences, BM
Anthropology, BMD
Applied Economics, M
Art History, Criticism and Conservation, B
Art Teacher Education, B
Art/Art Studies, General, B
Atmospheric Sciences and Meteorology, MD
Biochemistry, BMD
Biological and Biomedical Sciences, MD
Biology/Biological Sciences, B
Biomedical Engineering, MD
BioTechnology, BM
Broadcast Journalism, B
Business Administration, Management and
  Operations, M
Business Teacher Education, B
Business/Commerce, B
Business/Managerial Economics, B
Cell Biology and Anatomy, MD
Chemical Engineering, BMD
Chemistry, BMD
Child and Family Studies, M
Child Development, B
Civil Engineering, BMD
Communication Disorders, MD
Communication Studies/Speech Communication
  and Rhetoric, B
Computer and Information Sciences, B
Computer Engineering, BMD
Computer Science, BMD
Conservation Biology, D
Construction Engineering Technology/Technician, B
Counselor Education/School Counseling and
  Guidance Services, MDO
Criminology, B
Curriculum and Instruction, MDO
Drama and Dramatics/Theatre Arts, B
Ecology, D
Economics, M
Education, MDO
Educational Leadership and Administration, MDO
Educational Psychology, MDO
Electrical Engineering, MD
Electrical, Electronics and Communications
  Engineering, B
Elementary Education and Teaching, BMO
Engineering and Applied Sciences, MDO
Engineering Physics, B
English, MD
English Composition, B
English Language and Literature, B
English/Language Arts Teacher Education, B
Entrepreneurship/Entrepreneurial Studies, B
Environmental and Occupational Health, MD
Environmental Policy and Resource
  Management, M
Environmental Sciences, MD
Environmental/Environmental Health Engineering, B
Evolutionary Biology, D
Family and Consumer Sciences/Home Economics
  Teacher Education, B
Finance, B
Foods, Nutrition, and Wellness Studies, B
Foreign Language Teacher Education, BM
Forestry, B
French Language and Literature, BM
General Studies, B
Geochemistry, MD
Geography, BM

Geological Engineering, MO
Geological/Geophysical Engineering, B
Geology/Earth Science, BMD
Geophysics and Seismology, BMD
German Language and Literature, BM
Health Professions and Related Clinical Sciences, B
Health Teacher Education, B
Health/Medical Preparatory Programs, B
History, BMD
Hospitality Administration/Management, B
Housing and Human Environments, B
Human Development, M
Human Development and Family Studies, B
Human Resources Management/Personnel
    Administration, B
Hydrology and Water Resources Science, MD
International Business/Trade/Commerce, B
International Relations and Affairs, B
Journalism, BM
Legal and Justice Studies, M
Logistics and Materials Management, B
Marketing/Marketing Management, B
Mathematics, BM
Mathematics Teacher Education, BM
Mechanical Engineering, BMD
Metallurgical Engineering, BMDO
Mineral/Mining Engineering, MO
Mining and Mineral Engineering, B
Molecular Biology, MD
Molecular Pharmacology, MD
Music, BM
Music Performance, B
Music Teacher Education, B
Natural Resources and Conservation, B
Natural Resources Management/Development and
    Policy, B
Nursing, M
Nursing - Registered Nurse Training, B
Nutritional Sciences, M
Parks, Recreation, Leisure and Fitness Studies, B
Philosophy, BM
Physical Education Teaching and Coaching, B
Physics, BMD
Physiology, MD
Political Science and Government, BMD
Pre-Medicine/Pre-Medical Studies, B
Pre-Veterinary Studies, B
Psychology, BMD
Public Administration, M
Public Health, M
Reading Teacher Education, MD
Science Teacher Education/General Science
    Teacher Education, B
Science, Technology and Society, B
Secondary Education and Teaching, MO
Social Psychology, BD
Social Science Teacher Education, B
Social Studies Teacher Education, B
Social Work, BM
Sociology, BM
Spanish Language and Literature, BM
Special Education and Teaching, BMD
Speech and Rhetorical Studies, M
Speech-Language Pathology/Pathologist, B
Teacher Education and Professional
    Development, Specific Subject Areas, B
Technology Teacher Education/Industrial Arts
    Teacher Education, B
Trade and Industrial Teacher Education, B
Water Resources Engineering, B
Western European Studies, D
Wildlife and Wildlands Science and Management, B
Women's Studies, B

UNIVERSITY OF PHOENIX-NEVADA CAMPUS

Accounting, B
Business Administration and Management, B
Business Administration, Management and
    Operations, M
Business, Management, Marketing, and Related
    Support Services, B
Computer and Information Sciences, B
Counselor Education/School Counseling and
    Guidance Services, M
Curriculum and Instruction, M

Education, M
Educational Administration and Supervision, M
Electronic Commerce, M
Elementary Education and Teaching, M
Health Services Administration, M
Human Resources Management and Services, M
Human Services, M
Management, M
Management Information Systems and Services, M
Management of Technology, M
Marketing, M
Marketing/Marketing Management, B
Marriage and Family Therapy/Counseling, M
Organizational Management, M
Public Administration and Social Service
    Professions, B

WESTERN NEVADA COMMUNITY COLLEGE

Accounting, A
Accounting Technology/Technician and
    Bookkeeping, A
Administrative Assistant and Secretarial Science, A
Automobile/Automotive Mechanics
    Technology/Technician, A
Biology/Biological Sciences, A
Building/Construction
    Finishing, Management, and Inspection, A
Business Administration and Management, A
Business/Commerce, A
Business/Office Automation/Technology/Data
    Entry, A
Carpentry/Carpenter, A
Child Care and Support Services Management, A
Clinical/Medical Laboratory Technician, A
Computer and Information Sciences, A
Computer Programming/Programmer, A
Corrections, A
Criminal Justice/Law Enforcement Administration, A
Criminal Justice/Police Science, A
Drafting and Design Technology/Technician, A
Electrical and Power Transmission
    Installation/Installer, A
Electrical, Electronic and Communications
    Engineering Technology/Technician, A
Engineering, A
Environmental Studies, A
Fire Protection and Safety Technology/Technician, A
General Studies, A
Heating, Air Conditioning, Ventilation and
    Refrigeration Maintenance
    Technology/Technician, A
Industrial Technology/Technician, A
Legal Assistant/Paralegal, A
Liberal Arts and Sciences Studies and
    Humanities, A
Machine Tool Technology/Machinist, A
Management Information Systems and Services, A
Management Science, A
Marketing/Marketing Management, A
Mason/Masonry, A
Mathematics, A
Nursing - Registered Nurse Training, A
Parks, Recreation and Leisure Facilities
    Management, A
Physical Sciences, A
Pipefitting/Pipefitter and Sprinkler Fitter, A
Real Estate, A
Sheet Metal Technology/Sheetworking, A
Welding Technology/Welder, A

New Hampshire

CHESTER COLLEGE OF NEW ENGLAND

Creative Writing, B
Fine/Studio Arts, B
Graphic Design, B
Interdisciplinary Studies, B
Journalism, B
Photography, B

COLBY-SAWYER COLLEGE

Art Teacher Education, B
Art/Art Studies, General, B

Athletic Training and Sports Medicine, B
Biology/Biological Sciences, B
Business Administration and Management, B
Developmental and Child Psychology, B
Early Childhood Education and Teaching, B
English Language and Literature, B
English/Language Arts Teacher Education, B
Environmental Studies, B
Fine/Studio Arts, B
Graphic Design, B
Kinesiology and Exercise Science, B
Liberal Arts and Sciences Studies and
    Humanities, A
Mass Communication/Media Studies, B
Nursing - Registered Nurse Training, B
Psychology, B
Social Sciences, B
Social Studies Teacher Education, B
Sport and Fitness Administration/Management, B

DANIEL WEBSTER COLLEGE

Aeronautics/Aviation/Aerospace Science and
    Technology, AB
Air Traffic Controller, B
Airline/Commercial/Professional Pilot and Flight
    Crew, AB
Aviation/Airway Management and Operations, AB
Business Administration and Management, AB
Computer Programming/Programmer, AB
Computer Science, B
Engineering, B
Engineering Science, A
Information Science/Studies, AB
Liberal Arts and Sciences Studies and
    Humanities, A
Management Information Systems and Services, AB
Marketing/Marketing Management, A
Social Sciences, A
Sport and Fitness Administration/Management, B

DARTMOUTH COLLEGE

African Studies, B
African-American/Black Studies, B
Allopathic Medicine, PO
American Indian/Native American Studies, B
Ancient/Classical Greek Language and Literature, B
Animal Genetics, B
Anthropology, B
Arabic Language and Literature, B
Archeology, B
Art History, Criticism and Conservation, B
Asian Studies/Civilization, B
Astronomy, BMD
Biochemical Engineering, MD
Biochemistry, BDO
Biological and Biomedical Sciences, D
Biology/Biological Sciences, B
Biomedical Engineering, MDO
BioTechnology, MD
Business Administration, Management and
    Operations, MO
Chemistry, BD
Chinese Language and Literature, B
Classics and Classical
    Languages, Literatures, and Linguistics, B
Cognitive Psychology and Psycholinguistics, B
Cognitive Sciences, D
Comparative Literature, BM
Computer Engineering, MD
Computer Science, BMD
Creative Writing, B
Drama and Dramatics/Theatre Arts, B
East Asian
    Languages, Literatures, and Linguistics, B
Ecology, B
Economics, B
Electrical Engineering, MD
Engineering, B
Engineering and Applied Sciences, MDO
Engineering Management, MO
Engineering Physics, BMD
English Language and Literature, B
Environmental Studies, B
Evolutionary Biology, B
Film/Cinema Studies, B
Fine/Studio Arts, B

French Language and Literature, B
Genetics, D
Geography, B
Geology/Earth Science, B
Geosciences, MD
German Language and Literature, B
Health Services Research, MD
Hebrew Language and Literature, B
Hispanic-American, Puerto Rican, and Mexican-
   American/Chicano Studies, B
History, B
Italian Language and Literature, B
Japanese Language and Literature, B
Latin American Studies, B
Latin Language and Literature, B
Liberal Studies, M
Linguistics, B
Manufacturing Engineering, MD
Materials Engineering, MD
Materials Sciences, MD
Mathematics, BD
Mechanical Engineering, MD
Microbiology, D
Molecular Biology, B
Multi-/Interdisciplinary Studies, B
Music, BM
Near and Middle Eastern Studies, B
Neuroscience, DO
Pharmacology, DO
Philosophy, B
Physics, BMD
Physiology, DO
Political Science and Government, B
Psychology, BD
Public Health, M
Religion/Religious Studies, B
Romance Languages, Literatures, and Linguistics, B
Russian Language and Literature, B
Russian Studies, B
Sociology, B
Spanish Language and Literature, B
Toxicology, DO
Women's Studies, B

FRANKLIN PIERCE COLLEGE

Accounting, B
Adult and Continuing Education and Teaching, B
Advertising, B
American/United States Studies/Civilization, B
Anthropology, B
Applied Art, B
Archeology, B
Art Teacher Education, B
Art/Art Studies, General, B
Biology/Biological Sciences, B
Business Administration and Management, B
Business Administration, Management and
   Operations, M
Ceramic Arts and Ceramics, B
Clinical Psychology, B
Commercial and Advertising Art, B
Comparative Literature, B
Computer Programming/Programmer, B
Computer Science, B
Counselor Education/School Counseling and
   Guidance Services, B
Creative Writing, B
Criminal Justice/Law Enforcement Administration, B
Drama and Dramatics/Theatre Arts, B
Ecology, B
Economics, B
Education, B
Elementary Education and Teaching, B
English Language and Literature, B
Environmental Biology, B
Environmental Studies, B
Finance, B
Fine/Studio Arts, B
History, B
Journalism, B
Kindergarten/PreSchool Education and Teaching, B
Liberal Arts and Sciences Studies and
   Humanities, B
Management Information Systems and Services, M
Marketing/Marketing Management, B
Mass Communication/Media Studies, B

Mathematics, B
Music, B
Parks, Recreation and Leisure Facilities
   Management, B
Physical Therapy/Therapist, M
Political Science and Government, B
Pre-Dentistry Studies, B
Pre-Law Studies, B
Pre-Medicine/Pre-Medical Studies, B
Pre-Veterinary Studies, B
Psychology, B
Radio and Television, B
Secondary Education and Teaching, B
Social Work, B
Sociology, B
Sport and Fitness Administration/Management, B

GRANITE STATE COLLEGE

Behavioral Sciences, AB
Business Administration and Management, AB
Computer Programming/Programmer, B
Computer Systems Analysis/Analyst, B
Corrections and Criminal Justice, B
Criminal Justice/Law Enforcement Administration, B
Early Childhood Education and Teaching, AB
Finance, B
General Studies, A
Health/Health Care Administration/Management, B
Human Resources Management/Personnel
   Administration, B
Liberal Arts and Sciences Studies and
   Humanities, AB

HESSER COLLEGE

Accounting, AB
Business Administration and Management, AB
Business and Personal/Financial Services Marketing
   Operations, A
Child Care and Support Services Management, A
Commercial and Advertising Art, A
Computer and Information Sciences, A
Computer Engineering Technology/Technician, A
Computer Programming/Programmer, A
Computer Science, A
Computer Systems Analysis/Analyst, A
Corrections, A
Criminal Justice/Law Enforcement
   Administration, AB
Criminal Justice/Police Science, AB
Criminal Justice/Safety Studies, B
Human Services, A
Information Science/Studies, A
Interior Design, A
Kindergarten/PreSchool Education and Teaching, A
Legal Assistant/Paralegal, A
Liberal Arts and Sciences Studies and
   Humanities, A
Management Information Systems and Services, A
Marketing/Marketing Management, AB
Mass Communication/Media Studies, A
Medical Administrative Assistant/Secretary, A
Medical/Clinical Assistant, A
Physical Therapist Assistant, A
Psychology, A
Radio and Television, A
Sales, Distribution and Marketing Operations, A
Security and Loss Prevention Services, A
Social Work, A
Sport and Fitness Administration/Management, A

KEENE STATE COLLEGE

Acting, B
American/United States Studies/Civilization, B
Applied Mathematics, B
Architectural Technology/Technician, B
Art/Art Studies, General, B
Athletic Training and Sports Medicine, B
Biology Teacher Education, B
Biology/Biological Sciences, B
Business Administration and Management, B
Chemistry, AB
Chemistry Teacher Education, B
Cinematography and Film/Video Production, B
Commercial and Advertising Art, B
Communication Studies/Speech Communication
   and Rhetoric, B

Computer and Information Sciences, AB
Computer Science, AB
Computer Teacher Education, B
Counselor Education/School Counseling and
   Guidance Services, BMO
Curriculum and Instruction, BM
Dietetics/Dieticians, B
Drafting and Design Technology/Technician, AB
Drama and Dramatics/Theatre Arts, B
Early Childhood Education and Teaching, A
Ecology, B
Economics, B
Education, BMO
Educational Administration and Supervision, MO
Educational Leadership and Administration, BO
Electrical, Electronic and Communications
   Engineering Technology/Technician, AB
Electromechanical and Instrumentation and
   Maintenance Technologies/Technicians, B
Elementary Education and Teaching, B
Engineering Technologies/Technicians, A
English Language and Literature, B
English/Language Arts Teacher Education, B
Environmental Sciences, B
Environmental Studies, B
Family and Consumer Sciences/Home Economics
   Teacher Education, B
Fine/Studio Arts, B
Foods, Nutrition, and Wellness Studies, B
French Language and Literature, B
French Language Teacher Education, B
General Studies, B
Geography, B
Geography Teacher Education, B
Geology/Earth Science, B
Graphic Design, B
Health and Physical Education, B
Health Teacher Education, B
History, B
History Teacher Education, B
Industrial Technology/Technician, AB
Interdisciplinary Studies, B
Journalism, B
Kindergarten/PreSchool Education and
   Teaching, AB
Liberal Arts and Sciences Studies and
   Humanities, AB
Mass Communication/Media Studies, B
Mathematics, B
Mathematics and Computer Science, B
Mathematics Teacher Education, B
Multi-/Interdisciplinary Studies, B
Music, B
Music History, Literature, and Theory, B
Music Teacher Education, B
Natural Resources and Conservation, B
Occupational Safety and Health
   Technology/Technician, B
Physical Education Teaching and Coaching, B
Pre-Engineering, A
Psychology, B
Science Teacher Education/General Science
   Teacher Education, B
Secondary Education and Teaching, B
Social Science Teacher Education, B
Social Sciences, B
Social Studies Teacher Education, B
Sociology, B
Spanish Language and Literature, B
Spanish Language Teacher Education, B
Special Education and Teaching, BMO
Sport and Fitness Administration/Management, B
Substance Abuse/Addiction Counseling, A
Teacher Education and Professional
   Development, Specific Subject Areas, B
Technical Theatre/Theatre Design and
   Technology, B
Technology Education/Industrial Arts, B
Technology Teacher Education/Industrial Arts
   Teacher Education, B

Trade and Industrial Teacher Education, B

MAGDALEN COLLEGE

Liberal Arts and Sciences Studies and
   Humanities, B

McINTOSH COLLEGE

Accounting, A
Administrative Assistant and Secretarial Science, A
Business Administration and Management, A
Computer and Information Sciences, A
Criminal Justice/Law Enforcement Administration, A
Culinary Arts/Chef Training, A
Information Science/Studies, A
Legal Administrative Assistant/Secretary, A
Legal Assistant/Paralegal, A
Medical Administrative Assistant/Secretary, A
Medical/Clinical Assistant, A
Telecommunications Technology/Technician, A

NEW ENGLAND COLLEGE

Accounting, B
Advertising, B
Art History, Criticism and Conservation, B
Art/Art Studies, General, B
Biology/Biological Sciences, B
Business Administration and Management, B
Counseling Psychology, M
Criminal Justice/Law Enforcement Administration, B
Drama and Dramatics/Theatre Arts, B
Drawing, B
Education, BM
Educational Leadership and Administration, M
Elementary Education and Teaching, B
English Language and Literature, B
Environmental Studies, B
Fine/Studio Arts, B
Health and Physical Education, B
History, B
Journalism, B
Liberal Arts and Sciences Studies and
   Humanities, A
Management, M
Marketing/Marketing Management, B
Mass Communication/Media Studies, B
Parks, Recreation and Leisure Facilities
   Management, B
Parks, Recreation, Leisure and Fitness Studies, B
Philosophy, B
Photography, B
Physical Education Teaching and Coaching, B
Political Science and Government, B
Pre-Law Studies, B
Psychology, B
Public Policy Analysis, M
Public Relations/Image Management, B
Secondary Education and Teaching, B
Sociology, B
Special Education and Teaching, BM
Sport and Fitness Administration/Management, B
Teacher Education, Multiple Levels, B
Writing, M

NEW HAMPSHIRE COMMUNITY TECHNICAL COLLEGE, BERLIN/LACONIA

Accounting, A
Administrative Assistant and Secretarial Science, A
Automobile/Automotive Mechanics
   Technology/Technician, A
Business Administration and Management, A
Cartography, A
Computer and Information Sciences, A
Computer Engineering Technology/Technician, A
Culinary Arts/Chef Training, A
Diesel Mechanics Technology/Technician, A
Environmental Studies, A
Forestry, A
General Studies, A
Human Services, A
Industrial Technology/Technician, A
Kindergarten/PreSchool Education and Teaching, A
Liberal Arts and Sciences Studies and
   Humanities, A
Nursing - Registered Nurse Training, A

Survey Technology/Surveying, A
Water Quality and Wastewater Treatment
   Management and Recycling
   Technology/Technician, A

NEW HAMPSHIRE COMMUNITY TECHNICAL COLLEGE, MANCHESTER/STRATHAM

Accounting, A
Administrative Assistant and Secretarial Science, A
Athletic Training and Sports Medicine, A
Automobile/Automotive Mechanics
   Technology/Technician, A
Business Administration and Management, A
Child Development, A
Commercial and Advertising Art, A
Community Organization and Advocacy, A
Construction Engineering Technology/Technician, A
Drafting and Design Technology/Technician, A
Drafting/Design Engineering
   Technologies/Technicians, A
Heating, Air Conditioning, Ventilation and
   Refrigeration Maintenance
   Technology/Technician, A
Human Services, A
Information Science/Studies, A
Kindergarten/PreSchool Education and Teaching, A
Kinesiology and Exercise Science, A
Liberal Arts and Sciences Studies and
   Humanities, A
Management Information Systems and Services, A
Marketing/Marketing Management, A
Medical Administrative Assistant/Secretary, A
Nursing - Registered Nurse Training, A
Physical Therapy/Therapist, A
Welding Technology/Welder, A

NEW HAMPSHIRE COMMUNITY TECHNICAL COLLEGE, NASHUA/CLAREMONT

Accounting, A
Airframe Mechanics and Aircraft Maintenance
   Technology/Technician, A
Artificial Intelligence and Robotics, A
Autobody/Collision and Repair
   Technology/Technician, A
Automobile/Automotive Mechanics
   Technology/Technician, A
Avionics Maintenance Technology/Technician, A
Business Administration and Management, A
Child Development, A
Computer and Information Sciences, A
Computer Engineering Technology/Technician, A
Computer Science, A
Data Processing and Data Processing
   Technology/Technician, A
Drafting and Design Technology/Technician, A
Electrical, Electronic and Communications
   Engineering Technology/Technician, A
Electromechanical Technology/Electromechanical
   Engineering Technology, A
Engineering Technology, A
General Studies, A
Heavy Equipment Maintenance
   Technology/Technician, A
Human Services, A
Industrial Technology/Technician, A
Information Science/Studies, A
Kindergarten/PreSchool Education and Teaching, A
Law and Legal Studies, A
Legal Assistant/Paralegal, A
Liberal Arts and Sciences Studies and
   Humanities, A
Machine Tool Technology/Machinist, A
Ophthalmic Laboratory Technology/Technician, A
Quality Control Technology/Technician, A
Social Work, A

Telecommunications Technology/Technician, A

NEW HAMPSHIRE INSTITUTE OF ART

Fine/Studio Arts, B

NEW HAMPSHIRE TECHNICAL INSTITUTE

Accounting, A
Animation, Interactive Technology, Video Graphics
   and Special Effects, A
Architectural Engineering Technology/Technician, A
Business Administration and Management, A
Computer and Information Sciences, A
Computer Engineering Technology/Technician, A
Computer Programming, Specific Applications, A
Computer Systems Networking and
   Telecommunications, A
Criminal Justice/Law Enforcement Administration, A
Dental Assisting/Assistant, A
Dental Hygiene/Hygienist, A
Diagnostic Medical Sonography/Sonographer and
   Ultrasound Technician, A
Electrical, Electronic and Communications
   Engineering Technology/Technician, A
Emergency Medical Technology/Technician (EMT
   Paramedic), A
Engineering Technology, A
General Studies, A
Hotel/Motel Administration/Management, A
Human Resources Management/Personnel
   Administration, A
Human Services, A
Kindergarten/PreSchool Education and Teaching, A
Legal Assistant/Paralegal, A
Liberal Arts and Sciences Studies and
   Humanities, A
Marketing/Marketing Management, A
Mechanical Engineering/Mechanical
   Technology/Technician, A
Mental Health/Rehabilitation, A
Nursing - Registered Nurse Training, A
Real Estate, A
Sport and Fitness Administration/Management, A
Substance Abuse/Addiction Counseling, A
Teacher Assistant/Aide, A
Tourism and Travel Services Management, A
Visual and Performing Arts, A

PLYMOUTH STATE UNIVERSITY

Accounting, B
Applied Economics, B
Art Teacher Education, B
Art/Art Studies, General, B
Athletic Training and Sports Medicine, BM
Atmospheric Sciences and Meteorology, B
Biology/Biological Sciences, B
BioTechnology, B
Business Administration and Management, B
Business Administration, Management and
   Operations, M
Business/Commerce, B
Chemistry, B
City/Urban, Community and Regional Planning, B
Communication Studies/Speech Communication
   and Rhetoric, B
Computer Science, B
Counselor Education/School Counseling and
   Guidance Services, M
Criminal Justice/Safety Studies, B
Drama and Dramatics/Theatre Arts, B
Early Childhood Education and Teaching, B
Education, MO
Educational Administration and Supervision, M
Educational Leadership and Administration, M
Elementary Education and Teaching, BM
English Education, M
English Language and Literature, B
Environmental Biology, B
Fine/Studio Arts, B
French Language and Literature, B
Geography, B
Health and Physical Education, B
Health Education, M
History, B
Humanities/Humanistic Studies, B
Information Technology, B

Marketing/Marketing Management, B
Mathematics, B
Mathematics Teacher Education, M
Middle School Education, M
Multi-/Interdisciplinary Studies, B
Music, B
Music Teacher Education, B
Parks, Recreation, Leisure and Fitness Studies, B
Philosophy, B
Political Science and Government, B
Psychology, B
Public Administration, B
Public Health Education and Promotion, B
Reading Teacher Education, M
Secondary Education and Teaching, M
Social Sciences, B
Social Work, B
Spanish Language and Literature, B
Special Education and Teaching, M
Teacher Education and Professional
    Development, Specific Subject Areas, B

RIVIER COLLEGE

American Government and Politics (United States)
    , B
Art/Art Studies, General, AB
Biology Teacher Education, B
Biology/Biological Sciences, B
Business Administration and Management, AB
Business Administration, Management and
    Operations, M
Chemistry, B
Chemistry Teacher Education, B
Commercial and Advertising Art, B
Communication Studies/Speech Communication
    and Rhetoric, B
Computer Science, ABM
Counseling Psychology, M
Counselor Education/School Counseling and
    Guidance Services, M
Criminology, B
Curriculum and Instruction, M
Drawing, B
Early Childhood Education and Teaching, M
Education, BMO
Educational Administration and Supervision, M
Educational Leadership and Administration, O
Elementary Education and Teaching, BM
English, MO
English Language and Literature, B
English/Language Arts Teacher Education, B
Fine/Studio Arts, B
Foreign Language Teacher Education, BM
French Language and Literature, B
History, B
Human Resources Management and Services, M
Information Science/Studies, AB
Kindergarten/PreSchool Education and
    Teaching, AB
Law and Legal Studies, B
Liberal Arts and Sciences Studies and
    Humanities, AB
Management Information Systems and Services, M
Mathematics, BM
Mathematics Teacher Education, B
Modern Languages, B
Nursing, M
Nursing - Registered Nurse Training, AB
Nursing Administration, M
Nursing Education, M
Painting, B
Photography, B
Political Science and Government, B
Pre-Dentistry Studies, B
Pre-Law Studies, B
Pre-Medicine/Pre-Medical Studies, B
Pre-Veterinary Studies, B
Psychoanalysis and Psychotherapy, M
Psychology, B
Reading Teacher Education, M
Secondary Education and Teaching, BM
Social Science Teacher Education, B
Social Studies Teacher Education, M
Sociology, B
Spanish Language and Literature, B
Special Education and Teaching, BM

Writing, M

SAINT ANSELM COLLEGE

Accounting, B
Art/Art Studies, General, B
Biochemistry, B
Biological and Physical Sciences, B
Biology/Biological Sciences, B
Business/Commerce, B
Chemistry, B
Classics and Classical
    Languages, Literatures, and Linguistics, B
Computer Science, B
Criminal Justice/Safety Studies, B
Economics, B
Engineering, B
English Language and Literature, B
Environmental Studies, B
Finance, B
French Language and Literature, B
History, B
Liberal Arts and Sciences Studies and
    Humanities, B
Mathematics, B
Philosophy, B
Political Science and Government, B
Pre-Dentistry Studies, B
Pre-Law Studies, B
Pre-Medicine/Pre-Medical Studies, B
Psychology, B
Secondary Education and Teaching, B
Sociology, B
Spanish Language and Literature, B
Theology/Theological Studies, B

SOUTHERN NEW HAMPSHIRE UNIVERSITY

Accounting, ABM
Advertising, B
Baking and Pastry Arts/Baker/Pastry Chef, A
Business Administration and Management, AB
Business Administration, Management and
    Operations, MDO
Business and Personal/Financial Services Marketing
    Operations, AB
Business Education, M
Business Teacher Education, B
Business/Commerce, B
Business/Managerial Economics, B
Child Development, B
Clinical Psychology, O
Community Health and Preventive Medicine, M
Creative Writing, B
Culinary Arts/Chef Training, A
Curriculum and Instruction, M
Digital Communication and Media/Multimedia, B
Early Childhood Education and Teaching, B
Economics, BMDO
Education, MO
Elementary Education and Teaching, M
English as a Second Language, M
English Language and Literature, B
English/Language Arts Teacher Education, B
Environmental Studies, B
Fashion Merchandising, A
Finance, B
Finance and Banking, M
Graphic Design, B
History, B
Hospitality Administration/Management, B
Information Technology, AB
International Business/Trade/Commerce, ABMD
Liberal Arts and Sciences Studies and
    Humanities, AB
Management Information Systems and Services, M
Marketing/Marketing Management, AB
Organizational Management, M
Political Science and Government, B
Psychology, BMO
Resort Management, B
Retailing and Retail Operations, B
Sales and Marketing Operations/Marketing and
    Distribution Teacher Education, B
Secondary Education and Teaching, BM
Social Sciences, B
Social Studies Teacher Education, B

Special Education and Teaching, O
Sport and Fitness Administration/Management, BM
Substance Abuse/Addiction Counseling, O
Tourism and Travel Services Management, B

THOMAS MORE COLLEGE OF LIBERAL ARTS

Biology/Biological Sciences, B
Comparative Literature, B
Philosophy, B
Political Science and Government, B

UNIVERSITY OF NEW HAMPSHIRE

Accounting, BM
Adult and Continuing Education and Teaching, BM
Agricultural Business and Management, AB
Agricultural Teacher Education, B
Agriculture, B
Agronomy and Crop Science, B
Agronomy and Soil Sciences, M
American/United States Studies/Civilization, B
Animal Sciences, ABMD
Animal/Livestock Husbandry and Production, AB
Anthropology, B
Applied Mathematics, M
Art History, Criticism and Conservation, B
Art Teacher Education, B
Art/Art Studies, General, B
Athletic Training and Sports Medicine, B
Audiology/Audiologist and Speech-Language
    Pathology/Pathologist, B
Biochemistry, BMD
Biological and Physical Sciences, B
Biology/Biological Sciences, B
Biomedical Technology/Technician, B
Botany/Plant Biology, B
Building/Construction
    Finishing, Management, and Inspection, A
Business Administration and Management, AB
Business Administration, Management and
    Operations, M
Cell/Cellular Biology and Histology, B
Chemical Engineering, BMD
Chemistry, BMD
Chemistry Teacher Education, B
Child and Family Studies, M
Child Development, B
City/Urban, Community and Regional Planning, B
Civil Engineering, BMD
Civil Engineering Technology/Technician, A
Classics and Classical
    Languages, Literatures, and Linguistics, B
Clinical/Medical Laboratory Technician, B
Communication Disorders, BM
Community Organization and Advocacy, A
Comparative Literature, BM
Computer Engineering, B
Computer Science, BMD
Computer Software Technology/Technician, A
Construction Engineering Technology/Technician, A
Counselor Education/School Counseling and
    Guidance Services, M
Criminal Justice/Law Enforcement Administration, B
Culinary Arts/Chef Training, A
Dairy Science, AB
Dietetic Technician (DTR), A
Dietetics/Dieticians, AB
Drama and Dramatics/Theatre Arts, B
Early Childhood Education and Teaching, M
Ecology, B
Economics, BMD
Education, MDO
Educational Administration and Supervision, MO
Educational Leadership and Administration, M
Electrical Engineering, MD
Electrical, Electronics and Communications
    Engineering, B
Elementary Education and Teaching, BM
English, MD
English Education, M
English Language and Literature, B
English Literature (British and Commonwealth), B
English/Language Arts Teacher Education, B
Environmental Education, M
Environmental Policy and Resource
    Management, M

Environmental Sciences, B
Environmental Studies, B
Environmental/Environmental Health Engineering, B
Equestrian/Equine Studies, AB
European Studies/Civilization, B
Evolutionary Biology, B
Family and Consumer Economics and Related
   Services, B
Family and Consumer Sciences/Human Sciences, B
Finance, B
Fine/Studio Arts, B
Fish, Game and Wildlife Management, M
Foods, Nutrition, and Wellness Studies, AB
Forestry, BM
Forestry Technology/Technician, A
French Language and Literature, B
General Studies, A
Genetics, MD
Geography, B
Geology/Earth Science, B
Geosciences, M
German Language and Literature, B
Health Services Administration, M
Health/Health Care Administration/Management, B
Higher Education/Higher Education
   Administration, M
History, BMD
Horticultural Science, AB
Hospitality Administration/Management, B
Hotel/Motel Administration/Management, B
Humanities/Humanistic Studies, B
Hydrology and Water Resources Science, BM
Interdisciplinary Studies, B
International Relations and Affairs, B
International/Global Studies, B
Journalism, B
Kindergarten/PreSchool Education and Teaching, B
Kinesiology and Exercise Science, B
Kinesiology and Movement Studies, M
Landscape Architecture, A
Landscaping and Groundskeeping, A
Latin Language and Literature, B
Legal and Justice Studies, M
Liberal Arts and Sciences Studies and
   Humanities, A
Liberal Studies, M
Linguistics, BM
Logistics and Materials Management, D
Management of Technology, M
Marine Biology and Biological Oceanography, B
Marine Science/Merchant Marine Officer, B
Marriage and Family Therapy/Counseling, M
Mass Communication/Media Studies, B
Materials Sciences, AMD
Mathematics, BMD
Mathematics Teacher Education, BMD
Mechanical Engineering, BMD
Medical Microbiology and Bacteriology, B
Microbiology, MD
Modern Greek Language and Literature, B
Modern Languages, B
Molecular Biology, BMD
Museology/Museum Studies, M
Music, BM
Music History, Literature, and Theory, BM
Music Performance, B
Music Teacher Education, BM
Natural Resources and Conservation, BD
Natural Resources Management/Development and
   Policy, B
Natural Sciences, B
Nursing, M
Nursing - Registered Nurse Training, B
Nutritional Sciences, MD
Occupational Therapy/Therapist, BM
Ocean Engineering, BMD
Oceanography, Chemical and Physical, BM
Painting, M
Parks, Recreation, Leisure and Fitness Studies, B
Philosophy, B
Physical Education Teaching and Coaching, B
Physics, BMD
Piano and Organ, B
Plant Biology, MD
Political Science and Government, BM
Pre-Engineering, A

Pre-Medicine/Pre-Medical Studies, B
Pre-Veterinary Studies, B
Psychology, BD
Public Administration, M
Public Health, M
Reading Teacher Education, MD
Recreation and Park Management, M
Resource Management, M
Restaurant, Culinary, and Catering
   Management/Manager, A
Restaurant/Food Services Management, A
Romance Languages, Literatures, and Linguistics, B
Russian Language and Literature, B
Science Teacher Education/General Science
   Teacher Education, B
Secondary Education and Teaching, BM
Social Work, BM
Sociology, BMD
Soil Science and Agronomy, B
Spanish Language and Literature, BM
Special Education and Teaching, M
Statistics, BM
Survey Technology/Surveying, A
Therapeutic Recreation, M
Therapeutic Recreation/Recreational Therapy, B
Tourism and Travel Services Management, B
Trade and Industrial Teacher Education, B
Violin, Viola, Guitar and Other Stringed
   Instruments, B
Vocational and Technical Education, M
Voice and Opera, B
Water Resources, M
Wildlife and Wildlands Science and Management, B
Wildlife Biology, B
Wind and Percussion Instruments, B
Women's Studies, B
Writing, M
Zoology/Animal Biology, BMD

UNIVERSITY OF NEW HAMPSHIRE AT MANCHESTER

Biology/Biological Sciences, A
Business Administration and Management, AB
Electrical, Electronic and Communications
   Engineering Technology/Technician, B
English Language and Literature, B
Fine/Studio Arts, A
History, B
Humanities/Humanistic Studies, B
Liberal Arts and Sciences Studies and
   Humanities, A
Mass Communication/Media Studies, B
Mechanical Engineering/Mechanical
   Technology/Technician, B
Nursing Science, B
Psychology, B
Sign Language Interpretation and Translation, B

New Jersey
ASSUMPTION COLLEGE FOR SISTERS

Liberal Arts and Sciences Studies and
   Humanities, A
Theology/Theological Studies, A

ATLANTIC CAPE COMMUNITY COLLEGE

Accounting, A
Biology/Biological Sciences, A
Business Administration and Management, A
Chemistry, A
Child Development, A
Comparative Literature, A
Computer and Information Sciences and Support
   Services, A
Computer Programming/Programmer, A
Corrections, A
Culinary Arts/Chef Training, A
Data Entry/Microcomputer Applications, A
Education, A
Fine/Studio Arts, A
Foodservice Systems
   Administration/Management, A
General Studies, A
Health Services/Allied Health/Health Sciences, A

History, A
Hospitality Administration/Management, A
Humanities/Humanistic Studies, A
Legal Assistant/Paralegal, A
Liberal Arts and Sciences Studies and
   Humanities, A
Management Information Systems and Services, A
Mathematics, A
Nursing - Registered Nurse Training, A
Psychology, A
Respiratory Care Therapy/Therapist, A
Social Sciences, A
Social Work, A
Sociology, A
Visual and Performing Arts, A

BERGEN COMMUNITY COLLEGE

Accounting, A
Administrative Assistant and Secretarial Science, A
Automobile/Automotive Mechanics
   Technology/Technician, A
Biology/Biological Sciences, A
Broadcast Journalism, A
Business Administration and Management, A
Chemistry, A
Clinical/Medical Laboratory Technician, A
Commercial and Advertising Art, A
Comparative Literature, A
Computer Engineering Technology/Technician, A
Computer Programming/Programmer, A
Computer Science, A
Computer Typography and Composition Equipment
   Operator, A
Consumer Merchandising/Retailing Management, A
Criminal Justice/Law Enforcement Administration, A
Dance, A
Dental Hygiene/Hygienist, A
Drafting and Design Technology/Technician, A
Drama and Dramatics/Theatre Arts, A
Economics, A
Education, A
Electrical, Electronic and Communications
   Engineering Technology/Technician, A
Engineering Science, A
Finance, A
History, A
Hotel/Motel Administration/Management, A
Industrial Radiologic Technology/Technician, A
Industrial Technology/Technician, A
Kindergarten/PreSchool Education and Teaching, A
Kinesiology and Exercise Science, A
Legal Administrative Assistant/Secretary, A
Legal Assistant/Paralegal, A
Liberal Arts and Sciences Studies and
   Humanities, A
Mass Communication/Media Studies, A
Mathematics, A
Medical Administrative Assistant/Secretary, A
Medical/Clinical Assistant, A
Music, A
Nursing - Registered Nurse Training, A
Ornamental Horticulture, A
Parks, Recreation, Leisure and Fitness Studies, A
Philosophy, A
Photography, A
Physics, A
Political Science and Government, A
Psychology, A
Public Health (MPH, DPH), A
Real Estate, A
Respiratory Care Therapy/Therapist, A
Sociology, A
Special Products Marketing Operations, A
Tourism and Travel Services Management, A
Veterinary/Animal Health Technology/Technician and
   Veterinary Assistant, A
Women's Studies, A

BERKELEY COLLEGE

Accounting, A
Business Administration and Management, AB
Business/Commerce, A
Fashion Merchandising, A
Interior Design, A
International Business/Trade/Commerce, AB
Legal Assistant/Paralegal, A

Marketing/Marketing Management, A
System Administration/Administrator, A
Web Page, Digital/Multimedia and Information
  Resources Design, A

BETH MEDRASH GOVOHA

Rabbinical Studies, B

BLOOMFIELD COLLEGE

Accounting, B
Allied Health and Medical Assisting Services, B
Animation, Interactive Technology, Video Graphics
  and Special Effects, B
Applied Mathematics, B
Art Teacher Education, B
Biochemistry, B
Biology Teacher Education, B
Biology/Biological Sciences, B
Business Administration and Management, B
Cardiovascular Technology/Technologist, B
Chemistry, B
Chemistry Teacher Education, B
Clinical Laboratory Science/Medical
  Technology/Technologist, B
Communication Studies/Speech Communication
  and Rhetoric, B
Computer Graphics, B
Creative Writing, B
Criminal Justice/Law Enforcement Administration, B
CytoTechnology/Cytotechnologist, B
Drama and Dramatics/Theatre Arts, B
Early Childhood Education and Teaching, B
Economics, B
Elementary and Middle School
  Administration/Principalship, B
English Language and Literature, B
English/Language Arts Teacher Education, B
Environmental Biology, B
Film/Video and Photographic Arts, B
Finance, B
Fine/Studio Arts, B
History, B
History Teacher Education, B
Human Resources Management and Services, B
Human Resources Management/Personnel
  Administration, B
Information Science/Studies, B
Marketing/Marketing Management, B
Mathematics Teacher Education, B
Multi-/Interdisciplinary Studies, B
Music Management and Merchandising, B
Nuclear Medical Technology/Technologist, B
Nursing - Registered Nurse Training, B
Philosophy, B
Political Science and Government, B
Pre-Dentistry Studies, B
Pre-Medicine/Pre-Medical Studies, B
Pre-Veterinary Studies, B
Psychology, B
Public Administration, B
Public Policy Analysis, B
Purchasing, Procurement/Acquisitions and
  Contracts Management, B
Religion/Religious Studies, B
Respiratory Therapy Technician/Assistant, B
Science Teacher Education/General Science
  Teacher Education, B
Social Studies Teacher Education, B
Sociology, B
Special Education and Teaching, B
Toxicology, B
Web Page, Digital/Multimedia and Information
  Resources Design, B

BROOKDALE COMMUNITY COLLEGE

Accounting, A
Administrative Assistant and Secretarial Science, A
Architecture, A
Art/Art Studies, General, A
Audio Engineering, A
Automobile/Automotive Mechanics
  Technology/Technician, A
Biological and Physical Sciences, A
Business Administration and Management, A
Chemistry, A
Clinical/Medical Laboratory Technician, A

Commercial and Advertising Art, A
Computer Engineering Technology/Technician, A
Computer Programming/Programmer, A
Criminal Justice/Law Enforcement Administration, A
Culinary Arts/Chef Training, A
Design and Visual Communications, A
Drafting and Design Technology/Technician, A
Drama and Dramatics/Theatre Arts, A
Education, A
Educational/Instructional Media Design, A
Electrical, Electronic and Communications
  Engineering Technology/Technician, A
Engineering, A
English Language and Literature, A
Fashion Merchandising, A
Human Services, A
Humanities/Humanistic Studies, A
Interior Design, A
International Relations and Affairs, A
Journalism, A
Kindergarten/PreSchool Education and Teaching, A
Legal Assistant/Paralegal, A
Liberal Arts and Sciences Studies and
  Humanities, A
Library Science, A
Marketing/Marketing Management, A
Mass Communication/Media Studies, A
Mathematics, A
Mechanical Drafting and Mechanical Drafting
  CAD/CADD, A
Modern Languages, A
Multi-/Interdisciplinary Studies, A
Music, A
Nursing - Registered Nurse Training, A
Photography, A
Physics, A
Political Science and Government, A
Prepress/Desktop Publishing and Digital Imaging
  Design, A
Psychology, A
Public Relations/Image Management, A
Radio and Television Broadcasting
  Technology/Technician, A
Radiologic Technology/Science - Radiographer, A
Respiratory Care Therapy/Therapist, A
Social Sciences, A
Social Work, A
Sociology, A
Special Products Marketing Operations, A
Speech and Rhetorical Studies, A
Telecommunications Technology/Technician, A
Visual and Performing Arts, A

BURLINGTON COUNTY COLLEGE

Accounting, A
American Sign Language (ASL), A
Art/Art Studies, General, A
Automobile/Automotive Mechanics
  Technology/Technician, A
Biological and Physical Sciences, A
Biology/Biological Sciences, A
BioTechnology, A
Business Administration and Management, A
Chemical Engineering, A
Chemical Technology/Technician, A
Chemistry, A
Civil Engineering Technology/Technician, A
Commercial and Advertising Art, A
Communications Technology/Technician, A
Computer Graphics, A
Computer Science, A
Drafting and Design Technology/Technician, A
Drama and Dramatics/Theatre Arts, A
Education, A
Electrical, Electronic and Communications
  Engineering Technology/Technician, A
Engineering, A
English Language and Literature, A
Environmental Studies, A
Fashion/Apparel Design, A
Fire Science/Firefighting, A
Foodservice Systems
  Administration/Management, A
Graphic and Printing Equipment Operator
  Production, A

Health Information/Medical Records
  Technology/Technician, A
History, A
Hotel/Motel Administration/Management, A
Human Services, A
Information Technology, A
Journalism, A
Legal Assistant/Paralegal, A
Liberal Arts and Sciences Studies and
  Humanities, A
Management Information Systems and Services, A
Mathematics, A
Medical Radiologic Technology/Science - Radiation
  Therapist, A
Music, A
Nursing - Registered Nurse Training, A
Philosophy, A
Physics, A
Political Science and Government, A
Psychology, A
Sales, Distribution and Marketing Operations, A
Sign Language Interpretation and Translation, A
Sociology, A
Special Products Marketing Operations, A
Survey Technology/Surveying, A

CALDWELL COLLEGE

Accounting, BM
Art Therapy/Therapist, M
Art/Art Studies, General, B
Biology/Biological Sciences, B
Business Administration and Management, B
Business Administration, Management and
  Operations, M
Chemistry, B
Clinical Laboratory Science/Medical
  Technology/Technologist, B
Communication Studies/Speech Communication
  and Rhetoric, B
Computer and Information Sciences, B
Computer Science, B
Counseling Psychology, M
Counselor Education/School Counseling and
  Guidance Services, M
Criminal Justice/Safety Studies, B
Curriculum and Instruction, M
Educational Administration and Supervision, M
Elementary Education and Teaching, B
English Language and Literature, B
French Language and Literature, B
History, B
International Business/Trade/Commerce, B
Management Science, B
Marketing/Marketing Management, B
Mathematics, B
Multi-/Interdisciplinary Studies, B
Music, B
Pastoral Studies/Counseling, M
Political Science and Government, B
Psychology, BM
Social Sciences, B
Sociology, B
Spanish Language and Literature, B
Special Education and Teaching, M
Theology/Theological Studies, B

CAMDEN COUNTY COLLEGE

Accounting, A
Administrative Assistant and Secretarial Science, A
Animal Sciences, A
Applied Art, A
Art/Art Studies, General, A
Artificial Intelligence and Robotics, A
Automobile/Automotive Mechanics
  Technology/Technician, A
Business Administration and Management, A
Clinical/Medical Laboratory Technician, A
Computer and Information Sciences, A
Computer Engineering Technology/Technician, A
Computer Graphics, A
Computer Programming, A
Computer Programming, Specific Applications, A
Computer Programming/Programmer, A
Computer Typography and Composition Equipment
  Operator, A

Computer/Information Technology Services
Administration and Management, A
Criminal Justice/Law Enforcement Administration, A
Data Entry/Microcomputer Applications, A
Data Processing and Data Processing
Technology/Technician, A
Dental Hygiene/Hygienist, A
Dietetics/Dieticians, A
Drama and Dramatics/Theatre Arts, A
Electrical, Electronic and Communications
Engineering Technology/Technician, A
Engineering Science, A
Environmental Studies, A
Finance, A
Fire Science/Firefighting, A
Foods, Nutrition, and Wellness Studies, A
Forestry, A
Gerontology, A
Health and Medical Laboratory Technologies, A
Human Services, A
Information Technology, A
Kindergarten/PreSchool Education and Teaching, A
Kinesiology and Exercise Science, A
Laser and Optical Technology/Technician, A
Liberal Arts and Sciences Studies and
Humanities, A
Marketing/Marketing Management, A
Mass Communication/Media Studies, A
Mechanical Engineering/Mechanical
Technology/Technician, A
Medical Radiologic Technology/Science - Radiation
Therapist, A
Nursing - Registered Nurse Training, A
Occupational Safety and Health
Technology/Technician, A
Parks, Recreation, Leisure and Fitness Studies, A
Real Estate, A
Respiratory Care Therapy/Therapist, A
Special Products Marketing Operations, A
System Administration/Administrator, A
Web Page, Digital/Multimedia and Information
Resources Design, A
Web/Multimedia Management and Webmaster, A
Word Processing, A

CENTENARY COLLEGE

Accounting, BM
Biology/Biological Sciences, B
Business Administration and Management, B
Business Administration, Management and
Operations, M
Commercial and Advertising Art, B
Counseling Psychology, M
Criminology, B
Education, BM
Educational Leadership and Administration, M
Elementary Education and Teaching, B
English Language and Literature, B
Equestrian/Equine Studies, AB
Fashion/Apparel Design, B
History, B
Information Science/Studies, B
International Relations and Affairs, B
Liberal Arts and Sciences Studies and
Humanities, A
Marketing/Marketing Management, B
Mass Communication/Media Studies, B
Mathematics, B
Political Science and Government, B
Psychology, B
Secondary Education and Teaching, B
Sociology, B
Special Education and Teaching, BM
Sport and Fitness Administration/Management, B
Technical Theatre/Theatre Design and
Technology, B

THE COLLEGE OF NEW JERSEY

Accounting, B
Art Teacher Education, B
Art/Art Studies, General, B
Biology Teacher Education, B
Biology/Biological Sciences, B
Biomedical/Medical Engineering, B
Business Administration and Management, B
Business/Managerial Economics, B

Chemistry, B
Chemistry Teacher Education, B
Commercial and Advertising Art, B
Communication Disorders, M
Computer and Information Sciences, B
Computer Engineering, B
Counselor Education/School Counseling and
Guidance Services, M
Criminal Justice/Law Enforcement Administration, B
Early Childhood Education and Teaching, M
Economics, B
Education, BMO
Education/Teaching of Individuals with Hearing
Impairments, Including Deafness, B
Educational Administration and Supervision, M
Educational Leadership and Administration, M
Educational Media/Instructional Technology, MO
Electrical, Electronics and Communications
Engineering, B
Elementary Education and Teaching, BM
Engineering Science, B
English, M
English as a Second Language, MO
English Language and Literature, B
English/Language Arts Teacher Education, B
Finance, B
Fine/Studio Arts, B
Foreign Language Teacher Education, M
Health Education, M
History, B
History Teacher Education, B
Intermedia/Multimedia, B
International and Comparative Education, M
International Business/Trade/Commerce, B
International Relations and Affairs, B
Kindergarten/PreSchool Education and Teaching, B
Marriage and Family Therapy/Counseling, O
Mathematics, B
Mathematics Teacher Education, B
Mechanical Engineering, B
Music, B
Music Teacher Education, B
Nursing, MO
Nursing - Advanced Practice, MO
Nursing - Registered Nurse Training, B
Philosophy, B
Physical Education Teaching and Coaching, BM
Physics, B
Physics Teacher Education, B
Political Science and Government, B
Pre-Law Studies, B
Pre-Medicine/Pre-Medical Studies, B
Psychology, B
Reading Teacher Education, MO
School Nursing, O
Secondary Education and Teaching, BM
Sociology, B
Spanish Language and Literature, BM
Spanish Language Teacher Education, B
Special Education and Teaching, BM
Speech and Rhetorical Studies, B
Statistics, B
Substance Abuse/Addiction Counseling, MO
Technology Teacher Education/Industrial Arts
Teacher Education, B
Women's Studies, B

COLLEGE OF SAINT ELIZABETH

American/United States Studies/Civilization, B
Art/Art Studies, General, B
Biochemistry, B
Biology/Biological Sciences, B
Business Administration and Management, B
Business Administration, Management and
Operations, M
Chemistry, B
Communication Studies/Speech Communication
and Rhetoric, B
Computer Science, B
Counseling Psychology, M
Dietetics/Dieticians, B
Education, O
Educational Leadership and Administration, M
Educational Media/Instructional Technology, M
English Language and Literature, B
Health Services Administration, M

History, B
Human Resources Management/Personnel
Administration, B
International Relations and Affairs, B
Management, M
Mathematics, B
Multi-/Interdisciplinary Studies, B
Music, B
Nursing Science, B
Nutritional Sciences, O
Peace Studies and Conflict Resolution, B
Philosophy, B
Psychology, BM
Sociology, B
Spanish Language and Literature, B
Special Education and Teaching, B
Teacher Education, Multiple Levels, B
Theology and Religious Vocations, M
Theology/Theological Studies, B

COUNTY COLLEGE OF MORRIS

Administrative Assistant and Secretarial Science, A
Agricultural Business and Management, A
Airline/Commercial/Professional Pilot and Flight
Crew, A
Applied Art, A
Biology Technician/BioTechnology Laboratory
Technician, A
Business Administration and Management, A
Chemical Technology/Technician, A
Clinical/Medical Laboratory Technician, A
Commercial and Advertising Art, A
Criminal Justice/Police Science, A
Educational/Instructional Media Design, A
Electrical, Electronic and Communications
Engineering Technology/Technician, A
Engineering Science, A
Engineering Technology, A
Hotel/Motel Administration/Management, A
Interdisciplinary Studies, A
Kindergarten/PreSchool Education and Teaching, A
Kinesiology and Exercise Science, A
Liberal Arts and Sciences Studies and
Humanities, A
Management Information Systems and Services, A
Mechanical Engineering/Mechanical
Technology/Technician, A
Nursing - Registered Nurse Training, A
Parks, Recreation and Leisure Facilities
Management, A
Photographic and Film/Video Technology/Technician
and Assistant, A
Public Administration, A
Radio and Television Broadcasting
Technology/Technician, A
Respiratory Care Therapy/Therapist, A
Veterinary/Animal Health Technology/Technician and
Veterinary Assistant, A

CUMBERLAND COUNTY COLLEGE

Accounting, A
Administrative Assistant and Secretarial Science, A
Agricultural Business and Management, A
Agriculture, A
Artificial Intelligence and Robotics, A
Avionics Maintenance Technology/Technician, A
Biological and Physical Sciences, A
Broadcast Journalism, A
Business Administration and Management, A
Cinematography and Film/Video Production, A
Community Organization and Advocacy, A
Computer Science, A
Computer Systems Networking and
Telecommunications, A
Computer Typography and Composition Equipment
Operator, A
Corrections, A
Criminal Justice/Police Science, A
Drafting and Design Technology/Technician, A
Drama and Dramatics/Theatre Arts, A
Education, A
Elementary and Middle School
Administration/Principalship, A
Engineering, A
Fine/Studio Arts, A
Horticultural Science, A

Hospitality and Recreation Marketing Operations, A
Human Resources Management/Personnel
   Administration, A
Industrial Radiologic Technology/Technician, A
Industrial Technology/Technician, A
Information Science/Studies, A
Kindergarten/PreSchool Education and Teaching, A
Legal Administrative Assistant/Secretary, A
Liberal Arts and Sciences Studies and
   Humanities, A
Marketing/Marketing Management, A
Mathematics, A
Nursing - Registered Nurse Training, A
Ornamental Horticulture, A
Plastics Engineering Technology/Technician, A
Pre-Engineering, A
Social Work, A
System Administration/Administrator, A

DEVRY UNIVERSITY

Biomedical Technology/Technician, AB
Business Administration and Management, AB
Business Administration, Management and
   Operations, AB
Computer and Information Sciences, B
Computer Systems Networking and
   Telecommunications, AB
Electrical, Electronic and Communications
   Engineering Technology/Technician, AB
Health Information/Medical Records
   Technology/Technician, A
Information Science/Studies, A
Medical Informatics, B

DREW UNIVERSITY

African Studies, B
Anthropology, B
Art History, Criticism and Conservation, B
Art/Art Studies, General, B
Behavioral Sciences, B
Biochemistry, B
Bioethics/Medical Ethics, MDO
Biology/Biological Sciences, B
Chemistry, B
Chinese Studies, B
Classics and Classical
   Languages, Literatures, and Linguistics, B
Computer Science, B
Drama and Dramatics/Theatre Arts, B
Economics, B
English, MD
English Language and Literature, B
Ethics, MD
French Language and Literature, B
German Language and Literature, B
History, BMD
Holocaust Studies, O
Humanities/Humanistic Studies, MDO
Interdisciplinary Studies, MDO
Mathematics, B
Mathematics and Computer Science, B
Music, B
Near and Middle Eastern Studies, MD
Neuroscience, B
Philosophy, B
Physics, B
Political Science and Government, B
Psychology, B
Religion/Religious Studies, BMD
Russian Language and Literature, B
Sociology, B
Spanish Language and Literature, B
Theology and Religious Vocations, MDPO
Women's Studies, BM

ESSEX COUNTY COLLEGE

Accounting, A
Accounting Technology/Technician and
   Bookkeeping, A
Administrative Assistant and Secretarial Science, A
Architectural Engineering Technology/Technician, A
Art/Art Studies, General, A
Biology/Biological Sciences, A
Business Administration and Management, A
Business Teacher Education, A
Chemical Technology/Technician, A

Chemistry, A
Civil Engineering Technology/Technician, A
Communications Technology/Technician, A
Computer Programming, Specific Applications, A
Computer Programming/Programmer, A
Computer Science, A
Criminal Justice/Law Enforcement Administration, A
Criminal Justice/Police Science, A
Data Processing and Data Processing
   Technology/Technician, A
Dental Assisting/Assistant, A
Dental Hygiene/Hygienist, A
Electrical, Electronic and Communications
   Engineering Technology/Technician, A
Elementary Education and Teaching, A
Emergency Medical Technology/Technician (EMT
   Paramedic), A
Fire Science/Firefighting, A
Health Professions and Related Clinical Sciences, A
Health/Health Care Administration/Management, A
Hotel/Motel Administration/Management, A
Human Services, A
Industrial Production Technologies/Technicians, A
Information Science/Studies, A
Kindergarten/PreSchool Education and Teaching, A
Legal Assistant/Paralegal, A
Legal Professions and Studies, A
Liberal Arts and Sciences Studies and
   Humanities, A
Mathematics, A
Medical Administrative Assistant/Secretary, A
Medical Radiologic Technology/Science - Radiation
   Therapist, A
Music, A
Nursing - Registered Nurse Training, A
Opticianry/Ophthalmic Dispensing Optician, A
Physical Education Teaching and Coaching, A
Physical Therapist Assistant, A
Physical Therapy/Therapist, A
Pre-Engineering, A
Respiratory Care Therapy/Therapist, A
Secondary Education and Teaching, A
Social Sciences, A
Social Work, A

FAIRLEIGH DICKINSON
UNIVERSITY, COLLEGE AT FLORHAM

Accounting, BM
Allied Health
   Diagnostic, Intervention, and Treatment
   Professions, B
Biological and Biomedical Sciences, BM
Biology/Biological Sciences, B
Business Administration and Management, B
Business Administration, Management and
   Operations, MO
Business/Managerial Economics, B
Chemical Engineering, MO
Chemistry, BM
Clinical Laboratory Science/Medical
   Technology/Technologist, B
Clinical Psychology, M
Communication Studies/Speech Communication
   and Rhetoric, B
Computer and Information Sciences, B
Corporate and Organizational Communication, MO
Creative Writing, B
Drama and Dramatics/Theatre Arts, B
Economics, B
Education, MO
Educational Leadership and Administration, M
Educational Media/Instructional Technology, O
English Language and Literature, B
Entrepreneurship/Entrepreneurial Studies, MO
Finance, B
Finance and Banking, MO
French Language and Literature, B
Health Services Administration, MO
History, B
Hospitality Administration/Management, M
Hotel/Motel Administration/Management, B
Human Resources Management and Services, MO
Humanities/Humanistic Studies, B
Industrial and Organizational Psychology, MO
International Business/Trade/Commerce, MO
Management, M

Management of Technology, O
Marine Biology and Biological Oceanography, B
Marketing, MO
Marketing/Marketing Management, B
Mathematics, B
Medical Radiologic Technology/Science - Radiation
   Therapist, AB
Organizational Behavior Studies, MO
Organizational Management, O
Pharmacology, MO
Philosophy, B
Political Science and Government, B
Psychology, BMO
Public Administration, M
Reading Teacher Education, O
Sales, Distribution and Marketing Operations, B
Sociology, B
Spanish Language and Literature, B
Taxation, MO
Visual and Performing Arts, B
Writing, M

FAIRLEIGH DICKINSON
UNIVERSITY, METROPOLITAN CAMPUS

Accounting, BMO
Biochemistry, B
Biological and Biomedical Sciences, BM
Biological and Physical Sciences, B
Biology/Biological Sciences, B
Business Administration and Management, B
Business Administration, Management and
   Operations, MO
Business/Managerial Economics, B
Chemistry, B
Civil Engineering Technology/Technician, B
Clinical Laboratory Science/Medical
   Technology/Technologist, B
Clinical Psychology, MD
Communication and Media Studies, M
Communication Studies/Speech Communication
   and Rhetoric, B
Comparative Literature, M
Computer and Information Sciences, B
Computer and Information Sciences and Support
   Services, B
Computer Engineering, M
Computer Science, M
Construction Engineering Technology/Technician, B
Criminal Justice/Safety Studies, B
Curriculum and Instruction, M
Drama and Dramatics/Theatre Arts, B
Education, BMO
Educational Leadership and Administration, M
Educational Media/Instructional Technology, O
Electrical Engineering, M
Electrical, Electronic and Communications
   Engineering Technology/Technician, B
Electrical, Electronics and Communications
   Engineering, B
Electronic Commerce, M
Engineering and Applied Sciences, M
English, M
English Language and Literature, B
Entrepreneurship/Entrepreneurial Studies, MO
Environmental Studies, M
Experimental Psychology, MO
Finance, B
Finance and Banking, MO
French Language and Literature, B
General Studies, B
History, BM
Hospitality Administration/Management, M
Hotel/Motel Administration/Management, B
Human Resources Management and Services, MO
Humanities/Humanistic Studies, B
International Affairs, M
International Business/Trade/Commerce, M
International Relations and Affairs, B
Liberal Arts and Sciences Studies and
   Humanities, B
Management, MO
Management Information Systems and
   Services, MO
Marine Biology and Biological Oceanography, B
Marketing, MO
Marketing Research, B

Mathematics, B
Mechanical Engineering/Mechanical
Technology/Technician, B
Medical Radiologic Technology/Science - Radiation
Therapist, AB
Medical Technology, M
Multi-/Interdisciplinary Studies, B
Multilingual and Multicultural Education, M
Non-Profit/Public/Organizational Management, O
Nursing, MO
Nursing - Registered Nurse Training, B
Nursing Science, B
Pharmaceutical Administration, MO
Philosophy, B
Political Science and Government, BM
Psychology, BMDO
Public Administration, MO
Reading Teacher Education, O
School Psychology, MD
Science Teacher Education/General Science
Teacher Education, M
Sociology, B
Spanish Language and Literature, B
Special Education and Teaching, MO
Systems Science and Theory, M
Visual and Performing Arts, B

FELICIAN COLLEGE

Accounting, B
Art/Art Studies, General, AB
Behavioral Sciences, AB
Biochemistry, B
Biology/Biological Sciences, AB
Business Administration and Management, AB
Clinical Laboratory Science/Medical
Technology/Technologist, B
Clinical/Medical Laboratory Technician, A
Commercial and Advertising Art, AB
Computer Science, AB
CytoTechnology/Cytotechnologist, B
Education, BM
Elementary Education and Teaching, B
English Language and Literature, AB
Environmental Studies, B
Fine/Studio Arts, B
Gerontology, B
Health and Medical Laboratory Technologies, B
History, AB
Humanities/Humanistic Studies, AB
Interdisciplinary Studies, B
Liberal Arts and Sciences Studies and
Humanities, A
Marketing/Marketing Management, B
Mass Communication/Media Studies, B
Mathematics, AB
Mathematics Teacher Education, B
Mental Health/Rehabilitation, A
Natural Sciences, AB
Nursing, M
Nursing - Advanced Practice, M
Nursing - Registered Nurse Training, AB
Philosophy, AB
Political Science and Government, B
Pre-Law Studies, B
Pre-Medicine/Pre-Medical Studies, B
Psychology, AB
Religion/Religious Studies, AB
Religious Education, M
Social Sciences, AB
Sociology, AB
Special Education and Teaching, B
Teacher Education, Multiple Levels, B
Toxicology, B

GEORGIAN COURT UNIVERSITY

Accounting, B
Art History, Criticism and Conservation, B
Art/Art Studies, General, B
Biochemistry, B
Biological and Biomedical Sciences, M
Biology/Biological Sciences, B
Business Administration and Management, B
Business Administration, Management and
Operations, M
Chemistry, B

Communication Studies/Speech Communication
and Rhetoric, B
Computer and Information Sciences, B
Counseling Psychology, MO
Criminal Justice/Law Enforcement Administration, B
Education, MO
Educational Administration and Supervision, M
Educational Media/Instructional Technology, MO
Educational Psychology, O
Elementary Education and Teaching, B
English Language and Literature, B
Fine/Studio Arts, B
History, B
Humanities/Humanistic Studies, B
Liberal Arts and Sciences Studies and
Humanities, B
Mathematics, BM
Music, B
Natural Sciences, B
Physics, B
Psychology, B
Religion/Religious Studies, B
Social Work, B
Sociology, B
Spanish Language and Literature, B
Special Education and Teaching, BMO
Substance Abuse/Addiction Counseling, O
Theology and Religious Vocations, MO

GIBBS COLLEGE (MONTCLAIR)

Administrative Assistant and Secretarial Science, A
Computer Systems Networking and
Telecommunications, A
Executive Assistant/Executive Secretary, A
Hospitality Administration/Management, A
Legal Administrative Assistant/Secretary, A
Medical Administrative Assistant/Secretary, A

GLOUCESTER COUNTY COLLEGE

Accounting, A
Accounting Technology/Technician and
Bookkeeping, A
Automobile/Automotive Mechanics
Technology/Technician, A
Biology/Biological Sciences, A
Business Administration and Management, A
Chemical Engineering, A
Chemistry, A
Civil Engineering Technology/Technician, A
Communication Studies/Speech Communication
and Rhetoric, A
Computer Graphics, A
Computer Science, A
Consumer Merchandising/Retailing Management, A
Criminal Justice/Police Science, A
Data Processing and Data Processing
Technology/Technician, A
Diagnostic Medical Sonography/Sonographer and
Ultrasound Technician, A
Drafting and Design Technology/Technician, A
Drama and Dramatics/Theatre Arts, A
Education, A
Engineering Science, A
English Language and Literature, A
Environmental Engineering
Technology/Environmental Technology, A
Finance, A
Fine/Studio Arts, A
Health and Physical Education, A
History, A
Hospitality and Recreation Marketing Operations, A
Human Development and Family Studies, A
Information Science/Studies, A
Kinesiology and Exercise Science, A
Law and Legal Studies, A
Legal Administrative Assistant/Secretary, A
Legal Assistant/Paralegal, A
Liberal Arts and Sciences Studies and
Humanities, A
Marketing/Marketing Management, A
Mathematics, A
Medical Administrative Assistant/Secretary, A
Nuclear Medical Technology/Technologist, A
Nursing - Registered Nurse Training, A
Political Science and Government, A
Psychology, A

Respiratory Care Therapy/Therapist, A
Social Sciences, A
Sociology, A

HUDSON COUNTY COMMUNITY COLLEGE

Accounting, A
Business Administration and Management, A
Child Development, A
Computer Engineering Technology/Technician, A
Computer Science, A
Criminal Justice/Safety Studies, A
Culinary Arts/Chef Training, A
Data Processing and Data Processing
Technology/Technician, A
Electrical, Electronic and Communications
Engineering Technology/Technician, A
Engineering Science, A
Health Information/Medical Records
Technology/Technician, A
Human Services, A
Legal Assistant/Paralegal, A
Liberal Arts and Sciences Studies and
Humanities, A
Medical/Clinical Assistant, A

KEAN UNIVERSITY

Accounting, BM
Adult and Continuing Education and Teaching, M
Art Education, M
Art History, Criticism and Conservation, B
Art/Art Studies, General, B
Biology/Biological Sciences, B
BioTechnology, M
Business Administration and Management, B
Business Administration, Management and
Operations, MO
Chemistry, B
Clinical Laboratory Science/Medical
Technology/Technologist, B
Communication and Media Studies, MO
Communication Disorders, M
Communication Studies/Speech Communication
and Rhetoric, B
Community Health Nursing, M
Computational Sciences, M
Computer and Information Sciences, B
Computer Education, M
Computer Systems Networking and
Telecommunications, B
Counseling Psychology, MO
Counselor Education/School Counseling and
Guidance Services, MO
Criminal Justice/Law Enforcement Administration, B
Curriculum and Instruction, MO
Design and Visual Communications, B
Drama and Dramatics/Theatre Arts, B
Early Childhood Education and Teaching, MO
Economics, B
Education, MO
Educational Administration and Supervision, MO
Educational Leadership and Administration, M
Educational Media/Instructional Technology, M
Educational Psychology, M
Elementary Education and Teaching, BMO
English, M
English as a Second Language, MO
English Language and Literature, B
Environmental Policy and Resource
Management, M
Exercise and Sports Science, M
Finance, B
Fine/Studio Arts, B
Geology/Earth Science, B
Graphic Design, M
Health Information/Medical Records
Administration/Administrator, B
Health Services Administration, M
History, B
Industrial and Organizational Psychology, M
Industrial Design, B
Interior Design, B
Kindergarten/PreSchool Education and Teaching, B
Liberal Arts and Sciences Studies and
Humanities, B
Liberal Studies, M

Management Information Systems and Services, M
Management of Technology, M
Manufacturing Technology/Technician, B
Marketing/Marketing Management, B
Marriage and Family Therapy/Counseling, MO
Mathematics, BM
Mathematics Teacher Education, M
Middle School Education, MO
Multilingual and Multicultural Education, MO
Music, B
Music Teacher Education, B
Nursing, MO
Nursing Administration, M
Nursing Science, B
Occupational Therapy/Therapist, BM
Parks, Recreation and Leisure Facilities
    Management, B
Philosophy and Religious Studies, B
Physical Education Teaching and Coaching, B
Political Science and Government, BM
Printing Management, B
Psychology, BMO
Public Administration, BMO
Reading Teacher Education, MO
School Nursing, O
School Psychology, MO
Science Teacher Education/General Science
    Teacher Education, M
Science Technologies/Technicians, B
Secondary Education and Teaching, MO
Social Sciences, O
Social Work, BM
Sociology, B
Spanish Language and Literature, B
Special Education and Teaching, BM
Speech and Rhetorical Studies, M
Speech Teacher Education, B
Statistics, M
Substance Abuse/Addiction Counseling, M
Technology Teacher Education/Industrial Arts
    Teacher Education, B

MERCER COUNTY COMMUNITY COLLEGE

Accounting, A
Administrative Assistant and Secretarial Science, A
Airline Flight Attendant, A
Airline/Commercial/Professional Pilot and Flight
    Crew, A
Architectural Engineering Technology/Technician, A
Art History, Criticism and Conservation, A
Art/Art Studies, General, A
Automotive Engineering Technology/Technician, A
Aviation/Airway Management and Operations, A
Biology Technician/BioTechnology Laboratory
    Technician, A
Biology/Biological Sciences, A
Business Administration and Management, A
Ceramic Arts and Ceramics, A
Chemistry, A
Civil Engineering Technology/Technician, A
Clinical/Medical Laboratory Technician, A
Commercial and Advertising Art, A
Community Organization and Advocacy, A
Computer Graphics, A
Computer Science, A
Computer Systems Networking and
    Telecommunications, A
Corrections, A
Criminal Justice/Police Science, A
Culinary Arts/Chef Training, A
Dance, A
Drama and Dramatics/Theatre Arts, A
Electrical, Electronic and Communications
    Engineering Technology/Technician, A
Engineering Science, A
Fire Science/Firefighting, A
Funeral Service and Mortuary Science, A
Heating, Air Conditioning and Refrigeration
    Technology/Technician, A
Hotel/Motel Administration/Management, A
Humanities/Humanistic Studies, A
Legal Assistant/Paralegal, A
Liberal Arts and Sciences Studies and
    Humanities, A
Management Information Systems and Services, A

Mass Communication/Media Studies, A
Mathematics, A
Medical Radiologic Technology/Science - Radiation
    Therapist, A
Music, A
Nursing - Registered Nurse Training, A
Ornamental Horticulture, A
Photography, A
Physical Therapist Assistant, A
Physics, A
Plant Sciences, A
Public Health (MPH, DPH), A
Radio and Television Broadcasting
    Technology/Technician, A
Respiratory Care Therapy/Therapist, A
Sculpture, A
Teacher Assistant/Aide, A

MIDDLESEX COUNTY COLLEGE

Accounting, A
Administrative Assistant and Secretarial Science, A
Advertising, A
Applied Art, A
Art/Art Studies, General, A
Automobile/Automotive Mechanics
    Technology/Technician, A
Biological and Physical Sciences, A
Biology Technician/BioTechnology Laboratory
    Technician, A
Biology/Biological Sciences, A
Business Administration and Management, A
Chemistry, A
Child Development, A
Civil Engineering Technology/Technician, A
Clinical/Medical Laboratory Technician, A
Commercial and Advertising Art, A
Computer Engineering Technology/Technician, A
Computer Graphics, A
Computer Programming/Programmer, A
Computer Science, A
Computer Systems Networking and
    Telecommunications, A
Construction Engineering Technology/Technician, A
Consumer Merchandising/Retailing Management, A
Corrections, A
Criminal Justice/Law Enforcement Administration, A
Criminal Justice/Police Science, A
Culinary Arts/Chef Training, A
Dance, A
Dental Hygiene/Hygienist, A
Dietetics/Dieticians, A
Drafting and Design Technology/Technician, A
Drama and Dramatics/Theatre Arts, A
Education, A
Electrical, Electronic and Communications
    Engineering Technology/Technician, A
Engineering, A
Engineering Science, A
Engineering Technology, A
English Language and Literature, A
Fashion Merchandising, A
Fashion/Apparel Design, A
Fine/Studio Arts, A
Fire Science/Firefighting, A
General Studies, A
History, A
Hospitality Administration/Management, A
Hotel/Motel Administration/Management, A
Information Science/Studies, A
Journalism, A
Kindergarten/PreSchool Education and Teaching, A
Legal Administrative Assistant/Secretary, A
Legal Assistant/Paralegal, A
Marketing/Marketing Management, A
Mathematics, A
Mechanical Engineering/Mechanical
    Technology/Technician, A
Modern Languages, A
Music, A
Nursing - Registered Nurse Training, A
Photography, A
Physical Education Teaching and Coaching, A
Physical Sciences, A
Physics, A
Political Science and Government, A
Psychology, A

Radiologic Technology/Science - Radiographer, A
Respiratory Care Therapy/Therapist, A
Social Sciences, A
Sociology, A
Survey Technology/Surveying, A
Teacher Assistant/Aide, A

MONMOUTH UNIVERSITY

Accounting, M
Advertising and Public Relations, O
Anthropology, B
Art/Art Studies, General, B
Biology/Biological Sciences, B
Business Administration and Management, B
Business Administration, Management and
    Operations, MO
Chemistry, B
Clinical Laboratory Science/Medical
    Technology/Technologist, B
Communication and Media Studies, MO
Communication Studies/Speech Communication
    and Rhetoric, B
Computer and Information Sciences, B
Computer Science, M
Computer Software Engineering, B
Corporate and Organizational Communication, MO
Counseling Psychology, MO
Criminal Justice/Safety Studies, B
Criminology, MO
Education, BMO
Educational Administration and Supervision, MO
Elementary Education and Teaching, M
English Language and Literature, B
Environmental Biology, B
Fine Arts and Art Studies, B
Foreign Languages and Literatures, B
General Studies, A
Health Services Administration, MO
History, BM
Liberal Studies, M
Marine Biology and Biological Oceanography, B
Mathematics, B
Media Studies, O
Music, B
Nursing, MO
Nursing - Advanced Practice, O
Nursing Science, B
Political Science and Government, B
Psychology, BMO
Reading Teacher Education, MO
Real Estate, B
School Nursing, O
Secondary Education and Teaching, B
Social Sciences, B
Social Work, BM
Software Engineering, MO
Special Education and Teaching, BMO
Substance Abuse/Addiction Counseling, O

MONTCLAIR STATE UNIVERSITY

Accounting, M
Advertising and Public Relations, M
Anthropology, B
Applied Mathematics, M
Art Education, M
Art History, Criticism and Conservation, M
Athletic Training and Sports Medicine, B
Biochemistry, BM
Biological and Biomedical Sciences, MO
Biology/Biological Sciences, B
Broadcast Journalism, B
Business Administration and Management, B
Business Administration, Management and
    Operations, M
Chemistry, BM
Child and Family Studies, M
Classics and Classical
    Languages, Literatures, and Linguistics, B
Clinical Psychology, M
Communication and Media Studies, M
Communication Disorders, M
Communication Studies/Speech Communication
    and Rhetoric, B
Composition, M
Computer Science, BMO
Conflict Resolution and Mediation/Peace Studies, M

Consumer Economics, M
Corporate and Organizational Communication, M
Counselor Education/School Counseling and
   Guidance Services, M
Curriculum and Instruction, MD
Dance, B
Drama and Dramatics/Theatre Arts, B
Early Childhood Education and Teaching, M
Economics, BM
Education, MDO
Education/Teaching of Individuals with Multiple
   Disabilities, M
Educational Administration and Supervision, M
Educational Psychology, M
Elementary Education and Teaching, M
English, M
English as a Second Language, M
English Education, M
English Language and Literature, B
Environmental Policy and Resource
   Management, MD
Environmental Studies, M
Exercise and Sports Science, MO
Fashion/Apparel Design, B
Finance and Banking, M
Fine Arts and Art Studies, M
Fine/Studio Arts, B
Foods, Nutrition, and Wellness Studies, B
French Language and Literature, BM
Geography, B
Geological and Earth Sciences/Geosciences, B
Geosciences, MO
Health Education, MO
Health Services/Allied Health/Health Sciences, B
Health Teacher Education, B
History, BM
Home Economics, M
Home Economics Education, M
Hospitality Administration/Management, B
Human Services, M
Humanities/Humanistic Studies, B
Industrial and Organizational Psychology, M
Information Science/Studies, M
Information Technology, B
International Business/Trade/Commerce, M
Italian Language and Literature, B
Latin Language and Literature, B
Law and Legal Studies, B
Legal and Justice Studies, MO
Linguistics, BM
Management Information Systems and Services, M
Marketing, M
Marriage and Family Therapy/Counseling, M
Mathematics, BM
Mathematics Teacher Education, MD
Medical Informatics, B
Molecular Biology, BMO
Music, BM
Music Teacher Education, M
Music Theory and Composition, M
Music Therapy/Therapist, BM
Nutritional Sciences, MO
Parks, Recreation, Leisure and Fitness Studies, B
Performance, M
Philosophy, BMD
Physical Education Teaching and Coaching, BM
Physics, B
Political Science and Government, B
Psychology, BM
Reading Teacher Education, M
Religion/Religious Studies, B
Science Teacher Education/General Science
   Teacher Education, M
Social Psychology, M
Social Sciences, M
Sociology, BM
Spanish Language and Literature, BM
Special Education and Teaching, M
Speech and Interpersonal Communication, M
Sport and Fitness Administration/Management, M
Statistics, M
Theater, M
Theatre Literature, History and Criticism, B
Water Resources, O

Women's Studies, B

NEW JERSEY CITY UNIVERSITY

Accounting, M
Art Education, M
Art Teacher Education, B
Art/Art Studies, General, B
Biology/Biological Sciences, B
Business Administration and Management, B
Chemistry, B
Communication Studies/Speech Communication
   and Rhetoric, B
Community Health and Preventive Medicine, M
Computer and Information Sciences, B
Counseling Psychology, M
Criminal Justice/Safety Studies, B
Criminology, M
Early Childhood Education and Teaching, M
Economics, B
Educational Administration and Supervision, M
Educational Media/Instructional Technology, M
Educational Psychology, MO
Elementary Education and Teaching, BM
English as a Second Language, M
English Language and Literature, B
Fine Arts and Art Studies, M
Geology/Earth Science, B
Health Education, M
Health Services Administration, M
History, B
Kindergarten/PreSchool Education and Teaching, B
Mathematics, B
Mathematics Teacher Education, M
Multilingual and Multicultural Education, M
Music, BM
Music Teacher Education, BM
Nursing, M
Nursing Science, B
Performance, M
Philosophy, B
Physics, B
Political Science and Government, B
Psychology, BMO
Public Health (MPH, DPH), B
Reading Teacher Education, M
School Psychology, O
Secondary Education and Teaching, M
Sociology, B
Spanish Language and Literature, B
Special Education and Teaching, BM
Transcultural Nursing, M
Urban Education and Leadership, M
Urban Studies/Affairs, BM

NEW JERSEY INSTITUTE OF TECHNOLOGY

Actuarial Science, B
Applied Mathematics, BM
Applied Physics, MD
Architecture, BMO
Biological and Biomedical Sciences, MD
Biology/Biological Sciences, B
Biomedical Engineering, MD
Biomedical/Medical Engineering, B
Business Administration and Management, B
Business Administration, Management and
   Operations, M
Chemical Engineering, BMD
Chemistry, BMD
Civil Engineering, BMD
Computational Biology, M
Computer and Information Sciences, B
Computer and Information Sciences and Support
   Services, B
Computer Engineering, BMD
Computer Science, MD
Electrical Engineering, MD
Electrical, Electronics and Communications
   Engineering, B
Engineering and Applied Sciences, MDO
Engineering Management, M
Engineering Science, B
Engineering Technologies/Technicians, B
Engineering Technology, B
Environmental and Occupational Health, M

Environmental Engineering
   Technology/Environmental Technology, MD
Environmental Policy and Resource
   Management, MD
Environmental Sciences, MD
Environmental/Environmental Health Engineering, B
Geological/Geophysical Engineering, B
History, BM
History of Medicine, M
History of Science and Technology, M
Industrial Engineering, B
Industrial Hygiene, M
Industrial/Management Engineering, MD
Information Science/Studies, BMD
Internet and Interactive Multimedia, M
Management of Technology, MD
Manufacturing Engineering, BM
Materials Engineering, MD
Materials Sciences, MD
Mathematics, D
Mechanical Engineering, BMDO
Natural Resources and Conservation, B
Nursing - Registered Nurse Training, B
Nursing Science, B
Pharmaceutical Engineering, M
Physics, B
Public Health, M
Safety Engineering, M
Science, Technology and Society, B
Social Studies Teacher Education, M
Statistics, M
Technical and Business Writing, B
Technical Communication, M
Telecommunications, M
Transportation and Highway Engineering, MD
Transportation/Transportation Management, MD

OCEAN COUNTY COLLEGE

Accounting, A
Administrative Assistant and Secretarial Science, A
Business Administration and Management, A
Business/Commerce, A
Child Care and Support Services Management, A
Civil Engineering Technology/Technician, A
Clinical/Medical Laboratory Technician, A
Commercial and Advertising Art, A
Communications Technology/Technician, A
Computer and Information Sciences, A
Computer Programming/Programmer, A
Construction Engineering Technology/Technician, A
Criminal Justice/Police Science, A
Electrical, Electronic and Communications
   Engineering Technology/Technician, A
Engineering, A
Fire Protection and Safety Technology/Technician, A
General Studies, A
Information Science/Studies, A
Journalism, A
Legal Assistant/Paralegal, A
Liberal Arts and Sciences Studies and
   Humanities, A
Medical/Clinical Assistant, A
Nursing - Registered Nurse Training, A
Public Health (MPH, DPH), A
Real Estate, A
Social Work, A
Teacher Assistant/Aide, A

PASSAIC COUNTY COMMUNITY COLLEGE

Accounting, A
Administrative Assistant and Secretarial Science, A
Biological and Physical Sciences, A
Business Administration and Management, A
Consumer Merchandising/Retailing Management, A
Criminal Justice/Law Enforcement Administration, A
Electrical, Electronic and Communications
   Engineering Technology/Technician, A
English Language and Literature, A
Finance, A
Fire Science/Firefighting, A
Health Information/Medical Records
   Administration/Administrator, A
Hotel/Motel Administration/Management, A
Human Services, A
Humanities/Humanistic Studies, A

Industrial Radiologic Technology/Technician, A
Industrial Technology/Technician, A
Information Science/Studies, A
Kindergarten/PreSchool Education and Teaching, A
Marketing/Marketing Management, A
Mathematics, A
Medical Radiologic Technology/Science - Radiation
  Therapist, A
Natural Sciences, A
Nursing - Registered Nurse Training, A
Pre-Engineering, A
Psychology, A
Public Administration, A
Respiratory Care Therapy/Therapist, A

PRINCETON UNIVERSITY

Aerospace, Aeronautical and Astronautical
  Engineering, MD
Anthropology, BD
Applied Mathematics, D
Applied Physics, MD
Archeology, D
Architecture, BMD
Art History, Criticism and Conservation, B
Asian Studies/Civilization, D
Astrophysics, BD
Atmospheric Sciences and Meteorology, D
Biological and Biomedical Sciences, D
Biophysics, D
Chemical Engineering, BMD
Chemistry, BMD
Civil Engineering, BMD
Classics and Classical
  Languages, Literatures, and Linguistics, BD
Community College Education, D
Comparative Literature, BD
Composition, D
Computational Sciences, D
Computer Engineering, B
Computer Science, MD
Demography and Population Studies, DO
East Asian Studies, B
Ecology, BD
Economics, BD
Electrical Engineering, MD
Electrical, Electronics and Communications
  Engineering, B
Electronic Materials, D
English, D
English Language and Literature, B
Environmental Engineering
  Technology/Environmental Technology, D
Environmental Studies, MD
Evolutionary Biology, D
Finance and Banking, M
Financial Engineering, MD
French Language and Literature, BD
Geological and Earth Sciences/Geosciences, B
Geology/Earth Science, D
Geophysics and Seismology, D
Geosciences, D
German Language and Literature, BD
History, BD
History of Science and Technology, D
International Affairs, MDO
Italian Language and Literature, D
Mathematical Physics, D
Mathematics, BD
Mechanical Engineering, BMD
Molecular Biology, BD
Multi-/Interdisciplinary Studies, B
Music, BD
Musicology and Ethnomusicology, D
Near and Middle Eastern Studies, BMD
Neuroscience, D
Oceanography, Chemical and Physical, D
Operations Research, BMD
Philosophy, BD
Photonics, D
Physical Chemistry, D
Physics, BD
Plasma and High-Temperature Physics, D
Political Science and Government, BD
Polymer/Plastics Engineering, MD
Portuguese Language and Literature, D
Psychology, BD

Public Affairs, MDO
Public Policy Analysis, B
Religion/Religious Studies, BD
Slavic Languages, Literatures, and Linguistics, BD
Social Studies Teacher Education, D
Sociology, BD
Spanish Language and Literature, BD
Statistics, MD
Structural Engineering, MD
Transportation and Highway Engineering, MD
Water Resources Engineering, D

RABBINICAL COLLEGE OF AMERICA

Religion/Religious Studies, B

RAMAPO COLLEGE OF NEW JERSEY

Accounting, B
Allied Health
  Diagnostic, Intervention, and Treatment
    Professions, B
American/United States Studies/Civilization, B
Biochemistry, Biophysics and Molecular Biology, B
Bioinformatics, B
Biological and Biomedical Sciences, B
Biology/Biological Sciences, B
Business Administration and Management, B
Chemistry, B
Clinical Laboratory Science/Medical
  Technology/Technologist, B
Communication Studies/Speech Communication
  and Rhetoric, B
Comparative Literature, B
Computer and Information Sciences, B
Economics, B
Environmental Sciences, B
Environmental Studies, B
Fine/Studio Arts, B
History, B
Information Science/Studies, B
Interdisciplinary Studies, B
Intermedia/Multimedia, B
International Business/Trade/Commerce, B
International/Global Studies, B
Law and Legal Studies, B
Legal Professions and Studies, B
Liberal Studies, M
Mathematics, B
Multi-/Interdisciplinary Studies, B
Music, B
Nursing - Registered Nurse Training, B
Physics, B
Political Science and Government, B
Psychology, B
Social Sciences, B
Social Work, B
Sociology, B
Spanish Language and Literature, B
Theatre/Theatre Arts Management, B
Visual and Performing Arts, B

RARITAN VALLEY COMMUNITY COLLEGE

Accounting, A
Administrative Assistant and Secretarial Science, A
Aeronautics/Aviation/Aerospace Science and
  Technology, A
Artificial Intelligence and Robotics, A
Automobile/Automotive Mechanics
  Technology/Technician, A
Biology/Biological Sciences, A
Business Administration and Management, A
Chemistry, A
Commercial and Advertising Art, A
Computer Programming/Programmer, A
Computer Science, A
Construction Engineering Technology/Technician, A
Consumer Merchandising/Retailing Management, A
Criminal Justice/Law Enforcement Administration, A
Data Processing and Data Processing
  Technology/Technician, A
Diesel Mechanics Technology/Technician, A
Drafting/Design Engineering
  Technologies/Technicians, A
Drama and Dramatics/Theatre Arts, A
Education, A

Electrical, Electronic and Communications
  Engineering Technology/Technician, A
Electromechanical Technology/Electromechanical
  Engineering Technology, A
Elementary Education and Teaching, A
Engineering, A
Environmental Studies, A
Heating, Air Conditioning, Ventilation and
  Refrigeration Maintenance
  Technology/Technician, A
Hospitality and Recreation Marketing Operations, A
Hotel/Motel Administration/Management, A
Human Services, A
Industrial Technology/Technician, A
Information Science/Studies, A
Intermedia/Multimedia, A
International Business/Trade/Commerce, A
Kindergarten/PreSchool Education and Teaching, A
Legal Assistant/Paralegal, A
Liberal Arts and Sciences Studies and
  Humanities, A
Management Information Systems and Services, A
Marketing/Marketing Management, A
Mathematics, A
Music, A
Nursing - Registered Nurse Training, A
Ophthalmic Laboratory Technology/Technician, A
Real Estate, A
Respiratory Care Therapy/Therapist, A
Social Sciences, A
Tourism and Travel Services Management, A

THE RICHARD STOCKTON COLLEGE OF NEW JERSEY

Audiology/Audiologist and Speech-Language
  Pathology/Pathologist, B
Biochemistry, B
Biology/Biological Sciences, B
Business Administration and Management, B
Business Administration, Management and
  Operations, M
Chemistry, B
Communication Studies/Speech Communication
  and Rhetoric, B
Computer and Information Sciences, B
Computer Science, B
Criminology, B
Economics, B
Educational Media/Instructional Technology, M
English Language and Literature, B
Environmental Studies, B
Foreign Languages and Literatures, B
Geology/Earth Science, B
History, B
Holocaust Studies, M
Information Science/Studies, B
Interdisciplinary Studies, B
Liberal Arts and Sciences Studies and
  Humanities, B
Marine Biology and Biological Oceanography, B
Mathematics, B
Nursing, M
Nursing - Registered Nurse Training, B
Nursing Science, B
Occupational Therapy/Therapist, M
Philosophy, B
Physical Therapy/Therapist, M
Physics, B
Political Science and Government, B
Psychology, B
Public Health (MPH, DPH), B
Social Work, B
Sociology, B
Teacher Education, Multiple Levels, B
Visual and Performing Arts, B

RIDER UNIVERSITY

Accounting, BM
Actuarial Science, B
Advertising, B
American/United States Studies/Civilization, B
Bilingual and Multilingual Education, B
Biochemistry, B
Biology/Biological Sciences, B
Biopsychology, B
Business Administration and Management, AB

Business Administration, Management and
  Operations, M
Business Education, O
Business Teacher Education, B
Business/Managerial Economics, B
Chemistry, B
Composition, M
Computer Science, B
Counselor Education/School Counseling and
  Guidance Services, MO
Curriculum and Instruction, BM
Economics, B
Education, BMO
Educational Administration and Supervision, MO
Educational Leadership and Administration, BO
Elementary Education and Teaching, BO
English as a Second Language, O
English Education, O
English Language and Literature, B
Environmental Studies, B
Finance, B
Fine/Studio Arts, B
Foreign Language Teacher Education, O
French Language and Literature, B
General Studies, AB
Geology/Earth Science, B
German Language and Literature, B
History, B
Human Resources Management/Personnel
  Administration, B
Humanities/Humanistic Studies, A
Information Science/Studies, B
International Business/Trade/Commerce, B
Journalism, B
Kindergarten/PreSchool Education and Teaching, B
Liberal Arts and Sciences Studies and
  Humanities, AB
Management Science, B
Marine Science/Merchant Marine Officer, B
Marketing/Marketing Management, B
Mathematics, B
Mathematics Teacher Education, O
Music, BM
Music Teacher Education, BM
Music Theory and Composition, B
Occupational Health and Industrial Hygiene, B
Oceanography, Chemical and Physical, B
Performance, M
Philosophy, B
Physics, B
Piano and Organ, B
Political Science and Government, B
Psychology, B
Public Relations/Image Management, B
Radio and Television, B
Reading Teacher Education, MO
Religious/Sacred Music, B
Russian Language and Literature, B
Sacred Music, M
School Psychology, BO
Science Teacher Education/General Science
  Teacher Education, BO
Secondary Education and Teaching, B
Social Studies Teacher Education, O
Sociology, B
Spanish Language and Literature, B
Special Education and Teaching, M
Speech and Rhetorical Studies, B
Voice and Opera, B

ROWAN UNIVERSITY

Accounting, B
Advertising and Public Relations, M
Art Education, M
Art/Art Studies, General, B
Biochemistry, B
Biology/Biological Sciences, B
Business Administration and Management, B
Business Administration, Management and
  Operations, M
Chemical Engineering, B
Chemistry, B
Civil Engineering, B
Communication Studies/Speech Communication
  and Rhetoric, B
Computer and Information Sciences, B

Computer Science, B
Counseling Psychology, M
Criminal Justice/Police Science, B
Curriculum and Instruction, M
Drama and Dramatics/Theatre Arts, B
Economics, B
Education, MDO
Educational Administration and Supervision, M
Educational Leadership and Administration, D
Educational Media/Instructional Technology, M
Electrical, Electronics and Communications
  Engineering, B
Elementary Education and Teaching, BM
Engineering and Applied Sciences, M
English Language and Literature, B
Environmental Education, M
Environmental Studies, B
Fine/Studio Arts, B
Geography, B
Higher Education/Higher Education
  Administration, M
History, B
Jazz/Jazz Studies, B
Kindergarten/PreSchool Education and Teaching, B
Liberal Arts and Sciences Studies and
  Humanities, B
Library Science, M
Mathematics, BM
Mathematics Teacher Education, M
Mechanical Engineering, B
Music, M
Music Performance, B
Music Teacher Education, M
Music Theory and Composition, B
Nursing, B
Physical Education Teaching and Coaching, B
Physical Sciences, B
Political Science and Government, B
Psychology, BM
Reading Teacher Education, M
School Psychology, MO
Science Teacher Education/General Science
  Teacher Education, M
Secondary Education and Teaching, BM
Sociology, B
Spanish Language and Literature, B
Special Education and Teaching, BM
Student Personnel Services, M
Teacher Education and Professional
  Development, Specific Levels and Methods, B
Theater, M
Writing, M

RUTGERS, THE STATE UNIVERSITY OF NEW JERSEY, CAMDEN

Accounting, B
African-American/Black Studies, B
Art/Art Studies, General, B
Biological and Biomedical Sciences, M
Biology/Biological Sciences, B
Biomedical Technology/Technician, B
Business Administration and Management, B
Business Administration, Management and
  Operations, M
Chemistry, BM
Clinical Laboratory Science/Medical
  Technology/Technologist, B
Computer and Information Sciences, B
Criminal Justice/Safety Studies, B
Criminology, M
Drama and Dramatics/Theatre Arts, B
Economics, B
Engineering, B
English, M
English Language and Literature, B
Finance, B
French Language and Literature, B
German Language and Literature, B
Health Services Administration, M
History, BM
Hospitality Administration/Management, B
International Affairs, M
International Development, M
Law and Legal Studies, PO
Liberal Arts and Sciences Studies and
  Humanities, B

Liberal Studies, M
Marketing/Marketing Management, B
Mathematics, BM
Multi-/Interdisciplinary Studies, B
Music, B
Nursing - Registered Nurse Training, B
Philosophy, B
Physical Therapy/Therapist, M
Physics, B
Political Science and Government, B
Psychology, B
Public Administration, MO
Public History, M
Public Policy Analysis, MO
Social Work, B
Sociology, B
Spanish Language and Literature, B

RUTGERS, THE STATE UNIVERSITY OF NEW JERSEY, NEW BRUNSWICK/PISCATAWAY

Accounting, B
Adult and Continuing Education and Teaching, M
Aerospace, Aeronautical and Astronautical
  Engineering, MD
African Studies, BD
Agricultural Economics, M
Agricultural Engineering, M
Agricultural/Biological Engineering and
  Bioengineering, B
Agriculture, B
American/United States Studies/Civilization, B
Analytical Chemistry, MD
Ancient/Classical Greek Language and Literature, B
Animal Genetics, M
Animal Physiology, B
Animal Sciences, BMD
Animal/Livestock Husbandry and Production, B
Anthropology, BMD
Applied Mathematics, MD
Art History, Criticism and Conservation, BMD
Art/Art Studies, General, B
Astrophysics, B
Atmospheric Sciences and Meteorology, BMD
Biochemical Engineering, MD
Biochemistry, BMD
Bioengineering, M
Biological Anthropology, D
Biology/Biological Sciences, B
Biomedical Engineering, MD
Biomedical Sciences, B
Biomedical/Medical Engineering, B
Biometry/Biometrics, B
Biopsychology, D
BioTechnology, B
Business Administration and Management, B
Cell Biology and Anatomy, MD
Cell/Cellular Biology and Anatomical Sciences, B
Cell/Cellular Biology and Histology, B
Central/Middle and Eastern European Studies, B
Ceramic Arts and Ceramics, B
Ceramic Sciences and Engineering, BMD
Chemical Engineering, BMD
Chemistry, BMD
Chinese Language and Literature, B
Civil Engineering, BMD
Classics and Classical
  Languages, Literatures, and Linguistics, BMD
Clinical Laboratory Science/Medical
  Technology/Technologist, B
Clinical Microbiology, MD
Clinical Psychology, MD
Cognitive Sciences, D
Commercial and Advertising Art, B
Communication and Media Studies, MD
Communication Studies/Speech Communication
  and Rhetoric, B
Comparative Literature, BMD
Composition, MD
Computer Engineering, BMD
Computer Science, BMD
Condensed Matter Physics, MD
Counseling Psychology, M
Criminal Justice/Law Enforcement Administration, B
Dance, B
Design and Applied Arts, M

Developmental Biology and Embryology, MD
Developmental Education, M
Developmental Psychology, D
Drama and Dramatics/Theatre Arts, B
Drawing, B
Early Childhood Education and Teaching, MD
East Asian Studies, B
Ecology, BMD
Economics, BMD
Education, MD
Educational Administration and Supervision, MD
Educational Measurement and Evaluation, M
Educational Psychology, MD
Electrical Engineering, MD
Electrical, Electronics and Communications
   Engineering, B
Elementary Education and Teaching, MD
Engineering and Applied Sciences, MD
Engineering Science, B
English, D
English as a Second Language, M
English Education, M
English Language and Literature, B
Entomology, MD
Environmental Biology, MD
Environmental Design/Architecture, B
Environmental Engineering
   Technology/Environmental Technology, MD
Environmental Sciences, MD
Environmental Studies, B
Equestrian/Equine Studies, B
Ethnic and Cultural Studies, B
Evolutionary Biology, BMD
Family and Consumer Sciences/Human Sciences, B
Film/Cinema Studies, B
Finance, B
Fine Arts and Art Studies, M
Food Science, B
Food Science and Technology, MD
Foreign Language Teacher Education, MD
Foreign Languages and Literatures, B
Foundations and Philosophy of Education, MD
French Language and Literature, BMD
Gender Studies, MD
Genetics, MD
Geography, BMD
Geology/Earth Science, BMD
German Language and Literature, BMD
Hazardous Materials Management and Waste
   Technology/Technician, MD
Health Psychology, D
Hispanic-American, Puerto Rican, and Mexican-
   American/Chicano Studies, B
Historic Preservation and Conservation, D
History, BD
History of Medicine, D
History of Science and Technology, D
Horticultural Science, MD
Human Resources Management and Services, MD
Immunology, MD
Industrial and Labor Relations, MD
Industrial and Organizational Psychology, MD
Industrial Engineering, B
Industrial/Management Engineering, MD
Information Science/Studies, BMD
Inorganic Chemistry, MD
Interdisciplinary Studies, BD
International Affairs, D
Italian Language and Literature, BMD
Jazz/Jazz Studies, B
Jewish/Judaic Studies, B
Journalism, B
Kinesiology and Exercise Science, B
Labor and Industrial Relations, B
Latin American Studies, B
Latin Language and Literature, B
Legal and Justice Studies, D
Liberal Arts and Sciences Studies and
   Humanities, B
Library Science, M
Linguistics, BD
Management Science, B
Management Sciences and Quantitative Methods, B
Marine Biology and Biological Oceanography, BMD
Marketing/Marketing Management, B
Mass Communication/Media Studies, B

Materials Engineering, MD
Materials Sciences, MD
Mathematics, BMD
Mathematics Teacher Education, MD
Mechanical Engineering, BMD
Mechanics, MD
Medical Microbiology and Bacteriology, B
Medicinal and Pharmaceutical Chemistry, MD
Medieval and Renaissance Studies, BD
Microbiology, MD
Molecular Biology, BMD
Molecular Genetics, MD
Molecular Pharmacology, D
Multilingual and Multicultural Education, MD
Museology/Museum Studies, M
Music, BMDO
Music History, Literature, and Theory, MD
Music Teacher Education, MD
Natural Resources and Conservation, B
Natural Resources Management/Development and
   Policy, B
Near and Middle Eastern Studies, B
Neurobiology and Neurophysiology, D
Neuroscience, D
Nursing - Registered Nurse Training, B
Nutritional Sciences, BMD
Oceanography, Chemical and Physical, MD
Operations Research, D
Organic Chemistry, MD
Painting, BM
Pharmaceutical Sciences, MD
Pharmacy, BP
Philosophy, BD
Photography, B
Physical Chemistry, MD
Physics, BMD
Physiology, D
Plant Biology, MD
Plant Molecular Biology, MD
Plant Pathology/Phytopathology, MD
Plant Physiology, MD
Plant Sciences, BM
Political Science and Government, BMDO
Portuguese Language and Literature, B
Pre-Dentistry Studies, B
Pre-Law Studies, B
Pre-Medicine/Pre-Medical Studies, B
Printmaking, B
Psychology, BMD
Public Health, MDO
Public Health (MPH, DPH), B
Public Policy Analysis, MO
Quality Management, M
Reading Teacher Education, MD
Religion/Religious Studies, B
Russian Language and Literature, B
Russian Studies, B
School Psychology, MD
Science Teacher Education/General Science
   Teacher Education, MD
Sculpture, BM
Social Psychology, D
Social Sciences, B
Social Studies Teacher Education, MD
Social Work, BMDO
Sociology, BMD
Spanish Language and Literature, BMD
Special Education and Teaching, MD
Statistics, BMD
Systems Engineering, MD
Theater, M
Theoretical Physics, MD
Toxicology, MD
Translation and Interpretation, M
Turf and Turfgrass Management, B
Urban and Regional Planning, MDO
Urban Studies/Affairs, B
Virology, MD
Visual and Performing Arts, B
Water Resources, MD
Women's Studies, BMD

Writing, M

RUTGERS, THE STATE UNIVERSITY OF NEW JERSEY, NEWARK

Accounting, BMDO
African-American/Black Studies, B
Allied Health
   Diagnostic, Intervention, and Treatment
   Professions, B
American/United States Studies/Civilization, B
Analytical Chemistry, MD
Anthropology, B
Applied Mathematics, B
Applied Physics, MD
Art/Art Studies, General, B
Biochemistry, MD
Biological and Biomedical Sciences, BMD
Biology/Biological Sciences, B
Biopsychology, D
Botany/Plant Biology, B
Business Administration and Management, B
Business Administration, Management and
   Operations, MDO
Chemistry, BMD
Classics and Classical
   Languages, Literatures, and Linguistics, B
Clinical Laboratory Science/Medical
   Technology/Technologist, B
Cognitive Sciences, D
Computational Biology, M
Computer and Information Sciences, B
Criminal Justice/Safety Studies, B
Criminology, MD
Drama and Dramatics/Theatre Arts, B
Economics, BM
Engineering, B
English, M
English Language and Literature, B
Environmental Sciences, MD
Environmental Studies, B
Ethnic and Cultural Studies, B
Finance, B
Finance and Banking, MDO
Fine Arts and Art Studies, B
French Language and Literature, B
Geological/Geophysical Engineering, B
Geology/Earth Science, BM
German Language and Literature, B
Health Services Administration, M
Hispanic-American, Puerto Rican, and Mexican-
   American/Chicano Studies, B
History, BM
Human Resources Management and Services, M
Information Science/Studies, B
Inorganic Chemistry, MD
International Affairs, MD
International Business/Trade/Commerce, MD
Italian Language and Literature, B
Journalism, B
Law and Legal Studies, PO
Liberal Studies, M
Logistics and Materials Management, D
Management, D
Management Information Systems and
   Services, MD
Management Strategy and Policy, M
Marketing, MD
Marketing/Marketing Management, B
Mathematics, BD
Multi-/Interdisciplinary Studies, B
Music, B
Music History, Literature, and Theory, M
Neuroscience, D
Nursing, M
Nursing - Registered Nurse Training, B
Organic Chemistry, MD
Organizational Management, D
Philosophy, B
Physical Chemistry, MD
Physics, B
Political Science and Government, BMO
Psychology, BD
Public Administration, MD
Public Policy Analysis, M
Science, Technology and Society, B

Slavic, Baltic, and Albanian
  Languages, Literatures, and Linguistics, B
Social Psychology, D
Social Work, B
Sociology, B
Spanish Language and Literature, B
Taxation, M
Urban Studies/Affairs, MD
Women's Studies, B
Zoology/Animal Biology, B

SAINT PETER'S COLLEGE

Accounting, BMO
American/United States Studies/Civilization, B
Art History, Criticism and Conservation, B
Art/Art Studies, General, B
Banking and Financial Support Services, B
Biochemistry, B
Biological and Physical Sciences, B
Biology/Biological Sciences, B
Business Administration and Management, AB
Business Administration, Management and
  Operations, MO
Business/Managerial Economics, AB
Chemistry, B
Classics and Classical
  Languages, Literatures, and Linguistics, B
Communication Studies/Speech Communication
  and Rhetoric, B
Computer and Information Sciences, B
Computer Programming/Programmer, B
Criminal Justice/Safety Studies, B
Curriculum and Instruction, MO
Data Processing and Data Processing
  Technology/Technician, A
Economics, B
Education, MO
Educational Administration and Supervision, MO
Elementary Education and Teaching, BO
English Language and Literature, B
Finance, A
Finance and Banking, M
Fine/Studio Arts, B
Foreign Languages and Literatures, B
Health/Health Care Administration/Management, B
History, B
Humanities/Humanistic Studies, AB
Information Science/Studies, AB
International Business/Trade/Commerce, ABM
Liberal Arts and Sciences Studies and
  Humanities, B
Management, M
Management Information Systems and Services, M
Marketing, M
Marketing/Marketing Management, AB
Mathematics, B
Modern Languages, B
Natural Sciences, B
Nursing, M
Nursing Science, B
Philosophy, B
Physics, B
Political Science and Government, B
Psychology, B
Public Policy Analysis, AB
Reading Teacher Education, M
Religion/Religious Studies, B
Social Sciences, AB
Sociology, B
Spanish Language and Literature, B
Theology/Theological Studies, B
Urban Education and Leadership, M
Urban Studies/Affairs, AB
Visual and Performing Arts, B

SALEM COMMUNITY COLLEGE

Accounting, A
Biological and Physical Sciences, A
Biology/Biological Sciences, A
Business Administration and Management, A
Chemistry, A
Computer and Information Sciences, A
Computer Systems Networking and
  Telecommunications, A
Criminal Justice/Law Enforcement Administration, A
Early Childhood Education and Teaching, A

Education, A
English Language and Literature, A
Family and Community Services, A
Health and Physical Education, A
History, A
Human Resources Management/Personnel
  Administration, A
Humanities/Humanistic Studies, A
Journalism, A
Kinesiology and Exercise Science, A
Liberal Arts and Sciences Studies and
  Humanities, A
Management Information Systems and Services, A
Marketing/Marketing Management, A
Mathematics, A
Physics, A
Political Science and Government, A
Pre-Engineering, A
Psychology, A
Public Administration, A
Social Sciences, A
Sociology, A
Web/Multimedia Management and Webmaster, A

SETON HALL UNIVERSITY

Accounting, BMO
African-American/Black Studies, B
Allied Health and Medical Assisting Services, MD
Analytical Chemistry, MD
Anthropology, B
Art History, Criticism and Conservation, B
Art Teacher Education, B
Arts Management, M
Asian Studies/Civilization, BM
Athletic Training and Sports Medicine, M
Biochemistry, BMD
Biological and Biomedical Sciences, MD
Biology/Biological Sciences, B
Business Administration and Management, B
Business Administration, Management and
  Operations, MO
Business/Managerial Economics, B
Chemistry, BMD
Christian Studies, B
Classics and Classical
  Languages, Literatures, and Linguistics, B
Commercial and Advertising Art, B
Communication and Media Studies, M
Communication Disorders, M
Communication Studies/Speech Communication
  and Rhetoric, B
Computer and Information Sciences, B
Corporate and Organizational Communication, M
Counseling Psychology, D
Counselor Education/School Counseling and
  Guidance Services, M
Criminal Justice/Safety Studies, B
Economics, B
Education, MDO
Educational Administration and Supervision, MDO
Educational Leadership and Administration, DO
Educational Media/Instructional Technology, MO
Elementary Education and Teaching, BM
English, M
English as a Second Language, MO
English Language and Literature, B
Experimental Psychology, M
Finance, B
Finance and Banking, MO
Fine Arts and Art Studies, M
Foreign Languages and Literatures, B
French Language and Literature, B
Gerontological Nursing, M
Health Services Administration, MO
Higher Education/Higher Education
  Administration, D
History, B
Humanities/Humanistic Studies, B
Inorganic Chemistry, MD
International Affairs, MO
International Business/Trade/Commerce, MO
International Relations and Affairs, B
Italian Language and Literature, B
Jewish/Judaic Studies, M
Labor and Industrial Relations, B
Law and Legal Studies, MPO

Liberal Arts and Sciences Studies and
  Humanities, B
Management Information Systems and
  Services, BMO
Marketing, MO
Marketing/Marketing Management, B
Marriage and Family Therapy/Counseling, MDO
Mass Communication/Media Studies, M
Mathematics, B
Microbiology, M
Molecular Biology, MD
Multilingual and Multicultural Education, MO
Museology/Museum Studies, M
Music, BM
Music Performance, B
Non-Profit/Public/Organizational Management, M
Nursing, MO
Nursing - Adult, M
Nursing - Advanced Practice, M
Nursing - Registered Nurse Training, B
Nursing Administration, M
Nursing Education, MO
Occupational Therapy/Therapist, M
Organic Chemistry, MD
Pastoral Studies/Counseling, MP
Pediatric Nurse/Nursing, M
Pharmaceutical Administration, M
Philosophy, B
Physical Chemistry, MD
Physical Therapy/Therapist, D
Physician Assistant, M
Physics, B
Political Science and Government, B
Psychology, BMDO
Public Administration, M
Religion/Religious Studies, BM
Religious Education, B
School Nursing, M
School Psychology, O
Secondary Education and Teaching, BM
Social Work, B
Sociology, B
Spanish Language and Literature, B
Special Education and Teaching, B
Sport and Fitness
  Administration/Management, BMO
Taxation, M
Theology and Religious Vocations, MPO
Visual and Performing Arts, B
Women's Health Nursing, M

SOMERSET CHRISTIAN COLLEGE

Bible/Biblical Studies, A

STEVENS INSTITUTE OF TECHNOLOGY

Applied Mathematics, MD
Biochemistry, B
Biomedical/Medical Engineering, B
Business Administration and Management, B
Business Administration, Management and
  Operations, MDO
Chemical Engineering, BMDO
Chemistry, BMDO
Civil Engineering, BMDO
Computational Mathematics, B
Computer Engineering, BMDO
Computer Science, BMDO
Construction Engineering and Management, M
Electrical Engineering, MDO
Electrical, Electronics and Communications
  Engineering, B
Electronic Commerce, MO
Engineering and Applied Sciences, MDO
Engineering Physics, BMDO
Engineering/Industrial Management, B
English Language and Literature, B
Environmental Engineering
  Technology/Environmental Technology, MDO
Environmental/Environmental Health Engineering, B
History, B
History and Philosophy of Science and
  Technology, B
Humanities/Humanistic Studies, B
Industrial and Manufacturing Management, MO
Information Science/Studies, MO

Management Information Systems and
  Services, MDO
Management of Technology, MDO
Management Strategy and Policy, M
Marine Affairs, M
Materials Engineering, MDO
Materials Sciences, MDO
Mathematics, BMD
Mechanical Engineering, BMDO
Near and Middle Eastern Studies, B
Ocean Engineering, MD
Philosophy, B
Physics, BMDO
Pre-Dentistry Studies, B
Pre-Law Studies, B
Pre-Medicine/Pre-Medical Studies, B
Project Management, MO
Science Teacher Education/General Science
  Teacher Education, O
Software Engineering, O
Statistics, MO
Systems Engineering, B
Telecommunications Management, MDO

SUSSEX COUNTY COMMUNITY COLLEGE

Accounting, A
Administrative Assistant and Secretarial Science, A
Automotive Engineering Technology/Technician, A
Biological and Physical Sciences, A
Broadcast Journalism, A
Business Administration and Management, A
Commercial and Advertising Art, A
Computer and Information Sciences, A
Consumer Merchandising/Retailing Management, A
English Language and Literature, A
Environmental Studies, A
Fine/Studio Arts, A
Fire Protection, A
Human Services, A
Journalism, A
Legal Assistant/Paralegal, A
Liberal Arts and Sciences Studies and
  Humanities, A
Public Health (MPH, DPH), A
Respiratory Care Therapy/Therapist, A
Veterinary/Animal Health Technology/Technician and
  Veterinary Assistant, A

THOMAS EDISON STATE COLLEGE

Human Resources Management and Services, M
Insurance, M
Liberal Studies, M
Management, M
Project Management, M
Substance Abuse/Addiction Counseling, M

UNION COUNTY COLLEGE

Accounting Technology/Technician and
  Bookkeeping, A
Administrative Assistant and Secretarial Science, A
Allied Health
  Diagnostic, Intervention, and Treatment
  Professions, A
Biology/Biological Sciences, A
Business Administration and Management, A
Business and Personal/Financial Services Marketing
  Operations, A
Business/Commerce, A
Chemistry, A
Civil Engineering Technology/Technician, A
Clinical/Medical Laboratory Technician, A
Communication Studies/Speech Communication
  and Rhetoric, A
Criminal Justice/Police Science, A
Dental Hygiene/Hygienist, A
Electromechanical Technology/Electromechanical
  Engineering Technology, A
Engineering, A
Fire Protection and Safety Technology/Technician, A
Gerontology, A
Hotel/Motel Administration/Management, A
Industrial Technology/Technician, A
Information Science/Studies, A
Language Interpretation and Translation, A

Liberal Arts and Sciences Studies and
  Humanities, A
Licensed Practical/Vocational Nurse Training, A
Management Information Systems and Services, A
Mechanical Engineering/Mechanical
  Technology/Technician, A
Medical Radiologic Technology/Science - Radiation
  Therapist, A
Medical/Clinical Assistant, A
Nuclear Medical Technology/Technologist, A
Nursing - Registered Nurse Training, A
Occupational Therapist Assistant, A
Physical Sciences, A
Physical Therapist Assistant, A
Rehabilitation and Therapeutic Professions, A
Respiratory Care Therapy/Therapist, A
Sign Language Interpretation and Translation, A

WARREN COUNTY COMMUNITY COLLEGE

Accounting, A
Administrative Assistant and Secretarial Science, A
Biology/Biological Sciences, A
Business Administration and Management, A
Criminal Justice/Law Enforcement Administration, A
Data Processing and Data Processing
  Technology/Technician, A
Education, A
Environmental Studies, A
Fine/Studio Arts, A
Information Science/Studies, A
Legal Assistant/Paralegal, A
Liberal Arts and Sciences Studies and
  Humanities, A
Social Sciences, A

WESTMINSTER CHOIR COLLEGE OF RIDER UNIVERSITY

Conducting, B
Liberal Arts and Sciences Studies and
  Humanities, B
Music, B
Music Pedagogy, B
Music Teacher Education, B
Music Theory and Composition, B
Piano and Organ, B
Religious/Sacred Music, B
Voice and Opera, B

WILLIAM PATERSON UNIVERSITY OF NEW JERSEY

Accounting, B
African Studies, B
African-American/Black Studies, B
Anthropology, B
Applied Art, B
Applied Mathematics, B
Art History, Criticism and Conservation, B
Art Teacher Education, B
Art/Art Studies, General, B
Behavioral Sciences, B
Biological and Biomedical Sciences, M
Biology/Biological Sciences, B
BioTechnology, M
Business Administration and Management, B
Business Administration, Management and
  Operations, M
Business/Managerial Economics, B
Clinical Psychology, M
Commercial and Advertising Art, B
Communication and Media Studies, M
Communication Disorders, M
Comparative Literature, B
Computer Science, B
Counselor Education/School Counseling and
  Guidance Services, M
Drama and Dramatics/Theatre Arts, B
Ecology, BM
Education, BM
Educational Leadership and Administration, M
Elementary Education and Teaching, BM
English, M
English Language and Literature, B
Environmental Studies, B
Fine Arts and Art Studies, M

Fine/Studio Arts, B
Geography, B
Health Teacher Education, B
History, BM
Humanities/Humanistic Studies, B
International Business/Trade/Commerce, B
Jazz/Jazz Studies, B
Kinesiology and Exercise Science, B
Limnology, M
Mass Communication/Media Studies, B
Mathematics, B
Media Studies, M
Molecular Biology, M
Music, BM
Music Management and Merchandising, B
Music Teacher Education, B
Nursing, M
Nursing - Registered Nurse Training, B
Parks, Recreation, Leisure and Fitness Studies, B
Philosophy, B
Physical Education Teaching and Coaching, B
Physical Sciences, B
Physiology, M
Political Science and Government, B
Pre-Dentistry Studies, B
Pre-Law Studies, B
Pre-Medicine/Pre-Medical Studies, B
Psychology, B
Public Health (MPH, DPH), B
Public Policy Analysis, M
Reading Teacher Education, M
Secondary Education and Teaching, B
Social Sciences, B
Sociology, BM
Spanish Language and Literature, B
Special Education and Teaching, BM
Voice and Opera, B

New Mexico

THE ART CENTER DESIGN COLLEGE

Advertising, A
Art/Art Studies, General, A

CENTRAL NEW MEXICO COMMUNITY COLLEGE

Accounting, A
Administrative Assistant and Secretarial Science, A
Architectural Drafting and Architectural
  CAD/CADD, A
Banking and Financial Support Services, A
BioTechnology, A
Building/Construction
  Finishing, Management, and Inspection, A
Business Administration and Management, A
Child Care and Support Services Management, A
Clinical/Medical Laboratory Technician, A
Computer Systems Analysis/Analyst, A
Construction Trades, A
Cosmetology/Cosmetologist, A
Court Reporting/Court Reporter, A
Criminal Justice/Safety Studies, A
Culinary Arts/Chef Training, A
Data Processing and Data Processing
  Technology/Technician, A
Diagnostic Medical Sonography/Sonographer and
  Ultrasound Technician, A
Electrical, Electronic and Communications
  Engineering Technology/Technician, A
Electrical/Electronics Drafting and
  Electrical/Electronics CAD/CADD, A
Elementary Education and Teaching, A
Engineering, A
Engineering Technologies/Technicians, A
Environmental/Environmental Health Engineering, A
Fire Protection and Safety Technology/Technician, A
Health Information/Medical Records
  Administration/Administrator, A
Hospitality Administration/Management, A
Industrial Technology/Technician, A
Information Science/Studies, A
Laser and Optical Technology/Technician, A
Legal Assistant/Paralegal, A
Liberal Arts and Sciences Studies and
  Humanities, A

Nursing - Registered Nurse Training, A
Parks, Recreation, Leisure and Fitness Studies, A
Respiratory Care Therapy/Therapist, A
Vehicle Maintenance and Repair Technologies, A

CLOVIS COMMUNITY COLLEGE

Accounting, A
Administrative Assistant and Secretarial Science, A
Automobile/Automotive Mechanics
   Technology/Technician, A
Bilingual and Multilingual Education, A
Business Administration and Management, A
Business/Office Automation/Technology/Data
   Entry, A
Commercial and Advertising Art, A
Computer and Information Sciences, A
Computer Typography and Composition Equipment
   Operator, A
Corrections, A
Cosmetology/Cosmetologist, A
Criminal Justice/Police Science, A
Electromechanical Technology/Electromechanical
   Engineering Technology, A
Executive Assistant/Executive Secretary, A
Finance, A
Fine/Studio Arts, A
Health and Physical Education, A
Heating, Air Conditioning, Ventilation and
   Refrigeration Maintenance
   Technology/Technician, A
Legal Administrative Assistant/Secretary, A
Legal Assistant/Paralegal, A
Liberal Arts and Sciences Studies and
   Humanities, A
Library Assistant/Technician, A
Management Information Systems and Services, A
Mathematics, A
Medical Administrative Assistant/Secretary, A
Medical Office Assistant/Specialist, A
Medical Radiologic Technology/Science - Radiation
   Therapist, A
Nail Technician/Specialist and Manicurist, A
Nursing - Registered Nurse Training, A
Physical Sciences, A
Psychology, A
Sign Language Interpretation and Translation, A
Teacher Assistant/Aide, A
Technical and Business Writing, A
Web Page, Digital/Multimedia and Information
   Resources Design, A
Web/Multimedia Management and Webmaster, A

COLLEGE OF SANTA FE

Accounting, B
Acting, B
Art History, Criticism and Conservation, B
Art Therapy/Therapist, B
Arts Management, B
Business Administration and Management, AB
Business Administration, Management and
   Operations, M
Business Teacher Education, B
Computer Science, B
Counseling Psychology, B
Creative Writing, B
Criminal Justice/Law Enforcement Administration, B
Curriculum and Instruction, M
Drama and Dramatics/Theatre Arts, B
Dramatic/Theatre Arts and Stagecraft, B
Early Childhood Education and Teaching, B
Education, M
Elementary Education and Teaching, B
English Language and Literature, AB
English/Language Arts Teacher Education, B
Environmental Sciences, B
Film/Cinema Studies, B
Fine/Studio Arts, B
Humanities/Humanistic Studies, B
Industrial and Organizational Psychology, B
Intermedia/Multimedia, B
International Business/Trade/Commerce, B
Management Information Systems and Services, B
Multi-/Interdisciplinary Studies, B
Multilingual and Multicultural Education, M
Music, B
Natural Resources and Conservation, B

Natural Resources Management/Development and
   Policy, B
Painting, B
Pastoral Studies/Counseling, B
Photography, B
Political Science and Government, B
Printmaking, B
Psychology, B
Public Administration, B
Regional Studies (U.S., Canadian, Foreign), B
Religion/Religious Studies, B
Sculpture, B
Secondary Education and Teaching, B
Special Education and Teaching, M
Technical and Business Writing, B
Technical Theatre/Theatre Design and
   Technology, B
Theatre/Theatre Arts Management, B

COLLEGE OF THE SOUTHWEST

Accounting, B
Bilingual and Multilingual Education, B
Biology/Biological Sciences, B
Business Administration and Management, B
Business Teacher Education, B
Computer Science, B
Counselor Education/School Counseling and
   Guidance Services, M
Criminal Justice/Safety Studies, B
Curriculum and Instruction, M
Drama and Dramatics/Theatre Arts, B
Education, BM
Educational Administration and Supervision, M
Educational Measurement and Evaluation, M
Elementary Education and Teaching, B
English Language and Literature, B
Environmental Studies, B
History, B
Junior High/Intermediate/Middle School Education
   and Teaching, B
Marketing/Marketing Management, B
Mathematics, B
Physical Education Teaching and Coaching, B
Psychology, B
Science Teacher Education/General Science
   Teacher Education, B
Secondary Education and Teaching, B
Social Sciences, B
Special Education and Teaching, B

DOÑA ANA BRANCH COMMUNITY COLLEGE

Administrative Assistant and Secretarial Science, A
Architectural Engineering Technology/Technician, A
Automobile/Automotive Mechanics
   Technology/Technician, A
Business Administration and Management, A
Computer Engineering Technology/Technician, A
Computer Typography and Composition Equipment
   Operator, A
Consumer Merchandising/Retailing Management, A
Drafting and Design Technology/Technician, A
Electrical, Electronic and Communications
   Engineering Technology/Technician, A
Emergency Medical Technology/Technician (EMT
   Paramedic), A
Fashion Merchandising, A
Finance, A
Fire Science/Firefighting, A
Heating, Air Conditioning, Ventilation and
   Refrigeration Maintenance
   Technology/Technician, A
Hospitality Administration/Management, A
Hydrology and Water Resources Science, A
Industrial Radiologic Technology/Technician, A
Legal Assistant/Paralegal, A
Library Science, A
Nursing - Registered Nurse Training, A
Respiratory Care Therapy/Therapist, A
Welding Technology/Welder, A

EASTERN NEW MEXICO UNIVERSITY

Accounting, B
Agricultural Business and Management, B
Agricultural Teacher Education, B
Anthropology, BM

Art/Art Studies, General, AB
Audiology/Audiologist and Speech-Language
   Pathology/Pathologist, B
Biological and Biomedical Sciences, M
Biology/Biological Sciences, B
Business Administration and Management, B
Business Administration, Management and
   Operations, M
Business Teacher Education, B
Chemistry, BM
Child Care and Support Services Management, A
Clinical Laboratory Science/Medical
   Technology/Technologist, B
Communication and Media Studies, M
Communication Disorders, M
Communication Studies/Speech Communication
   and Rhetoric, B
Computer and Information Sciences, B
Counselor Education/School Counseling and
   Guidance Services, M
Criminal Justice/Safety Studies, B
Drama and Dramatics/Theatre Arts, B
Education, M
Elementary Education and Teaching, B
Engineering Technology, B
English, M
English Language and Literature, B
Family and Consumer Sciences/Human Sciences, B
Finance, B
General Studies, A
Geology/Earth Science, B
History, B
Human Resources Management/Personnel
   Administration, B
Kindergarten/PreSchool Education and Teaching, B
Liberal Arts and Sciences Studies and
   Humanities, B
Management Information Systems and Services, B
Marketing/Marketing Management, B
Mathematics, M
Multi-/Interdisciplinary Studies, B
Music, B
Music Teacher Education, B
Nursing - Registered Nurse Training, B
Physical Education Teaching and Coaching, BM
Physics, B
Political Science and Government, B
Psychology, ABM
Religion/Religious Studies, B
Sales and Marketing Operations/Marketing and
   Distribution Teacher Education, B
Social Sciences, B
Sociology, B
Spanish Language and Literature, B
Special Education and Teaching, BM
Statistics, B
Wildlife and Wildlands Science and Management, B

EASTERN NEW MEXICO UNIVERSITY-ROSWELL

Administrative Assistant and Secretarial Science, A
Airframe Mechanics and Aircraft Maintenance
   Technology/Technician, A
Automobile/Automotive Mechanics
   Technology/Technician, A
Banking and Financial Support Services, A
Business Administration and Management, A
Child Care and Support Services Management, A
Computer and Information Sciences, A
Criminal Justice/Safety Studies, A
Drafting and Design Technology/Technician, A
Electromechanical Technology/Electromechanical
   Engineering Technology, A
Emergency Medical Technology/Technician (EMT
   Paramedic), A
Fire Science/Firefighting, A
Human Services, A
Industrial Technology/Technician, A
Legal Assistant/Paralegal, A
Liberal Arts and Sciences Studies and
   Humanities, A
Medical Office Management/Administration, A
Nursing - Registered Nurse Training, A
Occupational Therapist Assistant, A
Social Work, A

Welding Technology/Welder, A

INSTITUTE OF AMERICAN INDIAN ARTS

Art/Art Studies, General, A
Ceramic Arts and Ceramics, A
Creative Writing, A
Drawing, A
Fiber, Textile and Weaving Arts, A
Fine/Studio Arts, A
Metal and Jewelry Arts, A
Museology/Museum Studies, A
Photography, A
Printmaking, A
Sculpture, A

INTERNATIONAL INSTITUTE OF THE AMERICAS

Accounting, A
Business Administration and Management, AB
Criminal Justice/Law Enforcement Administration, A
Health/Health Care Administration/Management, A

ITT TECHNICAL INSTITUTE

Animation, Interactive Technology, Video Graphics
    and Special Effects, B
Business Administration and Management, B
Computer and Information Systems Security, B
Computer Programming/Programmer, A
Criminal Justice/Law Enforcement Administration, B
E-Commerce/Electronic Commerce, B
Electrical, Electronic and Communications
    Engineering Technology/Technician, AB
System, Networking, and LAN/WAN
    Management/Manager, A
Web Page, Digital/Multimedia and Information
    Resources Design, A
Web/Multimedia Management and Webmaster, A

LUNA COMMUNITY COLLEGE

Accounting, A
Administrative Assistant and Secretarial Science, A
Architectural Drafting and Architectural
    CAD/CADD, A
Business Administration and Management, A
Civil Drafting and Civil Engineering CAD/CADD, A
Computer and Information Sciences, A
Criminal Justice/Police Science, A
Early Childhood Education and Teaching, A
Electrical, Electronic and Communications
    Engineering Technology/Technician, A
Licensed Practical/Vocational Nurse Training, A
Manufacturing Technology/Technician, A
Physical Therapy/Therapist, A
Technology Education/Industrial Arts, A

MESALANDS COMMUNITY COLLEGE

Animal Sciences, A
Automobile/Automotive Mechanics
    Technology/Technician, A
Business Administration and Management, A
Communication Studies/Speech Communication
    and Rhetoric, A
Diesel Mechanics Technology/Technician, A
Elementary Education and Teaching, A
Geology/Earth Science, A
History, A
Human Resources Management/Personnel
    Administration, A
Information Science/Studies, A
Metal and Jewelry Arts, A
Paleontology, A
Public Administration, A
Social Work, A

NATIONAL AMERICAN UNIVERSITY (ALBUQUERQUE)

Accounting, AB
Applied Art, AB
Business Administration and Management, AB
Engineering, B
Hospitality Administration/Management, AB
Hotel/Motel Administration/Management, AB
Information Science/Studies, AB

Management Information Systems and Services, AB

NATIONAL COLLEGE OF MIDWIFERY

Nurse Midwife/Nursing Midwifery, MD

NEW MEXICO HIGHLANDS UNIVERSITY

Accounting, B
American/United States Studies/Civilization, M
Anthropology, BM
Art Teacher Education, B
Art/Art Studies, General, B
Bilingual and Multilingual Education, B
Biological and Biomedical Sciences, M
Biology/Biological Sciences, B
Business Administration and Management, B
Business Administration, Management and
    Operations, M
Chemistry, BM
Cognitive Sciences, M
Commercial and Advertising Art, B
Computer Art and Design, M
Computer Programming/Programmer, B
Computer Science, BM
Counselor Education/School Counseling and
    Guidance Services, M
Criminal Justice/Safety Studies, B
Criminology, B
Curriculum and Instruction, M
Education, BM
Educational Administration and Supervision, M
Educational Leadership and Administration, M
Elementary Education and Teaching, AB
Engineering, B
English, M
English Language and Literature, B
Environmental Policy and Resource
    Management, M
Environmental Studies, B
Exercise and Sports Science, M
Film, Television, and Video Production, M
Health Teacher Education, B
Health/Health Care Administration/Management, B
Hispanic Studies, M
History, BM
Information Science/Studies, B
Internet and Interactive Multimedia, M
Journalism, B
Kindergarten/PreSchool Education and Teaching, B
Management Information Systems and Services, B
Marketing/Marketing Management, B
Mass Communication/Media Studies, B
Mathematics, B
Music, B
Music Teacher Education, B
Natural Resources Management/Development and
    Policy, B
Physical Education Teaching and Coaching, B
Political Science and Government, BM
Pre-Law Studies, B
Pre-Medicine/Pre-Medical Studies, B
Psychology, BM
Public Affairs, M
Science Teacher Education/General Science
    Teacher Education, B
Secondary Education and Teaching, B
Social Work, BM
Sociology, BM
Spanish Language and Literature, BM
Special Education and Teaching, BM
Teacher Assistant/Aide, A
Technology Education/Industrial Arts, B

NEW MEXICO INSTITUTE OF MINING AND TECHNOLOGY

Applied Mathematics, D
Astrophysics, MD
Atmospheric Sciences and Meteorology, MD
Biochemistry, M
Biological and Biomedical Sciences, M
Biology/Biological Sciences, B
Business Administration and Management, AB
Chemical Engineering, B
Chemistry, BMD
Civil Engineering, B
Computer Science, BMD

Electrical Engineering, M
Electrical, Electronics and Communications
    Engineering, B
Engineering Management, M
Engineering Mechanics, B
Environmental Engineering
    Technology/Environmental Technology, M
Environmental Sciences, D
Environmental Studies, B
Environmental/Environmental Health Engineering, B
General Studies, A
Geochemistry, MD
Geology/Earth Science, BMD
Geophysics and Seismology, BMD
Geosciences, MD
Hydrology and Water Resources Science, MD
Information Technology, B
Materials Engineering, BMD
Mathematical Physics, D
Mathematics, BMD
Mechanical Engineering, B
Mechanics, M
Mineral/Mining Engineering, M
Mining and Mineral Engineering, B
Operations Research, M
Petroleum Engineering, BMD
Physical Sciences, B
Physics, BMD
Psychology, B
Science Teacher Education/General Science
    Teacher Education, M
Technical and Business Writing, B

NEW MEXICO JUNIOR COLLEGE

Accounting, A
Administrative Assistant and Secretarial Science, A
Agriculture, A
Art Teacher Education, A
Art/Art Studies, General, A
Athletic Training and Sports Medicine, A
Automobile/Automotive Mechanics
    Technology/Technician, A
Biological and Physical Sciences, A
Biology/Biological Sciences, A
Business Administration and Management, A
Business Teacher Education, A
Carpentry/Carpenter, A
Chemistry, A
Clinical/Medical Laboratory Technician, A
Commercial and Advertising Art, A
Computer Graphics, A
Computer Programming/Programmer, A
Computer Science, A
Computer Typography and Composition Equipment
    Operator, A
Construction Engineering Technology/Technician, A
Cosmetology/Cosmetologist, A
Criminal Justice/Police Science, A
Data Processing and Data Processing
    Technology/Technician, A
Drafting and Design Technology/Technician, A
Drama and Dramatics/Theatre Arts, A
Education, A
Elementary Education and Teaching, A
Emergency Medical Technology/Technician (EMT
    Paramedic), A
Engineering, A
English Language and Literature, A
Environmental Education, A
Environmental Studies, A
Finance, A
Fire Science/Firefighting, A
History, A
Legal Administrative Assistant/Secretary, A
Liberal Arts and Sciences Studies and
    Humanities, A
Licensed Practical/Vocational Nurse Training, A
Machine Tool Technology/Machinist, A
Marketing/Marketing Management, A
Mathematics, A
Medical Administrative Assistant/Secretary, A
Medical/Clinical Assistant, A
Music, A
Nursing - Registered Nurse Training, A
Parks, Recreation, Leisure and Fitness Studies, A
Petroleum Technology/Technician, A

Physical Education Teaching and Coaching, A
Public Health (MPH, DPH), A
Real Estate, A
Technology Education/Industrial Arts, A
Trade and Industrial Teacher Education, A
Welding Technology/Welder, A

NEW MEXICO MILITARY INSTITUTE

Accounting, A
Army JROTC/ROTC, A
Art/Art Studies, General, A
Biological and Physical Sciences, A
Biology/Biological Sciences, A
Business Administration and Management, A
Chemistry, A
Civil Engineering Technology/Technician, A
Computer Programming/Programmer, A
Computer Science, A
Criminal Justice/Law Enforcement Administration, A
Criminal Justice/Police Science, A
Economics, A
Engineering, A
English Language and Literature, A
Finance, A
French Language and Literature, A
German Language and Literature, A
History, A
Humanities/Humanistic Studies, A
Liberal Arts and Sciences Studies and
   Humanities, A
Mathematics, A
Physical Education Teaching and Coaching, A
Physics, A
Pre-Engineering, A
Social Sciences, A
Spanish Language and Literature, A
Sport and Fitness Administration/Management, A

NEW MEXICO STATE UNIVERSITY

Accounting, BM
Aerospace, Aeronautical and Astronautical
   Engineering, B
Agribusiness, B
Agricultural Economics, BM
Agricultural Education, M
Agricultural Sciences, MD
Agricultural Teacher Education, B
Agriculture, B
Agronomy and Crop Science, B
Agronomy and Soil Sciences, MD
Animal Sciences, BMD
Anthropology, BM
Apparel and Textiles, B
Astronomy, MD
Athletic Training and Sports Medicine, B
Biochemistry, BMD
Biological and Biomedical Sciences, MD
Biology/Biological Sciences, B
Business Administration and Management, B
Business Administration, Management and
   Operations, MD
Business/Commerce, AB
Chemical Engineering, BMD
Chemistry, BMD
City/Urban, Community and Regional Planning, B
Civil Engineering, BMD
Communication and Media Studies, M
Communication Disorders, M
Community Organization and Advocacy, B
Computer and Information Sciences, B
Computer Engineering, MD
Computer Science, MD
Counseling Psychology, MDO
Counselor Education/School Counseling and
   Guidance Services, MDO
Criminal Justice/Safety Studies, AB
Criminology, M
Curriculum and Instruction, MDO
Dance, B
Drama and Dramatics/Theatre Arts, B
Early Childhood Education and Teaching, B
Economics, BM
Education, MDO
Education/Teaching of Individuals with Speech or
   Language Impairments, B
Educational Administration and Supervision, MD

Electrical Engineering, MD
Electrical, Electronics and Communications
   Engineering, B
Elementary Education and Teaching, B
Engineering and Applied Sciences, MD
Engineering Physics, B
Engineering Technology, AB
English, MD
English Language and Literature, B
Entomology, M
Environmental Engineering
   Technology/Environmental Technology, M
Environmental Health, B
Environmental Studies, B
Family and Consumer Sciences/Home Economics
   Teacher Education, B
Family and Consumer Sciences/Human
   Sciences, M
Finance, B
Fine Arts and Art Studies, M
Fine/Studio Arts, B
Fish, Game and Wildlife Management, M
Foods, Nutrition, and Wellness Studies, B
Foreign Languages and Literatures, B
General Studies, B
Geography, BM
Geology/Earth Science, BM
History, BM
Horticultural Science, BMD
Human Development and Family Studies, B
Industrial Engineering, B
Industrial/Management Engineering, MD
Information Science/Studies, B
Information Technology, B
Interdisciplinary Studies, BMD
International Business/Trade/Commerce, B
Journalism, B
Kindergarten/PreSchool Education and Teaching, B
Management Science, B
Marketing/Marketing Management, B
Mathematics, BMD
Mechanical Engineering, BMD
Medical Microbiology and Bacteriology, B
Microbiology, B
Molecular Biology, MD
Music, M
Music Performance, B
Music Teacher Education, B
Nursing, M
Nursing - Registered Nurse Training, B
Parks, Recreation and Leisure Facilities
   Management, B
Philosophy, B
Physical Education Teaching and Coaching, B
Physics, BMD
Plant Pathology/Phytopathology, BM
Plant Sciences, M
Political Science and Government, BM
Psychology, BMD
Public Health, M
Public Health (MPH, DPH), B
Public Health Education and Promotion, B
Range Science and Management, BMD
Reading Teacher Education, O
Secondary Education and Teaching, B
Social Work, BM
Sociology, BM
Soil Science and Agronomy, B
Spanish Language and Literature, M
Special Education and Teaching, BM
Statistics, M
Survey Technology/Surveying, B
Teacher Assistant/Aide, M
Tourism Promotion Operations, B
Visual and Performing Arts, B
Wildlife and Wildlands Science and Management, B
Wildlife Biology, B
Writing, M

NEW MEXICO STATE
UNIVERSITY-ALAMOGORDO

Administrative Assistant and Secretarial Science, A
Business/Commerce, A
Clinical/Medical Laboratory Technician, A
Commercial and Advertising Art, A
Criminal Justice/Safety Studies, A

Data Processing and Data Processing
   Technology/Technician, A
Education, A
Electrical, Electronic and Communications
   Engineering Technology/Technician, A
Engineering, A
Fire Science/Firefighting, A
General Office Occupations and Clerical Services, A
Legal Assistant/Paralegal, A
Liberal Arts and Sciences Studies and
   Humanities, A
Nursing - Registered Nurse Training, A
Social Work, A

NEW MEXICO STATE
UNIVERSITY-CARLSBAD

Administrative Assistant and Secretarial Science, A
Agriculture, A
Business Administration and Management, A
Computer Science, A
Criminal Justice/Law Enforcement Administration, A
Education, A
Electrical, Electronic and Communications
   Engineering Technology/Technician, A
Engineering Technology, A
Environmental Engineering
   Technology/Environmental Technology, A
Fire Science/Firefighting, A
Industrial Technology/Technician, A
Information Science/Studies, A
Legal Assistant/Paralegal, A
Liberal Arts and Sciences Studies and
   Humanities, A
Nursing - Registered Nurse Training, A
Social Work, A
Welding Technology/Welder, A

NEW MEXICO STATE
UNIVERSITY-GRANTS

Administrative Assistant and Secretarial Science, A
Business Administration and Management, A
Criminal Justice/Law Enforcement Administration, A
Data Processing and Data Processing
   Technology/Technician, A
Education, A
Electrical, Electronic and Communications
   Engineering Technology/Technician, A
Legal Assistant/Paralegal, A
Liberal Arts and Sciences Studies and
   Humanities, A

NORTHERN NEW MEXICO COMMUNITY
COLLEGE

BioTechnology, A
Business/Commerce, A
Computer and Information Sciences, A
Criminal Justice/Safety Studies, A
Electrical, Electronic and Communications
   Engineering Technology/Technician, A
Elementary Education and Teaching, A
Environmental Studies, A
Fine/Studio Arts, A
Human Services, A
Industrial Engineering, A
Industrial Radiologic Technology/Technician, A
Library Assistant/Technician, A
Medical Radiologic Technology/Science - Radiation
   Therapist, A

PIMA MEDICAL INSTITUTE

Radiologic Technology/Science - Radiographer, A

ST. JOHN'S COLLEGE

Ancient/Classical Greek Language and Literature, B
Asian Languages, M
Asian Studies/Civilization, M
Classics and Classical
   Languages, Literatures, and Linguistics, B
Comparative Literature, B
English Language and Literature, B
Ethics, B
European Studies/Civilization, B
Foreign Languages and Literatures, B
French Language and Literature, B
General Studies, B

History, B
Humanities/Humanistic Studies, B
Liberal Arts and Sciences Studies and
   Humanities, B
Liberal Studies, M
Mathematics, B
Philosophy, B
Philosophy and Religious Studies, B
Physical Sciences, B
Physics, B
Pre-Medicine/Pre-Medical Studies, B
Religion/Religious Studies, B

SAN JUAN COLLEGE

Accounting Technology/Technician and
   Bookkeeping, A
Administrative Assistant and Secretarial Science, A
Airline/Commercial/Professional Pilot and Flight
   Crew, A
Anthropology, A
Art/Art Studies, General, A
Autobody/Collision and Repair
   Technology/Technician, A
Automobile/Automotive Mechanics
   Technology/Technician, A
Banking and Financial Support Services, A
Biology/Biological Sciences, A
Business Administration and Management, A
Carpentry/Carpenter, A
Chemistry, A
Commercial and Advertising Art, A
Communication Studies/Speech Communication
   and Rhetoric, A
Computer Science, A
Criminal Justice/Police Science, A
Criminal Justice/Safety Studies, A
Diesel Mechanics Technology/Technician, A
Drafting and Design Technology/Technician, A
Drama and Dramatics/Theatre Arts, A
Economics, A
Education, A
Engineering, A
English Language and Literature, A
Fire Protection and Safety Technology/Technician, A
Foreign Languages and Literatures, A
General Studies, A
Geology/Earth Science, A
Health Information/Medical Records
   Technology/Technician, A
History, A
Human Services, A
Information Science/Studies, A
Instrumentation Technology/Technician, A
Kindergarten/PreSchool Education and Teaching, A
Legal Assistant/Paralegal, A
Mathematics, A
Music, A
Nursing - Registered Nurse Training, A
Parks, Recreation, Leisure and Fitness Studies, A
Philosophy, A
Physical Sciences, A
Physical Therapist Assistant, A
Physics, A
Political Science and Government, A
Pre-Medicine/Pre-Medical Studies, A
Psychology, A
Public Administration, A
Real Estate, A
Social Work, A
Sociology, A
Water Quality and Wastewater Treatment
   Management and Recycling
   Technology/Technician, A
Welding Technology/Welder, A

SANTA FE COMMUNITY COLLEGE

Accounting, A
Administrative Assistant and Secretarial Science, A
Area Studies, A
Art/Art Studies, General, A
Biology/Biological Sciences, A
Business Administration and Management, A
Computer and Information Sciences, A
Construction Engineering Technology/Technician, A
Criminal Justice/Safety Studies, A
Culinary Arts/Chef Training, A

Dance, A
Design and Visual Communications, A
Drafting and Design Technology/Technician, A
Electrical, Electronic and Communications
   Engineering Technology/Technician, A
Engineering, A
Entrepreneurship/Entrepreneurial Studies, A
General Studies, A
Health and Physical Education, A
Hotel/Motel Administration/Management, A
Interior Design, A
Kindergarten/PreSchool Education and Teaching, A
Legal Assistant/Paralegal, A
Natural Resources Management/Development and
   Policy, A
Nursing - Registered Nurse Training, A
Parks, Recreation, Leisure and Fitness Studies, A
Physical Sciences, A
Radio and Television Broadcasting
   Technology/Technician, A
Sign Language Interpretation and Translation, A
Social Work, A
Spanish Language and Literature, A
Survey Technology/Surveying, A
Visual and Performing Arts, A

SOUTHWESTERN INDIAN POLYTECHNIC INSTITUTE

Accounting, A
Administrative Assistant and Secretarial Science, A
Business Administration and Management, A
Civil Engineering Technology/Technician, A
Commercial and Advertising Art, A
Computer Science, A
Culinary Arts/Chef Training, A
Data Processing and Data Processing
   Technology/Technician, A
Drafting and Design Technology/Technician, A
Electrical, Electronic and Communications
   Engineering Technology/Technician, A
Engineering Technology, A
Laser and Optical Technology/Technician, A
Liberal Arts and Sciences Studies and
   Humanities, A
Marketing/Marketing Management, A
Natural Resources Management/Development and
   Policy, A

UNIVERSITY OF NEW MEXICO

Accounting, M
African-American/Black Studies, B
Allopathic Medicine, P
American/United States Studies/Civilization, BMD
Anthropology, BMD
Architecture, BM
Art Education, M
Art History, Criticism and Conservation, BMD
Art Teacher Education, B
Art/Art Studies, General, B
Asian Studies/Civilization, B
Astrophysics, B
Audiology/Audiologist and Speech-Language
   Pathology/Pathologist, B
Biochemistry, BMD
Biological and Biomedical Sciences, MD
Biology/Biological Sciences, B
Business Administration and Management, B
Business Administration, Management and
   Operations, MO
Cell Biology and Anatomy, MD
Chemical Engineering, BMD
Chemistry, BMD
Child and Family Studies, MD
Civil Engineering, BMD
Classics and Classical
   Languages, Literatures, and Linguistics, B
Clinical Psychology, MD
Clinical/Medical Laboratory Technician, B
Communication and Media Studies, MD
Communication Disorders, M
Community Organization and Advocacy, A
Comparative Literature, BMD
Computer and Information Sciences, B
Computer Engineering, BMD
Computer Science, MD
Corrections, B

Counselor Education/School Counseling and
   Guidance Services, MD
Dance, BM
Dental Hygiene/Hygienist, ABM
Drama and Dramatics/Theatre Arts, B
Early Childhood Education and Teaching, B
Economics, BMD
Education, MDO
Educational Administration and Supervision, MDO
Educational Media/Instructional Technology, MDO
Educational Psychology, MD
Electrical Engineering, MD
Electrical, Electronics and Communications
   Engineering, B
Elementary Education and Teaching, BM
Engineering and Applied Sciences, MD
Engineering Science, B
English, MD
English Language and Literature, B
Environmental Design/Architecture, B
Environmental Sciences, B
European Studies/Civilization, B
Family and Consumer Sciences/Human Sciences, B
Film/Cinema Studies, B
Finance and Banking, M
Fine Arts and Art Studies, M
Foods, Nutrition, and Wellness Studies, B
Foreign Languages and Literatures, B
Foundations and Philosophy of Education, MD
French Language and Literature, BMD
General Studies, B
Genetics, MD
Geography, BM
Geology/Earth Science, B
Geosciences, MD
German Language and Literature, BM
Health Education, M
Health Teacher Education, B
History, BMD
Human Development and Family Studies, B
Human Resources Management and Services, M
Humanities/Humanistic Studies, B
International Business/Trade/Commerce, M
Journalism, B
Landscape Architecture, M
Latin American Studies, BMDO
Law and Legal Studies, PO
Liberal Arts and Sciences Studies and
   Humanities, B
Linguistics, BMD
Management Information Systems and Services, M
Management of Technology, M
Management Strategy and Policy, M
Manufacturing Engineering, M
Marketing, M
Mathematics, BMD
Mechanical Engineering, BMD
Medical Radiologic Technology/Science - Radiation
   Therapist, AB
Microbiology, MD
Molecular Biology, MD
Multilingual and Multicultural Education, DO
Music, M
Music Performance, B
Music Teacher Education, B
Neuroscience, MD
Nuclear Engineering, BMD
Nursing, MDO
Nursing - Registered Nurse Training, B
Nutritional Sciences, M
Occupational Therapy/Therapist, M
Optics/Optical Sciences, MD
Organizational Management, M
Parks, Recreation, Leisure and Fitness Studies, B
Pathology/Experimental Pathology, MD
Pharmaceutical Sciences, MD
Pharmacy, BP
Philosophy, BMD
Physical Education Teaching and Coaching, BMDO
Physical Therapy/Therapist, M
Physician Assistant, B
Physics, BMD
Physiology, MD
Planetary Astronomy and Science, MD
Political Science and Government, BMD
Portuguese Language and Literature, BMD

Psychology, BMD
Public Administration, MO
Public Health, M
Recreation and Park Management, MO
Religion/Religious Studies, B
Russian Language and Literature, B
Russian Studies, B
Secondary Education and Teaching, B
Sign Language Interpretation and Translation, B
Sociology, BMD
Spanish Language and Literature, BMD
Special Education and Teaching, BMDO
Speech and Rhetorical Studies, B
Statistics, BMD
Taxation, M
Teacher Assistant/Aide, A
Technical Theatre/Theatre Design and
    Technology, B
Technology Teacher Education/Industrial Arts
    Teacher Education, B
Theater, M
Toxicology, MD
Urban and Regional Planning, MO
Water Resources, M
Women's Studies, B
Writing, M

UNIVERSITY OF NEW MEXICO-GALLUP

Accounting, A
Administrative Assistant and Secretarial Science, A
Art/Art Studies, General, A
Automobile/Automotive Mechanics
    Technology/Technician, A
Business Administration and Management, A
Clinical/Medical Laboratory Technician, A
Communication Studies/Speech Communication
    and Rhetoric, A
Community Organization and Advocacy, A
Construction Engineering Technology/Technician, A
Corrections, A
Cosmetology/Cosmetologist, A
Criminal Justice/Law Enforcement Administration, A
Education, A
Elementary Education and Teaching, AB
Entrepreneurship/Entrepreneurial Studies, A
General Studies, AB
Graphic and Printing Equipment Operator
    Production, A
Health Teacher Education, A
Kindergarten/PreSchool Education and Teaching, A
Legal Assistant/Paralegal, A
Liberal Arts and Sciences Studies and
    Humanities, A
Marketing/Marketing Management, A
Nursing - Registered Nurse Training, AB
Physical Education Teaching and Coaching, A
Physical Sciences, A
Welding Technology/Welder, A

UNIVERSITY OF NEW MEXICO-LOS ALAMOS BRANCH

Accounting, A
Administrative Assistant and Secretarial Science, A
Applied Art, A
Biological and Physical Sciences, A
Business Administration and Management, A
Computer Engineering Technology/Technician, A
Computer Programming/Programmer, A
Computer Science, A
Electrical, Electronic and Communications
    Engineering Technology/Technician, A
Engineering, A
Environmental Studies, A
Fine/Studio Arts, A
Liberal Arts and Sciences Studies and
    Humanities, A
Pre-Engineering, A

UNIVERSITY OF NEW MEXICO-VALENCIA CAMPUS

Administrative Assistant and Secretarial Science, A
Agriculture, A
Building/Construction
    Finishing, Management, and Inspection, A
Business Administration and Management, A
Computer Science, A

Computer Typography and Composition Equipment
    Operator, A
Construction Engineering Technology/Technician, A
Criminal Justice/Law Enforcement Administration, A
Education, A
Human Services, A
Information Science/Studies, A
Liberal Arts and Sciences Studies and
    Humanities, A
Pre-Engineering, A
Real Estate, A

UNIVERSITY OF PHOENIX-NEW MEXICO CAMPUS

Accounting, BM
Business Administration and Management, B
Business Administration, Management and
    Operations, M
Counseling Psychology, M
Criminal Justice/Law Enforcement Administration, B
Curriculum and Instruction, M
Education, M
Educational Administration and Supervision, M
Electronic Commerce, M
Health Services Administration, M
Health/Health Care Administration/Management, B
Human Resources Management and Services, M
Information Science/Studies, M
Information Technology, B
International Business/Trade/Commerce, M
Management Information Systems and
    Services, BM
Management of Technology, M
Management Science, B
Marketing, M
Marketing/Marketing Management, B
Marriage and Family Therapy/Counseling, M
Nursing, M
Nursing - Registered Nurse Training, B
Nursing Science, B
Organizational Management, M
Public Administration and Social Service
    Professions, B

WESTERN NEW MEXICO UNIVERSITY

Accounting, B
Administrative Assistant and Secretarial Science, A
Art Teacher Education, B
Art/Art Studies, General, B
Automobile/Automotive Mechanics
    Technology/Technician, A
Biological and Physical Sciences, B
Biology/Biological Sciences, B
Botany/Plant Biology, B
Business Administration and Management, B
Business Administration, Management and
    Operations, M
Business Teacher Education, B
Chemistry, B
Clinical Laboratory Science/Medical
    Technology/Technologist, B
Computer Science, B
Construction Engineering Technology/Technician, A
Counselor Education/School Counseling and
    Guidance Services, M
Criminal Justice/Law Enforcement
    Administration, AB
Criminal Justice/Police Science, AB
Drafting and Design Technology/Technician, A
Education, BM
Educational Administration and Supervision, M
Elementary Education and Teaching, BM
English Language and Literature, B
Geology/Earth Science, B
Hispanic-American, Puerto Rican, and Mexican-
    American/Chicano Studies, B
History, B
Humanities/Humanistic Studies, B
Interdisciplinary Studies, BM
International Business/Trade/Commerce, B
Kindergarten/PreSchool Education and Teaching, B
Legal Administrative Assistant/Secretary, A
Machine Tool Technology/Machinist, A
Marketing/Marketing Management, B
Mathematics, B
Music, B

Music Teacher Education, B
Nursing - Registered Nurse Training, A
Occupational Therapy/Therapist, A
Physical Education Teaching and Coaching, B
Physical Sciences, B
Pre-Law Studies, B
Pre-Veterinary Studies, B
Psychology, B
Public Administration, B
Reading Teacher Education, M
Science Teacher Education/General Science
    Teacher Education, B
Secondary Education and Teaching, BM
Social Sciences, B
Social Work, B
Sociology, B
Spanish Language and Literature, B
Special Education and Teaching, BM
Special Products Marketing Operations, B
Trade and Industrial Teacher Education, B
Welding Technology/Welder, A
Wildlife and Wildlands Science and Management, B
Zoology/Animal Biology, B

New York

ADELPHI UNIVERSITY

Accounting, BM
Anthropology, B
Art History, Criticism and Conservation, B
Art Teacher Education, B
Audiology/Audiologist and Speech-Language
    Pathology/Pathologist, B
Biochemistry, B
Biological and Biomedical Sciences, M
Biology/Biological Sciences, B
Business Administration and Management, B
Business Administration, Management and
    Operations, M
Business, Management, Marketing, and Related
    Support Services, B
Chemistry, B
Clinical Psychology, DO
Communication Disorders, MD
Computer and Information Sciences, B
Counseling Psychology, M
Criminal Justice/Law Enforcement Administration, B
Dance, B
Drama and Dramatics/Theatre Arts, B
Economics, B
Education, BMDO
Educational Leadership and Administration, MO
Educational Media/Instructional Technology, MO
Electronic Commerce, M
Elementary Education and Teaching, MO
English as a Second Language, MO
English Language and Literature, B
Environmental Studies, M
Finance, B
Finance and Banking, M
Fine Arts and Art Studies, BM
French Language and Literature, B
Health Education, MO
History, B
Human Resources Management and Services, MO
Humanities/Humanistic Studies, B
International/Global Studies, B
Latin American Studies, B
Liberal Arts and Sciences Studies and
    Humanities, A
Management, O
Management Information Systems and Services, M
Marketing, M
Mathematics, B
Multi-/Interdisciplinary Studies, B
Multilingual and Multicultural Education, M
Music, B
Nursing, BMO
Nursing - Registered Nurse Training, B
Philosophy, B
Physical Education Teaching and Coaching, BMO
Physics, B
Political Science and Government, B
Psychology, BMDO
Public Administration, O
Public Health, O

Reading Teacher Education, MO
School Psychology, M
Secondary Education and Teaching, M
Social Sciences, B
Social Work, BMD
Sociology, B
Spanish Language and Literature, B
Special Education and Teaching, MO
Visual and Performing Arts, B

ADIRONDACK COMMUNITY COLLEGE

Accounting, A
Administrative Assistant and Secretarial Science, A
Banking and Financial Support Services, A
Behavioral Sciences, A
Biological and Physical Sciences, A
Biology/Biological Sciences, A
Broadcast Journalism, A
Business Administration and Management, A
Business/Office Automation/Technology/Data
   Entry, A
Computer and Information Sciences, A
Computer Graphics, A
Computer Science, A
Computer Systems Networking and
   Telecommunications, A
Corrections, A
Criminal Justice/Law Enforcement Administration, A
Criminal Justice/Police Science, A
Culinary Arts/Chef Training, A
Data Processing and Data Processing
   Technology/Technician, A
Drafting and Design Technology/Technician, A
Drafting/Design Engineering
   Technologies/Technicians, A
Electrical, Electronic and Communications
   Engineering Technology/Technician, A
Engineering, A
Engineering Science, A
Executive Assistant/Executive Secretary, A
Finance, A
Food Technology and Processing, A
General Studies, A
Health Information/Medical Records
   Administration/Administrator, A
History, A
Hospitality Administration/Management, A
Humanities/Humanistic Studies, A
Information Science/Studies, A
Information Technology, A
Liberal Arts and Sciences Studies and
   Humanities, A
Marketing/Marketing Management, A
Mass Communication/Media Studies, A
Mathematics, A
Mathematics and Computer Science, A
Mechanical Drafting and Mechanical Drafting
   CAD/CADD, A
Mechanical Engineering/Mechanical
   Technology/Technician, A
Medical Administrative Assistant/Secretary, A
Music, A
Nursing - Registered Nurse Training, A
Occupational Therapist Assistant, A
Photography, A
Physical Therapist Assistant, A
Pre-Engineering, A
Radio and Television, A
Receptionist, A
Social Sciences, A
System Administration/Administrator, A
Tourism and Travel Services Management, A
Web Page, Digital/Multimedia and Information
   Resources Design, A
Word Processing, A

ALBANY COLLEGE OF PHARMACY OF UNION UNIVERSITY

Biomedical Sciences, B
Health Professions and Related Clinical Sciences, B
Pharmacy, BP
Pharmacy, Pharmaceutical Sciences, and Administration, B

ALFRED UNIVERSITY

Accounting, B
Applied Arts and Design, M

Art Teacher Education, B
Art/Art Studies, General, B
Athletic Training and Sports Medicine, B
Bioengineering, M
Biological and Physical Sciences, B
Biology/Biological Sciences, B
Business Administration and Management, B
Business Administration, Management and
   Operations, M
Business Teacher Education, B
Ceramic Arts and Ceramics, BM
Ceramic Sciences and Engineering, BMD
Chemistry, B
Communication, Journalism and Related
   Programs, B
Comparative Literature, B
Computer Art and Design, M
Counselor Education/School Counseling and
   Guidance Services, M
Criminal Justice/Law Enforcement Administration, B
Drama and Dramatics/Theatre Arts, B
Economics, B
Education, M
Electrical Engineering, M
Electrical, Electronics and Communications
   Engineering, B
Elementary Education and Teaching, B
English Language and Literature, B
Environmental Studies, B
Fine/Studio Arts, B
French Language and Literature, B
General Studies, B
Geology/Earth Science, B
German Language and Literature, B
Gerontology, B
History, B
Interdisciplinary Studies, B
Internet and Interactive Multimedia, M
Materials Sciences, BMD
Mathematics, B
Mechanical Engineering, BM
Modern Languages, B
Philosophy, B
Physics, B
Political Science and Government, B
Psychology, B
Public Administration, BM
Reading Teacher Education, M
School Psychology, MDO
Science Teacher Education/General Science
   Teacher Education, B
Sculpture, M
Secondary Education and Teaching, B
Sociology, B
Spanish Language and Literature, B

AMERICAN ACADEMY OF DRAMATIC ARTS

Drama and Dramatics/Theatre Arts, A

AMERICAN ACADEMY MCALLISTER INSTITUTE OF FUNERAL SERVICE

Funeral Service and Mortuary Science, A

THE ART INSTITUTE OF NEW YORK CITY

Animation, Interactive Technology, Video Graphics
   and Special Effects, A
Cinematography and Film/Video Production, A
Fashion/Apparel Design, A
Graphic Design, A
Restaurant, Culinary, and Catering
   Management/Manager, A

BARD COLLEGE

Acting, B
African Studies, B
American Government and Politics (United States)
   , B
American History (United States), B
American/United States Studies/Civilization, B
Ancient/Classical Greek Language and Literature, B
Anthropology, B
Archeology, B
Area Studies, B

Art History, Criticism and Conservation, B
Art/Art Studies, General, B
Asian History, B
Asian Studies/Civilization, B
Biochemistry, B
Biological and Physical Sciences, B
Biology/Biological Sciences, B
Central/Middle and Eastern European Studies, B
Chemistry, B
Chinese Language and Literature, B
Cinematography and Film/Video Production, B
Classics and Classical
   Languages, Literatures, and Linguistics, B
Comparative Literature, B
Computer Science, B
Creative Writing, B
Dance, B
Drama and Dramatics/Theatre Arts, B
Drawing, B
Ecology, B
Economics, B
Education, M
English Language and Literature, B
Environmental Biology, B
Environmental Policy, MO
Environmental Studies, B
Ethnic and Cultural Studies, B
European History, B
European Studies/Civilization, B
Film/Cinema Studies, B
Fine Arts and Art Studies, M
Fine/Studio Arts, B
French Language and Literature, B
German Language and Literature, B
Hebrew Language and Literature, B
History, B
History and Philosophy of Science and
   Technology, B
Humanities/Humanistic Studies, B
Interdisciplinary Studies, B
International Economics, B
International Relations and Affairs, B
Italian Language and Literature, B
Jazz/Jazz Studies, B
Jewish/Judaic Studies, B
Latin American Studies, B
Latin Language and Literature, B
Mathematics, B
Medieval and Renaissance Studies, B
Modern Greek Language and Literature, B
Modern Languages, B
Molecular Biology, B
Museology/Museum Studies, M
Music, B
Music History, Literature, and Theory, B
Music Performance, B
Music Theory and Composition, B
Natural Sciences, B
Painting, B
Philosophy, B
Photography, B
Physical Sciences, B
Physics, B
Playwriting and Screenwriting, B
Political Science and Government, B
Pre-Dentistry Studies, B
Pre-Law Studies, B
Pre-Medicine/Pre-Medical Studies, B
Pre-Veterinary Studies, B
Psychology, B
Religion/Religious Studies, B
Romance Languages, Literatures, and Linguistics, B
Russian Language and Literature, B
Russian Studies, B
Sculpture, B
Social Sciences, B
Sociology, B
Spanish Language and Literature, B
Theatre Literature, History and Criticism, B
Visual and Performing Arts, B
Voice and Opera, B

BARNARD COLLEGE

African Studies, B
American/United States Studies/Civilization, B
Ancient Studies/Civilization, B

Ancient/Classical Greek Language and Literature, B
Anthropology, B
Applied Mathematics, B
Architectural History and Criticism, B
Architecture, B
Area Studies, B
Art History, Criticism and Conservation, B
Asian Studies/Civilization, B
Astronomy, B
Astrophysics, B
Biochemistry, B
Biology/Biological Sciences, B
Biophysics, B
Biopsychology, B
Chemical Physics, B
Chemistry, B
Classics and Classical
 Languages, Literatures, and Linguistics, B
Comparative Literature, B
Computer and Information Sciences, B
Dance, B
Drama and Dramatics/Theatre Arts, B
Economics, B
English Language and Literature, B
Environmental Biology, B
Environmental Sciences, B
Environmental Studies, B
European Studies/Civilization, B
Film/Cinema Studies, B
French Language and Literature, B
French Studies, B
Geography, B
Geology/Earth Science, B
German Language and Literature, B
German Studies, B
History, B
Italian Language and Literature, B
Jazz/Jazz Studies, B
Latin American Studies, B
Latin Language and Literature, B
Linguistics, B
Mathematics, B
Mathematics and Statistics, B
Medieval and Renaissance Studies, B
Modern Greek Language and Literature, B
Multi-/Interdisciplinary Studies, B
Music, B
Near and Middle Eastern Studies, B
Philosophy, B
Physics, B
Political Science and Government, B
Psychology, B
Religion/Religious Studies, B
Russian Language and Literature, B
Russian Studies, B
Slavic Studies, B
Sociology, B
Spanish and Iberian Studies, B
Spanish Language and Literature, B
Statistics, B
Urban Studies/Affairs, B
Visual and Performing Arts, B
Women's Studies, B

BERKELEY COLLEGE-NEW YORK CITY CAMPUS

Accounting, AB
Business Administration and Management, AB
Business/Commerce, B
Fashion Merchandising, A
International Business/Trade/Commerce, AB
Legal Assistant/Paralegal, A
Marketing/Marketing Management, AB
Office Management and Supervision, AB

BERKELEY COLLEGE-WESTCHESTER CAMPUS

Accounting, AB
Business Administration and Management, AB
Business/Commerce, B
Fashion Merchandising, A
International Business/Trade/Commerce, AB
Legal Assistant/Paralegal, A
Marketing/Marketing Management, AB

Office Management and Supervision, AB

BERNARD M. BARUCH COLLEGE OF THE CITY UNIVERSITY OF NEW YORK

Accounting, BMD
Actuarial Science, B
Advertising, B
Arts Management, B
Business Administration and Management, B
Business Administration, Management and
 Operations, MDO
Business/Managerial Economics, B
Comparative Literature, B
Corporate and Organizational Communication, M
Creative Writing, B
Economics, BM
Education, B
Educational Administration and Supervision, MO
English Language and Literature, B
Entrepreneurship/Entrepreneurial Studies, M
Finance, B
Finance and Banking, MD
Health Services Administration, M
Higher Education/Higher Education
 Administration, M
History, B
Human Resources Management and Services, M
Human Resources Management/Personnel
 Administration, B
Industrial and Labor Relations, M
Industrial and Organizational Psychology, MDO
Information Science/Studies, B
Interdisciplinary Studies, B
International Business/Trade/Commerce, BM
Journalism, BM
Management Information Systems and
 Services, BMD
Management Strategy and Policy, MD
Marketing, MD
Marketing/Marketing Management, B
Mathematical and Computational Finance, M
Mathematics, B
Music, B
Natural Sciences, B
Operations Research, B
Organizational Behavior Studies, M
Organizational Management, D
Philosophy, B
Political Science and Government, B
Psychology, B
Public Administration, BM
Public Policy Analysis, B
Quantitative Analysis, M
Romance Languages, Literatures, and Linguistics, B
Sociology, B
Spanish Language and Literature, B
Statistics, BM
Taxation, M

BORICUA COLLEGE

Bilingual and Multilingual Education, B
Business Administration and Management, B
Elementary Education and Teaching, B
Human Services, BM
Kindergarten/PreSchool Education and Teaching, B
Latin American Studies, BM
Liberal Arts and Sciences Studies and
 Humanities, AB

BOROUGH OF MANHATTAN COMMUNITY COLLEGE OF THE CITY UNIVERSITY OF NEW YORK

Accounting, A
Administrative Assistant and Secretarial Science, A
Biological and Physical Sciences, A
Business Administration and Management, A
Child Development, A
Computer Programming/Programmer, A
Data Processing and Data Processing
 Technology/Technician, A
Emergency Medical Technology/Technician (EMT
 Paramedic), A
Engineering Science, A
Human Services, A
Kindergarten/PreSchool Education and Teaching, A

Liberal Arts and Sciences Studies and
 Humanities, A
Marketing/Marketing Management, A
Mathematics, A
Nursing - Registered Nurse Training, A
Public Health (MPH, DPH), A
Respiratory Care Therapy/Therapist, A

BRAMSON ORT COLLEGE

Accounting, A
Administrative Assistant and Secretarial Science, A
Business Administration and Management, A
Business Machine Repairer, A
Business Teacher Education, A
Computer Engineering Technology/Technician, A
Computer Programming/Programmer, A
Computer Science, A
Electrical, Electronic and Communications
 Engineering Technology/Technician, A
Electromechanical Technology/Electromechanical
 Engineering Technology, A
Information Science/Studies, A
Legal Administrative Assistant/Secretary, A
Marketing/Marketing Management, A

BRIARCLIFFE COLLEGE

Accounting, AB
Administrative Assistant and Secretarial Science, A
Business Administration and Management, A
Business Administration, Management and
 Operations, A
Commercial and Advertising Art, A
Computer Programming/Programmer, A
Electrical, Electronic and Communications
 Engineering Technology/Technician, A
Information Science/Studies, A
Legal Assistant/Paralegal, A
Telecommunications Technology/Technician, A
Visual and Performing Arts, A

BRONX COMMUNITY COLLEGE OF THE CITY UNIVERSITY OF NEW YORK

Accounting, A
Administrative Assistant and Secretarial Science, A
African-American/Black Studies, A
Art/Art Studies, General, A
Biology/Biological Sciences, A
Business Administration and Management, A
Business Teacher Education, A
Chemistry, A
Child Development, A
Clinical/Medical Laboratory Technician, A
Computer Science, A
Data Processing and Data Processing
 Technology/Technician, A
Electrical, Electronic and Communications
 Engineering Technology/Technician, A
History, A
Human Services, A
International Relations and Affairs, A
Legal Assistant/Paralegal, A
Liberal Arts and Sciences Studies and
 Humanities, A
Marketing/Marketing Management, A
Mathematics, A
Medical Administrative Assistant/Secretary, A
Music, A
Nuclear Medical Technology/Technologist, A
Nursing - Registered Nurse Training, A
Ornamental Horticulture, A
Pre-Engineering, A
Psychology, A

BROOKLYN COLLEGE OF THE CITY UNIVERSITY OF NEW YORK

Accounting, BM
African Studies, B
American/United States Studies/Civilization, B
Anthropology, B
Applied Physics, M
Art Education, M
Art History, Criticism and Conservation, BMD
Art Teacher Education, B
Art/Art Studies, General, B

Audiology/Audiologist and Speech-Language
  Pathology/Pathologist, B
Bilingual and Multilingual Education, B
Biological and Biomedical Sciences, MD
Biology Teacher Education, B
Biology/Biological Sciences, B
Broadcast Journalism, B
Caribbean Studies, B
Chemistry, BMD
Chemistry Teacher Education, B
Chinese Language and Literature, B
Cinematography and Film/Video Production, B
Classics and Classical
  Languages, Literatures, and Linguistics, B
Communication Disorders, MD
Communication Studies/Speech Communication
  and Rhetoric, B
Community Health and Preventive Medicine, M
Comparative Literature, B
Composition, M
Computational Mathematics, B
Computer and Information Sciences, B
Computer Graphics, B
Computer Science, MD
Counselor Education/School Counseling and
  Guidance Services, MO
Creative Writing, B
Developmental and Child Psychology, B
Early Childhood Education and Teaching, BM
Economics, BM
Education, BMO
Education/Teaching of Individuals with Speech or
  Language Impairments, B
Educational Leadership and Administration, O
Elementary Education and Teaching, BM
English, MD
English Education, M
English Language and Literature, B
English/Language Arts Teacher Education, B
Environmental Education, M
Environmental Studies, B
Exercise and Sports Science, M
Experimental Psychology, M
Film, Television, and Video Production, M
Film/Cinema Studies, B
Fine Arts and Art Studies, MD
Fine/Studio Arts, B
Foods, Nutrition, and Wellness Studies, B
Foreign Language Teacher Education, M
French Language and Literature, BMD
French Language Teacher Education, B
Geology/Earth Science, BMD
German Language and Literature, B
Health Education, M
Health Services Administration, M
Health Teacher Education, B
Hebrew Language and Literature, B
Hebrew Studies, M
Hispanic-American, Puerto Rican, and Mexican-
  American/Chicano Studies, B
History, BMD
Home Economics Education, M
Industrial and Organizational Psychology, BM
Information Science/Studies, BMD
Internet and Interactive Multimedia, O
Italian Language and Literature, B
Jewish/Judaic Studies, B
Journalism, B
Latin Language and Literature, B
Liberal Studies, M
Linguistics, B
Mathematics, BMD
Mathematics Teacher Education, BM
Middle School Education, M
Modern Greek Language and Literature, B
Multilingual and Multicultural Education, M
Music, BMD
Music Performance, B
Music Teacher Education, BMO
Music Theory and Composition, B
Musicology and Ethnomusicology, M
Nutritional Sciences, M
Painting, M
Performance, MO
Philosophy, B
Photography, M

Physical Education Teaching and Coaching, BM
Physics, BMD
Physics Teacher Education, B
Political Science and Government, BMDO
Portuguese Language and Literature, B
Printmaking, M
Psychology, BMD
Public Health, M
Public Policy Analysis, M
Radio and Television, B
Reading Teacher Education, M
Religion/Religious Studies, B
Russian Language and Literature, B
School Psychology, MO
Science Teacher Education/General Science
  Teacher Education, M
Sculpture, M
Secondary Education and Teaching, M
Social Studies Teacher Education, BM
Sociology, BMD
Spanish Language and Literature, BMD
Spanish Language Teacher Education, B
Special Education and Teaching, M
Speech and Interpersonal Communication, MD
Speech and Rhetorical Studies, MD
Speech Teacher Education, B
Speech-Language Pathology/Pathologist, B
Thanatology, M
Theater, MD
Theatre/Theatre Arts Management, B
Urban Studies/Affairs, M
Women's Studies, B

BROOME COMMUNITY COLLEGE

Accounting Technology/Technician and
  Bookkeeping, A
Business Administration and Management, A
Child Care and Support Services Management, A
Civil Engineering Technology/Technician, A
Clinical/Medical Laboratory Technician, A
Communication Studies/Speech Communication
  and Rhetoric, A
Communications Systems Installation and Repair
  Technology, A
Computer and Information Sciences, A
Computer Engineering Technology/Technician, A
Corrections, A
Criminal Justice/Police Science, A
Data Processing and Data Processing
  Technology/Technician, A
Dental Hygiene/Hygienist, A
Electrical, Electronic and Communications
  Engineering Technology/Technician, A
Emergency Medical Technology/Technician (EMT
  Paramedic), A
Engineering Science, A
Executive Assistant/Executive Secretary, A
Financial Planning and Services, A
Fire Science/Firefighting, A
General Merchandising, Sales, and Related
  Marketing Operations, A
Health Information/Medical Records
  Technology/Technician, A
Hotel/Motel Administration/Management, A
Industrial Production Technologies/Technicians, A
Information Science/Studies, A
International Finance, A
Legal Assistant/Paralegal, A
Liberal Arts and Sciences Studies and
  Humanities, A
Mechanical Engineering/Mechanical
  Technology/Technician, A
Medical Radiologic Technology/Science - Radiation
  Therapist, A
Medical/Clinical Assistant, A
Mental and Social Health Services and Allied
  Professions, A
Nursing - Registered Nurse Training, A
Physical Therapist Assistant, A
Quality Control Technology/Technician, A
Substance Abuse/Addiction Counseling, A

BRYANT AND STRATTON COLLEGE (ALBANY)

Accounting, A
Administrative Assistant and Secretarial Science, A

Business/Commerce, A
Criminal Justice/Law Enforcement Administration, A
Human Resources Management and Services, A
Information Technology, A
Legal Assistant/Paralegal, A
Medical Administrative Assistant/Secretary, A
Medical/Clinical Assistant, A

BRYANT AND STRATTON COLLEGE, AMHERST CAMPUS

Accounting, A
Administrative Assistant and Secretarial Science, A
Business Administration, Management and
  Operations, B
Business/Commerce, A
Graphic Design, A
Human Resources Management and Services, A
Information Technology, A
Legal Assistant/Paralegal, A

BRYANT AND STRATTON COLLEGE, BUFFALO CAMPUS

Accounting, A
Administrative Assistant and Secretarial Science, A
Business/Commerce, A
Criminal Justice/Law Enforcement Administration, A
Human Resources Management and Services, A
Information Technology, A
Medical Administrative Assistant/Secretary, A
Medical/Clinical Assistant, A

BRYANT AND STRATTON COLLEGE, LACKAWANNA CAMPUS

Accounting, A
Administrative Assistant and Secretarial Science, A
Business/Commerce, A
Criminal Justice/Law Enforcement Administration, A
Human Resources Management and Services, A
Information Technology, A
Medical Administrative Assistant/Secretary, A
Medical/Clinical Assistant, A

BRYANT AND STRATTON COLLEGE, NORTH CAMPUS

Accounting, A
Administrative Assistant and Secretarial Science, A
Business Administration and Management, A
Electrical, Electronic and Communications
  Engineering Technology/Technician, A
Information Science/Studies, A
Information Technology, A
Legal Administrative Assistant/Secretary, A
Legal Assistant/Paralegal, A

BRYANT AND STRATTON COLLEGE (ROCHESTER-GREECE CAMPUS)

Accounting, A
Administrative Assistant and Secretarial Science, A
Business/Commerce, A
Human Resources Management and Services, A
Information Technology, A
Medical Administrative Assistant/Secretary, A
Medical/Clinical Assistant, A

BRYANT AND STRATTON COLLEGE (ROCHESTER-HENRIETTA CAMPUS)

Accounting, A
Administrative Assistant and Secretarial Science, A
Business Administration and Management, A
Business/Commerce, A
Criminal Justice/Law Enforcement Administration, A
Graphic Design, A
Human Resources Management and Services, A
Information Technology, A
Legal Assistant/Paralegal, A
Medical Administrative Assistant/Secretary, A
Medical/Clinical Assistant, A

BRYANT AND STRATTON COLLEGE (SYRACUSE)

Accounting, A
Administrative Assistant and Secretarial Science, A
Business/Commerce, A
Hotel/Motel Administration/Management, A

Human Resources Management and Services, A
Information Technology, A
Medical Administrative Assistant/Secretary, A
Medical/Clinical Assistant, A
Tourism and Travel Services Management, A

BUFFALO STATE COLLEGE, STATE UNIVERSITY OF NEW YORK

Adult and Continuing Education and Teaching, MO
Anthropology, B
Applied Art, B
Applied Economics, M
Art Education, M
Art History, Criticism and Conservation, B
Art Teacher Education, B
Art/Art Studies, General, B
Audiology/Audiologist and Speech-Language
    Pathology/Pathologist, B
Biological and Biomedical Sciences, M
Biology/Biological Sciences, B
Broadcast Journalism, B
Business Administration and Management, B
Business Education, M
Business Teacher Education, B
Chemistry, BM
City/Urban, Community and Regional Planning, B
Commercial and Advertising Art, B
Communication Disorders, B
Communication Studies/Speech Communication
    and Rhetoric, B
Criminal Justice/Law Enforcement Administration, B
Criminology, M
Design and Visual Communications, B
Dietetics/Dieticians, B
Drama and Dramatics/Theatre Arts, B
Drawing, B
Early Childhood Education and Teaching, M
Economics, BM
Education/Teaching of Individuals with Speech or
    Language Impairments, B
Educational Leadership and Administration, O
Educational Media/Instructional Technology, M
Electrical, Electronic and Communications
    Engineering Technology/Technician, B
Electromechanical Technology/Electromechanical
    Engineering Technology, B
Elementary Education and Teaching, BM
Engineering, B
Engineering Technology, B
English, M
English Language and Literature, B
English/Language Arts Teacher Education, B
Fashion Merchandising, B
Fashion/Apparel Design, B
Fine/Studio Arts, B
Foreign Language Teacher Education, B
Forensic Science and Technology, B
French Language and Literature, B
General Studies, B
Geography, B
Geology/Earth Science, B
Historic Preservation and Conservation, MO
History, BM
Hospitality Administration/Management, B
Hotel/Motel Administration/Management, B
Human Resources Management and Services, O
Humanities/Humanistic Studies, B
Industrial Education, M
Industrial Technology/Technician, B
Industrial/Management Engineering, M
Information Science/Studies, B
Interdisciplinary Studies, M
Journalism, B
Kindergarten/PreSchool Education and Teaching, B
Kinesiology and Exercise Science, B
Liberal Arts and Sciences Studies and
    Humanities, B
Mass Communication/Media Studies, B
Mathematics, B
Mathematics Teacher Education, BM
Mechanical Engineering/Mechanical
    Technology/Technician, B
Multi-/Interdisciplinary Studies, B
Multilingual and Multicultural Education, M
Music, B

Music Teacher Education, B
Painting, B
Philosophy, B
Photography, B
Physics, B
Political Science and Government, B
Pre-Dentistry Studies, B
Pre-Law Studies, B
Pre-Medicine/Pre-Medical Studies, B
Pre-Veterinary Studies, B
Printmaking, B
Psychology, B
Public Relations/Image Management, B
Radio and Television, B
Reading Teacher Education, M
Science Teacher Education/General Science
    Teacher Education, BM
Sculpture, B
Secondary Education and Teaching, B
Social Studies Teacher Education, B
Social Work, B
Sociology, B
Spanish Language and Literature, B
Special Education and Teaching, BM
Special Products Marketing Operations, B
Student Personnel Services, M
Technology Education/Industrial Arts, B
Technology Teacher Education/Industrial Arts
    Teacher Education, B
Trade and Industrial Teacher Education, B
Urban Studies/Affairs, B
Vocational and Technical Education, M

CANISIUS COLLEGE

Accounting, BM
Accounting and Finance, B
Accounting Technology/Technician and
    Bookkeeping, B
Anthropology, B
Art History, Criticism and Conservation, B
Athletic Training and Sports Medicine, B
Biochemistry, B
Bioinformatics, B
Biological and Physical Sciences, B
Business Administration and Management, B
Business Administration, Management and
    Operations, BM
Business Education, M
Chemistry, B
Communication and Media Studies, B
Communication Disorders, M
Computer Science, B
Corporate and Organizational Communication, M
Counselor Education/School Counseling and
    Guidance Services, M
Creative Writing, B
Criminal Justice/Law Enforcement Administration, B
Digital Communication and Media/Multimedia, B
Drama and Dramatics/Theatre Arts, B
Early Childhood Education and Teaching, BM
Economics, B
Education, BM
Education/Teaching of Individuals in Early Childhood
    Special Education Programs, B
Educational Administration and Supervision, M
Engineering, B
English Language and Literature, B
Entrepreneurship/Entrepreneurial Studies, B
Environmental Sciences, B
European Studies/Civilization, B
Finance, B
Fine/Studio Arts, B
Forest Sciences and Biology, B
French Language and Literature, B
General Studies, B
German Language and Literature, B
Germanic Languages, Literatures, and Linguistics, B
Health Promotion, M
History, B
Information Technology, B
International Business/Trade/Commerce, B
International Relations and Affairs, B
Marketing, BM
Marketing/Marketing Management, B
Mathematics and Statistics, B
Neuroscience, B

Philosophy, B
Physical Education Teaching and Coaching, BM
Physics, B
Political Science and Government, B
Psychology, B
Reading Teacher Education, M
Rehabilitation Sciences, M
Religion/Religious Studies, B
Science Teacher Education/General Science
    Teacher Education, B
Secondary Education and Teaching, BM
Sociology, B
Spanish Language and Literature, B
Special Education and Teaching, M
Sport and Fitness Administration/Management, M
Student Personnel Services, M
Urban Studies/Affairs, B
Women's Studies, B

CAYUGA COUNTY COMMUNITY COLLEGE

Accounting, A
Business Administration and Management, A
Computer and Information Sciences, A
Computer Programming/Programmer, A
Computer Science, A
Computer/Information Technology Services
    Administration and Management, A
Consumer Merchandising/Retailing Management, A
Corrections, A
Criminal Justice/Law Enforcement Administration, A
Criminal Justice/Police Science, A
Data Processing and Data Processing
    Technology/Technician, A
Drafting and Design Technology/Technician, A
Drafting/Design Engineering
    Technologies/Technicians, A
Electrical, Electronic and Communications
    Engineering Technology/Technician, A
Humanities/Humanistic Studies, A
Information Science/Studies, A
Kindergarten/PreSchool Education and Teaching, A
Liberal Arts and Sciences Studies and
    Humanities, A
Marketing/Marketing Management, A
Mathematics, A
Nursing - Registered Nurse Training, A
Radio and Television, A
Radio and Television Broadcasting
    Technology/Technician, A
Telecommunications Technology/Technician, A

CAZENOVIA COLLEGE

Accounting, B
Business Administration and Management, AB
Comparative Literature, B
Criminal Justice/Safety Studies, AB
Design and Visual Communications, B
Early Childhood Education and Teaching, B
Education/Teaching of Individuals in Early Childhood
    Special Education Programs, B
Educational Administration and Supervision, B
English Language and Literature, B
Environmental Studies, B
Equestrian/Equine Studies, B
Fashion/Apparel Design, B
Fine/Studio Arts, B
Human Services, AB
Interior Design, B
Liberal Arts and Sciences Studies and
    Humanities, AB
Photography, B
Psychology, B
Social Sciences, B
Sport and Fitness Administration/Management, B
Visual and Performing Arts, B

CENTRAL YESHIVA TOMCHEI TMIMIM-LUBAVITCH

Rabbinical Studies, B

CITY COLLEGE OF THE CITY UNIVERSITY OF NEW YORK

African-American/Black Studies, B
Anthropology, BM

Architecture, BMO
Art History, Criticism and Conservation, BM
Art Teacher Education, B
Art/Art Studies, General, B
Asian Studies/Civilization, B
Atmospheric Sciences and Meteorology, MD
Biochemistry, BMD
Biological and Biomedical Sciences, MD
Biology Teacher Education, B
Biology/Biological Sciences, B
Biomedical Engineering, MD
Biomedical Sciences, B
Biomedical/Medical Engineering, B
Business Administration and Management, B
Ceramic Arts and Ceramics, M
Chemical Engineering, BMD
Chemistry, BMD
Chemistry Teacher Education, B
Cinematography and Film/Video Production, B
Civil Engineering, BMD
Clinical Psychology, D
Comparative Literature, B
Computer Science, BMD
Crafts, M
Creative Writing, B
Drama and Dramatics/Theatre Arts, B
Early Childhood Education and Teaching, BM
Economics, BM
Education, BMO
Educational Administration and Supervision, MO
Electrical Engineering, MD
Electrical, Electronics and Communications
    Engineering, B
Elementary Education and Teaching, BM
Engineering and Applied Sciences, MD
English, M
English Education, M
English Language and Literature, B
Environmental Sciences, D
Experimental Psychology, D
Fine Arts and Art Studies, M
French Language and Literature, B
Geography, B
Geology/Earth Science, B
Geosciences, MD
Graphic Design, BM
History, BM
Intermedia/Multimedia, B
International Affairs, M
International Relations and Affairs, B
International/Global Studies, B
Jazz/Jazz Studies, B
Jewelry/Metalsmithing, M
Jewish/Judaic Studies, B
Latin American Studies, B
Linguistics, B
Mass Communication/Media Studies, B
Mathematics, BM
Mathematics Teacher Education, BMO
Mechanical Engineering, BMD
Media Studies, M
Middle School Education, M
Multilingual and Multicultural Education, M
Museology/Museum Studies, M
Music, BM
Music Performance, B
Music Teacher Education, B
Music Theory and Composition, B
Painting, M
Philosophy, B
Physician Assistant, B
Physics, BMD
Physics Teacher Education, B
Political Science and Government, B
Pre-Dentistry Studies, B
Pre-Law Studies, B
Pre-Medicine/Pre-Medical Studies, B
Pre-Veterinary Studies, B
Printmaking, M
Psychology, BMD
Reading Teacher Education, BM
Romance Languages, Literatures, and Linguistics, B
Science Teacher Education/General Science
    Teacher Education, BM
Sculpture, M
Secondary Education and Teaching, BMO

Social Studies Teacher Education, BO
Sociology, BM
Spanish Language and Literature, BM
Special Education and Teaching, M
Urban Design, M
Women's Studies, B
Writing, M

CLARKSON UNIVERSITY

Accounting, B
Aerospace, Aeronautical and Astronautical
    Engineering, B
Analytical Chemistry, MD
Applied Mathematics, B
Biochemistry, B
Biology/Biological Sciences, B
Biophysics, B
BioTechnology, B
Business Administration and Management, B
Business Administration, Management and
    Operations, M
Cell/Cellular Biology and Histology, B
Chemical Engineering, BMD
Chemistry, BMD
Civil Engineering, BMD
Communication Studies/Speech Communication
    and Rhetoric, B
Computer and Information Sciences, B
Computer Engineering, BMD
Computer Science, BMD
Computer Software Engineering, B
Construction Engineering, B
Digital Communication and Media/Multimedia, B
Ecology, B
E-Commerce/Electronic Commerce, B
Electrical Engineering, MD
Electrical, Electronics and Communications
    Engineering, B
Engineering, B
Engineering and Applied Sciences, MD
Engineering Management, M
Environmental Engineering
    Technology/Environmental Technology, MD
Environmental Health, B
Environmental Sciences, MD
Environmental Studies, B
Environmental/Environmental Health Engineering, B
Finance, B
Health Services Research, M
History, B
Human Resources Management and Services, M
Human Resources Management/Personnel
    Administration, B
Humanities/Humanistic Studies, B
Industrial and Manufacturing Management, M
Industrial and Organizational Psychology, B
Information Resources Management/CIO Training, B
Information Science/Studies, M
Inorganic Chemistry, MD
Interdisciplinary Studies, BMD
International Business/Trade/Commerce, B
Liberal Arts and Sciences Studies and
    Humanities, B
Logistics and Materials Management, B
Management Information Systems and
    Services, BM
Manufacturing Engineering, B
Marketing/Marketing Management, B
Materials Engineering, B
Materials Sciences, B
Mathematics, BMD
Mechanical Engineering, BMD
Molecular Biology, B
Non-Profit/Public/Organizational Management, B
Occupational Health and Industrial Hygiene, B
Operations Management and Supervision, B
Organic Chemistry, MD
Physical Chemistry, MD
Physical Therapy/Therapist, M
Physics, BMD
Political Science and Government, B
Pre-Dentistry Studies, B
Pre-Law Studies, B
Pre-Medicine/Pre-Medical Studies, B
Pre-Veterinary Studies, B
Psychology, B

Social Sciences, B
Sociology, B
Statistics, B
Structural Engineering, B
Technical and Business Writing, B
Toxicology, B

CLINTON COMMUNITY COLLEGE

Accounting, A
Administrative Assistant and Secretarial Science, A
Biological and Physical Sciences, A
Business Administration and Management, A
Clinical/Medical Laboratory Technician, A
Community Organization and Advocacy, A
Computer/Information Technology Services
    Administration and Management, A
Consumer Merchandising/Retailing Management, A
Criminal Justice/Law Enforcement Administration, A
Criminal Justice/Police Science, A
Electrical, Electronic and Communications
    Engineering Technology/Technician, A
Humanities/Humanistic Studies, A
Industrial Technology/Technician, A
Liberal Arts and Sciences Studies and
    Humanities, A
Nursing - Registered Nurse Training, A
Physical Education Teaching and Coaching, A
Social Sciences, A

COCHRAN SCHOOL OF NURSING

Nursing - Registered Nurse Training, A

COLGATE UNIVERSITY

African Studies, B
African-American/Black Studies, B
American Indian/Native American Studies, B
Anthropology, B
Art History, Criticism and Conservation, B
Art/Art Studies, General, B
Asian Studies/Civilization, B
Astronomy, B
Astrophysics, B
Biochemistry, B
Biology/Biological Sciences, B
Chemistry, B
Chinese Language and Literature, B
Classics and Classical
    Languages, Literatures, and Linguistics, B
Computer Science, B
Drama and Dramatics/Theatre Arts, B
East Asian Studies, B
Economics, B
Education, B
English Language and Literature, B
Environmental Biology, B
Environmental Studies, B
French Language and Literature, B
Geography, B
Geology/Earth Science, B
German Language and Literature, B
History, B
Humanities/Humanistic Studies, B
International Relations and Affairs, B
Japanese Language and Literature, B
Latin American Studies, B
Latin Language and Literature, B
Mathematics, B
Modern Greek Language and Literature, B
Molecular Biology, B
Music, B
Natural Sciences, B
Neuroscience, B
Peace Studies and Conflict Resolution, B
Philosophy, B
Physical Sciences, B
Physics, B
Political Science and Government, B
Psychology, B
Religion/Religious Studies, B
Romance Languages, Literatures, and Linguistics, B
Russian Language and Literature, B
Russian Studies, B
Secondary Education and Teaching, M
Social Sciences, B
Sociology, B
Spanish Language and Literature, B

Women's Studies, B

COLLEGE OF MOUNT SAINT VINCENT

Allied Health and Medical Assisting Services, MO
Biochemistry, B
Biology/Biological Sciences, B
Business Administration and Management, AB
Business/Managerial Economics, B
Chemistry, B
Computer Science, B
Counseling Psychology, O
Economics, B
Education, BMO
Educational Media/Instructional Technology, O
Elementary Education and Teaching, B
English Language and Literature, B
French Language and Literature, B
Gerontological Nursing, M
Health Services Administration, O
History, B
Interdisciplinary Studies, AB
Kinesiology and Exercise Science, B
Liberal Arts and Sciences Studies and
   Humanities, B
Mass Communication/Media Studies, B
Mathematics, B
Middle School Education, O
Modern Languages, B
Multilingual and Multicultural Education, MO
Nursing, MO
Nursing - Adult, MO
Nursing - Advanced Practice, MO
Nursing - Registered Nurse Training, B
Nursing Administration, M
Philosophy, B
Physical Education Teaching and Coaching, B
Physics, B
Pre-Dentistry Studies, B
Pre-Law Studies, B
Pre-Medicine/Pre-Medical Studies, B
Psychology, B
Religion/Religious Studies, B
Social Sciences, B
Sociology, B
Spanish Language and Literature, B
Urban Education and Leadership, M
Urban Studies/Affairs, B

THE COLLEGE OF NEW ROCHELLE

Art Education, M
Art History, Criticism and Conservation, B
Art Teacher Education, B
Art Therapy/Therapist, BM
Biology/Biological Sciences, B
Broadcast Journalism, B
Business Administration and Management, B
Chemistry, B
Classics and Classical
   Languages, Literatures, and Linguistics, B
Communication and Media Studies, MO
Communication Disorders, M
Community Psychology, M
Counseling Psychology, M
Early Childhood Education and Teaching, M
Economics, B
Education, BMO
Education/Teaching of the Gifted and Talented, MO
Educational Administration and Supervision, MO
Elementary Education and Teaching, BM
English as a Second Language, MO
English Language and Literature, B
Environmental Studies, B
Fine Arts and Art Studies, M
Fine/Studio Arts, B
Foreign Languages, Literatures, and Linguistics, B
French Language and Literature, B
Gerontology, MO
Graphic Design, M
History, B
Human Resources Development, MO
International/Global Studies, B
Latin Language and Literature, B
Liberal Arts and Sciences Studies and
   Humanities, B
Mass Communication/Media Studies, B
Mathematics, B

Multi-/Interdisciplinary Studies, B
Multilingual and Multicultural Education, MO
Museum Education, O
Nursing, MO
Nursing - Registered Nurse Training, B
Nursing Administration, M
Nursing Education, O
Philosophy, B
Physics, B
Political Science and Government, B
Pre-Law Studies, B
Pre-Medicine/Pre-Medical Studies, B
Psychology, B
Reading Teacher Education, M
Religion/Religious Studies, B
School Psychology, M
Social Work, B
Sociology, B
Spanish Language and Literature, B
Special Education and Teaching, BM
Thanatology, O
Women's Studies, B

THE COLLEGE OF SAINT ROSE

Accounting, BM
American/United States Studies/Civilization, B
Art Education, MO
Art Teacher Education, B
Audiology/Audiologist and Speech-Language
   Pathology/Pathologist, B
Biochemistry, B
Biology Teacher Education, B
Biology/Biological Sciences, B
Business Administration and Management, B
Business Administration, Management and
   Operations, MO
Business Education, MO
Cell/Cellular Biology and Histology, B
Chemistry, B
Chemistry Teacher Education, B
Clinical Laboratory Science/Medical
   Technology/Technologist, B
Commercial and Advertising Art, B
Communication Disorders, BM
Communication Studies/Speech Communication
   and Rhetoric, B
Communications Technology/Technician, B
Computer and Information Sciences, B
Computer Science, M
Counselor Education/School Counseling and
   Guidance Services, M
Criminal Justice/Law Enforcement Administration, B
CytoTechnology/Cytotechnologist, B
Early Childhood Education and Teaching, M
Education, MO
Educational Administration and Supervision, MO
Educational Media/Instructional Technology, MO
Educational Psychology, M
Elementary Education and Teaching, BM
English, M
English Education, M
English Language and Literature, B
English/Language Arts Teacher Education, B
Environmental Studies, B
Fine/Studio Arts, B
Foreign Language Teacher Education, M
History, BM
Information Science/Studies, BM
Interdisciplinary Studies, B
Liberal Arts and Sciences Studies and
   Humanities, B
Mass Communication/Media Studies, M
Mathematics, B
Mathematics Teacher Education, BM
Multilingual and Multicultural Education, O
Music, BM
Music Teacher Education, BMO
Non-Profit/Public/Organizational Management, O
Political Science and Government, BM
Psychology, B
Reading Teacher Education, MO
Religion/Religious Studies, B
School Psychology, MO
Science Teacher Education/General Science
   Teacher Education, M
Secondary Education and Teaching, MO

Social Studies Teacher Education, BM
Social Work, B
Sociology, B
Spanish Language and Literature, B
Spanish Language Teacher Education, B
Special Education and Teaching, BM
Student Personnel Services, M
Trade and Industrial Teacher Education, B

COLLEGE OF STATEN ISLAND OF THE CITY UNIVERSITY OF NEW YORK

Accounting, B
African-American/Black Studies, B
American/United States Studies/Civilization, B
Anthropology, B
Architecture, A
Biochemistry, B
Biological and Biomedical Sciences, M
Biology/Biological Sciences, B
Business/Commerce, AB
Chemistry, BD
Cinematography and Film/Video Production, B
Clinical Laboratory Science/Medical
   Technology/Technologist, B
Clinical/Medical Laboratory Technician, A
Communication Studies/Speech Communication
   and Rhetoric, B
Computer and Information Sciences, B
Computer and Information Sciences and Support
   Services, B
Computer Programming/Programmer, A
Computer Science, MD
Construction Engineering Technology/Technician, A
Drama and Dramatics/Theatre Arts, B
Economics, B
Education, MO
Educational Leadership and Administration, O
Elementary Education and Teaching, M
Engineering, AB
English, M
English Language and Literature, B
Environmental Sciences, M
Film, Television, and Video Theory and Criticism, M
Fine Arts and Art Studies, B
Gerontological Nursing, MO
History, BM
Information Science/Studies, B
International Relations and Affairs, B
Liberal Arts and Sciences Studies and
   Humanities, AB
Liberal Studies, M
Mathematics, B
Media Studies, M
Molecular Pharmacology, D
Music, B
Neuroscience, MD
Nursing, BMO
Nursing - Adult, MO
Nursing - Registered Nurse Training, A
Philosophy, B
Physical Therapy/Therapist, BM
Physician Assistant, B
Physics, B
Political Science and Government, B
Psychology, B
Secondary Education and Teaching, M
Social Work, B
Sociology, B
Spanish Language and Literature, B
Special Education and Teaching, M
Women's Studies, B

THE COLLEGE OF WESTCHESTER

Accounting, A
Administrative Assistant and Secretarial Science, A
Business Administration and Management, A
Computer and Information Sciences, A
Computer Graphics, A
Computer Programming, A
Computer Programming, Specific Applications, A
Computer
   Programming, Vendor/Product Certification, A
Computer Programming/Programmer, A
Computer Software and Media Applications, A
Computer Systems Networking and
   Telecommunications, A

Computer Typography and Composition Equipment
    Operator, A
Computer/Information Technology Services
    Administration and Management, A
Data Entry/Microcomputer Applications, A
Data Processing and Data Processing
    Technology/Technician, A
Information Science/Studies, A
Information Technology, A
Management Information Systems and Services, A
Marketing/Marketing Management, A
Medical Administrative Assistant/Secretary, A
System Administration/Administrator, A
Web Page, Digital/Multimedia and Information
    Resources Design, A
Web/Multimedia Management and Webmaster, A
Word Processing, A

COLUMBIA COLLEGE

African-American/Black Studies, B
American/United States Studies/Civilization, B
Ancient Studies/Civilization, B
Ancient/Classical Greek Language and Literature, B
Anthropology, B
Archeology, B
Architecture, B
Architecture and Related Services, B
Art History, Criticism and Conservation, B
Asian-American Studies, B
Astronomy, B
Astrophysics, B
Atomic/Molecular Physics, B
Biochemistry, B
Biology/Biological Sciences, B
Biophysics, B
Biopsychology, B
Chemistry, B
Classical, Ancient Mediterranean and Near Eastern
    Studies and Archaeology, B
Classics and Classical
    Languages, Literatures, and Linguistics, B
Comparative Literature, B
Computer Science, B
Creative Writing, B
Dance, B
Drama and Dramatics/Theatre Arts, B
East Asian
    Languages, Literatures, and Linguistics, B
East Asian Studies, B
Economics, B
English Language and Literature, B
Environmental Biology, B
Environmental Studies, B
Film/Cinema Studies, B
French Language and Literature, B
French Studies, B
Geochemistry, B
Geology/Earth Science, B
German Language and Literature, B
German Studies, B
Hispanic-American, Puerto Rican, and Mexican-
    American/Chicano Studies, B
History, B
Italian Language and Literature, B
Italian Studies, B
Latin American Studies, B
Linguistics, B
Mathematics, B
Medieval and Renaissance Studies, B
Modern Greek Language and Literature, B
Music, B
Near and Middle Eastern Studies, B
Philosophy, B
Physics, B
Political Science and Government, B
Psychology, B
Religion/Religious Studies, B
Russian Language and Literature, B
Russian Studies, B
Slavic Languages, Literatures, and Linguistics, B
Sociology, B
Spanish Language and Literature, B
Statistics, B
Teacher Education, Multiple Levels, B
Urban Studies/Affairs, B
Visual and Performing Arts, B

Women's Studies, B

COLUMBIA-GREENE COMMUNITY COLLEGE

Accounting, A
Administrative Assistant and Secretarial Science, A
Art/Art Studies, General, A
Automobile/Automotive Mechanics
    Technology/Technician, A
Biological and Physical Sciences, A
Business Administration and Management, A
Computer and Information Sciences, A
Computer Graphics, A
Computer Science, A
Computer Systems Networking and
    Telecommunications, A
Criminal Justice/Law Enforcement Administration, A
Data Processing and Data Processing
    Technology/Technician, A
Human Services, A
Humanities/Humanistic Studies, A
Information Science/Studies, A
Interdisciplinary Studies, A
Kinesiology and Exercise Science, A
Liberal Arts and Sciences Studies and
    Humanities, A
Mathematics, A
Nursing - Registered Nurse Training, A
Real Estate, A
Social Sciences, A
Web/Multimedia Management and Webmaster, A

COLUMBIA UNIVERSITY, SCHOOL OF GENERAL STUDIES

African-American/Black Studies, B
Anthropology, B
Applied Art, B
Applied Mathematics, B
Architecture, B
Art History, Criticism and Conservation, B
Astronomy, B
Biology/Biological Sciences, B
Chemistry, B
Classics and Classical
    Languages, Literatures, and Linguistics, B
Comparative Literature, B
Computer Science, B
Dance, B
Drama and Dramatics/Theatre Arts, B
East Asian Studies, B
Ecology, B
Economics, B
English Composition, B
English Language and Literature, B
Environmental Biology, B
Evolutionary Biology, B
Film/Cinema Studies, B
French Language and Literature, B
Geology/Earth Science, B
German Language and Literature, B
Hispanic-American, Puerto Rican, and Mexican-
    American/Chicano Studies, B
History, B
Italian Language and Literature, B
Mathematics, B
Music, B
Near and Middle Eastern Studies, B
Philosophy, B
Physics, B
Political Science and Government, B
Psychology, B
Religion/Religious Studies, B
Russian Language and Literature, B
Slavic Languages, Literatures, and Linguistics, B
Sociology, B
Spanish Language and Literature, B
Statistics, B
Urban Studies/Affairs, B
Visual and Performing Arts, B

Women's Studies, B

COLUMBIA UNIVERSITY, THE FU FOUNDATION SCHOOL OF ENGINEERING AND APPLIED SCIENCE

Applied Mathematics, B
Biomedical/Medical Engineering, B
Chemical Engineering, B
Civil Engineering, B
Computer Engineering, B
Computer Science, B
Electrical, Electronics and Communications
    Engineering, B
Engineering Mechanics, B
Engineering Physics, B
Engineering/Industrial Management, B
Environmental/Environmental Health Engineering, B
Industrial Engineering, B
Materials Sciences, B
Mechanical Engineering, B
Operations Research, B

CONCORDIA COLLEGE

Administrative Assistant and Secretarial Science, A
Arts Management, B
Biology/Biological Sciences, B
Business Administration and Management, AB
Business Teacher Education, B
Ecology, B
Education, B
Elementary Education and Teaching, B
English Language and Literature, B
History, B
International Relations and Affairs, B
Junior High/Intermediate/Middle School Education
    and Teaching, B
Liberal Arts and Sciences Studies and
    Humanities, AB
Mathematics, B
Music, B
Music Teacher Education, B
Pre-Law Studies, B
Religion/Religious Studies, B
Religious/Sacred Music, B
Science Teacher Education/General Science
    Teacher Education, B
Secondary Education and Teaching, B
Social Sciences, B
Social Work, B

COOPER UNION FOR THE ADVANCEMENT OF SCIENCE AND ART

Architecture, B
Chemical Engineering, B
Civil Engineering, B
Electrical, Electronics and Communications
    Engineering, B
Engineering, B
Fine/Studio Arts, B
Mechanical Engineering, B
Visual and Performing Arts, B

CORNELL UNIVERSITY

Accounting, D
Adult and Continuing Education and Teaching, MD
Aerospace, Aeronautical and Astronautical
    Engineering, BMD
African Studies, MD
African-American/Black Studies, BMD
Agricultural and Extension Education Services, B
Agricultural and Horticultural Plant Breeding, B
Agricultural Animal Breeding, B
Agricultural Business and Management, B
Agricultural Economics, BMD
Agricultural Education, MD
Agricultural Engineering, MD
Agricultural Mechanics and Equipment/Machine
    Technology, B
Agricultural Teacher Education, B
Agricultural/Biological Engineering and
    Bioengineering, B
Agriculture, B
Agronomy and Crop Science, B
Agronomy and Soil Sciences, MD
American Indian/Native American Studies, B

American Literature (United States), B
American/United States Studies/Civilization, BMD
Analytical Chemistry, D
Anatomy, MD
Animal Physiology, B
Animal Sciences, BMD
Anthropology, BD
Apparel and Textiles, B
Applied Economics, BD
Applied Mathematics, BMD
Applied Physics, MD
Archeology, BMD
Architectural History and Criticism, BMD
Architecture, BMD
Architecture and Related Services, B
Art History, Criticism and Conservation, BD
Art/Art Studies, General, B
Artificial Intelligence and Robotics, MD
Asian History, B
Asian Languages, MD
Asian Studies/Civilization, BMD
Astronomy, BD
Astrophysics, D
Atmospheric Sciences and Meteorology, BMD
Biochemical Engineering, MD
Biochemistry, BD
Biochemistry, Biophysics and Molecular Biology, B
Bioengineering, MD
Biological and Biomedical Sciences, MD
Biology/Biological Sciences, B
Biomedical Engineering, MD
Biometry/Biometrics, BMD
Biophysics, BD
Biopsychology, D
Botany/Plant Biology, B
Building Science, M
Business Administration and Management, B
Business Administration, Management and
    Operations, MDO
Business Family and Consumer Sciences/Human
    Sciences, B
Business/Commerce, B
Cell Biology and Anatomy, MD
Cell/Cellular Biology and Histology, B
Chemical Engineering, BMD
Chemistry, BD
Child and Family Studies, D
Chinese Language and Literature, B
Chinese Studies, MD
City/Urban, Community and Regional Planning, B
Civil Engineering, BMD
Classics and Classical
    Languages, Literatures, and Linguistics, BD
Clothing and Textiles, MD
Cognitive Sciences, D
Communication and Media Studies, MD
Communication Studies/Speech Communication
    and Rhetoric, B
Community Organization and Advocacy, B
Comparative Literature, BD
Composition, D
Computational Sciences, MD
Computer and Information Sciences, B
Computer Art and Design, M
Computer Engineering, MD
Computer Science, BMD
Conflict Resolution and Mediation/Peace
    Studies, MD
Consumer Economics, BD
Creative Writing, B
Crop Production, B
Cultural Studies, D
Curriculum and Instruction, MD
Dairy Science, B
Dance, B
Developmental Biology and Embryology, MD
Developmental Psychology, D
Drama and Dramatics/Theatre Arts, B
East Asian
    Languages, Literatures, and Linguistics, B
East Asian Studies, BMD
East European and Russian Studies, MD
Ecology, MD
Ecology, Evolution, Systematics and Population
    Biology, B
Economics, BMD

Education, BMD
Educational Psychology, B
Electrical Engineering, MD
Electrical, Electronics and Communications
    Engineering, B
Engineering and Applied Sciences, MDO
Engineering Management, MD
Engineering Physics, BMD
English, MDO
English Language and Literature, B
Entomology, BMD
Environmental Design/Architecture, BM
Environmental Engineering
    Technology/Environmental Technology, BMD
Environmental Policy and Resource
    Management, MD
Environmental Sciences, MD
Environmental Studies, BMD
Environmental Toxicology, B
Environmental/Environmental Health Engineering, B
Epidemiology, MD
Ergonomics and Human Factors, M
Ethnic and Cultural Studies, MD
European History, B
Evolutionary Biology, D
Experimental Psychology, D
Facilities Planning and Management, M
Family and Consumer Sciences/Home Economics
    Teacher Education, B
Family and Consumer Sciences/Human Sciences, B
Family Resource Management Studies, B
Film/Cinema Studies, B
Finance and Banking, D
Fine Arts and Art Studies, M
Fine/Studio Arts, B
Fish, Game and Wildlife Management, MD
Floriculture/Floristry Operations and Management, B
Food Science, B
Food Science and Technology, MD
Foreign Language Teacher Education, MD
Forestry, MD
French Language and Literature, BD
Gay/Lesbian Studies, B
Gender Studies, MD
Genetics, BD
Geochemistry, MD
Geological/Geophysical Engineering, B
Geology/Earth Science, BMD
Geophysics and Seismology, MD
Geosciences, MD
Geotechnical Engineering, MD
German Language and Literature, BMD
German Studies, B
Health Services Administration, MD
Hispanic-American, Puerto Rican, and Mexican-
    American/Chicano Studies, B
Historic Preservation and Conservation, BM
History, BMD
History of Science and Technology, MD
Home Economics, MD
Horticultural Science, BMD
Hospitality Administration/Management, MD
Hotel/Motel Administration/Management, B
Housing and Human Environments, B
Human Development, D
Human Development and Family Studies, B
Human Nutrition, B
Human Resources Management and Services, MD
Human Services, B
Human-Computer Interaction, D
Humanities/Humanistic Studies, B
Hydrology and Water Resources Science, BMD
Immunology, MD
Industrial and Labor Relations, MD
Industrial/Management Engineering, MD
Infectious Diseases, MD
Information Science/Studies, BD
Inorganic Chemistry, D
Interdisciplinary Studies, B
Interior Design, M
International Affairs, D
International Agriculture, B
International Development, M
Italian Language and Literature, BD
Japanese Studies, MD
Jewish/Judaic Studies, MD

Labor and Industrial Relations, B
Landscape Architecture, BM
Latin American Studies, BMD
Law and Legal Studies, MDPO
Liberal Arts and Sciences Studies and
    Humanities, B
Linguistics, BMD
Manufacturing Engineering, D
Marine Biology and Biological Oceanography, B
Marine Geology, MD
Marine Sciences, MD
Marketing, D
Materials Engineering, BMD
Materials Sciences, BMD
Mathematics, BD
Mathematics Teacher Education, BM
Mechanical Engineering, BMD
Mechanics, MD
Medieval and Renaissance Studies, BMD
Microbiology, BD
Mineralogy, MD
Molecular Biology, BD
Molecular Medicine, MD
Multi-/Interdisciplinary Studies, B
Music, BMD
Music Theory and Composition, M
Musicology and Ethnomusicology, D
Natural Resource Economics, B
Natural Resources and Conservation, BMD
Near and Middle Eastern Studies, BMD
Neurobiology and Neurophysiology, MD
Nuclear Engineering, MD
Nutritional Sciences, BMD
Operations Research, BMD
Organic Chemistry, D
Organizational Behavior Studies, MD
Ornamental Horticulture, B
Paleontology, MD
Performance, D
Pharmacology, MD
Philosophy, BD
Physical Chemistry, D
Physics, BMD
Physics Teacher Education, B
Physiology, MD
Planetary Astronomy and Science, D
Plant Biology, MD
Plant Genetics, B
Plant Molecular Biology, MD
Plant Pathology/Phytopathology, BMD
Plant Physiology, MD
Plant Protection and Integrated Pest
    Management, B
Plant Sciences, BMD
Political Science and Government, BD
Polymer/Plastics Engineering, MD
Population Studies, MD
Pre-Law Studies, B
Psychology, BD
Public Administration and Social Service
    Professions, B
Public Affairs, M
Public Policy Analysis, BMD
Real Estate, M
Religion/Religious Studies, BD
Reproductive Biology, MD
Restaurant/Food Services Management, B
Romance
    Languages, Literatures, and Linguistics, BMD
Rural Planning and Studies, M
Rural Sociology, MD
Russian Studies, B
Scandinavian
    Languages, Literatures, and Linguistics, MD
Science Teacher Education/General Science
    Teacher Education, M
Science, Technology and Society, B
Semitic Languages, Literatures, and Linguistics, B
Slavic Languages, Literatures, and Linguistics, BMD
Slavic Studies, B
Social Psychology, MD
Social Work, D
Sociology, BMD
Soil Sciences, B
South and Southeast Asian Studies, MD
Spanish Language and Literature, BD

Statistics, BMD
Structural Biology, MD
Structural Engineering, MD
Systems Engineering, M
Textile Design, MD
Textile Science, B
Textile Sciences and Engineering, MD
Theater, D
Theoretical Chemistry, D
Theoretical Physics, MD
Toxicology, MD
Transportation and Highway Engineering, MD
Urban and Regional Planning, MD
Urban Design, M
Urban Studies/Affairs, B
Veterinary Medicine, MDP
Water Resources Engineering, MD
Western European Studies, MD
Women's Studies, BD
Writing, M
Zoology/Animal Biology, MD

CORNING COMMUNITY COLLEGE

Accounting, A
Administrative Assistant and Secretarial Science, A
Automobile/Automotive Mechanics Technology/Technician, A
Automotive Engineering Technology/Technician, A
Biological and Physical Sciences, A
Business Administration and Management, A
Chemical Technology/Technician, A
Child Care Provider/Assistant, A
Computer and Information Sciences, A
Computer Graphics, A
Computer Programming, A
Computer Programming/Programmer, A
Computer Science, A
Computer Systems Networking and Telecommunications, A
Computer Technology/Computer Systems Technology, A
Computer/Information Technology Services Administration and Management, A
Corrections and Criminal Justice, A
Criminal Justice/Law Enforcement Administration, A
Drafting and Design Technology/Technician, A
Education, A
Electrical, Electronic and Communications Engineering Technology/Technician, A
Elementary Education and Teaching, A
Emergency Medical Technology/Technician (EMT Paramedic), A
Fire Science/Firefighting, A
General Studies, A
Health and Physical Education, A
Human Services, A
Humanities/Humanistic Studies, A
Industrial Technology/Technician, A
Information Technology, A
Legal Assistant/Paralegal, A
Liberal Arts and Sciences Studies and Humanities, A
Machine Shop Technology/Assistant, A
Machine Tool Technology/Machinist, A
Mathematics, A
Mechanical Engineering/Mechanical Technology/Technician, A
Nursing - Registered Nurse Training, A
Optics/Optical Sciences, A
Pre-Engineering, A
Social Sciences, A
Substance Abuse/Addiction Counseling, A
Tourism and Travel Services Management, A

Word Processing, A

CROUSE HOSPITAL SCHOOL OF NURSING

Nursing - Registered Nurse Training, A

THE CULINARY INSTITUTE OF AMERICA

Baking and Pastry Arts/Baker/Pastry Chef, AB
Culinary Arts/Chef Training, AB

DAEMEN COLLEGE

Accounting, B
Applied Art, B
Art Teacher Education, B
Art/Art Studies, General, B
Biochemistry, B
Biology Teacher Education, B
Biology/Biological Sciences, B
Business Administration and Management, B
Design and Applied Arts, B
Early Childhood Education and Teaching, BM
Education, M
Elementary Education and Teaching, B
English Language and Literature, B
English/Language Arts Teacher Education, B
Fine/Studio Arts, B
French Language and Literature, B
French Language Teacher Education, B
Graphic Design, B
Health Services/Allied Health/Health Sciences, B
History, B
International Business/Trade/Commerce, M
Management, M
Mathematics, B
Mathematics Teacher Education, B
Medical/Surgical Nursing, MO
Middle School Education, M
Natural Sciences, B
Nursing, MO
Nursing - Advanced Practice, MO
Nursing - Registered Nurse Training, B
Nursing Administration, M
Physical Therapy/Therapist, D
Physician Assistant, BM
Political Science and Government, B
Psychology, B
Religion/Religious Studies, B
Social Studies Teacher Education, B
Social Work, B
Spanish Language and Literature, B
Spanish Language Teacher Education, B
Special Education and Teaching, BM

DARKEI NOAM RABBINICAL COLLEGE

Rabbinical Studies, B

DAVIS COLLEGE

Bible/Biblical Studies, AB

DEVRY INSTITUTE OF TECHNOLOGY

Biomedical Technology/Technician, B
Business Administration, Management and Operations, B
Computer and Information Sciences, B
Computer Engineering Technology/Technician, B
Computer Systems Analysis/Analyst, B
Computer Systems Networking and Telecommunications, AB
Electrical, Electronic and Communications Engineering Technology/Technician, AB
Information Science/Studies, B

DOMINICAN COLLEGE

Accounting, B
Allied Health and Medical Assisting Services, MD
American/United States Studies/Civilization, B
Athletic Training and Sports Medicine, B
Biology Teacher Education, B
Biology/Biological Sciences, B
Business Administration and Management, B
Computer and Information Sciences, B
Economics, B
Education, BM

Education/Teaching of Individuals with Multiple Disabilities, B
Elementary Education and Teaching, B
English Language and Literature, B
English/Language Arts Teacher Education, B
Finance, B
Health/Health Care Administration/Management, B
History, B
History Teacher Education, B
Human Resources Management/Personnel Administration, B
Humanities/Humanistic Studies, B
International Business/Trade/Commerce, B
Liberal Arts and Sciences Studies and Humanities, A
Management Information Systems and Services, B
Marketing/Marketing Management, B
Mathematics, B
Mathematics Teacher Education, B
Nursing, M
Nursing - Registered Nurse Training, B
Occupational Therapy/Therapist, BM
Physical Therapy/Therapist, MD
Pre-Law Studies, B
Psychology, B
Secondary Education and Teaching, B
Social Science Teacher Education, B
Social Sciences, B
Social Work, B
Spanish Language and Literature, B
Special Education and Teaching, BM

DOWLING COLLEGE

Accounting, B
Aerospace, Aeronautical and Astronautical Engineering, B
Anthropology, B
Applied Art, B
Art Teacher Education, B
Aviation/Airway Management and Operations, MO
Biological and Physical Sciences, B
Biology Teacher Education, B
Biology/Biological Sciences, B
Business Administration and Management, B
Business Administration, Management and Operations, MO
Business Teacher Education, B
Business, Management, Marketing, and Related Support Services, B
Commercial and Advertising Art, B
Communication Studies/Speech Communication and Rhetoric, B
Computer and Information Sciences, B
Computer and Information Sciences and Support Services, B
Economics, B
Education, BMDO
Educational Administration and Supervision, DO
Elementary Education and Teaching, B
Engineering, B
English Language and Literature, B
English/Language Arts Teacher Education, B
Finance, B
Finance and Banking, MO
Fine Arts and Art Studies, B
Fine/Studio Arts, B
Foreign Languages and Literatures, B
Health Professions and Related Clinical Sciences, B
History, B
Human Development, M
Humanities/Humanistic Studies, B
Interdisciplinary Studies, B
International Business/Trade/Commerce, B
Liberal Arts and Sciences Studies and Humanities, B
Liberal Studies, M
Management, M
Marine Biology and Biological Oceanography, B
Mathematics, BM
Mathematics Teacher Education, B
Music, B
Music Teacher Education, B
Natural Sciences, B
Philosophy, B
Political Science and Government, B
Psychology, B

Quality Management, MO
Reading Teacher Education, M
Romance Languages, Literatures, and Linguistics, B
Sales, Distribution and Marketing Operations, B
Secondary Education and Teaching, BM
Social Sciences, B
Social Studies Teacher Education, B
Sociology, B
Spanish Language Teacher Education, B
Special Education and Teaching, BM
Speech and Rhetorical Studies, B
Tourism and Travel Services Management, B
Transportation and Materials Moving, B

DUTCHESS COMMUNITY COLLEGE

Accounting, A
Administrative Assistant and Secretarial Science, A
Architectural Engineering Technology/Technician, A
Artificial Intelligence and Robotics, A
Biological and Physical Sciences, A
Business Administration and Management, A
Business Machine Repairer, A
Child Development, A
Clinical/Medical Laboratory Technician, A
Commercial and Advertising Art, A
Communication Studies/Speech Communication
    and Rhetoric, A
Computer and Information Sciences, A
Computer Science, A
Construction Engineering Technology/Technician, A
Consumer Merchandising/Retailing Management, A
Criminal Justice/Law Enforcement Administration, A
Criminal Justice/Safety Studies, A
Dietetics/Dieticians, A
Electrical, Electronic and Communications
    Engineering Technology/Technician, A
Electrical, Electronics and Communications
    Engineering, A
Electromechanical Technology/Electromechanical
    Engineering Technology, A
Elementary Education and Teaching, A
Emergency Medical Technology/Technician (EMT
    Paramedic), A
Engineering Science, A
Foods, Nutrition, and Wellness Studies, A
Humanities/Humanistic Studies, A
Information Science/Studies, A
Kindergarten/PreSchool Education and Teaching, A
Legal Assistant/Paralegal, A
Liberal Arts and Sciences Studies and
    Humanities, A
Mass Communication/Media Studies, A
Mathematics, A
Medical/Clinical Assistant, A
Mental Health/Rehabilitation, A
Nursing - Registered Nurse Training, A
Parks, Recreation, Leisure and Fitness Studies, A
Physical Therapist Assistant, A
Psychiatric/Mental Health Services Technician, A
Science Teacher Education/General Science
    Teacher Education, A
Social Sciences, A
Special Products Marketing Operations, A
Telecommunications Technology/Technician, A
Tourism and Travel Services Management, A

D'YOUVILLE COLLEGE

Accounting, B
Biology/Biological Sciences, B
Business Administration and Management, B
Business Teacher Education, B
Chiropractic, P
Dietetics/Dieticians, B
Education, BMO
Elementary Education and Teaching, BMO
English Language and Literature, B
Health Professions and Related Clinical Sciences, B
Health Services Administration, MO
Health Services/Allied Health/Health Sciences, B
Health/Health Care Administration/Management, B
History, B
Hospice Nursing, O
Information Technology, B
Interdisciplinary Studies, B
International Business/Trade/Commerce, BM

Liberal Arts and Sciences Studies and
    Humanities, B
Marketing/Marketing Management, B
Nursing, MO
Nursing - Advanced Practice, MO
Nursing - Registered Nurse Training, B
Nutritional Sciences, M
Occupational Therapy/Therapist, BM
Philosophy, B
Physical Therapy/Therapist, BMDO
Physician Assistant, B
Pre-Dentistry Studies, B
Pre-Law Studies, B
Pre-Medicine/Pre-Medical Studies, B
Pre-Veterinary Studies, B
Psychology, B
Science Teacher Education/General Science
    Teacher Education, B
Secondary Education and Teaching, BMO
Sociology, B
Special Education and Teaching, BM
Substance Abuse/Addiction Counseling, O
Teacher Education, Multiple Levels, B

ELLIS HOSPITAL SCHOOL OF NURSING

Nursing - Registered Nurse Training, A

ELMIRA BUSINESS INSTITUTE

Accounting, A
Administrative Assistant and Secretarial Science, A
Legal Administrative Assistant/Secretary, A
Medical Administrative Assistant/Secretary, A
Tourism and Travel Services Management, A

ELMIRA COLLEGE

Accounting, B
American/United States Studies/Civilization, B
Anthropology, B
Art Teacher Education, B
Art/Art Studies, General, B
Audiology/Audiologist and Speech-Language
    Pathology/Pathologist, B
Biochemistry, B
Biology Teacher Education, B
Biology/Biological Sciences, B
Business Administration and Management, B
Business/Managerial Economics, B
Chemistry, B
Chemistry Teacher Education, B
Classics and Classical
    Languages, Literatures, and Linguistics, B
Clinical Laboratory Science/Medical
    Technology/Technologist, B
Comparative Literature, B
Criminal Justice/Law Enforcement Administration, B
Drama and Dramatics/Theatre Arts, B
Economics, B
Education, B
Elementary Education and Teaching, B
English Language and Literature, B
English/Language Arts Teacher Education, B
Environmental Studies, B
European Studies/Civilization, B
Fine/Studio Arts, B
Foreign Language Teacher Education, B
Foreign Languages and Literatures, B
French Language and Literature, B
French Language Teacher Education, B
History, B
History Teacher Education, B
Human Services, B
Humanities/Humanistic Studies, B
Information Science/Studies, B
Interdisciplinary Studies, B
International Business/Trade/Commerce, B
International Relations and Affairs, B
Junior High/Intermediate/Middle School Education
    and Teaching, B
Liberal Arts and Sciences Studies and
    Humanities, B
Marketing/Marketing Management, B
Mathematics, B
Mathematics Teacher Education, B
Mental Health/Rehabilitation, B
Modern Languages, B

Music, B
Nursing - Registered Nurse Training, B
Nursing Science, B
Philosophy, B
Political Science and Government, B
Pre-Dentistry Studies, B
Pre-Law Studies, B
Pre-Medicine/Pre-Medical Studies, B
Pre-Veterinary Studies, B
Psychology, B
Religion/Religious Studies, B
Romance Languages, Literatures, and Linguistics, B
Science Teacher Education/General Science
    Teacher Education, B
Secondary Education and Teaching, B
Social Science Teacher Education, B
Social Sciences, B
Social Studies Teacher Education, B
Social Work, B
Sociology, B
Spanish Language and Literature, B
Spanish Language Teacher Education, B
Speech Teacher Education, B

ERIE COMMUNITY COLLEGE

Administrative Assistant and Secretarial Science, A
Building/Property Maintenance and Management, A
Business Administration and Management, A
Child Care and Support Services Management, A
Community Health Services/Liaison/Counseling, A
Criminal Justice/Law Enforcement Administration, A
Criminal Justice/Police Science, A
Culinary Arts/Chef Training, A
Humanities/Humanistic Studies, A
Industrial Production Technologies/Technicians, A
Information Science/Studies, A
Legal Assistant/Paralegal, A
Liberal Arts and Sciences Studies and
    Humanities, A
Medical Radiologic Technology/Science - Radiation
    Therapist, A
Nursing - Registered Nurse Training, A
Office Management and Supervision, A
Physical Education Teaching and Coaching, A
Public Administration and Social Service
    Professions, A
Substance Abuse/Addiction Counseling, A

ERIE COMMUNITY COLLEGE, NORTH CAMPUS

Business Administration and Management, A
Civil Engineering Technology/Technician, A
Clinical/Medical Laboratory Technician, A
Computer and Information Sciences, A
Construction Management, A
Construction Trades, A
Criminal Justice/Law Enforcement Administration, A
Criminal Justice/Police Science, A
Culinary Arts/Chef Training, A
Dental Hygiene/Hygienist, A
Dietician Assistant, A
Electrical, Electronic and Communications
    Engineering Technology/Technician, A
Engineering, A
Health Information/Medical Records
    Technology/Technician, A
Humanities/Humanistic Studies, A
Information Science/Studies, A
Liberal Arts and Sciences Studies and
    Humanities, A
Mechanical Engineering/Mechanical
    Technology/Technician, A
Medical Office Management/Administration, A
Nursing - Registered Nurse Training, A
Occupational Therapist Assistant, A
Office Management and Supervision, A
Opticianry/Ophthalmic Dispensing Optician, A
Physical Education Teaching and Coaching, A
Respiratory Care Therapy/Therapist, A

Restaurant, Culinary, and Catering
Management/Manager, A

ERIE COMMUNITY COLLEGE, SOUTH CAMPUS

Architectural Engineering Technology/Technician, A
Autobody/Collision and Repair
Technology/Technician, A
Automobile/Automotive Mechanics
Technology/Technician, A
Biomedical Technology/Technician, A
Business Administration and Management, A
Communication Studies/Speech Communication
and Rhetoric, A
Communications Systems Installation and Repair
Technology, A
Computer Technology/Computer Systems
Technology, A
Dental Laboratory Technology/Technician, A
Fire Services Administration, A
Graphic and Printing Equipment Operator
Production, A
Humanities/Humanistic Studies, A
Industrial Technology/Technician, A
Information Science/Studies, A
Liberal Arts and Sciences Studies and
Humanities, A
Mechanical Drafting and Mechanical Drafting
CAD/CADD, A
Office Management and Supervision, A
Parks, Recreation and Leisure Facilities
Management, A
Physical Education Teaching and Coaching, A
Public Administration and Social Service
Professions, A

EUGENE LANG COLLEGE THE NEW SCHOOL FOR LIBERAL ARTS

Anthropology, B
Comparative Literature, B
Creative Writing, B
Drama and Dramatics/Theatre Arts, B
Economics, B
Education, B
English Language and Literature, B
History, B
Humanities/Humanistic Studies, B
Interdisciplinary Studies, B
International Relations and Affairs, B
Liberal Arts and Sciences Studies and
Humanities, B
Music History, Literature, and Theory, B
Philosophy, B
Political Science and Government, B
Psychology, B
Religion/Religious Studies, B
Social Sciences, B
Sociology, B
Urban Studies/Affairs, B
Women's Studies, B

EUGENIO MARÍA DE HOSTOS COMMUNITY COLLEGE OF THE CITY UNIVERSITY OF NEW YORK

Accounting, A
Administrative Assistant and Secretarial Science, A
Business Administration and Management, A
Clinical/Medical Laboratory Technician, A
Data Entry/Microcomputer Applications, A
Data Processing and Data Processing
Technology/Technician, A
Dental Hygiene/Hygienist, A
Electrical and Electronic Engineering
Technologies/Technicians, A
Gerontology, A
Kindergarten/PreSchool Education and Teaching, A
Legal Assistant/Paralegal, A
Liberal Arts and Sciences Studies and
Humanities, A
Licensed Practical/Vocational Nurse Training, A
Medical Administrative Assistant/Secretary, A
Medical Radiologic Technology/Science - Radiation
Therapist, A
Nursing - Registered Nurse Training, A

Public Administration, A

EXCELSIOR COLLEGE

Accounting, B
Area Studies, B
Avionics Maintenance Technology/Technician, A
Biology/Biological Sciences, B
Business Administration and Management, AB
Business Administration, Management and
Operations, M
Chemical Engineering, AB
Chemistry, B
Comparative Literature, B
Computer Engineering Technology/Technician, AB
Computer Science, AB
Criminal Justice/Law Enforcement Administration, B
Economics, B
Electrical, Electronic and Communications
Engineering Technology/Technician, AB
Electromechanical Technology/Electromechanical
Engineering Technology, AB
Finance, B
Foreign Languages and Literatures, B
Geography, B
Geology/Earth Science, B
History, B
Human Resources Management/Personnel
Administration, B
Industrial Technology/Technician, AB
Information Science/Studies, B
Instrumentation Technology/Technician, AB
Insurance, B
International Business/Trade/Commerce, B
Laser and Optical Technology/Technician, AB
Liberal Arts and Sciences Studies and
Humanities, AB
Liberal Studies, M
Management Information Systems and Services, B
Manufacturing Technology/Technician, A
Marketing/Marketing Management, B
Mass Communication/Media Studies, B
Mathematics, B
Music, B
Nuclear Engineering Technology/Technician, AB
Nursing, MO
Nursing - Registered Nurse Training, AB
Nursing Administration, MO
Operations Management and Supervision, B
Philosophy, B
Physics, B
Political Science and Government, B
Psychology, B
Sociology, B

FARMINGDALE STATE UNIVERSITY OF NEW YORK

Airline/Commercial/Professional Pilot and Flight
Crew, B
Applied Mathematics, B
Architectural Engineering Technology/Technician, B
Automotive Engineering Technology/Technician, AB
Aviation/Airway Management and Operations, B
Biological and Biomedical Sciences, B
Building/Construction
Finishing, Management, and Inspection, B
Business Administration and Management, A
Clinical/Medical Laboratory Technician, A
Computer Engineering Technology/Technician, B
Computer Programming, B
Computer Programming/Programmer, AB
Computer Science, A
Construction Engineering Technology/Technician, B
Criminal Justice/Law Enforcement Administration, A
Data Processing and Data Processing
Technology/Technician, A
Dental Hygiene/Hygienist, AB
Design and Visual Communications, B
Electrical, Electronic and Communications
Engineering Technology/Technician, B
Engineering/Industrial Management, B
History and Philosophy of Science and
Technology, A
Information Science/Studies, A
Landscaping and Groundskeeping, A
Liberal Arts and Sciences Studies and
Humanities, A

Manufacturing Technology/Technician, B
Mechanical Engineering/Mechanical
Technology/Technician, AB
Nursing - Registered Nurse Training, A
Operations Management and Supervision, B
Ornamental Horticulture, A
Security and Loss Prevention Services, B

FASHION INSTITUTE OF TECHNOLOGY

Advertising, AB
Apparel and Textile Manufacture, AB
Apparel and Textiles, AB
Applied Arts and Design, M
Art History, Criticism and Conservation, BM
Arts Management, BM
Clothing and Textiles, M
Commercial and Advertising Art, AB
Commercial Photography, AB
Digital Communication and Media/Multimedia, B
Fashion Merchandising, AB
Fashion Modeling, A
Fashion/Apparel Design, AB
Fine/Studio Arts, AB
Graphic Design, B
Illustration, ABM
Industrial Design, B
Interior Design, AB
International Marketing, B
Management, M
Marketing, AM
Marketing Research, B
Metal and Jewelry Arts, A
Museology/Museum Studies, M
Special Products Marketing Operations, B

FINGER LAKES COMMUNITY COLLEGE

Accounting, A
Administrative Assistant and Secretarial Science, A
Architectural Engineering Technology/Technician, A
Banking and Financial Support Services, A
Biological and Physical Sciences, A
Biology Technician/BioTechnology Laboratory
Technician, A
Biology/Biological Sciences, A
Broadcast Journalism, A
Business Administration and Management, A
Chemistry, A
Commercial and Advertising Art, A
Computer and Information Sciences, A
Computer Science, A
Consumer Merchandising/Retailing Management, A
Criminal Justice/Law Enforcement Administration, A
Criminal Justice/Police Science, A
Data Processing and Data Processing
Technology/Technician, A
Drafting and Design Technology/Technician, A
Drama and Dramatics/Theatre Arts, A
Engineering Science, A
Environmental Studies, A
Fine/Studio Arts, A
Hotel/Motel Administration/Management, A
Human Services, A
Humanities/Humanistic Studies, A
Kindergarten/PreSchool Education and Teaching, A
Legal Assistant/Paralegal, A
Liberal Arts and Sciences Studies and
Humanities, A
Marketing/Marketing Management, A
Mass Communication/Media Studies, A
Mathematics, A
Mechanical Engineering/Mechanical
Technology/Technician, A
Music, A
Natural Resources and Conservation, A
Natural Resources Management/Development and
Policy, A
Nursing - Registered Nurse Training, A
Ornamental Horticulture, A
Parks, Recreation and Leisure Facilities
Management, A
Physical Education Teaching and Coaching, A
Physics, A
Political Science and Government, A
Pre-Engineering, A
Psychology, A

Social Sciences, A
Sociology, A
Substance Abuse/Addiction Counseling, A
Tourism and Travel Services Management, A

FIORELLO H. LAGUARDIA COMMUNITY COLLEGE OF THE CITY UNIVERSITY OF NEW YORK

Accounting, A
Administrative Assistant and Secretarial Science, A
Business Administration and Management, A
Computer and Information Sciences, A
Computer Engineering Technology/Technician, A
Computer Programming, A
Computer Programming, Specific Applications, A
Computer
   Programming, Vendor/Product Certification, A
Computer Programming/Programmer, A
Computer Science, A
Computer Systems Networking and
   Telecommunications, A
Data Entry/Microcomputer Applications, A
Dietetics/Dieticians, A
Education, A
Emergency Medical Technology/Technician (EMT
   Paramedic), A
Fine/Studio Arts, A
Funeral Service and Mortuary Science, A
Gerontology, A
Human Services, A
Information Science/Studies, A
Kindergarten/PreSchool Education and Teaching, A
Legal Administrative Assistant/Secretary, A
Legal Assistant/Paralegal, A
Liberal Arts and Sciences Studies and
   Humanities, A
Mental Health/Rehabilitation, A
Nursing - Registered Nurse Training, A
Occupational Therapy/Therapist, A
Photography, A
Physical Therapy/Therapist, A
Special Products Marketing Operations, A
System Administration/Administrator, A
Tourism and Travel Services Management, A
Veterinary/Animal Health Technology/Technician and
   Veterinary Assistant, A

FIVE TOWNS COLLEGE

Audio Engineering, AB
Broadcast Journalism, A
Business Administration and Management, AB
Cinematography and Film/Video Production, AB
Data Processing and Data Processing
   Technology/Technician, A
Drama and Dramatics/Theatre Arts, AB
Early Childhood Education and Teaching, M
Elementary Education and Teaching, B
Jazz/Jazz Studies, AB
Liberal Arts and Sciences Studies and
   Humanities, A
Marketing/Marketing Management, A
Mass Communication/Media Studies, A
Music, ABMD
Music Management and Merchandising, AB
Music Teacher Education, BM
Technical Theatre/Theatre Design and
   Technology, B
Violin, Viola, Guitar and Other Stringed
   Instruments, AB
Voice and Opera, AB
Wind and Percussion Instruments, AB

FORDHAM UNIVERSITY

Accounting, BM
Accounting and Computer Science, B
Adult and Continuing Education and Teaching, M
African Studies, B
African-American/Black Studies, B
American/United States Studies/Civilization, B
Anthropology, B
Art History, Criticism and Conservation, B
Art/Art Studies, General, B
Bilingual and Multilingual Education, B
Biological and Biomedical Sciences, MD
Biological and Physical Sciences, B
Biology/Biological Sciences, B

Broadcast Journalism, B
Business Administration and Management, B
Business Administration, Management and
   Operations, MO
Business/Managerial Economics, B
Central/Middle and Eastern European Studies, B
Chemistry, B
Classics and Classical
   Languages, Literatures, and Linguistics, BMD
Clinical Psychology, D
Commercial and Advertising Art, B
Communication and Media Studies, M
Comparative Literature, B
Computer and Information Sciences, B
Computer Science, BM
Corporate and Organizational Communication, M
Counseling Psychology, D
Counselor Education/School Counseling and
   Guidance Services, MO
Creative Writing, B
Criminal Justice/Law Enforcement Administration, B
Curriculum and Instruction, MD
Dance, B
Developmental Psychology, D
Drama and Dramatics/Theatre Arts, B
Early Childhood Education and Teaching, M
Economics, BMDO
Education, BMDO
Educational Administration and Supervision, MDO
Educational Psychology, MDO
Elementary Education and Teaching, BM
English, MD
English as a Second Language, M
English Language and Literature, B
Entrepreneurship/Entrepreneurial Studies, B
Ethics, O
Film/Cinema Studies, B
Finance, B
Finance and Banking, M
Fine/Studio Arts, B
French Language and Literature, B
French Studies, B
German Language and Literature, B
German Studies, B
Health/Medical Preparatory Programs, B
Hispanic-American, Puerto Rican, and Mexican-
   American/Chicano Studies, B
History, BMD
Human Resources Management and Services, M
Human Resources Management/Personnel
   Administration, B
Information Science/Studies, B
Interdisciplinary Studies, B
International Affairs, MO
International Business/Trade/Commerce, B
International Development, MO
International Economics, B
International Relations and Affairs, B
Italian Language and Literature, B
Italian Studies, B
Journalism, B
Latin American Studies, BO
Latin Language and Literature, B
Law and Legal Studies, MPO
Liberal Arts and Sciences Studies and
   Humanities, B
Liberal Studies, M
Management Information Systems and
   Services, BM
Marketing, M
Marketing/Marketing Management, B
Mass Communication/Media Studies, BM
Mathematics, B
Media Studies, M
Medieval and Renaissance Studies, BM
Modern Greek Language and Literature, B
Modern Languages, B
Multilingual and Multicultural Education, M
Music, B
Music History, Literature, and Theory, B
Natural Sciences, B
Near and Middle Eastern Studies, B
Pastoral Studies/Counseling, MO
Peace Studies and Conflict Resolution, B
Philosophy, BMD
Photography, B

Physical Sciences, B
Physics, B
Playwriting and Screenwriting, B
Political Science and Government, BM
Pre-Dentistry Studies, B
Pre-Law Studies, B
Pre-Medicine/Pre-Medical Studies, B
Pre-Pharmacy Studies, B
Pre-Veterinary Studies, B
Psychology, BD
Public Administration, B
Radio and Television, B
Reading Teacher Education, MO
Religion/Religious Studies, BMDO
Religious Education, MDO
Romance Languages, Literatures, and Linguistics, B
Russian Language and Literature, B
Russian Studies, B
School Psychology, DO
Secondary Education and Teaching, BM
Social Sciences, B
Social Work, BMDO
Sociology, BMD
Spanish and Iberian Studies, B
Spanish Language and Literature, B
Special Education and Teaching, MO
System Management, M
Taxation, M
Theology and Religious Vocations, MD
Theology/Theological Studies, B
Urban Studies/Affairs, B
Women's Studies, B

FULTON-MONTGOMERY COMMUNITY COLLEGE

Accounting, A
Administrative Assistant and Secretarial Science, A
Art/Art Studies, General, A
Automobile/Automotive Mechanics
   Technology/Technician, A
Behavioral Sciences, A
Biological and Physical Sciences, A
Biology/Biological Sciences, A
Business Administration and Management, A
Carpentry/Carpenter, A
Commercial and Advertising Art, A
Computer Engineering Technology/Technician, A
Computer Science, A
Computer Typography and Composition Equipment
   Operator, A
Construction Engineering Technology/Technician, A
Criminal Justice/Law Enforcement Administration, A
Data Processing and Data Processing
   Technology/Technician, A
Developmental and Child Psychology, A
Drama and Dramatics/Theatre Arts, A
Electrical, Electronic and Communications
   Engineering Technology/Technician, A
Elementary Education and Teaching, A
Engineering Science, A
English Language and Literature, A
Environmental Studies, A
Finance, A
Fine/Studio Arts, A
Graphic and Printing Equipment Operator
   Production, A
Health Teacher Education, A
History, A
Human Services, A
Humanities/Humanistic Studies, A
Information Science/Studies, A
Kindergarten/PreSchool Education and Teaching, A
Legal Administrative Assistant/Secretary, A
Liberal Arts and Sciences Studies and
   Humanities, A
Mass Communication/Media Studies, A
Mathematics, A
Medical Administrative Assistant/Secretary, A
Natural Resources and Conservation, A
Nursing - Registered Nurse Training, A
Physical Education Teaching and Coaching, A
Physical Sciences, A
Psychology, A
Social Sciences, A

Teacher Assistant/Aide, A

GENESEE COMMUNITY COLLEGE

Accounting, A
Administrative Assistant and Secretarial Science, A
Business Administration and Management, A
Clinical/Medical Laboratory Technician, A
Commercial and Advertising Art, A
Computer and Information Sciences, A
Computer Engineering Technology/Technician, A
Computer Graphics, A
Computer Software and Media Applications, A
Consumer Merchandising/Retailing Management, A
Criminal Justice/Law Enforcement Administration, A
Drafting and Design Technology/Technician, A
Drama and Dramatics/Theatre Arts, A
Education, A
Electrical, Electronic and Communications
    Engineering Technology/Technician, A
Elementary Education and Teaching, A
Engineering Science, A
Fashion Merchandising, A
Gerontology, A
Hotel/Motel Administration/Management, A
Human Services, A
Information Science/Studies, A
Kindergarten/PreSchool Education and Teaching, A
Legal Assistant/Paralegal, A
Liberal Arts and Sciences Studies and
    Humanities, A
Marketing/Marketing Management, A
Mass Communication/Media Studies, A
Mathematics, A
Nursing - Registered Nurse Training, A
Occupational Therapy/Therapist, A
Physical Education Teaching and Coaching, A
Physical Therapy/Therapist, A
Psychology, A
Respiratory Care Therapy/Therapist, A
Substance Abuse/Addiction Counseling, A
System Administration/Administrator, A
Tourism and Travel Services Management, A

GLOBE INSTITUTE OF TECHNOLOGY

Accounting, B
Banking and Financial Support Services, A
Business Administration and Management, AB
Computer and Information Sciences, AB
Computer Programming/Programmer, B
Finance, B
Health/Health Care Administration/Management, B
Hospitality Administration/Management, B
Management Information Systems and Services, A
Office Management and Supervision, A
Sport and Fitness Administration/Management, B

HAMILTON COLLEGE

African Studies, B
American/United States Studies/Civilization, B
Anthropology, B
Archeology, B
Art History, Criticism and Conservation, B
Art/Art Studies, General, B
Asian Studies/Civilization, B
Biochemistry, B
Biology/Biological Sciences, B
Chemistry, B
Classics and Classical
    Languages, Literatures, and Linguistics, B
Comparative Literature, B
Computer Science, B
Creative Writing, B
Dance, B
Drama and Dramatics/Theatre Arts, B
East Asian Studies, B
Economics, B
English Language and Literature, B
Fine/Studio Arts, B
French Language and Literature, B
Geology/Earth Science, B
German Language and Literature, B
History, B
International Relations and Affairs, B
Latin Language and Literature, B
Mass Communication/Media Studies, B
Mathematics, B

Medieval and Renaissance Studies, B
Modern Greek Language and Literature, B
Modern Languages, B
Molecular Biology, B
Music, B
Neuroscience, B
Philosophy, B
Physics, B
Physiological Psychology/Psychobiology, B
Political Science and Government, B
Psychology, B
Public Policy Analysis, B
Religion/Religious Studies, B
Russian Studies, B
Sociology, B
Spanish Language and Literature, B
Women's Studies, B

HARTWICK COLLEGE

Accounting, B
Anthropology, B
Art History, Criticism and Conservation, B
Art/Art Studies, General, B
Biochemistry, B
Biology/Biological Sciences, B
Business Administration and Management, B
Chemistry, B
Clinical Laboratory Science/Medical
    Technology/Technologist, B
Computer and Information Sciences, B
Computer Science, B
Drama and Dramatics/Theatre Arts, B
Economics, B
English Language and Literature, B
Environmental Sciences, B
French Language and Literature, B
Geology/Earth Science, B
German Language and Literature, B
History, B
Mathematics, B
Music, B
Music Teacher Education, B
Nursing - Registered Nurse Training, B
Philosophy, B
Physics, B
Political Science and Government, B
Pre-Law Studies, B
Pre-Medicine/Pre-Medical Studies, B
Pre-Veterinary Studies, B
Psychology, B
Religion/Religious Studies, B
Sociology, B
Spanish Language and Literature, B

HELENE FULD COLLEGE OF NURSING OF NORTH GENERAL HOSPITAL

Nursing - Registered Nurse Training, A

HERKIMER COUNTY COMMUNITY COLLEGE

Accounting, A
Art/Art Studies, General, A
Broadcast Journalism, A
Business Administration and Management, A
Computer and Information Sciences, A
Computer and Information Sciences and Support
    Services, A
Computer Systems Networking and
    Telecommunications, A
Corrections, A
Criminal Justice/Law Enforcement Administration, A
Criminal Justice/Police Science, A
Data Entry/Microcomputer Applications, A
Emergency Medical Technology/Technician (EMT
    Paramedic), A
English Language and Literature, A
Entrepreneurial and Small Business Operations, A
Fashion Merchandising, A
Fine/Studio Arts, A
General Studies, A
Health/Health Care Administration/Management, A
Human Resources Management and Services, A
Human Resources Management/Personnel
    Administration, A
Human Services, A
Humanities/Humanistic Studies, A

International Business/Trade/Commerce, A
Legal Assistant/Paralegal, A
Liberal Arts and Sciences Studies and
    Humanities, A
Marketing/Marketing Management, A
Mathematics, A
Photography, A
Physical Education Teaching and Coaching, A
Physical Therapy/Therapist, A
Radio and Television, A
Social Sciences, A
Telecommunications Technology/Technician, A
Tourism and Travel Services Management, A
Tourism and Travel Services Marketing
    Operations, A
Tourism Promotion Operations, A

HILBERT COLLEGE

Accounting, B
Banking and Financial Support Services, A
Business Administration and Management, AB
Criminal Justice/Law Enforcement
    Administration, AB
Criminal Justice/Police Science, B
English Language and Literature, B
Finance, B
Human Services, AB
Law and Legal Studies, AB
Legal Assistant/Paralegal, AB
Liberal Arts and Sciences Studies and
    Humanities, A
Management Information Systems and Services, A
Psychology, B

HOBART AND WILLIAM SMITH COLLEGES

African Studies, B
African-American/Black Studies, B
American/United States Studies/Civilization, B
Ancient/Classical Greek Language and Literature, B
Anthropology, B
Architecture, B
Art History, Criticism and Conservation, B
Art/Art Studies, General, B
Asian Studies/Civilization, B
Biochemistry, B
Biology/Biological Sciences, B
Chemistry, B
Chinese Language and Literature, B
Classics and Classical
    Languages, Literatures, and Linguistics, B
Comparative Literature, B
Computer Science, B
Dance, B
Drama and Dramatics/Theatre Arts, B
Economics, B
English Language and Literature, B
Environmental Studies, B
European Studies/Civilization, B
Fine/Studio Arts, B
French Language and Literature, B
Gay/Lesbian Studies, B
Geology/Earth Science, B
History, B
Interdisciplinary Studies, B
International Relations and Affairs, B
Japanese Language and Literature, B
Latin American Studies, B
Latin Language and Literature, B
Liberal Arts and Sciences Studies and
    Humanities, B
Mass Communication/Media Studies, B
Mathematics, B
Medieval and Renaissance Studies, B
Modern Languages, B
Music, B
Philosophy, B
Physics, B
Political Science and Government, B
Pre-Dentistry Studies, B
Pre-Law Studies, B
Pre-Medicine/Pre-Medical Studies, B
Pre-Veterinary Studies, B
Psychology, B
Public Policy Analysis, B
Religion/Religious Studies, B

Russian Language and Literature, B
Russian Studies, B
Sociology, B
Spanish Language and Literature, B
Urban Studies/Affairs, B
Women's Studies, B

HOFSTRA UNIVERSITY

Accounting, BMO
Actuarial Science, B
Administrative Assistant and Secretarial Science, B
African Studies, B
American/United States Studies/Civilization, B
Anthropology, B
Applied Mathematics, BM
Area Studies, B
Art Education, M
Art History, Criticism and Conservation, B
Art Teacher Education, B
Art Therapy/Therapist, M
Asian Studies/Civilization, B
Athletic Training and Sports Medicine, B
Audiology/Audiologist and Speech-Language
   Pathology/Pathologist, B
Biochemistry, B
Biological and Biomedical Sciences, M
Biology Teacher Education, B
Biology/Biological Sciences, B
Biomedical/Medical Engineering, B
Broadcast Journalism, B
Business Administration and Management, B
Business Administration, Management and
   Operations, BMO
Business Education, M
Business Teacher Education, B
Business/Commerce, B
Business/Managerial Economics, B
Caribbean Studies, B
Ceramic Arts and Ceramics, B
Chemistry, B
Chemistry Teacher Education, B
Civil Engineering, B
Classics and Classical
   Languages, Literatures, and Linguistics, B
Clinical Psychology, DO
Communication and Media Studies, B
Communication Disorders, MDO
Communication Studies/Speech Communication
   and Rhetoric, B
Community Health and Preventive Medicine, B
Community Psychology, DO
Comparative Literature, BM
Computer Engineering, B
Computer Science, BM
Counselor Education/School Counseling and
   Guidance Services, MO
Creative Writing, B
Dance, B
Design and Applied Arts, B
Drama and Dramatics/Theatre Arts, B
Early Childhood Education and Teaching, BMO
Econometrics and Quantitative Economics, B
Economics, B
Education, BMDO
Education/Teaching of the Gifted and Talented, O
Educational Administration and Supervision, MO
Educational Leadership and Administration, DO
Educational Measurement and Evaluation, M
Educational Media/Instructional Technology, M
Electrical, Electronics and Communications
   Engineering, B
Elementary Education and Teaching, BM
Engineering Management, M
Engineering Science, B
English, M
English as a Second Language, MO
English Education, M
English Language and Literature, B
English Literature (British and Commonwealth), B
English/Language Arts Teacher Education, B
Entrepreneurship/Entrepreneurial Studies, B
Environmental Studies, B
Environmental/Environmental Health Engineering, B
Film/Cinema Studies, B
Finance, B
Finance and Banking, MO

Fine Arts and Art Studies, M
Fine/Studio Arts, B
Foreign Language Teacher Education, BM
Foreign Languages, Literatures, and Linguistics, B
Foundations and Philosophy of Education, MO
French Language and Literature, BM
French Language Teacher Education, B
Geography, B
Geology/Earth Science, B
German Language and Literature, BM
German Language Teacher Education, B
Gerontology, MO
Health Education, M
Health Professions and Related Clinical Sciences, B
Health Services Administration, MO
Health Teacher Education, B
Hebrew Language and Literature, B
Hispanic-American, Puerto Rican, and Mexican-
   American/Chicano Studies, B
History, B
Human Resources Management and Services, MO
Humanities/Humanistic Studies, BM
Industrial and Organizational Psychology, MD
Industrial Engineering, B
Information Science/Studies, B
Interdisciplinary Studies, M
International Business/Trade/Commerce, BMO
Italian Language and Literature, B
Jazz/Jazz Studies, B
Jewish/Judaic Studies, B
Journalism, B
Kinesiology and Exercise Science, B
Labor Studies, B
Latin American Studies, B
Latin Language and Literature, B
Law and Legal Studies, MPO
Legal and Justice Studies, M
Liberal Arts and Sciences Studies and
   Humanities, B
Linguistics, M
Management Information Systems and
   Services, BMO
Manufacturing Engineering, B
Marketing, MO
Marketing Research, M
Marketing/Marketing Management, B
Marriage and Family Therapy/Counseling, MO
Mass Communication/Media Studies, B
Mathematics, BM
Mathematics and Computer Science, B
Mathematics and Statistics, B
Mathematics Teacher Education, BM
Mechanical Engineering, B
Metal and Jewelry Arts, B
Middle School Education, O
Multi-/Interdisciplinary Studies, B
Multilingual and Multicultural Education, MO
Music, B
Music History, Literature, and Theory, B
Music Management and Merchandising, B
Music Performance, B
Music Teacher Education, BM
Music Theory and Composition, B
Natural Sciences, B
Painting, B
Performance, M
Philosophy, B
Photography, B
Physical Education Teaching and Coaching, BMO
Physician Assistant, B
Physics, B
Physics Teacher Education, B
Political Science and Government, B
Pre-Dentistry Studies, B
Pre-Medicine/Pre-Medical Studies, B
Pre-Veterinary Studies, B
Psychology, BMDO
Public Relations/Image Management, B
Quantitative Analysis, MO
Radio and Television, B
Radio and Television Broadcasting
   Technology/Technician, B
Reading Teacher Education, MDO
Rehabilitation Counseling, MO
Russian Language and Literature, BM
School Psychology, DO

Science Teacher Education/General Science
   Teacher Education, BM
Secondary Education and Teaching, BM
Social Sciences, B
Social Studies Teacher Education, BM
Sociology, B
Spanish Language and Literature, BM
Spanish Language Teacher Education, B
Special Education and Teaching, MO
Speech and Interpersonal Communication, M
Speech and Rhetorical Studies, B
Statistics, B
Substance Abuse/Addiction Counseling, O
Taxation, MO
Teacher Education and Professional
   Development, Specific Subject Areas, B
Teacher Education, Multiple Levels, B
Writing, M

HOLY TRINITY ORTHODOX SEMINARY

Theology/Theological Studies, B

HOUGHTON COLLEGE

Accounting, B
Art Teacher Education, B
Art/Art Studies, General, B
Bible/Biblical Studies, AB
Biological and Physical Sciences, B
Biology/Biological Sciences, B
Business Administration and Management, B
Chemistry, B
Clinical Laboratory Science/Medical
   Technology/Technologist, B
Comparative Literature, B
Computer Science, B
Creative Writing, B
Elementary Education and Teaching, B
English Language and Literature, B
Environmental Biology, B
Ethnic and Cultural Studies, B
French Language and Literature, B
Health and Physical Education, B
History, B
Humanities/Humanistic Studies, B
Information Technology, B
International Relations and Affairs, B
Journalism, B
Liberal Arts and Sciences Studies and
   Humanities, AB
Mathematics, B
Music, B
Music Performance, B
Music Teacher Education, B
Music Theory and Composition, B
Natural Sciences, B
Parks, Recreation, Leisure and Fitness Studies, B
Pastoral Studies/Counseling, B
Philosophy, B
Physical Education Teaching and Coaching, B
Physics, B
Piano and Organ, B
Political Science and Government, B
Pre-Dentistry Studies, B
Pre-Law Studies, B
Pre-Medicine/Pre-Medical Studies, B
Pre-Veterinary Studies, B
Psychology, B
Religion/Religious Studies, B
Religious Education, AB
Secondary Education and Teaching, B
Sociology, B
Spanish Language and Literature, B
Special Education and Teaching, B
Theology/Theological Studies, B
Violin, Viola, Guitar and Other Stringed
   Instruments, B
Voice and Opera, B
Wind and Percussion Instruments, B

HUDSON VALLEY COMMUNITY COLLEGE

Accounting, A
Administrative Assistant and Secretarial Science, A
Automobile/Automotive Mechanics
   Technology/Technician, A

Biology Technician/BioTechnology Laboratory
Technician, A
Business Administration and Management, A
Chemical Technology/Technician, A
Civil Engineering Technology/Technician, A
Computer Programming, Specific Applications, A
Construction Engineering Technology/Technician, A
Criminal Justice/Law Enforcement Administration, A
Dental Hygiene/Hygienist, A
Early Childhood Education and Teaching, A
E-Commerce/Electronic Commerce, A
Electrical, Electronic and Communications
Engineering Technology/Technician, A
Electrical/Electronics Maintenance and Repair
Technology, A
Emergency Medical Technology/Technician (EMT
Paramedic), A
Engineering Science, A
Environmental Studies, A
Finance, A
Fine/Studio Arts, A
Forensic Science and Technology, A
Funeral Service and Mortuary Science, A
Health and Physical Education/Fitness, A
Health Information/Medical Records
Technology/Technician, A
Heating, Air Conditioning, Ventilation and
Refrigeration Maintenance
Technology/Technician, A
Human Services, A
Industrial Technology/Technician, A
Information Technology, A
Interdisciplinary Studies, A
Liberal Arts and Sciences Studies and
Humanities, A
Marketing/Marketing Management, A
Mechanical Engineering/Mechanical
Technology/Technician, A
Nursing - Registered Nurse Training, A
Public Administration, A
Radio and Television Broadcasting
Technology/Technician, A
Radiologic Technology/Science - Radiographer, A
Respiratory Care Therapy/Therapist, A
Substance Abuse/Addiction Counseling, A
System, Networking, and LAN/WAN
Management/Manager, A
Telecommunications Technology/Technician, A
Web Page, Digital/Multimedia and Information
Resources Design, A

HUNTER COLLEGE OF THE CITY
UNIVERSITY OF NEW YORK

Accounting, B
African-American/Black Studies, B
Ancient/Classical Greek Language and Literature, B
Anthropology, BM
Applied Mathematics, M
Archeology, B
Art History, Criticism and Conservation, BM
Art/Art Studies, General, B
Audiology/Audiologist and Speech-Language
Pathology/Pathologist, B
Biochemistry, M
Biological and Biomedical Sciences, MD
Biology Teacher Education, B
Biology/Biological Sciences, B
Biopsychology, M
BioTechnology, B
Chemistry, B
Chinese Language and Literature, B
Cinematography and Film/Video Production, B
Classics and Classical
Languages, Literatures, and Linguistics, BM
Clinical/Medical Laboratory Science and Allied
Professions, B
Cognitive Sciences, M
Communication Disorders, M
Community Health Nursing, MO
Comparative Literature, B
Computer Science, B
Counselor Education/School Counseling and
Guidance Services, M
Dance, B
Drama and Dramatics/Theatre Arts, B
Early Childhood Education and Teaching, M

Economics, BM
Education, MO
Education/Teaching of Individuals with Multiple
Disabilities, M
Educational Administration and Supervision, O
Elementary Education and Teaching, BM
English, M
English as a Second Language, M
English Education, M
English Language and Literature, B
English Literature (British and Commonwealth), B
Environmental and Occupational Health, M
Environmental Sciences, BM
Film/Cinema Studies, B
Fine Arts and Art Studies, M
Fine/Studio Arts, B
Foods, Nutrition, and Wellness Studies, B
Foreign Language Teacher Education, M
French Language and Literature, BM
Geographic Information Systems, MO
Geography, BMO
Geosciences, M
German Language and Literature, B
German Language Teacher Education, B
Gerontological Nursing, M
Health Teacher Education, B
Hebrew Language and Literature, B
Hispanic-American, Puerto Rican, and Mexican-
American/Chicano Studies, B
History, BM
Humanities/Humanistic Studies, B
Italian Language and Literature, BM
Jewish/Judaic Studies, B
Kindergarten/PreSchool Education and Teaching, B
Latin American Studies, B
Latin Language and Literature, B
Mass Communication/Media Studies, B
Maternity Nursing, M
Mathematics, BM
Mathematics Teacher Education, BM
Media Studies, M
Multilingual and Multicultural Education, M
Music, BM
Music Teacher Education, M
Nursing, MO
Nursing - Adult, M
Nursing - Advanced Practice, MO
Nursing - Registered Nurse Training, B
Pediatric Nurse/Nursing, MO
Philosophy, B
Physical Education Teaching and Coaching, B
Physical Therapy/Therapist, M
Physics, BMD
Political Science and Government, B
Psychiatric/Mental Health Nurse/Nursing, M
Psychology, BM
Public Health, MO
Public Health (MPH, DPH), B
Reading Teacher Education, M
Rehabilitation Counseling, M
Religion/Religious Studies, B
Romance
Languages, Literatures, and Linguistics, BM
Russian Language and Literature, B
Science Teacher Education/General Science
Teacher Education, BM
Secondary Education and Teaching, BM
Social Psychology, M
Social Studies Teacher Education, M
Social Work, MD
Sociology, BM
Spanish Language and Literature, BM
Special Education and Teaching, M
Statistics, B
Surgical Nursing, M
Survey Methodology, M
Theater, M
Urban Planning, MO
Urban Studies/Affairs, BM
Women's Studies, B

INSTITUTE OF DESIGN AND
CONSTRUCTION

Architectural Engineering Technology/Technician, A
Construction Engineering Technology/Technician, A
Drafting and Design Technology/Technician, A

Interior Architecture, A

INTERBORO INSTITUTE

Accounting, A
Administrative Assistant and Secretarial Science, A
Business Administration and Management, A
Legal Administrative Assistant/Secretary, A
Legal Assistant/Paralegal, A
Medical Administrative Assistant/Secretary, A
Ophthalmic Laboratory Technology/Technician, A

IONA COLLEGE

Accounting, B
Advertising, B
Applied Mathematics, B
Audiology/Audiologist and Speech-Language
Pathology/Pathologist, B
Biochemistry, B
Biology Teacher Education, B
Biology/Biological Sciences, B
Business Administration and Management, B
Business Administration, Management and
Operations, MO
Business Education, M
Chemistry, B
Clinical Laboratory Science/Medical
Technology/Technologist, B
Communication and Media Studies, MO
Communication Studies/Speech Communication
and Rhetoric, B
Computer Science, BM
Computer Systems Networking and
Telecommunications, B
Counselor Education/School Counseling and
Guidance Services, M
Criminal Justice/Law Enforcement Administration, B
Criminology, B
Drama and Dramatics/Theatre Arts, B
Early Childhood Education and Teaching, B
Economics, B
Education, B
Educational Administration and Supervision, M
Educational Media/Instructional Technology, MO
Elementary Education and Teaching, BM
English, M
English Education, M
English Language and Literature, B
English/Language Arts Teacher Education, B
Environmental Biology, B
Finance, B
Finance and Banking, MO
Foreign Language Teacher Education, M
French Language and Literature, B
French Language Teacher Education, B
Health Services Administration, MO
Health/Health Care Administration/Management, B
Health/Medical Psychology, B
History, BM
Human Resources Management and Services, MO
Interdisciplinary Studies, B
International Business/Trade/Commerce, BO
International/Global Studies, B
Italian Language and Literature, B
Journalism, BM
Liberal Arts and Sciences Studies and
Humanities, B
Management Information Systems and Services, B
Management of Technology, MO
Marketing, MO
Marketing/Marketing Management, B
Marriage and Family Therapy/Counseling, MO
Mass Communication/Media Studies, B
Mathematics, B
Mathematics Teacher Education, BM
Multilingual and Multicultural Education, M
Organizational Communication, B
Pastoral Studies/Counseling, MO
Philosophy, B
Physics, B
Political Science and Government, B
Psychology, BM
Public Relations/Image Management, B
Radio and Television, B
Radio and Television Broadcasting
Technology/Technician, B
Religion/Religious Studies, B

School Psychology, M
Science Teacher Education/General Science
   Teacher Education, BM
Secondary Education and Teaching, BM
Social Sciences, B
Social Studies Teacher Education, BM
Social Work, B
Sociology, B
Spanish Language and Literature, BM
Spanish Language Teacher Education, B
Teacher Education, Multiple Levels, B
Telecommunications, MO
Web Page, Digital/Multimedia and Information
   Resources Design, B

ISLAND DRAFTING AND TECHNICAL INSTITUTE

Architectural Drafting and Architectural
   CAD/CADD, A
Computer and Information Systems Security, A
Computer Systems Networking and
   Telecommunications, A
Computer Technology/Computer Systems
   Technology, A
Electrical, Electronic and Communications
   Engineering Technology/Technician, A
Management Information Systems and Services, A
Mechanical Drafting and Mechanical Drafting
   CAD/CADD, A
System Administration/Administrator, A

ITHACA COLLEGE

Accounting, B
Acting, B
Allied Health and Medical Assisting Services, MD
Anthropology, B
Applied Economics, B
Applied Mathematics, B
Art History, Criticism and Conservation, B
Art Teacher Education, B
Art/Art Studies, General, B
Arts Management, B
Athletic Training and Sports Medicine, B
Audiology/Audiologist and Speech-Language
   Pathology/Pathologist, B
Biochemistry, B
Biology Teacher Education, B
Biology/Biological Sciences, B
Broadcast Journalism, B
Business Administration and Management, B
Business/Commerce, B
Business/Managerial Economics, B
Chemistry, B
Chemistry Teacher Education, B
Cinematography and Film/Video Production, B
Communication and Media Studies, M
Communication Disorders, M
Communication, Journalism and Related
   Programs, B
Composition, M
Computer and Information Sciences, B
Computer Science, B
Creative Writing, B
Dance, B
Drama and Dramatics/Theatre Arts, B
Economics, B
Education/Teaching of Individuals with Speech or
   Language Impairments, B
Educational/Instructional Media Design, B
English Language and Literature, B
English/Language Arts Teacher Education, B
Environmental Studies, B
Exercise and Sports Science, M
Film/Cinema Studies, B
Finance, B
Fine/Studio Arts, B
Foods, Nutrition, and Wellness Studies, B
French Language and Literature, B
French Language Teacher Education, B
German Language and Literature, B
German Language Teacher Education, B
German Studies, B
Gerontology, B
Health and Physical Education, B
Health and Physical Education/Fitness, B
Health Teacher Education, B

Health/Health Care Administration/Management, B
Health/Medical Preparatory Programs, B
History, B
History Teacher Education, B
Hospital and Health Care Facilities
   Administration/Management, B
Industrial and Organizational Psychology, B
Interdisciplinary Studies, B
International Business/Trade/Commerce, B
Jazz/Jazz Studies, B
Journalism, B
Junior High/Intermediate/Middle School Education
   and Teaching, B
Kinesiology and Exercise Science, B
Labor and Industrial Relations, B
Liberal Arts and Sciences Studies and
   Humanities, B
Management, M
Marketing Research, B
Marketing/Marketing Management, B
Mass Communication/Media Studies, B
Mathematics, B
Mathematics and Computer Science, B
Mathematics Teacher Education, B
Multi-/Interdisciplinary Studies, B
Music, BM
Music Performance, B
Music Teacher Education, BM
Music Theory and Composition, BM
Occupational Therapy/Therapist, BM
Parks, Recreation, Leisure and Fitness Studies, B
Performance, M
Philosophy, B
Photography, B
Physical Education Teaching and Coaching, B
Physical Therapy/Therapist, BD
Physics, B
Physics Teacher Education, B
Piano and Organ, B
Political Science and Government, B
Pre-Law Studies, B
Pre-Medicine/Pre-Medical Studies, B
Psychology, B
Public Health Education and Promotion, B
Public Relations/Image Management, B
Radio and Television, B
Recording Arts Technology/Technician, B
Rehabilitation Therapy, B
Science Teacher Education/General Science
   Teacher Education, B
Secondary Education and Teaching, B
Social Sciences, B
Social Studies Teacher Education, B
Sociology, B
Spanish Language and Literature, B
Spanish Language Teacher Education, B
Speech and Rhetorical Studies, B
Sport and Fitness Administration/Management, B
Teacher Education, Multiple Levels, B
Technical Theatre/Theatre Design and
   Technology, B
Telecommunications Technology/Technician, B
Therapeutic Recreation/Recreational Therapy, B
Visual and Performing Arts, B
Voice and Opera, B

ITT TECHNICAL INSTITUTE (ALBANY)

Computer Engineering Technologies/Technicians, A
Computer Programming, Specific Applications, A
Computer Programming/Programmer, A
Electrical, Electronic and Communications
   Engineering Technology/Technician, A
System, Networking, and LAN/WAN
   Management/Manager, A
Web Page, Digital/Multimedia and Information
   Resources Design, A
Web/Multimedia Management and Webmaster, A

ITT TECHNICAL INSTITUTE (GETZVILLE)

CAD/CADD Drafting and/or Design
   Technology/Technician, A
Computer and Information Systems Security, A
Computer Programming/Programmer, A
Electrical, Electronic and Communications
   Engineering Technology/Technician, A

System, Networking, and LAN/WAN
   Management/Manager, A
Web Page, Digital/Multimedia and Information
   Resources Design, A

ITT TECHNICAL INSTITUTE (LIVERPOOL)

Computer Programming/Programmer, A
System, Networking, and LAN/WAN
   Management/Manager, A
Web Page, Digital/Multimedia and Information
   Resources Design, A
Web/Multimedia Management and Webmaster, A

JAMESTOWN BUSINESS COLLEGE

Accounting, A
Administrative Assistant and Secretarial Science, A
Business Administration and Management, A
Computer and Information Sciences, A
Legal Administrative Assistant/Secretary, A
Marketing/Marketing Management, A
Medical Administrative Assistant/Secretary, A

JAMESTOWN COMMUNITY COLLEGE

Accounting, A
Airline/Commercial/Professional Pilot and Flight
   Crew, A
Business Administration and Management, A
Clinical/Medical Laboratory Technician, A
Communication Studies/Speech Communication
   and Rhetoric, A
Computer and Information Sciences, A
Computer and Information Systems Security, A
Computer Engineering Technology/Technician, A
Computer Science, A
Criminal Justice/Police Science, A
Criminal Justice/Safety Studies, A
Electrical, Electronic and Communications
   Engineering Technology/Technician, A
Electrical, Electronics and Communications
   Engineering, A
Engineering, A
Fine/Studio Arts, A
Human Services, A
Humanities/Humanistic Studies, A
Mechanical Engineering/Mechanical
   Technology/Technician, A
Nursing - Registered Nurse Training, A
Occupational Therapist Assistant, A
Social Sciences, A

JEFFERSON COMMUNITY COLLEGE

Accounting, A
Administrative Assistant and Secretarial Science, A
Biology Technician/BioTechnology Laboratory
   Technician, A
Business Administration and Management, A
Chemical Technology/Technician, A
Computer Science, A
Computer Systems Networking and
   Telecommunications, A
Computer Typography and Composition Equipment
   Operator, A
Consumer Merchandising/Retailing Management, A
Criminal Justice/Law Enforcement Administration, A
Engineering Science, A
Forestry Technology/Technician, A
Health and Medical Laboratory Technologies, A
Hospitality Administration/Management, A
Hotel/Motel Administration/Management, A
Human Services, A
Humanities/Humanistic Studies, A
Information Science/Studies, A
Interdisciplinary Studies, A
Kindergarten/PreSchool Education and Teaching, A
Legal Assistant/Paralegal, A
Liberal Arts and Sciences Studies and
   Humanities, A
Marketing/Marketing Management, A
Mathematics, A
Medical Administrative Assistant/Secretary, A
Natural Sciences, A
Nursing - Registered Nurse Training, A
Pre-Engineering, A

Tourism and Travel Services Management, A

THE JEWISH THEOLOGICAL SEMINARY

Ancient Near Eastern and Biblical
   Languages, Literatures, and Linguistics, B
Bible/Biblical Studies, B
Comparative Literature, B
Ethnic and Cultural Studies, B
Hebrew Language and Literature, B
History, B
Jewish/Judaic Studies, BMDO
Music, B
Philosophy, B
Religion/Religious Studies, BMD
Religious Education, BMD
Sacred Music, MD
Talmudic Studies, B
Theology and Religious Vocations, MDO
Women's Studies, B

JOHN JAY COLLEGE OF CRIMINAL JUSTICE OF THE CITY UNIVERSITY OF NEW YORK

Behavioral Sciences, B
Corrections, AB
Corrections and Criminal Justice, B
Criminal Justice/Law Enforcement Administration, B
Criminal Justice/Police Science, AB
Criminology, MD
Fire Science/Firefighting, B
Fire Services Administration, B
Forensic Psychology, BMD
Forensic Science and Technology, BMD
Information Science/Studies, B
Law and Legal Studies, B
Legal and Justice Studies, D
Organizational Behavior Studies, D
Pre-Law Studies, B
Public Administration, BM
Public Policy Analysis, D
Securities Services Administration/Management, M
Security and Loss Prevention Services, AB

THE JUILLIARD SCHOOL

Dance, B
Drama and Dramatics/Theatre Arts, B
Music, BMDO
Music Performance, B

KATHARINE GIBBS SCHOOL (MELVILLE)

Administrative Assistant and Secretarial Science, A
Commercial and Advertising Art, A
Computer Systems Networking and
   Telecommunications, A
Hospitality Administration/Management, A

KATHARINE GIBBS SCHOOL (NEW YORK)

Accounting, A
Administrative Assistant and Secretarial Science, A
Hotel/Motel Administration/Management, A
Legal Administrative Assistant/Secretary, A
Marketing/Marketing Management, A
Medical Administrative Assistant/Secretary, A

KEUKA COLLEGE

Accounting, B
Biochemistry, B
Biology Teacher Education, B
Biology/Biological Sciences, B
Biomedical Sciences, B
Business Administration and Management, B
Clinical Laboratory Science/Medical
   Technology/Technologist, B
Communication Studies/Speech Communication
   and Rhetoric, B
Criminal Justice/Law Enforcement Administration, B
Early Childhood Education and Teaching, M
Education/Teaching of Individuals in Early Childhood
   Special Education Programs, B
Elementary Education and Teaching, B
English Language and Literature, B

English/Language Arts Teacher Education, B
Environmental Sciences, B
History, B
Hotel/Motel Administration/Management, B
Interdisciplinary Studies, B
Liberal Arts and Sciences Studies and
   Humanities, B
Management, M
Marketing/Marketing Management, B
Mathematics, B
Mathematics Teacher Education, B
Nursing - Registered Nurse Training, B
Occupational Therapy/Therapist, BM
Pre-Dentistry Studies, B
Pre-Law Studies, B
Pre-Medicine/Pre-Medical Studies, B
Pre-Veterinary Studies, B
Psychology, B
Secondary Education and Teaching, B
Social Sciences, B
Social Studies Teacher Education, B
Social Work, B
Sociology, B
Special Education and Teaching, B

THE KING'S COLLEGE

Business Administration and Management, B
Education, B
Elementary Education and Teaching, B
Finance, B
Marketing/Marketing Management, B

KINGSBOROUGH COMMUNITY COLLEGE OF THE CITY UNIVERSITY OF NEW YORK

Accounting, A
Administrative Assistant and Secretarial Science, A
Applied Art, A
Art/Art Studies, General, A
Biology/Biological Sciences, A
Broadcast Journalism, A
Business Administration and Management, A
Chemistry, A
Commercial and Advertising Art, A
Community Health Services/Liaison/Counseling, A
Computer and Information Sciences, A
Computer Science, A
Data Processing and Data Processing
   Technology/Technician, A
Drama and Dramatics/Theatre Arts, A
Early Childhood Education and Teaching, A
Education, A
Elementary Education and Teaching, A
Engineering Science, A
Fashion Merchandising, A
Health and Physical Education/Fitness, A
Human Services, A
Journalism, A
Labor and Industrial Relations, A
Liberal Arts and Sciences Studies and
   Humanities, A
Marine Technology, A
Marketing/Marketing Management, A
Mathematics, A
Mental Health/Rehabilitation, A
Music, A
Nursing - Registered Nurse Training, A
Parks, Recreation, Leisure and Fitness Studies, A
Physical Therapist Assistant, A
Physical Therapy/Therapist, A
Physics, A
Psychiatric/Mental Health Services Technician, A
Sport and Fitness Administration/Management, A
Teacher Assistant/Aide, A
Tourism and Travel Services Management, A

KOL YAAKOV TORAH CENTER

Jewish/Judaic Studies, B
Rabbinical Studies, B

Theology and Religious Vocations, O

LABORATORY INSTITUTE OF MERCHANDISING

Fashion Merchandising, AB
Marketing/Marketing Management, B

LE MOYNE COLLEGE

Accounting, B
Applied Mathematics, B
Biochemistry, B
Biological and Physical Sciences, B
Biology Teacher Education, B
Biology/Biological Sciences, B
Business Administration and Management, B
Business Administration, Management and
   Operations, M
Business/Commerce, B
Chemistry, B
Chemistry Teacher Education, B
Communication Studies/Speech Communication
   and Rhetoric, B
Creative Writing, B
Criminology, B
Drama and Dramatics/Theatre Arts, B
Economics, B
Education, M
Educational Administration and Supervision, B
Elementary and Middle School
   Administration/Principalship, B
Elementary Education and Teaching, B
English Language and Literature, B
English/Language Arts Teacher Education, B
Foreign Language Teacher Education, B
French Language and Literature, B
French Language Teacher Education, B
History, B
Information Science/Studies, B
International Relations and Affairs, B
Labor and Industrial Relations, B
Management Information Systems and Services, B
Management Science, B
Marketing/Marketing Management, B
Mathematics, B
Mathematics Teacher Education, B
Nursing, B
Peace Studies and Conflict Resolution, B
Philosophy, B
Physician Assistant, B
Physics, B
Physics Teacher Education, B
Political Science and Government, B
Pre-Dentistry Studies, B
Pre-Law Studies, B
Pre-Medicine/Pre-Medical Studies, B
Pre-Pharmacy Studies, B
Pre-Veterinary Studies, B
Psychology, B
Religion/Religious Studies, B
Science Teacher Education/General Science
   Teacher Education, B
Secondary Education and Teaching, B
Secondary School Administration/Principalship, B
Social Studies Teacher Education, B
Sociology, B
Spanish Language and Literature, B
Spanish Language Teacher Education, B
Superintendency and Educational System
   Administration, B

LEHMAN COLLEGE OF THE CITY UNIVERSITY OF NEW YORK

Accounting, BM
African-American/Black Studies, B
American/United States Studies/Civilization, B
Anthropology, B
Art History, Criticism and Conservation, B
Art Teacher Education, B
Art/Art Studies, General, B
Audiology/Audiologist and Speech-Language
   Pathology/Pathologist, B
Biochemistry, B
Biological and Biomedical Sciences, M
Biology/Biological Sciences, B
Business Administration and Management, B
Business Education, M

Business Teacher Education, B
Chemistry, B
Classics and Classical
   Languages, Literatures, and Linguistics, B
Communication Disorders, M
Communication, Journalism and Related
   Programs, B
Computer and Information Sciences, B
Computer Science, BM
Counselor Education/School Counseling and
   Guidance Services, M
Creative Writing, B
Dance, B
Dietetics/Dieticians, B
Drama and Dramatics/Theatre Arts, B
Early Childhood Education and Teaching, M
Economics, B
Education, M
Elementary Education and Teaching, M
English, M
English as a Second Language, M
English Education, M
English Language and Literature, B
Fine Arts and Art Studies, M
Foods, Nutrition, and Wellness Studies, B
French Language and Literature, B
Geography, B
Geology/Earth Science, B
Gerontological Nursing, M
Health Education, M
Health Promotion, M
Health Teacher Education, B
Health/Health Care Administration/Management, B
Hebrew Language and Literature, B
History, BM
Interdisciplinary Studies, B
Italian Language and Literature, B
Jewish/Judaic Studies, B
Latin American Studies, B
Latin Language and Literature, B
Linguistics, B
Mass Communication/Media Studies, B
Maternal/Child Health and Neonatal
   Nurse/Nursing, M
Mathematics, BM
Mathematics Teacher Education, M
Modern Greek Language and Literature, B
Multilingual and Multicultural Education, M
Music, B
Music Teacher Education, M
Nursing, M
Nursing - Adult, M
Nursing - Registered Nurse Training, B
Nutritional Sciences, M
Pediatric Nurse/Nursing, M
Philosophy, B
Physics, B
Plant Sciences, D
Political Science and Government, B
Psychology, B
Reading Teacher Education, M
Recreation and Park Management, M
Russian Language and Literature, B
Science Teacher Education/General Science
   Teacher Education, M
Social Studies Teacher Education, M
Social Work, B
Sociology, B
Spanish Language and Literature, BM
Special Education and Teaching, M
Speech and Rhetorical Studies, B
Speech-Language Pathology/Pathologist, B

LONG ISLAND BUSINESS INSTITUTE

Accounting, A
Administrative Assistant and Secretarial Science, A
Business Administration and Management, A

Court Reporting/Court Reporter, A

LONG ISLAND COLLEGE HOSPITAL SCHOOL OF NURSING

Nursing - Registered Nurse Training, A

LONG ISLAND UNIVERSITY, BRENTWOOD CAMPUS

Accounting, B
Business Administration and Management, B
Business Administration, Management and
   Operations, M
Counselor Education/School Counseling and
   Guidance Services, M
Criminal Justice/Safety Studies, B
Criminology, M
Education, M
Educational Administration and Supervision, M
Elementary Education and Teaching, M
Finance, B
Marketing/Marketing Management, B
Reading Teacher Education, M
Special Education and Teaching, M

LONG ISLAND UNIVERSITY, BROOKLYN CAMPUS

Accounting, BM
Art Teacher Education, B
Art/Art Studies, General, B
Athletic Training and Sports Medicine, BM
Bilingual and Multilingual Education, B
Biological and Biomedical Sciences, M
Biology/Biological Sciences, B
Business Administration and Management, AB
Business Administration, Management and
   Operations, M
Chemistry, BM
Chemistry Teacher Education, B
Clinical Laboratory Science/Medical
   Technology/Technologist, B
Clinical Psychology, D
Communication Disorders, M
Communication Disorders Sciences and Services, B
Communication Studies/Speech Communication
   and Rhetoric, B
Community Health and Preventive Medicine, M
Comparative Literature, M
Computer Art and Design, M
Computer Science, BM
Computer Teacher Education, B
Counselor Education/School Counseling and
   Guidance Services, MO
CytoTechnology/Cytotechnologist, B
Dance, B
Economics, BM
Education, BMO
Education/Teaching of Individuals with Speech or
   Language Impairments, B
Educational Leadership and Administration, M
Educational Media/Instructional Technology, M
Elementary Education and Teaching, BM
English, M
English as a Second Language, M
English Education, M
English Language and Literature, B
English/Language Arts Teacher Education, B
Exercise and Sports Science, M
Finance, B
Fine Arts and Art Studies, B
Foreign Languages and Literatures, B
Health Education, M
Health Professions and Related Clinical Sciences, B
Health Services Administration, M
History, BM
Human Resources Management and Services, M
Humanities/Humanistic Studies, B
Interdisciplinary Studies, B
International Affairs, O
Jazz/Jazz Studies, B
Journalism, B
Liberal Arts and Sciences Studies and
   Humanities, AB
Marketing/Marketing Management, B
Mathematics, B
Mathematics Teacher Education, BM

Modern Languages, B
Multi-/Interdisciplinary Studies, B
Multilingual and Multicultural Education, M
Music, B
Music Performance, B
Music Teacher Education, B
Music Theory and Composition, B
Nuclear Medical Technology/Technologist, B
Nursing, BMO
Nursing - Advanced Practice, MO
Nursing - Registered Nurse Training, B
Nursing Administration, M
Occupational Therapy/Therapist, B
Operations Research, B
Pharmaceutical Administration, M
Pharmaceutical Sciences, MD
Pharmacology, M
Pharmacy, B
Philosophy, B
Physical Education Teaching and Coaching, BM
Physical Sciences, B
Physical Therapy/Therapist, BD
Physician Assistant, B
Physics, B
Political Science and Government, BM
Psychology, BMD
Public Administration, M
Public Health (MPH, DPH), B
Reading Teacher Education, M
Respiratory Care Therapy/Therapist, B
School Psychology, M
Secondary Education and Teaching, B
Social Sciences, ABMO
Social Studies Teacher Education, B
Social Work, B
Sociology, B
Spanish Language Teacher Education, B
Special Education and Teaching, M
Speech and Rhetorical Studies, B
Taxation, M
Toxicology, M
Urban Studies/Affairs, M
Writing, M

LONG ISLAND UNIVERSITY, C.W. POST CAMPUS

Accounting, BMO
Acting, B
Allied Health and Medical Assisting Services, MO
American/United States Studies/Civilization, B
Applied Mathematics, BM
Art Education, M
Art History, Criticism and Conservation, B
Art Teacher Education, B
Art Therapy/Therapist, BM
Arts Management, B
Biological and Biomedical Sciences, M
Biology Teacher Education, B
Biology/Biological Sciences, B
Broadcast Journalism, B
Business Administration and Management, B
Business Administration, Management and
   Operations, MO
Cardiovascular Sciences, MO
Chemistry, B
Chemistry Teacher Education, B
Cinematography and Film/Video Production, B
Clinical Laboratory Science/Medical
   Technology/Technologist, B
Clinical Laboratory Sciences, M
Clinical Psychology, D
Clinical/Medical Laboratory Technician, B
Communication Disorders, M
Communication Studies/Speech Communication
   and Rhetoric, B
Computer and Information Sciences, B
Computer and Information Sciences and Support
   Services, B
Computer Art and Design, M
Computer Education, M
Computer Science, BM
Counselor Education/School Counseling and
   Guidance Services, M
Criminal Justice/Safety Studies, B
Criminology, M
CytoTechnology/Cytotechnologist, B

Dance, B
Drama and Dramatics/Theatre Arts, B
Early Childhood Education and Teaching, M
Economics, B
Education, BMO
Educational Administration and Supervision, MO
Educational Media/Instructional Technology, M
Elementary Education and Teaching, BM
Engineering Management, M
English, M
English as a Second Language, M
English Education, B
English Language and Literature, B
English/Language Arts Teacher Education, B
Environmental Policy and Resource
   Management, M
Environmental Sciences, BM
Environmental Studies, BM
Experimental Psychology, MO
Finance, B
Finance and Banking, MO
Fine Arts and Art Studies, BM
Fine/Studio Arts, B
Foreign Language Teacher Education, BM
Foreign Languages and Literatures, B
Forensic Science and Technology, B
French Language and Literature, B
French Language Teacher Education, B
Geography, B
Geology/Earth Science, B
Gerontology, MO
Health Information/Medical Records
   Administration/Administrator, B
Health Professions and Related Clinical Sciences, B
Health Services Administration, MO
Health Teacher Education, B
History, BM
Immunology, M
Information Science/Studies, BMDO
Information Technology, B
Interdisciplinary Studies, BM
Intermedia/Multimedia, B
International Affairs, M
International Business/Trade/Commerce, MO
International Relations and Affairs, B
Internet and Interactive Multimedia, M
Italian Language and Literature, B
Journalism, B
Kindergarten/PreSchool Education and Teaching, B
Liberal Arts and Sciences Studies and
   Humanities, B
Library Science, MDO
Management, MO
Management Information Systems and
   Services, MO
Marketing, MO
Marketing/Marketing Management, B
Mathematics, BM
Mathematics and Computer Science, B
Mathematics Teacher Education, BM
Medical Radiologic Technology/Science - Radiation
   Therapist, B
Medicinal and Pharmaceutical Chemistry, M
Microbiology, M
Middle School Education, M
Multilingual and Multicultural Education, M
Music, BM
Music Performance, B
Music Teacher Education, BM
Non-Profit/Public/Organizational Management, MO
Nuclear Medical Technology/Technologist, B
Nursing, BMO
Nursing - Advanced Practice, MO
Nursing - Registered Nurse Training, B
Nutritional Sciences, MO
Philosophy, B
Photography, B
Physical Education Teaching and Coaching, B
Physics, B
Political Science and Government, BM
Pre-Pharmacy Studies, B
Psychology, BMDO
Public Administration, BMO
Public Relations/Image Management, B
Reading Teacher Education, M

Science Teacher Education/General Science
   Teacher Education, M
Secondary Education and Teaching, BM
Securities Services Administration/Management, M
Social Sciences, M
Social Studies Teacher Education, B
Social Work, B
Sociology, B
Spanish Language and Literature, BM
Spanish Language Teacher Education, B
Special Education and Teaching, M
Taxation, MO
Theater, M
Visual and Performing Arts, B
Voice and Opera, B

LONG ISLAND UNIVERSITY, FRIENDS WORLD PROGRAM

Interdisciplinary Studies, B
Liberal Arts and Sciences Studies and
   Humanities, B
Multi-/Interdisciplinary Studies, B

MACHZIKEI HADATH RABBINICAL COLLEGE

Hebrew Language and Literature, B
Jewish/Judaic Studies, B
Theology and Religious Vocations, O

MANHATTAN COLLEGE

Accounting, B
Biochemistry, B
Biology/Biological Sciences, B
BioTechnology, B
Chemical Engineering, BM
Chemistry, B
Civil Engineering, BM
Classics and Classical
   Languages, Literatures, and Linguistics, B
Computer Engineering, BM
Computer Science, B
Counselor Education/School Counseling and
   Guidance Services, MO
Early Childhood Education and Teaching, O
Economics, B
Education, BMO
Educational Administration and Supervision, MO
Electrical Engineering, M
Electrical, Electronics and Communications
   Engineering, B
Elementary Education and Teaching, B
Engineering, B
Engineering and Applied Sciences, M
English Language and Literature, B
Environmental Engineering
   Technology/Environmental Technology, M
Environmental/Environmental Health Engineering, B
Finance, B
French Language and Literature, B
History, B
International Relations and Affairs, B
Junior High/Intermediate/Middle School Education
   and Teaching, B
Liberal Arts and Sciences Studies and
   Humanities, B
Management Science, B
Marketing/Marketing Management, B
Mathematics, B
Mechanical Engineering, BM
Nuclear Medical Technology/Technologist, B
Organizational Behavior Studies, B
Philosophy, B
Physical Education Teaching and Coaching, B
Physics, B
Political Science and Government, B
Psychology, B
Radiologic Technology/Science - Radiographer, B
Religion/Religious Studies, B
Sociology, B
Spanish Language and Literature, B
Special Education and Teaching, BMO
Teacher Education, Multiple Levels, B

Urban Studies/Affairs, B

MANHATTAN SCHOOL OF MUSIC

Composition, MD
Jazz/Jazz Studies, B
Music, BMDO
Performance, MD
Piano and Organ, B
Violin, Viola, Guitar and Other Stringed
   Instruments, B
Voice and Opera, B
Wind and Percussion Instruments, B

MANHATTANVILLE COLLEGE

American/United States Studies/Civilization, B
Art Education, M
Art History, Criticism and Conservation, B
Art Teacher Education, B
Asian Studies/Civilization, B
Biochemistry, B
Biology Teacher Education, B
Biology/Biological Sciences, B
Business Administration and Management, B
Chemistry, B
Chemistry Teacher Education, B
Classics and Classical
   Languages, Literatures, and Linguistics, B
Computer Science, B
Corporate and Organizational Communication, M
Dance, B
Early Childhood Education and Teaching, M
Economics, B
Education, BM
Educational Leadership and Administration, M
Elementary Education and Teaching, BM
English as a Second Language, M
English Education, M
English Language and Literature, B
English/Language Arts Teacher Education, B
Finance, B
Fine/Studio Arts, B
Foreign Language Teacher Education, M
French Language and Literature, B
French Language Teacher Education, B
German Studies, B
History, B
Human Resources Development, M
Human Resources Management and Services, M
International Relations and Affairs, B
Law and Legal Studies, B
Liberal Studies, M
Management Strategy and Policy, M
Mathematics, B
Mathematics Teacher Education, BM
Middle School Education, M
Music, B
Music Teacher Education, BM
Organizational Management, M
Philosophy, B
Physics, B
Political Science and Government, B
Pre-Medicine/Pre-Medical Studies, B
Psychology, B
Reading Teacher Education, M
Religion/Religious Studies, B
Romance Languages, Literatures, and Linguistics, B
Science Teacher Education/General Science
   Teacher Education, M
Secondary Education and Teaching, BM
Social Studies Teacher Education, BM
Sociology, B
Spanish Language and Literature, B
Spanish Language Teacher Education, B
Special Education and Teaching, M
Writing, M

MANNES COLLEGE THE NEW SCHOOL FOR MUSIC

Composition, MO
Conducting, B
Music, BMO
Music Theory and Composition, BMO
Performance, MO
Piano and Organ, B
Violin, Viola, Guitar and Other Stringed
   Instruments, B

Voice and Opera, B
Wind and Percussion Instruments, B

MARIA COLLEGE

Accounting, A
Business Administration and Management, A
Computer/Information Technology Services
 Administration and Management, A
Kindergarten/PreSchool Education and Teaching, A
Law and Legal Studies, A
Legal Assistant/Paralegal, A
Liberal Arts and Sciences Studies and
 Humanities, A
Licensed Practical/Vocational Nurse Training, A
Nursing - Registered Nurse Training, A
Occupational Therapist Assistant, A
Physical Therapist Assistant, A
Science Technologies/Technicians, A

MARIST COLLEGE

Accounting, B
Advertising, B
American/United States Studies/Civilization, B
Art History, Criticism and Conservation, B
Art/Art Studies, General, B
Athletic Training and Sports Medicine, B
Biochemistry, B
Biology Teacher Education, B
Biology/Biological Sciences, B
Biomedical Sciences, B
Broadcast Journalism, B
Business Administration and Management, B
Business Administration, Management and
 Operations, MO
Chemistry, B
Chemistry Teacher Education, B
Clinical Laboratory Science/Medical
 Technology/Technologist, B
Comparative Literature, B
Computational Mathematics, B
Computer Science, BMO
Corporate and Organizational Communication, M
Counseling Psychology, M
Criminal Justice/Law Enforcement Administration, B
Digital Communication and Media/Multimedia, B
Drama and Dramatics/Theatre Arts, B
Economics, B
Educational Psychology, M
Elementary Education and Teaching, B
English Language and Literature, B
English/Language Arts Teacher Education, B
Environmental Studies, B
Fashion Merchandising, B
Fashion/Apparel Design, B
Fine/Studio Arts, B
French Language and Literature, B
French Language Teacher Education, B
History, B
History Teacher Education, B
Industrial and Manufacturing Management, O
Information Science/Studies, B
Information Technology, B
Journalism, B
Management, O
Management Information Systems and
 Services, MO
Mathematics, B
Mathematics Teacher Education, B
Organizational Communication, B
Philosophy, B
Political Science and Government, B
Psychology, BMO
Public Administration, MO
Public Relations/Image Management, B
Radio and Television, B
School Psychology, MO
Secondary Education and Teaching, B
Social Studies Teacher Education, B
Social Work, B
Software Engineering, M
Spanish Language and Literature, B
Spanish Language Teacher Education, B

Special Education and Teaching, B

MARYMOUNT MANHATTAN COLLEGE

Accounting, B
Acting, B
Art History, Criticism and Conservation, B
Art/Art Studies, General, B
Audiology/Audiologist and Speech-Language
 Pathology/Pathologist, B
Biology/Biological Sciences, B
Business Administration and Management, B
Dance, B
Drama and Dramatics/Theatre Arts, B
English Language and Literature, B
Fine/Studio Arts, B
History, B
International Relations and Affairs, B
Liberal Arts and Sciences Studies and
 Humanities, B
Mass Communication/Media Studies, B
Political Science and Government, B
Psychology, B
Social Sciences, A
Sociology, B
Theatre Literature, History and Criticism, B

MEDAILLE COLLEGE

Accounting, B
Art/Art Studies, General, B
Biology/Biological Sciences, B
Business Administration and Management, AB
Business Administration, Management and
 Operations, M
Computer and Information Sciences, B
Computer Programming/Programmer, B
Counseling Psychology, M
Creative Writing, B
Criminal Justice/Safety Studies, B
Curriculum and Instruction, M
Education, BM
Elementary Education and Teaching, BM
English Language and Literature, B
Financial Planning and Services, B
Human Resources Management/Personnel
 Administration, B
Human Services, B
Junior High/Intermediate/Middle School Education
 and Teaching, B
Kindergarten/PreSchool Education and Teaching, B
Liberal Arts and Sciences Studies and
 Humanities, AB
Marketing/Marketing Management, B
Mass Communication/Media Studies, B
Organizational Management, B
Physiological Psychology/Psychobiology, B
Pre-Law Studies, B
Psychology, BM
Reading Teacher Education, M
Social Sciences, B
Sport and Fitness Administration/Management, B
Technical and Business Writing, B
Veterinary/Animal Health Technology/Technician and
 Veterinary Assistant, AB
Web Page, Digital/Multimedia and Information
 Resources Design, B
Youth Services/Administration, B

MEDGAR EVERS COLLEGE OF THE CITY UNIVERSITY OF NEW YORK

Accounting, B
Applied Mathematics, B
Biological and Physical Sciences, A
Biology/Biological Sciences, B
Business Administration and Management, AB
Computer Science, A
Computer/Information Technology Services
 Administration and Management, A
Education, AB
Environmental Studies, B
Information Science/Studies, B
Liberal Arts and Sciences Studies and
 Humanities, A
Licensed Practical/Vocational Nurse Training, A
Natural Sciences, A
Nursing - Registered Nurse Training, B
Pre-Engineering, A

Pre-Medicine/Pre-Medical Studies, B
Psychology, B
Public Administration, AB
Special Education and Teaching, B

MERCY COLLEGE

Accounting, B
Allied Health and Medical Assisting Services, M
Banking and Financial Support Services, A
Behavioral Sciences, B
Biology/Biological Sciences, B
Business Administration and Management, AB
Business/Corporate Communications, B
Business/Managerial Economics, B
Commercial and Advertising Art, AB
Communication Disorders, BM
Communication, Journalism and Related
 Programs, B
Computer Science, B
Computer/Information Technology Services
 Administration and Management, A
Counseling Psychology, MO
Counselor Education/School Counseling and
 Guidance Services, M
Criminal Justice/Law Enforcement Administration, B
Education, MO
Educational Administration and Supervision, MO
Educational Media/Instructional Technology, M
Electronic Commerce, M
Elementary Education and Teaching, B
English, M
English as a Second Language, M
English Language and Literature, B
English/Language Arts Teacher Education, B
Finance and Banking, M
Health Professions and Related Clinical Sciences, B
Health Services Administration, M
History, B
Human Resources Management and Services, M
Human Services, A
Information Science/Studies, B
International Business/Trade/Commerce, M
Junior High/Intermediate/Middle School Education
 and Teaching, B
Kindergarten/PreSchool Education and Teaching, B
Legal Professions and Studies, B
Liberal Arts and Sciences Studies and
 Humanities, A
Management, M
Marketing, B
Marriage and Family Therapy/Counseling, MO
Mathematics, B
Mathematics Teacher Education, B
Music, B
Nursing, M
Nursing - Advanced Practice, M
Nursing - Registered Nurse Training, B
Occupational Therapist Assistant, A
Occupational Therapy/Therapist, M
Organizational Management, M
Physical Therapy/Therapist, M
Physician Assistant, M
Psychology, BM
Public Administration and Social Service
 Professions, B
Reading Teacher Education, M
School Psychology, M
Social Sciences, B
Social Studies Teacher Education, B
Social Work, B
Sociology, B
Spanish Language and Literature, B
Spanish Language Teacher Education, B
Special Education and Teaching, B
Substance Abuse/Addiction Counseling, O
Teaching English as a Second or Foreign
 Language/ESL Language Instructor, B
Therapeutic Recreation/Recreational Therapy, B
Urban Education and Leadership, M

MESIVTA OF EASTERN PARKWAY RABBINICAL SEMINARY

Jewish/Judaic Studies, B
Rabbinical Studies, B
Religion/Religious Studies, B

Religious Education, B

MESIVTA TORAH VODAATH RABBINICAL SEMINARY

Jewish/Judaic Studies, B

METROPOLITAN COLLEGE OF NEW YORK

Business Administration and Management, B
Business/Commerce, A
Corporate and Organizational Communication, M
Electronic Commerce, M
Human Services, AB
Internet and Interactive Multimedia, M
Leisure Studies, M
Management, M
Media Studies, M
Public Administration, M
Sport and Fitness Administration/Management, M
Urban Studies/Affairs, B

MILDRED ELLEY

Administrative Assistant and Secretarial Science, A
Business Administration and Management, A
Information Technology, A
Legal Assistant/Paralegal, A
Medical/Clinical Assistant, A

MOHAWK VALLEY COMMUNITY COLLEGE

Accounting Technology/Technician and
    Bookkeeping, A
Administrative Assistant and Secretarial Science, A
Advertising, A
Airframe Mechanics and Aircraft Maintenance
    Technology/Technician, A
Appliance Installation and Repair
    Technology/Technician, A
Architectural Drafting and Architectural
    CAD/CADD, A
Art/Art Studies, General, A
Avionics Maintenance Technology/Technician, A
Banking and Financial Support Services, A
Building/Property Maintenance and Management, A
Business Administration and Management, A
Business and Personal/Financial Services Marketing
    Operations, A
Carpentry/Carpenter, A
Chemical Technology/Technician, A
Civil Engineering Technology/Technician, A
Commercial and Advertising Art, A
Commercial Photography, A
Communications Systems Installation and Repair
    Technology, A
Community Organization and Advocacy, A
Computer and Information Sciences, A
Computer and Information Sciences and Support
    Services, A
Computer Programming/Programmer, A
Criminal Justice/Law Enforcement Administration, A
Culinary Arts/Chef Training, A
Design and Applied Arts, A
Drafting and Design Technology/Technician, A
Drafting/Design Engineering
    Technologies/Technicians, A
Drama and Dramatics/Theatre Arts, A
Electrical and Electronic Engineering
    Technologies/Technicians, A
Electrical, Electronic and Communications
    Engineering Technology/Technician, A
Electrical/Electronics Maintenance and Repair
    Technology, A
Elementary Education and Teaching, A
Emergency Medical Technology/Technician (EMT
    Paramedic), A
Engineering, A
English Language and Literature, A
Entrepreneurship/Entrepreneurial Studies, A
Food Technology and Processing, A
Foodservice Systems
    Administration/Management, A
Forensic Science and Technology, A
General Office Occupations and Clerical Services, A
General Studies, A
Health and Medical Laboratory Technologies, A

Health Information/Medical Records
    Technology/Technician, A
Heating, Air Conditioning and Refrigeration
    Technology/Technician, A
Heating, Air Conditioning, Ventilation and
    Refrigeration Maintenance
    Technology/Technician, A
Heavy Equipment Maintenance
    Technology/Technician, A
Hotel/Motel Administration/Management, A
Human Services, A
Humanities/Humanistic Studies, A
Industrial Production Technologies/Technicians, A
Liberal Arts and Sciences Studies and
    Humanities, A
Machine Shop Technology/Assistant, A
Management Information Systems and Services, A
Mechanical Drafting and Mechanical Drafting
    CAD/CADD, A
Mechanical Engineering/Mechanical
    Technology/Technician, A
Medical Radiologic Technology/Science - Radiation
    Therapist, A
Medical/Clinical Assistant, A
Mental Health/Rehabilitation, A
Metallurgical Technology/Technician, A
Nursing - Registered Nurse Training, A
Nutritional Sciences, A
Office Management and Supervision, A
Parks, Recreation and Leisure Facilities
    Management, A
Photographic and Film/Video Technology/Technician
    and Assistant, A
Physical Education Teaching and Coaching, A
Public Administration, A
Respiratory Care Therapy/Therapist, A
Restaurant, Culinary, and Catering
    Management/Manager, A
Secondary Education and Teaching, A
Substance Abuse/Addiction Counseling, A
Surgical Technology/Technologist, A
Survey Technology/Surveying, A
Tool and Die Technology/Technician, A

MOLLOY COLLEGE

Accounting, B
Art/Art Studies, General, B
Audiology/Audiologist and Speech-Language
    Pathology/Pathologist, B
Biology Teacher Education, B
Biology/Biological Sciences, B
Business Administration and Management, B
Cardiovascular Technology/Technologist, A
Communication Studies/Speech Communication
    and Rhetoric, B
Computer Science, B
Criminal Justice/Safety Studies, B
Education, B
Elementary Education and Teaching, B
English Language and Literature, B
English/Language Arts Teacher Education, B
Environmental Studies, B
French Language and Literature, B
French Language Teacher Education, B
Health Informatics, O
Health Information/Medical Records
    Technology/Technician, A
History, B
Interdisciplinary Studies, B
Liberal Arts and Sciences Studies and
    Humanities, A
Mathematics, B
Mathematics Teacher Education, B
Music, B
Music Therapy/Therapist, B
Nuclear Medical Technology/Technologist, A
Nursing, MO
Nursing - Adult, O
Nursing - Advanced Practice, O
Nursing - Registered Nurse Training, B
Nursing Administration, O
Nursing Education, O
Peace Studies and Conflict Resolution, B
Pediatric Nurse/Nursing, O
Philosophy, B
Political Science and Government, B

Pre-Dentistry Studies, B
Pre-Law Studies, B
Pre-Medicine/Pre-Medical Studies, B
Pre-Veterinary Studies, B
Psychiatric/Mental Health Nurse/Nursing, O
Psychology, B
Religion/Religious Studies, B
Respiratory Care Therapy/Therapist, A
Secondary Education and Teaching, B
Social Studies Teacher Education, B
Social Work, B
Sociology, B
Spanish Language and Literature, B
Spanish Language Teacher Education, B
Special Education and Teaching, B

MONROE COLLEGE (BRONX)

Accounting, AB
Business Administration and Management, AB
Computer Science, A
Criminal Justice/Law Enforcement
    Administration, AB
Criminal Justice/Police Science, AB
Hospitality Administration/Management, A
Information Science/Studies, AB
Medical Administrative Assistant/Secretary, A

MONROE COLLEGE (NEW ROCHELLE)

Accounting, AB
Business Administration and Management, AB
Computer Science, A
Corrections and Criminal Justice, AB
Hospitality Administration/Management, A
Information Science/Studies, AB
Medical Administrative Assistant/Secretary, A

MONROE COMMUNITY COLLEGE

Accounting, A
Administrative Assistant and Secretarial Science, A
Art/Art Studies, General, A
Automobile/Automotive Mechanics
    Technology/Technician, A
Behavioral Sciences, A
Biological and Physical Sciences, A
Biology Technician/BioTechnology Laboratory
    Technician, A
Biology/Biological Sciences, A
Business Administration and Management, A
Chemical Engineering, A
Chemistry, A
Civil Engineering Technology/Technician, A
Commercial and Advertising Art, A
Computer and Information Sciences, A
Computer Engineering, A
Computer Engineering Technology/Technician, A
Computer Science, A
Construction Engineering Technology/Technician, A
Consumer Merchandising/Retailing Management, A
Corrections, A
Criminal Justice/Law Enforcement Administration, A
Criminal Justice/Police Science, A
Data Processing and Data Processing
    Technology/Technician, A
Dental Hygiene/Hygienist, A
Electrical, Electronic and Communications
    Engineering Technology/Technician, A
Engineering Science, A
Environmental Studies, A
Family and Consumer Sciences/Human Sciences, A
Fashion Merchandising, A
Fashion/Apparel Design, A
Fire Science/Firefighting, A
Food Technology and Processing, A
Forestry, A
Graphic and Printing Equipment Operator
    Production, A
Health Information/Medical Records
    Administration/Administrator, A
Heating, Air Conditioning, Ventilation and
    Refrigeration Maintenance
    Technology/Technician, A
History, A
Hotel/Motel Administration/Management, A
Human Services, A
Industrial Radiologic Technology/Technician, A
Industrial Technology/Technician, A

Information Science/Studies, A
Information Technology, A
Instrumentation Technology/Technician, A
Interior Design, A
International Business/Trade/Commerce, A
Landscape Architecture, A
Laser and Optical Technology/Technician, A
Legal Administrative Assistant/Secretary, A
Liberal Arts and Sciences Studies and
   Humanities, A
Management Information Systems and Services, A
Marketing/Marketing Management, A
Mass Communication/Media Studies, A
Mathematics, A
Mechanical Engineering/Mechanical
   Technology/Technician, A
Music, A
Nursing - Registered Nurse Training, A
Parks, Recreation, Leisure and Fitness Studies, A
Physical Education Teaching and Coaching, A
Physics, A
Political Science and Government, A
Pre-Pharmacy Studies, A
Quality Control Technology/Technician, A
Social Sciences, A
Special Products Marketing Operations, A
Telecommunications Technology/Technician, A
Tourism and Travel Services Management, A

MOUNT SAINT MARY COLLEGE

Accounting, B
Biology/Biological Sciences, B
Business Administration and Management, B
Business Administration, Management and
   Operations, M
Chemistry, B
Clinical Laboratory Science/Medical
   Technology/Technologist, B
Clinical/Medical Laboratory Technician, B
Computer and Information Sciences, B
Computer Science, B
Criminal Justice/Safety Studies, B
Early Childhood Education and Teaching, M
Education, BM
Elementary Education and Teaching, BM
English Language and Literature, B
Finance and Banking, M
History, B
Human Services, B
Information Technology, B
Interdisciplinary Studies, B
International Business/Trade/Commerce, B
International Relations and Affairs, B
Liberal Arts and Sciences Studies and
   Humanities, B
Marketing, B
Mass Communication/Media Studies, B
Mathematics, B
Middle School Education, M
Nursing, M
Nursing - Adult, M
Nursing - Advanced Practice, M
Nursing - Registered Nurse Training, B
Physical Therapy/Therapist, B
Political Science and Government, B
Pre-Law Studies, B
Psychology, B
Public Relations/Image Management, B
Reading Teacher Education, M
Secondary Education and Teaching, BM
Social Sciences, B
Social Work, B
Sociology, B
Special Education and Teaching, BM
Speech-Language Pathology/Pathologist, B
Teacher Education, Multiple Levels, B

NASSAU COMMUNITY COLLEGE

Accounting, A
Accounting Technology/Technician and
   Bookkeeping, A
Administrative Assistant and Secretarial Science, A
African-American/Black Studies, A
Art/Art Studies, General, A
Business Administration and Management, A
Civil Engineering Technology/Technician, A

Clinical/Medical Laboratory Technician, A
Commercial and Advertising Art, A
Communication Studies/Speech Communication
   and Rhetoric, A
Computer and Information Sciences, A
Computer Graphics, A
Computer Science, A
Computer Systems Networking and
   Telecommunications, A
Criminal Justice/Law Enforcement Administration, A
Criminal Justice/Safety Studies, A
Dance, A
Data Processing and Data Processing
   Technology/Technician, A
Design and Visual Communications, A
Drama and Dramatics/Theatre Arts, A
Engineering, A
Entrepreneurship/Entrepreneurial Studies, A
Fashion Merchandising, A
Fashion/Apparel Design, A
Funeral Service and Mortuary Science, A
General Studies, A
Hotel/Motel Administration/Management, A
Instrumentation Technology/Technician, A
Insurance, A
Interior Design, A
Kindergarten/PreSchool Education and Teaching, A
Legal Administrative Assistant/Secretary, A
Legal Assistant/Paralegal, A
Liberal Arts and Sciences Studies and
   Humanities, A
Management Information Systems and Services, A
Marketing/Marketing Management, A
Mass Communication/Media Studies, A
Mathematics, A
Medical Administrative Assistant/Secretary, A
Medical Radiologic Technology/Science - Radiation
   Therapist, A
Music Performance, A
Nursing - Registered Nurse Training, A
Photography, A
Physical Therapist Assistant, A
Public Health (MPH, DPH), A
Real Estate, A
Rehabilitation Therapy, A
Respiratory Care Therapy/Therapist, A
Security and Loss Prevention Services, A
Surgical Technology/Technologist, A
Technical Theatre/Theatre Design and
   Technology, A
Transportation and Materials Moving, A
Visual and Performing Arts, A

NAZARETH COLLEGE OF ROCHESTER

Accounting, B
American/United States Studies/Civilization, B
Anthropology, B
Art Education, M
Art History, Criticism and Conservation, B
Art Teacher Education, B
Art Therapy/Therapist, BM
Art/Art Studies, General, B
Audiology/Audiologist and Speech-Language
   Pathology/Pathologist, B
Biochemistry, B
Biology Teacher Education, B
Biology/Biological Sciences, B
Business Administration and Management, B
Business Education, M
Business Teacher Education, B
Ceramic Arts and Ceramics, B
Chemistry, B
Chemistry Teacher Education, B
Commercial and Advertising Art, B
Communication Disorders, M
Communication Studies/Speech Communication
   and Rhetoric, B
Comparative Literature, B
Creative Writing, B
Drama and Dramatics/Theatre Arts, B
Drawing, B
Early Childhood Education and Teaching, M
Economics, B
Education, BM
Educational Media/Instructional Technology, M
Elementary Education and Teaching, BM

English as a Second Language, M
English Language and Literature, B
English/Language Arts Teacher Education, B
Environmental Sciences, B
Environmental Studies, B
Fine/Studio Arts, B
Foreign Language Teacher Education, B
French Language and Literature, B
German Language and Literature, B
Gerontological Nursing, M
Gerontology, B
History, B
History Teacher Education, B
Human Resources Management/Personnel
   Administration, B
Information Science/Studies, B
Information Technology, B
Interdisciplinary Studies, B
International Relations and Affairs, B
Italian Language and Literature, B
Liberal Studies, M
Management, M
Management Information Systems and Services, B
Marketing/Marketing Management, B
Mathematics, B
Mathematics Teacher Education, B
Middle School Education, M
Modern Languages, B
Music, B
Music History, Literature, and Theory, B
Music Teacher Education, BM
Music Therapy/Therapist, B
Nursing, M
Nursing - Registered Nurse Training, B
Peace Studies and Conflict Resolution, B
Philosophy, B
Photography, B
Physical Therapy/Therapist, B
Political Science and Government, B
Pre-Dentistry Studies, B
Pre-Law Studies, B
Pre-Medicine/Pre-Medical Studies, B
Pre-Veterinary Studies, B
Psychology, B
Reading Teacher Education, M
Religion/Religious Studies, B
Science Teacher Education/General Science
   Teacher Education, B
Secondary Education and Teaching, BM
Social Sciences, B
Social Studies Teacher Education, B
Social Work, BM
Sociology, B
Spanish Language and Literature, B
Special Education and Teaching, B
Women's Studies, B

THE NEW SCHOOL FOR GENERAL STUDIES

Liberal Arts and Sciences Studies and
   Humanities, B

THE NEW SCHOOL FOR JAZZ AND CONTEMPORARY MUSIC

Jazz/Jazz Studies, B

NEW YORK CAREER INSTITUTE

Court Reporting/Court Reporter, A
Legal Assistant/Paralegal, A

NEW YORK CITY COLLEGE OF TECHNOLOGY OF THE CITY UNIVERSITY OF NEW YORK

Accounting, A
Architectural Drafting and Architectural
   CAD/CADD, A
Chemical Technology/Technician, A
Civil Engineering Technology/Technician, A
Commercial and Advertising Art, AB
Computer Science, A
Construction Engineering Technology/Technician, A
Data Processing and Data Processing
   Technology/Technician, A
Dental Hygiene/Hygienist, A
Dental Laboratory Technology/Technician, A

Drafting and Design Technology/Technician, A
Electrical, Electronic and Communications
  Engineering Technology/Technician, A
Electromechanical Technology/Electromechanical
  Engineering Technology, AB
Fashion Merchandising, A
Heating, Air Conditioning, Ventilation and
  Refrigeration Maintenance
  Technology/Technician, A
Hospitality Administration/Management, AB
Human Services, AB
Information Science/Studies, A
Legal Assistant/Paralegal, AB
Liberal Arts and Sciences Studies and
  Humanities, A
Marketing/Marketing Management, A
Mechanical Engineering/Mechanical
  Technology/Technician, A
Medical Radiologic Technology/Science - Radiation
  Therapist, A
Nursing - Registered Nurse Training, A
Ophthalmic Laboratory Technology/Technician, A
Technical Teacher Education, B
Technical Theatre/Theatre Design and
  Technology, B
Telecommunications Technology/Technician, AB
Trade and Industrial Teacher Education, B

NEW YORK COLLEGE OF HEALTH PROFESSIONS

Acupuncture and Oriental Medicine, M
Health Services/Allied Health/Health Sciences, AB
Massage Therapy/Therapeutic Massage, AB

NEW YORK INSTITUTE OF TECHNOLOGY

Accounting, BMO
Accounting Technology/Technician and
  Bookkeeping, A
Administrative Assistant and Secretarial Science, A
Advertising, B
Aeronautical/Aerospace Engineering
  Technology/Technician, B
Architecture, ABM
Architecture and Related Services, B
Art Teacher Education, B
Biology Teacher Education, B
Biology/Biological Sciences, B
Biomedical Technology/Technician, B
Business Administration and Management, AB
Business Administration, Management and
  Operations, MO
Business Teacher Education, B
Chemistry, B
Chemistry Teacher Education, B
Commercial and Advertising Art, B
Communication and Media Studies, M
Community Psychology, B
Computer and Information Sciences, B
Computer Engineering, M
Computer Science, M
Counseling Psychology, M
Counselor Education/School Counseling and
  Guidance Services, M
Criminal Justice/Law Enforcement Administration, B
Culinary Arts and Related Services, A
Data Processing and Data Processing
  Technology/Technician, A
Design and Applied Arts, B
Distance Education Development, O
Economics, BM
Education, BMO
Educational Leadership and Administration, O
Educational Media/Instructional Technology, MO
Electrical and Electronic Engineering
  Technologies/Technicians, AB
Electrical Engineering, M
Electrical, Electronic and Communications
  Engineering Technology/Technician, B
Electrical, Electronics and Communications
  Engineering, B
Electronic Commerce, M
Elementary Education and Teaching, BMO
Energy and Power Engineering, O
Energy Management and Policy, MO
Engineering and Applied Sciences, MO

English Language and Literature, B
English/Language Arts Teacher Education, B
Environmental Control Technologies/Technicians, B
Environmental Engineering
  Technology/Environmental Technology, ABM
Environmental Policy and Resource
  Management, O
Finance, B
Finance and Banking, MO
Fine/Studio Arts, B
Health Occupations Teacher Education, B
Health Services Administration, M
Hotel/Motel Administration/Management, B
Human Development, M
Human Resources Management and Services, MO
Human Resources Management/Personnel
  Administration, B
Industrial and Labor Relations, MO
Industrial Engineering, B
Information Science/Studies, B
Interior Design, B
International Business/Trade/Commerce, BMO
Management, M
Management Information Systems and
  Services, BMO
Management of Technology, M
Management Strategy and Policy, M
Marketing, MO
Marketing/Marketing Management, B
Mathematics Teacher Education, B
Mechanical Engineering, B
Mechanical Engineering Related
  Technologies/Technicians, B
Mechanical Engineering/Mechanical
  Technology/Technician, AB
Multi-/Interdisciplinary Studies, B
Nursing, B
Nursing - Registered Nurse Training, B
Nutritional Sciences, BMO
Occupational Therapy/Therapist, BM
Osteopathic Medicine, PO
Physical Therapy/Therapist, BMD
Physician Assistant, B
Physics, B
Physics Teacher Education, B
Political Science and Government, B
Pre-Medicine/Pre-Medical Studies, B
Project Management, M
Psychology, B
Radio and Television, B
Radio and Television Broadcasting
  Technology/Technician, B
Sales and Marketing Operations/Marketing and
  Distribution Teacher Education, B
Social Sciences, B
Social Studies Teacher Education, B
Sociology, B
Technical and Business Writing, B
Technical Teacher Education, AB
Technology Teacher Education/Industrial Arts
  Teacher Education, B
Telecommunications Technology/Technician, B
Trade and Industrial Teacher Education, B
Urban Design, M

NEW YORK SCHOOL OF INTERIOR DESIGN

Interior Design, ABM

NEW YORK UNIVERSITY

Accounting, BD
Actuarial Science, B
African Studies, M
African-American/Black Studies, B
Allopathic Medicine, PO
American/United States Studies/Civilization, MD
Anthropology, BMDO
Applied Arts and Design, M
Applied Economics, O
Archeology, BMDO
Area, Ethnic, Cultural, and Gender Studies, B
Art Education, MD
Art History, Criticism and Conservation, BMDO
Art Therapy/Therapist, M
Art/Art Studies, General, B
Arts Management, M

Biochemistry, BMDO
Biological and Biomedical Sciences, MDO
Biology Teacher Education, B
Biology/Biological Sciences, B
Business Administration and Management, B
Business Administration, Management and
  Operations, MDO
Business Education, MO
Business, Management, Marketing, and Related
  Support Services, B
Business/Managerial Economics, B
Cancer Biology/Oncology, DO
Cell Biology and Anatomy, MDO
Chemistry, BMD
Chemistry Teacher Education, B
Cinematography and Film/Video Production, B
City/Urban, Community and Regional Planning, B
Classics and Classical
  Languages, Literatures, and Linguistics, BMDO
Clinical Psychology, D
Clinical Research, M
Cognitive Sciences, D
Communication and Media Studies, MDO
Communication Disorders, MD
Communication Studies/Speech Communication
  and Rhetoric, B
Community Health and Preventive Medicine, MD
Community Psychology, D
Comparative Literature, BMD
Composition, MD
Computational Biology, D
Computer and Information Sciences, B
Computer Art and Design, M
Computer Programming/Programmer, A
Computer Science, BMD
Construction Engineering and Management, MO
Counseling Psychology, D
Counselor Education/School Counseling and
  Guidance Services, MDO
Dance, BMD
Dental and Oral Surgery, O
Dental Hygiene/Hygienist, AB
Dentistry, P
Design and Applied Arts, M
Developmental Psychology, D
Diagnostic Medical Sonography/Sonographer and
  Ultrasound Technician, A
Digital Communication and Media/Multimedia, B
Distance Education Development, M
Drama and Dramatics/Theatre Arts, B
Drama Therapy, M
Early Childhood Education and Teaching, MDO
East Asian Studies, B
Economics, BMDO
Education, BMDO
Education/Teaching of Individuals with Speech or
  Language Impairments, B
Educational Administration and Supervision, M
Educational Leadership and Administration, MDO
Educational Media/Instructional Technology, MDO
Educational Psychology, MDO
Elementary Education and Teaching, BMDO
Engineering, B
English, MD
English as a Second Language, MDO
English Education, MDO
English Language and Literature, B
English/Language Arts Teacher Education, B
Environmental and Occupational Health, MD
Environmental Education, M
Ethnomusicology, MD
European Studies/Civilization, B
Film, Television, and Video Production, M
Film, Television, and Video Theory and
  Criticism, MD
Film/Cinema Studies, B
Finance, B
Finance and Banking, D
Fine Arts and Art Studies, MDO
Fine/Studio Arts, B
Food Services Management, MD
Foods, Nutrition, and Wellness Studies, B
Foreign Language Teacher Education, BMO
Foundations and Philosophy of Education, MD
French Language and Literature, BMDO
French Language Teacher Education, B

General Studies, A
German Language and Literature, BMD
Gerontological Nursing, MO
Graphic Communications, B
Health Education, D
Health Informatics, MO
Health Information/Medical Records
  Technology/Technician, A
Health Services Administration, MO
Health/Health Care Administration/Management, AB
Hebrew Language and Literature, B
Higher Education/Higher Education
  Administration, MD
Historic Preservation and Conservation, O
History, BMDO
Hospitality Administration/Management, BMO
Hotel/Motel Administration/Management, B
Human Resources Development, M
Human Resources Management and Services, M
Human Services, A
Humanities/Humanistic Studies, BMO
Immunology, DO
Industrial and Organizational Psychology, MD
Information Science/Studies, B
Interdisciplinary Studies, BM
International Affairs, M
International and Comparative Education, MDO
International Business/Trade/Commerce, BM
International Public Health/International Health, M
International Relations and Affairs, B
Internet and Interactive Multimedia, M
Italian Language and Literature, BMD
Jewish/Judaic Studies, BMD
Journalism, BMO
Junior High/Intermediate/Middle School Education
  and Teaching, B
Kindergarten/PreSchool Education and Teaching, B
Kinesiology and Movement Studies, M
Latin American Studies, BMO
Latin Language and Literature, B
Law and Legal Studies, MDPO
Legal and Justice Studies, MDO
Liberal Arts and Sciences Studies and
  Humanities, AB
Linguistics, BMD
Management, MDO
Management Information Systems and
  Services, BMO
Management of Technology, MDO
Management Strategy and Policy, D
Marketing, MD
Marketing/Marketing Management, B
Mass Communication/Media Studies, B
Mathematical and Computational Finance, M
Mathematics, BMD
Mathematics and Statistics, B
Mathematics Teacher Education, BMD
Media Studies, MDO
Medieval and Renaissance Studies, B
Microbiology, MDO
Modern Greek Language and Literature, B
Molecular Biology, DO
Multilingual and Multicultural Education, MDO
Museology/Museum Studies, MO
Music, BMDO
Music Management and Merchandising, B
Music Performance, B
Music Teacher Education, BMDO
Music Theory and Composition, BMD
Music Therapy/Therapist, MD
Near and Middle Eastern Studies, BMD
Neuroscience, BDO
Non-Profit/Public/Organizational Management, MO
Nurse Midwife/Nursing Midwifery, MO
Nursing, MDO
Nursing - Adult, MO
Nursing - Advanced Practice, MO
Nursing - Registered Nurse Training, B
Nursing Education, M
Nutritional Sciences, MD
Occupational Therapy/Therapist, MD
Operations Research, B
Oral and Dental Sciences, MO
Organizational Behavior Studies, M
Organizational Management, O
Orthodontics, O

Parasitology, MDO
Pathology/Experimental Pathology, MDO
Pediatric Nurse/Nursing, MO
Pedodontics, O
Performance, MDO
Periodontics, O
Pharmacology, MDO
Philosophy, BMDO
Photography, B
Physical Therapist Assistant, A
Physical Therapy/Therapist, MD
Physics, BMD
Physics Teacher Education, B
Physiology, MDO
Piano and Organ, B
Playwriting and Screenwriting, B
Political Science and Government, BMDO
Portuguese Language and Literature, BMD
Pre-Dentistry Studies, B
Pre-Medicine/Pre-Medical Studies, B
Psychiatric/Mental Health Nurse/Nursing, MO
Psychoanalysis and Psychotherapy, O
Psychology, BMDO
Public Administration, MDO
Public Health, MD
Public History, O
Publishing, M
Radio and Television, B
Reading Teacher Education, M
Real Estate, BMO
Religion/Religious Studies, BMDO
Romance
  Languages, Literatures, and Linguistics, BM
Russian Language and Literature, BM
School Psychology, D
Science Teacher Education/General Science
  Teacher Education, M
Secondary Education and Teaching, B
Slavic Languages, Literatures, and Linguistics, M
Social Psychology, D
Social Sciences, B
Social Studies Teacher Education, BMD
Social Work, BMDO
Sociology, BMDO
Spanish Language and Literature, BMD
Special Education and Teaching, BMO
Speech and Rhetorical Studies, MO
Sport and Fitness
  Administration/Management, BMO
Statistics, BD
Structural Biology, D
Student Personnel Services, M
Taxation, O
Theater, MDO
Theatre Literature, History and Criticism, B
Tourism and Travel Services Management, B
Travel and Tourism, MO
Urban Planning, MO
Urban Studies/Affairs, B
Voice and Opera, B
Western European Studies, M
Writing, M

NIAGARA COUNTY COMMUNITY COLLEGE

Accounting, A
Administrative Assistant and Secretarial Science, A
Animal Sciences, A
Biological and Physical Sciences, A
Business Administration and Management, A
Chemical Technology/Technician, A
Computer Science, A
Consumer Merchandising/Retailing Management, A
Criminal Justice/Law Enforcement Administration, A
Culinary Arts/Chef Training, A
Design and Applied Arts, A
Drafting and Design Technology/Technician, A
Drafting/Design Engineering
  Technologies/Technicians, A
Drama and Dramatics/Theatre Arts, A
Electrical, Electronic and Communications
  Engineering Technology/Technician, A
Electroneurodiagnostic/Electroencephalographic
  Technology/Technologist, A
Fine/Studio Arts, A
General Studies, A

Hospitality Administration/Management, A
Human Services, A
Humanities/Humanistic Studies, A
Information Science/Studies, A
Liberal Arts and Sciences Studies and
  Humanities, A
Mass Communication/Media Studies, A
Mathematics, A
Medical/Clinical Assistant, A
Music, A
Natural Resources and Conservation, A
Nursing - Registered Nurse Training, A
Occupational Health and Industrial Hygiene, A
Physical Education Teaching and Coaching, A
Physical Therapist Assistant, A
Radiologic Technology/Science - Radiographer, A
Social Sciences, A
Surgical Technology/Technologist, A
Web Page, Digital/Multimedia and Information
  Resources Design, A

NIAGARA UNIVERSITY

Accounting, B
Biochemistry, B
Biology Teacher Education, B
Biology Technician/BioTechnology Laboratory
  Technician, B
Biology/Biological Sciences, B
Business Administration and Management, AB
Business Administration, Management and
  Operations, M
Business Teacher Education, B
Business/Commerce, B
Business/Managerial Economics, B
Chemistry, B
Chemistry Teacher Education, B
Computer Science, B
Counselor Education/School Counseling and
  Guidance Services, MO
Criminal Justice/Law Enforcement Administration, B
Criminology, BM
Drama and Dramatics/Theatre Arts, B
Economics, B
Education, BMO
Educational Administration and Supervision, MO
Elementary Education and Teaching, BM
English Language and Literature, B
Foundations and Philosophy of Education, M
French Language and Literature, B
French Language Teacher Education, B
History, B
Hospitality Administration/Management, B
Hotel/Motel Administration/Management, B
Human Resources Management and Services, B
Human Resources Management/Personnel
  Administration, B
Information Science/Studies, B
International Business/Trade/Commerce, B
International Relations and Affairs, B
Liberal Arts and Sciences Studies and
  Humanities, AB
Logistics and Materials Management, B
Marketing/Marketing Management, B
Mass Communication/Media Studies, B
Mathematics, B
Mathematics Teacher Education, B
Philosophy, B
Political Science and Government, B
Pre-Dentistry Studies, B
Pre-Engineering, A
Pre-Law Studies, B
Pre-Medicine/Pre-Medical Studies, B
Pre-Veterinary Studies, B
Psychology, B
Reading Teacher Education, M
Religion/Religious Studies, B
Restaurant/Food Services Management, B
School Psychology, M
Science Teacher Education/General Science
  Teacher Education, B
Secondary Education and Teaching, BM
Social Sciences, B
Social Studies Teacher Education, B
Social Work, B
Sociology, B
Spanish Language and Literature, B

Spanish Language Teacher Education, B
Special Education and Teaching, BM
Tourism and Travel Services Management, B
Transportation and Materials Moving, B

NORTH COUNTRY COMMUNITY COLLEGE

Biological and Physical Sciences, A
Business Administration and Management, A
Computer Graphics, A
Consumer Merchandising/Retailing Management, A
Criminal Justice/Safety Studies, A
General Office Occupations and Clerical Services, A
Interdisciplinary Studies, A
Kinesiology and Exercise Science, A
Liberal Arts and Sciences Studies and
   Humanities, A
Mathematics, A
Medical Radiologic Technology/Science - Radiation
   Therapist, A
Mental Health/Rehabilitation, A
Nursing - Registered Nurse Training, A
Parks, Recreation and Leisure Facilities
   Management, A

NYACK COLLEGE

Accounting, BM
Bible/Biblical Studies, B
Business Administration and Management, AB
Business Administration, Management and
   Operations, M
Communication Studies/Speech Communication
   and Rhetoric, B
Computer Science, B
Education, M
Elementary Education and Teaching, B
English Language and Literature, B
General Studies, A
History, B
Interdisciplinary Studies, B
Liberal Arts and Sciences Studies and
   Humanities, AB
Mathematics, B
Missions/Missionary Studies and Missiology, B
Music Teacher Education, B
Music Theory and Composition, B
Pastoral Studies/Counseling, B
Philosophy, B
Piano and Organ, B
Psychology, B
Religion/Religious Studies, B
Religious Education, B
Religious/Sacred Music, B
Secondary Education and Teaching, B
Social Sciences, B
Social Work, B
Teaching English as a Second or Foreign
   Language/ESL Language Instructor, B
Theology/Theological Studies, B
Voice and Opera, B

OHR SOMAYACH/JOSEPH TANENBAUM EDUCATIONAL CENTER

Rabbinical Studies, B

OLEAN BUSINESS INSTITUTE

Accounting, A
Administrative Assistant and Secretarial Science, A
Business Administration and Management, A
Legal Administrative Assistant/Secretary, A
Legal Assistant/Paralegal, A
Medical Administrative Assistant/Secretary, A

ONONDAGA COMMUNITY COLLEGE

Accounting, A
Administrative Assistant and Secretarial Science, A
Architectural Engineering Technology/Technician, A
Art/Art Studies, General, A
Automobile/Automotive Mechanics
   Technology/Technician, A
Biological and Physical Sciences, A
Business Administration and Management, A
Chemical Engineering, A
Commercial and Advertising Art, A
Computer and Information Sciences, A

Computer Engineering, A
Computer Engineering Technology/Technician, A
Computer Programming, Specific Applications, A
Computer Science, A
Computer Systems Networking and
   Telecommunications, A
Computer Typography and Composition Equipment
   Operator, A
Computer/Information Technology Services
   Administration and Management, A
Construction Engineering Technology/Technician, A
Criminal Justice/Law Enforcement Administration, A
Culinary Arts/Chef Training, A
Data Entry/Microcomputer Applications, A
Data Processing and Data Processing
   Technology/Technician, A
Dental Hygiene/Hygienist, A
Drafting and Design Technology/Technician, A
Electrical, Electronic and Communications
   Engineering Technology/Technician, A
Engineering Science, A
Finance, A
Fire Science/Firefighting, A
Health Information/Medical Records
   Administration/Administrator, A
Hotel/Motel Administration/Management, A
Human Services, A
Humanities/Humanistic Studies, A
Information Science/Studies, A
Information Technology, A
Insurance, A
Interior Design, A
Kindergarten/PreSchool Education and Teaching, A
Labor and Industrial Relations, A
Landscape Architecture, A
Liberal Arts and Sciences Studies and
   Humanities, A
Machine Tool Technology/Machinist, A
Management Information Systems and Services, A
Mathematics, A
Mechanical Engineering/Mechanical
   Technology/Technician, A
Music, A
Nursing - Registered Nurse Training, A
Parks, Recreation, Leisure and Fitness Studies, A
Photography, A
Physical Therapy/Therapist, A
Quality Control Technology/Technician, A
Radio and Television, A
Respiratory Care Therapy/Therapist, A
Special Products Marketing Operations, A
System Administration/Administrator, A
Telecommunications Technology/Technician, A
Web Page, Digital/Multimedia and Information
   Resources Design, A
Web/Multimedia Management and Webmaster, A

ORANGE COUNTY COMMUNITY COLLEGE

Accounting, A
Administrative Assistant and Secretarial Science, A
Architectural Engineering Technology/Technician, A
Biological and Physical Sciences, A
Biology/Biological Sciences, A
Business Administration and Management, A
Child Development, A
Clinical/Medical Laboratory Technician, A
Computer and Information Sciences, A
Computer Engineering, A
Computer Engineering Technology/Technician, A
Computer Programming/Programmer, A
Computer Science, A
Construction Engineering Technology/Technician, A
Consumer Merchandising/Retailing Management, A
Criminal Justice/Law Enforcement Administration, A
Criminal Justice/Police Science, A
Data Entry/Microcomputer Applications, A
Data Processing and Data Processing
   Technology/Technician, A
Dental Hygiene/Hygienist, A
Drafting and Design Technology/Technician, A
Electrical, Electronic and Communications
   Engineering Technology/Technician, A
Elementary Education and Teaching, A
Engineering Science, A
Finance, A

Humanities/Humanistic Studies, A
Industrial Radiologic Technology/Technician, A
Information Science/Studies, A
Information Technology, A
Kinesiology and Exercise Science, A
Liberal Arts and Sciences Studies and
   Humanities, A
Marketing/Marketing Management, A
Mental Health/Rehabilitation, A
Nursing - Registered Nurse Training, A
Occupational Therapy/Therapist, A
Parks, Recreation, Leisure and Fitness Studies, A
Physical Therapy/Therapist, A
Real Estate, A
Word Processing, A

PACE UNIVERSITY

Accounting, BM
Advertising, B
Art History, Criticism and Conservation, B
Art/Art Studies, General, B
Biochemistry, B
Biology Teacher Education, B
Biology/Biological Sciences, B
Business Administration and Management, B
Business Administration, Management and
   Operations, MDO
Business Teacher Education, B
Business/Commerce, B
Chemistry, B
Chemistry Teacher Education, B
Child Development, B
Clinical Laboratory Science/Medical
   Technology/Technologist, B
Clinical Psychology, D
Commercial and Advertising Art, A
Communication Disorders, B
Communication Studies/Speech Communication
   and Rhetoric, B
Communication, Journalism and Related
   Programs, B
Community Psychology, MD
Comparative Literature, B
Computer and Information Sciences, B
Computer Science, BMDO
Computer Systems Analysis/Analyst, B
Criminal Justice/Law Enforcement Administration, B
Curriculum and Instruction, M
Data Processing and Data Processing
   Technology/Technician, B
Design and Visual Communications, A
Drama and Dramatics/Theatre Arts, B
Ecology, B
Economics, BM
Education, BMO
Education/Teaching of Individuals with Speech or
   Language Impairments, B
Educational Administration and Supervision, MO
Elementary Education and Teaching, B
English Language and Literature, B
English/Language Arts Teacher Education, B
Entrepreneurship/Entrepreneurial Studies, B
Environmental Studies, B
Finance, B
Finance and Banking, M
Fine/Studio Arts, A
Foreign Languages and Literatures, B
Forensic Science and Technology, BM
French Language and Literature, B
French Language Teacher Education, B
Geology/Earth Science, B
Health Services Administration, M
History, B
History Teacher Education, B
Hotel/Motel Administration/Management, B
Human Resources Management/Personnel
   Administration, B
Information Science/Studies, BMDO
International Business/Trade/Commerce, BM
International Marketing, B
International Relations and Affairs, B
Investment Management, M
Liberal Arts and Sciences Studies and
   Humanities, AB
Management Information Systems and Services, M
Management Science, B

Management Strategy and Policy, M
Marketing, M
Marketing Research, M
Marketing/Marketing Management, B
Mathematics, B
Mathematics Teacher Education, B
Non-Profit/Public/Organizational Management, B
Nursing, MO
Nursing - Registered Nurse Training, B
Philosophy and Religious Studies, B
Physician Assistant, B
Physics, B
Physics Teacher Education, B
Political Science and Government, B
Psychology, BMD
Publishing, M
School Psychology, MD
Science Teacher Education/General Science
   Teacher Education, B
Social Sciences, B
Social Studies Teacher Education, B
Spanish Language and Literature, B
Spanish Language Teacher Education, B
Speech and Rhetorical Studies, B
Speech-Language Pathology/Pathologist, B
Taxation, M
Telecommunications, MO
Women's Studies, B

PARSONS THE NEW SCHOOL FOR DESIGN

Architecture, B
Art Teacher Education, B
Art/Art Studies, General, AB
Commercial and Advertising Art, AB
Drawing, AB
Environmental Design/Architecture, B
Fashion Merchandising, AB
Fashion/Apparel Design, AB
Industrial Design, B
Interior Design, AB
Photography, B
Sculpture, B

PAUL SMITH'S COLLEGE OF ARTS AND SCIENCES

Business Administration and Management, A
Culinary Arts/Chef Training, AB
Ecology, A
Environmental Studies, AB
Forestry, A
Forestry Technology/Technician, A
Hospitality Administration/Management, A
Hotel/Motel Administration/Management, AB
Liberal Arts and Sciences Studies and
   Humanities, A
Natural Resources Management/Development and
   Policy, B
Parks, Recreation and Leisure Facilities
   Management, A
Survey Technology/Surveying, A
Tourism and Travel Services Management, A

PHILLIPS BETH ISRAEL SCHOOL OF NURSING

Health Professions and Related Clinical Sciences, A
Nursing - Registered Nurse Training, A

PLAZA COLLEGE

Accounting, A
Administrative Assistant and Secretarial Science, A
Business Administration and Management, A
Computer Science, A

POLYTECHNIC UNIVERSITY, BROOKLYN CAMPUS

Agricultural/Biological Engineering and
   Bioengineering, B
Bioinformatics, BM
Biomedical Engineering, M
Building/Construction
   Finishing, Management, and Inspection, B
Business Administration, Management and
   Operations, M
Chemical Engineering, MD

Chemistry, BMD
Civil Engineering, BMD
Communication and Media Studies, MO
Computer Engineering, BMO
Computer Science, BMD
Construction Engineering and Management, M
Electrical Engineering, MD
Electrical, Electronics and Communications
   Engineering, B
Engineering Physics, M
Environmental Engineering
   Technology/Environmental Technology, M
Environmental Sciences, M
Financial Engineering, M
History of Science and Technology, M
Humanities/Humanistic Studies, M
Industrial/Management Engineering, M
Journalism, B
Liberal Arts and Sciences Studies and
   Humanities, B
Management, M
Management Information Systems and Services, B
Management of Technology, M
Manufacturing Engineering, M
Materials Sciences, M
Mathematics, BMD
Mechanical Engineering, BMD
Molecular Biochemistry, B
Organizational Behavior Studies, M
Physics, BMD
Polymer/Plastics Engineering, M
Psychology, M
Social Sciences, M
Systems Engineering, M
Telecommunications, M
Telecommunications Management, M
Transportation and Highway Engineering, M
Transportation/Transportation Management, M

PRATT INSTITUTE

Applied Art, B
Applied Arts and Design, MO
Architecture, BM
Art Education, M
Art History, Criticism and Conservation, BMO
Art Teacher Education, B
Art Therapy/Therapist, M
Art/Art Studies, General, B
Arts Management, M
Building/Construction
   Finishing, Management, and Inspection, AB
Ceramic Arts and Ceramics, BM
Cinematography and Film/Video Production, B
Commercial and Advertising Art, AB
Computer Graphics, B
Creative Writing, B
Dance Therapy/Therapist, M
Design and Applied Arts, B
Drawing, AB
Facilities Planning and Management, M
Fashion/Apparel Design, B
Film/Video and Photographic Arts, B
Fine Arts and Art Studies, BMO
Fine/Studio Arts, AB
Graphic Design, ABM
Illustration, AB
Industrial Design, BM
Information Science/Studies, MO
Interior Design, BM
Internet and Interactive Multimedia, M
Jewelry/Metalsmithing, M
Library Science, MO
Metal and Jewelry Arts, B
Painting, ABM
Photography, BM
Printmaking, BM
Sculpture, BM
Special Education and Teaching, M
Urban and Regional Planning, M
Urban Design, M

Urban Planning, M

PURCHASE COLLEGE, STATE UNIVERSITY OF NEW YORK

Anthropology, B
Art History, Criticism and Conservation, BM
Art/Art Studies, General, B
Biology/Biological Sciences, B
Chemistry, B
Cinematography and Film/Video Production, B
Communication Studies/Speech Communication
   and Rhetoric, B
Comparative Literature, B
Composition, M
Creative Writing, B
Dance, BM
Drama and Dramatics/Theatre Arts, B
Economics, B
Environmental Studies, B
Film/Cinema Studies, B
Fine Arts and Art Studies, M
French Language and Literature, B
History, B
Journalism, B
Liberal Arts and Sciences Studies and
   Humanities, B
Mathematics, B
Modern Languages, B
Music, BM
Philosophy, B
Playwriting and Screenwriting, B
Political Science and Government, B
Psychology, B
Sociology, B
Spanish Language and Literature, B
Technical Theatre/Theatre Design and
   Technology, B
Theater, M
Women's Studies, B

QUEENS COLLEGE OF THE CITY UNIVERSITY OF NEW YORK

Accounting, BM
Actuarial Science, B
African Studies, B
American/United States Studies/Civilization, B
Ancient/Classical Greek Language and Literature, B
Anthropology, B
Applied Mathematics, B
Art Education, M
Art History, Criticism and Conservation, BM
Art Teacher Education, B
Art/Art Studies, General, B
Biochemistry, M
Biological and Biomedical Sciences, M
Biology/Biological Sciences, B
Chemistry, BM
Clinical Psychology, M
Communication Disorders, BM
Comparative Literature, B
Computer Science, BM
Counselor Education/School Counseling and
   Guidance Services, M
Dance, B
Drama and Dramatics/Theatre Arts, B
Early Childhood Education and Teaching, M
East Asian Studies, B
Economics, B
Education, MO
Educational Administration and Supervision, O
Elementary Education and Teaching, BMO
English, M
English as a Second Language, M
English Education, MO
English Language and Literature, B
Environmental Biology, B
Environmental Sciences, BM
Environmental Studies, B
Exercise and Sports Science, M
Family and Consumer Sciences/Home Economics
   Teacher Education, B
Family and Consumer Sciences/Human
   Sciences, BM
Film/Cinema Studies, B
Finance, B

Fine Arts and Art Studies, M
Fine/Studio Arts, B
Foreign Language Teacher Education, MO
French Language and Literature, BM
Geological and Earth Sciences/Geosciences, B
Geology/Earth Science, BM
German Language and Literature, B
Hebrew Language and Literature, B
History, BM
Home Economics Education, M
Information Science/Studies, MO
Interdisciplinary Studies, B
International Business/Trade/Commerce, B
Italian Language and Literature, BM
Jewish/Judaic Studies, B
Kinesiology and Exercise Science, B
Labor and Industrial Relations, B
Latin American Studies, B
Latin Language and Literature, B
Liberal Studies, M
Library Science, MO
Linguistics, BM
Mass Communication/Media Studies, B
Mathematics, BM
Mathematics Teacher Education, MO
Modern Greek Language and Literature, B
Multi-/Interdisciplinary Studies, B
Multilingual and Multicultural Education, M
Music, M
Music Performance, B
Music Teacher Education, BMO
Philosophy, B
Physical Education Teaching and Coaching, B
Physics, BMD
Political Science and Government, B
Psychology, BM
Reading Teacher Education, M
Religion/Religious Studies, B
Romance
   Languages, Literatures, and Linguistics, M
Russian Language and Literature, B
School Psychology, MO
Science Teacher Education/General Science
   Teacher Education, MO
Secondary Education and Teaching, MO
Social Sciences, BM
Social Studies Teacher Education, BMO
Sociology, BM
Spanish Language and Literature, BM
Special Education and Teaching, M
Teaching English as a Second or Foreign
   Language/ESL Language Instructor, B
Urban Studies/Affairs, BM
Women's Studies, B
Writing, M

QUEENSBOROUGH COMMUNITY COLLEGE OF THE CITY UNIVERSITY OF NEW YORK

Accounting, A
Business Administration and Management, A
Business, Management, Marketing, and Related
   Support Services, A
Clinical/Medical Laboratory Technician, A
Communication, Journalism and Related
   Programs, A
Computer Engineering Technology/Technician, A
Electrical, Electronic and Communications
   Engineering Technology/Technician, A
Engineering Science, A
Environmental Design/Architecture, A
Environmental Health, A
Fine/Studio Arts, A
Information Science/Studies, A
Information Technology, A
Laser and Optical Technology/Technician, A
Liberal Arts and Sciences Studies and
   Humanities, A
Mechanical Engineering/Mechanical
   Technology/Technician, A
Musical Instrument Fabrication and Repair, A
Nursing - Registered Nurse Training, A
Public Health (MPH, DPH), A
Telecommunications Technology/Technician, A

Visual and Performing Arts, A

RABBINICAL ACADEMY MESIVTA RABBI CHAIM BERLIN

Ancient Near Eastern and Biblical
   Languages, Literatures, and Linguistics, B
Bible/Biblical Studies, B
Rabbinical Studies, B
Theology and Religious Vocations, O
Theology/Theological Studies, B

RABBINICAL COLLEGE BOBOVER YESHIVA B'NEI ZION

Theology/Theological Studies, B

RABBINICAL SEMINARY OF AMERICA

Rabbinical Studies, B
Theology/Theological Studies, B

RENSSELAER POLYTECHNIC INSTITUTE

Aerospace, Aeronautical and Astronautical
   Engineering, BMDO
Air Force JROTC/ROTC, B
Analytical Chemistry, MD
Applied Mathematics, BM
Applied Physics, MD
Applied Science and Technology, M
Architecture, BMD
Architecture and Related Services, B
Army JROTC/ROTC, B
Astrophysics, MD
Biochemistry, BMD
Bioinformatics, B
Biological and Biomedical Sciences, BMD
Biological and Physical Sciences, B
Biology/Biological Sciences, B
Biomedical Engineering, MD
Biomedical/Medical Engineering, B
Biophysics, BMD
Building Science, M
Building/Construction
   Finishing, Management, and Inspection, B
Business Administration and Management, B
Business Administration, Management and
   Operations, MDO
Cell Biology and Anatomy, MD
Ceramic Sciences and Engineering, MD
Chemical Engineering, BMD
Chemistry, BMD
Civil Engineering, BMDO
Cognitive Sciences, D
Communication and Media Studies, MD
Communication Studies/Speech Communication
   and Rhetoric, B
Computer and Information Sciences, B
Computer Art and Design, M
Computer Engineering, BMDO
Computer Science, BMD
Developmental Biology and Embryology, MD
Economics, BM
Electrical Engineering, MDO
Electrical, Electronics and Communications
   Engineering, B
Electronic Commerce, MD
Energy and Power Engineering, MDO
Engineering, B
Engineering and Applied Sciences, MDO
Engineering Management, MDO
Engineering Physics, BMD
Engineering Science, B
Entrepreneurship/Entrepreneurial Studies, M
Environmental Engineering
   Technology/Environmental Technology, MD
Environmental Policy and Resource
   Management, MD
Environmental Sciences, MD
Environmental/Environmental Health Engineering, B
Finance, B
Finance and Banking, M
Fine Arts and Art Studies, M
Geochemistry, MD
Geology/Earth Science, BMD
Geophysics and Seismology, MD
Geosciences, MD

Geotechnical Engineering, MD
Historic Preservation and Conservation, M
History of Science and Technology, MD
Hydrology and Water Resources Science, B
Industrial and Manufacturing Management, M
Industrial Engineering, B
Industrial/Management Engineering, MO
Information Science/Studies, M
Information Technology, B
Inorganic Chemistry, MD
Interdisciplinary Studies, B
Management Information Systems and
   Services, BM
Management of Technology, MD
Manufacturing Engineering, BMO
Marketing, M
Marketing/Marketing Management, B
Materials Engineering, BMDO
Materials Sciences, MDO
Mathematics, BMD
Mechanical Engineering, BMDO
Mechanics, MD
Metallurgy, MD
Microbiology, MD
Molecular Biology, MD
Navy/Marine Corps JROTC/ROTC, B
Nuclear Engineering, BMD
Operations Research, MO
Organic Chemistry, MD
Philosophy, B
Physical Chemistry, MD
Physics, MD
Polymer/Plastics Engineering, MD
Pre-Law Studies, B
Pre-Medicine/Pre-Medical Studies, B
Psychology, B
Rhetoric, MD
Science, Technology and Society, B
Social Sciences, B
Speech and Interpersonal Communication, MD
Statistics, MO
Structural Engineering, MD
Systems Engineering, BMDO
Technical Communication, M
Technology and Public Policy, MD
Transportation and Highway Engineering, MD
Visual and Performing Arts, B

ROBERTS WESLEYAN COLLEGE

Accounting, B
Art Teacher Education, B
Art/Art Studies, General, B
Biochemistry, B
Biological and Physical Sciences, B
Biology Teacher Education, B
Biology/Biological Sciences, B
Business Administration and Management, B
Chemistry, B
Chemistry Teacher Education, B
Child and Family Studies, M
Clinical Laboratory Science/Medical
   Technology/Technologist, B
Communication Studies/Speech Communication
   and Rhetoric, B
Computer and Information Sciences and Support
   Services, B
Computer Science, B
Criminal Justice/Law Enforcement Administration, B
Divinity/Ministry (BD, MDiv.), B
Education, BMO
Elementary Education and Teaching, B
English Language and Literature, B
English/Language Arts Teacher Education, B
Fine/Studio Arts, B
History, B
Human Resources Management/Personnel
   Administration, B
Human Services, M
Humanities/Humanistic Studies, B
Management, M
Management Information Systems and Services, B
Marketing/Marketing Management, B
Mathematics, B
Mathematics Teacher Education, B
Music, B
Music Teacher Education, B

Natural Sciences, A
Nursing, B
Nursing - Registered Nurse Training, B
Pastoral Studies/Counseling, B
Philosophy, B
Philosophy and Religious Studies, B
Physical Sciences, A
Physics, B
Physics Teacher Education, B
Piano and Organ, B
Pre-Dentistry Studies, B
Pre-Engineering, B
Pre-Law Studies, B
Pre-Medicine/Pre-Medical Studies, B
Pre-Pharmacy Studies, B
Pre-Theology/Pre-Ministerial Studies, B
Pre-Veterinary Studies, B
Psychology, B
Science Teacher Education/General Science
   Teacher Education, B
Secondary Education and Teaching, B
Social Studies Teacher Education, B
Social Work, BM
Sociology, B
Special Education and Teaching, B
Voice and Opera, B

ROCHESTER BUSINESS INSTITUTE

Accounting, A
Business Administration and Management, A
Computer Programming/Programmer, A
Data Processing and Data Processing
   Technology/Technician, A
Management Information Systems and Services, A

ROCHESTER INSTITUTE OF TECHNOLOGY

Accounting, BM
Advertising, B
Aerospace, Aeronautical and Astronautical
   Engineering, B
American Sign Language (ASL), AB
Animation, Interactive Technology, Video Graphics
   and Special Effects, B
Applied Art, AB
Applied Mathematics, ABM
Art Education, M
Art/Art Studies, General, AB
Biochemistry, B
Bioinformatics, BM
Biological and Biomedical Sciences, BM
Biology/Biological Sciences, AB
Biomedical/Medical Engineering, B
Biopsychology, B
BioTechnology, B
Business Administration and Management, AB
Business Administration, Management and
   Operations, M
Ceramic Arts and Ceramics, ABM
Chemistry, ABM
Cinematography and Film/Video Production, AB
Civil Engineering Technology/Technician, B
Clinical Laboratory Science/Medical
   Technology/Technologist, B
Clinical Laboratory Sciences, M
Commercial Photography, B
Communication and Media Studies, BM
Computer and Information Sciences, B
Computer and Information Systems Security, B
Computer Art and Design, M
Computer Engineering, BM
Computer Engineering Technology/Technician, B
Computer Graphics, B
Computer Science, ABM
Computer Software Engineering, B
Computer Systems Analysis/Analyst, B
Computer Systems Networking and
   Telecommunications, B
Crafts, M
Crafts/Craft Design, Folk Art and Artisanry, B
Criminal Justice/Law Enforcement Administration, B
Criminal Justice/Safety Studies, B
Data Modeling/Warehousing and Database
   Administration, B
Design and Visual Communications, B

Diagnostic Medical Sonography/Sonographer and
   Ultrasound Technician, B
Dietetics/Dieticians, AB
Economics, B
Educational Media/Instructional Technology, M
Electrical Engineering, M
Electrical, Electronic and Communications
   Engineering Technology/Technician, AB
Electrical, Electronics and Communications
   Engineering, B
Electromechanical Technology/Electromechanical
   Engineering Technology, B
Engineering, B
Engineering and Applied Sciences, MDO
Engineering Design, M
Engineering Management, M
Engineering Science, A
Engineering Technology, B
Engineering-Related Technologies, B
Environmental Policy and Resource
   Management, M
Environmental Sciences, BM
Film, Television, and Video Production, M
Finance, B
Finance and Banking, M
Fine Arts and Art Studies, M
Fine/Studio Arts, AB
Food Services Management, M
Foodservice Systems
   Administration/Management, B
Furniture Design and Manufacturing, AB
General Studies, AB
Gerontology, O
Graphic Communications, B
Graphic Design, ABM
Hazardous Materials Management and Waste
   Technology/Technician, B
Health Services Administration, MO
Hospitality Administration/Management, BM
Hospitality and Recreation Marketing Operations, B
Hotel/Motel Administration/Management, AB
Human Nutrition, B
Human Resources Development, MO
Illustration, B
Industrial and Manufacturing Management, M
Industrial Design, ABM
Industrial Engineering, B
Industrial Safety Technology/Technician, B
Industrial/Management Engineering, M
Information Science/Studies, M
Information Technology, B
Interdisciplinary Studies, BM
Interior Design, AB
International Business/Trade/Commerce, BM
International Relations and Affairs, B
Internet and Interactive Multimedia, O
Jewelry/Metalsmithing, M
Management Information Systems and Services, B
Manufacturing Engineering, M
Manufacturing Technology/Technician, B
Marketing/Marketing Management, B
Materials Engineering, M
Materials Sciences, M
Mathematics, B
Mathematics and Computer Science, B
Mechanical Engineering, BM
Mechanical Engineering/Mechanical
   Technology/Technician, AB
Media Studies, M
Medical Illustration and Informatics, M
Medical Illustration/Medical Illustrator, B
Metal and Jewelry Arts, AB
Natural Resources Management/Development and
   Policy, B
Occupational Safety and Health
   Technology/Technician, B
Ophthalmic Laboratory Technology/Technician, A
Optics/Optical Sciences, MD
Painting, M
Photographic and Film/Video Technology/Technician
   and Assistant, B
Photography, ABM
Photojournalism, B
Physician Assistant, B
Physics, AB
Polymer Chemistry, B

Pre-Dentistry Studies, B
Pre-Law Studies, B
Pre-Medicine/Pre-Medical Studies, B
Pre-Veterinary Studies, B
Printmaking, M
Psychology, B
Public Policy Analysis, BM
Public Relations, Advertising, and Applied
   Communication, B
Public Relations/Image Management, B
Publishing, BM
Resort Management, AB
Restaurant/Food Services Management, AB
School Psychology, MO
Sculpture, B
Secondary Education and Teaching, M
Sign Language Interpretation and Translation, AB
Software Engineering, M
Special Education and Teaching, MO
Special Products Marketing Operations, B
Statistics, BMO
System Administration/Administrator, B
System, Networking, and LAN/WAN
   Management/Manager, B
Systems Engineering, BMD
Technical Communication, O
Technology and Public Policy, M
Telecommunications, M
Telecommunications Technology/Technician, B
Tourism and Travel Services Management, AB
Tourism and Travel Services Marketing
   Operations, B
Travel and Tourism, M
Web Page, Digital/Multimedia and Information
   Resources Design, B
Web/Multimedia Management and Webmaster, B

ROCKLAND COMMUNITY COLLEGE

Accounting, A
Administrative Assistant and Secretarial Science, A
Advertising, A
Applied Art, A
Art/Art Studies, General, A
Automobile/Automotive Mechanics
   Technology/Technician, A
Biological and Physical Sciences, A
Business Administration and Management, A
Commercial and Advertising Art, A
Computer and Information Sciences, A
Computer Graphics, A
Computer Programming, A
Computer Programming, Specific Applications, A
Computer Programming/Programmer, A
Computer Systems Networking and
   Telecommunications, A
Computer/Information Technology Services
   Administration and Management, A
Criminal Justice/Law Enforcement Administration, A
Culinary Arts/Chef Training, A
Data Processing and Data Processing
   Technology/Technician, A
Developmental and Child Psychology, A
Dietetics/Dieticians, A
Drafting and Design Technology/Technician, A
Drama and Dramatics/Theatre Arts, A
Electrical, Electronic and Communications
   Engineering Technology/Technician, A
Emergency Medical Technology/Technician (EMT
   Paramedic), A
Finance, A
Fine/Studio Arts, A
Fire Science/Firefighting, A
Health Information/Medical Records
   Administration/Administrator, A
Hospitality Administration/Management, A
Human Services, A
Liberal Arts and Sciences Studies and
   Humanities, A
Marketing/Marketing Management, A
Mass Communication/Media Studies, A
Mathematics, A
Nursing - Registered Nurse Training, A
Occupational Therapy/Therapist, A
Photography, A
Respiratory Care Therapy/Therapist, A
System Administration/Administrator, A

Tourism and Travel Services Management, A

RUSSELL SAGE COLLEGE

Art Therapy/Therapist, B
Athletic Training and Sports Medicine, B
Biochemistry, B
Biology/Biological Sciences, B
Biopsychology, B
Business Administration and Management, B
Chemistry, B
Corrections and Criminal Justice, B
Drama and Dramatics/Theatre Arts, B
Elementary Education and Teaching, B
Engineering, B
English Language and Literature, B
Forensic Science and Technology, B
History, B
Interdisciplinary Studies, B
International/Global Studies, B
Mass Communication/Media Studies, B
Mathematics, B
Nursing - Registered Nurse Training, B
Nutritional Sciences, B
Occupational Therapy/Therapist, B
Physical Therapy/Therapist, B
Political Science and Government, B
Psychology, B
Sociology, B
Spanish Language and Literature, B

SAGE COLLEGE OF ALBANY

Accounting, B
Biological and Biomedical Sciences, B
Business Administration and Management, AB
Clinical Laboratory Science/Medical
    Technology/Technologist, B
Computer and Information Sciences, AB
Computer Science, A
Criminology, B
Fine/Studio Arts, A
Graphic Design, A
Health and Physical Education, B
Health Professions and Related Clinical Sciences, B
Humanities/Humanistic Studies, A
Information Science/Studies, A
Interior Design, AB
Law and Legal Studies, AB
Liberal Arts and Sciences Studies and
    Humanities, AB
Marketing/Marketing Management, A
Mass Communication/Media Studies, A
Multi-/Interdisciplinary Studies, B
Photography, A
Psychology, B
Social Sciences, A
System Administration/Administrator, AB

ST. BONAVENTURE UNIVERSITY

Accounting, BMO
Art Teacher Education, B
Biochemistry, B
Biology Teacher Education, B
Biology/Biological Sciences, B
Biophysics, B
Business Administration and Management, B
Business Administration, Management and
    Operations, MO
Business/Commerce, B
Business/Managerial Economics, B
Chemistry, B
Chemistry Teacher Education, B
Classics and Classical
    Languages, Literatures, and Linguistics, B
Computer Science, B
Counselor Education/School Counseling and
    Guidance Services, MO
Early Childhood Education and Teaching, B
Education, MO
Educational Leadership and Administration, MO
Elementary Education and Teaching, B
Engineering Physics, B
English, M
English Language and Literature, B
English/Language Arts Teacher Education, B
Environmental Studies, B
Finance, B

Finance and Banking, MO
Foreign Language Teacher Education, B
French Language and Literature, B
French Language Teacher Education, B
German Language Teacher Education, B
History, B
Interdisciplinary Studies, B
International Business/Trade/Commerce, B
Journalism, B
Junior High/Intermediate/Middle School Education
    and Teaching, B
Kindergarten/PreSchool Education and Teaching, B
Management, MO
Management Information Systems and Services, B
Management Science, B
Marketing, MO
Marketing/Marketing Management, B
Mass Communication/Media Studies, B
Mathematics, B
Mathematics Teacher Education, B
Modern Languages, B
Philosophy, B
Physical Education Teaching and Coaching, B
Physical Sciences, B
Physics, B
Physics Teacher Education, B
Political Science and Government, B
Pre-Dentistry Studies, B
Pre-Law Studies, B
Pre-Medicine/Pre-Medical Studies, B
Pre-Veterinary Studies, B
Psychology, B
Reading Teacher Education, M
Religious Education, B
Secondary Education and Teaching, B
Social Sciences, B
Social Studies Teacher Education, B
Sociology, B
Spanish Language and Literature, B
Spanish Language Teacher Education, B
Special Education and Teaching, B
Theology and Religious Vocations, MO
Visual and Performing Arts, B
Women's Studies, B

ST. FRANCIS COLLEGE

Accounting, B
Area Studies, B
Biology Teacher Education, B
Biology/Biological Sciences, B
Biomedical Sciences, B
Business Administration and Management, AB
Business Teacher Education, B
Chemistry, B
Chemistry Teacher Education, B
Clinical Laboratory Science/Medical
    Technology/Technologist, B
Communication Studies/Speech Communication
    and Rhetoric, B
Criminal Justice/Safety Studies, AB
Data Processing and Data Processing
    Technology/Technician, A
Economics, B
Education/Teaching of Individuals with Vision
    Impairments, Including Blindness, B
English Language and Literature, B
English/Language Arts Teacher Education, B
Ethnic, Cultural Minority, and Gender Studies, B
Health Professions and Related Clinical Sciences, B
History, B
Information Technology, B
Liberal Arts and Sciences Studies and
    Humanities, AB
Mathematics, B
Mathematics Teacher Education, B
Medical Radiologic Technology/Science - Radiation
    Therapist, B
Nursing, B
Philosophy, B
Physical Education Teaching and Coaching, B
Physician Assistant, B
Political Science and Government, B
Psychology, B
Religion/Religious Studies, B
Social Studies Teacher Education, B
Sociology, B

Spanish Language and Literature, B

ST. JOHN FISHER COLLEGE

Accounting, B
American/United States Studies/Civilization, B
Anthropology, B
Biochemistry, B
Biology/Biological Sciences, B
Business Administration and Management, B
Business Administration, Management and
    Operations, M
Chemistry, B
Computer Science, B
Counseling Psychology, M
Economics, B
Education, MO
Educational Administration and Supervision, M
Elementary Education and Teaching, BM
English Education, M
English Language and Literature, B
Finance, B
Foreign Language Teacher Education, M
French Language and Literature, B
German Language and Literature, B
Health and Physical Education/Fitness, B
History, B
Human Resources Development, M
Human Resources Management/Personnel
    Administration, B
Human Services, M
International Affairs, M
International Business/Trade/Commerce, B
International Relations and Affairs, B
Italian Language and Literature, B
Management Information Systems and Services, B
Marketing/Marketing Management, B
Mass Communication/Media Studies, B
Mathematics, B
Mathematics Teacher Education, BM
Middle School Education, MO
Multi-/Interdisciplinary Studies, B
Nursing - Advanced Practice, MO
Nursing - Registered Nurse Training, B
Philosophy, B
Physics, B
Political Science and Government, B
Psychology, B
Reading Teacher Education, M
Religion/Religious Studies, B
Science Teacher Education/General Science
    Teacher Education, BM
Social Studies Teacher Education, M
Sociology, B
Spanish Language and Literature, B
Special Education and Teaching, BMO
Technology Teacher Education/Industrial Arts
    Teacher Education, B

ST. JOHN'S UNIVERSITY

Accounting, ABMO
Actuarial Science, BM
African Studies, O
Anthropology, B
Applied Mathematics, M
Area Studies, B
Area, Ethnic, Cultural, and Gender Studies, B
Art Teacher Education, B
Asian Studies/Civilization, BMO
Audiology/Audiologist and Speech-Language
    Pathology/Pathologist, B
Bilingual, Multilingual, and Multicultural Education, B
Biological and Biomedical Sciences, MD
Biology Teacher Education, B
Biology/Biological Sciences, B
Business Administration and Management, B
Business Administration, Management and
    Operations, MO
Business/Managerial Economics, B
Chemistry, BM
Chemistry Teacher Education, B
Clinical Child Psychology, B
Clinical Laboratory Science/Medical
    Technology/Technologist, B
Clinical Psychology, MD
Commercial and Advertising Art, B
Communication Disorders, M

Communication Studies/Speech Communication and Rhetoric, B
Computer and Information Sciences, B
Computer Science, M
Counselor Education/School Counseling and Guidance Services, BMO
Criminal Justice/Law Enforcement Administration, AB
Criminology, BM
Curriculum and Instruction, B
CytoTechnology/Cytotechnologist, B
Data Processing and Data Processing Technology/Technician, A
Divinity/Ministry (BD, MDiv.), B
Early Childhood Education and Teaching, BM
East Asian Studies, BMO
Ecology, B
Economics, B
Education, MDO
Educational Administration and Supervision, MDO
Educational Leadership and Administration, BDO
Elementary Education and Teaching, BM
English, MD
English as a Second Language, M
English Language and Literature, B
English/Language Arts Teacher Education, B
Environmental Studies, B
Experimental Psychology, BM
Finance, B
Finance and Banking, MO
Fine Arts and Art Studies, B
Fine/Studio Arts, B
Foreign Language Teacher Education, B
French Language and Literature, B
French Language Teacher Education, B
Funeral Service and Mortuary Science, B
Graphic Design, B
Health/Health Care Administration/Management, B
Higher Education/Higher Education Administration, O
History, BMD
Hospital and Health Care Facilities Administration/Management, B
Hospitality Administration/Management, B
Hotel/Motel Administration/Management, B
Human Services, B
Illustration, B
Information Science/Studies, BMO
Insurance, BM
International Business/Trade/Commerce, BMO
International Relations and Affairs, B
Italian Language and Literature, B
Journalism, B
Junior High/Intermediate/Middle School Education and Teaching, B
Law and Legal Studies, BMPO
Legal and Justice Studies, M
Legal Assistant/Paralegal, AB
Liberal Arts and Sciences Studies and Humanities, AB
Library Science, BMO
Logistics and Materials Management, B
Management Information Systems and Services, BMO
Marketing, MO
Marketing/Marketing Management, B
Mathematics, BM
Mathematics Teacher Education, B
Medical Technology, M
Multilingual and Multicultural Education, M
Nursing - Registered Nurse Training, B
Pastoral Counseling and Specialized Ministries, B
Pastoral Studies/Counseling, O
Pathology/Pathologist Assistant, B
Pharmaceutical Administration, M
Pharmaceutical Sciences, MD
Pharmacy, BP
Pharmacy, Pharmaceutical Sciences, and Administration, B
Philosophy, B
Philosophy and Religious Studies, B
Photographic and Film/Video Technology/Technician and Assistant, B
Photography, B
Physical Sciences, B
Physician Assistant, B
Physics, B

Physics Teacher Education, B
Political Science and Government, BMO
Psychology, BMD
Public Administration, B
Purchasing, Procurement/Acquisitions and Contracts Management, B
Quantitative Analysis, MO
Reading Teacher Education, BO
Real Estate, B
Rehabilitation Counseling, MO
School Psychology, BMD
Science Teacher Education/General Science Teacher Education, B
Secondary Education and Teaching, BMO
Social Sciences, B
Social Studies Teacher Education, B
Sociology, BM
Spanish Language and Literature, BM
Spanish Language Teacher Education, B
Special Education and Teaching, BM
Speech and Rhetorical Studies, B
Sport and Fitness Administration/Management, B
Statistics, M
Taxation, BMO
Teaching English as a Second or Foreign Language/ESL Language Instructor, B
Telecommunications Technology/Technician, B
Theology and Religious Vocations, MPO
Theology/Theological Studies, B
Theoretical Physics, O
Toxicology, BM
Transportation and Materials Moving, B

ST. JOSEPH'S COLLEGE, NEW YORK

Accounting, B
Biology/Biological Sciences, B
Business Administration and Management, B
Chemistry, B
Child Development, B
Developmental and Child Psychology, B
Education, B
English Language and Literature, B
General Studies, B
Health/Health Care Administration/Management, B
History, B
Human Resources Management/Personnel Administration, B
Human Services, B
Mathematics, B
Mathematics and Computer Science, B
Nursing - Registered Nurse Training, B
Pre-Law Studies, B
Psychology, B
Public Health (MPH, DPH), B
Social Sciences, B
Spanish Language and Literature, B
Speech and Rhetorical Studies, B

ST. JOSEPH'S COLLEGE, SUFFOLK CAMPUS

Accounting, B
Adult and Continuing Education and Teaching, B
Behavioral Sciences, B
Biology/Biological Sciences, B
Business Administration and Management, B
Computer Science, B
Developmental and Child Psychology, B
Early Childhood Education and Teaching, BM
Economics, B
Education, B
Elementary Education and Teaching, B
English Language and Literature, B
Health/Health Care Administration/Management, B
History, B
Human Resources Management/Personnel Administration, B
Kindergarten/PreSchool Education and Teaching, B
Liberal Arts and Sciences Studies and Humanities, B
Mathematics, B
Nursing - Registered Nurse Training, B
Parks, Recreation, Leisure and Fitness Studies, B
Political Science and Government, B
Pre-Dentistry Studies, B
Pre-Law Studies, B
Pre-Medicine/Pre-Medical Studies, B

Pre-Veterinary Studies, B
Psychology, B
Secondary Education and Teaching, B
Social Sciences, B
Sociology, B
Spanish Language and Literature, B
Spanish Language Teacher Education, B
Special Education and Teaching, BM
Speech and Rhetorical Studies, B
Therapeutic Recreation/Recreational Therapy, B

SAINT JOSEPH'S HOSPITAL HEALTH CENTER SCHOOL OF NURSING

Nursing - Registered Nurse Training, A

ST. LAWRENCE UNIVERSITY

African Studies, B
American Literature (United States), B
Anthropology, B
Art History, Criticism and Conservation, B
Art/Art Studies, General, B
Asian Studies/Civilization, B
Biochemistry, B
Biology/Biological Sciences, B
Biophysics, B
Canadian Studies, B
Chemistry, B
Computer Science, B
Counselor Education/School Counseling and Guidance Services, MO
Creative Writing, B
Drama and Dramatics/Theatre Arts, B
Economics, B
Education, MO
Educational Administration and Supervision, MO
English Language and Literature, B
English Literature (British and Commonwealth), B
Environmental Studies, B
Fine/Studio Arts, B
Foreign Languages and Literatures, B
French Language and Literature, B
Geology/Earth Science, B
Geophysics and Seismology, B
German Language and Literature, B
History, B
Human Development, MO
International/Global Studies, B
Mathematics, B
Mathematics and Computer Science, B
Modern Languages, B
Music, B
Neurobiology and Neurophysiology, B
Neuroscience, B
Philosophy, B
Physics, B
Political Science and Government, B
Psychology, B
Religion/Religious Studies, B
Sociology, B
Spanish Language and Literature, B

ST. THOMAS AQUINAS COLLEGE

Accounting, B
Applied Mathematics, B
Art Therapy/Therapist, B
Art/Art Studies, General, B
Biology/Biological Sciences, B
Business Administration and Management, B
Business Administration, Management and Operations, M
Clinical Laboratory Science/Medical Technology/Technologist, B
Clinical/Medical Laboratory Technician, B
Commercial and Advertising Art, B
Criminal Justice/Law Enforcement Administration, B
Education, BMO
Elementary Education and Teaching, BM
Engineering Science, B
English Language and Literature, B
Finance, B
Finance and Banking, M
Fine/Studio Arts, B
History, B
Humanities/Humanistic Studies, B
Information Science/Studies, B
Journalism, B

Kindergarten/PreSchool Education and Teaching, B
Management, M
Marketing, M
Marketing/Marketing Management, B
Mass Communication/Media Studies, B
Mathematics, B
Middle School Education, M
Modern Languages, B
Natural Sciences, B
Parks, Recreation, Leisure and Fitness Studies, B
Philosophy, B
Pre-Medicine/Pre-Medical Studies, B
Psychology, B
Reading Teacher Education, MO
Religion/Religious Studies, B
Romance Languages, Literatures, and Linguistics, B
Secondary Education and Teaching, B
Social Sciences, B
Spanish Language and Literature, B
Special Education and Teaching, BMO

SAINT VINCENT CATHOLIC MEDICAL CENTERS SCHOOL OF NURSING

Nursing - Registered Nurse Training, A

SAMARITAN HOSPITAL SCHOOL OF NURSING

Nursing - Registered Nurse Training, A

SARAH LAWRENCE COLLEGE

Acting, B
African Studies, B
African-American/Black Studies, B
American History (United States), B
American Literature (United States), B
American/United States Studies/Civilization, B
Animal Genetics, B
Anthropology, B
Archeology, B
Architectural History and Criticism, B
Art History, Criticism and Conservation, B
Art/Art Studies, General, B
Asian History, B
Asian Studies/Civilization, B
Astronomy, B
Biological and Physical Sciences, B
Biology/Biological Sciences, B
Central/Middle and Eastern European Studies, B
Chemistry, B
Chinese Studies, B
Cinematography and Film/Video Production, B
Classics and Classical
   Languages, Literatures, and Linguistics, B
Comparative Literature, B
Computer Science, B
Creative Writing, B
Dance, BM
Developmental and Child Psychology, B
Directing and Theatrical Production, B
Drama and Dramatics/Theatre Arts, B
Drawing, B
Early Childhood Education and Teaching, B
East Asian Studies, B
Ecology, B
Economics, B
Education, BM
Elementary Education and Teaching, B
English Language and Literature, B
English Literature (British and Commonwealth), B
Environmental Studies, B
European History, B
European Studies/Civilization, B
Film/Cinema Studies, B
Fine/Studio Arts, B
Foreign Languages and Literatures, B
French Language and Literature, B
Gay/Lesbian Studies, B
Genetic Counseling/Counselor, M
Geology/Earth Science, B
German Language and Literature, B
History, BM
History and Philosophy of Science and
   Technology, B
Human Development, M
Human Development and Family Studies, B
Human Genetics, M

Human/Medical Genetics, B
Humanities/Humanistic Studies, B
Interdisciplinary Studies, BM
International Relations and Affairs, B
Italian Language and Literature, B
Japanese Language and Literature, B
Jazz/Jazz Studies, B
Kindergarten/PreSchool Education and Teaching, B
Latin American Studies, B
Latin Language and Literature, B
Liberal Arts and Sciences Studies and
   Humanities, B
Marine Biology and Biological Oceanography, B
Mathematics, B
Middle/Near Eastern and Semitic
   Languages, Literatures, and Linguistics, B
Modern Languages, B
Molecular Biology, B
Music, B
Music History, Literature, and Theory, B
Music Performance, B
Music Theory and Composition, B
Natural Sciences, B
Near and Middle Eastern Studies, B
Organic Chemistry, B
Painting, B
Philosophy, B
Philosophy and Religious Studies, B
Photography, B
Physics, B
Piano and Organ, B
Playwriting and Screenwriting, B
Political Science and Government, B
Pre-Dentistry Studies, B
Pre-Law Studies, B
Pre-Medicine/Pre-Medical Studies, B
Pre-Veterinary Studies, B
Printmaking, B
Psychology, B
Public Health, M
Public Policy Analysis, B
Religion/Religious Studies, B
Romance Languages, Literatures, and Linguistics, B
Russian Language and Literature, B
Sculpture, B
Social Sciences, B
Sociology, B
South Asian Studies, B
Spanish Language and Literature, B
Theater, M
Urban Studies/Affairs, B
Violin, Viola, Guitar and Other Stringed
   Instruments, B
Visual and Performing Arts, B
Voice and Opera, B
Wind and Percussion Instruments, B
Women's Studies, BM
Writing, M

SCHENECTADY COUNTY COMMUNITY COLLEGE

Accounting, A
Administrative Assistant and Secretarial Science, A
Aviation/Airway Management and Operations, A
Biological and Physical Sciences, A
Business Administration and Management, A
Computer and Information Sciences, A
Computer Programming, A
Computer Science, A
Computer/Information Technology Services
   Administration and Management, A
Counseling Psychology, A
Criminal Justice/Law Enforcement Administration, A
Culinary Arts/Chef Training, A
Drama and Dramatics/Theatre Arts, A
Education, A
Electrical, Electronic and Communications
   Engineering Technology/Technician, A
Fire Science/Firefighting, A
Foods, Nutrition, and Related Services, A
Hotel/Motel Administration/Management, A
Human Services, A
Humanities/Humanistic Studies, A
Information Technology, A
Legal Assistant/Paralegal, A

Liberal Arts and Sciences Studies and
   Humanities, A
Mathematics, A
Music, A
Music Management and Merchandising, A
Music Performance, A
Securities Services Administration/Management, A
Telecommunications Technology/Technician, A
Tourism and Travel Services Management, A

SCHOOL OF VISUAL ARTS

Advertising, B
Animation, Interactive Technology, Video Graphics
   and Special Effects, B
Art Education, M
Art Therapy/Therapist, M
Cinematography and Film/Video Production, B
Computer Art and Design, M
Computer Graphics, B
Design and Applied Arts, M
Drawing, B
Fine Arts and Art Studies, M
Fine/Studio Arts, B
Illustration, BM
Interior Design, B
Photography, BM

SH'OR YOSHUV RABBINICAL COLLEGE

Hebrew Language and Literature, B
Jewish/Judaic Studies, B
Rabbinical Studies, B

SIENA COLLEGE

Accounting, B
American/United States Studies/Civilization, B
Biology/Biological Sciences, B
Chemistry, B
Classics and Classical
   Languages, Literatures, and Linguistics, B
Computer and Information Sciences, B
Ecology, B
Economics, B
English Language and Literature, B
Finance, B
Fine/Studio Arts, B
French Language and Literature, B
History, B
Marketing/Marketing Management, B
Mathematics, B
Philosophy, B
Physics, B
Political Science and Government, B
Pre-Dentistry Studies, B
Pre-Law Studies, B
Pre-Medicine/Pre-Medical Studies, B
Psychology, B
Religion/Religious Studies, B
Secondary Education and Teaching, B
Social Work, B
Sociology, B
Spanish Language and Literature, B

SIMMONS INSTITUTE OF FUNERAL SERVICE

Funeral Service and Mortuary Science, A

SKIDMORE COLLEGE

American/United States Studies/Civilization, B
Anthropology, B
Area, Ethnic, Cultural, and Gender Studies, B
Art History, Criticism and Conservation, B
Asian Studies/Civilization, B
Biological and Biomedical Sciences, B
Biology/Biological Sciences, B
Business, Management, Marketing, and Related
   Support Services, B
Business/Commerce, B
Chemistry, B
Classics and Classical
   Languages, Literatures, and Linguistics, B
Computer and Information Sciences, B
Dance, B
Drama and Dramatics/Theatre Arts, B
Economics, B

Elementary Education and Teaching, B
English Language and Literature, B
Environmental Sciences, B
Environmental Studies, B
Fine Arts and Art Studies, B
French Language and Literature, B
Geology/Earth Science, B
German Language and Literature, B
History, B
International Relations and Affairs, B
Kinesiology and Exercise Science, B
Liberal Arts and Sciences Studies and
    Humanities, B
Liberal Studies, M
Mathematics, B
Music History, Literature, and Theory, B
Neuroscience, B
Philosophy, B
Physics, B
Political Science and Government, B
Psychology, B
Religion/Religious Studies, B
Social Sciences, B
Social Work, B
Sociology, B
Spanish Language and Literature, B
Women's Studies, B

STATE UNIVERSITY OF NEW YORK AT BINGHAMTON

Accounting, BMD
African Studies, B
African-American/Black Studies, B
Analytical Chemistry, D
Anthropology, BMD
Applied Physics, M
Arabic Language and Literature, B
Art History, Criticism and Conservation, BMD
Art/Art Studies, General, B
Asian-American Studies, B
Biochemistry, B
Biological and Biomedical Sciences, MD
Biology/Biological Sciences, B
Biomedical/Medical Engineering, B
Biopsychology, MD
Business Administration, Management and
    Operations, MD
Chemistry, BMD
Classics and Classical
    Languages, Literatures, and Linguistics, B
Clinical Psychology, MD
Cognitive Sciences, MD
Comparative Literature, BMD
Computer Engineering, B
Computer Science, BMD
Drama and Dramatics/Theatre Arts, B
Drawing, B
Early Childhood Education and Teaching, M
Economics, BMD
Education, MDO
Electrical Engineering, MD
Electrical, Electronics and Communications
    Engineering, B
Elementary Education and Teaching, M
Engineering and Applied Sciences, MD
English, MD
English Education, M
English Language and Literature, B
Environmental Studies, B
Film/Cinema Studies, B
Finance and Banking, MD
Fine/Studio Arts, B
Foreign Language Teacher Education, M
Foundations and Philosophy of Education, D
French Language and Literature, BM
Geography, BM
Geology/Earth Science, BMD
German Language and Literature, B
Health Services Administration, M
Hebrew Language and Literature, B
History, BMD
Human Development and Family Studies, B
Industrial Engineering, B
Industrial/Management Engineering, MD
Information Science/Studies, B
Inorganic Chemistry, D

Interdisciplinary Studies, B
International/Global Studies, B
Italian Language and Literature, BM
Jewish/Judaic Studies, B
Latin American Studies, B
Latin Language and Literature, B
Linguistics, B
Management Science, B
Mathematics, BMD
Mathematics Teacher Education, M
Mechanical Engineering, BMD
Medieval and Renaissance Studies, B
Music, BM
Music Performance, B
Nursing, MDO
Nursing - Registered Nurse Training, B
Organic Chemistry, D
Philosophy, BMD
Physical Chemistry, D
Physics, BM
Physiological Psychology/Psychobiology, B
Political Science and Government, BMD
Pre-Law Studies, B
Pre-Medicine/Pre-Medical Studies, B
Psychology, BMD
Public Administration, M
Public Policy Analysis, MD
Reading Teacher Education, M
Science Teacher Education/General Science
    Teacher Education, M
Secondary Education and Teaching, M
Social Sciences, MO
Social Studies Teacher Education, M
Sociology, BMD
Spanish Language and Literature, BMO
Special Education and Teaching, M
Statistics, MD
Systems Science and Theory, MD
Theater, M
Translation and Interpretation, O

STATE UNIVERSITY OF NEW YORK AT BUFFALO

Accounting, M
Adult Health Nurse/Nursing, B
Aerospace, Aeronautical and Astronautical
    Engineering, BMD
African-American/Black Studies, B
Allied Health and Medical Assisting Services, MDO
Allopathic Medicine, PO
American/United States Studies/Civilization, BMD
Anatomy, MD
Anthropology, BMD
Architecture, BMO
Art History, Criticism and Conservation, BM
Art/Art Studies, General, B
Asian Studies/Civilization, B
Audiology/Audiologist and Speech-Language
    Pathology/Pathologist, B
Biochemistry, BMD
Bioengineering, MD
Bioinformatics, B
Biological and Biomedical Sciences, MDO
Biology/Biological Sciences, B
Biophysics, BMD
Biostatistics, BMD
BioTechnology, BM
Business Administration and Management, B
Business Administration, Management and
    Operations, MDO
Cancer Biology/Oncology, D
Cell Biology and Anatomy, D
Chemical Engineering, BMD
Chemical Technology/Technician, B
Chemistry, BMD
Civil Engineering, BMD
Classics and Classical
    Languages, Literatures, and Linguistics, BMD
Clinical Laboratory Science/Medical
    Technology/Technologist, B
Clinical Laboratory Sciences, M
Clinical Psychology, D
Cognitive Sciences, D
Communication and Media Studies, MD
Communication Disorders, MD

Communication Studies/Speech Communication
    and Rhetoric, B
Community Health and Preventive Medicine, D
Comparative Literature, MD
Composition, MD
Computer Engineering, B
Computer Science, BMD
Counselor Education/School Counseling and
    Guidance Services, MDO
Critical Care Nursing, B
Dance, B
Dentistry, PO
Drama and Dramatics/Theatre Arts, B
Dramatic/Theatre Arts and Stagecraft, B
Early Childhood Education and Teaching, M
Economics, BMDO
Education, MDO
Educational Administration and Supervision, MDO
Educational Psychology, MDO
Electrical Engineering, MD
Electrical, Electronics and Communications
    Engineering, B
Electronic Commerce, O
Elementary Education and Teaching, MD
Engineering and Applied Sciences, MD
Engineering Physics, B
Engineering Science, B
English, MD
English as a Second Language, MD
English Education, MD
English Language and Literature, B
Environmental Design/Architecture, B
Environmental Engineering
    Technology/Environmental Technology, MD
Environmental/Environmental Health Engineering, B
Epidemiology, MD
Exercise and Sports Science, MD
Family Practice Nurse/Nurse Practitioner, B
Film/Cinema Studies, B
Finance and Banking, M
Fine Arts and Art Studies, M
Fine/Studio Arts, B
Foreign Language Teacher Education, MD
French Language and Literature, BMD
Geographic Information Systems, O
Geography, BMDO
Geology/Earth Science, BMD
German Language and Literature, B
Gerontological Nursing, M
Higher Education/Higher Education
    Administration, D
History, BMD
Human Resources Management and Services, O
Humanities/Humanistic Studies, M
Immunology, MD
Industrial Engineering, B
Industrial/Management Engineering, MD
Information Science/Studies, MDO
Italian Language and Literature, B
Japanese Studies, M
Kinesiology and Exercise Science, B
Law and Legal Studies, MPO
Library Science, MO
Linguistics, BMD
Logistics and Materials Management, M
Management, D
Management Information Systems and Services, M
Mass Communication/Media Studies, B
Materials Sciences, M
Maternal/Child Health and Neonatal
    Nurse/Nursing, BMO
Mathematics, BMD
Mathematics Teacher Education, MD
Mechanical Engineering, BMD
Media Studies, M
Medicinal and Pharmaceutical Chemistry, BMD
Microbiology, MD
Middle School Education, O
Molecular Biology, D
Molecular Pharmacology, BD
Multi-/Interdisciplinary Studies, B
Multilingual and Multicultural Education, MO
Music, BMD
Music History, Literature, and Theory, MD
Music Performance, B
Music Teacher Education, MO

Music Theory and Composition, MD
Musicology and Ethnomusicology, D
Neuroscience, MD
Nuclear Medical Technology/Technologist, B
Nurse Anesthetist, BM
Nursing, BMDO
Nursing - Adult, MO
Nursing - Advanced Practice, MO
Nursing - Registered Nurse Training, B
Nutritional Sciences, BMD
Occupational Therapy/Therapist, BM
Oral and Dental Sciences, M
Oral Biology, D
Orthodontics, MO
Pathology/Experimental Pathology, MD
Pediatric Nurse/Nursing, BM
Performance, M
Pharmaceutical Sciences, MD
Pharmacology, BMDO
Pharmacy, PO
Pharmacy Administration and Pharmacy Policy and
   Regulatory Affairs, B
Pharmacy, Pharmaceutical Sciences, and Administration, B
Philosophy, BMD
Physical Therapy/Therapist, D
Physics, BMD
Physiology, MD
Political Science and Government, BMD
Psychiatric/Mental Health Nurse/Nursing, BMO
Psychology, BMD
Public Health, M
Reading Teacher Education, D
Rehabilitation Counseling, M
Rehabilitation Sciences, MDO
Romance
   Languages, Literatures, and Linguistics, MD
School Psychology, M
Science Teacher Education/General Science
   Teacher Education, MD
Social Psychology, D
Social Sciences, M
Social Studies Teacher Education, M
Social Work, BMDO
Sociology, BMD
Spanish Language and Literature, BMD
Special Education and Teaching, D
Structural Biology, MD
Structural Engineering, BMD
Theoretical and Mathematical Physics, B
Toxicology, MDO
Transportation/Transportation Management, O
Urban and Regional Planning, MO
Urban Design, MO
Women's Health Nursing, MO
Women's Studies, B

STATE UNIVERSITY OF NEW YORK COLLEGE OF AGRICULTURE AND TECHNOLOGY AT COBLESKILL

Accounting, A
Agricultural Business and Management, AB
Agricultural Mechanization, AB
Agricultural/Biological Engineering and
   Bioengineering, A
Agriculture, A
Agronomy and Crop Science, AB
Animal Sciences, A
Biological and Physical Sciences, A
Biology Technician/BioTechnology Laboratory
   Technician, A
Business Administration and Management, A
Business/Corporate Communications, B
Chemical Technology/Technician, A
Child Care and Support Services Management, B
Clinical/Medical Laboratory Technician, A
Computer Programming/Programmer, A
Computer Science, A
Computer Technology/Computer Systems
   Technology, A
Culinary Arts/Chef Training, A
Dairy Science, AB
Data Processing and Data Processing
   Technology/Technician, A
Engineering Technology, A
Environmental Studies, AB
Equestrian/Equine Studies, A

Family and Community Services, A
Fishing and Fisheries Sciences and Management, B
Food Technology and Processing, A
Horticultural Science, AB
Hotel/Motel Administration/Management, A
Information Science/Studies, A
Information Technology, B
Institutional Food Workers, A
International Business/Trade/Commerce, A
Kindergarten/PreSchool Education and Teaching, A
Landscape Architecture, A
Landscaping and Groundskeeping, A
Liberal Arts and Sciences Studies and
   Humanities, A
Ornamental Horticulture, A
Parks, Recreation and Leisure Facilities
   Management, A
Plant Nursery Operations and Management, A
Plant Sciences, AB
Pre-Medicine/Pre-Medical Studies, A
Telecommunications Technology/Technician, A
Tourism and Travel Services Marketing
   Operations, B
Turf and Turfgrass Management, AB
Wildlife and Wildlands Science and
   Management, AB

STATE UNIVERSITY OF NEW YORK COLLEGE OF AGRICULTURE AND TECHNOLOGY AT MORRISVILLE

Accounting, A
Administrative Assistant and Secretarial Science, A
Agricultural Business and Management, A
Agricultural Mechanization, A
Agriculture, A
Agronomy and Crop Science, A
Animal Sciences, A
Architectural Engineering Technology/Technician, A
Automobile/Automotive Mechanics
   Technology/Technician, A
Biology Technician/BioTechnology Laboratory
   Technician, A
Biology/Biological Sciences, A
Business Administration and Management, A
Chemistry, A
Clinical/Medical Laboratory Technician, A
Computer Engineering Technology/Technician, A
Computer Programming/Programmer, A
Computer Science, A
Computer Typography and Composition Equipment
   Operator, A
Construction Engineering Technology/Technician, A
Dairy Science, A
Data Processing and Data Processing
   Technology/Technician, A
Dietetics/Dieticians, A
Drafting and Design Technology/Technician, A
Electrical, Electronic and Communications
   Engineering Technology/Technician, A
Engineering, A
Engineering Science, A
Engineering Technology, A
Environmental Studies, A
Equestrian/Equine Studies, AB
Food Technology and Processing, A
Foods, Nutrition, and Wellness Studies, A
Forestry, A
Forestry Technology/Technician, A
Horticultural Science, A
Hospitality Administration/Management, A
Hotel/Motel Administration/Management, A
Humanities/Humanistic Studies, A
Information Science/Studies, A
Journalism, A
Landscape Architecture, A
Landscaping and Groundskeeping, A
Legal Administrative Assistant/Secretary, A
Liberal Arts and Sciences Studies and
   Humanities, A
Marketing/Marketing Management, A
Mathematics, A
Mechanical Engineering/Mechanical
   Technology/Technician, A
Medical Administrative Assistant/Secretary, A
Natural Resources and Conservation, A

Natural Resources Management/Development and
   Policy, A
Nursing - Registered Nurse Training, A
Parks, Recreation and Leisure Facilities
   Management, A
Physics, A
Plastics Engineering Technology/Technician, A
Pre-Engineering, A
Social Sciences, A
Special Products Marketing Operations, A
Technical and Business Writing, A
Tourism and Travel Services Management, A
Wildlife and Wildlands Science and Management, A
Wood Science and Wood Products/Pulp and Paper
   Technology, A

STATE UNIVERSITY OF NEW YORK COLLEGE AT BROCKPORT

Accounting, B
Acting, B
African Studies, B
African-American/Black Studies, B
American Literature (United States), B
Anthropology, B
Art/Art Studies, General, B
Asian Studies/Civilization, B
Astronomy, B
Athletic Training and Sports Medicine, B
Atmospheric Sciences and Meteorology, B
Bilingual, Multilingual, and Multicultural Education, B
Biochemistry, B
Biological and Biomedical Sciences, M
Biology Teacher Education, B
Biology Technician/BioTechnology Laboratory
   Technician, B
Biology/Biological Sciences, B
BioTechnology, B
Broadcast Journalism, B
Business Administration and Management, B
Cell/Cellular and Molecular Biology, B
Cell/Cellular Biology and Histology, B
Ceramic Arts and Ceramics, B
Chemistry, B
Chemistry Teacher Education, B
Clinical Laboratory Science/Medical
   Technology/Technologist, B
Communication and Media Studies, BM
Communication Studies/Speech Communication
   and Rhetoric, B
Communication, Journalism and Related
   Programs, B
Comparative Literature, B
Computational Sciences, M
Computer Science, B
Corrections, B
Corrections and Criminal Justice, B
Counselor Education/School Counseling and
   Guidance Services, MO
Creative Writing, B
Criminal Justice/Law Enforcement Administration, B
Criminal Justice/Police Science, B
Criminology, B
Curriculum and Instruction, M
Dance, BM
Drama and Dramatics/Theatre Arts, B
Drawing, B
Early Childhood Education and Teaching, B
Economics, B
Education, BM
Educational Administration and Supervision, MO
Elementary Education and Teaching, B
English, M
English Education, M
English Language and Literature, B
English/Language Arts Teacher Education, B
Environmental Biology, B
Environmental Studies, B
European Studies/Civilization, B
Exercise Physiology, B
Finance, B
Fine Arts and Art Studies, M
Fine/Studio Arts, B
Foreign Language Teacher Education, B
French Language and Literature, B
French Language Teacher Education, B
Geological and Earth Sciences/Geosciences, B

Geology/Earth Science, B
Health and Physical Education, B
Health and Physical Education/Fitness, B
Health Education, M
Health Teacher Education, B
Health/Health Care Administration/Management, B
History, BM
History Teacher Education, B
Hydrology and Water Resources Science, B
Interdisciplinary Studies, B
International Business/Trade/Commerce, B
International Relations and Affairs, B
Journalism, B
Junior High/Intermediate/Middle School Education
   and Teaching, B
Kinesiology and Exercise Science, B
Latin American Studies, B
Leisure Studies, M
Liberal Studies, M
Marketing/Marketing Management, B
Mass Communication/Media Studies, B
Mathematics, BM
Mathematics Teacher Education, BM
Metal and Jewelry Arts, B
Meteorology, B
Middle School Education, M
Molecular Biology, B
Multilingual and Multicultural Education, M
Nursing - Registered Nurse Training, B
Organizational Communication, B
Painting, B
Parks, Recreation, Leisure and Fitness Studies, B
Philosophy, B
Physical Education Teaching and Coaching, BM
Physics, B
Physics Teacher Education, B
Political Science and Government, B
Pre-Dentistry Studies, B
Pre-Law Studies, B
Pre-Medicine/Pre-Medical Studies, B
Pre-Veterinary Studies, B
Psychology, BM
Public Administration, M
Public Health (MPH, DPH), B
Public Relations, Advertising, and Applied
   Communication, B
Public Relations/Image Management, B
Radio and Television, B
Radio, Television, and Digital Communication, B
Reading Teacher Education, M
Recreation and Park Management, M
Science Teacher Education/General Science
   Teacher Education, BM
Sculpture, B
Secondary Education and Teaching, B
Securities Services Administration/Management, B
Social Studies Teacher Education, BM
Social Work, BM
Sociology, B
Spanish Language and Literature, B
Spanish Language Teacher Education, B
Special Education and Teaching, M
Speech and Rhetorical Studies, B
Sport and Fitness Administration/Management, B
Substance Abuse/Addiction Counseling, B
Therapeutic Recreation/Recreational Therapy, B
Women's Studies, B

STATE UNIVERSITY OF NEW YORK COLLEGE AT CORTLAND

African-American/Black Studies, B
American/United States Studies/Civilization, O
Anthropology, B
Art History, Criticism and Conservation, B
Athletic Training and Sports Medicine, B
Audiology/Audiologist and Speech-Language
   Pathology/Pathologist, B
Biology Teacher Education, B
Biology/Biological Sciences, B
Chemistry, B
Chemistry Teacher Education, B
Communication Studies/Speech Communication
   and Rhetoric, B
Criminology, B
Early Childhood Education and Teaching, M
Economics, B

Education, MO
Education/Teaching of Individuals with Speech or
   Language Impairments, B
Educational Leadership and Administration, O
Elementary Education and Teaching, B
English, M
English as a Second Language, M
English Education, M
English Language and Literature, B
Environmental Biology, B
Environmental Sciences, B
Environmental Studies, B
Exercise and Sports Science, M
Fine/Studio Arts, B
Foreign Language Teacher Education, M
French Language and Literature, B
French Language Teacher Education, B
Geochemistry, B
Geography, B
Geology/Earth Science, B
German Language and Literature, B
Health Education, M
Health Teacher Education, B
History, BM
Human Services, B
International Relations and Affairs, B
International/Global Studies, B
Junior High/Intermediate/Middle School Education
   and Teaching, B
Kindergarten/PreSchool Education and Teaching, B
Kinesiology and Exercise Science, B
Mathematics, BM
Mathematics Teacher Education, BM
Parks, Recreation and Leisure Facilities
   Management, B
Parks, Recreation, Leisure and Fitness Studies, B
Philosophy, B
Physical Education Teaching and Coaching, BM
Physics, B
Physics Teacher Education, B
Political Science and Government, B
Pre-Dentistry Studies, B
Pre-Law Studies, B
Pre-Medicine/Pre-Medical Studies, B
Psychology, B
Public Health (MPH, DPH), B
Reading Teacher Education, BM
Recreation and Park Management, M
Science Teacher Education/General Science
   Teacher Education, BM
Secondary Education and Teaching, BM
Social Studies Teacher Education, BM
Social Work, B
Sociology, B
Spanish Language and Literature, B
Spanish Language Teacher Education, B
Special Education and Teaching, M
Speech and Rhetorical Studies, B
Therapeutic Recreation/Recreational Therapy, B

STATE UNIVERSITY OF NEW YORK COLLEGE OF ENVIRONMENTAL SCIENCE AND FORESTRY

Biochemistry, BMD
Biological and Physical Sciences, B
Biology Teacher Education, B
Biology/Biological Sciences, B
BioTechnology, B
Botany/Plant Biology, B
Chemical Engineering, B
Chemistry, BMD
Chemistry Teacher Education, B
City/Urban, Community and Regional Planning, B
Communication and Media Studies, MD
Conservation Biology, MD
Construction Engineering, B
Construction Engineering and Management, MD
Ecology, BMD
Entomology, BMD
Environmental Biology, BMD
Environmental Design/Architecture, B
Environmental Education, B
Environmental Engineering
   Technology/Environmental Technology, MD
Environmental Policy, MD

Environmental Policy and Resource
   Management, MD
Environmental Sciences, MD
Environmental Studies, BMD
Environmental/Environmental Health Engineering, B
Fish, Game and Wildlife Management, MD
Fishing and Fisheries Sciences and Management, B
Forest Engineering, B
Forest Management/Forest Resources
   Management, B
Forestry, BMD
Hydrology and Water Resources Science, BMD
Land Use Planning and
   Management/Development, B
Landscape Architecture, BM
Natural Resources and Conservation, BMD
Natural Resources Management/Development and
   Policy, BMD
Organic Chemistry, MD
Paper and Pulp Engineering, MD
Parks, Recreation, Leisure and Fitness Studies, B
Plant Pathology/Phytopathology, BMD
Plant Physiology, B
Plant Protection and Integrated Pest
   Management, B
Plant Sciences, BMD
Polymer Chemistry, B
Pre-Dentistry Studies, B
Pre-Law Studies, B
Pre-Medicine/Pre-Medical Studies, B
Pre-Veterinary Studies, B
Recreation and Park Management, MD
Resource Management, MD
Science Teacher Education/General Science
   Teacher Education, B
Urban and Regional Planning, MD
Urban Design, M
Water Resources, MD
Water Resources Engineering, B
Wildlife and Wildlands Science and Management, B
Wildlife Biology, B
Wood Science and Wood Products/Pulp and Paper
   Technology, B
Zoology/Animal Biology, B

STATE UNIVERSITY OF NEW YORK COLLEGE OF ENVIRONMENTAL SCIENCE & FORESTRY, RANGER SCHOOL

Forestry Technology/Technician, A
Survey Technology/Surveying, A

STATE UNIVERSITY OF NEW YORK COLLEGE AT GENESEO

Accounting, B
African-American/Black Studies, B
American/United States Studies/Civilization, B
Anthropology, B
Art History, Criticism and Conservation, B
Art/Art Studies, General, B
Biochemistry, B
Biology/Biological Sciences, B
Biophysics, B
Business Administration and Management, B
Chemistry, B
Communication Disorders, BM
Communication Studies/Speech Communication
   and Rhetoric, B
Comparative Literature, B
Computer Science, B
Drama and Dramatics/Theatre Arts, B
Early Childhood Education and Teaching, B
Economics, B
Education, BM
Education/Teaching of Individuals in Early Childhood
   Special Education Programs, B
Elementary Education and Teaching, BM
English Language and Literature, B
Fine/Studio Arts, B
French Language and Literature, B
Geochemistry, B
Geography, B
Geology/Earth Science, B
Geophysics and Seismology, B
History, B

International Relations and Affairs, B
Mathematics, B
Music, B
Natural Sciences, B
Philosophy, B
Physics, B
Political Science and Government, B
Pre-Dentistry Studies, B
Pre-Law Studies, B
Pre-Medicine/Pre-Medical Studies, B
Pre-Veterinary Studies, B
Psychology, B
Reading Teacher Education, M
Secondary Education and Teaching, M
Sociology, B
Spanish Language and Literature, B
Special Education and Teaching, BM
Visual and Performing Arts, B

STATE UNIVERSITY OF NEW YORK COLLEGE AT OLD WESTBURY

Accounting, BM
American/United States Studies/Civilization, B
Art/Art Studies, General, B
Bilingual and Multilingual Education, B
Biochemistry, B
Biology Teacher Education, B
Biology/Biological Sciences, B
Business Administration and Management, B
Chemistry, B
Chemistry Teacher Education, B
Communication Studies/Speech Communication
    and Rhetoric, B
Comparative Literature, B
Computer and Information Sciences, B
Computer Science, B
Criminology, B
Early Childhood Education and Teaching, B
Economics, B
Elementary Education and Teaching, B
Finance, B
Foreign Language Teacher Education, B
Foreign Languages and Literatures, B
Humanities/Humanistic Studies, B
Information Science/Studies, B
Junior High/Intermediate/Middle School Education
    and Teaching, B
Labor and Industrial Relations, B
Management Information Systems and Services, B
Marketing/Marketing Management, B
Mathematics, B
Mathematics Teacher Education, B
Philosophy, B
Psychology, B
Public Health (MPH, DPH), B
Religion/Religious Studies, B
Science Teacher Education/General Science
    Teacher Education, B
Secondary Education and Teaching, B
Social Sciences, B
Social Studies Teacher Education, B
Sociology, B
Spanish Language and Literature, B
Spanish Language Teacher Education, B
Special Education and Teaching, B
Visual and Performing Arts, B

STATE UNIVERSITY OF NEW YORK COLLEGE AT ONEONTA

Accounting, B
African-American/Black Studies, B
Anthropology, B
Art History, Criticism and Conservation, B
Art/Art Studies, General, B
Atmospheric Sciences and Meteorology, B
Biochemistry, B
Biological and Biomedical Sciences, M
Biology Teacher Education, B
Biology Technician/BioTechnology Laboratory
    Technician, B
Biology/Biological Sciences, B
Business/Managerial Economics, B
Cartography, B
Chemistry, B
Chemistry Teacher Education, B
Child Development, B

Computer Graphics, B
Computer Science, B
Consumer Services and Advocacy, B
Counselor Education/School Counseling and
    Guidance Services, MO
Criminal Justice/Safety Studies, B
Dietetics/Dieticians, B
Drama and Dramatics/Theatre Arts, B
Economics, B
Education, BMO
Educational Psychology, MO
Elementary Education and Teaching, BM
Engineering Science, B
English Language and Literature, B
English/Language Arts Teacher Education, B
Environmental Studies, B
Family and Consumer Sciences/Home Economics
    Teacher Education, B
Family and Consumer Sciences/Human
    Sciences, BM
Fashion Merchandising, B
Fine/Studio Arts, B
Foodservice Systems
    Administration/Management, B
French Language and Literature, B
French Language Teacher Education, B
Geography, B
Geology/Earth Science, B
Geosciences, M
Gerontology, B
Hispanic-American, Puerto Rican, and Mexican-
    American/Chicano Studies, B
History, B
Home Economics Education, M
Hydrology and Water Resources Science, B
Interdisciplinary Studies, B
International Relations and Affairs, B
Junior High/Intermediate/Middle School Education
    and Teaching, B
Kindergarten/PreSchool Education and Teaching, B
Liberal Arts and Sciences Studies and
    Humanities, B
Mass Communication/Media Studies, B
Mathematics, B
Mathematics Teacher Education, B
Middle School Education, M
Museology/Museum Studies, M
Music, B
Music Management and Merchandising, B
Ophthalmic/Optometric Services, B
Philosophy, B
Physics, B
Physics Teacher Education, B
Political Science and Government, B
Pre-Dentistry Studies, B
Pre-Law Studies, B
Pre-Medicine/Pre-Medical Studies, B
Pre-Veterinary Studies, B
Psychology, B
Reading Teacher Education, BM
Science Teacher Education/General Science
    Teacher Education, B
Secondary Education and Teaching, BM
Social Science Teacher Education, B
Sociology, B
Spanish Language and Literature, B
Spanish Language Teacher Education, B
Speech and Rhetorical Studies, B
Statistics, B

STATE UNIVERSITY OF NEW YORK COLLEGE AT POTSDAM

Anthropology, B
Archeology, B
Art History, Criticism and Conservation, B
Art/Art Studies, General, B
Biology Teacher Education, B
Biology/Biological Sciences, B
Business Administration and Management, B
Business/Managerial Economics, B
Chemistry, B
Chemistry Teacher Education, B
Composition, M
Computer and Information Sciences, B
Dance, B
Drama and Dramatics/Theatre Arts, B

Economics, B
Education, M
Educational Media/Instructional Technology, M
Elementary Education and Teaching, BM
English, M
English Language and Literature, B
English/Language Arts Teacher Education, B
French Language and Literature, B
French Language Teacher Education, B
Geology/Earth Science, B
Labor and Industrial Relations, B
Mathematics, BM
Mathematics Teacher Education, B
Music, M
Music History, Literature, and Theory, M
Music Performance, B
Music Teacher Education, BM
Music Theory and Composition, M
Performance, M
Philosophy, B
Physical Education Teaching and Coaching, B
Physics, B
Physics Teacher Education, B
Political Science and Government, B
Psychology, B
Reading Teacher Education, M
Science Teacher Education/General Science
    Teacher Education, B
Secondary Education and Teaching, M
Social Studies Teacher Education, B
Sociology, B
Spanish Language and Literature, B
Spanish Language Teacher Education, B
Special Education and Teaching, M
Speech and Rhetorical Studies, B

STATE UNIVERSITY OF NEW YORK COLLEGE OF TECHNOLOGY AT ALFRED

Accounting, A
Agricultural Business and Management, A
Agriculture, A
Animal Sciences, A
Architectural Engineering Technology/Technician, AB
Autobody/Collision and Repair
    Technology/Technician, A
Automobile/Automotive Mechanics
    Technology/Technician, A
Biological and Physical Sciences, A
Biology Technician/BioTechnology Laboratory
    Technician, A
Business Administration and Management, A
Carpentry/Carpenter, A
Civil Engineering Technology/Technician, A
Computer and Information Sciences, AB
Computer Engineering Technology/Technician, AB
Computer Graphics, A
Computer Hardware Engineering, B
Computer Installation and Repair
    Technology/Technician, A
Computer Science, A
Computer Typography and Composition Equipment
    Operator, A
Computer/Information Technology Services
    Administration and Management, B
Construction Engineering, AB
Construction Engineering Technology/Technician, A
Court Reporting/Court Reporter, A
Culinary Arts/Chef Training, A
Drafting and Design Technology/Technician, A
Drafting/Design Engineering
    Technologies/Technicians, A
Electrical, Electronic and Communications
    Engineering Technology/Technician, AB
Electrical/Electronics Equipment Installation and
    Repair, A
Electromechanical Technology/Electromechanical
    Engineering Technology, AB
Engineering Science, A
Environmental Studies, A
Finance, A
Health Information/Medical Records
    Administration/Administrator, A
Heating, Air Conditioning and Refrigeration
    Technology/Technician, A

Heating, Air Conditioning, Ventilation and
Refrigeration Maintenance
Technology/Technician, A
Heavy Equipment Maintenance
Technology/Technician, A
Human Services, A
Humanities/Humanistic Studies, A
Industrial Electronics Technology/Technician, A
Landscaping and Groundskeeping, A
Liberal Arts and Sciences Studies and
Humanities, A
Machine Tool Technology/Machinist, A
Management Information Systems and Services, B
Marketing/Marketing Management, A
Mason/Masonry, A
Mathematics, A
Mechanical Engineering/Mechanical
Technology/Technician, AB
Nursing - Registered Nurse Training, A
Pipefitting/Pipefitter and Sprinkler Fitter, A
Restaurant, Culinary, and Catering
Management/Manager, A
Sales, Distribution and Marketing Operations, A
Social Sciences, A
Sport and Fitness Administration/Management, A
Survey Technology/Surveying, A
System Administration/Administrator, B
Welding Technology/Welder, A

STATE UNIVERSITY OF NEW YORK COLLEGE OF TECHNOLOGY AT CANTON

Accounting, A
Automobile/Automotive Mechanics
Technology/Technician, A
Banking and Financial Support Services, B
Biological and Physical Sciences, A
Business Administration and Management, A
Business/Managerial Economics, A
Carpentry/Carpenter, A
Civil Engineering Technology/Technician, A
Clinical/Medical Laboratory Technician, A
Computer/Information Technology Services
Administration and Management, AB
Construction Engineering Technology/Technician, A
Corrections, A
Criminal Justice/Law Enforcement Administration, A
Criminal Justice/Police Science, AB
Electrical, Electronic and Communications
Engineering Technology/Technician, A
Engineering Science, A
Engineering Technology, A
Environmental Studies, A
Forestry Technology/Technician, A
Funeral Service and Mortuary Science, A
Health/Health Care Administration/Management, B
Heating, Air Conditioning, Ventilation and
Refrigeration Maintenance
Technology/Technician, A
Humanities/Humanistic Studies, A
Industrial Technology/Technician, A
Information Science/Studies, A
Interdisciplinary Studies, A
Kindergarten/PreSchool Education and Teaching, A
Liberal Arts and Sciences Studies and
Humanities, A
Mechanical Engineering/Mechanical
Technology/Technician, A
Nursing - Registered Nurse Training, A
Occupational Therapist Assistant, A
Office Management and Supervision, A
Physical Therapist Assistant, A
Pipefitting/Pipefitter and Sprinkler Fitter, A
Social Sciences, A
Veterinary/Animal Health Technology/Technician and
Veterinary Assistant, A

STATE UNIVERSITY OF NEW YORK COLLEGE OF TECHNOLOGY AT DELHI

Accounting, A
Architectural Engineering Technology/Technician, A
Building/Construction
Finishing, Management, and Inspection, A
Business Administration and Management, A
Computer/Information Technology Services
Administration and Management, B

Construction Engineering Technology/Technician, A
Culinary Arts/Chef Training, A
Electrical and Power Transmission
Installation/Installer, A
Engineering Science, A
Engineering Technology, A
General Studies, A
Health and Physical Education, A
Heating, Air Conditioning and Refrigeration
Technology/Technician, A
Heating, Air Conditioning, Ventilation and
Refrigeration Maintenance
Technology/Technician, A
Horticultural Science, A
Hospitality and Recreation Marketing Operations, A
Hotel/Motel Administration/Management, AB
Humanities/Humanistic Studies, A
Landscape Architecture, A
Landscaping and Groundskeeping, A
Marketing/Marketing Management, A
Mathematics, A
Nursing - Registered Nurse Training, A
Parks, Recreation and Leisure Facilities
Management, AB
Parks, Recreation, Leisure and Fitness Studies, A
Pipefitting/Pipefitter and Sprinkler Fitter, A
Restaurant, Culinary, and Catering
Management/Manager, AB
Social Sciences, A
Tourism and Travel Services Management, AB
Veterinary/Animal Health Technology/Technician and
Veterinary Assistant, AB
Web Page, Digital/Multimedia and Information
Resources Design, B
Welding Technology/Welder, A
Woodworking, A

STATE UNIVERSITY OF NEW YORK DOWNSTATE MEDICAL CENTER

Allopathic Medicine, MPO
Biological and Biomedical Sciences, MDO
Biomedical Engineering, MDO
Cell Biology and Anatomy, DO
Community Health and Preventive Medicine, M
Diagnostic Medical Sonography/Sonographer and
Ultrasound Technician, B
Genetics, D
Health Information/Medical Records
Administration/Administrator, B
Molecular Biology, DO
Neuroscience, DO
Nurse Anesthetist, M
Nursing, MO
Nursing - Advanced Practice, MO
Nursing - Registered Nurse Training, B
Occupational Therapy/Therapist, B
Physical Therapy/Therapist, B
Physician Assistant, B
Public Health, MO

STATE UNIVERSITY OF NEW YORK EMPIRE STATE COLLEGE

Art/Art Studies, General, AB
Biological and Physical Sciences, AB
Business Administration and Management, AB
Business Administration, Management and
Operations, M
Community Organization and Advocacy, AB
Economics, AB
Education, ABM
History, AB
Human Development and Family Studies, AB
Human Services, AB
Humanities/Humanistic Studies, AB
Industrial and Labor Relations, M
Interdisciplinary Studies, AB
Labor and Industrial Relations, AB
Liberal Studies, M
Mathematics, AB
Public Policy Analysis, M

Social Sciences, AB

STATE UNIVERSITY OF NEW YORK, FREDONIA

Accounting, B
American/United States Studies/Civilization, B
Applied Art, B
Art History, Criticism and Conservation, B
Art/Art Studies, General, B
Arts Management, B
Audio Engineering, B
Audiology/Audiologist and Speech-Language
Pathology/Pathologist, B
Biochemistry, B
Biological and Biomedical Sciences, M
Biological and Physical Sciences, B
Biology Technician/BioTechnology Laboratory
Technician, B
Biology/Biological Sciences, B
Biomedical Sciences, B
Broadcast Journalism, B
Business Administration and Management, B
Chemistry, BM
Clinical Laboratory Science/Medical
Technology/Technologist, B
Commercial and Advertising Art, B
Communication Disorders, BM
Computer Graphics, B
Computer Science, B
Criminal Justice/Law Enforcement Administration, B
Dance, B
Drama and Dramatics/Theatre Arts, B
Drawing, B
Economics, B
Education, BMO
Educational Administration and Supervision, O
Elementary Education and Teaching, BM
English, M
English Language and Literature, B
Environmental Studies, B
Film/Cinema Studies, B
Finance, B
Fine/Studio Arts, B
French Language and Literature, B
Geochemistry, B
Geology/Earth Science, B
Geophysics and Seismology, B
Gerontology, B
Health/Health Care Administration/Management, B
History, B
Information Science/Studies, B
Interdisciplinary Studies, B
Intermedia/Multimedia, B
Kindergarten/PreSchool Education and Teaching, B
Labor and Industrial Relations, B
Law and Legal Studies, B
Liberal Arts and Sciences Studies and
Humanities, B
Marketing/Marketing Management, B
Mass Communication/Media Studies, B
Mathematics, B
Mathematics Teacher Education, M
Music, BM
Music History, Literature, and Theory, B
Music Management and Merchandising, B
Music Teacher Education, BM
Music Therapy/Therapist, B
Philosophy, B
Physics, B
Piano and Organ, B
Political Science and Government, B
Pre-Law Studies, B
Pre-Medicine/Pre-Medical Studies, B
Pre-Veterinary Studies, B
Psychology, B
Radio and Television, B
Reading Teacher Education, M
Science Teacher Education/General Science
Teacher Education, B
Secondary Education and Teaching, BM
Social Sciences, M
Social Work, B
Sociology, B
Spanish Language and Literature, B
Violin, Viola, Guitar and Other Stringed
Instruments, B

Voice and Opera, B
Wind and Percussion Instruments, B
Women's Studies, B

STATE UNIVERSITY OF NEW YORK INSTITUTE OF TECHNOLOGY

Accounting, BM
Applied Mathematics, B
Business Administration and Management, B
Business Administration, Management and
  Operations, M
Civil Engineering Technology/Technician, B
Communication, Journalism and Related
  Programs, B
Computer and Information Sciences, B
Computer Engineering Technology/Technician, B
Computer Science, BM
Electrical, Electronic and Communications
  Engineering Technology/Technician, B
Engineering and Applied Sciences, M
Finance, B
General Studies, B
Health Information/Medical Records
  Administration/Administrator, B
Health Services Administration, M
Health/Health Care Administration/Management, B
Industrial Technology/Technician, B
Information Science/Studies, BM
Management of Technology, M
Mechanical Engineering/Mechanical
  Technology/Technician, B
Nursing, MO
Nursing - Adult, MO
Nursing - Advanced Practice, MO
Nursing - Registered Nurse Training, B
Nursing Administration, MO
Psychology, B
Sociology, BM
Telecommunications, M

STATE UNIVERSITY OF NEW YORK MARITIME COLLEGE

Atmospheric Sciences and Meteorology, B
Business Administration and Management, B
Electrical, Electronics and Communications
  Engineering, B
Engineering, B
Environmental Studies, B
Humanities/Humanistic Studies, B
Marine Science/Merchant Marine Officer, AB
Maritime Science, B
Mechanical Engineering, B
Naval Architecture and Marine Engineering, B
Navy/Marine Corps JROTC/ROTC, B
Oceanography, Chemical and Physical, B
Transportation/Transportation Management, M

STATE UNIVERSITY OF NEW YORK AT NEW PALTZ

Accounting, BM
African-American/Black Studies, B
Anthropology, B
Applied Mathematics, B
Art Education, M
Art History, Criticism and Conservation, B
Art Teacher Education, B
Art/Art Studies, General, B
Asian Studies/Civilization, B
Audiology/Audiologist and Speech-Language
  Pathology/Pathologist, B
Biochemistry, B
Biological and Biomedical Sciences, M
Biology/Biological Sciences, B
BioTechnology, B
Broadcast Journalism, B
Business Administration and Management, B
Business Administration, Management and
  Operations, M
Business/Managerial Economics, B
Ceramic Arts and Ceramics, BM
Chemistry, BM
City/Urban, Community and Regional Planning, B
Commercial and Advertising Art, B
Communication Disorders, BM
Computer Art and Design, M

Computer Engineering, BM
Computer Science, BM
Creative Writing, B
Criminology, B
Drama and Dramatics/Theatre Arts, B
Early Childhood Education and Teaching, M
Economics, B
Education, BMO
Educational Administration and Supervision, MO
Electrical Engineering, M
Electrical, Electronics and Communications
  Engineering, M
Elementary Education and Teaching, BM
Engineering Physics, B
English, M
English as a Second Language, M
English Language and Literature, B
Environmental Education, M
Environmental Studies, B
Finance, B
Finance and Banking, M
Fine Arts and Art Studies, M
Fine/Studio Arts, B
French Language and Literature, B
Geography, B
Geology/Earth Science, BM
German Language and Literature, B
Gerontological Nursing, M
History, B
Industrial and Organizational Psychology, B
International Business/Trade/Commerce, BM
International Economics, B
International Relations and Affairs, B
Jazz/Jazz Studies, B
Jewelry/Metalsmithing, M
Journalism, B
Kindergarten/PreSchool Education and Teaching, B
Latin American Studies, B
Management Science, B
Marketing, M
Marketing/Marketing Management, B
Mass Communication/Media Studies, B
Mathematics, BM
Mathematics Teacher Education, M
Metal and Jewelry Arts, M
Multilingual and Multicultural Education, M
Music, B
Music History, Literature, and Theory, B
Music Therapy/Therapist, B
Nursing, M
Nursing - Registered Nurse Training, B
Painting, BM
Philosophy, B
Photography, B
Physics, B
Physiological Psychology/Psychobiology, B
Political Science and Government, B
Printmaking, BM
Psychology, BM
Radio and Television, B
Reading Teacher Education, M
Science Teacher Education/General Science
  Teacher Education, BM
Sculpture, BM
Secondary Education and Teaching, BM
Social Work, B
Sociology, BMO
Spanish Language and Literature, B
Special Education and Teaching, BM
Women's Studies, B

STATE UNIVERSITY OF NEW YORK AT OSWEGO

Accounting, B
Accounting and Related Services, B
Agricultural Teacher Education, B
American/United States Studies/Civilization, B
Anthropology, B
Applied Mathematics, B
Art Education, M
Art/Art Studies, General, B
Atmospheric Sciences and Meteorology, B
Biology/Biological Sciences, B
Business Administration and Management, B
Business Administration, Management and
  Operations, M

Chemistry, BM
Cognitive Psychology and Psycholinguistics, B
Cognitive Sciences, B
Commercial and Advertising Art, B
Computer Science, B
Counseling Psychology, MO
Creative Writing, B
Criminal Justice/Law Enforcement Administration, B
Drama and Dramatics/Theatre Arts, B
Econometrics and Quantitative Economics, B
Economics, B
Education, BMO
Educational Administration and Supervision, MO
Elementary Education and Teaching, BM
English, M
English Language and Literature, B
Finance, B
Fine Arts and Art Studies, M
French Language and Literature, B
Geochemistry, B
Geology/Earth Science, B
German Language and Literature, B
Health Teacher Education, B
History, BM
Human Development and Family Studies, B
Human Resources Management/Personnel
  Administration, B
Human Services, M
Human-Computer Interaction, M
Information Science/Studies, B
International Economics, B
International Relations and Affairs, B
Journalism, B
Linguistics, B
Management Science, B
Marketing/Marketing Management, B
Mass Communication/Media Studies, B
Mathematics, B
Music, B
Philosophy, B
Philosophy and Religious Studies, B
Physics, B
Political Science and Government, B
Pre-Dentistry Studies, B
Pre-Law Studies, B
Pre-Medicine/Pre-Medical Studies, B
Pre-Veterinary Studies, B
Psychology, B
Public Relations/Image Management, B
Reading Teacher Education, M
Sales and Marketing Operations/Marketing and
  Distribution Teacher Education, B
School Psychology, MO
Science Teacher Education/General Science
  Teacher Education, B
Secondary Education and Teaching, BM
Sociology, B
Spanish Language and Literature, B
Special Education and Teaching, M
Sport and Fitness Administration/Management, B
Technology Teacher Education/Industrial Arts
  Teacher Education, B
Trade and Industrial Teacher Education, B
Vocational and Technical Education, M
Women's Studies, B
Zoology/Animal Biology, B

STATE UNIVERSITY OF NEW YORK AT PLATTSBURGH

Accounting, B
Anthropology, B
Art History, Criticism and Conservation, B
Audiology/Audiologist and Speech-Language
  Pathology/Pathologist, B
Biochemistry, B
Biology/Biological Sciences, B
Broadcast Journalism, B
Business Administration and Management, B
Business/Managerial Economics, B
Canadian Studies, B
Chemistry, B
Child Development, B
Clinical Laboratory Science/Medical
  Technology/Technologist, B
Communication Disorders, BM

Communication Studies/Speech Communication
  and Rhetoric, B
Computer Science, B
Counselor Education/School Counseling and
  Guidance Services, MO
Criminology, B
Curriculum and Instruction, M
Drama and Dramatics/Theatre Arts, B
Economics, B
Education, B
Educational Administration and Supervision, O
Elementary Education and Teaching, BM
English Education, M
English Language and Literature, B
Environmental Studies, B
Fine/Studio Arts, B
Foods, Nutrition, and Wellness Studies, B
French Language and Literature, B
Geography, B
Geology/Earth Science, B
History, B
Hotel/Motel Administration/Management, B
Interdisciplinary Studies, B
International Business/Trade/Commerce, B
Latin American Studies, B
Liberal Studies, M
Marketing/Marketing Management, B
Mass Communication/Media Studies, B
Mathematics, B
Mathematics Teacher Education, M
Music, B
Nursing - Registered Nurse Training, B
Philosophy, B
Physics, B
Political Science and Government, B
Psychology, BMO
Reading Teacher Education, M
School Psychology, MO
Science Teacher Education/General Science
  Teacher Education, M
Secondary Education and Teaching, BM
Social Studies Teacher Education, M
Social Work, B
Sociology, B
Spanish Language and Literature, B
Special Education and Teaching, BM

STATE UNIVERSITY OF NEW YORK UPSTATE MEDICAL UNIVERSITY

Allopathic Medicine, PO
Anatomy, MDO
Biochemistry, MDO
Biological and Biomedical Sciences, MDO
Cardiovascular Technology/Technologist, B
Cell Biology and Anatomy, MDO
Clinical Laboratory Science/Medical
  Technology/Technologist, B
CytoTechnology/Cytotechnologist, B
Developmental Biology and Embryology, DO
Immunology, MDO
Medical Radiologic Technology/Science - Radiation
  Therapist, B
Medical Technology, M
Microbiology, MDO
Molecular Biology, MDO
Neuroscience, D
Nursing, MO
Nursing - Advanced Practice, O
Nursing Science, B
Perfusion Technology/Perfusionist, B
Pharmacology, MDO
Physical Therapy/Therapist, MD
Physiology, MDO
Radiologic Technology/Science - Radiographer, B
Respiratory Care Therapy/Therapist, B

STONY BROOK UNIVERSITY, STATE UNIVERSITY OF NEW YORK

African-American/Black Studies, B
Allopathic Medicine, PO
American/United States Studies/Civilization, BO
Anatomy, D
Anthropology, BMD
Applied Mathematics, BMD
Art History, Criticism and Conservation, BMD

Asian-American Studies, B
Astronomy, B
Astronomy and Astrophysics, B
Athletic Training and Sports Medicine, B
Atmospheric Sciences and Meteorology, BMD
Biochemistry, BD
Biological and Biomedical Sciences, DO
Biology/Biological Sciences, B
Biomedical Engineering, MDO
Biomedical/Medical Engineering, B
Biophysics, D
Biopsychology, D
Business Administration and Management, B
Business Administration, Management and
  Operations, MO
Cell Biology and Anatomy, MD
Chemistry, BMD
Clinical Laboratory Science/Medical
  Technology/Technologist, B
Clinical Psychology, D
Community Health and Preventive Medicine, MO
Comparative Literature, BMD
Computer Education, MO
Computer Engineering, MD
Computer Hardware Engineering, B
Computer Science, BMDO
Cultural Studies, O
CytoTechnology/Cytotechnologist, B
Dentistry, PO
Developmental Biology and Embryology, D
Drama and Dramatics/Theatre Arts, B
Ecology, D
Economics, BMD
Educational Administration and Supervision, O
Educational Media/Instructional Technology, MO
Electrical Engineering, MD
Electrical, Electronics and Communications
  Engineering, B
Engineering, B
Engineering and Applied Sciences, MDO
English, MDO
English as a Second Language, MD
English Education, M
English Language and Literature, B
Environmental and Occupational Health, O
Environmental Policy and Resource
  Management, MO
Environmental Studies, B
Evolutionary Biology, D
Experimental Psychology, D
Fine Arts and Art Studies, M
Fine/Studio Arts, B
Foreign Language Teacher Education, M
French Language and Literature, BMD
Genetics, D
Geology/Earth Science, B
Geosciences, MD
German Language and Literature, BMD
Gerontological Nursing, M
Hazardous Materials Management and Waste
  Technology/Technician, O
Health Professions and Related Clinical Sciences, B
Health Psychology, D
Health Services Administration, MDO
Hispanic Studies, MD
History, BMD
Human Resources Management and Services, O
Humanities/Humanistic Studies, B
Immunology, D
Industrial and Manufacturing Management, MO
Information Science/Studies, B
Italian Language and Literature, BMD
Liberal Studies, M
Linguistics, BMD
Management Information Systems and Services, O
Management of Technology, MO
Marine Biology and Biological Oceanography, B
Marine Sciences, MD
Materials Engineering, MD
Materials Sciences, MD
Maternal/Child Health and Neonatal
  Nurse/Nursing, MO
Maternity Nursing, MO
Mathematics, BMD
Mechanical Engineering, BMDO
Medical Physics, D

Microbiology, D
Molecular Biology, MD
Molecular Genetics, D
Molecular Physiology, D
Multi-/Interdisciplinary Studies, B
Music, BMD
Neuroscience, D
Nurse Midwife/Nursing Midwifery, MO
Nursing, MO
Nursing - Adult, MO
Nursing - Advanced Practice, MO
Nursing - Registered Nurse Training, B
Occupational Therapy/Therapist, M
Oral and Dental Sciences, O
Oral Biology, D
Oral Pathology, D
Orthodontics, O
Pathology/Experimental Pathology, D
Pediatric Nurse/Nursing, MO
Performance, MD
Periodontics, O
Pharmacology, BD
Philosophy, BMD
Physical Education Teaching and Coaching, O
Physical Sciences, B
Physical Therapy/Therapist, MD
Physician Assistant, B
Physics, BMD
Physiology, D
Planetary Astronomy and Science, MD
Political Science and Government, BMD
Psychiatric/Mental Health Nurse/Nursing, MO
Psychology, BMD
Public Health, M
Public Policy Analysis, M
Religion/Religious Studies, B
Respiratory Care Therapy/Therapist, B
Romance
  Languages, Literatures, and Linguistics, M
Russian Language and Literature, BMD
Science Teacher Education/General Science
  Teacher Education, M
Slavic Languages, Literatures, and Linguistics, M
Social Psychology, D
Social Sciences, BM
Social Studies Teacher Education, M
Social Work, BMD
Sociology, BMD
Software Engineering, O
Spanish Language and Literature, B
Statistics, MD
Structural Biology, D
Substance Abuse/Addiction Counseling, M
Systems Engineering, M
Theater, M
Women's Health Nursing, MO
Women's Studies, BO

SUFFOLK COUNTY COMMUNITY COLLEGE

Accounting, A
Art/Art Studies, General, A
Automobile/Automotive Mechanics
  Technology/Technician, A
Biological and Physical Sciences, A
Biology/Biological Sciences, A
Business Administration and Management, A
Chemistry, A
Child Development, A
Civil Engineering Technology/Technician, A
Clinical Laboratory Science/Medical
  Technology/Technologist, A
Commercial and Advertising Art, A
Communications Systems Installation and Repair
  Technology, A
Community Organization and Advocacy, A
Computer Engineering Technology/Technician, A
Computer Programming/Programmer, A
Computer Science, A
Construction Engineering Technology/Technician, A
Consumer Merchandising/Retailing Management, A
Criminal Justice/Law Enforcement Administration, A
Criminal Justice/Police Science, A
Culinary Arts/Chef Training, A
Data Processing and Data Processing
  Technology/Technician, A

Dietetics/Dieticians, A
Drafting and Design Technology/Technician, A
Drama and Dramatics/Theatre Arts, A
Electrical, Electronic and Communications
   Engineering Technology/Technician, A
Engineering, A
Engineering Science, A
English Language and Literature, A
Horticultural Science, A
Human Services, A
Humanities/Humanistic Studies, A
Industrial Technology/Technician, A
Information Science/Studies, A
Information Technology, A
Insurance, A
Interior Design, A
Journalism, A
Kindergarten/PreSchool Education and Teaching, A
Legal Assistant/Paralegal, A
Liberal Arts and Sciences Studies and
   Humanities, A
Management Information Systems and Services, A
Marketing/Marketing Management, A
Mathematics, A
Mechanical Engineering/Mechanical
   Technology/Technician, A
Medical/Clinical Assistant, A
Music, A
Nursing - Registered Nurse Training, A
Opticianry/Ophthalmic Dispensing Optician, A
Parks, Recreation, Leisure and Fitness Studies, A
Photographic and Film/Video Technology/Technician
   and Assistant, A
Physical Therapy/Therapist, A
Real Estate, A
Sign Language Interpretation and Translation, A
Social Sciences, A
Substance Abuse/Addiction Counseling, A
Telecommunications Technology/Technician, A
Therapeutic Recreation/Recreational Therapy, A
Women's Studies, A

SULLIVAN COUNTY COMMUNITY COLLEGE

Accounting, A
Administrative Assistant and Secretarial Science, A
Baking and Pastry Arts/Baker/Pastry Chef, A
Business Administration and Management, A
Commercial and Advertising Art, A
Computer Graphics, A
Computer Programming, Specific Applications, A
Consumer Merchandising/Retailing Management, A
Corrections, A
Culinary Arts/Chef Training, A
Data Entry/Microcomputer Applications, A
Electrical, Electronic and Communications
   Engineering Technology/Technician, A
Elementary Education and Teaching, A
Engineering Science, A
Environmental Studies, A
Hospitality Administration/Management, A
Human Services, A
Information Science/Studies, A
Kindergarten/PreSchool Education and Teaching, A
Legal Assistant/Paralegal, A
Liberal Arts and Sciences Studies and
   Humanities, A
Marketing/Marketing Management, A
Mathematics, A
Nursing - Registered Nurse Training, A
Photography, A
Radio and Television, A
Sport and Fitness Administration/Management, A
Substance Abuse/Addiction Counseling, A
Survey Technology/Surveying, A
Tourism and Travel Services Management, A

SWEDISH INSTITUTE, COLLEGE OF HEALTH SCIENCES

Accounting, M
Acupuncture and Oriental Medicine, M

SYRACUSE UNIVERSITY

Accounting, BMDO
Acting, B
Advertising, B

Advertising and Public Relations, M
Aerospace, Aeronautical and Astronautical
   Engineering, BMD
African Studies, M
African-American/Black Studies, BM
American/United States Studies/Civilization, B
Anthropology, BMD
Apparel and Textiles, B
Applied Art, B
Applied Arts and Design, M
Architecture, BM
Area, Ethnic, Cultural, and Gender Studies, B
Art Education, MO
Art History, Criticism and Conservation, BM
Art Teacher Education, B
Art/Art Studies, General, B
Audiology/Audiologist and Speech-Language
   Pathology/Pathologist, B
Biochemistry, BD
Bioengineering, MD
Biological and Biomedical Sciences, MD
Biology Teacher Education, B
Biology/Biological Sciences, B
Biomedical Engineering, MD
Biomedical/Medical Engineering, B
Biophysics, BD
Broadcast Journalism, B
Business Administration and Management, B
Business Administration, Management and
   Operations, MDO
Ceramic Arts and Ceramics, BM
Chemical Engineering, BMD
Chemistry, BMD
Chemistry Teacher Education, B
Child and Family Studies, MD
Child Development, B
Cinematography and Film/Video Production, B
Civil Engineering, BMD
Classics and Classical
   Languages, Literatures, and Linguistics, B
Clinical Psychology, D
Commercial and Advertising Art, B
Communication and Media Studies, MDO
Communication Disorders, MD
Communication Studies/Speech Communication
   and Rhetoric, B
Communication Theory, M
Communication, Journalism and Related
   Programs, B
Comparative Literature, B
Composition, M
Computer and Information Sciences, B
Computer Art and Design, M
Computer Engineering, BMDO
Computer Graphics, B
Computer Science, MDO
Consumer Merchandising/Retailing Management, B
Consumer Services and Advocacy, B
Corporate and Organizational Communication, M
Counselor Education/School Counseling and
   Guidance Services, MDO
Curriculum and Instruction, MDO
Design and Visual Communications, B
Dietetics/Dieticians, B
Disability Studies, O
Drama and Dramatics/Theatre Arts, B
Early Childhood Education and Teaching, M
Economics, BMD
Education, BMDO
Educational Leadership and Administration, MDO
Educational Measurement and Evaluation, MDO
Educational Media/Instructional Technology, MO
Electrical Engineering, MDO
Electrical, Electronics and Communications
   Engineering, B
Elementary Education and Teaching, O
Engineering, B
Engineering and Applied Sciences, MDO
Engineering Management, M
Engineering Physics, B
English, MD
English Education, MDO
English Language and Literature, B
English Literature (British and Commonwealth), B
English/Language Arts Teacher Education, B
Entrepreneurship/Entrepreneurial Studies, B

Environmental Engineering
   Technology/Environmental Technology, MD
Environmental/Environmental Health Engineering, B
Exercise and Sports Science, M
Experimental Psychology, D
Family and Community Services, B
Family and Consumer Sciences/Home Economics
   Teacher Education, B
Family Systems, B
Fashion/Apparel Design, B
Fiber, Textile and Weaving Arts, B
Film, Television, and Video Production, M
Film/Video and Photographic Arts, B
Finance, B
Finance and Banking, D
Fine Arts and Art Studies, BM
Fine/Studio Arts, B
Foods, Nutrition, and Wellness Studies, B
Foreign Languages and Literatures, B
Foundations and Philosophy of Education, MDO
French Language and Literature, BM
Geography, BMD
Geology/Earth Science, BMD
German Language and Literature, B
Graphic Design, M
Health Services Administration, O
Higher Education/Higher Education
   Administration, MD
History, BMD
Hospitality Administration/Management, B
Housing and Human Environments, B
Human Development and Family Studies, B
Human Resources Development, D
Humanities/Humanistic Studies, B
Illustration, BM
Industrial and Manufacturing Management, D
Industrial Design, B
Information Science/Studies, BMDO
Interdisciplinary Studies, B
Interior Architecture, B
Interior Design, B
International Affairs, M
International Relations and Affairs, B
Internet and Interactive Multimedia, M
Italian Language and Literature, B
Jewelry/Metalsmithing, M
Journalism, BM
Kindergarten/PreSchool Education and Teaching, B
Kinesiology and Exercise Science, B
Latin American Studies, B
Law and Legal Studies, PO
Liberal Arts and Sciences Studies and
   Humanities, B
Library Science, MO
Linguistics, B
Logistics and Materials Management, BD
Management Information Systems and
   Services, MDO
Management Strategy and Policy, D
Marketing, D
Marketing/Marketing Management, B
Marriage and Family Therapy/Counseling, MD
Mass Communication/Media Studies, MD
Mathematics, BMD
Mathematics Teacher Education, BMD
Mechanical Engineering, BMD
Media Studies, M
Medieval and Renaissance Studies, B
Metal and Jewelry Arts, B
Modern Languages, B
Museology/Museum Studies, M
Music, BM
Music Management and Merchandising, B
Music Performance, B
Music Teacher Education, BM
Music Theory and Composition, B
Neuroscience, MD
Nutritional Sciences, BM
Organizational Behavior Studies, D
Painting, BM
Peace Studies and Conflict Resolution, B
Performance, M
Philosophy, BMD
Philosophy and Religious Studies, B
Photography, BM
Physical Education Teaching and Coaching, B

Physics, BMD
Physics Teacher Education, B
Piano and Organ, B
Political Science and Government, BMD
Pre-Dentistry Studies, B
Pre-Law Studies, B
Pre-Medicine/Pre-Medical Studies, B
Pre-Veterinary Studies, B
Printmaking, BM
Psychology, BD
Public Administration, BMDO
Public Health (MPH, DPH), B
Public Relations/Image Management, B
Quantitative Analysis, D
Radio and Television, B
Reading Teacher Education, MDO
Rehabilitation Counseling, M
Religion/Religious Studies, BMD
Restaurant/Food Services Management, B
Retailing and Retail Operations, B
Rhetoric, MD
Russian Language and Literature, B
Russian Studies, B
Sales, Distribution and Marketing Operations, B
School Psychology, D
Science Teacher Education/General Science
    Teacher Education, MD
Sculpture, BM
Social Psychology, D
Social Sciences, MD
Social Studies Teacher Education, BMO
Social Work, BM
Sociology, BMD
South Asian
    Languages, Literatures, and Linguistics, B
South Asian Studies, B
Spanish Language and Literature, BM
Special Education and Teaching, BMD
Speech and Rhetorical Studies, B
Sport and Fitness Administration/Management, B
Statistics, M
Structural Biology, D
Systems Science and Theory, M
Teacher Education and Professional
    Development, Specific Subject Areas, B
Teacher Education, Multiple Levels, B
Technical Theatre/Theatre Design and
    Technology, B
Telecommunications, MO
Telecommunications Management, MO
Telecommunications Technology/Technician, B
Textile Design, M
Transportation and Materials Moving, B
Violin, Viola, Guitar and Other Stringed
    Instruments, B
Voice and Opera, B
Wind and Percussion Instruments, B
Women's Studies, B
Writing, MD

TALMUDICAL INSTITUTE OF UPSTATE NEW YORK

Jewish/Judaic Studies, B
Rabbinical Studies, B

TALMUDICAL SEMINARY OHOLEI TORAH

Rabbinical Studies, B

TAYLOR BUSINESS INSTITUTE

Accounting, A
Administrative Assistant and Secretarial Science, A
Business Administration and Management, A
Tourism and Travel Services Management, A

TCI-THE COLLEGE OF TECHNOLOGY

Accounting, A
Administrative Assistant and Secretarial Science, A
Computer Engineering Technology/Technician, A
Construction Engineering Technology/Technician, A
Electrical, Electronic and Communications
    Engineering Technology/Technician, A

Heating, Air Conditioning and Refrigeration
    Technology/Technician, A

TOMPKINS CORTLAND COMMUNITY COLLEGE

Accounting, A
Administrative Assistant and Secretarial Science, A
Aeronautics/Aviation/Aerospace Science and
    Technology, A
Biological and Physical Sciences, A
Business Administration and Management, A
Child Care Provider/Assistant, A
Child Development, A
Commercial and Advertising Art, A
Computer and Information Sciences, A
Computer and Information Systems Security, A
Computer Graphics, A
Computer Hardware Engineering, A
Computer Programming, A
Computer Science, A
Computer Software Engineering, A
Computer/Information Technology Services
    Administration and Management, A
Construction Engineering Technology/Technician, A
Criminal Justice/Law Enforcement Administration, A
Data Entry/Microcomputer Applications, A
Electrical, Electronic and Communications
    Engineering Technology/Technician, A
Engineering Science, A
Environmental Studies, A
Hotel/Motel Administration/Management, A
Human Services, A
Humanities/Humanistic Studies, A
Information Science/Studies, A
International Business/Trade/Commerce, A
Kindergarten/PreSchool Education and Teaching, A
Legal Assistant/Paralegal, A
Liberal Arts and Sciences Studies and
    Humanities, A
Management Information Systems and Services, A
Marketing/Marketing Management, A
Mass Communication/Media Studies, A
Mathematics, A
Nursing - Registered Nurse Training, A
Parks, Recreation, Leisure and Fitness Studies, A
Radio and Television, A
Social Sciences, A
Sport and Fitness Administration/Management, A
Substance Abuse/Addiction Counseling, A
System Administration/Administrator, A
Tourism and Travel Services Management, A
Tourism and Travel Services Marketing
    Operations, A
Web Page, Digital/Multimedia and Information
    Resources Design, A
Women's Studies, A

TOURO COLLEGE

Accounting, B
Area, Ethnic, Cultural, and Gender Studies, B
Audiology/Audiologist and Speech-Language
    Pathology/Pathologist, B
Banking and Financial Support Services, A
Bible/Biblical Studies, B
Biological and Biomedical Sciences, MO
Biology/Biological Sciences, B
Business Administration and Management, B
Chemistry, B
Community Organization and Advocacy, AB
Comparative Literature, B
Computer Science, B
Economics, B
Education, B
English Language and Literature, B
Finance, B
Health Informatics, O
Health Information/Medical Records
    Administration/Administrator, B
Health Professions and Related Clinical Sciences, B
Health Services Administration, O
Hebrew Language and Literature, B
History, B
Human Services, B
Humanities/Humanistic Studies, B
Information Science/Studies, A
Interdisciplinary Studies, B

International Business/Trade/Commerce, B
Jewish/Judaic Studies, BM
Kindergarten/PreSchool Education and Teaching, B
Law and Legal Studies, MP
Liberal Arts and Sciences Studies and
    Humanities, AB
Marketing/Marketing Management, A
Mathematics, B
Occupational Therapy/Therapist, AM
Philosophy, B
Physical Therapy/Therapist, AM
Physician Assistant, B
Political Science and Government, B
Pre-Dentistry Studies, B
Pre-Law Studies, B
Pre-Medicine/Pre-Medical Studies, B
Prepress/Desktop Publishing and Digital Imaging
    Design, A
Psychology, B
Public Health (MPH, DPH), B
Social Sciences, A
Sociology, B
Special Education and Teaching, B

TROCAIRE COLLEGE

Administrative Assistant and Secretarial Science, A
Business Administration and Management, A
Environmental Studies, A
Health Information/Medical Records
    Administration/Administrator, A
Hotel/Motel Administration/Management, A
Industrial Radiologic Technology/Technician, A
Kindergarten/PreSchool Education and Teaching, A
Legal Administrative Assistant/Secretary, A
Liberal Arts and Sciences Studies and
    Humanities, A
Marketing/Marketing Management, A
Medical Administrative Assistant/Secretary, A
Medical/Clinical Assistant, A
Nursing - Registered Nurse Training, A
Radiologic Technology/Science - Radiographer, A
Surgical Technology/Technologist, A

ULSTER COUNTY COMMUNITY COLLEGE

Accounting, A
Administrative Assistant and Secretarial Science, A
Biological and Physical Sciences, A
Business Administration and Management, A
Commercial and Advertising Art, A
Community Organization and Advocacy, A
Computer Science, A
Consumer Merchandising/Retailing Management, A
Criminal Justice/Law Enforcement Administration, A
Data Processing and Data Processing
    Technology/Technician, A
Drafting and Design Technology/Technician, A
Elementary Education and Teaching, A
Engineering, A
Engineering Technology, A
Environmental Engineering
    Technology/Environmental Technology, A
Human Services, A
Humanities/Humanistic Studies, A
Industrial Technology/Technician, A
Information Science/Studies, A
Journalism, A
Liberal Arts and Sciences Studies and
    Humanities, A
Marketing/Marketing Management, A
Mass Communication/Media Studies, A
Mathematics, A
Nursing - Registered Nurse Training, A
Parks, Recreation, Leisure and Fitness Studies, A
Physical Sciences, A
Social Sciences, A

UNION COLLEGE

American/United States Studies/Civilization, B
Anthropology, B
Astronomy, B
Biochemistry, B
Biological and Biomedical Sciences, B
Biological and Physical Sciences, B
Biology/Biological Sciences, B
Chemistry, B

Classics and Classical
  Languages, Literatures, and Linguistics, B
Computer and Information Sciences, B
Economics, B
Electrical, Electronics and Communications
  Engineering, B
English Language and Literature, B
Fine/Studio Arts, B
Foreign Languages and Literatures, B
Geology/Earth Science, B
History, B
Humanities/Humanistic Studies, B
Liberal Arts and Sciences Studies and
  Humanities, B
Mathematics, B
Mechanical Engineering, B
Neuroscience, B
Philosophy, B
Physics, B
Political Science and Government, B
Psychology, B
Social Sciences, B
Sociology, B

UNITED STATES MERCHANT MARINE ACADEMY

Engineering/Industrial Management, B
Engineering-Related Technologies, B
Marine Science/Merchant Marine Officer, B
Marine Transportation, B
Maritime Science, B
Naval Architecture and Marine Engineering, B
Nuclear Engineering Technology/Technician, B
Transportation and Materials Moving, B

UNITED STATES MILITARY ACADEMY

Aerospace, Aeronautical and Astronautical
  Engineering, B
American/United States Studies/Civilization, B
Applied Mathematics, B
Arabic Language and Literature, B
Army JROTC/ROTC, B
Behavioral Sciences, B
Biological and Physical Sciences, B
Biology/Biological Sciences, B
Business Administration and Management, B
Central/Middle and Eastern European Studies, B
Chemical Engineering, B
Chemistry, B
Chinese Language and Literature, B
Civil Engineering, B
Comparative Literature, B
Computer Engineering, B
Computer Science, B
East Asian Studies, B
Economics, B
Electrical, Electronics and Communications
  Engineering, B
Engineering, B
Engineering Physics, B
Engineering/Industrial Management, B
Environmental Studies, B
Environmental/Environmental Health Engineering, B
European Studies/Civilization, B
French Language and Literature, B
Geography, B
German Language and Literature, B
History, B
Humanities/Humanistic Studies, B
Information Science/Studies, B
Interdisciplinary Studies, B
Latin American Studies, B
Mathematics, B
Mechanical Engineering, B
Modern Languages, B
Near and Middle Eastern Studies, B
Nuclear Engineering, B
Operations Research, B
Philosophy, B
Physics, B
Political Science and Government, B
Portuguese Language and Literature, B
Pre-Law Studies, B
Pre-Medicine/Pre-Medical Studies, B
Psychology, B
Public Policy Analysis, B

Russian Language and Literature, B
Spanish Language and Literature, B
Systems Engineering, B

UNIVERSITY AT ALBANY, STATE UNIVERSITY OF NEW YORK

Accounting, BM
Actuarial Science, B
African Studies, M
African-American/Black Studies, BM
Anthropology, BMD
Applied Mathematics, B
Art History, Criticism and Conservation, B
Art/Art Studies, General, B
Asian Studies/Civilization, B
Atmospheric Sciences and Meteorology, BMD
Biochemistry, BMD
Biological and Biomedical Sciences, MD
Biology Teacher Education, B
Biology/Biological Sciences, B
Biopsychology, D
Biostatistics, MD
BioTechnology, MD
Business Administration and Management, B
Business Administration, Management and
  Operations, MD
Cell Biology and Anatomy, MD
Central/Middle and Eastern European Studies, B
Chemistry, BMD
Chemistry Teacher Education, B
Chinese Language and Literature, B
Classics and Classical
  Languages, Literatures, and Linguistics, B
Clinical Psychology, D
Communication and Media Studies, MD
Computer and Information Sciences, B
Computer Science, BMD
Conservation Biology, M
Counseling Psychology, MDO
Counselor Education/School Counseling and
  Guidance Services, O
Criminal Justice/Law Enforcement Administration, B
Criminology, MDO
Curriculum and Instruction, MDO
Demography, O
Developmental Biology and Embryology, MD
Drama and Dramatics/Theatre Arts, B
East Asian Studies, B
Ecology, MD
Economics, BMDO
Education, MDO
Educational Administration and Supervision, MDO
Educational Measurement and Evaluation, D
Educational Media/Instructional Technology, MO
Educational Psychology, MDO
English, MDO
English Language and Literature, B
English/Language Arts Teacher Education, B
Environmental and Occupational Health, MD
Environmental Policy and Resource
  Management, M
Environmental Sciences, BM
Epidemiology, MD
Evolutionary Biology, MD
Experimental Psychology, D
Finance and Banking, M
Fine Arts and Art Studies, B
Foreign Language Teacher Education, B
Forensic Science and Technology, M
French Language and Literature, BMD
French Language Teacher Education, B
Genetics, MD
Geographic Information Systems, O
Geography, BMO
Geology/Earth Science, BMD
Geosciences, MD
Health Services Administration, M
Hispanic-American, Puerto Rican, and Mexican-
  American/Chicano Studies, B
History, BMDO
Human Resources Management and Services, M
Immunology, MD
Industrial and Organizational Psychology, D
Information Science/Studies, BMDO
Interdisciplinary Studies, B

Italian Language and Literature, BM
Japanese Studies, B
Jewish/Judaic Studies, B
Latin American Studies, BMO
Latin Language and Literature, B
Liberal Studies, M
Library Science, MDO
Linguistics, B
Management Information Systems and Services, M
Marketing, M
Mass Communication/Media Studies, B
Materials Sciences, MD
Mathematics, BMD
Mathematics and Computer Science, B
Mathematics Teacher Education, BM
Medieval and Renaissance Studies, B
Molecular Biology, BMD
Music, B
Neurobiology and Neurophysiology, MD
Neuroscience, MD
Organizational Management, D
Pathology/Experimental Pathology, MD
Philosophy, BMD
Physics, BMD
Political Science and Government, BMD
Psychology, BMDO
Public Administration, BMDO
Public Health, MD
Public History, O
Public Policy Analysis, BMDO
Reading Teacher Education, MDO
Rehabilitation Counseling, M
Religion/Religious Studies, B
Romance Languages, Literatures, and Linguistics, B
Russian Language and Literature, BMO
Russian Studies, B
School Psychology, DO
Science Teacher Education/General Science
  Teacher Education, BM
Slavic Languages, Literatures, and Linguistics, B
Social Psychology, D
Social Science Teacher Education, B
Social Work, BMDO
Sociology, BMDO
Spanish Language and Literature, BMD
Spanish Language Teacher Education, B
Special Education and Teaching, M
Speech and Rhetorical Studies, B
Statistics, MD
Structural Biology, MD
Taxation, M
Theater, M
Toxicology, MD
Translation and Interpretation, O
Urban and Regional Planning, M
Urban Studies/Affairs, BO
Women's Studies, BMD

UNIVERSITY OF ROCHESTER

African-American/Black Studies, B
Allopathic Medicine, PO
American Sign Language (ASL), B
Anatomy, MD
Anthropology, B
Applied Mathematics, B
Art History, Criticism and Conservation, BMD
Astronomy, MD
Biochemistry, MD
Biological and Biomedical Sciences, MDO
Biological and Physical Sciences, B
Biology/Biological Sciences, B
Biomedical Engineering, MD
Biomedical/Medical Engineering, B
Biophysics, MD
Biostatistics, MD
Business Administration, Management and
  Operations, MD
Chemical Engineering, BMD
Chemistry, BMD
Classics and Classical
  Languages, Literatures, and Linguistics, B
Clinical Psychology, D
Cognitive Sciences, BMD
Comparative Literature, B
Composition, MD
Computational Biology, MD

Computer Engineering, MD
Computer Science, BMD
Developmental Psychology, D
Economics, BMD
Education, MDO
Electrical Engineering, MD
Electrical, Electronics and Communications
    Engineering, B
Engineering and Applied Sciences, MD
Engineering Science, B
English, MD
English Language and Literature, B
Environmental Sciences, B
Environmental Studies, B
Epidemiology, MD
Film/Cinema Studies, B
Fine Arts and Art Studies, MD
Fine/Studio Arts, B
French Language and Literature, B
Genetics, MD
Geological/Geophysical Engineering, B
Geology/Earth Science, BMD
Geosciences, MD
German Language and Literature, B
Health Services Research, DO
History, BMD
Immunology, MDO
Japanese Language and Literature, B
Jazz/Jazz Studies, B
Linguistics, B
Marriage and Family Therapy/Counseling, M
Materials Sciences, MD
Mathematics, BMD
Mathematics and Statistics, B
Mechanical Engineering, BMD
Microbiology, MDO
Music, BMD
Music Teacher Education, BMD
Music Theory and Composition, BMD
Musicology and Ethnomusicology, MD
Neurobiology and Neurophysiology, MD
Neuroscience, MD
Nursing, MDO
Nursing - Registered Nurse Training, B
Optics/Optical Sciences, BMD
Oral and Dental Sciences, M
Pathology/Experimental Pathology, MD
Performance, MD
Pharmacology, MD
Philosophy, BMD
Physics, BMD
Physiology, MD
Political Science and Government, BMDO
Psychology, BMD
Public Health, MO
Religion/Religious Studies, B
Russian Language and Literature, B
Russian Studies, B
Social Psychology, D
Social Sciences, B
Spanish Language and Literature, B
Statistics, BMD
Toxicology, MD
Women's Studies, B

UTICA COLLEGE

Accounting, B
Biology Teacher Education, B
Biology/Biological Sciences, B
Business Administration and Management, B
Business Teacher Education, B
Business, Management, Marketing, and Related
    Support Services, B
Business/Managerial Economics, B
Chemistry, B
Chemistry Teacher Education, B
Communication Studies/Speech Communication
    and Rhetoric, B
Computer and Information Sciences, B
Computer Teacher Education, B
Criminal Justice/Law Enforcement Administration, B
Criminology, M
Developmental and Child Psychology, B
Economics, B
Elementary Education and Teaching, B
English Language and Literature, B

English/Language Arts Teacher Education, B
Health/Medical Preparatory Programs, B
History, B
History Teacher Education, B
International Business/Trade/Commerce, B
International Relations and Affairs, B
Journalism, B
Liberal Arts and Sciences Studies and
    Humanities, B
Mathematics, B
Mathematics Teacher Education, B
Nursing - Registered Nurse Training, B
Philosophy, B
Physics, B
Physics Teacher Education, B
Political Science and Government, B
Pre-Dentistry Studies, B
Pre-Law Studies, B
Pre-Medicine/Pre-Medical Studies, B
Pre-Veterinary Studies, B
Psychology, B
Public Relations/Image Management, B
Secondary Education and Teaching, B
Social Science Teacher Education, B
Social Sciences, B
Social Studies Teacher Education, B
Sociology, B
Therapeutic Recreation/Recreational Therapy, B

UTICA SCHOOL OF COMMERCE

Administrative Assistant and Secretarial Science, A
Business Administration and Management, A
Computer and Information Sciences and Support
    Services, A
Health Services Administration, A
Non-Profit/Public/Organizational Management, A

VASSAR COLLEGE

African Studies, B
American/United States Studies/Civilization, B
Ancient/Classical Greek Language and Literature, B
Anthropology, B
Art History, Criticism and Conservation, B
Asian Studies/Civilization, B
Astronomy, B
Biochemistry, B
Biological and Biomedical Sciences, M
Biology/Biological Sciences, B
Chemistry, BM
Chinese Language and Literature, B
Classics and Classical
    Languages, Literatures, and Linguistics, B
Cognitive Psychology and Psycholinguistics, B
Computer and Information Sciences, B
Drama and Dramatics/Theatre Arts, B
Economics, B
English Language and Literature, B
Environmental Sciences, B
Environmental Studies, B
Film/Cinema Studies, B
Fine/Studio Arts, B
French Language and Literature, B
Geography, B
Geology/Earth Science, B
German Language and Literature, B
History, B
Interdisciplinary Studies, B
International Relations and Affairs, B
Italian Language and Literature, B
Japanese Language and Literature, B
Jewish/Judaic Studies, B
Latin American Studies, B
Latin Language and Literature, B
Liberal Arts and Sciences Studies and
    Humanities, B
Mathematics, B
Medieval and Renaissance Studies, B
Multi-/Interdisciplinary Studies, B
Music, B
Philosophy, B
Physics, B
Physiological Psychology/Psychobiology, B
Political Science and Government, B
Psychology, B
Religion/Religious Studies, B
Russian Language and Literature, B

Science, Technology and Society, B
Sociology, B
Spanish Language and Literature, B
Urban Studies/Affairs, B
Visual and Performing Arts, B
Women's Studies, B

VAUGHN COLLEGE OF AERONAUTICS
AND TECHNOLOGY

Aeronautics/Aviation/Aerospace Science and
    Technology, A
Airframe Mechanics and Aircraft Maintenance
    Technology/Technician, AB
Airline/Commercial/Professional Pilot and Flight
    Crew, A
Aviation/Airway Management and Operations, B
Avionics Maintenance Technology/Technician, AB
Computer Graphics, AB
Engineering Technology, A
Machine Tool Technology/Machinist, A
Pre-Engineering, A

VILLA MARIA COLLEGE OF BUFFALO

Business Administration and Management, A
Education, A
Fine/Studio Arts, A
Graphic Design, A
Interior Design, AB
Jazz/Jazz Studies, A
Kindergarten/PreSchool Education and Teaching, A
Liberal Arts and Sciences Studies and
    Humanities, A
Music, A
Music Management and Merchandising, A
Physical Therapist Assistant, A
Public Health (MPH, DPH), A

WAGNER COLLEGE

Accounting, BM
Anthropology, B
Art/Art Studies, General, B
Arts Management, B
Biological and Biomedical Sciences, M
Biology/Biological Sciences, B
Business Administration and Management, B
Business Administration, Management and
    Operations, M
Chemistry, B
Computer and Information Sciences, B
Computer Science, B
Drama and Dramatics/Theatre Arts, B
Early Childhood Education and Teaching, M
Economics, B
Education, BM
Elementary Education and Teaching, BM
English Language and Literature, B
Finance, B
Finance and Banking, M
Health Services Administration, M
History, B
International Business/Trade/Commerce, M
International Relations and Affairs, B
Kindergarten/PreSchool Education and Teaching, B
Marketing, M
Mathematics, B
Medical Microbiology and Bacteriology, B
Microbiology, M
Middle School Education, M
Music, B
Nursing, M
Nursing - Advanced Practice, O
Nursing - Registered Nurse Training, B
Physician Assistant, BM
Physics, B
Political Science and Government, B
Pre-Dentistry Studies, B
Pre-Engineering, B
Pre-Law Studies, B
Pre-Medicine/Pre-Medical Studies, B
Pre-Theology/Pre-Ministerial Studies, B
Psychology, B
Public Administration, B
Reading Teacher Education, M
Secondary Education and Teaching, BM
Sociology, B

Spanish Language and Literature, B

WEBB INSTITUTE

Naval Architecture and Marine Engineering, B

WELLS COLLEGE

African-American/Black Studies, B
American/United States Studies/Civilization, B
Anthropology, B
Art History, Criticism and Conservation, B
Art/Art Studies, General, B
Biochemistry, B
Biology/Biological Sciences, B
Business Administration and Management, B
Chemistry, B
Computer Science, B
Creative Writing, B
Dance, B
Drama and Dramatics/Theatre Arts, B
Economics, B
Education, B
Elementary Education and Teaching, B
Engineering, B
English Language and Literature, B
Environmental Studies, B
Fine/Studio Arts, B
French Language and Literature, B
History, B
International Relations and Affairs, B
Mathematics, B
Molecular Biology, B
Music, B
Philosophy, B
Physics, B
Political Science and Government, B
Pre-Dentistry Studies, B
Pre-Law Studies, B
Pre-Medicine/Pre-Medical Studies, B
Pre-Veterinary Studies, B
Psychology, B
Public Policy Analysis, B
Religion/Religious Studies, B
Secondary Education and Teaching, B
Sociology, B
Spanish Language and Literature, B
Women's Studies, B

WESTCHESTER COMMUNITY COLLEGE

Accounting, A
Administrative Assistant and Secretarial Science, A
Applied Art, A
Automobile/Automotive Mechanics
   Technology/Technician, A
Biological and Physical Sciences, A
Business Administration and Management, A
Chemical Engineering, A
Child Care Provider/Assistant, A
Child Development, A
Civil Engineering Technology/Technician, A
Clinical Laboratory Science/Medical
   Technology/Technologist, A
Clinical/Medical Laboratory Technician, A
Computer and Information Sciences, A
Computer Science, A
Computer Systems Networking and
   Telecommunications, A
Consumer Merchandising/Retailing Management, A
Corrections, A
Criminal Justice/Law Enforcement Administration, A
Criminal Justice/Police Science, A
Culinary Arts/Chef Training, A
Dance, A
Data Processing and Data Processing
   Technology/Technician, A
Dietetics/Dieticians, A
Electrical, Electronic and Communications
   Engineering Technology/Technician, A
Emergency Medical Technology/Technician (EMT
   Paramedic), A
Engineering Science, A
Engineering Technology, A
Environmental Engineering
   Technology/Environmental Technology, A
Finance, A
Fine/Studio Arts, A

Food Technology and Processing, A
Hotel/Motel Administration/Management, A
Human Services, A
Humanities/Humanistic Studies, A
Industrial Radiologic Technology/Technician, A
Information Science/Studies, A
International Business/Trade/Commerce, A
Legal Administrative Assistant/Secretary, A
Legal Assistant/Paralegal, A
Liberal Arts and Sciences Studies and
   Humanities, A
Marketing/Marketing Management, A
Mass Communication/Media Studies, A
Mechanical Engineering/Mechanical
   Technology/Technician, A
Nursing - Registered Nurse Training, A
Public Administration, A
Respiratory Care Therapy/Therapist, A
Social Sciences, A
Special Products Marketing Operations, A
Substance Abuse/Addiction Counseling, A
Tourism and Travel Services Management, A
Tourism Promotion Operations, A

WOOD TOBE-COBURN SCHOOL

Accounting, A
Fashion Merchandising, A
Fashion/Apparel Design, A
Graphic Design, A
Marketing/Marketing Management, A
Medical/Clinical Assistant, A
Office Management and Supervision, A
System, Networking, and LAN/WAN
   Management/Manager, A
Tourism and Travel Services Marketing
   Operations, A

YESHIVA KARLIN STOLIN RABBINICAL INSTITUTE

Bible/Biblical Studies, B
Rabbinical Studies, B
Theology and Religious Vocations, O
Theology/Theological Studies, B

YESHIVA UNIVERSITY

Accounting, B
Audiology/Audiologist and Speech-Language
   Pathology/Pathologist, B
Biology/Biological Sciences, B
Business Administration and Management, B
Chemistry, B
Classics and Classical
   Languages, Literatures, and Linguistics, B
Clinical Psychology, D
Computer Science, B
Developmental Psychology, D
Drama and Dramatics/Theatre Arts, B
Economics, B
Education, B
Educational Administration and Supervision, MDO
Elementary Education and Teaching, B
English Language and Literature, B
Finance, B
French Language and Literature, B
Health Psychology, D
Hebrew Language and Literature, B
History, B
Interdisciplinary Studies, B
Jewish/Judaic Studies, BMD
Kindergarten/PreSchool Education and Teaching, B
Law and Legal Studies, MP
Management Information Systems and Services, B
Marketing/Marketing Management, B
Mass Communication/Media Studies, B
Mathematics, B
Music, B
Philosophy, B
Physics, B
Political Science and Government, B
Pre-Dentistry Studies, B
Pre-Law Studies, B
Pre-Medicine/Pre-Medical Studies, B
Psychology, BMD
Religious Education, MDO
School Psychology, D
Social Work, MDO

Sociology, B
Speech and Rhetorical Studies, B
Speech-Language Pathology/Pathologist, B

YESHIVAT MIKDASH MELECH

Ancient Near Eastern and Biblical
   Languages, Literatures, and Linguistics, B
Bible/Biblical Studies, B
Divinity/Ministry (BD, MDiv.), B
Hebrew Language and Literature, B
Philosophy, B
Rabbinical Studies, B
Religious Education, B

YESHIVATH ZICHRON MOSHE

Rabbinical Studies, B
Theology and Religious Vocations, O

YORK COLLEGE OF THE CITY UNIVERSITY OF NEW YORK

Accounting, B
African-American/Black Studies, B
Anthropology, B
Art/Art Studies, General, B
Biology Technician/BioTechnology Laboratory
   Technician, B
Biology/Biological Sciences, B
Business Administration and Management, B
Chemistry, B
Clinical Laboratory Science/Medical
   Technology/Technologist, B
Drama and Dramatics/Theatre Arts, B
Economics, B
English Language and Literature, B
Environmental Health, B
French Language and Literature, B
Geology/Earth Science, B
Gerontology, B
Health Teacher Education, B
History, B
Information Science/Studies, B
Italian Language and Literature, B
Liberal Arts and Sciences Studies and
   Humanities, B
Marketing/Marketing Management, B
Mathematics, B
Music, B
Nursing - Registered Nurse Training, B
Occupational Therapy/Therapist, B
Philosophy, B
Physical Education Teaching and Coaching, B
Physics, B
Political Science and Government, B
Psychology, B
Social Work, B
Sociology, B
Spanish Language and Literature, B
Speech and Rhetorical Studies, B

North Carolina

ALAMANCE COMMUNITY COLLEGE

Accounting Technology/Technician and
   Bookkeeping, A
Animal Sciences, A
Applied Horticulture/Horticultural Operations, A
Automobile/Automotive Mechanics
   Technology/Technician, A
Banking and Financial Support Services, A
BioTechnology, A
Business Administration and Management, A
Carpentry/Carpenter, A
Clinical/Medical Laboratory Technician, A
Commercial and Advertising Art, A
Computer Programming/Programmer, A
Criminal Justice/Safety Studies, A
Culinary Arts/Chef Training, A
Electrical, Electronic and Communications
   Engineering Technology/Technician, A
Electromechanical Technology/Electromechanical
   Engineering Technology, A
Executive Assistant/Executive Secretary, A
General Office Occupations and Clerical Services, A
Heating, Air Conditioning and Refrigeration
   Technology/Technician, A

Information Science/Studies, A
Kindergarten/PreSchool Education and Teaching, A
Legal Administrative Assistant/Secretary, A
Liberal Arts and Sciences Studies and
   Humanities, A
Machine Tool Technology/Machinist, A
Mechanical Engineering/Mechanical
   Technology/Technician, A
Medical Administrative Assistant/Secretary, A
Medical/Clinical Assistant, A
Nursing - Registered Nurse Training, A
Operations Management and Supervision, A
Real Estate, A
Social Work, A
Teacher Assistant/Aide, A
Welding Technology/Welder, A

APEX SCHOOL OF THEOLOGY

Religious Education, A
Theology and Religious Vocations, MP
Theology/Theological Studies, B

APPALACHIAN STATE UNIVERSITY

Accounting, BM
Advertising, B
American/United States Studies/Civilization, M
Anthropology, B
Apparel and Textiles, B
Applied Physics, M
Art Teacher Education, B
Art/Art Studies, General, B
Arts Management, B
Athletic Training and Sports Medicine, B
Audiology/Audiologist and Speech-Language
   Pathology/Pathologist, B
Biological and Biomedical Sciences, M
Biology Teacher Education, B
Biology/Biological Sciences, B
Business Administration and Management, B
Business Administration, Management and
   Operations, M
Business Teacher Education, B
Chemistry, B
Chemistry Teacher Education, B
Child Development, B
City/Urban, Community and Regional Planning, B
Clinical Laboratory Science/Medical
   Technology/Technologist, B
Clinical Psychology, M
Communication Disorders, BM
Community Psychology, M
Computer Science, BM
Counselor Education/School Counseling and
   Guidance Services, MO
Criminal Justice/Safety Studies, B
Curriculum and Instruction, M
Drama and Dance Teacher Education, B
Drama and Dramatics/Theatre Arts, B
Early Childhood Education and Teaching, M
Ecology, B
Economics, B
Education, MDO
Education/Teaching of Individuals with Specific
   Learning Disabilities, B
Educational Administration and Supervision, M
Educational Leadership and Administration, D
Educational Media/Instructional Technology, MO
Electrical, Electronic and Communications
   Engineering Technology/Technician, B
Elementary Education and Teaching, BM
English, M
English Education, M
English Language and Literature, B
English/Language Arts Teacher Education, B
Exercise and Sports Science, M
Experimental Psychology, M
Family and Consumer Sciences/Home Economics
   Teacher Education, B
Family and Consumer Sciences/Human
   Sciences, M
Finance, B
Fine/Studio Arts, B
Foods, Nutrition, and Wellness Studies, B
French Language and Literature, B
French Language Teacher Education, B
Geography, BM

Geology/Earth Science, B
Gerontology, BM
Graphic and Printing Equipment Operator
   Production, B
Graphic Design, B
Health Psychology, M
Health Teacher Education, B
Health/Health Care Administration/Management, B
Higher Education/Higher Education
   Administration, MO
History, BM
History Teacher Education, B
Home Economics, M
Hospitality Administration/Management, B
Human Development, M
Industrial and Organizational Psychology, M
Industrial Design, B
Industrial Education, M
Industrial Production Technologies/Technicians, B
Industrial Technology/Technician, B
Insurance, B
International Business/Trade/Commerce, B
Journalism, B
Junior High/Intermediate/Middle School Education
   and Teaching, B
Kindergarten/PreSchool Education and Teaching, B
Kinesiology and Exercise Science, B
Liberal Arts and Sciences Studies and
   Humanities, B
Library Science, BMO
Management Information Systems and Services, B
Marketing/Marketing Management, B
Marriage and Family Therapy/Counseling, M
Mathematics, BM
Mathematics Teacher Education, BM
Music, M
Music Management and Merchandising, B
Music Performance, B
Music Teacher Education, BM
Music Therapy/Therapist, B
Parks, Recreation and Leisure Facilities
   Management, B
Performance, M
Philosophy and Religious Studies, B
Physical Education Teaching and Coaching, BM
Physics, B
Physics Teacher Education, B
Political Science and Government, BM
Psychology, BMO
Public Administration, M
Public Health Education and Promotion, B
Public History, M
Public Relations/Image Management, B
Radio and Television, B
Reading Teacher Education, M
Romance
   Languages, Literatures, and Linguistics, M
School Psychology, MO
Secondary Education and Teaching, M
Social Sciences, M
Social Studies Teacher Education, B
Social Work, B
Sociology, B
Spanish Language and Literature, B
Spanish Language Teacher Education, B
Special Education and Teaching, M
Speech and Rhetorical Studies, B
Sport and Fitness Administration/Management, M
Statistics, B
Teacher Education and Professional
   Development, Specific Subject Areas, B
Technology Teacher Education/Industrial Arts
   Teacher Education, B

ASHEVILLE-BUNCOMBE TECHNICAL COMMUNITY COLLEGE

Accounting Technology/Technician and
   Bookkeeping, A
Automobile/Automotive Mechanics
   Technology/Technician, A
Business Administration and Management, A
Child Care and Support Services Management, A
Civil Engineering Technology/Technician, A
Clinical/Medical Laboratory Technician, A
Computer Programming/Programmer, A

Computer Systems Networking and
   Telecommunications, A
Criminal Justice/Police Science, A
Culinary Arts/Chef Training, A
Dental Hygiene/Hygienist, A
Drafting/Design Engineering
   Technologies/Technicians, A
Emergency Medical Technology/Technician (EMT
   Paramedic), A
Executive Assistant/Executive Secretary, A
Heating, Air Conditioning, Ventilation and
   Refrigeration Maintenance
   Technology/Technician, A
Hotel/Motel Administration/Management, A
Institutional Food Workers, A
Liberal Arts and Sciences Studies and
   Humanities, A
Machine Tool Technology/Machinist, A
Mechanical Engineering/Mechanical
   Technology/Technician, A
Medical Radiologic Technology/Science - Radiation
   Therapist, A
Nursing - Registered Nurse Training, A
Operations Management and Supervision, A
Social Work, A
Survey Technology/Surveying, A
Tool and Die Technology/Technician, A

BARBER-SCOTIA COLLEGE

Accounting, B
Biology/Biological Sciences, B
Business Administration and Management, B
Computer Science, B
Criminal Justice/Law Enforcement Administration, B
Elementary Education and Teaching, B
English Language and Literature, B
Finance, B
Hotel/Motel Administration/Management, B
Marketing/Marketing Management, B
Mass Communication/Media Studies, B
Mathematics, B
Political Science and Government, B
Pre-Law Studies, B
Sociology, B

BARTON COLLEGE

Accounting, B
Art Teacher Education, B
Athletic Training and Sports Medicine, B
Biology/Biological Sciences, B
Business Administration and Management, B
Chemistry, B
Computer and Information Sciences, B
Criminal Justice/Law Enforcement Administration, B
Drama and Dramatics/Theatre Arts, B
Economics, B
Education/Teaching of Individuals with Hearing
   Impairments, Including Deafness, B
Elementary Education and Teaching, B
English Language and Literature, B
Environmental Studies, B
Fine/Studio Arts, B
History, B
Human Resources Management/Personnel
   Administration, B
Junior High/Intermediate/Middle School Education
   and Teaching, B
Liberal Arts and Sciences Studies and
   Humanities, B
Marketing/Marketing Management, B
Mass Communication/Media Studies, B
Mathematics, B
Musical Instrument Fabrication and Repair, B
Nursing - Registered Nurse Training, B
Philosophy and Religious Studies, B
Physical Education Teaching and Coaching, B
Political Science and Government, B
Psychology, B
Social Work, B
Spanish Language and Literature, B
Special Education and Teaching, B

Sport and Fitness Administration/Management, B

BEAUFORT COUNTY COMMUNITY COLLEGE

Accounting, A
Administrative Assistant and Secretarial Science, A
Agricultural Mechanization, A
Automobile/Automotive Mechanics
   Technology/Technician, A
Business Administration and Management, A
Clinical/Medical Laboratory Technician, A
Computer Programming/Programmer, A
Computer Systems Networking and
   Telecommunications, A
Criminal Justice/Police Science, A
Drafting and Design Technology/Technician, A
Electrical, Electronic and Communications
   Engineering Technology/Technician, A
Heavy Equipment Maintenance
   Technology/Technician, A
Human Resources Management/Personnel
   Administration, A
Information Science/Studies, A
Kindergarten/PreSchool Education and Teaching, A
Liberal Arts and Sciences Studies and
   Humanities, A
Medical Administrative Assistant/Secretary, A
Medical Office Management/Administration, A
Nursing - Registered Nurse Training, A
Social Work, A
Welding Technology/Welder, A

BELMONT ABBEY COLLEGE

Accounting, B
Biology/Biological Sciences, B
Business Administration and Management, B
Clinical Laboratory Science/Medical
   Technology/Technologist, B
Economics, B
Education, B
Elementary Education and Teaching, B
English Language and Literature, B
History, B
Information Science/Studies, B
International Business/Trade/Commerce, B
Philosophy, B
Political Science and Government, B
Pre-Dentistry Studies, B
Pre-Law Studies, B
Pre-Medicine/Pre-Medical Studies, B
Pre-Pharmacy Studies, B
Pre-Veterinary Studies, B
Psychology, B
Secondary Education and Teaching, B
Sociology, B
Theology/Theological Studies, B
Therapeutic Recreation/Recreational Therapy, B

BENNETT COLLEGE FOR WOMEN

Accounting, B
Art/Art Studies, General, B
Arts Management, B
Biology/Biological Sciences, B
Business Administration and Management, B
Chemistry, B
Computer Science, B
Elementary Education and Teaching, B
English Language and Literature, B
Family and Consumer Sciences/Human Sciences, B
Interdisciplinary Studies, B
Junior High/Intermediate/Middle School Education
   and Teaching, B
Kindergarten/PreSchool Education and Teaching, B
Mass Communication/Media Studies, B
Mathematics, B
Music, B
Music Teacher Education, B
Political Science and Government, B
Psychology, B
Science Teacher Education/General Science
   Teacher Education, B
Social Work, B
Sociology, B

Special Education and Teaching, B

BLADEN COMMUNITY COLLEGE

Administrative Assistant and Secretarial Science, A
BioTechnology, A
Business Administration and Management, A
Child Care Provider/Assistant, A
Computer Programming, Specific Applications, A
Computer Programming/Programmer, A
Cosmetology/Cosmetologist, A
Criminal Justice/Police Science, A
Electrical, Electronic and Communications
   Engineering Technology/Technician, A
General Studies, A
Industrial Technology/Technician, A
Information Technology, A
Liberal Arts and Sciences Studies and
   Humanities, A
Nursing - Registered Nurse Training, A
Welding Technology/Welder, A

BLUE RIDGE COMMUNITY COLLEGE

Administrative Assistant and Secretarial Science, A
Art/Art Studies, General, A
Business Administration and Management, A
Computer Programming, A
Computer Programming/Programmer, A
Cosmetology/Cosmetologist, A
Drafting and Design Technology/Technician, A
Electrical, Electronic and Communications
   Engineering Technology/Technician, A
Environmental Engineering
   Technology/Environmental Technology, A
Horticultural Science, A
Industrial Technology/Technician, A
Information Science/Studies, A
Kindergarten/PreSchool Education and Teaching, A
Liberal Arts and Sciences Studies and
   Humanities, A
Machine Tool Technology/Machinist, A
Marketing/Marketing Management, A
Mechanical Engineering/Mechanical
   Technology/Technician, A
Nursing - Registered Nurse Training, A
Sign Language Interpretation and Translation, A
Surgical Technology/Technologist, A
System Administration/Administrator, A
Tourism and Travel Services Management, A

BREVARD COLLEGE

Art/Art Studies, General, B
Business Administration and Management, B
Dramatic/Theatre Arts and Stagecraft, B
Ecology, B
Education, B
Elementary Education and Teaching, B
English Language and Literature, B
Environmental Studies, B
General Studies, B
Health Services/Allied Health/Health Sciences, B
History, B
Interdisciplinary Studies, B
Junior High/Intermediate/Middle School Education
   and Teaching, B
Kinesiology and Exercise Science, B
Mathematics, B
Multi-/Interdisciplinary Studies, B
Music, B
Parks, Recreation, Leisure and Fitness Studies, B
Psychology, B
Religion/Religious Studies, B
Secondary Education and Teaching, B

BRUNSWICK COMMUNITY COLLEGE

Administrative Assistant and Secretarial Science, A
Applied Horticulture/Horticultural Operations, A
Aquaculture, A
Business Administration and Management, A
Child Care Provider/Assistant, A
Computer Programming, A
Computer Programming/Programmer, A
Computer/Information Technology Services
   Administration and Management, A
Electrical, Electronic and Communications
   Engineering Technology/Technician, A
Engineering Technology, A

Fishing and Fisheries Sciences and Management, A
Health Information/Medical Records
   Administration/Administrator, A
Industrial Technology/Technician, A
Liberal Arts and Sciences Studies and
   Humanities, A
Nursing - Registered Nurse Training, A
Teacher Assistant/Aide, A
Turf and Turfgrass Management, A

CABARRUS COLLEGE OF HEALTH SCIENCES

Health/Health Care Administration/Management, A
Medical/Clinical Assistant, A
Nurse/Nursing Assistant/Aide and Patient Care
   Assistant, A
Nursing - Registered Nurse Training, AB
Occupational Therapist Assistant, A
Surgical Technology/Technologist, A

CALDWELL COMMUNITY COLLEGE AND TECHNICAL INSTITUTE

Accounting, A
Aeronautics/Aviation/Aerospace Science and
   Technology, A
Art/Art Studies, General, A
Biological and Physical Sciences, A
Biomedical Technology/Technician, A
Business Administration and Management, A
Cardiovascular Technology/Technologist, A
Child Care and Support Services Management, A
Computer Programming, Specific Applications, A
Computer Systems Networking and
   Telecommunications, A
Cosmetology/Cosmetologist, A
Diagnostic Medical Sonography/Sonographer and
   Ultrasound Technician, A
Drafting and Design Technology/Technician, A
Electrical, Electronic and Communications
   Engineering Technology/Technician, A
Health/Health Care Administration/Management, A
Information Technology, A
Landscaping and Groundskeeping, A
Legal Assistant/Paralegal, A
Liberal Arts and Sciences Studies and
   Humanities, A
Medical Radiologic Technology/Science - Radiation
   Therapist, A
Music, A
Nuclear Medical Technology/Technologist, A
Nursing - Registered Nurse Training, A
Physical Therapy/Therapist, A
Pre-Engineering, A

CAMPBELL UNIVERSITY

Accounting, B
Accounting and Business/Management, B
Accounting and Finance, B
Acting, B
Advertising, B
Army JROTC/ROTC, B
Art/Art Studies, General, B
Athletic Training and Sports Medicine, B
Biochemistry, B
Biology Teacher Education, B
Biology/Biological Sciences, B
Broadcast Journalism, B
Business Administration and Management, B
Business Administration, Management and
   Operations, M
Business/Commerce, B
Chemistry, B
Child Development, B
Commercial and Advertising Art, B
Communication and Media Studies, B
Communication Studies/Speech Communication
   and Rhetoric, B
Communication, Journalism and Related
   Programs, B
Computer and Information Sciences, B
Counselor Education/School Counseling and
   Guidance Services, M
Criminal Justice/Law Enforcement Administration, B
Directing and Theatrical Production, B
Divinity/Ministry (BD, MDiv.), B
Drama and Dramatics/Theatre Arts, B

Economics, B
Education, BM
Educational Administration and Supervision, M
Educational Leadership and Administration, B
Elementary and Middle School
  Administration/Principalship, B
Elementary Education and Teaching, BM
Engineering, A
English Education, M
English Language and Literature, B
Family and Consumer Sciences/Home Economics
  Teacher Education, B
Family and Consumer Sciences/Human Sciences, B
Finance, B
Fine/Studio Arts, B
Foreign Languages and Literatures, B
French Language and Literature, B
General Studies, B
Graphic Design, B
Health and Physical Education, B
Health and Physical Education/Fitness, B
History, B
History Teacher Education, B
Interdisciplinary Studies, M
International Business/Trade/Commerce, B
International Relations and Affairs, B
Journalism, B
Junior High/Intermediate/Middle School Education
  and Teaching, B
Kinesiology and Exercise Science, B
Law and Legal Studies, P
Liberal Arts and Sciences Studies and
  Humanities, A
Marketing/Marketing Management, B
Mass Communication/Media Studies, B
Mathematics, B
Mathematics Teacher Education, BM
Middle School Education, M
Music, B
Music Pedagogy, B
Music Performance, B
Music Teacher Education, B
Music Theory and Composition, B
Pastoral Studies/Counseling, B
Pharmaceutical Sciences, M
Pharmaceutics and Drug Design, B
Pharmacology, B
Pharmacy, BMP
Pharmacy, Pharmaceutical Sciences, and
  Administration, B
Physical Education Teaching and Coaching, BM
Piano and Organ, B
Political Science and Government, B
Pre-Dentistry Studies, B
Pre-Engineering, A
Pre-Law Studies, B
Pre-Medicine/Pre-Medical Studies, B
Pre-Pharmacy Studies, B
Pre-Theology/Pre-Ministerial Studies, B
Pre-Veterinary Studies, B
Psychology, B
Public Administration, B
Public Relations, Advertising, and Applied
  Communication, B
Public Relations/Image Management, B
Radio and Television, B
Radio, Television, and Digital Communication, B
Religion/Religious Studies, B
Religious Education, M
Science Teacher Education/General Science
  Teacher Education, B
Secondary Education and Teaching, BM
Social Sciences, B
Social Studies Teacher Education, BM
Social Work, B
Spanish Language and Literature, B
Spanish Language Teacher Education, B
Sport and Fitness Administration/Management, B
Teacher Education, Multiple Levels, B
Teaching French as a Second or Foreign
  Language, B
Theatre/Theatre Arts Management, B
Theology and Religious Vocations, MDP

Youth Ministry, B

CAPE FEAR COMMUNITY COLLEGE

Accounting Technology/Technician and
  Bookkeeping, A
Architectural Engineering Technology/Technician, A
Automobile/Automotive Mechanics
  Technology/Technician, A
Business Administration and Management, A
Chemical Technology/Technician, A
Child Care and Support Services Management, A
Computer Systems Analysis/Analyst, A
Computer Systems Networking and
  Telecommunications, A
Computer Technology/Computer Systems
  Technology, A
Criminal Justice/Police Science, A
Dental Hygiene/Hygienist, A
Diagnostic Medical Sonography/Sonographer and
  Ultrasound Technician, A
Electrical, Electronic and Communications
  Engineering Technology/Technician, A
Electrical/Electronics Equipment Installation and
  Repair, A
Engineering/Industrial Management, A
Environmental Studies, A
Executive Assistant/Executive Secretary, A
Hotel/Motel Administration/Management, A
Industrial Production Technologies/Technicians, A
Institutional Food Workers, A
Instrumentation Technology/Technician, A
Interior Design, A
Landscaping and Groundskeeping, A
Liberal Arts and Sciences Studies and
  Humanities, A
Machine Shop Technology/Assistant, A
Marine Maintenance/Fitter and Ship Repair
  Technology/Technician, A
Marine Technology, A
Mechanical Engineering/Mechanical
  Technology/Technician, A
Medical Radiologic Technology/Science - Radiation
  Therapist, A
Nursing - Registered Nurse Training, A

CAROLINAS COLLEGE OF HEALTH SCIENCES

Medical Radiologic Technology/Science - Radiation
  Therapist, A
Nursing - Registered Nurse Training, A
Radiologic Technology/Science - Radiographer, A

CARTERET COMMUNITY COLLEGE

Administrative Assistant and Secretarial Science, A
Business Administration and Management, A
Computer Engineering Technology/Technician, A
Computer Software and Media Applications, A
Computer Systems Networking and
  Telecommunications, A
Criminal Justice/Law Enforcement Administration, A
Industrial Radiologic Technology/Technician, A
Information Technology, A
Interior Design, A
Legal Administrative Assistant/Secretary, A
Legal Assistant/Paralegal, A
Liberal Arts and Sciences Studies and
  Humanities, A
Licensed Practical/Vocational Nurse Training, A
Medical/Clinical Assistant, A
Photography, A
Respiratory Care Therapy/Therapist, A
Teacher Assistant/Aide, A
Therapeutic Recreation/Recreational Therapy, A

CATAWBA COLLEGE

Athletic Training and Sports Medicine, B
Biology/Biological Sciences, B
Business Administration and Management, B
Business/Managerial Economics, B
Chemistry, B
Clinical Laboratory Science/Medical
  Technology/Technologist, B
Computer Science, B
Drama and Dramatics/Theatre Arts, B
Education, BM

Elementary Education and Teaching, BM
English Language and Literature, B
Environmental Studies, B
French Language and Literature, B
History, B
Humanities/Humanistic Studies, B
Information Science/Studies, B
Interdisciplinary Studies, B
International Relations and Affairs, B
Junior High/Intermediate/Middle School Education
  and Teaching, B
Marketing/Marketing Management, B
Mass Communication/Media Studies, B
Mathematics, B
Music, B
Music Teacher Education, B
Parks, Recreation, Leisure and Fitness Studies, B
Philosophy, B
Physical Education Teaching and Coaching, B
Physician Assistant, B
Piano and Organ, B
Political Science and Government, B
Pre-Dentistry Studies, B
Pre-Law Studies, B
Pre-Medicine/Pre-Medical Studies, B
Pre-Veterinary Studies, B
Psychology, B
Reading Teacher Education, B
Religion/Religious Studies, B
Secondary Education and Teaching, B
Sociology, B
Spanish Language and Literature, B
Therapeutic Recreation/Recreational Therapy, B
Voice and Opera, B

CATAWBA VALLEY COMMUNITY COLLEGE

Accounting Technology/Technician and
  Bookkeeping, A
Administrative Assistant and Secretarial Science, A
Architectural Engineering Technology/Technician, A
Automobile/Automotive Mechanics
  Technology/Technician, A
Banking and Financial Support Services, A
Business Administration and Management, A
Business, Management, Marketing, and Related
  Support Services, A
Commercial and Advertising Art, A
Computer Engineering, A
Computer Engineering Technology/Technician, A
Computer Programming, Specific Applications, A
Computer Programming/Programmer, A
Computer Science, A
Computer Systems Networking and
  Telecommunications, A
Criminal Justice/Police Science, A
Criminology, A
Data Processing and Data Processing
  Technology/Technician, A
Dental Hygiene/Hygienist, A
Electrical, Electronic and Communications
  Engineering Technology/Technician, A
Emergency Medical Technology/Technician (EMT
  Paramedic), A
Engineering Technologies/Technicians, A
Fire Protection and Safety Technology/Technician, A
Funeral Service and Mortuary Science, A
Furniture Design and Manufacturing, A
Health and Medical Administrative Services, A
Health Information/Medical Records
  Technology/Technician, A
Industrial Technology/Technician, A
Information Technology, A
Legal Assistant/Paralegal, A
Liberal Arts and Sciences Studies and
  Humanities, A
Marketing/Marketing Management, A
Mechanical Engineering/Mechanical
  Technology/Technician, A
Medical Radiologic Technology/Science - Radiation
  Therapist, A
Nursing - Registered Nurse Training, A
Operations Management and Supervision, A
Photographic and Film/Video Technology/Technician
  and Assistant, A
Photography, A

Real Estate, A
Respiratory Care Therapy/Therapist, A
Retailing and Retail Operations, A
Speech-Language Pathology/Pathologist, A
Teacher Assistant/Aide, A

CENTRAL CAROLINA COMMUNITY COLLEGE

Accounting, A
Administrative Assistant and Secretarial Science, A
Automobile/Automotive Mechanics
  Technology/Technician, A
Business Administration and Management, A
Computer Programming, Specific Applications, A
Computer Programming/Programmer, A
Computer Systems Networking and
  Telecommunications, A
Computer/Information Technology Services
  Administration and Management, A
Criminal Justice/Law Enforcement Administration, A
Drafting and Design Technology/Technician, A
Electrical, Electronic and Communications
  Engineering Technology/Technician, A
Information Science/Studies, A
Information Technology, A
Instrumentation Technology/Technician, A
Kindergarten/PreSchool Education and Teaching, A
Laser and Optical Technology/Technician, A
Legal Administrative Assistant/Secretary, A
Legal Assistant/Paralegal, A
Liberal Arts and Sciences Studies and
  Humanities, A
Marketing/Marketing Management, A
Medical Administrative Assistant/Secretary, A
Medical/Clinical Assistant, A
Nursing - Registered Nurse Training, A
Operations Management and Supervision, A
Quality Control Technology/Technician, A
Radio and Television, A
Social Work, A
Telecommunications Technology/Technician, A
Veterinary/Animal Health Technology/Technician and
  Veterinary Assistant, A

CENTRAL PIEDMONT COMMUNITY COLLEGE

Accounting, A
Administrative Assistant and Secretarial Science, A
Advertising, A
Applied Art, A
Architectural Engineering Technology/Technician, A
Art/Art Studies, General, A
Automobile/Automotive Mechanics
  Technology/Technician, A
Biology/Biological Sciences, A
Business Administration and Management, A
Business Machine Repairer, A
Child Development, A
Civil Engineering Technology/Technician, A
Clinical Laboratory Science/Medical
  Technology/Technologist, A
Clinical/Medical Laboratory Technician, A
Commercial and Advertising Art, A
Computer Engineering Technology/Technician, A
Computer Programming, Specific Applications, A
Computer Programming/Programmer, A
Computer Science, A
Consumer Merchandising/Retailing Management, A
Criminal Justice/Law Enforcement Administration, A
Criminal Justice/Police Science, A
Culinary Arts/Chef Training, A
Dance, A
Data Processing and Data Processing
  Technology/Technician, A
Dental Hygiene/Hygienist, A
Drafting and Design Technology/Technician, A
Electrical, Electronic and Communications
  Engineering Technology/Technician, A
Electromechanical Technology/Electromechanical
  Engineering Technology, A
Engineering Technology, A
Environmental Engineering
  Technology/Environmental Technology, A
Fashion Merchandising, A
Finance, A
Fire Science/Firefighting, A

Food Science, A
Food Technology and Processing, A
Graphic and Printing Equipment Operator
  Production, A
Health Information/Medical Records
  Administration/Administrator, A
Health/Health Care Administration/Management, A
Horticultural Science, A
Hospitality Administration/Management, A
Hotel/Motel Administration/Management, A
Human Services, A
Industrial Technology/Technician, A
Insurance, A
Interior Design, A
Kindergarten/PreSchool Education and Teaching, A
Legal Administrative Assistant/Secretary, A
Legal Assistant/Paralegal, A
Liberal Arts and Sciences Studies and
  Humanities, A
Licensed Practical/Vocational Nurse Training, A
Machine Tool Technology/Machinist, A
Marketing/Marketing Management, A
Mechanical Engineering/Mechanical
  Technology/Technician, A
Medical Administrative Assistant/Secretary, A
Medical/Clinical Assistant, A
Music, A
Nursing - Registered Nurse Training, A
Physical Therapy/Therapist, A
Real Estate, A
Respiratory Care Therapy/Therapist, A
Sign Language Interpretation and Translation, A
Social Work, A
Special Products Marketing Operations, A
Survey Technology/Surveying, A
Tourism and Travel Services Management, A
Transportation and Materials Moving, A
Welding Technology/Welder, A

CHOWAN UNIVERSITY

Accounting, B
Agriculture, B
Art/Art Studies, General, B
Athletic Training and Sports Medicine, B
Biological and Physical Sciences, B
Biology/Biological Sciences, B
Business Administration and Management, B
Commercial and Advertising Art, B
Criminal Justice/Safety Studies, B
Elementary Education and Teaching, B
English Language and Literature, B
English/Language Arts Teacher Education, B
Environmental Biology, B
Fine/Studio Arts, B
Graphic and Printing Equipment Operator
  Production, AB
History, B
History Teacher Education, B
Information Science/Studies, B
Interdisciplinary Studies, B
Kinesiology and Exercise Science, B
Liberal Arts and Sciences Studies and
  Humanities, B
Marketing/Marketing Management, B
Mathematics, B
Mathematics Teacher Education, B
Music, AB
Music Management and Merchandising, A
Music Teacher Education, B
Physical Education Teaching and Coaching, B
Physical Sciences, B
Pre-Dentistry Studies, B
Pre-Law Studies, B
Pre-Medicine/Pre-Medical Studies, B
Pre-Veterinary Studies, B
Psychology, B
Religion/Religious Studies, B
Small Business Administration/Management, B
Sport and Fitness Administration/Management, B

CLEVELAND COMMUNITY COLLEGE

Accounting, A
Administrative Assistant and Secretarial Science, A
Biological and Physical Sciences, A
Business Administration and Management, A
Communications Technology/Technician, A

Computer Engineering Technology/Technician, A
Computer Programming, Specific Applications, A
Criminal Justice/Law Enforcement Administration, A
Criminal Justice/Safety Studies, A
Data Entry/Microcomputer Applications, A
Electrical, Electronic and Communications
  Engineering Technology/Technician, A
Electrician, A
Engineering Technologies/Technicians, A
Executive Assistant/Executive Secretary, A
Fashion Merchandising, A
Fire Protection and Safety Technology/Technician, A
Industrial Radiologic Technology/Technician, A
Information Science/Studies, A
Information Technology, A
Liberal Arts and Sciences Studies and
  Humanities, A
Management Information Systems and Services, A
Mechanical Engineering/Mechanical
  Technology/Technician, A
Medical Administrative Assistant/Secretary, A
Medical Radiologic Technology/Science - Radiation
  Therapist, A
Nursing - Registered Nurse Training, A
Operations Management and Supervision, A
Spanish Language and Literature, A
Special Education and Teaching, A
System Administration/Administrator, A
Teacher Assistant/Aide, A

COASTAL CAROLINA COMMUNITY COLLEGE

Accounting, A
Architectural Engineering Technology/Technician, A
Business Administration and Management, A
Child Care Provider/Assistant, A
Clinical/Medical Laboratory Technician, A
Computer Programming, Specific Applications, A
Computer Systems Analysis/Analyst, A
Computer Systems Networking and
  Telecommunications, A
Computer/Information Technology Services
  Administration and Management, A
Criminal Justice/Law Enforcement Administration, A
Dental Hygiene/Hygienist, A
Emergency Medical Technology/Technician (EMT
  Paramedic), A
Executive Assistant/Executive Secretary, A
Fire Science/Firefighting, A
Legal Assistant/Paralegal, A
Liberal Arts and Sciences Studies and
  Humanities, A
Medical Administrative Assistant/Secretary, A
Nursing - Registered Nurse Training, A
Surgical Technology/Technologist, A

COLLEGE OF THE ALBEMARLE

Administrative Assistant and Secretarial Science, A
Architectural Engineering Technology/Technician, A
Art/Art Studies, General, A
BioTechnology, A
Business Administration and Management, A
Computer Engineering Technology/Technician, A
Computer Programming, Specific Applications, A
Computer Programming/Programmer, A
Construction Trades, A
Crafts/Craft Design, Folk Art and Artisanry, A
Criminal Justice/Law Enforcement Administration, A
Culinary Arts/Chef Training, A
Data Entry/Microcomputer Applications, A
Drafting/Design Engineering
  Technologies/Technicians, A
Drama and Dramatics/Theatre Arts, A
Education, A
Information Science/Studies, A
Information Technology, A
Liberal Arts and Sciences Studies and
  Humanities, A
Licensed Practical/Vocational Nurse Training, A
Marine Technology, A
Medical Administrative Assistant/Secretary, A
Metal and Jewelry Arts, A
Music, A
Nursing - Registered Nurse Training, A

Teacher Assistant/Aide, A

CRAVEN COMMUNITY COLLEGE

Accounting, A
Automobile/Automotive Mechanics
  Technology/Technician, A
Business Administration and Management, A
Child Care and Support Services Management, A
Computer Programming, Specific Applications, A
Computer Systems Networking and
  Telecommunications, A
Criminal Justice/Law Enforcement Administration, A
Electrical, Electronic and Communications
  Engineering Technology/Technician, A
Electromechanical Technology/Electromechanical
  Engineering Technology, A
Executive Assistant/Executive Secretary, A
Heating, Air Conditioning, Ventilation and
  Refrigeration Maintenance
  Technology/Technician, A
Legal Administrative Assistant/Secretary, A
Liberal Arts and Sciences Studies and
  Humanities, A
Management Information Systems and Services, A
Mechanical Engineering/Mechanical
  Technology/Technician, A
Medical Administrative Assistant/Secretary, A
Nursing - Registered Nurse Training, A
Tool and Die Technology/Technician, A

DAVIDSON COLLEGE

Anthropology, B
Art/Art Studies, General, B
Biology/Biological Sciences, B
Chemistry, B
Classics and Classical
  Languages, Literatures, and Linguistics, B
Drama and Dramatics/Theatre Arts, B
Economics, B
English Language and Literature, B
French Language and Literature, B
German Language and Literature, B
History, B
Mathematics, B
Multi-/Interdisciplinary Studies, B
Music, B
Philosophy, B
Physics, B
Political Science and Government, B
Psychology, B
Religion/Religious Studies, B
Sociology, B
Spanish Language and Literature, B

DAVIDSON COUNTY COMMUNITY COLLEGE

Accounting, A
Administrative Assistant and Secretarial Science, A
Business Administration and Management, A
Clinical/Medical Laboratory Technician, A
Computer Engineering Technology/Technician, A
Computer Programming/Programmer, A
Criminal Justice/Law Enforcement Administration, A
Criminal Justice/Police Science, A
Data Processing and Data Processing
  Technology/Technician, A
Electrical, Electronic and Communications
  Engineering Technology/Technician, A
Emergency Medical Technology/Technician (EMT
  Paramedic), A
Engineering Technology, A
Fire Science/Firefighting, A
Health Information/Medical Records
  Administration/Administrator, A
Legal Assistant/Paralegal, A
Liberal Arts and Sciences Studies and
  Humanities, A
Medical/Clinical Assistant, A
Nursing - Registered Nurse Training, A
Plastics Engineering Technology/Technician, A

Pre-Engineering, A

DEVRY UNIVERSITY

Business Administration and Management, B
Business Administration, Management and
  Operations, BM
Computer and Information Sciences, B

DUKE UNIVERSITY

African-American/Black Studies, B
Allopathic Medicine, PO
Anatomy, BD
Ancient/Classical Greek Language and Literature, B
Anthropology, BDO
Art History, Criticism and Conservation, BD
Art/Art Studies, General, B
Asian Studies/Civilization, B
Biochemistry, DO
Bioinformatics, D
Biological and Biomedical Sciences, DO
Biological Anthropology, D
Biology/Biological Sciences, B
Biomedical Engineering, MD
Biomedical/Medical Engineering, B
Biopsychology, D
Business Administration, Management and
  Operations, MDO
Canadian Studies, B
Cancer Biology/Oncology, D
Cell Biology and Anatomy, DO
Chemistry, BD
Civil Engineering, BMD
Classics and Classical
  Languages, Literatures, and Linguistics, BD
Clinical Laboratory Sciences, M
Clinical Psychology, D
Clinical Research, M
Cognitive Sciences, D
Comparative Literature, BD
Composition, MD
Computer Engineering, MD
Computer Science, BMD
Demography, D
Design and Visual Communications, B
Developmental Biology and Embryology, DO
Developmental Psychology, D
Drama and Dramatics/Theatre Arts, B
East Asian Studies, MO
Ecology, MDO
Economics, BMDO
Education, MO
Electrical Engineering, MD
Electrical, Electronics and Communications
  Engineering, B
Engineering and Applied Sciences, MDO
Engineering Management, M
English, DO
English Language and Literature, B
Environmental and Occupational Health, M
Environmental Engineering
  Technology/Environmental Technology, MD
Environmental Policy, MD
Environmental Policy and Resource
  Management, MO
Environmental Sciences, MDO
Environmental Studies, B
Experimental Psychology, D
Forestry, M
French Language and Literature, BDO
Genetics, D
Genomic Sciences, D
Geology/Earth Science, BMD
German Language and Literature, BD
Gerontological Nursing, O
Health Informatics, O
Health Psychology, D
Health Services Administration, M
History, BMDO
History of Medicine, O
HIV/AIDS Nursing, O
Human Development, D
Humanities/Humanistic Studies, MO
Immunology, D
International Development, MO
International Relations and Affairs, B
Italian Language and Literature, B

Latin American Studies, DO
Latin Language and Literature, B
Law and Legal Studies, MDPO
Liberal Studies, M
Linguistics, B
Marine Affairs, M
Marine Sciences, MO
Materials Sciences, BMDO
Maternity Nursing, O
Mathematics, BD
Mechanical Engineering, BMDO
Medieval and Renaissance Studies, BO
Microbiology, D
Molecular Biology, DO
Molecular Biophysics, O
Molecular Genetics, D
Music, BMD
Musicology and Ethnomusicology, MD
Natural Resources and Conservation, MDO
Neurobiology and Neurophysiology, D
Neuroscience, DO
Nurse Anesthetist, MO
Nursing, MO
Nursing - Adult, O
Nursing - Advanced Practice, M
Nursing Administration, MO
Nursing Education, M
Oncology Nursing, O
Pathology/Experimental Pathology, MD
Pediatric Nurse/Nursing, MO
Performance, MD
Pharmacology, D
Philosophy, BMDO
Physical Therapy/Therapist, D
Physician Assistant, M
Physics, BMD
Political Science and Government, BMDO
Psychology, BDO
Public Policy Analysis, BMO
Religion/Religious Studies, BMD
Russian Language and Literature, B
Slavic Languages, Literatures, and Linguistics, BM
Sociology, BMD
Spanish Language and Literature, BDO
Statistics, D
Structural Biology, O
Theology and Religious Vocations, MPO
Toxicology, DO
Water Resources, MO
Women's Studies, BO

DURHAM TECHNICAL COMMUNITY COLLEGE

Accounting, A
Administrative Assistant and Secretarial Science, A
Architectural Engineering Technology/Technician, A
Automobile/Automotive Mechanics
  Technology/Technician, A
Business Administration and Management, A
Child Development, A
Computer Programming, A
Computer Programming/Programmer, A
Computer Typography and Composition Equipment
  Operator, A
Criminal Justice/Law Enforcement Administration, A
Criminal Justice/Police Science, A
Data Processing and Data Processing
  Technology/Technician, A
Dental Hygiene/Hygienist, A
Electrical, Electronic and Communications
  Engineering Technology/Technician, A
Fire Science/Firefighting, A
General Studies, A
Health Information/Medical Records
  Administration/Administrator, A
Information Science/Studies, A
Information Technology, A
Kindergarten/PreSchool Education and Teaching, A
Laser and Optical Technology/Technician, A
Legal Assistant/Paralegal, A
Liberal Arts and Sciences Studies and
  Humanities, A
Licensed Practical/Vocational Nurse Training, A
Machine Tool Technology/Machinist, A
Medical Administrative Assistant/Secretary, A
Nursing - Registered Nurse Training, A

Occupational Safety and Health
Technology/Technician, A
Occupational Therapy/Therapist, A
Operations Management and Supervision, A
Ophthalmic Laboratory Technology/Technician, A
Pharmacy, A
Real Estate, A
Respiratory Care Therapy/Therapist, A
Surgical Technology/Technologist, A
System Administration/Administrator, A
Teacher Assistant/Aide, A

EAST CAROLINA UNIVERSITY

Accounting, B
Accounting and Related Services, B
Adult and Continuing Education and Teaching, MO
Allied Health and Medical Assisting Services, MD
Allopathic Medicine, P
American/United States Studies/Civilization, M
Anatomy, D
Anthropology, BM
Apparel and Textiles, B
Applied Mathematics, M
Art History, Criticism and Conservation, B
Art Teacher Education, B
Art/Art Studies, General, B
Athletic Training and Sports Medicine, B
Audiology/Audiologist and Speech-Language
Pathology/Pathologist, B
Biochemistry, BD
Biological and Biomedical Sciences, MD
Biology/Biological Sciences, B
Biophysics, M
BioTechnology, M
Broadcast Journalism, B
Business Administration and Management, B
Business Administration, Management and
Operations, M
Business Teacher Education, B
Business/Office Automation/Technology/Data
Entry, B
Cell Biology and Anatomy, D
Chemistry, BM
Child and Family Studies, M
Child Development, B
City/Urban, Community and Regional Planning, B
Clinical Laboratory Science/Medical
Technology/Technologist, B
Clinical Psychology, M
Communication Disorders, MD
Communication Studies/Speech Communication
and Rhetoric, B
Composition, M
Computer Engineering Technology/Technician, B
Computer Science, BMO
Counselor Education/School Counseling and
Guidance Services, MO
Criminal Justice/Safety Studies, B
Criminology, M
Curriculum and Instruction, M
Dance, B
Dietetics/Dieticians, B
Drama and Dance Teacher Education, B
Drama and Dramatics/Theatre Arts, B
Economics, BM
Education, MDO
Education/Teaching of Individuals with Emotional
Disturbances, B
Education/Teaching of Individuals with Mental
Retardation, B
Education/Teaching of Individuals with Specific
Learning Disabilities, B
Educational Administration and Supervision, MDO
Educational Leadership and Administration, MDO
Educational Media/Instructional Technology, MO
Electrical, Electronic and Communications
Engineering Technology/Technician, B
Elementary Education and Teaching, BM
Engineering Technologies/Technicians, B
English, M
English Education, M
English Language and Literature, B
English/Language Arts Teacher Education, B
Environmental and Occupational Health, M
Environmental Engineering
Technology/Environmental Technology, B

Environmental Health, B
Exercise and Sports Science, MD
Family and Consumer Sciences/Home Economics
Teacher Education, B
Finance, B
Fine Arts and Art Studies, M
Fine/Studio Arts, B
French Language and Literature, B
French Language Teacher Education, B
Geography, BM
Geology/Earth Science, BM
German Language and Literature, B
German Language Teacher Education, B
Health and Physical Education/Fitness, B
Health Education, M
Health Information/Medical Records
Administration/Administrator, B
Health Professions and Related Clinical Sciences, B
Health Teacher Education, B
History, BM
Hotel/Motel Administration/Management, B
Human Development and Family Studies, B
Immunology, D
Industrial Production Technologies/Technicians, B
Industrial Technology/Technician, B
Industrial/Management Engineering, M
Information Science/Studies, M
Interior Design, B
International Affairs, M
Junior High/Intermediate/Middle School Education
and Teaching, B
Kindergarten/PreSchool Education and Teaching, B
Kinesiology and Exercise Science, B
Leisure Studies, M
Liberal Arts and Sciences Studies and
Humanities, B
Library Science, MO
Management, O
Management Information Systems and
Services, BO
Management of Technology, D
Manufacturing Technology/Technician, B
Marine Affairs, D
Marketing/Marketing Management, B
Marriage and Family Therapy/Counseling, M
Mathematics, BM
Mathematics Teacher Education, BM
Medical Physics, M
Microbiology, D
Middle School Education, M
Molecular Biology, M
Music, M
Music Performance, B
Music Teacher Education, BM
Music Theory and Composition, BM
Music Therapy/Therapist, BM
Nursing, MD
Nursing - Registered Nurse Training, B
Nutritional Sciences, M
Occupational Therapy/Therapist, BM
Parks, Recreation and Leisure Facilities
Management, B
Pathology/Experimental Pathology, D
Performance, M
Pharmacology, DO
Philosophy, B
Physical Education Teaching and Coaching, B
Physical Therapy/Therapist, M
Physician Assistant, BM
Physics, BMD
Physiology, M
Political Science and Government, BM
Psychology, BM
Public Administration, M
Public Health, M
Public Health Education and Promotion, B
Public/Applied History and Archival Administration, B
Reading Teacher Education, M
Recreation and Park Management, M
Rehabilitation Counseling, M
Rehabilitation Sciences, M
Resource Management, D
Sales and Marketing Operations/Marketing and
Distribution Teacher Education, B
School Psychology, O

Science Teacher Education/General Science
Teacher Education, BM
Social Studies Teacher Education, BM
Social Work, BM
Sociology, BM
Spanish Language and Literature, B
Spanish Language Teacher Education, B
Special Education and Teaching, M
Substance Abuse/Addiction Counseling, M
Therapeutic Recreation, M
Therapeutic Recreation/Recreational Therapy, B
Vocational and Technical Education, M
Vocational Rehabilitation Counseling/Counselor, B
Western European Studies, M
Women's Studies, B

ECPI TECHNICAL COLLEGE

Computer and Information Sciences, A
Computer Engineering Technology/Technician, A
Computer Science, A
Computer Technology/Computer Systems
Technology, A
Criminal Justice/Law Enforcement Administration, A
Licensed Practical/Vocational Nurse Training, A
Management Information Systems and Services, A
Medical/Clinical Assistant, A

EDGECOMBE COMMUNITY COLLEGE

Accounting, A
Administrative Assistant and Secretarial Science, A
Business Administration and Management, A
Criminal Justice/Law Enforcement Administration, A
Data Entry/Microcomputer Applications, A
Electrical, Electronic and Communications
Engineering Technology/Technician, A
Health Information/Medical Records
Administration/Administrator, A
Human Services, A
Information Technology, A
Kindergarten/PreSchool Education and Teaching, A
Liberal Arts and Sciences Studies and
Humanities, A
Licensed Practical/Vocational Nurse Training, A
Mechanical Drafting and Mechanical Drafting
CAD/CADD, A
Mechanical Engineering Related
Technologies/Technicians, A
Mechanical Engineering/Mechanical
Technology/Technician, A
Medical/Clinical Assistant, A
Nursing - Registered Nurse Training, A
Plastics Engineering Technology/Technician, A
Radiologic Technology/Science - Radiographer, A
Respiratory Care Therapy/Therapist, A
Respiratory Therapy Technician/Assistant, A
Social Work, A
Surgical Technology/Technologist, A
System Administration/Administrator, A
Word Processing, A

ELIZABETH CITY STATE UNIVERSITY

Accounting, B
Aeronautics/Aviation/Aerospace Science and
Technology, B
Applied Art, B
Art Teacher Education, B
Art/Art Studies, General, B
Avionics Maintenance Technology/Technician, B
Biology Teacher Education, B
Biology Technician/BioTechnology Laboratory
Technician, B
Biology/Biological Sciences, B
Business Administration and Management, B
Business Teacher Education, B
Chemistry, B
Chemistry Teacher Education, B
Computer Science, B
Criminal Justice/Law Enforcement Administration, B
Criminal Justice/Safety Studies, B
Education, B
Education/Teaching of Individuals with Specific
Learning Disabilities, B
Elementary Education and Teaching, BM
English Language and Literature, B
English/Language Arts Teacher Education, B
Fine/Studio Arts, B

Geology/Earth Science, B
History, B
History Teacher Education, B
Industrial Technology/Technician, B
Junior High/Intermediate/Middle School Education
and Teaching, B
Kindergarten/PreSchool Education and Teaching, B
Mathematics, B
Mathematics Teacher Education, B
Music, B
Music Management and Merchandising, B
Music Teacher Education, B
Oceanography, Chemical and Physical, B
Physical Education Teaching and Coaching, B
Physics, B
Political Science and Government, B
Psychology, B
Secondary Education and Teaching, B
Social Sciences, B
Social Work, B
Sociology, B
Special Education and Teaching, B
Technology Education/Industrial Arts, B
Technology Teacher Education/Industrial Arts
Teacher Education, B

ELON UNIVERSITY

Accounting, B
Art/Art Studies, General, B
Athletic Training and Sports Medicine, B
Biology/Biological Sciences, B
Broadcast Journalism, B
Business Administration and Management, B
Business Administration, Management and
Operations, M
Business/Corporate Communications, B
Chemistry, B
Clinical Laboratory Science/Medical
Technology/Technologist, B
Communication Studies/Speech Communication
and Rhetoric, B
Computer Science, B
Dance, B
Drama and Dramatics/Theatre Arts, B
Economics, B
Education, BM
Elementary Education and Teaching, BM
Engineering, B
English Language and Literature, B
Environmental Studies, B
Foreign Languages and Literatures, B
French Language and Literature, B
Health Teacher Education, B
History, B
Human Services, B
International Relations and Affairs, B
Journalism, B
Junior High/Intermediate/Middle School Education
and Teaching, B
Mathematics, B
Music, B
Music Performance, B
Music Teacher Education, B
Parks, Recreation, Leisure and Fitness Studies, B
Philosophy, B
Physical Education Teaching and Coaching, B
Physical Therapy/Therapist, D
Physics, B
Political Science and Government, B
Pre-Dentistry Studies, B
Pre-Law Studies, B
Pre-Medicine/Pre-Medical Studies, B
Pre-Veterinary Studies, B
Psychology, B
Public Administration, B
Religion/Religious Studies, B
Science Teacher Education/General Science
Teacher Education, B
Secondary Education and Teaching, B
Social Science Teacher Education, B
Social Studies Teacher Education, B
Sociology, B
Spanish Language and Literature, B
Special Education and Teaching, BM

Sport and Fitness Administration/Management, B

FAYETTEVILLE STATE UNIVERSITY

Accounting, B
Art/Art Studies, General, B
Biological and Biomedical Sciences, M
Biology Teacher Education, B
Biology/Biological Sciences, B
Business Administration and Management, B
Business Administration, Management and
Operations, M
Business Teacher Education, B
Business/Managerial Economics, B
Chemistry, B
Computer Science, B
Criminal Justice/Law Enforcement Administration, B
Dramatic/Theatre Arts and Stagecraft, B
Education, B
Educational Administration and Supervision, M
Educational Leadership and Administration, D
Elementary Education and Teaching, BM
English, M
English Language and Literature, B
English/Language Arts Teacher Education, B
Finance, B
Geography, B
Health Teacher Education, B
History, BM
Junior High/Intermediate/Middle School Education
and Teaching, B
Kindergarten/PreSchool Education and Teaching, B
Marketing/Marketing Management, B
Mathematics, BM
Mathematics Teacher Education, B
Middle School Education, M
Music Teacher Education, B
Nursing - Registered Nurse Training, B
Physical Education Teaching and Coaching, B
Political Science and Government, BM
Psychology, BM
Reading Teacher Education, M
Sales and Marketing Operations/Marketing and
Distribution Teacher Education, B
Secondary Education and Teaching, M
Social Science Teacher Education, B
Social Studies Teacher Education, M
Social Work, M
Sociology, BM
Spanish Language and Literature, B
Spanish Language Teacher Education, B

FAYETTEVILLE TECHNICAL
COMMUNITY COLLEGE

Accounting, A
Applied Horticulture/Horticultural Operations, A
Architectural Engineering Technology/Technician, A
Automobile/Automotive Mechanics
Technology/Technician, A
Banking and Financial Support Services, A
Biology Technician/BioTechnology Laboratory
Technician, A
Building/Construction
Finishing, Management, and Inspection, A
Business Administration and Management, A
Business Administration, Management and
Operations, A
Civil Engineering Technology/Technician, A
Commercial and Advertising Art, A
Computer and Information Systems Security, A
Computer Programming/Programmer, A
Corrections and Criminal Justice, A
Criminal Justice/Safety Studies, A
Culinary Arts/Chef Training, A
Dental Hygiene/Hygienist, A
Early Childhood Education and Teaching, A
E-Commerce/Electronic Commerce, A
Electrical, Electronic and Communications
Engineering Technology/Technician, A
Electrician, A
Elementary Education and Teaching, A
Emergency Medical Technology/Technician (EMT
Paramedic), A
Fire Protection, A
Fire Protection and Safety Technology/Technician, A
Forensic Science and Technology, A
Funeral Service and Mortuary Science, A

General Studies, A
Health Information/Medical Records
Technology/Technician, A
Heating, Air Conditioning, Ventilation and
Refrigeration Maintenance
Technology/Technician, A
Hotel/Motel Administration/Management, A
Human Resources Management/Personnel
Administration, A
Information Science/Studies, A
Information Technology, A
Language Interpretation and Translation, A
Legal Assistant/Paralegal, A
Liberal Arts and Sciences Studies and
Humanities, A
Machine Shop Technology/Assistant, A
Medical Office Management/Administration, A
Nuclear Medical Technology/Technologist, A
Nursing - Registered Nurse Training, A
Office Management and Supervision, A
Operations Management and Supervision, A
Physical Therapist Assistant, A
Public Administration, A
Radiologic Technology/Science - Radiographer, A
Respiratory Care Therapy/Therapist, A
Special Education and Teaching, A
Speech-Language Pathology/Pathologist, A
Surgical Technology/Technologist, A
Survey Technology/Surveying, A
System, Networking, and LAN/WAN
Management/Manager, A

FORSYTH TECHNICAL COMMUNITY
COLLEGE

Accounting, A
Administrative Assistant and Secretarial Science, A
Architectural Engineering Technology/Technician, A
Automobile/Automotive Mechanics
Technology/Technician, A
Business Administration and Management, A
Carpentry/Carpenter, A
Child Development, A
Commercial and Advertising Art, A
Computer Engineering Technology/Technician, A
Computer Science, A
Construction Engineering Technology/Technician, A
Criminal Justice/Law Enforcement Administration, A
Criminal Justice/Police Science, A
Data Processing and Data Processing
Technology/Technician, A
Drafting and Design Technology/Technician, A
Drafting/Design Engineering
Technologies/Technicians, A
Electrical, Electronic and Communications
Engineering Technology/Technician, A
Electromechanical Technology/Electromechanical
Engineering Technology, A
Engineering Technology, A
Finance, A
Funeral Service and Mortuary Science, A
Graphic and Printing Equipment Operator
Production, A
Heating, Air Conditioning, Ventilation and
Refrigeration Maintenance
Technology/Technician, A
Horticultural Science, A
Industrial Radiologic Technology/Technician, A
Industrial Technology/Technician, A
Kindergarten/PreSchool Education and Teaching, A
Legal Assistant/Paralegal, A
Machine Tool Technology/Machinist, A
Marketing/Marketing Management, A
Medical/Clinical Assistant, A
Nuclear Medical Technology/Technologist, A
Nursing - Registered Nurse Training, A
Ornamental Horticulture, A
Pipefitting/Pipefitter and Sprinkler Fitter, A
Real Estate, A
Respiratory Care Therapy/Therapist, A
Welding Technology/Welder, A

GARDNER-WEBB UNIVERSITY

Accounting, B
American Sign Language (ASL), B
Art/Art Studies, General, B
Athletic Training and Sports Medicine, B

Biology/Biological Sciences, B
Business Administration and Management, B
Business Administration, Management and
  Operations, M
Chemistry, B
Clinical Laboratory Science/Medical
  Technology/Technologist, B
Clinical/Medical Laboratory Technician, B
Computer Science, B
Counseling Psychology, M
Drama and Dramatics/Theatre Arts, B
Early Childhood Education and Teaching, B
Education, BM
Educational Administration and Supervision, M
Elementary Education and Teaching, BM
English, M
English Education, M
English Language and Literature, B
English/Language Arts Teacher Education, B
Exercise and Sports Science, M
Fine/Studio Arts, B
Foreign Language Teacher Education, B
French Language and Literature, B
French Language Teacher Education, B
Health and Physical Education, B
Health Teacher Education, B
History, B
Journalism, B
Kindergarten/PreSchool Education and Teaching, B
Management Information Systems and Services, B
Mass Communication/Media Studies, B
Mathematics, B
Mathematics Teacher Education, B
Middle School Education, M
Missions/Missionary Studies and Missiology, BP
Music Performance, B
Music Teacher Education, B
Nursing, MO
Nursing - Registered Nurse Training, AB
Pastoral Studies/Counseling, BDP
Physical Education Teaching and Coaching, BM
Physician Assistant, B
Political Science and Government, B
Pre-Dentistry Studies, B
Pre-Law Studies, B
Pre-Medicine/Pre-Medical Studies, B
Pre-Pharmacy Studies, B
Pre-Veterinary Studies, B
Psychology, BM
Radio and Television Broadcasting
  Technology/Technician, B
Religion/Religious Studies, B
Religious Education, BP
Religious/Sacred Music, B
Sacred Music, P
School Psychology, M
Secondary Education and Teaching, B
Social Sciences, B
Sociology, B
Spanish Language and Literature, B
Sport and Fitness Administration/Management, B
Theology and Religious Vocations, DPO
Youth Ministry, B

GASTON COLLEGE

Accounting, A
Architectural Engineering Technology/Technician, A
Art/Art Studies, General, A
Automobile/Automotive Mechanics
  Technology/Technician, A
Business Administration and Management, A
Civil Engineering Technology/Technician, A
Computer Programming/Programmer, A
Criminal Justice/Law Enforcement Administration, A
Data Processing and Data Processing
  Technology/Technician, A
Dietetics/Dieticians, A
Electrical, Electronic and Communications
  Engineering Technology/Technician, A
Fire Science/Firefighting, A
Information Science/Studies, A
Kindergarten/PreSchool Education and Teaching, A
Legal Assistant/Paralegal, A
Mechanical Drafting and Mechanical Drafting
  CAD/CADD, A

Mechanical Engineering/Mechanical
  Technology/Technician, A
Medical Office Management/Administration, A
Medical/Clinical Assistant, A
Nursing - Registered Nurse Training, A
Operations Management and Supervision, A
Veterinary/Animal Health Technology/Technician and
  Veterinary Assistant, A

GREENSBORO COLLEGE

Accounting, B
Acting, B
Art Teacher Education, B
Art/Art Studies, General, B
Athletic Training and Sports Medicine, B
Biology Teacher Education, B
Biology/Biological Sciences, B
Business Administration and Management, B
Business/Managerial Economics, B
Chemistry, B
Clinical Laboratory Science/Medical
  Technology/Technologist, B
Communication Studies/Speech Communication
  and Rhetoric, B
Drama and Dance Teacher Education, B
Drama and Dramatics/Theatre Arts, B
Early Childhood Education and Teaching, B
Education, B
Education/Teaching of Individuals with Emotional
  Disturbances, B
Education/Teaching of Individuals with Mental
  Retardation, B
Education/Teaching of Individuals with Specific
  Learning Disabilities, B
Elementary Education and Teaching, B
English as a Second Language, M
English Language and Literature, B
English/Language Arts Teacher Education, B
Foreign Language Teacher Education, B
French Language and Literature, B
Health and Physical Education/Fitness, B
History, B
Interdisciplinary Studies, B
Junior High/Intermediate/Middle School Education
  and Teaching, B
Kindergarten/PreSchool Education and Teaching, B
Kinesiology and Exercise Science, B
Mathematics, B
Mathematics Teacher Education, B
Music, B
Music Performance, B
Music Teacher Education, B
Physical Education Teaching and Coaching, B
Political Science and Government, B
Psychology, B
Religion/Religious Studies, B
Science Teacher Education/General Science
  Teacher Education, B
Secondary Education and Teaching, B
Social Studies Teacher Education, B
Sociology, B
Spanish Language and Literature, B
Spanish Language Teacher Education, B
Special Education and Teaching, B
Sport and Fitness Administration/Management, B
Technical Theatre/Theatre Design and
  Technology, B

GUILFORD COLLEGE

Accounting, B
African-American/Black Studies, B
Art/Art Studies, General, B
Athletic Training and Sports Medicine, B
Biological and Biomedical Sciences, B
Biology/Biological Sciences, B
Business Administration and Management, B
Chemistry, B
Computer and Information Sciences, B
Criminal Justice/Safety Studies, B
Drama and Dramatics/Theatre Arts, B
Economics, B
Elementary Education and Teaching, B
English Language and Literature, B
Environmental Studies, B
French Language and Literature, B
Geology/Earth Science, B

German Language and Literature, B
Health and Physical Education, B
Health/Medical Preparatory Programs, B
History, B
Information Science/Studies, B
Interdisciplinary Studies, B
International Relations and Affairs, B
Mathematics, B
Music, B
Peace Studies and Conflict Resolution, B
Philosophy, B
Physics, B
Political Science and Government, B
Psychology, B
Religion/Religious Studies, B
Secondary Education and Teaching, B
Sociology, B
Spanish Language and Literature, B
Sport and Fitness Administration/Management, B
Women's Studies, B

GUILFORD TECHNICAL COMMUNITY COLLEGE

Accounting, A
Airline/Commercial/Professional Pilot and Flight
  Crew, A
Architectural Engineering Technology/Technician, A
Automobile/Automotive Mechanics
  Technology/Technician, A
Aviation/Airway Management and Operations, A
Avionics Maintenance Technology/Technician, A
Biological and Physical Sciences, A
Biology Technician/BioTechnology Laboratory
  Technician, A
Building/Construction
  Finishing, Management, and Inspection, A
Business Administration and Management, A
Business Operations Support and Secretarial
  Services, A
Chemistry, A
Cinematography and Film/Video Production, A
Civil Engineering Technology/Technician, A
Clinical/Medical Laboratory Technician, A
Commercial and Advertising Art, A
Computer Programming/Programmer, A
Computer Systems Networking and
  Telecommunications, A
Computer/Information Technology Services
  Administration and Management, A
Cosmetology/Cosmetologist, A
Criminal Justice/Law Enforcement Administration, A
Criminal Justice/Police Science, A
Culinary Arts/Chef Training, A
Dental Hygiene/Hygienist, A
Drafting and Design Technology/Technician, A
Drama and Dramatics/Theatre Arts, A
Education, A
Electrical, Electronic and Communications
  Engineering Technology/Technician, A
Electrical/Electronics Equipment Installation and
  Repair, A
Emergency Medical Technology/Technician (EMT
  Paramedic), A
Fire Science/Firefighting, A
Heating, Air Conditioning, Ventilation and
  Refrigeration Maintenance
  Technology/Technician, A
Heavy Equipment Maintenance
  Technology/Technician, A
Human Services, A
Industrial Mechanics and Maintenance
  Technology, A
Industrial Technology/Technician, A
Information Science/Studies, A
Kindergarten/PreSchool Education and Teaching, A
Legal Assistant/Paralegal, A
Liberal Arts and Sciences Studies and
  Humanities, A
Machine Tool Technology/Machinist, A
Medical/Clinical Assistant, A
Nursing - Registered Nurse Training, A
Occupational Therapist Assistant, A
Physical Therapist Assistant, A
Respiratory Care Therapy/Therapist, A
Speech-Language Pathology/Pathologist, A
Surgical Technology/Technologist, A

Survey Technology/Surveying, A
Technology Education/Industrial Arts, A
Turf and Turfgrass Management, A
Web Page, Digital/Multimedia and Information
   Resources Design, A

HALIFAX COMMUNITY COLLEGE

Administrative Assistant and Secretarial Science, A
Art Teacher Education, A
Business Administration and Management, A
Business Teacher Education, A
Clinical/Medical Laboratory Technician, A
Commercial and Advertising Art, A
Corrections, A
Criminal Justice/Police Science, A
Education, A
Industrial Technology/Technician, A
Interior Design, A
Liberal Arts and Sciences Studies and
   Humanities, A
Marketing/Marketing Management, A
Medical Administrative Assistant/Secretary, A
Nursing - Registered Nurse Training, A

HAYWOOD COMMUNITY COLLEGE

Business Administration and Management, A
Ceramic Arts and Ceramics, A
Cosmetology/Cosmetologist, A
Crafts/Craft Design, Folk Art and Artisanry, A
Criminal Justice/Law Enforcement Administration, A
Education, A
Fiber, Textile and Weaving Arts, A
Forestry Technology/Technician, A
Horticultural Science, A
Industrial Technology/Technician, A
Information Science/Studies, A
Liberal Arts and Sciences Studies and
   Humanities, A
Machine Tool Technology/Machinist, A
Management Information Systems and Services, A
Medical/Clinical Assistant, A
Metal and Jewelry Arts, A
Nursing - Registered Nurse Training, A
Technology Education/Industrial Arts, A
Wildlife and Wildlands Science and Management, A
Wood Science and Wood Products/Pulp and Paper
   Technology, A

HERITAGE BIBLE COLLEGE

Buddhist Studies, AB
Christian Studies, AB
Theology/Theological Studies, AB

HIGH POINT UNIVERSITY

Accounting, B
American/United States Studies/Civilization, B
Art Teacher Education, B
Athletic Training and Sports Medicine, B
Biology/Biological Sciences, B
Business Administration and Management, B
Business Administration, Management and
   Operations, M
Chemistry, B
Clinical Laboratory Science/Medical
   Technology/Technologist, B
Community Organization and Advocacy, B
Comparative Literature, B
Computer and Information Sciences, B
Computer Science, B
Creative Writing, B
Criminal Justice/Safety Studies, B
Drama and Dramatics/Theatre Arts, B
Education, BM
Educational Leadership and Administration, M
Elementary Education and Teaching, BM
English Language and Literature, B
Exercise and Sports Science, M
Fine/Studio Arts, B
French Language and Literature, B
History, B
Human Services, B
Information Science/Studies, B
Interior Design, B
International Business/Trade/Commerce, B
International Relations and Affairs, B

Junior High/Intermediate/Middle School Education
   and Teaching, B
Kindergarten/PreSchool Education and Teaching, B
Kinesiology and Exercise Science, B
Marketing/Marketing Management, B
Mass Communication/Media Studies, B
Mathematics, B
Non-Profit/Public/Organizational Management, M
Parks, Recreation and Leisure Facilities
   Management, B
Parks, Recreation, Leisure and Fitness Studies, B
Philosophy, B
Physical Education Teaching and Coaching, B
Physician Assistant, B
Political Science and Government, B
Pre-Dentistry Studies, B
Pre-Law Studies, B
Pre-Medicine/Pre-Medical Studies, B
Pre-Veterinary Studies, B
Psychology, B
Religion/Religious Studies, B
Secondary Education and Teaching, B
Sociology, B
Spanish Language and Literature, B
Special Education and Teaching, B
Sport and Fitness Administration/Management, B

ISOTHERMAL COMMUNITY COLLEGE

Administrative Assistant and Secretarial Science, A
Automobile/Automotive Mechanics
   Technology/Technician, A
Biological and Physical Sciences, A
Broadcast Journalism, A
Business Administration and Management, A
Business Teacher Education, A
Commercial and Advertising Art, A
Computer Programming/Programmer, A
Computer Science, A
Cosmetology/Cosmetologist, A
Criminal Justice/Law Enforcement Administration, A
Criminal Justice/Police Science, A
Drafting and Design Technology/Technician, A
Drafting/Design Engineering
   Technologies/Technicians, A
Education, A
Electrical, Electronic and Communications
   Engineering Technology/Technician, A
Elementary Education and Teaching, A
Insurance, A
Kindergarten/PreSchool Education and Teaching, A
Liberal Arts and Sciences Studies and
   Humanities, A
Licensed Practical/Vocational Nurse Training, A
Machine Tool Technology/Machinist, A
Marketing/Marketing Management, A
Mechanical Engineering/Mechanical
   Technology/Technician, A
Music, A
Pharmacy, A
Plastics Engineering Technology/Technician, A
Pre-Engineering, A
Radio and Television, A
Real Estate, A
Teacher Assistant/Aide, A
Trade and Industrial Teacher Education, A
Welding Technology/Welder, A

JAMES SPRUNT COMMUNITY COLLEGE

Accounting, A
Administrative Assistant and Secretarial Science, A
Agribusiness, A
Animal Sciences, A
Business Administration and Management, A
Commercial and Advertising Art, A
Computer Systems Analysis/Analyst, A
Cosmetology/Cosmetologist, A
Criminal Justice/Police Science, A
Kindergarten/PreSchool Education and Teaching, A
Liberal Arts and Sciences Studies and
   Humanities, A
Medical/Clinical Assistant, A

Nursing - Registered Nurse Training, A

JOHN WESLEY COLLEGE

Bible/Biblical Studies, B
Business Administration and Management, B
Divinity/Ministry (BD, MDiv.), B
Elementary Education and Teaching, B
Liberal Arts and Sciences Studies and
   Humanities, A
Pastoral Studies/Counseling, B
Psychology, B
Religion/Religious Studies, B
Religious Education, B
Theology/Theological Studies, B

JOHNSON C. SMITH UNIVERSITY

Applied Mathematics, B
Biological and Physical Sciences, B
Biology/Biological Sciences, B
Business Administration and Management, B
Chemistry, B
Computer Engineering, B
Computer Science, B
Criminal Justice/Law Enforcement Administration, B
Early Childhood Education and Teaching, B
Economics, B
Education, B
Elementary Education and Teaching, B
Engineering, B
English Language and Literature, B
French Language and Literature, B
General Studies, B
Health and Physical Education, B
Health Teacher Education, B
History, B
Information Science/Studies, B
Liberal Arts and Sciences Studies and
   Humanities, B
Mass Communication/Media Studies, B
Mathematics, B
Mathematics Teacher Education, B
Music, B
Physical Education Teaching and Coaching, B
Physics, B
Political Science and Government, B
Pre-Medicine/Pre-Medical Studies, B
Psychology, B
Science Teacher Education/General Science
   Teacher Education, B
Secondary Education and Teaching, B
Social Sciences, B
Social Work, B
Sociology, B
Spanish Language and Literature, B

JOHNSON & WALES UNIVERSITY

Accounting, AB
Baking and Pastry Arts/Baker/Pastry Chef, A
Business Administration and Management, A
Culinary Arts/Chef Training, A
Fashion Merchandising, A
Food Service, Waiter/Waitress, and Dining Room
   Management/Manager, AB
Hotel/Motel Administration/Management, AB
Parks, Recreation and Leisure Facilities
   Management, AB
Parks, Recreation, Leisure and Fitness Studies, AB
Public Relations/Image Management, AB
Restaurant, Culinary, and Catering
   Management/Manager, AB
Sales, Distribution and Marketing Operations, AB
Tourism and Travel Services Management, B

JOHNSTON COMMUNITY COLLEGE

Accounting Technology/Technician and
   Bookkeeping, A
Administrative Assistant and Secretarial Science, A
Business Administration and Management, A
Commercial and Advertising Art, A
Computer Programming/Programmer, A
Criminal Justice/Police Science, A
Diesel Mechanics Technology/Technician, A
Electrical, Electronic and Communications
   Engineering Technology/Technician, A

Heating, Air Conditioning, Ventilation and
   Refrigeration Maintenance
   Technology/Technician, A
Kindergarten/PreSchool Education and Teaching, A
Landscaping and Groundskeeping, A
Legal Assistant/Paralegal, A
Liberal Arts and Sciences Studies and
   Humanities, A
Machine Tool Technology/Machinist, A
Medical Administrative Assistant/Secretary, A
Medical Radiologic Technology/Science - Radiation
   Therapist, A
Medical/Clinical Assistant, A
Nursing - Registered Nurse Training, A
Operations Management and Supervision, A

LEES-MCRAE COLLEGE

Athletic Training and Sports Medicine, B
Biological and Physical Sciences, B
Biology/Biological Sciences, B
Business Administration and Management, B
Criminal Justice/Law Enforcement Administration, B
Drama and Dramatics/Theatre Arts, B
Education, B
Elementary Education and Teaching, B
English Language and Literature, B
Environmental Studies, B
History, B
Humanities/Humanistic Studies, B
Information Science/Studies, B
Interdisciplinary Studies, B
International Relations and Affairs, B
Liberal Arts and Sciences Studies and
   Humanities, B
Mass Communication/Media Studies, B
Mathematics, B
Natural Sciences, B
Physical Education Teaching and Coaching, B
Pre-Law Studies, B
Pre-Medicine/Pre-Medical Studies, B
Pre-Veterinary Studies, B
Psychology, B
Religion/Religious Studies, B
Sales, Distribution and Marketing Operations, B
Social Sciences, B
Sociology, B
Wildlife Biology, B

LENOIR COMMUNITY COLLEGE

Accounting, A
Administrative Assistant and Secretarial Science, A
Agricultural Business and Management, A
Agriculture, A
Airline/Commercial/Professional Pilot and Flight
   Crew, A
Art/Art Studies, General, A
Aviation/Airway Management and Operations, A
Avionics Maintenance Technology/Technician, A
Business Administration and Management, A
Commercial and Advertising Art, A
Computer Programming/Programmer, A
Consumer Merchandising/Retailing Management, A
Cosmetology/Cosmetologist, A
Court Reporting/Court Reporter, A
Criminal Justice/Law Enforcement Administration, A
Criminal Justice/Police Science, A
Drafting and Design Technology/Technician, A
Drafting/Design Engineering
   Technologies/Technicians, A
Electrical, Electronic and Communications
   Engineering Technology/Technician, A
Elementary Education and Teaching, A
Finance, A
Fire Science/Firefighting, A
Food Technology and Processing, A
Graphic and Printing Equipment Operator
   Production, A
Heavy Equipment Maintenance
   Technology/Technician, A
Horticultural Science, A
Hydrology and Water Resources Science, A
Industrial Technology/Technician, A
Instrumentation Technology/Technician, A
Insurance, A
Landscape Architecture, A
Legal Administrative Assistant/Secretary, A

Liberal Arts and Sciences Studies and
   Humanities, A
Library Science, A
Marketing/Marketing Management, A
Medical Administrative Assistant/Secretary, A
Medical/Clinical Assistant, A
Mental Health/Rehabilitation, A
Nursing - Registered Nurse Training, A
Ornamental Horticulture, A
Pre-Engineering, A
Trade and Industrial Teacher Education, A
Welding Technology/Welder, A

LENOIR-RHYNE COLLEGE

Accounting, B
Adult and Continuing Education and Teaching, B
Art Teacher Education, B
Athletic Training and Sports Medicine, B
Biology/Biological Sciences, B
Business Administration and Management, B
Business Administration, Management and
   Operations, M
Business Teacher Education, B
Chemistry, B
Classics and Classical
   Languages, Literatures, and Linguistics, B
Clinical Laboratory Science/Medical
   Technology/Technologist, B
Computer Science, B
Counselor Education/School Counseling and
   Guidance Services, M
Drama and Dramatics/Theatre Arts, B
Early Childhood Education and Teaching, M
Ecology, B
Economics, B
Education, BM
Elementary Education and Teaching, B
English Language and Literature, B
Environmental Studies, B
French Language and Literature, B
German Language and Literature, B
History, B
Human Services, B
International Business/Trade/Commerce, B
International Relations and Affairs, B
Kindergarten/PreSchool Education and Teaching, B
Kinesiology and Exercise Science, B
Latin Language and Literature, B
Mass Communication/Media Studies, B
Mathematics, B
Modern Languages, B
Music, B
Music Teacher Education, B
Nursing - Registered Nurse Training, B
Occupational Therapy/Therapist, B
Pastoral Studies/Counseling, B
Philosophy, B
Physical Education Teaching and Coaching, B
Physical Sciences, B
Physician Assistant, B
Physics, B
Political Science and Government, B
Pre-Dentistry Studies, B
Pre-Law Studies, B
Pre-Medicine/Pre-Medical Studies, B
Pre-Veterinary Studies, B
Psychology, B
Reading Teacher Education, M
Religion/Religious Studies, B
Religious Education, B
Religious/Sacred Music, B
School Psychology, M
Science Teacher Education/General Science
   Teacher Education, B
Secondary Education and Teaching, B
Sociology, B
Spanish Language and Literature, B
Theology/Theological Studies, B

LIVINGSTONE COLLEGE

Accounting, B
Biology/Biological Sciences, B
Business Administration and Management, B
Chemistry, B
Computer Science, B
Education, B

Elementary Education and Teaching, B
English Language and Literature, B
History, B
Human Services, B
Information Science/Studies, B
Kindergarten/PreSchool Education and Teaching, B
Mathematics, B
Music, B
Music Teacher Education, B
Physical Education Teaching and Coaching, B
Political Science and Government, B
Psychology, B
Social Sciences, B
Social Work, B
Sociology, B
Sport and Fitness Administration/Management, B

LOUISBURG COLLEGE

Athletic Training and Sports Medicine, A
Biological and Physical Sciences, A
Biology Teacher Education, A
Biology/Biological Sciences, A
Business Administration and Management, A
Business Teacher Education, A
Business/Commerce, A
Chemistry, A
Chemistry Teacher Education, A
Clinical Laboratory Science/Medical
   Technology/Technologist, A
Computer Science, A
Dance, A
Economics, A
Elementary Education and Teaching, A
English Language and Literature, A
English/Language Arts Teacher Education, A
Health and Physical Education, A
History, A
Information Science/Studies, A
Liberal Arts and Sciences Studies and
   Humanities, A
Management Science, A
Mathematics, A
Mathematics Teacher Education, A
Nursing - Registered Nurse Training, A
Occupational Therapy/Therapist, A
Physical Therapy/Therapist, A
Physics, A
Political Science and Government, A
Pre-Engineering, A
Pre-Law Studies, A
Pre-Medicine/Pre-Medical Studies, A
Pre-Pharmacy Studies, A
Pre-Veterinary Studies, A
Psychology, A
Sales and Marketing Operations/Marketing and
   Distribution Teacher Education, A
Social Science Teacher Education, A
Social Work, A
Sociology, A
Special Education and Teaching, A
Speech and Rhetorical Studies, A
Sport and Fitness Administration/Management, A
Teacher Education, Multiple Levels, A

MARS HILL COLLEGE

Accounting, B
Adult and Continuing Education and Teaching, B
Art History, Criticism and Conservation, B
Art Teacher Education, B
Art/Art Studies, General, B
Athletic Training and Sports Medicine, B
Behavioral Sciences, B
Biological and Physical Sciences, B
Biology/Biological Sciences, B
Botany/Plant Biology, B
Business Administration and Management, B
Business/Managerial Economics, B
Chemistry, B
Computer and Information Sciences, B
Computer Science, B
Criminal Justice/Law Enforcement Administration, B
Drama and Dramatics/Theatre Arts, B
Ecology, B
Economics, B
Education, B
Elementary Education and Teaching, B

English Language and Literature, B
Entrepreneurship/Entrepreneurial Studies, B
Fashion Merchandising, B
Finance, B
Fine/Studio Arts, B
German Language and Literature, B
Graphic Design, B
History, B
Interdisciplinary Studies, B
International Business/Trade/Commerce, B
International Relations and Affairs, B
Junior High/Intermediate/Middle School Education
  and Teaching, B
Kindergarten/PreSchool Education and Teaching, B
Kinesiology and Exercise Science, B
Liberal Arts and Sciences Studies and
  Humanities, B
Marketing/Marketing Management, B
Mass Communication/Media Studies, B
Mathematics, B
Music, B
Music Performance, B
Music Teacher Education, B
Parks, Recreation, Leisure and Fitness Studies, B
Physical Education Teaching and Coaching, B
Political Science and Government, B
Pre-Law Studies, B
Pre-Medicine/Pre-Medical Studies, B
Pre-Veterinary Studies, B
Psychology, B
Religion/Religious Studies, B
Science Teacher Education/General Science
  Teacher Education, B
Secondary Education and Teaching, B
Social Sciences, B
Social Work, B
Sociology, B
Spanish Language and Literature, B
Special Education and Teaching, B
Sport and Fitness Administration/Management, B
Web/Multimedia Management and Webmaster, B
Women's Studies, B

MARTIN COMMUNITY COLLEGE

Accounting, A
Administrative Assistant and Secretarial Science, A
Automobile/Automotive Mechanics
  Technology/Technician, A
Business Administration and Management, A
Cosmetology/Cosmetologist, A
Dietician Assistant, A
Electrical and Power Transmission Installers, A
Electromechanical Technology/Electromechanical
  Engineering Technology, A
Equestrian/Equine Studies, A
General Studies, A
Heating, Air Conditioning and Refrigeration
  Technology/Technician, A
Heating, Air Conditioning, Ventilation and
  Refrigeration Maintenance
  Technology/Technician, A
Information Science/Studies, A
Liberal Arts and Sciences Studies and
  Humanities, A
Management Information Systems and Services, A
Medical Administrative Assistant/Secretary, A
Medical/Clinical Assistant, A
Physical Therapist Assistant, A

MAYLAND COMMUNITY COLLEGE

Accounting, A
Administrative Assistant and Secretarial Science, A
Business Administration and Management, A
Carpentry/Carpenter, A
Computer Programming/Programmer, A
Criminal Justice/Law Enforcement Administration, A
Criminal Justice/Police Science, A
Electrical, Electronic and Communications
  Engineering Technology/Technician, A
Electrical, Electronics and Communications
  Engineering, A
Finance, A
Horticultural Science, A
Information Technology, A
Kindergarten/PreSchool Education and Teaching, A

Liberal Arts and Sciences Studies and
  Humanities, A
Medical Administrative Assistant/Secretary, A
Medical/Clinical Assistant, A
Nursing - Registered Nurse Training, A
Plumbing Technology/Plumber, A

MCDOWELL TECHNICAL COMMUNITY COLLEGE

Accounting, A
Administrative Assistant and Secretarial Science, A
Automobile/Automotive Mechanics
  Technology/Technician, A
Business Administration and Management, A
Child Development, A
Commercial and Advertising Art, A
Computer Programming/Programmer, A
Construction Engineering Technology/Technician, A
Cosmetology/Cosmetologist, A
Criminal Justice/Law Enforcement Administration, A
Electrical, Electronic and Communications
  Engineering Technology/Technician, A
Heavy Equipment Maintenance
  Technology/Technician, A
Liberal Arts and Sciences Studies and
  Humanities, A
Machine Tool Technology/Machinist, A
Marketing/Marketing Management, A
Nursing - Registered Nurse Training, A
Photography, A
Teacher Assistant/Aide, A
Welding Technology/Welder, A

MEREDITH COLLEGE

Accounting, B
American/United States Studies/Civilization, B
Art Teacher Education, B
Biology/Biological Sciences, B
Business Administration and Management, B
Business Administration, Management and
  Operations, M
Business/Managerial Economics, B
Chemistry, B
Child Development, B
Communication Studies/Speech Communication
  and Rhetoric, B
Computer and Information Sciences, B
Computer Science, B
Dance, B
Dietetics/Dieticians, B
Drama and Dance Teacher Education, B
Drama and Dramatics/Theatre Arts, B
Economics, B
Education, M
English Language and Literature, B
Environmental Sciences, B
Environmental Studies, B
Family and Consumer Sciences/Human Sciences, B
Fashion Merchandising, B
Fashion/Apparel Design, B
Fine/Studio Arts, B
French Language and Literature, B
Graphic Design, B
Health/Medical Preparatory Programs, B
History, B
Interior Design, B
International Relations and Affairs, B
Kinesiology and Exercise Science, B
Mass Communication/Media Studies, B
Mathematics, B
Molecular Biology, B
Multi-/Interdisciplinary Studies, B
Music, BM
Music Pedagogy, B
Music Performance, B
Music Teacher Education, B
Music Theory and Composition, B
Nutritional Sciences, M
Physical Education Teaching and Coaching, B
Piano and Organ, B
Political Science and Government, B
Pre-Dentistry Studies, B
Pre-Medicine/Pre-Medical Studies, B
Pre-Pharmacy Studies, B
Pre-Veterinary Studies, B
Psychology, B

Public/Applied History and Archival Administration, B
Religion/Religious Studies, B
Social Work, B
Sociology, B
Spanish Language and Literature, B
Violin, Viola, Guitar and Other Stringed
  Instruments, B
Visual and Performing Arts, B
Voice and Opera, B
Wind and Percussion Instruments, B
Women's Studies, B

METHODIST COLLEGE

Accounting, AB
Army JROTC/ROTC, A
Art Teacher Education, B
Art/Art Studies, General, AB
Athletic Training and Sports Medicine, B
Behavioral Sciences, AB
Bible/Biblical Studies, B
Biological and Physical Sciences, B
Biology/Biological Sciences, AB
Business Administration and Management, AB
Chemistry, AB
Computer Science, AB
Creative Writing, B
Criminal Justice/Law Enforcement
  Administration, AB
Drama and Dramatics/Theatre Arts, AB
Economics, AB
Education, B
Elementary Education and Teaching, B
English Language and Literature, AB
Finance, AB
French Language and Literature, AB
German Language and Literature, A
Health/Health Care Administration/Management, AB
History, AB
Hospitality and Recreation Marketing Operations, B
International Relations and Affairs, B
Kindergarten/PreSchool Education and Teaching, B
Law and Legal Studies, B
Liberal Arts and Sciences Studies and
  Humanities, AB
Marketing Research, B
Mass Communication/Media Studies, AB
Mathematics, AB
Music, AB
Music Management and Merchandising, B
Music Teacher Education, B
Parks, Recreation and Leisure Facilities
  Management, B
Philosophy, A
Physical Education Teaching and Coaching, AB
Physician Assistant, B
Political Science and Government, AB
Pre-Dentistry Studies, B
Pre-Engineering, A
Pre-Law Studies, B
Pre-Medicine/Pre-Medical Studies, B
Pre-Veterinary Studies, B
Psychology, AB
Religion/Religious Studies, B
Religious Education, A
Science Teacher Education/General Science
  Teacher Education, B
Secondary Education and Teaching, B
Social Work, AB
Sociology, AB
Spanish Language and Literature, AB
Special Education and Teaching, B
Sport and Fitness Administration/Management, B
Teacher Education, Multiple Levels, B

MITCHELL COMMUNITY COLLEGE

Accounting, A
Administrative Assistant and Secretarial Science, A
Art/Art Studies, General, A
Biological and Physical Sciences, A
Business Administration and Management, A
Child Development, A
Computer Science, A
Criminal Justice/Law Enforcement Administration, A
Data Processing and Data Processing
  Technology/Technician, A
Drafting and Design Technology/Technician, A

Electrical, Electronic and Communications
   Engineering Technology/Technician, A
Elementary Education and Teaching, A
Engineering, A
Human Services, A
Industrial Technology/Technician, A
Kindergarten/PreSchool Education and Teaching, A
Liberal Arts and Sciences Studies and
   Humanities, A
Machine Tool Technology/Machinist, A
Mathematics, A
Medical/Clinical Assistant, A
Nursing - Registered Nurse Training, A
Physical Education Teaching and Coaching, A
Psychology, A
Social Work, A

MONTGOMERY COMMUNITY COLLEGE

Accounting, A
Administrative Assistant and Secretarial Science, A
Business Administration and Management, A
Ceramic Arts and Ceramics, A
Child Care and Support Services Management, A
Criminal Justice/Police Science, A
Emergency Medical Technology/Technician (EMT
   Paramedic), A
Forestry Technology/Technician, A
Liberal Arts and Sciences Studies and
   Humanities, A
Management Information Systems and Services, A
Medical/Clinical Assistant, A

MONTREAT COLLEGE

American/United States Studies/Civilization, B
Bible/Biblical Studies, B
Biology/Biological Sciences, B
Business Administration and Management, AB
Business Administration, Management and
   Operations, M
Computer and Information Sciences, B
Education, A
Elementary Education and Teaching, B
English Language and Literature, B
Environmental Studies, B
History, B
Human Services, B
Music Management and Merchandising, B
Music Performance, B
Parks, Recreation, Leisure and Fitness Studies, B

MOUNT OLIVE COLLEGE

Accounting, AB
Art/Art Studies, General, AB
Athletic Training and Sports Medicine, B
Biological and Physical Sciences, A
Biology/Biological Sciences, AB
Business Administration and Management, AB
Commercial and Advertising Art, B
Criminal Justice/Law Enforcement Administration, B
Divinity/Ministry (BD, MDiv.), AB
English Language and Literature, B
Environmental Studies, B
History, B
Human Services, B
Information Science/Studies, AB
Junior High/Intermediate/Middle School Education
   and Teaching, B
Liberal Arts and Sciences Studies and
   Humanities, AB
Mathematics, B
Music, A
Parks, Recreation, Leisure and Fitness Studies, AB
Psychology, AB
Public Health (MPH, DPH), B
Religion/Religious Studies, AB

NASH COMMUNITY COLLEGE

Accounting, A
Administrative Assistant and Secretarial Science, A
Architectural Engineering Technology/Technician, A
Business Administration and Management, A
Cosmetology/Cosmetologist, A
Criminal Justice/Police Science, A
Electrical, Electronic and Communications
   Engineering Technology/Technician, A
Information Technology, A

Kindergarten/PreSchool Education and Teaching, A
Legal Administrative Assistant/Secretary, A
Liberal Arts and Sciences Studies and
   Humanities, A
Marketing/Marketing Management, A
Medical Administrative Assistant/Secretary, A
Nursing - Registered Nurse Training, A
Physical Therapy/Therapist, A

NORTH CAROLINA AGRICULTURAL AND TECHNICAL STATE UNIVERSITY

Accounting, B
Administrative Assistant and Secretarial Science, B
Adult and Continuing Education and Teaching, M
African-American/Black Studies, M
Agricultural Business and Management, B
Agricultural Economics, BM
Agricultural Education, M
Agricultural Engineering, M
Agricultural Mechanization, B
Agricultural Sciences, M
Agricultural Teacher Education, B
Agriculture, B
Animal Sciences, B
Apparel and Textiles, B
Applied Economics, M
Applied Mathematics, B
Architectural Engineering, BM
Art Education, M
Art Teacher Education, M
Biological and Biomedical Sciences, M
Biology/Biological Sciences, B
Building/Construction
   Finishing, Management, and Inspection, B
Business Administration and Management, B
Business Teacher Education, B
Chemical Engineering, BM
Chemistry, BM
Child Development, B
Civil Engineering, BM
Computer Science, BM
Counselor Education/School Counseling and
   Guidance Services, M
Dietetics/Dieticians, B
Drama and Dramatics/Theatre Arts, B
Early Childhood Education and Teaching, M
Economics, B
Education, BM
Educational Administration and Supervision, M
Educational Media/Instructional Technology, M
Electrical Engineering, MD
Electrical, Electronics and Communications
   Engineering, B
Elementary Education and Teaching, BM
Engineering and Applied Sciences, MD
Engineering Physics, B
English, M
English Education, M
English Language and Literature, B
Environmental Engineering
   Technology/Environmental Technology, M
Environmental Sciences, M
Family and Consumer Sciences/Home Economics
   Teacher Education, B
Family and Consumer Sciences/Human Sciences, B
Food Science, B
Foods, Nutrition, and Wellness Studies, B
French Language and Literature, B
Health Education, M
Health Teacher Education, B
History, B
Human Resources Development, M
Human Resources Management and Services, M
Industrial Education, M
Industrial Engineering, B
Industrial Technology/Technician, B
Industrial/Management Engineering, MD
Kindergarten/PreSchool Education and Teaching, B
Landscape Architecture, B
Management of Technology, M
Mass Communication/Media Studies, B
Mathematics, B
Mathematics Teacher Education, M
Mechanical Engineering, BMD
Middle School Education, M
Music Teacher Education, B

Nursing - Registered Nurse Training, B
Nutritional Sciences, M
Occupational Safety and Health
   Technology/Technician, B
Parks, Recreation, Leisure and Fitness Studies, B
Physical Education Teaching and Coaching, BM
Physics, B
Plant Sciences, M
Political Science and Government, B
Psychology, B
Reading Teacher Education, M
Science Teacher Education/General Science
   Teacher Education, M
Social Sciences, B
Social Studies Teacher Education, M
Social Work, BM
Sociology, B
Special Education and Teaching, B
Speech and Rhetorical Studies, B
Systems Engineering, MD
Technology Education/Industrial Arts, B
Trade and Industrial Teacher Education, B
Transportation and Materials Moving, B
Vocational and Technical Education, M

NORTH CAROLINA CENTRAL UNIVERSITY

Accounting, B
Art Teacher Education, B
Art/Art Studies, General, B
Athletic Training and Sports Medicine, B
Biological and Biomedical Sciences, M
Biology Teacher Education, B
Biology/Biological Sciences, B
Business Administration and Management, B
Business Administration, Management and
   Operations, MO
Chemistry, B
Chemistry Teacher Education, B
Communication Disorders, M
Computer Science, B
Counselor Education/School Counseling and
   Guidance Services, M
Criminal Justice/Law Enforcement Administration, B
Criminology, M
Drama and Dramatics/Theatre Arts, B
Education, M
Educational Leadership and Administration, M
Educational Media/Instructional Technology, M
Elementary Education and Teaching, BM
English, M
English Language and Literature, B
English/Language Arts Teacher Education, B
Environmental Sciences, B
Family and Consumer Economics and Related
   Services, B
Family and Consumer Sciences/Home Economics
   Teacher Education, B
Family and Consumer Sciences/Human
   Sciences, BM
Fine/Studio Arts, B
French Language and Literature, B
French Language Teacher Education, B
Geography, B
Geosciences, M
Health and Physical Education, B
Health Teacher Education, B
History, BM
History Teacher Education, B
Hospitality Administration/Management, B
Information Science/Studies, BM
Jazz/Jazz Studies, B
Junior High/Intermediate/Middle School Education
   and Teaching, B
Kindergarten/PreSchool Education and Teaching, B
Law and Legal Studies, PO
Library Science, M
Mass Communication/Media Studies, B
Mathematics, BM
Mathematics Teacher Education, B
Music, B
Music Teacher Education, B
Nursing - Registered Nurse Training, B
Parks, Recreation and Leisure Facilities
   Management, B
Physical Education Teaching and Coaching, BM

Physics, B
Physics Teacher Education, B
Political Science and Government, B
Psychology, BM
Public Administration, M
Public Health Education and Promotion, B
Recreation and Park Management, M
Religious/Sacred Music, B
Social Work, B
Sociology, BM
Spanish Language and Literature, B
Spanish Language Teacher Education, B
Special Education and Teaching, M
Therapeutic Recreation, M

NORTH CAROLINA SCHOOL OF THE ARTS

Cinematography and Film/Video Production, B
Composition, M
Dance, B
Drama and Dramatics/Theatre Arts, B
Film, Television, and Video Production, M
Film/Cinema Studies, B
Music, M
Music Performance, B
Performance, M
Piano and Organ, B
Technical Theatre/Theatre Design and
  Technology, B
Theater, M
Visual and Performing Arts, B
Voice and Opera, B

NORTH CAROLINA STATE UNIVERSITY

Accounting, BM
Adult and Continuing Education and Teaching, MD
Aerospace, Aeronautical and Astronautical
  Engineering, BMD
Agribusiness, B
Agricultural and Extension Education Services, B
Agricultural and Food Products Processing, A
Agricultural Business and Management, A
Agricultural Economics, BM
Agricultural Education, M
Agricultural Engineering, MD
Agricultural Sciences, MD
Agricultural Teacher Education, B
Agricultural/Biological Engineering and
  Bioengineering, B
Agriculture, A
Agronomy and Crop Science, B
Agronomy and Soil Sciences, MD
American Government and Politics (United States)
  , B
Animal Sciences, B
Anthropology, B
Apparel and Textile Manufacture, B
Apparel and Textile Marketing Management, B
Applied Arts and Design, M
Applied Mathematics, BMD
Architecture, BM
Arts Management, B
Atmospheric Sciences and Meteorology, MD
Biochemistry, BMD
Bioengineering, MD
Bioinformatics, MD
Biological and Biomedical Sciences, MD
Biology Teacher Education, B
Biology/Biological Sciences, B
Biomedical Engineering, MD
Biomedical/Medical Engineering, B
Biometry/Biometrics, MD
BioTechnology, M
Botany/Plant Biology, BMD
Business Administration and Management, B
Business Administration, Management and
  Operations, M
Cell Biology and Anatomy, MD
Chemical Engineering, BMD
Chemistry, BMD
Chemistry Teacher Education, B
Civil Engineering, BMD
Clothing and Textiles, D
Communication and Media Studies, M
Communication Studies/Speech Communication
  and Rhetoric, B

Community College Education, MD
Community Psychology, M
Computer Engineering, BMD
Computer Science, BMD
Construction Engineering, B
Construction Management, B
Corporate and Organizational Communication, M
Counselor Education/School Counseling and
  Guidance Services, MD
Creative Writing, B
Criminology, B
Curriculum and Instruction, MD
Design and Applied Arts, BD
Design and Visual Communications, B
Developmental Education, M
Developmental Psychology, D
Ecology, BD
Economics, BMD
Education, BMDO
Educational Administration and Supervision, MD
Educational Measurement and Evaluation, D
Educational Media/Instructional Technology, MD
Electrical Engineering, BMD
Electrical, Electronics and Communications
  Engineering, B
Engineering, B
Engineering and Applied Sciences, MD
English, M
English Language and Literature, B
English/Language Arts Teacher Education, B
Entomology, MD
Environmental Design/Architecture, B
Environmental Sciences, B
Environmental Studies, B
Environmental/Environmental Health Engineering, B
Epidemiology, MD
Ergonomics and Human Factors, D
Experimental Psychology, D
Film/Cinema Studies, B
Finance, B
Fish, Game and Wildlife Management, M
Fishing and Fisheries Sciences and Management, B
Food Science, B
Food Science and Technology, MD
Foreign Language Teacher Education, B
Forest Management/Forest Resources
  Management, B
Forestry, MD
French Language and Literature, BM
French Language Teacher Education, B
Genetics, MD
Genomic Sciences, MD
Geographic Information Systems, M
Geology/Earth Science, B
Geosciences, MD
Graphic Design, BM
Health Occupations Teacher Education, B
Higher Education/Higher Education
  Administration, MD
History, BM
History Teacher Education, B
Horticultural Science, BMD
Human Resources Management/Personnel
  Administration, B
Hydrology and Water Resources Science, B
Immunology, MD
Industrial and Organizational Psychology, D
Industrial Design, BM
Industrial Engineering, B
Industrial/Management Engineering, MD
Information Technology, B
International Affairs, M
Junior High/Intermediate/Middle School Education
  and Teaching, B
Landscape Architecture, BM
Landscaping and Groundskeeping, A
Liberal Arts and Sciences Studies and
  Humanities, B
Liberal Studies, M
Management of Technology, D
Manufacturing Engineering, M
Marine Sciences, MD
Marketing/Marketing Management, B
Mass Communication/Media Studies, B
Materials Engineering, BMD
Materials Sciences, BMD

Mathematical and Computational Finance, M
Mathematics, BMD
Mathematics Teacher Education, BMD
Mechanical Engineering, BMD
Meteorology, BMD
Microbiology, BMD
Middle School Education, M
Molecular Toxicology, MD
Natural Resources and Conservation, BM
Natural Resources Management/Development and
  Policy, B
Nuclear Engineering, BMD
Nutritional Sciences, MD
Oceanography, Chemical and Physical, BMD
Operations Research, MD
Paleontology, B
Paper and Pulp Engineering, MD
Parks, Recreation and Leisure Facilities
  Management, BM
Parks, Recreation, Leisure and Fitness Studies, B
Pathology/Experimental Pathology, MD
Pharmacology, MD
Philosophy, B
Physics, BMD
Physics Teacher Education, B
Physiology, MD
Plant Pathology/Phytopathology, MD
Plant Protection and Integrated Pest
  Management, A
Political Science and Government, B
Polymer/Plastics Engineering, D
Poultry Science, BM
Psychology, BD
Public Administration, MD
Public History, M
Public Policy Analysis, B
Public Relations/Image Management, B
Recreation and Park Management, MD
Religion/Religious Studies, B
Rural Sociology, M
Sales and Marketing Operations/Marketing and
  Distribution Teacher Education, B
School Psychology, D
Science Teacher Education/General Science
  Teacher Education, BMD
Science, Technology and Society, B
Secondary Education and Teaching, B
Social Studies Teacher Education, B
Social Work, B
Sociology, BMD
Soil Science and Agronomy, B
Spanish Language and Literature, BM
Spanish Language Teacher Education, B
Special Education and Teaching, M
Sport and Fitness Administration/Management, BM
Statistics, BMD
Technical Communication, M
Technology Teacher Education/Industrial Arts
  Teacher Education, B
Textile Science, B
Textile Sciences and Engineering, BMD
Tourism and Travel Services Management, B
Toxicology, MD
Travel and Tourism, MD
Turf and Turfgrass Management, AB
Veterinary Medicine, MPO
Veterinary Sciences, MD
Wildlife and Wildlands Science and Management, B
Wood Science and Wood Products/Pulp and Paper
  Technology, B
Writing, M
Zoology/Animal Biology, BMD

NORTH CAROLINA WESLEYAN COLLEGE

Accounting, B
Anthropology, B
Biology/Biological Sciences, B
Business Administration and Management, B
Chemistry, B
Criminal Justice/Law Enforcement Administration, B
Drama and Dramatics/Theatre Arts, B
Education, B
Elementary Education and Teaching, B
English Language and Literature, B
Environmental Studies, B

History, B
Hotel/Motel Administration/Management, B
Information Science/Studies, B
Junior High/Intermediate/Middle School Education
and Teaching, B
Law and Legal Studies, B
Mathematics, B
Philosophy, B
Physical Education Teaching and Coaching, B
Political Science and Government, B
Pre-Medicine/Pre-Medical Studies, B
Psychology, B
Religion/Religious Studies, B
Secondary Education and Teaching, B
Sociology, B
Special Products Marketing Operations, B

PAMLICO COMMUNITY COLLEGE

Accounting, A
Administrative Assistant and Secretarial Science, A
Automobile/Automotive Mechanics
Technology/Technician, A
Business Administration and Management, A
Clinical/Medical Laboratory Technician, A
Computer Engineering Technology/Technician, A
Electrical, Electronic and Communications
Engineering Technology/Technician, A
Environmental Studies, A
Liberal Arts and Sciences Studies and
Humanities, A
Medical/Clinical Assistant, A
Neuroscience, A

PEACE COLLEGE

Biology/Biological Sciences, B
Business Administration and Management, B
Communication Studies/Speech Communication
and Rhetoric, B
Design and Visual Communications, B
English Language and Literature, B
Graphic Design, B
Human Resources Management/Personnel
Administration, B
Liberal Arts and Sciences Studies and
Humanities, AB
Music, A
Music Performance, B
Political Science and Government, B
Psychology, B
Spanish Language and Literature, B

PFEIFFER UNIVERSITY

Accounting, B
Arts Management, B
Athletic Training and Sports Medicine, B
Biology/Biological Sciences, B
Business Administration and Management, B
Business Administration, Management and
Operations, MO
Business/Managerial Economics, B
Chemistry, B
Communication Studies/Speech Communication
and Rhetoric, B
Criminal Justice/Law Enforcement Administration, B
Economics, B
Education, BM
Elementary Education and Teaching, BM
Engineering, B
English Language and Literature, B
Environmental Sciences, B
Environmental Studies, B
Exercise Physiology, B
Finance, B
Health Services Administration, MO
History, B
Human Services, B
International Business/Trade/Commerce, B
Journalism, B
Management Information Systems and Services, B
Marketing/Marketing Management, B
Mathematics, B
Mathematics and Computer Science, B
Music, B
Music Teacher Education, B
Organizational Communication, B
Organizational Management, MO

Physical Education Teaching and Coaching, B
Political Science and Government, B
Pre-Law Studies, B
Pre-Medicine/Pre-Medical Studies, B
Psychology, B
Public Relations/Image Management, B
Religion/Religious Studies, B
Religious Education, BM
Religious/Sacred Music, B
Science Teacher Education/General Science
Teacher Education, B
Social Sciences, B
Social Studies Teacher Education, B
Sociology, B
Special Education and Teaching, B
Sport and Fitness Administration/Management, B
Youth Ministry, B

PIEDMONT BAPTIST COLLEGE

Airline/Commercial/Professional Pilot and Flight
Crew, B
Avionics Maintenance Technology/Technician, AB
Bible/Biblical Studies, AB
Child Development, A
Education, AB
Elementary Education and Teaching, B
English Language and Literature, B
Kindergarten/PreSchool Education and Teaching, A
Music, B
Music Teacher Education, B
Pastoral Studies/Counseling, M
Physical Education Teaching and Coaching, B
Religion/Religious Studies, AB
Secondary Education and Teaching, B
Theology and Religious Vocations, M

PIEDMONT COMMUNITY COLLEGE

Accounting, A
Business Administration and Management, A
Cinematography and Film/Video Production, A
Computer Engineering Technology/Technician, A
Criminal Justice/Law Enforcement Administration, A
Electrical, Electronic and Communications
Engineering Technology/Technician, A
Liberal Arts and Sciences Studies and
Humanities, A
Medical Administrative Assistant/Secretary, A
Nursing - Registered Nurse Training, A
Social Sciences, A

PITT COMMUNITY COLLEGE

Accounting, A
Administrative Assistant and Secretarial Science, A
Architectural Engineering Technology/Technician, A
Business Administration and Management, A
Child Care and Support Services Management, A
Commercial and Advertising Art, A
Computer Programming, Specific Applications, A
Computer Systems Analysis/Analyst, A
Computer Systems Networking and
Telecommunications, A
Construction Trades, A
Criminal Justice/Police Science, A
Diagnostic Medical Sonography/Sonographer and
Ultrasound Technician, A
Electrical, Electronic and Communications
Engineering Technology/Technician, A
Electromechanical Technology/Electromechanical
Engineering Technology, A
Engineering/Industrial Management, A
Environmental Control Technologies/Technicians, A
Health Information/Medical Records
Technology/Technician, A
Health Professions and Related Clinical Sciences, A
Industrial Technology/Technician, A
Legal Assistant/Paralegal, A
Liberal Arts and Sciences Studies and
Humanities, A
Machine Shop Technology/Assistant, A
Machine Tool Technology/Machinist, A
Medical Administrative Assistant/Secretary, A
Medical Radiologic Technology/Science - Radiation
Therapist, A
Medical/Clinical Assistant, A
Mental and Social Health Services and Allied
Professions, A

Nuclear Medical Technology/Technologist, A
Nursing - Registered Nurse Training, A
Occupational Therapist Assistant, A
Operations Management and Supervision, A
Psychiatric/Mental Health Services Technician, A
Respiratory Care Therapy/Therapist, A
Retailing and Retail Operations, A

QUEENS UNIVERSITY OF CHARLOTTE

American Literature (United States), B
American/United States Studies/Civilization, B
Applied Mathematics, B
Art/Art Studies, General, B
Biochemistry, B
Biology/Biological Sciences, B
Business Administration and Management, B
Business Administration, Management and
Operations, M
Computer/Information Technology Services
Administration and Management, B
Corporate and Organizational Communication, M
Drama and Dramatics/Theatre Arts, B
Education, BM
Elementary Education and Teaching, BM
English Language and Literature, B
English/Language Arts Teacher Education, B
Environmental Biology, B
Fine/Studio Arts, B
Foreign Languages and Literatures, B
History, B
Information Science/Studies, B
International Relations and Affairs, B
Journalism, B
Mass Communication/Media Studies, B
Mathematics, B
Mathematics Teacher Education, B
Music, B
Music Therapy/Therapist, B
Nursing, M
Nursing Administration, M
Nursing Science, B
Philosophy, B
Piano and Organ, B
Political Science and Government, B
Pre-Law Studies, B
Pre-Medicine/Pre-Medical Studies, B
Pre-Veterinary Studies, B
Psychology, B
Religion/Religious Studies, B
Secondary Education and Teaching, B
Voice and Opera, B
Writing, M

RANDOLPH COMMUNITY COLLEGE

Accounting Technology/Technician and
Bookkeeping, A
Automobile/Automotive Mechanics
Technology/Technician, A
Business Administration and Management, A
Commercial and Advertising Art, A
Commercial Photography, A
Computer Systems Analysis/Analyst, A
Criminal Justice/Police Science, A
Electromechanical Technology/Electromechanical
Engineering Technology, A
Executive Assistant/Executive Secretary, A
Fine/Studio Arts, A
Graphic and Printing Equipment Operator
Production, A
Historic Preservation and Conservation, A
Information Technology, A
Interior Design, A
Liberal Arts and Sciences Studies and
Humanities, A
Machine Tool Technology/Machinist, A
Nursing - Registered Nurse Training, A
Photographic and Film/Video Technology/Technician
and Assistant, A
Photography, A
Plastics Engineering Technology/Technician, A
Speech-Language Pathology/Pathologist, A
System Administration/Administrator, A

Welding Technology/Welder, A

RICHMOND COMMUNITY COLLEGE

Accounting, A
Administrative Assistant and Secretarial Science, A
Business Administration and Management, A
Child Care and Support Services Management, A
Computer Engineering Technology/Technician, A
Computer Systems Analysis/Analyst, A
Criminal Justice/Law Enforcement Administration, A
Electrical, Electronic and Communications
 Engineering Technology/Technician, A
Human Services, A
Industrial Production Technologies/Technicians, A
Liberal Arts and Sciences Studies and
 Humanities, A
Machine Tool Technology/Machinist, A
Mechanical Engineering/Mechanical
 Technology/Technician, A
Medical/Clinical Assistant, A
Nursing - Registered Nurse Training, A

ROANOKE BIBLE COLLEGE

Bible/Biblical Studies, AB
Religion/Religious Studies, B
Theology/Theological Studies, B

ROANOKE-CHOWAN COMMUNITY COLLEGE

Administrative Assistant and Secretarial Science, A
Architectural Engineering Technology/Technician, A
Automobile/Automotive Mechanics
 Technology/Technician, A
Business Administration and Management, A
Computer Programming/Programmer, A
Construction Engineering Technology/Technician, A
Cosmetology/Cosmetologist, A
Criminal Justice/Law Enforcement Administration, A
Education, A
Electrical, Electronic and Communications
 Engineering Technology/Technician, A
Environmental Engineering
 Technology/Environmental Technology, A
Heating, Air Conditioning, Ventilation and
 Refrigeration Maintenance
 Technology/Technician, A
Kindergarten/PreSchool Education and Teaching, A
Liberal Arts and Sciences Studies and
 Humanities, A
Nursing - Registered Nurse Training, A

ROBESON COMMUNITY COLLEGE

Administrative Assistant and Secretarial Science, A
Business Administration and Management, A
Computer and Information Sciences, A
Computer and Information Sciences and Support
 Services, A
Computer Systems Networking and
 Telecommunications, A
Criminal Justice/Law Enforcement Administration, A
Early Childhood Education and Teaching, A
Electrical, Electronic and Communications
 Engineering Technology/Technician, A
Food Technology and Processing, A
Industrial Technology/Technician, A
Nursing - Registered Nurse Training, A
Respiratory Care Therapy/Therapist, A

ROCKINGHAM COMMUNITY COLLEGE

Accounting, A
Administrative Assistant and Secretarial Science, A
Art/Art Studies, General, A
Biological and Physical Sciences, A
Business Administration and Management, A
Business Machine Repairer, A
Carpentry/Carpenter, A
Child Development, A
Construction Engineering Technology/Technician, A
Consumer Services and Advocacy, A
Cosmetology/Cosmetologist, A
Criminal Justice/Law Enforcement Administration, A
Criminal Justice/Police Science, A
Electromechanical Technology/Electromechanical
 Engineering Technology, A

Heating, Air Conditioning, Ventilation and
 Refrigeration Maintenance
 Technology/Technician, A
Horticultural Science, A
Human Resources Management/Personnel
 Administration, A
Information Science/Studies, A
Labor and Industrial Relations, A
Legal Administrative Assistant/Secretary, A
Legal Assistant/Paralegal, A
Liberal Arts and Sciences Studies and
 Humanities, A
Licensed Practical/Vocational Nurse Training, A
Medical Administrative Assistant/Secretary, A
Medical/Clinical Assistant, A
Nursing - Registered Nurse Training, A
Occupational Therapist Assistant, A
Physical Therapist Assistant, A
Respiratory Care Therapy/Therapist, A
Teacher Assistant/Aide, A
Technology Education/Industrial Arts, A
Tourism and Travel Services Management, A

ROWAN-CABARRUS COMMUNITY COLLEGE

Accounting, A
Automobile/Automotive Mechanics
 Technology/Technician, A
Biomedical Technology/Technician, A
Business Administration and Management, A
Criminal Justice/Law Enforcement Administration, A
Electrical, Electronic and Communications
 Engineering Technology/Technician, A
Health and Medical Laboratory Technologies, A
Health Information/Medical Records
 Technology/Technician, A
Industrial Technology/Technician, A
Information Science/Studies, A
Kindergarten/PreSchool Education and Teaching, A
Legal Assistant/Paralegal, A
Liberal Arts and Sciences Studies and
 Humanities, A
Mechanical Drafting and Mechanical Drafting
 CAD/CADD, A
Nursing - Registered Nurse Training, A

ST. ANDREWS PRESBYTERIAN COLLEGE

Art/Art Studies, General, B
Biology/Biological Sciences, B
Business Administration and Management, B
Chemistry, B
Creative Writing, B
Elementary Education and Teaching, B
English Language and Literature, B
Equestrian/Equine Studies, B
Fine/Studio Arts, B
History, B
Interdisciplinary Studies, B
Liberal Arts and Sciences Studies and
 Humanities, B
Mass Communication/Media Studies, B
Mathematics, B
Philosophy, B
Physical Education Teaching and Coaching, B
Political Science and Government, B
Pre-Law Studies, B
Pre-Medicine/Pre-Medical Studies, B
Pre-Veterinary Studies, B
Psychology, B
Religion/Religious Studies, B
Therapeutic Recreation/Recreational Therapy, B

SAINT AUGUSTINE'S COLLEGE

Accounting, B
African-American/Black Studies, B
Art/Art Studies, General, B
Biology Teacher Education, B
Biology/Biological Sciences, B
Business Administration and Management, B
Business Teacher Education, B
Chemistry, B
Communication Studies/Speech Communication
 and Rhetoric, B
Computer and Information Sciences, B
Computer Science, B

Computer/Information Technology Services
 Administration and Management, B
Criminal Justice/Law Enforcement Administration, B
Dramatic/Theatre Arts and Stagecraft, B
Early Childhood Education and Teaching, B
Elementary Education and Teaching, B
English Language and Literature, B
English/Language Arts Teacher Education, B
Film/Cinema Studies, B
Forensic Science and Technology, B
Health and Physical Education/Fitness, B
History, B
International Business/Trade/Commerce, B
International Relations and Affairs, B
Mathematics, B
Mathematics Teacher Education, B
Music Performance, B
Music Teacher Education, B
Occupational Health and Industrial Hygiene, B
Organizational Behavior Studies, B
Physical Education Teaching and Coaching, B
Political Science and Government, B
Pre-Law Studies, B
Pre-Medicine/Pre-Medical Studies, B
Psychology, B
Real Estate, B
Social Studies Teacher Education, B
Sociology, B
Special Education and Teaching, B
Teacher Education, Multiple Levels, B
Visual and Performing Arts, B

SALEM COLLEGE

Accounting, B
American/United States Studies/Civilization, B
Art History, Criticism and Conservation, B
Arts Management, B
Biology/Biological Sciences, B
Business Administration and Management, B
Chemistry, B
Clinical Laboratory Science/Medical
 Technology/Technologist, B
Early Childhood Education and Teaching, M
Economics, B
Education, BM
Elementary Education and Teaching, M
English as a Second Language, M
English Language and Literature, B
Fine/Studio Arts, B
French Language and Literature, B
German Language and Literature, B
History, B
Interdisciplinary Studies, B
Interior Design, B
International Business/Trade/Commerce, B
International Relations and Affairs, B
Mass Communication/Media Studies, B
Mathematics, B
Music, B
Music Performance, B
Philosophy, B
Physician Assistant, B
Psychology, B
Reading Teacher Education, M
Religion/Religious Studies, B
Sociology, B
Spanish Language and Literature, B
Special Education and Teaching, M

SAMPSON COMMUNITY COLLEGE

Accounting, A
Administrative Assistant and Secretarial Science, A
Business Administration and Management, A
Computer and Information Sciences, A
Computer Programming/Programmer, A
Criminal Justice/Law Enforcement Administration, A
Horticultural Science, A
Industrial Technology/Technician, A
Information Technology, A
Liberal Arts and Sciences Studies and
 Humanities, A
Licensed Practical/Vocational Nurse Training, A
Nursing - Registered Nurse Training, A
Poultry Science, A
System Administration/Administrator, A

Word Processing, A

SANDHILLS COMMUNITY COLLEGE

Accounting, A
Administrative Assistant and Secretarial Science, A
Architectural Engineering Technology/Technician, A
Art Teacher Education, A
Art/Art Studies, General, A
Automobile/Automotive Mechanics
   Technology/Technician, A
Biological and Physical Sciences, A
Business Administration and Management, A
Business, Management, Marketing, and Related
   Support Services, A
Child Development, A
Civil Engineering Technology/Technician, A
Clinical/Medical Laboratory Technician, A
Computer Engineering, A
Computer Engineering Technology/Technician, A
Computer Programming, Specific Applications, A
Computer Programming/Programmer, A
Computer/Information Technology Services
   Administration and Management, A
Cosmetology/Cosmetologist, A
Criminal Justice/Law Enforcement Administration, A
Criminal Justice/Police Science, A
Culinary Arts/Chef Training, A
Fine/Studio Arts, A
Gerontology, A
Hotel/Motel Administration/Management, A
Human Services, A
Information Science/Studies, A
Kindergarten/PreSchool Education and Teaching, A
Landscaping and Groundskeeping, A
Liberal Arts and Sciences Studies and
   Humanities, A
Licensed Practical/Vocational Nurse Training, A
Mathematics, A
Medical Administrative Assistant/Secretary, A
Mental Health/Rehabilitation, A
Music, A
Music Teacher Education, A
Nurse/Nursing Assistant/Aide and Patient Care
   Assistant, A
Nursing - Registered Nurse Training, A
Pre-Engineering, A
Radiologic Technology/Science - Radiographer, A
Respiratory Care Therapy/Therapist, A
Science Teacher Education/General Science
   Teacher Education, A
Substance Abuse/Addiction Counseling, A
Surgical Technology/Technologist, A
Survey Technology/Surveying, A
System Administration/Administrator, A
Teacher Assistant/Aide, A
Turf and Turfgrass Management, A
Web/Multimedia Management and Webmaster, A

SHAW UNIVERSITY

Accounting, B
Athletic Training and Sports Medicine, B
Audiology/Audiologist and Speech-Language
   Pathology/Pathologist, B
Biology/Biological Sciences, B
Business Administration and Management, AB
Chemistry, B
Computer and Information Sciences, B
Computer Science, B
Criminal Justice/Safety Studies, AB
Curriculum and Instruction, M
Drama and Dramatics/Theatre Arts, B
Education/Teaching of Individuals with Mental
   Retardation, B
Elementary Education and Teaching, B
English Language and Literature, B
English/Language Arts Teacher Education, B
Environmental Studies, B
International Business/Trade/Commerce, B
International Relations and Affairs, B
Kindergarten/PreSchool Education and Teaching, B
Kinesiology and Exercise Science, B
Liberal Arts and Sciences Studies and
   Humanities, B
Mass Communication/Media Studies, B
Mathematics, B
Mathematics Teacher Education, B

Music, B
Parks, Recreation, Leisure and Fitness Studies, B
Philosophy, B
Physics, B
Political Science and Government, B
Psychology, B
Public Administration, B
Religion/Religious Studies, AB
Sales, Distribution and Marketing Operations, B
Social Work, B
Sociology, B
Spanish Language and Literature, B
Theology and Religious Vocations, MP
Therapeutic Recreation/Recreational Therapy, B

SOUTH COLLEGE-ASHEVILLE

Accounting, A
Business Administration and Management, A
Computer and Information Sciences, A
Legal Assistant/Paralegal, A
Medical/Clinical Assistant, A
Office Management and Supervision, A

SOUTH PIEDMONT COMMUNITY COLLEGE

Accounting Technology/Technician and
   Bookkeeping, A
Automobile/Automotive Mechanics
   Technology/Technician, A
Business Administration and Management, A
Commercial and Advertising Art, A
Computer Programming, Specific Applications, A
Computer Systems Analysis/Analyst, A
Computer Systems Networking and
   Telecommunications, A
Criminal Justice/Police Science, A
Drafting and Design Technology/Technician, A
Electrical, Electronic and Communications
   Engineering Technology/Technician, A
Electromechanical Technology/Electromechanical
   Engineering Technology, A
Executive Assistant/Executive Secretary, A
Health Information/Medical Records
   Technology/Technician, A
Heating, Air Conditioning and Refrigeration
   Technology/Technician, A
Legal Administrative Assistant/Secretary, A
Liberal Arts and Sciences Studies and
   Humanities, A
Machine Tool Technology/Machinist, A
Mechanical Engineering/Mechanical
   Technology/Technician, A
Medical Administrative Assistant/Secretary, A
Medical/Clinical Assistant, A
Operations Management and Supervision, A
Psychiatric/Mental Health Services Technician, A
Social Work, A

SOUTHEASTERN BAPTIST THEOLOGICAL SEMINARY

Divinity/Ministry (BD, MDiv.), A
Ethics, D
Missions/Missionary Studies and Missiology, D
Pastoral Studies/Counseling, A
Philosophy, D
Psychology, M
Religious Education, MP
Sacred Music, M
Theology and Religious Vocations, MDP
Theology/Theological Studies, A
Women's Studies, P

SOUTHEASTERN COMMUNITY COLLEGE

Administrative Assistant and Secretarial Science, A
Art/Art Studies, General, A
Biological and Physical Sciences, A
BioTechnology, A
Business Administration and Management, A
Clinical/Medical Laboratory Technician, A
Computer Engineering Technology/Technician, A
Cosmetology/Cosmetologist, A
Criminal Justice/Law Enforcement Administration, A
Electrical, Electronic and Communications
   Engineering Technology/Technician, A

Environmental Studies, A
Forestry Technology/Technician, A
Industrial Technology/Technician, A
Kindergarten/PreSchool Education and Teaching, A
Liberal Arts and Sciences Studies and
   Humanities, A
Music, A
Nursing - Registered Nurse Training, A
Parks, Recreation and Leisure Facilities
   Management, A
Parks, Recreation, Leisure and Fitness Studies, A
Teacher Assistant/Aide, A
Welding Technology/Welder, A

SOUTHWESTERN COMMUNITY COLLEGE

Accounting, A
Administrative Assistant and Secretarial Science, A
Automobile/Automotive Mechanics
   Technology/Technician, A
Business Administration and Management, A
Child Development, A
Clinical/Medical Laboratory Technician, A
Commercial and Advertising Art, A
Computer Engineering Technology/Technician, A
Cosmetology/Cosmetologist, A
Criminal Justice/Police Science, A
Culinary Arts/Chef Training, A
Electrical, Electronic and Communications
   Engineering Technology/Technician, A
Emergency Medical Technology/Technician (EMT
   Paramedic), A
Environmental Studies, A
Health Information/Medical Records
   Administration/Administrator, A
Health Information/Medical Records
   Technology/Technician, A
Information Science/Studies, A
Legal Assistant/Paralegal, A
Liberal Arts and Sciences Studies and
   Humanities, A
Licensed Practical/Vocational Nurse Training, A
Marketing/Marketing Management, A
Massage Therapy/Therapeutic Massage, A
Medical Radiologic Technology/Science - Radiation
   Therapist, A
Mental Health/Rehabilitation, A
Nursing - Registered Nurse Training, A
Parks, Recreation, Leisure and Fitness Studies, A
Physical Therapist Assistant, A
Physical Therapy/Therapist, A
Respiratory Care Therapy/Therapist, A
Substance Abuse/Addiction Counseling, A
System, Networking, and LAN/WAN
   Management/Manager, A
Trade and Industrial Teacher Education, A

STANLY COMMUNITY COLLEGE

Accounting Technology/Technician and
   Bookkeeping, A
Autobody/Collision and Repair
   Technology/Technician, A
Biomedical Technology/Technician, A
Business Administration and Management, A
Child Care and Support Services Management, A
Computer Hardware Engineering, A
Computer Programming, A
Computer Programming, Specific Applications, A
Computer Systems Networking and
   Telecommunications, A
Computer Technology/Computer Systems
   Technology, A
Computer/Information Technology Services
   Administration and Management, A
Cosmetology/Cosmetologist, A
Criminal Justice/Police Science, A
Electrical, Electronic and Communications
   Engineering Technology/Technician, A
Executive Assistant/Executive Secretary, A
Human Services, A
Industrial Technology/Technician, A
Information Science/Studies, A
Legal Administrative Assistant/Secretary, A
Management Information Systems and Services, A
Mechanical Drafting and Mechanical Drafting
   CAD/CADD, A

Medical Administrative Assistant/Secretary, A
Medical/Clinical Assistant, A
Nursing - Registered Nurse Training, A
Occupational Therapist Assistant, A
Physical Therapist Assistant, A
Respiratory Care Therapy/Therapist, A
System Administration/Administrator, A
Web Page, Digital/Multimedia and Information
   Resources Design, A
Web/Multimedia Management and Webmaster, A

SURRY COMMUNITY COLLEGE

Accounting, A
Administrative Assistant and Secretarial Science, A
Advertising, A
Agricultural Business and Management, A
Automobile/Automotive Mechanics
   Technology/Technician, A
Business Administration and Management, A
Child Care Provider/Assistant, A
Commercial and Advertising Art, A
Computer Engineering, A
Computer Engineering Technology/Technician, A
Computer Programming, A
Computer Programming/Programmer, A
Computer Systems Networking and
   Telecommunications, A
Construction Engineering Technology/Technician, A
Cosmetology/Cosmetologist, A
Criminal Justice/Law Enforcement Administration, A
Drafting and Design Technology/Technician, A
Electrical, Electronic and Communications
   Engineering Technology/Technician, A
Heating, Air Conditioning, Ventilation and
   Refrigeration Maintenance
   Technology/Technician, A
Horticultural Science, A
Information Science/Studies, A
Information Technology, A
Legal Assistant/Paralegal, A
Liberal Arts and Sciences Studies and
   Humanities, A
Licensed Practical/Vocational Nurse Training, A
Machine Tool Technology/Machinist, A
Medical Administrative Assistant/Secretary, A
Nursing - Registered Nurse Training, A
Poultry Science, A

TRI-COUNTY COMMUNITY COLLEGE

Accounting, A
Automobile/Automotive Mechanics
   Technology/Technician, A
Business Administration and Management, A
Early Childhood Education and Teaching, A
Electrical, Electronic and Communications
   Engineering Technology/Technician, A
Information Technology, A
Liberal Arts and Sciences Studies and
   Humanities, A
Medical/Clinical Assistant, A
Nursing - Registered Nurse Training, A
Welding Technology/Welder, A

THE UNIVERSITY OF NORTH CAROLINA AT ASHEVILLE

Accounting, B
Art/Art Studies, General, B
Atmospheric Sciences and Meteorology, B
Biology/Biological Sciences, B
Business Administration and Management, B
Chemistry, B
Classics and Classical
   Languages, Literatures, and Linguistics, B
Computer Science, B
Drama and Dramatics/Theatre Arts, B
Economics, B
English Language and Literature, B
Environmental Studies, B
Fine/Studio Arts, B
French Language and Literature, B
German Language and Literature, B
History, B
Journalism, B
Liberal Arts and Sciences Studies and
   Humanities, B
Liberal Studies, M

Mathematics, B
Music, B
Operations Management and Supervision, B
Philosophy, B
Physics, B
Political Science and Government, B
Psychology, B
Sociology, B
Spanish Language and Literature, B
Women's Studies, B

THE UNIVERSITY OF NORTH CAROLINA AT CHAPEL HILL

Accounting, MD
African-American/Black Studies, B
Allied Health and Medical Assisting Services, MD
Allopathic Medicine, PO
American/United States Studies/Civilization, B
Anthropology, BMD
Applied Mathematics, B
Archeology, MD
Area, Ethnic, Cultural, and Gender Studies, B
Art History, Criticism and Conservation, BMD
Asian Studies/Civilization, B
Astronomy, MD
Astrophysics, MD
Athletic Training and Sports Medicine, M
Atmospheric Sciences and Meteorology, MD
Biochemistry, MD
Biological and Biomedical Sciences, MDO
Biology/Biological Sciences, B
Biomedical Engineering, MD
Biophysics, MD
Biostatistics, BMD
Botany/Plant Biology, MD
Business Administration and Management, B
Business Administration, Management and
   Operations, MDO
Cell Biology and Anatomy, MD
Chemistry, BMD
Classics and Classical
   Languages, Literatures, and Linguistics, BMD
Clinical Laboratory Science/Medical
   Technology/Technologist, B
Clinical Psychology, D
Cognitive Sciences, D
Communication and Media Studies, MD
Communication Disorders, MD
Communication Studies/Speech Communication
   and Rhetoric, B
Community Health Nursing, M
Comparative Literature, BMD
Computer Science, BMD
Counselor Education/School Counseling and
   Guidance Services, M
Curriculum and Instruction, MD
Dental Hygiene/Hygienist, B
Dentistry, PO
Developmental Biology and Embryology, MD
Developmental Psychology, D
Drama and Dramatics/Theatre Arts, B
Early Childhood Education and Teaching, BMD
East European and Russian Studies, M
Ecology, MD
Economics, BMD
Education, MD
Educational Administration and Supervision, MD
Educational Leadership and Administration, D
Educational Measurement and Evaluation, MD
Educational Psychology, MD
Elementary Education and Teaching, B
English, MD
English Education, M
English Language and Literature, B
Environmental and Occupational Health, MD
Environmental Engineering
   Technology/Environmental Technology, MD
Environmental Health, B
Environmental Policy and Resource
   Management, MD
Environmental Sciences, BMD
Environmental Studies, B
Epidemiology, MD
European Studies/Civilization, B
Evolutionary Biology, MD
Exercise and Sports Science, M

Experimental Psychology, D
Finance and Banking, D
Fine Arts and Art Studies, M
Fine/Studio Arts, B
Folklore, M
Foods, Nutrition, and Wellness Studies, B
Foreign Language Teacher Education, M
French Language and Literature, MD
Genetics, MD
Geography, BMD
Geology/Earth Science, BMD
German Language and Literature, BMD
Health and Physical Education, B
Health Education, MD
Health Promotion, M
Health Services Administration, MDO
Health/Health Care Administration/Management, B
History, BMD
Human Resources Management/Personnel
   Administration, B
Immunology, MD
Industrial Hygiene, MD
Information Science/Studies, BMDO
Italian Language and Literature, MD
Junior High/Intermediate/Middle School Education
   and Teaching, B
Kinesiology and Movement Studies, MD
Latin American Studies, BO
Law and Legal Studies, PO
Leisure Studies, M
Liberal Arts and Sciences Studies and
   Humanities, B
Library Science, MDO
Linguistics, MD
Management Information Systems and Services, D
Management Strategy and Policy, D
Marine Sciences, MD
Marketing, D
Mass Communication/Media Studies, BMD
Materials Sciences, MD
Maternal and Child Health, MDO
Mathematics, BMD
Mathematics Teacher Education, M
Medical Radiologic Technology/Science - Radiation
   Therapist, B
Microbiology, MD
Molecular Biology, MD
Molecular Physiology, D
Music, BMD
Music Performance, B
Music Teacher Education, M
Neurobiology and Neurophysiology, D
Nursing, MD
Nursing - Registered Nurse Training, B
Nutritional Sciences, MD
Occupational Health Nursing, M
Occupational Therapy/Therapist, MD
Operations Research, MD
Oral and Dental Sciences, MD
Oral Biology, D
Organizational Behavior Studies, D
Parks, Recreation and Leisure Facilities
   Management, B
Pathology/Experimental Pathology, BD
Peace Studies and Conflict Resolution, B
Pharmaceutical Sciences, MD
Pharmacology, D
Philosophy, BMD
Physical Education Teaching and Coaching, M
Physical Sciences, B
Physical Therapy/Therapist, MD
Physics, BMD
Political Science and Government, BMD
Portuguese Language and Literature, MD
Psychology, BD
Public Administration, MO
Public Health, MDO
Public Policy Analysis, BD
Reading Teacher Education, MD
Recreation and Park Management, M
Rehabilitation Counseling, M
Religion/Religious Studies, BMD
Romance
   Languages, Literatures, and Linguistics, BMD
Russian Language and Literature, MD
Russian Studies, B

School Psychology, MD
Science Teacher Education/General Science
  Teacher Education, M
Secondary Education and Teaching, M
Slavic Languages, Literatures, and Linguistics, MD
Slavic, Baltic, and Albanian
  Languages, Literatures, and Linguistics, B
Social Psychology, D
Social Studies Teacher Education, M
Social Work, MDO
Sociology, BMD
Spanish Language and Literature, MD
Sport and Fitness Administration/Management, M
Statistics, MD
Theater, M
Toxicology, MD
Urban and Regional Planning, MDO
Women's Studies, B

THE UNIVERSITY OF NORTH CAROLINA AT CHARLOTTE

Accounting, BM
African-American/Black Studies, B
Anthropology, B
Applied Mathematics, D
Applied Physics, MD
Architecture, BM
Area, Ethnic, Cultural, and Gender Studies, B
Art Teacher Education, B
Art/Art Studies, General, B
Arts Management, M
Athletic Training and Sports Medicine, B
Biological and Biomedical Sciences, MD
Biology/Biological Sciences, B
Business Administration and Management, B
Business Administration, Management and
  Operations, M
Business/Managerial Economics, B
Chemistry, BM
Chemistry Teacher Education, B
Child Development, B
Civil Engineering, BM
Civil Engineering Technology/Technician, B
Clinical Laboratory Science/Medical
  Technology/Technologist, B
Clinical Psychology, M
Communication and Media Studies, M
Communication Studies/Speech Communication
  and Rhetoric, B
Community Health Nursing, MO
Community Psychology, M
Computer Engineering, BMD
Computer Science, BM
Counselor Education/School Counseling and
  Guidance Services, MD
Criminal Justice/Safety Studies, B
Criminology, M
Curriculum and Instruction, MD
Dance, B
Drama and Dance Teacher Education, B
Drama and Dramatics/Theatre Arts, B
Economics, BM
Education, M
Education/Teaching of Individuals with Mental
  Retardation, B
Educational Administration and Supervision, MO
Educational Leadership and Administration, MDO
Educational Media/Instructional Technology, M
Electrical Engineering, MD
Electrical, Electronic and Communications
  Engineering Technology/Technician, B
Electrical, Electronics and Communications
  Engineering, B
Elementary Education and Teaching, BM
Engineering and Applied Sciences, MD
Engineering Management, M
English, M
English Education, M
English Language and Literature, B
English/Language Arts Teacher Education, B
Environmental Engineering
  Technology/Environmental Technology, D
Finance, B
Fine/Studio Arts, B
French Language and Literature, B
French Language Teacher Education, B

Geography, BM
Geological and Earth Sciences/Geosciences, B
Geology/Earth Science, B
Geosciences, M
German Language and Literature, B
German Language Teacher Education, B
Gerontology, M
Health and Physical Education, B
Health Promotion, M
Health Services Administration, MO
History, BM
History Teacher Education, B
Human Development and Family Studies, B
Industrial and Organizational Psychology, M
Industrial Technology/Technician, B
Information Science/Studies, MD
International Business/Trade/Commerce, B
Junior High/Intermediate/Middle School Education
  and Teaching, B
Kindergarten/PreSchool Education and Teaching, B
Latin American Studies, B
Liberal Studies, M
Management Information Systems and Services, B
Mathematical and Computational Finance, M
Mathematics, BMD
Mathematics Teacher Education, BM
Mechanical Engineering, BMD
Mechanical Engineering/Mechanical
  Technology/Technician, B
Meteorology, B
Middle School Education, M
Music, B
Music Performance, B
Music Teacher Education, B
Nurse Anesthetist, M
Nursing, MO
Nursing - Adult, M
Nursing - Advanced Practice, M
Nursing - Registered Nurse Training, B
Operations Management and Supervision, B
Optics/Optical Sciences, MD
Philosophy, B
Physics, B
Political Science and Government, B
Psychology, BM
Public Administration, M
Public Policy Analysis, D
Reading Teacher Education, M
Religion/Religious Studies, BM
Secondary Education and Teaching, M
Social Work, BM
Sociology, BM
Spanish Language and Literature, BM
Spanish Language Teacher Education, B
Special Education and Teaching, MD
Systems Engineering, D
Systems Science and Theory, MD
Work and Family Studies, B

THE UNIVERSITY OF NORTH CAROLINA AT GREENSBORO

Accounting, BM
African-American/Black Studies, B
Apparel and Textiles, B
Applied Economics, M
Applied Mathematics, B
Archeology, B
Architecture, M
Art Education, M
Art Teacher Education, B
Art/Art Studies, General, B
Audiology/Audiologist and Speech-Language
  Pathology/Pathologist, B
Biochemistry, B
Biological and Biomedical Sciences, M
Biology Teacher Education, B
Biology/Biological Sciences, B
Business Administration and Management, B
Business Administration, Management and
  Operations, MO
Business Teacher Education, B
Chemistry, BM
Child and Family Studies, MD
Classics and Classical
  Languages, Literatures, and Linguistics, BM

Clinical Laboratory Science/Medical
  Technology/Technologist, B
Clinical Psychology, MD
Cognitive Sciences, MD
Communication and Media Studies, M
Communication Disorders, M
Community Health and Preventive Medicine, M
Composition, M
Computer and Information Sciences, B
Computer Science, BM
Counseling Psychology, MD
Counselor Education/School Counseling and
  Guidance Services, MDO
Curriculum and Instruction, D
Dance, BM
Developmental Psychology, MD
Drama and Dance Teacher Education, B
Drama and Dramatics/Theatre Arts, B
Early Childhood Education and Teaching, M
Economics, BD
Education, MDO
Education/Teaching of Individuals with Hearing
  Impairments, Including Deafness, B
Educational Administration and Supervision, M
Educational Leadership and Administration, MDO
Educational Measurement and Evaluation, MD
Elementary Education and Teaching, B
English, MDO
English Education, M
English Language and Literature, B
English/Language Arts Teacher Education, B
Exercise and Sports Science, MD
Family and Consumer Sciences/Human Sciences, B
Film, Television, and Video Production, M
Finance, B
Fine Arts and Art Studies, M
Fine/Studio Arts, B
Foodservice Systems
  Administration/Management, B
French Language and Literature, BM
French Language Teacher Education, B
Geography, BM
German Language and Literature, B
German Language Teacher Education, B
Gerontological Nursing, O
Higher Education/Higher Education
  Administration, MO
History, BMO
Home Economics, MD
Hospitality Administration/Management, B
Human Development, MD
Human Development and Family Studies, B
Information Science/Studies, M
Interdisciplinary Studies, B
Interior Design, BM
International Business/Trade/Commerce, O
Junior High/Intermediate/Middle School Education
  and Teaching, B
Kindergarten/PreSchool Education and Teaching, B
Kinesiology and Exercise Science, B
Liberal Arts and Sciences Studies and
  Humanities, B
Liberal Studies, M
Library Science, M
Management Information Systems and
  Services, BM
Marketing, MD
Marriage and Family Therapy/Counseling, O
Mass Communication/Media Studies, B
Mathematics, M
Mathematics Teacher Education, BM
Museology/Museum Studies, O
Music, BMD
Music History, Literature, and Theory, B
Music Performance, B
Music Teacher Education, BMD
Music Theory and Composition, B
Non-Profit/Public/Organizational Management, O
Nurse Anesthetist, MO
Nursing, MO
Nursing - Registered Nurse Training, B
Nursing Administration, M
Nutritional Sciences, MD
Parks, Recreation and Leisure Facilities
  Management, B
Parks, Recreation, Leisure and Fitness Studies, B

Performance, MD
Philosophy, B
Physical Education Teaching and Coaching, B
Physics, B
Political Science and Government, BMO
Psychology, BMD
Public Affairs, MO
Public Health Education and Promotion, B
Recreation and Park Management, M
Religion/Religious Studies, B
School Psychology, O
Social Psychology, MD
Social Science Teacher Education, B
Social Studies Teacher Education, B
Social Work, BM
Sociology, BM
Spanish Language and Literature, BM
Spanish Language Teacher Education, B
Special Education and Teaching, BM
Speech and Rhetorical Studies, B
Speech Teacher Education, B
Statistics, B
Technical and Business Writing, O
Textile Design, MD
Theater, M
Women's Studies, BO
Writing, M

THE UNIVERSITY OF NORTH CAROLINA AT PEMBROKE

Accounting, B
American Indian/Native American Studies, B
American/United States Studies/Civilization, B
Art Education, M
Art Teacher Education, B
Athletic Training and Sports Medicine, B
Biology Teacher Education, B
Biology/Biological Sciences, B
Business Administration and Management, B
Business Administration, Management and
    Operations, M
Chemistry, B
Computer Science, B
Counselor Education/School Counseling and
    ,Guidance Services, M
Criminal Justice/Safety Studies, B
Drama and Dramatics/Theatre Arts, B
Education, M
Education/Teaching of Individuals with Mental
    Retardation, B
Education/Teaching of Individuals with Specific
    Learning Disabilities, B
Educational Administration and Supervision, M
Elementary Education and Teaching, BM
English Education, M
English Language and Literature, B
English/Language Arts Teacher Education, B
Environmental Studies, B
Fine/Studio Arts, B
Health and Physical Education, B
History, B
Junior High/Intermediate/Middle School Education
    and Teaching, B
Kindergarten/PreSchool Education and Teaching, B
Mass Communication/Media Studies, B
Mathematics, B
Mathematics Teacher Education, BM
Middle School Education, M
Music, B
Music Teacher Education, B
Nursing - Registered Nurse Training, B
Parks, Recreation and Leisure Facilities
    Management, B
Philosophy and Religious Studies, B
Physical Education Teaching and Coaching, BM
Physics, B
Political Science and Government, B
Psychology, B
Public Administration, BM
Public Health Education and Promotion, B
Reading Teacher Education, M
Science Teacher Education/General Science
    Teacher Education, BM
Social Studies Teacher Education, BM
Social Work, B
Sociology, B

Spanish Language and Literature, B

THE UNIVERSITY OF NORTH CAROLINA WILMINGTON

Accounting, BM
Anthropology, B
Art History, Criticism and Conservation, B
Athletic Training and Sports Medicine, B
Biological and Biomedical Sciences, MD
Biology Teacher Education, B
Biology/Biological Sciences, B
Business Administration and Management, B
Business Administration, Management and
    Operations, M
Business/Managerial Economics, B
Chemistry, BM
Chemistry Teacher Education, B
Cinematography and Film/Video Production, B
Clinical Laboratory Science/Medical
    Technology/Technologist, B
Computer Education, M
Computer Science, BM
Creative Writing, B
Criminal Justice/Safety Studies, B
Curriculum and Instruction, M
Drama and Dramatics/Theatre Arts, B
Economics, B
Education, M
Education/Teaching of Individuals with Emotional
    Disturbances, B
Education/Teaching of Individuals with Mental
    Retardation, B
Education/Teaching of Individuals with Multiple
    Disabilities, B
Education/Teaching of Individuals with Specific
    Learning Disabilities, B
Educational Administration and Supervision, M
Educational Media/Instructional Technology, M
Elementary Education and Teaching, BM
English, M
English Language and Literature, B
English/Language Arts Teacher Education, B
Environmental Sciences, B
Environmental Studies, B
Finance, B
Fine/Studio Arts, B
French Language and Literature, B
French Language Teacher Education, B
Geography, B
Geology/Earth Science, BM
Geosciences, M
German Language and Literature, B
Health and Physical Education, B
History, BM
History Teacher Education, B
Junior High/Intermediate/Middle School Education
    and Teaching, B
Kindergarten/PreSchool Education and Teaching, B
Liberal Studies, M
Management Information Systems and Services, B
Marine Biology and Biological Oceanography, BMD
Marine Sciences, M
Marketing/Marketing Management, B
Mathematics, BM
Mathematics Teacher Education, B
Middle School Education, M
Music, B
Music Performance, B
Music Teacher Education, B
Nursing, M
Nursing - Registered Nurse Training, B
Parks, Recreation and Leisure Facilities
    Management, B
Philosophy and Religious Studies, B
Physical Education Teaching and Coaching, B
Physics, B
Physics Teacher Education, B
Political Science and Government, B
Psychology, BM
Public Administration, M
Reading Teacher Education, M
Secondary Education and Teaching, M
Social Work, BM
Sociology, B
Spanish Language and Literature, B
Spanish Language Teacher Education, B

Special Education and Teaching, M
Speech and Rhetorical Studies, B
Statistics, B
Systems Science and Theory, M
Teacher Education and Professional
    Development, Specific Subject Areas, B
Therapeutic Recreation/Recreational Therapy, B
Writing, M

UNIVERSITY OF PHOENIX-CHARLOTTE CAMPUS

Accounting, M
Business Administration, Management and
    Operations, M
Electronic Commerce, M
Health Services Administration, M
International Business/Trade/Commerce, M
Management of Technology, M

UNIVERSITY OF PHOENIX-RALEIGH CAMPUS

Business Administration and Management, B
Business/Commerce, B
Business/Corporate Communications, B
Criminal Justice/Law Enforcement Administration, B
Information Technology, B

VANCE-GRANVILLE COMMUNITY COLLEGE

Accounting, A
Administrative Assistant and Secretarial Science, A
Automobile/Automotive Mechanics
    Technology/Technician, A
Business Administration and Management, A
Carpentry/Carpenter, A
Child Development, A
Computer Engineering Technology/Technician, A
Construction Engineering Technology/Technician, A
Corrections, A
Cosmetology/Cosmetologist, A
Criminal Justice/Law Enforcement Administration, A
Criminal Justice/Police Science, A
Data Processing and Data Processing
    Technology/Technician, A
Education, A
Electrical, Electronic and Communications
    Engineering Technology/Technician, A
Elementary Education and Teaching, A
Heating, Air Conditioning, Ventilation and
    Refrigeration Maintenance
    Technology/Technician, A
Human Services, A
Industrial Radiologic Technology/Technician, A
Industrial Technology/Technician, A
Kindergarten/PreSchool Education and Teaching, A
Legal Administrative Assistant/Secretary, A
Liberal Arts and Sciences Studies and
    Humanities, A
Licensed Practical/Vocational Nurse Training, A
Medical Administrative Assistant/Secretary, A
Medical/Clinical Assistant, A
Nursing - Registered Nurse Training, A
Parks, Recreation, Leisure and Fitness Studies, A
Teacher Assistant/Aide, A
Welding Technology/Welder, A

WAKE FOREST UNIVERSITY

Accounting, BM
Allopathic Medicine, PO
Analytical Chemistry, MD
Anatomy, D
Ancient/Classical Greek Language and Literature, B
Anthropology, B
Art History, Criticism and Conservation, B
Biochemistry, D
Biological and Biomedical Sciences, MDO
Biology/Biological Sciences, B
Biomedical Engineering, MDO
Business Administration, Management and
    Operations, MO
Business/Commerce, B
Cancer Biology/Oncology, D
Chemistry, BMD
Classics and Classical
    Languages, Literatures, and Linguistics, B

Clinical Laboratory Science/Medical
    Technology/Technologist, B
Communication and Media Studies, M
Communication Studies/Speech Communication
    and Rhetoric, B
Computer and Information Sciences, B
Computer Science, M
Counselor Education/School Counseling and
    Guidance Services, M
Drama and Dramatics/Theatre Arts, B
Econometrics and Quantitative Economics, B
Economics, B
Education, M
Engineering, B
English, M
English Language and Literature, B
Exercise and Sports Science, M
Finance, B
Fine/Studio Arts, B
French Language and Literature, B
Genomic Sciences, D
German Language and Literature, B
Health Services Research, M
History, B
Human Genetics, D
Immunology, D
Inorganic Chemistry, MD
Kinesiology and Exercise Science, B
Latin Language and Literature, B
Law and Legal Studies, MPO
Liberal Studies, M
Management Information Systems and Services, B
Management Science, B
Mathematics, BM
Microbiology, D
Molecular Biology, D
Molecular Genetics, D
Molecular Medicine, MD
Music, B
Neurobiology and Neurophysiology, D
Neuroscience, D
Organic Chemistry, MD
Pastoral Studies/Counseling, M
Pathobiology, MD
Pharmacology, D
Philosophy, B
Physical Chemistry, MD
Physician Assistant, B
Physics, BMD
Physiology, D
Political Science and Government, B
Psychology, BM
Religion/Religious Studies, BM
Russian Language and Literature, B
Secondary Education and Teaching, M
Sociology, B
Spanish Language and Literature, B
Speech and Interpersonal Communication, M
Teacher Education, Multiple Levels, B

WAKE TECHNICAL COMMUNITY COLLEGE

Accounting, A
Architectural Engineering Technology/Technician, A
Artificial Intelligence and Robotics, A
Business Administration and Management, A
Civil Engineering Technology/Technician, A
Clinical/Medical Laboratory Technician, A
Computer and Information Sciences, A
Computer Engineering Technology/Technician, A
Computer Graphics, A
Computer Programming, Specific Applications, A
Computer Programming/Programmer, A
Computer Systems Networking and
    Telecommunications, A
Criminal Justice/Law Enforcement Administration, A
Criminal Justice/Police Science, A
Culinary Arts/Chef Training, A
Electrical and Power Transmission
    Installation/Installer, A
Electrical, Electronic and Communications
    Engineering Technology/Technician, A
Electromechanical Technology/Electromechanical
    Engineering Technology, A
Emergency Medical Technology/Technician (EMT
    Paramedic), A

Environmental Engineering
    Technology/Environmental Technology, A
General Studies, A
Heavy Equipment Maintenance
    Technology/Technician, A
Hotel/Motel Administration/Management, A
Human Resources Management/Personnel
    Administration, A
Industrial Technology/Technician, A
Instrumentation Technology/Technician, A
Kindergarten/PreSchool Education and Teaching, A
Landscape Architecture, A
Legal Administrative Assistant/Secretary, A
Liberal Arts and Sciences Studies and
    Humanities, A
Machine Tool Technology/Machinist, A
Management Information Systems and Services, A
Mechanical Drafting and Mechanical Drafting
    CAD/CADD, A
Mechanical Engineering/Mechanical
    Technology/Technician, A
Medical Administrative Assistant/Secretary, A
Medical Radiologic Technology/Science - Radiation
    Therapist, A
Nursing - Registered Nurse Training, A
Pharmacy Technician/Assistant, A
Plastics Engineering Technology/Technician, A
Pre-Engineering, A
Survey Technology/Surveying, A
System Administration/Administrator, A
Telecommunications Technology/Technician, A
Tool and Die Technology/Technician, A
Web Page, Digital/Multimedia and Information
    Resources Design, A
Web/Multimedia Management and Webmaster, A
Word Processing, A

WARREN WILSON COLLEGE

Art/Art Studies, General, B
Asian Studies/Civilization, B
Biology/Biological Sciences, B
Business Administration and Management, B
Chemistry, B
Creative Writing, B
Economics, B
Education, B
Elementary Education and Teaching, B
English Language and Literature, B
Entrepreneurial and Small Business Operations, B
Environmental Studies, B
History, B
Humanities/Humanistic Studies, B
Interdisciplinary Studies, B
International Business/Trade/Commerce, B
International/Global Studies, B
Latin American Studies, B
Mathematics, B
Non-Profit/Public/Organizational Management, B
Philosophy, B
Psychology, B
Secondary Education and Teaching, B
Social Work, B
Sociology, B
Spanish Language and Literature, B
Women's Studies, B
Writing, M

WAYNE COMMUNITY COLLEGE

Accounting Technology/Technician and
    Bookkeeping, A
Agribusiness, A
Agricultural Production Operations, A
Automobile/Automotive Mechanics
    Technology/Technician, A
Avionics Maintenance Technology/Technician, A
Biological and Physical Sciences, A
Business Administration and Management, A
Clinical/Medical Social Work, A
Computer Systems Analysis/Analyst, A
Criminal Justice/Police Science, A
Dental Hygiene/Hygienist, A
Electrical, Electronic and Communications
    Engineering Technology/Technician, A
Electromechanical Technology/Electromechanical
    Engineering Technology, A
Executive Assistant/Executive Secretary, A

Forestry Technology/Technician, A
Legal Administrative Assistant/Secretary, A
Liberal Arts and Sciences Studies and
    Humanities, A
Machine Tool Technology/Machinist, A
Mechanical Engineering/Mechanical
    Technology/Technician, A
Medical Administrative Assistant/Secretary, A
Medical Office Management/Administration, A
Medical/Clinical Assistant, A
Nursing - Registered Nurse Training, A
Parks, Recreation and Leisure Facilities
    Management, A
Poultry Science, A
Psychiatric/Mental Health Services Technician, A
Rehabilitation Therapy, A
Retailing and Retail Operations, A
Turf and Turfgrass Management, A

WESTERN CAROLINA UNIVERSITY

Accounting, BM
American/United States Studies/Civilization, M
Anthropology, B
Art Education, M
Art Teacher Education, B
Art/Art Studies, General, B
Biological and Biomedical Sciences, M
Biology/Biological Sciences, B
Business Administration and Management, B
Business Administration, Management and
    Operations, M
Chemistry, BM
Clinical Laboratory Science/Medical
    Technology/Technologist, B
Clinical Psychology, M
Communication Disorders, BM
Communication Studies/Speech Communication
    and Rhetoric, B
Community College Education, M
Community Psychology, M
Computer Science, BM
Construction Engineering and Management, M
Construction Management, B
Counselor Education/School Counseling and
    Guidance Services, M
Criminal Justice/Safety Studies, B
Dietetics/Dieticians, B
Drama and Dramatics/Theatre Arts, B
Early Childhood Education and Teaching, B
Education, MDO
Educational Administration and Supervision, M
Educational Leadership and Administration, DO
Electrical and Electronic Engineering
    Technologies/Technicians, B
Electrical, Electronic and Communications
    Engineering Technology/Technician, B
Electrical, Electronics and Communications
    Engineering, B
Elementary Education and Teaching, BM
Emergency Medical Technology/Technician (EMT
    Paramedic), B
English, M
English Education, M
English Language and Literature, B
English/Language Arts Teacher Education, B
Entrepreneurship/Entrepreneurial Studies, B
Environmental Health, B
Environmental Sciences, B
Finance, B
Fine Arts and Art Studies, M
Fine/Studio Arts, B
French Language Teacher Education, B
Geography, B
Geology/Earth Science, B
German Language and Literature, B
German Language Teacher Education, B
Health Information/Medical Records
    Administration/Administrator, B
Health Services Administration, M
History, BM
Home Economics Education, M
Hospitality Administration/Management, B
Human Resources Development, M
Industrial/Management Engineering, M
Interior Design, B
International Business/Trade/Commerce, B

Junior High/Intermediate/Middle School Education and Teaching, B
Liberal Arts and Sciences Studies and Humanities, B
Management Information Systems and Services, B
Manufacturing Technology/Technician, B
Marketing, B
Marketing/Marketing Management, B
Mathematics, BM
Mathematics Teacher Education, BM
Middle School Education, M
Music, BM
Music Performance, B
Music Teacher Education, B
Natural Resources Management/Development and Policy, B
Nursing, M
Nursing - Registered Nurse Training, B
Parks, Recreation and Leisure Facilities Management, B
Philosophy, B
Physical Education Teaching and Coaching, BM
Physical Therapy/Therapist, M
Political Science and Government, B
Project Management, M
Psychology, BM
Public Administration, B
Public Affairs, M
Reading Teacher Education, M
School Psychology, M
Science Teacher Education/General Science Teacher Education, BM
Secondary Education and Teaching, M
Social Sciences, B
Social Studies Teacher Education, BM
Social Work, B
Sociology, B
Spanish Language and Literature, B
Spanish Language Teacher Education, B
Special Education and Teaching, BM
Sport and Fitness Administration/Management, B
Therapeutic Recreation/Recreational Therapy, B

WESTERN PIEDMONT COMMUNITY COLLEGE

Accounting, A
Administrative Assistant and Secretarial Science, A
Art/Art Studies, General, A
Business Administration and Management, A
Civil Engineering Technology/Technician, A
Clinical/Medical Laboratory Technician, A
Computer Engineering Technology/Technician, A
Computer Programming/Programmer, A
Criminal Justice/Law Enforcement Administration, A
Criminal Justice/Police Science, A
Drafting and Design Technology/Technician, A
Electrical, Electronic and Communications Engineering Technology/Technician, A
Finance, A
Horticultural Science, A
Industrial Technology/Technician, A
Interior Design, A
Legal Administrative Assistant/Secretary, A
Legal Assistant/Paralegal, A
Liberal Arts and Sciences Studies and Humanities, A
Marketing/Marketing Management, A
Medical Administrative Assistant/Secretary, A
Medical/Clinical Assistant, A
Nursing - Registered Nurse Training, A
Pre-Engineering, A
Technology Education/Industrial Arts, A
Therapeutic Recreation/Recreational Therapy, A

WILKES COMMUNITY COLLEGE

Accounting Technology/Technician and Bookkeeping, A
Applied Horticulture/Horticultural Operations, A
Architectural Engineering Technology/Technician, A
Automobile/Automotive Mechanics Technology/Technician, A
Building/Construction Finishing, Management, and Inspection, A
Business Administration and Management, A
Child Care and Support Services Management, A
Computer Programming, Specific Applications, A

Computer Systems Analysis/Analyst, A
Computer Systems Networking and Telecommunications, A
Criminal Justice/Police Science, A
Diesel Mechanics Technology/Technician, A
Electrical, Electronic and Communications Engineering Technology/Technician, A
Electromechanical Technology/Electromechanical Engineering Technology, A
Executive Assistant/Executive Secretary, A
Hotel/Motel Administration/Management, A
Institutional Food Workers, A
Liberal Arts and Sciences Studies and Humanities, A
Medical/Clinical Assistant, A
Nursing - Registered Nurse Training, A
Psychiatric/Mental Health Services Technician, A
Radio and Television Broadcasting Technology/Technician, A
Speech-Language Pathology/Pathologist, A

WILSON TECHNICAL COMMUNITY COLLEGE

Accounting, A
Administrative Assistant and Secretarial Science, A
Business Administration and Management, A
Computer Programming/Programmer, A
Criminal Justice/Law Enforcement Administration, A
Electrical, Electronic and Communications Engineering Technology/Technician, A
Fire Science/Firefighting, A
General Studies, A
Industrial Technology/Technician, A
Information Science/Studies, A
Kindergarten/PreSchool Education and Teaching, A
Language Interpretation and Translation, A
Legal Assistant/Paralegal, A
Liberal Arts and Sciences Studies and Humanities, A
Mechanical Engineering/Mechanical Technology/Technician, A
Nursing - Registered Nurse Training, A
Sign Language Interpretation and Translation, A
Tool and Die Technology/Technician, A

WINGATE UNIVERSITY

Accounting, B
American/United States Studies/Civilization, B
Art Teacher Education, B
Art/Art Studies, General, B
Athletic Training and Sports Medicine, B
Biology Teacher Education, B
Biology/Biological Sciences, B
Business Administration and Management, B
Business Administration, Management and Operations, M
Chemistry, B
Computer Graphics, B
Economics, B
Elementary Education and Teaching, BM
English Language and Literature, B
Environmental Biology, B
Finance, B
Fine/Studio Arts, B
Health and Physical Education, B
History, B
Human Services, B
Junior High/Intermediate/Middle School Education and Teaching, B
Liberal Arts and Sciences Studies and Humanities, B
Management Information Systems and Services, B
Marketing/Marketing Management, B
Mass Communication/Media Studies, B
Mathematics, B
Music, B
Music Teacher Education, B
Parks, Recreation, Leisure and Fitness Studies, B
Pharmacy, P
Philosophy, B
Pre-Law Studies, B
Pre-Medicine/Pre-Medical Studies, B
Pre-Veterinary Studies, B
Psychology, B
Reading Teacher Education, B
Religion/Religious Studies, B

Social Studies Teacher Education, B
Sociology, B
Spanish Language and Literature, B
Sport and Fitness Administration/Management, B

WINSTON-SALEM STATE UNIVERSITY

Accounting, B
Art Teacher Education, B
Art/Art Studies, General, B
Biology/Biological Sciences, B
Business Administration and Management, B
Chemistry, B
Clinical Laboratory Science/Medical Technology/Technologist, B
Computer Science, B
Economics, B
Education, B
Education/Teaching of Individuals with Specific Learning Disabilities, B
Elementary Education and Teaching, BM
English Language and Literature, B
English/Language Arts Teacher Education, B
General Studies, B
Gerontology, B
History, B
Junior High/Intermediate/Middle School Education and Teaching, B
Kindergarten/PreSchool Education and Teaching, B
Kinesiology and Exercise Science, B
Management Information Systems and Services, B
Mass Communication/Media Studies, B
Mathematics, B
Mathematics Teacher Education, B
Molecular Biology, B
Music, B
Music Teacher Education, B
Nursing - Registered Nurse Training, B
Occupational Therapy/Therapist, BM
Physical Education Teaching and Coaching, B
Political Science and Government, B
Psychology, B
Social Sciences, B
Social Studies Teacher Education, B
Sociology, B
Spanish Language and Literature, B
Spanish Language Teacher Education, B
Special Education and Teaching, B
Sport and Fitness Administration/Management, B
Therapeutic Recreation/Recreational Therapy, B
Vocational Rehabilitation Counseling/Counselor, B

North Dakota

AAKERS BUSINESS COLLEGE

Accounting, A
Business Administration and Management, AB
Computer Systems Networking and Telecommunications, A
Criminal Justice/Law Enforcement Administration, A
Health Services/Allied Health/Health Sciences, A
Human Resources Management and Services, A
Law and Legal Studies, A

BISMARCK STATE COLLEGE

Administrative Assistant and Secretarial Science, A
Agricultural Business and Management, A
Autobody/Collision and Repair Technology/Technician, A
Automobile/Automotive Mechanics Technology/Technician, A
Business/Commerce, A
Business/Office Automation/Technology/Data Entry, A
Carpentry/Carpenter, A
Clinical/Medical Laboratory Technician, A
Commercial and Advertising Art, A
Computer Systems Networking and Telecommunications, A
Construction Engineering Technology/Technician, A
Emergency Medical Technology/Technician (EMT Paramedic), A
Energy Management and Systems Technology/Technician, A

Heating, Air Conditioning, Ventilation and
Refrigeration Maintenance
Technology/Technician, A
Hotel/Motel Administration/Management, A
Industrial Technology/Technician, A
Legal Administrative Assistant/Secretary, A
Liberal Arts and Sciences Studies and
Humanities, A
Licensed Practical/Vocational Nurse Training, A
Lineworker, A
Medical Administrative Assistant/Secretary, A
Surgical Technology/Technologist, A
Welding Technology/Welder, A

CANKDESKA CIKANA COMMUNITY COLLEGE

Accounting, A
Administrative Assistant and Secretarial Science, A
Art History, Criticism and Conservation, A
Art/Art Studies, General, A
Business Administration and Management, A
Business Teacher Education, A
Carpentry/Carpenter, A
Chemistry, A
Computer Science, A
Developmental and Child Psychology, A
English Language and Literature, A
Geography, A
Health Teacher Education, A
History, A
Liberal Arts and Sciences Studies and
Humanities, A
Marketing/Marketing Management, A
Mathematics, A
Parks, Recreation, Leisure and Fitness Studies, A
Trade and Industrial Teacher Education, A

DICKINSON STATE UNIVERSITY

Accounting, B
Administrative Assistant and Secretarial Science, A
Agricultural Business and Management, AB
Art Teacher Education, B
Art/Art Studies, General, B
Biology/Biological Sciences, B
Business Administration and Management, B
Business Teacher Education, B
Chemistry, B
Computer Science, B
Drama and Dramatics/Theatre Arts, B
Education, B
Elementary Education and Teaching, B
English Language and Literature, B
Environmental Studies, AB
Finance, B
Geography, B
Geology/Earth Science, B
History, B
International Business/Trade/Commerce, B
Liberal Arts and Sciences Studies and
Humanities, AB
Licensed Practical/Vocational Nurse Training, A
Marketing/Marketing Management, B
Mathematics, B
Medical Administrative Assistant/Secretary, A
Music, B
Music Teacher Education, B
Nursing - Registered Nurse Training, B
Physical Education Teaching and Coaching, B
Political Science and Government, B
Pre-Dentistry Studies, B
Pre-Law Studies, B
Pre-Medicine/Pre-Medical Studies, B
Pre-Veterinary Studies, B
Psychology, B
Science Teacher Education/General Science
Teacher Education, B
Secondary Education and Teaching, B
Social Sciences, B
Social Work, B
Spanish Language and Literature, B
Speech and Rhetorical Studies, B
Speech Teacher Education, B

Teacher Education, Multiple Levels, B

FORT BERTHOLD COMMUNITY COLLEGE

Accounting, A
Administrative Assistant and Secretarial Science, A
Biological and Physical Sciences, A
Business Administration and Management, A
Construction Engineering Technology/Technician, A
Environmental Studies, A
Farm/Farm and Ranch Management, A
Health Information/Medical Records
Administration/Administrator, A
Human Services, A
Information Science/Studies, A
Kindergarten/PreSchool Education and Teaching, A
Liberal Arts and Sciences Studies and
Humanities, A
Licensed Practical/Vocational Nurse Training, A
Marketing/Marketing Management, A
Mathematics, A

JAMESTOWN COLLEGE

Accounting, B
Actuarial Science, B
Applied Mathematics, B
Art/Art Studies, General, B
Biochemistry, B
Biology Teacher Education, B
Biology/Biological Sciences, B
Business Administration and Management, B
Business/Managerial Economics, B
Chemistry, B
Clinical Laboratory Science/Medical
Technology/Technologist, B
Communication Studies/Speech Communication
and Rhetoric, B
Computer Science, B
Counseling Psychology, B
Criminal Justice/Safety Studies, B
Drama and Dramatics/Theatre Arts, B
Educational Leadership and Administration, B
Elementary Education and Teaching, B
English Composition, B
English Language and Literature, B
English/Language Arts Teacher Education, B
Financial Planning and Services, B
Fine/Studio Arts, B
History, B
History Teacher Education, B
Industrial Radiologic Technology/Technician, B
International Business/Trade/Commerce, B
Management Information Systems and Services, B
Marketing/Marketing Management, B
Mathematics, B
Mathematics Teacher Education, B
Music, B
Music Performance, B
Music Teacher Education, B
Nursing - Registered Nurse Training, B
Philosophy, B
Physical Education Teaching and Coaching, B
Political Science and Government, B
Psychology, B
Radiologic Technology/Science - Radiographer, B
Religion/Religious Studies, B
Secondary Education and Teaching, B
Teacher Education, Multiple Levels, B

LAKE REGION STATE COLLEGE

Accounting, A
Accounting Technology/Technician and
Bookkeeping, A
Administrative Assistant and Secretarial Science, A
Agricultural Business and Management, A
Automobile/Automotive Mechanics
Technology/Technician, A
Avionics Maintenance Technology/Technician, A
Business Administration and Management, A
Child Care and Support Services Management, A
Child Care Provider/Assistant, A
Computer and Information Sciences, A
Computer Programming, Specific Applications, A
Computer
Programming, Vendor/Product Certification, A
Computer Science, A

Computer Systems Networking and
Telecommunications, A
Criminal Justice/Police Science, A
Diesel Mechanics Technology/Technician, A
Electrical, Electronics and Communications
Engineering, A
Electrical/Electronics Equipment Installation and
Repair, A
Executive Assistant/Executive Secretary, A
Fashion Merchandising, A
General Office Occupations and Clerical Services, A
Information Technology, A
Legal Administrative Assistant/Secretary, A
Legal Assistant/Paralegal, A
Liberal Arts and Sciences Studies and
Humanities, A
Licensed Practical/Vocational Nurse Training, A
Management Information Systems and Services, A
Marketing Research, A
Medical Administrative Assistant/Secretary, A
Nurse/Nursing Assistant/Aide and Patient Care
Assistant, A
Office Management and Supervision, A
Sales, Distribution and Marketing Operations, A
Sign Language Interpretation and Translation, A
Small Business Administration/Management, A
Technical Teacher Education, A

MAYVILLE STATE UNIVERSITY

Administrative Assistant and Secretarial Science, AB
Biology Teacher Education, B
Biology/Biological Sciences, B
Business Administration and Management, AB
Business Administration, Management and
Operations, B
Business Teacher Education, B
Chemistry, B
Chemistry Teacher Education, B
Child Care and Support Services Management, B
Child Care Provider/Assistant, A
Computer and Information Sciences, B
Computer and Information Sciences and Support
Services, B
Education, B
Elementary Education and Teaching, B
English Language and Literature, B
English/Language Arts Teacher Education, B
General Studies, B
Geography Teacher Education, B
Health and Physical Education, B
Health and Physical Education/Fitness, B
Health Teacher Education, B
History Teacher Education, B
Kinesiology and Exercise Science, B
Mathematics, B
Mathematics Teacher Education, B
Office Management and Supervision, B
Physical Education Teaching and Coaching, B
Physical Sciences, B
Physics Teacher Education, B
Pre-Dentistry Studies, B
Pre-Law Studies, B
Pre-Medicine/Pre-Medical Studies, B
Pre-Pharmacy Studies, B
Pre-Veterinary Studies, B
Psychology, B
Social Science Teacher Education, B
Social Sciences, B

MEDCENTER ONE COLLEGE OF NURSING

Nursing - Registered Nurse Training, B

MINOT STATE UNIVERSITY

Accounting, B
Art Teacher Education, B
Art/Art Studies, General, B
Biology Teacher Education, B
Biology/Biological Sciences, B
Business Administration and Management, B
Business Teacher Education, B
Chemistry, B
Chemistry Teacher Education, B
Clinical Laboratory Science/Medical
Technology/Technologist, B
Communication Disorders, BM

Computer Science, B
Criminal Justice/Safety Studies, B
Criminology, M
Digital Communication and Media/Multimedia, B
Economics, B
Education/Teaching of Individuals with Hearing
   Impairments, Including Deafness, B
Education/Teaching of Individuals with Mental
   Retardation, B
Education/Teaching of Individuals with Speech or
   Language Impairments, B
Elementary Education and Teaching, BM
English Language and Literature, B
English/Language Arts Teacher Education, B
Finance, B
French Language and Literature, B
French Language Teacher Education, B
General Studies, B
Geology/Earth Science, B
German Language and Literature, B
German Language Teacher Education, B
History, B
History Teacher Education, B
International Business/Trade/Commerce, B
Management, M
Management Information Systems and
   Services, BM
Marketing/Marketing Management, B
Mathematics, B
Mathematics Teacher Education, BM
Medical Radiologic Technology/Science - Radiation
   Therapist, B
Music, B
Music Teacher Education, BM
Nursing, B
Nursing - Registered Nurse Training, B
Physical Education Teaching and Coaching, B
Physical Sciences, B
Physics, B
Physics Teacher Education, B
Psychology, B
Radio and Television, B
School Psychology, O
Science Teacher Education/General Science
   Teacher Education, BM
Social Science Teacher Education, B
Social Sciences, B
Social Work, B
Sociology, B
Spanish Language and Literature, B
Spanish Language Teacher Education, B
Special Education and Teaching, ABM
Speech and Rhetorical Studies, B
Sport and Fitness Administration/Management, B
Substance Abuse/Addiction Counseling, B

MINOT STATE
UNIVERSITY-BOTTINEAU CAMPUS

Accounting Technology/Technician and
   Bookkeeping, A
Administrative Assistant and Secretarial Science, A
Applied Horticulture/Horticultural Business
   Services, A
Applied Horticulture/Horticultural Operations, A
Business Administration and Management, A
Computer Engineering, A
Computer Engineering Technology/Technician, A
Computer Systems Networking and
   Telecommunications, A
Environmental Engineering
   Technology/Environmental Technology, A
Executive Assistant/Executive Secretary, A
Forestry, A
General Office Occupations and Clerical Services, A
Greenhouse Operations and Management, A
Horticultural Science, A
Information Science/Studies, A
Information Technology, A
Liberal Arts and Sciences Studies and
   Humanities, A
Marketing/Marketing Management, A
Medical Administrative Assistant/Secretary, A
Medical Office Management/Administration, A
Medical/Clinical Assistant, A
Natural Resources and Conservation, A
Ornamental Horticulture, A

Receptionist, A
Surveying Engineering, A
System Administration/Administrator, A
Turf and Turfgrass Management, A
Water Quality and Wastewater Treatment
   Management and Recycling
   Technology/Technician, A
Web Page, Digital/Multimedia and Information
   Resources Design, A
Web/Multimedia Management and Webmaster, A

NORTH DAKOTA STATE COLLEGE OF
SCIENCE

Administrative Assistant and Secretarial Science, A
Agricultural Business and Management, A
Agricultural Mechanization, A
Agricultural Production Operations, A
Agricultural/Farm Supplies Retailing and
   Wholesaling, A
Architectural Engineering Technology/Technician, A
Autobody/Collision and Repair
   Technology/Technician, A
Automobile/Automotive Mechanics
   Technology/Technician, A
Business/Commerce, A
Civil Engineering Technology/Technician, A
Computer Programming, Specific Applications, A
Construction Engineering Technology/Technician, A
Dental Hygiene/Hygienist, A
Diesel Mechanics Technology/Technician, A
Electrical, Electronic and Communications
   Engineering Technology/Technician, A
Foodservice Systems
   Administration/Management, A
Health Information/Medical Records
   Technology/Technician, A
Heating, Air Conditioning and Refrigeration
   Technology/Technician, A
Heating, Air Conditioning, Ventilation and
   Refrigeration Maintenance
   Technology/Technician, A
Industrial Electronics Technology/Technician, A
Industrial Technology/Technician, A
Liberal Arts and Sciences Studies and
   Humanities, A
Licensed Practical/Vocational Nurse Training, A
Machine Shop Technology/Assistant, A
Occupational Therapist Assistant, A
Pharmacy Technician/Assistant, A
Psychiatric/Mental Health Services Technician, A
Small Engine Mechanics and Repair
   Technology/Technician, A
Technical Teacher Education, A
Vehicle Maintenance and Repair Technologies, A

NORTH DAKOTA STATE UNIVERSITY

Accounting, B
Agribusiness, B
Agricultural Business and Management, B
Agricultural Economics, BM
Agricultural Education, M
Agricultural Engineering, MD
Agricultural Mechanization, B
Agricultural Sciences, MD
Agricultural Teacher Education, B
Agricultural/Biological Engineering and
   Bioengineering, B
Agriculture, B
Agronomy and Soil Sciences, MD
Animal Sciences, BMD
Apparel and Textiles, B
Applied Mathematics, MD
Architecture, B
Art/Art Studies, General, B
Athletic Training and Sports Medicine, B
Biochemistry, MD
Biochemistry, Biophysics and Molecular Biology, B
Biological and Biomedical Sciences, MD
Biology Teacher Education, B
Biology/Biological Sciences, B
Biosystems Engineering, MD
BioTechnology, B
Botany/Plant Biology, BMD
Business Administration and Management, B
Business Administration, Management and
   Operations, M

Cell Biology and Anatomy, D
Chemistry, BMD
Chemistry Teacher Education, B
Child and Family Studies, MD
Civil Engineering, BMD
Classics and Classical
   Languages, Literatures, and Linguistics, B
Clinical Laboratory Science/Medical
   Technology/Technologist, B
Clinical Psychology, MD
Communication and Media Studies, MD
Computer Engineering, B
Computer Science, BMDO
Conservation Biology, MD
Construction Engineering, B
Construction Management, B
Corrections and Criminal Justice, B
Counselor Education/School Counseling and
   Guidance Services, MD
Criminology, MD
Crop Production, B
Dietetics/Dieticians, B
Drama and Dramatics/Theatre Arts, B
Ecology, MD
Education, MDO
Educational Administration and Supervision, MDO
Electrical Engineering, MD
Electrical, Electronics and Communications
   Engineering, B
Elementary Education and Teaching, B
Engineering, B
Engineering and Applied Sciences, MD
English, M
English Language and Literature, B
English/Language Arts Teacher Education, B
Entomology, MD
Environmental Design/Architecture, B
Environmental Engineering
   Technology/Environmental Technology, MD
Environmental Sciences, MD
Equestrian/Equine Studies, B
Exercise and Sports Science, M
Facilities Planning and Management, B
Family and Consumer Sciences/Home Economics
   Teacher Education, B
Family and Consumer Sciences/Human
   Sciences, M
Food Science, B
Food Science and Technology, MD
French Language and Literature, B
French Language Teacher Education, B
Genomic Sciences, MD
Geology/Earth Science, B
Gerontology, D
Health Teacher Education, B
History, BMD
History Teacher Education, B
Horticultural Science, B
Hospitality Administration/Management, B
Human Development, D
Human Development and Family Studies, B
Humanities/Humanistic Studies, B
Industrial Engineering, B
Industrial/Management Engineering, MD
Interior Design, B
International/Global Studies, B
Landscape Architecture, B
Logistics and Materials Management, D
Manufacturing Engineering, BMD
Mass Communication/Media Studies, BM
Mathematics, BMD
Mathematics Teacher Education, BM
Mechanical Engineering, BMD
Mechanics, MD
Microbiology, BMD
Molecular Biology, MD
Molecular Pathology, D
Multi-/Interdisciplinary Studies, B
Music, BMD
Music Teacher Education, BM
Natural Resources Management/Development and
   Policy, BMD
Nursing, MD
Nursing - Registered Nurse Training, B
Nutritional Sciences, M
Operations Research, M

Parks, Recreation, Leisure and Fitness Studies, B
Pathology/Experimental Pathology, D
Pharmaceutical Sciences, MD
Pharmacy, B
Philosophy, B
Physical Education Teaching and Coaching, BM
Physics, BMD
Physics Teacher Education, B
Plant Pathology/Phytopathology, MD
Plant Protection and Integrated Pest
   Management, B
Plant Sciences, MD
Political Science and Government, BMD
Polymer/Plastics Engineering, BMD
Psychology, BMD
Psychometrics and Quantitative Psychology, B
Radiologic Technology/Science - Radiographer, B
Range Science and Management, MD
Respiratory Care Therapy/Therapist, B
Science Teacher Education/General Science
   Teacher Education, BM
Security and Protective Services, B
Social Science Teacher Education, B
Social Sciences, BMD
Social Studies Teacher Education, M
Sociology, BM
Software Engineering, MDO
Soil Science and Agronomy, B
Spanish Language and Literature, B
Spanish Language Teacher Education, B
Speech and Interpersonal Communication, M
Speech and Rhetorical Studies, B
Speech Teacher Education, B
Sport and Fitness Administration/Management, BM
Statistics, BMDO
Transportation/Transportation Management, D
Turf and Turfgrass Management, B
Veterinary Sciences, MD
Veterinary/Animal Health Technology/Technician and
   Veterinary Assistant, B
Zoology/Animal Biology, BMD

SITTING BULL COLLEGE

Administrative Assistant and Secretarial Science, A
Agribusiness, A
American Indian/Native American Studies, A
Business Administration and Management, A
Carpentry/Carpenter, A
Child Care and Support Services Management, A
Education, A
Environmental Studies, A
Farm/Farm and Ranch Management, A
General Office Occupations and Clerical Services, A
Human Services, A
Liberal Arts and Sciences Studies and
   Humanities, A
Marketing/Marketing Management, A
Social Work, A
Teacher Assistant/Aide, A

TRINITY BIBLE COLLEGE

Administrative Assistant and Secretarial Science, AB
Bible/Biblical Studies, AB
Business Administration and Management, AB
Elementary Education and Teaching, B
Finance, B
Liberal Arts and Sciences Studies and
   Humanities, A
Music, A
Pastoral Studies/Counseling, B

TURTLE MOUNTAIN COMMUNITY COLLEGE

Accounting Technology/Technician and
   Bookkeeping, A
Administrative Assistant and Secretarial Science, A
Art/Art Studies, General, A
Biological and Physical Sciences, A
Biology/Biological Sciences, A
Business Administration and Management, A
Carpentry/Carpenter, A
Clinical Laboratory Science/Medical
   Technology/Technologist, A
Clinical/Medical Laboratory Technician, A
Computer Science, A
Elementary Education and Teaching, A

Emergency Medical Technology/Technician (EMT
   Paramedic), A
English Language and Literature, A
Environmental Studies, A
Health Information/Medical Records
   Administration/Administrator, A
History, A
Human Services, A
Journalism, A
Kindergarten/PreSchool Education and Teaching, A
Liberal Arts and Sciences Studies and
   Humanities, A
Marketing/Marketing Management, A
Mathematics, A
Natural Resources Management/Development and
   Policy, A
Nursing - Registered Nurse Training, A
Pharmacy, A
Physical Therapy/Therapist, A
Pre-Engineering, A
Social Sciences, A
Social Work, A
Trade and Industrial Teacher Education, A
Veterinary/Animal Health Technology/Technician and
   Veterinary Assistant, A
Wildlife and Wildlands Science and Management, A

UNITED TRIBES TECHNICAL COLLEGE

Administrative Assistant and Secretarial Science, A
Animation, Interactive Technology, Video Graphics
   and Special Effects, A
Art/Art Studies, General, A
Automobile/Automotive Mechanics
   Technology/Technician, A
Business Administration and Management, A
Business/Office Automation/Technology/Data
   Entry, A
Child Care Provider/Assistant, A
Community Health and Preventive Medicine, A
Computer Systems Analysis/Analyst, A
Construction Trades, A
Criminal Justice/Law Enforcement Administration, A
Early Childhood Education and Teaching, A
Education, A
Entrepreneurship/Entrepreneurial Studies, A
Environmental Sciences, A
Fine Arts and Art Studies, A
Foods, Nutrition, and Wellness Studies, A
General Office Occupations and Clerical Services, A
Health Information/Medical Records
   Technology/Technician, A
Hospitality Administration/Management, A
Licensed Practical/Vocational Nurse Training, A
Medical Administrative Assistant/Secretary, A

UNIVERSITY OF MARY

Accounting, AB
Athletic Training and Sports Medicine, B
Biology Teacher Education, B
Biology/Biological Sciences, B
Business Administration and Management, AB
Business Administration, Management and
   Operations, M
Business/Corporate Communications, B
Clinical Laboratory Science/Medical
   Technology/Technologist, B
Computer and Information Sciences, B
Criminal Justice/Police Science, B
Divinity/Ministry (BD, MDiv.), B
Early Childhood Education and Teaching, BM
Education, M
Education/Teaching of Individuals with Mental
   Retardation, B
Educational Administration and Supervision, M
Elementary Education and Teaching, BM
Engineering Science, B
English Language and Literature, B
English/Language Arts Teacher Education, B
General Studies, B
Health and Physical Education, B
Higher Education/Higher Education
   Administration, M
History Teacher Education, B
Kinesiology and Exercise Science, B
Management, M
Management Information Systems and Services, B

Management Science, B
Mass Communication/Media Studies, B
Mathematics, B
Mathematics Teacher Education, B
Music Performance, B
Music Teacher Education, B
Nursing, M
Nursing - Advanced Practice, M
Nursing - Registered Nurse Training, B
Nursing Administration, M
Nursing Education, M
Occupational Therapy/Therapist, M
Physical Education Teaching and Coaching, B
Physical Therapy/Therapist, MD
Psychology, B
Radiologic Technology/Science - Radiographer, B
Reading Teacher Education, M
Respiratory Care Therapy/Therapist, B
Secondary Education and Teaching, M
Social Science Teacher Education, B
Social Sciences, B
Social Work, B
Special Education and Teaching, M
Substance Abuse/Addiction Counseling, B
Theology/Theological Studies, B

UNIVERSITY OF NORTH DAKOTA

Accounting, B
Accounting and Finance, B
Aeronautics/Aviation/Aerospace Science and
   Technology, B
Air Traffic Controller, B
Allopathic Medicine, PO
American Indian/Native American Studies, B
Anatomy, MD
Anthropology, MD
Applied Economics, M
Art Teacher Education, B
Art/Art Studies, General, B
Athletic Training and Sports Medicine, B
Atmospheric Sciences and Meteorology, BM
Audiology/Audiologist and Speech-Language
   Pathology/Pathologist, B
Aviation, M
Aviation/Airway Management and Operations, B
Banking and Financial Support Services, B
Biochemistry, MD
Biological and Biomedical Sciences, BMDO
Biology/Biological Sciences, B
Botany/Plant Biology, MD
Business Administration, Management and
   Operations, M
Business Teacher Education, B
Business/Commerce, B
Business/Managerial Economics, B
Chemical Engineering, BM
Chemistry, BMD
Civil Engineering, BM
Classics and Classical
   Languages, Literatures, and Linguistics, B
Clinical Laboratory Science/Medical
   Technology/Technologist, B
Clinical Laboratory Sciences, M
Clinical Psychology, D
Clinical/Medical Laboratory Science and Allied
   Professions, B
Communication and Media Studies, MD
Communication Disorders, BMD
Communication Studies/Speech Communication
   and Rhetoric, B
Computer and Information Sciences, B
Computer Science, BM
Computer Systems Analysis/Analyst, B
Counseling Psychology, MD
Criminal Justice/Safety Studies, B
Criminology, D
CytoTechnology/Cytotechnologist, B
Dietetics/Dieticians, B
Drama and Dramatics/Theatre Arts, B
Early Childhood Education and Teaching, BM
Ecology, MD
Economics, B
Education, MDO
Educational Leadership and Administration, MDO
Educational Measurement and Evaluation, D
Educational Media/Instructional Technology, M

Electrical Engineering, M
Electrical, Electronics and Communications
   Engineering, B
Elementary Education and Teaching, BMD
Engineering and Applied Sciences, D
English, MD
English Language and Literature, B
Entomology, MD
Entrepreneurship/Entrepreneurial Studies, B
Environmental Biology, MD
Environmental Engineering
   Technology/Environmental Technology, M
Environmental/Environmental Health Engineering, B
Experimental Psychology, D
Finance, B
Fine Arts and Art Studies, M
Fish, Game and Wildlife Management, MD
Foreign Languages and Literatures, B
Forensic Science and Technology, B
French Language and Literature, B
General Studies, B
Genetics, MD
Geography, BM
Geological Engineering, M
Geological/Geophysical Engineering, B
Geology/Earth Science, BMD
Geosciences, MD
German Language and Literature, B
Graphic Design, B
History, BMD
Human Services, B
Immunology, MD
Industrial and Manufacturing Management, M
Industrial Technology/Technician, B
Information Science/Studies, B
Interdisciplinary Studies, B
International/Global Studies, B
Junior High/Intermediate/Middle School Education
   and Teaching, B
Kindergarten/PreSchool Education and Teaching, B
Kinesiology and Exercise Science, B
Kinesiology and Movement Studies, M
Law and Legal Studies, P
Liberal Arts and Sciences Studies and
   Humanities, B
Linguistics, M
Marketing/Marketing Management, B
Mathematics, BM
Mathematics Teacher Education, B
Mechanical Engineering, BM
Microbiology, MD
Multi-/Interdisciplinary Studies, B
Music, BM
Music Performance, B
Music Teacher Education, BM
Music Therapy/Therapist, B
Nursing, MD
Nursing - Registered Nurse Training, B
Occupational Safety and Health
   Technology/Technician, B
Occupational Therapy/Therapist, M
Parks, Recreation and Leisure Facilities
   Management, B
Parks, Recreation, Leisure and Fitness Studies, B
Pharmacology, MD
Philosophy, B
Physical Education Teaching and Coaching, B
Physical Therapy/Therapist, BMD
Physician Assistant, M
Physics, BMD
Physiology, MD
Planetary Astronomy and Science, M
Political Science and Government, B
Psychology, BMD
Public Administration, M
Reading Teacher Education, M
Religion/Religious Studies, B
Sales and Marketing Operations/Marketing and
   Distribution Teacher Education, B
Scandinavian
   Languages, Literatures, and Linguistics, B
Science Teacher Education/General Science
   Teacher Education, B
Secondary Education and Teaching, D
Social Sciences, B
Social Work, BM

Sociology, BM
Spanish Language and Literature, B
Special Education and Teaching, MD
Theater, M
Vocational and Technical Education, M
Wildlife Biology, B

VALLEY CITY STATE UNIVERSITY

Art Teacher Education, B
Art/Art Studies, General, B
Biology Teacher Education, B
Biology/Biological Sciences, B
Business Administration and Management, B
Business Teacher Education, B
Chemistry, B
Chemistry Teacher Education, B
Computer and Information Sciences, B
Computer and Information Sciences and Support
   Services, B
Education, B
Elementary Education and Teaching, B
English Language and Literature, B
English/Language Arts Teacher Education, B
Health Teacher Education, B
History, B
History Teacher Education, B
Human Resources Management/Personnel
   Administration, B
Mass Communication/Media Studies, B
Mathematics, B
Mathematics Teacher Education, B
Music, B
Music Teacher Education, B
Office Management and Supervision, B
Physical Education Teaching and Coaching, B
Pre-Dentistry Studies, B
Pre-Engineering, B
Pre-Law Studies, B
Pre-Medicine/Pre-Medical Studies, B
Pre-Pharmacy Studies, B
Pre-Veterinary Studies, B
Psychology, B
Science Teacher Education/General Science
   Teacher Education, B
Secondary Education and Teaching, B
Social Science Teacher Education, B
Social Sciences, B
Spanish Language and Literature, B
Spanish Language Teacher Education, B
Technical Teacher Education, B
Technology Teacher Education/Industrial Arts
   Teacher Education, B

WILLISTON STATE COLLEGE

Accounting Technology/Technician and
   Bookkeeping, A
Administrative Assistant and Secretarial Science, A
Agriculture, A
Automobile/Automotive Mechanics
   Technology/Technician, A
Computer and Information Sciences and Support
   Services, A
Data Processing and Data Processing
   Technology/Technician, A
Diesel Mechanics Technology/Technician, A
Entrepreneurial and Small Business Operations, A
Health Information/Medical Records
   Technology/Technician, A
Liberal Arts and Sciences Studies and
   Humanities, A
Licensed Practical/Vocational Nurse Training, A
Marketing/Marketing Management, A
Medical Transcription/Transcriptionist, A
Multi-/Interdisciplinary Studies, A
Physical Therapist Assistant, A

Ohio

ANTIOCH COLLEGE

African Studies, B
African-American/Black Studies, B
Anthropology, B
Behavioral Sciences, B
Biological and Physical Sciences, B
Biology/Biological Sciences, B

Biomedical Sciences, B
Business Administration and Management, B
Chemistry, B
Cinematography and Film/Video Production, B
Communication Studies/Speech Communication
   and Rhetoric, B
Comparative Literature, B
Computer Science, B
Creative Writing, B
Dance, B
Drama and Dramatics/Theatre Arts, B
Drawing, B
Economics, B
Education, B
English Language and Literature, B
Environmental Biology, B
Environmental Studies, B
European Studies/Civilization, B
French Language and Literature, B
Geology/Earth Science, B
German Language and Literature, B
History, B
Human Development and Family Studies, B
Humanities/Humanistic Studies, B
Interdisciplinary Studies, B
International Relations and Affairs, B
Japanese Language and Literature, B
Junior High/Intermediate/Middle School Education
   and Teaching, B
Mass Communication/Media Studies, B
Mathematics, B
Music, B
Natural Sciences, B
Peace Studies and Conflict Resolution, B
Philosophy, B
Physical Sciences, B
Physics, B
Political Science and Government, B
Pre-Law Studies, B
Pre-Medicine/Pre-Medical Studies, B
Pre-Veterinary Studies, B
Psychology, B
Religion/Religious Studies, B
Science Teacher Education/General Science
   Teacher Education, B
Sculpture, B
Secondary Education and Teaching, B
Social Sciences, B
Sociology, B
Spanish Language and Literature, B
Visual and Performing Arts, B
Women's Studies, B

ANTIOCH UNIVERSITY MCGREGOR

Business Administration and Management, B
Conflict Resolution and Mediation/Peace Studies, M
Education, M
Educational Administration and Supervision, M
Human Development and Family Studies, B
Human Resources Management/Personnel
   Administration, B
Human Services, B
Humanities/Humanistic Studies, B
Liberal Arts and Sciences Studies and
   Humanities, B
Liberal Studies, M
Management, M

ANTONELLI COLLEGE

Accounting and Business/Management, A
Commercial and Advertising Art, A
Computer and Information Sciences, A
Computer Systems Networking and
   Telecommunications, A
Graphic Design, A
Interior Design, A
Photography, A
Web/Multimedia Management and Webmaster, A

ART ACADEMY OF CINCINNATI

Art Education, M
Art History, Criticism and Conservation, B
Art/Art Studies, General, B
Drawing, B
Fine/Studio Arts, B
Graphic Design, AB

Illustration, B
Intermedia/Multimedia, B
Painting, B
Photography, B
Printmaking, B
Sculpture, B

THE ART INSTITUTE OF OHIO-CINCINNATI

Graphic Design, A
Interior Design, A

ASHLAND UNIVERSITY

Accounting, B
American/United States Studies/Civilization, B
Art Teacher Education, B
Art/Art Studies, General, AB
Athletic Training and Sports Medicine, B
Biology/Biological Sciences, B
Business Administration and Management, B
Business Administration, Management and
   Operations, M
Business Education, M
Chemistry, B
Child Development, B
Commercial and Advertising Art, B
Computer Education, M
Computer Science, B
Creative Writing, B
Criminal Justice/Law Enforcement
   Administration, AB
Curriculum and Instruction, M
Dietetics/Dieticians, B
Drama and Dramatics/Theatre Arts, B
Early Childhood Education and Teaching, M
Economics, B
Education, BMD
Education/Teaching of the Gifted and Talented, M
Educational Administration and Supervision, M
Educational Leadership and Administration, MD
Elementary Education and Teaching, B
English Language and Literature, B
Environmental Studies, B
Exercise and Sports Science, M
Family and Consumer Economics and Related
   Services, B
Family and Consumer Sciences/Home Economics
   Teacher Education, B
Family and Consumer Sciences/Human Sciences, B
Fashion Merchandising, B
Finance, B
Fine/Studio Arts, B
Foods, Nutrition, and Wellness Studies, B
Foundations and Philosophy of Education, M
French Language and Literature, B
Geology/Earth Science, B
Health Teacher Education, B
History, B
Hotel/Motel Administration/Management, B
Human Development and Family Studies, B
Information Science/Studies, B
International Relations and Affairs, B
Journalism, B
Junior High/Intermediate/Middle School Education
   and Teaching, B
Kindergarten/PreSchool Education and Teaching, B
Liberal Arts and Sciences Studies and
   Humanities, AB
Marketing Research, B
Marketing/Marketing Management, B
Mass Communication/Media Studies, B
Mathematics, B
Middle School Education, M
Music, B
Music Teacher Education, B
Parks, Recreation, Leisure and Fitness Studies, B
Philosophy, B
Physical Education Teaching and Coaching, BM
Physics, B
Political Science and Government, B
Pre-Dentistry Studies, B
Pre-Law Studies, B
Pre-Medicine/Pre-Medical Studies, B
Pre-Pharmacy Studies, B
Pre-Theology/Pre-Ministerial Studies, B
Pre-Veterinary Studies, B

Psychology, B
Radio and Television, AB
Reading Teacher Education, M
Religion/Religious Studies, B
Religious Education, B
Science Teacher Education/General Science
   Teacher Education, B
Secondary Education and Teaching, B
Social Sciences, B
Social Work, B
Sociology, B
Spanish Language and Literature, B
Special Education and Teaching, BM
Speech and Rhetorical Studies, B
Student Personnel Services, M
Therapeutic Recreation/Recreational Therapy, B
Toxicology, B

BALDWIN-WALLACE COLLEGE

Accounting, BM
Art History, Criticism and Conservation, B
Art Teacher Education, B
Athletic Training and Sports Medicine, B
Biology/Biological Sciences, B
Broadcast Journalism, B
Business Administration and Management, B
Business Administration, Management and
   Operations, M
Chemistry, B
Communication Disorders, B
Communication Studies/Speech Communication
   and Rhetoric, B
Computer and Information Sciences, B
Computer Science, B
Computer Systems Analysis/Analyst, B
Computer Systems Networking and
   Telecommunications, B
Criminal Justice/Law Enforcement Administration, B
Dramatic/Theatre Arts and Stagecraft, B
Early Childhood Education and Teaching, B
Econometrics and Quantitative Economics, B
Economics, B
Education, M
Education/Teaching of Individuals with Specific
   Learning Disabilities, B
Educational Administration and Supervision, M
Educational Leadership and Administration, B
Educational Media/Instructional Technology, M
Elementary Education and Teaching, B
English Language and Literature, B
Entrepreneurship/Entrepreneurial Studies, M
Film/Cinema Studies, B
Finance, B
Fine/Studio Arts, B
French Language and Literature, B
German Language and Literature, B
Health Services Administration, M
Health Teacher Education, B
History, B
Human Resources Management and Services, M
Human Resources Management/Personnel
   Administration, B
Information Science/Studies, B
International Business/Trade/Commerce, M
International/Global Studies, B
Junior High/Intermediate/Middle School Education
   and Teaching, B
Kinesiology and Exercise Science, B
Management, M
Management Information Systems and Services, B
Marketing/Marketing Management, B
Mass Communication/Media Studies, B
Mathematics, B
Music History, Literature, and Theory, B
Music Performance, B
Music Teacher Education, B
Music Theory and Composition, B
Music Therapy/Therapist, B
Neuroscience, B
Organizational Behavior Studies, B
Philosophy, B
Physical Education Teaching and Coaching, B
Physics, B
Physics Teacher Education, B
Piano and Organ, B
Political Science and Government, B

Pre-Engineering, B
Psychology, B
Public Health Education and Promotion, B
Public Relations/Image Management, B
Reading Teacher Education, M
Religion/Religious Studies, B
Science Teacher Education/General Science
   Teacher Education, B
Sociology, B
Spanish Language and Literature, B
Special Education and Teaching, M
Sport and Fitness Administration/Management, B
Web Page, Digital/Multimedia and Information
   Resources Design, B

BELMONT TECHNICAL COLLEGE

Accounting, A
Administrative Assistant and Secretarial Science, A
Business Administration and Management, A
Civil Engineering Technology/Technician, A
Computer Engineering Technology/Technician, A
Computer Programming/Programmer, A
Corrections, A
Electrical, Electronic and Communications
   Engineering Technology/Technician, A
Electromechanical Technology/Electromechanical
   Engineering Technology, A
Emergency Medical Technology/Technician (EMT
   Paramedic), A
Heating, Air Conditioning, Ventilation and
   Refrigeration Maintenance
   Technology/Technician, A
Historic Preservation and Conservation, A
Licensed Practical/Vocational Nurse Training, A
Medical/Clinical Assistant, A
Mental Health/Rehabilitation, A
Nursing - Registered Nurse Training, A
Welding Technology/Welder, A

BLUFFTON UNIVERSITY

Accounting, B
Apparel and Accessories Marketing Operations, B
Apparel and Textiles, B
Art/Art Studies, General, B
Biology/Biological Sciences, B
Business Administration and Management, B
Chemistry, B
Communication Studies/Speech Communication
   and Rhetoric, B
Computer Science, B
Creative Writing, B
Criminal Justice/Safety Studies, B
Economics, B
Education, M
Elementary Education and Teaching, B
English Language and Literature, B
Family and Consumer Sciences/Home Economics
   Teacher Education, B
Family and Consumer Sciences/Human Sciences, B
Foods, Nutrition, and Wellness Studies, B
Health and Physical Education, B
History, B
Information Science/Studies, B
Information Technology, B
Junior High/Intermediate/Middle School Education
   and Teaching, B
Kindergarten/PreSchool Education and Teaching, B
Mathematics, B
Multi-/Interdisciplinary Studies, B
Music, B
Music Teacher Education, B
Organizational Behavior Studies, B
Organizational Management, M
Parks, Recreation, Leisure and Fitness Studies, B
Physics, B
Pre-Medicine/Pre-Medical Studies, B
Psychology, B
Religion/Religious Studies, B
Social Sciences, B
Social Work, B
Sociology, B
Spanish Language and Literature, B
Sport and Fitness Administration/Management, B

Youth Ministry, B

BOWLING GREEN STATE UNIVERSITY

Accounting, BM
Acting, B
Adult Development and Aging, B
African Studies, B
American/United States Studies/Civilization, BMD
Apparel and Textiles, B
Applied Mathematics, B
Art History, Criticism and Conservation, B
Art Teacher Education, B
Asian Studies/Civilization, B
Astronomy, M
Athletic Training and Sports Medicine, B
Aviation/Airway Management and Operations, B
Biological and Biomedical Sciences, MDO
Biology Teacher Education, B
Biology/Biological Sciences, B
Broadcast Journalism, B
Business Administration, Management and
   Operations, M
Business Education, M
Business Teacher Education, B
Business, Management, Marketing, and Related
   Support Services, B
Business/Commerce, B
Business/Managerial Economics, B
Chemistry, BMD
Child and Family Studies, MD
Child Development, B
Cinematography and Film/Video Production, B
Classics and Classical
   Languages, Literatures, and Linguistics, B
Clinical Laboratory Science/Medical
   Technology/Technologist, B
Clinical Psychology, MD
Communication and Media Studies, MD
Communication Disorders, BMD
Communication Studies/Speech Communication
   and Rhetoric, B
Communication, Journalism and Related
   Programs, B
Composition, M
Computer and Information Sciences, B
Computer Science, M
Construction Engineering Technology/Technician, B
Counselor Education/School Counseling and
   Guidance Services, M
Crafts/Craft Design, Folk Art and Artisanry, B
Creative Writing, B
Criminal Justice/Safety Studies, B
Criminology, MD
Curriculum and Instruction, M
Dance, B
Demography and Population Studies, MD
Design and Visual Communications, B
Developmental Psychology, MD
Dietetics/Dieticians, B
Drafting/Design Engineering
   Technologies/Technicians, B
Drama and Dance Teacher Education, B
Drama and Dramatics/Theatre Arts, B
Dramatic/Theatre Arts and Stagecraft, B
Economics, BM
Education, BMDO
Education/Teaching of Individuals with Hearing
   Impairments, Including Deafness, B
Educational Administration and Supervision, MDO
Educational Leadership and Administration, D
Educational Media/Instructional Technology, M
Electrical, Electronic and Communications
   Engineering Technology/Technician, B
Elementary Education and Teaching, B
Engineering Technologies/Technicians, B
English, MD
English as a Second Language, M
English Language and Literature, B
English/Language Arts Teacher Education, B
Environmental Design/Architecture, B
Environmental Health, B
Ethnic, Cultural Minority, and Gender Studies, B
Experimental Psychology, MD
Family and Consumer Sciences/Human
   Sciences, M
Fashion Merchandising, B

Film/Cinema Studies, B
Finance, B
Fine Arts and Art Studies, BM
Fine/Studio Arts, B
Foods, Nutrition, and Wellness Studies, B
Foreign Language Teacher Education, BM
French Language and Literature, BM
Geography, B
Geology/Earth Science, BM
German Language and Literature, BMO
Gerontology, B
Health and Physical Education/Fitness, B
Health Professions and Related Clinical Sciences, B
Health Teacher Education, B
Health/Health Care Administration/Management, B
Higher Education/Higher Education
   Administration, D
History, BMDO
Hospitality Administration/Management, B
Human Development, M
Human Resources Management/Personnel
   Administration, B
Industrial and Organizational Psychology, MD
Industrial Technology/Technician, B
Interdisciplinary Studies, MD
Interior Architecture, B
International Business/Trade/Commerce, B
International Relations and Affairs, B
Jazz/Jazz Studies, B
Journalism, B
Junior High/Intermediate/Middle School Education
   and Teaching, B
Kindergarten/PreSchool Education and Teaching, B
Kinesiology and Movement Studies, M
Latin Teacher Education, B
Leisure Studies, M
Liberal Arts and Sciences Studies and
   Humanities, B
Logistics and Materials Management, B
Management Information Systems and Services, B
Manufacturing Engineering, M
Marketing, B
Mathematics, BMDO
Mathematics Teacher Education, BMO
Mechanical Engineering/Mechanical
   Technology/Technician, B
Medical Microbiology and Bacteriology, B
Multi-/Interdisciplinary Studies, B
Music, BM
Music History, Literature, and Theory, M
Music Performance, B
Music Teacher Education, BM
Music Theory and Composition, BM
Musicology and Ethnomusicology, B
Natural Resources Management/Development and
   Policy, B
Neuroscience, B
Nursing - Registered Nurse Training, B
Nutritional Sciences, M
Operations Management and Supervision, B
Organizational Management, M
Parks, Recreation, Leisure and Fitness Studies, B
Performance, M
Philosophy, BMD
Photography, B
Physical Education Teaching and Coaching, B
Physical Therapy/Therapist, B
Physics, BM
Piano and Organ, B
Political Science and Government, BO
Pre-Law Studies, B
Psychology, BMD
Public Administration, BM
Public Health, M
Public Relations/Image Management, B
Quality Control Technology/Technician, B
Reading Teacher Education, MO
Recreation and Park Management, M
Rehabilitation Counseling, M
Russian Language and Literature, B
Sales and Marketing Operations/Marketing and
   Distribution Teacher Education, B
School Psychology, MO
Science Teacher Education/General Science
   Teacher Education, BM
Social Psychology, MD

Social Studies Teacher Education, B
Social Work, B
Sociology, BMD
Spanish Language and Literature, BM
Special Education and Teaching, BM
Speech and Interpersonal Communication, MD
Speech and Rhetorical Studies, B
Sport and Fitness Administration/Management, BM
Statistics, BMDO
Student Personnel Services, M
Teacher Education and Professional
   Development, Specific Subject Areas, B
Technical and Business Writing, B
Technical Teacher Education, B
Technical Theatre/Theatre Design and
   Technology, B
Telecommunications Technology/Technician, B
Theater, MD
Tourism Promotion Operations, B
Vocational and Technical Education, M
Voice and Opera, B
Women's Studies, B
Writing, M

BOWLING GREEN STATE UNIVERSITY-FIRELANDS COLLEGE

Accounting Technology/Technician and
   Bookkeeping, A
Biological and Physical Sciences, A
Business Operations Support and Secretarial
   Services, A
Communications Technologies/Technicians and
   Support Services, A
Computer Engineering Technology/Technician, A
Computer Programming/Programmer, A
Computer Systems Networking and
   Telecommunications, A
Criminal Justice/Safety Studies, AB
Design and Visual Communications, B
Drafting/Design Engineering
   Technologies/Technicians, A
Education, A
Electrical, Electronic and Communications
   Engineering Technology/Technician, A
Engineering Technologies/Technicians, A
Family and Community Services, A
Health Information/Medical Records
   Administration/Administrator, A
Health Professions and Related Clinical Sciences, A
Human Services, A
Humanities/Humanistic Studies, A
Industrial Technology/Technician, AB
Interdisciplinary Studies, A
Kindergarten/PreSchool Education and Teaching, B
Liberal Arts and Sciences Studies and
   Humanities, A
Management Information Systems and Services, A
Nursing - Registered Nurse Training, A
Operations Management and Supervision, A
Pre-Engineering, A
Respiratory Care Therapy/Therapist, A
Social Sciences, A

BRADFORD SCHOOL

Accounting, A
Administrative Assistant and Secretarial Science, A
Computer Programming, Specific Applications, A
Computer Programming/Programmer, A
Graphic Design, A
Legal Administrative Assistant/Secretary, A
Legal Assistant/Paralegal, A
Medical/Clinical Assistant, A
Tourism and Travel Services Management, A

BROWN MACKIE COLLEGE-AKRON

Accounting, A
Business Administration and Management, A
Computer Software Technology/Technician, A
Computer Systems Networking and
   Telecommunications
Criminal Justice/Safety Studies, A
Health/Health Care Administration/Management, A
Legal Assistant/Paralegal, A
Medical/Clinical Assistant, A

Pharmacy Technician/Assistant, A

BROWN MACKIE COLLEGE-CINCINNATI

Accounting, A
Administrative Assistant and Secretarial Science, A
Audio Engineering, A
Business Administration and Management, A
Computer and Information Sciences, A
Computer Graphics, A
Computer Science, A
Laser and Optical Technology/Technician, A
Medical Administrative Assistant/Secretary, A
Medical/Clinical Assistant, A

BROWN MACKIE COLLEGE-FINDLAY

Accounting Technology/Technician and
   Bookkeeping, A
Business Administration and Management, A
Computer Software Technology/Technician, A
Criminal Justice/Safety Studies, A
Health/Health Care Administration/Management, A
Legal Assistant/Paralegal, A
Medical Office Management/Administration, A
Medical/Clinical Assistant, A
Pharmacy Technician/Assistant, A

BROWN MACKIE COLLEGE-NORTH CANTON

Accounting Technology/Technician and
   Bookkeeping, A
Business Administration and Management, A
CAD/CADD Drafting and/or Design
   Technology/Technician, A
Computer Systems Networking and
   Telecommunications, A
Criminal Justice/Safety Studies, A
Health/Health Care Administration/Management, A
Industrial Electronics Technology/Technician, A
Legal Assistant/Paralegal, A
Medical/Clinical Assistant, A
Pharmacy Technician/Assistant, A

BRYANT AND STRATTON COLLEGE (CLEVELAND)

Administrative Assistant and Secretarial Science, A
Business Administration and Management, B
Business/Commerce, A
Criminal Justice/Law Enforcement Administration, A
Electrical, Electronic and Communications
   Engineering Technology/Technician, AB
Human Resources Management and Services, A
Information Technology, A
Legal Administrative Assistant/Secretary, A
Legal Assistant/Paralegal, A

BRYANT AND STRATTON COLLEGE (PARMA)

Accounting, A
Administrative Assistant and Secretarial Science, A
Business Administration and Management, B
Business/Commerce, A
Criminal Justice/Law Enforcement Administration, A
Human Resources Management and Services, A
Information Technology, A
Legal Administrative Assistant/Secretary, A
Medical Administrative Assistant/Secretary, A
Medical/Clinical Assistant, A
Nursing - Registered Nurse Training, A

BRYANT AND STRATTON COLLEGE (WILLOUGHBY HILLS)

Accounting, A
Administrative Assistant and Secretarial Science, A
Business Administration and Management, A
Information Technology, A

CAPITAL UNIVERSITY

Accounting, B
Agricultural Business and Management, B
Art Teacher Education, B
Art Therapy/Therapist, B
Art/Art Studies, General, B
Athletic Training and Sports Medicine, B

Biochemistry, B
Biological and Biomedical Sciences, B
Biology Teacher Education, B
Biology/Biological Sciences, B
Business Administration and Management, B
Business Administration, Management and
   Operations, BMO
Business/Commerce, B
Business/Managerial Economics, B
Chemistry, B
Chemistry Teacher Education, B
Communication Studies/Speech Communication
   and Rhetoric, B
Community Health Nursing, M
Comparative Literature, B
Computer Engineering, B
Computer Science, B
Computer Teacher Education, B
Creative Writing, B
Criminal Justice/Safety Studies, B
Criminology, B
Drama and Dance Teacher Education, B
Drama and Dramatics/Theatre Arts, B
Early Childhood Education and Teaching, B
Economics, B
Education, B
Educational/Instructional Media Design, B
Elementary Education and Teaching, B
English Language and Literature, B
English/Language Arts Teacher Education, B
Environmental Sciences, B
Finance, B
Fine/Studio Arts, B
French Language and Literature, B
Health and Physical Education, B
Health and Physical Education/Fitness, B
Health Teacher Education, B
History, B
Human Resources Management/Personnel
   Administration, B
Interdisciplinary Studies, B
International Relations and Affairs, B
Jazz/Jazz Studies, B
Junior High/Intermediate/Middle School Education
   and Teaching, B
Kinesiology and Exercise Science, B
Law and Legal Studies, MPO
Legal and Justice Studies, M
Liberal Arts and Sciences Studies and
   Humanities, B
Marketing/Marketing Management, B
Mathematics, B
Mathematics Teacher Education, B
Multi-/Interdisciplinary Studies, B
Music, BM
Music Management and Merchandising, B
Music Performance, B
Music Teacher Education, BM
Music Theory and Composition, B
Nursing, BMO
Nursing - Registered Nurse Training, B
Nursing Administration, M
Organizational Communication, B
Philosophy, B
Philosophy and Religious Studies, B
Physical Education Teaching and Coaching, B
Piano and Organ, B
Political Science and Government, B
Pre-Dentistry Studies, B
Pre-Medicine/Pre-Medical Studies, B
Pre-Veterinary Studies, B
Psychology, B
Public Administration, B
Public Health/Community Nurse/Nursing, B
Public Relations/Image Management, B
Radio, Television, and Digital Communication, B
Religion/Religious Studies, B
Religious Education, B
School Nursing, M
Science Teacher Education/General Science
   Teacher Education, B
Secondary Education and Teaching, B
Social Studies Teacher Education, B
Social Work, B
Sociology, B
Spanish Language and Literature, B

Special Education and Teaching, B
Speech and Rhetorical Studies, B
Speech Teacher Education, B
Taxation, BMO
Violin, Viola, Guitar and Other Stringed
   Instruments, B
Voice and Opera, B
Wind and Percussion Instruments, B

CASE WESTERN RESERVE UNIVERSITY

Accounting, BMD
Aerospace, Aeronautical and Astronautical
   Engineering, BMD
Allopathic Medicine, PO
American/United States Studies/Civilization, B
Analytical Chemistry, MD
Anatomy, MDO
Anthropology, BMDO
Applied Mathematics, BMD
Art Education, M
Art History, Criticism and Conservation, BMD
Art Teacher Education, B
Asian Studies/Civilization, B
Astronomy, BMD
Biochemistry, BMDO
Bioethics/Medical Ethics, MDO
Biological and Biomedical Sciences, MDO
Biology/Biological Sciences, B
Biomedical Engineering, MDO
Biomedical/Medical Engineering, B
Biophysics, MDO
Biostatistics, MD
Business Administration and Management, B
Business Administration, Management and
   Operations, MDO
Cell Biology and Anatomy, MD
Ceramic Sciences and Engineering, M
Chemical Engineering, BMD
Chemistry, BMD
Civil Engineering, BMD
Classics and Classical
   Languages, Literatures, and Linguistics, B
Clinical Psychology, D
Clinical Research, M
Cognitive Sciences, B
Communication Disorders, BMDO
Comparative Literature, BM
Computer Engineering, BMD
Computer Science, BMD
Dance, M
Dental and Oral Surgery, O
Dentistry, P
Developmental Biology and Embryology, D
Dietetics/Dieticians, B
Drama and Dramatics/Theatre Arts, B
Economics, BM
Electrical Engineering, MD
Electrical, Electronics and Communications
   Engineering, B
Engineering, B
Engineering and Applied Sciences, MDO
Engineering Management, M
Engineering Physics, B
Engineering Science, B
English, MD
English Language and Literature, B
Environmental Studies, B
Epidemiology, MD
Evolutionary Biology, B
Experimental Psychology, D
Finance and Banking, MD
French Language and Literature, BMD
French Studies, B
Genetic Counseling/Counselor, M
Genetics, DO
Genomic Sciences, DO
Geology/Earth Science, BMD
Geosciences, MD
German Language and Literature, B
German Studies, B
Gerontological Nursing, M
Gerontology, BO
Health Informatics, M
History, BMD

History and Philosophy of Science and Technology, B
Human Genetics, DO
Human Nutrition, B
Human Resources Management and Services, MD
Immunology, MDO
Industrial and Labor Relations, MD
Industrial and Manufacturing Management, MD
Information Science/Studies, MD
Inorganic Chemistry, MD
International Relations and Affairs, B
International/Global Studies, B
Japanese Studies, B
Law and Legal Studies, MPO
Legal and Justice Studies, M
Logistics and Materials Management, M
Management Information Systems and Services, MDO
Management Strategy and Policy, MD
Marketing, MD
Materials Engineering, BMD
Materials Sciences, BMD
Mathematics, BMD
Mechanical Engineering, BMD
Mechanics, M
Medical Technology, M
Medical/Surgical Nursing, M
Microbiology, DO
Molecular Biology, DO
Museology/Museum Studies, MD
Music, BMD
Music Teacher Education, BMD
Natural Sciences, B
Neurobiology and Neurophysiology, D
Neuroscience, DO
Non-Profit/Public/Organizational Management, MO
Nurse Anesthetist, M
Nurse Midwife/Nursing Midwifery, M
Nursing, MDO
Nursing - Adult, M
Nursing - Advanced Practice, M
Nursing - Registered Nurse Training, B
Nutritional Sciences, BMD
Operations Research, D
Oral and Dental Sciences, MO
Organic Chemistry, MD
Organizational Behavior Studies, MD
Orthodontics, MO
Pathology/Experimental Pathology, MDO
Pediatric Nurse/Nursing, M
Pedodontics, O
Periodontics, MO
Pharmacology, MDO
Philosophy, B
Physical Chemistry, MD
Physics, MD
Physiology, MDO
Political Science and Government, BMD
Polymer/Plastics Engineering, BMDO
Psychiatric/Mental Health Nurse/Nursing, M
Psychology, BD
Public Health, MO
Religion/Religious Studies, B
Social Work, MDO
Sociology, BD
Spanish Language and Literature, B
Statistics, BMD
Surgical Nursing, M
Systems Engineering, BMD
Theater, M
Toxicology, MDO
Women's Health Nursing, M
Women's Studies, B

CEDARVILLE UNIVERSITY

Accounting, B
Administrative Assistant and Secretarial Science, B
American/United States Studies/Civilization, B
Athletic Training and Sports Medicine, B
Bible/Biblical Studies, B
Biological and Physical Sciences, B
Biology Teacher Education, B
Biology/Biological Sciences, B
Broadcast Journalism, B
Business Administration and Management, B
Chemistry, B

Clinical Laboratory Science/Medical Technology/Technologist, B
Communication Studies/Speech Communication and Rhetoric, B
Communications Technology/Technician, B
Computer Engineering, B
Computer Science, B
Criminal Justice/Law Enforcement Administration, B
Drama and Dramatics/Theatre Arts, B
Early Childhood Education and Teaching, B
Education, M
Electrical, Electronics and Communications Engineering, B
English Language and Literature, B
English/Language Arts Teacher Education, B
Environmental Biology, B
Finance, B
Fine/Studio Arts, B
Graphic Design, B
Health and Physical Education, B
Health Teacher Education, B
History, B
Information Science/Studies, B
Interdisciplinary Studies, B
International Business/Trade/Commerce, B
International Relations and Affairs, B
Kindergarten/PreSchool Education and Teaching, B
Kinesiology and Exercise Science, B
Marketing/Marketing Management, B
Mathematics, B
Mathematics Teacher Education, B
Mechanical Engineering, B
Missions/Missionary Studies and Missiology, B
Music, B
Music Pedagogy, B
Music Performance, B
Music Teacher Education, B
Music Theory and Composition, B
Nursing - Registered Nurse Training, B
Pastoral Counseling and Specialized Ministries, B
Pastoral Studies/Counseling, B
Philosophy, B
Physical Education Teaching and Coaching, B
Physics, B
Physics Teacher Education, B
Piano and Organ, B
Political Science and Government, B
Pre-Dentistry Studies, B
Pre-Law Studies, B
Pre-Medicine/Pre-Medical Studies, B
Pre-Veterinary Studies, B
Psychology, B
Public Administration, B
Radio and Television, B
Religion/Religious Studies, B
Religious Education, B
Religious/Sacred Music, B
Science Teacher Education/General Science Teacher Education, B
Secondary Education and Teaching, B
Social Studies Teacher Education, B
Social Work, B
Sociology, B
Spanish Language and Literature, B
Spanish Language Teacher Education, B
Special Education and Teaching, B
Speech and Rhetorical Studies, B
Sport and Fitness Administration/Management, B
Technical and Business Writing, B
Theology/Theological Studies, B
Voice and Opera, B
Youth Ministry, B

CENTRAL OHIO TECHNICAL COLLEGE

Accounting, A
Administrative Assistant and Secretarial Science, A
Business Administration and Management, A
Computer Programming/Programmer, A
Corrections, A
Criminal Justice/Law Enforcement Administration, A
Criminal Justice/Police Science, A
Diagnostic Medical Sonography/Sonographer and Ultrasound Technician, A
Drafting and Design Technology/Technician, A
Electrical, Electronic and Communications Engineering Technology/Technician, A

Electromechanical Technology/Electromechanical Engineering Technology, A
Human Services, A
Industrial Technology/Technician, A
Kindergarten/PreSchool Education and Teaching, A
Mechanical Engineering/Mechanical Technology/Technician, A
Medical Radiologic Technology/Science - Radiation Therapist, A
Nursing - Registered Nurse Training, A
Physical Therapist Assistant, A

CENTRAL STATE UNIVERSITY

Accounting, B
Art Teacher Education, B
Art/Art Studies, General, B
Biology/Biological Sciences, B
Business Administration and Management, B
Chemistry, B
Computer and Information Sciences, B
Economics, B
Education, M
Educational Leadership and Administration, M
Educational Media/Instructional Technology, M
English Language and Literature, B
English/Language Arts Teacher Education, B
Finance, B
Health Teacher Education, B
History, B
Hotel/Motel Administration/Management, B
Industrial Engineering, B
Industrial Technology/Technician, B
Jazz/Jazz Studies, B
Journalism, B
Junior High/Intermediate/Middle School Education and Teaching, B
Kindergarten/PreSchool Education and Teaching, B
Management Information Systems and Services, B
Marketing/Marketing Management, B
Mathematics, B
Mathematics Teacher Education, B
Music, B
Music Teacher Education, B
Parks, Recreation, Leisure and Fitness Studies, B
Physical Education Teaching and Coaching, B
Political Science and Government, B
Psychology, B
Radio and Television, B
Reading Teacher Education, M
Science Teacher Education/General Science Teacher Education, B
Social Studies Teacher Education, B
Social Work, B
Sociology, B
Special Education and Teaching, B
Water Resources Engineering, B

CHATFIELD COLLEGE

Business Administration and Management, A
Human Services, A
Kindergarten/PreSchool Education and Teaching, A
Liberal Arts and Sciences Studies and Humanities, A

CINCINNATI CHRISTIAN UNIVERSITY

Bible/Biblical Studies, AB
Divinity/Ministry (BD, MDiv.), B
Education, AB
Journalism, B
Kindergarten/PreSchool Education and Teaching, B
Pastoral Studies/Counseling, M
Piano and Organ, B
Psychology, B
Religion/Religious Studies, M
Religious Education, AB
Religious/Sacred Music, AB
Sign Language Interpretation and Translation, A
Theology and Religious Vocations, MP
Trade and Industrial Teacher Education, A

Voice and Opera, B

CINCINNATI COLLEGE OF MORTUARY SCIENCE

Funeral Service and Mortuary Science, AB

CINCINNATI STATE TECHNICAL AND COMMUNITY COLLEGE

Accounting, A
Administrative Assistant and Secretarial Science, A
Aeronautical/Aerospace Engineering
   Technology/Technician, A
Allied Health and Medical Assisting Services, A
Applied Horticulture/Horticultural Business
   Services, A
Architectural Engineering Technology/Technician, A
Automotive Engineering Technology/Technician, A
Biomedical Technology/Technician, A
Business Administration and Management, A
Business, Management, Marketing, and Related
   Support Services, A
Chemical Technology/Technician, A
Child Care Provider/Assistant, A
Cinematography and Film/Video Production, A
Civil Engineering Technology/Technician, A
Clinical/Medical Laboratory Technician, A
Commercial and Advertising Art, A
Computer and Information Sciences, A
Computer Engineering Technology/Technician, A
Computer Programming, Specific Applications, A
Computer Programming/Programmer, A
Criminal Justice/Police Science, A
Culinary Arts/Chef Training, A
Diagnostic Medical Sonography/Sonographer and
   Ultrasound Technician, A
Dietetics/Dieticians, A
Electrical and Electronic Engineering
   Technologies/Technicians, A
Electrical, Electronic and Communications
   Engineering Technology/Technician, A
Electromechanical Technology/Electromechanical
   Engineering Technology, A
Emergency Medical Technology/Technician (EMT
   Paramedic), A
Entrepreneurship/Entrepreneurial Studies, A
Environmental Engineering
   Technology/Environmental Technology, A
Executive Assistant/Executive Secretary, A
Fire Science/Firefighting, A
General Studies, A
Health Information/Medical Records
   Technology/Technician, A
Health Professions and Related Clinical Sciences, A
Heating, Air Conditioning and Refrigeration
   Technology/Technician, A
Hotel/Motel Administration/Management, A
Information Science/Studies, A
International Business/Trade/Commerce, A
Landscaping and Groundskeeping, A
Laser and Optical Technology/Technician, A
Liberal Arts and Sciences Studies and
   Humanities, A
Management Information Systems and Services, A
Marketing/Marketing Management, A
Mechanic and Repair Technologies/Technicians, A
Mechanical Engineering/Mechanical
   Technology/Technician, A
Medical/Clinical Assistant, A
Nursing, A
Nursing - Registered Nurse Training, A
Occupational Therapist Assistant, A
Office Management and Supervision, A
Parks, Recreation, Leisure and Fitness Studies, A
Plastics Engineering Technology/Technician, A
Purchasing, Procurement/Acquisitions and
   Contracts Management, A
Real Estate, A
Respiratory Care Therapy/Therapist, A
Restaurant, Culinary, and Catering
   Management/Manager, A
Science Technologies/Technicians, A
Security and Loss Prevention Services, A
Sign Language Interpretation and Translation, A
Surgical Technology/Technologist, A
Survey Technology/Surveying, A
Technical and Business Writing, A

Telecommunications Technology/Technician, A
Turf and Turfgrass Management, A

CIRCLEVILLE BIBLE COLLEGE

Behavioral Sciences, AB
Bible/Biblical Studies, AB
Business/Commerce, B
Counselor Education/School Counseling and
   Guidance Services, B
Education, AB
Elementary Education and Teaching, B
Missions/Missionary Studies and Missiology, AB
Pre-Theology/Pre-Ministerial Studies, B
Religion/Religious Studies, AB
Religious Education, AB
Religious/Sacred Music, AB
Theology/Theological Studies, AB

CLARK STATE COMMUNITY COLLEGE

Accounting, A
Administrative Assistant and Secretarial Science, A
Agricultural Business and Management, A
Agricultural Mechanization, A
Agriculture, A
Business Administration and Management, A
Civil Engineering Technology/Technician, A
Clinical/Medical Laboratory Technician, A
Commercial and Advertising Art, A
Computer Programming, A
Computer Programming/Programmer, A
Computer Systems Networking and
   Telecommunications, A
Corrections, A
Court Reporting/Court Reporter, A
Criminal Justice/Law Enforcement Administration, A
Criminal Justice/Police Science, A
Drafting and Design Technology/Technician, A
Drama and Dramatics/Theatre Arts, A
Electrical, Electronic and Communications
   Engineering Technology/Technician, A
Emergency Medical Technology/Technician (EMT
   Paramedic), A
Horticultural Science, A
Human Services, A
Industrial Technology/Technician, A
Information Science/Studies, A
Information Technology, A
Kindergarten/PreSchool Education and Teaching, A
Kinesiology and Exercise Science, A
Landscaping and Groundskeeping, A
Legal Assistant/Paralegal, A
Liberal Arts and Sciences Studies and
   Humanities, A
Licensed Practical/Vocational Nurse Training, A
Management Information Systems and Services, A
Mechanical Engineering/Mechanical
   Technology/Technician, A
Medical Administrative Assistant/Secretary, A
Nursing - Registered Nurse Training, A
Physical Therapy/Therapist, A
Social Work, A

THE CLEVELAND INSTITUTE OF ART

Ceramic Arts and Ceramics, B
Commercial and Advertising Art, B
Crafts/Craft Design, Folk Art and Artisanry, B
Drawing, B
Fiber, Textile and Weaving Arts, B
Graphic Design, B
Illustration, B
Industrial Design, B
Interior Design, B
Intermedia/Multimedia, B
Medical Illustration/Medical Illustrator, B
Metal and Jewelry Arts, B
Painting, B
Photography, B
Printmaking, B
Sculpture, B
Web Page, Digital/Multimedia and Information
   Resources Design, B

CLEVELAND INSTITUTE OF MUSIC

Audio Engineering, B
Music, B
Performance, MDO

Piano and Organ, B
Violin, Viola, Guitar and Other Stringed
   Instruments, B
Voice and Opera, B
Wind and Percussion Instruments, B

CLEVELAND STATE UNIVERSITY

Accounting, BM
Adult and Continuing Education and Teaching, MO
Allied Health and Medical Assisting Services, M
Analytical Chemistry, M
Anthropology, B
Applied Art, B
Applied Mathematics, M
Art History, Criticism and Conservation, M
Art/Art Studies, General, B
Audiology/Audiologist and Hearing Sciences, B
Bioethics/Medical Ethics, BMO
Biological and Biomedical Sciences, MD
Biology Technician/BioTechnology Laboratory
   Technician, B
Biology/Biological Sciences, B
Biomedical Engineering, D
Business Administration and Management, B
Business Administration, Management and
   Operations, BMDO
Business Statistics, B
Business/Managerial Economics, B
Chemical Engineering, BMD
Chemistry, BMD
Civil Engineering, BMD
Clinical Psychology, M
Communication and Media Studies, M
Communication Disorders, M
Communication Studies/Speech Communication
   and Rhetoric, B
Community Health Nursing, M
Community Health Services/Liaison/Counseling, B
Community Organization and Advocacy, B
Composition, M
Computer and Information Sciences, B
Computer Engineering, BMD
Computer Science, BM
Condensed Matter Physics, M
Counseling Psychology, M
Counselor Education/School Counseling and
   Guidance Services, MDO
Curriculum and Instruction, M
Dance, B
Drama and Dramatics/Theatre Arts, B
Early Childhood Education and Teaching, B
Economics, BMO
Education, BMDO
Educational Administration and Supervision, MDO
Educational Leadership and Administration, BD
Electrical Engineering, MD
Electrical, Electronic and Communications
   Engineering Technology/Technician, B
Electrical, Electronics and Communications
   Engineering, B
Elementary Education and Teaching, B
Engineering, B
Engineering and Applied Sciences, MD
Engineering Mechanics, B
Engineering Science, B
Engineering Technology, B
English, M
English Language and Literature, B
Environmental Engineering
   Technology/Environmental Technology, MD
Environmental Sciences, MD
Environmental Studies, BMO
Exercise and Sports Science, M
Experimental Psychology, M
Finance, B
Finance and Banking, O
Forensic Nursing, M
French Language and Literature, B
General Studies, B
Geology/Earth Science, BMD
Germanic Languages, Literatures, and Linguistics, B
Gerontology, B
Health Education, M
Health Professions and Related Clinical Sciences, B
Health Services Administration, M
History, M

Human Resources Management and Services, M
Industrial and Labor Relations, M
Industrial and Organizational Psychology, M
Industrial Engineering, B
Industrial Technology/Technician, B
Industrial/Management Engineering, MD
Information Science/Studies, B
Inorganic Chemistry, M
Interdisciplinary Studies, B
International Relations and Affairs, B
Junior High/Intermediate/Middle School Education
    and Teaching, B
Kinesiology and Exercise Science, B
Labor and Industrial Relations, B
Law and Legal Studies, MPO
Liberal Arts and Sciences Studies and
    Humanities, B
Linguistics, B
Management Information Systems and
    Services, MD
Marketing/Marketing Management, B
Mathematics, BM
Mechanical Engineering, BMD
Mechanical Engineering Related
    Technologies/Technicians, B
Medical Physics, M
Metallurgical Engineering, B
Multi-/Interdisciplinary Studies, B
Music, BM
Music History, Literature, and Theory, M
Music Teacher Education, M
Non-Profit/Public/Organizational Management, O
Nursing, MO
Nursing - Registered Nurse Training, B
Occupational Therapy/Therapist, BM
Optical Technologies, M
Organic Chemistry, M
Performance, M
Philosophy, BMO
Physical Chemistry, M
Physical Education Teaching and Coaching, BM
Physical Therapy/Therapist, BM
Physics, BM
Political Science and Government, B
Pre-Nursing Studies, B
Psychology, BMO
Public Administration, BMDO
Public Health, M
Public Relations/Image Management, B
Real Estate, O
Recreation and Park Management, M
Religion/Religious Studies, B
School Psychology, O
Science, Technology and Society, B
Social Sciences, BM
Social Work, BM
Sociology, BM
Spanish Language and Literature, BM
Special Education and Teaching, B
Sport and Fitness Administration/Management, BM
Sport Psychology, M
Taxation, M
Urban Design, M
Urban Education and Leadership, D
Urban Planning, MO
Urban Studies/Affairs, BMD

COLLEGE OF MOUNT ST. JOSEPH

Accounting, AB
Adult Development and Aging, B
Applied Mathematics, B
Art Teacher Education, B
Art/Art Studies, General, AB
Athletic Training and Sports Medicine, B
Biochemistry, B
Biology/Biological Sciences, B
Business Administration and Management, AB
Business, Management, Marketing, and Related
    Support Services, B
Chemistry, B
Clinical Laboratory Science/Medical
    Technology/Technologist, B
Communication Studies/Speech Communication
    and Rhetoric, AB
Computer and Information Sciences and Support
    Services, B

Computer Science, B
Criminology, B
Early Childhood Education and Teaching, M
Education, M
English Language and Literature, B
Fine/Studio Arts, B
Graphic Design, AB
History, B
Interior Design, AB
Junior High/Intermediate/Middle School Education
    and Teaching, B
Kindergarten/PreSchool Education and
    Teaching, AB
Legal Assistant/Paralegal, AB
Liberal Arts and Sciences Studies and
    Humanities, B
Management Information Systems and Services, AB
Mathematics, B
Middle School Education, M
Multilingual and Multicultural Education, M
Music, B
Natural Sciences, B
Nursing, M
Nursing - Registered Nurse Training, B
Nursing Science, B
Organizational Management, B
Pastoral Counseling and Specialized Ministries, B
Pastoral Studies/Counseling, M
Physical Therapy/Therapist, MD
Psychology, B
Reading Teacher Education, M
Religion/Religious Studies, B
Religious Education, B
Secondary Education and Teaching, M
Social Work, B
Sociology, B
Special Education and Teaching, B
Theology and Religious Vocations, M
Therapeutic Recreation/Recreational Therapy, B

THE COLLEGE OF WOOSTER

African-American/Black Studies, B
Archeology, B
Area, Ethnic, Cultural, and Gender Studies, B
Art History, Criticism and Conservation, B
Biochemistry, B
Biology/Biological Sciences, B
Business/Managerial Economics, B
Chemistry, B
Classics and Classical
    Languages, Literatures, and Linguistics, B
Communication Studies/Speech Communication
    and Rhetoric, B
Comparative Literature, B
Computer Science, B
Drama and Dramatics/Theatre Arts, B
Economics, B
English Language and Literature, B
Fine/Studio Arts, B
French Language and Literature, B
Geology/Earth Science, B
German Language and Literature, B
German Studies, B
History, B
Interdisciplinary Studies, B
International Relations and Affairs, B
Latin Language and Literature, B
Mass Communication/Media Studies, B
Mathematics, B
Molecular Biology, B
Multi-/Interdisciplinary Studies, B
Music, B
Music History, Literature, and Theory, B
Music Performance, B
Music Teacher Education, B
Music Theory and Composition, B
Music Therapy/Therapist, B
Philosophy, B
Physics, B
Political Science and Government, B
Psychology, B
Religion/Religious Studies, B
Russian Studies, B
Sociology, B
Spanish Language and Literature, B
Urban Studies/Affairs, B

Women's Studies, B

COLUMBUS COLLEGE OF ART & DESIGN

Fashion/Apparel Design, B
Fine/Studio Arts, B
Graphic Design, B
Illustration, B
Industrial Design, B
Interior Design, B
Photography, B

COLUMBUS STATE COMMUNITY COLLEGE

Accounting, A
Accounting and Computer Science, A
Accounting Technology/Technician and
    Bookkeeping, A
Administrative Assistant and Secretarial Science, A
Aircraft Powerplant Technology/Technician, A
Airframe Mechanics and Aircraft Maintenance
    Technology/Technician, A
Architectural Engineering Technology/Technician, A
Architectural Technology/Technician, A
Automobile/Automotive Mechanics
    Technology/Technician, A
Avionics Maintenance Technology/Technician, A
Building/Construction
    Finishing, Management, and Inspection, A
Business Administration and Management, A
Child Development, A
Civil Engineering Technology/Technician, A
Clinical Laboratory Science/Medical
    Technology/Technologist, A
Clinical/Medical Laboratory Assistant, A
Clinical/Medical Laboratory Technician, A
Commercial and Advertising Art, A
Computer Engineering Technology/Technician, A
Computer Programming/Programmer, A
Construction Management, A
Consumer Merchandising/Retailing Management, A
Corrections, A
Criminal Justice/Police Science, A
Culinary Arts/Chef Training, A
Dental Hygiene/Hygienist, A
Dental Laboratory Technology/Technician, A
Dietetic Technician (DTR), A
Dietetics/Dieticians, A
Electrical and Electronic Engineering
    Technologies/Technicians, A
Electrical, Electronic and Communications
    Engineering Technology/Technician, A
Electromechanical Technology/Electromechanical
    Engineering Technology, A
Emergency Care Attendant (EMT Ambulance), A
Emergency Medical Technology/Technician (EMT
    Paramedic), A
Environmental Engineering
    Technology/Environmental Technology, A
Finance, A
Food Technology and Processing, A
Gerontology, A
Health Information/Medical Records
    Administration/Administrator, A
Health Information/Medical Records
    Technology/Technician, A
Heating, Air Conditioning, Ventilation and
    Refrigeration Maintenance
    Technology/Technician, A
Histologic Technician, A
Hotel/Motel Administration/Management, A
Human Resources Management/Personnel
    Administration, A
Industrial Radiologic Technology/Technician, A
Kindergarten/PreSchool Education and Teaching, A
Landscape Architecture, A
Legal Administrative Assistant/Secretary, A
Legal Assistant/Paralegal, A
Liberal Arts and Sciences Studies and
    Humanities, A
Licensed Practical/Vocational Nurse Training, A
Logistics and Materials Management, A
Marketing/Marketing Management, A
Massage Therapy/Therapeutic Massage, A
Mechanical Engineering/Mechanical
    Technology/Technician, A

Medical Administrative Assistant/Secretary, A
Medical Insurance Coding Specialist/Coder, A
Mental Health/Rehabilitation, A
Nursing - Registered Nurse Training, A
Phlebotomy/Phlebotomist, A
Purchasing, Procurement/Acquisitions and
Contracts Management, A
Quality Control Technology/Technician, A
Radiologic Technology/Science - Radiographer, A
Real Estate, A
Respiratory Care Therapy/Therapist, A
Respiratory Therapy Technician/Assistant, A
Restaurant/Food Services Management, A
Sign Language Interpretation and Translation, A
Sport and Fitness Administration/Management, A
Substance Abuse/Addiction Counseling, A
Surgical Technology/Technologist, A
Technical and Business Writing, A
Tourism and Travel Services Management, A
Veterinary/Animal Health Technology/Technician and
Veterinary Assistant, A

CUYAHOGA COMMUNITY COLLEGE

Accounting, A
Administrative Assistant and Secretarial Science, A
Automobile/Automotive Mechanics
Technology/Technician, A
Avionics Maintenance Technology/Technician, A
Business Administration and Management, A
Clinical Laboratory Science/Medical
Technology/Technologist, A
Commercial and Advertising Art, A
Computer Engineering Technology/Technician, A
Computer Typography and Composition Equipment
Operator, A
Court Reporting/Court Reporter, A
Criminal Justice/Police Science, A
Engineering Technology, A
Finance, A
Fire Science/Firefighting, A
Industrial Radiologic Technology/Technician, A
Kindergarten/PreSchool Education and Teaching, A
Legal Assistant/Paralegal, A
Liberal Arts and Sciences Studies and
Humanities, A
Marketing/Marketing Management, A
Merchandising and Buying Operations, A
Nursing - Registered Nurse Training, A
Opticianry/Ophthalmic Dispensing Optician, A
Photography, A
Physician Assistant, A
Real Estate, A
Respiratory Care Therapy/Therapist, A
Restaurant, Culinary, and Catering
Management/Manager, A
Sales, Distribution and Marketing Operations, A
Selling Skills and Sales Operations, A
Surgical Technology/Technologist, A

DAVID N. MYERS UNIVERSITY

Accounting, AB
Administrative Assistant and Secretarial Science, AB
Business Administration and Management, AB
Business Administration, Management and
Operations, M
Computer Typography and Composition Equipment
Operator, B
Consumer Merchandising/Retailing Management, B
Economics, B
Finance, B
Health/Health Care Administration/Management, B
Legal Administrative Assistant/Secretary, A
Legal Assistant/Paralegal, AB
Marketing/Marketing Management, AB
Public Administration, AB
Real Estate, B
Social Sciences, B

DAVIS COLLEGE

Accounting, A
Administrative Assistant and Secretarial Science, A
Business Administration and Management, A
Commercial and Advertising Art, A
Computer Systems Networking and
Telecommunications, A

Data Processing and Data Processing
Technology/Technician, A
Fashion Merchandising, A
Information Technology, A
Interior Design, A
Legal Administrative Assistant/Secretary, A
Medical Administrative Assistant/Secretary, A
Medical/Clinical Assistant, A
System Administration/Administrator, A
Web Page, Digital/Multimedia and Information
Resources Design, A

DEFIANCE COLLEGE

Accounting, B
Art Teacher Education, B
Art/Art Studies, General, AB
Athletic Training and Sports Medicine, B
Biology/Biological Sciences, B
Business Administration and Management, AB
Business Administration, Management and
Operations, M
Business Teacher Education, B
Clinical Laboratory Science/Medical
Technology/Technologist, B
Computer Science, AB
Criminal Justice/Law Enforcement
Administration, AB
Criminal Justice/Police Science, AB
Ecology, B
Education, BM
Elementary Education and Teaching, B
English Language and Literature, B
Environmental Studies, AB
Forensic Science and Technology, B
Health Teacher Education, B
History, B
Kinesiology and Exercise Science, B
Liberal Arts and Sciences Studies and
Humanities, B
Mass Communication/Media Studies, B
Mathematics, B
Natural Sciences, B
Organizational Management, M
Physical Education Teaching and Coaching, B
Physical Sciences, B
Pre-Dentistry Studies, B
Pre-Law Studies, B
Pre-Medicine/Pre-Medical Studies, B
Pre-Veterinary Studies, B
Psychology, B
Religion/Religious Studies, B
Religious Education, B
Science Teacher Education/General Science
Teacher Education, B
Secondary Education and Teaching, B
Social Sciences, B
Social Work, B
Sport and Fitness Administration/Management, B

DENISON UNIVERSITY

African-American/Black Studies, B
Anthropology, B
Area Studies, B
Art History, Criticism and Conservation, B
Art/Art Studies, General, B
Biochemistry, B
Biology/Biological Sciences, B
Chemistry, B
Classics and Classical
Languages, Literatures, and Linguistics, B
Computer Science, B
Creative Writing, B
Dance, B
Drama and Dramatics/Theatre Arts, B
East Asian Studies, B
Economics, B
English Language and Literature, B
Environmental Studies, B
Film/Cinema Studies, B
Fine/Studio Arts, B
French Language and Literature, B
Geology/Earth Science, B
German Language and Literature, B
History, B
International Relations and Affairs, B
Latin American Studies, B

Mass Communication/Media Studies, B
Mathematics, B
Music, B
Organizational Behavior Studies, B
Philosophy, B
Physical Education Teaching and Coaching, B
Physics, B
Political Science and Government, B
Psychology, B
Religion/Religious Studies, B
Sociology, B
Spanish Language and Literature, B
Speech and Rhetorical Studies, B
Women's Studies, B

DEVRY UNIVERSITY (CLEVELAND)

Business Administration, Management and
Operations, M

DEVRY UNIVERSITY (COLUMBUS)

Biomedical Technology/Technician, B
Business Administration and Management, B
Business Administration, Management and
Operations, BM
Computer and Information Sciences, B
Computer Engineering Technology/Technician, B
Computer Systems Analysis/Analyst, B
Computer Systems Networking and
Telecommunications, AB
Electrical, Electronic and Communications
Engineering Technology/Technician, AB
Health Information/Medical Records
Technology/Technician, A
Information Science/Studies, B
Medical Informatics, B
Operations Management and Supervision, B

DEVRY UNIVERSITY (SEVEN HILLS)

Business Administration, Management and
Operations, M

EDISON STATE COMMUNITY COLLEGE

Accounting, A
Administrative Assistant and Secretarial Science, A
Advertising, A
Art/Art Studies, General, A
Business Administration and Management, A
Commercial and Advertising Art, A
Computer Engineering Technology/Technician, A
Computer Graphics, A
Computer Programming/Programmer, A
Computer Science, A
Consumer Merchandising/Retailing Management, A
Criminal Justice/Law Enforcement Administration, A
Criminal Justice/Police Science, A
Data Processing and Data Processing
Technology/Technician, A
Drafting and Design Technology/Technician, A
Drafting/Design Engineering
Technologies/Technicians, A
Electrical, Electronic and Communications
Engineering Technology/Technician, A
Elementary Education and Teaching, A
Engineering, A
Engineering Technology, A
English Language and Literature, A
Finance, A
Health Information/Medical Records
Administration/Administrator, A
Human Resources Management/Personnel
Administration, A
Human Services, A
Industrial Technology/Technician, A
Kindergarten/PreSchool Education and Teaching, A
Law and Legal Studies, A
Legal Assistant/Paralegal, A
Liberal Arts and Sciences Studies and
Humanities, A
Marketing/Marketing Management, A
Mathematics, A
Medical Administrative Assistant/Secretary, A
Nursing - Registered Nurse Training, A
Pre-Engineering, A
Quality Control Technology/Technician, A

Real Estate, A

ETI TECHNICAL COLLEGE OF NILES

Computer Programming, Specific Applications, A
Computer
    Programming, Vendor/Product Certification, A
Computer Software and Media Applications, A
Computer Software Engineering, A
Computer/Information Technology Services
    Administration and Management, A
Data Entry/Microcomputer Applications, A
Electrical, Electronic and Communications
    Engineering Technology/Technician, A
Legal Assistant/Paralegal, A
Medical/Clinical Assistant, A
Word Processing, A

FRANCISCAN UNIVERSITY OF STEUBENVILLE

Accounting, AB
Anthropology, B
Biology/Biological Sciences, B
Business Administration and Management, AB
Business Administration, Management and
    Operations, M
Chemistry, B
Child Development, A
Classics and Classical
    Languages, Literatures, and Linguistics, B
Communication Studies/Speech Communication
    and Rhetoric, B
Computer and Information Sciences, B
Computer Science, B
Counseling Psychology, M
Curriculum and Instruction, M
Drama and Dramatics/Theatre Arts, B
Economics, B
Education, M
Educational Administration and Supervision, M
Elementary Education and Teaching, B
English Language and Literature, B
French Language and Literature, B
General Studies, A
German Language and Literature, B
History, B
Humanities/Humanistic Studies, B
Law and Legal Studies, B
Mathematics, B
Nursing, M
Nursing - Registered Nurse Training, B
Philosophy, BM
Political Science and Government, B
Psychiatric/Mental Health Services Technician, B
Psychology, B
Religious Education, B
Social Work, B
Sociology, B
Spanish Language and Literature, B
Theology and Religious Vocations, M
Theology/Theological Studies, AB

FRANKLIN UNIVERSITY

Accounting, AB
Business Administration and Management, AB
Business Administration, Management and
    Operations, M
Computer and Information Sciences, AB
Computer Science, M
Corporate and Organizational Communication, M
Finance, B
Health/Health Care Administration/Management, B
Human Resources Management/Personnel
    Administration, B
Interdisciplinary Studies, B
Management Information Systems and Services, B
Management Science, B
Marketing, M
Marketing/Marketing Management, B
Operations Management and Supervision, B
Security and Protective Services, B

Web Page, Digital/Multimedia and Information
    Resources Design, B

GALLIPOLIS CAREER COLLEGE

Accounting, A
Administrative Assistant and Secretarial Science, A
Business Administration and Management, A
Business/Commerce, A
Computer Science, A
Computer Software and Media Applications, A
Data Entry/Microcomputer Applications, A
Management Information Systems and Services, A
Medical Administrative Assistant/Secretary, A

GOD'S BIBLE SCHOOL AND COLLEGE

Administrative Assistant and Secretarial Science, A
Bible/Biblical Studies, A
Business/Commerce, A
Christian Studies, AB
Elementary Education and Teaching, AB
Family and Community Services, B
General Studies, B
Missions/Missionary Studies and Missiology, AB
Music Teacher Education, B
Office Management and Supervision, A
Pastoral Studies/Counseling, B
Religious/Sacred Music, B
Theological and Ministerial Studies, B

HEIDELBERG COLLEGE

Accounting, B
Anthropology, B
Athletic Training and Sports Medicine, B
Biology/Biological Sciences, B
Business Administration and Management, B
Business Administration, Management and
    Operations, M
Chemistry, B
Computer Science, B
Counseling Psychology, M
Drama and Dramatics/Theatre Arts, B
Economics, B
Education, BM
Elementary Education and Teaching, B
English Language and Literature, B
Environmental Biology, B
Environmental Sciences, B
Environmental Studies, B
German Language and Literature, B
Health Teacher Education, B
Health/Health Care Administration/Management, B
History, B
Hydrology and Water Resources Science, B
Information Science/Studies, B
International Relations and Affairs, B
Mass Communication/Media Studies, B
Mathematics, B
Music, B
Music Management and Merchandising, B
Music Teacher Education, B
Philosophy, B
Physical Education Teaching and Coaching, B
Physics, B
Piano and Organ, B
Political Science and Government, B
Pre-Dentistry Studies, B
Pre-Law Studies, B
Pre-Medicine/Pre-Medical Studies, B
Pre-Veterinary Studies, B
Psychology, B
Public Administration, B
Public Relations/Image Management, B
Religion/Religious Studies, B
Science Teacher Education/General Science
    Teacher Education, B
Secondary Education and Teaching, B
Spanish Language and Literature, B
Special Education and Teaching, B
Violin, Viola, Guitar and Other Stringed
    Instruments, B
Voice and Opera, B

HIRAM COLLEGE

Accounting and Finance, B
Art History, Criticism and Conservation, B
Art/Art Studies, General, B

Biological and Biomedical Sciences, B
Biology/Biological Sciences, B
Business Administration and Management, B
Chemistry, B
Classics and Classical
    Languages, Literatures, and Linguistics, B
Computer Science, B
Drama and Dramatics/Theatre Arts, B
Economics, B
Elementary Education and Teaching, B
English Language and Literature, B
Environmental Studies, B
Fine/Studio Arts, B
French Language and Literature, B
German Language and Literature, B
History, B
Interdisciplinary Studies, B
International Business/Trade/Commerce, B
International Economics, B
Mass Communication/Media Studies, B
Mathematics, B
Music, B
Philosophy, B
Physics, B
Physiological Psychology/Psychobiology, B
Political Science and Government, B
Pre-Dentistry Studies, B
Pre-Law Studies, B
Pre-Medicine/Pre-Medical Studies, B
Pre-Veterinary Studies, B
Psychology, B
Public Health (MPH, DPH), B
Religion/Religious Studies, B
Secondary Education and Teaching, B
Sociology, B
Spanish Language and Literature, B

HOCKING COLLEGE

Accounting, A
Administrative Assistant and Secretarial Science, A
Business Administration and Management, A
Ceramic Sciences and Engineering, A
Child Development, A
Computer Engineering Technology/Technician, A
Computer Programming/Programmer, A
Computer Science, A
Consumer Merchandising/Retailing Management, A
Corrections, A
Criminal Justice/Law Enforcement Administration, A
Criminal Justice/Police Science, A
Culinary Arts/Chef Training, A
Dietetics/Dieticians, A
Drafting and Design Technology/Technician, A
Ecology, A
Electrical, Electronic and Communications
    Engineering Technology/Technician, A
Emergency Medical Technology/Technician (EMT
    Paramedic), A
Equestrian/Equine Studies, A
Fire Science/Firefighting, A
Fishing and Fisheries Sciences and Management, A
Food Science, A
Forestry, A
Forestry Technology/Technician, A
Health Information/Medical Records
    Administration/Administrator, A
Hospitality Administration/Management, A
Hotel/Motel Administration/Management, A
Industrial Technology/Technician, A
Land Use Planning and
    Management/Development, A
Licensed Practical/Vocational Nurse Training, A
Marketing/Marketing Management, A
Medical Administrative Assistant/Secretary, A
Medical/Clinical Assistant, A
Natural Resources and Conservation, A
Natural Resources Management/Development and
    Policy, A
Nursing - Registered Nurse Training, A
Occupational Therapist Assistant, A
Ophthalmic Laboratory Technology/Technician, A
Parks, Recreation and Leisure Facilities
    Management, A
Physical Therapist Assistant, A
Special Products Marketing Operations, A
Tourism and Travel Services Management, A

Wildlife and Wildlands Science and Management, A

HONDROS COLLEGE

Insurance, A
Real Estate, A

INTERNATIONAL COLLEGE OF BROADCASTING

Audio Engineering, A
Radio and Television, A

ITT TECHNICAL INSTITUTE (DAYTON)

Accounting and Business/Management, A
Business Administration and Management, A
CAD/CADD Drafting and/or Design
  Technology/Technician, A
Computer Programming/Programmer, A
Criminal Justice/Law Enforcement Administration, A
Electrical, Electronic and Communications
  Engineering Technology/Technician, A
System, Networking, and LAN/WAN
  Management/Manager, A
Web Page, Digital/Multimedia and Information
  Resources Design, A
Web/Multimedia Management and Webmaster, A

ITT TECHNICAL INSTITUTE (HILLIARD)

Accounting and Business/Management, A
Business Administration and Management, A
CAD/CADD Drafting and/or Design
  Technology/Technician, A
Criminal Justice/Law Enforcement Administration, A
Electrical, Electronic and Communications
  Engineering Technology/Technician, A
System, Networking, and LAN/WAN
  Management/Manager, A
Web Page, Digital/Multimedia and Information
  Resources Design, A

ITT TECHNICAL INSTITUTE (NORWOOD)

Accounting and Business/Management, A
Business Administration and Management, A
CAD/CADD Drafting and/or Design
  Technology/Technician, A
Computer Programming/Programmer, A
Criminal Justice/Law Enforcement Administration, A
Electrical, Electronic and Communications
  Engineering Technology/Technician, A
System, Networking, and LAN/WAN
  Management/Manager, A
Web Page, Digital/Multimedia and Information
  Resources Design, A
Web/Multimedia Management and Webmaster, A

ITT TECHNICAL INSTITUTE (STRONGSVILLE)

Accounting and Business/Management, A
Business Administration and Management, A
CAD/CADD Drafting and/or Design
  Technology/Technician, A
Computer Programming/Programmer, A
Criminal Justice/Law Enforcement Administration, A
Electrical, Electronic and Communications
  Engineering Technology/Technician, A
System, Networking, and LAN/WAN
  Management/Manager, A
Web Page, Digital/Multimedia and Information
  Resources Design, A
Web/Multimedia Management and Webmaster, A

ITT TECHNICAL INSTITUTE (WARRENSVILLE HEIGHTS)

Business Administration and Management, A
CAD/CADD Drafting and/or Design
  Technology/Technician, A
Criminal Justice/Law Enforcement Administration, A
Electrical, Electronic and Communications
  Engineering Technology/Technician, A
System, Networking, and LAN/WAN
  Management/Manager, A

Web Page, Digital/Multimedia and Information
  Resources Design, A

ITT TECHNICAL INSTITUTE (YOUNGSTOWN)

CAD/CADD Drafting and/or Design
  Technology/Technician, A
Computer and Information Systems Security, A
Computer Programming/Programmer, A
System, Networking, and LAN/WAN
  Management/Manager, A
Web Page, Digital/Multimedia and Information
  Resources Design, A
Web/Multimedia Management and Webmaster, A

JAMES A. RHODES STATE COLLEGE

Accounting, A
Administrative Assistant and Secretarial Science, A
Artificial Intelligence and Robotics, A
Business Administration and Management, A
Child Development, A
Civil Engineering Technology/Technician, A
Computer Graphics, A
Computer Programming/Programmer, A
Consumer Merchandising/Retailing Management, A
Corrections, A
Criminal Justice/Police Science, A
Dental Hygiene/Hygienist, A
Drafting and Design Technology/Technician, A
Drafting/Design Engineering
  Technologies/Technicians, A
Electrical, Electronic and Communications
  Engineering Technology/Technician, A
Emergency Medical Technology/Technician (EMT
  Paramedic), A
Engineering Technology, A
Fashion Merchandising, A
Finance, A
Human Services, A
Industrial Radiologic Technology/Technician, A
Industrial Technology/Technician, A
Information Science/Studies, A
Information Technology, A
Legal Administrative Assistant/Secretary, A
Legal Assistant/Paralegal, A
Marketing/Marketing Management, A
Mechanical Engineering/Mechanical
  Technology/Technician, A
Medical Administrative Assistant/Secretary, A
Nursing - Registered Nurse Training, A
Physical Therapy/Therapist, A
Quality Control Technology/Technician, A
Respiratory Care Therapy/Therapist, A

JEFFERSON COMMUNITY COLLEGE

Accounting, A
Administrative Assistant and Secretarial Science, A
Business Administration and Management, A
Child Care and Support Services Management, A
Computer Engineering, A
Consumer Merchandising/Retailing Management, A
Corrections, A
Criminal Justice/Police Science, A
Data Processing and Data Processing
  Technology/Technician, A
Dental Assisting/Assistant, A
Developmental and Child Psychology, A
Drafting and Design Technology/Technician, A
Electrical, Electronic and Communications
  Engineering Technology/Technician, A
Emergency Medical Technology/Technician (EMT
  Paramedic), A
Finance, A
Industrial Radiologic Technology/Technician, A
Industrial Technology/Technician, A
Legal Administrative Assistant/Secretary, A
Licensed Practical/Vocational Nurse Training, A
Mechanical Engineering/Mechanical
  Technology/Technician, A
Medical Administrative Assistant/Secretary, A
Medical/Clinical Assistant, A
Real Estate, A
Respiratory Care Therapy/Therapist, A

Special Products Marketing Operations, A

JOHN CARROLL UNIVERSITY

Accounting, BM
Art History, Criticism and Conservation, B
Asian Studies/Civilization, B
Biological and Biomedical Sciences, M
Biological and Physical Sciences, B
Biology/Biological Sciences, B
Business Administration and Management, B
Business Administration, Management and
  Operations, M
Chemistry, BM
Classics and Classical
  Languages, Literatures, and Linguistics, B
Comparative Literature, B
Computer Science, B
Corporate and Organizational Communication, M
Counseling Psychology, MO
Counselor Education/School Counseling and
  Guidance Services, MO
Early Childhood Education and Teaching, M
East Asian Studies, B
Economics, B
Education, BM
Educational Administration and Supervision, M
Educational Psychology, M
Elementary Education and Teaching, B
Engineering Physics, B
English, M
English Language and Literature, B
Environmental Studies, B
Finance, B
French Language and Literature, B
German Language and Literature, B
Gerontology, B
History, BM
Humanities/Humanistic Studies, BM
Interdisciplinary Studies, B
International Economics, B
International Relations and Affairs, B
Kindergarten/PreSchool Education and Teaching, B
Latin Language and Literature, B
Marketing/Marketing Management, B
Mass Communication/Media Studies, B
Mathematics, BM
Middle School Education, M
Modern Greek Language and Literature, B
Neuroscience, B
Philosophy, B
Physical Education Teaching and Coaching, B
Physics, BM
Political Science and Government, B
Pre-Dentistry Studies, B
Pre-Law Studies, B
Pre-Medicine/Pre-Medical Studies, B
Pre-Veterinary Studies, B
Psychology, B
Public Administration, B
Religion/Religious Studies, BM
Religious Education, B
Secondary Education and Teaching, BM
Sociology, B
Spanish Language and Literature, B
Special Education and Teaching, B
Teacher Education, Multiple Levels, B

KENT STATE UNIVERSITY

Accounting, BMD
Acting, B
Advertising, B
Aeronautics/Aviation/Aerospace Science and
  Technology, B
African-American/Black Studies, B
American/United States Studies/Civilization, B
Analytical Chemistry, MD
Anthropology, BM
Applied Mathematics, BMD
Architecture, BMO
Area Studies, B
Area, Ethnic, Cultural, and Gender Studies, B
Art Education, M
Art History, Criticism and Conservation, BM
Art Teacher Education, B
Asian Languages, M
Athletic Training and Sports Medicine, B

Audiology/Audiologist and Speech-Language Pathology/Pathologist, B
Aviation/Airway Management and Operations, B
Biochemistry, MD
Biological and Biomedical Sciences, BMD
Biological Anthropology, D
Biology/Biological Sciences, B
BioTechnology, B
Botany/Plant Biology, BM
Business Administration and Management, AB
Business Administration, Management and Operations, M
Business Teacher Education, B
Business/Managerial Economics, B
Cell Biology and Anatomy, MD
Central/Middle and Eastern European Studies, B
Ceramic Arts and Ceramics, B
Chemistry, BMD
Chemistry Teacher Education, B
Classics and Classical Languages, Literatures, and Linguistics, BM
Clinical Laboratory Science/Medical Technology/Technologist, B
Clinical Psychology, MD
Commercial and Advertising Art, B
Communication and Media Studies, MD
Communication Disorders, MD
Communication Theory, MD
Comparative Literature, M
Composition, MD
Computer Programming, Specific Applications, AB
Computer Programming/Programmer, AB
Computer Science, BMD
Computer Systems Analysis/Analyst, B
Counseling Psychology, M
Counselor Education/School Counseling and Guidance Services, MDO
Crafts, M
Crafts/Craft Design, Folk Art and Artisanry, B
Criminology, M
Curriculum and Instruction, MDO
Dance, B
Digital Communication and Media/Multimedia, B
Drama and Dramatics/Theatre Arts, B
Early Childhood Education and Teaching, M
Ecology, BMD
Economics, BM
Education, ABMDO
Education/Teaching of the Gifted and Talented, M
Educational Administration and Supervision, MDO
Educational Leadership and Administration, MDO
Educational Measurement and Evaluation, MD
Educational Media/Instructional Technology, M
Educational Psychology, MD
Engineering and Applied Sciences, M
English, MD
English as a Second Language, M
English Education, M
English Language and Literature, B
English/Language Arts Teacher Education, B
Environmental Design/Architecture, BO
Ethnic and Cultural Studies, B
Ethnomusicology, MD
Exercise and Sports Science, MD
Experimental Psychology, MD
Family and Consumer Sciences/Home Economics Teacher Education, B
Family and Consumer Sciences/Human Sciences, BMO
Fashion Merchandising, B
Fashion/Apparel Design, B
Finance, B
Finance and Banking, D
Financial Engineering, M
Fine Arts and Art Studies, M
Fine/Studio Arts, B
Foods, Nutrition, and Related Services, B
Foods, Nutrition, and Wellness Studies, B
Foreign Language Teacher Education, B
Foundations and Philosophy of Education, MD
French Language and Literature, BM
French Language Teacher Education, B
General Studies, B
Geography, BMD
Geology/Earth Science, BMD
German Language and Literature, BM

Gerontology, MO
Graphic Design, M
Health and Medical Administrative Services, AB
Health Education, MD
Health Services/Allied Health/Health Sciences, B
Health Teacher Education, B
Higher Education/Higher Education Administration, MDO
History, BMD
Hospitality Administration/Management, B
Human Development, D
Human Development and Family Studies, B
Human Nutrition, B
Illustration, M
Industrial Engineering, B
Industrial Technology/Technician, AB
Information Science/Studies, M
Inorganic Chemistry, MD
Interior Design, B
International Relations and Affairs, B
Journalism, BM
Junior High/Intermediate/Middle School Education and Teaching, B
Kindergarten/PreSchool Education and Teaching, B
Kinesiology and Exercise Science, B
Latin American Studies, B
Latin Language and Literature, B
Latin Teacher Education, B
Liberal Arts and Sciences Studies and Humanities, AB
Liberal Studies, M
Library Science, M
Linguistics of ASL and Other Sign Languages, B
Marketing, D
Marketing/Marketing Management, B
Mass Communication/Media Studies, BM
Mathematics, BMD
Metal and Jewelry Arts, B
Middle School Education, M
Molecular Biology, MD
Multi-/Interdisciplinary Studies, B
Music, BMD
Music Performance, B
Music Teacher Education, BMD
Music Theory and Composition, MD
Musicology and Ethnomusicology, MD
Natural Resources and Conservation, B
Neuroscience, MD
Nursing, MD
Nursing - Registered Nurse Training, AB
Nursing Administration, M
Nursing Education, M
Nutritional Sciences, M
Operations Management and Supervision, B
Organic Chemistry, MD
Parks, Recreation and Leisure Facilities Management, B
Peace Studies and Conflict Resolution, B
Pediatric Nurse/Nursing, M
Performance, M
Pharmacology, MD
Philosophy, BM
Photographic and Film/Video Technology/Technician and Assistant, B
Physical Chemistry, MD
Physical Education Teaching and Coaching, BMD
Physics, BMD
Physiology, MD
Piano and Organ, B
Political Science and Government, BMD
Pre-Dentistry Studies, B
Pre-Medicine/Pre-Medical Studies, B
Printmaking, B
Professional Studies, B
Psychology, BMD
Public Administration, M
Public Health, M
Public Policy Analysis, D
Public Relations/Image Management, B
Radio and Television, B
Radiologic Technology/Science - Radiographer, B
Reading Teacher Education, M
Rehabilitation Counseling, MO
Rhetoric, D
Russian Language and Literature, BM
Russian Studies, B

Sales and Marketing Operations/Marketing and Distribution Teacher Education, B
School Psychology, MDO
Science Teacher Education/General Science Teacher Education, B
Sculpture, B
Secondary Education and Teaching, M
Social Sciences, B
Social Studies Teacher Education, B
Social Work, B
Sociology, BMD
Spanish Language and Literature, BM
Spanish Language Teacher Education, B
Special Education and Teaching, BMDO
Speech and Rhetorical Studies, B
Student Personnel Services, MDO
System Management, D
Technology Teacher Education/Industrial Arts Teacher Education, B
Theater, M
Trade and Industrial Teacher Education, B
Translation and Interpretation, M
Vocational and Technical Education, MO
Writing, M
Zoology/Animal Biology, B

KENT STATE UNIVERSITY, ASHTABULA CAMPUS

Accounting, A
Administrative Assistant and Secretarial Science, A
Business Administration and Management, A
Computer Engineering Technology/Technician, A
Criminal Justice/Police Science, A
Electrical, Electronic and Communications Engineering Technology/Technician, A
Engineering Technology, A
Environmental Studies, A
Finance, A
Human Services, A
Industrial Technology/Technician, A
Kindergarten/PreSchool Education and Teaching, A
Legal Administrative Assistant/Secretary, A
Liberal Arts and Sciences Studies and Humanities, A
Marketing/Marketing Management, A
Materials Sciences, A
Mechanical Engineering/Mechanical Technology/Technician, A
Nursing - Registered Nurse Training, A
Physical Therapy/Therapist, A
Real Estate, A

KENT STATE UNIVERSITY, EAST LIVERPOOL CAMPUS

Accounting, A
Business Administration and Management, A
Computer and Information Sciences, A
Computer Engineering Technology/Technician, A
Criminal Justice/Law Enforcement Administration, A
Legal Administrative Assistant/Secretary, A
Liberal Arts and Sciences Studies and Humanities, A
Nursing - Registered Nurse Training, A
Occupational Therapy/Therapist, A
Physical Therapy/Therapist, A

KENT STATE UNIVERSITY, GEAUGA CAMPUS

Accounting Technology/Technician and Bookkeeping, A
Applied Horticulture/Horticultural Operations, A
Business Administration and Management, AB
Emergency Medical Technology/Technician (EMT Paramedic), A
Industrial Technology/Technician, A
Information Technology, A
Liberal Arts and Sciences Studies and Humanities, A
Nursing Science, B

KENT STATE UNIVERSITY, SALEM CAMPUS

Accounting, A
Administrative Assistant and Secretarial Science, A

Applied Horticulture/Horticultural Business
Services, A
Applied Horticulture/Horticultural Operations, A
Business Administration and Management, AB
Computer and Information Sciences, A
Education, AB
Environmental Studies, A
Family and Consumer Sciences/Human
Sciences, AB
Greenhouse Operations and Management, A
Horticultural Science, A
Human Services, A
Industrial Technology/Technician, A
Kindergarten/PreSchool Education and Teaching, A
Liberal Arts and Sciences Studies and
Humanities, A
Manufacturing Engineering, A
Medical Insurance Coding Specialist/Coder, A
Medical Insurance Specialist/Medical Biller, A
Medical Radiologic Technology/Science - Radiation
Therapist, AB
Nursing - Registered Nurse Training, B
Ornamental Horticulture, A
Turf and Turfgrass Management, A

KENT STATE
UNIVERSITY, STARK CAMPUS

Art/Art Studies, General, A
Biological and Physical Sciences, A
Business Administration and Management, A
Education, A
Interdisciplinary Studies, B
Liberal Arts and Sciences Studies and
Humanities, A

KENT STATE
UNIVERSITY, TRUMBULL CAMPUS

Automobile/Automotive Mechanics
Technology/Technician, A
Business Administration and Management, AB
Computer Engineering Technology/Technician, A
Criminal Justice/Law Enforcement
Administration, AB
Electrical, Electronic and Communications
Engineering Technology/Technician, A
English Language and Literature, B
Environmental Engineering
Technology/Environmental Technology, A
General Studies, B
Industrial Technology/Technician, AB
Liberal Arts and Sciences Studies and
Humanities, A
Mechanical Engineering/Mechanical
Technology/Technician, A
Nursing Science, B

KENT STATE
UNIVERSITY, TUSCARAWAS CAMPUS

Accounting, A
Administrative Assistant and Secretarial Science, A
Animation, Interactive Technology, Video Graphics
and Special Effects, A
Business Administration and Management, AB
Communications Technology/Technician, A
Computer Engineering Technology/Technician, A
Criminal Justice/Police Science, AB
Early Childhood Education and Teaching, A
Electrical, Electronic and Communications
Engineering Technology/Technician, A
Engineering Technology, A
Environmental Studies, A
Industrial Technology/Technician, AB
Liberal Arts and Sciences Studies and
Humanities, AB
Mechanical Engineering/Mechanical
Technology/Technician, A
Nursing - Registered Nurse Training, AB

KENYON COLLEGE

African Studies, B
African-American/Black Studies, B
American/United States Studies/Civilization, B
Ancient/Classical Greek Language and Literature, B
Anthropology, B
Art History, Criticism and Conservation, B

Art/Art Studies, General, B
Asian Studies/Civilization, B
Biochemistry, B
Biology/Biological Sciences, B
Chemistry, B
Classics and Classical
Languages, Literatures, and Linguistics, B
Comparative Literature, B
Creative Writing, B
Dance, B
Drama and Dramatics/Theatre Arts, B
Economics, B
English Language and Literature, B
Environmental Studies, B
Ethnic, Cultural Minority, and Gender Studies, B
Fine/Studio Arts, B
Foreign Languages and Literatures, B
French Language and Literature, B
German Language and Literature, B
History, B
Humanities/Humanistic Studies, B
Interdisciplinary Studies, B
International Relations and Affairs, B
International/Global Studies, B
Latin Language and Literature, B
Law and Legal Studies, B
Mathematics, B
Modern Greek Language and Literature, B
Modern Languages, B
Molecular Biology, B
Multi-/Interdisciplinary Studies, B
Music, B
Natural Sciences, B
Neuroscience, B
Philosophy, B
Physics, B
Political Science and Government, B
Pre-Dentistry Studies, B
Pre-Law Studies, B
Pre-Medicine/Pre-Medical Studies, B
Pre-Veterinary Studies, B
Psychology, B
Public Policy Analysis, B
Religion/Religious Studies, B
Romance Languages, Literatures, and Linguistics, B
Sociology, B
Spanish Language and Literature, B
Statistics, B
Women's Studies, B

KETTERING COLLEGE OF MEDICAL
ARTS

General Studies, A
Nuclear Medical Technology/Technologist, A
Nursing - Registered Nurse Training, A
Physician Assistant, AB
Public Health (MPH, DPH), B
Radiologic Technology/Science - Radiographer, AB
Respiratory Care Therapy/Therapist, AB

LAKE ERIE COLLEGE

Accounting, B
Art/Art Studies, General, B
Biology/Biological Sciences, B
Business Administration and Management, B
Business Administration, Management and
Operations, M
Chemistry, B
Dance, B
Drama and Dramatics/Theatre Arts, B
Education, M
Elementary Education and Teaching, B
English Language and Literature, B
Environmental Studies, B
Equestrian/Equine Studies, B
Fine/Studio Arts, B
French Language and Literature, B
German Language and Literature, B
Health Services Administration, M
International Business/Trade/Commerce, B
Italian Language and Literature, B
Legal Assistant/Paralegal, B
Management, M
Mathematics, B
Modern Languages, B
Music, B

Pre-Dentistry Studies, B
Pre-Law Studies, B
Pre-Medicine/Pre-Medical Studies, B
Pre-Veterinary Studies, B
Psychology, B
Reading Teacher Education, M
Social Sciences, B
Sociology, B
Spanish Language and Literature, B
Teacher Education, Multiple Levels, B

LAKELAND COMMUNITY COLLEGE

Accounting, A
Administrative Assistant and Secretarial Science, A
Biological and Physical Sciences, A
BioTechnology, A
Business Administration and Management, A
Civil Engineering Technology/Technician, A
Clinical/Medical Laboratory Technician, A
Commercial and Advertising Art, A
Computer Graphics, A
Computer Programming, A
Computer Programming, Specific Applications, A
Computer Systems Networking and
Telecommunications, A
Corrections, A
Criminal Justice/Law Enforcement Administration, A
Criminal Justice/Police Science, A
Dental Hygiene/Hygienist, A
Electrical, Electronic and Communications
Engineering Technology/Technician, A
Engineering Technology, A
Fire Science/Firefighting, A
Hospitality Administration/Management, A
Human Services, A
Industrial Technology/Technician, A
Information Science/Studies, A
Kindergarten/PreSchool Education and Teaching, A
Legal Assistant/Paralegal, A
Liberal Arts and Sciences Studies and
Humanities, A
Machine Tool Technology/Machinist, A
Mechanical Engineering/Mechanical
Technology/Technician, A
Nursing - Registered Nurse Training, A
Ophthalmic Laboratory Technology/Technician, A
Radiologic Technology/Science - Radiographer, A
Respiratory Care Therapy/Therapist, A
System Administration/Administrator, A
Tourism and Travel Services Management, A
Web Page, Digital/Multimedia and Information
Resources Design, A
Web/Multimedia Management and Webmaster, A

LAURA AND ALVIN SIEGAL COLLEGE
OF JUDAIC STUDIES

Ancient Near Eastern and Biblical
Languages, Literatures, and Linguistics, B
Bible/Biblical Studies, B
Hebrew Language and Literature, B
History, B
Humanities/Humanistic Studies, M
Jewish/Judaic Studies, BM
Religion/Religious Studies, B
Religious Education, M
Theology/Theological Studies, B

LORAIN COUNTY COMMUNITY
COLLEGE

Accounting, A
Administrative Assistant and Secretarial Science, A
Art/Art Studies, General, A
Artificial Intelligence and Robotics, A
Athletic Training and Sports Medicine, A
Biological and Physical Sciences, A
Biology/Biological Sciences, A
Business Administration and Management, A
Chemistry, A
Civil Engineering Technology/Technician, A
Clinical/Medical Laboratory Technician, A
Computer and Information Sciences, A
Computer Engineering Technology/Technician, A
Computer Programming, A
Computer Programming, Specific Applications, A
Computer
Programming, Vendor/Product Certification, A

Computer Programming/Programmer, A
Computer Science, A
Computer Systems Networking and
    Telecommunications, A
Computer Technology/Computer Systems
    Technology, A
Consumer Merchandising/Retailing Management, A
Corrections, A
Cosmetology and Related Personal Grooming
    Arts, A
Cosmetology/Cosmetologist, A
Criminal Justice/Police Science, A
Data Entry/Microcomputer Applications, A
Diagnostic Medical Sonography/Sonographer and
    Ultrasound Technician, A
Drafting and Design Technology/Technician, A
Drafting/Design Engineering
    Technologies/Technicians, A
Drama and Dramatics/Theatre Arts, A
Education, A
Electrical, Electronic and Communications
    Engineering Technology/Technician, A
Elementary Education and Teaching, A
Engineering, A
Engineering Technology, A
Finance, A
Fire Science/Firefighting, A
History, A
Human Services, A
Industrial Radiologic Technology/Technician, A
Industrial Technology/Technician, A
Information Science/Studies, A
Information Technology, A
Journalism, A
Kindergarten/PreSchool Education and Teaching, A
Liberal Arts and Sciences Studies and
    Humanities, A
Machine Tool Technology/Machinist, A
Marketing/Marketing Management, A
Mass Communication/Media Studies, A
Mathematics, A
Music, A
Nuclear Medical Technology/Technologist, A
Nursing - Registered Nurse Training, A
Pharmacy, A
Physical Education Teaching and Coaching, A
Physical Therapist Assistant, A
Physics, A
Plastics Engineering Technology/Technician, A
Political Science and Government, A
Pre-Engineering, A
Psychology, A
Quality Control Technology/Technician, A
Real Estate, A
Social Sciences, A
Social Work, A
Sociology, A
Sport and Fitness Administration/Management, A
Surgical Technology/Technologist, A
Tourism and Travel Services Management, A
Urban Studies/Affairs, A
Word Processing, A

LOURDES COLLEGE

Accounting, B
Art History, Criticism and Conservation, AB
Art/Art Studies, General, AB
Biology/Biological Sciences, AB
Business Administration and Management, AB
Chemistry, AB
Criminal Justice/Law Enforcement
    Administration, AB
Education, M
Educational Media/Instructional Technology, M
English Language and Literature, AB
History, AB
Junior High/Intermediate/Middle School Education
    and Teaching, B
Kindergarten/PreSchool Education and
    Teaching, AB
Liberal Arts and Sciences Studies and
    Humanities, AB
Management Science, B
Music, A
Natural Sciences, A
Nursing - Registered Nurse Training, B

Organizational Management, M
Pre-Medicine/Pre-Medical Studies, B
Psychology, AB
Religion/Religious Studies, AB
Social Work, B
Sociology, AB

MALONE COLLEGE

Accounting, B
Art Teacher Education, B
Bible/Biblical Studies, B
Biology/Biological Sciences, B
Business Administration and Management, B
Business Administration, Management and
    Operations, BM
Chemistry, B
Clinical Laboratory Science/Medical
    Technology/Technologist, B
Communication, Journalism and Related
    Programs, B
Community Psychology, M
Computer Science, B
Counselor Education/School Counseling and
    Guidance Services, M
Curriculum and Instruction, M
Early Childhood Education and Teaching, B
Education, M
Education/Teaching of Individuals with Specific
    Learning Disabilities, B
Educational Media/Instructional Technology, M
English Language and Literature, B
English/Language Arts Teacher Education, B
Fine/Studio Arts, B
Health and Physical Education, B
Health Teacher Education, B
History, B
Junior High/Intermediate/Middle School Education
    and Teaching, B
Kinesiology and Exercise Science, B
Liberal Arts and Sciences Studies and
    Humanities, B
Mathematics, B
Music, B
Music Teacher Education, B
Nursing, M
Nursing - Advanced Practice, M
Nursing - Registered Nurse Training, B
Parks, Recreation, Leisure and Fitness Studies, B
Pastoral Counseling and Specialized Ministries, B
Pastoral Studies/Counseling, M
Physical Education Teaching and Coaching, B
Political Science and Government, B
Psychology, B
Public Health, B
Public Health Education and Promotion, B
Reading Teacher Education, M
Recording Arts Technology/Technician, B
Religious Education, B
Religious/Sacred Music, B
Science Teacher Education/General Science
    Teacher Education, B
Social Studies Teacher Education, B
Social Work, B
Spanish Language and Literature, B
Spanish Language Teacher Education, B
Special Education and Teaching, M
Sport and Fitness Administration/Management, B
Theology and Religious Vocations, M
Youth Ministry, B
Zoology/Animal Biology, B

MARIETTA COLLEGE

Accounting, B
Art/Art Studies, General, B
Athletic Training and Sports Medicine, B
Biochemistry, B
Biology/Biological Sciences, B
Business Administration and Management, AB
Business/Corporate Communications, B
Chemistry, B
Commercial and Advertising Art, B
Communication Studies/Speech Communication
    and Rhetoric, B
Computer Science, B
Corporate and Organizational Communication, M
Drama and Dramatics/Theatre Arts, B

Economics, B
Education, BM
Elementary Education and Teaching, B
English Language and Literature, B
Environmental Sciences, B
Environmental Studies, B
Fine/Studio Arts, B
Geology/Earth Science, B
Graphic Design, B
History, B
Human Resources Management/Personnel
    Administration, B
Information Science/Studies, B
International Business/Trade/Commerce, B
Journalism, B
Liberal Arts and Sciences Studies and
    Humanities, AB
Liberal Studies, M
Marketing/Marketing Management, B
Mathematics, B
Music, B
Petroleum Engineering, B
Philosophy, B
Physician Assistant, M
Physics, B
Political Science and Government, B
Psychology, BM
Public Relations, Advertising, and Applied
    Communication, B
Radio and Television, B
Secondary Education and Teaching, B
Spanish Language and Literature, B
Speech and Rhetorical Studies, B

MARION TECHNICAL COLLEGE

Accounting, A
Administrative Assistant and Secretarial Science, A
Business Administration and Management, A
Clinical/Medical Laboratory Technician, A
Computer
    Programming, Vendor/Product Certification, A
Computer Software and Media Applications, A
Computer Systems Networking and
    Telecommunications, A
Data Entry/Microcomputer Applications, A
Data Processing and Data Processing
    Technology/Technician, A
Drafting and Design Technology/Technician, A
Electrical, Electronic and Communications
    Engineering Technology/Technician, A
Engineering Technology, A
Finance, A
Human Services, A
Industrial Radiologic Technology/Technician, A
Industrial Technology/Technician, A
Information Technology, A
Legal Assistant/Paralegal, A
Marketing/Marketing Management, A
Mechanical Engineering/Mechanical
    Technology/Technician, A
Medical Administrative Assistant/Secretary, A
Nursing - Registered Nurse Training, A
Physical Therapist Assistant, A
Radiologic Technology/Science - Radiographer, A
Social Work, A
Telecommunications Technology/Technician, A

MEDCENTRAL COLLEGE OF NURSING

Nursing - Registered Nurse Training, B

MERCY COLLEGE OF NORTHWEST OHIO

General Studies, A
Health Information/Medical Records
    Technology/Technician, A
Health/Health Care Administration/Management, B
Massage Therapy/Therapeutic Massage, A
Medical Radiologic Technology/Science - Radiation
    Therapist, A
Nursing - Registered Nurse Training, AB

MIAMI-JACOBS COLLEGE

Accounting, A
Administrative Assistant and Secretarial Science, A
Computer Programming/Programmer, A

Information Science/Studies, A
Information Technology, A
Legal Administrative Assistant/Secretary, A
Medical Administrative Assistant/Secretary, A
Medical/Clinical Assistant, A

MIAMI UNIVERSITY

Accounting, BM
Aerospace, Aeronautical and Astronautical
   Engineering, B
African-American/Black Studies, B
American/United States Studies/Civilization, B
Analytical Chemistry, MD
Ancient/Classical Greek Language and Literature, B
Anthropology, B
Architecture, BM
Art Education, M
Art History, Criticism and Conservation, B
Art Teacher Education, B
Art/Art Studies, General, B
Athletic Training and Sports Medicine, B
Audiology/Audiologist and Speech-Language
   Pathology/Pathologist, B
Biochemistry, BMD
Biology Teacher Education, B
Biology/Biological Sciences, B
Botany/Plant Biology, BMD
Business Administration and Management, B
Business Administration, Management and
   Operations, M
Business/Commerce, B
Business/Managerial Economics, B
Chemical Engineering, B
Chemistry, BMD
Child and Family Studies, M
Child Development, B
City/Urban, Community and Regional Planning, B
Classics and Classical
   Languages, Literatures, and Linguistics, B
Clinical Laboratory Science/Medical
   Technology/Technologist, B
Clinical Psychology, D
Communication and Media Studies, M
Communication Disorders, M
Computer and Information Sciences, B
Computer Systems Analysis/Analyst, B
Creative Writing, B
Curriculum and Instruction, M
Dietetics/Dieticians, B
Drama and Dramatics/Theatre Arts, B
Early Childhood Education and Teaching, M
Economics, BM
Education, MDO
Educational Administration and Supervision, D
Educational Leadership and Administration, M
Educational Psychology, MO
Electrical, Electronics and Communications
   Engineering, B
Elementary Education and Teaching, BM
Engineering and Applied Sciences, MO
Engineering Physics, B
Engineering Technology, B
Engineering/Industrial Management, B
English, MD
English Education, M
English Language and Literature, B
English/Language Arts Teacher Education, B
Environmental Design/Architecture, B
Environmental Sciences, M
Exercise and Sports Science, M
Experimental Psychology, D
Family and Consumer Economics and Related
   Services, B
Family and Consumer Sciences/Home Economics
   Teacher Education, B
Family and Consumer Sciences/Human Sciences, B
Finance, B
Finance and Banking, M
Fine Arts and Art Studies, M
Fine/Studio Arts, B
French Language and Literature, BM
Geography, BM
Geology/Earth Science, BMD
German Language and Literature, B
Gerontology, M
Graphic Design, B

Health and Physical Education, B
Health Teacher Education, B
History, BMD
Human Development and Family Studies, B
Human Resources Management/Personnel
   Administration, B
Industrial Engineering, B
Inorganic Chemistry, MD
Interdisciplinary Studies, B
Interior Design, B
International Relations and Affairs, B
Italian Studies, B
Journalism, B
Junior High/Intermediate/Middle School Education
   and Teaching, B
Kindergarten/PreSchool Education and Teaching, B
Kinesiology and Exercise Science, B
Latin Language and Literature, B
Linguistics, B
Management, M
Management Information Systems and
   Services, BM
Management Science, B
Marketing, M
Marketing/Marketing Management, B
Mass Communication/Media Studies, BM
Mathematics, BM
Mathematics Teacher Education, M
Mechanical Engineering, B
Medical Microbiology and Bacteriology, B
Microbiology, MD
Modern Greek Language and Literature, B
Multi-/Interdisciplinary Studies, B
Music, B
Music Performance, B
Music Teacher Education, BM
Nursing - Registered Nurse Training, B
Operations Management and Supervision, B
Operations Research, BM
Organic Chemistry, MD
Organizational Behavior Studies, B
Paper and Pulp Engineering, M
Performance, M
Philosophy, BM
Physical Chemistry, M
Physical Education Teaching and Coaching, B
Physics, BM
Political Science and Government, BMD
Pre-Dentistry Studies, B
Pre-Law Studies, B
Pre-Medicine/Pre-Medical Studies, B
Pre-Veterinary Studies, B
Psychology, BD
Public Administration, B
Purchasing, Procurement/Acquisitions and
   Contracts Management, B
Reading Teacher Education, M
Religion/Religious Studies, BM
Rhetoric, MD
Russian Language and Literature, B
School Psychology, MO
Science Teacher Education/General Science
   Teacher Education, B
Secondary Education and Teaching, BM
Social Psychology, D
Social Studies Teacher Education, B
Social Work, BM
Sociology, B
Software Engineering, O
Spanish Language and Literature, BM
Special Education and Teaching, BM
Speech and Rhetorical Studies, BM
Speech-Language Pathology/Pathologist, B
Sport and Fitness Administration/Management, B
Statistics, BM
Student Personnel Services, M
Systems Science and Theory, BM
Technical and Business Writing, BM
Theater, B
Women's Studies, B
Wood Science and Wood Products/Pulp and Paper
   Technology, B
Writing, M

Zoology/Animal Biology, BMD

MIAMI UNIVERSITY HAMILTON

Accounting, B
American/United States Studies/Civilization, B
Anthropology, B
Architectural History and Criticism, B
Architecture, B
Art Teacher Education, B
Art/Art Studies, General, B
Athletic Training and Sports Medicine, B
Audiology/Audiologist and Speech-Language
   Pathology/Pathologist, B
Biochemistry, B
Botany/Plant Biology, B
Business Administration and Management, A
Business Administration, Management and
   Operations, B
Business/Commerce, B
Business/Managerial Economics, B
Chemistry, B
Chemistry Teacher Education, B
City/Urban, Community and Regional Planning, B
Classics and Classical
   Languages, Literatures, and Linguistics, B
Clinical Laboratory Science/Medical
   Technology/Technologist, B
Communication Studies/Speech Communication
   and Rhetoric, B
Computer and Information Sciences, B
Computer Engineering, B
Computer Science, B
Computer Systems Analysis/Analyst, B
Computer Technology/Computer Systems
   Technology, A
Creative Writing, B
Dietetics/Dieticians, B
Early Childhood Education and Teaching, B
Econometrics and Quantitative Economics, B
Economics, B
Electrical and Electronic Engineering
   Technologies/Technicians, A
Electromechanical Technology/Electromechanical
   Engineering Technology, B
Engineering Physics, B
Engineering Technology, B
Engineering/Industrial Management, B
English Composition, B
English Language and Literature, B
English/Language Arts Teacher Education, B
Environmental Sciences, B
Environmental Studies, B
Ethnic, Cultural Minority, and Gender Studies, B
Exercise Physiology, B
Finance, B
French Language and Literature, B
French Language Teacher Education, B
General Studies, A
Geography, B
Geology/Earth Science, B
German Language and Literature, B
German Language Teacher Education, B
Gerontology, B
Graphic Design, B
Health Teacher Education, B
History, B
Human Resources Management and Services, B
Interior Design, B
International/Global Studies, B
Journalism, B
Latin Language and Literature, B
Latin Teacher Education, B
Linguistics, B
Management Information Systems and Services, A
Marketing, B
Marketing/Marketing Management, A
Mass Communication/Media Studies, B
Mathematics, B
Mathematics and Statistics, B
Mathematics Teacher Education, B
Mechanical Engineering/Mechanical
   Technology/Technician, AB
Microbiology, B
Multi-/Interdisciplinary Studies, B
Music, B
Music Teacher Education, B

Office Management and Supervision, B
Philosophy, B
Physical Education Teaching and Coaching, B
Physics, B
Physics Teacher Education, B
Political Science and Government, B
Psychology, B
Public Administration, B
Purchasing, Procurement/Acquisitions and
   Contracts Management, A
Real Estate, A
Russian Language and Literature, B
Science Teacher Education/General Science
   Teacher Education, B
Social Studies Teacher Education, B
Social Work, B
Sociology, B
Spanish Language and Literature, B
Spanish Language Teacher Education, B
Special Education and Teaching, B
Speech-Language Pathology/Pathologist, B
Statistics, B
Teacher Education, Multiple Levels, B
Technical and Business Writing, B
Theatre/Theatre Arts Management, B
Work and Family Studies, B
Zoology/Animal Biology, B

MIAMI UNIVERSITY-MIDDLETOWN CAMPUS

Accounting, A
Administrative Assistant and Secretarial Science, A
Anthropology, A
Art/Art Studies, General, A
Biological and Physical Sciences, A
Botany/Plant Biology, A
Business Administration and Management, A
Business/Commerce, A
Business/Managerial Economics, A
Chemical Engineering, A
Chemistry, A
Communication Studies/Speech Communication
   and Rhetoric, A
Computer and Information Sciences, A
Computer Engineering Technology/Technician, A
Computer Science, A
Economics, A
Education, A
Electrical, Electronic and Communications
   Engineering Technology/Technician, A
Electromechanical Technology/Electromechanical
   Engineering Technology, A
Elementary Education and Teaching, A
Engineering, A
Engineering Technology, AB
English Language and Literature, A
Geography, A
History, A
Industrial Technology/Technician, A
Information Science/Studies, A
Interdisciplinary Studies, A
Kindergarten/PreSchool Education and Teaching, A
Legal Administrative Assistant/Secretary, A
Liberal Arts and Sciences Studies and
   Humanities, A
Management Information Systems and Services, A
Marketing/Marketing Management, A
Mass Communication/Media Studies, A
Mathematics, A
Mechanical Engineering/Mechanical
   Technology/Technician, A
Medical Administrative Assistant/Secretary, A
Nursing - Registered Nurse Training, AB
Office Management and Supervision, A
Philosophy, A
Physics, A
Political Science and Government, A
Pre-Engineering, A
Psychology, A
Real Estate, A
Social Sciences, A
Social Work, A
Sociology, A
Spanish Language and Literature, A
Systems Science and Theory, A

Zoology/Animal Biology, A

MOUNT CARMEL COLLEGE OF NURSING

Nursing, M
Nursing - Adult, M
Nursing Education, M

MOUNT UNION COLLEGE

Accounting, B
American/United States Studies/Civilization, B
Art/Art Studies, General, B
Asian Studies/Civilization, B
Astronomy, B
Athletic Training and Sports Medicine, B
Biochemistry, Biophysics and Molecular Biology, B
Biology/Biological Sciences, B
Business Administration and Management, B
Chemistry, B
Communication Studies/Speech Communication
   and Rhetoric, B
Computer Science, B
Design and Visual Communications, B
Drama and Dramatics/Theatre Arts, B
Early Childhood Education and Teaching, B
Economics, B
English Composition, B
English Language and Literature, B
Environmental Biology, B
French Language and Literature, B
Geology/Earth Science, B
German Language and Literature, B
History, B
Information Science/Studies, B
Interdisciplinary Studies, B
International Business/Trade/Commerce, B
Japanese Language and Literature, B
Junior High/Intermediate/Middle School Education
   and Teaching, B
Kinesiology and Exercise Science, B
Mass Communication/Media Studies, B
Mathematics, B
Music, B
Music Performance, B
Music Teacher Education, B
Philosophy, B
Physical Education Teaching and Coaching, B
Physics, B
Political Science and Government, B
Psychology, B
Religion/Religious Studies, B
Sociology, B
Spanish Language and Literature, B
Sport and Fitness Administration/Management, B

MOUNT VERNON NAZARENE UNIVERSITY

Accounting, B
Art Teacher Education, B
Art/Art Studies, General, B
Bible/Biblical Studies, B
Biological and Physical Sciences, B
Biology/Biological Sciences, B
Broadcast Journalism, B
Business Teacher Education, B
Business/Commerce, AB
Chemistry, B
Child Care and Support Services Management, A
Clinical Laboratory Science/Medical
   Technology/Technologist, B
Communication Studies/Speech Communication
   and Rhetoric, B
Computer and Information Sciences, B
Criminal Justice/Law Enforcement Administration, B
Data Processing and Data Processing
   Technology/Technician, B
Drama and Dramatics/Theatre Arts, B
Early Childhood Education and Teaching, B
Education, BM
Elementary Education and Teaching, B
English Language and Literature, B
English/Language Arts Teacher Education, B
Family and Consumer Sciences/Home Economics
   Teacher Education, B
Family and Consumer Sciences/Human
   Sciences, AB

Fine Arts and Art Studies, B
General Studies, A
Graphic Design, B
Health and Physical Education, A
Health Teacher Education, B
History, B
Human Services, A
Journalism, B
Junior High/Intermediate/Middle School Education
   and Teaching, B
Kindergarten/PreSchool Education and Teaching, B
Kinesiology and Exercise Science, B
Management, M
Marketing/Marketing Management, B
Mathematics, B
Mathematics Teacher Education, B
Music, AB
Music Teacher Education, B
Natural Resources and Conservation, B
Philosophy, B
Physical Education Teaching and Coaching, B
Physical Therapy/Therapist, B
Pre-Dentistry Studies, B
Pre-Law Studies, B
Pre-Medicine/Pre-Medical Studies, B
Pre-Pharmacy Studies, B
Pre-Veterinary Studies, B
Psychology, B
Religious Education, B
Religious/Sacred Music, AB
Science Teacher Education/General Science
   Teacher Education, B
Secondary Education and Teaching, B
Social Sciences, B
Social Studies Teacher Education, B
Social Work, B
Sociology, B
Spanish Language and Literature, B
Spanish Language Teacher Education, B
Special Education and Teaching, B
Sport and Fitness Administration/Management, B
Theology and Religious Vocations, M
Theology/Theological Studies, B
Youth Ministry, B

MUSKINGUM COLLEGE

Accounting, B
American/United States Studies/Civilization, B
Applied Art, B
Art Teacher Education, B
Art/Art Studies, General, B
Biology/Biological Sciences, B
Broadcast Journalism, B
Business Administration and Management, B
Business Teacher Education, B
Chemistry, B
Clinical Laboratory Science/Medical
   Technology/Technologist, B
Computer Science, B
Criminal Justice/Law Enforcement Administration, B
Drama and Dramatics/Theatre Arts, B
Early Childhood Education and Teaching, B
Economics, B
Education, BM
Elementary Education and Teaching, B
English Language and Literature, B
Environmental Sciences, B
Environmental Studies, B
French Language and Literature, B
Geology/Earth Science, B
German Language and Literature, B
Health Teacher Education, B
History, B
Humanities/Humanistic Studies, B
Interdisciplinary Studies, B
International Business/Trade/Commerce, B
International Relations and Affairs, B
Journalism, B
Junior High/Intermediate/Middle School Education
   and Teaching, B
Kindergarten/PreSchool Education and Teaching, B
Mass Communication/Media Studies, B
Mathematics, B
Molecular Biology, B
Music, B
Music Teacher Education, B

Natural Resources and Conservation, B
Neuroscience, B
Philosophy, B
Physical Education Teaching and Coaching, B
Physics, B
Political Science and Government, B
Pre-Dentistry Studies, B
Pre-Law Studies, B
Pre-Medicine/Pre-Medical Studies, B
Pre-Pharmacy Studies, B
Pre-Veterinary Studies, B
Psychology, B
Public Policy Analysis, B
Radio and Television, B
Religion/Religious Studies, B
Science Teacher Education/General Science
   Teacher Education, B
Secondary Education and Teaching, B
Social Sciences, B
Sociology, B
Spanish Language and Literature, B
Special Education and Teaching, B

NORTH CENTRAL STATE COLLEGE

Accounting, A
Administrative Assistant and Secretarial Science, A
Business Administration and Management, A
Computer Systems Networking and
   Telecommunications, A
Criminal Justice/Law Enforcement Administration, A
Criminal Justice/Safety Studies, A
Drafting and Design Technology/Technician, A
Electrical, Electronic and Communications
   Engineering Technology/Technician, A
Finance, A
Heating, Air Conditioning, Ventilation and
   Refrigeration Maintenance
   Technology/Technician, A
Human Services, A
Industrial Technology/Technician, A
Information Science/Studies, A
Kindergarten/PreSchool Education and Teaching, A
Legal Assistant/Paralegal, A
Machine Tool Technology/Machinist, A
Mechanical Engineering/Mechanical
   Technology/Technician, A
Nursing - Registered Nurse Training, A
Operations Management and Supervision, A
Pharmacy Technician/Assistant, A
Physical Therapist Assistant, A
Quality Control Technology/Technician, A
Radiologic Technology/Science - Radiographer, A
Respiratory Care Therapy/Therapist, A
Therapeutic Recreation/Recreational Therapy, A
Welding Technology/Welder, A

NORTHWEST STATE COMMUNITY
COLLEGE

Accounting, A
Business Administration and Management, A
Business, Management, Marketing, and Related
   Support Services, A
Business/Commerce, A
Child Development, A
Computer Programming/Programmer, A
Corrections, A
Criminal Justice/Law Enforcement Administration, A
Criminal Justice/Police Science, A
Criminal Justice/Safety Studies, A
Design and Visual Communications, A
Education, A
Electrical, Electronic and Communications
   Engineering Technology/Technician, A
Engineering, A
Executive Assistant/Executive Secretary, A
Health Professions and Related Clinical Sciences, A
Human Development and Family Studies, A
Legal Administrative Assistant/Secretary, A
Legal Assistant/Paralegal, A
Machine Tool Technology/Machinist, A
Marketing/Marketing Management, A
Mechanical Engineering, A
Mechanical Engineering/Mechanical
   Technology/Technician, A
Medical Administrative Assistant/Secretary, A
Nursing - Registered Nurse Training, A

Plastics Engineering Technology/Technician, A
Precision Metal Working, A
Quality Control Technology/Technician, A
Sheet Metal Technology/Sheetworking, A
Social Work, A
Tool and Die Technology/Technician, A
Transportation/Transportation Management, A

NOTRE DAME COLLEGE

Accounting, BO
Art Teacher Education, B
Art/Art Studies, General, B
Biochemistry, B
Biology/Biological Sciences, B
Business Administration and Management, AB
Chemistry, B
Communication Studies/Speech Communication
   and Rhetoric, B
Early Childhood Education and Teaching, B
Education, O
Education/Teaching of Individuals with Specific
   Learning Disabilities, B
Elementary Education and Teaching, B
English Language and Literature, B
Environmental Sciences, B
Finance and Banking, O
Fine/Studio Arts, B
Graphic Communications, B
History, B
Human Resources Management/Personnel
   Administration, B
Information Science/Studies, B
Junior High/Intermediate/Middle School Education
   and Teaching, B
Kindergarten/PreSchool Education and Teaching, B
Management, O
Management Information Systems and Services, O
Marketing/Marketing Management, B
Mathematics, B
Multi-/Interdisciplinary Studies, B
Pastoral Studies/Counseling, ABO
Political Science and Government, B
Pre-Law Studies, B
Pre-Medicine/Pre-Medical Studies, B
Psychology, B
Public Administration, B
Public Relations, Advertising, and Applied
   Communication, B
Reading Teacher Education, M
Spanish Language Teacher Education, B
Special Education and Teaching, M
Sport and Fitness Administration/Management, B
Theology/Theological Studies, B

OBERLIN COLLEGE

African-American/Black Studies, B
Anthropology, B
Archeology, B
Art History, Criticism and Conservation, B
Art/Art Studies, General, B
Biochemistry, B
Biology/Biological Sciences, B
Chemistry, B
Classics and Classical
   Languages, Literatures, and Linguistics, B
Comparative Literature, B
Computer Science, B
Creative Writing, B
Dance, B
Drama and Dramatics/Theatre Arts, B
East Asian Studies, B
Ecology, B
Economics, B
English Language and Literature, B
Environmental Studies, B
Fine/Studio Arts, B
French Language and Literature, B
Geology/Earth Science, B
German Language and Literature, B
History, B
Interdisciplinary Studies, B
Jazz/Jazz Studies, B
Jewish/Judaic Studies, B
Latin American Studies, B
Latin Language and Literature, B
Law and Legal Studies, B

Mathematics, B
Modern Greek Language and Literature, B
Music, BM
Music History, Literature, and Theory, B
Music Teacher Education, B
Music Theory and Composition, B
Near and Middle Eastern Studies, B
Neuroscience, B
Philosophy, B
Physics, B
Physiological Psychology/Psychobiology, B
Piano and Organ, B
Political Science and Government, B
Psychology, B
Religion/Religious Studies, B
Romance Languages, Literatures, and Linguistics, B
Russian Language and Literature, B
Russian Studies, B
Sociology, B
Spanish Language and Literature, B
Violin, Viola, Guitar and Other Stringed
   Instruments, B
Voice and Opera, B
Wind and Percussion Instruments, B
Women's Studies, B

OHIO BUSINESS COLLEGE (LORAIN)

Accounting, A
Administrative Assistant and Secretarial Science, A
Business Administration and Management, A
Computer and Information Sciences, A
Legal Administrative Assistant/Secretary, A
Medical Administrative Assistant/Secretary, A

OHIO BUSINESS COLLEGE
(SANDUSKY)

Accounting, A
Administrative Assistant and Secretarial Science, A
Business Administration and Management, A
Computer Programming/Programmer, A
Data Entry/Microcomputer Applications, A
Health/Medical Claims Examiner, A
Legal Administrative Assistant/Secretary, A
Medical Administrative Assistant/Secretary, A

OHIO DOMINICAN UNIVERSITY

Accounting, B
Art Teacher Education, B
Biology/Biological Sciences, B
Business Administration and Management, AB
Business/Corporate Communications, B
Chemistry, AB
Chemistry Teacher Education, B
Communication Studies/Speech Communication
   and Rhetoric, B
Computer and Information Sciences, B
Computer Science, B
Criminal Justice/Law Enforcement Administration, B
Early Childhood Education and Teaching, B
Economics, B
English Language and Literature, B
Finance, B
Fine/Studio Arts, B
Foreign Language Teacher Education, B
General Studies, AB
Gerontology, A
Graphic Design, B
History, B
Information Science/Studies, B
Interdisciplinary Studies, AB
International Business/Trade/Commerce, B
Junior High/Intermediate/Middle School Education
   and Teaching, B
Kindergarten/PreSchool Education and Teaching, B
Law and Legal Studies, A
Liberal Arts and Sciences Studies and
   Humanities, B
Library Assistant/Technician, A
Mathematics, B
Mathematics Teacher Education, B
Peace Studies and Conflict Resolution, B
Philosophy, B
Physics Teacher Education, B
Political Science and Government, B
Psychology, B
Public Relations/Image Management, B

School Librarian/School Library Media Specialist, B
Science Teacher Education/General Science
  Teacher Education, B
Secondary Education and Teaching, B
Social Studies Teacher Education, B
Social Work, B
Sociology, B
Special Education and Teaching, B
Sport and Fitness Administration/Management, B
Teacher Education, Multiple Levels, B
Teaching English as a Second or Foreign
  Language/ESL Language Instructor, B
Theology/Theological Studies, AB

OHIO INSTITUTE OF PHOTOGRAPHY AND TECHNOLOGY

Criminal Justice/Law Enforcement Administration, A
Graphic Design, A
Medical Office Management/Administration, A
Photography, A

OHIO NORTHERN UNIVERSITY

Accounting, B
Art Teacher Education, B
Art/Art Studies, General, B
Athletic Training and Sports Medicine, B
Biochemistry, B
Biology Teacher Education, B
Biology/Biological Sciences, B
Business Administration and Management, B
Business/Commerce, B
Ceramic Arts and Ceramics, B
Chemistry, B
Chemistry Teacher Education, B
Civil Engineering, B
Clinical Laboratory Science/Medical
  Technology/Technologist, B
Commercial and Advertising Art, B
Communication Studies/Speech Communication
  and Rhetoric, B
Communication, Journalism and Related
  Programs, B
Computer Engineering, B
Computer Science, B
Creative Writing, B
Criminal Justice/Law Enforcement Administration, B
Criminal Justice/Police Science, B
Criminal Justice/Safety Studies, B
Design and Visual Communications, B
Drama and Dramatics/Theatre Arts, B
Early Childhood Education and Teaching, B
Education, B
Electrical, Electronics and Communications
  Engineering, B
Elementary Education and Teaching, B
Engineering, B
English Language and Literature, B
English/Language Arts Teacher Education, B
Environmental Studies, B
Fine/Studio Arts, B
Foreign Language Teacher Education, B
French Language and Literature, B
French Language Teacher Education, B
General Studies, B
German Language Teacher Education, B
Germanic Languages, Literatures, and Linguistics, B
Graphic Design, B
Health and Physical Education, B
Health and Physical Education/Fitness, B
Health Teacher Education, B
History, B
History Teacher Education, B
Industrial Technology/Technician, B
International Business/Trade/Commerce, B
International Relations and Affairs, B
Journalism, B
Junior High/Intermediate/Middle School Education
  and Teaching, B
Kindergarten/PreSchool Education and Teaching, B
Kinesiology and Exercise Science, B
Law and Legal Studies, P
Management Science, B
Management Sciences and Quantitative Methods, B
Mass Communication/Media Studies, B
Mathematics, B
Mathematics Teacher Education, B

Mechanical Engineering, B
Medicinal and Pharmaceutical Chemistry, B
Molecular Biology, B
Music, B
Music Management and Merchandising, B
Music Performance, B
Music Teacher Education, B
Organizational Communication, B
Painting, B
Pharmacy, BP
Pharmacy, Pharmaceutical Sciences, and
  Administration, B
Philosophy, B
Physical Education Teaching and Coaching, B
Physics, B
Physics Teacher Education, B
Political Science and Government, B
Pre-Dentistry Studies, B
Pre-Law Studies, B
Pre-Medicine/Pre-Medical Studies, B
Pre-Theology/Pre-Ministerial Studies, B
Pre-Veterinary Studies, B
Printmaking, B
Psychology, B
Public Relations/Image Management, B
Radio and Television, B
Religion/Religious Studies, B
Science Teacher Education/General Science
  Teacher Education, B
Sculpture, B
Secondary Education and Teaching, B
Social Studies Teacher Education, B
Sociology, B
Spanish Language and Literature, B
Spanish Language Teacher Education, B
Sport and Fitness Administration/Management, B
Statistics, B
Teacher Education, Multiple Levels, B
Technical and Business Writing, B
Technology Education/Industrial Arts, B
Theatre/Theatre Arts Management, B
Visual and Performing Arts, B

THE OHIO STATE UNIVERSITY

Accounting, BMD
Actuarial Science, B
Aerospace, Aeronautical and Astronautical
  Engineering, BMD
African Studies, BM
African-American/Black Studies, BM
Agricultural and Food Products Processing, B
Agricultural Business and Management, B
Agricultural Economics, BMD
Agricultural Education, MD
Agricultural Engineering, MD
Agricultural Sciences, MD
Agricultural Teacher Education, B
Agricultural/Biological Engineering and
  Bioengineering, B
Agronomy and Crop Science, B
Agronomy and Soil Sciences, MD
Allied Health and Medical Assisting Services, M
Allopathic Medicine, P
Anatomy, MD
Animal Genetics, B
Animal Sciences, BMD
Anthropology, BMD
Apparel and Textiles, B
Arabic Language and Literature, B
Architecture, BM
Art Education, MD
Art History, Criticism and Conservation, BMD
Art Teacher Education, B
Art/Art Studies, General, B
Arts Management, M
Asian Languages, MD
Asian-American Studies, B
Astronomy, BMD
Athletic Training and Sports Medicine, B
Atmospheric Sciences and Meteorology, MD
Audiology/Audiologist and Speech-Language
  Pathology/Pathologist, B
Aviation/Airway Management and Operations, B
Avionics Maintenance Technology/Technician, B
Biochemistry, BMD
Bioengineering, MD
Biological and Biomedical Sciences, MD

Biological Anthropology, MD
Biology/Biological Sciences, B
Biomedical Engineering, MD
Biophysics, MD
Biopsychology, D
Biostatistics, D
BioTechnology, B
Botany/Plant Biology, B
Business Administration and Management, B
Business Administration, Management and
  Operations, MD
Business Family and Consumer Sciences/Human
  Sciences, B
Business/Managerial Economics, B
Cell Biology and Anatomy, MD
Ceramic Arts and Ceramics, B
Ceramic Sciences and Engineering, B
Chemical Engineering, BMD
Chemistry, BMD
Child and Family Studies, MD
Chinese Language and Literature, B
City/Urban, Community and Regional Planning, B
Civil Engineering, BMD
Classics and Classical
  Languages, Literatures, and Linguistics, BMD
Clinical Laboratory Science/Medical
  Technology/Technologist, B
Clinical Psychology, D
Clothing and Textiles, MD
Cognitive Sciences, D
Commercial and Advertising Art, B
Communication and Media Studies, MD
Communication Disorders, MD
Communication Studies/Speech Communication
  and Rhetoric, B
Communication, Journalism and Related
  Programs, B
Comparative Literature, B
Computer and Information Sciences, B
Computer Engineering, B
Computer Science, BMD
Consumer Economics, MD
Counseling Psychology, D
Creative Writing, B
Criminal Justice/Safety Studies, B
Criminology, B
Dance, BM
Dental Hygiene/Hygienist, B
Dentistry, PO
Design and Visual Communications, B
Development Economics and International
  Development, B
Developmental Biology and Embryology, MD
Developmental Psychology, D
Dietetics/Dieticians, B
Drama and Dance Teacher Education, B
Drama and Dramatics/Theatre Arts, B
Drawing, B
East Asian Studies, B
East European and Russian Studies, M
Ecology, MD
Economics, BMD
Education, MD
Educational Leadership and Administration, MD
Electrical Engineering, MD
Electrical, Electronics and Communications
  Engineering, B
Engineering and Applied Sciences, MD
Engineering Physics, B
English, MD
English Language and Literature, B
Entomology, BMD
Environmental Education, B
Environmental Sciences, MD
Environmental Studies, B
Ethnic and Cultural Studies, B
Ethnic, Cultural Minority, and Gender Studies, B
Evolutionary Biology, MD
Experimental Psychology, D
Family Resource Management Studies, B
Finance, B
Fine Arts and Art Studies, M
Fine/Studio Arts, B
Fishing and Fisheries Sciences and Management, B
Food Engineering, MD
Food Science, B

Food Science and Technology, MD
Food Services Management, MD
Foods, Nutrition, and Wellness Studies, B
Forestry, B
French Language and Literature, BMD
Genetics, MD
Geodetic Sciences, MD
Geography, BMD
Geology/Earth Science, BMD
German Language and Literature, BMD
Health Information/Medical Records
   Administration/Administrator, B
Health Professions and Related Clinical Sciences, B
Health Services Administration, M
Hebrew Language and Literature, B
History, BMD
Home Economics, MD
Home Economics Education, MD
Horticultural Science, BMD
Hospitality Administration/Management, B
Human Development, MD
Human Development and Family Studies, B
Human Resources Management and Services, MD
Human Resources Management/Personnel
   Administration, B
Humanities/Humanistic Studies, B
Immunology, MD
Industrial and Labor Relations, MD
Industrial Design, BM
Industrial Engineering, B
Industrial/Management Engineering, MD
Information Science/Studies, BMD
Insurance, B
Interdisciplinary Studies, MD
Interior Design, BM
International Business/Trade/Commerce, B
International Relations and Affairs, B
Islamic Studies, B
Italian Language and Literature, BMD
Japanese Language and Literature, B
Jazz/Jazz Studies, B
Jewish/Judaic Studies, B
Journalism, BM
Kinesiology and Exercise Science, B
Landscape Architecture, BM
Latin American Studies, B
Law and Legal Studies, PO
Linguistics, BMD
Logistics and Materials Management, B
Management Information Systems and
   Services, BMD
Marketing/Marketing Management, B
Materials Engineering, BMD
Materials Sciences, BMD
Mathematics, BMD
Mathematics and Statistics, B
Mechanical Engineering, BMD
Mechanics, MD
Medical Microbiology and Bacteriology, B
Medical Radiologic Technology/Science - Radiation
   Therapist, B
Medicinal and Pharmaceutical Chemistry, MD
Metallurgical Engineering, BMD
Microbiology, MD
Modern Greek Language and Literature, B
Molecular Biology, MD
Molecular Genetics, MD
Music, BMD
Music History, Literature, and Theory, B
Music Performance, B
Music Teacher Education, B
Music Theory and Composition, B
Natural Resources and Conservation, MD
Natural Resources Management/Development and
   Policy, B
Near and Middle Eastern Languages, M
Near and Middle Eastern Studies, B
Neuroscience, D
Nuclear Engineering, MD
Nursing, MD
Nursing - Registered Nurse Training, B
Nursing Science, B
Nutritional Sciences, MD
Occupational Therapy/Therapist, BM
Operations Management and Supervision, B
Optics/Optical Sciences, MDO

Optometry, P
Oral and Dental Sciences, MDO
Painting, B
Pathobiology, MD
Pathology/Experimental Pathology, M
Peace Studies and Conflict Resolution, B
Pharmaceutical Administration, MD
Pharmaceutical Sciences, MD
Pharmacognosy, MD
Pharmacology, MD
Pharmacy, BP
Philosophy, BMD
Physical Education Teaching and Coaching, BMD
Physical Therapy/Therapist, BM
Physics, BMD
Physiology, MD
Piano and Organ, B
Plant Biology, MD
Plant Pathology/Phytopathology, BMD
Plant Sciences, B
Political Science and Government, BMD
Portuguese Language and Literature, BMD
Printmaking, B
Psychology, BMD
Public Health, MDO
Public Policy Analysis, MD
Radiologic Technology/Science - Radiographer, B
Real Estate, B
Religion/Religious Studies, B
Respiratory Care Therapy/Therapist, B
Rural Sociology, MD
Russian Language and Literature, B
Russian Studies, B
Sculpture, B
Slavic Languages, Literatures, and Linguistics, MD
Social Psychology, D
Social Sciences, B
Social Work, BMD
Sociology, BMD
Soil Science and Agronomy, B
Spanish Language and Literature, BMD
Special Education and Teaching, B
Statistics, MD
Survey Technology/Surveying, B
Surveying Engineering, MD
Systems Engineering, BMD
Technical Teacher Education, B
Technology Teacher Education/Industrial Arts
   Teacher Education, B
Theater, MD
Toxicology, MD
Turf and Turfgrass Management, B
Urban and Regional Planning, MD
Veterinary Medicine, PO
Veterinary Sciences, MD
Virology, MD
Vocational and Technical Education, D
Voice and Opera, B
Western European Studies, B
Wildlife and Wildlands Science and Management, B
Women's Studies, BM
Zoology/Animal Biology, B

THE OHIO STATE UNIVERSITY AGRICULTURAL TECHNICAL INSTITUTE

Agribusiness, A
Agricultural Business and Management, A
Agricultural Business Technology, A
Agricultural Communication/Journalism, A
Agricultural Economics, A
Agricultural Mechanization, A
Agricultural Power Machinery Operation, A
Agricultural Teacher Education, A
Agronomy and Crop Science, A
Animal Sciences, A
Animal/Livestock Husbandry and Production, A
Biology Technician/BioTechnology Laboratory
   Technician, A
Building/Construction Site Management/Manager, A
Clinical/Medical Laboratory Technician, A
Construction Engineering Technology/Technician, A
Construction Management, A
Crop Production, A
Dairy Husbandry and Production, A
Dairy Science, A

Environmental Sciences, A
Equestrian/Equine Studies, A
Floriculture/Floristry Operations and Management, A
Greenhouse Operations and Management, A
Health and Medical Laboratory Technologies, A
Heavy Equipment Maintenance
   Technology/Technician, A
Horse Husbandry/Equine Science and
   Management, A
Horticultural Science, A
Hydraulics and Fluid Power Technology, A
Industrial Technology/Technician, A
Landscaping and Groundskeeping, A
Livestock Management, A
Natural Resources Management/Development and
   Policy, A
Plant Nursery Operations and Management, A
Soil Science and Agronomy, A
Turf and Turfgrass Management, A

THE OHIO STATE UNIVERSITY AT LIMA

Biology/Biological Sciences, B
Business Administration and Management, B
Early Childhood Education and Teaching, M
Education, M
Elementary Education and Teaching, B
English Language and Literature, B
Financial Planning and Services, B
Health Services/Allied Health/Health Sciences, B
History, B
Hospitality Administration/Management, B
Liberal Arts and Sciences Studies and
   Humanities, A
Mathematics, B
Middle School Education, M
Psychology, B
Social Work, M

THE OHIO STATE UNIVERSITY-MANSFIELD CAMPUS

Business Administration and Management, B
Early Childhood Education and Teaching, BM
Elementary Education and Teaching, B
English Language and Literature, B
History, B
Kindergarten/PreSchool Education and Teaching, B
Liberal Arts and Sciences Studies and
   Humanities, A
Middle School Education, M
Psychology, B
Social Work, M

THE OHIO STATE UNIVERSITY AT MARION

Business Administration and Management, B
Early Childhood Education and Teaching, M
Education, M
Elementary Education and Teaching, B
English Language and Literature, B
History, B
Liberal Arts and Sciences Studies and
   Humanities, A
Middle School Education, M
Nursing, MD
Psychology, B

THE OHIO STATE UNIVERSITY-NEWARK CAMPUS

Business Administration and Management, B
Early Childhood Education and Teaching, M
Education, M
Elementary Education and Teaching, B
English Language and Literature, B
History, B
Liberal Arts and Sciences Studies and
   Humanities, A
Middle School Education, M
Psychology, B
Social Work, M

OHIO UNIVERSITY

Accounting Technology/Technician and
   Bookkeeping, A
Acting, B

Administrative Assistant and Secretarial Science, A
Advertising, B
Aeronautical/Aerospace Engineering
   Technology/Technician, B
Aeronautics/Aviation/Aerospace Science and
   Technology, B
African Languages, Literatures, and Linguistics, B
African Studies, BM
African-American/Black Studies, B
Ancient/Classical Greek Language and Literature, B
Anthropology, B
Apparel and Textiles, B
Applied Economics, M
Applied Mathematics, B
Art Education, M
Art History, Criticism and Conservation, BM
Art Teacher Education, B
Artificial Intelligence and Robotics, D
Asian Studies/Civilization, B
Astronomy, MD
Astrophysics, B
Athletic Training and Sports Medicine, M
Atmospheric Sciences and Meteorology, B
Atomic/Molecular Physics, B
Audiology/Audiologist and Hearing Sciences, A
Audiology/Audiologist and Speech-Language
   Pathology/Pathologist, B
Aviation/Airway Management and Operations, B
Biochemistry, MD
Biological and Biomedical Sciences, MD
Biological and Physical Sciences, A
Biology Teacher Education, B
Biology/Biological Sciences, B
Botany/Plant Biology, B
Broadcast Journalism, B
Business Administration and Management, AB
Business Administration, Management and
   Operations, M
Business, Management, Marketing, and Related
   Support Services, B
Business/Commerce, B
Cell Biology and Anatomy, MD
Cell/Cellular Biology and Histology, B
Ceramic Arts and Ceramics, BM
Chemical Engineering, BMD
Chemistry, B
Child and Family Studies, M
Child Development, AB
Cinematography and Film/Video Production, B
Civil Engineering, BMD
Classics and Classical
   Languages, Literatures, and Linguistics, B
Clinical Psychology, D
Commercial and Advertising Art, B
Communication and Media Studies, MD
Communication Disorders, MD
Communication Disorders Sciences and Services, B
Communication Studies/Speech Communication
   and Rhetoric, B
Communication, Journalism and Related
   Programs, B
Comparative and Interdisciplinary Arts, D
Composition, M
Computer Education, M
Computer Engineering, B
Computer Science, BMD
Conducting, B
Construction Engineering and Management, M
Counselor Education/School Counseling and
   Guidance Services, MD
Creative Writing, B
Criminal Justice/Law Enforcement Administration, B
Criminal Justice/Police Science, A
Criminal Justice/Safety Studies, B
Criminology, B
Curriculum and Instruction, BMD
Dance, B
Design and Applied Arts, B
Design and Visual Communications, B
Directing and Theatrical Production, B
Drama and Dramatics/Theatre Arts, B
Dramatic/Theatre Arts and Stagecraft, B
Drawing, B
Early Childhood Education and Teaching, B
Ecology, MD
Economics, BM

Education, BMD
Education/Teaching of Individuals with Multiple
   Disabilities, B
Educational Administration and Supervision, MD
Educational Leadership and Administration, MD
Educational Measurement and Evaluation, MD
Educational Media/Instructional Technology, D
Electrical Engineering, MD
Electrical, Electronic and Communications
   Engineering Technology/Technician, A
Electrical, Electronics and Communications
   Engineering, B
Elementary and Middle School
   Administration/Principalship, B
Elementary Education and Teaching, B
Engineering, B
Engineering and Applied Sciences, MD
Engineering Technologies/Technicians, B
English, MD
English as a Second Language, M
English Language and Literature, B
Environmental Biology, BMD
Environmental Engineering
   Technology/Environmental Technology, AMD
Environmental Studies, M
Environmental/Environmental Health Engineering, A
Equestrian/Equine Studies, A
European Studies/Civilization, B
Evolutionary Biology, MD
Exercise and Sports Science, MD
Experimental Psychology, D
Family and Consumer Sciences/Human
   Sciences, BM
Family Resource Management Studies, B
Film, Television, and Video Production, M
Film, Television, and Video Theory and Criticism, M
Film/Cinema Studies, B
Finance and Banking, M
Fine Arts and Art Studies, M
Fine/Studio Arts, B
Foods, Nutrition, and Wellness Studies, B
French Language and Literature, BM
French Language Teacher Education, B
General Studies, B
Geochemistry, M
Geography, BM
Geological and Earth Sciences/Geosciences, B
Geology/Earth Science, BM
Geophysics and Seismology, M
Geotechnical Engineering, MD
German Language and Literature, B
German Language Teacher Education, B
Hazardous Materials Information Systems
   Technology/Technician, A
Hazardous Materials Management and Waste
   Technology/Technician, A
Health and Physical Education, B
Health Services Administration, M
Higher Education/Higher Education
   Administration, MD
History, MD
Housing and Human Environments, B
Human Development and Family Studies, B
Human Services, A
Humanities/Humanistic Studies, A
Hydrology and Water Resources Science, M
Industrial and Organizational Psychology, D
Industrial Engineering, B
Industrial Technology/Technician, B
Industrial/Management Engineering, M
Interdisciplinary Studies, BD
International Affairs, M
International Development, M
International Economics, B
International Relations and Affairs, B
Journalism, BMD
Junior High/Intermediate/Middle School Education
   and Teaching, B
Kindergarten/PreSchool Education and Teaching, B
Kinesiology and Exercise Science, B
Latin American Studies, BM
Latin Language and Literature, B
Liberal Arts and Sciences Studies and
   Humanities, AB
Linguistics, BM
Manufacturing Engineering, M

Materials Sciences, D
Mathematics, BMD
Mathematics Teacher Education, BMD
Mechanical Engineering, BMD
Mechanical Engineering/Mechanical
   Technology/Technician, B
Media Studies, MD
Medical Microbiology and Bacteriology, B
Medical/Clinical Assistant, A
Microbiology, MD
Middle School Education, MD
Molecular Biology, MD
Multi-/Interdisciplinary Studies, A
Multilingual and Multicultural Education, M
Music, BMO
Music History, Literature, and Theory, BM
Music Management and Merchandising, B
Music Performance, B
Music Teacher Education, BM
Music Theory and Composition, BM
Music Therapy/Therapist, M
Neuroscience, MD
Nutritional Sciences, M
Osteopathic Medicine, PO
Painting, BM
Parks, Recreation and Leisure Facilities
   Management, B
Parks, Recreation, Leisure and Fitness Studies, B
Performance, MO
Philosophy, BM
Photographic and Film/Video Technology/Technician
   and Assistant, B
Photography, M
Physical Education Teaching and Coaching, BM
Physical Sciences, B
Physical Therapy/Therapist, D
Physics, BMD
Physiology, MD
Piano and Organ, B
Plant Biology, MD
Playwriting and Screenwriting, B
Political Science and Government, BM
Pre-Law Studies, B
Printmaking, BM
Psychology, BD
Public Administration, M
Public Administration and Social Service
   Professions, B
Public Relations/Image Management, B
Radio and Television, AB
Radio and Television Broadcasting
   Technology/Technician, B
Reading Teacher Education, BMD
Recreation and Park Management, M
Rehabilitation Counseling, M
Russian Language and Literature, B
Science Teacher Education/General Science
   Teacher Education, BM
Sculpture, BM
Secondary Education and Teaching, BM
Security and Protective Services, A
Social Sciences, ABM
Social Studies Teacher Education, BD
Social Work, BM
Sociology, BM
South and Southeast Asian Studies, M
Southeast Asian Studies, B
Spanish Language and Literature, BM
Spanish Language Teacher Education, B
Special Education and Teaching, BMD
Speech and Interpersonal Communication, MD
Speech and Rhetorical Studies, B
Sport and Fitness Administration/Management, BM
Structural Engineering, M
Student Personnel Services, M
Systems Engineering, BM
Teacher Education and Professional
   Development, Specific Subject Areas, B
Teaching English as a Second or Foreign
   Language/ESL Language Instructor, B
Technical Theatre/Theatre Design and
   Technology, B
Technology and Public Policy, M
Telecommunications Technology/Technician, B
Theater, M
Theatre Literature, History and Criticism, B

Theatre/Theatre Arts Management, B
Tourism and Travel Services Management, A
Tourism and Travel Services Marketing
  Operations, A
Transportation and Highway Engineering, M
Visual and Performing Arts, B
Voice and Opera, B
Water Resources Engineering, M
Wildlife Biology, B
Zoology/Animal Biology, B

OHIO UNIVERSITY-CHILLICOTHE

Administrative Assistant and Secretarial Science, A
Biological and Physical Sciences, A
Business Administration and Management, AB
Criminal Justice/Law Enforcement Administration, B
Criminal Justice/Police Science, A
Education/Teaching of Individuals with Hearing
  Impairments, Including Deafness, A
Elementary Education and Teaching, B
Environmental Studies, A
Environmental/Environmental Health Engineering, A
Human Services, A
Legal Assistant/Paralegal, A
Liberal Arts and Sciences Studies and
  Humanities, AB
Nursing - Registered Nurse Training, AB

OHIO UNIVERSITY-EASTERN

Accounting, B
Animal Physiology, B
Art Teacher Education, B
Art/Art Studies, General, B
Behavioral Sciences, B
Biological and Physical Sciences, B
Botany/Plant Biology, B
Business Administration and Management, B
Chemical Engineering, B
Chemistry, B
Civil Engineering, B
Clinical Laboratory Science/Medical
  Technology/Technologist, B
Commercial and Advertising Art, B
Comparative Literature, B
Computer Science, B
Consumer Merchandising/Retailing Management, B
Counselor Education/School Counseling and
  Guidance Services, B
Creative Writing, B
Criminal Justice/Law Enforcement Administration, B
Developmental and Child Psychology, B
Drama and Dramatics/Theatre Arts, B
Economics, B
Education, B
Educational Leadership and Administration, B
Electrical, Electronics and Communications
  Engineering, B
Elementary Education and Teaching, B
Engineering, B
English Language and Literature, B
European Studies/Civilization, B
Forestry, B
Geography, B
Geology/Earth Science, B
Health Teacher Education, B
Health/Health Care Administration/Management, B
History, B
Humanities/Humanistic Studies, B
Industrial Engineering, B
Information Science/Studies, B
International Business/Trade/Commerce, B
International Relations and Affairs, B
Journalism, B
Kindergarten/PreSchool Education and Teaching, B
Kinesiology and Exercise Science, B
Liberal Arts and Sciences Studies and
  Humanities, AB
Library Science, B
Linguistics, B
Management Information Systems and Services, B
Marketing/Marketing Management, B
Mass Communication/Media Studies, B
Mathematics, B
Mechanical Engineering, B
Medical Microbiology and Bacteriology, B
Natural Sciences, B

Nursing - Registered Nurse Training, B
Occupational Therapy/Therapist, B
Parks, Recreation and Leisure Facilities
  Management, B
Pharmacy, B
Philosophy, B
Physical Education Teaching and Coaching, B
Physical Sciences, B
Political Science and Government, B
Pre-Dentistry Studies, B
Pre-Law Studies, B
Pre-Medicine/Pre-Medical Studies, B
Psychology, B
Public Administration, B
Public Health (MPH, DPH), B
Public Relations/Image Management, B
Science Teacher Education/General Science
  Teacher Education, B
Social Sciences, B
Social Work, B
Sociology, B
Speech and Rhetorical Studies, B
Telecommunications Technology/Technician, B
Women's Studies, B

OHIO UNIVERSITY-LANCASTER

Accounting, A
Administrative Assistant and Secretarial Science, A
Art/Art Studies, General, A
Biological and Physical Sciences, A
Business Administration and Management, AB
Business Teacher Education, B
Child Development, A
Computer Engineering Technology/Technician, A
Computer Science, A
Criminal Justice/Law Enforcement Administration, B
Criminal Justice/Police Science, A
Drafting and Design Technology/Technician, A
Education, B
Electrical, Electronic and Communications
  Engineering Technology/Technician, A
Elementary Education and Teaching, B
Industrial Design, A
Industrial Technology/Technician, A
Legal Administrative Assistant/Secretary, A
Liberal Arts and Sciences Studies and
  Humanities, AB
Medical Administrative Assistant/Secretary, A

OHIO UNIVERSITY-SOUTHERN CAMPUS

Accounting and Business/Management, A
Accounting Technology/Technician and
  Bookkeeping, A
Biological and Physical Sciences, A
Business Administration and Management, B
Computer Science, A
Criminal Justice/Law Enforcement
  Administration, AB
Early Childhood Education and Teaching, AB
Education, B
General Office Occupations and Clerical Services, A
Health Services Administration, B
Health/Health Care Administration/Management, B
Human Services, A
Interdisciplinary Studies, A
Kindergarten/PreSchool Education and Teaching, A
Liberal Arts and Sciences Studies and
  Humanities, A
Multi-/Interdisciplinary Studies, B
Nursing - Registered Nurse Training, AB
Organizational Communication, B
Radio and Television Broadcasting
  Technology/Technician, A
Tourism and Travel Services Marketing
  Operations, A

OHIO UNIVERSITY-ZANESVILLE

Biological and Physical Sciences, A
Broadcast Journalism, A
Criminal Justice/Law Enforcement Administration, B
Elementary Education and Teaching, B
Liberal Arts and Sciences Studies and
  Humanities, AB
Nursing - Registered Nurse Training, AB
Public Relations/Image Management, B

Radio and Television, A
Social Sciences, A

OHIO VALLEY COLLEGE OF TECHNOLOGY

Accounting, A
Data Processing and Data Processing
  Technology/Technician, A
Dental Assisting/Assistant, A
Executive Assistant/Executive Secretary, A
Information Technology, A
Medical Administrative Assistant/Secretary, A
Medical/Clinical Assistant, A

OHIO WESLEYAN UNIVERSITY

Accounting, B
African-American/Black Studies, B
Ancient Studies/Civilization, B
Animal Genetics, B
Anthropology, B
Art History, Criticism and Conservation, B
Art Teacher Education, B
Art Therapy/Therapist, B
Astronomy, B
Astrophysics, B
Biology Teacher Education, B
Biology/Biological Sciences, B
Botany/Plant Biology, B
Broadcast Journalism, B
Business Administration and Management, B
Business Teacher Education, B
Business/Managerial Economics, B
Chemistry, B
Chemistry Teacher Education, B
Classics and Classical
  Languages, Literatures, and Linguistics, B
Comparative Literature, B
Computer Science, B
Creative Writing, B
Drama and Dance Teacher Education, B
Drama and Dramatics/Theatre Arts, B
Early Childhood Education and Teaching, B
East Asian Studies, B
Economics, B
Education, B
Elementary Education and Teaching, B
Engineering, B
Engineering Science, B
English Language and Literature, B
Environmental Studies, B
Ethnic and Cultural Studies, B
Fine/Studio Arts, B
Foreign Language Teacher Education, B
French Language and Literature, B
French Language Teacher Education, B
General Studies, B
Genetics, B
Geography, B
Geology/Earth Science, B
German Language and Literature, B
German Language Teacher Education, B
Health Teacher Education, B
History, B
History Teacher Education, B
Humanities/Humanistic Studies, B
International Business/Trade/Commerce, B
International Relations and Affairs, B
Journalism, B
Junior High/Intermediate/Middle School Education
  and Teaching, B
Kindergarten/PreSchool Education and Teaching, B
Latin American Studies, B
Latin Teacher Education, B
Mathematics, B
Mathematics Teacher Education, B
Medical Microbiology and Bacteriology, B
Medieval and Renaissance Studies, B
Multi-/Interdisciplinary Studies, B
Music, B
Music Performance, B
Music Teacher Education, B
Neuroscience, B
Philosophy, B
Physical Education Teaching and Coaching, B
Physics, B
Physics Teacher Education, B

Political Science and Government, B
Pre-Dentistry Studies, B
Pre-Law Studies, B
Pre-Medicine/Pre-Medical Studies, B
Pre-Theology/Pre-Ministerial Studies, B
Pre-Veterinary Studies, B
Psychology, B
Psychology Teacher Education, B
Public Administration, B
Religion/Religious Studies, B
Secondary Education and Teaching, B
Social Studies Teacher Education, B
Sociology, B
Spanish Language and Literature, B
Spanish Language Teacher Education, B
Statistics, B
Teacher Education, Multiple Levels, B
Urban Studies/Affairs, B
Women's Studies, B
Zoology/Animal Biology, B

OTTERBEIN COLLEGE

Accounting, B
Art Teacher Education, B
Art/Art Studies, General, B
Athletic Training and Sports Medicine, B
Audiology/Audiologist and Speech-Language
    Pathology/Pathologist, B
Biochemistry, B
Biology/Biological Sciences, B
Business Administration and Management, B
Business Administration, Management and
    Operations, M
Business/Managerial Economics, B
Chemistry, B
Comparative Literature, B
Computer Science, B
Drama and Dramatics/Theatre Arts, B
Economics, B
Education, BM
Elementary Education and Teaching, B
English Language and Literature, B
Environmental Biology, B
Environmental Sciences, B
Equestrian/Equine Studies, B
Finance, B
French Language and Literature, B
Health Teacher Education, B
History, B
International Business/Trade/Commerce, B
International Relations and Affairs, B
Journalism, B
Junior High/Intermediate/Middle School Education
    and Teaching, B
Marketing/Marketing Management, B
Mathematics, B
Molecular Biology, B
Multi-/Interdisciplinary Studies, B
Music, B
Music History, Literature, and Theory, B
Music Management and Merchandising, B
Music Performance, B
Music Teacher Education, B
Nursing, MO
Nursing - Adult, MO
Nursing - Advanced Practice, O
Nursing - Registered Nurse Training, B
Nursing Administration, M
Philosophy, B
Physical Education Teaching and Coaching, B
Physical Sciences, B
Physics, B
Piano and Organ, B
Political Science and Government, B
Pre-Dentistry Studies, B
Pre-Law Studies, B
Pre-Medicine/Pre-Medical Studies, B
Pre-Veterinary Studies, B
Psychology, B
Public Relations/Image Management, B
Radio and Television, B
Religion/Religious Studies, B
Science Teacher Education/General Science
    Teacher Education, B
Secondary Education and Teaching, B
Sociology, B

Spanish Language and Literature, B
Sport and Fitness Administration/Management, B
Violin, Viola, Guitar and Other Stringed
    Instruments, B
Voice and Opera, B
Wind and Percussion Instruments, B

OWENS COMMUNITY COLLEGE

Accounting Technology/Technician and
    Bookkeeping, A
Agricultural Business and Management, A
Automotive Engineering Technology/Technician, A
Business/Commerce, A
CAD/CADD Drafting and/or Design
    Technology/Technician, A
Commercial and Advertising Art, A
Criminal Justice/Law Enforcement Administration, A
Criminal Justice/Police Science, A
Drafting/Design Engineering
    Technologies/Technicians, A
Early Childhood Education and Teaching, A
Electrical, Electronic and Communications
    Engineering Technology/Technician, A
Fashion Merchandising, A
Fire Protection and Safety Technology/Technician, A
Food Technology and Processing, A
General Studies, A
Health Information/Medical Records
    Technology/Technician, A
Management Information Systems and Services, A
Manufacturing Technology/Technician, A
Marketing/Marketing Management, A
Mechanical Engineering/Mechanical
    Technology/Technician, A
Nursing - Registered Nurse Training, A
Occupational Therapist Assistant, A
Physical Therapist Assistant, A
Survey Technology/Surveying, A
Telecommunications Technology/Technician, A

PONTIFICAL COLLEGE JOSEPHINUM

Classics and Classical
    Languages, Literatures, and Linguistics, B
English Language and Literature, B
History, B
Humanities/Humanistic Studies, B
Latin American Studies, B
Philosophy, B
Theology and Religious Vocations, MP

PROFESSIONAL SKILLS INSTITUTE

Physical Therapist Assistant, A

REMINGTON COLLEGE-CLEVELAND
WEST CAMPUS

Business Administration and Management, A
Computer Systems Networking and
    Telecommunications, A
Criminal Justice/Law Enforcement Administration, A

RETS TECH CENTER

Computer Engineering Technology/Technician, A
Computer Programming/Programmer, A
Computer Science, A
Electrical, Electronic and Communications
    Engineering Technology/Technician, A
Legal Assistant/Paralegal, A
Medical/Clinical Assistant, A

SCHOOL OF ADVERTISING ART

Commercial and Advertising Art, A

SHAWNEE STATE UNIVERSITY

Accounting, A
Applied Mathematics, B
Art Teacher Education, B
Art/Art Studies, General, AB
Athletic Training and Sports Medicine, B
Biological and Physical Sciences, B
Biology/Biological Sciences, AB
Business Administration and Management, AB
CAD/CADD Drafting and/or Design
    Technology/Technician, A
Ceramic Arts and Ceramics, B
Chemistry, B

Clinical/Medical Laboratory Technician, A
Computer Engineering Technology/Technician, B
Dental Hygiene/Hygienist, A
Drama and Dramatics/Theatre Arts, B
Drawing, B
Early Childhood Education and Teaching, B
Education, B
Electromechanical Technology/Electromechanical
    Engineering Technology, A
Elementary Education and Teaching, B
Emergency Medical Technology/Technician (EMT
    Paramedic), A
English Language and Literature, B
English/Language Arts Teacher Education, B
Environmental Engineering
    Technology/Environmental Technology, B
Fine/Studio Arts, B
General Studies, AB
Geography Teacher Education, B
Graphic Design, B
History, B
History Teacher Education, B
Humanities/Humanistic Studies, A
International Relations and Affairs, B
Junior High/Intermediate/Middle School Education
    and Teaching, B
Kindergarten/PreSchool Education and Teaching, B
Legal Administrative Assistant/Secretary, A
Legal Assistant/Paralegal, A
Management Information Systems and Services, AB
Mathematics, B
Mathematics Teacher Education, B
Medical Radiologic Technology/Science - Radiation
    Therapist, A
Music, A
Natural Sciences, AB
Nursing - Registered Nurse Training, AB
Occupational Therapy/Therapist, AB
Office Management and Supervision, A
Painting, B
Photography, B
Physical Sciences, B
Physical Therapy/Therapist, A
Physics Teacher Education, B
Plastics Engineering Technology/Technician, AB
Pre-Engineering, A
Pre-Law Studies, B
Pre-Medicine/Pre-Medical Studies, B
Pre-Veterinary Studies, A
Psychology, B
Psychology Teacher Education, B
Respiratory Care Therapy/Therapist, A
Science Teacher Education/General Science
    Teacher Education, B
Secondary Education and Teaching, B
Social Sciences, AB
Social Studies Teacher Education, B
Sociology, B
Special Education and Teaching, B
Sport and Fitness Administration/Management, B
Teacher Education, Multiple Levels, B

SINCLAIR COMMUNITY COLLEGE

Accounting, A
Administrative Assistant and Secretarial Science, A
African Studies, A
Applied Art, A
Architectural Engineering Technology/Technician, A
Art/Art Studies, General, A
Artificial Intelligence and Robotics, A
Automobile/Automotive Mechanics
    Technology/Technician, A
Aviation/Airway Management and Operations, A
BioTechnology, A
Business Administration and Management, A
Child Development, A
Civil Engineering Technology/Technician, A
Commercial and Advertising Art, A
Computer and Information Sciences, A
Computer Engineering, A
Computer Graphics, A
Computer Hardware Engineering, A
Computer Programming, A
Computer Programming, Specific Applications, A
Computer
    Programming, Vendor/Product Certification, A

Computer Software Engineering, A
Computer Systems Networking and
 Telecommunications, A
Computer/Information Technology Services
 Administration and Management, A
Consumer Merchandising/Retailing Management, A
Corrections, A
Criminal Justice/Law Enforcement Administration, A
Criminal Justice/Police Science, A
Culinary Arts/Chef Training, A
Dance, A
Data Entry/Microcomputer Applications, A
Dental Hygiene/Hygienist, A
Dietetics/Dieticians, A
Drafting and Design Technology/Technician, A
Drama and Dramatics/Theatre Arts, A
Education, A
Electrical, Electronic and Communications
 Engineering Technology/Technician, A
Electromechanical Technology/Electromechanical
 Engineering Technology, A
Emergency Medical Technology/Technician (EMT
 Paramedic), A
Engineering, A
Finance, A
Fine/Studio Arts, A
Fire Science/Firefighting, A
Foods, Nutrition, and Wellness Studies, A
Gerontology, A
Graphic and Printing Equipment Operator
 Production, A
Health Information/Medical Records
 Administration/Administrator, A
Hotel/Motel Administration/Management, A
Human Services, A
Industrial Radiologic Technology/Technician, A
Industrial Technology/Technician, A
Information Science/Studies, A
Information Technology, A
Interior Design, A
Kindergarten/PreSchool Education and Teaching, A
Labor and Industrial Relations, A
Legal Administrative Assistant/Secretary, A
Legal Assistant/Paralegal, A
Liberal Arts and Sciences Studies and
 Humanities, A
Logistics and Materials Management, A
Machine Tool Technology/Machinist, A
Marketing/Marketing Management, A
Mass Communication/Media Studies, A
Mechanical Engineering/Mechanical
 Technology/Technician, A
Medical Administrative Assistant/Secretary, A
Medical/Clinical Assistant, A
Mental Health/Rehabilitation, A
Music, A
Nursing - Registered Nurse Training, A
Occupational Therapy/Therapist, A
Physical Education Teaching and Coaching, A
Physical Therapy/Therapist, A
Plastics Engineering Technology/Technician, A
Public Administration, A
Quality Control Technology/Technician, A
Radiologic Technology/Science - Radiographer, A
Real Estate, A
Respiratory Care Therapy/Therapist, A
Sign Language Interpretation and Translation, A
Special Products Marketing Operations, A
Surgical Technology/Technologist, A
Survey Technology/Surveying, A
System Administration/Administrator, A
Tourism and Travel Services Management, A
Transportation and Materials Moving, A
Web/Multimedia Management and Webmaster, A
Word Processing, A

SOUTHERN STATE COMMUNITY COLLEGE

Accounting Technology/Technician and
 Bookkeeping, A
Agricultural Production Operations, A
Business/Commerce, A
Computer Programming, Specific Applications, A
Corrections, A
Criminal Justice/Law Enforcement Administration, A
Drafting and Design Technology/Technician, A

Emergency Medical Technology/Technician (EMT
 Paramedic), A
Executive Assistant/Executive Secretary, A
Human Services, A
Kindergarten/PreSchool Education and Teaching, A
Liberal Arts and Sciences Studies and
 Humanities, A
Medical/Clinical Assistant, A
Nursing - Registered Nurse Training, A
Real Estate, A

SOUTHWESTERN COLLEGE OF BUSINESS (CINCINNATI)

Accounting, A
Administrative Assistant and Secretarial Science, A
Business Administration and Management, A
Computer Science, A
Medical/Clinical Assistant, A

SOUTHWESTERN COLLEGE OF BUSINESS (CINCINNATI)

Accounting, A
Administrative Assistant and Secretarial Science, A
Business Administration and Management, A
Clinical/Medical Laboratory Technician, A
Computer Programming/Programmer, A
Computer Science, A
Information Science/Studies, A
Labor and Industrial Relations, A
Medical Administrative Assistant/Secretary, A
Medical/Clinical Assistant, A
Real Estate, A

SOUTHWESTERN COLLEGE OF BUSINESS (DAYTON)

Accounting, A
Administrative Assistant and Secretarial Science, A
Business Administration and Management, A
Computer Science, A
Medical/Clinical Assistant, A

SOUTHWESTERN COLLEGE OF BUSINESS (FRANKLIN)

Administrative Assistant and Secretarial Science, A
Business Administration and Management, A
Computer Science, A
Medical Administrative Assistant/Secretary, A

STARK STATE COLLEGE OF TECHNOLOGY

Accounting, A
Administrative Assistant and Secretarial Science, A
Architectural Engineering Technology/Technician, A
Automobile/Automotive Mechanics
 Technology/Technician, A
Biomedical Technology/Technician, A
Business Administration and Management, A
Child Development, A
Civil Engineering Technology/Technician, A
Clinical/Medical Laboratory Technician, A
Computer and Information Sciences, A
Computer Engineering, A
Computer Hardware Engineering, A
Computer Programming, A
Computer Programming, Specific Applications, A
Computer
 Programming, Vendor/Product Certification, A
Computer Programming/Programmer, A
Computer Software and Media Applications, A
Computer Software Engineering, A
Computer Systems Networking and
 Telecommunications, A
Computer/Information Technology Services
 Administration and Management, A
Consumer Merchandising/Retailing Management, A
Court Reporting/Court Reporter, A
Data Entry/Microcomputer Applications, A
Dental Hygiene/Hygienist, A
Drafting and Design Technology/Technician, A
Environmental Studies, A
Finance, A
Fire Science/Firefighting, A
Food Technology and Processing, A
Health Information/Medical Records
 Administration/Administrator, A

Human Services, A
Industrial Technology/Technician, A
Information Technology, A
International Business/Trade/Commerce, A
Legal Administrative Assistant/Secretary, A
Management Information Systems and Services, A
Marketing/Marketing Management, A
Mechanical Engineering/Mechanical
 Technology/Technician, A
Medical/Clinical Assistant, A
Nursing - Registered Nurse Training, A
Occupational Therapy/Therapist, A
Operations Management and Supervision, A
Physical Therapy/Therapist, A
Respiratory Care Therapy/Therapist, A
Survey Technology/Surveying, A
Web Page, Digital/Multimedia and Information
 Resources Design, A
Web/Multimedia Management and Webmaster, A
Word Processing, A

STAUTZENBERGER COLLEGE

Business, Management, Marketing, and Related
 Support Services, A
Computer Systems Networking and
 Telecommunications, A
Legal Assistant/Paralegal, A
Massage Therapy/Therapeutic Massage, A
Medical Office Assistant/Specialist, A
Medical/Clinical Assistant, A
Veterinary/Animal Health Technology/Technician and
 Veterinary Assistant, A
Web Page, Digital/Multimedia and Information
 Resources Design, A

TERRA STATE COMMUNITY COLLEGE

Accounting, A
Administrative Assistant and Secretarial Science, A
Architectural Engineering Technology/Technician, A
Automobile/Automotive Mechanics
 Technology/Technician, A
Automotive Engineering Technology/Technician, A
Banking and Financial Support Services, A
Business Administration and Management, A
Chemistry, A
Commercial and Advertising Art, A
Computer and Information Sciences, A
Criminal Justice/Police Science, A
Electromechanical Technology/Electromechanical
 Engineering Technology, A
Engineering, A
Engineering Technology, A
English Language and Literature, A
Entrepreneurship/Entrepreneurial Studies, A
Finance, A
General Office Occupations and Clerical Services, A
General Studies, A
Heating, Air Conditioning and Refrigeration
 Technology/Technician, A
Heating, Air Conditioning, Ventilation and
 Refrigeration Maintenance
 Technology/Technician, A
Industrial Technology/Technician, A
Information Science/Studies, A
Kindergarten/PreSchool Education and Teaching, A
Marketing/Marketing Management, A
Mathematics, A
Mechanical Engineering/Mechanical
 Technology/Technician, A
Medical Administrative Assistant/Secretary, A
Plastics Engineering Technology/Technician, A
Psychology, A
Quality Control Technology/Technician, A
Robotics Technology/Technician, A
Sign Language Interpretation and Translation, A
Social Work, A
Technical and Business Writing, A
Tool and Die Technology/Technician, A
Welding Technology/Welder, A

TIFFIN UNIVERSITY

Accounting, AB
Arts Management, B
Business Administration and Management, AB
Business Administration, Management and
 Operations, M

Communication Studies/Speech Communication
and Rhetoric, B
Computer and Information Sciences and Support
Services, B
Computer Programming/Programmer, A
Corrections, B
Criminal Justice/Law Enforcement Administration, B
Criminal Justice/Police Science, AB
Criminal Justice/Safety Studies, B
Criminology, M
English Language and Literature, B
Finance, B
Forensic Psychology, BM
Forensic Science and Technology, B
History, B
Human Services, B
Information Science/Studies, B
International Relations and Affairs, B
Marketing/Marketing Management, B
Pre-Law Studies, B
Psychology, B

TRUMBULL BUSINESS COLLEGE

Accounting, A
Administrative Assistant and Secretarial Science, A
Computer/Information Technology Services
Administration and Management, A
Legal Administrative Assistant/Secretary, A
Management Information Systems and Services, A
Medical Administrative Assistant/Secretary, A
Word Processing, A

UNION INSTITUTE & UNIVERSITY

Business/Commerce, B
Communication Studies/Speech Communication
and Rhetoric, B
Criminal Justice/Law Enforcement Administration, B
Education, BMO
Fine Arts and Art Studies, M
History, B
Humanities/Humanistic Studies, B
Interdisciplinary Studies, MD
Liberal Arts and Sciences Studies and
Humanities, B
Psychology, BD
Public Administration, B
Public Health (MPH, DPH), B
Social Sciences, B
Social Work, B
Writing, M

THE UNIVERSITY OF AKRON

Accounting, BMO
Accounting Technology/Technician and
Bookkeeping, A
Acting, B
Administrative Assistant and Secretarial Science, A
Agricultural Teacher Education, B
Airline Flight Attendant, A
Allied Health
Diagnostic, Intervention, and Treatment
Professions, A
American Government and Politics (United States)
, B
Animal Physiology, B
Apparel and Textiles, B
Applied Art, B
Applied Mathematics, BMD
Art History, Criticism and Conservation, B
Art Teacher Education, B
Art/Art Studies, General, B
Arts Management, M
Athletic Training and Sports Medicine, B
Atomic/Molecular Physics, B
Audiology/Audiologist and Hearing Sciences, B
Audiology/Audiologist and Speech-Language
Pathology/Pathologist, B
Automotive Engineering Technology/Technician, A
Aviation/Airway Management and Operations, A
Banking and Financial Support Services, A
Behavioral Sciences, B
Bilingual and Multilingual Education, B
Biological and Biomedical Sciences, M
Biological and Physical Sciences, B
Biology Teacher Education, B
Biology/Biological Sciences, B

Biomedical Engineering, MD
Biomedical/Medical Engineering, B
Botany/Plant Biology, B
Broadcast Journalism, B
Business Administration and Management, B
Business Operations Support and Secretarial
Services, A
Business Teacher Education, B
Business, Management, Marketing, and Related
Support Services, A
Business/Commerce, B
Business/Office Automation/Technology/Data
Entry, A
Cartography, B
Ceramic Arts and Ceramics, B
Chemical Engineering, BMD
Chemical Technology/Technician, A
Chemistry, BMD
Chemistry Teacher Education, B
Child and Family Studies, M
Child Development, B
Civil Engineering, BMD
Classics and Classical
Languages, Literatures, and Linguistics, B
Clinical/Medical Laboratory Science and Allied
Professions, A
Clothing and Textiles, M
Cognitive Sciences, MD
Commercial and Advertising Art, B
Commercial Photography, A
Communication and Media Studies, M
Communication Disorders, BMD
Communication Studies/Speech Communication
and Rhetoric, B
Communication, Journalism and Related
Programs, B
Community Organization and Advocacy, AB
Comparative Literature, B
Composition, M
Computer Engineering, B
Computer Science, BM
Computer Systems Analysis/Analyst, A
Computer Teacher Education, B
Computer/Information Technology Services
Administration and Management, A
Construction Engineering Technology/Technician, A
Corrections, B
Counseling Psychology, MD
Counselor Education/School Counseling and
Guidance Services, MD
Crafts/Craft Design, Folk Art and Artisanry, B
Criminal Justice/Law Enforcement Administration, B
Criminal Justice/Police Science, A
Criminal Justice/Safety Studies, B
Culinary Arts/Chef Training, A
Dance, B
Data Processing and Data Processing
Technology/Technician, A
Design and Applied Arts, B
Developmental and Child Psychology, B
Dietetics/Dieticians, B
Drafting and Design Technology/Technician, A
Drafting/Design Engineering
Technologies/Technicians, A
Drama and Dance Teacher Education, B
Drama and Dramatics/Theatre Arts, B
Dramatic/Theatre Arts and Stagecraft, B
Drawing, B
Ecology, B
Economics, BM
Education, ABMD
Education/Teaching of Individuals with Mental
Retardation, B
Education/Teaching of Individuals with Multiple
Disabilities, B
Education/Teaching of Individuals with Specific
Learning Disabilities, B
Education/Teaching of Individuals with Speech or
Language Impairments, B
Educational Administration and Supervision, MD
Educational Media/Instructional Technology, M
Electrical Engineering, MD
Electrical, Electronic and Communications
Engineering Technology/Technician, AB
Electrical, Electronics and Communications
Engineering, B

Electromechanical Technology/Electromechanical
Engineering Technology, A
Electronic Commerce, M
Elementary Education and Teaching, BMD
Engineering, B
Engineering and Applied Sciences, MDO
Engineering Management, M
Engineering Physics, B
Engineering Technologies/Technicians, A
Engineering Technology, B
English, M
English Language and Literature, B
English/Language Arts Teacher Education, B
Entrepreneurship/Entrepreneurial Studies, AM
Environmental Health, A
Executive Assistant/Executive Secretary, A
Exercise and Sports Science, M
Family and Consumer Economics and Related
Services, B
Family and Consumer Sciences/Home Economics
Teacher Education, B
Family and Consumer Sciences/Human Sciences, B
Family Systems, B
Fashion Merchandising, AB
Finance, B
Finance and Banking, MO
Finance and Financial Management Services, B
Fine Arts and Art Studies, B
Fine/Studio Arts, B
Fire Protection, B
Fire Protection and Safety Technology/Technician, A
Food Science, B
Food Science and Technology, M
Foods, Nutrition, and Wellness Studies, B
Foreign Language Teacher Education, B
French Language and Literature, B
French Language Teacher Education, B
General Merchandising, Sales, and Related
Marketing Operations, B
Geographic Information Systems, M
Geography, BM
Geological and Earth Sciences/Geosciences, B
Geological/Geophysical Engineering, B
Geology/Earth Science, BM
Geophysics and Seismology, BM
Geosciences, M
German Language and Literature, B
German Language Teacher Education, B
Gerontology, B
Health and Medical Administrative Services, A
Health and Physical Education/Fitness, B
Health Teacher Education, B
Higher Education/Higher Education
Administration, MD
History, BMD
History Teacher Education, B
Home Economics, M
Hospitality Administration/Management, A
Hospitality and Recreation Marketing Operations, A
Hotel/Motel Administration/Management, A
Housing and Human Environments, B
Human Resources Management and Services, M
Human Resources Management/Personnel
Administration, B
Humanities/Humanistic Studies, B
Industrial and Labor Relations, M
Industrial and Organizational Psychology, MD
Industrial Production Technologies/Technicians, B
Industrial Technology/Technician, AB
Interdisciplinary Studies, AB
Interior Design, B
International Business/Trade/Commerce, BMO
International Finance, B
International Marketing, B
Jazz/Jazz Studies, B
Junior High/Intermediate/Middle School Education
and Teaching, B
Kindergarten/PreSchool Education and Teaching, B
Labor and Industrial Relations, A
Law and Legal Studies, PO
Legal Administrative Assistant/Secretary, A
Legal Assistant/Paralegal, A
Liberal Arts and Sciences Studies and
Humanities, AB
Logistics and Materials Management, A
Management, MO

Management Information Systems and
  Services, BM
Management of Technology, M
Marketing, BMO
Marketing/Marketing Management, B
Marriage and Family Therapy/Counseling, M
Mass Communication/Media Studies, B
Mathematics, BM
Mathematics and Computer Science, B
Mathematics and Statistics, B
Mathematics Teacher Education, B
Mechanical Engineering, BMD
Mechanical Engineering/Mechanical
  Technology/Technician, AB
Medical Administrative Assistant/Secretary, A
Medical Microbiology and Bacteriology, B
Medical Office Management/Administration, A
Medical Radiologic Technology/Science - Radiation
  Therapist, A
Medical/Clinical Assistant, A
Merchandising and Buying Operations, A
Metal and Jewelry Arts, B
Multi-/Interdisciplinary Studies, A
Music, BM
Music History, Literature, and Theory, BM
Music Performance, B
Music Teacher Education, BM
Music Theory and Composition, BM
Musicology and Ethnomusicology, B
Natural Sciences, B
Nursing, BMD
Nursing - Registered Nurse Training, B
Nursing Science, B
Nutritional Sciences, M
Opticianry/Ophthalmic Dispensing Optician, A
Painting, B
Performance, M
Philosophy, B
Photography, B
Physical Education Teaching and Coaching, BM
Physical Science Technologies/Technicians, A
Physics, BM
Physics Teacher Education, B
Piano and Organ, B
Political Science and Government, BM
Polymer Chemistry, B
Polymer/Plastics Engineering, BMD
Pre-Law Studies, B
Printmaking, B
Psychology, BMD
Public Administration, MO
Public Administration and Social Service
  Professions, A
Public Health, M
Public Relations, Advertising, and Applied
  Communication, B
Quality Management, M
Respiratory Care Therapy/Therapist, A
Restaurant, Culinary, and Catering
  Management/Manager, A
School Psychology, M
Science Teacher Education/General Science
  Teacher Education, B
Sculpture, B
Secondary Education and Teaching, BMD
Selling Skills and Sales Operations, A
Social Science Teacher Education, B
Social Sciences, B
Social Studies Teacher Education, B
Social Work, BM
Sociology, BMD
Spanish Language and Literature, BM
Spanish Language Teacher Education, B
Special Education and Teaching, BM
Specialized Merchandising, Sales, and Marketing
  Operations, B
Speech and Rhetorical Studies, B
Speech Teacher Education, B
Speech-Language Pathology/Pathologist, B
Statistics, BM
Substance Abuse/Addiction Counseling, A
Surgical Technology/Technologist, A
Survey Technology/Surveying, AB
Taxation, M
Teacher Assistant/Aide, A

Teacher Education and Professional
  Development, Specific Levels and Methods, B
Teacher Education and Professional
  Development, Specific Subject Areas, B
Teacher Education, Multiple Levels, B
Technical Teacher Education, B
Technical Theatre/Theatre Design and
  Technology, B
Theater, M
Tourism and Travel Services Management, A
Urban Planning, M
Urban Studies/Affairs, MD
Violin, Viola, Guitar and Other Stringed
  Instruments, B
Visual and Performing Arts, B
Vocational and Technical Education, M
Voice and Opera, B
Wind and Percussion Instruments, B
Writing, M
Zoology/Animal Biology, B

THE UNIVERSITY OF AKRON-WAYNE COLLEGE

Accounting, A
Accounting Technology/Technician and
  Bookkeeping, A
Administrative Assistant and Secretarial Science, A
Business Administration and Management, A
Business/Office Automation/Technology/Data
  Entry, A
Computer Science, A
Computer Systems Networking and
  Telecommunications, A
Data Processing and Data Processing
  Technology/Technician, A
Engineering, A
Environmental Health, A
Executive Assistant/Executive Secretary, A
General Studies, A
Interdisciplinary Studies, A
Legal Administrative Assistant/Secretary, A
Liberal Arts and Sciences Studies and
  Humanities, A
Management Information Systems and Services, A
Medical Administrative Assistant/Secretary, A
Medical Office Management/Administration, A
Occupational Safety and Health
  Technology/Technician, A
Social Work, A

UNIVERSITY OF CINCINNATI

Accounting, ABMD
Administrative Assistant and Secretarial Science, A
Aerospace, Aeronautical and Astronautical
  Engineering, BMD
African-American/Black Studies, B
Allopathic Medicine, MPO
Analytical Chemistry, MD
Anthropology, BM
Applied Arts and Design, M
Applied Mathematics, MD
Architectural Engineering, B
Architectural Engineering Technology/Technician, AB
Architecture, BM
Art Education, M
Art History, Criticism and Conservation, BM
Art Teacher Education, B
Art/Art Studies, General, B
Artificial Intelligence and Robotics, A
Arts Management, MO
Asian Studies/Civilization, B
Audiology/Audiologist and Speech-Language
  Pathology/Pathologist, B
Biochemistry, BMD
Bioinformatics, MD
Biological and Biomedical Sciences, MDO
Biological and Physical Sciences, A
Biology/Biological Sciences, B
Biomedical Engineering, MD
Biophysics, D
Biostatistics, MD
Broadcast Journalism, B
Building/Construction
  Finishing, Management, and Inspection, B
Business Administration and Management, AB

Business Administration, Management and
  Operations, MDO
Cell Biology and Anatomy, D
Ceramic Sciences and Engineering, MD
Chemical Engineering, BMD
Chemistry, BMD
Child Development, A
City/Urban, Community and Regional Planning, B
Civil Engineering, BMD
Civil Engineering Technology/Technician, AB
Classics and Classical
  Languages, Literatures, and Linguistics, BMD
Clinical Laboratory Science/Medical
  Technology/Technologist, B
Clinical Psychology, D
Clinical/Medical Laboratory Technician, A
Commercial and Advertising Art, B
Communication and Media Studies, M
Communication Disorders, MD
Comparative Literature, B
Composition, MD
Computer and Information Sciences, AB
Computer Engineering, BMD
Computer Engineering Technology/Technician, A
Computer Programming/Programmer, AB
Computer Science, BMD
Construction Engineering, B
Construction Engineering and Management, M
Construction Engineering Technology/Technician, AB
Counselor Education/School Counseling and
  Guidance Services, MDO
Court Reporting/Court Reporter, A
Criminal Justice/Law Enforcement
  Administration, AB
Criminal Justice/Police Science, AB
Criminology, MD
Curriculum and Instruction, MD
Dance, B
Data Processing and Data Processing
  Technology/Technician, A
Developmental Biology and Embryology, MD
Drafting and Design Technology/Technician, A
Drama and Dramatics/Theatre Arts, B
Early Childhood Education and Teaching, M
Economics, BM
Education, BMDO
Educational Administration and Supervision, MO
Educational Leadership and Administration, D
Electrical Engineering, MD
Electrical, Electronic and Communications
  Engineering Technology/Technician, AB
Electrical, Electronics and Communications
  Engineering, B
Electronic Commerce, M
Elementary Education and Teaching, BM
Energy Management and Systems
  Technology/Technician, A
Engineering, B
Engineering and Applied Sciences, MDO
Engineering Mechanics, B
Engineering Science, AB
English, MD
English as a Second Language, MDO
English Language and Literature, B
Environmental and Occupational Health, MD
Environmental Engineering
  Technology/Environmental Technology, AMD
Environmental Sciences, MD
Environmental Studies, A
Epidemiology, MD
Ergonomics and Human Factors, MD
Experimental Psychology, D
Fashion/Apparel Design, B
Finance, AB
Finance and Banking, MD
Fine Arts and Art Studies, M
Fire Protection and Safety Technology/Technician, B
Fire Science/Firefighting, A
Foods, Nutrition, and Wellness Studies, B
Foundations and Philosophy of Education, MD
French Language and Literature, BMD
Genetic Counseling/Counselor, M
Genomic Sciences, MD
Geography, BMD
Geology/Earth Science, BMD
German Language and Literature, BMD

Graphic Design, M
Health and Medical Laboratory Technologies, B
Health Education, M
Health Physics/Radiological Health, M
Health Teacher Education, B
Health/Health Care Administration/Management, B
Heating, Air Conditioning, Ventilation and
   Refrigeration Maintenance
   Technology/Technician, A
History, BMD
Human Services, A
Humanities/Humanistic Studies, AB
Immunology, MD
Industrial and Labor Relations, M
Industrial and Manufacturing Management, MD
Industrial Design, BM
Industrial Engineering, B
Industrial Hygiene, MD
Industrial Radiologic Technology/Technician, A
Industrial Technology/Technician, A
Industrial/Management Engineering, MDO
Information Science/Studies, AB
Inorganic Chemistry, MD
Insurance, AB
Interdisciplinary Studies, D
Interior Design, BM
International Business/Trade/Commerce, M
International Relations and Affairs, B
Jazz/Jazz Studies, B
Jewish/Judaic Studies, B
Kindergarten/PreSchool Education and Teaching, B
Latin American Studies, B
Law and Legal Studies, PO
Legal Administrative Assistant/Secretary, A
Legal Assistant/Paralegal, A
Liberal Arts and Sciences Studies and
   Humanities, AB
Linguistics, B
Management Information Systems and
   Services, BMO
Management of Technology, M
Marketing, MD
Marketing/Marketing Management, AB
Mass Communication/Media Studies, B
Materials Engineering, MD
Materials Sciences, MD
Mathematics, BMD
Mathematics Teacher Education, M
Mechanical Engineering, BMD
Mechanical Engineering/Mechanical
   Technology/Technician, AB
Mechanics, MD
Medical Administrative Assistant/Secretary, A
Medical Microbiology and Bacteriology, B
Medical Physics, M
Metallurgical Engineering, BMD
Metallurgical Technology/Technician, B
Microbiology, MD
Molecular Biology, MD
Molecular Genetics, MD
Molecular Medicine, D
Molecular Toxicology, MD
Music, BMDO
Music History, Literature, and Theory, BMD
Music Teacher Education, BM
Music Theory and Composition, MD
Musicology and Ethnomusicology, D
Natural Sciences, AB
Neuroscience, D
Nuclear Engineering, BMD
Nuclear Medical Technology/Technologist, B
Nurse Anesthetist, M
Nurse Midwife/Nursing Midwifery, M
Nursing, MDO
Nursing - Advanced Practice, M
Nursing - Registered Nurse Training, AB
Nutritional Sciences, M
Occupational Safety and Health
   Technology/Technician, A
Operations Research, B
Organic Chemistry, MD
Organizational Management, M
Pathobiology, D
Pathology/Experimental Pathology, D
Pediatric Nurse/Nursing, M
Performance, MDO

Pharmaceutical Sciences, MD
Pharmacology, BD
Pharmacy, BP
Philosophy, BMD
Physical Chemistry, MD
Physical Education Teaching and Coaching, B
Physical Therapy/Therapist, A
Physics, BMD
Physiology, D
Piano and Organ, B
Political Science and Government, BMD
Polymer/Plastics Engineering, MD
Pre-Law Studies, B
Pre-Medicine/Pre-Medical Studies, B
Pre-Veterinary Studies, B
Psychology, BD
Public Health (MPH, DPH), B
Public Policy Analysis, B
Quality Control Technology/Technician, A
Quantitative Analysis, MD
Radio and Television, B
Reading Teacher Education, MD
Real Estate, ABM
Rehabilitation Sciences, M
Romance
   Languages, Literatures, and Linguistics, BMD
School Psychology, MD
Science Teacher Education/General Science
   Teacher Education, A
Secondary Education and Teaching, BMD
Social Sciences, AB
Social Studies Teacher Education, M
Social Work, ABM
Sociology, BMD
Spanish Language and Literature, BMD
Special Education and Teaching, BMD
Statistics, MD
Taxation, M
Technology Education/Industrial Arts, A
Textile Design, M
Theater, MO
Toxicology, MD
Transportation and Materials Moving, AB
Urban and Regional Planning, MO
Urban Studies/Affairs, B
Violin, Viola, Guitar and Other Stringed
   Instruments, B
Voice and Opera, B
Wind and Percussion Instruments, B
Women's Studies, MO

UNIVERSITY OF CINCINNATI CLERMONT COLLEGE

Accounting, A
Administrative Assistant and Secretarial Science, A
Avionics Maintenance Technology/Technician, A
Business Administration and Management, A
Computer and Information Sciences, A
Computer Graphics, A
Computer Programming/Programmer, A
Court Reporting/Court Reporter, A
Criminal Justice/Law Enforcement Administration, A
Electrical, Electronic and Communications
   Engineering Technology/Technician, A
Elementary Education and Teaching, A
Hospitality Administration/Management, A
Information Science/Studies, A
Legal Administrative Assistant/Secretary, A
Legal Assistant/Paralegal, A
Liberal Arts and Sciences Studies and
   Humanities, A
Medical Administrative Assistant/Secretary, A
Pharmacy, A
Social Work, A

UNIVERSITY OF CINCINNATI RAYMOND WALTERS COLLEGE

Accounting, A
Administrative Assistant and Secretarial Science, A
Automobile/Automotive Mechanics
   Technology/Technician, A
Biology/Biological Sciences, A
Business Administration and Management, A
Chemical Technology/Technician, A
Chemistry, A

Clinical Laboratory Science/Medical
   Technology/Technologist, A
Commercial and Advertising Art, A
Computer Engineering Technology/Technician, A
Computer Programming/Programmer, A
Computer Science, A
Dental Hygiene/Hygienist, A
Dietetics/Dieticians, A
Economics, A
Education, A
Emergency Medical Technology/Technician (EMT
   Paramedic), A
Environmental Studies, A
Health and Medical Laboratory Technologies, A
Industrial Radiologic Technology/Technician, A
Industrial Technology/Technician, A
Information Science/Studies, A
Legal Administrative Assistant/Secretary, A
Liberal Arts and Sciences Studies and
   Humanities, A
Library Science, A
Management Information Systems and Services, A
Marketing/Marketing Management, A
Medical Administrative Assistant/Secretary, A
Nuclear Medical Technology/Technologist, A
Nursing - Registered Nurse Training, A
Pharmacy, A
Physical Therapy/Therapist, A
Pre-Engineering, A
Real Estate, A
Social Work, A
Urban Studies/Affairs, A
Veterinary/Animal Health Technology/Technician and
   Veterinary Assistant, A

UNIVERSITY OF DAYTON

Accounting, B
Aerospace, Aeronautical and Astronautical
   Engineering, MD
Agricultural Engineering, M
American/United States Studies/Civilization, B
Applied Art, B
Applied Mathematics, BM
Art Education, M
Art History, Criticism and Conservation, B
Art Teacher Education, B
Biochemistry, B
Biological and Biomedical Sciences, MD
Biology/Biological Sciences, B
Broadcast Journalism, B
Business Administration and Management, B
Business Administration, Management and
   Operations, MO
Business/Managerial Economics, B
Chemical Engineering, BM
Chemistry, BM
Civil Engineering, BM
Clinical Psychology, M
Commercial and Advertising Art, B
Communication and Media Studies, M
Community Psychology, M
Computer Engineering, BMD
Computer Engineering Technology/Technician, B
Computer Science, BM
Counselor Education/School Counseling and
   Guidance Services, M
Criminal Justice/Law Enforcement Administration, B
Dietetics/Dieticians, B
Drama and Dramatics/Theatre Arts, B
Early Childhood Education and Teaching, M
Economics, B
Education, BMDO
Educational Administration and Supervision, M
Educational Leadership and Administration, MD
Educational Media/Instructional Technology, M
Electrical Engineering, MD
Electrical, Electronic and Communications
   Engineering Technology/Technician, B
Electrical, Electronics and Communications
   Engineering, B
Elementary Education and Teaching, B
Engineering and Applied Sciences, MD
Engineering Management, M
English, M
English Language and Literature, B
Environmental Biology, B

Environmental Engineering
  Technology/Environmental Technology, M
Environmental Studies, B
Exercise and Sports Science, M
Experimental Psychology, M
Finance, B
Fine/Studio Arts, B
Foods, Nutrition, and Wellness Studies, B
French Language and Literature, B
General Studies, B
Geology/Earth Science, B
German Language and Literature, B
Health Teacher Education, B
History, B
Human Development, M
Industrial Technology/Technician, B
Industrial/Management Engineering, M
Information Science/Studies, B
International Business/Trade/Commerce, B
International Relations and Affairs, B
Journalism, B
Kindergarten/PreSchool Education and Teaching, B
Kinesiology and Exercise Science, B
Law and Legal Studies, PO
Management Information Systems and Services, B
Marketing/Marketing Management, B
Mass Communication/Media Studies, B
Materials Engineering, MD
Mathematics, B
Mechanical Engineering, BMD
Mechanical Engineering/Mechanical
  Technology/Technician, B
Mechanics, M
Middle School Education, M
Music, B
Music Teacher Education, B
Music Therapy/Therapist, B
Optical Technologies, MD
Pastoral Studies/Counseling, M
Philosophy, B
Photography, B
Physical Education Teaching and Coaching, BM
Physical Sciences, B
Physics, B
Political Science and Government, BM
Pre-Dentistry Studies, B
Pre-Law Studies, B
Pre-Medicine/Pre-Medical Studies, B
Psychology, BM
Public Administration, M
Public Relations/Image Management, B
Radio and Television, B
Reading Teacher Education, M
Religion/Religious Studies, B
Religious Education, B
School Psychology, M
Science Teacher Education/General Science
  Teacher Education, B
Secondary Education and Teaching, BM
Sociology, B
Spanish Language and Literature, B
Special Education and Teaching, BM
Sport and Fitness Administration/Management, B
Structural Engineering, M
Student Personnel Services, M
Theology and Religious Vocations, MD
Transportation and Highway Engineering, M

THE UNIVERSITY OF FINDLAY

Accounting, AB
Administrative Assistant and Secretarial Science, A
Art Teacher Education, B
Art/Art Studies, General, B
Athletic Training and Sports Medicine, BM
Bilingual and Multilingual Education, B
Biological and Physical Sciences, B
Biology/Biological Sciences, B
Broadcast Journalism, B
Business Administration and Management, AB
Business Administration, Management and
  Operations, M
Business Teacher Education, B
Business/Corporate Communications, B
Clinical Laboratory Science/Medical
  Technology/Technologist, B
Community Organization and Advocacy, A

Computer Science, AB
Computer Systems Networking and
  Telecommunications, B
Creative Writing, B
Criminal Justice/Law Enforcement
  Administration, AB
Drama and Dramatics/Theatre Arts, B
Early Childhood Education and Teaching, M
Economics, B
Education, BM
Educational Administration and Supervision, M
Educational Leadership and Administration, M
Educational Media/Instructional Technology, M
Elementary Education and Teaching, BM
English as a Second Language, M
English Language and Literature, B
Environmental Policy and Resource
  Management, M
Environmental Studies, AB
Equestrian/Equine Studies, AB
Farm/Farm and Ranch Management, B
Finance and Banking, M
History, B
Hotel/Motel Administration/Management, B
Human Resources Management and Services, M
Human Resources Management/Personnel
  Administration, AB
Humanities/Humanistic Studies, A
International Business/Trade/Commerce, BM
Japanese Language and Literature, B
Journalism, B
Liberal Studies, M
Logistics and Materials Management, B
Management, M
Marketing, M
Marketing/Marketing Management, B
Mathematics, B
Multilingual and Multicultural Education, M
Nuclear Medical Technology/Technologist, AB
Occupational Therapy/Therapist, BM
Philosophy, B
Physical Education Teaching and Coaching, B
Physical Therapy/Therapist, BM
Physician Assistant, B
Political Science and Government, B
Pre-Law Studies, B
Pre-Medicine/Pre-Medical Studies, B
Pre-Veterinary Studies, B
Psychology, B
Public Administration, M
Public Relations/Image Management, B
Religion/Religious Studies, AB
Sales, Distribution and Marketing Operations, AB
Science Teacher Education/General Science
  Teacher Education, B
Secondary Education and Teaching, B
Social Sciences, AB
Social Work, B
Sociology, B
Spanish Language and Literature, B
Special Education and Teaching, BM
Teaching English as a Second or Foreign
  Language/ESL Language Instructor, B

UNIVERSITY OF NORTHWESTERN OHIO

Accounting, AB
Administrative Assistant and Secretarial Science, A
Agricultural Business and Management, A
Automobile/Automotive Mechanics
  Technology/Technician, A
Business Administration and Management, AB
Computer Programming/Programmer, A
Diesel Mechanics Technology/Technician, A
Health/Health Care Administration/Management, B
Heating, Air Conditioning, Ventilation and
  Refrigeration Maintenance
  Technology/Technician, A
Legal Administrative Assistant/Secretary, A
Legal Assistant/Paralegal, A
Marketing/Marketing Management, AB
Medical Administrative Assistant/Secretary, A
Medical/Clinical Assistant, A

Pharmacy Technician/Assistant, A

UNIVERSITY OF PHOENIX-CINCINNATI CAMPUS

Accounting, M
Business Administration and Management, B
Business Administration, Management and
  Operations, M
Electronic Commerce, M
Information Science/Studies, M
Information Technology, B
International Business/Trade/Commerce, M
Management of Technology, M
Organizational Management, M

UNIVERSITY OF PHOENIX-CLEVELAND CAMPUS

Business Administration and Management, B
Business Administration, Management and
  Operations, M
Electronic Commerce, M
Health/Health Care Administration/Management, B
Information Technology, B
International Business/Trade/Commerce, M
Management Information Systems and Services, M
Management of Technology, M
Nursing, M
Organizational Management, M

UNIVERSITY OF PHOENIX-COLUMBUS OHIO CAMPUS

Business Administration, Management and
  Operations, M
Management Science, B

UNIVERSITY OF RIO GRANDE

Accounting, AB
Accounting Technology/Technician and
  Bookkeeping, A
Administrative Assistant and Secretarial Science, A
American/United States Studies/Civilization, B
Art Teacher Education, B
Art/Art Studies, General, AB
Biology Teacher Education, B
Biology/Biological Sciences, AB
Business Administration and Management, AB
Business Teacher Education, B
Business/Corporate Communications, B
Business/Office Automation/Technology/Data
  Entry, A
Chemistry, AB
Clinical Laboratory Science/Medical
  Technology/Technologist, B
Clinical/Medical Laboratory Technician, A
Communication Studies/Speech Communication
  and Rhetoric, AB
Computer Science, AB
Drafting and Design Technology/Technician, AB
Ecology, B
Economics, B
Education, BM
Education/Teaching of Individuals with Mental
  Retardation, B
Education/Teaching of Individuals with Specific
  Learning Disabilities, B
Elementary Education and Teaching, B
Energy Management and Systems
  Technology/Technician, A
English Language and Literature, AB
English/Language Arts Teacher Education, B
General Studies, B
Graphic Design, B
Health and Physical Education, B
Health Teacher Education, B
History, AB
History Teacher Education, B
Humanities/Humanistic Studies, B
Industrial Technology/Technician, AB
Information Technology, B
International Business/Trade/Commerce, B
Kindergarten/PreSchool Education and Teaching, A
Legal Administrative Assistant/Secretary, A
Marketing/Marketing Management, B
Mass Communication/Media Studies, AB
Mathematics, AB

Mathematics Teacher Education, B
Mechanical Engineering/Mechanical
   Technology/Technician, AB
Medical Administrative Assistant/Secretary, A
Music, AB
Music Teacher Education, B
Nursing - Registered Nurse Training, A
Physical Education Teaching and Coaching, AB
Physical Sciences, B
Physics Teacher Education, B
Political Science and Government, B
Pre-Dentistry Studies, B
Pre-Law Studies, B
Pre-Medicine/Pre-Medical Studies, B
Pre-Theology/Pre-Ministerial Studies, B
Pre-Veterinary Studies, B
Psychology, A
Public Relations/Image Management, B
Radiologic Technology/Science - Radiographer, A
Robotics Technology/Technician, AB
Science Teacher Education/General Science
   Teacher Education, B
Secondary Education and Teaching, B
Social Science Teacher Education, B
Social Sciences, B
Social Work, AB
Sociology, AB
Speech Teacher Education, B
Teacher Education, Multiple Levels, B
Technical Theatre/Theatre Design and
   Technology, A
Visual and Performing Arts, B

THE UNIVERSITY OF TOLEDO

Accounting, ABM
Administrative Assistant and Secretarial Science, A
Adult and Continuing Education and Teaching, B
Adult Development and Aging, A
African-American/Black Studies, B
Allied Health
   Diagnostic, Intervention, and Treatment
   Professions, B
American/United States Studies/Civilization, B
Analytical Chemistry, MD
Anthropology, BM
Applied Art, B
Applied Mathematics, M
Architectural Drafting and Architectural
   CAD/CADD, A
Art History, Criticism and Conservation, B
Art Teacher Education, B
Art/Art Studies, General, AB
Asian Studies/Civilization, B
Astronomy, B
Audiology/Audiologist and Speech-Language
   Pathology/Pathologist, B
Biochemistry, MD
Bioengineering, MD
Biological and Biomedical Sciences, MD
Biological and Physical Sciences, B
Biology/Biological Sciences, AB
Biomedical/Medical Engineering, B
Business Administration and Management, AB
Business Administration, Management and
   Operations, BMD
Business Education, MDO
Business Teacher Education, B
Business, Management, Marketing, and Related
   Support Services, B
Business/Commerce, AB
Business/Managerial Economics, B
Business/Office Automation/Technology/Data
   Entry, A
Cardiovascular Technology/Technologist, A
Chemical Engineering, BMD
Chemical Technology/Technician, A
Chemistry, BMD
Civil Engineering, BMD
Civil Engineering Technology/Technician, AB
Classics and Classical
   Languages, Literatures, and Linguistics, B
Clinical Laboratory Science/Medical
   Technology/Technologist, AB
Clinical Psychology, D
Communication Disorders, BM

Communication Studies/Speech Communication
   and Rhetoric, B
Community Organization and Advocacy, B
Community Psychology, M
Comparative Literature, B
Computer Engineering, B
Computer Programming, Specific Applications, A
Computer Programming/Programmer, AB
Computer Science, BMD
Computer Systems Analysis/Analyst, A
Computer Typography and Composition Equipment
   Operator, A
Construction Engineering Technology/Technician, AB
Consumer Merchandising/Retailing Management, A
Corrections, A
Counselor Education/School Counseling and
   Guidance Services, MDO
Criminal Justice/Police Science, A
Criminal Justice/Safety Studies, B
Criminology, A
Curriculum and Instruction, MDO
Data Processing and Data Processing
   Technology/Technician, A
Developmental and Child Psychology, B
Drafting and Design Technology/Technician, A
Drama and Dramatics/Theatre Arts, B
Drawing, B
Early Childhood Education and Teaching, MDO
Ecology, MD
Economics, BM
Education, BMDO
Education/Teaching of Individuals with Emotional
   Disturbances, B
Education/Teaching of Individuals with Hearing
   Impairments, Including Deafness, B
Education/Teaching of Individuals with Multiple
   Disabilities, B
Education/Teaching of Individuals with Specific
   Learning Disabilities, B
Education/Teaching of Individuals with Speech or
   Language Impairments, B
Education/Teaching of Individuals with Vision
   Impairments, Including Blindness, B
Educational Administration and Supervision, MDO
Educational Measurement and Evaluation, D
Educational Media/Instructional Technology, DO
Educational Psychology, MD
Educational/Instructional Media Design, B
Electrical Engineering, MD
Electrical, Electronic and Communications
   Engineering Technology/Technician, AB
Electrical, Electronics and Communications
   Engineering, B
Electromechanical Technology/Electromechanical
   Engineering Technology, B
Elementary Education and Teaching, BDO
Emergency Medical Technology/Technician (EMT
   Paramedic), A
Engineering, B
Engineering and Applied Sciences, M
Engineering Physics, B
English, M
English as a Second Language, M
English Education, M
English Language and Literature, B
English/Language Arts Teacher Education, B
Entrepreneurship/Entrepreneurial Studies, B
Environmental Engineering
   Technology/Environmental Technology, A
Environmental Studies, AB
European Studies/Civilization, B
Exercise and Sports Science, MD
Experimental Psychology, BMD
Film/Cinema Studies, B
Finance, B
Finance and Banking, M
Fine/Studio Arts, B
Fire Protection and Safety Technology/Technician, A
Foreign Language Teacher Education, M
Foundations and Philosophy of Education, MDO
French Language and Literature, BM
French Language Teacher Education, B
General Studies, AB
Geography, BM
Geology/Earth Science, BMD
German Language and Literature, BM

German Language Teacher Education, B
Gerontology, A
Health Education, D
Health Information/Medical Records
   Administration/Administrator, B
Health Teacher Education, B
Higher Education/Higher Education
   Administration, MD
History, BMD
Hospital and Health Care Facilities
   Administration/Management, B
Human Development and Family Studies, A
Human Resources Management/Personnel
   Administration, B
Human Services, MDO
Humanities/Humanistic Studies, B
Industrial and Manufacturing Management, D
Industrial Engineering, AB
Industrial Technology/Technician, AB
Industrial/Management Engineering, MD
Information Science/Studies, AB
Inorganic Chemistry, MD
International Business/Trade/Commerce, B
International Relations and Affairs, B
Journalism, B
Kindergarten/PreSchool Education and Teaching, B
Kinesiology and Exercise Science, B
Kinesiology and Movement Studies, MD
Latin American Studies, B
Law and Legal Studies, PO
Legal Administrative Assistant/Secretary, A
Legal Assistant/Paralegal, A
Leisure Studies, M
Liberal Arts and Sciences Studies and
   Humanities, AB
Liberal Studies, M
Linguistics, B
Logistics and Materials Management, AB
Management Information Systems and
   Services, BMD
Management Sciences and Quantitative Methods, B
Marketing, M
Marketing Research, B
Marketing/Marketing Management, B
Mass Communication/Media Studies, B
Mathematics, BMD
Mathematics Teacher Education, BM
Mechanical Engineering, BMD
Mechanical Engineering/Mechanical
   Technology/Technician, AB
Medical/Clinical Assistant, A
Medicinal and Pharmaceutical Chemistry, MD
Medieval and Renaissance Studies, B
Mental and Social Health Services and Allied
   Professions, B
Mental Health/Rehabilitation, A
Multi-/Interdisciplinary Studies, AB
Music, BM
Music Teacher Education, BM
Natural Sciences, AB
Near and Middle Eastern Studies, B
Nursing, B
Nursing - Registered Nurse Training, AB
Operations Management and Supervision, B
Organic Chemistry, MD
Organizational Behavior Studies, B
Parks, Recreation, Leisure and Fitness Studies, B
Performance, M
Pharmaceutical Administration, M
Pharmaceutical Sciences, M
Pharmacology, M
Pharmacy, BP
Pharmacy, Pharmaceutical Sciences, and Administration, B
Philosophy, BM
Physical Chemistry, MD
Physical Education Teaching and Coaching, BMD
Physical Sciences, B
Physical Therapy/Therapist, B
Physics, BMD
Political Science and Government, ABM
Pre-Dentistry Studies, B
Pre-Law Studies, B
Pre-Medicine/Pre-Medical Studies, B
Pre-Veterinary Studies, B
Psychiatric/Mental Health Services Technician, A
Psychology, BMD

Public Administration, M
Public Health, M
Public Health Education and Promotion, B
Public Policy Analysis, B
Recreation and Park Management, M
Rehabilitation Sciences, M
Religion/Religious Studies, B
Respiratory Care Therapy/Therapist, A
School Psychology, MO
Science Teacher Education/General Science
   Teacher Education, BM
Secondary Education and Teaching, BMDO
Social Sciences, A
Social Studies Teacher Education, BM
Social Work, AB
Sociology, BM
Spanish Language and Literature, BM
Spanish Language Teacher Education, B
Special Education and Teaching, BMDO
Speech-Language Pathology/Pathologist, B
Statistics, M
Structural Engineering, B
Substance Abuse/Addiction Counseling, A
Teacher Education and Professional
   Development, Specific Levels and Methods, B
Teacher Education and Professional
   Development, Specific Subject Areas, B
Trade and Industrial Teacher Education, B
Transportation and Materials Moving, A
Urban and Regional Planning, M
Urban Studies/Affairs, B
Vocational and Technical Education, MO
Welding Technology/Welder, A
Women's Studies, B

URBANA UNIVERSITY

Accounting, AB
Adult and Continuing Education and Teaching, B
Athletic Training and Sports Medicine, B
Biology/Biological Sciences, B
Business Administration and Management, AB
Business Administration, Management and
   Operations, M
Business/Managerial Economics, AB
Chemistry, B
Criminal Justice/Law Enforcement
   Administration, AB
Education, BM
Elementary Education and Teaching, B
English Language and Literature, B
Health Teacher Education, B
History, B
Human Resources Management/Personnel
   Administration, AB
Junior High/Intermediate/Middle School Education
   and Teaching, B
Liberal Arts and Sciences Studies and
   Humanities, AB
Marketing/Marketing Management, AB
Mass Communication/Media Studies, B
Philosophy, B
Pre-Dentistry Studies, B
Pre-Law Studies, B
Pre-Medicine/Pre-Medical Studies, B
Pre-Veterinary Studies, B
Psychology, B
Religion/Religious Studies, B
Science Teacher Education/General Science
   Teacher Education, B
Secondary Education and Teaching, B
Sociology, B

URSULINE COLLEGE

Accounting, B
American/United States Studies/Civilization, B
Art History, Criticism and Conservation, B
Art Teacher Education, B
Art Therapy/Therapist, M
Behavioral Sciences, B
Biological and Biomedical Sciences, B
Biology/Biological Sciences, B
BioTechnology, B
Business Administration and Management, B
Business Administration, Management and
   Operations, B
Christian Studies, B

Early Childhood Education and Teaching, B
Education, M
Educational Administration and Supervision, M
English Language and Literature, B
English/Language Arts Teacher Education, B
Environmental Biology, B
Fashion Merchandising, B
Fashion/Apparel Design, B
Fine/Studio Arts, B
Graphic Design, B
Health and Medical Administrative Services, B
Health Services Administration, B
Health Services/Allied Health/Health Sciences, B
Health/Health Care Administration/Management, B
Historic Preservation and Conservation, B
History, B
Hospital and Health Care Facilities
   Administration/Management, B
Human Resources Management/Personnel
   Administration, B
Humanities/Humanistic Studies, B
Interior Design, B
Junior High/Intermediate/Middle School Education
   and Teaching, B
Legal Assistant/Paralegal, B
Liberal Studies, M
Management, M
Management Information Systems and Services, B
Marketing/Marketing Management, B
Mathematics, B
Mathematics Teacher Education, B
Multi-/Interdisciplinary Studies, B
Nursing, M
Nursing - Registered Nurse Training, B
Philosophy, B
Psychology, B
Public Relations/Image Management, B
Religion/Religious Studies, B
Science Teacher Education/General Science
   Teacher Education, B
Social Studies Teacher Education, B
Social Work, B
Sociology, B
Special Education and Teaching, B
Theology and Religious Vocations, M
Work and Family Studies, B

VIRGINIA MARTI COLLEGE OF ART AND DESIGN

Commercial and Advertising Art, A
Fashion Merchandising, A
Fashion/Apparel Design, A
Interior Design, A
Metal and Jewelry Arts, A

WALSH UNIVERSITY

Accounting, AB
Athletic Training and Sports Medicine, B
Behavioral Sciences, B
Biological and Physical Sciences, B
Biology/Biological Sciences, B
Business Administration and Management, AB
Business Administration, Management and
   Operations, M
Chemistry, B
Communication and Media Studies, B
Computer Science, B
Counseling Psychology, M
Counselor Education/School Counseling and
   Guidance Services, M
Education, BM
Elementary Education and Teaching, B
English Language and Literature, B
Finance, AB
French Language and Literature, B
History, B
Human Services, AB
Kindergarten/PreSchool Education and Teaching, B
Liberal Arts and Sciences Studies and
   Humanities, AB
Marketing/Marketing Management, AB
Mathematics, B
Modern Languages, B
Nursing - Registered Nurse Training, AB
Pastoral Studies/Counseling, BM
Philosophy, B

Physical Education Teaching and Coaching, B
Physical Therapy/Therapist, M
Political Science and Government, B
Pre-Dentistry Studies, B
Pre-Medicine/Pre-Medical Studies, B
Pre-Veterinary Studies, B
Psychology, B
Religion/Religious Studies, B
Science Teacher Education/General Science
   Teacher Education, B
Secondary Education and Teaching, B
Sociology, B
Spanish Language and Literature, B
Special Education and Teaching, B
Theology/Theological Studies, B

WASHINGTON STATE COMMUNITY COLLEGE

Accounting, A
Administrative Assistant and Secretarial Science, A
Automobile/Automotive Mechanics
   Technology/Technician, A
Biological and Physical Sciences, A
Biology/Biological Sciences, A
Business Administration and Management, A
Chemical Engineering, A
Clinical/Medical Laboratory Technician, A
Computer Engineering Technology/Technician, A
Data Processing and Data Processing
   Technology/Technician, A
Drafting and Design Technology/Technician, A
Education, A
Electrical, Electronic and Communications
   Engineering Technology/Technician, A
Engineering, A
Heating, Air Conditioning, Ventilation and
   Refrigeration Maintenance
   Technology/Technician, A
Industrial Technology/Technician, A
Kindergarten/PreSchool Education and Teaching, A
Liberal Arts and Sciences Studies and
   Humanities, A
Licensed Practical/Vocational Nurse Training, A
Marketing/Marketing Management, A
Mathematics, A
Mechanical Engineering/Mechanical
   Technology/Technician, A
Medical Administrative Assistant/Secretary, A
Nursing - Registered Nurse Training, A
Physical Sciences, A
Radio and Television, A
Social Work, A

WILBERFORCE UNIVERSITY

Accounting, B
Accounting and Finance, B
Biology/Biological Sciences, B
Business Administration and Management, B
Business/Managerial Economics, B
Chemistry, B
Comparative Literature, B
Computer Engineering, B
Computer Science, B
Economics, B
Electrical, Electronics and Communications
   Engineering, B
Engineering Physics, B
Finance, B
Fine/Studio Arts, B
Health/Health Care Administration/Management, B
Information Science/Studies, B
Liberal Arts and Sciences Studies and
   Humanities, B
Marketing/Marketing Management, B
Mass Communication/Media Studies, B
Mathematics, B
Music Theory and Composition, B
Political Science and Government, B
Psychology, B
Rehabilitation Therapy, B
Sociology, B
Voice and Opera, B

WILMINGTON COLLEGE

Accounting, B
Agricultural Business and Management, B

Agricultural Teacher Education, B
Agriculture, B
Art Teacher Education, B
Athletic Training and Sports Medicine, B
Biological and Physical Sciences, B
Biology/Biological Sciences, B
Business Administration and Management, B
Business Teacher Education, B
Business/Managerial Economics, B
Chemistry, B
Computer Science, B
Criminal Justice/Law Enforcement Administration, B
Drama and Dramatics/Theatre Arts, B
Economics, B
Education, BM
Elementary Education and Teaching, B
English Language and Literature, B
Health Teacher Education, B
History, B
Liberal Arts and Sciences Studies and
  Humanities, B
Marketing/Marketing Management, B
Mass Communication/Media Studies, B
Mathematics, B
Modern Languages, B
Music Teacher Education, B
Philosophy, B
Physical Education Teaching and Coaching, B
Political Science and Government, B
Pre-Dentistry Studies, B
Pre-Law Studies, B
Pre-Medicine/Pre-Medical Studies, B
Pre-Veterinary Studies, B
Psychology, B
Reading Teacher Education, M
Religion/Religious Studies, B
Science Teacher Education/General Science
  Teacher Education, B
Secondary Education and Teaching, B
Social Sciences, B
Social Work, B
Spanish Language and Literature, B
Special Education and Teaching, M
Sport and Fitness Administration/Management, B

WITTENBERG UNIVERSITY

American/United States Studies/Civilization, B
Art/Art Studies, General, B
Biochemistry, Biophysics and Molecular Biology, B
Biology/Biological Sciences, B
Business Administration and Management, B
Business/Managerial Economics, B
Chemistry, B
Communication Studies/Speech Communication
  and Rhetoric, B
Computer Science, B
Dance, B
Drama and Dramatics/Theatre Arts, B
East Asian Studies, B
Economics, B
Education, B
English Language and Literature, B
Environmental Studies, B
French Language and Literature, B
Geography, B
Geology/Earth Science, B
German Language and Literature, B
History, B
Liberal Arts and Sciences Studies and
  Humanities, B
Mathematics, B
Music, B
Music Performance, B
Music Teacher Education, B
Music Theory and Composition, B
Philosophy, B
Physical Sciences, B
Physics, B
Political Science and Government, B
Psychology, B
Religion/Religious Studies, B
Religious/Sacred Music, B
Russian Studies, B
Sociology, B
Spanish Language and Literature, B

Urban Studies/Affairs, B

WRIGHT STATE UNIVERSITY

Accounting, BM
Accounting Technology/Technician and
  Bookkeeping, A
Administration of Special Education, B
Administrative Assistant and Secretarial Science, A
Adult and Continuing Education and Teaching, O
Adult Health Nurse/Nursing, B
African-American/Black Studies, B
Allopathic Medicine, P
Anatomy, BM
Anthropology, B
Applied Economics, M
Applied Mathematics, BM
Area Studies, B
Art History, Criticism and Conservation, B
Art Teacher Education, B
Art Therapy/Therapist, B
Art/Art Studies, General, B
Arts Management, B
Biochemistry, BM
Biological and Biomedical Sciences, MD
Biological and Physical Sciences, B
Biology/Biological Sciences, AB
Biomedical Engineering, M
Biomedical Technology/Technician, B
Biomedical/Medical Engineering, B
Biophysics, M
Business Administration and Management, B
Business Administration, Management and
  Operations, MO
Business Education, M
Business Teacher Education, B
Business/Commerce, B
Business/Managerial Economics, B
Chemistry, ABM
City/Urban, Community and Regional Planning, B
Classics and Classical
  Languages, Literatures, and Linguistics, B
Clinical Laboratory Science/Medical
  Technology/Technologist, B
Clinical Psychology, D
Communication Studies/Speech Communication
  and Rhetoric, AB
Community Health Nursing, M
Community Psychology, B
Computer and Information Sciences, B
Computer Education, M
Computer Engineering, BMD
Computer Science, BMD
Computer Teacher Education, B
Construction Engineering Technology/Technician, A
Counselor Education/School Counseling and
  Guidance Services, BM
Criminal Justice/Police Science, B
Criminology, BM
Curriculum and Instruction, BMO
Dance, B
Data Processing and Data Processing
  Technology/Technician, A
Drafting and Design Technology/Technician, A
Drama and Dramatics/Theatre Arts, B
Drawing, B
Early Childhood Education and Teaching, M
Economics, BMO
Education, BMO
Education/Teaching of Individuals with Emotional
  Disturbances, B
Education/Teaching of Individuals with Mental
  Retardation, B
Education/Teaching of Individuals with Multiple
  Disabilities, B
Education/Teaching of Individuals with Orthopedic
  and Other Physical Health Impairments, B
Education/Teaching of Individuals with Specific
  Learning Disabilities, B
Education/Teaching of the Gifted and Talented, BM
Educational Administration and Supervision, MO
Educational Leadership and Administration, BMO
Educational, Instructional, and Curriculum
  Supervision, B
Electrical Engineering, M
Electrical, Electronic and Communications
  Engineering Technology/Technician, A

Electrical, Electronics and Communications
  Engineering, B
Electromechanical Technology/Electromechanical
  Engineering Technology, A
Elementary Education and Teaching, BM
Engineering, B
Engineering and Applied Sciences, MD
Engineering Physics, B
Engineering Science, B
English, M
English as a Second Language, M
English Language and Literature, B
English/Language Arts Teacher Education, B
Environmental Engineering
  Technology/Environmental Technology, B
Environmental Health, B
Environmental Sciences, BMD
Environmental Studies, M
Ergonomics and Human Factors, MD
Film/Cinema Studies, B
Finance, B
Finance and Banking, MO
Foreign Language Teacher Education, B
Foreign Languages and Literatures, B
French Language and Literature, B
General Office Occupations and Clerical Services, A
Geochemistry, M
Geography, AB
Geology/Earth Science, BM
Geophysics and Seismology, BM
German Language and Literature, B
Health Education, M
Health Promotion, M
Health Services Administration, M
Health Teacher Education, B
Health/Health Care Administration/Management, B
Health/Medical Preparatory Programs, B
Higher Education/Higher Education
  Administration, BMO
History, ABM
Human Resources Management/Personnel
  Administration, B
Humanities/Humanistic Studies, BM
Hydrology and Water Resources Science, BM
Immunology, M
Industrial and Organizational Psychology, BMD
Industrial Technology/Technician, A
Information Science/Studies, B
Interdisciplinary Studies, M
International and Comparative Education, M
International Business/Trade/Commerce, M
International Relations and Affairs, B
Junior High/Intermediate/Middle School Education
  and Teaching, B
Kindergarten/PreSchool Education and Teaching, B
Legal Administrative Assistant/Secretary, A
Liberal Arts and Sciences Studies and
  Humanities, B
Library Science, M
Linguistics, B
Logistics and Materials Management, BM
Management Information Systems and
  Services, ABMO
Management Science, B
Marketing, MO
Marketing/Marketing Management, AB
Mass Communication/Media Studies, B
Materials Engineering, BM
Materials Sciences, M
Mathematics, BM
Mathematics Teacher Education, BM
Mechanical Engineering, BM
Medical Administrative Assistant/Secretary, A
Medical Physics, M
Mental and Social Health Services and Allied
  Professions, B
Microbiological Sciences and Immunology, B
Microbiology, M
Middle School Education, M
Military Technologies, B
Modern Greek Language and Literature, B
Modern Languages, B
Molecular Biology, M
Multi-/Interdisciplinary Studies, B
Music, B
Music History, Literature, and Theory, B

Music Performance, B
Music Teacher Education, BM
Music Theory and Composition, B
Nursing, BMO
Nursing - Adult, M
Nursing - Advanced Practice, M
Nursing - Registered Nurse Training, B
Nursing Administration, M
Occupational Safety and Health
   Technology/Technician, A
Office Management and Supervision, B
Operations Management and Supervision, B
Organizational Communication, B
Pediatric Nurse/Nursing, M
Performance, M
Pharmacology, M
Pharmacology and Toxicology, B
Philosophy, B
Photography, B
Physical Education Teaching and Coaching, BM
Physics, BM
Physiology, M
Political Science and Government, B
Pre-Dentistry Studies, B
Pre-Law Studies, B
Pre-Medicine/Pre-Medical Studies, B
Pre-Pharmacy Studies, B
Pre-Veterinary Studies, B
Project Management, M
Psychology, ABMD
Public Administration, BM
Public Health, M
Public Health/Community Nurse/Nursing, B
Purchasing, Procurement/Acquisitions and
   Contracts Management, B
Reading Teacher Education, B
Recreation and Park Management, M
Rehabilitation Counseling, M
Religion/Religious Studies, B
Rhetoric, M
Sales and Marketing Operations/Marketing and
   Distribution Teacher Education, B
School Nursing, M
Science Teacher Education/General Science
   Teacher Education, BM
Secondary Education and Teaching, BM
Social Studies Teacher Education, B
Social Work, AB
Sociology, AB
Spanish Language and Literature, B
Special Education and Teaching, BM
Statistics, BM
Systems Engineering, B
Systems Science and Theory, B
Teacher Education and Professional
   Development, Specific Levels and Methods, B
Teacher Education and Professional
   Development, Specific Subject Areas, B
Teacher Education, Multiple Levels, B
Teaching English as a Second or Foreign
   Language/ESL Language Instructor, B
Technical Teacher Education, B
Technical Theatre/Theatre Design and
   Technology, B
Toxicology, M
Trade and Industrial Teacher Education, B
Urban Studies/Affairs, BM
Vocational and Technical Education, M
Vocational Rehabilitation Counseling/Counselor, B
Water Quality and Wastewater Treatment
   Management and Recycling
   Technology/Technician, A
Women's Studies, B
Writing, M

WRIGHT STATE
UNIVERSITY, LAKE CAMPUS

Accounting, A
Administrative Assistant and Secretarial Science, A
Biology/Biological Sciences, A
Business Administration and Management, A
Chemistry, A
Computer Typography and Composition Equipment
   Operator, A
Consumer Merchandising/Retailing Management, A
Drafting and Design Technology/Technician, A

Electrical, Electronic and Communications
   Engineering Technology/Technician, A
Elementary Education and Teaching, A
Engineering, A
Engineering Technology, A
English Language and Literature, A
Finance, A
Geography, A
History, A
Industrial Technology/Technician, A
Legal Administrative Assistant/Secretary, A
Liberal Arts and Sciences Studies and
   Humanities, A
Management Information Systems and Services, A
Marketing/Marketing Management, A
Mass Communication/Media Studies, A
Mechanical Engineering/Mechanical
   Technology/Technician, A
Medical Administrative Assistant/Secretary, A
Pre-Engineering, A
Psychology, A
Social Work, A
Sociology, A

XAVIER UNIVERSITY

Accounting, BM
Advertising, AB
Art/Art Studies, General, B
Athletic Training and Sports Medicine, B
Biological and Physical Sciences, B
Biology Teacher Education, B
Biology/Biological Sciences, B
Business Administration and Management, AB
Business Administration, Management and
   Operations, MO
Business/Managerial Economics, B
Chemical Engineering, B
Chemistry, B
Chemistry Teacher Education, B
Classics and Classical
   Languages, Literatures, and Linguistics, B
Clinical Laboratory Science/Medical
   Technology/Technologist, B
Clinical Psychology, D
Computer Science, B
Corrections, A
Counselor Education/School Counseling and
   Guidance Services, M
Criminal Justice/Safety Studies, AB
Criminology, M
Early Childhood Education and Teaching, M
Economics, B
Education, BM
Educational Administration and Supervision, M
Electronic Commerce, M
Elementary Education and Teaching, BM
English, M
English Language and Literature, AB
Entrepreneurship/Entrepreneurial Studies, BM
Finance, B
Finance and Banking, M
Fine/Studio Arts, B
French Language and Literature, AB
German Language and Literature, AB
Health Services Administration, MO
History, AB
Human Resources Development, M
Human Resources Management/Personnel
   Administration, B
International Business/Trade/Commerce, BM
International Relations and Affairs, B
Junior High/Intermediate/Middle School Education
   and Teaching, M
Liberal Arts and Sciences Studies and
   Humanities, AB
Management Information Systems and
   Services, BM
Marketing, M
Marketing/Marketing Management, B
Mathematics, B
Montessori Teacher Education, B
Multilingual and Multicultural Education, M
Music, B
Music Teacher Education, B
Natural Sciences, B
Nursing, MO

Nursing Administration, MO
Nursing Science, B
Occupational Therapy/Therapist, B
Philosophy, B
Physics, B
Physics Teacher Education, B
Political Science and Government, AB
Psychology, ABMD
Public Relations/Image Management, AB
Radio and Television, AB
Reading Teacher Education, M
Science Teacher Education/General Science
   Teacher Education, B
Secondary Education and Teaching, M
Social Work, B
Sociology, AB
Spanish Language and Literature, AB
Special Education and Teaching, BM
Sport and Fitness Administration/Management, BM
Teacher Education and Professional
   Development, Specific Levels and Methods, B
Theology and Religious Vocations, M
Theology/Theological Studies, AB

YOUNGSTOWN STATE UNIVERSITY

Accounting, ABM
Advertising, B
African-American/Black Studies, B
American/United States Studies/Civilization, B
Anthropology, B
Art History, Criticism and Conservation, B
Art Teacher Education, B
Art/Art Studies, General, B
Astronomy, B
Athletic Training and Sports Medicine, B
Biological and Biomedical Sciences, M
Biology Teacher Education, B
Biology/Biological Sciences, B
Business Administration and Management, AB
Business Administration, Management and
   Operations, M
Business Teacher Education, B
Business/Commerce, AB
Business/Managerial Economics, B
Chemical Engineering, BM
Chemistry, BM
Child Care and Support Services Management, A
Child Development, AB
Civil Engineering, BM
Civil Engineering Technology/Technician, AB
Clinical Laboratory Science/Medical
   Technology/Technologist, B
Clinical/Medical Laboratory Technician, A
Community Health Services/Liaison/Counseling, B
Composition, M
Computer Programming/Programmer, AB
Computer Science, B
Counselor Education/School Counseling and
   Guidance Services, M
Criminal Justice/Law Enforcement Administration, B
Criminal Justice/Safety Studies, AB
Criminology, M
Data Processing and Data Processing
   Technology/Technician, A
Dental Hygiene/Hygienist, A
Dietetics/Dieticians, AB
Dietician Assistant, A
Drafting and Design Technology/Technician, A
Drama and Dance Teacher Education, B
Early Childhood Education and Teaching, BM
Economics, BM
Education, BMD
Education/Teaching of the Gifted and Talented, M
Educational Administration and Supervision, MD
Educational Leadership and Administration, D
Electrical Engineering, M
Electrical, Electronic and Communications
   Engineering Technology/Technician, AB
Electrical, Electronics and Communications
   Engineering, B
Elementary Education and Teaching, BM
Emergency Medical Technology/Technician (EMT
   Paramedic), A
Engineering, B
Engineering and Applied Sciences, M
Engineering Technology, B

English, M
English Language and Literature, B
English/Language Arts Teacher Education, B
Environmental Engineering
   Technology/Environmental Technology, M
Environmental Studies, MO
Family and Community Services, B
Family and Consumer Sciences/Home Economics
   Teacher Education, B
Family and Consumer Sciences/Human Sciences, B
Fashion Merchandising, B
Finance, AB
Finance and Banking, M
Fine/Studio Arts, B
Foods, Nutrition, and Wellness Studies, B
Foreign Language Teacher Education, B
Foreign Languages and Literatures, B
Forensic Science and Technology, B
Foundations and Philosophy of Education, MD
French Language and Literature, B
French Language Teacher Education, B
General Studies, B
Geography, B
Geology/Earth Science, B
Graphic Design, B
Health and Physical Education, B
Health Services Administration, M
Health Teacher Education, B
History, BM
Hospital and Health Care Facilities
   Administration/Management, B
Hospitality Administration/Management, AB
Human Development and Family Studies, B
Human Services, M
Industrial Engineering, B
Industrial/Management Engineering, M
Italian Language and Literature, B
Journalism, B
Junior High/Intermediate/Middle School Education
   and Teaching, B
Kinesiology and Exercise Science, B
Labor and Industrial Relations, A
Legal Administrative Assistant/Secretary, A
Liberal Arts and Sciences Studies and
   Humanities, AB
Management Information Systems and Services, B
Marketing, M
Marketing/Marketing Management, AB
Mathematics, BM
Mathematics Teacher Education, B
Mechanical Engineering, BM
Mechanical Engineering/Mechanical
   Technology/Technician, AB
Medical/Clinical Assistant, A
Middle School Education, M
Music, BM
Music History, Literature, and Theory, BM
Music Performance, B
Music Teacher Education, BM
Music Theory and Composition, BM
Nursing, M
Nursing - Registered Nurse Training, B
Operations Management and Supervision, B
Painting, B
Pediatric Nurse/Nursing, B
Performance, M
Philosophy, B
Photography, B
Physical Education Teaching and Coaching, B
Physical Therapy/Therapist, M
Physics, B
Political Science and Government, B
Pre-Dentistry Studies, B
Pre-Law Studies, B
Pre-Medicine/Pre-Medical Studies, B
Pre-Pharmacy Studies, B
Pre-Veterinary Studies, B
Printmaking, B
Psychology, B
Public Health (MPH, DPH), B
Radio and Television, B
Reading Teacher Education, M
Religion/Religious Studies, B
Respiratory Care Therapy/Therapist, B
Science Teacher Education/General Science
   Teacher Education, B

Secondary Education and Teaching, BM
Social Science Teacher Education, B
Social Sciences, B
Social Studies Teacher Education, B
Social Work, B
Sociology, B
Spanish Language and Literature, B
Spanish Language Teacher Education, B
Special Education and Teaching, BM
Speech and Rhetorical Studies, B
Technical and Business Writing, B

ZANE STATE COLLEGE

Accounting, A
Administrative Assistant and Secretarial Science, A
Business Administration and Management, A
Child Care Provider/Assistant, A
Clinical/Medical Laboratory Assistant, A
Computer Programming, Specific Applications, A
Criminal Justice/Law Enforcement Administration, A
Culinary Arts/Chef Training, A
Data Entry/Microcomputer Applications, A
Drafting and Design Technology/Technician, A
Electrical, Electronic and Communications
   Engineering Technology/Technician, A
Environmental Studies, A
Human Resources Management/Personnel
   Administration, A
Industrial Radiologic Technology/Technician, A
Industrial Technology/Technician, A
Legal Assistant/Paralegal, A
Marketing/Marketing Management, A
Medical/Clinical Assistant, A
Mental Health/Rehabilitation, A
Natural Resources Management/Development and
   Policy, A
Occupational Therapy/Therapist, A
Parks, Recreation and Leisure Facilities
   Management, A
Parks, Recreation, Leisure and Fitness Studies, A
Physical Therapist Assistant, A
Social Work, A
Tourism and Travel Services Management, A
Web Page, Digital/Multimedia and Information
   Resources Design, A

Oklahoma

BACONE COLLEGE

Accounting, AB
Administrative Assistant and Secretarial Science, A
American Indian/Native American Studies, A
Art/Art Studies, General, A
Business Administration and Management, AB
Cardiopulmonary Technology/Technologist, A
Computer Science, A
Drama and Dramatics/Theatre Arts, A
Early Childhood Education and Teaching, B
Education, AB
Elementary Education and Teaching, B
Entrepreneurship/Entrepreneurial Studies, B
Finance, B
General Studies, A
History, A
Horticultural Science, A
Humanities/Humanistic Studies, A
Journalism, A
Liberal Arts and Sciences Studies and
   Humanities, A
Mass Communication/Media Studies, A
Mathematics, A
Medical Radiologic Technology/Science - Radiation
   Therapist, A
Natural Resources Management/Development and
   Policy, A
Nursing - Registered Nurse Training, AB
Physical Education Teaching and Coaching, B
Physical Sciences, A
Political Science and Government, A
Sales, Distribution and Marketing Operations, B
Sociology, A

Substance Abuse/Addiction Counseling, A

CAMERON UNIVERSITY

Accounting, B
Agriculture, B
Allied Health
   Diagnostic, Intervention, and Treatment
   Professions, A
Art/Art Studies, General, B
Biology/Biological Sciences, B
Business Administration and Management, AB
Business Administration, Management and
   Operations, M
Chemistry, B
Child Care and Support Services Management, A
Clinical Laboratory Science/Medical
   Technology/Technologist, B
Clinical/Medical Laboratory Technician, B
Communication Studies/Speech Communication
   and Rhetoric, AB
Computer and Information Sciences, B
Criminal Justice/Police Science, AB
Digital Communication and Media/Multimedia, A
Drafting and Design Technology/Technician, B
Education, BM
Educational Leadership and Administration, M
Electrical, Electronic and Communications
   Engineering Technology/Technician, AB
Elementary Education and Teaching, B
Engineering Technologies/Technicians, AB
English Language and Literature, B
Family and Consumer Sciences/Human Sciences, B
Health and Physical Education, B
History, B
Industrial Technology/Technician, A
Management Information Systems and Services, A
Mathematics, B
Mechanical Drafting and Mechanical Drafting
   CAD/CADD, A
Music, B
Natural Sciences, B
Physics, B
Political Science and Government, B
Psychology, BM
Respiratory Care Therapy/Therapist, A
Romance Languages, Literatures, and Linguistics, B
Sociology, B
Teacher Education and Professional
   Development, Specific Subject Areas, B
Visual and Performing Arts, B

CARL ALBERT STATE COLLEGE

Accounting, A
Administrative Assistant and Secretarial Science, A
Agricultural Business and Management, A
Art Teacher Education, A
Biology/Biological Sciences, A
Business Administration and Management, A
Business Teacher Education, A
Computer Science, A
Elementary Education and Teaching, A
English Language and Literature, A
Hotel/Motel Administration/Management, A
Journalism, A
Kindergarten/PreSchool Education and Teaching, A
Legal Administrative Assistant/Secretary, A
Mathematics, A
Medical Administrative Assistant/Secretary, A
Music, A
Nursing - Registered Nurse Training, A
Physical Education Teaching and Coaching, A
Physical Sciences, A
Physical Therapist Assistant, A
Pre-Engineering, A
Psychology, A
Social Sciences, A
Speech and Rhetorical Studies, A
Technology Education/Industrial Arts, A
Zoology/Animal Biology, A

COMMUNITY CARE COLLEGE

Business Administration, Management and
   Operations, A
Dental Assisting/Assistant, A
Health/Health Care Administration/Management, A
Massage Therapy/Therapeutic Massage, A

Medical/Clinical Assistant, A
Pharmacy Technician/Assistant, A
Surgical Technology/Technologist, A
Veterinary/Animal Health Technology/Technician and
  Veterinary Assistant, A

CONNORS STATE COLLEGE

Animal Sciences, A
Biology/Biological Sciences, A
Business Administration and Management, A
Chemistry, A
Child Development, A
Computer Science, A
Criminal Justice/Police Science, A
Education, A
Engineering, A
Family and Consumer Sciences/Human Sciences, A
General Studies, A
Health Services/Allied Health/Health Sciences, A
History, A
Horticultural Science, A
Journalism, A
Mathematics, A
Nursing - Registered Nurse Training, A
Pre-Nursing Studies, A
Psychology, A
Social Work, A
Sociology, A

EAST CENTRAL UNIVERSITY

Accounting, B
Advertising, B
Art Teacher Education, B
Art/Art Studies, General, B
Biology Teacher Education, B
Biology/Biological Sciences, B
Business Administration and Management, B
Business Teacher Education, B
Business/Managerial Economics, B
Business/Office Automation/Technology/Data
  Entry, B
Cartography, B
Chemistry, B
Chemistry Teacher Education, B
Clinical/Medical Laboratory Technician, B
Comparative Literature, B
Computer Science, B
Consumer Merchandising/Retailing Management, B
Corrections, B
Counselor Education/School Counseling and
  Guidance Services, BM
Criminal Justice/Law Enforcement Administration, B
Criminal Justice/Police Science, B
Criminology, M
Drafting and Design Technology/Technician, B
Early Childhood Education and Teaching, B
Ecology, B
Education, BM
Electrical, Electronic and Communications
  Engineering Technology/Technician, B
Elementary Education and Teaching, B
English Language and Literature, B
English/Language Arts Teacher Education, B
Entrepreneurship/Entrepreneurial Studies, B
Environmental Health, B
Environmental Sciences, B
Environmental Studies, B
Family and Consumer Sciences/Home Economics
  Teacher Education, B
Family and Consumer Sciences/Human Sciences, B
Fashion Merchandising, B
Finance, B
General Studies, B
Health Information/Medical Records
  Administration/Administrator, B
Health Teacher Education, B
History, B
History Teacher Education, B
Human Resources Management and Services, M
Human Resources Management/Personnel
  Administration, B
Human Services, B
Hydrology and Water Resources Science, B
Juvenile Corrections, B
Kindergarten/PreSchool Education and Teaching, B
Law and Legal Studies, B

Management Information Systems and Services, B
Marketing/Marketing Management, B
Mass Communication/Media Studies, B
Mathematics, B
Mathematics Teacher Education, B
Medical Staff Services Technology/Technician, B
Music, B
Music Teacher Education, B
Nursing - Registered Nurse Training, B
Physical Education Teaching and Coaching, B
Physics, B
Physics Teacher Education, B
Piano and Organ, B
Political Science and Government, B
Pre-Dentistry Studies, B
Pre-Law Studies, B
Pre-Medicine/Pre-Medical Studies, B
Pre-Pharmacy Studies, B
Pre-Veterinary Studies, B
Psychology, BM
Public Relations, Advertising, and Applied
  Communication, B
Public Relations/Image Management, B
Radio and Television, B
Rehabilitation Counseling, M
Science Teacher Education/General Science
  Teacher Education, B
Secondary Education and Teaching, B
Social Work, B
Sociology, B
Special Education and Teaching, B
Speech and Rhetorical Studies, B
Speech Teacher Education, B
Theatre/Theatre Arts Management, B
Voice and Opera, B

EASTERN OKLAHOMA STATE COLLEGE

Accounting, A
Administrative Assistant and Secretarial Science, A
Agricultural Business and Management, A
Agricultural Economics, A
Agricultural Teacher Education, A
Agronomy and Crop Science, A
Animal Sciences, A
Art Teacher Education, A
Art/Art Studies, General, A
Biology/Biological Sciences, A
Business Administration and Management, A
Business Teacher Education, A
Chemistry, A
Clinical Laboratory Science/Medical
  Technology/Technologist, A
Clinical/Medical Laboratory Technician, A
Computer Engineering Technology/Technician, A
Computer Science, A
Corrections, A
Criminal Justice/Law Enforcement Administration, A
Drama and Dramatics/Theatre Arts, A
Economics, A
Education, A
Electrical, Electronic and Communications
  Engineering Technology/Technician, A
Elementary Education and Teaching, A
English Language and Literature, A
Environmental Studies, A
Farm/Farm and Ranch Management, A
Fashion Merchandising, A
Forestry, A
Forestry Technology/Technician, A
History, A
Horticultural Science, A
Journalism, A
Legal Administrative Assistant/Secretary, A
Marketing/Marketing Management, A
Mathematics, A
Medical/Clinical Assistant, A
Music, A
Nursing - Registered Nurse Training, A
Physical Education Teaching and Coaching, A
Physical Sciences, A
Political Science and Government, A
Pre-Engineering, A
Psychology, A
Range Science and Management, A

Science Teacher Education/General Science
  Teacher Education, A
Sociology, A
Speech and Rhetorical Studies, A
Survey Technology/Surveying, A
Technology Education/Industrial Arts, A
Wildlife and Wildlands Science and Management, A

HILLSDALE FREE WILL BAPTIST COLLEGE

Bible/Biblical Studies, A
Business/Commerce, AB
Elementary Education and Teaching, A
English Language and Literature, A
General Studies, A
Interdisciplinary Studies, AB
Liberal Arts and Sciences Studies and
  Humanities, A
Mathematics, A
Missions/Missionary Studies and Missiology, AB
Music, A
Nursing - Registered Nurse Training, A
Pastoral Studies/Counseling, M
Physical Education Teaching and Coaching, A
Psychology, A
Religious Education, AB
Religious/Sacred Music, AB
Theology/Theological Studies, B

ITT TECHNICAL INSTITUTE

Business Administration and Management, B
CAD/CADD Drafting and/or Design
  Technology/Technician, A
Computer and Information Systems Security, B
Criminal Justice/Law Enforcement Administration, B
Electrical, Electronic and Communications
  Engineering Technology/Technician, AB
System, Networking, and LAN/WAN
  Management/Manager, A
Web Page, Digital/Multimedia and Information
  Resources Design, A

LANGSTON UNIVERSITY

Accounting, B
Administrative Assistant and Secretarial Science, B
Agricultural Economics, B
Agricultural Teacher Education, B
Animal Sciences, B
Art Teacher Education, B
Art/Art Studies, General, B
Biology/Biological Sciences, B
Broadcast Journalism, B
Business Administration and Management, B
Chemistry, B
Clinical Laboratory Science/Medical
  Technology/Technologist, B
Computer Science, B
Corrections, B
Criminal Justice/Law Enforcement Administration, B
Criminal Justice/Police Science, B
Developmental and Child Psychology, B
Dietetics/Dieticians, B
Drafting and Design Technology/Technician, A
Drama and Dramatics/Theatre Arts, B
Economics, B
Education, BM
Electrical, Electronic and Communications
  Engineering Technology/Technician, A
Elementary Education and Teaching, BM
English as a Second Language, M
English Language and Literature, B
Family and Consumer Sciences/Home Economics
  Teacher Education, B
Family and Consumer Sciences/Human Sciences, B
Foods, Nutrition, and Wellness Studies, B
Gerontology, B
Health/Health Care Administration/Management, B
History, B
Hotel/Motel Administration/Management, B
Industrial Technology/Technician, B
Journalism, B
Kindergarten/PreSchool Education and Teaching, B
Liberal Arts and Sciences Studies and
  Humanities, B
Mass Communication/Media Studies, B
Mathematics, B

Multilingual and Multicultural Education, M
Music, B
Music Teacher Education, B
Nursing - Registered Nurse Training, B
Physical Education Teaching and Coaching, B
Physical Therapy/Therapist, B
Pre-Dentistry Studies, B
Pre-Law Studies, B
Pre-Medicine/Pre-Medical Studies, B
Pre-Veterinary Studies, B
Psychology, B
Radio and Television, B
Rehabilitation Counseling, M
Secondary Education and Teaching, B
Sociology, B
Special Education and Teaching, B
Teaching English as a Second or Foreign
   Language/ESL Language Instructor, B
Technology Education/Industrial Arts, B
Urban Education and Leadership, M
Urban Studies/Affairs, B
Voice and Opera, B

METROPOLITAN COLLEGE (TULSA)

Court Reporting/Court Reporter, AB
Legal Assistant/Paralegal, A

MID-AMERICA CHRISTIAN UNIVERSITY

Behavioral Sciences, B
Bible/Biblical Studies, B
Business Administration and Management, B
Divinity/Ministry (BD, MDiv.), B
Elementary Education and Teaching, B
English Language and Literature, B
Liberal Arts and Sciences Studies and
   Humanities, A
Music, B
Music Teacher Education, B
Piano and Organ, B
Religion/Religious Studies, B
Religious/Sacred Music, B
Secondary Education and Teaching, B
Theology/Theological Studies, B
Voice and Opera, B

MURRAY STATE COLLEGE

Administrative Assistant and Secretarial Science, A
Agricultural Teacher Education, A
Agriculture, A
Animal Sciences, A
Art/Art Studies, General, A
Biological and Physical Sciences, A
Business Administration and Management, A
Business Teacher Education, A
Chemistry, A
Child Development, A
Computer Science, A
Drafting and Design Technology/Technician, A
Electrical, Electronic and Communications
   Engineering Technology/Technician, A
Elementary Education and Teaching, A
Engineering, A
Engineering Technology, A
English Language and Literature, A
Equestrian/Equine Studies, A
History, A
Information Science/Studies, A
Liberal Arts and Sciences Studies and
   Humanities, A
Mathematics, A
Metallurgical Technology/Technician, A
Natural Resources and Conservation, A
Nursing - Registered Nurse Training, A
Physical Education Teaching and Coaching, A
Physical Therapy/Therapist, A
Pre-Engineering, A
Public Health (MPH, DPH), A
Veterinary/Animal Health Technology/Technician and
   Veterinary Assistant, A

NORTHEASTERN OKLAHOMA AGRICULTURAL AND MECHANICAL COLLEGE

Accounting, A
Administrative Assistant and Secretarial Science, A

Agricultural Business and Management, A
Agricultural Economics, A
Agronomy and Crop Science, A
American Indian/Native American Studies, A
Animal Sciences, A
Apparel and Textiles, A
Art Teacher Education, A
Art/Art Studies, General, A
Biology/Biological Sciences, A
Botany/Plant Biology, A
Broadcast Journalism, A
Business Administration and Management, A
Chemistry, A
Child Development, A
Computer Programming/Programmer, A
Computer Science, A
Computer Typography and Composition Equipment
   Operator, A
Construction Engineering Technology/Technician, A
Criminal Justice/Law Enforcement Administration, A
Dairy Science, A
Drafting and Design Technology/Technician, A
Drama and Dramatics/Theatre Arts, A
Economics, A
Electrical, Electronic and Communications
   Engineering Technology/Technician, A
Elementary Education and Teaching, A
Forestry, A
Graphic and Printing Equipment Operator
   Production, A
Horticultural Science, A
Hotel/Motel Administration/Management, A
Journalism, A
Legal Administrative Assistant/Secretary, A
Marketing/Marketing Management, A
Mathematics, A
Mechanical Engineering/Mechanical
   Technology/Technician, A
Medical Administrative Assistant/Secretary, A
Music, A
Nursing - Registered Nurse Training, A
Philosophy, A
Photography, A
Physical Education Teaching and Coaching, A
Physical Sciences, A
Physical Therapy/Therapist, A
Piano and Organ, A
Plastics Engineering Technology/Technician, A
Political Science and Government, A
Pre-Engineering, A
Psychology, A
Social Sciences, A
Social Work, A
Sociology, A
Technology Education/Industrial Arts, A
Trade and Industrial Teacher Education, A
Welding Technology/Welder, A
Wildlife and Wildlands Science and Management, A
Wildlife Biology, A

NORTHEASTERN STATE UNIVERSITY

Accounting, BM
American Indian/Native American Studies, B
American/United States Studies/Civilization, M
Art Teacher Education, B
Art/Art Studies, General, B
Audiology/Audiologist and Speech-Language
   Pathology/Pathologist, B
Biology/Biological Sciences, B
Business Administration and Management, B
Business Administration, Management and
   Operations, M
Business Teacher Education, B
Cell/Cellular Biology and Histology, B
Chemistry, B
Clinical Laboratory Science/Medical
   Technology/Technologist, B
Commercial and Advertising Art, B
Communication and Media Studies, M
Communication Disorders, BM
Computer Science, B
Counseling Psychology, M
Counselor Education/School Counseling and
   Guidance Services, M
Criminal Justice/Law Enforcement Administration, B
Criminal Justice/Police Science, B

Criminology, M
Drama and Dramatics/Theatre Arts, B
Early Childhood Education and Teaching, M
Education, BM
Educational Administration and Supervision, M
Electrical, Electronic and Communications
   Engineering Technology/Technician, B
Elementary Education and Teaching, B
Engineering Physics, B
English, M
English Language and Literature, B
Family and Consumer Sciences/Home Economics
   Teacher Education, B
Family and Consumer Sciences/Human Sciences, B
Fashion Merchandising, B
Finance, B
Finance and Banking, M
Fine/Studio Arts, B
Foods, Nutrition, and Wellness Studies, B
Geography, B
Health Teacher Education, B
Health/Health Care Administration/Management, B
Higher Education/Higher Education
   Administration, M
History, B
Human Resources Management/Personnel
   Administration, B
Industrial and Manufacturing Management, M
Industrial Technology/Technician, B
Journalism, B
Kindergarten/PreSchool Education and Teaching, B
Library Science, B
Marketing/Marketing Management, B
Mathematics, B
Medical Microbiology and Bacteriology, B
Music, B
Music Teacher Education, B
Nursing - Registered Nurse Training, B
Ophthalmic/Optometric Services, B
Optometry, P
Physical Education Teaching and Coaching, B
Physics, B
Piano and Organ, B
Political Science and Government, B
Pre-Dentistry Studies, B
Pre-Law Studies, B
Pre-Medicine/Pre-Medical Studies, B
Pre-Veterinary Studies, B
Psychology, BM
Reading Teacher Education, BM
Secondary Education and Teaching, B
Social Work, B
Sociology, B
Spanish Language and Literature, B
Special Education and Teaching, BM
Technology Education/Industrial Arts, B
Tourism and Travel Services Management, B
Trade and Industrial Teacher Education, B
Voice and Opera, B
Wildlife Biology, B
Zoology/Animal Biology, B

NORTHERN OKLAHOMA COLLEGE

Accounting, A
Administrative Assistant and Secretarial Science, A
Agricultural Business and Management, A
Biological and Physical Sciences, A
Broadcast Journalism, A
Business Administration and Management, A
Commercial and Advertising Art, A
Computer Science, A
Construction Engineering Technology/Technician, A
Criminal Justice/Law Enforcement Administration, A
Drafting and Design Technology/Technician, A
Elementary Education and Teaching, A
Engineering, A
Graphic and Printing Equipment Operator
   Production, A
Information Science/Studies, A
Liberal Arts and Sciences Studies and
   Humanities, A

Nursing - Registered Nurse Training, A

NORTHWESTERN OKLAHOMA STATE UNIVERSITY

Accounting, B
Adult and Continuing Education and Teaching, M
Agricultural Business and Management, B
Agriculture, B
Biology/Biological Sciences, B
Business Administration and Management, B
Business Teacher Education, B
Chemistry, B
Computer Science, B
Computer Systems Networking and
   Telecommunications, B
Counseling Psychology, M
Counselor Education/School Counseling and
   Guidance Services, M
Criminal Justice/Police Science, B
Education, M
Elementary Education and Teaching, BM
English Language and Literature, B
Health Teacher Education, B
History, B
Information Science/Studies, B
Kindergarten/PreSchool Education and Teaching, B
Mass Communication/Media Studies, B
Mathematics, B
Music, B
Music Teacher Education, B
Nursing - Registered Nurse Training, B
Physical Education Teaching and Coaching, B
Physics, B
Political Science and Government, B
Pre-Dentistry Studies, B
Pre-Law Studies, B
Pre-Medicine/Pre-Medical Studies, B
Psychology, B
Reading Teacher Education, M
Science Teacher Education/General Science
   Teacher Education, B
Secondary Education and Teaching, BM
Social Sciences, B
Social Work, B
Sociology, B
Spanish Language and Literature, B
Special Education and Teaching, B
Speech and Rhetorical Studies; B
Speech Teacher Education, B

OKLAHOMA BAPTIST UNIVERSITY

Accounting, B
Advertising, B
Ancient Near Eastern and Biblical
   Languages, Literatures, and Linguistics, B
Applied Art, B
Art Teacher Education, B
Art/Art Studies, General, B
Athletic Training and Sports Medicine, B
Bible/Biblical Studies, B
Biological and Physical Sciences, B
Biology Teacher Education, B
Biology/Biological Sciences, B
Broadcast Journalism, B
Business Administration and Management, B
Chemistry, B
Chemistry Teacher Education, B
Child Development, B
Computer and Information Sciences, B
Computer Programming, Specific Applications, B
Computer Science, B
Computer Systems Analysis/Analyst, B
Developmental and Child Psychology, B
Divinity/Ministry (BD, MDiv.), B
Drama and Dance Teacher Education, B
Drama and Dramatics/Theatre Arts, B
Education, B
Education/Teaching of Individuals with Emotional
   Disturbances, B
Education/Teaching of Individuals with Mental
   Retardation, B
Education/Teaching of Individuals with Specific
   Learning Disabilities, B
Elementary Education and Teaching, B
English Composition, B
English Language and Literature, B

English/Language Arts Teacher Education, B
Finance, B
Fine/Studio Arts, B
French Language and Literature, B
French Language Teacher Education, B
German Language and Literature, B
German Language Teacher Education, B
Health and Physical Education, B
History, B
History Teacher Education, B
Human Resources Management/Personnel
   Administration, B
Humanities/Humanistic Studies, B
Information Science/Studies, B
Interdisciplinary Studies, B
International Business/Trade/Commerce, B
International Marketing, B
Journalism, B
Kindergarten/PreSchool Education and Teaching, B
Kinesiology and Exercise Science, B
Management Information Systems and Services, B
Marketing/Marketing Management, B
Marriage and Family Therapy/Counseling, B
Mass Communication/Media Studies, B
Mathematics, B
Mathematics Teacher Education, B
Missions/Missionary Studies and Missiology, B
Museology/Museum Studies, B
Music, B
Music Teacher Education, B
Music Theory and Composition, B
Natural Sciences, B
Nursing - Registered Nurse Training, B
Parks, Recreation, Leisure and Fitness Studies, B
Pastoral Studies/Counseling, B
Philosophy, B
Physical Education Teaching and Coaching, B
Physical Sciences, B
Physics, B
Piano and Organ, B
Political Science and Government, B
Pre-Dentistry Studies, B
Pre-Law Studies, B
Pre-Medicine/Pre-Medical Studies, B
Pre-Pharmacy Studies, B
Pre-Veterinary Studies, B
Psychology, B
Public Relations/Image Management, B
Radio and Television, B
Religion/Religious Studies, B
Religious Education, B
Religious/Sacred Music, B
Science Teacher Education/General Science
   Teacher Education, B
Secondary Education and Teaching, B
Social Science Teacher Education, B
Social Sciences, B
Social Studies Teacher Education, B
Social Work, B
Sociology, B
Spanish Language and Literature, B
Spanish Language Teacher Education, B
Special Education and Teaching, B
Speech and Rhetorical Studies, B
Speech Teacher Education, B
Telecommunications Technology/Technician, B
Theology/Theological Studies, B
Voice and Opera, B
Wind and Percussion Instruments, B

OKLAHOMA CHRISTIAN UNIVERSITY

Accounting, B
Advertising, B
American Government and Politics (United States)
   , B
Art/Art Studies, General, B
Bible/Biblical Studies, B
Biochemistry, B
Biology/Biological Sciences, B
Broadcast Journalism, B
Business Administration and Management, B
Business/Commerce, B
Chemistry, B
Child Development, B
Clinical Laboratory Science/Medical
   Technology/Technologist, B

Commercial and Advertising Art, B
Computer Engineering, B
Computer Science, B
Creative Writing, B
Drama and Dramatics/Theatre Arts, B
Early Childhood Education and Teaching, B
Electrical, Electronics and Communications
   Engineering, B
Elementary Education and Teaching, B
Engineering, B
English Language and Literature, B
English/Language Arts Teacher Education, B
Family and Community Services, B
History, B
Information Science/Studies, B
Interior Design, B
Journalism, B
Kindergarten/PreSchool Education and Teaching, B
Liberal Arts and Sciences Studies and
   Humanities, B
Marketing/Marketing Management, B
Mass Communication/Media Studies, B
Mathematics, B
Mathematics Teacher Education, B
Mechanical Engineering, B
Missions/Missionary Studies and Missiology, B
Music, B
Music Teacher Education, B
Pastoral Studies/Counseling, M
Physical Education Teaching and Coaching, B
Pre-Law Studies, B
Psychology, B
Public Relations/Image Management, B
Radio and Television, B
Religion/Religious Studies, B
Religious Education, B
Science Teacher Education/General Science
   Teacher Education, B
Secondary Education and Teaching, B
Social Studies Teacher Education, B
Spanish Language and Literature, B
Speech and Rhetorical Studies, B
Teaching English as a Second or Foreign
   Language/ESL Language Instructor, B
Theology and Religious Vocations, MP
Voice and Opera, B
Wind and Percussion Instruments, B

OKLAHOMA CITY COMMUNITY COLLEGE

Accounting, A
Airframe Mechanics and Aircraft Maintenance
   Technology/Technician, A
Applied Art, A
Area Studies, A
Art/Art Studies, General, A
Automobile/Automotive Mechanics
   Technology/Technician, A
Avionics Maintenance Technology/Technician, A
Biology/Biological Sciences, A
Biomedical Technology/Technician, A
Broadcast Journalism, A
Business Administration and Management, A
Chemistry, A
Child Development, A
Commercial and Advertising Art, A
Comparative Literature, A
Computer Engineering Technology/Technician, A
Computer Science, A
Drafting and Design Technology/Technician, A
Drama and Dramatics/Theatre Arts, A
Electrical, Electronic and Communications
   Engineering Technology/Technician, A
Emergency Medical Technology/Technician (EMT
   Paramedic), A
Finance, A
Fine/Studio Arts, A
Gerontology, A
Health Information/Medical Records
   Administration/Administrator, A
History, A
Humanities/Humanistic Studies, A
Insurance, A
Liberal Arts and Sciences Studies and
   Humanities, A
Mass Communication/Media Studies, A

Mathematics, A
Modern Languages, A
Music, A
Nursing - Registered Nurse Training, A
Occupational Therapy/Therapist, A
Orthoptics/Orthoptist, A
Physical Therapy/Therapist, A
Physics, A
Political Science and Government, A
Pre-Engineering, A
Psychology, A
Respiratory Care Therapy/Therapist, A
Sociology, A
Surgical Technology/Technologist, A

OKLAHOMA CITY UNIVERSITY

Accounting, BM
Advertising, B
American/United States Studies/Civilization, B
Art History, Criticism and Conservation, B
Art Teacher Education, B
Arts Management, BM
Biochemistry, B
Biological and Physical Sciences, B
Biology/Biological Sciences, B
Biophysics, B
Broadcast Journalism, B
Business Administration and Management, B
Business Administration, Management and
    Operations, MO
Business/Commerce, B
Business/Managerial Economics, B
Chemistry, B
Cinematography and Film/Video Production, B
Commercial and Advertising Art, B
Comparative Literature, M
Composition, M
Computer Science, BM
Corporate and Organizational Communication, M
Corrections, B
Criminal Justice/Law Enforcement Administration, B
Criminal Justice/Police Science, B
Criminology, M
Curriculum and Instruction, M
Dance, B
Drama and Dramatics/Theatre Arts, B
Early Childhood Education and Teaching, M
Education, BM
Elementary Education and Teaching, BM
English as a Second Language, M
English Language and Literature, B
Finance, B
Finance and Banking, M
Fine Arts and Art Studies, M
Fine/Studio Arts, B
French Language and Literature, B
German Language and Literature, B
Health Services Administration, M
History, B
Humanities/Humanistic Studies, B
International Affairs, M
International Business/Trade/Commerce, BM
Journalism, B
Kindergarten/PreSchool Education and Teaching, B
Kinesiology and Exercise Science, B
Law and Legal Studies, PO
Liberal Arts and Sciences Studies and
    Humanities, B
Liberal Studies, M
Management, M
Management Information Systems and
    Services, BM
Marketing, M
Marketing/Marketing Management, B
Mass Communication/Media Studies, B
Mathematics, B
Montessori Teacher Education, B
Music, BM
Music Management and Merchandising, B
Music Teacher Education, B
Music Theory and Composition, B
Nursing - Registered Nurse Training, B
Performance, M
Philosophy, BM
Physical Education Teaching and Coaching, B
Physics, B

Piano and Organ, B
Political Science and Government, B
Pre-Dentistry Studies, B
Pre-Law Studies, B
Pre-Medicine/Pre-Medical Studies, B
Pre-Nursing Studies, B
Pre-Pharmacy Studies, B
Pre-Veterinary Studies, B
Psychology, B
Public Administration, M
Public Relations/Image Management, B
Radio and Television, B
Religion/Religious Studies, BM
Religious Education, BM
Religious/Sacred Music, B
Science Teacher Education/General Science
    Teacher Education, B
Secondary Education and Teaching, B
Sociology, B
Spanish Language and Literature, B
Speech and Rhetorical Studies, B
Speech Teacher Education, B
Technical Theatre/Theatre Design and
    Technology, B
Theater, M
Violin, Viola, Guitar and Other Stringed
    Instruments, B
Voice and Opera, B
Wind and Percussion Instruments, B
Writing, M

OKLAHOMA PANHANDLE STATE UNIVERSITY

Accounting, B
Agricultural Business and Management, B
Agricultural Teacher Education, B
Agriculture, A
Agronomy and Crop Science, B
Animal Sciences, B
Biological and Physical Sciences, B
Biology/Biological Sciences, B
Business Administration and Management, AB
Business Teacher Education, B
Chemistry, B
Clinical Laboratory Science/Medical
    Technology/Technologist, B
Computer and Information Sciences, A
Elementary Education and Teaching, B
English Language and Literature, B
Farm/Farm and Ranch Management, A
General Studies, A
History, B
Humanities/Humanistic Studies, B
Industrial Technology/Technician, AB
Information Science/Studies, AB
Mathematics, B
Natural Sciences, B
Nursing - Registered Nurse Training, AB
Parks, Recreation, Leisure and Fitness Studies, AB
Physical Education Teaching and Coaching, B
Psychology, B
Science Teacher Education/General Science
    Teacher Education, B
Secondary Education and Teaching, B
Social Sciences, B
Technology Education/Industrial Arts, B
Technology Teacher Education/Industrial Arts
    Teacher Education, B

OKLAHOMA STATE UNIVERSITY

Accounting, BMD
Aeronautics/Aviation/Aerospace Science and
    Technology, B
Aerospace, Aeronautical and Astronautical
    Engineering, BM
Agricultural Business and Management, B
Agricultural Communication/Journalism, B
Agricultural Economics, BMD
Agricultural Education, MD
Agricultural Engineering, MD
Agricultural Sciences, MD
Agricultural Teacher Education, B
Agriculture, B
Agronomy and Soil Sciences, MD
American/United States Studies/Civilization, B
Animal Sciences, BMD

Applied Mathematics, M
Applied Science and Technology, M
Architectural Engineering, BM
Architecture, BM
Art/Art Studies, General, B
Athletic Training and Sports Medicine, B
Biochemistry, BMD
Biochemistry, Biophysics and Molecular Biology, B
Bioengineering, MD
Biology/Biological Sciences, B
Biomedical/Medical Engineering, B
Botany/Plant Biology, BMD
Broadcast Journalism, B
Business Administration, Management and
    Operations, M
Business/Commerce, B
Business/Managerial Economics, B
Cell/Cellular and Molecular Biology, B
Chemical Engineering, BMD
Chemistry, BMD
Child and Family Studies, MD
Civil Engineering, BMD
Clinical Psychology, D
Clothing and Textiles, MD
Communication Disorders, BM
Computer Engineering, MD
Computer Science, BMD
Construction Management, B
Corrections, M
Counselor Education/School Counseling and
    Guidance Services, MD
Curriculum and Instruction, MD
Design and Applied Arts, MD
Drama and Dramatics/Theatre Arts, B
Ecology, MD
Economics, BMD
Education, BMDO
Educational Administration and Supervision, M
Educational Leadership and Administration, MD
Educational Psychology, MD
Electrical Engineering, MD
Electrical, Electronic and Communications
    Engineering Technology/Technician, B
Electrical, Electronics and Communications
    Engineering, B
Elementary Education and Teaching, B
Emergency Medical Services, M
Engineering, B
Engineering and Applied Sciences, MD
Engineering Management, M
Engineering Technology, B
English, MD
English Language and Literature, B
Entomology, BMD
Environmental Engineering
    Technology/Environmental Technology, MD
Environmental Sciences, MD
Environmental Studies, B
Experimental Psychology, D
Family and Consumer Sciences/Human
    Sciences, MD
Finance, B
Finance and Banking, MD
Fire Protection and Safety Technology/Technician, B
Fire Protection Engineering, M
Food Engineering, MD
Food Science and Technology, MD
Forestry, BM
French Language and Literature, B
Geography, BM
Geology/Earth Science, BM
German Language and Literature, B
Gerontology, M
Health Education, MD
Health Services Administration, M
Higher Education/Higher Education
    Administration, MD
History, BMD
Home Economics, MD
Horticultural Science, BMD
Hospitality Administration/Management, MD
Hotel/Motel Administration/Management, B
Human Development and Family Studies, B
Industrial and Manufacturing Management, D
Industrial Education, MD
Industrial Engineering, B

Industrial/Management Engineering, MD
International Affairs, M
Journalism, B
Landscape Architecture, BMD
Leisure Studies, MD
Liberal Arts and Sciences Studies and
    Humanities, B
Management, D
Management Information Systems and
    Services, BMD
Management of Technology, M
Management Science, B
Manufacturing Engineering, M
Marketing, D
Marketing/Marketing Management, B
Mass Communication/Media Studies, M
Mathematics, BMD
Mechanical Engineering, BMD
Mechanical Engineering/Mechanical
    Technology/Technician, B
Microbiology, MD
Molecular Biology, MD
Molecular Genetics, MD
Music, BM
Music Teacher Education, B
Natural Resources and Conservation, MD
Nutritional Sciences, MD
Operations Research, D
Philosophy, BM
Photonics, MD
Physical Education Teaching and Coaching, BMD
Physics, BMD
Physiology, B
Plant Pathology/Phytopathology, MD
Plant Sciences, BD
Political Science and Government, BM
Pre-Veterinary Studies, B
Psychology, BMD
Public Health (MPH, DPH), B
Russian Language and Literature, B
Secondary Education and Teaching, B
Sociology, BMD
Spanish Language and Literature, B
Speech and Rhetorical Studies, B
Statistics, BMD
Student Personnel Services, MD
Systems Engineering, M
Technical and Business Writing, MD
Telecommunications Management, MD
Theater, M
Veterinary Medicine, P
Veterinary Sciences, MD
Vocational and Technical Education, MD
Writing, MD
Zoology/Animal Biology, BMD

OKLAHOMA STATE UNIVERSITY, OKLAHOMA CITY

Accounting, A
Architectural Engineering Technology/Technician, A
Business Administration and Management, A
Business/Office Automation/Technology/Data
    Entry, A
Civil Engineering Technology/Technician, A
Computer and Information Sciences, A
Construction Engineering Technology/Technician, A
Criminal Justice/Police Science, A
Data Entry/Microcomputer Applications, A
Early Childhood Education and Teaching, A
Education, A
Electrical and Power Transmission
    Installation/Installer, A
Electrical, Electronic and Communications
    Engineering Technology/Technician, A
Engineering, A
Fire Science/Firefighting, A
Horticultural Science, A
Industrial Design, A
Landscape Architecture, A
Management Information Systems and Services, A
Medical/Health Management and Clinical
    Assistant/Specialist, A
Nursing - Registered Nurse Training, A
Occupational Safety and Health
    Technology/Technician, A
Quality Control Technology/Technician, A

Sign Language Interpretation and Translation, A
Special Products Marketing Operations, A
Substance Abuse/Addiction Counseling, A
Survey Technology/Surveying, A
Turf and Turfgrass Management, A
Veterinary/Animal Health Technology/Technician and
    Veterinary Assistant, A

OKLAHOMA STATE UNIVERSITY, OKMULGEE

Accounting, A
Administrative Assistant and Secretarial Science, A
Architectural Engineering Technology/Technician, A
Artificial Intelligence and Robotics, A
Automobile/Automotive Mechanics
    Technology/Technician, A
Avionics Maintenance Technology/Technician, A
Business Administration and Management, A
Commercial and Advertising Art, A
Computer Graphics, A
Construction Engineering Technology/Technician, A
Culinary Arts/Chef Training, A
Dietetics/Dieticians, A
Drafting and Design Technology/Technician, A
Electrical, Electronic and Communications
    Engineering Technology/Technician, A
Food Technology and Processing, A
Graphic and Printing Equipment Operator
    Production, A
Heating, Air Conditioning, Ventilation and
    Refrigeration Maintenance
    Technology/Technician, A
Heavy Equipment Maintenance
    Technology/Technician, A
Hospitality Administration/Management, A
Industrial Technology/Technician, A
Information Science/Studies, A
Legal Administrative Assistant/Secretary, A
Machine Tool Technology/Machinist, A
Marketing/Marketing Management, A
Medical Administrative Assistant/Secretary, A
Metal and Jewelry Arts, A
Photography, A
Pipefitting/Pipefitter and Sprinkler Fitter, A
Special Products Marketing Operations, A

OKLAHOMA WESLEYAN UNIVERSITY

Accounting, AB
Administrative Assistant and Secretarial Science, A
Athletic Training and Sports Medicine, B
Behavioral Sciences, AB
Biological and Physical Sciences, B
Biology/Biological Sciences, AB
Business Administration and Management, AB
Business Teacher Education, B
Chemistry, AB
Divinity/Ministry (BD, MDiv.), B
Education, B
Elementary Education and Teaching, B
English Language and Literature, B
History, B
Information Science/Studies, AB
Kinesiology and Exercise Science, B
Liberal Arts and Sciences Studies and
    Humanities, B
Linguistics, AB
Mass Communication/Media Studies, B
Mathematics, B
Music, B
Music Performance, B
Natural Sciences, B
Nursing - Registered Nurse Training, B
Physical Education Teaching and Coaching, B
Physical Therapy/Therapist, B
Political Science and Government, B
Pre-Dentistry Studies, B
Pre-Law Studies, B
Pre-Medicine/Pre-Medical Studies, B
Pre-Veterinary Studies, B
Religion/Religious Studies, B
Science Teacher Education/General Science
    Teacher Education, B
Secondary Education and Teaching, B
Social Sciences, B
Teaching English as a Second or Foreign
    Language/ESL Language Instructor, B

Theology/Theological Studies, B

ORAL ROBERTS UNIVERSITY

Accounting, BM
Art Teacher Education, B
Bible/Biblical Studies, B
Biochemistry, B
Biology/Biological Sciences, B
Biomedical Technology/Technician, B
Biomedical/Medical Engineering, B
Business Administration and Management, B
Business Administration, Management and
    Operations, M
Chemistry, B
Clinical/Medical Laboratory Technician, B
Commercial and Advertising Art, B
Communication Studies/Speech Communication
    and Rhetoric, B
Computer Engineering, B
Computer Science, B
Curriculum and Instruction, M
Drama and Dramatics/Theatre Arts, B
Early Childhood Education and Teaching, BM
Education, BMD
Educational Administration and Supervision, MD
Educational Leadership and Administration, B
Electrical, Electronics and Communications
    Engineering, B
Elementary Education and Teaching, B
Engineering Mechanics, B
English as a Second Language, M
English Language and Literature, B
English Literature (British and Commonwealth), B
English/Language Arts Teacher Education, B
Film/Cinema Studies, B
Finance, B
Finance and Banking, M
Fine/Studio Arts, B
Foreign Language Teacher Education, B
French Language and Literature, B
French Language Teacher Education, B
German Language and Literature, B
German Language Teacher Education, B
History, B
Hospitality and Recreation Marketing Operations, B
Human Resources Management and Services, M
International Business/Trade/Commerce, B
International Relations and Affairs, B
International/Global Studies, B
Journalism, B
Kindergarten/PreSchool Education and Teaching, B
Kinesiology and Exercise Science, B
Liberal Arts and Sciences Studies and
    Humanities, B
Management Information Systems and Services, B
Management Science, B
Marketing, M
Marketing/Marketing Management, B
Mathematics, B
Mathematics Teacher Education, B
Mechanical Engineering, B
Missions/Missionary Studies and Missiology, BMDP
Music, B
Music Performance, B
Music Teacher Education, B
Music Theory and Composition, B
Non-Profit/Public/Organizational Management, M
Nursing - Registered Nurse Training, B
Pastoral Studies/Counseling, BM
Philosophy, B
Physical Education Teaching and Coaching, B
Physics, B
Political Science and Government, B
Pre-Dentistry Studies, B
Pre-Engineering, B
Pre-Law Studies, B
Pre-Medicine/Pre-Medical Studies, B
Psychology, B
Public Health (MPH, DPH), B
Public Relations/Image Management, B
Radio and Television, B
Religion/Religious Studies, B
Religious Education, M
Religious/Sacred Music, B
Science Teacher Education/General Science
    Teacher Education, B

Social Studies Teacher Education, B
Social Work, B
Spanish Language and Literature, B
Spanish Language Teacher Education, B
Special Education and Teaching, B
Speech and Rhetorical Studies, B
Teacher Education, Multiple Levels, B
Teaching English as a Second or Foreign
  Language/ESL Language Instructor, B
Theology and Religious Vocations, MDP
Theology/Theological Studies, B

REDLANDS COMMUNITY COLLEGE

Administrative Assistant and Secretarial Science, A
Agricultural Business and Management, A
Agricultural Teacher Education, A
Agriculture, A
Animal Sciences, A
Art/Art Studies, General, A
Biological and Physical Sciences, A
Biology/Biological Sciences, A
Business Administration and Management, A
Child Development, A
Commercial and Advertising Art, A
Computer Programming/Programmer, A
Computer Science, A
Construction Engineering Technology/Technician, A
Corrections, A
Criminal Justice/Law Enforcement Administration, A
Criminal Justice/Police Science, A
Drafting and Design Technology/Technician, A
Education, A
Electrical, Electronic and Communications
  Engineering Technology/Technician, A
Elementary Education and Teaching, A
Emergency Medical Technology/Technician (EMT
  Paramedic), A
English Language and Literature, A
Equestrian/Equine Studies, A
Kindergarten/PreSchool Education and Teaching, A
Liberal Arts and Sciences Studies and
  Humanities, A
Mathematics, A
Nursing - Registered Nurse Training, A
Physical Education Teaching and Coaching, A
Physical Sciences, A
Psychology, A
Social Sciences, A

ROGERS STATE UNIVERSITY

Accounting, A
Administrative Assistant and Secretarial Science, A
Agricultural Business and Management, A
American Indian/Native American Studies, A
Art/Art Studies, General, A
Biology/Biological Sciences, AB
Broadcast Journalism, A
Business Administration and Management, A
Chemistry, A
Commercial and Advertising Art, A
Computer Engineering Technology/Technician, A
Computer Programming/Programmer, A
Computer Science, A
Criminal Justice/Law Enforcement Administration, A
Criminal Justice/Police Science, A
Elementary Education and Teaching, A
Emergency Medical Technology/Technician (EMT
  Paramedic), A
Engineering Technologies/Technicians, AB
Equestrian/Equine Studies, A
Farm/Farm and Ranch Management, A
History, A
Information Science/Studies, A
Legal Administrative Assistant/Secretary, A
Legal Assistant/Paralegal, A
Liberal Arts and Sciences Studies and
  Humanities, AB
Management Information Systems and Services, B
Mathematics, A
Nursing, A
Nursing - Registered Nurse Training, A
Physical Sciences, A
Political Science and Government, A
Radio and Television, A
Secondary Education and Teaching, A
Social Sciences, AB

Substance Abuse/Addiction Counseling, A

ROSE STATE COLLEGE

Accounting, A
Administrative Assistant and Secretarial Science, A
Art/Art Studies, General, A
Avionics Maintenance Technology/Technician, A
Biology/Biological Sciences, A
Broadcast Journalism, A
Business Administration and Management, A
Business/Commerce, A
Chemistry, A
Clinical/Medical Laboratory Technician, A
Court Reporting/Court Reporter, A
Criminal Justice/Law Enforcement Administration, A
Dental Assisting/Assistant, A
Dental Hygiene/Hygienist, A
Developmental and Child Psychology, A
Drafting and Design Technology/Technician, A
Drama and Dramatics/Theatre Arts, A
Electrical, Electronic and Communications
  Engineering Technology/Technician, A
Elementary Education and Teaching, A
English Language and Literature, A
Environmental Engineering
  Technology/Environmental Technology, A
Family and Consumer Sciences/Human Sciences, A
Health and Medical Laboratory Technologies, A
History, A
Industrial Radiologic Technology/Technician, A
Information Science/Studies, A
Journalism, A
Kindergarten/PreSchool Education and Teaching, A
Kinesiology and Exercise Science, A
Legal Administrative Assistant/Secretary, A
Liberal Arts and Sciences Studies and
  Humanities, A
Library Science, A
Management Information Systems and Services, A
Mathematics, A
Medical Radiologic Technology/Science - Radiation
  Therapist, A
Modern Languages, A
Music, A
Nursing - Registered Nurse Training, A
Parks, Recreation and Leisure Facilities
  Management, A
Physical Education Teaching and Coaching, A
Physical Therapy/Therapist, A
Physics, A
Political Science and Government, A
Pre-Engineering, A
Pre-Pharmacy Studies, A
Psychology, A
Respiratory Care Therapy/Therapist, A
Sociology, A
Speech and Rhetorical Studies, A

ST. GREGORY'S UNIVERSITY

Accounting, B
Art/Art Studies, General, A
Biology Teacher Education, B
Biology/Biological Sciences, B
Biomedical Sciences, B
Broadcast Journalism, B
Business Administration and Management, AB
Chemistry, B
Communication and Media Studies, B
Conservation Biology, B
Criminal Justice/Police Science, B
Criminal Justice/Safety Studies, A
Dance, B
English Language and Literature, B
English/Language Arts Teacher Education, B
Fine/Studio Arts, AB
History, B
Humanities/Humanistic Studies, AB
Journalism, B
Liberal Arts and Sciences Studies and
  Humanities, AB
Management Information Systems and Services, B
Management Science, B
Marketing/Marketing Management, B
Mathematics, B
Mathematics and Computer Science, B
Mathematics Teacher Education, B

Natural Resources and Conservation, B
Natural Sciences, B
Pastoral Studies/Counseling, B
Philosophy, B
Photojournalism, B
Political Science and Government, B
Pre-Dentistry Studies, B
Pre-Engineering, A
Pre-Law Studies, B
Pre-Medicine/Pre-Medical Studies, B
Pre-Nursing Studies, B
Pre-Pharmacy Studies, B
Pre-Theology/Pre-Ministerial Studies, A
Psychology, B
Social Sciences, B
Social Studies Teacher Education, B
Sociology, B
Theology/Theological Studies, B
Visual and Performing Arts, B

SEMINOLE STATE COLLEGE

Accounting, A
Administrative Assistant and Secretarial Science, A
Art/Art Studies, General, A
Behavioral Sciences, A
Biology/Biological Sciences, A
Business Administration and Management, A
Clinical/Medical Laboratory Technician, A
Computer Science, A
Criminal Justice/Police Science, A
Elementary Education and Teaching, A
English Language and Literature, A
Liberal Arts and Sciences Studies and
  Humanities, A
Mathematics, A
Nursing - Registered Nurse Training, A
Physical Education Teaching and Coaching, A
Physical Sciences, A
Pre-Engineering, A
Social Sciences, A

SOUTHEASTERN OKLAHOMA STATE UNIVERSITY

Accounting, B
Airline/Commercial/Professional Pilot and Flight
  Crew, B
Art Teacher Education, B
Art/Art Studies, General, B
Aviation, M
Aviation/Airway Management and Operations, BM
Biology/Biological Sciences, B
BioTechnology, B
Botany/Plant Biology, B
Business Administration and Management, B
Business Administration, Management and
  Operations, M
Chemistry, B
Communication Studies/Speech Communication
  and Rhetoric, B
Communication, Journalism and Related
  Programs, B
Computer and Information Sciences, B
Counselor Education/School Counseling and
  Guidance Services, M
Criminal Justice/Safety Studies, B
Drama and Dramatics/Theatre Arts, B
Economics, B
Education, BM
Educational Administration and Supervision, M
Educational Leadership and Administration, M
Educational Media/Instructional Technology, M
Elementary Education and Teaching, BM
English Language and Literature, B
English/Language Arts Teacher Education, B
Environmental Sciences, B
Finance, B
General Studies, B
Health and Medical Laboratory Technologies, B
Health Teacher Education, B
History, B
Industrial and Manufacturing Management, M
Industrial Technology/Technician, B
Information Science/Studies, B
Kindergarten/PreSchool Education and Teaching, B
Management Information Systems and Services, B
Management Science, B

Marketing/Marketing Management, B
Mathematics, B
Mathematics Teacher Education, B
Music, B
Music Performance, B
Music Teacher Education, B
Natural Resources and Conservation, B
Occupational Safety and Health
    Technology/Technician, B
Office Management and Supervision, B
Parks, Recreation, Leisure and Fitness Studies, B
Physical Education Teaching and Coaching, B
Political Science and Government, B
Psychology, B
Science Teacher Education/General Science
    Teacher Education, B
Secondary Education and Teaching, BM
Social Studies Teacher Education, B
Sociology, B
Spanish Language and Literature, B
Spanish Language Teacher Education, B
Special Education and Teaching, B
Wildlife and Wildlands Science and Management, B
Zoology/Animal Biology, B

SOUTHERN NAZARENE UNIVERSITY

Accounting, B
American/United States Studies/Civilization, B
Athletic Training and Sports Medicine, B
Aviation/Airway Management and Operations, B
Biochemistry, B
Biology/Biological Sciences, B
Broadcast Journalism, B
Business Administration and Management, B
Business Administration, Management and
    Operations, M
Business/Commerce, A
Chemistry, B
Communication Studies/Speech Communication
    and Rhetoric, A
Counseling Psychology, M
Early Childhood Education and Teaching, B
Education, BM
Elementary Education and Teaching, B
English Language and Literature, B
English/Language Arts Teacher Education, B
Environmental Studies, B
Finance, B
Gerontology, B
History, B
Human Development and Family Studies, B
International Relations and Affairs, B
Journalism, B
Junior High/Intermediate/Middle School Education
    and Teaching, B
Kinesiology and Exercise Science, B
Liberal Arts and Sciences Studies and
    Humanities, B
Management Information Systems and Services, B
Management Science, B
Marketing/Marketing Management, B
Marriage and Family Therapy/Counseling, M
Mass Communication/Media Studies, B
Mathematics, B
Mathematics Teacher Education, B
Missions/Missionary Studies and Missiology, B
Music Management and Merchandising, B
Music Performance, B
Music Teacher Education, B
Nursing, M
Nursing - Registered Nurse Training, B
Philosophy, B
Physical Education Teaching and Coaching, B
Physics, B
Piano and Organ, B
Political Science and Government, B
Pre-Dentistry Studies, B
Pre-Law Studies, B
Pre-Medicine/Pre-Medical Studies, B
Pre-Pharmacy Studies, B
Psychology, BM
Religion/Religious Studies, M
Religious Education, B
Science Teacher Education/General Science
    Teacher Education, B
Secondary Education and Teaching, B

Social Science Teacher Education, B
Social Studies Teacher Education, B
Social Work, B
Sociology, B
Spanish Language and Literature, B
Spanish Language Teacher Education, B
Speech and Rhetorical Studies, B
Speech Teacher Education, B
Sport and Fitness Administration/Management, B
Theology and Religious Vocations, M
Theology/Theological Studies, B
Urban Studies/Affairs, B
Voice and Opera, B
Youth Ministry, B

SOUTHWESTERN CHRISTIAN UNIVERSITY

Behavioral Sciences, B
Bible/Biblical Studies, B
Divinity/Ministry (BD, MDiv.), B
Interdisciplinary Studies, A
Pastoral Studies/Counseling, BM
Religion/Religious Studies, B
Religious Education, B
Religious/Sacred Music, B
Social Work, B
Theology/Theological Studies, B

SOUTHWESTERN OKLAHOMA STATE UNIVERSITY

Accounting, B
Art Education, M
Art Teacher Education, B
Biology/Biological Sciences, B
Biophysics, B
Business Administration and Management, B
Business Administration, Management and
    Operations, M
Chemistry, B
Clinical Laboratory Science/Medical
    Technology/Technologist, B
Commercial and Advertising Art, B
Computer and Information Sciences, B
Computer Science, B
Counselor Education/School Counseling and
    Guidance Services, M
Criminal Justice/Law Enforcement Administration, B
Early Childhood Education and Teaching, M
Education, BM
Educational Administration and Supervision, M
Educational Measurement and Evaluation, M
Elementary Education and Teaching, BM
Engineering Physics, B
Engineering Technology, B
English Education, M
English Language and Literature, B
English/Language Arts Teacher Education, B
Finance, B
Health Information/Medical Records
    Administration/Administrator, B
Health/Health Care Administration/Management, B
History, B
History Teacher Education, B
Industrial Technology/Technician, B
Kinesiology and Movement Studies, M
Marketing/Marketing Management, B
Mass Communication/Media Studies, B
Mathematics, B
Mathematics Teacher Education, M
Music, BM
Music Management and Merchandising, B
Music Teacher Education, B
Music Therapy/Therapist, B
Nursing - Registered Nurse Training, B
Parks, Recreation, Leisure and Fitness Studies, B
Pharmacy, BP
Physical Education Teaching and Coaching, B
Physics, B
Piano and Organ, B
Political Science and Government, B
Pre-Dentistry Studies, B
Pre-Law Studies, B
Pre-Medicine/Pre-Medical Studies, B
Pre-Veterinary Studies, B
Psychology, B
Recreation and Park Management, M

Religious/Sacred Music, B
School Psychology, M
Science Teacher Education/General Science
    Teacher Education, BM
Secondary Education and Teaching, B
Social Science Teacher Education, B
Social Studies Teacher Education, M
Social Work, B
Special Education and Teaching, BM
Technology Education/Industrial Arts, B
Technology Teacher Education/Industrial Arts
    Teacher Education, B
Therapeutic Recreation/Recreational Therapy, B
Vocational and Technical Education, M
Voice and Opera, B
Wind and Percussion Instruments, B

SOUTHWESTERN OKLAHOMA STATE UNIVERSITY AT SAYRE

Business Administration and Management, A
Clinical/Medical Laboratory Technician, A
Computer Science, A
Corrections, A
Criminal Justice/Safety Studies, A
General Studies, A
Medical Radiologic Technology/Science - Radiation
    Therapist, A
Nursing - Registered Nurse Training, A
Occupational Therapist Assistant, A
Physical Therapist Assistant, A

SPARTAN COLLEGE OF AERONAUTICS AND TECHNOLOGY

Airline/Commercial/Professional Pilot and Flight
    Crew, A
Avionics Maintenance Technology/Technician, A
Communications Technology/Technician, A
Electrical, Electronic and Communications
    Engineering Technology/Technician, A
Instrumentation Technology/Technician, A
Quality Control Technology/Technician, A

TULSA COMMUNITY COLLEGE

Accounting, A
Administrative Assistant and Secretarial Science, A
Advertising, A
Aeronautics/Aviation/Aerospace Science and
    Technology, A
Agriculture, A
Airframe Mechanics and Aircraft Maintenance
    Technology/Technician, A
American/United States Studies/Civilization, A
Applied Horticulture/Horticultural Operations, A
Architecture, A
Art/Art Studies, General, A
Artificial Intelligence and Robotics, A
Astronomy, A
Automobile/Automotive Mechanics
    Technology/Technician, A
Avionics Maintenance Technology/Technician, A
Behavioral Sciences, A
Biology/Biological Sciences, A
Biomedical Technology/Technician, A
Botany/Plant Biology, A
Business Administration and Management, A
Business and Personal/Financial Services Marketing
    Operations, A
Business Teacher Education, A
Chemistry, A
Child Care and Support Services Management, A
Child Development, A
Civil Engineering Technology/Technician, A
Clinical/Medical Laboratory Technician, A
Computer and Information Sciences, A
Computer and Information Systems Security, A
Computer Graphics, A
Computer Hardware Engineering, A
Computer Programming, A
Computer Programming, Specific Applications, A
Computer
    Programming, Vendor/Product Certification, A
Computer Science, A
Computer Software and Media Applications, A
Computer Software Engineering, A
Computer Systems Networking and
    Telecommunications, A

Computer/Information Technology Services
　Administration and Management, A
Construction Engineering Technology/Technician, A
Corrections, A
Creative Writing, A
Criminal Justice/Law Enforcement Administration, A
Criminal Justice/Police Science, A
Data Entry/Microcomputer Applications, A
Data Modeling/Warehousing and Database
　Administration, A
Dental Assisting/Assistant, A
Dental Hygiene/Hygienist, A
Drafting and Design Technology/Technician, A
Drama and Dramatics/Theatre Arts, A
Ecology, A
Economics, A
Education, A
Electrical, Electronic and Communications
　Engineering Technology/Technician, A
Elementary and Middle School
　Administration/Principalship, A
Elementary Education and Teaching, A
Emergency Medical Technology/Technician (EMT
　Paramedic), A
Engineering, A
English Language and Literature, A
Environmental Engineering
　Technology/Environmental Technology, A
Fashion/Apparel Design, A
Fire Protection and Safety Technology/Technician, A
Fire Science/Firefighting, A
Forestry, A
French Language and Literature, A
Geography, A
Geology/Earth Science, A
German Language and Literature, A
Health Information/Medical Records
　Administration/Administrator, A
Health Teacher Education, A
Heating, Air Conditioning, Ventilation and
　Refrigeration Maintenance
　Technology/Technician, A
History, A
Horticultural Science, A
Hotel/Motel Administration/Management, A
Human Resources Management/Personnel
　Administration, A
Human Services, A
Humanities/Humanistic Studies, A
Industrial Radiologic Technology/Technician, A
Industrial Technology/Technician, A
Information Science/Studies, A
Information Technology, A
Insurance, A
Interior Design, A
International Business/Trade/Commerce, A
International Relations and Affairs, A
Italian Language and Literature, A
Japanese Language and Literature, A
Journalism, A
Kindergarten/PreSchool Education and Teaching, A
Labor and Industrial Relations, A
Landscape Architecture, A
Landscaping and Groundskeeping, A
Latin Language and Literature, A
Law and Legal Studies, A
Legal Administrative Assistant/Secretary, A
Legal Assistant/Paralegal, A
Liberal Arts and Sciences Studies and
　Humanities, A
Library Science, A
Management Information Systems and Services, A
Management Science, A
Marketing/Marketing Management, A
Mass Communication/Media Studies, A
Materials Sciences, A
Mathematics, A
Mechanical Engineering/Mechanical
　Technology/Technician, A
Medical Administrative Assistant/Secretary, A
Medical/Clinical Assistant, A
Music, A
Music Teacher Education, A
Nursing - Registered Nurse Training, A
Occupational Safety and Health
　Technology/Technician, A

Occupational Therapist Assistant, A
Occupational Therapy/Therapist, A
Oceanography, Chemical and Physical, A
Ornamental Horticulture, A
Petroleum Technology/Technician, A
Philosophy, A
Physical Education Teaching and Coaching, A
Physical Sciences, A
Physical Therapy/Therapist, A
Physician Assistant, A
Physics, A
Plant Protection and Integrated Pest
　Management, A
Political Science and Government, A
Pre-Dentistry Studies, A
Pre-Engineering, A
Pre-Medicine/Pre-Medical Studies, A
Pre-Pharmacy Studies, A
Prepress/Desktop Publishing and Digital Imaging
　Design, A
Pre-Veterinary Studies, A
Psychology, A
Public Health (MPH, DPH), A
Purchasing, Procurement/Acquisitions and
　Contracts Management, A
Quality Control Technology/Technician, A
Radio and Television, A
Radiologic Technology/Science - Radiographer, A
Religion/Religious Studies, A
Respiratory Care Therapy/Therapist, A
Russian Language and Literature, A
Sign Language Interpretation and Translation, A
Social Sciences, A
Social Work, A
Sociology, A
Spanish Language and Literature, A
Speech and Rhetorical Studies, A
Surgical Technology/Technologist, A
Survey Technology/Surveying, A
System Administration/Administrator, A
Telecommunications Technology/Technician, A
Therapeutic Recreation/Recreational Therapy, A
Tourism and Travel Services Management, A
Veterinary/Animal Health Technology/Technician and
　Veterinary Assistant, A
Web Page, Digital/Multimedia and Information
　Resources Design, A
Web/Multimedia Management and Webmaster, A
Word Processing, A
Zoology/Animal Biology, A

TULSA WELDING SCHOOL

Welding Technology/Welder, A

UNIVERSITY OF CENTRAL OKLAHOMA

Accounting, B
Actuarial Science, B
Adult and Continuing Education and Teaching, BM
Advertising, B
American/United States Studies/Civilization, M
Apparel and Textiles, B
Applied Mathematics, BM
Applied Physics, M
Art Teacher Education, B
Art/Art Studies, General, B
Audiology/Audiologist and Speech-Language
　Pathology/Pathologist, B
Biological and Biomedical Sciences, M
Biology/Biological Sciences, B
Biomedical/Medical Engineering, B
Broadcast Journalism, B
Business Administration and Management, B
Business Administration, Management and
　Operations, M
Business Teacher Education, B
Business/Commerce, B
Business/Managerial Economics, B
Chemistry, BM
Child Development, B
Clinical Laboratory Science/Medical
　Technology/Technologist, B
Commercial and Advertising Art, B
Communication Disorders, M
Communication Studies/Speech Communication
　and Rhetoric, B
Computer Science, B

Consumer Merchandising/Retailing Management, B
Counseling Psychology, M
Counselor Education/School Counseling and
　Guidance Services, BM
Criminal Justice/Law Enforcement Administration, B
Criminal Justice/Safety Studies, B
Criminology, M
Dance, B
Design and Applied Arts, M
Dietetics/Dieticians, B
Drama and Dramatics/Theatre Arts, B
Early Childhood Education and Teaching, M
Economics, B
Education, M
Educational Administration and Supervision, M
Educational Leadership and Administration, B
Educational Media/Instructional Technology, M
Educational/Instructional Media Design, B
Elementary Education and Teaching, BM
English, M
English as a Second Language, M
English Language and Literature, B
English/Language Arts Teacher Education, B
Family and Consumer Sciences/Home Economics
　Teacher Education, B
Family and Consumer Sciences/Human Sciences, B
Fashion Merchandising, B
Finance, B
Foods, Nutrition, and Wellness Studies, B
Forensic Science and Technology, B
French Language and Literature, B
Funeral Service and Mortuary Science, B
Geography, B
German Language and Literature, B
Gerontology, M
Health and Physical Education/Fitness, B
Health Education, M
Health Occupations Teacher Education, B
Higher Education/Higher Education
　Administration, M
History, BM
History Teacher Education, B
Home Economics, M
Home Economics Education, M
Hotel/Motel Administration/Management, B
Human Development, M
Human Resources Management/Personnel
　Administration, B
Interior Design, BM
International Affairs, M
Journalism, B
Kindergarten/PreSchool Education and Teaching, B
Liberal Arts and Sciences Studies and
　Humanities, B
Marketing/Marketing Management, B
Mathematics, BM
Mathematics Teacher Education, B
Museology/Museum Studies, M
Music, BM
Music Teacher Education, BM
Nursing - Registered Nurse Training, B
Nutritional Sciences, M
Occupational Safety and Health
　Technology/Technician, B
Performance, M
Philosophy, B
Photography, B
Physical Education Teaching and Coaching, B
Physics, B
Piano and Organ, B
Political Science and Government, BM
Psychology, BM
Public Relations/Image Management, B
Radio and Television, B
Reading Teacher Education, BM
Real Estate, B
Science Teacher Education/General Science
　Teacher Education, B
Secondary Education and Teaching, BM
Social Studies Teacher Education, B
Sociology, B
Spanish Language and Literature, B
Special Education and Teaching, BM
Statistics, M
Teacher Education and Professional
　Development, Specific Subject Areas, B

Trade and Industrial Teacher Education, B
Urban Studies/Affairs, M
Violin, Viola, Guitar and Other Stringed
  Instruments, B
Voice and Opera, B
Wind and Percussion Instruments, B
Writing, M

UNIVERSITY OF OKLAHOMA

Accounting, BM
Adult and Continuing Education and Teaching, MD
Advertising, B
Advertising and Public Relations, M
Aeronautics/Aviation/Aerospace Science and
  Technology, B
Aerospace, Aeronautical and Astronautical
  Engineering, BMD
African-American/Black Studies, B
American Indian/Native American Studies, BM
Anthropology, BMD
Architecture, BMO
Architecture and Related Services, B
Area Studies, B
Art History, Criticism and Conservation, BM
Art/Art Studies, General, B
Astronomy, B
Astrophysics, BMD
Atmospheric Sciences and Meteorology, B
Biochemistry, MD
Bioengineering, MD
Biomedical/Medical Engineering, B
Botany/Plant Biology, BMD
Broadcast Journalism, B
Business Administration and Management, B
Business Administration, Management and
  Operations, MDO
Business/Managerial Economics, B
Ceramic Arts and Ceramics, M
Chemical Engineering, BMD
Chemistry, BMD
Chinese Language and Literature, B
Cinematography and Film/Video Production, B
Civil Engineering, BMD
Classics and Classical
  Languages, Literatures, and Linguistics, B
Clinical/Medical Laboratory Technician, B
Communication and Media Studies, MD
Communication Studies/Speech Communication
  and Rhetoric, B
Communication, Journalism and Related
  Programs, B
Community Psychology, M
Composition, MD
Computer and Information Sciences, B
Computer Engineering, BMD
Computer Science, MD
Counseling Psychology, D
Counselor Education/School Counseling and
  Guidance Services, M
Criminology, B
Curriculum and Instruction, MD
Dance, BM
Design and Applied Arts, M
Design and Visual Communications, B
Drama and Dramatics/Theatre Arts, B
Early Childhood Education and Teaching, B
Economics, BMD
Education, MDO
Educational Administration and Supervision, MD
Educational Psychology, MD
Electrical Engineering, MD
Electrical, Electronics and Communications
  Engineering, B
Elementary Education and Teaching, B
Engineering, B
Engineering and Applied Sciences, MD
Engineering Physics, BMD
English, MD
English Language and Literature, B
English/Language Arts Teacher Education, B
Entrepreneurship/Entrepreneurial Studies, B
Environmental and Occupational Health, M
Environmental Design/Architecture, B
Environmental Engineering
  Technology/Environmental Technology, M
Environmental Sciences, BMD

Environmental/Environmental Health Engineering, B
Exercise and Sports Science, MD
Film, Television, and Video Production, M
Finance, B
Fine Arts and Art Studies, M
Fine/Studio Arts, B
Foreign Language Teacher Education, B
Foundations and Philosophy of Education, MD
French Language and Literature, BMDO
Geography, BMD
Geological and Earth Sciences/Geosciences, B
Geological Engineering, MD
Geology/Earth Science, BMD
Geophysics and Seismology, BM
Geotechnical Engineering, M
German Language and Literature, BMO
Hazardous Materials Management and Waste
  Technology/Technician, M
Health and Medical Laboratory Technologies, B
Health and Physical Education, B
Higher Education/Higher Education
  Administration, MD
History, BMD
History of Science and Technology, MD
Human Resources Management and Services, B
Human Services, M
Industrial Engineering, B
Industrial/Management Engineering, MD
Information Science/Studies, MO
Interdisciplinary Studies, MD
Interior Design, B
International Affairs, M
International Business/Trade/Commerce, B
Journalism, BM
Landscape Architecture, MO
Law and Legal Studies, PO
Liberal Arts and Sciences Studies and
  Humanities, B
Liberal Studies, M
Library Science, BMO
Linguistics, B
Management, M
Management Information Systems and
  Services, BM
Marketing/Marketing Management, B
Mass Communication/Media Studies, M
Mathematics, BMDO
Mathematics Teacher Education, B
Mechanical Engineering, BMD
Meteorology, MD
Microbiology, BMD
Multi-/Interdisciplinary Studies, B
Music, BMD
Music Performance, B
Music Teacher Education, MD
Music Theory and Composition, BM
Musicology and Ethnomusicology, M
Natural Resources and Conservation, M
Organizational Behavior Studies, M
Painting, M
Performance, MD
Petroleum Engineering, BMD
Philosophy, BMD
Photography, BM
Physics, BMD
Piano and Organ, B
Political Science and Government, BMD
Printmaking, M
Professional Studies, B
Psychology, BMD
Public Administration, BM
Public Relations/Image Management, B
Religion/Religious Studies, B
Russian Language and Literature, B
School Psychology, M
Science Teacher Education/General Science
  Teacher Education, B
Social Studies Teacher Education, B
Social Work, BM
Sociology, BMD
Spanish Language and Literature, BMDO
Special Education and Teaching, BMD
Structural Engineering, M
Teacher Education and Professional
  Development, Specific Subject Areas, B
Telecommunications, M

Theater, M
Urban and Regional Planning, MO
Violin, Viola, Guitar and Other Stringed
  Instruments, B
Visual and Performing Arts, B
Voice and Opera, B
Water Resources, M
Wind and Percussion Instruments, B
Women's Studies, B
Writing, M
Zoology/Animal Biology, BMD

UNIVERSITY OF OKLAHOMA HEALTH SCIENCES CENTER

Allied Health and Medical Assisting Services, MDO
Allopathic Medicine, PO
Audiology/Audiologist and Hearing Sciences, B
Audiology/Audiologist and Speech-Language
  Pathology/Pathologist, B
Biochemistry, MD
Biological and Biomedical Sciences, MDO
Biopsychology, MD
Biostatistics, MD
Cell Biology and Anatomy, MD
Communication Disorders, BMDO
Communication Disorders Sciences and Services, B
Dental Hygiene/Hygienist, B
Dentistry, P
Dietetics/Dieticians, B
Environmental and Occupational Health, MDO
Epidemiology, MD
Genetic Counseling/Counselor, M
Health Education, D
Health Physics/Radiological Health, MD
Health Promotion, MD
Health Services Administration, MDO
Immunology, MD
Medical Physics, MD
Microbiology, MD
Molecular Biology, MD
Neuroscience, MD
Nuclear Medical Technology/Technologist, B
Nursing, MO
Nursing - Registered Nurse Training, B
Nutritional Sciences, M
Occupational Therapy/Therapist, M
Orthodontics, M
Pathology/Experimental Pathology, D
Periodontics, M
Pharmaceutical Sciences, MDO
Pharmacy, P
Physical Therapy/Therapist, M
Physiology, MD
Public Health, MD
Radiation Biology/Radiobiology, MD
Radiologic Technology/Science - Radiographer, B
Rehabilitation Sciences, M
Special Education and Teaching, M
Speech-Language Pathology/Pathologist, B

UNIVERSITY OF PHOENIX-OKLAHOMA CITY CAMPUS

Accounting, BM
Business Administration and Management, B
Business Administration, Management and
  Operations, M
Electronic Commerce, M
Health Services Administration, M
Health/Health Care Administration/Management, B
Human Resources Management and Services, M
Information Science/Studies, M
Information Technology, B
Management Information Systems and
  Services, BM
Management of Technology, M
Management Science, B
Nursing, M
Nursing - Registered Nurse Training, B
Organizational Management, M

UNIVERSITY OF PHOENIX-TULSA CAMPUS

Accounting, B
Business Administration and Management, B

Business Administration, Management and
Operations, M
Computer and Information Sciences, B
Corrections and Criminal Justice, B
Electronic Commerce, M
Health Services Administration, M
Health/Health Care Administration/Management, B
Human Resources Management and Services, M
Management Information Systems and
Services, BM
Management of Technology, M
Management Science, B
Marketing/Marketing Management, B
Nursing - Registered Nurse Training, B
Organizational Management, M

UNIVERSITY OF SCIENCE AND ARTS OF OKLAHOMA

American Indian/Native American Studies, B
Art/Art Studies, General, B
Biology/Biological Sciences, B
Business/Commerce, B
Chemistry, B
Clinical/Medical Laboratory Technician, B
Communication Studies/Speech Communication
and Rhetoric, B
Computer and Information Sciences, B
Drama and Dramatics/Theatre Arts, B
Early Childhood Education and Teaching, B
Economics, B
Education/Teaching of Individuals with Hearing
Impairments, Including Deafness, B
Elementary Education and Teaching, B
English Language and Literature, B
Fine/Studio Arts, B
Health and Physical Education, B
History, B
Mathematics, B
Music, B
Natural Sciences, B
Physics, B
Political Science and Government, B
Psychology, B
Sociology, B
Speech-Language Pathology/Pathologist, B

UNIVERSITY OF TULSA

Accounting, B
Anthropology, BMO
Applied Mathematics, B
Art History, Criticism and Conservation, B
Arts Management, B
Athletic Training and Sports Medicine, B
Audiology/Audiologist and Speech-Language
Pathology/Pathologist, B
Biochemistry, B
Biological and Biomedical Sciences, MDO
Biology/Biological Sciences, B
Business Administration and Management, B
Business Administration, Management and
Operations, MO
Chemical Engineering, BMD
Chemistry, BM
Clinical Psychology, MDO
Communication Disorders, M
Communication Studies/Speech Communication
and Rhetoric, B
Computer Science, BMD
Drama and Dramatics/Theatre Arts, B
Economics, B
Education, BM
Electrical Engineering, M
Electrical, Electronics and Communications
Engineering, B
Elementary Education and Teaching, B
Engineering and Applied Sciences, MDO
Engineering Management, M
Engineering Physics, B
English, MDO
English Language and Literature, B
Environmental Studies, B
Film/Cinema Studies, B
Finance, B
Finance and Banking, M
Financial Engineering, M
Fine Arts and Art Studies, M

Fine/Studio Arts, B
French Language and Literature, B
Geology/Earth Science, BM
Geophysics and Seismology, B
Geosciences, MD
German Language and Literature, B
History, BMO
Industrial and Organizational Psychology, MDO
Information Science/Studies, B
International Business/Trade/Commerce, BM
Investment Management, M
Kinesiology and Exercise Science, B
Law and Legal Studies, MPO
Legal Professions and Studies, B
Liberal Arts and Sciences Studies and
Humanities, B
Management Information Systems and Services, B
Management of Technology, M
Marketing/Marketing Management, B
Mathematics, BM
Mathematics Teacher Education, M
Mechanical Engineering, BMD
Music, B
Music Teacher Education, B
Nursing - Registered Nurse Training, B
Petroleum Engineering, BMD
Philosophy, B
Physics, B
Piano and Organ, B
Political Science and Government, B
Psychology, BMDO
Religion/Religious Studies, B
Science Teacher Education/General Science
Teacher Education, M
Sociology, B
Spanish Language and Literature, B
Sport and Fitness Administration/Management, B
Taxation, M
Voice and Opera, B

VATTEROTT COLLEGE (OKLAHOMA CITY)

Computer Programming/Programmer, A
Electrical and Electronic Engineering
Technologies/Technicians, A
Heating, Air Conditioning and Refrigeration
Technology/Technician, A
Information Technology, A
Medical Office Assistant/Specialist, A

VATTEROTT COLLEGE (TULSA)

Computer Programming/Programmer, A
Electrical, Electronic and Communications
Engineering Technology/Technician, A
Heating, Air Conditioning and Refrigeration
Technology/Technician, A
Medical Administrative Assistant/Secretary, A

WESTERN OKLAHOMA STATE COLLEGE

Accounting Technology/Technician and
Bookkeeping, A
Aviation/Airway Management and Operations, A
Child Development, A
Computer/Information Technology Services
Administration and Management, A
Criminal Justice/Police Science, A
Emergency Medical Technology/Technician (EMT
Paramedic), A
Fire Protection, A
General Studies, A
Liberal Arts and Sciences Studies and
Humanities, A
Mechanics and Repairers, A
Medical Radiologic Technology/Science - Radiation
Therapist, A
Nursing - Registered Nurse Training, A

Oregon

THE ART INSTITUTE OF PORTLAND

Advertising, B
Animation, Interactive Technology, Video Graphics
and Special Effects, B
Fashion/Apparel Design, AB

Graphic Design, AB
Interior Design, AB
Intermedia/Multimedia, AB
Web Page, Digital/Multimedia and Information
Resources Design, AB

BLUE MOUNTAIN COMMUNITY COLLEGE

Accounting, A
Administrative Assistant and Secretarial Science, A
Agricultural Business and Management, A
Animal Sciences, A
Automobile/Automotive Mechanics
Technology/Technician, A
Business Administration and Management, A
Civil Drafting and Civil Engineering CAD/CADD, A
Civil Engineering Technology/Technician, A
Dental Assisting/Assistant, A
Diesel Mechanics Technology/Technician, A
Electrical, Electronic and Communications
Engineering Technology/Technician, A
Health and Physical Education, A
Health Information/Medical Records
Technology/Technician, A
Industrial Technology/Technician, A
Information Science/Studies, A
Liberal Arts and Sciences Studies and
Humanities, A
Licensed Practical/Vocational Nurse Training, A
Marketing/Marketing Management, A
Mathematics, A
Medical Administrative Assistant/Secretary, A
Nursing - Registered Nurse Training, A
Social Work, A

CASCADE COLLEGE

Bible/Biblical Studies, B
Business Administration and Management, B
Communication and Media Studies, B
Early Childhood Education and Teaching, B
Elementary Education and Teaching, B
English Language and Literature, B
Liberal Arts and Sciences Studies and
Humanities, B
Marketing/Marketing Management, B
Psychology, B

CENTRAL OREGON COMMUNITY COLLEGE

Accounting, A
Administrative Assistant and Secretarial Science, A
Art/Art Studies, General, A
Automobile/Automotive Mechanics
Technology/Technician, A
Biological and Physical Sciences, A
Business Administration and Management, A
Cartography, A
Computer and Information Sciences, A
Computer Science, A
Criminal Justice/Law Enforcement Administration, A
Culinary Arts/Chef Training, A
Dental Assisting/Assistant, A
Early Childhood Education and Teaching, A
Education, A
Emergency Medical Technology/Technician (EMT
Paramedic), A
Fire Science/Firefighting, A
Forestry, A
Forestry Technology/Technician, A
Health Information/Medical Records
Technology/Technician, A
Hospitality Administration/Management, A
Hospitality and Recreation Marketing Operations, A
Hotel/Motel Administration/Management, A
Humanities/Humanistic Studies, A
Industrial Technology/Technician, A
Kinesiology and Exercise Science, A
Liberal Arts and Sciences Studies and
Humanities, A
Licensed Practical/Vocational Nurse Training, A
Marketing/Marketing Management, A
Mathematics, A
Medical/Clinical Assistant, A
Nursing - Registered Nurse Training, A
Physical Sciences, A
Pre-Engineering, A

Social Sciences, A
Sport and Fitness Administration/Management, A
Tourism Promotion Operations, A
Welding Technology/Welder, A

CHEMEKETA COMMUNITY COLLEGE

Accounting, A
Administrative Assistant and Secretarial Science, A
Agricultural Teacher Education, A
Art Teacher Education, A
Automobile/Automotive Mechanics
   Technology/Technician, A
Business Administration and Management, A
Civil Engineering Technology/Technician, A
Computer Engineering Technology/Technician, A
Computer Programming/Programmer, A
Computer Science, A
Construction Engineering Technology/Technician, A
Criminal Justice/Law Enforcement Administration, A
Dental Hygiene/Hygienist, A
Drafting and Design Technology/Technician, A
Drafting/Design Engineering
   Technologies/Technicians, A
Economics, A
Education, A
Electrical, Electronic and Communications
   Engineering Technology/Technician, A
Emergency Medical Technology/Technician (EMT
   Paramedic), A
Engineering, A
English Language and Literature, A
Finance, A
Fire Science/Firefighting, A
Forestry, A
Forestry Technology/Technician, A
Graphic and Printing Equipment Operator
   Production, A
Health Information/Medical Records
   Administration/Administrator, A
Health Teacher Education, A
Health/Health Care Administration/Management, A
Hospitality Administration/Management, A
Hotel/Motel Administration/Management, A
Human Services, A
Humanities/Humanistic Studies, A
Industrial Technology/Technician, A
Kindergarten/PreSchool Education and Teaching, A
Liberal Arts and Sciences Studies and
   Humanities, A
Licensed Practical/Vocational Nurse Training, A
Mathematics, A
Medical Administrative Assistant/Secretary, A
Medical/Clinical Assistant, A
Nursing - Registered Nurse Training, A
Physical Education Teaching and Coaching, A
Political Science and Government, A
Real Estate, A
Science Teacher Education/General Science
   Teacher Education, A
Social Sciences, A
Teacher Assistant/Aide, A
Welding Technology/Welder, A

CLACKAMAS COMMUNITY COLLEGE

Accounting, A
Autobody/Collision and Repair
   Technology/Technician, A
Automobile/Automotive Mechanics
   Technology/Technician, A
Community Organization and Advocacy, A
Computer Technology/Computer Systems
   Technology, A
Corrections, A
Criminal Justice/Police Science, A
Drafting and Design Technology/Technician, A
General Studies, A
Liberal Arts and Sciences Studies and
   Humanities, A
Machine Tool Technology/Machinist, A
Nursing - Registered Nurse Training, A
Office Management and Supervision, A
Ornamental Horticulture, A

Water Quality and Wastewater Treatment
   Management and Recycling
   Technology/Technician, A

CLATSOP COMMUNITY COLLEGE

Accounting, A
Administrative Assistant and Secretarial Science, A
Business Administration and Management, A
Business/Office Automation/Technology/Data
   Entry, A
Computer Engineering Technology/Technician, A
Computer Systems Networking and
   Telecommunications, A
Criminal Justice/Law Enforcement Administration, A
Fire Science/Firefighting, A
Legal Administrative Assistant/Secretary, A
Liberal Arts and Sciences Studies and
   Humanities, A
Medical Administrative Assistant/Secretary, A
Nursing - Registered Nurse Training, A

CONCORDIA UNIVERSITY

Biological and Physical Sciences, B
Biology/Biological Sciences, B
Business Administration and Management, AB
Chemistry, B
Curriculum and Instruction, M
Drama and Dramatics/Theatre Arts, B
Education, BM
Educational Administration and Supervision, M
Elementary Education and Teaching, BM
English Language and Literature, B
English/Language Arts Teacher Education, B
Environmental Studies, B
Health/Health Care Administration/Management, B
Humanities/Humanistic Studies, B
Interdisciplinary Studies, B
Kindergarten/PreSchool Education and Teaching, B
Liberal Arts and Sciences Studies and
   Humanities, AB
Mathematics Teacher Education, B
Natural Sciences, B
Nursing - Registered Nurse Training, B
Physical Education Teaching and Coaching, B
Physical Sciences, B
Pre-Medicine/Pre-Medical Studies, B
Pre-Theology/Pre-Ministerial Studies, B
Psychology, B
Religion/Religious Studies, B
Religious Education, B
Science Teacher Education/General Science
   Teacher Education, B
Secondary Education and Teaching, BM
Social Sciences, B
Social Studies Teacher Education, B
Social Work, B
Sport and Fitness Administration/Management, B
Theology/Theological Studies, B

CORBAN COLLEGE

Accounting, B
Bible/Biblical Studies, AB
Biology Teacher Education, B
Business Administration and Management, AB
Business Teacher Education, B
Business, Management, Marketing, and Related
   Support Services, B
Communication Studies/Speech Communication
   and Rhetoric, B
Community Organization and Advocacy, B
Computer Science, B
Divinity/Ministry (BD, MDiv.), B
Education, B
Elementary Education and Teaching, B
English Language and Literature, B
English/Language Arts Teacher Education, B
Family Psychology, B
Finance, B
Health Services/Allied Health/Health Sciences, B
Humanities/Humanistic Studies, B
Industrial and Organizational Psychology, B
Interdisciplinary Studies, B
Journalism, B
Liberal Arts and Sciences Studies and
   Humanities, B
Management Information Systems and Services, B

Mathematics, B
Mathematics Teacher Education, B
Missions/Missionary Studies and Missiology, B
Music, B
Music Performance, B
Music Teacher Education, B
Pastoral Studies/Counseling, B
Physical Education Teaching and Coaching, B
Pre-Law Studies, B
Pre-Theology/Pre-Ministerial Studies, B
Psychology, B
Public Health (MPH, DPH), B
Religion/Religious Studies, B
Religious Education, B
Religious/Sacred Music, B
Secondary Education and Teaching, B
Social Science Teacher Education, B
Social Sciences, B
Social Studies Teacher Education, B
Sport and Fitness Administration/Management, B
Theology/Theological Studies, B
Voice and Opera, B

DEVRY UNIVERSITY

Business Administration and Management, B
Business Administration, Management and
   Operations, BM
Computer and Information Sciences, B

EASTERN OREGON UNIVERSITY

Accounting, B
Administrative Assistant and Secretarial Science, A
Agricultural Business and Management, B
Agricultural Economics, B
Agronomy and Crop Science, B
Anthropology, B
Art/Art Studies, General, B
Biological and Physical Sciences, B
Biology/Biological Sciences, B
Business/Managerial Economics, B
Chemistry, B
City/Urban, Community and Regional Planning, B
Computer Science, B
Drama and Dramatics/Theatre Arts, B
Economics, B
Education, BM
Elementary Education and Teaching, M
English Language and Literature, B
Fire Science/Firefighting, B
History, B
Liberal Arts and Sciences Studies and
   Humanities, B
Mathematics, B
Music, B
Natural Resources Management/Development and
   Policy, B
Physical Education Teaching and Coaching, B
Physics, B
Pre-Dentistry Studies, B
Pre-Law Studies, B
Pre-Medicine/Pre-Medical Studies, B
Pre-Veterinary Studies, B
Psychology, B
Secondary Education and Teaching, M
Sociology, B
Special Education and Teaching, B

EUGENE BIBLE COLLEGE

Bible/Biblical Studies, B
Divinity/Ministry (BD, MDiv.), B
Missions/Missionary Studies and Missiology, B
Pastoral Studies/Counseling, B
Religious Education, B
Religious/Sacred Music, B
Youth Ministry, B

GEORGE FOX UNIVERSITY

Acting, B
Art/Art Studies, General, B
Athletic Training and Sports Medicine, B
Behavioral Sciences, B
Bible/Biblical Studies, B
Biology/Biological Sciences, B
Broadcast Journalism, B
Business Administration and Management, B

Business Administration, Management and
Operations, M
Chemistry, B
Cinematography and Film/Video Production, B
Clinical Psychology, BMD
Cognitive Psychology and Psycholinguistics, B
Cognitive Sciences, B
Communication Studies/Speech Communication
and Rhetoric, B
Computer and Information Sciences, B
Counseling Psychology, M
Counselor Education/School Counseling and
Guidance Services, M
Directing and Theatrical Production, B
Drama and Dramatics/Theatre Arts, B
Economics, B
Education, MD
Educational Leadership and Administration, MD
Electrical, Electronics and Communications
Engineering, B
Elementary Education and Teaching, B
Engineering, B
English Language and Literature, B
Family and Consumer Sciences/Human Sciences, B
Fashion Merchandising, B
Film/Cinema Studies, B
Finance, B
Fine/Studio Arts, B
Foods, Nutrition, and Wellness Studies, B
Foundations and Philosophy of Education, MD
Graphic Design, B
Health and Physical Education, B
Health Teacher Education, B
History, B
Industrial Design, B
Information Science/Studies, B
Interdisciplinary Studies, B
Intermedia/Multimedia, B
International Business/Trade/Commerce, B
International/Global Studies, B
Management Information Systems and Services, B
Marketing/Marketing Management, B
Marriage and Family Therapy/Counseling, M
Mathematics, B
Mechanical Engineering, B
Missions/Missionary Studies and Missiology, B
Music, B
Music Performance, B
Music Teacher Education, B
Music Theory and Composition, B
Nursing - Registered Nurse Training, B
Organizational Management, M
Pastoral Studies/Counseling, BD
Philosophy, B
Physical Education Teaching and Coaching, B
Psychology, BMD
Public Relations/Image Management, B
Radio and Television, B
Religion/Religious Studies, BP
Religious Education, BM
School Psychology, M
Social Work, B
Sociology, B
Spanish Language and Literature, B
Sport and Fitness Administration/Management, B
Technical Theatre/Theatre Design and
Technology, B
Theology and Religious Vocations, MDP
Youth Ministry, B

HEALD COLLEGE-PORTLAND

Accounting, A
Administrative Assistant and Secretarial Science, A
Business Administration and Management, A
Information Science/Studies, A
Medical Administrative Assistant/Secretary, A

ITT TECHNICAL INSTITUTE

Animation, Interactive Technology, Video Graphics
and Special Effects, B
Business Administration and Management, B
CAD/CADD Drafting and/or Design
Technology/Technician, A
Computer and Information Systems Security, B
Computer Programming/Programmer, A

Computer Systems Networking and
Telecommunications, B
Criminal Justice/Law Enforcement Administration, B
E-Commerce/Electronic Commerce, B
Electrical, Electronic and Communications
Engineering Technology/Technician, AB
Robotics Technology/Technician, B
System, Networking, and LAN/WAN
Management/Manager, A
Web Page, Digital/Multimedia and Information
Resources Design, A
Web/Multimedia Management and Webmaster, A

LANE COMMUNITY COLLEGE

Accounting, A
Administrative Assistant and Secretarial Science, A
Agricultural Mechanization, A
Airline/Commercial/Professional Pilot and Flight
Crew, A
Automobile/Automotive Mechanics
Technology/Technician, A
Avionics Maintenance Technology/Technician, A
Broadcast Journalism, A
Business Administration and Management, A
Child Development, A
Cinematography and Film/Video Production, A
Commercial and Advertising Art, A
Community Organization and Advocacy, A
Computer Engineering Technology/Technician, A
Computer Programming/Programmer, A
Construction Engineering Technology/Technician, A
Criminal Justice/Law Enforcement Administration, A
Culinary Arts/Chef Training, A
Dental Hygiene/Hygienist, A
Drafting and Design Technology/Technician, A
Electrical, Electronic and Communications
Engineering Technology/Technician, A
Energy Management and Systems
Technology/Technician, A
Food Technology and Processing, A
Heating, Air Conditioning, Ventilation and
Refrigeration Maintenance
Technology/Technician, A
Heavy Equipment Maintenance
Technology/Technician, A
Hospitality Administration/Management, A
Hotel/Motel Administration/Management, A
Industrial Technology/Technician, A
Kindergarten/PreSchool Education and Teaching, A
Liberal Arts and Sciences Studies and
Humanities, A
Nursing - Registered Nurse Training, A
Radio and Television, A
Real Estate, A
Respiratory Care Therapy/Therapist, A
Special Products Marketing Operations, A
Substance Abuse/Addiction Counseling, A
Welding Technology/Welder, A

LEWIS & CLARK COLLEGE

Anthropology, B
Art/Art Studies, General, B
Biochemistry, B
Biology/Biological Sciences, B
Chemistry, B
Communication Disorders, M
Communication Studies/Speech Communication
and Rhetoric, B
Computer Science, B
Counseling Psychology, MO
Cultural Studies, M
Drama and Dramatics/Theatre Arts, B
East Asian Studies, B
Economics, B
Education, MDO
Educational Administration and Supervision, MD
Elementary Education and Teaching, M
English Language and Literature, B
Environmental Studies, B
Foreign Languages and Literatures, B
French Language and Literature, B
German Language and Literature, B
Hispanic-American, Puerto Rican, and Mexican-
American/Chicano Studies, B
History, B
International Relations and Affairs, B

Law and Legal Studies, MP
Liberal Studies, B
Marriage and Family Therapy/Counseling, M
Mathematics, B
Modern Languages, B
Music, B
Philosophy, B
Physics, B
Political Science and Government, B
Pre-Engineering, B
Psychology, B
Religion/Religious Studies, B
School Psychology, MO
Secondary Education and Teaching, M
Sociology, B
Spanish Language and Literature, B
Special Education and Teaching, M
Substance Abuse/Addiction Counseling, M

LINFIELD COLLEGE

Accounting, B
Anthropology, B
Area, Ethnic, Cultural, and Gender Studies, B
Art/Art Studies, General, B
Athletic Training and Sports Medicine, B
Biology/Biological Sciences, B
Business/Commerce, B
Chemistry, B
Communication Studies/Speech Communication
and Rhetoric, B
Computer Science, B
Creative Writing, B
Drama and Dramatics/Theatre Arts, B
Economics, B
Elementary Education and Teaching, B
English Language and Literature, B
Environmental Studies, B
Finance, B
French Language and Literature, B
German Language and Literature, B
Health and Physical Education, B
History, B
International Business/Trade/Commerce, B
Japanese Language and Literature, B
Kinesiology and Exercise Science, B
Mathematics, B
Music, B
Philosophy, B
Physical Sciences, B
Physics, B
Political Science and Government, B
Psychology, B
Religion/Religious Studies, B
Sociology, B
Spanish Language and Literature, B

LINN-BENTON COMMUNITY COLLEGE

Accounting, A
Administrative Assistant and Secretarial Science, A
Agricultural Business and Management, A
Agricultural Teacher Education, A
Agriculture, A
Animal Sciences, A
Art/Art Studies, General, A
Automobile/Automotive Mechanics
Technology/Technician, A
Biological and Physical Sciences, A
Biology/Biological Sciences, A
Business Administration and Management, A
Chemistry, A
Child Care and Support Services Management, A
Civil Engineering Technology/Technician, A
Commercial and Advertising Art, A
Computer and Information Sciences, A
Computer Programming, Specific Applications, A
Criminal Justice/Police Science, A
Criminal Justice/Safety Studies, A
Culinary Arts and Related Services, A
Culinary Arts/Chef Training, A
Dairy Husbandry and Production, A
Diesel Mechanics Technology/Technician, A
Drafting and Design Technology/Technician, A
Drama and Dramatics/Theatre Arts, A
Economics, A
Education, A
Elementary Education and Teaching, A

Engineering, A
English Language and Literature, A
Family and Consumer Sciences/Human Sciences, A
Foreign Languages and Literatures, A
Graphic Communications, A
Horse Husbandry/Equine Science and
   Management, A
Horticultural Science, A
Industrial Technology/Technician, A
Journalism, A
Juvenile Corrections, A
Legal Administrative Assistant/Secretary, A
Liberal Arts and Sciences Studies and
   Humanities, A
Machine Tool Technology/Machinist, A
Management Information Systems and Services, A
Mathematics, A
Medical Administrative Assistant/Secretary, A
Medical/Clinical Assistant, A
Metallurgical Technology/Technician, A
Multi-/Interdisciplinary Studies, A
Nursing - Registered Nurse Training, A
Photography, A
Physical Education Teaching and Coaching, A
Physical Sciences, A
Physics, A
Pre-Engineering, A
Prepress/Desktop Publishing and Digital Imaging
   Design, A
Restaurant, Culinary, and Catering
   Management/Manager, A
Speech and Rhetorical Studies, A
System Administration/Administrator, A
Teacher Assistant/Aide, A
Technical and Business Writing, A
Water Quality and Wastewater Treatment
   Management and Recycling
   Technology/Technician, A

MARYLHURST UNIVERSITY

Art Therapy/Therapist, MO
Art/Art Studies, General, B
Biological and Physical Sciences, B
Business Administration and Management, B
Business Administration, Management and
   Operations, M
Corporate and Organizational Communication, M
Counseling Psychology, O
Creative Writing, B
Divinity/Ministry (BD, MDiv.), B
Education, B
English Literature (British and Commonwealth), B
Environmental Studies, B
Ethnic, Cultural Minority, and Gender Studies, B
Gerontology, M
History, B
Interdisciplinary Studies, BM
Interior Design, B
Liberal Studies, M
Mass Communication/Media Studies, B
Music, B
Pastoral Studies/Counseling, B
Psychology, B
Public Relations/Image Management, B
Real Estate, B
Religion/Religious Studies, B
Social Sciences, B
Theology and Religious Vocations, MP

MOUNT ANGEL SEMINARY

Comparative Literature, B
Liberal Arts and Sciences Studies and
   Humanities, B
Philosophy, B
Theology and Religious Vocations, MP

MT. HOOD COMMUNITY COLLEGE

Accounting, A
Administrative Assistant and Secretarial Science, A
Architectural Engineering Technology/Technician, A
Automobile/Automotive Mechanics
   Technology/Technician, A
Avionics Maintenance Technology/Technician, A
Broadcast Journalism, A
Business Administration and Management, A
Business Teacher Education, A

Civil Engineering Technology/Technician, A
Commercial and Advertising Art, A
Computer Engineering Technology/Technician, A
Cosmetology/Cosmetologist, A
Dental Hygiene/Hygienist, A
Electrical, Electronic and Communications
   Engineering Technology/Technician, A
Environmental Health, A
Fire Science/Firefighting, A
Food Science, A
Forestry Technology/Technician, A
Funeral Service and Mortuary Science, A
Horticultural Science, A
Hospitality Administration/Management, A
Industrial Technology/Technician, A
Journalism, A
Kindergarten/PreSchool Education and Teaching, A
Legal Administrative Assistant/Secretary, A
Liberal Arts and Sciences Studies and
   Humanities, A
Marketing/Marketing Management, A
Mechanical Engineering/Mechanical
   Technology/Technician, A
Medical Administrative Assistant/Secretary, A
Medical/Clinical Assistant, A
Mental Health/Rehabilitation, A
Nursing - Registered Nurse Training, A
Occupational Therapy/Therapist, A
Ornamental Horticulture, A
Physical Therapy/Therapist, A
Radio and Television, A
Respiratory Care Therapy/Therapist, A
Surgical Technology/Technologist, A
Tourism and Travel Services Management, A

MULTNOMAH BIBLE COLLEGE AND BIBLICAL SEMINARY

Ancient/Classical Greek Language and Literature, B
Bible/Biblical Studies, B
Communication Studies/Speech Communication
   and Rhetoric, B
Hebrew Language and Literature, B
History, B
Journalism, B
Missions/Missionary Studies and Missiology, B
Pastoral Counseling and Specialized Ministries, B
Pastoral Studies/Counseling, BM
Religious Education, B
Religious/Sacred Music, B
Theology and Religious Vocations, MPO
Theology/Theological Studies, B
Youth Ministry, B

NORTHWEST CHRISTIAN COLLEGE

Area, Ethnic, Cultural, and Gender Studies, B
Bible/Biblical Studies, B
Business Administration, Management and
   Operations, BM
Communication Studies/Speech Communication
   and Rhetoric, B
Computer and Information Sciences, B
Counselor Education/School Counseling and
   Guidance Services, M
Health Services Administration, B
Human Services, B
Liberal Arts and Sciences Studies and
   Humanities, B
Management Information Systems and Services, B
Music Management and Merchandising, B
Psychology, B
Social Sciences, B
Teacher Education, Multiple Levels, B
Theological and Ministerial Studies, B

OREGON COAST COMMUNITY COLLEGE

General Studies, A
Liberal Arts and Sciences Studies and
   Humanities, A
Marine Biology and Biological Oceanography, A

Nursing - Registered Nurse Training, A

OREGON COLLEGE OF ART & CRAFT

Crafts/Craft Design, Folk Art and Artisanry, B
Fine Arts and Art Studies, B

OREGON HEALTH & SCIENCE UNIVERSITY

Allopathic Medicine, PO
Biochemistry, DO
Bioinformatics, MDO
Biological and Biomedical Sciences, MDO
Biopsychology, MDO
Biostatistics, MO
Cell Biology and Anatomy, DO
Community Health Nursing, MO
Dentistry, PO
Developmental Biology and Embryology, DO
Epidemiology, MO
Genetics, D
Gerontological Nursing, MDO
Immunology, D
Medical Informatics, MDO
Medical Radiologic Technology/Science - Radiation
   Therapist, B
Microbiology, D
Molecular Biology, DO
Neuroscience, MDO
Nurse Midwife/Nursing Midwifery, MO
Nursing, MDO
Nursing - Adult, MO
Nursing - Advanced Practice, MO
Nursing - Registered Nurse Training, B
Oral and Dental Sciences, MO
Oral Pathology, O
Pediatric Nurse/Nursing, MO
Pharmacology, DO
Physiology, DO
Psychiatric/Mental Health Nurse/Nursing, MO

OREGON INSTITUTE OF TECHNOLOGY

Accounting, B
Business Administration and Management, B
Civil Engineering, B
Communication Studies/Speech Communication
   and Rhetoric, B
Computer and Information Sciences, B
Computer Engineering Technology/Technician, AB
Computer Programming/Programmer, AB
Counseling Psychology, B
Dental Hygiene/Hygienist, B
Electrical, Electronic and Communications
   Engineering Technology/Technician, AB
Environmental Studies, B
Industrial Radiologic Technology/Technician, B
Laser and Optical Technology/Technician, B
Liberal Arts and Sciences Studies and
   Humanities, A
Management Information Systems and Services, B
Mechanical Engineering/Mechanical
   Technology/Technician, B
Pre-Medicine/Pre-Medical Studies, B
Radiologic Technology/Science - Radiographer, B
Survey Technology/Surveying, B

OREGON STATE UNIVERSITY

Actuarial Science, B
Adult and Continuing Education and Teaching, M
Agricultural Business and Management, B
Agricultural Economics, BMD
Agricultural Education, M
Agricultural Sciences, MD
Agricultural/Biological Engineering and
   Bioengineering, B
Agriculture, B
Agronomy and Crop Science, B
Agronomy and Soil Sciences, MD
American/United States Studies/Civilization, B
Analytical Chemistry, MD
Animal Sciences, BMD
Anthropology, BM
Apparel and Textiles, B
Applied Art, B
Applied Mathematics, B
Art History, Criticism and Conservation, B

Art/Art Studies, General, B
Athletic Training and Sports Medicine, B
Atmospheric Sciences and Meteorology, MD
Biochemistry, BMD
Bioengineering, MD
Biological and Physical Sciences, B
Biology/Biological Sciences, B
Biometry/Biometrics, MD
Biophysics, BMD
Botany/Plant Biology, BMD
Building/Construction
    Finishing, Management, and Inspection, B
Business Administration and Management, B
Business Administration, Management and
    Operations, MO
Cell Biology and Anatomy, MD
Cell/Cellular Biology and Histology, B
Chemical Engineering, BMD
Chemistry, BMD
Child and Family Studies, MD
Civil Engineering, BMD
Clinical Laboratory Science/Medical
    Technology/Technologist, B
Clothing and Textiles, MD
Comparative Literature, B
Computer Engineering, B
Computer Science, BMD
Construction Engineering, B
Construction Engineering and Management, MD
Counselor Education/School Counseling and
    Guidance Services, MD
Economics, BMD
Education, MD
Electrical Engineering, MD
Electrical, Electronics and Communications
    Engineering, B
Elementary Education and Teaching, M
Engineering, B
Engineering and Applied Sciences, MD
Engineering Physics, B
English, M
English Language and Literature, B
Entomology, B
Environmental and Occupational Health, M
Environmental Biology, B
Environmental Engineering
    Technology/Environmental Technology, MD
Environmental Health, B
Environmental Policy and Resource
    Management, M
Environmental Sciences, MD
Environmental Studies, B
Environmental/Environmental Health Engineering, B
Ethnic and Cultural Studies, B
Evolutionary Biology, B
Exercise and Sports Science, MD
Family and Community Services, B
Family and Consumer Economics and Related
    Services, B
Family and Consumer Sciences/Human
    Sciences, BM
Fashion Merchandising, B
Fashion/Apparel Design, B
Finance, B
Fish, Game and Wildlife Management, MD
Fishing and Fisheries Sciences and Management, B
Food Science, B
Food Science and Technology, MD
Foods, Nutrition, and Wellness Studies, B
Forest Engineering, B
Forest Management/Forest Resources
    Management, B
Forest Resources Production and Management, B
Forestry, BMD
French Language and Literature, B
General Merchandising, Sales, and Related
    Marketing Operations, B
Genetics, MD
Geography, BMD
Geological/Geophysical Engineering, B
Geology/Earth Science, BMD
Geophysics and Seismology, BMD
Geosciences, MD
German Language and Literature, B
Gerontology, M
Health Education, M

Health Physics/Radiological Health, MD
Health Services Administration, M
Health/Health Care Administration/Management, B
History, BMD
History and Philosophy of Science and
    Technology, B
Horticultural Science, BMD
Human Development, MD
Human Development and Family Studies, B
Industrial Engineering, B
Industrial/Management Engineering, MD
Information Science/Studies, B
Inorganic Chemistry, MD
Interdisciplinary Studies, BM
Interior Design, B
International Business/Trade/Commerce, B
International Relations and Affairs, B
International/Global Studies, B
Kindergarten/PreSchool Education and Teaching, B
Kinesiology and Exercise Science, B
Kinesiology and Movement Studies, M
Liberal Arts and Sciences Studies and
    Humanities, B
Management Information Systems and Services, B
Manufacturing Engineering, M
Marine Affairs, M
Marine Sciences, M
Marketing/Marketing Management, B
Materials Sciences, MD
Mathematics, BMD
Mathematics Teacher Education, MD
Mechanical Engineering, BMD
Medical Microbiology and Bacteriology, B
Metallurgical Engineering, B
Microbiology, BMD
Mining and Mineral Engineering, B
Molecular Biology, MD
Molecular Toxicology, MD
Music, B
Music Teacher Education, M
Natural Resources Management/Development and
    Policy, B
Nuclear Engineering, BMD
Nutritional Sciences, MD
Occupational Safety and Health
    Technology/Technician, B
Ocean Engineering, M
Oceanography, Chemical and Physical, MD
Operations Research, M
Organic Chemistry, MD
Paper and Pulp Engineering, MD
Parks, Recreation and Leisure Facilities
    Management, B
Parks, Recreation, Leisure and Fitness Studies, B
Pathology/Experimental Pathology, M
Pharmaceutical Sciences, MDP
Pharmacy, MDP
Philosophy, B
Physical Chemistry, MD
Physical Education Teaching and Coaching, BM
Physical Sciences, B
Physics, BMD
Plant Pathology/Phytopathology, MD
Plant Physiology, MD
Political Science and Government, B
Pre-Pharmacy Studies, B
Psychology, B
Public Health, MD
Public Health (MPH, DPH), B
Radiation Protection/Health Physics Technician, B
Range Science and Management, BMD
Science Teacher Education/General Science
    Teacher Education, MD
Sociology, B
Soil Science and Agronomy, B
Spanish Language and Literature, B
Special Products Marketing Operations, B
Speech and Rhetorical Studies, B
Statistics, MD
Student Personnel Services, M
Toxicology, MD
Veterinary Medicine, P
Veterinary Sciences, MD
Vocational and Technical Education, M
Water Resources Engineering, MD
Wildlife and Wildlands Science and Management, B

Wood Science and Wood Products/Pulp and Paper
    Technology, B
Zoology/Animal Biology, BMD

PACIFIC NORTHWEST COLLEGE OF ART

Design and Visual Communications, B
Fine/Studio Arts, B
Graphic Design, B
Illustration, B
Intermedia/Multimedia, B
Painting, B
Photography, B
Printmaking, B
Sculpture, B

PACIFIC UNIVERSITY

Accounting, B
Art Teacher Education, B
Art/Art Studies, General, B
Athletic Training and Sports Medicine, B
Biology/Biological Sciences, B
Broadcast Journalism, B
Business Administration and Management, B
Chemistry, B
Chinese Language and Literature, B
Comparative Literature, B
Computer Science, B
Creative Writing, B
Drama and Dramatics/Theatre Arts, B
Early Childhood Education and Teaching, M
Economics, B
Education, BM
Elementary Education and Teaching, BM
English Language and Literature, B
Environmental Studies, B
Finance, B
French Language and Literature, B
German Language and Literature, B
History, B
Humanities/Humanistic Studies, B
International Relations and Affairs, B
Japanese Language and Literature, B
Journalism, B
Kindergarten/PreSchool Education and Teaching, B
Kinesiology and Exercise Science, B
Liberal Arts and Sciences Studies and
    Humanities, B
Marketing/Marketing Management, B
Mass Communication/Media Studies, B
Mathematics, B
Middle School Education, M
Modern Languages, B
Music, B
Music Performance, B
Music Teacher Education, B
Occupational Therapy/Therapist, M
Optometry, P
Philosophy, B
Physical Therapy/Therapist, D
Physician Assistant, M
Physics, B
Political Science and Government, B
Pre-Dentistry Studies, B
Pre-Medicine/Pre-Medical Studies, B
Psychology, BMD
Public Health (MPH, DPH), B
Radio and Television, B
Secondary Education and Teaching, BM
Social Work, B
Sociology, B
Spanish Language and Literature, B
Special Education and Teaching, M
Telecommunications Technology/Technician, B
Vision Science/Physiological Optics, M

PIONEER PACIFIC COLLEGE

Accounting, A
Business Administration and Management, AB
Criminal Justice/Police Science, AB
Health/Health Care Administration/Management, AB
Information Science/Studies, A
Information Technology, B
Legal Assistant/Paralegal, A
Medical/Clinical Assistant, A
Sales, Distribution and Marketing Operations, A

Web/Multimedia Management and Webmaster, A

PORTLAND COMMUNITY COLLEGE

Accounting, A
Administrative Assistant and Secretarial Science, A
Aeronautics/Aviation/Aerospace Science and
   Technology, A
Automobile/Automotive Mechanics
   Technology/Technician, A
Avionics Maintenance Technology/Technician, A
Biological and Physical Sciences, A
Biology Technician/BioTechnology Laboratory
   Technician, A
Business Administration and Management, A
Carpentry/Carpenter, A
Child Development, A
Civil Engineering Technology/Technician, A
Clinical/Medical Laboratory Technician, A
Commercial and Advertising Art, A
Computer Engineering Technology/Technician, A
Computer Programming/Programmer, A
Construction Engineering Technology/Technician, A
Criminal Justice/Law Enforcement Administration, A
Dental Hygiene/Hygienist, A
Dietetics/Dieticians, A
Drafting and Design Technology/Technician, A
Educational/Instructional Media Design, A
Electrical, Electronic and Communications
   Engineering Technology/Technician, A
Elementary Education and Teaching, A
Engineering, A
Engineering Technology, A
Family and Consumer Economics and Related
   Services, A
Family and Consumer Sciences/Human Sciences, A
Fire Science/Firefighting, A
Gerontology, A
Health and Medical Laboratory Technologies, A
Health Information/Medical Records
   Administration/Administrator, A
Industrial Design, A
Industrial Radiologic Technology/Technician, A
Information Science/Studies, A
Landscape Architecture, A
Laser and Optical Technology/Technician, A
Legal Administrative Assistant/Secretary, A
Legal Assistant/Paralegal, A
Liberal Arts and Sciences Studies and
   Humanities, A
Library Science, A
Machine Tool Technology/Machinist, A
Marketing/Marketing Management, A
Mechanical Engineering/Mechanical
   Technology/Technician, A
Medical Administrative Assistant/Secretary, A
Medical/Clinical Assistant, A
Nursing - Registered Nurse Training, A
Ophthalmic Laboratory Technology/Technician, A
Physical Sciences, A
Pre-Engineering, A
Real Estate, A
Sign Language Interpretation and Translation, A
Trade and Industrial Teacher Education, A
Welding Technology/Welder, A

PORTLAND STATE UNIVERSITY

Accounting, B
Adult and Continuing Education and Teaching, D
Advertising, B
African Studies, B
American Indian/Native American Studies, B
Anthropology, BMD
Applied Art, B
Applied Economics, M
Architecture, B
Art History, Criticism and Conservation, B
Art/Art Studies, General, B
Artificial Intelligence and Robotics, O
Biochemistry, B
Biological and Biomedical Sciences, MD
Biological and Physical Sciences, B
Biological Anthropology, MD
Biology/Biological Sciences, B
Business Administration and Management, B
Business Administration, Management and
   Operations, MD

Central/Middle and Eastern European Studies, B
Chemistry, BMD
Child Development, B
Chinese Language and Literature, B
City/Urban, Community and Regional Planning, B
Civil Engineering, BMD
Commercial and Advertising Art, B
Communication Disorders, M
Computer and Information Sciences, B
Computer Engineering, BMD
Computer Science, BMD
Conflict Resolution and Mediation/Peace Studies, M
Counselor Education/School Counseling and
   Guidance Services, MD
Criminal Justice/Law Enforcement Administration, B
Criminology, MD
Curriculum and Instruction, MD
Drama and Dramatics/Theatre Arts, B
Drawing, B
Early Childhood Education and Teaching, M
East Asian Studies, B
Economics, BMD
Education, MD
Educational Administration and Supervision, MD
Educational Media/Instructional Technology, M
Electrical Engineering, MD
Electrical, Electronics and Communications
   Engineering, B
Elementary Education and Teaching, M
Engineering and Applied Sciences, MDO
Engineering Management, MDO
English, MO
English as a Second Language, M
English Language and Literature, B
Environmental Engineering
   Technology/Environmental Technology, MD
Environmental Policy and Resource
   Management, M
Environmental Sciences, MD
Environmental Studies, BM
Finance, B
Finance and Banking, M
Fine Arts and Art Studies, M
Foreign Language Teacher Education, M
French Language and Literature, BM
Geography, BMD
Geology/Earth Science, BMD
German Language and Literature, BM
Gerontology, O
Health Education, M
Health Promotion, M
Health Services Administration, M
Health Teacher Education, B
Higher Education/Higher Education
   Administration, D
History, BM
Human Resources Management/Personnel
   Administration, M
Humanities/Humanistic Studies, B
Industrial and Manufacturing Management, M
International Business/Trade/Commerce, M
International Relations and Affairs, B
Japanese Language and Literature, B
Japanese Studies, M
Latin American Studies, B
Liberal Arts and Sciences Studies and
   Humanities, B
Linguistics, B
Logistics and Materials Management, B
Management of Technology, MDO
Manufacturing Engineering, M
Marketing/Marketing Management, B
Mathematics, BMDO
Mathematics Teacher Education, D
Mechanical Engineering, BMD
Music, BM
Music Teacher Education, M
Near and Middle Eastern Studies, B
Painting, M
Performance, M
Philosophy, B
Physics, BMD
Political Science and Government, BMD
Printmaking, M
Psychology, BMD
Public Administration, MD

Public Health, MO
Reading Teacher Education, M
Russian Language and Literature, B
Science Teacher Education/General Science
   Teacher Education, M
Sculpture, BM
Secondary Education and Teaching, M
Social Sciences, B
Social Studies Teacher Education, M
Social Work, MD
Sociology, BMD
Software Engineering, M
Spanish Language and Literature, BM
Special Education and Teaching, MD
Speech and Interpersonal Communication, MO
Speech and Rhetorical Studies, B
Statistics, M
Systems Engineering, MO
Systems Science and Theory, MDO
Theater, MO
Urban and Regional Planning, M
Urban Studies/Affairs, BMD
Women's Studies, B

REED COLLEGE

American/United States Studies/Civilization, B
Anthropology, B
Art/Art Studies, General, B
Biochemistry, B
Biology/Biological Sciences, B
Chemistry, B
Chinese Language and Literature, B
Classics and Classical
   Languages, Literatures, and Linguistics, B
Comparative Literature, B
Dance, B
Drama and Dramatics/Theatre Arts, B
Economics, B
English Language and Literature, B
Fine/Studio Arts, B
French Language and Literature, B
German Language and Literature, B
History, B
International Relations and Affairs, B
Liberal Studies, M
Linguistics, B
Mathematics, B
Music, B
Philosophy, B
Physics, B
Political Science and Government, B
Psychology, B
Religion/Religious Studies, B
Russian Language and Literature, B
Sociology, B
Spanish Language and Literature, B

ROGUE COMMUNITY COLLEGE

Automobile/Automotive Mechanics
   Technology/Technician, A
Business Administration and Management, A
Child Development, A
Computer Science, A
Construction Management, A
Criminal Justice/Law Enforcement Administration, A
Education, A
Electrical, Electronic and Communications
   Engineering Technology/Technician, A
Fire Science/Firefighting, A
Heavy Equipment Maintenance
   Technology/Technician, A
Human Services, A
Humanities/Humanistic Studies, A
Industrial Technology/Technician, A
Liberal Arts and Sciences Studies and
   Humanities, A
Manufacturing Technology/Technician, A
Nursing - Registered Nurse Training, A
Social Sciences, A
Substance Abuse/Addiction Counseling, A
Welding Technology/Welder, A

SOUTHERN OREGON UNIVERSITY

Accounting, B
Anthropology, B
Art/Art Studies, General, B

Biochemistry, B
Biology/Biological Sciences, B
Business Administration and Management, B
Business Administration, Management and
   Operations, M
Business Statistics, B
Chemistry, B
Communication Studies/Speech Communication
   and Rhetoric, B
Computer Science, BM
Criminology, B
Drama and Dramatics/Theatre Arts, B
Economics, B
Education, M
Elementary Education and Teaching, M
English Language and Literature, B
Environmental Education, M
Environmental Studies, B
French Language and Literature, B
Geography, B
Geology/Earth Science, B
German Language and Literature, B
Health Teacher Education, B
History, B
Hotel/Motel Administration/Management, B
Human Services, M
Interdisciplinary Studies, B
International Relations and Affairs, B
Liberal Arts and Sciences Studies and
   Humanities, B
Marketing/Marketing Management, B
Mathematics, BM
Mathematics and Computer Science, B
Music, BM
Music Management and Merchandising, B
Nursing - Registered Nurse Training, B
Performance, M
Physical Education Teaching and Coaching, B
Physics, B
Political Science and Government, B
Pre-Law Studies, B
Pre-Medicine/Pre-Medical Studies, B
Psychology, BM
Secondary Education and Teaching, M
Social Sciences, BM
Sociology, B
Spanish Language and Literature, B

SOUTHWESTERN OREGON COMMUNITY COLLEGE

Accounting, A
Adult Development and Aging, A
Athletic Training and Sports Medicine, A
Business Administration and Management, A
Child Care Provider/Assistant, A
Computer Systems Analysis/Analyst, A
Computer Systems Networking and
   Telecommunications, A
Corrections, A
Criminal Justice/Police Science, A
Criminal Justice/Safety Studies, A
Engineering, A
Environmental Studies, A
Fire Science/Firefighting, A
Forestry, A
Health and Physical Education, A
Industrial Technology/Technician, A
Liberal Arts and Sciences Studies and
   Humanities, A
Machine Tool Technology/Machinist, A
Management Information Systems and Services, A
Marketing/Marketing Management, A
Mathematics, A
Medical/Clinical Assistant, A
Natural Sciences, A
Nursing - Registered Nurse Training, A
Office Management and Supervision, A
Restaurant, Culinary, and Catering
   Management/Manager, A
Social Work, A
Substance Abuse/Addiction Counseling, A
Turf and Turfgrass Management, A

Welding Technology/Welder, A

TILLAMOOK BAY COMMUNITY COLLEGE

Accounting, A
Accounting Technology/Technician and
   Bookkeeping, A
Administrative Assistant and Secretarial Science, A
Business/Office Automation/Technology/Data
   Entry, A
Criminal Justice/Law Enforcement Administration, A
Early Childhood Education and Teaching, A
Emergency Medical Technology/Technician (EMT
   Paramedic), A
General Studies, A
Liberal Arts and Sciences Studies and
   Humanities, A
Management Science, A
Marketing, A
Nursing, A
Office Management and Supervision, A
Substance Abuse/Addiction Counseling, A

TREASURE VALLEY COMMUNITY COLLEGE

Administrative Assistant and Secretarial Science, A
Agricultural Business and Management, A
Agricultural Mechanization, A
Agriculture, A
Agronomy and Crop Science, A
Biological and Physical Sciences, A
Biology/Biological Sciences, A
Business Administration and Management, A
Chemistry, A
Commercial and Advertising Art, A
Computer Science, A
Criminal Justice/Law Enforcement Administration, A
Criminal Justice/Police Science, A
Drafting and Design Technology/Technician, A
Drama and Dramatics/Theatre Arts, A
Economics, A
Education, A
Engineering, A
English Language and Literature, A
Forestry, A
Forestry Technology/Technician, A
History, A
Humanities/Humanistic Studies, A
Legal Administrative Assistant/Secretary, A
Liberal Arts and Sciences Studies and
   Humanities, A
Mass Communication/Media Studies, A
Mathematics, A
Medical Administrative Assistant/Secretary, A
Music, A
Music Teacher Education, A
Natural Resources Management/Development and
   Policy, A
Nursing - Registered Nurse Training, A
Physical Education Teaching and Coaching, A
Political Science and Government, A
Range Science and Management, A
Social Sciences, A
Sociology, A
Survey Technology/Surveying, A
Welding Technology/Welder, A
Wildlife and Wildlands Science and Management, A

UMPQUA COMMUNITY COLLEGE

Accounting, A
Administrative Assistant and Secretarial Science, A
Agriculture, A
Anthropology, A
Art History, Criticism and Conservation, A
Art Teacher Education, A
Art/Art Studies, General, A
Automobile/Automotive Mechanics
   Technology/Technician, A
Behavioral Sciences, A
Biological and Physical Sciences, A
Biology/Biological Sciences, A
Business Administration and Management, A
Chemistry, A
Child Development, A
Civil Engineering Technology/Technician, A
Computer Engineering Technology/Technician, A

Computer Science, A
Cosmetology/Cosmetologist, A
Criminal Justice/Law Enforcement Administration, A
Drama and Dramatics/Theatre Arts, A
Economics, A
Education, A
Electrical, Electronic and Communications
   Engineering Technology/Technician, A
Elementary Education and Teaching, A
Emergency Medical Technology/Technician (EMT
   Paramedic), A
Engineering, A
English Language and Literature, A
Fire Science/Firefighting, A
Forestry, A
Health Teacher Education, A
History, A
Human Resources Management/Personnel
   Administration, A
Humanities/Humanistic Studies, A
Journalism, A
Kindergarten/PreSchool Education and Teaching, A
Legal Administrative Assistant/Secretary, A
Liberal Arts and Sciences Studies and
   Humanities, A
Marketing/Marketing Management, A
Mathematics, A
Medical Administrative Assistant/Secretary, A
Music, A
Music Teacher Education, A
Natural Sciences, A
Nursing - Registered Nurse Training, A
Physical Education Teaching and Coaching, A
Physical Sciences, A
Political Science and Government, A
Pre-Engineering, A
Prepress/Desktop Publishing and Digital Imaging
   Design, A
Psychology, A
Social Sciences, A
Social Work, A
Sociology, A

UNIVERSITY OF OREGON

Accounting, BMD
Advertising, B
Anthropology, BMD
Applied Art, B
Architecture, BM
Art History, Criticism and Conservation, BMD
Art/Art Studies, General, B
Arts Management, M
Asian Languages, MD
Asian Studies/Civilization, BM
Audiology/Audiologist and Speech-Language
   Pathology/Pathologist, B
Biochemistry, BMD
Biological and Biomedical Sciences, MD
Biological and Physical Sciences, B
Biology/Biological Sciences, B
Biopsychology, MD
Broadcast Journalism, B
Business Administration and Management, B
Business Administration, Management and
   Operations, M
Central/Middle and Eastern European Studies, B
Ceramic Arts and Ceramics, B
Chemistry, BMD
Chinese Language and Literature, B
Chinese Studies, MD
City/Urban, Community and Regional Planning, B
Classics and Classical
   Languages, Literatures, and Linguistics, BM
Clinical Psychology, D
Cognitive Sciences, MD
Commercial and Advertising Art, B
Communication and Media Studies, MD
Communication Disorders, B
Community Organization and Advocacy, B
Comparative Literature, BMD
Computer and Information Sciences, B
Computer Science, BMD
Dance, BM
Developmental Psychology, MD
Drama and Dramatics/Theatre Arts, B
Drawing, B

East Asian
   Languages, Literatures, and Linguistics, B
East Asian Studies, B
Ecology, MD
Economics, BMD
Education, BMD
Educational Leadership and Administration, B
English, MD
English Language and Literature, B
Environmental Sciences, B
Environmental Studies, BMD
Ethnic and Cultural Studies, B
Ethnic, Cultural Minority, and Gender Studies, B
Evolutionary Biology, MD
Family and Consumer Sciences/Human Sciences, B
Fiber, Textile and Weaving Arts, B
Finance, B
Finance and Banking, D
Fine Arts and Art Studies, M
Fine/Studio Arts, B
Folklore, M
French Language and Literature, BM
Genetics, D
Geography, BMD
Geology/Earth Science, BMD
German Language and Literature, BMD
Hebrew Language and Literature, B
Historic Preservation and Conservation, M
History, BMD
Human Services, B
Humanities/Humanistic Studies, B
Information Science/Studies, MD
Interdisciplinary Studies, M
Interior Architecture, B
Interior Design, M
Intermedia/Multimedia, B
International Affairs, M
International Business/Trade/Commerce, B
International Relations and Affairs, B
Italian Language and Literature, BM
Japanese Language and Literature, B
Japanese Studies, MD
Jazz/Jazz Studies, B
Jewish/Judaic Studies, B
Journalism, BMD
Landscape Architecture, BM
Latin Language and Literature, B
Law and Legal Studies, PO
Liberal Arts and Sciences Studies and
   Humanities, B
Linguistics, BMD
Management, D
Management Information Systems and Services, M
Marine Biology and Biological Oceanography, MD
Marketing, D
Marketing/Marketing Management, B
Mass Communication/Media Studies, B
Mathematics, BMD
Mathematics and Computer Science, B
Metal and Jewelry Arts, B
Modern Greek Language and Literature, B
Molecular Biology, D
Music, BMD
Music Performance, B
Music Teacher Education, BMD
Neuroscience, D
Painting, B
Philosophy, BMD
Photography, B
Physics, BMD
Physiology, BMD
Political Science and Government, BMD
Pre-Dentistry Studies, B
Pre-Medicine/Pre-Medical Studies, B
Printmaking, B
Psychology, BMD
Public Administration, B
Public Policy Analysis, BM
Public Relations/Image Management, B
Quantitative Analysis, M
Radio and Television, B
Religion/Religious Studies, B
Romance
   Languages, Literatures, and Linguistics, BMD
Russian Language and Literature, BM
Sculpture, B

Social Psychology, MD
Sociology, BMD
Spanish Language and Literature, BM
Theater, MD
Urban and Regional Planning, M
Women's Studies, B
Writing, M

UNIVERSITY OF PHOENIX-OREGON CAMPUS

Business Administration and Management, B
Business Administration, Management and
   Operations, M
Education, M
Information Technology, B
Management, M
Management Information Systems and Services, M
Management of Technology, M
Management Science, B
Marketing/Marketing Management, B
Organizational Management, M
Public Administration and Social Service
   Professions, B

UNIVERSITY OF PORTLAND

Accounting, B
Arts Management, B
Biology/Biological Sciences, B
Business Administration and Management, B
Business Administration, Management and
   Operations, M
Chemistry, B
Civil Engineering, B
Communication and Media Studies, M
Computer Engineering, B
Computer Science, B
Corporate and Organizational Communication, M
Criminal Justice/Safety Studies, B
Drama and Dramatics/Theatre Arts, B
Early Childhood Education and Teaching, M
Education, BM
Electrical, Electronics and Communications
   Engineering, B
Elementary Education and Teaching, B
Engineering, B
Engineering and Applied Sciences, M
Engineering Science, B
Engineering/Industrial Management, B
English Language and Literature, B
Environmental Studies, B
Finance, B
History, B
Interdisciplinary Studies, B
International Business/Trade/Commerce, B
Journalism, B
Marketing/Marketing Management, B
Mass Communication/Media Studies, B
Mathematics, B
Mechanical Engineering, B
Music, BM
Music Teacher Education, B
Nursing, MO
Nursing - Advanced Practice, O
Nursing - Registered Nurse Training, B
Nursing Administration, O
Nursing Education, O
Pastoral Studies/Counseling, M
Philosophy, B
Physics, B
Political Science and Government, B
Pre-Dentistry Studies, B
Pre-Law Studies, B
Pre-Medicine/Pre-Medical Studies, B
Psychology, B
Religious Education, M
Secondary Education and Teaching, BM
Social Work, B
Sociology, B
Spanish Language and Literature, B
Special Education and Teaching, M
Theater, M
Theology/Theological Studies, B

WARNER PACIFIC COLLEGE

American/United States Studies/Civilization, B
Bible/Biblical Studies, AB

Biological and Physical Sciences, B
Biology/Biological Sciences, B
Business Administration and Management, B
Divinity/Ministry (BD, MDiv.), AB
Education, B
Elementary Education and Teaching, B
English Language and Literature, B
History, B
Human Development and Family Studies, B
Junior High/Intermediate/Middle School Education
   and Teaching, B
Kindergarten/PreSchool Education and Teaching, B
Kinesiology and Exercise Science, B
Liberal Arts and Sciences Studies and
   Humanities, B
Music, B
Music Management and Merchandising, B
Music Teacher Education, B
Nursing - Registered Nurse Training, A
Pastoral Studies/Counseling, B
Physical Education Teaching and Coaching, B
Physical Sciences, B
Pre-Law Studies, B
Pre-Medicine/Pre-Medical Studies, B
Pre-Veterinary Studies, B
Psychology, B
Public Health (MPH, DPH), B
Religion/Religious Studies, BM
Religious Education, AB
Science Teacher Education/General Science
   Teacher Education, B
Secondary Education and Teaching, B
Social Sciences, AB
Social Work, B
Theology/Theological Studies, B

WESTERN OREGON UNIVERSITY

Anthropology, B
Art/Art Studies, General, B
Biology/Biological Sciences, B
Business/Commerce, B
Chemistry, B
Computer Science, B
Corrections, BM
Criminal Justice/Law Enforcement Administration, B
Criminal Justice/Police Science, B
Dance, B
Drama and Dramatics/Theatre Arts, B
Early Childhood Education and Teaching, M
Economics, B
Education, M
Education/Teaching of Individuals with Multiple
   Disabilities, M
Educational Media/Instructional Technology, M
Educational/Instructional Media Design, B
English Language and Literature, B
Fire Services Administration, B
Geography, B
German Language and Literature, B
Health Education, M
History, B
Humanities/Humanistic Studies, B
Intercultural/Multicultural and Diversity Studies, B
Interdisciplinary Studies, B
International Relations and Affairs, B
Liberal Arts and Sciences Studies and
   Humanities, A
Mathematics, B
Mathematics Teacher Education, M
Multilingual and Multicultural Education, M
Music, B
Natural Sciences, B
Philosophy, B
Political Science and Government, B
Psychology, B
Public Administration, B
Rehabilitation Counseling, M
Science Teacher Education/General Science
   Teacher Education, M
Secondary Education and Teaching, BM
Sign Language Interpretation and Translation, B
Social Sciences, B
Social Studies Teacher Education, M
Sociology, B

Spanish Language and Literature, B

WILLAMETTE UNIVERSITY

American/United States Studies/Civilization, B
Anthropology, B
Art History, Criticism and Conservation, B
Art/Art Studies, General, B
Asian Studies/Civilization, B
Biology/Biological Sciences, B
Business Administration, Management and
   Operations, MO
Chemistry, B
Classics and Classical
   Languages, Literatures, and Linguistics, B
Comparative Literature, B
Computer Science, B
Drama and Dramatics/Theatre Arts, B
Economics, B
Education, M
English Language and Literature, B
Environmental Sciences, B
Fine/Studio Arts, B
French Language and Literature, B
German Language and Literature, B
History, B
Humanities/Humanistic Studies, B
International/Global Studies, B
Japanese Studies, B
Kinesiology and Exercise Science, B
Latin American Studies, B
Law and Legal Studies, MPO
Mathematics, B
Music, B
Music Performance, B
Music Theory and Composition, B
Non-Profit/Public/Organizational Management, M
Philosophy, B
Physics, B
Piano and Organ, B
Political Science and Government, B
Psychology, B
Public Administration, MO
Religion/Religious Studies, B
Science Technologies/Technicians, B
Sociology, B
Spanish Language and Literature, B
Speech and Rhetorical Studies, B
Violin, Viola, Guitar and Other Stringed
   Instruments, B
Voice and Opera, B
Women's Studies, B

Pennsylvania

ACADEMY OF MEDICAL ARTS AND BUSINESS

Child Care and Support Services Management, A
Child Care Provider/Assistant, A
Computer Programming, A
Computer Programming, Specific Applications, A
Computer
   Programming, Vendor/Product Certification, A
Data Entry/Microcomputer Applications, A
Data Processing and Data Processing
   Technology/Technician, A
Dental Assisting/Assistant, A
Legal Assistant/Paralegal, A
Medical Administrative Assistant/Secretary, A
Medical Office Management/Administration, A
Medical/Clinical Assistant, A
Word Processing, A

ALBRIGHT COLLEGE

Accounting, B
American/United States Studies/Civilization, B
Apparel and Textiles, B
Art Teacher Education, B
Art/Art Studies, General, B
Biochemistry, B
Biology/Biological Sciences, B
Business Administration and Management, B
Chemistry, B
Communication Studies/Speech Communication
   and Rhetoric, B
Computer Science, B

Criminology, B
Design and Visual Communications, B
Drama and Dramatics/Theatre Arts, B
Early Childhood Education and Teaching, M
Economics, B
Education, M
Elementary Education and Teaching, BM
English as a Second Language, M
English Language and Literature, B
Environmental Sciences, B
Finance, B
Forestry, B
French Language and Literature, B
History, B
Industrial and Organizational Psychology, B
Information Science/Studies, B
Interdisciplinary Studies, B
International Business/Trade/Commerce, B
Kindergarten/PreSchool Education and Teaching, B
Latin American Studies, B
Marketing/Marketing Management, B
Mathematics, B
Multi-/Interdisciplinary Studies, B
Music, B
Natural Resources Management/Development and
   Policy, B
Philosophy, B
Physics, B
Physiological Psychology/Psychobiology, B
Political Science and Government, B
Pre-Law Studies, B
Psychology, B
Religion/Religious Studies, B
Secondary Education and Teaching, B
Sociology, B
Spanish Language and Literature, B
Special Education and Teaching, BM
Women's Studies, B

ALLEGHENY COLLEGE

Applied Economics, B
Art History, Criticism and Conservation, B
Art/Art Studies, General, B
Biochemistry, B
Biology/Biological Sciences, B
Business/Managerial Economics, B
Chemistry, B
Communication Studies/Speech Communication
   and Rhetoric, B
Computer Science, B
Computer Software Engineering, B
Creative Writing, B
Drama and Dramatics/Theatre Arts, B
Economics, B
Education, B
English Language and Literature, B
Environmental Sciences, B
Environmental Studies, B
Fine Arts and Art Studies, B
Fine/Studio Arts, B
French Language and Literature, B
Geology/Earth Science, B
German Language and Literature, B
Health/Medical Preparatory Programs, B
History, B
International Relations and Affairs, B
International/Global Studies, B
Journalism, B
Mass Communication/Media Studies, B
Mathematics, B
Multi-/Interdisciplinary Studies, B
Music, B
Music Performance, B
Neuroscience, B
Philosophy, B
Physics, B
Political Science and Government, B
Pre-Dentistry Studies, B
Pre-Law Studies, B
Pre-Medicine/Pre-Medical Studies, B
Pre-Nursing Studies, B
Pre-Pharmacy Studies, B
Pre-Veterinary Studies, B
Psychology, B
Religion/Religious Studies, B
Spanish Language and Literature, B

Technical and Business Writing, B
Women's Studies, B

ALVERNIA COLLEGE

Accounting, AB
Biochemistry, B
Biological and Physical Sciences, B
Biology Teacher Education, B
Biology/Biological Sciences, B
Biomedical Technology/Technician, B
Business Administration and Management, AB
Business Administration, Management and
   Operations, M
Chemistry, B
Chemistry Teacher Education, B
Clinical Laboratory Science/Medical
   Technology/Technologist, B
Communication Studies/Speech Communication
   and Rhetoric, B
Criminal Justice/Law Enforcement Administration, B
Education, BM
Elementary Education and Teaching, B
English Language and Literature, B
English/Language Arts Teacher Education, B
Forensic Science and Technology, B
Health/Health Care Administration/Management, B
History, B
Information Science/Studies, AB
Kindergarten/PreSchool Education and Teaching, B
Liberal Arts and Sciences Studies and
   Humanities, AB
Liberal Studies, M
Marketing/Marketing Management, B
Mathematics, B
Mathematics Teacher Education, B
Nursing - Registered Nurse Training, AB
Occupational Therapy/Therapist, BM
Philosophy, B
Physical Therapy/Therapist, A
Political Science and Government, B
Pre-Law Studies, B
Pre-Medicine/Pre-Medical Studies, B
Psychology, B
Religion/Religious Studies, B
Science Teacher Education/General Science
   Teacher Education, B
Social Sciences, B
Social Work, B
Sport and Fitness Administration/Management, B
Substance Abuse/Addiction Counseling, B
Theology/Theological Studies, B

ANTONELLI INSTITUTE

Commercial and Advertising Art, A
Photography, A

ARCADIA UNIVERSITY

Accounting, B
Acting, B
Art Education, M
Art History, Criticism and Conservation, B
Art Teacher Education, B
Art/Art Studies, General, B
Biology/Biological Sciences, B
Business Administration and Management, B
Ceramic Arts and Ceramics, B
Chemistry, B
Commercial and Advertising Art, B
Community Health and Preventive Medicine, MO
Comparative Literature, B
Computer and Information Sciences, B
Computer Education, MO
Computer Programming/Programmer, B
Computer Science, B
Conflict Resolution and Mediation/Peace Studies, M
Counseling Psychology, M
Criminal Justice/Law Enforcement Administration, B
Drama and Dramatics/Theatre Arts, B
Drawing, B
Early Childhood Education and Teaching, BMO
Education, BMDO
Educational Leadership and Administration, MO
Educational Media/Instructional Technology, M
Educational Psychology, O
Elementary Education and Teaching, BMO
English, M

English Education, MO
English Language and Literature, B
Environmental Biology, B
Environmental Education, MO
Finance, B
Fine/Studio Arts, B
Genetic Counseling/Counselor, M
Health Education, M
Health/Health Care Administration/Management, B
History, B
Human Resources Management/Personnel
   Administration, B
Human Services, B
Humanities/Humanistic Studies, M
Interior Design, B
International Business/Trade/Commerce, B
International/Global Studies, B
Kindergarten/PreSchool Education and Teaching, B
Liberal Arts and Sciences Studies and
   Humanities, B
Management Information Systems and Services, B
Marketing/Marketing Management, B
Mass Communication/Media Studies, B
Mathematics, B
Mathematics Teacher Education, MO
Medical Illustration/Medical Illustrator, B
Metal and Jewelry Arts, B
Music Teacher Education, M
Natural Sciences, B
Philosophy, B
Photography, B
Physical Therapy/Therapist, D
Physiological Psychology/Psychobiology, B
Political Science and Government, B
Pre-Dentistry Studies, B
Pre-Law Studies, B
Pre-Medicine/Pre-Medical Studies, B
Pre-Veterinary Studies, B
Psychology, BM
Reading Teacher Education, MO
Science Teacher Education/General Science
   Teacher Education, MO
Secondary Education and Teaching, BMO
Social Studies Teacher Education, M
Sociology, B
Spanish Language and Literature, B
Special Education and Teaching, MDO
Theater, M

THE ART INSTITUTE OF PHILADELPHIA

Animation, Interactive Technology, Video Graphics
   and Special Effects, AB
Cinematography and Film/Video Production, A
Culinary Arts/Chef Training, A
Fashion Merchandising, AB
Fashion/Apparel Design, AB
Film/Video and Photographic Arts, B
Graphic Design, AB
Industrial Design, B
Interior Design, AB
Intermedia/Multimedia, AB
Photographic and Film/Video Technology/Technician
   and Assistant, B
Photography, AB
Prepress/Desktop Publishing and Digital Imaging
   Design, AB

THE ART INSTITUTE OF PITTSBURGH

Advertising, B
Applied Art, A
Architectural Drafting and Architectural
   CAD/CADD, B
Baking and Pastry Arts/Baker/Pastry Chef, AB
CAD/CADD Drafting and/or Design
   Technology/Technician, B
Cinematography and Film/Video Production, AB
Commercial and Advertising Art, AB
Commercial Photography, AB
Computer Graphics, AB
Cooking and Related Culinary Arts, AB
Culinary Arts and Related Services, AB
Culinary Arts/Chef Training, AB
Design and Visual Communications, AB
Digital Communication and Media/Multimedia, AB
Film/Video and Photographic Arts, AB

Food Preparation/Professional Cooking/Kitchen
   Assistant, AB
Food Service, Waiter/Waitress, and Dining Room
   Management/Manager, B
Graphic Design, AB
Hospitality Administration/Management, AB
Hotel/Motel Administration/Management, AB
Illustration, AB
Industrial Design, AB
Institutional Food Workers, AB
Interior Design, AB
Intermedia/Multimedia, AB
Painting, AB
Personal and Culinary Services, AB
Photography, AB
Public Relations/Image Management, B
Radio and Television, AB
Resort Management, AB
Restaurant, Culinary, and Catering
   Management/Manager, B
Restaurant/Food Services Management, AB
Web Page, Digital/Multimedia and Information
   Resources Design, AB
Web/Multimedia Management and Webmaster, AB

BAPTIST BIBLE COLLEGE OF PENNSYLVANIA

Administrative Assistant and Secretarial Science, AB
Bible/Biblical Studies, B
Counselor Education/School Counseling and
   Guidance Services, M
Divinity/Ministry (BD, MDiv.), B
Education, B
Elementary Education and Teaching, B
Music, B
Music Teacher Education, B
Pastoral Studies/Counseling, BMD
Piano and Organ, B
Psychology, B
Religious Education, BM
Religious/Sacred Music, B
Secondary Education and Teaching, B
Speech Teacher Education, B

BEREAN INSTITUTE

Accounting, A
Administrative Assistant and Secretarial Science, A
Computer Science, A
Court Reporting/Court Reporter, A
Electrical, Electronic and Communications
   Engineering Technology/Technician, A
Legal Administrative Assistant/Secretary, A
Medical Administrative Assistant/Secretary, A

BERKS TECHNICAL INSTITUTE

Computer and Information Sciences, A
Computer Graphics, A
Computer Programming, A
Computer Programming/Programmer, A
Drafting and Design Technology/Technician, A
Information Technology, A
Medical/Clinical Assistant, A
System Administration/Administrator, A

BLOOMSBURG UNIVERSITY OF PENNSYLVANIA

Accounting, B
Allied Health and Medical Assisting Services, A
Anthropology, B
Art History, Criticism and Conservation, B
Audiology/Audiologist and Speech-Language
   Pathology/Pathologist, B
Biological and Biomedical Sciences, M
Biological and Physical Sciences, B
Biology/Biological Sciences, B
Business Administration and Management, B
Business Administration, Management and
   Operations, M
Business Education, M
Business/Commerce, B
Business/Managerial Economics, B
Chemistry, B
Clinical Laboratory Science/Medical
   Technology/Technologist, B
Clinical/Medical Laboratory Technician, B

Communication Disorders, MD
Communication Studies/Speech Communication
   and Rhetoric, B
Computer and Information Sciences, B
Computer Science, B
Criminal Justice/Safety Studies, B
Curriculum and Instruction, M
Drama and Dramatics/Theatre Arts, B
Early Childhood Education and Teaching, BM
Economics, B
Education, M
Education/Teaching of Individuals with Speech or
   Language Impairments, B
Educational Media/Instructional Technology, M
Electrical, Electronics and Communications
   Engineering, B
Elementary Education and Teaching, BM
English Language and Literature, B
Exercise and Sports Science, M
Fine/Studio Arts, B
French Language and Literature, B
Geography, B
Geology/Earth Science, B
German Language and Literature, B
Health and Physical Education/Fitness, B
Health Physics/Radiological Health, M
Health/Medical Physics, B
History, B
Mass Communication/Media Studies, B
Mathematics, B
Medical Radiologic Technology/Science - Radiation
   Therapist, B
Multi-/Interdisciplinary Studies, B
Music, B
Nursing, M
Nursing - Registered Nurse Training, B
Philosophy, B
Physics, B
Political Science and Government, B
Psychology, B
Reading Teacher Education, M
Science Teacher Education/General Science
   Teacher Education, M
Sign Language Interpretation and Translation, B
Social Sciences, B
Social Work, B
Sociology, B
Spanish Language and Literature, B
Special Education and Teaching, BM

BRADLEY ACADEMY FOR THE VISUAL ARTS

Advertising, A
Animation, Interactive Technology, Video Graphics
   and Special Effects, A
Apparel and Textiles, A
Commercial and Advertising Art, A
Computer Graphics, A
Design and Visual Communications, A
Fashion Merchandising, A
Interior Design, A
Web Page, Digital/Multimedia and Information
   Resources Design, A
Web/Multimedia Management and Webmaster, A

BRYN ATHYN COLLEGE OF THE NEW CHURCH

Biology/Biological Sciences, B
Education, B
English Language and Literature, B
History, B
Interdisciplinary Studies, B
Liberal Arts and Sciences Studies and
   Humanities, A
Religion/Religious Studies, BM
Theology and Religious Vocations, MP

BRYN MAWR COLLEGE

Ancient/Classical Greek Language and Literature, B
Anthropology, B
Archeology, BMD
Art History, Criticism and Conservation, BMD
Art/Art Studies, General, B
Astronomy, B
Biology/Biological Sciences, B
Chemistry, BMD

Classics and Classical
Languages, Literatures, and Linguistics, BMD
Clinical Psychology, D
Comparative Literature, B
Developmental Psychology, D
East Asian Studies, B
Economics, B
English Language and Literature, B
French Language and Literature, BMD
Geology/Earth Science, B
German Language and Literature, B
History, B
Italian Language and Literature, B
Latin Language and Literature, B
Mathematics, BMD
Middle/Near Eastern and Semitic
Languages, Literatures, and Linguistics, B
Music, B
Philosophy, B
Physics, BMD
Political Science and Government, B
Psychology, BD
Religion/Religious Studies, B
Romance Languages, Literatures, and Linguistics, B
Russian Language and Literature, BMD
Social Work, MD
Sociology, B
Spanish Language and Literature, B
Urban Studies/Affairs, B

BUCKNELL UNIVERSITY

Accounting, B
Animal Behavior and Ethology, M
Anthropology, B
Area Studies, B
Art History, Criticism and Conservation, B
Art/Art Studies, General, B
Biological and Biomedical Sciences, M
Biology/Biological Sciences, B
Biomedical/Medical Engineering, B
Biopsychology, B
Business Administration and Management, B
Chemical Engineering, BM
Chemistry, BM
Civil Engineering, BM
Classics and Classical
Languages, Literatures, and Linguistics, B
Computer and Information Sciences, B
Computer Engineering, B
Counselor Education/School Counseling and
Guidance Services, M
Curriculum and Instruction, M
Drama and Dramatics/Theatre Arts, B
East Asian Studies, B
Economics, B
Education, BM
Educational Administration and Supervision, M
Educational Measurement and Evaluation, M
Educational Statistics and Research Methods, B
Electrical Engineering, M
Electrical, Electronics and Communications
Engineering, B
Elementary Education and Teaching, B
Engineering and Applied Sciences, M
English, M
English Language and Literature, B
Environmental Studies, B
Fine/Studio Arts, B
French Language and Literature, B
Geography, B
Geological and Earth Sciences/Geosciences, B
Geology/Earth Science, B
German Language and Literature, B
History, B
Humanities/Humanistic Studies, B
Interdisciplinary Studies, B
International Relations and Affairs, B
Kindergarten/PreSchool Education and Teaching, B
Latin American Studies, B
Mathematics, BM
Mechanical Engineering, BM
Multi-/Interdisciplinary Studies, B
Music, B
Music History, Literature, and Theory, B
Music Performance, B
Music Teacher Education, B

Music Theory and Composition, B
Philosophy, B
Physics, B
Political Science and Government, B
Psychology, BM
Reading Teacher Education, M
Religion/Religious Studies, B
Russian Language and Literature, B
School Psychology, M
Secondary Education and Teaching, B
Sociology, B
Spanish Language and Literature, B
Women's Studies, B

BUCKS COUNTY COMMUNITY COLLEGE

Accounting, A
Administrative Assistant and Secretarial Science, A
American/United States Studies/Civilization, A
Art/Art Studies, General, A
Biology/Biological Sciences, A
Business Administration and Management, A
Chemistry, A
Cinematography and Film/Video Production, A
Commercial and Advertising Art, A
Computer and Information Sciences, A
Computer Engineering Technology/Technician, A
Computer Programming, A
Computer Programming, Specific Applications, A
Computer Programming/Programmer, A
Computer Science, A
Computer/Information Technology Services
Administration and Management, A
Consumer Merchandising/Retailing Management, A
Corrections, A
Criminal Justice/Law Enforcement Administration, A
Criminal Justice/Police Science, A
Culinary Arts/Chef Training, A
Data Processing and Data Processing
Technology/Technician, A
Drama and Dramatics/Theatre Arts, A
Education, A
Engineering, A
Entrepreneurship/Entrepreneurial Studies, A
Environmental Studies, A
Health Teacher Education, A
Historic Preservation and Conservation, A
Hospitality Administration/Management, A
Hotel/Motel Administration/Management, A
Humanities/Humanistic Studies, A
Information Science/Studies, A
Information Technology, A
Journalism, A
Kindergarten/PreSchool Education and Teaching, A
Legal Assistant/Paralegal, A
Liberal Arts and Sciences Studies and
Humanities, A
Marketing/Marketing Management, A
Mass Communication/Media Studies, A
Mathematics, A
Medical/Clinical Assistant, A
Music, A
Nursing - Registered Nurse Training, A
Physical Education Teaching and Coaching, A
Psychology, A
Public Health (MPH, DPH), A
Radio and Television, A
Social Sciences, A
Social Work, A
Sport and Fitness Administration/Management, A
Teacher Assistant/Aide, A
Visual and Performing Arts, A
Woodworking, A

BUSINESS INSTITUTE OF PENNSYLVANIA (MEADVILLE)

Business Operations Support and Secretarial
Services, A
Data Entry/Microcomputer Applications, A
Executive Assistant/Executive Secretary, A
Health Information/Medical Records
Technology/Technician, A
Legal Administrative Assistant/Secretary, A
Medical Administrative Assistant/Secretary, A

Medical Office Assistant/Specialist, A

BUSINESS INSTITUTE OF PENNSYLVANIA (SHARON)

Administrative Assistant and Secretarial Science, A
Business Administration and Management, A
Business/Office Automation/Technology/Data
Entry, A
Computer Programming/Programmer, A
Executive Assistant/Executive Secretary, A
Health Information/Medical Records
Administration/Administrator, A
Legal Administrative Assistant/Secretary, A
Medical Administrative Assistant/Secretary, A
Medical/Clinical Assistant, A

BUTLER COUNTY COMMUNITY COLLEGE

Accounting, A
Administrative Assistant and Secretarial Science, A
Architectural Drafting and Architectural
CAD/CADD, A
Architectural Engineering Technology/Technician, A
Biology/Biological Sciences, A
Business Administration and Management, A
Civil Engineering Technology/Technician, A
Commercial and Advertising Art, A
Computer and Information Sciences, A
Computer Programming/Programmer, A
Criminal Justice/Police Science, A
Criminology, A
Dietetics/Dieticians, A
Drafting and Design Technology/Technician, A
Drafting/Design Engineering
Technologies/Technicians, A
Education, A
Electrical, Electronic and Communications
Engineering Technology/Technician, A
Elementary Education and Teaching, A
Emergency Medical Technology/Technician (EMT
Paramedic), A
English Language and Literature, A
Executive Assistant/Executive Secretary, A
Food Technology and Processing, A
General Office Occupations and Clerical Services, A
General Studies, A
Hospitality Administration/Management, A
Humanities/Humanistic Studies, A
Instrumentation Technology/Technician, A
Kindergarten/PreSchool Education and Teaching, A
Kinesiology and Exercise Science, A
Legal Administrative Assistant/Secretary, A
Liberal Arts and Sciences Studies and
Humanities, A
Machine Tool Technology/Machinist, A
Marketing/Marketing Management, A
Mass Communication/Media Studies, A
Mathematics, A
Mechanical Drafting and Mechanical Drafting
CAD/CADD, A
Medical Administrative Assistant/Secretary, A
Medical/Clinical Assistant, A
Nursing - Registered Nurse Training, A
Parks, Recreation and Leisure Facilities
Management, A
Physical Education Teaching and Coaching, A
Physical Sciences, A
Physical Therapist Assistant, A
Pre-Engineering, A
Psychology, A
Quality Control Technology/Technician, A
Sport and Fitness Administration/Management, A
Therapeutic Recreation/Recreational Therapy, A
Tourism and Travel Services Management, A

CABRINI COLLEGE

Accounting, B
American/United States Studies/Civilization, B
Biology Teacher Education, B
Biology/Biological Sciences, B
Business Administration and Management, B
Business, Management, Marketing, and Related
Support Services, B
Chemistry, B
Chemistry Teacher Education, B

Communication Studies/Speech Communication
and Rhetoric, B
Computer and Information Sciences, B
Computer and Information Sciences and Support
Services, B
Criminology, B
Education, BM
Educational Leadership and Administration, O
Educational Media/Instructional Technology, M
Elementary Education and Teaching, B
English Language and Literature, B
English/Language Arts Teacher Education, B
Finance, B
Fine/Studio Arts, B
French Language and Literature, B
Graphic Design, B
History, B
Human Resources Management/Personnel
Administration, B
Information Technology, B
Kindergarten/PreSchool Education and Teaching, B
Kinesiology and Exercise Science, B
Liberal Arts and Sciences Studies and
Humanities, B
Marketing/Marketing Management, B
Mathematics, B
Mathematics Teacher Education, B
Organizational Management, M
Philosophy, B
Political Science and Government, B
Project Management, O
Psychology, B
Religion/Religious Studies, B
Social Studies Teacher Education, B
Social Work, B
Sociology, B
Spanish Language and Literature, B
Special Education and Teaching, B

CALIFORNIA UNIVERSITY OF PENNSYLVANIA

Accounting, AB
Anthropology, B
Art/Art Studies, General, B
Athletic Training and Sports Medicine, M
Biological and Biomedical Sciences, M
Biological and Physical Sciences, B
Biology/Biological Sciences, B
Business Administration and Management, AB
Business Administration, Management and
Operations, M
Business/Commerce, A
Chemistry, B
Clinical/Medical Laboratory Technician, B
Communication and Media Studies, M
Communication Disorders, M
Communication Studies/Speech Communication
and Rhetoric, B
Computer Education, M
Computer Programming/Programmer, A
Counselor Education/School Counseling and
Guidance Services, M
Drafting and Design Technology/Technician, A
Drama and Dramatics/Theatre Arts, B
Economics, B
Education, BM
Educational Administration and Supervision, M
Electrical, Electronic and Communications
Engineering Technology/Technician, B
Elementary Education and Teaching, BM
English Language and Literature, B
Environmental Studies, B
Exercise and Sports Science, M
French Language and Literature, B
Geography, BM
Geology/Earth Science, B
Geosciences, M
German Language and Literature, B
Gerontology, B
History, B
Industrial Technology/Technician, B
Kindergarten/PreSchool Education and
Teaching, AB
Liberal Arts and Sciences Studies and
Humanities, B
Management of Technology, M

Mathematics, B
Mathematics Teacher Education, M
Nursing - Registered Nurse Training, B
Occupational Therapist Assistant, A
Parks, Recreation and Leisure Facilities
Management, B
Philosophy, B
Physics, B
Political Science and Government, B
Psychology, B
Reading Teacher Education, M
School Psychology, M
Science Teacher Education/General Science
Teacher Education, M
Social Sciences, BM
Social Work, BM
Sociology, B
Spanish Language and Literature, B
Special Education and Teaching, BM
Vocational and Technical Education, M

CAMBRIA-ROWE BUSINESS COLLEGE (JOHNSTOWN)

Accounting, A
Administrative Assistant and Secretarial Science, A
Business Administration and Management, A
Legal Administrative Assistant/Secretary, A
Medical Administrative Assistant/Secretary, A

CAREER TRAINING ACADEMY (NEW KENSINGTON)

Massage Therapy/Therapeutic Massage, A
Medical/Clinical Assistant, A

CARLOW UNIVERSITY

Accounting, B
Art Education, M
Art History, Criticism and Conservation, B
Art Teacher Education, B
Art/Art Studies, General, B
Auditing, B
Biology/Biological Sciences, B
Business/Commerce, B
Chemical Engineering, B
Chemistry, B
Communication Studies/Speech Communication
and Rhetoric, B
Computer Science, B
Counseling Psychology, M
Creative Writing, B
Design and Visual Communications, B
Early Childhood Education and Teaching, M
Education, M
Educational Leadership and Administration, M
Elementary Education and Teaching, B
English Language and Literature, B
Environmental Biology, B
Health Services Administration, M
History, B
Human Resources Development, M
Human Resources Management/Personnel
Administration, B
Information Science/Studies, B
International Business/Trade/Commerce, B
Kindergarten/PreSchool Education and Teaching, B
Liberal Arts and Sciences Studies and
Humanities, B
Management of Technology, M
Mathematics, B
Non-Profit/Public/Organizational Management, M
Nursing, MO
Nursing - Advanced Practice, MO
Nursing - Registered Nurse Training, B
Nursing Administration, MO
Philosophy, B
Political Science and Government, B
Psychology, B
Public Health (MPH, DPH), B
Public Policy Analysis, B
Social Studies Teacher Education, B
Social Work, B
Sociology, B
Spanish Language and Literature, B
Special Education and Teaching, B
Special Products Marketing Operations, B
Technical and Business Writing, B

Theology/Theological Studies, B

CARNEGIE MELLON UNIVERSITY

Accounting, D
Anthropology, B
Applied Mathematics, B
Architectural History and Criticism, B
Architectural Technology/Technician, B
Architecture, BMD
Architecture and Related Services, B
Art/Art Studies, General, B
Artificial Intelligence and Robotics, MD
Arts Management, M
Astrophysics, B
Behavioral Sciences, B
Biochemistry, D
Bioengineering, MD
Biological and Biomedical Sciences, BMD
Biology/Biological Sciences, B
Biomedical Engineering, MD
Biomedical/Medical Engineering, B
Biophysics, BD
Biopsychology, BD
Building Science, MD
Business Administration and Management, B
Business/Managerial Economics, B
Cell Biology and Anatomy, D
Chemical Engineering, BMD
Chemical Physics, B
Chemistry, BMD
Chinese Language and Literature, B
Civil Engineering, BMDO
Cognitive Sciences, BD
Communication and Media Studies, BM
Comparative Literature, MD
Composition, M
Computational Biology, MD
Computational Mathematics, B
Computational Sciences, MD
Computer Art and Design, M
Computer Engineering, BMD
Computer Science, BMD
Construction Engineering and Management, M
Creative Writing, B
Design and Applied Arts, D
Developmental Biology and Embryology, D
Developmental Psychology, D
Drama and Dramatics/Theatre Arts, B
Economics, BMD
Education, MD
Electrical Engineering, MD
Electronic Commerce, M
Engineering, B
Engineering and Applied Sciences, MD
English, MD
English Language and Literature, B
Environmental Engineering
Technology/Environmental Technology, MDO
Ethics, B
Ethnic, Cultural Minority, and Gender Studies, B
European History, B
European Studies/Civilization, B
Film, Television, and Video Production, M
Finance and Banking, D
Fine Arts and Art Studies, M
Foreign Languages and Literatures, B
French Language and Literature, B
Genetics, D
German Language and Literature, B
Health Services Administration, M
History, BMD
Human-Computer Interaction, MD
Industrial and Manufacturing Management, MD
Industrial Design, B
Information Science/Studies, BMD
International Relations and Affairs, B
Japanese Language and Literature, B
Latin American Studies, B
Liberal Arts and Sciences Studies and
Humanities, B
Linguistics, MD
Logic, B
Management, M
Management Information Systems and
Services, MD
Management of Technology, M

Marketing, D
Materials Engineering, MD
Materials Sciences, BMD
Mathematical and Computational Finance, MD
Mathematical Statistics and Probability, B
Mathematics, MD
Mathematics and Statistics, B
Mechanical Engineering, BMD
Media Studies, M
Molecular Biology, D
Music, M
Music Performance, B
Music Teacher Education, M
Music Theory and Composition, B
Natural Resources Management/Development and
    Policy, B
Neurobiology and Neurophysiology, D
Operations Research, BD
Organizational Behavior Studies, D
Organizational Management, D
Performance, M
Philosophy, BMD
Physics, BD
Piano and Organ, B
Political Science and Government, B
Polymer/Plastics Engineering, M
Project Management, M
Psychology, BD
Public Administration, M
Public Policy Analysis, BMO
Rhetoric, MD
Science, Technology and Society, B
Securities Services Administration/Management, M
Social Psychology, D
Social Sciences, BD
Software Engineering, MD
Spanish Language and Literature, B
Statistics, BMD
Sustainable Development, M
Systems Science and Theory, B
Teaching English as a Second or Foreign
    Language/ESL Language Instructor, B
Technical and Business Writing, BM
Technology and Public Policy, D
Theater, M
Violin, Viola, Guitar and Other Stringed
    Instruments, B
Voice and Opera, B
Writing, M

CEDAR CREST COLLEGE

Accounting, B
Animal Genetics, B
Art/Art Studies, General, B
Behavioral Sciences, B
Biochemistry, B
Biological and Physical Sciences, B
Biology/Biological Sciences, B
Biomedical Sciences, B
Biomedical Technology/Technician, B
Biomedical/Medical Engineering, B
Business Administration and Management, B
Business/Managerial Economics, B
Chemistry, B
Clinical Laboratory Science/Medical
    Technology/Technologist, B
Communication Studies/Speech Communication
    and Rhetoric, B
Computer and Information Sciences, B
Dance, B
Drama and Dramatics/Theatre Arts, B
Education, BM
Elementary Education and Teaching, B
English Language and Literature, B
Environmental Biology, B
Environmental Studies, B
Experimental Psychology, B
Fine/Studio Arts, B
Foods, Nutrition, and Wellness Studies, AB
Forensic Science and Technology, B
Gerontology, B
Health/Health Care Administration/Management, B
History, B
Information Science/Studies, B
International Relations and Affairs, B

Junior High/Intermediate/Middle School Education
    and Teaching, B
Legal Assistant/Paralegal, B
Liberal Arts and Sciences Studies and
    Humanities, B
Mathematics, B
Molecular Biology, B
Music, B
Natural Sciences, B
Neuroscience, B
Nuclear Medical Technology/Technologist, B
Nursing Science, B
Political Science and Government, B
Pre-Dentistry Studies, B
Pre-Law Studies, B
Pre-Medicine/Pre-Medical Studies, B
Pre-Veterinary Studies, B
Psychology, B
Public Health (MPH, DPH), B
Science Teacher Education/General Science
    Teacher Education, B
Secondary Education and Teaching, B
Social Work, B
Spanish Language and Literature, B

CENTRAL PENNSYLVANIA COLLEGE

Accounting, A
Accounting and Related Services, A
Business Administration and Management, AB
Child Development, A
Computer Programming, A
Consumer Merchandising/Retailing Management, A
Criminal Justice/Law Enforcement
    Administration, AB
Executive Assistant/Executive Secretary, A
Finance, A
Hotel/Motel Administration/Management, A
Information Science/Studies, AB
Legal Administrative Assistant/Secretary, A
Legal Assistant/Paralegal, A
Marketing/Marketing Management, A
Mass Communication/Media Studies, AB
Medical Administrative Assistant/Secretary, A
Medical/Clinical Assistant, A
Ophthalmic Laboratory Technology/Technician, A
Physical Therapist Assistant, A
Sales, Distribution and Marketing Operations, A
Tourism and Travel Services Management, A
Web/Multimedia Management and Webmaster, A

CHATHAM COLLEGE

Accounting, B
Area, Ethnic, Cultural, and Gender Studies, B
Art History, Criticism and Conservation, B
Arts Management, B
Biochemistry, B
Bioinformatics, B
Biology/Biological Sciences, B
Business Administration and Management, B
Business Administration, Management and
    Operations, M
Chemistry, B
Chemistry Teacher Education, B
Communication Studies/Speech Communication
    and Rhetoric, B
Community Psychology, M
Computer and Information Sciences, B
Counseling Psychology, BM
Creative Writing, B
Drama and Dramatics/Theatre Arts, B
Economics, B
Education, M
Elementary Education and Teaching, BM
Engineering, B
English as a Second Language, M
English Education, M
English Language and Literature, B
English/Language Arts Teacher Education, B
Environmental Education, M
Environmental Studies, B
Fine/Studio Arts, B
French Language and Literature, BM
Health Professions and Related Clinical Sciences, B
History, B
Industrial and Organizational Psychology, M
International Business/Trade/Commerce, B

International Relations and Affairs, B
International/Global Studies, B
Kinesiology and Exercise Science, B
Landscape Architecture, BM
Management Information Systems and Services, B
Marketing/Marketing Management, B
Mathematics, B
Mathematics Teacher Education, BM
Music, B
Physical Therapy/Therapist, BD
Physician Assistant, M
Physics, B
Physics Teacher Education, B
Political Science and Government, B
Psychology, B
Public Policy Analysis, B
Science Teacher Education/General Science
    Teacher Education, M
Secondary Education and Teaching, M
Social Studies Teacher Education, BM
Social Work, B
Spanish Language and Literature, BM
Special Education and Teaching, BM
Women's Studies, B
Writing, M

CHESTNUT HILL COLLEGE

Accounting, AB
Accounting and Business/Management, AB
Biochemistry, B
Biology/Biological Sciences, AB
Business Administration and Management, AB
Business/Corporate Communications, AB
Chemistry, AB
Child Care and Support Services Management, AB
Clinical Psychology, DO
Communication, Journalism and Related
    Programs, B
Communications Technologies/Technicians and
    Support Services, B
Computer and Information Sciences, B
Computer Science, B
Computer/Information Technology Services
    Administration and Management, B
Counseling Psychology, MO
Criminal Justice/Law Enforcement
    Administration, AB
Early Childhood Education and Teaching, BM
Education, M
Educational Leadership and Administration, M
Educational Media/Instructional Technology, MO
Elementary Education and Teaching, BM
English Language and Literature, B
Environmental Studies, B
Film, Television, and Video Production, O
Forensic Science and Technology, B
French Language and Literature, AB
Gerontology, O
Health/Health Care Administration/Management, AB
History, B
Human Resources Management/Personnel
    Administration, AB
Human Services, ABMO
International Business/Trade/Commerce, B
Internet and Interactive Multimedia, O
Liberal Arts and Sciences Studies and
    Humanities, B
Marketing/Marketing Management, AB
Mathematics and Computer Science, B
Molecular Biology, B
Multi-/Interdisciplinary Studies, B
Music, B
Music Teacher Education, B
Pastoral Studies/Counseling, O
Political Science and Government, B
Psychology, ABMDO
Religion/Religious Studies, MO
Sociology, B
Spanish Language and Literature, AB
Teacher Education, Multiple Levels, B

CHEYNEY UNIVERSITY OF PENNSYLVANIA

Adult and Continuing Education and Teaching, M
Apparel and Textiles, B
Art/Art Studies, General, B

Biological and Physical Sciences, B
Biology/Biological Sciences, B
Business Administration and Management, B
Chemistry, B
Clinical Laboratory Science/Medical
    Technology/Technologist, B
Communications Technology/Technician, B
Computer Science, B
Drama and Dramatics/Theatre Arts, B
Early Childhood Education and Teaching, O
Economics, B
Education, BMO
Educational Administration and Supervision, MO
Elementary Education and Teaching, BM
English Language and Literature, B
Family and Consumer Sciences/Home Economics
    Teacher Education, B
French Language and Literature, B
Geography, B
Hotel/Motel Administration/Management, B
Industrial Technology/Technician, B
Kindergarten/PreSchool Education and Teaching, B
Mass Communication/Media Studies, B
Mathematics, B
Mathematics Teacher Education, O
Music, B
Parks, Recreation, Leisure and Fitness Studies, B
Political Science and Government, B
Psychology, B
Secondary Education and Teaching, B
Social Sciences, B
Sociology, B
Spanish Language and Literature, B
Special Education and Teaching, BM

CHI INSTITUTE

Clinical Laboratory Science/Medical
    Technology/Technologist, A
Commercial and Advertising Art, A
Computer Engineering Technology/Technician, A
Computer Graphics, A
Computer Programming, Specific Applications, A
Computer Programming/Programmer, A
Computer Systems Networking and
    Telecommunications, A
Computer Typography and Composition Equipment
    Operator, A
Computer/Information Technology Services
    Administration and Management, A
Electrical, Electronic and Communications
    Engineering Technology/Technician, A
Health Information/Medical Records
    Administration/Administrator, A
Heating, Air Conditioning, Ventilation and
    Refrigeration Maintenance
    Technology/Technician, A
Medical Administrative Assistant/Secretary, A
Medical/Clinical Assistant, A
System Administration/Administrator, A

CHI INSTITUTE, RETS CAMPUS

Electrical, Electronic and Communications
    Engineering Technology/Technician, A

CLARION UNIVERSITY OF PENNSYLVANIA

Accounting, B
Anthropology, B
Art/Art Studies, General, B
Audiology/Audiologist and Speech-Language
    Pathology/Pathologist, B
Biological and Biomedical Sciences, M
Biological and Physical Sciences, B
Biology/Biological Sciences, B
Business Administration and Management, AB
Business Administration, Management and
    Operations, M
Business/Managerial Economics, B
Chemistry, B
Clinical Laboratory Science/Medical
    Technology/Technologist, B
Communication and Media Studies, M
Communication Disorders, B
Communication Studies/Speech Communication
    and Rhetoric, B
Computer and Information Sciences, B

Drama and Dramatics/Theatre Arts, B
Economics, B
Education, BMO
Elementary Education and Teaching, BM
English, M
English Language and Literature, B
Environmental Studies, B
Finance, B
French Language and Literature, B
Geography, B
Geology/Earth Science, B
History, B
Humanities/Humanistic Studies, B
Information Science/Studies, B
International Business/Trade/Commerce, B
Kindergarten/PreSchool Education and Teaching, B
Labor and Industrial Relations, B
Legal Administrative Assistant/Secretary, A
Liberal Arts and Sciences Studies and
    Humanities, AB
Library Science, BMO
Management Science, B
Marketing/Marketing Management, B
Mathematics, B
Molecular Biology, B
Music Management and Merchandising, B
Music Performance, B
Music Teacher Education, B
Nursing, M
Nursing - Registered Nurse Training, AB
Occupational Therapist Assistant, A
Philosophy, B
Physics, B
Political Science and Government, B
Psychology, B
Radiologic Technology/Science - Radiographer, B
Reading Teacher Education, BM
Real Estate, B
Rehabilitation Sciences, M
Science Teacher Education/General Science
    Teacher Education, BM
Social Psychology, B
Social Sciences, B
Social Studies Teacher Education, B
Sociology, B
Spanish Language and Literature, B
Special Education and Teaching, BM
Speech and Rhetorical Studies, B

COLLEGE MISERICORDIA

Accounting, B
Allied Health and Medical Assisting Services, M
Biochemistry, B
Biology/Biological Sciences, B
Business Administration and Management, B
Chemistry, B
Clinical Laboratory Science/Medical
    Technology/Technologist, B
Communication Disorders, B
Communication Studies/Speech Communication
    and Rhetoric, B
Computer Science, B
Curriculum and Instruction, M
Education, M
Elementary Education and Teaching, B
English Language and Literature, B
History, B
Information Science/Studies, B
Interdisciplinary Studies, B
Kindergarten/PreSchool Education and Teaching, B
Liberal Arts and Sciences Studies and
    Humanities, B
Management Information Systems and Services, B
Marketing/Marketing Management, B
Mathematics, B
Medical Radiologic Technology/Science - Radiation
    Therapist, B
Nursing, M
Nursing - Registered Nurse Training, B
Occupational Therapy/Therapist, M
Organizational Management, M
Philosophy, B
Physical Therapy/Therapist, M
Psychology, B
Public Health (MPH, DPH), B
Social Work, B

Special Education and Teaching, B
Sport and Fitness Administration/Management, B

COMMONWEALTH TECHNICAL INSTITUTE

Accounting, A
Architectural Drafting and Architectural
    CAD/CADD, A
Computer Science, A
Culinary Arts/Chef Training, A
Dental Laboratory Technology/Technician, A
Mechanical Drafting and Mechanical Drafting
    CAD/CADD, A
Medical Office Assistant/Specialist, A

COMMUNITY COLLEGE OF ALLEGHENY COUNTY

Accounting Technology/Technician and
    Bookkeeping, A
Administrative Assistant and Secretarial Science, A
Airline/Commercial/Professional Pilot and Flight
    Crew, A
Applied Horticulture/Horticultural Operations, A
Architectural Drafting and Architectural
    CAD/CADD, A
Art/Art Studies, General, A
Athletic Training and Sports Medicine, A
Automotive Engineering Technology/Technician, A
Aviation/Airway Management and Operations, A
Banking and Financial Support Services, A
Biology/Biological Sciences, A
Building/Property Maintenance and Management, A
Business Administration and Management, A
Business Machine Repairer, A
Business/Office Automation/Technology/Data
    Entry, A
Carpentry/Carpenter, A
Chemical Technology/Technician, A
Chemistry, A
Child Care Provider/Assistant, A
Child Development, A
Civil Drafting and Civil Engineering CAD/CADD, A
Civil Engineering Technology/Technician, A
Clinical/Medical Laboratory Technician, A
Commercial and Advertising Art, A
Communications Technologies/Technicians and
    Support Services, A
Community Health Services/Liaison/Counseling, A
Computer Engineering Technology/Technician, A
Computer Systems Networking and
    Telecommunications, A
Computer Technology/Computer Systems
    Technology, A
Construction Engineering Technology/Technician, A
Construction Trades, A
Corrections, A
Cosmetology and Related Personal Grooming
    Arts, A
Court Reporting/Court Reporter, A
Criminal Justice/Police Science, A
Culinary Arts/Chef Training, A
Diagnostic Medical Sonography/Sonographer and
    Ultrasound Technician, A
Dietician Assistant, A
Drafting and Design Technology/Technician, A
Drafting/Design Engineering
    Technologies/Technicians, A
Drama and Dramatics/Theatre Arts, A
Electrical, Electronic and Communications
    Engineering Technology/Technician, A
Electroneurodiagnostic/Electroencephalographic
    Technology/Technologist, A
Energy Management and Systems
    Technology/Technician, A
Engineering Technologies/Technicians, A
English Language and Literature, A
Entrepreneurship/Entrepreneurial Studies, A
Environmental Engineering
    Technology/Environmental Technology, A
Fire Protection and Safety Technology/Technician, A
Foodservice Systems
    Administration/Management, A
Foreign Languages and Literatures, A
General Studies, A
Greenhouse Operations and Management, A
Health and Physical Education, A

Health Information/Medical Records
Technology/Technician, A
Health Professions and Related Clinical Sciences, A
Health Unit Coordinator/Ward Clerk, A
Heating, Air Conditioning, Ventilation and
Refrigeration Maintenance
Technology/Technician, A
Hotel/Motel Administration/Management, A
Housing and Human Environments, A
Human Development and Family Studies, A
Human Resources Management/Personnel
Administration, A
Humanities/Humanistic Studies, A
Industrial Technology/Technician, A
Insurance, A
Journalism, A
Landscaping and Groundskeeping, A
Legal Administrative Assistant/Secretary, A
Legal Assistant/Paralegal, A
Liberal Arts and Sciences Studies and
Humanities, A
Licensed Practical/Vocational Nurse Training, A
Machine Shop Technology/Assistant, A
Management Information Systems and Services, A
Marketing/Marketing Management, A
Mathematics, A
Mechanical Drafting and Mechanical Drafting
CAD/CADD, A
Medical Administrative Assistant/Secretary, A
Medical Radiologic Technology/Science - Radiation
Therapist, A
Medical/Clinical Assistant, A
Music, A
Nuclear Medical Technology/Technologist, A
Nurse/Nursing Assistant/Aide and Patient Care
Assistant, A
Nursing - Registered Nurse Training, A
Occupational Therapist Assistant, A
Office Management and Supervision, A
Ornamental Horticulture, A
Perioperative/Operating Room and Surgical
Nurse/Nursing, A
Pharmacy Technician/Assistant, A
Physical Therapist Assistant, A
Physics, A
Plant Nursery Operations and Management, A
Psychiatric/Mental Health Services Technician, A
Psychology, A
Quality Control Technology/Technician, A
Real Estate, A
Respiratory Care Therapy/Therapist, A
Restaurant, Culinary, and Catering
Management/Manager, A
Retailing and Retail Operations, A
Robotics Technology/Technician, A
Science Technologies/Technicians, A
Sheet Metal Technology/Sheetworking, A
Sign Language Interpretation and Translation, A
Social Sciences, A
Social Work, A
Sociology, A
Solar Energy Technology/Technician, A
Substance Abuse/Addiction Counseling, A
Surgical Technology/Technologist, A
Teacher Education and Professional
Development, Specific Levels and Methods, A
Teacher Education and Professional
Development, Specific Subject Areas, A
Therapeutic Recreation/Recreational Therapy, A
Tourism Promotion Operations, A
Turf and Turfgrass Management, A
Visual and Performing Arts, A
Welding Technology/Welder, A

COMMUNITY COLLEGE OF BEAVER COUNTY

Accounting, A
Administrative Assistant and Secretarial Science, A
Aeronautics/Aviation/Aerospace Science and
Technology, A
Air Traffic Controller, A
Airline/Commercial/Professional Pilot and Flight
Crew, A
Architectural Engineering Technology/Technician, A
Avionics Maintenance Technology/Technician, A
Biology/Biological Sciences, A

Business Administration and Management, A
Clinical/Medical Laboratory Technician, A
Communications Technology/Technician, A
Computer and Information Sciences, A
Computer Programming/Programmer, A
Computer Typography and Composition Equipment
Operator, A
Criminal Justice/Law Enforcement Administration, A
Criminal Justice/Police Science, A
Culinary Arts/Chef Training, A
Data Processing and Data Processing
Technology/Technician, A
Drafting and Design Technology/Technician, A
Education, A
Electrical, Electronic and Communications
Engineering Technology/Technician, A
Information Science/Studies, A
Liberal Arts and Sciences Studies and
Humanities, A
Licensed Practical/Vocational Nurse Training, A
Marketing/Marketing Management, A
Medical Administrative Assistant/Secretary, A
Nursing - Registered Nurse Training, A
Public Relations/Image Management, A
Technology Education/Industrial Arts, A
Telecommunications Technology/Technician, A

COMMUNITY COLLEGE OF PHILADELPHIA

Accounting, A
Administrative Assistant and Secretarial Science, A
Architectural Engineering Technology/Technician, A
Art/Art Studies, General, A
Automobile/Automotive Mechanics
Technology/Technician, A
Biological and Physical Sciences, A
Biomedical Technology/Technician, A
Business Administration and Management, A
Business Teacher Education, A
Chemical Engineering, A
Clinical/Medical Laboratory Technician, A
Communications Technology/Technician, A
Community Organization and Advocacy, A
Computer Engineering Technology/Technician, A
Computer Science, A
Construction Engineering Technology/Technician, A
Consumer Merchandising/Retailing Management, A
Criminal Justice/Law Enforcement Administration, A
Culinary Arts/Chef Training, A
Data Processing and Data Processing
Technology/Technician, A
Dental Hygiene/Hygienist, A
Dietetics/Dieticians, A
Drafting and Design Technology/Technician, A
Education, A
Electrical, Electronic and Communications
Engineering Technology/Technician, A
Engineering, A
Engineering Technology, A
Environmental Engineering
Technology/Environmental Technology, A
Fashion Merchandising, A
Finance, A
Fire Science/Firefighting, A
Foods, Nutrition, and Wellness Studies, A
Gerontology, A
Health Information/Medical Records
Administration/Administrator, A
Hotel/Motel Administration/Management, A
Industrial Radiologic Technology/Technician, A
International Business/Trade/Commerce, A
Kindergarten/PreSchool Education and Teaching, A
Legal Administrative Assistant/Secretary, A
Legal Assistant/Paralegal, A
Liberal Arts and Sciences Studies and
Humanities, A
Library Science, A
Marketing/Marketing Management, A
Medical Administrative Assistant/Secretary, A
Medical/Clinical Assistant, A
Mental Health/Rehabilitation, A
Music, A
Nursing - Registered Nurse Training, A
Photography, A
Pre-Engineering, A
Real Estate, A

Respiratory Care Therapy/Therapist, A
Sign Language Interpretation and Translation, A
Special Products Marketing Operations, A

CONSOLIDATED SCHOOL OF BUSINESS (LANCASTER)

Accounting, A
Business Administration and Management, A
Health/Health Care Administration/Management, A
Legal Administrative Assistant/Secretary, A
Medical Administrative Assistant/Secretary, A
Office Management and Supervision, A
Tourism and Travel Services Management, A

CONSOLIDATED SCHOOL OF BUSINESS (YORK)

Accounting, A
Business Administration and Management, A
Health/Health Care Administration/Management, A
Legal Administrative Assistant/Secretary, A
Medical Administrative Assistant/Secretary, A
Office Management and Supervision, A
Tourism and Travel Services Management, A

THE CURTIS INSTITUTE OF MUSIC

Music, BM
Piano and Organ, B
Violin, Viola, Guitar and Other Stringed
Instruments, B
Voice and Opera, B
Wind and Percussion Instruments, B

DEAN INSTITUTE OF TECHNOLOGY

Electromechanical Technology/Electromechanical
Engineering Technology, A
Heating, Air Conditioning and Refrigeration
Technology/Technician, A

DELAWARE COUNTY COMMUNITY COLLEGE

Accounting Technology/Technician and
Bookkeeping, A
Anthropology, A
Architectural Engineering Technology/Technician, A
Automobile/Automotive Mechanics
Technology/Technician, A
Biological and Physical Sciences, A
Biomedical Technology/Technician, A
Building/Property Maintenance and Management, A
Business Administration and Management, A
Business Administration, Management and
Operations, A
Commercial and Advertising Art, A
Communication Studies/Speech Communication
and Rhetoric, A
Communication, Journalism and Related
Programs, A
Computer and Information Sciences, A
Computer Programming, Specific Applications, A
Computer Systems Networking and
Telecommunications, A
Computer Technology/Computer Systems
Technology, A
Construction Engineering Technology/Technician, A
Criminal Justice/Police Science, A
Drafting and Design Technology/Technician, A
Electrical, Electronic and Communications
Engineering Technology/Technician, A
Energy Management and Systems
Technology/Technician, A
Engineering, A
Entrepreneurship/Entrepreneurial Studies, A
Fire Protection and Safety Technology/Technician, A
General Studies, A
Health Unit Manager/Ward Supervisor, A
Heating, Air Conditioning and Refrigeration
Technology/Technician, A
Heating, Air Conditioning, Ventilation and
Refrigeration Maintenance
Technology/Technician, A
Hotel/Motel Administration/Management, A
Information Science/Studies, A
Journalism, A
Legal Assistant/Paralegal, A

Liberal Arts and Sciences Studies and Humanities, A
Machine Tool Technology/Machinist, A
Management Information Systems and Services, A
Mechanical Engineering Related Technologies/Technicians, A
Mechanical Engineering/Mechanical Technology/Technician, A
Medical/Clinical Assistant, A
Nursing - Registered Nurse Training, A
Office Management and Supervision, A
Psychology, A
Respiratory Care Therapy/Therapist, A
Robotics Technology/Technician, A
Science Technologies/Technicians, A
Sociology, A
Surgical Technology/Technologist, A
Teacher Assistant/Aide, A
Teacher Education, Multiple Levels, A
Web Page, Digital/Multimedia and Information Resources Design, A

DELAWARE VALLEY COLLEGE

Accounting, B
Agribusiness, B
Agronomy and Crop Science, B
Animal Sciences, B
Applied Horticulture/Horticultural Business Services, B
Biology/Biological Sciences, B
Business Administration and Management, B
Business/Commerce, A
Chemistry, B
Computer and Information Sciences, A
Computer and Information Sciences and Support Services, B
Computer Programming/Programmer, A
Criminal Justice/Law Enforcement Administration, B
Crop Production, B
Culinary Arts and Related Services, A
Dairy Science, B
Educational Leadership and Administration, M
English Language and Literature, B
Food Science, B
Horticultural Science, B
Management Information Systems and Services, B
Marketing/Marketing Management, B
Mathematics, B
Ornamental Horticulture, B
Secondary Education and Teaching, B
Turf and Turfgrass Management, B
Wildlife and Wildlands Science and Management, B
Zoology/Animal Biology, B

DESALES UNIVERSITY

Accounting, B
Biological Anthropology, O
Biology/Biological Sciences, B
Business Administration and Management, B
Business Administration, Management and Operations, M
Chemistry, B
Cinematography and Film/Video Production, B
Clinical Laboratory Science/Medical Technology/Technologist, B
Computer Education, M
Computer Science, B
Criminal Justice/Law Enforcement Administration, B
Criminal Justice/Safety Studies, B
Criminology, M
Dance, B
Drama and Dramatics/Theatre Arts, B
E-Commerce/Electronic Commerce, B
Education, MO
Educational Media/Instructional Technology, O
Elementary Education and Teaching, B
English as a Second Language, O
English Education, M
English Language and Literature, B
Environmental Sciences, B
Environmental Studies, B
Finance, B
Health/Medical Preparatory Programs, B
History, B
Human Resources Management/Personnel Administration, B

Information Science/Studies, M
Kinesiology and Exercise Science, B
Liberal Arts and Sciences Studies and Humanities, B
Management Information Systems and Services, B
Marketing, B
Marketing/Marketing Management, B
Mass Communication/Media Studies, B
Mathematics, B
Mathematics Teacher Education, M
Multilingual and Multicultural Education, O
Nursing, MO
Nursing - Advanced Practice, M
Nursing - Registered Nurse Training, B
Nursing Education, M
Pharmacy Administration and Pharmacy Policy and Regulatory Affairs, B
Philosophy, B
Physician Assistant, M
Political Science and Government, B
Pre-Dentistry Studies, B
Pre-Medicine/Pre-Medical Studies, B
Pre-Veterinary Studies, B
Psychology, B
Science Teacher Education/General Science Teacher Education, M
Spanish Language and Literature, B
Special Education and Teaching, MO
Sport and Fitness Administration/Management, B
Theology/Theological Studies, B

DEVRY UNIVERSITY (CHESTERBROOK)

Business Administration, Management and Operations, M

DEVRY UNIVERSITY (FORT WASHINGTON)

Biomedical Technology/Technician, B
Business Administration and Management, B
Business Administration, Management and Operations, M
Computer and Information Sciences, B
Computer Engineering Technology/Technician, AB
Electrical, Electronic and Communications Engineering Technology/Technician, B
Health Information/Medical Records Technology/Technician, A
Medical Informatics, B
System, Networking, and LAN/WAN Management/Manager, A

DEVRY UNIVERSITY (PITTSBURGH)

Business Administration, Management and Operations, M

DICKINSON COLLEGE

American/United States Studies/Civilization, B
Anthropology, B
Archeology, B
Biochemistry, B
Biology/Biological Sciences, B
Chemistry, B
Classics and Classical Languages, Literatures, and Linguistics, B
Computer Science, B
Dance, B
Drama and Dramatics/Theatre Arts, B
East Asian Studies, B
Economics, B
Engineering, B
English Language and Literature, B
Environmental Sciences, B
Environmental Studies, B
Fine/Studio Arts, B
French Language and Literature, B
Geology/Earth Science, B
German Language and Literature, B
History, B
International Business/Trade/Commerce, B
International Relations and Affairs, B
Italian Language and Literature, B
Jewish/Judaic Studies, B
Law and Legal Studies, B
Mathematics, B

Medieval and Renaissance Studies, B
Multi-/Interdisciplinary Studies, B
Music, B
Neuroscience, B
Philosophy, B
Physics, B
Political Science and Government, B
Pre-Dentistry Studies, B
Pre-Law Studies, B
Pre-Medicine/Pre-Medical Studies, B
Psychology, B
Public Policy Analysis, B
Religion/Religious Studies, B
Russian Language and Literature, B
Russian Studies, B
Sociology, B
Spanish Language and Literature, B
Women's Studies, B

DOUGLAS EDUCATION CENTER

Administrative Assistant and Secretarial Science, A
Business Administration and Management, A
Design and Visual Communications, A
Medical Administrative Assistant/Secretary, A
Medical Office Management/Administration, A
Medical/Clinical Assistant, A

DREXEL UNIVERSITY

Accounting, BM
Allied Health and Medical Assisting Services, MDO
Allopathic Medicine, PO
Applied Arts and Design, M
Architectural Engineering, B
Architecture, BM
Area Studies, B
Art Therapy/Therapist, M
Arts Management, M
Biochemical Engineering, M
Biochemistry, MDO
Biological and Biomedical Sciences, MDO
Biological and Physical Sciences, B
Biology/Biological Sciences, B
Biomedical Engineering, MD
Biomedical/Medical Engineering, B
Biopsychology, MDO
Biostatistics, M
Business Administration, Management and Operations, MDO
Business, Management, Marketing, and Related Support Services, B
Business/Commerce, B
Business/Managerial Economics, B
Cancer Biology/Oncology, MD
Cell Biology and Anatomy, MDO
Chemical Engineering, BMD
Chemistry, BMD
Cinematography and Film/Video Production, B
Civil Engineering, BMD
Clinical Psychology, MDO
Commercial and Advertising Art, B
Communication and Media Studies, M
Communication, Journalism and Related Programs, B
Computer Engineering, BM
Computer Science, BMD
Culinary Arts/Chef Training, B
Curriculum and Instruction, M
Dance Therapy/Therapist, M
Design and Applied Arts, B
Education, MDO
Educational Administration and Supervision, O
Educational Leadership and Administration, D
Educational Media/Instructional Technology, DO
Electrical Engineering, MD
Electrical, Electronics and Communications Engineering, B
Emergency Medical Services, M
Engineering, B
Engineering and Applied Sciences, MD
Engineering Management, MD
English as a Second Language, O
English Language and Literature, B
Environmental Engineering Technology/Environmental Technology, MD
Environmental Policy, M
Environmental Sciences, MD

Environmental Studies, B
Environmental/Environmental Health Engineering, B
Fashion/Apparel Design, B
Finance, B
Finance and Banking, M
Food Science and Technology, MD
Forensic Psychology, D
General Studies, B
Genetics, MDO
Geological Engineering, M
Health Physics/Radiological Health, MD
Health Psychology, DO
Health/Health Care Administration/Management, B
Higher Education/Higher Education
    Administration, M
History, B
History of Science and Technology, M
Hospitality Administration/Management, B
Human Genetics, MDO
Human Resources Management/Personnel
    Administration, B
Humanities/Humanistic Studies, B
Immunology, MD
Industrial Engineering, B
Information Science/Studies, BMDO
Interior Design, BM
International Business/Trade/Commerce, B
Library Science, MDO
Management Information Systems and Services, B
Manufacturing Engineering, MD
Marketing, M
Marketing/Marketing Management, B
Marriage and Family Therapy/Counseling, MD
Materials Engineering, BMD
Mathematics, BMD
Mechanical Engineering, BMD
Mechanics, MD
Medical Physics, MD
Microbiology, MD
Molecular Biology, MDO
Music, B
Music Therapy/Therapist, M
Neuroscience, D
Nurse Anesthetist, M
Nursing, M
Nutritional Sciences, BMD
Pathobiology, DO
Pharmacology, MDO
Photography, B
Physical Therapy/Therapist, MDO
Physician Assistant, M
Physics, BMD
Playwriting and Screenwriting, B
Psychology, BMDO
Public Health, M
Publishing, M
Quantitative Analysis, M
Social Sciences, B
Sociology, B
Software Engineering, M
Taxation, BM
Teacher Education and Professional
    Development, Specific Subject Areas, B
Technical and Business Writing, BM
Telecommunications, M
Textile Design, M
Veterinary Sciences, M
Web Page, Digital/Multimedia and Information
    Resources Design, B

DUBOIS BUSINESS COLLEGE

Accounting, A
Administrative Assistant and Secretarial Science, A
Business/Office Automation/Technology/Data
    Entry, A
Legal Administrative Assistant/Secretary, A
Medical Administrative Assistant/Secretary, A

DUFF'S BUSINESS INSTITUTE

Accounting, A
Administrative Assistant and Secretarial Science, A
Business Administration and Management, A
Computer Programming/Programmer, A
Court Reporting/Court Reporter, A
Fashion Merchandising, A
Legal Administrative Assistant/Secretary, A

Legal Assistant/Paralegal, A
Medical Administrative Assistant/Secretary, A
Medical/Clinical Assistant, A

DUQUESNE UNIVERSITY

Accounting, B
Accounting and Related Services, B
Allied Health and Medical Assisting Services, MDO
Ancient/Classical Greek Language and Literature, B
Art History, Criticism and Conservation, B
Athletic Training and Sports Medicine, B
Biochemistry, BMD
Bioethics/Medical Ethics, MDO
Biological and Biomedical Sciences, MDO
Biology/Biological Sciences, B
Business Administration, Management and
    Operations, BMO
Business, Management, Marketing, and Related
    Support Services, B
Business/Commerce, B
Business/Corporate Communications, B
Business/Managerial Economics, B
Chemistry, BMD
Classics and Classical
    Languages, Literatures, and Linguistics, B
Clinical Psychology, D
Communication and Media Studies, MD
Communication Disorders, M
Communication Studies/Speech Communication
    and Rhetoric, B
Composition, M
Computer Science, B
Computer Software and Media Applications, B
Conflict Resolution and Mediation/Peace Studies, O
Counselor Education/School Counseling and
    Guidance Services, MD
Curriculum and Instruction, D
Drama and Dramatics/Theatre Arts, B
Early Childhood Education and Teaching, BM
Economics, B
Education, BMDO
Educational Administration and Supervision, M
Educational Leadership and Administration, D
Educational Media/Instructional Technology, MD
Elementary Education and Teaching, BM
English, MD
English as a Second Language, M
English Language and Literature, B
English/Language Arts Teacher Education, B
Entrepreneurship/Entrepreneurial Studies, B
Environmental Policy and Resource
    Management, MO
Environmental Sciences, BMO
Finance, B
Fine/Studio Arts, B
Foreign Languages and Literatures, B
Forensic Nursing, O
Foundations and Philosophy of Education, M
French Language Teacher Education, B
General Studies, B
Health Services Administration, M
Health/Health Care Administration/Management, B
History, BM
International Business/Trade/Commerce, B
International Relations and Affairs, B
Internet and Interactive Multimedia, MO
Investments and Securities, B
Journalism, B
Latin Language and Literature, B
Latin Teacher Education, B
Law and Legal Studies, PO
Liberal Arts and Sciences Studies and
    Humanities, B
Liberal Studies, M
Logistics and Materials Management, B
Management Information Systems and
    Services, BM
Management Science, B
Management Sciences and Quantitative Methods, B
Marketing/Marketing Management, B
Mathematics, BM
Mathematics Teacher Education, B
Medicinal and Pharmaceutical Chemistry, MD
Museology/Museum Studies, M
Music, BMO
Music Performance, B

Music Teacher Education, BM
Music Theory and Composition, M
Music Therapy/Therapist, B
Non-Profit/Public/Organizational Management, B
Nursing, MDO
Nursing - Advanced Practice, MO
Nursing - Registered Nurse Training, B
Nursing Administration, MO
Nursing Education, MO
Occupational Therapy/Therapist, M
Operations Management and Supervision, B
Performance, MO
Pharmaceutical Administration, M
Pharmaceutical Sciences, MDO
Pharmacology, MD
Pharmacy, P
Pharmacy, Pharmaceutical Sciences, and Administration, B
Philosophy, BMD
Physical Therapy/Therapist, D
Physician Assistant, B
Physics, B
Political Science and Government, B
Psychiatric/Mental Health Nurse/Nursing, O
Psychology, BD
Public Administration, MO
Public Policy Analysis, MO
Public Relations, Advertising, and Applied
    Communication, B
Public Relations/Image Management, B
Reading Teacher Education, M
Rehabilitation Sciences, MD
Rhetoric, MD
Sacred Music, M
School Psychology, MDO
Science Teacher Education/General Science
    Teacher Education, B
Secondary Education and Teaching, BM
Social Studies Teacher Education, B
Sociology, B
Spanish Language and Literature, B
Spanish Language Teacher Education, B
Special Education and Teaching, BM
Speech-Language Pathology/Pathologist, B
Taxation, M
Theology and Religious Vocations, MD
Theology/Theological Studies, B
Toxicology, MD
Web Page, Digital/Multimedia and Information
    Resources Design, B
Web/Multimedia Management and Webmaster, B

EAST STROUDSBURG UNIVERSITY OF PENNSYLVANIA

Athletic Training and Sports Medicine, B
Audiology/Audiologist and Speech-Language
    Pathology/Pathologist, B
Biochemistry, B
Biological and Biomedical Sciences, M
Biological and Physical Sciences, B
Biology/Biological Sciences, B
BioTechnology, B
Business Administration and Management, B
Chemistry, B
Clinical Laboratory Science/Medical
    Technology/Technologist, B
Communication Disorders, M
Communication Studies/Speech Communication
    and Rhetoric, B
Communications Technology/Technician, AB
Computer and Information Sciences, B
Computer and Information Systems Security, B
Computer Science, M
Drama and Dramatics/Theatre Arts, B
Early Childhood Education and Teaching, B
Economics, B
Education, M
Educational Media/Instructional Technology, M
Elementary Education and Teaching, BM
English Language and Literature, B
Environmental Biology, B
Exercise and Sports Science, M
French Language and Literature, B
Geography, B
Geology/Earth Science, B
Graphic Design, B
Health and Physical Education/Fitness, B

Health Education, M
Health Services Administration, B
Health Teacher Education, B
History, BM
Hospitality Administration/Management, BM
Humanities/Humanistic Studies, B
Kinesiology and Exercise Science, B
Liberal Arts and Sciences Studies and
  Humanities, B
Marine Biology and Biological Oceanography, B
Mathematics, B
Nursing - Registered Nurse Training, B
Parks, Recreation and Leisure Facilities
  Management, B
Philosophy, B
Physical Education Teaching and Coaching, BM
Physical Sciences, B
Physics, B
Political Science and Government, BM
Psychology, B
Public Health, M
Reading Teacher Education, M
Rehabilitation and Therapeutic Professions, B
Rehabilitation Sciences, M
Rehabilitation Therapy, B
Science Teacher Education/General Science
  Teacher Education, M
Secondary Education and Teaching, BM
Social Science Teacher Education, B
Social Sciences, B
Social Studies Teacher Education, M
Sociology, B
Spanish Language and Literature, B
Special Education and Teaching, BM
Sport and Fitness Administration/Management, M
Travel and Tourism, M
Visual and Performing Arts, B

EASTERN UNIVERSITY

Accounting, B
Art History, Criticism and Conservation, B
Astronomy, B
Bible/Biblical Studies, B
Biochemistry, B
Biology/Biological Sciences, B
Business Administration, Management and
  Operations, MO
Chemistry, B
Communication Studies/Speech Communication
  and Rhetoric, B
Counseling Psychology, M
Counselor Education/School Counseling and
  Guidance Services, M
Creative Writing, B
Economics, M
Education, MO
Educational Psychology, M
Elementary Education and Teaching, B
English as a Second Language, O
English Language and Literature, B
English/Language Arts Teacher Education, B
Environmental Studies, B
Finance, B
French Language and Literature, B
Health and Physical Education, B
Health Education, M
History, B
Hospital and Health Care Facilities
  Administration/Management, B
Intermedia/Multimedia, B
Liberal Arts and Sciences Studies and
  Humanities, A
Management Information Systems and Services, B
Management Science, B
Marketing/Marketing Management, B
Mathematics, B
Missions/Missionary Studies and Missiology, B
Multilingual and Multicultural Education, M
Music, B
Non-Profit/Public/Organizational Management, M
Nursing - Registered Nurse Training, B
Philosophy, B
Political Science and Government, B
Psychology, B
Secondary Education and Teaching, B
Social Work, B

Sociology, B
Spanish Language and Literature, B
Theology/Theological Studies, B

EDINBORO UNIVERSITY OF PENNSYLVANIA

Anthropology, B
Art History, Criticism and Conservation, B
Art Teacher Education, B
Art/Art Studies, General, B
Biochemistry, B
Biological and Biomedical Sciences, M
Biological and Physical Sciences, B
Biology/Biological Sciences, B
Broadcast Journalism, B
Business Administration and Management, AB
Chemistry, B
Clinical Psychology, M
Clinical/Medical Laboratory Technician, B
Communication and Media Studies, M
Communication Disorders, BM
Communication Studies/Speech Communication
  and Rhetoric, B
Computer and Information Sciences, AB
Counselor Education/School Counseling and
  Guidance Services, MO
Criminal Justice/Police Science, A
Criminal Justice/Safety Studies, B
Developmental Education, O
Drama and Dramatics/Theatre Arts, B
Early Childhood Education and Teaching, M
Economics, B
Education, MO
Educational Administration and Supervision, MO
Educational Leadership and Administration, M
Educational Psychology, M
Electrical, Electronic and Communications
  Engineering Technology/Technician, B
Elementary Education and Teaching, BM
English Education, M
English Language and Literature, B
Environmental Studies, B
Fine Arts and Art Studies, M
Fine/Studio Arts, B
Foreign Languages, Literatures, and Linguistics, B
Geography, B
Geology/Earth Science, B
German Language and Literature, B
Health and Physical Education, B
History, B
Humanities/Humanistic Studies, B
Industrial Technology/Technician, A
Journalism, B
Kindergarten/PreSchool Education and
  Teaching, AB
Latin American Studies, B
Liberal Arts and Sciences Studies and
  Humanities, AB
Management Information Systems and
  Services, MO
Mathematics, B
Mathematics Teacher Education, M
Music, B
Nursing, M
Nursing - Advanced Practice, M
Nursing - Registered Nurse Training, B
Nutritional Sciences, B
Operations Management and Supervision, B
Philosophy, B
Physical Education Teaching and Coaching, B
Physics, B
Political Science and Government, B
Psychology, BM
Reading Teacher Education, MO
School Psychology, O
Science Teacher Education/General Science
  Teacher Education, M
Secondary Education and Teaching, M
Social Sciences, BM
Social Studies Teacher Education, BM
Social Work, ABM
Sociology, B
Spanish Language and Literature, B
Special Education and Teaching, ABM
Sport and Fitness Administration/Management, B

Women's Studies, B

ELIZABETHTOWN COLLEGE

Accounting, B
Anthropology, B
Art/Art Studies, General, B
Biochemistry, B
Biology/Biological Sciences, B
BioTechnology, B
Business Administration and Management, B
Chemistry, B
Communication Studies/Speech Communication
  and Rhetoric, B
Computer Engineering, B
Computer Science, B
Criminal Justice/Safety Studies, B
Directing and Theatrical Production, B
Economics, B
Education, B
Elementary Education and Teaching, B
Engineering, B
Engineering Physics, B
English Language and Literature, B
Environmental Studies, B
French Language and Literature, B
German Language and Literature, B
History, B
Industrial Engineering, B
International Business/Trade/Commerce, B
Kindergarten/PreSchool Education and Teaching, B
Mathematics, B
Modern Languages, B
Music, B
Music Teacher Education, B
Music Therapy/Therapist, B
Occupational Therapy/Therapist, B
Peace Studies and Conflict Resolution, B
Philosophy, B
Physics, B
Political Science and Government, B
Pre-Dentistry Studies, B
Pre-Law Studies, B
Pre-Medicine/Pre-Medical Studies, B
Pre-Veterinary Studies, B
Psychology, B
Religion/Religious Studies, B
Science Teacher Education/General Science
  Teacher Education, B
Secondary Education and Teaching, B
Social Sciences, B
Social Work, B
Sociology, B
Spanish Language and Literature, B
Technical Theatre/Theatre Design and
  Technology, B
Theatre/Theatre Arts Management, B

ERIE BUSINESS CENTER, MAIN

Accounting, A
Administrative Assistant and Secretarial Science, A
Computer and Information Sciences, A
Computer Programming, A
Computer Science, A
Computer Systems Networking and
  Telecommunications, A
Information Science/Studies, A
Legal Administrative Assistant/Secretary, A
Legal Assistant/Paralegal, A
Marketing/Marketing Management, A
Medical Administrative Assistant/Secretary, A
Medical Transcription/Transcriptionist, A
Medical/Clinical Assistant, A
Tourism and Travel Services Management, A
Web Page, Digital/Multimedia and Information
  Resources Design, A

ERIE BUSINESS CENTER SOUTH

Accounting, A
Administrative Assistant and Secretarial Science, A
Advertising, A
Business Administration and Management, A
Computer Science, A
Health Information/Medical Records
  Administration/Administrator, A
Legal Administrative Assistant/Secretary, A
Marketing/Marketing Management, A

Medical Administrative Assistant/Secretary, A
Tourism and Travel Services Management, A

ERIE INSTITUTE OF TECHNOLOGY

Electrical, Electronic and Communications
   Engineering Technology/Technician, A

FRANKLIN AND MARSHALL COLLEGE

African Studies, B
American/United States Studies/Civilization, B
Ancient/Classical Greek Language and Literature, B
Animal Behavior and Ethology, B
Anthropology, B
Art History, Criticism and Conservation, B
Astronomy, B
Astrophysics, B
Biochemistry, B
Biology/Biological Sciences, B
Business Administration and Management, B
Chemistry, B
Classics and Classical
   Languages, Literatures, and Linguistics, B
Creative Writing, B
Dance, B
Drama and Dramatics/Theatre Arts, B
Economics, B
English Language and Literature, B
Environmental Sciences, B
Environmental Studies, B
Fine/Studio Arts, B
French Language and Literature, B
Geology/Earth Science, B
German Language and Literature, B
German Studies, B
History, B
Latin Language and Literature, B
Mathematics, B
Multi-/Interdisciplinary Studies, B
Music, B
Neuroscience, B
Philosophy, B
Physics, B
Political Science and Government, B
Psychology, B
Religion/Religious Studies, B
Sociology, B
Spanish Language and Literature, B

GANNON UNIVERSITY

Accounting, BO
Accounting Technology/Technician and
   Bookkeeping, A
Advertising, B
Area Studies, B
Athletic Training and Sports Medicine, B
Bioinformatics, B
Biological and Physical Sciences, B
Biology Technician/BioTechnology Laboratory
   Technician, B
Biology/Biological Sciences, B
Business Administration and Management, B
Business Administration, Management and
   Operations, M
Business Teacher Education, B
Business/Commerce, A
Chemistry, B
Clinical Laboratory Science/Medical
   Technology/Technologist, B
Computer and Information Sciences, B
Computer Programming/Programmer, B
Computer Science, M
Counseling Psychology, D
Counselor Education/School Counseling and
   Guidance Services, MO
Criminal Justice/Safety Studies, AB
Curriculum and Instruction, M
Dietetics/Dieticians, B
Drama and Dramatics/Theatre Arts, B
Early Childhood Education and Teaching, ABMO
Education, MO
Educational Administration and Supervision, O
Educational Leadership and Administration, MO
Educational Media/Instructional Technology, MO
Electrical Engineering, M
Electrical, Electronics and Communications
   Engineering, B

Elementary Education and Teaching, B
Engineering Management, M
English, M
English as a Second Language, O
English Literature (British and Commonwealth), B
Environmental and Occupational Health, MO
Environmental Education, MO
Environmental Engineering
   Technology/Environmental Technology, M
Environmental Sciences, BO
Environmental Studies, M
Environmental/Environmental Health Engineering, B
Finance, B
Finance and Banking, O
Foreign Language Teacher Education, B
Foreign Languages and Literatures, B
Funeral Service and Mortuary Science, B
Gerontology, O
Health Professions and Related Clinical Sciences, B
Health/Medical Preparatory Programs, B
History, B
Human Resources Management and Services, O
Industrial Engineering, B
Information Science/Studies, M
Insurance, B
International Business/Trade/Commerce, B
Law and Legal Studies, B
Legal Assistant/Paralegal, AB
Liberal Arts and Sciences Studies and
   Humanities, AB
Management, O
Management Information Systems and Services, B
Marketing, O
Marketing/Marketing Management, B
Mathematics, B
Mechanical Engineering, BM
Medical Radiologic Technology/Science - Radiation
   Therapist, AB
Medical/Surgical Nursing, M
Multi-/Interdisciplinary Studies, B
Nurse Anesthetist, MO
Nursing, MO
Nursing - Advanced Practice, MO
Nursing - Registered Nurse Training, B
Nursing Administration, M
Occupational Therapy/Therapist, MO
Ophthalmic/Optometric Services, B
Pastoral Studies/Counseling, MO
Philosophy, B
Physical Therapy/Therapist, MD
Physician Assistant, BM
Political Science and Government, B
Pre-Dentistry Studies, B
Pre-Law Studies, B
Pre-Medicine/Pre-Medical Studies, B
Pre-Veterinary Studies, B
Psychology, B
Public Administration, MO
Public Health (MPH, DPH), B
Radio and Television, B
Reading Teacher Education, MO
Respiratory Care Therapy/Therapist, AB
Science Teacher Education/General Science
   Teacher Education, MO
Secondary Education and Teaching, B
Social Studies Teacher Education, B
Social Work, B
Software Engineering, M
Special Education and Teaching, B
Specialized Merchandising, Sales, and Marketing
   Operations, B
Teacher Education, Multiple Levels, B
Theology/Theological Studies, B
Visual and Performing Arts, B

GENEVA COLLEGE

Accounting, B
Applied Mathematics, B
Audiology/Audiologist and Speech-Language
   Pathology/Pathologist, B
Aviation/Airway Management and Operations, B
Bible/Biblical Studies, AB
Biology/Biological Sciences, B
Business Administration and Management, AB
Business Administration, Management and
   Operations, M

Business Teacher Education, B
Chemical Engineering, B
Chemistry, B
Communication Studies/Speech Communication
   and Rhetoric, B
Computer Science, B
Counseling Psychology, M
Counselor Education/School Counseling and
   Guidance Services, M
Creative Writing, B
Education, M
Educational Administration and Supervision, M
Educational Leadership and Administration, M
Elementary Education and Teaching, B
Engineering, AB
English Language and Literature, B
Higher Education/Higher Education
   Administration, M
History, B
Human Development and Family Studies, B
Human Services, B
Liberal Arts and Sciences Studies and
   Humanities, B
Marriage and Family Therapy/Counseling, M
Mathematics Teacher Education, B
Music, B
Music Management and Merchandising, B
Music Performance, B
Music Teacher Education, B
Organizational Management, M
Philosophy, B
Physics, B
Political Science and Government, B
Pre-Theology/Pre-Ministerial Studies, B
Psychology, BM
Radio and Television, B
Radio and Television Broadcasting
   Technology/Technician, B
Secondary Education and Teaching, B
Social Work, B
Sociology, B
Spanish Language and Literature, B
Special Education and Teaching, BM
Speech and Rhetorical Studies, B

GETTYSBURG COLLEGE

Accounting, B
African-American/Black Studies, B
American History (United States), B
American/United States Studies/Civilization, B
Ancient/Classical Greek Language and Literature, B
Anthropology, B
Area Studies, B
Area, Ethnic, Cultural, and Gender Studies, B
Art History, Criticism and Conservation, B
Art/Art Studies, General, B
Asian History, B
Biochemistry, B
Biological and Physical Sciences, B
Biology/Biological Sciences, B
Broadcast Journalism, B
Business Administration and Management, B
Business Administration, Management and
   Operations, B
Chemistry, B
Classics and Classical
   Languages, Literatures, and Linguistics, B
Comparative Literature, B
Computer Science, B
Creative Writing, B
Drama and Dramatics/Theatre Arts, B
East Asian Studies, B
Economics, B
Education, B
Elementary Education and Teaching, B
Engineering, B
English Composition, B
English Language and Literature, B
Environmental Sciences, B
Environmental Studies, B
European History, B
European Studies/Civilization, B
Fine/Studio Arts, B
French Language and Literature, B
German Language and Literature, B

Hispanic-American, Puerto Rican, and Mexican-
   American/Chicano Studies, B
History, B
Interdisciplinary Studies, B
International Business/Trade/Commerce, B
International Economics, B
International Relations and Affairs, B
Italian Language and Literature, B
Japanese Language and Literature, B
Japanese Studies, B
Journalism, B
Junior High/Intermediate/Middle School Education
   and Teaching, B
Latin American Studies, B
Latin Language and Literature, B
Liberal Arts and Sciences Studies and
   Humanities, B
Marine Biology and Biological Oceanography, B
Mathematics, B
Modern Languages, B
Molecular Biology, B
Music, B
Music Teacher Education, B
Non-Profit/Public/Organizational Management, B
Peace Studies and Conflict Resolution, B
Philosophy, B
Physical Education Teaching and Coaching, B
Physics, B
Political Science and Government, B
Pre-Dentistry Studies, B
Pre-Law Studies, B
Pre-Medicine/Pre-Medical Studies, B
Pre-Nursing Studies, B
Pre-Pharmacy Studies, B
Pre-Veterinary Studies, B
Psychology, B
Public Health (MPH, DPH), B
Religion/Religious Studies, B
Romance Languages, Literatures, and Linguistics, B
Science Teacher Education/General Science
   Teacher Education, B
Secondary Education and Teaching, B
Social Sciences, B
Sociology, B
South Asian Studies, B
Spanish Language and Literature, B
Visual and Performing Arts, B
Women's Studies, B

GRATZ COLLEGE

Education, M
Jewish/Judaic Studies, BM
Library Science, O
Music, MO
Near and Middle Eastern Studies, O
Religious Education, MO
Social Work, MO

GROVE CITY COLLEGE

Accounting, B
Biochemistry, B
Biology/Biological Sciences, B
Business Administration and Management, B
Business/Managerial Economics, B
Chemistry, B
Comparative Literature, B
Computer and Information Sciences, B
Divinity/Ministry (BD, MDiv.), B
Economics, B
Electrical and Electronic Engineering
   Technologies/Technicians, B
Electrical, Electronics and Communications
   Engineering, B
Elementary Education and Teaching, B
English Language and Literature, B
Entrepreneurship/Entrepreneurial Studies, B
Finance, B
French Language and Literature, B
History, B
International Business/Trade/Commerce, B
Kindergarten/PreSchool Education and Teaching, B
Marketing/Marketing Management, B
Mass Communication/Media Studies, B
Mathematics, B
Mechanical Engineering, B

Mechanical Engineering Related
   Technologies/Technicians, B
Modern Languages, B
Molecular Biology, B
Music, B
Music Management and Merchandising, B
Music Performance, B
Music Teacher Education, B
Philosophy, B
Physics, B
Political Science and Government, B
Pre-Dentistry Studies, B
Pre-Law Studies, B
Pre-Medicine/Pre-Medical Studies, B
Pre-Veterinary Studies, B
Psychology, B
Religion/Religious Studies, B
Science Teacher Education/General Science
   Teacher Education, B
Secondary Education and Teaching, B
Sociology, B
Spanish Language and Literature, B

GWYNEDD-MERCY COLLEGE

Accounting, AB
Allied Health
   Diagnostic, Intervention, and Treatment
   Professions, AB
Biological and Biomedical Sciences, A
Biology/Biological Sciences, B
Business Administration and Management, AB
Business Teacher Education, B
Cardiovascular Technology/Technologist, AB
Clinical Laboratory Science/Medical
   Technology/Technologist, B
Computer and Information Sciences, B
Computer Programming/Programmer, A
Counselor Education/School Counseling and
   Guidance Services, M
Education, BM
Educational Administration and Supervision, M
Elementary Education and Teaching, B
English Language and Literature, B
Forensic Psychology, B
Gerontology, B
Health Information/Medical Records
   Administration/Administrator, AB
Health Information/Medical Records
   Technology/Technician, AB
Health Services/Allied Health/Health Sciences, B
History, B
History Teacher Education, B
Hospital and Health Care Facilities
   Administration/Management, B
Liberal Arts and Sciences Studies and
   Humanities, A
Mathematics, B
Mathematics Teacher Education, B
Nursing, M
Nursing - Advanced Practice, M
Nursing - Registered Nurse Training, AB
Pre-Law Studies, B
Psychology, B
Public Health (MPH, DPH), B
Public Relations/Image Management, B
Reading Teacher Education, M
Respiratory Care Therapy/Therapist, AB
Science Teacher Education/General Science
   Teacher Education, B
Secondary Education and Teaching, B
Social Work, B
Sociology, B
Special Education and Teaching, BM
Teacher Education, Multiple Levels, B

HARCUM COLLEGE

Allied Health
   Diagnostic, Intervention, and Treatment
   Professions, A
Animal Sciences, A
Business Administration and Management, A
Child Development, A
Clinical/Medical Laboratory Technician, A
Consumer Merchandising/Retailing Management, A
Dental Assisting/Assistant, A
Dental Hygiene/Hygienist, A

Fashion Merchandising, A
Fashion/Apparel Design, A
Information Science/Studies, A
Interdisciplinary Studies, A
Interior Design, A
Kindergarten/PreSchool Education and Teaching, A
Liberal Arts and Sciences Studies and
   Humanities, A
Medical Radiologic Technology/Science - Radiation
   Therapist, A
Nursing - Registered Nurse Training, A
Occupational Therapist Assistant, A
Physical Therapist Assistant, A
Psychology, A
Public Health (MPH, DPH), A
Sport and Fitness Administration/Management, A
Veterinary/Animal Health Technology/Technician and
   Veterinary Assistant, A

HARRISBURG AREA COMMUNITY
COLLEGE

Accounting, A
Actuarial Science, A
Administrative Assistant and Secretarial Science, A
Agricultural Business and Management, A
Architectural Engineering Technology/Technician, A
Architecture, A
Art/Art Studies, General, A
Automobile/Automotive Mechanics
   Technology/Technician, A
Automotive Engineering Technology/Technician, A
Banking and Financial Support Services, A
Biology/Biological Sciences, A
Business Administration and Management, A
Business Teacher Education, A
Business, Management, Marketing, and Related
   Support Services, A
Business/Commerce, A
Cardiovascular Technology/Technologist, A
Chemistry, A
Civil Engineering Technology/Technician, A
Clinical/Medical Laboratory Assistant, A
Clinical/Medical Laboratory Technician, A
Commercial and Advertising Art, A
Computer and Information Sciences, A
Computer and Information Sciences and Support
   Services, A
Computer Installation and Repair
   Technology/Technician, A
Computer Systems Networking and
   Telecommunications, A
Construction Engineering Technology/Technician, A
Consumer Merchandising/Retailing Management, A
Criminal Justice/Law Enforcement Administration, A
Criminal Justice/Police Science, A
Culinary Arts/Chef Training, A
Dental Hygiene/Hygienist, A
Design and Visual Communications, A
Dietetics/Dieticians, A
Drama and Dramatics/Theatre Arts, A
Education, A
Electrical, Electronic and Communications
   Engineering Technology/Technician, A
Elementary Education and Teaching, A
Emergency Medical Technology/Technician (EMT
   Paramedic), A
Engineering, A
Engineering Technologies/Technicians, A
Engineering Technology, A
Environmental Studies, A
Fire Science/Firefighting, A
Foods, Nutrition, and Wellness Studies, A
Health Information/Medical Records
   Administration/Administrator, A
Heating, Air Conditioning and Refrigeration
   Technology/Technician, A
Hospital and Health Care Facilities
   Administration/Management, A
Hotel/Motel Administration/Management, A
Human Services, A
Industrial Mechanics and Maintenance
   Technology, A
Information Technology, A
Institutional Food Workers, A
International Relations and Affairs, A
Journalism, A

Kindergarten/PreSchool Education and Teaching, A
Legal Administrative Assistant/Secretary, A
Legal Assistant/Paralegal, A
Liberal Arts and Sciences Studies and
   Humanities, A
Management Information Systems and Services, A
Management Science, A
Marketing/Marketing Management, A
Mass Communication/Media Studies, A
Mathematics, A
Mechanical Engineering/Mechanical
   Technology/Technician, A
Medical Office Assistant/Specialist, A
Medical Radiologic Technology/Science - Radiation
   Therapist, A
Music, A
Nuclear Medical Technology/Technologist, A
Nursing - Registered Nurse Training, A
Opticianry/Ophthalmic Dispensing Optician, A
Pharmacy Technician/Assistant, A
Photography, A
Physical Education Teaching and Coaching, A
Physical Sciences, A
Psychology, A
Real Estate, A
Respiratory Care Therapy/Therapist, A
Respiratory Therapy Technician/Assistant, A
Science Teacher Education/General Science
   Teacher Education, A
Social Sciences, A
Social Work, A
Tourism and Travel Services Management, A
Tourism and Travel Services Marketing
   Operations, A
Web/Multimedia Management and Webmaster, A

HAVERFORD COLLEGE

African Studies, B
Anthropology, B
Archeology, B
Art History, Criticism and Conservation, B
Art/Art Studies, General, B
Astronomy, B
Biochemistry, B
Biology/Biological Sciences, B
Biophysics, B
Chemistry, B
Classics and Classical
   Languages, Literatures, and Linguistics, B
Comparative Literature, B
Computer Science, B
East Asian Studies, B
Econometrics and Quantitative Economics, B
Economics, B
Education, B
English Language and Literature, B
French Language and Literature, B
Geology/Earth Science, B
German Language and Literature, B
History, B
Italian Language and Literature, B
Latin American Studies, B
Latin Language and Literature, B
Mathematics, B
Modern Greek Language and Literature, B
Music, B
Neuroscience, B
Peace Studies and Conflict Resolution, B
Philosophy, B
Physics, B
Political Science and Government, B
Pre-Law Studies, B
Pre-Medicine/Pre-Medical Studies, B
Pre-Veterinary Studies, B
Psychology, B
Religion/Religious Studies, B
Romance Languages, Literatures, and Linguistics, B
Russian Language and Literature, B
Sociology, B
Spanish Language and Literature, B
Urban Studies/Affairs, B
Women's Studies, B

HOLY FAMILY UNIVERSITY

Accounting, B
Art/Art Studies, General, B

Biochemistry, B
Biology/Biological Sciences, B
Business Administration and Management, B
Business Administration, Management and
   Operations, M
Chemistry, B
Clinical/Medical Laboratory Technician, B
Communication Studies/Speech Communication
   and Rhetoric, B
Comparative Literature, B
Computer and Information Sciences, B
Counseling Psychology, M
Criminal Justice/Law Enforcement Administration, B
Economics, B
Education, BM
Elementary Education and Teaching, BM
English Language and Literature, B
Fire Science/Firefighting, B
French Language and Literature, B
History, B
Human Resources Management and Services, M
Humanities/Humanistic Studies, B
Industrial and Organizational Psychology, B
International Business/Trade/Commerce, B
Kindergarten/PreSchool Education and Teaching, B
Liberal Arts and Sciences Studies and
   Humanities, B
Management Information Systems and Services, M
Marketing/Marketing Management, B
Mathematics, B
Medical Radiologic Technology/Science - Radiation
   Therapist, A
Nursing, M
Nursing Science, B
Physiological Psychology/Psychobiology, B
Pre-Dentistry Studies, B
Pre-Law Studies, B
Pre-Medicine/Pre-Medical Studies, B
Pre-Pharmacy Studies, B
Pre-Veterinary Studies, B
Psychology, B
Radiologic Technology/Science - Radiographer, B
Reading Teacher Education, M
Religion/Religious Studies, B
Religious Education, B
Secondary Education and Teaching, BM
Social Sciences, B
Social Studies Teacher Education, B
Social Work, B
Sociology, B
Spanish Language and Literature, B
Special Education and Teaching, B
Sport and Fitness Administration/Management, B

HUSSIAN SCHOOL OF ART

Advertising, A
Commercial and Advertising Art, A

ICM SCHOOL OF BUSINESS & MEDICAL CAREERS

Accounting, A
Administrative Assistant and Secretarial Science, A
Business Administration and Management, A
Computer Engineering Technology/Technician, A
Computer Programming/Programmer, A
Computer Science, A
Criminal Justice/Law Enforcement Administration, A
Fashion Merchandising, A
Legal Administrative Assistant/Secretary, A
Medical Administrative Assistant/Secretary, A
Medical/Clinical Assistant, A
Occupational Therapy/Therapist, A
Tourism and Travel Services Management, A

IMMACULATA UNIVERSITY

Accounting, AB
Biochemistry, B
Biology/Biological Sciences, B
Biopsychology, B
Business Administration and Management, AB
Chemistry, B
Clinical Psychology, D
Communication Studies/Speech Communication
   and Rhetoric, B
Computer Science, B
Computer Teacher Education, B

Counseling Psychology, MO
Criminology, B
Dietetics/Dieticians, B
Economics, B
Educational Administration and Supervision, MDO
Elementary Education and Teaching, BO
English Language and Literature, B
Environmental Studies, B
Family and Consumer Sciences/Home Economics
   Teacher Education, B
Fashion Merchandising, B
Finance, B
Foods, Nutrition, and Wellness Studies, B
French Language and Literature, B
Health Services/Allied Health/Health Sciences, A
Health/Health Care Administration/Management, B
History, B
Human Resources Management/Personnel
   Administration, B
Information Science/Studies, AB
Intercultural/Multicultural and Diversity Studies, A
International Business/Trade/Commerce, B
International Relations and Affairs, B
Kinesiology and Exercise Science, B
Mathematics, B
Mathematics and Computer Science, AB
Modern Languages, B
Multilingual and Multicultural Education, M
Music, B
Music Performance, B
Music Teacher Education, B
Music Therapy/Therapist, BM
Nursing, M
Nursing Science, B
Nutritional Sciences, M
Organizational Management, M
Pre-Dentistry Studies, B
Pre-Law Studies, B
Pre-Veterinary Studies, B
Psychology, BMDO
Public Policy Analysis, B
Religious/Sacred Music, A
School Psychology, D
Secondary Education and Teaching, O
Social Work, B
Sociology, B
Spanish Language and Literature, B
Special Education and Teaching, O
Theology/Theological Studies, B

INDIANA UNIVERSITY OF PENNSYLVANIA

Accounting, B
Adult and Continuing Education and Teaching, M
Anthropology, B
Applied Mathematics, BM
Art Teacher Education, B
Art/Art Studies, General, B
Biochemistry, B
Biological and Biomedical Sciences, M
Biological and Physical Sciences, B
Biology/Biological Sciences, B
Business Administration and Management, AB
Business Administration, Management and
   Operations, M
Business Teacher Education, B
Chemistry, BM
City/Urban, Community and Regional Planning, B
Clinical Laboratory Science/Medical
   Technology/Technologist, B
Clinical Psychology, D
Communication Disorders, M
Communication Studies/Speech Communication
   and Rhetoric, B
Composition, M
Computer and Information Sciences, B
Consumer Economics, B
Counselor Education/School Counseling and
   Guidance Services, M
Criminology, ABMD
Curriculum and Instruction, MD
Dietetics/Dieticians, B
Drama and Dramatics/Theatre Arts, B
Early Childhood Education and Teaching, M
Economics, B
Education, MDO

Education/Teaching of Individuals with Hearing
Impairments, Including Deafness, B
Education/Teaching of Individuals with Orthopedic
and Other Physical Health Impairments, B
Education/Teaching of Individuals with Speech or
Language Impairments, B
Educational Administration and Supervision, MDO
Educational Media/Instructional Technology, M
Educational Psychology, MO
Elementary Education and Teaching, B
English, MD
English as a Second Language, MD
English Education, M
English Language and Literature, B
English/Language Arts Teacher Education, B
Environmental and Occupational Health, M
Environmental Health, B
Environmental Studies, B
Exercise and Sports Science, M
Facilities Planning and Management, M
Family and Consumer Sciences/Home Economics
Teacher Education, B
Fashion Merchandising, B
Finance, B
Fine Arts and Art Studies, M
Foods, Nutrition, and Wellness Studies, B
French Language and Literature, B
General Studies, AB
Geography, BM
Geology/Earth Science, B
German Language and Literature, B
Health and Physical Education, B
Health Education, M
Higher Education/Higher Education
Administration, M
History, BM
Hotel/Motel Administration/Management, B
Human Development and Family Studies, B
Human Resources Development, M
Human Resources Management/Personnel
Administration, B
Industrial and Labor Relations, M
Interior Architecture, B
Intermedia/Multimedia, B
International Business/Trade/Commerce, B
International Relations and Affairs, B
Journalism, B
Kindergarten/PreSchool Education and Teaching, B
Linguistics, D
Management Information Systems and Services, B
Marketing/Marketing Management, B
Mathematics, BM
Mathematics Teacher Education, BM
Music, BM
Music History, Literature, and Theory, M
Music Performance, B
Music Teacher Education, BM
Music Theory and Composition, M
Nuclear Medical Technology/Technologist, B
Nursing, M
Nursing - Registered Nurse Training, B
Nutritional Sciences, M
Occupational Safety and Health
Technology/Technician, B
Office Management and Supervision, B
Performance, M
Philosophy, B
Physical Education Teaching and Coaching, BM
Physics, BM
Political Science and Government, BM
Psychology, BMD
Public Affairs, M
Reading Teacher Education, M
Religion/Religious Studies, B
Respiratory Care Therapy/Therapist, B
Rhetoric, D
Russian Language and Literature, B
School Psychology, DO
Science Teacher Education/General Science
Teacher Education, B
Secondary Education and Teaching, B
Social Studies Teacher Education, B
Sociology, BM
Spanish Language and Literature, B
Special Education and Teaching, BM
Sport and Fitness Administration/Management, M

Trade and Industrial Teacher Education, B
Writing, MD

INTERNATIONAL ACADEMY OF DESIGN & TECHNOLOGY

Culinary Arts/Chef Training, A
Management Information Systems and Services, A

JOHNSON COLLEGE

Architectural Drafting and Architectural
CAD/CADD, A
Automobile/Automotive Mechanics
Technology/Technician, A
Biomedical Technology/Technician, A
Building/Home/Construction Inspection/Inspector, A
Cabinetmaking and Millwork/Millwright, A
Carpentry/Carpenter, A
Diesel Mechanics Technology/Technician, A
Electrical, Electronic and Communications
Engineering Technology/Technician, A
Electrician, A
Industrial Electronics Technology/Technician, A
Industrial Mechanics and Maintenance
Technology, A
Information Technology, A
Machine Shop Technology/Assistant, A
Machine Tool Technology/Machinist, A
Medical Radiologic Technology/Science - Radiation
Therapist, A
Precision Production Trades, A
Sales, Distribution and Marketing Operations, A
Veterinary/Animal Health Technology/Technician and
Veterinary Assistant, A

JUNIATA COLLEGE

Accounting, B
Anthropology, B
Art History, Criticism and Conservation, B
Biochemistry, B
Biology Teacher Education, B
Biology/Biological Sciences, B
Botany/Plant Biology, B
Business Administration and Management, B
Business/Commerce, B
Cell/Cellular Biology and Histology, B
Chemistry, B
Chemistry Teacher Education, B
Communication Studies/Speech Communication
and Rhetoric, B
Communication, Journalism and Related
Programs, B
Computer and Information Sciences, B
Criminal Justice/Safety Studies, B
Criminology, B
Early Childhood Education and Teaching, B
Ecology, B
Economics, B
Education, B
Education/Teaching of Individuals in Early Childhood
Special Education Programs, B
Elementary Education and Teaching, B
Engineering, B
Engineering Physics, B
English Language and Literature, B
English/Language Arts Teacher Education, B
Environmental Sciences, B
Environmental Studies, B
Finance, B
Fine/Studio Arts, B
Foreign Language Teacher Education, B
Foreign Languages and Literatures, B
French Language and Literature, B
French Language Teacher Education, B
Geology/Earth Science, B
German Language and Literature, B
German Language Teacher Education, B
Health Communication, B
Health/Medical Preparatory Programs, B
History, B
Human Resources Management/Personnel
Administration, B
Humanities/Humanistic Studies, B
Information Resources Management/CIO Training, B
Information Technology, B
International Business/Trade/Commerce, B
International Relations and Affairs, B

Kindergarten/PreSchool Education and Teaching, B
Liberal Arts and Sciences Studies and
Humanities, B
Marine Biology and Biological Oceanography, B
Marketing/Marketing Management, B
Mathematics, B
Mathematics Teacher Education, B
Microbiology, B
Molecular Biology, B
Museology/Museum Studies, B
Natural Sciences, B
Peace Studies and Conflict Resolution, B
Philosophy, B
Philosophy and Religious Studies, B
Physical Sciences, B
Physics, B
Physics Teacher Education, B
Political Science and Government, B
Pre-Dentistry Studies, B
Pre-Law Studies, B
Pre-Medicine/Pre-Medical Studies, B
Pre-Nursing Studies, B
Pre-Pharmacy Studies, B
Pre-Theology/Pre-Ministerial Studies, B
Pre-Veterinary Studies, B
Psychology, B
Public Administration, B
Religion/Religious Studies, B
Russian Language and Literature, B
Science Teacher Education/General Science
Teacher Education, B
Secondary Education and Teaching, B
Social Sciences, B
Social Studies Teacher Education, B
Social Work, B
Sociology, B
Spanish Language and Literature, B
Spanish Language Teacher Education, B
Special Education and Teaching, B
Teacher Education, Multiple Levels, B
Theatre/Theatre Arts Management, B
Zoology/Animal Biology, B

KEYSTONE COLLEGE

Accounting, AB
Accounting and Business/Management, B
Accounting and Related Services, B
Art Teacher Education, B
Art/Art Studies, General, AB
Biological and Physical Sciences, B
Biology/Biological Sciences, AB
Business Administration and Management, AB
Business/Commerce, AB
Communication and Media Studies, A
Communication Studies/Speech Communication
and Rhetoric, AB
Communication, Journalism and Related
Programs, A
Computer Programming/Programmer, A
Computer/Information Technology Services
Administration and Management, A
Criminal Justice/Law Enforcement Administration, B
Criminal Justice/Safety Studies, A
Culinary Arts and Related Services, A
Culinary Arts/Chef Training, A
Data Processing and Data Processing
Technology/Technician, A
Diagnostic Medical Sonography/Sonographer and
Ultrasound Technician, A
Drawing, A
Early Childhood Education and Teaching, AB
Elementary Education and Teaching, B
Environmental Biology, B
Environmental Studies, AB
Family and Community Services, B
Fine/Studio Arts, B
Food Preparation/Professional Cooking/Kitchen
Assistant, A
Forensic Science and Technology, B
Forestry, A
Forestry Technology/Technician, A
Graphic Design, A
Hotel/Motel Administration/Management, A
Human Resources Management/Personnel
Administration, A
Illustration, A

Information Technology, AB
Journalism, A
Kindergarten/PreSchool Education and Teaching, A
Landscape Architecture, A
Liberal Arts and Sciences Studies and
  Humanities, A
Mathematics Teacher Education, B
Medical Radiologic Technology/Science - Radiation
  Therapist, A
Natural Resources Management/Development and
  Policy, B
Occupational Therapy/Therapist, A
Painting, A
Parks, Recreation and Leisure Facilities
  Management, AB
Photography, A
Physical Therapy/Therapist, B
Pre-Nursing Studies, A
Printmaking, A
Public Relations, Advertising, and Applied
  Communication, A
Radio and Television, A
Radio, Television, and Digital Communication, A
Radiologic Technology/Science - Radiographer, A
Restaurant, Culinary, and Catering
  Management/Manager, A
Restaurant/Food Services Management, A
Sculpture, A
Social Studies Teacher Education, B
Sport and Fitness Administration/Management, AB
Teacher Education, Multiple Levels, AB
Therapeutic Recreation/Recreational Therapy, A
Water, Wetlands, and Marine Resources
  Management, A
Wildlife and Wildlands Science and Management, A
Wildlife Biology, A

KING'S COLLEGE

Accounting, B
Athletic Training and Sports Medicine, B
Biological and Physical Sciences, B
Biology/Biological Sciences, B
Business Administration and Management, AB
Business Administration, Management and
  Operations, M
Chemistry, B
Clinical Laboratory Science/Medical
  Technology/Technologist, B
Communication and Media Studies, B
Computer and Information Sciences, AB
Computer Science, B
Criminal Justice/Safety Studies, AB
Drama and Dramatics/Theatre Arts, B
Early Childhood Education and Teaching, B
Economics, B
Elementary Education and Teaching, B
English Language and Literature, B
Environmental Sciences, B
Environmental Studies, B
Finance, B
French Language and Literature, B
Health Professions and Related Clinical Sciences, B
Health Services Administration, M
History, B
Human Resources Management/Personnel
  Administration, AB
International Business/Trade/Commerce, B
Marketing/Marketing Management, B
Mathematics, B
Neuroscience, B
Philosophy, B
Physician Assistant, M
Political Science and Government, B
Pre-Dentistry Studies, B
Pre-Law Studies, B
Pre-Medicine/Pre-Medical Studies, B
Pre-Pharmacy Studies, B
Pre-Veterinary Studies, B
Psychology, B
Reading Teacher Education, M
Secondary Education and Teaching, B
Sociology, B
Spanish Language and Literature, B
Special Education and Teaching, B

Theology/Theological Studies, B

KUTZTOWN UNIVERSITY OF PENNSYLVANIA

Accounting, B
Anthropology, B
Art Education, MO
Art Teacher Education, B
Biological and Physical Sciences, B
Biology/Biological Sciences, B
Business Administration and Management, B
Business Administration, Management and
  Operations, M
Business/Managerial Economics, B
Chemistry, B
Clinical Laboratory Science/Medical
  Technology/Technologist, B
College Student Counseling and Personnel
  Services, B
Commercial and Advertising Art, B
Computer Science, M
Counseling Psychology, BM
Counselor Education/School Counseling and
  Guidance Services, BM
Crafts/Craft Design, Folk Art and Artisanry, B
Criminal Justice/Safety Studies, B
Curriculum and Instruction, M
Digital Communication and Media/Multimedia, B
Drama and Dramatics/Theatre Arts, B
Early Childhood Education and Teaching, O
Economics, B
Education, BMO
Education/Teaching of Individuals with Speech or
  Language Impairments, B
Education/Teaching of Individuals with Vision
  Impairments, Including Blindness, B
Educational Administration and Supervision, M
Educational Media/Instructional Technology, MO
Educational/Instructional Media Design, B
Elementary Education and Teaching, BMO
English, M
English Education, M
English Language and Literature, B
Environmental Sciences, B
Environmental Studies, B
Finance, B
Fine/Studio Arts, B
French Language and Literature, B
General Studies, B
Geography, B
Geology/Earth Science, B
German Language and Literature, B
History, B
Human Resources Management/Personnel
  Administration, B
Information Technology, B
International Business/Trade/Commerce, B
Kindergarten/PreSchool Education and Teaching, B
Liberal Arts and Sciences Studies and
  Humanities, B
Library Science, BMO
Marketing/Marketing Management, B
Marriage and Family Therapy/Counseling, M
Mathematics, BM
Mathematics Teacher Education, M
Media Studies, M
Music, B
Nursing - Registered Nurse Training, B
Nursing Science, B
Oceanography, Chemical and Physical, B
Philosophy, B
Physics, B
Political Science and Government, B
Psychology, B
Public Administration, BM
Reading Teacher Education, M
Russian Language and Literature, B
School Nursing, O
Science Teacher Education/General Science
  Teacher Education, M
Secondary Education and Teaching, BMO
Social Sciences, B
Social Studies Teacher Education, M
Social Work, BM
Sociology, B
Spanish Language and Literature, B

Special Education and Teaching, BO
Speech and Rhetorical Studies, B
Telecommunications Technology/Technician, B
Visual and Performing Arts, B

LA ROCHE COLLEGE

Accounting, B
Biology Teacher Education, B
Biology/Biological Sciences, B
Business Administration and Management, B
Chemistry, B
Chemistry Teacher Education, B
Communication Studies/Speech Communication
  and Rhetoric, B
Community Health Nursing, M
Computer and Information Sciences, B
Criminal Justice/Safety Studies, B
Dance, B
Elementary Education and Teaching, B
English Language and Literature, B
English/Language Arts Teacher Education, B
Finance, B
General Studies, B
Graphic Design, B
History, B
Human Resources Management and Services, M
Human Services, B
Interior Design, B
International Business/Trade/Commerce, B
International Relations and Affairs, B
Liberal Arts and Sciences Studies and
  Humanities, B
Marketing, B
Mathematics, B
Mathematics Teacher Education, B
Medical Radiologic Technology/Science - Radiation
  Therapist, AB
Nurse Anesthetist, M
Nursing, M
Nursing - Advanced Practice, M
Nursing Administration, M
Nursing Science, AB
Psychology, B
Religion/Religious Studies, B
Religious Education, B
Respiratory Care Therapy/Therapist, B
Sociology, B
Spanish Language Teacher Education, B
Technical and Business Writing, B

LA SALLE UNIVERSITY

Accounting, B
Air Force JROTC/ROTC, B
Applied Mathematics, B
Army JROTC/ROTC, B
Art History, Criticism and Conservation, B
Audiology/Audiologist and Speech-Language
  Pathology/Pathologist, B
Biochemistry, B
Biology/Biological Sciences, B
Broadcast Journalism, B
Business Administration and Management, B
Business Administration, Management and
  Operations, MO
Business Teacher Education, B
Business/Managerial Economics, B
Chemistry, B
Classics and Classical
  Languages, Literatures, and Linguistics, B
Clinical Psychology, MD
Communication Disorders, M
Community Health Nursing, M
Computer and Information Sciences, B
Computer Programming/Programmer, B
Computer Science, BM
Corporate and Organizational Communication, M
Counseling Psychology, M
Criminal Justice/Safety Studies, B
East European and Russian Studies, M
Economics, B
Education, BM
Elementary Education and Teaching, B
English Language and Literature, B
Environmental Studies, B
Film/Cinema Studies, B
Finance, B

French Language and Literature, B
Geology/Earth Science, B
German Language and Literature, B
Health Informatics, O
Hispanic Studies, M
History, BM
Human Resources Management/Personnel
   Administration, B
Information Science/Studies, B
Italian Language and Literature, B
Journalism, B
Latin American Studies, M
Liberal Arts and Sciences Studies and
   Humanities, AB
Management Information Systems and Services, B
Management of Technology, M
Marketing/Marketing Management, B
Marriage and Family Therapy/Counseling, D
Mass Communication/Media Studies, B
Mathematics, B
Medical/Surgical Nursing, M
Modern Languages, B
Nursing, MO
Nursing - Adult, M
Nursing - Advanced Practice, M
Nursing - Registered Nurse Training, B
Nursing Administration, M
Nursing Education, O
Nutritional Sciences, B
Pastoral Studies/Counseling, M
Philosophy, B
Political Science and Government, B
Pre-Dentistry Studies, B
Pre-Medicine/Pre-Medical Studies, B
Pre-Veterinary Studies, B
Psychology, BD
Public Administration, B
Public Relations/Image Management, B
Radio and Television, B
Rehabilitation Counseling, D
Religion/Religious Studies, BM
Religious Education, B
Russian Language and Literature, B
Russian Studies, B
School Nursing, O
Science Teacher Education/General Science
   Teacher Education, B
Secondary Education and Teaching, B
Social Sciences, B
Social Work, B
Sociology, B
Spanish Language and Literature, B
Special Education and Teaching, B
Theology and Religious Vocations, M

LACKAWANNA COLLEGE

Accounting Technology/Technician and
   Bookkeeping, A
Administrative Assistant and Secretarial Science, A
Banking and Financial Support Services, A
BioTechnology, A
Business Administration and Management, A
Business/Commerce, A
Communication Studies/Speech Communication
   and Rhetoric, A
Communications Technology/Technician, A
Computer and Information Sciences, A
Criminal Justice/Safety Studies, A
Diagnostic Medical Sonography/Sonographer and
   Ultrasound Technician, A
Early Childhood Education and Teaching, A
Education, A
Emergency Medical Technology/Technician (EMT
   Paramedic), A
General Studies, A
Humanities/Humanistic Studies, A
Industrial Technology/Technician, A
Legal Assistant/Paralegal, A
Liberal Arts and Sciences Studies and
   Humanities, A
Management Information Systems and Services, A
Mass Communication/Media Studies, A
Medical Administrative Assistant/Secretary, A

Mental Health/Rehabilitation, A

LAFAYETTE COLLEGE

American/United States Studies/Civilization, B
Anthropology, B
Art History, Criticism and Conservation, B
Art/Art Studies, General, B
Biochemistry, B
Biology/Biological Sciences, B
Business/Managerial Economics, B
Chemical Engineering, B
Chemistry, B
Civil Engineering, B
Computer Science, B
Economics, B
Electrical, Electronics and Communications
   Engineering, B
Engineering, B
English Language and Literature, B
Environmental/Environmental Health Engineering, B
Fine/Studio Arts, B
French Language and Literature, B
Geology/Earth Science, B
German Language and Literature, B
History, B
International Relations and Affairs, B
Mathematics, B
Mechanical Engineering, B
Music, B
Music History, Literature, and Theory, B
Philosophy, B
Physics, B
Political Science and Government, B
Psychology, B
Religion/Religious Studies, B
Russian Studies, B
Sociology, B
Spanish Language and Literature, B

LANCASTER BIBLE COLLEGE

Administrative Assistant and Secretarial Science, A
Bible/Biblical Studies, AB
Computer and Information Sciences, B
Counselor Education/School Counseling and
   Guidance Services, BM
Early Childhood Education and Teaching, AB
Education, B
Elementary Education and Teaching, B
Missions/Missionary Studies and Missiology, B
Music Teacher Education, B
Pastoral Counseling and Specialized Ministries, B
Pastoral Studies/Counseling, BM
Physical Education Teaching and Coaching, B
Religious Education, B
Religious/Sacred Music, B
Social Work, B
Theology and Religious Vocations, M
Youth Ministry, B

LANSDALE SCHOOL OF BUSINESS

Accounting, A
Administrative Assistant and Secretarial Science, A
Computer Engineering Technology/Technician, A
Legal Assistant/Paralegal, A
Medical Administrative Assistant/Secretary, A
Medical/Clinical Assistant, A

LAUREL BUSINESS INSTITUTE

Accounting, A
Administrative Assistant and Secretarial Science, A
Banking and Financial Support Services, A
Business Administration and Management, A
Business/Office Automation/Technology/Data
   Entry, A
Child Development, A
Computer and Information Sciences, A
Computer and Information Systems Security, A
Computer Software and Media Applications, A
Computer Systems Networking and
   Telecommunications, A
Computer/Information Technology Services
   Administration and Management, A
Consumer Merchandising/Retailing Management, A
Data Entry/Microcomputer Applications, A
Executive Assistant/Executive Secretary, A
General Office Occupations and Clerical Services, A

Home Health Aide/Home Attendant, A
Information Technology, A
Insurance, A
Legal Administrative Assistant/Secretary, A
Management Information Systems and Services, A
Medical Administrative Assistant/Secretary, A
Medical Transcription/Transcriptionist, A
Medical/Clinical Assistant, A
System Administration/Administrator, A
Web Page, Digital/Multimedia and Information
   Resources Design, A
Word Processing, A

LEBANON VALLEY COLLEGE

Accounting, AB
Actuarial Science, B
American/United States Studies/Civilization, B
Art History, Criticism and Conservation, B
Biochemistry, B
Biochemistry, Biophysics and Molecular Biology, B
Biology Teacher Education, B
Biology/Biological Sciences, B
Business Administration and Management, AB
Business Administration, Management and
   Operations, M
Chemistry, B
Chemistry Teacher Education, B
Clinical/Medical Laboratory Science and Allied
   Professions, B
Computer Science, B
Digital Communication and Media/Multimedia, B
Economics, B
Elementary Education and Teaching, B
English Language and Literature, B
English/Language Arts Teacher Education, B
Fine/Studio Arts, B
French Language and Literature, B
French Language Teacher Education, B
General Studies, A
German Language and Literature, B
German Language Teacher Education, B
Health Professions and Related Clinical Sciences, B
Health Services/Allied Health/Health Sciences, B
Health/Health Care Administration/Management, B
History, B
Liberal Arts and Sciences Studies and
   Humanities, AB
Mathematics, B
Mathematics Teacher Education, B
Multi-/Interdisciplinary Studies, B
Music, B
Music Management and Merchandising, B
Music Performance, B
Music Teacher Education, BM
Philosophy, B
Physics, B
Physics Teacher Education, B
Physiological Psychology/Psychobiology, B
Political Science and Government, B
Pre-Law Studies, B
Pre-Medicine/Pre-Medical Studies, B
Pre-Veterinary Studies, B
Psychology, B
Recording Arts Technology/Technician, B
Religion/Religious Studies, B
Science Teacher Education/General Science
   Teacher Education, BM
Secondary Education and Teaching, B
Social Studies Teacher Education, B
Sociology, B
Spanish Language and Literature, B
Spanish Language Teacher Education, B

LEHIGH CARBON COMMUNITY COLLEGE

Accounting, A
Accounting Technology/Technician and
   Bookkeeping, A
Administrative Assistant and Secretarial Science, A
Adult Development and Aging, A
Airline/Commercial/Professional Pilot and Flight
   Crew, A
Art/Art Studies, General, A
Aviation/Airway Management and Operations, A
Avionics Maintenance Technology/Technician, A
Biology/Biological Sciences, A

Biomedical Technology/Technician, A
BioTechnology, A
Business Administration and Management, A
Chemical Technology/Technician, A
Child Care Provider/Assistant, A
Clinical/Medical Laboratory Technician, A
Commercial and Advertising Art, A
Communication Studies/Speech Communication
  and Rhetoric, A
Computer Engineering Technology/Technician, A
Computer Technology/Computer Systems
  Technology, A
Construction Engineering Technology/Technician, A
Corrections, A
Criminal Justice/Law Enforcement Administration, A
Criminal Justice/Police Science, A
Culinary Arts/Chef Training, A
Digital Communication and Media/Multimedia, A
Drafting and Design Technology/Technician, A
Education, A
Electrical, Electronic and Communications
  Engineering Technology/Technician, A
Electrical, Electronics and Communications
  Engineering, A
Engineering, A
Executive Assistant/Executive Secretary, A
Forensic Science and Technology, A
General Office Occupations and Clerical Services, A
General Studies, A
Health Information/Medical Records
  Technology/Technician, A
Heating, Air Conditioning, Ventilation and
  Refrigeration Maintenance
  Technology/Technician, A
Horticultural Science, A
Hotel/Motel Administration/Management, A
Human Resources Management/Personnel
  Administration, A
Humanities/Humanistic Studies, A
Industrial Technology/Technician, A
Information Science/Studies, A
Interior Architecture, A
Kindergarten/PreSchool Education and Teaching, A
Legal Administrative Assistant/Secretary, A
Legal Assistant/Paralegal, A
Liberal Arts and Sciences Studies and
  Humanities, A
Licensed Practical/Vocational Nurse Training, A
Lineworker, A
Logistics and Materials Management, A
Manufacturing Technology/Technician, A
Mathematics, A
Mechanical Engineering, A
Mechanical Engineering/Mechanical
  Technology/Technician, A
Medical Transcription/Transcriptionist, A
Medical/Clinical Assistant, A
Nursing - Registered Nurse Training, A
Occupational Therapist Assistant, A
Operations Management and Supervision, A
Physical Sciences, A
Physical Therapist Assistant, A
Real Estate, A
Respiratory Care Therapy/Therapist, A
Restaurant/Food Services Management, A
Social Sciences, A
Social Work, A
Special Education and Teaching, A
Sport and Fitness Administration/Management, A
Tourism and Travel Services Marketing
  Operations, A
Tourism Promotion Operations, A
Veterinary/Animal Health Technology/Technician and
  Veterinary Assistant, A

LEHIGH UNIVERSITY

Accounting, BM
African-American/Black Studies, B
American/United States Studies/Civilization, BM
Anthropology, BM
Applied Mathematics, MD
Architecture, B
Art History, Criticism and Conservation, B
Art/Art Studies, General, B
Asian Studies/Civilization, B
Astronomy, B

Astrophysics, B
Biochemistry, BD
Biological and Biomedical Sciences, BD
Biological and Physical Sciences, B
Biology/Biological Sciences, B
Biomedical/Medical Engineering, B
Biopsychology, B
Business Administration and Management, B
Business Administration, Management and
  Operations, MDO
Business/Commerce, B
Business/Managerial Economics, B
Chemical Engineering, BMDO
Chemistry, BMD
Civil Engineering, BMD
Classics and Classical
  Languages, Literatures, and Linguistics, B
Communication, Journalism and Related
  Programs, B
Computer and Information Sciences and Support
  Services, B
Computer Engineering, BMD
Computer Science, BMD
Counseling Psychology, MDO
Counselor Education/School Counseling and
  Guidance Services, MO
Design and Applied Arts, B
Design and Visual Communications, B
Drama and Dramatics/Theatre Arts, B
Dramatic/Theatre Arts and Stagecraft, B
Ecology, B
Economics, MD
Education, BMDO
Educational Leadership and Administration, MDO
Educational Media/Instructional Technology, MD
Electrical Engineering, MD
Electrical, Electronics and Communications
  Engineering, B
Elementary Education and Teaching, MO
Engineering, B
Engineering and Applied Sciences, MDO
Engineering Mechanics, B
Engineering Physics, B
English, MD
English Language and Literature, B
Environmental Engineering
  Technology/Environmental Technology, MD
Environmental Sciences, BMD
Environmental Studies, B
Environmental/Environmental Health Engineering, B
Finance, B
Finance and Banking, M
French Language and Literature, B
Geological and Earth Sciences/Geosciences, B
Geology/Earth Science, MD
Geosciences, MD
German Language and Literature, B
Health Services Research, M
History, BMD
Human Development, MD
Human Services, M
Industrial Engineering, B
Industrial/Management Engineering, MD
Information Science/Studies, BM
International Relations and Affairs, B
Journalism, B
Management, O
Management Information Systems and Services, B
Manufacturing Engineering, MO
Marketing/Marketing Management, B
Materials Engineering, BMD
Materials Sciences, MD
Mathematics, BMD
Mechanical Engineering, BMD
Mechanics, MD
Molecular Biology, BD
Music, B
Music Theory and Composition, B
Neuroscience, B
Organizational Management, O
Philosophy, B
Photonics, M
Physical and Theoretical Chemistry, B
Physics, BMD
Political Science and Government, BM
Polymer/Plastics Engineering, MD

Pre-Dentistry Studies, B
Pre-Medicine/Pre-Medical Studies, B
Project Management, O
Psychology, BMD
Quantitative Analysis, M
Religion/Religious Studies, B
Russian Studies, B
School Psychology, DO
Science Technologies/Technicians, B
Secondary Education and Teaching, MO
Social Sciences, B
Sociology, BM
Spanish Language and Literature, B
Special Education and Teaching, MDO
Statistics, BM
Structural Engineering, B
Systems Engineering, MDO
Urban Studies/Affairs, B

LEHIGH VALLEY COLLEGE

Accounting, A
Business Administration and Management, A
Computer and Information Sciences, A
Computer Programming/Programmer, A
Criminal Justice/Law Enforcement Administration, A
Design and Visual Communications, A
Hospitality Administration/Management, A
Information Science/Studies, A
Legal Assistant/Paralegal, A
Marketing/Marketing Management, A
Massage Therapy/Therapeutic Massage, A
Medical Administrative Assistant/Secretary, A
Photography, A
Tourism and Travel Services Management, A

LINCOLN TECHNICAL INSTITUTE (ALLENTOWN)

Drafting and Design Technology/Technician, A
Electrical, Electronic and Communications
  Engineering Technology/Technician, A

LINCOLN TECHNICAL INSTITUTE (PHILADELPHIA)

Automobile/Automotive Mechanics
  Technology/Technician, A
Drafting and Design Technology/Technician, A

LINCOLN UNIVERSITY

Accounting, B
Actuarial Science, B
Anthropology, B
Art Teacher Education, B
Biology/Biological Sciences, B
Business Administration and Management, B
Chemistry, B
Chinese Language and Literature, B
Communication Studies/Speech Communication
  and Rhetoric, B
Computer and Information Sciences, B
Criminal Justice/Safety Studies, B
Economics, B
Education, B
Elementary Education and Teaching, B
English Language and Literature, B
English/Language Arts Teacher Education, B
Environmental Studies, B
Finance, B
Foreign Language Teacher Education, B
French Language and Literature, B
Health and Physical Education, B
Health and Physical Education/Fitness, B
History, B
Human Services, BM
Industrial and Organizational Psychology, B
International Relations and Affairs, B
Japanese Language and Literature, B
Journalism, B
Kindergarten/PreSchool Education and Teaching, B
Mathematics, B
Mathematics Teacher Education, B
Music, B
Music Teacher Education, B
Philosophy, B
Physical Sciences, B
Physics, B

Physiological Psychology/Psychobiology, B
Political Science and Government, B
Psychology, B
Public Administration, B
Religion/Religious Studies, B
Secondary Education and Teaching, B
Sociology, B
Spanish Language and Literature, B
Special Education and Teaching, B

LOCK HAVEN UNIVERSITY OF PENNSYLVANIA

Accounting, B
Anthropology, B
Art/Art Studies, General, B
Athletic Training and Sports Medicine, B
Biological and Physical Sciences, B
Biology/Biological Sciences, B
Business Administration and Management, B
Business/Managerial Economics, B
Chemistry, B
Computer and Information Sciences, B
Computer Science, B
Criminal Justice/Law Enforcement Administration, B
Curriculum and Instruction, B
Drama and Dramatics/Theatre Arts, B
Economics, B
Education, BM
Elementary Education and Teaching, BM
Engineering, B
English Language and Literature, B
French Language and Literature, B
Geography, B
Geology/Earth Science, B
German Language and Literature, B
Health Professions and Related Clinical Sciences, A
History, B
Humanities/Humanistic Studies, B
International Relations and Affairs, B
Journalism, B
Kindergarten/PreSchool Education and Teaching, B
Latin American Studies, B
Legal Assistant/Paralegal, B
Liberal Arts and Sciences Studies and
    Humanities, B
Liberal Studies, M
Management Information Systems and Services, A
Mathematics, B
Music, B
Natural Sciences, B
Nursing - Registered Nurse Training, A
Parks, Recreation, Leisure and Fitness Studies, B
Philosophy, B
Physical Education Teaching and Coaching, B
Physical Sciences, B
Physician Assistant, M
Physics, B
Political Science and Government, B
Pre-Dentistry Studies, B
Pre-Medicine/Pre-Medical Studies, B
Pre-Veterinary Studies, B
Psychology, B
Public Health (MPH, DPH), B
Secondary Education and Teaching, B
Social Sciences, B
Social Work, B
Sociology, B
Spanish Language and Literature, B
Special Education and Teaching, B
Speech and Rhetorical Studies, B

LUZERNE COUNTY COMMUNITY COLLEGE

Accounting, A
Administrative Assistant and Secretarial Science, A
Airline/Commercial/Professional Pilot and Flight
    Crew, A
Architectural Engineering, A
Architectural Engineering Technology/Technician, A
Automobile/Automotive Mechanics
    Technology/Technician, A
Aviation/Airway Management and Operations, A
Baking and Pastry Arts/Baker/Pastry Chef, A
Banking and Financial Support Services, A
Biological and Physical Sciences, A
Building/Property Maintenance and Management, A

Business Administration and Management, A
Child Care Provider/Assistant, A
Commercial and Advertising Art, A
Commercial Photography, A
Computer and Information Sciences, A
Computer Graphics, A
Computer Programming, A
Computer Science, A
Computer Systems Networking and
    Telecommunications, A
Computer Technology/Computer Systems
    Technology, A
Court Reporting/Court Reporter, A
Criminal Justice/Law Enforcement Administration, A
Culinary Arts/Chef Training, A
Data Entry/Microcomputer Applications, A
Data Processing and Data Processing
    Technology/Technician, A
Dental Assisting/Assistant, A
Dental Hygiene/Hygienist, A
Drafting and Design Technology/Technician, A
Drafting/Design Engineering
    Technologies/Technicians, A
Drawing, A
Early Childhood Education and Teaching, A
Education, A
Electrical, Electronic and Communications
    Engineering Technology/Technician, A
Electrician, A
Emergency Medical Technology/Technician (EMT
    Paramedic), A
Engineering Technology, A
Executive Assistant/Executive Secretary, A
Fire Science/Firefighting, A
Food Technology and Processing, A
Funeral Service and Mortuary Science, A
General Studies, A
Graphic and Printing Equipment Operator
    Production, A
Graphic Design, A
Health and Physical Education, A
Health/Health Care Administration/Management, A
Heating, Air Conditioning, Ventilation and
    Refrigeration Maintenance
    Technology/Technician, A
Horticultural Science, A
Hospitality and Recreation Marketing Operations, A
Hotel/Motel Administration/Management, A
Human Services, A
Humanities/Humanistic Studies, A
Industrial Design, A
International Business/Trade/Commerce, A
Journalism, A
Legal Assistant/Paralegal, A
Liberal Arts and Sciences Studies and
    Humanities, A
Mathematics, A
Medical Administrative Assistant/Secretary, A
Nursing - Registered Nurse Training, A
Ophthalmic/Optometric Services, A
Painting, A
Photography, A
Physical Education Teaching and Coaching, A
Plumbing Technology/Plumber, A
Pre-Pharmacy Studies, A
Radio and Television Broadcasting
    Technology/Technician, A
Real Estate, A
Respiratory Care Therapy/Therapist, A
Social Sciences, A
Surgical Technology/Technologist, A
Tourism and Travel Services Management, A
Tourism and Travel Services Marketing
    Operations, A

LYCOMING COLLEGE

Accounting, B
Actuarial Science, B
American/United States Studies/Civilization, B
Anthropology, B
Archeology, B
Art History, Criticism and Conservation, B
Art Teacher Education, B
Art/Art Studies, General, B
Astronomy, B
Biology/Biological Sciences, B

Business Administration and Management, B
Chemistry, B
Clinical Laboratory Science/Medical
    Technology/Technologist, B
Commercial and Advertising Art, B
Comparative Literature, B
Computer Science, B
Creative Writing, B
Criminal Justice/Law Enforcement Administration, B
Drama and Dramatics/Theatre Arts, B
Economics, B
Education, B
Elementary Education and Teaching, B
English Language and Literature, B
Finance, B
Fine/Studio Arts, B
French Language and Literature, B
German Language and Literature, B
History, B
Interdisciplinary Studies, B
International Business/Trade/Commerce, B
International Relations and Affairs, B
Marketing/Marketing Management, B
Mass Communication/Media Studies, B
Mathematics, B
Music, B
Music Teacher Education, B
Philosophy, B
Physics, B
Political Science and Government, B
Pre-Dentistry Studies, B
Pre-Law Studies, B
Pre-Medicine/Pre-Medical Studies, B
Pre-Veterinary Studies, B
Psychology, B
Religion/Religious Studies, B
Secondary Education and Teaching, B
Sociology, B
Spanish Language and Literature, B
Special Education and Teaching, B

MANOR COLLEGE

Accounting, A
Administrative Assistant and Secretarial Science, A
Animal Sciences, A
Biological and Physical Sciences, A
Business Administration and Management, A
Child Development, A
Clinical/Medical Laboratory Technician, A
Computer and Information Sciences, A
Computer Science, A
CytoTechnology/Cytotechnologist, A
Dental Hygiene/Hygienist, A
Education, A
Elementary Education and Teaching, A
Human Services, A
International Business/Trade/Commerce, A
Kindergarten/PreSchool Education and Teaching, A
Legal Administrative Assistant/Secretary, A
Legal Assistant/Paralegal, A
Liberal Arts and Sciences Studies and
    Humanities, A
Management Information Systems and Services, A
Medical Administrative Assistant/Secretary, A
Occupational Therapy/Therapist, A
Physical Therapy/Therapist, A
Psychology, A
Public Health (MPH, DPH), A
Veterinary/Animal Health Technology/Technician and
    Veterinary Assistant, A

MANSFIELD UNIVERSITY OF PENNSYLVANIA

Accounting, B
Anthropology, B
Applied Art, B
Art Education, M
Art Teacher Education, B
Art/Art Studies, General, B
Biochemistry, B
Biological and Physical Sciences, B
Biology Teacher Education, B
Biology/Biological Sciences, B
Broadcast Journalism, B
Business Administration and Management, B
Cartography, B

Cell/Cellular Biology and Histology, B
Chemistry, B
Chemistry Teacher Education, B
City/Urban, Community and Regional Planning, B
Clinical Laboratory Science/Medical
    Technology/Technologist, B
Clinical Psychology, B
Computer and Information Sciences, B
Computer Science, B
Criminal Justice/Law Enforcement
    Administration, AB
Dietetics/Dieticians, B
Economics, B
Education, BM
Elementary Education and Teaching, BM
English Language and Literature, B
English/Language Arts Teacher Education, B
Environmental Biology, B
Environmental Studies, B
Fishing and Fisheries Sciences and Management, B
Food Technology and Processing, B
French Language and Literature, B
French Language Teacher Education, B
Geography, B
Geology/Earth Science, B
German Language and Literature, B
German Language Teacher Education, B
History, B
Human Resources Management/Personnel
    Administration, B
Human Services, B
Information Science/Studies, ABM
International Business/Trade/Commerce, B
International Relations and Affairs, B
Journalism, B
Kindergarten/PreSchool Education and Teaching, B
Liberal Arts and Sciences Studies and
    Humanities, B
Library Science, M
Marketing/Marketing Management, B
Mass Communication/Media Studies, B
Mathematics, B
Mathematics Teacher Education, B
Music, BM
Music Management and Merchandising, B
Music Performance, B
Music Teacher Education, B
Music Therapy/Therapist, B
Nursing, M
Nursing - Registered Nurse Training, B
Performance, M
Philosophy, B
Physical Sciences, B
Physics, B
Physics Teacher Education, B
Piano and Organ, B
Political Science and Government, B
Pre-Law Studies, B
Pre-Medicine/Pre-Medical Studies, B
Psychology, B
Public Relations/Image Management, B
Radio and Television, B
Radiologic Technology/Science - Radiographer, A
Respiratory Care Therapy/Therapist, A
Science Teacher Education/General Science
    Teacher Education, B
Secondary Education and Teaching, BM
Social Science Teacher Education, B
Social Sciences, B
Social Studies Teacher Education, B
Social Work, B
Sociology, B
Spanish Language and Literature, B
Spanish Language Teacher Education, B
Special Education and Teaching, B
Speech and Rhetorical Studies, B
Tourism and Travel Services Management, B
Voice and Opera, B

MARYWOOD UNIVERSITY

Accounting, B
Advertising, B
Applied Art, B
Art Education, M
Art Teacher Education, B
Art Therapy/Therapist, BM

Arts Management, B
Athletic Training and Sports Medicine, B
Audiology/Audiologist and Speech-Language
    Pathology/Pathologist, B
Aviation/Airway Management and Operations, B
Biology Teacher Education, B
Biology Technician/BioTechnology Laboratory
    Technician, B
Biology/Biological Sciences, B
Broadcast Journalism, B
Business Administration and Management, B
Business Administration, Management and
    Operations, M
Clinical Laboratory Science/Medical
    Technology/Technologist, B
Clinical Psychology, MD
Communication and Media Studies, M
Communication Disorders, M
Community Organization and Advocacy, B
Computer and Information Sciences, B
Counseling Psychology, BM
Counselor Education/School Counseling and
    Guidance Services, M
Criminal Justice/Law Enforcement Administration, B
Criminal Justice/Safety Studies, B
Criminology, BM
Design and Visual Communications, B
Developmental and Child Psychology, B
Dietetics/Dieticians, B
Directing and Theatrical Production, B
Drama and Dramatics/Theatre Arts, B
Early Childhood Education and Teaching, M
Ecology, Evolution, Systematics and Population
    Biology, B
Education, BM
Educational Leadership and Administration, M
Educational Media/Instructional Technology, M
Electronic Commerce, M
Elementary Education and Teaching, BM
English Language and Literature, B
English/Language Arts Teacher Education, B
Environmental Sciences, B
Family and Consumer Sciences/Home Economics
    Teacher Education, B
Family and Consumer Sciences/Human Sciences, B
Film, Television, and Video Production, M
Finance and Banking, M
Financial Planning and Services, B
Fine Arts and Art Studies, M
Fine/Studio Arts, B
Food Science and Technology, M
Foods, Nutrition, and Related Services, B
French Language and Literature, B
French Language Teacher Education, B
Graphic Design, BM
Health Professions and Related Clinical Sciences, B
Health Promotion, MD
Health Services Administration, BM
Health Services/Allied Health/Health Sciences, B
Health/Health Care Administration/Management, B
History, B
History Teacher Education, B
Hospital and Health Care Facilities
    Administration/Management, B
Hotel/Motel Administration/Management, B
Human Development, D
Human Services, B
Industrial and Organizational Psychology, B
Information Science/Studies, M
Interdisciplinary Studies, BM
International Business/Trade/Commerce, B
Investment Management, M
Jewelry/Metalsmithing, M
Legal Assistant/Paralegal, AB
Library Science, M
Management, M
Management Information Systems and Services, M
Marketing/Marketing Management, B
Mathematics, B
Mathematics Teacher Education, B
Media Studies, M
Mental Health Counseling/Counselor, B
Multi-/Interdisciplinary Studies, B
Music, B
Music Performance, B
Music Teacher Education, BM

Music Therapy/Therapist, B
Musicology and Ethnomusicology, M
Nursing - Registered Nurse Training, B
Nursing Administration, M
Nutritional Sciences, MD
Painting, M
Parks, Recreation, Leisure and Fitness Studies, B
Photography, BM
Physician Assistant, BM
Pre-Law Studies, B
Pre-Nursing Studies, B
Printmaking, M
Psychology, BM
Public Administration, BMO
Public Health, M
Public Relations/Image Management, B
Reading Teacher Education, M
Religion/Religious Studies, B
Religious Education, B
Religious/Sacred Music, B
Sacred Music, M
School Psychology, M
Science Teacher Education/General Science
    Teacher Education, B
Sculpture, M
Secondary Education and Teaching, B
Social Sciences, B
Social Work, BMDO
Spanish Language and Literature, B
Spanish Language Teacher Education, B
Special Education and Teaching, BM
Substance Abuse/Addiction Counseling, M
Teacher Education and Professional
    Development, Specific Subject Areas, B
Textile Design, M
Visual and Performing Arts, B

MCCANN SCHOOL OF BUSINESS & TECHNOLOGY

Accounting, A
Administrative Assistant and Secretarial Science, A
Business Administration and Management, A
Computer and Information Sciences, A
Computer Programming, Specific Applications, A
Computer Science, A
Legal Assistant/Paralegal, A
Marketing/Marketing Management, A
Medical Office Management/Administration, A
System Administration/Administrator, A

MEDIAN SCHOOL OF ALLIED HEALTH CAREERS

Medical Administrative Assistant/Secretary, A
Orthotist/Prosthetist, A

MERCYHURST COLLEGE

Accounting, B
Administrative Assistant and Secretarial Science, AB
Advertising, B
Anthropology, B
Apparel and Textiles, B
Archeology, B
Art Teacher Education, B
Art Therapy/Therapist, B
Art/Art Studies, General, B
Arts Management, B
Athletic Training and Sports Medicine, B
Biochemistry, B
Biological Anthropology, M
Biology Teacher Education, B
Biology/Biological Sciences, B
Broadcast Journalism, B
Business Administration and Management, AB
Business Teacher Education, B
Business, Management, Marketing, and Related
    Support Services, B
Chemistry, B
Chemistry Teacher Education, B
Clinical Laboratory Science/Medical
    Technology/Technologist, B
Computer and Information Sciences, B
Computer Science, B
Corrections, B
Corrections and Criminal Justice, B
Creative Writing, B

Criminal Justice/Law Enforcement
 Administration, AB
Criminal Justice/Police Science, AB
Criminal Justice/Safety Studies, AB
Criminology, M
Culinary Arts/Chef Training, AB
Dance, B
Dietetics/Dieticians, B
Early Childhood Education and Teaching, AB
Education, B
Educational Leadership and Administration, O
Elementary Education and Teaching, B
English Language and Literature, B
English/Language Arts Teacher Education, B
Family and Consumer Sciences/Home Economics
 Teacher Education, B
Family and Consumer Sciences/Human Sciences, B
Fashion Merchandising, B
Fiber, Textile and Weaving Arts, B
Finance, B
Fine/Studio Arts, B
Foreign Language Teacher Education, B
Foreign Languages and Literatures, B
Forensic Science and Technology, BM
French Language and Literature, B
Geology/Earth Science, B
German Language and Literature, B
Gerontology, B
Health Information/Medical Records
 Technology/Technician, B
Health/Medical Preparatory Programs, B
History, B
Hospitality Administration/Management, B
Hotel/Motel Administration/Management, AB
Human Development and Family Studies, B
Human Resources Management/Personnel
 Administration, B
Humanities/Humanistic Studies, B
Information Science/Studies, B
Insurance, A
Interior Design, B
Journalism, B
Liberal Arts and Sciences Studies and
 Humanities, AB
Marketing/Marketing Management, B
Mass Communication/Media Studies, B
Mathematics, B
Mathematics Teacher Education, B
Medical Administrative Assistant/Secretary, B
Medical Transcription/Transcriptionist, B
Multi-/Interdisciplinary Studies, B
Multilingual and Multicultural Education, M
Music, B
Music Performance, B
Music Teacher Education, B
Nursing - Registered Nurse Training, AB
Office Management and Supervision, A
Organizational Management, MO
Paleontology, B
Petroleum Technology/Technician, B
Philosophy, B
Physical Therapist Assistant, B
Physical Therapy/Therapist, A
Physics, B
Political Science and Government, B
Pre-Dentistry Studies, B
Pre-Law Studies, B
Pre-Medicine/Pre-Medical Studies, B
Pre-Veterinary Studies, B
Psychology, B
Public Relations/Image Management, B
Purchasing, Procurement/Acquisitions and
 Contracts Management, B
Radio and Television, B
Religion/Religious Studies, B
Religious Education, AB
Science Teacher Education/General Science
 Teacher Education, B
Sculpture, B
Secondary Education and Teaching, B
Securities Services Administration/Management, MO
Social Science Teacher Education, B
Social Sciences, B
Social Work, B
Sociology, B
Spanish Language and Literature, B

Special Education and Teaching, BMO
Sport and Fitness Administration/Management, B
Statistics, B
Voice and Opera, B
Wind and Percussion Instruments, B

MESSIAH COLLEGE

Accounting, B
Art History, Criticism and Conservation, B
Art Teacher Education, B
Athletic Training and Sports Medicine, B
Bible/Biblical Studies, B
Biochemistry, B
Biology Teacher Education, B
Biology/Biological Sciences, B
Biopsychology, B
Business Administration and Management, B
Business, Management, Marketing, and Related
 Support Services, B
Business/Managerial Economics, B
Chemistry, B
Chemistry Teacher Education, B
Civil Engineering, B
Clinical Nutrition/Nutritionist, B
Communication Studies/Speech Communication
 and Rhetoric, B
Computer Science, B
Criminal Justice/Safety Studies, B
Drama and Dramatics/Theatre Arts, B
Early Childhood Education and Teaching, B
E-Commerce/Electronic Commerce, B
Economics, B
Elementary Education and Teaching, B
Engineering, B
English Language and Literature, B
English/Language Arts Teacher Education, B
Entrepreneurship/Entrepreneurial Studies, B
Environmental Sciences, B
Environmental Studies, B
Family and Community Services, B
Fine/Studio Arts, B
French Language and Literature, B
French Language Teacher Education, B
German Language and Literature, B
German Language Teacher Education, B
History, B
Human Resources Management/Personnel
 Administration, B
Humanities/Humanistic Studies, B
Information Science/Studies, B
International Business/Trade/Commerce, B
Journalism, B
Kinesiology and Exercise Science, B
Marketing/Marketing Management, B
Mathematics, B
Mathematics Teacher Education, B
Music, B
Music Teacher Education, B
Nursing - Registered Nurse Training, B
Parks, Recreation, Leisure and Fitness Studies, B
Philosophy, B
Physical Education Teaching and Coaching, B
Physics, B
Political Science and Government, B
Psychology, B
Radio and Television, B
Religion/Religious Studies, B
Religious Studies, B
Social Studies Teacher Education, B
Social Work, B
Sociology, B
Spanish Language and Literature, B
Spanish Language Teacher Education, B
Therapeutic Recreation/Recreational Therapy, B

MILLERSVILLE UNIVERSITY OF PENNSYLVANIA

Anthropology, B
Area Studies, B
Art Education, M
Art Teacher Education, B
Art/Art Studies, General, B
Atmospheric Sciences and Meteorology, B
Biological and Biomedical Sciences, M
Biology/Biological Sciences, B
Business Administration and Management, B

Business Administration, Management and
 Operations, M
Chemical Technology/Technician, A
Chemistry, B
Clinical Psychology, M
Communication Studies/Speech Communication
 and Rhetoric, B
Computer and Information Sciences, AB
Computer Science, AB
Counseling Psychology, M
Early Childhood Education and Teaching, BM
Economics, B
Education, M
Elementary Education and Teaching, BM
English, M
English Education, M
English Language and Literature, B
English/Language Arts Teacher Education, B
Foreign Language Teacher Education, B
Foundations and Philosophy of Education, M
French Language and Literature, BM
Geography, B
Geology/Earth Science, B
Geosciences, M
German Language and Literature, BM
Gerontology, A
History, ABM
Industrial Production Technologies/Technicians, B
Industrial Technology/Technician, AB
Liberal Arts and Sciences Studies and
 Humanities, A
Mathematics, B
Mathematics Teacher Education, BM
Music, B
Music Teacher Education, B
Nursing, M
Nursing - Registered Nurse Training, B
Nursing Science, B
Occupational Safety and Health
 Technology/Technician, B
Oceanography, Chemical and Physical, B
Philosophy, B
Physics, B
Political Science and Government, B
Psychology, BM
Reading Teacher Education, BM
School Psychology, M
Science Teacher Education/General Science
 Teacher Education, B
Social Sciences, B
Social Studies Teacher Education, B
Social Work, B
Sociology, B
Spanish Language and Literature, BM
Special Education and Teaching, BM
Sport and Fitness Administration/Management, M

MONTGOMERY COUNTY COMMUNITY COLLEGE

Accounting, A
Accounting Technology/Technician and
 Bookkeeping, A
Administrative Assistant and Secretarial Science, A
Architectural Drafting and Architectural
 CAD/CADD, A
Art/Art Studies, General, A
Automotive Engineering Technology/Technician, A
Baking and Pastry Arts/Baker/Pastry Chef, A
Biology/Biological Sciences, A
BioTechnology, A
Business Administration and Management, A
Business/Commerce, A
Business/Corporate Communications, A
Child Care and Support Services Management, A
Clinical/Medical Laboratory Technician, A
Commercial and Advertising Art, A
Communication Studies/Speech Communication
 and Rhetoric, A
Communications Technologies/Technicians and
 Support Services, A
Computer and Information Sciences, A
Computer Engineering Technology/Technician, A
Computer Programming/Programmer, A
Computer Systems Networking and
 Telecommunications, A
Criminal Justice/Police Science, A

Culinary Arts/Chef Training, A
Dental Hygiene/Hygienist, A
Electrical, Electronic and Communications
   Engineering Technology/Technician, A
Electromechanical Technology/Electromechanical
   Engineering Technology, A
Elementary Education and Teaching, A
Engineering Science, A
Engineering Technologies/Technicians, A
Fire Protection and Safety Technology/Technician, A
Hospitality and Recreation Marketing Operations, A
Humanities/Humanistic Studies, A
Information Science/Studies, A
Liberal Arts and Sciences Studies and
   Humanities, A
Management Information Systems and Services, A
Mathematics, A
Mechanical Drafting and Mechanical Drafting
   CAD/CADD, A
Mechanical Engineering/Mechanical
   Technology/Technician, A
Medical Radiologic Technology/Science - Radiation
   Therapist, A
Nursing - Registered Nurse Training, A
Physical Education Teaching and Coaching, A
Physical Sciences, A
Psychiatric/Mental Health Services Technician, A
Radiologic Technology/Science - Radiographer, A
Real Estate, A
Respiratory Care Therapy/Therapist, A
Sales, Distribution and Marketing Operations, A
Secondary Education and Teaching, A
Social Sciences, A
Surgical Technology/Technologist, A
Teacher Assistant/Aide, A

MOORE COLLEGE OF ART & DESIGN

Art History, Criticism and Conservation, B
Art Teacher Education, B
Art/Art Studies, General, B
Fashion/Apparel Design, B
Fiber, Textile and Weaving Arts, B
Fine/Studio Arts, B
Graphic Design, B
Illustration, B
Interior Design, B
Photography, B

MORAVIAN COLLEGE

Accounting, B
Art History, Criticism and Conservation, B
Art Teacher Education, B
Art/Art Studies, General, B
Biochemistry, B
Biology Teacher Education, B
Biology/Biological Sciences, B
Business Administration and Management, B
Business Administration, Management and
   Operations, M
Chemistry, B
Chemistry Teacher Education, B
Classics and Classical
   Languages, Literatures, and Linguistics, B
Clinical Laboratory Science/Medical
   Technology/Technologist, B
Clinical Psychology, B
Computer Science, B
Creative Writing, B
Criminal Justice/Law Enforcement Administration, B
Curriculum and Instruction, M
Drama and Dramatics/Theatre Arts, B
Economics, B
Education, BM
Elementary Education and Teaching, B
English Language and Literature, B
Environmental Studies, B
Experimental Psychology, B
Fine/Studio Arts, B
Foreign Language Teacher Education, B
French Language and Literature, B
French Language Teacher Education, B
Geology/Earth Science, B
German Language and Literature, B
German Language Teacher Education, B
German Studies, B
Graphic Design, B

History, B
History Teacher Education, B
Industrial and Organizational Psychology, B
International Business/Trade/Commerce, B
Mathematics, B
Mathematics Teacher Education, B
Music, B
Music Performance, B
Music Teacher Education, B
Music Theory and Composition, B
Natural Resources Management/Development and
   Policy, B
Nursing - Registered Nurse Training, B
Philosophy, B
Physics, B
Physics Teacher Education, B
Political Science and Government, B
Psychology, B
Religion/Religious Studies, B
Religious/Sacred Music, B
Science Teacher Education/General Science
   Teacher Education, B
Secondary Education and Teaching, B
Social Psychology, B
Social Sciences, B
Social Studies Teacher Education, B
Sociology, B
Spanish Language and Literature, B
Spanish Language Teacher Education, B
Theatre Literature, History and Criticism, B

MOUNT ALOYSIUS COLLEGE

Accounting, AB
Accounting and Business/Management, AB
Behavioral Sciences, AB
Business Administration and Management, AB
Child Care and Support Services Management, A
Computer Science, A
Corrections, M
Criminal Justice/Safety Studies, AB
Criminology, B
English Language and Literature, B
General Studies, A
Health Services Administration, M
Health Services/Allied Health/Health Sciences, B
History, B
Humanities/Humanistic Studies, B
Information Science/Studies, B
Kindergarten/PreSchool Education and
   Teaching, AB
Legal Assistant/Paralegal, A
Liberal Arts and Sciences Studies and
   Humanities, AB
Medical Office Assistant/Specialist, B
Medical/Clinical Assistant, A
Nursing - Registered Nurse Training, A
Nursing Science, A
Occupational Therapist Assistant, A
Occupational Therapy/Therapist, B
Pharmacy Technician/Assistant, A
Physical Therapist Assistant, A
Physical Therapy/Therapist, B
Political Science and Government, B
Pre-Law Studies, B
Professional Studies, B
Psychology, BM
Radiologic Technology/Science - Radiographer, AB
Sign Language Interpretation and Translation, AB
Social Sciences, B
Surgical Technology/Technologist, A

MUHLENBERG COLLEGE

Accounting, B
American/United States Studies/Civilization, B
Anthropology, B
Art/Art Studies, General, B
Biochemistry, B
Biology/Biological Sciences, B
Business Administration and Management, B
Chemistry, B
Computer Science, B
Dance, B
Drama and Dramatics/Theatre Arts, B
Economics, B
English Language and Literature, B
Environmental Sciences, B

French Language and Literature, B
German Language and Literature, B
History, B
International Relations and Affairs, B
Mathematics, B
Music, B
Natural Sciences, B
Neuroscience, B
Philosophy, B
Physical Sciences, B
Physics, B
Political Science and Government, B
Psychology, B
Religion/Religious Studies, B
Russian Studies, B
Social Sciences, B
Sociology, B
Spanish Language and Literature, B

NEUMANN COLLEGE

Accounting, B
Athletic Training and Sports Medicine, B
Biology/Biological Sciences, B
Business Administration and Management, B
Communication Studies/Speech Communication
   and Rhetoric, B
Computer and Information Sciences, B
Criminal Justice/Safety Studies, B
Education, M
Elementary Education and Teaching, B
English Language and Literature, B
Environmental Studies, B
International Business/Trade/Commerce, B
Kindergarten/PreSchool Education and Teaching, B
Liberal Arts and Sciences Studies and
   Humanities, AB
Management Strategy and Policy, M
Marketing/Marketing Management, B
Nursing, M
Nursing - Registered Nurse Training, B
Pastoral Studies/Counseling, MO
Physical Therapy/Therapist, MD
Political Science and Government, B
Psychology, B
Sport and Fitness Administration/Management, BM

NEW CASTLE SCHOOL OF TRADES

Automotive Engineering Technology/Technician, A
Construction Engineering Technology/Technician, A
Electrical, Electronic and Communications
   Engineering Technology/Technician, A
Heating, Air Conditioning and Refrigeration
   Technology/Technician, A
Machine Tool Technology/Machinist, A

NEWPORT BUSINESS INSTITUTE (LOWER BURRELL)

Accounting, A
Business Administration and Management, A
Computer Programming/Programmer, A
Consumer Merchandising/Retailing Management, A
Data Entry/Microcomputer Applications, A
Executive Assistant/Executive Secretary, A
Legal Administrative Assistant/Secretary, A
Medical Administrative Assistant/Secretary, A
Medical Office Management/Administration, A
Medical/Clinical Assistant, A
Tourism and Travel Services Management, A
Word Processing, A

NEWPORT BUSINESS INSTITUTE (WILLIAMSPORT)

Administrative Assistant and Secretarial Science, A
Business Administration and Management, A
Legal Administrative Assistant/Secretary, A
Medical Administrative Assistant/Secretary, A

NORTHAMPTON COUNTY AREA COMMUNITY COLLEGE

Accounting Technology/Technician and
   Bookkeeping, A
Acting, A
Administrative Assistant and Secretarial Science, A
Architectural Engineering Technology/Technician, A

Automobile/Automotive Mechanics
Technology/Technician, A
Biology/Biological Sciences, A
BioTechnology, A
Business Administration and Management, A
Business/Commerce, A
CAD/CADD Drafting and/or Design
Technology/Technician, A
Chemical Technology/Technician, A
Chemistry, A
Child Care Provider/Assistant, A
Communication Disorders, A
Communication Studies/Speech Communication
and Rhetoric, A
Computer and Information Systems Security, A
Computer Installation and Repair
Technology/Technician, A
Computer Programming/Programmer, A
Computer Science, A
Computer Systems Networking and
Telecommunications, A
Criminal Justice/Safety Studies, A
Dental Hygiene/Hygienist, A
Diagnostic Medical Sonography/Sonographer and
Ultrasound Technician, A
Education, A
Electrical, Electronic and Communications
Engineering Technology/Technician, A
Electrician, A
Electromechanical Technology/Electromechanical
Engineering Technology, A
Engineering, A
Fine/Studio Arts, A
Fire Services Administration, A
Food Preparation/Professional Cooking/Kitchen
Assistant, A
Funeral Service and Mortuary Science, A
General Studies, A
Graphic Design, A
Heating, Air Conditioning, Ventilation and
Refrigeration Maintenance
Technology/Technician, A
Hotel/Motel Administration/Management, A
Industrial Electronics Technology/Technician, A
Interior Design, A
Journalism, A
Legal Administrative Assistant/Secretary, A
Legal Assistant/Paralegal, A
Liberal Arts and Sciences Studies and
Humanities, A
Mathematics, A
Medical Administrative Assistant/Secretary, A
Nursing - Registered Nurse Training, A
Physics, A
Quality Control Technology/Technician, A
Radio and Television Broadcasting
Technology/Technician, A
Radiologic Technology/Science - Radiographer, A
Restaurant/Food Services Management, A
Social Work, A
Sport and Fitness Administration/Management, A
Surgical Technology/Technologist, A
Teacher Assistant/Aide, A
Veterinary/Animal Health Technology/Technician and
Veterinary Assistant, A
Web Page, Digital/Multimedia and Information
Resources Design, A

OAKBRIDGE ACADEMY OF ARTS

Commercial and Advertising Art, A
Commercial Photography, A
Computer Graphics, A

PACE INSTITUTE

Accounting, A
Administrative Assistant and Secretarial Science, A
Business Administration and Management, A
Computer Programming/Programmer, A
Computer Systems Networking and
Telecommunications, A
Fashion Merchandising, A
Legal Assistant/Paralegal, A
Medical/Clinical Assistant, A

Tourism and Travel Services Management, A

PEIRCE COLLEGE

Accounting, A
Accounting and Business/Management, A
Accounting and Related Services, A
Accounting Technology/Technician and
Bookkeeping, A
Business Administration and Management, AB
Business Administration, Management and
Operations, A
Business/Commerce, A
Computer Engineering Technology/Technician, A
Computer Programming, Specific Applications, A
Computer Technology/Computer Systems
Technology, A
Information Science/Studies, B
Legal Administrative Assistant/Secretary, A
Legal Assistant/Paralegal, AB
Legal Professions and Studies, A
Management Information Systems and Services, A
Marketing/Marketing Management, A
Office Management and Supervision, A
Pre-Law Studies, A
System, Networking, and LAN/WAN
Management/Manager, A

PENN COMMERCIAL BUSINESS AND TECHNICAL SCHOOL

Administrative Assistant and Secretarial Science, A
Business Administration and Management, A
Drafting and Design Technology/Technician, A
Legal Administrative Assistant/Secretary, A
Legal Assistant/Paralegal, A
Medical Administrative Assistant/Secretary, A
Medical/Clinical Assistant, A

PENN FOSTER CAREER SCHOOL

Accounting Technology/Technician and
Bookkeeping, A
Business/Commerce, A
Child Care and Support Services Management, A
Civil Engineering Technology/Technician, A
Computer and Information Sciences and Support
Services, A
Computer Science, A
Criminal Justice/Police Science, A
Electrical, Electronic and Communications
Engineering Technology/Technician, A
Hotel/Motel Administration/Management, A
Industrial Engineering, A
Legal Assistant/Paralegal, A
Mechanical Engineering/Mechanical
Technology/Technician, A
Veterinary/Animal Health Technology/Technician and
Veterinary Assistant, A

PENNCO TECH

Autobody/Collision and Repair
Technology/Technician, A
Automobile/Automotive Mechanics
Technology/Technician, A
Computer Programming/Programmer, A
Drafting and Design Technology/Technician, A
Electrical, Electronic and Communications
Engineering Technology/Technician, A

PENNSYLVANIA COLLEGE OF ART & DESIGN

Fine/Studio Arts, B
Graphic Design, B
Illustration, B
Photography, B

PENNSYLVANIA COLLEGE OF TECHNOLOGY

Accounting, B
Accounting Technology/Technician and
Bookkeeping, A
Administrative Assistant and Secretarial Science, A
Adult Health Nurse/Nursing, B
Aeronautical/Aerospace Engineering
Technology/Technician, A
Aircraft Powerplant Technology/Technician, A

Allied Health
Diagnostic, Intervention, and Treatment
Professions, A
Applied Horticulture/Horticultural Business
Services, A
Architectural Engineering Technology/Technician, A
Autobody/Collision and Repair
Technology/Technician, A
Automotive Engineering Technology/Technician, AB
Avionics Maintenance Technology/Technician, AB
Baking and Pastry Arts/Baker/Pastry Chef, A
Banking and Financial Support Services, A
Biology/Biological Sciences, A
Biomedical Technology/Technician, A
Broadcast Journalism, A
Business Administration and Management, AB
Business Administration, Management and
Operations, B
Business/Office Automation/Technology/Data
Entry, A
Cabinetmaking and Millwork/Millwright, A
Cardiovascular Technology/Technologist, B
Carpentry/Carpenter, A
Child Care and Support Services Management, A
Child Care Provider/Assistant, A
Civil Engineering Technology/Technician, AB
Commercial and Advertising Art, AB
Computer and Information Sciences, A
Computer and Information Sciences and Support
Services, A
Computer Programming, Specific Applications, A
Computer Systems Analysis/Analyst, B
Computer Systems Networking and
Telecommunications, AB
Computer Technology/Computer Systems
Technology, A
Computer/Information Technology Services
Administration and Management, A
Construction Engineering Technology/Technician, AB
Culinary Arts/Chef Training, AB
Dental Hygiene/Hygienist, AB
Diesel Mechanics Technology/Technician, A
Dietician Assistant, A
Drafting and Design Technology/Technician, A
Drafting/Design Engineering
Technologies/Technicians, A
Electrical and Electronic Engineering
Technologies/Technicians, AB
Electrical, Electronic and Communications
Engineering Technology/Technician, A
Electrician, A
Emergency Medical Technology/Technician (EMT
Paramedic), A
Engineering Science, A
Engineering Technologies/Technicians, B
Environmental Control Technologies/Technicians, A
Environmental Engineering
Technology/Environmental Technology, AB
Forestry Technology/Technician, A
General Office Occupations and Clerical Services, A
General Studies, A
Graphic and Printing Equipment Operator
Production, AB
Health and Medical Administrative Services, B
Health and Physical Education/Fitness, A
Health Information/Medical Records
Administration/Administrator, A
Health Professions and Related Clinical Sciences, B
Heating, Air Conditioning and Refrigeration
Technology/Technician, AB
Heavy Equipment Maintenance
Technology/Technician, A
Heavy/Industrial Equipment Maintenance
Technologies, A
Industrial Electronics Technology/Technician, A
Industrial Mechanics and Maintenance
Technology, A
Industrial Production Technologies/Technicians, AB
Industrial Technology/Technician, AB
Information Technology, A
Institutional Food Workers, A
Instrumentation Technology/Technician, A
Laser and Optical Technology/Technician, A
Law and Legal Studies, B
Legal Assistant/Paralegal, A
Legal Professions and Studies, B

Liberal Arts and Sciences Studies and
Humanities, A
Licensed Practical/Vocational Nurse Training, A
Machine Shop Technology/Assistant, A
Management Information Systems and Services, B
Manufacturing Technology/Technician, AB
Mason/Masonry, A
Mass Communication/Media Studies, A
Mechanic and Repair Technologies/Technicians, A
Mechanical Drafting and Mechanical Drafting
CAD/CADD, B
Mechanical Engineering/Mechanical
Technology/Technician, B
Medical Administrative Assistant/Secretary, A
Medical Radiologic Technology/Science - Radiation
Therapist, A
Mental and Social Health Services and Allied
Professions, B
Multi-/Interdisciplinary Studies, A
Nursing - Registered Nurse Training, A
Occupational Therapist Assistant, A
Ornamental Horticulture, A
Physical Sciences, A
Plant Nursery Operations and Management, A
Plastics Engineering Technology/Technician, AB
Platemaker/Imager, A
Plumbing Technology/Plumber, A
Psychiatric/Mental Health Services Technician, AB
Quality Control Technology/Technician, A
Solar Energy Technology/Technician, A
Survey Technology/Surveying, A
Teacher Education and Professional
Development, Specific Subject Areas, A
Technical and Business Writing, B
Tool and Die Technology/Technician, A
Tourism and Travel Services Management, A
Turf and Turfgrass Management, A
Vehicle and Vehicle Parts and Accessories
Marketing Operations, A
Vehicle Maintenance and Repair Technologies, A
Web Page, Digital/Multimedia and Information
Resources Design, A
Welding Technology/Welder, A
Woodworking, A

PENNSYLVANIA CULINARY INSTITUTE

Culinary Arts/Chef Training, A
Hotel/Motel Administration/Management, A

PENNSYLVANIA HIGHLAND COMMUNITY COLLEGE

Accounting, A
Banking and Financial Support Services, A
Computer and Information Sciences, A
Computer Programming, A
Computer Programming, Specific Applications, A
Computer Programming/Programmer, A
Computer/Information Technology Services
Administration and Management, A
Construction Engineering Technology/Technician, A
Consumer Merchandising/Retailing Management, A
Court Reporting/Court Reporter, A
Electrical, Electronic and Communications
Engineering Technology/Technician, A
Environmental Engineering
Technology/Environmental Technology, A
Geography, A
Health/Health Care Administration/Management, A
Heating, Air Conditioning and Refrigeration
Technology/Technician, A
Hospitality Administration/Management, A
Human Services, A
Industrial Technology/Technician, A
Liberal Arts and Sciences Studies and
Humanities, A
Management Information Systems and Services, A
System Administration/Administrator, A
Web/Multimedia Management and Webmaster, A

PENNSYLVANIA INSTITUTE OF TECHNOLOGY

Allied Health and Medical Assisting Services, A
Architectural Engineering Technology/Technician, A
Business Administration and Management, A
Electrical, Electronic and Communications
Engineering Technology/Technician, A

Engineering Technology, A
General Office Occupations and Clerical Services, A
Mechanical Engineering Related
Technologies/Technicians, A
Mechanical Engineering/Mechanical
Technology/Technician, A
Medical Office Management/Administration, A
Web Page, Digital/Multimedia and Information
Resources Design, A

THE PENNSYLVANIA STATE UNIVERSITY ABINGTON COLLEGE

Accounting, B
Acting, B
Actuarial Science, B
Adult and Continuing Education Administration, B
Advertising, B
Aerospace, Aeronautical and Astronautical
Engineering, B
African-American/Black Studies, B
Agribusiness, B
Agricultural and Extension Education Services, B
Agricultural Business and Management, A
Agricultural Mechanization, B
Agricultural/Biological Engineering and
Bioengineering, B
Agriculture, B
American/United States Studies/Civilization, B
Animal Sciences, B
Anthropology, B
Applied Economics, B
Archeology, B
Architectural Engineering, B
Art History, Criticism and Conservation, B
Art Teacher Education, B
Art/Art Studies, General, B
Astronomy, B
Atmospheric Sciences and Meteorology, B
Biochemistry, B
Biological and Biomedical Sciences, B
Biological and Physical Sciences, B
Biology Technician/BioTechnology Laboratory
Technician, B
Biology/Biological Sciences, B
Biomedical/Medical Engineering, B
Business/Commerce, AB
Business/Corporate Communications, B
Business/Managerial Economics, B
Chemical Engineering, B
Chemistry, B
Civil Engineering, B
Classics and Classical
Languages, Literatures, and Linguistics, B
Communication Disorders, B
Communication Studies/Speech Communication
and Rhetoric, B
Communication, Journalism and Related
Programs, B
Comparative Literature, B
Computer and Information Sciences, B
Computer Engineering, B
Criminal Justice/Law Enforcement Administration, B
Criminal Justice/Safety Studies, B
East Asian Studies, B
Economics, B
Electrical, Electronic and Communications
Engineering Technology/Technician, A
Electrical, Electronics and Communications
Engineering, B
Elementary Education and Teaching, B
Engineering Science, B
English Language and Literature, B
Environmental/Environmental Health Engineering, B
Film/Cinema Studies, B
Finance, B
Food Science, B
Foreign Language Teacher Education, B
Forest Sciences and Biology, B
Forestry Technology/Technician, B
French Language and Literature, B
Geography, B
Geological and Earth Sciences/Geosciences, B
Geology/Earth Science, B
German Language and Literature, B
Graphic Design, B
Health/Health Care Administration/Management, B

History, B
Horticultural Science, B
Hospitality Administration/Management, B
Human Development and Family Studies, B
Human Nutrition, B
Industrial Engineering, B
Information Science/Studies, B
International Relations and Affairs, B
Italian Language and Literature, B
Japanese Language and Literature, B
Jewish/Judaic Studies, B
Journalism, B
Kinesiology and Exercise Science, B
Labor and Industrial Relations, B
Landscaping and Groundskeeping, B
Latin American Studies, B
Liberal Arts and Sciences Studies and
Humanities, AB
Management Information Systems and Services, B
Marketing/Marketing Management, B
Materials Sciences, B
Mathematics, B
Mechanical Engineering, B
Medical Microbiology and Bacteriology, B
Medieval and Renaissance Studies, B
Mining and Mineral Engineering, B
Natural Resources and Conservation, B
Nuclear Engineering, B
Nursing - Registered Nurse Training, B
Organizational Behavior Studies, B
Parks, Recreation and Leisure Facilities
Management, B
Petroleum Engineering, B
Philosophy, B
Physics, B
Political Science and Government, B
Pre-Medicine/Pre-Medical Studies, B
Psychology, B
Rehabilitation and Therapeutic Professions, B
Religion/Religious Studies, B
Russian Language and Literature, B
Secondary Education and Teaching, B
Social Psychology, B
Sociology, B
Soil Science and Agronomy, B
Spanish Language and Literature, B
Special Education and Teaching, B
Statistics, B
Technical Theatre/Theatre Design and
Technology, B
Toxicology, B
Turf and Turfgrass Management, B
Visual and Performing Arts, B
Women's Studies, B

THE PENNSYLVANIA STATE UNIVERSITY ALTOONA COLLEGE

Accounting, B
Acting, B
Actuarial Science, B
Adult and Continuing Education Administration, B
Advertising, B
Aerospace, Aeronautical and Astronautical
Engineering, B
African-American/Black Studies, B
Agribusiness, B
Agricultural and Extension Education Services, B
Agricultural Business and Management, A
Agricultural/Biological Engineering and
Bioengineering, B
Agriculture, B
Agronomy and Crop Science, B
Animal Sciences, B
Anthropology, B
Applied Economics, B
Archeology, B
Architectural Engineering, B
Art History, Criticism and Conservation, B
Art Teacher Education, B
Art/Art Studies, General, B
Astronomy, B
Atmospheric Sciences and Meteorology, B
Biochemistry, B
Biological and Biomedical Sciences, B
Biological and Physical Sciences, AB

Biology Technician/BioTechnology Laboratory Technician, B
Biology/Biological Sciences, B
Biomedical Technology/Technician, A
Biomedical/Medical Engineering, B
Business Administration and Management, B
Business/Commerce, AB
Business/Managerial Economics, B
Chemical Engineering, B
Chemistry, B
Civil Engineering, B
Classics and Classical Languages, Literatures, and Linguistics, B
Communication Disorders, B
Communication Studies/Speech Communication and Rhetoric, B
Communication, Journalism and Related Programs, B
Comparative Literature, B
Computer and Information Sciences, B
Computer Engineering, B
Criminal Justice/Law Enforcement Administration, B
Criminal Justice/Safety Studies, AB
East Asian Studies, B
Economics, B
Electrical, Electronic and Communications Engineering Technology/Technician, A
Electrical, Electronics and Communications Engineering, B
Elementary Education and Teaching, B
Engineering Science, B
English Language and Literature, B
Environmental Studies, B
Environmental/Environmental Health Engineering, B
Film/Cinema Studies, B
Finance, B
Food Science, B
Foreign Language Teacher Education, B
Forest Sciences and Biology, B
Forestry Technology/Technician, B
French Language and Literature, B
Geography, B
Geological and Earth Sciences/Geosciences, B
Geology/Earth Science, B
German Language and Literature, B
Graphic Design, B
Health/Health Care Administration/Management, B
History, B
Horticultural Science, B
Hospitality Administration/Management, B
Human Development and Family Studies, AB
Human Nutrition, B
Industrial Engineering, B
Information Science/Studies, AB
International Relations and Affairs, B
Italian Language and Literature, B
Japanese Language and Literature, B
Jewish/Judaic Studies, B
Journalism, B
Kinesiology and Exercise Science, B
Labor and Industrial Relations, B
Landscaping and Groundskeeping, B
Latin American Studies, B
Liberal Arts and Sciences Studies and Humanities, AB
Management Information Systems and Services, B
Marketing/Marketing Management, B
Materials Sciences, B
Mathematics, B
Mechanical Engineering, B
Mechanical Engineering/Mechanical Technology/Technician, A
Medical Microbiology and Bacteriology, B
Medieval and Renaissance Studies, B
Metallurgical Technology/Technician, A
Mining and Mineral Engineering, B
Music, B
Natural Resources and Conservation, B
Nuclear Engineering, B
Nursing - Registered Nurse Training, AB
Organizational Behavior Studies, B
Parks, Recreation and Leisure Facilities Management, B
Petroleum Engineering, B
Philosophy, B
Physics, B

Political Science and Government, B
Pre-Medicine/Pre-Medical Studies, B
Psychology, B
Rehabilitation and Therapeutic Professions, B
Religion/Religious Studies, B
Russian Language and Literature, B
Secondary Education and Teaching, B
Sociology, B
Soil Science and Agronomy, B
Spanish Language and Literature, B
Special Education and Teaching, B
Statistics, B
Technical Theatre/Theatre Design and Technology, B
Telecommunications Technology/Technician, A
Toxicology, B
Turf and Turfgrass Management, B
Visual and Performing Arts, B

THE PENNSYLVANIA STATE UNIVERSITY BEAVER CAMPUS OF THE COMMONWEALTH COLLEGE

Accounting, B
Acting, B
Actuarial Science, B
Adult and Continuing Education Administration, B
Advertising, B
Aerospace, Aeronautical and Astronautical Engineering, B
African-American/Black Studies, B
Agribusiness, B
Agricultural and Extension Education Services, B
Agricultural Business and Management, A
Agricultural Mechanization, B
Agricultural/Biological Engineering and Bioengineering, B
Agriculture, B
Agronomy and Crop Science, B
Animal Sciences, B
Anthropology, B
Applied Economics, B
Archeology, B
Architectural Engineering, B
Art History, Criticism and Conservation, B
Art Teacher Education, B
Art/Art Studies, General, B
Astronomy, B
Atmospheric Sciences and Meteorology, B
Biochemistry, B
Biological and Biomedical Sciences, B
Biological and Physical Sciences, AB
Biology Technician/BioTechnology Laboratory Technician, B
Biology/Biological Sciences, B
Biomedical/Medical Engineering, B
Business Administration and Management, B
Business/Commerce, A
Business/Managerial Economics, B
Chemical Engineering, B
Chemistry, B
Civil Engineering, B
Classics and Classical Languages, Literatures, and Linguistics, B
Communication Disorders, B
Communication Studies/Speech Communication and Rhetoric, B
Communication, Journalism and Related Programs, B
Comparative Literature, B
Computer and Information Sciences, B
Computer Engineering, B
Criminal Justice/Law Enforcement Administration, B
East Asian Studies, B
Economics, B
Electrical, Electronics and Communications Engineering, B
Elementary Education and Teaching, B
Engineering Science, B
English Language and Literature, B
Environmental/Environmental Health Engineering, B
Film/Cinema Studies, B
Finance, B
Food Science, B
Foreign Language Teacher Education, B
Forest Sciences and Biology, B
Forestry Technology/Technician, B

French Language and Literature, B
Geography, B
Geological and Earth Sciences/Geosciences, B
Geology/Earth Science, B
German Language and Literature, B
Graphic Design, B
Health/Health Care Administration/Management, B
History, B
Horticultural Science, B
Hospitality Administration/Management, AB
Human Development and Family Studies, B
Human Nutrition, B
Industrial Engineering, B
Information Science/Studies, B
International Relations and Affairs, B
Italian Language and Literature, B
Japanese Language and Literature, B
Jewish/Judaic Studies, B
Journalism, B
Kinesiology and Exercise Science, B
Labor and Industrial Relations, B
Landscaping and Groundskeeping, B
Latin American Studies, B
Liberal Arts and Sciences Studies and Humanities, AB
Logistics and Materials Management, B
Management Information Systems and Services, B
Marketing/Marketing Management, B
Materials Sciences, B
Mathematics, B
Mechanical Engineering, B
Medical Microbiology and Bacteriology, B
Medieval and Renaissance Studies, B
Mining and Mineral Engineering, B
Music, B
Natural Resources and Conservation, B
Nuclear Engineering, B
Nursing - Registered Nurse Training, B
Organizational Behavior Studies, B
Parks, Recreation and Leisure Facilities Management, B
Petroleum Engineering, B
Philosophy, B
Physics, B
Political Science and Government, B
Pre-Medicine/Pre-Medical Studies, B
Psychology, B
Rehabilitation and Therapeutic Professions, B
Religion/Religious Studies, B
Russian Language and Literature, B
Secondary Education and Teaching, B
Sociology, B
Soil Science and Agronomy, B
Spanish Language and Literature, B
Special Education and Teaching, B
Statistics, B
Technical Theatre/Theatre Design and Technology, B
Toxicology, B
Turf and Turfgrass Management, B
Visual and Performing Arts, B
Women's Studies, B

THE PENNSYLVANIA STATE UNIVERSITY BERKS CAMPUS OF THE BERKS-LEHIGH VALLEY COLLEGE

Accounting, B
Acting, B
Actuarial Science, B
Adult and Continuing Education Administration, B
Advertising, B
Aerospace, Aeronautical and Astronautical Engineering, B
African-American/Black Studies, B
Agribusiness, B
Agricultural and Extension Education Services, B
Agricultural Business and Management, A
Agricultural Mechanization, B
Agricultural/Biological Engineering and Bioengineering, B
Agriculture, B
Agronomy and Crop Science, B
American/United States Studies/Civilization, B
Animal Sciences, B
Anthropology, B
Applied Economics, B

Archeology, B
Architectural Engineering, B
Art History, Criticism and Conservation, B
Art Teacher Education, B
Art/Art Studies, General, B
Astronomy, B
Atmospheric Sciences and Meteorology, B
Biochemistry, B
Biological and Biomedical Sciences, B
Biological and Physical Sciences, B
Biology Technician/BioTechnology Laboratory
    Technician, B
Biology/Biological Sciences, B
Biomedical Technology/Technician, A
Biomedical/Medical Engineering, B
Business Administration and Management, B
Business/Commerce, AB
Business/Managerial Economics, B
Chemical Engineering, B
Chemistry, B
Civil Engineering, B
Classics and Classical
    Languages, Literatures, and Linguistics, B
Communication Disorders, B
Communication Studies/Speech Communication
    and Rhetoric, B
Communication, Journalism and Related
    Programs, B
Comparative Literature, B
Computer and Information Sciences, B
Computer Engineering, B
Criminal Justice/Law Enforcement Administration, B
East Asian Studies, B
Economics, B
Electrical, Electronic and Communications
    Engineering Technology/Technician, A
Electrical, Electronics and Communications
    Engineering, B
Elementary Education and Teaching, B
Engineering Science, B
English Language and Literature, B
Environmental/Environmental Health Engineering, B
Film/Cinema Studies, B
Finance, B
Food Science, B
Foreign Language Teacher Education, B
Foreign Languages and Literatures, B
Forest Sciences and Biology, B
Forestry Technology/Technician, B
French Language and Literature, B
Geography, B
Geological and Earth Sciences/Geosciences, B
Geology/Earth Science, B
German Language and Literature, B
Graphic Design, B
Health/Health Care Administration/Management, B
History, B
Horticultural Science, B
Hospitality Administration/Management, AB
Human Development and Family Studies, B
Human Nutrition, B
Industrial Engineering, B
Information Science/Studies, AB
International Relations and Affairs, B
Italian Language and Literature, B
Japanese Language and Literature, B
Jewish/Judaic Studies, B
Journalism, B
Kinesiology and Exercise Science, B
Labor and Industrial Relations, B
Landscape Architecture, B
Landscaping and Groundskeeping, B
Latin American Studies, B
Liberal Arts and Sciences Studies and
    Humanities, AB
Management Information Systems and Services, B
Marketing/Marketing Management, B
Materials Sciences, B
Mathematics, B
Mechanical Engineering, B
Mechanical Engineering/Mechanical
    Technology/Technician, A
Medical Microbiology and Bacteriology, B
Medieval and Renaissance Studies, B
Metallurgical Technology/Technician, A
Mining and Mineral Engineering, B

Music, B
Natural Resources and Conservation, B
Nuclear Engineering, B
Nursing - Registered Nurse Training, B
Occupational Therapist Assistant, B
Organizational Behavior Studies, B
Parks, Recreation and Leisure Facilities
    Management, B
Petroleum Engineering, B
Philosophy, B
Physics, B
Political Science and Government, B
Pre-Medicine/Pre-Medical Studies, B
Psychology, B
Rehabilitation and Therapeutic Professions, B
Religion/Religious Studies, B
Russian Language and Literature, B
Secondary Education and Teaching, B
Sociology, B
Soil Science and Agronomy, B
Spanish Language and Literature, B
Special Education and Teaching, B
Statistics, B
Technical and Business Writing, B
Technical Theatre/Theatre Design and
    Technology, B
Telecommunications Technology/Technician, A
Toxicology, B
Turf and Turfgrass Management, B
Visual and Performing Arts, B
Women's Studies, B

THE PENNSYLVANIA STATE UNIVERSITY DELAWARE COUNTY CAMPUS OF THE COMMONWEALTH COLLEGE

Accounting, B
Acting, B
Actuarial Science, B
Adult and Continuing Education Administration, B
Advertising, B
Aerospace, Aeronautical and Astronautical
    Engineering, B
African-American/Black Studies, B
Agribusiness, B
Agricultural and Extension Education Services, B
Agricultural Business and Management, A
Agricultural Mechanization, B
Agricultural/Biological Engineering and
    Bioengineering, B
Agriculture, B
Agronomy and Crop Science, B
American/United States Studies/Civilization, B
Animal Sciences, B
Anthropology, B
Applied Economics, B
Archeology, B
Architectural Engineering, B
Art History, Criticism and Conservation, B
Art Teacher Education, B
Art/Art Studies, General, B
Astronomy, B
Atmospheric Sciences and Meteorology, B
Biochemistry, B
Biological and Biomedical Sciences, B
Biological and Physical Sciences, B
Biology Technician/BioTechnology Laboratory
    Technician, B
Biology/Biological Sciences, B
Biomedical/Medical Engineering, B
Business Administration and Management, B
Business/Commerce, A
Business/Managerial Economics, B
Chemical Engineering, B
Chemistry, B
Civil Engineering, B
Classics and Classical
    Languages, Literatures, and Linguistics, B
Communication Disorders, B
Communication Studies/Speech Communication
    and Rhetoric, B
Communication, Journalism and Related
    Programs, B
Comparative Literature, B
Computer and Information Sciences, B
Computer Engineering, B

Criminal Justice/Law Enforcement Administration, B
East Asian Studies, B
Economics, B
Electrical, Electronic and Communications
    Engineering Technology/Technician, A
Electrical, Electronics and Communications
    Engineering, B
Elementary Education and Teaching, B
Engineering Science, B
English Language and Literature, B
Environmental/Environmental Health Engineering, B
Film/Cinema Studies, B
Finance, B
Food Science, B
Foreign Language Teacher Education, B
Forest Sciences and Biology, B
Forestry Technology/Technician, B
French Language and Literature, B
Geography, B
Geological and Earth Sciences/Geosciences, B
Geology/Earth Science, B
German Language and Literature, B
Graphic Design, B
Health/Health Care Administration/Management, B
History, B
Horticultural Science, B
Hospitality Administration/Management, B
Human Development and Family Studies, AB
Human Nutrition, B
Industrial Engineering, B
Information Science/Studies, B
International Relations and Affairs, B
Italian Language and Literature, B
Japanese Language and Literature, B
Jewish/Judaic Studies, B
Journalism, B
Kinesiology and Exercise Science, B
Labor and Industrial Relations, B
Landscape Architecture, B
Landscaping and Groundskeeping, B
Latin American Studies, B
Liberal Arts and Sciences Studies and
    Humanities, AB
Logistics and Materials Management, B
Management Information Systems and Services, B
Marketing/Marketing Management, B
Materials Sciences, B
Mathematics, B
Mechanical Engineering, B
Medical Microbiology and Bacteriology, B
Medieval and Renaissance Studies, B
Mining and Mineral Engineering, B
Music, B
Natural Resources and Conservation, B
Nuclear Engineering, B
Nursing - Registered Nurse Training, B
Organizational Behavior Studies, B
Parks, Recreation and Leisure Facilities
    Management, B
Petroleum Engineering, B
Philosophy, B
Physics, B
Political Science and Government, B
Pre-Medicine/Pre-Medical Studies, B
Psychology, B
Rehabilitation and Therapeutic Professions, B
Religion/Religious Studies, B
Russian Language and Literature, B
Secondary Education and Teaching, B
Sociology, B
Soil Science and Agronomy, B
Spanish Language and Literature, B
Special Education and Teaching, B
Statistics, B
Technical Theatre/Theatre Design and
    Technology, B
Turf and Turfgrass Management, B
Visual and Performing Arts, B
Women's Studies, B

THE PENNSYLVANIA STATE UNIVERSITY DUBOIS CAMPUS OF THE COMMONWEALTH COLLEGE

Accounting, B
Acting, B
Actuarial Science, B

Adult and Continuing Education Administration, B
Advertising, B
Aerospace, Aeronautical and Astronautical
    Engineering, B
African-American/Black Studies, B
Agribusiness, B
Agricultural and Extension Education Services, B
Agricultural Business and Management, A
Agricultural Mechanization, B
Agricultural/Biological Engineering and
    Bioengineering, B
Agriculture, B
Agronomy and Crop Science, B
Animal Sciences, B
Anthropology, B
Applied Economics, B
Archeology, B
Architectural Engineering, B
Art History, Criticism and Conservation, B
Art Teacher Education, B
Art/Art Studies, General, B
Astronomy, B
Atmospheric Sciences and Meteorology, B
Biochemistry, B
Biological and Biomedical Sciences, B
Biological and Physical Sciences, AB
Biology Technician/BioTechnology Laboratory
    Technician, B
Biology/Biological Sciences, B
Biomedical Technology/Technician, A
Biomedical/Medical Engineering, B
Business Administration and Management, B
Business/Commerce, A
Business/Managerial Economics, B
Chemical Engineering, B
Chemistry, B
Civil Engineering, B
Classics and Classical
    Languages, Literatures, and Linguistics, B
Clinical/Medical Laboratory Technician, B
Communication Disorders, B
Communication Studies/Speech Communication
    and Rhetoric, B
Communication, Journalism and Related
    Programs, B
Comparative Literature, B
Computer and Information Sciences, B
Computer Engineering, B
Criminal Justice/Law Enforcement Administration, B
East Asian Studies, B
Economics, B
Electrical, Electronic and Communications
    Engineering Technology/Technician, A
Electrical, Electronics and Communications
    Engineering, B
Elementary Education and Teaching, B
Engineering Science, B
English Language and Literature, B
Environmental/Environmental Health Engineering, B
Film/Cinema Studies, B
Finance, B
Food Science, B
Foreign Language Teacher Education, B
Forest Sciences and Biology, B
Forestry Technology/Technician, B
French Language and Literature, B
Geography, B
Geological and Earth Sciences/Geosciences, B
Geology/Earth Science, B
German Language and Literature, B
Graphic Design, B
Health/Health Care Administration/Management, B
History, B
Horticultural Science, B
Hospitality Administration/Management, B
Human Development and Family Studies, AB
Human Nutrition, B
Industrial Engineering, B
Information Science/Studies, AB
International Business/Trade/Commerce, B
International Relations and Affairs, B
Italian Language and Literature, B
Japanese Language and Literature, B
Jewish/Judaic Studies, B
Journalism, B
Kinesiology and Exercise Science, B

Labor and Industrial Relations, B
Landscaping and Groundskeeping, B
Latin American Studies, B
Liberal Arts and Sciences Studies and
    Humanities, AB
Management Information Systems and Services, B
Marketing/Marketing Management, B
Materials Sciences, B
Mathematics, B
Mechanical Engineering, B
Mechanical Engineering/Mechanical
    Technology/Technician, A
Medical Microbiology and Bacteriology, B
Medieval and Renaissance Studies, B
Metallurgical Technology/Technician, A
Mining and Mineral Engineering, B
Music, B
Natural Resources and Conservation, B
Nuclear Engineering, B
Nursing - Registered Nurse Training, B
Occupational Therapist Assistant, A
Organizational Behavior Studies, B
Parks, Recreation and Leisure Facilities
    Management, B
Petroleum Engineering, B
Philosophy, B
Physical Therapist Assistant, A
Physics, B
Political Science and Government, B
Pre-Medicine/Pre-Medical Studies, B
Psychology, B
Rehabilitation and Therapeutic Professions, B
Religion/Religious Studies, B
Russian Language and Literature, B
Secondary Education and Teaching, B
Sociology, B
Soil Science and Agronomy, B
Spanish Language and Literature, B
Special Education and Teaching, B
Statistics, B
Technical Theatre/Theatre Design and
    Technology, B
Telecommunications Technology/Technician, A
Toxicology, B
Turf and Turfgrass Management, B
Visual and Performing Arts, B
Wildlife and Wildlands Science and Management, A
Women's Studies, B

THE PENNSYLVANIA STATE UNIVERSITY AT ERIE, THE BEHREND COLLEGE

Accounting, B
Acting, B
Actuarial Science, B
Adult and Continuing Education Administration, B
Advertising, B
Aerospace, Aeronautical and Astronautical
    Engineering, B
African-American/Black Studies, B
Agribusiness, B
Agricultural and Extension Education Services, B
Agricultural Business and Management, A
Agricultural Mechanization, B
Agricultural/Biological Engineering and
    Bioengineering, B
Agriculture, B
Animal Sciences, B
Anthropology, B
Applied Economics, B
Archeology, B
Architectural Engineering, B
Art History, Criticism and Conservation, B
Art Teacher Education, B
Art/Art Studies, General, B
Astronomy, B
Atmospheric Sciences and Meteorology, B
Biochemistry, B
Biological and Biomedical Sciences, B
Biological and Physical Sciences, B
Biology Technician/BioTechnology Laboratory
    Technician, B
Biology/Biological Sciences, B
Biomedical Technology/Technician, A
Biomedical/Medical Engineering, B
Business Administration and Management, B

Business Administration, Management and
    Operations, M
Business/Commerce, A
Business/Managerial Economics, B
Chemical Engineering, B
Chemistry, B
Civil Engineering, B
Classics and Classical
    Languages, Literatures, and Linguistics, B
Communication and Media Studies, B
Communication Disorders, B
Communication Studies/Speech Communication
    and Rhetoric, B
Communication, Journalism and Related
    Programs, B
Comparative Literature, B
Computer and Information Sciences, B
Computer Engineering, B
Computer Science, B
Computer Software Engineering, B
Creative Writing, B
Criminal Justice/Law Enforcement Administration, B
East Asian Studies, B
Economics, B
Electrical, Electronic and Communications
    Engineering Technology/Technician, AB
Electrical, Electronics and Communications
    Engineering, B
Elementary Education and Teaching, B
Engineering Science, B
English Language and Literature, B
Environmental/Environmental Health Engineering, B
Film/Cinema Studies, B
Finance, B
Food Science, B
Foreign Language Teacher Education, B
Forest Sciences and Biology, B
Forestry Technology/Technician, B
French Language and Literature, B
Geography, B
Geological and Earth Sciences/Geosciences, B
Geology/Earth Science, B
German Language and Literature, B
Graphic Design, B
Health/Health Care Administration/Management, B
History, B
Horticultural Science, B
Hospitality Administration/Management, B
Human Development and Family Studies, B
Human Nutrition, B
Industrial Engineering, B
Information Science/Studies, B
International Business/Trade/Commerce, B
International Relations and Affairs, B
Italian Language and Literature, B
Japanese Language and Literature, B
Jewish/Judaic Studies, B
Journalism, B
Kinesiology and Exercise Science, B
Labor and Industrial Relations, B
Landscaping and Groundskeeping, B
Latin American Studies, B
Liberal Arts and Sciences Studies and
    Humanities, AB
Management Information Systems and Services, B
Manufacturing Technology/Technician, A
Marketing/Marketing Management, B
Materials Sciences, B
Mathematics, B
Mechanical Engineering, B
Mechanical Engineering/Mechanical
    Technology/Technician, AB
Medical Microbiology and Bacteriology, B
Medieval and Renaissance Studies, B
Metallurgical Technology/Technician, A
Mining and Mineral Engineering, B
Multi-/Interdisciplinary Studies, B
Music, B
Natural Resources and Conservation, B
Nuclear Engineering, B
Nursing - Registered Nurse Training, B
Organizational Behavior Studies, B
Parks, Recreation and Leisure Facilities
    Management, B
Petroleum Engineering, B
Philosophy, B

Physical Sciences, B
Physics, B
Plastics Engineering Technology/Technician, A
Political Science and Government, B
Polymer/Plastics Engineering, B
Pre-Medicine/Pre-Medical Studies, B
Project Management, M
Psychology, B
Rehabilitation and Therapeutic Professions, B
Religion/Religious Studies, B
Russian Language and Literature, B
Secondary Education and Teaching, B
Sociology, B
Soil Science and Agronomy, B
Spanish Language and Literature, B
Special Education and Teaching, B
Statistics, B
Technical Theatre/Theatre Design and
   Technology, B
Telecommunications Technology/Technician, A
Toxicology, B
Turf and Turfgrass Management, B
Visual and Performing Arts, B
Women's Studies, B

THE PENNSYLVANIA STATE UNIVERSITY FAYETTE CAMPUS OF THE COMMONWEALTH COLLEGE

Accounting, B
Acting, B
Actuarial Science, B
Adult and Continuing Education Administration, B
Advertising, B
Aerospace, Aeronautical and Astronautical
   Engineering, B
African-American/Black Studies, B
Agribusiness, B
Agricultural and Extension Education Services, B
Agricultural Business and Management, A
Agricultural Mechanization, B
Agricultural/Biological Engineering and
   Bioengineering, B
Agriculture, B
Agronomy and Crop Science, B
Animal Sciences, B
Anthropology, B
Applied Economics, B
Archeology, B
Architectural Engineering, B
Architectural Engineering Technology/Technician, A
Art History, Criticism and Conservation, B
Art Teacher Education, B
Art/Art Studies, General, B
Astronomy, B
Atmospheric Sciences and Meteorology, B
Biochemistry, B
Biological and Biomedical Sciences, B
Biological and Physical Sciences, AB
Biology Technician/BioTechnology Laboratory
   Technician, B
Biology/Biological Sciences, B
Biomedical Technology/Technician, A
Biomedical/Medical Engineering, B
Business Administration and Management, B
Business/Commerce, A
Business/Managerial Economics, B
Chemical Engineering, B
Chemistry, B
Civil Engineering, B
Classics and Classical
   Languages, Literatures, and Linguistics, B
Communication Disorders, B
Communication Studies/Speech Communication
   and Rhetoric, B
Communication, Journalism and Related
   Programs, B
Comparative Literature, B
Computer and Information Sciences, B
Computer Engineering, B
Criminal Justice/Law Enforcement Administration, B
Criminal Justice/Safety Studies, B
East Asian Studies, B
Economics, B
Electrical, Electronic and Communications
   Engineering Technology/Technician, A

Electrical, Electronics and Communications
   Engineering, B
Elementary Education and Teaching, B
Engineering Science, B
English Language and Literature, B
Environmental/Environmental Health Engineering, B
Film/Cinema Studies, B
Finance, B
Food Science, B
Foreign Language Teacher Education, B
Forest Sciences and Biology, B
Forestry Technology/Technician, B
French Language and Literature, B
Geography, B
Geological and Earth Sciences/Geosciences, B
Geology/Earth Science, B
German Language and Literature, B
Graphic Design, B
Health/Health Care Administration/Management, B
History, B
Horticultural Science, B
Hospitality Administration/Management, B
Human Development and Family Studies, AB
Human Nutrition, B
Industrial Engineering, B
Information Science/Studies, B
International Relations and Affairs, B
Italian Language and Literature, B
Japanese Language and Literature, B
Jewish/Judaic Studies, B
Journalism, B
Kinesiology and Exercise Science, B
Labor and Industrial Relations, B
Landscaping and Groundskeeping, B
Latin American Studies, B
Liberal Arts and Sciences Studies and
   Humanities, AB
Logistics and Materials Management, B
Management Information Systems and Services, B
Manufacturing Engineering, A
Marketing/Marketing Management, B
Materials Sciences, B
Mathematics, B
Mechanical Engineering, B
Medical Microbiology and Bacteriology, B
Medieval and Renaissance Studies, B
Metallurgical Technology/Technician, A
Mining and Mineral Engineering, B
Natural Resources and Conservation, B
Nuclear Engineering, B
Nursing - Registered Nurse Training, AB
Organizational Behavior Studies, B
Parks, Recreation and Leisure Facilities
   Management, B
Petroleum Engineering, B
Philosophy, B
Physics, B
Political Science and Government, B
Pre-Medicine/Pre-Medical Studies, B
Psychology, B
Rehabilitation and Therapeutic Professions, B
Religion/Religious Studies, B
Russian Language and Literature, B
Secondary Education and Teaching, B
Sociology, B
Soil Science and Agronomy, B
Spanish Language and Literature, B
Special Education and Teaching, B
Statistics, B
Technical Theatre/Theatre Design and
   Technology, B
Telecommunications Technology/Technician, A
Toxicology, B
Turf and Turfgrass Management, B
Visual and Performing Arts, B
Women's Studies, B

THE PENNSYLVANIA STATE UNIVERSITY HARRISBURG CAMPUS

Adult and Continuing Education and Teaching, D
American/United States Studies/Civilization, BM
Applied Mathematics, B
Business Administration and Management, B
Business Administration, Management and
   Operations, MO
Business/Commerce, A

Clinical Psychology, BM
Communication Studies/Speech Communication
   and Rhetoric, B
Community Psychology, M
Computer and Information Sciences, B
Computer Science, M
Criminal Justice/Safety Studies, B
Criminology, M
Curriculum and Instruction, BM
Education, MD
Electrical Engineering, M
Electrical, Electronics and Communications
   Engineering, B
Elementary Education and Teaching, B
Engineering and Applied Sciences, M
English Language and Literature, B
Environmental Engineering
   Technology/Environmental Technology, M
Environmental Sciences, M
Environmental/Environmental Health Engineering, B
Finance, B
Health Education, M
Health Services Administration, M
Health Teacher Education, B
Health/Health Care Administration/Management, B
Humanities/Humanistic Studies, BM
Information Science/Studies, B
International Business/Trade/Commerce, B
Liberal Arts and Sciences Studies and
   Humanities, A
Management Information Systems and
   Services, BMO
Management Science, B
Marketing/Marketing Management, B
Mechanical Engineering, B
Nursing - Registered Nurse Training, B
Organizational Behavior Studies, B
Psychology, BM
Public Administration, BMD
Public Policy Analysis, B
Social Studies Teacher Education, B
Sociology, B
Structural Engineering, B
Teacher Education and Professional
   Development, Specific Subject Areas, B

THE PENNSYLVANIA STATE UNIVERSITY HAZLETON CAMPUS OF THE COMMONWEALTH COLLEGE

Accounting, B
Acting, B
Actuarial Science, B
Adult and Continuing Education Administration, B
Advertising, B
Aerospace, Aeronautical and Astronautical
   Engineering, B
African-American/Black Studies, B
Agribusiness, B
Agricultural and Extension Education Services, B
Agricultural Business and Management, A
Agricultural Mechanization, B
Agricultural/Biological Engineering and
   Bioengineering, B
Agriculture, B
Agronomy and Crop Science, B
Animal Sciences, B
Anthropology, B
Applied Economics, B
Archeology, B
Architectural Engineering, B
Art History, Criticism and Conservation, B
Art Teacher Education, B
Art/Art Studies, General, B
Astronomy, B
Atmospheric Sciences and Meteorology, B
Biochemistry, B
Biological and Biomedical Sciences, B
Biological and Physical Sciences, B
Biology Technician/BioTechnology Laboratory
   Technician, B
Biology/Biological Sciences, B
Biomedical Technology/Technician, A
Biomedical/Medical Engineering, B
Business Administration and Management, B
Business/Commerce, A
Business/Managerial Economics, B

Chemical Engineering, B
Chemistry, B
Civil Engineering, B
Classics and Classical
  Languages, Literatures, and Linguistics, B
Clinical/Medical Laboratory Technician, A
Communication Disorders, B
Communication Studies/Speech Communication
  and Rhetoric, B
Communication, Journalism and Related
  Programs, B
Comparative Literature, B
Computer and Information Sciences, B
Computer Engineering, B
Criminal Justice/Law Enforcement Administration, B
East Asian Studies, B
Economics, B
Electrical, Electronic and Communications
  Engineering Technology/Technician, A
Electrical, Electronics and Communications
  Engineering, B
Elementary Education and Teaching, B
Engineering Science, B
English Language and Literature, B
Environmental/Environmental Health Engineering, B
Film/Cinema Studies, B
Finance, B
Food Science, B
Forest Sciences and Biology, B
Forestry Technology/Technician, B
French Language and Literature, B
Geography, B
Geological and Earth Sciences/Geosciences, B
Geology/Earth Science, B
German Language and Literature, B
Graphic Design, B
Health/Health Care Administration/Management, B
History, B
Horticultural Science, B
Hospitality Administration/Management, B
Human Development and Family Studies, B
Human Nutrition, B
Industrial Engineering, B
Information Science/Studies, A
International Relations and Affairs, B
Italian Language and Literature, B
Japanese Language and Literature, B
Jewish/Judaic Studies, B
Journalism, B
Kinesiology and Exercise Science, B
Labor and Industrial Relations, B
Landscaping and Groundskeeping, B
Latin American Studies, B
Liberal Arts and Sciences Studies and
  Humanities, A
Logistics and Materials Management, B
Management Information Systems and Services, B
Manufacturing Engineering, A
Marketing/Marketing Management, B
Materials Sciences, B
Mathematics, B
Mechanical Engineering, B
Mechanical Engineering/Mechanical
  Technology/Technician, A
Medical Microbiology and Bacteriology, B
Medieval and Renaissance Studies, B
Metallurgical Technology/Technician, A
Mining and Mineral Engineering, B
Music, B
Natural Resources and Conservation, B
Nuclear Engineering, B
Nursing - Registered Nurse Training, B
Organizational Behavior Studies, B
Parks, Recreation and Leisure Facilities
  Management, B
Petroleum Engineering, B
Philosophy, B
Physical Therapist Assistant, A
Physics, B
Political Science and Government, B
Pre-Medicine/Pre-Medical Studies, B
Psychology, B
Rehabilitation and Therapeutic Professions, B
Religion/Religious Studies, B
Russian Language and Literature, B
Secondary Education and Teaching, B

Sociology, B
Soil Science and Agronomy, B
Spanish Language and Literature, B
Special Education and Teaching, B
Statistics, B
Technical Theatre/Theatre Design and
  Technology, B
Telecommunications Technology/Technician, A
Toxicology, B
Turf and Turfgrass Management, B
Visual and Performing Arts, B
Women's Studies, B

THE PENNSYLVANIA STATE UNIVERSITY, LEHIGH VALLEY CAMPUS OF THE BERKS-LEHIGH VALLEY COLLEGE

Accounting, B
Acting, B
Actuarial Science, B
Adult and Continuing Education Administration, B
Advertising, B
Aerospace, Aeronautical and Astronautical
  Engineering, B
African-American/Black Studies, B
Agribusiness, B
Agricultural and Extension Education Services, B
Agricultural Business and Management, A
Agricultural Mechanization, B
Agricultural/Biological Engineering and
  Bioengineering, B
Agriculture, B
American/United States Studies/Civilization, B
Animal Sciences, B
Anthropology, B
Applied Economics, B
Archeology, B
Architectural Engineering, B
Art History, Criticism and Conservation, B
Art Teacher Education, B
Art/Art Studies, General, B
Astronomy, B
Atmospheric Sciences and Meteorology, B
Biochemistry, B
Biological and Biomedical Sciences, B
Biological and Physical Sciences, B
Biology Technician/BioTechnology Laboratory
  Technician, B
Biology/Biological Sciences, B
Biomedical/Medical Engineering, B
Business/Commerce, AB
Business/Managerial Economics, B
Chemical Engineering, B
Chemistry, B
Civil Engineering, B
Classics and Classical
  Languages, Literatures, and Linguistics, B
Communication Disorders, B
Communication Studies/Speech Communication
  and Rhetoric, B
Communication, Journalism and Related
  Programs, B
Comparative Literature, B
Computer and Information Sciences, B
Computer Engineering, B
Criminal Justice/Law Enforcement Administration, B
East Asian Studies, B
Economics, B
Electrical, Electronics and Communications
  Engineering, B
Elementary Education and Teaching, B
Engineering Science, B
English Language and Literature, B
Environmental/Environmental Health Engineering, B
Film/Cinema Studies, B
Finance, B
Food Science, B
Foreign Languages and Literatures, B
Forest Sciences and Biology, B
Forestry Technology/Technician, B
French Language and Literature, B
Geography, B
Geological and Earth Sciences/Geosciences, B
Geology/Earth Science, B
German Language and Literature, B
Graphic Design, B

Health/Health Care Administration/Management, B
History, B
Horticultural Science, B
Hospitality Administration/Management, B
Human Development and Family Studies, B
Human Nutrition, B
Industrial Engineering, B
Information Science/Studies, AB
International Business/Trade/Commerce, B
International Relations and Affairs, B
Italian Language and Literature, B
Japanese Language and Literature, B
Jewish/Judaic Studies, B
Journalism, B
Kinesiology and Exercise Science, B
Labor and Industrial Relations, B
Landscape Architecture, B
Landscaping and Groundskeeping, B
Latin American Studies, B
Liberal Arts and Sciences Studies and
  Humanities, AB
Logistics and Materials Management, B
Management Information Systems and Services, B
Management Sciences and Quantitative Methods, B
Marketing/Marketing Management, B
Materials Sciences, B
Mathematics, B
Mechanical Engineering, B
Medical Microbiology and Bacteriology, B
Medieval and Renaissance Studies, B
Mining and Mineral Engineering, B
Natural Resources and Conservation, B
Nuclear Engineering, B
Nursing - Registered Nurse Training, B
Organizational Behavior Studies, B
Parks, Recreation and Leisure Facilities
  Management, B
Petroleum Engineering, B
Philosophy, B
Physics, B
Political Science and Government, B
Pre-Medicine/Pre-Medical Studies, B
Psychology, B
Rehabilitation and Therapeutic Professions, B
Religion/Religious Studies, B
Russian Language and Literature, B
Secondary Education and Teaching, B
Sociology, B
Soil Science and Agronomy, B
Spanish Language and Literature, B
Special Education and Teaching, B
Statistics, B
Technical and Business Writing, B
Technical Theatre/Theatre Design and
  Technology, B
Turf and Turfgrass Management, B
Visual and Performing Arts, B
Women's Studies, B

THE PENNSYLVANIA STATE UNIVERSITY MCKEESPORT CAMPUS OF THE COMMONWEALTH COLLEGE

Accounting, B
Acting, B
Actuarial Science, B
Adult and Continuing Education Administration, B
Advertising, B
Aerospace, Aeronautical and Astronautical
  Engineering, B
African-American/Black Studies, B
Agribusiness, B
Agricultural and Extension Education Services, B
Agricultural Business and Management, A
Agricultural Mechanization, B
Agricultural/Biological Engineering and
  Bioengineering, B
Agriculture, B
Agronomy and Crop Science, B
Animal Sciences, B
Anthropology, B
Applied Economics, B
Archeology, B
Architectural Engineering, B
Art History, Criticism and Conservation, B
Art Teacher Education, B
Art/Art Studies, General, B

Astronomy, B
Atmospheric Sciences and Meteorology, B
Biochemistry, B
Biological and Biomedical Sciences, B
Biological and Physical Sciences, AB
Biology Technician/BioTechnology Laboratory
    Technician, B
Biology/Biological Sciences, B
Biomedical/Medical Engineering, B
Business Administration and Management, B
Business/Commerce, A
Business/Managerial Economics, B
Chemical Engineering, B
Chemistry, B
Civil Engineering, B
Classics and Classical
    Languages, Literatures, and Linguistics, B
Communication Disorders, B
Communication Studies/Speech Communication
    and Rhetoric, B
Communication, Journalism and Related
    Programs, B
Comparative Literature, B
Computer and Information Sciences, B
Computer Engineering, B
Criminal Justice/Law Enforcement Administration, B
East Asian Studies, B
Economics, B
Electrical, Electronics and Communications
    Engineering, B
Elementary Education and Teaching, B
Engineering Science, B
English Language and Literature, B
Environmental/Environmental Health Engineering, B
Film/Cinema Studies, B
Finance, B
Food Science, B
Foreign Language Teacher Education, B
Forest Sciences and Biology, B
Forestry Technology/Technician, B
French Language and Literature, B
Geography, B
Geological and Earth Sciences/Geosciences, B
Geology/Earth Science, B
German Language and Literature, B
Graphic Design, B
Health/Health Care Administration/Management, B
History, B
Horticultural Science, B
Hospitality Administration/Management, B
Human Development and Family Studies, B
Human Nutrition, B
Industrial Engineering, B
Information Science/Studies, B
International Relations and Affairs, B
Italian Language and Literature, B
Japanese Language and Literature, B
Jewish/Judaic Studies, B
Journalism, B
Kinesiology and Exercise Science, B
Labor and Industrial Relations, B
Landscaping and Groundskeeping, B
Latin American Studies, B
Liberal Arts and Sciences Studies and
    Humanities, AB
Logistics and Materials Management, B
Management Information Systems and Services, B
Manufacturing Engineering, A
Marketing/Marketing Management, B
Materials Sciences, B
Mathematics, B
Mechanical Engineering, B
Medical Microbiology and Bacteriology, B
Medieval and Renaissance Studies, B
Mining and Mineral Engineering, B
Music, B
Natural Resources and Conservation, B
Nuclear Engineering, B
Nursing - Registered Nurse Training, B
Organizational Behavior Studies, B
Parks, Recreation and Leisure Facilities
    Management, B
Petroleum Engineering, B
Philosophy, B
Physics, B
Political Science and Government, B

Pre-Medicine/Pre-Medical Studies, B
Psychology, B
Rehabilitation and Therapeutic Professions, B
Religion/Religious Studies, B
Russian Language and Literature, B
Secondary Education and Teaching, B
Sociology, B
Soil Science and Agronomy, B
Spanish Language and Literature, B
Special Education and Teaching, B
Statistics, B
Technical Theatre/Theatre Design and
    Technology, B
Toxicology, B
Turf and Turfgrass Management, B
Visual and Performing Arts, B
Women's Studies, B

THE PENNSYLVANIA STATE UNIVERSITY MONT ALTO CAMPUS OF THE COMMONWEALTH COLLEGE

Accounting, B
Acting, B
Actuarial Science, B
Adult and Continuing Education Administration, B
Advertising, B
Aerospace, Aeronautical and Astronautical
    Engineering, B
African-American/Black Studies, B
Agribusiness, B
Agricultural and Extension Education Services, B
Agricultural Business and Management, A
Agricultural Mechanization, B
Agricultural/Biological Engineering and
    Bioengineering, B
Agriculture, B
Agronomy and Crop Science, B
Animal Sciences, B
Anthropology, B
Applied Economics, B
Archeology, B
Architectural Engineering, B
Art History, Criticism and Conservation, B
Art Teacher Education, B
Art/Art Studies, General, B
Astronomy, B
Atmospheric Sciences and Meteorology, B
Biochemistry, B
Biological and Biomedical Sciences, B
Biological and Physical Sciences, B
Biology Technician/BioTechnology Laboratory
    Technician, B
Biology/Biological Sciences, B
Biomedical/Medical Engineering, B
Business Administration and Management, B
Business/Commerce, A
Business/Managerial Economics, B
Chemical Engineering, B
Chemistry, B
Civil Engineering, B
Classics and Classical
    Languages, Literatures, and Linguistics, B
Communication Disorders, B
Communication Studies/Speech Communication
    and Rhetoric, B
Communication, Journalism and Related
    Programs, B
Comparative Literature, B
Computer and Information Sciences, B
Computer Engineering, B
Criminal Justice/Law Enforcement Administration, B
East Asian Studies, B
Economics, B
Electrical, Electronics and Communications
    Engineering, B
Elementary Education and Teaching, B
Engineering Science, B
English Language and Literature, B
Environmental/Environmental Health Engineering, B
Film/Cinema Studies, B
Finance, B
Food Science, B
Foreign Language Teacher Education, B
Forest Sciences and Biology, B
Forestry Technology/Technician, AB
French Language and Literature, B

Geography, B
Geological and Earth Sciences/Geosciences, B
Geology/Earth Science, B
German Language and Literature, B
Graphic Design, B
Health/Health Care Administration/Management, B
History, B
Horticultural Science, B
Hospitality Administration/Management, B
Human Development and Family Studies, AB
Human Nutrition, B
Industrial Engineering, B
Information Science/Studies, B
International Relations and Affairs, B
Italian Language and Literature, B
Japanese Language and Literature, B
Jewish/Judaic Studies, B
Journalism, B
Kinesiology and Exercise Science, B
Labor and Industrial Relations, B
Landscaping and Groundskeeping, B
Latin American Studies, B
Liberal Arts and Sciences Studies and
    Humanities, AB
Management Information Systems and Services, B
Marketing/Marketing Management, B
Materials Sciences, B
Mathematics, B
Mechanical Engineering, B
Medical Microbiology and Bacteriology, B
Medieval and Renaissance Studies, B
Mining and Mineral Engineering, B
Music, B
Natural Resources and Conservation, B
Nuclear Engineering, B
Nursing - Registered Nurse Training, AB
Occupational Therapist Assistant, A
Occupational Therapy/Therapist, B
Organizational Behavior Studies, B
Parks, Recreation and Leisure Facilities
    Management, B
Petroleum Engineering, B
Philosophy, B
Physical Therapist Assistant, A
Physics, B
Political Science and Government, B
Pre-Medicine/Pre-Medical Studies, B
Psychology, B
Rehabilitation and Therapeutic Professions, B
Religion/Religious Studies, B
Russian Language and Literature, B
Secondary Education and Teaching, B
Sociology, B
Soil Science and Agronomy, B
Spanish Language and Literature, B
Special Education and Teaching, B
Statistics, B
Technical Theatre/Theatre Design and
    Technology, B
Toxicology, B
Turf and Turfgrass Management, B
Visual and Performing Arts, B
Women's Studies, B

THE PENNSYLVANIA STATE UNIVERSITY NEW KENSINGTON CAMPUS OF THE COMMONWEALTH COLLEGE

Accounting, B
Acting, B
Actuarial Science, B
Adult and Continuing Education Administration, B
Advertising, B
Aerospace, Aeronautical and Astronautical
    Engineering, B
African-American/Black Studies, B
Agribusiness, B
Agricultural and Extension Education Services, B
Agricultural Business and Management, AB
Agricultural Mechanization, B
Agricultural/Biological Engineering and
    Bioengineering, B
Agriculture, B
Agronomy and Crop Science, B
Animal Sciences, B
Anthropology, B

Applied Economics, B
Archeology, B
Architectural Engineering, B
Art History, Criticism and Conservation, B
Art Teacher Education, B
Art/Art Studies, General, B
Astronomy, B
Atmospheric Sciences and Meteorology, B
Biochemistry, B
Biological and Biomedical Sciences, B
Biological and Physical Sciences, AB
Biology Technician/BioTechnology Laboratory
    Technician, B
Biology/Biological Sciences, B
Biomedical Technology/Technician, A
Biomedical/Medical Engineering, B
Business Administration and Management, B
Business/Commerce, A
Business/Managerial Economics, B
Chemical Engineering, B
Chemistry, B
Civil Engineering, B
Classics and Classical
    Languages, Literatures, and Linguistics, B
Communication Disorders, B
Communication Studies/Speech Communication
    and Rhetoric, B
Communication, Journalism and Related
    Programs, B
Comparative Literature, B
Computer and Information Sciences, B
Computer Engineering, B
Computer Engineering Technology/Technician, A
Criminal Justice/Law Enforcement Administration, B
East Asian Studies, B
Economics, B
Electrical, Electronic and Communications
    Engineering Technology/Technician, A
Electrical, Electronics and Communications
    Engineering, B
Elementary Education and Teaching, B
Engineering Science, B
English Language and Literature, B
Environmental/Environmental Health Engineering, B
Film/Cinema Studies, B
Finance, B
Food Science, B
Forest Sciences and Biology, B
Forestry Technology/Technician, B
French Language and Literature, B
Geography, B
Geological and Earth Sciences/Geosciences, B
Geology/Earth Science, B
German Language and Literature, B
Graphic Design, B
Health/Health Care Administration/Management, B
History, B
Horticultural Science, B
Hospitality Administration/Management, B
Human Development and Family Studies, AB
Human Nutrition, B
Industrial Engineering, B
Information Science/Studies, AB
International Relations and Affairs, B
Italian Language and Literature, B
Japanese Language and Literature, B
Jewish/Judaic Studies, B
Journalism, B
Kinesiology and Exercise Science, B
Labor and Industrial Relations, B
Landscaping and Groundskeeping, B
Latin American Studies, B
Liberal Arts and Sciences Studies and
    Humanities, AB
Logistics and Materials Management, B
Management Information Systems and Services, B
Marketing/Marketing Management, B
Materials Sciences, B
Mathematics, B
Mechanical Engineering, B
Mechanical Engineering/Mechanical
    Technology/Technician, A
Medical Microbiology and Bacteriology, B
Medical Radiologic Technology/Science - Radiation
    Therapist, A
Medieval and Renaissance Studies, B

Metallurgical Technology/Technician, A
Mining and Mineral Engineering, B
Music, B
Natural Resources and Conservation, B
Nuclear Engineering, B
Nursing - Registered Nurse Training, B
Organizational Behavior Studies, B
Parks, Recreation and Leisure Facilities
    Management, B
Petroleum Engineering, B
Philosophy, B
Physics, B
Political Science and Government, B
Pre-Medicine/Pre-Medical Studies, B
Psychology, B
Rehabilitation and Therapeutic Professions, B
Religion/Religious Studies, B
Russian Language and Literature, B
Secondary Education and Teaching, B
Sociology, B
Soil Science and Agronomy, B
Spanish Language and Literature, B
Special Education and Teaching, B
Statistics, B
Technical Theatre/Theatre Design and
    Technology, B
Telecommunications Technology/Technician, A
Toxicology, B
Turf and Turfgrass Management, B
Visual and Performing Arts, B
Women's Studies, B

THE PENNSYLVANIA STATE UNIVERSITY SCHUYLKILL CAMPUS OF THE CAPITAL COLLEGE

Accounting, B
Acting, B
Actuarial Science, B
Adult and Continuing Education Administration, B
Advertising, B
Aerospace, Aeronautical and Astronautical
    Engineering, B
African-American/Black Studies, B
Agribusiness, B
Agricultural and Extension Education Services, B
Agricultural Business and Management, A
Agricultural Mechanization, B
Agricultural/Biological Engineering and
    Bioengineering, B
Agriculture, B
American/United States Studies/Civilization, B
Animal Sciences, B
Anthropology, B
Applied Economics, B
Archeology, B
Architectural Engineering, B
Art History, Criticism and Conservation, B
Art Teacher Education, B
Art/Art Studies, General, B
Astronomy, B
Atmospheric Sciences and Meteorology, B
Biochemistry, B
Biological and Biomedical Sciences, B
Biological and Physical Sciences, AB
Biology Technician/BioTechnology Laboratory
    Technician, B
Biology/Biological Sciences, B
Biomedical Technology/Technician, A
Biomedical/Medical Engineering, B
Business/Commerce, AB
Business/Managerial Economics, B
Chemical Engineering, B
Chemistry, B
Civil Engineering, B
Classics and Classical
    Languages, Literatures, and Linguistics, B
Clinical/Medical Laboratory Technician, A
Communication Disorders, B
Communication Studies/Speech Communication
    and Rhetoric, B
Communication, Journalism and Related
    Programs, B
Comparative Literature, B
Computer and Information Sciences, AB
Computer Engineering, B
Criminal Justice/Law Enforcement Administration, B

Criminal Justice/Safety Studies, B
East Asian Studies, B
Economics, B
Electrical, Electronic and Communications
    Engineering Technology/Technician, A
Electrical, Electronics and Communications
    Engineering, B
Elementary Education and Teaching, B
Engineering Science, B
English Language and Literature, B
Environmental/Environmental Health Engineering, B
Film/Cinema Studies, B
Finance, B
Food Science, B
Forest Sciences and Biology, B
Forestry Technology/Technician, B
French Language and Literature, B
Geography, B
Geological and Earth Sciences/Geosciences, B
Geology/Earth Science, B
German Language and Literature, B
Graphic Design, B
Health/Health Care Administration/Management, B
History, B
Horticultural Science, B
Hospitality Administration/Management, B
Human Development and Family Studies, AB
Human Nutrition, B
Industrial Engineering, B
Information Science/Studies, AB
International Business/Trade/Commerce, B
International Relations and Affairs, B
Italian Language and Literature, B
Japanese Language and Literature, B
Jewish/Judaic Studies, B
Journalism, B
Kinesiology and Exercise Science, B
Labor and Industrial Relations, B
Landscape Architecture, B
Landscaping and Groundskeeping, B
Latin American Studies, B
Liberal Arts and Sciences Studies and
    Humanities, AB
Logistics and Materials Management, B
Management Information Systems and Services, B
Management Sciences and Quantitative Methods, B
Marketing/Marketing Management, B
Materials Sciences, B
Mathematics, B
Mechanical Engineering, B
Medical Microbiology and Bacteriology, B
Medical Radiologic Technology/Science - Radiation
    Therapist, A
Medieval and Renaissance Studies, B
Metallurgical Technology/Technician, A
Mining and Mineral Engineering, B
Natural Resources and Conservation, B
Nuclear Engineering, B
Nursing - Registered Nurse Training, B
Organizational Behavior Studies, B
Parks, Recreation and Leisure Facilities
    Management, B
Petroleum Engineering, B
Philosophy, B
Physics, B
Political Science and Government, B
Pre-Medicine/Pre-Medical Studies, B
Psychology, B
Rehabilitation and Therapeutic Professions, B
Religion/Religious Studies, B
Russian Language and Literature, B
Secondary Education and Teaching, B
Sociology, B
Soil Science and Agronomy, B
Spanish Language and Literature, B
Special Education and Teaching, B
Statistics, B
Technical Theatre/Theatre Design and
    Technology, B
Telecommunications Technology/Technician, A
Turf and Turfgrass Management, B
Visual and Performing Arts, B

Women's Studies, B

THE PENNSYLVANIA STATE UNIVERSITY SHENANGO CAMPUS OF THE COMMONWEALTH COLLEGE

Accounting, B
Acting, B
Actuarial Science, B
Adult and Continuing Education Administration, B
Advertising, B
Aerospace, Aeronautical and Astronautical Engineering, B
African-American/Black Studies, B
Agribusiness, B
Agricultural and Extension Education Services, B
Agricultural Business and Management, A
Agricultural Mechanization, B
Agricultural/Biological Engineering and Bioengineering, B
Agriculture, B
Agronomy and Crop Science, B
Animal Sciences, B
Anthropology, B
Applied Economics, B
Archeology, B
Architectural Engineering, B
Art History, Criticism and Conservation, B
Art Teacher Education, B
Art/Art Studies, General, B
Astronomy, B
Atmospheric Sciences and Meteorology, B
Biochemistry, B
Biological and Biomedical Sciences, B
Biological and Physical Sciences, AB
Biology Technician/BioTechnology Laboratory Technician, B
Biology/Biological Sciences, B
Biomedical Technology/Technician, A
Biomedical/Medical Engineering, B
Business Administration and Management, B
Business/Commerce, A
Business/Managerial Economics, B
Chemical Engineering, B
Chemistry, B
Civil Engineering, B
Classics and Classical Languages, Literatures, and Linguistics, B
Communication Disorders, B
Communication Studies/Speech Communication and Rhetoric, B
Communication, Journalism and Related Programs, B
Comparative LIterature, B
Computer and Information Sciences, B
Computer Engineering, B
Criminal Justice/Law Enforcement Administration, B
East Asian Studies, B
Economics, B
Electrical, Electronic and Communications Engineering Technology/Technician, A
Electrical, Electronics and Communications Engineering, B
Elementary Education and Teaching, B
Engineering Science, B
English Language and Literature, B
Environmental/Environmental Health Engineering, B
Film/Cinema Studies, B
Finance, B
Food Science, B
Foreign Language Teacher Education, B
Forest Sciences and Biology, B
Forestry Technology/Technician, B
French Language and Literature, B
Geography, B
Geological and Earth Sciences/Geosciences, B
Geology/Earth Science, B
German Language and Literature, B
Graphic Design, B
Health/Health Care Administration/Management, B
History, B
Horticultural Science, B
Hospitality Administration/Management, B
Human Development and Family Studies, AB
Human Nutrition, B
Industrial Engineering, B
Information Science/Studies, B

International Relations and Affairs, B
Italian Language and Literature, B
Japanese Language and Literature, B
Jewish/Judaic Studies, B
Journalism, B
Kinesiology and Exercise Science, B
Labor and Industrial Relations, B
Landscaping and Groundskeeping, B
Latin American Studies, B
Liberal Arts and Sciences Studies and Humanities, AB
Logistics and Materials Management, B
Management Information Systems and Services, B
Marketing/Marketing Management, B
Materials Sciences, B
Mathematics, B
Mechanical Engineering, B
Mechanical Engineering/Mechanical Technology/Technician, A
Medical Microbiology and Bacteriology, B
Medieval and Renaissance Studies, B
Metallurgical Technology/Technician, A
Mining and Mineral Engineering, B
Music, B
Natural Resources and Conservation, B
Nuclear Engineering, B
Nursing - Registered Nurse Training, B
Organizational Behavior Studies, B
Parks, Recreation and Leisure Facilities Management, B
Petroleum Engineering, B
Philosophy, B
Physical Therapist Assistant, A
Physics, B
Political Science and Government, B
Pre-Medicine/Pre-Medical Studies, B
Psychology, B
Rehabilitation and Therapeutic Professions, B
Religion/Religious Studies, B
Russian Language and Literature, B
Secondary Education and Teaching, B
Sociology, B
Soil Science and Agronomy, B
Spanish Language and Literature, B
Special Education and Teaching, B
Statistics, B
Technical Theatre/Theatre Design and Technology, B
Telecommunications Technology/Technician, A
Toxicology, B
Turf and Turfgrass Management, B
Visual and Performing Arts, B
Women's Studies, B

THE PENNSYLVANIA STATE UNIVERSITY UNIVERSITY PARK CAMPUS

Accounting, BMD
Acoustics, MD
Acting, B
Actuarial Science, B
Adult and Continuing Education Administration, B
Adult and Continuing Education and Teaching, MD
Advertising, B
Aerospace, Aeronautical and Astronautical Engineering, BMD
African-American/Black Studies, B
Agribusiness, B
Agricultural and Extension Education Services, B
Agricultural Business and Management, A
Agricultural Economics, MD
Agricultural Education, MD
Agricultural Engineering, MD
Agricultural Mechanization, B
Agricultural Sciences, MD
Agricultural/Biological Engineering and Bioengineering, B
Agriculture, B
Agronomy and Crop Science, B
Agronomy and Soil Sciences, MD
Animal Sciences, BMD
Anthropology, BMD
Applied Economics, B
Archeology, B
Architectural Engineering, BMD
Architecture, BM

Art Education, MD
Art History, Criticism and Conservation, BMD
Art Teacher Education, B
Art/Art Studies, General, B
Astronomy, BMD
Astrophysics, MD
Atmospheric Sciences and Meteorology, B
Biochemistry, BMD
Bioengineering, MD
Biological and Biomedical Sciences, BMD
Biological and Physical Sciences, B
Biology Technician/BioTechnology Laboratory Technician, B
Biology/Biological Sciences, B
Biomedical Engineering, MD
Biomedical/Medical Engineering, B
Biopsychology, MD
BioTechnology, M
Business Administration, Management and Operations, M
Business/Commerce, A
Business/Managerial Economics, B
Cell Biology and Anatomy, D
Ceramic Sciences and Engineering, MD
Chemical Engineering, BMD
Chemistry, BMD
Child and Family Studies, MD
Civil Engineering, BMD
Classics and Classical Languages, Literatures, and Linguistics, B
Clinical Psychology, MD
Cognitive Sciences, MD
Communication and Media Studies, MD
Communication Disorders, BMD
Communication Studies/Speech Communication and Rhetoric, B
Communication, Journalism and Related Programs, B
Comparative Literature, BMD
Composition, M
Computer and Information Sciences, B
Computer Engineering, BMD
Computer Science, MD
Counseling Psychology, D
Counselor Education/School Counseling and Guidance Services, MD
Criminal Justice/Law Enforcement Administration, B
Criminology, MD
Curriculum and Instruction, MD
Developmental Biology and Embryology, D
Developmental Psychology, MD
Dietician Assistant, A
Early Childhood Education and Teaching, MD
East Asian Studies, B
Ecology, MD
Economics, BMD
Education, MD
Educational Leadership and Administration, MD
Educational Media/Instructional Technology, MD
Educational Psychology, MD
Electrical Engineering, MD
Electrical, Electronics and Communications Engineering, B
Elementary Education and Teaching, BMD
Engineering and Applied Sciences, MD
Engineering Management, M
Engineering Science, B
English, MD
English as a Second Language, M
English Language and Literature, B
Entomology, MD
Environmental and Occupational Health, M
Environmental Engineering Technology/Environmental Technology, MD
Environmental Policy and Resource Management, M
Environmental Sciences, M
Environmental/Environmental Health Engineering, B
Evolutionary Biology, MD
Film/Cinema Studies, B
Finance, B
Finance and Banking, D
Fine Arts and Art Studies, M
Fish, Game and Wildlife Management, MD
Food Science, B
Food Science and Technology, MD

Foreign Language Teacher Education, B
Forest Sciences and Biology, B
Forestry, MD
Forestry Technology/Technician, B
Foundations and Philosophy of Education, MD
French Language and Literature, BMD
Genetics, MD
Geographic Information Systems, M
Geography, BMD
Geological and Earth Sciences/Geosciences, B
Geology/Earth Science, B
Geosciences, MD
German Language and Literature, BMD
Graphic Design, B
Health Services Administration, MD
Health/Health Care Administration/Management, B
Higher Education/Higher Education
    Administration, MD
History, BMD
Horticultural Science, BMD
Hospitality Administration/Management, ABMD
Human Development, MD
Human Development and Family Studies, AB
Human Nutrition, B
Human Resources Development, M
Industrial and Labor Relations, B
Industrial and Manufacturing Management, MD
Industrial and Organizational Psychology, MD
Industrial Engineering, B
Industrial/Management Engineering, MD
Information Science/Studies, BMD
International Business/Trade/Commerce, B
International Relations and Affairs, B
Italian Language and Literature, B
Japanese Language and Literature, B
Jewish/Judaic Studies, B
Journalism, B
Kinesiology and Exercise Science, B
Kinesiology and Movement Studies, MD
Labor and Industrial Relations, B
Landscape Architecture, BM
Landscaping and Groundskeeping, B
Latin American Studies, B
Leisure Studies, MD
Liberal Arts and Sciences Studies and
    Humanities, AB
Linguistics, D
Logistics and Materials Management, MD
Management Information Systems and
    Services, BMD
Management Sciences and Quantitative Methods, B
Manufacturing Engineering, M
Marketing, D
Marketing/Marketing Management, B
Mass Communication/Media Studies, D
Materials Engineering, MD
Materials Sciences, BMD
Mathematics, BMD
Mechanical Engineering, BMD
Mechanics, MD
Media Studies, M
Medical Microbiology and Bacteriology, B
Medieval and Renaissance Studies, B
Metallurgical Engineering, MD
Meteorology, MD
Microbiology, MD
Mineral/Mining Engineering, MD
Mining and Mineral Engineering, B
Molecular Biology, MD
Multilingual and Multicultural Education, MD
Music, BM
Music History, Literature, and Theory, M
Music Performance, B
Music Teacher Education, BMD
Music Theory and Composition, M
Musicology and Ethnomusicology, M
Natural Resources and Conservation, B
Nuclear Engineering, BMD
Nursing, MD
Nursing - Registered Nurse Training, B
Nutritional Sciences, MD
Organizational Behavior Studies, B
Parks, Recreation and Leisure Facilities
    Management, B
Pathobiology, MD
Performance, M

Petroleum Engineering, BMD
Philosophy, BMD
Photography, M
Physics, BMD
Physiology, MD
Plant Pathology/Phytopathology, MD
Plant Physiology, MD
Political Science and Government, BMD
Polymer/Plastics Engineering, MD
Pre-Medicine/Pre-Medical Studies, B
Psychology, BMD
Quality Management, M
Reading Teacher Education, MD
Real Estate, D
Rehabilitation and Therapeutic Professions, B
Religion/Religious Studies, B
Rural Sociology, MD
Russian Language and Literature, BM
School Psychology, MD
Science Teacher Education/General Science
    Teacher Education, MD
Secondary Education and Teaching, B
Social Psychology, MD
Social Studies Teacher Education, MD
Sociology, ABMD
Soil Science and Agronomy, B
Spanish Language and Literature, BMD
Special Education and Teaching, BMD
Statistics, BMD
Structural Engineering, MD
Student Personnel Services, M
Technical Theatre/Theatre Design and
    Technology, B
Telecommunications, M
Theater, M
Toxicology, B
Transportation and Highway Engineering, MD
Turf and Turfgrass Management, B
Urban and Regional Planning, M
Veterinary Sciences, MD
Visual and Performing Arts, B
Vocational and Technical Education, MD
Water Resources Engineering, MD
Women's Studies, B
Writing, MD

THE PENNSYLVANIA STATE UNIVERSITY WILKES-BARRE CAMPUS OF THE COMMONWEALTH COLLEGE

Accounting, B
Acting, B
Actuarial Science, B
Adult and Continuing Education Administration, B
Advertising, B
Aerospace, Aeronautical and Astronautical
    Engineering, B
African-American/Black Studies, B
Agribusiness, B
Agricultural and Extension Education Services, B
Agricultural Business and Management, A
Agricultural Mechanization, B
Agricultural/Biological Engineering and
    Bioengineering, B
Agriculture, B
Agronomy and Crop Science, B
Animal Sciences, B
Anthropology, B
Applied Economics, B
Archeology, B
Architectural Engineering, B
Art History, Criticism and Conservation, B
Art Teacher Education, B
Art/Art Studies, General, B
Astronomy, B
Atmospheric Sciences and Meteorology, B
Biochemistry, B
Biological and Biomedical Sciences, B
Biological and Physical Sciences, B
Biology Technician/BioTechnology Laboratory
    Technician, B
Biology/Biological Sciences, B
Biomedical/Medical Engineering, B
Business Administration and Management, B
Business/Commerce, A
Business/Managerial Economics, B
Chemical Engineering, B

Chemistry, B
Civil Engineering, B
Classics and Classical
    Languages, Literatures, and Linguistics, B
Communication Disorders, B
Communication Studies/Speech Communication
    and Rhetoric, B
Communication, Journalism and Related
    Programs, B
Comparative Literature, B
Computer and Information Sciences, B
Computer Engineering, B
Criminal Justice/Law Enforcement Administration, B
Criminal Justice/Safety Studies, B
Economics, B
Electrical, Electronic and Communications
    Engineering Technology/Technician, A
Electrical, Electronics and Communications
    Engineering, B
Elementary Education and Teaching, B
Engineering Science, B
English Language and Literature, B
Environmental/Environmental Health Engineering, B
Film/Cinema Studies, B
Finance, B
Food Science, B
Forest Sciences and Biology, B
Forestry Technology/Technician, B
French Language and Literature, B
Geography, B
Geological and Earth Sciences/Geosciences, B
Geology/Earth Science, B
German Language and Literature, B
Graphic Design, B
Health/Health Care Administration/Management, B
History, B
Horticultural Science, B
Hospitality Administration/Management, B
Human Development and Family Studies, B
Human Nutrition, B
Industrial Engineering, B
Information Science/Studies, B
International Relations and Affairs, B
Italian Language and Literature, B
Japanese Language and Literature, B
Jewish/Judaic Studies, B
Journalism, B
Kinesiology and Exercise Science, B
Labor and Industrial Relations, B
Landscape Architecture, B
Landscaping and Groundskeeping, B
Latin American Studies, B
Liberal Arts and Sciences Studies and
    Humanities, AB
Management Information Systems and Services, B
Manufacturing Engineering, A
Marketing/Marketing Management, B
Materials Sciences, B
Mathematics, B
Mechanical Engineering, B
Medical Microbiology and Bacteriology, B
Medieval and Renaissance Studies, B
Metallurgical Technology/Technician, A
Mining and Mineral Engineering, B
Music, B
Natural Resources and Conservation, B
Nuclear Engineering, B
Nursing - Registered Nurse Training, B
Organizational Behavior Studies, B
Parks, Recreation and Leisure Facilities
    Management, B
Petroleum Engineering, B
Philosophy, B
Physics, B
Political Science and Government, B
Pre-Medicine/Pre-Medical Studies, B
Psychology, B
Rehabilitation and Therapeutic Professions, B
Religion/Religious Studies, B
Russian Language and Literature, B
Secondary Education and Teaching, B
Sociology, B
Soil Science and Agronomy, B
Spanish Language and Literature, B
Special Education and Teaching, B
Statistics, B

Survey Technology/Surveying, AB
Technical Theatre/Theatre Design and
   Technology, B
Telecommunications Technology/Technician, A
Toxicology, B
Turf and Turfgrass Management, B
Visual and Performing Arts, B
Women's Studies, B

THE PENNSYLVANIA STATE UNIVERSITY WORTHINGTON SCRANTON CAMPUS OF THE COMMONWEALTH COLLEGE

Accounting, B
Acting, B
Actuarial Science, B
Adult and Continuing Education Administration, B
Advertising, B
Aerospace, Aeronautical and Astronautical
   Engineering, B
African-American/Black Studies, B
Agribusiness, B
Agricultural and Extension Education Services, B
Agricultural Business and Management, A
Agricultural Mechanization, B
Agricultural/Biological Engineering and
   Bioengineering, B
Agriculture, B
Agronomy and Crop Science, B
American/United States Studies/Civilization, B
Animal Sciences, B
Anthropology, B
Applied Economics, B
Archeology, B
Architectural Engineering, B
Architectural Engineering Technology/Technician, A
Art History, Criticism and Conservation, B
Art Teacher Education, B
Art/Art Studies, General, B
Astronomy, B
Atmospheric Sciences and Meteorology, B
Biochemistry, B
Biological and Biomedical Sciences, B
Biological and Physical Sciences, B
Biology Technician/BioTechnology Laboratory
   Technician, B
Biology/Biological Sciences, B
Biomedical/Medical Engineering, B
Business Administration and Management, B
Business/Commerce, A
Business/Managerial Economics, B
Chemical Engineering, B
Chemistry, B
Civil Engineering, B
Classics and Classical
   Languages, Literatures, and Linguistics, B
Communication Disorders, B
Communication Studies/Speech Communication
   and Rhetoric, B
Communication, Journalism and Related
   Programs, B
Comparative Literature, B
Computer and Information Sciences, B
Computer Engineering, B
Criminal Justice/Law Enforcement Administration, B
East Asian Studies, B
Economics, B
Electrical, Electronic and Communications
   Engineering Technology/Technician, A
Electrical, Electronics and Communications
   Engineering, B
Elementary Education and Teaching, B
Engineering Science, B
English Language and Literature, B
Environmental/Environmental Health Engineering, B
Film/Cinema Studies, B
Finance, B
Food Science, B
Foreign Language Teacher Education, B
Forest Sciences and Biology, B
Forestry Technology/Technician, B
French Language and Literature, B
Geography, B
Geological and Earth Sciences/Geosciences, B
Geology/Earth Science, B
German Language and Literature, B

Graphic Design, B
Health/Health Care Administration/Management, B
History, B
Horticultural Science, B
Hospitality Administration/Management, B
Human Development and Family Studies, AB
Human Nutrition, B
Industrial Engineering, B
Information Science/Studies, B
International Relations and Affairs, B
Italian Language and Literature, B
Japanese Language and Literature, B
Jewish/Judaic Studies, B
Journalism, B
Kinesiology and Exercise Science, B
Labor and Industrial Relations, B
Landscaping and Groundskeeping, B
Latin American Studies, B
Liberal Arts and Sciences Studies and
   Humanities, AB
Management Information Systems and Services, B
Marketing/Marketing Management, B
Materials Sciences, B
Mathematics, B
Mechanical Engineering, B
Medical Microbiology and Bacteriology, B
Medieval and Renaissance Studies, B
Mining and Mineral Engineering, B
Music, B
Natural Resources and Conservation, B
Nuclear Engineering, B
Nursing - Registered Nurse Training, AB
Organizational Behavior Studies, B
Parks, Recreation and Leisure Facilities
   Management, B
Petroleum Engineering, B
Philosophy, B
Physics, B
Political Science and Government, B
Pre-Medicine/Pre-Medical Studies, B
Psychology, B
Rehabilitation and Therapeutic Professions, B
Religion/Religious Studies, B
Russian Language and Literature, B
Secondary Education and Teaching, B
Sociology, B
Soil Science and Agronomy, B
Spanish Language and Literature, B
Special Education and Teaching, B
Statistics, B
Technical Theatre/Theatre Design and
   Technology, B
Turf and Turfgrass Management, B
Visual and Performing Arts, B
Women's Studies, B

THE PENNSYLVANIA STATE UNIVERSITY YORK CAMPUS OF THE COMMONWEALTH COLLEGE

Accounting, B
Acting, B
Actuarial Science, B
Adult and Continuing Education Administration, B
Advertising, B
Aerospace, Aeronautical and Astronautical
   Engineering, B
African-American/Black Studies, B
Agribusiness, B
Agricultural and Extension Education Services, B
Agricultural Business and Management, A
Agricultural Mechanization, B
Agricultural/Biological Engineering and
   Bioengineering, B
Agriculture, B
Agronomy and Crop Science, B
American/United States Studies/Civilization, B
Animal Sciences, B
Anthropology, B
Applied Economics, B
Archeology, B
Architectural Engineering, B
Art History, Criticism and Conservation, B
Art Teacher Education, B
Art/Art Studies, General, B
Astronomy, B
Atmospheric Sciences and Meteorology, B

Biochemistry, B
Biological and Biomedical Sciences, B
Biological and Physical Sciences, B
Biology Technician/BioTechnology Laboratory
   Technician, B
Biology/Biological Sciences, B
Biomedical Technology/Technician, A
Biomedical/Medical Engineering, B
Business Administration and Management, B
Business/Commerce, A
Business/Managerial Economics, B
Chemical Engineering, B
Chemistry, B
Civil Engineering, B
Classics and Classical
   Languages, Literatures, and Linguistics, B
Communication Disorders, B
Communication Studies/Speech Communication
   and Rhetoric, B
Communication, Journalism and Related
   Programs, B
Comparative Literature, B
Computer and Information Sciences, B
Computer Engineering, B
Criminal Justice/Law Enforcement Administration, B
East Asian Studies, B
Economics, B
Electrical, Electronic and Communications
   Engineering Technology/Technician, A
Electrical, Electronics and Communications
   Engineering, B
Elementary Education and Teaching, B
Engineering Science, B
English Language and Literature, B
Environmental/Environmental Health Engineering, B
Film/Cinema Studies, B
Finance, B
Food Science, B
Foreign Language Teacher Education, B
Forest Sciences and Biology, B
Forestry Technology/Technician, B
French Language and Literature, B
Geography, B
Geological and Earth Sciences/Geosciences, B
Geology/Earth Science, B
German Language and Literature, B
Graphic Design, B
Health/Health Care Administration/Management, B
History, B
Horticultural Science, B
Hospitality Administration/Management, B
Human Development and Family Studies, AB
Human Nutrition, B
Industrial Engineering, B
Industrial Technology/Technician, A
Information Science/Studies, B
International Relations and Affairs, B
Italian Language and Literature, B
Japanese Language and Literature, B
Jewish/Judaic Studies, B
Journalism, B
Kinesiology and Exercise Science, B
Labor and Industrial Relations, B
Landscaping and Groundskeeping, B
Latin American Studies, B
Liberal Arts and Sciences Studies and
   Humanities, AB
Logistics and Materials Management, B
Management Information Systems and Services, B
Manufacturing Engineering, A
Marketing/Marketing Management, B
Materials Sciences, B
Mathematics, B
Mechanical Engineering, B
Mechanical Engineering/Mechanical
   Technology/Technician, A
Medical Microbiology and Bacteriology, B
Medieval and Renaissance Studies, B
Metallurgical Technology/Technician, A
Mining and Mineral Engineering, B
Music, B
Natural Resources and Conservation, B
Nuclear Engineering, B
Nursing - Registered Nurse Training, B
Organizational Behavior Studies, B

Parks, Recreation and Leisure Facilities
    Management, B
Petroleum Engineering, B
Philosophy, B
Physics, B
Political Science and Government, B
Pre-Medicine/Pre-Medical Studies, B
Psychology, B
Rehabilitation and Therapeutic Professions, B
Religion/Religious Studies, B
Russian Language and Literature, B
Secondary Education and Teaching, B
Sociology, B
Soil Science and Agronomy, B
Spanish Language and Literature, B
Special Education and Teaching, B
Statistics, B
Technical Theatre/Theatre Design and
    Technology, B
Telecommunications Technology/Technician, A
Toxicology, B
Turf and Turfgrass Management, B
Visual and Performing Arts, B
Women's Studies, B

PHILADELPHIA BIBLICAL UNIVERSITY

Bible/Biblical Studies, B
Business Administration and Management, B
Curriculum and Instruction, M
Education, M
Educational Administration and Supervision, M
Elementary Education and Teaching, B
English/Language Arts Teacher Education, B
Kindergarten/PreSchool Education and Teaching, B
Mathematics Teacher Education, B
Music, B
Organizational Management, M
Pastoral Studies/Counseling, M
Physical Education Teaching and Coaching, B
Religion/Religious Studies, B
Social Studies Teacher Education, B
Social Work, B
Theology and Religious Vocations, MP

PHILADELPHIA UNIVERSITY

Accounting, B
Apparel and Accessories Marketing Operations, B
Apparel and Textiles, B
Architecture, B
Biochemistry, B
Biology/Biological Sciences, B
Biopsychology, B
Business Administration and Management, B
Business Administration, Management and
    Operations, MO
Chemistry, B
Clothing and Textiles, M
Commercial and Advertising Art, B
Computer and Information Sciences, B
Computer Art and Design, M
Computer Science, B
Conservation Biology, B
E-Commerce/Electronic Commerce, B
Educational Media/Instructional Technology, M
Environmental Biology, B
Fashion Merchandising, B
Fashion/Apparel Design, B
Fiber, Textile and Weaving Arts, B
Finance, B
Finance and Banking, M
Graphic Design, B
Health Services Administration, M
Industrial Design, B
Information Science/Studies, B
Interior Architecture, B
Interior Design, B
International Business/Trade/Commerce, BM
Landscape Architecture, B
Management Information Systems and Services, B
Marketing, M
Marketing/Marketing Management, B
Nurse Midwife/Nursing Midwifery, MO
Occupational Therapy/Therapist, M
Physician Assistant, BM
Pre-Medicine/Pre-Medical Studies, B
Psychology, B

Taxation, M
Textile Design, M
Textile Sciences and Engineering, BMD

PITTSBURGH INSTITUTE OF AERONAUTICS

Airframe Mechanics and Aircraft Maintenance
    Technology/Technician, A
Avionics Maintenance Technology/Technician, A
Electrical, Electronic and Communications
    Engineering Technology/Technician, A

PITTSBURGH INSTITUTE OF MORTUARY SCIENCE, INCORPORATED

Funeral Service and Mortuary Science, A

POINT PARK UNIVERSITY

Accounting, AB
Advertising, B
Area, Ethnic, Cultural, and Gender Studies, B
Arts Management, B
Behavioral Sciences, B
Biology Teacher Education, B
Biology Technician/BioTechnology Laboratory
    Technician, B
Biology/Biological Sciences, B
BioTechnology, B
Broadcast Journalism, B
Business Administration and Management, AB
Business Administration, Management and
    Operations, BM
Business/Corporate Communications, B
Cinematography and Film/Video Production, B
Civil Engineering Technology/Technician, AB
Communication and Media Studies, BM
Computer/Information Technology Services
    Administration and Management, B
Criminal Justice/Law Enforcement Administration, B
Criminal Justice/Safety Studies, B
Criminology, M
Curriculum and Instruction, M
Dance, B
Design and Applied Arts, B
Drama and Dance Teacher Education, B
Drama and Dramatics/Theatre Arts, B
Early Childhood Education and Teaching, AB
Education, BM
Educational Administration and Supervision, M
Electrical, Electronic and Communications
    Engineering Technology/Technician, AB
Elementary Education and Teaching, B
Engineering Management, M
English Language and Literature, B
English/Language Arts Teacher Education, B
Environmental Sciences, B
Funeral Service and Mortuary Science, AB
General Studies, B
Health/Health Care Administration/Management, AB
History, B
Human Resources Management/Personnel
    Administration, B
Information Technology, AB
Journalism, BM
Law and Legal Studies, B
Mass Communication/Media Studies, BM
Mathematics Teacher Education, B
Mechanical Engineering/Mechanical
    Technology/Technician, AB
Performance, M
Photography, B
Photojournalism, B
Political Science and Government, B
Psychology, B
Public Administration, AB
Public Relations/Image Management, B
Radio and Television, B
Respiratory Care Therapy/Therapist, A
Secondary Education and Teaching, B
Security and Protective Services, B
Social Science Teacher Education, B
Social Sciences, B
Teacher Education and Professional
    Development, Specific Subject Areas, B

Theater, M

READING AREA COMMUNITY COLLEGE

Accounting, A
Administrative Assistant and Secretarial Science, A
Behavioral Sciences, A
Biology/Biological Sciences, A
Business Administration and Management, A
Business Teacher Education, A
Chemistry, A
Child Development, A
Clinical Laboratory Science/Medical
    Technology/Technologist, A
Clinical/Medical Laboratory Technician, A
Communications Technology/Technician, A
Computer Programming/Programmer, A
Computer Science, A
Consumer Merchandising/Retailing Management, A
Culinary Arts/Chef Training, A
Data Processing and Data Processing
    Technology/Technician, A
Education, A
Electrical, Electronic and Communications
    Engineering Technology/Technician, A
Elementary Education and Teaching, A
Engineering, A
Engineering Science, A
Engineering Technology, A
Finance, A
Health and Medical Laboratory Technologies, A
Health Information/Medical Records
    Administration/Administrator, A
Human Resources Management/Personnel
    Administration, A
Human Services, A
Humanities/Humanistic Studies, A
Industrial Radiologic Technology/Technician, A
Industrial Technology/Technician, A
Information Science/Studies, A
Kindergarten/PreSchool Education and Teaching, A
Law and Legal Studies, A
Legal Administrative Assistant/Secretary, A
Liberal Arts and Sciences Studies and
    Humanities, A
Licensed Practical/Vocational Nurse Training, A
Machine Tool Technology/Machinist, A
Marketing/Marketing Management, A
Mechanical Engineering/Mechanical
    Technology/Technician, A
Medical Administrative Assistant/Secretary, A
Mental Health/Rehabilitation, A
Nursing - Registered Nurse Training, A
Political Science and Government, A
Pre-Engineering, A
Pre-Pharmacy Studies, A
Psychology, A
Public Administration, A
Respiratory Care Therapy/Therapist, A
Social Sciences, A
Social Work, A
Telecommunications Technology/Technician, A
Tourism and Travel Services Management, A

THE RESTAURANT SCHOOL AT WALNUT HILL COLLEGE

Culinary Arts/Chef Training, A
Hotel/Motel Administration/Management, A

ROBERT MORRIS UNIVERSITY

Accounting, BM
Actuarial Science, B
Applied Mathematics, B
Business Administration and Management, B
Business Administration, Management and
    Operations, M
Business Education, M
Business Teacher Education, B
Business/Managerial Economics, B
Computer Engineering, B
Computer Software Engineering, B
Computer/Information Technology Services
    Administration and Management, B
Design and Visual Communications, B
Economics, B
Education, MDO

Educational Leadership and Administration, MD
Educational Media/Instructional Technology, DO
Elementary Education and Teaching, B
Engineering, B
Engineering Management, MD
Engineering/Industrial Management, B
English Language and Literature, B
Entrepreneurship/Entrepreneurial Studies, B
Environmental Studies, B
Finance, B
Finance and Banking, M
Health and Medical Administrative Services, B
Health Services Administration, B
Health/Health Care Administration/Management, B
Hospitality Administration/Management, B
Human Resources Management/Personnel
   Administration, B
Industrial Engineering, B
Information Science/Studies, BMD
Internet and Interactive Multimedia, M
Logistics and Materials Management, B
Management Information Systems and
   Services, BMD
Manufacturing Engineering, B
Marketing/Marketing Management, B
Mass Communication/Media Studies, B
Multi-/Interdisciplinary Studies, B
Non-Profit/Public/Organizational Management, M
Nursing, M
Nursing - Registered Nurse Training, B
Operations Management and Supervision, B
Organizational Behavior Studies, B
Psychology, B
Social Sciences, B
Sport and Fitness Administration/Management, BM
Taxation, M

ROSEDALE TECHNICAL INSTITUTE

Automobile/Automotive Mechanics
   Technology/Technician, A
Diesel Mechanics Technology/Technician, A
Electrician, A

ROSEMONT COLLEGE

Accounting, B
Art History, Criticism and Conservation, B
Biochemistry, B
Biology/Biological Sciences, B
Business Administration and Management, B
Business Administration, Management and
   Operations, M
Chemistry, B
Communication Studies/Speech Communication
   and Rhetoric, B
Counseling Psychology, M
Counselor Education/School Counseling and
   Guidance Services, M
Criminology, M
Curriculum and Instruction, M
Economics, B
Educational Media/Instructional Technology, M
Elementary Education and Teaching, M
English, M
English Language and Literature, B
Fine/Studio Arts, B
French Language and Literature, B
German Language and Literature, B
History, B
Human Services, M
Humanities/Humanistic Studies, B
Italian Language and Literature, B
Management, M
Mathematics, B
Middle School Education, M
Non-Profit/Public/Organizational Management, M
Philosophy, B
Political Science and Government, B
Project Management, M
Psychology, B
Publishing, M
Religion/Religious Studies, B
Social Sciences, B
Sociology, B
Spanish Language and Literature, B

Women's Studies, B

ST. CHARLES BORROMEO SEMINARY, OVERBROOK

Philosophy, B
Religion/Religious Studies, M
Theology and Religious Vocations, MP

SAINT FRANCIS UNIVERSITY

Accounting, AB
Accounting and Finance, B
American/United States Studies/Civilization, B
Anthropology, B
Biological and Biomedical Sciences, M
Biology Teacher Education, B
Biology/Biological Sciences, B
Business Administration and Management, AB
Business Administration, Management and
   Operations, M
Chemistry, B
Chemistry Teacher Education, B
Clinical Laboratory Science/Medical
   Technology/Technologist, B
Comparative Literature, B
Computer Programming/Programmer, AB
Computer Science, B
Criminal Justice/Law Enforcement Administration, B
Criminology, B
Culinary Arts/Chef Training, A
Data Processing and Data Processing
   Technology/Technician, A
Drafting and Design Technology/Technician, A
Economics, B
Education, ABM
Educational Leadership and Administration, M
Elementary Education and Teaching, B
Emergency Medical Technology/Technician (EMT
   Paramedic), A
Engineering, B
English Language and Literature, B
English/Language Arts Teacher Education, B
Environmental Sciences, B
Environmental Studies, B
Finance, B
Fine Arts and Art Studies, A
Foreign Language Teacher Education, B
Forensic Science and Technology, B
French Language and Literature, B
French Language Teacher Education, B
Health Education, M
History, B
History Teacher Education, B
Human Resources Management and Services, M
Human Resources Management/Personnel
   Administration, B
International Business/Trade/Commerce, B
International Relations and Affairs, B
Journalism, B
Labor and Industrial Relations, B
Management Information Systems and Services, B
Marine Biology and Biological Oceanography, B
Marketing/Marketing Management, B
Mass Communication/Media Studies, B
Mathematics, B
Mathematics and Computer Science, B
Mathematics Teacher Education, B
Modern Languages, B
Nursing - Registered Nurse Training, B
Occupational Therapy/Therapist, BM
Pastoral Studies/Counseling, B
Philosophy, B
Physical Therapy/Therapist, BD
Physician Assistant, BM
Political Science and Government, B
Pre-Dentistry Studies, B
Pre-Law Studies, B
Pre-Medicine/Pre-Medical Studies, B
Pre-Veterinary Studies, B
Psychology, B
Public Administration, B
Public Relations/Image Management, B
Real Estate, A
Religion/Religious Studies, B
Science Teacher Education/General Science
   Teacher Education, B
Secondary Education and Teaching, B

Social Studies Teacher Education, B
Social Work, B
Sociology, B
Spanish Language and Literature, B

SAINT JOSEPH'S UNIVERSITY

Accounting, ABM
Actuarial Science, B
Biochemistry, B
Biological and Biomedical Sciences, M
Biology/Biological Sciences, AB
Business Administration and Management, AB
Business Administration, Management and
   Operations, MO
Chemistry, AB
Communication Studies/Speech Communication
   and Rhetoric, B
Computer and Information Sciences, B
Computer Science, ABM
Criminal Justice/Law Enforcement
   Administration, AB
Criminology, BMO
Economics, B
Education, BMD
Educational Leadership and Administration, D
Educational Media/Instructional Technology, M
Elementary Education and Teaching, BM
English Language and Literature, B
Environmental and Occupational Health, MO
Environmental Policy and Resource
   Management, MO
Environmental Sciences, B
Finance, AB
Finance and Banking, M
French Language and Literature, B
French Studies, B
German Language and Literature, B
Gerontology, MO
Health Education, M
Health Professions and Related Clinical Sciences, B
Health Services Administration, MO
Health/Health Care Administration/Management, AB
History, B
Hospital and Health Care Facilities
   Administration/Management, B
Human Resources Management and Services, M
Human Services, BM
Humanities/Humanistic Studies, B
Industrial and Organizational Psychology, B
Information Science/Studies, B
Interdisciplinary Studies, B
International Business/Trade/Commerce, BM
International Relations and Affairs, B
Italian Language and Literature, B
Legal Professions and Studies, B
Liberal Arts and Sciences Studies and
   Humanities, AB
Management, M
Management Information Systems and
   Services, ABM
Management Science, B
Marketing, BMO
Marketing/Marketing Management, AB
Mathematics, B
Mathematics Teacher Education, M
Nurse Anesthetist, M
Organizational Management, M
Philosophy, B
Physics, B
Political Science and Government, B
Psychology, BM
Public Administration, B
Purchasing, Procurement/Acquisitions and
   Contracts Management, AB
Reading Teacher Education, M
Religion/Religious Studies, B
Secondary Education and Teaching, BM
Social Sciences, B
Sociology, B
Spanish Language and Literature, B
Special Education and Teaching, BM
Theology/Theological Studies, B
Visual and Performing Arts, B

Writing, M

SAINT VINCENT COLLEGE

Accounting, BM
Anthropology, B
Art History, Criticism and Conservation, B
Art Teacher Education, B
Biochemistry, B
Bioinformatics, B
Biology/Biological Sciences, B
Business Administration and Management, B
Business Teacher Education, B
Business, Management, Marketing, and Related
   Support Services, B
Chemistry, B
Communication Studies/Speech Communication
   and Rhetoric, B
Computer and Information Sciences, B
Curriculum and Instruction, M
Drama and Dramatics/Theatre Arts, B
Economics, B
Education, M
Educational Media/Instructional Technology, M
Engineering, B
English Language and Literature, B
Environmental Education, M
Environmental Sciences, B
Environmental Studies, B
Finance, B
Fine/Studio Arts, B
French Language and Literature, B
History, B
International Business/Trade/Commerce, B
Liberal Arts and Sciences Studies and
   Humanities, B
Marketing/Marketing Management, B
Mathematics, B
Music, B
Music Performance, B
Music Teacher Education, B
Occupational Therapy/Therapist, B
Pharmacy, B
Philosophy, B
Physical Therapy/Therapist, B
Physician Assistant, B
Physics, B
Physics Teacher Education, B
Political Science and Government, B
Psychology, B
Public Policy Analysis, B
Religious Education, B
Sociology, B
Spanish Language and Literature, B
Special Education and Teaching, M
Theology/Theological Studies, B

SCHUYLKILL INSTITUTE OF BUSINESS AND TECHNOLOGY

Administrative Assistant and Secretarial Science, A
Business Administration and Management, A
Commercial and Advertising Art, A
Computer and Information Sciences and Support
   Services, A
Drafting and Design Technology/Technician, A
Electrical, Electronic and Communications
   Engineering Technology/Technician, A
Legal Assistant/Paralegal, A
Medical Office Management/Administration, A

SETON HILL UNIVERSITY

Accounting, B
Acting, B
Actuarial Science, B
Art History, Criticism and Conservation, B
Art Teacher Education, B
Art Therapy/Therapist, BMO
Arts Management, B
Biochemistry, B
Biology Teacher Education, B
Biology/Biological Sciences, B
Business Administration and Management, B
Business Administration, Management and
   Operations, M
Business/Managerial Economics, B
Ceramic Arts and Ceramics, B
Chemistry, B

Chemistry Teacher Education, B
Child Care and Support Services Management, B
Child Development, B
Clinical Laboratory Science/Medical
   Technology/Technologist, B
Commercial and Advertising Art, B
Communication Studies/Speech Communication
   and Rhetoric, B
Community Health Services/Liaison/Counseling, B
Community Psychology, B
Computer Science, B
Creative Writing, B
Criminal Justice/Law Enforcement Administration, B
Dietetics/Dieticians, B
Drama and Dramatics/Theatre Arts, B
Dramatic/Theatre Arts and Stagecraft, B
Drawing, B
Economics, B
Educational Media/Instructional Technology, M
Educational/Instructional Media Design, B
Elementary Education and Teaching, BMO
Engineering, B
English Language and Literature, B
English/Language Arts Teacher Education, B
Entrepreneurship/Entrepreneurial Studies, B
Family and Consumer Sciences/Home Economics
   Teacher Education, B
Family and Consumer Sciences/Human Sciences, B
Finance, B
Fine/Studio Arts, B
Foreign Language Teacher Education, B
Forensic Science and Technology, B
French Language Teacher Education, B
General Studies, B
History, B
Hospitality Administration/Management, B
Human Resources Management/Personnel
   Administration, B
Human Services, B
International Business/Trade/Commerce, B
International Relations and Affairs, B
Journalism, B
Kindergarten/PreSchool Education and Teaching, B
Management Information Systems and Services, B
Marketing/Marketing Management, B
Marriage and Family Therapy/Counseling, BM
Mathematics, B
Mathematics Teacher Education, B
Metal and Jewelry Arts, B
Music, B
Music Performance, B
Music Teacher Education, B
Music Theory and Composition, B
Nursing - Registered Nurse Training, B
Painting, B
Physician Assistant, BM
Physics, B
Piano and Organ, B
Political Science and Government, B
Pre-Dentistry Studies, B
Pre-Law Studies, B
Pre-Medicine/Pre-Medical Studies, B
Pre-Veterinary Studies, B
Printmaking, B
Psychology, B
Religion/Religious Studies, B
Religious/Sacred Music, B
Sales, Distribution and Marketing Operations, B
Sculpture, B
Social Studies Teacher Education, B
Social Work, B
Sociology, B
Spanish Language and Literature, B
Spanish Language Teacher Education, B
Special Education and Teaching, BMO
Technical Theatre/Theatre Design and
   Technology, B
Theatre/Theatre Arts Management, B
Violin, Viola, Guitar and Other Stringed
   Instruments, B
Voice and Opera, B
Wind and Percussion Instruments, B

Writing, M

SHIPPENSBURG UNIVERSITY OF PENNSYLVANIA

Accounting, B
Applied History, MO
Art/Art Studies, General, B
Biological and Biomedical Sciences, M
Biology/Biological Sciences, B
Business Administration and Management, B
Business Administration, Management and
   Operations, M
Business/Commerce, B
Chemistry, B
Communication and Media Studies, M
Computer and Information Sciences, B
Computer Science, M
Computer Systems Analysis/Analyst, B
Counselor Education/School Counseling and
   Guidance Services, MO
Criminal Justice/Safety Studies, B
Criminology, M
Curriculum and Instruction, M
Economics, B
Education, MO
Educational Administration and Supervision, M
Elementary Education and Teaching, B
English Language and Literature, B
Environmental Studies, BM
Finance, B
French Language and Literature, B
Geography, B
Geology/Earth Science, B
Gerontology, MO
Health/Health Care Administration/Management, B
History, BMO
Information Science/Studies, M
Journalism, B
Kinesiology and Exercise Science, B
Management Science, B
Marketing/Marketing Management, B
Mathematics, B
Multi-/Interdisciplinary Studies, B
Organizational Management, M
Physics, B
Political Science and Government, B
Psychology, BM
Public Administration, BM
Reading Teacher Education, M
Social Work, B
Sociology, BM
Spanish Language and Literature, B
Special Education and Teaching, M
Speech and Rhetorical Studies, B

SLIPPERY ROCK UNIVERSITY OF PENNSYLVANIA

Anthropology, B
Art/Art Studies, General, B
Athletic Training and Sports Medicine, B
Biology/Biological Sciences, B
Business Administration and Management, B
Business Administration, Management and
   Operations, M
Chemistry, B
Clinical/Medical Laboratory Technician, B
Clinical/Medical Social Work, B
Communication Studies/Speech Communication
   and Rhetoric, B
Computer and Information Sciences, B
Counselor Education/School Counseling and
   Guidance Services, M
CytoTechnology/Cytotechnologist, B
Dance, B
Drama and Dramatics/Theatre Arts, B
Early Childhood Education and Teaching, M
Economics, B
Education, M
Educational Administration and Supervision, M
Elementary Education and Teaching, BM
English, M
English Language and Literature, B
Environmental Education, M
Environmental Policy and Resource
   Management, M
Environmental Sciences, B

Environmental Studies, B
Exercise and Sports Science, M
French Language and Literature, B
Geography, B
Geology/Earth Science, B
Health and Physical Education, B
History, BM
Information Technology, B
Mathematics, B
Mathematics Teacher Education, M
Modern Languages, B
Music, B
Music Performance, B
Music Therapy/Therapist, B
Natural Resources and Conservation, B
Nursing, M
Nursing - Registered Nurse Training, B
Occupational Safety and Health
    Technology/Technician, B
Parks, Recreation and Leisure Facilities
    Management, B
Philosophy, B
Physical Therapy/Therapist, D
Physics, B
Political Science and Government, B
Psychology, B
Public Health (MPH, DPH), B
Reading Teacher Education, M
Rehabilitation Sciences, M
Science Teacher Education/General Science
    Teacher Education, M
Science, Technology and Society, B
Secondary Education and Teaching, M
Social Work, B
Sociology, B
Spanish Language and Literature, B
Special Education and Teaching, BM
Sport and Fitness Administration/Management, M
Student Personnel Services, M
Sustainable Development, M

SOUTH HILLS SCHOOL OF BUSINESS & TECHNOLOGY (ALTOONA)

Accounting, A
Legal Administrative Assistant/Secretary, A
Marketing/Marketing Management, A
Medical Administrative Assistant/Secretary, A

SOUTH HILLS SCHOOL OF BUSINESS & TECHNOLOGY (STATE COLLEGE)

Accounting, A
Administrative Assistant and Secretarial Science, A
Business Administration and Management, A
Computer and Information Sciences, A
Computer Programming, Specific Applications, A
Diagnostic Medical Sonography/Sonographer and
    Ultrasound Technician, A
Engineering Technology, A
Health Information/Medical Records
    Technology/Technician, A
Legal Administrative Assistant/Secretary, A
Marketing/Marketing Management, A
Medical Administrative Assistant/Secretary, A
Office Management and Supervision, A

SUSQUEHANNA UNIVERSITY

Accounting, B
Art History, Criticism and Conservation, B
Art/Art Studies, General, B
Biochemistry, B
Biology/Biological Sciences, B
Broadcast Journalism, B
Business Administration and Management, B
Business/Managerial Economics, B
Chemistry, B
Communication Studies/Speech Communication
    and Rhetoric, B
Computer Science, B
Creative Writing, B
Drama and Dramatics/Theatre Arts, B
Ecology, B
Economics, B
Elementary Education and Teaching, B
English Language and Literature, B
Entrepreneurship/Entrepreneurial Studies, B
Finance, B

French Language and Literature, B
Geology/Earth Science, B
German Language and Literature, B
Graphic Design, B
History, B
Human Resources Management/Personnel
    Administration, B
Information Science/Studies, B
International Relations and Affairs, B
Journalism, B
Kindergarten/PreSchool Education and Teaching, B
Marketing/Marketing Management, B
Mass Communication/Media Studies, B
Mathematics, B
Music, B
Music Teacher Education, B
Philosophy, B
Physics, B
Piano and Organ, B
Political Science and Government, B
Pre-Dentistry Studies, B
Pre-Law Studies, B
Pre-Medicine/Pre-Medical Studies, B
Pre-Veterinary Studies, B
Psychology, B
Public Relations/Image Management, B
Radio and Television, B
Religion/Religious Studies, B
Religious/Sacred Music, B
Secondary Education and Teaching, B
Sociology, B
Spanish Language and Literature, B
Speech and Rhetorical Studies, B
Violin, Viola, Guitar and Other Stringed
    Instruments, B
Voice and Opera, B
Wind and Percussion Instruments, B

SWARTHMORE COLLEGE

Ancient/Classical Greek Language and Literature, B
Anthropology, B
Art History, Criticism and Conservation, B
Asian Studies/Civilization, B
Astronomy, B
Astrophysics, B
Biochemistry, B
Biological and Biomedical Sciences, B
Biology/Biological Sciences, B
Chemical Physics, B
Chemistry, B
Chinese Language and Literature, B
Classics and Classical
    Languages, Literatures, and Linguistics, B
Comparative Literature, B
Computer and Information Sciences, B
Dance, B
Drama and Dramatics/Theatre Arts, B
Economics, B
Education, B
Engineering, B
English Language and Literature, B
Film/Video and Photographic Arts, B
Fine/Studio Arts, B
French Language and Literature, B
German Language and Literature, B
German Studies, B
History, B
Latin Language and Literature, B
Linguistics, B
Mathematics, B
Mathematics and Computer Science, B
Medieval and Renaissance Studies, B
Music, B
Philosophy, B
Physics, B
Physiological Psychology/Psychobiology, B
Political Science and Government, B
Psychology, B
Religion/Religious Studies, B
Russian Language and Literature, B
Social Sciences, B
Sociology, B
Spanish Language and Literature, B

Visual and Performing Arts, B

TALMUDICAL YESHIVA OF PHILADELPHIA

Rabbinical Studies, B
Theology/Theological Studies, B

TEMPLE UNIVERSITY

Accounting, BMD
Acting, B
Actuarial Science, BM
Advertising, B
African-American/Black Studies, BMD
Allied Health and Medical Assisting Services, MD
Allopathic Medicine, PO
American/United States Studies/Civilization, B
Anatomy, D
Anthropology, BMD
Applied Horticulture/Horticultural Operations, A
Applied Mathematics, BMD
Architecture, B
Art Education, M
Art History, Criticism and Conservation, BMD
Art Teacher Education, B
Art/Art Studies, General, B
Arts Management, MD
Asian Studies/Civilization, B
Audiology/Audiologist and Speech-Language
    Pathology/Pathologist, B
Biochemistry, BMD
Biological and Biomedical Sciences, MDO
Biology/Biological Sciences, B
Biophysics, B
Business Administration and Management, B
Business Administration, Management and
    Operations, MDO
Business Teacher Education, B
Business/Commerce, B
Cell Biology and Anatomy, D
Ceramic Arts and Ceramics, BM
Chemistry, BMD
City/Urban, Community and Regional Planning, B
Civil Engineering, BM
Civil Engineering Technology/Technician, B
Classics and Classical
    Languages, Literatures, and Linguistics, B
Clinical Psychology, D
Cognitive Sciences, D
Communication and Media Studies, MD
Communication Disorders, M
Composition, MD
Computational Sciences, MD
Computer and Information Sciences, B
Computer Engineering, M
Computer Science, MD
Conducting, B
Counseling Psychology, MD
Crafts, M
Criminal Justice/Safety Studies, B
Criminology, MD
Dance, BMD
Dental and Oral Surgery, O
Dentistry, PO
Developmental Psychology, D
Drama and Dramatics/Theatre Arts, B
Early Childhood Education and Teaching, M
E-Commerce/Electronic Commerce, B
Economics, BMD
Education, MD
Educational Administration and Supervision, MD
Educational Psychology, MD
Electrical Engineering, M
Electrical, Electronics and Communications
    Engineering, B
Electronic Commerce, M
Elementary Education and Teaching, BM
Engineering and Applied Sciences, MD
Engineering Technology, B
English, MD
English Language and Literature, B
English/Language Arts Teacher Education, B
Entrepreneurship/Entrepreneurial Studies, B
Environmental and Occupational Health, M
Environmental Engineering
    Technology/Environmental Technology, BM
Environmental Sciences, B

Environmental Studies, B
Experimental Psychology, D
Fiber, Textile and Weaving Arts, B
Film, Television, and Video Production, M
Film/Cinema Studies, B
Finance, B
Finance and Banking, MD
Fine Arts and Art Studies, M
Foreign Language Teacher Education, B
French Language and Literature, B
General Studies, AB
Genetics, DO
Geography, BM
Geology/Earth Science, BM
German Language and Literature, B
Graphic Design, BM
Health Education, M
Health Information/Medical Records
   Administration/Administrator, B
Health Services Administration, MD
Health Teacher Education, B
Hebrew Language and Literature, B
History, BMD
Horticultural Science, B
Hospitality Administration/Management, BM
Human Resources Management and Services, MD
Immunology, MDO
Industrial and Organizational Psychology, M
Information Science/Studies, MD
Information Technology, B
Insurance, BMD
Interdisciplinary Studies, B
International Business/Trade/Commerce, BMD
Italian Language and Literature, B
Jazz/Jazz Studies, B
Jewelry/Metalsmithing, M
Jewish/Judaic Studies, B
Journalism, BM
Kinesiology and Movement Studies, MD
Labor and Industrial Relations, B
Landscape Architecture, B
Latin American Studies, B
Law and Legal Studies, MPO
Legal Professions and Studies, B
Leisure Studies, M
Liberal Studies, M
Linguistics, BM
Management, MD
Management Information Systems and
   Services, BMD
Management Strategy and Policy, MD
Marketing, MD
Marketing/Marketing Management, B
Mass Communication/Media Studies, D
Mathematics, BMD
Mathematics Teacher Education, BD
Mechanical Engineering, BM
Media Studies, MD
Medicinal and Pharmaceutical Chemistry, MD
Metal and Jewelry Arts, B
Microbiology, MDO
Molecular Biology, DO
Multi-/Interdisciplinary Studies, B
Music, BMD
Music History, Literature, and Theory, BM
Music Pedagogy, B
Music Performance, B
Music Teacher Education, BMD
Music Theory and Composition, BM
Music Therapy/Therapist, BMD
Nursing, M
Nursing - Registered Nurse Training, B
Occupational Therapy/Therapist, M
Operations Research, D
Oral and Dental Sciences, MO
Organizational Behavior Studies, B
Orthodontics, O
Painting, BM
Parks, Recreation, Leisure and Fitness Studies, B
Pathology/Experimental Pathology, D
Performance, MD
Periodontics, O
Pharmaceutical Sciences, MD
Pharmacology, MDO
Pharmacy, P
Philosophy, BMD

Photography, BM
Physical Education Teaching and Coaching, BMD
Physical Therapy/Therapist, MD
Physics, BMD
Physiology, MDO
Piano and Organ, B
Podiatric Medicine, PO
Political Science and Government, BMD
Printmaking, BM
Psychology, BD
Public Health, MD
Public Health Education and Promotion, B
Public Relations/Image Management, B
Radio and Television, B
Reading Teacher Education, MD
Real Estate, B
Recreation and Park Management, M
Religion/Religious Studies, BMD
Russian Language and Literature, B
School Psychology, MD
Science Teacher Education/General Science
   Teacher Education, BD
Sculpture, BM
Secondary Education and Teaching, M
Social Psychology, D
Social Studies Teacher Education, B
Social Work, BM
Sociology, BMD
Spanish Language and Literature, BMD
Special Education and Teaching, M
Speech and Rhetorical Studies, B
Sport and Fitness Administration/Management, M
Statistics, MD
Taxation, M
Textile Design, M
Theater, M
Therapeutic Recreation, M
Therapeutic Recreation/Recreational Therapy, B
Trade and Industrial Teacher Education, B
Travel and Tourism, MD
Urban and Regional Planning, M
Urban Education and Leadership, MD
Urban Studies/Affairs, M
Violin, Viola, Guitar and Other Stringed
   Instruments, B
Vocational and Technical Education, M
Voice and Opera, B
Wind and Percussion Instruments, B
Women's Studies, B
Writing, M

THADDEUS STEVENS COLLEGE OF TECHNOLOGY

Architectural Engineering Technology/Technician, A
Automobile/Automotive Mechanics
   Technology/Technician, A
Carpentry/Carpenter, A
Computer
   Programming, Vendor/Product Certification, A
Construction Engineering Technology/Technician, A
Data Entry/Microcomputer Applications, A
Drafting and Design Technology/Technician, A
Drafting/Design Engineering
   Technologies/Technicians, A
Electrical, Electronic and Communications
   Engineering Technology/Technician, A
Graphic and Printing Equipment Operator
   Production, A
Heating, Air Conditioning, Ventilation and
   Refrigeration Maintenance
   Technology/Technician, A
Information Science/Studies, A
Legal Administrative Assistant/Secretary, A
Machine Tool Technology/Machinist, A
Pipefitting/Pipefitter and Sprinkler Fitter, A
System Administration/Administrator, A
Technology Education/Industrial Arts, A
Web Page, Digital/Multimedia and Information
   Resources Design, A
Word Processing, A

THIEL COLLEGE

Accounting, AB
Actuarial Science, B
Art/Art Studies, General, B

Audiology/Audiologist and Speech-Language
   Pathology/Pathologist, B
Biology/Biological Sciences, B
Business Administration and Management, B
Chemical Engineering, B
Chemistry, B
Clinical Laboratory Science/Medical
   Technology/Technologist, B
Communication Studies/Speech Communication
   and Rhetoric, B
Computer Science, B
Criminal Justice/Safety Studies, B
CytoTechnology/Cytotechnologist, B
E-Commerce/Electronic Commerce, B
Elementary Education and Teaching, B
Engineering Physics, B
English Language and Literature, B
Environmental Studies, B
Funeral Service and Mortuary Science, B
History, B
Information Science/Studies, B
International Business/Trade/Commerce, B
Liberal Arts and Sciences Studies and
   Humanities, A
Management Information Systems and Services, AB
Mass Communication/Media Studies, B
Mathematics, B
Philosophy, B
Physics, B
Political Science and Government, B
Pre-Dentistry Studies, B
Pre-Law Studies, B
Pre-Medicine/Pre-Medical Studies, B
Pre-Veterinary Studies, B
Psychology, B
Religion/Religious Studies, B
Religious Education, B
Secondary Education and Teaching, B
Sociology, B
Spanish Language and Literature, B
Web Page, Digital/Multimedia and Information
   Resources Design, B

THOMAS JEFFERSON UNIVERSITY

Allopathic Medicine, PO
Biochemistry, MD
Biological and Biomedical Sciences, MDO
Biomedical Engineering, D
BioTechnology, BD
Cardiovascular Technology/Technologist, B
Cell Biology and Anatomy, D
Clinical Laboratory Science/Medical
   Technology/Technologist, B
Clinical Laboratory Sciences, M
Clinical Research, O
CytoTechnology/Cytotechnologist, B
Developmental Biology and Embryology, MD
Genetics, D
Health Services Research, O
Immunology, D
Industrial Radiologic Technology/Technician, B
Microbiology, MD
Molecular Biology, D
Molecular Pharmacology, D
Neuroscience, D
Nursing, M
Nursing - Registered Nurse Training, B
Occupational Therapy/Therapist, BM
Pathology/Experimental Pathology, D
Pharmacology, M
Physical Therapy/Therapist, BMD
Physiology, D
Public Health, M
Structural Biology, D

THOMPSON INSTITUTE

Accounting, A
Business Administration and Management, A
Computer Programming/Programmer, A
Computer Systems Networking and
   Telecommunications, A
Drafting and Design Technology/Technician, A
Electrical, Electronic and Communications
   Engineering Technology/Technician, A
Health Information/Medical Records
   Administration/Administrator, A

Medical/Clinical Assistant, A

TRIANGLE TECH, INC.-DUBOIS SCHOOL

Carpentry/Carpenter, A
Drafting and Design Technology/Technician, A
Electrical, Electronic and Communications
   Engineering Technology/Technician, A
Welding Technology/Welder, A

TRIANGLE TECH, INC.-ERIE SCHOOL

Architectural Engineering Technology/Technician, A
Drafting and Design Technology/Technician, A
Drafting/Design Engineering
   Technologies/Technicians, A
Electrical, Electronic and Communications
   Engineering Technology/Technician, A

TRIANGLE TECH, INC.-GREENSBURG SCHOOL

Carpentry/Carpenter, A
Construction Trades, A
Drafting and Design Technology/Technician, A
Electrical/Electronics Equipment Installation and
   Repair, A
Electrical/Electronics Maintenance and Repair
   Technology, A
Heating, Air Conditioning and Refrigeration
   Technology/Technician, A
Heating, Air Conditioning, Ventilation and
   Refrigeration Maintenance
   Technology/Technician, A
Mechanical Drafting and Mechanical Drafting
   CAD/CADD, A

TRIANGLE TECH, INC.-PITTSBURGH SCHOOL

Architectural Engineering Technology/Technician, A
Carpentry/Carpenter, A
Drafting and Design Technology/Technician, A
Drafting/Design Engineering
   Technologies/Technicians, A
Electrical, Electronic and Communications
   Engineering Technology/Technician, A
Heating, Air Conditioning, Ventilation and
   Refrigeration Maintenance
   Technology/Technician, A

THE UNIVERSITY OF THE ARTS

Acting, B
Art Education, M
Ceramic Arts and Ceramics, M
Cinematography and Film/Video Production, B
Communication and Media Studies, B
Communication Studies/Speech Communication
   and Rhetoric, B
Communication, Journalism and Related
   Programs, B
Crafts/Craft Design, Folk Art and Artisanry, B
Dance, B
Digital Communication and Media/Multimedia, B
Drama and Dance Teacher Education, B
Drama and Dramatics/Theatre Arts, B
Dramatic/Theatre Arts and Stagecraft, B
Film/Video and Photographic Arts, B
Graphic Design, B
Illustration, B
Industrial Design, BM
Museology/Museum Studies, M
Museum Education, M
Music, M
Music Performance, B
Music Teacher Education, M
Music Theory and Composition, B
Painting, BM
Photography, B
Printmaking, BM
Sculpture, BM
Technical Theatre/Theatre Design and
   Technology, B
Visual and Performing Arts, B

UNIVERSITY OF PENNSYLVANIA

Accounting, BMD
Actuarial Science, B

African Studies, B
African-American/Black Studies, B
Allopathic Medicine, PO
American/United States Studies/Civilization, BMDO
Anthropology, BMD
Archeology, MD
Architecture, BMDO
Art History, Criticism and Conservation, BMD
Astrophysics, MD
Biochemistry, BDO
Bioengineering, MDO
Bioethics/Medical Ethics, MO
Bioinformatics, B
Biological and Biomedical Sciences, MDO
Biological Anthropology, MD
Biology/Biological Sciences, B
Biomedical Sciences, B
Biomedical/Medical Engineering, B
Biophysics, B
Biostatistics, MD
BioTechnology, M
Business Administration and Management, B
Business Administration, Management and
   Operations, BMDO
Cancer Biology/Oncology, DO
Cell Biology and Anatomy, DO
Chemical Engineering, BMDO
Chemistry, BMD
Classics and Classical
   Languages, Literatures, and Linguistics, BMD
Clinical Psychology, D
Cognitive Sciences, B
Communication and Media Studies, D
Communication Studies/Speech Communication
   and Rhetoric, B
Community Health Services/Liaison/Counseling, B
Community Psychology, D
Comparative Literature, BMD
Computational Biology, DO
Computer Art and Design, M
Computer Engineering, B
Computer Graphics, B
Computer Science, MD
Computer Systems Networking and
   Telecommunications, B
Counseling Psychology, M
Criminology, MD
Dentistry, PO
Developmental Biology and Embryology, DO
Drama and Dramatics/Theatre Arts, B
Early Childhood Education and Teaching, M
East Asian
   Languages, Literatures, and Linguistics, B
East Asian Studies, BMD
Ecology, D
E-Commerce/Electronic Commerce, B
Economics, BMDO
Education, MDO
Educational Administration and Supervision, MD
Educational Leadership and Administration, MD
Educational Measurement and Evaluation, MD
Educational Psychology, MD
Electrical Engineering, MD
Electrical, Electronics and Communications
   Engineering, B
Elementary Education and Teaching, BM
Engineering, B
Engineering and Applied Sciences, MDO
English, MD
English as a Second Language, MD
English Language and Literature, B
Environmental Design/Architecture, B
Environmental Studies, BM
Environmental/Environmental Health Engineering, B
Epidemiology, MD
Evolutionary Biology, D
Film/Cinema Studies, B
Finance, B
Finance and Banking, MD
Fine Arts and Art Studies, M
Fine/Studio Arts, B
Folklore, MD
French Language and Literature, BMD
Genetics, DO
Genomic Sciences, DO
Geology/Earth Science, BMD

German Language and Literature, BMD
Health Education, MD
Health Professions and Related Clinical Sciences, B
Health Services Administration, MD
Health/Health Care Administration/Management, B
Historic Preservation and Conservation, MO
History, BMD
History and Philosophy of Science and
   Technology, B
History of Science and Technology, MD
Human Development, MD
Human Resources Management/Personnel
   Administration, B
Immunology, DO
Information Science/Studies, MD
Insurance, BMD
International Affairs, M
International and Comparative Education, MD
International Business/Trade/Commerce, BMO
International Relations and Affairs, B
International/Global Studies, B
Italian Language and Literature, BMD
Jewish/Judaic Studies, B
Landscape Architecture, MO
Latin American Studies, B
Law and Legal Studies, MDPO
Legal Professions and Studies, B
Liberal Arts and Sciences Studies and
   Humanities, B
Liberal Studies, M
Linguistics, BMD
Logic, B
Management, MD
Management Information Systems and
   Services, BMD
Management of Technology, M
Management Sciences and Quantitative Methods, B
Marketing, MD
Marketing/Marketing Management, B
Materials Engineering, BMDO
Materials Sciences, BMDO
Maternal/Child Health and Neonatal
   Nurse/Nursing, MO
Maternity Nursing, M
Mathematics, BMD
Mechanical Engineering, BMD
Mechanics, MD
Medical Physics, M
Medical/Surgical Nursing, M
Microbiology, DO
Molecular Biology, DO
Molecular Biophysics, DO
Multilingual and Multicultural Education, MD
Music, BMD
Natural Sciences, B
Near and Middle Eastern Languages, MD
Near and Middle Eastern Studies, MD
Neurobiology and Neurophysiology, D
Neuroscience, BDO
Nurse Anesthetist, M
Nurse Midwife/Nursing Midwifery, M
Nursing, BMDO
Nursing - Adult, M
Nursing - Advanced Practice, MO
Nursing - Registered Nurse Training, B
Nursing Administration, MDO
Occupational Health Nursing, M
Oncology Nursing, M
Operations Management and Supervision, B
Organizational Behavior Studies, M
Organizational Management, M
Parasitology, DO
Pediatric Nurse/Nursing, M
Pharmacology, DO
Philosophy, BMDO
Physics, BMD
Physiology, DO
Plant Biology, D
Political Science and Government, BMDO
Population Studies, MD
Psychiatric/Mental Health Nurse/Nursing, M
Psychology, BD
Public Affairs, M
Public Policy Analysis, BMD
Reading Teacher Education, MD
Real Estate, BMD

Religion/Religious Studies, BD
Romance
    Languages, Literatures, and Linguistics, BMD
Russian Language and Literature, B
Sales, Distribution and Marketing Operations, B
School Psychology, D
Secondary Education and Teaching, M
Semitic Languages, Literatures, and Linguistics, B
Social Work, MDO
Sociology, BMD
South and Southeast Asian Studies, MD
South Asian Studies, B
Spanish Language and Literature, BMD
Statistics, BMD
Structural Biology, DO
Systems Engineering, BMD
Telecommunications, M
Telecommunications Management, M
Transportation/Transportation Management, B
Urban and Regional Planning, MDO
Urban Studies/Affairs, B
Veterinary Medicine, PO
Virology, DO
Visual and Performing Arts, B
Women's Health Nursing, M
Women's Studies, B
Writing, MD

UNIVERSITY OF PHOENIX-PHILADELPHIA CAMPUS

Business Administration and Management, B
Business Administration, Management and
    Operations, M
Criminal Justice/Law Enforcement Administration, B
Information Technology, B
International Business/Trade/Commerce, M
Management of Technology, M
Management Science, B

UNIVERSITY OF PHOENIX-PITTSBURGH CAMPUS

Business Administration and Management, B
Business Administration, Management and
    Operations, M
Corrections and Criminal Justice, B
Information Technology, B
Management Information Systems and Services, B
Management of Technology, M
Management Science, B
Organizational Management, M

UNIVERSITY OF PITTSBURGH

Accounting, B
African-American/Black Studies, B
Allopathic Medicine, P
Anthropology, BMD
Applied Mathematics, BM
Architectural History and Criticism, MD
Art History, Criticism and Conservation, BMD
Audiology/Audiologist and Speech-Language
    Pathology/Pathologist, B
Biochemistry, MD
Bioengineering, MDO
Bioethics/Medical Ethics, M
Bioinformatics, MDO
Biological and Biomedical Sciences, MD
Biological and Physical Sciences, B
Biology/Biological Sciences, B
Biomedical/Medical Engineering, B
Biostatistics, MD
Business Administration, Management and
    Operations, MDO
Business/Commerce, B
Cell Biology and Anatomy, MD
Chemical Engineering, BMDO
Chemistry, BMD
Child Development, B
Chinese Language and Literature, B
Civil Engineering, BMD
Classics and Classical
    Languages, Literatures, and Linguistics, BMD
Clinical Laboratory Science/Medical
    Technology/Technologist, B
Clinical Research, MO
Cognitive Sciences, D
Communication and Media Studies, MD

Communication Disorders, MD
Communication Studies/Speech Communication
    and Rhetoric, B
Community Health and Preventive Medicine, MDO
Composition, MD
Computer and Information Sciences and Support
    Services, B
Computer Engineering, B
Computer Science, BMD
Corrections, B
Creative Writing, B
Criminology, M
Cultural Studies, D
Dental and Oral Surgery, O
Dental Hygiene/Hygienist, B
Dentistry, MPO
Developmental Biology and Embryology, D
Developmental Psychology, MD
Dietetics/Dieticians, B
Drama and Dramatics/Theatre Arts, B
Early Childhood Education and Teaching, M
East Asian Studies, M
Ecology, BMD
Economics, BMDO
Education, MD
Educational Leadership and Administration, MD
Educational Measurement and Evaluation, MD
Educational Psychology, B
Electrical Engineering, MD
Electrical, Electronics and Communications
    Engineering, MD
Elementary Education and Teaching, M
Engineering, B
Engineering and Applied Sciences, MDO
Engineering Physics, B
English, MD
English as a Second Language, O
English Education, MD
English Language and Literature, B
English Literature (British and Commonwealth), B
Environmental and Occupational Health, M
Environmental Engineering
    Technology/Environmental Technology, MD
Environmental Policy, M
Epidemiology, MD
Ethnic, Cultural Minority, and Gender Studies, B
Ethnomusicology, MD
Evolutionary Biology, MD
Exercise and Sports Science, MD
Film/Cinema Studies, B
Finance, B
Fine/Studio Arts, B
Foreign Language Teacher Education, MD
Foundations and Philosophy of Education, MD
French Language and Literature, BMD
Genetic Counseling/Counselor, M
Geographic Information Systems, M
Geological and Earth Sciences/Geosciences, B
Geology/Earth Science, BMD
German Language and Literature, BMD
Gerontology, O
Health Education, MO
Health Information/Medical Records
    Administration/Administrator, B
Health Professions and Related Clinical Sciences, B
Health Services Administration, MDO
Higher Education/Higher Education
    Administration, MD
Hispanic Studies, MD
History, BMD
History and Philosophy of Science and
    Technology, B
History of Science and Technology, MD
Human Genetics, MD
Human Resources Development, M
Human Resources Management and Services, O
Humanities/Humanistic Studies, B
Immunology, MD
Industrial Engineering, B
Industrial/Management Engineering, MD
Infectious Diseases, MD
Information Science/Studies, BMDO
Interdisciplinary Studies, B
International Affairs, MDO
International and Comparative Education, MD
International Business/Trade/Commerce, MO

International Development, M
Italian Language and Literature, BM
Japanese Language and Literature, B
Latin American Studies, O
Law and Legal Studies, BMPO
Legal and Justice Studies, MO
Liberal Arts and Sciences Studies and
    Humanities, B
Library Science, MDO
Linguistics, BMD
Management, M
Management Information Systems and
    Services, MO
Marketing/Marketing Management, B
Marriage and Family Therapy/Counseling, O
Materials Engineering, BMD
Materials Sciences, MD
Mathematical and Computational Finance, M
Mathematics, BMD
Mathematics and Statistics, B
Mathematics Teacher Education, MD
Mechanical Engineering, BMD
Medical Microbiology and Bacteriology, B
Metallurgical Engineering, BMD
Microbiology, MD
Military and Defense Studies, MO
Molecular Biology, BD
Molecular Biophysics, D
Molecular Genetics, MD
Molecular Pathology, MD
Molecular Pharmacology, D
Molecular Physiology, MD
Music, BMD
Music History, Literature, and Theory, MD
Music Theory and Composition, MD
Musicology and Ethnomusicology, MD
Neurobiology and Neurophysiology, MD
Neuroscience, BD
Non-Profit/Public/Organizational Management, M
Nurse Anesthetist, M
Nursing, MD
Nursing - Advanced Practice, M
Nursing - Registered Nurse Training, B
Nursing Administration, M
Nursing Education, M
Occupational Therapy/Therapist, BM
Oral and Dental Sciences, MO
Orthodontics, MO
Pathology/Experimental Pathology, MD
Pediatric Nurse/Nursing, M
Performance, MD
Periodontics, MO
Petroleum Engineering, MDO
Pharmacy, BP
Philosophy, BMD
Physical Education Teaching and Coaching, B
Physical Sciences, B
Physical Therapy/Therapist, D
Physics, BMD
Planetary Astronomy and Science, MD
Political Science and Government, BMDO
Psychiatric/Mental Health Nurse/Nursing, M
Psychology, BMD
Public Administration, BMDO
Public Health, MDO
Public Policy Analysis, MDO
Reading Teacher Education, MD
Rehabilitation and Therapeutic Professions, B
Rehabilitation Sciences, MDO
Religion/Religious Studies, BMD
Russian Language and Literature, B
Science Teacher Education/General Science
    Teacher Education, MD
Secondary Education and Teaching, MD
Securities Services Administration/Management, MD
Slavic Languages, Literatures, and Linguistics, BMD
Social Sciences, B
Social Studies Teacher Education, MD
Social Work, BMDO
Sociology, BMD
Spanish Language and Literature, BMD
Special Education and Teaching, MD
Speech and Rhetorical Studies, B
Statistics, BMD
Telecommunications, MDO
Theater, MD

Urban and Regional Planning, MO
Urban Studies/Affairs, B
Virology, MD
Women's Studies, MDO
Writing, M

UNIVERSITY OF PITTSBURGH AT BRADFORD

Applied Mathematics, B
Athletic Training and Sports Medicine, B
Biology/Biological Sciences, B
Business Administration and Management, B
Chemistry, B
Computer Science, B
Creative Writing, B
Criminal Justice/Law Enforcement Administration, B
Economics, B
English Language and Literature, B
Entrepreneurship/Entrepreneurial Studies, B
Environmental Studies, B
History, B
Information Science/Studies, A
Liberal Arts and Sciences Studies and
   Humanities, A
Nursing - Registered Nurse Training, AB
Physical Sciences, B
Political Science and Government, B
Psychology, B
Public Relations/Image Management, B
Radiologic Technology/Science - Radiographer, B
Social Sciences, B
Sociology, B
Sport and Fitness Administration/Management, B

UNIVERSITY OF PITTSBURGH AT GREENSBURG

Accounting, B
American/United States Studies/Civilization, B
Anthropology, B
Applied Mathematics, B
Biology/Biological Sciences, B
Business Administration and Management, B
Comparative Literature, B
Computer and Information Sciences, B
Creative Writing, B
Criminal Justice/Law Enforcement Administration, B
Criminal Justice/Police Science, B
Education, B
English Language and Literature, B
Environmental Biology, B
Humanities/Humanistic Studies, B
Journalism, B
Mass Communication/Media Studies, B
Natural Sciences, B
Political Science and Government, B
Pre-Law Studies, B
Psychology, B
Social Sciences, B

UNIVERSITY OF PITTSBURGH AT JOHNSTOWN

Accounting, B
American/United States Studies/Civilization, B
Biology Teacher Education, B
Biology/Biological Sciences, B
Biopsychology, B
Business Administration and Management, B
Business/Managerial Economics, B
Chemistry, B
Chemistry Teacher Education, B
Civil Engineering Technology/Technician, B
Comparative Literature, B
Computer Science, B
Creative Writing, B
Drama and Dramatics/Theatre Arts, B
Ecology, B
Economics, B
Education, B
Electrical, Electronic and Communications
   Engineering Technology/Technician, B
Elementary Education and Teaching, B
Emergency Medical Technology/Technician (EMT
   Paramedic), A
Engineering Technology, B
English Language and Literature, B

English/Language Arts Teacher Education, B
Environmental Biology, B
Environmental Studies, B
Finance, B
Geography, B
Geology/Earth Science, B
History, B
History Teacher Education, B
Humanities/Humanistic Studies, B
Journalism, B
Mass Communication/Media Studies, B
Mathematics, B
Mathematics Teacher Education, B
Mechanical Engineering/Mechanical
   Technology/Technician, B
Natural Sciences, B
Political Science and Government, B
Pre-Dentistry Studies, B
Pre-Law Studies, B
Pre-Medicine/Pre-Medical Studies, B
Pre-Veterinary Studies, B
Psychology, B
Respiratory Care Therapy/Therapist, A
Science Teacher Education/General Science
   Teacher Education, B
Secondary Education and Teaching, B
Social Sciences, B
Social Studies Teacher Education, B
Sociology, B
Surgical Technology/Technologist, A

UNIVERSITY OF PITTSBURGH AT TITUSVILLE

Accounting, A
Business/Commerce, A
Human Services, A
Liberal Arts and Sciences Studies and
   Humanities, A
Management Information Systems and Services, A
Natural Sciences, A
Nursing - Registered Nurse Training, A
Physical Therapist Assistant, A

UNIVERSITY OF THE SCIENCES IN PHILADELPHIA

Biochemistry, BMD
Bioinformatics, BM
Biology/Biological Sciences, B
BioTechnology, M
Cell Biology and Anatomy, M
Chemistry, BMD
Clinical Laboratory Science/Medical
   Technology/Technologist, B
Computer Science, B
Environmental Sciences, B
Health Psychology, M
Health Services Administration, MD
Health Services/Allied Health/Health Sciences, B
Health/Medical Psychology, B
Marketing/Marketing Management, B
Medicinal and Pharmaceutical Chemistry, BMD
Microbiology, B
Pharmaceutical Administration, M
Pharmaceutical Sciences, MD
Pharmaceutics and Drug Design, B
Pharmacology, MD
Pharmacology and Toxicology, B
Pharmacy, P
Pharmacy, Pharmaceutical Sciences, and Administration, B
Physical Therapy/Therapist, D
Psychology, B
Technical and Business Writing, M
Toxicology, MD

THE UNIVERSITY OF SCRANTON

Accounting, BM
Ancient/Classical Greek Language and Literature, B
Biochemistry, M
Biology/Biological Sciences, B
Biomathematics and Bioinformatics, B
Biophysics, B
Business Administration and Management, AB
Business Administration, Management and
   Operations, BM
Chemistry, BM

Clinical Laboratory Science/Medical
   Technology/Technologist, B
Communication Studies/Speech Communication
   and Rhetoric, B
Communications Technologies/Technicians and
   Support Services, B
Community Psychology, M
Computer and Information Sciences and Support
   Services, B
Computer Engineering, AB
Computer Science, B
Counseling Psychology, O
Counselor Education/School Counseling and
   Guidance Services, M
Criminal Justice/Safety Studies, AB
Curriculum and Instruction, M
Drama and Dramatics/Theatre Arts, B
Early Childhood Education and Teaching, BM
Economics, B
Education, M
Educational Administration and Supervision, M
Electrical, Electronics and Communications
   Engineering, B
Elementary Education and Teaching, BM
English Language and Literature, B
Entrepreneurship/Entrepreneurial Studies, B
Finance, B
Finance and Banking, M
Foreign Languages and Literatures, B
French Language and Literature, B
German Language and Literature, B
Gerontology, B
Health Services Administration, M
Health/Health Care Administration/Management, AB
History, BM
Human Resources Development, M
Human Resources Management and Services, M
Human Resources Management/Personnel
   Administration, B
Human Services, AB
Information Science/Studies, AB
International Business/Trade/Commerce, BM
International Relations and Affairs, B
Italian Language and Literature, B
Kindergarten/PreSchool Education and Teaching, B
Kinesiology and Exercise Science, B
Latin Language and Literature, B
Management, M
Management Information Systems and Services, M
Management of Technology, M
Management Science, B
Marketing, M
Marketing/Marketing Management, B
Mathematics, B
Mathematics and Statistics, B
Neuroscience, B
Nurse Anesthetist, MO
Nursing, MO
Nursing - Adult, M
Nursing - Advanced Practice, MO
Nursing - Registered Nurse Training, B
Occupational Therapy/Therapist, M
Operations Management and Supervision, B
Organizational Management, M
Philosophy, B
Physical Therapy/Therapist, MD
Physics, B
Political Science and Government, AB
Psychology, B
Reading Teacher Education, M
Rehabilitation Counseling, M
Religion/Religious Studies, B
Secondary Education and Teaching, BM
Sociology, AB
Software Engineering, M
Spanish Language and Literature, B
Special Education and Teaching, BM
Theology and Religious Vocations, M

URSINUS COLLEGE

American/United States Studies/Civilization, B
Anthropology, B
Art/Art Studies, General, B
Biological and Physical Sciences, B
Biology/Biological Sciences, B
Business Administration and Management, B

Chemistry, B
Civil Engineering, B
Classics and Classical
  Languages, Literatures, and Linguistics, B
Computer Science, B
East Asian Studies, B
Economics, B
Electrical, Electronics and Communications
  Engineering, B
English Language and Literature, B
Environmental Studies, B
Fine Arts and Art Studies, B
French Language and Literature, B
German Language and Literature, B
Health and Physical Education, B
History, B
International Relations and Affairs, B
Mass Communication/Media Studies, B
Mathematics, B
Mechanical Engineering, B
Metallurgical Engineering, B
Multi-/Interdisciplinary Studies, B
Neuroscience, B
Philosophy, B
Philosophy and Religious Studies, B
Physics, B
Political Science and Government, B
Psychology, B
Social Sciences, B
Sociology, B
Spanish Language and Literature, B

VALLEY FORGE CHRISTIAN COLLEGE

Bible/Biblical Studies, AB
Elementary Education and Teaching, B
Kindergarten/PreSchool Education and Teaching, A
Religious Education, B
Religious/Sacred Music, B
Theology/Theological Studies, B

VALLEY FORGE MILITARY COLLEGE

Biological and Physical Sciences, A
Business Administration and Management, A
Criminal Justice/Law Enforcement Administration, A
Engineering, A
Liberal Arts and Sciences Studies and
  Humanities, A

VILLANOVA UNIVERSITY

Accounting, BM
Art History, Criticism and Conservation, B
Artificial Intelligence and Robotics, O
Astronomy, B
Astrophysics, B
Biological and Biomedical Sciences, M
Biology/Biological Sciences, B
Business Administration and Management, B
Business Administration, Management and
  Operations, MO
Business/Managerial Economics, B
Chemical Engineering, BM
Chemistry, BM
Civil Engineering, BM
Classics and Classical
  Languages, Literatures, and Linguistics, BM
Computer Engineering, BMO
Computer Science, BMO
Counselor Education/School Counseling and
  Guidance Services, M
Criminal Justice/Law Enforcement Administration, B
Criminology, M
Economics, B
Education, BM
Educational Leadership and Administration, M
Electrical Engineering, MO
Electrical, Electronics and Communications
  Engineering, B
Elementary Education and Teaching, BM
Engineering and Applied Sciences, MDO
English, M
English Language and Literature, B
Environmental Engineering
  Technology/Environmental Technology, M
Finance, B
French Language and Literature, B
Geography, B

German Language and Literature, B
Gerontological Nursing, MO
Health Services Administration, M
Hispanic Studies, M
History, BM
Human Resources Development, M
Human Services, B
Information Science/Studies, B
Interdisciplinary Studies, D
International Business/Trade/Commerce, B
Italian Language and Literature, B
Law and Legal Studies, PO
Liberal Arts and Sciences Studies and
  Humanities, AB
Liberal Studies, M
Management Information Systems and Services, B
Management of Technology, M
Manufacturing Engineering, O
Marketing/Marketing Management, B
Mass Communication/Media Studies, B
Mathematics, BM
Mechanical Engineering, BMO
Natural Sciences, AB
Nurse Anesthetist, MO
Nursing, MDO
Nursing - Adult, MO
Nursing - Advanced Practice, MO
Nursing - Registered Nurse Training, B
Nursing Administration, MO
Nursing Education, MO
Pediatric Nurse/Nursing, MO
Philosophy, BD
Physics, B
Political Science and Government, BM
Psychology, BM
Public Administration, M
Religion/Religious Studies, B
Secondary Education and Teaching, BM
Sociology, B
Spanish Language and Literature, B
Statistics, M
Taxation, MO
Theater, M
Theology and Religious Vocations, M
Transportation and Highway Engineering, M
Water Resources Engineering, M

WASHINGTON & JEFFERSON COLLEGE

Accounting, B
Art Teacher Education, B
Art/Art Studies, General, B
Biochemistry, B
Biology/Biological Sciences, B
Business/Commerce, B
Cell/Cellular Biology and Anatomical Sciences, B
Chemistry, B
Economics, B
Education, B
English Language and Literature, B
French Language and Literature, B
German Language and Literature, B
History, B
Information Technology, B
International Business/Trade/Commerce, B
Liberal Arts and Sciences Studies and
  Humanities, B
Mathematics, B
Music, B
Philosophy, B
Physics, B
Political Science and Government, B
Psychology, B
Sociology, B
Spanish Language and Literature, B
Theatre Literature, History and Criticism, B

WAYNESBURG COLLEGE

Accounting, B
Advertising, B
Art/Art Studies, General, B
Arts Management, B
Athletic Training and Sports Medicine, B
Biology Teacher Education, B
Biology/Biological Sciences, B
Business Administration and Management, AB

Business Administration, Management and
  Operations, MO
Chemistry, B
Chemistry Teacher Education, B
Commercial and Advertising Art, B
Communication Studies/Speech Communication
  and Rhetoric, B
Computer and Information Sciences, B
Computer Science, B
Creative Writing, B
Criminal Justice/Law Enforcement Administration, B
Elementary Education and Teaching, B
Engineering, B
English Language and Literature, B
English/Language Arts Teacher Education, B
Environmental Studies, B
Finance, B
Forensic Science and Technology, B
Graphic Design, B
Health/Health Care Administration/Management, B
History, B
International Business/Trade/Commerce, B
Journalism, B
Kinesiology and Exercise Science, B
Liberal Arts and Sciences Studies and
  Humanities, A
Marine Biology and Biological Oceanography, B
Marketing/Marketing Management, B
Mathematics, B
Mathematics Teacher Education, B
Nursing - Registered Nurse Training, B
Pre-Dentistry Studies, B
Pre-Engineering, B
Pre-Law Studies, B
Pre-Medicine/Pre-Medical Studies, B
Pre-Theology/Pre-Ministerial Studies, B
Pre-Veterinary Studies, B
Psychology, B
Public Administration, B
Radio and Television, B
Science Teacher Education/General Science
  Teacher Education, B
Secondary Education and Teaching, B
Social Sciences, B
Social Studies Teacher Education, B
Sociology, B
Special Education and Teaching, B

WEST CHESTER UNIVERSITY OF PENNSYLVANIA

Accounting, B
American/United States Studies/Civilization, B
Anthropology, BMO
Art/Art Studies, General, B
Astronomy, M
Athletic Training and Sports Medicine, BM
Audiology/Audiologist and Speech-Language
  Pathology/Pathologist, B
Biochemistry, B
Biological and Biomedical Sciences, M
Biology Teacher Education, B
Biology/Biological Sciences, B
Business Administration and Management, B
Business Administration, Management and
  Operations, M
Business/Managerial Economics, B
Chemistry, BM
Chemistry Teacher Education, B
City/Urban, Community and Regional Planning, B
Classics and Classical
  Languages, Literatures, and Linguistics, M
Clinical Nutrition/Nutritionist, B
Clinical Psychology, M
Communication and Media Studies, M
Communication Disorders, M
Communication Studies/Speech Communication
  and Rhetoric, B
Comparative Literature, B
Computer and Information Sciences, B
Computer Science, MO
Counselor Education/School Counseling and
  Guidance Services, M
Criminal Justice/Safety Studies, B
Criminology, M
Dietetics/Dieticians, B
Drama and Dramatics/Theatre Arts, B

Ecology, B
Economics, M
Education, MO
Educational Measurement and Evaluation, M
Educational Media/Instructional Technology, O
Electronic Commerce, M
Elementary Education and Teaching, BM
English, M
English as a Second Language, M
English Language and Literature, B
English/Language Arts Teacher Education, B
Environmental and Occupational Health, M
Environmental Health, B
Environmental Studies, B
Exercise and Sports Science, M
Finance, B
Finance and Banking, M
Fine/Studio Arts, B
Foreign Language Teacher Education, BM
French Language and Literature, BM
French Language Teacher Education, B
Geography, BM
Geology/Earth Science, BM
German Language and Literature, BM
Gerontology, MO
Health and Physical Education, B
Health Education, M
Health Psychology, O
Health Services Administration, MO
Health Teacher Education, B
Health/Health Care Administration/Management, B
History, BM
History Teacher Education, B
Industrial and Organizational Psychology, M
International Relations and Affairs, B
Kinesiology and Exercise Science, B
Kinesiology and Movement Studies, MO
Latin Language and Literature, B
Liberal Arts and Sciences Studies and
  Humanities, B
Management, M
Mathematics, BM
Mathematics Teacher Education, B
Molecular Biology, B
Music, BM
Music History, Literature, and Theory, B
Music Performance, B
Music Teacher Education, BM
Music Theory and Composition, B
Nursing, M
Nursing - Registered Nurse Training, B
Nursing Education, M
Philosophy, BM
Physical Education Teaching and Coaching, BMO
Physics, B
Physics Teacher Education, B
Piano and Organ, B
Political Science and Government, B
Pre-Medicine/Pre-Medical Studies, B
Psychology, BM
Public Administration, M
Public Health, BMO
Public Health (MPH, DPH), B
Public Health Education and Promotion, B
Reading Teacher Education, M
Russian Language and Literature, B
Sales, Distribution and Marketing Operations, B
Science Teacher Education/General Science
  Teacher Education, BM
Secondary Education and Teaching, M
Social Studies Teacher Education, B
Social Work, BM
Sociology, BMO
Spanish Language and Literature, BM
Spanish Language Teacher Education, B
Special Education and Teaching, BM
Speech and Rhetorical Studies, B
Sport and Fitness Administration/Management, M
Urban and Regional Planning, M
Voice and Opera, B
Women's Studies, B

WESTERN SCHOOL OF HEALTH AND BUSINESS CAREERS (PITTSBURGH)

Child Care and Support Services Management, A
Clinical/Medical Laboratory Technician, A

Diagnostic Medical Sonography/Sonographer and
  Ultrasound Technician, A
Legal Assistant/Paralegal, A
Medical Radiologic Technology/Science - Radiation
  Therapist, A
Medical/Clinical Assistant, A
Pharmacy Technician/Assistant, A
Respiratory Care Therapy/Therapist, A
Surgical Technology/Technologist, A
Veterinary/Animal Health Technology/Technician and
  Veterinary Assistant, A

WESTMINSTER COLLEGE

Accounting, B
Art/Art Studies, General, B
Behavioral Sciences, B
Biology Technician/BioTechnology Laboratory
  Technician, B
Biology/Biological Sciences, B
Broadcast Journalism, B
Business Administration and Management, B
Chemistry, B
Classics and Classical
  Languages, Literatures, and Linguistics, B
Computer Science, B
Counselor Education/School Counseling and
  Guidance Services, MO
Creative Writing, B
Criminal Justice/Law Enforcement Administration, B
Drama and Dramatics/Theatre Arts, B
Economics, B
Education, BMO
Educational Administration and Supervision, MO
Elementary Education and Teaching, B
English Language and Literature, B
Environmental Studies, B
French Language and Literature, B
German Language and Literature, B
History, B
Information Science/Studies, B
Interdisciplinary Studies, B
International Business/Trade/Commerce, B
International Economics, B
International Relations and Affairs, B
Labor and Industrial Relations, B
Latin Language and Literature, B
Mass Communication/Media Studies, B
Mathematics, B
Modern Languages, B
Molecular Biology, B
Music, B
Music Teacher Education, B
Philosophy, B
Physics, B
Physiological Psychology/Psychobiology, B
Political Science and Government, B
Pre-Dentistry Studies, B
Pre-Law Studies, B
Pre-Medicine/Pre-Medical Studies, B
Pre-Veterinary Studies, B
Psychology, B
Public Relations/Image Management, B
Radio and Television, B
Reading Teacher Education, MO
Religion/Religious Studies, B
Religious Education, B
Religious/Sacred Music, B
Sociology, B
Spanish Language and Literature, B
Telecommunications Technology/Technician, B
Voice and Opera, B

WESTMORELAND COUNTY COMMUNITY COLLEGE

Accounting, A
Administrative Assistant and Secretarial Science, A
Architectural Engineering Technology/Technician, A
Artificial Intelligence and Robotics, A
Business Administration and Management, A
Child Development, A
Commercial and Advertising Art, A
Computer and Information Sciences, A
Computer Engineering Technology/Technician, A
Computer Graphics, A
Computer Science, A
Consumer Merchandising/Retailing Management, A

Criminal Justice/Law Enforcement Administration, A
Criminal Justice/Police Science, A
Culinary Arts/Chef Training, A
Data Processing and Data Processing
  Technology/Technician, A
Dental Hygiene/Hygienist, A
Dietetics/Dieticians, A
Drafting and Design Technology/Technician, A
Drafting/Design Engineering
  Technologies/Technicians, A
Electrical, Electronic and Communications
  Engineering Technology/Technician, A
Engineering, A
Environmental Engineering
  Technology/Environmental Technology, A
Fashion Merchandising, A
Fashion/Apparel Design, A
Finance, A
Fire Science/Firefighting, A
Graphic and Printing Equipment Operator
  Production, A
Health Information/Medical Records
  Administration/Administrator, A
Health Teacher Education, A
Heating, Air Conditioning, Ventilation and
  Refrigeration Maintenance
  Technology/Technician, A
Horticultural Science, A
Hospitality Administration/Management, A
Hotel/Motel Administration/Management, A
Human Services, A
Information Science/Studies, A
Legal Administrative Assistant/Secretary, A
Legal Assistant/Paralegal, A
Liberal Arts and Sciences Studies and
  Humanities, A
Licensed Practical/Vocational Nurse Training, A
Marketing/Marketing Management, A
Mechanical Engineering/Mechanical
  Technology/Technician, A
Medical Administrative Assistant/Secretary, A
Nuclear/Nuclear Power Technology/Technician, A
Nursing - Registered Nurse Training, A
Ophthalmic Laboratory Technology/Technician, A
Photography, A
Public Administration, A
Publishing, A
Real Estate, A
Special Products Marketing Operations, A
Tourism and Travel Services Management, A
Welding Technology/Welder, A

WIDENER UNIVERSITY

Accounting, BM
Adult and Continuing Education and Teaching, M
Advertising, B
Anthropology, B
Behavioral Sciences, B
Biochemistry, B
Biology Teacher Education, B
Biology/Biological Sciences, B
Business Administration and Management, B
Business Administration, Management and
  Operations, BMO
Business/Managerial Economics, B
Chemical Engineering, BM
Chemistry, B
Chemistry Teacher Education, B
Civil Engineering, BM
Clinical Psychology, DO
Computer and Information Sciences, B
Computer Engineering, M
Computer Science, B
Counselor Education/School Counseling and
  Guidance Services, M
Criminal Justice/Law Enforcement Administration, B
Criminology, MO
Early Childhood Education and Teaching, BM
Economics, B
Education, MD
Educational Administration and Supervision, MD
Educational Leadership and Administration, MD
Educational Media/Instructional Technology, M
Educational Psychology, M
Educational/Instructional Media Design, B

Electrical, Electronics and Communications
  Engineering, B
Elementary Education and Teaching, BM
Engineering, B
Engineering and Applied Sciences, MO
Engineering Management, M
Engineering/Industrial Management, B
English Education, M
English Language and Literature, B
English/Language Arts Teacher Education, B
Environmental Studies, B
Financial Planning and Services, B
Fine Arts and Art Studies, B
Foreign Languages and Literatures, B
Foundations and Philosophy of Education, M
French Language and Literature, B
French Language Teacher Education, B
Health Education, M
Health Services Administration, MO
Health Services/Allied Health/Health Sciences, B
History, B
History Teacher Education, B
Hospitality Administration/Management, B
Hotel/Motel Administration/Management, B
Human Resources Management and
  Services, BMO
Humanities/Humanistic Studies, B
Industrial Radiologic Technology/Technician, A
Information Science/Studies, B
International Business/Trade/Commerce, B
International Relations and Affairs, B
Kindergarten/PreSchool Education and Teaching, B
Law and Legal Studies, MDPO
Legal Assistant/Paralegal, A
Liberal Studies, M
Management Information Systems and Services, B
Marketing/Marketing Management, B
Mass Communication/Media Studies, B
Mathematics, B
Mathematics Teacher Education, BM
Mechanical Engineering, BM
Middle School Education, M
Modern Languages, B
Nursing, MDO
Nursing - Registered Nurse Training, B
Operations Management and Supervision, B
Physical Therapy/Therapist, MD
Physics, B
Political Science and Government, B
Pre-Dentistry Studies, B
Pre-Medicine/Pre-Medical Studies, B
Pre-Veterinary Studies, B
Psychology, BO
Psychology Teacher Education, B
Public Administration, MO
Reading Teacher Education, MD
Science Teacher Education/General Science
  Teacher Education, BM
Social Sciences, B
Social Studies Teacher Education, BM
Social Work, BM
Sociology, B
Software Engineering, M
Spanish Language and Literature, B
Spanish Language Teacher Education, B
Special Education and Teaching, BM
Sport and Fitness Administration/Management, B
Taxation, M
Telecommunications, M

WILKES UNIVERSITY

Accounting, BM
Biochemistry, B
Biology/Biological Sciences, B
Business Administration and Management, B
Business Administration, Management and
  Operations, M
Chemistry, B
Clinical Laboratory Science/Medical
  Technology/Technologist, B
Communication Studies/Speech Communication
  and Rhetoric, B
Computer and Information Sciences, B
Computer Education, M
Criminal Justice/Safety Studies, B
Drama and Dramatics/Theatre Arts, B

Education, BM
Educational Leadership and Administration, M
Educational Measurement and Evaluation, M
Educational Media/Instructional Technology, M
Electrical Engineering, M
Electrical, Electronics and Communications
  Engineering, B
Elementary Education and Teaching, BM
Engineering, B
Engineering and Applied Sciences, M
Engineering/Industrial Management, B
English Language and Literature, B
Entrepreneurship/Entrepreneurial Studies, B
Environmental/Environmental Health Engineering, B
Finance and Banking, M
French Language and Literature, B
Geology/Earth Science, B
Health Services Administration, M
History, B
Human Resources Management and Services, M
Information Science/Studies, B
International Business/Trade/Commerce, M
International Relations and Affairs, B
Liberal Arts and Sciences Studies and
  Humanities, B
Marketing, M
Mathematics, BM
Mathematics Teacher Education, M
Mechanical Engineering, B
Multi-/Interdisciplinary Studies, B
Music Performance, B
Music Teacher Education, B
Nursing, M
Nursing - Registered Nurse Training, B
Pharmacy, P
Pharmacy, Pharmaceutical Sciences, and
  Administration, B
Philosophy, B
Political Science and Government, B
Psychology, B
Secondary Education and Teaching, M
Sociology, B
Spanish Language and Literature, B
Special Education and Teaching, M
Writing, M

THE WILLIAMSON FREE SCHOOL OF MECHANICAL TRADES

Carpentry/Carpenter, A
Construction Engineering Technology/Technician, A
Electrical, Electronic and Communications
  Engineering Technology/Technician, A
Energy Management and Systems
  Technology/Technician, A
Horticultural Science, A
Landscaping and Groundskeeping, A
Machine Tool Technology/Machinist, A
Turf and Turfgrass Management, A

WILSON COLLEGE

Accounting, AB
Art/Art Studies, General, B
Behavioral Sciences, B
Biology/Biological Sciences, B
Business Administration and Management, AB
Chemistry, B
Elementary Education and Teaching, AB
English Language and Literature, B
Environmental Studies, B
Equestrian/Equine Studies, B
French Language and Literature, B
International Relations and Affairs, B
Kinesiology and Exercise Science, B
Liberal Arts and Sciences Studies and
  Humanities, A
Management Information Systems and Services, A
Mass Communication/Media Studies, AB
Mathematics, B
Philosophy and Religious Studies, B
Physiological Psychology/Psychobiology, B
Rehabilitation and Therapeutic Professions, B
Social Sciences, B
Spanish Language and Literature, B

Veterinary/Animal Health Technology/Technician and
  Veterinary Assistant, B

YESHIVA BETH MOSHE

Jewish/Judaic Studies, B
Theology and Religious Vocations, O

YORK COLLEGE OF PENNSYLVANIA

Accounting, B
Behavioral Sciences, B
Biology/Biological Sciences, AB
Business Administration and Management, AB
Business Administration, Management and
  Operations, M
Business, Management, Marketing, and Related
  Support Services, B
Business/Managerial Economics, B
Chemistry, AB
Clinical Laboratory Science/Medical
  Technology/Technologist, B
Computer and Information Sciences, B
Computer and Information Sciences and Support
  Services, B
Computer Science, B
Corrections, B
Criminal Justice/Police Science, AB
Education, M
Elementary Education and Teaching, B
Engineering, B
Engineering/Industrial Management, B
English Language and Literature, B
English/Language Arts Teacher Education, B
Finance, B
Fine Arts and Art Studies, AB
Health/Health Care Administration/Management, B
History, B
International Business/Trade/Commerce, B
International Relations and Affairs, B
Liberal Arts and Sciences Studies and
  Humanities, A
Marketing/Marketing Management, B
Mass Communication/Media Studies, B
Mathematics, AB
Mathematics Teacher Education, B
Mechanical Engineering, B
Music, AB
Music Teacher Education, B
Nuclear Medical Technology/Technologist, B
Nursing, M
Nursing - Registered Nurse Training, B
Parks, Recreation, Leisure and Fitness Studies, B
Philosophy, AB
Physical Sciences, B
Physics, A
Political Science and Government, AB
Pre-Dentistry Studies, B
Pre-Law Studies, B
Pre-Medicine/Pre-Medical Studies, B
Pre-Veterinary Studies, B
Psychology, B
Public Administration, B
Public Relations/Image Management, B
Radio and Television, AB
Respiratory Care Therapy/Therapist, AB
Science Teacher Education/General Science
  Teacher Education, B
Secondary Education and Teaching, B
Social Science Teacher Education, B
Social Studies Teacher Education, B
Sociology, B
Spanish Language and Literature, B
Special Education and Teaching, B
Speech and Rhetorical Studies, B
Sport and Fitness Administration/Management, B

YORK TECHNICAL INSTITUTE

Artificial Intelligence and Robotics, A
Computer and Information Sciences, A
Computer and Information Systems Security, A
Computer Systems Networking and
  Telecommunications, A
Computer/Information Technology Services
  Administration and Management, A
Information Technology, A
Management Information Systems and Services, A
System Administration/Administrator, A

Web Page, Digital/Multimedia and Information
Resources Design, A

YORKTOWNE BUSINESS INSTITUTE

Accounting, A
Administrative Assistant and Secretarial Science, A
Business/Commerce, A
Culinary Arts/Chef Training, A
Executive Assistant/Executive Secretary, A
Hospitality Administration/Management, A
Management Information Systems and Services, A
Medical Administrative Assistant/Secretary, A
Medical/Clinical Assistant, A

Puerto Rico

AMERICAN UNIVERSITY OF PUERTO RICO

Accounting, AB
Administrative Assistant and Secretarial Science, AB
Business Administration and Management, AB
Education, B
Elementary Education and Teaching, B
Liberal Arts and Sciences Studies and
Humanities, A
Physical Education Teaching and Coaching, B
Purchasing, Procurement/Acquisitions and
Contracts Management, B
Special Education and Teaching, B

BAYAMON CENTRAL UNIVERSITY

Accounting, BM
Administrative Assistant and Secretarial Science, AB
Biological and Physical Sciences, B
Biology/Biological Sciences, B
Business Administration and Management, B
Business Administration, Management and
Operations, M
Business/Commerce, AB
Chemistry, B
Computer Science, A
Counselor Education/School Counseling and
Guidance Services, M
Early Childhood Education and Teaching, M
Education, M
Educational Administration and Supervision, M
Educational/Instructional Media Design, AB
Elementary Education and Teaching, BM
English/Language Arts Teacher Education, B
Environmental Studies, B
Human Resources Management/Personnel
Administration, B
Journalism, B
Kindergarten/PreSchool Education and Teaching, B
Management, M
Management Information Systems and Services, AB
Marketing, M
Marketing/Marketing Management, B
Mathematics Teacher Education, B
Nursing - Registered Nurse Training, AB
Occupational Safety and Health
Technology/Technician, B
Pastoral Studies/Counseling, M
Philosophy, B
Physical Education Teaching and Coaching, B
Psychology, BM
Public Administration, B
Religion/Religious Studies, BM
Science Teacher Education/General Science
Teacher Education, B
Social Work, B
Spanish Language Teacher Education, B
Special Education and Teaching, BM
Theology and Religious Vocations, MP

CARIBBEAN UNIVERSITY

Accounting, AB
Administrative Assistant and Secretarial Science, AB
Biology Teacher Education, B
Business Administration and Management, AB
Business and Personal/Financial Services Marketing
Operations, B
Civil Engineering, B
Civil Engineering Technology/Technician, A
Computer Programming, B

Computer Programming/Programmer, AB
Computer Science, B
Criminal Justice/Law Enforcement Administration, B
Criminal Justice/Police Science, A
Criminology, B
Drafting and Design Technology/Technician, B
Education, AB
Educational Leadership and Administration, B
Electrical and Electronic Engineering
Technologies/Technicians, B
Elementary and Middle School
Administration/Principalship, B
Elementary Education and Teaching, B
Engineering/Industrial Management, B
English/Language Arts Teacher Education, B
Executive Assistant/Executive Secretary, B
Finance, A
General Merchandising, Sales, and Related
Marketing Operations, B
Human Resources Management/Personnel
Administration, B
Human Services, B
Industrial Engineering, B
Information Science/Studies, B
Kindergarten/PreSchool Education and
Teaching, AB
Legal Administrative Assistant/Secretary, A
Liberal Arts and Sciences Studies and
Humanities, B
Mathematics Teacher Education, B
Medical Administrative Assistant/Secretary, A
Nursing, B
Nursing - Registered Nurse Training, B
Pre-Law Studies, B
Pre-Medicine/Pre-Medical Studies, B
Real Estate, A
Sales, Distribution and Marketing Operations, B
Secondary Education and Teaching, B
Social Work, B
Special Education and Teaching, B
Survey Technology/Surveying, A
Teacher Education, Multiple Levels, B

CARLOS ALBIZU UNIVERSITY

Clinical Psychology, D
Industrial and Organizational Psychology, MD
Psychology, MD

COLEGIO BIBLICO PENTECOSTAL

Bible/Biblical Studies, B
Pastoral Studies/Counseling, B
Religious Education, B

COLEGIO PENTECOSTAL MIZPA

Theology and Religious Vocations, M

COLUMBIA COLLEGE (CAGUAS)

Administrative Assistant and Secretarial Science, A
Business Administration and Management, A
Business/Commerce, B
Electrical, Electronic and Communications
Engineering Technology/Technician, A
Management Information Systems and Services, A
Nursing - Registered Nurse Training, A
Nursing Science, B

CONSERVATORY OF MUSIC OF PUERTO RICO

Music, B
Music Teacher Education, B
Piano and Organ, B
Violin, Viola, Guitar and Other Stringed
Instruments, B
Voice and Opera, B
Wind and Percussion Instruments, B

ELECTRONIC DATA PROCESSING COLLEGE OF PUERTO RICO

Administrative Assistant and Secretarial Science, A
Business Administration and Management, AB
Computer Programming/Programmer, AB

Electrical, Electronic and Communications
Engineering Technology/Technician, A

ESCUELA DE ARTES PLASTICAS DE PUERTO RICO

Art Teacher Education, B
Commercial and Advertising Art, B
Industrial Design, B
Painting, B
Printmaking, B
Sculpture, B

HUERTAS JUNIOR COLLEGE

Accounting, A
Administrative Assistant and Secretarial Science, A
Business Administration and Management, A
Computer Science, A
Dental Hygiene/Hygienist, A
Pharmacy, A

HUMACAO COMMUNITY COLLEGE

Accounting, A
Administrative Assistant and Secretarial Science, A
Computer Programming/Programmer, A

INSTITUTO COMERCIAL DE PUERTO RICO JUNIOR COLLEGE

Accounting, A
Administrative Assistant and Secretarial Science, A
Business Administration and Management, A
Hotel/Motel Administration/Management, A
Information Science/Studies, A

INTER AMERICAN UNIVERSITY OF PUERTO RICO, AGUADILLA CAMPUS

Accounting, AB
Administrative Assistant and Secretarial Science, AB
Biology Teacher Education, B
Biology/Biological Sciences, B
Business Administration and Management, AB
Computer Hardware Technology/Technician, A
Computer Science, AB
Criminal Justice/Safety Studies, B
Early Childhood Education and Teaching, B
Electrical, Electronic and Communications
Engineering Technology/Technician, B
Elementary Education and Teaching, B
Hotel/Motel Administration/Management, B
Kindergarten/PreSchool Education and Teaching, B
Management Information Systems and Services, B
Marketing/Marketing Management, B
Microbiology, B
Nursing, AB
Parks, Recreation and Leisure Facilities
Management, B
Pharmacy Technician/Assistant, A
Social Psychology, B
Spanish Language Teacher Education, B
Teaching English as a Second or Foreign
Language/ESL Language Instructor, B

INTER AMERICAN UNIVERSITY OF PUERTO RICO, ARECIBO CAMPUS

Accounting, AB
Administrative Assistant and Secretarial Science, AB
Biology/Biological Sciences, B
Business Administration and Management, AB
Chemistry, AB
Computer Science, AB
Counselor Education/School Counseling and
Guidance Services, M
Criminal Justice/Law Enforcement Administration, B
Education, BM
Educational Administration and Supervision, M
Elementary Education and Teaching, AB
Kindergarten/PreSchool Education and Teaching, B
Marketing/Marketing Management, B
Medical Microbiology and Bacteriology, B
Nurse Anesthetist, M
Nursing - Registered Nurse Training, AB
Secondary Education and Teaching, B
Social Work, B
Special Education and Teaching, B

Teaching English as a Second or Foreign Language/ESL Language Instructor, B

INTER AMERICAN UNIVERSITY OF PUERTO RICO, BARRANQUITAS CAMPUS

Accounting, AB
Administrative Assistant and Secretarial Science, AB
Biology/Biological Sciences, AB
Business Administration and Management, AB
Computer and Information Sciences, AB
Computer Programming, AB
Computer Science, A
Criminal Justice/Law Enforcement Administration, B
Education, AB
Education/Teaching of Individuals with Multiple Disabilities, AB
Elementary and Middle School Administration/Principalship, AB
Elementary Education and Teaching, AB
Floriculture/Floristry Operations and Management, A
Microbiology, AB
Nursing - Registered Nurse Training, A
Plant Nursery Operations and Management, A
Radiation Biology/Radiobiology, AB
Secondary Education and Teaching, B

INTER AMERICAN UNIVERSITY OF PUERTO RICO, BAYAMÓN CAMPUS

Accounting, AB
Administrative Assistant and Secretarial Science, AB
Aeronautics/Aviation/Aerospace Science and Technology, B
Aerospace, Aeronautical and Astronautical Engineering, B
Air Traffic Controller, B
Airline/Commercial/Professional Pilot and Flight Crew, B
Applied Mathematics, B
Aviation/Airway Management and Operations, B
Biochemistry, B
Biological and Biomedical Sciences, B
Biology/Biological Sciences, B
Business Administration and Management, AB
Business, Management, Marketing, and Related Support Services, B
Business/Managerial Economics, B
Business/Office Automation/Technology/Data Entry, B
Chemical Technology/Technician, B
Chemistry, B
Communication Studies/Speech Communication and Rhetoric, B
Communications Technology/Technician, B
Computer and Information Sciences and Support Services, B
Computer Installation and Repair Technology/Technician, AB
Computer Programming/Programmer, B
Computer Science, AB
Computer Systems Analysis/Analyst, B
Electrical, Electronic and Communications Engineering Technology/Technician, B
Electrical, Electronics and Communications Engineering, B
Engineering, B
Entrepreneurship/Entrepreneurial Studies, B
Environmental Biology, B
Environmental Control Technologies/Technicians, B
Executive Assistant/Executive Secretary, B
Finance, B
Forensic Science and Technology, B
Human Resources Management/Personnel Administration, B
Industrial Engineering, B
Management Information Systems and Services, AB
Management Science, B
Marketing Research, B
Marketing/Marketing Management, B
Mass Communication/Media Studies, AB
Mathematics, B
Mechanical Engineering, B
Medical Microbiology and Bacteriology, B
Pre-Medicine/Pre-Medical Studies, B

Telecommunications Technology/Technician, AB

INTER AMERICAN UNIVERSITY OF PUERTO RICO, FAJARDO CAMPUS

Accounting, A
Administrative Assistant and Secretarial Science, AB
Art Teacher Education, B
Aviation/Airway Management and Operations, B
Avionics Maintenance Technology/Technician, B
Biology/Biological Sciences, B
Business Administration and Management, AB
Business Teacher Education, AB
Clinical Laboratory Science/Medical Technology/Technologist, B
Computer Science, AB
Criminal Justice/Law Enforcement Administration, B
Criminal Justice/Police Science, A
Economics, B
Education, B
Electrical, Electronics and Communications Engineering, B
Elementary Education and Teaching, AB
History, B
Hotel/Motel Administration/Management, B
Marketing/Marketing Management, A
Music, B
Nursing - Registered Nurse Training, AB
Physical Education Teaching and Coaching, B
Social Work, B
Sociology, B
Special Education and Teaching, B
Teaching English as a Second or Foreign Language/ESL Language Instructor, B
Tourism and Travel Services Management, B

INTER AMERICAN UNIVERSITY OF PUERTO RICO, GUAYAMA CAMPUS

Accounting, AB
Administrative Assistant and Secretarial Science, AB
Business Administration and Management, AB
Chemical Engineering, B
Chemistry, AB
Computer Science, A
Criminal Justice/Law Enforcement Administration, B
Elementary Education and Teaching, AB
Human Resources Management/Personnel Administration, B
Kindergarten/PreSchool Education and Teaching, B
Landscaping and Groundskeeping, A
Nursing - Registered Nurse Training, AB
Physical Education Teaching and Coaching, B
Special Education and Teaching, B
Teaching English as a Second or Foreign Language/ESL Language Instructor, B

INTER AMERICAN UNIVERSITY OF PUERTO RICO, METROPOLITAN CAMPUS

Accounting, ABM
Administrative Assistant and Secretarial Science, AB
Behavioral Sciences, B
Biology Teacher Education, B
Biology/Biological Sciences, B
Biomedical Sciences, B
Business Administration and Management, AB
Business Education, M
Business/Managerial Economics, B
Chemistry, B
Chemistry Teacher Education, B
Clinical Laboratory Science/Medical Technology/Technologist, B
Comparative Literature, B
Computer Engineering Technology/Technician, B
Computer Programming/Programmer, B
Computer Science, BM
Counselor Education/School Counseling and Guidance Services, M
Criminal Justice/Law Enforcement Administration, B
Criminology, M
Economics, B
Education, BMD
Educational Administration and Supervision, M
Educational Media/Instructional Technology, M
Elementary Education and Teaching, BM

Emergency Medical Technology/Technician (EMT Paramedic), A
English as a Second Language, M
English Language and Literature, B
Environmental Studies, B
Finance, B
Finance and Banking, M
Health and Physical Education, B
Health Education, M
Higher Education/Higher Education Administration, M
History, B
History Teacher Education, B
Human Resources Development, M
Human Resources Management and Services, M
Industrial and Labor Relations, M
Industrial and Manufacturing Management, M
Information Science/Studies, B
International Business/Trade/Commerce, M
Junior High/Intermediate/Middle School Education and Teaching, B
Kindergarten/PreSchool Education and Teaching, B
Law and Legal Studies, P
Management Information Systems and Services, B
Marketing, M
Marketing/Marketing Management, B
Mathematics, B
Mathematics Teacher Education, B
Medical Technology, M
Music, B
Nursing - Registered Nurse Training, AB
Physical Education Teaching and Coaching, BM
Physics, B
Physics Teacher Education, B
Political Science and Government, B
Pre-Medicine/Pre-Medical Studies, B
Psychology, BM
Science Teacher Education/General Science Teacher Education, M
Social Studies Teacher Education, B
Social Work, BM
Sociology, B
Spanish Language and Literature, BM
Spanish Language Teacher Education, B
Special Education and Teaching, BM
Teaching English as a Second or Foreign Language/ESL Language Instructor, B
Theology and Religious Vocations, D
Vocational and Technical Education, M

INTER AMERICAN UNIVERSITY OF PUERTO RICO, PONCE CAMPUS

Accounting, AB
Administrative Assistant and Secretarial Science, AB
Biology/Biological Sciences, B
Business Administration and Management, AB
Communication, Journalism and Related Programs, B
Computer Science, AB
Criminal Justice/Law Enforcement Administration, B
Education, B
Elementary Education and Teaching, B
Environmental Sciences, B
Finance, B
Hotel/Motel Administration/Management, B
Human Resources Management/Personnel Administration, B
Information Science/Studies, B
International Business/Trade/Commerce, B
Journalism, B
Kindergarten/PreSchool Education and Teaching, B
Marketing/Marketing Management, B
Nursing - Registered Nurse Training, A
Secondary Education and Teaching, B
Special Education and Teaching, B
Tourism and Travel Services Management, A

INTER AMERICAN UNIVERSITY OF PUERTO RICO, SAN GERMÁN CAMPUS

Accounting, ABM
Administrative Assistant and Secretarial Science, AB
Applied Art, B
Applied Mathematics, BM
Art History, Criticism and Conservation, B
Art Teacher Education, B

Art/Art Studies, General, B
Behavioral Sciences, B
Biology/Biological Sciences, B
Biomedical Sciences, B
Business Administration and Management, AB
Business Administration, Management and
Operations, MD
Business Education, M
Business/Managerial Economics, B
Ceramic Arts and Ceramics, BM
Chemistry, B
Clinical Laboratory Science/Medical
Technology/Technologist, B
Comparative Literature, B
Computer Programming/Programmer, B
Computer Science, B
Counseling Psychology, MD
Counselor Education/School Counseling and
Guidance Services, M
Drawing, B
Economics, B
Education, B
Educational Administration and Supervision, M
Electrical, Electronic and Communications
Engineering Technology/Technician, B
Elementary Education and Teaching, B
English as a Second Language, M
English Language and Literature, B
Entrepreneurship/Entrepreneurial Studies, D
Environmental Sciences, M
Environmental Studies, B
Finance, B
Finance and Banking, M
Fine Arts and Art Studies, M
Health Information/Medical Records
Administration/Administrator, A
Human Resources Development, M
Human Resources Management and Services, MD
Human Resources Management/Personnel
Administration, B
Industrial and Labor Relations, MD
Industrial Radiologic Technology/Technician, A
Information Science/Studies, B
International Business/Trade/Commerce, D
Kindergarten/PreSchool Education and Teaching, B
Kinesiology and Movement Studies, M
Library Science, M
Linguistics, B
Management, D
Management Information Systems and Services, M
Marketing, BM
Marketing/Marketing Management, B
Mathematics, B
Medical Microbiology and Bacteriology, B
Music, B
Music Teacher Education, BM
Natural Sciences, B
Nursing - Registered Nurse Training, B
Painting, M
Photography, BM
Physical Education Teaching and Coaching, BM
Piano and Organ, B
Political Science and Government, B
Printmaking, M
Psychology, BMD
Public Administration, B
Public Health (MPH, DPH), B
School Psychology, MD
Science Teacher Education/General Science
Teacher Education, BM
Sculpture, BM
Secondary Education and Teaching, B
Social Sciences, B
Sociology, B
Spanish Language and Literature, B
Special Education and Teaching, M
Teaching English as a Second or Foreign
Language/ESL Language Instructor, B
Violin, Viola, Guitar and Other Stringed
Instruments, B
Voice and Opera, B

Wind and Percussion Instruments, B

POLYTECHNIC UNIVERSITY OF PUERTO RICO

Architecture, B
Business Administration and Management, B
Business Administration, Management and
Operations, M
Chemical Engineering, B
Civil Engineering, BM
Computer Engineering, BM
Electrical Engineering, M
Electrical, Electronics and Communications
Engineering, B
Engineering Management, M
Environmental Policy and Resource
Management, M
Environmental/Environmental Health Engineering, B
Finance, B
Industrial and Manufacturing Management, M
Industrial Engineering, B
Manufacturing Engineering, M
Marketing/Marketing Management, B
Mechanical Engineering, B
Survey Technology/Surveying, B

PONTIFICAL CATHOLIC UNIVERSITY OF PUERTO RICO

Accounting, BM
Administrative Assistant and Secretarial Science, AB
Art Teacher Education, B
Art/Art Studies, General, AB
Biological and Physical Sciences, B
Biology Teacher Education, B
Biology/Biological Sciences, B
Business Administration and Management, AB
Business Administration, Management and
Operations, MDO
Business Teacher Education, B
Chemistry, BM
Clinical Laboratory Science/Medical
Technology/Technologist, B
Clinical Psychology, M
Computer Programming/Programmer, A
Computer Science, B
Computer Teacher Education, B
Criminal Justice/Law Enforcement Administration, B
Criminology, BM
Curriculum and Instruction, M
Economics, B
Education, ABMD
Educational Media/Instructional Technology, M
Elementary Education and Teaching, B
English as a Second Language, M
English Language and Literature, B
English/Language Arts Teacher Education, B
Environmental Studies, B
Family and Consumer Sciences/Home Economics
Teacher Education, B
Family and Consumer Sciences/Human Sciences, B
Fashion/Apparel Design, B
Finance, B
Finance and Banking, M
French Language and Literature, B
Gerontology, AB
Health Teacher Education, B
Hispanic Studies, M
Hispanic-American, Puerto Rican, and Mexican-
American/Chicano Studies, B
History, BM
History Teacher Education, B
Human Resources Management and Services, M
Human Resources Management/Personnel
Administration, B
Human Services, MD
Industrial and Organizational Psychology, M
International Business/Trade/Commerce, B
Kindergarten/PreSchool Education and Teaching, B
Law and Legal Studies, PO
Liberal Arts and Sciences Studies and
Humanities, B
Marketing, M
Marketing/Marketing Management, B
Mass Communication/Media Studies, B
Maternal/Child Health and Neonatal
Nurse/Nursing, M

Mathematics, B
Mathematics Teacher Education, B
Medical/Surgical Nursing, M
Music, B
Music Teacher Education, B
Nursing, M
Nursing - Registered Nurse Training, B
Philosophy, B
Physical Education Teaching and Coaching, B
Physics, B
Political Science and Government, B
Pre-Law Studies, B
Pre-Medicine/Pre-Medical Studies, B
Psychiatric/Mental Health Nurse/Nursing, M
Psychology, BD
Public Administration, BM
Public Relations/Image Management, B
Publishing, B
Radio and Television, B
Religious Education, M
School Psychology, M
Science Teacher Education/General Science
Teacher Education, B
Secondary Education and Teaching, B
Social Studies Teacher Education, B
Social Work, BM
Sociology, B
Spanish Language and Literature, B
Special Education and Teaching, B
Theology and Religious Vocations, M
Theology/Theological Studies, B
Tourism and Travel Services Management, B
Tourism and Travel Services Marketing
Operations, A

RAMÍREZ COLLEGE OF BUSINESS AND TECHNOLOGY

Accounting, A
Administrative Assistant and Secretarial Science, A
Business Administration and Management, A
Dental Hygiene/Hygienist, A

TECHNOLOGICAL COLLEGE OF SAN JUAN

Accounting, A
Administrative Assistant and Secretarial Science, A
Computer and Information Sciences, A
Computer Programming/Programmer, A
Electrical, Electronic and Communications
Engineering Technology/Technician, A
Liberal Arts and Sciences Studies and
Humanities, A
Nursing - Registered Nurse Training, A

UNIVERSIDAD ADVENTISTA DE LAS ANTILLAS

Administrative Assistant and Secretarial Science, AB
Bible/Biblical Studies, AB
Biology Teacher Education, B
Biology/Biological Sciences, B
Business Administration and Management, AB
Chemistry, B
Computer Science, AB
Elementary Education and Teaching, B
Health Information/Medical Records
Administration/Administrator, A
History, B
History Teacher Education, B
Mathematics Teacher Education, B
Medical Administrative Assistant/Secretary, A
Music, B
Music Teacher Education, B
Nursing - Registered Nurse Training, AB
Pastoral Studies/Counseling, B
Religious Education, B
Respiratory Care Therapy/Therapist, AB
Secondary Education and Teaching, B
Social Studies Teacher Education, B
Spanish Language and Literature, B
Spanish Language Teacher Education, B

Theology/Theological Studies, B

UNIVERSIDAD CENTRAL DEL CARIBE

Allopathic Medicine, PO

UNIVERSIDAD DEL ESTE

Accounting, A
Administrative Assistant and Secretarial Science, A
Biological and Physical Sciences, A
Business Administration and Management, A
Computer Programming/Programmer, A
Health Information/Medical Records
   Administration/Administrator, A
Industrial Radiologic Technology/Technician, A
Legal Assistant/Paralegal, A
Liberal Arts and Sciences Studies and
   Humanities, A
Marketing/Marketing Management, A
Pharmacy, A
Social Work, A

UNIVERSIDAD METROPOLITANA

Accounting, BMO
Administrative Assistant and Secretarial Science, B
Applied Mathematics, B
Bilingual and Multilingual Education, B
Biology/Biological Sciences, B
Business Administration and Management, B
Business Administration, Management and
   Operations, MO
Computer Science, B
Criminal Justice/Safety Studies, B
Curriculum and Instruction, M
Early Childhood Education and Teaching, M
Economics, B
Education, M
Educational Administration and Supervision, M
Elementary Education and Teaching, B
Environmental Education, M
Environmental Policy and Resource
   Management, M
Environmental Studies, B
Human Resources Management and Services, M
Human Resources Management/Personnel
   Administration, B
Information Science/Studies, B
Kindergarten/PreSchool Education and Teaching, B
Leisure Studies, M
Marketing, M
Marketing/Marketing Management, B
Natural Resources Management/Development and
   Policy, M
Natural Sciences, AB
Nursing - Registered Nurse Training, AB
Parks, Recreation, Leisure and Fitness Studies, B
Physical Education Teaching and Coaching, M
Physics Teacher Education, B
Pre-Medicine/Pre-Medical Studies, B
Psychology, B
Recreation and Park Management, M
Respiratory Care Therapy/Therapist, B
Science Teacher Education/General Science
   Teacher Education, B
Secondary Education and Teaching, B
Social Sciences, B
Special Education and Teaching, BM

UNIVERSIDAD DEL TURABO

Accounting, BM
Administrative Assistant and Secretarial Science, AB
Applied Mathematics, B
Biology/Biological Sciences, B
Business Administration and Management, B
Business Administration, Management and
   Operations, M
Chemistry, B
Computer Science, A
Criminology, BM
Education, BM
Educational Administration and Supervision, M
Electrical, Electronics and Communications
   Engineering, B
Elementary Education and Teaching, B
Engineering Mechanics, B
English as a Second Language, M
English Language and Literature, B

Environmental Studies, M
History, B
Human Resources Development, M
Human Resources Management and Services, M
Human Services, M
Humanities/Humanistic Studies, B
Industrial Engineering, B
Liberal Arts and Sciences Studies and
   Humanities, B
Logistics and Materials Management, M
Management, M
Marketing, M
Mass Communication/Media Studies, B
Mathematics, B
Mechanical Engineering, B
Multilingual and Multicultural Education, M
Natural Sciences, B
Physical Education Teaching and Coaching, B
Psychology, B
Public Administration, AB
Social Sciences, B
Social Work, B
Spanish Language and Literature, B
Special Education and Teaching, BM

UNIVERSITY OF PHOENIX-PUERTO RICO CAMPUS

Accounting, M
Business Administration and Management, B
Business Administration, Management and
   Operations, M
Curriculum and Instruction, M
Early Childhood Education and Teaching, M
Education, M
Educational Administration and Supervision, M
Electronic Commerce, M
Health Services Administration, M
Human Resources Management and Services, M
International Business/Trade/Commerce, M
Management of Technology, M
Marketing, M
Marketing/Marketing Management, B
Marriage and Family Therapy/Counseling, M

UNIVERSITY OF PUERTO RICO, AGUADILLA UNIVERSITY COLLEGE

Accounting, B
Administrative Assistant and Secretarial Science, AB
Biological and Physical Sciences, A
Business Administration and Management, AB
Computer Programming/Programmer, A
Electrical, Electronic and Communications
   Engineering Technology/Technician, AB
Environmental Studies, A
Liberal Arts and Sciences Studies and
   Humanities, A
Quality Control Technology/Technician, AB

UNIVERSITY OF PUERTO RICO AT ARECIBO

Accounting, B
Animal Sciences, A
Business Administration and Management, AB
Computer Science, AB
Elementary Education and Teaching, AB
Finance, B
Humanities/Humanistic Studies, A
Industrial Technology/Technician, B
Medical Microbiology and Bacteriology, B
Natural Sciences, A
Office Management and Supervision, AB
Radio and Television Broadcasting
   Technology/Technician, AB

UNIVERSITY OF PUERTO RICO AT BAYAMÓN

Accounting, AB
Administrative Assistant and Secretarial Science, AB
Biological and Physical Sciences, A
Business Administration and Management, AB
Civil Engineering Technology/Technician, A
Computer Science, AB
Construction Engineering Technology/Technician, A
Education, A

Electrical, Electronic and Communications
   Engineering Technology/Technician, AB
European Studies/Civilization, A
Finance, AB
Humanities/Humanistic Studies, A
Industrial Technology/Technician, A
Instrumentation Technology/Technician, A
Kindergarten/PreSchool Education and Teaching, B
Marketing/Marketing Management, AB
Materials Sciences, B
Mechanical Engineering/Mechanical
   Technology/Technician, A
Natural Sciences, A
Physical Education Teaching and Coaching, AB
Pre-Engineering, A
Social Sciences, A
Special Education and Teaching, B
Survey Technology/Surveying, A

UNIVERSITY OF PUERTO RICO AT CAROLINA

Administrative Assistant and Secretarial Science, A
Advertising, A
Automobile/Automotive Mechanics
   Technology/Technician, A
Commercial and Advertising Art, A
Criminal Justice/Police Science, A
Education, A
Finance, A
Hotel/Motel Administration/Management, AB
Humanities/Humanistic Studies, A
Interior Design, A
Mechanical Engineering/Mechanical
   Technology/Technician, A
Natural Sciences, A
Physical Education Teaching and Coaching, A
Public Administration, A
Social Sciences, A

UNIVERSITY OF PUERTO RICO, CAYEY UNIVERSITY COLLEGE

Accounting, B
Administrative Assistant and Secretarial Science, AB
Army JROTC/ROTC, B
Biology Teacher Education, B
Biology/Biological Sciences, B
Business Administration and Management, B
Chemistry, B
Chemistry Teacher Education, B
Economics, B
Elementary Education and Teaching, B
English Language and Literature, B
English/Language Arts Teacher Education, B
History, B
History Teacher Education, B
Humanities/Humanistic Studies, B
Mathematics, B
Mathematics Teacher Education, B
Mental Health/Rehabilitation, B
Natural Sciences, B
Office Management and Supervision, B
Physical Education Teaching and Coaching, B
Physics Teacher Education, B
Psychology, B
Science Teacher Education/General Science
   Teacher Education, B
Secondary Education and Teaching, B
Social Science Teacher Education, B
Social Sciences, B
Social Studies Teacher Education, B
Sociology, B
Spanish and Iberian Studies, B
Spanish Language and Literature, B
Spanish Language Teacher Education, B
Teaching English as a Second or Foreign
   Language/ESL Language Instructor, B

UNIVERSITY OF PUERTO RICO AT HUMACAO

Accounting, AB
Administrative Assistant and Secretarial Science, AB
Biology/Biological Sciences, B
Business Administration and Management, AB
Business/Commerce, B
Chemical Technology/Technician, A

Chemistry, B
Electrical, Electronic and Communications
  Engineering Technology/Technician, A
Elementary Education and Teaching, B
Human Resources Management/Personnel
  Administration, B
Marine Biology and Biological Oceanography, B
Mathematics and Computer Science, B
Medical Microbiology and Bacteriology, B
Nursing - Registered Nurse Training, AB
Occupational Therapist Assistant, AB
Physical Therapist Assistant, A
Physics, B
Social Work, B
Teaching English as a Second or Foreign
  Language/ESL Language Instructor, B
Wildlife and Wildlands Science and Management, B

UNIVERSITY OF PUERTO RICO, MAYAGÜEZ CAMPUS

Accounting, B
Administrative Assistant and Secretarial Science, B
Agricultural Business and Management, B
Agricultural Economics, BM
Agricultural Education, M
Agricultural Mechanization, B
Agricultural Sciences, M
Agricultural Teacher Education, B
Agriculture, B
Agronomy and Crop Science, B
Agronomy and Soil Sciences, M
Animal Sciences, BM
Applied Mathematics, M
Art/Art Studies, General, B
Biological and Biomedical Sciences, M
Biology Technician/BioTechnology Laboratory
  Technician, B
Biology/Biological Sciences, B
Business Administration and Management, B
Business Administration, Management and
  Operations, M
Chemical Engineering, BMD
Chemistry, BM
Civil Engineering, BMD
Clinical Laboratory Science/Medical
  Technology/Technologist, B
Comparative Literature, B
Computational Sciences, M
Computer Engineering, BM
Computer Science, B
Economics, B
Electrical Engineering, M
Electrical, Electronics and Communications
  Engineering, B
Engineering and Applied Sciences, MD
English, M
English Language and Literature, B
Finance, B
Finance and Banking, M
Food Science and Technology, M
French Language and Literature, B
Geology/Earth Science, BM
Hispanic Studies, M
Hispanic-American, Puerto Rican, and Mexican-
  American/Chicano Studies, B
History, B
Horticultural Science, BM
Human Resources Management and Services, M
Human Resources Management/Personnel
  Administration, B
Humanities/Humanistic Studies, B
Industrial and Manufacturing Management, M
Industrial Engineering, B
Industrial/Management Engineering, M
Information Science/Studies, BD
Latin American Studies, B
Marine Sciences, MD
Marketing, M
Marketing/Marketing Management, B
Mathematics, BM
Mechanical Engineering, BM
Medical Microbiology and Bacteriology, B
Nursing - Registered Nurse Training, B
Oceanography, Chemical and Physical, MD
Philosophy, B
Physical Education Teaching and Coaching, B

Physical Sciences, B
Physics, BM
Political Science and Government, B
Pre-Medicine/Pre-Medical Studies, B
Pre-Veterinary Studies, B
Psychology, B
Social Sciences, B
Sociology, B
Statistics, M
Survey Technology/Surveying, B

UNIVERSITY OF PUERTO RICO, MEDICAL SCIENCES CAMPUS

Allied Health and Medical Assisting Services, MO
Allopathic Medicine, P
Anatomy, MD
Audiology/Audiologist and Speech-Language
  Pathology/Pathologist, B
Biochemistry, MD
Biological and Biomedical Sciences, MD
Biostatistics, M
Clinical Laboratory Sciences, M
Communication Disorders, M
Demography, M
Dental and Oral Surgery, M
Dental Assisting/Assistant, A
Dental Hygiene/Hygienist, A
Dentistry, P
Environmental and Occupational Health, MD
Epidemiology, M
Gerontology, MO
Health and Medical Laboratory Technologies, B
Health Education, M
Health Informatics, M
Health Services Administration, M
Health Services Research, M
Health Teacher Education, B
Human Development, MO
Industrial Hygiene, M
Maternal and Child Health, M
Medical Radiologic Technology/Science - Radiation
  Therapist, A
Medical Technology, O
Microbiology, MD
Nuclear Medical Technology/Technologist, B
Nurse Anesthetist, M
Nurse Midwife/Nursing Midwifery, MO
Nursing, M
Nursing - Advanced Practice, M
Nursing - Registered Nurse Training, B
Nursing Administration, M
Nursing Education, M
Nutritional Sciences, MDO
Occupational Therapy/Therapist, B
Ophthalmic Laboratory Technology/Technician, A
Oral and Dental Sciences, MO
Orthodontics, M
Pedodontics, M
Pharmaceutical Sciences, M
Pharmacology, MD
Pharmacy, BMP
Physical Therapy/Therapist, BM
Physiology, MD
Public Health, M
Public Health (MPH, DPH), B
Special Education and Teaching, O
Toxicology, MD
Veterinary/Animal Health Technology/Technician and
  Veterinary Assistant, B
Zoology/Animal Biology, MD

UNIVERSITY OF PUERTO RICO AT PONCE

Accounting, AB
Administrative Assistant and Secretarial Science, AB
Athletic Training and Sports Medicine, B
Business Administration and Management, AB
Civil Engineering Technology/Technician, A
Computer Science, AB
Drafting and Design Technology/Technician, A
Elementary Education and Teaching, B
Industrial Technology/Technician, A
Liberal Arts and Sciences Studies and
  Humanities, A
Natural Sciences, A
Occupational Therapy/Therapist, A

Physical Therapy/Therapist, A

UNIVERSITY OF PUERTO RICO, RÍO PIEDRAS

Accounting, B
Administrative Assistant and Secretarial Science, B
American History (United States), B
Anthropology, B
Applied Physics, M
Architecture, M
Art History, Criticism and Conservation, B
Art/Art Studies, General, B
Biological and Biomedical Sciences, MD
Biological and Physical Sciences, B
Biology/Biological Sciences, B
Business Administration and Management, B
Business Administration, Management and
  Operations, MD
Business Statistics, B
Business/Commerce, B
Business/Managerial Economics, B
Chemistry, BMD
Child Development, B
Comparative Literature, BM
Computer and Information Sciences, B
Computer Science, B
Counselor Education/School Counseling and
  Guidance Services, MD
Curriculum and Instruction, MD
Dietetics/Dieticians, B
Drama and Dramatics/Theatre Arts, B
Drawing, B
Early Childhood Education and Teaching, M
Economics, BM
Education, MD
Educational Administration and Supervision, MD
Educational Measurement and Evaluation, M
Elementary Education and Teaching, B
English, MD
English as a Second Language, M
English Education, M
English Language and Literature, B
Entrepreneurship/Entrepreneurial Studies, B
Environmental Design/Architecture, B
Environmental Studies, B
European History, B
Family and Consumer Sciences/Human
  Sciences, BM
Finance, B
Foods, Nutrition, and Wellness Studies, B
Foreign Language Teacher Education, M
Foreign Languages and Literatures, B
French Language and Literature, B
General Studies, B
Geography, B
Hispanic Studies, MD
History, MD
Human Resources Management/Personnel
  Administration, B
Humanities/Humanistic Studies, B
Information Science/Studies, M
Interdisciplinary Studies, B
Intermedia/Multimedia, B
Labor and Industrial Relations, B
Law and Legal Studies, MP
Library Science, MO
Linguistics, M
Marketing/Marketing Management, B
Mass Communication/Media Studies, BM
Mathematics, BMD
Mathematics Teacher Education, M
Music, B
Natural Sciences, B
Nutritional Sciences, M
Painting, B
Philosophy, BM
Physics, MD
Political Science and Government, B
Psychology, BMD
Public Administration, M
Rehabilitation Counseling, M
Science Teacher Education/General Science
  Teacher Education, M
Sculpture, B
Secondary Education and Teaching, BM
Social Sciences, B

Social Studies Teacher Education, M
Social Work, BMD
Sociology, BM
Spanish Language and Literature, B
Special Education and Teaching, M
Translation and Interpretation, MO
Urban and Regional Planning, M

UNIVERSITY OF PUERTO RICO AT UTUADO

Agricultural Production Operations, A
Animal Sciences, A
Business Administration and Management, A
Education, A
Elementary Education and Teaching, B
Food Science, A
General Office Occupations and Clerical Services, A
Horticultural Science, A
Natural Sciences, A
Office Management and Supervision, B
Plant Protection and Integrated Pest
    Management, A
Social Sciences, A

UNIVERSITY OF THE SACRED HEART

Accounting, B
Administrative Assistant and Secretarial Science, B
Advertising, B
Advertising and Public Relations, M
Bilingual and Multilingual Education, B
Biology/Biological Sciences, B
Business Administration and Management, B
Business Administration, Management and
    Operations, M
Chemistry, B
Clinical Laboratory Science/Medical
    Technology/Technologist, B
Communication and Media Studies, M
Communication Studies/Speech Communication
    and Rhetoric, B
Comparative Literature, B
Computer Science, B
Criminal Justice/Safety Studies, B
Cultural Studies, M
Drama and Dramatics/Theatre Arts, B
Education, BM
Educational Media/Instructional Technology, M
Elementary Education and Teaching, B
Environmental and Occupational Health, M
Foreign Languages, Literatures, and Linguistics, B
Human Resources Management and Services, M
Humanities/Humanistic Studies, B
Information Science/Studies, B
Interdisciplinary Studies, B
Journalism, BM
Kinesiology and Exercise Science, B
Management Information Systems and Services, M
Marketing, M
Marketing/Marketing Management, B
Mass Communication/Media Studies, BM
Medical Technology, O
Non-Profit/Public/Organizational Management, M
Nursing - Registered Nurse Training, AB
Office Management and Supervision, B
Psychology, B
Secondary Education and Teaching, B
Social Sciences, B
Social Work, B
Taxation, M
Telecommunications Technology/Technician, B
Tourism and Travel Services Management, B
Tourism and Travel Services Marketing
    Operations, B
Visual and Performing Arts, B

Rhode Island

BROWN UNIVERSITY

Aerospace, Aeronautical and Astronautical
    Engineering, MD
African-American/Black Studies, B
Allopathic Medicine, PO
American/United States Studies/Civilization, BMD
Anthropology, BMD
Applied Mathematics, BMD

Archeology, BMD
Architectural History and Criticism, B
Art History, Criticism and Conservation, BMD
Art/Art Studies, General, B
Behavioral Sciences, B
Biochemistry, BMDO
Biological and Biomedical Sciences, MDO
Biology/Biological Sciences, B
Biomedical Engineering, MD
Biomedical Sciences, B
Biomedical/Medical Engineering, B
Biophysics, B
Biostatistics, MDO
BioTechnology, MD
Cancer Biology/Oncology, D
Cell Biology and Anatomy, MDO
Chemical Engineering, BMD
Chemistry, BMD
Civil Engineering, B
Classics and Classical
    Languages, Literatures, and Linguistics, BMD
Cognitive Psychology and Psycholinguistics, B
Cognitive Sciences, MD
Community Health and Preventive Medicine, MDO
Comparative Literature, BMD
Computer Engineering, B
Computer Science, BMD
Creative Writing, B
Demography and Population Studies, D
Development Economics and International
    Development, B
Developmental Biology and Embryology, MD
Drama and Dramatics/Theatre Arts, B
East Asian Studies, B
Ecology, D
Economics, BMD
Education, BM
Electrical Engineering, MD
Electrical, Electronics and Communications
    Engineering, B
Elementary Education and Teaching, M
Engineering, B
Engineering and Applied Sciences, MD
Engineering Physics, B
English, MD
English Education, M
English Language and Literature, B
Environmental Sciences, B
Environmental Studies, BM
Epidemiology, MDO
Evolutionary Biology, D
Film/Cinema Studies, B
Fine/Studio Arts, B
French Language and Literature, BMD
French Studies, B
Geochemistry, B
Geology/Earth Science, B
Geophysics and Seismology, B
Geosciences, MD
German Language and Literature, BMD
German Studies, B
Health Services Research, MD
Hebrew Studies, MD
Hispanic Studies, MD
Hispanic-American, Puerto Rican, and Mexican-
    American/Chicano Studies, B
History, BMD
History of Science and Technology, MD
Immunology, MD
International Relations and Affairs, B
Italian Language and Literature, BMD
Italian Studies, B
Jewish/Judaic Studies, B
Latin American Studies, BMD
Linguistics, BMD
Marine Biology and Biological Oceanography, B
Materials Engineering, B
Materials Sciences, MD
Mathematics, BMD
Mathematics and Computer Science, B
Mechanical Engineering, BMD
Mechanics, MD
Medieval and Renaissance Studies, B
Microbiology, MD
Molecular Biology, BMDO
Molecular Pharmacology, MDO

Multilingual and Multicultural Education, M
Music, BMD
Musicology and Ethnomusicology, B
Near and Middle Eastern Studies, B
Neuroscience, BD
Organizational Behavior Studies, B
Pathobiology, MD
Pathology/Experimental Pathology, D
Philosophy, BMD
Physics, BMD
Physiology, MDO
Political Science and Government, BMD
Psychology, BMD
Public Health, M
Public Policy Analysis, M
Religion/Religious Studies, BMD
Russian Language and Literature, MD
Russian Studies, B
Science Teacher Education/General Science
    Teacher Education, M
Secondary Education and Teaching, M
Slavic Languages, Literatures, and Linguistics, MD
Social Studies Teacher Education, M
Sociology, BMD
South Asian Studies, B
Spanish Language and Literature, B
Theater, M
Toxicology, D
Urban Studies/Affairs, B
Visual and Performing Arts, B
Western European Studies, MD
Women's Studies, B
Writing, M

BRYANT UNIVERSITY

Accounting, BMO
Accounting Technology/Technician and
    Bookkeeping, B
Actuarial Science, B
Business Administration and Management, B
Business Administration, Management and
    Operations, MO
Communication Studies/Speech Communication
    and Rhetoric, B
Computer and Information Sciences, B
Economics, B
Electronic Commerce, MO
English Language and Literature, B
Finance, B
Finance and Banking, MO
Finance and Financial Management Services, B
History, B
Industrial and Manufacturing Management, M
Information Science/Studies, M
Information Technology, B
International Business/Trade/Commerce, B
International Relations and Affairs, B
Management, MO
Management Information Systems and
    Services, MO
Marketing, MO
Marketing/Marketing Management, B
Psychology, B
Taxation, MO

COMMUNITY COLLEGE OF RHODE ISLAND

Accounting, A
Administrative Assistant and Secretarial Science, A
Adult Development and Aging, A
Art/Art Studies, General, A
Banking and Financial Support Services, A
Biological and Physical Sciences, A
Business Administration and Management, A
Business/Commerce, A
Chemical Technology/Technician, A
Clinical/Medical Laboratory Technician, A
Computer Engineering Technology/Technician, A
Computer Programming/Programmer, A
Criminal Justice/Police Science, A
Dental Hygiene/Hygienist, A
Drama and Dramatics/Theatre Arts, A
Electrical, Electronic and Communications
    Engineering Technology/Technician, A
Engineering, A
Fashion Merchandising, A

Fire Science/Firefighting, A
General Studies, A
Instrumentation Technology/Technician, A
Kindergarten/PreSchool Education and Teaching, A
Labor and Industrial Relations, A
Legal Administrative Assistant/Secretary, A
Legal Assistant/Paralegal, A
Liberal Arts and Sciences Studies and
   Humanities, A
Marketing/Marketing Management, A
Medical Administrative Assistant/Secretary, A
Medical Radiologic Technology/Science - Radiation
   Therapist, A
Music, A
Nursing - Registered Nurse Training, A
Occupational Therapist Assistant, A
Physical Therapist Assistant, A
Psychiatric/Mental Health Services Technician, A
Rehabilitation and Therapeutic Professions, A
Respiratory Care Therapy/Therapist, A
Retailing and Retail Operations, A
Social Work, A
Special Education and Teaching, A
Substance Abuse/Addiction Counseling, A
Technical Theatre/Theatre Design and
   Technology, A
Urban Studies/Affairs, A

JOHNSON & WALES UNIVERSITY

Accounting, ABM
Advertising, AB
Baking and Pastry Arts/Baker/Pastry Chef, AB
Business Administration and Management, AB
CAD/CADD Drafting and/or Design
   Technology/Technician, A
Computer and Information Sciences, B
Computer Engineering, B
Computer Engineering Technology/Technician, A
Computer Graphics, AB
Computer Programming/Programmer, A
Computer/Information Technology Services
   Administration and Management, AB
Consumer Merchandising/Retailing
   Management, AB
Criminal Justice/Law Enforcement
   Administration, AB
Culinary Arts/Chef Training, AB
Education, M
Educational Leadership and Administration, D
Electrical, Electronic and Communications
   Engineering Technology/Technician, AB
Electrical, Electronics and Communications
   Engineering, B
Equestrian/Equine Studies, AB
Farm/Farm and Ranch Management, AB
Fashion Merchandising, A
Finance, B
Finance and Banking, M
Food Technology and Processing, B
Foodservice Systems
   Administration/Management, B
Hospitality Administration/Management, BM
Hospitality and Recreation Marketing
   Operations, AB
Hotel/Motel Administration/Management, AB
Information Science/Studies, B
International Business/Trade/Commerce, M
International Trade, M
Legal Assistant/Paralegal, AB
Marketing, M
Marketing/Marketing Management, AB
Mass Communication/Media Studies, B
Organizational Management, M
Parks, Recreation and Leisure Facilities
   Management, AB
Parks, Recreation, Leisure and Fitness Studies, AB
Public Relations/Image Management, B
Restaurant, Culinary, and Catering
   Management/Manager, AB
Retailing and Retail Operations, AB
Sales, Distribution and Marketing Operations, AB
Special Products Marketing Operations, AB
Tourism and Travel Services Management, AB

Tourism and Travel Services Marketing
   Operations, AB

NEW ENGLAND INSTITUTE OF TECHNOLOGY

Architectural Engineering Technology/Technician, AB
Automobile/Automotive Mechanics
   Technology/Technician, A
Business Administration and Management, AB
Computer and Information Sciences, AB
Computer Technology/Computer Systems
   Technology, A
Construction Engineering Technology/Technician, A
Electrical, Electronic and Communications
   Engineering Technology/Technician, AB
Electrical, Electronics and Communications
   Engineering, B
Heating, Air Conditioning, Ventilation and
   Refrigeration Maintenance
   Technology/Technician, A
Industrial Technology/Technician, AB
Interior Design, A
Marine Maintenance/Fitter and Ship Repair
   Technology/Technician, A
Medical/Clinical Assistant, A
Occupational Therapist Assistant, A
Pipefitting/Pipefitter and Sprinkler Fitter, A
Radio and Television Broadcasting
   Technology/Technician, AB
Surgical Technology/Technologist, A

PROVIDENCE COLLEGE

Accounting, B
American/United States Studies/Civilization, B
Art History, Criticism and Conservation, B
Biochemistry, B
Biology/Biological Sciences, B
Business Administration and Management, B
Business Administration, Management and
   Operations, M
Business/Managerial Economics, B
Chemistry, B
Computer Education, M
Computer Science, B
Counselor Education/School Counseling and
   Guidance Services, M
Econometrics and Quantitative Economics, B
Economics, B
Education, M
Educational Administration and Supervision, M
English Language and Literature, B
Finance, B
Fine/Studio Arts, B
French Language and Literature, B
General Studies, B
Health/Health Care Administration/Management, B
History, BM
Human Services, B
Humanities/Humanistic Studies, B
Interdisciplinary Studies, B
International/Global Studies, B
Italian Language and Literature, B
Liberal Arts and Sciences Studies and
   Humanities, B
Marketing/Marketing Management, B
Mathematics, B
Mathematics Teacher Education, M
Music, B
Pastoral Studies/Counseling, M
Philosophy, B
Political Science and Government, B
Psychology, B
Reading Teacher Education, M
Religion/Religious Studies, M
Secondary Education and Teaching, B
Social Sciences, B
Social Work, B
Sociology, B
Spanish Language and Literature, B
Special Education and Teaching, BM
Systems Science and Theory, B
Theology and Religious Vocations, M
Theology/Theological Studies, B

Visual and Performing Arts, B

RHODE ISLAND COLLEGE

Accounting, BM
African-American/Black Studies, B
Anthropology, B
Art Education, M
Art History, Criticism and Conservation, B
Art Teacher Education, B
Arts Management, M
Biological and Biomedical Sciences, M
Biology Teacher Education, B
Biology/Biological Sciences, B
Business Administration and Management, B
Chemistry, B
Chemistry Teacher Education, B
Clinical Laboratory Science/Medical
   Technology/Technologist, B
Communication Studies/Speech Communication
   and Rhetoric, B
Computer and Information Sciences, B
Counselor Education/School Counseling and
   Guidance Services, MO
Criminal Justice/Safety Studies, B
Dance, B
Drama and Dramatics/Theatre Arts, B
Early Childhood Education and Teaching, BM
Economics, B
Education, BD
Educational Administration and Supervision, MO
Elementary Education and Teaching, BM
English, M
English as a Second Language, M
English Language and Literature, B
English/Language Arts Teacher Education, B
Film/Cinema Studies, B
Finance, B
Fine Arts and Art Studies, M
Fine/Studio Arts, B
Foreign Language Teacher Education, M
Foreign Languages and Literatures, B
French Language and Literature, BM
French Language Teacher Education, B
Geography, B
Health Education, M
Health Teacher Education, B
History, BM
History Teacher Education, B
Industrial Technology/Technician, B
Kindergarten/PreSchool Education and Teaching, B
Labor and Industrial Relations, B
Liberal Arts and Sciences Studies and
   Humanities, B
Management Information Systems and Services, B
Marketing/Marketing Management, B
Mathematics, BMO
Mathematics Teacher Education, B
Multilingual and Multicultural Education, M
Music, B
Music Performance, B
Music Teacher Education, BM
Nursing, B
Nursing - Registered Nurse Training, B
Philosophy, B
Physical Education Teaching and Coaching, B
Physics, B
Physics Teacher Education, B
Political Science and Government, B
Psychology, BM
Public Administration, B
Reading Teacher Education, M
Science Teacher Education/General Science
   Teacher Education, BM
Secondary Education and Teaching, BM
Social Science Teacher Education, B
Social Work, BM
Sociology, B
Spanish Language and Literature, B
Spanish Language Teacher Education, B
Special Education and Teaching, BMO
Teacher Education and Professional
   Development, Specific Levels and Methods, B
Teacher Education, Multiple Levels, B
Technical Teacher Education, B
Technology Teacher Education/Industrial Arts
   Teacher Education, B

Theater, M
Vocational and Technical Education, M
Women's Studies, B

RHODE ISLAND SCHOOL OF DESIGN

Applied Arts and Design, M
Architecture, BM
Art Education, M
Ceramic Arts and Ceramics, BM
Computer Art and Design, M
Fashion/Apparel Design, B
Fiber, Textile and Weaving Arts, B
Film/Cinema Studies, B
Fine Arts and Art Studies, B
Furniture Design and Manufacturing, B
Graphic Design, BM
Illustration, B
Industrial Design, BM
Interior Architecture, B
Interior Design, M
Jewelry/Metalsmithing, M
Landscape Architecture, M
Metal and Jewelry Arts, B
Painting, BM
Photography, BM
Printmaking, BM
Sculpture, BM
Textile Design, M

ROGER WILLIAMS UNIVERSITY

Accounting, B
American/United States Studies/Civilization, B
Anthropology, B
Architecture, BM
Art History, Criticism and Conservation, B
Art/Art Studies, General, B
Biology/Biological Sciences, B
Building/Construction
   Finishing, Management, and Inspection, B
Business Administration and Management, AB
Chemistry, B
Communication and Media Studies, B
Computer Science, B
Creative Writing, B
Criminal Justice/Law Enforcement
   Administration, AB
Criminology, M
Dance, B
Drama and Dramatics/Theatre Arts, B
Education, M
Elementary Education and Teaching, BM
English Language and Literature, B
Environmental Sciences, B
Finance, B
Financial Planning and Services, B
Foreign Languages and Literatures, B
Forensic Psychology, M
Graphic Design, B
Health/Health Care Administration/Management, B
Historic Preservation and Conservation, B
History, B
International Business/Trade/Commerce, B
Law and Legal Studies, PO
Legal Assistant/Paralegal, B
Legal Professions and Studies, B
Liberal Arts and Sciences Studies and
   Humanities, AB
Management Information Systems and Services, B
Manufacturing Technology/Technician, B
Marine Biology and Biological Oceanography, B
Marketing/Marketing Management, B
Mathematics, B
Multi-/Interdisciplinary Studies, B
Philosophy, B
Political Science and Government, B
Pre-Dentistry Studies, B
Pre-Medicine/Pre-Medical Studies, B
Pre-Veterinary Studies, B
Psychology, B
Public Administration, BM
Reading Teacher Education, M
Secondary Education and Teaching, B
Social Sciences, B
Sociology, B

Visual and Performing Arts, B

SALVE REGINA UNIVERSITY

Accounting, B
American/United States Studies/Civilization, B
Anthropology, B
Art History, Criticism and Conservation, B
Art Therapy/Therapist, O
Biology Teacher Education, B
Biology/Biological Sciences, B
Business Administration and Management, AB
Business Administration, Management and
   Operations, MO
Ceramic Arts and Ceramics, B
Chemistry, B
Clinical Laboratory Science/Medical
   Technology/Technologist, B
Communications Technology/Technician, B
Counseling Psychology, MO
Criminal Justice/Law Enforcement Administration, B
CytoTechnology/Cytotechnologist, B
Drama and Dance Teacher Education, B
Drama and Dramatics/Theatre Arts, B
Early Childhood Education and Teaching, B
Economics, B
Elementary Education and Teaching, B
English Language and Literature, B
English/Language Arts Teacher Education, B
Finance, B
Fine/Studio Arts, B
French Language and Literature, B
French Language Teacher Education, B
Graphic Design, B
Health Services Administration, MO
Historic Preservation and Conservation, B
History, B
History Teacher Education, B
Human Resources Development, O
Human Resources Management and Services, O
Humanities/Humanistic Studies, MDO
Information Science/Studies, B
International Affairs, MO
Law Enforcement, MO
Liberal Arts and Sciences Studies and
   Humanities, AB
Management, MO
Mathematics, B
Mathematics Teacher Education, B
Military and Defense Studies, M
Music, B
Music Teacher Education, B
Nursing - Registered Nurse Training, B
Painting, B
Philosophy, B
Photography, B
Political Science and Government, B
Psychology, B
Rehabilitation Counseling, MO
Religion/Religious Studies, B
Secondary Education and Teaching, B
Social Work, B
Sociology, B
Spanish Language and Literature, B
Spanish Language Teacher Education, B
Special Education and Teaching, B

UNIVERSITY OF RHODE ISLAND

Accounting, BM
Adult and Continuing Education and Teaching, M
Agricultural Economics, MD
Animal Sciences, BM
Anthropology, B
Apparel and Accessories Marketing Operations, B
Apparel and Textiles, B
Applied Economics, B
Applied Mathematics, D
Aquaculture, M
Art History, Criticism and Conservation, B
Art/Art Studies, General, B
Biochemistry, MD
Biological and Biomedical Sciences, MD
Biology/Biological Sciences, B
Biomedical/Medical Engineering, B
Business Administration and Management, B
Business Administration, Management and
   Operations, MD

Cell Biology and Anatomy, MD
Chemical Engineering, BMD
Chemistry, BMD
Child and Family Studies, M
Civil Engineering, BMD
Classics and Classical
   Languages, Literatures, and Linguistics, B
Clinical Laboratory Science/Medical
   Technology/Technologist, B
Clinical Laboratory Sciences, M
Clinical Psychology, D
Clothing and Textiles, M
Communication Disorders, BM
Communication Studies/Speech Communication
   and Rhetoric, B
Comparative Literature, B
Computer and Information Sciences, B
Computer Engineering, BMD
Computer Science, MD
Consumer Economics, B
Counseling Psychology, M
Dental Hygiene/Hygienist, B
Dietetics/Dieticians, B
Econometrics and Quantitative Economics, B
Economics, BMD
Education, M
Electrical Engineering, MD
Electrical, Electronics and Communications
   Engineering, B
Elementary Education and Teaching, BM
Engineering and Applied Sciences, MD
English, MD
English Language and Literature, B
Entomology, MD
Environmental Engineering
   Technology/Environmental Technology, MD
Environmental Policy and Resource
   Management, MD
Environmental Studies, B
Experimental Psychology, D
Finance, B
Finance and Banking, M
Fish, Game and Wildlife Management, MD
Fishing and Fisheries Sciences and Management, B
Food Science and Technology, MD
Foods, Nutrition, and Wellness Studies, B
French Language and Literature, BMD
Geology/Earth Science, B
Geosciences, M
Geotechnical Engineering, MD
German Language and Literature, B
Health Education, M
Health/Health Care Administration/Management, B
History, BM
Home Economics Education, M
Human Development and Family Studies, B
Human Services, B
Industrial and Labor Relations, M
Industrial Engineering, B
Industrial/Management Engineering, M
Information Science/Studies, M
Interdisciplinary Studies, B
International Business/Trade/Commerce, BM
International Development, O
Italian Language and Literature, B
Journalism, B
Landscape Architecture, B
Latin American Studies, B
Liberal Arts and Sciences Studies and
   Humanities, B
Library Science, M
Management, M
Management Information Systems and Services, B
Manufacturing Engineering, M
Marine Affairs, M
Marine Biology and Biological Oceanography, B
Marketing, M
Marketing/Marketing Management, B
Mathematics, BMD
Mechanical Engineering, BMD
Mechanics, M
Medical Microbiology and Bacteriology, B
Medicinal and Pharmaceutical Chemistry, MD
Microbiology, MD
Molecular Biology, MD
Music, BM

Music Performance, B
Music Teacher Education, B
Music Theory and Composition, B
Natural Resources and Conservation, BMD
Natural Resources Management/Development and
   Policy, B
Nursing, MD
Nursing - Registered Nurse Training, B
Nursing Administration, M
Nursing Education, M
Nutritional Sciences, MD
Ocean Engineering, BMD
Oceanography, Chemical and Physical, MD
Pharmaceutical Administration, M
Pharmaceutical Sciences, MD
Pharmacognosy, MD
Pharmacology, MD
Pharmacy, BP
Philosophy, BM
Physical Education Teaching and Coaching, BM
Physical Therapy/Therapist, M
Physics, BMD
Plant Pathology/Phytopathology, MD
Plant Sciences, MD
Political Science and Government, BMO
Psychology, BMD
Public Administration, M
Public Policy Analysis, BM
Quantitative Analysis, D
Reading Teacher Education, M
Recreation and Park Management, M
School Psychology, MD
Secondary Education and Teaching, BM
Sociology, B
Spanish Language and Literature, BM
Sport and Fitness Administration/Management, M
Statistics, MD
Structural Engineering, MD
Systems Engineering, MD
Toxicology, MD
Transportation and Highway Engineering, MD
Turf and Turfgrass Management, B
Urban and Regional Planning, M
Wildlife and Wildlands Science and Management, B
Women's Studies, B
Zoology/Animal Biology, B

South Carolina

AIKEN TECHNICAL COLLEGE

Accounting, A
Administrative Assistant and Secretarial Science, A
Biological and Physical Sciences, A
Business Administration and Management, A
Computer Engineering Technology/Technician, A
Electrical, Electronic and Communications
   Engineering Technology/Technician, A
Electromechanical Technology/Electromechanical
   Engineering Technology, A
Engineering Technology, A
Human Services, A
Industrial Technology/Technician, A
Interdisciplinary Studies, A
Liberal Arts and Sciences Studies and
   Humanities, A
Machine Tool Technology/Machinist, A
Marketing/Marketing Management, A
Nuclear/Nuclear Power Technology/Technician, A

ALLEN UNIVERSITY

Biology/Biological Sciences, B
Business Administration and Management, B
Chemistry, B
Education, B
Elementary Education and Teaching, B
English Language and Literature, B
Humanities/Humanistic Studies, B
Mathematics, B
Music, B
Religion/Religious Studies, B
Social Sciences, B

ANDERSON UNIVERSITY

Accounting, B
Art Teacher Education, B

Art/Art Studies, General, B
Biology Teacher Education, B
Biology/Biological Sciences, B
Business Administration and Management, B
Ceramic Arts and Ceramics, B
Commercial and Advertising Art, B
Creative Writing, B
Criminal Justice/Law Enforcement Administration, B
CytoTechnology/Cytotechnologist, B
Drama and Dramatics/Theatre Arts, B
Drawing, B
Education, B
Elementary Education and Teaching, B
English Language and Literature, B
English/Language Arts Teacher Education, B
Finance, B
Fine/Studio Arts, B
History, B
History Teacher Education, B
Human Resources Management/Personnel
   Administration, B
Human Services, B
Interior Design, B
Journalism, B
Kindergarten/PreSchool Education and Teaching, B
Liberal Arts and Sciences Studies and
   Humanities, A
Management Information Systems and Services, B
Marketing/Marketing Management, B
Mass Communication/Media Studies, B
Mathematics, B
Mathematics Teacher Education, B
Music, B
Music Performance, B
Music Teacher Education, B
Physical Education Teaching and Coaching, B
Psychology, B
Public Relations/Image Management, B
Religion/Religious Studies, B
Religious/Sacred Music, B
Secondary Education and Teaching, B
Spanish Language and Literature, B
Spanish Language Teacher Education, B
Special Education and Teaching, B
Speech and Rhetorical Studies, B

BENEDICT COLLEGE

Accounting, B
Administrative Assistant and Secretarial Science, B
Art Teacher Education, B
Art/Art Studies, General, B
Biology/Biological Sciences, B
Broadcast Journalism, B
Business Administration and Management, B
Chemistry, B
Child Development, B
Commercial and Advertising Art, B
Computer and Information Sciences, B
Computer Science, B
Criminal Justice/Law Enforcement Administration, B
Elementary Education and Teaching, B
English Language and Literature, B
Environmental Health, B
Finance, B
History, B
Journalism, B
Kindergarten/PreSchool Education and Teaching, B
Marketing/Marketing Management, B
Mathematics, B
Music, B
Parks, Recreation, Leisure and Fitness Studies, B
Philosophy, B
Physics, B
Political Science and Government, B
Pre-Dentistry Studies, B
Pre-Law Studies, B
Pre-Medicine/Pre-Medical Studies, B
Religion/Religious Studies, B
Social Work, B
Sociology, B

BOB JONES UNIVERSITY

Accounting, B
Actuarial Science, B
Apparel and Textiles, B
Applied Horticulture/Horticultural Operations, A

Art Teacher Education, B
Art/Art Studies, General, B
Aviation/Airway Management and Operations, B
Bible/Biblical Studies, B
Biology/Biological Sciences, B
Biophysics, B
Broadcast Journalism, B
Building/Construction Site Management/Manager, B
Business Administration and Management, B
Carpentry/Carpenter, A
Chemistry, B
Child Care and Support Services Management, AB
Cinematography and Film/Video Production, B
Commercial and Advertising Art, B
Communication Disorders, B
Communication Studies/Speech Communication
   and Rhetoric, B
Computer and Information Sciences, B
Computer Engineering, B
Computer Technology/Computer Systems
   Technology, B
Corrections and Criminal Justice, B
Cosmetology/Cosmetologist, A
Counseling Psychology, B
Creative Writing, B
Drama and Dramatics/Theatre Arts, B
Early Childhood Education and Teaching, B
Education/Teaching of Individuals with Emotional
   Disturbances, B
Education/Teaching of Individuals with Specific
   Learning Disabilities, B
Electrical, Electronics and Communications
   Engineering, B
Elementary Education and Teaching, B
Engineering Science, B
English Language and Literature, B
English/Language Arts Teacher Education, B
Family and Consumer Economics and Related
   Services, B
Finance, B
Foods, Nutrition, and Wellness Studies, B
French Language and Literature, B
General Office Occupations and Clerical Services, A
German Language and Literature, B
Health and Physical Education, B
Health/Medical Preparatory Programs, B
History, B
Hospitality Administration/Management, AB
Housing and Human Environments, B
Human Resources Management/Personnel
   Administration, B
Humanities/Humanistic Studies, B
International Business/Trade/Commerce, AB
International Relations and Affairs, B
Journalism, B
Junior High/Intermediate/Middle School Education
   and Teaching, B
Landscaping and Groundskeeping, B
Marketing/Marketing Management, B
Mathematics, B
Mathematics Teacher Education, B
Mechanic and Repair Technologies/Technicians, AB
Missions/Missionary Studies and Missiology, AB
Music, B
Music Performance, B
Music Teacher Education, B
Nursing - Registered Nurse Training, B
Office Management and Supervision, B
Operations Management and Supervision, B
Operations Research, B
Physics, B
Piano and Organ, B
Political Science and Government, B
Pre-Law Studies, B
Pre-Medicine/Pre-Medical Studies, B
Pre-Veterinary Studies, B
Radio and Television, B
Religious Education, B
Restaurant, Culinary, and Catering
   Management/Manager, A
Science Teacher Education/General Science
   Teacher Education, B
Social Studies Teacher Education, B
Spanish Language and Literature, B
Spanish Language Teacher Education, B
Special Education and Teaching, B

Speech and Rhetorical Studies, B
Speech-Language Pathology/Pathologist, B
Technical and Business Writing, B
Theological and Ministerial Studies, AB

CENTRAL CAROLINA TECHNICAL COLLEGE

Accounting, A
Administrative Assistant and Secretarial Science, A
Business Administration and Management, A
Child Care and Support Services Management, A
Civil Engineering Technology/Technician, A
Criminal Justice/Safety Studies, A
Data Processing and Data Processing Technology/Technician, A
Environmental Control Technologies/Technicians, A
Industrial Electronics Technology/Technician, A
Legal Assistant/Paralegal, A
Liberal Arts and Sciences Studies and Humanities, A
Mechanical Drafting and Mechanical Drafting CAD/CADD, A
Multi-/Interdisciplinary Studies, A
Natural Resources Management/Development and Policy, A
Nursing - Registered Nurse Training, A
Sales, Distribution and Marketing Operations, A
Surgical Technology/Technologist, A

CHARLESTON SOUTHERN UNIVERSITY

Accounting, BM
American History (United States), B
Applied Mathematics, B
Athletic Training and Sports Medicine, B
Biochemistry, B
Biological and Biomedical Sciences, B
Biological and Physical Sciences, B
Biology Teacher Education, B
Biology/Biological Sciences, B
Business Administration and Management, AB
Business Administration, Management and Operations, BM
Business/Managerial Economics, B
Chemistry, B
Computer Programming/Programmer, AB
Computer Science, B
Criminal Justice/Law Enforcement Administration, B
Criminal Justice/Safety Studies, B
Criminology, M
Dramatic/Theatre Arts and Stagecraft, B
Early Childhood Education and Teaching, B
Economics, B
Education, BM
Educational Administration and Supervision, M
Educational Leadership and Administration, B
Elementary and Middle School Administration/Principalship, B
Elementary Education and Teaching, BM
Engineering, B
Engineering Technology, B
English Education, M
English Language and Literature, B
English/Language Arts Teacher Education, B
Environmental Studies, B
European History, B
Finance, B
Finance and Banking, M
Health Services Administration, M
Health/Medical Preparatory Programs, B
History, B
History Teacher Education, B
Humanities/Humanistic Studies, B
Kindergarten/PreSchool Education and Teaching, B
Liberal Arts and Sciences Studies and Humanities, A
Management Information Systems and Services, BM
Marketing/Marketing Management, B
Mathematics, B
Mathematics Teacher Education, B
Music, B
Music Performance, B
Music Teacher Education, B
Music Therapy/Therapist, B

Natural Resources Management/Development and Policy, B
Natural Sciences, AB
Nursing - Registered Nurse Training, B
Organizational Management, M
Pastoral Studies/Counseling, B
Physical Education Teaching and Coaching, B
Physical Sciences, B
Political Science and Government, B
Pre-Dentistry Studies, B
Pre-Engineering, A
Pre-Law Studies, B
Pre-Medicine/Pre-Medical Studies, B
Pre-Pharmacy Studies, B
Psychology, B
Religion/Religious Studies, B
Religious/Sacred Music, B
Science Teacher Education/General Science Teacher Education, BM
Science Technologies/Technicians, B
Secondary Education and Teaching, BM
Secondary School Administration/Principalship, B
Social Sciences, B
Social Studies Teacher Education, BM
Sociology, B
Spanish Language and Literature, B
Spanish Language Teacher Education, B
Speech and Rhetorical Studies, B
Teacher Education, Multiple Levels, B
Voice and Opera, B
Youth Ministry, B

THE CITADEL, THE MILITARY COLLEGE OF SOUTH CAROLINA

Biology Teacher Education, B
Biology/Biological Sciences, B
Business Administration and Management, B
Business Administration, Management and Operations, M
Chemistry, B
Civil Engineering, B
Computer Science, BM
Counselor Education/School Counseling and Guidance Services, M
Criminal Justice/Law Enforcement Administration, B
Education, MO
Educational Administration and Supervision, MO
Electrical, Electronics and Communications Engineering, B
English, M
English Language and Literature, B
English/Language Arts Teacher Education, B
French Language and Literature, B
German Language and Literature, B
Health Education, M
History, BM
History Teacher Education, B
Information Science/Studies, M
Mathematics, B
Mathematics Teacher Education, BM
Physical Education Teaching and Coaching, BM
Physics, B
Political Science and Government, B
Psychology, BM
Reading Teacher Education, M
School Psychology, MO
Science Teacher Education/General Science Teacher Education, BM
Secondary Education and Teaching, M
Social Studies Teacher Education, BM
Spanish Language and Literature, B

CLAFLIN UNIVERSITY

African-American/Black Studies, B
American/United States Studies/Civilization, B
Art Teacher Education, B
Art/Art Studies, General, B
Biochemistry, B
Bioinformatics, B
Biology/Biological Sciences, B
Business Administration and Management, B
Business, Management, Marketing, and Related Support Services, B
Chemistry, B
Computer Science, B
Computer Software Engineering, B

Criminal Justice/Law Enforcement Administration, B
Early Childhood Education and Teaching, B
Elementary Education and Teaching, B
English Language and Literature, B
Environmental Sciences, B
Health and Physical Education, B
History, B
Junior High/Intermediate/Middle School Education and Teaching, B
Management Information Systems and Services, B
Marketing/Marketing Management, B
Mass Communication/Media Studies, B
Mathematics, B
Mathematics Teacher Education, B
Music, B
Music Teacher Education, B
Organizational Behavior Studies, B
Philosophy and Religious Studies, B
Sociology, B

CLEMSON UNIVERSITY

Accounting, BM
Agricultural Business and Management, B
Agricultural Economics, BM
Agricultural Education, M
Agricultural Mechanization, B
Agricultural Sciences, MD
Agricultural Teacher Education, B
Agricultural/Biological Engineering and Bioengineering, B
Animal Sciences, BMD
Applied Economics, MD
Applied Mathematics, MD
Aquaculture, MD
Architecture, BM
Astronomy, MD
Astrophysics, MD
Atmospheric Sciences and Meteorology, MD
Biochemistry, BMD
Bioengineering, MD
Biological and Biomedical Sciences, MD
Biology/Biological Sciences, B
Biomedical/Medical Engineering, B
Biophysics, MD
Biosystems Engineering, MD
Business Administration and Management, B
Business Administration, Management and Operations, M
Business, Management, Marketing, and Related Support Services, B
Ceramic Sciences and Engineering, B
Chemical Engineering, BMD
Chemistry, BMD
Civil Engineering, BMD
Communication and Media Studies, MD
Communication, Journalism and Related Programs, B
Community College Education, M
Computational Sciences, MD
Computer and Information Sciences, B
Computer Art and Design, M
Computer Engineering, BMD
Computer Programming/Programmer, B
Computer Science, BMD
Construction Engineering and Management, M
Construction Management, B
Counselor Education/School Counseling and Guidance Services, BM
Curriculum and Instruction, D
Early Childhood Education and Teaching, B
Economics, BMD
Education, MDO
Educational Administration and Supervision, MO
Educational Leadership and Administration, D
Electrical Engineering, MD
Electrical, Electronics and Communications Engineering, B
Electronic Commerce, M
Elementary Education and Teaching, BM
Engineering and Applied Sciences, MD
Engineering Mechanics, B
Engineering/Industrial Management, B
English, M
English Education, M
English Language and Literature, B
Entomology, MD

Environmental and Occupational Health, D
Environmental Design/Architecture, D
Environmental Engineering
    Technology/Environmental Technology, MD
Environmental Sciences, MD
Environmental Studies, MD
Ergonomics and Human Factors, D
Finance, B
Fine Arts and Art Studies, M
Fish, Game and Wildlife Management, MD
Fishing and Fisheries Sciences and Management, B
Food Science, B
Food Science and Technology, MD
Forest Management/Forest Resources
    Management, B
Forestry, MD
Genetics, BMD
Geology/Earth Science, BM
Graphic Communications, B
Health Physics/Radiological Health, D
Health Professions and Related Clinical Sciences, B
Health Services Administration, M
Historic Preservation and Conservation, M
History, BM
Horticultural Science, B
Human Development, M
Human Resources Development, BM
Hydrology and Water Resources Science, M
Industrial and Manufacturing Management, MD
Industrial and Organizational Psychology, D
Industrial Design, B
Industrial Education, M
Industrial Engineering, B
Industrial/Management Engineering, MD
Information Science/Studies, B
International Business/Trade/Commerce, B
International Public Health/International Health, B
Landscape Architecture, BM
Management, MD
Management Information Systems and Services, B
Management Strategy and Policy, D
Manufacturing Engineering, M
Marketing/Marketing Management, B
Mass Communication/Media Studies, B
Materials Engineering, BMD
Materials Sciences, MD
Mathematics, BMD
Mathematics Teacher Education, BM
Mechanical Engineering, BMD
Microbiology, BMD
Middle School Education, M
Modern Languages, B
Molecular Biology, MD
Natural Resources and Conservation, B
Nursing, M
Nursing - Registered Nurse Training, B
Nutritional Sciences, M
Operations Research, MD
Parks, Recreation and Leisure Facilities
    Management, B
Philosophy, B
Physics, BMD
Plant Biology, MD
Plant Sciences, MD
Political Science and Government, B
Polymer Chemistry, B
Polymer/Plastics Engineering, MD
Psychology, BM
Public Administration, M
Public Health (MPH, DPH), B
Public Policy Analysis, DO
Reading Teacher Education, M
Real Estate, M
Recreation and Park Management, MD
Rhetoric, D
Science Teacher Education/General Science
    Teacher Education, BM
Science Technologies/Technicians, B
Secondary Education and Teaching, BM
Social Studies Teacher Education, M
Sociology, BM
Special Education and Teaching, BM
Speech and Rhetorical Studies, B
Statistics, MD
Textile Sciences and Engineering, BMD
Travel and Tourism, MD

Turf and Turfgrass Management, B
Urban and Regional Planning, MD
Veterinary Sciences, MD
Visual and Performing Arts, B
Vocational and Technical Education, MD
Wildlife Biology, B
Writing, M
Zoology/Animal Biology, MD

COASTAL CAROLINA UNIVERSITY

Accounting, B
Applied Mathematics, B
Biology/Biological Sciences, B
Business Administration and Management, B
Chemistry, B
Computer and Information Sciences, B
Drama and Dramatics/Theatre Arts, B
Dramatic/Theatre Arts and Stagecraft, B
Early Childhood Education and Teaching, BM
Economics, B
Education, M
Educational Media/Instructional Technology, M
Elementary Education and Teaching, BM
English Language and Literature, B
Finance, B
Fine/Studio Arts, B
History, B
Junior High/Intermediate/Middle School Education
    and Teaching, B
Liberal Arts and Sciences Studies and
    Humanities, B
Marine Biology and Biological Oceanography, B
Marine Sciences, M
Marketing/Marketing Management, B
Music, B
Philosophy, B
Physical Education Teaching and Coaching, B
Physics, B
Political Science and Government, B
Psychology, B
Public Health Education and Promotion, B
Resort Management, B
Secondary Education and Teaching, BM
Sociology, B
Spanish Language and Literature, B
Special Education and Teaching, B

COKER COLLEGE

Acting, B
Art Teacher Education, B
Art/Art Studies, General, B
Biology Teacher Education, B
Biology/Biological Sciences, B
Business Administration and Management, B
Chemistry, B
Chemistry Teacher Education, B
Clinical Laboratory Science/Medical
    Technology/Technologist, B
Computer Science, B
Corrections, B
Counseling Psychology, B
Criminal Justice/Law Enforcement Administration, B
Criminology, B
Dance, B
Drama and Dramatics/Theatre Arts, B
Dramatic/Theatre Arts and Stagecraft, B
Early Childhood Education and Teaching, B
Education, B
Elementary Education and Teaching, B
English Language and Literature, B
English/Language Arts Teacher Education, B
Fine/Studio Arts, B
French Language and Literature, B
Graphic Design, B
Health and Physical Education, B
Health and Physical Education/Fitness, B
History, B
History Teacher Education, B
Kinesiology and Exercise Science, B
Mass Communication/Media Studies, B
Mathematics, B
Mathematics Teacher Education, B
Music, B
Music Teacher Education, B
Parks, Recreation, Leisure and Fitness Studies, B
Photography, B

Physical Education Teaching and Coaching, B
Piano and Organ, B
Political Science and Government, B
Psychology, B
Social Work, B
Sociology, B
Sport and Fitness Administration/Management, B
Technical Theatre/Theatre Design and
    Technology, B
Therapeutic Recreation/Recreational Therapy, B
Voice and Opera, B

COLLEGE OF CHARLESTON

Accounting, BM
Anthropology, B
Art History, Criticism and Conservation, B
Arts Management, B
Athletic Training and Sports Medicine, B
Biochemistry, B
Biology/Biological Sciences, B
Business Administration and Management, B
Business Administration, Management and
    Operations, M
Chemistry, B
Classics and Classical
    Languages, Literatures, and Linguistics, B
Communication Studies/Speech Communication
    and Rhetoric, B
Computer and Information Sciences, B
Computer Science, M
Corporate and Organizational Communication, O
Drama and Dramatics/Theatre Arts, B
Early Childhood Education and Teaching, BM
Economics, B
Education, MO
Elementary Education and Teaching, BM
English, M
English as a Second Language, O
English Language and Literature, B
Environmental Sciences, M
Fine/Studio Arts, B
Foreign Language Teacher Education, M
French Language and Literature, B
Geology/Earth Science, B
German Language and Literature, B
Historic Preservation and Conservation, B
History, BM
Hospitality Administration/Management, B
Information Science/Studies, B
International Business/Trade/Commerce, B
Junior High/Intermediate/Middle School Education
    and Teaching, B
Latin American Studies, B
Legal and Justice Studies, MO
Marine Biology and Biological Oceanography, BM
Mathematics, BMO
Mathematics Teacher Education, M
Music, B
Philosophy, B
Physical Education Teaching and Coaching, B
Physics, B
Political Science and Government, B
Pre-Dentistry Studies, B
Pre-Medicine/Pre-Medical Studies, B
Psychology, B
Public Administration, M
Religion/Religious Studies, B
Science Teacher Education/General Science
    Teacher Education, M
Sociology, B
Spanish Language and Literature, B
Special Education and Teaching, BM
Urban Studies/Affairs, B

COLUMBIA COLLEGE

Accounting, B
Applied Art, B
Biology/Biological Sciences, B
Business Administration and Management, B
Chemistry, B
Communication Studies/Speech Communication
    and Rhetoric, B
Communication, Journalism and Related
    Programs, B
Computer and Information Sciences and Support
    Services, B

Conflict Resolution and Mediation/Peace Studies, MO
Dance, B
Drama and Dance Teacher Education, B
Education, M
Elementary Education and Teaching, BM
English Language and Literature, B
Fine/Studio Arts, B
French Language and Literature, B
History, B
Human Development and Family Studies, B
Journalism, B
Kindergarten/PreSchool Education and Teaching, B
Liberal Arts and Sciences Studies and Humanities, B
Mathematics, B
Multi-/Interdisciplinary Studies, B
Music, B
Music Performance, B
Music Teacher Education, B
Organizational Behavior Studies, O
Piano and Organ, B
Political Science and Government, B
Psychology, B
Public Administration and Social Service Professions, B
Public Relations/Image Management, B
Religion/Religious Studies, B
Religious Education, B
Social Sciences, B
Social Work, B
Spanish Language and Literature, B
Special Education and Teaching, B
Speech-Language Pathology/Pathologist, B
Voice and Opera, B

COLUMBIA INTERNATIONAL UNIVERSITY

Ancient Near Eastern and Biblical Languages, Literatures, and Linguistics, B
Bible/Biblical Studies, AB
Communication Studies/Speech Communication and Rhetoric, B
Counselor Education/School Counseling and Guidance Services, M
Cultural Studies, MPO
Curriculum and Instruction, M
Early Childhood Education and Teaching, M
Education, MDO
Educational Administration and Supervision, MD
Elementary Education and Teaching, M
English as a Second Language, MO
General Studies, B
Humanities/Humanistic Studies, B
Intercultural/Multicultural and Diversity Studies, B
Missions/Missionary Studies and Missiology, MDPO
Multilingual and Multicultural Education, M
Near and Middle Eastern Studies, B
Nursing - Registered Nurse Training, B
Pastoral Studies/Counseling, BMDPO
Pre-Theology/Pre-Ministerial Studies, B
Psychology, B
Religious Education, BMPO
Religious/Sacred Music, B
Teacher Education, Multiple Levels, B
Theology and Religious Vocations, MDPO
Youth Ministry, B

CONVERSE COLLEGE

Accounting, B
Applied Art, B
Art History, Criticism and Conservation, B
Art Teacher Education, B
Art Therapy/Therapist, B
Art/Art Studies, General, B
Biochemistry, B
Biology/Biological Sciences, B
Business Administration and Management, B
Chemistry, B
Computer Science, B
Curriculum and Instruction, O
Drama and Dramatics/Theatre Arts, B
Early Childhood Education and Teaching, M
Economics, B
Education, BMO
Education/Teaching of the Gifted and Talented, M

Educational Administration and Supervision, O
Educational Leadership and Administration, M
Elementary Education and Teaching, BM
English, M
English Education, M
English Language and Literature, B
Fine/Studio Arts, B
French Language and Literature, B
History, BM
Interior Design, B
International Business/Trade/Commerce, B
Kindergarten/PreSchool Education and Teaching, B
Liberal Studies, M
Marketing/Marketing Management, B
Marriage and Family Therapy/Counseling, O
Mathematics, B
Mathematics Teacher Education, M
Modern Languages, B
Music, BM
Music History, Literature, and Theory, B
Music Teacher Education, BM
Music Therapy/Therapist, B
Performance, M
Piano and Organ, B
Political Science and Government, BM
Psychology, B
Religion/Religious Studies, B
Science Teacher Education/General Science Teacher Education, M
Secondary Education and Teaching, BM
Sign Language Interpretation and Translation, B
Social Studies Teacher Education, M
Sociology, B
Spanish Language and Literature, B
Special Education and Teaching, BM
Violin, Viola, Guitar and Other Stringed Instruments, B
Voice and Opera, B

DENMARK TECHNICAL COLLEGE

Administrative Assistant and Secretarial Science, A
Automobile/Automotive Mechanics Technology/Technician, A
Business Administration and Management, A
Computer and Information Sciences, A
Criminal Justice/Law Enforcement Administration, A
Engineering Technology, A
Human Services, A
Kindergarten/PreSchool Education and Teaching, A

ERSKINE COLLEGE

American/United States Studies/Civilization, B
Art/Art Studies, General, B
Athletic Training and Sports Medicine, B
Behavioral Sciences, B
Bible/Biblical Studies, B
Biological and Physical Sciences, B
Biology/Biological Sciences, B
Business Administration and Management, B
Chemistry, B
Clinical Laboratory Science/Medical Technology/Technologist, B
Elementary Education and Teaching, B
English Language and Literature, B
French Language and Literature, B
History, B
Kindergarten/PreSchool Education and Teaching, B
Mathematics, B
Music, B
Music Teacher Education, B
Natural Sciences, B
Philosophy, B
Physical Education Teaching and Coaching, B
Physics, B
Psychology, B
Religion/Religious Studies, B
Religious Education, B
Religious/Sacred Music, B
Social Studies Teacher Education, B
Spanish Language and Literature, B
Special Education and Teaching, B

Sport and Fitness Administration/Management, B

FLORENCE-DARLINGTON TECHNICAL COLLEGE

Accounting, A
Administrative Assistant and Secretarial Science, A
Automobile/Automotive Mechanics Technology/Technician, A
Biological and Physical Sciences, A
Business Administration and Management, A
Chemical Engineering, A
Civil Engineering Technology/Technician, A
Clinical/Medical Laboratory Technician, A
Computer Engineering Technology/Technician, A
Criminal Justice/Law Enforcement Administration, A
Dental Hygiene/Hygienist, A
Drafting and Design Technology/Technician, A
Electrical, Electronic and Communications Engineering Technology/Technician, A
Electromechanical Technology/Electromechanical Engineering Technology, A
Engineering Technology, A
Funeral Service and Mortuary Science, A
Health Information/Medical Records Administration/Administrator, A
Heating, Air Conditioning, Ventilation and Refrigeration Maintenance Technology/Technician, A
Human Services, A
Industrial Radiologic Technology/Technician, A
Legal Assistant/Paralegal, A
Liberal Arts and Sciences Studies and Humanities, A
Machine Tool Technology/Machinist, A
Marketing/Marketing Management, A
Nursing - Registered Nurse Training, A
Occupational Therapy/Therapist, A
Physical Therapy/Therapist, A
Respiratory Care Therapy/Therapist, A
Trade and Industrial Teacher Education, A

FORREST JUNIOR COLLEGE

Business Administration and Management, A

FRANCIS MARION UNIVERSITY

Accounting, B
Art Teacher Education, B
Art/Art Studies, General, B
Biology/Biological Sciences, B
Business Administration and Management, B
Business Administration, Management and Operations, M
Chemistry, B
Clinical Psychology, M
Community Psychology, M
Computer and Information Sciences, B
Drama and Dramatics/Theatre Arts, B
Early Childhood Education and Teaching, BM
Economics, B
Education, M
Elementary Education and Teaching, BM
English Language and Literature, B
Finance, B
Foreign Languages and Literatures, B
French Language and Literature, B
Geography, B
Health Services Administration, M
History, B
International Relations and Affairs, B
Liberal Arts and Sciences Studies and Humanities, B
Management Information Systems and Services, B
Marketing/Marketing Management, B
Mass Communication/Media Studies, B
Mathematics, B
Nursing - Registered Nurse Training, B
Physics, B
Political Science and Government, B
Pre-Law Studies, B
Psychology, BM
School Psychology, M
Secondary Education and Teaching, M
Sociology, B
Spanish Language and Literature, B

Special Education and Teaching, M

FURMAN UNIVERSITY

Accounting, B
Art History, Criticism and Conservation, B
Art/Art Studies, General, B
Asian Studies/Civilization, B
Biochemistry, B
Biology/Biological Sciences, B
Business Administration and Management, B
Chemistry, BM
Classics and Classical
　Languages, Literatures, and Linguistics, B
Communication Studies/Speech Communication
　and Rhetoric, B
Computer Science, B
Drama and Dramatics/Theatre Arts, B
Early Childhood Education and Teaching, M
Economics, B
Education, BM
Educational Administration and Supervision, M
Elementary Education and Teaching, BM
English Language and Literature, B
Environmental Studies, B
Fine/Studio Arts, B
French Language and Literature, B
Geology/Earth Science, B
German Language and Literature, B
History, B
Information Technology, B
Kindergarten/PreSchool Education and Teaching, B
Kinesiology and Exercise Science, B
Latin Language and Literature, B
Mathematics, B
Modern Greek Language and Literature, B
Music, B
Music Teacher Education, B
Neuroscience, B
Philosophy, B
Physics, B
Piano and Organ, B
Political Science and Government, B
Pre-Dentistry Studies, B
Pre-Law Studies, B
Pre-Medicine/Pre-Medical Studies, B
Pre-Veterinary Studies, B
Psychology, B
Reading Teacher Education, M
Religion/Religious Studies, B
Religious/Sacred Music, B
Secondary Education and Teaching, B
Sociology, B
Spanish Language and Literature, B
Special Education and Teaching, BM
Urban Studies/Affairs, B
Voice and Opera, B

GREENVILLE TECHNICAL COLLEGE

Accounting, A
Administrative Assistant and Secretarial Science, A
Airframe Mechanics and Aircraft Maintenance
　Technology/Technician, A
Architectural Engineering Technology/Technician, A
Automobile/Automotive Mechanics
　Technology/Technician, A
Avionics Maintenance Technology/Technician, A
Business Administration and Management, A
Clinical/Medical Laboratory Technician, A
Computer Programming/Programmer, A
Construction Engineering Technology/Technician, A
Criminal Justice/Law Enforcement Administration, A
Criminal Justice/Police Science, A
Dental Hygiene/Hygienist, A
Drafting and Design Technology/Technician, A
Electrical, Electronic and Communications
　Engineering Technology/Technician, A
Emergency Medical Technology/Technician (EMT
　Paramedic), A
Fire Science/Firefighting, A
Heating, Air Conditioning, Ventilation and
　Refrigeration Maintenance
　Technology/Technician, A
Hospitality Administration/Management, A
Industrial Radiologic Technology/Technician, A
Industrial Technology/Technician, A
Legal Assistant/Paralegal, A

Liberal Arts and Sciences Studies and
　Humanities, A
Machine Tool Technology/Machinist, A
Marketing/Marketing Management, A
Materials Sciences, A
Mechanical Engineering/Mechanical
　Technology/Technician, A
Nursing - Registered Nurse Training, A
Physical Therapy/Therapist, A
Pre-Engineering, A
Public Health (MPH, DPH), A
Respiratory Care Therapy/Therapist, A
Special Products Marketing Operations, A

HORRY-GEORGETOWN TECHNICAL COLLEGE

Administrative Assistant and Secretarial Science, A
Agriculture, A
Business Administration and Management, A
Civil Engineering Technology/Technician, A
Computer Engineering Technology/Technician, A
Computer Programming, Specific Applications, A
Computer/Information Technology Services
　Administration and Management, A
Criminal Justice/Law Enforcement Administration, A
Culinary Arts/Chef Training, A
Data Entry/Microcomputer Applications, A
Electrical, Electronic and Communications
　Engineering Technology/Technician, A
Forestry Technology/Technician, A
Heating, Air Conditioning, Ventilation and
　Refrigeration Maintenance
　Technology/Technician, A
Hotel/Motel Administration/Management, A
Industrial Radiologic Technology/Technician, A
Landscaping and Groundskeeping, A
Legal Assistant/Paralegal, A
Licensed Practical/Vocational Nurse Training, A
Machine Tool Technology/Machinist, A
Nursing - Registered Nurse Training, A
Parks, Recreation and Leisure Facilities
　Management, A
Pre-Engineering, A
Web Page, Digital/Multimedia and Information
　Resources Design, A
Web/Multimedia Management and Webmaster, A
Word Processing, A

ITT TECHNICAL INSTITUTE

Animation, Interactive Technology, Video Graphics
　and Special Effects, B
CAD/CADD Drafting and/or Design
　Technology/Technician, A
Computer and Information Systems Security, B
Computer Programming/Programmer, A
E-Commerce/Electronic Commerce, B
Electrical, Electronic and Communications
　Engineering Technology/Technician, AB
System, Networking, and LAN/WAN
　Management/Manager, A
Web Page, Digital/Multimedia and Information
　Resources Design, A
Web/Multimedia Management and Webmaster, A

LANDER UNIVERSITY

Art/Art Studies, General, B
Athletic Training and Sports Medicine, B
Biology/Biological Sciences, B
Business Administration and Management, B
Chemistry, B
Computer and Information Sciences, B
Curriculum and Instruction, M
Early Childhood Education and Teaching, B
Education, M
Elementary Education and Teaching, BM
English Language and Literature, B
Environmental Sciences, B
History, B
Interdisciplinary Studies, B
Kinesiology and Exercise Science, B
Liberal Arts and Sciences Studies and
　Humanities, B
Mathematics, B
Music, B
Nursing - Registered Nurse Training, B
Physical Education Teaching and Coaching, B

Political Science and Government, B
Psychology, B
Secondary Education and Teaching, B
Sociology, B
Spanish Language and Literature, B
Special Education and Teaching, B

LIMESTONE COLLEGE

Accounting, B
Art Teacher Education, B
Athletic Training and Sports Medicine, B
Biology Teacher Education, B
Biology/Biological Sciences, B
Business Administration and Management, AB
Business/Commerce, AB
Business/Managerial Economics, B
Chemistry, B
Computer Programming/Programmer, AB
Computer Science, AB
Corrections, B
Corrections and Criminal Justice, B
Criminal Justice/Safety Studies, B
Drama and Dramatics/Theatre Arts, B
Education, B
Elementary Education and Teaching, B
English Language and Literature, B
English/Language Arts Teacher Education, B
Fine/Studio Arts, B
Graphic Design, B
Health and Physical Education/Fitness, B
History, B
Human Resources Development, B
Information Science/Studies, AB
Jazz/Jazz Studies, B
Liberal Arts and Sciences Studies and
　Humanities, B
Marketing/Marketing Management, B
Marriage and Family Therapy/Counseling, B
Mathematics, B
Mathematics Teacher Education, B
Music, B
Music Teacher Education, B
Physical Education Teaching and Coaching, B
Pre-Dentistry Studies, B
Pre-Law Studies, B
Pre-Medicine/Pre-Medical Studies, B
Pre-Nursing Studies, B
Pre-Pharmacy Studies, B
Pre-Veterinary Studies, B
Psychology, B
Social Studies Teacher Education, B
Social Work, B
Sport and Fitness Administration/Management, B
Web/Multimedia Management and Webmaster, AB

MEDICAL UNIVERSITY OF SOUTH CAROLINA

Allied Health and Medical Assisting Services, MDO
Allopathic Medicine, PO
Anatomy, D
Biochemistry, DO
Bioengineering, MD
Biological and Biomedical Sciences, MDO
Biometry/Biometrics, MDO
Biostatistics, MD
Cell Biology and Anatomy, DO
Clinical Research, M
Communication Disorders, M
Dentistry, PO
Epidemiology, MDO
Gerontological Nursing, MO
Health Services Administration, BMDO
Immunology, MDO
Maternal/Child Health and Neonatal
　Nurse/Nursing, MO
Maternity Nursing, MO
Medical Technology, M
Microbiology, MDO
Molecular Biology, DO
Molecular Pharmacology, DO
Neuroscience, MDO
Nurse Anesthetist, M
Nurse Midwife/Nursing Midwifery, M
Nursing, MDO
Nursing - Adult, MO
Nursing - Advanced Practice, MO

Nursing - Registered Nurse Training, B
Nursing Administration, MO
Nursing Education, M
Occupational Therapy/Therapist, M
Pathobiology, DO
Pathology/Experimental Pathology, MDO
Perfusion Technology/Perfusionist, B
Periodontics, M
Pharmaceutical Sciences, D
Pharmacy, P
Physical Therapy/Therapist, D
Physician Assistant, M
Physiology, MDO
Psychiatric/Mental Health Nurse/Nursing, MO
Rehabilitation Sciences, MD

MIDLANDS TECHNICAL COLLEGE

Accounting, A
Administrative Assistant and Secretarial Science, A
Architectural Engineering Technology/Technician, A
Automobile/Automotive Mechanics
   Technology/Technician, A
Business Administration and Management, A
Business/Commerce, A
Cartography, A
Chemical Technology/Technician, A
Child Care Provider/Assistant, A
Civil Engineering Technology/Technician, A
Clinical/Medical Laboratory Technician, A
Commercial and Advertising Art, A
Computer and Information Sciences and Support
   Services, A
Computer Installation and Repair
   Technology/Technician, A
Computer Systems Networking and
   Telecommunications, A
Construction Engineering Technology/Technician, A
Court Reporting/Court Reporter, A
Criminal Justice/Safety Studies, A
Data Processing and Data Processing
   Technology/Technician, A
Dental Assisting/Assistant, A
Dental Hygiene/Hygienist, A
Electrical, Electronic and Communications
   Engineering Technology/Technician, A
Engineering Technology, A
Fashion Merchandising, A
Gerontology, A
Graphic and Printing Equipment Operator
   Production, A
Health Information/Medical Records
   Technology/Technician, A
Health Professions and Related Clinical Sciences, A
Heating, Air Conditioning, Ventilation and
   Refrigeration Maintenance
   Technology/Technician, A
Industrial Electronics Technology/Technician, A
Industrial Mechanics and Maintenance
   Technology, A
Legal Assistant/Paralegal, A
Liberal Arts and Sciences Studies and
   Humanities, A
Licensed Practical/Vocational Nurse Training, A
Mechanical Drafting and Mechanical Drafting
   CAD/CADD, A
Mechanical Engineering/Mechanical
   Technology/Technician, A
Medical Radiologic Technology/Science - Radiation
   Therapist, A
Medical/Clinical Assistant, A
Multi-/Interdisciplinary Studies, A
Nuclear Medical Technology/Technologist, A
Nursing - Registered Nurse Training, A
Occupational Therapist Assistant, A
Pharmacy Technician/Assistant, A
Physical Therapist Assistant, A
Precision Production, A
Respiratory Care Therapy/Therapist, A
Sales, Distribution and Marketing Operations, A
Surgical Technology/Technologist, A
Youth Services/Administration, A

MORRIS COLLEGE

Biology Teacher Education, B
Biology/Biological Sciences, B
Broadcast Journalism, B

Business Administration and Management, B
Business Administration, Management and
   Operations, B
Community Health Services/Liaison/Counseling, B
Criminal Justice/Law Enforcement Administration, B
Early Childhood Education and Teaching, B
Elementary Education and Teaching, B
English Language and Literature, B
English/Language Arts Teacher Education, B
History, B
Journalism, B
Liberal Arts and Sciences Studies and
   Humanities, B
Mathematics, B
Mathematics Teacher Education, B
Parks, Recreation, Leisure and Fitness Studies, B
Political Science and Government, B
Religious Education, B
Social Studies Teacher Education, B
Sociology, B
Theology/Theological Studies, B

NEWBERRY COLLEGE

Art/Art Studies, General, B
Athletic Training and Sports Medicine, B
Biology/Biological Sciences, B
Business Administration and Management, B
Chemistry, B
Computer Science, B
Drama and Dramatics/Theatre Arts, B
Education, B
Elementary Education and Teaching, B
English Language and Literature, B
French Language and Literature, B
German Language and Literature, B
History, B
Kindergarten/PreSchool Education and Teaching, B
Mass Communication/Media Studies, B
Mathematics, B
Music, B
Music Teacher Education, B
Philosophy, B
Physical Education Teaching and Coaching, B
Piano and Organ, B
Political Science and Government, B
Pre-Dentistry Studies, B
Pre-Law Studies, B
Pre-Medicine/Pre-Medical Studies, B
Pre-Veterinary Studies, B
Psychology, B
Religion/Religious Studies, B
Religious/Sacred Music, B
Secondary Education and Teaching, B
Sociology, B
Spanish Language and Literature, B
Special Education and Teaching, B
Speech and Rhetorical Studies, B
Veterinary/Animal Health Technology/Technician and
   Veterinary Assistant, B
Voice and Opera, B

NORTH GREENVILLE COLLEGE

Accounting and Business/Management, B
Ancient Near Eastern and Biblical
   Languages, Literatures, and Linguistics, B
Art/Art Studies, General, A
Bible/Biblical Studies, B
Biology/Biological Sciences, B
Business Administration and Management, B
Business/Managerial Economics, B
Drama and Dramatics/Theatre Arts, A
Elementary Education and Teaching, B
English Language and Literature, B
Humanities/Humanistic Studies, B
Interdisciplinary Studies, B
Journalism, B
Kindergarten/PreSchool Education and Teaching, B
Liberal Arts and Sciences Studies and
   Humanities, A
Mass Communication/Media Studies, B
Multi-/Interdisciplinary Studies, B
Music, B
Music History, Literature, and Theory, B
Music Teacher Education, B
Pastoral Studies/Counseling, B
Piano and Organ, B

Psychology, B
Religion/Religious Studies, B
Religious Education, B
Religious/Sacred Music, B
Sport and Fitness Administration/Management, B
Theatre/Theatre Arts Management, B
Theology/Theological Studies, B
Voice and Opera, B

NORTHEASTERN TECHNICAL COLLEGE

Accounting, A
Administrative Assistant and Secretarial Science, A
Business Administration and Management, A
Computer Programming/Programmer, A
Computer Science, A
Data Processing and Data Processing
   Technology/Technician, A
Drafting/Design Engineering
   Technologies/Technicians, A
Electrical, Electronic and Communications
   Engineering Technology/Technician, A
Liberal Arts and Sciences Studies and
   Humanities, A
Machine Tool Technology/Machinist, A
Marketing/Marketing Management, A

ORANGEBURG-CALHOUN TECHNICAL COLLEGE

Accounting, A
Administrative Assistant and Secretarial Science, A
Automobile/Automotive Mechanics
   Technology/Technician, A
Business/Commerce, A
Clinical/Medical Laboratory Technician, A
Computer Programming, A
Criminal Justice/Safety Studies, A
Electrical, Electronic and Communications
   Engineering Technology/Technician, A
Instrumentation Technology/Technician, A
Kindergarten/PreSchool Education and Teaching, A
Legal Assistant/Paralegal, A
Liberal Arts and Sciences Studies and
   Humanities, A
Machine Tool Technology/Machinist, A
Medical Radiologic Technology/Science - Radiation
   Therapist, A
Nursing - Registered Nurse Training, A

PIEDMONT TECHNICAL COLLEGE

Accounting, A
Administrative Assistant and Secretarial Science, A
Automobile/Automotive Mechanics
   Technology/Technician, A
Biological and Physical Sciences, A
Building/Construction
   Finishing, Management, and Inspection, A
Business Administration and Management, A
Business/Commerce, A
Carpentry/Carpenter, A
Child Development, A
Commercial and Advertising Art, A
Computer Programming/Programmer, A
Construction Engineering Technology/Technician, A
Criminal Justice/Law Enforcement Administration, A
Criminal Justice/Safety Studies, A
Data Processing and Data Processing
   Technology/Technician, A
Drafting and Design Technology/Technician, A
Electrical, Electronic and Communications
   Engineering Technology/Technician, A
Engineering, A
Engineering Technology, A
Funeral Service and Mortuary Science, A
Heating, Air Conditioning, Ventilation and
   Refrigeration Maintenance
   Technology/Technician, A
Human Services, A
Legal Administrative Assistant/Secretary, A
Liberal Arts and Sciences Studies and
   Humanities, A
Machine Tool Technology/Machinist, A
Marketing/Marketing Management, A
Mechanical Drafting and Mechanical Drafting
   CAD/CADD, A

Mechanical Engineering/Mechanical
   Technology/Technician, A
Medical Administrative Assistant/Secretary, A
Medical Radiologic Technology/Science - Radiation
   Therapist, A
Nursing - Registered Nurse Training, A
Office Management and Supervision, A
Respiratory Care Therapy/Therapist, A
Social Work, A

PRESBYTERIAN COLLEGE

Art/Art Studies, General, B
Biology/Biological Sciences, B
Business Administration and Management, B
Chemistry, B
Computer Science, B
Drama and Dramatics/Theatre Arts, B
Economics, B
Education, B
English Language and Literature, B
French Language and Literature, B
German Language and Literature, B
History, B
Junior High/Intermediate/Middle School Education
   and Teaching, B
Kindergarten/PreSchool Education and Teaching, B
Mathematics, B
Modern Languages, B
Music, B
Music Teacher Education, B
Physics, B
Political Science and Government, B
Psychology, B
Religion/Religious Studies, B
Sociology, B
Spanish Language and Literature, B

SOUTH CAROLINA STATE UNIVERSITY

Accounting, B
Administrative Assistant and Secretarial Science, B
Agribusiness, M
Agricultural Business and Management, B
Art Teacher Education, B
Audiology/Audiologist and Speech-Language
   Pathology/Pathologist, B
Biology/Biological Sciences, B
Business Administration and Management, B
Business Teacher Education, B
Business/Managerial Economics, B
Chemistry, B
Child and Family Studies, M
Civil Engineering Technology/Technician, B
Communication Disorders, M
Computer Science, B
Counselor Education/School Counseling and
   Guidance Services, MDO
Criminal Justice/Law Enforcement Administration, B
Drama and Dramatics/Theatre Arts, B
Early Childhood Education and Teaching, M
Economics, B
Education, BMDO
Educational Administration and Supervision, MDO
Electrical, Electronic and Communications
   Engineering Technology/Technician, B
Elementary Education and Teaching, BM
English Language and Literature, B
Family and Consumer Sciences/Home Economics
   Teacher Education, B
Family and Consumer Sciences/Human
   Sciences, BM
Fashion Merchandising, B
Foods, Nutrition, and Wellness Studies, B
French Language and Literature, B
Health Teacher Education, B
History, B
Industrial Technology/Technician, B
Kindergarten/PreSchool Education and Teaching, B
Marketing/Marketing Management, B
Mathematics, B
Mathematics Teacher Education, M
Mechanical Engineering/Mechanical
   Technology/Technician, B
Music Management and Merchandising, B
Music Teacher Education, B
Nuclear Engineering, B
Nursing - Registered Nurse Training, B

Nutritional Sciences, M
Physical Education Teaching and Coaching, B
Physics, B
Political Science and Government, B
Pre-Dentistry Studies, B
Pre-Law Studies, B
Pre-Medicine/Pre-Medical Studies, B
Pre-Veterinary Studies, B
Psychology, B
Rehabilitation Counseling, M
Science Teacher Education/General Science
   Teacher Education, M
Secondary Education and Teaching, M
Social Work, B
Sociology, B
Spanish Language and Literature, B
Special Education and Teaching, BM
Technology Education/Industrial Arts, B
Trade and Industrial Teacher Education, B

SOUTH UNIVERSITY

Accounting, A
Business Administration and Management, AB
Criminal Justice/Law Enforcement Administration, B
Health/Health Care Administration/Management, B
Information Technology, AB
Law and Legal Studies, B
Legal Assistant/Paralegal, A
Medical/Clinical Assistant, A

SOUTHERN METHODIST COLLEGE

Bible/Biblical Studies, AB
Missions/Missionary Studies and Missiology, AB

SOUTHERN WESLEYAN UNIVERSITY

Accounting, B
Biology/Biological Sciences, B
Business Administration and Management, AB
Business Administration, Management and
   Operations, M
Business/Commerce, AB
Chemistry, B
Clinical Laboratory Science/Medical
   Technology/Technologist, B
Computer and Information Sciences, B
Divinity/Ministry (BD, MDiv.), B
Education, BM
Education/Teaching of Individuals with Emotional
   Disturbances, B
Education/Teaching of Individuals with Mental
   Retardation, B
Education/Teaching of Individuals with Specific
   Learning Disabilities, B
Elementary Education and Teaching, B
English Language and Literature, B
Health and Physical Education, B
History, B
Human Resources Management/Personnel
   Administration, B
Kindergarten/PreSchool Education and Teaching, B
Management, M
Mathematics, B
Mathematics Teacher Education, B
Music, B
Music Teacher Education, B
Parks, Recreation, Leisure and Fitness Studies, B
Pastoral Studies/Counseling, M
Physical Education Teaching and Coaching, B
Pre-Medicine/Pre-Medical Studies, B
Psychology, B
Religion/Religious Studies, B
Religious/Sacred Music, B
Science Teacher Education/General Science
   Teacher Education, B
Social Sciences, B
Special Education and Teaching, B
Sport and Fitness Administration/Management, B
Theology/Theological Studies, B

SPARTANBURG METHODIST COLLEGE

Administrative Assistant and Secretarial Science, A
Criminal Justice/Law Enforcement Administration, A
Information Technology, A

Liberal Arts and Sciences Studies and
   Humanities, A

SPARTANBURG TECHNICAL COLLEGE

Accounting, A
Administrative Assistant and Secretarial Science, A
Architectural Engineering Technology/Technician, A
Automobile/Automotive Mechanics
   Technology/Technician, A
Biological and Physical Sciences, A
Business Administration and Management, A
Civil Engineering Technology/Technician, A
Clinical/Medical Laboratory Technician, A
Computer and Information Sciences, A
Drafting and Design Technology/Technician, A
Electrical, Electronic and Communications
   Engineering Technology/Technician, A
Engineering Technology, A
Heating, Air Conditioning, Ventilation and
   Refrigeration Maintenance
   Technology/Technician, A
Horticultural Science, A
Liberal Arts and Sciences Studies and
   Humanities, A
Machine Tool Technology/Machinist, A
Marketing/Marketing Management, A
Mechanical Engineering/Mechanical
   Technology/Technician, A
Medical Administrative Assistant/Secretary, A
Medical Radiologic Technology/Science - Radiation
   Therapist, A
Respiratory Care Therapy/Therapist, A
Robotics Technology/Technician, A
Sign Language Interpretation and Translation, A
Trade and Industrial Teacher Education, A

TECHNICAL COLLEGE OF THE LOWCOUNTRY

Accounting, A
Administrative Assistant and Secretarial Science, A
Automobile/Automotive Mechanics
   Technology/Technician, A
Biological and Physical Sciences, A
Business Administration and Management, A
Carpentry/Carpenter, A
Computer Engineering Technology/Technician, A
Computer Typography and Composition Equipment
   Operator, A
Construction Engineering Technology/Technician, A
Criminal Justice/Law Enforcement Administration, A
Data Processing and Data Processing
   Technology/Technician, A
Electrical, Electronic and Communications
   Engineering Technology/Technician, A
Environmental Studies, A
Fashion Merchandising, A
Heating, Air Conditioning, Ventilation and
   Refrigeration Maintenance
   Technology/Technician, A
Horticultural Science, A
Human Services, A
Kindergarten/PreSchool Education and Teaching, A
Legal Administrative Assistant/Secretary, A
Legal Assistant/Paralegal, A
Liberal Arts and Sciences Studies and
   Humanities, A
Licensed Practical/Vocational Nurse Training, A
Marketing/Marketing Management, A
Nursing - Registered Nurse Training, A

TRI-COUNTY TECHNICAL COLLEGE

Accounting, A
Administrative Assistant and Secretarial Science, A
Apparel and Textiles, A
Business Administration and Management, A
Clinical/Medical Laboratory Technician, A
Computer Programming/Programmer, A
Criminal Justice/Law Enforcement Administration, A
Data Processing and Data Processing
   Technology/Technician, A
Drafting and Design Technology/Technician, A
Electrical, Electronic and Communications
   Engineering Technology/Technician, A
Electromechanical Technology/Electromechanical
   Engineering Technology, A

Heating, Air Conditioning, Ventilation and
Refrigeration Maintenance
Technology/Technician, A
Liberal Arts and Sciences Studies and
Humanities, A
Machine Tool Technology/Machinist, A
Medical/Clinical Assistant, A
Nursing - Registered Nurse Training, A
Public Health (MPH, DPH), A
Quality Control Technology/Technician, A
Radio and Television, A
Veterinary/Animal Health Technology/Technician and
Veterinary Assistant, A

TRIDENT TECHNICAL COLLEGE

Accounting, A
Administrative Assistant and Secretarial Science, A
Airframe Mechanics and Aircraft Maintenance
Technology/Technician, A
Automobile/Automotive Mechanics
Technology/Technician, A
Biological and Physical Sciences, A
Broadcast Journalism, A
Business Administration and Management, A
Child Care Provider/Assistant, A
Civil Engineering Technology/Technician, A
Clinical/Medical Laboratory Technician, A
Commercial and Advertising Art, A
Computer Engineering Technology/Technician, A
Computer Graphics, A
Computer Programming, Specific Applications, A
Computer Systems Networking and
Telecommunications, A
Computer/Information Technology Services
Administration and Management, A
Criminal Justice/Law Enforcement Administration, A
Culinary Arts/Chef Training, A
Dental Hygiene/Hygienist, A
Electrical, Electronic and Communications
Engineering Technology/Technician, A
Engineering Technology, A
Horticultural Science, A
Hotel/Motel Administration/Management, A
Human Services, A
Industrial Technology/Technician, A
Law and Legal Studies, A
Legal Assistant/Paralegal, A
Liberal Arts and Sciences Studies and
Humanities, A
Machine Tool Technology/Machinist, A
Marketing/Marketing Management, A
Mechanical Engineering/Mechanical
Technology/Technician, A
Medical Administrative Assistant/Secretary, A
Nursing - Registered Nurse Training, A
Occupational Therapy/Therapist, A
Physical Therapy/Therapist, A
Respiratory Care Therapy/Therapist, A
Telecommunications Technology/Technician, A
Veterinary/Animal Health Technology/Technician and
Veterinary Assistant, A
Web Page, Digital/Multimedia and Information
Resources Design, A
Web/Multimedia Management and Webmaster, A

UNIVERSITY OF SOUTH CAROLINA

Accounting, BMO
Advertising, B
African-American/Black Studies, B
Allopathic Medicine, PO
Anthropology, BMD
Aquatic Biology/Limnology, B
Art Education, M
Art History, Criticism and Conservation, BM
Art Teacher Education, B
Astronomy, MD
Biochemistry, MD
Biological and Biomedical Sciences, MD
Biology/Biological Sciences, B
Biostatistics, MD
Broadcast Journalism, B
Business Administration and Management, B
Business Administration, Management and
Operations, MDO
Business Education, M
Business/Managerial Economics, B

Cell Biology and Anatomy, MD
Chemical Engineering, BMD
Chemistry, BMD
Civil Engineering, BMD
Classics and Classical
Languages, Literatures, and Linguistics, B
Clinical Psychology, MD
Communication Disorders, MD
Community Health Nursing, MO
Community Psychology, MD
Comparative Literature, MD
Composition, M
Computer and Information Sciences, B
Computer Engineering, BMD
Computer Science, MD
Consumer Economics, M
Counselor Education/School Counseling and
Guidance Services, DO
Criminal Justice/Law Enforcement Administration, B
Criminology, MO
Curriculum and Instruction, D
Developmental Biology and Embryology, MD
Drama and Dramatics/Theatre Arts, B
Early Childhood Education and Teaching, MD
Ecology, MD
Economics, BMDO
Education, MDO
Educational Administration and Supervision, MDO
Educational Measurement and Evaluation, MD
Educational Media/Instructional Technology, M
Educational Psychology, MD
Electrical Engineering, MD
Electrical, Electronics and Communications
Engineering, B
Elementary Education and Teaching, MD
Engineering and Applied Sciences, MD
English, MDO
English as a Second Language, O
English Education, M
English Language and Literature, B
Environmental and Occupational Health, MD
Environmental Policy and Resource
Management, MO
Environmental Sciences, M
Epidemiology, MD
European Studies/Civilization, B
Evolutionary Biology, MD
Exercise and Sports Science, MD
Experimental Psychology, BMD
Finance, B
Fine Arts and Art Studies, M
Fine/Studio Arts, B
Foreign Language Teacher Education, MD
Foundations and Philosophy of Education, D
French Language and Literature, BM
Genetic Counseling/Counselor, M
Geography, BMD
Geology/Earth Science, BMD
Geophysics and Seismology, B
Geosciences, MD
German Language and Literature, BM
Gerontology, O
Hazardous Materials Management and Waste
Technology/Technician, MD
Health Education, MDO
Health Promotion, MDO
Health Services Administration, MDO
Higher Education/Higher Education
Administration, M
Historic Preservation and Conservation, M
History, BMDO
Hospitality Administration/Management, BM
Human Resources Management and Services, MO
Industrial Hygiene, MD
Information Science/Studies, MO
Insurance, B
International Affairs, MD
International Business/Trade/Commerce, M
International Relations and Affairs, B
Italian Language and Literature, B
Journalism, BMD
Kinesiology and Exercise Science, B
Latin American Studies, B
Law and Legal Studies, PO
Liberal Arts and Sciences Studies and
Humanities, B

Library Science, MO
Linguistics, MDO
Management Science, B
Marine Biology and Biological Oceanography, B
Marine Science/Merchant Marine Officer, B
Marine Sciences, MD
Marketing/Marketing Management, B
Mathematics, BMD
Mathematics Teacher Education, M
Mechanical Engineering, BMD
Media Studies, M
Medical/Surgical Nursing, M
Molecular Biology, MD
Museology/Museum Studies, MO
Music, BMDO
Music History, Literature, and Theory, M
Music Teacher Education, BMD
Music Theory and Composition, M
Nurse Anesthetist, M
Nursing, MDO
Nursing - Adult, M
Nursing - Advanced Practice, MO
Nursing - Registered Nurse Training, B
Nursing Administration, M
Oceanography, Chemical and Physical, B
Office Management and Supervision, B
Pediatric Nurse/Nursing, M
Performance, MDO
Pharmaceutical Sciences, MD
Pharmacy, P
Philosophy, BMD
Physical Education Teaching and Coaching, BMD
Physics, BMD
Political Science and Government, BMD
Psychiatric/Mental Health Nurse/Nursing, MO
Psychology, MD
Public Administration, MO
Public Health, MO
Public History, MO
Public Relations/Image Management, B
Reading Teacher Education, MD
Real Estate, B
Rehabilitation Counseling, MO
Rehabilitation Sciences, O
Religion/Religious Studies, BM
School Psychology, D
Science Teacher Education/General Science
Teacher Education, M
Secondary Education and Teaching, MD
Social Studies Teacher Education, M
Social Work, MDO
Sociology, BMD
Software Engineering, M
Spanish Language and Literature, BM
Special Education and Teaching, MD
Speech and Rhetorical Studies, M
Sport and Fitness Administration/Management, BM
Statistics, BMDO
Student Personnel Services, M
Theater, M
Travel and Tourism, M
Vocational and Technical Education, M
Women's Health Nursing, MO
Women's Studies, BO
Writing, M

UNIVERSITY OF SOUTH CAROLINA
AIKEN

Applied Mathematics, B
Biology/Biological Sciences, B
Business Administration and Management, B
Chemistry, B
Clinical Psychology, M
Communication Studies/Speech Communication
and Rhetoric, B
Computer Science, B
Early Childhood Education and Teaching, B
Education, M
Educational Media/Instructional Technology, M
Elementary Education and Teaching, BM
English Language and Literature, B
Fine/Studio Arts, B
History, B
Kindergarten/PreSchool Education and Teaching, B
Kinesiology and Exercise Science, B

Liberal Arts and Sciences Studies and
 Humanities, B
Music Teacher Education, B
Nursing - Registered Nurse Training, B
Political Science and Government, B
Psychology, B
Secondary Education and Teaching, B
Sociology, B
Special Education and Teaching, B

UNIVERSITY OF SOUTH CAROLINA BEAUFORT

Biology/Biological Sciences, B
Business Administration and Management, B
Education, B
English Language and Literature, B
Foreign Languages and Literatures, B
History, B
Hospitality Administration/Management, B
Liberal Arts and Sciences Studies and
 Humanities, AB
Psychology, B
Social Sciences, B

UNIVERSITY OF SOUTH CAROLINA LANCASTER

Administrative Assistant and Secretarial Science, A
Biological and Physical Sciences, A
Business Administration and Management, A
Criminal Justice/Law Enforcement Administration, A
Liberal Arts and Sciences Studies and
 Humanities, A
Nursing - Registered Nurse Training, A

UNIVERSITY OF SOUTH CAROLINA SALKEHATCHIE

Biological and Physical Sciences, A
Liberal Arts and Sciences Studies and
 Humanities, A
Mathematics, A

UNIVERSITY OF SOUTH CAROLINA SUMTER

Interdisciplinary Studies, A
Liberal Arts and Sciences Studies and
 Humanities, A

UNIVERSITY OF SOUTH CAROLINA UNION

Biological and Physical Sciences, A
Liberal Arts and Sciences Studies and
 Humanities, A

UNIVERSITY OF SOUTH CAROLINA UPSTATE

Biology/Biological Sciences, B
Business Administration and Management, B
Chemistry, B
Communication Studies/Speech Communication
 and Rhetoric, B
Computer and Information Sciences, B
Criminal Justice/Law Enforcement Administration, B
Early Childhood Education and Teaching, M
Education, M
Elementary Education and Teaching, BM
English Language and Literature, B
French Language and Literature, B
History, B
Interdisciplinary Studies, B
Kindergarten/PreSchool Education and Teaching, B
Mathematics, B
Nursing - Registered Nurse Training, AB
Physical Education Teaching and Coaching, B
Political Science and Government, B
Psychology, B
Secondary Education and Teaching, B
Sociology, B
Spanish Language and Literature, B
Special Education and Teaching, M

VOORHEES COLLEGE

Accounting, B
Biology/Biological Sciences, B
Business Administration and Management, B

Chemistry, B
Computer Science, B
Criminal Justice/Law Enforcement Administration, B
Education, B
Elementary Education and Teaching, B
English Language and Literature, B
Kindergarten/PreSchool Education and Teaching, B
Kinesiology and Exercise Science, B
Mathematics, B
Physical Education Teaching and Coaching, B
Political Science and Government, B
Sociology, B

WILLIAMSBURG TECHNICAL COLLEGE

Administrative Assistant and Secretarial Science, A
Business/Commerce, A
Computer Programming, Specific Applications, A
Data Entry/Microcomputer Applications, A
Drafting and Design Technology/Technician, A
Heating, Air Conditioning, Ventilation and
 Refrigeration Maintenance
 Technology/Technician, A
Information Technology, A
Liberal Arts and Sciences Studies and
 Humanities, A

WINTHROP UNIVERSITY

Art Education, M
Art History, Criticism and Conservation, B
Art/Art Studies, General, B
Arts Management, M
Biological and Biomedical Sciences, M
Biology/Biological Sciences, B
Business Administration and Management, B
Business Administration, Management and
 Operations, M
Business Teacher Education, B
Chemistry, B
Clinical Laboratory Science/Medical
 Technology/Technologist, B
Communication Disorders, B
Computer Science, B
Counselor Education/School Counseling and
 Guidance Services, M
Dance, B
Drama and Dramatics/Theatre Arts, B
Education, M
Educational Leadership and Administration, M
Elementary Education and Teaching, B
English, M
English Language and Literature, B
Family and Consumer Sciences/Home Economics
 Teacher Education, B
Fine Arts and Art Studies, M
Foods, Nutrition, and Wellness Studies, B
History, BM
Kindergarten/PreSchool Education and Teaching, B
Liberal Studies, M
Mass Communication/Media Studies, B
Mathematics, B
Middle School Education, M
Modern Languages, B
Music, BM
Music Teacher Education, BM
Nutritional Sciences, M
Performance, M
Philosophy, B
Physical Education Teaching and Coaching, BM
Political Science and Government, B
Project Management, MO
Psychology, BMO
Reading Teacher Education, M
Religion/Religious Studies, B
Secondary Education and Teaching, M
Social Work, B
Sociology, B
Software Engineering, MO
Spanish Language and Literature, M
Special Education and Teaching, BM
Sport and Fitness Administration/Management, B
Technical and Business Writing, B

WOFFORD COLLEGE

Accounting, B
Art History, Criticism and Conservation, B
Biology/Biological Sciences, B

Business/Managerial Economics, B
Chemistry, B
Computer Science, B
Creative Writing, B
Drama and Dramatics/Theatre Arts, B
Economics, B
English Language and Literature, B
Finance, B
French Language and Literature, B
German Language and Literature, B
History, B
Humanities/Humanistic Studies, B
International Business/Trade/Commerce, B
International Relations and Affairs, B
Mathematics, B
Neuroscience, B
Philosophy, B
Physics, B
Political Science and Government, B
Pre-Dentistry Studies, B
Pre-Law Studies, B
Pre-Medicine/Pre-Medical Studies, B
Pre-Veterinary Studies, B
Psychology, B
Religion/Religious Studies, B
Sociology, B
Spanish Language and Literature, B

YORK TECHNICAL COLLEGE

Accounting, A
Administrative Assistant and Secretarial Science, A
Automobile/Automotive Mechanics
 Technology/Technician, A
Business Administration and Management, A
Business/Commerce, A
Child Care and Support Services Management, A
Child Care Provider/Assistant, A
Clinical/Medical Laboratory Technician, A
Commercial and Advertising Art, A
Computer and Information Sciences and Support
 Services, A
Computer Engineering Technology/Technician, A
Data Processing and Data Processing
 Technology/Technician, A
Dental Assisting/Assistant, A
Dental Hygiene/Hygienist, A
Electrical and Electronic Engineering
 Technologies/Technicians, A
Electrical, Electronic and Communications
 Engineering Technology/Technician, A
Electrical/Electronics Equipment Installation and
 Repair, A
General Office Occupations and Clerical Services, A
Heating, Air Conditioning, Ventilation and
 Refrigeration Maintenance
 Technology/Technician, A
Industrial Electronics Technology/Technician, A
Industrial Mechanics and Maintenance
 Technology, A
Legal Administrative Assistant/Secretary, A
Liberal Arts and Sciences Studies and
 Humanities, A
Licensed Practical/Vocational Nurse Training, A
Machine Tool Technology/Machinist, A
Mechanical Drafting and Mechanical Drafting
 CAD/CADD, A
Mechanical Engineering/Mechanical
 Technology/Technician, A
Medical Administrative Assistant/Secretary, A
Medical Radiologic Technology/Science - Radiation
 Therapist, A
Medical/Clinical Assistant, A
Multi-/Interdisciplinary Studies, A
Nursing - Registered Nurse Training, A
Radio and Television Broadcasting
 Technology/Technician, A
Surgical Technology/Technologist, A
Welding Technology/Welder, A

South Dakota

AUGUSTANA COLLEGE

Accounting, B
American Sign Language (ASL), B
Art Teacher Education, B

Art/Art Studies, General, B
Athletic Training and Sports Medicine, B
Audiology/Audiologist and Speech-Language
  Pathology/Pathologist, B
Biology/Biological Sciences, B
Business Administration and Management, B
Business/Corporate Communications, B
Chemistry, B
Clinical Laboratory Science/Medical
  Technology/Technologist, B
Communication Studies/Speech Communication
  and Rhetoric, B
Community Health Nursing, M
Computer Science, B
Drama and Dramatics/Theatre Arts, B
Economics, B
Education, M
Education/Teaching of Individuals with Hearing
  Impairments, Including Deafness, B
Elementary Education and Teaching, BM
Engineering Physics, B
English Language and Literature, B
Foreign Languages and Literatures, B
French Language and Literature, B
German Language and Literature, B
Health/Health Care Administration/Management, B
History, B
International Relations and Affairs, B
Journalism, B
Kinesiology and Exercise Science, B
Liberal Arts and Sciences Studies and
  Humanities, B
Management Information Systems and Services, B
Mathematics, B
Music, B
Music Teacher Education, B
Nursing, M
Nursing - Registered Nurse Training, B
Philosophy, B
Physical Education Teaching and Coaching, B
Physics, B
Political Science and Government, B
Pre-Dentistry Studies, B
Pre-Law Studies, B
Pre-Medicine/Pre-Medical Studies, B
Pre-Veterinary Studies, B
Psychology, B
Religion/Religious Studies, B
Secondary Education and Teaching, BM
Social Studies Teacher Education, B
Social Work, B
Sociology, B
Spanish Language and Literature, B
Special Education and Teaching, B
Speech Teacher Education, B
Sport and Fitness Administration/Management, B
Teacher Education, Multiple Levels, B

BLACK HILLS STATE UNIVERSITY

Accounting, B
Administrative Assistant and Secretarial Science, A
American Indian/Native American Studies, B
Art/Art Studies, General, B
Biology/Biological Sciences, B
Business Administration and Management, B
Business Administration, Management and
  Operations, M
Business Teacher Education, B
Chemistry, B
Commercial and Advertising Art, B
Computer and Information Sciences, A
Computer Programming/Programmer, A
Computer Science, A
Curriculum and Instruction, M
Drafting and Design Technology/Technician, A
Education, M
Elementary Education and Teaching, B
English Language and Literature, B
Environmental Studies, B
General Studies, A
Health and Physical Education, B
Health/Health Care Administration/Management, B
History, B
Hospital and Health Care Facilities
  Administration/Management, B

Human Resources Management/Personnel
  Administration, B
Human Services, B
Industrial Technology/Technician, B
Junior High/Intermediate/Middle School Education
  and Teaching, B
Kindergarten/PreSchool Education and Teaching, B
Marketing/Marketing Management, B
Mass Communication/Media Studies, AB
Mathematics, B
Mathematics Teacher Education, B
Music, B
Music Performance, B
Parks, Recreation, Leisure and Fitness Studies, B
Physical Sciences, B
Political Science and Government, B
Psychology, B
Sales, Distribution and Marketing Operations, B
Science Teacher Education/General Science
  Teacher Education, B
Secondary Education and Teaching, B
Social Sciences, B
Sociology, B
Spanish Language and Literature, B
Special Education and Teaching, B
Speech and Rhetorical Studies, B
Sport and Fitness Administration/Management, B
Tourism and Travel Services Management, AB
Voice and Opera, B

COLORADO TECHNICAL UNIVERSITY
SIOUX FALLS CAMPUS

Accounting, AB
Business Administration and Management, AB
Business Administration, Management and
  Operations, M
Computer Science, B
Criminal Justice/Safety Studies, AB
Finance, B
Health Services Administration, M
Human Resources Management and Services, M
Human Resources Management/Personnel
  Administration, B
Information Science/Studies, AB
Management Information Systems and
  Services, ABM
Marketing/Marketing Management, B
Medical/Clinical Assistant, A
Organizational Management, M
Sales, Distribution and Marketing Operations, B

DAKOTA STATE UNIVERSITY

Accounting, B
Biology Teacher Education, B
Biology/Biological Sciences, B
Business Administration and Management, AB
Business Teacher Education, B
Chemical Technology/Technician, B
Computer and Information Sciences, B
Computer and Information Systems Security, B
Computer Graphics, B
Computer Programming/Programmer, A
Computer Science, M
Computer Teacher Education, B
Education, M
Educational Media/Instructional Technology, M
Elementary Education and Teaching, B
English Language and Literature, B
English/Language Arts Teacher Education, B
Finance, B
General Studies, A
Health Information/Medical Records
  Administration/Administrator, B
Health Information/Medical Records
  Technology/Technician, A
Information Science/Studies, ABM
Information Technology, B
Kinesiology and Exercise Science, B
Management Information Systems and Services, M
Marketing/Marketing Management, B
Mathematics and Statistics, B
Mathematics Teacher Education, B
Office Management and Supervision, A
Physical Education Teaching and Coaching, B
Physical Sciences, B
Respiratory Care Therapy/Therapist, AB

Special Education and Teaching, B
Web Page, Digital/Multimedia and Information
  Resources Design, B

DAKOTA WESLEYAN UNIVERSITY

Accounting, B
Adult and Continuing Education and Teaching, B
Art Teacher Education, B
Art/Art Studies, General, B
Athletic Training and Sports Medicine, B
Behavioral Sciences, B
Biochemistry, B
Biology Teacher Education, B
Biology/Biological Sciences, B
Business Administration and Management, AB
Business Teacher Education, B
Computer Software and Media Applications, B
Criminal Justice/Law Enforcement
  Administration, AB
Drama and Dramatics/Theatre Arts, B
Education, B
Elementary Education and Teaching, B
English Language and Literature, B
English/Language Arts Teacher Education, B
Finance, B
History, B
History Teacher Education, B
Human Services, B
Junior High/Intermediate/Middle School Education
  and Teaching, B
Liberal Arts and Sciences Studies and
  Humanities, B
Marketing/Marketing Management, B
Mathematics, B
Mathematics Teacher Education, B
Music, B
Music Teacher Education, B
Nursing - Registered Nurse Training, A
Philosophy, B
Physical Education Teaching and Coaching, B
Psychology, B
Religion/Religious Studies, B
Science Teacher Education/General Science
  Teacher Education, B
Secondary Education and Teaching, B
Social Studies Teacher Education, B
Sociology, B
Spanish Language and Literature, B
Special Education and Teaching, B
Teacher Education, Multiple Levels, B
Theology/Theological Studies, B
Wildlife and Wildlands Science and Management, B

KILIAN COMMUNITY COLLEGE

Accounting, A
Administrative Assistant and Secretarial Science, A
Business Administration and Management, A
Computer Science, A
Computer Software and Media Applications, A
Counseling Psychology, A
Criminal Justice/Law Enforcement Administration, A
Information Technology, A
Liberal Arts and Sciences Studies and
  Humanities, A
Medical Insurance Coding Specialist/Coder, A
Medical Office Management/Administration, A
Medical Transcription/Transcriptionist, A
Social Work, A

LAKE AREA TECHNICAL INSTITUTE

Accounting, A
Agricultural Business and Management, A
Automobile/Automotive Mechanics
  Technology/Technician, A
Avionics Maintenance Technology/Technician, A
Biology Technician/BioTechnology Laboratory
  Technician, A
Carpentry/Carpenter, A
Clinical/Medical Laboratory Technician, A
Computer Programming, A
Computer Programming, Specific Applications, A
Computer Programming/Programmer, A
Computer Systems Networking and
  Telecommunications, A
Cosmetology/Cosmetologist, A
Data Entry/Microcomputer Applications, A

Dental Assisting/Assistant, A
Drafting and Design Technology/Technician, A
Electrical, Electronic and Communications
  Engineering Technology/Technician, A
Finance, A
Information Technology, A
Licensed Practical/Vocational Nurse Training, A
Machine Tool Technology/Machinist, A
Marketing/Marketing Management, A
Medical/Clinical Assistant, A
Occupational Therapist Assistant, A
Physical Therapist Assistant, A
System Administration/Administrator, A
Web/Multimedia Management and Webmaster, A
Welding Technology/Welder, A

MITCHELL TECHNICAL INSTITUTE

Accounting, A
Administrative Assistant and Secretarial Science, A
Agricultural Business and Management, A
Agricultural Production Operations, A
Appliance Installation and Repair
  Technology/Technician, A
Architectural Drafting and Architectural
  CAD/CADD, A
Carpentry/Carpenter, A
Clinical/Medical Laboratory Technician, A
Communications Technologies/Technicians and
  Support Services, A
Computer and Information Sciences, A
Computer and Information Sciences and Support
  Services, A
Computer Software and Media Applications, A
Computer Systems Networking and
  Telecommunications, A
Computer Technology/Computer Systems
  Technology, A
Computer/Information Technology Services
  Administration and Management, A
Construction Trades, A
Culinary Arts/Chef Training, A
Data Entry/Microcomputer Applications, A
Drafting and Design Technology/Technician, A
Electrical and Electronic Engineering
  Technologies/Technicians, A
Electrical and Power Transmission
  Installation/Installer, A
Electrical, Electronic and Communications
  Engineering Technology/Technician, A
Electrician, A
Electromechanical Technology/Electromechanical
  Engineering Technology, A
Engineering Technologies/Technicians, A
Farm/Farm and Ranch Management, A
Heating, Air Conditioning and Refrigeration
  Technology/Technician, A
Heating, Air Conditioning, Ventilation and
  Refrigeration Maintenance
  Technology/Technician, A
Industrial Electronics Technology/Technician, A
Information Science/Studies, A
Lineworker, A
Management Information Systems and Services, A
Medical Administrative Assistant/Secretary, A
Medical/Clinical Assistant, A
Radiologic Technology/Science - Radiographer, A
System, Networking, and LAN/WAN
  Management/Manager, A
Telecommunications Technology/Technician, A

MOUNT MARTY COLLEGE

Accounting, AB
Biology/Biological Sciences, B
Business Administration and Management, AB
Chemistry, B
Chemistry Teacher Education, B
Clinical Laboratory Science/Medical
  Technology/Technologist, B
Computer Science, B
Criminal Justice/Safety Studies, B
Education, B
Elementary Education and Teaching, B
English Language and Literature, B
English/Language Arts Teacher Education, B
Foods, Nutrition, and Wellness Studies, B
General Studies, AB

History, B
History Teacher Education, B
Human Services, B
Information Technology, B
Liberal Arts and Sciences Studies and
  Humanities, AB
Mathematics, B
Mathematics Teacher Education, B
Medical Radiologic Technology/Science - Radiation
  Therapist, B
Music, B
Music Teacher Education, B
Nurse Anesthetist, M
Nursing, M
Nursing - Registered Nurse Training, B
Parks, Recreation and Leisure Facilities
  Management, B
Physical Education Teaching and Coaching, B
Psychology, B
Religion/Religious Studies, AB
Secondary Education and Teaching, B
Special Education and Teaching, B

NATIONAL AMERICAN UNIVERSITY
(RAPID CITY)

Accounting, AB
Athletic Training and Sports Medicine, B
Business Administration and Management, AB
Business Administration, Management and
  Operations, M
Computer Engineering Technology/Technician, A
Computer Programming/Programmer, AB
Equestrian/Equine Studies, AB
Finance, B
Information Science/Studies, AB
International Business/Trade/Commerce, B
Legal Assistant/Paralegal, A
Liberal Arts and Sciences Studies and
  Humanities, A
Management Information Systems and Services, B
Marketing/Marketing Management, B
Operations Management and Supervision, B
Pre-Law Studies, B
System, Networking, and LAN/WAN
  Management/Manager, B
Veterinary/Animal Health Technology/Technician and
  Veterinary Assistant, A

NATIONAL AMERICAN
UNIVERSITY-SIOUX FALLS BRANCH

Accounting, AB
Business Administration and Management, AB
Computer
  Programming, Vendor/Product Certification, B
Computer Programming/Programmer, AB
Customer Service Support/Call Center/Teleservice
  Operation, AB
Information Science/Studies, AB
Information Technology, AB
Legal Assistant/Paralegal, AB
Management Information Systems and Services, AB
Massage Therapy/Therapeutic Massage, A
Medical/Clinical Assistant, A
Web Page, Digital/Multimedia and Information
  Resources Design, B

NORTHERN STATE UNIVERSITY

Accounting, B
Administrative Assistant and Secretarial Science, AB
Art Teacher Education, B
Art/Art Studies, General, B
Audiology/Audiologist and Speech-Language
  Pathology/Pathologist, B
Biological and Physical Sciences, B
Biology/Biological Sciences, B
Business Administration and Management, AB
Business Teacher Education, B
Business/Managerial Economics, B
Chemistry, B
Clinical Laboratory Science/Medical
  Technology/Technologist, B
Clinical/Medical Laboratory Technician, B
Commercial and Advertising Art, A
Community Organization and Advocacy, B
Counselor Education/School Counseling and
  Guidance Services, M

Criminal Justice/Police Science, B
Data Processing and Data Processing
  Technology/Technician, A
Drama and Dramatics/Theatre Arts, B
Economics, B
Education, BM
Educational Administration and Supervision, M
Educational Media/Instructional Technology, M
Electrical, Electronic and Communications
  Engineering Technology/Technician, AB
Elementary Education and Teaching, BM
English Education, M
English Language and Literature, B
Environmental Studies, B
Finance, B
French Language and Literature, B
German Language and Literature, B
Health Education, M
Health Teacher Education, B
History, B
International Business/Trade/Commerce, B
Liberal Arts and Sciences Studies and
  Humanities, A
Management Information Systems and Services, B
Marketing/Marketing Management, B
Mathematics, B
Music, B
Music Teacher Education, B
Physical Education Teaching and Coaching, BM
Political Science and Government, B
Pre-Dentistry Studies, B
Pre-Engineering, A
Pre-Law Studies, B
Pre-Medicine/Pre-Medical Studies, B
Psychology, B
Public Administration, B
Reading Teacher Education, M
Secondary Education and Teaching, BM
Social Work, A
Sociology, B
Spanish Language and Literature, B
Special Education and Teaching, BM
Speech and Rhetorical Studies, B
Technology Education/Industrial Arts, B
Voice and Opera, B

OGLALA LAKOTA COLLEGE

Accounting, A
Administrative Assistant and Secretarial Science, A
Agriculture, A
American Indian/Native American Studies, AB
Bilingual and Multilingual Education, B
Business Administration and Management, AB
Carpentry/Carpenter, A
Computer Science, A
Counselor Education/School Counseling and
  Guidance Services, AB
Criminal Justice/Law Enforcement
  Administration, A
Educational Administration and Supervision, M
Electrical, Electronic and Communications
  Engineering Technology/Technician, A
Elementary Education and Teaching, AB
Family and Consumer Sciences/Human Sciences, A
History, B
Human Services, AB
Kindergarten/PreSchool Education and
  Teaching, AB
Legal Assistant/Paralegal, AB
Liberal Arts and Sciences Studies and
  Humanities, A
Management, M
Mass Communication/Media Studies, A
Natural Resources Management/Development and
  Policy, A
Nursing - Registered Nurse Training, A
Social Work, AB
Special Education and Teaching, B

PRESENTATION COLLEGE

Biology/Biological Sciences, AB
Business Administration and Management, AB
Chemistry, A
Clinical/Medical Laboratory Technician, A
Communication Studies/Speech Communication
  and Rhetoric, AB

English Language and Literature, A
General Studies, A
Medical Radiologic Technology/Science - Radiation
  Therapist, AB
Medical Transcription/Transcriptionist, A
Medical/Clinical Assistant, A
Nursing - Registered Nurse Training, AB
Religion/Religious Studies, A
Social Work, B
Surgical Technology/Technologist, A

SINTE GLESKA UNIVERSITY

Accounting, A
American Indian/Native American Studies, A
Art/Art Studies, General, A
Business Administration and Management, AB
Business Teacher Education, A
Criminal Justice/Law Enforcement Administration, B
Data Processing and Data Processing
  Technology/Technician, A
Education, AM
Elementary Education and Teaching, BM
Human Services, AB
Kindergarten/PreSchool Education and Teaching, B
Liberal Arts and Sciences Studies and
  Humanities, A
Natural Resources Management/Development and
  Policy, A
Trade and Industrial Teacher Education, A

SISSETON-WAHPETON COMMUNITY COLLEGE

Accounting, A
American Indian/Native American Studies, A
Business Administration and Management, A
Electrical, Electronic and Communications
  Engineering Technology/Technician, A
Hospitality Administration/Management, A
Information Science/Studies, A
Kindergarten/PreSchool Education and Teaching, A
Liberal Arts and Sciences Studies and
  Humanities, A
Natural Sciences, A
Nursing - Registered Nurse Training, A
Nutritional Sciences, A
Substance Abuse/Addiction Counseling, A

SOUTH DAKOTA SCHOOL OF MINES AND TECHNOLOGY

Atmospheric Sciences and Meteorology, MD
Chemical Engineering, BMD
Chemistry, BMD
Civil Engineering, BMD
Computer Engineering, B
Computer Science, BM
Electrical Engineering, MD
Electrical, Electronics and Communications
  Engineering, B
Engineering and Applied Sciences, MD
Environmental Sciences, D
Environmental/Environmental Health Engineering, B
General Studies, A
Geological Engineering, MD
Geological/Geophysical Engineering, B
Geology/Earth Science, BMD
Industrial Engineering, B
Interdisciplinary Studies, B
Management of Technology, M
Materials Engineering, MD
Materials Sciences, MD
Mathematics, B
Mechanical Engineering, BMD
Metallurgical Engineering, BMD
Mining and Mineral Engineering, B
Paleontology, M
Physics, BMD
Water Resources, D

SOUTH DAKOTA STATE UNIVERSITY

Agribusiness, B
Agricultural Economics, B
Agricultural Engineering, MD
Agricultural Mechanization, B
Agricultural Sciences, MD
Agricultural Teacher Education, B

Agricultural/Biological Engineering and
  Bioengineering, B
Agriculture, AB
Agronomy and Crop Science, B
Agronomy and Soil Sciences, MD
Analytical Chemistry, MD
Animal Sciences, BMD
Applied Horticulture/Horticultural Operations, B
Art Teacher Education, B
Art/Art Studies, General, B
Athletic Training and Sports Medicine, B
Atmospheric Sciences and Meteorology, D
Biochemistry, BMD
Biological and Biomedical Sciences, MD
Biology/Biological Sciences, B
Chemistry, BMD
Child Development, B
Civil Engineering, BM
Clinical Laboratory Science/Medical
  Technology/Technologist, B
Communication and Media Studies, M
Computer and Information Sciences, B
Computer Graphics, B
Computer Science, M
Computer Software Engineering, B
Computer Teacher Education, B
Construction Engineering Technology/Technician, B
Consumer Services and Advocacy, B
Counselor Education/School Counseling and
  Guidance Services, M
Curriculum and Instruction, M
Dairy Science, BMD
Dietetics/Dieticians, B
Drama and Dramatics/Theatre Arts, B
Economics, BM
Education, BM
Educational Administration and Supervision, M
Electrical Engineering, M
Electrical, Electronic and Communications
  Engineering Technology/Technician, B
Electrical, Electronics and Communications
  Engineering, B
Engineering and Applied Sciences, MD
Engineering Physics, B
Engineering/Industrial Management, B
English, M
English Language and Literature, B
Entomology, M
Environmental Engineering
  Technology/Environmental Technology, M
Environmental Sciences, D
Environmental/Environmental Health Engineering, B
Family and Consumer Sciences/Home Economics
  Teacher Education, B
Fashion Merchandising, B
Fish, Game and Wildlife Management, MD
Food Science, B
Foods, Nutrition, and Wellness Studies, B
French Language and Literature, B
Geography, BM
German Language and Literature, B
Health and Physical Education, B
Health Education, M
History, B
Home Economics, M
Hotel/Motel Administration/Management, B
Human Development and Family Studies, B
Industrial Safety Technology/Technician, B
Industrial Technology/Technician, B
Industrial/Management Engineering, M
Information Science/Studies, B
Inorganic Chemistry, MD
Interior Design, B
Journalism, BM
Kindergarten/PreSchool Education and Teaching, B
Landscaping and Groundskeeping, B
Mass Communication/Media Studies, B
Mathematics, BM
Mechanical Engineering, BM
Medical Microbiology and Bacteriology, B
Microbiology, M
Music, B
Music Management and Merchandising, B
Music Teacher Education, B
Nursing, M
Nursing - Registered Nurse Training, B

Organic Chemistry, MD
Parks, Recreation and Leisure Facilities
  Management, B
Parks, Recreation, Leisure and Fitness Studies, B
Pharmaceutical Sciences, M
Pharmacy, BP
Physical Chemistry, MD
Physical Education Teaching and Coaching, BM
Physics, MD
Plant Pathology/Phytopathology, M
Plant Sciences, MD
Political Science and Government, B
Pre-Dentistry Studies, B
Pre-Law Studies, B
Pre-Medicine/Pre-Medical Studies, B
Pre-Veterinary Studies, B
Psychology, B
Range Science and Management, B
Recreation and Park Management, M
Rural Sociology, MD
Secondary Education and Teaching, B
Sociology, B
Spanish Language and Literature, B
Speech and Rhetorical Studies, B
Theater, M
Visual and Performing Arts, B
Water Resources, D
Wildlife and Wildlands Science and Management, B

SOUTHEAST TECHNICAL INSTITUTE

Accounting, A
Architectural Engineering Technology/Technician, A
Artificial Intelligence and Robotics, A
Autobody/Collision and Repair
  Technology/Technician, A
Automobile/Automotive Mechanics
  Technology/Technician, A
Biomedical Technology/Technician, A
Business Administration and Management, A
Cardiovascular Technology/Technologist, A
Civil Engineering Technology/Technician, A
Clinical/Medical Laboratory Technician, A
Commercial and Advertising Art, A
Computer and Information Sciences, A
Computer Graphics, A
Computer Programming, A
Computer Programming, Specific Applications, A
Computer
  Programming, Vendor/Product Certification, A
Computer Programming/Programmer, A
Computer Software and Media Applications, A
Computer Software Engineering, A
Computer Systems Networking and
  Telecommunications, A
Computer Technology/Computer Systems
  Technology, A
Computer/Information Technology Services
  Administration and Management, A
Diesel Mechanics Technology/Technician, A
Drafting and Design Technology/Technician, A
Electrical, Electronic and Communications
  Engineering Technology/Technician, A
Electromechanical Technology/Electromechanical
  Engineering Technology, A
Engineering Technology, A
Finance, A
Graphic and Printing Equipment Operator
  Production, A
Health Unit Coordinator/Ward Clerk, A
Heating, Air Conditioning, Ventilation and
  Refrigeration Maintenance
  Technology/Technician, A
Horticultural Science, A
Industrial Technology/Technician, A
Information Science/Studies, A
Information Technology, A
Laser and Optical Technology/Technician, A
Machine Tool Technology/Machinist, A
Management Information Systems and Services, A
Marketing/Marketing Management, A
Mechanical Engineering/Mechanical
  Technology/Technician, A
Medical Transcription/Transcriptionist, A
Nuclear Medical Technology/Technologist, A
Nursing, A
Sign Language Interpretation and Translation, A

Surgical Technology/Technologist, A
Survey Technology/Surveying, A
System Administration/Administrator, A
Turf and Turfgrass Management, A
Web Page, Digital/Multimedia and Information
   Resources Design, A
Web/Multimedia Management and Webmaster, A

UNIVERSITY OF SIOUX FALLS

Accounting, B
Administrative Assistant and Secretarial Science, AB
Applied Art, B
Applied Mathematics, B
Art Teacher Education, B
Behavioral Sciences, B
Biology/Biological Sciences, B
Business Administration and Management, AB
Business Administration, Management and
   Operations, M
Chemistry, B
Clinical Laboratory Science/Medical
   Technology/Technologist, B
Commercial and Advertising Art, B
Computer Science, B
Developmental and Child Psychology, A
Drama and Dramatics/Theatre Arts, AB
Economics, AB
Education, BM
Educational Leadership and Administration, M
Educational Media/Instructional Technology, M
Elementary Education and Teaching, B
English Language and Literature, B
Health Teacher Education, B
History, B
Humanities/Humanistic Studies, A
Industrial Radiologic Technology/Technician, B
Information Science/Studies, B
Interdisciplinary Studies, AB
Junior High/Intermediate/Middle School Education
   and Teaching, B
Kindergarten/PreSchool Education and Teaching, A
Kinesiology and Exercise Science, B
Liberal Arts and Sciences Studies and
   Humanities, B
Management Information Systems and Services, B
Marketing/Marketing Management, AB
Mass Communication/Media Studies, B
Mathematics, B
Music, B
Music Management and Merchandising, B
Music Teacher Education, B
Pastoral Studies/Counseling, B
Philosophy, B
Physical Education Teaching and Coaching, B
Piano and Organ, B
Political Science and Government, B
Pre-Dentistry Studies, B
Pre-Engineering, A
Pre-Law Studies, B
Pre-Medicine/Pre-Medical Studies, B
Pre-Veterinary Studies, B
Psychology, B
Public Relations/Image Management, B
Radio and Television, B
Reading Teacher Education, M
Religion/Religious Studies, AB
Science Teacher Education/General Science
   Teacher Education, B
Secondary Education and Teaching, B
Social Sciences, AB
Social Work, B
Sociology, B
Speech and Rhetorical Studies, B
Voice and Opera, B

THE UNIVERSITY OF SOUTH DAKOTA

Accounting, BMO
Allied Health and Medical Assisting Services, M
Allopathic Medicine, P
American Indian/Native American Studies, B
Anthropology, B
Art Teacher Education, B
Art/Art Studies, General, B
Biological and Biomedical Sciences, MD
Biology Teacher Education, B
Biology/Biological Sciences, B

Business Administration and Management, B
Business Administration, Management and
   Operations, MO
Business/Managerial Economics, B
Cardiovascular Sciences, MD
Cell Biology and Anatomy, MD
Chemistry, BM
Classics and Classical
   Languages, Literatures, and Linguistics, B
Clinical Psychology, MD
Communication Disorders, BM
Computer and Information Sciences, B
Computer Science, M
Counselor Education/School Counseling and
   Guidance Services, MDO
Criminal Justice/Law Enforcement Administration, B
Curriculum and Instruction, BMDO
Dental Hygiene/Hygienist, AB
Drama and Dance Teacher Education, B
Drama and Dramatics/Theatre Arts, B
Economics, B
Education, BMDO
Educational Administration and Supervision, MDO
Educational Media/Instructional Technology, MO
Educational Psychology, MDO
Elementary Education and Teaching, BM
English, MD
English Language and Literature, B
English/Language Arts Teacher Education, B
Finance, B
Fine Arts and Art Studies, M
Foreign Language Teacher Education, B
French Language and Literature, B
French Language Teacher Education, B
General Studies, A
Geology/Earth Science, B
German Language and Literature, B
German Language Teacher Education, B
Health Education, M
Health Teacher Education, B
History, BMO
History Teacher Education, B
Hospital and Health Care Facilities
   Administration/Management, B
Immunology, MD
Interdisciplinary Studies, MO
Junior High/Intermediate/Middle School Education
   and Teaching, B
Law and Legal Studies, PO
Liberal Arts and Sciences Studies and
   Humanities, B
Marketing/Marketing Management, B
Mass Communication/Media Studies, BM
Mathematics, BM
Mathematics Teacher Education, B
Microbiology, MD
Molecular Biology, MD
Music, BM
Music Teacher Education, B
Neuroscience, MD
Nursing - Registered Nurse Training, A
Occupational Therapy/Therapist, M
Parks, Recreation, Leisure and Fitness Studies, B
Pharmacology, MD
Philosophy, B
Physical Education Teaching and Coaching, BM
Physical Therapy/Therapist, M
Physician Assistant, M
Physics, B
Physics Teacher Education, B
Physiology, MD
Political Science and Government, BMO
Psychology, BMD
Public Administration, M
Science Teacher Education/General Science
   Teacher Education, B
Secondary Education and Teaching, BM
Social Science Teacher Education, B
Social Work, B
Sociology, BM
Spanish Language and Literature, B
Spanish Language Teacher Education, B
Special Education and Teaching, BM
Speech and Interpersonal Communication, M
Speech Teacher Education, B
Substance Abuse/Addiction Counseling, B

Theater, M

WESTERN DAKOTA TECHNICAL INSTITUTE

Agricultural Business and Management, A
Animal/Livestock Husbandry and Production, A
Automobile/Automotive Mechanics
   Technology/Technician, A
Business Administration and Management, A
Computer Installation and Repair
   Technology/Technician, A
Criminal Justice/Police Science, A
Drafting and Design Technology/Technician, A
Electrical, Electronic and Communications
   Engineering Technology/Technician, A
Electrical/Electronics Equipment Installation and
   Repair, A
Farm/Farm and Ranch Management, A
Industrial Electronics Technology/Technician, A
Legal Assistant/Paralegal, A
Machine Shop Technology/Assistant, A
Management Information Systems and Services, A
Medical Transcription/Transcriptionist, A

Tennessee

AMERICAN ACADEMY OF NUTRITION, COLLEGE OF NUTRITION

Foods, Nutrition, and Wellness Studies, A

AMERICAN BAPTIST COLLEGE OF AMERICAN BAPTIST THEOLOGICAL SEMINARY

Bible/Biblical Studies, AB
Theology/Theological Studies, B

AQUINAS COLLEGE

Elementary Education and Teaching, B
English Language and Literature, B
Liberal Arts and Sciences Studies and
   Humanities, A
Management Information Systems and Services, B
Nursing - Registered Nurse Training, AB
Theology/Theological Studies, B

ARGOSY UNIVERSITY/NASHVILLE

Counseling Psychology, M

AUSTIN PEAY STATE UNIVERSITY

Agriculture, B
Art/Art Studies, General, B
Biological and Biomedical Sciences, M
Biology/Biological Sciences, B
Business Administration and Management, AB
Business Administration, Management and
   Operations, M
Business/Commerce, B
Business/Office Automation/Technology/Data
   Entry, A
Chemistry, B
Clinical Laboratory Science/Medical
   Technology/Technologist, B
Clinical Psychology, M
Communication and Media Studies, M
Computer and Information Sciences, B
Counselor Education/School Counseling and
   Guidance Services, O
Criminal Justice/Law Enforcement Administration, B
Curriculum and Instruction, M
Data Processing and Data Processing
   Technology/Technician, A
Education, MO
Educational Administration and Supervision, O
Educational Leadership and Administration, M
Elementary Education and Teaching, O
Engineering Technology, B
English, M
English Education, M
English Language and Literature, B
Environmental Studies, B
Exercise and Sports Science, M
Foreign Languages and Literatures, B
Geology/Earth Science, B
Health and Physical Education, B

Health Education, M
History, B
Interdisciplinary Studies, B
Liberal Arts and Sciences Studies and
   Humanities, A
Mass Communication/Media Studies, B
Mathematics, B
Music, BM
Music Teacher Education, M
Nursing, M
Nursing - Registered Nurse Training, B
Philosophy, B
Physics, B
Political Science and Government, B
Psychology, BM
Radiologic Technology/Science - Radiographer, B
Reading Teacher Education, M
School Psychology, M
Secondary Education and Teaching, O
Social Work, B
Sociology, B
Spanish Language and Literature, B
Special Education and Teaching, B
Technology Education/Industrial Arts, A
Theater, M

BAPTIST COLLEGE OF HEALTH SCIENCES

Diagnostic Medical Sonography/Sonographer and
   Ultrasound Technician, B
Health Services/Allied Health/Health Sciences, B
Health/Health Care Administration/Management, B
Medical Radiologic Technology/Science - Radiation
   Therapist, B
Nuclear Medical Technology/Technologist, B
Nursing - Registered Nurse Training, B
Radiologic Technology/Science - Radiographer, B
Respiratory Care Therapy/Therapist, B

BELMONT UNIVERSITY

Accounting, B
Advertising, B
Allied Health and Medical Assisting Services, MD
Ancient Near Eastern and Biblical
   Languages, Literatures, and Linguistics, B
Applied Mathematics, B
Art Teacher Education, B
Art/Art Studies, General, B
Bible/Biblical Studies, B
Bilingual and Multilingual Education, B
Biochemistry, B
Biological and Physical Sciences, B
Biology/Biological Sciences, B
Broadcast Journalism, B
Business Administration and Management, B
Business Administration, Management and
   Operations, M
Business Teacher Education, B
Business/Managerial Economics, B
Chemistry, B
Clinical Laboratory Science/Medical
   Technology/Technologist, B
Composition, M
Computer Programming/Programmer, B
Computer Science, B
Consumer Merchandising/Retailing Management, B
Counselor Education/School Counseling and
   Guidance Services, B
Developmental and Child Psychology, B
Divinity/Ministry (BD, MDiv.), B
Drama and Dramatics/Theatre Arts, B
Economics, B
Education, BM
Educational Media/Instructional Technology, M
Elementary Education and Teaching, BM
Engineering Science, B
English, M
English Education, M
English Language and Literature, B
European Studies/Civilization, B
Finance, B
Fine/Studio Arts, B
Health and Physical Education, B
Health Teacher Education, B
Health/Health Care Administration/Management, B
History, B

Information Science/Studies, B
International Business/Trade/Commerce, B
Journalism, B
Marketing/Marketing Management, B
Mass Communication/Media Studies, B
Mathematics, B
Mathematics Teacher Education, M
Middle School Education, M
Modern Greek Language and Literature, B
Music, BM
Music History, Literature, and Theory, B
Music Management and Merchandising, B
Music Teacher Education, BM
Nursing, M
Nursing - Registered Nurse Training, B
Occupational Therapy/Therapist, MD
Parks, Recreation, Leisure and Fitness Studies, B
Pastoral Studies/Counseling, B
Performance, M
Philosophy, B
Physical Education Teaching and Coaching, B
Physical Therapy/Therapist, D
Physics, B
Piano and Organ, B
Political Science and Government, B
Psychology, B
Public Relations, Advertising, and Applied
   Communication, B
Radio and Television, B
Religious/Sacred Music, B
Sacred Music, M
Sales, Distribution and Marketing Operations, B
Science Teacher Education/General Science
   Teacher Education, M
Secondary Education and Teaching, M
Social Studies Teacher Education, M
Social Work, B
Sociology, B
Spanish Language and Literature, B
Special Education and Teaching, B
Speech and Rhetorical Studies, B
Sport and Fitness Administration/Management, M
Voice and Opera, B
Writing, M

BETHEL COLLEGE

Accounting, B
Biology Teacher Education, B
Biology/Biological Sciences, B
Business Administration and Management, B
Chemistry, B
Drama and Dramatics/Theatre Arts, B
Education, BM
Educational Administration and Supervision, M
Elementary Education and Teaching, BM
English Education, M
English Language and Literature, B
English/Language Arts Teacher Education, B
Health and Physical Education, B
History, B
History Teacher Education, B
Human Services, B
Interdisciplinary Studies, B
Liberal Arts and Sciences Studies and
   Humanities, B
Mathematics, B
Physical Education Teaching and Coaching, BM
Physician Assistant, B
Pre-Dentistry Studies, B
Pre-Medicine/Pre-Medical Studies, B
Psychology, B
Science Teacher Education/General Science
   Teacher Education, M
Social Studies Teacher Education, M
Special Education and Teaching, BM
Teacher Education, Multiple Levels, B

BRYAN COLLEGE

Athletic Training and Sports Medicine, B
Bible/Biblical Studies, B
Biology/Biological Sciences, B
Business Administration and Management, AB
Business/Corporate Communications, B
Christian Studies, B
Communication, Journalism and Related
   Programs, B

Communications Technology/Technician, B
Comparative Literature, B
Computer Science, B
Education, B
Elementary Education and Teaching, B
English Language and Literature, B
Health and Physical Education, B
History, B
Junior High/Intermediate/Middle School Education
   and Teaching, B
Kindergarten/PreSchool Education and Teaching, B
Kinesiology and Exercise Science, B
Liberal Arts and Sciences Studies and
   Humanities, AB
Mass Communication/Media Studies, B
Mathematics, B
Music, B
Music Management and Merchandising, B
Music Pedagogy, B
Music Performance, B
Music Teacher Education, B
Musical Instrument Fabrication and Repair, B
Physical Education Teaching and Coaching, B
Piano and Organ, B
Political Communication, B
Pre-Medicine/Pre-Medical Studies, B
Psychology, B
Religious Education, B
Religious/Sacred Music, B
Science Teacher Education/General Science
   Teacher Education, B
Secondary Education and Teaching, B
Spanish Language and Literature, B
Voice and Opera, B
Wind and Percussion Instruments, B

CARSON-NEWMAN COLLEGE

Accounting, B
Ancient Near Eastern and Biblical
   Languages, Literatures, and Linguistics, B
Art Teacher Education, B
Art/Art Studies, General, B
Athletic Training and Sports Medicine, B
Bible/Biblical Studies, B
Biology/Biological Sciences, B
Broadcast Journalism, B
Business Administration and Management, B
Business Teacher Education, B
Business/Managerial Economics, B
Chemistry, B
Child Development, B
Clinical Laboratory Science/Medical
   Technology/Technologist, B
Commercial and Advertising Art, B
Comparative Literature, B
Computer Science, B
Consumer Services and Advocacy, B
Counselor Education/School Counseling and
   Guidance Services, M
Creative Writing, B
Curriculum and Instruction, M
Developmental and Child Psychology, B
Dietetics/Dieticians, B
Divinity/Ministry (BD, MDiv.), A
Drama and Dramatics/Theatre Arts, B
Drawing, B
Economics, B
Education, BM
Elementary Education and Teaching, BM
English as a Second Language, M
English Language and Literature, B
Family and Consumer Economics and Related
   Services, B
Family and Consumer Sciences/Home Economics
   Teacher Education, B
Family and Consumer Sciences/Human Sciences, B
Fashion Merchandising, B
Film/Cinema Studies, B
Foods, Nutrition, and Wellness Studies, B
French Language and Literature, B
History, B
Hospital and Health Care Facilities
   Administration/Management, B
Human Services, B
Information Science/Studies, B
Interdisciplinary Studies, B

Interior Design, B
International Economics, B
Journalism, B
Kindergarten/PreSchool Education and Teaching, B
Kinesiology and Exercise Science, B
Liberal Arts and Sciences Studies and
 Humanities, B
Management Information Systems and Services, B
Marketing/Marketing Management, B
Mass Communication/Media Studies, B
Mathematics, B
Music, B
Music Teacher Education, B
Music Theory and Composition, B
Nursing, M
Nursing - Advanced Practice, M
Nursing - Registered Nurse Training, B
Parks, Recreation, Leisure and Fitness Studies, B
Philosophy, B
Photography, B
Physical Education Teaching and Coaching, B
Piano and Organ, B
Political Science and Government, B
Psychology, B
Religion/Religious Studies, B
Secondary Education and Teaching, BM
Sociology, B
Spanish Language and Literature, B
Special Education and Teaching, B
Speech and Rhetorical Studies, B
Voice and Opera, B

CHATTANOOGA STATE TECHNICAL COMMUNITY COLLEGE

Accounting, A
Administrative Assistant and Secretarial Science, A
Advertising, A
Airline/Commercial/Professional Pilot and Flight
 Crew, A
Applied Art, A
Artificial Intelligence and Robotics, A
Automobile/Automotive Mechanics
 Technology/Technician, A
Aviation/Airway Management and Operations, A
Avionics Maintenance Technology/Technician, A
Biology/Biological Sciences, A
Broadcast Journalism, A
Business Administration and Management, A
Chemical Engineering, A
Chemistry, A
Child Development, A
Civil Engineering Technology/Technician, A
Commercial and Advertising Art, A
Computer Engineering Technology/Technician, A
Computer Programming/Programmer, A
Computer Science, A
Consumer Merchandising/Retailing Management, A
Criminal Justice/Law Enforcement Administration, A
Data Processing and Data Processing
 Technology/Technician, A
Dental Hygiene/Hygienist, A
Drafting and Design Technology/Technician, A
Drafting/Design Engineering
 Technologies/Technicians, A
Electrical, Electronic and Communications
 Engineering Technology/Technician, A
Emergency Medical Technology/Technician (EMT
 Paramedic), A
Energy Management and Systems
 Technology/Technician, A
Engineering, A
Environmental Engineering
 Technology/Environmental Technology, A
Finance, A
Fire Science/Firefighting, A
Food Technology and Processing, A
Forestry, A
Forestry Technology/Technician, A
Graphic and Printing Equipment Operator
 Production, A
Health Information/Medical Records
 Administration/Administrator, A
Heating, Air Conditioning, Ventilation and
 Refrigeration Maintenance
 Technology/Technician, A
Hotel/Motel Administration/Management, A

Industrial Radiologic Technology/Technician, A
Information Science/Studies, A
Instrumentation Technology/Technician, A
Kindergarten/PreSchool Education and Teaching, A
Legal Administrative Assistant/Secretary, A
Liberal Arts and Sciences Studies and
 Humanities, A
Machine Tool Technology/Machinist, A
Mass Communication/Media Studies, A
Mechanical Engineering/Mechanical
 Technology/Technician, A
Medical Administrative Assistant/Secretary, A
Nuclear Medical Technology/Technologist, A
Nuclear/Nuclear Power Technology/Technician, A
Nursing - Registered Nurse Training, A
Occupational Therapy/Therapist, A
Physical Therapy/Therapist, A
Radio and Television, A
Respiratory Care Therapy/Therapist, A
Sign Language Interpretation and Translation, A
Survey Technology/Surveying, A
Transportation and Materials Moving, A
Welding Technology/Welder, A
Wildlife and Wildlands Science and Management, A

CHRISTIAN BROTHERS UNIVERSITY

Biology Teacher Education, B
Biology/Biological Sciences, B
Business Administration and Management, B
Business Administration, Management and
 Operations, M
Chemical Engineering, B
Chemistry, B
Chemistry Teacher Education, B
Civil Engineering, B
Computer Science, B
Education, B
Electrical, Electronics and Communications
 Engineering, B
Elementary Education and Teaching, B
Engineering and Applied Sciences, M
Engineering Physics, B
English Language and Literature, B
English/Language Arts Teacher Education, B
Environmental/Environmental Health Engineering, B
History, B
History Teacher Education, B
Liberal Studies, M
Mathematics, B
Mathematics Teacher Education, B
Mechanical Engineering, B
Natural Sciences, B
Philosophy, B
Physics, B
Physics Teacher Education, B
Psychology, B
Public Relations/Image Management, B
Religion/Religious Studies, B

CLEVELAND STATE COMMUNITY COLLEGE

Administrative Assistant and Secretarial Science, A
Business Administration and Management, A
Child Development, A
Community Organization and Advocacy, A
General Studies, A
Industrial Technology/Technician, A
Kindergarten/PreSchool Education and Teaching, A
Liberal Arts and Sciences Studies and
 Humanities, A
Nursing - Registered Nurse Training, A
Public Administration and Social Service
 Professions, A
Technology Education/Industrial Arts, A

COLUMBIA STATE COMMUNITY COLLEGE

Accounting, A
Administrative Assistant and Secretarial Science, A
Agricultural Business and Management, A
Art/Art Studies, General, A
Biology/Biological Sciences, A
Business/Commerce, A
Chemistry, A
Clinical/Medical Laboratory Technician, A
Dental Hygiene/Hygienist, A

Economics, A
Electrical, Electronic and Communications
 Engineering Technology/Technician, A
Elementary Education and Teaching, A
Geography, A
History, A
Industrial Radiologic Technology/Technician, A
Information Science/Studies, A
Kindergarten/PreSchool Education and Teaching, A
Liberal Arts and Sciences Studies and
 Humanities, A
Mass Communication/Media Studies, A
Mathematics, A
Music, A
Nursing - Registered Nurse Training, A
Pharmacy, A
Physical Education Teaching and Coaching, A
Physical Therapy/Therapist, A
Physics, A
Political Science and Government, A
Pre-Engineering, A
Psychology, A
Respiratory Care Therapy/Therapist, A
Sociology, A
Speech and Rhetorical Studies, A
Veterinary/Animal Health Technology/Technician and
 Veterinary Assistant, A

CRICHTON COLLEGE

Bible/Biblical Studies, B
Biology/Biological Sciences, B
Business Administration and Management, B
Chemistry, B
Chemistry Teacher Education, B
Elementary Education and Teaching, B
English Language and Literature, B
English/Language Arts Teacher Education, B
General Studies, B
History, B
Liberal Arts and Sciences Studies and
 Humanities, B
Management Information Systems and Services, B
Mathematics Teacher Education, B
Non-Profit/Public/Organizational Management, B
Psychology, B
Secondary Education and Teaching, B
Youth Ministry, B

CUMBERLAND UNIVERSITY

Accounting, B
American/United States Studies/Civilization, B
Athletic Training and Sports Medicine, B
Biology Teacher Education, B
Biology/Biological Sciences, AB
Business Administration, Management and
 Operations, M
Business/Commerce, AB
Criminal Justice/Law Enforcement Administration, B
Drama and Dramatics/Theatre Arts, B
Education, ABM
Elementary Education and Teaching, B
English Language and Literature, B
Fine/Studio Arts, B
Geography Teacher Education, B
Health/Medical Preparatory Programs, B
History, B
History Teacher Education, B
Human Resources Management and Services, M
Liberal Arts and Sciences Studies and
 Humanities, AB
Mathematics, B
Mathematics Teacher Education, B
Music, B
Music Teacher Education, B
Nursing - Registered Nurse Training, B
Organizational Management, M
Parks, Recreation, Leisure and Fitness Studies, B
Physical Education Teaching and Coaching, B
Political Science and Government, B
Pre-Dentistry Studies, B
Pre-Law Studies, B
Pre-Medicine/Pre-Medical Studies, B
Pre-Pharmacy Studies, B
Pre-Veterinary Studies, B
Psychology, B
Psychology Teacher Education, B

Public Administration, M
Secondary Education and Teaching, B
Social Sciences, B
Sociology, B
Special Education and Teaching, B
Visual and Performing Arts, B

DRAUGHONS JUNIOR COLLEGE (CLARKSVILLE)

Accounting, A
Administrative Assistant and Secretarial Science, A
Business Administration and Management, A
Computer Programming/Programmer, A
Computer Science, A
Criminal Justice/Safety Studies, A
Fashion Merchandising, A
Health Information/Medical Records
   Administration/Administrator, A
Information Science/Studies, A
Legal Administrative Assistant/Secretary, A
Medical/Clinical Assistant, A
Pharmacy Technician/Assistant, A
Radio and Television, A
Retailing and Retail Operations, A

DRAUGHONS JUNIOR COLLEGE (NASHVILLE)

Accounting, A
Administrative Assistant and Secretarial Science, A
Broadcast Journalism, A
Business Administration and Management, A
Computer Programming/Programmer, A
Computer Science, A
Fashion Merchandising, A
Health Information/Medical Records
   Administration/Administrator, A
Information Science/Studies, A
Law and Legal Studies, A
Medical/Clinical Assistant, A
Radio and Television, A

DYERSBURG STATE COMMUNITY COLLEGE

Business Administration and Management, A
Child Development, A
Computer/Information Technology Services
   Administration and Management, A
Criminal Justice/Police Science, A
Electrical, Electronic and Communications
   Engineering Technology/Technician, A
Health Information/Medical Records
   Technology/Technician, A
Liberal Arts and Sciences Studies and
   Humanities, A
Nursing - Registered Nurse Training, A

EAST TENNESSEE STATE UNIVERSITY

Accounting, BM
Allied Health and Medical Assisting Services, MDO
Allopathic Medicine, P
Anatomy, MD
Art Education, M
Art History, Criticism and Conservation, M
Art/Art Studies, General, B
Biochemistry, MD
Biological and Biomedical Sciences, MD
Biology/Biological Sciences, B
Biophysics, MD
Business Administration and Management, B
Business Administration, Management and
   Operations, MO
Business/Managerial Economics, B
Chemistry, BM
Child Development, B
Clinical Psychology, M
Communication and Media Studies, M
Communication Disorders, MD
Community Health and Preventive Medicine, M
Computer and Information Sciences, B
Computer Art and Design, M
Computer Science, M
Counselor Education/School Counseling and
   Guidance Services, M
Criminal Justice/Law Enforcement Administration, B
Criminology, M

Curriculum and Instruction, M
Dental Hygiene/Hygienist, B
Early Childhood Education and Teaching, M
Economics, BM
Education, MDO
Educational Leadership and Administration, MDO
Educational Media/Instructional Technology, M
Elementary Education and Teaching, M
Engineering Technology, B
English, M
English Language and Literature, B
Environmental and Occupational Health, M
Environmental Health, B
Epidemiology, O
Exercise and Sports Science, M
Family and Consumer Sciences/Human Sciences, B
Finance, B
Finance and Banking, M
Fine Arts and Art Studies, M
Foreign Languages and Literatures, B
General Studies, B
Geography, B
Gerontology, O
Health and Physical Education, B
Health Professions and Related Clinical
   Sciences, AB
Health Services Administration, MO
History, BM
Human Development, M
Information Science/Studies, M
Liberal Studies, M
Manufacturing Engineering, M
Marketing/Marketing Management, B
Marriage and Family Therapy/Counseling, M
Mass Communication/Media Studies, B
Mathematics, BM
Microbiology, MD
Multi-/Interdisciplinary Studies, B
Music, B
Nursing, MDO
Nursing - Advanced Practice, O
Nursing - Registered Nurse Training, B
Nutritional Sciences, M
Pharmacology, MD
Philosophy, B
Physical Education Teaching and Coaching, M
Physical Therapy/Therapist, D
Physics, B
Physiology, MD
Political Science and Government, B
Psychology, BM
Public Health, MO
Public Health (MPH, DPH), B
Reading Teacher Education, M
Secondary Education and Teaching, M
Social Work, BM
Sociology, BM
Software Engineering, M
Special Education and Teaching, BM
Speech and Rhetorical Studies, B
Sport and Fitness Administration/Management, M
Survey Technology/Surveying, B
Urban and Regional Planning, M
Urban Studies/Affairs, M
Vocational and Technical Education, M

ELECTRONIC COMPUTER PROGRAMMING COLLEGE

Business/Office Automation/Technology/Data
   Entry, A
Computer Technology/Computer Systems
   Technology, A
Health Information/Medical Records
   Technology/Technician, A

FISK UNIVERSITY

Accounting, B
Art/Art Studies, General, B
Biological and Biomedical Sciences, M
Biology/Biological Sciences, B
Business Administration and Management, B
Chemistry, BM
Clinical Psychology, M
Computer Science, B
Drama and Dramatics/Theatre Arts, B
Economics, B

English Language and Literature, B
Finance, B
French Language and Literature, B
Health/Health Care Administration/Management, B
History, B
Mathematics, B
Music, B
Music Teacher Education, B
Philosophy, B
Physics, BM
Political Science and Government, B
Psychology, BM
Public Administration, B
Religion/Religious Studies, B
Sociology, BM
Spanish Language and Literature, B
Speech and Rhetorical Studies, B

FOUNTAINHEAD COLLEGE OF TECHNOLOGY

Communications Technology/Technician, A
Computer and Information Systems Security, B
Computer Engineering Technology/Technician, A
Electrical, Electronic and Communications
   Engineering Technology/Technician, A
Industrial Technology/Technician, A
Information Science/Studies, A

FREE WILL BAPTIST BIBLE COLLEGE

Administrative Assistant and Secretarial Science, A
Athletic Training and Sports Medicine, B
Bible/Biblical Studies, B
Business Administration and Management, AB
Education, B
Elementary Education and Teaching, B
English Language and Literature, B
Music Teacher Education, B
Physical Education Teaching and Coaching, B
Religious Education, B
Religious/Sacred Music, B
Secondary Education and Teaching, B

FREED-HARDEMAN UNIVERSITY

Accounting, B
Agricultural Business and Management, B
Apparel and Textiles, B
Art Teacher Education, B
Art/Art Studies, General, B
Behavioral Sciences, B
Bible/Biblical Studies, B
Biochemistry, B
Biological and Physical Sciences, B
Biology Teacher Education, B
Biology/Biological Sciences, B
Biophysics, B
Business Administration and Management, B
Business Administration, Management and
   Operations, M
Business/Managerial Economics, B
Chemistry, B
Child Development, B
Commercial and Advertising Art, B
Computer and Information Sciences, B
Computer Science, B
Counselor Education/School Counseling and
   Guidance Services, M
Curriculum and Instruction, M
Drama and Dramatics/Theatre Arts, B
Education, BMO
Educational Leadership and Administration, O
Elementary Education and Teaching, B
English Language and Literature, B
English/Language Arts Teacher Education, B
Family and Consumer Sciences/Human Sciences, B
Fashion Merchandising, B
Finance, B
Health and Physical Education, B
Health Services Administration, B
Health Teacher Education, B
History, B
Human Resources Management/Personnel
   Administration, B
Humanities/Humanistic Studies, B
Information Science/Studies, B
Interdisciplinary Studies, B

Liberal Arts and Sciences Studies and
  Humanities, B
Marketing/Marketing Management, B
Mathematics, B
Mathematics Teacher Education, B
Missions/Missionary Studies and Missiology, B
Music, B
Music Teacher Education, B
Pastoral Studies/Counseling, M
Philosophy, B
Physical Education Teaching and Coaching, B
Physical Sciences, B
Psychology, B
Public Relations/Image Management, B
Radio and Television, B
Science Teacher Education/General Science
  Teacher Education, B
Secondary Education and Teaching, B
Social Sciences, B
Social Work, B
Special Education and Teaching, B
Theology and Religious Vocations, MP

ITT TECHNICAL INSTITUTE (KNOXVILLE)

Accounting and Business/Management, B
Animation, Interactive Technology, Video Graphics
  and Special Effects, B
Business Administration and Management, B
CAD/CADD Drafting and/or Design
  Technology/Technician, A
Computer and Information Systems Security, B
Computer Programming/Programmer, A
Computer Software Technology/Technician, B
Computer Systems Networking and
  Telecommunications, B
Criminal Justice/Law Enforcement Administration, B
E-Commerce/Electronic Commerce, B
Electrical, Electronic and Communications
  Engineering Technology/Technician, AB
System, Networking, and LAN/WAN
  Management/Manager, A
Web Page, Digital/Multimedia and Information
  Resources Design, A
Web/Multimedia Management and Webmaster, A

ITT TECHNICAL INSTITUTE (MEMPHIS)

Accounting and Business/Management, B
Animation, Interactive Technology, Video Graphics
  and Special Effects, B
Business Administration and Management, B
CAD/CADD Drafting and/or Design
  Technology/Technician, A
Computer and Information Systems Security, B
Computer Programming/Programmer, A
Computer Systems Networking and
  Telecommunications, B
Criminal Justice/Law Enforcement Administration, B
E-Commerce/Electronic Commerce, B
Electrical, Electronic and Communications
  Engineering Technology/Technician, AB
System, Networking, and LAN/WAN
  Management/Manager, A
Web Page, Digital/Multimedia and Information
  Resources Design, A

ITT TECHNICAL INSTITUTE (NASHVILLE)

Accounting and Business/Management, B
Animation, Interactive Technology, Video Graphics
  and Special Effects, B
Business Administration and Management, B
CAD/CADD Drafting and/or Design
  Technology/Technician, A
Computer and Information Systems Security, B
Computer Programming/Programmer, A
Computer Software Technology/Technician, B
Computer Systems Networking and
  Telecommunications, B
Criminal Justice/Law Enforcement Administration, B
E-Commerce/Electronic Commerce, B
Electrical, Electronic and Communications
  Engineering Technology/Technician, AB
System, Networking, and LAN/WAN
  Management/Manager, A

Web Page, Digital/Multimedia and Information
  Resources Design, A
Web/Multimedia Management and Webmaster, A

JACKSON STATE COMMUNITY COLLEGE

Agricultural Business and Management, A
Business Administration and Management, A
Child Development, A
Clinical/Medical Laboratory Technician, A
Commercial and Advertising Art, A
Computer Science, A
Electromechanical Technology/Electromechanical
  Engineering Technology, A
Industrial Technology/Technician, A
Liberal Arts and Sciences Studies and
  Humanities, A
Management Information Systems and Services, A
Medical Radiologic Technology/Science - Radiation
  Therapist, A
Nursing - Registered Nurse Training, A
Physical Therapist Assistant, A
Respiratory Care Therapy/Therapist, A
Tool and Die Technology/Technician, A

JOHN A. GUPTON COLLEGE

Funeral Service and Mortuary Science, A

JOHNSON BIBLE COLLEGE

Bible/Biblical Studies, B
Education, M
Educational Media/Instructional Technology, M
Elementary Education and Teaching, B
Junior High/Intermediate/Middle School Education
  and Teaching, B
Kindergarten/PreSchool Education and
  Teaching, AB
Marriage and Family Therapy/Counseling, M
Religious/Sacred Music, B
Teacher Assistant/Aide, A
Theology and Religious Vocations, M

KING COLLEGE

Accounting, B
American/United States Studies/Civilization, B
Applied Mathematics, B
Bible/Biblical Studies, B
Biochemistry, B
Biological and Physical Sciences, B
Biology Teacher Education, B
Biology/Biological Sciences, B
Biophysics, B
Business Administration and Management, B
Business Administration, Management and
  Operations, M
Chemistry, B
Chemistry Teacher Education, B
Clinical Laboratory Science/Medical
  Technology/Technologist, B
Computer Science, B
Economics, B
Education, B
Elementary Education and Teaching, B
English Language and Literature, B
English/Language Arts Teacher Education, B
Finance, B
French Language and Literature, B
French Language Teacher Education, B
Health Professions and Related Clinical Sciences, B
History, B
History Teacher Education, B
Information Science/Studies, B
International Business/Trade/Commerce, B
Junior High/Intermediate/Middle School Education
  and Teaching, B
Kindergarten/PreSchool Education and Teaching, B
Mathematics, B
Mathematics Teacher Education, B
Modern Languages, B
Music, B
Nursing - Registered Nurse Training, B
Physics, B
Physics Teacher Education, B
Political Science and Government, B
Pre-Law Studies, B

Pre-Medicine/Pre-Medical Studies, B
Pre-Pharmacy Studies, B
Pre-Veterinary Studies, B
Psychology, B
Religion/Religious Studies, B
Secondary Education and Teaching, B
Spanish Language and Literature, B
Spanish Language Teacher Education, B
Speech Teacher Education, B
Technical and Business Writing, B

LAMBUTH UNIVERSITY

Accounting, B
Art History, Criticism and Conservation, B
Art Teacher Education, B
Art/Art Studies, General, B
Athletic Training and Sports Medicine, B
Audiology/Audiologist and Speech-Language
  Pathology/Pathologist, B
Biology Teacher Education, B
Biology/Biological Sciences, B
Business Administration and Management, B
Business Teacher Education, B
Chemistry, B
Chemistry Teacher Education, B
Computer and Information Sciences, B
Criminal Justice/Law Enforcement Administration, B
Design and Visual Communications, B
Drama and Dramatics/Theatre Arts, B
Economics, B
Education, B
Education/Teaching of Individuals with Hearing
  Impairments, Including Deafness, B
Elementary Education and Teaching, B
English Language and Literature, B
English/Language Arts Teacher Education, B
Environmental Sciences, B
Environmental Studies, B
Family and Consumer Sciences/Human Sciences, B
Fashion Merchandising, B
Fine/Studio Arts, B
Foods, Nutrition, and Wellness Studies, B
Foreign Languages and Literatures, B
French Language and Literature, B
German Language and Literature, B
Health and Physical Education/Fitness, B
Health Teacher Education, B
History, B
History Teacher Education, B
Interior Design, B
International Relations and Affairs, B
Junior High/Intermediate/Middle School Education
  and Teaching, B
Liberal Arts and Sciences Studies and
  Humanities, B
Marketing/Marketing Management, B
Mass Communication/Media Studies, B
Mathematics, B
Mathematics Teacher Education, B
Modern Languages, B
Multi-/Interdisciplinary Studies, B
Music, B
Music Performance, B
Music Teacher Education, B
Parks, Recreation, Leisure and Fitness Studies, B
Philosophy and Religious Studies, B
Physical Education Teaching and Coaching, B
Political Science and Government, B
Pre-Dentistry Studies, B
Pre-Law Studies, B
Pre-Medicine/Pre-Medical Studies, B
Pre-Nursing Studies, B
Pre-Pharmacy Studies, B
Pre-Theology/Pre-Ministerial Studies, B
Pre-Veterinary Studies, B
Psychology, B
Public Relations, Advertising, and Applied
  Communication, B
Religion/Religious Studies, B
Religious/Sacred Music, B
Secondary Education and Teaching, B
Sociology, B
Spanish Language and Literature, B
Special Education and Teaching, B
Sport and Fitness Administration/Management, B
Teacher Education, Multiple Levels, B

Visual and Performing Arts, B

LANE COLLEGE

Biology/Biological Sciences, B
Business Administration and Management, B
Chemistry, B
Communication and Media Studies, B
Computer and Information Sciences, B
Criminal Justice/Safety Studies, B
English Language and Literature, B
French Language and Literature, B
History, B
Interdisciplinary Studies, B
Mathematics, B
Multi-/Interdisciplinary Studies, B
Music, B
Physical Education Teaching and Coaching, B
Physics, B
Religion/Religious Studies, B
Sociology, B

LEE UNIVERSITY

Accounting, B
Bible/Biblical Studies, B
Biological and Physical Sciences, B
Biology/Biological Sciences, B
Business Administration and Management, B
Business Teacher Education, B
Chemistry, B
Clinical Laboratory Science/Medical
    Technology/Technologist, B
Counseling Psychology, M
Counselor Education/School Counseling and
    Guidance Services, M
Education, BM
Educational Leadership and Administration, M
Elementary Education and Teaching, BM
English Language and Literature, B
Health Teacher Education, B
History, B
Human Development and Family Studies, B
Information Science/Studies, B
Interdisciplinary Studies, B
International Relations and Affairs, B
Mass Communication/Media Studies, B
Mathematics, B
Modern Languages, B
Music, B
Music Teacher Education, BM
Natural Sciences, B
Pastoral Studies/Counseling, B
Physical Education Teaching and Coaching, B
Piano and Organ, B
Psychology, B
Religion/Religious Studies, M
Religious Education, B
Sacred Music, M
Secondary Education and Teaching, BM
Sociology, B
Special Education and Teaching, BM
Theology and Religious Vocations, M
Theology/Theological Studies, B
Voice and Opera, B

LEMOYNE-OWEN COLLEGE

Accounting, B
Art/Art Studies, General, B
Biology/Biological Sciences, B
Business Administration and Management, B
Chemistry, B
Computer Science, B
Education, B
Elementary Education and Teaching, B
English Language and Literature, B
History, B
Humanities/Humanistic Studies, B
Mathematics, B
Natural Sciences, B
Physical Education Teaching and Coaching, B
Political Science and Government, B
Secondary Education and Teaching, B
Social Sciences, B
Social Work, B
Sociology, B

Teacher Education, Multiple Levels, B

LINCOLN MEMORIAL UNIVERSITY

Accounting, B
Art Teacher Education, B
Art/Art Studies, General, B
Athletic Training and Sports Medicine, B
Biology Teacher Education, B
Biology/Biological Sciences, B
Business Administration and Management, AB
Business Administration, Management and
    Operations, M
Business/Managerial Economics, B
Chemistry, B
Chemistry Teacher Education, B
Clinical Laboratory Science/Medical
    Technology/Technologist, B
Computer and Information Sciences, B
Counselor Education/School Counseling and
    Guidance Services, M
Criminal Justice/Law Enforcement Administration, B
Curriculum and Instruction, MO
Economics, B
Education, BMO
Educational Administration and Supervision, MO
Elementary Education and Teaching, B
English Language and Literature, B
Environmental Studies, B
Finance, B
Health and Physical Education, B
Health Teacher Education, B
History, B
History Teacher Education, B
Humanities/Humanistic Studies, B
Kindergarten/PreSchool Education and Teaching, B
Kinesiology and Exercise Science, B
Liberal Arts and Sciences Studies and
    Humanities, B
Marketing/Marketing Management, B
Mass Communication/Media Studies, B
Mathematics, B
Mathematics Teacher Education, B
Nursing - Registered Nurse Training, AB
Physical Education Teaching and Coaching, B
Pre-Law Studies, B
Pre-Medicine/Pre-Medical Studies, B
Pre-Veterinary Studies, B
Psychology, B
Science Teacher Education/General Science
    Teacher Education, B
Secondary Education and Teaching, B
Social Work, B
Veterinary/Animal Health Technology/Technician and
    Veterinary Assistant, A

LIPSCOMB UNIVERSITY

Accounting, BM
American Government and Politics (United States)
    , B
American/United States Studies/Civilization, B
Athletic Training and Sports Medicine, B
Bible/Biblical Studies, B
Biochemistry, B
Biology Teacher Education, B
Biology/Biological Sciences, B
Business Administration and Management, B
Business Administration, Management and
    Operations, M
Business/Managerial Economics, B
Chemistry, B
Commercial and Advertising Art, B
Computer Science, B
Dietetics/Dieticians, B
Divinity/Ministry (BD, MDiv.), B
Education, BM
Elementary Education and Teaching, B
Engineering, B
Engineering Science, B
English Language and Literature, B
Environmental Studies, B
Family and Consumer Economics and Related
    Services, B
Family and Consumer Sciences/Human Sciences, B
Fashion Merchandising, B
Finance, B
Finance and Banking, M

Fine/Studio Arts, B
French Language and Literature, B
French Language Teacher Education, B
German Language and Literature, B
Health Services Administration, M
Health Teacher Education, B
History, B
Information Science/Studies, B
Junior High/Intermediate/Middle School Education
    and Teaching, B
Kinesiology and Exercise Science, B
Liberal Arts and Sciences Studies and
    Humanities, B
Management, M
Marketing/Marketing Management, B
Mass Communication/Media Studies, B
Mathematics, B
Music, B
Music Teacher Education, B
Non-Profit/Public/Organizational Management, M
Nursing - Registered Nurse Training, B
Philosophy, B
Physical Education Teaching and Coaching, B
Physics, B
Political Science and Government, B
Pre-Dentistry Studies, B
Pre-Law Studies, B
Pre-Medicine/Pre-Medical Studies, B
Pre-Veterinary Studies, B
Psychology, B
Public Administration, B
Public Relations/Image Management, B
Religion/Religious Studies, M
Secondary Education and Teaching, B
Social Work, B
Spanish Language and Literature, B
Speech and Rhetorical Studies, B
Theology and Religious Vocations, MP
Theology/Theological Studies, B
Urban Studies/Affairs, B

MARTIN METHODIST COLLEGE

Administrative Assistant and Secretarial Science, A
Advertising, A
Agricultural Business and Management, A
American/United States Studies/Civilization, A
Animal Physiology, A
Art Teacher Education, A
Art/Art Studies, General, A
Behavioral Sciences, A
Biological and Physical Sciences, A
Biology/Biological Sciences, A
Broadcast Journalism, A
Business Administration and Management, AB
Business Teacher Education, A
Chemistry, A
Clinical/Medical Laboratory Technician, A
Community Organization and Advocacy, A
Computer Programming/Programmer, A
Computer Science, A
Counselor Education/School Counseling and
    Guidance Services, A
Criminal Justice/Law Enforcement Administration, A
Criminal Justice/Police Science, A
Divinity/Ministry (BD, MDiv.), B
Drama and Dramatics/Theatre Arts, A
Economics, A
Education, A
Elementary Education and Teaching, B
English Language and Literature, AB
Health Teacher Education, A
Health/Health Care Administration/Management, AB
History, A
Human Services, AB
Humanities/Humanistic Studies, A
Interior Design, A
Kindergarten/PreSchool Education and Teaching, A
Legal Administrative Assistant/Secretary, A
Liberal Arts and Sciences Studies and
    Humanities, A
Maritime Science, A
Marketing/Marketing Management, A
Marriage and Family Therapy/Counseling, A
Mass Communication/Media Studies, A
Mathematics, A
Medical Administrative Assistant/Secretary, A

Music, A
Music Teacher Education, A
Parks, Recreation and Leisure Facilities
  Management, A
Pharmacy, A
Philosophy, A
Physical Education Teaching and Coaching, A
Physical Sciences, A
Physical Therapy/Therapist, A
Psychology, A
Public Health (MPH, DPH), A
Religion/Religious Studies, AB
Science Teacher Education/General Science
  Teacher Education, A
Social Work, A
Sociology, A
Teacher Assistant/Aide, A
Theology/Theological Studies, A
Wildlife and Wildlands Science and Management, A
Wildlife Biology, A

MARYVILLE COLLEGE

American Sign Language (ASL), B
Art History, Criticism and Conservation, B
Art Teacher Education, B
Atomic/Molecular Physics, B
Biochemistry, B
Biology Teacher Education, B
Biology/Biological Sciences, B
Business Administration and Management, B
Chemistry, B
Chemistry Teacher Education, B
Computer and Information Sciences, B
Computer Science, B
Developmental and Child Psychology, B
Drama and Dramatics/Theatre Arts, B
Economics, B
Education, B
Engineering, B
English Language and Literature, B
English/Language Arts Teacher Education, B
Environmental Studies, B
Fine/Studio Arts, B
Health and Physical Education, B
Health Teacher Education, B
History, B
History Teacher Education, B
International Business/Trade/Commerce, B
International Relations and Affairs, B
Mathematics, B
Mathematics and Computer Science, B
Mathematics Teacher Education, B
Multi-/Interdisciplinary Studies, B
Music Performance, B
Music Teacher Education, B
Nursing - Registered Nurse Training, B
Parks, Recreation, Leisure and Fitness Studies, B
Physical Education Teaching and Coaching, B
Physics Teacher Education, B
Piano and Organ, B
Political Science and Government, B
Psychology, B
Religion/Religious Studies, B
Sign Language Interpretation and Translation, B
Social Studies Teacher Education, B
Sociology, B
Spanish Language and Literature, B
Spanish Language Teacher Education, B
Teaching English as a Second or Foreign
  Language/ESL Language Instructor, B
Technical and Business Writing, B
Voice and Opera, B
Wind and Percussion Instruments, B

MEDVANCE INSTITUTE

Administrative Assistant and Secretarial Science, A
Clinical/Medical Laboratory Technician, A

MEMPHIS COLLEGE OF ART

Advertising, B
Applied Art, B
Applied Arts and Design, M
Art/Art Studies, General, B
Ceramic Arts and Ceramics, B
Commercial and Advertising Art, B
Commercial Photography, B

Computer Art and Design, M
Computer Graphics, B
Design and Visual Communications, B
Drawing, B
Fine Arts and Art Studies, BM
Fine/Studio Arts, B
Graphic Communications, B
Graphic Design, B
Illustration, B
Intermedia/Multimedia, B
Metal and Jewelry Arts, B
Painting, BM
Photography, BM
Printmaking, BM
Sculpture, BM
Textile Design, M

MID-AMERICA BAPTIST THEOLOGICAL SEMINARY

Theology and Religious Vocations, MDP
Theology/Theological Studies, A

MIDDLE TENNESSEE STATE UNIVERSITY

Accounting, BM
Aeronautics/Aviation/Aerospace Science and
  Technology, B
Aerospace, Aeronautical and Astronautical
  Engineering, M
Agribusiness, B
Animal Sciences, B
Anthropology, B
Apparel and Textiles, B
Art Teacher Education, B
Art/Art Studies, General, B
Athletic Training and Sports Medicine, B
Aviation, M
Biological and Biomedical Sciences, M
Biological and Physical Sciences, B
Biology/Biological Sciences, B
Business Administration and Management, B
Business Education, M
Business Teacher Education, B
Business/Managerial Economics, B
Chemistry, BMD
Child and Family Studies, M
Computer Science, BM
Counselor Education/School Counseling and
  Guidance Services, MO
Criminal Justice/Law Enforcement Administration, B
Criminal Justice/Police Science, A
Criminology, M
Curriculum and Instruction, MO
Drama and Dramatics/Theatre Arts, B
Early Childhood Education and Teaching, M
Economics, BMD
Education, MDO
Educational Administration and Supervision, MO
Elementary Education and Teaching, MO
Engineering Technology, B
Engineering/Industrial Management, B
English, MD
English as a Second Language, M
English Language and Literature, B
Environmental Engineering
  Technology/Environmental Technology, B
Exercise and Sports Science, D
Family Resource Management Studies, B
Finance, B
Finance and Banking, MD
Foods, Nutrition, and Wellness Studies, B
Foreign Language Teacher Education, M
Foreign Languages and Literatures, B
Geology/Earth Science, B
Geosciences, O
Gerontology, O
Health and Physical Education, B
Health Education, MD
Health Services Administration, O
Health Teacher Education, B
Historic Preservation and Conservation, D
History, BMD
Industrial and Labor Relations, M
Industrial and Organizational Psychology, BM
Industrial Education, M
Industrial Technology/Technician, B

Interdisciplinary Studies, B
Interior Design, B
International Relations and Affairs, B
Kindergarten/PreSchool Education and Teaching, B
Liberal Arts and Sciences Studies and
  Humanities, B
Management, M
Management Information Systems and
  Services, BM
Marketing, M
Marketing/Marketing Management, B
Mass Communication/Media Studies, BM
Mathematics, BM
Mathematics Teacher Education, M
Middle School Education, M
Multi-/Interdisciplinary Studies, B
Music, BM
Music Management and Merchandising, B
Nursing, M
Nursing - Registered Nurse Training, B
Nutritional Sciences, M
Office Management and Supervision, B
Parks, Recreation and Leisure Facilities
  Management, B
Philosophy, B
Physical Education Teaching and Coaching, MD
Physics, B
Plant Sciences, B
Political Science and Government, B
Psychology, BM
Public Relations/Image Management, B
Reading Teacher Education, M
Recreation and Park Management, MD
Sales and Marketing Operations/Marketing and
  Distribution Teacher Education, B
Sales, Distribution and Marketing Operations, B
School Psychology, O
Science Teacher Education/General Science
  Teacher Education, M
Social Work, B
Sociology, BMO
Special Education and Teaching, BMO
Technology Teacher Education/Industrial Arts
  Teacher Education, B
Transportation/Transportation Management, M

MILLIGAN COLLEGE

Accounting, B
Bible/Biblical Studies, B
Biology/Biological Sciences, B
Business Administration and Management, B
Chemistry, B
Communication and Media Studies, B
Computer and Information Sciences, B
Computer Science, B
Early Childhood Education and Teaching, B
Education, BM
English Language and Literature, B
Fine/Studio Arts, B
Health and Physical Education, B
History, B
Humanities/Humanistic Studies, B
Mathematics, B
Music, B
Music Teacher Education, B
Nursing - Registered Nurse Training, B
Occupational Therapy/Therapist, M
Pastoral Studies/Counseling, B
Psychology, B
Public Administration and Social Service
  Professions, B
Public Health (MPH, DPH), B
Sociology, B

MOTLOW STATE COMMUNITY COLLEGE

Business Administration and Management, A
Education/Teaching of Individuals in Early Childhood
  Special Education Programs, A
Liberal Arts and Sciences Studies and
  Humanities, A
Nursing - Registered Nurse Training, A

NASHVILLE AUTO DIESEL COLLEGE

Autobody/Collision and Repair
  Technology/Technician, A

Automobile/Automotive Mechanics
Technology/Technician, A
Diesel Mechanics Technology/Technician, A

NASHVILLE STATE TECHNICAL COMMUNITY COLLEGE

Accounting, A
Administrative Assistant and Secretarial Science, A
Architectural Engineering Technology/Technician, A
Automobile/Automotive Mechanics
Technology/Technician, A
Business Administration and Management, A
Civil Engineering Technology/Technician, A
Commercial and Advertising Art, A
Computer Engineering Technology/Technician, A
Computer Systems Networking and
Telecommunications, A
Criminal Justice/Police Science, A
Culinary Arts/Chef Training, A
Electrical, Electronic and Communications
Engineering Technology/Technician, A
Industrial Engineering, A
Industrial Technology/Technician, A
Information Science/Studies, A
Kindergarten/PreSchool Education and Teaching, A
Occupational Therapy/Therapist, A
Photography, A
Sign Language Interpretation and Translation, A

NATIONAL COLLEGE OF BUSINESS & TECHNOLOGY (BRISTOL)

Accounting, A
Administrative Assistant and Secretarial Science, A
Business Administration and Management, A
Computer and Information Sciences, A
Medical/Clinical Assistant, A

NATIONAL COLLEGE OF BUSINESS & TECHNOLOGY (NASHVILLE)

Administrative Assistant and Secretarial Science, A
Business Administration and Management, A
Computer and Information Sciences, A
Medical/Clinical Assistant, A

NORTH CENTRAL INSTITUTE

Aircraft Powerplant Technology/Technician, A
Airframe Mechanics and Aircraft Maintenance
Technology/Technician, A

NORTHEAST STATE TECHNICAL COMMUNITY COLLEGE

Accounting, A
Administrative Assistant and Secretarial Science, A
Automobile/Automotive Mechanics
Technology/Technician, A
Business Administration and Management, A
Cardiovascular Technology/Technologist, A
Chemistry, A
Computer Programming, A
Computer Programming/Programmer, A
Computer Systems Networking and
Telecommunications, A
Data Processing and Data Processing
Technology/Technician, A
Drafting and Design Technology/Technician, A
Electrical, Electronic and Communications
Engineering Technology/Technician, A
Emergency Medical Technology/Technician (EMT
Paramedic), A
Engineering Technology, A
Industrial Technology/Technician, A
Instrumentation Technology/Technician, A
Kindergarten/PreSchool Education and Teaching, A
Liberal Arts and Sciences Studies and
Humanities, A
Machine Tool Technology/Machinist, A
Medical/Clinical Assistant, A
Surgical Technology/Technologist, A

Welding Technology/Welder, A

NOSSI COLLEGE OF ART

Commercial and Advertising Art, A
Photography, A

O'MORE COLLEGE OF DESIGN

Commercial and Advertising Art, B
Fashion Merchandising, B
Fashion/Apparel Design, B
Interior Design, B

PELLISSIPPI STATE TECHNICAL COMMUNITY COLLEGE

Accounting, A
Accounting Technology/Technician and
Bookkeeping, A
Administrative Assistant and Secretarial Science, A
Automobile/Automotive Mechanics
Technology/Technician, A
Business Administration and Management, A
Business Machine Repairer, A
Chemical Engineering, A
Chemical Technology/Technician, A
Cinematography and Film/Video Production, A
Civil Engineering Technology/Technician, A
Commercial and Advertising Art, A
Computer and Information Sciences, A
Computer Engineering Technology/Technician, A
Computer Graphics, A
Computer Programming/Programmer, A
Computer Science, A
Computer Software and Media Applications, A
Computer Systems Networking and
Telecommunications, A
Construction Engineering Technology/Technician, A
Data Entry/Microcomputer Applications, A
Data Processing and Data Processing
Technology/Technician, A
Drafting and Design Technology/Technician, A
Electrical, Electronic and Communications
Engineering Technology/Technician, A
Environmental Engineering
Technology/Environmental Technology, A
Finance, A
Geography, A
Hospitality Administration/Management, A
Hotel/Motel Administration/Management, A
Industrial Technology/Technician, A
Interior Design, A
Legal Administrative Assistant/Secretary, A
Legal Assistant/Paralegal, A
Liberal Arts and Sciences Studies and
Humanities, A
Machine Tool Technology/Machinist, A
Marketing/Marketing Management, A
Mechanical Engineering/Mechanical
Technology/Technician, A
Technology Education/Industrial Arts, A

REMINGTON COLLEGE-MEMPHIS CAMPUS

Business Administration and Management, A
Computer Systems Networking and
Telecommunications, A
Electrical, Electronic and Communications
Engineering Technology/Technician, A
Information Science/Studies, A
Operations Management and Supervision, B

RHODES COLLEGE

Accounting, M
Anthropology, B
Art History, Criticism and Conservation, B
Art/Art Studies, General, B
Biochemistry, B
Biology/Biological Sciences, B
Business Administration and Management, B
Chemistry, B
Classics and Classical
Languages, Literatures, and Linguistics, B
Computer Science, B
Drama and Dramatics/Theatre Arts, B
Economics, B
English Language and Literature, B

Fine/Studio Arts, B
French Language and Literature, B
German Language and Literature, B
History, B
Interdisciplinary Studies, B
International Business/Trade/Commerce, B
International Economics, B
International Relations and Affairs, B
Latin Language and Literature, B
Mathematics, B
Modern Greek Language and Literature, B
Music, B
Philosophy, B
Physics, B
Political Science and Government, B
Psychology, B
Religion/Religious Studies, B
Russian Studies, B
Sociology, B
Spanish Language and Literature, B
Urban Studies/Affairs, B

ROANE STATE COMMUNITY COLLEGE

Accounting, A
Administrative Assistant and Secretarial Science, A
Art Teacher Education, A
Art/Art Studies, General, A
Biology/Biological Sciences, A
Business Administration and Management, A
Business Teacher Education, A
Chemistry, A
Clinical/Medical Laboratory Technician, A
Computer Engineering Technology/Technician, A
Computer Science, A
Corrections, A
Criminal Justice/Law Enforcement Administration, A
Criminal Justice/Police Science, A
Dental Hygiene/Hygienist, A
Education, A
Elementary Education and Teaching, A
Emergency Medical Technology/Technician (EMT
Paramedic), A
Engineering, A
Environmental Health, A
Health Information/Medical Records
Administration/Administrator, A
Industrial Radiologic Technology/Technician, A
Kindergarten/PreSchool Education and Teaching, A
Laser and Optical Technology/Technician, A
Legal Administrative Assistant/Secretary, A
Liberal Arts and Sciences Studies and
Humanities, A
Mathematics, A
Medical Administrative Assistant/Secretary, A
Music Teacher Education, A
Nursing - Registered Nurse Training, A
Occupational Therapy/Therapist, A
Pharmacy Technician/Assistant, A
Physical Education Teaching and Coaching, A
Physical Sciences, A
Physical Therapy/Therapist, A
Pre-Engineering, A
Respiratory Care Therapy/Therapist, A
Social Sciences, A
Technology Teacher Education/Industrial Arts
Teacher Education, A

SEWANEE: THE UNIVERSITY OF THE SOUTH

American/United States Studies/Civilization, B
Anthropology, B
Applied Art, B
Art History, Criticism and Conservation, B
Art/Art Studies, General, B
Asian Studies/Civilization, B
Biology/Biological Sciences, B
Chemistry, B
Classics and Classical
Languages, Literatures, and Linguistics, B
Comparative Literature, B
Computer Science, B
Drama and Dramatics/Theatre Arts, B
Drawing, B
Economics, B
English Language and Literature, B
Environmental Studies, B

European Studies/Civilization, B
Fine/Studio Arts, B
Forestry, B
French Language and Literature, B
Geology/Earth Science, B
German Language and Literature, B
History, B
International Relations and Affairs, B
Latin Language and Literature, B
Mathematics, B
Medieval and Renaissance Studies, B
Modern Greek Language and Literature, B
Music, B
Music History, Literature, and Theory, B
Natural Resources Management/Development and
    Policy, B
Philosophy, B
Physics, B
Political Science and Government, B
Psychology, B
Religion/Religious Studies, B
Russian Language and Literature, B
Russian Studies, B
Social Sciences, B
Spanish Language and Literature, B
Theology and Religious Vocations, MDP

SOUTH COLLEGE

Accounting, A
Administrative Assistant and Secretarial Science, A
Business Administration and Management, A
Computer Science, A
Elementary Education and Teaching, A
Hotel/Motel Administration/Management, A
Information Science/Studies, A
Legal Administrative Assistant/Secretary, A
Legal Assistant/Paralegal, A
Medical Administrative Assistant/Secretary, A
Medical/Clinical Assistant, A
Nursing - Registered Nurse Training, A
Physical Therapist Assistant, A
Radiologic Technology/Science - Radiographer, A

SOUTHERN ADVENTIST UNIVERSITY

Accounting, ABM
Actuarial Science, B
Advertising, B
Animation, Interactive Technology, Video Graphics
    and Special Effects, B
Archeology, B
Art/Art Studies, General, B
Automobile/Automotive Mechanics
    Technology/Technician, A
Biochemistry, B
Biology/Biological Sciences, B
Broadcast Journalism, B
Business Administration and Management, B
Business Administration, Management and
    Operations, M
Chemistry, B
Cinematography and Film/Video Production, AB
Clinical Laboratory Science/Medical
    Technology/Technologist, B
Computer Graphics, B
Computer Science, AB
Counselor Education/School Counseling and
    Guidance Services, M
Curriculum and Instruction, M
Dental Hygiene/Hygienist, A
Education, M
Educational Administration and Supervision, M
Elementary Education and Teaching, B
Engineering, A
English Language and Literature, B
English/Language Arts Teacher Education, B
Family Systems, B
Finance and Banking, M
Foods, Nutrition, and Wellness Studies, A
Foreign Languages and Literatures, B
French Language and Literature, B
General Studies, A
Graphic Design, B
Health Services Administration, M
Health/Health Care Administration/Management, B
History, B
Human Resources Management and Services, M

International Business/Trade/Commerce, B
Journalism, B
Kindergarten/PreSchool Education and Teaching, B
Kinesiology and Exercise Science, B
Management, M
Management Information Systems and Services, B
Management Science, B
Marketing, M
Marketing/Marketing Management, B
Marriage and Family Therapy/Counseling, M
Mass Communication/Media Studies, B
Mathematics, B
Missions/Missionary Studies and Missiology, M
Music, B
Music Performance, B
Music Teacher Education, B
Music Theory and Composition, B
Non-Profit/Public/Organizational Management, B
Nursing, MO
Nursing - Adult, M
Nursing - Advanced Practice, M
Nursing - Registered Nurse Training, A
Nursing Administration, M
Nursing Science, B
Occupational Therapy/Therapist, A
Photography, B
Physical Education Teaching and Coaching, B
Physical Therapy/Therapist, A
Physician Assistant, A
Physics, B
Psychology, BM
Public Relations/Image Management, B
Radio and Television Broadcasting
    Technology/Technician, A
Reading Teacher Education, M
Religion/Religious Studies, BM
Religious Education, BM
Respiratory Care Therapy/Therapist, A
Social Work, B
Spanish Language and Literature, B
Speech-Language Pathology/Pathologist, A
Sport and Fitness Administration/Management, B
Theology/Theological Studies, B

SOUTHWEST TENNESSEE COMMUNITY COLLEGE

Accounting, A
Administrative Assistant and Secretarial Science, A
Applied Horticulture/Horticultural Business
    Services, A
Architectural Engineering Technology/Technician, A
Automobile/Automotive Mechanics
    Technology/Technician, A
Biomedical Technology/Technician, A
Business Administration and Management, A
Business/Commerce, A
Cartography, A
Clinical/Medical Laboratory Technician, A
Commercial and Advertising Art, A
Computer Engineering Technology/Technician, A
Court Reporting/Court Reporter, A
Criminal Justice/Safety Studies, A
Dietician Assistant, A
Electrical, Electronic and Communications
    Engineering Technology/Technician, A
Electrical/Electronics Equipment Installation and
    Repair, A
Fire Science/Firefighting, A
General Studies, A
Health Professions and Related Clinical Sciences, A
Heavy Equipment Maintenance
    Technology/Technician, A
Industrial Technology/Technician, A
Kindergarten/PreSchool Education and Teaching, A
Legal Assistant/Paralegal, A
Management Information Systems and Services, A
Mechanical Engineering/Mechanical
    Technology/Technician, A
Medical Radiologic Technology/Science - Radiation
    Therapist, A
Medical/Clinical Assistant, A
Nursing - Registered Nurse Training, A

Physical Therapist Assistant, A

TENNESSEE STATE UNIVERSITY

Accounting, B
Administrative Assistant and Secretarial Science, AB
Adult and Continuing Education and Teaching, BM
African Studies, B
Agricultural Sciences, MD
Agriculture, B
Allied Health and Medical Assisting Services, M
Animal Sciences, B
Architectural Engineering, B
Art/Art Studies, General, B
Audiology/Audiologist and Speech-Language
    Pathology/Pathologist, B
Biological and Biomedical Sciences, MD
Biology/Biological Sciences, B
Business Administration and Management, B
Business Administration, Management and
    Operations, M
Business Teacher Education, B
Business/Managerial Economics, B
Chemistry, BM
Child and Family Studies, MD
Civil Engineering, B
Clinical Laboratory Science/Medical
    Technology/Technologist, B
Clinical Psychology, B
Computer Science, B
Consumer Services and Advocacy, B
Counseling Psychology, D
Counselor Education/School Counseling and
    Guidance Services, M
Criminal Justice/Law Enforcement Administration, B
Criminology, M
Curriculum and Instruction, MD
Dental Hygiene/Hygienist, AB
Education, BMD
Educational Administration and Supervision, MD
Educational Leadership and Administration, B
Electrical, Electronics and Communications
    Engineering, B
Elementary Education and Teaching, BMD
Engineering, B
Engineering and Applied Sciences, MD
English, M
English Language and Literature, B
Exercise and Sports Science, M
Family and Consumer Economics and Related
    Services, B
Food Technology and Processing, B
French Language and Literature, B
Health Information/Medical Records
    Administration/Administrator, B
Health Teacher Education, B
Health/Health Care Administration/Management, B
History, B
Humanities/Humanistic Studies, B
Industrial Engineering, B
Industrial Technology/Technician, B
Kindergarten/PreSchool Education and
    Teaching, AB
Liberal Arts and Sciences Studies and
    Humanities, B
Mass Communication/Media Studies, B
Mathematics, BM
Mechanical Engineering, B
Music, B
Music Teacher Education, M
Nursing, MD
Nursing - Registered Nurse Training, AB
Parks, Recreation, Leisure and Fitness Studies, B
Physical Education Teaching and Coaching, BM
Physical Therapy/Therapist, B
Physics, B
Political Science and Government, B
Psychology, BMD
Public Administration, BMD
Reading Teacher Education, BM
Respiratory Care Therapy/Therapist, B
School Psychology, MD
Secondary Education and Teaching, M
Social Work, B
Sociology, B
Spanish Language and Literature, B
Special Education and Teaching, BMD

Technology Education/Industrial Arts, B
Transportation and Materials Moving, B
Vocational and Technical Education, M

TENNESSEE TECHNOLOGICAL UNIVERSITY

Accounting, B
Agricultural Business and Management, B
Agricultural Teacher Education, B
Agricultural/Biological Engineering and Bioengineering, B
Agronomy and Crop Science, B
Animal Sciences, B
Apparel and Textiles, B
Art Teacher Education, B
Art/Art Studies, General, B
Biochemistry, B
Biological and Biomedical Sciences, M
Biology/Biological Sciences, B
Business Administration and Management, B
Business Administration, Management and Operations, M
Chemical Engineering, BMD
Chemistry, BM
Child Development, B
Civil Engineering, BMD
Computer Engineering, B
Computer Science, BM
Curriculum and Instruction, MO
Dietetics/Dieticians, B
Early Childhood Education and Teaching, MO
Economics, B
Education, BMDO
Education/Teaching of the Gifted and Talented, D
Educational Leadership and Administration, MO
Educational Psychology, MO
Electrical Engineering, MD
Electrical, Electronics and Communications Engineering, B
Elementary Education and Teaching, BMO
Engineering and Applied Sciences, MD
English, M
English Language and Literature, B
Environmental Biology, M
Environmental Sciences, D
Family and Consumer Sciences/Home Economics Teacher Education, B
Family and Consumer Sciences/Human Sciences, B
Fashion Merchandising, B
Finance, B
Fish, Game and Wildlife Management, M
Foods, Nutrition, and Wellness Studies, B
French Language and Literature, B
Geology/Earth Science, B
German Language and Literature, B
Health Education, M
Health Teacher Education, B
History, B
Horticultural Science, B
Industrial Engineering, B
Industrial Technology/Technician, B
Industrial/Management Engineering, MD
Information Science/Studies, B
International Business/Trade/Commerce, B
Journalism, B
Kindergarten/PreSchool Education and Teaching, B
Labor and Industrial Relations, B
Landscaping and Groundskeeping, B
Library Science, M
Marketing/Marketing Management, B
Mathematics, BM
Mechanical Engineering, BMD
Music, B
Music Teacher Education, B
Nursing, M
Nursing - Registered Nurse Training, B
Operations Management and Supervision, B
Physical Education Teaching and Coaching, BM
Physics, B
Political Science and Government, B
Pre-Dentistry Studies, B
Pre-Law Studies, B
Pre-Medicine/Pre-Medical Studies, B
Pre-Veterinary Studies, B
Psychology, B
Reading Teacher Education, MO

Secondary Education and Teaching, BMO
Social Work, B
Sociology, B
Spanish Language and Literature, B
Special Education and Teaching, BMO
Student Personnel Services, MO
Technical and Business Writing, B
Turf and Turfgrass Management, B
Web Page, Digital/Multimedia and Information Resources Design, B
Wildlife and Wildlands Science and Management, B

TENNESSEE TEMPLE UNIVERSITY

Administrative Assistant and Secretarial Science, B
Bible/Biblical Studies, B
Biological and Physical Sciences, B
Biology Teacher Education, B
Biology/Biological Sciences, B
Business Administration and Management, B
Communication Studies/Speech Communication and Rhetoric, B
Counseling Psychology, B
Curriculum and Instruction, M
Education, M
Educational Administration and Supervision, M
Elementary Education and Teaching, B
English Language and Literature, B
English/Language Arts Teacher Education, B
Geology/Earth Science, B
History, B
History Teacher Education, B
Information Science/Studies, B
Interdisciplinary Studies, B
Marketing/Marketing Management, B
Mathematics, B
Mathematics Teacher Education, B
Missions/Missionary Studies and Missiology, B
Office Management and Supervision, B
Pastoral Studies/Counseling, B
Political Science and Government, B
Pre-Law Studies, B
Psychology, B
Religious Education, B
Science Teacher Education/General Science Teacher Education, B
Sign Language Interpretation and Translation, A
Theological and Ministerial Studies, B
Youth Ministry, B

TENNESSEE WESLEYAN COLLEGE

Accounting, B
Athletic Training and Sports Medicine, B
Behavioral Sciences, B
Biology Teacher Education, B
Biology/Biological Sciences, B
Business Administration and Management, B
Chemistry, B
Chemistry Teacher Education, B
Education, B
Elementary Education and Teaching, B
English Language and Literature, B
English/Language Arts Teacher Education, B
Finance, B
Health and Physical Education, B
History, B
History Teacher Education, B
Human Resources Management/Personnel Administration, B
Human Services, B
Interdisciplinary Studies, B
Kinesiology and Exercise Science, B
Mathematics, B
Mathematics Teacher Education, B
Music, B
Music Teacher Education, B
Nursing - Registered Nurse Training, B
Ophthalmic and Optometric Support Services and Allied Professions, B
Parks, Recreation, Leisure and Fitness Studies, B
Physical Education Teaching and Coaching, B
Pre-Dentistry Studies, B
Pre-Law Studies, B
Pre-Medicine/Pre-Medical Studies, B
Pre-Pharmacy Studies, B
Pre-Theology/Pre-Ministerial Studies, B
Pre-Veterinary Studies, B

Psychology, B
Public Health (MPH, DPH), B
Religion/Religious Studies, B
Secondary Education and Teaching, B
Sport and Fitness Administration/Management, B
Teacher Education, Multiple Levels, B

TREVECCA NAZARENE UNIVERSITY

Accounting, B
Behavioral Sciences, B
Biological and Physical Sciences, B
Biology Teacher Education, B
Biology/Biological Sciences, B
Broadcast Journalism, A
Business Administration and Management, B
Business Administration, Management and Operations, M
Chemistry, B
Chemistry Teacher Education, B
Child Development, A
Clinical Laboratory Science/Medical Technology/Technologist, B
Communication Studies/Speech Communication and Rhetoric, B
Counseling Psychology, M
Counselor Education/School Counseling and Guidance Services, M
Curriculum and Instruction, M
Drama and Dramatics/Theatre Arts, B
Education, MD
Educational Leadership and Administration, M
Elementary Education and Teaching, M
English Language and Literature, B
English/Language Arts Teacher Education, B
General Studies, A
History, B
History Teacher Education, B
Information Science/Studies, ABM
Kinesiology and Exercise Science, B
Library Science, M
Marketing/Marketing Management, B
Marriage and Family Therapy/Counseling, M
Mass Communication/Media Studies, B
Mathematics, B
Mathematics Teacher Education, B
Music, B
Music Management and Merchandising, B
Music Teacher Education, B
Organizational Management, M
Physical Education Teaching and Coaching, B
Physician Assistant, M
Physics, B
Psychology, B
Radio and Television Broadcasting Technology/Technician, B
Religion/Religious Studies, BM
Religious/Sacred Music, B
Secondary Education and Teaching, BM
Social Sciences, B
Teacher Education, Multiple Levels, B

TUSCULUM COLLEGE

Accounting, B
Adult and Continuing Education and Teaching, M
Art Teacher Education, B
Art/Art Studies, General, B
Athletic Training and Sports Medicine, B
Biology/Biological Sciences, B
Business Administration and Management, B
Clinical Laboratory Science/Medical Technology/Technologist, B
Computer Science, B
Education, BM
Elementary Education and Teaching, B
English Language and Literature, B
Environmental Studies, B
History, B
Information Science/Studies, B
Junior High/Intermediate/Middle School Education and Teaching, B
Kindergarten/PreSchool Education and Teaching, B
Mathematics, B
Museology/Museum Studies, B
Organizational Management, M
Physical Education Teaching and Coaching, B
Pre-Law Studies, B

Pre-Medicine/Pre-Medical Studies, B
Pre-Veterinary Studies, B
Psychology, B
Secondary Education and Teaching, B
Special Education and Teaching, B
Sport and Fitness Administration/Management, B
Telecommunications Technology/Technician, B

UNION UNIVERSITY

Accounting, B
Advertising, B
Ancient Near Eastern and Biblical
    Languages, Literatures, and Linguistics, B
Art Teacher Education, B
Art/Art Studies, General, B
Athletic Training and Sports Medicine, B
Bible/Biblical Studies, B
Biological and Physical Sciences, B
Biology/Biological Sciences, B
Broadcast Journalism, B
Business Administration and Management, B
Business Administration, Management and
    Operations, M
Business Teacher Education, B
Business/Managerial Economics, B
Chemistry, B
Clinical Laboratory Science/Medical
    Technology/Technologist, B
Computer Science, B
Cultural Studies, M
Drama and Dramatics/Theatre Arts, B
Economics, B
Education, BMDO
Educational Administration and Supervision, O
Educational Leadership and Administration, DO
Elementary Education and Teaching, B
English Language and Literature, B
Family and Community Services, B
Finance, B
Foreign Languages and Literatures, B
French Language and Literature, B
History, B
Information Science/Studies, B
Journalism, B
Kindergarten/PreSchool Education and Teaching, B
Kinesiology and Exercise Science, B
Marketing/Marketing Management, B
Mass Communication/Media Studies, B
Mathematics, B
Music, B
Music Management and Merchandising, B
Music Performance, B
Music Teacher Education, B
Nursing, MO
Nursing - Registered Nurse Training, B
Nursing Education, MO
Parks, Recreation and Leisure Facilities
    Management, B
Philosophy, B
Philosophy and Religious Studies, B
Physical Education Teaching and Coaching, B
Physics, B
Piano and Organ, B
Political Science and Government, B
Pre-Dentistry Studies, B
Pre-Law Studies, B
Pre-Medicine/Pre-Medical Studies, B
Pre-Pharmacy Studies, B
Psychology, B
Public Relations/Image Management, B
Radio and Television, B
Religion/Religious Studies, B
Religious/Sacred Music, B
Science Teacher Education/General Science
    Teacher Education, B
Secondary Education and Teaching, B
Social Work, B
Sociology, B
Spanish Language and Literature, B
Special Education and Teaching, B
Speech and Rhetorical Studies, B
Sport and Fitness Administration/Management, B
Teaching English as a Second or Foreign
    Language/ESL Language Instructor, B
Theology and Religious Vocations, B
Theology/Theological Studies, B

Voice and Opera, B

UNIVERSITY OF MEMPHIS

Accounting, BMD
Adult and Continuing Education and Teaching, D
African-American/Black Studies, B
Anthropology, BM
Applied Mathematics, M
Archeology, M
Architecture, B
Art History, Criticism and Conservation, BM
Art/Art Studies, General, B
Biochemistry, Biophysics and Molecular Biology, B
Biological and Biomedical Sciences, MD
Biology/Biological Sciences, B
Biomedical Engineering, MD
Biomedical/Medical Engineering, B
Business Administration, Management and
    Operations, MDO
Business/Managerial Economics, B
Ceramic Arts and Ceramics, M
Chemistry, BMD
Civil Engineering, BMD
Clinical Psychology, D
Communication and Media Studies, MD
Communication Disorders, MD
Communication Studies/Speech Communication
    and Rhetoric, B
Composition, MD
Computer Engineering, BMD
Computer Engineering Technology/Technician, B
Computer Science, BMD
Consumer Merchandising/Retailing Management, B
Counseling Psychology, D
Counselor Education/School Counseling and
    Guidance Services, MD
Criminal Justice/Law Enforcement Administration, B
Criminology, BM
Curriculum and Instruction, MD
Drama and Dramatics/Theatre Arts, B
Early Childhood Education and Teaching, MD
Economics, BMD
Education, MDO
Educational Administration and Supervision, MDO
Educational Leadership and Administration, MD
Educational Measurement and Evaluation, MD
Educational Media/Instructional Technology, MD
Educational Psychology, MD
Electrical Engineering, MD
Electrical, Electronic and Communications
    Engineering Technology/Technician, B
Electrical, Electronics and Communications
    Engineering, B
Elementary Education and Teaching, M
Energy and Power Engineering, M
Engineering and Applied Sciences, MD
English, MD
English Language and Literature, B
Environmental Engineering
    Technology/Environmental Technology, M
Exercise and Sports Science, M
Experimental Psychology, D
Family and Consumer Sciences/Human
    Sciences, M
Film, Television, and Video Production, M
Finance, B
Finance and Banking, MD
Fine Arts and Art Studies, M
Foreign Languages and Literatures, B
French Language and Literature, M
General Studies, B
Geography, BM
Geology/Earth Science, BMD
Geophysics and Seismology, M
Geosciences, D
Graphic Design, M
Health Promotion, M
Health Services Administration, M
Higher Education/Higher Education
    Administration, D
History, BMD
Hospitality Administration/Management, B
Human Development and Family Studies, B
Industrial/Management Engineering, M
Insurance, B
Interdisciplinary Studies, B

Interior Design, M
International Business/Trade/Commerce, BM
International Relations and Affairs, B
Journalism, BM
Kinesiology and Exercise Science, B
Law and Legal Studies, PO
Legal Assistant/Paralegal, B
Leisure Studies, M
Liberal Arts and Sciences Studies and
    Humanities, B
Liberal Studies, M
Management, MD
Management Information Systems and
    Services, BMD
Management Science, B
Manufacturing Engineering, M
Manufacturing Technology/Technician, B
Marketing, MD
Marketing/Marketing Management, B
Mathematics, BMD
Mechanical Engineering, BMD
Microbiology, B
Molecular Biology, B
Multi-/Interdisciplinary Studies, B
Music, BMD
Music History, Literature, and Theory, M
Music Management and Merchandising, B
Music Teacher Education, MD
Musicology and Ethnomusicology, M
Non-Profit/Public/Organizational Management, M
Nursing - Registered Nurse Training, B
Nutritional Sciences, M
Painting, M
Performance, D
Philosophy, BMD
Photography, M
Physical Education Teaching and Coaching, BM
Physics, BM
Political Science and Government, BM
Printmaking, M
Professional Studies, B
Psychology, BMD
Public Administration, M
Public Policy Analysis, M
Reading Teacher Education, MD
Real Estate, BM
Sacred Music, MD
Sales, Distribution and Marketing Operations, B
School Psychology, MD
Sculpture, M
Secondary Education and Teaching, M
Social Work, B
Sociology, BM
Spanish Language and Literature, M
Special Education and Teaching, BMD
Sport and Fitness Administration/Management, B
Statistics, M
Structural Engineering, M
Systems Engineering, B
Taxation, M
Teacher Education, Multiple Levels, B
Theater, M
Transportation and Highway Engineering, M
Urban and Regional Planning, M
Water Resources Engineering, M
Writing, MD

UNIVERSITY OF PHOENIX-NASHVILLE CAMPUS

Accounting, B
Business Administration and Management, B
Business Administration, Management and
    Operations, M
Business, Management, Marketing, and Related
    Support Services, B
Computer and Information Sciences, B
Electronic Commerce, M
Health Services Administration, M
Health/Health Care Administration/Management, B
Management Information Systems and Services, M
Management of Technology, M
Marketing/Marketing Management, B

Nursing Administration, B

THE UNIVERSITY OF TENNESSEE

Accounting, BMD
Adult and Continuing Education and Teaching, M
Advertising, B
Advertising and Public Relations, MD
Aerospace, Aeronautical and Astronautical
   Engineering, BMDO
Agricultural Business and Management, B
Agricultural Economics, BM
Agricultural Education, M
Agricultural Engineering, M
Agricultural Sciences, MD
Agricultural Teacher Education, B
Agricultural/Biological Engineering and
   Bioengineering, B
Analytical Chemistry, MD
Anatomy, D
Animal Behavior and Ethology, MD
Animal Sciences, BMD
Anthropology, BMD
Applied Mathematics, M
Archeology, MD
Architecture, BM
Area, Ethnic, Cultural, and Gender Studies, B
Art Education, M
Art History, Criticism and Conservation, B
Art Teacher Education, B
Artificial Intelligence and Robotics, M
Audiology/Audiologist and Hearing Sciences, B
Aviation, M
Biochemistry, BMD
Bioethics/Medical Ethics, MD
Biological and Biomedical Sciences, MD
Biology/Biological Sciences, B
Biomedical Engineering, MD
Biosystems Engineering, MD
Botany/Plant Biology, B
Business Administration and Management, B
Business Administration, Management and
   Operations, MDO
Business Teacher Education, B
Business/Commerce, B
Business/Managerial Economics, B
Ceramic Arts and Ceramics, M
Chemical Engineering, BMDO
Chemistry, BMD
Child and Family Studies, MD
Civil Engineering, BMD
Classics and Classical
   Languages, Literatures, and Linguistics, B
Clinical Laboratory Science/Medical
   Technology/Technologist, B
Clinical Psychology, D
Clothing and Textiles, MD
Commercial and Advertising Art, B
Communication and Media Studies, MD
Communication Disorders, MD
Community Health and Preventive Medicine, MD
Composition, M
Computer Engineering, B
Computer Science, BMD
Consumer Economics, BMD
Counseling Psychology, M
Counselor Education/School Counseling and
   Guidance Services, MDO
Criminology, MD
Curriculum and Instruction, MDO
Drama and Dramatics/Theatre Arts, B
Early Childhood Education and Teaching, MD
Ecology, BMD
Economics, BMD
Education, MDO
Educational Administration and Supervision, MDO
Educational Leadership and Administration, D
Educational Measurement and Evaluation, D
Educational Media/Instructional Technology, MDO
Educational Psychology, MD
Electrical Engineering, MDO
Electrical, Electronics and Communications
   Engineering, B
Elementary Education and Teaching, MO
Engineering and Applied Sciences, MDO
Engineering Management, M
Engineering Physics, B

Engineering Science, B
English, MD
English as a Second Language, MDO
English Education, MO
English Language and Literature, B
Entomology, MD
Environmental Engineering
   Technology/Environmental Technology, M
Environmental Policy and Resource
   Management, MD
Ergonomics and Human Factors, M
Ethnic and Cultural Studies, B
Evolutionary Biology, MD
Exercise and Sports Science, MD
Experimental Psychology, MD
Family and Consumer Sciences/Home Economics
   Teacher Education, B
Family Systems, B
Finance, B
Finance and Banking, MD
Fine Arts and Art Studies, M
Fine/Studio Arts, B
Fish, Game and Wildlife Management, M
Food Science, B
Food Science and Technology, MD
Foods, Nutrition, and Wellness Studies, B
Foreign Language Teacher Education, MO
Forestry, BM
Foundations and Philosophy of Education, MD
French Language and Literature, BMD
Genetics, MD
Genomic Sciences, MD
Geography, BMD
Geology/Earth Science, BMD
German Language and Literature, BMD
Gerontology, M
Graphic Design, M
Health Education, M
Health Promotion, M
Health Services Administration, M
Health Teacher Education, B
History, BMD
Home Economics, D
Hospitality Administration/Management, M
Hotel/Motel Administration/Management, B
Human Development and Family Studies, B
Human Resources Development, M
Industrial and Manufacturing Management, M
Industrial and Organizational Psychology, D
Industrial Engineering, B
Industrial/Management Engineering, MDO
Information Science/Studies, MD
Inorganic Chemistry, MD
Interior Design, B
Italian Language and Literature, BD
Journalism, BMD
Kinesiology and Exercise Science, B
Kinesiology and Movement Studies, MD
Law and Legal Studies, PO
Leisure Studies, M
Linguistics, D
Logistics and Materials Management, BMD
Management, MD
Manufacturing Engineering, M
Marketing, MD
Marketing/Marketing Management, B
Materials Engineering, BMD
Materials Sciences, MD
Mathematics, BMD
Mathematics Teacher Education, MO
Mechanical Engineering, BMDO
Mechanics, MD
Media Studies, MD
Medical Microbiology and Bacteriology, B
Microbiology, MD
Multi-/Interdisciplinary Studies, B
Multilingual and Multicultural Education, D
Music, BM
Music Teacher Education, BM
Music Theory and Composition, M
Musicology and Ethnomusicology, M
Nuclear Engineering, BMDO
Nursing, MD
Nursing - Registered Nurse Training, B
Nutritional Sciences, MO
Organic Chemistry, MD

Ornamental Horticulture, B
Painting, M
Parks, Recreation and Leisure Facilities
   Management, B
Performance, M
Philosophy, BMD
Photography, M
Physical Chemistry, MD
Physics, BMD
Physiology, MD
Plant Pathology/Phytopathology, MD
Plant Physiology, MD
Plant Protection and Integrated Pest
   Management, B
Plant Sciences, BM
Political Science and Government, BMD
Polymer/Plastics Engineering, MD
Portuguese Language and Literature, D
Printmaking, M
Psychology, BMD
Public Administration, BMO
Public Health, MO
Radio and Television, B
Reading Teacher Education, MDO
Recreation and Park Management, M
Rehabilitation Counseling, M
Religion/Religious Studies, BM
Rural Sociology, M
Russian Language and Literature, BD
School Psychology, DO
Science Teacher Education/General Science
   Teacher Education, MO
Sculpture, M
Secondary Education and Teaching, M
Social Studies Teacher Education, MO
Social Work, BMD
Sociology, BMD
Spanish Language and Literature, BMD
Special Education and Teaching, BMO
Speech and Interpersonal Communication, MD
Speech and Rhetorical Studies, B
Speech-Language Pathology/Pathologist, B
Sport and Fitness Administration/Management, BM
Sports Medicine, MD
Statistics, BMD
Student Personnel Services, M
Technical Teacher Education, B
Theater, M
Theoretical Chemistry, D
Therapeutic Recreation, M
Transportation/Transportation Management, MD
Travel and Tourism, M
Veterinary Medicine, P
Wildlife and Wildlands Science and Management, B

THE UNIVERSITY OF TENNESSEE AT CHATTANOOGA

Accounting, B
Applied Mathematics, B
Art Teacher Education, B
Art/Art Studies, General, B
Biology/Biological Sciences, B
Business Administration and Management, B
Business Administration, Management and
   Operations, M
Chemistry, B
Clinical Laboratory Science/Medical
   Technology/Technologist, B
Computer Science, BM
Counselor Education/School Counseling and
   Guidance Services, M
Criminal Justice/Law Enforcement Administration, B
Criminal Justice/Police Science, B
Criminology, M
Drama and Dramatics/Theatre Arts, B
Economics, B
Education, MDO
Educational Administration and Supervision, M
Educational Leadership and Administration, D
Educational Media/Instructional Technology, O
Elementary Education and Teaching, M
Engineering, B
Engineering and Applied Sciences, M
Engineering Management, M
Engineering/Industrial Management, B
English, M

English Language and Literature, B
Environmental Sciences, M
Environmental Studies, B
Experimental Psychology, M
Family and Consumer Sciences/Human Sciences, B
Fine/Studio Arts, B
French Language and Literature, B
Geology/Earth Science, B
History, B
Human Services, B
Humanities/Humanistic Studies, B
Industrial and Organizational Psychology, M
Junior High/Intermediate/Middle School Education
   and Teaching, B
Kinesiology and Exercise Science, B
Latin Language and Literature, B
Legal Assistant/Paralegal, B
Mass Communication/Media Studies, B
Mathematics, B
Modern Greek Language and Literature, B
Music, BM
Nurse Anesthetist, M
Nursing, M
Nursing - Adult, M
Nursing - Advanced Practice, M
Nursing - Registered Nurse Training, B
Nursing Administration, M
Nursing Education, M
Parks, Recreation, Leisure and Fitness Studies, B
Philosophy and Religious Studies, B
Physical Education Teaching and Coaching, M
Physical Therapy/Therapist, BD
Physics, B
Political Science and Government, B
Psychology, BM
Public Administration, M
School Psychology, O
Science Teacher Education/General Science
   Teacher Education, B
Secondary Education and Teaching, BM
Social Work, B
Sociology, B
Spanish Language and Literature, B
Special Education and Teaching, BM

THE UNIVERSITY OF TENNESSEE AT MARTIN

Accounting, BM
Agricultural Business and Management, B
Agricultural Production Operations, B
Agricultural Teacher Education, B
Agriculture, B
Agronomy and Crop Science, B
Animal Sciences, B
Animal/Livestock Husbandry and Production, B
Anthropology, B
Art Teacher Education, B
Athletic Training and Sports Medicine, B
Biology Teacher Education, B
Biology/Biological Sciences, B
Broadcast Journalism, B
Business Administration and Management, B
Business Administration, Management and
   Operations, M
Business Teacher Education, B
Business/Managerial Economics, B
Cell/Cellular and Molecular Biology, B
Chemistry, B
Chemistry Teacher Education, B
Child and Family Studies, M
Child Development, B
Commercial and Advertising Art, B
Computer Science, B
Counselor Education/School Counseling and
   Guidance Services, M
Criminal Justice/Law Enforcement Administration, B
Curriculum and Instruction, M
Dance, B
Design and Visual Communications, B
Dietetics/Dieticians, B
Drama and Dramatics/Theatre Arts, B
Economics, B
Education, M
Educational Administration and Supervision, M
Elementary Education and Teaching, BM
Engineering, B

English Language and Literature, B
English/Language Arts Teacher Education, B
Environmental Biology, B
Environmental Studies, B
Family and Consumer Sciences/Home Economics
   Teacher Education, B
Family and Consumer Sciences/Human
   Sciences, BM
Fashion Merchandising, B
Finance, B
Fishing and Fisheries Sciences and Management, B
Food Science and Technology, M
Forestry, B
French Language and Literature, B
French Language Teacher Education, B
General Office Occupations and Clerical Services, B
Geography, B
Geography Teacher Education, B
Geology/Earth Science, B
German Language Teacher Education, B
Graphic Design, B
Health and Physical Education, B
History, B
History Teacher Education, B
Human Resources Management/Personnel
   Administration, B
Industrial and Organizational Psychology, B
Interdisciplinary Studies, B
Interior Design, B
International Business/Trade/Commerce, B
International Relations and Affairs, B
Journalism, B
Kindergarten/PreSchool Education and Teaching, B
Landscaping and Groundskeeping, B
Management Information Systems and Services, B
Management Science, B
Marketing/Marketing Management, B
Mass Communication/Media Studies, B
Mathematics, B
Mathematics Teacher Education, B
Music, B
Music Pedagogy, B
Music Performance, B
Music Teacher Education, B
Natural Resources Management/Development and
   Policy, B
Nursing - Registered Nurse Training, B
Nutritional Sciences, M
Operations Management and Supervision, B
Parks, Recreation and Leisure Facilities
   Management, B
Philosophy, B
Piano and Organ, B
Political Science and Government, B
Pre-Dentistry Studies, B
Pre-Medicine/Pre-Medical Studies, B
Pre-Pharmacy Studies, B
Pre-Veterinary Studies, B
Professional Studies, B
Psychology, B
Public Administration, B
Public Health (MPH, DPH), B
Public Relations/Image Management, B
Science Teacher Education/General Science
   Teacher Education, B
Secondary Education and Teaching, M
Social Work, B
Sociology, B
Soil Science and Agronomy, B
Spanish Language and Literature, B
Spanish Language Teacher Education, B
Special Education and Teaching, B
Sport and Fitness Administration/Management, B
Statistics, B
Teacher Education, Multiple Levels, B
Tourism and Travel Services Management, B
Visual and Performing Arts, B
Voice and Opera, B
Wildlife and Wildlands Science and Management, B

VANDERBILT UNIVERSITY

African Studies, B
African-American/Black Studies, B
Allopathic Medicine, MDPO
American/United States Studies/Civilization, B
Analytical Chemistry, MD

Anthropology, BMD
Art/Art Studies, General, B
Astronomy, BM
Biochemistry, MDO
Bioinformatics, MD
Biological and Biomedical Sciences, MDO
Biological Anthropology, D
Biology/Biological Sciences, B
Biomedical Engineering, MDO
Biomedical/Medical Engineering, B
Biophysics, DO
Business Administration, Management and
   Operations, MO
Cancer Biology/Oncology, MD
Cell Biology and Anatomy, MDO
Chemical Engineering, BMD
Chemistry, BMD
Child and Family Studies, M
Civil Engineering, BMD
Classics and Classical
   Languages, Literatures, and Linguistics, BMD
Clinical Research, M
Cognitive Psychology and Psycholinguistics, B
Communication Disorders, MD
Comparative Literature, MD
Computer Engineering, B
Computer Science, BMD
Counselor Education/School Counseling and
   Guidance Services, M
Curriculum and Instruction, M
Drama and Dramatics/Theatre Arts, B
Early Childhood Education and Teaching, M
East Asian Studies, B
Ecology, B
Economics, BMD
Education, BMD
Educational Administration and Supervision, MD
Educational Leadership and Administration, D
Educational Measurement and Evaluation, MD
Electrical Engineering, MD
Electrical, Electronics and Communications
   Engineering, B
Elementary Education and Teaching, BM
Engineering, B
Engineering and Applied Sciences, MDO
Engineering Science, B
English, MD
English Education, M
English Language and Literature, B
Environmental Engineering
   Technology/Environmental Technology, MD
Environmental Policy and Resource
   Management, MD
Environmental Sciences, M
European Studies/Civilization, B
Finance and Banking, D
Fine Arts and Art Studies, M
Foreign Language Teacher Education, M
French Language and Literature, BMD
Geology/Earth Science, B
German Language and Literature, BMD
Gerontological Nursing, M
Higher Education/Higher Education
   Administration, MD
History, BMD
Human Development, M
Human Development and Family Studies, B
Human Resources Development, M
Human Resources Management/Personnel
   Administration, B
Immunology, MDO
Inorganic Chemistry, MD
Interdisciplinary Studies, B
International and Comparative Education, M
Kindergarten/PreSchool Education and Teaching, B
Latin American Studies, BMO
Law and Legal Studies, MPO
Liberal Studies, M
Management, D
Management of Technology, MD
Marketing, D
Mass Communication/Media Studies, B
Materials Sciences, MD
Maternity Nursing, M
Mathematics, BMD
Mathematics Teacher Education, M

Mechanical Engineering, BMD
Medical Physics, M
Microbiology, MDO
Molecular Biology, BDO
Molecular Physiology, DO
Music, B
Neuroscience, D
Nurse Midwife/Nursing Midwifery, M
Nursing, MDO
Nursing - Adult, M
Nursing - Advanced Practice, M
Nursing Administration, M
Occupational Health Nursing, M
Organic Chemistry, MD
Organizational Management, MD
Pathology/Experimental Pathology, DO
Pediatric Nurse/Nursing, M
Pharmacology, DO
Philosophy, BMD
Physical Chemistry, MD
Physics, BMD
Piano and Organ, B
Political Science and Government, BMD
Portuguese Language and Literature, BMD
Psychiatric/Mental Health Nurse/Nursing, M
Psychology, BMD
Public Policy Analysis, MD
Reading Teacher Education, M
Religion/Religious Studies, BMD
Russian Language and Literature, B
Science Teacher Education/General Science
    Teacher Education, M
Secondary Education and Teaching, BM
Sociology, BMD
Spanish Language and Literature, BMD
Special Education and Teaching, BMD
Theology and Religious Vocations, MPO
Theoretical Chemistry, M
Urban Studies/Affairs, B
Violin, Viola, Guitar and Other Stringed
    Instruments, B
Voice and Opera, B
Wind and Percussion Instruments, B
Women's Health Nursing, M

VOLUNTEER STATE COMMUNITY COLLEGE

Business Administration and Management, A
Fire Science/Firefighting, A
Health Information/Medical Records
    Technology/Technician, A
Health Professions and Related Clinical Sciences, A
Legal Assistant/Paralegal, A
Liberal Arts and Sciences Studies and
    Humanities, A
Medical Radiologic Technology/Science - Radiation
    Therapist, A
Ophthalmic Technician/Technologist, A
Physical Therapist Assistant, A
Respiratory Care Therapy/Therapist, A
Technology Education/Industrial Arts, A

WALTERS STATE COMMUNITY COLLEGE

Administrative Assistant and Secretarial Science, A
Agricultural Mechanization, A
Art Teacher Education, A
Art/Art Studies, General, A
Business Administration and Management, A
Child Development, A
Clinical/Medical Laboratory Technician, A
Computer and Information Sciences, A
Computer Science, A
Criminal Justice/Law Enforcement Administration, A
Education, A
Industrial Radiologic Technology/Technician, A
Information Technology, A
Interdisciplinary Studies, A
Liberal Arts and Sciences Studies and
    Humanities, A
Medical Administrative Assistant/Secretary, A
Music Teacher Education, A
Nursing - Registered Nurse Training, A
Physical Education Teaching and Coaching, A

Pre-Engineering, A

WATKINS COLLEGE OF ART AND DESIGN

Film/Cinema Studies, B
Fine/Studio Arts, B
Graphic Design, B
Interior Design, AB
Photography, B

WILLIAMSON CHRISTIAN COLLEGE

Bible/Biblical Studies, B
Business Administration and Management, AB
Pre-Theology/Pre-Ministerial Studies, B
Theological and Ministerial Studies, B
Theology and Religious Vocations, B

Texas

ABILENE CHRISTIAN UNIVERSITY

Accounting, BM
Agribusiness, B
Animal Sciences, B
Architecture and Related Services, A
Art Teacher Education, B
Art/Art Studies, General, B
Bible/Biblical Studies, B
Biochemistry, B
Biology Teacher Education, B
Biology/Biological Sciences, B
Chemistry, B
Clinical Laboratory Science/Medical
    Technology/Technologist, B
Clinical Psychology, M
Commercial and Advertising Art, B
Communication and Media Studies, M
Communication Disorders, M
Communication, Journalism and Related
    Programs, B
Computer Hardware Engineering, B
Computer Science, B
Conflict Resolution and Mediation/Peace Studies, O
Counseling Psychology, M
Dietetics/Dieticians, B
Digital Communication and Media/Multimedia, B
Drama and Dramatics/Theatre Arts, B
Education, MO
Educational Administration and Supervision, MO
Educational Measurement and Evaluation, M
Elementary Education and Teaching, BMO
Engineering, B
Engineering Physics, B
Engineering Science, B
English, M
English Language and Literature, B
English/Language Arts Teacher Education, B
Environmental Sciences, B
Family and Consumer Sciences/Human Sciences, B
Finance, B
Fine Arts and Art Studies, B
Fine/Studio Arts, B
Gerontological Nursing, O
Gerontology, MO
Health and Medical Laboratory Technologies, B
Health and Physical Education, B
Health/Medical Preparatory Programs, B
History, B
History Teacher Education, B
Human Development and Family Studies, B
Human Resources Development, M
Human Services, MO
Industrial and Organizational Psychology, B
Interdisciplinary Studies, B
Interior Design, B
International/Global Studies, B
Journalism, B
Junior High/Intermediate/Middle School Education
    and Teaching, B
Liberal Arts and Sciences Studies and
    Humanities, B
Liberal Studies, M
Marketing/Marketing Management, B
Marriage and Family Therapy/Counseling, M
Mathematics, B
Mathematics Teacher Education, B

Missions/Missionary Studies and Missiology, BM
Multi-/Interdisciplinary Studies, B
Music, B
Music Teacher Education, B
Nursing, M
Nursing - Registered Nurse Training, B
Ophthalmic Laboratory Technology/Technician, B
Pastoral Studies/Counseling, BMD
Physical Education Teaching and Coaching, B
Physics, B
Piano and Organ, B
Political Science and Government, B
Pre-Dentistry Studies, B
Pre-Law Studies, B
Pre-Medicine/Pre-Medical Studies, B
Pre-Pharmacy Studies, B
Pre-Veterinary Studies, B
Psychology, BM
Reading Teacher Education, BM
Rhetoric, M
School Psychology, M
Science Teacher Education/General Science
    Teacher Education, B
Secondary Education and Teaching, BM
Social Sciences, B
Social Studies Teacher Education, B
Social Work, B
Sociology, B
Spanish Language and Literature, B
Spanish Language Teacher Education, B
Special Education and Teaching, B
Speech and Interpersonal Communication, M
Speech and Rhetorical Studies, B
Speech-Language Pathology/Pathologist, B
Sport and Fitness Administration/Management, B
Theology and Religious Vocations, BMP
Voice and Opera, B
Writing, M

ALVIN COMMUNITY COLLEGE

Accounting, A
Administrative Assistant and Secretarial Science, A
Aeronautics/Aviation/Aerospace Science and
    Technology, A
Art/Art Studies, General, A
Biology/Biological Sciences, A
Business Administration and Management, A
Chemical Technology/Technician, A
Child Development, A
Computer Engineering Technology/Technician, A
Computer Programming/Programmer, A
Corrections, A
Court Reporting/Court Reporter, A
Criminal Justice/Police Science, A
Drafting and Design Technology/Technician, A
Drama and Dramatics/Theatre Arts, A
Electrical, Electronic and Communications
    Engineering Technology/Technician, A
Emergency Medical Technology/Technician (EMT
    Paramedic), A
Law and Legal Studies, A
Legal Administrative Assistant/Secretary, A
Legal Assistant/Paralegal, A
Liberal Arts and Sciences Studies and
    Humanities, A
Marketing/Marketing Management, A
Mathematics, A
Medical Administrative Assistant/Secretary, A
Mental Health/Rehabilitation, A
Music, A
Nursing - Registered Nurse Training, A
Physical Education Teaching and Coaching, A
Physical Sciences, A
Radio and Television, A
Respiratory Care Therapy/Therapist, A
Substance Abuse/Addiction Counseling, A
Voice and Opera, A

AMARILLO COLLEGE

Accounting, A
Administrative Assistant and Secretarial Science, A
Airframe Mechanics and Aircraft Maintenance
    Technology/Technician, A
Architectural Engineering Technology/Technician, A
Art/Art Studies, General, A

Automobile/Automotive Mechanics
Technology/Technician, A
Behavioral Sciences, A
Bible/Biblical Studies, A
Biology/Biological Sciences, A
Broadcast Journalism, A
Business Administration and Management, A
Business Teacher Education, A
Chemical Technology/Technician, A
Chemistry, A
Child Development, A
Clinical Laboratory Science/Medical
Technology/Technologist, A
Commercial and Advertising Art, A
Computer Engineering Technology/Technician, A
Computer Programming/Programmer, A
Computer Science, A
Computer Systems Analysis/Analyst, A
Corrections, A
Criminal Justice/Law Enforcement Administration, A
Criminal Justice/Police Science, A
Dental Hygiene/Hygienist, A
Drafting and Design Technology/Technician, A
Drama and Dramatics/Theatre Arts, A
Electrical, Electronic and Communications
Engineering Technology/Technician, A
Elementary Education and Teaching, A
Emergency Medical Technology/Technician (EMT
Paramedic), A
Engineering, A
English Language and Literature, A
Environmental Health, A
Fine/Studio Arts, A
Fire Science/Firefighting, A
Funeral Service and Mortuary Science, A
General Studies, A
Geology/Earth Science, A
Health Information/Medical Records
Administration/Administrator, A
Heating, Air Conditioning, Ventilation and
Refrigeration Maintenance
Technology/Technician, A
Heavy Equipment Maintenance
Technology/Technician, A
History, A
Industrial Radiologic Technology/Technician, A
Information Science/Studies, A
Instrumentation Technology/Technician, A
Interior Design, A
Journalism, A
Laser and Optical Technology/Technician, A
Legal Administrative Assistant/Secretary, A
Liberal Arts and Sciences Studies and
Humanities, A
Licensed Practical/Vocational Nurse Training, A
Machine Tool Technology/Machinist, A
Mass Communication/Media Studies, A
Mathematics, A
Medical Administrative Assistant/Secretary, A
Modern Languages, A
Music, A
Music Teacher Education, A
Natural Sciences, A
Nuclear Medical Technology/Technologist, A
Nursing - Registered Nurse Training, A
Occupational Therapy/Therapist, A
Photography, A
Physical Education Teaching and Coaching, A
Physical Sciences, A
Physical Therapy/Therapist, A
Physics, A
Pre-Engineering, A
Pre-Pharmacy Studies, A
Psychology, A
Public Relations/Image Management, A
Radio and Television, A
Radiologic Technology/Science - Radiographer, A
Real Estate, A
Religion/Religious Studies, A
Respiratory Care Therapy/Therapist, A
Social Sciences, A
Social Work, A
Speech and Rhetorical Studies, A
Substance Abuse/Addiction Counseling, A
Telecommunications Technology/Technician, A
Tourism and Travel Services Management, A

Visual and Performing Arts, A

AMBERTON UNIVERSITY

Accounting, B
Business Administration and Management, B
Business Administration, Management and
Operations, M
Computer and Information Sciences, B
Counseling Psychology, M
Counselor Education/School Counseling and
Guidance Services, B
Human Development and Family Studies, B
Human Resources Development, M
Human Resources Management and Services, M
Human Resources Management/Personnel
Administration, B
Interdisciplinary Studies, BM
Management, M
Management Information Systems and Services, B
Marketing/Marketing Management, B

AMERICAN INTERCONTINENTAL
UNIVERSITY

Business Administration and Management, AB
Commercial and Advertising Art, AB
Information Technology, B

ANGELINA COLLEGE

Accounting, A
Administrative Assistant and Secretarial Science, A
Art Teacher Education, A
Art/Art Studies, General, A
Automobile/Automotive Mechanics
Technology/Technician, A
Biological and Physical Sciences, A
Biology/Biological Sciences, A
Business Administration and Management, A
Child Care and Support Services Management, A
Child Care Provider/Assistant, A
Child Development, A
Clinical Laboratory Science/Medical
Technology/Technologist, A
Clinical/Medical Laboratory Technician, A
Computer Engineering Technology/Technician, A
Computer Programming/Programmer, A
Computer Science, A
Criminal Justice/Law Enforcement Administration, A
Data Processing and Data Processing
Technology/Technician, A
Developmental and Child Psychology, A
Electrical, Electronic and Communications
Engineering Technology/Technician, A
Electrical/Electronics Equipment Installation and
Repair, A
Electromechanical Technology/Electromechanical
Engineering Technology, A
Elementary Education and Teaching, A
Emergency Medical Technology/Technician (EMT
Paramedic), A
Engineering, A
Engineering Technology, A
English Language and Literature, A
Environmental Engineering
Technology/Environmental Technology, A
Health Teacher Education, A
History, A
Human Services, A
Humanities/Humanistic Studies, A
Industrial Radiologic Technology/Technician, A
Journalism, A
Legal Assistant/Paralegal, A
Liberal Arts and Sciences Studies and
Humanities, A
Licensed Practical/Vocational Nurse Training, A
Mathematics, A
Music, A
Music Teacher Education, A
Nursing - Registered Nurse Training, A
Physical Education Teaching and Coaching, A
Physical Sciences, A
Physical Therapist Assistant, A
Piano and Organ, A
Pre-Pharmacy Studies, A
Real Estate, A
Respiratory Care Therapy/Therapist, A

Science Teacher Education/General Science
Teacher Education, A
Social Sciences, A
Social Work, A
Speech Teacher Education, A
System Administration/Administrator, A
Teacher Assistant/Aide, A
Teacher Education, Multiple Levels, A
Voice and Opera, A
Water Quality and Wastewater Treatment
Management and Recycling
Technology/Technician, A
Welding Technology/Welder, A

ANGELO STATE UNIVERSITY

Accounting, BM
Agricultural Sciences, M
Animal Sciences, BM
Art/Art Studies, General, B
Athletic Training and Sports Medicine, B
Biochemistry, B
Biological and Biomedical Sciences, M
Biological and Physical Sciences, B
Biology/Biological Sciences, B
Business Administration and Management, B
Chemistry, B
Clinical Laboratory Science/Medical
Technology/Technologist, B
Communication and Media Studies, M
Communication Studies/Speech Communication
and Rhetoric, B
Computer and Information Sciences, B
Counselor Education/School Counseling and
Guidance Services, M
Criminal Justice/Safety Studies, B
Curriculum and Instruction, M
Drama and Dramatics/Theatre Arts, B
Education, M
Educational Administration and Supervision, M
Educational Measurement and Evaluation, M
English, M
English Language and Literature, B
Finance, B
Fine/Studio Arts, B
French Language and Literature, B
General Studies, B
German Language and Literature, B
Health and Physical Education, B
History, BM
Interdisciplinary Studies, BM
Journalism, BM
Kinesiology and Movement Studies, M
Liberal Arts and Sciences Studies and
Humanities, B
Management, M
Management Information Systems and Services, B
Marketing/Marketing Management, B
Mathematics, B
Medical/Surgical Nursing, M
Multi-/Interdisciplinary Studies, B
Music, B
Nursing - Registered Nurse Training, AB
Physical Therapy/Therapist, M
Physics, B
Political Science and Government, B
Psychology, BM
Public Administration, M
Reading Teacher Education, M
Real Estate, B
Social Sciences, B
Sociology, B
Spanish Language and Literature, B
Visual and Performing Arts, B

ARGOSY UNIVERSITY/DALLAS

Accounting, M
Business Administration, Management and
Operations, M
Clinical Psychology, MD
Counseling Psychology, M
Forensic Psychology, M
Psychology, BD

ARLINGTON BAPTIST COLLEGE

Bible/Biblical Studies, B
Early Childhood Education and Teaching, B

Education, B
Elementary Education and Teaching, B
English/Language Arts Teacher Education, B
Junior High/Intermediate/Middle School Education
   and Teaching, B
Music, B
Music Teacher Education, B
Religion/Religious Studies, B
Theology and Religious Vocations, B

THE ART INSTITUTE OF DALLAS

Animation, Interactive Technology, Video Graphics
   and Special Effects, AB
Cinematography and Film/Video Production, A
Commercial and Advertising Art, B
Computer Graphics, A
Culinary Arts/Chef Training, A
Fashion/Apparel Design, A
Graphic Design, AB
Interior Design, AB
Restaurant, Culinary, and Catering
   Management/Manager, A
Web Page, Digital/Multimedia and Information
   Resources Design, AB

THE ART INSTITUTE OF HOUSTON

Animation, Interactive Technology, Video Graphics
   and Special Effects, AB
Baking and Pastry Arts/Baker/Pastry Chef, A
Culinary Arts/Chef Training, A
Graphic Design, AB
Interior Design, B
Restaurant, Culinary, and Catering
   Management/Manager, A
Web Page, Digital/Multimedia and Information
   Resources Design, A

AUSTIN BUSINESS COLLEGE

Data Entry/Microcomputer Applications, A
Management Information Systems and Services, A

AUSTIN COLLEGE

American/United States Studies/Civilization, B
Art Education, M
Art/Art Studies, General, B
Biochemistry, B
Biology/Biological Sciences, B
Business Administration and Management, B
Chemistry, B
Classics and Classical
   Languages, Literatures, and Linguistics, B
Communication Studies/Speech Communication
   and Rhetoric, B
Computer Science, B
Economics, B
Education, M
Elementary Education and Teaching, M
English Language and Literature, B
Environmental Studies, B
French Language and Literature, B
German Language and Literature, B
History, B
International Economics, B
International Relations and Affairs, B
Latin American Studies, B
Latin Language and Literature, B
Mathematics, B
Middle School Education, M
Multi-/Interdisciplinary Studies, B
Music, B
Music Teacher Education, M
Philosophy, B
Physical Education Teaching and Coaching, BM
Physics, B
Political Science and Government, B
Psychology, B
Religion/Religious Studies, B
Secondary Education and Teaching, M
Sociology, B
Spanish Language and Literature, B

AUSTIN COMMUNITY COLLEGE

Accounting, A
Administrative Assistant and Secretarial Science, A
Art/Art Studies, General, A

Astronomy, A
Automobile/Automotive Mechanics
   Technology/Technician, A
Biology/Biological Sciences, A
Business Administration and Management, A
Chemistry, A
Clinical/Medical Laboratory Technician, A
Commercial and Advertising Art, A
Computer and Information Sciences, A
Computer Programming, A
Computer Programming/Programmer, A
Computer Science, A
Computer Systems Networking and
   Telecommunications, A
Construction Engineering Technology/Technician, A
Consumer Merchandising/Retailing Management, A
Criminal Justice/Law Enforcement Administration, A
Criminal Justice/Police Science, A
Data Entry/Microcomputer Applications, A
Developmental and Child Psychology, A
Drafting and Design Technology/Technician, A
Economics, A
Electrical, Electronic and Communications
   Engineering Technology/Technician, A
Emergency Medical Technology/Technician (EMT
   Paramedic), A
English Language and Literature, A
Fashion Merchandising, A
Finance, A
Fire Science/Firefighting, A
French Language and Literature, A
Geology/Earth Science, A
German Language and Literature, A
Graphic and Printing Equipment Operator
   Production, A
Heating, Air Conditioning, Ventilation and
   Refrigeration Maintenance
   Technology/Technician, A
History, A
Hospitality and Recreation Marketing Operations, A
Hotel/Motel Administration/Management, A
Human Services, A
Industrial Radiologic Technology/Technician, A
Industrial Technology/Technician, A
Information Science/Studies, A
Information Technology, A
Insurance, A
Japanese Language and Literature, A
Journalism, A
Legal Administrative Assistant/Secretary, A
Legal Assistant/Paralegal, A
Liberal Arts and Sciences Studies and
   Humanities, A
Marketing/Marketing Management, A
Mass Communication/Media Studies, A
Mathematics, A
Medical/Clinical Assistant, A
Music, A
Nursing - Registered Nurse Training, A
Occupational Therapy/Therapist, A
Photography, A
Physical Sciences, A
Physics, A
Political Science and Government, A
Pre-Engineering, A
Psychology, A
Quality Control Technology/Technician, A
Radio and Television, A
Real Estate, A
Russian Language and Literature, A
Sign Language Interpretation and Translation, A
Social Work, A
Sociology, A
Spanish Language and Literature, A
Speech and Rhetorical Studies, A
Surgical Technology/Technologist, A
Survey Technology/Surveying, A
System Administration/Administrator, A
Technical and Business Writing, A

Welding Technology/Welder, A

AUSTIN GRADUATE SCHOOL OF THEOLOGY

Bible/Biblical Studies, B
Theology and Religious Vocations, M

BAPTIST MISSIONARY ASSOCIATION THEOLOGICAL SEMINARY

Theology and Religious Vocations, MP
Theology/Theological Studies, AB

BAPTIST UNIVERSITY OF THE AMERICAS

Bible/Biblical Studies, B
Ethnic and Cultural Studies, A

BAYLOR UNIVERSITY

Accounting, BMO
Acting, B
Airline/Commercial/Professional Pilot and Flight
   Crew, B
Allied Health and Medical Assisting Services, MD
American/United States Studies/Civilization, BM
Ancient Near Eastern and Biblical
   Languages, Literatures, and Linguistics, B
Ancient/Classical Greek Language and Literature, B
Anthropology, B
Applied Mathematics, B
Archeology, B
Architecture, B
Art History, Criticism and Conservation, B
Art Teacher Education, B
Art/Art Studies, General, B
Asian Studies/Civilization, B
Athletic Training and Sports Medicine, B
Biochemistry, B
Bioinformatics, B
Biological and Biomedical Sciences, MD
Biology Teacher Education, B
Biology/Biological Sciences, B
Biomedical Engineering, M
Business Administration and Management, B
Business Administration, Management and
   Operations, MO
Business Statistics, B
Business Teacher Education, B
Business, Management, Marketing, and Related
   Support Services, B
Business/Commerce, B
Business/Managerial Economics, B
Chemistry, BMD
Chemistry Teacher Education, B
Classics and Classical
   Languages, Literatures, and Linguistics, B
Clinical Laboratory Science/Medical
   Technology/Technologist, B
Clinical Psychology, MD
Communication and Media Studies, M
Communication Disorders, BM
Communication Studies/Speech Communication
   and Rhetoric, B
Composition, M
Computer Engineering, M
Computer Science, BM
Computer Teacher Education, B
Curriculum and Instruction, MDO
Drama and Dance Teacher Education, B
Drama and Dramatics/Theatre Arts, B
Economics, BM
Education, BMDO
Education/Teaching of Individuals with Speech or
   Language Impairments, B
Educational Administration and Supervision, MO
Educational Psychology, MDO
Electrical Engineering, M
Electrical, Electronics and Communications
   Engineering, B
Elementary Education and Teaching, B
Engineering, B
Engineering and Applied Sciences, M
English, MD
English Composition, B
English Language and Literature, B
English/Language Arts Teacher Education, B

Entrepreneurship/Entrepreneurial Studies, B
Environmental Biology, M
Environmental Studies, BM
Exercise and Sports Science, D
Family and Consumer Sciences/Human Sciences, B
Fashion Merchandising, B
Fashion/Apparel Design, B
Finance, B
Financial Planning and Services, B
Fine/Studio Arts, B
Foreign Language Teacher Education, B
Forensic Science and Technology, B
Forestry, B
French Language and Literature, B
French Language Teacher Education, B
Geological and Earth Sciences/Geosciences, B
Geology/Earth Science, BMD
Geophysics and Seismology, B
Geosciences, M
German Language and Literature, B
German Language Teacher Education, B
Health and Physical Education, B
Health Education, MD
Health Occupations Teacher Education, B
Health Services Administration, M
Health Teacher Education, B
Health/Medical Preparatory Programs, B
History, BM
Human Development and Family Studies, B
Human Nutrition, B
Human Resources Management/Personnel
    Administration, B
Humanities/Humanistic Studies, B
Insurance, B
Interdisciplinary Studies, MD
Interior Design, B
International Affairs, M
International Business/Trade/Commerce, BM
International Relations and Affairs, B
Journalism, BM
Kindergarten/PreSchool Education and Teaching, B
Latin American Studies, B
Latin Language and Literature, B
Latin Teacher Education, B
Law and Legal Studies, PO
Limnology, M
Linguistics, B
Management Information Systems and
    Services, BMO
Marketing/Marketing Management, B
Maternal/Child Health and Neonatal
    Nurse/Nursing, M
Mathematics, BMD
Mathematics Teacher Education, B
Mechanical Engineering, BM
Multi-/Interdisciplinary Studies, B
Museology/Museum Studies, BM
Music, BMO
Music History, Literature, and Theory, BM
Music Pedagogy, B
Music Performance, B
Music Teacher Education, BM
Music Theory and Composition, BM
Neuroscience, BMD
Nursing, M
Nursing - Advanced Practice, M
Nursing - Registered Nurse Training, B
Nursing Administration, M
Nutritional Sciences, D
Operations Management and Supervision, B
Pediatric Nurse/Nursing, M
Performance, M
Philosophy, BMD
Physical Education Teaching and Coaching, BMD
Physical Therapy/Therapist, MD
Physics, BMD
Physics Teacher Education, B
Political Science and Government, BMDO
Pre-Dentistry Studies, B
Pre-Law Studies, B
Pre-Medicine/Pre-Medical Studies, B
Pre-Nursing Studies, B
Psychology, BMD
Public Administration, BM
Public Policy Analysis, M
Radio and Television, B

Reading Teacher Education, B
Real Estate, B
Religion/Religious Studies, BMD
Religious/Sacred Music, B
Russian Language and Literature, B
Sacred Music, M
Sales, Distribution and Marketing Operations, B
Science Teacher Education/General Science
    Teacher Education, B
Secondary Education and Teaching, B
Slavic Studies, B
Social Science Teacher Education, B
Social Studies Teacher Education, B
Social Work, BMO
Sociology, BMD
Spanish Language and Literature, BM
Spanish Language Teacher Education, B
Special Education and Teaching, B
Specialized Merchandising, Sales, and Marketing
    Operations, B
Speech Teacher Education, B
Sport and Fitness Administration/Management, B
Statistics, BMD
Teacher Education and Professional
    Development, Specific Subject Areas, B
Technical Theatre/Theatre Design and
    Technology, B
Theater, M
Theology and Religious Vocations, MDPO
Urban Studies/Affairs, B

BLINN COLLEGE

Accounting, A
Administrative Assistant and Secretarial Science, A
Agriculture, A
Biology/Biological Sciences, A
Business Administration and Management, A
Chemistry, A
Child Development, A
Comparative Literature, A
Computer Science, A
Computer Systems Networking and
    Telecommunications, A
Criminal Justice/Law Enforcement Administration, A
Dental Hygiene/Hygienist, A
Drama and Dramatics/Theatre Arts, A
English Language and Literature, A
Fire Science/Firefighting, A
French Language and Literature, A
German Language and Literature, A
Health Information/Medical Records
    Technology/Technician, A
History, A
Industrial Radiologic Technology/Technician, A
Legal Administrative Assistant/Secretary, A
Mass Communication/Media Studies, A
Mathematics, A
Mental Health/Rehabilitation, A
Music, A
Nursing - Registered Nurse Training, A
Philosophy, A
Physical Education Teaching and Coaching, A
Physical Therapist Assistant, A
Physics, A
Psychology, A
Real Estate, A
Spanish Language and Literature, A
Speech and Rhetorical Studies, A

BRAZOSPORT COLLEGE

Accounting, A
Administrative Assistant and Secretarial Science, A
Agricultural Business and Management, A
Architecture, A
Art/Art Studies, General, A
Automobile/Automotive Mechanics
    Technology/Technician, A
Biology/Biological Sciences, A
Business Administration and Management, A
Business/Commerce, A
Chemical Technology/Technician, A
Chemistry, A
Child Care and Support Services Management, A
Child Development, A
Computer and Information Sciences, A
Computer Hardware Technology/Technician, A

Computer Programming, A
Computer Programming, Specific Applications, A
Computer Programming/Programmer, A
Computer Technology/Computer Systems
    Technology, A
Construction Engineering Technology/Technician, A
Construction/Heavy Equipment/Earthmoving
    Equipment Operation, A
Corrections and Criminal Justice, A
Criminal Justice/Police Science, A
Data Processing and Data Processing
    Technology/Technician, A
Drafting and Design Technology/Technician, A
Drama and Dramatics/Theatre Arts, A
Economics, A
Education, A
Electrical, Electronic and Communications
    Engineering Technology/Technician, A
Electrician, A
Elementary Education and Teaching, A
Emergency Medical Technology/Technician (EMT
    Paramedic), A
Engineering, A
English Language and Literature, A
Environmental Health, A
Ethnic, Cultural Minority, and Gender Studies, A
Family and Consumer Sciences/Human Sciences, A
Finance, A
Fine/Studio Arts, A
Foreign Languages and Literatures, A
General Studies, A
Geology/Earth Science, A
Health and Physical Education, A
Health Professions and Related Clinical Sciences, A
Heating, Air Conditioning, Ventilation and
    Refrigeration Maintenance
    Technology/Technician, A
History, A
Information Technology, A
Instrumentation Technology/Technician, A
Journalism, A
Legal Assistant/Paralegal, A
Liberal Arts and Sciences Studies and
    Humanities, A
Library Science, A
Machine Tool Technology/Machinist, A
Marketing/Marketing Management, A
Mathematics, A
Music, A
Nursing - Registered Nurse Training, A
Occupational Safety and Health
    Technology/Technician, A
Physical Education Teaching and Coaching, A
Physics, A
Pipefitting/Pipefitter and Sprinkler Fitter, A
Political Science and Government, A
Pre-Medicine/Pre-Medical Studies, A
Psychology, A
Public Administration, A
Purchasing, Procurement/Acquisitions and
    Contracts Management, A
Quality Control Technology/Technician, A
Secondary Education and Teaching, A
Sheet Metal Technology/Sheetworking, A
Social Sciences, A
Sociology, A
Speech and Rhetorical Studies, A
Theology/Theological Studies, A
Welding Technology/Welder, A

BROOKHAVEN COLLEGE

Accounting, A
Automobile/Automotive Mechanics
    Technology/Technician, A
Business Administration and Management, A
Child Development, A
Emergency Medical Technology/Technician (EMT
    Paramedic), A
Fashion Merchandising, A
Liberal Arts and Sciences Studies and
    Humanities, A
Marketing/Marketing Management, A
Nursing - Registered Nurse Training, A

Radiologic Technology/Science - Radiographer, A

BROWN MACKIE COLLEGE-DALLAS

Business Administration and Management, A

BROWN MACKIE COLLEGE-FORT WORTH

Accounting Technology/Technician and Bookkeeping, A
Business Administration and Management, A
Legal Assistant/Paralegal, A

CEDAR VALLEY COLLEGE

Accounting, A
Administrative Assistant and Secretarial Science, A
Automobile/Automotive Mechanics Technology/Technician, A
Business Administration and Management, A
Computer Programming, Specific Applications, A
Computer Programming/Programmer, A
Criminal Justice/Law Enforcement Administration, A
Data Processing and Data Processing Technology/Technician, A
Heating, Air Conditioning, Ventilation and Refrigeration Maintenance Technology/Technician, A
Liberal Arts and Sciences Studies and Humanities, A
Management Information Systems and Services, A
Marketing/Marketing Management, A
Music, A
Radio and Television Broadcasting Technology/Technician, A
Real Estate, A

CENTRAL TEXAS COLLEGE

Administrative Assistant and Secretarial Science, A
Agriculture, A
Aircraft Powerplant Technology/Technician, A
Airline/Commercial/Professional Pilot and Flight Crew, A
Automobile/Automotive Mechanics Technology/Technician, A
Biology/Biological Sciences, A
Business Administration and Management, A
Chemistry, A
Child Care and Support Services Management, A
Clinical/Medical Laboratory Technician, A
Commercial and Advertising Art, A
Computer and Information Sciences, A
Computer Programming, A
Computer Programming, Specific Applications, A
Computer Programming, Vendor/Product Certification, A
Computer Programming/Programmer, A
Cosmetology/Cosmetologist, A
Criminal Justice/Police Science, A
Criminal Justice/Safety Studies, A
Data Processing and Data Processing Technology/Technician, A
Drafting and Design Technology/Technician, A
Electrical, Electronic and Communications Engineering Technology/Technician, A
Emergency Medical Technology/Technician (EMT Paramedic), A
Engineering, A
Environmental Studies, A
Equestrian/Equine Studies, A
Farm/Farm and Ranch Management, A
Geology/Earth Science, A
Graphic and Printing Equipment Operator Production, A
Heating, Air Conditioning, Ventilation and Refrigeration Maintenance Technology/Technician, A
Hotel/Motel Administration/Management, A
Interdisciplinary Studies, A
Journalism, A
Legal Assistant/Paralegal, A
Liberal Arts and Sciences Studies and Humanities, A
Licensed Practical/Vocational Nurse Training, A
Marketing/Marketing Management, A
Mathematics, A
Medical Administrative Assistant/Secretary, A

Medical Radiologic Technology/Science - Radiation Therapist, A
Music, A
Nursing - Registered Nurse Training, A
Office Management and Supervision, A
Physical Education Teaching and Coaching, A
Radio and Television, A
Social Sciences, A
Substance Abuse/Addiction Counseling, A
Welding Technology/Welder, A

CISCO JUNIOR COLLEGE

Accounting, A
Agricultural Business and Management, A
Agriculture, A
Automobile/Automotive Mechanics Technology/Technician, A
Biology/Biological Sciences, A
Business Administration and Management, A
Business Teacher Education, A
Chemistry, A
Child Development, A
Clinical Laboratory Science/Medical Technology/Technologist, A
Computer Programming/Programmer, A
Computer Science, A
Construction Engineering Technology/Technician, A
Consumer Merchandising/Retailing Management, A
Cosmetology/Cosmetologist, A
Criminal Justice/Police Science, A
Dairy Science, A
Data Processing and Data Processing Technology/Technician, A
Developmental and Child Psychology, A
Drafting and Design Technology/Technician, A
Education, A
Electrical, Electronic and Communications Engineering Technology/Technician, A
Finance, A
Fire Science/Firefighting, A
French Language and Literature, A
History, A
Human Services, A
Kindergarten/PreSchool Education and Teaching, A
Marketing/Marketing Management, A
Mathematics, A
Nursing - Registered Nurse Training, A
Physical Education Teaching and Coaching, A
Psychology, A
Real Estate, A
Welding Technology/Welder, A

CLARENDON COLLEGE

Accounting, A
Agribusiness, A
Agricultural Economics, A
Agriculture, A
Architecture, A
Art/Art Studies, General, A
Behavioral Sciences, A
Biology/Biological Sciences, A
Business Administration and Management, A
Chemistry, A
Computer and Information Sciences, A
Drama and Dramatics/Theatre Arts, A
Economics, A
Education, A
Elementary Education and Teaching, A
Engineering, A
English Language and Literature, A
Environmental Sciences, A
Farm/Farm and Ranch Management, A
Finance, A
General Studies, A
Health Services/Allied Health/Health Sciences, A
History, A
Horse Husbandry/Equine Science and Management, A
Kinesiology and Exercise Science, A
Liberal Arts and Sciences Studies and Humanities, A
Marketing/Marketing Management, A
Mass Communication/Media Studies, A
Mathematics, A
Music, A
Nursing - Registered Nurse Training, A

Physical Education Teaching and Coaching, A
Physical Therapy/Therapist, A
Pre-Dentistry Studies, A
Pre-Law Studies, A
Pre-Medicine/Pre-Medical Studies, A
Psychology, A
Secondary Education and Teaching, A
Social Sciences, A
Social Work, A
Sociology, A
Speech and Rhetorical Studies, A

COASTAL BEND COLLEGE

Accounting, A
Administrative Assistant and Secretarial Science, A
Agriculture, A
Applied Art, A
Art Teacher Education, A
Art/Art Studies, General, A
Automobile/Automotive Mechanics Technology/Technician, A
Biological and Physical Sciences, A
Biology/Biological Sciences, A
Business Administration and Management, A
Chemistry, A
Child Development, A
Commercial and Advertising Art, A
Computer and Information Sciences, A
Computer Engineering Technology/Technician, A
Computer Programming, A
Computer Programming, Specific Applications, A
Computer Programming, Vendor/Product Certification, A
Computer Science, A
Computer Systems Networking and Telecommunications, A
Cosmetology/Cosmetologist, A
Criminal Justice/Law Enforcement Administration, A
Criminal Justice/Police Science, A
Data Entry/Microcomputer Applications, A
Data Processing and Data Processing Technology/Technician, A
Dental Hygiene/Hygienist, A
Developmental and Child Psychology, A
Drafting and Design Technology/Technician, A
Drama and Dramatics/Theatre Arts, A
Economics, A
Education, A
Elementary Education and Teaching, A
Engineering, A
English Language and Literature, A
Environmental Engineering Technology/Environmental Technology, A
Finance, A
Fine/Studio Arts, A
French Language and Literature, A
Geology/Earth Science, A
German Language and Literature, A
Health Teacher Education, A
History, A
Information Technology, A
Journalism, A
Legal Administrative Assistant/Secretary, A
Liberal Arts and Sciences Studies and Humanities, A
Licensed Practical/Vocational Nurse Training, A
Mathematics, A
Music, A
Music Teacher Education, A
Nursing - Registered Nurse Training, A
Parks, Recreation, Leisure and Fitness Studies, A
Petroleum Technology/Technician, A
Pharmacy, A
Physical Education Teaching and Coaching, A
Physical Sciences, A
Physics, A
Political Science and Government, A
Psychology, A
Public Relations/Image Management, A
Sociology, A
Speech and Rhetorical Studies, A
System Administration/Administrator, A
Voice and Opera, A
Welding Technology/Welder, A

Word Processing, A

COLLEGE OF BIBLICAL STUDIES-HOUSTON

Bible/Biblical Studies, AB
Christian Studies, AB
Divinity/Ministry (BD, MDiv.), AB

COLLEGE OF THE MAINLAND

Accounting Technology/Technician and
    Bookkeeping, A
Administrative Assistant and Secretarial Science, A
Business Administration and Management, A
Chemical Technology/Technician, A
Child Development, A
Computer Programming/Programmer, A
Computer Systems Networking and
    Telecommunications, A
Criminal Justice/Law Enforcement Administration, A
Criminal Justice/Safety Studies, A
Criminology, A
Drama and Dramatics/Theatre Arts, A
Emergency Medical Technology/Technician (EMT
    Paramedic), A
Fine/Studio Arts, A
Fire Protection and Safety Technology/Technician, A
General Studies, A
Liberal Arts and Sciences Studies and
    Humanities, A
Mathematics, A
Music, A
Natural Sciences, A
Nursing - Registered Nurse Training, A
Pre-Engineering, A
Public Administration and Social Service
    Professions, A
Social Work, A
Sociology, A
Web Page, Digital/Multimedia and Information
    Resources Design, A

THE COLLEGE OF SAINT THOMAS MORE

Liberal Arts and Sciences Studies and
    Humanities, AB

COLLIN COUNTY COMMUNITY COLLEGE DISTRICT

Biology Technician/BioTechnology Laboratory
    Technician, A
Business Administration and Management, A
Business/Office Automation/Technology/Data
    Entry, A
Commercial and Advertising Art, A
Computer and Information Sciences, A
Computer Engineering Technology/Technician, A
Computer Programming/Programmer, A
Computer Systems Networking and
    Telecommunications, A
Dental Hygiene/Hygienist, A
Drafting and Design Technology/Technician, A
Educational/Instructional Media Design, A
Electrical, Electronic and Communications
    Engineering Technology/Technician, A
Electrical/Electronics Drafting and
    Electrical/Electronics CAD/CADD, A
Electrical/Electronics Equipment Installation and
    Repair, A
Emergency Medical Technology/Technician (EMT
    Paramedic), A
Environmental Engineering
    Technology/Environmental Technology, A
Family and Community Services, A
Fire Protection and Safety Technology/Technician, A
Hospitality Administration/Management, A
Interior Design, A
Legal Assistant/Paralegal, A
Liberal Arts and Sciences Studies and
    Humanities, A
Music Management and Merchandising, A
Nursing - Registered Nurse Training, A
Real Estate, A
Respiratory Care Therapy/Therapist, A
Sales, Distribution and Marketing Operations, A
Sign Language Interpretation and Translation, A

Telecommunications Technology/Technician, A
Water Quality and Wastewater Treatment
    Management and Recycling
    Technology/Technician, A

COMMONWEALTH INSTITUTE OF FUNERAL SERVICE

Funeral Service and Mortuary Science, A

COMPUTER CAREER CENTER

Accounting, A
Computer and Information Sciences, A

CONCORDIA UNIVERSITY AT AUSTIN

Biology/Biological Sciences, B
Business Administration and Management, B
Business/Commerce, B
Computer Science, B
Criminal Justice/Law Enforcement Administration, B
Education, M
Elementary Education and Teaching, B
English Language and Literature, B
Environmental Studies, B
General Studies, A
History, B
Human Resources Development, B
Junior High/Intermediate/Middle School Education
    and Teaching, B
Kinesiology and Exercise Science, B
Liberal Arts and Sciences Studies and
    Humanities, AB
Mass Communication/Media Studies, B
Mathematics, B
Religion/Religious Studies, B
Religious Education, B
Religious/Sacred Music, B
Secondary Education and Teaching, B
Social Sciences, AB

COURT REPORTING INSTITUTE OF DALLAS

Court Reporting/Court Reporter, A

THE CRISWELL COLLEGE

Bible/Biblical Studies, AB
Pastoral Studies/Counseling, M
Psychology, B
Religion/Religious Studies, AB
Theology and Religious Vocations, MP
Theology/Theological Studies, AB
Urban Studies/Affairs, B

DALLAS BAPTIST UNIVERSITY

Accounting, BM
Aeronautics/Aviation/Aerospace Science and
    Technology, B
Army JROTC/ROTC, B
Art/Art Studies, General, B
Bible/Biblical Studies, AB
Biology/Biological Sciences, B
Business Administration and Management, AB
Business Administration, Management and
    Operations, M
Business/Managerial Economics, B
Christian Studies, B
Communication Studies/Speech Communication
    and Rhetoric, B
Computer and Information Sciences, B
Computer Science, B
Conflict Resolution and Mediation/Peace Studies, M
Counseling Psychology, M
Counselor Education/School Counseling and
    Guidance Services, M
Criminal Justice/Law Enforcement Administration, B
Criminology, M
Divinity/Ministry (BD, MDiv.), B
Early Childhood Education and Teaching, M
Education, BM
Educational Leadership and Administration, M
Electronic Commerce, M
Elementary Education and Teaching, BM
Engineering Management, M
English Language and Literature, B
Entrepreneurship/Entrepreneurial Studies, M
Experimental Psychology, M

Finance, B
Finance and Banking, M
General Studies, B
Health Services Administration, M
Health/Health Care Administration/Management, B
Higher Education/Higher Education
    Administration, M
History, B
Human Resources Management and Services, M
Interdisciplinary Studies, BM
International Business/Trade/Commerce, M
Kindergarten/PreSchool Education and Teaching, B
Liberal Arts and Sciences Studies and
    Humanities, AB
Liberal Studies, M
Management, M
Management Information Systems and
    Services, BM
Management of Technology, M
Marketing, M
Marketing/Marketing Management, B
Mathematics, B
Missions/Missionary Studies and Missiology, M
Modern Languages, B
Multi-/Interdisciplinary Studies, B
Music, AB
Music Management and Merchandising, B
Music Teacher Education, B
Music Theory and Composition, B
Natural Sciences, B
Organizational Management, M
Pastoral Studies/Counseling, BM
Philosophy, B
Physical Education Teaching and Coaching, B
Piano and Organ, B
Political Science and Government, B
Psychology, B
Reading Teacher Education, M
Religious Education, ABM
Religious/Sacred Music, B
Science Teacher Education/General Science
    Teacher Education, B
Secondary Education and Teaching, B
Sociology, B

DALLAS CHRISTIAN COLLEGE

Bible/Biblical Studies, B
Business Administration and Management, B
Education, B

DALLAS INSTITUTE OF FUNERAL SERVICE

Funeral Service and Mortuary Science, A

DEL MAR COLLEGE

Accounting, A
Accounting Technology/Technician and
    Bookkeeping, A
Administrative Assistant and Secretarial Science, A
Applied Art, A
Architectural Engineering Technology/Technician, A
Art Teacher Education, A
Art/Art Studies, General, A
Automobile/Automotive Mechanics
    Technology/Technician, A
Biology/Biological Sciences, A
Building/Property Maintenance and Management, A
Business Administration and Management, A
Business Machine Repairer, A
Business/Commerce, A
Chemical Technology/Technician, A
Chemistry, A
Child Development, A
Clinical Laboratory Science/Medical
    Technology/Technologist, A
Clinical/Medical Laboratory Technician, A
Community Organization and Advocacy, A
Computer and Information Sciences, A
Computer Programming, A
Computer Programming, Specific Applications, A
Computer
    Programming, Vendor/Product Certification, A
Computer Programming/Programmer, A
Computer Science, A
Computer Systems Networking and
    Telecommunications, A

Computer Typography and Composition Equipment
Operator, A
Consumer Merchandising/Retailing Management, A
Cosmetology/Cosmetologist, A
Court Reporting/Court Reporter, A
Criminal Justice/Law Enforcement Administration, A
Criminal Justice/Police Science, A
Culinary Arts/Chef Training, A
Data Entry/Microcomputer Applications, A
Dental Hygiene/Hygienist, A
Diagnostic Medical Sonography/Sonographer and
Ultrasound Technician, A
Drafting and Design Technology/Technician, A
Drama and Dramatics/Theatre Arts, A
E-Commerce/Electronic Commerce, A
Education, A
Electrical, Electronic and Communications
Engineering Technology/Technician, A
Elementary Education and Teaching, A
Emergency Medical Technology/Technician (EMT
Paramedic), A
English Language and Literature, A
Finance, A
Fine/Studio Arts, A
Fire Protection and Safety Technology/Technician, A
Fire Science/Firefighting, A
General Office Occupations and Clerical Services, A
Geography, A
Geology/Earth Science, A
Health Information/Medical Records
Technology/Technician, A
Health Teacher Education, A
Heavy Equipment Maintenance
Technology/Technician, A
History, A
Hotel/Motel Administration/Management, A
Industrial Radiologic Technology/Technician, A
Information Science/Studies, A
Information Technology, A
Interdisciplinary Studies, A
Journalism, A
Kindergarten/PreSchool Education and Teaching, A
Law and Legal Studies, A
Legal Administrative Assistant/Secretary, A
Liberal Arts and Sciences Studies and
Humanities, A
Machine Tool Technology/Machinist, A
Management Information Systems and Services, A
Mathematics, A
Medical Administrative Assistant/Secretary, A
Medical Radiologic Technology/Science - Radiation
Therapist, A
Mental Health/Rehabilitation, A
Music, A
Music Teacher Education, A
Nursing - Registered Nurse Training, A
Occupational Safety and Health
Technology/Technician, A
Occupational Therapist Assistant, A
Parks, Recreation, Leisure and Fitness Studies, A
Physical Education Teaching and Coaching, A
Physics, A
Political Science and Government, A
Pre-Engineering, A
Psychology, A
Public Administration, A
Public Policy Analysis, A
Radio and Television, A
Real Estate, A
Respiratory Care Therapy/Therapist, A
Sign Language Interpretation and Translation, A
Social Work, A
Sociology, A
Special Products Marketing Operations, A
Speech and Rhetorical Studies, A
System Administration/Administrator, A
Trade and Industrial Teacher Education, A
Transportation/Transportation Management, A
Voice and Opera, A
Web Page, Digital/Multimedia and Information
Resources Design, A
Web/Multimedia Management and Webmaster, A
Welding Technology/Welder, A

Word Processing, A

DEVRY UNIVERSITY (HOUSTON)

Biomedical Technology/Technician, B
Business Administration and Management, B
Business Administration, Management and
Operations, BM
Computer and Information Sciences, B
Computer Engineering Technology/Technician, B
Computer Systems Networking and
Telecommunications, B
Electrical, Electronic and Communications
Engineering Technology/Technician, AB
Health Information/Medical Records
Technology/Technician, A

DEVRY UNIVERSITY (IRVING)

Biomedical Technology/Technician, B
Business Administration, Management and
Operations, BM
Computer Engineering Technology/Technician, B
Computer Systems Analysis/Analyst, B
Computer Systems Networking and
Telecommunications, AB
Electrical, Electronic and Communications
Engineering Technology/Technician, AB
Health Information/Medical Records
Technology/Technician, A
Information Science/Studies, B
Medical Informatics, B
Operations Management and Supervision, B

DEVRY UNIVERSITY (PLANO)

Business Administration, Management and
Operations, M

EAST TEXAS BAPTIST UNIVERSITY

Accounting, B
Athletic Training and Sports Medicine, B
Bible/Biblical Studies, B
Biology Teacher Education, B
Biology/Biological Sciences, B
Business Administration and Management, B
Business/Commerce, B
Chemistry, B
Chemistry Teacher Education, B
Clinical Laboratory Science/Medical
Technology/Technologist, B
Drama and Dance Teacher Education, B
Drama and Dramatics/Theatre Arts, B
Education, B
Elementary Education and Teaching, B
English Language and Literature, B
English/Language Arts Teacher Education, B
Health and Physical Education, B
History, B
History Teacher Education, B
Liberal Arts and Sciences Studies and
Humanities, AB
Management Information Systems and Services, B
Mass Communication/Media Studies, B
Mathematics, B
Mathematics Teacher Education, B
Music, B
Music Teacher Education, B
Nursing, B
Nursing - Registered Nurse Training, B
Pastoral Studies/Counseling, B
Physical Education Teaching and Coaching, B
Piano and Organ, B
Psychology, B
Religion/Religious Studies, B
Religious Education, B
Religious/Sacred Music, B
Science Teacher Education/General Science
Teacher Education, B
Social Studies Teacher Education, B
Sociology, B
Spanish Language and Literature, B
Spanish Language Teacher Education, B
Speech and Rhetorical Studies, B
Speech Teacher Education, B
Voice and Opera, B

Youth Ministry, B

EASTFIELD COLLEGE

Accounting, A
Autobody/Collision and Repair
Technology/Technician, A
Automobile/Automotive Mechanics
Technology/Technician, A
Business Administration and Management, A
Child Care and Support Services Management, A
Computer and Information Sciences, A
Computer Engineering Technology/Technician, A
Computer Hardware Engineering, A
Computer Programming, A
Computer Programming/Programmer, A
Computer Systems Networking and
Telecommunications, A
Computer/Information Technology Services
Administration and Management, A
Criminal Justice/Safety Studies, A
Data Entry/Microcomputer Applications, A
Data Processing and Data Processing
Technology/Technician, A
Drafting and Design Technology/Technician, A
Electrical, Electronic and Communications
Engineering Technology/Technician, A
Electrical/Electronics Drafting and
Electrical/Electronics CAD/CADD, A
Executive Assistant/Executive Secretary, A
Graphic and Printing Equipment Operator
Production, A
Heating, Air Conditioning, Ventilation and
Refrigeration Maintenance
Technology/Technician, A
Legal Administrative Assistant/Secretary, A
Liberal Arts and Sciences Studies and
Humanities, A
Psychiatric/Mental Health Services Technician, A
Sign Language Interpretation and Translation, A
Social Work, A
Substance Abuse/Addiction Counseling, A
System Administration/Administrator, A
Word Processing, A

EL CENTRO COLLEGE

Accounting, A
Administrative Assistant and Secretarial Science, A
Apparel and Textiles, A
Baking and Pastry Arts/Baker/Pastry Chef, A
BioTechnology, A
Business Administration and Management, A
Business/Office Automation/Technology/Data
Entry, A
Cardiovascular Technology/Technologist, A
Clinical Laboratory Science/Medical
Technology/Technologist, A
Clinical/Medical Laboratory Technician, A
Computer Programming/Programmer, A
Computer Science, A
Computer/Information Technology Services
Administration and Management, A
Criminal Justice/Police Science, A
Criminal Justice/Safety Studies, A
Culinary Arts/Chef Training, A
Data Processing and Data Processing
Technology/Technician, A
Diagnostic Medical Sonography/Sonographer and
Ultrasound Technician, A
Drafting and Design Technology/Technician, A
Emergency Medical Technology/Technician (EMT
Paramedic), A
Fashion/Apparel Design, A
Food Science, A
Food Technology and Processing, A
General Office Occupations and Clerical Services, A
Health Information/Medical Records
Administration/Administrator, A
Hospitality Administration/Management, A
Hotel/Motel Administration/Management, A
Information Science/Studies, A
Information Technology, A
Interior Design, A
Law and Legal Studies, A
Legal Administrative Assistant/Secretary, A
Legal Assistant/Paralegal, A

Liberal Arts and Sciences Studies and
    Humanities, A
Licensed Practical/Vocational Nurse Training, A
Medical Administrative Assistant/Secretary, A
Medical Radiologic Technology/Science - Radiation
    Therapist, A
Medical Transcription/Transcriptionist, A
Medical/Clinical Assistant, A
Nursing - Registered Nurse Training, A
Radiologic Technology/Science - Radiographer, A
Respiratory Care Therapy/Therapist, A
Special Products Marketing Operations, A
Surgical Technology/Technologist, A
Teacher Assistant/Aide, A

EL PASO COMMUNITY COLLEGE

Accounting, A
Administrative Assistant and Secretarial Science, A
Architectural Engineering Technology/Technician, A
Art/Art Studies, General, A
Automobile/Automotive Mechanics
    Technology/Technician, A
Biology/Biological Sciences, A
Broadcast Journalism, A
Building/Construction
    Finishing, Management, and Inspection, A
Business Administration and Management, A
Chemistry, A
Child Development, A
Clinical/Medical Laboratory Technician, A
Commercial and Advertising Art, A
Computer and Information Sciences, A
Computer Graphics, A
Computer Programming, A
Computer Programming, Specific Applications, A
Computer Programming/Programmer, A
Computer Software and Media Applications, A
Computer Systems Networking and
    Telecommunications, A
Corrections, A
Court Reporting/Court Reporter, A
Criminal Justice/Police Science, A
Data Entry/Microcomputer Applications, A
Data Modeling/Warehousing and Database
    Administration, A
Dental Hygiene/Hygienist, A
Dietetics/Dieticians, A
Drafting and Design Technology/Technician, A
Drama and Dramatics/Theatre Arts, A
Education, A
Electrical, Electronic and Communications
    Engineering Technology/Technician, A
Elementary Education and Teaching, A
English Language and Literature, A
Fashion Merchandising, A
Fashion/Apparel Design, A
Finance, A
Fire Science/Firefighting, A
Geology/Earth Science, A
Health Information/Medical Records
    Administration/Administrator, A
Health Teacher Education, A
Heating, Air Conditioning, Ventilation and
    Refrigeration Maintenance
    Technology/Technician, A
History, A
Human Services, A
Industrial Radiologic Technology/Technician, A
Information Technology, A
Interior Design, A
International Business/Trade/Commerce, A
Liberal Arts and Sciences Studies and
    Humanities, A
Management Information Systems and Services, A
Mass Communication/Media Studies, A
Mathematics, A
Medical/Clinical Assistant, A
Mental Health/Rehabilitation, A
Music, A
Nursing - Registered Nurse Training, A
Ophthalmic Laboratory Technology/Technician, A
Photography, A
Physical Therapist Assistant, A
Physics, A
Political Science and Government, A
Pre-Engineering, A

Psychology, A
Public Health (MPH, DPH), A
Real Estate, A
Respiratory Care Therapy/Therapist, A
Sign Language Interpretation and Translation, A
Social Sciences, A
Sociology, A
Speech and Rhetorical Studies, A
System Administration/Administrator, A
Technology Education/Industrial Arts, A
Tourism and Travel Services Management, A
Web Page, Digital/Multimedia and Information
    Resources Design, A
Web/Multimedia Management and Webmaster, A
Word Processing, A

FRANK PHILLIPS COLLEGE

Accounting, A
Administrative Assistant and Secretarial Science, A
Agricultural Business and Management, A
Agricultural Economics, A
Agricultural Mechanization, A
Agricultural Teacher Education, A
Agriculture, A
Agronomy and Crop Science, A
Airline/Commercial/Professional Pilot and Flight
    Crew, A
Anatomy, A
Art Teacher Education, A
Art/Art Studies, General, A
Athletic Training and Sports Medicine, A
Biological and Physical Sciences, A
Biology/Biological Sciences, A
Botany/Plant Biology, A
Business Administration and Management, A
Business Machine Repairer, A
Business Teacher Education, A
Business/Managerial Economics, A
Chemistry, A
Computer and Information Sciences, A
Computer Engineering Technology/Technician, A
Computer Science, A
Cosmetology/Cosmetologist, A
Criminal Justice/Law Enforcement Administration, A
Criminal Justice/Police Science, A
Data Processing and Data Processing
    Technology/Technician, A
Developmental and Child Psychology, A
Economics, A
Education, A
Electrical, Electronic and Communications
    Engineering Technology/Technician, A
Elementary Education and Teaching, A
Engineering, A
Engineering Technology, A
English Language and Literature, A
Farm/Farm and Ranch Management, A
Finance, A
Fire Science/Firefighting, A
Heating, Air Conditioning, Ventilation and
    Refrigeration Maintenance
    Technology/Technician, A
History, A
Horticultural Science, A
Information Science/Studies, A
Legal Administrative Assistant/Secretary, A
Liberal Arts and Sciences Studies and
    Humanities, A
Mathematics, A
Music, A
Music Teacher Education, A
Natural Resources Management/Development and
    Policy, A
Nursing - Registered Nurse Training, A
Petroleum Technology/Technician, A
Physical Education Teaching and Coaching, A
Physical Sciences, A
Piano and Organ, A
Political Science and Government, A
Pre-Engineering, A
Pre-Pharmacy Studies, A
Psychology, A
Sociology, A
Survey Technology/Surveying, A
Welding Technology/Welder, A

Zoology/Animal Biology, A

GALVESTON COLLEGE

Administrative Assistant and Secretarial Science, A
Behavioral Sciences, A
Biological and Physical Sciences, A
Business Administration and Management, A
Computer and Information Sciences, A
Computer Science, A
Criminal Justice/Police Science, A
Culinary Arts/Chef Training, A
Data Entry/Microcomputer Applications, A
Drama and Dramatics/Theatre Arts, A
Education, A
Emergency Medical Technology/Technician (EMT
    Paramedic), A
English Language and Literature, A
History, A
Hotel/Motel Administration/Management, A
Humanities/Humanistic Studies, A
Information Technology, A
Liberal Arts and Sciences Studies and
    Humanities, A
Licensed Practical/Vocational Nurse Training, A
Management Information Systems and Services, A
Mathematics, A
Medical Radiologic Technology/Science - Radiation
    Therapist, A
Modern Languages, A
Music, A
Natural Sciences, A
Nuclear Medical Technology/Technologist, A
Nursing - Registered Nurse Training, A
Physical Education Teaching and Coaching, A
Social Sciences, A
Social Work, A
Web Page, Digital/Multimedia and Information
    Resources Design, A
Word Processing, A

GRAYSON COUNTY COLLEGE

Accounting, A
Administrative Assistant and Secretarial Science, A
Art Teacher Education, A
Art/Art Studies, General, A
Autobody/Collision and Repair
    Technology/Technician, A
Biology/Biological Sciences, A
Business Administration and Management, A
Chemistry, A
Clinical Laboratory Science/Medical
    Technology/Technologist, A
Clinical/Medical Laboratory Technician, A
Computer Engineering Technology/Technician, A
Computer Science, A
Cosmetology/Cosmetologist, A
Criminal Justice/Law Enforcement Administration, A
Criminal Justice/Police Science, A
Drafting and Design Technology/Technician, A
Drama and Dramatics/Theatre Arts, A
Education, A
Electrical, Electronic and Communications
    Engineering Technology/Technician, A
Elementary Education and Teaching, A
Geology/Earth Science, A
Heating, Air Conditioning, Ventilation and
    Refrigeration Maintenance
    Technology/Technician, A
Landscaping and Groundskeeping, A
Legal Administrative Assistant/Secretary, A
Liberal Arts and Sciences Studies and
    Humanities, A
Machine Tool Technology/Machinist, A
Management Information Systems and Services, A
Mathematics, A
Music, A
Nursing - Registered Nurse Training, A
Physical Education Teaching and Coaching, A
Physics, A
Pre-Engineering, A
Psychology, A
Real Estate, A
Sociology, A
Speech and Rhetorical Studies, A

Welding Technology/Welder, A

HALLMARK INSTITUTE OF AERONAUTICS

Aircraft Powerplant Technology/Technician, A
Airframe Mechanics and Aircraft Maintenance
  Technology/Technician, A

HALLMARK INSTITUTE OF TECHNOLOGY

Accounting, A
Administrative Assistant and Secretarial Science, A
Airframe Mechanics and Aircraft Maintenance
  Technology/Technician, A
Electrical, Electronic and Communications
  Engineering Technology/Technician, A
Medical Administrative Assistant/Secretary, A

HARDIN-SIMMONS UNIVERSITY

Accounting, B
Agricultural Business and Management, B
Agronomy and Crop Science, B
Animal Sciences, B
Art Teacher Education, B
Athletic Training and Sports Medicine, B
Audiology/Audiologist and Speech-Language
  Pathology/Pathologist, B
Bible/Biblical Studies, B
Biochemistry, Biophysics and Molecular Biology, B
Biology/Biological Sciences, B
Broadcast Journalism, B
Business Administration and Management, B
Business Administration, Management and
  Operations, M
Business Teacher Education, B
Chemistry, B
Communication Studies/Speech Communication
  and Rhetoric, B
Composition, M
Computer Programming/Programmer, B
Computer Teacher Education, B
Corrections, B
Counselor Education/School Counseling and
  Guidance Services, M
Criminal Justice/Police Science, B
Drama and Dance Teacher Education, B
Drama and Dramatics/Theatre Arts, B
Early Childhood Education and Teaching, B
Economics, B
Education, BM
Education/Teaching of the Gifted and Talented, M
English, M
English Language and Literature, B
English/Language Arts Teacher Education, B
Environmental Policy and Resource
  Management, M
Environmental Sciences, B
Finance, B
Fine/Studio Arts, B
Geology/Earth Science, B
Graphic Design, B
Health and Physical Education, B
History, BM
History Teacher Education, B
Kinesiology and Exercise Science, B
Management Science, B
Marketing/Marketing Management, B
Marriage and Family Therapy/Counseling, M
Maternal/Child Health and Neonatal
  Nurse/Nursing, M
Mathematics, BD
Mathematics Teacher Education, B
Missions/Missionary Studies and Missiology, B
Music, BM
Music History, Literature, and Theory, B
Music Management and Merchandising, B
Music Performance, B
Music Teacher Education, BM
Music Theory and Composition, BM
Nursing, M
Nursing - Advanced Practice, M
Nursing - Registered Nurse Training, B
Pastoral Studies/Counseling, M
Performance, M
Philosophy, B
Physical Education Teaching and Coaching, BM

Physical Therapy/Therapist, D
Physics, B
Piano and Organ, B
Political Science and Government, B
Pre-Dentistry Studies, B
Pre-Law Studies, B
Pre-Medicine/Pre-Medical Studies, B
Pre-Pharmacy Studies, B
Psychology, BM
Radio and Television, B
Reading Teacher Education, BM
Recreation and Park Management, M
Religion/Religious Studies, M
Religious/Sacred Music, B
Sacred Music, M
Science Teacher Education/General Science
  Teacher Education, BD
Social Studies Teacher Education, B
Social Work, B
Sociology, B
Spanish Language and Literature, B
Spanish Language Teacher Education, B
Speech and Rhetorical Studies, B
Speech Teacher Education, B
Sport and Fitness Administration/Management, M
Theological and Ministerial Studies, B
Theology and Religious Vocations, P
Theology/Theological Studies, B
Violin, Viola, Guitar and Other Stringed
  Instruments, B
Voice and Opera, B

HILL COLLEGE OF THE HILL JUNIOR COLLEGE DISTRICT

Accounting, A
Administrative Assistant and Secretarial Science, A
Agricultural Business and Management, A
Agricultural Economics, A
Agriculture, A
Animal Sciences, A
Applied Art, A
Art History, Criticism and Conservation, A
Art Teacher Education, A
Art/Art Studies, General, A
Artificial Intelligence and Robotics, A
Autobody/Collision and Repair
  Technology/Technician, A
Automobile/Automotive Mechanics
  Technology/Technician, A
Behavioral Sciences, A
Biological and Physical Sciences, A
Biology/Biological Sciences, A
Botany/Plant Biology, A
Business Administration and Management, A
Business/Managerial Economics, A
Ceramic Arts and Ceramics, A
Chemistry, A
Child Care Provider/Assistant, A
Child Development, A
Civil Engineering Technology/Technician, A
Commercial and Advertising Art, A
Computer Programming, A
Computer Programming/Programmer, A
Computer Science, A
Computer Typography and Composition Equipment
  Operator, A
Cosmetology/Cosmetologist, A
Criminal Justice/Law Enforcement Administration, A
Criminal Justice/Police Science, A
Dairy Science, A
Data Processing and Data Processing
  Technology/Technician, A
Developmental and Child Psychology, A
Drafting and Design Technology/Technician, A
Drama and Dramatics/Theatre Arts, A
Economics, A
Education, A
Electrical, Electronic and Communications
  Engineering Technology/Technician, A
Elementary Education and Teaching, A
Engineering, A
Engineering Science, A
English Language and Literature, A
Family and Consumer Sciences/Human Sciences, A
Farm/Farm and Ranch Management, A
Finance, A

Fire Science/Firefighting, A
Geography, A
Geology/Earth Science, A
Health Teacher Education, A
Heating, Air Conditioning, Ventilation and
  Refrigeration Maintenance
  Technology/Technician, A
History, A
Horticultural Science, A
Humanities/Humanistic Studies, A
Information Science/Studies, A
Journalism, A
Liberal Arts and Sciences Studies and
  Humanities, A
Licensed Practical/Vocational Nurse Training, A
Machine Tool Technology/Machinist, A
Mass Communication/Media Studies, A
Mathematics, A
Music, A
Music History, Literature, and Theory, A
Music Teacher Education, A
Music Theory and Composition, A
Photography, A
Physical Education Teaching and Coaching, A
Physical Sciences, A
Physics, A
Piano and Organ, A
Political Science and Government, A
Pre-Engineering, A
Psychology, A
Public Health (MPH, DPH), A
Public Policy Analysis, A
Real Estate, A
Social Sciences, A
Social Work, A
Sociology, A
Spanish Language and Literature, A
Speech and Rhetorical Studies, A
Voice and Opera, A
Welding Technology/Welder, A
Zoology/Animal Biology, A

HOUSTON BAPTIST UNIVERSITY

Accounting, B
Art Teacher Education, B
Bible/Biblical Studies, B
Bilingual and Multilingual Education, B
Biology Teacher Education, B
Biology/Biological Sciences, B
Business Administration and Management, B
Business/Commerce, B
Business/Managerial Economics, B
Chemistry, B
Child Development, B
Christian Studies, B
Communication and Media Studies, B
Communication Studies/Speech Communication
  and Rhetoric, B
Computer and Information Sciences, B
Computer Science, B
Counseling Psychology, M
Counselor Education/School Counseling and
  Guidance Services, BM
Curriculum and Instruction, M
Developmental and Child Psychology, B
Early Childhood Education and Teaching, B
Economics, B
Education, BM
Educational Administration and Supervision, M
Educational Measurement and Evaluation, M
Elementary Education and Teaching, B
Engineering Science, B
English as a Second Language, M
English Language and Literature, B
English/Language Arts Teacher Education, B
Entrepreneurship/Entrepreneurial Studies, B
Finance, B
Fine/Studio Arts, B
Foreign Languages, Literatures, and Linguistics, B
French Language and Literature, B
Health and Physical Education, B
Health Services Administration, M
History, B
Human Resources Management and Services, M
Information Science/Studies, B
Interdisciplinary Studies, B

International Business/Trade/Commerce, B
Junior High/Intermediate/Middle School Education
and Teaching, B
Kindergarten/PreSchool Education and Teaching, B
Kinesiology and Exercise Science, B
Liberal Arts and Sciences Studies and
Humanities, B
Liberal Studies, M
Management, M
Management Information Systems and Services, M
Marketing/Marketing Management, B
Mass Communication/Media Studies, B
Mathematics, B
Mathematics Teacher Education, B
Molecular Biology, B
Music, B
Music Performance, B
Music Teacher Education, B
Music Theory and Composition, B
Nursing - Registered Nurse Training, AB
Pastoral Studies/Counseling, M
Physical Education Teaching and Coaching, B
Physics, B
Political Science and Government, B
Pre-Law Studies, B
Psychology, BM
Public Policy Analysis, B
Reading Teacher Education, M
Religion/Religious Studies, B
Religious/Sacred Music, B
Romance Languages, Literatures, and Linguistics, B
Science Teacher Education/General Science
Teacher Education, B
Secondary Education and Teaching, B
Social Studies Teacher Education, B
Sociology, B
Spanish Language and Literature, B
Special Education and Teaching, B
Speech and Rhetorical Studies, B
Theology and Religious Vocations, M

HOUSTON COMMUNITY COLLEGE SYSTEM

Accounting, A
Administrative Assistant and Secretarial Science, A
Agriculture, A
Automobile/Automotive Mechanics
Technology/Technician, A
Business Administration and Management, A
Business/Corporate Communications, A
Cartography, A
Child Care and Support Services Management, A
Child Development, A
Civil Engineering Technology/Technician, A
Clinical/Medical Laboratory Technician, A
Commercial and Advertising Art, A
Commercial Photography, A
Computer and Information Sciences, A
Computer Engineering Technology/Technician, A
Computer Science, A
Construction Engineering Technology/Technician, A
Court Reporting/Court Reporter, A
Criminal Justice/Police Science, A
Drafting and Design Technology/Technician, A
Drama and Dramatics/Theatre Arts, A
Electrical, Electronic and Communications
Engineering Technology/Technician, A
Emergency Medical Technology/Technician (EMT
Paramedic), A
Engineering Technology, A
Family and Consumer Sciences/Human Sciences, A
Fashion Merchandising, A
Fashion/Apparel Design, A
Finance, A
Fire Science/Firefighting, A
Graphic and Printing Equipment Operator
Production, A
Health Information/Medical Records
Administration/Administrator, A
Health Information/Medical Records
Technology/Technician, A
Health/Health Care Administration/Management, A
Horticultural Science, A
Hotel/Motel Administration/Management, A
Human Resources Management/Personnel
Administration, A

Industrial Radiologic Technology/Technician, A
Industrial Technology/Technician, A
Insurance, A
Interior Design, A
Kinesiology and Exercise Science, A
Legal Assistant/Paralegal, A
Liberal Arts and Sciences Studies and
Humanities, A
Logistics and Materials Management, A
Marketing/Marketing Management, A
Mass Communication/Media Studies, A
Medical Administrative Assistant/Secretary, A
Medical Radiologic Technology/Science - Radiation
Therapist, A
Mental Health/Rehabilitation, A
Music Management and Merchandising, A
Music Theory and Composition, A
Nuclear Medical Technology/Technologist, A
Nursing - Registered Nurse Training, A
Occupational Safety and Health
Technology/Technician, A
Occupational Therapist Assistant, A
Physical Therapist Assistant, A
Psychiatric/Mental Health Services Technician, A
Radio and Television Broadcasting
Technology/Technician, A
Real Estate, A
Respiratory Care Therapy/Therapist, A
Sign Language Interpretation and Translation, A
Social Sciences, A
Technical and Business Writing, A
Tourism and Travel Services Management, A
Transportation and Materials Moving, A

HOWARD COLLEGE

Accounting, A
Agriculture, A
Art/Art Studies, General, A
Automobile/Automotive Mechanics
Technology/Technician, A
Behavioral Sciences, A
Biology/Biological Sciences, A
Business Administration and Management, A
Chemistry, A
Child Development, A
Computer and Information Sciences, A
Computer Programming/Programmer, A
Computer Science, A
Cosmetology/Cosmetologist, A
Criminal Justice/Police Science, A
Dental Hygiene/Hygienist, A
Drafting and Design Technology/Technician, A
Drama and Dramatics/Theatre Arts, A
English Language and Literature, A
Finance, A
Health Information/Medical Records
Administration/Administrator, A
Licensed Practical/Vocational Nurse Training, A
Mathematics, A
Music Teacher Education, A
Nursing - Registered Nurse Training, A
Ornamental Horticulture, A
Physical Education Teaching and Coaching, A
Respiratory Care Therapy/Therapist, A
Social Sciences, A
Speech and Rhetorical Studies, A
Substance Abuse/Addiction Counseling, A

HOWARD PAYNE UNIVERSITY

Accounting, B
American/United States Studies/Civilization, B
Ancient Near Eastern and Biblical
Languages, Literatures, and Linguistics, B
Applied Art, B
Art Teacher Education, B
Art/Art Studies, General, B
Athletic Training and Sports Medicine, B
Behavioral Sciences, B
Bible/Biblical Studies, AB
Biology Teacher Education, B
Biology/Biological Sciences, B
Business Administration and Management, B
Business Teacher Education, B
Business/Commerce, B
Chemistry, B

Communication Studies/Speech Communication
and Rhetoric, B
Computer Science, B
Drama and Dance Teacher Education, B
Drama and Dramatics/Theatre Arts, B
Education, B
Elementary Education and Teaching, B
English Language and Literature, B
English/Language Arts Teacher Education, B
European Studies/Civilization, B
Finance, B
Fine/Studio Arts, B
General Studies, B
Health and Physical Education, B
Health Professions and Related Clinical Sciences, A
Health/Health Care Administration/Management, B
History, B
History Teacher Education, B
Information Science/Studies, B
Kindergarten/PreSchool Education and Teaching, B
Kinesiology and Exercise Science, B
Legal Assistant/Paralegal, B
Liberal Arts and Sciences Studies and
Humanities, B
Marketing/Marketing Management, B
Mathematics, B
Mathematics Teacher Education, B
Modern Languages, B
Music, B
Music Performance, B
Music Teacher Education, B
Parks, Recreation, Leisure and Fitness Studies, B
Philosophy, B
Physical Education Teaching and Coaching, B
Piano and Organ, B
Political Science and Government, B
Pre-Law Studies, B
Pre-Medicine/Pre-Medical Studies, B
Psychology, B
Public Health (MPH, DPH), A
Public Relations/Image Management, B
Religion/Religious Studies, AB
Religious Education, B
Religious/Sacred Music, B
Science Teacher Education/General Science
Teacher Education, B
Secondary Education and Teaching, B
Social Science Teacher Education, B
Social Sciences, B
Social Studies Teacher Education, B
Social Work, B
Sociology, B
Spanish Language and Literature, B
Spanish Language Teacher Education, B
Speech and Rhetorical Studies, B
Speech Teacher Education, B
Sport and Fitness Administration/Management, B
Teacher Education, Multiple Levels, B
Teaching English as a Second or Foreign
Language/ESL Language Instructor, B
Telecommunications Technology/Technician, B
Theology/Theological Studies, B
Violin, Viola, Guitar and Other Stringed
Instruments, B
Voice and Opera, B

HUSTON-TILLOTSON UNIVERSITY

Accounting, B
American Government and Politics (United States)
, B
Biology/Biological Sciences, B
Business Administration and Management, B
Chemistry, B
Computer Science, B
Education, B
Elementary Education and Teaching, B
English Language and Literature, B
Mathematics, B
Music, B
Physical Education Teaching and Coaching, B
Political Science and Government, B
Pre-Medicine/Pre-Medical Studies, B
Psychology, B
Secondary Education and Teaching, B
Social Studies Teacher Education, B

Sociology, B

ITT TECHNICAL INSTITUTE (ARLINGTON)

CAD/CADD Drafting and/or Design
   Technology/Technician, A
Computer Programming/Programmer, A
Electrical, Electronic and Communications
   Engineering Technology/Technician, A
System, Networking, and LAN/WAN
   Management/Manager, A
Web Page, Digital/Multimedia and Information
   Resources Design, A
Web/Multimedia Management and Webmaster, A

ITT TECHNICAL INSTITUTE (AUSTIN)

CAD/CADD Drafting and/or Design
   Technology/Technician, A
Computer Programming/Programmer, A
Electrical, Electronic and Communications
   Engineering Technology/Technician, A
System, Networking, and LAN/WAN
   Management/Manager, A
Web Page, Digital/Multimedia and Information
   Resources Design, A
Web/Multimedia Management and Webmaster, A

ITT TECHNICAL INSTITUTE (HOUSTON)

CAD/CADD Drafting and/or Design
   Technology/Technician, A
Computer Programming/Programmer, A
Electrical, Electronic and Communications
   Engineering Technology/Technician, A
System, Networking, and LAN/WAN
   Management/Manager, A
Web Page, Digital/Multimedia and Information
   Resources Design, A
Web/Multimedia Management and Webmaster, A

ITT TECHNICAL INSTITUTE (HOUSTON)

CAD/CADD Drafting and/or Design
   Technology/Technician, A
Computer Programming/Programmer, A
Electrical, Electronic and Communications
   Engineering Technology/Technician, A
System, Networking, and LAN/WAN
   Management/Manager, A
Web Page, Digital/Multimedia and Information
   Resources Design, A
Web/Multimedia Management and Webmaster, A

ITT TECHNICAL INSTITUTE (HOUSTON)

CAD/CADD Drafting and/or Design
   Technology/Technician, A
Computer Programming/Programmer, A
Electrical, Electronic and Communications
   Engineering Technology/Technician, A
System, Networking, and LAN/WAN
   Management/Manager, A
Web Page, Digital/Multimedia and Information
   Resources Design, A
Web/Multimedia Management and Webmaster, A

ITT TECHNICAL INSTITUTE (RICHARDSON)

CAD/CADD Drafting and/or Design
   Technology/Technician, A
Computer Programming/Programmer, A
Electrical, Electronic and Communications
   Engineering Technology/Technician, A
System, Networking, and LAN/WAN
   Management/Manager, A
Web Page, Digital/Multimedia and Information
   Resources Design, A
Web/Multimedia Management and Webmaster, A

ITT TECHNICAL INSTITUTE (SAN ANTONIO)

CAD/CADD Drafting and/or Design
   Technology/Technician, A
Computer Programming/Programmer, A
Electrical, Electronic and Communications
   Engineering Technology/Technician, A
System, Networking, and LAN/WAN
   Management/Manager, A

Web Page, Digital/Multimedia and Information
   Resources Design, A
Web/Multimedia Management and Webmaster, A

JACKSONVILLE COLLEGE

Biological and Physical Sciences, A
Liberal Arts and Sciences Studies and
   Humanities, A

JARVIS CHRISTIAN COLLEGE

Accounting, B
Biology/Biological Sciences, B
Business Administration and Management, B
Business Teacher Education, B
Chemistry, B
Computer Science, B
Economics, B
Elementary Education and Teaching, B
English Language and Literature, B
Health and Physical Education, B
History, B
Kindergarten/PreSchool Education and Teaching, B
Marketing/Marketing Management, B
Mathematics, B
Music, B
Music Teacher Education, B
Physical Education Teaching and Coaching, B
Physics, B
Reading Teacher Education, B
Religion/Religious Studies, B
Secondary Education and Teaching, B
Sociology, B
Special Education and Teaching, B

KD STUDIO

Acting, A
Music, A

KILGORE COLLEGE

Accounting, A
Accounting Technology/Technician and
   Bookkeeping, A
Administrative Assistant and Secretarial Science, A
Aerospace, Aeronautical and Astronautical
   Engineering, A
Agriculture, A
Art/Art Studies, General, A
Automobile/Automotive Mechanics
   Technology/Technician, A
Biological and Physical Sciences, A
Business Administration and Management, A
Business/Commerce, A
Chemistry, A
Child Care and Support Services Management, A
Clinical Laboratory Science/Medical
   Technology/Technologist, A
Clinical/Medical Laboratory Technician, A
Commercial and Advertising Art, A
Commercial Photography, A
Computer and Information Sciences, A
Computer Programming/Programmer, A
Computer Systems Networking and
   Telecommunications, A
Corrections, A
Criminal Justice/Law Enforcement Administration, A
Criminal Justice/Police Science, A
Criminal Justice/Safety Studies, A
Dance, A
Data Processing and Data Processing
   Technology/Technician, A
Design and Visual Communications, A
Diesel Mechanics Technology/Technician, A
Drafting and Design Technology/Technician, A
Drama and Dramatics/Theatre Arts, A
Electrical, Electronic and Communications
   Engineering Technology/Technician, A
Elementary Education and Teaching, A
Emergency Medical Technology/Technician (EMT
   Paramedic), A
English Language and Literature, A
Executive Assistant/Executive Secretary, A
Fashion Merchandising, A
Finance, A
Fire Science/Firefighting, A
Forestry, A
General Studies, A

Geology/Earth Science, A
Graphic and Printing Equipment Operator
   Production, A
Health Teacher Education, A
Heating, Air Conditioning, Ventilation and
   Refrigeration Maintenance
   Technology/Technician, A
Industrial Technology/Technician, A
Journalism, A
Legal Assistant/Paralegal, A
Machine Tool Technology/Machinist, A
Management Information Systems and Services, A
Mathematics, A
Medical Radiologic Technology/Science - Radiation
   Therapist, A
Medical/Clinical Assistant, A
Metallurgical Technology/Technician, A
Music, A
Nursing - Registered Nurse Training, A
Occupational Safety and Health
   Technology/Technician, A
Operations Management and Supervision, A
Physical Education Teaching and Coaching, A
Physical Therapist Assistant, A
Physics, A
Pre-Pharmacy Studies, A
Psychology, A
Religion/Religious Studies, A
Social Sciences, A
Speech and Rhetorical Studies, A
Trade and Industrial Teacher Education, A

KINGWOOD COLLEGE

Accounting, A
Biology/Biological Sciences, A
Business Administration and Management, A
Computer and Information Sciences, A
Computer Engineering Technology/Technician, A
Computer Graphics, A
Computer Typography and Composition Equipment
   Operator, A
Education, A
English Language and Literature, A
Foreign Languages and Literatures, A
Information Science/Studies, A
Licensed Practical/Vocational Nurse Training, A
Mathematics, A
Occupational Therapy/Therapist, A
Psychology, A
Social Sciences, A
Visual and Performing Arts, A

LAMAR STATE COLLEGE-ORANGE

Accounting, A
Administrative Assistant and Secretarial Science, A
Architectural Engineering Technology/Technician, A
Business Administration and Management, A
Clinical/Medical Laboratory Technician, A
Comparative Literature, A
Computer Science, A
Data Processing and Data Processing
   Technology/Technician, A
Environmental Studies, A
Information Science/Studies, A
Liberal Arts and Sciences Studies and
   Humanities, A
Mass Communication/Media Studies, A
Mathematics, A
Nursing - Registered Nurse Training, A
Real Estate, A

LAMAR STATE COLLEGE-PORT ARTHUR

Accounting Technology/Technician and
   Bookkeeping, A
Administrative Assistant and Secretarial Science, A
Automobile/Automotive Mechanics
   Technology/Technician, A
Business Administration and Management, A
Business/Commerce, A
Child Development, A
Computer Systems Networking and
   Telecommunications, A
Cosmetology/Cosmetologist, A
Criminal Justice/Safety Studies, A

Data Processing and Data Processing
Technology/Technician, A
Electrical and Electronic Engineering
Technologies/Technicians, A
Electrical, Electronic and Communications
Engineering Technology/Technician, A
Family and Consumer Sciences/Human Sciences, A
General Studies, A
Heating, Air Conditioning, Ventilation and
Refrigeration Maintenance
Technology/Technician, A
Legal Assistant/Paralegal, A
Liberal Arts and Sciences Studies and
Humanities, A
Licensed Practical/Vocational Nurse Training, A
Medical Administrative Assistant/Secretary, A
Nursing - Registered Nurse Training, A
Occupational Safety and Health
Technology/Technician, A
Social Sciences, A
Surgical Technology/Technologist, A

LAMAR UNIVERSITY

Accounting, BM
Administrative Assistant and Secretarial Science, AB
Applied Art, B
Applied Arts and Design, M
Applied Mathematics, B
Art History, Criticism and Conservation, M
Art Teacher Education, B
Art/Art Studies, General, B
Artificial Intelligence and Robotics, A
Audiology/Audiologist and Speech-Language
Pathology/Pathologist, B
Automobile/Automotive Mechanics
Technology/Technician, A
Biological and Biomedical Sciences, M
Biology/Biological Sciences, B
Broadcast Journalism, B
Business Administration and Management, B
Business Administration, Management and
Operations, M
Business Machine Repairer, A
Chemical Engineering, BMD
Chemistry, BM
Child Development, A
Civil Engineering, BMD
Clinical Laboratory Science/Medical
Technology/Technologist, B
Clinical Psychology, BM
Commercial and Advertising Art, B
Communication Disorders, BM
Community Psychology, M
Computer Programming/Programmer, B
Computer Science, BM
Corrections, AB
Cosmetology/Cosmetologist, A
Counselor Education/School Counseling and
Guidance Services, BMO
Criminal Justice/Law Enforcement Administration, B
Criminal Justice/Police Science, B
Criminology, M
Dance, B
Data Processing and Data Processing
Technology/Technician, A
Dental Hygiene/Hygienist, A
Design and Applied Arts, M
Dietetics/Dieticians, B
Drafting and Design Technology/Technician, A
Drama and Dramatics/Theatre Arts, B
Economics, B
Education, ABMDO
Educational Administration and Supervision, MO
Educational Leadership and Administration, BD
Educational Media/Instructional Technology, O
Electrical Engineering, MD
Electrical, Electronic and Communications
Engineering Technology/Technician, A
Electrical, Electronics and Communications
Engineering, B
Elementary Education and Teaching, B
Energy Management and Systems
Technology/Technician, A
Engineering and Applied Sciences, MD
Engineering Management, M
Engineering Science, B

English, M
English Language and Literature, B
Environmental Engineering
Technology/Environmental Technology, M
Environmental Studies, BM
Family and Consumer Sciences/Home Economics
Teacher Education, B
Family and Consumer Sciences/Human
Sciences, BMO
Fashion Merchandising, B
Fashion/Apparel Design, B
Finance, B
Fine Arts and Art Studies, M
Fine/Studio Arts, B
Fire Science/Firefighting, A
Food Science, AB
French Language and Literature, B
Geology/Earth Science, B
Health Teacher Education, B
Heating, Air Conditioning, Ventilation and
Refrigeration Maintenance
Technology/Technician, A
History, BM
Home Economics, O
Industrial and Organizational Psychology, M
Industrial Engineering, B
Industrial Radiologic Technology/Technician, A
Industrial Technology/Technician, A
Industrial/Management Engineering, MD
Information Science/Studies, BM
Interdisciplinary Studies, B
Interior Design, B
Jazz/Jazz Studies, B
Journalism, B
Kindergarten/PreSchool Education and Teaching, B
Kinesiology and Movement Studies, M
Legal Administrative Assistant/Secretary, A
Liberal Arts and Sciences Studies and
Humanities, B
Licensed Practical/Vocational Nurse Training, A
Machine Tool Technology/Machinist, A
Management Strategy and Policy, M
Marine Technology, B
Marketing/Marketing Management, B
Mass Communication/Media Studies, B
Mathematics, BM
Mechanical Engineering, BMD
Medical Administrative Assistant/Secretary, A
Music, B
Music Teacher Education, BM
Nursing, MO
Nursing - Registered Nurse Training, AB
Nursing Administration, MO
Nursing Education, M
Occupational Safety and Health
Technology/Technician, A
Oceanography, Chemical and Physical, B
Performance, M
Photography, M
Physical Education Teaching and Coaching, B
Physics, B
Piano and Organ, B
Political Science and Government, BM
Pre-Dentistry Studies, B
Psychology, BM
Public Administration, M
Public Health (MPH, DPH), B
Radio and Television, B
Real Estate, A
Respiratory Care Therapy/Therapist, A
Secondary Education and Teaching, B
Social Work, B
Sociology, B
Spanish Language and Literature, B
Special Education and Teaching, BMD
Special Products Marketing Operations, A
Teacher Assistant/Aide, A
Theater, M
Violin, Viola, Guitar and Other Stringed
Instruments, B
Voice and Opera, B
Welding Technology/Welder, A

LAREDO COMMUNITY COLLEGE

Administrative Assistant and Secretarial Science, A
Child Development, A

Clinical/Medical Laboratory Technician, A
Computer Programming, A
Computer Programming/Programmer, A
Computer Software and Media Applications, A
Computer Systems Networking and
Telecommunications, A
Construction Engineering Technology/Technician, A
Criminal Justice/Police Science, A
Data Entry/Microcomputer Applications, A
Data Processing and Data Processing
Technology/Technician, A
Electrical, Electronic and Communications
Engineering Technology/Technician, A
Emergency Medical Technology/Technician (EMT
Paramedic), A
Fashion Merchandising, A
Fire Science/Firefighting, A
Hotel/Motel Administration/Management, A
Industrial Radiologic Technology/Technician, A
Information Science/Studies, A
Information Technology, A
International Business/Trade/Commerce, A
Liberal Arts and Sciences Studies and
Humanities, A
Marketing/Marketing Management, A
Medical/Clinical Assistant, A
Nursing - Registered Nurse Training, A
Physical Therapy/Therapist, A
Radiologic Technology/Science - Radiographer, A
Real Estate, A
Social Sciences, A

LEE COLLEGE

Accounting Technology/Technician and
Bookkeeping, A
Administrative Assistant and Secretarial Science, A
American/United States Studies/Civilization, A
Art/Art Studies, General, A
Biology/Biological Sciences, A
Business Administration and Management, A
Chemistry, A
Communication Studies/Speech Communication
and Rhetoric, A
Computer Programming/Programmer, A
Computer Systems Analysis/Analyst, A
Criminal Justice/Police Science, A
Data Processing and Data Processing
Technology/Technician, A
Drafting and Design Technology/Technician, A
Drama and Dramatics/Theatre Arts, A
Economics, A
Education, A
Electrical, Electronic and Communications
Engineering Technology/Technician, A
Emergency Medical Technology/Technician (EMT
Paramedic), A
English Language and Literature, A
Environmental Studies, A
Executive Assistant/Executive Secretary, A
Fashion Merchandising, A
French Language and Literature, A
Geology/Earth Science, A
German Language and Literature, A
Health Information/Medical Records
Technology/Technician, A
Heating, Air Conditioning, Ventilation and
Refrigeration Maintenance
Technology/Technician, A
History, A
Humanities/Humanistic Studies, A
Information Science/Studies, A
Instrumentation Technology/Technician, A
International Business/Trade/Commerce, A
Journalism, A
Kinesiology and Exercise Science, A
Legal Assistant/Paralegal, A
Liberal Arts and Sciences Studies and
Humanities, A
Licensed Practical/Vocational Nurse Training, A
Logistics and Materials Management, A
Machine Tool Technology/Machinist, A
Mathematics, A
Music, A
Natural Sciences, A
Nurse/Nursing Assistant/Aide and Patient Care
Assistant, A

Office Management and Supervision, A
Operations Management and Supervision, A
Photography, A
Physical Education Teaching and Coaching, A
Physics, A
Political Science and Government, A
Pre-Engineering, A
Prepress/Desktop Publishing and Digital Imaging
　Design, A
Psychology, A
Radio and Television, A
Sociology, A
Spanish Language and Literature, A
Speech and Rhetorical Studies, A
Substance Abuse/Addiction Counseling, A
Telecommunications Technology/Technician, A
Visual and Performing Arts, A
Welding Technology/Welder, A

LETOURNEAU UNIVERSITY

Accounting, B
Airframe Mechanics and Aircraft Maintenance
　Technology/Technician, B
Airline/Commercial/Professional Pilot and Flight
　Crew, B
Avionics Maintenance Technology/Technician, B
Bible/Biblical Studies, B
Biology/Biological Sciences, B
Biomedical/Medical Engineering, B
Business Administration and Management, B
Business Administration, Management and
　Operations, M
Chemistry, B
Computer Engineering, B
Computer Engineering Technology/Technician, B
Computer Science, B
Drafting and Design Technology/Technician, A
Electrical, Electronic and Communications
　Engineering Technology/Technician, B
Electrical, Electronics and Communications
　Engineering, B
Elementary Education and Teaching, B
Engineering, B
Engineering Technology, B
English Language and Literature, B
Finance, B
History, B
Information Science/Studies, B
Interdisciplinary Studies, B
International Business/Trade/Commerce, B
Management Information Systems and Services, B
Marketing/Marketing Management, B
Mathematics, B
Mechanical Engineering, B
Mechanical Engineering/Mechanical
　Technology/Technician, B
Missions/Missionary Studies and Missiology, B
Natural Sciences, B
Physical Education Teaching and Coaching, B
Pre-Dentistry Studies, B
Pre-Law Studies, B
Pre-Medicine/Pre-Medical Studies, B
Pre-Veterinary Studies, B
Psychology, B
Religion/Religious Studies, B
Secondary Education and Teaching, B
Sport and Fitness Administration/Management, B
Welding Technology/Welder, B

LON MORRIS COLLEGE

Accounting, A
Applied Art, A
Art History, Criticism and Conservation, A
Art Teacher Education, A
Art/Art Studies, General, A
Bible/Biblical Studies, A
Biology/Biological Sciences, A
Botany/Plant Biology, A
Business Administration and Management, A
Chemistry, A
Commercial and Advertising Art, A
Comparative Literature, A
Computer Science, A
Creative Writing, A
Dance, A
Divinity/Ministry (BD, MDiv.), A

Drama and Dramatics/Theatre Arts, A
Drawing, A
Economics, A
Education, A
Elementary Education and Teaching, A
Engineering, A
English Language and Literature, A
European Studies/Civilization, A
Fine/Studio Arts, A
History, A
Humanities/Humanistic Studies, A
Liberal Arts and Sciences Studies and
　Humanities, A
Mass Communication/Media Studies, A
Mathematics, A
Modern Languages, A
Music, A
Music Teacher Education, A
Philosophy, A
Physical Education Teaching and Coaching, A
Physics, A
Piano and Organ, A
Political Science and Government, A
Pre-Engineering, A
Psychology, A
Religion/Religious Studies, A
Religious Education, A
Romance Languages, Literatures, and Linguistics, A
Social Sciences, A
Sociology, A
Spanish Language and Literature, A
Speech and Rhetorical Studies, A
Theology/Theological Studies, A
Voice and Opera, A

LUBBOCK CHRISTIAN UNIVERSITY

Accounting, B
Agricultural Business and Management, B
Agriculture, AB
Ancient Near Eastern and Biblical
　Languages, Literatures, and Linguistics, B
Animal Sciences, B
Applied Art, B
Art Teacher Education, B
Bible/Biblical Studies, B
Biology/Biological Sciences, B
Business Administration and Management, B
Chemistry, B
Clinical Laboratory Science/Medical
　Technology/Technologist, B
Computer and Information Sciences, B
Computer Science, B
Criminal Justice/Safety Studies, B
Design and Visual Communications, B
Early Childhood Education and Teaching, B
Education, B
Elementary Education and Teaching, B
Engineering, B
Family and Community Services, B
Finance, B
Health and Physical Education, B
Humanities/Humanistic Studies, B
Junior High/Intermediate/Middle School Education
　and Teaching, B
Kinesiology and Exercise Science, B
Marketing/Marketing Management, B
Mass Communication/Media Studies, B
Mathematics, B
Missions/Missionary Studies and Missiology, B
Music, B
Music Teacher Education, B
Nursing, B
Physical Education Teaching and Coaching, B
Plant Protection and Integrated Pest
　Management, B
Plant Sciences, B
Pre-Law Studies, B
Psychology, B
Secondary Education and Teaching, B
Social Work, B
Special Education and Teaching, B
Sport and Fitness Administration/Management, B
Theology and Religious Vocations, BM

Youth Ministry, B

MCLENNAN COMMUNITY COLLEGE

Accounting, A
Administrative Assistant and Secretarial Science, A
Art Teacher Education, A
Business Administration and Management, A
Clinical/Medical Laboratory Technician, A
Computer Engineering Technology/Technician, A
Criminal Justice/Law Enforcement Administration, A
Criminal Justice/Police Science, A
Developmental and Child Psychology, A
Finance, A
Health Information/Medical Records
　Administration/Administrator, A
Industrial Radiologic Technology/Technician, A
Information Science/Studies, A
Kindergarten/PreSchool Education and Teaching, A
Legal Administrative Assistant/Secretary, A
Legal Assistant/Paralegal, A
Liberal Arts and Sciences Studies and
　Humanities, A
Medical Administrative Assistant/Secretary, A
Mental Health/Rehabilitation, A
Music, A
Nursing - Registered Nurse Training, A
Physical Education Teaching and Coaching, A
Physical Therapy/Therapist, A
Real Estate, A
Respiratory Care Therapy/Therapist, A
Sign Language Interpretation and Translation, A

MCMURRY UNIVERSITY

Accounting, B
Art Teacher Education, B
Art/Art Studies, General, B
Athletic Training and Sports Medicine, B
Biochemistry, B
Biological and Physical Sciences, B
Biology/Biological Sciences, B
Business Administration and Management, B
Business/Commerce, B
Business/Managerial Economics, B
Ceramic Arts and Ceramics, B
Chemistry, B
Communication Studies/Speech Communication
　and Rhetoric, B
Computer and Information Sciences, B
Computer Software and Media Applications, B
Creative Writing, B
Drama and Dramatics/Theatre Arts, B
Elementary Education and Teaching, B
English Language and Literature, B
Environmental Sciences, B
Finance, B
Graphic Design, B
History, B
Information Science/Studies, B
Junior High/Intermediate/Middle School Education
　and Teaching, B
Management Information Systems and Services, B
Marketing/Marketing Management, B
Mathematics, B
Mathematics and Computer Science, B
Music Performance, B
Music Teacher Education, B
Nursing - Registered Nurse Training, B
Painting, B
Philosophy, B
Physical Education Teaching and Coaching, B
Physics, B
Piano and Organ, B
Political Science and Government, B
Psychology, B
Religion/Religious Studies, B
Religious/Sacred Music, B
Secondary Education and Teaching, B
Sociology, B
Spanish Language and Literature, B
Speech and Rhetorical Studies, B

MIDLAND COLLEGE

Airline/Commercial/Professional Pilot and Flight
　Crew, A
Anthropology, A
Art/Art Studies, General, A

Automobile/Automotive Mechanics Technology/Technician, A
Behavioral Sciences, A
Biology/Biological Sciences, A
Business/Commerce, A
Business/Office Automation/Technology/Data Entry, A
Chemistry, A
Child Care Provider/Assistant, A
Commercial and Advertising Art, A
Comparative Literature, A
Computer Programming, Specific Applications, A
Criminal Justice/Police Science, A
Data Modeling/Warehousing and Database Administration, A
Developmental and Child Psychology, A
Drafting and Design Technology/Technician, A
Drawing, A
Economics, A
Electrical, Electronic and Communications Engineering Technology/Technician, A
Emergency Medical Technology/Technician (EMT Paramedic), A
English Language and Literature, A
Fine/Studio Arts, A
Fire Science/Firefighting, A
Fire Services Administration, A
Foreign Languages and Literatures, A
French Language and Literature, A
Geology/Earth Science, A
German Language and Literature, A
Health Information/Medical Records Technology/Technician, A
Heating, Air Conditioning, Ventilation and Refrigeration Maintenance Technology/Technician, A
History, A
Journalism, A
Legal Assistant/Paralegal, A
Liberal Arts and Sciences Studies and Humanities, A
Mass Communication/Media Studies, A
Mathematics, A
Medical Radiologic Technology/Science - Radiation Therapist, A
Modern Languages, A
Music, A
Music Teacher Education, A
Nursing - Registered Nurse Training, A
Physical Education Teaching and Coaching, A
Physics, A
Political Science and Government, A
Pre-Engineering, A
Psychology, A
Radiologic Technology/Science - Radiographer, A
Respiratory Care Therapy/Therapist, A
Sociology, A
Spanish Language and Literature, A
Speech and Rhetorical Studies, A
Substance Abuse/Addiction Counseling, A
System Administration/Administrator, A
System, Networking, and LAN/WAN Management/Manager, A
Veterinary/Animal Health Technology/Technician and Veterinary Assistant, A
Welding Technology/Welder, A

MIDWESTERN STATE UNIVERSITY

Accounting, B
Applied Art, B
Art/Art Studies, General, B
Athletic Training and Sports Medicine, B
Biological and Biomedical Sciences, M
Biology/Biological Sciences, B
Business Administration and Management, B
Business Administration, Management and Operations, M
Business/Commerce, B
Business/Managerial Economics, B
Chemistry, B
Clinical Laboratory Science/Medical Technology/Technologist, B
Computer Engineering, B
Computer Science, M
Counselor Education/School Counseling and Guidance Services, M

Criminal Justice/Law Enforcement Administration, B
Criminology, M
Curriculum and Instruction, M
Dental Hygiene/Hygienist, B
Drama and Dramatics/Theatre Arts, B
Early Childhood Education and Teaching, B
Economics, B
Education, M
Educational Administration and Supervision, M
Engineering Technology, B
English, M
English Language and Literature, B
Environmental Sciences, B
Finance, B
Geology/Earth Science, B
Health and Physical Education/Fitness, B
Health Physics/Radiological Health, M
Health Services Administration, M
History, BM
Human Resources Development, M
Humanities/Humanistic Studies, B
Information Science/Studies, B
Interdisciplinary Studies, B
International Business/Trade/Commerce, B
International/Global Studies, B
Kinesiology and Exercise Science, B
Kinesiology and Movement Studies, M
Liberal Arts and Sciences Studies and Humanities, AB
Management Information Systems and Services, B
Manufacturing Technology/Technician, B
Marketing/Marketing Management, B
Mass Communication/Media Studies, B
Mathematics, B
Mechanical Engineering/Mechanical Technology/Technician, B
Multi-/Interdisciplinary Studies, B
Music, B
Music Performance, B
Music Teacher Education, B
Nursing, M
Nursing - Advanced Practice, M
Nursing - Registered Nurse Training, B
Nursing Education, M
Physics, B
Political Science and Government, BM
Pre-Dentistry Studies, B
Pre-Engineering, B
Pre-Law Studies, B
Pre-Medicine/Pre-Medical Studies, B
Pre-Pharmacy Studies, B
Pre-Veterinary Studies, B
Psychology, BM
Public Administration, M
Radiologic Technology/Science - Radiographer, AB
Reading Teacher Education, M
Respiratory Care Therapy/Therapist, B
Secondary Education and Teaching, B
Social Sciences, B
Social Work, B
Sociology, B
Spanish Language and Literature, B
Special Education and Teaching, M
Sport and Fitness Administration/Management, B

MONTGOMERY COLLEGE

Accounting and Business/Management, A
Animation, Interactive Technology, Video Graphics and Special Effects, A
Business Administration and Management, A
CAD/CADD Drafting and/or Design Technology/Technician, A
Computer and Information Systems Security, A
Computer Programming/Programmer, A
Computer Software Technology/Technician, A
Computer Systems Networking and Telecommunications, A
Criminal Justice/Law Enforcement Administration, A
Drafting/Design Engineering Technologies/Technicians, A
E-Commerce/Electronic Commerce, A
Electrical, Electronic and Communications Engineering Technology/Technician, A
Human Services, A
Information Technology, A
Robotics Technology/Technician, A

System, Networking, and LAN/WAN Management/Manager, A
Web Page, Digital/Multimedia and Information Resources Design, A
Web/Multimedia Management and Webmaster, A

MOUNTAIN VIEW COLLEGE

Accounting, A
Artificial Intelligence and Robotics, A
Aviation/Airway Management and Operations, A
Avionics Maintenance Technology/Technician, A
Computer Programming/Programmer, A
Criminal Justice/Law Enforcement Administration, A
Drafting and Design Technology/Technician, A
Electrical, Electronic and Communications Engineering Technology/Technician, A
Electromechanical Technology/Electromechanical Engineering Technology, A
Engineering Technology, A
Health Information/Medical Records Technology/Technician, A
Information Science/Studies, A
Legal Administrative Assistant/Secretary, A
Liberal Arts and Sciences Studies and Humanities, A
Quality Control Technology/Technician, A

MTI COLLEGE OF BUSINESS AND TECHNOLOGY (HOUSTON)

Administrative Assistant and Secretarial Science, A
Business/Office Automation/Technology/Data Entry, A
Computer and Information Systems Security, A
Medical Office Assistant/Specialist, A
System Administration/Administrator, A
System, Networking, and LAN/WAN Management/Manager, A

MTI COLLEGE OF BUSINESS AND TECHNOLOGY (HOUSTON)

Administrative Assistant and Secretarial Science, A
Business Operations Support and Secretarial Services, A
Computer Technology/Computer Systems Technology, A
Medical Office Assistant/Specialist, A

NAVARRO COLLEGE

Accounting, A
Administrative Assistant and Secretarial Science, A
Agricultural Mechanization, A
Airline/Commercial/Professional Pilot and Flight Crew, A
Art/Art Studies, General, A
Avionics Maintenance Technology/Technician, A
Biological and Physical Sciences, A
Biology/Biological Sciences, A
Broadcast Journalism, A
Business Administration and Management, A
Chemistry, A
Clinical/Medical Laboratory Technician, A
Commercial and Advertising Art, A
Computer Graphics, A
Computer Programming/Programmer, A
Computer Science, A
Consumer Merchandising/Retailing Management, A
Corrections, A
Criminal Justice/Law Enforcement Administration, A
Criminal Justice/Police Science, A
Dance, A
Data Processing and Data Processing Technology/Technician, A
Dental Hygiene/Hygienist, A
Developmental and Child Psychology, A
Drafting and Design Technology/Technician, A
Drama and Dramatics/Theatre Arts, A
Education, A
Elementary Education and Teaching, A
Engineering, A
English Language and Literature, A
Fire Science/Firefighting, A
Industrial Design, A
Industrial Technology/Technician, A
Journalism, A
Law and Legal Studies, A

Legal Administrative Assistant/Secretary, A
Legal Assistant/Paralegal, A
Licensed Practical/Vocational Nurse Training, A
Marketing/Marketing Management, A
Mathematics, A
Music, A
Nursing - Registered Nurse Training, A
Occupational Therapy/Therapist, A
Pharmacy, A
Physical Education Teaching and Coaching, A
Physical Sciences, A
Physics, A
Pre-Engineering, A
Psychology, A
Radio and Television, A
Real Estate, A
Social Sciences, A
Sociology, A
Speech and Rhetorical Studies, A
Voice and Opera, A

NORTH CENTRAL TEXAS COLLEGE

Administrative Assistant and Secretarial Science, A
Agricultural Mechanization, A
Animal/Livestock Husbandry and Production, A
Automobile/Automotive Mechanics
    Technology/Technician, A
Biological and Physical Sciences, A
Business Administration and Management, A
Business and Personal/Financial Services Marketing
    Operations, A
Computer Engineering Technology/Technician, A
Computer Graphics, A
Computer Programming, A
Computer Programming, Specific Applications, A
Computer
    Programming, Vendor/Product Certification, A
Computer Programming/Programmer, A
Computer Science, A
Computer/Information Technology Services
    Administration and Management, A
Criminal Justice/Law Enforcement Administration, A
Criminal Justice/Police Science, A
Data Processing and Data Processing
    Technology/Technician, A
Drafting and Design Technology/Technician, A
Electrical, Electronic and Communications
    Engineering Technology/Technician, A
Emergency Medical Technology/Technician (EMT
    Paramedic), A
Engineering Technology, A
Equestrian/Equine Studies, A
Farm/Farm and Ranch Management, A
Health Information/Medical Records
    Administration/Administrator, A
Industrial Mechanics and Maintenance
    Technology, A
Information Science/Studies, A
Legal Administrative Assistant/Secretary, A
Legal Assistant/Paralegal, A
Liberal Arts and Sciences Studies and
    Humanities, A
Machine Shop Technology/Assistant, A
Machine Tool Technology/Machinist, A
Management Information Systems and Services, A
Merchandising and Buying Operations, A
Nursing - Registered Nurse Training, A
Occupational Therapy/Therapist, A
Pre-Engineering, A
Real Estate, A
Retailing and Retail Operations, A
Sales, Distribution and Marketing Operations, A
Welding Technology/Welder, A
Word Processing, A

NORTH HARRIS COLLEGE

Accounting, A
Administrative Assistant and Secretarial Science, A
Art Teacher Education, A
Art/Art Studies, General, A
Automobile/Automotive Mechanics
    Technology/Technician, A
Biological and Physical Sciences, A
Child Development, A
Computer and Information Sciences, A
Computer Science, A

Cosmetology/Cosmetologist, A
Criminal Justice/Law Enforcement Administration, A
Criminal Justice/Police Science, A
Drafting and Design Technology/Technician, A
Drama and Dramatics/Theatre Arts, A
Education, A
Electrical, Electronic and Communications
    Engineering Technology/Technician, A
Emergency Medical Technology/Technician (EMT
    Paramedic), A
Finance, A
Heating, Air Conditioning, Ventilation and
    Refrigeration Maintenance
    Technology/Technician, A
Human Services, A
Information Science/Studies, A
Interior Design, A
Journalism, A
Law and Legal Studies, A
Legal Administrative Assistant/Secretary, A
Liberal Arts and Sciences Studies and
    Humanities, A
Management Information Systems and Services, A
Marketing/Marketing Management, A
Mathematics, A
Music, A
Nursing - Registered Nurse Training, A
Photography, A
Physical Education Teaching and Coaching, A
Political Science and Government, A
Pre-Engineering, A
Respiratory Care Therapy/Therapist, A
Sociology, A
Speech and Rhetorical Studies, A
Tourism and Travel Services Management, A
Welding Technology/Welder, A

NORTH LAKE COLLEGE

Accounting, A
Administrative Assistant and Secretarial Science, A
Business Administration and Management, A
Carpentry/Carpenter, A
Communications Technology/Technician, A
Computer Programming/Programmer, A
Construction Engineering Technology/Technician, A
Data Processing and Data Processing
    Technology/Technician, A
Electrical, Electronic and Communications
    Engineering Technology/Technician, A
Heating, Air Conditioning, Ventilation and
    Refrigeration Maintenance
    Technology/Technician, A
Information Science/Studies, A
Kinesiology and Exercise Science, A
Legal Administrative Assistant/Secretary, A
Liberal Arts and Sciences Studies and
    Humanities, A
Real Estate, A

NORTHEAST TEXAS COMMUNITY COLLEGE

Accounting, A
Administrative Assistant and Secretarial Science, A
Agriculture, A
Automobile/Automotive Mechanics
    Technology/Technician, A
Computer Science, A
Cosmetology/Cosmetologist, A
Criminal Justice/Law Enforcement Administration, A
Dairy Science, A
Dental Hygiene/Hygienist, A
Education, A
Education/Teaching of Individuals in Early Childhood
    Special Education Programs, A
Elementary Education and Teaching, A
Finance, A
Information Science/Studies, A
Junior High/Intermediate/Middle School Education
    and Teaching, A
Legal Administrative Assistant/Secretary, A
Mathematics Teacher Education, A
Medical Administrative Assistant/Secretary, A
Nursing - Registered Nurse Training, A
Poultry Science, A
Range Science and Management, A

Secondary Education and Teaching, A

NORTHWEST VISTA COLLEGE

Biology Technician/BioTechnology Laboratory
    Technician, A
Business Administration, Management and
    Operations, A
Community Health and Preventive Medicine, A
Computer and Information Sciences, A
Computer and Information Systems Security, A
Computer Programming/Programmer, A
Computer Science, A
Computer/Information Technology Services
    Administration and Management, A
Criminal Justice/Safety Studies, A
International/Global Studies, A
Liberal Arts and Sciences Studies and
    Humanities, A
Management Information Systems and Services, A
Pre-Engineering, A
Recording Arts Technology/Technician, A
Water Quality and Wastewater Treatment
    Management and Recycling
    Technology/Technician, A

NORTHWOOD
UNIVERSITY, TEXAS CAMPUS

Accounting, AB
Advertising, AB
Banking and Financial Support Services, AB
Business Administration and Management, AB
Computer and Information Sciences, B
Entrepreneurship/Entrepreneurial Studies, B
Fashion Merchandising, AB
Hotel/Motel Administration/Management, AB
International Business/Trade/Commerce, B
Management Information Systems and Services, AB
Marketing/Marketing Management, B
Sport and Fitness Administration/Management, AB
Vehicle and Vehicle Parts and Accessories
    Marketing Operations, AB

ODESSA COLLEGE

Accounting, A
Administrative Assistant and Secretarial Science, A
Agriculture, A
Applied Art, A
Art/Art Studies, General, A
Athletic Training and Sports Medicine, A
Automobile/Automotive Mechanics
    Technology/Technician, A
Biology/Biological Sciences, A
Business Administration and Management, A
Chemistry, A
Child Development, A
Clinical/Medical Laboratory Technician, A
Computer and Information Sciences, A
Computer Science, A
Computer Systems Networking and
    Telecommunications, A
Construction Engineering Technology/Technician, A
Cosmetology/Cosmetologist, A
Criminal Justice/Law Enforcement Administration, A
Criminal Justice/Police Science, A
Culinary Arts/Chef Training, A
Data Processing and Data Processing
    Technology/Technician, A
Drafting and Design Technology/Technician, A
Education, A
Electrical, Electronic and Communications
    Engineering Technology/Technician, A
Emergency Medical Technology/Technician (EMT
    Paramedic), A
English Language and Literature, A
Fashion Merchandising, A
Fire Science/Firefighting, A
Geology/Earth Science, A
Hazardous Materials Management and Waste
    Technology/Technician, A
Heating, Air Conditioning, Ventilation and
    Refrigeration Maintenance
    Technology/Technician, A
History, A
Human Services, A
Industrial Radiologic Technology/Technician, A
Information Science/Studies, A

Kindergarten/PreSchool Education and Teaching, A
Legal Administrative Assistant/Secretary, A
Liberal Arts and Sciences Studies and
   Humanities, A
Machine Tool Technology/Machinist, A
Mathematics, A
Modern Languages, A
Music, A
Nursing - Registered Nurse Training, A
Petroleum Technology/Technician, A
Photography, A
Physical Education Teaching and Coaching, A
Physical Therapy/Therapist, A
Physics, A
Political Science and Government, A
Pre-Engineering, A
Psychology, A
Radio and Television, A
Respiratory Care Therapy/Therapist, A
Social Sciences, A
Sociology, A
Speech and Rhetorical Studies, A
Substance Abuse/Addiction Counseling, A
Surgical Technology/Technologist, A
Teacher Assistant/Aide, A
Welding Technology/Welder, A

OUR LADY OF THE LAKE UNIVERSITY OF SAN ANTONIO

Accounting, B
American/United States Studies/Civilization, B
Art/Art Studies, General, B
Audiology/Audiologist and Speech-Language
   Pathology/Pathologist, B
Biology/Biological Sciences, B
Business Administration and Management, B
Business Administration, Management and
   Operations, M
Chemistry, B
Communication Disorders, M
Communication Studies/Speech Communication
   and Rhetoric, B
Computer Systems Networking and
   Telecommunications, B
Counseling Psychology, MD
Counselor Education/School Counseling and
   Guidance Services, M
Curriculum and Instruction, M
Drama and Dramatics/Theatre Arts, B
Education, MD
Educational Administration and Supervision, M
Educational Leadership and Administration, D
Educational Media/Instructional Technology, M
English, M
English Language and Literature, B
Family and Community Services, B
Fashion Merchandising, B
Fine Arts and Art Studies, B
Health Services Administration, M
Hispanic-American, Puerto Rican, and Mexican-
   American/Chicano Studies, B
History, B
Human Development, M
Human Resources Management/Personnel
   Administration, B
Kindergarten/PreSchool Education and Teaching, B
Liberal Arts and Sciences Studies and
   Humanities, B
Marketing/Marketing Management, B
Marriage and Family Therapy/Counseling, M
Mathematics, B
Natural Sciences, B
Philosophy, B
Political Science and Government, B
Psychology, BMD
Religion/Religious Studies, B
School Psychology, M
Social Sciences, B
Social Work, BM
Sociology, BM
Spanish Language and Literature, B
Special Education and Teaching, BM

PALO ALTO COLLEGE

Agriculture, A
Architectural Engineering Technology/Technician, A

Art/Art Studies, General, A
Aviation/Airway Management and Operations, A
Avionics Maintenance Technology/Technician, A
Biology/Biological Sciences, A
Business Administration and Management, A
Chemistry, A
Computer and Information Sciences, A
Computer Engineering Technology/Technician, A
Computer Science, A
Economics, A
Education, A
Engineering, A
English Language and Literature, A
Finance, A
Geology/Earth Science, A
History, A
Horticultural Science, A
Information Science/Studies, A
Information Technology, A
Journalism, A
Law and Legal Studies, A
Liberal Arts and Sciences Studies and
   Humanities, A
Library Science, A
Mathematics, A
Modern Languages, A
Music, A
Philosophy, A
Physical Education Teaching and Coaching, A
Physics, A
Psychology, A
Public Health (MPH, DPH), A
Sociology, A
Speech and Rhetorical Studies, A
Trade and Industrial Teacher Education, A

PANOLA COLLEGE

Business/Commerce, A
Health Information/Medical Records
   Technology/Technician, A
Industrial Technology/Technician, A
Information Science/Studies, A
Nursing - Registered Nurse Training, A

PARIS JUNIOR COLLEGE

Agricultural Mechanization, A
Art/Art Studies, General, A
Biological and Physical Sciences, A
Business Administration and Management, A
Business Teacher Education, A
Computer Engineering Technology/Technician, A
Computer Typography and Composition Equipment
   Operator, A
Cosmetology/Cosmetologist, A
Drafting and Design Technology/Technician, A
Education, A
Electrical, Electronic and Communications
   Engineering Technology/Technician, A
Elementary Education and Teaching, A
Engineering, A
Heating, Air Conditioning, Ventilation and
   Refrigeration Maintenance
   Technology/Technician, A
Information Science/Studies, A
Liberal Arts and Sciences Studies and
   Humanities, A
Mathematics, A
Medical Insurance Coding Specialist/Coder, A
Metal and Jewelry Arts, A
Nursing - Registered Nurse Training, A
Radiologic Technology/Science - Radiographer, A
Surgical Technology/Technologist, A
Welding Technology/Welder, A

PAUL QUINN COLLEGE

Accounting, B
Administrative Assistant and Secretarial Science, B
Biology/Biological Sciences, B
Business Administration and Management, B
Computer Science, B
Criminal Justice/Law Enforcement Administration, B
Education, B
Elementary Education and Teaching, B
English Language and Literature, B
History, B
Mass Communication/Media Studies, B

Mathematics, B
Physical Education Teaching and Coaching, B
Pre-Medicine/Pre-Medical Studies, B
Religion/Religious Studies, B
Secondary Education and Teaching, B
Social Work, B
Sociology, B

PRAIRIE VIEW A&M UNIVERSITY

Accounting, BM
Agricultural Economics, M
Agricultural Sciences, M
Agricultural Teacher Education, B
Agriculture, B
Agronomy and Soil Sciences, M
Animal Sciences, M
Architecture, BM
Biological and Biomedical Sciences, M
Biology/Biological Sciences, B
Business Administration and Management, B
Business Administration, Management and
   Operations, M
Chemical Engineering, B
Chemistry, BM
Civil Engineering, B
Clinical Laboratory Science/Medical
   Technology/Technologist, B
Clinical Psychology, D
Community Health Services/Liaison/Counseling, B
Computer Science, BM
Computer Technology/Computer Systems
   Technology, B
Counselor Education/School Counseling and
   Guidance Services, MD
Criminal Justice/Safety Studies, B
Curriculum and Instruction, M
Drafting and Design Technology/Technician, B
Drama and Dramatics/Theatre Arts, B
Education, MD
Educational Administration and Supervision, M
Educational Leadership and Administration, MD
Electrical Engineering, MD
Electrical, Electronic and Communications
   Engineering Technology/Technician, B
Electrical, Electronics and Communications
   Engineering, B
Engineering and Applied Sciences, MD
Engineering Technology, B
English, M
English Language and Literature, B
Family and Community Services, B
Family and Consumer Sciences/Human
   Sciences, M
Finance, B
Foods, Nutrition, and Wellness Studies, B
Forensic Psychology, MD
Health Education, M
History, B
Home Economics, M
Industrial Technology/Technician, B
Interdisciplinary Studies, B
Legal and Justice Studies, MD
Management Information Systems and Services, M
Marketing/Marketing Management, B
Marriage and Family Therapy/Counseling, M
Mathematics, BM
Mechanical Engineering, B
Music, B
Nursing, M
Nursing - Registered Nurse Training, B
Physical Education Teaching and Coaching, M
Physics, B
Piano and Organ, B
Political Science and Government, B
Psychology, B
Social Work, B
Sociology, BM
Spanish Language and Literature, B
Special Education and Teaching, M
Trade and Industrial Teacher Education, B
Urban Design, M
Voice and Opera, B

Wind and Percussion Instruments, B

RANGER COLLEGE

Administrative Assistant and Secretarial Science, A
Automobile/Automotive Mechanics
  Technology/Technician, A
Computer Engineering Technology/Technician, A
Liberal Arts and Sciences Studies and
  Humanities, A
Science Teacher Education/General Science
  Teacher Education, A
Welding Technology/Welder, A

RICE UNIVERSITY

Ancient/Classical Greek Language and Literature, B
Anthropology, BMD
Applied Mathematics, BMD
Applied Physics, MD
Architecture, BMD
Art History, Criticism and Conservation, B
Art/Art Studies, General, B
Asian Studies/Civilization, B
Astronomy, BMD
Astrophysics, B
Biochemistry, BMD
Bioengineering, MDO
Biology/Biological Sciences, B
Biomedical Engineering, MD
Biomedical/Medical Engineering, B
Biostatistics, D
Business Administration and Management, B
Business Administration, Management and
  Operations, MO
Cell Biology and Anatomy, MD
Chemical Engineering, BMD
Chemistry, BMD
Civil Engineering, BMD
Classics and Classical
  Languages, Literatures, and Linguistics, B
Cognitive Sciences, MD
Composition, MD
Computational Sciences, MD
Computer and Information Sciences, B
Computer Engineering, BMD
Computer Science, MD
Ecology, BMD
Economics, BMD
Education, M
Electrical Engineering, MD
Electrical, Electronics and Communications
  Engineering, B
Engineering and Applied Sciences, MDO
English, MD
English Language and Literature, B
Environmental Engineering
  Technology/Environmental Technology, MD
Environmental Policy and Resource
  Management, M
Environmental Sciences, MD
Environmental/Environmental Health Engineering, B
Evolutionary Biology, BMD
Fine/Studio Arts, B
French Language and Literature, BMD
Geology/Earth Science, B
Geophysics and Seismology, BM
Geosciences, MD
German Language and Literature, B
History, BMD
Industrial and Organizational Psychology, MD
Inorganic Chemistry, D
Kinesiology and Exercise Science, B
Latin American Studies, B
Latin Language and Literature, B
Linguistics, BMD
Materials Engineering, B
Materials Sciences, BMD
Mathematical and Computational Finance, D
Mathematics, BMD
Mechanical Engineering, BMD
Multi-/Interdisciplinary Studies, B
Music, BMD
Music History, Literature, and Theory, BM
Music Performance, B
Music Theory and Composition, BM
Neuroscience, B
Organic Chemistry, D

Performance, MD
Philosophy, BMD
Physical and Theoretical Chemistry, B
Physical Chemistry, D
Physics, BMD
Political Science and Government, BMD
Psychology, BMD
Public Policy Analysis, B
Religion/Religious Studies, BD
Russian Language and Literature, B
Russian Studies, B
Sociology, B
Spanish Language and Literature, BM
Statistics, BMD
Urban Design, M
Visual and Performing Arts, B
Women's Studies, B

RICHLAND COLLEGE

Accounting, A
Administrative Assistant and Secretarial Science, A
Artificial Intelligence and Robotics, A
Business Administration and Management, A
Computer Programming/Programmer, A
Data Processing and Data Processing
  Technology/Technician, A
Drafting/Design Engineering
  Technologies/Technicians, A
Electrical, Electronic and Communications
  Engineering Technology/Technician, A
Engineering, A
Horticultural Science, A
Industrial Technology/Technician, A
International Business/Trade/Commerce, A
Liberal Arts and Sciences Studies and
  Humanities, A
Mechanical Engineering/Mechanical
  Technology/Technician, A
Ornamental Horticulture, A

ST. EDWARD'S UNIVERSITY

Accounting, BM
Art Teacher Education, B
Art/Art Studies, General, B
Biochemistry, B
Bioinformatics, B
Biology Teacher Education, B
Biology/Biological Sciences, B
Business Administration and Management, B
Chemistry, B
Communication and Media Studies, B
Computer and Information Sciences, B
Computer Art and Design, M
Computer Science, B
Conflict Resolution and Mediation/Peace Studies, O
Counseling Psychology, M
Criminal Justice/Safety Studies, B
Criminology, B
Drama and Dance Teacher Education, B
Drama and Dramatics/Theatre Arts, B
Economics, B
English Composition, B
English Language and Literature, B
Entrepreneurship/Entrepreneurial Studies, BMO
Ethics, M
Finance, B
Finance and Banking, MO
Forensic Science and Technology, B
Graphic Design, B
History, B
History Teacher Education, B
Human Resources Management and Services, MO
Human Services, MO
International Business/Trade/Commerce, BMO
International Relations and Affairs, B
Kinesiology and Exercise Science, B
Latin American Studies, B
Liberal Arts and Sciences Studies and
  Humanities, B
Liberal Studies, MO
Management, MO
Management Information Systems and
  Services, MO
Marketing, MO
Marketing/Marketing Management, B
Mathematics, B

Mathematics Teacher Education, B
Multi-/Interdisciplinary Studies, B
Organizational Management, M
Parks, Recreation, Leisure and Fitness Studies, B
Philosophy, B
Photography, B
Physical Education Teaching and Coaching, B
Political Science and Government, B
Psychology, B
Religious Education, B
Social Studies Teacher Education, B
Social Work, B
Sociology, B
Spanish Language and Literature, B
Spanish Language Teacher Education, B
Sport and Fitness Administration/Management, O
Teacher Education and Professional
  Development, Specific Subject Areas, B

ST. MARY'S UNIVERSITY OF SAN ANTONIO

Accounting, BM
Art Teacher Education, B
Biochemistry, B
Biology/Biological Sciences, B
Business Administration and Management, B
Business Administration, Management and
  Operations, MO
Business Teacher Education, B
Chemistry, B
Clinical Psychology, M
Communication and Media Studies, M
Communication Studies/Speech Communication
  and Rhetoric, B
Community Psychology, M
Computer Engineering, BM
Computer Science, BMO
Counseling Psychology, DO
Counselor Education/School Counseling and
  Guidance Services, MD
Criminal Justice/Law Enforcement Administration, B
Criminology, B
Economics, B
Education, BMO
Educational Leadership and Administration, MO
Electrical Engineering, M
Electrical, Electronics and Communications
  Engineering, B
Engineering, B
Engineering and Applied Sciences, MO
Engineering Management, M
Engineering Science, B
English, M
English Language and Literature, B
Finance, B
Finance and Banking, M
French Language and Literature, B
Geology/Earth Science, B
Health and Physical Education, B
History, B
Human Resources Management/Personnel
  Administration, B
Human Services, MDO
Industrial and Organizational Psychology, M
Industrial Engineering, B
Industrial/Management Engineering, MO
Information Science/Studies, BM
International Affairs, MO
International Business/Trade/Commerce, BM
Kinesiology and Exercise Science, B
Law and Legal Studies, PO
Marketing/Marketing Management, B
Marriage and Family Therapy/Counseling, MDO
Mass Communication/Media Studies, B
Mathematics, B
Music, B
Operations Research, M
Pastoral Studies/Counseling, M
Philosophy, B
Physics, B
Political Science and Government, BMO
Pre-Dentistry Studies, B
Psychology, BM
Public Administration, MO
Reading Teacher Education, BM
Sales, Distribution and Marketing Operations, B

School Psychology, M
Social Studies Teacher Education, B
Sociology, B
Software Engineering, M
Spanish Language and Literature, B
Speech and Rhetorical Studies, B
Statistics, B
Substance Abuse/Addiction Counseling, MO
Taxation, M
Theology and Religious Vocations, MO
Theology/Theological Studies, B

ST. PHILIP'S COLLEGE

Accounting, A
Administrative Assistant and Secretarial Science, A
Aircraft Powerplant Technology/Technician, A
Airframe Mechanics and Aircraft Maintenance
   Technology/Technician, A
Art/Art Studies, General, A
Autobody/Collision and Repair
   Technology/Technician, A
Automobile/Automotive Mechanics
   Technology/Technician, A
Biology/Biological Sciences, A
Biomedical Technology/Technician, A
Building/Construction
   Finishing, Management, and Inspection, A
Business Administration and Management, A
CAD/CADD Drafting and/or Design
   Technology/Technician, A
Chemistry, A
Clinical/Medical Laboratory Technician, A
Communications Technology/Technician, A
Computer and Information Systems Security, A
Computer Systems Networking and
   Telecommunications, A
Computer Technology/Computer Systems
   Technology, A
Construction Engineering Technology/Technician, A
Criminal Justice/Law Enforcement Administration, A
Culinary Arts/Chef Training, A
Data Entry/Microcomputer Applications, A
Diesel Mechanics Technology/Technician, A
Drama and Dramatics/Theatre Arts, A
Dramatic/Theatre Arts and Stagecraft, A
Early Childhood Education and Teaching, A
E-Commerce/Electronic Commerce, A
Economics, A
Education, A
Electrical/Electronics Equipment Installation and
   Repair, A
Electromechanical Technology/Electromechanical
   Engineering Technology, A
English Language and Literature, A
Environmental Sciences, A
Geology/Earth Science, A
Health Information/Medical Records
   Technology/Technician, A
Heating, Air Conditioning, Ventilation and
   Refrigeration Maintenance
   Technology/Technician, A
History, A
Home Furnishings and Equipment Installers, A
Hotel/Motel Administration/Management, A
Interior Architecture, A
Interior Design, A
Kinesiology and Exercise Science, A
Leatherworking and Upholstery, A
Legal Administrative Assistant/Secretary, A
Liberal Arts and Sciences Studies and
   Humanities, A
Licensed Practical/Vocational Nurse Training, A
Mathematics, A
Medical Administrative Assistant/Secretary, A
Medical Radiologic Technology/Science - Radiation
   Therapist, A
Music, A
Occupational Therapist Assistant, A
Philosophy, A
Physical Therapist Assistant, A
Political Science and Government, A
Pre-Dentistry Studies, A
Pre-Engineering, A
Pre-Law Studies, A
Pre-Medicine/Pre-Medical Studies, A
Pre-Nursing Studies, A

Pre-Pharmacy Studies, A
Psychology, A
Respiratory Care Therapy/Therapist, A
Restaurant/Food Services Management, A
Social Work, A
Sociology, A
Spanish Language and Literature, A
Speech and Rhetorical Studies, A
System, Networking, and LAN/WAN
   Management/Manager, A
Teacher Assistant/Aide, A
Tourism and Travel Services Management, A
Urban Studies/Affairs, A
Web/Multimedia Management and Webmaster, A
Welding Technology/Welder, A

SAM HOUSTON STATE UNIVERSITY

Accounting, B
Advertising, B
Agribusiness, B
Agricultural Business and Management, B
Agricultural Mechanization, B
Agricultural Sciences, M
Agricultural Teacher Education, B
Agriculture, B
Animal Sciences, B
Art Teacher Education, B
Art/Art Studies, General, B
Biological and Biomedical Sciences, M
Biological and Physical Sciences, B
Biology/Biological Sciences, B
Building/Construction
   Finishing, Management, and Inspection, B
Business Administration and Management, B
Business Administration, Management and
   Operations, M
Business Teacher Education, B
Business/Commerce, B
Business/Managerial Economics, B
Chemistry, BM
Clinical Laboratory Science/Medical
   Technology/Technologist, B
Clinical Psychology, BMD
Commercial and Advertising Art, B
Community Health Services/Liaison/Counseling, B
Computational Sciences, M
Computer and Information Sciences, B
Computer Science, M
Conducting, B
Construction Engineering Technology/Technician, B
Corrections, B
Corrections and Criminal Justice, B
Counseling Psychology, B
Counselor Education/School Counseling and
   Guidance Services, BMD
Criminal Justice/Law Enforcement Administration, B
Criminal Justice/Police Science, B
Criminal Justice/Safety Studies, B
Criminology, MD
Curriculum and Instruction, B
Dance, BM
Digital Communication and Media/Multimedia, B
Drafting and Design Technology/Technician, B
Drama and Dramatics/Theatre Arts, B
Early Childhood Education and Teaching, M
Education, B
Educational Administration and Supervision, M
Educational Leadership and Administration, D
Electrical, Electronic and Communications
   Engineering Technology/Technician, B
Elementary Education and Teaching, M
English, M
English Language and Literature, B
English/Language Arts Teacher Education, B
Environmental Studies, B
Family and Consumer Sciences/Home Economics
   Teacher Education, B
Family and Consumer Sciences/Human
   Sciences, BM
Fashion Merchandising, B
Finance, B
Finance and Banking, M
Fine Arts and Art Studies, M
Fine/Studio Arts, B
Foods, Nutrition, and Wellness Studies, B
Foreign Language Teacher Education, B

Forensic Psychology, B
Forensic Science and Technology, BM
French Language and Literature, B
Geography, B
Geology/Earth Science, B
German Language and Literature, B
Health and Physical Education/Fitness, B
Health Teacher Education, B
History, BM
Horticultural Science, B
Human Resources Management/Personnel
   Administration, B
Humanities/Humanistic Studies, MD
Industrial Education, M
Industrial Technology/Technician, B
Industrial/Management Engineering, M
Information Science/Studies, M
Interior Design, B
International Business/Trade/Commerce, B
Journalism, B
Kinesiology and Exercise Science, B
Kinesiology and Movement Studies, M
Library Science, M
Marketing/Marketing Management, B
Mathematics, BM
Mathematics Teacher Education, B
Multi-/Interdisciplinary Studies, B
Music, BM
Music Performance, B
Music Teacher Education, BM
Music Therapy/Therapist, B
Operations Management and Supervision, B
Painting, B
Performance, M
Philosophy, B
Photography, B
Physical Education Teaching and Coaching, B
Physician Assistant, B
Physics, B
Political Science and Government, BM
Pre-Dentistry Studies, B
Pre-Law Studies, B
Pre-Medicine/Pre-Medical Studies, B
Pre-Nursing Studies, B
Pre-Pharmacy Studies, B
Psychology, BMD
Public Administration, M
Public Relations/Image Management, B
Radio and Television, B
Reading Teacher Education, BM
Respiratory Care Therapy/Therapist, B
School Psychology, M
Secondary Education and Teaching, M
Sociology, BM
Spanish Language and Literature, B
Special Education and Teaching, M
Speech and Rhetorical Studies, B
Statistics, BM
Technology Teacher Education/Industrial Arts
   Teacher Education, B

SAN ANTONIO COLLEGE

Biological and Physical Sciences, A
Business Administration and Management, A
Business Machine Repairer, A
Child Care and Support Services Management, A
Child Care Provider/Assistant, A
Child Development, A
Civil Engineering Technology/Technician, A
Commercial and Advertising Art, A
Computer Engineering Technology/Technician, A
Computer Graphics, A
Computer Programming, A
Computer Programming, Specific Applications, A
Computer
   Programming, Vendor/Product Certification, A
Computer Programming/Programmer, A
Computer/Information Technology Services
   Administration and Management, A
Corrections, A
Court Reporting/Court Reporter, A
Criminal Justice/Law Enforcement Administration, A
Criminal Justice/Police Science, A
Data Entry/Microcomputer Applications, A
Data Processing and Data Processing
   Technology/Technician, A

Dental Hygiene/Hygienist, A
Developmental and Child Psychology, A
Drafting and Design Technology/Technician, A
Electrical, Electronic and Communications
   Engineering Technology/Technician, A
Engineering Technology, A
Fire Science/Firefighting, A
Funeral Service and Mortuary Science, A
Industrial Technology/Technician, A
Legal Administrative Assistant/Secretary, A
Liberal Arts and Sciences Studies and
   Humanities, A
Mechanical Engineering/Mechanical
   Technology/Technician, A
Medical/Clinical Assistant, A
Metal and Jewelry Arts, A
Nursing - Registered Nurse Training, A
Psychology, A
Public Administration, A
Radio and Television, A
Real Estate, A
Speech Teacher Education, A
System Administration/Administrator, A
Web Page, Digital/Multimedia and Information
   Resources Design, A
Word Processing, A

SCHREINER UNIVERSITY

Accounting, B
Biochemistry, B
Biology/Biological Sciences, B
Business/Commerce, B
Chemistry, B
Comparative Literature, B
Drama and Dramatics/Theatre Arts, B
Early Childhood Education and Teaching, B
Education, BM
Elementary Education and Teaching, B
Engineering, B
English Language and Literature, B
English/Language Arts Teacher Education, B
Graphic Design, B
History, B
History Teacher Education, B
Humanities/Humanistic Studies, B
Kinesiology and Exercise Science, B
Law and Legal Studies, B
Liberal Arts and Sciences Studies and
   Humanities, AB
Management Information Systems and Services, B
Mathematics, B
Mathematics Teacher Education, B
Music, B
Physical Education Teaching and Coaching, B
Political Science and Government, B
Pre-Dentistry Studies, B
Pre-Engineering, A
Pre-Law Studies, B
Pre-Medicine/Pre-Medical Studies, B
Psychology, B
Religion/Religious Studies, B
Teacher Education and Professional
   Development, Specific Subject Areas, B

SOUTH PLAINS COLLEGE

Accounting, A
Administrative Assistant and Secretarial Science, A
Advertising, A
Agricultural Economics, A
Agriculture, A
Agronomy and Crop Science, A
Art/Art Studies, General, A
Audio Engineering, A
Automobile/Automotive Mechanics
   Technology/Technician, A
Biological and Physical Sciences, A
Biology/Biological Sciences, A
Business Administration and Management, A
Carpentry/Carpenter, A
Chemistry, A
Child Development, A
Commercial and Advertising Art, A
Computer Engineering Technology/Technician, A
Computer Programming/Programmer, A
Computer Science, A
Consumer Merchandising/Retailing Management, A

Cosmetology/Cosmetologist, A
Criminal Justice/Law Enforcement Administration, A
Criminal Justice/Police Science, A
Data Processing and Data Processing
   Technology/Technician, A
Developmental and Child Psychology, A
Dietetics/Dieticians, A
Drafting and Design Technology/Technician, A
Education, A
Electrical, Electronic and Communications
   Engineering Technology/Technician, A
Engineering, A
Fashion Merchandising, A
Fire Science/Firefighting, A
Health Information/Medical Records
   Administration/Administrator, A
Health/Health Care Administration/Management, A
Heating, Air Conditioning, Ventilation and
   Refrigeration Maintenance
   Technology/Technician, A
Industrial Radiologic Technology/Technician, A
Journalism, A
Legal Administrative Assistant/Secretary, A
Liberal Arts and Sciences Studies and
   Humanities, A
Licensed Practical/Vocational Nurse Training, A
Machine Tool Technology/Machinist, A
Marketing/Marketing Management, A
Mass Communication/Media Studies, A
Medical Administrative Assistant/Secretary, A
Mental Health/Rehabilitation, A
Music, A
Nursing - Registered Nurse Training, A
Petroleum Technology/Technician, A
Physical Education Teaching and Coaching, A
Physical Therapy/Therapist, A
Pre-Engineering, A
Real Estate, A
Respiratory Care Therapy/Therapist, A
Social Work, A
Special Products Marketing Operations, A
Surgical Technology/Technologist, A
Telecommunications Technology/Technician, A
Welding Technology/Welder, A

SOUTH TEXAS COLLEGE

Accounting, A
Automobile/Automotive Mechanics
   Technology/Technician, A
Behavioral Sciences, A
Business Administration and Management, A
Clinical Laboratory Science/Medical
   Technology/Technologist, A
Computer Science, A
Computer Typography and Composition Equipment
   Operator, A
Developmental and Child Psychology, A
Education, A
Emergency Medical Technology/Technician (EMT
   Paramedic), A
Heating, Air Conditioning, Ventilation and
   Refrigeration Maintenance
   Technology/Technician, A
Heavy Equipment Maintenance
   Technology/Technician, A
Hospitality Administration/Management, A
Hotel/Motel Administration/Management, A
Human Services, A
Industrial Radiologic Technology/Technician, A
Industrial Technology/Technician, A
Information Science/Studies, A
Interdisciplinary Studies, A
Legal Administrative Assistant/Secretary, A
Legal Assistant/Paralegal, A
Liberal Arts and Sciences Studies and
   Humanities, A
Machine Tool Technology/Machinist, A
Nursing - Registered Nurse Training, A
Occupational Therapy/Therapist, A
Plastics Engineering Technology/Technician, A

SOUTHERN METHODIST UNIVERSITY

Accounting, BM
Advertising, B
African-American/Black Studies, B
Anthropology, BMD

Applied Economics, BM
Applied Mathematics, MD
Applied Science and Technology, MD
Art History, Criticism and Conservation, BM
Art/Art Studies, General, B
Audiology/Audiologist and Speech-Language
   Pathology/Pathologist, B
Biochemistry, B
Biological and Biomedical Sciences, MD
Biology/Biological Sciences, B
Broadcast Journalism, B
Business Administration and Management, B
Business Administration, Management and
   Operations, MO
Business/Commerce, B
Chemistry, BMD
Civil Engineering, BMD
Clinical Psychology, MD
Composition, M
Computational Sciences, MD
Computer Engineering, BMD
Computer Science, BMD
Counseling Psychology, M
Dance, BM
Drama and Dramatics/Theatre Arts, B
Econometrics and Quantitative Economics, B
Economics, BMDO
Education, M
Electrical Engineering, MD
Electrical, Electronics and Communications
   Engineering, B
Elementary Education and Teaching, B
Engineering and Applied Sciences, MD
Engineering Management, M
English, M
English Language and Literature, B
Environmental Engineering
   Technology/Environmental Technology, MD
Environmental Sciences, M
Environmental Studies, B
Environmental/Environmental Health Engineering, B
European Studies/Civilization, B
Facilities Planning and Management, M
Film, Television, and Video Production, M
Film/Cinema Studies, B
Film/Video and Photographic Arts, B
Finance, B
Financial Planning and Services, B
Fine Arts and Art Studies, M
Fine/Studio Arts, B
Foreign Languages and Literatures, B
French Language and Literature, B
Geology/Earth Science, BMD
Geophysics and Seismology, BMD
German Language and Literature, B
German Studies, B
Hispanic-American, Puerto Rican, and Mexican-
   American/Chicano Studies, B
History, BMD
Humanities/Humanistic Studies, B
Information Science/Studies, MD
Interdisciplinary Studies, M
International Relations and Affairs, B
International/Global Studies, B
Italian Studies, B
Journalism, B
Latin American Studies, B
Law and Legal Studies, MDPO
Management Science, B
Manufacturing Engineering, M
Marketing/Marketing Management, B
Mass Communication/Media Studies, B
Mathematics, BMD
Mechanical Engineering, BMD
Medieval and Renaissance Studies, BM
Multilingual and Multicultural Education, M
Music, BMO
Music History, Literature, and Theory, M
Music Teacher Education, M
Music Theory and Composition, BM
Music Therapy/Therapist, B
Operations Research, MD
Organizational Behavior Studies, B
Performance, MO
Philosophy, B
Physics, BMD

Piano and Organ, B
Political Science and Government, B
Psychology, BMD
Public Policy Analysis, B
Public Relations/Image Management, B
Radio and Television, B
Real Estate, B
Religion/Religious Studies, BMD
Russian Language and Literature, B
Russian Studies, B
Sacred Music, M
Social Sciences, B
Sociology, B
Software Engineering, M
Spanish and Iberian Studies, B
Spanish Language and Literature, B
Speech-Language Pathology/Pathologist, B
Statistics, BMD
Systems Engineering, M
Systems Science and Theory, MD
Taxation, M
Telecommunications, M
Telecommunications Technology/Technician, B
Theater, M
Theology and Religious Vocations, MDP

SOUTHWEST TEXAS JUNIOR COLLEGE

Agricultural Mechanization, A
Automobile/Automotive Mechanics
    Technology/Technician, A
Avionics Maintenance Technology/Technician, A
Biological and Physical Sciences, A
Business Administration and Management, A
Computer Engineering Technology/Technician, A
Cosmetology/Cosmetologist, A
Criminal Justice/Law Enforcement Administration, A
Data Processing and Data Processing
    Technology/Technician, A
Education, A
Engineering, A
Farm/Farm and Ranch Management, A
Liberal Arts and Sciences Studies and
    Humanities, A
Teacher Assistant/Aide, A

SOUTHWESTERN ADVENTIST UNIVERSITY

Accounting, BM
Administrative Assistant and Secretarial Science, AB
Biology/Biological Sciences, B
Broadcast Journalism, B
Business Administration and Management, B
Business Administration, Management and
    Operations, M
Chemistry, B
Clinical Laboratory Science/Medical
    Technology/Technologist, B
Computer Science, B
Criminal Justice/Law Enforcement Administration, B
Education, M
Elementary Education and Teaching, BM
English Language and Literature, B
Health and Physical Education, B
Health/Health Care Administration/Management, B
History, B
Information Science/Studies, AB
International Business/Trade/Commerce, B
International Relations and Affairs, B
Journalism, B
Kinesiology and Exercise Science, B
Mass Communication/Media Studies, B
Mathematics, B
Music, B
Nursing - Registered Nurse Training, AB
Physics, B
Psychology, B
Religion/Religious Studies, B
Social Sciences, B

Social Work, B

SOUTHWESTERN ASSEMBLIES OF GOD UNIVERSITY

Accounting, B
Ancient Near Eastern and Biblical
    Languages, Literatures, and Linguistics, B
Bible/Biblical Studies, AB
Business Administration and Management, AB
Business/Commerce, A
Communication Studies/Speech Communication
    and Rhetoric, A
Counseling Psychology, MO
Curriculum and Instruction, M
Divinity/Ministry (BD, MDiv.), B
Education, AMO
Educational Administration and Supervision, M
Elementary Education and Teaching, B
General Studies, AB
Missions/Missionary Studies and Missiology, B
Music, AB
Pastoral Studies/Counseling, B
Psychology, A
Religion/Religious Studies, B
Religious Education, BM
Religious/Sacred Music, B
Secondary Education and Teaching, B
Social Sciences, A
Theology and Religious Vocations, MO

SOUTHWESTERN CHRISTIAN COLLEGE

Accounting, A
Applied Mathematics, A
Bible/Biblical Studies, AB
Business Administration and Management, A
Computer Science, A
Developmental and Child Psychology, A
Humanities/Humanistic Studies, A
Liberal Arts and Sciences Studies and
    Humanities, A
Nursing - Registered Nurse Training, B
Pre-Engineering, A
Psychology, A
Religion/Religious Studies, AB

SOUTHWESTERN UNIVERSITY

Accounting, B
American/United States Studies/Civilization, B
Animal Behavior and Ethology, B
Animal Sciences, B
Anthropology, B
Art History, Criticism and Conservation, B
Art Teacher Education, B
Art/Art Studies, General, B
Biochemistry, B
Biology/Biological Sciences, B
Business Administration and Management, B
Chemistry, B
Classics and Classical
    Languages, Literatures, and Linguistics, B
Communication Studies/Speech Communication
    and Rhetoric, B
Comparative Literature, B
Computational Mathematics, B
Computer Science, B
Drama and Dramatics/Theatre Arts, B
Economics, B
English Language and Literature, B
Environmental Studies, B
Fine/Studio Arts, B
French Language and Literature, B
German Language and Literature, B
History, B
International Relations and Affairs, B
Kinesiology and Exercise Science, B
Latin American Studies, B
Latin Language and Literature, B
Mass Communication/Media Studies, B
Mathematics, B
Music, B
Philosophy, B
Physical Sciences, B
Physics, B
Political Science and Government, B
Psychology, B

Religion/Religious Studies, B
Science Teacher Education/General Science
    Teacher Education, B
Social Sciences, B
Social Studies Teacher Education, B
Sociology, B
Spanish Language and Literature, B
Speech-Language Pathology/Pathologist, B
Women's Studies, B

STEPHEN F. AUSTIN STATE UNIVERSITY

Accounting, BM
Agribusiness, B
Agricultural Education, M
Agricultural Mechanization, B
Agricultural Production Operations, B
Agriculture, B
Agronomy and Crop Science, B
Animal Sciences, B
Applied Horticulture/Horticultural Operations, B
Art History, Criticism and Conservation, B
Art/Art Studies, General, B
Athletic Training and Sports Medicine, M
Audiology/Audiologist and Hearing Sciences, B
Audiology/Audiologist and Speech-Language
    Pathology/Pathologist, B
Biological and Biomedical Sciences, M
Biology/Biological Sciences, B
BioTechnology, M
Business Administration and Management, B
Business Administration, Management and
    Operations, M
Business/Commerce, B
Business/Managerial Economics, B
Chemistry, BM
Clinical Laboratory Science/Medical
    Technology/Technologist, B
Communication and Media Studies, M
Communication Disorders, M
Communication Studies/Speech Communication
    and Rhetoric, B
Community Health Services/Liaison/Counseling, B
Computer and Information Sciences, B
Computer Science, M
Corrections, B
Counselor Education/School Counseling and
    Guidance Services, M
Criminal Justice/Police Science, B
Criminal Justice/Safety Studies, B
Dance, B
Data Processing and Data Processing
    Technology/Technician, B
Design and Applied Arts, M
Drama and Dramatics/Theatre Arts, B
Early Childhood Education and Teaching, M
Economics, B
Education, MD
Educational Leadership and Administration, MD
Elementary Education and Teaching, M
English, M
English Language and Literature, B
Environmental Sciences, M
Environmental Studies, B
Family and Consumer Sciences/Human Sciences, B
Fashion Merchandising, B
Finance, B
Fine Arts and Art Studies, M
Foods, Nutrition, and Wellness Studies, B
Forest Management/Forest Resources
    Management, B
Forestry, BMD
French Language and Literature, B
Geography, B
Geology/Earth Science, BM
Gerontology, B
Health and Physical Education, B
History, BM
Home Economics, M
Horticultural Science, B
Hospitality Administration/Management, B
Human Development and Family Studies, B
Humanities/Humanistic Studies, B
Interdisciplinary Studies, BM
Interior Architecture, B
International Business/Trade/Commerce, B

Journalism, B
Kinesiology and Movement Studies, M
Legal Assistant/Paralegal, B
Management, M
Marketing, M
Marketing/Marketing Management, B
Mass Communication/Media Studies, M
Mathematics, BM
Mathematics Teacher Education, M
Multi-/Interdisciplinary Studies, B
Music, BM
Music Performance, B
Music Teacher Education, B
Natural Resources and Conservation, B
Nursing - Registered Nurse Training, B
Office Management and Supervision, B
Painting, M
Physics, BM
Political Science and Government, B
Poultry Science, B
Psychology, BM
Public Administration, BM
Radio and Television, B
Rehabilitation Therapy, B
School Psychology, M
Sculpture, M
Secondary Education and Teaching, MD
Social Sciences, B
Social Work, BM
Sociology, B
Spanish Language and Literature, B
Special Education and Teaching, M
Speech and Rhetorical Studies, B
Statistics, M
Wildlife and Wildlands Science and Management, B

SUL ROSS STATE UNIVERSITY

Accounting, B
Administrative Assistant and Secretarial Science, AB
Agricultural Business and Management, B
Animal Health, B
Animal Sciences, ABM
Art Education, M
Art History, Criticism and Conservation, M
Art/Art Studies, General, B
Biological and Biomedical Sciences, M
Biology/Biological Sciences, B
Business Administration and Management, B
Business Administration, Management and
   Operations, M
Chemistry, BM
Counselor Education/School Counseling and
   Guidance Services, M
Criminal Justice/Law Enforcement Administration, B
Criminology, M
Drama and Dramatics/Theatre Arts, B
Education, M
Educational Administration and Supervision, M
Educational Measurement and Evaluation, M
Elementary Education and Teaching, BM
English, M
English Language and Literature, B
Environmental Studies, B
Equestrian/Equine Studies, B
Fine Arts and Art Studies, M
Fish, Game and Wildlife Management, M
Geology/Earth Science, BM
Hispanic-American, Puerto Rican, and Mexican-
   American/Chicano Studies, B
History, BM
Industrial Education, M
International Trade, M
Management, M
Mass Communication/Media Studies, B
Mathematics, B
Multilingual and Multicultural Education, M
Music, B
Nursing - Registered Nurse Training, A
Physical Education Teaching and Coaching, BM
Political Science and Government, BM
Pre-Dentistry Studies, B
Pre-Law Studies, B
Pre-Medicine/Pre-Medical Studies, B
Pre-Veterinary Studies, B
Psychology, BM
Public Administration, M

Range Science and Management, BM
Reading Teacher Education, M
Secondary Education and Teaching, M
Social Sciences, B
Spanish Language and Literature, B
Technology Education/Industrial Arts, B
Veterinary/Animal Health Technology/Technician and
   Veterinary Assistant, A
Wildlife and Wildlands Science and Management, B

TARLETON STATE UNIVERSITY

Accounting, BM
Agricultural and Domestic Animals Services, B
Agricultural Economics, B
Agricultural Production Operations, B
Agricultural Sciences, M
Agricultural Teacher Education, B
Agriculture, Agriculture Operations and Related
   Sciences, B
Agronomy and Crop Science, B
Animal Sciences, BM
Animal/Livestock Husbandry and Production, B
Art/Art Studies, General, B
Aviation/Airway Management and Operations, B
Biological and Biomedical Sciences, M
Biology/Biological Sciences, B
Business Administration and Management, B
Business Administration, Management and
   Operations, M
Business/Commerce, B
Chemistry, B
Clinical Laboratory Science/Medical
   Technology/Technologist, B
Computer and Information Sciences, B
Counseling Psychology, M
Counselor Education/School Counseling and
   Guidance Services, BM
Criminal Justice/Safety Studies, B
Criminology, M
Curriculum and Instruction, BM
Drama and Dramatics/Theatre Arts, B
Economics, BM
Education, BMDO
Educational Administration and Supervision, MO
Educational Leadership and Administration, BD
Elementary Education and Teaching, B
Engineering Physics, B
English, M
English Language and Literature, B
Environmental Sciences, M
Environmental Studies, B
Family and Consumer Sciences/Human Sciences, B
Farm/Farm and Ranch Management, B
Finance, B
Finance and Banking, M
Fine/Studio Arts, B
Geology/Earth Science, B
Health Education, MO
Histologic Technology/Histotechnologist, A
History, BM
Horticultural Science, B
Human Nutrition, B
Human Resources Management/Personnel
   Administration, B
Hydrology and Water Resources Science, B
Industrial Production Technologies/Technicians, B
Interdisciplinary Studies, B
International Agriculture, B
International Business/Trade/Commerce, B
Junior High/Intermediate/Middle School Education
   and Teaching, B
Kinesiology and Exercise Science, B
Liberal Arts and Sciences Studies and
   Humanities, B
Management Information Systems and
   Services, BM
Manufacturing Technology/Technician, B
Marketing, M
Mathematics, BM
Multi-/Interdisciplinary Studies, B
Music, B
Music Teacher Education, B
Nursing - Registered Nurse Training, B
Office Management and Supervision, B
Ornamental Horticulture, B
Physical Education Teaching and Coaching, BMO

Physical Therapy/Therapist, B
Physics, B
Political Science and Government, BM
Pre-Dentistry Studies, B
Pre-Medicine/Pre-Medical Studies, B
Pre-Pharmacy Studies, B
Pre-Veterinary Studies, B
Psychology, B
Range Science and Management, B
Reading Teacher Education, O
School Psychology, M
Science Teacher Education/General Science
   Teacher Education, B
Secondary Education and Teaching, BMO
Social Work, B
Sociology, B
Spanish Language and Literature, B
Special Education and Teaching, O
Speech and Rhetorical Studies, B
Teacher Education, Multiple Levels, B
Teaching English as a Second or Foreign
   Language/ESL Language Instructor, B
Technical and Business Writing, B
Technology Education/Industrial Arts, B
Wildlife and Wildlands Science and Management, B

TARRANT COUNTY COLLEGE DISTRICT

Accounting, A
Administrative Assistant and Secretarial Science, A
Architectural Engineering Technology/Technician, A
Automobile/Automotive Mechanics
   Technology/Technician, A
Avionics Maintenance Technology/Technician, A
Business Administration and Management, A
Clinical Laboratory Science/Medical
   Technology/Technologist, A
Clinical/Medical Laboratory Technician, A
Computer Programming/Programmer, A
Computer Science, A
Construction Engineering Technology/Technician, A
Consumer Merchandising/Retailing Management, A
Criminal Justice/Law Enforcement Administration, A
Dental Hygiene/Hygienist, A
Developmental and Child Psychology, A
Dietetics/Dieticians, A
Drafting and Design Technology/Technician, A
Educational/Instructional Media Design, A
Electrical, Electronic and Communications
   Engineering Technology/Technician, A
Electromechanical Technology/Electromechanical
   Engineering Technology, A
Emergency Medical Technology/Technician (EMT
   Paramedic), A
Fashion Merchandising, A
Fire Science/Firefighting, A
Food Technology and Processing, A
Graphic and Printing Equipment Operator
   Production, A
Health Information/Medical Records
   Administration/Administrator, A
Heating, Air Conditioning, Ventilation and
   Refrigeration Maintenance
   Technology/Technician, A
Horticultural Science, A
Industrial Radiologic Technology/Technician, A
Legal Assistant/Paralegal, A
Liberal Arts and Sciences Studies and
   Humanities, A
Machine Tool Technology/Machinist, A
Marketing/Marketing Management, A
Mechanical Engineering/Mechanical
   Technology/Technician, A
Mental Health/Rehabilitation, A
Nursing - Registered Nurse Training, A
Physical Therapy/Therapist, A
Quality Control Technology/Technician, A
Respiratory Care Therapy/Therapist, A
Sign Language Interpretation and Translation, A
Surgical Technology/Technologist, A
Welding Technology/Welder, A

TEMPLE COLLEGE

Administrative Assistant and Secretarial Science, A
Art/Art Studies, General, A

Automobile/Automotive Mechanics Technology/Technician, A
Business Administration and Management, A
Clinical Laboratory Science/Medical Technology/Technologist, A
Clinical/Medical Laboratory Technician, A
Computer Programming/Programmer, A
Computer Science, A
Criminal Justice/Law Enforcement Administration, A
Criminal Justice/Police Science, A
Data Processing and Data Processing Technology/Technician, A
Dental Hygiene/Hygienist, A
Drafting and Design Technology/Technician, A
Electrical, Electronic and Communications Engineering Technology/Technician, A
Industrial Technology/Technician, A
Liberal Arts and Sciences Studies and Humanities, A
Licensed Practical/Vocational Nurse Training, A
Medical Administrative Assistant/Secretary, A
Nursing - Registered Nurse Training, A
Respiratory Care Therapy/Therapist, A

TEXARKANA COLLEGE

Administrative Assistant and Secretarial Science, A
Agriculture, A
Art/Art Studies, General, A
Automobile/Automotive Mechanics Technology/Technician, A
Biology/Biological Sciences, A
Business Administration and Management, A
Chemistry, A
Computer Programming/Programmer, A
Computer Science, A
Consumer Merchandising/Retailing Management, A
Cosmetology/Cosmetologist, A
Criminal Justice/Law Enforcement Administration, A
Criminal Justice/Police Science, A
Data Entry/Microcomputer Applications, A
Data Processing and Data Processing Technology/Technician, A
Drafting and Design Technology/Technician, A
Drama and Dramatics/Theatre Arts, A
Electrical, Electronic and Communications Engineering Technology/Technician, A
Emergency Medical Technology/Technician (EMT Paramedic), A
Engineering, A
Finance, A
Heating, Air Conditioning, Ventilation and Refrigeration Maintenance Technology/Technician, A
Information Technology, A
Journalism, A
Liberal Arts and Sciences Studies and Humanities, A
Licensed Practical/Vocational Nurse Training, A
Mathematics, A
Music, A
Nursing - Registered Nurse Training, A
Physics, A
Real Estate, A
Substance Abuse/Addiction Counseling, A
Welding Technology/Welder, A
Wood Science and Wood Products/Pulp and Paper Technology, A

TEXAS A&M INTERNATIONAL UNIVERSITY

Accounting, BM
Bilingual and Multilingual Education, B
Biological and Biomedical Sciences, M
Biology Teacher Education, B
Biology/Biological Sciences, B
Business Administration and Management, B
Business Administration, Management and Operations, M
Business/Managerial Economics, B
Chemistry, B
Communication Studies/Speech Communication and Rhetoric, B
Counseling Psychology, M
Criminal Justice/Safety Studies, B
Criminology, M
Curriculum and Instruction, M

Early Childhood Education and Teaching, M
Education, M
Educational Administration and Supervision, M
English, M
English Language and Literature, B
English/Language Arts Teacher Education, B
Finance, B
Finance and Banking, M
Health and Physical Education, B
History, BM
History Teacher Education, B
Information Science/Studies, B
Interdisciplinary Studies, M
International Trade, M
Kindergarten/PreSchool Education and Teaching, B
Management Information Systems and Services, M
Marketing/Marketing Management, B
Mathematics, BM
Mathematics Teacher Education, B
Multilingual and Multicultural Education, M
Nursing - Registered Nurse Training, B
Perioperative/Operating Room and Surgical Nurse/Nursing, B
Physical Education Teaching and Coaching, B
Physical Sciences, B
Physics, M
Political Science and Government, BM
Psychology, BM
Public Administration, M
Reading Teacher Education, BM
Science Teacher Education/General Science Teacher Education, B
Social Sciences, BM
Social Studies Teacher Education, B
Sociology, BM
Spanish Language and Literature, BM
Spanish Language Teacher Education, B
Special Education and Teaching, BM

TEXAS A&M UNIVERSITY

Accounting, BMD
Aerospace, Aeronautical and Astronautical Engineering, BMD
Agribusiness, B
Agricultural and Food Products Processing, B
Agricultural Animal Breeding, B
Agricultural Business and Management, B
Agricultural Economics, BMD
Agricultural Education, MD
Agricultural Engineering, MD
Agricultural Production Operations, B
Agricultural Sciences, MD
Agricultural/Biological Engineering and Bioengineering, B
Agricultural/Farm Supplies Retailing and Wholesaling, B
Agriculture, B
Agronomy and Crop Science, B
Agronomy and Soil Sciences, MD
American/United States Studies/Civilization, B
Anatomy, MD
Animal Sciences, BMD
Animal/Livestock Husbandry and Production, B
Anthropology, BMD
Applied Horticulture/Horticultural Operations, B
Applied Mathematics, B
Applied Physics, D
Aquaculture, B
Architecture, BMD
Atmospheric Sciences and Meteorology, B
Biochemistry, BMD
Bioengineering, MD
Biological and Biomedical Sciences, MD
Biology/Biological Sciences, B
Biomedical Engineering, MD
Biomedical Sciences, B
Biomedical/Medical Engineering, B
Biophysics, MD
Biopsychology, MD
BioTechnology, M
Botany/Plant Biology, BMD
Business Administration and Management, B
Business Administration, Management and Operations, M
Cartography, B
Cell Biology and Anatomy, D

Cell/Cellular and Molecular Biology, B
Chemical Engineering, BMD
Chemistry, BMD
Civil Engineering, BMD
Clinical Psychology, MD
Cognitive Sciences, MD
Communication and Media Studies, MD
Community Health Services/Liaison/Counseling, B
Computer Engineering, BMD
Computer Science, BMD
Construction Engineering and Management, MD
Construction Engineering Technology/Technician, B
Counseling Psychology, D
Counselor Education/School Counseling and Guidance Services, M
Curriculum and Instruction, BMD
Dairy Science, BM
Developmental Psychology, MD
Digital Communication and Media/Multimedia, B
Drama and Dramatics/Theatre Arts, B
Ecology, B
Economics, BMD
Education, MD
Education/Teaching of the Gifted and Talented, MD
Educational Administration and Supervision, MD
Educational Measurement and Evaluation, MD
Educational Media/Instructional Technology, M
Educational Psychology, MD
Electrical Engineering, MD
Electrical, Electronic and Communications Engineering Technology/Technician, B
Electrical, Electronics and Communications Engineering, B
Engineering and Applied Sciences, MD
Engineering Technology, B
English, MD
English as a Second Language, MD
English Education, MD
English Language and Literature, B
Entomology, BMD
Environmental Design/Architecture, B
Environmental Engineering Technology/Environmental Technology, MD
Environmental Sciences, B
Environmental Studies, B
Epidemiology, M
Farm/Farm and Ranch Management, B
Finance, B
Finance and Banking, MD
Fish, Game and Wildlife Management, MD
Fishing and Fisheries Sciences and Management, B
Food Science, B
Food Science and Technology, MD
Foods, Nutrition, and Wellness Studies, B
Forest Management/Forest Resources Management, B
Forestry, BMD
Foundations and Philosophy of Education, MD
French Language and Literature, B
Genetics, MD
Genomic Sciences, D
Geography, BMD
Geological and Earth Sciences/Geosciences, B
Geology/Earth Science, BMD
Geophysics and Seismology, BMD
Geotechnical Engineering, MD
German Language and Literature, B
Health and Physical Education, B
Health Education, MD
Health Physics/Radiological Health, M
History, BMD
Horticultural Science, BMD
Human Development, MD
Human Resources Development, MD
Human Resources Management and Services, M
Hydraulics and Fluid Power Technology, MD
Hydrology and Water Resources Science, MD
Industrial and Manufacturing Management, D
Industrial and Organizational Psychology, MD
Industrial Engineering, B
Industrial/Management Engineering, MD
Interdisciplinary Studies, B
International Affairs, M
International/Global Studies, B
Journalism, BM
Kinesiology and Movement Studies, MD

Landscape Architecture, BMD
Management, MD
Management Information Systems and
  Services, MD
Management Science, B
Manufacturing Technology/Technician, B
Marketing, MD
Marketing/Marketing Management, B
Materials Engineering, MD
Mathematics, BMD
Mathematics Teacher Education, MD
Mechanical Engineering, BMD
Mechanical Engineering/Mechanical
  Technology/Technician, B
Meteorology, MD
Microbiology, BMD
Molecular Biology, D
Molecular Genetics, B
Multi-/Interdisciplinary Studies, B
Multilingual and Multicultural Education, MD
Museology/Museum Studies, B
Music, B
Natural Resources and Conservation, BM
Neuroscience, MD
Nuclear Engineering, BMD
Nutritional Sciences, MD
Ocean Engineering, BMD
Oceanography, Chemical and Physical, MD
Ornamental Horticulture, B
Parasitology, M
Parks, Recreation and Leisure Facilities
  Management, B
Parks, Recreation, Leisure and Fitness Studies, B
Pathobiology, MD
Pathology/Experimental Pathology, MD
Petroleum Engineering, BMD
Philosophy, BMD
Physical Education Teaching and Coaching, MD
Physics, BMD
Physiology, MD
Plant Biology, MD
Plant Pathology/Phytopathology, MD
Plant Protection and Integrated Pest
  Management, B
Plant Sciences, MD
Political Science and Government, BMD
Poultry Science, BMD
Pre-Veterinary Studies, B
Project Management, MD
Psychology, BMD
Public Affairs, M
Public Health, MD
Public Relations, Advertising, and Applied
  Communication, B
Range Science and Management, BMD
Reading Teacher Education, MD
Real Estate, M
Recreation and Park Management, MD
Reproductive Biology, D
Russian Language and Literature, B
Sales, Distribution and Marketing Operations, B
School Psychology, MD
Science Teacher Education/General Science
  Teacher Education, MD
Social Psychology, MD
Social Studies Teacher Education, MD
Sociology, BMD
Spanish Language and Literature, BM
Special Education and Teaching, MD
Speech and Rhetorical Studies, B
Statistics, MD
Structural Engineering, MD
Tourism and Travel Services Management, B
Toxicology, MD
Transportation and Highway Engineering, MD
Urban and Regional Planning, MD
Urban Education and Leadership, MD
Urban Forestry, B
Urban Planning, M
Veterinary Medicine, MPO
Veterinary Sciences, MDO
Water Resources Engineering, MD
Wildlife and Wildlands Science and Management, B

Zoology/Animal Biology, BMD

TEXAS A&M UNIVERSITY-COMMERCE

Accounting, B
Administrative Assistant and Secretarial Science, B
Advertising, B
Agricultural Economics, B
Agricultural Education, M
Agricultural Sciences, M
Agricultural Teacher Education, B
Agriculture, B
Agronomy and Crop Science, B
Animal Sciences, B
Anthropology, B
Art History, Criticism and Conservation, BM
Art Teacher Education, B
Art/Art Studies, General, B
Biological and Biomedical Sciences, M
Biology/Biological Sciences, BM
Business Administration and Management, B
Business Administration, Management and
  Operations, M
Business Teacher Education, B
Chemistry, BM
Commercial and Advertising Art, B
Composition, M
Computer Science, BM
Construction Engineering, B
Counseling Psychology, MD
Counselor Education/School Counseling and
  Guidance Services, BMD
Criminal Justice/Law Enforcement Administration, B
Criminal Justice/Police Science, B
Curriculum and Instruction, D
Drama and Dramatics/Theatre Arts, B
Drawing, B
Early Childhood Education and Teaching, M
Economics, BM
Education, BMD
Educational Administration and Supervision, MD
Educational Media/Instructional Technology, M
Educational Psychology, D
Elementary Education and Teaching, BMD
English, MD
English Education, D
English Language and Literature, B
Finance, B
Fine Arts and Art Studies, M
French Language and Literature, B
Geography, B
Geology/Earth Science, B
Geosciences, M
Graphic and Printing Equipment Operator
  Production, B
Health Education, MD
Health Teacher Education, B
Higher Education/Higher Education
  Administration, MD
History, BM
Human Resources Management/Personnel
  Administration, B
Industrial Engineering, B
Industrial/Management Engineering, M
Information Science/Studies, B
Interdisciplinary Studies, B
Journalism, B
Kindergarten/PreSchool Education and Teaching, B
Kinesiology and Movement Studies, MD
Labor and Industrial Relations, B
Legal Administrative Assistant/Secretary, B
Liberal Arts and Sciences Studies and
  Humanities, B
Management Information Systems and Services, B
Management of Technology, M
Marketing/Marketing Management, B
Mathematics, BM
Music, BM
Music Teacher Education, BM
Music Theory and Composition, M
Performance, M
Photography, B
Physical Education Teaching and Coaching, BMD
Physics, BM
Piano and Organ, B
Political Science and Government, B
Psychology, BMD

Radio and Television, B
Reading Teacher Education, BM
Sculpture, B
Secondary Education and Teaching, BMD
Social Sciences, BM
Social Studies Teacher Education, M
Social Work, BM
Sociology, BM
Spanish Language and Literature, BMD
Special Education and Teaching, BMD
Speech and Rhetorical Studies, M
Technology Education/Industrial Arts, B
Theater, M
Trade and Industrial Teacher Education, B
Voice and Opera, B

TEXAS A&M UNIVERSITY-CORPUS CHRISTI

Accounting, BM
Art/Art Studies, General, B
Biological and Biomedical Sciences, M
Biology/Biological Sciences, B
Business Administration and Management, B
Business Administration, Management and
  Operations, M
Cartography, B
Chemistry, B
Clinical Laboratory Science/Medical
  Technology/Technologist, B
Communication Studies/Speech Communication
  and Rhetoric, B
Computer Science, BM
Counselor Education/School Counseling and
  Guidance Services, MD
Criminal Justice/Law Enforcement Administration, B
Curriculum and Instruction, M
Early Childhood Education and Teaching, M
Education, MD
Educational Administration and Supervision, M
Educational Leadership and Administration, D
Educational Media/Instructional Technology, M
Elementary Education and Teaching, M
Engineering Technology, B
English, M
English Language and Literature, B
Environmental Sciences, M
Environmental Studies, B
Finance, B
Fine Arts and Art Studies, M
Fine/Studio Arts, B
Geology/Earth Science, B
History, BM
Information Science/Studies, B
Interdisciplinary Studies, B
Management, M
Marketing/Marketing Management, B
Mathematics, B
Music, B
Nursing, M
Nursing - Registered Nurse Training, B
Nursing Administration, M
Physical Education Teaching and Coaching, B
Political Science and Government, B
Psychology, BM
Public Administration, M
Public Health (MPH, DPH), B
Reading Teacher Education, M
Secondary Education and Teaching, M
Sociology, B
Spanish Language and Literature, B
Special Education and Teaching, M
Survey Technology/Surveying, B
Trade and Industrial Teacher Education, B
Vocational and Technical Education, M

TEXAS A&M UNIVERSITY AT GALVESTON

Biological and Physical Sciences, B
Business Administration and Management, B
Marine Biology and Biological Oceanography, B
Marine Science/Merchant Marine Officer, B
Marine Sciences, M
Maritime Science, B
Multi-/Interdisciplinary Studies, B
Natural Resources and Conservation, B
Naval Architecture and Marine Engineering, B

Ocean Engineering, B
Oceanography, Chemical and Physical, B
Transportation and Materials Moving, B

TEXAS A&M UNIVERSITY-KINGSVILLE

Accounting, B
Adult and Continuing Education and Teaching, M
Agribusiness, M
Agricultural Business and Management, B
Agricultural Education, M
Agricultural Sciences, MD
Agricultural Teacher Education, B
Agriculture, B
Agronomy and Crop Science, B
Agronomy and Soil Sciences, MD
Animal Sciences, BM
Anthropology, B
Art/Art Studies, General, B
Bilingual and Multilingual Education, B
Biological and Biomedical Sciences, M
Biology/Biological Sciences, B
Business Administration and Management, B
Business Administration, Management and
    Operations, M
Business/Managerial Economics, B
Chemical Engineering, BM
Chemistry, BM
Child Development, B
Civil Engineering, BM
Communication Disorders, BM
Computer Science, BM
Counselor Education/School Counseling and
    Guidance Services, M
Criminology, B
Dietetics/Dieticians, B
Drama and Dramatics/Theatre Arts, B
Early Childhood Education and Teaching, M
Economics, B
Education, BMD
Educational Administration and Supervision, MD
Electrical Engineering, M
Electrical, Electronics and Communications
    Engineering, B
Elementary Education and Teaching, BM
Engineering and Applied Sciences, MD
English, M
English as a Second Language, M
English Language and Literature, B
Environmental Engineering
    Technology/Environmental Technology, MD
Environmental/Environmental Health Engineering, B
Family and Consumer Sciences/Home Economics
    Teacher Education, B
Family and Consumer Sciences/Human Sciences, B
Fashion Merchandising, B
Finance, B
Fine Arts and Art Studies, M
Fish, Game and Wildlife Management, MD
Food Science, B
Foods, Nutrition, and Wellness Studies, B
Foreign Language Teacher Education, M
Geography, B
Geology/Earth Science, BM
Gerontology, M
Health Education, M
Health Teacher Education, B
Higher Education/Higher Education
    Administration, D
History, BM
Home Economics, M
Horticultural Science, B
Hotel/Motel Administration/Management, B
Human Services, B
Industrial Engineering, B
Industrial Technology/Technician, B
Industrial/Management Engineering, M
Information Science/Studies, B
Interior Design, B
International Business/Trade/Commerce, B
Journalism, B
Kindergarten/PreSchool Education and Teaching, B
Kinesiology and Movement Studies, M
Marketing/Marketing Management, B
Mass Communication/Media Studies, B
Mathematics, BM
Mechanical Engineering, BM

Multilingual and Multicultural Education, MD
Music, B
Music Teacher Education, BM
Petroleum Engineering, BM
Physical Education Teaching and Coaching, B
Physics, B
Plant Sciences, MD
Political Science and Government, BM
Pre-Dentistry Studies, B
Pre-Law Studies, B
Pre-Medicine/Pre-Medical Studies, B
Pre-Veterinary Studies, B
Psychology, BM
Public Administration, B
Range Science and Management, BM
Reading Teacher Education, M
Real Estate, B
Secondary Education and Teaching, BM
Social Work, B
Sociology, BM
Spanish Language and Literature, BM
Special Education and Teaching, M
Speech and Rhetorical Studies, B
Wildlife and Wildlands Science and Management, B

TEXAS A&M UNIVERSITY SYSTEM HEALTH SCIENCE CENTER

Anatomy, D
Biochemistry, D
Biological and Biomedical Sciences, MDO
Cardiovascular Sciences, D
Dental and Oral Surgery, PO
Dental Hygiene/Hygienist, BM
Dentistry, P
Environmental and Occupational Health, M
Epidemiology, M
Genetics, D
Health Education, M
Health Services Administration, M
Immunology, D
Medical Microbiology and Bacteriology, D
Microbiology, D
Molecular Biology, D
Neurobiology and Neurophysiology, D
Neuroscience, D
Oral and Dental Sciences, MDO
Oral Biology, MD
Oral Pathology, MDO
Orthodontics, MO
Pathology/Experimental Pathology, DO
Pedodontics, MO
Periodontics, MO
Pharmacology, D
Physiology, D
Public Health, M
Toxicology, D
Virology, D

TEXAS A&M UNIVERSITY-TEXARKANA

Accounting, BM
Adult and Continuing Education and Teaching, M
Biology/Biological Sciences, B
Business Administration and Management, B
Business Administration, Management and
    Operations, M
Business/Commerce, B
Counseling Psychology, M
Criminal Justice/Safety Studies, B
Education, M
Educational Administration and Supervision, M
Elementary Education and Teaching, M
English Language and Literature, B
Finance, B
General Studies, B
History, B
Human Resources Management/Personnel
    Administration, B
Interdisciplinary Studies, BM
International Business/Trade/Commerce, B
Management Information Systems and Services, B
Marketing/Marketing Management, B
Mass Communication/Media Studies, B
Mathematics, B
Multi-/Interdisciplinary Studies, B
Nursing - Registered Nurse Training, B
Psychology, BM

Secondary Education and Teaching, M
Special Education and Teaching, M

TEXAS CHIROPRACTIC COLLEGE

Biology/Biological Sciences, B
Chiropractic, P
Public Health, B

TEXAS CHRISTIAN UNIVERSITY

Accounting, BM
Advertising, B
Advertising and Public Relations, M
Allied Health and Medical Assisting Services, M
Anthropology, B
Art History, Criticism and Conservation, BM
Art Teacher Education, B
Astronomy, MD
Astronomy and Astrophysics, B
Ballet, B
Bilingual and Multilingual Education, B
Biochemistry, B
Biological and Biomedical Sciences, MO
Biology/Biological Sciences, B
Broadcast Journalism, B
Business Administration, Management and
    Operations, M
Chemistry, BMD
Communication Disorders, M
Communication Studies/Speech Communication
    and Rhetoric, B
Composition, M
Computer and Information Sciences, B
Counselor Education/School Counseling and
    Guidance Services, BMO
Criminal Justice/Safety Studies, B
Dietetics and Clinical Nutrition Services, B
Dietetics/Dieticians, B
Drama and Dramatics/Theatre Arts, B
Early Childhood Education and Teaching, BM
Ecology, M
E-Commerce/Electronic Commerce, B
Economics, B
Education, MO
Education/Teaching of Individuals with Hearing
    Impairments, Including Deafness, B
Education/Teaching of the Gifted and Talented, B
Educational Administration and Supervision, M
Educational Leadership and Administration, BO
Educational Measurement and Evaluation, M
Educational Psychology, O
Elementary Education and Teaching, BMO
Engineering, B
English, MD
English Language and Literature, B
English/Language Arts Teacher Education, B
Environmental Sciences, BMO
Fashion Merchandising, B
Finance, B
Fine Arts and Art Studies, M
Fine/Studio Arts, B
French Language and Literature, B
General Studies, B
Geology/Earth Science, BM
Geosciences, M
Health and Physical Education, B
Health and Physical Education/Fitness, B
History, BMD
Interior Design, B
International Business/Trade/Commerce, BM
International Economics, B
International Finance, B
International Marketing, B
International Relations and Affairs, B
Journalism, BM
Kinesiology and Movement Studies, M
Latin American Studies, B
Liberal Arts and Sciences Studies and
    Humanities, B
Liberal Studies, M
Management Science, B
Marketing/Marketing Management, B
Mass Communication/Media Studies, B
Mathematics, BM
Mathematics Teacher Education, B
Middle School Education, M
Military Studies, B

Movement Therapy and Movement Education, B
Music, BMO
Music Performance, B
Music Teacher Education, BM
Music Theory and Composition, BM
Musicology and Ethnomusicology, M
Neuroscience, B
Nurse Anesthetist, M
Nursing, M
Nursing - Adult, M
Nursing - Registered Nurse Training, B
Painting, B
Pastoral Studies/Counseling, D
Performance, MO
Philosophy, B
Photography, B
Physical Education Teaching and Coaching, B
Physics, BMD
Piano and Organ, B
Political Science and Government, B
Printmaking, B
Psychology, BMD
Public Health (MPH, DPH), B
Radio and Television, B
Real Estate, B
Religion/Religious Studies, B
Science Teacher Education/General Science
    Teacher Education, B
Sculpture, B
Secondary Education and Teaching, BMO
Social Studies Teacher Education, B
Social Work, B
Sociology, B
Spanish Language and Literature, B
Special Education and Teaching, BM
Speech and Interpersonal Communication, M
Speech-Language Pathology/Pathologist, B
Technical Teacher Education, B
Theatre Literature, History and Criticism, B
Theology and Religious Vocations, MDPO

TEXAS COLLEGE

Art/Art Studies, General, B
Biology/Biological Sciences, B
Business Administration and Management, B
Business/Commerce, B
Computer Science, B
Elementary Education and Teaching, B
English Language and Literature, B
Health and Physical Education, B
History, B
Mathematics, B
Music, B
Political Science and Government, B
Social Work, B
Sociology, B

TEXAS CULINARY ACADEMY

Culinary Arts/Chef Training, A

TEXAS LUTHERAN UNIVERSITY

Accounting, B
Art Teacher Education, B
Art/Art Studies, General, B
Athletic Training and Sports Medicine, B
Biology/Biological Sciences, B
Business Administration and Management, B
Chemistry, B
Communication Studies/Speech Communication
    and Rhetoric, B
Computer Science, B
Drama and Dramatics/Theatre Arts, B
Economics, B
Education, B
Elementary Education and Teaching, B
English Language and Literature, B
Finance, B
Health and Physical Education/Fitness, B
History, B
History Teacher Education, B
Information Science/Studies, B
International Relations and Affairs, B
Junior High/Intermediate/Middle School Education
    and Teaching, B
Kinesiology and Exercise Science, B
Mathematics, B

Mathematics Teacher Education, B
Molecular Biology, B
Music, B
Music Teacher Education, B
Philosophy, B
Physical Education Teaching and Coaching, B
Physics, B
Political Science and Government, B
Pre-Dentistry Studies, B
Pre-Law Studies, B
Pre-Medicine/Pre-Medical Studies, B
Pre-Veterinary Studies, B
Psychology, B
Social Studies Teacher Education, B
Sociology, B
Spanish Language and Literature, B
Sport and Fitness Administration/Management, B
Teacher Education, Multiple Levels, B
Theology/Theological Studies, B

TEXAS SOUTHERN UNIVERSITY

Accounting, B
African-American/Black Studies, B
Air Traffic Controller, B
Apparel and Textiles, B
Architectural Engineering Technology/Technician, B
Art Teacher Education, B
Art/Art Studies, General, B
Aviation/Airway Management and Operations, B
Banking and Financial Support Services, B
Bilingual and Multilingual Education, B
Biological and Biomedical Sciences, M
Biological and Physical Sciences, B
Biology/Biological Sciences, B
Biomedical Technology/Technician, B
Business Administration and Management, B
Business Administration, Management and
    Operations, M
Business Education, M
Business Teacher Education, B
Chemistry, BM
Child Development, B
Civil Engineering Technology/Technician, B
Clinical Laboratory Science/Medical
    Technology/Technologist, B
Communication and Media Studies, M
Communication Disorders, B
Communication Studies/Speech Communication
    and Rhetoric, B
Computer and Information Sciences, B
Computer Engineering Technology/Technician, B
Computer Programming/Programmer, B
Computer Science, B
Construction Engineering Technology/Technician, B
Counselor Education/School Counseling and
    Guidance Services, BMD
Criminal Justice/Law Enforcement Administration, B
Curriculum and Instruction, BMD
Dietetics/Dieticians, B
Drafting and Design Technology/Technician, B
Drama and Dramatics/Theatre Arts, B
Early Childhood Education and Teaching, M
Economics, B
Education, BMD
Educational Administration and Supervision, MD
Educational Leadership and Administration, B
Educational Measurement and Evaluation, D
Educational Media/Instructional Technology, M
Electrical, Electronic and Communications
    Engineering Technology/Technician, B
Elementary Education and Teaching, BM
Engineering Technology, B
English, M
English Language and Literature, B
Environmental Engineering
    Technology/Environmental Technology, B
Environmental Health, B
Environmental Sciences, B
Family and Consumer Sciences/Human
    Sciences, BM
Fashion Merchandising, B
Fashion/Apparel Design, B
Finance, B
Fine/Studio Arts, B
Foods, Nutrition, and Wellness Studies, B
Foreign Languages and Literatures, B

French Language and Literature, B
General Studies, B
German Language and Literature, B
Health and Physical Education, B
Health Education, B
Health Information/Medical Records
    Administration/Administrator, B
Health Teacher Education, B
Health/Health Care Administration/Management, B
Higher Education/Higher Education
    Administration, MD
History, BMO
Human Services, M
Industrial Technology/Technician, B
Insurance, B
Interdisciplinary Studies, B
Jazz/Jazz Studies, B
Journalism, BM
Kindergarten/PreSchool Education and Teaching, B
Law and Legal Studies, PO
Liberal Arts and Sciences Studies and
    Humanities, B
Marketing/Marketing Management, B
Mass Communication/Media Studies, B
Mathematics, BM
Media Studies, M
Multi-/Interdisciplinary Studies, B
Multilingual and Multicultural Education, M
Music, BM
Music Teacher Education, B
Nursing - Registered Nurse Training, B
Occupational Safety and Health
    Technology/Technician, B
Office Management and Supervision, B
Operations Management and Supervision, B
Pharmacy, BMP
Photography, B
Physical Education Teaching and Coaching, BM
Physical Therapy/Therapist, B
Physics, B
Piano and Organ, B
Political Science and Government, B
Pre-Dentistry Studies, B
Pre-Medicine/Pre-Medical Studies, B
Pre-Pharmacy Studies, B
Psychology, BM
Public Administration, BMO
Public Health (MPH, DPH), B
Radio and Television, B
Radio, Television, and Digital Communication, B
Reading Teacher Education, BM
Respiratory Care Therapy/Therapist, B
Science, Technology and Society, B
Secondary Education and Teaching, BM
Social and Philosophical Foundations of
    Education, B
Social Work, B
Sociology, BM
Spanish Language and Literature, B
Special Education and Teaching, BM
Speech and Interpersonal Communication, M
Speech and Rhetorical Studies, B
Technology Teacher Education/Industrial Arts
    Teacher Education, B
Telecommunications Technology/Technician, B
Toxicology, MD
Transportation and Highway Engineering, M
Urban and Regional Planning, MO
Urban Education and Leadership, D
Visual and Performing Arts, B
Voice and Opera, B
Wind and Percussion Instruments, B

TEXAS SOUTHMOST COLLEGE

Accounting, A
Administrative Assistant and Secretarial Science, A
Art/Art Studies, General, A
Automobile/Automotive Mechanics
    Technology/Technician, A
Business Administration and Management, A
Child Development, A
Clinical/Medical Laboratory Technician, A
Computer Typography and Composition Equipment
    Operator, A
Construction Engineering Technology/Technician, A
Consumer Merchandising/Retailing Management, A

Criminal Justice/Law Enforcement Administration, A
Criminal Justice/Police Science, A
Data Processing and Data Processing
  Technology/Technician, A
Drafting and Design Technology/Technician, A
Electrical, Electronic and Communications
  Engineering Technology/Technician, A
Emergency Medical Technology/Technician (EMT
  Paramedic), A
Finance, A
Fire Science/Firefighting, A
Hotel/Motel Administration/Management, A
Industrial Radiologic Technology/Technician, A
Legal Administrative Assistant/Secretary, A
Liberal Arts and Sciences Studies and
  Humanities, A
Music, A
Nursing - Registered Nurse Training, A
Respiratory Care Therapy/Therapist, A
Social Work, A
Substance Abuse/Addiction Counseling, A

TEXAS STATE TECHNICAL COLLEGE HARLINGEN

Administrative Assistant and Secretarial Science, A
Airframe Mechanics and Aircraft Maintenance
  Technology/Technician, A
Autobody/Collision and Repair
  Technology/Technician, A
Biomedical Technology/Technician, A
Chemical Engineering, A
Commercial and Advertising Art, A
Computer and Information Sciences, A
Computer Graphics, A
Computer Programming, A
Computer Programming, Specific Applications, A
Computer
  Programming, Vendor/Product Certification, A
Computer Programming/Programmer, A
Computer Science, A
Computer Software and Media Applications, A
Computer Systems Networking and
  Telecommunications, A
Computer Technology/Computer Systems
  Technology, A
Computer/Information Technology Services
  Administration and Management, A
Construction Engineering Technology/Technician, A
Data Processing and Data Processing
  Technology/Technician, A
Dental Assisting/Assistant, A
Dental Hygiene/Hygienist, A
Dental Laboratory Technology/Technician, A
Drafting and Design Technology/Technician, A
Electrical, Electronic and Communications
  Engineering Technology/Technician, A
Electromechanical Technology/Electromechanical
  Engineering Technology, A
Environmental Engineering
  Technology/Environmental Technology, A
Farm/Farm and Ranch Management, A
Food Technology and Processing, A
Health Information/Medical Records
  Administration/Administrator, A
Heating, Air Conditioning, Ventilation and
  Refrigeration Maintenance
  Technology/Technician, A
Industrial Technology/Technician, A
Information Technology, A
Institutional Food Workers, A
Instrumentation Technology/Technician, A
Legal Administrative Assistant/Secretary, A
Machine Tool Technology/Machinist, A
Management Information Systems and Services, A
Surgical Technology/Technologist, A
System Administration/Administrator, A
Web Page, Digital/Multimedia and Information
  Resources Design, A
Web/Multimedia Management and Webmaster, A
Welding Technology/Welder, A
Word Processing, A

TEXAS STATE TECHNICAL COLLEGE WACO

Aeronautics/Aviation/Aerospace Science and
  Technology, A

Agricultural and Food Products Processing, A
Aircraft Powerplant Technology/Technician, A
Airframe Mechanics and Aircraft Maintenance
  Technology/Technician, A
Airline/Commercial/Professional Pilot and Flight
  Crew, A
Audio Engineering, A
Autobody/Collision and Repair
  Technology/Technician, A
Automobile/Automotive Mechanics
  Technology/Technician, A
Avionics Maintenance Technology/Technician, A
Biomedical Technology/Technician, A
Chemical Engineering, A
Chemical Technology/Technician, A
Commercial and Advertising Art, A
Computer and Information Sciences, A
Computer Engineering Technology/Technician, A
Computer Programming/Programmer, A
Computer Science, A
Computer Technology/Computer Systems
  Technology, A
Culinary Arts/Chef Training, A
Dental Assisting/Assistant, A
Diesel Mechanics Technology/Technician, A
Drafting and Design Technology/Technician, A
Educational/Instructional Media Design, A
Electrical, Electronic and Communications
  Engineering Technology/Technician, A
Electrical/Electronics Drafting and
  Electrical/Electronics CAD/CADD, A
Food Technology and Processing, A
Graphic and Printing Equipment Operator
  Production, A
Heating, Air Conditioning and Refrigeration
  Technology/Technician, A
Heating, Air Conditioning, Ventilation and
  Refrigeration Maintenance
  Technology/Technician, A
Heavy Equipment Maintenance
  Technology/Technician, A
Industrial Technology/Technician, A
Information Science/Studies, A
Institutional Food Workers, A
Instrumentation Technology/Technician, A
Laser and Optical Technology/Technician, A
Machine Tool Technology/Machinist, A
Mechanical Engineering/Mechanical
  Technology/Technician, A
Nuclear/Nuclear Power Technology/Technician, A
Occupational Safety and Health
  Technology/Technician, A
Ornamental Horticulture, A
Photographic and Film/Video Technology/Technician
  and Assistant, A
Quality Control Technology/Technician, A
Turf and Turfgrass Management, A
Welding Technology/Welder, A

TEXAS STATE TECHNICAL COLLEGE WEST TEXAS

Airframe Mechanics and Aircraft Maintenance
  Technology/Technician, A
Automobile/Automotive Mechanics
  Technology/Technician, A
Computer Engineering Technology/Technician, A
Computer Programming/Programmer, A
Computer Systems Networking and
  Telecommunications, A
Diesel Mechanics Technology/Technician, A
Drafting and Design Technology/Technician, A
Electrical, Electronic and Communications
  Engineering Technology/Technician, A
Emergency Medical Technology/Technician (EMT
  Paramedic), A
Environmental Engineering
  Technology/Environmental Technology, A
Health Information/Medical Records
  Technology/Technician, A
Machine Tool Technology/Machinist, A
Robotics Technology/Technician, A

TEXAS STATE UNIVERSITY-SAN MARCOS

Accounting, BM
Advertising, B

Agribusiness, B
Agricultural Education, M
Agriculture, B
Allied Health and Medical Assisting Services, M
American/United States Studies/Civilization, B
Animal Physiology, B
Animal Sciences, B
Anthropology, B
Applied Mathematics, BM
Aquatic Biology/Limnology, B
Art/Art Studies, General, B
Asian Studies/Civilization, B
Athletic Training and Sports Medicine, B
Audiology/Audiologist and Speech-Language
  Pathology/Pathologist, B
Biochemistry, BM
Biological and Biomedical Sciences, M
Biology/Biological Sciences, B
Botany/Plant Biology, B
Business Administration and Management, B
Business Administration, Management and
  Operations, M
Business/Managerial Economics, B
Cartography, B
Chemistry, BM
Child and Family Studies, M
City/Urban, Community and Regional Planning, B
Clinical Laboratory Science/Medical
  Technology/Technologist, B
Communication and Media Studies, M
Communication Disorders, M
Community Health Services/Liaison/Counseling, B
Computer and Information Sciences, B
Computer Science, M
Construction Engineering Technology/Technician, B
Corrections, B
Counselor Education/School Counseling and
  Guidance Services, M
Criminal Justice/Police Science, B
Criminal Justice/Safety Studies, B
Criminology, M
Dance, B
Data Processing and Data Processing
  Technology/Technician, B
Developmental Education, M
Drama and Dramatics/Theatre Arts, B
Early Childhood Education and Teaching, M
Economics, B
Education, M
Educational Administration and Supervision, M
Elementary Education and Teaching, M
Engineering Technology, B
English, M
English Language and Literature, B
Environmental Sciences, B
Environmental Studies, M
European Studies/Civilization, B
Family and Consumer Sciences/Human Sciences, B
Fashion Merchandising, B
Finance, B
Fine/Studio Arts, B
Fish, Game and Wildlife Management, M
Foods, Nutrition, and Wellness Studies, B
French Language and Literature, B
Geographic Information Systems, MD
Geography, BMD
German Language and Literature, B
Graphic Design, B
Health and Physical Education, B
Health Education, M
Health Information/Medical Records
  Administration/Administrator, B
Health Psychology, M
Health Services Administration, M
Health Services Research, M
Health Services/Allied Health/Health Sciences, B
Health/Health Care Administration/Management, B
History, BM
Hospital and Health Care Facilities
  Administration/Management, B
Human Development and Family Studies, B
Industrial Engineering, B
Industrial Technology/Technician, B
Industrial/Management Engineering, M
Interdisciplinary Studies, M
Interior Design, B

International Affairs, M
International Relations and Affairs, B
International/Global Studies, B
Jazz/Jazz Studies, B
Journalism, B
Land Use Planning and
   Management/Development, B
Legal and Justice Studies, M
Leisure Studies, M
Management Information Systems and Services, B
Management of Technology, M
Manufacturing Engineering, B
Manufacturing Technology/Technician, B
Marine Biology and Biological Oceanography, BM
Marketing/Marketing Management, B
Mass Communication/Media Studies, BM
Mathematics, BM
Mathematics Teacher Education, M
Medical Radiologic Technology/Science - Radiation
   Therapist, B
Microbiology, B
Multi-/Interdisciplinary Studies, B
Multilingual and Multicultural Education, M
Music, B
Music Performance, B
Music Teacher Education, M
Near and Middle Eastern Studies, B
Parks, Recreation and Leisure Facilities
   Management, B
Performance, M
Philosophy, B
Physical Education Teaching and Coaching, M
Physical Therapy/Therapist, M
Physics, BM
Political Science and Government, BM
Prepress/Desktop Publishing and Digital Imaging
   Design, B
Psychology, BM
Public Administration, BM
Public Relations/Image Management, B
Radio and Television, B
Reading Teacher Education, M
Recording Arts Technology/Technician, B
Recreation and Park Management, M
Respiratory Care Therapy/Therapist, B
Russian Studies, B
School Psychology, M
Science Teacher Education/General Science
   Teacher Education, M
Secondary Education and Teaching, M
Social Studies Teacher Education, D
Social Work, BM
Sociology, BM
Software Engineering, M
Spanish Language and Literature, BM
Special Education and Teaching, M
Speech and Rhetorical Studies, B
Sport and Fitness Administration/Management, B
Technical Communication, M
Theater, M
Vocational and Technical Education, M
Water, Wetlands, and Marine Resources
   Management, B
Wildlife Biology, B
Writing, M
Zoology/Animal Biology, B

TEXAS TECH UNIVERSITY

Accounting, BMDO
Acting, B
Advertising, B
Agribusiness, M
Agricultural Business and Management, B
Agricultural Communication/Journalism, B
Agricultural Economics, BMDO
Agricultural Education, MD
Agricultural Production Operations, B
Agricultural Sciences, MDO
Agronomy and Crop Science, B
Agronomy and Soil Sciences, MD
Animal Sciences, BMD
Animal/Livestock Husbandry and Production, B
Anthropology, BM
Apparel and Textiles, B
Applied Economics, MDO
Applied Horticulture/Horticultural Operations, B

Applied Physics, M
Architectural Engineering Technology/Technician, B
Architecture, BMO
Art Education, M
Art History, Criticism and Conservation, B
Art/Art Studies, General, B
Atmospheric Sciences and Meteorology, M
Audiology/Audiologist and Hearing Sciences, B
Biochemistry, B
Bioinformatics, M
Biological and Biomedical Sciences, MD
Biological and Physical Sciences, B
Biology/Biological Sciences, B
BioTechnology, M
Business Administration and Management, B
Business Administration, Management and
   Operations, BMDO
Business/Commerce, B
Cell/Cellular and Molecular Biology, B
Cell/Cellular Biology and Histology, B
Chemical Engineering, BMD
Chemistry, BMD
Child and Family Studies, MD
Child Development, B
Civil Engineering, BMD
Classics and Classical
   Languages, Literatures, and Linguistics, BM
Clinical Psychology, D
Commercial and Advertising Art, B
Communication and Media Studies, M
Community Health Services/Liaison/Counseling, B
Composition, M
Computer and Information Sciences, B
Computer Engineering, B
Computer Science, MD
Consumer Economics, MD
Counseling Psychology, MD
Counselor Education/School Counseling and
   Guidance Services, MDO
Curriculum and Instruction, MDO
Dance, BMD
Dietetics/Dieticians, B
Drama and Dramatics/Theatre Arts, B
Economics, BMD
Education, MDO
Educational Administration and Supervision, O
Educational Leadership and Administration, MDO
Educational Media/Instructional Technology, MD
Educational Psychology, MDO
Electrical Engineering, MD
Electrical, Electronic and Communications
   Engineering Technology/Technician, B
Electrical, Electronics and Communications
   Engineering, B
Electronic Commerce, M
Elementary Education and Teaching, M
Engineering, B
Engineering and Applied Sciences, MD
Engineering Management, M
Engineering Physics, B
Engineering Technology, B
English, MD
English Education, M
English Language and Literature, B
Entomology, M
Entrepreneurship/Entrepreneurial Studies, M
Environmental Design/Architecture, MD
Environmental Engineering
   Technology/Environmental Technology, M
Environmental Policy and Resource Management, D
Environmental Sciences, MD
Environmental/Environmental Health Engineering, B
Exercise and Sports Science, M
Experimental Psychology, MD
Family and Consumer Sciences/Human Sciences, B
Family Resource Management Studies, B
Family Systems, B
Fashion Merchandising, B
Fashion/Apparel Design, B
Finance, B
Finance and Banking, MD
Fine Arts and Art Studies, MD
Fine/Studio Arts, B
Fish, Game and Wildlife Management, MD
Fishing and Fisheries Sciences and Management, B
Food Science, B

Food Science and Technology, MD
Foods, Nutrition, and Wellness Studies, B
French Language and Literature, BM
General Studies, B
Geography, B
Geology/Earth Science, B
Geophysics and Seismology, B
Geosciences, MD
German Language and Literature, BM
Gerontology, M
Graphic Design, B
Health and Physical Education, B
Health Services Administration, MO
Health Services/Allied Health/Health Sciences, B
Higher Education/Higher Education
   Administration, MD
Historic Preservation and Conservation, M
History, BMD
Home Economics, MD
Home Economics Education, MD
Horticultural Science, BM
Hospitality Administration/Management, MD
Hotel/Motel Administration/Management, B
Human Development, MD
Human Development and Family Studies, B
Humanities/Humanistic Studies, M
Industrial and Manufacturing Management, MD
Industrial Engineering, B
Industrial/Management Engineering, MD
Interdisciplinary Studies, BMD
Interior Architecture, B
International Business/Trade/Commerce, BM
Journalism, B
Kinesiology and Exercise Science, B
Landscape Architecture, BM
Latin American Studies, B
Law and Legal Studies, PO
Liberal Arts and Sciences Studies and
   Humanities, B
Linguistics, M
Management Information Systems and
   Services, BMD
Manufacturing Engineering, M
Marketing, MD
Marketing/Marketing Management, B
Marriage and Family Therapy/Counseling, MD
Mass Communication/Media Studies, MD
Mathematics, BMD
Mechanical Engineering, BMD
Medical Microbiology and Bacteriology, B
Microbiology, M
Molecular Biology, B
Multi-/Interdisciplinary Studies, B
Multilingual and Multicultural Education, M
Museology/Museum Studies, M
Music, BMD
Music History, Literature, and Theory, M
Music Performance, B
Music Teacher Education, MD
Music Theory and Composition, BM
Natural Resources and Conservation, B
Nutritional Sciences, MD
Parks, Recreation, Leisure and Fitness Studies, B
Performance, MD
Petroleum Engineering, BMD
Philosophy, BM
Photojournalism, B
Physics, BMD
Plant Protection and Integrated Pest
   Management, B
Plant Sciences, MD
Political Science and Government, BMDO
Psychology, BMD
Public Administration, M
Public Relations/Image Management, B
Quantitative Analysis, MD
Radio and Television, B
Range Science and Management, BMD
Reading Teacher Education, M
Rhetoric, D
Romance
   Languages, Literatures, and Linguistics, M
Russian Studies, B
Secondary Education and Teaching, M
Social Work, B
Sociology, BM

Software Engineering, M
Spanish Language and Literature, BMD
Special Education and Teaching, MDO
Speech and Rhetorical Studies, B
Systems Engineering, M
Taxation, M
Technical and Business Writing, MD
Technical Theatre/Theatre Design and
    Technology, B
Telecommunications, M
Textile Sciences and Engineering, B
Theater, MD
Toxicology, MD
Wildlife and Wildlands Science and Management, B
Work and Family Studies, B
Zoology/Animal Biology, BMD

TEXAS WESLEYAN UNIVERSITY

Accounting, B
Advertising, B
Art Teacher Education, B
Art/Art Studies, General, B
Athletic Training and Sports Medicine, B
Behavioral Sciences, B
Bilingual and Multilingual Education, B
Biochemistry, B
Biological and Biomedical Sciences, B
Biology Teacher Education, B
Biology/Biological Sciences, B
Business Administration and Management, B
Business Administration, Management and
    Operations, M
Business Teacher Education, B
Business, Management, Marketing, and Related
    Support Services, B
Business/Managerial Economics, B
Chemistry, B
Computer and Information Sciences, B
Counseling Psychology, B
Criminal Justice/Safety Studies, B
Drama and Dance Teacher Education, B
Drama and Dramatics/Theatre Arts, B
Economics, B
Education, BM
Elementary Education and Teaching, B
Engineering, B
English Language and Literature, B
English/Language Arts Teacher Education, B
Foreign Language Teacher Education, B
Gerontological Nursing, M
Health and Physical Education, B
Health Services Administration, M
History, B
History Teacher Education, B
Humanities/Humanistic Studies, B
Industrial and Organizational Psychology, B
International Business/Trade/Commerce, B
International Relations and Affairs, B
Journalism, B
Law and Legal Studies, P
Legal Professions and Studies, B
Management Information Systems and Services, B
Marketing/Marketing Management, B
Mass Communication/Media Studies, B
Mathematics, B
Mathematics Teacher Education, B
Multi-/Interdisciplinary Studies, B
Music, B
Music Teacher Education, B
Nurse Anesthetist, M
Physical Education Teaching and Coaching, B
Political Science and Government, B
Pre-Dentistry Studies, B
Pre-Law Studies, B
Pre-Medicine/Pre-Medical Studies, B
Psychology, B
Public Health, M
Radio and Television, B
Reading Teacher Education, B
Religion/Religious Studies, B
Religious Education, B
School Psychology, B
Science Teacher Education/General Science
    Teacher Education, B
Social Sciences, B
Social Studies Teacher Education, B

Sociology, B
Spanish Language and Literature, B
Speech and Rhetorical Studies, B
Speech Teacher Education, B
Sport and Fitness Administration/Management, B
Teaching English as a Second or Foreign
    Language/ESL Language Instructor, B
Technology Teacher Education/Industrial Arts
    Teacher Education, B
Visual and Performing Arts, B
Voice and Opera, B
Wind and Percussion Instruments, B

TEXAS WOMAN'S UNIVERSITY

Accounting, B
Allied Health and Medical Assisting Services, MD
Audiology/Audiologist and Speech-Language
    Pathology/Pathologist, MD
Biological and Biomedical Sciences, MD
Biology/Biological Sciences, B
Business Administration and Management, B
Business Administration, Management and
    Operations, M
Chemistry, BM
Child and Family Studies, MD
Child Development, B
Clinical Laboratory Science/Medical
    Technology/Technologist, B
Communication Disorders, M
Community Health Services/Liaison/Counseling, B
Computer and Information Sciences, B
Counseling Psychology, MD
Counselor Education/School Counseling and
    Guidance Services, M
Criminal Justice/Safety Studies, B
Dance, BMD
Dental Hygiene/Hygienist, B
Drama and Dramatics/Theatre Arts, B
Early Childhood Education and Teaching, MD
Education, MD
Educational Administration and Supervision, M
Elementary Education and Teaching, M
English, MD
English Language and Literature, B
Exercise and Sports Science, M
Family and Consumer Sciences/Human Sciences, B
Fashion Merchandising, B
Fashion/Apparel Design, B
Fine Arts and Art Studies, M
Food Science and Technology, MD
Foods, Nutrition, and Wellness Studies, B
Health Education, MD
Health Services Administration, M
History, BM
Hospitality Administration/Management, M
Human Development and Family Studies, B
Institutional Food Workers, B
Interdisciplinary Studies, B
Journalism, B
Kinesiology and Exercise Science, B
Kinesiology and Movement Studies, MD
Legal Assistant/Paralegal, B
Library Science, MD
Marketing/Marketing Management, B
Marriage and Family Therapy/Counseling, MD
Mathematics, BM
Mathematics Teacher Education, M
Molecular Biology, D
Music, BM
Music Therapy/Therapist, B
Nursing, MD
Nursing - Advanced Practice, M
Nursing - Registered Nurse Training, B
Nursing Education, M
Nutritional Sciences, BMD
Occupational Therapy/Therapist, MD
Physical Therapy/Therapist, MD
Political Science and Government, BM
Psychology, BMD
Public Administration and Social Service
    Professions, B
Reading Teacher Education, MD
Rhetoric, D
School Psychology, MD
Science Teacher Education/General Science
    Teacher Education, M

Social Work, B
Sociology, BMD
Special Education and Teaching, MD
Theater, M
Women's Studies, M

TOMBALL COLLEGE

Accounting, A
Business Administration and Management, A
Computer Programming/Programmer, A
Electrical, Electronic and Communications
    Engineering Technology/Technician, A
Human Services, A
Legal Administrative Assistant/Secretary, A
Medical Administrative Assistant/Secretary, A
Nursing - Registered Nurse Training, A
Occupational Therapy/Therapist, A
Veterinary/Animal Health Technology/Technician and
    Veterinary Assistant, A

TRINITY UNIVERSITY

Accounting, BM
Acting, B
Anthropology, B
Art History, Criticism and Conservation, B
Art/Art Studies, General, B
Asian Studies/Civilization, B
Biochemistry, B
Biology/Biological Sciences, B
Business Administration and Management, B
Business Administration, Management and
    Operations, M
Chemistry, B
Chinese Language and Literature, B
Classics and Classical
    Languages, Literatures, and Linguistics, B
Communication Studies/Speech Communication
    and Rhetoric, B
Computer and Information Sciences, B
Drama and Dramatics/Theatre Arts, B
Economics, B
Education, M
Educational Administration and Supervision, M
Engineering Science, B
English Language and Literature, B
European Studies/Civilization, B
Finance, B
French Language and Literature, B
Geology/Earth Science, B
German Language and Literature, B
Health Services Administration, M
History, B
Humanities/Humanistic Studies, B
International Business/Trade/Commerce, B
Latin American Studies, B
Management Science, B
Marketing/Marketing Management, B
Mathematics, B
Music, B
Music Performance, B
Music Theory and Composition, B
Philosophy, B
Physics, B
Political Science and Government, B
Pre-Dentistry Studies, B
Pre-Law Studies, B
Pre-Medicine/Pre-Medical Studies, B
Pre-Veterinary Studies, B
Psychology, B
Religion/Religious Studies, B
Russian Language and Literature, B
School Psychology, M
Sociology, B
Spanish Language and Literature, B
Speech and Rhetorical Studies, B
Technical Theatre/Theatre Design and
    Technology, B
Urban Studies/Affairs, B
Voice and Opera, B

TRINITY VALLEY COMMUNITY COLLEGE

Accounting, A
Agricultural Teacher Education, A
Animal Sciences, A
Art/Art Studies, General, A

Automobile/Automotive Mechanics
   Technology/Technician, A
Biology/Biological Sciences, A
Business Administration and Management, A
Business Teacher Education, A
Chemistry, A
Child Development, A
Computer Science, A
Corrections, A
Cosmetology/Cosmetologist, A
Criminal Justice/Law Enforcement Administration, A
Criminal Justice/Police Science, A
Dance, A
Data Processing and Data Processing
   Technology/Technician, A
Developmental and Child Psychology, A
Drafting and Design Technology/Technician, A
Drama and Dramatics/Theatre Arts, A
Education, A
Elementary Education and Teaching, A
Emergency Medical Technology/Technician (EMT
   Paramedic), A
English Language and Literature, A
Farm/Farm and Ranch Management, A
Fashion Merchandising, A
Finance, A
Geology/Earth Science, A
Heating, Air Conditioning, Ventilation and
   Refrigeration Maintenance
   Technology/Technician, A
History, A
Horticultural Science, A
Insurance, A
Journalism, A
Kindergarten/PreSchool Education and Teaching, A
Legal Administrative Assistant/Secretary, A
Liberal Arts and Sciences Studies and
   Humanities, A
Licensed Practical/Vocational Nurse Training, A
Marketing/Marketing Management, A
Mathematics, A
Music, A
Nursing - Registered Nurse Training, A
Physical Education Teaching and Coaching, A
Physical Sciences, A
Political Science and Government, A
Pre-Engineering, A
Psychology, A
Range Science and Management, A
Real Estate, A
Religion/Religious Studies, A
Sociology, A
Spanish Language and Literature, A
Speech and Rhetorical Studies, A
Surgical Technology/Technologist, A
Welding Technology/Welder, A

TYLER JUNIOR COLLEGE

Accounting, A
Administrative Assistant and Secretarial Science, A
Agricultural Business and Management, A
Agricultural Economics, A
Agricultural Teacher Education, A
Agriculture, A
Art/Art Studies, General, A
Behavioral Sciences, A
Business Administration and Management, A
Clinical/Medical Laboratory Technician, A
Commercial and Advertising Art, A
Computer and Information Sciences, A
Computer Engineering Technology/Technician, A
Computer Graphics, A
Computer Programming, A
Computer Science, A
Computer Systems Networking and
   Telecommunications, A
Criminal Justice/Law Enforcement Administration, A
Criminal Justice/Police Science, A
Data Entry/Microcomputer Applications, A
Dental Hygiene/Hygienist, A
Developmental and Child Psychology, A
Drafting and Design Technology/Technician, A
Electrical, Electronic and Communications
   Engineering Technology/Technician, A
Environmental Engineering
   Technology/Environmental Technology, A

Farm/Farm and Ranch Management, A
Fashion Merchandising, A
Finance, A
Fire Science/Firefighting, A
Graphic and Printing Equipment Operator
   Production, A
Health/Health Care Administration/Management, A
Heating, Air Conditioning, Ventilation and
   Refrigeration Maintenance
   Technology/Technician, A
Horticultural Science, A
Human Resources Management/Personnel
   Administration, A
Industrial Radiologic Technology/Technician, A
Information Technology, A
Legal Administrative Assistant/Secretary, A
Liberal Arts and Sciences Studies and
   Humanities, A
Licensed Practical/Vocational Nurse Training, A
Marketing/Marketing Management, A
Medical Administrative Assistant/Secretary, A
Modern Languages, A
Music, A
Nursing - Registered Nurse Training, A
Ophthalmic Laboratory Technology/Technician, A
Ornamental Horticulture, A
Parks, Recreation, Leisure and Fitness Studies, A
Petroleum Technology/Technician, A
Photography, A
Plastics Engineering Technology/Technician, A
Psychology, A
Real Estate, A
Respiratory Care Therapy/Therapist, A
Sign Language Interpretation and Translation, A
Social Sciences, A
Speech and Rhetorical Studies, A
Survey Technology/Surveying, A
Welding Technology/Welder, A

UNIVERSAL TECHNICAL INSTITUTE

Automobile/Automotive Mechanics
   Technology/Technician, A
Diesel Mechanics Technology/Technician, A

UNIVERSITY OF DALLAS

Accounting, M
American/United States Studies/Civilization, M
Art History, Criticism and Conservation, B
Art Teacher Education, B
Art/Art Studies, General, B
Biochemistry, B
Biology/Biological Sciences, B
Business Administration, Management and
   Operations, M
Ceramic Arts and Ceramics, B
Chemistry, B
Classics and Classical
   Languages, Literatures, and Linguistics, B
Comparative Literature, D
Drama and Dramatics/Theatre Arts, B
Economics, B
Education, B
Elementary Education and Teaching, B
English, M
English Language and Literature, B
Entrepreneurship/Entrepreneurial Studies, M
Finance and Banking, M
Fine Arts and Art Studies, M
Fine/Studio Arts, B
French Language and Literature, B
German Language and Literature, B
Health Services Administration, M
History, B
Human Resources Management and Services, M
Humanities/Humanistic Studies, M
International Business/Trade/Commerce, M
Management, M
Management Information Systems and Services, M
Management Strategy and Policy, M
Marketing, M
Mathematics, B
Non-Profit/Public/Organizational Management, M
Organizational Management, M
Painting, B
Pastoral Studies/Counseling, M
Philosophy, BMD

Physics, B
Political Science and Government, MD
Pre-Dentistry Studies, B
Pre-Law Studies, B
Pre-Medicine/Pre-Medical Studies, B
Pre-Theology/Pre-Ministerial Studies, B
Printmaking, B
Project Management, M
Psychology, BM
Sculpture, B
Secondary Education and Teaching, B
Spanish Language and Literature, B
Sport and Fitness Administration/Management, M
Theology and Religious Vocations, M
Theology/Theological Studies, B

UNIVERSITY OF HOUSTON

Accounting, BMD
Advertising and Public Relations, M
Aerospace, Aeronautical and Astronautical
   Engineering, MD
Anthropology, BM
Applied Mathematics, B
Architecture, BM
Architecture and Related Services, B
Art Education, M
Art History, Criticism and Conservation, B
Art/Art Studies, General, B
Audiology/Audiologist and Speech-Language
   Pathology/Pathologist, B
Bilingual and Multilingual Education, B
Biochemistry, BMD
Biological and Biomedical Sciences, MD
Biology/Biological Sciences, B
Biomedical Engineering, M
Biomedical/Medical Engineering, B
Business Administration and Management, B
Business Administration, Management and
   Operations, MDO
Business Family and Consumer Sciences/Human
   Sciences, B
Business Statistics, B
Business/Corporate Communications, B
Chemical Engineering, BMD
Chemistry, BMD
Civil Engineering, BMD
Civil Engineering Technology/Technician, B
Classics and Classical
   Languages, Literatures, and Linguistics, B
Clinical Laboratory Science/Medical
   Technology/Technologist, B
Clinical Psychology, D
Communication and Media Studies, M
Communication Disorders, BM
Communication Studies/Speech Communication
   and Rhetoric, B
Community Health Services/Liaison/Counseling, B
Composition, MD
Computer and Information Sciences, B
Computer Engineering, BMD
Computer Engineering Technology/Technician, B
Computer Science, MD
Computer Systems Analysis/Analyst, B
Construction Engineering Technology/Technician, B
Counseling Psychology, MD
Creative Writing, B
Curriculum and Instruction, MD
Drafting and Design Technology/Technician, B
Drama and Dramatics/Theatre Arts, B
Early Childhood Education and Teaching, M
Economics, BMD
Education, BMD
Education/Teaching of the Gifted and Talented, M
Educational Administration and Supervision, MD
Educational Psychology, MD
Electrical Engineering, MD
Electrical, Electronics and Communications
   Engineering, B
Electromechanical Technology/Electromechanical
   Engineering Technology, B
Elementary Education and Teaching, M
Engineering and Applied Sciences, MDO
English, MD
English as a Second Language, M
English Language and Literature, B
Entrepreneurship/Entrepreneurial Studies, D

Environmental Design/Architecture, B
Environmental Engineering
  Technology/Environmental Technology, MD
Environmental Studies, B
Exercise and Sports Science, M
Family and Consumer Sciences/Human
  Sciences, BM
Finance, B
Finance and Banking, MD
Fine Arts and Art Studies, M
Fine/Studio Arts, B
Foods, Nutrition, and Wellness Studies, B
Foundations and Philosophy of Education, MD
French Language and Literature, BMDO
Geology/Earth Science, BMD
Geophysics and Seismology, BMD
German Language and Literature, B
German Studies, B
Graphic Communications, B
Graphic Design, M
Health and Physical Education, B
Health Education, MD
Higher Education/Higher Education
  Administration, M
History, BMD
Hospitality Administration/Management, M
Hotel/Motel Administration/Management, B
Human Development, M
Human Development and Family Studies, B
Human Nutrition, B
Industrial and Organizational Psychology, D
Industrial Engineering, B
Industrial Technology/Technician, B
Industrial/Management Engineering, MDO
Information Science/Studies, BMD
Information Technology, B
Interdisciplinary Studies, B
Interior Architecture, B
Interior Design, BM
Italian Language and Literature, B
Journalism, B
Kinesiology and Exercise Science, B
Kinesiology and Movement Studies, D
Latin Language and Literature, B
Law and Legal Studies, MPO
Linguistics, M
Logistics and Materials Management, M
Management Information Systems and Services, B
Marketing, D
Marketing/Marketing Management, B
Mass Communication/Media Studies, BM
Materials Engineering, MD
Mathematics, BMD
Mathematics Teacher Education, M
Mechanical Engineering, BMD
Multilingual and Multicultural Education, M
Music, BMD
Music Performance, B
Music Teacher Education, MD
Music Theory and Composition, BM
Operations Management and Supervision, B
Optometry, P
Organizational Behavior Studies, B
Organizational Communication, B
Painting, BM
Performance, MD
Petroleum Engineering, M
Pharmaceutical Administration, M
Pharmaceutical Sciences, MD
Pharmacology, MD
Pharmacy, BMDP
Philosophy, BM
Photography, BM
Physical Education Teaching and Coaching, MD
Physics, BMD
Political Science and Government, BMD
Pre-Dentistry Studies, B
Pre-Law Studies, B
Pre-Medicine/Pre-Medical Studies, B
Pre-Veterinary Studies, B
Printmaking, B
Psychology, BD
Public History, M
Public Relations/Image Management, B
Reading Teacher Education, M
Russian Studies, B

Sales, Distribution and Marketing Operations, B
Science Teacher Education/General Science
  Teacher Education, M
Sculpture, BM
Secondary Education and Teaching, M
Social Psychology, D
Social Studies Teacher Education, M
Social Work, MD
Sociology, BM
Spanish and Iberian Studies, B
Spanish Language and Literature, BMDO
Special Education and Teaching, MD
Speech and Interpersonal Communication, M
Speech and Rhetorical Studies, B
Statistics, B
Systems Engineering, MD
Theater, M
Vision Science/Physiological Optics, MD
Western European Studies, B
Writing, MD

UNIVERSITY OF HOUSTON-CLEAR LAKE

Accounting, BM
Anthropology, B
Art/Art Studies, General, B
Behavioral Sciences, B
Biological and Biomedical Sciences, M
Biology/Biological Sciences, B
Business Administration and Management, B
Business Administration, Management and
  Operations, BMO
Business/Commerce, B
Chemistry, BM
Clinical Psychology, BM
Communication Studies/Speech Communication
  and Rhetoric, B
Computer and Information Sciences, B
Computer Engineering, BM
Computer Science, M
Computer Software Engineering, B
Computer Systems Networking and
  Telecommunications, B
Counselor Education/School Counseling and
  Guidance Services, BM
Criminology, M
Cultural Studies, M
Curriculum and Instruction, BM
Early Childhood Education and Teaching, BM
Education, M
Educational Administration and Supervision, M
Educational Leadership and Administration, B
Educational Media/Instructional Technology, M
Educational/Instructional Media Design, B
English, M
English Language and Literature, B
Environmental Policy and Resource
  Management, M
Environmental Sciences, BM
Exercise and Sports Science, M
Finance, B
Finance and Banking, M
Foundations and Philosophy of Education, M
Geography, B
Health and Physical Education, B
Health Services Administration, M
Health/Health Care Administration/Management, B
History, BM
Human Resources Development, B
Human Resources Management and Services, M
Humanities/Humanistic Studies, BM
Information Science/Studies, BM
Intercultural/Multicultural and Diversity Studies, B
Legal Assistant/Paralegal, B
Library Science, BM
Management Information Systems and
  Services, BM
Management Strategy and Policy, M
Marketing/Marketing Management, B
Marriage and Family Therapy/Counseling, BM
Mathematics, BM
Multi-/Interdisciplinary Studies, B
Multilingual and Multicultural Education, M
Parks, Recreation and Leisure Facilities
  Management, B
Physical Sciences, B

Political Science and Government, B
Psychology, BM
Public Administration, BM
Reading Teacher Education, BM
School Psychology, BM
Social Work, B
Sociology, B
Software Engineering, M
Statistics, B
Systems Engineering, BM

UNIVERSITY OF HOUSTON-DOWNTOWN

Accounting, B
Applied Mathematics, B
Biological and Physical Sciences, B
Biology/Biological Sciences, B
Business Administration and Management, B
Business/Commerce, B
Chemistry, B
Civil Engineering Technology/Technician, B
Computer and Information Sciences, B
Computer Engineering Technology/Technician, B
Criminal Justice/Safety Studies, B
Engineering, B
English Language and Literature, B
Finance, B
Humanities/Humanistic Studies, B
Interdisciplinary Studies, B
Liberal Arts and Sciences Studies and
  Humanities, B
Management Information Systems and Services, B
Marketing/Marketing Management, B
Mechanical Engineering/Mechanical
  Technology/Technician, B
Medical Microbiology and Bacteriology, B
Office Management and Supervision, B
Physics, B
Psychology, B
Purchasing, Procurement/Acquisitions and
  Contracts Management, B
Real Estate, B
Social Sciences, B
Technical and Business Writing, B

UNIVERSITY OF HOUSTON-VICTORIA

Accounting, B
Biology/Biological Sciences, B
Business Administration and Management, B
Business Administration, Management and
  Operations, M
Computer Science, B
Education, BM
History, B
Humanities/Humanistic Studies, B
Interdisciplinary Studies, M
Marketing/Marketing Management, B
Mathematics, B
Psychology, M
Social Sciences, B

UNIVERSITY OF THE INCARNATE WORD

Accounting, B
Adult and Continuing Education and Teaching, BM
American Indian/Native American Studies, B
Area, Ethnic, Cultural, and Gender Studies, B
Art Teacher Education, B
Art/Art Studies, General, B
Athletic Training and Sports Medicine, B
Biological and Biomedical Sciences, M
Biology/Biological Sciences, B
Business Administration and Management, B
Business Administration, Management and
  Operations, MO
Business/Commerce, B
Chemistry, AB
Child Care and Support Services Management, B
Clinical Laboratory Science/Medical
  Technology/Technologist, B
Commercial and Advertising Art, B
Communication and Media Studies, M
Communication Studies/Speech Communication
  and Rhetoric, B
Computer Graphics, B
Developmental and Child Psychology, B

Drama and Dramatics/Theatre Arts, B
Early Childhood Education and Teaching, M
Education, BM
Educational Media/Instructional Technology, M
Elementary Education and Teaching, B
Engineering, B
English, M
English Language and Literature, B
Entrepreneurship/Entrepreneurial Studies, D
Environmental Studies, B
Fashion Merchandising, AB
Fashion/Apparel Design, AB
Finance, B
Foods, Nutrition, and Wellness Studies, B
Health Informatics, M
History, B
Housing and Human Environments, B
Human Resources Management/Personnel
    Administration, B
Information Technology, B
Interdisciplinary Studies, BM
Interior Design, AB
International and Comparative Education, MD
International Business/Trade/Commerce, BM
Kindergarten/PreSchool Education and Teaching, B
Liberal Arts and Sciences Studies and
    Humanities, B
Management Information Systems and Services, B
Management Science, B
Marketing/Marketing Management, B
Mass Communication/Media Studies, B
Mathematics, BM
Mathematics Teacher Education, D
Music, B
Music Management and Merchandising, B
Music Performance, B
Music Teacher Education, B
Music Therapy/Therapist, B
Nuclear Medical Technology/Technologist, B
Nursing, MO
Nursing - Registered Nurse Training, B
Nutritional Sciences, BM
Organizational Behavior Studies, B
Organizational Management, MD
Philosophy, B
Physical Education Teaching and Coaching, BMO
Political Science and Government, B
Pre-Dentistry Studies, B
Pre-Law Studies, B
Pre-Medicine/Pre-Medical Studies, B
Pre-Pharmacy Studies, B
Psychology, B
Reading Teacher Education, BM
Religion/Religious Studies, BM
Secondary Education and Teaching, B
Sociology, B
Spanish Language and Literature, B
Spanish Language Teacher Education, B
Special Education and Teaching, BM
Speech and Rhetorical Studies, B
Sport and Fitness
    Administration/Management, BMO
Urban Studies/Affairs, M

UNIVERSITY OF MARY HARDIN-BAYLOR

Accounting, B
Art/Art Studies, General, B
Athletic Training and Sports Medicine, B
Bible/Biblical Studies, B
Biology/Biological Sciences, B
Business Administration and Management, B
Business Administration, Management and
    Operations, M
Business/Commerce, B
Chemistry, B
Chemistry Teacher Education, B
Christian Studies, B
Clinical Laboratory Science/Medical
    Technology/Technologist, B
Communication Studies/Speech Communication
    and Rhetoric, B
Computer and Information Sciences, B
Computer Graphics, B
Computer Science, B
Counseling Psychology, M

Criminal Justice/Law Enforcement Administration, B
Drama and Dramatics/Theatre Arts, B
Economics, B
Education, BM
Educational Administration and Supervision, M
Educational Psychology, M
Elementary Education and Teaching, B
English Language and Literature, B
Finance, B
Fine/Studio Arts, B
General Studies, B
History, B
Information Science/Studies, B
Junior High/Intermediate/Middle School Education
    and Teaching, B
Kindergarten/PreSchool Education and Teaching, B
Management Information Systems and
    Services, BM
Marketing/Marketing Management, B
Mass Communication/Media Studies, B
Mathematics, B
Mathematics Teacher Education, B
Music Performance, B
Music Teacher Education, B
Music Theory and Composition, B
Nursing - Registered Nurse Training, B
Parks, Recreation, Leisure and Fitness Studies, B
Pastoral Studies/Counseling, B
Physical Education Teaching and Coaching, B
Political Science and Government, B
Psychology, BM
Reading Teacher Education, M
Religion/Religious Studies, BM
Religious/Sacred Music, B
Science Teacher Education/General Science
    Teacher Education, B
Social Studies Teacher Education, B
Social Work, B
Sociology, B
Spanish Language and Literature, B
Special Education and Teaching, B
Sport and Fitness Administration/Management, B
Theology/Theological Studies, B

UNIVERSITY OF NORTH TEXAS

Accounting, BMD
Advertising, B
Anthropology, BM
Applied Economics, M
Art Education, MD
Art History, Criticism and Conservation, BM
Art/Art Studies, General, B
Audiology/Audiologist and Speech-Language
    Pathology/Pathologist, B
Banking and Financial Support Services, B
Behavioral Sciences, B
Biochemistry, BMD
Biological and Biomedical Sciences, MD
Biology/Biological Sciences, B
Broadcast Journalism, B
Business Administration, Management and
    Operations, MD
Business/Commerce, B
Business/Managerial Economics, B
Ceramic Arts and Ceramics, BM
Chemistry, BMD
Child and Family Studies, MD
Child Development, B
City/Urban, Community and Regional Planning, B
Civil Engineering Technology/Technician, B
Clinical Laboratory Science/Medical
    Technology/Technologist, B
Clinical Psychology, D
Clothing and Textiles, M
Communication and Media Studies, M
Communication Disorders, MD
Communication Studies/Speech Communication
    and Rhetoric, B
Community Health and Preventive Medicine, M
Composition, MD
Computer and Information Sciences, B
Computer Education, MD
Computer Engineering, B
Computer Science, MD
Computer Teacher Education, B
Construction Engineering Technology/Technician, B

Counseling Psychology, MD
Counselor Education/School Counseling and
    Guidance Services, MD
Criminal Justice/Safety Studies, B
Criminology, M
Curriculum and Instruction, D
CytoTechnology/Cytotechnologist, B
Dance, B
Drama and Dramatics/Theatre Arts, B
Drawing, B
Early Childhood Education and Teaching, MD
Economics, BM
Education, MDO
Educational Administration and Supervision, MD
Educational Measurement and Evaluation, D
Electrical, Electronic and Communications
    Engineering Technology/Technician, B
Elementary Education and Teaching, M
Engineering and Applied Sciences, M
Engineering Technology, B
English, MD
English Composition, B
English Language and Literature, B
Environmental Sciences, MD
Experimental Psychology, MD
Facilities Planning and Management, M
Fashion Merchandising, B
Fashion/Apparel Design, B
Fiber, Textile and Weaving Arts, B
Film, Television, and Video Production, M
Finance, B
Finance and Banking, MD
Financial Planning and Services, B
Fine Arts and Art Studies, MD
French Language and Literature, BM
General Studies, B
Geography, BM
Geology/Earth Science, B
German Language and Literature, B
Gerontology, BMO
Graphic Design, M
Health and Physical Education, B
Health Promotion, M
Health Psychology, D
Health Services Administration, M
Higher Education/Higher Education
    Administration, D
History, BMD
Hospitality Administration/Management, BM
Human Development, MD
Human Development and Family Studies, B
Industrial and Labor Relations, MD
Industrial and Manufacturing Management, MD
Industrial and Organizational Psychology, M
Information Science/Studies, BMD
Insurance, BMD
Interdisciplinary Studies, BM
Interior Design, M
International/Global Studies, B
Jazz/Jazz Studies, B
Jewelry/Metalsmithing, M
Journalism, BM
Kinesiology and Exercise Science, B
Kinesiology and Movement Studies, M
Landscape Architecture, B
Leisure Studies, MO
Library Science, BMD
Logistics and Materials Management, B
Management Information Systems and
    Services, BMD
Management Strategy and Policy, D
Marketing, MD
Marketing/Marketing Management, B
Materials Sciences, MD
Mathematics, BMD
Mechanical Engineering/Mechanical
    Technology/Technician, B
Metal and Jewelry Arts, B
Molecular Biology, MD
Multi-/Interdisciplinary Studies, B
Music, BMD
Music History, Literature, and Theory, B
Music Performance, B
Music Teacher Education, BMD
Music Theory and Composition, BMD
Musicology and Ethnomusicology, MD

Nuclear/Nuclear Power Technology/Technician, B
Operations Management and Supervision, B
Organizational Behavior Studies, B
Organizational Management, D
Painting, BM
Parks, Recreation and Leisure Facilities
   Management, B
Performance, MD
Philosophy, BMD
Photography, BM
Photojournalism, B
Physics, BMD
Piano and Organ, B
Political Science and Government, BMD
Printmaking, BM
Psychology, BMD
Public Administration, BM
Public Health Education and Promotion, B
Public Relations/Image Management, B
Radio and Television, B
Reading Teacher Education, MD
Real Estate, BMD
Recreation and Park Management, MO
Rehabilitation and Therapeutic Professions, B
Rehabilitation Counseling, M
Rehabilitation Sciences, M
Rehabilitation Therapy, B
Religion/Religious Studies, MD
Sales, Distribution and Marketing Operations, B
School Psychology, MD
Sculpture, BM
Secondary Education and Teaching, M
Social Sciences, B
Social Work, B
Sociology, BMD
Spanish Language and Literature, BM
Special Education and Teaching, MD
Textile Design, M
Theater, M
Violin, Viola, Guitar and Other Stringed
   Instruments, B
Vocational and Technical Education, MD
Voice and Opera, B
Wind and Percussion Instruments, B
Work and Family Studies, B

UNIVERSITY OF PHOENIX-DALLAS CAMPUS

Accounting, M
Business Administration, Management and
   Operations, M
E-Commerce/Electronic Commerce, B
Electronic Commerce, M
Management, M
Management Information Systems and Services, B
Management of Technology, M
Management Science, B
Marketing, M
Marketing/Marketing Management, B
Organizational Management, M

UNIVERSITY OF PHOENIX-HOUSTON CAMPUS

Accounting, M
Business Administration and Management, B
Business Administration, Management and
   Operations, M
Computer and Information Sciences, B
Electronic Commerce, M
Health Services Administration, M
Human Resources Management and Services, M
International Business/Trade/Commerce, M
Management Information Systems and Services, B
Management of Technology, O
Management Science, B
Organizational Management, M

UNIVERSITY OF ST. THOMAS

Accounting, B
Biology/Biological Sciences, B
Business Administration and Management, B
Business Administration, Management and
   Operations, M
Chemistry, B
Communication Studies/Speech Communication
   and Rhetoric, B

Drama and Dramatics/Theatre Arts, B
Economics, B
Education, BM
Elementary Education and Teaching, B
English Language and Literature, B
Environmental Studies, B
Finance, B
Fine/Studio Arts, B
French Language and Literature, B
General Studies, B
History, B
International Relations and Affairs, B
Liberal Arts and Sciences Studies and
   Humanities, B
Liberal Studies, M
Management Information Systems and Services, B
Marketing/Marketing Management, B
Mathematics, B
Music, B
Music Teacher Education, B
Pastoral Studies/Counseling, B
Philosophy, BMD
Political Science and Government, B
Pre-Dentistry Studies, B
Pre-Law Studies, B
Pre-Medicine/Pre-Medical Studies, B
Pre-Pharmacy Studies, B
Pre-Veterinary Studies, B
Psychology, B
Secondary Education and Teaching, B
Spanish Language and Literature, B
Theology and Religious Vocations, BMP
Theology/Theological Studies, B

THE UNIVERSITY OF TEXAS AT ARLINGTON

Accounting, BMD
Advertising, B
Aerospace, Aeronautical and Astronautical
   Engineering, BMD
Anthropology, BM
Architecture, BMO
Art History, Criticism and Conservation, B
Art/Art Studies, General, B
Athletic Training and Sports Medicine, B
Banking and Financial Support Services, B
Biochemistry, B
Biological and Biomedical Sciences, MD
Biology/Biological Sciences, B
Biomedical Engineering, MD
Business Administration and Management, B
Business Administration, Management and
   Operations, MD
Business/Managerial Economics, B
Chemistry, BMD
Child Development, B
Civil Engineering, BMD
Classics and Classical
   Languages, Literatures, and Linguistics, B
Clinical Laboratory Science/Medical
   Technology/Technologist, B
Communication and Media Studies, M
Computer and Information Sciences, B
Computer Engineering, BMD
Computer Science, BMD
Computer Software Engineering, B
Criminal Justice/Safety Studies, B
Criminology, M
Curriculum and Instruction, M
Digital Communication and Media/Multimedia, B
Drama and Dramatics/Theatre Arts, B
Economics, BM
Education, M
Educational Administration and Supervision, M
Electrical Engineering, MD
Electrical, Electronics and Communications
   Engineering, B
Engineering and Applied Sciences, MD
English, MD
English as a Second Language, M
English Language and Literature, B
Environmental Engineering
   Technology/Environmental Technology, MD
Environmental Sciences, MD
Exercise and Sports Science, M
Experimental Psychology, D

Finance and Banking, M
Fine/Studio Arts, B
Foreign Languages and Literatures, B
French Language and Literature, BM
Geology/Earth Science, BMD
Geosciences, D
German Language and Literature, B
Health and Physical Education, B
Health Services Administration, M
History, BMD
Human Resources Management and Services, M
Humanities/Humanistic Studies, M
Industrial Engineering, B
Industrial/Management Engineering, MD
Interdisciplinary Studies, BM
Interior Architecture, B
International Business/Trade/Commerce, B
Journalism, B
Landscape Architecture, M
Linguistics, MD
Logistics and Materials Management, M
Management, M
Management Information Systems and
   Services, BMD
Marketing, MD
Marketing Research, M
Marketing/Marketing Management, B
Materials Engineering, MD
Materials Sciences, MD
Mathematics, BMD
Mechanical Engineering, BMD
Microbiology, B
Multi-/Interdisciplinary Studies, B
Music, BM
Nursing, MD
Nursing - Advanced Practice, M
Nursing - Registered Nurse Training, B
Nursing Administration, M
Nursing Education, M
Philosophy, B
Physical Education Teaching and Coaching, M
Physics, BMD
Political Science and Government, BM
Psychology, BMD
Public Administration, M
Public Affairs, D
Public Relations/Image Management, B
Quantitative Analysis, MD
Radio and Television, B
Real Estate, BM
Rhetoric, D
Russian Language and Literature, B
Social Work, BMD
Sociology, BM
Software Engineering, MD
Spanish Language and Literature, BM
Speech and Rhetorical Studies, B
Systems Engineering, MD
Taxation, M
Urban and Regional Planning, MO

THE UNIVERSITY OF TEXAS AT AUSTIN

Accounting, BMD
Advertising, B
Advertising and Public Relations, MD
Aerospace, Aeronautical and Astronautical
   Engineering, BMD
American/United States Studies/Civilization, BMD
Analytical Chemistry, MD
Ancient Studies/Civilization, B
Ancient/Classical Greek Language and Literature, B
Animal Behavior and Ethology, D
Anthropology, BMD
Apparel and Textiles, B
Applied Mathematics, MD
Arabic Language and Literature, BMD
Archeology, BMD
Architectural Engineering, BM
Architecture, BMDO
Art Education, M
Art History, Criticism and Conservation, BMD
Art/Art Studies, General, B
Asian Languages, MD
Asian Studies/Civilization, BMDO
Astronomy, BMD

Athletic Training and Sports Medicine, B
Biochemistry, BMD
Biological and Biomedical Sciences, MD
Biology/Biological Sciences, B
Biomedical Engineering, MDO
Biomedical/Medical Engineering, B
Biopsychology, MDO
Botany/Plant Biology, B
Business Administration and Management, B
Business Administration, Management and
  Operations, BMO
Business/Commerce, B
Cell Biology and Anatomy, D
Chemical Engineering, BMD
Chemistry, BMD
Child and Family Studies, MD
Civil Engineering, BMD
Classics and Classical
  Languages, Literatures, and Linguistics, BMD
Clinical Laboratory Science/Medical
  Technology/Technologist, B
Cognitive Sciences, D
Communication and Media Studies, MDO
Communication Disorders, BMD
Communication Studies/Speech Communication
  and Rhetoric, B
Comparative Literature, MD
Computational Sciences, MD
Computer and Information Sciences, B
Computer Engineering, MD
Computer Science, MD
Counseling Psychology, D
Counselor Education/School Counseling and
  Guidance Services, M
Curriculum and Instruction, MD
Czech Language and Literature, B
Dance, B
Design and Applied Arts, M
Design and Visual Communications, B
Developmental Biology and Embryology, D
Drama and Dramatics/Theatre Arts, B
East Asian
  Languages, Literatures, and Linguistics, B
East European and Russian Studies, MO
Ecology, BD
Economics, BMD
Education, MD
Educational Administration and Supervision, MD
Educational Psychology, MD
Electrical Engineering, MD
Electrical, Electronics and Communications
  Engineering, B
Engineering and Applied Sciences, MDO
English, MD
English Language and Literature, B
Environmental Engineering
  Technology/Environmental Technology, M
Ethnic, Cultural Minority, and Gender Studies, B
Evolutionary Biology, D
Family and Consumer Sciences/Human
  Sciences, BMD
Film, Television, and Video Production, M
Finance, B
Finance and Banking, D
Fine Arts and Art Studies, M
Fine/Studio Arts, B
Folklore, MD
Foods, Nutrition, and Wellness Studies, B
Foreign Language Teacher Education, MD
Foreign Languages and Literatures, B
French Language and Literature, BMD
Genetics, D
Geography, BMDO
Geological and Earth Sciences/Geosciences, B
Geology/Earth Science, BMD
Geophysics and Seismology, B
Geosciences, MD
Geotechnical Engineering, MD
German Language and Literature, BMD
Health and Physical Education, B
Health Education, MD
Health Services/Allied Health/Health Sciences, B
Hebrew Language and Literature, BMD
History, BMD
Human Development, D
Human Development and Family Studies, B

Human Resources Development, M
Humanities/Humanistic Studies, B
Hydrology and Water Resources Science, B
Immunology, D
Industrial/Management Engineering, MD
Information Science/Studies, MD
Inorganic Chemistry, MD
Interior Design, B
Iranian/Persian
  Languages, Literatures, and Linguistics, B
Islamic Studies, B
Italian Language and Literature, B
Jewish/Judaic Studies, B
Journalism, BMD
Kinesiology and Movement Studies, MD
Latin American Studies, BMDO
Latin Language and Literature, B
Law and Legal Studies, MPO
Liberal Arts and Sciences Studies and
  Humanities, B
Library Science, MD
Linguistics, BMD
Management, D
Management Information Systems and Services, BD
Manufacturing Engineering, MO
Marine Sciences, MD
Marketing, D
Marketing/Marketing Management, B
Materials Engineering, MD
Materials Sciences, MD
Mathematics, BMD
Mathematics Teacher Education, MD
Mechanical Engineering, BMD
Mechanics, MD
Media Studies, MD
Microbiology, BMD
Mineral Economics, M
Mineral/Mining Engineering, M
Molecular Biology, BD
Multi-/Interdisciplinary Studies, B
Music, BMD
Music History, Literature, and Theory, B
Music Performance, B
Music Theory and Composition, B
Natural Resources Management/Development and
  Policy, M
Near and Middle Eastern Languages, MD
Near and Middle Eastern Studies, BMDO
Neurobiology and Neurophysiology, MDO
Neuroscience, MDO
Nursing, MD
Nursing - Registered Nurse Training, B
Nutritional Sciences, MD
Operations Research, MD
Organic Chemistry, MD
Petroleum Engineering, BMD
Pharmaceutical Sciences, MD
Pharmacy, P
Philosophy, BMD
Physical Chemistry, MD
Physics, BMD
Plant Biology, MD
Political Science and Government, BMD
Portuguese Language and Literature, BMD
Psychology, BD
Public Affairs, MDO
Public History, MD
Public Policy Analysis, D
Public Relations/Image Management, B
Radio and Television, B
Religion/Religious Studies, B
Romance
  Languages, Literatures, and Linguistics, MD
Russian Language and Literature, B
Russian Studies, B
Scandinavian
  Languages, Literatures, and Linguistics, B
School Psychology, D
Science Teacher Education/General Science
  Teacher Education, MD
Semitic Languages, Literatures, and Linguistics, B
Slavic Languages, Literatures, and Linguistics, MD
Social Work, BMD
Sociology, BMD
Spanish Language and Literature, BMD
Special Education and Teaching, MD

Sport and Fitness Administration/Management, B
Statistics, M
Technology and Public Policy, M
Theater, MD
Turkish Language and Literature, B
Urban and Regional Planning, MDO
Urban Studies/Affairs, B
Visual and Performing Arts, B
Water Resources Engineering, M
Writing, M
Zoology/Animal Biology, B

THE UNIVERSITY OF TEXAS AT BROWNSVILLE

Accounting, B
Applied Art, B
Art/Art Studies, General, B
Bilingual and Multilingual Education, B
Biological and Biomedical Sciences, M
Biology/Biological Sciences, B
Business Administration and Management, B
Business Administration, Management and
  Operations, M
Chemistry, B
Communication Studies/Speech Communication
  and Rhetoric, B
Community Health Nursing, M
Computer and Information Sciences, B
Corrections, B
Counselor Education/School Counseling and
  Guidance Services, M
Criminal Justice/Law Enforcement Administration, B
Criminal Justice/Police Science, B
Curriculum and Instruction, M
Early Childhood Education and Teaching, M
Education, M
Educational Administration and Supervision, M
Educational Media/Instructional Technology, M
Electrical, Electronic and Communications
  Engineering Technology/Technician, B
Elementary Education and Teaching, M
Engineering Physics, B
English, M
English as a Second Language, M
English Language and Literature, B
Environmental Sciences, B
Finance, B
Health Services/Allied Health/Health Sciences, B
History, BM
Information Science/Studies, B
Interdisciplinary Studies, M
Kindergarten/PreSchool Education and Teaching, B
Kinesiology and Exercise Science, B
Liberal Arts and Sciences Studies and
  Humanities, B
Manufacturing Technology/Technician, B
Marketing/Marketing Management, B
Mathematics, BM
Mechanical Engineering/Mechanical
  Technology/Technician, B
Multi-/Interdisciplinary Studies, B
Multilingual and Multicultural Education, M
Music, B
Nursing - Registered Nurse Training, B
Physics, M
Political Science and Government, BM
Psychology, BM
Public Administration, M
Public Policy Analysis, M
Reading Teacher Education, M
Sociology, B
Spanish Language and Literature, BM
Special Education and Teaching, BM

THE UNIVERSITY OF TEXAS AT DALLAS

Accounting, BM
American/United States Studies/Civilization, B
Applied Economics, MD
Applied Mathematics, BMD
Audiology/Audiologist and Speech-Language
  Pathology/Pathologist, B
Biochemistry, B
Biology/Biological Sciences, B
BioTechnology, M

Business Administration, Management and
Operations, M
Business/Commerce, B
Cell Biology and Anatomy, MD
Chemistry, BMD
Child and Family Studies, M
Cognitive Psychology and Psycholinguistics, B
Cognitive Sciences, MD
Communication and Media Studies, D
Communication Disorders, MD
Comparative Literature, B
Computer and Information Sciences, B
Computer Engineering, BMD
Computer Science, BMD
Computer Software Engineering, B
Criminology, B
Economics, BMD
Electrical Engineering, MD
Electrical, Electronics and Communications
Engineering, B
Engineering and Applied Sciences, MD
Ethnic, Cultural Minority, and Gender Studies, B
Finance, B
Geographic Information Systems, MD
Geography, B
Geology/Earth Science, B
Geosciences, MD
Health Services Administration, M
History, B
Humanities/Humanistic Studies, BMD
Interdisciplinary Studies, BM
International Business/Trade/Commerce, BMD
Management, MD
Management Information Systems and Services, M
Mathematics, BMD
Mathematics Teacher Education, M
Molecular Biology, BMD
Neuroscience, BMD
Physics, BMD
Political Science and Government, BD
Psychology, B
Public Administration, B
Public Affairs, MD
Science Teacher Education/General Science
Teacher Education, M
Sociology, BM
Software Engineering, MD
Statistics, BMD
Telecommunications, MD
Visual and Performing Arts, B

THE UNIVERSITY OF TEXAS AT EL PASO

Accounting, BM
Allied Health and Medical Assisting Services, M
Anthropology, B
Applied Mathematics, B
Art Teacher Education, B
Audiology/Audiologist and Speech-Language
Pathology/Pathologist, B
Bioinformatics, M
Biological and Biomedical Sciences, MD
Biology/Biological Sciences, B
Botany/Plant Biology, B
Broadcast Journalism, B
Business Administration and Management, B
Business Administration, Management and
Operations, M
Ceramic Arts and Ceramics, B
Chemistry, BM
Civil Engineering, BMD
Clinical Laboratory Science/Medical
Technology/Technologist, B
Clinical Psychology, M
Commercial and Advertising Art, B
Communication and Media Studies, M
Communication Disorders, M
Community Health Nursing, M
Community Organization and Advocacy, B
Computer Engineering, MD
Computer Science, BM
Creative Writing, B
Criminal Justice/Law Enforcement Administration, B
Curriculum and Instruction, M
Drama and Dramatics/Theatre Arts, B
Drawing, B

Economics, BM
Education, MD
Educational Leadership and Administration, MD
Electrical Engineering, MD
Electrical, Electronics and Communications
Engineering, B
Engineering and Applied Sciences, MD
English, M
English Education, M
English Language and Literature, B
Environmental Engineering
Technology/Environmental Technology, MD
Environmental Sciences, D
Exercise and Sports Science, M
Experimental Psychology, M
Finance, B
Fine Arts and Art Studies, M
Fine/Studio Arts, B
French Language and Literature, B
Geography, B
Geology/Earth Science, BMD
Geophysics and Seismology, BM
German Language and Literature, B
Health Education, M
Health/Health Care Administration/Management, B
Hispanic-American, Puerto Rican, and Mexican-
American/Chicano Studies, B
History, BMD
Industrial Engineering, B
Industrial/Management Engineering, M
Information Science/Studies, BM
Interdisciplinary Studies, BM
Journalism, B
Kinesiology and Movement Studies, M
Latin American Studies, B
Linguistics, BM
Marketing/Marketing Management, B
Mass Communication/Media Studies, B
Materials Engineering, D
Materials Sciences, D
Mathematics, BM
Mechanical Engineering, BM
Medical Microbiology and Bacteriology, B
Metallurgical Engineering, BM
Music, BM
Music Teacher Education, M
Nurse Midwife/Nursing Midwifery, M
Nursing, M
Nursing - Advanced Practice, M
Nursing - Registered Nurse Training, B
Nursing Administration, M
Philosophy, B
Physical Education Teaching and Coaching, M
Physical Therapy/Therapist, M
Physics, BM
Political Science and Government, BM
Printmaking, B
Psychology, BMD
Public Health (MPH, DPH), B
Real Estate, B
Rhetoric, M
Sculpture, B
Social Work, B
Sociology, BM
Spanish Language and Literature, BM
Speech and Rhetorical Studies, B
Statistics, BM
Theater, M
Women's Health Nursing, M
Writing, M
Zoology/Animal Biology, B

THE UNIVERSITY OF TEXAS HEALTH SCIENCE CENTER AT HOUSTON

Allopathic Medicine, PO
Biochemistry, MDO
Biological and Biomedical Sciences, MDO
Biometry/Biometrics, MDO
Biophysics, MDO
Cancer Biology/Oncology, MDO
Cell Biology and Anatomy, MDO
Dental Hygiene/Hygienist, B
Dentistry, P
Developmental Biology and Embryology, MDO
Genetic Counseling/Counselor, M
Genetics, MDO

Health Informatics, MD
Human Genetics, MDO
Immunology, MDO
Medical Physics, MDO
Microbiology, MDO
Molecular Biology, MDO
Molecular Genetics, MDO
Molecular Pathology, MDO
Neuroscience, MDO
Nursing, MDO
Nursing - Registered Nurse Training, B
Oral and Dental Sciences, M
Public Health, MDO
Toxicology, MDO
Virology, MDO

THE UNIVERSITY OF TEXAS HEALTH SCIENCE CENTER AT SAN ANTONIO

Allopathic Medicine, P
Biochemistry, MD
Biological and Biomedical Sciences, MDPO
Cell Biology and Anatomy, D
Clinical Laboratory Science/Medical
Technology/Technologist, B
Clinical Laboratory Sciences, M
Dental Hygiene/Hygienist, BM
Dentistry, MPO
Immunology, MD
Medical Physics, MD
Microbiology, MD
Molecular Medicine, MD
Nursing, MD
Nursing - Registered Nurse Training, B
Occupational Therapy/Therapist, BM
Oral and Dental Sciences, MO
Pharmacology, D
Physical Therapy/Therapist, M
Physician Assistant, BM
Physiology, MD
Respiratory Care Therapy/Therapist, B
Science Teacher Education/General Science
Teacher Education, M
Structural Biology, D

THE UNIVERSITY OF TEXAS MEDICAL BRANCH

Allied Health and Medical Assisting Services, M
Allopathic Medicine, P
Bacteriology, DO
Biochemistry, MD
Biological and Biomedical Sciences, MDO
Cell Biology and Anatomy, MD
Clinical Laboratory Science/Medical
Technology/Technologist, B
Community Health and Preventive Medicine, MD
Genetics, MD
Humanities/Humanistic Studies, MDO
Immunology, MD
Infectious Diseases, DO
Microbiology, MD
Molecular Biology, D
Molecular Biophysics, MD
Neuroscience, D
Nursing, MD
Nursing - Registered Nurse Training, B
Occupational Therapy/Therapist, M
Pathology/Experimental Pathology, D
Pharmacology, MD
Physical Therapy/Therapist, M
Physician Assistant, M
Physiology, MD
Respiratory Care Therapy/Therapist, B
Structural Biology, D
Toxicology, D
Virology, DO

THE UNIVERSITY OF TEXAS-PAN AMERICAN

Accounting, B
American/United States Studies/Civilization, B
Anthropology, B
Art/Art Studies, General, B
Audiology/Audiologist and Speech-Language
Pathology/Pathologist, B
Biological and Biomedical Sciences, M

Biology/Biological Sciences, B
Business Administration and Management, B
Business Administration, Management and
    Operations, MD
Chemistry, B
Clinical Laboratory Science/Medical
    Technology/Technologist, B
Commercial and Advertising Art, B
Communication and Media Studies, M
Communication Disorders, BM
Communication Studies/Speech Communication
    and Rhetoric, B
Computer Science, BM
Corrections, B
Counselor Education/School Counseling and
    Guidance Services, M
Criminal Justice/Law Enforcement Administration, B
Criminal Justice/Police Science, B
Criminology, M
Dietetics/Dieticians, B
Drama and Dramatics/Theatre Arts, B
Early Childhood Education and Teaching, M
Economics, B
Education, MD
Education/Teaching of the Gifted and Talented, M
Educational Leadership and Administration, MD
Educational Measurement and Evaluation, M
Educational Psychology, M
Electrical, Electronics and Communications
    Engineering, B
Elementary Education and Teaching, BM
Engineering, B
English, M
English as a Second Language, M
English Language and Literature, B
Ethnomusicology, M
Finance, B
Fine Arts and Art Studies, M
Fine/Studio Arts, B
General Studies, B
Health and Physical Education, B
Hispanic-American, Puerto Rican, and Mexican-
    American/Chicano Studies, B
History, BM
Human Services, B
Interdisciplinary Studies, BM
International Business/Trade/Commerce, B
Journalism, B
Kinesiology and Movement Studies, M
Management Information Systems and
    Services, BMD
Manufacturing Engineering, B
Marketing/Marketing Management, B
Mass Communication/Media Studies, B
Mathematics, BM
Mechanical Engineering, B
Multi-/Interdisciplinary Studies, B
Multilingual and Multicultural Education, M
Music, BM
Music Teacher Education, M
Nursing, M
Nursing - Adult, M
Nursing - Advanced Practice, M
Nursing - Registered Nurse Training, B
Occupational Therapy/Therapist, BM
Pediatric Nurse/Nursing, M
Performance, M
Philosophy, B
Physics, B
Political Science and Government, B
Pre-Dentistry Studies, B
Pre-Medicine/Pre-Medical Studies, B
Pre-Pharmacy Studies, B
Psychology, BM
Public Administration, M
Reading Teacher Education, M
Rehabilitation and Therapeutic Professions, B
Rehabilitation Counseling, M
Rehabilitation Therapy, B
School Psychology, M
Science Teacher Education/General Science
    Teacher Education, B
Secondary Education and Teaching, M
Social Sciences, B
Social Work, BM
Sociology, BM

Spanish Language and Literature, BM
Special Education and Teaching, M
Speech and Rhetorical Studies, B
Theater, M

THE UNIVERSITY OF TEXAS OF THE PERMIAN BASIN

Accounting, BM
Art/Art Studies, General, B
Biological and Biomedical Sciences, M
Biology/Biological Sciences, B
Business Administration and Management, B
Business Administration, Management and
    Operations, M
Chemistry, B
Clinical Psychology, M
Computer Science, B
Counselor Education/School Counseling and
    Guidance Services, M
Criminology, BM
Early Childhood Education and Teaching, M
Economics, B
Education, M
Educational Administration and Supervision, M
English, M
English as a Second Language, M
English Language and Literature, B
Environmental Studies, B
Finance, B
Foundations and Philosophy of Education, M
Geology/Earth Science, BM
History, BM
Humanities/Humanistic Studies, B
Interdisciplinary Studies, B
Kinesiology and Exercise Science, B
Kinesiology and Movement Studies, M
Marketing/Marketing Management, B
Mass Communication/Media Studies, B
Mathematics, B
Political Science and Government, B
Psychology, BM
Reading Teacher Education, M
Sociology, B
Spanish Language and Literature, B
Special Education and Teaching, M
Speech and Rhetorical Studies, B

THE UNIVERSITY OF TEXAS AT SAN ANTONIO

Accounting, BMD
Actuarial Science, B
Adult and Continuing Education and Teaching, M
American/United States Studies/Civilization, B
Anthropology, BM
Architecture, BM
Art History, Criticism and Conservation, BM
Art/Art Studies, General, B
Biological and Biomedical Sciences, MD
Biological and Physical Sciences, B
Biology/Biological Sciences, B
Biomedical Engineering, D
BioTechnology, M
Business Administration and Management, B
Business Administration, Management and
    Operations, D
Business/Commerce, B
Business/Managerial Economics, B
Cell Biology and Anatomy, D
Chemistry, BM
Civil Engineering, BM
Classics and Classical
    Languages, Literatures, and Linguistics, B
Clinical Laboratory Science/Medical
    Technology/Technologist, B
Communication Studies/Speech Communication
    and Rhetoric, B
Computer Engineering, B
Computer Science, MD
Counselor Education/School Counseling and
    Guidance Services, M
Criminal Justice/Safety Studies, B
Criminology, M
Cultural Studies, D
Curriculum and Instruction, M
Early Childhood Education and Teaching, M
Economics, M

Education, M
Educational Leadership and Administration, MD
Educational Media/Instructional Technology, M
Educational Psychology, M
Electrical Engineering, MD
Electrical, Electronics and Communications
    Engineering, B
Elementary Education and Teaching, M
Engineering and Applied Sciences, MD
English, MD
English as a Second Language, M
English Language and Literature, B
Entrepreneurship/Entrepreneurial Studies, B
Environmental Engineering
    Technology/Environmental Technology, D
Environmental Sciences, BMD
Finance, B
Finance and Banking, MD
Fine Arts and Art Studies, M
French Language and Literature, B
Geography, B
Geology/Earth Science, BMD
Germanic Languages, Literatures, and Linguistics, B
Health and Physical Education, B
Health Services/Allied Health/Health Sciences, B
Higher Education/Higher Education
    Administration, M
Hispanic-American, Puerto Rican, and Mexican-
    American/Chicano Studies, B
History, BM
Human Resources Management/Personnel
    Administration, B
Humanities/Humanistic Studies, B
Information Science/Studies, MD
Interdisciplinary Studies, M
Interior Architecture, B
Interior Design, B
International Business/Trade/Commerce, B
Management, M
Management Information Systems and
    Services, BM
Management Science, B
Marketing, M
Marketing/Marketing Management, B
Mass Communication/Media Studies, B
Mathematics, B
Mathematics Teacher Education, M
Mechanical Engineering, BM
Molecular Biology, D
Multilingual and Multicultural Education, MD
Music, BM
Music Management and Merchandising, B
Music Performance, B
Music Theory and Composition, B
Neurobiology and Neurophysiology, D
Operations Management and Supervision, B
Organizational Management, D
Philosophy, B
Physics, B
Political Science and Government, BM
Psychology, BM
Public Administration, M
Reading Teacher Education, M
Sociology, BM
Spanish Language and Literature, BM
Special Education and Teaching, M
Statistics, BM
Taxation, M
Tourism and Travel Services Management, B

THE UNIVERSITY OF TEXAS SOUTHWESTERN MEDICAL CENTER AT DALLAS

Allopathic Medicine, PO
Biochemistry, D
Biological and Biomedical Sciences, DO
Biomedical Engineering, MD
Cell Biology and Anatomy, D
Clinical Laboratory Science/Medical
    Technology/Technologist, B
Clinical Psychology, D
Developmental Biology and Embryology, D
Dietetics/Dieticians, B
Genetics, D
Immunology, D
Medical Illustration and Informatics, M

Microbiology, D
Molecular Biophysics, D
Neuroscience, D
Orthotist/Prosthetist, B
Physical Therapy/Therapist, M
Physician Assistant, M
Radiation Biology/Radiobiology, MD
Rehabilitation and Therapeutic Professions, B
Rehabilitation Counseling, M

THE UNIVERSITY OF TEXAS AT TYLER

Accounting, B
Art/Art Studies, General, B
Biological and Biomedical Sciences, M
Biology/Biological Sciences, B
Business Administration and Management, B
Business Administration, Management and
    Operations, M
Chemistry, B
Civil Engineering, B
Clinical Laboratory Science/Medical
    Technology/Technologist, B
Clinical Psychology, M
Communication and Media Studies, M
Computer and Information Sciences, B
Computer Science, BM
Counseling Psychology, M
Criminal Justice/Safety Studies, B
Criminology, M
Curriculum and Instruction, M
Drama and Dramatics/Theatre Arts, B
Early Childhood Education and Teaching, M
Economics, B
Education, M
Educational Leadership and Administration, M
Electrical, Electronics and Communications
    Engineering, B
Engineering and Applied Sciences, M
Engineering Technology, B
English, M
English Education, M
English Language and Literature, B
Exercise and Sports Science, M
Finance, B
Fine Arts and Art Studies, M
Foreign Languages and Literatures, B
General Studies, B
Health and Physical Education, B
Health Education, M
Health Professions and Related Clinical Sciences, B
Health Services Administration, M
History, BM
Human Resources Development, BM
Industrial and Manufacturing Management, M
Industrial Education, M
Industrial Technology/Technician, B
Information Science/Studies, M
Interdisciplinary Studies, BM
Journalism, B
Kinesiology and Exercise Science, B
Kinesiology and Movement Studies, M
Liberal Arts and Sciences Studies and
    Humanities, B
Management, M
Marketing/Marketing Management, B
Mathematics, BM
Mechanical Engineering, B
Multi-/Interdisciplinary Studies, B
Music, BM
Nursing, MO
Nursing - Advanced Practice, M
Nursing - Registered Nurse Training, B
Nursing Administration, M
Nursing Education, M
Political Science and Government, BM
Psychology, BM
Public Administration, M
Reading Teacher Education, M
School Psychology, M
Science Teacher Education/General Science
    Teacher Education, M
Secondary Education and Teaching, M
Social Sciences, M
Social Studies Teacher Education, M
Sociology, BM
Spanish Language and Literature, B

Special Education and Teaching, M
Speech and Rhetorical Studies, B
Vocational and Technical Education, M

VERNON COLLEGE

Accounting, A
Administrative Assistant and Secretarial Science, A
Automobile/Automotive Mechanics
    Technology/Technician, A
Business Administration and Management, A
Child Care and Support Services Management, A
Cosmetology/Cosmetologist, A
Criminal Justice/Law Enforcement Administration, A
Data Processing and Data Processing
    Technology/Technician, A
Drafting and Design Technology/Technician, A
Farm/Farm and Ranch Management, A
Health Information/Medical Records
    Technology/Technician, A
Law and Legal Studies, A
Liberal Arts and Sciences Studies and
    Humanities, A
Licensed Practical/Vocational Nurse Training, A
Machine Tool Technology/Machinist, A

VICTORIA COLLEGE

Accounting, A
Administrative Assistant and Secretarial Science, A
Business Administration and Management, A
Clinical/Medical Laboratory Technician, A
Computer Programming/Programmer, A
Computer Systems Networking and
    Telecommunications, A
Criminal Justice/Police Science, A
Drafting and Design Technology/Technician, A
Electrical, Electronic and Communications
    Engineering Technology/Technician, A
Emergency Medical Technology/Technician (EMT
    Paramedic), A
Industrial Technology/Technician, A
Information Science/Studies, A
Legal Assistant/Paralegal, A
Liberal Arts and Sciences Studies and
    Humanities, A
Nursing - Registered Nurse Training, A

WADE COLLEGE

Computer Graphics, A
Design and Visual Communications, A
Fashion Merchandising, A
Fashion/Apparel Design, A
Interior Design, A

WAYLAND BAPTIST UNIVERSITY

Art/Art Studies, General, B
Biology/Biological Sciences, B
Business Administration and Management, AB
Business Administration, Management and
    Operations, M
Chemistry, B
Christian Studies, AB
Criminal Justice/Safety Studies, B
Drama and Dramatics/Theatre Arts, B
Education, ABM
Elementary Education and Teaching, B
English Language and Literature, B
Health Services Administration, M
History, B
Human Resources Management and Services, M
Human Services, B
Interdisciplinary Studies, M
International Business/Trade/Commerce, M
Management Information Systems and Services, M
Mass Communication/Media Studies, B
Mathematics, B
Music, B
Music Teacher Education, B
Pastoral Studies/Counseling, M
Physical Education Teaching and Coaching, B
Physical Sciences, B
Political Science and Government, B
Psychology, B
Religion/Religious Studies, M
Religious Education, B
Religious/Sacred Music, B
Social Sciences, AB

Spanish Language and Literature, B
Theology and Religious Vocations, B
Trade and Industrial Teacher Education, B

WEATHERFORD COLLEGE

Administrative Assistant and Secretarial Science, A
Biological and Physical Sciences, A
Business Administration and Management, A
Computer Graphics, A
Computer Programming/Programmer, A
Corrections, A
Cosmetology/Cosmetologist, A
Criminal Justice/Law Enforcement Administration, A
Emergency Medical Technology/Technician (EMT
    Paramedic), A
Fire Science/Firefighting, A
Information Science/Studies, A
Liberal Arts and Sciences Studies and
    Humanities, A
Nursing - Registered Nurse Training, A
Pharmacy Technician/Assistant, A
Respiratory Care Therapy/Therapist, A

WEST TEXAS A&M UNIVERSITY

Accounting, BM
Advertising, B
Agribusiness, B
Agricultural Business and Management, B
Agricultural Economics, M
Agricultural Sciences, MD
Agriculture, B
Agronomy and Crop Science, B
Animal Sciences, BM
Art/Art Studies, General, B
Biological and Biomedical Sciences, M
Biology/Biological Sciences, B
BioTechnology, B
Broadcast Journalism, B
Business Administration and Management, B
Business Administration, Management and
    Operations, M
Business/Commerce, B
Business/Managerial Economics, B
Chemistry, BM
Clinical Laboratory Science/Medical
    Technology/Technologist, B
Commercial and Advertising Art, B
Communication and Media Studies, M
Communication Disorders, BM
Computer and Information Sciences, B
Counselor Education/School Counseling and
    Guidance Services, M
Criminal Justice/Law Enforcement Administration, B
Criminology, M
Curriculum and Instruction, M
Dance, B
Drama and Dramatics/Theatre Arts, B
Economics, BM
Education, M
Educational Administration and Supervision, M
Educational Measurement and Evaluation, M
Educational Media/Instructional Technology, M
Engineering and Applied Sciences, M
English, M
English Language and Literature, B
Environmental Sciences, BM
Equestrian/Equine Studies, B
Exercise and Sports Science, M
Finance, B
Finance and Banking, M
Fine Arts and Art Studies, M
Fine/Studio Arts, B
General Studies, B
Geography, B
Geology/Earth Science, B
Health and Physical Education, B
History, BM
Industrial Technology/Technician, B
Interdisciplinary Studies, BM
Journalism, B
Management Information Systems and Services, B
Marketing/Marketing Management, B
Mass Communication/Media Studies, B
Mathematics, BM
Mechanical Engineering, B
Multi-/Interdisciplinary Studies, B

Music, BM
Music Performance, B
Music Theory and Composition, B
Music Therapy/Therapist, B
Nursing, M
Nursing - Registered Nurse Training, B
Performance, M
Physics, B
Plant Protection and Integrated Pest
  Management, B
Plant Sciences, M
Political Science and Government, BM
Pre-Law Studies, B
Psychology, BM
Public Administration, B
Reading Teacher Education, M
Social Sciences, B
Social Work, B
Sociology, B
Spanish Language and Literature, B
Special Education and Teaching, M
Speech and Rhetorical Studies, B
Wildlife and Wildlands Science and Management, B

WESTERN TECHNICAL COLLEGE

Automobile/Automotive Mechanics
  Technology/Technician, A
Computer Engineering Technology/Technician, A
Heating, Air Conditioning, Ventilation and
  Refrigeration Maintenance
  Technology/Technician, A

WESTERN TEXAS COLLEGE

Accounting, A
Administrative Assistant and Secretarial Science, A
Agricultural Teacher Education, A
Agriculture, A
Art Teacher Education, A
Art/Art Studies, General, A
Automobile/Automotive Mechanics
  Technology/Technician, A
Business Administration and Management, A
Computer Engineering Technology/Technician, A
Computer Science, A
Corrections, A
Criminal Justice/Law Enforcement Administration, A
Criminal Justice/Police Science, A
Education, A
Journalism, A
Landscape Architecture, A
Liberal Arts and Sciences Studies and
  Humanities, A
Licensed Practical/Vocational Nurse Training, A
Marketing/Marketing Management, A
Mass Communication/Media Studies, A
Parks, Recreation and Leisure Facilities
  Management, A
Welding Technology/Welder, A

WESTWOOD COLLEGE-DALLAS

Architectural Drafting and Architectural
  CAD/CADD, A
Computer Systems Networking and
  Telecommunications, A
Graphic Design, A

WESTWOOD COLLEGE-FORT WORTH

Architectural Drafting and Architectural
  CAD/CADD, A
Computer Systems Networking and
  Telecommunications, A
Graphic Design, A
Intermedia/Multimedia, A

WESTWOOD COLLEGE-HOUSTON
SOUTH CAMPUS

Architectural Drafting and Architectural
  CAD/CADD, A
Computer Systems Networking and
  Telecommunications, A
Graphic Design, A

WHARTON COUNTY JUNIOR COLLEGE

Administrative Assistant and Secretarial Science, A
Agriculture, A

Art/Art Studies, General, A
Automobile/Automotive Mechanics
  Technology/Technician, A
Behavioral Sciences, A
Biology/Biological Sciences, A
Business Administration and Management, A
Chemistry, A
Clinical/Medical Laboratory Technician, A
Computer Science, A
Criminal Justice/Law Enforcement Administration, A
Data Processing and Data Processing
  Technology/Technician, A
Dental Hygiene/Hygienist, A
Drafting and Design Technology/Technician, A
Drama and Dramatics/Theatre Arts, A
Electrical, Electronic and Communications
  Engineering Technology/Technician, A
English Language and Literature, A
Farm/Farm and Ranch Management, A
Health Information/Medical Records
  Administration/Administrator, A
Industrial Radiologic Technology/Technician, A
Mathematics, A
Music, A
Nursing - Registered Nurse Training, A
Ornamental Horticulture, A
Physical Education Teaching and Coaching, A
Physical Therapy/Therapist, A
Pre-Engineering, A
Spanish Language and Literature, A
Speech and Rhetorical Studies, A

WILEY COLLEGE

Administrative Assistant and Secretarial Science, AB
Biology/Biological Sciences, B
Business Administration and Management, B
Business Teacher Education, B
Chemistry, B
Computer and Information Sciences, AB
Computer Science, AB
Elementary Education and Teaching, B
English Language and Literature, B
History, B
Hotel/Motel Administration/Management, B
Mass Communication/Media Studies, B
Mathematics, B
Music, B
Music Teacher Education, B
Philosophy, B
Physical Education Teaching and Coaching, B
Physical Sciences, B
Physics, B
Pre-Dentistry Studies, B
Pre-Law Studies, B
Pre-Medicine/Pre-Medical Studies, B
Religion/Religious Studies, B
Social Sciences, B
Social Work, B
Sociology, B
Special Education and Teaching, B

United States Virgin Islands
UNIVERSITY OF THE VIRGIN ISLANDS

Accounting, AB
Administrative Assistant and Secretarial Science, A
Biology/Biological Sciences, B
Business Administration and Management, AB
Business Administration, Management and
  Operations, M
Chemistry, B
Computer Science, A
Criminal Justice/Police Science, A
Data Processing and Data Processing
  Technology/Technician, A
Drama and Dramatics/Theatre Arts, B
Education, MO
Elementary Education and Teaching, B
English Language and Literature, B
Hotel/Motel Administration/Management, A
Humanities/Humanistic Studies, B
Marine Biology and Biological Oceanography, B
Mathematics, B
Music Teacher Education, B
Nursing - Registered Nurse Training, AB

Physics, A
Psychology, B
Public Administration, M
School Psychology, O
Social Sciences, B
Social Work, B
Speech and Rhetorical Studies, B
Trade and Industrial Teacher Education, B

Utah
BRIGHAM YOUNG UNIVERSITY

Accounting, BMO
Accounting and Related Services, B
Acting, B
Actuarial Science, B
Advertising, B
Agribusiness, B
Agricultural Business and Management, B
Agricultural Economics, B
Agricultural Sciences, MD
Agronomy and Soil Sciences, M
American/United States Studies/Civilization, B
Analytical Chemistry, MD
Ancient Near Eastern and Biblical
  Languages, Literatures, and Linguistics, B
Ancient/Classical Greek Language and Literature, B
Animal Sciences, M
Animation, Interactive Technology, Video Graphics
  and Special Effects, B
Anthropology, BM
Applied Economics, B
Arabic Language and Literature, B
Art Education, M
Art History, Criticism and Conservation, BM
Art Teacher Education, B
Art/Art Studies, General, B
Asian Languages, M
Asian Studies/Civilization, B
Astronomy, BMD
Athletic Training and Sports Medicine, BM
Audiology/Audiologist and Speech-Language
  Pathology/Pathologist, B
Ballet, B
Biochemistry, BMD
Bioinformatics, B
Biological and Biomedical Sciences, MD
Biological and Physical Sciences, B
Biology/Biological Sciences, B
Biomedical Sciences, B
Biophysics, B
Biostatistics, B
BioTechnology, B
Botany/Plant Biology, B
Broadcast Journalism, B
Business Administration and Management, B
Business Administration, Management and
  Operations, MO
Business Family and Consumer Sciences/Human
  Sciences, B
Business Statistics, B
Business/Commerce, B
Cartography, B
Central/Middle and Eastern European Studies, B
Ceramic Arts and Ceramics, B
Chemical Engineering, BMD
Chemistry, BMD
Chemistry Teacher Education, B
Child and Family Studies, MD
Child Care and Support Services Management, B
Child Care Provider/Assistant, B
Child Development, B
Chinese Language and Literature, B
Cinematography and Film/Video Production, B
Civil Engineering, BMD
Classical, Ancient Mediterranean and Near Eastern
  Studies and Archaeology, B
Classics and Classical
  Languages, Literatures, and Linguistics, B
Clinical Laboratory Science/Medical
  Technology/Technologist, B
Clinical Psychology, D
Communication and Media Studies, M
Communication Disorders, M
Communication, Journalism and Related
  Programs, B

Comparative and Interdisciplinary Arts, M
Comparative Literature, BM
Composition, M
Computer Engineering, B
Computer Science, BMD
Conservation Biology, B
Construction Engineering and Management, M
Counseling Psychology, MDO
Crafts/Craft Design, Folk Art and Artisanry, B
Dance, B
Design and Visual Communications, B
Developmental Biology and Embryology, MD
Dietetics/Dieticians, B
Directing and Theatrical Production, B
Drama and Dance Teacher Education, B
Drama and Dramatics/Theatre Arts, B
Dramatic/Theatre Arts and Stagecraft, B
Drawing, B
Early Childhood Education and Teaching, B
Ecology, Evolution, Systematics and Population
  Biology, B
Economics, B
Education, BMDO
Educational Leadership and Administration, MDO
Educational Media/Instructional Technology, MD
Educational Psychology, MD
Electrical Engineering, MD
Electrical, Electronics and Communications
  Engineering, B
Elementary Education and Teaching, B
Engineering and Applied Sciences, MDO
Engineering Technology, B
English, M
English as a Second Language, MO
English Composition, B
English Language and Literature, B
English/Language Arts Teacher Education, B
Entrepreneurship/Entrepreneurial Studies, B
Environmental Sciences, B
Exercise and Sports Science, MD
Family and Consumer Economics and Related
  Services, B
Family and Consumer Sciences/Home Economics
  Teacher Education, B
Family and Consumer Sciences/Human Sciences, B
Family and Consumer Sciences/Human Sciences
  Business Services, B
Family Resource Management Studies, B
Family Systems, B
Film, Television, and Video Production, MD
Film/Cinema Studies, B
Film/Video and Photographic Arts, B
Financial Planning and Services, B
Fine Arts and Art Studies, M
Fine/Studio Arts, B
Fish, Game and Wildlife Management, MD
Food Science, B
Food Science and Technology, M
Food Technology and Processing, B
Foreign Language Teacher Education, BM
Foundations and Philosophy of Education, MDO
French Language and Literature, BM
French Language Teacher Education, B
General Merchandising, Sales, and Related
  Marketing Operations, B
Geography, BM
Geological and Earth Sciences/Geosciences, B
Geology/Earth Science, BM
German Language and Literature, BM
German Language Teacher Education, B
Graphic Design, B
Health and Physical Education, B
Health and Physical Education/Fitness, B
Health Education, M
Health Promotion, MD
Hebrew Language and Literature, B
History, BM
History Teacher Education, B
Home Furnishings and Equipment Installers, B
Horticultural Science, M
Human Development, MD
Human Development and Family Studies, B
Human Resources Development, B
Human Resources Management/Personnel
  Administration, B
Humanities/Humanistic Studies, BM

Illustration, B
Industrial Design, BM
Information Science/Studies, M
Information Technology, B
Inorganic Chemistry, MD
Interior Design, B
International Finance, B
International Marketing, B
International Relations and Affairs, B
Italian Language and Literature, B
Japanese Language and Literature, B
Jazz/Jazz Studies, B
Journalism, B
Kinesiology and Exercise Science, B
Korean Language and Literature, B
Language Interpretation and Translation, B
Latin American Studies, B
Latin Language and Literature, B
Latin Teacher Education, B
Law and Legal Studies, MPO
Liberal Arts and Sciences Studies and
  Humanities, B
Linguistic, Comparative, and Related Language
  Studies and Services, B
Linguistics, BMO
Logistics and Materials Management, B
Management Information Systems and
  Services, BMO
Manufacturing Engineering, B
Marketing/Marketing Management, B
Marriage and Family Therapy/Counseling, MD
Mass Communication/Media Studies, BM
Mathematics, BMD
Mathematics Teacher Education, BM
Mechanical Engineering, BMDO
Microbiology, BMD
Molecular Biology, BMD
Music, BM
Music History, Literature, and Theory, B
Music Pedagogy, B
Music Performance, B
Music Teacher Education, BM
Music Theory and Composition, B
Musicology and Ethnomusicology, M
Near and Middle Eastern Languages, M
Neuroscience, BMD
Norwegian Language and Literature, B
Nursing, M
Nursing - Registered Nurse Training, B
Nutritional Sciences, BM
Organic Chemistry, MD
Organizational Communication, B
Painting, B
Parks, Recreation, Leisure and Fitness Studies, B
Performance, M
Philosophy, B
Photography, B
Physical Chemistry, MD
Physical Education Teaching and Coaching, BM
Physics, BMD
Physics Teacher Education, B
Physiology, BMD
Piano and Organ, B
Plant Genetics, B
Plant Sciences, M
Playwriting and Screenwriting, B
Political Science and Government, B
Portuguese Language and Literature, BM
Pre-Nursing Studies, B
Printmaking, B
Psychology, BMD
Psychology Teacher Education, B
Public Administration, MO
Public Policy Analysis, B
Public Relations, Advertising, and Applied
  Communication, B
Radio, Television, and Digital Communication, B
Range Science and Management, B
Recreation and Park Management, M
Religious Education, M
Retailing and Retail Operations, B
Russian Language and Literature, B
School Psychology, O
Science Teacher Education/General Science
  Teacher Education, BM
Sculpture, B

Social Psychology, B
Social Science Teacher Education, B
Social Work, BM
Sociology, BMD
Soil Sciences, B
Spanish Language and Literature, BM
Spanish Language Teacher Education, B
Special Education and Teaching, BMDO
Speech and Rhetorical Studies, B
Speech Teacher Education, B
Statistics, BM
Swedish Language and Literature, B
Teacher Education and Professional
  Development, Specific Levels and Methods, B
Teacher Education and Professional
  Development, Specific Subject Areas, B
Teaching English as a Second or Foreign
  Language/ESL Language Instructor, B
Technical Theatre/Theatre Design and
  Technology, B
Technology Teacher Education/Industrial Arts
  Teacher Education, B
Theater, MD
Therapeutic Recreation/Recreational Therapy, B
Veterinary/Animal Health Technology/Technician and
  Veterinary Assistant, B
Violin, Viola, Guitar and Other Stringed
  Instruments, B
Visual and Performing Arts, B
Voice and Opera, B
Wildlife and Wildlands Science and Management, B
Work and Family Studies, B
Zoology/Animal Biology, B

CALIFORNIA COLLEGE FOR HEALTH SCIENCES

Accounting, AB
Business/Commerce, AB
Community Health and Preventive Medicine, M
Finance, AB
Health Information/Medical Records
  Administration/Administrator, A
Health Promotion, M
Health Services Administration, M
Health/Health Care Administration/Management, B
Kindergarten/PreSchool Education and Teaching, A
Public Health, M
Public Health (MPH, DPH), A
Respiratory Care Therapy/Therapist, AB

COLLEGE OF EASTERN UTAH

Administrative Assistant and Secretarial Science, A
Automobile/Automotive Mechanics
  Technology/Technician, A
Business Administration and Management, A
Carpentry/Carpenter, A
Child Development, A
Computer Graphics, A
Construction Engineering Technology/Technician, A
Cosmetology/Cosmetologist, A
Kindergarten/PreSchool Education and Teaching, A
Liberal Arts and Sciences Studies and
  Humanities, A
Machine Tool Technology/Machinist, A
Mining Technology/Technician, A
Nursing - Registered Nurse Training, A
Pre-Engineering, A
Welding Technology/Welder, A

DIXIE STATE COLLEGE OF UTAH

Accounting, A
Administrative Assistant and Secretarial Science, A
Agriculture, A
Airline/Commercial/Professional Pilot and Flight
  Crew, A
Architectural Drafting and Architectural
  CAD/CADD, A
Art History, Criticism and Conservation, A
Art/Art Studies, General, A
Autobody/Collision and Repair
  Technology/Technician, A
Automobile/Automotive Mechanics
  Technology/Technician, A
Aviation/Airway Management and Operations, A
Biology/Biological Sciences, A
BioTechnology, A

Botany/Plant Biology, A
Broadcast Journalism, A
Business Administration and Management, AB
Cartography, A
Ceramic Arts and Ceramics, A
Chemistry, A
Child Care and Support Services Management, A
Commercial and Advertising Art, A
Communication Studies/Speech Communication
    and Rhetoric, A
Computer Science, AB
Criminal Justice/Safety Studies, A
Dance, A
Data Processing and Data Processing
    Technology/Technician, A
Dental Hygiene/Hygienist, A
Diesel Mechanics Technology/Technician, A
Drama and Dramatics/Theatre Arts, A
Drawing, A
Ecology, A
Economics, A
Elementary Education and Teaching, AB
Emergency Medical Technology/Technician (EMT
    Paramedic), A
Engineering, A
English Language and Literature, A
Environmental Studies, A
Foreign Languages and Literatures, A
Forestry, A
Geology/Earth Science, A
Health Professions and Related Clinical Sciences, A
History, A
Humanities/Humanistic Studies, A
Interior Design, A
Journalism, A
Kindergarten/PreSchool Education and Teaching, A
Liberal Arts and Sciences Studies and
    Humanities, A
Marine Biology and Biological Oceanography, A
Mathematics, A
Mechanical Drafting and Mechanical Drafting
    CAD/CADD, A
Music, A
Natural Resources and Conservation, A
Natural Resources Management/Development and
    Policy, A
Nursing - Registered Nurse Training, AB
Painting, A
Philosophy, A
Photographic and Film/Video Technology/Technician
    and Assistant, A
Photography, A
Physical Education Teaching and Coaching, A
Physics, A
Plant Pathology/Phytopathology, A
Plant Protection and Integrated Pest
    Management, A
Political Science and Government, A
Pre-Law Studies, A
Printmaking, A
Psychology, A
Radio and Television, A
Radio, Television, and Digital Communication, B
Range Science and Management, A
Sculpture, A
Secondary Education and Teaching, A
Social Work, A
Sociology, A
Soil Science and Agronomy, A
Tourism and Travel Services Marketing
    Operations, A
Water Resources Engineering, A
Web Page, Digital/Multimedia and Information
    Resources Design, A
Wildlife and Wildlands Science and Management, A
Zoology/Animal Biology, A

ITT TECHNICAL INSTITUTE

Animation, Interactive Technology, Video Graphics
    and Special Effects, B
CAD/CADD Drafting and/or Design
    Technology/Technician, A
Computer and Information Systems Security, A
Computer Programming/Programmer, A
Computer Software Technology/Technician, B

Computer Systems Networking and
    Telecommunications, B
Criminal Justice/Law Enforcement Administration, B
E-Commerce/Electronic Commerce, B
Electrical, Electronic and Communications
    Engineering Technology/Technician, AB
System, Networking, and LAN/WAN
    Management/Manager, A
Web Page, Digital/Multimedia and Information
    Resources Design, A
Web/Multimedia Management and Webmaster, A

LDS BUSINESS COLLEGE

Accounting, A
Accounting and Business/Management, A
Accounting Technology/Technician and
    Bookkeeping, A
Administrative Assistant and Secretarial Science, A
Computer and Information Sciences and Support
    Services, A
Entrepreneurship/Entrepreneurial Studies, A
Executive Assistant/Executive Secretary, A
Health Information/Medical Records
    Administration/Administrator, A
Information Technology, A
Interior Design, A
Legal Administrative Assistant/Secretary, A
Liberal Arts and Sciences Studies and
    Humanities, A
Medical Administrative Assistant/Secretary, A
Medical Insurance Coding Specialist/Coder, A
Medical Office Assistant/Specialist, A
Medical Transcription/Transcriptionist, A
Medical/Clinical Assistant, A
Sales, Distribution and Marketing Operations, A
System, Networking, and LAN/WAN
    Management/Manager, A
Web Page, Digital/Multimedia and Information
    Resources Design, A

MIDWIVES COLLEGE OF UTAH

Direct Entry Midwifery (LM, CPM), B

MOUNTAIN WEST COLLEGE

Accounting, A
Administrative Assistant and Secretarial Science, A
Business Administration and Management, A
Computer Systems Networking and
    Telecommunications, A
Information Science/Studies, A
Legal Assistant/Paralegal, A
Medical/Clinical Assistant, A
Tourism and Travel Services Management, A

NEUMONT UNIVERSITY

Computer and Information Sciences, B
Computer Programming, B
Computer Programming, Specific Applications, B
Computer
    Programming, Vendor/Product Certification, B
Computer Programming/Programmer, B
Computer Science, B
Computer Software and Media Applications, B
Data Modeling/Warehousing and Database
    Administration, B
Information Technology, B
Web Page, Digital/Multimedia and Information
    Resources Design, B

SALT LAKE COMMUNITY COLLEGE

Accounting, A
Airline/Commercial/Professional Pilot and Flight
    Crew, A
Architectural Engineering Technology/Technician, A
Autobody/Collision and Repair
    Technology/Technician, A
Avionics Maintenance Technology/Technician, A
Biology Technician/BioTechnology Laboratory
    Technician, A
Biology/Biological Sciences, A
Building/Construction
    Finishing, Management, and Inspection, A
Business Administration and Management, A
Chemistry, A
Clinical/Medical Laboratory Technician, A

Computer and Information Sciences, A
Computer Science, A
Cosmetology/Cosmetologist, A
Criminal Justice/Law Enforcement Administration, A
Dental Hygiene/Hygienist, A
Diesel Mechanics Technology/Technician, A
Drafting and Design Technology/Technician, A
Economics, A
Electrical, Electronic and Communications
    Engineering Technology/Technician, A
Engineering, A
Engineering Technology, A
English Language and Literature, A
Environmental Engineering
    Technology/Environmental Technology, A
Finance and Financial Management Services, A
General Studies, A
Graphic Design, A
Heating, Air Conditioning, Ventilation and
    Refrigeration Maintenance
    Technology/Technician, A
Heavy Equipment Maintenance
    Technology/Technician, A
History, A
Human Development and Family Studies, A
Humanities/Humanistic Studies, A
Industrial Radiologic Technology/Technician, A
Information Science/Studies, A
Information Technology, A
Instrumentation Technology/Technician, A
International Relations and Affairs, A
International/Global Studies, A
Kinesiology and Exercise Science, A
Legal Assistant/Paralegal, A
Marketing/Marketing Management, A
Mass Communication/Media Studies, A
Medical/Clinical Assistant, A
Music, A
Nursing - Registered Nurse Training, A
Occupational Therapist Assistant, A
Photographic and Film/Video Technology/Technician
    and Assistant, A
Physical Sciences, A
Physical Therapist Assistant, A
Physics, A
Political Science and Government, A
Psychology, A
Public Health (MPH, DPH), A
Quality Control Technology/Technician, A
Radio and Television Broadcasting
    Technology/Technician, A
Radiologic Technology/Science - Radiographer, A
Sign Language Interpretation and Translation, A
Social Work, A
Sociology, A
Survey Technology/Surveying, A
Teacher Assistant/Aide, A
Telecommunications Technology/Technician, A
Welding Technology/Welder, A

SNOW COLLEGE

Accounting, A
Administrative Assistant and Secretarial Science, A
Agricultural Business and Management, A
Agricultural Economics, A
Agriculture, A
Agronomy and Crop Science, A
Animal Physiology, A
Animal Sciences, A
Art/Art Studies, General, A
Automobile/Automotive Mechanics
    Technology/Technician, A
Biology/Biological Sciences, A
Botany/Plant Biology, A
Building/Construction
    Finishing, Management, and Inspection, A
Business Administration and Management, A
Business Teacher Education, A
Carpentry/Carpenter, A
Chemistry, A
Child Development, A
Computer Science, A
Construction Engineering Technology/Technician, A
Criminal Justice/Law Enforcement Administration, A
Dance, A
Drama and Dramatics/Theatre Arts, A

Economics, A
Education, A
Electrical, Electronic and Communications
   Engineering Technology/Technician, A
Elementary Education and Teaching, A
Engineering, A
Entomology, A
Family and Community Services, A
Family and Consumer Sciences/Human Sciences, A
Farm/Farm and Ranch Management, A
Foods, Nutrition, and Wellness Studies, A
Forestry, A
French Language and Literature, A
Geography, A
Geology/Earth Science, A
History, A
Humanities/Humanistic Studies, A
Information Science/Studies, A
Japanese Language and Literature, A
Kindergarten/PreSchool Education and Teaching, A
Liberal Arts and Sciences Studies and
   Humanities, A
Mass Communication/Media Studies, A
Mathematics, A
Music, A
Music History, Literature, and Theory, A
Music Teacher Education, A
Natural Resources Management/Development and
   Policy, A
Natural Sciences, A
Philosophy, A
Physical Education Teaching and Coaching, A
Physical Sciences, A
Physics, A
Political Science and Government, A
Pre-Engineering, A
Range Science and Management, A
Science Teacher Education/General Science
   Teacher Education, A
Sociology, A
Soil Science and Agronomy, A
Spanish Language and Literature, A
Trade and Industrial Teacher Education, A
Voice and Opera, A
Wildlife and Wildlands Science and Management, A
Zoology/Animal Biology, A

SOUTHERN UTAH UNIVERSITY

Accounting, BM
Agriculture, A
Art Teacher Education, B
Art/Art Studies, General, B
Automobile/Automotive Mechanics
   Technology/Technician, A
Biology/Biological Sciences, B
Botany/Plant Biology, B
Business Administration and Management, B
Business Administration, Management and
   Operations, M
Business Teacher Education, B
Carpentry/Carpenter, A
Chemistry, B
Child Development, A
Computer Science, B
Construction Engineering Technology/Technician, B
Criminal Justice/Law Enforcement Administration, A
Dance, B
Drafting and Design Technology/Technician, A
Drama and Dramatics/Theatre Arts, B
Economics, B
Education, BM
Electrical, Electronic and Communications
   Engineering Technology/Technician, AB
Elementary Education and Teaching, B
English Language and Literature, B
Family and Community Services, B
Family and Consumer Sciences/Home Economics
   Teacher Education, B
Family and Consumer Sciences/Human Sciences, B
Fine Arts and Art Studies, M
French Language and Literature, B
Geology/Earth Science, B
German Language and Literature, B
History, B
Information Science/Studies, A
Interior Design, A

Mass Communication/Media Studies, B
Mathematics, B
Music, B
Music Teacher Education, B
Performance, M
Physical Education Teaching and Coaching, B
Physical Sciences, B
Political Science and Government, B
Pre-Engineering, A
Psychology, B
Secondary Education and Teaching, B
Social Sciences, B
Sociology, B
Spanish Language and Literature, B
Special Education and Teaching, B
Speech and Rhetorical Studies, B
Technology Education/Industrial Arts, B
Zoology/Animal Biology, B

STEVENS-HENAGER COLLEGE

Accounting, A
Administrative Assistant and Secretarial Science, A
Business Machine Repairer, A
Legal Administrative Assistant/Secretary, A
Medical Administrative Assistant/Secretary, A

UNIVERSITY OF PHOENIX-UTAH
CAMPUS

Accounting, BM
Business Administration and Management, B
Business Administration, Management and
   Operations, M
Corrections and Criminal Justice, B
Counseling Psychology, M
Counselor Education/School Counseling and
   Guidance Services, M
Curriculum and Instruction, M
Education, M
Educational Media/Instructional Technology, M
Electronic Commerce, M
Elementary Education and Teaching, M
Finance, B
Health Services Administration, M
Health/Health Care Administration/Management, B
Information Technology, B
International Business/Trade/Commerce, M
Management, M
Management Information Systems and
   Services, BM
Management of Technology, M
Management Science, M
Marketing, M
Marketing/Marketing Management, B
Nursing, M
Nursing - Registered Nurse Training, B
Organizational Management, M
Public Administration and Social Service
   Professions, B
Secondary Education and Teaching, M

UNIVERSITY OF UTAH

Accounting, BMD
Allopathic Medicine, P
Anatomy, MD
Anthropology, BMD
Arabic Language and Literature, BMD
Architecture, BMO
Architecture and Related Services, B
Art History, Criticism and Conservation, BM
Art/Art Studies, General, B
Asian Studies/Civilization, B
Atmospheric Sciences and Meteorology, B
Audiology/Audiologist and Speech-Language
   Pathology/Pathologist, B
Ballet, B
Behavioral Sciences, B
Biochemistry, MD
Bioengineering, MD
Biological and Biomedical Sciences, MD
Biology Teacher Education, B
Biology/Biological Sciences, B
Biomedical Sciences, B
Biomedical/Medical Engineering, B
Biostatistics, M
Broadcast Journalism, B
Business Administration and Management, B

Business Administration, Management and
   Operations, MDO
Business, Management, Marketing, and Related
   Support Services, B
Business/Commerce, B
Cancer Biology/Oncology, MD
Cell/Cellular Biology and Histology, B
Ceramic Arts and Ceramics, M
Chemical Engineering, BMD
Chemistry, BMD
Child and Family Studies, M
Child Development, B
Chinese Language and Literature, B
Civil Engineering, BMD
Classics and Classical
   Languages, Literatures, and Linguistics, B
Clinical Laboratory Science/Medical
   Technology/Technologist, B
Clinical/Medical Laboratory Technician, B
Communication and Media Studies, MD
Communication Disorders, MD
Communication Studies/Speech Communication
   and Rhetoric, B
Comparative Literature, MD
Computer Engineering, BM
Computer Science, BMD
Consumer Economics, M
Dance, BM
Developmental and Child Psychology, B
Drama and Dance Teacher Education, B
Drama and Dramatics/Theatre Arts, B
Ecology, MD
Economics, BMD
Education, BMDO
Educational Leadership and Administration, MDO
Educational Psychology, MD
Electrical Engineering, MDO
Electrical, Electronics and Communications
   Engineering, B
Elementary Education and Teaching, B
Engineering, B
Engineering and Applied Sciences, MDO
English, MD
English Language and Literature, B
Environmental Engineering
   Technology/Environmental Technology, MD
Environmental Health, B
Environmental Studies, B
Environmental/Environmental Health Engineering, B
Evolutionary Biology, MD
Exercise and Sports Science, MD
Family and Community Services, B
Family and Consumer Economics and Related
   Services, B
Family and Consumer Sciences/Home Economics
   Teacher Education, B
Family and Consumer Sciences/Human Sciences, B
Family Resource Management Studies, B
Film, Television, and Video Production, M
Film/Cinema Studies, B
Finance, B
Finance and Banking, MD
Fine Arts and Art Studies, M
Food Science, B
Foreign Language Teacher Education, M
Foreign Languages and Literatures, B
Foundations and Philosophy of Education, MD
French Language and Literature, BM
French Language Teacher Education, B
Genetics, MD
Geography, BMD
Geological and Earth Sciences/Geosciences, B
Geological Engineering, MD
Geological/Geophysical Engineering, B
Geology/Earth Science, BMD
Geophysics and Seismology, BMD
German Language and Literature, BMD
German Language Teacher Education, B
Gerontological Nursing, MO
Gerontology, MO
Graphic Design, M
Health and Physical Education, B
Health Education, MD
Health Professions and Related Clinical Sciences, B
Health Promotion, MD
Health Services/Allied Health/Health Sciences, B

Health Teacher Education, B
History, BMD
History Teacher Education, B
Human Development and Family Studies, B
Human Genetics, MD
Humanities/Humanistic Studies, B
Illustration, M
International/Global Studies, B
Japanese Language and Literature, B
Journalism, B
Kindergarten/PreSchool Education and Teaching, B
Kinesiology and Exercise Science, B
Law and Legal Studies, MPO
Leisure Studies, MD
Liberal Arts and Sciences Studies and
 Humanities, B
Linguistics, BM
Management Information Systems and Services, B
Marketing, B
Marketing/Marketing Management, B
Mass Communication/Media Studies, B
Materials Engineering, BMD
Materials Sciences, BMD
Mathematics, BMD
Mathematics Teacher Education, B
Mechanical Engineering, BMD
Medical Informatics, MD
Medical Technology, M
Medicinal and Pharmaceutical Chemistry, MD
Metallurgical Engineering, BMD
Meteorology, BMD
Mineral/Mining Engineering, MD
Mining and Mineral Engineering, B
Modern Greek Language and Literature, B
Music, BMD
Music Teacher Education, B
Near and Middle Eastern Languages, M
Near and Middle Eastern Studies, BMD
Neurobiology and Neurophysiology, MD
Neuroscience, D
Nuclear Engineering, MD
Nursing, MD
Nursing - Registered Nurse Training, B
Nutritional Sciences, M
Occupational Therapy/Therapist, BM
Painting, M
Parks, Recreation and Leisure Facilities
 Management, B
Parks, Recreation, Leisure and Fitness Studies, B
Pathology/Experimental Pathology, MD
Petroleum Engineering, MD
Pharmacology, MDO
Pharmacy, BMP
Pharmacy, Pharmaceutical Sciences, and Administration, B
Philosophy, BMD
Photography, M
Physical Chemistry, D
Physical Education Teaching and Coaching, B
Physical Sciences, B
Physical Therapy/Therapist, BMD
Physician Assistant, M
Physics, BMD
Physics Teacher Education, B
Physiology, D
Political Science and Government, BMD
Pre-Pharmacy Studies, B
Printmaking, M
Psychology, BMD
Public Administration, MO
Public Health, MD
Public Relations/Image Management, B
Radio and Television, B
Recreation and Park Management, MD
Russian Language and Literature, B
Science Teacher Education/General Science
 Teacher Education, BM
Sculpture, M
Secondary Education and Teaching, B
Social Science Teacher Education, B
Social Sciences, B
Social Studies Teacher Education, B
Social Work, BMDO
Sociology, BMD
Spanish Language and Literature, BMD
Spanish Language Teacher Education, B
Special Education and Teaching, BMD

Speech and Rhetorical Studies, B
Statistics, M
Toxicology, MDO
Urban Studies/Affairs, B
Visual and Performing Arts, B
Women's Studies, B
Writing, M

UTAH CAREER COLLEGE

Business Administration and Management, A
Computer Graphics, A
Kinesiology and Exercise Science, A
Legal Assistant/Paralegal, A
Massage Therapy/Therapeutic Massage, A
Medical/Clinical Assistant, A
Nursing - Registered Nurse Training, A
Pharmacy Technician/Assistant, A
Veterinary/Animal Health Technology/Technician and
 Veterinary Assistant, A

UTAH STATE UNIVERSITY

Accounting, BM
Administrative Assistant and Secretarial Science, AB
Aeronautical/Aerospace Engineering
 Technology/Technician, B
Aerospace, Aeronautical and Astronautical
 Engineering, BMD
Agricultural Business and Management, B
Agricultural Economics, B
Agricultural Education, M
Agricultural Engineering, MD
Agricultural Sciences, MD
Agricultural Teacher Education, B
Agricultural/Biological Engineering and
 Bioengineering, B
Agriculture, B
Agronomy and Crop Science, B
Agronomy and Soil Sciences, MD
Airframe Mechanics and Aircraft Maintenance
 Technology/Technician, AB
American/United States Studies/Civilization, BM
Animal Physiology, B
Animal Sciences, BMD
Anthropology, B
Applied Economics, M
Applied Mathematics, M
Area Studies, B
Art/Art Studies, General, B
Asian Studies/Civilization, B
Audiology/Audiologist and Speech-Language
 Pathology/Pathologist, B
Biochemistry, MD
Biological and Biomedical Sciences, MD
Biology Teacher Education, B
Biology/Biological Sciences, B
Botany/Plant Biology, B
Business Administration and Management, B
Business Administration, Management and
 Operations, M
Business Education, MD
Business Teacher Education, B
Business/Commerce, B
Chemistry, BMD
Chemistry Teacher Education, B
Child and Family Studies, MD
Civil Engineering, BMDO
Clinical Laboratory Science/Medical
 Technology/Technologist, B
Clinical Psychology, D
Communication and Media Studies, M
Communication Disorders, MDO
Computer and Information Sciences, B
Computer and Information Sciences and Support
 Services, B
Computer Engineering, B
Computer Engineering Technology/Technician, B
Computer Science, MD
Consumer Economics, M
Counseling Psychology, D
Counselor Education/School Counseling and
 Guidance Services, M
Curriculum and Instruction, BD
Dairy Science, BM
Dance, B
Drafting and Design Technology/Technician, A
Drama and Dramatics/Theatre Arts, B

Ecology, BMD
Economics, BMD
Education, MDO
Educational Measurement and Evaluation, D
Educational Media/Instructional Technology, MDO
Electrical Engineering, MDO
Electrical, Electronics and Communications
 Engineering, B
Elementary Education and Teaching, BM
Engineering and Applied Sciences, MDO
English, B
English Language and Literature, B
Entomology, B
Environmental Engineering
 Technology/Environmental Technology, MDO
Environmental Policy and Resource
 Management, MD
Environmental/Environmental Health Engineering, B
Family and Consumer Economics and Related
 Services, B
Family and Consumer Sciences/Home Economics
 Teacher Education, B
Fashion Merchandising, B
Finance, B
Fine Arts and Art Studies, M
Fish, Game and Wildlife Management, MD
Folklore, M
Food Science and Technology, MD
Foods, Nutrition, and Related Services, B
Forestry, BMD
French Language and Literature, B
General Studies, A
Geography, BMD
Geology/Earth Science, BM
German Language and Literature, B
Health Education, M
Health Teacher Education, B
History, BM
Home Economics Education, M
Horticultural Science, B
Housing and Human Environments, B
Human Development, MD
Human Development and Family Studies, AB
Human Resources Management and Services, M
Human Resources Management/Personnel
 Administration, B
Industrial Education, M
Industrial Production Technologies/Technicians, B
Information Science/Studies, B
Interior Design, BM
International Agriculture, B
Journalism, B
Kindergarten/PreSchool Education and Teaching, B
Landscape Architecture, BM
Liberal Arts and Sciences Studies and
 Humanities, B
Management Information Systems and
 Services, MD
Marketing/Marketing Management, B
Mathematics, BMD
Mathematics Teacher Education, B
Mechanical Engineering, BMD
Medical Microbiology and Bacteriology, B
Meteorology, MD
Microbiology, M
Molecular Biology, MD
Multi-/Interdisciplinary Studies, B
Multilingual and Multicultural Education, M
Music, B
Music Teacher Education, B
Music Therapy/Therapist, B
Natural Resources and Conservation, BM
Nutritional Sciences, MD
Occupational Safety and Health
 Technology/Technician, B
Operations Management and Supervision, B
Ornamental Horticulture, AB
Parks, Recreation, Leisure and Fitness Studies, B
Philosophy, B
Physical Education Teaching and Coaching, BM
Physics, BMD
Physics Teacher Education, B
Plant Sciences, BMD
Political Science and Government, BM
Pre-Dentistry Studies, B
Pre-Law Studies, B

Pre-Medicine/Pre-Medical Studies, B
Pre-Veterinary Studies, B
Psychology, BMD
Public Health, B
Range Science and Management, BMD
Recreation and Park Management, MD
Rehabilitation Counseling, M
Sales and Marketing Operations/Marketing and
    Distribution Teacher Education, B
School Psychology, M
Science Teacher Education/General Science
    Teacher Education, B
Secondary Education and Teaching, BM
Social Studies Teacher Education, B
Social Work, B
Sociology, BMD
Soil Science and Agronomy, B
Spanish Language and Literature, B
Special Education and Teaching, BMDO
Speech and Rhetorical Studies, B
Statistics, BM
Teacher Education and Professional
    Development, Specific Subject Areas, B
Teacher Education, Multiple Levels, B
Technical Teacher Education, B
Technology Teacher Education/Industrial Arts
    Teacher Education, B
Theater, M
Tool and Die Technology/Technician, B
Toxicology, MD
Urban and Regional Planning, M
Veterinary Sciences, MD
Water Resources Engineering, MD
Wildlife and Wildlands Science and Management, B
Zoology/Animal Biology, B

UTAH VALLEY STATE COLLEGE

Accounting, AB
Airline/Commercial/Professional Pilot and Flight
    Crew, AB
Autobody/Collision and Repair
    Technology/Technician, A
Automobile/Automotive Mechanics
    Technology/Technician, A
Banking and Financial Support Services, A
Behavioral Sciences, AB
Biology Teacher Education, B
Biology/Biological Sciences, AB
Building/Home/Construction Inspection/Inspector, A
Business Administration and Management, AB
Business Teacher Education, B
Business/Commerce, AB
Business/Office Automation/Technology/Data
    Entry, A
Cabinetmaking and Millwork/Millwright, A
Chemistry, AB
Chemistry Teacher Education, B
Commercial and Advertising Art, A
Communication Studies/Speech Communication
    and Rhetoric, A
Community Health and Preventive Medicine, A
Computer and Information Sciences, A
Computer Science, AB
Construction Trades, A
Criminal Justice/Law Enforcement
    Administration, AB
Culinary Arts/Chef Training, A
Dance, A
Data Processing and Data Processing
    Technology/Technician, AB
Dental Hygiene/Hygienist, A
Diesel Mechanics Technology/Technician, A
Digital Communication and Media/Multimedia, AB
Drafting and Design Technology/Technician, A
Drama and Dance Teacher Education, B
Drama and Dramatics/Theatre Arts, A
Early Childhood Education and Teaching, AB
Electrical, Electronic and Communications
    Engineering Technology/Technician, A
Electromechanical Technology/Electromechanical
    Engineering Technology, A
English Language and Literature, AB
English/Language Arts Teacher Education, B
Environmental Engineering
    Technology/Environmental Technology, A
Executive Assistant/Executive Secretary, A

Fire Science/Firefighting, A
Fire Services Administration, B
General Studies, A
Geology/Earth Science, AB
Health and Physical Education, A
Health and Physical Education/Fitness, AB
Health Services Administration, B
Health Teacher Education, B
Heating, Air Conditioning, Ventilation and
    Refrigeration Maintenance
    Technology/Technician, A
History, B
Hospitality Administration/Management, AB
Humanities/Humanistic Studies, A
Information Technology, AB
International Business/Trade/Commerce, B
Legal Assistant/Paralegal, AB
Lineworker, A
Machine Tool Technology/Machinist, A
Management Information Systems and Services, B
Manufacturing Technology/Technician, A
Marketing/Marketing Management, B
Mathematics, AB
Mathematics Teacher Education, B
Music, A
Natural Sciences, A
Nursing - Registered Nurse Training, AB
Operations Management and Supervision, B
Parks, Recreation, Leisure and Fitness Studies, AB
Philosophy, AB
Physical Education Teaching and Coaching, B
Physical Sciences, A
Physics, AB
Political Science and Government, B
Pre-Engineering, A
Science Teacher Education/General Science
    Teacher Education, B
Spanish Language and Literature, B
Spanish Language Teacher Education, B

WEBER STATE UNIVERSITY

Accounting, BM
Administrative Assistant and Secretarial Science, AB
Aerospace, Aeronautical and Astronautical
    Engineering, B
Air Force JROTC/ROTC, B
Applied Mathematics, B
Archeology, A
Art Teacher Education, B
Art/Art Studies, General, B
Athletic Training and Sports Medicine, B
Autobody/Collision and Repair
    Technology/Technician, A
Automobile/Automotive Mechanics
    Technology/Technician, AB
Automotive Engineering Technology/Technician, B
Bilingual and Multilingual Education, B
Biology Teacher Education, B
Biology Technician/BioTechnology Laboratory
    Technician, A
Botany/Plant Biology, B
Business Administration and Management, B
Business Administration, Management and
    Operations, M
Business Teacher Education, B
Business/Managerial Economics, B
Chemical Technology/Technician, A
Chemistry, B
Chemistry Teacher Education, B
Child Care and Support Services Management, A
Child Development, AB
Clinical Laboratory Science/Medical
    Technology/Technologist, AB
Clinical/Medical Laboratory Technician, AB
Commercial and Advertising Art, B
Computer and Information Sciences, AB
Computer Engineering Technology/Technician, A
Computer Science, AB
Computer Systems Networking and
    Telecommunications, B
Corrections, AB
Criminal Justice/Police Science, AB
Criminal Justice/Safety Studies, AB
Curriculum and Instruction, M
Dance, B
Dental Hygiene/Hygienist, AB

Design and Visual Communications, B
Diagnostic Medical Sonography/Sonographer and
    Ultrasound Technician, B
Diesel Mechanics Technology/Technician, A
Drafting and Design Technology/Technician, A
Drama and Dance Teacher Education, B
Drama and Dramatics/Theatre Arts, B
Economics, B
Education, M
Electrical, Electronic and Communications
    Engineering Technology/Technician, AB
Elementary Education and Teaching, B
Emergency Medical Technology/Technician (EMT
    Paramedic), A
English Language and Literature, B
English/Language Arts Teacher Education, B
Family Systems, B
Fashion Merchandising, A
Finance, B
French Language and Literature, B
French Language Teacher Education, B
Geography, B
Geology/Earth Science, B
German Language and Literature, B
German Language Teacher Education, B
Gerontology, B
Health and Physical Education, B
Health Information/Medical Records
    Technology/Technician, A
Health/Health Care Administration/Management, B
History, B
History Teacher Education, B
Human Resources Management/Personnel
    Administration, B
Industrial Technology/Technician, AB
Information Science/Studies, AB
Interior Design, A
Journalism, B
Kindergarten/PreSchool Education and Teaching, B
Kinesiology and Exercise Science, B
Legal and Justice Studies, M
Liberal Arts and Sciences Studies and
    Humanities, AB
Logistics and Materials Management, B
Machine Tool Technology/Machinist, A
Management Information Systems and Services, AB
Marketing/Marketing Management, AB
Mathematics, B
Mechanical Engineering/Mechanical
    Technology/Technician, AB
Medical Microbiology and Bacteriology, B
Medical Radiologic Technology/Science - Radiation
    Therapist, AB
Music, B
Music Performance, B
Music Teacher Education, B
Nuclear Medical Technology/Technologist, B
Nursing - Registered Nurse Training, AB
Office Management and Supervision, B
Photography, B
Physical Education Teaching and Coaching, B
Physics, B
Physics Teacher Education, B
Piano and Organ, B
Political Science and Government, B
Psychology, B
Public Relations/Image Management, B
Radio and Television, B
Respiratory Care Therapy/Therapist, AB
Science Teacher Education/General Science
    Teacher Education, B
Secondary Education and Teaching, B
Social Science Teacher Education, B
Social Studies Teacher Education, B
Social Work, B
Sociology, B
Spanish Language and Literature, B
Spanish Language Teacher Education, B
Technical and Business Writing, B
Technology Education/Industrial Arts, A
Zoology/Animal Biology, B

WESTERN GOVERNORS UNIVERSITY

Business/Commerce, AB
Computer Engineering, A
Education, MO

Educational Administration and Supervision, O
Educational Media/Instructional Technology, MO
Information Science/Studies, AB
Information Technology, A
System Administration/Administrator, A

WESTMINSTER COLLEGE

Accounting, B
Airline/Commercial/Professional Pilot and Flight
    Crew, B
Art/Art Studies, General, B
Aviation/Airway Management and Operations, B
Biology Teacher Education, B
Biology/Biological Sciences, B
Business Administration and Management, B
Business Administration, Management and
    Operations, MO
Business/Commerce, B
Business/Managerial Economics, B
Chemistry, B
Chemistry Teacher Education, B
Communication and Media Studies, M
Communication Studies/Speech Communication
    and Rhetoric, B
Computer Science, B
Education, M
Elementary Education and Teaching, B
English Language and Literature, B
Environmental Studies, B
Finance, B
History, B
Human Resources Management/Personnel
    Administration, B
International Business/Trade/Commerce, B
Kindergarten/PreSchool Education and Teaching, B
Management Information Systems and Services, B
Marketing/Marketing Management, B
Mathematics, B
Nursing, M
Nursing - Registered Nurse Training, B
Philosophy, B
Physics, B
Political Science and Government, B
Psychology, B
Social Science Teacher Education, B
Social Sciences, B
Sociology, B
Special Education and Teaching, B
Writing, M

Vermont

BENNINGTON COLLEGE

Acting, B
Allied Health and Medical Assisting Services, O
American Government and Politics (United States)
    , B
American History (United States), B
American Literature (United States), B
American/United States Studies/Civilization, B
Animation, Interactive Technology, Video Graphics
    and Special Effects, B
Anthropology, B
Architecture, B
Art Education, M
Asian Studies/Civilization, B
Astronomy, B
Biochemistry, B
Biology/Biological Sciences, B
Cell/Cellular and Molecular Biology, B
Ceramic Arts and Ceramics, B
Chemistry, B
Chinese Language and Literature, B
Cinematography and Film/Video Production, B
Computer Science, B
Creative Writing, B
Dance, BM
Design and Visual Communications, B
Directing and Theatrical Production, B
Drama and Dramatics/Theatre Arts, B
Drawing, B
Early Childhood Education and Teaching, BM
Ecology, B
Education, BM
Elementary Education and Teaching, BM

English, M
English Composition, B
English Education, M
English Language and Literature, B
English Literature (British and Commonwealth), B
Environmental Biology, B
Environmental Studies, B
European History, B
European Studies/Civilization, B
Evolutionary Biology, B
Film/Cinema Studies, B
Fine/Studio Arts, B
Foreign Language Teacher Education, BM
Foreign Languages and Literatures, B
French Language and Literature, BM
Gay/Lesbian Studies, B
History, B
Humanities/Humanistic Studies, B
Interdisciplinary Studies, B
Intermedia/Multimedia, B
International Relations and Affairs, B
International/Global Studies, B
Italian Studies, B
Japanese Language and Literature, B
Jazz/Jazz Studies, B
Journalism, B
Junior High/Intermediate/Middle School Education
    and Teaching, B
Liberal Arts and Sciences Studies and
    Humanities, B
Mathematics, B
Mathematics Teacher Education, M
Multilingual and Multicultural Education, M
Music, BM
Music History, Literature, and Theory, B
Music Performance, B
Music Teacher Education, M
Music Theory and Composition, B
Musicology and Ethnomusicology, B
Painting, B
Peace Studies and Conflict Resolution, B
Philosophy, B
Photography, B
Physical Sciences, B
Physics, B
Piano and Organ, B
Playwriting and Screenwriting, B
Political Science and Government, B
Pre-Law Studies, B
Pre-Medicine/Pre-Medical Studies, B
Printmaking, B
Psychology, B
Science Teacher Education/General Science
    Teacher Education, M
Sculpture, B
Secondary Education and Teaching, BM
Social Sciences, B
Social Studies Teacher Education, M
Sociology, B
Spanish Language and Literature, BM
Technical Theatre/Theatre Design and
    Technology, B
Theater, M
Theatre Literature, History and Criticism, B
Violin, Viola, Guitar and Other Stringed
    Instruments, B
Visual and Performing Arts, B
Voice and Opera, B
Women's Studies, B
Writing, M
Zoology/Animal Biology, B

BURLINGTON COLLEGE

Animation, Interactive Technology, Video Graphics
    and Special Effects, B
Art/Art Studies, General, AB
Cinematography and Film/Video Production, AB
City/Urban, Community and Regional Planning, B
Comparative Literature, B
Film/Cinema Studies, AB
Human Services, B
Humanities/Humanistic Studies, AB
Interdisciplinary Studies, AB
Land Use Planning and
    Management/Development, B
Latin American Studies, B

Law and Legal Studies, B
Legal Assistant/Paralegal, A
Liberal Arts and Sciences Studies and
    Humanities, AB
Natural Resources Management/Development and
    Policy, B
Photographic and Film/Video Technology/Technician
    and Assistant, A
Psychology, B
Women's Studies, B

CASTLETON STATE COLLEGE

Accounting, B
American Literature (United States), B
Art/Art Studies, General, B
Athletic Training and Sports Medicine, B
Biological and Physical Sciences, B
Biology/Biological Sciences, B
Business Administration and Management, B
Business/Commerce, A
Chemistry, A
Comparative Literature, B
Computer and Information Sciences, B
Computer Programming/Programmer, A
Criminal Justice/Law Enforcement
    Administration, AB
Criminology, B
Curriculum and Instruction, M
Developmental and Child Psychology, B
Drama and Dramatics/Theatre Arts, B
Education, MO
Educational Leadership and Administration, MO
Environmental Studies, B
Finance, B
Forensic Psychology, M
General Studies, A
Geology/Earth Science, B
Health and Physical Education, B
History, B
Journalism, B
Kinesiology and Exercise Science, B
Marketing/Marketing Management, B
Mathematics, B
Mathematics Teacher Education, B
Music, B
Music Teacher Education, B
Natural Sciences, B
Nursing - Registered Nurse Training, A
Physical Education Teaching and Coaching, B
Psychology, BM
Public Health (MPH, DPH), B
Public Relations/Image Management, B
Radio and Television, B
Reading Teacher Education, MO
Science Teacher Education/General Science
    Teacher Education, B
Social Sciences, B
Social Studies Teacher Education, B
Social Work, B
Sociology, B
Spanish Language and Literature, B
Special Education and Teaching, MO

CHAMPLAIN COLLEGE

Accounting, AB
Animation, Interactive Technology, Video Graphics
    and Special Effects, AB
Business Administration and Management, AB
Business/Commerce, AB
Commercial and Advertising Art, AB
Communication and Media Studies, AB
Communication, Journalism and Related
    Programs, AB
Computer and Information Sciences, AB
Computer and Information Systems Security, AB
Computer Graphics, AB
Computer Software and Media Applications, B
Computer Software Engineering, B
Computer Systems Networking and
    Telecommunications, AB
Computer/Information Technology Services
    Administration and Management, AB
Creative Writing, B
Criminal Justice/Law Enforcement
    Administration, AB
Criminal Justice/Safety Studies, AB

Design and Visual Communications, AB
Digital Communication and Media/Multimedia, AB
Early Childhood Education and Teaching, A
E-Commerce/Electronic Commerce, AB
Elementary Education and Teaching, B
Forensic Science and Technology, B
Graphic Design, AB
Hospitality Administration/Management, AB
Hospitality and Recreation Marketing
   Operations, AB
Hotel/Motel Administration/Management, AB
Human Services, AB
Information Science/Studies, AB
Intermedia/Multimedia, AB
International Business/Trade/Commerce, AB
Journalism, B
Junior High/Intermediate/Middle School Education
   and Teaching, B
Kindergarten/PreSchool Education and
   Teaching, AB
Legal Assistant/Paralegal, AB
Liberal Arts and Sciences Studies and
   Humanities, A
Management of Technology, M
Marketing/Marketing Management, AB
Mass Communication/Media Studies, AB
Pre-Law Studies, B
Professional Studies, B
Public Relations, Advertising, and Applied
   Communication, AB
Public Relations/Image Management, AB
Radiologic Technology/Science - Radiographer, AB
Sales, Distribution and Marketing Operations, AB
Secondary Education and Teaching, B
Social Work, AB
System Administration/Administrator, B
System, Networking, and LAN/WAN
   Management/Manager, AB
Technical and Business Writing, B
Telecommunications Technology/Technician, AB
Tourism and Travel Services Management, AB
Tourism and Travel Services Marketing
   Operations, AB
Tourism Promotion Operations, AB
Web Page, Digital/Multimedia and Information
   Resources Design, AB
Web/Multimedia Management and Webmaster, AB

COLLEGE OF ST. JOSEPH

Accounting, AB
American/United States Studies/Civilization, B
Business Administration and Management, AB
Business Administration, Management and
   Operations, M
Clinical Psychology, M
Communication Studies/Speech Communication
   and Rhetoric, B
Community Psychology, M
Counseling Psychology, M
Counselor Education/School Counseling and
   Guidance Services, M
Education, BM
Elementary Education and Teaching, BM
English Education, M
English Language and Literature, B
Finance, B
History, B
Human Services, B
Information Science/Studies, AB
Journalism, B
Kindergarten/PreSchool Education and Teaching, B
Liberal Arts and Sciences Studies and
   Humanities, AB
Mathematics Teacher Education, M
Parks, Recreation and Leisure Facilities
   Management, B
Political Science and Government, B
Pre-Law Studies, B
Psychology, BM
Reading Teacher Education, M
School Psychology, M
Secondary Education and Teaching, BM
Social Studies Teacher Education, M

Special Education and Teaching, BM

COMMUNITY COLLEGE OF VERMONT

Accounting, A
Administrative Assistant and Secretarial Science, A
Business Administration and Management, A
Child Development, A
Community Organization and Advocacy, A
Computer Science, A
Data Entry/Microcomputer Applications, A
Developmental and Child Psychology, A
Education, A
Human Services, A
Industrial Technology/Technician, A
Information Technology, A
Liberal Arts and Sciences Studies and
   Humanities, A
Social Sciences, A
Teacher Assistant/Aide, A

GODDARD COLLEGE

Botany/Plant Biology, B
Comparative and Interdisciplinary Arts, M
Counseling Psychology, M
Education, M
Environmental Studies, M
Foods, Nutrition, and Wellness Studies, B
Health Promotion, M
Industrial and Organizational Psychology, M
Interdisciplinary Studies, BM
Liberal Arts and Sciences Studies and
   Humanities, B
Nutritional Sciences, B
Writing, M

GREEN MOUNTAIN COLLEGE

Anthropology, B
Art/Art Studies, General, B
Arts Management, B
Biology/Biological Sciences, B
Business/Managerial Economics, B
Communication Studies/Speech Communication
   and Rhetoric, B
Creative Writing, B
Elementary Education and Teaching, B
English Language and Literature, B
Environmental Studies, B
Fine/Studio Arts, B
History, B
Hospitality Administration/Management, B
Liberal Arts and Sciences Studies and
   Humanities, B
Natural Resources Management/Development and
   Policy, B
Parks, Recreation and Leisure Facilities
   Management, B
Parks, Recreation, Leisure and Fitness Studies, B
Philosophy, B
Psychology, B
Resort Management, B
Secondary Education and Teaching, B
Sociology, B
Special Education and Teaching, B
Visual and Performing Arts, B

JOHNSON STATE COLLEGE

Accounting, AB
Acting, B
Alternative and Complementary Medicine and
   Medical Systems, B
Anthropology, B
Art Teacher Education, B
Art/Art Studies, General, B
Athletic Training and Sports Medicine, B
Biology Teacher Education, B
Biology/Biological Sciences, B
Business Administration and Management, AB
Business/Commerce, B
Comparative Literature, B
Counselor Education/School Counseling and
   Guidance Services, M
Creative Writing, B
Curriculum and Instruction, M
Dance, B
Drama and Dance Teacher Education, B
Drama and Dramatics/Theatre Arts, B

Education, BM
Education/Teaching of the Gifted and Talented, M
Educational Psychology, M
Elementary Education and Teaching, B
English Language and Literature, B
English/Language Arts Teacher Education, B
Environmental Education, B
Environmental Studies, B
Fine Arts and Art Studies, M
Fine/Studio Arts, B
General Studies, A
Health and Physical Education, B
History, B
History Teacher Education, B
Hospitality Administration/Management, B
Humanities/Humanistic Studies, B
Information Science/Studies, AB
Jazz/Jazz Studies, B
Journalism, B
Junior High/Intermediate/Middle School Education
   and Teaching, B
Kinesiology and Exercise Science, B
Liberal Arts and Sciences Studies and
   Humanities, AB
Management Information Systems and Services, AB
Marketing/Marketing Management, B
Mathematics, B
Mathematics Teacher Education, B
Music, B
Music Management and Merchandising, B
Music Performance, B
Music Teacher Education, B
Natural Resources Management/Development and
   Policy, B
Painting, M
Parks, Recreation, Leisure and Fitness Studies, B
Physical Education Teaching and Coaching, B
Political Science and Government, B
Pre-Medicine/Pre-Medical Studies, B
Psychology, B
Public Health (MPH, DPH), B
Reading Teacher Education, M
Sculpture, M
Secondary Education and Teaching, B
Social Science Teacher Education, B
Social Studies Teacher Education, B
Sociology, B
Special Education and Teaching, M
Sport and Fitness Administration/Management, B
Technical Theatre/Theatre Design and
   Technology, A
Tourism and Travel Services Management, B
Visual and Performing Arts, B

LANDMARK COLLEGE

Liberal Arts and Sciences Studies and
   Humanities, A

LYNDON STATE COLLEGE

Accounting, B
Athletic Training and Sports Medicine, B
Atmospheric Sciences and Meteorology, B
Biological and Physical Sciences, B
Business Administration and Management, AB
Commercial and Advertising Art, B
Communication Studies/Speech Communication
   and Rhetoric, A
Computer and Information Sciences, AB
Computer Science, A
Counselor Education/School Counseling and
   Guidance Services, M
Curriculum and Instruction, M
Education, M
Elementary Education and Teaching, B
English Language and Literature, B
English/Language Arts Teacher Education, A
Entrepreneurship/Entrepreneurial Studies, AB
Health and Physical Education, B
Journalism, B
Liberal Arts and Sciences Studies and
   Humanities, AB
Mathematics, AB
Mathematics Teacher Education, B
Parks, Recreation and Leisure Facilities
   Management, B
Parks, Recreation, Leisure and Fitness Studies, B

Physical Education Teaching and Coaching, B
Physical Sciences, B
Psychology, B
Radio and Television, B
Radio and Television Broadcasting
  Technology/Technician, A
Reading Teacher Education, BM
Science Teacher Education/General Science
  Teacher Education, BM
Social Science Teacher Education, B
Social Sciences, B
Special Education and Teaching, BM
Sport and Fitness Administration/Management, B

MARLBORO COLLEGE

African Studies, B
American/United States Studies/Civilization, B
Anthropology, B
Applied Mathematics, B
Art History, Criticism and Conservation, B
Art/Art Studies, General, B
Asian Studies/Civilization, B
Astronomy, B
Astrophysics, B
Behavioral Sciences, B
Bible/Biblical Studies, B
Biochemistry, B
Biology/Biological Sciences, B
Botany/Plant Biology, B
Cell/Cellular Biology and Histology, B
Central/Middle and Eastern European Studies, B
Ceramic Arts and Ceramics, B
Chemistry, B
Classics and Classical
  Languages, Literatures, and Linguistics, B
Comparative Literature, B
Computer Education, MO
Computer Science, BM
Creative Writing, B
Dance, B
Developmental and Child Psychology, B
Drama and Dramatics/Theatre Arts, B
Drawing, B
East Asian Studies, B
Ecology, B
Economics, B
Education, M
English Language and Literature, B
Environmental Biology, B
Environmental Studies, B
Ethnic and Cultural Studies, B
Ethnic, Cultural Minority, and Gender Studies, B
European Studies/Civilization, B
Experimental Psychology, B
Film/Cinema Studies, B
Fine/Studio Arts, B
French Language and Literature, B
German Language and Literature, B
History, B
Humanities/Humanistic Studies, B
Information Science/Studies, M
Interdisciplinary Studies, B
International Economics, B
International Relations and Affairs, B
Internet and Interactive Multimedia, M
Italian Language and Literature, B
Latin American Studies, B
Latin Language and Literature, B
Linguistics, B
Management, M
Mathematics, B
Medieval and Renaissance Studies, B
Modern Greek Language and Literature, B
Modern Languages, B
Molecular Biology, B
Music, B
Music History, Literature, and Theory, B
Natural Resources and Conservation, B
Natural Sciences, B
Philosophy, B
Photography, B
Physics, B
Political Science and Government, B
Portuguese Language and Literature, B
Pre-Law Studies, B
Pre-Medicine/Pre-Medical Studies, B

Pre-Veterinary Studies, B
Psychology, B
Religion/Religious Studies, B
Romance Languages, Literatures, and Linguistics, B
Russian Studies, B
Sculpture, B
Social Sciences, B
Sociology, B
Spanish Language and Literature, B
Women's Studies, B

MIDDLEBURY COLLEGE

American Literature (United States), B
American/United States Studies/Civilization, B
Art History, Criticism and Conservation, B
Biochemistry, B
Biology/Biological Sciences, B
Central/Middle and Eastern European Studies, B
Chemistry, B
Chinese Language and Literature, B
Cinematography and Film/Video Production, B
Classics and Classical
  Languages, Literatures, and Linguistics, B
Computer Science, B
Dance, B
Drama and Dramatics/Theatre Arts, B
East Asian Studies, B
Economics, B
English, M
English Language and Literature, B
Environmental Studies, B
European Studies/Civilization, B
Fine/Studio Arts, B
French Language and Literature, BMD
Geography, B
Geology/Earth Science, B
German Language and Literature, BMD
History, B
International Relations and Affairs, B
Italian Language and Literature, BMD
Japanese Language and Literature, B
Latin American Studies, B
Liberal Arts and Sciences Studies and
  Humanities, B
Mathematics, B
Modern Languages, B
Molecular Biology, B
Music, B
Neuroscience, B
Philosophy, B
Physics, B
Political Science and Government, B
Psychology, B
Religion/Religious Studies, B
Russian Language and Literature, BMD
Russian Studies, B
Sociology, B
Spanish Language and Literature, BMD
Women's Studies, B

NEW ENGLAND CULINARY INSTITUTE

Baking and Pastry Arts/Baker/Pastry Chef, A
Culinary Arts/Chef Training, A
Hotel/Motel Administration/Management, B
Restaurant, Culinary, and Catering
  Management/Manager, AB

NEW ENGLAND CULINARY INSTITUTE AT ESSEX

Baking and Pastry Arts/Baker/Pastry Chef, A
Culinary Arts/Chef Training, A
Hotel/Motel Administration/Management, AB

NORWICH UNIVERSITY

Architecture, B
Athletic Training and Sports Medicine, B
Biology/Biological Sciences, B
Business Administration and Management, B
Business Administration, Management and
  Operations, M
Chemical Technology/Technician, B
Chemistry, B
Civil Engineering, B
Communication Studies/Speech Communication
  and Rhetoric, B

Computer Science, B
Criminal Justice/Law Enforcement Administration, B
Criminology, M
Economics, B
Educational/Instructional Media Design, B
Electrical, Electronics and Communications
  Engineering, B
English Language and Literature, B
Environmental Studies, B
Geology/Earth Science, B
Health Services Administration, M
History, B
Information Science/Studies, B
International Affairs, M
International Business/Trade/Commerce, M
International Relations and Affairs, B
Management Information Systems and Services, M
Mathematics, B
Mechanical Engineering, B
Nursing - Registered Nurse Training, B
Peace Studies and Conflict Resolution, B
Physical Education Teaching and Coaching, B
Physics, B
Political Science and Government, B
Psychology, B

SAINT MICHAEL'S COLLEGE

Accounting, B
American/United States Studies/Civilization, B
Art Education, O
Art Teacher Education, B
Art/Art Studies, General, B
Biochemistry, B
Biology/Biological Sciences, B
Business Administration and Management, B
Business Administration, Management and
  Operations, MO
Chemistry, B
Classics and Classical
  Languages, Literatures, and Linguistics, B
Clinical Psychology, M
Computer Science, B
Curriculum and Instruction, MO
Drama and Dramatics/Theatre Arts, B
Economics, B
Education, BMO
Educational Administration and Supervision, MO
Educational Media/Instructional Technology, MO
Elementary Education and Teaching, B
English as a Second Language, MO
English Language and Literature, B
French Language and Literature, B
History, B
Information Science/Studies, B
Journalism, B
Mathematics, B
Modern Languages, B
Music, B
Philosophy, B
Physical Sciences, B
Physics, B
Political Science and Government, B
Pre-Dentistry Studies, B
Pre-Law Studies, B
Pre-Medicine/Pre-Medical Studies, B
Pre-Veterinary Studies, B
Psychology, B
Reading Teacher Education, M
Religion/Religious Studies, B
Secondary Education and Teaching, B
Sociology, B
Spanish Language and Literature, B
Special Education and Teaching, MO
Theology and Religious Vocations, MO

SOUTHERN VERMONT COLLEGE

Business Administration and Management, AB
Child Development, A
Communication Studies/Speech Communication
  and Rhetoric, B
Comparative Literature, B
Creative Writing, B
Criminal Justice/Law Enforcement
  Administration, AB
English Language and Literature, B
Environmental Studies, B

Human Services, B
Liberal Arts and Sciences Studies and
  Humanities, AB
Mass Communication/Media Studies, B
Nursing - Registered Nurse Training, AB
Pre-Law Studies, B
Psychology, B

STERLING COLLEGE

Administration of Special Education, B
Agricultural and Domestic Animals Services, AB
Agricultural and Horticultural Plant Breeding, AB
Agricultural Animal Breeding, AB
Agricultural Business and Management, B
Agricultural Communication/Journalism, B
Agricultural Production Operations, AB
Agricultural Public Services, AB
Agricultural Teacher Education, B
Agriculture, AB
Agriculture, Agriculture Operations and Related
  Sciences, AB
Agronomy and Crop Science, B
Animal Health, AB
Animal Nutrition, AB
Animal Sciences, AB
Animal Training, B
Animal/Livestock Husbandry and Production, AB
Applied Horticulture/Horticultural Operations, AB
Area, Ethnic, Cultural, and Gender Studies, B
Biological and Physical Sciences, AB
Canadian Studies, B
Conservation Biology, B
Crop Production, AB
Cultural Resource Management and Policy
  Analysis, B
Curriculum and Instruction, B
Dairy Husbandry and Production, AB
Dairy Science, B
Ecology, AB
Ecology, Evolution, Systematics and Population
  Biology, B
Education, B
Educational Leadership and Administration, B
Educational, Instructional, and Curriculum
  Supervision, B
Energy Management and Systems
  Technology/Technician, B
Environmental Biology, B
Environmental Design/Architecture, B
Environmental Engineering
  Technology/Environmental Technology, B
Environmental Studies, AB
Equestrian/Equine Studies, B
Ethnic, Cultural Minority, and Gender Studies, B
Family and Consumer Sciences/Human
  Sciences, AB
Farm/Farm and Ranch Management, B
Fishing and Fisheries Sciences and
  Management, AB
Forest Management/Forest Resources
  Management, AB
Forest Resources Production and Management, AB
Forest Sciences and Biology, AB
Forestry, AB
Greenhouse Operations and Management, AB
Horse Husbandry/Equine Science and
  Management, B
Horticultural Science, B
Intercultural/Multicultural and Diversity Studies, B
International Agriculture, B
International and Comparative Education, B
International/Global Studies, B
Land Use Planning and
  Management/Development, B
Liberal Arts and Sciences Studies and
  Humanities, AB
Livestock Management, AB
Multi-/Interdisciplinary Studies, AB
Natural Resources and Conservation, AB
Natural Resources Conservation and Research, AB
Natural Resources Management/Development and
  Policy, AB
Natural Sciences, AB
Parks, Recreation and Leisure Facilities
  Management, B
Parks, Recreation, Leisure and Fitness Studies, B

Plant Protection and Integrated Pest
  Management, AB
Plant Sciences, AB
Poultry Science, B
Range Science and Management, AB
Scandinavian Studies, B
Science Teacher Education/General Science
  Teacher Education, B
Social and Philosophical Foundations of
  Education, B
Soil Science and Agronomy, AB
Soil Sciences, AB
Solar Energy Technology/Technician, B
Systems Science and Theory, B
Waldorf/Steiner Teacher Education, B
Water, Wetlands, and Marine Resources
  Management, B
Wildlife and Wildlands Science and
  Management, AB
Wildlife Biology, B
Wood Science and Wood Products/Pulp and Paper
  Technology, B

UNIVERSITY OF VERMONT

Agricultural Economics, BM
Agricultural Sciences, MD
Agriculture, B
Agronomy and Crop Science, B
Agronomy and Soil Sciences, MD
Allied Health and Medical Assisting Services, MD
Allopathic Medicine, PO
Anatomy, DO
Ancient/Classical Greek Language and Literature, B
Animal Sciences, BMD
Anthropology, B
Applied Economics, BM
Applied Horticulture/Horticultural Business
  Services, B
Applied Horticulture/Horticultural Operations, B
Art History, Criticism and Conservation, B
Art Teacher Education, B
Asian Studies/Civilization, B
Athletic Training and Sports Medicine, B
Biochemistry, BMDO
Biological and Biomedical Sciences, MDO
Biology/Biological Sciences, B
Biomedical Engineering, M
Biophysics, MDO
Biostatistics, M
Botany/Plant Biology, BMD
Business Administration and Management, B
Business Administration, Management and
  Operations, M
Canadian Studies, B
Cell Biology and Anatomy, MD
Chemistry, BMD
Child and Family Studies, M
Civil Engineering, BMD
Classics and Classical
  Languages, Literatures, and Linguistics, BM
Clinical Laboratory Science/Medical
  Technology/Technologist, B
Clinical Psychology, D
Communication and Media Studies, M
Communication Disorders, B
Computer and Information Sciences, B
Computer Science, BMD
Computer Systems Analysis/Analyst, B
Consumer Economics, M
Counseling Psychology, M
Counselor Education/School Counseling and
  Guidance Services, M
Curriculum and Instruction, M
Dairy Husbandry and Production, B
Development Economics and International
  Development, B
Dietetics/Dieticians, B
Drama and Dramatics/Theatre Arts, B
Early Childhood Education and Teaching, B
Economics, B
Education, BMD
Education/Teaching of Individuals in Early Childhood
  Special Education Programs, B
Educational Administration and Supervision, M
Educational Leadership and Administration, MD
Electrical Engineering, MD

Electrical, Electronics and Communications
  Engineering, B
Elementary Education and Teaching, B
Engineering and Applied Sciences, MD
Engineering/Industrial Management, B
English, M
English Language and Literature, B
English/Language Arts Teacher Education, B
Environmental Engineering
  Technology/Environmental Technology, MD
Environmental Sciences, B
Environmental Studies, B
Environmental/Environmental Health Engineering, B
European Studies/Civilization, B
Family and Consumer Sciences/Home Economics
  Teacher Education, B
Film/Cinema Studies, B
Fine/Studio Arts, B
Foreign Language Teacher Education, BM
Forestry, B
French Language and Literature, BM
Geography, B
Geology/Earth Science, BM
German Language and Literature, BM
Historic Preservation and Conservation, M
History, BM
Horticultural Science, MD
Industrial Engineering, B
Information Science/Studies, B
Interdisciplinary Studies, B
Italian Studies, B
Junior High/Intermediate/Middle School Education
  and Teaching, B
Kindergarten/PreSchool Education and Teaching, B
Latin American Studies, B
Latin Language and Literature, B
Liberal Arts and Sciences Studies and
  Humanities, B
Materials Sciences, MD
Mathematics, BMD
Mathematics Teacher Education, BM
Mechanical Engineering, BMD
Medical Microbiology and Bacteriology, B
Medical Radiologic Technology/Science - Radiation
  Therapist, B
Microbiology, MDO
Molecular Biology, BMD
Molecular Genetics, BMDO
Molecular Physiology, MDO
Movement Therapy and Movement Education, B
Music, B
Music History, Literature, and Theory, B
Music Performance, B
Music Teacher Education, B
Natural Resources and Conservation, BMD
Natural Resources Management/Development and
  Policy, MD
Neurobiology and Neurophysiology, DO
Neuroscience, DO
Nuclear Medical Technology/Technologist, B
Nursing, M
Nursing - Registered Nurse Training, B
Nutritional Sciences, BM
Parks, Recreation and Leisure Facilities
  Management, B
Pathology/Experimental Pathology, MO
Pharmacology, MDO
Philosophy, B
Physical Education Teaching and Coaching, B
Physical Therapy/Therapist, D
Physics, BM
Plant Sciences, BMD
Political Science and Government, B
Psychology, BD
Public Administration, M
Public Relations, Advertising, and Applied
  Communication, B
Reading Teacher Education, M
Religion/Religious Studies, B
Russian Language and Literature, B
Russian Studies, B
Science Teacher Education/General Science
  Teacher Education, BM
Secondary Education and Teaching, B
Social Science Teacher Education, B
Social Work, BM

Sociology, B
Spanish Language and Literature, B
Special Education and Teaching, M
Statistics, BM
Wildlife Biology, B
Women's Studies, B
Zoology/Animal Biology, B

VERMONT TECHNICAL COLLEGE

Agribusiness, A
Architectural Engineering Technology/Technician, AB
Automotive Engineering Technology/Technician, A
Business Administration and Management, AB
Civil Engineering Technology/Technician, A
Computer Engineering Technology/Technician, AB
Computer Software Engineering, AB
Construction Engineering Technology/Technician, A
Construction Management, A
Dairy Science, A
Dental Hygiene/Hygienist, A
Electrical, Electronic and Communications
  Engineering Technology/Technician, A
Electromechanical Technology/Electromechanical
  Engineering Technology, B
Information Technology, B
Landscaping and Groundskeeping, A
Licensed Practical/Vocational Nurse Training, A
Mechanical Engineering/Mechanical
  Technology/Technician, A
Nursing - Registered Nurse Training, A
Respiratory Care Therapy/Therapist, A
Veterinary/Animal Health Technology/Technician and
  Veterinary Assistant, A

WOODBURY COLLEGE

Community Psychology, AB
General Studies, A
Legal Assistant/Paralegal, AB
Peace Studies and Conflict Resolution, A

Virginia

ARGOSY UNIVERSITY/WASHINGTON D.C.

Business Administration, Management and
  Operations, MD
Clinical Psychology, MD
Counseling Psychology, MD
Curriculum and Instruction, MD
Education, MD
Educational Leadership and Administration, MD
Forensic Psychology, M
Psychology, BMD

THE ART INSTITUTE OF WASHINGTON

Advertising, B
Commercial and Advertising Art, AB
Computer Graphics, A
Culinary Arts/Chef Training, A
Design and Visual Communications, B
Digital Communication and Media/Multimedia, B
Interior Design, B
Intermedia/Multimedia, AB
Web Page, Digital/Multimedia and Information
  Resources Design, B

AVERETT UNIVERSITY

Accounting, B
Air Transportation, B
Applied Mathematics, B
Art Education, M
Art Teacher Education, B
Art/Art Studies, General, B
Athletic Training and Sports Medicine, B
Aviation/Airway Management and Operations, B
Avionics Maintenance Technology/Technician, B
Biological and Physical Sciences, B
Biology Teacher Education, B
Biology/Biological Sciences, B
Business Administration and Management, AB
Business Administration, Management and
  Operations, M
Chemistry, B
Chemistry Teacher Education, B

Clinical Laboratory Science/Medical
  Technology/Technologist, B
Clinical Psychology, B
Cognitive Psychology and Psycholinguistics, B
Computer Science, BM
Corrections and Criminal Justice, B
Criminal Justice/Law Enforcement Administration, B
Curriculum and Instruction, M
Drama and Dramatics/Theatre Arts, B
Ecology, B
Education, M
Elementary Education and Teaching, M
English Education, M
English Language and Literature, B
English/Language Arts Teacher Education, B
Environmental Biology, B
Environmental Sciences, B
Equestrian/Equine Studies, B
Finance, B
General Studies, A
Health and Physical Education, B
Health and Physical Education/Fitness, B
Health Teacher Education, B
History, B
History Teacher Education, B
Industrial and Organizational Psychology, B
Information Science/Studies, B
Interdisciplinary Studies, B
International Marketing, B
Journalism, B
Liberal Arts and Sciences Studies and
  Humanities, AB
Management Science, B
Marketing/Marketing Management, B
Mathematics, B
Mathematics and Computer Science, B
Mathematics Teacher Education, BM
Music, B
Music Performance, B
Physical Education Teaching and Coaching, BM
Physiological Psychology/Psychobiology, B
Political Science and Government, B
Pre-Medicine/Pre-Medical Studies, B
Psychology, B
Radiologic Technology/Science - Radiographer, B
Reading Teacher Education, M
Religion/Religious Studies, B
Religious Education, B
Religious/Sacred Music, B
Science Teacher Education/General Science
  Teacher Education, M
Social Science Teacher Education, B
Social Studies Teacher Education, BM
Sociology, B
Special Education and Teaching, M
Sport and Fitness Administration/Management, B
Teacher Education and Professional
  Development, Specific Subject Areas, B
Teacher Education, Multiple Levels, B
Theater, M
Theatre Literature, History and Criticism, B

AVIATION INSTITUTE OF MAINTENANCE-MANASSAS

Airframe Mechanics and Aircraft Maintenance
  Technology/Technician, A

AVIATION INSTITUTE OF MAINTENANCE-VIRGINIA BEACH

Airframe Mechanics and Aircraft Maintenance
  Technology/Technician, A

BLUE RIDGE COMMUNITY COLLEGE

Accounting, A
Administrative Assistant and Secretarial Science, A
Business Administration and Management, A
Computer Systems Networking and
  Telecommunications, A
Drafting/Design Engineering
  Technologies/Technicians, A
Electrical, Electronic and Communications
  Engineering Technology/Technician, A
Information Science/Studies, A
Information Technology, A
Nursing - Registered Nurse Training, A

Veterinary/Animal Health Technology/Technician and
  Veterinary Assistant, A

BLUEFIELD COLLEGE

Accounting, B
Art/Art Studies, General, B
Athletic Training and Sports Medicine, B
Bible/Biblical Studies, B
Biology Teacher Education, B
Biology/Biological Sciences, B
Business Administration and Management, B
Business Teacher Education, B
Chemistry, B
Chemistry Teacher Education, B
Computer Science, B
Criminal Justice/Law Enforcement Administration, B
Divinity/Ministry (BD, MDiv.), B
Drama and Dramatics/Theatre Arts, B
Education, B
Elementary Education and Teaching, B
English Language and Literature, B
English/Language Arts Teacher Education, B
Health Teacher Education, B
History, B
History Teacher Education, B
Interdisciplinary Studies, B
Junior High/Intermediate/Middle School Education
  and Teaching, B
Kindergarten/PreSchool Education and Teaching, B
Kinesiology and Exercise Science, B
Liberal Arts and Sciences Studies and
  Humanities, B
Mass Communication/Media Studies, B
Mathematics, B
Mathematics Teacher Education, B
Music, B
Music Teacher Education, B
Philosophy, B
Physical Education Teaching and Coaching, B
Psychology, B
Religion/Religious Studies, B
Religious/Sacred Music, B
Science Teacher Education/General Science
  Teacher Education, B
Secondary Education and Teaching, B
Social Sciences, B
Social Studies Teacher Education, B
Theology/Theological Studies, B

BRIDGEWATER COLLEGE

American History (United States), B
Athletic Training and Sports Medicine, B
Biology/Biological Sciences, B
Business Administration and Management, B
Chemistry, B
Clinical Laboratory Science/Medical
  Technology/Technologist, B
Computer Science, B
Economics, B
English Language and Literature, B
Environmental Sciences, B
Family and Consumer Sciences/Human Sciences, B
Fine/Studio Arts, B
Foods, Nutrition, and Wellness Studies, B
French Language and Literature, B
Health and Physical Education, B
History, B
International Relations and Affairs, B
Kinesiology and Exercise Science, B
Liberal Arts and Sciences Studies and
  Humanities, B
Management Information Systems and Services, B
Marketing/Marketing Management, B
Mass Communication/Media Studies, B
Mathematics, B
Music History, Literature, and Theory, B
Philosophy and Religious Studies, B
Physical Education Teaching and Coaching, B
Physics, B
Political Science and Government, B
Psychology, B
Public Relations/Image Management, B
Sociology, B

Spanish Language and Literature, B

BRYANT AND STRATTON COLLEGE, RICHMOND

Accounting, A
Administrative Assistant and Secretarial Science, A
Business Administration and Management, B
Business/Commerce, A
Criminal Justice/Law Enforcement Administration, A
Human Resources Management and Services, A
Information Technology, A
Legal Administrative Assistant/Secretary, A
Legal Assistant/Paralegal, A
Medical Administrative Assistant/Secretary, A
Medical/Clinical Assistant, A

BRYANT AND STRATTON COLLEGE, VIRGINIA BEACH

Accounting, A
Administrative Assistant and Secretarial Science, A
Business Administration and Management, AB
Consumer Merchandising/Retailing Management, A
Hotel/Motel Administration/Management, A
Information Science/Studies, A
Legal Administrative Assistant/Secretary, A
Legal Assistant/Paralegal, A
Medical Administrative Assistant/Secretary, A
Medical/Clinical Assistant, A
Tourism and Travel Services Management, A

CENTRAL VIRGINIA COMMUNITY COLLEGE

Accounting, A
Administrative Assistant and Secretarial Science, A
Architectural Engineering Technology/Technician, A
Biological and Physical Sciences, A
Business Administration and Management, A
Civil Engineering Technology/Technician, A
Clinical/Medical Laboratory Technician, A
Commercial and Advertising Art, A
Consumer Merchandising/Retailing Management, A
Criminal Justice/Law Enforcement Administration, A
Drafting and Design Technology/Technician, A
Education, A
Electrical, Electronic and Communications
   Engineering Technology/Technician, A
Engineering Technology, A
Finance, A
General Studies, A
Information Science/Studies, A
Liberal Arts and Sciences Studies and
   Humanities, A
Management Information Systems and Services, A
Marketing/Marketing Management, A
Mechanical Engineering/Mechanical
   Technology/Technician, A
Radiologic Technology/Science - Radiographer, A
Respiratory Care Therapy/Therapist, A

CHRISTENDOM COLLEGE

Classics and Classical
   Languages, Literatures, and Linguistics, B
Comparative Literature, B
French Language and Literature, B
History, B
Liberal Arts and Sciences Studies and
   Humanities, A
Philosophy, B
Political Science and Government, B
Theology and Religious Vocations, M
Theology/Theological Studies, B

CHRISTOPHER NEWPORT UNIVERSITY

Accounting, B
Applied Physics, M
Art Education, M
Biology/Biological Sciences, B
Business Administration and Management, B
Business/Managerial Economics, B
Chemistry, B
Communication Studies/Speech Communication
   and Rhetoric, B
Comparative Literature, B
Computer and Information Sciences, B
Computer Engineering, B

Computer Science, BM
Drama and Dramatics/Theatre Arts, B
Economics, B
Education, BM
Elementary Education and Teaching, M
English Education, M
English Language and Literature, B
Environmental Sciences, M
Environmental Studies, B
Finance, B
Fine/Studio Arts, B
Foreign Language Teacher Education, M
French Language and Literature, BM
German Language and Literature, B
History, BM
Horticultural Science, B
Information Science/Studies, B
Interdisciplinary Studies, B
International Business/Trade/Commerce, B
Junior High/Intermediate/Middle School Education
   and Teaching, B
Law and Legal Studies, B
Marketing/Marketing Management, B
Mathematics, B
Mathematics Teacher Education, M
Music, B
Music History, Literature, and Theory, B
Music Teacher Education, M
Music Theory and Composition, B
Philosophy, B
Physics, BM
Political Science and Government, B
Pre-Law Studies, B
Science Teacher Education/General Science
   Teacher Education, M
Social Work, B
Sociology, B
Spanish Language and Literature, BM
Theater, M

THE COLLEGE OF WILLIAM AND MARY

Accounting, M
African-American/Black Studies, B
American/United States Studies/Civilization, BMDO
Anthropology, BMD
Applied Science and Technology, MD
Art History, Criticism and Conservation, B
Art/Art Studies, General, B
Biological and Biomedical Sciences, M
Biological Anthropology, D
Biology/Biological Sciences, B
Biopsychology, B
Business Administration and Management, B
Business Administration, Management and
   Operations, MO
Chemistry, BM
Classics and Classical
   Languages, Literatures, and Linguistics, B
Clinical Psychology, D
Computational Sciences, M
Computer and Information Sciences, B
Computer Science, MD
Counselor Education/School Counseling and
   Guidance Services, MD
Curriculum and Instruction, MD
Drama and Dramatics/Theatre Arts, B
East Asian Studies, B
Economics, B
Education, MDO
Education/Teaching of the Gifted and Talented, M
Educational Leadership and Administration, MD
Educational Media/Instructional Technology, D
Elementary Education and Teaching, M
English Language and Literature, B
Environmental Studies, B
Ethnic and Cultural Studies, B
European Studies/Civilization, B
Experimental Psychology, M
French Language and Literature, B
Geology/Earth Science, B
German Language and Literature, B
History, BMD
Interdisciplinary Studies, B
International Relations and Affairs, B
Latin American Studies, B

Latin Language and Literature, B
Law and Legal Studies, MPO
Linguistics, B
Marine Sciences, MD
Marriage and Family Therapy/Counseling, M
Mathematics, B
Medieval and Renaissance Studies, B
Modern Greek Language and Literature, B
Modern Languages, B
Multi-/Interdisciplinary Studies, B
Music, B
Operations Research, M
Philosophy, B
Physical Education Teaching and Coaching, B
Physics, BMD
Political Science and Government, B
Psychology, BMD
Public Policy Analysis, BMO
Reading Teacher Education, M
Religion/Religious Studies, B
Russian Studies, B
School Psychology, MO
Secondary Education and Teaching, M
Sociology, B
Spanish Language and Literature, B
Special Education and Teaching, M
Substance Abuse/Addiction Counseling, M
Women's Studies, B

DABNEY S. LANCASTER COMMUNITY COLLEGE

Administrative Assistant and Secretarial Science, A
Biological and Physical Sciences, A
Business Administration and Management, A
Computer Programming/Programmer, A
Criminal Justice/Law Enforcement Administration, A
Data Processing and Data Processing
   Technology/Technician, A
Drafting and Design Technology/Technician, A
Drafting/Design Engineering
   Technologies/Technicians, A
Education, A
Electrical, Electronic and Communications
   Engineering Technology/Technician, A
Forestry Technology/Technician, A
Information Science/Studies, A
Legal Administrative Assistant/Secretary, A
Liberal Arts and Sciences Studies and
   Humanities, A
Medical Administrative Assistant/Secretary, A
Nursing - Registered Nurse Training, A
Wood Science and Wood Products/Pulp and Paper
   Technology, A

DANVILLE COMMUNITY COLLEGE

Accounting, A
Administrative Assistant and Secretarial Science, A
Biological and Physical Sciences, A
Business Administration and Management, A
Computer Programming/Programmer, A
Education, A
Engineering Technology, A
Liberal Arts and Sciences Studies and
   Humanities, A
Marketing/Marketing Management, A

DEVRY UNIVERSITY (ARLINGTON)

Business Administration and Management, B
Business Administration, Management and
   Operations, BM
Computer and Information Sciences, B
Computer Engineering Technology/Technician, B
Computer Programming, Specific Applications, B
Computer Systems Analysis/Analyst, B
Computer Systems Networking and
   Telecommunications, AB
Electrical, Electronic and Communications
   Engineering Technology/Technician, AB

Information Science/Studies, B

DEVRY UNIVERSITY (MCLEAN)

Business Administration, Management and
Operations, M

EASTERN MENNONITE UNIVERSITY

Accounting, B
Art Teacher Education, B
Art/Art Studies, General, B
Bible/Biblical Studies, AB
Biochemistry, B
Biology Teacher Education, B
Biology/Biological Sciences, B
Business Administration and Management, B
Business Administration, Management and
Operations, M
Chemistry, B
Chemistry Teacher Education, B
Clinical Laboratory Science/Medical
Technology/Technologist, B
Communication Studies/Speech Communication
and Rhetoric, B
Computer Science, B
Computer Systems Analysis/Analyst, B
Conflict Resolution and Mediation/Peace
Studies, MO
Development Economics and International
Development, B
Drama and Dramatics/Theatre Arts, B
Economics, B
Education, M
Education/Teaching of Individuals with Emotional
Disturbances, B
Education/Teaching of Individuals with Mental
Retardation, B
Education/Teaching of Individuals with Specific
Learning Disabilities, B
Elementary Education and Teaching, B
English Language and Literature, B
English/Language Arts Teacher Education, B
Environmental Sciences, B
French Language and Literature, B
French Language Teacher Education, B
General Studies, A
German Language and Literature, B
German Language Teacher Education, B
Health Teacher Education, B
History, B
International Agriculture, B
International Business/Trade/Commerce, B
Junior High/Intermediate/Middle School Education
and Teaching, B
Kindergarten/PreSchool Education and Teaching, B
Liberal Arts and Sciences Studies and
Humanities, B
Mathematics, B
Mathematics Teacher Education, B
Multi-/Interdisciplinary Studies, B
Music, B
Music Teacher Education, B
Nursing - Registered Nurse Training, B
Pastoral Studies/Counseling, MO
Peace Studies and Conflict Resolution, B
Philosophy and Religious Studies, B
Physical Education Teaching and Coaching, B
Pre-Dentistry Studies, B
Pre-Medicine/Pre-Medical Studies, B
Pre-Veterinary Studies, B
Psychology, B
Religion/Religious Studies, M
Secondary Education and Teaching, B
Social Science Teacher Education, B
Social Sciences, B
Social Work, B
Sociology, B
Spanish Language and Literature, B
Spanish Language Teacher Education, B
Sport and Fitness Administration/Management, B
Theology and Religious Vocations, MPO
Theology/Theological Studies, B

EASTERN SHORE COMMUNITY COLLEGE

Administrative Assistant and Secretarial Science, A
Biological and Physical Sciences, A

Business Administration and Management, A
Computer/Information Technology Services
Administration and Management, A
Education, A
Electrical, Electronic and Communications
Engineering Technology/Technician, A
Liberal Arts and Sciences Studies and
Humanities, A
Management Information Systems and Services, A
Nursing - Registered Nurse Training, A

ECPI COLLEGE OF TECHNOLOGY (NEWPORT NEWS)

Accounting, A
Communications Technology/Technician, A
Computer and Information Sciences, A
Computer Engineering Technology/Technician, A
Computer Science, A
Computer Typography and Composition Equipment
Operator, A
Electrical, Electronic and Communications
Engineering Technology/Technician, A
Electromechanical Technology/Electromechanical
Engineering Technology, A
Engineering Technology, A
Health Information/Medical Records
Administration/Administrator, A
Health/Health Care Administration/Management, A
Information Science/Studies, A
Mechanical Engineering/Mechanical
Technology/Technician, A
Medical Administrative Assistant/Secretary, A
Telecommunications Technology/Technician, A

ECPI COLLEGE OF TECHNOLOGY (VIRGINIA BEACH)

Accounting, A
Biomedical Technology/Technician, A
Business Machine Repairer, A
Communications Technology/Technician, A
Computer and Information Sciences, A
Computer Engineering Technology/Technician, A
Computer Programming/Programmer, A
Computer Science, A
Computer Typography and Composition Equipment
Operator, A
Data Processing and Data Processing
Technology/Technician, A
Electrical, Electronic and Communications
Engineering Technology/Technician, A
Electromechanical Technology/Electromechanical
Engineering Technology, A
Engineering Technology, A
Health Information/Medical Records
Administration/Administrator, A
Health/Health Care Administration/Management, A
Information Science/Studies, A
Mechanical Engineering/Mechanical
Technology/Technician, A
Medical Administrative Assistant/Secretary, A
Telecommunications Technology/Technician, A

ECPI TECHNICAL COLLEGE (GLEN ALLEN)

Computer and Information Systems Security, A
Computer Programming/Programmer, A
Computer Technology/Computer Systems
Technology, A
Data Entry/Microcomputer Applications, A
Telecommunications Technology/Technician, A
Web Page, Digital/Multimedia and Information
Resources Design, A

ECPI TECHNICAL COLLEGE (RICHMOND)

Accounting, A
Business Machine Repairer, A
Communications Technology/Technician, A
Computer and Information Sciences, A
Computer and Information Systems Security, A
Computer Programming/Programmer, A
Computer Science, A
Computer Technology/Computer Systems
Technology, A

Computer Typography and Composition Equipment
Operator, A
Data Entry/Microcomputer Applications, A
Data Processing and Data Processing
Technology/Technician, A
Electrical, Electronic and Communications
Engineering Technology/Technician, A
Electromechanical Technology/Electromechanical
Engineering Technology, A
Engineering Technology, A
Health Information/Medical Records
Administration/Administrator, A
Health/Health Care Administration/Management, A
Information Science/Studies, A
Mechanical Engineering/Mechanical
Technology/Technician, A
Medical Administrative Assistant/Secretary, A
Telecommunications Technology/Technician, A
Trade and Industrial Teacher Education, A
Web Page, Digital/Multimedia and Information
Resources Design, A

ECPI TECHNICAL COLLEGE (ROANOKE)

Accounting, A
Communications Technology/Technician, A
Computer and Information Sciences, A
Computer and Information Systems Security, A
Computer Engineering Technology/Technician, A
Computer Science, A
Computer Technology/Computer Systems
Technology, A
Computer Typography and Composition Equipment
Operator, A
Data Entry/Microcomputer Applications, A
Electrical, Electronic and Communications
Engineering Technology/Technician, A
Electromechanical Technology/Electromechanical
Engineering Technology, A
Engineering Technology, A
Health Information/Medical Records
Administration/Administrator, A
Health/Health Care Administration/Management, A
Information Science/Studies, A
Mechanical Engineering/Mechanical
Technology/Technician, A
Medical Administrative Assistant/Secretary, A
Medical/Clinical Assistant, A
Telecommunications Technology/Technician, A

EMORY & HENRY COLLEGE

Accounting, B
Applied Mathematics, B
Art/Art Studies, General, B
Biology/Biological Sciences, B
Business Administration and Management, B
Chemistry, B
Clinical Laboratory Science/Medical
Technology/Technologist, B
Community Organization and Advocacy, B
Computer Science, B
Creative Writing, B
Drama and Dramatics/Theatre Arts, B
East Asian Studies, B
Economics, B
English Education, M
English Language and Literature, B
Environmental Studies, B
European Studies/Civilization, B
French Language and Literature, B
Geography, B
Health and Physical Education, B
History, B
Interdisciplinary Studies, B
International Relations and Affairs, B
Mass Communication/Media Studies, B
Mathematics, B
Music, B
Near and Middle Eastern Studies, B
Philosophy, B
Physics, B
Political Science and Government, B
Pre-Dentistry Studies, B
Pre-Law Studies, B
Pre-Medicine/Pre-Medical Studies, B
Pre-Veterinary Studies, B

Psychology, B
Religion/Religious Studies, B
Sociology, B
Spanish Language and Literature, B

FERRUM COLLEGE

Accounting, B
Agriculture, B
Applied Horticulture/Horticultural Operations, B
Art/Art Studies, General, B
Biology/Biological Sciences, B
Business Administration and Management, B
Chemistry, B
Clinical Laboratory Science/Medical
 Technology/Technologist, B
Computer Science, B
Criminal Justice/Safety Studies, B
Drama and Dramatics/Theatre Arts, B
Education, B
English Language and Literature, B
Environmental Studies, B
Fine/Studio Arts, B
History, B
Horticultural Science, B
Information Science/Studies, B
International Relations and Affairs, B
Liberal Arts and Sciences Studies and
 Humanities, B
Mathematics, B
Parks, Recreation, Leisure and Fitness Studies, B
Philosophy, B
Physical Education Teaching and Coaching, B
Political Science and Government, B
Psychology, B
Religion/Religious Studies, B
Russian Language and Literature, B
Social Work, B
Sociology, B
Spanish Language and Literature, B
Sport and Fitness Administration/Management, B
Tourism and Travel Services Management, B

GEORGE MASON UNIVERSITY

Accounting, B
Anthropology, B
Applied Physics, M
Art History, Criticism and Conservation, B
Art/Art Studies, General, B
Atmospheric Sciences and Meteorology, D
Bioinformatics, MD
Biological and Biomedical Sciences, MD
Biology/Biological Sciences, B
Business Administration and Management, B
Business Administration, Management and
 Operations, M
Business, Management, Marketing, and Related
 Support Services, B
Cell Biology and Anatomy, M
Chemistry, BM
Civil Engineering, BM
Clinical Laboratory Science/Medical
 Technology/Technologist, B
Clinical Psychology, D
Communication and Media Studies, M
Community College Education, DO
Computational Sciences, MDO
Computer and Information Sciences, B
Computer Engineering, BMD
Computer Science, MD
Conflict Resolution and Mediation/Peace
 Studies, MD
Counselor Education/School Counseling and
 Guidance Services, M
Criminal Justice/Police Science, B
Cultural Studies, D
Dance, BM
Developmental Psychology, MD
Drama and Dramatics/Theatre Arts, B
Early Childhood Education and Teaching, M
Ecology, M
Economics, BMD
Education, MD
Educational Leadership and Administration, M
Educational Measurement and Evaluation, M
Educational Media/Instructional Technology, M
Electrical Engineering, MD

Electrical, Electronics and Communications
 Engineering, B
Engineering and Applied Sciences, MDO
Engineering Physics, M
English, M
English as a Second Language, M
English Language and Literature, B
Environmental Sciences, MD
Evolutionary Biology, M
Exercise and Sports Science, M
Experimental Psychology, M
Finance, B
Fine/Studio Arts, B
Foreign Language Teacher Education, M
Foreign Languages and Literatures, B
Geodetic Sciences, O
Geographic Information Systems, MD
Geography, BM
Geology/Earth Science, B
Graphic Design, M
Health Professions and Related Clinical Sciences, B
Health Teacher Education, B
History, BMD
Human Resources Management and Services, M
Industrial and Organizational Psychology, MD
Information Science/Studies, MDO
Interdisciplinary Studies, BM
International Affairs, M
International Relations and Affairs, B
Law and Legal Studies, MPO
Liberal Arts and Sciences Studies and
 Humanities, B
Liberal Studies, M
Linguistics, M
Logistics and Materials Management, M
Management of Technology, MD
Marketing/Marketing Management, B
Mathematics, BM
Medical/Surgical Nursing, M
Microbiology, D
Middle School Education, M
Molecular Biology, MD
Multilingual and Multicultural Education, M
Music, M
Music Performance, B
Music Teacher Education, M
Neuroscience, D
Nursing, MD
Nursing - Advanced Practice, M
Nursing - Registered Nurse Training, B
Nursing Administration, M
Operations Research, M
Organizational Management, M
Philosophy, B
Physical Education Teaching and Coaching, B
Physics, BM
Political Science and Government, B
Psychology, BMD
Public Administration, B
Public Affairs, M
Public Policy Analysis, MD
Reading Teacher Education, M
Religion/Religious Studies, B
Russian Studies, B
School Psychology, M
Secondary Education and Teaching, M
Social Sciences, D
Social Work, BM
Sociology, BM
Software Engineering, M
Solid State and Low-Temperature Physics, B
Special Education and Teaching, M
Speech and Rhetorical Studies, B
Statistics, M
Systems Engineering, BM
Systems Science and Theory, M
Telecommunications, M
Transportation/Transportation Management, M
Urban Education and Leadership, M
Visual and Performing Arts, B
Writing, M

GERMANNA COMMUNITY COLLEGE

Biological and Physical Sciences, A
Business Administration and Management, A
Criminal Justice/Police Science, A

Dental Hygiene/Hygienist, A
Education, A
General Studies, A
Information Technology, A
Liberal Arts and Sciences Studies and
 Humanities, A
Nursing - Registered Nurse Training, A

HAMPDEN-SYDNEY COLLEGE

Ancient/Classical Greek Language and Literature, B
Applied Mathematics, B
Biochemistry, B
Biology/Biological Sciences, B
Biophysics, B
Business/Managerial Economics, B
Chemistry, B
Classics and Classical
 Languages, Literatures, and Linguistics, B
Computer Science, B
Econometrics and Quantitative Economics, B
Economics, B
English Language and Literature, B
Fine/Studio Arts, B
French Language and Literature, B
German Language and Literature, B
History, B
Humanities/Humanistic Studies, B
International Relations and Affairs, B
Latin Language and Literature, B
Mathematics, B
Mathematics and Computer Science, B
Philosophy, B
Physics, B
Political Science and Government, B
Psychology, B
Religion/Religious Studies, B
Spanish Language and Literature, B

HAMPTON UNIVERSITY

Accounting, B
Advertising, B
Air Traffic Controller, B
Applied Mathematics, M
Architecture, B
Army JROTC/ROTC, B
Art Teacher Education, B
Art/Art Studies, General, B
Audiology/Audiologist and Speech-Language
 Pathology/Pathologist, B
Aviation/Airway Management and Operations, B
Avionics Maintenance Technology/Technician, AB
Biological and Biomedical Sciences, M
Biology/Biological Sciences, B
Broadcast Journalism, B
Building/Construction
 Finishing, Management, and Inspection, B
Business Administration and Management, B
Business Administration, Management and
 Operations, M
Business Teacher Education, B
Ceramic Arts and Ceramics, B
Chemical Engineering, B
Chemistry, BM
Child Development, B
Commercial and Advertising Art, B
Communication Disorders, BM
Computer Science, BM
Construction Engineering Technology/Technician, B
Counselor Education/School Counseling and
 Guidance Services, M
Criminal Justice/Law Enforcement Administration, B
Developmental and Child Psychology, B
Drama and Dramatics/Theatre Arts, B
Drawing, B
Economics, B
Education, BM
Electrical, Electronic and Communications
 Engineering Technology/Technician, B
Electrical, Electronics and Communications
 Engineering, B
Elementary Education and Teaching, BM
English Language and Literature, B
Environmental Studies, B
Family and Consumer Sciences/Home Economics
 Teacher Education, B
Fashion Merchandising, B

Fashion/Apparel Design, B
Finance, B
Fire Science/Firefighting, B
General Studies, B
Health Teacher Education, B
History, B
Hotel/Motel Administration/Management, B
Information Science/Studies, B
Interior Design, B
Jazz/Jazz Studies, B
Journalism, B
Junior High/Intermediate/Middle School Education
    and Teaching, B
Kindergarten/PreSchool Education and Teaching, B
Legal Assistant/Paralegal, B
Marine Biology and Biological Oceanography, B
Marine Science/Merchant Marine Officer, B
Marketing/Marketing Management, B
Mass Communication/Media Studies, B
Mathematics, B
Modern Languages, B
Molecular Biology, B
Museology/Museum Studies, M
Music, B
Music Teacher Education, B
Navy/Marine Corps JROTC/ROTC, B
Nursing, M
Nursing - Registered Nurse Training, B
Photography, B
Physical Education Teaching and Coaching, B
Physical Sciences, B
Physical Therapy/Therapist, BD
Physics, BMD
Political Science and Government, B
Pre-Dentistry Studies, B
Pre-Law Studies, B
Pre-Medicine/Pre-Medical Studies, B
Pre-Veterinary Studies, B
Psychology, B
Public Relations/Image Management, B
Religion/Religious Studies, B
Sales, Distribution and Marketing Operations, B
Secondary Education and Teaching, B
Social Sciences, B
Social Work, B
Sociology, B
Special Education and Teaching, BM
Sport and Fitness Administration/Management, B
Student Personnel Services, B
Therapeutic Recreation/Recreational Therapy, B

HOLLINS UNIVERSITY

Art History, Criticism and Conservation, B
Art/Art Studies, General, B
Arts Management, B
Biology/Biological Sciences, B
Business/Commerce, B
Chemistry, B
Classics and Classical
    Languages, Literatures, and Linguistics, B
Computer Science, O
Creative Writing, B
Dance, BM
Drama and Dramatics/Theatre Arts, B
Economics, B
Education, BM
English, M
English Language and Literature, B
Film, Television, and Video Production, M
Film, Television, and Video Theory and Criticism, M
Film/Video and Photographic Arts, B
Fine Arts and Art Studies, M
French Language and Literature, B
German Language and Literature, B
History, B
Humanities/Humanistic Studies, M
Interdisciplinary Studies, BM
International Relations and Affairs, B
Liberal Studies, MO
Mass Communication/Media Studies, B
Mathematics, B
Music, B
Performance, M
Philosophy, B
Physics, B
Political Science and Government, B

Psychology, B
Religion/Religious Studies, B
Social Sciences, M
Sociology, B
Spanish Language and Literature, B
Women's Studies, B
Writing, M

ITT TECHNICAL INSTITUTE
(CHANTILLY)

Animation, Interactive Technology, Video Graphics
    and Special Effects, B
Business Administration and Management, B
CAD/CADD Drafting and/or Design
    Technology/Technician, A
Computer and Information Systems Security, A
Computer Programming/Programmer, A
Computer Software Technology/Technician, B
Computer Systems Networking and
    Telecommunications, B
Criminal Justice/Law Enforcement Administration, B
Electrical, Electronic and Communications
    Engineering Technology/Technician, AB
Web Page, Digital/Multimedia and Information
    Resources Design, A
Web/Multimedia Management and Webmaster, A

ITT TECHNICAL INSTITUTE (NORFOLK)

Accounting and Business/Management, B
Animation, Interactive Technology, Video Graphics
    and Special Effects, B
Business Administration and Management, B
CAD/CADD Drafting and/or Design
    Technology/Technician, A
Computer Programming/Programmer, A
Criminal Justice/Law Enforcement Administration, B
E-Commerce/Electronic Commerce, B
Electrical, Electronic and Communications
    Engineering Technology/Technician, AB
Information Technology, B
Robotics Technology/Technician, B
System, Networking, and LAN/WAN
    Management/Manager, A
Web Page, Digital/Multimedia and Information
    Resources Design, A
Web/Multimedia Management and Webmaster, A

ITT TECHNICAL INSTITUTE
(RICHMOND)

Animation, Interactive Technology, Video Graphics
    and Special Effects, B
Business Administration and Management, B
CAD/CADD Drafting and/or Design
    Technology/Technician, A
Computer and Information Systems Security, B
Computer Programming/Programmer, A
Criminal Justice/Law Enforcement Administration, B
Electrical, Electronic and Communications
    Engineering Technology/Technician, AB
System, Networking, and LAN/WAN
    Management/Manager, A
Web Page, Digital/Multimedia and Information
    Resources Design, A
Web/Multimedia Management and Webmaster, A

ITT TECHNICAL INSTITUTE
(SPRINGFIELD)

Business Administration and Management, B
CAD/CADD Drafting and/or Design
    Technology/Technician, A
Computer and Information Systems Security, B
Computer Programming/Programmer, A
Computer Software Technology/Technician, B
Criminal Justice/Law Enforcement Administration, B
Electrical, Electronic and Communications
    Engineering Technology/Technician, AB
System, Networking, and LAN/WAN
    Management/Manager, A
Web Page, Digital/Multimedia and Information
    Resources Design, A

J. SARGEANT REYNOLDS
COMMUNITY COLLEGE

Accounting Technology/Technician and
    Bookkeeping, A

Administrative Assistant and Secretarial Science, A
Architectural Engineering Technology/Technician, A
Biological and Physical Sciences, A
Business Administration and Management, A
Child Care and Support Services Management, A
Civil Engineering Technology/Technician, A
Clinical/Medical Laboratory Technician, A
Community Organization and Advocacy, A
Computer and Information Sciences, A
Computer Engineering Technology/Technician, A
Computer Programming, A
Computer Programming/Programmer, A
Construction Engineering Technology/Technician, A
Criminal Justice/Safety Studies, A
Culinary Arts/Chef Training, A
Data Processing and Data Processing
    Technology/Technician, A
Dental Laboratory Technology/Technician, A
Dietetics/Dieticians, A
Electrical, Electronic and Communications
    Engineering Technology/Technician, A
Engineering, A
Executive Assistant/Executive Secretary, A
Fashion Merchandising, A
Fire Science/Firefighting, A
Hospitality Administration/Management, A
Hotel/Motel Administration/Management, A
Information Technology, A
Landscaping and Groundskeeping, A
Legal Assistant/Paralegal, A
Liberal Arts and Sciences Studies and
    Humanities, A
Marketing/Marketing Management, A
Music, A
Nursing - Registered Nurse Training, A
Occupational Therapist Assistant, A
Opticianry/Ophthalmic Dispensing Optician, A
Ornamental Horticulture, A
Respiratory Care Therapy/Therapist, A
Social Sciences, A

JAMES MADISON UNIVERSITY

Accounting, BM
Anthropology, B
Applied Science and Technology, M
Art Education, M
Art History, Criticism and Conservation, BM
Art/Art Studies, General, B
Biological and Biomedical Sciences, M
Biology/Biological Sciences, B
BioTechnology, B
Business Administration and Management, B
Business Administration, Management and
    Operations, M
Business Teacher Education, B
Business/Managerial Economics, B
Ceramic Arts and Ceramics, M
Chemistry, B
Communication Disorders, MD
Communication Studies/Speech Communication
    and Rhetoric, B
Community Health Services/Liaison/Counseling, B
Composition, M
Computer and Information Sciences, B
Computer Science, M
Counseling Psychology, MO
Dietetics/Dieticians, B
Drama and Dramatics/Theatre Arts, B
Early Childhood Education and Teaching, M
Econometrics and Quantitative Economics, B
Economics, B
Education, M
Educational Leadership and Administration, M
English, M
English Language and Literature, B
Finance, B
Fine Arts and Art Studies, M
Foods, Nutrition, and Wellness Studies, B
Foreign Languages and Literatures, B
Geography, B
Geology/Earth Science, B
Health and Physical Education, B
Health Education, M
History, BM
Hospitality Administration/Management, B
Information Science/Studies, B

International Business/Trade/Commerce, B
International Relations and Affairs, B
Jewelry/Metalsmithing, M
Kinesiology and Movement Studies, M
Liberal Arts and Sciences Studies and
  Humanities, B
Marketing/Marketing Management, B
Mathematics, BM
Middle School Education, M
Music, M
Music Performance, B
Music Teacher Education, M
Music Theory and Composition, M
Nursing, M
Nursing - Registered Nurse Training, B
Occupational Therapy/Therapist, M
Painting, M
Performance, M
Philosophy and Religious Studies, B
Photography, M
Physician Assistant, M
Physics, B
Political Science and Government, B
Printmaking, M
Psychology, BMDO
Public Administration, BM
Public Health, M
Reading Teacher Education, M
School Psychology, MO
Science, Technology and Society, B
Sculpture, M
Secondary Education and Teaching, M
Social Sciences, B
Social Work, B
Sociology, B
Special Education and Teaching, M
Speech-Language Pathology/Pathologist, B
Statistics, BM
Technical and Business Writing, BM
Textile Design, M
Vocational and Technical Education, M

JEFFERSON COLLEGE OF HEALTH SCIENCES

Athletic Training and Sports Medicine, B
Biomedical Sciences, B
Emergency Medical Technology/Technician (EMT
  Paramedic), A
Fire Protection and Safety Technology/Technician, A
Health/Health Care Administration/Management, B
Licensed Practical/Vocational Nurse Training, B
Nursing - Registered Nurse Training, AB
Occupational Therapist Assistant, A
Physical Therapist Assistant, A
Physician Assistant, B
Public Health (MPH, DPH), A
Radiologic Technology/Science - Radiographer, B
Respiratory Care Therapy/Therapist, AB

JOHN TYLER COMMUNITY COLLEGE

Administrative Assistant and Secretarial Science, A
Architectural Engineering Technology/Technician, A
Biology Technician/BioTechnology Laboratory
  Technician, A
Business/Commerce, A
Electrical, Electronics and Communications
  Engineering, A
Environmental Engineering
  Technology/Environmental Technology, A
Funeral Service and Mortuary Science, A
Human Services, A
Liberal Arts and Sciences Studies and
  Humanities, A
Management Information Systems and Services, A
Mechanical Engineering/Mechanical
  Technology/Technician, A
Nursing - Registered Nurse Training, A
Physical Therapy/Therapist, A

LIBERTY UNIVERSITY

Accounting, B
Aeronautics/Aviation/Aerospace Science and
  Technology, B
Athletic Training and Sports Medicine, B
Biochemistry, Biophysics and Molecular Biology, B
Biology Teacher Education, B

Biology/Biological Sciences, B
Business Administration and Management, B
Business Administration, Management and
  Operations, M
Business Teacher Education, B
Business/Commerce, B
Communication and Media Studies, M
Communication Studies/Speech Communication
  and Rhetoric, B
Computer and Information Sciences, B
Computer Teacher Education, B
Counseling Psychology, MD
Counselor Education/School Counseling and
  Guidance Services, M
Criminal Justice/Law Enforcement Administration, B
Curriculum and Instruction, M
Developmental and Child Psychology, B
Early Childhood Education and Teaching, M
Economics, B
Education, MDO
Education/Teaching of the Gifted and Talented, M
Educational Administration and Supervision, M
Educational Leadership and Administration, D
Elementary Education and Teaching, BM
English Language and Literature, B
English/Language Arts Teacher Education, B
Family and Consumer Sciences/Home Economics
  Teacher Education, B
Family and Consumer Sciences/Human Sciences, B
Fashion Merchandising, B
General Studies, AB
Health and Physical Education, B
Health Services/Allied Health/Health Sciences, B
Health Teacher Education, B
History, B
History Teacher Education, B
Human Development and Family Studies, B
Interdisciplinary Studies, B
Kinesiology and Exercise Science, B
Law and Legal Studies, P
Management Information Systems and Services, B
Mathematics, B
Mathematics Teacher Education, B
Multi-/Interdisciplinary Studies, B
Music, B
Music Teacher Education, B
Nursing, MD
Nursing - Registered Nurse Training, B
Pastoral Studies/Counseling, D
Philosophy, B
Physical Education Teaching and Coaching, B
Political Science and Government, B
Psychology, B
Public Health Education and Promotion, B
Reading Teacher Education, M
Religion/Religious Studies, ABMDP
Secondary Education and Teaching, M
Social Science Teacher Education, B
Social Sciences, B
Spanish Language and Literature, B
Spanish Language Teacher Education, B
Special Education and Teaching, BM
Sport and Fitness Administration/Management, B
Teacher Education, Multiple Levels, B
Teaching English as a Second or Foreign
  Language/ESL Language Instructor, B
Theology and Religious Vocations, MDP

LONGWOOD UNIVERSITY

Accounting, B
Anthropology, B
Applied Mathematics, B
Army JROTC/ROTC, B
Art History, Criticism and Conservation, B
Art Teacher Education, B
Art/Art Studies, General, B
Athletic Training and Sports Medicine, B
Biology/Biological Sciences, B
Biophysics, B
Business Administration and Management, B
Business/Managerial Economics, B
Chemistry, B
Clinical Laboratory Science/Medical
  Technology/Technologist, B
Clinical/Medical Laboratory Technician, B
Commercial and Advertising Art, B

Communication Disorders, BM
Communication Studies/Speech Communication
  and Rhetoric, B
Community Health Services/Liaison/Counseling, B
Computer Science, B
Counselor Education/School Counseling and
  Guidance Services, M
Criminal Justice/Law Enforcement Administration, B
Criminology, M
Developmental and Child Psychology, B
Drama and Dramatics/Theatre Arts, B
Drawing, B
Economics, B
Education, BM
Educational Administration and Supervision, M
Educational Media/Instructional Technology, M
Elementary Education and Teaching, BM
English, M
English Education, M
English Language and Literature, B
Environmental Studies, B
Experimental Psychology, B
Finance, B
Fine/Studio Arts, B
French Language and Literature, B
Geography, B
Geology/Earth Science, B
German Language and Literature, B
Health Teacher Education, B
History, B
Interior Design, B
International Economics, B
International Relations and Affairs, B
Journalism, B
Kindergarten/PreSchool Education and Teaching, B
Kinesiology and Exercise Science, B
Liberal Arts and Sciences Studies and
  Humanities, B
Library Science, B
Management Information Systems and Services, B
Marketing/Marketing Management, B
Mathematics, B
Modern Languages, B
Music, B
Music Teacher Education, B
Natural Sciences, B
Physical Education Teaching and Coaching, B
Physics, B
Political Science and Government, B
Pre-Dentistry Studies, B
Pre-Law Studies, B
Pre-Medicine/Pre-Medical Studies, B
Pre-Pharmacy Studies, B
Pre-Veterinary Studies, B
Printmaking, B
Psychology, B
Public Health (MPH, DPH), B
Reading Teacher Education, BM
Science Teacher Education/General Science
  Teacher Education, B
Sculpture, B
Secondary Education and Teaching, BM
Social Work, B
Sociology, B
Spanish Language and Literature, B
Special Education and Teaching, B
Sport and Fitness Administration/Management, B
Therapeutic Recreation/Recreational Therapy, B
Writing, M

LORD FAIRFAX COMMUNITY COLLEGE

Accounting, A
Administrative Assistant and Secretarial Science, A
Agricultural Business and Management, A
Applied Horticulture/Horticultural Operations, A
Biological and Physical Sciences, A
Business Administration and Management, A
Civil Engineering Technology/Technician, A
Commercial and Advertising Art, A
Communication Studies/Speech Communication
  and Rhetoric, A
Computer and Information Sciences, A
Computer Programming/Programmer, A
Dental Hygiene/Hygienist, A
Education, A

Environmental Engineering
   Technology/Environmental Technology, A
Information Science/Studies, A
Liberal Arts and Sciences Studies and
   Humanities, A
Mechanical Engineering/Mechanical
   Technology/Technician, A
Natural Resources Management/Development and
   Policy, A
Nursing - Registered Nurse Training, A
Office Management and Supervision, A
Philosophy, A

LYNCHBURG COLLEGE

Accounting, B
Art/Art Studies, General, B
Athletic Training and Sports Medicine, B
Biological and Biomedical Sciences, B
Biology/Biological Sciences, B
Business Administration and Management, B
Business Administration, Management and
   Operations, M
Chemistry, B
Communication Studies/Speech Communication
   and Rhetoric, B
Computer Science, B
Counselor Education/School Counseling and
   Guidance Services, M
Creative Writing, B
Drama and Dramatics/Theatre Arts, B
Economics, B
Education, BM
Educational Leadership and Administration, M
Elementary Education and Teaching, BM
English Education, M
English Language and Literature, B
Environmental Studies, B
French Language and Literature, B
Health Teacher Education, B
History, B
International Relations and Affairs, B
Journalism, B
Kindergarten/PreSchool Education and Teaching, B
Kinesiology and Exercise Science, B
Marketing/Marketing Management, B
Mass Communication/Media Studies, B
Mathematics, B
Music, B
Music Performance, B
Music Theory and Composition, B
Nursing - Registered Nurse Training, B
Organizational Communication, B
Philosophy, B
Physical Education Teaching and Coaching, B
Physics, B
Political Science and Government, B
Pre-Dentistry Studies, B
Pre-Law Studies, B
Pre-Medicine/Pre-Medical Studies, B
Pre-Veterinary Studies, B
Psychology, B
Religion/Religious Studies, B
Secondary Education and Teaching, B
Sociology, B
Spanish Language and Literature, B
Special Education and Teaching, BM
Speech and Rhetorical Studies, B
Sport and Fitness Administration/Management, B

MARY BALDWIN COLLEGE

Applied Mathematics, B
Art/Art Studies, General, B
Arts Management, B
Asian Studies/Civilization, B
Biochemistry, B
Biology/Biological Sciences, B
Business Administration and Management, B
Chemistry, B
Clinical Laboratory Science/Medical
   Technology/Technologist, B
Communication Studies/Speech Communication
   and Rhetoric, B
Communication, Journalism and Related
   Programs, B
Computer and Information Sciences, B
Drama and Dramatics/Theatre Arts, B

Economics, B
Education, M
Elementary Education and Teaching, M
English Language and Literature, B
French Language and Literature, B
German Language and Literature, B
Health/Health Care Administration/Management, B
History, B
International Relations and Affairs, B
Mathematics, B
Middle School Education, M
Music, B
Philosophy, B
Physics, B
Political Science and Government, B
Psychology, B
Religion/Religious Studies, B
Social Work, B
Sociology, B
Spanish Language and Literature, B

MARYMOUNT UNIVERSITY

Accounting, B
Allied Health and Medical Assisting Services, MDO
Biology/Biological Sciences, B
Business Administration and Management, B
Business Administration, Management and
   Operations, BMO
Cell/Cellular and Molecular Biology, B
Communication Studies/Speech Communication
   and Rhetoric, B
Computer and Information Sciences, B
Computer Science, BMO
Counseling Psychology, MO
Counselor Education/School Counseling and
   Guidance Services, M
Criminal Justice/Safety Studies, B
Criminology, B
Economics, B
Education, MO
Educational Leadership and Administration, MO
Educational Psychology, B
Elementary Education and Teaching, M
English, M
English as a Second Language, M
English Language and Literature, B
Environmental Sciences, B
Fashion Merchandising, B
Fashion/Apparel Design, B
Finance, B
Fine/Studio Arts, B
Forensic Psychology, M
Graphic Design, B
Health Promotion, M
Health Services Administration, M
History, B
Human Resources Management and Services, MO
Humanities/Humanistic Studies, M
Information Science/Studies, B
Interior Design, BM
International Business/Trade/Commerce, BO
Kinesiology and Exercise Science, B
Legal and Justice Studies, MO
Legal Assistant/Paralegal, B
Liberal Arts and Sciences Studies and
   Humanities, AB
Management, MO
Management Information Systems and
   Services, MO
Management Strategy and Policy, O
Marketing/Marketing Management, B
Mathematics, B
Medical/Surgical Nursing, MO
Mental and Social Health Services and Allied
   Professions, B
Nursing, M
Nursing - Advanced Practice, MO
Nursing - Registered Nurse Training, B
Nursing Administration, MO
Nursing Education, M
Organizational Management, MO
Pastoral Studies/Counseling, MO
Philosophy, B
Physical Therapy/Therapist, MD
Political Science and Government, B
Psychology, B

Religion/Religious Studies, B
Secondary Education and Teaching, M
Sociology, B
Special Education and Teaching, M
Sport and Fitness Administration/Management, B

MOUNTAIN EMPIRE COMMUNITY COLLEGE

Accounting, A
Administrative Assistant and Secretarial Science, A
Biological and Physical Sciences, A
Biology/Biological Sciences, A
Business Administration and Management, A
Business Teacher Education, A
Chemistry, A
Computer Systems Networking and
   Telecommunications, A
Corrections, A
Criminal Justice/Law Enforcement Administration, A
Criminal Justice/Police Science, A
Data Entry/Microcomputer Applications, A
Drafting and Design Technology/Technician, A
Education, A
Electrical, Electronic and Communications
   Engineering Technology/Technician, A
Elementary Education and Teaching, A
Engineering Technology, A
English Language and Literature, A
Environmental Studies, A
Forestry, A
Hydrology and Water Resources Science, A
Industrial Technology/Technician, A
Information Science/Studies, A
Information Technology, A
Land Use Planning and
   Management/Development, A
Legal Administrative Assistant/Secretary, A
Liberal Arts and Sciences Studies and
   Humanities, A
Management Information Systems and Services, A
Marketing/Marketing Management, A
Mathematics, A
Mining Technology/Technician, A
Nursing - Registered Nurse Training, A
Pre-Engineering, A
Public Administration, A

NATIONAL COLLEGE OF BUSINESS & TECHNOLOGY (BLUEFIELD)

Accounting, A
Administrative Assistant and Secretarial Science, A
Business Administration and Management, A
Computer and Information Sciences, A
Medical/Clinical Assistant, A

NATIONAL COLLEGE OF BUSINESS & TECHNOLOGY (CHARLOTTESVILLE)

Accounting, A
Administrative Assistant and Secretarial Science, A
Business/Commerce, A
Computer and Information Sciences, A
Medical/Clinical Assistant, A

NATIONAL COLLEGE OF BUSINESS & TECHNOLOGY (DANVILLE)

Accounting, A
Administrative Assistant and Secretarial Science, A
Business Administration and Management, A
Computer and Information Sciences, A
Medical/Clinical Assistant, A

NATIONAL COLLEGE OF BUSINESS & TECHNOLOGY (HARRISONBURG)

Accounting, A
Administrative Assistant and Secretarial Science, A
Business Administration and Management, A
Computer and Information Sciences, A
Medical/Clinical Assistant, A

NATIONAL COLLEGE OF BUSINESS & TECHNOLOGY (LYNCHBURG)

Accounting, A
Administrative Assistant and Secretarial Science, A
Business Administration and Management, A

Computer and Information Sciences, A
Medical/Clinical Assistant, A

NATIONAL COLLEGE OF BUSINESS & TECHNOLOGY (MARTINSVILLE)

Accounting, A
Administrative Assistant and Secretarial Science, A
Business Administration and Management, A
Computer and Information Sciences, A

NATIONAL COLLEGE OF BUSINESS & TECHNOLOGY (SALEM)

Accounting, AB
Accounting Technology/Technician and
 Bookkeeping, A
Administrative Assistant and Secretarial Science, A
Business/Commerce, AB
Computer and Information Sciences, A
Executive Assistant/Executive Secretary, A
Hospitality Administration/Management, A
Hotel/Motel Administration/Management, A
Marketing/Marketing Management, A
Medical/Clinical Assistant, A
Office Management and Supervision, A
Tourism and Travel Services Marketing
 Operations, A

NEW RIVER COMMUNITY COLLEGE

Accounting, A
Administrative Assistant and Secretarial Science, A
Architectural Engineering Technology/Technician, A
Automobile/Automotive Mechanics
 Technology/Technician, A
Biological and Physical Sciences, A
Business Administration and Management, A
Child Development, A
Community Organization and Advocacy, A
Computer Engineering Technology/Technician, A
Computer Graphics, A
Computer Typography and Composition Equipment
 Operator, A
Criminal Justice/Law Enforcement Administration, A
Criminal Justice/Police Science, A
Drafting and Design Technology/Technician, A
Education, A
Electrical, Electronic and Communications
 Engineering Technology/Technician, A
Engineering, A
Forensic Science and Technology, A
General Studies, A
Gerontology, A
Information Science/Studies, A
Instrumentation Technology/Technician, A
Legal Assistant/Paralegal, A
Liberal Arts and Sciences Studies and
 Humanities, A
Licensed Practical/Vocational Nurse Training, A
Machine Tool Technology/Machinist, A
Marketing/Marketing Management, A
Medical Administrative Assistant/Secretary, A
Sign Language Interpretation and Translation, A
Welding Technology/Welder, A

NORFOLK STATE UNIVERSITY

Accounting, B
Architectural Engineering Technology/Technician, A
Art/Art Studies, General, B
Biology/Biological Sciences, B
Business Teacher Education, B
Business/Commerce, B
Chemistry, B
Clinical Laboratory Science/Medical
 Technology/Technologist, B
Clinical Psychology, M
Communication and Media Studies, M
Communication, Journalism and Related
 Programs, B
Community Psychology, M
Composition, M
Computer and Information Sciences, B
Computer Engineering, M
Computer Engineering Technology/Technician, B
Computer Science, M
Construction Engineering Technology/Technician, B
Criminology, M

Drafting and Design Technology/Technician, B
Early Childhood Education and Teaching, M
Education, M
Education/Teaching of Individuals with Multiple
 Disabilities, M
Educational Administration and Supervision, M
Educational Leadership and Administration, M
Electrical Engineering, M
Electrical, Electronic and Communications
 Engineering Technology/Technician, B
Electrical, Electronics and Communications
 Engineering, B
English Language and Literature, B
Family and Consumer Sciences/Human Sciences, B
Fine Arts and Art Studies, M
Health Information/Medical Records
 Administration/Administrator, B
Health/Health Care Administration/Management, B
History, B
Journalism, B
Kindergarten/PreSchool Education and Teaching, B
Kinesiology and Exercise Science, B
Materials Sciences, M
Mathematics, B
Media Studies, M
Multi-/Interdisciplinary Studies, B
Music, BM
Music Teacher Education, M
Music Theory and Composition, M
Nursing - Registered Nurse Training, AB
Office Management and Supervision, B
Optical Technologies, M
Performance, M
Physics, B
Political Science and Government, B
Psychology, BMD
Secondary Education and Teaching, M
Social Work, BMD
Sociology, BM
Special Education and Teaching, M
Trade and Industrial Teacher Education, B
Urban Education and Leadership, M
Urban Studies/Affairs, M

NORTHERN VIRGINIA COMMUNITY COLLEGE

Accounting, A
Administrative Assistant and Secretarial Science, A
Airline/Commercial/Professional Pilot and Flight
 Crew, A
Applied Art, A
Architectural Engineering Technology/Technician, A
Art History, Criticism and Conservation, A
Art/Art Studies, General, A
Automobile/Automotive Mechanics
 Technology/Technician, A
Avionics Maintenance Technology/Technician, A
Biological and Physical Sciences, A
Business Administration and Management, A
Civil Engineering Technology/Technician, A
Clinical/Medical Laboratory Technician, A
Commercial and Advertising Art, A
Computer Graphics, A
Computer Science, A
Criminal Justice/Law Enforcement Administration, A
Criminal Justice/Police Science, A
Dental Hygiene/Hygienist, A
Dietetics/Dieticians, A
Electrical, Electronic and Communications
 Engineering Technology/Technician, A
Emergency Medical Technology/Technician (EMT
 Paramedic), A
Engineering, A
Fire Science/Firefighting, A
Gerontology, A
Health Information/Medical Records
 Administration/Administrator, A
Heating, Air Conditioning, Ventilation and
 Refrigeration Maintenance
 Technology/Technician, A
Horticultural Science, A
Hotel/Motel Administration/Management, A
Human Services, A
Industrial Radiologic Technology/Technician, A
Information Science/Studies, A
Interior Design, A

International Business/Trade/Commerce, A
Kindergarten/PreSchool Education and Teaching, A
Legal Assistant/Paralegal, A
Liberal Arts and Sciences Studies and
 Humanities, A
Marketing/Marketing Management, A
Mathematics, A
Mechanical Engineering/Mechanical
 Technology/Technician, A
Music, A
Nursing - Registered Nurse Training, A
Parks, Recreation, Leisure and Fitness Studies, A
Photography, A
Physical Therapy/Therapist, A
Pre-Engineering, A
Psychology, A
Purchasing, Procurement/Acquisitions and
 Contracts Management, A
Religion/Religious Studies, A
Respiratory Care Therapy/Therapist, A
Special Products Marketing Operations, A
Speech and Rhetorical Studies, A
Substance Abuse/Addiction Counseling, A
Tourism and Travel Services Management, A
Veterinary/Animal Health Technology/Technician and
 Veterinary Assistant, A

OLD DOMINION UNIVERSITY

Accounting, BM
Acting, B
Aerospace, Aeronautical and Astronautical
 Engineering, MD
Allied Health and Medical Assisting Services, MD
Analytical Chemistry, M
Anthropology, B
Art History, Criticism and Conservation, B
Art Teacher Education, B
Art/Art Studies, General, B
Asian Studies/Civilization, B
Athletic Training and Sports Medicine, M
Audiology/Audiologist and Speech-Language
 Pathology/Pathologist, B
Biochemistry, BM
Biological and Biomedical Sciences, MD
Biology Teacher Education, B
Biology/Biological Sciences, B
Business Administration and Management, B
Business Administration, Management and
 Operations, MD
Business Education, M
Business/Managerial Economics, B
Chemistry, BM
Chemistry Teacher Education, B
Civil Engineering, BMD
Civil Engineering Technology/Technician, B
Clinical Laboratory Science/Medical
 Technology/Technologist, B
Clinical Psychology, D
Communication Disorders, M
Communication, Journalism and Related
 Programs, B
Community College Education, MD
Community Health and Preventive Medicine, M
Computer and Information Sciences, B
Computer Engineering, BMD
Computer Engineering Technologies/Technicians, B
Computer Science, MD
Counselor Education/School Counseling and
 Guidance Services, MO
Criminology, B
Curriculum and Instruction, M
CytoTechnology/Cytotechnologist, B
Dance, B
Dental Hygiene/Hygienist, BM
Drama and Dance Teacher Education, B
Drama and Dramatics/Theatre Arts, B
Early Childhood Education and Teaching, M
Ecology, D
Economics, BM
Education, MDO
Educational Administration and Supervision, O
Educational Leadership and Administration, MDO
Educational Media/Instructional Technology, MD
Electrical and Electronic Engineering
 Technologies/Technicians, B
Electrical Engineering, MD

Electrical, Electronics and Communications
Engineering, B
Elementary Education and Teaching, M
Engineering and Applied Sciences, MD
Engineering Management, MD
Engineering Technologies/Technicians, B
English, M
English Language and Literature, B
English/Language Arts Teacher Education, B
Environmental and Occupational Health, M
Environmental Engineering
Technology/Environmental Technology, MD
Environmental Health, B
Environmental/Environmental Health Engineering, B
Ergonomics and Human Factors, D
Exercise and Sports Science, M
Experimental Psychology, D
Finance, B
Fine Arts and Art Studies, M
Fine/Studio Arts, B
Foreign Language Teacher Education, B
Foreign Languages and Literatures, B
French Language and Literature, B
French Language Teacher Education, B
Geography, B
Geology/Earth Science, B
German Language and Literature, B
German Language Teacher Education, B
Graphic Design, B
Health Promotion, M
Health Services Administration, M
Health Services Research, D
Health Services/Allied Health/Health Sciences, B
Higher Education/Higher Education
Administration, MDO
History, BM
History Teacher Education, B
Humanities/Humanistic Studies, M
Industrial and Organizational Psychology, D
International Affairs, MD
International Business/Trade/Commerce, B
International Development, M
International Relations and Affairs, B
Kinesiology and Exercise Science, B
Library Science, M
Linguistics, M
Management Information Systems and Services, B
Manufacturing Engineering, M
Marine Biology and Biological Oceanography, B
Marketing/Marketing Management, B
Materials Engineering, M
Materials Sciences, M
Mathematics, BMD
Mathematics Teacher Education, B
Mechanical Engineering, BMD
Mechanical Engineering Related
Technologies/Technicians, B
Mental and Social Health Services and Allied
Professions, B
Middle School Education, M
Multi-/Interdisciplinary Studies, B
Music, B
Music Performance, B
Music Teacher Education, B
Nuclear Engineering Technology/Technician, B
Nuclear Medical Technology/Technologist, B
Nursing, M
Nursing - Registered Nurse Training, B
Oceanography, Chemical and Physical, BMD
Ophthalmic Technician/Technologist, B
Organic Chemistry, M
Parks, Recreation and Leisure Facilities
Management, B
Philosophy, B
Physical Chemistry, M
Physical Education Teaching and Coaching, BM
Physical Therapy/Therapist, D
Physics, BMD
Physics Teacher Education, B
Political Science and Government, B
Psychology, BMD
Public Administration, M
Public Health, M
Reading Teacher Education, M
Recreation and Park Management, M

Sales and Marketing Operations/Marketing and
Distribution Teacher Education, B
Secondary Education and Teaching, M
Sociology, BM
Spanish Language and Literature, B
Spanish Language Teacher Education, B
Special Education and Teaching, MD
Speech and Rhetorical Studies, B
Sport and Fitness Administration/Management, BM
Systems Engineering, M
Travel and Tourism, M
Urban and Regional Planning, M
Urban Education and Leadership, D
Urban Studies/Affairs, MD
Vocational and Technical Education, M
Women's Studies, B
Writing, M

PATRICK HENRY COLLEGE

English Language and Literature, B
History, B
Journalism, B
Liberal Arts and Sciences Studies and
Humanities, B
Political Science and Government, B

PATRICK HENRY COMMUNITY COLLEGE

Accounting, A
Administrative Assistant and Secretarial Science, A
Biological and Physical Sciences, A
Business Administration and Management, A
Computer Programming, A
Computer Programming/Programmer, A
Computer Systems Networking and
Telecommunications, A
Data Entry/Microcomputer Applications, A
Data Processing and Data Processing
Technology/Technician, A
Electrical, Electronic and Communications
Engineering Technology/Technician, A
Engineering Technology, A
Industrial Technology/Technician, A
Information Technology, A
Liberal Arts and Sciences Studies and
Humanities, A
Nursing - Registered Nurse Training, A

PAUL D. CAMP COMMUNITY COLLEGE

Administrative Assistant and Secretarial Science, A
Business Administration and Management, A
Criminal Justice/Law Enforcement Administration, A
Data Processing and Data Processing
Technology/Technician, A
Education, A
Liberal Arts and Sciences Studies and
Humanities, A

PIEDMONT VIRGINIA COMMUNITY COLLEGE

Accounting, A
Administrative Assistant and Secretarial Science, A
Biological and Physical Sciences, A
BioTechnology, A
Business Administration and Management, A
Carpentry/Carpenter, A
Clinical/Medical Laboratory Technician, A
Computer Engineering Technology/Technician, A
Computer Programming, Specific Applications, A
Computer Programming/Programmer, A
Computer Science, A
Computer Systems Networking and
Telecommunications, A
Criminal Justice/Police Science, A
Data Processing and Data Processing
Technology/Technician, A
Education, A
Electrician, A
Emergency Medical Technology/Technician (EMT
Paramedic), A
Engineering, A
General Studies, A
Heating, Air Conditioning and Refrigeration
Technology/Technician, A

Liberal Arts and Sciences Studies and
Humanities, A
Management Information Systems and Services, A
Marketing/Marketing Management, A
Mason/Masonry, A
Mechanical Drafting and Mechanical Drafting
CAD/CADD, A
Nursing - Registered Nurse Training, A
Plumbing Technology/Plumber, A
Respiratory Care Therapy/Therapist, A
Visual and Performing Arts, A
Web/Multimedia Management and Webmaster, A

RADFORD UNIVERSITY

Accounting, B
Anthropology, B
Art/Art Studies, General, B
Athletic Training and Sports Medicine, B
Biology/Biological Sciences, B
Business Administration, Management and
Operations, M
Chemistry, B
Clinical Laboratory Science/Medical
Technology/Technologist, B
Clinical Psychology, M
Communication Disorders, M
Communication Disorders Sciences and Services, B
Communication, Journalism and Related
Programs, B
Computer Science, B
Corporate and Organizational Communication, M
Counseling Psychology, M
Counselor Education/School Counseling and
Guidance Services, M
Criminal Justice/Law Enforcement Administration, B
Criminology, M
Dance, B
Drama and Dramatics/Theatre Arts, B
Economics, B
Education, M
Educational Leadership and Administration, M
Educational Media/Instructional Technology, M
English, M
English Language and Literature, B
Experimental Psychology, M
Finance, B
Fine Arts and Art Studies, M
Foods, Nutrition, and Wellness Studies, B
Foreign Languages and Literatures, B
General Studies, B
Geography, B
Geology/Earth Science, B
Health and Physical Education, B
History, B
Industrial and Organizational Psychology, M
Information Science/Studies, B
Interdisciplinary Studies, B
Interior Design, B
Intermedia/Multimedia, B
Kinesiology and Exercise Science, B
Liberal Arts and Sciences Studies and
Humanities, B
Marketing/Marketing Management, B
Mathematics, B
Music, BM
Music Therapy/Therapist, M
Nursing, M
Nursing - Registered Nurse Training, B
Parks, Recreation, Leisure and Fitness Studies, B
Philosophy and Religious Studies, B
Physical Education Teaching and Coaching, B
Physical Sciences, B
Political Science and Government, B
Psychology, BMO
Reading Teacher Education, M
School Psychology, O
Social Sciences, B
Social Work, BM
Sociology, B

RANDOLPH-MACON COLLEGE

Accounting, B
Ancient/Classical Greek Language and Literature, B
Art History, Criticism and Conservation, B
Arts Management, B
Biology/Biological Sciences, B

Business/Managerial Economics, B
Chemistry, B
Classics and Classical
  Languages, Literatures, and Linguistics, B
Computer Science, B
Drama and Dramatics/Theatre Arts, B
Economics, B
English Language and Literature, B
Environmental Studies, B
Fine/Studio Arts, B
French Language and Literature, B
German Language and Literature, B
History, B
International Relations and Affairs, B
International/Global Studies, B
Latin Language and Literature, B
Mathematics, B
Music, B
Philosophy, B
Physics, B
Political Science and Government, B
Psychology, B
Religion/Religious Studies, B
Sociology, B
Spanish Language and Literature, B
Women's Studies, B

RANDOLPH-MACON WOMAN'S COLLEGE

American/United States Studies/Civilization, B
Ancient/Classical Greek Language and Literature, B
Art History, Criticism and Conservation, B
Art/Art Studies, General, B
Biology/Biological Sciences, B
Chemistry, B
Classics and Classical
  Languages, Literatures, and Linguistics, B
Communication Studies/Speech Communication
  and Rhetoric, B
Creative Writing, B
Dance, B
Drama and Dramatics/Theatre Arts, B
Economics, B
Elementary Education and Teaching, B
Engineering Physics, B
English Language and Literature, B
Environmental Studies, B
Fine/Studio Arts, B
French Language and Literature, B
German Language and Literature, B
Health Professions and Related Clinical Sciences, B
History, B
International Relations and Affairs, B
Latin Language and Literature, B
Liberal Arts and Sciences Studies and
  Humanities, B
Mathematics, B
Museology/Museum Studies, B
Music History, Literature, and Theory, B
Music Performance, B
Music Theory and Composition, B
Philosophy, B
Physics, B
Political Science and Government, B
Psychology, B
Religion/Religious Studies, B
Russian Studies, B
Sociology, B
Spanish Language and Literature, B

RAPPAHANNOCK COMMUNITY COLLEGE

Accounting, A
Administrative Assistant and Secretarial Science, A
Biological and Physical Sciences, A
Business Administration and Management, A
Criminal Justice/Police Science, A
Engineering Technology, A
Information Science/Studies, A
Liberal Arts and Sciences Studies and
  Humanities, A
Nursing - Registered Nurse Training, A

REGENT UNIVERSITY

Business Administration, Management and
  Operations, MO

Communication Studies/Speech Communication
  and Rhetoric, B
Counseling Psychology, MDO
Counselor Education/School Counseling and
  Guidance Services, MDO
Divinity/Ministry (BD, MDiv.), B
Education, MDO
Family and Consumer Sciences/Human Sciences, B
International Business/Trade/Commerce, B
Law and Legal Studies, PO
Management, M
Management Strategy and Policy, D
Missions/Missionary Studies and Missiology, MP
Organizational Behavior Studies, B
Organizational Management, MDO
Political Science and Government, B
Psychology, B
Public Administration, MO
Public Policy Analysis, M
Theology and Religious Vocations, MDPO

RICHARD BLAND COLLEGE OF THE COLLEGE OF WILLIAM AND MARY

Liberal Arts and Sciences Studies and
  Humanities, A

ROANOKE COLLEGE

Art History, Criticism and Conservation, B
Art/Art Studies, General, B
Athletic Training and Sports Medicine, B
Biochemistry, B
Biology/Biological Sciences, B
Business Administration and Management, B
Chemistry, B
Clinical Laboratory Science/Medical
  Technology/Technologist, B
Computer Science, B
Criminal Justice/Safety Studies, B
Drama and Dramatics/Theatre Arts, B
Economics, B
English Language and Literature, B
Environmental Sciences, B
Environmental Studies, B
French Language and Literature, B
Health and Physical Education, B
History, B
Information Science/Studies, B
International Relations and Affairs, B
Mathematics, B
Music, B
Philosophy, B
Philosophy and Religious Studies, B
Physics, B
Political Science and Government, B
Psychology, B
Religion/Religious Studies, B
Sociology, B
Spanish Language and Literature, B

SAINT PAUL'S COLLEGE

Biology/Biological Sciences, B
Business Administration and Management, B
Computer Science, B
Criminal Justice/Law Enforcement Administration, B
Elementary Education and Teaching, B
English Language and Literature, B
Environmental Studies, B
Liberal Arts and Sciences Studies and
  Humanities, B
Marine Science/Merchant Marine Officer, B
Mathematics, B
Political Science and Government, B
Social Sciences, B
Sociology, B

SHENANDOAH UNIVERSITY

Acting, B
Allied Health and Medical Assisting Services, MDO
American/United States Studies/Civilization, B
Arts Management, BM
Athletic Training and Sports Medicine, M
Biology/Biological Sciences, B
Business Administration and Management, B
Business Administration, Management and
  Operations, MO

Chemistry, B
Communication Studies/Speech Communication
  and Rhetoric, B
Composition, M
Criminal Justice/Law Enforcement Administration, B
Dance, BM
Drama and Dramatics/Theatre Arts, B
Dramatic/Theatre Arts and Stagecraft, B
Education, M
Educational Administration and Supervision, D
Educational Leadership and Administration, D
Educational Psychology, B
Elementary Education and Teaching, O
English as a Second Language, O
English Language and Literature, B
Environmental Studies, B
Health Psychology, O
Health Services Administration, O
History, B
Kinesiology and Exercise Science, B
Liberal Arts and Sciences Studies and
  Humanities, B
Management Information Systems and Services, O
Mathematics, B
Middle School Education, O
Music, BMDO
Music Performance, B
Music Teacher Education, BMD
Music Theory and Composition, B
Music Therapy/Therapist, BMO
Nurse Midwife/Nursing Midwifery, O
Nursing, MO
Nursing - Advanced Practice, O
Nursing - Registered Nurse Training, B
Occupational Therapy/Therapist, M
Performance, MD
Pharmacy, P
Physical Education Teaching and Coaching, B
Physical Therapy/Therapist, D
Physician Assistant, M
Piano and Organ, B
Political Science and Government, B
Psychology, B
Public Administration, BO
Religion/Religious Studies, B
Respiratory Care Therapy/Therapist, AB
Sacred Music, MO
Secondary Education and Teaching, O
Sociology, B
Spanish Language and Literature, B
Technical Theatre/Theatre Design and
  Technology, B
Visual and Performing Arts, B
Women's Studies, O

SOUTHERN VIRGINIA UNIVERSITY

Art/Art Studies, General, B
Biology/Biological Sciences, B
Business Administration and Management, B
Computer and Information Sciences, B
Drama and Dramatics/Theatre Arts, B
English Language and Literature, B
Family and Consumer Sciences/Human Sciences, B
Health and Physical Education, B
History, B
Liberal Arts and Sciences Studies and
  Humanities, B
Music, B
Parks, Recreation and Leisure Facilities
  Management, B
Philosophy, B
Spanish Language and Literature, B
Web Page, Digital/Multimedia and Information
  Resources Design, B

SOUTHSIDE VIRGINIA COMMUNITY COLLEGE

Administrative Assistant and Secretarial Science, A
Biological and Physical Sciences, A
Business Administration and Management, A
Criminal Justice/Law Enforcement Administration, A
Drafting and Design Technology/Technician, A
Education, A
Electrical, Electronic and Communications
  Engineering Technology/Technician, A
General Studies, A

Human Services, A
Information Science/Studies, A
Information Technology, A
Liberal Arts and Sciences Studies and
   Humanities, A
Nursing - Registered Nurse Training, A
Respiratory Care Therapy/Therapist, A

SOUTHWEST VIRGINIA COMMUNITY COLLEGE

Accounting, A
Administrative Assistant and Secretarial Science, A
Biological and Physical Sciences, A
Business Administration and Management, A
Criminal Justice/Police Science, A
Drafting and Design Technology/Technician, A
Education, A
Electrical, Electronic and Communications
   Engineering Technology/Technician, A
Engineering, A
Human Services, A
Industrial Radiologic Technology/Technician, A
Information Science/Studies, A
Land Use Planning and
   Management/Development, A
Liberal Arts and Sciences Studies and
   Humanities, A
Mining Technology/Technician, A
Music, A
Nursing - Registered Nurse Training, A
Respiratory Care Therapy/Therapist, A

STRATFORD UNIVERSITY

Accounting, M
Business Administration and Management, AB
Business Administration, Management and
   Operations, M
Computer Programming, A
Computer Programming/Programmer, A
Computer Systems Networking and
   Telecommunications, A
Culinary Arts/Chef Training, A
Entrepreneurship/Entrepreneurial Studies, M
Hospitality Administration/Management, B
Hotel/Motel Administration/Management, A
Information Technology, B
Software Engineering, M

SWEET BRIAR COLLEGE

Anthropology, B
Art History, Criticism and Conservation, B
Biochemistry, Biophysics and Molecular Biology, B
Biology/Biological Sciences, B
Business, Management, Marketing, and Related
   Support Services, B
Chemistry, B
Classics and Classical
   Languages, Literatures, and Linguistics, B
Computer Science, B
Creative Writing, B
Dance, B
Drama and Dramatics/Theatre Arts, B
Economics, B
Engineering Science, B
English Language and Literature, B
Environmental Sciences, B
Environmental Studies, B
Fine/Studio Arts, B
Foreign Languages and Literatures, B
French Language and Literature, B
German Language and Literature, B
History, B
International Relations and Affairs, B
Italian Language and Literature, B
Liberal Arts and Sciences Studies and
   Humanities, B
Mathematics, B
Music, B
Philosophy, B
Physics, B
Political Science and Government, B
Psychology, B
Religion/Religious Studies, B
Sociology, B
Spanish Language and Literature, B

Theoretical and Mathematical Physics, B

THOMAS NELSON COMMUNITY COLLEGE

Accounting, A
Administrative Assistant and Secretarial Science, A
Automobile/Automotive Mechanics
   Technology/Technician, A
Biological and Physical Sciences, A
Business Administration and Management, A
Clinical/Medical Laboratory Technician, A
Commercial and Advertising Art, A
Computer Science, A
Criminal Justice/Police Science, A
Drafting and Design Technology/Technician, A
Electrical, Electronic and Communications
   Engineering Technology/Technician, A
Engineering, A
Fire Science/Firefighting, A
Information Science/Studies, A
Kindergarten/PreSchool Education and Teaching, A
Liberal Arts and Sciences Studies and
   Humanities, A
Mechanical Engineering/Mechanical
   Technology/Technician, A
Nursing - Registered Nurse Training, A
Ophthalmic Laboratory Technology/Technician, A
Photography, A
Public Administration, A
Social Sciences, A

TIDEWATER COMMUNITY COLLEGE

Accounting, A
Administrative Assistant and Secretarial Science, A
Advertising, A
Automobile/Automotive Mechanics
   Technology/Technician, A
Biological and Physical Sciences, A
Business Administration and Management, A
Civil Engineering, A
Commercial and Advertising Art, A
Computer Programming/Programmer, A
Drafting and Design Technology/Technician, A
Education, A
Electrical, Electronic and Communications
   Engineering Technology/Technician, A
Engineering, A
Finance, A
Fine/Studio Arts, A
Graphic Design, A
Horticultural Science, A
Information Technology, A
Interior Design, A
Kindergarten/PreSchool Education and Teaching, A
Legal Assistant/Paralegal, A
Liberal Arts and Sciences Studies and
   Humanities, A
Marketing/Marketing Management, A
Music, A
Nursing - Registered Nurse Training, A
Real Estate, A

UNIVERSITY OF MANAGEMENT AND TECHNOLOGY

Business Administration and Management, AB
Business Administration, Management and
   Operations, ABMO
Business/Commerce, AB
Computer Science, M
Information Science/Studies, M
Management, M
Management Information Systems and
   Services, ABM
Marketing/Marketing Management, AB
Project Management, MO
Public Administration, M
Purchasing, Procurement/Acquisitions and
   Contracts Management, AB
Software Engineering, M
Telecommunications Management, M

UNIVERSITY OF MARY WASHINGTON

American/United States Studies/Civilization, B
Art History, Criticism and Conservation, B
Art/Art Studies, General, B

Biology/Biological Sciences, B
Business Administration and Management, B
Business Administration, Management and
   Operations, M
Chemistry, B
Classics and Classical
   Languages, Literatures, and Linguistics, B
Computer Science, B
Drama and Dramatics/Theatre Arts, B
Economics, B
Education, M
Elementary Education and Teaching, B
English Language and Literature, B
Environmental Studies, B
Fine/Studio Arts, B
French Language and Literature, B
Geography, B
Geology/Earth Science, B
German Language and Literature, B
Historic Preservation and Conservation, B
History, B
Interdisciplinary Studies, B
International Relations and Affairs, B
Latin Language and Literature, B
Liberal Arts and Sciences Studies and
   Humanities, B
Mathematics, B
Modern Languages, B
Music, B
Music Teacher Education, B
Philosophy, B
Physics, B
Political Science and Government, B
Pre-Dentistry Studies, B
Pre-Law Studies, B
Pre-Medicine/Pre-Medical Studies, B
Pre-Veterinary Studies, B
Psychology, B
Religion/Religious Studies, B
Secondary Education and Teaching, B
Sociology, B
Spanish Language and Literature, B

UNIVERSITY OF NORTHERN VIRGINIA

Accounting, M
Business Administration, Management and
   Operations, D
Computer Science, M
Counselor Education/School Counseling and
   Guidance Services, M
Early Childhood Education and Teaching, M
Educational Leadership and Administration, M
Educational Media/Instructional Technology, M
English as a Second Language, M
Finance and Banking, M
Management, M
Management Information Systems and Services, M
Marketing, M
Project Management, M
Public Administration, M

UNIVERSITY OF PHOENIX-NORTHERN VIRGINIA CAMPUS

Business Administration and Management, B
Business, Management, Marketing, and Related
   Support Services, B
Computer and Information Sciences, B

UNIVERSITY OF PHOENIX-RICHMOND CAMPUS

Business Administration and Management, B
Information Technology, B

UNIVERSITY OF RICHMOND

Accounting, B
American/United States Studies/Civilization, B
Art History, Criticism and Conservation, B
Art Teacher Education, B
Art/Art Studies, General, B
Biological and Biomedical Sciences, MO
Biology/Biological Sciences, B
Business Administration and Management, B
Business Administration, Management and
   Operations, MO
Business/Managerial Economics, B

Central/Middle and Eastern European Studies, B
Chemistry, B
Classics and Classical
  Languages, Literatures, and Linguistics, B
Computer Science, B
Criminal Justice/Law Enforcement Administration, B
Drama and Dramatics/Theatre Arts, B
Economics, B
English, M
English Language and Literature, B
Environmental Studies, B
European Studies/Civilization, B
Finance, B
Fine/Studio Arts, B
French Language and Literature, B
German Language and Literature, B
Health Teacher Education, B
History, BMO
Human Resources Management/Personnel
  Administration, A
Interdisciplinary Studies, B
International Business/Trade/Commerce, B
International Economics, B
International Relations and Affairs, B
Journalism, B
Junior High/Intermediate/Middle School Education
  and Teaching, B
Latin American Studies, B
Latin Language and Literature, B
Law and Legal Studies, PO
Legal Administrative Assistant/Secretary, A
Liberal Studies, M
Management Information Systems and Services, B
Marketing/Marketing Management, B
Mathematics, B
Modern Greek Language and Literature, B
Molecular Biology, B
Music, B
Music History, Literature, and Theory, B
Philosophy, B
Physical Education Teaching and Coaching, B
Physics, B
Political Science and Government, B
Psychology, BM
Religion/Religious Studies, B
Secondary Education and Teaching, B
Sociology, B
Spanish Language and Literature, B
Speech and Rhetorical Studies, B
Urban Studies/Affairs, B
Women's Studies, B

UNIVERSITY OF VIRGINIA

Accounting, M
Aerospace, Aeronautical and Astronautical
  Engineering, BMD
African-American/Black Studies, B
Allopathic Medicine, MDPO
Anthropology, BMD
Applied Mathematics, B
Archeology, MD
Architectural History and Criticism, BMD
Architecture, BM
Area Studies, B
Art History, Criticism and Conservation, MD
Art/Art Studies, General, B
Astronomy, BMD
Audiology/Audiologist and Speech-Language
  Pathology/Pathologist, B
Biochemistry, DO
Bioethics/Medical Ethics, M
Biological and Biomedical Sciences, MD
Biological Anthropology, MD
Biology/Biological Sciences, B
Biomedical Engineering, MD
Biomedical/Medical Engineering, B
Biophysics, MDO
Business Administration, Management and
  Operations, MDO
Business/Commerce, B
Cell Biology and Anatomy, DO
Chemical Engineering, BMD
Chemistry, BMD
City/Urban, Community and Regional Planning, B
Civil Engineering, BMD

Classics and Classical
  Languages, Literatures, and Linguistics, BMD
Clinical Psychology, D
Clinical Research, M
Communication Disorders, BM
Comparative Literature, B
Computer and Information Sciences, B
Computer Engineering, BMD
Computer Science, MD
Counselor Education/School Counseling and
  Guidance Services, MDO
Curriculum and Instruction, MDO
Drama and Dramatics/Theatre Arts, B
East Asian Studies, MO
Economics, BMDO
Education, MDO
Educational Administration and Supervision, MDO
Educational Measurement and Evaluation, MD
Educational Psychology, MDO
Electrical Engineering, MD
Electrical, Electronics and Communications
  Engineering, B
Engineering, B
Engineering and Applied Sciences, MDO
Engineering Physics, MD
English, MD
English Language and Literature, B
Environmental Sciences, BMD
Ethnic and Cultural Studies, B
Fine Arts and Art Studies, MD
French Language and Literature, BMD
German Language and Literature, BMD
Health Education, MD
Health Informatics, M
Health Services Administration, M
Health Services Research, M
Higher Education/Higher Education
  Administration, DO
History, BMDO
Immunology, DO
International Affairs, MD
International Relations and Affairs, B
Italian Language and Literature, BM
Kinesiology and Movement Studies, MD
Landscape Architecture, M
Law and Legal Studies, MDPO
Liberal Arts and Sciences Studies and
  Humanities, B
Linguistics, M
Management Information Systems and Services, M
Materials Sciences, MD
Mathematics, BMD
Mechanical Engineering, BMD
Mechanics, M
Microbiology, DO
Molecular Genetics, DO
Molecular Physiology, MDO
Multi-/Interdisciplinary Studies, B
Music, BMD
Neuroscience, DO
Nuclear Engineering, B
Nursing, MDO
Nursing - Registered Nurse Training, B
Pharmacology, DO
Philosophy, BMDO
Physical Education Teaching and Coaching, BMD
Physics, BMD
Physiology, DO
Political Science and Government, BMDO
Psychology, BMD
Public Health, M
Religion/Religious Studies, BMD
Romance
  Languages, Literatures, and Linguistics, MD
School Psychology, D
Science Teacher Education/General Science
  Teacher Education, M
Slavic Languages, Literatures, and Linguistics, BMD
Sociology, BMDO
Spanish Language and Literature, BMD
Special Education and Teaching, MDO
Speech and Rhetorical Studies, B
Statistics, MD
Systems Engineering, BMDO
Theater, M
Urban and Regional Planning, M

Writing, M

THE UNIVERSITY OF VIRGINIA'S COLLEGE AT WISE

Accounting, B
Art/Art Studies, General, B
Biology/Biological Sciences, B
Business Administration and Management, B
Chemistry, B
Clinical Laboratory Science/Medical
  Technology/Technologist, B
Communication Studies/Speech Communication
  and Rhetoric, B
Computer and Information Sciences, B
Criminal Justice/Safety Studies, B
Drama and Dramatics/Theatre Arts, B
Economics, B
English Language and Literature, B
Environmental Studies, B
Family Practice Nurse/Nurse Practitioner, B
Foreign Languages and Literatures, B
French Language and Literature, B
History, B
Interdisciplinary Studies, B
Liberal Arts and Sciences Studies and
  Humanities, B
Mathematics, B
Political Science and Government, B
Psychology, B
Sociology, B
Spanish Language and Literature, B

VIRGINIA COMMONWEALTH UNIVERSITY

Accounting, BMD
Adult and Continuing Education and Teaching, M
Advertising and Public Relations, M
African-American/Black Studies, B
Allied Health and Medical Assisting Services, MDO
Allopathic Medicine, PO
Anatomy, MDO
Anthropology, B
Applied Arts and Design, M
Applied Mathematics, M
Applied Physics, M
Area Studies, B
Art Education, M
Art History, Criticism and Conservation, BMD
Art Teacher Education, B
Biochemistry, MDO
Bioengineering, D
Bioinformatics, B
Biological and Biomedical Sciences, MDO
Biological and Physical Sciences, B
Biology/Biological Sciences, B
Biomedical Engineering, MDO
Biomedical/Medical Engineering, B
Biostatistics, MDO
Business Administration and Management, B
Business Administration, Management and
  Operations, MDO
Business/Managerial Economics, B
Ceramic Arts and Ceramics, M
Chemical Engineering, B
Chemistry, BMD
Clinical Laboratory Science/Medical
  Technology/Technologist, B
Clinical Laboratory Sciences, M
Clinical Psychology, D
Composition, M
Computer and Information Sciences, B
Computer Engineering, B
Computer Science, M
Counseling Psychology, MDO
Counselor Education/School Counseling and
  Guidance Services, M
Crafts/Craft Design, Folk Art and Artisanry, B
Criminal Justice/Law Enforcement Administration, B
Criminology, MO
Curriculum and Instruction, MO
Dance, B
Dental Hygiene/Hygienist, B
Dentistry, PO
Design and Visual Communications, B
Drama and Dramatics/Theatre Arts, B
Early Childhood Education and Teaching, M

Economics, M
Education, MDO
Educational Administration and Supervision, MO
Electrical, Electronics and Communications
  Engineering, B
Engineering and Applied Sciences, MDO
English, M
English Language and Literature, B
Environmental and Occupational Health, M
Environmental Policy and Resource
  Management, M
Environmental Sciences, M
Environmental Studies, BM
Epidemiology, D
Fashion/Apparel Design, B
Finance and Banking, M
Finance and Financial Management Services, B
Fine Arts and Art Studies, M
Foreign Languages and Literatures, B
Forensic Science and Technology, BM
General Studies, B
Genetic Counseling/Counselor, M
Genetics, D
Gerontology, MO
Health Physics/Radiological Health, D
Health Services Administration, MDO
Health Services Research, D
Health Teacher Education, B
History, BM
Human Genetics, DO
Human Resources Management and Services, M
Immunology, MO
Industrial and Labor Relations, M
Information Science/Studies, B
Insurance, M
Interdisciplinary Studies, M
Interior Design, BM
International/Global Studies, B
Internet and Interactive Multimedia, M
Jewelry/Metalsmithing, M
Management Information Systems and
  Services, MD
Marketing, M
Marketing/Marketing Management, B
Mass Communication/Media Studies, BM
Mathematics, BMO
Mechanical Engineering, B
Microbiology, MDO
Middle School Education, M
Molecular Biology, D
Molecular Biophysics, MO
Music, M
Music Performance, B
Music Teacher Education, M
Neuroscience, MD
Nurse Anesthetist, M
Nursing, MDO
Nursing - Adult, M
Nursing - Advanced Practice, MO
Nursing - Registered Nurse Training, B
Nursing Administration, M
Occupational Therapy/Therapist, M
Operations Research, M
Painting, BM
Parks, Recreation and Leisure Facilities
  Management, B
Pathology/Experimental Pathology, MDO
Pediatric Nurse/Nursing, M
Performance, M
Pharmaceutical Sciences, MDP
Pharmacology, MDO
Pharmacy, PO
Philosophy, B
Photography, BM
Physical Education Teaching and Coaching, M
Physical Therapy/Therapist, D
Physics, BM
Physiology, MDO
Political Science and Government, B
Printmaking, M
Psychiatric/Mental Health Nurse/Nursing, M
Psychology, BD
Public Administration, MO
Public Health, MDO
Public Policy Analysis, D
Quantitative Analysis, M

Radiologic Technology/Science - Radiographer, B
Reading Teacher Education, M
Real Estate, MO
Recreation and Park Management, M
Rehabilitation Counseling, MO
Religion/Religious Studies, B
Rhetoric, M
Sculpture, BM
Secondary Education and Teaching, MO
Social Studies Teacher Education, M
Social Work, BMDO
Sociology, BMO
Special Education and Teaching, M
Statistics, MO
Taxation, M
Theater, M
Toxicology, M
Urban and Regional Planning, MO
Urban Education and Leadership, D
Urban Planning, M
Urban Studies/Affairs, B
Women's Health Nursing, M
Writing, M

VIRGINIA HIGHLANDS COMMUNITY COLLEGE

Accounting, A
Administrative Assistant and Secretarial Science, A
Biological and Physical Sciences, A
Business Administration and Management, A
Criminal Justice/Police Science, A
Data Processing and Data Processing
  Technology/Technician, A
Drafting and Design Technology/Technician, A
Drama and Dramatics/Theatre Arts, A
Education, A
Electrical, Electronic and Communications
  Engineering Technology/Technician, A
Engineering Technology, A
Heating, Air Conditioning, Ventilation and
  Refrigeration Maintenance
  Technology/Technician, A
Human Services, A
Industrial Radiologic Technology/Technician, A
Information Science/Studies, A
Liberal Arts and Sciences Studies and
  Humanities, A
Machine Tool Technology/Machinist, A
Nursing - Registered Nurse Training, A
Physical Therapy/Therapist, A

VIRGINIA INTERMONT COLLEGE

Art Teacher Education, B
Art/Art Studies, General, B
Biology Teacher Education, B
Biology/Biological Sciences, B
Business Administration and Management, B
Commercial and Advertising Art, A
Computer and Information Sciences, B
Criminal Justice/Law Enforcement Administration, B
Culinary Arts/Chef Training, AB
Dance, B
Drama and Dramatics/Theatre Arts, B
Education, B
Elementary Education and Teaching, B
English Language and Literature, B
English/Language Arts Teacher Education, B
Environmental Studies, B
Equestrian/Equine Studies, B
General Studies, B
Health and Physical Education, B
History, B
Interdisciplinary Studies, B
International Business/Trade/Commerce, B
Law and Legal Studies, B
Legal Assistant/Paralegal, B
Liberal Arts and Sciences Studies and
  Humanities, AB
Marketing/Marketing Management, B
Photography, B
Physical Education Teaching and Coaching, B
Political Science and Government, B
Pre-Law Studies, B
Pre-Medicine/Pre-Medical Studies, B
Pre-Veterinary Studies, B
Psychology, B

Public Administration, B
Religion/Religious Studies, B
Restaurant, Culinary, and Catering
  Management/Manager, B
Secondary Education and Teaching, B
Social Studies Teacher Education, B
Social Work, B
Sport and Fitness Administration/Management, B

VIRGINIA MILITARY INSTITUTE

Biology/Biological Sciences, B
Chemistry, B
Civil Engineering, B
Computer Science, B
Economics, B
Electrical, Electronics and Communications
  Engineering, B
English Language and Literature, B
History, B
International Relations and Affairs, B
Mathematics, B
Mechanical Engineering, B
Modern Languages, B
Physics, B
Psychology, B

VIRGINIA POLYTECHNIC INSTITUTE AND STATE UNIVERSITY

Accounting, BMD
Adult and Continuing Education and Teaching, MDO
Aerospace, Aeronautical and Astronautical
  Engineering, BMD
Agribusiness, M
Agricultural Economics, BMD
Agricultural Engineering, MD
Agricultural Sciences, MD
Agronomy and Crop Science, B
Agronomy and Soil Sciences, MD
Animal Sciences, BMD
Apparel and Textiles, B
Applied Economics, MD
Applied Mathematics, MD
Applied Physics, MD
Architecture, BM
Art/Art Studies, General, B
Arts Management, M
Biochemistry, BMD
Bioengineering, MD
Bioinformatics, D
Biological and Biomedical Sciences, MD
Biology/Biological Sciences, B
Biomedical Engineering, MDO
Botany/Plant Biology, MD
Business Administration and Management, B
Business Administration, Management and
  Operations, MD
Business Family and Consumer Sciences/Human
  Sciences, B
Business/Managerial Economics, B
Chemical Engineering, BMD
Chemistry, BMD
Child and Family Studies, MD
Civil Engineering, BMD
Clinical Psychology, D
Clothing and Textiles, MD
Communication Studies/Speech Communication
  and Rhetoric, B
Computational Biology, D
Computer and Information Sciences, B
Computer Engineering, BMD
Computer Science, BMD
Construction Management, B
Consumer Economics, MD
Counselor Education/School Counseling and
  Guidance Services, MDO
Curriculum and Instruction, MDO
Dairy Science, BMD
Design and Applied Arts, M
Developmental Biology and Embryology, MD
Developmental Psychology, D
Drama and Dramatics/Theatre Arts, B
Ecology, MD
Economics, BMD
Educational Administration and Supervision, DO
Educational Leadership and Administration, MDO
Educational Measurement and Evaluation, D

Educational Media/Instructional Technology, MDO
Electrical Engineering, MD
Electrical, Electronics and Communications
   Engineering, B
Engineering and Applied Sciences, MD
Engineering Management, M
Engineering Mechanics, B
English, M
English Language and Literature, B
Entomology, MD
Environmental Design/Architecture, D
Environmental Engineering
   Technology/Environmental Technology, M
Environmental Sciences, M
Environmental Studies, B
Evolutionary Biology, MD
Family and Consumer Sciences/Home Economics
   Teacher Education, B
Finance, B
Finance and Banking, MD
Fish, Game and Wildlife Management, MD
Food Science, B
Food Science and Technology, MD
Foods, Nutrition, and Wellness Studies, B
Forestry, BMD
French Language and Literature, B
Genetics, MD
Geography, BM
Geology/Earth Science, BMD
Geophysics and Seismology, MD
German Language and Literature, B
Gerontology, MD
Health Education, M
History, BM
History of Science and Technology, MD
Horticultural Science, BMD
Hospitality Administration/Management, MD
Hotel/Motel Administration/Management, B
Human Development, M
Human Development and Family Studies, B
Human Resources Development, MD
Industrial and Organizational Psychology, D
Industrial Design, B
Industrial Engineering, B
Industrial/Management Engineering, MD
Information Science/Studies, BM
Interdisciplinary Studies, B
Interior Design, BMD
International Affairs, M
International Relations and Affairs, B
Landscape Architecture, BM
Logistics and Materials Management, MD
Management, D
Management Information Systems and
   Services, MDO
Management Science, B
Marketing, MD
Marketing/Marketing Management, B
Marriage and Family Therapy/Counseling, MD
Materials Engineering, BMD
Materials Sciences, MD
Mathematical Physics, MD
Mathematics, BMD
Mechanical Engineering, BMD
Mechanics, MD
Microbiology, MD
Mineral/Mining Engineering, MD
Mining and Mineral Engineering, B
Music, B
Natural Resources and Conservation, MD
Nutritional Sciences, MD
Ocean Engineering, BM
Operations Research, MD
Philosophy, BM
Physical Education Teaching and Coaching, M
Physics, BMD
Plant Pathology/Phytopathology, MD
Plant Physiology, MD
Political Science and Government, BM
Poultry Science, BMD
Psychology, BMD
Public Administration, MDO
Public Policy Analysis, BMDO
Recreation and Park Management, MD
Secondary Education and Teaching, B
Sociology, BMD

Spanish Language and Literature, B
Special Education and Teaching, DO
Statistics, BMD
Theater, M
Travel and Tourism, MD
Urban and Regional Planning, M
Veterinary Medicine, P
Veterinary Sciences, MD
Vocational and Technical Education, MD
Zoology/Animal Biology, MD

VIRGINIA STATE UNIVERSITY

Accounting, B
Agriculture, B
Biological and Biomedical Sciences, M
Biology/Biological Sciences, B
Business Administration and Management, B
Business Administration, Management and
   Operations, M
Business Teacher Education, B
Business/Managerial Economics, B
Chemistry, B
Computer Engineering, B
Computer Science, B
Counselor Education/School Counseling and
   Guidance Services, M
Criminal Justice/Safety Studies, B
Economics, M
Education, MO
Educational Administration and Supervision, M
Engineering Technology, B
English, M
English Language and Literature, B
Family and Consumer Economics and Related
   Services, B
Finance and Banking, M
History, BM
Hospitality Administration/Management, B
Interdisciplinary Studies, BM
Liberal Arts and Sciences Studies and
   Humanities, B
Licensed Practical/Vocational Nurse Training, A
Management Science, B
Manufacturing Engineering, B
Marketing/Marketing Management, B
Mass Communication/Media Studies, B
Mathematics, BM
Mathematics Teacher Education, M
Mechanical Engineering/Mechanical
   Technology/Technician, B
Music, B
Physics, BM
Political Science and Government, B
Psychology, BM
Public Administration, B
Social Work, B
Sociology, B
Technology Education/Industrial Arts, B
Visual and Performing Arts, B
Vocational and Technical Education, MO

VIRGINIA UNION UNIVERSITY

Accounting, B
Biology/Biological Sciences, B
Business Administration and Management, B
Business Teacher Education, B
Chemistry, B
Criminology, B
Drama Therapy, B
Elementary Education and Teaching, B
English Language and Literature, B
History, B
Jazz/Jazz Studies, B
Journalism, B
Kindergarten/PreSchool Education and Teaching, B
Management Information Systems and Services, B
Marketing/Marketing Management, B
Mathematics, B
Music, B
Political Science and Government, B
Psychology, B
Social Work, B
Sociology, B
Special Education and Teaching, B

Theology and Religious Vocations, DP

VIRGINIA UNIVERSITY OF LYNCHBURG

Religion/Religious Studies, P

VIRGINIA WESLEYAN COLLEGE

American/United States Studies/Civilization, B
Art Teacher Education, B
Art/Art Studies, General, B
Biology/Biological Sciences, B
Business Administration and Management, B
Chemistry, B
Classics and Classical
   Languages, Literatures, and Linguistics, B
Communication and Media Studies, B
Computer Science, B
Criminology, B
Drama and Dramatics/Theatre Arts, B
Elementary Education and Teaching, B
English Language and Literature, B
Environmental Studies, B
Foreign Language Teacher Education, B
Foreign Languages and Literatures, B
French Language and Literature, B
Geology/Earth Science, B
German Language and Literature, B
History, B
Human Services, B
Humanities/Humanistic Studies, B
Interdisciplinary Studies, B
International Relations and Affairs, B
Junior High/Intermediate/Middle School Education
   and Teaching, B
Liberal Arts and Sciences Studies and
   Humanities, B
Mathematics, B
Music, B
Natural Sciences, B
Parks, Recreation, Leisure and Fitness Studies, B
Philosophy, B
Political Science and Government, B
Pre-Dentistry Studies, B
Pre-Law Studies, B
Pre-Medicine/Pre-Medical Studies, B
Pre-Veterinary Studies, B
Psychology, B
Religion/Religious Studies, B
Secondary Education and Teaching, B
Social Sciences, B
Social Studies Teacher Education, B
Sociology, B
Spanish Language and Literature, B
Women's Studies, B

VIRGINIA WESTERN COMMUNITY COLLEGE

Accounting, A
Administrative Assistant and Secretarial Science, A
Art/Art Studies, General, A
Automobile/Automotive Mechanics
   Technology/Technician, A
Biological and Physical Sciences, A
Business Administration and Management, A
Child Development, A
Civil Engineering Technology/Technician, A
Commercial and Advertising Art, A
Computer Science, A
Criminal Justice/Law Enforcement Administration, A
Data Processing and Data Processing
   Technology/Technician, A
Dental Hygiene/Hygienist, A
Education, A
Electrical, Electronic and Communications
   Engineering Technology/Technician, A
Engineering, A
Industrial Radiologic Technology/Technician, A
Kindergarten/PreSchool Education and Teaching, A
Liberal Arts and Sciences Studies and
   Humanities, A
Mechanical Engineering/Mechanical
   Technology/Technician, A
Mental Health/Rehabilitation, A
Nursing - Registered Nurse Training, A
Pre-Engineering, A
Radio and Television, A

Radiologic Technology/Science - Radiographer, A

WASHINGTON AND LEE UNIVERSITY

Accounting, B
Anthropology, B
Archeology, B
Art History, Criticism and Conservation, B
Biochemistry, B
Biology/Biological Sciences, B
Business Administration and Management, B
Chemical Engineering, B
Chemistry, B
Classics and Classical
   Languages, Literatures, and Linguistics, B
Computer and Information Sciences, B
Computer Science, B
Drama and Dramatics/Theatre Arts, B
East Asian Studies, B
Economics, B
Engineering Physics, B
English Language and Literature, B
Fine/Studio Arts, B
Foreign Languages and Literatures, B
French Language and Literature, B
Geological and Earth Sciences/Geosciences, B
Geology/Earth Science, B
German Language and Literature, B
History, B
Journalism, B
Law and Legal Studies, MP
Mathematics, B
Medieval and Renaissance Studies, B
Multi-/Interdisciplinary Studies, B
Music, B
Neuroscience, B
Philosophy, B
Physics, B
Political Science and Government, B
Psychology, B
Public Policy Analysis, B
Religion/Religious Studies, B
Russian Studies, B
Sociology, B
Spanish Language and Literature, B

WESTWOOD COLLEGE-ANNANDALE CAMPUS

Animation, Interactive Technology, Video Graphics
   and Special Effects, B
Architectural Drafting and Architectural
   CAD/CADD, A
Graphic Design, A
Interior Design, B
Intermedia/Multimedia, A

WORLD COLLEGE

Electrical, Electronic and Communications
   Engineering Technology/Technician, B

WYTHEVILLE COMMUNITY COLLEGE

Accounting, A
Administrative Assistant and Secretarial Science, A
Biological and Physical Sciences, A
Business Administration and Management, A
Civil Engineering Technology/Technician, A
Clinical/Medical Laboratory Technician, A
Corrections, A
Criminal Justice/Law Enforcement Administration, A
Criminal Justice/Police Science, A
Dental Hygiene/Hygienist, A
Drafting and Design Technology/Technician, A
Education, A
Electrical, Electronic and Communications
   Engineering Technology/Technician, A
Information Science/Studies, A
Liberal Arts and Sciences Studies and
   Humanities, A
Machine Tool Technology/Machinist, A
Mass Communication/Media Studies, A
Mechanical Engineering/Mechanical
   Technology/Technician, A
Medical Administrative Assistant/Secretary, A
Nursing - Registered Nurse Training, A
Physical Therapy/Therapist, A

Real Estate, A

Washington

ANTIOCH UNIVERSITY SEATTLE

Education, M
Environmental Policy and Resource
   Management, M
Industrial and Organizational Psychology, M
Liberal Arts and Sciences Studies and
   Humanities, B
Management, M
Organizational Management, M
Psychology, M

ARGOSY UNIVERSITY/SEATTLE

Business Administration, Management and
   Operations, MD
Business/Commerce, B
Clinical Psychology, MD
Counseling Psychology, M
Curriculum and Instruction, MD
Education, MD
Educational Leadership and Administration, MD
Psychology, B

THE ART INSTITUTE OF SEATTLE

Animation, Interactive Technology, Video Graphics
   and Special Effects, AB
Audio Engineering, A
Cinematography and Film/Video Production, A
Culinary Arts/Chef Training, A
Fashion Merchandising, A
Fashion/Apparel Design, A
Graphic Design, AB
Industrial Design, A
Interior Design, AB
Intermedia/Multimedia, AB
Photography, A

BASTYR UNIVERSITY

Acupuncture and Oriental Medicine, MDO
Dietetics/Dieticians, B
Foods, Nutrition, and Wellness Studies, B
Health Psychology, M
Herbalism/Herbalist, B
Kinesiology and Exercise Science, B
Naturopathic Medicine/Naturopathy, DO
Nurse Midwife/Nursing Midwifery, O
Nutritional Sciences, M
Psychology, B
Public Health (MPH, DPH), B

BATES TECHNICAL COLLEGE

Accounting Technology/Technician and
   Bookkeeping, A
Administrative Assistant and Secretarial Science, A
Architectural Engineering Technology/Technician, A
Autobody/Collision and Repair
   Technology/Technician, A
Automobile/Automotive Mechanics
   Technology/Technician, A
Biology Technician/BioTechnology Laboratory
   Technician, A
Biomedical Technology/Technician, A
Building/Property Maintenance and Management, A
Carpentry/Carpenter, A
Child Care Provider/Assistant, A
Civil Engineering Technology/Technician, A
Computer Programming/Programmer, A
Computer Systems Networking and
   Telecommunications, A
Computer Technology/Computer Systems
   Technology, A
Court Reporting/Court Reporter, A
Culinary Arts/Chef Training, A
Data Modeling/Warehousing and Database
   Administration, A
Data Processing and Data Processing
   Technology/Technician, A
Dental Laboratory Technology/Technician, A
Diesel Mechanics Technology/Technician, A
Electrical and Power Transmission
   Installation/Installer, A

Electrical, Electronic and Communications
   Engineering Technology/Technician, A
Electrical/Electronics Equipment Installation and
   Repair, A
Electrician, A
Fire Science/Firefighting, A
Heating, Air Conditioning, Ventilation and
   Refrigeration Maintenance
   Technology/Technician, A
Industrial Electronics Technology/Technician, A
Information Science/Studies, A
Legal Administrative Assistant/Secretary, A
Licensed Practical/Vocational Nurse Training, A
Manufacturing Technology/Technician, A
Mechanical Engineering/Mechanical
   Technology/Technician, A
Occupational Safety and Health
   Technology/Technician, A
Radio and Television Broadcasting
   Technology/Technician, A
Retailing and Retail Operations, A
Small Engine Mechanics and Repair
   Technology/Technician, A
Survey Technology/Surveying, A
Web/Multimedia Management and Webmaster, A

BELLEVUE COMMUNITY COLLEGE

Accounting, A
Administrative Assistant and Secretarial Science, A
Business Administration and Management, A
Computer Programming/Programmer, A
Criminal Justice/Law Enforcement Administration, A
Criminal Justice/Police Science, A
Data Processing and Data Processing
   Technology/Technician, A
Educational/Instructional Media Design, A
Fashion Merchandising, A
Fire Science/Firefighting, A
Industrial Radiologic Technology/Technician, A
Information Science/Studies, A
Interior Design, A
Kindergarten/PreSchool Education and Teaching, A
Liberal Arts and Sciences Studies and
   Humanities, A
Marketing/Marketing Management, A
Nursing - Registered Nurse Training, A
Parks, Recreation, Leisure and Fitness Studies, A
Real Estate, A

BELLINGHAM TECHNICAL COLLEGE

Data Entry/Microcomputer Applications, A
Information Technology, A
System Administration/Administrator, A
Web Page, Digital/Multimedia and Information
   Resources Design, A
Web/Multimedia Management and Webmaster, A

BIG BEND COMMUNITY COLLEGE

Accounting Technology/Technician and
   Bookkeeping, A
Airline/Commercial/Professional Pilot and Flight
   Crew, A
Automobile/Automotive Mechanics
   Technology/Technician, A
Avionics Maintenance Technology/Technician, A
Civil Engineering Technology/Technician, A
Heavy/Industrial Equipment Maintenance
   Technologies, A
Industrial Electronics Technology/Technician, A
Information Science/Studies, A
Liberal Arts and Sciences Studies and
   Humanities, A
Licensed Practical/Vocational Nurse Training, A
Nursing - Registered Nurse Training, A
Office Management and Supervision, A
Teacher Assistant/Aide, A
Welding Technology/Welder, A

CASCADIA COMMUNITY COLLEGE

Liberal Arts and Sciences Studies and
   Humanities, A

Science Technologies/Technicians, A

CENTRAL WASHINGTON UNIVERSITY

Accounting, BM
Aeronautics/Aviation/Aerospace Science and
Technology, B
Anthropology, B
Art Teacher Education, B
Art/Art Studies, General, B
Asian Studies/Civilization, B
Biological and Biomedical Sciences, M
Biology Teacher Education, B
Biology/Biological Sciences, B
Business Administration and Management, B
Business Education, M
Business Teacher Education, B
Chemistry, BM
Chemistry Teacher Education, B
Child and Family Studies, M
Community Health Services/Liaison/Counseling, B
Computer and Information Sciences, B
Counseling Psychology, M
Counselor Education/School Counseling and
Guidance Services, M
Criminal Justice/Law Enforcement Administration, B
Curriculum and Instruction, M
Drama and Dance Teacher Education, B
Drama and Dramatics/Theatre Arts, B
Early Childhood Education and Teaching, B
Economics, B
Education, M
Educational Administration and Supervision, M
Electrical, Electronic and Communications
Engineering Technology/Technician, B
Elementary Education and Teaching, BM
Emergency Medical Technology/Technician (EMT
Paramedic), B
Engineering and Applied Sciences, M
English, M
English as a Second Language, M
English Language and Literature, B
English/Language Arts Teacher Education, B
Experimental Psychology, M
Family and Consumer Sciences/Human Sciences, B
Fashion Merchandising, B
Fine Arts and Art Studies, M
Foods, Nutrition, and Wellness Studies, B
Foreign Languages and Literatures, B
French Language Teacher Education, B
Geography, B
Geology/Earth Science, BM
German Language Teacher Education, B
Gerontology, B
Health Education, M
Health Teacher Education, B
History, BM
History Teacher Education, B
Home Economics, M
Home Economics Education, M
Industrial and Organizational Psychology, M
Industrial Technology/Technician, B
Industrial/Management Engineering, M
Information Science/Studies, M
Interdisciplinary Studies, M
Journalism, B
Kindergarten/PreSchool Education and Teaching, B
Kinesiology and Exercise Science, B
Management, M
Mass Communication/Media Studies, B
Mathematics, BM
Mathematics Teacher Education, B
Mechanical Engineering/Mechanical
Technology/Technician, B
Music, BM
Music Management and Merchandising, B
Music Teacher Education, B
Music Theory and Composition, B
Natural Resources Management/Development and
Policy, BM
Nutritional Sciences, M
Occupational Safety and Health
Technology/Technician, B
Office Management and Supervision, B
Operations Management and Supervision, B
Parks, Recreation, Leisure and Fitness Studies, B
Philosophy, B

Physical Education Teaching and Coaching, BM
Physics, B
Piano and Organ, B
Political Science and Government, B
Psychology, BM
Public Policy Analysis, B
Public Relations/Image Management, B
Radio and Television, B
Reading Teacher Education, M
Recreation and Park Management, M
Religion/Religious Studies, B
School Psychology, M
Science Teacher Education/General Science
Teacher Education, B
Social Science Teacher Education, B
Sociology, B
Spanish Language Teacher Education, B
Special Education and Teaching, BM
Sport and Fitness Administration/Management, B
Technology Teacher Education/Industrial Arts
Teacher Education, B
Textile Design, M
Theater, M
Trade and Industrial Teacher Education, B
Voice and Opera, B

CENTRALIA COLLEGE

Administrative Assistant and Secretarial Science, A
Applied Art, A
Art/Art Studies, General, A
Biological and Physical Sciences, A
Biology/Biological Sciences, A
Botany/Plant Biology, A
Broadcast Journalism, A
Business Administration and Management, A
Business and Personal/Financial Services Marketing
Operations, A
Business/Commerce, A
Chemistry, A
Child Care and Support Services Management, A
Child Development, A
Civil Engineering Technology/Technician, A
Commercial and Advertising Art, A
Computer and Information Sciences, A
Computer Programming, A
Computer Systems Networking and
Telecommunications, A
Consumer Merchandising/Retailing Management, A
Corrections, A
Criminal Justice/Law Enforcement Administration, A
Diesel Mechanics Technology/Technician, A
Drama and Dramatics/Theatre Arts, A
Electrical, Electronic and Communications
Engineering Technology/Technician, A
Engineering, A
English Language and Literature, A
French Language and Literature, A
Geology/Earth Science, A
German Language and Literature, A
Heavy Equipment Maintenance
Technology/Technician, A
History, A
Humanities/Humanistic Studies, A
Kindergarten/PreSchool Education and Teaching, A
Legal Administrative Assistant/Secretary, A
Liberal Arts and Sciences Studies and
Humanities, A
Licensed Practical/Vocational Nurse Training, A
Marketing/Marketing Management, A
Mass Communication/Media Studies, A
Mathematics, A
Medical Administrative Assistant/Secretary, A
Music, A
Natural Sciences, A
Nursing - Registered Nurse Training, A
Parks, Recreation, Leisure and Fitness Studies, A
Physical Sciences, A
Political Science and Government, A
Pre-Dentistry Studies, A
Pre-Engineering, A
Pre-Law Studies, A
Pre-Medicine/Pre-Medical Studies, A
Pre-Pharmacy Studies, A
Pre-Veterinary Studies, A
Psychology, A
Radio and Television, A

Receptionist, A
Retailing and Retail Operations, A
Sales, Distribution and Marketing Operations, A
Social Sciences, A
Sociology, A
Spanish Language and Literature, A
Survey Technology/Surveying, A
System Administration/Administrator, A
Teacher Assistant/Aide, A
Welding Technology/Welder, A
Work and Family Studies, A
Zoology/Animal Biology, A

CITY UNIVERSITY

Accounting, BM
Art Education, M
Business Administration and Management, B
Business Administration, Management and
Operations, MO
Computer and Information Sciences and Support
Services, B
Computer Programming/Programmer, B
Computer Science, MO
Counseling Psychology, M
Curriculum and Instruction, M
Education, MO
Educational Administration and Supervision, MO
Educational Leadership and Administration, M
Educational Media/Instructional Technology, M
Electronic Commerce, MO
Elementary Education and Teaching, B
English as a Second Language, M
Finance and Banking, MO
General Studies, AB
Human Resources Management and Services, M
International Business/Trade/Commerce, BM
Internet and Interactive Multimedia, MO
Management, MO
Management Information Systems and
Services, MO
Management of Technology, MO
Marketing, MO
Mass Communication/Media Studies, B
Project Management, MO
Psychology, B
Reading Teacher Education, M
School Psychology, M
Special Education and Teaching, B
System Management, M

CLARK COLLEGE

Accounting Technology/Technician and
Bookkeeping, A
Applied Horticulture/Horticultural Operations, A
Automobile/Automotive Mechanics
Technology/Technician, A
Baking and Pastry Arts/Baker/Pastry Chef, A
Business Administration and Management, A
Business/Office Automation/Technology/Data
Entry, A
Computer Programming/Programmer, A
Computer Systems Networking and
Telecommunications, A
Construction Engineering Technology/Technician, A
Culinary Arts/Chef Training, A
Data Entry/Microcomputer Applications, A
Dental Hygiene/Hygienist, A
Diesel Mechanics Technology/Technician, A
Early Childhood Education and Teaching, A
Electrical, Electronic and Communications
Engineering Technology/Technician, A
Emergency Medical Technology/Technician (EMT
Paramedic), A
Executive Assistant/Executive Secretary, A
Graphic Communications, A
Human Resources Management/Personnel
Administration, A
Landscaping and Groundskeeping, A
Legal Assistant/Paralegal, A
Liberal Arts and Sciences Studies and
Humanities, A
Machine Tool Technology/Machinist, A
Manufacturing Technology/Technician, A
Medical Administrative Assistant/Secretary, A
Medical/Clinical Assistant, A
Nursing - Registered Nurse Training, A

Retailing and Retail Operations, A
Selling Skills and Sales Operations, A
Sport and Fitness Administration/Management, A
Substance Abuse/Addiction Counseling, A
Telecommunications Technology/Technician, A
Web/Multimedia Management and Webmaster, A
Welding Technology/Welder, A

CLOVER PARK TECHNICAL COLLEGE

Accounting Technology/Technician and
    Bookkeeping, A
Agriculture, A
Airline/Commercial/Professional Pilot and Flight
    Crew, A
Architectural Engineering Technology/Technician, A
Automobile/Automotive Mechanics
    Technology/Technician, A
Avionics Maintenance Technology/Technician, A
Business Machine Repairer, A
Clinical/Medical Laboratory Assistant, A
Computer and Information Sciences and Support
    Services, A
Computer and Information Systems Security, A
Computer Programming/Programmer, A
Computer Systems Networking and
    Telecommunications, A
Early Childhood Education and Teaching, A
Environmental Engineering
    Technology/Environmental Technology, A
Graphic and Printing Equipment Operator
    Production, A
Heating, Air Conditioning, Ventilation and
    Refrigeration Maintenance
    Technology/Technician, A
Heavy Equipment Maintenance
    Technology/Technician, A
Interior Design, A
Landscaping and Groundskeeping, A
Legal Administrative Assistant/Secretary, A
Machine Tool Technology/Machinist, A
Marketing/Marketing Management, A
Massage Therapy/Therapeutic Massage, A
Mechanical Engineering/Mechanical
    Technology/Technician, A
Office Management and Supervision, A
Radio and Television Broadcasting
    Technology/Technician, A
Rehabilitation and Therapeutic Professions, A
Security and Protective Services, A
Teacher Assistant/Aide, A
Web Page, Digital/Multimedia and Information
    Resources Design, A

COLUMBIA BASIN COLLEGE

Administrative Assistant and Secretarial Science, A
Agricultural Business and Management, A
Agricultural Mechanization, A
Automobile/Automotive Mechanics
    Technology/Technician, A
Carpentry/Carpenter, A
Computer and Information Sciences, A
Computer Programming, A
Computer Science, A
Computer Software and Media Applications, A
Computer Systems Networking and
    Telecommunications, A
Criminal Justice/Police Science, A
Criminal Justice/Safety Studies, A
Electrical, Electronic and Communications
    Engineering Technology/Technician, A
Engineering, A
Environmental Engineering
    Technology/Environmental Technology, A
Fire Science/Firefighting, A
Kindergarten/PreSchool Education and Teaching, A
Legal Assistant/Paralegal, A
Liberal Arts and Sciences Studies and
    Humanities, A
Machine Tool Technology/Machinist, A
Marketing/Marketing Management, A
Nuclear/Nuclear Power Technology/Technician, A
Nursing - Registered Nurse Training, A
Quality Control Technology/Technician, A
Real Estate, A
Web Page, Digital/Multimedia and Information
    Resources Design, A

Welding Technology/Welder, A

CORNISH COLLEGE OF THE ARTS

Acting, B
Art/Art Studies, General, B
Dance, B
Directing and Theatrical Production, B
Drama and Dramatics/Theatre Arts, B
Fine Arts and Art Studies, B
Fine/Studio Arts, B
Graphic Design, B
Illustration, B
Interior Design, B
Jazz/Jazz Studies, B
Music, B
Piano and Organ, B
Technical Theatre/Theatre Design and
    Technology, B
Violin, Viola, Guitar and Other Stringed
    Instruments, B

CROWN COLLEGE

Criminal Justice/Safety Studies, A
Legal Administrative Assistant/Secretary, A
Legal Assistant/Paralegal, A
Public Administration, B

DEVRY UNIVERSITY (BELLEVUE)

Business Administration, Management and
    Operations, M

DEVRY UNIVERSITY (FEDERAL WAY)

Biomedical/Medical Engineering, B
Business Administration, Management and
    Operations, BM
Computer and Information Sciences, B
Computer Engineering Technology/Technician, B
Computer Programming, Specific Applications, B
Computer Systems Analysis/Analyst, B
Computer Systems Networking and
    Telecommunications, AB
Electrical, Electronic and Communications
    Engineering Technology/Technician, AB
Information Science/Studies, B
Medical Informatics, B
System, Networking, and LAN/WAN
    Management/Manager, B

DIGIPEN INSTITUTE OF TECHNOLOGY

Computer Engineering, B
Intermedia/Multimedia, AB

EASTERN WASHINGTON UNIVERSITY

Accounting, B
Adult and Continuing Education and Teaching, M
Anthropology, B
Art History, Criticism and Conservation, B
Art Teacher Education, B
Athletic Training and Sports Medicine, B
Audiology/Audiologist and Speech-Language
    Pathology/Pathologist, B
Biochemistry, B
Biological and Biomedical Sciences, M
Biological and Physical Sciences, B
Biology/Biological Sciences, B
BioTechnology, B
Business Administration and Management, B
Business Administration, Management and
    Operations, MO
Business Teacher Education, B
Business/Managerial Economics, B
Chemistry, B
Chemistry Teacher Education, B
Child Care and Support Services Management, B
Child Development, B
City/Urban, Community and Regional Planning, B
Communication and Media Studies, M
Communication Disorders, M
Communication Studies/Speech Communication
    and Rhetoric, B
Communication, Journalism and Related
    Programs, B
Community College Education, M
Comparative Literature, B
Composition, M

Computer and Information Sciences, B
Computer Education, M
Computer Engineering Technology/Technician, B
Computer Science, M
Computer Software and Media Applications, B
Computer Teacher Education, B
Construction Engineering Technology/Technician, B
Corrections, B
Counseling Psychology, M
Counselor Education/School Counseling and
    Guidance Services, M
Creative Writing, B
Criminal Justice/Law Enforcement Administration, B
Curriculum and Instruction, M
Dental Hygiene/Hygienist, B
Developmental and Child Psychology, B
Digital Communication and Media/Multimedia, B
Drafting/Design Engineering
    Technologies/Technicians, B
Drama and Dance Teacher Education, B
Drama and Dramatics/Theatre Arts, B
Early Childhood Education and Teaching, BM
Economics, B
Education, BM
Education/Teaching of Individuals in Early Childhood
    Special Education Programs, B
Educational Administration and Supervision, M
Educational Leadership and Administration, M
Educational Media/Instructional Technology, M
Electrical, Electronic and Communications
    Engineering Technology/Technician, B
Elementary Education and Teaching, BM
Engineering Technology, B
English, M
English Language and Literature, B
English/Language Arts Teacher Education, B
Environmental Biology, B
Environmental Sciences, B
Finance, B
Fine/Studio Arts, B
Foreign Language Teacher Education, M
Foundations and Philosophy of Education, M
French Language and Literature, B
French Language Teacher Education, B
Geography, B
Geology/Earth Science, B
German Language Teacher Education, B
Health and Physical Education, B
Health Teacher Education, B
Health/Health Care Administration/Management, B
Higher Education/Higher Education
    Administration, M
History, BM
Human Resources Management/Personnel
    Administration, B
Humanities/Humanistic Studies, B
Interdisciplinary Studies, BM
International Relations and Affairs, B
Journalism, B
Kinesiology and Exercise Science, B
Liberal Arts and Sciences Studies and
    Humanities, B
Management Information Systems and Services, B
Manufacturing Technology/Technician, B
Marketing/Marketing Management, B
Mathematics, BM
Mathematics Teacher Education, BM
Mechanical Engineering/Mechanical
    Technology/Technician, B
Music, BM
Music History, Literature, and Theory, M
Music Performance, B
Music Teacher Education, BM
Music Theory and Composition, B
Natural Sciences, B
Nursing, M
Nursing - Registered Nurse Training, B
Nursing Education, M
Occupational Therapy/Therapist, M
Organizational Communication, B
Parks, Recreation and Leisure Facilities
    Management, B
Parks, Recreation, Leisure and Fitness Studies, B
Performance, B
Philosophy, B
Physical Education Teaching and Coaching, BM

Physical Sciences, B
Physical Therapy/Therapist, BD
Physics, B
Physics Teacher Education, B
Piano and Organ, B
Political Science and Government, B
Pre-Dentistry Studies, B
Pre-Law Studies, B
Pre-Medicine/Pre-Medical Studies, B
Pre-Veterinary Studies, B
Psychology, BM
Public Administration, BMO
Reading Teacher Education, BM
School Librarian/School Library Media Specialist, B
School Psychology, M
Science Teacher Education/General Science
    Teacher Education, BM
Social Studies Teacher Education, BM
Social Work, BMO
Sociology, B
Spanish Language and Literature, B
Spanish Language Teacher Education, B
Special Education and Teaching, BM
Teacher Education and Professional
    Development, Specific Subject Areas, B
Teaching English as a Second or Foreign
    Language/ESL Language Instructor, B
Therapeutic Recreation/Recreational Therapy, B
Urban and Regional Planning, MO
Voice and Opera, B
Writing, M

EDMONDS COMMUNITY COLLEGE

Accounting Technology/Technician and
    Bookkeeping, A
Administrative Assistant and Secretarial Science, A
Applied Horticulture/Horticultural Operations, A
Audiovisual Communications
    Technologies/Technicians, A
Building/Home/Construction Inspection/Inspector, A
Business Administration and Management, A
Clinical/Medical Laboratory Assistant, A
Computer and Information Sciences and Support
    Services, A
Computer and Information Systems Security, A
Computer Programming, Specific Applications, A
Computer
    Programming, Vendor/Product Certification, A
Computer Programming/Programmer, A
Computer Systems Networking and
    Telecommunications, A
Computer Technology/Computer Systems
    Technology, A
Construction Engineering Technology/Technician, A
Culinary Arts/Chef Training, A
Data Entry/Microcomputer Applications, A
Data Modeling/Warehousing and Database
    Administration, A
Data Processing and Data Processing
    Technology/Technician, A
Early Childhood Education and Teaching, A
E-Commerce/Electronic Commerce, A
Electrical, Electronic and Communications
    Engineering Technology/Technician, A
Electrocardiograph Technology/Technician, A
Entrepreneurship/Entrepreneurial Studies, A
Fashion Merchandising, A
Fire Services Administration, A
Health Aide, A
Health Information/Medical Records
    Technology/Technician, A
Health Professions and Related Clinical Sciences, A
Human Resources Management/Personnel
    Administration, A
International Business/Trade/Commerce, A
Landscaping and Groundskeeping, A
Legal Administrative Assistant/Secretary, A
Legal Assistant/Paralegal, A
Liberal Arts and Sciences Studies and
    Humanities, A
Marketing/Marketing Management, A
Medical Administrative Assistant/Secretary, A
Medical Reception/Receptionist, A
Mental and Social Health Services and Allied
    Professions, A

Nurse/Nursing Assistant/Aide and Patient Care
    Assistant, A
Office Management and Supervision, A
Pharmacy Technician/Assistant, A
Phlebotomy/Phlebotomist, A
Plant Nursery Operations and Management, A
Prepress/Desktop Publishing and Digital Imaging
    Design, A
Substance Abuse/Addiction Counseling, A
System Administration/Administrator, A
Tourism and Travel Services Marketing
    Operations, A
Vocational Rehabilitation Counseling/Counselor, A
Web Page, Digital/Multimedia and Information
    Resources Design, A
Web/Multimedia Management and Webmaster, A

EVERETT COMMUNITY COLLEGE

Accounting, A
Animal Sciences, A
Anthropology, A
Art/Art Studies, General, A
Atmospheric Sciences and Meteorology, A
Avionics Maintenance Technology/Technician, A
Biology/Biological Sciences, A
Botany/Plant Biology, A
Business Administration and Management, A
Chemistry, A
Cinematography and Film/Video Production, A
Civil Engineering Technology/Technician, A
Commercial and Advertising Art, A
Computer Science, A
Consumer Merchandising/Retailing Management, A
Cosmetology/Cosmetologist, A
Criminal Justice/Law Enforcement Administration, A
Criminal Justice/Police Science, A
Data Processing and Data Processing
    Technology/Technician, A
Dental Hygiene/Hygienist, A
Drafting and Design Technology/Technician, A
Drama and Dramatics/Theatre Arts, A
Drawing, A
Ecology, A
Economics, A
Education, A
Elementary Education and Teaching, A
Engineering, A
Engineering Science, A
Engineering Technology, A
English Language and Literature, A
Environmental Studies, A
Fire Science/Firefighting, A
Funeral Service and Mortuary Science, A
Geology/Earth Science, A
German Language and Literature, A
History, A
Human Services, A
Industrial Technology/Technician, A
Japanese Language and Literature, A
Journalism, A
Kindergarten/PreSchool Education and Teaching, A
Liberal Arts and Sciences Studies and
    Humanities, A
Licensed Practical/Vocational Nurse Training, A
Marketing/Marketing Management, A
Mathematics, A
Medical Administrative Assistant/Secretary, A
Medical/Clinical Assistant, A
Modern Languages, A
Music, A
Nursing - Registered Nurse Training, A
Occupational Therapy/Therapist, A
Oceanography, Chemical and Physical, A
Ophthalmic Laboratory Technology/Technician, A
Pharmacy Technician/Assistant, A
Philosophy, A
Photography, A
Physical Education Teaching and Coaching, A
Physical Therapist Assistant, A
Physics, A
Political Science and Government, A
Pre-Engineering, A
Psychology, A
Russian Language and Literature, A
Sociology, A
Spanish Language and Literature, A

Speech and Rhetorical Studies, A
Technology Education/Industrial Arts, A
Welding Technology/Welder, A
Wildlife Biology, A
Zoology/Animal Biology, A

THE EVERGREEN STATE COLLEGE

American Indian/Native American Studies, B
Area, Ethnic, Cultural, and Gender Studies, B
Art/Art Studies, General, B
Biological and Physical Sciences, B
Biology/Biological Sciences, B
Business Administration and Management, B
Cinematography and Film/Video Production, B
Classics and Classical
    Languages, Literatures, and Linguistics, B
Computer and Information Sciences, B
Drama and Dramatics/Theatre Arts, B
Education, M
Environmental Studies, BM
Fine/Studio Arts, B
Humanities/Humanistic Studies, B
Intercultural/Multicultural and Diversity Studies, B
Intermedia/Multimedia, B
International/Global Studies, B
Liberal Arts and Sciences Studies and
    Humanities, B
Multi-/Interdisciplinary Studies, B
Natural Sciences, B
Physical Sciences, B
Political Science and Government, B
Public Administration, M
Social Sciences, B
Visual and Performing Arts, B

GONZAGA UNIVERSITY

Accounting, BMO
Art/Art Studies, General, B
Asian Studies/Civilization, B
Biochemistry, B
Biology/Biological Sciences, B
Broadcast Journalism, B
Business Administration and Management, B
Business Administration, Management and
    Operations, MO
Business/Managerial Economics, B
Chemistry, B
Civil Engineering, B
Comparative Literature, B
Computer Engineering, B
Computer Science, B
Counseling Psychology, M
Criminal Justice/Law Enforcement Administration, B
Curriculum and Instruction, M
Drama and Dramatics/Theatre Arts, B
Economics, B
Education, MD
Educational Administration and Supervision, M
Educational Leadership and Administration, D
Electrical, Electronics and Communications
    Engineering, B
Elementary Education and Teaching, B
Engineering, B
English as a Second Language, M
English Language and Literature, B
Finance, B
French Language and Literature, B
German Language and Literature, B
History, B
Information Science/Studies, B
International Business/Trade/Commerce, B
International Relations and Affairs, B
Italian Language and Literature, B
Journalism, B
Kinesiology and Exercise Science, B
Law and Legal Studies, PO
Liberal Arts and Sciences Studies and
    Humanities, B
Marketing/Marketing Management, B
Mass Communication/Media Studies, B
Mathematics, B
Mechanical Engineering, B
Music, B
Music Teacher Education, B
Nurse Anesthetist, M
Nursing, M

Nursing - Registered Nurse Training, B
Organizational Management, M
Pastoral Studies/Counseling, M
Philosophy, BM
Physical Education Teaching and Coaching, B
Physics, B
Political Science and Government, B
Psychology, B
Public Relations/Image Management, B
Religion/Religious Studies, BMP
Secondary Education and Teaching, B
Sociology, B
Spanish Language and Literature, B
Special Education and Teaching, BM
Speech and Rhetorical Studies, B
Sport and Fitness Administration/Management, BM
Theology and Religious Vocations, P

GRAYS HARBOR COLLEGE

Accounting Technology/Technician and
   Bookkeeping, A
Automobile/Automotive Mechanics
   Technology/Technician, A
Business Administration and Management, A
Carpentry/Carpenter, A
Child Care and Support Services Management, A
Corrections, A
Criminal Justice/Police Science, A
Diesel Mechanics Technology/Technician, A
General Studies, A
Human Services, A
Industrial Technology/Technician, A
Information Science/Studies, A
Liberal Arts and Sciences Studies and
   Humanities, A
Machine Tool Technology/Machinist, A
Natural Resources and Conservation, A
Nursing - Registered Nurse Training, A
Office Management and Supervision, A
Welding Technology/Welder, A

GREEN RIVER COMMUNITY COLLEGE

Accounting Technology/Technician and
   Bookkeeping, A
Air Traffic Controller, A
Airline/Commercial/Professional Pilot and Flight
   Crew, A
Autobody/Collision and Repair
   Technology/Technician, A
Automobile/Automotive Mechanics
   Technology/Technician, A
Carpentry/Carpenter, A
Child Care and Support Services Management, A
Court Reporting/Court Reporter, A
Criminal Justice/Police Science, A
Drafting and Design Technology/Technician, A
Forestry Technology/Technician, A
Information Science/Studies, A
Legal Administrative Assistant/Secretary, A
Liberal Arts and Sciences Studies and
   Humanities, A
Licensed Practical/Vocational Nurse Training, A
Machine Tool Technology/Machinist, A
Marketing/Marketing Management, A
Mechanical Engineering/Mechanical
   Technology/Technician, A
Medical Administrative Assistant/Secretary, A
Occupational Therapist Assistant, A
Office Management and Supervision, A
Physical Therapist Assistant, A
Water Quality and Wastewater Treatment
   Management and Recycling
   Technology/Technician, A
Welding Technology/Welder, A

HENRY COGSWELL COLLEGE

Business Administration and Management, B
Computer Science, B
Design and Visual Communications, B
Electrical, Electronics and Communications
   Engineering, B
Mechanical Engineering, B

HERITAGE UNIVERSITY

Bilingual and Multilingual Education, B
Biological and Biomedical Sciences, M

Biological and Physical Sciences, AB
Biology/Biological Sciences, B
Business Administration and Management, AB
Computer Science, AB
Counselor Education/School Counseling and
   Guidance Services, M
Education, BM
Educational Administration and Supervision, M
Elementary Education and Teaching, B
English, M
English as a Second Language, M
English Language and Literature, B
Environmental Studies, B
History, B
Interdisciplinary Studies, AB
Kindergarten/PreSchool Education and Teaching, A
Liberal Arts and Sciences Studies and
   Humanities, A
Mathematics, AB
Multilingual and Multicultural Education, M
Natural Resources Management/Development and
   Policy, A
Nursing - Registered Nurse Training, A
Political Science and Government, B
Psychology, AB
Public Administration, B
Reading Teacher Education, M
Science Teacher Education/General Science
   Teacher Education, B
Secondary Education and Teaching, B
Social Sciences, AB
Social Work, B
Sociology, B
Spanish Language and Literature, B
Special Education and Teaching, M

HIGHLINE COMMUNITY COLLEGE

Accounting, A
Administrative Assistant and Secretarial Science, A
Art/Art Studies, General, A
Behavioral Sciences, A
Biological and Physical Sciences, A
Business Administration and Management, A
Clinical/Medical Laboratory Science and Allied
   Professions, A
Computer Engineering Technology/Technician, A
Computer Programming/Programmer, A
Computer Systems Networking and
   Telecommunications, A
Computer Typography and Composition Equipment
   Operator, A
Criminal Justice/Law Enforcement Administration, A
Criminal Justice/Police Science, A
Data Entry/Microcomputer Applications, A
Dental Hygiene/Hygienist, A
Drafting and Design Technology/Technician, A
Education, A
Engineering, A
Engineering Technology, A
English Language and Literature, A
Ethnic and Cultural Studies, A
Graphic and Printing Equipment Operator
   Production, A
Hotel/Motel Administration/Management, A
Human Services, A
Humanities/Humanistic Studies, A
Industrial Technology/Technician, A
Interior Design, A
International Business/Trade/Commerce, A
Journalism, A
Kindergarten/PreSchool Education and Teaching, A
Legal Administrative Assistant/Secretary, A
Legal Assistant/Paralegal, A
Library Science, A
Marine Technology, A
Mathematics, A
Medical/Clinical Assistant, A
Music, A
Natural Sciences, A
Nursing - Registered Nurse Training, A
Plastics Engineering Technology/Technician, A
Pre-Engineering, A
Psychology, A
Respiratory Care Therapy/Therapist, A
Romance Languages, Literatures, and Linguistics, A
Social Sciences, A

Tourism and Travel Services Management, A
Transportation and Materials Moving, A
Web Page, Digital/Multimedia and Information
   Resources Design, A

ITT TECHNICAL INSTITUTE (BOTHELL)

Animation, Interactive Technology, Video Graphics
   and Special Effects, B
Business Administration and Management, B
CAD/CADD Drafting and/or Design
   Technology/Technician, A
Computer and Information Systems Security, B
Computer Programming/Programmer, A
Computer Systems Networking and
   Telecommunications, B
Criminal Justice/Law Enforcement Administration, B
E-Commerce/Electronic Commerce, B
Electrical, Electronic and Communications
   Engineering Technology/Technician, AB
System, Networking, and LAN/WAN
   Management/Manager, A
Web Page, Digital/Multimedia and Information
   Resources Design, A
Web/Multimedia Management and Webmaster, A

ITT TECHNICAL INSTITUTE (SEATTLE)

Animation, Interactive Technology, Video Graphics
   and Special Effects, B
Business Administration and Management, B
CAD/CADD Drafting and/or Design
   Technology/Technician, A
Computer and Information Systems Security, B
Computer Programming/Programmer, A
Criminal Justice/Law Enforcement Administration, B
Electrical, Electronic and Communications
   Engineering Technology/Technician, AB
System, Networking, and LAN/WAN
   Management/Manager, A
Web Page, Digital/Multimedia and Information
   Resources Design, A
Web/Multimedia Management and Webmaster, A

ITT TECHNICAL INSTITUTE (SPOKANE)

Animation, Interactive Technology, Video Graphics
   and Special Effects, B
CAD/CADD Drafting and/or Design
   Technology/Technician, A
Computer and Information Systems Security, B
Computer Programming/Programmer, A
Criminal Justice/Law Enforcement Administration, B
E-Commerce/Electronic Commerce, B
Electrical, Electronic and Communications
   Engineering Technology/Technician, AB
System, Networking, and LAN/WAN
   Management/Manager, A
Web Page, Digital/Multimedia and Information
   Resources Design, A
Web/Multimedia Management and Webmaster, A

LAKE WASHINGTON TECHNICAL
COLLEGE

Accounting, A
Administrative Assistant and Secretarial Science, A
Autobody/Collision and Repair
   Technology/Technician, A
Automobile/Automotive Mechanics
   Technology/Technician, A
Child Development, A
Computer Engineering Technology/Technician, A
Computer Science, A
Culinary Arts/Chef Training, A
Dental Assisting/Assistant, A
Dental Hygiene/Hygienist, A
Diesel Mechanics Technology/Technician, A
Drafting and Design Technology/Technician, A
Electrical, Electronic and Communications
   Engineering Technology/Technician, A
Environmental Studies, A
Horticultural Science, A
Hotel/Motel Administration/Management, A
Legal Administrative Assistant/Secretary, A
Machine Tool Technology/Machinist, A

Medical/Clinical Assistant, A

LOWER COLUMBIA COLLEGE

Accounting, A
Accounting Technology/Technician and
   Bookkeeping, A
Administrative Assistant and Secretarial Science, A
Anthropology, A
Art/Art Studies, General, A
Automobile/Automotive Mechanics
   Technology/Technician, A
Biology/Biological Sciences, A
Business Administration and Management, A
Business/Commerce, A
CAD/CADD Drafting and/or Design
   Technology/Technician, A
Computer and Information Sciences, A
Computer Engineering Technology/Technician, A
Computer Programming/Programmer, A
Computer Science, A
Computer Systems Analysis/Analyst, A
Computer Systems Networking and
   Telecommunications, A
Computer Technology/Computer Systems
   Technology, A
Corrections, A
Criminal Justice/Law Enforcement Administration, A
Criminal Justice/Police Science, A
Criminal Justice/Safety Studies, A
Data Entry/Microcomputer Applications, A
Data Processing and Data Processing
   Technology/Technician, A
Diesel Mechanics Technology/Technician, A
Drama and Dramatics/Theatre Arts, A
Early Childhood Education and Teaching, A
Economics, A
Electrical, Electronic and Communications
   Engineering Technology/Technician, A
Electrician, A
Engineering, A
Engineering Technology, A
English Language and Literature, A
Environmental Studies, A
Fire Science/Firefighting, A
Fire Services Administration, A
Foreign Languages and Literatures, A
Geography, A
Geology/Earth Science, A
Heavy Equipment Maintenance
   Technology/Technician, A
History, A
Industrial Mechanics and Maintenance
   Technology, A
Industrial Technology/Technician, A
Information Science/Studies, A
Information Technology, A
Instrumentation Technology/Technician, A
Kindergarten/PreSchool Education and Teaching, A
Legal Administrative Assistant/Secretary, A
Liberal Arts and Sciences Studies and
   Humanities, A
Licensed Practical/Vocational Nurse Training, A
Lineworker, A
Machine Tool Technology/Machinist, A
Management Information Systems and Services, A
Mathematics, A
Mechanical Engineering/Mechanical
   Technology/Technician, A
Medical Administrative Assistant/Secretary, A
Medical Reception/Receptionist, A
Medical Transcription/Transcriptionist, A
Medical/Clinical Assistant, A
Music, A
Nurse/Nursing Assistant/Aide and Patient Care
   Assistant, A
Nursing - Registered Nurse Training, A
Office Management and Supervision, A
Philosophy, A
Photography, A
Physical Education Teaching and Coaching, A
Physics, A
Political Science and Government, A
Pre-Engineering, A
Pre-Law Studies, A
Psychology, A
Receptionist, A

Social Sciences, A
Sociology, A
Speech and Rhetorical Studies, A
Substance Abuse/Addiction Counseling, A
Teacher Assistant/Aide, A
Welding Technology/Welder, A
Wood Science and Wood Products/Pulp and Paper
   Technology, A
Word Processing, A

NORTH SEATTLE COMMUNITY COLLEGE

Accounting Technology/Technician and
   Bookkeeping, A
Administrative Assistant and Secretarial Science, A
Allied Health and Medical Assisting Services, A
Architectural Drafting and Architectural
   CAD/CADD, A
Art/Art Studies, General, A
Biomedical Technology/Technician, A
Business/Corporate Communications, A
Civil Drafting and Civil Engineering CAD/CADD, A
Communications Systems Installation and Repair
   Technology, A
Computer and Information Systems Security, A
Computer Systems Networking and
   Telecommunications, A
Early Childhood Education and Teaching, A
Electrical, Electronic and Communications
   Engineering Technology/Technician, A
Electrical/Electronics Drafting and
   Electrical/Electronics CAD/CADD, A
Heating, Air Conditioning, Ventilation and
   Refrigeration Maintenance
   Technology/Technician, A
Industrial Technology/Technician, A
Liberal Arts and Sciences Studies and
   Humanities, A
Licensed Practical/Vocational Nurse Training, A
Mechanical Drafting and Mechanical Drafting
   CAD/CADD, A
Medical/Clinical Assistant, A
Music, A
Nursing - Registered Nurse Training, A
Pharmacy Technician/Assistant, A
Real Estate, A
Telecommunications Technology/Technician, A
Watchmaking and Jewelrymaking, A
Web Page, Digital/Multimedia and Information
   Resources Design, A

NORTHWEST AVIATION COLLEGE

Aeronautics/Aviation/Aerospace Science and
   Technology, A

NORTHWEST COLLEGE OF ART

Art/Art Studies, General, B
Commercial and Advertising Art, B

NORTHWEST INDIAN COLLEGE

American Indian/Native American Studies, A
Biology/Biological Sciences, A
Construction Engineering Technology/Technician, A
Education, A
General Studies, A
Human Services, A
Kindergarten/PreSchool Education and Teaching, A
Management Information Systems and Services, A
Substance Abuse/Addiction Counseling, A

NORTHWEST UNIVERSITY

Accounting, B
Bible/Biblical Studies, B
Biology Teacher Education, B
Business Administration and Management, B
Comparative Literature, B
Divinity/Ministry (BD, MDiv.), B
Drama and Dramatics/Theatre Arts, B
Education, B
Elementary Education and Teaching, B
English Composition, B
English Language and Literature, B
English/Language Arts Teacher Education, B
Environmental Sciences, B
General Studies, A

History, B
Intercultural/Multicultural and Diversity Studies, B
Interdisciplinary Studies, B
Marketing/Marketing Management, B
Missions/Missionary Studies and Missiology, B
Music, B
Music Performance, B
Music Teacher Education, B
Nursing - Registered Nurse Training, B
Organizational Communication, B
Pastoral Studies/Counseling, B
Philosophy, B
Physical Education Teaching and Coaching, B
Political Science and Government, B
Psychology, B
Public Health (MPH, DPH), B
Religion/Religious Studies, B
Religious Education, B
Religious/Sacred Music, B
Secondary Education and Teaching, B
Teaching English as a Second or Foreign
   Language/ESL Language Instructor, B
Youth Ministry, B

OLYMPIC COLLEGE

Accounting Technology/Technician and
   Bookkeeping, A
Administrative Assistant and Secretarial Science, A
Aesthetician/Esthetician and Skin Care Specialist, A
Animation, Interactive Technology, Video Graphics
   and Special Effects, A
Audiovisual Communications
   Technologies/Technicians, A
Automobile/Automotive Mechanics
   Technology/Technician, A
Barbering/Barber, A
Business Administration and Management, A
Child Care and Support Services Management, A
Computer and Information Sciences, A
Computer Graphics, A
Computer Programming, A
Computer Programming/Programmer, A
Computer Software and Media Applications, A
Computer Systems Networking and
   Telecommunications, A
Cosmetology, Barber/Styling, and Nail Instructor, A
Cosmetology/Cosmetologist, A
Criminal Justice/Law Enforcement Administration, A
Criminal Justice/Police Science, A
Culinary Arts and Related Services, A
Culinary Arts/Chef Training, A
Digital Communication and Media/Multimedia, A
Drafting and Design Technology/Technician, A
Early Childhood Education and Teaching, A
Education/Teaching of Individuals in Early Childhood
   Special Education Programs, A
Electrical, Electronic and Communications
   Engineering Technology/Technician, A
Engineering, A
Fire Science/Firefighting, A
Fire Services Administration, A
Industrial Technology/Technician, A
Information Science/Studies, A
Information Technology, A
Legal Administrative Assistant/Secretary, A
Liberal Arts and Sciences Studies and
   Humanities, A
Licensed Practical/Vocational Nurse Training, A
Marine Maintenance/Fitter and Ship Repair
   Technology/Technician, A
Medical/Clinical Assistant, A
Nail Technician/Specialist and Manicurist, A
Nursing - Registered Nurse Training, A
Office Management and Supervision, A
Photographic and Film/Video Technology/Technician
   and Assistant, A
Recording Arts Technology/Technician, A
System Administration/Administrator, A
System, Networking, and LAN/WAN
   Management/Manager, A
Web/Multimedia Management and Webmaster, A

PACIFIC LUTHERAN UNIVERSITY

Accounting, B
Anthropology, B
Art History, Criticism and Conservation, B

Art Teacher Education, B
Art/Art Studies, General, B
Biochemistry, B
Biology/Biological Sciences, B
Broadcast Journalism, B
Business Administration and Management, B
Business Administration, Management and
  Operations, M
Chemistry, B
Chinese Language and Literature, B
Classics and Classical
  Languages, Literatures, and Linguistics, B
Comparative Literature, B
Computer Engineering, B
Computer Science, B
Curriculum and Instruction, M
Drama and Dramatics/Theatre Arts, B
Economics, B
Education, BM
Educational Administration and Supervision, M
Electrical, Electronics and Communications
  Engineering, B
Elementary Education and Teaching, BM
Engineering Physics, B
Engineering Science, B
English Language and Literature, B
Environmental Studies, B
Finance, B
Fine/Studio Arts, B
French Language and Literature, B
Geology/Earth Science, B
German Language and Literature, B
History, B
International Business/Trade/Commerce, B
International Relations and Affairs, B
Journalism, B
Kindergarten/PreSchool Education and Teaching, B
Management Information Systems and Services, B
Marketing/Marketing Management, B
Marriage and Family Therapy/Counseling, M
Mass Communication/Media Studies, B
Mathematics, B
Modern Languages, B
Music Teacher Education, B
Nursing, M
Nursing - Advanced Practice, M
Nursing - Registered Nurse Training, B
Nursing Administration, M
Philosophy, B
Physical Education Teaching and Coaching, B
Piano and Organ, B
Political Science and Government, B
Psychology, B
Radio and Television, B
Reading Teacher Education, B
Religion/Religious Studies, B
Religious/Sacred Music, B
Scandinavian
  Languages, Literatures, and Linguistics, B
Science Teacher Education/General Science
  Teacher Education, B
Secondary Education and Teaching, BM
Social Work, B
Sociology, B
Spanish Language and Literature, B
Special Education and Teaching, B
Therapeutic Recreation/Recreational Therapy, B
Voice and Opera, B
Women's Studies, B
Writing, M

PENINSULA COLLEGE

Accounting, A
Automobile/Automotive Mechanics
  Technology/Technician, A
Biological and Physical Sciences, A
Business Administration and Management, A
Child Care and Support Services Management, A
Child Development, A
Civil Engineering Technology/Technician, A
Commercial Fishing, A
Computer
  Programming, Vendor/Product Certification, A
Criminal Justice/Law Enforcement Administration, A
Data Entry/Microcomputer Applications, A
Diesel Mechanics Technology/Technician, A

Electrical, Electronic and Communications
  Engineering Technology/Technician, A
Engineering Technology, A
Fishing and Fisheries Sciences and Management, A
Nursing - Registered Nurse Training, A
Office Management and Supervision, A
Substance Abuse/Addiction Counseling, A
Web Page, Digital/Multimedia and Information
  Resources Design, A

PIERCE COLLEGE

Accounting, A
Administrative Assistant and Secretarial Science, A
Business Administration and Management, A
Clinical/Medical Laboratory Technician, A
Computer Programming/Programmer, A
Computer Typography and Composition Equipment
  Operator, A
Criminal Justice/Law Enforcement Administration, A
Dental Hygiene/Hygienist, A
Electrical, Electronic and Communications
  Engineering Technology/Technician, A
Fire Science/Firefighting, A
Industrial Technology/Technician, A
Information Science/Studies, A
Kindergarten/PreSchool Education and Teaching, A
Legal Administrative Assistant/Secretary, A
Legal Assistant/Paralegal, A
Liberal Arts and Sciences Studies and
  Humanities, A
Marketing/Marketing Management, A
Mental Health/Rehabilitation, A
Substance Abuse/Addiction Counseling, A
Veterinary/Animal Health Technology/Technician and
  Veterinary Assistant, A

PIMA MEDICAL INSTITUTE

Radiologic Technology/Science - Radiographer, A

PUGET SOUND CHRISTIAN COLLEGE

Bible/Biblical Studies, B
Divinity/Ministry (BD, MDiv.), B
Education, A
Music, B
Pastoral Studies/Counseling, B
Religious Education, B
Religious/Sacred Music, B
Social Sciences, B
Theology/Theological Studies, B

RENTON TECHNICAL COLLEGE

Accounting, A
Administrative Assistant and Secretarial Science, A
Automobile/Automotive Mechanics
  Technology/Technician, A
Business Administration and Management, A
Civil Engineering Technology/Technician, A
Clinical Laboratory Science/Medical
  Technology/Technologist, A
Communications Technology/Technician, A
Computer Science, A
Culinary Arts/Chef Training, A
Electrical, Electronic and Communications
  Engineering Technology/Technician, A
Heating, Air Conditioning, Ventilation and
  Refrigeration Maintenance
  Technology/Technician, A
Legal Administrative Assistant/Secretary, A
Machine Tool Technology/Machinist, A
Medical Administrative Assistant/Secretary, A
Medical/Clinical Assistant, A
Musical Instrument Fabrication and Repair, A
Surgical Technology/Technologist, A
Survey Technology/Surveying, A
Teacher Assistant/Aide, A

SAINT MARTIN'S UNIVERSITY

Accounting, B
Biology/Biological Sciences, B
Business Administration and Management, B
Business Administration, Management and
  Operations, M
Chemistry, B
Civil Engineering, BM
Community Organization and Advocacy, B

Community Psychology, M
Computer Science, B
Counseling Psychology, M
Criminal Justice/Law Enforcement Administration, B
Drama and Dramatics/Theatre Arts, B
Economics, B
Education, BM
Elementary Education and Teaching, B
Engineering Management, M
English Language and Literature, B
Finance, B
History, B
Humanities/Humanistic Studies, B
Information Science/Studies, B
Management Information Systems and Services, B
Marketing/Marketing Management, B
Mathematics, B
Mechanical Engineering, B
Political Science and Government, B
Pre-Dentistry Studies, B
Pre-Law Studies, B
Pre-Medicine/Pre-Medical Studies, B
Pre-Pharmacy Studies, B
Pre-Veterinary Studies, B
Psychology, B
Religion/Religious Studies, B
Secondary Education and Teaching, B
Special Education and Teaching, BM

SEATTLE CENTRAL COMMUNITY COLLEGE

Accounting, A
Administrative Assistant and Secretarial Science, A
Biological and Physical Sciences, A
Biology Technician/BioTechnology Laboratory
  Technician, A
Carpentry/Carpenter, A
Cinematography and Film/Video Production, A
Commercial and Advertising Art, A
Computer Typography and Composition Equipment
  Operator, A
Cosmetology/Cosmetologist, A
Culinary Arts/Chef Training, A
Drafting and Design Technology/Technician, A
Fashion/Apparel Design, A
Graphic and Printing Equipment Operator
  Production, A
Hospitality Administration/Management, A
Hotel/Motel Administration/Management, A
Human Services, A
Kindergarten/PreSchool Education and Teaching, A
Liberal Arts and Sciences Studies and
  Humanities, A
Marine Technology, A
Nursing - Registered Nurse Training, A
Ophthalmic Laboratory Technology/Technician, A
Photography, A
Respiratory Care Therapy/Therapist, A
Sign Language Interpretation and Translation, A
Substance Abuse/Addiction Counseling, A

SEATTLE PACIFIC UNIVERSITY

Accounting, B
Apparel and Textiles, B
Art Teacher Education, B
Art/Art Studies, General, B
Biochemistry, B
Biology Teacher Education, B
Biology/Biological Sciences, B
Business Administration and Management, B
Business Administration, Management and
  Operations, M
Chemistry, B
Classics and Classical
  Languages, Literatures, and Linguistics, B
Clinical Psychology, D
Communication Studies/Speech Communication
  and Rhetoric, B
Computer Science, B
Computer Systems Analysis/Analyst, B
Computer/Information Technology Services
  Administration and Management, B
Counselor Education/School Counseling and
  Guidance Services, B
Drama and Dramatics/Theatre Arts, B
Economics, BM

Education, MD
Educational Leadership and Administration, MD
Electrical, Electronics and Communications
  Engineering, B
Engineering Science, B
English as a Second Language, M
English Language and Literature, B
English/Language Arts Teacher Education, B
European Studies/Civilization, B
Family and Consumer Economics and Related
  Services, B
Family and Consumer Sciences/Home Economics
  Teacher Education, B
Foods, Nutrition, and Wellness Studies, B
French Language and Literature, B
General Studies, B
German Language and Literature, B
History, B
Kinesiology and Exercise Science, B
Latin American Studies, B
Latin Language and Literature, B
Liberal Arts and Sciences Studies and
  Humanities, B
Management Information Systems and Services, M
Marriage and Family Therapy/Counseling, M
Mathematics, B
Mathematics and Statistics, B
Mathematics Teacher Education, B
Music, B
Music Teacher Education, B
Nursing, MO
Nursing - Advanced Practice, O
Nursing - Registered Nurse Training, B
Nursing Administration, M
Philosophy, B
Physical Education Teaching and Coaching, B
Physics, B
Political Science and Government, B
Pre-Dentistry Studies, B
Pre-Law Studies, B
Pre-Medicine/Pre-Medical Studies, B
Psychology, B
Reading Teacher Education, M
Religious Education, B
Russian Language and Literature, B
Science Teacher Education/General Science
  Teacher Education, B
Secondary Education and Teaching, M
Social Science Teacher Education, B
Sociology, B
Spanish Language and Literature, B
Special Education and Teaching, B
Sport and Fitness Administration/Management, M
Theology/Theological Studies, B

SEATTLE UNIVERSITY

Accounting, BM
Adult and Continuing Education and Teaching, MO
Applied Mathematics, B
Art History, Criticism and Conservation, B
Art/Art Studies, General, B
Biochemistry, B
Biological and Physical Sciences, B
Biology/Biological Sciences, B
Business Administration and Management, B
Business Administration, Management and
  Operations, MO
Business/Managerial Economics, B
Chemistry, B
Civil Engineering, B
Clinical Laboratory Science/Medical
  Technology/Technologist, B
Community Health Nursing, M
Computer Science, B
Counselor Education/School Counseling and
  Guidance Services, MO
Creative Writing, B
Criminal Justice/Law Enforcement Administration, B
Curriculum and Instruction, MO
Diagnostic Medical Sonography/Sonographer and
  Ultrasound Technician, B
Drama and Dramatics/Theatre Arts, B
East Asian Studies, B
Economics, B
Education, MDO
Educational Administration and Supervision, MO

Educational Leadership and Administration, D
Educational Measurement and Evaluation, O
Electrical, Electronics and Communications
  Engineering, B
Engineering and Applied Sciences, M
English as a Second Language, MO
English Language and Literature, B
Environmental Studies, B
Environmental/Environmental Health Engineering, B
Finance, B
Finance and Banking, MO
Fine/Studio Arts, B
Forensic Science and Technology, B
French Language and Literature, B
German Language and Literature, B
History, B
Humanities/Humanistic Studies, B
Industrial Engineering, B
Insurance, B
International Business/Trade/Commerce, BMO
International Economics, B
International Relations and Affairs, B
Journalism, B
Law and Legal Studies, PO
Liberal Arts and Sciences Studies and
  Humanities, B
Management Information Systems and Services, B
Marketing/Marketing Management, B
Mass Communication/Media Studies, B
Mathematics, B
Mechanical Engineering, B
Non-Profit/Public/Organizational Management, M
Nursing, M
Nursing - Advanced Practice, M
Nursing - Registered Nurse Training, B
Nursing Administration, M
Operations Management and Supervision, B
Pastoral Studies/Counseling, M
Philosophy, B
Photography, B
Physics, B
Political Science and Government, B
Psychology, BM
Public Administration, BM
Public Relations/Image Management, B
Reading Teacher Education, MO
Religion/Religious Studies, B
School Psychology, O
Social Work, B
Sociology, B
Software Engineering, M
Spanish Language and Literature, B
Special Education and Teaching, MO
Theology and Religious Vocations, MPO
Transpersonal and Humanistic Psychology, M
Western European Studies, B

SHORELINE COMMUNITY COLLEGE

Accounting, A
Audio Engineering, A
Automobile/Automotive Mechanics
  Technology/Technician, A
Biology Technician/BioTechnology Laboratory
  Technician, A
Business Administration and Management, A
Chemical Engineering, A
Child Development, A
Cinematography and Film/Video Production, A
Civil Engineering Technology/Technician, A
Clinical/Medical Laboratory Technician, A
Commercial and Advertising Art, A
Computer and Information Sciences, A
Computer Graphics, A
Consumer Merchandising/Retailing Management, A
Cosmetology/Cosmetologist, A
Dental Hygiene/Hygienist, A
Dietetics/Dieticians, A
Drafting and Design Technology/Technician, A
Education, A
Engineering Technology, A
Environmental Engineering
  Technology/Environmental Technology, A
Graphic and Printing Equipment Operator
  Production, A
Health and Medical Laboratory Technologies, A

Health Information/Medical Records
  Administration/Administrator, A
Human Development and Family Studies, A
Industrial Technology/Technician, A
International Business/Trade/Commerce, A
Kindergarten/PreSchool Education and Teaching, A
Liberal Arts and Sciences Studies and
  Humanities, A
Machine Tool Technology/Machinist, A
Marine Biology and Biological Oceanography, A
Marine Technology, A
Marketing/Marketing Management, A
Mechanical Engineering/Mechanical
  Technology/Technician, A
Medical Administrative Assistant/Secretary, A
Music, A
Nursing - Registered Nurse Training, A
Oceanography, Chemical and Physical, A
Photography, A
Pre-Engineering, A
Purchasing, Procurement/Acquisitions and
  Contracts Management, A
Teacher Assistant/Aide, A

SKAGIT VALLEY COLLEGE

Accounting, A
Administrative Assistant and Secretarial Science, A
Agriculture, A
Anthropology, A
Applied Horticulture/Horticultural Operations, A
Art History, Criticism and Conservation, A
Art/Art Studies, General, A
Automobile/Automotive Mechanics
  Technology/Technician, A
Biological and Physical Sciences, A
Biology/Biological Sciences, A
Business Administration and Management, A
Chemistry, A
Child Development, A
Commercial and Advertising Art, A
Comparative Literature, A
Computer and Information Sciences, A
Computer Engineering Technology/Technician, A
Computer Science, A
Computer Technology/Computer Systems
  Technology, A
Criminal Justice/Police Science, A
Culinary Arts/Chef Training, A
Diesel Mechanics Technology/Technician, A
Economics, A
Electrical, Electronic and Communications
  Engineering Technology/Technician, A
English Language and Literature, A
Environmental Engineering
  Technology/Environmental Technology, A
Ethnic and Cultural Studies, A
Family and Community Services, A
Fire Science/Firefighting, A
Food Technology and Processing, A
Foreign Languages and Literatures, A
Geography, A
Geology/Earth Science, A
Heavy Equipment Maintenance
  Technology/Technician, A
History, A
Hotel/Motel Administration/Management, A
Human Services, A
Humanities/Humanistic Studies, A
Journalism, A
Kindergarten/PreSchool Education and Teaching, A
Legal Assistant/Paralegal, A
Liberal Arts and Sciences Studies and
  Humanities, A
Licensed Practical/Vocational Nurse Training, A
Marine Technology, A
Mathematics, A
Medical Administrative Assistant/Secretary, A
Medical/Clinical Assistant, A
Music, A
Natural Sciences, A
Nursing - Registered Nurse Training, A
Office Management and Supervision, A
Parks, Recreation and Leisure Facilities
  Management, A
Parks, Recreation, Leisure and Fitness Studies, A
Philosophy, A

Physical Education Teaching and Coaching, A
Political Science and Government, A
Pre-Engineering, A
Psychology, A
Social Sciences, A
Sociology, A
Spanish Language and Literature, A
Speech and Rhetorical Studies, A
Telecommunications Technology/Technician, A
Welding Technology/Welder, A

SOUTH PUGET SOUND COMMUNITY COLLEGE

Accounting, A
Administrative Assistant and Secretarial Science, A
Automobile/Automotive Mechanics
    Technology/Technician, A
Business Administration and Management, A
Communications Technology/Technician, A
Computer and Information Sciences, A
Computer Programming/Programmer, A
Culinary Arts/Chef Training, A
Data Processing and Data Processing
    Technology/Technician, A
Dental Hygiene/Hygienist, A
Drafting and Design Technology/Technician, A
Electrical, Electronic and Communications
    Engineering Technology/Technician, A
Fire Science/Firefighting, A
Food Technology and Processing, A
Horticultural Science, A
Information Science/Studies, A
Kindergarten/PreSchool Education and Teaching, A
Landscaping and Groundskeeping, A
Legal Administrative Assistant/Secretary, A
Legal Assistant/Paralegal, A
Liberal Arts and Sciences Studies and
    Humanities, A
Licensed Practical/Vocational Nurse Training, A
Medical Administrative Assistant/Secretary, A
Medical/Clinical Assistant, A
Nursing - Registered Nurse Training, A
Purchasing, Procurement/Acquisitions and
    Contracts Management, A
Sign Language Interpretation and Translation, A
Special Products Marketing Operations, A
Telecommunications Technology/Technician, A
Welding Technology/Welder, A

SOUTH SEATTLE COMMUNITY COLLEGE

Accounting, A
Administrative Assistant and Secretarial Science, A
Airframe Mechanics and Aircraft Maintenance
    Technology/Technician, A
Artificial Intelligence and Robotics, A
Automobile/Automotive Mechanics
    Technology/Technician, A
Avionics Maintenance Technology/Technician, A
Biological and Physical Sciences, A
Business Administration and Management, A
Computer Engineering Technology/Technician, A
Computer Programming/Programmer, A
Cosmetology/Cosmetologist, A
Culinary Arts/Chef Training, A
Drafting and Design Technology/Technician, A
Engineering, A
Engineering Technology, A
Food Science, A
Food Technology and Processing, A
Heavy Equipment Maintenance
    Technology/Technician, A
Horticultural Science, A
Hospitality Administration/Management, A
Landscape Architecture, A
Landscaping and Groundskeeping, A
Liberal Arts and Sciences Studies and
    Humanities, A
Machine Tool Technology/Machinist, A
Quality Control Technology/Technician, A
Special Products Marketing Operations, A
Trade and Industrial Teacher Education, A

Welding Technology/Welder, A

SPOKANE COMMUNITY COLLEGE

Accounting Technology/Technician and
    Bookkeeping, A
Administrative Assistant and Secretarial Science, A
Agricultural Business and Management, A
Agronomy and Crop Science, A
Applied Horticulture/Horticultural Operations, A
Architectural Engineering Technology/Technician, A
Artificial Intelligence and Robotics, A
Automobile/Automotive Mechanics
    Technology/Technician, A
Avionics Maintenance Technology/Technician, A
Biomedical Technology/Technician, A
Business Administration and Management, A
Carpentry/Carpenter, A
Civil Engineering Technology/Technician, A
Computer Programming/Programmer, A
Computer Typography and Composition Equipment
    Operator, A
Construction Engineering Technology/Technician, A
Corrections, A
Cosmetology/Cosmetologist, A
Criminal Justice/Police Science, A
Culinary Arts/Chef Training, A
Data Processing and Data Processing
    Technology/Technician, A
Dental Hygiene/Hygienist, A
Dietetics/Dieticians, A
Drafting and Design Technology/Technician, A
Drafting/Design Engineering
    Technologies/Technicians, A
Electrical, Electronic and Communications
    Engineering Technology/Technician, A
Fire Science/Firefighting, A
Food Technology and Processing, A
Forestry, A
Health Information/Medical Records
    Administration/Administrator, A
Heating, Air Conditioning, Ventilation and
    Refrigeration Maintenance
    Technology/Technician, A
Heavy Equipment Maintenance
    Technology/Technician, A
Hotel/Motel Administration/Management, A
Hydrology and Water Resources Science, A
Industrial Technology/Technician, A
Landscaping and Groundskeeping, A
Legal Administrative Assistant/Secretary, A
Legal Assistant/Paralegal, A
Liberal Arts and Sciences Studies and
    Humanities, A
Licensed Practical/Vocational Nurse Training, A
Machine Tool Technology/Machinist, A
Marketing/Marketing Management, A
Mechanical Engineering/Mechanical
    Technology/Technician, A
Medical Administrative Assistant/Secretary, A
Natural Resources Management/Development and
    Policy, A
Nursing - Registered Nurse Training, A
Ophthalmic Laboratory Technology/Technician, A
Ornamental Horticulture, A
Parks, Recreation and Leisure Facilities
    Management, A
Respiratory Care Therapy/Therapist, A
Surgical Technology/Technologist, A
Welding Technology/Welder, A
Wildlife and Wildlands Science and Management, A

SPOKANE FALLS COMMUNITY COLLEGE

Accounting Technology/Technician and
    Bookkeeping, A
Administrative Assistant and Secretarial Science, A
Art/Art Studies, General, A
Business Administration and Management, A
Business and Personal/Financial Services Marketing
    Operations, A
Child Care and Support Services Management, A
Commercial and Advertising Art, A
Commercial Photography, A
Consumer Merchandising/Retailing Management, A
Fashion Merchandising, A
General Office Occupations and Clerical Services, A

Gerontology, A
Heavy Equipment Maintenance
    Technology/Technician, A
Information Science/Studies, A
Interior Design, A
International Business/Trade/Commerce, A
Leatherworking and Upholstery, A
Liberal Arts and Sciences Studies and
    Humanities, A
Library Assistant/Technician, A
Marketing/Marketing Management, A
Mass Communication/Media Studies, A
Music, A
Orthotist/Prosthetist, A
Physical Therapist Assistant, A
Real Estate, A
Sign Language Interpretation and Translation, A
Social Work, A
Sport and Fitness Administration/Management, A
Substance Abuse/Addiction Counseling, A
Vocational Rehabilitation Counseling/Counselor, A

TACOMA COMMUNITY COLLEGE

Accounting, A
Administrative Assistant and Secretarial Science, A
American/United States Studies/Civilization, A
Anthropology, A
Art/Art Studies, General, A
Behavioral Sciences, A
Biological and Physical Sciences, A
Biology/Biological Sciences, A
Botany/Plant Biology, A
Business Administration and Management, A
Business/Managerial Economics, A
Chemistry, A
Comparative Literature, A
Computer and Information Sciences, A
Computer Programming, Specific Applications, A
Computer Science, A
Computer Systems Networking and
    Telecommunications, A
Criminal Justice/Law Enforcement Administration, A
Criminal Justice/Police Science, A
Data Processing and Data Processing
    Technology/Technician, A
Economics, A
Education, A
Emergency Medical Technology/Technician (EMT
    Paramedic), A
Engineering, A
English Language and Literature, A
Environmental Studies, A
Fine/Studio Arts, A
Forestry, A
General Studies, A
Geology/Earth Science, A
Health Information/Medical Records
    Administration/Administrator, A
History, A
Human Services, A
Humanities/Humanistic Studies, A
Information Science/Studies, A
Information Technology, A
International Business/Trade/Commerce, A
International Relations and Affairs, A
Japanese Language and Literature, A
Journalism, A
Liberal Arts and Sciences Studies and
    Humanities, A
Management Information Systems and Services, A
Mathematics, A
Medical Administrative Assistant/Secretary, A
Museology/Museum Studies, A
Music, A
Nursing - Registered Nurse Training, A
Occupational Therapy/Therapist, A
Oceanography, Chemical and Physical, A
Pharmacy Technician/Assistant, A
Philosophy, A
Physical Education Teaching and Coaching, A
Physical Sciences, A
Physical Therapy/Therapist, A
Physics, A
Political Science and Government, A
Pre-Engineering, A
Pre-Pharmacy Studies, A

Psychology, A
Radiologic Technology/Science - Radiographer, A
Respiratory Care Therapy/Therapist, A
Romance Languages, Literatures, and Linguistics, A
Russian Language and Literature, A
Social Sciences, A
Sociology, A
Spanish Language and Literature, A
Speech and Rhetorical Studies, A
Substance Abuse/Addiction Counseling, A
System Administration/Administrator, A
Web Page, Digital/Multimedia and Information
   Resources Design, A
Wildlife and Wildlands Science and Management, A
Wildlife Biology, A
Wood Science and Wood Products/Pulp and Paper
   Technology, A
Word Processing, A
Zoology/Animal Biology, A

TRINITY LUTHERAN COLLEGE

Bible/Biblical Studies, AB
Pastoral Studies/Counseling, B
Religious Education, B

UNIVERSITY OF PHOENIX-SPOKANE CAMPUS

Business Administration and Management, B
Business Administration, Management and
   Operations, M
Criminal Justice/Law Enforcement Administration, B
Health/Health Care Administration/Management, B
Information Technology, B

UNIVERSITY OF PHOENIX-WASHINGTON CAMPUS

Accounting, B
Business Administration and Management, B
Business Administration, Management and
   Operations, M
Criminal Justice/Law Enforcement Administration, B
Health Services Administration, M
Health/Health Care Administration/Management, B
Human Resources Management and Services, M
Information Technology, B
Management, M
Management Information Systems and Services, M
Management of Technology, M
Management Science, B
Organizational Management, M
Public Administration and Social Service
   Professions, B

UNIVERSITY OF PUGET SOUND

Art/Art Studies, General, B
Asian Studies/Civilization, B
Biology/Biological Sciences, B
Business/Commerce, B
Chemistry, B
Classics and Classical
   Languages, Literatures, and Linguistics, B
Communication Studies/Speech Communication
   and Rhetoric, B
Computer Programming, Specific Applications, B
Computer Science, B
Counselor Education/School Counseling and
   Guidance Services, M
Creative Writing, B
Drama and Dramatics/Theatre Arts, B
Economics, B
Education, M
Educational Administration and Supervision, M
Elementary Education and Teaching, M
English Language and Literature, B
French Language and Literature, B
Geology/Earth Science, B
German Language and Literature, B
History, B
Interdisciplinary Studies, B
International Business/Trade/Commerce, B
International Economics, B
International Relations and Affairs, B
Kinesiology and Exercise Science, B
Mathematics, B
Middle School Education, M

Music, B
Music Management and Merchandising, B
Music Performance, B
Music Teacher Education, BM
Natural Sciences, B
Occupational Therapy/Therapist, M
Pastoral Studies/Counseling, M
Philosophy, B
Physical Therapy/Therapist, D
Physics, B
Political Science and Government, B
Pre-Dentistry Studies, B
Pre-Law Studies, B
Pre-Medicine/Pre-Medical Studies, B
Pre-Veterinary Studies, B
Psychology, B
Religion/Religious Studies, B
Science, Technology and Society, B
Secondary Education and Teaching, M
Sociology, B
Spanish Language and Literature, B

UNIVERSITY OF WASHINGTON

Accounting, B
Aerospace, Aeronautical and Astronautical
   Engineering, BMD
African-American/Black Studies, B
Air Force JROTC/ROTC, B
Allopathic Medicine, PO
American Indian/Native American Studies, B
Ancient/Classical Greek Language and Literature, B
Anthropology, BMD
Applied Mathematics, BMD
Applied Physics, MD
Architecture, BMO
Army JROTC/ROTC, B
Art History, Criticism and Conservation, BMD
Art/Art Studies, General, B
Asian Languages, MD
Asian Studies/Civilization, BM
Astronomy, BMD
Atmospheric Sciences and Meteorology, BMD
Audiology/Audiologist and Speech-Language
   Pathology/Pathologist, B
Bacteriology, MD
Bilingual and Multilingual Education, B
Biochemistry, BD
Bioengineering, MD
Bioinformatics, M
Biological and Biomedical Sciences, MD
Biological Anthropology, MD
Biology Teacher Education, B
Biology/Biological Sciences, B
Biophysics, D
Biostatistics, BMD
BioTechnology, D
Botany/Plant Biology, BMD
Building/Construction
   Finishing, Management, and Inspection, B
Business Administration and Management, B
Business Administration, Management and
   Operations, MDO
Business/Commerce, B
Canadian Studies, B
Cell Biology and Anatomy, D
Cell/Cellular Biology and Histology, B
Ceramic Arts and Ceramics, B
Ceramic Sciences and Engineering, B
Chemical Engineering, BMD
Chemistry, BMD
Chinese Language and Literature, B
Chinese Studies, MD
City/Urban, Community and Regional Planning, B
Civil Engineering, BMD
Classics and Classical
   Languages, Literatures, and Linguistics, BMD
Clinical Laboratory Science/Medical
   Technology/Technologist, B
Clinical Laboratory Sciences, M
Clinical Psychology, D
Commercial and Advertising Art, B
Communication and Media Studies, MD
Communication Disorders, MD
Communication Studies/Speech Communication
   and Rhetoric, B
Comparative Literature, BMD

Computer and Information Sciences, B
Computer Engineering, B
Computer Science, BMD
Construction Engineering and Management, MD
Counselor Education/School Counseling and
   Guidance Services, MD
Creative Writing, B
Criminal Justice/Law Enforcement Administration, B
Curriculum and Instruction, MD
Dance, BM
Data Processing and Data Processing
   Technology/Technician, B
Dental Hygiene/Hygienist, B
Dentistry, PO
Drama and Dramatics/Theatre Arts, B
East Asian Studies, B
East European and Russian Studies, M
Economics, BMD
Education, BMDO
Educational Administration and Supervision, O
Educational Leadership and Administration, MD
Educational Measurement and Evaluation, MD
Educational Psychology, MD
Electrical Engineering, MD
Electrical, Electronics and Communications
   Engineering, B
Elementary Education and Teaching, B
Engineering, B
Engineering and Applied Sciences, MD
English, MD
English as a Second Language, M
English Education, M
English Language and Literature, B
Environmental and Occupational Health, MD
Environmental Engineering
   Technology/Environmental Technology, MD
Environmental Health, B
Environmental Policy and Resource
   Management, MD
Environmental Studies, B
Epidemiology, MD
Ergonomics and Human Factors, M
Ethnic and Cultural Studies, B
European Studies/Civilization, B
Fiber, Textile and Weaving Arts, B
Fine Arts and Art Studies, M
Fish, Game and Wildlife Management, MD
Fishing and Fisheries Sciences and Management, B
Forest Engineering, B
Forest Management/Forest Resources
   Management, B
Forest Sciences and Biology, B
Forestry, BMDO
French Language and Literature, BMD
General Studies, B
Genetics, MD
Genomic Sciences, D
Geography, BMD
Geology/Earth Science, BMD
Geophysics and Seismology, BMD
Geotechnical Engineering, MD
German Language and Literature, BMD
Health Informatics, M
Health Services Administration, MO
Health Services Research, MD
Hispanic Studies, M
Hispanic-American, Puerto Rican, and Mexican-
   American/Chicano Studies, B
Historic Preservation and Conservation, O
History, BMD
History and Philosophy of Science and
   Technology, B
Horticultural Science, MD
Human Development, MD
Humanities/Humanistic Studies, B
Hydraulics and Fluid Power Technology, MD
Hydrology and Water Resources Science, MD
Immunology, D
Industrial Design, B
Industrial Engineering, B
Industrial Hygiene, M
Industrial/Management Engineering, MD
Information Science/Studies, BMD
Interdisciplinary Studies, B
Interior Architecture, B
International Affairs, MO

International Business/Trade/Commerce, B
International Public Health/International Health, M
International Relations and Affairs, B
International Trade, O
Italian Language and Literature, BMD
Japanese Language and Literature, B
Japanese Studies, MD
Jewish/Judaic Studies, B
Landscape Architecture, BM
Latin American Studies, B
Latin Language and Literature, B
Law and Legal Studies, MDPO
Legal and Justice Studies, D
Liberal Arts and Sciences Studies and
  Humanities, B
Library Science, MD
Linguistics, BMD
Logistics and Materials Management, O
Management Information Systems and Services, B
Management Science, B
Marine Affairs, MO
Marine Geology, MD
Materials Engineering, BMD
Materials Sciences, MD
Maternal and Child Health, M
Maternal/Child Health and Neonatal
  Nurse/Nursing, B
Mathematics, BMD
Mechanical Engineering, BMD
Medical Informatics, M
Medical Microbiology and Bacteriology, B
Medicinal and Pharmaceutical Chemistry, D
Metal and Jewelry Arts, B
Metallurgical Engineering, B
Microbiology, D
Molecular Biology, BD
Molecular Medicine, MD
Museology/Museum Studies, M
Music, BMD
Music History, Literature, and Theory, B
Music Performance, B
Music Teacher Education, BMD
Music Theory and Composition, B
Musical Instrument Fabrication and Repair, B
Musicology and Ethnomusicology, B
Natural Resources Management/Development and
  Policy, B
Navy/Marine Corps JROTC/ROTC, B
Near and Middle Eastern Studies, BMD
Neurobiology and Neurophysiology, D
Neuroscience, D
Nursing, MDO
Nursing - Registered Nurse Training, B
Nutritional Sciences, MD
Occupational Therapy/Therapist, BM
Oceanography, Chemical and Physical, BMD
Oral and Dental Sciences, MDO
Orthotist/Prosthetist, B
Painting, B
Paper and Pulp Engineering, MD
Parasitology, MD
Pathobiology, MD
Pathology/Experimental Pathology, MD
Pharmaceutical Sciences, MD
Pharmacology, MD
Pharmacy, BP
Philosophy, BMD
Photography, B
Physical Therapy/Therapist, BD
Physician Assistant, B
Physics, BMD
Physiology, D
Piano and Organ, B
Political Science and Government, BMD
Portuguese Language and Literature, M
Printmaking, B
Psychology, BD
Public Administration, B
Public Affairs, MO
Public Health, MDO
Public Health (MPH, DPH), B
Public Health/Community Nurse/Nursing, B
Rehabilitation Sciences, M
Religion/Religious Studies, BM
Resource Management, MD

Romance
  Languages, Literatures, and Linguistics, BMD
Russian Language and Literature, BMD
Russian Studies, B
Scandinavian
  Languages, Literatures, and Linguistics, BMD
Scandinavian Studies, B
School Psychology, MD
Science Teacher Education/General Science
  Teacher Education, BM
Sculpture, B
Secondary Education and Teaching, B
Slavic Languages, Literatures, and Linguistics, BMD
Social Sciences, B
Social Work, BMDO
Sociology, BMD
South and Southeast Asian Studies, M
South Asian Studies, B
Southeast Asian Studies, B
Spanish Language and Literature, BM
Special Education and Teaching, MD
Speech and Rhetorical Studies, B
Statistics, BMD
Structural Biology, D
Structural Engineering, MD
Sustainable Development, M
Taxation, M
Teacher Education, Multiple Levels, B
Teaching English as a Second or Foreign
  Language/ESL Language Instructor, B
Technical and Business Writing, B
Technical Communication, MD
Theater, MD
Toxicology, MD
Transportation and Highway Engineering, MD
Transportation/Transportation Management, O
Urban and Regional Planning, MD
Urban Design, MDO
Veterinary Sciences, M
Violin, Viola, Guitar and Other Stringed
  Instruments, B
Voice and Opera, B
Wildlife and Wildlands Science and Management, B
Women's Studies, BMD
Wood Science and Wood Products/Pulp and Paper
  Technology, B
Zoology/Animal Biology, BD

UNIVERSITY OF WASHINGTON, BOTHELL

Business Administration and Management, B
Computer and Information Sciences, B
Environmental Sciences, B
Multi-/Interdisciplinary Studies, B
Nursing - Registered Nurse Training, B

UNIVERSITY OF WASHINGTON, TACOMA

Business Administration and Management, B
Computer and Information Sciences, B
Education, B
Environmental Sciences, B
Multi-/Interdisciplinary Studies, B
Nursing - Registered Nurse Training, B
Social Work, B
Urban Studies/Affairs, B

WALLA WALLA COLLEGE

Accounting, B
Ancient Near Eastern and Biblical
  Languages, Literatures, and Linguistics, B
Art Teacher Education, B
Art/Art Studies, General, B
Automobile/Automotive Mechanics
  Technology/Technician, AB
Avionics Maintenance Technology/Technician, AB
Biological and Biomedical Sciences, M
Biology/Biological Sciences, B
Biomedical Technology/Technician, B
Biomedical/Medical Engineering, B
Biophysics, B
Business Administration and Management, AB
Business Teacher Education, B
Chemistry, B
Civil Engineering, B

Clinical Laboratory Science/Medical
  Technology/Technologist, B
Commercial and Advertising Art, AB
Computer Programming/Programmer, A
Computer Science, B
Counseling Psychology, M
Curriculum and Instruction, M
Economics, B
Education, M
Educational Leadership and Administration, M
Electrical, Electronics and Communications
  Engineering, B
Electromechanical Technology/Electromechanical
  Engineering Technology, A
Elementary Education and Teaching, B
Engineering, B
Engineering Technology, B
English Language and Literature, B
Environmental Studies, B
French Language and Literature, B
German Language and Literature, B
Health and Physical Education, B
History, B
Humanities/Humanistic Studies, B
Journalism, B
Kinesiology and Exercise Science, B
Management Information Systems and Services, B
Marketing/Marketing Management, B
Mass Communication/Media Studies, B
Mathematics, B
Mechanical Engineering, B
Modern Languages, B
Music, B
Music Teacher Education, B
Nursing - Registered Nurse Training, B
Philosophy, B
Physical Education Teaching and Coaching, B
Physics, B
Piano and Organ, B
Pre-Dentistry Studies, B
Pre-Law Studies, B
Pre-Medicine/Pre-Medical Studies, B
Pre-Veterinary Studies, B
Psychology, B
Public Health (MPH, DPH), B
Public Health Education and Promotion, B
Public Relations/Image Management, B
Radio and Television, B
Reading Teacher Education, M
Religion/Religious Studies, B
Social Work, BM
Sociology, B
Spanish Language and Literature, B
Special Education and Teaching, M
Speech and Rhetorical Studies, B
Teacher Education, Multiple Levels, B
Technology Education/Industrial Arts, B
Theology/Theological Studies, B
Voice and Opera, B

WALLA WALLA COMMUNITY COLLEGE

Accounting Technology/Technician and
  Bookkeeping, A
Administrative Assistant and Secretarial Science, A
Agricultural Business and Management, A
Agricultural Mechanization, A
Agricultural Production Operations, A
Autobody/Collision and Repair
  Technology/Technician, A
Automobile/Automotive Mechanics
  Technology/Technician, A
Business Administration and Management, A
Carpentry/Carpenter, A
Child Care and Support Services Management, A
Civil Engineering Technology/Technician, A
Computer Technology/Computer Systems
  Technology, A
Corrections, A
Cosmetology/Cosmetologist, A
Criminal Justice/Safety Studies, A
Data Entry/Microcomputer Applications, A
Fire Services Administration, A
General Office Occupations and Clerical Services, A

Heating, Air Conditioning, Ventilation and
Refrigeration Maintenance
Technology/Technician, A
Information Science/Studies, A
Legal Administrative Assistant/Secretary, A
Liberal Arts and Sciences Studies and
Humanities, A
Licensed Practical/Vocational Nurse Training, A
Machine Tool Technology/Machinist, A
Medical Administrative Assistant/Secretary, A
Nursing - Registered Nurse Training, A
Office Management and Supervision, A
Teacher Assistant/Aide, A
Turf and Turfgrass Management, A
Welding Technology/Welder, A

WASHINGTON STATE UNIVERSITY

Accounting, BM
Agribusiness, M
Agricultural Communication/Journalism, B
Agricultural Economics, MD
Agricultural Mechanization, B
Agricultural Sciences, MD
Agricultural Teacher Education, B
Agriculture, B
Agriculture, Agriculture Operations and Related
Sciences, B
Agronomy and Crop Science, B
Agronomy and Soil Sciences, MD
American/United States Studies/Civilization, BMD
Analytical Chemistry, MD
Animal Sciences, BMD
Anthropology, BMD
Apparel and Textiles, B
Architecture, BM
Art History, Criticism and Conservation, B
Asian Studies/Civilization, B
Athletic Training and Sports Medicine, B
Bilingual and Multilingual Education, B
Biochemistry, BMD
Biochemistry, Biophysics and Molecular Biology, B
Bioengineering, MD
Biological and Biomedical Sciences, MD
Biology Teacher Education, B
Biology/Biological Sciences, B
Biophysics, BMD
BioTechnology, B
Botany/Plant Biology, MD
Business Administration and Management, B
Business Administration, Management and
Operations, MDO
Business/Commerce, B
Business/Managerial Economics, B
Cell Biology and Anatomy, MD
Ceramic Arts and Ceramics, M
Chemical Engineering, BMD
Chemistry, BMD
Chemistry Teacher Education, B
Civil Engineering, BMD
Clinical Psychology, D
Clothing and Textiles, M
Communication and Media Studies, MD
Communication Studies/Speech Communication
and Rhetoric, B
Computer Art and Design, M
Computer Engineering, B
Computer Science, BMD
Construction Engineering and Management, M
Counseling Psychology, MD
Criminal Justice/Law Enforcement Administration, B
Criminology, MD
Crop Production, B
Curriculum and Instruction, D
Digital Communication and Media/Multimedia, B
Drama and Dramatics/Theatre Arts, B
Ecology, B
E-Commerce/Electronic Commerce, B
Economics, BMDO
Education, BMD
Educational Leadership and Administration, MD
Electrical Engineering, MD
Electrical, Electronics and Communications
Engineering, B
Elementary Education and Teaching, BM
Engineering and Applied Sciences, MD
English, MD

English Education, M
English Language and Literature, B
English/Language Arts Teacher Education, B
Entomology, BMD
Entrepreneurship/Entrepreneurial Studies, B
Environmental Engineering
Technology/Environmental Technology, M
Environmental Sciences, BMD
Ethnic, Cultural Minority, and Gender Studies, B
Family and Consumer Sciences/Home Economics
Teacher Education, B
Family and Consumer Sciences/Human Sciences, B
Finance, B
Fine Arts and Art Studies, M
Fine/Studio Arts, B
Food Science, B
Food Science and Technology, MD
Foods, Nutrition, and Wellness Studies, B
Foreign Language Teacher Education, B
Foreign Languages and Literatures, B
Forestry, B
French Language and Literature, B
French Language Teacher Education, B
Genetics, BMD
Geology/Earth Science, BMD
German Language and Literature, B
German Language Teacher Education, B
Health and Physical Education, B
Health Teacher Education, B
History, BMD
History Teacher Education, B
Horticultural Science, BMD
Hospitality Administration/Management, B
Human Development, M
Human Development and Family Studies, B
Human Nutrition, B
Human Resources Management/Personnel
Administration, M
Humanities/Humanistic Studies, B
Inorganic Chemistry, MD
Insurance, B
Interior Design, BM
International Business/Trade/Commerce, BO
Kindergarten/PreSchool Education and Teaching, B
Kinesiology and Exercise Science, B
Landscape Architecture, BMD
Linguistics, B
Management Information Systems and
Services, BM
Management of Technology, M
Management Science, B
Marketing/Marketing Management, B
Materials Engineering, BM
Materials Sciences, BMD
Mathematics, BMD
Mathematics Teacher Education, BD
Mechanical Engineering, BMD
Microbiology, BMD
Molecular Biology, MD
Multilingual and Multicultural Education, M
Music, BM
Music Performance, B
Music Teacher Education, B
Music Theory and Composition, B
Natural Resources and Conservation, BMD
Neuroscience, BMD
Nursing, M
Nursing - Registered Nurse Training, B
Nutritional Sciences, MD
Operations Management and Supervision, B
Organic Chemistry, MD
Painting, M
Parks, Recreation, Leisure and Fitness Studies, B
Pathology/Experimental Pathology, MD
Pharmacology, MD
Pharmacology and Toxicology, B
Pharmacy, P
Philosophy, B
Photography, M
Physical Chemistry, M
Physical Education Teaching and Coaching, B
Physical Sciences, B
Physics, BMD
Plant Molecular Biology, MD
Plant Pathology/Phytopathology, MD

Plant Protection and Integrated Pest
Management, B
Plant Sciences, B
Political Science and Government, BMD
Pre-Law Studies, B
Pre-Medicine/Pre-Medical Studies, B
Printmaking, M
Psychology, BMD
Reading Teacher Education, BMD
Real Estate, B
Religion/Religious Studies, B
Russian Language and Literature, B
Science Teacher Education/General Science
Teacher Education, B
Sculpture, M
Secondary Education and Teaching, BM
Social Sciences, B
Social Studies Teacher Education, B
Sociology, BMD
Soil Science and Agronomy, B
Spanish Language and Literature, BM
Spanish Language Teacher Education, B
Special Education and Teaching, B
Sport and Fitness Administration/Management, B
Statistics, M
Systems Engineering, MD
Taxation, M
Teaching English as a Second or Foreign
Language/ESL Language Instructor, B
Toxicology, MD
Urban and Regional Planning, M
Veterinary Medicine, PO
Veterinary Sciences, MD
Wildlife and Wildlands Science and Management, B
Women's Studies, B
Zoology/Animal Biology, BMD

WENATCHEE VALLEY COLLEGE

Accounting, A
Administrative Assistant and Secretarial Science, A
Agricultural Mechanization, A
Applied Art, A
Athletic Training and Sports Medicine, A
Automobile/Automotive Mechanics
Technology/Technician, A
Biology/Biological Sciences, A
Business Administration and Management, A
Carpentry/Carpenter, A
Chemistry, A
Clinical/Medical Laboratory Technician, A
Commercial and Advertising Art, A
Economics, A
Education, A
Fire Science/Firefighting, A
Heating, Air Conditioning, Ventilation and
Refrigeration Maintenance
Technology/Technician, A
History, A
Industrial Radiologic Technology/Technician, A
Kindergarten/PreSchool Education and Teaching, A
Legal Administrative Assistant/Secretary, A
Liberal Arts and Sciences Studies and
Humanities, A
Licensed Practical/Vocational Nurse Training, A
Mathematics, A
Medical Administrative Assistant/Secretary, A
Medical/Clinical Assistant, A
Music, A
Music Teacher Education, A
Nursing - Registered Nurse Training, A
Parks, Recreation, Leisure and Fitness Studies, A
Physical Education Teaching and Coaching, A
Pre-Engineering, A
Sociology, A
Substance Abuse/Addiction Counseling, A
Trade and Industrial Teacher Education, A

WESTERN WASHINGTON UNIVERSITY

Accounting, B
Accounting and Computer Science, B
Adult and Continuing Education and Teaching, M
American/United States Studies/Civilization, B
Anthropology, BM
Archeology, B
Art History, Criticism and Conservation, B
Art Teacher Education, B

Asian Studies/Civilization, B
Audiology/Audiologist and Speech-Language
  Pathology/Pathologist, B
Biochemistry, B
Biological and Biomedical Sciences, M
Biological and Physical Sciences, B
Biology/Biological Sciences, B
Business Administration and Management, B
Business Administration, Management and
  Operations, M
Canadian Studies, B
Cell/Cellular and Molecular Biology, B
Cell/Cellular Biology and Histology, B
Ceramic Arts and Ceramics, B
Chemistry, BM
Chemistry Teacher Education, B
Classics and Classical
  Languages, Literatures, and Linguistics, B
Communication Disorders, M
Communication Studies/Speech Communication
  and Rhetoric, B
Community Health Services/Liaison/Counseling, B
Comparative Literature, B
Computer Science, BM
Counseling Psychology, M
Counselor Education/School Counseling and
  Guidance Services, BM
Creative Writing, B
Design and Visual Communications, B
Developmental and Child Psychology, B
Drama and Dramatics/Theatre Arts, B
Drawing, B
East Asian Studies, B
Economics, B
Education, BM
Education/Teaching of the Gifted and Talented, M
Educational Administration and Supervision, M
Educational Leadership and Administration, B
Electrical, Electronic and Communications
  Engineering Technology/Technician, B
Elementary Education and Teaching, BM
Engineering, B
Engineering Technology, B
English, M
English Language and Literature, B
Environmental Biology, B
Environmental Education, BM
Environmental Sciences, BM
Environmental Studies, B
Ethnic and Cultural Studies, B
Experimental Psychology, M
Fiber, Textile and Weaving Arts, B
Finance, B
Fine/Studio Arts, B
French Language and Literature, B
General Studies, B
Geography, BM
Geology/Earth Science, BM
Geophysics and Seismology, B
German Language and Literature, B
Graphic Design, B
Health Teacher Education, B
Higher Education/Higher Education
  Administration, M
History, BM
Human Resources Management/Personnel
  Administration, B
Human Services, B
Humanities/Humanistic Studies, B
Industrial Design, B
Industrial Technology/Technician, B
Interdisciplinary Studies, B
Intermedia/Multimedia, B
International Business/Trade/Commerce, B
Jazz/Jazz Studies, B
Journalism, B
Kindergarten/PreSchool Education and Teaching, B
Kinesiology and Exercise Science, B
Kinesiology and Movement Studies, M
Latin American Studies, B
Liberal Arts and Sciences Studies and
  Humanities, B
Linguistics, B
Management Information Systems and Services, B
Manufacturing Technology/Technician, B
Marine Biology and Biological Oceanography, B

Marketing/Marketing Management, B
Mathematics, BM
Music, BM
Music History, Literature, and Theory, B
Music Teacher Education, B
Operations Management and Supervision, B
Painting, B
Parks, Recreation, Leisure and Fitness Studies, B
Philosophy, B
Physical Education Teaching and Coaching, BM
Physics, B
Plastics Engineering Technology/Technician, B
Political Science and Government, BM
Printmaking, B
Psychology, BM
Rehabilitation Counseling, M
Science Teacher Education/General Science
  Teacher Education, BM
Sculpture, B
Secondary Education and Teaching, BM
Sociology, B
Spanish Language and Literature, B
Special Education and Teaching, BM
Student Personnel Services, M
Teacher Education, Multiple Levels, B
Theater, M
Visual and Performing Arts, B
Women's Studies, B

WHATCOM COMMUNITY COLLEGE

Accounting, A
Administrative Assistant and Secretarial Science, A
Business Administration and Management, A
Commercial and Advertising Art, A
Computer Engineering Technology/Technician, A
Computer Science, A
Criminal Justice/Police Science, A
Kindergarten/PreSchool Education and Teaching, A
Legal Assistant/Paralegal, A
Liberal Arts and Sciences Studies and
  Humanities, A
Medical Administrative Assistant/Secretary, A
Medical/Clinical Assistant, A
Nursing - Registered Nurse Training, A
Physical Therapist Assistant, A

WHITMAN COLLEGE

Anthropology, B
Art/Art Studies, General, B
Asian Studies/Civilization, B
Astronomy, B
Biochemistry, B
Biology/Biological Sciences, B
Biophysics, B
Chemistry, B
Classics and Classical
  Languages, Literatures, and Linguistics, B
Drama and Dramatics/Theatre Arts, B
Economics, B
English Language and Literature, B
Film/Cinema Studies, B
French Language and Literature, B
Geology/Earth Science, B
German Language and Literature, B
History, B
Mathematics, B
Molecular Biology, B
Music, B
Philosophy, B
Physics, B
Political Science and Government, B
Psychology, B
Religion/Religious Studies, B
Sociology, B
Spanish Language and Literature, B

WHITWORTH COLLEGE

Accounting, B
American/United States Studies/Civilization, B
Art Teacher Education, B
Art/Art Studies, General, B
Arts Management, B
Athletic Training and Sports Medicine, B
Biology/Biological Sciences, B
Business Administration and Management, B

Business Administration, Management and
  Operations, M
Chemistry, B
Computer Science, B
Counselor Education/School Counseling and
  Guidance Services, M
Drama and Dramatics/Theatre Arts, B
Economics, B
Education, M
Education/Teaching of the Gifted and Talented, M
Educational Administration and Supervision, M
Elementary Education and Teaching, BM
English Language and Literature, B
Fine/Studio Arts, B
French Language and Literature, B
History, B
International Business/Trade/Commerce, BM
International Relations and Affairs, B
Journalism, B
Mass Communication/Media Studies, B
Mathematics, B
Music, B
Music Teacher Education, B
Nursing, M
Nursing - Registered Nurse Training, B
Peace Studies and Conflict Resolution, B
Philosophy, B
Physical Education Teaching and Coaching, B
Physics, B
Piano and Organ, B
Political Science and Government, B
Pre-Dentistry Studies, B
Pre-Law Studies, B
Pre-Medicine/Pre-Medical Studies, B
Pre-Veterinary Studies, B
Psychology, B
Religion/Religious Studies, B
Secondary Education and Teaching, BM
Sociology, B
Spanish Language and Literature, B
Special Education and Teaching, BM
Speech and Rhetorical Studies, B
Voice and Opera, B

YAKIMA VALLEY COMMUNITY COLLEGE

Accounting, A
Administrative Assistant and Secretarial Science, A
Agricultural Business and Management, A
Agricultural Mechanization, A
Agriculture, A
Agronomy and Crop Science, A
Animal Sciences, A
Automobile/Automotive Mechanics
  Technology/Technician, A
Broadcast Journalism, A
Business Administration and Management, A
Child Development, A
Civil Engineering Technology/Technician, A
Computer Engineering Technology/Technician, A
Computer Graphics, A
Computer Science, A
Criminal Justice/Law Enforcement Administration, A
Criminal Justice/Police Science, A
Dental Hygiene/Hygienist, A
Electrical, Electronic and Communications
  Engineering Technology/Technician, A
Family and Consumer Economics and Related
  Services, A
Fire Science/Firefighting, A
Hotel/Motel Administration/Management, A
Industrial Radiologic Technology/Technician, A
Industrial Technology/Technician, A
Instrumentation Technology/Technician, A
Kindergarten/PreSchool Education and Teaching, A
Legal Administrative Assistant/Secretary, A
Liberal Arts and Sciences Studies and
  Humanities, A
Management Information Systems and Services, A
Marketing/Marketing Management, A
Medical Administrative Assistant/Secretary, A
Nursing - Registered Nurse Training, A
Occupational Therapy/Therapist, A
Pre-Engineering, A
Special Products Marketing Operations, A
Substance Abuse/Addiction Counseling, A

Tourism and Travel Services Management, A
Veterinary/Animal Health Technology/Technician and
    Veterinary Assistant, A

West Virginia

ALDERSON-BROADDUS COLLEGE

Accounting, B
Allied Health and Medical Assisting Services, M
Athletic Training and Sports Medicine, B
Biology/Biological Sciences, B
Business Administration and Management, AB
Comparative Literature, B
Computer Science, AB
Creative Writing, B
CytoTechnology/Cytotechnologist, B
Drama and Dramatics/Theatre Arts, B
Education, B
Elementary Education and Teaching, B
Emergency Medical Services, M
Environmental Studies, B
Family and Community Services, B
Finance, B
General Studies, A
History, B
Interdisciplinary Studies, B
Liberal Arts and Sciences Studies and
    Humanities, B
Management Information Systems and Services, B
Marketing/Marketing Management, B
Mass Communication/Media Studies, B
Mathematics, B
Music, B
Music Teacher Education, B
Natural Sciences, AB
Nursing - Registered Nurse Training, B
Physical Education Teaching and Coaching, B
Physician Assistant, B
Political Science and Government, B
Pre-Dentistry Studies, B
Pre-Law Studies, B
Pre-Medicine/Pre-Medical Studies, B
Pre-Veterinary Studies, B
Psychology, B
Public Health (MPH, DPH), B
Radiologic Technology/Science - Radiographer, B
Religion/Religious Studies, B
Religious/Sacred Music, B
Science Teacher Education/General Science
    Teacher Education, B
Secondary Education and Teaching, B
Sociology, B
Therapeutic Recreation/Recreational Therapy, B
Visual and Performing Arts, B

AMERICAN PUBLIC UNIVERSITY SYSTEM

African Studies, B
American/United States Studies/Civilization, B
Army JROTC/ROTC, B
Asian Studies/Civilization, B
Business Administration and Management, B
Business Administration, Management and
    Operations, M
Business and Personal/Financial Services Marketing
    Operations, M
Computer Science, B
Criminal Justice/Safety Studies, B
Criminology, M
English Language and Literature, B
Environmental Studies, B
General Studies, A
History, B
Information Technology, B
Latin American Studies, B
Management Science, B
Military and Defense Studies, M
Philosophy, B
Political Science and Government, M
Psychology, B
Public Administration, BM
Public Health, M
Securities Services Administration/Management, M
Sport and Fitness Administration/Management, B

Work and Family Studies, B

APPALACHIAN BIBLE COLLEGE

Bible/Biblical Studies, AB
Theology/Theological Studies, AB

BETHANY COLLEGE

Accounting, B
Art/Art Studies, General, B
Biology/Biological Sciences, B
Business/Managerial Economics, B
Chemistry, B
Communication Studies/Speech Communication
    and Rhetoric, B
Computer Science, B
Drama and Dramatics/Theatre Arts, B
Economics, B
Education, B
English Language and Literature, B
Environmental Studies, B
Fine/Studio Arts, B
French Language and Literature, B
German Language and Literature, B
History, B
Horse Husbandry/Equine Science and
    Management, B
Interdisciplinary Studies, B
International Relations and Affairs, B
Mathematics, B
Music, B
Physical Education Teaching and Coaching, B
Physics, B
Political Science and Government, B
Pre-Dentistry Studies, B
Pre-Law Studies, B
Pre-Medicine/Pre-Medical Studies, B
Pre-Veterinary Studies, B
Psychology, B
Religion/Religious Studies, B
Social Work, B
Spanish Language and Literature, B
Sport and Fitness Administration/Management, B

BLUEFIELD STATE COLLEGE

Accounting, AB
Administrative Assistant and Secretarial Science, AB
Architectural Engineering Technology/Technician, AB
Biological and Physical Sciences, AB
Business Administration and Management, B
Business/Commerce, A
Civil Engineering Technology/Technician, AB
Communications Technology/Technician, A
Computer and Information Sciences, AB
Corrections, AB
Criminal Justice/Police Science, A
Criminal Justice/Safety Studies, B
Electrical, Electronic and Communications
    Engineering Technology/Technician, AB
Elementary Education and Teaching, B
General Studies, B
Hotel/Motel Administration/Management, A
Humanities/Humanistic Studies, B
Interdisciplinary Studies, A
Legal Assistant/Paralegal, A
Liberal Arts and Sciences Studies and
    Humanities, A
Marketing/Marketing Management, AB
Mechanical Engineering/Mechanical
    Technology/Technician, AB
Medical Radiologic Technology/Science - Radiation
    Therapist, A
Medical/Clinical Assistant, A
Mining Technology/Technician, B
Nursing - Registered Nurse Training, A
Psychology, A
Social Sciences, B

COMMUNITY AND TECHNICAL COLLEGE OF SHEPHERD

Automobile/Automotive Mechanics
    Technology/Technician, A
Business, Management, Marketing, and Related
    Support Services, A
Criminal Justice/Safety Studies, A
Culinary Arts/Chef Training, A

Design and Visual Communications, A
Electromechanical Technology/Electromechanical
    Engineering Technology, A
Emergency Medical Technology/Technician (EMT
    Paramedic), A
Fashion Merchandising, A
Fire Science/Firefighting, A
General Office Occupations and Clerical Services, A
General Studies, A
Heating, Air Conditioning, Ventilation and
    Refrigeration Maintenance
    Technology/Technician, A
Information Technology, A
Legal Assistant/Paralegal, A

COMMUNITY & TECHNICAL COLLEGE AT WEST VIRGINIA UNIVERSITY INSTITUTE OF TECHNOLOGY

Accounting, A
Administrative Assistant and Secretarial Science, A
Automobile/Automotive Mechanics
    Technology/Technician, A
Automotive Engineering Technology/Technician, A
Business Administration and Management, A
Civil Engineering Technology/Technician, A
Corrections, A
Culinary Arts/Chef Training, A
Data Processing and Data Processing
    Technology/Technician, A
Dental Hygiene/Hygienist, A
Drafting and Design Technology/Technician, A
Electrical, Electronic and Communications
    Engineering Technology/Technician, A
Graphic and Printing Equipment Operator
    Production, A
Health/Health Care Administration/Management, A
Legal Administrative Assistant/Secretary, A
Liberal Arts and Sciences Studies and
    Humanities, A
Mechanical Engineering/Mechanical
    Technology/Technician, A
Medical Administrative Assistant/Secretary, A
Respiratory Care Therapy/Therapist, A
Surgical Technology/Technologist, A

CONCORD UNIVERSITY

Accounting, B
Art Teacher Education, B
Biology/Biological Sciences, B
Business Administration and Management, AB
Business Teacher Education, B
Ceramic Arts and Ceramics, B
Chemistry, B
Clinical Laboratory Science/Medical
    Technology/Technologist, B
Commercial and Advertising Art, B
Computer Science, B
Education, B
Elementary Education and Teaching, B
English Language and Literature, B
Geography, B
Health Teacher Education, B
History, B
Hospitality Administration/Management, B
Hotel/Motel Administration/Management, B
Information Science/Studies, B
Kindergarten/PreSchool Education and Teaching, B
Library Science, B
Mass Communication/Media Studies, B
Mathematics, B
Music Teacher Education, B
Parks, Recreation and Leisure Facilities
    Management, B
Physical Education Teaching and Coaching, B
Political Science and Government, B
Pre-Medicine/Pre-Medical Studies, B
Pre-Veterinary Studies, B
Psychology, B
Secondary Education and Teaching, B
Social Work, B
Sociology, B
Special Education and Teaching, B
Special Products Marketing Operations, B

Tourism and Travel Services Management, B

DAVIS & ELKINS COLLEGE

Accounting, B
Accounting and Business/Management, A
Art Teacher Education, B
Biology/Biological Sciences, B
Business Administration and Management, B
Business Teacher Education, B
Chemistry, B
Communication Studies/Speech Communication
   and Rhetoric, B
Comparative Literature, B
Computer Science, B
Criminal Justice/Police Science, A
Criminology, B
Drama and Dramatics/Theatre Arts, B
Economics, B
Elementary Education and Teaching, B
English Language and Literature, B
Environmental Sciences, B
Forestry, B
History, B
Hospitality Administration/Management, AB
Information Science/Studies, B
International Business/Trade/Commerce, B
International Marketing, B
Kinesiology and Exercise Science, B
Management Information Systems and Services, AB
Marketing/Marketing Management, B
Mathematics, B
Mathematics Teacher Education, B
Music, B
Music Teacher Education, B
Natural Sciences, B
Nursing - Registered Nurse Training, A
Physical Education Teaching and Coaching, B
Political Science and Government, B
Pre-Dentistry Studies, B
Pre-Law Studies, B
Pre-Medicine/Pre-Medical Studies, B
Pre-Veterinary Studies, B
Psychology, B
Religion/Religious Studies, B
Religious Education, B
Secondary Education and Teaching, B
Sociology, B
Spanish Language and Literature, B
Sport and Fitness Administration/Management, B
Technical Theatre/Theatre Design and
   Technology, B
Tourism and Travel Services Management, B

EASTERN WEST VIRGINIA COMMUNITY AND TECHNICAL COLLEGE

Administrative Assistant and Secretarial Science, A
Child Care Provider/Assistant, A
General Studies, A
Heavy/Industrial Equipment Maintenance
   Technologies, A
Liberal Arts and Sciences Studies and
   Humanities, A
Multi-/Interdisciplinary Studies, A
Science Technologies/Technicians, A

FAIRMONT STATE COMMUNITY & TECHNICAL COLLEGE

Aeronautical/Aerospace Engineering
   Technology/Technician, A
American Sign Language (ASL), A
Architectural Engineering Technology/Technician, A
Business/Commerce, A
Child Development, A
Civil Engineering Technology/Technician, A
Communications Technology/Technician, A
Drafting/Design Engineering
   Technologies/Technicians, A
Electrical and Electronic Engineering
   Technologies/Technicians, A
Electrical, Electronic and Communications
   Engineering Technology/Technician, A
Emergency Medical Technology/Technician (EMT
   Paramedic), A
Finance, A

Food Service, Waiter/Waitress, and Dining Room
   Management/Manager, A
General Studies, A
Graphic Communications, A
Mechanical Engineering/Mechanical
   Technology/Technician, A
Nursing - Registered Nurse Training, A
Physician Assistant, A

FAIRMONT STATE UNIVERSITY

Accounting, AB
Administrative Assistant and Secretarial Science, A
Art Teacher Education, B
Aviation/Airway Management and Operations, AB
Avionics Maintenance Technology/Technician, AB
Biology/Biological Sciences, B
Business Administration and Management, AB
Business Teacher Education, B
Chemistry, B
Child Development, A
Civil Engineering Technology/Technician, AB
Clinical/Medical Laboratory Technician, A
Commercial and Advertising Art, AB
Community Organization and Advocacy, A
Computer Science, B
Construction Engineering Technology/Technician, A
Consumer Merchandising/Retailing Management, A
Criminal Justice/Police Science, AB
Drafting and Design Technology/Technician, A
Drama and Dramatics/Theatre Arts, B
Economics, B
Education, B
Electrical, Electronic and Communications
   Engineering Technology/Technician, AB
Elementary Education and Teaching, B
Engineering Technology, AB
English Language and Literature, B
Family and Consumer Economics and Related
   Services, AB
Family and Consumer Sciences/Home Economics
   Teacher Education, B
Family and Consumer Sciences/Human Sciences, B
Fashion Merchandising, A
Finance, AB
French Language and Literature, B
Graphic and Printing Equipment Operator
   Production, AB
Health Information/Medical Records
   Administration/Administrator, A
History, B
Human Services, B
Industrial Technology/Technician, AB
Information Science/Studies, A
Institutional Food Workers, A
Interior Design, A
Liberal Arts and Sciences Studies and
   Humanities, A
Mathematics, B
Mechanical Engineering/Mechanical
   Technology/Technician, AB
Music Teacher Education, B
Nursing - Registered Nurse Training, AB
Occupational Safety and Health
   Technology/Technician, B
Physical Education Teaching and Coaching, B
Physical Therapy/Therapist, A
Political Science and Government, B
Psychology, B
Public Health (MPH, DPH), B
Real Estate, A
Science Teacher Education/General Science
   Teacher Education, B
Secondary Education and Teaching, B
Sign Language Interpretation and Translation, A
Sociology, B
Special Education and Teaching, B
Speech and Rhetorical Studies, B
Technology Education/Industrial Arts, B
Veterinary/Animal Health Technology/Technician and
   Veterinary Assistant, A

GLENVILLE STATE COLLEGE

Accounting, B
Behavioral Sciences, B
Biology Teacher Education, B
Biology/Biological Sciences, B

Business Administration and Management, B
Business Teacher Education, B
Business/Commerce, AB
Chemistry, B
Chemistry Teacher Education, B
Computer Science, B
Criminal Justice/Law Enforcement Administration, A
Education, B
Elementary Education and Teaching, B
English Language and Literature, B
English/Language Arts Teacher Education, B
Forestry Technology/Technician, B
History, B
Information Science/Studies, B
Kindergarten/PreSchool Education and Teaching, B
Liberal Arts and Sciences Studies and
   Humanities, A
Marketing/Marketing Management, B
Mathematics Teacher Education, B
Multi-/Interdisciplinary Studies, B
Music Teacher Education, B
Nursing - Registered Nurse Training, B
Physical Education Teaching and Coaching, B
Science Teacher Education/General Science
   Teacher Education, B
Secondary Education and Teaching, B
Social Studies Teacher Education, B
Special Education and Teaching, B

HUNTINGTON JUNIOR COLLEGE

Accounting, A
Administrative Assistant and Secretarial Science, A
Business Administration and Management, A
Computer Programming/Programmer, A
Computer Science, A
Court Reporting/Court Reporter, A
Dental Assisting/Assistant, A
Fashion Merchandising, A
Legal Administrative Assistant/Secretary, A
Medical Administrative Assistant/Secretary, A
Medical/Clinical Assistant, A

MARSHALL COMMUNITY AND TECHNICAL COLLEGE

Accounting Technology/Technician and
   Bookkeeping, A
Administrative Assistant and Secretarial Science, A
Business/Commerce, A
Computer Engineering Technology/Technician, A
Criminal Justice/Police Science, A
Dental Laboratory Technology/Technician, A
Electrical, Electronic and Communications
   Engineering Technology/Technician, A
Emergency Medical Technology/Technician (EMT
   Paramedic), A
Finance, A
Health Information/Medical Records
   Technology/Technician, A
Hospitality Administration/Management, A
Interior Design, A
Legal Assistant/Paralegal, A
Liberal Arts and Sciences Studies and
   Humanities, A
Manufacturing Technology/Technician, A
Medical Radiologic Technology/Science - Radiation
   Therapist, A
Medical Transcription/Transcriptionist, A
Medical/Clinical Assistant, A
Multi-/Interdisciplinary Studies, A
Physical Science Technologies/Technicians, A
Physical Therapist Assistant, A
Respiratory Care Therapy/Therapist, A
Science Technologies/Technicians, A

MARSHALL UNIVERSITY

Accounting, B
Adult and Continuing Education Administration, B
Adult and Continuing Education and Teaching, M
Allopathic Medicine, P
Anthropology, M
Art/Art Studies, General, B
Biological and Biomedical Sciences, MD
Biology/Biological Sciences, B
Business Administration and Management, B
Business Administration, Management and
   Operations, M

Business/Managerial Economics, B
Chemistry, BM
Clinical Laboratory Science/Medical
　Technology/Technologist, B
Clinical Psychology, M
Clinical/Medical Laboratory Technician, A
Communication and Media Studies, M
Communication Disorders, BM
Computer and Information Sciences, B
Computer Engineering Technology/Technician, B
Counselor Education/School Counseling and
　Guidance Services, BMO
Criminal Justice/Safety Studies, B
Criminology, M
CytoTechnology/Cytotechnologist, B
Dietetics/Dieticians, B
Early Childhood Education and Teaching, M
Economics, B
Education, MDO
Educational Leadership and Administration, MDO
Elementary Education and Teaching, BM
Engineering and Applied Sciences, M
English, M
English Language and Literature, B
Environmental Sciences, BM
Exercise and Sports Science, M
Family and Consumer Sciences/Human
　Sciences, BM
Finance, B
Fine Arts and Art Studies, M
Foreign Languages and Literatures, B
Forensic Science and Technology, M
General Studies, B
Geography, BM
Geology/Earth Science, B
Health Education, M
Health Services Administration, M
History, BM
Human Resources Management and Services, M
Humanities/Humanistic Studies, BM
Industrial and Organizational Psychology, M
Information Science/Studies, M
International Relations and Affairs, B
Journalism, BM
Management of Technology, M
Marketing/Marketing Management, B
Mass Communication/Media Studies, M
Mathematics, BM
Multi-/Interdisciplinary Studies, B
Music, M
Nursing, M
Nursing - Registered Nurse Training, AB
Occupational Safety and Health
　Technology/Technician, B
Parks, Recreation and Leisure Facilities
　Management, B
Physical Education Teaching and Coaching, BM
Physics, BM
Political Science and Government, BM
Psychology, BMD
Reading Teacher Education, MO
School Psychology, O
Secondary Education and Teaching, BM
Social Work, B
Sociology, BM
Special Education and Teaching, M
Speech and Rhetorical Studies, B
Speech-Language Pathology/Pathologist, B
Systems Science and Theory, B
Vocational and Technical Education, M

MOUNTAIN STATE COLLEGE

Accounting and Business/Management, A
Administrative Assistant and Secretarial Science, A
Computer and Information Sciences, A
Legal Assistant/Paralegal, A
Medical Transcription/Transcriptionist, A
Medical/Clinical Assistant, A

MOUNTAIN STATE UNIVERSITY

Accounting, B
Administrative Assistant and Secretarial Science, A
Allied Health and Medical Assisting Services, M
Aviation/Airway Management and Operations, AB
Banking and Financial Support Services, A
Behavioral Sciences, B

Business Administration and Management, A
Business/Commerce, AB
Computer Science, AB
Computer Systems Networking and
　Telecommunications, B
Criminal Justice/Law Enforcement Administration, B
Criminal Justice/Safety Studies, AB
Criminology, M
Culinary Arts/Chef Training, AB
Diagnostic Medical Sonography/Sonographer and
　Ultrasound Technician, AB
E-Commerce/Electronic Commerce, B
Elementary Education and Teaching, A
Emergency Medical Technology/Technician (EMT
　Paramedic), A
Engineering, A
English Language and Literature, B
Entrepreneurship/Entrepreneurial Studies, B
Environmental Studies, AB
Fire Science/Firefighting, A
Forensic Science and Technology, B
Health/Health Care Administration/Management, B
Hospitality Administration/Management, AB
Hospitality and Recreation Marketing Operations, B
Human Resources Management and Services, B
Humanities/Humanistic Studies, B
Information Science/Studies, AB
Information Technology, A
Interdisciplinary Studies, AM
Law and Legal Studies, AB
Legal Assistant/Paralegal, A
Liberal Arts and Sciences Studies and
　Humanities, AB
Library Science, AB
Logistics and Materials Management, B
Management Science, AB
Management Strategy and Policy, M
Marketing/Marketing Management, AB
Mass Communication/Media Studies, B
Mathematics and Computer Science, B
Medical Radiologic Technology/Science - Radiation
　Therapist, A
Medical/Clinical Assistant, A
Natural Resources and Conservation, B
Non-Profit/Public/Organizational Management, B
Nurse Anesthetist, MO
Nursing, MO
Nursing - Advanced Practice, M
Nursing - Registered Nurse Training, B
Nursing Administration, M
Nursing Education, M
Occupational Health and Industrial Hygiene, B
Occupational Therapist Assistant, A
Office Management and Supervision, A
Organizational Behavior Studies, B
Physical Sciences, B
Physical Therapist Assistant, A
Physician Assistant, M
Pre-Medicine/Pre-Medical Studies, B
Psychology, B
Public Health Education and Promotion, B
Radiologic Technology/Science - Radiographer, A
Respiratory Care Therapy/Therapist, AB
Secondary Education and Teaching, A
Social Work, B
Tourism and Travel Services Management, A
Tourism and Travel Services Marketing
　Operations, A
Web Page, Digital/Multimedia and Information
　Resources Design, A

NATIONAL INSTITUTE OF TECHNOLOGY

Electrical, Electronic and Communications
　Engineering Technology/Technician, A
Medical/Clinical Assistant, A

NEW RIVER COMMUNITY AND TECHNICAL COLLEGE

Accounting, A
Administrative Assistant and Secretarial Science, A
Biological and Physical Sciences, A
Business/Commerce, A
Communications Technology/Technician, A
Computer and Information Sciences, A
Corrections, A

Criminal Justice/Police Science, A
Hotel/Motel Administration/Management, A
Interdisciplinary Studies, A
Legal Assistant/Paralegal, A
Liberal Arts and Sciences Studies and
　Humanities, A
Marketing/Marketing Management, A
Medical/Clinical Assistant, A
Psychology, A

OHIO VALLEY UNIVERSITY

Accounting, B
Bible/Biblical Studies, AB
Business Administration and Management, B
Education, B
Elementary Education and Teaching, B
English/Language Arts Teacher Education, B
Human Resources Management/Personnel
　Administration, B
Liberal Arts and Sciences Studies and
　Humanities, AB
Marketing/Marketing Management, B
Mathematics Teacher Education, B
Physical Education Teaching and Coaching, B
Professional Studies, A
Psychology, B
Religion/Religious Studies, B
Science Teacher Education/General Science
　Teacher Education, B
Science Technologies/Technicians, A
Secondary Education and Teaching, B
Social Studies Teacher Education, B
Teacher Education, Multiple Levels, B

POTOMAC STATE COLLEGE OF WEST VIRGINIA UNIVERSITY

Accounting, A
Administrative Assistant and Secretarial Science, A
Agricultural Business and Management, A
Agricultural Economics, A
Agricultural Mechanization, A
Agricultural Teacher Education, A
Agriculture, A
Agronomy and Crop Science, A
Animal Sciences, A
Biological and Physical Sciences, A
Biology/Biological Sciences, A
Business Administration and Management, A
Business/Managerial Economics, A
Chemistry, A
Civil Engineering Technology/Technician, A
Computer and Information Sciences, A
Computer Engineering Technology/Technician, A
Computer Programming, Specific Applications, A
Computer Programming/Programmer, A
Computer Science, A
Computer Systems Networking and
　Telecommunications, A
Criminal Justice/Safety Studies, A
Data Processing and Data Processing
　Technology/Technician, A
Economics, A
Education, A
Electrical, Electronic and Communications
　Engineering Technology/Technician, A
Elementary Education and Teaching, A
Engineering, A
English Language and Literature, A
Forestry, A
Forestry Technology/Technician, A
Geology/Earth Science, A
History, A
Horticultural Science, A
Information Technology, A
Journalism, A
Kindergarten/PreSchool Education and Teaching, A
Liberal Arts and Sciences Studies and
　Humanities, A
Mathematics, A
Mechanical Engineering/Mechanical
　Technology/Technician, A
Medical Administrative Assistant/Secretary, A
Music, A
Music Teacher Education, A
Parks, Recreation and Leisure Facilities
　Management, A

Physical Education Teaching and Coaching, A
Political Science and Government, A
Pre-Engineering, A
Psychology, A
Social Work, A
Sociology, A
System Administration/Administrator, A
Wildlife and Wildlands Science and Management, A
Wood Science and Wood Products/Pulp and Paper
  Technology, A

SALEM INTERNATIONAL UNIVERSITY

Airline/Commercial/Professional Pilot and Flight
  Crew, B
Asian Studies/Civilization, B
Athletic Training and Sports Medicine, B
Biological and Biomedical Sciences, M
Biology Technician/BioTechnology Laboratory
  Technician, B
Biology/Biological Sciences, B
BioTechnology, M
Business Administration and Management, AB
Computer Science, B
Criminal Justice/Law Enforcement Administration, B
Education, BM
Elementary Education and Teaching, BM
Environmental Studies, B
Equestrian/Equine Studies, B
Human Services, B
International Business/Trade/Commerce, B
Japanese Language and Literature, B
Liberal Arts and Sciences Studies and
  Humanities, AB
Management, M
Mass Communication/Media Studies, AB
Mathematics, B
Molecular Biology, BM
Physical Education Teaching and Coaching, B
Psychology, B
Public Health (MPH, DPH), B
Radio and Television, AB
Secondary Education and Teaching, BM
Sport and Fitness Administration/Management, B
Teacher Education, Multiple Levels, B
Telecommunications Technology/Technician, AB

SHEPHERD UNIVERSITY

Accounting, B
Art/Art Studies, General, B
Biology/Biological Sciences, B
Business Administration and Management, B
Chemistry, B
Communication Studies/Speech Communication
  and Rhetoric, B
Computer and Information Sciences, B
Curriculum and Instruction, M
Economics, B
Elementary Education and Teaching, B
English Language and Literature, B
Environmental Studies, B
Family and Consumer Sciences/Human Sciences, B
General Studies, B
History, B
Mathematics, B
Music, B
Parks, Recreation, Leisure and Fitness Studies, B
Political Science and Government, B
Psychology, B
Secondary Education and Teaching, B
Social Work, B
Sociology, B

SOUTHERN WEST VIRGINIA COMMUNITY AND TECHNICAL COLLEGE

Accounting, A
Administrative Assistant and Secretarial Science, A
Automobile/Automotive Mechanics
  Technology/Technician, A
Business Administration and Management, A
Clinical/Medical Laboratory Technician, A
Communications Technology/Technician, A
Computer Programming, Specific Applications, A
Criminal Justice/Law Enforcement Administration, A
Drafting and Design Technology/Technician, A
Engineering Technology, A

Finance, A
Industrial Radiologic Technology/Technician, A
Information Science/Studies, A
Liberal Arts and Sciences Studies and
  Humanities, A
Nursing - Registered Nurse Training, A

UNIVERSITY OF CHARLESTON

Accounting, AB
Art/Art Studies, General, B
Athletic Training and Sports Medicine, B
Biology Teacher Education, B
Biology/Biological Sciences, B
Business Administration and Management, AB
Business Administration, Management and
  Operations, BM
Chemistry, B
Computer and Information Sciences, AB
Education, B
Elementary Education and Teaching, B
Environmental Biology, B
Environmental Sciences, B
Finance, B
General Studies, B
Health Teacher Education, B
History, B
Information Science/Studies, B
Marketing/Marketing Management, B
Music Teacher Education, B
Nursing - Registered Nurse Training, AB
Pre-Pharmacy Studies, B
Psychology, B
Public Policy Analysis, B
Radiologic Technology/Science - Radiographer, B
Science Teacher Education/General Science
  Teacher Education, B
Social Studies Teacher Education, B

VALLEY COLLEGE

Business Administration and Management, A

WEST LIBERTY STATE COLLEGE

Accounting, B
Art Teacher Education, B
Banking and Financial Support Services, B
Biology/Biological Sciences, B
Business Administration and Management, B
Business/Managerial Economics, B
Chemistry, B
Clinical Laboratory Science/Medical
  Technology/Technologist, B
Commercial and Advertising Art, B
Criminal Justice/Law Enforcement Administration, B
Dental Hygiene/Hygienist, AB
Education, B
Elementary Education and Teaching, B
English Language and Literature, B
Health Teacher Education, B
History, B
Information Science/Studies, B
Interdisciplinary Studies, B
Kindergarten/PreSchool Education and Teaching, B
Kinesiology and Exercise Science, B
Marketing/Marketing Management, B
Mass Communication/Media Studies, B
Mathematics, B
Music Teacher Education, B
Nursing - Registered Nurse Training, B
Physical Education Teaching and Coaching, B
Political Science and Government, B
Pre-Dentistry Studies, B
Pre-Law Studies, B
Pre-Medicine/Pre-Medical Studies, B
Psychology, B
Public Health (MPH, DPH), B
Secondary Education and Teaching, B
Social Sciences, B
Sociology, B

WEST VIRGINIA BUSINESS COLLEGE (WHEELING)

Accounting, A
Administrative Assistant and Secretarial Science, A
Business Administration and Management, A

Legal Assistant/Paralegal, A

WEST VIRGINIA JUNIOR COLLEGE (BRIDGEPORT)

Accounting, A
Administrative Assistant and Secretarial Science, A
Business Administration and Management, A
Legal Assistant/Paralegal, A

WEST VIRGINIA JUNIOR COLLEGE (CHARLESTON)

Accounting, A
Administrative Assistant and Secretarial Science, A
Business Administration and Management, A
Computer Typography and Composition Equipment
  Operator, A
Data Processing and Data Processing
  Technology/Technician, A
Law and Legal Studies, A
Medical Administrative Assistant/Secretary, A
Medical/Clinical Assistant, A

WEST VIRGINIA JUNIOR COLLEGE (MORGANTOWN)

Accounting, A
Business Administration and Management, A
Legal Administrative Assistant/Secretary, A

WEST VIRGINIA NORTHERN COMMUNITY COLLEGE

Accounting Technology/Technician and
  Bookkeeping, A
Administrative Assistant and Secretarial Science, A
Applied Horticulture/Horticultural Operations, A
Banking and Financial Support Services, A
Business Administration and Management, A
Computer Programming/Programmer, A
Criminal Justice/Police Science, A
Electrical, Electronic and Communications
  Engineering Technology/Technician, A
Health Information/Medical Records
  Technology/Technician, A
Heating, Air Conditioning, Ventilation and
  Refrigeration Maintenance
  Technology/Technician, A
Hospitality Administration/Management, A
Industrial Technology/Technician, A
Information Technology, A
Institutional Food Workers, A
Liberal Arts and Sciences Studies and
  Humanities, A
Nursing - Registered Nurse Training, A
Social Work, A
Word Processing, A

WEST VIRGINIA STATE COMMUNITY AND TECHNICAL COLLEGE

Accounting, A
Architectural Drafting and Architectural
  CAD/CADD, A
Banking and Financial Support Services, A
Behavioral Sciences, A
Business Administration, Management and
  Operations, A
CAD/CADD Drafting and/or Design
  Technology/Technician, A
Chemical Technology/Technician, A
Computer Science, A
Criminal Justice/Safety Studies, A
Electrical and Electronic Engineering
  Technologies/Technicians, A
Electrical/Electronics Maintenance and Repair
  Technology, A
General Office Occupations and Clerical Services, A
General Studies, A
Gerontology, A
Health Services/Allied Health/Health Sciences, A
Heating, Air Conditioning, Ventilation and
  Refrigeration Maintenance
  Technology/Technician, A
Legal Assistant/Paralegal, A
Marketing, A
Meteorology, A

Nuclear Medical Technology/Technologist, A

WEST VIRGINIA STATE UNIVERSITY

Accounting, AB
Administrative Assistant and Secretarial Science, A
Advertising, A
Applied Mathematics, B
Architectural Engineering Technology/Technician, A
Art Teacher Education, B
Art/Art Studies, General, AB
Biology/Biological Sciences, B
BioTechnology, M
Business Administration and Management, AB
Business Teacher Education, B
Chemical Engineering, A
Chemistry, B
Communication Studies/Speech Communication and Rhetoric, AB
Computer Programming/Programmer, A
Computer Science, A
Criminal Justice/Law Enforcement Administration, AB
Drafting and Design Technology/Technician, A
Economics, B
Education, B
Electrical, Electronic and Communications Engineering Technology/Technician, A
Elementary Education and Teaching, B
English Language and Literature, B
Fashion Merchandising, A
Finance, A
Gerontology, A
Health Teacher Education, B
History, B
Hotel/Motel Administration/Management, A
Kindergarten/PreSchool Education and Teaching, B
Liberal Arts and Sciences Studies and Humanities, A
Marketing/Marketing Management, A
Mathematics, B
Medical/Clinical Assistant, A
Music Teacher Education, B
Nuclear Medical Technology/Technologist, A
Parks, Recreation, Leisure and Fitness Studies, B
Physical Education Teaching and Coaching, B
Political Science and Government, B
Pre-Dentistry Studies, B
Pre-Engineering, A
Pre-Medicine/Pre-Medical Studies, B
Pre-Veterinary Studies, B
Psychology, B
Science Teacher Education/General Science Teacher Education, B
Secondary Education and Teaching, B
Social Work, B
Sociology, B
Therapeutic Recreation/Recreational Therapy, B

WEST VIRGINIA UNIVERSITY

Accounting, BM
Advertising, B
Aerospace, Aeronautical and Astronautical Engineering, BMD
African Studies, MD
African-American/Black Studies, MD
Agricultural Economics, BM
Agricultural Education, M
Agricultural Sciences, MD
Agricultural Teacher Education, B
Agronomy and Soil Sciences, MD
Allopathic Medicine, PO
American/United States Studies/Civilization, MD
Analytical Chemistry, MD
Anatomy, MD
Animal Sciences, BMD
Anthropology, B
Applied Mathematics, MD
Applied Physics, MD
Art Education, M
Art History, Criticism and Conservation, M
Art/Art Studies, General, B
Athletic Training and Sports Medicine, M
Audiology/Audiologist and Speech-Language Pathology/Pathologist, B
Bacteriology, MD
Biochemistry, MD

Biological and Biomedical Sciences, MDO
Biology/Biological Sciences, B
Business Administration and Management, B
Business Administration, Management and Operations, MO
Business/Managerial Economics, B
Cancer Biology/Oncology, MDO
Cell Biology and Anatomy, MD
Ceramic Arts and Ceramics, M
Chemical Engineering, BMD
Chemistry, BMD
Child and Family Studies, M
Civil Engineering, BMD
Clinical Laboratory Science/Medical Technology/Technologist, B
Clinical Psychology, MD
Communication and Media Studies, M
Communication Disorders, M
Communication Theory, M
Communication, Journalism and Related Programs, B
Community Health and Preventive Medicine, M
Comparative Literature, M
Composition, MD
Computer and Information Sciences, B
Computer and Information Sciences and Support Services, B
Computer Engineering, BD
Computer Science, BMD
Condensed Matter Physics, MD
Corporate and Organizational Communication, M
Counseling Psychology, MD
Criminalistics and Criminal Science, B
Curriculum and Instruction, MD
Dental Hygiene/Hygienist, B
Dentistry, P
Developmental Biology and Embryology, MD
Developmental Psychology, D
Drama and Dramatics/Theatre Arts, B
East Asian Studies, MD
Economics, MD
Education, MD
Education/Teaching of Individuals with Multiple Disabilities, M
Education/Teaching of the Gifted and Talented, M
Educational Administration and Supervision, MD
Educational Leadership and Administration, MD
Educational Psychology, MD
Electrical Engineering, MD
Electrical, Electronics and Communications Engineering, B
Elementary Education and Teaching, BM
Engineering and Applied Sciences, MD
English, MD
English as a Second Language, M
English Language and Literature, B
Entomology, M
Environmental and Occupational Health, D
Environmental Biology, MD
Environmental Education, M
Environmental Engineering Technology/Environmental Technology, MD
Environmental Policy and Resource Management, M
Environmental Studies, B
Evolutionary Biology, MD
Exercise and Sports Science, MD
Exercise Physiology, B
Family and Consumer Sciences/Human Sciences, B
Finance, B
Fine Arts and Art Studies, M
Fish, Game and Wildlife Management, M
Food Science and Technology, MD
Foreign Languages and Literatures, B
Forensic Science and Technology, B
Forest Management/Forest Resources Management, B
Forestry, BMD
French Language and Literature, M
General Studies, B
Genetics, MD
Geographic Information Systems, MD
Geography, BMD
Geology/Earth Science, BMD
Geophysics and Seismology, MD
German Language and Literature, M

Graphic Design, M
Health and Physical Education, B
Health Promotion, M
Higher Education/Higher Education Administration, M
History, BMD
History of Science and Technology, MD
Horticultural Science, M
Human Genetics, MD
Human Services, M
Hydrology and Water Resources Science, MD
Immunology, MD
Industrial and Labor Relations, M
Industrial Engineering, B
Industrial Hygiene, M
Industrial/Management Engineering, MD
Inorganic Chemistry, MD
Interdisciplinary Studies, B
International Affairs, M
International Relations and Affairs, B
Journalism, BM
Kinesiology and Exercise Science, B
Landscape Architecture, B
Latin American Studies, M
Law and Legal Studies, PO
Legal and Justice Studies, M
Liberal Arts and Sciences Studies and Humanities, B
Liberal Studies, M
Linguistics, M
Marketing, M
Marketing/Marketing Management, B
Mass Communication/Media Studies, B
Mathematics, BMD
Mathematics Teacher Education, M
Mechanical Engineering, BMD
Medicinal and Pharmaceutical Chemistry, MD
Microbiology, MD
Mineral/Mining Engineering, MD
Mining and Mineral Engineering, B
Molecular Biology, MD
Music, BMD
Music History, Literature, and Theory, M
Music Teacher Education, MD
Music Theory and Composition, M
Natural Resources and Conservation, D
Natural Resources Management/Development and Policy, BD
Neurobiology and Neurophysiology, MD
Nursing, MDO
Nursing - Registered Nurse Training, B
Nutritional Sciences, M
Occupational Therapy/Therapist, BM
Oral and Dental Sciences, M
Organic Chemistry, MD
Orthodontics, M
Painting, M
Paleontology, MD
Parasitology, MD
Parks, Recreation and Leisure Facilities Management, B
Parks, Recreation, Leisure and Fitness Studies, B
Performance, MD
Petroleum Engineering, BMD
Pharmaceutical Administration, MD
Pharmaceutical Sciences, MDO
Pharmacology, MD
Pharmacy, MDP
Philosophy, B
Physical Chemistry, MD
Physical Education Teaching and Coaching, BMD
Physical Therapy/Therapist, BM
Physics, BMD
Physiology, MD
Plant Pathology/Phytopathology, M
Plant Sciences, BMD
Plasma and High-Temperature Physics, MD
Political Science and Government, BMD
Printmaking, M
Psychology, BMD
Public Administration, MO
Public Health, M
Public Policy Analysis, MD
Reading Teacher Education, M
Recreation and Park Management, M
Rehabilitation Counseling, M

Reproductive Biology, MD
Safety Engineering, M
Sculpture, M
Secondary Education and Teaching, BM
Social Work, BM
Sociology, BM
Software Engineering, M
Spanish Language and Literature, M
Special Education and Teaching, MD
Sport and Fitness Administration/Management, BM
Sport Psychology, MD
Statistics, M
Theater, M
Theoretical Chemistry, MD
Theoretical Physics, MD
Toxicology, MD
Urban and Regional Planning, MD
Urban Planning, M
Veterinary Sciences, M
Virology, MD
Visual and Performing Arts, B
Vocational and Technical Education, MD
Wildlife and Wildlands Science and Management, B
Wood Science and Wood Products/Pulp and Paper
   Technology, B
Writing, M

WEST VIRGINIA UNIVERSITY INSTITUTE OF TECHNOLOGY

Accounting, B
Aerospace, Aeronautical and Astronautical
   Engineering, B
Biology/Biological Sciences, B
Business Administration and Management, B
Chemical Engineering, B
Chemistry, B
City/Urban, Community and Regional Planning, B
Civil Engineering, B
Civil Engineering Technology/Technician, B
Community Organization and Advocacy, B
Computer Programming/Programmer, B
Computer Science, B
Data Processing and Data Processing
   Technology/Technician, B
Electrical, Electronics and Communications
   Engineering, B
Engineering, B
Engineering and Applied Sciences, M
Engineering Physics, B
Engineering Technology, B
Graphic and Printing Equipment Operator
   Production, B
Health Teacher Education, B
Health/Health Care Administration/Management, B
History, B
Industrial Technology/Technician, B
Labor and Industrial Relations, B
Mathematics, B
Mechanical Engineering, B
Multi-/Interdisciplinary Studies, B
Nursing - Registered Nurse Training, B
Physical Education Teaching and Coaching, B
Public Administration, B

WEST VIRGINIA UNIVERSITY AT PARKERSBURG

Accounting, A
Administrative Assistant and Secretarial Science, A
Automobile/Automotive Mechanics
   Technology/Technician, A
Business Administration and Management, AB
Chemical Engineering, A
Criminal Justice/Law Enforcement Administration, A
Data Processing and Data Processing
   Technology/Technician, A
Drafting and Design Technology/Technician, A
Education, A
Electrical, Electronic and Communications
   Engineering Technology/Technician, A
Electromechanical Technology/Electromechanical
   Engineering Technology, A
Elementary Education and Teaching, B
Environmental Engineering
   Technology/Environmental Technology, A
Finance, A

Liberal Arts and Sciences Studies and
   Humanities, A
Machine Tool Technology/Machinist, A
Marketing/Marketing Management, A
Mechanical Engineering/Mechanical
   Technology/Technician, A
Nursing - Registered Nurse Training, A
Pre-Engineering, A
Social Work, A
Welding Technology/Welder, A

WEST VIRGINIA WESLEYAN COLLEGE

Accounting, B
Art History, Criticism and Conservation, B
Art Teacher Education, B
Art/Art Studies, General, B
Athletic Training and Sports Medicine, B
Biology/Biological Sciences, B
Business Administration and Management, B
Business Administration, Management and
   Operations, M
Business/Managerial Economics, B
Ceramic Arts and Ceramics, B
Chemistry, B
Commercial and Advertising Art, B
Communication Studies/Speech Communication
   and Rhetoric, B
Comparative Literature, B
Computer and Information Sciences, B
Computer Science, B
Creative Writing, B
Criminal Justice/Law Enforcement Administration, B
Drama and Dramatics/Theatre Arts, B
Drawing, B
Economics, B
Education, B
Education/Teaching of Individuals with Specific
   Learning Disabilities, B
Elementary Education and Teaching, B
Engineering Mechanics, B
Engineering Physics, B
English Language and Literature, B
English/Language Arts Teacher Education, B
Environmental Sciences, B
Finance, B
Fine/Studio Arts, B
Health and Physical Education, B
Health Teacher Education, B
History, B
Information Science/Studies, B
International Relations and Affairs, B
Junior High/Intermediate/Middle School Education
   and Teaching, B
Kindergarten/PreSchool Education and Teaching, B
Marketing/Marketing Management, B
Mathematics, B
Mathematics Teacher Education, B
Music, B
Music Teacher Education, B
Nursing - Registered Nurse Training, B
Painting, B
Philosophy, B
Philosophy and Religious Studies, B
Physical Education Teaching and Coaching, B
Physics, B
Political Science and Government, B
Pre-Dentistry Studies, B
Pre-Law Studies, B
Pre-Medicine/Pre-Medical Studies, B
Pre-Pharmacy Studies, B
Pre-Veterinary Studies, B
Psychology, B
Public Relations/Image Management, B
Religion/Religious Studies, B
Religious Education, B
Secondary Education and Teaching, B
Sociology, B
Special Education and Teaching, B
Speech and Rhetorical Studies, B
Sport and Fitness Administration/Management, B
Teacher Education, Multiple Levels, B

WHEELING JESUIT UNIVERSITY

Accounting, BM
Biology Teacher Education, B
Biology/Biological Sciences, B

Business Administration and Management, B
Business Administration, Management and
   Operations, M
Chemistry, B
Chemistry Teacher Education, B
Communication, Journalism and Related
   Programs, B
Computer Programming/Programmer, B
Computer Science, B
Criminal Justice/Law Enforcement Administration, B
Digital Communication and Media/Multimedia, B
Education, B
Education/Teaching of Individuals with Specific
   Learning Disabilities, B
Elementary Education and Teaching, B
English Language and Literature, B
English/Language Arts Teacher Education, B
Environmental Studies, B
Foreign Language Teacher Education, B
French Language and Literature, B
French Language Teacher Education, B
Health/Health Care Administration/Management, B
History, B
History Teacher Education, B
International Business/Trade/Commerce, B
International Relations and Affairs, B
Journalism, B
Junior High/Intermediate/Middle School Education
   and Teaching, B
Liberal Arts and Sciences Studies and
   Humanities, B
Management Science, B
Marketing/Marketing Management, B
Mathematics, B
Mathematics Teacher Education, BM
Nuclear Medical Technology/Technologist, B
Nursing, M
Nursing - Registered Nurse Training, B
Nursing Administration, B
Philosophy, B
Physical Therapy/Therapist, BD
Physics, B
Physics Teacher Education, B
Political Science and Government, B
Pre-Dentistry Studies, B
Pre-Law Studies, B
Pre-Medicine/Pre-Medical Studies, B
Pre-Veterinary Studies, B
Psychology, B
Public Relations/Image Management, B
Religion/Religious Studies, B
Respiratory Care Therapy/Therapist, B
Science Teacher Education/General Science
   Teacher Education, BM
Secondary Education and Teaching, B
Social Studies Teacher Education, B
Spanish Language and Literature, B
Spanish Language Teacher Education, B
Theology and Religious Vocations, M
Theology/Theological Studies, B

Wisconsin

ALVERNO COLLEGE

Adult and Continuing Education and Teaching, M
Art Teacher Education, B
Art Therapy/Therapist, B
Art/Art Studies, General, B
Biology/Biological Sciences, B
Business Administration and Management, B
Business Administration, Management and
   Operations, B
Chemistry, B
Communication Studies/Speech Communication
   and Rhetoric, B
Communications Technologies/Technicians and
   Support Services, B
Community Organization and Advocacy, B
Computer and Information Sciences, B
Computer Science, B
Education, BM
Educational Administration and Supervision, M
Educational Leadership and Administration, M
Educational Media/Instructional Technology, M
Elementary Education and Teaching, B
English Language and Literature, B

English/Language Arts Teacher Education, B
Environmental Studies, B
General Studies, B
History, B
International Business/Trade/Commerce, B
International Relations and Affairs, B
International/Global Studies, B
Junior High/Intermediate/Middle School Education
and Teaching, B
Liberal Arts and Sciences Studies and
Humanities, AB
Marketing/Marketing Management, B
Mathematics, B
Mathematics Teacher Education, B
Molecular Biology, B
Music, AB
Music Teacher Education, B
Music Therapy/Therapist, B
Nursing, B
Nursing - Registered Nurse Training, B
Philosophy, B
Political Science and Government, B
Psychology, B
Reading Teacher Education, M
Religion/Religious Studies, B
Science Teacher Education/General Science
Teacher Education, BM
Social Science Teacher Education, B
Social Sciences, B
Social Studies Teacher Education, B
Teacher Assistant/Aide, A

BELLIN COLLEGE OF NURSING

Nursing - Registered Nurse Training, B

BELOIT COLLEGE

Anthropology, B
Art History, Criticism and Conservation, B
Art Teacher Education, B
Asian Studies/Civilization, B
Biochemistry, B
Biology/Biological Sciences, B
Business Administration and Management, B
Business/Managerial Economics, B
Cell/Cellular Biology and Histology, B
Chemistry, B
Classics and Classical
Languages, Literatures, and Linguistics, B
Comparative Literature, B
Computer Science, B
Creative Writing, B
Drama and Dramatics/Theatre Arts, B
Economics, B
Education, B
Elementary Education and Teaching, B
Engineering, B
English Language and Literature, B
Environmental Biology, B
Environmental Studies, B
European Studies/Civilization, B
Fine/Studio Arts, B
French Language and Literature, B
Geology/Earth Science, B
German Language and Literature, B
History, B
Interdisciplinary Studies, B
International Relations and Affairs, B
Latin American Studies, B
Mass Communication/Media Studies, B
Mathematics, B
Modern Languages, B
Molecular Biology, B
Museology/Museum Studies, B
Music, B
Music Teacher Education, B
Philosophy, B
Physics, B
Political Science and Government, B
Pre-Dentistry Studies, B
Pre-Law Studies, B
Pre-Medicine/Pre-Medical Studies, B
Psychology, B
Religion/Religious Studies, B
Romance Languages, Literatures, and Linguistics, B
Russian Language and Literature, B
Russian Studies, B

Science Teacher Education/General Science
Teacher Education, B
Secondary Education and Teaching, B
Sociology, B
Spanish Language and Literature, B
Women's Studies, B

BLACKHAWK TECHNICAL COLLEGE

Accounting, A
Administrative Assistant and Secretarial Science, A
Avionics Maintenance Technology/Technician, A
Computer and Information Sciences, A
Criminal Justice/Police Science, A
Culinary Arts/Chef Training, A
Dental Hygiene/Hygienist, A
Drafting/Design Engineering
Technologies/Technicians, A
Electrical, Electronic and Communications
Engineering Technology/Technician, A
Electromechanical Technology/Electromechanical
Engineering Technology, A
Fire Science/Firefighting, A
Industrial Technology/Technician, A
Legal Administrative Assistant/Secretary, A
Marketing/Marketing Management, A
Nursing - Registered Nurse Training, A
Physical Therapy/Therapist, A
Radiologic Technology/Science - Radiographer, A

BRYANT AND STRATTON COLLEGE

Accounting, A
Administrative Assistant and Secretarial Science, A
Business/Commerce, A
Criminal Justice/Law Enforcement Administration, A
Human Resources Management and Services, A
Information Technology, A
Medical Administrative Assistant/Secretary, A
Medical/Clinical Assistant, A

BRYANT AND STRATTON
COLLEGE, WAUWATOSA CAMPUS

Business Administration and Management, B
Business/Commerce, A
Criminal Justice/Law Enforcement Administration, A
Graphic Design, A
Human Resources Management and Services, A
Legal Assistant/Paralegal, A
Medical Office Assistant/Specialist, A
Nursing - Registered Nurse Training, A
Physician Assistant, A

CARDINAL STRITCH UNIVERSITY

Accounting, B
Applied Arts and Design, M
Art Teacher Education, B
Art/Art Studies, General, B
Biology/Biological Sciences, B
Business Administration and Management, AB
Business Administration, Management and
Operations, M
Business/Managerial Economics, B
Chemistry, B
Clinical Psychology, M
Commercial and Advertising Art, B
Communication Studies/Speech Communication
and Rhetoric, B
Computer Education, M
Computer Science, B
Creative Writing, B
Divinity/Ministry (BD, MDiv.), B
Drama and Dramatics/Theatre Arts, B
Education, BMD
Educational Leadership and Administration, MD
Elementary Education and Teaching, B
English Language and Literature, B
Finance and Banking, M
Fine/Studio Arts, B
French Language and Literature, B
General Studies, M
Graphic Design, M
Health Services Administration, M
History, B
Interdisciplinary Studies, A
International Business/Trade/Commerce, B
Kindergarten/PreSchool Education and Teaching, B

Liberal Arts and Sciences Studies and
Humanities, AB
Mathematics, B
Mathematics and Computer Science, B
Music, B
Nursing, M
Nursing - Registered Nurse Training, AB
Political Science and Government, B
Pre-Dentistry Studies, B
Pre-Law Studies, B
Pre-Medicine/Pre-Medical Studies, B
Pre-Veterinary Studies, B
Psychology, BM
Public Relations/Image Management, B
Reading Teacher Education, M
Religion/Religious Studies, BM
Religious Education, B
Science Teacher Education/General Science
Teacher Education, B
Secondary Education and Teaching, B
Social Sciences, B
Sociology, B
Spanish Language and Literature, B
Special Education and Teaching, BM

CARROLL COLLEGE

Accounting, B
Actuarial Science, B
Animal Behavior and Ethology, B
Applied Mathematics, B
Art Teacher Education, B
Art/Art Studies, General, B
Athletic Training and Sports Medicine, B
Biochemistry, B
Biology Teacher Education, B
Biology/Biological Sciences, B
Business Administration and Management, B
Chemistry, B
Chemistry Teacher Education, B
Clinical Laboratory Science/Medical
Technology/Technologist, B
Commercial and Advertising Art, B
Communication Studies/Speech Communication
and Rhetoric, B
Computer and Information Sciences, B
Computer Science, B
Computer Software Engineering, B
Creative Writing, B
Criminal Justice/Law Enforcement Administration, B
Drama and Dramatics/Theatre Arts, B
Early Childhood Education and Teaching, B
Education, BM
Elementary Education and Teaching, B
English Language and Literature, B
English/Language Arts Teacher Education, B
Environmental Sciences, B
Finance, B
Fine/Studio Arts, B
Foreign Language Teacher Education, B
Forensic Science and Technology, B
French Language Teacher Education, B
German Language Teacher Education, B
Graphic Communications, B
Health and Physical Education, B
Health Teacher Education, B
History, B
History Teacher Education, B
Information Science/Studies, B
International Relations and Affairs, B
Journalism, B
Junior High/Intermediate/Middle School Education
and Teaching, B
Kindergarten/PreSchool Education and Teaching, B
Kinesiology and Exercise Science, B
Management Information Systems and Services, B
Marketing/Marketing Management, B
Mathematics, B
Mathematics Teacher Education, B
Music, B
Music Teacher Education, B
Natural Resources and Conservation, B
Nursing - Registered Nurse Training, B
Organizational Behavior Studies, B
Organizational Communication, B
Photography, B
Physical Education Teaching and Coaching, B

Physical Therapy/Therapist, M
Physics Teacher Education, B
Political Science and Government, B
Pre-Dentistry Studies, B
Pre-Medicine/Pre-Medical Studies, B
Pre-Pharmacy Studies, B
Pre-Veterinary Studies, B
Printing Management, B
Psychology, B
Psychology Teacher Education, B
Public Relations, Advertising, and Applied
    Communication, B
Religion/Religious Studies, B
Science Teacher Education/General Science
    Teacher Education, B
Secondary Education and Teaching, B
Social Science Teacher Education, B
Social Studies Teacher Education, B
Sociology, B
Software Engineering, M
Spanish Language and Literature, B
Spanish Language Teacher Education, B
System, Networking, and LAN/WAN
    Management/Manager, B

CARTHAGE COLLEGE

Accounting, B
Art Education, M
Athletic Training and Sports Medicine, B
Biology/Biological Sciences, B
Business Administration and Management, B
Chemistry, B
Classics and Classical
    Languages, Literatures, and Linguistics, B
Communication Studies/Speech Communication
    and Rhetoric, B
Computer Science, B
Counselor Education/School Counseling and
    Guidance Services, M
Criminal Justice/Law Enforcement Administration, B
Drama and Dramatics/Theatre Arts, B
Economics, B
Education, MO
Education/Teaching of the Gifted and Talented, M
Educational Leadership and Administration, M
Elementary Education and Teaching, B
Engineering, B
English Education, M
English Language and Literature, B
Environmental Sciences, B
Environmental Studies, B
Fine/Studio Arts, B
French Language and Literature, B
Geography, B
German Language and Literature, B
Graphic Design, B
History, B
International Economics, B
Marketing/Marketing Management, B
Mathematics, B
Music, B
Music Teacher Education, B
Natural Sciences, B
Neuroscience, B
Occupational Therapy/Therapist, B
Philosophy, B
Physical Education Teaching and Coaching, B
Physics, B
Political Science and Government, B
Pre-Dentistry Studies, B
Pre-Law Studies, B
Pre-Medicine/Pre-Medical Studies, B
Pre-Veterinary Studies, B
Psychology, B
Reading Teacher Education, MO
Religion/Religious Studies, B
Science Teacher Education/General Science
    Teacher Education, M
Secondary Education and Teaching, B
Social Sciences, B
Social Studies Teacher Education, M
Social Work, B
Sociology, B
Spanish Language and Literature, B
Special Education and Teaching, B
Speech and Rhetorical Studies, B

Sport and Fitness Administration/Management, B

CHIPPEWA VALLEY TECHNICAL COLLEGE

Accounting, A
Administrative Assistant and Secretarial Science, A
Agricultural Business and Management, A
Architectural Engineering Technology/Technician, A
Automobile/Automotive Mechanics
    Technology/Technician, A
Child Development, A
Civil Engineering Technology/Technician, A
Clinical/Medical Laboratory Technician, A
Computer and Information Sciences, A
Construction Engineering Technology/Technician, A
Criminal Justice/Police Science, A
Culinary Arts/Chef Training, A
Dairy Science, A
Data Processing and Data Processing
    Technology/Technician, A
Dental Hygiene/Hygienist, A
Diagnostic Medical Sonography/Sonographer and
    Ultrasound Technician, A
Drafting and Design Technology/Technician, A
Drafting/Design Engineering
    Technologies/Technicians, A
Electrical, Electronic and Communications
    Engineering Technology/Technician, A
Electromechanical Technology/Electromechanical
    Engineering Technology, A
Fire Science/Firefighting, A
Health and Medical Laboratory Technologies, A
Health Information/Medical Records
    Administration/Administrator, A
Heating, Air Conditioning, Ventilation and
    Refrigeration Maintenance
    Technology/Technician, A
Hospitality Administration/Management, A
Legal Assistant/Paralegal, A
Machine Tool Technology/Machinist, A
Marketing/Marketing Management, A
Medical Radiologic Technology/Science - Radiation
    Therapist, A
Nursing - Registered Nurse Training, A
Quality Control Technology/Technician, A
Real Estate, A
Substance Abuse/Addiction Counseling, A
Welding Technology/Welder, A

COLLEGE OF MENOMINEE NATION

Business Administration and Management, A
Computer Science, A
Education, A
Liberal Arts and Sciences Studies and
    Humanities, A
Licensed Practical/Vocational Nurse Training, A
Natural Resources and Conservation, A
Political Science and Government, A
Social Work, A

COLUMBIA COLLEGE OF NURSING

Nursing - Registered Nurse Training, B

CONCORDIA UNIVERSITY WISCONSIN

Accounting, B
Allied Health and Medical Assisting Services, M
Ancient Near Eastern and Biblical
    Languages, Literatures, and Linguistics, B
Art Education, M
Art Teacher Education, B
Art/Art Studies, General, B
Athletic Training and Sports Medicine, B
Biology/Biological Sciences, B
Business Administration and Management, B
Business Administration, Management and
    Operations, M
Business Teacher Education, B
Child and Family Studies, M
Commercial and Advertising Art, B
Computer Science, B
Corporate and Organizational Communication, M
Counselor Education/School Counseling and
    Guidance Services, M
Criminal Justice/Law Enforcement Administration, B
Curriculum and Instruction, M

Early Childhood Education and Teaching, M
Economics, B
Education, BM
Educational Administration and Supervision, M
Elementary Education and Teaching, B
English Language and Literature, B
Exercise Physiology, B
Finance and Banking, M
General Studies, B
German Language and Literature, B
German Language Teacher Education, B
Gerontological Nursing, M
Graphic Design, B
Health and Physical Education, B
Health and Physical Education/Fitness, B
Health Services Administration, M
Health/Health Care Administration/Management, B
Hebrew Language and Literature, B
History, B
History Teacher Education, B
Human Resources Management and Services, M
Humanities/Humanistic Studies, B
Industrial Radiologic Technology/Technician, B
Interior Design, B
International Business/Trade/Commerce, M
Junior High/Intermediate/Middle School Education
    and Teaching, B
Kindergarten/PreSchool Education and Teaching, B
Legal Assistant/Paralegal, B
Liberal Arts and Sciences Studies and
    Humanities, B
Management, M
Management Information Systems and Services, M
Marketing, M
Marketing/Marketing Management, B
Mass Communication/Media Studies, B
Mathematics, B
Medical Office Assistant/Specialist, B
Missions/Missionary Studies and Missiology, B
Modern Greek Language and Literature, B
Music, B
Music Teacher Education, B
Nursing, M
Nursing - Advanced Practice, M
Nursing - Registered Nurse Training, B
Nursing Education, M
Occupational Therapy/Therapist, BM
Pastoral Studies/Counseling, B
Physical Education Teaching and Coaching, B
Physical Therapy/Therapist, BMD
Pre-Dentistry Studies, A
Pre-Law Studies, B
Pre-Medicine/Pre-Medical Studies, A
Pre-Nursing Studies, A
Psychology, B
Public Administration, M
Reading Teacher Education, M
Religion/Religious Studies, B
Sacred Music, M
Science Teacher Education/General Science
    Teacher Education, B
Secondary Education and Teaching, B
Social Work, B
Spanish Language and Literature, B
Spanish Language Teacher Education, B
Sport and Fitness Administration/Management, B
Student Personnel Services, M
Teacher Education, Multiple Levels, B
Teaching English as a Second or Foreign
    Language/ESL Language Instructor, B
Theology/Theological Studies, B
Youth Ministry, B

DEVRY UNIVERSITY (MILWAUKEE)

Business Administration and Management, B
Business Administration, Management and
    Operations, BM
Computer and Information Sciences, B

DEVRY UNIVERSITY (WAUKESHA)

Business Administration, Management and
    Operations, M

EDGEWOOD COLLEGE

Accounting, B
Art Teacher Education, B

Art Therapy/Therapist, B
Art/Art Studies, General, B
Biology/Biological Sciences, B
Business Administration and Management, B
Business Administration, Management and
  Operations, M
Chemistry, B
Clinical Laboratory Science/Medical
  Technology/Technologist, B
Commercial and Advertising Art, B
Criminal Justice/Law Enforcement Administration, B
CytoTechnology/Cytotechnologist, B
Developmental and Child Psychology, B
Drama and Dramatics/Theatre Arts, B
Economics, B
Education, BMDO
Educational Administration and Supervision, MO
Educational Leadership and Administration, D
Elementary Education and Teaching, B
English Language and Literature, B
French Language and Literature, B
History, B
Information Science/Studies, B
International Relations and Affairs, B
Kindergarten/PreSchool Education and Teaching, B
Liberal Arts and Sciences Studies and
  Humanities, AB
Marriage and Family Therapy/Counseling, M
Mass Communication/Media Studies, B
Mathematics, B
Music, B
Natural Sciences, B
Nursing, M
Nursing - Registered Nurse Training, B
Political Science and Government, B
Pre-Dentistry Studies, B
Pre-Engineering, A
Pre-Law Studies, B
Pre-Medicine/Pre-Medical Studies, B
Pre-Veterinary Studies, B
Psychology, B
Public Administration, B
Public Policy Analysis, B
Religion/Religious Studies, BM
Social Sciences, B
Sociology, B
Spanish Language and Literature, B
Special Education and Teaching, MO

FOX VALLEY TECHNICAL COLLEGE

Accounting, A
Administrative Assistant and Secretarial Science, A
Agricultural Business and Management, A
Airline/Commercial/Professional Pilot and Flight
  Crew, A
Automobile/Automotive Mechanics
  Technology/Technician, A
Business Administration and Management, A
Child Development, A
Commercial and Advertising Art, A
Computer Programming/Programmer, A
Computer Typography and Composition Equipment
  Operator, A
Consumer Merchandising/Retailing Management, A
Criminal Justice/Law Enforcement Administration, A
Criminal Justice/Police Science, A
Culinary Arts/Chef Training, A
Drafting and Design Technology/Technician, A
Drafting/Design Engineering
  Technologies/Technicians, A
Electrical, Electronic and Communications
  Engineering Technology/Technician, A
Finance, A
Fire Science/Firefighting, A
Forestry Technology/Technician, A
Graphic and Printing Equipment Operator
  Production, A
Hospitality Administration/Management, A
Industrial Technology/Technician, A
Insurance, A
Interior Design, A
Legal Administrative Assistant/Secretary, A
Marketing/Marketing Management, A
Mechanical Engineering/Mechanical
  Technology/Technician, A
Natural Resources and Conservation, A

Nursing - Registered Nurse Training, A
Occupational Therapy/Therapist, A
Special Products Marketing Operations, A
Welding Technology/Welder, A
Wood Science and Wood Products/Pulp and Paper
  Technology, A

GATEWAY TECHNICAL COLLEGE

Accounting, A
Administrative Assistant and Secretarial Science, A
Airline/Commercial/Professional Pilot and Flight
  Crew, A
Applied Horticulture/Horticultural Operations, A
Artificial Intelligence and Robotics, A
Automobile/Automotive Mechanics
  Technology/Technician, A
Banking and Financial Support Services, A
Child Development, A
Civil Engineering Technology/Technician, A
Communications Technology/Technician, A
Computer Graphics, A
Computer Programming, Specific Applications, A
Computer Systems Networking and
  Telecommunications, A
Corrections, A
Court Reporting/Court Reporter, A
Criminal Justice/Police Science, A
Dental Hygiene/Hygienist, A
Drafting/Design Engineering
  Technologies/Technicians, A
Electrical, Electronic and Communications
  Engineering Technology/Technician, A
Electromechanical Technology/Electromechanical
  Engineering Technology, A
Fire Science/Firefighting, A
Health Information/Medical Records
  Administration/Administrator, A
Heating, Air Conditioning and Refrigeration
  Technology/Technician, A
Human Services, A
Hydraulics and Fluid Power Technology, A
Industrial Technology/Technician, A
Interior Design, A
Legal Administrative Assistant/Secretary, A
Logistics and Materials Management, A
Machine Tool Technology/Machinist, A
Management Information Systems and Services, A
Marketing/Marketing Management, A
Nursing - Registered Nurse Training, A
Operations Management and Supervision, A
Physical Therapist Assistant, A
Physical Therapy/Therapist, A
Quality Control Technology/Technician, A
Radio and Television Broadcasting
  Technology/Technician, A
Surgical Technology/Technologist, A
Technical and Business Writing, A

HERZING COLLEGE

Computer and Information Sciences, AB
Computer Programming, A
Computer Systems Networking and
  Telecommunications, A
Drafting and Design Technology/Technician, AB
Electrical, Electronic and Communications
  Engineering Technology/Technician, AB

ITT TECHNICAL INSTITUTE (GREEN BAY)

Animation, Interactive Technology, Video Graphics
  and Special Effects, B
Business Administration and Management, B
CAD/CADD Drafting and/or Design
  Technology/Technician, A
Computer and Information Systems Security, B
Computer Programming/Programmer, A
Computer Software Technology/Technician, B
Computer Systems Networking and
  Telecommunications, B
Criminal Justice/Law Enforcement Administration, B
E-Commerce/Electronic Commerce, B
Electrical, Electronic and Communications
  Engineering Technology/Technician, AB
System, Networking, and LAN/WAN
  Management/Manager, A

Web Page, Digital/Multimedia and Information
  Resources Design, A
Web/Multimedia Management and Webmaster, A

ITT TECHNICAL INSTITUTE (GREENFIELD)

Animation, Interactive Technology, Video Graphics
  and Special Effects, B
Business Administration and Management, B
CAD/CADD Drafting and/or Design
  Technology/Technician, A
Computer and Information Systems Security, B
Computer Programming/Programmer, A
Criminal Justice/Law Enforcement Administration, B
E-Commerce/Electronic Commerce, B
Electrical, Electronic and Communications
  Engineering Technology/Technician, AB
System, Networking, and LAN/WAN
  Management/Manager, A
Web Page, Digital/Multimedia and Information
  Resources Design, A
Web/Multimedia Management and Webmaster, A

LAC COURTE OREILLES OJIBWA COMMUNITY COLLEGE

Administrative Assistant and Secretarial Science, A
American Indian/Native American Studies, A
Business Administration and Management, A
Liberal Arts and Sciences Studies and
  Humanities, A
Medical/Clinical Assistant, A
Natural Resources Management/Development and
  Policy, A
Nursing - Registered Nurse Training, A
Social Work, A
Substance Abuse/Addiction Counseling, A

LAKELAND COLLEGE

Accounting, B
Art/Art Studies, General, B
Biochemistry, B
Biology/Biological Sciences, B
Business Administration and Management, B
Business Administration, Management and
  Operations, M
Business Teacher Education, B
Chemistry, B
Computer Science, B
Criminal Justice/Safety Studies, B
Education, M
Elementary Education and Teaching, B
English Composition, B
English Language and Literature, B
German Language and Literature, B
History, B
International Business/Trade/Commerce, B
Junior High/Intermediate/Middle School Education
  and Teaching, B
Kindergarten/PreSchool Education and Teaching, B
Marketing/Marketing Management, B
Mathematics, B
Music, B
Music Teacher Education, B
Non-Profit/Public/Organizational Management, B
Psychology, B
Religion/Religious Studies, B
Resort Management, B
Science Teacher Education/General Science
  Teacher Education, B
Secondary Education and Teaching, B
Sociology, B
Spanish Language and Literature, B
Theology and Religious Vocations, M

LAKESHORE TECHNICAL COLLEGE

Accounting, A
Administrative Assistant and Secretarial Science, A
Computer and Information Sciences, A
Computer Programming, A
Computer Programming/Programmer, A
Computer Systems Analysis/Analyst, A
Court Reporting/Court Reporter, A
Criminal Justice/Police Science, A
Dental Hygiene/Hygienist, A

Drafting/Design Engineering
 Technologies/Technicians, A
Electrical, Electronic and Communications
 Engineering Technology/Technician, A
Electromechanical Technology/Electromechanical
 Engineering Technology, A
Finance, A
Legal Assistant/Paralegal, A
Management Science, A
Marketing/Marketing Management, A
Medical Administrative Assistant/Secretary, A
Nursing - Registered Nurse Training, A
Quality Control Technology/Technician, A
Radiologic Technology/Science - Radiographer, A

LAWRENCE UNIVERSITY

Ancient/Classical Greek Language and Literature, B
Anthropology, B
Archeology, B
Art History, Criticism and Conservation, B
Art Teacher Education, B
Biochemistry, B
Biology/Biological Sciences, B
Chemistry, B
Chinese Language and Literature, B
Classics and Classical
 Languages, Literatures, and Linguistics, B
Cognitive Psychology and Psycholinguistics, B
Cognitive Sciences, B
Computer Science, B
Drama and Dramatics/Theatre Arts, B
East Asian Studies, B
Ecology, B
Economics, B
English Language and Literature, B
Environmental Studies, B
Ethnic, Cultural Minority, and Gender Studies, B
Fine/Studio Arts, B
French Language and Literature, B
Geology/Earth Science, B
German Language and Literature, B
History, B
International Economics, B
International Relations and Affairs, B
Japanese Language and Literature, B
Latin Language and Literature, B
Linguistics, B
Mathematics, B
Mathematics and Computer Science, B
Music, B
Music Pedagogy, B
Music Performance, B
Music Teacher Education, B
Music Theory and Composition, B
Neuroscience, B
Philosophy, B
Physics, B
Piano and Organ, B
Political Science and Government, B
Pre-Dentistry Studies, B
Pre-Law Studies, B
Pre-Medicine/Pre-Medical Studies, B
Pre-Veterinary Studies, B
Psychology, B
Religion/Religious Studies, B
Russian Language and Literature, B
Russian Studies, B
Secondary Education and Teaching, B
Slavic Studies, B
Social Psychology, B
Spanish Language and Literature, B
Violin, Viola, Guitar and Other Stringed
 Instruments, B
Voice and Opera, B
Wind and Percussion Instruments, B

MADISON AREA TECHNICAL COLLEGE

Accounting, A
Administrative Assistant and Secretarial Science, A
Agricultural Mechanization, A
Architectural Engineering Technology/Technician, A
Automobile/Automotive Mechanics
 Technology/Technician, A
Biology Technician/BioTechnology Laboratory
 Technician, A
Business Administration and Management, A

Business Teacher Education, A
Child Development, A
Civil Engineering Technology/Technician, A
Clinical/Medical Laboratory Technician, A
Commercial and Advertising Art, A
Communications Technology/Technician, A
Computer Engineering Technology/Technician, A
Computer Programming/Programmer, A
Computer Typography and Composition Equipment
 Operator, A
Court Reporting/Court Reporter, A
Criminal Justice/Police Science, A
Culinary Arts/Chef Training, A
Data Processing and Data Processing
 Technology/Technician, A
Dental Hygiene/Hygienist, A
Dietetics/Dieticians, A
Drafting/Design Engineering
 Technologies/Technicians, A
Electrical, Electronic and Communications
 Engineering Technology/Technician, A
Emergency Medical Technology/Technician (EMT
 Paramedic), A
Fashion Merchandising, A
Finance, A
Fire Science/Firefighting, A
Graphic and Printing Equipment Operator
 Production, A
Health and Medical Laboratory Technologies, A
Hospitality Administration/Management, A
Human Services, A
Industrial Radiologic Technology/Technician, A
Insurance, A
Interior Design, A
Liberal Arts and Sciences Studies and
 Humanities, A
Marketing/Marketing Management, A
Medical Administrative Assistant/Secretary, A
Nursing - Registered Nurse Training, A
Occupational Therapy/Therapist, A
Parks, Recreation, Leisure and Fitness Studies, A
Photography, A
Real Estate, A
Respiratory Care Therapy/Therapist, A
Tourism and Travel Services Management, A
Veterinary/Animal Health Technology/Technician and
 Veterinary Assistant, A
Welding Technology/Welder, A

MARANATHA BAPTIST BIBLE COLLEGE

Administrative Assistant and Secretarial Science, AB
Bible/Biblical Studies, B
Business Administration and Management, B
Business Teacher Education, B
Education, B
Elementary Education and Teaching, B
Humanities/Humanistic Studies, B
Kindergarten/PreSchool Education and
 Teaching, AB
Liberal Arts and Sciences Studies and
 Humanities, B
Music, B
Music Teacher Education, B
Nursing - Registered Nurse Training, B
Physical Education Teaching and Coaching, B
Religion/Religious Studies, AB
Religious Education, B
Religious/Sacred Music, B
Science Teacher Education/General Science
 Teacher Education, B
Secondary Education and Teaching, B
Speech and Rhetorical Studies, B
Theology and Religious Vocations, M

MARIAN COLLEGE OF FOND DU LAC

Accounting, B
Art Teacher Education, B
Art Therapy/Therapist, B
Biological and Physical Sciences, B
Biology Teacher Education, B
Biology/Biological Sciences, B
Business Administration and Management, B
Business Administration, Management and
 Operations, M
Business/Managerial Economics, B

Chemistry, B
Chemistry Teacher Education, B
Clinical Laboratory Science/Medical
 Technology/Technologist, B
Communication Studies/Speech Communication
 and Rhetoric, B
Criminal Justice/Law Enforcement Administration, B
CytoTechnology/Cytotechnologist, B
Education, BMD
Educational Leadership and Administration, MD
Elementary Education and Teaching, B
English Language and Literature, B
English/Language Arts Teacher Education, B
Finance, B
Fine/Studio Arts, B
Foreign Languages and Literatures, B
History, B
History Teacher Education, B
Information Technology, B
International Relations and Affairs, B
Junior High/Intermediate/Middle School Education
 and Teaching, B
Kindergarten/PreSchool Education and Teaching, B
Liberal Arts and Sciences Studies and
 Humanities, B
Marketing/Marketing Management, B
Mathematics, B
Mathematics Teacher Education, B
Medical Radiologic Technology/Science - Radiation
 Therapist, B
Music, B
Music Management and Merchandising, B
Music Teacher Education, B
Nursing, M
Nursing - Adult, M
Nursing - Registered Nurse Training, B
Nursing Education, M
Organizational Management, M
Political Science and Government, B
Pre-Dentistry Studies, B
Pre-Law Studies, B
Pre-Medicine/Pre-Medical Studies, B
Pre-Veterinary Studies, B
Psychology, B
Quality Management, M
Science Teacher Education/General Science
 Teacher Education, B
Secondary Education and Teaching, B
Social Sciences, B
Social Work, B
Sociology, B
Spanish Language and Literature, B
Spanish Language Teacher Education, B
Sport and Fitness Administration/Management, B

MARQUETTE UNIVERSITY

Accounting, BM
Advertising, B
Advertising and Public Relations, M
African-American/Black Studies, B
Analytical Chemistry, MD
Anthropology, B
Athletic Training and Sports Medicine, B
Audiology/Audiologist and Speech-Language
 Pathology/Pathologist, B
Biochemistry, B
Bioinformatics, M
Biological and Biomedical Sciences, MD
Biology/Biological Sciences, B
Biomedical Engineering, MD
Biomedical Sciences, B
Biomedical/Medical Engineering, B
Broadcast Journalism, B
Business Administration and Management, B
Business Administration, Management and
 Operations, MO
Business/Managerial Economics, B
Cell Biology and Anatomy, MD
Chemistry, BMD
Civil Engineering, BMD
Classics and Classical
 Languages, Literatures, and Linguistics, B
Clinical Psychology, M
Clinical/Medical Laboratory Technician, B
Communication and Media Studies, M
Communication Disorders, M

Communication Studies/Speech Communication and Rhetoric, B
Communication, Journalism and Related Programs, B
Computational Mathematics, B
Computer Engineering, BMD
Computer Science, BM
Construction Engineering and Management, MD
Creative Writing, B
Criminology, AB
Dental Hygiene/Hygienist, B
Dentistry, P
Developmental Biology and Embryology, MD
Drama and Dramatics/Theatre Arts, B
Ecology, MD
Economics, BM
Education, BMDO
Electrical Engineering, MD
Electrical, Electronics and Communications Engineering, B
Elementary Education and Teaching, B
Engineering, B
Engineering and Applied Sciences, MD
Engineering Management, M
English, MD
English Language and Literature, B
English/Language Arts Teacher Education, B
Environmental Engineering Technology/Environmental Technology, MD
Environmental/Environmental Health Engineering, B
Ethics, MD
Evolutionary Biology, MD
Finance, B
Foreign Language Teacher Education, BM
Foreign Languages, Literatures, and Linguistics, B
French Language and Literature, B
Genetics, MD
Geotechnical Engineering, MD
German Language and Literature, B
Gerontological Nursing, O
History, BMD
Human Resources Development, M
Human Resources Management and Services, M
Human Resources Management/Personnel Administration, B
Industrial Engineering, B
Information Science/Studies, B
Inorganic Chemistry, MD
Intercultural/Multicultural and Diversity Studies, B
Interdisciplinary Studies, BD
International Affairs, MO
International Business/Trade/Commerce, B
International Relations and Affairs, B
International/Global Studies, B
Journalism, BM
Junior High/Intermediate/Middle School Education and Teaching, B
Kinesiology and Exercise Science, B
Law and Legal Studies, PO
Management Information Systems and Services, B
Management of Technology, M
Marketing/Marketing Management, B
Mass Communication/Media Studies, BM
Maternal/Child Health and Neonatal Nurse/Nursing, O
Mathematics, BMD
Mathematics Teacher Education, BM
Mechanical Engineering, BMD
Media Studies, M
Medieval and Renaissance Studies, M
Microbiology, MD
Molecular Biology, BMD
Multi-/Interdisciplinary Studies, B
Neurobiology and Neurophysiology, MD
Nurse Midwife/Nursing Midwifery, O
Nursing, MDO
Nursing - Adult, O
Nursing - Advanced Practice, M
Nursing - Registered Nurse Training, B
Oral and Dental Sciences, M
Organic Chemistry, MD
Orthodontics, M
Pediatric Nurse/Nursing, O
Philosophy, BMD
Physical Chemistry, MD
Physical Therapy/Therapist, BM

Physician Assistant, BM
Physics, B
Physiology, MD
Political Science and Government, BMO
Pre-Dentistry Studies, B
Pre-Law Studies, B
Pre-Medicine/Pre-Medical Studies, B
Psychology, BMD
Public Relations/Image Management, B
Religion/Religious Studies, B
Science Teacher Education/General Science Teacher Education, B
Secondary Education and Teaching, B
Social Science Teacher Education, B
Social Studies Teacher Education, B
Social Work, B
Sociology, B
Spanish Language and Literature, BM
Speech and Interpersonal Communication, M
Speech and Rhetorical Studies, B
Statistics, BM
Structural Engineering, MD
Teacher Education and Professional Development, Specific Subject Areas, B
Theology and Religious Vocations, MD
Transportation and Highway Engineering, MD
Water Resources Engineering, MD
Women's Studies, B

MID-STATE TECHNICAL COLLEGE

Accounting, A
Administrative Assistant and Secretarial Science, A
Business Administration and Management, A
Civil Engineering Technology/Technician, A
Computer and Information Sciences, A
Computer Engineering Technology/Technician, A
Computer Programming, A
Computer Programming, Specific Applications, A
Corrections, A
Criminal Justice/Police Science, A
Data Entry/Microcomputer Applications, A
Drafting/Design Engineering Technologies/Technicians, A
Electrical, Electronic and Communications Engineering Technology/Technician, A
Hotel/Motel Administration/Management, A
Industrial Technology/Technician, A
Information Science/Studies, A
Instrumentation Technology/Technician, A
Marketing/Marketing Management, A
Nursing - Registered Nurse Training, A
Quality Control Technology/Technician, A
Respiratory Care Therapy/Therapist, A

MILWAUKEE AREA TECHNICAL COLLEGE

Accounting Technology/Technician and Bookkeeping, A
Administrative Assistant and Secretarial Science, A
Agricultural Business and Management, A
Automobile/Automotive Mechanics Technology/Technician, A
Baking and Pastry Arts/Baker/Pastry Chef, A
Barbering/Barber, A
Biomedical Technology/Technician, A
Business Administration and Management, A
Business, Management, Marketing, and Related Support Services, A
Cardiovascular Technology/Technologist, A
Chemical Engineering, A
Child Development, A
Civil Engineering Technology/Technician, A
Clinical/Medical Laboratory Technician, A
Commercial and Advertising Art, A
Communications Technology/Technician, A
Computer and Information Sciences, A
Computer Graphics, A
Computer Programming, A
Computer Programming, Specific Applications, A
Computer Programming, Vendor/Product Certification, A
Computer Science, A
Computer Systems Analysis/Analyst, A
Computer/Information Technology Services Administration and Management, A
Construction Engineering Technology/Technician, A

Consumer Merchandising/Retailing Management, A
Cooking and Related Culinary Arts, A
Cosmetology and Related Personal Grooming Arts, A
Cosmetology/Cosmetologist, A
Criminal Justice/Law Enforcement Administration, A
Criminal Justice/Police Science, A
Culinary Arts/Chef Training, A
Data Entry/Microcomputer Applications, A
Data Processing and Data Processing Technology/Technician, A
Dental Assisting/Assistant, A
Dental Hygiene/Hygienist, A
Dietetic Technician (DTR), A
Dietetics/Dieticians, A
Drafting and Design Technology/Technician, A
E-Commerce/Electronic Commerce, A
Educational/Instructional Media Design, A
Electrical, Electronic and Communications Engineering Technology/Technician, A
Electrical/Electronics Equipment Installation and Repair, A
Electrocardiograph Technology/Technician, A
Electromechanical Technology/Electromechanical Engineering Technology, A
Environmental Engineering Technology/Environmental Technology, A
Environmental Health, A
Fashion Merchandising, A
Film/Cinema Studies, A
Finance, A
Fire Science/Firefighting, A
Food Technology and Processing, A
Funeral Service and Mortuary Science, A
Furniture Design and Manufacturing, A
Graphic and Printing Equipment Operator Production, A
Hair Styling/Stylist and Hair Design, A
Health Unit Coordinator/Ward Clerk, A
Heating, Air Conditioning and Refrigeration Technology/Technician, A
Heating, Air Conditioning, Ventilation and Refrigeration Maintenance Technology/Technician, A
Hospitality and Recreation Marketing Operations, A
Hotel/Motel Administration/Management, A
Human Services, A
Hydrology and Water Resources Science, A
Industrial Design, A
Industrial Radiologic Technology/Technician, A
Industrial Technology/Technician, A
Information Technology, A
Landscaping and Groundskeeping, A
Legal Administrative Assistant/Secretary, A
Legal Assistant/Paralegal, A
Liberal Arts and Sciences Studies and Humanities, A
Licensed Practical/Vocational Nurse Training, A
Machine Tool Technology/Machinist, A
Marketing/Marketing Management, A
Mechanical Engineering/Mechanical Technology/Technician, A
Medical Administrative Assistant/Secretary, A
Music, A
Nursing - Registered Nurse Training, A
Occupational Therapy/Therapist, A
Opticianry/Ophthalmic Dispensing Optician, A
Photography, A
Physical Therapy/Therapist, A
Pre-Engineering, A
Publishing, A
Radio and Television Broadcasting Technology/Technician, A
Real Estate, A
Respiratory Care Therapy/Therapist, A
Substance Abuse/Addiction Counseling, A
Survey Technology/Surveying, A
System Administration/Administrator, A
Tool and Die Technology/Technician, A
Tourism and Travel Services Marketing Operations, A
Transportation and Materials Moving, A
Transportation/Transportation Management, A
Web/Multimedia Management and Webmaster, A
Welding Technology/Welder, A

Word Processing, A

MILWAUKEE INSTITUTE OF ART AND DESIGN

Art/Art Studies, General, B
Commercial and Advertising Art, B
Drawing, B
Fine/Studio Arts, B
Industrial Design, B
Interior Design, B
Painting, B
Photography, B
Printmaking, B
Sculpture, B

MILWAUKEE SCHOOL OF ENGINEERING

Architectural Engineering, B
Biomedical Engineering, M
Biomedical/Medical Engineering, B
Business Administration and Management, B
Business Administration, Management and
   Operations, M
Business/Commerce, B
Cardiovascular Sciences, M
Clinical Laboratory Sciences, M
Communication, Journalism and Related
   Programs, B
Computer Engineering, B
Computer Software Engineering, B
Construction Management, B
Electrical, Electronics and Communications
   Engineering, B
Engineering and Applied Sciences, M
Engineering Management, M
Environmental Engineering
   Technology/Environmental Technology, M
Industrial Engineering, B
International Business/Trade/Commerce, B
Management Information Systems and Services, B
Mechanical Engineering, B
Medical Informatics, M
Nursing - Registered Nurse Training, B
Structural Engineering, M

MORAINE PARK TECHNICAL COLLEGE

Accounting, A
Administrative Assistant and Secretarial Science, A
Automobile/Automotive Mechanics
   Technology/Technician, A
Business and Personal/Financial Services Marketing
   Operations, A
Child Care Provider/Assistant, A
Chiropractic, A
Civil Engineering Technology/Technician, A
Clinical/Medical Laboratory Assistant, A
Computer Programming, Specific Applications, A
Computer Systems Networking and
   Telecommunications, A
Construction Trades, A
Corrections and Criminal Justice, A
Cosmetology, Barber/Styling, and Nail Instructor, A
Culinary Arts/Chef Training, A
Drafting/Design Engineering
   Technologies/Technicians, A
Early Childhood Education and Teaching, A
Electrical and Power Transmission
   Installation/Installer, A
Electromechanical Technology/Electromechanical
   Engineering Technology, A
Engineering Technology, A
Graphic and Printing Equipment Operator
   Production, A
Health Information/Medical Records
   Technology/Technician, A
Heating, Air Conditioning and Refrigeration
   Technology/Technician, A
Legal Administrative Assistant/Secretary, A
Licensed Practical/Vocational Nurse Training, A
Machine Shop Technology/Assistant, A
Management Information Systems and Services, A
Marketing/Marketing Management, A
Medical Radiologic Technology/Science - Radiation
   Therapist, A
Medical Transcription/Transcriptionist, A
Medical/Clinical Assistant, A

Nuclear Medical Technology/Technologist, A
Nurse/Nursing Assistant/Aide and Patient Care
   Assistant, A
Nursing - Registered Nurse Training, A
Radiologic Technology/Science - Radiographer, A
Respiratory Care Therapy/Therapist, A
Substance Abuse/Addiction Counseling, A
Surgical Technology/Technologist, A
Tool and Die Technology/Technician, A
Web Page, Digital/Multimedia and Information
   Resources Design, A
Welding Technology/Welder, A

MOUNT MARY COLLEGE

Accounting, B
Art Teacher Education, B
Art Therapy/Therapist, BM
Art/Art Studies, General, B
Behavioral Sciences, B
Bilingual and Multilingual Education, B
Biology Teacher Education, B
Biology/Biological Sciences, B
Business Administration and Management, B
Business Teacher Education, B
Chemistry, B
Chemistry Teacher Education, B
Commercial and Advertising Art, B
Communication Studies/Speech Communication
   and Rhetoric, B
Computer Science, B
Corrections and Criminal Justice, B
Counselor Education/School Counseling and
   Guidance Services, M
Dietetics/Dieticians, B
Education, BM
Elementary Education and Teaching, B
English Language and Literature, B
English/Language Arts Teacher Education, B
Fashion Merchandising, B
Fashion/Apparel Design, B
French Language and Literature, B
French Language Teacher Education, B
Gerontology, M
Graphic Design, B
Health Education, M
History, B
History Teacher Education, B
Interior Design, B
International Relations and Affairs, B
Kindergarten/PreSchool Education and Teaching, B
Liberal Arts and Sciences Studies and
   Humanities, B
Marketing/Marketing Management, B
Mathematics, B
Mathematics Teacher Education, B
Music, B
Music Teacher Education, B
Nursing - Registered Nurse Training, B
Nutritional Sciences, M
Occupational Therapy/Therapist, BM
Philosophy, B
Pre-Dentistry Studies, B
Pre-Law Studies, B
Pre-Medicine/Pre-Medical Studies, B
Pre-Veterinary Studies, B
Psychology, B
Public Relations/Image Management, B
Religion/Religious Studies, B
Religious Education, B
Secondary Education and Teaching, B
Social Work, B
Spanish Language and Literature, B
Spanish Language Teacher Education, B
Technical and Business Writing, B

NICOLET AREA TECHNICAL COLLEGE

Accounting, A
Administrative Assistant and Secretarial Science, A
Automobile/Automotive Mechanics
   Technology/Technician, A
Business Administration and Management, A
Child Development, A
Computer and Information Sciences, A
Computer Science, A
Criminal Justice/Police Science, A
Culinary Arts/Chef Training, A

Data Processing and Data Processing
   Technology/Technician, A
Hotel/Motel Administration/Management, A
Kindergarten/PreSchool Education and Teaching, A
Liberal Arts and Sciences Studies and
   Humanities, A
Machine Tool Technology/Machinist, A
Marketing/Marketing Management, A
Medical Administrative Assistant/Secretary, A
Nursing - Registered Nurse Training, A
Physical Therapist Assistant, A
Real Estate, A
Survey Technology/Surveying, A
Welding Technology/Welder, A

NORTHCENTRAL TECHNICAL COLLEGE

Accounting, A
Administrative Assistant and Secretarial Science, A
Architectural Engineering Technology/Technician, A
Automobile/Automotive Mechanics
   Technology/Technician, A
Business Administration and Management, A
Criminal Justice/Police Science, A
Dental Hygiene/Hygienist, A
Drafting and Design Technology/Technician, A
Drafting/Design Engineering
   Technologies/Technicians, A
Electrical, Electronic and Communications
   Engineering Technology/Technician, A
Electromechanical Technology/Electromechanical
   Engineering Technology, A
Graphic and Printing Equipment Operator
   Production, A
Human Services, A
Industrial Radiologic Technology/Technician, A
Industrial Technology/Technician, A
Information Science/Studies, A
Kindergarten/PreSchool Education and Teaching, A
Laser and Optical Technology/Technician, A
Legal Administrative Assistant/Secretary, A
Licensed Practical/Vocational Nurse Training, A
Machine Tool Technology/Machinist, A
Marketing/Marketing Management, A
Medical Administrative Assistant/Secretary, A
Nursing - Registered Nurse Training, A
Radiologic Technology/Science - Radiographer, A
Sign Language Interpretation and Translation, A

NORTHEAST WISCONSIN TECHNICAL COLLEGE

Accounting, A
Accounting and Related Services, A
Accounting Technology/Technician and
   Bookkeeping, A
Administrative Assistant and Secretarial Science, A
Agribusiness, A
Agricultural Business and Management, A
Agricultural Mechanization, A
Agriculture, A
Apparel and Accessories Marketing Operations, A
Architectural Engineering Technology/Technician, A
Autobody/Collision and Repair
   Technology/Technician, A
Automobile/Automotive Mechanics
   Technology/Technician, A
Automotive Engineering Technology/Technician, A
Business Administration and Management, A
Business Administration, Management and
   Operations, A
Business, Management, Marketing, and Related
   Support Services, A
Carpentry/Carpenter, A
Child Care and Support Services Management, A
Civil Engineering Technology/Technician, A
Clinical/Medical Laboratory Technician, A
Communications Technologies/Technicians and
   Support Services, A
Computer and Information Sciences and Support
   Services, A
Computer Programming/Programmer, A
Corrections, A
Criminal Justice/Police Science, A
Data Processing and Data Processing
   Technology/Technician, A
Dental Assisting/Assistant, A

Dental Hygiene/Hygienist, A
Diesel Mechanics Technology/Technician, A
Drafting and Design Technology/Technician, A
Drafting/Design Engineering
    Technologies/Technicians, A
Electrical, Electronic and Communications
    Engineering Technology/Technician, A
Electromechanical Technology/Electromechanical
    Engineering Technology, A
Emergency Medical Technology/Technician (EMT
    Paramedic), A
Environmental Studies, A
Farm/Farm and Ranch Management, A
Fashion Merchandising, A
Finance, A
Finance and Financial Management Services, A
Fire Science/Firefighting, A
Fire Services Administration, A
General Merchandising, Sales, and Related
    Marketing Operations, A
General Office Occupations and Clerical Services, A
Health Information/Medical Records
    Technology/Technician, A
Heating, Air Conditioning and Refrigeration
    Technology/Technician, A
Heating, Air Conditioning, Ventilation and
    Refrigeration Maintenance
    Technology/Technician, A
Heavy/Industrial Equipment Maintenance
    Technologies, A
Industrial Design, A
Industrial Technology/Technician, A
Instrumentation Technology/Technician, A
Legal Administrative Assistant/Secretary, A
Legal Assistant/Paralegal, A
Licensed Practical/Vocational Nurse Training, A
Lineworker, A
Logistics and Materials Management, A
Machine Shop Technology/Assistant, A
Machine Tool Technology/Machinist, A
Marine Maintenance/Fitter and Ship Repair
    Technology/Technician, A
Marketing/Marketing Management, A
Mass Communication/Media Studies, A
Mechanic and Repair Technologies/Technicians, A
Mechanical Drafting and Mechanical Drafting
    CAD/CADD, A
Mechanical Engineering/Mechanical
    Technology/Technician, A
Medical Administrative Assistant/Secretary, A
Medical Office Management/Administration, A
Medical/Clinical Assistant, A
Nurse/Nursing Assistant/Aide and Patient Care
    Assistant, A
Nursing - Registered Nurse Training, A
Petroleum Technology/Technician, A
Physical Therapist Assistant, A
Physical Therapy/Therapist, A
Precision Metal Working, A
Precision Production, A
Precision Systems Maintenance and Repair
    Technologies, A
Quality Control Technology/Technician, A
Respiratory Care Therapy/Therapist, A
Surgical Technology/Technologist, A
Systems Science and Theory, A
Telecommunications Technology/Technician, A
Tourism and Travel Services Management, A
Transportation and Materials Moving, A
Vehicle and Vehicle Parts and Accessories
    Marketing Operations, A
Watchmaking and Jewelrymaking, A
Welding Technology/Welder, A

NORTHLAND COLLEGE

American Indian/Native American Studies, B
Applied Mathematics, B
Art Teacher Education, B
Art/Art Studies, General, B
Atmospheric Sciences and Meteorology, B
Biological and Physical Sciences, B
Biology/Biological Sciences, B
Business Administration and Management, B
Business/Managerial Economics, B
Chemistry, B
Creative Writing, B

Ecology, B
Economics, B
Education, B
Elementary Education and Teaching, B
English Language and Literature, B
Environmental Biology, B
Environmental Education, B
Environmental Studies, B
Fine/Studio Arts, B
Forestry, B
Geology/Earth Science, B
History, B
Hydrology and Water Resources Science, B
Information Science/Studies, B
Interdisciplinary Studies, B
Junior High/Intermediate/Middle School Education
    and Teaching, B
Land Use Planning and
    Management/Development, B
Mathematics, B
Music, B
Music Teacher Education, B
Natural Resources and Conservation, B
Natural Resources Management/Development and
    Policy, B
Natural Sciences, B
Parks, Recreation and Leisure Facilities
    Management, B
Parks, Recreation, Leisure and Fitness Studies, B
Peace Studies and Conflict Resolution, B
Philosophy, B
Pre-Dentistry Studies, B
Pre-Law Studies, B
Pre-Medicine/Pre-Medical Studies, B
Pre-Veterinary Studies, B
Psychology, B
Religion/Religious Studies, B
Science Teacher Education/General Science
    Teacher Education, B
Secondary Education and Teaching, B
Social Sciences, B
Sociology, B
Therapeutic Recreation/Recreational Therapy, B
Wildlife and Wildlands Science and Management, B
Wildlife Biology, B
Zoology/Animal Biology, B

RIPON COLLEGE

Anthropology, B
Art/Art Studies, General, B
Biochemistry, B
Biology/Biological Sciences, B
Business Administration and Management, B
Chemistry, B
Communication Studies/Speech Communication
    and Rhetoric, B
Computer Science, B
Drama and Dramatics/Theatre Arts, B
Early Childhood Education and Teaching, B
Economics, B
Education, B
Elementary Education and Teaching, B
English Language and Literature, B
Environmental Studies, B
French Language and Literature, B
German Language and Literature, B
History, B
Interdisciplinary Studies, B
Latin American Studies, B
Mathematics, B
Music, B
Music Teacher Education, B
Philosophy, B
Physical Education Teaching and Coaching, B
Physical Sciences, B
Physiological Psychology/Psychobiology, B
Political Science and Government, B
Pre-Dentistry Studies, B
Pre-Law Studies, B
Pre-Medicine/Pre-Medical Studies, B
Pre-Veterinary Studies, B
Psychology, B
Religion/Religious Studies, B
Romance Languages, Literatures, and Linguistics, B
Secondary Education and Teaching, B
Sociology, B

Spanish Language and Literature, B

ST. NORBERT COLLEGE

Accounting, B
Art/Art Studies, General, B
Biological and Physical Sciences, B
Biology/Biological Sciences, B
Business Administration and Management, B
Chemistry, B
Commercial and Advertising Art, B
Communication Studies/Speech Communication
    and Rhetoric, B
Computer and Information Sciences, B
Economics, B
Education, M
Elementary Education and Teaching, B
English Language and Literature, B
Environmental Sciences, B
Environmental Studies, B
French Language and Literature, B
Geology/Earth Science, B
German Language and Literature, B
History, B
Humanities/Humanistic Studies, B
International Business/Trade/Commerce, B
International Relations and Affairs, B
Mathematics, B
Music, B
Music Teacher Education, B
Philosophy, B
Physics, B
Political Science and Government, B
Psychology, B
Religion/Religious Studies, B
Sociology, B
Spanish Language and Literature, B
Theology and Religious Vocations, M

SILVER LAKE COLLEGE

Accounting, B
Art Teacher Education, B
Art/Art Studies, General, B
Biology/Biological Sciences, B
Business Administration and Management, B
Commercial and Advertising Art, A
Computer and Information Sciences, B
Education, M
Education/Teaching of Individuals with Mental
    Retardation, B
Education/Teaching of Individuals with Specific
    Learning Disabilities, B
Educational Administration and Supervision, M
Educational Leadership and Administration, M
Elementary Education and Teaching, B
English Language and Literature, B
General Studies, A
History, B
Human Resources Management/Personnel
    Administration, B
Information Science/Studies, B
Interdisciplinary Studies, B
Kindergarten/PreSchool Education and Teaching, B
Management, M
Mathematics, B
Music, B
Music Teacher Education, BM
Organizational Behavior Studies, M
Psychology, B
Social Sciences, B
Theology/Theological Studies, B
Web Page, Digital/Multimedia and Information
    Resources Design, B

SOUTHWEST WISCONSIN TECHNICAL COLLEGE

Accounting, A
Administrative Assistant and Secretarial Science, A
Agribusiness, A
Agricultural Mechanization, A
Autobody/Collision and Repair
    Technology/Technician, A
Automobile/Automotive Mechanics
    Technology/Technician, A
Child Development, A
Computer Programming/Programmer, A
Cosmetology/Cosmetologist, A

Culinary Arts/Chef Training, A
Dairy Science, A
Data Processing and Data Processing
    Technology/Technician, A
Dental Assisting/Assistant, A
Drafting and Design Technology/Technician, A
Drafting/Design Engineering
    Technologies/Technicians, A
Electrical, Electronic and Communications
    Engineering Technology/Technician, A
Electromechanical Technology/Electromechanical
    Engineering Technology, A
Finance, A
Food Technology and Processing, A
Human Services, A
Legal Administrative Assistant/Secretary, A
Licensed Practical/Vocational Nurse Training, A
Machine Tool Technology/Machinist, A
Marketing/Marketing Management, A
Mason/Masonry, A
Medical Transcription/Transcriptionist, A
Medical/Clinical Assistant, A
Nurse/Nursing Assistant/Aide and Patient Care
    Assistant, A
Nursing - Registered Nurse Training, A
Welding Technology/Welder, A

UNIVERSITY OF PHOENIX-WISCONSIN CAMPUS

Business Administration and Management, B
Business Administration, Management and
    Operations, M
Electronic Commerce, M
Health Services Administration, M
Information Technology, B
Management, M
Management Information Systems and Services, M
Management of Technology, M
Management Science, B
Organizational Management, M

UNIVERSITY OF WISCONSIN-BARABOO/SAUK COUNTY

Liberal Arts and Sciences Studies and
    Humanities, A

UNIVERSITY OF WISCONSIN-BARRON COUNTY

Liberal Arts and Sciences Studies and
    Humanities, A

UNIVERSITY OF WISCONSIN-EAU CLAIRE

Accounting, B
American Indian/Native American Studies, B
Art/Art Studies, General, B
Athletic Training and Sports Medicine, B
Biological and Biomedical Sciences, M
Biomedical Sciences, B
Business Administration and Management, B
Business Administration, Management and
    Operations, M
Chemistry, B
Communication Disorders, BM
Communication Studies/Speech Communication
    and Rhetoric, B
Computer and Information Sciences, B
Criminal Justice/Safety Studies, B
Drama and Dramatics/Theatre Arts, B
Economics, B
Education, M
Elementary Education and Teaching, BM
English, M
English Education, M
English Language and Literature, B
Environmental and Occupational Health, M
Environmental Health, B
Finance, B
French Language and Literature, B
Geography, B
Geology/Earth Science, B
Germanic Languages, Literatures, and Linguistics, B
Health/Health Care Administration/Management, B
History, BM
Information Resources Management/CIO Training, B

Journalism, B
Kinesiology and Exercise Science, B
Latin American Studies, B
Liberal Arts and Sciences Studies and
    Humanities, A
Marketing/Marketing Management, B
Mass Communication/Media Studies, B
Mathematics, B
Mathematics Teacher Education, M
Molecular Biology, B
Music, B
Music Therapy/Therapist, B
Nursing, M
Nursing - Registered Nurse Training, B
Philosophy, B
Physics, B
Political Science and Government, B
Psychology, BMO
Public Health, M
Reading Teacher Education, M
Religion/Religious Studies, B
School Psychology, MO
Science Teacher Education/General Science
    Teacher Education, BM
Secondary Education and Teaching, M
Social Studies Teacher Education, BM
Social Work, B
Sociology, B
Spanish Language and Literature, B
Special Education and Teaching, BM
Teacher Education and Professional
    Development, Specific Subject Areas, B

UNIVERSITY OF WISCONSIN-FOND DU LAC

Liberal Arts and Sciences Studies and
    Humanities, A

UNIVERSITY OF WISCONSIN-FOX VALLEY

Liberal Arts and Sciences Studies and
    Humanities, A

UNIVERSITY OF WISCONSIN-GREEN BAY

Accounting, B
Art/Art Studies, General, AB
Biology/Biological Sciences, AB
Biomedical Sciences, B
Business Administration and Management, AB
Chemistry, AB
Communication, Journalism and Related
    Programs, B
Computer Science, B
Developmental and Child Psychology, B
Drama and Dramatics/Theatre Arts, AB
Economics, AB
Education, M
Elementary Education and Teaching, B
English Language and Literature, AB
Environmental Policy, M
Environmental Sciences, ABM
Environmental Studies, AB
French Language and Literature, AB
General Studies, B
Geology/Earth Science, AB
Germanic
    Languages, Literatures, and Linguistics, AB
History, AB
Humanities/Humanistic Studies, AB
Information Science/Studies, AB
Interdisciplinary Studies, AB
Management, M
Mathematics, AB
Music, B
Nursing Science, B
Nutritional Sciences, B
Philosophy, AB
Political Science and Government, AB
Pre-Dentistry Studies, B
Psychology, AB
Social Work, ABM
Spanish Language and Literature, AB

Urban Studies/Affairs, AB

UNIVERSITY OF WISCONSIN-LA CROSSE

Accounting, B
Archeology, B
Art/Art Studies, General, B
Athletic Training and Sports Medicine, BM
Biological and Biomedical Sciences, M
Biology/Biological Sciences, B
Business Administration and Management, B
Business Administration, Management and
    Operations, M
Cell Biology and Anatomy, M
Chemistry, B
Clinical Laboratory Science/Medical
    Technology/Technologist, B
Clinical Microbiology, M
Communication Studies/Speech Communication
    and Rhetoric, B
Community Health and Preventive Medicine, M
Computer and Information Sciences, B
Drama and Dramatics/Theatre Arts, B
Economics, B
Education, M
Elementary Education and Teaching, BM
English Language and Literature, B
Exercise and Sports Science, M
Finance, B
French Language and Literature, B
General Studies, B
Geography, B
German Language and Literature, B
Health Education, M
Health Teacher Education, B
History, B
International Business/Trade/Commerce, B
Kinesiology and Exercise Science, B
Management Information Systems and Services, B
Marine Sciences, M
Marketing/Marketing Management, B
Mathematics, B
Microbiology, BM
Molecular Biology, M
Music, B
Nuclear Medical Technology/Technologist, B
Nurse Anesthetist, M
Parks, Recreation and Leisure Facilities
    Management, B
Philosophy, B
Physical Education Teaching and Coaching, M
Physical Therapy/Therapist, BM
Physician Assistant, BM
Physics, B
Physiology, M
Political Science and Government, B
Psychology, BMO
Public Health, M
Reading Teacher Education, M
Recreation and Park Management, M
Rehabilitation and Therapeutic Professions, B
Rehabilitation Sciences, M
School Psychology, MO
Science Teacher Education/General Science
    Teacher Education, B
Secondary Education and Teaching, M
Social Studies Teacher Education, B
Sociology, B
Software Engineering, M
Spanish Language and Literature, B
Special Education and Teaching, M
Sport and Fitness Administration/Management, M
Student Personnel Services, M
Therapeutic Recreation, M
Therapeutic Recreation/Recreational Therapy, B

UNIVERSITY OF WISCONSIN-MADISON

Accounting, B
Actuarial Science, BM
Adult and Continuing Education and Teaching, MD
Advertising, B
African Languages, Literatures, and Linguistics, B
African Studies, BMD
African-American/Black Studies, BM
Agricultural Business and Management, B
Agricultural Economics, BMD

Agricultural Engineering, MD
Agricultural Sciences, MD
Agricultural Teacher Education, B
Agricultural/Biological Engineering and
Bioengineering, B
Agriculture, B
Agronomy and Crop Science, B
Agronomy and Soil Sciences, MD
Allopathic Medicine, P
American/United States Studies/Civilization, B
Anatomy, MD
Animal Genetics, B
Animal Sciences, BMD
Anthropology, BMD
Apparel and Textiles, B
Applied Art, B
Applied Economics, MD
Applied Mathematics, B
Art Education, M
Art History, Criticism and Conservation, BMD
Art Teacher Education, B
Art/Art Studies, General, B
Arts Management, M
Asian Languages, MD
Asian Studies/Civilization, BMD
Astronomy, BD
Atmospheric Sciences and Meteorology, MD
Bacteriology, M
Biochemistry, BMD
Bioengineering, MD
Biological and Biomedical Sciences, MDO
Biological Anthropology, MD
Biology/Biological Sciences, B
Biomedical Engineering, MD
Biomedical/Medical Engineering, B
Biometry/Biometrics, M
Biophysics, D
Biopsychology, D
Botany/Plant Biology, BMD
Broadcast Journalism, B
Building/Construction
Finishing, Management, and Inspection, B
Business Administration and Management, B
Business Administration, Management and
Operations, MD
Cancer Biology/Oncology, D
Cartography, B
Cell Biology and Anatomy, MD
Cell/Cellular Biology and Histology, B
Chemical Engineering, BMD
Chemistry, BMD
Child and Family Studies, MD
Child Development, B
Chinese Language and Literature, B
Chinese Studies, MD
Civil Engineering, BMD
Classics and Classical
Languages, Literatures, and Linguistics, BMD
Clinical Laboratory Science/Medical
Technology/Technologist, B
Clinical Psychology, D
Cognitive Sciences, D
Communication and Media Studies, MD
Communication Disorders, BMD
Community Health and Preventive Medicine, MD
Comparative Literature, BMD
Composition, MD
Computer Engineering, B
Computer Science, BMD
Conservation Biology, M
Consumer Economics, MD
Consumer Services and Advocacy, B
Counseling Psychology, D
Counselor Education/School Counseling and
Guidance Services, M
Curriculum and Instruction, MD
Dairy Science, BMD
Design and Applied Arts, MD
Developmental and Child Psychology, B
Developmental Psychology, D
Dietetics/Dieticians, B
Drama and Dramatics/Theatre Arts, B
Ecology, MD
Economics, D
Education, MDO
Educational Administration and Supervision, O

Educational Leadership and Administration, MDO
Educational Psychology, MD
Electrical Engineering, MD
Electrical, Electronics and Communications
Engineering, B
Elementary Education and Teaching, B
Energy and Power Engineering, M
Engineering, B
Engineering and Applied Sciences, MDO
Engineering Mechanics, B
Engineering Physics, BMD
English, MD
English Education, M
English Language and Literature, B
Entomology, BMD
Entrepreneurship/Entrepreneurial Studies, M
Environmental Biology, MD
Environmental Engineering
Technology/Environmental Technology, MD
Environmental Policy and Resource
Management, MD
Environmental Sciences, MD
Environmental/Environmental Health Engineering, B
Ethnomusicology, MD
Experimental Psychology, B
Family and Consumer Economics and Related
Services, B
Family and Consumer Sciences/Home Economics
Teacher Education, B
Family and Consumer Sciences/Human
Sciences, BMD
Farm/Farm and Ranch Management, B
Fashion Merchandising, B
Finance, B
Finance and Banking, MD
Fine Arts and Art Studies, M
Food Science, B
Food Science and Technology, MD
Foods, Nutrition, and Wellness Studies, B
Foreign Language Teacher Education, M
Forestry, BMD
French Language and Literature, BMDO
Genetics, MD
Geographic Information Systems, MO
Geography, BMDO
Geological Engineering, MD
Geology/Earth Science, BMD
Geophysics and Seismology, BMD
German Language and Literature, BMD
Hebrew Language and Literature, BMD
Hebrew Studies, MD
Hispanic-American, Puerto Rican, and Mexican-
American/Chicano Studies, B
History, BMD
History and Philosophy of Science and
Technology, B
History of Science and Technology, MD
Horticultural Science, BMD
Human Development, MD
Human Resources Management and Services, MD
Hydrology and Water Resources Science, B
Industrial and Labor Relations, MD
Industrial and Manufacturing Management, MD
Industrial Engineering, B
Industrial/Management Engineering, MD
Information Science/Studies, MDO
Insurance, BMD
Interior Design, B
International Business/Trade/Commerce, M
International Relations and Affairs, B
Investment Management, MD
Italian Language and Literature, BMD
Japanese Language and Literature, B
Japanese Studies, MD
Journalism, BMD
Kindergarten/PreSchool Education and Teaching, B
Kinesiology and Movement Studies, MD
Labor and Industrial Relations, B
Landscape Architecture, BM
Latin American Studies, BM
Latin Language and Literature, B
Law and Legal Studies, MD
Legal and Justice Studies, M
Library Science, MDO
Limnology, MD
Linguistics, BMD

Logistics and Materials Management, M
Management Information Systems and
Services, MD
Manufacturing Engineering, M
Marine Sciences, MD
Marketing Research, M
Mass Communication/Media Studies, BMD
Materials Sciences, MD
Mathematics, BMD
Mathematics Teacher Education, M
Mechanical Engineering, BMD
Mechanics, MD
Medical Microbiology and Bacteriology, BD
Medical Physics, MD
Metallurgical Engineering, BMD
Microbiology, D
Mining and Mineral Engineering, B
Modern Greek Language and Literature, B
Molecular Biology, BMD
Music, BMD
Music Teacher Education, BMD
Music Theory and Composition, MD
Musicology and Ethnomusicology, MD
Natural Resources Management/Development and
Policy, BMD
Neurobiology and Neurophysiology, D
Neuroscience, MD
Nuclear Engineering, BMD
Nursing, MD
Nursing - Registered Nurse Training, B
Nutritional Sciences, MD
Occupational Therapy/Therapist, B
Oceanography, Chemical and Physical, MD
Parks, Recreation, Leisure and Fitness Studies, B
Pathology/Experimental Pathology, D
Performance, MD
Pharmaceutical Administration, MD
Pharmaceutical Sciences, MD
Pharmacology, BMD
Pharmacy, BP
Philosophy, BMD
Physical Education Teaching and Coaching, B
Physician Assistant, B
Physics, MD
Physiology, MD
Plant Pathology/Phytopathology, MD
Plant Sciences, MD
Political Science and Government, BMD
Polymer/Plastics Engineering, M
Portuguese Language and Literature, BMD
Poultry Science, B
Psychology, BD
Public Affairs, M
Public Relations/Image Management, B
Radio and Television, B
Real Estate, BMD
Recreation and Park Management, M
Rehabilitation Counseling, MD
Rehabilitation Sciences, M
Rural Sociology, M
Russian Language and Literature, B
Scandinavian
Languages, Literatures, and Linguistics, BMD
Science Teacher Education/General Science
Teacher Education, BM
Secondary Education and Teaching, B
Slavic Languages, Literatures, and Linguistics, BMD
Social Psychology, D
Social Sciences, M
Social Studies Teacher Education, M
Social Work, BMD
Sociology, BMD
South and Southeast Asian Studies, M
Southeast Asian Studies, B
Spanish Language and Literature, BMD
Special Education and Teaching, BMD
Statistics, BMD
Survey Technology/Surveying, B
Sustainable Development, M
Systems Engineering, MD
Theater, MD
Toxicology, BMD
Urban and Regional Planning, MD
Urban Studies/Affairs, B
Veterinary Medicine, P
Veterinary Sciences, MD

Vocational and Technical Education, MD
Water Resources, M
Wildlife and Wildlands Science and Management, B
Women's Studies, B
Zoology/Animal Biology, BMD

UNIVERSITY OF WISCONSIN-MANITOWOC

Liberal Arts and Sciences Studies and
  Humanities, A

UNIVERSITY OF WISCONSIN-MARATHON COUNTY

Liberal Arts and Sciences Studies and
  Humanities, A

UNIVERSITY OF WISCONSIN-MARINETTE

Liberal Arts and Sciences Studies and
  Humanities, A

UNIVERSITY OF WISCONSIN-MARSHFIELD/WOOD COUNTY

Liberal Arts and Sciences Studies and
  Humanities, A

UNIVERSITY OF WISCONSIN-MILWAUKEE

Accounting, B
African-American/Black Studies, B
Allied Health and Medical Assisting Services, MD
American Indian/Native American Studies, B
Anthropology, BMDO
Applied Mathematics, B
Architecture, BMDO
Art Education, M
Art History, Criticism and Conservation, BMO
Art Teacher Education, B
Art/Art Studies, General, B
Atmospheric Sciences and Meteorology, B
Audiology/Audiologist and Speech-Language
  Pathology/Pathologist, B
Bilingual and Multilingual Education, B
Biochemistry, B
Biological and Biomedical Sciences, MD
Biological Anthropology, M
Biology/Biological Sciences, B
Broadcast Journalism, B
Business Administration and Management, B
Business Administration, Management and
  Operations, MDO
Ceramic Arts and Ceramics, B
Chemistry, BMD
Civil Engineering, B
Classics and Classical
  Languages, Literatures, and Linguistics, BM
Clinical Laboratory Science/Medical
  Technology/Technologist, B
Clinical Laboratory Sciences, M
Clinical Psychology, MD
Communication and Media Studies, MO
Communication Disorders, M
Comparative Literature, BMDO
Computer Science, BMD
Criminal Justice/Law Enforcement Administration, B
Criminal Justice/Police Science, B
Criminology, M
Curriculum and Instruction, M
Dance, BM
Drama and Dramatics/Theatre Arts, B
Early Childhood Education and Teaching, M
Ecology, B
Economics, BMD
Education, BMDO
Educational Administration and Supervision, MO
Educational Psychology, MO
Electrical, Electronics and Communications
  Engineering, B
Elementary Education and Teaching, BM
Engineering, B
Engineering and Applied Sciences, MDO
English, MDO
English Language and Literature, B

Ethnic and Cultural Studies, B
Fiber, Textile and Weaving Arts, B
Film, Television, and Video Production, M
Film/Cinema Studies, B
Finance, B
Fine Arts and Art Studies, M
Fine/Studio Arts, B
Forestry, B
Foundations and Philosophy of Education, M
French Language and Literature, BM
Geography, BMDO
Geology/Earth Science, BMD
German Language and Literature, BM
Health Informatics, M
Health Information/Medical Records
  Administration/Administrator, B
Health/Health Care Administration/Management, B
Hebrew Language and Literature, B
Hebrew Studies, M
History, BMDO
Human Resources Development, MO
Human Resources Management/Personnel
  Administration, B
Industrial and Labor Relations, MO
Industrial Engineering, B
Information Science/Studies, MO
Interdisciplinary Studies, BD
International Relations and Affairs, B
Italian Language and Literature, BM
Journalism, BM
Kindergarten/PreSchool Education and Teaching, B
Kinesiology and Movement Studies, M
Labor and Industrial Relations, B
Latin American Studies, B
Latin Language and Literature, B
Liberal Studies, M
Library Science, MO
Linguistics, B
Management Information Systems and Services, B
Marketing/Marketing Management, B
Mass Communication/Media Studies, BM
Materials Engineering, B
Mathematics, BMD
Mechanical Engineering, B
Metal and Jewelry Arts, B
Middle School Education, M
Modern Greek Language and Literature, B
Museology/Museum Studies, O
Music, BMO
Music History, Literature, and Theory, B
Music Teacher Education, B
Music Therapy/Therapist, B
Natural Resources and Conservation, B
Nursing, MDO
Nursing - Registered Nurse Training, B
Occupational Therapy/Therapist, BM
Parks, Recreation, Leisure and Fitness Studies, B
Peace Studies and Conflict Resolution, B
Philosophy, BM
Physical Therapy/Therapist, B
Physics, BMD
Political Science and Government, BMD
Pre-Dentistry Studies, B
Pre-Law Studies, B
Pre-Medicine/Pre-Medical Studies, B
Psychology, BMD
Public Administration, MO
Public Health (MPH, DPH), B
Reading Teacher Education, M
Real Estate, B
Religion/Religious Studies, B
Russian Language and Literature, B
Russian Studies, B
Sculpture, B
Secondary Education and Teaching, BM
Slavic Languages, Literatures, and Linguistics, BM
Social Work, BMO
Sociology, BM
Spanish Language and Literature, BM
Special Education and Teaching, BM
Statistics, B
Theater, M
Therapeutic Recreation/Recreational Therapy, B
Urban Education and Leadership, MD
Urban Planning, MO
Urban Studies/Affairs, BMDO

Violin, Viola, Guitar and Other Stringed
  Instruments, B
Voice and Opera, B
Wind and Percussion Instruments, B
Women's Studies, B
Zoology/Animal Biology, B

UNIVERSITY OF WISCONSIN-OSHKOSH

Accounting, B
Anthropology, B
Art Teacher Education, B
Art/Art Studies, General, B
Audiology/Audiologist and Speech-Language
  Pathology/Pathologist, B
Biological and Biomedical Sciences, M
Biology/Biological Sciences, B
Broadcast Journalism, B
Business Administration and Management, B
Business Administration, Management and
  Operations, M
Chemistry, B
Clinical Laboratory Science/Medical
  Technology/Technologist, B
Computer Science, B
Counselor Education/School Counseling and
  Guidance Services, M
Criminal Justice/Law Enforcement Administration, B
Curriculum and Instruction, M
Drama and Dramatics/Theatre Arts, B
Early Childhood Education and Teaching, M
Economics, B
Education, BM
Educational Leadership and Administration, M
Elementary Education and Teaching, B
English, M
English Language and Literature, B
Experimental Psychology, M
Finance, B
Fine/Studio Arts, B
French Language and Literature, B
Geography, B
Geology/Earth Science, B
German Language and Literature, B
Health Services Administration, M
History, B
Human Services, B
Industrial and Organizational Psychology, M
International Relations and Affairs, B
Journalism, B
Kindergarten/PreSchool Education and Teaching, B
Liberal Arts and Sciences Studies and
  Humanities, AB
Management Information Systems and
  Services, BM
Marketing/Marketing Management, B
Mass Communication/Media Studies, B
Mathematics, B
Mathematics Teacher Education, M
Medical Microbiology and Bacteriology, B
Music, B
Music Teacher Education, B
Music Therapy/Therapist, B
Nursing, M
Nursing - Adult, M
Nursing - Advanced Practice, M
Nursing - Registered Nurse Training, B
Philosophy, B
Physical Education Teaching and Coaching, B
Physics, B
Political Science and Government, BM
Pre-Dentistry Studies, B
Pre-Law Studies, B
Pre-Medicine/Pre-Medical Studies, B
Pre-Veterinary Studies, B
Psychology, BM
Radio and Television, B
Reading Teacher Education, M
Religion/Religious Studies, B
Secondary Education and Teaching, B
Social Work, BM
Sociology, B
Spanish Language and Literature, B
Special Education and Teaching, BM
Teaching English as a Second or Foreign
  Language/ESL Language Instructor, B

Urban Studies/Affairs, B

UNIVERSITY OF WISCONSIN-PARKSIDE

Accounting, B
Art/Art Studies, General, B
Biological and Biomedical Sciences, B
Business Administration and Management, B
Business Administration, Management and
    Operations, M
Chemistry, B
Communication Studies/Speech Communication
    and Rhetoric, B
Computer Science, BM
Creative Writing, B
Criminal Justice/Law Enforcement Administration, B
Drama and Dramatics/Theatre Arts, B
Economics, B
English Language and Literature, B
Finance, B
French Language and Literature, B
Geography, B
Geology/Earth Science, B
German Language and Literature, B
History, B
Humanities/Humanistic Studies, B
Information Science/Studies, M
Interdisciplinary Studies, B
International Relations and Affairs, B
Mathematics, B
Molecular Biology, BM
Music, B
Nursing - Registered Nurse Training, B
Philosophy, B
Physics, B
Political Science and Government, B
Pre-Dentistry Studies, B
Pre-Law Studies, B
Pre-Medicine/Pre-Medical Studies, B
Pre-Pharmacy Studies, B
Pre-Veterinary Studies, B
Psychology, B
Sociology, B
Spanish Language and Literature, B
Sport and Fitness Administration/Management, B

UNIVERSITY OF WISCONSIN-PLATTEVILLE

Accounting, B
Adult and Continuing Education and Teaching, M
Agricultural Business and Management, B
Agricultural Teacher Education, B
Agronomy and Crop Science, B
Animal Sciences, B
Art/Art Studies, General, B
Biological and Physical Sciences, B
Biology/Biological Sciences, B
Broadcast Journalism, B
Building/Construction
    Finishing, Management, and Inspection, B
Business Administration and Management, B
Business/Managerial Economics, B
Cartography, B
Civil Engineering, B
Commercial and Advertising Art, B
Computer Science, BM
Computer Software Engineering, B
Counselor Education/School Counseling and
    Guidance Services, M
Criminal Justice/Law Enforcement Administration, B
Criminology, M
Economics, B
Education, BM
Electrical, Electronics and Communications
    Engineering, B
Elementary Education and Teaching, BM
Engineering and Applied Sciences, M
English Language and Literature, B
Environmental/Environmental Health Engineering, B
Geology/Earth Science, B
German Language and Literature, B
History, B
Industrial Design, B
Industrial Engineering, B
Industrial Technology/Technician, B
International Relations and Affairs, B

Junior High/Intermediate/Middle School Education
    and Teaching, B
Kindergarten/PreSchool Education and Teaching, B
Land Use Planning and
    Management/Development, B
Liberal Arts and Sciences Studies and
    Humanities, AB
Mass Communication/Media Studies, B
Mathematics, B
Mechanical Engineering, B
Middle School Education, M
Music, B
Ornamental Horticulture, B
Philosophy, B
Political Science and Government, B
Project Management, M
Psychology, B
Science Teacher Education/General Science
    Teacher Education, B
Secondary Education and Teaching, BM
Social Sciences, B
Spanish Language and Literature, B
Speech and Rhetorical Studies, B
Technology Education/Industrial Arts, B
Telecommunications Technology/Technician, B
Vocational and Technical Education, M

UNIVERSITY OF WISCONSIN-RICHLAND

Biological and Physical Sciences, A
Liberal Arts and Sciences Studies and
    Humanities, A

UNIVERSITY OF WISCONSIN-RIVER FALLS

Accounting, B
Agricultural Business and Management, B
Agricultural Education, M
Agricultural Sciences, M
Agricultural Teacher Education, B
Agricultural/Biological Engineering and
    Bioengineering, B
Agriculture, B
Agronomy and Crop Science, B
Animal Sciences, B
Art Teacher Education, B
Art/Art Studies, General, B
Biochemistry, B
Biology Teacher Education, B
Biology/Biological Sciences, B
BioTechnology, B
Broadcast Journalism, B
Business Administration and Management, B
Chemistry, B
Chemistry Teacher Education, B
Communication Disorders, BM
Computer and Information Sciences, B
Computer Science, B
Computer Teacher Education, B
Counselor Education/School Counseling and
    Guidance Services, MO
Dairy Science, B
Drama and Dramatics/Theatre Arts, B
Economics, B
Education, BM
Elementary Education and Teaching, BM
Engineering Technology, B
English Language and Literature, B
English/Language Arts Teacher Education, B
Environmental Studies, B
Equestrian/Equine Studies, B
Finance, B
Food Science, B
French Language and Literature, B
French Language Teacher Education, B
Geography, B
Geology/Earth Science, B
German Language and Literature, B
German Language Teacher Education, B
History, B
History Teacher Education, B
Horticultural Science, B
Information Science/Studies, B
Journalism, B
Land Use Planning and
    Management/Development, B

Liberal Arts and Sciences Studies and
    Humanities, B
Management, M
Management Information Systems and Services, B
Marketing/Marketing Management, B
Mathematics, B
Mathematics Teacher Education, BM
Music, B
Music Teacher Education, B
Natural Resources and Conservation, B
Natural Sciences, B
Physical Education Teaching and Coaching, B
Physical Sciences, B
Physics, B
Physics Teacher Education, B
Political Science and Government, B
Pre-Dentistry Studies, B
Pre-Law Studies, B
Pre-Medicine/Pre-Medical Studies, B
Pre-Pharmacy Studies, B
Pre-Veterinary Studies, B
Psychology, B
Public Relations/Image Management, B
Radio and Television, B
Reading Teacher Education, M
School Psychology, MO
Science Teacher Education/General Science
    Teacher Education, BM
Secondary Education and Teaching, B
Social Science Teacher Education, B
Social Sciences, B
Social Studies Teacher Education, BM
Social Work, B
Sociology, B
Soil Science and Agronomy, B
Spanish Language and Literature, B
Spanish Language Teacher Education, B
Speech and Rhetorical Studies, B
Teaching English as a Second or Foreign
    Language/ESL Language Instructor, B

UNIVERSITY OF WISCONSIN-ROCK COUNTY

Liberal Arts and Sciences Studies and
    Humanities, A

UNIVERSITY OF WISCONSIN-SHEBOYGAN

Liberal Arts and Sciences Studies and
    Humanities, A

UNIVERSITY OF WISCONSIN-STEVENS POINT

Accounting, B
Actuarial Science, B
Advertising and Public Relations, M
Arts Management, B
Athletic Training and Sports Medicine, B
Audiology/Audiologist and Speech-Language
    Pathology/Pathologist, B
Biology/Biological Sciences, B
Business Administration and Management, B
Business Administration, Management and
    Operations, M
Chemistry, B
Clinical Laboratory Science/Medical
    Technology/Technologist, B
Commercial and Advertising Art, B
Communication and Media Studies, M
Communication Disorders, M
Communication Studies/Speech Communication
    and Rhetoric, B
Computer and Information Sciences, B
Corporate and Organizational Communication, M
Counselor Education/School Counseling and
    Guidance Services, M
Dance, B
Dietetics/Dieticians, B
Drama and Dramatics/Theatre Arts, B
Economics, B
Education, BM
Educational Administration and Supervision, M
Elementary Education and Teaching, BM
English, M
English Language and Literature, B

Family and Consumer Economics and Related
   Services, B
Family and Consumer Sciences/Home Economics
   Teacher Education, B
Family and Consumer Sciences/Human
   Sciences, M
Fine/Studio Arts, B
Forestry, B
French Language and Literature, B
General Studies, B
Geography, B
German Language and Literature, B
Health and Physical Education, B
Health Promotion, M
History, BM
Human Development, M
Hydrology and Water Resources Science, B
Interior Design, B
International Relations and Affairs, B
Kindergarten/PreSchool Education and Teaching, B
Liberal Arts and Sciences Studies and
   Humanities, A
Mass Communication/Media Studies, M
Mathematics, B
Music, B
Music Teacher Education, BM
Natural Resources and Conservation, BM
Natural Resources Management/Development and
   Policy, B
Natural Sciences, B
Nutritional Sciences, M
Philosophy, B
Physical Education Teaching and Coaching, B
Physics, B
Political Science and Government, B
Polymer Chemistry, B
Psychology, B
Public Administration, B
Reading Teacher Education, M
Science Teacher Education/General Science
   Teacher Education, M
Secondary Education and Teaching, B
Social Sciences, B
Sociology, B
Soil Science and Agronomy, B
Spanish Language and Literature, B
Special Education and Teaching, M
Speech and Interpersonal Communication, M
Web Page, Digital/Multimedia and Information
   Resources Design, B
Wildlife and Wildlands Science and Management, B
Wood Science and Wood Products/Pulp and Paper
   Technology, B

UNIVERSITY OF WISCONSIN-STOUT

Apparel and Textiles, B
Applied Mathematics, B
Art Teacher Education, B
Business Administration and Management, B
Business, Management, Marketing, and Related
   Support Services, B
Child and Family Studies, M
Computer Systems Networking and
   Telecommunications, B
Construction Engineering Technology/Technician, B
Counseling Psychology, M
Customer Service Management, B
Design and Applied Arts, B
Dietetics/Dieticians, B
Early Childhood Education and Teaching, B
Education, M
Engineering Technology, B
Engineering/Industrial Management, B
Family and Consumer Sciences/Home Economics
   Teacher Education, B
Food Science and Technology, M
Foods, Nutrition, and Related Services, B
Foodservice Systems
   Administration/Management, B
Hospitality Administration/Management, BM
Human Development, M
Human Development and Family Studies, B
Human Resources Development, M
Industrial Production Technologies/Technicians, B
Management of Technology, M
Manufacturing Engineering, B

Marriage and Family Therapy/Counseling, M
Nutritional Sciences, M
Operations Management and Supervision, B
Printing Management, B
Psychology, BM
Rehabilitation Counseling, M
Safety Engineering, M
Sales and Marketing Operations/Marketing and
   Distribution Teacher Education, B
Sales, Distribution and Marketing Operations, B
School Psychology, MO
Science Technologies/Technicians, B
Technical and Business Writing, B
Technical Teacher Education, B
Technology Teacher Education/Industrial Arts
   Teacher Education, B
Travel and Tourism, M
Vocational and Technical Education, MO
Vocational Rehabilitation Counseling/Counselor, B

UNIVERSITY OF WISCONSIN-SUPERIOR

Accounting, B
Art Education, M
Art History, Criticism and Conservation, BM
Art Teacher Education, B
Art Therapy/Therapist, BM
Biological and Physical Sciences, B
Biology Teacher Education, B
Biology/Biological Sciences, B
Broadcast Journalism, B
Business Administration and Management, B
Business Teacher Education, B
Business/Managerial Economics, B
Chemistry, B
Chemistry Teacher Education, B
Communication and Media Studies, M
Community Psychology, M
Computer and Information Sciences, B
Computer Science, B
Counselor Education/School Counseling and
   Guidance Services, M
Criminal Justice/Safety Studies, B
Curriculum and Instruction, M
Drama and Dramatics/Theatre Arts, B
Economics, B
Education, BM
Educational Administration and Supervision, MO
Educational Leadership and Administration, B
Elementary Education and Teaching, B
English Language and Literature, B
English/Language Arts Teacher Education, B
Finance, B
Fine Arts and Art Studies, M
Fine/Studio Arts, B
General Studies, A
Health and Physical Education, B
Health and Physical Education/Fitness, B
History, B
History Teacher Education, B
Information Science/Studies, B
International Relations and Affairs, B
Journalism, B
Kinesiology and Exercise Science, B
Law and Legal Studies, B
Marketing/Marketing Management, B
Mass Communication/Media Studies, BM
Mathematics, B
Mathematics Teacher Education, B
Multi-/Interdisciplinary Studies, B
Music, B
Music Performance, B
Music Teacher Education, B
Peace Studies and Conflict Resolution, B
Physical Education Teaching and Coaching, B
Physical Sciences, B
Political Science and Government, B
Pre-Law Studies, B
Psychology, B
Radio and Television, B
Reading Teacher Education, BM
Sales, Distribution and Marketing Operations, B
Science Teacher Education/General Science
   Teacher Education, B
Social Psychology, B
Social Science Teacher Education, B

Social Sciences, B
Social Studies Teacher Education, B
Social Work, B
Sociology, B
Special Education and Teaching, BM
Speech and Interpersonal Communication, M
Speech and Rhetorical Studies, B
Theater, M
Transportation/Transportation Management, B
Visual and Performing Arts, B

UNIVERSITY OF WISCONSIN-WASHINGTON COUNTY

Liberal Arts and Sciences Studies and
   Humanities, A

UNIVERSITY OF WISCONSIN-WAUKESHA

Liberal Arts and Sciences Studies and
   Humanities, A

UNIVERSITY OF WISCONSIN-WHITEWATER

Accounting, BM
Art History, Criticism and Conservation, B
Art Teacher Education, B
Art/Art Studies, General, B
Biological and Physical Sciences, B
Biology/Biological Sciences, B
Business Administration and Management, B
Business Administration, Management and
   Operations, M
Business Education, M
Business Teacher Education, B
Business/Commerce, B
Business/Managerial Economics, B
Chemistry, B
Communication and Media Studies, M
Communication Disorders, M
Communication Studies/Speech Communication
   and Rhetoric, B
Community Psychology, M
Computer and Information Sciences, B
Corporate and Organizational Communication, M
Counselor Education/School Counseling and
   Guidance Services, M
Curriculum and Instruction, M
Drama and Dramatics/Theatre Arts, B
Early Childhood Education and Teaching, B
Economics, B
Education, BM
Educational Administration and Supervision, M
Elementary Education and Teaching, B
English Language and Literature, B
Environmental and Occupational Health, M
Environmental Engineering
   Technology/Environmental Technology, B
Finance, B
Finance and Banking, M
French Language and Literature, B
Geography, B
German Language and Literature, B
Higher Education/Higher Education
   Administration, M
History, B
Human Resources Management and Services, M
Human Resources Management/Personnel
   Administration, B
Information Technology, B
International Business/Trade/Commerce, M
International Relations and Affairs, B
International/Global Studies, B
Journalism, B
Liberal Arts and Sciences Studies and
   Humanities, AB
Management, M
Management Information Systems and
   Services, BM
Management of Technology, M
Marketing, M
Marketing/Marketing Management, B
Mass Communication/Media Studies, M
Mathematics, B
Music, B
Music Teacher Education, B

Occupational Safety and Health
    Technology/Technician, B
Operations Management and Supervision, B
Physical Education Teaching and Coaching, B
Physics, B
Political Science and Government, B
Psychology, BMO
Public Administration, BM
Public Policy Analysis, B
Reading Teacher Education, M
School Psychology, MO
Science Teacher Education/General Science
    Teacher Education, B
Secondary Education and Teaching, BM
Social Sciences, B
Social Work, B
Sociology, B
Spanish Language and Literature, B
Special Education and Teaching, BM
Speech and Rhetorical Studies, B
Speech-Language Pathology/Pathologist, B
Women's Studies, B

VITERBO UNIVERSITY

Accounting, B
Art Teacher Education, B
Art/Art Studies, General, B
Arts Management, B
Biochemistry, B
Biology Teacher Education, B
Biology/Biological Sciences, B
Business Administration and Management, B
Business Administration, Management and
    Operations, B
Business Teacher Education, B
Chemistry, B
Chemistry Teacher Education, B
Computer and Information Sciences, B
Computer Teacher Education, B
Criminal Justice/Safety Studies, B
Design and Visual Communications, B
Dietetics/Dieticians, B
Divinity/Ministry (BD, MDiv.), B
Drama and Dance Teacher Education, B
Drama and Dramatics/Theatre Arts, B
Education, M
Elementary Education and Teaching, B
English Language and Literature, B
English/Language Arts Teacher Education, B
Fine/Studio Arts, B
Graphic Design, B
Liberal Arts and Sciences Studies and
    Humanities, B
Management Information Systems and Services, B
Marketing/Marketing Management, B
Mathematics, B
Mathematics Teacher Education, B
Multi-/Interdisciplinary Studies, B
Music, B
Music Pedagogy, B
Music Performance, B
Music Teacher Education, B
Nursing, M
Nursing - Registered Nurse Training, B
Philosophy and Religious Studies, B
Pre-Theology/Pre-Ministerial Studies, B
Psychology, B
Religion/Religious Studies, B
Religious Education, B
Science Teacher Education/General Science
    Teacher Education, B
Social Sciences, B
Social Studies Teacher Education, B
Social Work, B
Sociology, B
Spanish Language and Literature, B
Spanish Language Teacher Education, B
Speech Teacher Education, B
Technology Teacher Education/Industrial Arts
    Teacher Education, B
Visual and Performing Arts, B

Web Page, Digital/Multimedia and Information
    Resources Design, B

WAUKESHA COUNTY TECHNICAL COLLEGE

Accounting, A
Administrative Assistant and Secretarial Science, A
Architectural Drafting and Architectural
    CAD/CADD, A
Autobody/Collision and Repair
    Technology/Technician, A
Automobile/Automotive Mechanics
    Technology/Technician, A
Computer and Information Sciences and Support
    Services, A
Computer Installation and Repair
    Technology/Technician, A
Computer Programming/Programmer, A
Computer Systems Analysis/Analyst, A
Computer Systems Networking and
    Telecommunications, A
Criminal Justice/Police Science, A
Dental Hygiene/Hygienist, A
Early Childhood Education and Teaching, A
Electrical, Electronic and Communications
    Engineering Technology/Technician, A
Electrical/Electronics Drafting and
    Electrical/Electronics CAD/CADD, A
Electromechanical and Instrumentation and
    Maintenance Technologies/Technicians, A
Financial Planning and Services, A
Fire Protection and Safety Technology/Technician, A
Graphic Communications, A
Graphic Design, A
Hospitality Administration/Management, A
Interior Design, A
Manufacturing Technology/Technician, A
Marketing/Marketing Management, A
Mechanical Drafting and Mechanical Drafting
    CAD/CADD, A
Mental and Social Health Services and Allied
    Professions, A
Multi-/Interdisciplinary Studies, A
Nursing - Registered Nurse Training, A
Operations Management and Supervision, A
Restaurant, Culinary, and Catering
    Management/Manager, A
Retailing and Retail Operations, A
Surgical Technology/Technologist, A
Teacher Assistant/Aide, A
Telecommunications Technology/Technician, A

WESTERN TECHNICAL COLLEGE

Accounting, A
Administrative Assistant and Secretarial Science, A
Agricultural Mechanization, A
Architectural Engineering Technology/Technician, A
Automobile/Automotive Mechanics
    Technology/Technician, A
Business Administration and Management, A
Business Administration, Management and
    Operations, A
Child Care Provider/Assistant, A
Child Development, A
Clinical/Medical Laboratory Technician, A
Commercial and Advertising Art, A
Communications Technologies/Technicians and
    Support Services, A
Computer Programming/Programmer, A
Consumer Merchandising/Retailing Management, A
Criminal Justice/Police Science, A
Data Processing and Data Processing
    Technology/Technician, A
Dental Hygiene/Hygienist, A
Drafting/Design Engineering
    Technologies/Technicians, A
Electrical, Electronic and Communications
    Engineering Technology/Technician, A
Electromechanical Technology/Electromechanical
    Engineering Technology, A
Electroneurodiagnostic/Electroencephalographic
    Technology/Technologist, A
Fashion Merchandising, A
Finance, A
Fire Protection and Safety Technology/Technician, A
Food Technology and Processing, A

Heating, Air Conditioning, Ventilation and
    Refrigeration Maintenance
    Technology/Technician, A
Hospital and Health Care Facilities
    Administration/Management, A
Human Resources Management/Personnel
    Administration, A
Interior Design, A
Legal Assistant/Paralegal, A
Marketing/Marketing Management, A
Mass Communication/Media Studies, A
Medical Administrative Assistant/Secretary, A
Nursing - Registered Nurse Training, A
Occupational Therapy/Therapist, A
Office Management and Supervision, A
Physical Therapist Assistant, A
Precision Production, A
Public Health, A
Radiologic Technology/Science - Radiographer, A
Respiratory Care Therapy/Therapist, A
Retailing and Retail Operations, A
Sales, Distribution and Marketing Operations, A
Surgical Technology/Technologist, A
System Administration/Administrator, A

WISCONSIN INDIANHEAD TECHNICAL COLLEGE

Accounting, A
Administrative Assistant and Secretarial Science, A
Agricultural/Farm Supplies Retailing and
    Wholesaling, A
Architectural Engineering Technology/Technician, A
Business and Personal/Financial Services Marketing
    Operations, A
Business Operations Support and Secretarial
    Services, A
Child Care and Support Services Management, A
Communications Systems Installation and Repair
    Technology, A
Computer Programming, Specific Applications, A
Computer Systems Networking and
    Telecommunications, A
Corrections and Criminal Justice, A
Court Reporting/Court Reporter, A
Criminal Justice/Police Science, A
Electromechanical Technology/Electromechanical
    Engineering Technology, A
Emergency Medical Technology/Technician (EMT
    Paramedic), A
Engineering Technologies/Technicians, A
Finance, A
General Merchandising, Sales, and Related
    Marketing Operations, A
Heating, Air Conditioning and Refrigeration
    Technology/Technician, A
Management Information Systems and Services, A
Mechanical Engineering/Mechanical
    Technology/Technician, A
Medical Administrative Assistant/Secretary, A
Occupational Therapy/Therapist, A
Quality Control Technology/Technician, A
Retailing and Retail Operations, A

WISCONSIN LUTHERAN COLLEGE

Art/Art Studies, General, B
Biochemistry, B
Biology/Biological Sciences, B
Business/Managerial Economics, B
Chemistry, B
Communication Studies/Speech Communication
    and Rhetoric, B
Communication, Journalism and Related
    Programs, B
Drama and Dramatics/Theatre Arts, B
Elementary Education and Teaching, B
English Language and Literature, B
History, B
Interdisciplinary Studies, B
Mathematics, B
Multi-/Interdisciplinary Studies, B
Music, B
Political Science and Government, B
Psychology, B
Social Sciences, B
Spanish Language and Literature, B

Theology/Theological Studies, B

Wyoming

CASPER COLLEGE

Accounting, A
Administrative Assistant and Secretarial Science, A
Agricultural Business and Management, A
Agricultural Mechanization, A
Agriculture, A
Airline/Commercial/Professional Pilot and Flight Crew, A
Animal Sciences, A
Anthropology, A
Applied Art, A
Art/Art Studies, General, A
Automobile/Automotive Mechanics Technology/Technician, A
Biology/Biological Sciences, A
Business Administration and Management, A
Carpentry/Carpenter, A
Ceramic Arts and Ceramics, A
Chemistry, A
Clinical Laboratory Science/Medical Technology/Technologist, A
Commercial and Advertising Art, A
Computer Programming/Programmer, A
Computer Science, A
Construction Engineering Technology/Technician, A
Consumer Merchandising/Retailing Management, A
Corrections, A
Criminal Justice/Law Enforcement Administration, A
Criminal Justice/Police Science, A
Dance, A
Data Processing and Data Processing Technology/Technician, A
Drafting and Design Technology/Technician, A
Drama and Dramatics/Theatre Arts, A
Economics, A
Education, A
Electrical, Electronic and Communications Engineering Technology/Technician, A
Elementary Education and Teaching, A
Emergency Medical Technology/Technician (EMT Paramedic), A
Engineering, A
English Language and Literature, A
Fire Science/Firefighting, A
French Language and Literature, A
Geology/Earth Science, A
German Language and Literature, A
History, A
Hospitality Administration/Management, A
Italian Language and Literature, A
Journalism, A
Kindergarten/PreSchool Education and Teaching, A
Legal Assistant/Paralegal, A
Liberal Arts and Sciences Studies and Humanities, A
Machine Tool Technology/Machinist, A
Marketing/Marketing Management, A
Mass Communication/Media Studies, A
Mathematics, A
Music, A
Music Teacher Education, A
Nursing - Registered Nurse Training, A
Nutritional Sciences, A
Occupational Therapy/Therapist, A
Pharmacy Technician/Assistant, A
Photography, A
Physical Education Teaching and Coaching, A
Physical Sciences, A
Physics, A
Political Science and Government, A
Psychology, A
Respiratory Care Therapy/Therapist, A
Social Sciences, A
Social Work, A
Sociology, A
Spanish Language and Literature, A
Speech and Rhetorical Studies, A
Technology Education/Industrial Arts, A
Welding Technology/Welder, A
Wildlife and Wildlands Science and Management, A

Women's Studies, A

CENTRAL WYOMING COLLEGE

Accounting, A
Accounting Technology/Technician and Bookkeeping, A
Acting, A
Agribusiness, A
Agricultural Business and Management, A
Agriculture, A
American Indian/Native American Studies, A
Art/Art Studies, General, A
Automobile/Automotive Mechanics Technology/Technician, A
Biology/Biological Sciences, A
Business Administration and Management, A
Business/Office Automation/Technology/Data Entry, A
Child Care and Support Services Management, A
Computer Science, A
Computer Systems Networking and Telecommunications, A
Computer Technology/Computer Systems Technology, A
Criminal Justice/Law Enforcement Administration, A
Digital Communication and Media/Multimedia, A
Drama and Dramatics/Theatre Arts, A
Elementary Education and Teaching, A
English Language and Literature, A
Environmental Sciences, A
Equestrian/Equine Studies, A
General Studies, A
Horse Husbandry/Equine Science and Management, A
Human Services, A
Management Information Systems and Services, A
Music, A
Nursing - Registered Nurse Training, A
Parts, Warehousing, and Inventory Management Operations, A
Physical Sciences, A
Pre-Law Studies, A
Psychology, A
Radio and Television Broadcasting Technology/Technician, A
Range Science and Management, A
Secondary Education and Teaching, A
Social Sciences, A
Surgical Technology/Technologist, A
Technical Theatre/Theatre Design and Technology, A
Web Page, Digital/Multimedia and Information Resources Design, A
Welding Technology/Welder, A

EASTERN WYOMING COLLEGE

Accounting, A
Administrative Assistant and Secretarial Science, A
Agribusiness, A
Agricultural Economics, A
Agricultural Teacher Education, A
Agriculture, A
Animal Sciences, A
Art/Art Studies, General, A
Biology/Biological Sciences, A
Business Administration and Management, A
Business Teacher Education, A
Communication Studies/Speech Communication and Rhetoric, A
Cosmetology/Cosmetologist, A
Criminal Justice/Police Science, A
Criminal Justice/Safety Studies, A
Economics, A
Elementary Education and Teaching, A
English Language and Literature, A
Environmental Biology, A
Farm/Farm and Ranch Management, A
Foreign Languages and Literatures, A
General Studies, A
Health/Medical Preparatory Programs, A
History, A
Liberal Arts and Sciences Studies and Humanities, A
Management Information Systems and Services, A
Mathematics, A
Mathematics Teacher Education, A

Music, A
Music Teacher Education, A
Office Management and Supervision, A
Physical Education Teaching and Coaching, A
Political Science and Government, A
Pre-Dentistry Studies, A
Pre-Medicine/Pre-Medical Studies, A
Pre-Pharmacy Studies, A
Pre-Veterinary Studies, A
Psychology, A
Range Science and Management, A
Secondary Education and Teaching, A
Sociology, A
Statistics, A
Veterinary/Animal Health Technology/Technician and Veterinary Assistant, A
Welding Technology/Welder, A
Wildlife and Wildlands Science and Management, A

LARAMIE COUNTY COMMUNITY COLLEGE

Accounting, A
Agribusiness, A
Agricultural Business Technology, A
Agricultural Production Operations, A
Agriculture, A
Anthropology, A
Art/Art Studies, General, A
Autobody/Collision and Repair Technology/Technician, A
Automobile/Automotive Mechanics Technology/Technician, A
Biological and Physical Sciences, A
Biology/Biological Sciences, A
Business Administration and Management, A
Business Operations Support and Secretarial Services, A
Business/Commerce, A
Carpentry/Carpenter, A
Chemistry, A
Civil Engineering Technology/Technician, A
Communication Studies/Speech Communication and Rhetoric, A
Computer and Information Sciences, A
Computer and Information Sciences and Support Services, A
Computer Hardware Technology/Technician, A
Computer Programming/Programmer, A
Computer Science, A
Computer Systems Analysis/Analyst, A
Construction Engineering Technology/Technician, A
Construction Trades, A
Corrections, A
Criminal Justice/Law Enforcement Administration, A
Customer Service Support/Call Center/Teleservice Operation, A
Data Modeling/Warehousing and Database Administration, A
Dental Assisting/Assistant, A
Dental Hygiene/Hygienist, A
Diagnostic Medical Sonography/Sonographer and Ultrasound Technician, A
Diesel Mechanics Technology/Technician, A
Digital Communication and Media/Multimedia, A
Drama and Dramatics/Theatre Arts, A
Early Childhood Education and Teaching, A
Economics, A
Education, A
Engineering, A
Engineering Technology, A
English Language and Literature, A
Entrepreneurship/Entrepreneurial Studies, A
Equestrian/Equine Studies, A
Health/Medical Preparatory Programs, A
History, A
Humanities/Humanistic Studies, A
Industrial Radiologic Technology/Technician, A
Information Technology, A
Journalism, A
Mass Communication/Media Studies, A
Mathematics, A
Multi-/Interdisciplinary Studies, A
Music, A
Nurse/Nursing Assistant/Aide and Patient Care Assistant, A
Nursing - Registered Nurse Training, A

Philosophy, A
Physical Education Teaching and Coaching, A
Political Science and Government, A
Pre-Dentistry Studies, A
Pre-Engineering, A
Pre-Law Studies, A
Pre-Medicine/Pre-Medical Studies, A
Pre-Pharmacy Studies, A
Pre-Veterinary Studies, A
Psychology, A
Public Administration, A
Radiologic Technology/Science - Radiographer, A
Religion/Religious Studies, A
Social Sciences, A
Sociology, A
Spanish Language and Literature, A
Teacher Education and Professional
 Development, Specific Levels and Methods, A
Visual and Performing Arts, A
Web Page, Digital/Multimedia and Information
 Resources Design, A
Web/Multimedia Management and Webmaster, A
Wildlife and Wildlands Science and Management, A

NORTHWEST COLLEGE

Accounting, A
Administrative Assistant and Secretarial Science, A
Agricultural Business and Management, A
Agricultural Economics, A
Agricultural Mechanization, A
Agricultural Teacher Education, A
Agriculture, A
Agronomy and Crop Science, A
American/United States Studies/Civilization, A
Animal Sciences, A
Art Teacher Education, A
Art/Art Studies, General, A
Biological and Physical Sciences, A
Biology/Biological Sciences, A
Botany/Plant Biology, A
Business Administration and Management, A
Business Teacher Education, A
Chemistry, A
Commercial and Advertising Art, A
Drafting and Design Technology/Technician, A
Early Childhood Education and Teaching, A
Ecology, A
Economics, A
Education, A
Elementary Education and Teaching, A
Engineering, A
English Language and Literature, A
Environmental Studies, A
Equestrian/Equine Studies, A
Farm/Farm and Ranch Management, A
Forestry, A
Graphic and Printing Equipment Operator
 Production, A
Health Teacher Education, A
History, A
Humanities/Humanistic Studies, A
Information Science/Studies, A
Journalism, A
Kindergarten/PreSchool Education and Teaching, A
Kinesiology and Exercise Science, A
Liberal Arts and Sciences Studies and
 Humanities, A
Licensed Practical/Vocational Nurse Training, A
Marketing/Marketing Management, A
Mass Communication/Media Studies, A
Mathematics, A
Modern Languages, A
Music, A
Music Teacher Education, A
Natural Resources Management/Development and
 Policy, A
Natural Sciences, A
Nursing - Registered Nurse Training, A
Parks, Recreation and Leisure Facilities
 Management, A
Parks, Recreation, Leisure and Fitness Studies, A
Photography, A
Physical Anthropology, A
Physical Education Teaching and Coaching, A
Physical Sciences, A
Physics, A

Political Science and Government, A
Pre-Engineering, A
Prepress/Desktop Publishing and Digital Imaging
 Design, A
Psychology, A
Range Science and Management, A
Science Teacher Education/General Science
 Teacher Education, A
Social Sciences, A
Sociology, A
Speech and Rhetorical Studies, A
Tourism and Travel Services Management, A
Trade and Industrial Teacher Education, A
Welding Technology/Welder, A
Wildlife and Wildlands Science and Management, A

SHERIDAN COLLEGE-SHERIDAN AND GILLETTE

Administrative Assistant and Secretarial Science, A
Agricultural Business and Management, A
Agriculture, A
Art/Art Studies, General, A
Biological and Physical Sciences, A
Biology/Biological Sciences, A
Business Administration and Management, A
Business/Commerce, A
Computer Programming, Specific Applications, A
Computer Software and Media Applications, A
Computer Systems Networking and
 Telecommunications, A
Criminal Justice/Law Enforcement Administration, A
Criminal Justice/Police Science, A
Data Entry/Microcomputer Applications, A
Dental Hygiene/Hygienist, A
Diesel Mechanics Technology/Technician, A
Drafting and Design Technology/Technician, A
Education, A
Elementary Education and Teaching, A
Engineering, A
Engineering Technology, A
English Language and Literature, A
Foreign Languages and Literatures, A
General Studies, A
Health and Physical Education, A
Heavy Equipment Maintenance
 Technology/Technician, A
History, A
Hospitality Administration/Management, A
Humanities/Humanistic Studies, A
Information Science/Studies, A
Liberal Arts and Sciences Studies and
 Humanities, A
Machine Tool Technology/Machinist, A
Mathematics, A
Music, A
Nursing - Registered Nurse Training, A
Respiratory Care Therapy/Therapist, A
Sign Language Interpretation and Translation, A
Social Sciences, A
System Administration/Administrator, A
Web Page, Digital/Multimedia and Information
 Resources Design, A
Web/Multimedia Management and Webmaster, A
Welding Technology/Welder, A

UNIVERSITY OF WYOMING

Accounting, BM
Adult and Continuing Education and Teaching, MDO
Agribusiness, B
Agricultural Communication/Journalism, B
Agricultural Economics, M
Agricultural Sciences, MD
Agricultural Teacher Education, B
Agriculture, Agriculture Operations and Related
 Sciences, B
Agronomy and Soil Sciences, MD
American/United States Studies/Civilization, BM
Animal Sciences, BMD
Anthropology, BMD
Applied Economics, M
Applied Mathematics, B
Architectural Engineering, B
Art/Art Studies, General, B
Astronomy and Astrophysics, B
Atmospheric Sciences and Meteorology, MD

Audiology/Audiologist and Speech-Language
 Pathology/Pathologist, B
Biology/Biological Sciences, B
Botany/Plant Biology, BMD
Business Administration and Management, B
Business Administration, Management and
 Operations, M
Business/Managerial Economics, B
Chemical Engineering, BMD
Chemistry, BMD
Civil Engineering, BMD
Communication and Media Studies, M
Communication Disorders, M
Communication Studies/Speech Communication
 and Rhetoric, B
Computer Engineering, B
Computer Science, BMD
Consumer Economics, M
Counselor Education/School Counseling and
 Guidance Services, MD
Criminal Justice/Safety Studies, B
Curriculum and Instruction, MD
Dental Hygiene/Hygienist, B
Distance Education Development, D
Drama and Dramatics/Theatre Arts, B
Economics, MD
Education, O
Educational Leadership and Administration, MDO
Educational Media/Instructional Technology, MDO
Electrical Engineering, MD
Electrical, Electronics and Communications
 Engineering, B
Elementary Education and Teaching, B
Engineering and Applied Sciences, MD
English, M
English Language and Literature, B
Entomology, MD
Environmental Engineering
 Technology/Environmental Technology, M
Environmental Studies, B
Family and Consumer Sciences/Human Sciences, B
Finance, B
Finance and Banking, M
Food Science and Technology, M
French Language and Literature, BM
Geography, BM
Geological and Earth Sciences/Geosciences, B
Geology/Earth Science, BMD
Geophysics and Seismology, MD
German Language and Literature, BM
Health Education, M
Health Services/Allied Health/Health Sciences, B
Health Teacher Education, B
History, BM
Humanities/Humanistic Studies, B
International Affairs, M
International Relations and Affairs, B
Journalism, B
Kinesiology and Exercise Science, B
Law and Legal Studies, PO
Management Information Systems and Services, B
Management Science, B
Marketing/Marketing Management, B
Mathematics, BMD
Mathematics Teacher Education, M
Mechanical Engineering, BMD
Microbiology, B
Molecular Biology, BMD
Multi-/Interdisciplinary Studies, B
Music, BM
Music History, Literature, and Theory, M
Music Performance, B
Music Teacher Education, BM
Music Theory and Composition, B
Natural Resources and Conservation, BMD
Nursing, M
Nursing - Registered Nurse Training, B
Nutritional Sciences, M
Parks, Recreation and Leisure Facilities
 Management, B
Pathobiology, M
Performance, M
Petroleum Engineering, MD
Pharmacy, P
Philosophy, BM
Physical Education Teaching and Coaching, BM

Physics, B
Physiology, MD
Political Science and Government, BM
Psychology, BMD
Public Administration, M
Range Science and Management, BMD
Reproductive Biology, MD
Rural Planning and Studies, M
Russian Language and Literature, B
Science Teacher Education/General Science
    Teacher Education, M
Secondary Education and Teaching, B
Social Sciences, B
Social Work, BM
Sociology, BM
Spanish Language and Literature, BM
Special Education and Teaching, BMO
Statistics, BMD
Technology Teacher Education/Industrial Arts
    Teacher Education, B
Trade and Industrial Teacher Education, B
Water Resources, MD
Women's Studies, B
Zoology/Animal Biology, BMD

WESTERN WYOMING COMMUNITY COLLEGE

Accounting, A
Administrative Assistant and Secretarial Science, A
Anthropology, A
Archeology, A
Art/Art Studies, General, A
Automobile/Automotive Mechanics
    Technology/Technician, A
Biological and Physical Sciences, A
Biology/Biological Sciences, A
Business Administration and Management, A
Chemistry, A
Communication Studies/Speech Communication
    and Rhetoric, A
Computer and Information Sciences, A
Computer Programming, Specific Applications, A
Computer Science, A
Criminal Justice/Law Enforcement Administration, A
Criminology, A
Dance, A
Data Entry/Microcomputer Applications, A
Data Processing and Data Processing
    Technology/Technician, A
Diesel Mechanics Technology/Technician, A
Drama and Dramatics/Theatre Arts, A
Early Childhood Education and Teaching, A
Economics, A
Education, A
Electrical, Electronic and Communications
    Engineering Technology/Technician, A
Electrical/Electronics Equipment Installation and
    Repair, A
Electrician, A
Elementary Education and Teaching, A
Engineering Technology, A
English Language and Literature, A
Environmental Sciences, A
Forestry, A
General Studies, A
Geography, A
Geology/Earth Science, A
Health Services/Allied Health/Health Sciences, A
Health/Medical Preparatory Programs, A
Heavy Equipment Maintenance
    Technology/Technician, A
History, A
Human Services, A
Humanities/Humanistic Studies, A
Industrial Electronics Technology/Technician, A
Industrial Mechanics and Maintenance
    Technology, A
Information Science/Studies, A
Information Technology, A
Instrumentation Technology/Technician, A
International Relations and Affairs, A
Journalism, A
Kinesiology and Exercise Science, A
Legal Administrative Assistant/Secretary, A
Liberal Arts and Sciences Studies and
    Humanities, A

Licensed Practical/Vocational Nurse Training, A
Marketing/Marketing Management, A
Mathematics, A
Mechanics and Repairers, A
Medical Administrative Assistant/Secretary, A
Medical Office Assistant/Specialist, A
Medical Office Computer Specialist/Assistant, A
Medical/Clinical Assistant, A
Mining Technology/Technician, A
Music, A
Nurse/Nursing Assistant/Aide and Patient Care
    Assistant, A
Photography, A
Political Science and Government, A
Pre-Dentistry Studies, A
Pre-Engineering, A
Pre-Law Studies, A
Pre-Medicine/Pre-Medical Studies, A
Pre-Nursing Studies, A
Pre-Pharmacy Studies, A
Pre-Veterinary Studies, A
Psychology, A
Secondary Education and Teaching, A
Social Sciences, A
Social Work, A
Sociology, A
Spanish Language and Literature, A
Special Education and Teaching, A
Teacher Education, Multiple Levels, A
Technical Theatre/Theatre Design and
    Technology, A
Visual and Performing Arts, A
Web Page, Digital/Multimedia and Information
    Resources Design, A
Web/Multimedia Management and Webmaster, A
Welding Technology/Welder, A
Wildlife and Wildlands Science and Management, A
Word Processing, A

WYOTECH

Automobile/Automotive Mechanics
    Technology/Technician, A

CANADIAN COLLEGES: ALBERTA

ALBERTA COLLEGE OF ART & DESIGN

Art/Art Studies, General, B
Ceramic Arts and Ceramics, B
Commercial and Advertising Art, B
Computer Graphics, B
Design and Visual Communications, B
Drawing, B
Fiber, Textile and Weaving Arts, B
Fine/Studio Arts, B
Graphic Design, B
Illustration, B
Intermedia/Multimedia, B
Metal and Jewelry Arts, B
Painting, B
Photography, B
Printmaking, B

ALLIANCE UNIVERSITY COLLEGE

Bible/Biblical Studies, B
Missions/Missionary Studies and Missiology, BO
Pastoral Studies/Counseling, P
Religion/Religious Studies, M
Religious Education, BMP
Religious/Sacred Music, B
Theology and Religious Vocations, MPO
Theology/Theological Studies, B

ATHABASCA UNIVERSITY

Accounting, B
Adult and Continuing Education and Teaching, M
Allied Health and Medical Assisting Services, MO
Anthropology, B
Applied Art, B
Biological and Physical Sciences, B
Business Administration and Management, B
Business Administration, Management and
    Operations, MO

Canadian Studies, BM
Communication and Media Studies, B
Computer and Information Sciences, B
Criminal Justice/Police Science, B
Cultural Studies, M
Distance Education Development, MO
Education, MO
English Language and Literature, B
French Language and Literature, B
Gender Studies, M
General Studies, B
History, BM
Human Resources Management/Personnel
    Administration, B
Information Science/Studies, BM
Interdisciplinary Studies, M
International Development, M
Labor and Industrial Relations, B
Liberal Arts and Sciences Studies and
    Humanities, B
Management, O
Management Information Systems and Services, M
Management of Technology, MO
Marketing/Marketing Management, B
Nursing - Advanced Practice, MO
Nursing - Registered Nurse Training, B
Nursing Administration, M
Organizational Behavior Studies, B
Organizational Management, M
Political Science and Government, B
Project Management, MO
Psychology, B
Public Administration, B
Sociology, B
Women's Studies, B

CONCORDIA UNIVERSITY COLLEGE OF ALBERTA

Biology/Biological Sciences, B
Business Administration and Management, B
Canadian Studies, B
Chemistry, B
Education, B
Elementary Education and Teaching, B
English Language and Literature, B
Environmental Biology, B
Environmental Health, B
Environmental Sciences, B
Environmental Studies, B
Foreign Languages and Literatures, B
French Language and Literature, B
French Studies, B
History, B
Human Resources Management and Services, A
Mathematics, B
Music, B
Non-Profit/Public/Organizational Management, B
Philosophy, B
Political Science and Government, B
Pre-Theology/Pre-Ministerial Studies, B
Psychology, B
Public Health, B
Religion/Religious Studies, B
Religious Education, B
Social Sciences, B
Sociology, B
Theology and Religious Vocations, B
Visual and Performing Arts, B

THE KING'S UNIVERSITY COLLEGE

Biology/Biological Sciences, B
Business Administration and Management, B
Chemistry, B
Computer Science, B
Elementary Education and Teaching, B
English Language and Literature, B
Environmental Studies, B
History, B
Music, B
Philosophy, B
Psychology, B
Social Sciences, B
Sociology, B

Theology/Theological Studies, B

NEWMAN THEOLOGICAL COLLEGE

Educational Administration and Supervision, O
Religious Education, MO
Theology and Religious Vocations, MP

PRAIRIE BIBLE INSTITUTE

Ancient Near Eastern and Biblical
   Languages, Literatures, and Linguistics, B
Bible/Biblical Studies, AB
Drama and Dramatics/Theatre Arts, AB
Education, B
International Relations and Affairs, B
Missions/Missionary Studies and Missiology, AB
Music, B
Musicology and Ethnomusicology, B
Pastoral Counseling and Specialized Ministries, B
Pastoral Studies/Counseling, B
Pre-Theology/Pre-Ministerial Studies, B
Religious Education, B
Theological and Ministerial Studies, B
Theology and Religious Vocations, B
Theology/Theological Studies, B

ROCKY MOUNTAIN COLLEGE

Bible/Biblical Studies, B
Counseling Psychology, B
Education, B
Missions/Missionary Studies and Missiology, B
Music, B
Pastoral Studies/Counseling, B
Religious Education, B
Social Sciences, B
Theology/Theological Studies, B
Youth Ministry, B

SOUTHERN ALBERTA INSTITUTE OF TECHNOLOGY

Business Administration and Management, B
Business Administration, Management and
   Operations, B
Geography, B
Information Science/Studies, B
Petroleum Engineering, B

TAYLOR UNIVERSITY COLLEGE AND SEMINARY

Bible/Biblical Studies, B
Cultural Studies, M
Divinity/Ministry (BD, MDiv.), B
Education, A
English Language and Literature, B
Liberal Arts and Sciences Studies and
   Humanities, B
Missions/Missionary Studies and Missiology, M
Music, B
Religion/Religious Studies, B
Theology and Religious Vocations, MP

UNIVERSITY OF ALBERTA

Accounting, BD
Adult and Continuing Education and Teaching, BMD
Aerospace, Aeronautical and Astronautical
   Engineering, B
Agricultural Business and Management, B
Agricultural Economics, BMDO
Agricultural Sciences, MDO
Agricultural/Biological Engineering and
   Bioengineering, B
Agriculture, B
Agronomy and Crop Science, B
Agronomy and Soil Sciences, MDO
American Indian/Native American Studies, B
Animal Genetics, B
Animal Physiology, B
Animal Sciences, B
Anthropology, BMD
Apparel and Textiles, B
Applied Mathematics, BMD
Arabic Language and Literature, B
Archeology, MD
Art History, Criticism and Conservation, BM
Art Teacher Education, B
Art/Art Studies, General, B

Astrophysics, MD
Athletic Training and Sports Medicine, B
Atmospheric Sciences and Meteorology, B
Bilingual and Multilingual Education, B
Biochemistry, BMD
Bioinformatics, B
Biological and Biomedical Sciences, MDO
Biological and Physical Sciences, B
Biological Anthropology, MDO
Biology Technician/BioTechnology Laboratory
   Technician, B
Biology/Biological Sciences, B
Biomedical Engineering, MD
Biostatistics, M
BioTechnology, MD
Botany/Plant Biology, B
Business Administration and Management, B
Business Administration, Management and
   Operations, MDO
Business Teacher Education, B
Canadian Studies, B
Cancer Biology/Oncology, MD
Cartography, B
Cell Biology and Anatomy, MD
Cell/Cellular Biology and Histology, B
Central/Middle and Eastern European Studies, B
Chemical Engineering, BMD
Chemistry, BMD
Child Development, B
Chinese Language and Literature, B
Chinese Studies, M
Civil Engineering, BMD
Classics and Classical
   Languages, Literatures, and Linguistics, BMD
Clinical Laboratory Sciences, MD
Clinical Psychology, B
Clinical/Medical Laboratory Technician, B
Clothing and Textiles, MD
Communication and Media Studies, M
Communication Disorders, M
Comparative Literature, B
Composition, M
Computer Engineering, BMD
Computer Science, BMD
Condensed Matter Physics, MD
Conservation Biology, MD
Construction Engineering, B
Construction Engineering and Management, MD
Counseling Psychology, MD
Counselor Education/School Counseling and
   Guidance Services, M
Criminal Justice/Law Enforcement Administration, B
Criminology, BM
Dairy Science, B
Dance, B
Demography and Population Studies, MD
Dental Hygiene/Hygienist, BO
Dentistry, P
Design and Applied Arts, M
Developmental and Child Psychology, B
Drama and Dramatics/Theatre Arts, B
Drawing, B
East Asian Studies, BM
East European and Russian Studies, MD
Ecology, MD
Economics, BMD
Education, B
Educational Administration and Supervision, MDO
Educational Leadership and Administration, MDO
Educational Media/Instructional Technology, M
Educational Psychology, MD
Electrical Engineering, MD
Electrical, Electronics and Communications
   Engineering, B
Elementary Education and Teaching, BMD
Energy and Power Engineering, MD
Engineering, B
Engineering Management, M
Engineering Physics, B
English, MD
English as a Second Language, M
English Language and Literature, B
Entomology, B
Entrepreneurial and Small Business Operations, B
Environmental and Occupational Health, MD
Environmental Biology, BMD

Environmental Engineering
   Technology/Environmental Technology, MD
Environmental Policy and Resource Management, D
Environmental Sciences, BMD
Environmental Studies, B
Environmental/Environmental Health Engineering, B
Epidemiology, MD
Ethnic, Cultural Minority, and Gender Studies, B
Evolutionary Biology, MD
Exercise and Sports Science, MD
Experimental Psychology, B
Family and Consumer Economics and Related
   Services, B
Family and Consumer Sciences/Home Economics
   Teacher Education, B
Family and Consumer Sciences/Human
   Sciences, BMD
Farm/Farm and Ranch Management, B
Film/Cinema Studies, B
Finance, B
Finance and Banking, MD
Fine Arts and Art Studies, M
Fine/Studio Arts, B
Folklore, MD
Food Science, B
Foods, Nutrition, and Wellness Studies, B
Forest Management/Forest Resources
   Management, B
Forestry, BMD
French Language and Literature, BMD
Genetics, MD
Geography, B
Geology/Earth Science, B
Geophysics and Seismology, BMD
Geosciences, MD
Geotechnical Engineering, MD
German Language and Literature, BMD
Health Physics/Radiological Health, MD
Health Promotion, MO
Health Services Administration, MDO
Health Services Research, M
Hebrew Language and Literature, B
Hispanic Studies, MD
History, BMD
Human Resources Management/Personnel
   Administration, B
Humanities/Humanistic Studies, B
Immunology, BMD
Industrial and Labor Relations, D
Industrial Design, B
Information Science/Studies, BM
Interdisciplinary Studies, B
International Business/Trade/Commerce, BM
International Relations and Affairs, B
Italian Language and Literature, BM
Japanese Language and Literature, B
Japanese Studies, M
Kindergarten/PreSchool Education and Teaching, B
Kinesiology and Exercise Science, B
Labor and Industrial Relations, B
Land Use Planning and
   Management/Development, B
Latin American Studies, B
Latin Language and Literature, B
Law and Legal Studies, BMPO
Liberal Arts and Sciences Studies and
   Humanities, B
Library Science, M
Linguistics, BMD
Management, D
Management Information Systems and Services, B
Marketing, D
Marketing/Marketing Management, B
Materials Engineering, MD
Mathematical and Computational Finance, MD
Mathematical Physics, MD
Mathematics, BMDO
Mechanical Engineering, BMDO
Medical Microbiology and Bacteriology, BMD
Medical Physics, MD
Metallurgical Engineering, B
Microbiology, MD
Mineral/Mining Engineering, MD
Mining and Mineral Engineering, B
Modern Greek Language and Literature, B
Modern Languages, B

Molecular Biology, BMD
Multilingual and Multicultural Education, M
Music, BMD
Music History, Literature, and Theory, B
Music Teacher Education, B
Natural Resources and Conservation, BMDO
Natural Resources Management/Development and
    Policy, B
Neuroscience, MD
Nursing, MD
Nursing - Registered Nurse Training, B
Occupational Therapy/Therapist, BM
Oral and Dental Sciences, MD
Organizational Management, D
Orthodontics, MD
Painting, M
Paleontology, B
Parks, Recreation and Leisure Facilities
    Management, B
Parks, Recreation, Leisure and Fitness Studies, B
Pathology/Experimental Pathology, MD
Petroleum Engineering, BMD
Pharmaceutical Sciences, MD
Pharmacology, BMD
Pharmacy, BMD
Philosophy, BMD
Physical Education Teaching and Coaching, BMD
Physical Sciences, B
Physical Therapy/Therapist, BM
Physics, BMD
Physiology, BMDO
Piano and Organ, B
Plant Biology, MD
Political Science and Government, BMD
Pre-Dentistry Studies, B
Pre-Law Studies, B
Pre-Medicine/Pre-Medical Studies, B
Pre-Veterinary Studies, B
Printmaking, BM
Psychology, BMD
Public Health, MDO
Range Science and Management, B
Reading Teacher Education, B
Recreation and Park Management, MD
Rehabilitation Sciences, D
Religion/Religious Studies, B
Romance Languages, Literatures, and Linguistics, B
Rural Sociology, MDO
Russian Language and Literature, B
Russian Studies, B
Scandinavian
    Languages, Literatures, and Linguistics, B
School Psychology, MD
Science Teacher Education/General Science
    Teacher Education, B
Sculpture, BM
Secondary Education and Teaching, BMD
Slavic Languages, Literatures, and Linguistics, BMD
Sociology, BMD
Spanish Language and Literature, B
Special Education and Teaching, BMD
Special Products Marketing Operations, B
Sport and Fitness Administration/Management, BM
Statistics, BMDO
Structural Engineering, MD
Systems Engineering, MD
Teaching English as a Second or Foreign
    Language/ESL Language Instructor, B
Technical Theatre/Theatre Design and
    Technology, B
Technology Education/Industrial Arts, B
Telecommunications, MD
Theater, M
Trade and Industrial Teacher Education, B
Urban Studies/Affairs, B
Violin, Viola, Guitar and Other Stringed
    Instruments, B
Vision Science/Physiological Optics, MD
Voice and Opera, B
Water Resources Engineering, MD
Wildlife and Wildlands Science and Management, B
Wind and Percussion Instruments, B
Women's Studies, B

Zoology/Animal Biology, B

UNIVERSITY OF CALGARY

Accounting, B
Actuarial Science, B
Allopathic Medicine, P
American Indian/Native American Studies, B
Analytical Chemistry, MD
Anthropology, BMD
Applied Mathematics, B
Archeology, BMD
Architecture, M
Art History, Criticism and Conservation, B
Art Teacher Education, B
Art/Art Studies, General, B
Astronomy, MD
Astrophysics, B
Biochemistry, BMD
Biological and Biomedical Sciences, MD
Biology/Biological Sciences, B
Biomedical Engineering, MD
Biomedical Sciences, B
BioTechnology, M
Botany/Plant Biology, B
Business Administration and Management, B
Business Administration, Management and
    Operations, MO
Canadian Studies, B
Cardiovascular Sciences, MD
Cell/Cellular Biology and Histology, B
Chemical Engineering, BMD
Chemistry, BMD
Civil Engineering, BMD
Classics and Classical
    Languages, Literatures, and Linguistics, BMD
Clinical Psychology, MD
Communication and Media Studies, MD
Communication Studies/Speech Communication
    and Rhetoric, B
Community Health and Preventive Medicine, MDO
Computer Engineering, BMD
Computer Science, BMD
Counseling Psychology, MD
Curriculum and Instruction, MDO
Dance, B
Drama and Dance Teacher Education, B
Drama and Dramatics/Theatre Arts, B
East Asian Studies, B
Ecology, B
Economics, BMD
Education, B
Education/Teaching of the Gifted and
    Talented, MDO
Educational Administration and Supervision, D
Educational Leadership and Administration, MDO
Educational Measurement and Evaluation, MDO
Educational Media/Instructional Technology, MDO
Educational Psychology, MD
Electrical Engineering, MD
Electrical, Electronics and Communications
    Engineering, B
Elementary Education and Teaching, B
Engineering and Applied Sciences, MD
English, MD
English as a Second Language, MDO
English Language and Literature, B
Environmental Design/Architecture, MD
Environmental Policy and Resource
    Management, MD
Environmental Studies, B
Epidemiology, MD
Finance, B
Fine Arts and Art Studies, M
Foundations and Philosophy of Education, MDO
French Language and Literature, BMD
General Studies, B
Geography, BMD
Geological/Geophysical Engineering, B
Geology/Earth Science, BMD
Geophysics and Seismology, BMD
Geotechnical Engineering, MD
German Language and Literature, BM
Higher Education/Higher Education
    Administration, D
History, BMD
Hotel/Motel Administration/Management, B

Human Development, MD
Humanities/Humanistic Studies, B
Industrial Design, M
Industrial Engineering, B
Infectious Diseases, MD
Inorganic Chemistry, MD
Insurance, B
International Relations and Affairs, B
Kinesiology and Exercise Science, B
Kinesiology and Movement Studies, MD
Latin American Studies, B
Law and Legal Studies, BMP
Liberal Arts and Sciences Studies and
    Humanities, B
Linguistics, BMD
Management, D
Management Information Systems and Services, B
Management Strategy and Policy, MD
Manufacturing Engineering, MD
Marketing/Marketing Management, B
Mathematics, BMD
Mechanical Engineering, BMD
Medieval and Renaissance Studies, B
Microbiology, MD
Military and Defense Studies, MD
Molecular Biology, BMD
Music, BMD
Neuroscience, MD
Nursing, MDO
Nursing - Registered Nurse Training, B
Organic Chemistry, MD
Parks, Recreation, Leisure and Fitness Studies, B
Petroleum Engineering, MD
Philosophy, BMD
Physical Chemistry, MD
Physics, BMD
Political Science and Government, BMD
Psychology, BMD
Religion/Religious Studies, BMD
Russian Language and Literature, B
School Psychology, MD
Secondary Education and Teaching, B
Social Work, BMDO
Sociology, BMD
Software Engineering, M
Spanish Language and Literature, BMD
Special Education and Teaching, MD
Statistics, BMD
Theater, M
Theoretical Chemistry, MD
Tourism and Travel Services Management, B
Urban and Regional Planning, M
Urban Design, M
Urban Studies/Affairs, B
Vocational and Technical Education, MDO
Women's Studies, B
Zoology/Animal Biology, B

UNIVERSITY OF LETHBRIDGE

Accounting, BMO
Agricultural Business and Management, B
Agricultural Sciences, M
Agriculture, B
American Indian/Native American
    Languages, Literatures, and Linguistics, B
American Indian/Native American Studies, BM
Anthropology, BM
Archeology, M
Art Teacher Education, B
Art/Art Studies, General, B
Biochemistry, BM
Biological and Biomedical Sciences, M
Biological and Physical Sciences, B
Biology/Biological Sciences, B
BioTechnology, B
Business Administration and Management, B
Business Teacher Education, B
Canadian Studies, BM
Chemistry, BM
Computational Sciences, D
Computer and Information Sciences, B
Computer Science, BM
Counseling Psychology, BM
Digital Communication and Media/Multimedia, B
Drama and Dance Teacher Education, B
Drama and Dramatics/Theatre Arts, B

Economics, BM
Education, BMO
Educational Leadership and Administration, B
English, M
English Language and Literature, B
Environmental Sciences, BM
Exercise and Sports Science, M
Finance, B
Finance and Banking, M
Fine Arts and Art Studies, M
Foreign Language Teacher Education, B
French Language and Literature, BM
Geography, BM
German Language and Literature, BM
Health Teacher Education, B
History, BM
Human Resources Management and Services, M
Human Resources Management/Personnel
   Administration, B
Humanities/Humanistic Studies, B
Indian/Native American Education, B
International Business/Trade/Commerce, BM
Kinesiology and Exercise Science, B
Kinesiology and Movement Studies, M
Management, M
Management Information Systems and
   Services, BM
Marketing/Marketing Management, B
Mathematics, BM
Mathematics Teacher Education, B
Modern Languages, B
Molecular Biology, D
Music, BM
Music Teacher Education, B
Neuroscience, BMD
Nursing, M
Nursing - Registered Nurse Training, B
Parks, Recreation, Leisure and Fitness Studies, B
Philosophy, BM
Physical Education Teaching and Coaching, B
Physics, BM
Political Science and Government, BM
Psychology, BM
Public Administration, B
Religion/Religious Studies, BM
Science Teacher Education/General Science
   Teacher Education, B
Social Sciences, B
Social Studies Teacher Education, B
Social Work, M
Sociology, BM
Spanish Language and Literature, M
Special Education and Teaching, B
Substance Abuse/Addiction Counseling, B
Teacher Education, Multiple Levels, B
Technical Theatre/Theatre Design and
   Technology, B
Technology Teacher Education/Industrial Arts
   Teacher Education, B
Urban Studies/Affairs, BM

VANGUARD COLLEGE

Bible/Biblical Studies, B
Religious/Sacred Music, B
Theology/Theological Studies, B

British Columbia

BRITISH COLUMBIA INSTITUTE OF TECHNOLOGY

Accounting, AB
Accounting Technology/Technician and
   Bookkeeping, A
Administrative Assistant and Secretarial Science, A
Aeronautical/Aerospace Engineering
   Technology/Technician, A
Aircraft Powerplant Technology/Technician, A
Airframe Mechanics and Aircraft Maintenance
   Technology/Technician, A
Allied Health
   Diagnostic, Intervention, and Treatment
   Professions, A
Architectural Drafting and Architectural
   CAD/CADD, A
Architectural Engineering Technology/Technician, A

Autobody/Collision and Repair
   Technology/Technician, A
Automobile/Automotive Mechanics
   Technology/Technician, A
Avionics Maintenance Technology/Technician, A
Biology Technician/BioTechnology Laboratory
   Technician, A
BioTechnology, AB
Building/Construction
   Finishing, Management, and Inspection, A
Business Administration and Management, AB
Cabinetmaking and Millwork/Millwright, A
Cardiovascular Technology/Technologist, A
Carpentry/Carpenter, A
Chemical Technology/Technician, A
Civil Drafting and Civil Engineering CAD/CADD, A
Civil Engineering Technology/Technician, A
Clinical/Medical Laboratory Technician, A
Commercial and Advertising Art, A
Computer Science, AB
Computer Systems Analysis/Analyst, AB
Construction Engineering Technology/Technician, A
Construction Trades, A
Critical Care Nursing, B
Data Processing and Data Processing
   Technology/Technician, A
Diesel Mechanics Technology/Technician, A
Drafting and Design Technology/Technician, A
Electrical and Power Transmission
   Installation/Installer, A
Electrical, Electronic and Communications
   Engineering Technology/Technician, AB
Engineering, A
Entrepreneurship/Entrepreneurial Studies, A
Environmental Engineering
   Technology/Environmental Technology, B
Environmental Health, AB
Environmental/Environmental Health Engineering, A
Finance, A
Finance and Financial Management Services, A
Financial Planning and Services, A
Fire Protection and Safety Technology/Technician, A
Forensic Science and Technology, A
Forest Management/Forest Resources
   Management, A
Forestry Technology/Technician, A
Health and Medical Administrative Services, A
Health and Medical Laboratory Technologies, A
Health Professions and Related Clinical Sciences, A
Health/Health Care Administration/Management, AB
Heating, Air Conditioning, Ventilation and
   Refrigeration Maintenance
   Technology/Technician, A
Heavy Equipment Maintenance
   Technology/Technician, A
Human Resources Management/Personnel
   Administration, A
Industrial Mechanics and Maintenance
   Technology, A
Industrial Technology/Technician, A
Information Science/Studies, A
Interior Design, A
International Business/Trade/Commerce, A
Machine Tool Technology/Machinist, A
Management Science, A
Marketing/Marketing Management, A
Mechanical Drafting and Mechanical Drafting
   CAD/CADD, A
Mechanical Engineering/Mechanical
   Technology/Technician, A
Medical Administrative Assistant/Secretary, A
Medical Radiologic Technology/Science - Radiation
   Therapist, AB
Mining Technology/Technician, A
Naval Architecture and Marine Engineering, A
Nuclear Medical Technology/Technologist, A
Nursing, AB
Nursing - Registered Nurse Training, AB
Nursing Administration, A
Occupational and Environmental Health Nursing, B
Occupational Health and Industrial Hygiene, A
Operations Management and Supervision, A
Pediatric Nurse/Nursing, AB
Perioperative/Operating Room and Surgical
   Nurse/Nursing, AB
Petroleum Technology/Technician, A

Pipefitting/Pipefitter and Sprinkler Fitter, A
Plastics Engineering Technology/Technician, A
Precision Systems Maintenance and Repair
   Technologies, A
Radio and Television Broadcasting
   Technology/Technician, A
Real Estate, A
Robotics Technology/Technician, A
Science Technologies/Technicians, A
Sheet Metal Technology/Sheetworking, A
Small Engine Mechanics and Repair
   Technology/Technician, A
Survey Technology/Surveying, AB
Taxation, A
Tourism and Travel Services Management, A
Trade and Industrial Teacher Education, A
Transportation and Highway Engineering, A
Vehicle Maintenance and Repair Technologies, A
Welding Technology/Welder, A
Wildlife and Wildlands Science and Management, A

COLUMBIA BIBLE COLLEGE

Bible/Biblical Studies, B
Intercultural/Multicultural and Diversity Studies, B
Kindergarten/PreSchool Education and Teaching, B
Missions/Missionary Studies and Missiology, B
Pastoral Studies/Counseling, B
Pre-Theology/Pre-Ministerial Studies, B
Religion/Religious Studies, B

KWANTLEN UNIVERSITY COLLEGE

Accounting, B
Anthropology, A
Community Psychology, AB
Criminology, AB
English Composition, A
English Language and Literature, A
Entrepreneurship/Entrepreneurial Studies, B
Fashion/Apparel Design, B
Geography, A
Geological and Earth Sciences/Geosciences, A
Graphic Design, B
History, A
Information Technology, B
Interior Design, B
Journalism, B
Music, A
Music Theory and Composition, A
Nursing - Registered Nurse Training, B
Philosophy, A
Piano and Organ, A
Political Science and Government, A
Psychology, A
Social Psychology, AB
Social Sciences, A
Sociology, A
Violin, Viola, Guitar and Other Stringed
   Instruments, A
Voice and Opera, A

MALASPINA UNIVERSITY-COLLEGE

Anthropology, B
Biology/Biological Sciences, B
Business Administration, Management and
   Operations, M
Business/Commerce, B
Child Care and Support Services Management, B
Computer and Information Sciences, B
Creative Writing, B
Education, B
Fishing and Fisheries Sciences and Management, B
History, B
Liberal Arts and Sciences Studies and
   Humanities, B
Nursing, B
Psychology, B
Sociology, B
Tourism and Travel Services Management, B

OPEN LEARNING AGENCY

Art/Art Studies, General, A
Biological and Biomedical Sciences, B
Business Administration and Management, B
Business Administration, Management and
   Operations, B
Design and Applied Arts, B

Electrical and Electronic Engineering
  Technologies/Technicians, B
Fine/Studio Arts, B
General Studies, B
Jazz/Jazz Studies, B
Music Performance, B
Music Therapy/Therapist, B
Psychiatric/Mental Health Nurse/Nursing, B
Respiratory Care Therapy/Therapist, B
Tourism Promotion Operations, B

ROYAL ROADS UNIVERSITY

Advertising and Public Relations, M
Business Administration and Management, B
Business Administration, Management and
  Operations, M
Conflict Resolution and Mediation/Peace Studies, M
Corporate and Organizational Communication, M
Educational Leadership and Administration, M
Educational Media/Instructional Technology, M
Environmental Policy and Resource
  Management, M
Environmental Studies, B
Human Resources Management and Services, M
Management, M
Organizational Management, M

SIMON FRASER UNIVERSITY

Actuarial Science, B
Anthropology, MD
Applied Mathematics, BMD
Archeology, BMD
Art/Art Studies, General, B
Biochemistry, BMD
Biological and Biomedical Sciences, MDO
Biological and Physical Sciences, B
Biology/Biological Sciences, B
Biophysics, MD
Business Administration and Management, B
Business Administration, Management and
  Operations, MO
Canadian Studies, B
Chemical Physics, B
Chemistry, BMD
Clinical Psychology, B
Cognitive Sciences, B
Communication and Media Studies, MD
Communication Studies/Speech Communication
  and Rhetoric, B
Comparative and Interdisciplinary Arts, M
Computer Science, BMD
Counselor Education/School Counseling and
  Guidance Services, M
Criminology, BMD
Curriculum and Instruction, MD
Dance, B
Drama and Dramatics/Theatre Arts, B
Economics, BMD
Education, BMD
Educational Administration and Supervision, M
Educational Psychology, MD
Engineering and Applied Sciences, MD
Engineering Science, B
English, MD
English Language and Literature, B
Entomology, M
Environmental Policy and Resource
  Management, MD
Environmental Sciences, B
Film/Cinema Studies, B
French Language and Literature, BM
General Studies, B
Geography, BMD
Geology/Earth Science, B
Geosciences, M
Gerontology, M
History, BMD
Humanities/Humanistic Studies, B
Information Science/Studies, M
Interdisciplinary Studies, D
International Business/Trade/Commerce, M
Internet and Interactive Multimedia, M
Kinesiology and Exercise Science, B
Kinesiology and Movement Studies, MD
Latin American Studies, M

Liberal Arts and Sciences Studies and
  Humanities, B
Liberal Studies, M
Linguistics, BMD
Management, M
Management Information Systems and
  Services, BM
Management of Technology, M
Management Science, B
Marketing, M
Mathematics, BMD
Molecular Biochemistry, B
Molecular Biology, BMD
Music, B
Philosophy, BMD
Physical Chemistry, MD
Physics, BMD
Political Science and Government, BMD
Psychology, BMD
Publishing, M
Social Sciences, B
Sociology, BMD
Software Engineering, M
Statistics, BMD
Toxicology, O
Visual and Performing Arts, B
Women's Studies, BM

SUMMIT PACIFIC COLLEGE

Bible/Biblical Studies, B
Kindergarten/PreSchool Education and Teaching, B
Pastoral Studies/Counseling, B
Religious Education, B
Religious/Sacred Music, B
Theology/Theological Studies, B

THOMPSON RIVERS UNIVERSITY

Accounting, B
Anesthesiologist Assistant, A
Animal Sciences, B
Animal/Livestock Husbandry and Production, A
Biochemistry, B
Biology/Biological Sciences, B
Business Administration and Management, B
Business/Commerce, B
Canadian Studies, B
Cardiovascular Technology/Technologist, A
Carpentry/Carpenter, A
Cell/Cellular and Molecular Biology, B
Cell/Cellular Biology and Histology, B
Chemistry, B
Child Care and Support Services Management, A
Communications Systems Installation and Repair
  Technology, A
Computer and Information Sciences, B
Computer Engineering, A
Computer Graphics, A
Computer Installation and Repair
  Technology/Technician, A
Computer Programming/Programmer, B
Computer Science, B
Computer Systems Analysis/Analyst, B
Computer Technology/Computer Systems
  Technology, A
Drafting and Design Technology/Technician, A
Drama and Dramatics/Theatre Arts, B
Dramatic/Theatre Arts and Stagecraft, B
Early Childhood Education and Teaching, A
Ecology, B
Economics, B
Electrical, Electronics and Communications
  Engineering, A
Electrical/Electronics Equipment Installation and
  Repair, A
Electrician, A
Elementary Education and Teaching, B
Engineering, A
English Language and Literature, B
Environmental Biology, B
Executive Assistant/Executive Secretary, A
Finance, B
Fine/Studio Arts, B
Geography, B
Graphic Design, A
Health Services/Allied Health/Health Sciences, B
History, B

Hospitality Administration/Management, B
Hospitality and Recreation Marketing Operations, A
Hotel/Motel Administration/Management, A
Human Resources Management and Services, B
Human Resources Management/Personnel
  Administration, B
Industrial Electronics Technology/Technician, A
Journalism, B
Licensed Practical/Vocational Nurse Training, A
Manufacturing Technology/Technician, A
Marketing/Marketing Management, B
Mathematics, B
Molecular Biology, B
Natural Resources and Conservation, B
Nursing - Registered Nurse Training, B
Nursing Science, B
Office Management and Supervision, A
Perfusion Technology/Perfusionist, A
Physics, B
Pipefitting/Pipefitter and Sprinkler Fitter, A
Plumbing Technology/Plumber, A
Political Science and Government, B
Pre-Dentistry Studies, B
Pre-Medicine/Pre-Medical Studies, B
Pre-Pharmacy Studies, A
Prepress/Desktop Publishing and Digital Imaging
  Design, A
Pre-Veterinary Studies, B
Psychology, B
Public Relations, Advertising, and Applied
  Communication, B
Resort Management, A
Respiratory Care Therapy/Therapist, B
Respiratory Therapy Technician/Assistant, A
Sales, Distribution and Marketing Operations, A
Social Sciences, B
Social Work, B
Sociology, B
Sport and Fitness Administration/Management, A
System Administration/Administrator, A
System, Networking, and LAN/WAN
  Management/Manager, A
Tourism and Travel Services Marketing
  Operations, A
Tourism Promotion Operations, A
Veterinary/Animal Health Technology/Technician and
  Veterinary Assistant, A
Visual and Performing Arts, B
Web Page, Digital/Multimedia and Information
  Resources Design, A
Zoology/Animal Biology, B

TRINITY WESTERN UNIVERSITY

Airline/Commercial/Professional Pilot and Flight
  Crew, B
Applied Mathematics, B
Bible/Biblical Studies, B
Biological and Physical Sciences, B
Biology/Biological Sciences, B
Business Administration and Management, B
Chemistry, B
Communication Studies/Speech Communication
  and Rhetoric, B
Computer Science, B
Counseling Psychology, M
Divinity/Ministry (BD, MDiv.), B
Drama and Dramatics/Theatre Arts, B
Education, B
Educational Leadership and Administration, M
Elementary Education and Teaching, B
English as a Second Language, M
English Language and Literature, B
Environmental Biology, B
Environmental Sciences, B
Environmental Studies, B
General Studies, B
Geography, B
Health and Physical Education, B
History, B
Human Services, B
Humanities/Humanistic Studies, B
International Relations and Affairs, B
Liberal Arts and Sciences Studies and
  Humanities, B
Linguistics, B
Mathematics, B

Mathematics and Computer Science, B
Missions/Missionary Studies and Missiology, B
Music, B
Natural Sciences, B
Nursing - Registered Nurse Training, B
Organizational Management, M
Pastoral Studies/Counseling, M
Philosophy, B
Physical Education Teaching and Coaching, B
Political Science and Government, B
Pre-Dentistry Studies, B
Pre-Law Studies, B
Pre-Medicine/Pre-Medical Studies, B
Pre-Veterinary Studies, B
Psychology, B
Religion/Religious Studies, B
Secondary Education and Teaching, B
Social Sciences, B
Theology and Religious Vocations, MP
Visual and Performing Arts, B

THE UNIVERSITY OF BRITISH COLUMBIA

Accounting, BD
Adult and Continuing Education and Teaching, M
Agricultural and Food Products Processing, B
Agricultural Economics, AM
Agricultural Sciences, MD
Agriculture, B
Agronomy and Soil Sciences, MD
Allopathic Medicine, MPO
Anatomy, MD
Animal Genetics, B
Animal Sciences, BMD
Animal/Livestock Husbandry and Production, B
Anthropology, BMD
Applied Mathematics, BMD
Archeology, BM
Architecture, M
Art Education, M
Art History, Criticism and Conservation, BMDO
Art Teacher Education, B
Asian Studies/Civilization, BMD
Astronomy, BMD
Atmospheric Sciences and Meteorology, BMD
Biochemistry, BMD
Biochemistry, Biophysics and Molecular Biology, B
Biological and Biomedical Sciences, MDO
Biological Anthropology, D
Biology/Biological Sciences, B
Biomedical/Medical Engineering, B
Biophysics, B
BioTechnology, B
Botany/Plant Biology, MD
Business Administration and Management, B
Business Administration, Management and
   Operations, B
Business Teacher Education, B
Business/Commerce, B
Canadian Government and Politics, B
Canadian Studies, B
Cell Biology and Anatomy, MD
Cell/Cellular Biology and Histology, B
Central/Middle and Eastern European Studies, B
Chemical Engineering, BMD
Chemistry, BMD
Child and Family Studies, MD
Chinese Language and Literature, B
Civil Engineering, BMD
Classics and Classical
   Languages, Literatures, and Linguistics, BMD
Clinical Psychology, BMD
Clinical/Medical Laboratory Technician, B
Cognitive Sciences, BMD
Communication Disorders, BMD
Community Health and Preventive Medicine, M
Comparative Literature, MD
Computer Engineering, BMD
Computer Science, BMD
Counseling Psychology, MD
Counselor Education/School Counseling and
   Guidance Services, B
Creative Writing, B
Curriculum and Instruction, MD
Dental Hygiene/Hygienist, B
Dentistry, P

Developmental and Child Psychology, B
Developmental Psychology, MD
Dietetics/Dieticians, B
Drama and Dramatics/Theatre Arts, B
Early Childhood Education and Teaching, M
East European and Russian Studies, MD
Economics, BMD
Education, BMDO
Educational Administration and Supervision, M
Educational Leadership and Administration, BD
Educational Measurement and Evaluation, MD
Electrical Engineering, MD
Electrical, Electronics and Communications
   Engineering, B
Elementary Education and Teaching, B
Engineering and Applied Sciences, MD
Engineering Physics, BM
Engineering Technologies/Technicians, B
English, MD
English as a Second Language, MD
English Language and Literature, B
Environmental and Occupational Health, MD
Environmental Biology, B
Environmental Engineering
   Technology/Environmental Technology, B
Environmental Studies, B
Epidemiology, MD
Ethnic and Cultural Studies, B
European Studies/Civilization, B
Experimental Psychology, B
Family and Consumer Sciences/Home Economics
   Teacher Education, B
Family and Consumer Sciences/Human Sciences, B
Film, Television, and Video Production, M
Film, Television, and Video Theory and Criticism, M
Film/Cinema Studies, B
Finance, B
Finance and Banking, D
Fine Arts and Art Studies, MDO
Fine/Studio Arts, B
Food Science, B
Food Science and Technology, BMD
Foods, Nutrition, and Related Services, B
Foods, Nutrition, and Wellness Studies, B
Forensic Psychology, MD
Forest Management/Forest Resources
   Management, B
Forestry, BMD
Foundations and Philosophy of Education, MD
French Language and Literature, BMD
Genetics, MD
Geography, BMD
Geological Engineering, MD
Geological/Geophysical Engineering, B
Geology/Earth Science, BMD
Geophysics and Seismology, BMD
German Language and Literature, B
Health Services Administration, M
Health Services Research, MD
Higher Education/Higher Education
   Administration, M
Hispanic Studies, MD
History, BMD
Home Economics Education, M
Horticultural Science, B
Human Nutrition, B
Human Resources Management and Services, B
Immunology, MD
Industrial Education, M
Information Science/Studies, MDO
Interdisciplinary Studies, B
International Affairs, M
International Business/Trade/Commerce, BD
International Relations and Affairs, B
Italian Language and Literature, B
Japanese Language and Literature, B
Journalism, M
Kindergarten/PreSchool Education and Teaching, B
Kinesiology and Exercise Science, B
Kinesiology and Movement Studies, MD
Labor and Industrial Relations, B
Landscape Architecture, BM
Latin American Studies, B
Latin Language and Literature, B
Law and Legal Studies, MD

Liberal Arts and Sciences Studies and
   Humanities, B
Library Science, MDO
Linguistics, BMD
Management, D
Management Information Systems and Services, BD
Management Strategy and Policy, D
Marine Biology and Biological Oceanography, B
Marine Sciences, MD
Marketing, D
Marketing/Marketing Management, B
Materials Engineering, BMD
Materials Sciences, MD
Mathematics, BMD
Mathematics Teacher Education, M
Mechanical Engineering, BMD
Mechanical Engineering/Mechanical
   Technology/Technician, B
Medical Microbiology and Bacteriology, B
Metallurgical Engineering, BMD
Metallurgy, MD
Microbiology, MD
Mineral/Mining Engineering, MD
Mining and Mineral Engineering, B
Molecular Biology, MD
Music, BMD
Music History, Literature, and Theory, B
Music Teacher Education, BM
Music Theory and Composition, B
Natural Resources and Conservation, B
Natural Resources Management/Development and
   Policy, BMD
Neuroscience, MD
Nursing, MD
Nursing - Registered Nurse Training, B
Nutritional Sciences, MD
Occupational Therapy/Therapist, B
Oceanography, Chemical and Physical, BMD
Operations Research, M
Oral and Dental Sciences, MDO
Organizational Behavior Studies, D
Parks, Recreation and Leisure Facilities
   Management, B
Pathology/Experimental Pathology, MD
Periodontics, O
Pharmaceutical Sciences, MDP
Pharmacology, BMD
Pharmacy, BMDP
Philosophy, BMD
Physical Education Teaching and Coaching, M
Physical Therapy/Therapist, B
Physics, BMD
Physiology, BMD
Piano and Organ, B
Plant Sciences, MD
Political Science and Government, BMD
Pre-Dentistry Studies, B
Pre-Law Studies, B
Pre-Medicine/Pre-Medical Studies, B
Pre-Veterinary Studies, B
Psychology, BMD
Public History, MDO
Reading Teacher Education, BMD
Real Estate, B
Rehabilitation Sciences, MD
Rehabilitation Therapy, B
Religion/Religious Studies, BMD
Reproductive Biology, MD
Romance Languages, Literatures, and Linguistics, B
Russian Language and Literature, B
Russian Studies, B
School Psychology, MDO
Science Teacher Education/General Science
   Teacher Education, BM
Secondary Education and Teaching, B
Slavic Languages, Literatures, and Linguistics, B
Social Psychology, MD
Social Sciences, B
Social Studies Teacher Education, M
Social Work, BMD
Sociology, BMD
Software Engineering, M
Soil Science and Agronomy, B
South Asian
   Languages, Literatures, and Linguistics, B
South Asian Studies, B

Spanish Language and Literature, B
Special Education and Teaching, BMDO
Statistics, BMD
Teaching English as a Second or Foreign
  Language/ESL Language Instructor, B
Theater, MD
Theatre/Theatre Arts Management, B
Transportation and Materials Moving, B
Transportation/Transportation Management, D
Urban and Regional Planning, MD
Urban Studies/Affairs, B
Violin, Viola, Guitar and Other Stringed
  Instruments, B
Visual and Performing Arts, B
Voice and Opera, B
Wildlife and Wildlands Science and Management, B
Women's Studies, B
Wood Science and Wood Products/Pulp and Paper
  Technology, B
Writing, MO
Zoology/Animal Biology, BMD

UNIVERSITY COLLEGE OF THE FRASER VALLEY

Adult and Continuing Education Administration, B
Adult and Continuing Education and Teaching, B
Anthropology, B
Aviation/Airway Management and Operations, B
Biology/Biological Sciences, B
Business Administration and Management, B
Chemistry, B
Child Care and Support Services Management, B
Computer and Information Sciences, B
Computer Systems Analysis/Analyst, B
Criminal Justice/Safety Studies, B
Drama and Dramatics/Theatre Arts, A
English Language and Literature, B
Geography, B
History, B
Interdisciplinary Studies, B
Latin American Studies, A
Mass Communication/Media Studies, A
Mathematics, B
Nursing - Registered Nurse Training, B
Physical Education Teaching and Coaching, B
Physics, B
Psychology, B
Social Work, B
Sociology, B
Statistics, B

UNIVERSITY OF NORTHERN BRITISH COLUMBIA

Accounting, B
Anthropology, B
Aquatic Biology/Limnology, B
Biochemistry, Biophysics and Molecular Biology, B
Biological and Physical Sciences, B
Biology/Biological Sciences, B
Botany/Plant Biology, B
Business Administration and Management, B
Business/Commerce, B
Canadian Studies, B
Chemistry, B
Community Health and Preventive Medicine, M
Computer and Information Sciences, B
Computer Science, BM
Disability Studies, M
Economics, B
Education, M
Elementary Education and Teaching, B
English Language and Literature, B
Environmental Sciences, B
Environmental Studies, BMD
Environmental/Environmental Health Engineering, B
Finance, B
Fishing and Fisheries Sciences and Management, B
Forest Sciences and Biology, B
Gender Studies, M
General Studies, B
Geography, B
History, BM
Interdisciplinary Studies, M
International Affairs, M
International Business/Trade/Commerce, B
International/Global Studies, B

Land Use Planning and
  Management/Development, B
Liberal Arts and Sciences Studies and
  Humanities, B
Marketing/Marketing Management, B
Mathematics, BM
Mathematics and Computer Science, B
Multi-/Interdisciplinary Studies, B
Natural Resources and Conservation, MD
Natural Sciences, B
Nursing - Registered Nurse Training, B
Parks, Recreation and Leisure Facilities
  Management, B
Parks, Recreation, Leisure and Fitness Studies, B
Physics, B
Political Science and Government, BM
Psychology, BMD
Public Health/Community Nurse/Nursing, B
Secondary Education and Teaching, B
Social Psychology, B
Social Work, BM
Wildlife and Wildlands Science and Management, B
Wildlife Biology, B
Women's Studies, B
Youth Services/Administration, B

UNIVERSITY OF PHOENIX-VANCOUVER CAMPUS

Business Administration and Management, B
Business Administration, Management and
  Operations, M
Curriculum and Instruction, M
Education, M
Educational Administration and Supervision, M
Human Resources Management and Services, M
International Business/Trade/Commerce, M
Management, M
Management Information Systems and Services, M
Management of Technology, M
Marketing/Marketing Management, B

UNIVERSITY OF VICTORIA

Ancient/Classical Greek Language and Literature, B
Anthropology, BM
Applied Mathematics, MD
Art Education, M
Art History, Criticism and Conservation, BMD
Art Teacher Education, B
Asian Studies/Civilization, BM
Astronomy, BMD
Astrophysics, MD
Atmospheric Sciences and Meteorology, B
Biochemistry, BMD
Biological and Biomedical Sciences, MD
Biology/Biological Sciences, B
Botany/Plant Biology, B
Business Administration, Management and
  Operations, MO
Business/Commerce, B
Cell Biology and Anatomy, MD
Central/Middle and Eastern European Studies, B
Chemistry, BMD
Child and Family Studies, M
Child Development, B
Chinese Language and Literature, B
Classics and Classical
  Languages, Literatures, and Linguistics, BM
Clinical Psychology, MD
Comparative Literature, B
Composition, M
Computer Art and Design, M
Computer Engineering, B
Computer Science, BMD
Computer Software Engineering, B
Condensed Matter Physics, MD
Conflict Resolution and Mediation/Peace Studies, M
Counselor Education/School Counseling and
  Guidance Services, M
Creative Writing, B
Curriculum and Instruction, M
Developmental Biology and Embryology, MD
Developmental Psychology, MD
Drama and Dramatics/Theatre Arts, B
Ecology, BMD
Economics, BMD
Education, BMD

Educational Leadership and Administration, M
Educational Psychology, MD
Electrical Engineering, MD
Electrical, Electronics and Communications
  Engineering, B
Elementary Education and Teaching, B
Engineering and Applied Sciences, MD
English, MD
English Education, MD
English Language and Literature, B
Environmental Studies, B
Exercise and Sports Science, M
Experimental Psychology, MD
Finance and Banking, M
Fine Arts and Art Studies, M
Fine/Studio Arts, B
Foreign Language Teacher Education, M
French Language and Literature, BM
French Studies, B
Geochemistry, MD
Geography, BMD
Geology/Earth Science, B
Geophysics and Seismology, BMD
Geosciences, MD
German Language and Literature, BM
German Studies, B
Health and Physical Education/Fitness, B
Health/Health Care Administration/Management, B
Hispanic Studies, M
History, BMD
Hotel/Motel Administration/Management, B
Human Development, M
Human Resources Management and Services, M
International Business/Trade/Commerce, B
Italian Language and Literature, BM
Italian Studies, B
Japanese Language and Literature, B
Kindergarten/PreSchool Education and Teaching, B
Kinesiology and Exercise Science, B
Latin Language and Literature, B
Law and Legal Studies, MDPO
Leisure Studies, M
Liberal Arts and Sciences Studies and
  Humanities, B
Linguistics, BMD
Management, M
Marine Biology and Biological Oceanography, BMD
Marine Geology, MD
Mathematics, BMD
Mathematics Teacher Education, M
Mechanical Engineering, BMD
Medical Microbiology and Bacteriology, B
Medical Physics, MD
Medieval and Renaissance Studies, B
Microbiology, MD
Modern Languages, B
Music, BMD
Music History, Literature, and Theory, B
Music Teacher Education, BM
Music Theory and Composition, B
Musicology and Ethnomusicology, MD
Nursing, M
Nursing - Registered Nurse Training, B
Nursing Science, B
Oceanography, Chemical and Physical, BMD
Pacific Area/Pacific Rim Studies, B
Painting, M
Performance, M
Philosophy, BM
Photography, M
Physical Education Teaching and Coaching, BM
Physics, BMD
Physiology, MD
Piano and Organ, B
Political Science and Government, BM
Pre-Dentistry Studies, B
Pre-Law Studies, B
Pre-Medicine/Pre-Medical Studies, B
Pre-Veterinary Studies, B
Psychology, BMD
Public Administration, BMO
Public Policy Analysis, M
Reading Teacher Education, MD
Romance Languages, Literatures, and Linguistics, B
Russian Language and Literature, B
Russian Studies, B

Science Teacher Education/General Science
    Teacher Education, M
Sculpture, M
Secondary Education and Teaching, B
Slavic Languages, Literatures, and Linguistics, B
Social Psychology, MD
Social Studies Teacher Education, M
Social Work, BM
Sociology, BMD
Spanish Language and Literature, B
Special Education and Teaching, B
Sport and Fitness Administration/Management, B
Statistics, BMD
Teaching English as a Second or Foreign
    Language/ESL Language Instructor, B
Technical and Business Writing, B
Theater, MD
Theoretical Physics, MD
Voice and Opera, B
Women's Studies, B
Zoology/Animal Biology, B

Manitoba

BRANDON UNIVERSITY

American Indian/Native American Studies, B
Biology/Biological Sciences, B
Botany/Plant Biology, B
Business Administration and Management, B
Canadian Studies, B
Chemistry, B
Computer Science, B
Counselor Education/School Counseling and
    Guidance Services, BMO
Curriculum and Instruction, MO
Economics, B
Education, BMO
Educational Administration and Supervision, MO
Elementary Education and Teaching, B
English Language and Literature, B
French Language and Literature, B
General Studies, B
Geography, B
Geology/Earth Science, B
History, B
Junior High/Intermediate/Middle School Education
    and Teaching, B
Kindergarten/PreSchool Education and Teaching, B
Liberal Arts and Sciences Studies and
    Humanities, B
Mathematics, B
Mathematics and Computer Science, B
Mental Health/Rehabilitation, B
Music, BM
Music History, Literature, and Theory, B
Music Performance, B
Music Teacher Education, BM
Music Theory and Composition, B
Nursing Science, B
Performance, M
Philosophy, B
Physics, B
Political Science and Government, B
Pre-Dentistry Studies, B
Pre-Law Studies, B
Pre-Medicine/Pre-Medical Studies, B
Pre-Veterinary Studies, B
Psychiatric/Mental Health Nurse/Nursing, B
Psychology, B
Religion/Religious Studies, B
Rural Planning and Studies, MO
Sociology, B
Special Education and Teaching, MO
Voice and Opera, B
Zoology/Animal Biology, B

CANADIAN MENNONITE UNIVERSITY

Bible/Biblical Studies, B
Biology/Biological Sciences, A
Computer Science, B
Conducting, B
Development Economics and International
    Development, B
Divinity/Ministry (BD, MDiv.), B
Economics, B

English Language and Literature, B
Geography, B
History, B
International Relations and Affairs, B
Mathematics, B
Microbiology, A
Missions/Missionary Studies and Missiology, B
Music, B
Music History, Literature, and Theory, B
Music Performance, B
Music Theory and Composition, B
Music Therapy/Therapist, B
Musicology and Ethnomusicology, B
Pastoral Studies/Counseling, B
Peace Studies and Conflict Resolution, B
Philosophy, B
Piano and Organ, B
Political Science and Government, B
Pre-Nursing Studies, B
Psychology, B
Religion/Religious Studies, B
Religious Education, B
Theology/Theological Studies, B
Voice and Opera, B
Youth Ministry, B

COLLÈGE UNIVERSITAIRE DE SAINT-BONIFACE

Canadian Studies, M
Education, M

PROVIDENCE COLLEGE AND THEOLOGICAL SEMINARY

Airline/Commercial/Professional Pilot and Flight
    Crew, B
Bible/Biblical Studies, B
Business Administration and Management, B
Communication and Media Studies, B
Divinity/Ministry (BD, MDiv.), B
Drama and Dramatics/Theatre Arts, B
Education, B
English as a Second Language, O
History, B
Humanities/Humanistic Studies, B
Liberal Arts and Sciences Studies and
    Humanities, B
Missions/Missionary Studies and Missiology, BM
Music, B
Parks, Recreation, Leisure and Fitness Studies, B
Pastoral Studies/Counseling, BM
Religion/Religious Studies, B
Religious Education, BM
Social Sciences, B
Teaching English as a Second or Foreign
    Language/ESL Language Instructor, B
Theology and Religious Vocations, MDPO
Theology/Theological Studies, B
Youth Ministry, B

STEINBACH BIBLE COLLEGE

Bible/Biblical Studies, B
Music, B
Religion/Religious Studies, B

UNIVERSITY OF MANITOBA

Accounting, B
Actuarial Science, B
Adult and Continuing Education and Teaching, M
Agricultural Economics, BMD
Agricultural Sciences, MD
Agricultural/Biological Engineering and
    Bioengineering, B
Agriculture, B
Agronomy and Crop Science, B
Agronomy and Soil Sciences, MD
American Indian/Native American Studies, M
Anatomy, MD
Animal Genetics, B
Animal Sciences, BMD
Anthropology, BMD
Apparel and Textiles, B
Applied Mathematics, B
Architecture, BM
Art History, Criticism and Conservation, B
Art/Art Studies, General, B

Astronomy, B
Biochemistry, MD
Biological and Biomedical Sciences, MDO
Biology/Biological Sciences, B
Biosystems Engineering, MD
Botany/Plant Biology, BMD
Business Administration and Management, B
Business Administration, Management and
    Operations, MD
Business/Managerial Economics, B
Canadian Studies, BM
Chemistry, BMD
Child and Family Studies, M
Child Development, B
Civil Engineering, BMD
Classics and Classical
    Languages, Literatures, and Linguistics, BM
Clinical Psychology, D
Clothing and Textiles, M
Community Health and Preventive Medicine, MD
Computational Sciences, M
Computer Engineering, BMD
Computer Science, BMD
Counselor Education/School Counseling and
    Guidance Services, M
Curriculum and Instruction, M
Dental and Oral Surgery, M
Dental Hygiene/Hygienist, B
Dentistry, P
Disability Studies, M
Drama and Dramatics/Theatre Arts, B
Ecology, B
Economics, BMD
Education, BMD
Educational Administration and Supervision, M
Educational Psychology, M
Electrical Engineering, MD
Electrical, Electronics and Communications
    Engineering, B
Elementary Education and Teaching, B
Engineering and Applied Sciences, MD
Engineering Science, B
English, MD
English as a Second Language, M
English Education, M
English Language and Literature, B
Entomology, BMD
Environmental Design/Architecture, B
Environmental Studies, B
Family and Consumer Sciences/Human Sciences, B
Film/Cinema Studies, B
Finance, B
Food Science, B
Food Science and Technology, M
Foods, Nutrition, and Wellness Studies, B
Foundations and Philosophy of Education, M
French Language and Literature, BMD
Geography, BMD
Geological/Geophysical Engineering, B
Geology/Earth Science, BMD
Geophysics and Seismology, MD
German Language and Literature, BM
History, BMD
Home Economics, M
Horticultural Science, MD
Human Genetics, MD
Immunology, MD
Industrial Engineering, B
Industrial/Management Engineering, MD
Interdisciplinary Studies, MD
Interior Design, BM
Italian Language and Literature, MD
Jewish/Judaic Studies, B
Kindergarten/PreSchool Education and Teaching, B
Labor and Industrial Relations, B
Landscape Architecture, M
Latin Language and Literature, B
Law and Legal Studies, B
Legal and Justice Studies, M
Linguistics, MD
Mathematics, BMD
Mechanical Engineering, BMD
Medical Microbiology and Bacteriology, BMD
Medieval and Renaissance Studies, B
Microbiology, MD
Modern Greek Language and Literature, B

Music, BM
Natural Resources Management/Development and Policy, MD
Northern Studies, M
Nursing, M
Nursing - Registered Nurse Training, B
Nutritional Sciences, MD
Occupational Therapy/Therapist, B
Oral and Dental Sciences, M
Oral Biology, MD
Orthodontics, M
Pathology/Experimental Pathology, M
Periodontics, M
Pharmaceutical Sciences, MD
Pharmacology, MD
Pharmacy, B
Philosophy, BM
Physical Education Teaching and Coaching, BM
Physical Therapy/Therapist, B
Physics, BMD
Physiology, MDO
Political Science and Government, BM
Pre-Dentistry Studies, B
Pre-Law Studies, B
Pre-Medicine/Pre-Medical Studies, B
Pre-Veterinary Studies, B
Psychology, BMD
Public Administration, BM
Recreation and Park Management, M
Rehabilitation Sciences, M
Rehabilitation Therapy, B
Religion/Religious Studies, BMD
Russian Language and Literature, B
Russian Studies, B
Science Teacher Education/General Science Teacher Education, B
Secondary Education and Teaching, B
Slavic Languages, Literatures, and Linguistics, BM
Social Work, BM
Sociology, BMD
South Asian Studies, B
Spanish Language and Literature, BMD
Special Education and Teaching, M
Statistics, BMD
Theology and Religious Vocations, P
Urban and Regional Planning, M
Women's Studies, B
Zoology/Animal Biology, BMD

THE UNIVERSITY OF WINNIPEG

Anthropology, B
Applied Mathematics, B
Art History, Criticism and Conservation, B
Biochemistry, B
Biology/Biological Sciences, B
Business Administration and Management, B
Canadian Studies, B
Chemistry, B
Classics and Classical Languages, Literatures, and Linguistics, B
Criminal Justice/Police Science, B
Data Processing and Data Processing Technology/Technician, B
Development Economics and International Development, B
Developmental and Child Psychology, B
Drama and Dramatics/Theatre Arts, B
Ecology, B
Economics, B
Education, B
Elementary Education and Teaching, B
English Language and Literature, B
Environmental Studies, B
French Language and Literature, B
French Studies, B
Geography, B
German Language and Literature, B
German Studies, B
History, BM
Information Science/Studies, B
Interdisciplinary Studies, B
Italian Studies, B
Journalism, B
Latin Language and Literature, B
Marriage and Family Therapy/Counseling, MO
Mathematics, B

Modern Greek Language and Literature, B
Molecular Biology, B
Music, B
Peace Studies and Conflict Resolution, B
Philosophy, B
Physics, B
Political Science and Government, B
Pre-Dentistry Studies, B
Pre-Law Studies, B
Pre-Medicine/Pre-Medical Studies, B
Pre-Nursing Studies, B
Pre-Pharmacy Studies, B
Pre-Veterinary Studies, B
Psychology, B
Public Administration, M
Religion/Religious Studies, BM
Secondary Education and Teaching, B
Sociology, B
Spanish and Iberian Studies, B
Statistics, B
Theology and Religious Vocations, MPO
Theology/Theological Studies, B
Urban Studies/Affairs, B
Women's Studies, B

WILLIAM AND CATHERINE BOOTH COLLEGE

Bible/Biblical Studies, B
Pastoral Studies/Counseling, B
Religious Education, B
Social Work, B
Theology/Theological Studies, B

New Brunswick

ATLANTIC BAPTIST UNIVERSITY

Bible/Biblical Studies, B
Biology/Biological Sciences, B
Business Administration and Management, B
Education, B
English Language and Literature, B
History, B
Interdisciplinary Studies, B
Mass Communication/Media Studies, B
Psychology, B
Religion/Religious Studies, B
Sociology, B
Teacher Education, Multiple Levels, B

BETHANY BIBLE COLLEGE

Bible/Biblical Studies, B
Divinity/Ministry (BD, MDiv.), B
Elementary Education and Teaching, B
Music, B
Religion/Religious Studies, B
Religious Education, B

MOUNT ALLISON UNIVERSITY

Accounting, B
American/United States Studies/Civilization, B
Ancient/Classical Greek Language and Literature, B
Anthropology, B
Applied Mathematics, B
Art History, Criticism and Conservation, B
Biochemistry, B
Biological and Biomedical Sciences, M
Biological and Physical Sciences, B
Biology/Biological Sciences, B
Biopsychology, B
Business Administration and Management, B
Business/Commerce, B
Business/Managerial Economics, B
Canadian Studies, B
Chemistry, BM
Classics and Classical Languages, Literatures, and Linguistics, B
Comparative Literature, B
Computer Science, B
Drama and Dramatics/Theatre Arts, B
Drawing, B
Economics, B
English Language and Literature, B
Environmental Studies, B
Fine/Studio Arts, B
French Language and Literature, B

Geography, B
Geology/Earth Science, B
German Language and Literature, B
History, B
Humanities/Humanistic Studies, B
Interdisciplinary Studies, B
International Business/Trade/Commerce, B
International Relations and Affairs, B
Latin Language and Literature, B
Liberal Arts and Sciences Studies and Humanities, B
Mathematics, B
Mathematics and Computer Science, B
Medieval and Renaissance Studies, B
Modern Languages, B
Music, B
Music History, Literature, and Theory, B
Music Performance, B
Natural Sciences, B
Philosophy, B
Photography, B
Physics, B
Physiological Psychology/Psychobiology, B
Piano and Organ, B
Political Science and Government, B
Pre-Dentistry Studies, B
Pre-Law Studies, B
Pre-Medicine/Pre-Medical Studies, B
Pre-Pharmacy Studies, B
Pre-Theology/Pre-Ministerial Studies, B
Pre-Veterinary Studies, B
Printmaking, B
Psychology, B
Religion/Religious Studies, B
Romance Languages, Literatures, and Linguistics, B
Sculpture, B
Sociology, B
Spanish Language and Literature, B
Violin, Viola, Guitar and Other Stringed Instruments, B
Voice and Opera, B
Wind and Percussion Instruments, B

ST. THOMAS UNIVERSITY

Adult Development and Aging, B
American Indian/Native American Studies, B
Anthropology, B
Criminology, B
Economics, B
Education, B
English Language and Literature, B
French Language and Literature, B
Gerontology, B
History, B
Interdisciplinary Studies, B
Journalism, B
Mathematics, B
Philosophy, B
Political Science and Government, B
Psychology, B
Religion/Religious Studies, B
Social Work, B
Sociology, B
Spanish Language and Literature, B

UNIVERSITÉ DE MONCTON

Accounting, B
Adult and Continuing Education and Teaching, B
Astronomy, M
Biochemistry, BM
Biological and Biomedical Sciences, M
Biological and Physical Sciences, B
Biology/Biological Sciences, B
Business Administration and Management, B
Business Administration, Management and Operations, MO
Chemistry, BM
Child Development, B
Civil Engineering, BM
Comparative Literature, B
Computer Science, BMO
Counselor Education/School Counseling and Guidance Services, M
Drama and Dramatics/Theatre Arts, B
Economics, BM
Education, BM

Educational Administration and Supervision, M
Educational Psychology, M
Electrical Engineering, M
Electrical, Electronics and Communications
    Engineering, B
Elementary Education and Teaching, B
Engineering, B
Engineering and Applied Sciences, M
English Language and Literature, B
Family and Consumer Economics and Related
    Services, B
Finance, B
Fine/Studio Arts, B
Food Science and Technology, M
Food Technology and Processing, B
Foods, Nutrition, and Wellness Studies, B
Forest Engineering, B
French Language and Literature, BMD
Geography, B
History, BM
Industrial Engineering, B
Industrial/Management Engineering, M
Kindergarten/PreSchool Education and Teaching, B
Language Interpretation and Translation, B
Law and Legal Studies, BMPO
Liberal Arts and Sciences Studies and
    Humanities, B
Linguistics, B
Marketing/Marketing Management, B
Mass Communication/Media Studies, B
Mathematics, BM
Mechanical Engineering, BM
Modern Languages, B
Music, B
Music Teacher Education, B
Nursing Science, B
Nutritional Sciences, M
Operations Management and Supervision, B
Parks, Recreation, Leisure and Fitness Studies, B
Philosophy, B
Physical Education Teaching and Coaching, B
Physics, BM
Political Science and Government, B
Psychology, BM
Public Administration, MO
Radiologic Technology/Science - Radiographer, B
Secondary Education and Teaching, B
Social Sciences, B
Social Work, BM
Sociology, B
Sport and Fitness Administration/Management, B
Technology Education/Industrial Arts, B

UNIVERSITY OF NEW BRUNSWICK FREDERICTON

Accounting, B
Adult and Continuing Education and Teaching, BM
American/United States Studies/Civilization, M
Animal Physiology, B
Anthropology, BM
Applied Mathematics, B
Art Teacher Education, B
Biochemistry, B
Biological and Biomedical Sciences, MD
Biological and Physical Sciences, B
Biology/Biological Sciences, B
Biophysics, B
Botany/Plant Biology, B
Business Administration and Management, B
Business Administration, Management and
    Operations, M
Business Teacher Education, B
Business/Managerial Economics, B
Canadian Studies, B
Chemical Engineering, BMD
Chemistry, BMD
Civil Engineering, BMD
Classics and Classical
    Languages, Literatures, and Linguistics, BM
Clinical Psychology, B
Comparative Literature, B
Computer Engineering, BMD
Computer Science, BMD
Construction Engineering, B
Construction Engineering and Management, MD

Counselor Education/School Counseling and
    Guidance Services, BM
Curriculum and Instruction, M
Data Processing and Data Processing
    Technology/Technician, B
Developmental and Child Psychology, B
Drama and Dramatics/Theatre Arts, B
Ecology, B
Economics, BM
Education, BM
Educational Administration and Supervision, M
Educational Psychology, M
Electrical Engineering, MD
Electrical, Electronics and Communications
    Engineering, B
Elementary Education and Teaching, B
Engineering, B
Engineering and Applied Sciences, MDO
English, MD
English Language and Literature, B
Entomology, B
Environmental Engineering
    Technology/Environmental Technology, MD
Exercise and Sports Science, M
Family and Consumer Sciences/Home Economics
    Teacher Education, B
Finance, B
Fire Science/Firefighting, B
Forest Engineering, B
Forestry, BMD
French Language and Literature, BM
Geochemistry, B
Geodetic Sciences, MDO
Geological/Geophysical Engineering, B
Geology/Earth Science, BMD
Geophysics and Seismology, B
Geotechnical Engineering, MD
German Language and Literature, BM
Health Teacher Education, B
History, BMD
Human Resources Management/Personnel
    Administration, B
Hydrology and Water Resources Science, MD
Information Science/Studies, B
International Business/Trade/Commerce, B
International Relations and Affairs, B
Kindergarten/PreSchool Education and Teaching, B
Kinesiology and Exercise Science, B
Latin Language and Literature, B
Law and Legal Studies, BPO
Liberal Arts and Sciences Studies and
    Humanities, B
Linguistics, B
Marketing/Marketing Management, B
Materials Sciences, MD
Mathematics, BMD
Mechanical Engineering, BMD
Mechanics, MD
Medical Microbiology and Bacteriology, B
Modern Greek Language and Literature, B
Modern Languages, B
Molecular Biology, B
Music Teacher Education, B
Nursing - Registered Nurse Training, B
Operations Research, B
Parks, Recreation, Leisure and Fitness Studies, B
Philosophy, BM
Physical Education Teaching and Coaching, BM
Physics, BMD
Physiological Psychology/Psychobiology, B
Political Science and Government, BM
Pre-Dentistry Studies, B
Pre-Law Studies, B
Pre-Medicine/Pre-Medical Studies, B
Pre-Veterinary Studies, B
Psychology, BD
Public Administration, M
Recreation and Park Management, M
Romance Languages, Literatures, and Linguistics, B
Russian Language and Literature, BM
Science Teacher Education/General Science
    Teacher Education, B
Secondary Education and Teaching, B
Sociology, BMD
Spanish Language and Literature, BM
Special Education and Teaching, BM

Sport and Fitness Administration/Management, M
Statistics, BMD
Structural Engineering, MD
Survey Technology/Surveying, B
Surveying Engineering, MD
Teaching English as a Second or Foreign
    Language/ESL Language Instructor, B
Transportation and Highway Engineering, MD
Vocational and Technical Education, M
Water Resources, MD
Wildlife and Wildlands Science and Management, B
Wildlife Biology, B
Zoology/Animal Biology, B

UNIVERSITY OF NEW BRUNSWICK SAINT JOHN

Accounting, B
Applied Mathematics, B
Biological and Biomedical Sciences, MD
Biology/Biological Sciences, B
Business Administration and Management, B
Business Administration, Management and
    Operations, M
Chemical Engineering, B
Civil Engineering, B
Communication Studies/Speech Communication
    and Rhetoric, B
Computer Engineering Technology/Technician, B
Computer Science, B
Economics, B
Education, B
Electrical, Electronics and Communications
    Engineering, B
Electronic Commerce, M
Elementary Education and Teaching, B
English Language and Literature, B
Forest Engineering, B
Forestry, B
French Language and Literature, B
Geological/Geophysical Engineering, B
History, B
Hospitality Administration/Management, B
Human Resources Management/Personnel
    Administration, B
International Business/Trade/Commerce, M
International Relations and Affairs, B
Kinesiology and Exercise Science, B
Marine Biology and Biological Oceanography, B
Mechanical Engineering, B
Natural Resources Management/Development and
    Policy, M
Naval Architecture and Marine Engineering, B
Nursing - Registered Nurse Training, B
Philosophy, B
Political Science and Government, B
Psychology, BM
Public Health (MPH, DPH), B
Sociology, B
Statistics, B
Survey Technology/Surveying, B

Nova Scotia

ACADIA UNIVERSITY

Applied Mathematics, M
Biological and Biomedical Sciences, M
Biology/Biological Sciences, B
Business Administration and Management, B
Canadian Studies, B
Chemistry, BM
Classics and Classical
    Languages, Literatures, and Linguistics, B
Clinical Psychology, M
Computer Science, BM
Counselor Education/School Counseling and
    Guidance Services, M
Curriculum and Instruction, M
Dietetics/Dieticians, B
Drama and Dramatics/Theatre Arts, B
Economics, B
Education, BM
Educational Leadership and Administration, M
Educational Media/Instructional Technology, M
Elementary Education and Teaching, B
English, M

English Language and Literature, B
Environmental Studies, B
Food Science, B
Foods, Nutrition, and Wellness Studies, B
French Language and Literature, B
Geology/Earth Science, BM
History, B
Kinesiology and Exercise Science, B
Kinesiology and Movement Studies, M
Latin Language and Literature, B
Mathematics, B
Mathematics Teacher Education, M
Music, B
Music Teacher Education, B
Pastoral Studies/Counseling, M
Philosophy, B
Physics, B
Piano and Organ, B
Political Science and Government, BM
Pre-Dentistry Studies, B
Pre-Law Studies, B
Pre-Medicine/Pre-Medical Studies, B
Pre-Veterinary Studies, B
Psychology, BM
Recreation and Park Management, M
Science Teacher Education/General Science
   Teacher Education, M
Secondary Education and Teaching, M
Social Studies Teacher Education, M
Sociology, BM
Special Education and Teaching, M
Statistics, M
Theology and Religious Vocations, MDP
Violin, Viola, Guitar and Other Stringed
   Instruments, B
Voice and Opera, B
Wind and Percussion Instruments, B

CAPE BRETON UNIVERSITY

Accounting, B
American Indian/Native American Studies, B
Anthropology, B
Art Education, O
Biological and Physical Sciences, B
Biology/Biological Sciences, B
Business Administration and Management, B
Business Administration, Management and
   Operations, M
Business/Commerce, B
Business/Managerial Economics, B
Chemical Technology/Technician, B
Chemistry, B
Communication Studies/Speech Communication
   and Rhetoric, B
Community Organization and Advocacy, B
Computer and Information Sciences, B
Computer Science, B
Counselor Education/School Counseling and
   Guidance Services, O
Economics, B
Education, O
Educational Media/Instructional Technology, O
Electrical/Electronics Equipment Installation and
   Repair, B
Engineering, B
English Language and Literature, B
Environmental Engineering
   Technology/Environmental Technology, B
Environmental Health, B
Environmental Studies, B
Finance, B
French Language and Literature, B
History, B
Hospitality Administration/Management, B
Hospitality and Recreation Marketing Operations, B
Information Science/Studies, B
Labor and Industrial Relations, B
Liberal Arts and Sciences Studies and
   Humanities, B
Management Information Systems and Services, B
Marketing/Marketing Management, B
Mathematics, B
Nursing - Registered Nurse Training, B
Organizational Behavior Studies, B
Parks, Recreation, Leisure and Fitness Studies, B
Petroleum Technology/Technician, B

Philosophy, B
Political Science and Government, B
Pre-Dentistry Studies, B
Pre-Law Studies, B
Pre-Medicine/Pre-Medical Studies, B
Pre-Veterinary Studies, B
Psychology, B
Religion/Religious Studies, B
Sales, Distribution and Marketing Operations, B
Sociology, B
Speech and Rhetorical Studies, B
Sport and Fitness Administration/Management, B
Tourism and Travel Services Management, B
Tourism Promotion Operations, B

DALHOUSIE UNIVERSITY

Accounting, B
Acting, B
Agricultural Engineering, MD
Agricultural Sciences, M
Agricultural/Biological Engineering and
   Bioengineering, B
Allopathic Medicine, PO
Anatomy, MD
Anthropology, BMD
Applied Mathematics, MD
Architecture, BMO
Atmospheric Sciences and Meteorology, B
Biochemistry, MDO
Biochemistry, Biophysics and Molecular Biology, B
Bioengineering, MD
Bioinformatics, B
Biological and Biomedical Sciences, MDO
Biology/Biological Sciences, B
Biomedical Engineering, M
Biomedical/Medical Engineering, B
Biophysics, MDO
Business Administration and Management, B
Business Administration, Management and
   Operations, MO
Business/Commerce, B
Canadian Studies, B
Chemical Engineering, BMD
Chemistry, BMD
City/Urban, Community and Regional Planning, B
Civil Engineering, BMD
Classics and Classical
   Languages, Literatures, and Linguistics, BMD
Clinical Psychology, D
Communication Disorders, M
Communication, Journalism and Related
   Programs, B
Community Health and Preventive Medicine, M
Comparative Literature, B
Computer Education, M
Computer Engineering, BMD
Computer Science, BMD
Computer Software Engineering, B
Computer/Information Technology Services
   Administration and Management, B
Dental and Oral Surgery, O
Dental Hygiene/Hygienist, BO
Dentistry, P
Development Economics and International
   Development, B
Diagnostic Medical Sonography/Sonographer and
   Ultrasound Technician, B
Drama and Dramatics/Theatre Arts, B
Dramatic/Theatre Arts and Stagecraft, B
Economics, BMD
Electrical Engineering, MD
Electrical, Electronics and Communications
   Engineering, B
Electronic Commerce, M
Engineering, B
Engineering and Applied Sciences, MDO
English, MD
English Language and Literature, B
Entrepreneurship/Entrepreneurial Studies, B
Environmental Design/Architecture, B
Environmental Sciences, B
Environmental Studies, BM
Environmental/Environmental Health Engineering, B
Epidemiology, M
European Studies/Civilization, B
Fashion/Apparel Design, B

Finance, B
Food Science, B
Food Science and Technology, MD
French Language and Literature, BMD
General Merchandising, Sales, and Related
   Marketing Operations, B
Geology/Earth Science, B
Geosciences, MD
German Language and Literature, BM
Health Education, M
Health Information/Medical Records
   Administration/Administrator, B
Health Professions and Related Clinical Sciences, B
Health Services Administration, MO
Health Services/Allied Health/Health Sciences, B
History, BMD
History and Philosophy of Science and
   Technology, B
Human-Computer Interaction, M
Immunology, MDO
Industrial Engineering, B
Industrial/Management Engineering, MD
Information Science/Studies, MO
Interdisciplinary Studies, D
International Business/Trade/Commerce, B
International Development, M
International Relations and Affairs, B
Italian Studies, B
Kinesiology and Exercise Science, B
Kinesiology and Movement Studies, M
Law and Legal Studies, MDO
Leisure Studies, M
Library Science, MO
Linguistics, B
Management Information Systems and Services, M
Management Science, B
Marine Affairs, M
Marine Biology and Biological Oceanography, B
Marketing/Marketing Management, B
Mathematics, BMD
Mechanical Engineering, BMD
Medical Microbiology and Bacteriology, B
Metallurgical Engineering, BMD
Meteorology, B
Microbiological Sciences and Immunology, B
Microbiology, MDO
Mineral/Mining Engineering, MD
Mining and Mineral Engineering, B
Multi-/Interdisciplinary Studies, B
Music, B
Music History, Literature, and Theory, B
Music Performance, B
Music Theory and Composition, B
Neurobiology and Neurophysiology, MD
Neuroscience, BMD
Non-Profit/Public/Organizational Management, B
Nuclear Medical Technology/Technologist, B
Nursing, MO
Nursing - Registered Nurse Training, B
Occupational Therapy/Therapist, BM
Oceanography, Chemical and Physical, BMD
Oral and Dental Sciences, MO
Parks, Recreation, Leisure and Fitness Studies, B
Pathology/Experimental Pathology, M
Pharmaceutical Sciences, MD
Pharmacology, MDO
Pharmacy, B
Pharmacy, Pharmaceutical Sciences, and Administration, B
Philosophy, BMD
Physical Therapy/Therapist, B
Physics, BMD
Physiology, MDO
Political Science and Government, BMD
Pre-Dentistry Studies, B
Pre-Law Studies, B
Pre-Medicine/Pre-Medical Studies, B
Pre-Pharmacy Studies, B
Pre-Veterinary Studies, B
Psychology, BMD
Public Administration, MO
Public Affairs, M
Public Health (MPH, DPH), B
Public Health Education and Promotion, B
Radiologic Technology/Science - Radiographer, B
Religion/Religious Studies, B
Respiratory Care Therapy/Therapist, B

Respiratory Therapy Technician/Assistant, B
Rural Planning and Studies, MO
Russian Language and Literature, B
Russian Studies, B
Science, Technology and Society, B
Small Business Administration/Management, B
Social Work, BM
Sociology, BMD
Spanish Language and Literature, B
Statistics, BMD
Theatre Literature, History and Criticism, B
Therapeutic Recreation/Recreational Therapy, B
Urban and Regional Planning, MO
Women's Studies, BM

MOUNT SAINT VINCENT UNIVERSITY

Accounting, B
Adult and Continuing Education and Teaching, M
Adult Development and Aging, B
Anthropology, B
Applied Mathematics, B
Art Teacher Education, B
Biological and Physical Sciences, B
Biology/Biological Sciences, B
Business Administration and Management, B
Chemistry, B
Child and Family Studies, M
Child Development, B
Comparative Literature, B
Computer and Information Sciences, B
Computer Systems Analysis/Analyst, B
Curriculum and Instruction, M
Developmental and Child Psychology, B
Dietetics/Dieticians, B
Economics, B
Education, BM
Educational Psychology, M
Elementary Education and Teaching, BM
English as a Second Language, M
English Language and Literature, B
Family and Consumer Economics and Related
    Services, B
Family and Consumer Sciences/Human Sciences, B
Fine/Studio Arts, B
Foods, Nutrition, and Wellness Studies, B
Foundations and Philosophy of Education, M
French Language and Literature, B
German Language and Literature, B
Gerontology, BM
History, B
Hospitality Administration/Management, B
Hotel/Motel Administration/Management, B
Humanities/Humanistic Studies, B
Information Science/Studies, B
Interdisciplinary Studies, B
Kindergarten/PreSchool Education and Teaching, B
Liberal Arts and Sciences Studies and
    Humanities, B
Linguistics, B
Management Information Systems and Services, B
Marketing Research, B
Marketing/Marketing Management, B
Mathematics, B
Mathematics and Computer Science, B
Middle School Education, M
Modern Languages, B
Nutritional Sciences, BM
Peace Studies and Conflict Resolution, B
Philosophy, B
Political Science and Government, B
Psychology, B
Public Relations/Image Management, B
Reading Teacher Education, BM
Religion/Religious Studies, B
School Psychology, M
Secondary Education and Teaching, B
Social Sciences, B
Sociology, B
Spanish Language and Literature, B
Special Education and Teaching, M
Special Products Marketing Operations, B
Statistics, B
Tourism and Travel Services Management, B
Tourism and Travel Services Marketing
    Operations, B

Women's Studies, BM

NOVA SCOTIA AGRICULTURAL COLLEGE

Agricultural Business and Management, B
Agricultural Economics, B
Agricultural Mechanization, B
Agricultural Sciences, M
Agriculture, B
Animal Sciences, B
Applied Horticulture/Horticultural Operations, B
Engineering, B
Environmental Studies, B
Plant Sciences, B
Pre-Veterinary Studies, B

NSCAD UNIVERSITY

Art History, Criticism and Conservation, B
Art/Art Studies, General, B
Ceramic Arts and Ceramics, B
Commercial and Advertising Art, B
Crafts, M
Crafts/Craft Design, Folk Art and Artisanry, B
Design and Applied Arts, BM
Design and Visual Communications, B
Drawing, B
Fiber, Textile and Weaving Arts, B
Film/Cinema Studies, B
Fine Arts and Art Studies, M
Fine/Studio Arts, B
Graphic Design, B
Metal and Jewelry Arts, B
Painting, B
Photography, B
Printmaking, B
Sculpture, B

ST. FRANCIS XAVIER UNIVERSITY

Accounting, B
Adult and Continuing Education and Teaching, M
Anthropology, B
Biological and Biomedical Sciences, M
Biological and Physical Sciences, B
Biology/Biological Sciences, B
Business Administration and Management, B
Canadian Studies, B
Chemistry, BM
Classics and Classical
    Languages, Literatures, and Linguistics, B
Computer and Information Sciences, B
Cultural Studies, M
Economics, B
Education, BMO
Elementary Education and Teaching, B
English Language and Literature, B
Environmental Studies, B
Ethnic and Cultural Studies, B
Foods, Nutrition, and Wellness Studies, B
French Language and Literature, B
Geology/Earth Science, BM
Geosciences, M
History, B
Hydrology and Water Resources Science, B
Information Science/Studies, B
Jazz/Jazz Studies, B
Kinesiology and Exercise Science, B
Liberal Arts and Sciences Studies and
    Humanities, B
Management Information Systems and Services, B
Mathematics, B
Modern Languages, B
Music, B
Nursing - Registered Nurse Training, B
Nursing Science, B
Philosophy, B
Physical Education Teaching and Coaching, B
Physical Sciences, B
Physics, BM
Political Science and Government, B
Pre-Dentistry Studies, B
Pre-Law Studies, B
Pre-Medicine/Pre-Medical Studies, B
Pre-Veterinary Studies, B
Psychology, B
Religion/Religious Studies, B
Secondary Education and Teaching, B

Sociology, B
Women's Studies, B

SAINT MARY'S UNIVERSITY

Accounting, B
Anthropology, B
Asian Studies/Civilization, B
Astronomy, BM
Astrophysics, B
Biology/Biological Sciences, B
Business Administration and Management, B
Business Administration, Management and
    Operations, MD
Business/Managerial Economics, B
Canadian Studies, BM
Chemistry, B
Classics and Classical
    Languages, Literatures, and Linguistics, B
Computer Science, B
Criminology, BM
Data Processing and Data Processing
    Technology/Technician, B
Economics, B
Engineering, B
English Language and Literature, B
Finance, B
French Language and Literature, B
Geography, B
Geology/Earth Science, B
German Language and Literature, B
History, BM
Human Resources Management/Personnel
    Administration, B
Interdisciplinary Studies, B
International Development, M
International Relations and Affairs, B
Marketing/Marketing Management, B
Mathematics, B
Modern Languages, B
Philosophy, BM
Physics, B
Political Science and Government, B
Psychology, BM
Religion/Religious Studies, B
Sociology, B
Women's Studies, BM

UNIVERSITÉ SAINTE-ANNE

Biology/Biological Sciences, B
Business Administration and Management, B
Canadian Studies, B
Chemistry, B
Drama and Dramatics/Theatre Arts, B
Education, B
Elementary Education and Teaching, B
English Language and Literature, B
European Studies/Civilization, B
French Language and Literature, B
French Language Teacher Education, B
History, B
Mathematics, B
Physics, B
Pre-Veterinary Studies, B
Public Administration, B
Secondary Education and Teaching, B

UNIVERSITY OF KING'S COLLEGE

Anthropology, B
Biochemistry, B
Biology/Biological Sciences, B
Chemistry, B
Classics and Classical
    Languages, Literatures, and Linguistics, B
Computer Science, B
Development Economics and International
    Development, B
Drama and Dramatics/Theatre Arts, B
Economics, B
English Language and Literature, B
European Studies/Civilization, B
French Language and Literature, B
Geology/Earth Science, B
German Language and Literature, B
History, B
Journalism, B
Linguistics, B

Marine Biology and Biological Oceanography, B
Mathematics, B
Medical Microbiology and Bacteriology, B
Multi-/Interdisciplinary Studies, B
Music, B
Neuroscience, B
Philosophy, B
Physics, B
Political Science and Government, B
Psychology, B
Religion/Religious Studies, B
Russian Language and Literature, B
Science, Technology and Society, B
Sociology, B
Spanish Language and Literature, B
Statistics, B
Women's Studies, B

Prince Edward Island

UNIVERSITY OF PRINCE EDWARD ISLAND

Anatomy, MD
Anthropology, B
Bacteriology, MD
Biological and Biomedical Sciences, M
Biology/Biological Sciences, B
Business Administration and Management, B
Canadian Studies, B
Chemistry, BM
Computer Science, B
Economics, B
Education, BM
Educational Leadership and Administration, M
Elementary Education and Teaching, B
English Language and Literature, B
Epidemiology, MD
Family and Consumer Economics and Related
   Services, B
Foods, Nutrition, and Wellness Studies, B
French Language and Literature, B
Geography, M
German Language and Literature, B
History, B
Hospitality Administration/Management, B
Immunology, MD
Mathematics, B
Medical Radiologic Technology/Science - Radiation
   Therapist, B
Music, B
Music Teacher Education, B
Nursing - Registered Nurse Training, B
Parasitology, MD
Pathology/Experimental Pathology, MD
Pharmacology, MD
Philosophy, B
Physics, B
Physiology, MD
Political Science and Government, B
Pre-Dentistry Studies, B
Pre-Medicine/Pre-Medical Studies, B
Pre-Veterinary Studies, B
Psychology, B
Religion/Religious Studies, B
Science Teacher Education/General Science
   Teacher Education, M
Secondary Education and Teaching, B
Sociology, B
Spanish Language and Literature, B
Toxicology, MD
Veterinary Medicine, P
Veterinary Sciences, MD
Virology, MD

Newfoundland and Labrador

MEMORIAL UNIVERSITY OF NEWFOUNDLAND

Accounting, B
Acting, B
Adult and Continuing Education and Teaching, BMO
Allopathic Medicine, P
Anthropology, BMD
Applied Mathematics, B

Applied Science and Technology, M
Aquaculture, M
Archeology, B
Area Studies, B
Art History, Criticism and Conservation, B
Art/Art Studies, General, B
Athletic Training and Sports Medicine, B
Biochemistry, BMD
Biological and Biomedical Sciences, MDO
Biological and Physical Sciences, B
Biology/Biological Sciences, B
Biopsychology, MD
Business Administration and Management, B
Business Administration, Management and
   Operations, M
Canadian Studies, B
Cartography, B
Cell/Cellular Biology and Histology, B
Chemical Engineering, B
Chemistry, BMD
Civil Engineering, BMD
Classics and Classical
   Languages, Literatures, and Linguistics, BM
Community Health and Preventive Medicine, MDO
Comparative Literature, B
Computational Sciences, M
Computer Engineering, MD
Computer Programming/Programmer, B
Computer Science, BMD
Condensed Matter Physics, M
Counselor Education/School Counseling and
   Guidance Services, B
Criminal Justice/Police Science, B
Criminology, B
Curriculum and Instruction, M
Dietetics/Dieticians, B
Drama and Dramatics/Theatre Arts, B
Drawing, B
Ecology, B
Economics, BM
Education, BMDO
Educational Leadership and Administration, M
Educational Media/Instructional Technology, M
Educational Psychology, M
Electrical Engineering, MD
Electrical, Electronics and Communications
   Engineering, B
Elementary Education and Teaching, B
Engineering, B
Engineering and Applied Sciences, MD
English, MD
English Language and Literature, B
Entomology, B
Environmental Biology, B
Environmental Engineering
   Technology/Environmental Technology, M
Environmental Sciences, M
Environmental Studies, B
Epidemiology, MDO
Ethnic, Cultural Minority, and Gender Studies, B
Experimental Psychology, MD
Finance, B
Fish, Game and Wildlife Management, M
Folklore, MD
Food Science, B
Food Science and Technology, MD
Foods, Nutrition, and Wellness Studies, B
Forest Sciences and Biology, B
French Language and Literature, BM
Gender Studies, D
Geography, BMD
Geological/Geophysical Engineering, B
Geology/Earth Science, BMD
Geophysics and Seismology, BMD
Geosciences, MD
German Language and Literature, BM
History, BMD
Human Genetics, MDO
Humanities/Humanistic Studies, BM
Industrial and Labor Relations, M
Industrial Engineering, B
Information Science/Studies, B
Junior High/Intermediate/Middle School Education
   and Teaching, B
Kinesiology and Exercise Science, B
Kinesiology and Movement Studies, M

Labor and Industrial Relations, B
Latin Language and Literature, B
Linguistics, BMD
Marine Affairs, MD
Marine Biology and Biological Oceanography, BM
Marine Science/Merchant Marine Officer, B
Marine Sciences, M
Marketing/Marketing Management, B
Mathematics, BMD
Mechanical Engineering, BMD
Medical Microbiology and Bacteriology, B
Medieval and Renaissance Studies, B
Modern Greek Language and Literature, B
Music, BO
Music History, Literature, and Theory, B
Music Teacher Education, B
Music Theory and Composition, B
Natural Resources and Conservation, M
Naval Architecture and Marine Engineering, B
Neuroscience, B
Nursing, M
Nursing - Registered Nurse Training, B
Ocean Engineering, BMD
Oceanography, Chemical and Physical, BMD
Organizational Behavior Studies, B
Painting, B
Parks, Recreation, Leisure and Fitness Studies, B
Performance, O
Pharmaceutical Sciences, M
Pharmacy, B
Philosophy, BM
Photography, B
Physical Education Teaching and Coaching, BM
Physics, BMD
Piano and Organ, B
Political Science and Government, BM
Pre-Medicine/Pre-Medical Studies, B
Printmaking, B
Psychology, BMD
Religion/Religious Studies, BM
Russian Language and Literature, B
Science Teacher Education/General Science
   Teacher Education, B
Sculpture, B
Secondary Education and Teaching, B
Social Psychology, M
Social Sciences, B
Social Work, BMD
Sociology, BMD
Spanish Language and Literature, B
Special Education and Teaching, B
Statistics, BMD
Technical Theatre/Theatre Design and
   Technology, B
Theatre Literature, History and Criticism, B
Trade and Industrial Teacher Education, B
Violin, Viola, Guitar and Other Stringed
   Instruments, B
Voice and Opera, B
Wind and Percussion Instruments, B
Women's Studies, BM
Zoology/Animal Biology, B

Ontario

BROCK UNIVERSITY

Accounting, BM
Adult and Continuing Education and Teaching, B
Ancient/Classical Greek Language and Literature, B
Applied Mathematics, B
Archeology, B
Art/Art Studies, General, B
Biochemistry, B
Biological and Biomedical Sciences, M
Biological and Physical Sciences, B
Biology/Biological Sciences, B
Biomedical Sciences, B
BioTechnology, BMD
Business Administration and Management, B
Business/Commerce, B
Business/Corporate Communications, B
Business/Managerial Economics, B
Canadian Studies, B
Cell Biology and Anatomy, M
Chemistry, BM
Child and Family Studies, M

Classics and Classical
  Languages, Literatures, and Linguistics, B
Communication Disorders, B
Communication Studies/Speech Communication
  and Rhetoric, B
Comparative Literature, B
Computer Engineering Technology/Technician, B
Computer Programming/Programmer, B
Computer Science, B
Computer Software Engineering, B
Cultural Studies, M
Curriculum and Instruction, M
Drama and Dramatics/Theatre Arts, B
Drawing, B
Ecology, M
Economics, B
Education, BMD
Educational Administration and Supervision, M
Elementary Education and Teaching, B
English Language and Literature, B
European Studies/Civilization, B
Film/Cinema Studies, B
Finance, B
Fine/Studio Arts, B
French Language and Literature, B
French Studies, B
Geography, B
Geology/Earth Science, B
Geosciences, M
German Language and Literature, B
German Studies, B
Health/Health Care Administration/Management, B
History, B
Human Development, M
Human Resources Management/Personnel
  Administration, B
Humanities/Humanistic Studies, B
Information Science/Studies, B
Interdisciplinary Studies, B
International Affairs, M
International Business/Trade/Commerce, B
International Economics, B
Italian Language and Literature, B
Italian Studies, B
Kinesiology and Exercise Science, B
Labor and Industrial Relations, B
Legal and Justice Studies, M
Liberal Arts and Sciences Studies and
  Humanities, B
Linguistics, B
Marketing/Marketing Management, B
Mass Communication/Media Studies, B
Mathematics, B
Mathematics Teacher Education, B
Molecular Biology, M
Movement Therapy and Movement Education, B
Music, B
Music Teacher Education, B
Neuroscience, B
Nursing Science, B
Parks, Recreation, Leisure and Fitness Studies, B
Philosophy, BM
Physical Education Teaching and Coaching, B
Physical Sciences, B
Physics, BM
Political Science and Government, BM
Psychology, BM
Public Administration, BM
Public Health (MPH, DPH), B
Russian Studies, B
Sales, Distribution and Marketing Operations, B
Science Teacher Education/General Science
  Teacher Education, B
Secondary Education and Teaching, B
Social Psychology, M
Social Sciences, B
Sociology, B
Spanish Language and Literature, B
Sport and Fitness Administration/Management, B
Statistics, B
Teaching English as a Second or Foreign
  Language/ESL Language Instructor, B
Tourism and Travel Services Management, B
Transpersonal and Humanistic Psychology, M

Women's Studies, B

CARLETON UNIVERSITY

Accounting, B
Aerospace, Aeronautical and Astronautical
  Engineering, BMD
African Studies, B
Anthropology, BM
Applied Mathematics, B
Architecture, BM
Art History, Criticism and Conservation, BM
Asian Studies/Civilization, B
Biochemistry, B
Biological and Biomedical Sciences, MD
Biological and Physical Sciences, B
Biology Technician/BioTechnology Laboratory
  Technician, B
Biology/Biological Sciences, B
Botany/Plant Biology, B
Business Administration and Management, B
Business Administration, Management and
  Operations, MD
Canadian Studies, BMD
Central/Middle and Eastern European Studies, B
Chemistry, BMD
Child Development, B
City/Urban, Community and Regional Planning, B
Civil Engineering, BMD
Classics and Classical
  Languages, Literatures, and Linguistics, B
Cognitive Psychology and Psycholinguistics, B
Cognitive Sciences, D
Communication and Media Studies, MD
Comparative Literature, BD
Computer Engineering, B
Computer Programming/Programmer, B
Computer Science, BMD
Computer Software and Media Applications, B
Criminal Justice/Law Enforcement Administration, B
Criminal Justice/Police Science, B
Criminology, B
Drama and Dramatics/Theatre Arts, B
East Asian Studies, B
East European and Russian Studies, M
Ecology, B
Economics, BMD
Electrical Engineering, MD
Electrical, Electronics and Communications
  Engineering, B
Engineering, B
Engineering and Applied Sciences, MD
English, M
English Language and Literature, B
Environmental Engineering
  Technology/Environmental Technology, MD
Environmental Studies, B
Environmental/Environmental Health Engineering, B
European Studies/Civilization, B
Film, Television, and Video Production, M
Film/Cinema Studies, B
Finance, B
French Language and Literature, BM
Geography, BMD
Geology/Earth Science, B
Geosciences, MD
German Language and Literature, B
History, BMD
Human Resources Management/Personnel
  Administration, B
Humanities/Humanistic Studies, B
Industrial Design, B
Information Science/Studies, BMD
Interdisciplinary Studies, B
International Affairs, M
International Business/Trade/Commerce, B
International Relations and Affairs, B
Italian Language and Literature, B
Journalism, BMD
Labor and Industrial Relations, B
Latin American Studies, B
Latin Language and Literature, B
Legal and Justice Studies, M
Linguistics, BM
Management, D
Management Information Systems and Services, B
Marketing/Marketing Management, B

Mass Communication/Media Studies, B
Materials Engineering, M
Mathematics, BMD
Mechanical Engineering, BMD
Medieval and Renaissance Studies, B
Modern Greek Language and Literature, B
Modern Languages, B
Music, B
Near and Middle Eastern Studies, B
Operations Research, B
Philosophy, BM
Physics, BMD
Political Science and Government, BMD
Pre-Law Studies, B
Psychology, BMD
Public Administration, BMD
Public Policy Analysis, MD
Religion/Religious Studies, B
Russian Language and Literature, B
Russian Studies, B
Social Work, BM
Sociology, BMD
Spanish Language and Literature, B
Statistics, B
Systems Engineering, BM
Systems Science and Theory, MD
Teaching English as a Second or Foreign
  Language/ESL Language Instructor, B
Telecommunications Management, M
Urban Studies/Affairs, B

COLLÈGE DOMINICAIN DE PHILOSOPHIE ET DE THÉOLOGIE

Pastoral Studies/Counseling, BM
Philosophy, BMD
Theology and Religious Vocations, MDO
Theology/Theological Studies, B

EMMANUEL BIBLE COLLEGE

Divinity/Ministry (BD, MDiv.), B
Religious Education, B
Religious/Sacred Music, B
Theology/Theological Studies, B

HERITAGE BAPTIST COLLEGE AND HERITAGE THEOLOGICAL SEMINARY

Bible/Biblical Studies, B
Religious Education, B
Religious/Sacred Music, B
Theology and Religious Vocations, MO
Theology/Theological Studies, B

LAKEHEAD UNIVERSITY

Accounting, B
Anthropology, B
Art/Art Studies, General, B
Athletic Training and Sports Medicine, B
Biological and Biomedical Sciences, M
Biological and Physical Sciences, B
Biology/Biological Sciences, B
Business Administration and Management, B
Chemical Engineering, B
Chemistry, BM
Civil Engineering, B
Civil Engineering Technology/Technician, B
Clinical Psychology, BMD
Computer Engineering, B
Computer Science, BM
Curriculum and Instruction, M
Economics, BM
Education, BMD
Educational Administration and Supervision, M
Electrical, Electronic and Communications
  Engineering Technology/Technician, B
Electrical, Electronics and Communications
  Engineering, B
Elementary Education and Teaching, B
Engineering, B
Engineering and Applied Sciences, M
English, M
English Language and Literature, B
Environmental Biology, B
Environmental Studies, B
Exercise and Sports Science, M
Experimental Psychology, M

Finance, B
Forestry, BM
French Language and Literature, B
Geography, B
Geology/Earth Science, BM
Gerontology, BM
History, BM
Human Resources Management/Personnel
　Administration, B
Hydrology and Water Resources Science, B
Information Science/Studies, B
Labor and Industrial Relations, B
Liberal Arts and Sciences Studies and
　Humanities, B
Management Information Systems and Services, B
Marketing/Marketing Management, B
Mathematics, BM
Mechanical Engineering, B
Mechanical Engineering/Mechanical
　Technology/Technician, B
Molecular Biology, B
Music, B
Natural Sciences, B
Nursing - Registered Nurse Training, B
Parks, Recreation, Leisure and Fitness Studies, B
Philosophy, BM
Physical Education Teaching and Coaching, BM
Physics, BM
Plant Sciences, B
Political Science and Government, B
Psychology, BMD
Science Teacher Education/General Science
　Teacher Education, B
Secondary Education and Teaching, B
Social Work, BM
Sociology, BM
Statistics, M
Women's Studies, BM

LAURENTIAN UNIVERSITY

Adult and Continuing Education and Teaching, B
American Indian/Native American Studies, B
Anthropology, B
Applied Physics, M
Astronomy, B
Behavioral Sciences, B
Biochemistry, BM
Biological and Biomedical Sciences, M
Biology/Biological Sciences, B
Biophysics, B
Business Administration and Management, B
Business Administration, Management and
　Operations, M
Chemistry, BM
Classics and Classical
　Languages, Literatures, and Linguistics, B
Computer Science, B
Drama and Dramatics/Theatre Arts, B
Economics, B
Education, B
Engineering and Applied Sciences, M
English Language and Literature, B
Ethnic, Cultural Minority, and Gender Studies, B
Film/Cinema Studies, B
French Language and Literature, B
Geography, B
Geological/Geophysical Engineering, B
Geology/Earth Science, BM
History, BM
Human Development, M
Humanities/Humanistic Studies, M
Italian Language and Literature, B
Kinesiology and Exercise Science, B
Language Interpretation and Translation, B
Law and Legal Studies, B
Liberal Arts and Sciences Studies and
　Humanities, B
Mathematics, B
Metallurgical Engineering, B
Metallurgy, M
Mineral/Mining Engineering, M
Mining and Mineral Engineering, B
Modern Languages, B
Music, B
Nursing - Registered Nurse Training, B
Philosophy, B

Physical Education Teaching and Coaching, B
Physics, B
Political Science and Government, B
Psychology, B
Public Health Education and Promotion, B
Religion/Religious Studies, B
Social Work, BM
Sociology, BM
Spanish Language and Literature, B
Sport and Fitness Administration/Management, B
Women's Studies, B

MASTER'S COLLEGE AND SEMINARY

Bible/Biblical Studies, B
Divinity/Ministry (BD, MDiv.), B
Missions/Missionary Studies and Missiology, B
Religious Education, B
Theology and Religious Vocations, B
Theology/Theological Studies, B
Youth Ministry, B

MCMASTER UNIVERSITY

Analytical Chemistry, MD
Anthropology, BMD
Applied Mathematics, B
Art History, Criticism and Conservation, B
Art/Art Studies, General, B
Astrophysics, BD
Biochemistry, BMD
Biological and Biomedical Sciences, MD
Biological and Physical Sciences, B
Biology Technician/BioTechnology Laboratory
　Technician, B
Biology/Biological Sciences, B
Business Administration and Management, B
Business Administration, Management and
　Operations, MD
Cancer Biology/Oncology, MD
Cardiovascular Sciences, MD
Cell Biology and Anatomy, MD
Chemical Engineering, BMD
Chemistry, BMD
Civil Engineering, BMD
Classics and Classical
　Languages, Literatures, and Linguistics, BMD
Communication, Journalism and Related
　Programs, B
Comparative Literature, B
Computer Engineering, B
Computer Science, BMD
Cultural Studies, MD
Drama and Dramatics/Theatre Arts, B
Economics, BMD
Electrical Engineering, MD
Electrical, Electronics and Communications
　Engineering, B
Engineering and Applied Sciences, MD
Engineering Physics, BMD
Engineering/Industrial Management, B
English, MD
English Language and Literature, B
Environmental Studies, B
French Language and Literature, BM
Genetics, MD
Geochemistry, D
Geography, BMD
Geology/Earth Science, BMD
Geosciences, MD
German Language and Literature, B
Gerontology, B
Health Physics/Radiological Health, MD
Health Services Research, MD
Hispanic-American, Puerto Rican, and Mexican-
　American/Chicano Studies, B
History, BMD
Human Resources Management and Services, MD
Immunology, MD
Industrial and Labor Relations, M
Industrial Engineering, B
Inorganic Chemistry, MD
Intermedia/Multimedia, B
International Affairs, D
Japanese Language and Literature, B
Kinesiology and Exercise Science, B
Kinesiology and Movement Studies, MD
Labor and Industrial Relations, B

Latin American Studies, B
Linguistics, B
Management Information Systems and Services, D
Materials Engineering, BMD
Materials Sciences, BMD
Mathematics, BMD
Mechanical Engineering, BMD
Medical Physics, MD
Modern Languages, B
Molecular Biology, BMD
Music, BM
Music History, Literature, and Theory, B
Music Teacher Education, B
Neuroscience, MD
Nuclear Engineering, D
Nurse Midwife/Nursing Midwifery, B
Nursing, MD
Nursing - Registered Nurse Training, B
Occupational Therapy/Therapist, M
Organic Chemistry, MD
Pharmacology, BMD
Philosophy, BMD
Physical Chemistry, MD
Physical Sciences, B
Physical Therapy/Therapist, M
Physics, BD
Physiology, MD
Political Science and Government, BMD
Psychology, BMD
Public Administration, M
Public Affairs, M
Public Policy Analysis, MD
Rehabilitation Sciences, M
Religion/Religious Studies, BMD
Religious Education, B
Russian Language and Literature, B
Russian Studies, B
Social Work, BM
Sociology, BMD
Software Engineering, MD
Statistics, BM
Theology and Religious Vocations, MPO
Virology, MD
Women's Studies, B

NER ISRAEL YESHIVA COLLEGE OF TORONTO

Jewish/Judaic Studies, B
Theology/Theological Studies, B

NIPISSING UNIVERSITY

Biology/Biological Sciences, B
Business Administration and Management, B
Business and Personal/Financial Services Marketing
　Operations, B
Classics and Classical
　Languages, Literatures, and Linguistics, B
Computer Science, B
Economics, B
Education, BMO
English Language and Literature, B
Environmental Biology, B
Environmental Studies, B
Geography, B
History, B
Liberal Arts and Sciences Studies and
　Humanities, B
Mathematics, B
Nursing - Registered Nurse Training, B
Philosophy, B
Psychology, B
Sociology, B
Women's Studies, B

QUEEN'S UNIVERSITY AT KINGSTON

Allopathic Medicine, P
Anatomy, MD
Art History, Criticism and Conservation, B
Biochemistry, BMD
Biological and Biomedical Sciences, MD
Biology/Biological Sciences, B
Business Administration, Management and
　Operations, M
Business/Commerce, B
Canadian Studies, B
Cartography, B

Cell Biology and Anatomy, MD
Chemical Engineering, BMD
Chemistry, BMD
Civil Engineering, BMD
Classics and Classical
  Languages, Literatures, and Linguistics, M
Clinical Psychology, MD
Cognitive Sciences, BMD
Computer Engineering, BMD
Computer Science, BMD
Developmental Psychology, MD
Drama and Dramatics/Theatre Arts, B
Economics, B
Education, BMD
Electrical Engineering, MD
Electrical, Electronics and Communications
  Engineering, B
Elementary Education and Teaching, B
Engineering, B
Engineering and Applied Sciences, MD
Engineering Physics, B
English, MD
English Language and Literature, B
Environmental Sciences, B
Epidemiology, M
Exercise and Sports Science, MD
Film/Cinema Studies, B
French Language and Literature, BMD
Geography, BMD
Geological/Geophysical Engineering, B
Geology/Earth Science, BMD
German Language and Literature, BMD
German Studies, B
Health and Physical Education, B
History, B
Immunology, MD
Indian/Native American Education, B
Industrial and Labor Relations, M
Law and Legal Studies, MPO
Linguistics, B
Mathematics, BMD
Mechanical Engineering, BMD
Microbiology, MD
Mineral/Mining Engineering, MD
Mining and Mineral Engineering, B
Music, B
Nursing, M
Nursing - Registered Nurse Training, B
Occupational Therapy/Therapist, B
Pathology/Experimental Pathology, MD
Pharmacology, MD
Philosophy, BMD
Physical Education Teaching and Coaching, B
Physical Therapy/Therapist, B
Physics, BMD
Physiology, MD
Political Science and Government, BMD
Psychology, BMD
Public Policy Analysis, MO
Rehabilitation Sciences, MD
Religion/Religious Studies, BM
Science Teacher Education/General Science
  Teacher Education, B
Social Psychology, MD
Sociology, BMD
Spanish Language and Literature, BM
Sport Psychology, M
Statistics, BMD
Teacher Education, Multiple Levels, B
Technical Teacher Education, B
Theology and Religious Vocations, MP
Theology/Theological Studies, B
Toxicology, MD
Urban and Regional Planning, M
Women's Studies, B

REDEEMER UNIVERSITY COLLEGE

Accounting, B
Art/Art Studies, General, B
Bible/Biblical Studies, B
Biological and Physical Sciences, B
Biology/Biological Sciences, B
Business Administration and Management, B
Computer Science, B
Drama and Dramatics/Theatre Arts, B
Education, B

Elementary Education and Teaching, B
English Language and Literature, B
French Language and Literature, B
Health and Physical Education, B
History, B
Human Resources Management/Personnel
  Administration, B
Humanities/Humanistic Studies, B
Kinesiology and Exercise Science, B
Liberal Arts and Sciences Studies and
  Humanities, B
Mathematics, B
Music, B
Natural Sciences, B
Parks, Recreation, Leisure and Fitness Studies, B
Philosophy, B
Political Science and Government, B
Pre-Dentistry Studies, B
Pre-Law Studies, B
Pre-Medicine/Pre-Medical Studies, B
Pre-Theology/Pre-Ministerial Studies, B
Pre-Veterinary Studies, B
Psychology, B
Religion/Religious Studies, B
Social Work, B
Sociology, B
Teacher Education, Multiple Levels, B
Theology/Theological Studies, B

ROYAL MILITARY COLLEGE OF CANADA

Astronomy, B
Business Administration and Management, B
Business Administration, Management and
  Operations, M
Chemical Engineering, BMD
Chemistry, BMD
Civil Engineering, BMD
Computer Engineering, BMD
Computer Science, BM
Electrical Engineering, MD
Electrical, Electronics and Communications
  Engineering, B
Engineering and Applied Sciences, MD
English Language and Literature, B
Environmental Engineering
  Technology/Environmental Technology, MD
Environmental Sciences, MD
French Language and Literature, B
History, B
Materials Sciences, MD
Mathematics, M
Mechanical Engineering, BMD
Military and Defense Studies, M
Military Technologies, B
Nuclear Engineering, MD
Physics, BM
Social Sciences, B
Software Engineering, MD

RYERSON UNIVERSITY

Acting, B
Aerospace, Aeronautical and Astronautical
  Engineering, B
Architecture, B
Arts Management, M
Biology/Biological Sciences, B
Business Administration and Management, B
Chemical Engineering, B
Chemistry, B
Child Care and Support Services Management, B
Cinematography and Film/Video Production, B
City/Urban, Community and Regional Planning, B
Civil Engineering, B
Computer Engineering, B
Computer Science, B
Criminal Justice/Safety Studies, B
Dance, B
Early Childhood Education and Teaching, B
Electrical, Electronics and Communications
  Engineering, B
Family Practice Nurse/Nurse Practitioner, B
Fashion/Apparel Design, B
Film/Video and Photographic Arts, B
Finance, B
General Studies, B

Geography, B
Graphic Communications, B
Health Information/Medical Records
  Administration/Administrator, B
Health Unit Manager/Ward Supervisor, B
Health/Medical Physics, B
Hospitality Administration/Management, B
Hotel/Motel Administration/Management, B
Human Nutrition, B
Humanities/Humanistic Studies, B
Industrial Engineering, B
Information Technology, B
Interior Design, B
International Economics, B
Journalism, B
Marketing/Marketing Management, B
Mechanical Engineering, B
Multi-/Interdisciplinary Studies, B
Nurse Midwife/Nursing Midwifery, B
Nursing - Registered Nurse Training, B
Nursing Administration, B
Occupational Health and Industrial Hygiene, B
Photography, B
Political Science and Government, B
Psychology, B
Public Administration, B
Public Health (MPH, DPH), B
Radio and Television, B
Sales, Distribution and Marketing Operations, B
Social Work, B
Sociology, B
Technical Theatre/Theatre Design and
  Technology, B
Urban Studies/Affairs, B

SAINT PAUL UNIVERSITY

Bible/Biblical Studies, B
Divinity/Ministry (BD, MDiv.), B
Family and Community Services, B
Marriage and Family Therapy/Counseling, BM
Missions/Missionary Studies and Missiology, MO
Pastoral Studies/Counseling, MDO
Philosophy, B
Religion/Religious Studies, B
Theology and Religious Vocations, MDO
Theology/Theological Studies, B

TRENT UNIVERSITY

American Indian/Native American Studies, BMD
Anthropology, BM
Applied Mathematics, B
Biochemistry, B
Biological and Biomedical Sciences, MD
Biological and Physical Sciences, B
Biology/Biological Sciences, B
Business Administration and Management, B
Canadian Studies, BM
Chemistry, BM
Classics and Classical
  Languages, Literatures, and Linguistics, B
Comparative Literature, B
Computer Science, BM
Economics, B
Education, B
Elementary Education and Teaching, B
English Language and Literature, B
Environmental Policy and Resource
  Management, MD
Environmental Studies, B
French Language and Literature, B
Geography, BMD
German Language and Literature, B
Hispanic-American, Puerto Rican, and Mexican-
  American/Chicano Studies, B
History, BM
Humanities/Humanistic Studies, B
Interdisciplinary Studies, B
International Relations and Affairs, B
Latin Language and Literature, B
Liberal Arts and Sciences Studies and
  Humanities, B
Mathematics, B
Modern Greek Language and Literature, B
Modern Languages, B
Natural Sciences, B
Nursing - Registered Nurse Training, B

Philosophy, B
Physical Sciences, B
Physics, BM
Political Science and Government, B
Psychology, B
Secondary Education and Teaching, B
Social Sciences, B
Sociology, B
Spanish Language and Literature, B
Women's Studies, B

TYNDALE UNIVERSITY COLLEGE & SEMINARY

Bible/Biblical Studies, B
Business/Commerce, B
Divinity/Ministry (BD, MDiv.), B
English Language and Literature, B
History, B
Hospitality and Recreation Marketing Operations, B
Human Services, B
Liberal Arts and Sciences Studies and
   Humanities, B
Missions/Missionary Studies and Missiology, PO
Parks, Recreation, Leisure and Fitness Studies, B
Pastoral Studies/Counseling, BP
Philosophy, B
Psychology, B
Religious Education, B
Theology and Religious Vocations, MPO

UNIVERSITY OF GUELPH

Agribusiness, M
Agricultural Business and Management, B
Agricultural Economics, BMD
Agricultural Sciences, MDO
Agriculture, B
Agronomy and Crop Science, B
Agronomy and Soil Sciences, MD
Anatomy, MD
Animal Sciences, BMD
Anthropology, BMD
Applied Economics, B
Applied Mathematics, D
Aquaculture, M
Art History, Criticism and Conservation, B
Atmospheric Sciences and Meteorology, BMD
Biochemistry, BMD
Bioengineering, MD
Biological and Biomedical Sciences, MD
Biology/Biological Sciences, B
Biomedical Sciences, B
Biomedical/Medical Engineering, B
Biophysics, BMD
BioTechnology, MD
Business Administration, Management and
   Operations, M
Chemical Engineering, B
Chemistry, BMD
Child and Family Studies, MD
Child Development, B
Classics and Classical
   Languages, Literatures, and Linguistics, B
Cognitive Sciences, M
Comparative Literature, D
Computer and Information Sciences, B
Computer Science, BMD
Consumer Economics, M
Criminal Justice/Law Enforcement Administration, B
Developmental Psychology, D
Drama and Dramatics/Theatre Arts, B
Ecology, BMD
Econometrics and Quantitative Economics, B
Economics, BMD
Engineering and Applied Sciences, MD
English, M
English Language and Literature, B
Entomology, MD
Environmental Biology, BMD
Environmental Engineering
   Technology/Environmental Technology, BMD
Environmental Policy and Resource
   Management, MD
Environmental Sciences, MD
Environmental Studies, B
Environmental Toxicology, B
Epidemiology, MD

European Studies/Civilization, B
Evolutionary Biology, MD
Experimental Psychology, M
Fine Arts and Art Studies, M
Fine/Studio Arts, B
Food Science, B
Food Science and Technology, MD
French Studies, B
Geography, BMD
Gerontology, B
History, BMD
Horticultural Science, BMD
Hospitality Administration/Management, M
Hotel/Motel Administration/Management, B
Human Development, MD
Human Nutrition, B
Human Resources Management/Personnel
   Administration, B
Immunology, MD
Industrial and Organizational Psychology, MD
Infectious Diseases, MD
Information Science/Studies, B
International Development, M
Landscape Architecture, BM
Management, M
Marketing/Marketing Management, B
Mathematics, BMD
Medical Technology, MD
Microbiology, BMD
Molecular Biology, B
Molecular Genetics, B
Music, B
Natural Resources and Conservation, MD
Natural Resources Management/Development and
   Policy, M
Neuroscience, MD
Non-Profit/Public/Organizational Management, B
Nutritional Sciences, BMD
Pathology/Experimental Pathology, MDO
Pharmacology, MD
Philosophy, BMD
Physical Sciences, B
Physics, BMD
Physiology, MD
Plant Pathology/Phytopathology, MD
Political Science and Government, BM
Poultry Science, MD
Psychology, BMD
Real Estate, B
Rural Planning and Studies, MDO
Social Psychology, MD
Sociology, BMD
Spanish Language and Literature, B
Statistics, BMD
Theater, MD
Theoretical and Mathematical Physics, B
Tourism and Travel Services Management, B
Toxicology, MD
Veterinary Medicine, MD
Veterinary Sciences, MDO
Vision Science/Physiological Optics, MD
Water Resources Engineering, BMD
Wildlife Biology, B
Women's Studies, B
Zoology/Animal Biology, B

UNIVERSITY OF OTTAWA

Accounting, B
Aerospace, Aeronautical and Astronautical
   Engineering, MD
Allopathic Medicine, MDP
Applied Art, B
Applied Mathematics, B
Art/Art Studies, General, B
Behavioral Sciences, B
Bilingual and Multilingual Education, B
Biochemistry, BMD
Biological and Biomedical Sciences, MD
Biological and Physical Sciences, B
Biology Technician/BioTechnology Laboratory
   Technician, B
Biology/Biological Sciences, B
Biomedical Sciences, B
Business Administration and Management, B
Business Administration, Management and
   Operations, M

Business/Managerial Economics, B
Canadian Studies, BD
Cell Biology and Anatomy, MD
Chemical Engineering, BMD
Chemistry, BMD
Christian Studies, B
Civil Engineering, BMD
Classics and Classical
   Languages, Literatures, and Linguistics, BMD
Communication and Media Studies, BM
Communication Disorders, M
Community Health and Preventive Medicine, MO
Comparative Literature, B
Computer and Information Sciences, B
Computer Engineering, BMD
Computer Science, BMD
Criminal Justice/Law Enforcement Administration, B
Criminology, BMD
Developmental and Child Psychology, B
Dietetics/Dieticians, A
Drama and Dramatics/Theatre Arts, B
Economics, BMD
Education, BMDO
Electrical Engineering, MD
Electrical, Electronics and Communications
   Engineering, B
Electronic Commerce, O
Elementary Education and Teaching, B
Engineering, B
Engineering and Applied Sciences, MDO
Engineering Management, MO
Engineering Science, B
Engineering/Industrial Management, B
English, MD
English Language and Literature, B
Environmental Sciences, B
Environmental Studies, AB
Epidemiology, M
Ethnic and Cultural Studies, B
Finance, B
Finance and Banking, O
Fine/Studio Arts, B
Foods, Nutrition, and Wellness Studies, A
French Language and Literature, BMD
Geography, BMD
Geology/Earth Science, B
Geophysics and Seismology, A
Geosciences, MD
German Language and Literature, B
Health Services Administration, M
Health Services Research, O
Health Services/Allied Health/Health Sciences, B
History, BMD
Human Resources Management/Personnel
   Administration, B
Humanities/Humanistic Studies, B
Immunology, MD
Information Science/Studies, BO
Interdisciplinary Studies, BDO
International Business/Trade/Commerce, B
International Relations and Affairs, B
Italian Language and Literature, B
Journalism, B
Kindergarten/PreSchool Education and Teaching, B
Kinesiology and Movement Studies, M
Latin Language and Literature, B
Law and Legal Studies, MD
Legal Professions and Studies, B
Liberal Arts and Sciences Studies and
   Humanities, B
Linguistics, BMD
Management Information Systems and Services, B
Marketing/Marketing Management, B
Mass Communication/Media Studies, B
Mathematics, BMD
Mechanical Engineering, BMD
Medical Microbiology and Bacteriology, B
Medieval and Renaissance Studies, B
Microbiology, MD
Modern Languages, B
Molecular Biology, MD
Music, BMO
Music History, Literature, and Theory, B
Music Teacher Education, BO
Natural Sciences, B
Nursing, MDO

Nursing - Registered Nurse Training, B
Occupational Therapy/Therapist, B
Ophthalmic/Optometric Services, B
Parks, Recreation, Leisure and Fitness Studies, B
Pastoral Studies/Counseling, B
Philosophy, BMD
Photography, B
Physical Education Teaching and Coaching, B
Physical Sciences, B
Physical Therapy/Therapist, B
Physics, BMD
Physiology, B
Political Science and Government, BMD
Pre-Law Studies, B
Pre-Medicine/Pre-Medical Studies, A
Project Management, O
Psychology, BD
Public Administration, BO
Public Health, D
Public Policy Analysis, B
Rehabilitation Sciences, M
Rehabilitation Therapy, B
Religion/Religious Studies, BMD
Russian Language and Literature, B
Secondary Education and Teaching, B
Slavic Languages, Literatures, and Linguistics, A
Slavic Studies, B
Social Sciences, B
Social Work, M
Sociology, BM
Spanish Language and Literature, BMD
Special Education and Teaching, B
Statistics, BMD
Systems Science and Theory, BMO
Teaching English as a Second or Foreign
   Language/ESL Language Instructor, B
Teaching English or French as a Second or Foreign
   Language, B
Theater, M
Theology/Theological Studies, B
Translation and Interpretation, MD
Voice and Opera, B
Women's Studies, BM

UNIVERSITY OF TORONTO

Accounting, BMDO
Actuarial Science, B
Aerospace, Aeronautical and Astronautical
   Engineering, BMD
African Studies, B
Allopathic Medicine, MDPO
American Indian/Native American Studies, B
American/United States Studies/Civilization, B
Ancient Near Eastern and Biblical
   Languages, Literatures, and Linguistics, B
Animal Behavior and Ethology, B
Animal Genetics, B
Animal Physiology, B
Anthropology, BMD
Applied Mathematics, B
Arabic Language and Literature, B
Archeology, B
Architecture, BM
Art History, Criticism and Conservation, BMD
Art/Art Studies, General, B
Arts Management, B
Asian Studies/Civilization, B
Astronomy, BMD
Biochemistry, BMD
Biological and Biomedical Sciences, MDO
Biological and Physical Sciences, B
Biology/Biological Sciences, B
Biomedical Engineering, MD
Biomedical/Medical Engineering, B
Biophysics, BMD
Botany/Plant Biology, BMD
Business Administration and Management, B
Business Administration, Management and
   Operations, MDO
Canadian Studies, B
Central/Middle and Eastern European Studies, B
Chemical Engineering, BMD
Chemistry, BMD
Civil Engineering, BMD
Classical, Ancient Mediterranean and Near Eastern
   Studies and Archaeology, B

Classics and Classical
   Languages, Literatures, and Linguistics, BMD
Communication Disorders, MD
Comparative Literature, BMD
Computer Engineering, BMD
Computer Science, BMD
Computer Software Engineering, B
Computer Systems Networking and
   Telecommunications, B
Criminal Justice/Police Science, B
Criminology, BMDO
Dental and Oral Surgery, M
Dentistry, P
Digital Communication and Media/Multimedia, B
Drama and Dramatics/Theatre Arts, B
East Asian Studies, BMD
East European and Russian Studies, MO
Ecology, B
E-Commerce/Electronic Commerce, B
Economics, BMDO
Education, BMD
Electrical Engineering, MD
Electrical, Electronics and Communications
   Engineering, B
Engineering, B
Engineering and Applied Sciences, MD
Engineering Science, B
English, MD
English Language and Literature, B
Environmental Studies, B
Ethnic and Cultural Studies, B
European Studies/Civilization, B
Film/Cinema Studies, B
Finance, B
Fine/Studio Arts, B
Foods, Nutrition, and Wellness Studies, B
Forensic Science and Technology, B
Forest Management/Forest Resources
   Management, B
Forestry, BMD
French Language and Literature, BMD
French Language Teacher Education, B
Genetic Counseling/Counselor, M
Genetics, MD
Geography, BMD
Geological/Geophysical Engineering, B
Geology/Earth Science, BMD
Geophysics and Seismology, B
German Language and Literature, BMD
Health and Physical Education, B
Health Teacher Education, B
History, BMD
History and Philosophy of Science and
   Technology, B
History of Science and Technology, MD
Humanities/Humanistic Studies, B
Hydrology and Water Resources Science, B
Immunology, MD
Industrial and Labor Relations, MD
Industrial Engineering, B
Industrial/Management Engineering, MD
Information Science/Studies, MDO
International Relations and Affairs, B
Islamic Studies, B
Italian Language and Literature, BMD
Jewish/Judaic Studies, B
Labor and Industrial Relations, B
Latin American Studies, B
Latin Language and Literature, B
Law and Legal Studies, MDPO
Library Science, MDO
Linguistics, BMD
Manufacturing Engineering, B
Mass Communication/Media Studies, B
Materials Engineering, BMD
Materials Sciences, BMD
Mathematics, BMD
Mechanical Engineering, BMD
Medical Microbiology and Bacteriology, B
Medieval and Renaissance Studies, BMD
Metallurgical Engineering, B
Microbiology, B
Mining and Mineral Engineering, B
Modern Greek Language and Literature, B
Modern Languages, B
Molecular Biology, B

Museology/Museum Studies, M
Music, BMD
Music History, Literature, and Theory, B
Music Teacher Education, BMD
Near and Middle Eastern Studies, BMD
Neuroscience, B
Nurse Midwife/Nursing Midwifery, B
Nursing, MDO
Nursing - Registered Nurse Training, B
Nutritional Sciences, MDO
Operations Research, B
Oral and Dental Sciences, MD
Oral Pathology, M
Orthodontics, M
Paleontology, B
Pathobiology, MDO
Peace Studies and Conflict Resolution, B
Periodontics, M
Petroleum Engineering, B
Pharmaceutical Sciences, MD
Pharmacology, BMD
Pharmacy, B
Philosophy, BMD
Physical Education Teaching and Coaching, MD
Physical Sciences, B
Physics, BMD
Physiology, MD
Political Science and Government, BMDO
Portuguese Language and Literature, BMD
Psychology, BMD
Public Administration, B
Public Health, MDO
Public Relations/Image Management, B
Radiologic Technology/Science - Radiographer, B
Rehabilitation Sciences, M
Religion/Religious Studies, BMD
Romance Languages, Literatures, and Linguistics, B
Russian Language and Literature, B
Russian Studies, B
Science Teacher Education/General Science
   Teacher Education, B
Slavic Languages, Literatures, and Linguistics, BMD
Social Work, MD
Sociology, BMD
South and Southeast Asian Studies, MD
South Asian Studies, B
Spanish Language and Literature, BMD
Statistics, BMD
Teaching French as a Second or Foreign
   Language, B
Theater, MD
Theology/Theological Studies, B
Toxicology, B
Transportation and Highway Engineering, B
Urban and Regional Planning, M
Urban Studies/Affairs, B
Visual and Performing Arts, B
Women's Studies, B
Wood Science and Wood Products/Pulp and Paper
   Technology, B
Zoology/Animal Biology, BMD

UNIVERSITY OF WATERLOO

Accounting, BMD
Accounting and Finance, B
Actuarial Science, BM
Anthropology, B
Applied Economics, B
Applied Mathematics, BMD
Architecture, BM
Art History, Criticism and Conservation, B
Arts Management, B
Atmospheric Sciences and Meteorology, B
Atomic/Molecular Physics, B
Biochemistry, B
Biochemistry, Biophysics and Molecular Biology, B
Bioinformatics, B
Biological and Biomedical Sciences, MD
Biological and Physical Sciences, B
Biology Teacher Education, B
Biology/Biological Sciences, B
Biostatistics, M
BioTechnology, B
Business Administration and Management, B
Business Administration, Management and
   Operations, BM

Canadian Studies, B
Chemical Engineering, BMD
Chemical Physics, B
Chemistry, BMD
Chemistry Teacher Education, B
City/Urban, Community and Regional Planning, B
Civil Engineering, BMD
Classics and Classical
  Languages, Literatures, and Linguistics, B
Communication Studies/Speech Communication
  and Rhetoric, B
Computational Mathematics, B
Computer Engineering, BMD
Computer Science, BMD
Computer Software Engineering, B
Cultural Resource Management and Policy
  Analysis, B
Digital Communication and Media/Multimedia, B
Drama and Dramatics/Theatre Arts, B
Ecology, B
Economics, BMD
Education, B
Electrical Engineering, MD
Electrical, Electronics and Communications
  Engineering, B
Engineering, B
Engineering and Applied Sciences, MD
Engineering Management, MD
English, MD
English Language and Literature, B
Entrepreneurship/Entrepreneurial Studies, M
Environmental Policy and Resource
  Management, M
Environmental Sciences, B
Environmental Studies, B
Environmental/Environmental Health Engineering, B
Film/Cinema Studies, B
Finance and Banking, M
Fine Arts and Art Studies, M
Fine/Studio Arts, B
French Language and Literature, BM
French Language Teacher Education, B
French Studies, B
Geochemistry, B
Geography, BMD
Geological/Geophysical Engineering, B
Geology/Earth Science, B
Geophysics and Seismology, B
Geosciences, MD
German Language and Literature, BMD
Health Education, MD
Health/Medical Preparatory Programs, B
History, BMD
Human Development and Family Studies, B
Human Resources Management/Personnel
  Administration, B
Information Science/Studies, MD
Interdisciplinary Studies, B
International Business/Trade/Commerce, B
International Relations and Affairs, B
International/Global Studies, B
Kinesiology and Exercise Science, B
Kinesiology and Movement Studies, MD
Leisure Studies, MD
Liberal Arts and Sciences Studies and
  Humanities, B
Management of Technology, MD
Mathematics, BMD
Mathematics and Computer Science, B
Mathematics Teacher Education, B
Mechanical Engineering, BMD
Medical Informatics, B
Medieval and Renaissance Studies, B
Multi-/Interdisciplinary Studies, B
Music, B
Operations Research, BMD
Ophthalmic/Optometric Services, B
Optometry, MDP
Parks, Recreation and Leisure Facilities
  Management, B
Parks, Recreation, Leisure and Fitness Studies, B
Philosophy, BMD
Physics, BMD
Physics Teacher Education, B
Planetary Astronomy and Science, B
Political Science and Government, BM

Psychology, BMD
Public Health (MPH, DPH), B
Public History, M
Recreation and Park Management, MD
Rehabilitation and Therapeutic Professions, B
Religion/Religious Studies, B
Respiratory Care Therapy/Therapist, B
Russian Language and Literature, BM
Russian Studies, B
Slavic Studies, B
Social Sciences, B
Social Work, B
Sociology, BMD
Software Engineering, M
Spanish Language and Literature, B
Speech and Rhetorical Studies, B
Statistics, BMD
Systems Engineering, BMD
Taxation, M
Technical and Business Writing, M
Therapeutic Recreation/Recreational Therapy, B
Travel and Tourism, M
Urban and Regional Planning, MD
Vision Science/Physiological Optics, MDP
Women's Studies, B

THE UNIVERSITY OF WESTERN ONTARIO

Accounting, M
Actuarial Science, B
Allopathic Medicine, MP
American/United States Studies/Civilization, B
Anatomy, BMD
Ancient/Classical Greek Language and Literature, B
Animal Genetics, B
Animal Physiology, B
Anthropology, BMD
Applied Mathematics, BMD
Art History, Criticism and Conservation, B
Art Teacher Education, B
Art/Art Studies, General, B
Astronomy, BMD
Astrophysics, B
Bible/Biblical Studies, B
Biochemistry, BMD
Bioinformatics, B
Biological and Biomedical Sciences, MDO
Biological and Physical Sciences, B
Biological Anthropology, M
Biology/Biological Sciences, B
Biophysics, BMD
Biostatistics, MD
BioTechnology, M
Business Administration and Management, B
Business Administration, Management and
  Operations, MDO
Business Teacher Education, B
Cell Biology and Anatomy, MD
Cell/Cellular Biology and Histology, B
Chemical Engineering, B
Chemistry, BMD
City/Urban, Community and Regional Planning, B
Civil Engineering, B
Classics and Classical
  Languages, Literatures, and Linguistics, BM
Communication Disorders, M
Comparative Literature, BMD
Computer and Information Sciences, B
Computer Science, BMD
Computer Software Engineering, B
Counselor Education/School Counseling and
  Guidance Services, M
Criminology, B
Curriculum and Instruction, M
Demography and Population Studies, B
Dentistry, P
Dietetics/Dieticians, B
East Asian Studies, B
Ecology, B
Economics, BMD
Education, BM
Educational Psychology, M
Electrical, Electronics and Communications
  Engineering, B
Elementary Education and Teaching, B
Engineering and Applied Sciences, MD

Engineering Science, B
English, MD
English Language and Literature, B
English/Language Arts Teacher Education, B
Entrepreneurship/Entrepreneurial Studies, M
Environmental Sciences, MD
Environmental Studies, B
Environmental/Environmental Health Engineering, B
Epidemiology, MD
Ethnic, Cultural Minority, and Gender Studies, B
European Studies/Civilization, B
Family and Consumer Sciences/Human Sciences, B
Film/Cinema Studies, B
Finance and Banking, M
Fine/Studio Arts, B
Foods, Nutrition, and Wellness Studies, B
French Language and Literature, BMD
Geography, BMD
Geology/Earth Science, BMD
Geophysics and Seismology, BMD
Geosciences, MD
German Language and Literature, B
History, BMD
Immunology, BMD
Information Science/Studies, BMD
Interdisciplinary Studies, BMD
International/Global Studies, B
Journalism, BM
Junior High/Intermediate/Middle School Education
  and Teaching, B
Kindergarten/PreSchool Education and Teaching, B
Kinesiology and Exercise Science, B
Kinesiology and Movement Studies, MD
Latin Language and Literature, B
Law and Legal Studies, BMPO
Library Science, MD
Licensed Practical/Vocational Nurse Training, B
Linguistics, B
Mass Communication/Media Studies, B
Materials Engineering, B
Mathematics, BMD
Mathematics Teacher Education, B
Mechanical Engineering, B
Media Studies, MD
Medical Microbiology and Bacteriology, B
Microbiology, BMD
Modern Languages, B
Molecular Biology, MD
Music, BMD
Music History, Literature, and Theory, B
Music Performance, B
Music Teacher Education, B
Music Theory and Composition, B
Natural Resources Management/Development and
  Policy, B
Neuroscience, MD
Nursing, MD
Nursing - Registered Nurse Training, B
Nursing Administration, B
Occupational Therapy/Therapist, BM
Oral and Dental Sciences, M
Pathology/Experimental Pathology, MD
Peace Studies and Conflict Resolution, B
Pharmacology, B
Pharmacology and Toxicology, B
Philosophy, BMD
Physical Education Teaching and Coaching, B
Physical Therapy/Therapist, BM
Physics, BMD
Physiology, MDO
Piano and Organ, B
Planetary Astronomy and Science, B
Plant Biology, MD
Plant Sciences, BMD
Political Science and Government, BMD
Psychology, BMD
Public Administration, B
Public Health (MPH, DPH), B
Religion/Religious Studies, B
Russian Language and Literature, B
Secondary Education and Teaching, B
Social Work, B
Sociology, BMD
Spanish Language and Literature, BMD
Special Education and Teaching, BM
Statistics, BMD

Theology/Theological Studies, B
Toxicology, B
Urban Studies/Affairs, B
Violin, Viola, Guitar and Other Stringed
    Instruments, B
Voice and Opera, B
Wind and Percussion Instruments, B
Women's Studies, B
Zoology/Animal Biology, BMD

UNIVERSITY OF WINDSOR

Accounting, B
Accounting and Finance, B
Acting, B
Anthropology, B
Applied Mathematics, B
Art History, Criticism and Conservation, B
Art Teacher Education, B
Art/Art Studies, General, B
Artificial Intelligence and Robotics, B
Arts Management, B
Athletic Training and Sports Medicine, B
Biochemistry, BMD
Bioinformatics, B
Biological and Biomedical Sciences, MD
Biological and Physical Sciences, B
Biology Teacher Education, B
Biology/Biological Sciences, B
Biophysics, B
Biopsychology, BM
BioTechnology, B
Broadcast Journalism, B
Business Administration and Management, B
Business Administration, Management and
    Operations, MO
Business/Commerce, B
Business/Managerial Economics, B
Chemical Technology/Technician, B
Chemistry, BMD
Chemistry Teacher Education, B
City/Urban, Community and Regional Planning, B
Civil Engineering, BMD
Classics and Classical
    Languages, Literatures, and Linguistics, B
Clinical Child Psychology, B
Clinical Psychology, BD
Communication and Media Studies, M
Communication Studies/Speech Communication
    and Rhetoric, B
Communications Technologies/Technicians and
    Support Services, B
Comparative Literature, B
Computer and Information Sciences, B
Computer Engineering, B
Computer Programming, Specific Applications, B
Computer Science, BMD
Computer Software and Media Applications, B
Computer Systems Networking and
    Telecommunications, B
Counselor Education/School Counseling and
    Guidance Services, B
Creative Writing, B
Criminal Justice/Safety Studies, B
Criminology, B
Development Economics and International
    Development, B
Developmental and Child Psychology, B
Drama and Dance Teacher Education, B
Drama and Dramatics/Theatre Arts, B
Drawing, B
Economics, BM
Education, BMD
Educational Leadership and Administration, B
Electrical Engineering, MD
Electrical, Electronics and Communications
    Engineering, B
Elementary Education and Teaching, B
Engineering, B
Engineering and Applied Sciences, MD
Engineering Mechanics, B
English, M
English Language and Literature, B
English/Language Arts Teacher Education, B
Environmental Biology, B
Environmental Engineering
    Technology/Environmental Technology, MD

Environmental Sciences, BMD
Environmental Studies, B
Environmental/Environmental Health Engineering, B
Family and Consumer Economics and Related
    Services, B
Family Practice Nurse/Nurse Practitioner, B
Film/Cinema Studies, B
Finance, B
Fine Arts and Art Studies, M
Fine/Studio Arts, B
Foreign Language Teacher Education, B
Forensic Science and Technology, B
French Language and Literature, B
French Language Teacher Education, B
French Studies, B
General Studies, B
Geography Teacher Education, B
Geology/Earth Science, B
Geosciences, MD
German Language and Literature, B
German Language Teacher Education, B
German Studies, B
Health and Medical Laboratory Technologies, B
Health and Physical Education, B
Health Teacher Education, B
Hispanic-American, Puerto Rican, and Mexican-
    American/Chicano Studies, B
History, BM
History Teacher Education, B
Human Resources Management/Personnel
    Administration, B
Humanities/Humanistic Studies, B
Industrial Engineering, B
Industrial/Management Engineering, MD
Information Science/Studies, B
Information Technology, B
Intermedia/Multimedia, B
International Relations and Affairs, B
Italian Language and Literature, B
Italian Studies, B
Japanese Language and Literature, B
Journalism, B
Kindergarten/PreSchool Education and Teaching, B
Kinesiology and Exercise Science, B
Kinesiology and Movement Studies, M
Labor and Industrial Relations, B
Labor Studies, B
Latin Language and Literature, B
Law and Legal Studies, B
Legal and Justice Studies, M
Linguistics, B
Management Information Systems and Services, B
Management Science, B
Manufacturing Engineering, MD
Marketing Research, B
Marketing/Marketing Management, B
Mass Communication/Media Studies, B
Materials Engineering, BMD
Mathematics, BMD
Mathematics and Computer Science, B
Mathematics Teacher Education, B
Mechanical Engineering, BMD
Medical Microbiology and Bacteriology, B
Modern Greek Language and Literature, B
Modern Languages, B
Music, B
Music History, Literature, and Theory, B
Music Performance, B
Music Teacher Education, B
Music Theory and Composition, B
Music Therapy/Therapist, B
Natural Resources Management/Development and
    Policy, B
Neuroscience, B
Nursing, M
Nursing - Registered Nurse Training, B
Nursing Administration, B
Organizational Communication, B
Painting, B
Parks, Recreation, Leisure and Fitness Studies, B
Philosophy, BM
Physical Education Teaching and Coaching, B
Physics, BMD
Physics Teacher Education, B
Political Science and Government, BM
Pre-Dentistry Studies, B

Pre-Law Studies, B
Pre-Medicine/Pre-Medical Studies, B
Pre-Pharmacy Studies, B
Printmaking, B
Psychology, BMD
Public Administration, B
Radio and Television, B
Romance Languages, Literatures, and Linguistics, B
Russian Language and Literature, B
Science Teacher Education/General Science
    Teacher Education, B
Science, Technology and Society, B
Sculpture, B
Secondary Education and Teaching, B
Slavic Languages, Literatures, and Linguistics, B
Social Psychology, MD
Social Sciences, B
Social Work, BM
Sociology, BMD
Spanish Language and Literature, B
Special Education and Teaching, B
Speech Teacher Education, B
Sport and Fitness Administration/Management, B
Statistics, BMD
Teacher Education, Multiple Levels, B
Teaching French as a Second or Foreign
    Language, B
Visual and Performing Arts, B
Women's Studies, B
Writing, M

WILFRID LAURIER UNIVERSITY

Anthropology, B
Archeology, B
Art/Art Studies, General, B
Biology/Biological Sciences, B
BioTechnology, B
Business Administration and Management, B
Business Administration, Management and
    Operations, M
Canadian Studies, B
Chemistry, B
Classics and Classical
    Languages, Literatures, and Linguistics, B
Cognitive Psychology and Psycholinguistics, B
Community Psychology, BM
Computer and Information Sciences, B
Computer Programming/Programmer, B
Computer Science, B
Developmental and Child Psychology, B
Drama and Dramatics/Theatre Arts, B
Early Childhood Education and Teaching, B
Economics, BM
English, MD
English Language and Literature, B
Ethics, M
Experimental Psychology, BM
Film/Cinema Studies, B
French Language and Literature, B
French Studies, B
Geography, BMD
German Language and Literature, B
German Studies, B
History, BMD
International Relations and Affairs, B
Kinesiology and Exercise Science, B
Latin Language and Literature, B
Mass Communication/Media Studies, B
Mathematics, B
Modern Greek Language and Literature, B
Music, B
Music Therapy/Therapist, B
Pastoral Studies/Counseling, M
Philosophy, BD
Physical Education Teaching and Coaching, B
Physics, B
Political Science and Government, BM
Psychology, BM
Religion/Religious Studies, BM
Social Work, MD
Sociology, B
Spanish Language and Literature, B
Statistics, B
Theology and Religious Vocations, MDPO

Women's Studies, B

YORK UNIVERSITY

Accounting, B
Acting, B
Actuarial Science, B
Aeronautics/Aviation/Aerospace Science and
    Technology, B
Aerospace, Aeronautical and Astronautical
    Engineering, B
African Studies, B
Ancient Near Eastern and Biblical
    Languages, Literatures, and Linguistics, B
Anthropology, BMD
Applied Art, B
Applied Mathematics, BM
Art History, Criticism and Conservation, BM
Art Teacher Education, B
Art/Art Studies, General, B
Astronomy, BMD
Atmospheric Sciences and Meteorology, B
Behavioral Sciences, B
Bilingual and Multilingual Education, B
Biological and Biomedical Sciences, MD
Biological and Physical Sciences, B
Biology Teacher Education, B
Biology/Biological Sciences, B
BioTechnology, B
Business Administration and Management, B
Business Administration, Management and
    Operations, MDO
Business Statistics, B
Business/Commerce, B
Business/Managerial Economics, B
Canadian Studies, B
Chemistry, BMD
Chemistry Teacher Education, B
Cinematography and Film/Video Production, B
Classics and Classical
    Languages, Literatures, and Linguistics, B
Commercial and Advertising Art, B
Communication and Media Studies, MD
Communication Studies/Speech Communication
    and Rhetoric, B
Comparative Literature, B
Composition, M
Computer and Information Sciences, B
Computer Engineering, B
Computer Hardware Engineering, B
Computer Programming/Programmer, B
Computer Science, BMD
Computer Software Engineering, B
Creative Writing, B
Curriculum and Instruction, B
Dance, BM
Design and Applied Arts, M
Design and Visual Communications, B
Development Economics and International
    Development, B
Disability Studies, M
Drama and Dance Teacher Education, B
Drama and Dramatics/Theatre Arts, B
Drawing, B
East Asian Studies, B
Ecology, B
Economics, BMD
Education, BMD
Elementary Education and Teaching, B
Engineering, B
Engineering Physics, B
English, MD
English Language and Literature, B
English/Language Arts Teacher Education, B
Entrepreneurship/Entrepreneurial Studies, B
Environmental Biology, B
Environmental Education, B
Environmental Policy and Resource
    Management, MDO
Environmental Sciences, B
Environmental Studies, B
Ethnic and Cultural Studies, B
Ethnomusicology, MD
European Studies/Civilization, B
Film, Television, and Video Production, M
Film/Cinema Studies, B
Finance, B

Fine Arts and Art Studies, M
Fine/Studio Arts, B
French Language and Literature, BM
French Studies, B
Geography, BMD
Geology/Earth Science, B
Geosciences, MD
Geotechnical Engineering, B
German Language and Literature, B
German Studies, B
Gerontology, B
Health and Physical Education, B
Health Services/Allied Health/Health Sciences, B
Hebrew Language and Literature, B
History, BMD
History Teacher Education, B
Hospital and Health Care Facilities
    Administration/Management, B
Human Resources Management and Services, M
Human Resources Management/Personnel
    Administration, B
Humanities/Humanistic Studies, BMD
Information Technology, B
Interdisciplinary Studies, BM
International Business/Trade/Commerce, B
International Marketing, B
International Relations and Affairs, B
Italian Language and Literature, B
Italian Studies, B
Japanese Language and Literature, B
Jewish/Judaic Studies, B
Junior High/Intermediate/Middle School Education
    and Teaching, B
Kindergarten/PreSchool Education and Teaching, B
Kinesiology and Movement Studies, MD
Labor and Industrial Relations, B
Language Interpretation and Translation, B
Latin American Studies, B
Latin Language and Literature, B
Law and Legal Studies, BMDO
Liberal Arts and Sciences Studies and
    Humanities, B
Liberal Studies, M
Linguistics, B
Management Information Systems and Services, B
Marketing/Marketing Management, B
Mass Communication/Media Studies, B
Mathematics, BMD
Mathematics and Computer Science, B
Mathematics Teacher Education, B
Modern Greek Language and Literature, B
Modern Languages, B
Molecular Biology, B
Music, B
Music History, Literature, and Theory, B
Music Performance, B
Music Teacher Education, B
Music Theory and Composition, B
Musicology and Ethnomusicology, BMD
Natural Sciences, B
Nursing, M
Nursing - Registered Nurse Training, B
Nursing Science, B
Operations Research, B
Organizational Behavior Studies, B
Painting, B
Philosophy, BMD
Photography, B
Physical Education Teaching and Coaching, B
Physical Sciences, B
Physics, BMD
Physics Teacher Education, B
Piano and Organ, B
Planetary Astronomy and Science, MD
Playwriting and Screenwriting, B
Political Science and Government, BMD
Pre-Dentistry Studies, B
Pre-Law Studies, B
Pre-Medicine/Pre-Medical Studies, B
Pre-Pharmacy Studies, B
Pre-Veterinary Studies, B
Printmaking, B
Psychology, BMD
Public Administration, B
Public Health (MPH, DPH), B
Public Policy Analysis, B

Rehabilitation Therapy, B
Religion/Religious Studies, B
Romance Languages, Literatures, and Linguistics, B
Russian Language and Literature, B
Russian Studies, B
Sales, Distribution and Marketing Operations, B
Science Teacher Education/General Science
    Teacher Education, B
Science, Technology and Society, B
Sculpture, B
Secondary Education and Teaching, B
Sign Language Interpretation and Translation, B
Social Science Teacher Education, B
Social Sciences, B
Social Studies Teacher Education, B
Social Work, BM
Sociology, BMD
Spanish and Iberian Studies, B
Spanish Language and Literature, B
Special Education and Teaching, B
Speech Teacher Education, B
Sport and Fitness Administration/Management, B
Statistics, BMD
Teacher Education, Multiple Levels, B
Teaching English as a Second or Foreign
    Language/ESL Language Instructor, B
Technical and Business Writing, B
Theater, M
Translation and Interpretation, M
Urban Studies/Affairs, B
Visual and Performing Arts, B
Voice and Opera, B
Women's Studies, BMD

Quebec

BISHOP'S UNIVERSITY

Accounting, B
Art Teacher Education, B
Art/Art Studies, General, B
Arts Management, B
Biochemistry, B
Biological and Physical Sciences, B
Biology Teacher Education, B
Biology/Biological Sciences, B
Business Administration and Management, B
Business/Managerial Economics, B
Canadian Studies, B
Chemistry, B
Chemistry Teacher Education, B
Classics and Classical
    Languages, Literatures, and Linguistics, B
Comparative Literature, B
Computer and Information Sciences, B
Computer Programming/Programmer, B
Computer Science, B
Computer Teacher Education, B
Drama and Dance Teacher Education, B
Drama and Dramatics/Theatre Arts, B
Economics, B
Education, BMO
Elementary Education and Teaching, B
English as a Second Language, O
English Language and Literature, B
English/Language Arts Teacher Education, B
Environmental Studies, B
Film/Cinema Studies, B
Finance, B
Fine/Studio Arts, B
French Language and Literature, B
French Language Teacher Education, B
Geography, B
Geography Teacher Education, B
German Language and Literature, B
Gerontology, B
History, B
History Teacher Education, B
Human Resources Management/Personnel
    Administration, B
Humanities/Humanistic Studies, B
International Business/Trade/Commerce, B
International Relations and Affairs, B
Italian Language and Literature, B
Liberal Arts and Sciences Studies and
    Humanities, B
Management Information Systems and Services, B

Marketing/Marketing Management, B
Mathematics, B
Mathematics Teacher Education, B
Modern Languages, B
Music, B
Music Teacher Education, B
Natural Sciences, B
Neuroscience, B
Philosophy, B
Physics, B
Physics Teacher Education, B
Political Science and Government, B
Psychology, B
Religion/Religious Studies, B
Science Teacher Education/General Science
  Teacher Education, B
Secondary Education and Teaching, B
Social Sciences, B
Sociology, B
Spanish Language and Literature, B
Spanish Language Teacher Education, B
Teaching French as a Second or Foreign
  Language, B
Web Page, Digital/Multimedia and Information
  Resources Design, B
Women's Studies, B

CONCORDIA UNIVERSITY

Accounting, BO
Acting, B
Actuarial Science, B
Adult and Continuing Education and Teaching, MO
Aerospace, Aeronautical and Astronautical
  Engineering, M
Anthropology, BM
Applied Mathematics, B
Art Education, MD
Art History, Criticism and Conservation, BMD
Art Teacher Education, B
Art Therapy/Therapist, BM
Art/Art Studies, General, B
Athletic Training and Sports Medicine, B
Aviation/Airway Management and Operations, O
Behavioral Sciences, B
Biochemistry, B
Biological and Biomedical Sciences, MDO
Biology/Biological Sciences, B
BioTechnology, O
Business Administration and Management, B
Business Administration, Management and
  Operations, MDO
Business/Managerial Economics, B
Cell/Cellular Biology and Histology, B
Ceramic Arts and Ceramics, B
Chemistry, BMD
Child and Family Studies, M
Cinematography and Film/Video Production, B
Civil Engineering, BMDO
Classics and Classical
  Languages, Literatures, and Linguistics, B
Clinical Psychology, MDO
Commercial and Advertising Art, B
Communication and Media Studies, MDO
Communication Studies/Speech Communication
  and Rhetoric, B
Comparative Literature, B
Computer Art and Design, O
Computer Engineering, BMD
Computer Science, BMDO
Construction Engineering and Management, MDO
Creative Writing, B
Dance, B
Design and Applied Arts, O
Developmental and Child Psychology, B
Drama and Dance Teacher Education, B
Drama and Dramatics/Theatre Arts, B
Drawing, B
Ecology, B
Economics, BMDO
Education, MDO
Educational Media/Instructional Technology, MDO
Electrical Engineering, MD
Electrical, Electronics and Communications
  Engineering, B
Electronic Commerce, O
Elementary Education and Teaching, B

Engineering and Applied Sciences, MDO
English, M
English Language and Literature, B
Entrepreneurship/Entrepreneurial Studies, B
Environmental Biology, B
Environmental Engineering
  Technology/Environmental Technology, O
Environmental Studies, BO
Environmental/Environmental Health Engineering, B
Ethnic and Cultural Studies, B
European Studies/Civilization, B
Exercise and Sports Science, M
Fiber, Textile and Weaving Arts, B
Film, Television, and Video Production, M
Film, Television, and Video Theory and Criticism, M
Film/Cinema Studies, B
Finance, B
Fine Arts and Art Studies, M
Fine/Studio Arts, B
French Language and Literature, BMO
Genomic Sciences, O
Geography, BO
German Language and Literature, B
Health Services Administration, O
History, BMD
Human Resources Management/Personnel
  Administration, B
Humanities/Humanistic Studies, D
Industrial Engineering, B
Industrial/Management Engineering, MDO
Information Science/Studies, M
Interdisciplinary Studies, B
International Business/Trade/Commerce, B
Investment Management, MO
Italian Language and Literature, B
Jazz/Jazz Studies, B
Jewish/Judaic Studies, M
Journalism, BO
Kindergarten/PreSchool Education and Teaching, B
Kinesiology and Exercise Science, B
Language Interpretation and Translation, B
Linguistics, BM
Management, O
Management Information Systems and Services, B
Marketing Research, B
Marketing/Marketing Management, B
Mass Communication/Media Studies, B
Mathematics, BMD
Mathematics Teacher Education, M
Mechanical Engineering, BMDO
Media Studies, M
Modern Languages, B
Molecular Biology, B
Music, BO
Music Performance, B
Neuroscience, B
Organizational Management, M
Painting, B
Parks, Recreation, Leisure and Fitness Studies, B
Performance, O
Philosophy, BM
Photography, B
Physics, B
Playwriting and Screenwriting, B
Political Science and Government, B
Printmaking, B
Psychology, BMD
Public Administration, BM
Public Affairs, O
Public Policy Analysis, BM
Religion/Religious Studies, BMD
Rural Planning and Studies, O
Sculpture, B
Social Sciences, B
Sociology, BM
Software Engineering, MDO
South Asian Studies, B
Spanish Language and Literature, B
Sport and Fitness Administration/Management, O
Statistics, B
Systems Engineering, MO
Teaching English as a Second or Foreign
  Language/ESL Language Instructor, B
Technical Theatre/Theatre Design and
  Technology, B
Theology and Religious Vocations, M

Theology/Theological Studies, B
Therapeutic Recreation/Recreational Therapy, B
Translation and Interpretation, O
Urban and Regional Planning, O
Urban Studies/Affairs, B
Women's Studies, B
Writing, M

HEC MONTREAL

Accounting, BMO
Applied Economics, BM
Arts Management, O
Business Administration and Management, B
Business Administration, Management and
  Operations, MD
Business Statistics, B
Business/Commerce, B
Business/Managerial Economics, B
Computer Systems Analysis/Analyst, B
Consumer Merchandising/Retailing Management, B
Corporate and Organizational Communication, O
Electronic Commerce, MO
Entrepreneurship/Entrepreneurial Studies, B
Finance, B
Finance and Banking, M
Financial Engineering, M
Human Resources Management and Services, M
Human Resources Management/Personnel
  Administration, B
Industrial and Manufacturing Management, M
Information Science/Studies, B
International Business/Trade/Commerce, BM
International Economics, B
International Finance, B
Logistics and Materials Management, M
Management, O
Management Information Systems and
  Services, BM
Management Science, B
Management Strategy and Policy, M
Marketing, M
Marketing/Marketing Management, B
Sales, Distribution and Marketing Operations, B
Taxation, MO

MCGILL UNIVERSITY

Accounting, BMO
Aerospace, Aeronautical and Astronautical
  Engineering, M
African Studies, B
Agribusiness, B
Agricultural Business and Management, B
Agricultural Economics, BM
Agricultural Engineering, MD
Agricultural Sciences, MDO
Agricultural/Biological Engineering and
  Bioengineering, B
Agronomy and Soil Sciences, MD
Allopathic Medicine, MDPO
Anatomy, MD
Animal Genetics, B
Animal Physiology, B
Animal Sciences, BMD
Anthropology, BMD
Applied Mathematics, BM
Architecture, BMDO
Area Studies, B
Art History, Criticism and Conservation, BMD
Atmospheric Sciences and Meteorology, BMD
Biochemistry, BMD
Bioengineering, MD
Bioethics/Medical Ethics, M
Biological and Biomedical Sciences, MD
Biology Teacher Education, B
Biology/Biological Sciences, B
Biomedical Engineering, MD
Biostatistics, MDO
BioTechnology, MO
Botany/Plant Biology, B
Business Administration and Management, B
Business Administration, Management and
  Operations, MDO
Business Teacher Education, B
Business/Managerial Economics, B
Canadian Studies, B
Cell Biology and Anatomy, MD

Central/Middle and Eastern European Studies, B
Chemical Engineering, BMD
Chemistry, BMD
Chemistry Teacher Education, B
Civil Engineering, MD
Classics and Classical
   Languages, Literatures, and Linguistics, B
Clinical Psychology, D
Communication and Media Studies, MD
Communication Disorders, MD
Community Health and Preventive Medicine, M
Composition, MD
Computational Sciences, M
Computer and Information Sciences, B
Computer Engineering, BMD
Computer Science, BMD
Counseling Psychology, MD
Curriculum and Instruction, M
Dental and Oral Surgery, MD
Dentistry, MDPO
Developmental Psychology, MDO
Dietetics/Dieticians, B
Drama and Dramatics/Theatre Arts, B
Early Childhood Education and Teaching, B
East Asian Studies, BMD
Ecology, B
Economics, BMD
Education, BMDO
Educational Administration and Supervision, M
Educational Leadership and Administration, O
Educational Psychology, MD
Electrical Engineering, MD
Electrical, Electronics and Communications
   Engineering, B
Elementary Education and Teaching, B
Engineering, B
Engineering and Applied Sciences, MDO
English, MD
English Language and Literature, B
English/Language Arts Teacher Education, B
Entomology, MD
Entrepreneurship/Entrepreneurial Studies, BM
Environmental and Occupational Health, MDO
Environmental Biology, B
Environmental Engineering
   Technology/Environmental Technology, MD
Environmental Studies, B
Epidemiology, MDO
Experimental Psychology, MD
Finance, B
Finance and Banking, M
Fish, Game and Wildlife Management, MD
Food Engineering, MD
Food Science, B
Food Science and Technology, MD
Foods, Nutrition, and Wellness Studies, B
Foreign Language Teacher Education, MD
Foreign Languages and Literatures, B
Forensic Science and Technology, O
Forestry, MD
Foundations and Philosophy of Education, MD
French Language and Literature, BMD
French Language Teacher Education, B
Genetic Counseling/Counselor, M
Geography, BMD
Geology/Earth Science, B
Geophysics and Seismology, B
Geosciences, MD
Geotechnical Engineering, MD
German Language and Literature, BMD
Health Physics/Radiological Health, MD
Health Services Administration, M
Hispanic Studies, MD
History, BMD
History of Medicine, MD
History Teacher Education, B
Human Genetics, MD
Human Resources Management/Personnel
   Administration, B
Humanities/Humanistic Studies, B
Hydraulics and Fluid Power Technology, MD
Immunology, MD
Industrial and Manufacturing Management, M
Information Science/Studies, BMDO
International Agriculture, B
International Business/Trade/Commerce, BM

International Development, M
Italian Language and Literature, BMD
Jazz/Jazz Studies, B
Jewish/Judaic Studies, BMD
Kindergarten/PreSchool Education and Teaching, B
Kinesiology and Exercise Science, B
Kinesiology and Movement Studies, MDO
Labor and Industrial Relations, B
Latin American Studies, B
Law and Legal Studies, MDO
Library Science, MDO
Linguistics, BMD
Management, O
Management Information Systems and Services, M
Management Science, B
Management Strategy and Policy, M
Marine Biology and Biological Oceanography, B
Marketing, M
Marketing Research, B
Materials Engineering, BMD
Mathematics, BMD
Mathematics and Computer Science, B
Mathematics Teacher Education, B
Mechanical Engineering, BMD
Mechanics, MD
Medical Microbiology and Bacteriology, B
Medical Physics, MD
Metallurgical Engineering, MD
Meteorology, MD
Microbiology, MD
Mineral/Mining Engineering, MDO
Mining and Mineral Engineering, B
Molecular Biology, B
Music, BMD
Music History, Literature, and Theory, B
Music Performance, B
Music Teacher Education, BMD
Music Theory and Composition, BMD
Musicology and Ethnomusicology, MD
Natural Resources and Conservation, BMD
Natural Resources Management/Development and
   Policy, M
Near and Middle Eastern Studies, BMDO
Neuroscience, MD
Nursing, MDO
Nursing - Advanced Practice, O
Nursing - Registered Nurse Training, B
Nutritional Sciences, BMD
Occupational Therapy/Therapist, B
Oceanography, Chemical and Physical, MD
Organizational Behavior Studies, B
Parasitology, MDO
Pathology/Experimental Pathology, MD
Performance, MD
Pharmacology, MD
Philosophy, BMD
Philosophy and Religious Studies, B
Physical Education Teaching and Coaching, BMDO
Physical Therapy/Therapist, B
Physics, BMD
Physics Teacher Education, B
Physiological Psychology/Psychobiology, B
Physiology, MD
Piano and Organ, B
Planetary Astronomy and Science, MD
Plant Sciences, BMDO
Political Science and Government, BMD
Psychology, BMD
Rehabilitation Sciences, MD
Religion/Religious Studies, BMD
Religious Education, B
Russian Language and Literature, BMD
Russian Studies, B
Sales, Distribution and Marketing Operations, B
School Psychology, MDO
Science Teacher Education/General Science
   Teacher Education, B
Secondary Education and Teaching, B
Social Science Teacher Education, B
Social Studies Teacher Education, B
Social Work, BMDO
Sociology, BMD
Soil Science and Agronomy, B
Spanish Language and Literature, B
Statistics, BMD
Structural Engineering, MD

Teaching English as a Second or Foreign
   Language/ESL Language Instructor, B
Theology and Religious Vocations, MD
Transportation/Transportation Management, M
Urban and Regional Planning, MD
Urban Studies/Affairs, B
Voice and Opera, B
Water Resources Engineering, MD
Wildlife and Wildlands Science and Management, B
Wildlife Biology, B
Women's Studies, B
Zoology/Animal Biology, B

TÉLÉ-UNIVERSITÉ

Business Administration and Management, B
Computer Science, D
Distance Education Development, M
Education, B
Finance and Banking, M
Liberal Arts and Sciences Studies and
   Humanities, B
Mass Communication/Media Studies, B

UNIVERSITÉ LAVAL

Accounting, MO
Actuarial Science, B
Advertising and Public Relations, O
Aerospace, Aeronautical and Astronautical
   Engineering, M
Agricultural Economics, BM
Agricultural Engineering, M
Agricultural Sciences, MDO
Agronomy and Crop Science, B
Agronomy and Soil Sciences, MD
Allopathic Medicine, PO
Anatomy, MDO
Animal Sciences, MD
Anthropology, ABMD
Archeology, BMD
Architecture, BM
Art History, Criticism and Conservation, ABMD
Art Teacher Education, B
Biochemistry, BMDO
Biological and Biomedical Sciences, MDO
Biology/Biological Sciences, B
Business Administration and Management, B
Business Administration, Management and
   Operations, MO
Cancer Biology/Oncology, O
Cardiovascular Sciences, O
Cell Biology and Anatomy, MD
Chemical Engineering, BMD
Chemistry, BMD
Civil Engineering, BMDO
Classics and Classical
   Languages, Literatures, and Linguistics, B
Clinical Psychology, D
Commercial and Advertising Art, B
Communication Disorders, M
Community Health and Preventive Medicine, MDO
Community Psychology, D
Comparative Literature, ABMD
Composition, M
Computer Engineering, BMD
Computer Science, BMD
Computer Software Engineering, B
Consumer Economics, O
Consumer Services and Advocacy, B
Counselor Education/School Counseling and
   Guidance Services, BMD
Curriculum and Instruction, MD
Dentistry, P
Drama and Dramatics/Theatre Arts, AB
Econometrics and Quantitative Economics, B
Economics, BMD
Education, MDO
Educational Administration and Supervision, MD
Educational Leadership and Administration, O
Educational Measurement and Evaluation, MD
Educational Media/Instructional Technology, MD
Educational Psychology, MD
Electrical Engineering, MD
Electrical, Electronics and Communications
   Engineering, B
Electronic Commerce, MO
Elementary Education and Teaching, B

Emergency Medical Services, O
Engineering, B
Engineering and Applied Sciences, MDO
Engineering Physics, B
English, MD
English Language and Literature, AB
Entrepreneurship/Entrepreneurial Studies, O
Environmental and Occupational Health, O
Environmental Engineering
   Technology/Environmental Technology, M
Environmental Sciences, M
Environmental Studies, BM
Environmental/Environmental Health Engineering, B
Epidemiology, MD
Ethics, O
Ethnic and Cultural Studies, MD
Ethnic, Cultural Minority, and Gender Studies, A
Facilities Planning and Management, M
Film, Television, and Video Theory and
   Criticism, MD
Finance and Banking, M
Fine Arts and Art Studies, M
Fine/Studio Arts, B
Food Science, B
Food Science and Technology, MD
Foods, Nutrition, and Wellness Studies, B
Forest Management/Forest Resources
   Management, B
Forestry, BMD
French Language and Literature, ABM
French Language Teacher Education, B
Geodetic Sciences, MD
Geography, ABMD
Geography Teacher Education, B
Geological/Geophysical Engineering, B
Geology/Earth Science, BMD
Geosciences, MD
Gerontology, O
Graphic Design, M
Health Physics/Radiological Health, O
History, BMD
History Teacher Education, B
Immunology, MD
Industrial and Labor Relations, MD
Industrial/Management Engineering, O
Infectious Diseases, O
Insurance, A
Interdisciplinary Studies, B
International Affairs, M
International Business/Trade/Commerce, M
Jazz/Jazz Studies, A
Journalism, O
Kindergarten/PreSchool Education and Teaching, B
Kinesiology and Exercise Science, B
Kinesiology and Movement Studies, MD
Labor and Industrial Relations, AB
Language Interpretation and Translation, B
Law and Legal Studies, BMDO
Legal and Justice Studies, O
Linguistics, BMD
Management, MDO
Management Information Systems and Services, M
Management of Technology, O
Marketing, M
Mass Communication/Media Studies, BM
Mathematics, BMD
Mathematics and Computer Science, B
Mathematics Teacher Education, B
Mechanical Engineering, BMD
Medical Microbiology and Bacteriology, B
Metallurgical Engineering, BMD
Microbiology, MD
Mineral/Mining Engineering, MD
Mining and Mineral Engineering, B
Modern Languages, B
Molecular Biology, MD
Multi-/Interdisciplinary Studies, B
Museology/Museum Studies, O
Music, BMD
Music Teacher Education, BM
Musicology and Ethnomusicology, M
Neurobiology and Neurophysiology, MD
Nursing, MO
Nursing - Registered Nurse Training, B
Nutritional Sciences, BMD
Occupational Therapy/Therapist, B

Oceanography, Chemical and Physical, D
Oral and Dental Sciences, MO
Organizational Management, M
Pathology/Experimental Pathology, O
Pharmaceutical Sciences, MDO
Pharmacy, B
Pharmacy, Pharmaceutical Sciences, and Administration, B
Philosophy, ABMD
Physical Education Teaching and Coaching, B
Physical Therapy/Therapist, B
Physics, BMD
Physiology, MD
Plant Biology, MD
Political Science and Government, ABMD
Pre-Dentistry Studies, B
Pre-Law Studies, B
Pre-Medicine/Pre-Medical Studies, B
Pre-Pharmacy Studies, B
Psychology, BD
Rabbinical Studies, AB
Religion/Religious Studies, MD
Rural Planning and Studies, O
Science Teacher Education/General Science
   Teacher Education, B
Secondary Education and Teaching, B
Social Work, BMD
Sociology, BMD
Software Engineering, O
Spanish Language and Literature, BMD
Statistics, BM
Survey Technology/Surveying, B
Teaching English as a Second or Foreign
   Language/ESL Language Instructor, B
Teaching French as a Second or Foreign
   Language, B
Technical Teacher Education, B
Theater, MD
Theology and Religious Vocations, MD
Theology/Theological Studies, AB
Translation and Interpretation, MO
Urban and Regional Planning, MD
Urban Forestry, B
Women's Studies, O

UNIVERSITÉ DE MONTRÉAL

Actuarial Science, B
Allopathic Medicine, PO
Anthropology, BMD
Applied Mathematics, B
Archeology, B
Architecture, B
Art History, Criticism and Conservation, BMD
Art/Art Studies, General, B
Audiology/Audiologist and Speech-Language
   Pathology/Pathologist, B
Bible/Biblical Studies, B
Biochemistry, BMDO
Bioethics/Medical Ethics, MO
Biological and Biomedical Sciences, MDO
Biology/Biological Sciences, B
Biomedical Engineering, MDO
Biomedical Sciences, B
Biophysics, MD
Cell Biology and Anatomy, MD
Chemical Engineering, B
Chemistry, BMD
Classics and Classical
   Languages, Literatures, and Linguistics, B
Communication and Media Studies, MD
Communication Disorders, M
Community Health and Preventive Medicine, MDO
Comparative Literature, BMD
Composition, MD
Computer Science, BMDO
Criminology, BMD
Curriculum and Instruction, MDO
Dental Hygiene/Hygienist, O
Developmental and Child Psychology, B
Developmental Psychology, M
East Asian Studies, B
Ecology, B
Economics, BMD
Education, BMDO
Educational Administration and Supervision, MDO
Educational Psychology, MDO
Elementary Education and Teaching, B

Emergency Medical Services, O
English, MD
English Language and Literature, B
Environmental and Occupational Health, MO
Environmental Design/Architecture, MDO
Environmental Policy and Resource
   Management, O
Ergonomics and Human Factors, O
Ethnomusicology, MD
Film, Television, and Video Theory and Criticism, M
Film/Cinema Studies, B
Foods, Nutrition, and Wellness Studies, B
French Language and Literature, BMD
Geography, BMDO
Geology/Earth Science, B
German Language and Literature, BMD
Health Promotion, O
Health Services Administration, MO
Hispanic-American, Puerto Rican, and Mexican-
   American/Chicano Studies, B
History, BMD
Human Resources Management/Personnel
   Administration, B
Human Services, D
Immunology, MD
Industrial and Labor Relations, MD
Industrial Design, B
Infectious Diseases, O
Information Science/Studies, MD
Interdisciplinary Studies, B
Jazz/Jazz Studies, B
Kindergarten/PreSchool Education and Teaching, B
Kinesiology and Movement Studies, MDO
Labor and Industrial Relations, B
Landscape Architecture, B
Law and Legal Studies, BMDPO
Library Science, MD
Linguistics, BMDO
Management Information Systems and Services, O
Mass Communication/Media Studies, B
Maternal/Child Health and Neonatal
   Nurse/Nursing, O
Mathematics, BMD
Medical Microbiology and Bacteriology, B
Microbiology, MDO
Modern Languages, B
Molecular Biology, MD
Museology/Museum Studies, M
Music, BMDO
Musicology and Ethnomusicology, MD
Neuroscience, MD
Nuclear/Nuclear Power Technology/Technician, O
Nurse Anesthetist, O
Nursing, MDO
Nursing - Registered Nurse Training, B
Nutritional Sciences, MD
Occupational Therapy/Therapist, B
Operations Research, B
Ophthalmic/Optometric Services, B
Optometry, P
Oral and Dental Sciences, MO
Oral Biology, M
Orthodontics, MO
Pathology/Experimental Pathology, MD
Pedodontics, MO
Performance, O
Pharmaceutical Sciences, MDO
Pharmacology, MD
Pharmacy, B
Philosophy, BMD
Physical Education Teaching and Coaching, BMDO
Physical Therapy/Therapist, B
Physics, BMD
Physiology, MD
Political Science and Government, BMD
Population Studies, MD
Pre-Dentistry Studies, B
Pre-Medicine/Pre-Medical Studies, B
Psychology, BMD
Rehabilitation Therapy, B
Religion/Religious Studies, B
Secondary Education and Teaching, B
Social Sciences, B
Social Work, BO
Sociology, BMD
Spanish Language and Literature, BMD

Special Education and Teaching, BO
Sport and Fitness Administration/Management, M
Statistics, BMD
Theology and Religious Vocations, MDO
Theology/Theological Studies, B
Toxicology, O
Urban Studies/Affairs, B
Veterinary Medicine, P
Veterinary Sciences, MDO
Virology, D
Vision Science/Physiological Optics, MO

UNIVERSITÉ DU QUÉBEC EN ABITIBI-TÉMISCAMINGUE

Accounting, B
Behavioral Sciences, B
Business Administration and Management, B
Business Administration, Management and
    Operations, M
Business Teacher Education, B
Education, BMD
Electrical, Electronics and Communications
    Engineering, B
Electromechanical Technology/Electromechanical
    Engineering Technology, B
Elementary Education and Teaching, B
Engineering, O
Engineering Mechanics, B
Kindergarten/PreSchool Education and Teaching, B
Mechanical Engineering, B
Mechanical Engineering/Mechanical
    Technology/Technician, B
Mining and Mineral Engineering, B
Nursing - Registered Nurse Training, B
Project Management, M
Psychology, B
Secondary Education and Teaching, B
Social Sciences, B
Social Work, B
Special Education and Teaching, B

UNIVERSITÉ DU QUÉBEC ÀCHICOUTIMI

Accounting, B
Art Teacher Education, B
Art/Art Studies, General, B
Biology/Biological Sciences, B
Business Administration and Management, B
Business Administration, Management and
    Operations, M
Business Teacher Education, B
Canadian Studies, M
Chemistry, B
Comparative Literature, BM
Computer Engineering, B
Computer Science, B
Education, MD
Elementary Education and Teaching, B
Engineering, B
Engineering and Applied Sciences, MD
English Language and Literature, B
Environmental Policy and Resource
    Management, M
Ethics, O
Fine Arts and Art Studies, M
French Language and Literature, BO
Genetics, M
Geography, B
Geological/Geophysical Engineering, B
Geology/Earth Science, B
Geosciences, M
History, B
Information Science/Studies, B
Kindergarten/PreSchool Education and Teaching, B
Linguistics, BM
Management Information Systems and Services, B
Mathematics, B
Mineralogy, D
Modern Languages, B
Nursing - Registered Nurse Training, B
Physical Education Teaching and Coaching, B
Physical Sciences, B
Physics, B
Political Science and Government, B
Project Management, M
Psychology, B

Religious Education, B
Science Teacher Education/General Science
    Teacher Education, B
Secondary Education and Teaching, B
Social Sciences, B
Social Work, B
Special Education and Teaching, B
Teaching English as a Second or Foreign
    Language/ESL Language Instructor, B
Theology and Religious Vocations, MD
Theology/Theological Studies, B
Trade and Industrial Teacher Education, B

UNIVERSITE DU QUEBEC, ECOLE DE TECHNOLOGIE SUPERIEURE

Artificial Intelligence and Robotics, B
Construction Engineering, B
Electrical, Electronics and Communications
    Engineering, B
Engineering, B
Engineering and Applied Sciences, MDO
Mechanical Engineering, B

UNIVERSITÉ DU QUÉBEC ÀMONTRÉAL

Accounting, BMO
Actuarial Science, O
Art History, Criticism and Conservation, BMD
Art/Art Studies, General, B
Atmospheric Sciences and Meteorology, MDO
Biochemistry, B
Biological and Biomedical Sciences, MD
Biology/Biological Sciences, B
Business Administration and Management, B
Business Administration, Management and
    Operations, MDO
Chemistry, BM
Commercial and Advertising Art, B
Communication and Media Studies, MD
Comparative Literature, BMD
Counselor Education/School Counseling and
    Guidance Services, B
Dance, BM
Drama and Dramatics/Theatre Arts, B
Economics, BMD
Education, BMDO
Elementary Education and Teaching, B
Environmental and Occupational Health, O
Environmental Design/Architecture, B
Environmental Education, O
Environmental Sciences, MD
Ergonomics and Human Factors, O
Fashion/Apparel Design, B
Finance and Banking, O
Fine Arts and Art Studies, M
Geographic Information Systems, O
Geography, BM
Geology/Earth Science, BM
Geosciences, MDO
History, BMD
Hotel/Motel Administration/Management, B
Kindergarten/PreSchool Education and Teaching, B
Kinesiology and Movement Studies, M
Law and Legal Studies, BM
Linguistics, BMD
Management Information Systems and
    Services, BM
Mass Communication/Media Studies, B
Mathematics, BMD
Meteorology, MDO
Mineralogy, D
Museology/Museum Studies, M
Music, B
Music History, Literature, and Theory, B
Music Teacher Education, B
Music Therapy/Therapist, B
Natural Resources and Conservation, O
Parks, Recreation, Leisure and Fitness Studies, B
Philosophy, BMD
Physical Education Teaching and Coaching, B
Physics, B
Political Science and Government, BMD
Project Management, MO
Psychology, BD
Public Administration, M
Religion/Religious Studies, BMD
Religious Education, B

Science Teacher Education/General Science
    Teacher Education, B
Science, Technology and Society, B
Secondary Education and Teaching, B
Social Work, BM
Sociology, BMD
Special Education and Teaching, B
Teaching English as a Second or Foreign
    Language/ESL Language Instructor, B
Theater, M
Trade and Industrial Teacher Education, B
Urban Studies/Affairs, BMD

UNIVERSITÉ DU QUÉBEC EN OUTAOUAIS

Accounting, BO
Adult and Continuing Education and Teaching, O
Art/Art Studies, General, B
Business Administration and Management, B
Computer Engineering, B
Computer Science, BMO
Design and Visual Communications, B
Education, BMDO
Educational Psychology, M
Elementary Education and Teaching, B
Finance and Banking, M
Fine/Studio Arts, B
Human Resources Management and Services, B
Industrial and Labor Relations, MO
International Business/Trade/Commerce, B
Kindergarten/PreSchool Education and Teaching, B
Labor and Industrial Relations, B
Language Interpretation and Translation, B
Management Information Systems and Services, B
Nursing, MO
Nursing - Registered Nurse Training, B
Project Management, MO
Psychology, B
Secondary Education and Teaching, B
Social Sciences, B
Social Work, BM
Sociology, B
Software Engineering, O
Special Education and Teaching, B
Urban and Regional Planning, M

UNIVERSITÉ DU QUÉBEC ÀRIMOUSKI

Accounting, B
Biology/Biological Sciences, B
Business Administration and Management, B
Business Teacher Education, B
Chemistry, B
Comparative Literature, BM
Computer Science, B
Education, MD
Elementary Education and Teaching, B
Engineering, B
Ethics, M
Fish, Game and Wildlife Management, MO
French Language and Literature, B
Geography, B
History, B
Kindergarten/PreSchool Education and Teaching, B
Marine Affairs, M
Mathematics, B
Nursing - Registered Nurse Training, B
Oceanography, Chemical and Physical, MD
Project Management, M
Public Administration, O
Religion/Religious Studies, B
Religious Education, B
Science Teacher Education/General Science
    Teacher Education, B
Secondary Education and Teaching, B
Sociology, B
Special Education and Teaching, B
Theology/Theological Studies, B
Trade and Industrial Teacher Education, B

UNIVERSITÉ DU QUÉBEC ÀTROIS-RIVIÈRES

Accounting, BO
Adult and Continuing Education and Teaching, B
Adult Health Nurse/Nursing, B
Art Teacher Education, B
Art/Art Studies, General, B

Artificial Intelligence and Robotics, B
Biochemistry, B
Biology/Biological Sciences, B
Biomedical Sciences, B
Biophysics, BMD
Business Administration and Management, B
Business Administration, Management and
    Operations, MD
Business/Managerial Economics, B
Canadian Studies, MD
Chemical Engineering, B
Chemistry, BM
Comparative Literature, M
Computer Engineering, B
Computer Programming/Programmer, B
Computer Science, BM
Computer Systems Analysis/Analyst, B
Economics, B
Education, BMO
Education/Teaching of Individuals with Mental
    Retardation, B
Educational Administration and Supervision, D
Educational Psychology, M
Electrical Engineering, MD
Electrical, Electronics and Communications
    Engineering, B
Elementary Education and Teaching, B
Energy Management and Policy, MD
Engineering Mechanics, B
Engineering/Industrial Management, B
English/Language Arts Teacher Education, B
Entrepreneurship/Entrepreneurial Studies, BM
Environmental Sciences, MD
Family Practice Nurse/Nurse Practitioner, B
Finance and Banking, O
French Language and Literature, B
Geography, B
Health and Physical Education, B
History, B
Human Resources Management/Personnel
    Administration, B
Industrial and Labor Relations, O
Industrial Engineering, B
Industrial/Management Engineering, MO
Information Science/Studies, B
Kindergarten/PreSchool Education and Teaching, B
Leisure Studies, MO
Mass Communication/Media Studies, B
Mathematics, BM
Mathematics Teacher Education, B
Mechanical Engineering, B
Nurse Midwife/Nursing Midwifery, B
Nursing, MO
Nursing - Registered Nurse Training, B
Operations Research, B
Paper and Pulp Engineering, MD
Parks, Recreation, Leisure and Fitness Studies, B
Philosophy, BMD
Physical Education Teaching and Coaching, M
Physics, B
Project Management, MO
Psychology, BMD
Public Health (MPH, DPH), B
Public Health/Community Nurse/Nursing, B
Secondary Education and Teaching, B
Theology/Theological Studies, B
Travel and Tourism, MO

UNIVERSITÉ DE SHERBROOKE

Accounting, BM
Allopathic Medicine, P
Athletic Training and Sports Medicine, B
Biochemistry, BMD
Biological and Biomedical Sciences, MD
Biology Technician/BioTechnology Laboratory
    Technician, B
Biology/Biological Sciences, B
Biophysics, MD
BioTechnology, P
Business Administration and Management, B
Business Administration, Management and
    Operations, MDO
Canadian Studies, MD
Cell Biology and Anatomy, MD
Chemical Engineering, BMD
Chemistry, BMD

Civil Engineering, BMD
Clinical Laboratory Sciences, MD
Communication and Media Studies, B
Comparative Literature, MD
Computer and Information Sciences, B
Computer Engineering, B
Computer Programming/Programmer, B
Computer Science, B
Conflict Resolution and Mediation/Peace
    Studies, MO
Counselor Education/School Counseling and
    Guidance Services, B
Ecology, B
Economics, BM
Education, BMO
Educational Administration and Supervision, M
Electrical Engineering, MD
Electrical, Electronics and Communications
    Engineering, B
Elementary Education and Teaching, BMO
Engineering, B
Engineering and Applied Sciences, MDO
Engineering Management, MO
English Language and Literature, B
Environmental Engineering
    Technology/Environmental Technology, M
Environmental Sciences, MO
Ethics, O
Finance, B
Finance and Banking, M
French Language and Literature, BMD
Geography, BMD
Gerontology, M
Higher Education/Higher Education
    Administration, MO
History, BM
Immunology, MD
Information Science/Studies, B
Information Technology, B
Interdisciplinary Studies, B
International Business/Trade/Commerce, M
Kindergarten/PreSchool Education and Teaching, B
Kinesiology and Exercise Science, B
Kinesiology and Movement Studies, M
Law and Legal Studies, BMDPO
Linguistics, M
Management, O
Management Information Systems and Services, M
Marketing, M
Marketing/Marketing Management, B
Mathematics, BMD
Mechanical Engineering, BMD
Medical Microbiology and Bacteriology, B
Microbiology, MD
Music, B
Nursing - Registered Nurse Training, B
Organizational Behavior Studies, M
Pharmacology, MD
Philosophy, BMD
Physical Education Teaching and Coaching, BMO
Physics, BMD
Physiology, MD
Pre-Medicine/Pre-Medical Studies, B
Psychology, BM
Radiation Biology/Radiobiology, MD
Religion/Religious Studies, M
Secondary Education and Teaching, B
Social Work, BM
Special Education and Teaching, BMO
Taxation, MO
Theater, M
Theology and Religious Vocations, MDO
Theology/Theological Studies, B

Saskatchewan

BRIERCREST COLLEGE

Accounting, B
Bible/Biblical Studies, B
Business Administration and Management, B
Child Development, B
Divinity/Ministry (BD, MDiv.), B
Ethnic and Cultural Studies, B
Missions/Missionary Studies and Missiology, B
Pastoral Studies/Counseling, B
Religion/Religious Studies, B

Religious/Sacred Music, B
Theology/Theological Studies, B

CENTRAL PENTECOSTAL COLLEGE

Bible/Biblical Studies, B
Christian Studies, B
Missions/Missionary Studies and Missiology, B
Pastoral Counseling and Specialized Ministries, B
Pastoral Studies/Counseling, B
Religious/Sacred Music, B
Theological and Ministerial Studies, B
Theology and Religious Vocations, B
Theology/Theological Studies, B
Youth Ministry, B

COLLEGE OF EMMANUEL AND ST. CHAD

Theology and Religious Vocations, MP
Theology/Theological Studies, B

UNIVERSITY OF REGINA

Accounting, B
Acting, B
Actuarial Science, B
Adult and Continuing Education and Teaching, BMO
American History (United States), B
American Indian/Native American
    Languages, Literatures, and Linguistics, B
American Indian/Native American Studies, BM
Analytical Chemistry, MD
Anthropology, BM
Art History, Criticism and Conservation, B
Art Teacher Education, B
Art/Art Studies, General, B
Asian History, B
Bilingual and Multilingual Education, B
Biochemistry, BMD
Biological and Biomedical Sciences, MD
Biological and Physical Sciences, B
Biology Teacher Education, B
Biology/Biological Sciences, B
Business Administration and Management, AB
Business Administration, Management and
    Operations, M
Business Teacher Education, B
Canadian History, B
Canadian Studies, BMD
Ceramic Arts and Ceramics, B
Chemical Technology/Technician, B
Chemistry, BMD
Chemistry Teacher Education, B
Chinese Language and Literature, B
Cinematography and Film/Video Production, B
Classics and Classical
    Languages, Literatures, and Linguistics, B
Computer Engineering, MD
Computer Science, BMD
Computer Software Engineering, B
Criminal Justice/Law Enforcement Administration, B
Criminal Justice/Police Science, B
Criminal Justice/Safety Studies, B
Curriculum and Instruction, M
Drama and Dramatics/Theatre Arts, B
Dramatic/Theatre Arts and Stagecraft, B
Drawing, B
Early Childhood Education and Teaching, B
Economics, BM
Education, BMDO
Educational Administration and Supervision, MO
Educational Psychology, BMDO
Electrical, Electronic and Communications
    Engineering Technology/Technician, B
Electrical, Electronics and Communications
    Engineering, B
Elementary Education and Teaching, B
Engineering, B
Engineering and Applied Sciences, MD
English, MD
English Language and Literature, B
English/Language Arts Teacher Education, B
Environmental Biology, B
Environmental Engineering
    Technology/Environmental Technology, MD
Environmental Studies, B
Environmental/Environmental Health Engineering, B
Ethnic, Cultural Minority, and Gender Studies, B

European History, B
Film/Cinema Studies, B
Finance, B
Fine Arts and Art Studies, BM
French Language and Literature, BM
French Language Teacher Education, B
Geography, BM
Geology/Earth Science, BMD
German Language and Literature, B
Health Teacher Education, B
History, BM
Human Resources Development, M
Human Resources Management and Services, M
Humanities/Humanistic Studies, B
Indian/Native American Education, B
Industrial Engineering, B
Industrial/Management Engineering, MD
Inorganic Chemistry, MD
Intermedia/Multimedia, B
Japanese Language and Literature, B
Journalism, B
Junior High/Intermediate/Middle School Education
    and Teaching, B
Kindergarten/PreSchool Education and Teaching, B
Kinesiology and Exercise Science, B
Kinesiology and Movement Studies, MD
Kinesiotherapy/Kinesiotherapist, B
Liberal Arts and Sciences Studies and
    Humanities, B
Linguistics, BM
Manufacturing Engineering, M
Marketing/Marketing Management, B
Mathematics, BMD
Mathematics and Computer Science, B
Mathematics and Statistics, B
Mathematics Teacher Education, B
Music, BMD
Music History, Literature, and Theory, B
Music Performance, B
Music Teacher Education, B
Music Theory and Composition, BM
Musicology and Ethnomusicology, BMD
Organic Chemistry, MD
Painting, B
Petroleum Engineering, BMD
Philosophy, BM
Physical Chemistry, MD
Physical Education Teaching and Coaching, B
Physics, BMD
Physics Teacher Education, B
Political Science and Government, BM
Pre-Dentistry Studies, B
Pre-Law Studies, B
Pre-Medicine/Pre-Medical Studies, B
Pre-Pharmacy Studies, B
Pre-Veterinary Studies, B
Printmaking, B
Psychology, BMD
Public Administration, ABM
Public Policy Analysis, M
Religion/Religious Studies, BM
Science Teacher Education/General Science
    Teacher Education, B
Sculpture, B
Secondary Education and Teaching, B
Social Sciences, BM
Social Studies Teacher Education, B
Social Work, BMD
Sociology, BM
Spanish Language and Literature, B
Sport and Fitness Administration/Management, B
Statistics, BMD
Systems Engineering, BMD
Technical Theatre/Theatre Design and
    Technology, B
Technology Teacher Education/Industrial Arts
    Teacher Education, B

Trade and Industrial Teacher Education, B
Visual and Performing Arts, B
Women's Studies, B

UNIVERSITY OF SASKATCHEWAN

Accounting, BM
Agribusiness, B
Agricultural Economics, BMD
Agricultural Engineering, MD
Agricultural Sciences, MD
Agricultural/Biological Engineering and
    Bioengineering, B
Agriculture, B
Agronomy and Crop Science, B
Agronomy and Soil Sciences, MD
Allopathic Medicine, P
American Indian/Native American Studies, B
American/United States Studies/Civilization, B
Anatomy, BMD
Animal Physiology, B
Animal Sciences, BMD
Anthropology, BM
Archeology, BMD
Art History, Criticism and Conservation, B
Astronomy, B
Biochemistry, BMDO
Bioinformatics, B
Biological and Biomedical Sciences, MDO
Biology/Biological Sciences, B
Biomedical Engineering, MD
BioTechnology, BM
Business Administration, Management and
    Operations, M
Business/Commerce, B
Business/Managerial Economics, B
Canadian Studies, MD
Cell Biology and Anatomy, MD
Chemical Engineering, BMD
Chemistry, BMD
Civil Engineering, BMD
Classics and Classical
    Languages, Literatures, and Linguistics, B
Community Health and Preventive Medicine, MD
Computer Science, BMD
Curriculum and Instruction, MDO
Dentistry, P
Drama and Dramatics/Theatre Arts, B
East European and Russian Studies, M
Economics, M
Education, BMDO
Educational Administration and Supervision, MDO
Educational Psychology, MDO
Electrical Engineering, MD
Elementary Education and Teaching, B
Engineering, B
Engineering and Applied Sciences, MDO
Engineering Physics, BMD
English, MD
English Language and Literature, B
Environmental Engineering
    Technology/Environmental Technology, MDO
Environmental Studies, B
Epidemiology, MD
Family and Consumer Sciences/Home Economics
    Teacher Education, B
Finance, B
Finance and Banking, M
Fine Arts and Art Studies, M
Fine/Studio Arts, B
Food Science, B
Food Science and Technology, MD
Foundations and Philosophy of Education, MDO
French Language and Literature, BM
Gender Studies, MD
Geography, BMD
Geological/Geophysical Engineering, B
Geology/Earth Science, BMDO

Geophysics and Seismology, B
German Language and Literature, BM
Health Services Administration, M
Hebrew Language and Literature, B
History, BMD
Horticultural Science, B
Human Resources Management/Personnel
    Administration, B
Industrial and Labor Relations, M
Information Science/Studies, B
International Business/Trade/Commerce, M
International Relations and Affairs, B
Kinesiology and Exercise Science, B
Kinesiology and Movement Studies, MDO
Land Use Planning and
    Management/Development, B
Latin Language and Literature, B
Law and Legal Studies, MP
Linguistics, B
Marketing, M
Marketing/Marketing Management, B
Mathematics, BMD
Mechanical Engineering, BMD
Medical Microbiology and Bacteriology, B
Microbiology, BMD
Modern Greek Language and Literature, B
Music, BM
Music Teacher Education, B
Nursing, M
Nursing - Registered Nurse Training, B
Nursing Administration, B
Nutritional Sciences, B
Operations Management and Supervision, B
Organizational Behavior Studies, M
Pathology/Experimental Pathology, MD
Pharmaceutical Sciences, MD
Pharmacology, MD
Pharmacy, B
Philosophy, BM
Physical Education Teaching and Coaching, B
Physical Therapy/Therapist, B
Physics, MD
Physiology, BMD
Plant Sciences, BMD
Political Science and Government, BM
Pre-Dentistry Studies, B
Pre-Law Studies, B
Pre-Medicine/Pre-Medical Studies, B
Pre-Pharmacy Studies, B
Pre-Veterinary Studies, B
Psychology, BMD
Public Administration, B
Range Science and Management, B
Religion/Religious Studies, BM
Reproductive Biology, MD
Russian Language and Literature, B
Secondary Education and Teaching, B
Slavic Languages, Literatures, and Linguistics, B
Sociology, BMD
Soil Science and Agronomy, B
Spanish Language and Literature, B
Special Education and Teaching, MDO
Sport and Fitness Administration/Management, B
Statistics, BMD
Teaching English as a Second or Foreign
    Language/ESL Language Instructor, B
Technical Teacher Education, B
Theater, M
Theoretical and Mathematical Physics, B
Toxicology, BMDO
Trade and Industrial Teacher Education, B
Ukrainian Language and Literature, B
Urban Studies/Affairs, B
Veterinary Medicine, MDP
Veterinary Sciences, MD
Women's Studies, BMD

ACCOUNTING

Alabama

Alabama Agricultural and Mechanical University, B
Alabama Southern Community College, A
Alabama State University, BM
Athens State University, B
Auburn University, BM
Auburn University Montgomery, B
Birmingham-Southern College, B
Calhoun Community College, A
Faulkner University, AB
Gadsden State Community College-Ayers
  Campus, A
George C. Wallace Community College, A
George Corley Wallace State Community College, A
Huntingdon College, B
J. F. Drake State Technical College, A
Jacksonville State University, B
Lawson State Community College, A
Northwest-Shoals Community College, A
Oakwood College, AB
Samford University, B
South University, A
Spring Hill College, B
Talladega College, B
Troy University, B
Tuskegee University, B
The University of Alabama, BMD
The University of Alabama at Birmingham, B
The University of Alabama in Huntsville, BMO
University of Mobile, B
University of Montevallo, B
University of North Alabama, B
University of South Alabama, BM
The University of West Alabama, AB
Wallace State Community College, A

Alaska

Charter College, A
University of Alaska Anchorage, AB
University of Alaska Anchorage, Matanuska-Susitna
  College, A
University of Alaska Fairbanks, B

Arizona

Arizona State University, BMDO
Arizona State University West, BO
Central Arizona College, A
Chandler-Gilbert Community College, A
Chaparral College, AB
Coconino Community College, A
Everest College, A
GateWay Community College, A
Grand Canyon University, B
International Institute of the Americas (Mesa), A
International Institute of the Americas (Phoenix), A
International Institute of the Americas (Tucson), A
International Institute of the Americas (West Valley)
  , A
Lamson College, A
Mesa Community College, A
Mohave Community College, A

Northern Arizona University, B
Paradise Valley Community College, A
Phoenix College, A
Pima Community College, A
Prescott College, B
Scottsdale Community College, A
The University of Arizona, BM
University of Phoenix Online Campus, BM
University of Phoenix-Phoenix Campus, M
University of Phoenix-Southern Arizona
  Campus, BM
Western International University, B
Yavapai College, A

Arkansas

Arkansas State University, BM
Arkansas Tech University, B
Harding University, B
Henderson State University, B
Hendrix College, BM
John Brown University, B
Lyon College, B
National Park Community College, A
NorthWest Arkansas Community College, A
Ouachita Baptist University, B
Ouachita Technical College, A
Southern Arkansas University-Magnolia, B
University of Arkansas, BM
University of Arkansas at Fort Smith, B
University of Arkansas at Little Rock, B
University of Arkansas at Monticello, B
University of Arkansas at Pine Bluff, B
University of Central Arkansas, BM
University of the Ozarks, B

California

Allan Hancock College, A
American River College, A
Azusa Pacific University, B
Bakersfield College, A
Barstow College, A
Berkeley City College, A
Butte College, A
Cabrillo College, A
California Baptist University, B
California Lutheran University, B
California State Polytechnic University, Pomona, B
California State University, Chico, BM
California State University, Dominguez Hills, B
California State University, East Bay, BM
California State University, Fresno, BM
California State University, Fullerton, BM
California State University, Long Beach, B
California State University, Los Angeles, M
California State University, Northridge, B
California State University, Sacramento, BM
California State University, San Bernardino, B
California State University, San Marcos, B
Cañada College, A
Cerritos College, A
Chabot College, A
Chaffey College, A
Chapman University, B
City College of San Francisco, A

Claremont McKenna College, B
College of Alameda, A
College of the Canyons, A
College of Marin, A
College of San Mateo, A
College of the Sequoias, A
College of the Siskiyous, A
Compton Community College, A
Cosumnes River College (Sacramento), A
Crafton Hills College, A
Cuyamaca College, A
Cypress College, A
De Anza College, A
East Los Angeles College, A
El Camino College, A
Empire College, A
Evergreen Valley College, A
Folsom Lake College, A
Foothill College, A
Fresno Pacific University, B
Fullerton College, A
Gavilan College, A
Glendale Community College, A
Golden Gate University, BM
Golden West College, A
Grossmont College, A
Heald College-Fresno, A
Heald College-Hayward, A
Heald College-Rancho Cordova, A
Heald College-Salinas, A
Heald College-San Francisco, A
Heald College-San Jose, A
Heald College-Stockton, A
Humboldt State University, B
Humphreys College, AB
Imperial Valley College, A
Irvine Valley College, A
John F. Kennedy University, B
La Sierra University, B
Lake Tahoe Community College, A
Laney College, A
Las Positas College, A
Lassen Community College District, A
Lincoln University, B
Long Beach City College, A
Los Angeles City College, A
Los Angeles Harbor College, A
Los Angeles Mission College, A
Los Angeles Pierce College, A
Los Angeles Southwest College, A
Los Angeles Trade-Technical College, A
Los Angeles Valley College, A
Los Medanos College, A
Loyola Marymount University, B
The Master's College and Seminary, B
Mendocino College, A
Merced College, A
Merritt College, A
MiraCosta College, A
Mission College, A
Modesto Junior College, A
Monterey Peninsula College, A
Moorpark College, A
Mount St. Mary's College, B

Mt. San Antonio College, A
MTI College of Business and Technology, A
Napa Valley College, A
National University, BM
Ohlone College, A
Orange Coast College, A
Oxnard College, A
Pacific Union College, B
Palo Verde College, A
Palomar College, A
Pasadena City College, A
Pepperdine University, B
Point Loma Nazarene University, B
Reedley College, A
Sacramento City College, A
Saddleback College, A
Saint Mary's College of California, B
San Bernardino Valley College, A
San Diego City College, A
San Diego Mesa College, A
San Diego Miramar College, A
San Diego State University, BM
San Francisco State University, B
San Joaquin Delta College, A
San Jose City College, A
San Jose State University, BM
Santa Ana College, A
Santa Barbara City College, A
Santa Clara University, B
Santa Monica College, A
Santiago Canyon College, A
Shasta College, A
Sierra College, A
Skyline College, A
Solano Community College, A
Southwestern College, A
Taft College, A
University of California, Berkeley, D
University of La Verne, B
University of Phoenix-Bay Area Campus, BM
University of Phoenix-Central Valley Campus, B
University of Phoenix-Sacramento Valley Campus, B
University of Phoenix-San Diego Campus, B
University of Phoenix-Southern California
   Campus, BM
University of Redlands, B
University of San Diego, BM
University of San Francisco, B
University of Southern California, BM
Vanguard University of Southern California, B
Ventura College, A
West Hills Community College, A
West Los Angeles College, A
West Valley College, A
Westwood College-Inland Empire, B
Woodbury University, B
Yuba College, A

Colorado

Aims Community College, A
Blair College, A
CollegeAmerica-Fort Collins, B
Colorado Christian University, B
Colorado Mountain College, A
Colorado Mountain College, Alpine Campus, A
Colorado Mountain College, Timberline Campus, A
Colorado Northwestern Community College, A
Colorado State University, BM
Colorado State University-Pueblo, B
Community College of Aurora, A
Community College of Denver, A
Fort Lewis College, B
Front Range Community College, A
Johnson & Wales University, AB
Lamar Community College, A
Mesa State College, B
Metropolitan State College of Denver, B
Morgan Community College, A
National American University (Colorado Springs)
   , AB
National American University (Denver), AB
Northeastern Junior College, A
Parks College (Denver), A
Pueblo Community College, A
Red Rocks Community College, A
Regis University, BM

Trinidad State Junior College, A
University of Colorado at Boulder, BM
University of Colorado at Colorado Springs, BM
University of Colorado at Denver and Health
   Sciences Center - Downtown Denver Campus, M
University of Denver, BM
University of Phoenix-Denver Campus, B
University of Phoenix-Southern Colorado
   Campus, B
Western State College of Colorado, B

Connecticut

Albertus Magnus College, B
Asnuntuck Community College, A
Briarwood College, A
Capital Community College, A
Central Connecticut State University, B
Eastern Connecticut State University, BM
Fairfield University, BMO
Gateway Community College, A
Housatonic Community College, A
Manchester Community College, A
Middlesex Community College, A
Mitchell College, A
Naugatuck Valley Community College, A
Northwestern Connecticut Community College, A
Norwalk Community College, A
Post University, AB
Quinebaug Valley Community College, A
Quinnipiac University, BM
Sacred Heart University, AB
Southern Connecticut State University, B
Three Rivers Community College, A
Tunxis Community College, A
University of Bridgeport, B
University of Connecticut, BMD
University of Hartford, BMO
University of New Haven, BM
Western Connecticut State University, BM
Yale University, D

Delaware

Delaware State University, B
Delaware Technical & Community College, Jack F.
   Owens Campus, A
Delaware Technical & Community College,
   Stanton/Wilmington Campus, A
Delaware Technical & Community College, Terry
   Campus, A
Goldey-Beacom College, AB
University of Delaware, BM
Wesley College, B
Wilmington College, B

District of Columbia

American University, M
The Catholic University of America, BM
Gallaudet University, B
The George Washington University, BMD
Georgetown University, B
Howard University, BM
Potomac College, AB
Southeastern University, M
Strayer University, ABM
University of the District of Columbia, AB

Florida

Argosy University/Sarasota, MD
Barry University, B
Bethune-Cookman College, B
Brevard Community College, A
Broward Community College, A
Chipola College, A
Clearwater Christian College, B
College of Business and Technology, A
Daytona Beach Community College, A
Edison College, A
Flagler College, B
Florida Agricultural and Mechanical University, BM
Florida Atlantic University, BM
Florida Community College at Jacksonville, A
Florida Gulf Coast University, BM
Florida Institute of Technology, B
Florida International University, BM
Florida Memorial College, B

Florida Metropolitan University-Brandon
   Campus, AB
Florida Metropolitan University-Jacksonville
   Campus, AB
Florida Metropolitan University-Lakeland
   Campus, AB
Florida Metropolitan University-Melbourne
   Campus, AB
Florida Metropolitan University-North Orlando
   Campus, AB
Florida Metropolitan University-Pinellas Campus, AB
Florida Metropolitan University-Pompano Beach
   Campus, AB
Florida Metropolitan University-South Orlando
   Campus, ABM
Florida Metropolitan University-Tampa
   Campus, ABM
Florida National College, A
Florida Southern College, BM
Florida State University, BM
Gulf Coast Community College, A
Hillsborough Community College, A
Indian River Community College, A
International College, AB
Jacksonville University, B
Johnson & Wales University, AB
Jones College (Jacksonville), AB
Keiser College (Daytona Beach), A
Keiser College (Fort Lauderdale), A
Keiser College (Sarasota), A
Keiser College (Tallahassee), A
Lynn University, B
Manatee Community College, A
Northwood University, Florida Campus, AB
Nova Southeastern University, BM
Okaloosa-Walton College, A
Palm Beach Community College, A
Pensacola Junior College, A
Saint Leo University, BM
St. Thomas University, BMO
Santa Fe Community College, A
Seminole Community College, A
South Florida Community College, A
South University (West Palm Beach), A
Southeastern University, B
Southwest Florida College (Fort Myers), A
Stetson University, BM
University of Central Florida, BM
University of Florida, BMDO
University of Miami, BM
University of North Florida, BM
University of Phoenix-Central Florida Campus, BM
University of Phoenix-North Florida Campus, BM
University of Phoenix-South Florida Campus, BM
University of Phoenix-West Florida Campus, B
University of South Florida, BM
The University of Tampa, BM
University of West Florida, BM
Valencia Community College, A
Webber International University, ABM
Webster College (Holiday), A
Webster College (Ocala), A

Georgia

Abraham Baldwin Agricultural College, A
Albany State University, B
Albany Technical College, A
Appalachian Technical College, A
Athens Technical College, A
Atlanta Technical College, A
Augusta State University, B
Augusta Technical College, A
Bainbridge College, A
Berry College, B
Brenau University, BM
Brewton-Parker College, B
Central Georgia Technical College, A
Chattahoochee Technical College, A
Clark Atlanta University, B
Clayton State University, AB
Columbus State University, B
Columbus Technical College, A
Coosa Valley Technical College, A
Darton College, A
DeKalb Technical College, A
Emory University, BD

Flint River Technical College, A
Fort Valley State University, B
Georgia College & State University, BM
Georgia Highlands College, A
Georgia Institute of Technology, MD
Georgia Southern University, BM
Georgia Southwestern State University, B
Georgia State University, BMDO
Griffin Technical College, A
Gwinnett Technical College, A
Kennesaw State University, B
LaGrange College, B
Lanier Technical College, A
Macon State College, A
Middle Georgia Technical College, A
Morehouse College, B
Moultrie Technical College, A
North Georgia College & State University, B
North Metro Technical College, A
Northwestern Technical College, A
Ogeechee Technical College, A
Oglethorpe University, B
Paine College, B
Reinhardt College, B
Sandersville Technical College, A
Savannah State University, B
Savannah Technical College, A
Shorter College, B
South Georgia College, A
South Georgia Technical College, A
South University, A
Southeastern Technical College, A
Southwest Georgia Technical College, A
Swainsboro Technical College, A
Thomas University, B
University of Georgia, BMO
University of Phoenix-Atlanta Campus, B
University of Phoenix-Columbus Georgia
  Campus, B
University of West Georgia, M
Valdosta State University, B
Valdosta Technical College, A
Waycross College, A
West Central Technical College, A
West Georgia Technical College, A

Guam

Guam Community College, A
University of Guam, B

Hawaii

Brigham Young University-Hawaii, AB
Chaminade University of Honolulu, B
Hawaii Business College, A
Hawaii Community College, A
Hawaii Pacific University, ABM
Heald College-Honolulu, A
Kapiolani Community College, A
Kauai Community College, A
Leeward Community College, A
Maui Community College, A
University of Hawaii at Manoa, BMD
University of Phoenix-Hawaii Campus, B

Idaho

Albertson College of Idaho, B
Boise State University, BM
Brigham Young University -Idaho, A
College of Southern Idaho, A
Eastern Idaho Technical College, A
Idaho State University, B
Northwest Nazarene University, B
University of Idaho, BM
University of Phoenix-Idaho Campus, BM

Illinois

American InterContinental University Online, M
Argosy University/Schaumburg, D
Augustana College, B
Aurora University, B
Benedictine University, B
Black Hawk College, A
Blackburn College, B
Bradley University, BM
Carl Sandburg College, A
Chicago State University, B

City Colleges of Chicago, Harold Washington
  College, A
City Colleges of Chicago, Harry S. Truman
  College, A
City Colleges of Chicago, Kennedy-King College, A
City Colleges of Chicago, Malcolm X College, A
City Colleges of Chicago, Olive-Harvey College, A
City Colleges of Chicago, Richard J. Daley
  College, A
City Colleges of Chicago, Wilbur Wright College, A
College of DuPage, A
Concordia University, B
Danville Area Community College, A
DePaul University, BM
DeVry University (Oakbrook Terrace), M
Dominican University, BM
East-West University, B
Eastern Illinois University, BO
Elgin Community College, A
Elmhurst College, BM
Eureka College, B
Gem City College, A
Governors State University, BM
Greenville College, B
Highland Community College, A
Illinois Central College, A
Illinois College, B
Illinois Eastern Community Colleges, Olney Central
  College, A
Illinois State University, BM
Illinois Valley Community College, A
Illinois Wesleyan University, B
John A. Logan College, A
John Wood Community College, A
Joliet Junior College, A
Judson College, B
Kankakee Community College, A
Lewis and Clark Community College, A
Lewis University, B
Lincoln College, A
Lincoln College-Normal, A
Loyola University Chicago, BM
MacCormac College, A
MacMurray College, B
McKendree College, B
Midstate College, A
Millikin University, B
Monmouth College, B
Morton College, A
National-Louis University, B
North Central College, B
North Park University, B
Northeastern Illinois University, BM
Northern Illinois University, BM
Northwestern Business College, A
Northwestern University, D
Oakton Community College, A
Olivet Nazarene University, B
Quincy University, B
Richland Community College, A
Rock Valley College, A
Rockford Business College, A
Rockford College, B
Roosevelt University, BM
Saint Xavier University, B
Sauk Valley Community College, A
Shawnee Community College, A
South Suburban College, A
Southeastern Illinois College, A
Southern Illinois University Carbondale, BMDO
Southern Illinois University Edwardsville, BM
Southwestern Illinois College, A
Spoon River College, A
Trinity Christian College, B
Trinity International University, B
Triton College, A
University of Illinois at Chicago, BMO
University of Illinois at Springfield, BM
University of Illinois at Urbana-Champaign, BMD
University of Phoenix-Chicago Campus, B
University of St. Francis, B
Western Illinois University, BM
Westwood College-Chicago Du Page, B
Westwood College-Chicago O'Hare Airport, B

William Rainey Harper College, A

Indiana

Anderson University, BM
Ball State University, BM
Bethel College, B
Butler University, B
Calumet College of Saint Joseph, AB
Franklin College, B
Goshen College, B
Grace College, B
Huntington University, B
Indiana Business College (Anderson), A
Indiana Business College (Columbus), A
Indiana Business College (Evansville), A
Indiana Business College (Fort Wayne), A
Indiana Business College (Indianapolis), A
Indiana Business College (Indianapolis), A
Indiana Business College (Lafayette), A
Indiana Business College (Marion), A
Indiana Business College (Muncie), A
Indiana Business College (Terre Haute), A
Indiana State University, B
Indiana Tech, AB
Indiana University Bloomington, BMD
Indiana University Kokomo, O
Indiana University Northwest, BMO
Indiana University-Purdue University Fort Wayne, B
Indiana University South Bend, M
Indiana University Southeast, O
Indiana Wesleyan University, AB
International Business College (Fort Wayne), AB
Ivy Tech Community College-Lafayette, A
Manchester College, ABM
Marian College, AB
Martin University, B
Oakland City University, AB
Purdue University, BMD
Purdue University Calumet, BM
Purdue University North Central, A
Saint Joseph's College, B
Saint Mary-of-the-Woods College, B
Taylor University, B
Tri-State University, AB
University of Evansville, B
University of Indianapolis, BM
University of Notre Dame, BM
University of Saint Francis, B
University of Southern Indiana, BM
Valparaiso University, B
Vincennes University, A
Vincennes University Jasper Campus, A

Iowa

AIB College of Business, A
Ashford University, B
Briar Cliff University, B
Buena Vista University, B
Central College, B
Clarke College, B
Coe College, B
Des Moines Area Community College, A
Dordt College, B
Drake University, B
Ellsworth Community College, A
Graceland University, B
Grand View College, B
Hamilton College (Cedar Falls), AB
Hamilton College (Cedar Rapids), AB
Hawkeye Community College, A
Iowa Central Community College, A
Iowa Lakes Community College, A
Iowa State University of Science and
  Technology, BM
Iowa Wesleyan College, B
Iowa Western Community College, A
Kaplan University, A
Kirkwood Community College, A
Loras College, B
Luther College, B
Marshalltown Community College, A
Morningside College, B
Mount Mercy College, B
Muscatine Community College, A
North Iowa Area Community College, A
Northeast Iowa Community College, A

Northwest Iowa Community College, A
Northwestern College, B
St. Ambrose University, BM
Scott Community College, A
Simpson College, B
Southeastern Community College, North Campus, A
Southwestern Community College, A
University of Dubuque, AB
The University of Iowa, BMDO
University of Northern Iowa, BM
Upper Iowa University, BM
Wartburg College, B
William Penn University, B

Kansas

Allen County Community College, A
Baker University, B
Barton County Community College, A
Benedictine College, B
Bethany College, B
Brown Mackie College-Kansas City, A
Brown Mackie College-Salina, A
Butler Community College, A
Central Christian College of Kansas, B
Coffeyville Community College, A
Colby Community College, A
Cowley County Community College and Area
   Vocational-Technical School, A
Dodge City Community College, A
Donnelly College, A
Emporia State University, B
Fort Hays State University, BM
Fort Scott Community College, A
Friends University, AB
Garden City Community College, A
Highland Community College, A
Independence Community College, A
Kansas State University, BM
Kansas Wesleyan University, B
Labette Community College, A
McPherson College, B
MidAmerica Nazarene University, B
Neosho County Community College, A
Newman University, B
Pittsburg State University, BM
Pratt Community College, A
Seward County Community College, A
Tabor College, B
University of Kansas, BMD
University of Saint Mary, B
Washburn University, B
Wichita State University, BM

Kentucky

Asbury College, B
Ashland Community and Technical College, A
Bellarmine University, B
Big Sandy Community and Technical College, A
Brescia University, B
Campbellsville University, B
Draughons Junior College, A
Eastern Kentucky University, B
Georgetown College, B
Jefferson Community and Technical College, A
Kentucky Wesleyan College, B
Lexington Community College, A
Madisonville Community College, A
Maysville Community and Technical College, A
Morehead State University, B
Murray State University, BM
National College of Business & Technology
   (Danville), A
National College of Business & Technology
   (Florence), A
National College of Business & Technology
   (Lexington), A
National College of Business & Technology
   (Louisville), A
National College of Business & Technology
   (Pikeville), A
National College of Business & Technology
   (Richmond), A
Northern Kentucky University, BM
St. Catharine College, A
Southwestern College of Business, A
Spalding University, B

Spencerian College, A
Sullivan University, AB
Thomas More College, AB
Transylvania University, B
Union College, B
University of the Cumberlands, B
University of Kentucky, BM
University of Louisville, BM
West Kentucky Community and Technical College, A
Western Kentucky University, B

Louisiana

Centenary College of Louisiana, B
Delgado Community College, A
Dillard University, B
Elaine P. Nunez Community College, A
Grambling State University, B
Louisiana College, B
Louisiana State University and Agricultural and
   Mechanical College, BMD
Louisiana State University in Shreveport, B
Louisiana Tech University, BMD
Loyola University New Orleans, B
McNeese State University, B
Nicholls State University, B
Northwestern State University of Louisiana, B
Our Lady of Holy Cross College, B
Southeastern Louisiana University, B
Southern University and Agricultural and Mechanical
   College, BM
Southern University at New Orleans, B
Southern University at Shreveport, A
Tulane University, B
University of Louisiana at Lafayette, B
University of Louisiana at Monroe, B
University of New Orleans, BM
University of Phoenix-Louisiana Campus, BM
Xavier University of Louisiana, B

Maine

Andover College, A
Beal College, A
Central Maine Community College, A
Husson College, AB
Kennebec Valley Community College, A
Northern Maine Community College, A
Saint Joseph's College of Maine, B
Thomas College, AB
University of Maine, M
The University of Maine at Augusta, B
University of Maine at Machias, B
University of Maine at Presque Isle, B
University of Southern Maine, BMO
York County Community College, A

Maryland

Anne Arundel Community College, A
Baltimore City Community College, A
Bowie State University, B
Carroll Community College, A
Cecil Community College, A
Chesapeake College, A
College of Southern Maryland, A
Columbia Union College, AB
Frederick Community College, A
Frostburg State University, B
Hagerstown Business College, A
Howard Community College, A
Loyola College in Maryland, B
Morgan State University, B
Mount St. Mary's University, B
Prince George's Community College, A
Salisbury University, B
Sojourner-Douglass College, B
Towson University, BM
University of Baltimore, BM
University of Maryland, College Park, B
University of Maryland Eastern Shore, B
University of Maryland University College, BMO
University of Phoenix-Maryland Campus, B
Villa Julie College, AB

Massachusetts

American International College, B
Assumption College, B
Atlantic Union College, B

Babson College, B
Bay State College, A
Becker College, AB
Bentley College, BMO
Boston College, BM
Boston University, BDO
Bridgewater State College, BM
Bristol Community College, A
Bunker Hill Community College, A
Cape Cod Community College, A
Clark University, M
College of the Holy Cross, B
Elms College, B
Fisher College, A
Fitchburg State College, BM
Framingham State College, B
Gordon College, B
Greenfield Community College, A
Holyoke Community College, A
Lasell College, B
Marian Court College, A
Massachusetts Bay Community College, A
Massachusetts College of Liberal Arts, B
Massasoit Community College, A
Middlesex Community College, A
Mount Wachusett Community College, A
New England College of Finance, A
Newbury College, AB
Nichols College, BM
North Shore Community College, A
Northeastern University, BMO
Northern Essex Community College, A
Quincy College, A
Quinsigamond Community College, A
Roxbury Community College, A
Salem State College, B
Simmons College, B
Springfield Technical Community College, A
Stonehill College, BM
Suffolk University, BMO
University of Massachusetts Amherst, BM
University of Massachusetts Dartmouth, BO
University of Phoenix-Boston Campus, M
Western New England College, BM
Westfield State College, B
Worcester State College, M

Michigan

Adrian College, B
Alma College, B
Alpena Community College, A
Andrews University, BM
Aquinas College, B
Baker College of Allen Park, A
Baker College of Auburn Hills, AB
Baker College of Cadillac, AB
Baker College of Clinton Township, A
Baker College of Flint, AB
Baker College of Jackson, AB
Baker College of Muskegon, AB
Baker College of Owosso, AB
Baker College of Port Huron, AB
Bay de Noc Community College, A
Calvin College, B
Central Michigan University, BM
Cleary University, BM
Cornerstone University, B
Davenport University (Dearborn), ABM
Davenport University (Midland), A
Delta College, A
Eastern Michigan University, BM
Ferris State University, AB
Gogebic Community College, A
Grace Bible College, B
Grand Valley State University, BM
Henry Ford Community College, A
Hillsdale College, B
Hope College, B
Kellogg Community College, A
Kettering University, B
Kirtland Community College, A
Kuyper College, B
Lake Superior State University, AB
Lansing Community College, A
Lewis College of Business, A
Macomb Community College, A

Madonna University, B
Marygrove College, A
Michigan State University, BMD
Michigan Technological University, B
Mid Michigan Community College, A
Monroe County Community College, A
Montcalm Community College, A
Muskegon Community College, A
North Central Michigan College, A
Northern Michigan University, B
Northwood University, AB
Oakland Community College, A
Oakland University, BMO
Olivet College, B
Rochester College, B
Saginaw Valley State University, B
St. Clair County Community College, A
Schoolcraft College, A
Siena Heights University, AB
Spring Arbor University, B
University of Detroit Mercy, B
University of Michigan-Dearborn, BM
University of Michigan-Flint, B
University of Phoenix-Metro Detroit Campus, B
University of Phoenix-West Michigan Campus, B
Walsh College of Accountancy and Business
    Administration, BM
Washtenaw Community College, A
Wayne County Community College District, A
Wayne State University, BM
West Shore Community College, A
Western Michigan University, BM

Minnesota

Academy College, A
Alexandria Technical College, A
Anoka-Ramsey Community College, A
Anoka-Ramsey Community College, Cambridge
    Campus, A
Anoka Technical College, A
Augsburg College, B
Bemidji State University, B
Central Lakes College, A
Century College, A
College of Saint Benedict, B
College of St. Catherine, B
The College of St. Scholastica, B
Concordia College, B
Concordia University, St. Paul, B
Dakota County Technical College, A
Duluth Business University, A
Globe College, AB
Gustavus Adolphus College, B
Inver Hills Community College, A
Itasca Community College, A
Lake Superior College, A
Metropolitan State University, B
Minneapolis Business College, A
Minnesota School of Business, AB
Minnesota School of Business-Brooklyn Center, AB
Minnesota School of Business-Plymouth, AB
Minnesota School of Business-Richfield, AB
Minnesota School of Business-St. Cloud, AB
Minnesota School of Business-Shakopee, AB
Minnesota State College-Southeast Technical, A
Minnesota State Community and Technical
    College-Fergus Falls, A
Minnesota State University Mankato, B
Minnesota State University Moorhead, B
Minnesota West Community and Technical
    College, A
National American University (Roseville), B
Normandale Community College, A
North Hennepin Community College, A
Northland Community and Technical College-Thief
    River Falls, A
Northwest Technical College, A
Northwestern College, B
Rasmussen College Eagan, A
Rasmussen College Eden Prairie, A
Rasmussen College Mankato, A
Rasmussen College St. Cloud, A
Ridgewater College, A
St. Cloud State University, B
St. Cloud Technical College, A
Saint John's University, B

Saint Mary's University of Minnesota, B
Saint Paul College-A Community & Technical
    College, A
South Central Technical College, A
Southwest Minnesota State University, AB
University of Minnesota, Crookston, AB
University of Minnesota, Duluth, B
University of Minnesota, Twin Cities Campus, BMD
University of St. Thomas, BM
Vermilion Community College, A
Winona State University, B

Mississippi

Alcorn State University, B
Belhaven College, B
Coahoma Community College, A
Copiah-Lincoln Community College, A
Delta State University, B
East Central Community College, A
East Mississippi Community College, A
Hinds Community College, A
Itawamba Community College, A
Jackson State University, BM
Jones County Junior College, A
Millsaps College, BM
Mississippi College, BM
Mississippi Delta Community College, A
Mississippi Gulf Coast Community College, A
Mississippi State University, BM
Mississippi University for Women, B
Mississippi Valley State University, B
Northeast Mississippi Community College, A
Northwest Mississippi Community College, A
Southwest Mississippi Community College, A
Tougaloo College, B
University of Mississippi, BMD
University of Southern Mississippi, BM

Missouri

Avila University, B
Central Methodist University, B
Central Missouri State University, M
College of the Ozarks, B
Columbia College, B
Culver-Stockton College, B
Drury University, B
East Central College, A
Evangel University, AB
Fontbonne University, B
Harris-Stowe State University, B
Hickey College, A
Lincoln University, BM
Lindenwood University, BM
Longview Community College, A
Maple Woods Community College, A
Maryville University of Saint Louis, BMO
Metropolitan Community College-Business &
    Technology College, A
Mineral Area College, A
Missouri Baptist University, B
Missouri Southern State University, AB
Missouri State University, BM
Missouri State University-West Plains, A
Missouri Valley College, B
Missouri Western State University, B
National American University, AB
North Central Missouri College, A
Northwest Missouri State University, BM
Ozarks Technical Community College, A
Park University, B
Penn Valley Community College, A
Saint Charles Community College, A
St. Louis Community College at Florissant Valley, A
St. Louis Community College at Forest Park, A
St. Louis Community College at Meramec, A
Saint Louis University, M
Sanford-Brown College (Fenton), A
Sanford-Brown College (Hazelwood), A
Sanford-Brown College (St. Charles), A
Southeast Missouri State University, BM
Southwest Baptist University, AB
Springfield College, A
State Fair Community College, A
Stephens College, B
Three Rivers Community College, A
Truman State University, BM

University of Missouri-Columbia, BMD
University of Missouri-Kansas City, BM
University of Missouri-St. Louis, BMO
Washington University in St. Louis, B
Webster University, B
Westminster College, B
William Jewell College, B
William Woods University, BM

Montana

Carroll College, B
Flathead Valley Community College, A
Montana State University, M
Montana State University-Billings, B
Montana State University-Great Falls College of
    Technology, A
Montana Tech of The University of Montana, B
Rocky Mountain College, B
University of Great Falls, B
The University of Montana-Missoula, BM

Nebraska

Bellevue University, B
Central Community College-Columbus Campus, A
Central Community College-Grand Island
    Campus, A
Central Community College-Hastings Campus, A
College of Saint Mary, A
Concordia University, B
Creighton University, B
Dana College, B
Doane College, B
Grace University, B
Hamilton College-Lincoln, A
Hamilton College-Omaha, A
Hastings College, B
Metropolitan Community College, A
Midland Lutheran College, AB
Nebraska Wesleyan University, B
Northeast Community College, A
Peru State College, B
Southeast Community College, Beatrice Campus, A
Union College, AB
University of Nebraska-Lincoln, BMDO
University of Nebraska at Omaha, BM
Wayne State College, B
York College, B

Nevada

Community College of Southern Nevada, A
Las Vegas College, A
Morrison University, AB
Truckee Meadows Community College, A
University of Nevada, Las Vegas, BM
University of Nevada, Reno, BM
University of Phoenix-Nevada Campus, B
Western Nevada Community College, A

New Hampshire

Franklin Pierce College, B
Hesser College, AB
McIntosh College, A
New England College, B
New Hampshire Community Technical College,
    Berlin/Laconia, A
New Hampshire Community Technical College,
    Manchester/Stratham, A
New Hampshire Community Technical College,
    Nashua/Claremont, A
New Hampshire Technical Institute, A
Plymouth State University, B
Saint Anselm College, B
Southern New Hampshire University, ABM
University of New Hampshire, BM

New Jersey

Atlantic Cape Community College, A
Bergen Community College, A
Berkeley College, A
Bloomfield College, B
Brookdale Community College, A
Burlington County College, A
Caldwell College, BM
Camden County College, A
Centenary College, BM

The College of New Jersey, B
Cumberland County College, A
Essex County College, A
Fairleigh Dickinson University, College at
    Florham, BM
Fairleigh Dickinson University, Metropolitan
    Campus, BMO
Felician College, B
Georgian Court University, B
Gloucester County College, A
Hudson County Community College, A
Kean University, BM
Mercer County Community College, A
Middlesex County College, A
Monmouth University, M
Montclair State University, M
New Jersey City University, M
Ocean County College, A
Passaic County Community College, A
Ramapo College of New Jersey, B
Raritan Valley Community College, A
Rider University, BM
Rowan University, B
Rutgers, The State University of New Jersey,
    Camden, B
Rutgers, The State University of New Jersey, New
    Brunswick/Piscataway, B
Rutgers, The State University of New Jersey,
    Newark, BMDO
Saint Peter's College, BMO
Salem Community College, A
Seton Hall University, BMO
Sussex County Community College, A
Warren County Community College, A
William Paterson University of New Jersey, B

New Mexico

Central New Mexico Community College, A
Clovis Community College, A
College of Santa Fe, B
College of the Southwest, B
Eastern New Mexico University, B
International Institute of the Americas, A
Luna Community College, A
National American University (Albuquerque), AB
New Mexico Highlands University, B
New Mexico Junior College, A
New Mexico Military Institute, A
New Mexico State University, BM
Santa Fe Community College, A
Southwestern Indian Polytechnic Institute, A
University of New Mexico, M
University of New Mexico-Gallup, A
University of New Mexico-Los Alamos Branch, A
University of Phoenix-New Mexico Campus, BM
Western New Mexico University, B

New York

Adelphi University, BM
Adirondack Community College, A
Alfred University, B
Berkeley College-New York City Campus, AB
Berkeley College-Westchester Campus, AB
Bernard M. Baruch College of the City University of
    New York, BMD
Borough of Manhattan Community College of the
    City University of New York, A
Bramson ORT College, A
Briarcliffe College, AB
Bronx Community College of the City University of
    New York, A
Brooklyn College of the City University of New
    York, BM
Bryant and Stratton College (Albany), A
Bryant and Stratton College, Amherst Campus, A
Bryant and Stratton College, Buffalo Campus, A
Bryant and Stratton College, Lackawanna
    Campus, A
Bryant and Stratton College, North Campus, A
Bryant and Stratton College (Rochester-Greece
    Campus), A
Bryant and Stratton College (Rochester-Henrietta
    Campus), A
Bryant and Stratton College (Syracuse), A
Canisius College, BM
Cayuga County Community College, A

Cazenovia College, B
Clarkson University, B
Clinton Community College, A
The College of Saint Rose, BM
College of Staten Island of the City University of
    New York, B
The College of Westchester, A
Columbia-Greene Community College, A
Cornell University, D
Corning Community College, A
Daemen College, B
Dominican College, B
Dowling College, B
Dutchess Community College, A
D'Youville College, B
Elmira Business Institute, A
Elmira College, B
Eugenio María de Hostos Community College of the
    City University of New York, A
Excelsior College, B
Finger Lakes Community College, A
Fiorello H. LaGuardia Community College of the
    City University of New York, A
Fordham University, BM
Fulton-Montgomery Community College, A
Genesee Community College, A
Globe Institute of Technology, B
Hartwick College, B
Herkimer County Community College, A
Hilbert College, B
Hofstra University, BMO
Houghton College, B
Hudson Valley Community College, A
Hunter College of the City University of New York, B
Interboro Institute, A
Iona College, B
Ithaca College, B
Jamestown Business College, A
Jamestown Community College, A
Jefferson Community College, A
Katharine Gibbs School (New York), A
Keuka College, B
Kingsborough Community College of the City
    University of New York, A
Le Moyne College, B
Lehman College of the City University of New
    York, BM
Long Island Business Institute, A
Long Island University, Brentwood Campus, B
Long Island University, Brooklyn Campus, BM
Long Island University, C.W. Post Campus, BMO
Manhattan College, B
Maria College, A
Marist College, B
Marymount Manhattan College, B
Medaille College, B
Medgar Evers College of the City University of New
    York, B
Mercy College, B
Molloy College, B
Monroe College (Bronx), AB
Monroe College (New Rochelle), AB
Monroe Community College, A
Mount Saint Mary College, B
Nassau Community College, A
Nazareth College of Rochester, B
New York City College of Technology of the City
    University of New York, A
New York Institute of Technology, BMO
New York University, BD
Niagara County Community College, A
Niagara University, B
Nyack College, BM
Olean Business Institute, A
Onondaga Community College, A
Orange County Community College, A
Pace University, BM
Plaza College, A
Queens College of the City University of New
    York, BM
Queensborough Community College of the City
    University of New York, A
Roberts Wesleyan College, B
Rochester Business Institute, A
Rochester Institute of Technology, BM
Rockland Community College, A

Sage College of Albany, B
St. Bonaventure University, BMO
St. Francis College, B
St. John Fisher College, B
St. John's University, ABMO
St. Joseph's College, New York, B
St. Joseph's College, Suffolk Campus, B
St. Thomas Aquinas College, B
Schenectady County Community College, A
Siena College, B
State University of New York at Binghamton, BMD
State University of New York at Buffalo, M
State University of New York College of Agriculture
    and Technology at Cobleskill, A
State University of New York College of Agriculture
    and Technology at Morrisville, A
State University of New York College at
    Brockport, B
State University of New York College at Geneseo, B
State University of New York College at Old
    Westbury, BM
State University of New York College at Oneonta, B
State University of New York College of Technology
    at Alfred, A
State University of New York College of Technology
    at Canton, A
State University of New York College of Technology
    at Delhi, A
State University of New York, Fredonia, B
State University of New York Institute of
    Technology, BM
State University of New York at New Paltz, BM
State University of New York at Oswego, B
State University of New York at Plattsburgh, B
Suffolk County Community College, A
Sullivan County Community College, A
Swedish Institute, College of Health Sciences, M
Syracuse University, BMDO
Taylor Business Institute, A
TCI-The College of Technology, A
Tompkins Cortland Community College, A
Touro College, B
Ulster County Community College, A
University at Albany, State University of New
    York, BM
Utica College, B
Wagner College, BM
Westchester Community College, A
Wood Tobe-Coburn School, A
Yeshiva University, B
York College of the City University of New York, B

North Carolina

Appalachian State University, BM
Barber-Scotia College, B
Barton College, B
Beaufort County Community College, A
Belmont Abbey College, B
Bennett College For Women, B
Caldwell Community College and Technical
    Institute, A
Campbell University, B
Central Carolina Community College, A
Central Piedmont Community College, A
Chowan University, B
Cleveland Community College, A
Coastal Carolina Community College, A
Craven Community College, A
Davidson County Community College, A
Durham Technical Community College, A
East Carolina University, B
Edgecombe Community College, A
Elizabeth City State University, B
Elon University, B
Fayetteville State University, B
Fayetteville Technical Community College, A
Forsyth Technical Community College, A
Gardner-Webb University, B
Gaston College, A
Greensboro College, B
Guilford College, B
Guilford Technical Community College, A
High Point University, B
James Sprunt Community College, A
Johnson & Wales University, AB
Lenoir Community College, A

Lenoir-Rhyne College, B
Livingstone College, B
Mars Hill College, B
Martin Community College, A
Mayland Community College, A
McDowell Technical Community College, A
Meredith College, B
Methodist College, AB
Mitchell Community College, A
Montgomery Community College, A
Mount Olive College, AB
Nash Community College, A
North Carolina Agricultural and Technical State
    University, B
North Carolina Central University, B
North Carolina State University, BM
North Carolina Wesleyan College, B
Pamlico Community College, A
Pfeiffer University, B
Piedmont Community College, A
Pitt Community College, A
Richmond Community College, A
Rockingham Community College, A
Rowan-Cabarrus Community College, A
Saint Augustine's College, B
Salem College, B
Sampson Community College, A
Sandhills Community College, A
Shaw University, B
South College-Asheville, A
Southwestern Community College, A
Surry Community College, A
Tri-County Community College, A
The University of North Carolina at Asheville, B
The University of North Carolina at Chapel Hill, MD
The University of North Carolina at Charlotte, BM
The University of North Carolina at Greensboro, BM
The University of North Carolina at Pembroke, B
The University of North Carolina Wilmington, BM
University of Phoenix-Charlotte Campus, M
Vance-Granville Community College, A
Wake Forest University, BM
Wake Technical Community College, A
Western Carolina University, BM
Western Piedmont Community College, A
Wilson Technical Community College, A
Wingate University, B
Winston-Salem State University, B

North Dakota

Aakers Business College, A
Cankdeska Cikana Community College, A
Dickinson State University, B
Fort Berthold Community College, A
Jamestown College, B
Lake Region State College, A
Minot State University, B
North Dakota State University, B
University of Mary, AB
University of North Dakota, B

Ohio

Ashland University, B
Baldwin-Wallace College, BM
Belmont Technical College, A
Bluffton University, B
Bowling Green State University, BM
Bradford School, A
Brown Mackie College-Akron, A
Brown Mackie College-Cincinnati, A
Bryant and Stratton College (Parma), A
Bryant and Stratton College (Willoughby Hills), A
Capital University, B
Case Western Reserve University, BMD
Cedarville University, B
Central Ohio Technical College, A
Central State University, B
Cincinnati State Technical and Community
    College, A
Clark State Community College, A
Cleveland State University, BMD
College of Mount St. Joseph, AB
Columbus State Community College, A
Cuyahoga Community College, A
David N. Myers University, AB
Davis College, A

Defiance College, B
Edison State Community College, A
Franciscan University of Steubenville, AB
Franklin University, AB
Gallipolis Career College, A
Heidelberg College, B
Hocking College, A
James A. Rhodes State College, A
Jefferson Community College, A
John Carroll University, BM
Kent State University, BMD
Kent State University, Ashtabula Campus, A
Kent State University, East Liverpool Campus, A
Kent State University, Salem Campus, A
Kent State University, Tuscarawas Campus, A
Lake Erie College, B
Lakeland Community College, A
Lorain County Community College, A
Lourdes College, B
Malone College, B
Marietta College, B
Marion Technical College, A
Miami-Jacobs College, A
Miami University, BM
Miami University Hamilton, B
Miami University-Middletown Campus, A
Mount Union College, B
Mount Vernon Nazarene University, B
Muskingum College, B
North Central State College, A
Northwest State Community College, A
Notre Dame College, BO
Ohio Business College (Lorain), A
Ohio Business College (Sandusky), A
Ohio Dominican University, B
Ohio Northern University, B
The Ohio State University, BMD
Ohio University-Eastern, A
Ohio University-Lancaster, A
Ohio Valley College of Technology, A
Ohio Wesleyan University, B
Otterbein College, B
Shawnee State University, A
Sinclair Community College, A
Southwestern College of Business (Cincinnati), A
Southwestern College of Business (Cincinnati), A
Southwestern College of Business (Dayton), A
Stark State College of Technology, A
Terra State Community College, A
Tiffin University, AB
Trumbull Business College, A
The University of Akron, BMO
The University of Akron-Wayne College, A
University of Cincinnati, ABMD
University of Cincinnati Clermont College, A
University of Cincinnati Raymond Walters College, A
University of Dayton, B
The University of Findlay, AB
University of Northwestern Ohio, AB
University of Phoenix-Cincinnati Campus, M
University of Rio Grande, AB
The University of Toledo, ABM
Urbana University, AB
Ursuline College, B
Walsh University, AB
Washington State Community College, A
Wilberforce University, B
Wilmington College, B
Wright State University, BM
Wright State University, Lake Campus, A
Xavier University, BM
Youngstown State University, ABM
Zane State College, A

Oklahoma

Bacone College, AB
Cameron University, B
Carl Albert State College, A
East Central University, B
Eastern Oklahoma State College, A
Langston University, B
Northeastern Oklahoma Agricultural and Mechanical
    College, A
Northeastern State University, BM
Northern Oklahoma College, A
Northwestern Oklahoma State University, B

Oklahoma Baptist University, B
Oklahoma Christian University, B
Oklahoma City Community College, A
Oklahoma City University, BM
Oklahoma Panhandle State University, B
Oklahoma State University, BMD
Oklahoma State University, Oklahoma City, A
Oklahoma State University, Okmulgee, A
Oklahoma Wesleyan University, AB
Oral Roberts University, BM
Rogers State University, A
Rose State College, A
St. Gregory's University, B
Seminole State College, A
Southeastern Oklahoma State University, B
Southern Nazarene University, B
Southwestern Oklahoma State University, B
Tulsa Community College, A
University of Central Oklahoma, B
University of Oklahoma, BM
University of Phoenix-Oklahoma City Campus, BM
University of Phoenix-Tulsa Campus, B
University of Tulsa, B

Oregon

Blue Mountain Community College, A
Central Oregon Community College, A
Chemeketa Community College, A
Clackamas Community College, A
Clatsop Community College, A
Corban College, B
Eastern Oregon University, B
Heald College-Portland, A
Lane Community College, A
Linfield College, B
Linn-Benton Community College, A
Mt. Hood Community College, A
Oregon Institute of Technology, B
Pacific University, B
Pioneer Pacific College, A
Portland Community College, A
Portland State University, B
Southern Oregon University, B
Southwestern Oregon Community College, A
Tillamook Bay Community College, A
Umpqua Community College, A
University of Oregon, BMD
University of Portland, B

Pennsylvania

Albright College, B
Alvernia College, AB
Arcadia University, B
Berean Institute, A
Bloomsburg University of Pennsylvania, B
Bucknell University, B
Bucks County Community College, A
Butler County Community College, A
Cabrini College, B
California University of Pennsylvania, AB
Cambria-Rowe Business College (Johnstown), A
Carlow University, B
Carnegie Mellon University, D
Cedar Crest College, B
Central Pennsylvania College, A
Chatham College, B
Chestnut Hill College, AB
Clarion University of Pennsylvania, B
College Misericordia, B
Commonwealth Technical Institute, A
Community College of Beaver County, A
Community College of Philadelphia, A
Consolidated School of Business (Lancaster), A
Consolidated School of Business (York), A
Delaware Valley College, B
DeSales University, B
Drexel University, BM
DuBois Business College, A
Duff's Business Institute, A
Duquesne University, B
Eastern University, B
Elizabethtown College, B
Erie Business Center, Main, A
Erie Business Center South, A
Gannon University, BO
Geneva College, B

Gettysburg College, B
Grove City College, B
Gwynedd-Mercy College, AB
Harrisburg Area Community College, A
Holy Family University, B
ICM School of Business & Medical Careers, A
Immaculata University, AB
Indiana University of Pennsylvania, B
Juniata College, B
Keystone College, AB
King's College, B
Kutztown University of Pennsylvania, B
La Roche College, B
La Salle University, B
Lansdale School of Business, A
Laurel Business Institute, A
Lebanon Valley College, AB
Lehigh Carbon Community College, A
Lehigh University, BM
Lehigh Valley College, A
Lincoln University, B
Lock Haven University of Pennsylvania, B
Luzerne County Community College, A
Lycoming College, B
Manor College, A
Mansfield University of Pennsylvania, B
Marywood University, B
McCann School of Business & Technology, A
Mercyhurst College, B
Messiah College, B
Montgomery County Community College, A
Moravian College, B
Mount Aloysius College, AB
Muhlenberg College, B
Neumann College, B
Newport Business Institute (Lower Burrell), A
Pace Institute, A
Peirce College, A
Pennsylvania College of Technology, B
Pennsylvania Highland Community College, A
The Pennsylvania State University Abington
   College, B
The Pennsylvania State University Altoona
   College, B
The Pennsylvania State University Beaver Campus
   of the Commonwealth College, B
The Pennsylvania State University Berks Campus of
   the Berks-Lehigh Valley College, B
The Pennsylvania State University Delaware County
   Campus of the Commonwealth College, B
The Pennsylvania State University DuBois Campus
   of the Commonwealth College, B
The Pennsylvania State University at Erie, The
   Behrend College, B
The Pennsylvania State University Fayette Campus
   of the Commonwealth College, B
The Pennsylvania State University Hazleton
   Campus of the Commonwealth College, B
The Pennsylvania State University, Lehigh Valley
   Campus of the Berks-Lehigh Valley College, B
The Pennsylvania State University McKeesport
   Campus of the Commonwealth College, B
The Pennsylvania State University Mont Alto
   Campus of the Commonwealth College, B
The Pennsylvania State University New Kensington
   Campus of the Commonwealth College, B
The Pennsylvania State University Schuylkill
   Campus of the Capital College, B
The Pennsylvania State University Shenango
   Campus of the Commonwealth College, B
The Pennsylvania State University University Park
   Campus, BMD
The Pennsylvania State University Wilkes-Barre
   Campus of the Commonwealth College, B
The Pennsylvania State University Worthington
   Scranton Campus of the Commonwealth
   College, B
The Pennsylvania State University York Campus of
   the Commonwealth College, B
Philadelphia University, B
Point Park University, AB
Reading Area Community College, A
Robert Morris University, BM
Rosemont College, B
Saint Francis University, AB
Saint Joseph's University, ABM

Saint Vincent College, BM
Seton Hill University, B
Shippensburg University of Pennsylvania, B
South Hills School of Business & Technology
   (Altoona), A
South Hills School of Business & Technology (State
   College), A
Susquehanna University, B
Temple University, BMD
Thiel College, AB
Thompson Institute, A
University of Pennsylvania, BMD
University of Pittsburgh, B
University of Pittsburgh at Greensburg, B
University of Pittsburgh at Johnstown, B
University of Pittsburgh at Titusville, A
The University of Scranton, BM
Villanova University, BM
Washington & Jefferson College, B
Waynesburg College, B
West Chester University of Pennsylvania, B
Westminster College, B
Westmoreland County Community College, A
Widener University, BM
Wilkes University, BM
Wilson College, AB
York College of Pennsylvania, B
Yorktowne Business Institute, A

Puerto Rico

American University of Puerto Rico, AB
Bayamon Central University, BM
Caribbean University, AB
Huertas Junior College, A
Humacao Community College, A
Instituto Comercial de Puerto Rico Junior College, A
Inter American University of Puerto Rico, Aguadilla
   Campus, AB
Inter American University of Puerto Rico, Arecibo
   Campus, AB
Inter American University of Puerto Rico,
   Barranquitas Campus, AB
Inter American University of Puerto Rico, Bayamón
   Campus, AB
Inter American University of Puerto Rico, Fajardo
   Campus, A
Inter American University of Puerto Rico, Guayama
   Campus, AB
Inter American University of Puerto Rico,
   Metropolitan Campus, ABM
Inter American University of Puerto Rico, Ponce
   Campus, AB
Inter American University of Puerto Rico, San
   Germán Campus, ABM
Pontifical Catholic University of Puerto Rico, BM
Ramírez College of Business and Technology, A
Technological College of San Juan, A
Universidad del Este, A
Universidad Metropolitana, BMO
Universidad del Turabo, BM
University of Phoenix-Puerto Rico Campus, M
University of Puerto Rico, Aguadilla University
   College, B
University of Puerto Rico at Arecibo, B
University of Puerto Rico at Bayamón, AB
University of Puerto Rico, Cayey University
   College, B
University of Puerto Rico at Humacao, AB
University of Puerto Rico, Mayagüez Campus, B
University of Puerto Rico at Ponce, AB
University of Puerto Rico, Río Piedras, B
University of the Sacred Heart, B

Rhode Island

Bryant University, BMO
Community College of Rhode Island, A
Johnson & Wales University, ABM
Providence College, B
Rhode Island College, BM
Roger Williams University, B
Salve Regina University, B
University of Rhode Island, BM

South Carolina

Aiken Technical College, A
Anderson University, B

Benedict College, B
Bob Jones University, B
Central Carolina Technical College, A
Charleston Southern University, BM
Clemson University, BM
Coastal Carolina University, B
College of Charleston, BM
Columbia College, B
Converse College, B
Florence-Darlington Technical College, A
Francis Marion University, B
Furman University, B
Greenville Technical College, A
Limestone College, B
Midlands Technical College, A
Northeastern Technical College, A
Orangeburg-Calhoun Technical College, A
Piedmont Technical College, A
South Carolina State University, B
South University, A
Southern Wesleyan University, B
Spartanburg Technical College, A
Technical College of the Lowcountry, A
Tri-County Technical College, A
Trident Technical College, A
University of South Carolina, BMO
Voorhees College, B
Wofford College, B
York Technical College, A

South Dakota

Augustana College, B
Black Hills State University, B
Colorado Technical University Sioux Falls
   Campus, AB
Dakota State University, B
Dakota Wesleyan University, B
Kilian Community College, A
Lake Area Technical Institute, A
Mitchell Technical Institute, A
Mount Marty College, AB
National American University (Rapid City), AB
National American University-Sioux Falls
   Branch, AB
Northern State University, B
Oglala Lakota College, A
Sinte Gleska University, A
Sisseton-Wahpeton Community College, A
Southeast Technical Institute, A
University of Sioux Falls, B
The University of South Dakota, BMO

Tennessee

Belmont University, B
Bethel College, B
Carson-Newman College, B
Chattanooga State Technical Community College, A
Columbia State Community College, A
Cumberland University, B
Draughons Junior College (Clarksville), A
Draughons Junior College (Nashville), A
East Tennessee State University, BM
Fisk University, B
Freed-Hardeman University, B
King College, B
Lambuth University, B
Lee University, B
LeMoyne-Owen College, B
Lincoln Memorial University, B
Lipscomb University, BM
Middle Tennessee State University, BM
Milligan College, B
Nashville State Technical Community College, A
National College of Business & Technology (Bristol)
   , A
Northeast State Technical Community College, A
Pellissippi State Technical Community College, A
Rhodes College, M
Roane State Community College, A
South College, A
Southern Adventist University, ABM
Southwest Tennessee Community College, A
Tennessee State University, B
Tennessee Technological University, B
Tennessee Wesleyan College, B
Trevecca Nazarene University, B

Tusculum College, B
Union University, B
University of Memphis, BMD
University of Phoenix-Nashville Campus, B
The University of Tennessee, BMD
The University of Tennessee at Chattanooga, M
The University of Tennessee at Martin, BM

Texas

Abilene Christian University, BM
Alvin Community College, A
Amarillo College, A
Amberton University, B
Angelina College, A
Angelo State University, BM
Argosy University/Dallas, M
Austin Community College, A
Baylor University, BMO
Blinn College, A
Brazosport College, A
Brookhaven College, A
Cedar Valley College, A
Cisco Junior College, A
Clarendon College, A
Coastal Bend College, A
Computer Career Center, A
Dallas Baptist University, BM
Del Mar College, A
East Texas Baptist University, B
Eastfield College, A
El Centro College, A
El Paso Community College, A
Frank Phillips College, A
Grayson County College, A
Hallmark Institute of Technology, A
Hardin-Simmons University, B
Hill College of the Hill Junior College District, A
Houston Baptist University, B
Houston Community College System, A
Howard College, A
Howard Payne University, B
Huston-Tillotson University, B
Jarvis Christian College, B
Kilgore College, A
Kingwood College, A
Lamar State College-Orange, A
Lamar University, BM
LeTourneau University, B
Lon Morris College, A
Lubbock Christian University, B
McLennan Community College, A
McMurry University, B
Midwestern State University, B
Mountain View College, A
Navarro College, A
North Harris College, A
North Lake College, A
Northeast Texas Community College, A
Northwood University, Texas Campus, AB
Odessa College, A
Our Lady of the Lake University of San Antonio, B
Paul Quinn College, B
Prairie View A&M University, BM
Richland College, A
St. Edward's University, BM
St. Mary's University of San Antonio, BM
St. Philip's College, A
Sam Houston State University, B
Schreiner University, B
South Plains College, A
South Texas College, A
Southern Methodist University, BM
Southwestern Adventist University, BM
Southwestern Assemblies of God University, B
Southwestern Christian College, A
Southwestern University, B
Stephen F. Austin State University, BM
Sul Ross State University, B
Tarleton State University, BM
Tarrant County College District, A
Texas A&M International University, BM
Texas A&M University, BMD
Texas A&M University-Commerce, B
Texas A&M University-Corpus Christi, BM
Texas A&M University-Kingsville, B
Texas A&M University-Texarkana, BM

Texas Christian University, BM
Texas Lutheran University, B
Texas Southern University, B
Texas Southmost College, A
Texas State University-San Marcos, BM
Texas Tech University, BMDO
Texas Wesleyan University, B
Texas Woman's University, B
Tomball College, A
Trinity University, BM
Trinity Valley Community College, A
Tyler Junior College, A
University of Dallas, M
University of Houston, BMD
University of Houston-Clear Lake, BM
University of Houston-Downtown, B
University of Houston-Victoria, B
University of the Incarnate Word, B
University of Mary Hardin-Baylor, B
University of North Texas, BMD
University of Phoenix-Dallas Campus, M
University of Phoenix-Houston Campus, M
University of St. Thomas, B
The University of Texas at Arlington, BMD
The University of Texas at Austin, BMD
The University of Texas at Brownsville, B
The University of Texas at Dallas, BM
The University of Texas at El Paso, BM
The University of Texas-Pan American, B
The University of Texas of the Permian Basin, BM
The University of Texas at San Antonio, BMD
The University of Texas at Tyler, B
Vernon College, A
Victoria College, A
West Texas A&M University, BM
Western Texas College, A

United States Virgin Islands

University of the Virgin Islands, AB

Utah

Brigham Young University, BMO
California College for Health Sciences, AB
Dixie State College of Utah, A
LDS Business College, A
Mountain West College, A
Salt Lake Community College, A
Snow College, A
Southern Utah University, BM
Stevens-Henager College, A
University of Phoenix-Utah Campus, BM
University of Utah, BMD
Utah State University, BM
Utah Valley State College, AB
Weber State University, BM
Westminster College, B

Vermont

Castleton State College, B
Champlain College, AB
College of St. Joseph, AB
Community College of Vermont, A
Johnson State College, AB
Lyndon State College, B
Saint Michael's College, B

Virginia

Averett University, B
Blue Ridge Community College, A
Bluefield College, B
Bryant and Stratton College, Richmond, A
Bryant and Stratton College, Virginia Beach, A
Central Virginia Community College, A
Christopher Newport University, B
The College of William and Mary, M
Danville Community College, A
Eastern Mennonite University, B
ECPI College of Technology (Newport News), A
ECPI College of Technology (Virginia Beach), A
ECPI Technical College (Richmond), A
ECPI Technical College (Roanoke), A
Emory & Henry College, B
Ferrum College, B
George Mason University, B
Hampton University, B
James Madison University, BM

Liberty University, B
Longwood University, B
Lord Fairfax Community College, A
Lynchburg College, B
Marymount University, B
Mountain Empire Community College, A
National College of Business & Technology
  (Bluefield), A
National College of Business & Technology
  (Charlottesville), A
National College of Business & Technology
  (Danville), A
National College of Business & Technology
  (Harrisonburg), A
National College of Business & Technology
  (Lynchburg), A
National College of Business & Technology
  (Martinsville), A
National College of Business & Technology (Salem)
  , AB
New River Community College, A
Norfolk State University, B
Northern Virginia Community College, A
Old Dominion University, BM
Patrick Henry Community College, A
Piedmont Virginia Community College, A
Radford University, B
Randolph-Macon College, B
Rappahannock Community College, A
Southwest Virginia Community College, A
Stratford University, M
Thomas Nelson Community College, A
Tidewater Community College, A
University of Northern Virginia, M
University of Richmond, B
University of Virginia, M
The University of Virginia's College at Wise, B
Virginia Commonwealth University, BMD
Virginia Highlands Community College, A
Virginia Polytechnic Institute and State
  University, BMD
Virginia State University, B
Virginia Union University, B
Virginia Western Community College, A
Washington and Lee University, B
Wytheville Community College, A

Washington

Bellevue Community College, A
Central Washington University, BM
City University, BM
Eastern Washington University, B
Everett Community College, A
Gonzaga University, BMO
Highline Community College, A
Lake Washington Technical College, A
Lower Columbia College, A
Northwest University, B
Pacific Lutheran University, B
Peninsula College, A
Pierce College, A
Renton Technical College, A
Saint Martin's University, B
Seattle Central Community College, A
Seattle Pacific University, B
Seattle University, BM
Shoreline Community College, A
Skagit Valley College, A
South Puget Sound Community College, A
South Seattle Community College, A
Tacoma Community College, A
University of Phoenix-Washington Campus, B
University of Washington, B
Walla Walla College, B
Washington State University, BM
Wenatchee Valley College, A
Western Washington University, A
Whatcom Community College, A
Whitworth College, B
Yakima Valley Community College, A

West Virginia

Alderson-Broaddus College, B
Bethany College, B
Bluefield State College, AB

Community & Technical College at West Virginia University Institute of Technology, A
Concord University, B
Davis & Elkins College, B
Fairmont State University, AB
Glenville State College, B
Huntington Junior College, A
Marshall University, B
Mountain State University, B
New River Community and Technical College, A
Ohio Valley University, B
Potomac State College of West Virginia University, A
Shepherd University, B
Southern West Virginia Community and Technical College, A
University of Charleston, AB
West Liberty State College, B
West Virginia Business College (Wheeling), A
West Virginia Junior College (Bridgeport), A
West Virginia Junior College (Charleston), A
West Virginia Junior College (Morgantown), A
West Virginia State Community and Technical College, A
West Virginia State University, AB
West Virginia University, BM
West Virginia University Institute of Technology, B
West Virginia University at Parkersburg, A
West Virginia Wesleyan College, B
Wheeling Jesuit University, BM

Wisconsin

Blackhawk Technical College, A
Bryant and Stratton College, A
Cardinal Stritch University, B
Carroll College, B
Carthage College, B
Chippewa Valley Technical College, A
Concordia University Wisconsin, B
Edgewood College, B
Fox Valley Technical College, A
Gateway Technical College, A
Lakeland College, B
Lakeshore Technical College, A
Madison Area Technical College, A
Marian College of Fond du Lac, B
Marquette University, BM
Mid-State Technical College, A
Moraine Park Technical College, A
Mount Mary College, B
Nicolet Area Technical College, A
Northcentral Technical College, A
Northeast Wisconsin Technical College, A
St. Norbert College, B
Silver Lake College, B
Southwest Wisconsin Technical College, A
University of Wisconsin-Eau Claire, B
University of Wisconsin-Green Bay, B
University of Wisconsin-La Crosse, B
University of Wisconsin-Madison, B
University of Wisconsin-Milwaukee, B
University of Wisconsin-Oshkosh, B
University of Wisconsin-Parkside, B
University of Wisconsin-Platteville, B
University of Wisconsin-River Falls, B
University of Wisconsin-Stevens Point, B
University of Wisconsin-Superior, B
University of Wisconsin-Whitewater, BM
Viterbo University, B
Waukesha County Technical College, A
Western Technical College, A
Wisconsin Indianhead Technical College, A

Wyoming

Casper College, A
Central Wyoming College, A
Eastern Wyoming College, A
Laramie County Community College, A
Northwest College, A
University of Wyoming, BM
Western Wyoming Community College, A

Alberta

Athabasca University, B
University of Alberta, BD
University of Calgary, B

University of Lethbridge, BMO

British Columbia

British Columbia Institute of Technology, AB
Kwantlen University College, B
Thompson Rivers University, B
The University of British Columbia, BD
University of Northern British Columbia, B

Manitoba

University of Manitoba, B

New Brunswick

Mount Allison University, B
Université de Moncton, B
University of New Brunswick Fredericton, B
University of New Brunswick Saint John, B

Newfoundland and Labrador

Memorial University of Newfoundland, B

Nova Scotia

Cape Breton University, B
Dalhousie University, B
Mount Saint Vincent University, B
St. Francis Xavier University, B
Saint Mary's University, B

Ontario

Brock University, BM
Carleton University, B
Lakehead University, B
Redeemer University College, B
University of Ottawa, B
University of Toronto, BMDO
University of Waterloo, BMD
The University of Western Ontario, M
University of Windsor, B
York University, B

Quebec

Bishop's University, B
Concordia University, BO
HEC Montreal, BMO
McGill University, BMO
Université Laval, MO
Université du Québec en Abitibi-Témiscamingue, B
Université du Québec àChicoutimi, B
Université du Québec àMontréal, BMO
Université du Québec en Outaouais, BO
Université du Québec àRimouski, B
Université du Québec àTrois-Rivières, BO
Université de Sherbrooke, BM

Saskatchewan

Briercrest College, B
University of Regina, B
University of Saskatchewan, BM

ACCOUNTING AND BUSINESS/MANAGEMENT

Alabama

Miles College, B

Alaska

Alaska Pacific University, B

Arkansas

ITT Technical Institute, B

California

Westwood College-Anaheim, B
Westwood College-Inland Empire, B
Westwood College-Los Angeles, B

Colorado

National American University (Colorado Springs), AB
Westwood College-Denver North, B

Westwood College-Denver South, B

Florida

Florida Agricultural and Mechanical University, B
ITT Technical Institute (Miami), B

Illinois

Illinois State University, B
Westwood College-Chicago Du Page, B
Westwood College-Chicago Loop Campus, AB
Westwood College-Chicago O'Hare Airport, B
Westwood College-Chicago River Oaks, B

Indiana

ITT Technical Institute (Fort Wayne), B
ITT Technical Institute (Indianapolis), B
Sawyer College (Hammond), A

Kansas

Central Christian College of Kansas, AB

Louisiana

ITT Technical Institute, B

Massachusetts

Babson College, B

Missouri

ITT Technical Institute (Árnold), B
ITT Technical Institute (Earth City), B
ITT Technical Institute (Kansas City), B

Montana

University of Great Falls, B

Nebraska

ITT Technical Institute, B

North Carolina

Campbell University, B

Ohio

Antonelli College, A
ITT Technical Institute (Dayton), A
ITT Technical Institute (Hilliard), A
ITT Technical Institute (Norwood), A
ITT Technical Institute (Strongsville), A
Ohio University-Southern Campus, A

Pennsylvania

Chestnut Hill College, AB
Keystone College, B
Mount Aloysius College, AB
Peirce College, A

South Carolina

North Greenville College, B

Tennessee

ITT Technical Institute (Knoxville), B
ITT Technical Institute (Memphis), B
ITT Technical Institute (Nashville), B

Texas

Montgomery College, A

Utah

LDS Business College, A

Virginia

ITT Technical Institute (Norfolk), B

West Virginia

Davis & Elkins College, A
Mountain State College, A

ACCOUNTING AND COMPUTER SCIENCE

California

California State University, Chico, B

San Jose State University, B

Maine

Husson College, B

New York

Fordham University, B

Ohio

Columbus State Community College, A

Washington

Western Washington University, B

ACCOUNTING AND FINANCE

Colorado

Jones International University, B

Connecticut

Albertus Magnus College, B

Florida

Palm Beach Atlantic University, B

Illinois

American InterContinental University Online, B

Iowa

Drake University, B

Massachusetts

Babson College, B

Michigan

Jackson Community College, A
Kettering University, B

New York

Canisius College, B

North Carolina

Campbell University, B

North Dakota

University of North Dakota, B

Ohio

Hiram College, B
Wilberforce University, B

Pennsylvania

Saint Francis University, B

Ontario

University of Waterloo, B
University of Windsor, B

ACCOUNTING AND RELATED SERVICES

California

California State University, Sacramento, B
Saint Mary's College of California, B

Indiana

Saint Mary-of-the-Woods College, B

Michigan

Central Michigan University, B

Mississippi

Virginia College at Jackson, A

Missouri

Maryville University of Saint Louis, B
Park University, AB

Montana

Montana State University-Billings, A
Rocky Mountain College, B

New York

State University of New York at Oswego, B

North Carolina

East Carolina University, B

Pennsylvania

Central Pennsylvania College, A
Duquesne University, B
Keystone College, B
Peirce College, A

Utah

Brigham Young University, B

Wisconsin

Northeast Wisconsin Technical College, A

ACCOUNTING TECHNOLOGY/TECHNICIAN AND BOOKKEEPING

Alabama

Bishop State Community College, A
H. Councill Trenholm State Technical College, A
Jefferson State Community College, A
Virginia College at Birmingham, A

Alaska

Ilisagvik College, A
University of Alaska Fairbanks, A

Arizona

Glendale Community College, A
Northland Pioneer College, A

California

Cuyamaca College, A

Colorado

Institute of Business & Medical Careers, A
Pikes Peak Community College, A

Connecticut

Goodwin College, A

Florida

Brown Mackie College-Miami, A
Central Florida Community College, A
Miami Dade College, A
North Florida Community College, A
Polk Community College, A
St. Johns River Community College, A
St. Petersburg College, A
Tallahassee Community College, A

Georgia

Brown Mackie College-Atlanta, A
Georgia Southwestern State University, A

Idaho

Lewis-Clark State College, AB

Illinois

College of Lake County, A
Elgin Community College, A
John Wood Community College, A
Lake Land College, A
McHenry County College, A
Parkland College, A
Robert Morris College, A
St. Augustine College, A
Waubonsee Community College, A

Indiana

Brown Mackie College-Fort Wayne, A
Brown Mackie College-Merrillville, A

Brown Mackie College-Michigan City, A
International Business College (Indianapolis), A
Ivy Tech Community College-Bloomington, A
Ivy Tech Community College-Central Indiana, A
Ivy Tech Community College-Columbus, A
Ivy Tech Community College-East Central, A
Ivy Tech Community College-Kokomo, A
Ivy Tech Community College-Lafayette, A
Ivy Tech Community College-North Central, A
Ivy Tech Community College-Northeast, A
Ivy Tech Community College-Northwest, A
Ivy Tech Community College-Southeast, A
Ivy Tech Community College-Southern Indiana, A
Ivy Tech Community College-Southwest, A
Ivy Tech Community College-Wabash Valley, A
Ivy Tech Community College-Whitewater, A

Iowa

Iowa Lakes Community College, A
North Iowa Area Community College, A

Kansas

Johnson County Community College, A

Kentucky

Brown Mackie College-Hopkinsville, A
Brown Mackie College-Louisville, A
Brown Mackie College-Northern Kentucky, A
Madisonville Community College, A

Louisiana

Louisiana Technical College, A

Maryland

Allegany College of Maryland, A
Hagerstown Community College, A
Harford Community College, A
Montgomery College, A
Wor-Wic Community College, A

Michigan

Baker College of Flint, A
Bay de Noc Community College, A
Cleary University, A
Davenport University (Midland), A
Kalamazoo Valley Community College, A
Kellogg Community College, A
Lake Michigan College, A
Mott Community College, A
Northwestern Michigan College, A
Southwestern Michigan College, A

Minnesota

Dakota County Technical College, A
Minneapolis Community and Technical College, A
St. Cloud Technical College, A

Missouri

Blue River Community College, A
Metropolitan Community College-Business & Technology College, A
Moberly Area Community College, A

Montana

Montana State University-Billings, A
The University of Montana-Helena College of Technology, A
The University of Montana-Missoula, A

Nevada

Western Nevada Community College, A

New Jersey

Essex County College, A
Gloucester County College, A
Union County College, A

New Mexico

San Juan College, A

New York

Broome Community College, A
Canisius College, B
Mohawk Valley Community College, A

Nassau Community College, A
New York Institute of Technology, A

North Carolina

Alamance Community College, A
Asheville-Buncombe Technical Community
    College, A
Cape Fear Community College, A
Catawba Valley Community College, A
Johnston Community College, A
Randolph Community College, A
South Piedmont Community College, A
Stanly Community College, A
Wayne Community College, A
Wilkes Community College, A

North Dakota

Lake Region State College, A
Minot State University-Bottineau Campus, A
Turtle Mountain Community College, A
Williston State College, A

Ohio

Bowling Green State University-Firelands College, A
Brown Mackie College-Findlay, A
Brown Mackie College-North Canton, A
Columbus State Community College, A
Kent State University, Geauga Campus, A
Ohio University, A
Ohio University-Southern Campus, A
Owens Community College, A
Southern State Community College, A
The University of Akron, A
The University of Akron-Wayne College, A
University of Rio Grande, A
Wright State University, A

Oklahoma

Western Oklahoma State College, A

Oregon

Tillamook Bay Community College, A

Pennsylvania

Community College of Allegheny County, A
Delaware County Community College, A
Gannon University, A
Lackawanna College, A
Lehigh Carbon Community College, A
Montgomery County Community College, A
Northampton County Area Community College, A
Peirce College, A
Penn Foster Career School, A
Pennsylvania College of Technology, A

Rhode Island

Bryant University, B

Tennessee

Pellissippi State Technical Community College, A

Texas

Brown Mackie College-Fort Worth, A
College of the Mainland, A
Del Mar College, A
Kilgore College, A
Lamar State College-Port Arthur, A
Lee College, A

Utah

LDS Business College, A

Virginia

J. Sargeant Reynolds Community College, A
National College of Business & Technology (Salem)
    , A

Washington

Bates Technical College, A
Big Bend Community College, A
Clark College, A
Clover Park Technical College, A
Edmonds Community College, A
Grays Harbor College, A

Green River Community College, A
Lower Columbia College, A
North Seattle Community College, A
Olympic College, A
Spokane Community College, A
Spokane Falls Community College, A
Walla Walla Community College, A

West Virginia

Marshall Community and Technical College, A
West Virginia Northern Community College, A

Wisconsin

Milwaukee Area Technical College, A
Northeast Wisconsin Technical College, A

Wyoming

Central Wyoming College, A

British Columbia

British Columbia Institute of Technology, A

ACOUSTICS

District of Columbia

The Catholic University of America, MD

Pennsylvania

The Pennsylvania State University University Park
    Campus, MD

ACTING

California

California Institute of the Arts, B
California State University, Long Beach, B
Santa Barbara City College, A
University of Southern California, B

Connecticut

University of Connecticut, B

Florida

Barry University, B
Florida State University, B
New World School of the Arts, AB
Palm Beach Atlantic University, B

Illinois

Columbia College Chicago, B
DePaul University, B

Iowa

Coe College, B
Drake University, B
University of Northern Iowa, B

Kansas

Central Christian College of Kansas, A

Massachusetts

Boston University, B
Emerson College, B
Framingham State College, B
Simon's Rock College of Bard, B

Michigan

Western Michigan University, B

Minnesota

St. Cloud State University, B

Missouri

College of the Ozarks, B

Montana

Carroll College, B

New Hampshire

Keene State College, B

New Mexico

College of Santa Fe, B

New York

Bard College, B
Ithaca College, B
Long Island University, C.W. Post Campus, B
Marymount Manhattan College, B
Sarah Lawrence College, B
State University of New York College at
    Brockport, B
Syracuse University, B

North Carolina

Campbell University, B
Greensboro College, B

Ohio

Bowling Green State University, B
Kent State University, B
Ohio University, B
The University of Akron, B

Oregon

George Fox University, B

Pennsylvania

Arcadia University, B
Northampton County Area Community College, A
The Pennsylvania State University Abington
    College, B
The Pennsylvania State University Altoona
    College, B
The Pennsylvania State University Beaver Campus
    of the Commonwealth College, B
The Pennsylvania State University Berks Campus of
    the Berks-Lehigh Valley College, B
The Pennsylvania State University Delaware County
    Campus of the Commonwealth College, B
The Pennsylvania State University DuBois Campus
    of the Commonwealth College, B
The Pennsylvania State University at Erie, The
    Behrend College, B
The Pennsylvania State University Fayette Campus
    of the Commonwealth College, B
The Pennsylvania State University Hazleton
    Campus of the Commonwealth College, B
The Pennsylvania State University, Lehigh Valley
    Campus of the Berks-Lehigh Valley College, B
The Pennsylvania State University McKeesport
    Campus of the Commonwealth College, B
The Pennsylvania State University Mont Alto
    Campus of the Commonwealth College, B
The Pennsylvania State University New Kensington
    Campus of the Commonwealth College, B
The Pennsylvania State University Schuylkill
    Campus of the Capital College, B
The Pennsylvania State University Shenango
    Campus of the Commonwealth College, B
The Pennsylvania State University University Park
    Campus, B
The Pennsylvania State University Wilkes-Barre
    Campus of the Commonwealth College, B
The Pennsylvania State University Worthington
    Scranton Campus of the Commonwealth
    College, B
The Pennsylvania State University York Campus of
    the Commonwealth College, B
Seton Hill University, B
Temple University, B
The University of the Arts, B

South Carolina

Coker College, B

Texas

Baylor University, B
KD Studio, A
Texas Tech University, B

Trinity University, B

Utah

Brigham Young University, B

Vermont

Bennington College, B
Johnson State College, B

Virginia

Old Dominion University, B
Shenandoah University, B

Washington

Cornish College of the Arts, B

Wyoming

Central Wyoming College, A

Newfoundland and Labrador

Memorial University of Newfoundland, B

Nova Scotia

Dalhousie University, B

Ontario

Ryerson University, B
University of Windsor, B
York University, B

Quebec

Concordia University, B

Saskatchewan

University of Regina, B

ACTUARIAL SCIENCE

California

The Master's College and Seminary, B

Connecticut

Quinnipiac University, B
University of Connecticut, BMD

Florida

Florida Agricultural and Mechanical University, B
University of Central Florida, BMO

Georgia

Georgia State University, BM

Illinois

Bradley University, B
Elmhurst College, B
North Central College, B
Roosevelt University, B
University of Illinois at Urbana-Champaign, B

Indiana

Ball State University, BM
Butler University, B
Indiana University Northwest, B
Valparaiso University, B

Iowa

Drake University, B
Northwestern College, B*
The University of Iowa, BMD
University of Northern Iowa, B

Kansas

Tabor College, B

Kentucky

Bellarmine University, B

Massachusetts

Boston University, M
Worcester Polytechnic Institute, B

Michigan

Central Michigan University, B
Eastern Michigan University, B

Ferris State University, B
Michigan Technological University, B
University of Michigan-Flint, B

Minnesota

University of Minnesota, Duluth, B
University of Minnesota, Twin Cities Campus, B
University of St. Thomas, B

Missouri

Maryville University of Saint Louis, B

Nebraska

University of Nebraska-Lincoln, BM

New Jersey

New Jersey Institute of Technology, B
Rider University, B

New York

Bernard M. Baruch College of the City University of
  New York, B
Hofstra University, B
New York University, B
Queens College of the City University of New
  York, B
St. John's University, BM
University at Albany, State University of New York, B

North Dakota

Jamestown College, B

Ohio

The Ohio State University, B

Oklahoma

University of Central Oklahoma, B

Oregon

Oregon State University, B

Pennsylvania

Harrisburg Area Community College, A
Lebanon Valley College, B
Lincoln University, B
Lycoming College, B
The Pennsylvania State University Abington
  College, B
The Pennsylvania State University Altoona
  College, B
The Pennsylvania State University Beaver Campus
  of the Commonwealth College, B
The Pennsylvania State University Berks Campus of
  the Berks-Lehigh Valley College, B
The Pennsylvania State University Delaware County
  Campus of the Commonwealth College, B
The Pennsylvania State University DuBois Campus
  of the Commonwealth College, B
The Pennsylvania State University at Erie, The
  Behrend College, B
The Pennsylvania State University Fayette Campus
  of the Commonwealth College, B
The Pennsylvania State University Hazleton
  Campus of the Commonwealth College, B
The Pennsylvania State University, Lehigh Valley
  Campus of the Berks-Lehigh Valley College, B
The Pennsylvania State University McKeesport
  Campus of the Commonwealth College, B
The Pennsylvania State University Mont Alto
  Campus of the Commonwealth College, B
The Pennsylvania State University New Kensington
  Campus of the Commonwealth College, B
The Pennsylvania State University Schuylkill
  Campus of the Capital College, B
The Pennsylvania State University Shenango
  Campus of the Commonwealth College, B
The Pennsylvania State University University Park
  Campus, B
The Pennsylvania State University Wilkes-Barre
  Campus of the Commonwealth College, B
The Pennsylvania State University Worthington
  Scranton Campus of the Commonwealth
  College, B

The Pennsylvania State University York Campus of
  the Commonwealth College, B
Robert Morris University, B
Saint Joseph's University, B
Seton Hill University, B
Temple University, BM
Thiel College, B
University of Pennsylvania, B

Rhode Island

Bryant University, B

South Carolina

Bob Jones University, B

Tennessee

Southern Adventist University, B

Texas

The University of Texas at San Antonio, B

Utah

Brigham Young University, B

Wisconsin

Carroll College, B
University of Wisconsin-Madison, BM
University of Wisconsin-Stevens Point, B

Alberta

University of Calgary, B

British Columbia

Simon Fraser University, B

Manitoba

University of Manitoba, B

Ontario

University of Toronto, B
University of Waterloo, BM
The University of Western Ontario, B
York University, B

Quebec

Concordia University, B
Université Laval, B
Université de Montréal, B
Université du Québec àMontréal, O

Saskatchewan

University of Regina, B

ACUPUNCTURE AND ORIENTAL MEDICINE

Connecticut

University of Bridgeport, M

New York

New York College of Health Professions, M
Swedish Institute, College of Health Sciences, M

Washington

Bastyr University, MDO

ADMINISTRATION OF SPECIAL EDUCATION

Ohio

Wright State University, B

Vermont

Sterling College, B

ADMINISTRATIVE ASSISTANT AND SECRETARIAL SCIENCE

Alabama

Alabama Southern Community College, A
Alabama State University, AB

Bevill State Community College, A
Bishop State Community College, A
Central Alabama Community College, A
Chattahoochee Valley Community College, A
Enterprise-Ozark Community College, A
Faulkner University, A
Gadsden State Community College, A
George C. Wallace Community College, A
H. Councill Trenholm State Technical College, A
Herzing College, A
J. F. Drake State Technical College, A
James H. Faulkner State Community College, A
Jefferson Davis Community College, A
Jefferson State Community College, A
Lawson State Community College, A
Northeast Alabama Community College, A
Northwest-Shoals Community College, A
Oakwood College, AB
Reid State Technical College, A
Shelton State Community College, A
Southern Union State Community College, A
Virginia College at Birmingham, A
Virginia College at Huntsville, A
Wallace State Community College, A

Alaska

University of Alaska Anchorage, Kenai Peninsula
    College, A
University of Alaska Anchorage, Kodiak College, A
University of Alaska Anchorage, Matanuska-Susitna
    College, A
University of Alaska Fairbanks, A
University of Alaska, Prince William Sound
    Community College, A
University of Alaska Southeast, A
University of Alaska Southeast, Ketchikan
    Campus, A

Arizona

Arizona Western College, A
Central Arizona College, A
Chaparral College, A
Cochise College (Douglas), A
Cochise College (Sierra Vista), A
Diné College, A
Glendale Community College, A
Lamson College, A
Mesa Community College, A
Northland Pioneer College, A
Paradise Valley Community College, A
Phoenix College, A
Pima Community College, A
Scottsdale Community College, A
South Mountain Community College, A
Yavapai College, A

Arkansas

Arkansas State University, A
Arkansas Tech University, A
Henderson State University, A
National Park Community College, A
North Arkansas College, A
NorthWest Arkansas Community College, A
Ouachita Technical College, A
Ozarka College, A
Phillips Community College of the University of
    Arkansas, A
Pulaski Technical College, A
Rich Mountain Community College, A
South Arkansas Community College, A
Southern Arkansas University-Magnolia, A
University of Arkansas Community College at
    Morrilton, A
University of Arkansas at Fort Smith, A
Williams Baptist College, A

California

Allan Hancock College, A
American River College, A
Antelope Valley College, A
Bakersfield College, A
Barstow College, A
Butte College, A
Cañada College, A
Cerritos College, A
Chabot College, A

Chaffey College, A
Citrus College, A
College of Alameda, A
College of the Canyons, A
College of the Desert, A
College of Marin, A
College of the Redwoods, A
College of San Mateo, A
College of the Sequoias, A
Columbia College, A
Compton Community College, A
Contra Costa College, A
Crafton Hills College, A
Cuesta College, A
Cypress College, A
De Anza College, A
East Los Angeles College, A
El Camino College, A
Empire College, A
Feather River College, A
Fresno City College, A
Gavilan College, A
Glendale Community College, A
Golden West College, A
Grossmont College, A
Hartnell College, A
Heald College-Fresno, A
Heald College-Hayward, A
Heald College-Rancho Cordova, A
Heald College-San Francisco, A
Humphreys College, AB
Imperial Valley College, A
Irvine Valley College, A
Lake Tahoe Community College, A
Laney College, A
Las Positas College, A
Lassen Community College District, A
Long Beach City College, A
Los Angeles City College, A
Los Angeles Harbor College, A
Los Angeles Mission College, A
Los Angeles Southwest College, A
Los Angeles Valley College, A
Los Medanos College, A
Mendocino College, A
Merced College, A
Merritt College, A
MiraCosta College, A
Mission College, A
Modesto Junior College, A
Monterey Peninsula College, A
Mt. San Antonio College, A
Mt. San Jacinto College, A
Napa Valley College, A
Ohlone College, A
Orange Coast College, A
Oxnard College, A
Palo Verde College, A
Palomar College, A
Pasadena City College, A
Porterville College, A
Reedley College, A
Sacramento City College, A
Saddleback College, A
San Bernardino Valley College, A
San Diego City College, A
San Diego Mesa College, A
San Diego Miramar College, A
San Jose City College, A
Santa Ana College, A
Santa Barbara City College, A
Santa Monica College, A
Shasta College, A
Sierra College, A
Skyline College, A
Southwestern College, A
Taft College, A
Victor Valley College, A
West Hills Community College, A
West Los Angeles College, A
West Valley College, A
Yuba College, A

Colorado

Aims Community College, A
Arapahoe Community College, A

Blair College, A
Community College of Denver, A
Lamar Community College, A
Mesa State College, AB
Morgan Community College, A
Northeastern Junior College, A
Otero Junior College, A
Parks College (Denver), A
Pueblo Community College, A
Red Rocks Community College, A
Trinidad State Junior College, A

Connecticut

Asnuntuck Community College, A
Briarwood College, A
Capital Community College, A
Gibbs College, A
Housatonic Community College, A
Manchester Community College, A
Middlesex Community College, A
Naugatuck Valley Community College, A
Northwestern Connecticut Community College, A
Norwalk Community College, A
Quinebaug Valley Community College, A
Three Rivers Community College, A
Tunxis Community College, A

Delaware

Delaware Technical & Community College, Jack F.
    Owens Campus, A
Delaware Technical & Community College,
    Stanton/Wilmington Campus, A
Delaware Technical & Community College, Terry
    Campus, A

District of Columbia

University of the District of Columbia, A

Florida

Broward Community College, A
Clearwater Christian College, AB
Daytona Beach Community College, A
Florida Agricultural and Mechanical University, B
Florida Community College at Jacksonville, A
Florida National College, A
Gulf Coast Community College, A
Hillsborough Community College, A
Hobe Sound Bible College, A
Indian River Community College, A
Jones College (Jacksonville), AB
Lake City Community College, A
Manatee Community College, A
Miami Dade College, A
Okaloosa-Walton College, A
Palm Beach Community College, A
Pensacola Junior College, A
St. Johns River Community College, A
Seminole Community College, A
South Florida Community College, A
South University (West Palm Beach), A
Southwest Florida College (Fort Myers), A
Tallahassee Community College, A
Trinity Baptist College, A
Valencia Community College, A
Webster College (Ocala), A

Georgia

Abraham Baldwin Agricultural College, A
Albany State University, B
Altamaha Technical College, A
Appalachian Technical College, A
Athens Technical College, A
Augusta Technical College, A
Bainbridge College, A
Central Georgia Technical College, A
Chattahoochee Technical College, A
Clayton State University, A
Columbus Technical College, A
Darton College, A
DeKalb Technical College, A
East Central Technical College, A
Flint River Technical College, A
Fort Valley State University, AB
Georgia Southwestern State University, A
Gordon College, A

Griffin Technical College, A
Gwinnett Technical College, A
Lanier Technical College, A
Macon State College, A
Middle Georgia Technical College, A
Moultrie Technical College, A
North Georgia Technical College, A
North Metro Technical College, A
Northwestern Technical College, A
Ogeechee Technical College, A
Okefenokee Technical College, A
Sandersville Technical College, A
Savannah Technical College, A
South Georgia College, A
South Georgia Technical College, A
Southeastern Technical College, A
Southwest Georgia Technical College, A
Swainsboro Technical College, A
Valdosta State University, B
Valdosta Technical College, A
Waycross College, A
West Central Technical College, A
West Georgia Technical College, A

Guam

Guam Community College, A

Hawaii

Hawaii Community College, A
Heald College-Honolulu, A
Kauai Community College, A
Leeward Community College, A
Maui Community College, A

Idaho

Brigham Young University -Idaho, A
Eastern Idaho Technical College, A
Idaho State University, A
Lewis-Clark State College, AB
North Idaho College, A
University of Idaho, B

Illinois

Black Hawk College, A
Carl Sandburg College, A
City Colleges of Chicago, Harold Washington
  College, A
City Colleges of Chicago, Kennedy-King College, A
City Colleges of Chicago, Malcolm X College, A
City Colleges of Chicago, Richard J. Daley
  College, A
College of DuPage, A
College of Lake County, A
East-West University, B
Elgin Community College, A
Gem City College, A
Heartland Community College, A
Highland Community College, A
Illinois Central College, A
Illinois Eastern Community Colleges, Frontier
  Community College, A
Illinois Eastern Community Colleges, Olney Central
  College, A
Illinois Eastern Community Colleges, Wabash Valley
  College, A
Illinois Valley Community College, A
John Wood Community College, A
Joliet Junior College, A
Kankakee Community College, A
Kishwaukee College, A
Lake Land College, A
Lewis and Clark Community College, A
Lincoln Christian College, AB
Lincoln Land Community College, A
MacCormac College, A
McHenry County College, A
Midstate College, A
Moraine Valley Community College, A
Morton College, A
Northwestern Business College, A
Oakton Community College, A
Parkland College, A
Rend Lake College, A
Richland Community College, A
Robert Morris College, A
St. Augustine College, A

Sauk Valley Community College, A
Shawnee Community College, A
South Suburban College, A
Southeastern Illinois College, A
Southwestern Illinois College, A
Spoon River College, A
Triton College, A
Waubonsee Community College, A
William Rainey Harper College, A

Indiana

Ball State University, A
Grace College, A
Indiana Business College (Anderson), A
Indiana Business College (Columbus), A
Indiana Business College (Evansville), A
Indiana Business College (Fort Wayne), A
Indiana Business College (Indianapolis), A
Indiana Business College (Indianapolis), A
Indiana Business College (Lafayette), A
Indiana Business College (Marion), A
Indiana Business College (Muncie), A
Indiana Business College (Terre Haute), A
International Business College (Fort Wayne), AB
International Business College (Indianapolis), A
Oakland City University, A
Vincennes University, A
Vincennes University Jasper Campus, A

Iowa

AIB College of Business, A
Clinton Community College, A
Des Moines Area Community College, A
Dordt College, A
Ellsworth Community College, A
Faith Baptist Bible College and Theological
  Seminary, A
Hamilton College (Cedar Rapids), A
Hawkeye Community College, A
Iowa Central Community College, A
Iowa Lakes Community College, A
Iowa Western Community College, A
Kirkwood Community College, A
Marshalltown Community College, A
Muscatine Community College, A
North Iowa Area Community College, A
Northwest Iowa Community College, A
Scott Community College, A
Southeastern Community College, North Campus, A
Southeastern Community College, South
  Campus, A
Southwestern Community College, A

Kansas

Allen County Community College, A
Barton County Community College, A
Butler Community College, A
Cloud County Community College, A
Coffeyville Community College, A
Cowley County Community College and Area
  Vocational-Technical School, A
Dodge City Community College, A
Fort Hays State University, AB
Fort Scott Community College, A
Garden City Community College, A
Highland Community College, A
Hutchinson Community College and Area Vocational
  School, A
Independence Community College, A
Johnson County Community College, A
Kansas City Kansas Community College, A
Labette Community College, A
Neosho County Community College, A
Pratt Community College, A
Seward County Community College, A
Tabor College, AB
Washburn University, A

Kentucky

Ashland Community and Technical College, A
Campbellsville University, AB
Daymar College (Owensboro), A
Draughons Junior College, A
Eastern Kentucky University, AB
Elizabethtown Community and Technical College, A
Hazard Community and Technical College, A

Henderson Community College, A
Hopkinsville Community College, A
Kentucky Christian University, A
Madisonville Community College, A
Maysville Community and Technical College, A
Murray State University, A
National College of Business & Technology
  (Danville), A
National College of Business & Technology
  (Florence), A
National College of Business & Technology
  (Lexington), A
National College of Business & Technology
  (Louisville), A
National College of Business & Technology
  (Pikeville), A
National College of Business & Technology
  (Richmond), A
St. Catharine College, A
Southeast Kentucky Community and Technical
  College, A
Sullivan University, A
West Kentucky Community and Technical College, A

Louisiana

Delgado Community College, A
Elaine P. Nunez Community College, A
Louisiana State University at Eunice, A
Louisiana Technical College, A
Northwestern State University of Louisiana, A
Southeastern Louisiana University, A
Southern University at New Orleans, AB

Maine

Andover College, A
Beal College, A
Central Maine Community College, A
Eastern Maine Community College, A
Kennebec Valley Community College, A
Northern Maine Community College, A

Maryland

Allegany College of Maryland, A
Anne Arundel Community College, A
Baltimore City Community College, A
Cecil Community College, A
Chesapeake College, A
Garrett College, A
Hagerstown Business College, A
Harford Community College, A
Howard Community College, A
Wor-Wic Community College, A

Massachusetts

Atlantic Union College, A
Bay State College, A
Bristol Community College, A
Cape Cod Community College, A
Gibbs College, A
Greenfield Community College, A
Holyoke Community College, A
Marian Court College, A
Massasoit Community College, A
North Shore Community College, A
Northern Essex Community College, A
Quinsigamond Community College, A
Roxbury Community College, A
Salem State College, B
Springfield Technical Community College, A

Michigan

Alpena Community College, A
Baker College of Auburn Hills, A
Baker College of Cadillac, A
Baker College of Clinton Township, A
Baker College of Flint, AB
Baker College of Jackson, A
Baker College of Muskegon, AB
Baker College of Owosso, AB
Baker College of Port Huron, AB
Bay Mills Community College, A
Bay de Noc Community College, A
Davenport University (Dearborn), A
Davenport University (Midland), A
Delta College, A

Gogebic Community College, A
Grand Rapids Community College, A
Henry Ford Community College, A
Jackson Community College, A
Kellogg Community College, A
Kirtland Community College, A
Kuyper College, A
Lake Michigan College, A
Lansing Community College, A
Lewis College of Business, A
Macomb Community College, A
Mid Michigan Community College, A
Monroe County Community College, A
Montcalm Community College, A
Mott Community College, A
Muskegon Community College, A
North Central Michigan College, A
St. Clair County Community College, A
Schoolcraft College, A
Southwestern Michigan College, A
Washtenaw Community College, A
Wayne County Community College District, A

Minnesota

Alexandria Technical College, A
Anoka-Ramsey Community College, A
Anoka-Ramsey Community College, Cambridge
    Campus, A
Anoka Technical College, A
Central Lakes College, A
Century College, A
Dakota County Technical College, A
Duluth Business University, A
Hibbing Community College, A
Inver Hills Community College, A
Mesabi Range Community and Technical College, A
Minneapolis Business College, A
Minneapolis Community and Technical College, A
Minnesota School of Business, A
Minnesota School of Business-Brooklyn Center, A
Minnesota School of Business-Plymouth, A
Minnesota School of Business-Richfield, A
Minnesota School of Business-St. Cloud, A
Minnesota State College-Southeast Technical, A
Minnesota State Community and Technical
    College-Fergus Falls, A
Minnesota West Community and Technical
    College, A
North Central University, A
Northland Community and Technical College-Thief
    River Falls, A
Northwest Technical College, A
Pillsbury Baptist Bible College, AB
Pine Technical College, A
Rainy River Community College, A
Rasmussen College Eden Prairie, A
Rasmussen College Mankato, A
Rasmussen College St. Cloud, A
Ridgewater College, A
Riverland Community College, A
Rochester Community and Technical College, A
St. Cloud Technical College, A
Saint Paul College-A Community & Technical
    College, A
South Central Technical College, A

Mississippi

Alcorn State University, B
Coahoma Community College, A
Copiah-Lincoln Community College-Natchez
    Campus, A
East Mississippi Community College, A
Hinds Community College, A
Holmes Community College, A
Itawamba Community College, A
Jackson State University, B
Meridian Community College, A
Mississippi Delta Community College, A
Mississippi Gulf Coast Community College, A
Northeast Mississippi Community College, A
Pearl River Community College, A
Southeastern Baptist College, A
Southwest Mississippi Community College, A

Virginia College at Jackson, A

Missouri

Baptist Bible College, AB
Blue River Community College, A
Central Missouri State University, A
Crowder College, A
East Central College, A
Evangel University, AB
Jefferson College, A
Longview Community College, A
Maple Woods Community College, A
Mineral Area College, A
Moberly Area Community College, A
North Central Missouri College, A
Northwest Missouri State University, B
Ozarks Technical Community College, A
Penn Valley Community College, A
Saint Charles Community College, A
St. Louis Community College at Florissant Valley, A
St. Louis Community College at Forest Park, A
St. Louis Community College at Meramec, A
Sanford-Brown College (Hazelwood), A
Sanford-Brown College (St. Charles), A
Southeast Missouri State University, B
Springfield College, A
State Fair Community College, A
Three Rivers Community College, A
Vatterott College (St. Joseph), A

Montana

Blackfeet Community College, A
Chief Dull Knife College, A
Dawson Community College, A
Flathead Valley Community College, A
Fort Belknap College, A
Fort Peck Community College, A
Miles Community College, A
Montana State University-Billings, A
Montana State University-Great Falls College of
    Technology, A
Montana Tech of The University of Montana, A
Salish Kootenai College, A
Stone Child College, A
The University of Montana-Missoula, B
The University of Montana-Western, A

Nebraska

Central Community College-Columbus Campus, A
Central Community College-Grand Island
    Campus, A
Central Community College-Hastings Campus, A
Hamilton College-Lincoln, A
Hamilton College-Omaha, A
Metropolitan Community College, A
Mid-Plains Community College, A
Midland Lutheran College, B
Nebraska Christian College, A
Northeast Community College, A
Southeast Community College, Beatrice Campus, A
Southeast Community College, Lincoln Campus, A

Nevada

Community College of Southern Nevada, A
Las Vegas College, A
Morrison University, A
Truckee Meadows Community College, A
Western Nevada Community College, A

New Hampshire

McIntosh College, A
New Hampshire Community Technical College,
    Berlin/Laconia, A
New Hampshire Community Technical College,
    Manchester/Stratham, A

New Jersey

Bergen Community College, A
Brookdale Community College, A
Camden County College, A
County College of Morris, A
Cumberland County College, A
Essex County College, A
Gibbs College (Montclair), A
Mercer County Community College, A

Middlesex County College, A
Ocean County College, A
Passaic County Community College, A
Raritan Valley Community College, A
Sussex County Community College, A
Union County College, A
Warren County Community College, A

New Mexico

Central New Mexico Community College, A
Clovis Community College, A
Doña Ana Branch Community College, A
Eastern New Mexico University-Roswell, A
Luna Community College, A
New Mexico Junior College, A
New Mexico State University-Alamogordo, A
New Mexico State University-Carlsbad, A
New Mexico State University-Grants, A
San Juan College, A
Santa Fe Community College, A
Southwestern Indian Polytechnic Institute, A
University of New Mexico-Gallup, A
University of New Mexico-Los Alamos Branch, A
University of New Mexico-Valencia Campus, A
Western New Mexico University, A

New York

Adirondack Community College, A
Borough of Manhattan Community College of the
    City University of New York, A
Bramson ORT College, A
Briarcliffe College, A
Bronx Community College of the City University of
    New York, A
Bryant and Stratton College (Albany), A
Bryant and Stratton College, Amherst Campus, A
Bryant and Stratton College, Buffalo Campus, A
Bryant and Stratton College, Lackawanna
    Campus, A
Bryant and Stratton College, North Campus, A
Bryant and Stratton College (Rochester-Greece
    Campus), A
Bryant and Stratton College (Rochester-Henrietta
    Campus), A
Bryant and Stratton College (Syracuse), A
Clinton Community College, A
The College of Westchester, A
Columbia-Greene Community College, A
Concordia College, A
Corning Community College, A
Dutchess Community College, A
Elmira Business Institute, A
Erie Community College, A
Eugenio María de Hostos Community College of the
    City University of New York, A
Finger Lakes Community College, A
Fiorello H. LaGuardia Community College of the
    City University of New York, A
Fulton-Montgomery Community College, A
Genesee Community College, A
Hofstra University, B
Hudson Valley Community College, A
Interboro Institute, A
Jamestown Business College, A
Jefferson Community College, A
Katharine Gibbs School (Melville), A
Katharine Gibbs School (New York), A
Kingsborough Community College of the City
    University of New York, A
Long Island Business Institute, A
Mildred Elley, A
Mohawk Valley Community College, A
Monroe Community College, A
Nassau Community College, A
New York Institute of Technology, A
Niagara County Community College, A
Olean Business Institute, A
Onondaga Community College, A
Orange County Community College, A
Plaza College, A
Rockland Community College, A
Schenectady County Community College, A
State University of New York College of Agriculture
    and Technology at Morrisville, A
Sullivan County Community College, A
Taylor Business Institute, A

TCI-The College of Technology, A
Tompkins Cortland Community College, A
Trocaire College, A
Ulster County Community College, A
Utica School of Commerce, A
Westchester Community College, A

North Carolina

Beaufort County Community College, A
Bladen Community College, A
Blue Ridge Community College, A
Brunswick Community College, A
Carteret Community College, A
Catawba Valley Community College, A
Central Carolina Community College, A
Central Piedmont Community College, A
Cleveland Community College, A
College of The Albemarle, A
Davidson County Community College, A
Durham Technical Community College, A
Edgecombe Community College, A
Forsyth Technical Community College, A
Halifax Community College, A
Isothermal Community College, A
James Sprunt Community College, A
Johnston Community College, A
Lenoir Community College, A
Martin Community College, A
Mayland Community College, A
McDowell Technical Community College, A
Mitchell Community College, A
Montgomery Community College, A
Nash Community College, A
North Carolina Agricultural and Technical State
  University, B
Pamlico Community College, A
Pitt Community College, A
Richmond Community College, A
Roanoke-Chowan Community College, A
Robeson Community College, A
Rockingham Community College, A
Sampson Community College, A
Sandhills Community College, A
Southeastern Community College, A
Southwestern Community College, A
Surry Community College, A
Vance-Granville Community College, A
Western Piedmont Community College, A
Wilson Technical Community College, A

North Dakota

Bismarck State College, A
Cankdeska Cikana Community College, A
Dickinson State University, A
Fort Berthold Community College, A
Lake Region State College, A
Mayville State University, AB
Minot State University-Bottineau Campus, A
North Dakota State College of Science, A
Sitting Bull College, A
Trinity Bible College, AB
Turtle Mountain Community College, A
United Tribes Technical College, A
Williston State College, A

Ohio

Belmont Technical College, A
Bradford School, A
Brown Mackie College-Cincinnati, A
Bryant and Stratton College (Cleveland), A
Bryant and Stratton College (Parma), A
Bryant and Stratton College (Willoughby Hills), A
Cedarville University, B
Central Ohio Technical College, A
Cincinnati State Technical and Community
  College, A
Clark State Community College, A
Columbus State Community College, A
Cuyahoga Community College, A
David N. Myers University, AB
Davis College, A
Edison State Community College, A
Gallipolis Career College, A
God's Bible School and College, A
Hocking College, A
James A. Rhodes State College, A

Jefferson Community College, A
Kent State University, Ashtabula Campus, A
Kent State University, Salem Campus, A
Kent State University, Tuscarawas Campus, A
Lakeland Community College, A
Lorain County Community College, A
Marion Technical College, A
Miami-Jacobs College, A
Miami University-Middletown Campus, A
North Central State College, A
Ohio Business College (Lorain), A
Ohio Business College (Sandusky), A
Ohio University, A
Ohio University-Chillicothe, A
Ohio University-Lancaster, A
Sinclair Community College, A
Southwestern College of Business (Cincinnati), A
Southwestern College of Business (Cincinnati), A
Southwestern College of Business (Dayton), A
Southwestern College of Business (Franklin), A
Stark State College of Technology, A
Terra State Community College, A
Trumbull Business College, A
The University of Akron, A
The University of Akron-Wayne College, A
University of Cincinnati, A
University of Cincinnati Clermont College, A
University of Cincinnati Raymond Walters College, A
The University of Findlay, A
University of Northwestern Ohio, A
University of Rio Grande, A
The University of Toledo, A
Washington State Community College, A
Wright State University, A
Wright State University, Lake Campus, A
Zane State College, A

Oklahoma

Bacone College, A
Carl Albert State College, A
Eastern Oklahoma State College, A
Langston University, B
Murray State College, A
Northeastern Oklahoma Agricultural and Mechanical
  College, A
Northern Oklahoma College, A
Oklahoma State University, Okmulgee, A
Oklahoma Wesleyan University, A
Redlands Community College, A
Rogers State University, A
Rose State College, A
Seminole State College, A
Tulsa Community College, A

Oregon

Blue Mountain Community College, A
Central Oregon Community College, A
Chemeketa Community College, A
Clatsop Community College, A
Eastern Oregon University, A
Heald College-Portland, A
Lane Community College, A
Linn-Benton Community College, A
Mt. Hood Community College, A
Portland Community College, A
Tillamook Bay Community College, A
Treasure Valley Community College, A
Umpqua Community College, A

Pennsylvania

Baptist Bible College of Pennsylvania, AB
Berean Institute, A
Bucks County Community College, A
Business Institute of Pennsylvania (Sharon), A
Butler County Community College, A
Cambria-Rowe Business College (Johnstown), A
Community College of Allegheny County, A
Community College of Beaver County, A
Community College of Philadelphia, A
Douglas Education Center, A
DuBois Business College, A
Duff's Business Institute, A
Erie Business Center, Main, A
Erie Business Center South, A
Harrisburg Area Community College, A
ICM School of Business & Medical Careers, A

Lackawanna College, A
Lancaster Bible College, A
Lansdale School of Business, A
Laurel Business Institute, A
Lehigh Carbon Community College, A
Luzerne County Community College, A
Manor College, A
McCann School of Business & Technology, A
Mercyhurst College, AB
Montgomery County Community College, A
Newport Business Institute (Williamsport), A
Northampton County Area Community College, A
Pace Institute, A
Penn Commercial Business and Technical School, A
Pennsylvania College of Technology, A
Reading Area Community College, A
Schuylkill Institute of Business and Technology, A
South Hills School of Business & Technology (State
  College), A
Westmoreland County Community College, A
Yorktowne Business Institute, A

Puerto Rico

American University of Puerto Rico, AB
Bayamon Central University, AB
Caribbean University, AB
Columbia College (Caguas), A
Electronic Data Processing College of Puerto
  Rico, A
Huertas Junior College, A
Humacao Community College, A
Instituto Comercial de Puerto Rico Junior College, A
Inter American University of Puerto Rico, Aguadilla
  Campus, AB
Inter American University of Puerto Rico, Arecibo
  Campus, AB
Inter American University of Puerto Rico,
  Barranquitas Campus, AB
Inter American University of Puerto Rico, Bayamón
  Campus, AB
Inter American University of Puerto Rico, Fajardo
  Campus, AB
Inter American University of Puerto Rico, Guayama
  Campus, AB
Inter American University of Puerto Rico,
  Metropolitan Campus, AB
Inter American University of Puerto Rico, Ponce
  Campus, AB
Inter American University of Puerto Rico, San
  Germán Campus, AB
Pontifical Catholic University of Puerto Rico, AB
Ramírez College of Business and Technology, A
Technological College of San Juan, A
Universidad Adventista de las Antillas, AB
Universidad del Este, A
Universidad Metropolitana, B
Universidad del Turabo, AB
University of Puerto Rico, Aguadilla University
  College, AB
University of Puerto Rico at Bayamón, AB
University of Puerto Rico at Carolina, A
University of Puerto Rico, Cayey University
  College, AB
University of Puerto Rico at Humacao, AB
University of Puerto Rico, Mayagüez Campus, B
University of Puerto Rico at Ponce, AB
University of Puerto Rico, Río Piedras, B
University of the Sacred Heart, B

Rhode Island

Community College of Rhode Island, A

South Carolina

Aiken Technical College, A
Benedict College, B
Central Carolina Technical College, A
Denmark Technical College, A
Florence-Darlington Technical College, A
Greenville Technical College, A
Horry-Georgetown Technical College, A
Midlands Technical College, A
Northeastern Technical College, A
Orangeburg-Calhoun Technical College, A
Piedmont Technical College, A
South Carolina State University, B
Spartanburg Methodist College, A

Spartanburg Technical College, A
Technical College of the Lowcountry, A
Tri-County Technical College, A
Trident Technical College, A
University of South Carolina Lancaster, A
Williamsburg Technical College, A
York Technical College, A

South Dakota

Black Hills State University, A
Kilian Community College, A
Mitchell Technical Institute, A
Northern State University, AB
Oglala Lakota College, A
University of Sioux Falls, AB

Tennessee

Chattanooga State Technical Community College, A
Cleveland State Community College, A
Columbia State Community College, A
Draughons Junior College (Clarksville), A
Draughons Junior College (Nashville), A
Free Will Baptist Bible College, A
Martin Methodist College, A
MedVance Institute, A
Nashville State Technical Community College, A
National College of Business & Technology (Bristol), A
National College of Business & Technology (Nashville), A
Northeast State Technical Community College, A
Pellissippi State Technical Community College, A
Roane State Community College, A
South College, A
Southwest Tennessee Community College, A
Tennessee State University, AB
Tennessee Temple University, B
Walters State Community College, A

Texas

Alvin Community College, A
Amarillo College, A
Angelina College, A
Austin Community College, A
Blinn College, A
Brazosport College, A
Cedar Valley College, A
Central Texas College, A
Coastal Bend College, A
College of the Mainland, A
Del Mar College, A
El Centro College, A
El Paso Community College, A
Frank Phillips College, A
Galveston College, A
Grayson County College, A
Hallmark Institute of Technology, A
Hill College of the Hill Junior College District, A
Houston Community College System, A
Kilgore College, A
Lamar State College-Orange, A
Lamar State College-Port Arthur, A
Lamar University, AB
Laredo Community College, A
Lee College, A
McLennan Community College, A
MTI College of Business and Technology (Houston), A
MTI College of Business and Technology (Houston), A
Navarro College, A
North Central Texas College, A
North Harris College, A
North Lake College, A
Northeast Texas Community College, A
Odessa College, A
Paul Quinn College, B
Ranger College, A
Richland College, A
St. Philip's College, A
South Plains College, A
Southwestern Adventist University, AB
Sul Ross State University, AB
Tarrant County College District, A
Temple College, A
Texarkana College, A

Texas A&M University-Commerce, B
Texas Southmost College, A
Texas State Technical College Harlingen, A
Tyler Junior College, A
Vernon College, A
Victoria College, A
Weatherford College, A
Western Texas College, A
Wharton County Junior College, A
Wiley College, AB

United States Virgin Islands

University of the Virgin Islands, A

Utah

College of Eastern Utah, A
Dixie State College of Utah, A
LDS Business College, A
Mountain West College, A
Snow College, A
Stevens-Henager College, A
Utah State University, AB
Weber State University, AB

Vermont

Community College of Vermont, A

Virginia

Blue Ridge Community College, A
Bryant and Stratton College, Richmond, A
Bryant and Stratton College, Virginia Beach, A
Central Virginia Community College, A
Dabney S. Lancaster Community College, A
Danville Community College, A
Eastern Shore Community College, A
J. Sargeant Reynolds Community College, A
John Tyler Community College, A
Lord Fairfax Community College, A
Mountain Empire Community College, A
National College of Business & Technology (Bluefield), A
National College of Business & Technology (Charlottesville), A
National College of Business & Technology (Danville), A
National College of Business & Technology (Harrisonburg), A
National College of Business & Technology (Lynchburg), A
National College of Business & Technology (Martinsville), A
National College of Business & Technology (Salem), A
New River Community College, A
Northern Virginia Community College, A
Patrick Henry Community College, A
Paul D. Camp Community College, A
Piedmont Virginia Community College, A
Rappahannock Community College, A
Southside Virginia Community College, A
Southwest Virginia Community College, A
Thomas Nelson Community College, A
Tidewater Community College, A
Virginia Highlands Community College, A
Virginia Western Community College, A
Wytheville Community College, A

Washington

Bates Technical College, A
Bellevue Community College, A
Centralia College, A
Columbia Basin College, A
Edmonds Community College, A
Highline Community College, A
Lake Washington Technical College, A
Lower Columbia College, A
North Seattle Community College, A
Olympic College, A
Pierce College, A
Renton Technical College, A
Seattle Central Community College, A
Skagit Valley College, A
South Puget Sound Community College, A
South Seattle Community College, A
Spokane Community College, A

Spokane Falls Community College, A
Tacoma Community College, A
Walla Walla Community College, A
Wenatchee Valley College, A
Whatcom Community College, A
Yakima Valley Community College, A

West Virginia

Bluefield State College, AB
Community & Technical College at West Virginia University Institute of Technology, A
Eastern West Virginia Community and Technical College, A
Fairmont State University, A
Huntington Junior College, A
Marshall Community and Technical College, A
Mountain State College, A
Mountain State University, A
New River Community and Technical College, A
Potomac State College of West Virginia University, A
Southern West Virginia Community and Technical College, A
West Virginia Business College (Wheeling), A
West Virginia Junior College (Bridgeport), A
West Virginia Junior College (Charleston), A
West Virginia Northern Community College, A
West Virginia State University, A
West Virginia University at Parkersburg, A

Wisconsin

Blackhawk Technical College, A
Bryant and Stratton College, A
Chippewa Valley Technical College, A
Fox Valley Technical College, A
Gateway Technical College, A
Lac Courte Oreilles Ojibwa Community College, A
Lakeshore Technical College, A
Madison Area Technical College, A
Maranatha Baptist Bible College, AB
Mid-State Technical College, A
Milwaukee Area Technical College, A
Moraine Park Technical College, A
Nicolet Area Technical College, A
Northcentral Technical College, A
Northeast Wisconsin Technical College, A
Southwest Wisconsin Technical College, A
Waukesha County Technical College, A
Western Technical College, A
Wisconsin Indianhead Technical College, A

Wyoming

Casper College, A
Eastern Wyoming College, A
Northwest College, A
Sheridan College-Sheridan and Gillette, A
Western Wyoming Community College, A

British Columbia

British Columbia Institute of Technology, A

ADULT AND CONTINUING EDUCATION ADMINISTRATION

Pennsylvania

The Pennsylvania State University Abington College, B
The Pennsylvania State University Altoona College, B
The Pennsylvania State University Beaver Campus of the Commonwealth College, B
The Pennsylvania State University Berks Campus of the Berks-Lehigh Valley College, B
The Pennsylvania State University Delaware County Campus of the Commonwealth College, B
The Pennsylvania State University DuBois Campus of the Commonwealth College, B
The Pennsylvania State University at Erie, The Behrend College, B
The Pennsylvania State University Fayette Campus of the Commonwealth College, B
The Pennsylvania State University Hazleton Campus of the Commonwealth College, B

The Pennsylvania State University, Lehigh Valley Campus of the Berks-Lehigh Valley College, B

The Pennsylvania State University McKeesport Campus of the Commonwealth College, B

The Pennsylvania State University Mont Alto Campus of the Commonwealth College, B

The Pennsylvania State University New Kensington Campus of the Commonwealth College, B

The Pennsylvania State University Schuylkill Campus of the Capital College, B

The Pennsylvania State University Shenango Campus of the Commonwealth College, B

The Pennsylvania State University University Park Campus, B

The Pennsylvania State University Wilkes-Barre Campus of the Commonwealth College, B

The Pennsylvania State University Worthington Scranton Campus of the Commonwealth College, B

The Pennsylvania State University York Campus of the Commonwealth College, B

West Virginia

Marshall University, B

British Columbia

University College of the Fraser Valley, B

ADULT AND CONTINUING EDUCATION AND TEACHING

Alabama

Auburn University, BMD
The University of West Alabama, M

Alaska

University of Alaska Anchorage, M

Arizona

University of Phoenix Online Campus, M
University of Phoenix-Phoenix Campus, M

Arkansas

Arkansas Baptist College, B
University of Arkansas, MDO
University of Arkansas at Little Rock, M

California

Biola University, B
San Diego Christian College, B
San Francisco State University, MO
University of Phoenix-Sacramento Valley Campus, M
University of Phoenix-San Diego Campus, M
University of San Francisco, B

Colorado

Regis University, MO
University of Denver, MD
University of Phoenix-Denver Campus, M

Connecticut

University of Connecticut, MD

Florida

Florida Agricultural and Mechanical University, M
Florida Atlantic University, MDO
Florida International University, MD
Florida State University, MDO
Lynn University, B
Nova Southeastern University, D
University of South Florida, MDO

Georgia

Armstrong Atlantic State University, M
Morehouse College, B
University of Georgia, MDO

Valdosta State University, D

Idaho

University of Idaho, MDO

Illinois

DePaul University, B
National-Louis University, MDO
Northern Illinois University, MD
University of St. Francis, M

Indiana

Ball State University, MD
Martin University, B

Iowa

Drake University, M
Iowa Wesleyan College, B

Kansas

Kansas State University, MD
Tabor College, B

Kentucky

Morehead State University, MO

Louisiana

Louisiana College, B
Northwestern State University of Louisiana, M

Maine

University of Southern Maine, MO

Maryland

Coppin State University, M

Massachusetts

American International College, B
Atlantic Union College, B
Curry College, MO
Massachusetts College of Liberal Arts, B
Suffolk University, MO

Michigan

Grand Valley State University, M
Marygrove College, M
Michigan State University, MD
University of Phoenix-Metro Detroit Campus, M
Wayne State University, M

Minnesota

University of Minnesota, Twin Cities Campus, MDO

Mississippi

University of Southern Mississippi, MDO

Missouri

University of Missouri-Columbia, MDO
University of Missouri-St. Louis, MD

Nevada

University of Nevada, Las Vegas, B

New Hampshire

Franklin Pierce College, B
University of New Hampshire, BM

New Jersey

Kean University, M
Rutgers, The State University of New Jersey, New Brunswick/Piscataway, M

New York

Buffalo State College, State University of New York, MO
Cornell University, MD
Fordham University, M
St. Joseph's College, Suffolk Campus, B

North Carolina

East Carolina University, MO
Lenoir-Rhyne College, B
Mars Hill College, B

North Carolina Agricultural and Technical State University, M
North Carolina State University, MD

Ohio

Cleveland State University, MO
The University of Toledo, B
Urbana University, B
Wright State University, O

Oklahoma

Northwestern Oklahoma State University, M
University of Central Oklahoma, BM
University of Oklahoma, MD

Oregon

Oregon State University, M
Portland State University, D

Pennsylvania

Cheyney University of Pennsylvania, M
Indiana University of Pennsylvania, M
The Pennsylvania State University Harrisburg Campus, D
The Pennsylvania State University University Park Campus, MD
Widener University, M

Rhode Island

University of Rhode Island, M

South Dakota

Dakota Wesleyan University, B

Tennessee

Tennessee State University, BM
Tusculum College, M
University of Memphis, D
The University of Tennessee, M

Texas

Texas A&M University-Kingsville, M
Texas A&M University-Texarkana, M
University of the Incarnate Word, BM
The University of Texas at San Antonio, M

Virginia

Virginia Commonwealth University, M
Virginia Polytechnic Institute and State University, MDO

Washington

Eastern Washington University, M
Seattle University, MO
Western Washington University, M

West Virginia

Marshall University, M

Wisconsin

Alverno College, M
University of Wisconsin-Madison, MD
University of Wisconsin-Platteville, M

Wyoming

University of Wyoming, MDO

Alberta

Athabasca University, M
University of Alberta, BMD

British Columbia

The University of British Columbia, M
University College of the Fraser Valley, B

Manitoba

University of Manitoba, M

New Brunswick

Université de Moncton, B
University of New Brunswick Fredericton, BM

Newfoundland and Labrador

Memorial University of Newfoundland, BMO

Nova Scotia

Mount Saint Vincent University, M
St. Francis Xavier University, M

Ontario

Brock University, B
Laurentian University, B

Quebec

Concordia University, MO
Université du Québec en Outaouais, O
Université du Québec àTrois-Rivières, B

Saskatchewan

University of Regina, BMO

ADULT DEVELOPMENT AND AGING

California

Santa Rosa Junior College, A

Colorado

University of Northern Colorado, B

Georgia

Albany Technical College, A
Central Georgia Technical College, A

Indiana

Saint Mary-of-the-Woods College, AB

Michigan

Madonna University, AB

Ohio

Bowling Green State University, B
College of Mount St. Joseph, B
The University of Toledo, A

Oregon

Southwestern Oregon Community College, A

Pennsylvania

Lehigh Carbon Community College, A

Rhode Island

Community College of Rhode Island, A

New Brunswick

St. Thomas University, B

Nova Scotia

Mount Saint Vincent University, B

ADULT HEALTH NURSE/NURSING

Kentucky

Northern Kentucky University, B

New York

State University of New York at Buffalo, B

Ohio

Wright State University, B

Pennsylvania

Pennsylvania College of Technology, B

Quebec

Université du Québec àTrois-Rivières, B

ADVERTISING

Alabama

The University of Alabama, B

Arizona

The Art Institute of Phoenix, B
Northern Arizona University, B

Arkansas

Harding University, B
University of Arkansas at Little Rock, B

California

Academy of Art University, AB
American River College, A
Art Center College of Design, B
The Art Institute of California-Los Angeles, B
The Art Institute of California-Orange County, B
The Art Institute of California-San Diego, AB
The Art Institute of California-San Francisco, B
California State University, East Bay, B
California State University, Fullerton, B
Chabot College, A
Chapman University, B
Cosumnes River College (Sacramento), A
Cypress College, A
El Camino College, A
Grossmont College, A
Long Beach City College, A
Los Angeles City College, A
Los Angeles Valley College, A
Mt. San Antonio College, A
Notre Dame de Namur University, B
Palomar College, A
Pasadena City College, A
Pepperdine University, B
Sacramento City College, A
San Diego State University, B
San Jose State University, B
Santa Rosa Junior College, A
Yuba College, A

Colorado

The Art Institute of Colorado, B
Colorado State University-Pueblo, B
Johnson & Wales University, A
Platt College, B
University of Colorado at Boulder, B

Connecticut

Quinnipiac University, B

District of Columbia

University of the District of Columbia, A

Florida

The Art Institute of Tampa, B
Barry University, B
Daytona Beach Community College, A
Florida Southern College, B
Florida State University, B
Johnson & Wales University, A
Manatee Community College, A
Miami International University of Art & Design, B
Northwood University, Florida Campus, AB
University of Central Florida, B
University of Florida, B
University of Miami, B

Georgia

The Art Institute of Atlanta, B
University of Georgia, B

Wesleyan College, B

Hawaii

Hawaii Pacific University, B

Idaho

Boise State University, B
Brigham Young University -Idaho, A

Illinois

American Academy of Art, B
Bradley University, B
Columbia College Chicago, B
DePaul University, B
The Illinois Institute of Art-Schaumburg, B
Parkland College, A
South Suburban College, A
University of Illinois at Urbana-Champaign, B

Indiana

Ball State University, B
University of Southern Indiana, B
Vincennes University, A

Iowa

Clarke College, B
Drake University, B
Iowa State University of Science and Technology, B
St. Ambrose University, B
Simpson College, B

Kansas

Highland Community College, A

Kentucky

University of Kentucky, B
Western Kentucky University, B

Louisiana

Louisiana College, B

Maine

New England School of Communications, AB
Saint Joseph's College of Maine, B

Massachusetts

Eastern Nazarene College, B
Emerson College, B
Simmons College, B
Western New England College, B

Michigan

Central Michigan University, B
Ferris State University, B
Grand Valley State University, B
Michigan State University, B
Muskegon Community College, A
Northwood University, AB
St. Clair County Community College, A

Minnesota

Concordia College, B
Metropolitan State University, B
Minneapolis College of Art and Design, B
Minnesota State University Moorhead, B
St. Cloud State University, B
St. Cloud Technical College, A
Winona State University, B

Mississippi

Mississippi Delta Community College, A
Mississippi Gulf Coast Community College, A
Southwest Mississippi Community College, A
University of Mississippi, B
University of Southern Mississippi, B

Missouri

Drury University, B
Fontbonne University, B
Northwest Missouri State University, B
St. Louis Community College at Meramec, A
Stephens College, B
University of Missouri-Columbia, B
Washington University in St. Louis, B

Webster University, B
William Woods University, B

Nebraska

Hastings College, B
University of Nebraska-Lincoln, B
Wayne State College, B

Nevada

University of Nevada, Reno, B

New Hampshire

Franklin Pierce College, B
New England College, B
Southern New Hampshire University, B

New Jersey

Middlesex County College, A
Rider University, B

New Mexico

The Art Center Design College, A

New York

Bernard M. Baruch College of the City University of
New York, B
Fashion Institute of Technology, AB
Iona College, B
Marist College, B
Mohawk Valley Community College, A
New York Institute of Technology, B
Pace University, B
Rochester Institute of Technology, B
Rockland Community College, A
School of Visual Arts, B
Syracuse University, B

North Carolina

Appalachian State University, B
Campbell University, B
Central Piedmont Community College, A
Surry Community College, A

Ohio

Edison State Community College, A
Kent State University, B
Ohio University, B
Xavier University, AB
Youngstown State University, B

Oklahoma

East Central University, B
Oklahoma Baptist University, B
Oklahoma Christian University, B
Oklahoma City University, B
Tulsa Community College, A
University of Central Oklahoma, B
University of Oklahoma, B

Oregon

The Art Institute of Portland, B
Portland State University, B
University of Oregon, B

Pennsylvania

The Art Institute of Pittsburgh, B
Bradley Academy for the Visual Arts, A
Erie Business Center South, A
Gannon University, B
Hussian School of Art, A
Marywood University, B
Mercyhurst College, B
The Pennsylvania State University Abington
College, B
The Pennsylvania State University Altoona
College, B
The Pennsylvania State University Beaver Campus
of the Commonwealth College, B
The Pennsylvania State University Berks Campus of
the Berks-Lehigh Valley College, B
The Pennsylvania State University Delaware County
Campus of the Commonwealth College, B
The Pennsylvania State University DuBois Campus
of the Commonwealth College, B

The Pennsylvania State University at Erie, The
Behrend College, B
The Pennsylvania State University Fayette Campus
of the Commonwealth College, B
The Pennsylvania State University Hazleton
Campus of the Commonwealth College, B
The Pennsylvania State University, Lehigh Valley
Campus of the Berks-Lehigh Valley College, B
The Pennsylvania State University McKeesport
Campus of the Commonwealth College, B
The Pennsylvania State University Mont Alto
Campus of the Commonwealth College, B
The Pennsylvania State University New Kensington
Campus of the Commonwealth College, B
The Pennsylvania State University Schuylkill
Campus of the Capital College, B
The Pennsylvania State University Shenango
Campus of the Commonwealth College, B
The Pennsylvania State University University Park
Campus, B
The Pennsylvania State University Wilkes-Barre
Campus of the Commonwealth College, B
The Pennsylvania State University Worthington
Scranton Campus of the Commonwealth
College, B
The Pennsylvania State University York Campus of
the Commonwealth College, B
Point Park University, B
Temple University, B
Waynesburg College, B
Widener University, B

Puerto Rico

University of Puerto Rico at Carolina, A
University of the Sacred Heart, B

Rhode Island

Johnson & Wales University, AB

South Carolina

University of South Carolina, B

Tennessee

Belmont University, B
Chattanooga State Technical Community College, A
Martin Methodist College, A
Memphis College of Art, B
Southern Adventist University, B
Union University, B
The University of Tennessee, B

Texas

Northwood University, Texas Campus, AB
Sam Houston State University, B
South Plains College, A
Southern Methodist University, B
Texas A&M University-Commerce, B
Texas Christian University, B
Texas State University-San Marcos, B
Texas Tech University, B
Texas Wesleyan University, B
University of North Texas, B
The University of Texas at Arlington, B
The University of Texas at Austin, B
West Texas A&M University, B

Utah

Brigham Young University, B

Virginia

The Art Institute of Washington, B
Hampton University, B
Tidewater Community College, A

West Virginia

West Virginia State University, A
West Virginia University, B

Wisconsin

Marquette University, B
University of Wisconsin-Madison, B

ADVERTISING AND PUBLIC RELATIONS

Alabama

The University of Alabama, M

California

Academy of Art University, M
California State University, Fullerton, M
Golden Gate University, MO
San Diego State University, M
University of Southern California, M

Colorado

Colorado State University, M
University of Denver, M

Connecticut

University of New Haven, M

Florida

University of Florida, MD
University of Miami, M

Georgia

Savannah College of Art and Design, M

Illinois

Northwestern University, M
University of Illinois at Urbana-Champaign, M

Indiana

Ball State University, M

Kentucky

Morehead State University, M

Maryland

Towson University, O

Massachusetts

Boston University, MO
Emerson College, M

Michigan

Michigan State University, M
Wayne State University, M

Mississippi

University of Southern Mississippi, M

Montana

Montana State University-Billings, M

New Jersey

Monmouth University, O
Montclair State University, M
Rowan University, M

New York

Syracuse University, M

Oklahoma

University of Oklahoma, M

Puerto Rico

University of the Sacred Heart, M

Tennessee

The University of Tennessee, MD

Texas

Texas Christian University, M
University of Houston, M

The University of Texas at Austin, MD

Virginia

Virginia Commonwealth University, M

Wisconsin

Marquette University, M
University of Wisconsin-Stevens Point, M

British Columbia

Royal Roads University, M

Quebec

Université Laval, O

AERONAUTICAL/AEROSPACE ENGINEERING TECHNOLOGY/TECHNICIAN

Alabama

Calhoun Community College, A

Arizona

GateWay Community College, A

California

Santa Rosa Junior College, A

Indiana

Purdue University, A

Massachusetts

Northeastern University, B

Missouri

Central Missouri State University, B
Saint Louis University, B

New York

New York Institute of Technology, B

Ohio

Cincinnati State Technical and Community College, A
Ohio University, B

Pennsylvania

Pennsylvania College of Technology, A

Utah

Utah State University, B

West Virginia

Fairmont State Community & Technical College, A

British Columbia

British Columbia Institute of Technology, A

AERONAUTICS/AVIATION/ AEROSPACE SCIENCE AND TECHNOLOGY

Alabama

Community College of the Air Force, A

Arizona

Arizona State University, B
Arizona State University at the Polytechnic Campus, B
Embry-Riddle Aeronautical University, B

Arkansas

Henderson State University, B

California

Orange Coast College, A
San Bernardino Valley College, A

San Jose State University, B

Delaware

Delaware Technical & Community College, Terry Campus, A

District of Columbia

University of the District of Columbia, B

Florida

Embry-Riddle Aeronautical University, B
Embry-Riddle Aeronautical University, Extended Campus, AB
Miami Dade College, A

Indiana

Indiana State University, A
Purdue University, AB

Kansas

Hesston College, A
Kansas State University, B

Louisiana

Louisiana Tech University, B
University of Louisiana at Monroe, B

Minnesota

Augsburg College, B
Northland Community and Technical College-Thief River Falls, A
Vermilion Community College, A

Mississippi

Delta State University, B

Nebraska

University of Nebraska at Omaha, B

New Hampshire

Daniel Webster College, AB

New Jersey

Raritan Valley Community College, A

New York

Tompkins Cortland Community College, A
Vaughn College of Aeronautics and Technology, A

North Carolina

Caldwell Community College and Technical Institute, A
Elizabeth City State University, B

North Dakota

University of North Dakota, B

Ohio

Kent State University, B
Ohio University, B

Oklahoma

Oklahoma State University, B
Tulsa Community College, A
University of Oklahoma, B

Oregon

Portland Community College, A

Pennsylvania

Community College of Beaver County, A

Puerto Rico

Inter American University of Puerto Rico, Bayamón Campus, B

Tennessee

Middle Tennessee State University, B

Texas

Alvin Community College, A
Dallas Baptist University, B

Texas State Technical College Waco, A

Virginia

Liberty University, B

Washington

Central Washington University, B
Northwest Aviation College, A

Ontario

York University, B

AEROSPACE, AERONAUTICAL AND ASTRONAUTICAL ENGINEERING

Alabama

Auburn University, BMD
Tuskegee University, B
The University of Alabama, BMD
The University of Alabama in Huntsville, M

Arizona

Arizona State University, MD
Arizona State University at the Polytechnic Campus, M
Embry-Riddle Aeronautical University, B
The University of Arizona, BMD

California

Allan Hancock College, A
California Institute of Technology, BMDO
California Polytechnic State University, San Luis Obispo, BM
California State Polytechnic University, Pomona, B
California State University, Long Beach, BM
California State University, Northridge, M
San Diego State University, BMD
San Jose State University, BM
Stanford University, BMDO
University of California, Davis, BMDO
University of California, Irvine, BMD
University of California, Los Angeles, BMD
University of California, San Diego, BMD
University of Southern California, BMDO

Colorado

United States Air Force Academy, B
University of Colorado at Boulder, BMD
University of Colorado at Colorado Springs, M

Connecticut

University of Connecticut, MD

District of Columbia

The George Washington University, MDO

Florida

Embry-Riddle Aeronautical University, BM
Embry-Riddle Aeronautical University, Extended Campus, M
Florida Institute of Technology, BMD
University of Central Florida, BM
University of Florida, BMDO
University of Miami, B

Georgia

Georgia Institute of Technology, BMD

Illinois

Illinois Institute of Technology, BMD
University of Illinois at Urbana-Champaign, BMD

Indiana

Purdue University, BMD
University of Notre Dame, BMD

Iowa

Iowa State University of Science and Technology, BMD

Kansas

University of Kansas, BMD
Wichita State University, BMD

Maryland

Prince George's Community College, A
United States Naval Academy, B
University of Maryland, College Park, BMD

Massachusetts

Boston University, BMD
Eastern Nazarene College, B
Massachusetts Institute of Technology, BMDO
Worcester Polytechnic Institute, B

Michigan

University of Michigan, BMD
Western Michigan University, B

Minnesota

University of Minnesota, Twin Cities Campus, BMD

Mississippi

Mississippi State University, BM

Missouri

Saint Louis University, BM
University of Missouri-Columbia, MD
University of Missouri-Rolla, BMD
Washington University in St. Louis, B
Webster University, M

New Jersey

Princeton University, MD
Rutgers, The State University of New Jersey, New Brunswick/Piscataway, MD

New Mexico

New Mexico State University, B

New York

Clarkson University, B
Cornell University, BMD
Dowling College, B
Rensselaer Polytechnic Institute, BMDO
Rochester Institute of Technology, B
State University of New York at Buffalo, BMD
Syracuse University, BMD
United States Military Academy, B

North Carolina

North Carolina State University, BMD

Ohio

Case Western Reserve University, BMD
Miami University, B
The Ohio State University, BMD
University of Cincinnati, BMD
University of Dayton, MD

Oklahoma

Oklahoma State University, BM
University of Oklahoma, BMD

Pennsylvania

The Pennsylvania State University Abington College, B
The Pennsylvania State University Altoona College, B
The Pennsylvania State University Beaver Campus of the Commonwealth College, B
The Pennsylvania State University Berks Campus of the Berks-Lehigh Valley College, B
The Pennsylvania State University Delaware County Campus of the Commonwealth College, B
The Pennsylvania State University DuBois Campus of the Commonwealth College, B
The Pennsylvania State University at Erie, The Behrend College, B
The Pennsylvania State University Fayette Campus of the Commonwealth College, B
The Pennsylvania State University Hazleton Campus of the Commonwealth College, B

The Pennsylvania State University, Lehigh Valley Campus of the Berks-Lehigh Valley College, B
The Pennsylvania State University McKeesport Campus of the Commonwealth College, B
The Pennsylvania State University Mont Alto Campus of the Commonwealth College, B
The Pennsylvania State University New Kensington Campus of the Commonwealth College, B
The Pennsylvania State University Schuylkill Campus of the Capital College, B
The Pennsylvania State University Shenango Campus of the Commonwealth College, B
The Pennsylvania State University University Park Campus, BMD
The Pennsylvania State University Wilkes-Barre Campus of the Commonwealth College, B
The Pennsylvania State University Worthington Scranton Campus of the Commonwealth College, B
The Pennsylvania State University York Campus of the Commonwealth College, B

Puerto Rico

Inter American University of Puerto Rico, Bayamón Campus, B

Rhode Island

Brown University, MD

Tennessee

Middle Tennessee State University, M
The University of Tennessee, BMDO

Texas

Kilgore College, A
Texas A&M University, BMD
University of Houston, MD
The University of Texas at Arlington, BMD
The University of Texas at Austin, BMD

Utah

Utah State University, BMD
Weber State University, B

Virginia

Old Dominion University, MD
University of Virginia, BMD
Virginia Polytechnic Institute and State University, BMD

Washington

University of Washington, BMD

West Virginia

West Virginia University, BMD
West Virginia University Institute of Technology, B

Alberta

University of Alberta, B

Ontario

Carleton University, BMD
Ryerson University, B
University of Ottawa, MD
University of Toronto, BMD
York University, B

Quebec

Concordia University, M
McGill University, M
Université Laval, M

AESTHETICIAN/ESTHETICIAN AND SKIN CARE SPECIALIST

Colorado

Colorado Northwestern Community College, A

Washington

Olympic College, A

AFRICAN-AMERICAN/BLACK STUDIES

Alabama

Talladega College, B
The University of Alabama at Birmingham, B

Arizona

Arizona State University, B

California

California State University, Dominguez Hills, B
California State University, East Bay, B
California State University, Fresno, B
California State University, Fullerton, B
California State University, Long Beach, B
California State University, Los Angeles, B
California State University, Northridge, B
City College of San Francisco, A
Claremont McKenna College, B
College of Alameda, A
Compton Community College, A
Contra Costa College, A
El Camino College, A
Fresno City College, A
Laney College, A
Los Angeles City College, A
Los Angeles Valley College, A
Loyola Marymount University, B
Merritt College, A
Pasadena City College, A
Pitzer College, B
Pomona College, B
San Diego City College, A
San Diego Mesa College, A
San Diego State University, B
San Francisco State University, B
San Jose State University, B
Santa Ana College, A
Santa Barbara City College, A
Scripps College, B
Solano Community College, A
Sonoma State University, B
Southwestern College, A
University of California, Berkeley, BD
University of California, Davis, B
University of California, Irvine, B
University of California, Los Angeles, BM
University of California, Riverside, B
University of California, Santa Barbara, B
University of Southern California, B
Yuba College, A

Colorado

Metropolitan State College of Denver, B
University of Northern Colorado, B

Connecticut

Wesleyan University, B
Yale University, BMD

Delaware

University of Delaware, B

District of Columbia

Howard University, B

Florida

Florida Agricultural and Mechanical University, BM
Manatee Community College, A
University of Miami, B
University of South Florida, B

Georgia

Atlanta Metropolitan College, A
Clark Atlanta University, MD
Emory University, B
Georgia State University, B
Mercer University, B
Morehouse College, B
Savannah State University, B

University of Georgia, B

Illinois

Chicago State University, B
City Colleges of Chicago, Olive-Harvey College, A
DePaul University, B
Eastern Illinois University, B
Knox College, B
Northwestern University, B
Roosevelt University, B
University of Chicago, B
University of Illinois at Chicago, B
Western Illinois University, B

Indiana

DePauw University, B
Earlham College, B
Indiana State University, B
Indiana University Bloomington, BM
Indiana University Northwest, B
Martin University, B
Purdue University, B

Iowa

Coe College, B
Luther College, B
The University of Iowa, BM

Kansas

University of Kansas, B

Kentucky

University of Louisville, B

Maine

Bates College, B
Bowdoin College, B
Colby College, B

Maryland

Morgan State University, BM
University of Maryland, Baltimore County, B
University of Maryland, College Park, B

Massachusetts

Amherst College, B
Boston University, M
Brandeis University, B
Hampshire College, B
Harvard University, B
Mount Holyoke College, B
Northeastern University, B
Simmons College, B
Simon's Rock College of Bard, B
Smith College, B
Suffolk University, B
Tufts University, B
University of Massachusetts Amherst, BMD
University of Massachusetts Boston, B
Wellesley College, B

Michigan

Eastern Michigan University, B
Michigan State University, MD
University of Michigan, B
University of Michigan-Flint, B
Wayne State University, B

Minnesota

University of Minnesota, Twin Cities Campus, B

Mississippi

Tougaloo College, B

Missouri

St. Louis Community College at Forest Park, A
Washington University in St. Louis, B

Montana

The University of Montana-Missoula, B

Nebraska

University of Nebraska at Omaha, B

Nevada

University of Nevada, Las Vegas, B

New Hampshire

Dartmouth College, B

New Jersey

Rutgers, The State University of New Jersey, Camden, B
Rutgers, The State University of New Jersey, Newark, B
Seton Hall University, B
William Paterson University of New Jersey, B

New Mexico

University of New Mexico, B

New York

Bronx Community College of the City University of New York, A
City College of the City University of New York, B
Colgate University, B
College of Staten Island of the City University of New York, B
Columbia College, B
Columbia University, School of General Studies, B
Cornell University, BMD
Fordham University, B
Hobart and William Smith Colleges, B
Hunter College of the City University of New York, B
Lehman College of the City University of New York, B
Nassau Community College, A
New York University, B
Sarah Lawrence College, B
State University of New York at Binghamton, B
State University of New York at Buffalo, B
State University of New York College at Brockport, B
State University of New York College at Cortland, B
State University of New York College at Geneseo, B
State University of New York College at Oneonta, B
State University of New York at New Paltz, B
Stony Brook University, State University of New York, B
Syracuse University, BM
University at Albany, State University of New York, BM
University of Rochester, B
Wells College, B
York College of the City University of New York, B

North Carolina

Duke University, B
Guilford College, B
North Carolina Agricultural and Technical State University, M
Saint Augustine's College, B
The University of North Carolina at Chapel Hill, B
The University of North Carolina at Charlotte, B
The University of North Carolina at Greensboro, B

Ohio

Antioch College, B
The College of Wooster, B
Denison University, B
Kent State University, B
Kenyon College, B
Miami University, B
Oberlin College, B
The Ohio State University, BM
Ohio University, B
Ohio Wesleyan University, B
University of Cincinnati, B
The University of Toledo, B
Wright State University, B
Youngstown State University, B

Oklahoma

University of Oklahoma, B

Pennsylvania

Gettysburg College, B
Lehigh University, B

The Pennsylvania State University Abington College, B
The Pennsylvania State University Altoona College, B
The Pennsylvania State University Beaver Campus of the Commonwealth College, B
The Pennsylvania State University Berks Campus of the Berks-Lehigh Valley College, B
The Pennsylvania State University Delaware County Campus of the Commonwealth College, B
The Pennsylvania State University DuBois Campus of the Commonwealth College, B
The Pennsylvania State University at Erie, The Behrend College, B
The Pennsylvania State University Fayette Campus of the Commonwealth College, B
The Pennsylvania State University Hazleton Campus of the Commonwealth College, B
The Pennsylvania State University, Lehigh Valley Campus of the Berks-Lehigh Valley College, B
The Pennsylvania State University McKeesport Campus of the Commonwealth College, B
The Pennsylvania State University Mont Alto Campus of the Commonwealth College, B
The Pennsylvania State University New Kensington Campus of the Commonwealth College, B
The Pennsylvania State University Schuylkill Campus of the Capital College, B
The Pennsylvania State University Shenango Campus of the Commonwealth College, B
The Pennsylvania State University University Park Campus, B
The Pennsylvania State University Wilkes-Barre Campus of the Commonwealth College, B
The Pennsylvania State University Worthington Scranton Campus of the Commonwealth College, B
The Pennsylvania State University York Campus of the Commonwealth College, B
Temple University, BMD
University of Pennsylvania, B
University of Pittsburgh, B

Rhode Island

Brown University, B
Rhode Island College, B

South Carolina

Claflin University, B
University of South Carolina, B

Tennessee

University of Memphis, B
Vanderbilt University, B

Texas

Southern Methodist University, B
Texas Southern University, B

Virginia

The College of William and Mary, B
University of Virginia, B
Virginia Commonwealth University, B

Washington

University of Washington, B

West Virginia

West Virginia University, MD

Wisconsin

Marquette University, B
University of Wisconsin-Madison, BM
University of Wisconsin-Milwaukee, B

AFRICAN LANGUAGES, LITERATURES, AND LINGUISTICS

California

University of California, Los Angeles, B

Massachusetts

Harvard University, B

Ohio

Ohio University, B

Wisconsin

University of Wisconsin-Madison, B

AFRICAN STUDIES

Alabama

Miles College, B

California

Los Angeles Southwest College, A
MiraCosta College, A
Pasadena City College, A
Solano Community College, A
Southwestern College, A
Stanford University, B
University of California, Los Angeles, BMO

Colorado

Colorado State University, M

Connecticut

Connecticut College, B
University of Connecticut, M
Yale University, BM

District of Columbia

Howard University, MD

Florida

Florida International University, M
University of Florida, O
University of South Florida, M

Georgia

Emory University, B
Fort Valley State University, B
Kennesaw State University, B

Illinois

DePaul University, B
Illinois Wesleyan University, B
Northwestern University, BO
University of Chicago, B
University of Illinois at Urbana-Champaign, M

Indiana

Indiana University Bloomington, B

Iowa

The University of Iowa, B

Kansas

University of Kansas, B

Kentucky

University of Louisville, M

Louisiana

Tulane University, B

Maine

Bowdoin College, B

Maryland

Morgan State University, B
University of Maryland, Baltimore County, B

Massachusetts

Boston University, O
Brandeis University, B
Harvard University, B

Wellesley College, B

Michigan

Michigan State University, MD
Western Michigan University, B

Minnesota

Carleton College, B
University of Minnesota, Twin Cities Campus, B

Missouri

Washington University in St. Louis, B

New Hampshire

Dartmouth College, B

New Jersey

Drew University, B
Rutgers, The State University of New Jersey, New
    Brunswick/Piscataway, BD
William Paterson University of New Jersey, B

New York

Bard College, B
Barnard College, B
Brooklyn College of the City University of New
    York, B
Colgate University, B
Cornell University, MD
Fordham University, B
Hamilton College, B
Hobart and William Smith Colleges, B
Hofstra University, B
New York University, M
Queens College of the City University of New
    York, B
St. John's University, O
St. Lawrence University, B
Sarah Lawrence College, B
State University of New York at Binghamton, B
State University of New York College at
    Brockport, B
Syracuse University, M
University at Albany, State University of New
    York, M
Vassar College, B

Ohio

Antioch College, B
Bowling Green State University, B
Kenyon College, B
The Ohio State University, BM
Ohio University, BM
Sinclair Community College, A

Oregon

Portland State University, B

Pennsylvania

Franklin and Marshall College, B
Haverford College, B
University of Pennsylvania, B

Tennessee

Tennessee State University, B
Vanderbilt University, B

Vermont

Marlboro College, B

West Virginia

American Public University System, B
West Virginia University, MD

Wisconsin

University of Wisconsin-Madison, BMD

Ontario

Carleton University, B
University of Toronto, B

York University, B

Quebec

McGill University, B

AGRIBUSINESS

Alabama

Alabama Agricultural and Mechanical University, M

Arizona

Arizona State University at the Polytechnic
    Campus, M
Eastern Arizona College, A
Glendale Community College, A
Yavapai College, A

Arkansas

Arkansas State University, B
Arkansas Tech University, B
University of Arkansas, B

California

Allan Hancock College, A

Colorado

Adams State College, B
Colorado State University, B

Delaware

University of Delaware, B

Florida

Florida Agricultural and Mechanical University, M
University of Florida, M

Georgia

Ogeechee Technical College, A

Illinois

Black Hawk College, A
Illinois State University, BM
University of Illinois at Urbana-Champaign, B

Iowa

Iowa Lakes Community College, A
Northwestern College, B

Kentucky

Morehead State University, A

Louisiana

University of Louisiana at Lafayette, B

Maine

University of Maine, B

Maryland

College of Southern Maryland, A

Michigan

Andrews University, B

Minnesota

South Central Technical College, A

Mississippi

Copiah-Lincoln Community College, A
Mississippi State University, B

Missouri

Central Missouri State University, B
College of the Ozarks, B
Crowder College, A
Lindenwood University, B
Mineral Area College, A
Missouri State University, B

Southeast Missouri State University, B

New Mexico

New Mexico State University, B

North Carolina

James Sprunt Community College, A
North Carolina State University, B
Wayne Community College, A

North Dakota

North Dakota State University, B
Sitting Bull College, A

Ohio

The Ohio State University Agricultural Technical
Institute, A

Pennsylvania

Delaware Valley College, B
The Pennsylvania State University Abington
College, B
The Pennsylvania State University Altoona
College, B
The Pennsylvania State University Beaver Campus
of the Commonwealth College, B
The Pennsylvania State University Berks Campus of
the Berks-Lehigh Valley College, B
The Pennsylvania State University Delaware County
Campus of the Commonwealth College, B
The Pennsylvania State University DuBois Campus
of the Commonwealth College, B
The Pennsylvania State University at Erie, The
Behrend College, B
The Pennsylvania State University Fayette Campus
of the Commonwealth College, B
The Pennsylvania State University Hazleton
Campus of the Commonwealth College, B
The Pennsylvania State University, Lehigh Valley
Campus of the Berks-Lehigh Valley College, B
The Pennsylvania State University McKeesport
Campus of the Commonwealth College, B
The Pennsylvania State University Mont Alto
Campus of the Commonwealth College, B
The Pennsylvania State University New Kensington
Campus of the Commonwealth College, B
The Pennsylvania State University Schuylkill
Campus of the Capital College, B
The Pennsylvania State University Shenango
Campus of the Commonwealth College, B
The Pennsylvania State University University Park
Campus, B
The Pennsylvania State University Wilkes-Barre
Campus of the Commonwealth College, B
The Pennsylvania State University Worthington
Scranton Campus of the Commonwealth
College, B
The Pennsylvania State University York Campus of
the Commonwealth College, B

South Carolina

South Carolina State University, M

South Dakota

South Dakota State University, B

Tennessee

Middle Tennessee State University, B

Texas

Abilene Christian University, B
Clarendon College, A
Sam Houston State University, B
Stephen F. Austin State University, B
Texas A&M University, B
Texas A&M University-Kingsville, M
Texas State University-San Marcos, B
Texas Tech University, M

West Texas A&M University, B

Utah

Brigham Young University, B

Vermont

Vermont Technical College, A

Virginia

Virginia Polytechnic Institute and State University, M

Washington

Washington State University, M

Wisconsin

Northeast Wisconsin Technical College, A
Southwest Wisconsin Technical College, A

Wyoming

Central Wyoming College, A
Eastern Wyoming College, A
Laramie County Community College, A
University of Wyoming, B

Ontario

University of Guelph, M

Quebec

McGill University, B

Saskatchewan

University of Saskatchewan, B

AGRICULTURAL AND DOMESTIC ANIMALS SERVICES

Texas

Tarleton State University, B

Vermont

Sterling College, AB

AGRICULTURAL AND EXTENSION EDUCATION SERVICES

Colorado

Colorado State University, B

Indiana

Vincennes University, A

New York

Cornell University, B

North Carolina

North Carolina State University, B

Pennsylvania

The Pennsylvania State University Abington
College, B
The Pennsylvania State University Altoona
College, B
The Pennsylvania State University Beaver Campus
of the Commonwealth College, B
The Pennsylvania State University Berks Campus of
the Berks-Lehigh Valley College, B
The Pennsylvania State University Delaware County
Campus of the Commonwealth College, B
The Pennsylvania State University DuBois Campus
of the Commonwealth College, B
The Pennsylvania State University at Erie, The
Behrend College, B
The Pennsylvania State University Fayette Campus
of the Commonwealth College, B
The Pennsylvania State University Hazleton
Campus of the Commonwealth College, B

The Pennsylvania State University, Lehigh Valley
Campus of the Berks-Lehigh Valley College, B
The Pennsylvania State University McKeesport
Campus of the Commonwealth College, B
The Pennsylvania State University Mont Alto
Campus of the Commonwealth College, B
The Pennsylvania State University New Kensington
Campus of the Commonwealth College, B
The Pennsylvania State University Schuylkill
Campus of the Capital College, B
The Pennsylvania State University Shenango
Campus of the Commonwealth College, B
The Pennsylvania State University University Park
Campus, B
The Pennsylvania State University Wilkes-Barre
Campus of the Commonwealth College, B
The Pennsylvania State University Worthington
Scranton Campus of the Commonwealth
College, B
The Pennsylvania State University York Campus of
the Commonwealth College, B

AGRICULTURAL AND FOOD PRODUCTS PROCESSING

Florida

University of Florida, B

Kansas

Kansas State University, B

North Carolina

North Carolina State University, A

Ohio

The Ohio State University, B

Texas

Texas A&M University, B
Texas State Technical College Waco, A

British Columbia

The University of British Columbia, B

AGRICULTURAL AND HORTICULTURAL PLANT BREEDING

Colorado

Colorado State University, B

Delaware

Delaware State University, B

New York

Cornell University, B

Vermont

Sterling College, AB

AGRICULTURAL ANIMAL BREEDING

Nevada

University of Nevada, Reno, B

New York

Cornell University, B

Texas

Texas A&M University, B

Vermont

Sterling College, AB

AGRICULTURAL/BIOLOGICAL ENGINEERING AND BIOENGINEERING

Alabama

Auburn University, B

Arizona

The University of Arizona, B

Arkansas

University of Arkansas, B

California

California Polytechnic State University, San Luis Obispo, B
California State Polytechnic University, Pomona, B
University of California, Los Angeles, B

Delaware

University of Delaware, B

Florida

University of Florida, B

Georgia

Fort Valley State University, B
University of Georgia, B

Idaho

University of Idaho, B

Illinois

University of Illinois at Urbana-Champaign, B

Indiana

Purdue University, B

Iowa

Dordt College, B
Iowa State University of Science and Technology, B

Kansas

Kansas State University, B

Kentucky

University of Kentucky, B

Maine

University of Maine, B

Maryland

University of Maryland, College Park, B

Michigan

Michigan State University, B

Minnesota

University of Minnesota, Twin Cities Campus, B

Mississippi

Mississippi State University, B

Missouri

University of Missouri-Rolla, B

Nebraska

University of Nebraska-Lincoln, B

New Jersey

Rutgers, The State University of New Jersey, New Brunswick/Piscataway, B

New York

Cornell University, B
Polytechnic University, Brooklyn Campus, B

State University of New York College of Agriculture and Technology at Cobleskill, A

North Carolina

North Carolina State University, B

North Dakota

North Dakota State University, B

Ohio

The Ohio State University, B

Oregon

Oregon State University, B

Pennsylvania

The Pennsylvania State University Abington College, B
The Pennsylvania State University Altoona College, B
The Pennsylvania State University Beaver Campus of the Commonwealth College, B
The Pennsylvania State University Berks Campus of the Berks-Lehigh Valley College, B
The Pennsylvania State University Delaware County Campus of the Commonwealth College, B
The Pennsylvania State University DuBois Campus of the Commonwealth College, B
The Pennsylvania State University at Erie, The Behrend College, B
The Pennsylvania State University Fayette Campus of the Commonwealth College, B
The Pennsylvania State University Hazleton Campus of the Commonwealth College, B
The Pennsylvania State University, Lehigh Valley Campus of the Berks-Lehigh Valley College, B
The Pennsylvania State University McKeesport Campus of the Commonwealth College, B
The Pennsylvania State University Mont Alto Campus of the Commonwealth College, B
The Pennsylvania State University New Kensington Campus of the Commonwealth College, B
The Pennsylvania State University Schuylkill Campus of the Capital College, B
The Pennsylvania State University Shenango Campus of the Commonwealth College, B
The Pennsylvania State University University Park Campus, B
The Pennsylvania State University Wilkes-Barre Campus of the Commonwealth College, B
The Pennsylvania State University Worthington Scranton Campus of the Commonwealth College, B
The Pennsylvania State University York Campus of the Commonwealth College, B

South Carolina

Clemson University, B

South Dakota

South Dakota State University, B

Tennessee

Tennessee Technological University, B
The University of Tennessee, B

Texas

Texas A&M University, B

Utah

Utah State University, B

Wisconsin

University of Wisconsin-Madison, B
University of Wisconsin-River Falls, B

Alberta

University of Alberta, B

Manitoba

University of Manitoba, B

Nova Scotia

Dalhousie University, B

Quebec

McGill University, B

Saskatchewan

University of Saskatchewan, B

AGRICULTURAL BUSINESS AND MANAGEMENT

Alabama

Enterprise-Ozark Community College, A
Jefferson State Community College, A
Tuskegee University, B

Arizona

Arizona State University at the Polytechnic Campus, B
Arizona Western College, A
Cochise College (Douglas), A
Mesa Community College, A
Yavapai College, A

Arkansas

North Arkansas College, A
Phillips Community College of the University of Arkansas, A
Southern Arkansas University-Magnolia, B

California

Bakersfield College, A
Butte College, A
California Polytechnic State University, San Luis Obispo, B
California State Polytechnic University, Pomona, B
California State University, Chico, B
California State University, Fresno, B
City College of San Francisco, A
College of the Desert, A
College of the Redwoods, A
College of the Sequoias, A
Cosumnes River College (Sacramento), A
Hartnell College, A
Imperial Valley College, A
Lassen Community College District, A
Merced College, A
Modesto Junior College, A
Mt. San Antonio College, A
Oxnard College, A
Porterville College, A
Reedley College, A
San Diego State University, B
San Joaquin Delta College, A
Santa Rosa Junior College, A
Shasta College, A
University of California, Davis, B
West Hills Community College, A
Yuba College, A

Colorado

Fort Lewis College, B
Lamar Community College, A
Northeastern Junior College, A
Otero Junior College, A

Delaware

Delaware State University, B
Delaware Technical & Community College, Jack F. Owens Campus, A
University of Delaware, B

Florida

Florida Agricultural and Mechanical University, B
Florida Southern College, B
Indian River Community College, A
South Florida Community College, A

Georgia

Abraham Baldwin Agricultural College, A
Clayton State University, A
Coastal Georgia Community College, A
South Georgia College, A

University of Georgia, B

Hawaii

University of Hawaii at Hilo, B

Idaho

Brigham Young University -Idaho, A
College of Southern Idaho, A
University of Idaho, B

Illinois

Carl Sandburg College, A
Danville Area Community College, A
Highland Community College, A
Illinois Central College, A
Illinois Eastern Community Colleges, Wabash Valley
 College, A
Illinois Valley Community College, A
John Wood Community College, A
Joliet Junior College, A
Kaskaskia College, A
Kishwaukee College, A
Lake Land College, A
Parkland College, A
Rend Lake College, A
Richland Community College, A
Shawnee Community College, A

Indiana

Vincennes University, A

Iowa

Des Moines Area Community College, A
Dordt College, AB
Ellsworth Community College, A
Hawkeye Community College, A
Iowa Lakes Community College, A
Iowa State University of Science and Technology, B
Iowa Western Community College, A
Kirkwood Community College, A
Northeast Iowa Community College, A
Southeastern Community College, North Campus, A
Southwestern Community College, A
Upper Iowa University, B

Kansas

Barton County Community College, A
Butler Community College, A
Central Christian College of Kansas, A
Cloud County Community College, A
Coffeyville Community College, A
Colby Community College, A
Dodge City Community College, A
Fort Hays State University, B
Fort Scott Community College, A
Garden City Community College, A
Highland Community College, A
Kansas State University, B
McPherson College, B
Pratt Community College, A
Tabor College, B

Kentucky

Berea College, B
Eastern Kentucky University, B
Murray State University, B
St. Catharine College, A

Louisiana

Louisiana State University and Agricultural and
 Mechanical College, B
Louisiana Tech University, B
Nicholls State University, B
University of Louisiana at Monroe, B

Maryland

University of Maryland Eastern Shore, B

Massachusetts

Simon's Rock College of Bard, B

Michigan

Andrews University, AB
Michigan State University, B

St. Clair County Community College, A

Minnesota

Ridgewater College, A
Southwest Minnesota State University, AB
University of Minnesota, Crookston, AB
University of Minnesota, Twin Cities Campus, B
Vermilion Community College, A

Mississippi

Alcorn State University, B
Copiah-Lincoln Community College, A
Hinds Community College, A
Itawamba Community College, A
Mississippi Delta Community College, A
Mississippi Gulf Coast Community College, A
Northwest Mississippi Community College, A

Missouri

Central Missouri State University, B
Lincoln University, B
North Central Missouri College, A
Northwest Missouri State University, B
State Fair Community College, A
Three Rivers Community College, A
Truman State University, B
University of Missouri-Columbia, B

Montana

Dawson Community College, A
Montana State University, B
Montana State University-Northern, A
Rocky Mountain College, B

Nebraska

Central Community College-Columbus Campus, A
Central Community College-Hastings Campus, A
Grace University, B
Nebraska College of Technical Agriculture, A
Northeast Community College, A
Southeast Community College, Beatrice Campus, A
University of Nebraska at Kearney, B
University of Nebraska-Lincoln, B
Wayne State College, B

New Hampshire

University of New Hampshire, AB

New Jersey

County College of Morris, A
Cumberland County College, A

New Mexico

Eastern New Mexico University, B

New York

Cornell University, B
State University of New York College of Agriculture
 and Technology at Cobleskill, AB
State University of New York College of Agriculture
 and Technology at Morrisville, A
State University of New York College of Technology
 at Alfred, A

North Carolina

Lenoir Community College, A
North Carolina Agricultural and Technical State
 University, B
North Carolina State University, A
Surry Community College, A

North Dakota

Bismarck State College, A
Dickinson State University, AB
Lake Region State College, A
North Dakota State College of Science, A
North Dakota State University, B

Ohio

Capital University, B
Clark State Community College, A
The Ohio State University, B
The Ohio State University Agricultural Technical
 Institute, A

Owens Community College, A
University of Northwestern Ohio, A
Wilmington College, B

Oklahoma

Carl Albert State College, A
Eastern Oklahoma State College, A
Northeastern Oklahoma Agricultural and Mechanical
 College, A
Northern Oklahoma College, A
Northwestern Oklahoma State University, B
Oklahoma Panhandle State University, B
Oklahoma State University, B
Redlands Community College, A
Rogers State University, A

Oregon

Blue Mountain Community College, A
Eastern Oregon University, B
Linn-Benton Community College, A
Oregon State University, B
Treasure Valley Community College, A

Pennsylvania

Harrisburg Area Community College, A
The Pennsylvania State University Abington
 College, A
The Pennsylvania State University Altoona
 College, A
The Pennsylvania State University Beaver Campus
 of the Commonwealth College, A
The Pennsylvania State University Berks Campus of
 the Berks-Lehigh Valley College, A
The Pennsylvania State University Delaware County
 Campus of the Commonwealth College, A
The Pennsylvania State University DuBois Campus
 of the Commonwealth College, A
The Pennsylvania State University at Erie, The
 Behrend College, A
The Pennsylvania State University Fayette Campus
 of the Commonwealth College, A
The Pennsylvania State University Hazleton
 Campus of the Commonwealth College, A
The Pennsylvania State University, Lehigh Valley
 Campus of the Berks-Lehigh Valley College, A
The Pennsylvania State University McKeesport
 Campus of the Commonwealth College, A
The Pennsylvania State University Mont Alto
 Campus of the Commonwealth College, A
The Pennsylvania State University New Kensington
 Campus of the Commonwealth College, AB
The Pennsylvania State University Schuylkill
 Campus of the Capital College, A
The Pennsylvania State University Shenango
 Campus of the Commonwealth College, A
The Pennsylvania State University University Park
 Campus, A
The Pennsylvania State University Wilkes-Barre
 Campus of the Commonwealth College, A
The Pennsylvania State University Worthington
 Scranton Campus of the Commonwealth
 College, A
The Pennsylvania State University York Campus of
 the Commonwealth College, A

Puerto Rico

University of Puerto Rico, Mayagüez Campus, B

South Carolina

Clemson University, B
South Carolina State University, B

South Dakota

Lake Area Technical Institute, A
Mitchell Technical Institute, A
Western Dakota Technical Institute, A

Tennessee

Columbia State Community College, A
Freed-Hardeman University, B
Jackson State Community College, A
Martin Methodist College, A
Tennessee Technological University, B
The University of Tennessee, B

The University of Tennessee at Martin, B

Texas

Brazosport College, A
Cisco Junior College, A
Frank Phillips College, A
Hardin-Simmons University, B
Hill College of the Hill Junior College District, A
Lubbock Christian University, B
Sam Houston State University, B
Sul Ross State University, B
Texas A&M University, B
Texas A&M University-Kingsville, B
Texas Tech University, B
Tyler Junior College, A
West Texas A&M University, B

Utah

Brigham Young University, B
Snow College, A
Utah State University, B

Vermont

Sterling College, B

Virginia

Lord Fairfax Community College, A

Washington

Columbia Basin College, A
Spokane Community College, A
Walla Walla Community College, A
Yakima Valley Community College, A

West Virginia

Potomac State College of West Virginia
    University, A

Wisconsin

Chippewa Valley Technical College, A
Fox Valley Technical College, A
Milwaukee Area Technical College, A
Northeast Wisconsin Technical College, A
University of Wisconsin-Madison, B
University of Wisconsin-Platteville, B
University of Wisconsin-River Falls, B

Wyoming

Casper College, A
Central Wyoming College, A
Northwest College, A
Sheridan College-Sheridan and Gillette, A

Alberta

University of Alberta, B
University of Lethbridge, B

Nova Scotia

Nova Scotia Agricultural College, B

Ontario

University of Guelph, B

Quebec

McGill University, B

AGRICULTURAL BUSINESS TECHNOLOGY

Iowa

Iowa Lakes Community College, A
North Iowa Area Community College, A

Mississippi

Copiah-Lincoln Community College, A

Ohio

The Ohio State University Agricultural Technical
    Institute, A

Wyoming

Laramie County Community College, A

AGRICULTURAL COMMUNICATION/JOURNALISM

Arkansas

University of Arkansas, B

Georgia

University of Georgia, B

Illinois

University of Illinois at Urbana-Champaign, B

Michigan

Michigan State University, B

Missouri

University of Missouri-Columbia, B

Nebraska

University of Nebraska-Lincoln, B

Ohio

The Ohio State University Agricultural Technical
    Institute, A

Oklahoma

Oklahoma State University, B

Texas

Texas Tech University, B

Vermont

Sterling College, B

Washington

Washington State University, B

Wyoming

University of Wyoming, B

AGRICULTURAL ECONOMICS

Alabama

Alabama Agricultural and Mechanical University, B
Auburn University, BMD
James H. Faulkner State Community College, A
Tuskegee University, M

Arizona

The University of Arizona, BM

Arkansas

University of Arkansas, BM
University of Arkansas at Pine Bluff, B

California

Butte College, A
California Polytechnic State University, San Luis
    Obispo, M
Lassen Community College District, A
University of California, Berkeley, D
University of California, Davis, MDO
University of California, Santa Barbara, MD

Colorado

Colorado State University, BMD
Northeastern Junior College, A

Connecticut

University of Connecticut, BMD

Delaware

University of Delaware, BM

Florida

University of Florida, BMD

Georgia

Abraham Baldwin Agricultural College, A
Fort Valley State University, B

University of Georgia, BMD

Hawaii

University of Hawaii at Manoa, B

Idaho

Brigham Young University -Idaho, A
University of Idaho, BM

Illinois

Southern Illinois University Carbondale, BMO
University of Illinois at Urbana-Champaign, BMD

Indiana

Purdue University, BMD

Iowa

Iowa Lakes Community College, A
Iowa State University of Science and
    Technology, MD
North Iowa Area Community College, A

Kansas

Coffeyville Community College, A
Colby Community College, A
Dodge City Community College, A
Fort Scott Community College, A
Garden City Community College, A
Highland Community College, A
Kansas State University, BMD
McPherson College, B
Pratt Community College, A

Kentucky

University of Kentucky, BMD

Louisiana

Louisiana State University and Agricultural and
    Mechanical College, MD
Southern University and Agricultural and Mechanical
    College, B

Maine

University of Maine, BM

Maryland

University of Maryland, College Park, BMD

Massachusetts

University of Massachusetts Amherst, MD

Michigan

Michigan State University, BMD

Minnesota

University of Minnesota, Twin Cities Campus, MD
Vermilion Community College, A

Mississippi

Alcorn State University, BM
Copiah-Lincoln Community College, A
Hinds Community College, A
Mississippi Delta Community College, A
Mississippi State University, BMD
Northwest Mississippi Community College, A

Missouri

Central Missouri State University, B
Northwest Missouri State University, BM
Truman State University, B
University of Missouri-Columbia, BMD

Montana

Montana State University, M

Nebraska

University of Nebraska-Lincoln, BMD

Nevada

University of Nevada, Reno, BM

New Jersey

Rutgers, The State University of New Jersey, New Brunswick/Piscataway, M

New Mexico

New Mexico State University, BM

New York

Cornell University, BMD

North Carolina

North Carolina Agricultural and Technical State University, BM
North Carolina State University, BM

North Dakota

North Dakota State University, BM

Ohio

The Ohio State University, BMD
The Ohio State University Agricultural Technical Institute, A

Oklahoma

Eastern Oklahoma State College, A
Langston University, B
Northeastern Oklahoma Agricultural and Mechanical College, A
Oklahoma State University, BMD

Oregon

Eastern Oregon University, B
Oregon State University, BMD

Pennsylvania

The Pennsylvania State University University Park Campus, MD

Puerto Rico

University of Puerto Rico, Mayagüez Campus, BM

Rhode Island

University of Rhode Island, MD

South Carolina

Clemson University, BM

South Dakota

South Dakota State University, B

Tennessee

The University of Tennessee, BM

Texas

Clarendon College, A
Frank Phillips College, A
Hill College of the Hill Junior College District, A
Prairie View A&M University, M
South Plains College, A
Tarleton State University, B
Texas A&M University, BMD
Texas A&M University-Commerce, B
Texas Tech University, BMDO
Tyler Junior College, A
West Texas A&M University, M

Utah

Brigham Young University, B
Snow College, A
Utah State University, B

Vermont

University of Vermont, BM

Virginia

Virginia Polytechnic Institute and State University, BMD

Washington

Washington State University, MD

West Virginia

Potomac State College of West Virginia University, A

West Virginia University, BM

Wisconsin

University of Wisconsin-Madison, BMD

Wyoming

Eastern Wyoming College, A
Northwest College, A
University of Wyoming, M

Alberta

University of Alberta, BMDO

British Columbia

The University of British Columbia, AM

Manitoba

University of Manitoba, BMD

Nova Scotia

Nova Scotia Agricultural College, B

Ontario

University of Guelph, BMD

Quebec

McGill University, BM
Université Laval, BM

Saskatchewan

University of Saskatchewan, BMD

AGRICULTURAL EDUCATION

Arizona

The University of Arizona, M

Arkansas

Arkansas State University, MO
University of Arkansas, M

Florida

Florida Agricultural and Mechanical University, M
University of Florida, MD

Georgia

University of Georgia, M

Idaho

University of Idaho, M

Illinois

University of Illinois at Urbana-Champaign, M

Indiana

Purdue University, MDO

Iowa

Iowa State University of Science and Technology, MD

Kentucky

Eastern Kentucky University, M

Louisiana

Louisiana State University and Agricultural and Mechanical College, MD

Minnesota

University of Minnesota, Twin Cities Campus, MD

Mississippi

Alcorn State University, M
Mississippi State University, M

Missouri

Northwest Missouri State University, M
University of Missouri-Columbia, MDO

Nebraska

University of Nebraska-Lincoln, M

New Mexico

New Mexico State University, M

New York

Cornell University, MD

North Carolina

North Carolina Agricultural and Technical State University, M
North Carolina State University, M

North Dakota

North Dakota State University, M

Ohio

The Ohio State University, MD

Oklahoma

Oklahoma State University, MD

Oregon

Oregon State University, M

Pennsylvania

The Pennsylvania State University University Park Campus, MD

Puerto Rico

University of Puerto Rico, Mayagüez Campus, M

South Carolina

Clemson University, M

Tennessee

The University of Tennessee, M

Texas

Stephen F. Austin State University, M
Texas A&M University, MD
Texas A&M University-Commerce, M
Texas A&M University-Kingsville, M
Texas State University-San Marcos, M
Texas Tech University, MD

Utah

Utah State University, M

West Virginia

West Virginia University, M

Wisconsin

University of Wisconsin-River Falls, M

AGRICULTURAL ENGINEERING

Arizona

The University of Arizona, MD

Colorado

Colorado State University, MD

Florida

University of Florida, MDO

Georgia

University of Georgia, MD

Idaho

University of Idaho, MD

Illinois

University of Illinois at Urbana-Champaign, MD

Indiana

Purdue University, MD

Iowa

Iowa State University of Science and Technology, MD

Kansas

Kansas State University, MD

Kentucky

University of Kentucky, MD

Louisiana

Louisiana State University and Agricultural and
Mechanical College, MD

Maryland

University of Maryland, College Park, MD

Michigan

Michigan State University, MD

Minnesota

University of Minnesota, Twin Cities Campus, MD

Missouri

University of Missouri-Columbia, MD

Nebraska

University of Nebraska-Lincoln, M

New Jersey

Rutgers, The State University of New Jersey, New
Brunswick/Piscataway, M

New York

Cornell University, MD

North Carolina

North Carolina Agricultural and Technical State
University, M
North Carolina State University, MD

North Dakota

North Dakota State University, MD

Ohio

The Ohio State University, MD
University of Dayton, M

Oklahoma

Oklahoma State University, MD

Pennsylvania

The Pennsylvania State University University Park
Campus, MD

South Dakota

South Dakota State University, MD

Tennessee

The University of Tennessee, M

Texas

Texas A&M University, MD

Utah

Utah State University, MD

Virginia

Virginia Polytechnic Institute and State
University, MD

Wisconsin

University of Wisconsin-Madison, MD

Nova Scotia

Dalhousie University, MD

Quebec

McGill University, MD
Université Laval, M

Saskatchewan

University of Saskatchewan, MD

AGRICULTURAL/FARM SUPPLIES RETAILING AND WHOLESALING

Iowa

Iowa Lakes Community College, A
Muscatine Community College, A

Western Iowa Tech Community College, A

Mississippi

Copiah-Lincoln Community College, A

North Dakota

North Dakota State College of Science, A

Texas

Texas A&M University, B

Wisconsin

Wisconsin Indianhead Technical College, A

AGRICULTURAL MECHANICS AND EQUIPMENT/MACHINE TECHNOLOGY

Illinois

Black Hawk College, A

Iowa

Iowa Lakes Community College, A

New York

Cornell University, B

AGRICULTURAL MECHANIZATION

Arizona

Mesa Community College, A

California

College of the Sequoias, A
Cosumnes River College (Sacramento), A
Cuesta College, A
Imperial Valley College, A
Lassen Community College District, A
Modesto Junior College, A
Mt. San Antonio College, A
Oxnard College, A
Reedley College, A
San Joaquin Delta College, A
Santa Rosa Junior College, A
Sierra College, A
West Hills Community College, A
Yuba College, A

Colorado

Aims Community College, A
Northeastern Junior College, A

Florida

South Florida Community College, A

Georgia

Abraham Baldwin Agricultural College, A
Clayton State University, A
Southwest Georgia Technical College, A

Hawaii

Maui Community College, A

Idaho

University of Idaho, B

Illinois

Black Hawk College, A
Carl Sandburg College, A
Highland Community College, A
Illinois Central College, A
Kishwaukee College, A
Lake Land College, A
Parkland College, A
Rend Lake College, A
Southeastern Illinois College, A
Spoon River College, A

University of Illinois at Urbana-Champaign, B

Indiana

Purdue University, B
Vincennes University, A

Iowa

Hawkeye Community College, A
Indian Hills Community College, A
Iowa Lakes Community College, A
Iowa State University of Science and Technology, B

Kansas

Coffeyville Community College, A
Cowley County Community College and Area
Vocational-Technical School, A
Dodge City Community College, A
Fort Scott Community College, A
Garden City Community College, A
Hutchinson Community College and Area Vocational
School, A
Kansas State University, B
Pratt Community College, A

Maryland

Garrett College, A

Michigan

Andrews University, AB
St. Clair County Community College, A

Minnesota

Ridgewater College, A
South Central Technical College, A

Mississippi

Hinds Community College, A
Northwest Mississippi Community College, A

Missouri

College of the Ozarks, B
Longview Community College, A
Northwest Missouri State University, B
State Fair Community College, A
Three Rivers Community College, A
University of Missouri-Columbia, B

Montana

Fort Peck Community College, A
Miles Community College, A
Montana State University, B
Montana State University-Northern, A
The University of Montana-Helena College of
Technology, A

Nebraska

Nebraska College of Technical Agriculture, A
Northeast Community College, A
Southeast Community College, Beatrice Campus, A
University of Nebraska-Lincoln, B

New York

State University of New York College of Agriculture
and Technology at Cobleskill, AB
State University of New York College of Agriculture
and Technology at Morrisville, A

North Carolina

Beaufort County Community College, A
North Carolina Agricultural and Technical State
University, B

North Dakota

North Dakota State College of Science, A
North Dakota State University, B

Ohio

Clark State Community College, A
The Ohio State University Agricultural Technical
Institute, A

Oregon

Lane Community College, A
Treasure Valley Community College, A

Pennsylvania

The Pennsylvania State University Abington
College, B

The Pennsylvania State University Beaver Campus of the Commonwealth College, B
The Pennsylvania State University Berks Campus of the Berks-Lehigh Valley College, B
The Pennsylvania State University Delaware County Campus of the Commonwealth College, B
The Pennsylvania State University DuBois Campus of the Commonwealth College, B
The Pennsylvania State University at Erie, The Behrend College, B
The Pennsylvania State University Fayette Campus of the Commonwealth College, B
The Pennsylvania State University Hazleton Campus of the Commonwealth College, B
The Pennsylvania State University, Lehigh Valley Campus of the Berks-Lehigh Valley College, B
The Pennsylvania State University McKeesport Campus of the Commonwealth College, B
The Pennsylvania State University Mont Alto Campus of the Commonwealth College, B
The Pennsylvania State University New Kensington Campus of the Commonwealth College, B
The Pennsylvania State University Schuylkill Campus of the Capital College, B
The Pennsylvania State University Shenango Campus of the Commonwealth College, B
The Pennsylvania State University University Park Campus, B
The Pennsylvania State University Wilkes-Barre Campus of the Commonwealth College, B
The Pennsylvania State University Worthington Scranton Campus of the Commonwealth College, B
The Pennsylvania State University York Campus of the Commonwealth College, B

Puerto Rico

University of Puerto Rico, Mayagüez Campus, B

South Carolina

Clemson University, B

South Dakota

South Dakota State University, B

Tennessee

Walters State Community College, A

Texas

Frank Phillips College, A
Navarro College, A
North Central Texas College, A
Paris Junior College, A
Sam Houston State University, B
Southwest Texas Junior College, A
Stephen F. Austin State University, B

Washington

Columbia Basin College, A
Walla Walla Community College, A
Washington State University, B
Wenatchee Valley College, A
Yakima Valley Community College, A

West Virginia

Potomac State College of West Virginia University, A

Wisconsin

Madison Area Technical College, A
Northeast Wisconsin Technical College, A
Southwest Wisconsin Technical College, A
Western Technical College, A

Wyoming

Casper College, A
Northwest College, A

Nova Scotia

Nova Scotia Agricultural College, B

AGRICULTURAL POWER MACHINERY OPERATION

Iowa

Iowa Lakes Community College, A

Minnesota

University of Minnesota, Crookston, B

Ohio

The Ohio State University Agricultural Technical Institute, A

AGRICULTURAL PRODUCTION OPERATIONS

Arkansas

University of Arkansas at Monticello, A

California

Modesto Junior College, A

Florida

Hillsborough Community College, A

Hawaii

University of Hawaii at Manoa, B

Illinois

Black Hawk College, A
Illinois Eastern Community Colleges, Wabash Valley College, A
John Wood Community College, A
Kishwaukee College, A
Lake Land College, A
Lincoln Land Community College, A
Rend Lake College, A

Iowa

Iowa Lakes Community College, A
Muscatine Community College, A
North Iowa Area Community College, A

Kansas

Allen County Community College, A

Kentucky

Eastern Kentucky University, B
Western Kentucky University, A

Michigan

Northwestern Michigan College, A

Minnesota

South Central Technical College, A

Nebraska

Northeast Community College, A

North Carolina

Wayne Community College, A

North Dakota

North Dakota State College of Science, A

Ohio

Southern State Community College, A

Puerto Rico

University of Puerto Rico at Utuado, A

South Dakota

Mitchell Technical Institute, A

Tennessee

The University of Tennessee at Martin, B

Texas

Stephen F. Austin State University, B
Tarleton State University, B

Texas A&M University, B
Texas Tech University, B

Vermont

Sterling College, AB

Washington

Walla Walla Community College, A

Wyoming

Laramie County Community College, A

AGRICULTURAL PUBLIC SERVICES

Vermont

Sterling College, AB

AGRICULTURAL SCIENCES

Alabama

Alabama Agricultural and Mechanical University, MD
Auburn University, MD
Tuskegee University, M

Arizona

The University of Arizona, MD

Arkansas

Arkansas State University, MO
University of Arkansas, MD

California

California Polytechnic State University, San Luis Obispo, M
California State Polytechnic University, Pomona, M
California State University, Fresno, M
University of California, Davis, M

Colorado

Colorado State University, MD

Connecticut

University of Connecticut, MD

Delaware

University of Delaware, MD

Florida

University of Florida, MDO

Georgia

University of Georgia, MD

Hawaii

University of Hawaii at Manoa, MD

Idaho

University of Idaho, M

Illinois

Illinois State University, M
Southern Illinois University Carbondale, MO
University of Illinois at Urbana-Champaign, MDO

Indiana

Purdue University, MD

Iowa

Iowa State University of Science and Technology, MD

Kansas

Kansas State University, MD

Kentucky

Murray State University, M
University of Kentucky, MD

Western Kentucky University, M

Louisiana

Louisiana State University and Agricultural and
  Mechanical College, MD
Southern University and Agricultural and Mechanical
  College, M

Maine

University of Maine, MD

Maryland

University of Maryland, College Park, MDP
University of Maryland Eastern Shore, MD

Michigan

Michigan State University, MD

Minnesota

University of Minnesota, Twin Cities Campus, MD

Mississippi

Alcorn State University, M
Mississippi State University, MD

Missouri

Missouri State University, M
Northwest Missouri State University, M
University of Missouri-Columbia, MDO

Montana

Montana State University, MD

Nebraska

University of Nebraska-Lincoln, MD

Nevada

University of Nevada, Reno, MD

New Mexico

New Mexico State University, MD

North Carolina

North Carolina Agricultural and Technical State
  University, M
North Carolina State University, MD

North Dakota

North Dakota State University, MD

Ohio

The Ohio State University, MD

Oklahoma

Oklahoma State University, MD

Oregon

Oregon State University, MD

Pennsylvania

The Pennsylvania State University University Park
  Campus, MD

Puerto Rico

University of Puerto Rico, Mayagüez Campus, M

South Carolina

Clemson University, MD

South Dakota

South Dakota State University, MD

Tennessee

Tennessee State University, MD
The University of Tennessee, MD

Texas

Angelo State University, M
Prairie View A&M University, M
Sam Houston State University, M
Tarleton State University, M
Texas A&M University, MD

Texas A&M University-Commerce, M
Texas A&M University-Kingsville, MD
Texas Tech University, MDO
West Texas A&M University, MD

Utah

Brigham Young University, MD
Utah State University, MD

Vermont

University of Vermont, MD

Virginia

Virginia Polytechnic Institute and State
  University, MD

Washington

Washington State University, MD

West Virginia

West Virginia University, MD

Wisconsin

University of Wisconsin-Madison, MD
University of Wisconsin-River Falls, M

Wyoming

University of Wyoming, MD

Alberta

University of Alberta, MDO
University of Lethbridge, M

British Columbia

The University of British Columbia, MD

Manitoba

University of Manitoba, MD

Nova Scotia

Dalhousie University, M
Nova Scotia Agricultural College, M

Ontario

University of Guelph, MDO

Quebec

McGill University, MDO
Université Laval, MDO

Saskatchewan

University of Saskatchewan, MD

AGRICULTURAL TEACHER EDUCATION

Alabama

Auburn University, B
Northwest-Shoals Community College, A

Arizona

The University of Arizona, B

Arkansas

Arkansas State University, B
Southern Arkansas University-Magnolia, B
University of Arkansas, B
University of Arkansas at Pine Bluff, B

California

California State Polytechnic University, Pomona, B
California State University, Chico, B
California State University, Fresno, B
College of the Sequoias, A
Victor Valley College, A

Colorado

Colorado State University, B
Lamar Community College, A

Northeastern Junior College, A

Connecticut

University of Connecticut, B

Delaware

University of Delaware, B

Florida

University of Florida, B

Georgia

South Georgia College, A
University of Georgia, B

Idaho

University of Idaho, B

Illinois

Spoon River College, A
University of Illinois at Urbana-Champaign, B

Indiana

Purdue University, B

Iowa

Dordt College, B
Iowa Lakes Community College, A
Iowa State University of Science and Technology, B
Kirkwood Community College, A

Kansas

Coffeyville Community College, A
Colby Community College, A
Fort Scott Community College, A
Highland Community College, A
Pratt Community College, A

Kentucky

Murray State University, B

Louisiana

Louisiana Tech University, B
McNeese State University, B
Southern University and Agricultural and Mechanical
  College, B

Maryland

University of Maryland Eastern Shore, B

Michigan

Andrews University, B

Minnesota

University of Minnesota, Crookston, B
University of Minnesota, Twin Cities Campus, B
Vermilion Community College, A

Mississippi

Hinds Community College, A
Mississippi State University, B
Northeast Mississippi Community College, A

Missouri

College of the Ozarks, B
Missouri State University, B
Northwest Missouri State University, B
University of Missouri-Columbia, B

Montana

Montana State University, B

Nebraska

University of Nebraska-Lincoln, B

Nevada

University of Nevada, Reno, B

New Hampshire

University of New Hampshire, B

New Mexico

Eastern New Mexico University, B
New Mexico State University, B

New York

Cornell University, B
State University of New York at Oswego, B

North Carolina

North Carolina Agricultural and Technical State
    University, B
North Carolina State University, B

North Dakota

North Dakota State University, B

Ohio

The Ohio State University, B
The Ohio State University Agricultural Technical
    Institute, A
The University of Akron, B
Wilmington College, B

Oklahoma

Eastern Oklahoma State College, A
Langston University, B
Murray State College, A
Oklahoma Panhandle State University, B
Oklahoma State University, B
Redlands Community College, A

Oregon

Chemeketa Community College, A
Linn-Benton Community College, A

Puerto Rico

University of Puerto Rico, Mayagüez Campus, B

South Carolina

Clemson University, B

South Dakota

South Dakota State University, B

Tennessee

Tennessee Technological University, B
The University of Tennessee, B
The University of Tennessee at Martin, B

Texas

Frank Phillips College, A
Prairie View A&M University, B
Sam Houston State University, B
Tarleton State University, B
Texas A&M University-Commerce, B
Texas A&M University-Kingsville, B
Trinity Valley Community College, A
Tyler Junior College, A
Western Texas College, A

Utah

Utah State University, B

Vermont

Sterling College, B

Washington

Washington State University, B

West Virginia

Potomac State College of West Virginia
    University, A
West Virginia University, B

Wisconsin

University of Wisconsin-Madison, B
University of Wisconsin-Platteville, B
University of Wisconsin-River Falls, B

Wyoming

Eastern Wyoming College, A
Northwest College, A

University of Wyoming, B

AGRICULTURE

Alabama

Auburn University, B
Calhoun Community College, A
Chattahoochee Valley Community College, A
Tuskegee University, B
Wallace State Community College, A

Arizona

Arizona Western College, A
Central Arizona College, A
Eastern Arizona College, A
Northland Pioneer College, A
The University of Arizona, B
Yavapai College, A

Arkansas

Arkansas Northeastern College, A
Arkansas State University, B
Arkansas State University-Beebe, A
North Arkansas College, A
Southern Arkansas University-Magnolia, B
University of Arkansas at Monticello, B
University of Arkansas at Pine Bluff, B

California

Bakersfield College, A
Butte College, A
California Polytechnic State University, San Luis
    Obispo, B
California State Polytechnic University, Pomona, B
California State University, Stanislaus, B
Cerritos College, A
College of the Sequoias, A
Fullerton College, A
Imperial Valley College, A
Lassen Community College District, A
Los Angeles Pierce College, A
Mendocino College, A
Merced College, A
Modesto Junior College, A
Mt. San Antonio College, A
Napa Valley College, A
Palo Verde College, A
Reedley College, A
San Joaquin Delta College, A
Santa Rosa Junior College, A
Ventura College, A
Yuba College, A

Colorado

Colorado State University, B
Fort Lewis College, A
Lamar Community College, A
Northeastern Junior College, A

Connecticut

University of Connecticut, B

Delaware

Delaware State University, B
University of Delaware, AB

Florida

Chipola College, A
Daytona Beach Community College, A
Florida Agricultural and Mechanical University, B
Miami Dade College, A
Pensacola Junior College, A

Georgia

Abraham Baldwin Agricultural College, A
Andrew College, A
Bainbridge College, A
Clayton State University, A
Dalton State College, A
Darton College, A
East Georgia College, A
Georgia Highlands College, A
Gordon College, A

Macon State College, A
South Georgia College, A
University of Georgia, B
Waycross College, A
Young Harris College, A

Guam

University of Guam, B

Hawaii

Hawaii Community College, A
University of Hawaii at Hilo, B

Idaho

Brigham Young University -Idaho, A
College of Southern Idaho, A
North Idaho College, A
University of Idaho, B

Illinois

Danville Area Community College, A
Illinois State University, B
Illinois Valley Community College, A
John A. Logan College, A
Rend Lake College, A
Shawnee Community College, A
Southern Illinois University Carbondale, B
University of Illinois at Urbana-Champaign, B
Western Illinois University, B

Indiana

Purdue University, AB

Iowa

Dordt College, B
Iowa Lakes Community College, A
Iowa State University of Science and Technology, B
Kirkwood Community College, A

Kansas

Barton County Community College, A
Coffeyville Community College, A
Colby Community College, A
Cowley County Community College and Area
    Vocational-Technical School, A
Fort Hays State University, B
Fort Scott Community College, A
Garden City Community College, A
Highland Community College, A
Hutchinson Community College and Area Vocational
    School, A
Pratt Community College, A
Seward County Community College, A

Kentucky

Berea College, B
Eastern Kentucky University, B
Morehead State University, B
Murray State University, AB
Owensboro Community and Technical College, A
St. Catharine College, A
Western Kentucky University, B

Louisiana

McNeese State University, B
University of Louisiana at Lafayette, B

Maryland

University of Maryland, College Park, B
University of Maryland Eastern Shore, B

Massachusetts

Hampshire College, B

Michigan

Andrews University, AB
Macomb Community College, A

St. Clair County Community College, A

Minnesota

University of Minnesota, Crookston, AB
University of Minnesota, Twin Cities Campus, B

Mississippi

Alcorn State University, B
Copiah-Lincoln Community College, A
Holmes Community College, A
Jones County Junior College, A
Mississippi State University, B
Northeast Mississippi Community College, A
Northwest Mississippi Community College, A

Missouri

Crowder College, A
Lincoln University, B
Missouri State University, B
Missouri State University-West Plains, A
Northwest Missouri State University, B
Southeast Missouri State University, B
State Fair Community College, A
Truman State University, B
University of Missouri-Columbia, B

Montana

Chief Dull Knife College, A

Nebraska

Northeast Community College, A
Southeast Community College, Beatrice Campus, A
University of Nebraska-Lincoln, B
Western Nebraska Community College, A

New Hampshire

University of New Hampshire, B

New Jersey

Cumberland County College, A
Rutgers, The State University of New Jersey, New
Brunswick/Piscataway, B

New Mexico

New Mexico Junior College, A
New Mexico State University, B
New Mexico State University-Carlsbad, A
University of New Mexico-Valencia Campus, A

New York

Cornell University, B
State University of New York College of Agriculture
and Technology at Cobleskill, A
State University of New York College of Agriculture
and Technology at Morrisville, A
State University of New York College of Technology
at Alfred, A

North Carolina

Chowan University, B
Lenoir Community College, A
North Carolina Agricultural and Technical State
University, B
North Carolina State University, A

North Dakota

North Dakota State University, B
Williston State College, A

Ohio

Clark State Community College, A
Wilmington College, B

Oklahoma

Cameron University, B
Murray State College, A
Northwestern Oklahoma State University, B
Oklahoma Panhandle State University, A
Oklahoma State University, B
Redlands Community College, A

Tulsa Community College, A

Oregon

Linn-Benton Community College, A
Oregon State University, B
Treasure Valley Community College, A
Umpqua Community College, A

Pennsylvania

The Pennsylvania State University Abington
College, B
The Pennsylvania State University Altoona
College, B
The Pennsylvania State University Beaver Campus
of the Commonwealth College, B
The Pennsylvania State University Berks Campus of
the Berks-Lehigh Valley College, B
The Pennsylvania State University Delaware County
Campus of the Commonwealth College, B
The Pennsylvania State University DuBois Campus
of the Commonwealth College, B
The Pennsylvania State University at Erie, The
Behrend College, B
The Pennsylvania State University Fayette Campus
of the Commonwealth College, B
The Pennsylvania State University Hazleton
Campus of the Commonwealth College, B
The Pennsylvania State University, Lehigh Valley
Campus of the Berks-Lehigh Valley College, B
The Pennsylvania State University McKeesport
Campus of the Commonwealth College, B
The Pennsylvania State University Mont Alto
Campus of the Commonwealth College, B
The Pennsylvania State University New Kensington
Campus of the Commonwealth College, B
The Pennsylvania State University Schuylkill
Campus of the Capital College, B
The Pennsylvania State University Shenango
Campus of the Commonwealth College, B
The Pennsylvania State University University Park
Campus, B
The Pennsylvania State University Wilkes-Barre
Campus of the Commonwealth College, B
The Pennsylvania State University Worthington
Scranton Campus of the Commonwealth
College, B
The Pennsylvania State University York Campus of
the Commonwealth College, B

Puerto Rico

University of Puerto Rico, Mayagüez Campus, B

South Carolina

Horry-Georgetown Technical College, A

South Dakota

Oglala Lakota College, A
South Dakota State University, AB

Tennessee

Austin Peay State University, B
Tennessee State University, B
The University of Tennessee at Martin, B

Texas

Blinn College, A
Central Texas College, A
Cisco Junior College, A
Clarendon College, A
Coastal Bend College, A
Frank Phillips College, A
Hill College of the Hill Junior College District, A
Houston Community College System, A
Howard College, A
Kilgore College, A
Lubbock Christian University, AB
Northeast Texas Community College, A
Odessa College, A
Palo Alto College, A
Prairie View A&M University, B
Sam Houston State University, B
South Plains College, A
Stephen F. Austin State University, B
Texarkana College, A
Texas A&M University, B

Texas A&M University-Commerce, B
Texas A&M University-Kingsville, B
Texas State University-San Marcos, B
Tyler Junior College, A
West Texas A&M University, B
Western Texas College, A
Wharton County Junior College, A

Utah

Dixie State College of Utah, A
Snow College, A
Southern Utah University, A
Utah State University, B

Vermont

Sterling College, AB
University of Vermont, B

Virginia

Ferrum College, B
Virginia State University, B

Washington

Clover Park Technical College, A
Skagit Valley College, A
Washington State University, B
Yakima Valley Community College, A

West Virginia

Potomac State College of West Virginia
University, A

Wisconsin

Northeast Wisconsin Technical College, A
University of Wisconsin-Madison, B
University of Wisconsin-River Falls, B

Wyoming

Casper College, A
Central Wyoming College, A
Eastern Wyoming College, A
Laramie County Community College, A
Northwest College, A
Sheridan College-Sheridan and Gillette, A

Alberta

University of Alberta, B
University of Lethbridge, B

British Columbia

The University of British Columbia, B

Manitoba

University of Manitoba, B

Nova Scotia

Nova Scotia Agricultural College, B

Ontario

University of Guelph, B

Saskatchewan

University of Saskatchewan, B

AGRICULTURE, AGRICULTURE OPERATIONS AND RELATED SCIENCES

California

University of California, Davis, B

Georgia

University of Georgia, B

Kentucky

Eastern Kentucky University, A
University of Kentucky, B

Maryland

University of Maryland, College Park, B

Michigan

Michigan State University, B

Texas

Tarleton State University, B

Vermont

Sterling College, AB

Washington

Washington State University, B

Wyoming

University of Wyoming, B

AGRONOMY AND CROP SCIENCE

Alabama

Auburn University, B
Tuskegee University, B

Arizona

Mesa Community College, A

Arkansas

University of Arkansas at Pine Bluff, B

California

Butte College, A
California Polytechnic State University, San Luis
   Obispo, B
California State Polytechnic University, Pomona, B
California State University, Chico, B
California State University, Fresno, B
College of the Redwoods, A
Cosumnes River College (Sacramento), A
Hartnell College, A
Lassen Community College District, A
Merced College, A
Modesto Junior College, A
Mt. San Antonio College, A
Sierra College, A
West Hills Community College, A
Yuba College, A

Colorado

Colorado State University, B
Lamar Community College, A
Northeastern Junior College, A

Connecticut

University of Connecticut, B

Delaware

Delaware State University, B
University of Delaware, B

Florida

Chipola College, A
University of Florida, B

Georgia

Fort Valley State University, B

Idaho

Brigham Young University -Idaho, A

Illinois

Shawnee Community College, A
University of Illinois at Urbana-Champaign, B

Indiana

Purdue University, B

Iowa

Hawkeye Community College, A
Iowa Lakes Community College, A
Iowa State University of Science and Technology, B
Kirkwood Community College, A

Southeastern Community College, North Campus, A

Kansas

Colby Community College, A
Cowley County Community College and Area
   Vocational-Technical School, A
Dodge City Community College, A
Fort Hays State University, B
Fort Scott Community College, A
Highland Community College, A
Kansas State University, B

Kentucky

University of Kentucky, B

Maine

Southern Maine Community College, A

Maryland

University of Maryland, College Park, B

Michigan

Andrews University, AB

Minnesota

Southwest Minnesota State University, B
University of Minnesota, Crookston, AB
University of Minnesota, Twin Cities Campus, B
Vermilion Community College, A

Mississippi

Alcorn State University, B
Hinds Community College, A
Mississippi State University, B
Northeast Mississippi Community College, A

Missouri

College of the Ozarks, B
Missouri State University, B
Northwest Missouri State University, B
Truman State University, B

Nebraska

Nebraska College of Technical Agriculture, A
Northeast Community College, A
Southeast Community College, Beatrice Campus, A
University of Nebraska-Lincoln, B

New Hampshire

University of New Hampshire, B

New Mexico

New Mexico State University, B

New York

Cornell University, B
State University of New York College of Agriculture
   and Technology at Cobleskill, AB
State University of New York College of Agriculture
   and Technology at Morrisville, A

North Carolina

North Carolina State University, B

Ohio

The Ohio State University, B
The Ohio State University Agricultural Technical
   Institute, A

Oklahoma

Eastern Oklahoma State College, A
Northeastern Oklahoma Agricultural and Mechanical
   College, A
Oklahoma Panhandle State University, B

Oregon

Eastern Oregon University, B
Oregon State University, B

Treasure Valley Community College, A

Pennsylvania

Delaware Valley College, B
The Pennsylvania State University Altoona
   College, B
The Pennsylvania State University Beaver Campus
   of the Commonwealth College, B
The Pennsylvania State University Berks Campus of
   the Berks-Lehigh Valley College, B
The Pennsylvania State University Delaware County
   Campus of the Commonwealth College, B
The Pennsylvania State University DuBois Campus
   of the Commonwealth College, B
The Pennsylvania State University Fayette Campus
   of the Commonwealth College, B
The Pennsylvania State University Hazleton
   Campus of the Commonwealth College, B
The Pennsylvania State University McKeesport
   Campus of the Commonwealth College, B
The Pennsylvania State University Mont Alto
   Campus of the Commonwealth College, B
The Pennsylvania State University New Kensington
   Campus of the Commonwealth College, B
The Pennsylvania State University Shenango
   Campus of the Commonwealth College, B
The Pennsylvania State University University Park
   Campus, B
The Pennsylvania State University Wilkes-Barre
   Campus of the Commonwealth College, B
The Pennsylvania State University Worthington
   Scranton Campus of the Commonwealth
   College, B
The Pennsylvania State University York Campus of
   the Commonwealth College, B

Puerto Rico

University of Puerto Rico, Mayagüez Campus, B

South Dakota

South Dakota State University, B

Tennessee

Tennessee Technological University, B
The University of Tennessee at Martin, B

Texas

Frank Phillips College, A
Hardin-Simmons University, B
South Plains College, A
Stephen F. Austin State University, B
Tarleton State University, B
Texas A&M University, B
Texas A&M University-Commerce, B
Texas A&M University-Kingsville, B
Texas Tech University, B
West Texas A&M University, B

Utah

Snow College, A
Utah State University, B

Vermont

Sterling College, B
University of Vermont, B

Virginia

Virginia Polytechnic Institute and State University, B

Washington

Spokane Community College, A
Washington State University, B
Yakima Valley Community College, A

West Virginia

Potomac State College of West Virginia
   University, A

Wisconsin

University of Wisconsin-Madison, B
University of Wisconsin-Platteville, B

University of Wisconsin-River Falls, B

Wyoming

Northwest College, A

Alberta

University of Alberta, B

Manitoba

University of Manitoba, B

Ontario

University of Guelph, B

Quebec

Université Laval, B

Saskatchewan

University of Saskatchewan, B

AGRONOMY AND SOIL SCIENCES

Alabama

Alabama Agricultural and Mechanical University, MD
Auburn University, MD
Tuskegee University, M

Arizona

The University of Arizona, MD

Arkansas

University of Arkansas, MD

California

University of California, Davis, MD
University of California, Riverside, MD

Colorado

Colorado State University, MD

Connecticut

University of Connecticut, MD

Delaware

University of Delaware, MD

Florida

University of Florida, MD

Georgia

University of Georgia, MD

Idaho

University of Idaho, MD

Illinois

Southern Illinois University Carbondale, M
University of Illinois at Urbana-Champaign, MD

Indiana

Purdue University, MD

Iowa

Iowa State University of Science and
Technology, MD

Kansas

Kansas State University, MD

Kentucky

University of Kentucky, MD

Louisiana

Louisiana State University and Agricultural and
Mechanical College, MD

Maine

University of Maine, MD

Maryland

University of Maryland, College Park, MD

Massachusetts

University of Massachusetts Amherst, MD

Michigan

Michigan State University, MD

Minnesota

University of Minnesota, Twin Cities Campus, MD

Mississippi

Alcorn State University, M
Mississippi State University, MD

Missouri

University of Missouri-Columbia, MD

Nebraska

University of Nebraska-Lincoln, MD

New Hampshire

University of New Hampshire, M

New Mexico

New Mexico State University, MD

New York

Cornell University, MD

North Carolina

North Carolina State University, MD

North Dakota

North Dakota State University, MD

Ohio

The Ohio State University, MD

Oklahoma

Oklahoma State University, MD

Oregon

Oregon State University, MD

Pennsylvania

The Pennsylvania State University University Park
Campus, MD

Puerto Rico

University of Puerto Rico, Mayagüez Campus, M

South Dakota

South Dakota State University, MD

Texas

Prairie View A&M University, M
Texas A&M University, MD
Texas A&M University-Kingsville, MD
Texas Tech University, MD

Utah

Brigham Young University, M
Utah State University, MD

Vermont

University of Vermont, MD

Virginia

Virginia Polytechnic Institute and State
University, MD

Washington

Washington State University, MD

West Virginia

West Virginia University, MD

Wisconsin

University of Wisconsin-Madison, MD

Wyoming

University of Wyoming, MD

Alberta

University of Alberta, MDO

British Columbia

The University of British Columbia, MD

Manitoba

University of Manitoba, MD

Ontario

University of Guelph, MD

Quebec

McGill University, MD
Université Laval, MD

Saskatchewan

University of Saskatchewan, MD

AIR FORCE JROTC/ROTC

Iowa

The University of Iowa, B

New York

Rensselaer Polytechnic Institute, B

Pennsylvania

La Salle University, B

Utah

Weber State University, B

Washington

University of Washington, B

AIR TRAFFIC CONTROLLER

Alabama

Community College of the Air Force, A

Alaska

University of Alaska Anchorage, A

California

Mt. San Antonio College, A

Florida

Embry-Riddle Aeronautical University, B
Florida Memorial College, B
Miami Dade College, A

Georgia

Georgia Aviation & Technical College, A

Maryland

Cecil Community College, A
University of Maryland Eastern Shore, B

Minnesota

Anoka Technical College, A
Inver Hills Community College, A
St. Cloud State University, B

New Hampshire

Daniel Webster College, B

North Dakota

University of North Dakota, B

Pennsylvania

Community College of Beaver County, A

Puerto Rico

Inter American University of Puerto Rico, Bayamón
Campus, B

Texas

Texas Southern University, B

Virginia

Hampton University, B

Washington

Green River Community College, A

AIR TRANSPORTATION

Florida

Florida Institute of Technology, B

Virginia

Averett University, B

AIRCRAFT POWERPLANT TECHNOLOGY/TECHNICIAN

Arizona

Pima Community College, A

California

Antelope Valley College, A
San Joaquin Valley College, A

Colorado

Colorado Northwestern Community College, A

Florida

Embry-Riddle Aeronautical University, B
Embry-Riddle Aeronautical University, Extended
  Campus, A
Florida Community College at Jacksonville, A

Georgia

Georgia Southwestern State University, A

Idaho

Idaho State University, A

Louisiana

Louisiana Technical College, A

Minnesota

Minneapolis Community and Technical College, A

Missouri

Linn State Technical College, A

Ohio

Columbus State Community College, A

Pennsylvania

Pennsylvania College of Technology, A

Tennessee

North Central Institute, A

Texas

Central Texas College, A
Hallmark Institute of Aeronautics, A
St. Philip's College, A
Texas State Technical College Waco, A

British Columbia

British Columbia Institute of Technology, A

AIRFRAME MECHANICS AND AIRCRAFT MAINTENANCE TECHNOLOGY/TECHNICIAN

Alabama

Community College of the Air Force, A
Enterprise-Ozark Community College, A

Alaska

University of Alaska Anchorage, A
University of Alaska Fairbanks, A

Arizona

Chandler-Gilbert Community College, A
Cochise College (Douglas), A

Arkansas

Southern Arkansas University Tech, A

California

Antelope Valley College, A
City College of San Francisco, A
College of San Mateo, A
Glendale Community College, A
Merced College, A
Mt. San Antonio College, A
Sacramento City College, A
San Diego Miramar College, A
San Joaquin Valley College, A
Solano Community College, A
West Los Angeles College, A

Colorado

Colorado Northwestern Community College, A

Delaware

Wilmington College, B

Florida

Florida Community College at Jacksonville, A

Georgia

Clayton State University, A
Georgia Southwestern State University, A
Middle Georgia Technical College, A

Illinois

Lewis University, AB
Southwestern Illinois College, A

Indiana

Ivy Tech Community College-Wabash Valley, A
Vincennes University, A

Kansas

Cowley County Community College and Area
  Vocational-Technical School, A
Johnson County Community College, A
Kansas State University, A

Massachusetts

Wentworth Institute of Technology, A

Michigan

Southwestern Michigan College, A

Minnesota

Minneapolis Community and Technical College, A

Missouri

Aviation Institute of Maintenance-Kansas City, A

Montana

The University of Montana-Helena College of
  Technology, A

New Hampshire

New Hampshire Community Technical College,
  Nashua/Claremont, A

New Mexico

Eastern New Mexico University-Roswell, A

New York

Mohawk Valley Community College, A
Vaughn College of Aeronautics and Technology, AB

Ohio

Columbus State Community College, A

Oklahoma

Oklahoma City Community College, A
Tulsa Community College, A

Pennsylvania

Pittsburgh Institute of Aeronautics, A

South Carolina

Greenville Technical College, A
Trident Technical College, A

Tennessee

North Central Institute, A

Texas

Amarillo College, A
Hallmark Institute of Aeronautics, A
Hallmark Institute of Technology, A
LeTourneau University, B
St. Philip's College, A
Texas State Technical College Harlingen, A
Texas State Technical College Waco, A
Texas State Technical College West Texas, A

Utah

Utah State University, AB

Virginia

Aviation Institute of Maintenance-Manassas, A
Aviation Institute of Maintenance-Virginia Beach, A

Washington

South Seattle Community College, A

British Columbia

British Columbia Institute of Technology, A

AIRLINE/COMMERCIAL/PROFESSION PILOT AND FLIGHT CREW

Alabama

Auburn University, B
Wallace State Community College, A

Alaska

University of Alaska Anchorage, A

Arizona

Cochise College (Douglas), A
Embry-Riddle Aeronautical University, B

California

College of San Mateo, A
Compton Community College, A
Cypress College, A
Glendale Community College, A
Long Beach City College, A
Mt. San Antonio College, A
Orange Coast College, A
Pasadena City College, A

Colorado

Colorado Northwestern Community College, A

Delaware

Delaware State University, B

Florida

Broward Community College, A
Embry-Riddle Aeronautical University, B
Everglades University (Boca Raton), B
Florida Community College at Jacksonville, A
Indian River Community College, A
Jacksonville University, B
Lynn University, B
Miami Dade College, A

Palm Beach Community College, A

Georgia

Georgia Aviation & Technical College, A

Illinois

Lewis University, B
Quincy University, B
Southern Illinois University Carbondale, A
University of Illinois at Urbana-Champaign, B

Indiana

Indiana State University, B
Vincennes University, A

Iowa

Indian Hills Community College, A
Iowa Central Community College, A
Iowa Lakes Community College, A
Scott Community College, A
University of Dubuque, AB

Kansas

Central Christian College of Kansas, A
Kansas State University, AB

Kentucky

Eastern Kentucky University, B

Massachusetts

Bridgewater State College, B
North Shore Community College, A

Michigan

Andrews University, AB
Baker College of Flint, A
Baker College of Muskegon, A
Cornerstone University, B
Eastern Michigan University, B
Jackson Community College, A
Lansing Community College, A
Northwestern Michigan College, A
Western Michigan University, B

Minnesota

Academy College, A
Inver Hills Community College, A
Lake Superior College, A
St. Cloud State University, B
Vermilion Community College, A

Mississippi

Delta State University, B

Missouri

Saint Louis University, B

Montana

Rocky Mountain College, B

Nebraska

Grace University, B

New Hampshire

Daniel Webster College, AB

New Jersey

County College of Morris, A
Mercer County Community College, A

New Mexico

San Juan College, A

New York

Farmingdale State University of New York, B
Jamestown Community College, A
Vaughn College of Aeronautics and Technology, A

North Carolina

Guilford Technical Community College, A
Lenoir Community College, A

Piedmont Baptist College, B

Oklahoma

Southeastern Oklahoma State University, B
Spartan College of Aeronautics and Technology, A

Oregon

Lane Community College, A

Pennsylvania

Community College of Allegheny County, A
Community College of Beaver County, A
Lehigh Carbon Community College, A
Luzerne County Community College, A

Puerto Rico

Inter American University of Puerto Rico, Bayamón
    Campus, B

Tennessee

Chattanooga State Technical Community College, A

Texas

Baylor University, B
Central Texas College, A
Frank Phillips College, A
LeTourneau University, B
Midland College, A
Navarro College, A
Texas State Technical College Waco, A

Utah

Dixie State College of Utah, A
Salt Lake Community College, A
Utah Valley State College, AB
Westminster College, B

Virginia

Northern Virginia Community College, A

Washington

Big Bend Community College, A
Clover Park Technical College, A
Green River Community College, A

West Virginia

Salem International University, B

Wisconsin

Fox Valley Technical College, A
Gateway Technical College, A

Wyoming

Casper College, A

British Columbia

Trinity Western University, B

Manitoba

Providence College and Theological Seminary, B

AIRLINE FLIGHT ATTENDANT

California

Cypress College, A

New Jersey

Mercer County Community College, A

Ohio

The University of Akron, A

ALLIED HEALTH AND MEDICAL ASSISTING SERVICES

Alabama

Alabama State University, M
The University of Alabama at Birmingham, MDO

University of South Alabama, MD

Arizona

Midwestern University, Glendale Campus, MPO
Northern Arizona University, MDO

Arkansas

Arkansas State University, MO

California

Loma Linda University, MD
University of Southern California, MD

Colorado

National American University (Colorado Springs), A
Regis University, MD

Connecticut

Quinnipiac University, M
University of Connecticut, M

Florida

Florida Agricultural and Mechanical University, M
Florida Gulf Coast University, M
Florida National College, A
Nova Southeastern University, MD
University of Florida, MD
University of North Florida, MO

Georgia

Emory University, MD
Georgia Southern University, MO
Georgia State University, MDO
Medical College of Georgia, MD

Idaho

Idaho State University, MDO

Illinois

University of Illinois at Chicago, MD
University of St. Francis, M

Indiana

University of Saint Francis, M

Kansas

University of Kansas, MDO
Washburn University, AB
Wichita State University, MO

Kentucky

Eastern Kentucky University, M
University of Kentucky, MD

Louisiana

Louisiana State University Health Sciences
    Center, M

Maryland

Towson University, M

Massachusetts

Boston University, MD
Northeastern University, MDPO
University of Massachusetts Lowell, MD

Michigan

Andrews University, M
Ferris State University, M
Grand Valley State University, MD
Oakland University, MDO

University of Detroit Mercy, MO

Minnesota

Minneapolis Business College, A
Minnesota State University Mankato, MO

Mississippi

Jackson State University, M
University of Mississippi Medical Center, M

Missouri

Barnes-Jewish College of Nursing and Allied
Health, MO
Maryville University of Saint Louis, M
Saint Louis University, MDO
Washington University in St. Louis, MDO

Nebraska

Creighton University, MDPO
University of Nebraska Medical Center, MDO

New Jersey

Bloomfield College, B
Seton Hall University, MD

New York

College of Mount Saint Vincent, MO
Dominican College, MD
Ithaca College, MD
Long Island University, C.W. Post Campus, MO
Mercy College, M
State University of New York at Buffalo, MDO

North Carolina

East Carolina University, MD
The University of North Carolina at Chapel Hill, MD

Ohio

Cincinnati State Technical and Community
College, A
Cleveland State University, M
The Ohio State University, M

Oklahoma

University of Oklahoma Health Sciences
Center, MDO

Pennsylvania

Bloomsburg University of Pennsylvania, A
College Misericordia, M
Drexel University, MDO
Duquesne University, MDO
Pennsylvania Institute of Technology, A
Temple University, MD

Puerto Rico

University of Puerto Rico, Medical Sciences
Campus, MO

South Carolina

Medical University of South Carolina, MDO

South Dakota

The University of South Dakota, M

Tennessee

Belmont University, MD
East Tennessee State University, MDO
Tennessee State University, M

Texas

Baylor University, MD
Texas Christian University, M
Texas State University-San Marcos, M
Texas Woman's University, MD
The University of Texas at El Paso, M

The University of Texas Medical Branch, M

Vermont

Bennington College, O
University of Vermont, MD

Virginia

Marymount University, MDO
Old Dominion University, MD
Shenandoah University, MDO
Virginia Commonwealth University, MDO

Washington

North Seattle Community College, A

West Virginia

Alderson-Broaddus College, M
Mountain State University, M

Wisconsin

Concordia University Wisconsin, M
University of Wisconsin-Milwaukee, MD

Alberta

Athabasca University, MO

ALLIED HEALTH DIAGNOSTIC, INTERVENTION, AND TREATMENT PROFESSIONS

California

Sonoma College (Petaluma), A

Connecticut

University of Connecticut, B

Indiana

Ivy Tech Community College-Wabash Valley, A

Michigan

Oakland Community College, A

New Jersey

Fairleigh Dickinson University, College at
Florham, B
Ramapo College of New Jersey, B
Rutgers, The State University of New Jersey,
Newark, B
Union County College, A

Ohio

The University of Akron, A
The University of Toledo, B

Oklahoma

Cameron University, A

Pennsylvania

Gwynedd-Mercy College, AB
Harcum College, A
Pennsylvania College of Technology, A

British Columbia

British Columbia Institute of Technology, A

ALLOPATHIC MEDICINE

Alabama

The University of Alabama at Birmingham, MDPO
University of South Alabama, P

Arizona

The University of Arizona, PO

California

Charles R. Drew University of Medicine and
Science, P
Loma Linda University, MDPO
Stanford University, P
University of California, Davis, MPO

University of California, Irvine, PO
University of California, Los Angeles, PO
University of California, San Diego, PO
University of Southern California, PO

Connecticut

Yale University, P

District of Columbia

The George Washington University, PO
Georgetown University, PO
Howard University, DPO

Florida

Florida State University, DP
University of Florida, PO
University of Miami, PO
University of South Florida, P

Georgia

Emory University, PO
Medical College of Georgia, PO
Mercer University, MP

Hawaii

University of Hawaii at Manoa, P

Illinois

Loyola University Chicago, MDPO
Northwestern University, PO
Rush University, PO
Southern Illinois University Carbondale, PO
University of Chicago, PO
University of Illinois at Chicago, PO
University of Illinois at Urbana-Champaign, O

Indiana

Indiana University-Purdue University
Indianapolis, PO

Iowa

The University of Iowa, PO

Kansas

University of Kansas, PO

Kentucky

University of Kentucky, PO
University of Louisville, PO

Louisiana

Louisiana State University Health Sciences
Center, MPO
Tulane University, PO

Maryland

The Johns Hopkins University, PO

Massachusetts

Boston University, PO
Harvard University, PO
Tufts University, PO

Michigan

Michigan State University, P
University of Michigan, PO
Wayne State University, PO

Minnesota

University of Minnesota, Duluth, P
University of Minnesota, Twin Cities Campus, PO

Mississippi

University of Mississippi Medical Center, PO

Missouri

Saint Louis University, MDP
University of Missouri-Columbia, PO
University of Missouri-Kansas City, PO

Washington University in St. Louis, PO

Nebraska

Creighton University, PO
University of Nebraska Medical Center, PO

New Hampshire

Dartmouth College, PO

New Mexico

University of New Mexico, P

New York

New York University, PO
State University of New York at Buffalo, PO
State University of New York Downstate Medical
 Center, MPO
State University of New York Upstate Medical
 University, PO
Stony Brook University, State University of New
 York, PO
University of Rochester, PO

North Carolina

Duke University, PO
East Carolina University, P
The University of North Carolina at Chapel Hill, PO
Wake Forest University, PO

North Dakota

University of North Dakota, PO

Ohio

Case Western Reserve University, PO
The Ohio State University, P
University of Cincinnati, MPO
Wright State University, P

Oklahoma

University of Oklahoma Health Sciences Center, PO

Oregon

Oregon Health & Science University, PO

Pennsylvania

Drexel University, PO
Temple University, PO
Thomas Jefferson University, PO
University of Pennsylvania, PO
University of Pittsburgh, P

Puerto Rico

Universidad Central del Caribe, PO
University of Puerto Rico, Medical Sciences
 Campus, P

Rhode Island

Brown University, PO

South Carolina

Medical University of South Carolina, PO
University of South Carolina, PO

South Dakota

The University of South Dakota, P

Tennessee

East Tennessee State University, P
Vanderbilt University, MDPO

Texas

The University of Texas Health Science Center at
 Houston, PO
The University of Texas Health Science Center at
 San Antonio, P
The University of Texas Medical Branch, P

The University of Texas Southwestern Medical
 Center at Dallas, PO

Utah

University of Utah, P

Vermont

University of Vermont, PO

Virginia

University of Virginia, MDPO
Virginia Commonwealth University, PO

Washington

University of Washington, PO

West Virginia

Marshall University, P
West Virginia University, PO

Wisconsin

University of Wisconsin-Madison, P

Alberta

University of Calgary, P

British Columbia

The University of British Columbia, MPO

Newfoundland and Labrador

Memorial University of Newfoundland, P

Nova Scotia

Dalhousie University, PO

Ontario

Queen's University at Kingston, P
University of Ottawa, MDP
University of Toronto, MDPO
The University of Western Ontario, MP

Quebec

McGill University, MDPO
Université Laval, PO
Université de Montréal, PO
Université de Sherbrooke, P

Saskatchewan

University of Saskatchewan, P

ALTERNATIVE AND COMPLEMENTARY MEDICINE AND MEDICAL SYSTEMS

Florida

Everglades University (Sarasota), B

Vermont

Johnson State College, B

AMERICAN GOVERNMENT AND POLITICS (UNITED STATES)

Arizona

Northern Arizona University, B

California

Chapman University, B
Claremont McKenna College, B

The Master's College and Seminary, B

District of Columbia

Gallaudet University, B

Florida

Manatee Community College, A

Massachusetts

Bridgewater State College, B
Framingham State College, B
Quincy College, A

Missouri

Drury University, B

Montana

The University of Montana-Missoula, B

New Hampshire

Rivier College, B

New York

Bard College, B

North Carolina

North Carolina State University, B

Ohio

The University of Akron, B

Oklahoma

Oklahoma Christian University, B

Tennessee

Lipscomb University, B

Texas

Huston-Tillotson University, B

Vermont

Bennington College, B

AMERICAN HISTORY (UNITED STATES)

California

Chapman University, B

Florida

Ave Maria University, B

Massachusetts

Framingham State College, B

New York

Bard College, B
Sarah Lawrence College, B

Pennsylvania

Gettysburg College, B

Puerto Rico

University of Puerto Rico, Río Piedras, B

South Carolina

Charleston Southern University, B

Vermont

Bennington College, B

Virginia

Bridgewater College, B

Saskatchewan

University of Regina, B

AMERICAN INDIAN/NATIVE AMERICAN LANGUAGES, LITERATURES, AND LINGUISTICS

Idaho
Idaho State University, A

Minnesota
Bemidji State University, B

Alberta
University of Lethbridge, B

Saskatchewan
University of Regina, B

AMERICAN INDIAN/NATIVE AMERICAN STUDIES

Alaska
University of Alaska Fairbanks, B

Arizona
Arizona State University, B
Diné College, A
Northern Arizona University, B
Pima Community College, A
The University of Arizona, MDO

California
California State University, East Bay, B
Fresno City College, A
Humboldt State University, B
Santa Barbara City College, A
Sonoma State University, B
Stanford University, B
University of California, Berkeley, B
University of California, Davis, BMD
University of California, Los Angeles, BMO
University of California, Riverside, B

Colorado
Fort Lewis College, B

Idaho
North Idaho College, A

Iowa
The University of Iowa, B

Kansas
Haskell Indian Nations University, B
University of Kansas, M

Michigan
Saginaw Chippewa Tribal College, A

Minnesota
Bemidji State University, B
Fond du Lac Tribal and Community College, A
Itasca Community College, A
University of Minnesota, Duluth, B
University of Minnesota, Twin Cities Campus, B

Montana
Blackfeet Community College, A
Fort Belknap College, A
Fort Peck Community College, A
Montana State University, M
Salish Kootenai College, A

The University of Montana-Missoula, B

Nebraska
Creighton University, B
Nebraska Indian Community College, A

New Hampshire
Dartmouth College, B

New York
Colgate University, B
Cornell University, B

North Carolina
The University of North Carolina at Pembroke, B

North Dakota
Sitting Bull College, A
University of North Dakota, B

Oklahoma
Bacone College, A
Northeastern Oklahoma Agricultural and Mechanical College, A
Northeastern State University, B
Rogers State University, A
University of Oklahoma, BM
University of Science and Arts of Oklahoma, B

Oregon
Portland State University, B

South Dakota
Black Hills State University, B
Oglala Lakota College, AB
Sinte Gleska University, A
Sisseton-Wahpeton Community College, A
The University of South Dakota, B

Texas
University of the Incarnate Word, B

Washington
The Evergreen State College, B
Northwest Indian College, A
University of Washington, B

Wisconsin
Lac Courte Oreilles Ojibwa Community College, A
Northland College, B
University of Wisconsin-Eau Claire, B
University of Wisconsin-Milwaukee, B

Wyoming
Central Wyoming College, A

Alberta
University of Alberta, B
University of Calgary, B
University of Lethbridge, BM

Manitoba
Brandon University, B
University of Manitoba, M

New Brunswick
St. Thomas University, B

Nova Scotia
Cape Breton University, B

Ontario
Laurentian University, B
Trent University, BMD

University of Toronto, B

Saskatchewan
University of Regina, BM
University of Saskatchewan, B

AMERICAN LITERATURE (UNITED STATES)

California
University of California, Los Angeles, B
University of Southern California, B

Florida
Ave Maria University, B

Kansas
Haskell Indian Nations University, A

Massachusetts
Simon's Rock College of Bard, B

Missouri
Washington University in St. Louis, B

Montana
University of Great Falls, B

New York
Cornell University, B
St. Lawrence University, B
Sarah Lawrence College, B
State University of New York College at Brockport, B

North Carolina
Queens University of Charlotte, B

Vermont
Bennington College, B
Castleton State College, B
Middlebury College, B

AMERICAN SIGN LANGUAGE

Iowa
The University of Iowa, B

AMERICAN SIGN LANGUAGE (ASL)

Idaho
Idaho State University, A

Indiana
Bethel College, AB

Michigan
Madonna University, AB

Minnesota
North Central University, AB

New Jersey
Burlington County College, A

New York
Rochester Institute of Technology, AB
University of Rochester, B

North Carolina
Gardner-Webb University, B

South Dakota
Augustana College, B

Tennessee
Maryville College, B

West Virginia

Fairmont State Community & Technical College, A

AMERICAN/UNITED STATES STUDIES/CIVILIZATION

Alabama

Huntingdon College, B
The University of Alabama, BM

Arizona

Arizona State University West, B

Arkansas

Harding University, B
University of Arkansas, B

California

California State University, Chico, B
California State University, Fullerton, BM
California State University, Long Beach, B
California State University, San Bernardino, B
Claremont McKenna College, B
Cosumnes River College (Sacramento), A
El Camino College, A
Foothill College, A
Los Angeles City College, A
Mills College, B
Mount St. Mary's College, B
Occidental College, B
Pepperdine University, M
Pitzer College, B
Pomona College, B
Saddleback College, A
Saint Mary's College of California, B
San Diego State University, B
San Francisco State University, B
San Jose State University, B
Scripps College, B
Sonoma State University, B
Stanford University, B
University of California, Berkeley, B
University of California, Davis, B
University of California, Los Angeles, B
University of California, Santa Cruz, B
University of Southern California, BD

Colorado

Colorado State University, B
Western State College of Colorado, B

Connecticut

Connecticut College, B
Fairfield University, BM
Naugatuck Valley Community College, A
Saint Joseph College, B
Trinity College, BM
University of Connecticut, B
Wesleyan University, B
Western Connecticut State University, B
Yale University, BMD

Delaware

University of Delaware, M
Wesley College, B

District of Columbia

American University, BO
The George Washington University, BMD
Georgetown University, B

Florida

Eckerd College, B
Florida State University, BMO
Manatee Community College, A
Miami Dade College, A
Nova Southeastern University, B
Stetson University, B
University of Florida, B
University of Miami, B

University of South Florida, BM

Georgia

Emory University, B
Oglethorpe University, B
Wesleyan College, B

Hawaii

University of Hawaii at Manoa, BMD

Idaho

Idaho State University, B
University of Idaho, B

Illinois

DePaul University, B
Dominican University, B
Elmhurst College, B
Illinois Wesleyan University, B
Knox College, B
Lake Forest College, B
Lewis University, B
Northwestern University, B
University of Chicago, B
Wheaton College, M

Indiana

Franklin College, B
Purdue University, MD
University of Notre Dame, B
Valparaiso University, B

Iowa

Coe College, B
Drake University, M
The University of Iowa, BMD
University of Northern Iowa, B

Kansas

University of Kansas, BMDO

Kentucky

Georgetown College, B
Lindsey Wilson College, B

Louisiana

Tulane University, B
University of Louisiana at Lafayette, D

Maine

Bates College, B
Colby College, B
University of New England, B
University of Southern Maine, M

Maryland

Anne Arundel Community College, A
Goucher College, B
University of Maryland, Baltimore County, B
University of Maryland, College Park, BMD
Washington College, B

Massachusetts

Amherst College, B
Boston University, BD
Brandeis University, BMD
Emmanuel College, B
Greenfield Community College, A
Hampshire College, B
Harvard University, BD
Holyoke Community College, A
Lesley University, B
Mount Holyoke College, B
Mount Ida College, B
Pine Manor College, B
Simon's Rock College of Bard, B
Smith College, B
Stonehill College, B
Tufts University, B
University of Massachusetts Boston, BM
University of Massachusetts Lowell, B
Wellesley College, B
Wheaton College, B

Williams College, B

Michigan

Albion College, B
Eastern Michigan University, M
Hillsdale College, B
Michigan State University, BMD
Oakland University, B
University of Michigan, BMD
University of Michigan-Dearborn, B
University of Michigan-Flint, M
Wayne State University, B
Western Michigan University, B

Minnesota

Carleton College, B
Minnesota State University Moorhead, B
St. Cloud State University, B
St. Olaf College, B
University of Minnesota, Twin Cities Campus, BD

Mississippi

Mississippi Delta Community College, A
University of Mississippi, BM
University of Southern Mississippi, B

Missouri

Saint Louis University, BMD
Southeast Missouri State University, B
University of Missouri-Kansas City, B
Washington University in St. Louis, B

Nebraska

Creighton University, B

New Hampshire

Franklin Pierce College, B
Keene State College, B
University of New Hampshire, B

New Jersey

College of Saint Elizabeth, B
Ramapo College of New Jersey, B
Rider University, B
Rutgers, The State University of New Jersey, New Brunswick/Piscataway, B
Rutgers, The State University of New Jersey, Newark, B
Saint Peter's College, B

New Mexico

New Mexico Highlands University, M
University of New Mexico, BMD

New York

Bard College, B
Barnard College, B
Brooklyn College of the City University of New York, B
The College of Saint Rose, B
College of Staten Island of the City University of New York, B
Columbia College, B
Cornell University, BMD
Dominican College, B
Elmira College, B
Fordham University, B
Hamilton College, B
Hobart and William Smith Colleges, B
Hofstra University, B
Lehman College of the City University of New York, B
Long Island University, C.W. Post Campus, B
Manhattanville College, B
Marist College, B
Nazareth College of Rochester, B
New York University, MD
Queens College of the City University of New York, B
St. John Fisher College, B
Sarah Lawrence College, B
Siena College, B
Skidmore College, B
State University of New York at Buffalo, BMD
State University of New York College at Cortland, O

State University of New York College at Geneseo, B
State University of New York College at Old
  Westbury, B
State University of New York, Fredonia, B
State University of New York at Oswego, B
Stony Brook University, State University of New
  York, BO
Syracuse University, B
Union College, B
United States Military Academy, B
Vassar College, B
Wells College, B

North Carolina

Appalachian State University, M
East Carolina University, M
High Point University, B
Meredith College, B
Montreat College, B
Queens University of Charlotte, B
Salem College, B
The University of North Carolina at Chapel Hill, B
The University of North Carolina at Pembroke, B
Western Carolina University, M
Wingate University, B

Ohio

Ashland University, B
Bowling Green State University, BMD
Case Western Reserve University, B
Cedarville University, B
Kent State University, B
Kenyon College, B
Miami University, B
Miami University Hamilton, B
Mount Union College, B
Muskingum College, B
University of Dayton, B
University of Rio Grande, B
The University of Toledo, B
Ursuline College, B
Wittenberg University, B
Youngstown State University, B

Oklahoma

Northeastern State University, M
Oklahoma City University, B
Oklahoma State University, B
Southern Nazarene University, B
Tulsa Community College, A
University of Central Oklahoma, M

Oregon

Oregon State University, B
Reed College, B
Warner Pacific College, B
Willamette University, B

Pennsylvania

Albright College, B
Bucks County Community College, A
Cabrini College, B
Dickinson College, B
Franklin and Marshall College, B
Gettysburg College, B
Lafayette College, B
Lebanon Valley College, B
Lehigh University, BM
Lycoming College, B
Muhlenberg College, B
The Pennsylvania State University Abington
  College, B
The Pennsylvania State University Berks Campus of
  the Berks-Lehigh Valley College, B
The Pennsylvania State University Delaware County
  Campus of the Commonwealth College, B
The Pennsylvania State University Harrisburg
  Campus, BM
The Pennsylvania State University, Lehigh Valley
  Campus of the Berks-Lehigh Valley College, B
The Pennsylvania State University Schuylkill
  Campus of the Capital College, B
The Pennsylvania State University Worthington
  Scranton Campus of the Commonwealth
  College, B

The Pennsylvania State University York Campus of
  the Commonwealth College, B
Saint Francis University, B
Temple University, B
University of Pennsylvania, BMDO
University of Pittsburgh at Greensburg, B
University of Pittsburgh at Johnstown, B
Ursinus College, B
West Chester University of Pennsylvania, B

Rhode Island

Brown University, BMD
Providence College, B
Roger Williams University, B
Salve Regina University, B

South Carolina

Claflin University, B
Erskine College, B

Tennessee

Cumberland University, B
King College, B
Lipscomb University, B
Martin Methodist College, A
Sewanee: The University of the South, B
Vanderbilt University, B

Texas

Austin College, B
Baylor University, BM
Howard Payne University, B
Lee College, A
Our Lady of the Lake University of San Antonio, B
Southwestern University, B
Texas A&M University, B
Texas State University-San Marcos, B
University of Dallas, M
The University of Texas at Austin, BMD
The University of Texas at Dallas, B
The University of Texas-Pan American, B
The University of Texas at San Antonio, B

Utah

Brigham Young University, B
Utah State University, BM

Vermont

Bennington College, B
College of St. Joseph, B
Marlboro College, B
Middlebury College, B
Saint Michael's College, B

Virginia

The College of William and Mary, BMDO
Randolph-Macon Woman's College, B
Shenandoah University, B
University of Mary Washington, B
University of Richmond, B
Virginia Wesleyan College, B

Washington

Tacoma Community College, A
Washington State University, BMD
Western Washington University, B
Whitworth College, B

West Virginia

American Public University System, B
West Virginia University, MD

Wisconsin

University of Wisconsin-Madison, B

Wyoming

Northwest College, A
University of Wyoming, BM

New Brunswick

Mount Allison University, B
University of New Brunswick Fredericton, M

Ontario

University of Toronto, B
The University of Western Ontario, B

Saskatchewan

University of Saskatchewan, B

ANALYTICAL CHEMISTRY

California

California State University, Fullerton, M
California State University, Los Angeles, M

District of Columbia

The George Washington University, MD
Georgetown University, MD
Howard University, MD

Florida

Florida Institute of Technology, B
Florida State University, MD
University of South Florida, MD

Georgia

University of Georgia, MD

Illinois

Governors State University, M
Illinois Institute of Technology, MD

Indiana

Indiana University Bloomington, D
Purdue University, MD

Kansas

Kansas State University, M

Kentucky

University of Louisville, MD

Louisiana

Southern University and Agricultural and Mechanical
  College, M

Maryland

University of Maryland, College Park, MD

Massachusetts

Northeastern University, D
Tufts University, MD

Michigan

University of Michigan, D

Mississippi

University of Southern Mississippi, MD

Missouri

University of Missouri-Columbia, MD
University of Missouri-Kansas City, MD

Nebraska

University of Nebraska-Lincoln, D

New Jersey

Rutgers, The State University of New Jersey, New
  Brunswick/Piscataway, MD
Rutgers, The State University of New Jersey,
  Newark, MD
Seton Hall University, MD

New York

Clarkson University, MD
Cornell University, D
Rensselaer Polytechnic Institute, MD

State University of New York at Binghamton, D

North Carolina

Wake Forest University, MD

Ohio

Case Western Reserve University, MD
Cleveland State University, M
Kent State University, MD
Miami University, MD
University of Cincinnati, MD
The University of Toledo, MD

Oregon

Oregon State University, MD

South Dakota

South Dakota State University, MD

Tennessee

The University of Tennessee, MD
Vanderbilt University, MD

Texas

The University of Texas at Austin, MD

Utah

Brigham Young University, MD

Virginia

Old Dominion University, M

Washington

Washington State University, MD

West Virginia

West Virginia University, MD

Wisconsin

Marquette University, MD

Alberta

University of Calgary, MD

Ontario

McMaster University, MD

Saskatchewan

University of Regina, MD

ANATOMY

Arizona

The University of Arizona, D

Arkansas

University of Arkansas for Medical Sciences, MDO

California

Cañada College, A
Loma Linda University, MD
University of California, Irvine, MDO
University of California, Los Angeles, D

Colorado

Northeastern Junior College, A

District of Columbia

Howard University, BMD

Florida

University of Florida, D
University of South Florida, D

Georgia

Medical College of Georgia, D
University of Georgia, M

Hawaii

University of Hawaii at Manoa, MD

Illinois

Loyola University Chicago, MDO
Rush University, MDO

University of Chicago, D
University of Illinois at Chicago, MDO

Indiana

Indiana University Bloomington, MD
Indiana University-Purdue University
Indianapolis, MDO
Purdue University, MD

Iowa

Palmer College of Chiropractic, M
The University of Iowa, D

Kansas

Kansas State University, MD
University of Kansas, MDO

Kentucky

University of Kentucky, D
University of Louisville, MD

Louisiana

Louisiana State University Health Sciences
Center, MDO
Tulane University, B

Maryland

The Johns Hopkins University, D

Massachusetts

Boston University, MDO

Michigan

Andrews University, B
Wayne State University, MD

Minnesota

Minnesota State University Mankato, B
University of Minnesota, Duluth, MD

Mississippi

University of Mississippi Medical Center, MDO

Missouri

Saint Louis University, MD

Nebraska

University of Nebraska Medical Center, MD

New York

Cornell University, MD
State University of New York at Buffalo, MD
State University of New York Upstate Medical
University, MDO
Stony Brook University, State University of New
York, D
University of Rochester, MD

North Carolina

Duke University, BD
East Carolina University, D
Wake Forest University, D

North Dakota

University of North Dakota, MD

Ohio

Case Western Reserve University, MDO
The Ohio State University, MD
Wright State University, BM

Pennsylvania

Temple University, D

Puerto Rico

University of Puerto Rico, Medical Sciences
Campus, MD

South Carolina

Medical University of South Carolina, D

Tennessee

East Tennessee State University, MD
The University of Tennessee, D

Texas

Frank Phillips College, A
Texas A&M University, MD

Texas A&M University System Health Science
Center, D

Utah

University of Utah, MD

Vermont

University of Vermont, DO

Virginia

Virginia Commonwealth University, MDO

West Virginia

West Virginia University, MD

Wisconsin

University of Wisconsin-Madison, MD

British Columbia

The University of British Columbia, MD

Manitoba

University of Manitoba, MD

Nova Scotia

Dalhousie University, MD

Ontario

Queen's University at Kingston, MD
University of Guelph, MD
The University of Western Ontario, BMD

Prince Edward Island

University of Prince Edward Island, MD

Quebec

McGill University, MD
Université Laval, MDO

Saskatchewan

University of Saskatchewan, BMD

ANCIENT/CLASSICAL GREEK LANGUAGE AND LITERATURE

California

California State University, Long Beach, B
Santa Clara University, B
Stanford University, B
University of California, Berkeley, B
University of California, Los Angeles, B
University of California, Santa Cruz, B

Connecticut

Yale University, B

Georgia

University of Georgia, B

Illinois

Loyola University Chicago, B
Rockford College, B
University of Chicago, B

Indiana

DePauw University, B
Indiana University Bloomington, B
University of Notre Dame, B

Iowa

The University of Iowa, B

Kentucky

Asbury College, B

Massachusetts

Amherst College, B
Boston University, B
Brandeis University, B
Smith College, B

Wellesley College, B

Minnesota

Carleton College, B
St. Olaf College, B
University of St. Thomas, B

Missouri

Washington University in St. Louis, B

Nebraska

Creighton University, B
University of Nebraska-Lincoln, B

New Hampshire

Dartmouth College, B

New Jersey

Rutgers, The State University of New Jersey, New
    Brunswick/Piscataway, B

New Mexico

St. John's College, B

New York

Bard College, B
Barnard College, B
Columbia College, B
Hobart and William Smith Colleges, B
Hunter College of the City University of New York, B
Queens College of the City University of New
    York, B
Vassar College, B

North Carolina

Duke University, B
Wake Forest University, B

Ohio

Kenyon College, B
Miami University, B
Ohio University, B

Oregon

Multnomah Bible College and Biblical Seminary, B

Pennsylvania

Bryn Mawr College, B
Duquesne University, B
Franklin and Marshall College, B
Gettysburg College, B
Swarthmore College, B
The University of Scranton, B

Texas

Baylor University, B
Rice University, B
The University of Texas at Austin, B

Utah

Brigham Young University, B

Vermont

University of Vermont, B

Virginia

Hampden-Sydney College, B
Randolph-Macon College, B
Randolph-Macon Woman's College, B

Washington

University of Washington, B

Wisconsin

Lawrence University, B

British Columbia

University of Victoria, B

New Brunswick

Mount Allison University, B

Ontario

Brock University, B
The University of Western Ontario, B

ANCIENT NEAR EASTERN AND BIBLICAL LANGUAGES, LITERATURES, AND LINGUISTICS

California

Bethany University, B
The Master's College and Seminary, B

Idaho

Northwest Nazarene University, B

Illinois

Concordia University, B
University of Chicago, B

Indiana

Indiana Wesleyan University, AB
Taylor University, B

Kentucky

Mid-Continent University, B

Maryland

Baltimore Hebrew University, AB

Massachusetts

Harvard University, B

Michigan

Concordia University, B
Cornerstone University, B
Hope College, B

Minnesota

North Central University, A

Missouri

Central Bible College, B
Ozark Christian College, B

Nebraska

York College, B

New York

The Jewish Theological Seminary, B
Rabbinical Academy Mesivta Rabbi Chaim Berlin, B
Yeshivat Mikdash Melech, B

Ohio

Laura and Alvin Siegal College of Judaic Studies, B

Oklahoma

Oklahoma Baptist University, B

South Carolina

Columbia International University, B
North Greenville College, B

Tennessee

Belmont University, B
Carson-Newman College, B
Union University, B

Texas

Baylor University, B
Howard Payne University, B
Lubbock Christian University, B

Southwestern Assemblies of God University, B

Utah

Brigham Young University, B

Washington

Walla Walla College, B

Wisconsin

Concordia University Wisconsin, B

Alberta

Prairie Bible Institute, B

Ontario

University of Toronto, B
York University, B

ANCIENT STUDIES/CIVILIZATION

California

Santa Clara University, B
Stanford University, B

Illinois

Rockford College, B

Iowa

The University of Iowa, B

Kansas

University of Kansas, B

Maryland

University of Maryland, Baltimore County, B

Massachusetts

Mount Holyoke College, B
Wheaton College, B

Michigan

Michigan State University, B

Minnesota

St. Olaf College, B

Missouri

Missouri State University, B

New York

Barnard College, B
Columbia College, B

Ohio

Ohio Wesleyan University, B

Texas

The University of Texas at Austin, B

ANESTHESIOLOGIST ASSISTANT

British Columbia

Thompson Rivers University, A

ANIMAL BEHAVIOR AND ETHOLOGY

Arizona

Arizona State University, MD

California

University of California, Davis, MD

Colorado

University of Colorado at Boulder, MD

Minnesota

University of Minnesota, Twin Cities Campus, MD

Pennsylvania

Bucknell University, M
Franklin and Marshall College, B

Tennessee

The University of Tennessee, MD

Texas

Southwestern University, B
The University of Texas at Austin, D

Wisconsin

Carroll College, B

Ontario

University of Toronto, B

ANIMAL GENETICS

Alabama

Jacksonville State University, B

Indiana

Ball State University, B

Massachusetts

Harvard University, B
Worcester Polytechnic Institute, B

Minnesota

University of Minnesota, Twin Cities Campus, B

Missouri

Missouri Southern State University, B

New Hampshire

Dartmouth College, B

New Jersey

Rutgers, The State University of New Jersey, New
   Brunswick/Piscataway, B

New York

Sarah Lawrence College, B

Ohio

The Ohio State University, B
Ohio Wesleyan University, B

Pennsylvania

Cedar Crest College, B

Wisconsin

University of Wisconsin-Madison, B

Alberta

University of Alberta, B

British Columbia

The University of British Columbia, B

Manitoba

University of Manitoba, B

Ontario

University of Toronto, B
The University of Western Ontario, B

Quebec

McGill University, B

ANIMAL HEALTH

California

Santa Rosa Junior College, A

Georgia

University of Georgia, B

Texas

Sul Ross State University, B

Vermont

Sterling College, AB

ANIMAL/LIVESTOCK HUSBANDRY AND PRODUCTION

California

Feather River College, A

Connecticut

University of Connecticut, A

Illinois

Black Hawk College, A
John Wood Community College, A

Indiana

Saint Mary-of-the-Woods College, AB

Iowa

Dordt College, B
Iowa Lakes Community College, A
Iowa Western Community College, A

Kansas

Pratt Community College, A

Kentucky

Hopkinsville Community College, A

Minnesota

Ridgewater College, A

New Hampshire

University of New Hampshire, AB

New Jersey

Rutgers, The State University of New Jersey, New
   Brunswick/Piscataway, B

Ohio

The Ohio State University Agricultural Technical
   Institute, A

South Dakota

Western Dakota Technical Institute, A

Tennessee

The University of Tennessee at Martin, B

Texas

North Central Texas College, A
Tarleton State University, B
Texas A&M University, B
Texas Tech University, B

Vermont

Sterling College, AB

British Columbia

Thompson Rivers University, A
The University of British Columbia, B

ANIMAL NUTRITION

Vermont

Sterling College, AB

ANIMAL PHYSIOLOGY

Arizona

The University of Arizona, B

California

California State University, Fresno, B
Chabot College, A

San Francisco State University, B
Santa Rosa Junior College, A
Sonoma State University, B
University of California, San Diego, B
University of California, Santa Barbara, B

Connecticut

University of Connecticut, B

Illinois

Joliet Junior College, A

Massachusetts

Boston University, B

Minnesota

Minnesota State University Mankato, B
University of Minnesota, Twin Cities Campus, B

New Jersey

Rutgers, The State University of New Jersey, New
   Brunswick/Piscataway, B

New York

Cornell University, B

Ohio

Ohio University-Eastern, B
The University of Akron, B

Tennessee

Martin Methodist College, A

Texas

Texas State University-San Marcos, B

Utah

Snow College, A
Utah State University, B

Alberta

University of Alberta, B

New Brunswick

University of New Brunswick Fredericton, B

Ontario

University of Toronto, B
The University of Western Ontario, B

Quebec

McGill University, B

Saskatchewan

University of Saskatchewan, B

ANIMAL SCIENCES

Alabama

Alabama Agricultural and Mechanical University, BM
Auburn University, BMD
Tuskegee University, BM

Arizona

The University of Arizona, BMD

Arkansas

Arkansas State University, B
Arkansas State University-Beebe, A
University of Arkansas, BMD
University of Arkansas at Pine Bluff, B

California

Bakersfield College, A
Butte College, A
California Polytechnic State University, San Luis
   Obispo, B
California State Polytechnic University, Pomona, BM
California State University, Chico, B
California State University, Fresno, BM
College of the Sequoias, A

Cosumnes River College (Sacramento), A
Hartnell College, A
Los Angeles Pierce College, A
Mendocino College, A
Merced College, A
Modesto Junior College, A
Moorpark College, A
Mt. San Antonio College, A
Reedley College, A
San Joaquin Delta College, A
Santa Rosa Junior College, A
Shasta College, A
Sierra College, A
University of California, Davis, BMD
West Hills Community College, A
Yuba College, A

Colorado

Colorado State University, BMD
Lamar Community College, A
Northeastern Junior College, A
University of Denver, B

Connecticut

University of Connecticut, ABMD

Delaware

Delaware State University, B
University of Delaware, BMD

Florida

Florida Agricultural and Mechanical University, BM
University of Florida, BMD

Georgia

Abraham Baldwin Agricultural College, A
Berry College, B
Fort Valley State University, BM
South Georgia College, A
University of Georgia, BMD

Hawaii

University of Hawaii at Hilo, B
University of Hawaii at Manoa, BM

Idaho

Brigham Young University -Idaho, A
University of Idaho, BMD

Illinois

Black Hawk College, A
Shawnee Community College, A
Southern Illinois University Carbondale, BM
University of Illinois at Urbana-Champaign, BMD

Indiana

Purdue University, BMD

Iowa

Dordt College, B
Hawkeye Community College, A
Iowa Lakes Community College, A
Iowa State University of Science and
   Technology, BMD
Kirkwood Community College, A

Kansas

Coffeyville Community College, A
Colby Community College, A
Dodge City Community College, A
Fort Hays State University, B
Fort Scott Community College, A
Highland Community College, A
Kansas State University, BMD
Pratt Community College, A

Kentucky

St. Catharine College, A
University of Kentucky, BMD

Louisiana

Louisiana State University and Agricultural and
   Mechanical College, BMD
Louisiana Tech University, B

Southern University and Agricultural and Mechanical
   College, B
University of Louisiana at Lafayette, B

Maine

University of Maine, BM

Maryland

University of Maryland, College Park, BMD

Massachusetts

Becker College, A
Mount Ida College, B
University of Massachusetts Amherst, BMD

Michigan

Michigan State University, BMD

Minnesota

University of Minnesota, Crookston, AB
University of Minnesota, Twin Cities Campus, BMD

Mississippi

Alcorn State University, BM
Mississippi State University, B
Northwest Mississippi Community College, A

Missouri

College of the Ozarks, B
Missouri State University, B
Northwest Missouri State University, B
Truman State University, B
University of Missouri-Columbia, BMD

Montana

Montana State University, BMD

Nebraska

Nebraska College of Technical Agriculture, A
Northeast Community College, A
Southeast Community College, Beatrice Campus, A
University of Nebraska-Lincoln, BMD

Nevada

University of Nevada, Reno, BM

New Hampshire

University of New Hampshire, ABMD

New Jersey

Camden County College, A
Rutgers, The State University of New Jersey, New
   Brunswick/Piscataway, BMD

New Mexico

Mesalands Community College, A
New Mexico State University, BMD

New York

Cornell University, BMD
Niagara County Community College, A
State University of New York College of Agriculture
   and Technology at Cobleskill, A
State University of New York College of Agriculture
   and Technology at Morrisville, A
State University of New York College of Technology
   at Alfred, A

North Carolina

Alamance Community College, A
James Sprunt Community College, A
North Carolina Agricultural and Technical State
   University, B

North Carolina State University, B

North Dakota

North Dakota State University, BMD

Ohio

The Ohio State University, BMD
The Ohio State University Agricultural Technical
   Institute, A

Oklahoma

Connors State College, A
Eastern Oklahoma State College, A
Langston University, B
Murray State College, A
Northeastern Oklahoma Agricultural and Mechanical
   College, A
Oklahoma Panhandle State University, B
Oklahoma State University, BMD
Redlands Community College, A

Oregon

Blue Mountain Community College, A
Linn-Benton Community College, A
Oregon State University, BMD

Pennsylvania

Delaware Valley College, B
Harcum College, A
Manor College, A
The Pennsylvania State University Abington
   College, B
The Pennsylvania State University Altoona
   College, B
The Pennsylvania State University Beaver Campus
   of the Commonwealth College, B
The Pennsylvania State University Berks Campus of
   the Berks-Lehigh Valley College, B
The Pennsylvania State University Delaware County
   Campus of the Commonwealth College, B
The Pennsylvania State University DuBois Campus
   of the Commonwealth College, B
The Pennsylvania State University at Erie, The
   Behrend College, B
The Pennsylvania State University Fayette Campus
   of the Commonwealth College, B
The Pennsylvania State University Hazleton
   Campus of the Commonwealth College, B
The Pennsylvania State University, Lehigh Valley
   Campus of the Berks-Lehigh Valley College, B
The Pennsylvania State University McKeesport
   Campus of the Commonwealth College, B
The Pennsylvania State University Mont Alto
   Campus of the Commonwealth College, B
The Pennsylvania State University New Kensington
   Campus of the Commonwealth College, B
The Pennsylvania State University Schuylkill
   Campus of the Capital College, B
The Pennsylvania State University Shenango
   Campus of the Commonwealth College, B
The Pennsylvania State University University Park
   Campus, BMD
The Pennsylvania State University Wilkes-Barre
   Campus of the Commonwealth College, B
The Pennsylvania State University Worthington
   Scranton Campus of the Commonwealth
   College, B
The Pennsylvania State University York Campus of
   the Commonwealth College, B

Puerto Rico

University of Puerto Rico at Arecibo, A
University of Puerto Rico, Mayagüez Campus, BM
University of Puerto Rico at Utuado, A

Rhode Island

University of Rhode Island, BM

South Carolina

Clemson University, BMD

South Dakota

South Dakota State University, BMD

Tennessee

Middle Tennessee State University, B
Tennessee State University, B

Tennessee Technological University, B
The University of Tennessee, BMD
The University of Tennessee at Martin, B

Texas

Abilene Christian University, B
Angelo State University, BM
Hardin-Simmons University, B
Hill College of the Hill Junior College District, A
Lubbock Christian University, B
Prairie View A&M University, M
Sam Houston State University, B
Southwestern University, B
Stephen F. Austin State University, B
Sul Ross State University, ABM
Tarleton State University, BM
Texas A&M University, BMD
Texas A&M University-Commerce, B
Texas A&M University-Kingsville, BM
Texas State University-San Marcos, B
Texas Tech University, BMD
Trinity Valley Community College, A
West Texas A&M University, BM

Utah

Brigham Young University, M
Snow College, A
Utah State University, BMD

Vermont

Sterling College, AB
University of Vermont, BMD

Virginia

Virginia Polytechnic Institute and State
    University, BMD

Washington

Everett Community College, A
Washington State University, BMD
Yakima Valley Community College, A

West Virginia

Potomac State College of West Virginia
    University, A
West Virginia University, BMD

Wisconsin

University of Wisconsin-Madison, BMD
University of Wisconsin-Platteville, B
University of Wisconsin-River Falls, B

Wyoming

Casper College, A
Eastern Wyoming College, A
Northwest College, A
University of Wyoming, BMD

Alberta

University of Alberta, B

British Columbia

Thompson Rivers University, B
The University of British Columbia, BMD

Manitoba

University of Manitoba, BMD

Nova Scotia

Nova Scotia Agricultural College, B

Ontario

University of Guelph, BMD

Quebec

McGill University, BMD
Université Laval, MD

Saskatchewan

University of Saskatchewan, BMD

ANIMAL TRAINING

Massachusetts

Becker College, A

Vermont

Sterling College, B

ANIMATION, INTERACTIVE TECHNOLOGY, VIDEO GRAPHICS AND SPECIAL EFFECTS

Arizona

The Art Center Design College, B
The Art Institute of Phoenix, B
ITT Technical Institute (Tempe), B
ITT Technical Institute (Tucson), B

Arkansas

ITT Technical Institute, B

California

Academy of Art University, AB
The Art Institute of California-Inland Empire, B
The Art Institute of California-Los Angeles, B
The Art Institute of California-Orange County, B
The Art Institute of California-San Francisco, B
Brooks College (Long Beach), A
Cogswell Polytechnical College, B
ITT Technical Institute (Anaheim), B
ITT Technical Institute (Lathrop), B
ITT Technical Institute (Oxnard), B
ITT Technical Institute (Rancho Cordova), B
ITT Technical Institute (San Bernardino), B
ITT Technical Institute (San Diego), B
ITT Technical Institute (Sylmar), B
ITT Technical Institute (Torrance), B
ITT Technical Institute (West Covina), B
National University, A
Platt College San Diego, AB
Western Career College (Walnut Creek), AB
Westwood College-Anaheim, B
Westwood College-Inland Empire, B

Colorado

ITT Technical Institute, B
Westwood College-Denver North, B
Westwood College-Denver South, B

Delaware

Delaware College of Art and Design, A

Florida

The Art Institute of Tampa, AB
Full Sail Real World Education, B
ITT Technical Institute (Fort Lauderdale), B
ITT Technical Institute (Jacksonville), B
ITT Technical Institute (Lake Mary), B
ITT Technical Institute (Miami), B
ITT Technical Institute (Tampa), B
Miami International University of Art & Design, B

Georgia

The Art Institute of Atlanta, B
ITT Technical Institute (Duluth), B
Savannah College of Art and Design, B
Westwood College-Atlanta Midtown, B
Westwood College-Atlanta Northlake, B

Idaho

ITT Technical Institute, B

Illinois

The Illinois Institute of Art-Chicago, AB
The Illinois Institute of Art-Schaumburg, B
North Central College, B
Northwestern Business College, A

School of the Art Institute of Chicago, B

Indiana

ITT Technical Institute (Fort Wayne), B
ITT Technical Institute (Indianapolis), B
ITT Technical Institute (Newburgh), B

Iowa

University of Dubuque, B

Kentucky

ITT Technical Institute (Louisville), B
Louisville Technical Institute, A

Louisiana

ITT Technical Institute, B

Maine

New England School of Communications, AB

Maryland

Hagerstown Community College, A

Massachusetts

Massachusetts College of Art, B
The New England Institute of Art, B

Minnesota

The Art Institutes International Minnesota, B
Brown College, B
Globe College, A
ITT Technical Institute, B

Missouri

ITT Technical Institute (Arnold), B
ITT Technical Institute (Earth City), B

Nebraska

ITT Technical Institute, B

Nevada

ITT Technical Institute, B
Nevada State College at Henderson, B

New Hampshire

New Hampshire Technical Institute, A

New Jersey

Bloomfield College, B

New Mexico

ITT Technical Institute, B

New York

The Art Institute of New York City, A
Rochester Institute of Technology, B
School of Visual Arts, B

North Dakota

United Tribes Technical College, A

Ohio

Kent State University, Tuscarawas Campus, A

Oregon

The Art Institute of Portland, B
ITT Technical Institute, B

Pennsylvania

The Art Institute of Philadelphia, AB
Bradley Academy for the Visual Arts, A

South Carolina

ITT Technical Institute, B

Tennessee

ITT Technical Institute (Knoxville), B
ITT Technical Institute (Memphis), B
ITT Technical Institute (Nashville), B

Southern Adventist University, B

Texas

The Art Institute of Dallas, AB
The Art Institute of Houston, AB
Montgomery College, A

Utah

Brigham Young University, B
ITT Technical Institute, B

Vermont

Bennington College, B
Burlington College, B
Champlain College, AB

Virginia

ITT Technical Institute (Chantilly), B
ITT Technical Institute (Norfolk), B
ITT Technical Institute (Richmond), B
Westwood College-Annandale Campus, B

Washington

The Art Institute of Seattle, AB
ITT Technical Institute (Bothell), B
ITT Technical Institute (Seattle), B
ITT Technical Institute (Spokane), B
Olympic College, A

Wisconsin

ITT Technical Institute (Green Bay), B
ITT Technical Institute (Greenfield), B

ANTHROPOLOGY

Alabama

Auburn University, B
Jacksonville State University, B
The University of Alabama, BMD
The University of Alabama at Birmingham, BM
University of South Alabama, B

Alaska

University of Alaska Anchorage, B
University of Alaska Fairbanks, BMD

Arizona

Arizona State University, BMDO
Cochise College (Douglas), A
Cochise College (Sierra Vista), A
Eastern Arizona College, A
Northern Arizona University, BM
Pima Community College, A
Prescott College, B
The University of Arizona, BMD

Arkansas

Hendrix College, B
University of Arkansas, BM
University of Arkansas at Little Rock, B

California

Bakersfield College, A
Biola University, B
California Institute of Integral Studies, MD
California State Polytechnic University, Pomona, B
California State University, Bakersfield, BM
California State University, Chico, BM
California State University, Dominguez Hills, B
California State University, East Bay, BM
California State University, Fresno, B
California State University, Fullerton, BM
California State University, Long Beach, BM
California State University, Los Angeles, BM
California State University, Northridge, BM
California State University, Sacramento, BM
California State University, San Bernardino, B
California State University, Stanislaus, B
Cañada College, A
Cerritos College, A
Chaffey College, A
Claremont McKenna College, B
College of Alameda, A

College of the Desert, A
Columbia College, A
Contra Costa College, A
Crafton Hills College, A
Cypress College, A
East Los Angeles College, A
El Camino College, A
Foothill College, A
Fresno City College, A
Fullerton College, A
Hartnell College, A
Humboldt State University, B
Imperial Valley College, A
Los Angeles Southwest College, A
Los Medanos College, A
Mills College, B
Monterey Peninsula College, A
Moorpark College, A
Occidental College, B
Orange Coast College, A
Oxnard College, A
Palomar College, A
Pasadena City College, A
Pitzer College, B
Pomona College, B
Saddleback College, A
Saint Mary's College of California, B
San Bernardino Valley College, A
San Diego City College, A
San Diego Miramar College, A
San Diego State University, BM
San Francisco State University, BM
San Joaquin Delta College, A
San Jose State University, B
Santa Ana College, A
Santa Barbara City College, A
Santa Clara University, B
Santa Monica College, A
Santa Rosa Junior College, A
Santiago Canyon College, A
Scripps College, B
Skyline College, A
Sonoma State University, B
Southwestern College, A
Stanford University, BMD
University of California, Berkeley, BD
University of California, Davis, BMD
University of California, Irvine, BMD
University of California, Los Angeles, BMD
University of California, Riverside, BMD
University of California, San Diego, BD
University of California, Santa Barbara, BMD
University of California, Santa Cruz, BMD
University of La Verne, B
University of Redlands, B
University of San Diego, B
University of Southern California, BMDO
Vanguard University of Southern California, B
West Los Angeles College, A
Westmont College, B

Colorado

The Colorado College, B
Colorado State University, BM
Fort Lewis College, B
Mesa State College, B
Metropolitan State College of Denver, B
University of Colorado at Boulder, BMD
University of Colorado at Colorado Springs, B
University of Colorado at Denver and Health Sciences Center - Downtown Denver Campus, BM
University of Denver, BM
Western State College of Colorado, B

Connecticut

Central Connecticut State University, B
Connecticut College, B
Trinity College, B
University of Connecticut, BMD
Wesleyan University, B
Western Connecticut State University, B

Yale University, BMD

Delaware

University of Delaware, B

District of Columbia

American University, BMDO
The Catholic University of America, BMD
The George Washington University, BMD
Georgetown University, B
Howard University, B
University of the District of Columbia, B

Florida

Daytona Beach Community College, A
Eckerd College, B
Florida Atlantic University, BM
Florida State University, BMD
Gulf Coast Community College, A
Indian River Community College, A
Miami Dade College, A
New College of Florida, B
Rollins College, B
University of Central Florida, B
University of Florida, BMDO
University of Miami, B
University of North Florida, B
University of South Florida, BMD
University of West Florida, BM

Georgia

Agnes Scott College, B
Berry College, B
Darton College, A
East Georgia College, A
Emory University, BD
Gainesville College, A
Georgia Perimeter College, A
Georgia Southern University, B
Georgia State University, BM
Spelman College, B
University of Georgia, BMD
University of West Georgia, B

Guam

University of Guam, B

Hawaii

Brigham Young University-Hawaii, B
Hawaii Pacific University, B
University of Hawaii at Hilo, B
University of Hawaii at Manoa, BMD
University of Hawaii-West Oahu, B

Idaho

Albertson College of Idaho, B
Boise State University, B
College of Southern Idaho, A
Idaho State University, BM
North Idaho College, A
University of Idaho, BM

Illinois

Augustana College, B
DePaul University, B
Illinois State University, B
Judson College, B
Knox College, B
Lake Forest College, B
Loyola University Chicago, B
National-Louis University, B
North Central College, B
North Park University, B
Northeastern Illinois University, B
Northern Illinois University, BM
Northwestern University, BDO
Principia College, B
Rockford College, B
Southern Illinois University Carbondale, BMD
Southern Illinois University Edwardsville, B
University of Chicago, BD
University of Illinois at Chicago, BMD
University of Illinois at Springfield, B
University of Illinois at Urbana-Champaign, BMD

Wheaton College, B

Indiana

Ball State University, BM
Butler University, B
DePauw University, B
Hanover College, B
Indiana State University, B
Indiana University Bloomington, BMD
Indiana University-Purdue University Fort Wayne, B
Indiana University-Purdue University Indianapolis, B
Purdue University, MD
University of Indianapolis, B
University of Notre Dame, B
Vincennes University, A

Iowa

Cornell College, B
Drake University, B
Grinnell College, B
Iowa State University of Science and
    Technology, BM
Luther College, B
The University of Iowa, BMD
University of Northern Iowa, B

Kansas

Barton County Community College, A
Kansas State University, B
University of Kansas, BMD
Washburn University, B
Wichita State University, BM

Kentucky

Centre College, B
Eastern Kentucky University, B
Northern Kentucky University, B
Transylvania University, B
University of Kentucky, BMD
University of Louisville, B
Western Kentucky University, B

Louisiana

Louisiana State University and Agricultural and
    Mechanical College, BMD
Northwestern State University of Louisiana, B
Tulane University, BMD
University of Louisiana at Lafayette, B
University of New Orleans, B

Maine

Bates College, B
Bowdoin College, B
Colby College, B
University of Maine, B
University of Maine at Farmington, B
University of Southern Maine, B

Maryland

The Johns Hopkins University, BD
St. Mary's College of Maryland, B
University of Maryland, Baltimore County, B
University of Maryland, College Park, BM
Washington College, B

Massachusetts

Amherst College, B
Boston University, BMD
Brandeis University, BMD
Bridgewater State College, B
College of the Holy Cross, B
Framingham State College, B
Hampshire College, B
Harvard University, BMD
Massachusetts College of Liberal Arts, B
Massachusetts Institute of Technology, B
Mount Holyoke College, B
Northeastern University, B
Simon's Rock College of Bard, B
Smith College, B
Tufts University, B
University of Massachusetts Amherst, BMD
University of Massachusetts Boston, B
Wellesley College, B
Wheaton College, B

Williams College, B

Michigan

Albion College, B
Alma College, B
Central Michigan University, B
Eastern Michigan University, B
Grand Valley State University, B
Kalamazoo College, B
Kellogg Community College, A
Michigan State University, BMD
Muskegon Community College, A
Oakland University, B
University of Michigan, BD
University of Michigan-Dearborn, B
University of Michigan-Flint, B
Wayne State University, BMD
Western Michigan University, BM

Minnesota

Carleton College, B
Gustavus Adolphus College, B
Hamline University, B
Macalester College, B
Minnesota State University Mankato, BM
Minnesota State University Moorhead, B
St. Cloud State University, B
University of Minnesota, Duluth, BM
University of Minnesota, Morris, B
University of Minnesota, Twin Cities Campus, BMD

Mississippi

Millsaps College, B
Mississippi State University, BMD
University of Mississippi, BM
University of Southern Mississippi, BM

Missouri

Missouri State University, B
Southeast Missouri State University, B
University of Missouri-Columbia, BMD
University of Missouri-St. Louis, B
Washington University in St. Louis, BMD
Webster University, B
Westminster College, B

Montana

Montana State University, B
The University of Montana-Missoula, BMD

Nebraska

University of Nebraska-Lincoln, BM
Western Nebraska Community College, A

Nevada

Community College of Southern Nevada, A
Great Basin College, A
University of Nevada, Las Vegas, BMD
University of Nevada, Reno, BMD

New Hampshire

Dartmouth College, B
Franklin Pierce College, B
University of New Hampshire, B

New Jersey

Drew University, B
Monmouth University, B
Montclair State University, B
Princeton University, BD
Rutgers, The State University of New Jersey, New
    Brunswick/Piscataway, BMD
Rutgers, The State University of New Jersey,
    Newark, B
Seton Hall University, B
William Paterson University of New Jersey, B

New Mexico

Eastern New Mexico University, BM
New Mexico Highlands University, BM
New Mexico State University, BM
San Juan College, A

University of New Mexico, BMD

New York

Adelphi University, B
Bard College, B
Barnard College, B
Brooklyn College of the City University of New
    York, B
Buffalo State College, State University of New
    York, B
Canisius College, B
City College of the City University of New York, BM
Colgate University, B
College of Staten Island of the City University of
    New York, B
Columbia College, B
Columbia University, School of General Studies, B
Cornell University, BD
Dowling College, B
Elmira College, B
Eugene Lang College The New School for Liberal
    Arts, B
Fordham University, B
Hamilton College, B
Hartwick College, B
Hobart and William Smith Colleges, B
Hofstra University, B
Hunter College of the City University of New
    York, BM
Ithaca College, B
Lehman College of the City University of New
    York, B
Nazareth College of Rochester, B
New York University, BMDO
Purchase College, State University of New York, B
Queens College of the City University of New
    York, B
St. John Fisher College, B
St. John's University, B
St. Lawrence University, B
Sarah Lawrence College, B
Skidmore College, B
State University of New York at Binghamton, BMD
State University of New York at Buffalo, BMD
State University of New York College at
    Brockport, B
State University of New York College at Cortland, B
State University of New York College at Geneseo, B
State University of New York College at Oneonta, B
State University of New York College at Potsdam, B
State University of New York at New Paltz, B
State University of New York at Oswego, B
State University of New York at Plattsburgh, B
Stony Brook University, State University of New
    York, BMD
Syracuse University, BMD
Union College, B
University at Albany, State University of New
    York, BMD
University of Rochester, B
Vassar College, B
Wagner College, B
Wells College, B
York College of the City University of New York, B

North Carolina

Appalachian State University, B
Davidson College, B
Duke University, BDO
East Carolina University, BM
North Carolina State University, B
North Carolina Wesleyan College, B
The University of North Carolina at Chapel
    Hill, BMD
The University of North Carolina at Charlotte, B
The University of North Carolina Wilmington, B
Wake Forest University, B
Western Carolina University, B

North Dakota

University of North Dakota, B

Ohio

Antioch College, B
Case Western Reserve University, BMDO
Cleveland State University, B

Denison University, B
Franciscan University of Steubenville, B
Heidelberg College, B
Kent State University, BM
Kenyon College, B
Miami University, B
Miami University Hamilton, B
Miami University-Middletown Campus, A
Oberlin College, B
The Ohio State University, BMD
Ohio University, B
Ohio Wesleyan University, B
University of Cincinnati, BM
The University of Toledo, BM
Wright State University, B
Youngstown State University, B

Oklahoma

University of Oklahoma, BMD
University of Tulsa, BMO

Oregon

Eastern Oregon University, B
Lewis & Clark College, B
Linfield College, B
Oregon State University, BM
Portland State University, BMD
Reed College, B
Southern Oregon University, B
Umpqua Community College, A
University of Oregon, BMD
Western Oregon University, B
Willamette University, B

Pennsylvania

Bloomsburg University of Pennsylvania, B
Bryn Mawr College, B
Bucknell University, B
California University of Pennsylvania, B
Carnegie Mellon University, B
Clarion University of Pennsylvania, B
Delaware County Community College, A
Dickinson College, B
Edinboro University of Pennsylvania, B
Elizabethtown College, B
Franklin and Marshall College, B
Gettysburg College, B
Haverford College, B
Indiana University of Pennsylvania, B
Juniata College, B
Kutztown University of Pennsylvania, B
Lafayette College, B
Lehigh University, BM
Lincoln University, B
Lock Haven University of Pennsylvania, B
Lycoming College, B
Mansfield University of Pennsylvania, B
Mercyhurst College, B
Millersville University of Pennsylvania, B
Muhlenberg College, B
The Pennsylvania State University Abington
    College, B
The Pennsylvania State University Altoona
    College, B
The Pennsylvania State University Beaver Campus
    of the Commonwealth College, B
The Pennsylvania State University Berks Campus of
    the Berks-Lehigh Valley College, B
The Pennsylvania State University Delaware County
    Campus of the Commonwealth College, B
The Pennsylvania State University DuBois Campus
    of the Commonwealth College, B
The Pennsylvania State University at Erie, The
    Behrend College, B
The Pennsylvania State University Fayette Campus
    of the Commonwealth College, B
The Pennsylvania State University Hazleton
    Campus of the Commonwealth College, B
The Pennsylvania State University, Lehigh Valley
    Campus of the Berks-Lehigh Valley College, B
The Pennsylvania State University McKeesport
    Campus of the Commonwealth College, B
The Pennsylvania State University Mont Alto
    Campus of the Commonwealth College, B
The Pennsylvania State University New Kensington
    Campus of the Commonwealth College, B

The Pennsylvania State University Schuylkill
    Campus of the Capital College, B
The Pennsylvania State University Shenango
    Campus of the Commonwealth College, B
The Pennsylvania State University University Park
    Campus, BMD
The Pennsylvania State University Wilkes-Barre
    Campus of the Commonwealth College, B
The Pennsylvania State University Worthington
    Scranton Campus of the Commonwealth
    College, B
The Pennsylvania State University York Campus of
    the Commonwealth College, B
Saint Francis University, B
Saint Vincent College, B
Slippery Rock University of Pennsylvania, B
Swarthmore College, B
Temple University, BMD
University of Pennsylvania, BMD
University of Pittsburgh, BMD
University of Pittsburgh at Greensburg, B
Ursinus College, B
West Chester University of Pennsylvania, BMO
Widener University, B

Puerto Rico

University of Puerto Rico, Río Piedras, B

Rhode Island

Brown University, BMD
Rhode Island College, B
Roger Williams University, B
Salve Regina University, B
University of Rhode Island, B

South Carolina

College of Charleston, B
University of South Carolina, BMD

South Dakota

The University of South Dakota, B

Tennessee

Middle Tennessee State University, B
Rhodes College, B
Sewanee: The University of the South, B
University of Memphis, BM
The University of Tennessee, BMD
The University of Tennessee at Martin, B
Vanderbilt University, BMD

Texas

Baylor University, B
Midland College, A
Rice University, BMD
Southern Methodist University, BMD
Southwestern University, B
Texas A&M University, BMD
Texas A&M University-Commerce, B
Texas A&M University-Kingsville, B
Texas Christian University, B
Texas State University-San Marcos, B
Texas Tech University, BM
Trinity University, B
University of Houston, BM
University of Houston-Clear Lake, B
University of North Texas, BM
The University of Texas at Arlington, BM
The University of Texas at Austin, BMD
The University of Texas at El Paso, B
The University of Texas-Pan American, B
The University of Texas at San Antonio, BM

Utah

Brigham Young University, BM
University of Utah, BMD
Utah State University, B

Vermont

Bennington College, B
Green Mountain College, B
Johnson State College, B
Marlboro College, B

University of Vermont, B

Virginia

The College of William and Mary, BMD
George Mason University, B
James Madison University, B
Longwood University, B
Old Dominion University, B
Radford University, B
Sweet Briar College, B
University of Virginia, BMD
Virginia Commonwealth University, B
Washington and Lee University, B

Washington

Central Washington University, B
Eastern Washington University, B
Everett Community College, A
Lower Columbia College, A
Pacific Lutheran University, B
Skagit Valley College, A
Tacoma Community College, A
University of Washington, BMD
Washington State University, BMD
Western Washington University, BM
Whitman College, B

West Virginia

Marshall University, M
West Virginia University, B

Wisconsin

Beloit College, B
Lawrence University, B
Marquette University, B
Ripon College, B
University of Wisconsin-Madison, BMD
University of Wisconsin-Milwaukee, BMDO
University of Wisconsin-Oshkosh, B

Wyoming

Casper College, A
Laramie County Community College, A
University of Wyoming, BMD
Western Wyoming Community College, A

Alberta

Athabasca University, B
University of Alberta, BMD
University of Calgary, BMD
University of Lethbridge, BM

British Columbia

Kwantlen University College, A
Malaspina University-College, B
Simon Fraser University, MD
The University of British Columbia, BMD
University College of the Fraser Valley, B
University of Northern British Columbia, B
University of Victoria, BM

Manitoba

University of Manitoba, BMD
The University of Winnipeg, B

New Brunswick

Mount Allison University, B
St. Thomas University, B
University of New Brunswick Fredericton, BM

Newfoundland and Labrador

Memorial University of Newfoundland, BMD

Nova Scotia

Cape Breton University, B
Dalhousie University, BMD
Mount Saint Vincent University, B
St. Francis Xavier University, B
Saint Mary's University, B
University of King's College, B

Ontario

Carleton University, BM
Lakehead University, B

Laurentian University, B
McMaster University, BMD
Trent University, BM
University of Guelph, BMD
University of Toronto, BMD
University of Waterloo, B
The University of Western Ontario, BMD
University of Windsor, B
Wilfrid Laurier University, B
York University, BMD

Prince Edward Island

University of Prince Edward Island, B

Quebec

Concordia University, BM
McGill University, BMD
Université Laval, ABMD
Université de Montréal, BMD

Saskatchewan

University of Regina, BM
University of Saskatchewan, BM

APPAREL AND ACCESSORIES MARKETING OPERATIONS

California

California Design College, A
FIDM/The Fashion Institute of Design & Merchandising, Los Angeles Campus, A
FIDM/The Fashion Institute of Design & Merchandising, San Diego Campus, A
FIDM/The Fashion Institute of Design & Merchandising, San Francisco Campus, A

Georgia

Clayton State University, A

Illinois

The Illinois Institute of Art-Chicago, B

Montana

The University of Montana-Missoula, A

Ohio

Bluffton University, B

Pennsylvania

Philadelphia University, B

Rhode Island

University of Rhode Island, B

Wisconsin

Northeast Wisconsin Technical College, A

APPAREL AND TEXTILE MANUFACTURE

New York

Fashion Institute of Technology, AB

North Carolina

North Carolina State University, B

APPAREL AND TEXTILE MARKETING MANAGEMENT

Alabama

Community College of the Air Force, A

Florida

Florida State University, B

Michigan

Delta College, A
Wayne State University, B

North Carolina

North Carolina State University, B

APPAREL AND TEXTILES

Alabama

Auburn University, B
Central Alabama Community College, A
H. Councill Trenholm State Technical College, A
Jacksonville State University, B
Lawson State Community College, A
The University of Alabama, B

Arizona

Northland Pioneer College, A

Arkansas

University of Arkansas, B
University of Arkansas at Pine Bluff, B

California

Academy of Art University, AB
Antelope Valley College, A
Brooks College (Long Beach), A
California State University, Long Beach, B
California State University, Sacramento, B
FIDM/The Fashion Institute of Design & Merchandising, Los Angeles Campus, A
FIDM/The Fashion Institute of Design & Merchandising, Orange County Campus, A
FIDM/The Fashion Institute of Design & Merchandising, San Francisco Campus, A
Los Angeles City College, A
Modesto Junior College, A
Monterey Peninsula College, A
Mt. San Antonio College, A
San Francisco State University, B
University of California, Davis, B

Colorado

Colorado State University, B

Delaware

Delaware State University, B

District of Columbia

Gallaudet University, B
University of the District of Columbia, B

Florida

The Art Institute of Fort Lauderdale, A
Florida State University, B
Indian River Community College, A
Palm Beach Community College, A

Georgia

Georgia Southern University, B
University of Georgia, B

Idaho

Brigham Young University -Idaho, A
University of Idaho, B

Illinois

The Illinois Institute of Art-Chicago, A
Northern Illinois University, B
Olivet Nazarene University, B
Southern Illinois University Carbondale, B
University of Illinois at Urbana-Champaign, B

Indiana

Indiana State University, B
Indiana University Bloomington, B

Purdue University, B

Iowa

Iowa State University of Science and Technology, B
University of Northern Iowa, B

Kansas

Kansas State University, B

Kentucky

Kentucky State University, B
Murray State University, B
University of Kentucky, B
Western Kentucky University, B

Louisiana

University of Louisiana at Lafayette, B

Massachusetts

Framingham State College, B

Michigan

Michigan State University, B
Western Michigan University, B

Minnesota

Minnesota State University Mankato, B
University of Minnesota, Twin Cities Campus, B

Mississippi

Hinds Community College, A
Mississippi University for Women, B
University of Southern Mississippi, B

Missouri

Central Missouri State University, B
College of the Ozarks, B
Missouri State University, B
Northwest Missouri State University, B
University of Missouri-Columbia, B

Nebraska

University of Nebraska-Lincoln, B

New Mexico

New Mexico State University, B

New York

Cornell University, B
Fashion Institute of Technology, AB
Syracuse University, B

North Carolina

Appalachian State University, B
East Carolina University, B
North Carolina Agricultural and Technical State University, B
The University of North Carolina at Greensboro, B

North Dakota

North Dakota State University, B

Ohio

Bluffton University, B
Bowling Green State University, B
The Ohio State University, B
Ohio University, B
The University of Akron, B

Oklahoma

Northeastern Oklahoma Agricultural and Mechanical College, A
University of Central Oklahoma, B

Oregon

Oregon State University, B

Pennsylvania

Albright College, B
Bradley Academy for the Visual Arts, A
Cheyney University of Pennsylvania, B
Mercyhurst College, B

Philadelphia University, B

Rhode Island

University of Rhode Island, B

South Carolina

Bob Jones University, B
Tri-County Technical College, A

Tennessee

Freed-Hardeman University, B
Middle Tennessee State University, B
Tennessee Technological University, B

Texas

El Centro College, A
Texas Southern University, B
Texas Tech University, B
The University of Texas at Austin, B

Virginia

Virginia Polytechnic Institute and State University, B

Washington

Seattle Pacific University, B
Washington State University, B

Wisconsin

University of Wisconsin-Madison, B
University of Wisconsin-Stout, B

Alberta

University of Alberta, B

Manitoba

University of Manitoba, B

APPLIANCE INSTALLATION AND REPAIR TECHNOLOGY/TECHNICIAN

Minnesota

Dunwoody College of Technology, A

New York

Mohawk Valley Community College, A

South Dakota

Mitchell Technical Institute, A

APPLIED ART

Alabama

Huntingdon College, B
Jefferson Davis Community College, A

California

Academy of Art University, AB
Allan Hancock College, A
Azusa Pacific University, B
Butte College, A
California College of the Arts, B
California Polytechnic State University, San Luis
    Obispo, B
California State University, Dominguez Hills, B
College of Marin, A
Cosumnes River College (Sacramento), A
Cuesta College, A
Cypress College, A
Evergreen Valley College, A
Glendale Community College, A
Lassen Community College District, A
Los Angeles City College, A
Merced College, A
Newschool of Architecture & Design, A
Otis College of Art and Design, B
Palomar College, A
Porterville College, A

Skyline College, A

Colorado

Colorado State University-Pueblo, B
Mesa State College, B

Connecticut

Tunxis Community College, A

Delaware

University of Delaware, B

District of Columbia

Howard University, B

Florida

The Art Institute of Fort Lauderdale, A
Edison College, A
New World School of the Arts, AB
St. Johns River Community College, A

Illinois

American Academy of Art, B
Chicago State University, B
DePaul University, B
Lincoln College, A
Lincoln College-Normal, A

Indiana

Indiana University Bloomington, B
Oakland City University, B

Iowa

Iowa Lakes Community College, A
Kirkwood Community College, A

Kansas

Coffeyville Community College, A
Friends University, AB
Pratt Community College, A

Louisiana

McNeese State University, B

Maine

University of Maine at Presque Isle, A

Maryland

Anne Arundel Community College, A
Howard Community College, A
Villa Julie College, A

Massachusetts

Elms College, B
Hampshire College, B
School of the Museum of Fine Arts, Boston, B
Springfield College, B

Michigan

Henry Ford Community College, A
Marygrove College, B
Muskegon Community College, A
Olivet College, B
Washtenaw Community College, A

Minnesota

Bemidji State University, B
Minnesota State University Mankato, B
Minnesota State University Moorhead, B
Ridgewater College, A
St. Cloud State University, B
Winona State University, B

Mississippi

Jones County Junior College, A
Mississippi Delta Community College, A

Missouri

Lindenwood University, B
Truman State University, B

Washington University in St. Louis, B

Montana

The University of Montana-Western, AB

Nebraska

Peru State College, B

New Hampshire

Franklin Pierce College, B

New Jersey

Camden County College, A
County College of Morris, A
Middlesex County College, A
William Paterson University of New Jersey, B

New Mexico

National American University (Albuquerque), AB
University of New Mexico-Los Alamos Branch, A

New York

Buffalo State College, State University of New
    York, B
Columbia University, School of General Studies, B
Daemen College, B
Dowling College, B
Kingsborough Community College of the City
    University of New York, A
Pratt Institute, B
Rochester Institute of Technology, AB
Rockland Community College, A
State University of New York, Fredonia, B
Syracuse University, B
Westchester Community College, A

North Carolina

Central Piedmont Community College, A
Elizabeth City State University, B

Ohio

Cleveland State University, B
Muskingum College, B
Sinclair Community College, A
The University of Akron, B
University of Dayton, B
The University of Toledo, B

Oklahoma

Oklahoma Baptist University, B
Oklahoma City Community College, A

Oregon

Oregon State University, B
Portland State University, B
University of Oregon, B

Pennsylvania

The Art Institute of Pittsburgh, A
Mansfield University of Pennsylvania, B
Marywood University, B

Puerto Rico

Inter American University of Puerto Rico, San
    Germán Campus, B

South Carolina

Columbia College, B
Converse College, B

South Dakota

University of Sioux Falls, B

Tennessee

Chattanooga State Technical Community College, A
Memphis College of Art, B
Sewanee: The University of the South, B

Texas

Coastal Bend College, A
Del Mar College, A
Hill College of the Hill Junior College District, A
Howard Payne University, B

Lamar University, B
Lon Morris College, A
Lubbock Christian University, B
Midwestern State University, B
Odessa College, A
The University of Texas at Brownsville, B

Virginia

Northern Virginia Community College, A

Washington

Centralia College, A
Wenatchee Valley College, A

Wisconsin

University of Wisconsin-Madison, B

Wyoming

Casper College, A

Alberta

Athabasca University, B

Ontario

University of Ottawa, B
York University, B

APPLIED ARTS AND DESIGN

California

Academy of Art University, M
California Institute of the Arts, MO
California State University, Los Angeles, M
San Diego State University, M
San Jose State University, M

Connecticut

Yale University, M

Florida

Florida Atlantic University, M

Georgia

Savannah College of Art and Design, M

Illinois

Illinois Institute of Technology, MD
Southern Illinois University Carbondale, M
University of Illinois at Urbana-Champaign, MD

Indiana

Indiana University Bloomington, M

Iowa

Iowa State University of Science and Technology, M

Louisiana

Louisiana Tech University, M

Massachusetts

Massachusetts College of Art, M
Suffolk University, M

Michigan

Western Michigan University, M

Minnesota

Minneapolis College of Art and Design, M

New York

Alfred University, M
Fashion Institute of Technology, M
New York University, M
Pratt Institute, MO

Syracuse University, M

North Carolina

North Carolina State University, M

Ohio

University of Cincinnati, M

Pennsylvania

Drexel University, M

Rhode Island

Rhode Island School of Design, M

Tennessee

Memphis College of Art, M

Texas

Lamar University, M

Virginia

Virginia Commonwealth University, M

Wisconsin

Cardinal Stritch University, M

APPLIED ECONOMICS

California

San Jose State University, M
University of California, Santa Cruz, M
University of San Francisco, B

District of Columbia

American University, O

Florida

Florida State University, B

Georgia

University of Georgia, MD

Illinois

Roosevelt University, M

Iowa

University of Northern Iowa, B

Maryland

The Johns Hopkins University, M

Massachusetts

Northeastern University, MD
Western New England College, B

Michigan

Eastern Michigan University, M
Michigan State University, B
University of Michigan, M
Western Michigan University, D

Minnesota

The College of St. Scholastica, B
St. Cloud State University, M
University of Minnesota, Twin Cities Campus, MD

Mississippi

Mississippi State University, D

Montana

Montana State University, M

Nevada

University of Nevada, Reno, M

New Hampshire

Plymouth State University, B

New York

Buffalo State College, State University of New
York, M

Cornell University, BD
Ithaca College, B
New York University, O

North Carolina

North Carolina Agricultural and Technical State
University, M
The University of North Carolina at Greensboro, M

North Dakota

University of North Dakota, M

Ohio

Ohio University, M
Wright State University, M

Oregon

Portland State University, M

Pennsylvania

Allegheny College, B
The Pennsylvania State University Abington
College, B
The Pennsylvania State University Altoona
College, B
The Pennsylvania State University Beaver Campus
of the Commonwealth College, B
The Pennsylvania State University Berks Campus of
the Berks-Lehigh Valley College, B
The Pennsylvania State University Delaware County
Campus of the Commonwealth College, B
The Pennsylvania State University DuBois Campus
of the Commonwealth College, B
The Pennsylvania State University at Erie, The
Behrend College, B
The Pennsylvania State University Fayette Campus
of the Commonwealth College, B
The Pennsylvania State University Hazleton
Campus of the Commonwealth College, B
The Pennsylvania State University, Lehigh Valley
Campus of the Berks-Lehigh Valley College, B
The Pennsylvania State University McKeesport
Campus of the Commonwealth College, B
The Pennsylvania State University Mont Alto
Campus of the Commonwealth College, B
The Pennsylvania State University New Kensington
Campus of the Commonwealth College, B
The Pennsylvania State University Schuylkill
Campus of the Capital College, B
The Pennsylvania State University Shenango
Campus of the Commonwealth College, B
The Pennsylvania State University University Park
Campus, B
The Pennsylvania State University Wilkes-Barre
Campus of the Commonwealth College, B
The Pennsylvania State University Worthington
Scranton Campus of the Commonwealth
College, B
The Pennsylvania State University York Campus of
the Commonwealth College, B

Rhode Island

University of Rhode Island, B

South Carolina

Clemson University, MD

Texas

Southern Methodist University, BM
Texas Tech University, MDO
University of North Texas, M
The University of Texas at Dallas, MD

Utah

Brigham Young University, B
Utah State University, M

Vermont

University of Vermont, BM

Virginia

Virginia Polytechnic Institute and State
University, MD

Wisconsin

University of Wisconsin-Madison, MD

Wyoming

University of Wyoming, M

Ontario

University of Guelph, B
University of Waterloo, B

Quebec

HEC Montreal, BM

APPLIED HISTORY

California

Sonoma State University, M

Pennsylvania

Shippensburg University of Pennsylvania, MO

APPLIED HORTICULTURE/HORTICULTURAL BUSINESS SERVICES

Massachusetts

University of Massachusetts Amherst, A

Minnesota

Dakota County Technical College, A

North Dakota

Minot State University-Bottineau Campus, A

Ohio

Cincinnati State Technical and Community
College, A
Kent State University, Salem Campus, A

Pennsylvania

Delaware Valley College, B
Pennsylvania College of Technology, A

Tennessee

Southwest Tennessee Community College, A

Vermont

University of Vermont, B

APPLIED HORTICULTURE/HORTICULTURAL OPERATIONS

Arizona

Glendale Community College, A

Arkansas

Arkansas Northeastern College, A

California

Santa Barbara City College, A

Colorado

Colorado State University, B

Connecticut

University of Connecticut, A

Georgia

Georgia Southwestern State University, A
University of Georgia, B

Illinois

John Wood Community College, A
Kaskaskia College, A
Kishwaukee College, A
McHenry County College, A

Rend Lake College, A

Indiana

Oakland City University, A

Iowa

Iowa State University of Science and Technology, B

Louisiana

Delgado Community College, A

Maine

The University of Maine at Augusta, A

Maryland

Montgomery College, A

Massachusetts

North Shore Community College, A

Michigan

Oakland Community College, A

Minnesota

Anoka Technical College, A

Missouri

College of the Ozarks, B
Mineral Area College, A

Nebraska

Central Community College-Hastings Campus, A
Northeast Community College, A

North Carolina

Alamance Community College, A
Brunswick Community College, A
Fayetteville Technical Community College, A
Wilkes Community College, A

North Dakota

Minot State University-Bottineau Campus, A

Ohio

Kent State University, Geauga Campus, A
Kent State University, Salem Campus, A

Oklahoma

Tulsa Community College, A

Pennsylvania

Community College of Allegheny County, A
Temple University, A

South Carolina

Bob Jones University, A

South Dakota

South Dakota State University, B

Texas

Stephen F. Austin State University, B
Texas A&M University, B
Texas Tech University, B

Vermont

Sterling College, AB
University of Vermont, B

Virginia

Ferrum College, B
Lord Fairfax Community College, A

Washington

Clark College, A
Edmonds Community College, A
Skagit Valley College, A

Spokane Community College, A

West Virginia

West Virginia Northern Community College, A

Wisconsin

Gateway Technical College, A

Nova Scotia

Nova Scotia Agricultural College, B

APPLIED MATHEMATICS

Alabama

Auburn University, B
Oakwood College, B
The University of Alabama, D
The University of Alabama at Birmingham, D
The University of Alabama in Huntsville, D

Alaska

University of Alaska Fairbanks, B

Arizona

Arizona State University, BMD
The University of Arizona, MD

Arkansas

University of Arkansas at Little Rock, M

California

California Institute of Technology, BMD
California State Polytechnic University, Pomona, BM
California State University, Chico, B
California State University, East Bay, B
California State University, Fullerton, BM
California State University, Long Beach, BMD
Chabot College, A
Fresno Pacific University, B
Humboldt State University, B
The Master's College and Seminary, B
Pacific Union College, B
San Diego Miramar College, A
San Diego State University, BM
San Francisco State University, B
San Jose State University, B
Santa Clara University, M
Sonoma State University, B
University of California, Berkeley, BD
University of California, Davis, BMD
University of California, Los Angeles, B
University of California, San Diego, BM
University of California, Santa Barbara, M
University of California, Santa Cruz, BMD
University of Southern California, MD

Colorado

Colorado State University, B
Mesa State College, B
Northeastern Junior College, A
University of Colorado at Boulder, BMD
University of Colorado at Colorado Springs, BM
University of Colorado at Denver and Health
Sciences Center - Downtown Denver
Campus, MD
University of Denver, M

Connecticut

Quinnipiac University, B
University of Connecticut, BM
University of New Haven, B
Yale University, BMD

Delaware

University of Delaware, MD

District of Columbia

American University, B
The George Washington University, BM

Howard University, MD

Florida

Florida Atlantic University, M
Florida Institute of Technology, BMD
Florida International University, B
Florida State University, BMD
University of Central Florida, O
University of South Florida, D

Georgia

Clark Atlanta University, M
Columbus State University, B
Georgia Institute of Technology, BM
South Georgia College, A
University of Georgia, M
Valdosta State University, B

Hawaii

Hawaii Pacific University, AB

Idaho

University of Idaho, B

Illinois

DePaul University, B
Illinois Institute of Technology, BMD
Lincoln College, A
Millikin University, B
North Central College, B
Northern Illinois University, B
Northwestern University, BMD
University of Chicago, BMD
University of Illinois at Chicago, MD
University of Illinois at Urbana-Champaign, M

Indiana

Indiana University Bloomington, MD
Indiana University-Purdue University Fort Wayne, M
Indiana University-Purdue University
    Indianapolis, MD
Indiana University South Bend, BM
Oakland City University, B
Saint Mary's College, B
University of Notre Dame, M

Iowa

Grand View College, B
Iowa State University of Science and
    Technology, MD
The University of Iowa, BD
University of Northern Iowa, B

Kansas

University of Kansas, MD
Wichita State University, D

Kentucky

Asbury College, B
Brescia University, B
Eastern Kentucky University, B
Kentucky State University, B
University of Louisville, D

Louisiana

Nicholls State University, M
Tulane University, M

Maryland

Bowie State University, B
The Johns Hopkins University, BMD
Loyola College in Maryland, B
Towson University, M
University of Maryland, Baltimore County, BMD
University of Maryland, College Park, MD

Massachusetts

Harvard University, BMD
Salem State College, B
Simon's Rock College of Bard, B
University of Massachusetts Amherst, M
University of Massachusetts Lowell, BM

Worcester Polytechnic Institute, BM

Michigan

Ferris State University, B
Grand Valley State University, B
Kettering University, B
Michigan State University, BMD
Michigan Technological University, B
Muskegon Community College, A
Oakland University, MD
University of Michigan, B
University of Michigan-Dearborn, M
Wayne State University, MD
Western Michigan University, BM

Minnesota

Metropolitan State University, B
University of Minnesota, Duluth, M
Winona State University, B

Missouri

Central Methodist University, A
Central Missouri State University, M
Maryville University of Saint Louis, B
University of Missouri-Columbia, M
University of Missouri-Rolla, BM
University of Missouri-St. Louis, BMD
Washington University in St. Louis, B

Montana

Montana Tech of The University of Montana, B
The University of Montana-Missoula, B

Nebraska

Creighton University, B
Wayne State College, B

Nevada

University of Nevada, Las Vegas, BM

New Hampshire

Keene State College, B
University of New Hampshire, M

New Jersey

Bloomfield College, B
Montclair State University, M
New Jersey Institute of Technology, BM
Princeton University, D
Rutgers, The State University of New Jersey, New
    Brunswick/Piscataway, MD
Rutgers, The State University of New Jersey,
    Newark, B
Stevens Institute of Technology, MD
William Paterson University of New Jersey, B

New Mexico

New Mexico Institute of Mining and Technology, D

New York

Barnard College, B
Clarkson University, B
Columbia University, School of General Studies, B
Columbia University, The Fu Foundation School of
    Engineering and Applied Science, B
Cornell University, BMD
Farmingdale State University of New York, B
Hofstra University, BM
Hunter College of the City University of New
    York, M
Iona College, B
Ithaca College, B
Le Moyne College, B
Long Island University, C.W. Post Campus, BM
Medgar Evers College of the City University of New
    York, B
Queens College of the City University of New
    York, B
Rensselaer Polytechnic Institute, BM
Rochester Institute of Technology, ABM
St. John's University, M
St. Thomas Aquinas College, B
State University of New York Institute of
    Technology, B

State University of New York at New Paltz, B
State University of New York at Oswego, B
Stony Brook University, State University of New
    York, BMD
United States Military Academy, B
University at Albany, State University of New York, B
University of Rochester, B

North Carolina

East Carolina University, M
Johnson C. Smith University, B
North Carolina Agricultural and Technical State
    University, B
North Carolina State University, BMD
Queens University of Charlotte, B
The University of North Carolina at Chapel Hill, B
The University of North Carolina at Charlotte, D
The University of North Carolina at Greensboro, B

North Dakota

Jamestown College, B
North Dakota State University, MD

Ohio

Bowling Green State University, B
Case Western Reserve University, BMD
Cleveland State University, M
College of Mount St. Joseph, B
Kent State University, BMD
Ohio University, B
Shawnee State University, B
The University of Akron, BMD
University of Cincinnati, MD
University of Dayton, BM
The University of Toledo, M
Wright State University, BM

Oklahoma

Oklahoma State University, M
University of Central Oklahoma, BM
University of Tulsa, B

Oregon

Oregon State University, B

Pennsylvania

Carnegie Mellon University, B
Geneva College, B
Indiana University of Pennsylvania, BM
La Salle University, B
Lehigh University, MD
The Pennsylvania State University Harrisburg
    Campus, B
Robert Morris University, B
Temple University, BMD
University of Pittsburgh, BM
University of Pittsburgh at Bradford, B
University of Pittsburgh at Greensburg, B

Puerto Rico

Inter American University of Puerto Rico, Bayamón
    Campus, B
Inter American University of Puerto Rico, San
    Germán Campus, BM
Universidad Metropolitana, B
Universidad del Turabo, B
University of Puerto Rico, Mayagüez Campus, M

Rhode Island

Brown University, BMD
University of Rhode Island, D

South Carolina

Charleston Southern University, B
Clemson University, MD
Coastal Carolina University, B
University of South Carolina Aiken, B

South Dakota

University of Sioux Falls, B

Tennessee

Belmont University, B
King College, B

University of Memphis, M
The University of Tennessee, M
The University of Tennessee at Chattanooga, B

Texas

Baylor University, B
Lamar University, B
Rice University, BMD
Southern Methodist University, MD
Southwestern Christian College, A
Texas A&M University, B
Texas State University-San Marcos, BM
University of Houston, B
University of Houston-Downtown, B
The University of Texas at Austin, MD
The University of Texas at Dallas, BMD
The University of Texas at El Paso, B

Utah

Utah State University, M
Weber State University, B

Vermont

Marlboro College, B

Virginia

Averett University, B
Emory & Henry College, B
Hampden-Sydney College, B
Hampton University, M
Longwood University, B
Mary Baldwin College, B
University of Virginia, B
Virginia Commonwealth University, M
Virginia Polytechnic Institute and State
    University, MD

Washington

Seattle University, B
University of Washington, BMD

West Virginia

West Virginia State University, B
West Virginia University, MD

Wisconsin

Carroll College, B
Northland College, B
University of Wisconsin-Madison, B
University of Wisconsin-Milwaukee, B
University of Wisconsin-Stout, B

Wyoming

University of Wyoming, B

Alberta

University of Alberta, BMD
University of Calgary, B

British Columbia

Simon Fraser University, BMD
Trinity Western University, B
The University of British Columbia, BMD
University of Victoria, MD

Manitoba

University of Manitoba, B
The University of Winnipeg, B

New Brunswick

Mount Allison University, B
University of New Brunswick Fredericton, B
University of New Brunswick Saint John, B

Newfoundland and Labrador

Memorial University of Newfoundland, B

Nova Scotia

Acadia University, M
Dalhousie University, MD

Mount Saint Vincent University, B

Ontario

Brock University, B
Carleton University, B
McMaster University, B
Trent University, B
University of Guelph, D
University of Ottawa, B
University of Toronto, B
University of Waterloo, BMD
The University of Western Ontario, BMD
University of Windsor, B
York University, BM

Quebec

Concordia University, B
McGill University, BM
Université de Montréal, B

APPLIED PHYSICS

Arizona

Northern Arizona University, M
The University of Arizona, M

Arkansas

University of Arkansas, M

California

California Institute of Technology, MD
Stanford University, MD
University of California, San Diego, MD

Colorado

Colorado School of Mines, D

Connecticut

Yale University, MD

Florida

University of South Florida, D

Illinois

DePaul University, M
Southern Illinois University Carbondale, MD

Iowa

Iowa State University of Science and
    Technology, MD

Kansas

Pittsburg State University, M

Maryland

The Johns Hopkins University, M
University of Maryland, Baltimore County, MD

Massachusetts

Harvard University, MD
University of Massachusetts Boston, M
University of Massachusetts Lowell, MD

Michigan

University of Michigan, D

Missouri

University of Missouri-St. Louis, M

New Jersey

New Jersey Institute of Technology, MD
Princeton University, MD
Rutgers, The State University of New Jersey,
    Newark, MD

New York

Brooklyn College of the City University of New
    York, M
Cornell University, MD
Rensselaer Polytechnic Institute, MD

State University of New York at Binghamton, M

North Carolina

Appalachian State University, M
The University of North Carolina at Charlotte, MD

Oklahoma

University of Central Oklahoma, M

Puerto Rico

University of Puerto Rico, Río Piedras, M

Texas

Rice University, MD
Texas A&M University, D
Texas Tech University, M

Virginia

Christopher Newport University, M
George Mason University, M
Virginia Commonwealth University, M
Virginia Polytechnic Institute and State
    University, MD

Washington

University of Washington, MD

West Virginia

West Virginia University, MD

Ontario

Laurentian University, M

APPLIED SCIENCE AND TECHNOLOGY

Arkansas

University of Arkansas at Little Rock, MD

California

University of California, Berkeley, D
University of California, Davis, MD

Colorado

Colorado State University-Pueblo, M
University of Colorado at Denver and Health
    Sciences Center - Downtown Denver Campus, M

District of Columbia

American University, M

Louisiana

Louisiana State University and Agricultural and
    Mechanical College, M
Southeastern Louisiana University, M

Massachusetts

Harvard University, O

Minnesota

Capella University, M

Mississippi

University of Mississippi, MD

Missouri

Missouri State University, M

New York

Rensselaer Polytechnic Institute, M

Oklahoma

Oklahoma State University, M

Texas

Southern Methodist University, MD

Virginia

The College of William and Mary, MD
James Madison University, M

Newfoundland and Labrador

Memorial University of Newfoundland, M

AQUACULTURE

Alabama

Auburn University, BMD

Arizona

Yavapai College, A

Colorado

Trinidad State Junior College, A

Florida

Hillsborough Community College, A
University of Florida, MD

Indiana

Purdue University, MD

Kentucky

Kentucky State University, M

Maine

University of New England, B

North Carolina

Brunswick Community College, A

Rhode Island

University of Rhode Island, M

South Carolina

Clemson University, MD

Texas

Texas A&M University, B

Newfoundland and Labrador

Memorial University of Newfoundland, M

Ontario

University of Guelph, M

AQUATIC BIOLOGY/LIMNOLOGY

California

University of California, Santa Barbara, B

Florida

Florida Institute of Technology, B
Stetson University, B

South Carolina

University of South Carolina, B

Texas

Texas State University-San Marcos, B

British Columbia

University of Northern British Columbia, B

ARABIC LANGUAGE AND LITERATURE

California

University of California, Los Angeles, B

District of Columbia

Georgetown University, BMD

Illinois

University of Chicago, B

Indiana

University of Notre Dame, B

Massachusetts

Brandeis University, B
Harvard University, BMD

Michigan

University of Michigan, BMD

Missouri

Washington University in St. Louis, B

New Hampshire

Dartmouth College, B

New York

State University of New York at Binghamton, B
United States Military Academy, B

Ohio

The Ohio State University, B

Texas

The University of Texas at Austin, BMD

Utah

Brigham Young University, B
University of Utah, BMD

Alberta

University of Alberta, B

Ontario

University of Toronto, B

ARCHEOLOGY

Arizona

Northern Arizona University, M

California

Claremont McKenna College, B
Palomar College, A
Saint Mary's College of California, B
Stanford University, B
University of California, Berkeley, MD
University of California, Los Angeles, BMD
University of California, San Diego, B
University of California, Santa Barbara, MD

Connecticut

Wesleyan University, B
Yale University, BM

District of Columbia

The George Washington University, B

Florida

Florida State University, M

Illinois

Illinois State University, M
University of Chicago, MD
Wheaton College, BM

Indiana

University of Evansville, B
University of Indianapolis, B

Maine

Bates College, B
Bowdoin College, B

Maryland

Baltimore Hebrew University, AB

Massachusetts

Boston University, BMD
Bridgewater State College, B
Harvard University, BMD

Tufts University, BM
University of Massachusetts Boston, M
Wellesley College, B

Michigan

Michigan Technological University, MD
University of Michigan, D

Minnesota

Minnesota State University Moorhead, B
University of Minnesota, Twin Cities Campus, MD

Missouri

University of Missouri-Columbia, BMD
Washington University in St. Louis, BMD

New Hampshire

Dartmouth College, B
Franklin Pierce College, B

New Jersey

Princeton University, D

New York

Bard College, B
Columbia College, B
Cornell University, BMD
Hamilton College, B
Hunter College of the City University of New York, B
New York University, BMDO
Sarah Lawrence College, B
State University of New York College at Potsdam, B

North Carolina

The University of North Carolina at Chapel Hill, MD
The University of North Carolina at Greensboro, B

Ohio

The College of Wooster, B
Oberlin College, B

Pennsylvania

Bryn Mawr College, BMD
Dickinson College, B
Haverford College, B
Lycoming College, B
Mercyhurst College, B
The Pennsylvania State University Abington College, B
The Pennsylvania State University Altoona College, B
The Pennsylvania State University Beaver Campus of the Commonwealth College, B
The Pennsylvania State University Berks Campus of the Berks-Lehigh Valley College, B
The Pennsylvania State University Delaware County Campus of the Commonwealth College, B
The Pennsylvania State University DuBois Campus of the Commonwealth College, B
The Pennsylvania State University at Erie, The Behrend College, B
The Pennsylvania State University Fayette Campus of the Commonwealth College, B
The Pennsylvania State University Hazleton Campus of the Commonwealth College, B
The Pennsylvania State University, Lehigh Valley Campus of the Berks-Lehigh Valley College, B
The Pennsylvania State University McKeesport Campus of the Commonwealth College, B
The Pennsylvania State University Mont Alto Campus of the Commonwealth College, B
The Pennsylvania State University New Kensington Campus of the Commonwealth College, B
The Pennsylvania State University Schuylkill Campus of the Capital College, B
The Pennsylvania State University Shenango Campus of the Commonwealth College, B
The Pennsylvania State University University Park Campus, B
The Pennsylvania State University Wilkes-Barre Campus of the Commonwealth College, B
The Pennsylvania State University Worthington Scranton Campus of the Commonwealth College, B

The Pennsylvania State University York Campus of
  the Commonwealth College, B
University of Pennsylvania, MD

Rhode Island

Brown University, BMD

Tennessee

Southern Adventist University, B
University of Memphis, M
The University of Tennessee, MD

Texas

Baylor University, B
The University of Texas at Austin, BMD

Utah

Weber State University, A

Virginia

University of Virginia, MD
Washington and Lee University, B

Washington

Western Washington University, B

Wisconsin

Lawrence University, B
University of Wisconsin-La Crosse, B

Wyoming

Western Wyoming Community College, A

Alberta

University of Alberta, MD
University of Calgary, BMD
University of Lethbridge, M

British Columbia

Simon Fraser University, BMD
The University of British Columbia, BM

Newfoundland and Labrador

Memorial University of Newfoundland, B

Ontario

Brock University, B
University of Toronto, B
Wilfrid Laurier University, B

Quebec

Université Laval, BMD
Université de Montréal, B

Saskatchewan

University of Saskatchewan, BMD

ARCHITECTURAL DRAFTING AND ARCHITECTURAL CAD/CADD

Arizona

Glendale Community College, A
Pima Community College, A
Yavapai College, A

California

Western Career College (San Jose), A
Western Career College (Walnut Creek), A
Westwood College-Anaheim, A
Westwood College-Inland Empire, A
Westwood College-Long Beach, A

Colorado

IntelliTec College (Grand Junction), A
Westwood College-Denver North, A
Westwood College-Denver South, A

Florida

Florida Community College at Jacksonville, A
Florida Technical College (Orlando), A

Indian River Community College, A
Miami Dade College, A
New England Institute of Technology at Palm
  Beach, A
North Florida Community College, A

Georgia

Westwood College-Atlanta Midtown, A
Westwood College-Atlanta Northlake, A

Illinois

College of Lake County, A
Kaskaskia College, A
Lincoln Land Community College, A
Westwood College-Chicago Du Page, A
Westwood College-Chicago Loop Campus, A
Westwood College-Chicago O'Hare Airport, A
Westwood College-Chicago River Oaks, A

Indiana

Indiana State University, A
Indiana University-Purdue University Indianapolis, A

Iowa

Clinton Community College, A

Kentucky

Lexington Community College, A
Louisville Technical Institute, A
Spencerian College-Lexington, A
Western Kentucky University, A

Maryland

Montgomery College, A

Michigan

Baker College of Flint, A
Baker College of Muskegon, A
Macomb Community College, A

Minnesota

Anoka Technical College, A
Dakota County Technical College, A
Dunwoody College of Technology, A
Hennepin Technical College, A
Lake Superior College, A
Normandale Community College, A
Northwest Technical Institute, A
St. Cloud Technical College, A
South Central Technical College, A

Montana

Montana Tech of The University of Montana, A

New Mexico

Central New Mexico Community College, A
Luna Community College, A

New York

Island Drafting and Technical Institute, A
Mohawk Valley Community College, A
New York City College of Technology of the City
  University of New York, A

Ohio

The University of Toledo, A

Pennsylvania

The Art Institute of Pittsburgh, B
Butler County Community College, A
Commonwealth Technical Institute, A
Community College of Allegheny County, A
Johnson College, A
Montgomery County Community College, A

South Dakota

Mitchell Technical Institute, A

Texas

Westwood College-Dallas, A
Westwood College-Fort Worth, A

Westwood College-Houston South Campus, A

Utah

Dixie State College of Utah, A

Virginia

Westwood College-Annandale Campus, A

Washington

North Seattle Community College, A

West Virginia

West Virginia State Community and Technical
  College, A

Wisconsin

Waukesha County Technical College, A

British Columbia

British Columbia Institute of Technology, A

ARCHITECTURAL ENGINEERING

Alabama

Auburn University, B

California

California Polytechnic State University, San Luis
  Obispo, B

Colorado

University of Colorado at Boulder, BMD

Florida

University of Miami, BMD

Illinois

Illinois Institute of Technology, BMD

Kansas

Kansas State University, BM
University of Kansas, BMD

Louisiana

University of Louisiana at Lafayette, M

Massachusetts

Harvard University, B
Tufts University, B

Michigan

Andrews University, B
University of Detroit Mercy, M

Missouri

University of Missouri-Rolla, B

Nebraska

University of Nebraska-Lincoln, BM
University of Nebraska at Omaha, B

North Carolina

North Carolina Agricultural and Technical State
  University, BM

Ohio

University of Cincinnati, B

Oklahoma

Oklahoma State University, BM

Pennsylvania

Drexel University, B
Luzerne County Community College, A
The Pennsylvania State University Abington
  College, B
The Pennsylvania State University Altoona
  College, B
The Pennsylvania State University Beaver Campus
  of the Commonwealth College, B

The Pennsylvania State University Berks Campus of the Berks-Lehigh Valley College, B
The Pennsylvania State University Delaware County Campus of the Commonwealth College, B
The Pennsylvania State University DuBois Campus of the Commonwealth College, B
The Pennsylvania State University at Erie, The Behrend College, B
The Pennsylvania State University Fayette Campus of the Commonwealth College, B
The Pennsylvania State University Hazleton Campus of the Commonwealth College, B
The Pennsylvania State University, Lehigh Valley Campus of the Berks-Lehigh Valley College, B
The Pennsylvania State University McKeesport Campus of the Commonwealth College, B
The Pennsylvania State University Mont Alto Campus of the Commonwealth College, B
The Pennsylvania State University New Kensington Campus of the Commonwealth College, B
The Pennsylvania State University Schuylkill Campus of the Capital College, B
The Pennsylvania State University Shenango Campus of the Commonwealth College, B
The Pennsylvania State University University Park Campus, BMD
The Pennsylvania State University Wilkes-Barre Campus of the Commonwealth College, B
The Pennsylvania State University Worthington Scranton Campus of the Commonwealth College, B
The Pennsylvania State University York Campus of the Commonwealth College, B

Tennessee

Tennessee State University, B

Texas

The University of Texas at Austin, BM

Wisconsin

Milwaukee School of Engineering, B

Wyoming

University of Wyoming, B

ARCHITECTURAL ENGINEERING TECHNOLOGY/TECHNICIAN

Alaska

University of Alaska Anchorage, A

Arizona

Phoenix College, A

California

Allan Hancock College, A
Bakersfield College, A
Cerritos College, A
Chabot College, A
College of the Desert, A
College of Marin, A
College of the Redwoods, A
College of San Mateo, A
College of the Sequoias, A
Cosumnes River College (Sacramento), A
East Los Angeles College, A
El Camino College, A
Fullerton College, A
Golden West College, A
Hartnell College, A
Laney College, A
Long Beach City College, A
Los Angeles City College, A
Los Angeles Harbor College, A
Los Angeles Pierce College, A
Los Angeles Trade-Technical College, A
MiraCosta College, A
Modesto Junior College, A
Mt. San Antonio College, A
Newschool of Architecture & Design, A
Orange Coast College, A

Pasadena City College, A
Saddleback College, A
San Bernardino Valley College, A
San Diego Mesa College, A
Santa Monica College, A
Southwestern College, A

Colorado

Arapahoe Community College, A
Front Range Community College, A
Pikes Peak Community College, A

Connecticut

Norwalk Community College, A
Three Rivers Community College, A
University of Hartford, B

Delaware

Delaware Technical & Community College, Jack F. Owens Campus, A
Delaware Technical & Community College, Stanton/Wilmington Campus, A
Delaware Technical & Community College, Terry Campus, A

District of Columbia

University of the District of Columbia, A

Florida

Broward Community College, A
Daytona Beach Community College, A
Florida Agricultural and Mechanical University, B
Florida Community College at Jacksonville, A
Hillsborough Community College, A
Miami Dade College, A
St. Petersburg College, A
Seminole Community College, A

Georgia

Clayton State University, A
Southern Polytechnic State University, B

Guam

Guam Community College, A

Hawaii

Honolulu Community College, A

Idaho

Brigham Young University -Idaho, A

Illinois

City Colleges of Chicago, Harold Washington College, A
City Colleges of Chicago, Kennedy-King College, A
City Colleges of Chicago, Richard J. Daley College, A
City Colleges of Chicago, Wilbur Wright College, A
Illinois Central College, A
Lake Land College, A
Oakton Community College, A
South Suburban College, A
Triton College, A
William Rainey Harper College, A

Indiana

Indiana State University, B
Indiana University-Purdue University Fort Wayne, A
Indiana University-Purdue University Indianapolis, B
Purdue University, AB
Purdue University Calumet, A
Purdue University North Central, A
Vincennes University, A

Iowa

Hawkeye Community College, A
Iowa Western Community College, A

Western Iowa Tech Community College, A

Kansas

Fort Scott Community College, A

Kentucky

Eastern Kentucky University, B
Lexington Community College, A
Louisville Technical Institute, A
Northern Kentucky University, A

Louisiana

Delgado Community College, A
Grambling State University, B

Maine

Southern Maine Community College, A

Maryland

Anne Arundel Community College, A
Chesapeake College, A

Massachusetts

Benjamin Franklin Institute of Technology, A
Fitchburg State College, B
Massasoit Community College, A
Springfield Technical Community College, A
Wentworth Institute of Technology, AB

Michigan

Baker College of Cadillac, A
Baker College of Clinton Township, A
Baker College of Owosso, A
Baker College of Port Huron, A
Delta College, A
Ferris State University, A
Grand Rapids Community College, A
Lansing Community College, A
Monroe County Community College, A
Mott Community College, A
Oakland Community College, A
St. Clair County Community College, A
Washtenaw Community College, A

Minnesota

Minnesota State Community and Technical College-Fergus Falls, A
Northland Community and Technical College-Thief River Falls, A
Northwest Technical College, A
St. Cloud Technical College, A
Vermilion Community College, A

Mississippi

Mississippi Delta Community College, A
University of Southern Mississippi, B

Missouri

Ranken Technical College, AB
St. Louis Community College at Meramec, A
Washington University in St. Louis, B

Nebraska

Metropolitan Community College, A
Southeast Community College, Milford Campus, A

Nevada

Truckee Meadows Community College, A

New Hampshire

New Hampshire Technical Institute, A

New Jersey

Essex County College, A
Mercer County Community College, A

New Mexico

Doña Ana Branch Community College, A

New York

Dutchess Community College, A
Erie Community College, South Campus, A
Farmingdale State University of New York, B

Finger Lakes Community College, A
Institute of Design and Construction, A
Onondaga Community College, A
Orange County Community College, A
State University of New York College of Agriculture
    and Technology at Morrisville, A
State University of New York College of Technology
    at Alfred, AB
State University of New York College of Technology
    at Delhi, A

North Carolina

Cape Fear Community College, A
Catawba Valley Community College, A
Central Piedmont Community College, A
Coastal Carolina Community College, A
College of The Albemarle, A
Durham Technical Community College, A
Fayetteville Technical Community College, A
Forsyth Technical Community College, A
Gaston College, A
Guilford Technical Community College, A
Nash Community College, A
Pitt Community College, A
Roanoke-Chowan Community College, A
Sandhills Community College, A
Wake Technical Community College, A
Wilkes Community College, A

North Dakota

North Dakota State College of Science, A

Ohio

Cincinnati State Technical and Community
    College, A
Columbus State Community College, A
Sinclair Community College, A
Stark State College of Technology, A
Terra State Community College, A
University of Cincinnati, AB

Oklahoma

Oklahoma State University, Oklahoma City, A
Oklahoma State University, Okmulgee, A

Oregon

Mt. Hood Community College, A

Pennsylvania

Butler County Community College, A
Community College of Beaver County, A
Community College of Philadelphia, A
Delaware County Community College, A
Harrisburg Area Community College, A
Luzerne County Community College, A
Northampton County Area Community College, A
Pennsylvania College of Technology, A
Pennsylvania Institute of Technology, A
The Pennsylvania State University Fayette Campus
    of the Commonwealth College, A
The Pennsylvania State University Worthington
    Scranton Campus of the Commonwealth
    College, A
Thaddeus Stevens College of Technology, A
Triangle Tech, Inc.-Erie School, A
Triangle Tech, Inc.-Pittsburgh School, A
Westmoreland County Community College, A

Rhode Island

New England Institute of Technology, AB

South Carolina

Greenville Technical College, A
Midlands Technical College, A

Spartanburg Technical College, A

South Dakota

Southeast Technical Institute, A

Tennessee

Nashville State Technical Community College, A
Southwest Tennessee Community College, A

Texas

Amarillo College, A
Del Mar College, A
El Paso Community College, A
Lamar State College-Orange, A
Palo Alto College, A
Tarrant County College District, A
Texas Southern University, B
Texas Tech University, B

Utah

Salt Lake Community College, A

Vermont

Vermont Technical College, AB

Virginia

Central Virginia Community College, A
J. Sargeant Reynolds Community College, A
John Tyler Community College, A
New River Community College, A
Norfolk State University, A
Northern Virginia Community College, A

Washington

Bates Technical College, A
Clover Park Technical College, A
Spokane Community College, A

West Virginia

Bluefield State College, AB
Fairmont State Community & Technical College, A
West Virginia State University, A

Wisconsin

Chippewa Valley Technical College, A
Madison Area Technical College, A
Northcentral Technical College, A
Northeast Wisconsin Technical College, A
Western Technical College, A
Wisconsin Indianhead Technical College, A

British Columbia

British Columbia Institute of Technology, A

ARCHITECTURAL HISTORY
AND CRITICISM

Arizona

Arizona State University, D

California

University of California, Berkeley, MD

Georgia

Savannah College of Art and Design, BM

Kansas

University of Kansas, B

Massachusetts

Mount Holyoke College, B

New York

Barnard College, B
Cornell University, BMD

Sarah Lawrence College, B

Ohio

Miami University Hamilton, B

Pennsylvania

Carnegie Mellon University, B
University of Pittsburgh, MD

Rhode Island

Brown University, B

Virginia

University of Virginia, BMD

ARCHITECTURAL
TECHNOLOGY/TECHNICIAN

California

Western Career College (Walnut Creek), A

Illinois

City Colleges of Chicago, Wilbur Wright College, A
Rend Lake College, A

Maine

The University of Maine at Augusta, A

Minnesota

Dakota County Technical College, A

Missouri

Washington University in St. Louis, B

New Hampshire

Keene State College, B

Ohio

Columbus State Community College, A

Pennsylvania

Carnegie Mellon University, B

ARCHITECTURE

Alabama

Auburn University, BMO
Tuskegee University, B

Arizona

Arizona State University, BMO
The University of Arizona, BM

Arkansas

University of Arkansas, B

California

Academy of Art University, M
California College of the Arts, BM
California Polytechnic State University, San Luis
    Obispo, BM
California State Polytechnic University, Pomona, BM
Newschool of Architecture & Design, BM
San Diego Mesa College, A
Southern California Institute of Architecture, BM
University of California, Berkeley, BMDO
University of California, Los Angeles, BMD
University of San Francisco, B
University of Southern California, BMO
Western Career College (Walnut Creek), A
Woodbury University, B

Colorado

University of Colorado at Denver and Health
    Sciences Center - Downtown Denver
    Campus, MD

Western State College of Colorado, B

Connecticut

Connecticut College, B
University of Hartford, M
Yale University, BMO

District of Columbia

The Catholic University of America, BM
Howard University, B
University of the District of Columbia, B

Florida

Florida Agricultural and Mechanical University, BM
Florida Atlantic University, B
Florida International University, M
University of Florida, BMD
University of Miami, BM
University of South Florida, M

Georgia

Georgia Institute of Technology, BMDO
Savannah College of Art and Design, BM
Southern Polytechnic State University, B

Hawaii

University of Hawaii at Manoa, BD

Idaho

University of Idaho, BM

Illinois

Columbia College Chicago, M
Illinois Institute of Technology, BMD
Judson College, B
Sauk Valley Community College, A
Southern Illinois University Carbondale, B
University of Illinois at Chicago, BM
University of Illinois at Urbana-Champaign, MO

Indiana

Ball State University, BM
University of Notre Dame, BM

Iowa

Coe College, B
Cornell College, B
Iowa State University of Science and
 Technology, BMO

Kansas

Allen County Community College, A
Barton County Community College, A
Central Christian College of Kansas, A
Kansas State University, BM
University of Kansas, BMO

Kentucky

University of Kentucky, BM

Louisiana

Louisiana State University and Agricultural and
 Mechanical College, BM
Louisiana Tech University, B
Southern University and Agricultural and Mechanical
 College, B
Tulane University, BM
University of Louisiana at Lafayette, B

Maine

Central Maine Community College, A

Maryland

Howard Community College, A
Morgan State University, M
University of Maryland, College Park, BMO

Massachusetts

Boston Architectural College, BM
Harvard University, MD
Massachusetts College of Art, B
Massachusetts Institute of Technology, BMD
Northeastern University, BM
Smith College, B

Wellesley College, B
Wentworth Institute of Technology, B

Michigan

Andrews University, BM
Eastern Michigan University, B
Hope College, B
Lawrence Technological University, BM
Oakland Community College, A
University of Detroit Mercy, B
University of Michigan, BMDO
Western Michigan University, B

Minnesota

University of Minnesota, Twin Cities Campus, BM

Mississippi

Copiah-Lincoln Community College, A
Mississippi State University, BM

Missouri

Drury University, B
University of Missouri-Columbia, M
Washington University in St. Louis, BMO

Montana

Montana State University, M

Nebraska

University of Nebraska-Lincoln, BMO

Nevada

University of Nevada, Las Vegas, BM

New Jersey

Brookdale Community College, A
New Jersey Institute of Technology, BMO
Princeton University, BMD

New Mexico

University of New Mexico, BM

New York

Barnard College, B
City College of the City University of New
 York, BMO
College of Staten Island of the City University of
 New York, A
Columbia College, B
Columbia University, School of General Studies, B
Cooper Union for the Advancement of Science and
 Art, B
Cornell University, BMD
Hobart and William Smith Colleges, B
New York Institute of Technology, ABM
Parsons The New School for Design, B
Pratt Institute, BM
Rensselaer Polytechnic Institute, BMD
State University of New York at Buffalo, BMO
Syracuse University, BM

North Carolina

North Carolina State University, BM
The University of North Carolina at Charlotte, BM
The University of North Carolina at Greensboro, M

North Dakota

North Dakota State University, B

Ohio

Kent State University, BMO
Miami University, BM
Miami University Hamilton, B
The Ohio State University, BM
University of Cincinnati, BM

Oklahoma

Oklahoma State University, BM
Tulsa Community College, A

University of Oklahoma, BMO

Oregon

Portland State University, B
University of Oregon, BM

Pennsylvania

Carnegie Mellon University, BMD
Drexel University, BM
Harrisburg Area Community College, A
Lehigh University, B
The Pennsylvania State University University Park
 Campus, BM
Philadelphia University, B
Temple University, B
University of Pennsylvania, BMDO

Puerto Rico

Polytechnic University of Puerto Rico, B
University of Puerto Rico, Río Piedras, M

Rhode Island

Rhode Island School of Design, BM
Roger Williams University, BM

South Carolina

Clemson University, BM

Tennessee

University of Memphis, B
The University of Tennessee, BM

Texas

Baylor University, B
Brazosport College, A
Clarendon College, A
Prairie View A&M University, BM
Rice University, BMD
Texas A&M University, BMD
Texas Tech University, BMO
University of Houston, BM
The University of Texas at Arlington, BMO
The University of Texas at Austin, BMDO
The University of Texas at San Antonio, BM

Utah

University of Utah, BMO

Vermont

Bennington College, B
Norwich University, B

Virginia

Hampton University, B
University of Virginia, BM
Virginia Polytechnic Institute and State
 University, BM

Washington

University of Washington, BMO
Washington State University, BM

Wisconsin

University of Wisconsin-Milwaukee, BMDO

Alberta

University of Calgary, M

British Columbia

The University of British Columbia, M

Manitoba

University of Manitoba, BM

Nova Scotia

Dalhousie University, BMO

Ontario

Carleton University, BM
Ryerson University, B
University of Toronto, BM

University of Waterloo, BM

Quebec

McGill University, BMDO
Université Laval, BM
Université de Montréal, B

ARCHITECTURE AND RELATED SERVICES

California

Western Career College (Walnut Creek), A

Florida

Florida International University, B

Georgia

Georgia Institute of Technology, B

Illinois

School of the Art Institute of Chicago, B
University of Illinois at Urbana-Champaign, B

Kentucky

Louisville Technical Institute, A

Louisiana

University of Louisiana at Lafayette, B

Missouri

Washington University in St. Louis, B

New York

Columbia College, B
Cornell University, B
New York Institute of Technology, B
Rensselaer Polytechnic Institute, B

Oklahoma

University of Oklahoma, B

Pennsylvania

Carnegie Mellon University, B

Texas

Abilene Christian University, A
University of Houston, B

Utah

University of Utah, B

AREA, ETHNIC, CULTURAL, AND GENDER STUDIES

California

Claremont McKenna College, B
Saint Mary's College of California, B
University of California, Irvine, B

Hawaii

Brigham Young University-Hawaii, B

Illinois

Columbia College Chicago, B
University of Chicago, B

Iowa

Coe College, B

Maryland

University of Maryland, Baltimore County, B

Massachusetts

Brandeis University, B
Emmanuel College, B

Minnesota

Bethel University, B

Missouri

Washington University in St. Louis, B

New York

New York University, B
St. John's University, B

Skidmore College, B
Syracuse University, B
Touro College, B

North Carolina

The University of North Carolina at Chapel Hill, B
The University of North Carolina at Charlotte, B

Ohio

The College of Wooster, B
Kent State University, B

Oregon

Linfield College, B
Northwest Christian College, B

Pennsylvania

Chatham College, B
Gettysburg College, B
Point Park University, B

Tennessee

The University of Tennessee, B

Texas

University of the Incarnate Word, B

Vermont

Sterling College, B

Washington

The Evergreen State College, B

AREA STUDIES

Alaska

University of Alaska Fairbanks, B

California

Claremont McKenna College, B
University of California, Los Angeles, B

Colorado

United States Air Force Academy, B

Hawaii

Hawaii Pacific University, B

Illinois

Illinois Wesleyan University, B
Lewis University, B
Northwestern University, B
University of Illinois at Urbana-Champaign, B

Maine

Colby College, B

Massachusetts

Boston University, B
Bridgewater State College, B

Michigan

Hope College, B
University of Michigan-Dearborn, B

Missouri

Washington University in St. Louis, B

Montana

The University of Montana-Missoula, B

New Mexico

Santa Fe Community College, A

New York

Bard College, B
Barnard College, B
Excelsior College, B
Hofstra University, B
St. Francis College, B

St. John's University, B

Ohio

Denison University, B
Kent State University, B
Wright State University, B

Oklahoma

Oklahoma City Community College, A
University of Oklahoma, B

Pennsylvania

Bucknell University, B
Drexel University, B
Gannon University, B
Gettysburg College, B
Millersville University of Pennsylvania, B

Utah

Utah State University, B

Virginia

University of Virginia, B
Virginia Commonwealth University, B

Newfoundland and Labrador

Memorial University of Newfoundland, B

Quebec

McGill University, B

ARMY JROTC/ROTC

Alabama

Jacksonville State University, B

California

Sacramento City College, A

Georgia

Georgia Military College, A

Idaho

Brigham Young University -Idaho, A

Iowa

The University of Iowa, B

Minnesota

Minnesota State University Mankato, B

Missouri

Northwest Missouri State University, B

New Mexico

New Mexico Military Institute, A

New York

Rensselaer Polytechnic Institute, B
United States Military Academy, B

North Carolina

Campbell University, B
Methodist College, A

Pennsylvania

La Salle University, B

Puerto Rico

University of Puerto Rico, Cayey University College, B

Texas

Dallas Baptist University, B

Virginia

Hampton University, B
Longwood University, B

Washington

University of Washington, B

West Virginia

American Public University System, B

ART/ART STUDIES, GENERAL

Alabama

Alabama Southern Community College, A
Alabama State University, B
Athens State University, B
Auburn University Montgomery, B
Birmingham-Southern College, B
Huntingdon College, B
Jacksonville State University, B
Judson College, B
Lawson State Community College, A
Northwest-Shoals Community College, A
Troy University, B
The University of Alabama in Huntsville, B
University of Mobile, B
University of Montevallo, B
University of South Alabama, B

Alaska

University of Alaska Anchorage, B
University of Alaska Fairbanks, B

Arizona

Arizona State University, B
Arizona Western College, A
Cochise College (Douglas), A
Cochise College (Sierra Vista), A
Diné College, A
Eastern Arizona College, A
Grand Canyon University, B
Mesa Community College, A
Mohave Community College, A
Northern Arizona University, B
Phoenix College, A
Prescott College, B
South Mountain Community College, A

Arkansas

Arkansas State University, B
Arkansas Tech University, B
Henderson State University, B
Hendrix College, B
Lyon College, B
National Park Community College, A
Phillips Community College of the University of
    Arkansas, A
Southern Arkansas University-Magnolia, B
University of Arkansas, B
University of Arkansas at Little Rock, B
University of Arkansas at Monticello, B
University of Arkansas at Pine Bluff, B
University of Central Arkansas, B
University of the Ozarks, B
Williams Baptist College, B

California

Allan Hancock College, A
American River College, A
Art Center College of Design, B
Bakersfield College, A
Berkeley City College, A
Butte College, A
California College of the Arts, B
California Institute of the Arts, B
California Lutheran University, B
California State Polytechnic University, Pomona, B
California State University, Bakersfield, B
California State University Channel Islands, B
California State University, Chico, B
California State University, Dominguez Hills, B
California State University, Fresno, B
California State University, Fullerton, B
California State University, Long Beach, B
California State University, Los Angeles, B
California State University, Monterey Bay, B
California State University, Northridge, B
California State University, Sacramento, B
California State University, San Bernardino, B
California State University, Stanislaus, B
Cañada College, A

Cerritos College, A
Cerro Coso Community College, A
Chabot College, A
Chaffey College, A
Chapman University, B
Citrus College, A
City College of San Francisco, A
Claremont McKenna College, B
College of Alameda, A
College of the Canyons, A
College of the Desert, A
College of Marin, A
College of San Mateo, A
College of the Sequoias, A
Columbia College, A
Compton Community College, A
Concordia University, B
Contra Costa College, A
Cosumnes River College (Sacramento), A
Crafton Hills College, A
Cuesta College, A
Cypress College, A
De Anza College, A
Dominican University of California, B
East Los Angeles College, A
El Camino College, A
Folsom Lake College, A
Foothill College, A
Fresno City College, A
Fullerton College, A
Gavilan College, A
Glendale Community College, A
Golden West College, A
Grossmont College, A
Hartnell College, A
Humboldt State University, B
Imperial Valley College, A
Irvine Valley College, A
La Sierra University, B
Laguna College of Art & Design, B
Lake Tahoe Community College, A
Laney College, A
Lassen Community College District, A
Long Beach City College, A
Los Angeles City College, A
Los Angeles Pierce College, A
Los Angeles Valley College, A
Los Medanos College, A
Mendocino College, A
Merced College, A
Mills College, B
MiraCosta College, A
Mission College, A
Modesto Junior College, A
Monterey Peninsula College, A
Moorpark College, A
Mount St. Mary's College, B
Mt. San Jacinto College, A
Napa Valley College, A
Newschool of Architecture & Design, A
Ohlone College, A
Orange Coast College, A
Otis College of Art and Design, B
Pacific Union College, B
Palomar College, A
Pasadena City College, A
Pepperdine University, B
Pitzer College, B
Point Loma Nazarene University, B
Pomona College, B
Porterville College, A
Reedley College, A
Sacramento City College, A
Saddleback College, A
Saint Mary's College of California, B
San Bernardino Valley College, A
San Diego City College, A
San Diego Mesa College, A
San Diego Miramar College, A
San Francisco State University, B
San Joaquin Delta College, A
San Jose State University, B
Santa Ana College, A
Santa Monica College, A
Santa Rosa Junior College, A
Santiago Canyon College, A

Scripps College, B
Shasta College, A
Sierra College, A
Skyline College, A
Solano Community College, A
Sonoma State University, B
Southwestern College, A
Stanford University, B
Taft College, A
University of California, Berkeley, B
University of California, Irvine, B
University of California, Los Angeles, B
University of California, San Diego, B
University of California, Santa Barbara, B
University of California, Santa Cruz, B
University of La Verne, B
University of the Pacific, B
University of San Diego, B
University of San Francisco, B
University of Southern California, B
Victor Valley College, A
West Hills Community College, A
West Los Angeles College, A
West Valley College, A
Westmont College, B
Whittier College, B
Yuba College, A

Colorado

Adams State College, B
The Art Institute of Colorado, AB
Colorado Christian University, B
Colorado Northwestern Community College, A
Colorado State University-Pueblo, B
Fort Lewis College, B
Lamar Community College, A
Mesa State College, AB
Metropolitan State College of Denver, B
Northeastern Junior College, A
Red Rocks Community College, A
University of Colorado at Colorado Springs, B
University of Denver, B
Western State College of Colorado, B

Connecticut

Albertus Magnus College, B
Central Connecticut State University, B
Connecticut College, B
Eastern Connecticut State University, B
Fairfield University, B
Housatonic Community College, A
Northwestern Connecticut Community College, A
Norwalk Community College, A
Quinebaug Valley Community College, A
Trinity College, B
Tunxis Community College, A
Wesleyan University, B
Yale University, B

Delaware

Delaware State University, B
University of Delaware, B

District of Columbia

American University, B
The Catholic University of America, B
Corcoran College of Art and Design, B
Gallaudet University, B
The George Washington University, B
Howard University, B
University of the District of Columbia, B

Florida

Chipola College, A
Daytona Beach Community College, A
Edison College, A
Florida Agricultural and Mechanical University, B
Florida Atlantic University, B
Florida Southern College, B
Gulf Coast Community College, A
Hillsborough Community College, A
Jacksonville University, B
Manatee Community College, A
Miami Dade College, A
Miami International University of Art & Design, A

Okaloosa-Walton College, A
Palm Beach Community College, A
Pensacola Junior College, A
St. Johns River Community College, A
Stetson University, B
University of Central Florida, B
University of Miami, B
University of North Florida, B
University of South Florida, B
The University of Tampa, B
University of West Florida, B

Georgia

Abraham Baldwin Agricultural College, A
Agnes Scott College, B
Albany State University, B
Armstrong Atlantic State University, B
Atlanta Metropolitan College, A
Bainbridge College, A
Berry College, B
Clark Atlanta University, B
Clayton State University, A
Coastal Georgia Community College, A
Columbus State University, B
Covenant College, B
Darton College, A
East Georgia College, A
Georgia College & State University, B
Georgia Highlands College, A
Georgia Perimeter College, A
Georgia Southern University, B
Georgia Southwestern State University, B
Georgia State University, B
Gordon College, A
Kennesaw State University, B
Macon State College, A
Mercer University, B
Morehouse College, B
North Georgia College & State University, B
Oglethorpe University, B
Piedmont College, B
Reinhardt College, B
Shorter College, B
Spelman College, B
University of Georgia, B
University of West Georgia, B
Valdosta State University, B
Young Harris College, A

Guam

University of Guam, B

Hawaii

Brigham Young University-Hawaii, B
University of Hawaii at Hilo, B
University of Hawaii at Manoa, B

Idaho

Albertson College of Idaho, B
Boise State University, B
Brigham Young University -Idaho, A
College of Southern Idaho, A
Idaho State University, AB
North Idaho College, A
Northwest Nazarene University, B
University of Idaho, B

Illinois

American Academy of Art, B
Augustana College, B
Blackburn College, B
Bradley University, B
City Colleges of Chicago, Harold Washington
   College, A
City Colleges of Chicago, Harry S. Truman
   College, A
City Colleges of Chicago, Malcolm X College, A
City Colleges of Chicago, Olive-Harvey College, A
City Colleges of Chicago, Richard J. Daley
   College, A
City Colleges of Chicago, Wilbur Wright College, A
College of Lake County, A
Columbia College Chicago, B
Concordia University, B
Danville Area Community College, A

DePaul University, B
Eastern Illinois University, B
Elgin Community College, A
Elmhurst College, B
Eureka College, B
Governors State University, B
Greenville College, B
Highland Community College, A
Illinois College, B
Illinois State University, B
Illinois Wesleyan University, B
John A. Logan College, A
Joliet Junior College, A
Judson College, B
Kishwaukee College, A
Knox College, B
Lewis and Clark Community College, A
Lewis University, B
Lincoln Land Community College, A
MacMurray College, B
McHenry County College, A
McKendree College, B
Monmouth College, B
Morton College, A
National-Louis University, B
North Central College, B
North Park University, B
Northeastern Illinois University, B
Northern Illinois University, B
Northwestern University, B
Oakton Community College, A
Olivet Nazarene University, B
Parkland College, A
Rend Lake College, A
Roosevelt University, B
Saint Xavier University, B
Sauk Valley Community College, A
School of the Art Institute of Chicago, B
Southern Illinois University Carbondale, B
Southern Illinois University Edwardsville, B
Spoon River College, A
Springfield College in Illinois, A
Trinity Christian College, B
Triton College, A
University of Chicago, B
Waubonsee Community College, A
Western Illinois University, B
Wheaton College, B
William Rainey Harper College, A

Indiana

Ancilla College, A
Ball State University, B
Bethel College, B
Earlham College, B
Goshen College, B
Grace College, B
Hanover College, B
Huntington University, B
Indiana State University, B
Indiana University Bloomington, B
Indiana University Northwest, B
Indiana University South Bend, B
Indiana University Southeast, B
Indiana Wesleyan University, AB
Manchester College, AB
Marian College, AB
Oakland City University, B
Purdue University, B
Saint Mary-of-the-Woods College, B
Saint Mary's College, B
Taylor University, B
University of Evansville, B
University of Indianapolis, B
University of Saint Francis, B
University of Southern Indiana, B
Valparaiso University, B
Vincennes University, A
Wabash College, B

Iowa

Briar Cliff University, B
Buena Vista University, B
Central College, B
Clarke College, B
Coe College, B

Cornell College, B
Drake University, B
Ellsworth Community College, A
Graceland University, B
Grand View College, B
Grinnell College, B
Iowa Lakes Community College, A
Iowa State University of Science and Technology, B
Iowa Wesleyan College, B
Kirkwood Community College, A
Luther College, B
Morningside College, B
Mount Mercy College, B
Northwestern College, B
St. Ambrose University, B
Simpson College, B
The University of Iowa, B
University of Northern Iowa, B
Upper Iowa University, B
Wartburg College, B

Kansas

Allen County Community College, A
Barton County Community College, A
Benedictine College, B
Bethany College, B
Butler Community College, A
Central Christian College of Kansas, A
Cloud County Community College, A
Coffeyville Community College, A
Cowley County Community College and Area
   Vocational-Technical School, A
Dodge City Community College, A
Emporia State University, B
Fort Hays State University, B
Friends University, AB
Highland Community College, A
Kansas State University, B
Kansas Wesleyan University, B
Labette Community College, A
McPherson College, B
Newman University, B
Ottawa University, B
Pittsburg State University, B
Pratt Community College, A
Seward County Community College, A
Sterling College, B
University of Saint Mary, B
Washburn University, B
Wichita State University, B

Kentucky

Bellarmine University, B
Berea College, B
Brescia University, B
Campbellsville University, B
Centre College, B
Eastern Kentucky University, B
Lindsey Wilson College, AB
Northern Kentucky University, B
Pikeville College, B
St. Catharine College, A
Transylvania University, B

Louisiana

Centenary College of Louisiana, B
Dillard University, B
Grambling State University, B
Louisiana College, B
Louisiana State University in Shreveport, B
Louisiana Tech University, B
Loyola University New Orleans, B
McNeese State University, B
Nicholls State University, B
Northwestern State University of Louisiana, B
Southeastern Louisiana University, B
Southern University and Agricultural and Mechanical
   College, B
Southern University at New Orleans, B
Tulane University, B
University of Louisiana at Lafayette, B
University of Louisiana at Monroe, B

Xavier University of Louisiana, B

Maine

Bates College, B
Bowdoin College, B
Colby College, B
College of the Atlantic, B
University of Maine, B
University of Maine at Farmington, B
University of Maine at Machias, B
University of Maine at Presque Isle, B
University of Southern Maine, B

Maryland

Anne Arundel Community College, A
Bowie State University, B
Cecil Community College, A
Chesapeake College, A
College of Notre Dame of Maryland, B
College of Southern Maryland, A
Frederick Community College, A
Garrett College, A
Goucher College, B
Hood College, B
Howard Community College, A
Loyola College in Maryland, B
Maryland Institute College of Art, B
McDaniel College, B
Morgan State University, B
Mount St. Mary's University, B
St. Mary's College of Maryland, B
Salisbury University, B
Towson University, B
University of Maryland, Baltimore County, B
Villa Julie College, A
Washington College, B

Massachusetts

Amherst College, B
Anna Maria College, B
Atlantic Union College, B
Brandeis University, B
Bunker Hill Community College, A
Cape Cod Community College, A
Elms College, B
Emmanuel College, B
Framingham State College, B
Gordon College, B
Greenfield Community College, A
Harvard University, B
Lesley University, B
Massachusetts College of Liberal Arts, B
Middlesex Community College, A
Mount Wachusett Community College, A
Northeastern University, B
Quinsigamond Community College, A
Salem State College, B
School of the Museum of Fine Arts, Boston, B
Simmons College, B
Smith College, B
Suffolk University, A
University of Massachusetts Boston, B
Westfield State College, B

Michigan

Adrian College, AB
Albion College, B
Alma College, B
Andrews University, B
Aquinas College, B
Calvin College, B
Central Michigan University, B
Concordia University, B
Delta College, A
Eastern Michigan University, B
Finlandia University, B
Grand Rapids Community College, A
Grand Valley State University, B
Henry Ford Community College, A
Hillsdale College, B
Kalamazoo College, B
Kellogg Community College, A
Kirtland Community College, A
Lansing Community College, A
Madonna University, AB
Marygrove College, B

Michigan State University, B
Mid Michigan Community College, A
Monroe County Community College, A
Muskegon Community College, A
Northern Michigan University, B
Northwestern Michigan College, A
Olivet College, B
Saginaw Valley State University, B
St. Clair County Community College, A
Siena Heights University, AB
Spring Arbor University, B
Wayne State University, B
Western Michigan University, B

Minnesota

Anoka-Ramsey Community College, A
Anoka-Ramsey Community College, Cambridge
   Campus, A
Augsburg College, B
Bemidji State University, B
Bethany Lutheran College, B
Bethel University, B
College of Saint Benedict, B
College of St. Catherine, B
Concordia College, B
Gustavus Adolphus College, B
Hamline University, B
Minnesota State University Mankato, B
Minnesota State University Moorhead, B
Ridgewater College, A
St. Cloud State University, B
Saint John's University, B
St. Olaf College, B
Southwest Minnesota State University, B
University of Minnesota, Duluth, B
University of Minnesota, Twin Cities Campus, B
Vermilion Community College, A
Winona State University, B

Mississippi

Belhaven College, B
Coahoma Community College, A
East Central Community College, A
East Mississippi Community College, A
Hinds Community College, A
Itawamba Community College, A
Jackson State University, B
Millsaps College, B
Mississippi College, B
Mississippi Gulf Coast Community College, A
Mississippi University for Women, B
Mississippi Valley State University, B
Northeast Mississippi Community College, A
Northwest Mississippi Community College, A
Tougaloo College, B
University of Mississippi, B
William Carey College, B

Missouri

College of the Ozarks, B
Columbia College, B
Crowder College, A
Culver-Stockton College, B
Drury University, B
Evangel University, B
Fontbonne University, B
Hannibal-LaGrange College, B
Jefferson College, A
Lindenwood University, B
Missouri State University, B
Missouri Valley College, B
Missouri Western State University, B
Northwest Missouri State University, B
St. Louis Community College at Florissant Valley, A
St. Louis Community College at Forest Park, A
St. Louis Community College at Meramec, A
Southeast Missouri State University, B
Southwest Baptist University, B
State Fair Community College, A
Truman State University, B
University of Missouri-Columbia, B
University of Missouri-Kansas City, B
Washington University in St. Louis, B
Webster University, B
William Jewell College, B

William Woods University, B

Montana

Carroll College, A
Montana State University, B
Montana State University-Billings, B
Rocky Mountain College, B
University of Great Falls, B
The University of Montana-Missoula, B

Nebraska

Chadron State College, B
College of Saint Mary, B
Concordia University, B
Creighton University, B
Dana College, B
Doane College, B
Hastings College, B
Midland Lutheran College, B
Nebraska Wesleyan University, B
Northeast Community College, A
Peru State College, B
Southeast Community College, Beatrice Campus, A
Union College, A
University of Nebraska at Kearney, B
University of Nebraska at Omaha, B
Wayne State College, B
Western Nebraska Community College, A

Nevada

Community College of Southern Nevada, A
Great Basin College, A
Sierra Nevada College, B
University of Nevada, Las Vegas, B
University of Nevada, Reno, B

New Hampshire

Colby-Sawyer College, B
Franklin Pierce College, B
Keene State College, B
New England College, B
Plymouth State University, B
Rivier College, AB
Saint Anselm College, B
University of New Hampshire, B

New Jersey

Brookdale Community College, A
Burlington County College, A
Caldwell College, B
Camden County College, A
The College of New Jersey, B
College of Saint Elizabeth, B
Drew University, B
Essex County College, A
Felician College, AB
Georgian Court University, B
Kean University, B
Mercer County Community College, A
Middlesex County College, A
Monmouth University, B
New Jersey City University, B
Rowan University, B
Rutgers, The State University of New Jersey,
   Camden, B
Rutgers, The State University of New Jersey, New
   Brunswick/Piscataway, B
Rutgers, The State University of New Jersey,
   Newark, B
Saint Peter's College, B
William Paterson University of New Jersey, B

New Mexico

The Art Center Design College, A
Eastern New Mexico University, AB
Institute of American Indian Arts, A
New Mexico Highlands University, B
New Mexico Junior College, A
New Mexico Military Institute, A
San Juan College, A
Santa Fe Community College, A
University of New Mexico, B
University of New Mexico-Gallup, A

Western New Mexico University, B

New York

Alfred University, B
Bard College, B
Bronx Community College of the City University of New York, A
Brooklyn College of the City University of New York, B
Buffalo State College, State University of New York, B
City College of the City University of New York, B
Colgate University, B
Columbia-Greene Community College, A
Cornell University, B
Daemen College, B
Elmira College, B
Fordham University, B
Fulton-Montgomery Community College, A
Hamilton College, B
Hartwick College, B
Herkimer County Community College, A
Hobart and William Smith Colleges, B
Houghton College, B
Hunter College of the City University of New York, B
Ithaca College, B
Kingsborough Community College of the City University of New York, A
Lehman College of the City University of New York, B
Long Island University, Brooklyn Campus, B
Marist College, B
Marymount Manhattan College, B
Medaille College, B
Mohawk Valley Community College, A
Molloy College, B
Monroe Community College, A
Nassau Community College, A
Nazareth College of Rochester, B
New York University, B
Onondaga Community College, A
Pace University, B
Parsons The New School for Design, AB
Pratt Institute, B
Purchase College, State University of New York, B
Queens College of the City University of New York, B
Roberts Wesleyan College, B
Rochester Institute of Technology, AB
Rockland Community College, A
St. Lawrence University, B
St. Thomas Aquinas College, B
Sarah Lawrence College, B
State University of New York at Binghamton, B
State University of New York at Buffalo, B
State University of New York College at Brockport, B
State University of New York College at Geneseo, B
State University of New York College at Old Westbury, B
State University of New York College at Oneonta, B
State University of New York College at Potsdam, B
State University of New York Empire State College, AB
State University of New York, Fredonia, B
State University of New York at New Paltz, B
State University of New York at Oswego, B
Suffolk County Community College, A
Syracuse University, B
University at Albany, State University of New York, B
Wagner College, B
Wells College, B
York College of the City University of New York, B

North Carolina

Appalachian State University, B
Bennett College For Women, B
Blue Ridge Community College, A
Brevard College, B
Caldwell Community College and Technical Institute, A
Campbell University, B
Central Piedmont Community College, A
Chowan University, B
College of The Albemarle, A
Davidson College, B

Duke University, B
East Carolina University, B
Elizabeth City State University, B
Elon University, B
Fayetteville State University, B
Gardner-Webb University, B
Gaston College, A
Greensboro College, B
Guilford College, B
Lenoir Community College, A
Mars Hill College, B
Methodist College, AB
Mitchell Community College, A
Mount Olive College, AB
North Carolina Central University, B
Queens University of Charlotte, B
Rockingham Community College, A
St. Andrews Presbyterian College, B
Saint Augustine's College, B
Sandhills Community College, A
Southeastern Community College, A
The University of North Carolina at Asheville, B
The University of North Carolina at Charlotte, B
The University of North Carolina at Greensboro, B
Warren Wilson College, B
Western Carolina University, B
Western Piedmont Community College, A
Wingate University, B
Winston-Salem State University, B

North Dakota

Cankdeska Cikana Community College, A
Dickinson State University, B
Jamestown College, B
Minot State University, B
North Dakota State University, B
Turtle Mountain Community College, A
United Tribes Technical College, A
University of North Dakota, B
Valley City State University, B

Ohio

Art Academy of Cincinnati, B
Ashland University, AB
Bluffton University, B
Capital University, B
Central State University, B
Cleveland State University, B
College of Mount St. Joseph, AB
Defiance College, AB
Denison University, B
Edison State Community College, A
Hiram College, B
Kent State University, Stark Campus, A
Kenyon College, B
Lake Erie College, B
Lorain County Community College, A
Lourdes College, AB
Marietta College, B
Miami University, B
Miami University Hamilton, B
Miami University-Middletown Campus, A
Mount Union College, B
Mount Vernon Nazarene University, B
Muskingum College, B
Notre Dame College, B
Oberlin College, B
Ohio Northern University, B
The Ohio State University, B
Ohio University-Eastern, B
Ohio University-Lancaster, A
Otterbein College, B
Shawnee State University, AB
Sinclair Community College, A
The University of Akron, B
University of Cincinnati, B
The University of Findlay, B
University of Rio Grande, AB
The University of Toledo, AB
Wittenberg University, B
Wright State University, B
Xavier University, B

Youngstown State University, B

Oklahoma

Bacone College, A
Cameron University, B
East Central University, B
Eastern Oklahoma State College, A
Langston University, B
Murray State College, A
Northeastern Oklahoma Agricultural and Mechanical College, A
Northeastern State University, B
Oklahoma Baptist University, B
Oklahoma Christian University, B
Oklahoma City Community College, A
Oklahoma State University, B
Redlands Community College, A
Rogers State University, B
Rose State College, A
St. Gregory's University, A
Seminole State College, A
Southeastern Oklahoma State University, B
Tulsa Community College, A
University of Central Oklahoma, B
University of Oklahoma, B
University of Science and Arts of Oklahoma, B

Oregon

Central Oregon Community College, A
Eastern Oregon University, B
George Fox University, B
Lewis & Clark College, B
Linfield College, B
Linn-Benton Community College, A
Marylhurst University, B
Oregon State University, B
Pacific University, B
Portland State University, B
Reed College, B
Southern Oregon University, B
Umpqua Community College, A
University of Oregon, B
Western Oregon University, B
Willamette University, B

Pennsylvania

Albright College, B
Allegheny College, B
Arcadia University, B
Bryn Mawr College, B
Bucknell University, B
Bucks County Community College, A
California University of Pennsylvania, B
Carlow University, B
Carnegie Mellon University, B
Cedar Crest College, B
Cheyney University of Pennsylvania, B
Clarion University of Pennsylvania, B
Community College of Allegheny County, A
Community College of Philadelphia, A
Edinboro University of Pennsylvania, B
Elizabethtown College, B
Gettysburg College, B
Harrisburg Area Community College, A
Haverford College, B
Holy Family University, B
Indiana University of Pennsylvania, B
Keystone College, AB
Lafayette College, B
Lehigh Carbon Community College, A
Lehigh University, B
Lock Haven University of Pennsylvania, B
Lycoming College, B
Mansfield University of Pennsylvania, B
Mercyhurst College, B
Millersville University of Pennsylvania, B
Montgomery County Community College, A
Moore College of Art & Design, B
Moravian College, B
Muhlenberg College, B
The Pennsylvania State University Abington College, B
The Pennsylvania State University Altoona College, B
The Pennsylvania State University Beaver Campus of the Commonwealth College, B

The Pennsylvania State University Berks Campus of the Berks-Lehigh Valley College, B
The Pennsylvania State University Delaware County Campus of the Commonwealth College, B
The Pennsylvania State University DuBois Campus of the Commonwealth College, B
The Pennsylvania State University at Erie, The Behrend College, B
The Pennsylvania State University Fayette Campus of the Commonwealth College, B
The Pennsylvania State University Hazleton Campus of the Commonwealth College, B
The Pennsylvania State University, Lehigh Valley Campus of the Berks-Lehigh Valley College, B
The Pennsylvania State University McKeesport Campus of the Commonwealth College, B
The Pennsylvania State University Mont Alto Campus of the Commonwealth College, B
The Pennsylvania State University New Kensington Campus of the Commonwealth College, B
The Pennsylvania State University Schuylkill Campus of the Capital College, B
The Pennsylvania State University Shenango Campus of the Commonwealth College, B
The Pennsylvania State University University Park Campus, B
The Pennsylvania State University Wilkes-Barre Campus of the Commonwealth College, B
The Pennsylvania State University Worthington Scranton Campus of the Commonwealth College, B
The Pennsylvania State University York Campus of the Commonwealth College, B
Shippensburg University of Pennsylvania, B
Slippery Rock University of Pennsylvania, B
Susquehanna University, B
Temple University, B
Thiel College, B
Ursinus College, B
Washington & Jefferson College, B
Waynesburg College, B
West Chester University of Pennsylvania, B
Westminster College, B
Wilson College, B

Puerto Rico

Inter American University of Puerto Rico, San Germán Campus, B
Pontifical Catholic University of Puerto Rico, AB
University of Puerto Rico, Mayagüez Campus, B
University of Puerto Rico, Río Piedras, B

Rhode Island

Brown University, B
Community College of Rhode Island, A
Roger Williams University, B
University of Rhode Island, B

South Carolina

Anderson University, B
Benedict College, B
Bob Jones University, B
Claflin University, B
Coker College, B
Converse College, B
Erskine College, B
Francis Marion University, B
Furman University, B
Lander University, B
Newberry College, B
North Greenville College, A
Presbyterian College, B
Winthrop University, B

South Dakota

Augustana College, B
Black Hills State University, B
Dakota Wesleyan University, B
Northern State University, B
Sinte Gleska University, A
South Dakota State University, B

The University of South Dakota, B

Tennessee

Austin Peay State University, B
Belmont University, B
Carson-Newman College, B
Columbia State Community College, A
East Tennessee State University, B
Fisk University, B
Freed-Hardeman University, B
Lambuth University, B
LeMoyne-Owen College, B
Lincoln Memorial University, B
Martin Methodist College, A
Memphis College of Art, B
Middle Tennessee State University, B
Rhodes College, B
Roane State Community College, A
Sewanee: The University of the South, B
Southern Adventist University, B
Tennessee State University, B
Tennessee Technological University, B
Tusculum College, B
Union University, B
University of Memphis, B
The University of Tennessee at Chattanooga, B
Vanderbilt University, B
Walters State Community College, A

Texas

Abilene Christian University, B
Alvin Community College, A
Amarillo College, A
Angelina College, A
Angelo State University, B
Austin College, B
Austin Community College, A
Baylor University, B
Brazosport College, A
Clarendon College, A
Coastal Bend College, A
Dallas Baptist University, B
Del Mar College, A
El Paso Community College, A
Frank Phillips College, A
Grayson County College, A
Hill College of the Hill Junior College District, A
Howard College, A
Howard Payne University, B
Kilgore College, A
Lamar University, B
Lee College, A
Lon Morris College, A
McMurry University, B
Midland College, A
Midwestern State University, B
Navarro College, A
North Harris College, A
Odessa College, A
Our Lady of the Lake University of San Antonio, B
Palo Alto College, A
Paris Junior College, A
Rice University, B
St. Edward's University, B
St. Philip's College, A
Sam Houston State University, B
South Plains College, A
Southern Methodist University, B
Southwestern University, B
Stephen F. Austin State University, B
Sul Ross State University, B
Tarleton State University, B
Temple College, A
Texarkana College, A
Texas A&M University-Commerce, B
Texas A&M University-Corpus Christi, B
Texas A&M University-Kingsville, B
Texas College, B
Texas Lutheran University, B
Texas Southern University, B
Texas Southmost College, A
Texas State University-San Marcos, B
Texas Tech University, B
Texas Wesleyan University, B
Trinity University, B
Trinity Valley Community College, A

Tyler Junior College, A
University of Dallas, B
University of Houston, B
University of Houston-Clear Lake, B
University of the Incarnate Word, B
University of Mary Hardin-Baylor, B
University of North Texas, B
The University of Texas at Arlington, B
The University of Texas at Austin, B
The University of Texas at Brownsville, B
The University of Texas-Pan American, B
The University of Texas of the Permian Basin, B
The University of Texas at San Antonio, B
The University of Texas at Tyler, B
Wayland Baptist University, B
West Texas A&M University, B
Western Texas College, A
Wharton County Junior College, A

Utah

Brigham Young University, B
Dixie State College of Utah, A
Snow College, A
Southern Utah University, B
University of Utah, B
Utah State University, B
Weber State University, B
Westminster College, B

Vermont

Burlington College, AB
Castleton State College, B
Green Mountain College, B
Johnson State College, B
Marlboro College, B
Saint Michael's College, B

Virginia

Averett University, B
Bluefield College, B
The College of William and Mary, B
Eastern Mennonite University, B
Emory & Henry College, B
Ferrum College, B
George Mason University, B
Hampton University, B
Hollins University, B
James Madison University, B
Longwood University, B
Lynchburg College, B
Mary Baldwin College, B
Norfolk State University, B
Northern Virginia Community College, A
Old Dominion University, B
Radford University, B
Randolph-Macon Woman's College, B
Roanoke College, B
Southern Virginia University, B
University of Mary Washington, B
University of Richmond, B
University of Virginia, B
The University of Virginia's College at Wise, B
Virginia Intermont College, B
Virginia Polytechnic Institute and State University, B
Virginia Wesleyan College, B
Virginia Western Community College, A

Washington

Central Washington University, B
Centralia College, A
Cornish College of the Arts, B
Everett Community College, A
The Evergreen State College, B
Gonzaga University, B
Highline Community College, A
Lower Columbia College, A
North Seattle Community College, A
Northwest College of Art, B
Pacific Lutheran University, B
Seattle Pacific University, B
Seattle University, B
Skagit Valley College, A
Spokane Falls Community College, A
Tacoma Community College, A
University of Puget Sound, B
University of Washington, B

Walla Walla College, B
Whitman College, B
Whitworth College, B

West Virginia

Bethany College, B
Marshall University, B
Shepherd University, B
University of Charleston, B
West Virginia State University, AB
West Virginia University, B
West Virginia Wesleyan College, B

Wisconsin

Alverno College, B
Cardinal Stritch University, B
Carroll College, B
Concordia University Wisconsin, B
Edgewood College, B
Lakeland College, B
Milwaukee Institute of Art and Design, B
Mount Mary College, B
Northland College, B
Ripon College, B
St. Norbert College, B
Silver Lake College, B
University of Wisconsin-Eau Claire, B
University of Wisconsin-Green Bay, AB
University of Wisconsin-La Crosse, B
University of Wisconsin-Madison, B
University of Wisconsin-Milwaukee, B
University of Wisconsin-Oshkosh, B
University of Wisconsin-Parkside, B
University of Wisconsin-Platteville, B
University of Wisconsin-River Falls, B
University of Wisconsin-Whitewater, B
Viterbo University, B
Wisconsin Lutheran College, B

Wyoming

Casper College, A
Central Wyoming College, A
Eastern Wyoming College, A
Laramie County Community College, A
Northwest College, A
Sheridan College-Sheridan and Gillette, A
University of Wyoming, B
Western Wyoming Community College, A

Alberta

Alberta College of Art & Design, B
University of Alberta, B
University of Calgary, B
University of Lethbridge, B

British Columbia

Open Learning Agency, A
Simon Fraser University, B

Manitoba

University of Manitoba, B

Newfoundland and Labrador

Memorial University of Newfoundland, B

Nova Scotia

NSCAD University, B

Ontario

Brock University, B
Lakehead University, B
McMaster University, B
Redeemer University College, B
University of Ottawa, B
University of Toronto, B
The University of Western Ontario, B
University of Windsor, B
Wilfrid Laurier University, B
York University, B

Quebec

Bishop's University, B
Concordia University, B
Université de Montréal, B

Université du Québec àChicoutimi, B
Université du Québec àMontréal, B
Université du Québec en Outaouais, B
Université du Québec àTrois-Rivières, B

Saskatchewan

University of Regina, B

ART EDUCATION

Alabama

The University of Alabama at Birmingham, M
University of South Alabama, M

Arizona

The University of Arizona, M

Arkansas

University of Arkansas at Little Rock, M

California

California State University, Long Beach, M
California State University, Northridge, M
Stanford University, MD

Colorado

The Colorado College, M

Connecticut

Central Connecticut State University, M
Southern Connecticut State University, M

Florida

Florida Atlantic University, M
Florida International University, MD
Florida State University, MDO
University of Central Florida, M
University of Florida, M

Georgia

Columbus State University, M
Georgia Southern University, MO
Georgia State University, MO
LaGrange College, M
University of Georgia, MDO
University of West Georgia, M

Idaho

Boise State University, M
University of Idaho, M

Illinois

Eastern Illinois University, M
Rockford College, M
School of the Art Institute of Chicago, MO
Southern Illinois University Edwardsville, M
University of Illinois at Urbana-Champaign, MD

Indiana

Ball State University, M
Indiana University Bloomington, M
Indiana University-Purdue University Indianapolis, M
Purdue University, D
University of Indianapolis, M

Iowa

Iowa State University of Science and Technology, M
The University of Iowa, MD
University of Northern Iowa, M

Kansas

Pittsburg State University, M
University of Kansas, M
Wichita State University, M

Kentucky

Eastern Kentucky University, M
Morehead State University, M
University of Kentucky, M
University of Louisville, M

Western Kentucky University, M

Maryland

Maryland Institute College of Art, M
Salisbury University, M
Towson University, M

Massachusetts

Boston University, M
Bridgewater State College, M
Endicott College, M
Fitchburg State College, MO
Harvard University, M
Lesley University, MO
Massachusetts College of Art, M
University of Massachusetts Amherst, M
University of Massachusetts Dartmouth, M

Michigan

Eastern Michigan University, M
Wayne State University, M

Minnesota

Minnesota State University Mankato, M
University of Minnesota, Twin Cities Campus, MD

Mississippi

Mississippi College, M
University of Mississippi, M
University of Southern Mississippi, M
William Carey College, M

Missouri

Maryville University of Saint Louis, M
Missouri State University, M
Southeast Missouri State University, M
University of Missouri-Columbia, MDO

Nebraska

University of Nebraska at Kearney, M

New Jersey

Kean University, M
Montclair State University, M
New Jersey City University, M
Rowan University, M

New Mexico

University of New Mexico, M

New York

Brooklyn College of the City University of New
    York, M
Buffalo State College, State University of New
    York, M
The College of New Rochelle, M
The College of Saint Rose, MO
Hofstra University, M
Long Island University, C.W. Post Campus, M
Manhattanville College, M
Nazareth College of Rochester, M
New York University, MD
Pratt Institute, M
Queens College of the City University of New
    York, M
Rochester Institute of Technology, M
School of Visual Arts, M
State University of New York at New Paltz, M
State University of New York at Oswego, M
Syracuse University, MO

North Carolina

North Carolina Agricultural and Technical State
    University, M
The University of North Carolina at Greensboro, M
The University of North Carolina at Pembroke, M
Western Carolina University, M

Ohio

Art Academy of Cincinnati, M
Case Western Reserve University, M
Kent State University, M
Miami University, M
The Ohio State University, MD

Ohio University, M
University of Cincinnati, M
University of Dayton, M

Oklahoma

Southwestern Oklahoma State University, M

Pennsylvania

Arcadia University, M
Carlow University, M
Kutztown University of Pennsylvania, MO
Mansfield University of Pennsylvania, M
Marywood University, M
Millersville University of Pennsylvania, M
The Pennsylvania State University University Park
　Campus, MD
Temple University, M
The University of the Arts, M

Rhode Island

Rhode Island College, M
Rhode Island School of Design, M

South Carolina

University of South Carolina, M
Winthrop University, M

Tennessee

East Tennessee State University, M
The University of Tennessee, M

Texas

Austin College, M
Sul Ross State University, M
Texas Tech University, M
University of Houston, M
University of North Texas, MD
The University of Texas at Austin, M

Utah

Brigham Young University, M

Vermont

Bennington College, M
Saint Michael's College, O

Virginia

Averett University, M
Christopher Newport University, M
James Madison University, M
Virginia Commonwealth University, M

Washington

City University, M

West Virginia

West Virginia University, M

Wisconsin

Carthage College, M
Concordia University Wisconsin, M
University of Wisconsin-Madison, M
University of Wisconsin-Milwaukee, M
University of Wisconsin-Superior, M

British Columbia

The University of British Columbia, M
University of Victoria, M

Nova Scotia

Cape Breton University, O

Quebec

Concordia University, MD

ART HISTORY, CRITICISM AND CONSERVATION

Alabama

Birmingham-Southern College, B
Troy University, B
The University of Alabama, BM

The University of Alabama at Birmingham, M

Arizona

Northern Arizona University, B
The University of Arizona, BMD

Arkansas

University of Arkansas at Little Rock, BM

California

California State University, Chico, BM
California State University, Dominguez Hills, B
California State University, East Bay, B
California State University, Fullerton, BM
California State University, Long Beach, BM
California State University, Northridge, M
California State University, San Bernardino, B
Cañada College, A
Chapman University, B
Claremont McKenna College, B
De Anza College, A
Dominican University of California, B
El Camino College, A
Foothill College, A
Glendale Community College, A
Grossmont College, A
Humboldt State University, B
Loyola Marymount University, B
Mills College, B
Monterey Peninsula College, A
Occidental College, B
Pacific Union College, B
Pasadena City College, A
Pitzer College, B
Pomona College, B
Saint Mary's College of California, B
San Diego State University, BM
San Francisco State University, M
San Jose State University, BM
Santa Barbara City College, A
Santa Clara University, B
Scripps College, B
Skyline College, A
Sonoma State University, B
Stanford University, B
University of California, Berkeley, BD
University of California, Davis, BM
University of California, Irvine, BMD
University of California, Los Angeles, BMD
University of California, Riverside, BM
University of California, San Diego, B
University of California, Santa Barbara, BDO
University of California, Santa Cruz, B
University of La Verne, B
University of the Pacific, B
University of Redlands, B
University of San Francisco, B
University of Southern California, BMDO

Colorado

The Colorado College, B
Colorado State University, B
University of Colorado at Boulder, M
University of Denver, BM
Western State College of Colorado, B

Connecticut

Albertus Magnus College, B
Connecticut College, B
Saint Joseph College, B
Southern Connecticut State University, B
Trinity College, B
University of Connecticut, BM
University of Hartford, B
Wesleyan University, B
Yale University, BD

Delaware

University of Delaware, BMD

District of Columbia

American University, BM
The Catholic University of America, B
Gallaudet University, B
The George Washington University, BMD

Georgetown University, B
Howard University, M
Trinity (Washington) University, B

Florida

Florida International University, B
Florida State University, BMDO
Jacksonville University, B
Manatee Community College, A
New College of Florida, B
Palm Beach Community College, A
Rollins College, B
University of Florida, BMD
University of Miami, BM
University of South Florida, M

Georgia

Emory University, BD
Georgia State University, M
Oglethorpe University, B
Savannah College of Art and Design, BM
University of Georgia, BMD
Wesleyan College, B

Hawaii

University of Hawaii at Manoa, M

Idaho

Boise State University, B

Illinois

Augustana College, B
Blackburn College, B
Bradley University, B
DePaul University, B
Dominican University, B
Governors State University, B
Illinois State University, M
Knox College, B
Lake Forest College, B
Lincoln College, A
MacMurray College, B
Northern Illinois University, B
Northwestern University, BD
Principia College, B
Rockford College, B
Roosevelt University, B
School of the Art Institute of Chicago, BMO
University of Chicago, BMD
University of Illinois at Chicago, BMD
University of Illinois at Urbana-Champaign, BMD

Indiana

DePauw University, B
Hanover College, B
Indiana University Bloomington, BMDO
Indiana University-Purdue University Indianapolis, B
Marian College, B
University of Evansville, B
University of Notre Dame, BM

Iowa

Clarke College, B
Cornell College, B
Drake University, B
Iowa Lakes Community College, A
The University of Iowa, BMD
University of Northern Iowa, B

Kansas

Baker University, B
University of Kansas, BMD
Washburn University, B
Wichita State University, B

Kentucky

Berea College, B
Centre College, B
St. Catharine College, A
Thomas More College, A
Transylvania University, B
University of Kentucky, BM

University of Louisville, BMD

Louisiana

Louisiana State University and Agricultural and
 Mechanical College, M
Tulane University, BM
University of New Orleans, B

Maine

Bowdoin College, B
Colby College, B
University of Maine, B

Maryland

The Johns Hopkins University, BMD
Maryland Institute College of Art, B
McDaniel College, B
Morgan State University, B
University of Maryland, Baltimore County, B
University of Maryland, College Park, BMD

Massachusetts

Boston College, B
Boston University, BMDO
Bridgewater State College, B
Clark University, B
College of the Holy Cross, B
Framingham State College, B
Harvard University, BD
Massachusetts College of Art, B
Mount Holyoke College, B
Pine Manor College, B
Simon's Rock College of Bard, B
Smith College, B
Tufts University, BM
University of Massachusetts Amherst, BM
University of Massachusetts Dartmouth, B
Wellesley College, B
Wheaton College, B
Williams College, BM

Michigan

Andrews University, B
Aquinas College, B
Calvin College, B
Eastern Michigan University, B
Grand Valley State University, B
Hope College, B
Kalamazoo College, B
Michigan State University, B
Muskegon Community College, A
Oakland University, B
University of Michigan, BD
University of Michigan-Dearborn, B
Wayne State University, BM
Western Michigan University, B

Minnesota

Augsburg College, B
Carleton College, B
College of St. Catherine, B
Concordia College, B
Gustavus Adolphus College, B
Hamline University, B
Macalester College, B
Minnesota State University Mankato, B
Minnesota State University Moorhead, B
St. Cloud State University, B
St. Olaf College, B
University of Minnesota, Duluth, B
University of Minnesota, Morris, B
University of Minnesota, Twin Cities Campus, BMD
University of St. Thomas, BM
Vermilion Community College, A

Mississippi

Mississippi College, B
University of Mississippi, BM

Missouri

Drury University, B
Kansas City Art Institute, B
Lindenwood University, B
Saint Louis University, B
Truman State University, B

University of Missouri-Columbia, BMD
University of Missouri-Kansas City, BMD
University of Missouri-St. Louis, B
Washington University in St. Louis, BMD
Webster University, B

Montana

The University of Montana-Missoula, B

Nebraska

Hastings College, B
University of Nebraska-Lincoln, BM
University of Nebraska at Omaha, B

Nevada

University of Nevada, Las Vegas, B
University of Nevada, Reno, B

New Hampshire

Dartmouth College, B
New England College, B
University of New Hampshire, B

New Jersey

Drew University, B
Georgian Court University, B
Kean University, B
Mercer County Community College, A
Montclair State University, M
Princeton University, B
Rutgers, The State University of New Jersey, New
 Brunswick/Piscataway, BMD
Saint Peter's College, B
Seton Hall University, B
William Paterson University of New Jersey, B

New Mexico

College of Santa Fe, B
University of New Mexico, BMD

New York

Adelphi University, B
Bard College, B
Barnard College, B
Brooklyn College of the City University of New
 York, BMD
Buffalo State College, State University of New
 York, B
Canisius College, B
City College of the City University of New York, BM
Colgate University, B
The College of New Rochelle, B
Columbia College, B
Columbia University, School of General Studies, B
Cornell University, BD
Fashion Institute of Technology, BM
Fordham University, B
Hamilton College, B
Hartwick College, B
Hobart and William Smith Colleges, B
Hofstra University, B
Hunter College of the City University of New
 York, BM
Ithaca College, B
Lehman College of the City University of New
 York, B
Long Island University, C.W. Post Campus, B
Manhattanville College, B
Marist College, B
Marymount Manhattan College, B
Nazareth College of Rochester, B
New York University, BMDO
Pace University, B
Pratt Institute, BMO
Purchase College, State University of New York, BM
Queens College of the City University of New
 York, BM
St. Lawrence University, B
Sarah Lawrence College, B
Skidmore College, B
State University of New York at Binghamton, BMD
State University of New York at Buffalo, BM
State University of New York College at Cortland, B
State University of New York College at Geneseo, B
State University of New York College at Oneonta, B

State University of New York College at Potsdam, B
State University of New York, Fredonia, B
State University of New York at New Paltz, B
State University of New York at Plattsburgh, B
Stony Brook University, State University of New
 York, BMD
Syracuse University, BM
University at Albany, State University of New York, B
University of Rochester, BMD
Vassar College, B
Wells College, B

North Carolina

Duke University, BD
East Carolina University, B
Mars Hill College, B
Salem College, B
The University of North Carolina at Chapel
 Hill, BMD
The University of North Carolina Wilmington, B
Wake Forest University, B

North Dakota

Cankdeska Cikana Community College, A

Ohio

Art Academy of Cincinnati, B
Baldwin-Wallace College, B
Bowling Green State University, B
Case Western Reserve University, BMD
Cleveland State University, M
The College of Wooster, B
Denison University, B
Hiram College, B
John Carroll University, B
Kent State University, BM
Kenyon College, B
Lourdes College, AB
Miami University, B
Oberlin College, B
The Ohio State University, BMD
Ohio University, BM
Ohio Wesleyan University, B
The University of Akron, B
University of Cincinnati, BM
University of Dayton, B
The University of Toledo, B
Ursuline College, B
Wright State University, B
Youngstown State University, B

Oklahoma

Oklahoma City University, B
University of Oklahoma, BM
University of Tulsa, B

Oregon

Oregon State University, B
Portland State University, B
Umpqua Community College, A
University of Oregon, BMD
Willamette University, B

Pennsylvania

Allegheny College, B
Arcadia University, B
Bloomsburg University of Pennsylvania, B
Bryn Mawr College, BMD
Bucknell University, B
Carlow University, B
Chatham College, B
Duquesne University, B
Eastern University, B
Edinboro University of Pennsylvania, B
Franklin and Marshall College, B
Gettysburg College, B
Haverford College, B
Juniata College, B
La Salle University, B
Lafayette College, B
Lebanon Valley College, B
Lehigh University, B
Lycoming College, B
Messiah College, B
Moore College of Art & Design, B

Moravian College, B
The Pennsylvania State University Abington
    College, B
The Pennsylvania State University Altoona
    College, B
The Pennsylvania State University Beaver Campus
    of the Commonwealth College, B
The Pennsylvania State University Berks Campus of
    the Berks-Lehigh Valley College, B
The Pennsylvania State University Delaware County
    Campus of the Commonwealth College, B
The Pennsylvania State University DuBois Campus
    of the Commonwealth College, B
The Pennsylvania State University at Erie, The
    Behrend College, B
The Pennsylvania State University Fayette Campus
    of the Commonwealth College, B
The Pennsylvania State University Hazleton
    Campus of the Commonwealth College, B
The Pennsylvania State University, Lehigh Valley
    Campus of the Berks-Lehigh Valley College, B
The Pennsylvania State University McKeesport
    Campus of the Commonwealth College, B
The Pennsylvania State University Mont Alto
    Campus of the Commonwealth College, B
The Pennsylvania State University New Kensington
    Campus of the Commonwealth College, B
The Pennsylvania State University Schuylkill
    Campus of the Capital College, B
The Pennsylvania State University Shenango
    Campus of the Commonwealth College, B
The Pennsylvania State University University Park
    Campus, BMD
The Pennsylvania State University Wilkes-Barre
    Campus of the Commonwealth College, B
The Pennsylvania State University Worthington
    Scranton Campus of the Commonwealth
    College, B
The Pennsylvania State University York Campus of
    the Commonwealth College, B
Rosemont College, B
Saint Vincent College, B
Seton Hill University, B
Susquehanna University, B
Swarthmore College, B
Temple University, BMD
University of Pennsylvania, BMD
University of Pittsburgh, BMD
Villanova University, B

Puerto Rico

Inter American University of Puerto Rico, San
    Germán Campus, B
University of Puerto Rico, Río Piedras, B

Rhode Island

Brown University, BMD
Providence College, B
Rhode Island College, B
Roger Williams University, B
Salve Regina University, B
University of Rhode Island, B

South Carolina

College of Charleston, B
Converse College, B
Furman University, B
University of South Carolina, BM
Winthrop University, B
Wofford College, B

Tennessee

East Tennessee State University, M
Lambuth University, B
Maryville College, B
Rhodes College, B
Sewanee: The University of the South, B
University of Memphis, BM
The University of Tennessee, B

Texas

Baylor University, B
Hill College of the Hill Junior College District, A
Lamar University, M
Lon Morris College, A

Rice University, B
Southern Methodist University, BM
Southwestern University, B
Stephen F. Austin State University, B
Sul Ross State University, M
Texas A&M University-Commerce, BM
Texas Christian University, BM
Texas Tech University, B
Trinity University, B
University of Dallas, B
University of Houston, B
University of North Texas, BM
The University of Texas at Arlington, B
The University of Texas at Austin, BMD
The University of Texas at San Antonio, BM

Utah

Brigham Young University, BM
Dixie State College of Utah, A
University of Utah, BM

Vermont

Marlboro College, B
Middlebury College, B
University of Vermont, B

Virginia

The College of William and Mary, B
George Mason University, B
Hollins University, B
James Madison University, BM
Longwood University, B
Northern Virginia Community College, A
Old Dominion University, B
Randolph-Macon College, B
Randolph-Macon Woman's College, B
Roanoke College, B
Sweet Briar College, B
University of Mary Washington, B
University of Richmond, B
University of Virginia, MD
Virginia Commonwealth University, BMD
Washington and Lee University, B

Washington

Eastern Washington University, B
Pacific Lutheran University, B
Seattle University, B
Skagit Valley College, A
University of Washington, BMD
Washington State University, B
Western Washington University, B

West Virginia

West Virginia University, M
West Virginia Wesleyan College, B

Wisconsin

Beloit College, B
Lawrence University, B
University of Wisconsin-Madison, BMD
University of Wisconsin-Milwaukee, BMO
University of Wisconsin-Superior, BM
University of Wisconsin-Whitewater, B

Alberta

University of Alberta, BM
University of Calgary, B

British Columbia

The University of British Columbia, BMDO
University of Victoria, BMD

Manitoba

University of Manitoba, B
The University of Winnipeg, B

New Brunswick

Mount Allison University, B

Newfoundland and Labrador

Memorial University of Newfoundland, B

Nova Scotia

NSCAD University, B

Ontario

Carleton University, BM
McMaster University, B
Queen's University at Kingston, B
University of Guelph, B
University of Toronto, BMD
University of Waterloo, B
The University of Western Ontario, B
University of Windsor, B
York University, BM

Quebec

Concordia University, BMD
McGill University, BMD
Université Laval, ABMD
Université de Montréal, BMD
Université du Québec àMontréal, BMD

Saskatchewan

University of Regina, B
University of Saskatchewan, B

ART TEACHER EDUCATION

Alabama

Alabama State University, B
Birmingham-Southern College, B
Huntingdon College, B
Troy University, B
University of Montevallo, B
Wallace State Community College, A

Arizona

Eastern Arizona College, A
Grand Canyon University, B
Northern Arizona University, B
The University of Arizona, B

Arkansas

Arkansas State University, B
Arkansas Tech University, B
Harding University, B
Henderson State University, B
Ouachita Baptist University, B
Southern Arkansas University-Magnolia, B
University of Arkansas at Pine Bluff, B
University of the Ozarks, B
Williams Baptist College, B

California

Bakersfield College, A
California Lutheran University, B
California State University, Chico, B
California State University, Fullerton, B
California State University, Long Beach, B
Compton Community College, A
Humboldt State University, B
Los Angeles Mission College, A
Mount St. Mary's College, B
Oxnard College, A
Palomar College, A
Point Loma Nazarene University, B
Westmont College, B

Colorado

Colorado State University, B
Colorado State University-Pueblo, B
Northeastern Junior College, A
Rocky Mountain College of Art & Design, B
Trinidad State Junior College, A
University of Denver, B

Western State College of Colorado, B

Connecticut

Central Connecticut State University, B
Southern Connecticut State University, B

Delaware

Delaware State University, B

District of Columbia

The Catholic University of America, B
Gallaudet University, B
University of the District of Columbia, B

Florida

Flagler College, B
Florida Agricultural and Mechanical University, B
Florida International University, B
Florida Southern College, B
Florida State University, B
Indian River Community College, A
Palm Beach Atlantic University, B
Pensacola Junior College, A
University of Central Florida, B
University of Florida, B
University of North Florida, B
University of South Florida, B

Georgia

Armstrong Atlantic State University, B
Brenau University, B
Clark Atlanta University, B
Clayton State University, A
Columbus State University, B
Georgia Southern University, B
Georgia State University, B
Kennesaw State University, B
North Georgia College & State University, B
Shorter College, B
University of Georgia, B
Valdosta State University, B
Young Harris College, A

Guam

University of Guam, B

Hawaii

Brigham Young University-Hawaii, B

Idaho

Boise State University, B
Northwest Nazarene University, B
University of Idaho, B

Illinois

Augustana College, B
Chicago State University, B
Concordia University, B
Elmhurst College, B
John A. Logan College, A
Kishwaukee College, A
Lewis University, B
Lincoln College, A
Lincoln College-Normal, A
McKendree College, B
Millikin University, B
North Central College, B
North Park University, B
Northern Illinois University, B
Olivet Nazarene University, B
Parkland College, A
Saint Xavier University, B
School of the Art Institute of Chicago, B
Trinity Christian College, B
University of Illinois at Chicago, B
University of Illinois at Urbana-Champaign, B
Waubonsee Community College, A

Indiana

Ancilla College, A
Anderson University, B
Ball State University, B
Calumet College of Saint Joseph, B
Goshen College, B

Grace College, B
Huntington University, B
Indiana State University, B
Indiana University Bloomington, B
Indiana University-Purdue University Fort Wayne, B
Indiana University-Purdue University Indianapolis, B
Indiana Wesleyan University, B
Manchester College, B
Marian College, B
Oakland City University, B
Saint Joseph's College, B
Saint Mary-of-the-Woods College, B
Saint Mary's College, B
Taylor University, B
University of Evansville, B
University of Indianapolis, B
University of Saint Francis, B
Valparaiso University, B
Vincennes University, A

Iowa

Buena Vista University, B
Clarke College, B
Coe College, B
Ellsworth Community College, A
Graceland University, B
Iowa Lakes Community College, A
Iowa Wesleyan College, B
Kirkwood Community College, A
Loras College, B
Morningside College, B
Mount Mercy College, B
Northwestern College, B
St. Ambrose University, B
Simpson College, B
The University of Iowa, B
University of Northern Iowa, B
Upper Iowa University, B
Waldorf College, B
Wartburg College, B

Kansas

Baker University, B
Bethany College, B
Central Christian College of Kansas, A
Fort Hays State University, B
Friends University, B
Independence Community College, A
Kansas Wesleyan University, B
McPherson College, B
Ottawa University, B
Pittsburg State University, B
Pratt Community College, A
Tabor College, B
University of Kansas, B
Wichita State University, B

Kentucky

Asbury College, B
Berea College, B
Brescia University, B
Campbellsville University, B
Eastern Kentucky University, B
Kentucky State University, B
Kentucky Wesleyan College, B
Lindsey Wilson College, B
Murray State University, B
St. Catharine College, A
Thomas More College, B
Transylvania University, B
University of the Cumberlands, B
University of Kentucky, B
Western Kentucky University, B

Louisiana

Centenary College of Louisiana, B
Dillard University, B
Grambling State University, B
Louisiana College, B
Louisiana State University in Shreveport, B
Louisiana Tech University, B
McNeese State University, B
Nicholls State University, B
Southeastern Louisiana University, B

Xavier University of Louisiana, B

Maine

University of Maine, B
University of Maine at Presque Isle, B
University of Southern Maine, B

Maryland

Maryland Institute College of Art, B
Towson University, B
University of Maryland, College Park, B
University of Maryland Eastern Shore, B

Massachusetts

Anna Maria College, B
Atlantic Union College, B
Boston University, B
Bridgewater State College, B
Framingham State College, B
Massachusetts College of Art, B
Montserrat College of Art, B
Salem State College, B
School of the Museum of Fine Arts, Boston, B
University of Massachusetts Dartmouth, B
Westfield State College, B

Michigan

Adrian College, B
Alma College, B
Andrews University, B
Aquinas College, B
Calvin College, B
Central Michigan University, B
Concordia University, B
Eastern Michigan University, B
Grand Valley State University, B
Hope College, B
Kellogg Community College, A
Madonna University, B
Michigan State University, B
Muskegon Community College, A
Northern Michigan University, B
Olivet College, B
Saginaw Valley State University, B
Siena Heights University, B
University of Michigan, B
University of Michigan-Flint, B
Wayne State University, B
Western Michigan University, B

Minnesota

Augsburg College, B
Bemidji State University, B
Bethel University, B
College of St. Catherine, B
Concordia College, B
Gustavus Adolphus College, B
Minnesota State University Mankato, B
Minnesota State University Moorhead, B
Northwestern College, B
St. Cloud State University, B
Southwest Minnesota State University, B
University of Minnesota, Duluth, B
University of Minnesota, Twin Cities Campus, B
Vermilion Community College, A
Winona State University, B

Mississippi

Copiah-Lincoln Community College, A
Delta State University, B
East Central Community College, A
Itawamba Community College, A
Jones County Junior College, A
Mississippi College, B
Mississippi Delta Community College, A
Mississippi Gulf Coast Community College, A
Mississippi University for Women, B
Northeast Mississippi Community College, A
William Carey College, B

Missouri

Central Missouri State University, B
College of the Ozarks, B
Culver-Stockton College, B
Evangel University, B

Fontbonne University, B
Hannibal-LaGrange College, B
Lincoln University, B
Lindenwood University, B
Maryville University of Saint Louis, B
Missouri State University, B
Missouri Western State University, B
Northwest Missouri State University, B
Southeast Missouri State University, B
Southwest Baptist University, B
University of Missouri-Columbia, B
Washington University in St. Louis, B
William Woods University, B

Montana

Montana State University-Billings, B
Rocky Mountain College, B
University of Great Falls, B
The University of Montana-Missoula, B
The University of Montana-Western, B

Nebraska

Chadron State College, B
Concordia University, B
Dana College, B
Hastings College, B
Midland Lutheran College, B
Northeast Community College, A
Peru State College, B
Union College, B
University of Nebraska-Lincoln, B
Wayne State College, B
Western Nebraska Community College, A
York College, B

Nevada

University of Nevada, Reno, B

New Hampshire

Colby-Sawyer College, B
Franklin Pierce College, B
Plymouth State University, B
University of New Hampshire, B

New Jersey

Bloomfield College, B
The College of New Jersey, B
New Jersey City University, B
Seton Hall University, B
William Paterson University of New Jersey, B

New Mexico

New Mexico Highlands University, B
New Mexico Junior College, A
University of New Mexico, B
Western New Mexico University, B

New York

Adelphi University, B
Alfred University, B
Brooklyn College of the City University of New
   York, B
Buffalo State College, State University of New
   York, B
City College of the City University of New York, B
The College of New Rochelle, B
The College of Saint Rose, B
Daemen College, B
Dowling College, B
Elmira College, B
Hofstra University, B
Houghton College, B
Ithaca College, B
Lehman College of the City University of New
   York, B
Long Island University, Brooklyn Campus, B
Long Island University, C.W. Post Campus, B
Manhattanville College, B
Nazareth College of Rochester, B
New York Institute of Technology, B
Parsons The New School for Design, B
Pratt Institute, B
Queens College of the City University of New
   York, B
Roberts Wesleyan College, B

St. Bonaventure University, B
St. John's University, B
State University of New York at New Paltz, B
Syracuse University, B

North Carolina

Appalachian State University, B
Barton College, B
East Carolina University, B
Elizabeth City State University, B
Greensboro College, B
Halifax Community College, A
High Point University, B
Lenoir-Rhyne College, B
Mars Hill College, B
Meredith College, B
Methodist College, B
North Carolina Agricultural and Technical State
   University, B
North Carolina Central University, B
Sandhills Community College, A
The University of North Carolina at Charlotte, B
The University of North Carolina at Greensboro, B
The University of North Carolina at Pembroke, B
Western Carolina University, B
Wingate University, B
Winston-Salem State University, B

North Dakota

Dickinson State University, B
Minot State University, B
University of North Dakota, B
Valley City State University, B

Ohio

Ashland University, B
Baldwin-Wallace College, B
Bowling Green State University, B
Capital University, B
Case Western Reserve University, B
Central State University, B
College of Mount St. Joseph, B
Defiance College, B
Kent State University, B
Malone College, B
Miami University, B
Miami University Hamilton, B
Mount Vernon Nazarene University, B
Muskingum College, B
Notre Dame College, B
Ohio Dominican University, B
Ohio Northern University, B
The Ohio State University, B
Ohio University, B
Ohio University-Eastern, B
Ohio Wesleyan University, B
Otterbein College, B
Shawnee State University, B
The University of Akron, B
University of Cincinnati, B
University of Dayton, B
The University of Findlay, B
University of Rio Grande, B
The University of Toledo, B
Ursuline College, B
Wilmington College, B
Wright State University, B
Youngstown State University, B

Oklahoma

Carl Albert State College, A
East Central University, B
Eastern Oklahoma State College, A
Langston University, B
Northeastern Oklahoma Agricultural and Mechanical
   College, A
Northeastern State University, B
Oklahoma Baptist University, B
Oklahoma City University, B
Oral Roberts University, B
Southeastern Oklahoma State University, B
Southwestern Oklahoma State University, B

University of Central Oklahoma, B

Oregon

Chemeketa Community College, A
Pacific University, B
Umpqua Community College, A

Pennsylvania

Albright College, B
Arcadia University, B
Carlow University, B
Edinboro University of Pennsylvania, B
Indiana University of Pennsylvania, B
Keystone College, B
Kutztown University of Pennsylvania, B
Lincoln University, B
Lycoming College, B
Mansfield University of Pennsylvania, B
Marywood University, B
Mercyhurst College, B
Messiah College, B
Millersville University of Pennsylvania, B
Moore College of Art & Design, B
Moravian College, B
The Pennsylvania State University Abington
   College, B
The Pennsylvania State University Altoona
   College, B
The Pennsylvania State University Beaver Campus
   of the Commonwealth College, B
The Pennsylvania State University Berks Campus of
   the Berks-Lehigh Valley College, B
The Pennsylvania State University Delaware County
   Campus of the Commonwealth College, B
The Pennsylvania State University DuBois Campus
   of the Commonwealth College, B
The Pennsylvania State University at Erie, The
   Behrend College, B
The Pennsylvania State University Fayette Campus
   of the Commonwealth College, B
The Pennsylvania State University Hazleton
   Campus of the Commonwealth College, B
The Pennsylvania State University, Lehigh Valley
   Campus of the Berks-Lehigh Valley College, B
The Pennsylvania State University McKeesport
   Campus of the Commonwealth College, B
The Pennsylvania State University Mont Alto
   Campus of the Commonwealth College, B
The Pennsylvania State University New Kensington
   Campus of the Commonwealth College, B
The Pennsylvania State University Schuylkill
   Campus of the Capital College, B
The Pennsylvania State University Shenango
   Campus of the Commonwealth College, B
The Pennsylvania State University University Park
   Campus, B
The Pennsylvania State University Wilkes-Barre
   Campus of the Commonwealth College, B
The Pennsylvania State University Worthington
   Scranton Campus of the Commonwealth
   College, B
The Pennsylvania State University York Campus of
   the Commonwealth College, B
Saint Vincent College, B
Seton Hill University, B
Temple University, B
Washington & Jefferson College, B

Puerto Rico

Escuela de Artes Plasticas de Puerto Rico, B
Inter American University of Puerto Rico, Fajardo
   Campus, B
Inter American University of Puerto Rico, San
   Germán Campus, B
Pontifical Catholic University of Puerto Rico, B

Rhode Island

Rhode Island College, B

South Carolina

Anderson University, B
Benedict College, B
Bob Jones University, B
Claflin University, B
Coker College, B

Converse College, B
Francis Marion University, B
Limestone College, B
South Carolina State University, B
University of South Carolina, B

South Dakota

Augustana College, B
Dakota Wesleyan University, B
Northern State University, B
South Dakota State University, B
University of Sioux Falls, B
The University of South Dakota, B

Tennessee

Belmont University, B
Carson-Newman College, B
Freed-Hardeman University, B
Lambuth University, B
Lincoln Memorial University, B
Martin Methodist College, A
Maryville College, B
Middle Tennessee State University, B
Roane State Community College, A
Tennessee Technological University, B
Tusculum College, B
Union University, B
The University of Tennessee, B
The University of Tennessee at Chattanooga, B
The University of Tennessee at Martin, B
Walters State Community College, A

Texas

Abilene Christian University, B
Angelina College, A
Baylor University, B
Coastal Bend College, A
Del Mar College, A
Frank Phillips College, A
Grayson County College, A
Hardin-Simmons University, B
Hill College of the Hill Junior College District, A
Houston Baptist University, B
Howard Payne University, B
Lamar University, B
Lon Morris College, A
Lubbock Christian University, B
McLennan Community College, A
McMurry University, B
North Harris College, A
St. Edward's University, B
St. Mary's University of San Antonio, B
Sam Houston State University, B
Southwestern University, B
Texas A&M University-Commerce, B
Texas Christian University, B
Texas Lutheran University, B
Texas Southern University, B
Texas Wesleyan University, B
University of Dallas, B
University of the Incarnate Word, B
The University of Texas at El Paso, B
Western Texas College, A

Utah

Brigham Young University, B
Southern Utah University, B
Weber State University, B

Vermont

Johnson State College, B
Saint Michael's College, B
University of Vermont, B

Virginia

Averett University, B
Eastern Mennonite University, B
Hampton University, B
Longwood University, B
Old Dominion University, B
University of Richmond, B
Virginia Commonwealth University, B
Virginia Intermont College, B

Virginia Wesleyan College, B

Washington

Central Washington University, B
Eastern Washington University, B
Pacific Lutheran University, B
Seattle Pacific University, B
Walla Walla College, B
Western Washington University, B
Whitworth College, B

West Virginia

Concord University, B
Davis & Elkins College, B
Fairmont State University, B
West Liberty State College, B
West Virginia State University, B
West Virginia Wesleyan College, B

Wisconsin

Alverno College, B
Beloit College, B
Cardinal Stritch University, B
Carroll College, B
Concordia University Wisconsin, B
Edgewood College, B
Lawrence University, B
Marian College of Fond du Lac, B
Mount Mary College, B
Northland College, B
Silver Lake College, B
University of Wisconsin-Madison, B
University of Wisconsin-Milwaukee, B
University of Wisconsin-Oshkosh, B
University of Wisconsin-River Falls, B
University of Wisconsin-Stout, B
University of Wisconsin-Superior, B
University of Wisconsin-Whitewater, B
Viterbo University, B

Wyoming

Northwest College, A

Alberta

University of Alberta, B
University of Calgary, B
University of Lethbridge, B

British Columbia

The University of British Columbia, B
University of Victoria, B

New Brunswick

University of New Brunswick Fredericton, B

Nova Scotia

Mount Saint Vincent University, B

Ontario

The University of Western Ontario, B
University of Windsor, B
York University, B

Quebec

Bishop's University, B
Concordia University, B
Université Laval, B
Université du Québec àChicoutimi, B
Université du Québec àTrois-Rivières, B

Saskatchewan

University of Regina, B

ART THERAPY/THERAPIST

Alabama

Spring Hill College, B

Arizona

Prescott College, B

Arkansas

Harding University, B

California

California Institute of Integral Studies, M
Notre Dame de Namur University, M

Colorado

Naropa University, M

Connecticut

Albertus Magnus College, BM

District of Columbia

The George Washington University, MO
Howard University, B

Illinois

Millikin University, B
School of the Art Institute of Chicago, M
Southern Illinois University Edwardsville, MO

Indiana

Goshen College, B
Saint Mary-of-the-Woods College, MO
University of Indianapolis, B

Kansas

Emporia State University, M

Kentucky

Brescia University, B
University of Louisville, M

Massachusetts

Anna Maria College, B
Emmanuel College, B
Endicott College, B
Lesley University, BMD
Springfield College, BMO

Michigan

Marygrove College, B

Missouri

Webster University, B

New Jersey

Caldwell College, M

New Mexico

College of Santa Fe, B

New York

The College of New Rochelle, BM
Hofstra University, M
Long Island University, C.W. Post Campus, BM
Nazareth College of Rochester, BM
New York University, M
Pratt Institute, M
Russell Sage College, B
St. Thomas Aquinas College, B
School of Visual Arts, M

Ohio

Capital University, B
Ohio Wesleyan University, B
Ursuline College, M
Wright State University, B

Oregon

Marylhurst University, MO

Pennsylvania

Drexel University, M
Marywood University, BM
Mercyhurst College, B

Seton Hill University, BMO

Rhode Island

Salve Regina University, O

South Carolina

Converse College, B

Wisconsin

Alverno College, B
Edgewood College, B
Marian College of Fond du Lac, B
Mount Mary College, BM
University of Wisconsin-Superior, BM

Quebec

Concordia University, BM

ARTIFICIAL INTELLIGENCE AND ROBOTICS

California

Cuesta College, A
San Diego City College, A
University of California, San Diego, MD
University of Southern California, M

District of Columbia

The Catholic University of America, MD

Florida

Remington College-Pinellas Campus, A

Georgia

Clayton State University, A
University of Georgia, M

Illinois

Illinois Central College, A

Indiana

Vincennes University, A

Iowa

Des Moines Area Community College, A
Indian Hills Community College, A
Kirkwood Community College, A
Southeastern Community College, North Campus, A

Kentucky

Louisville Technical Institute, A

Maryland

Cecil Community College, A

Massachusetts

Harvard University, B

Michigan

Henry Ford Community College, A
St. Clair County Community College, A
Washtenaw Community College, A

Mississippi

Northeast Mississippi Community College, A

Missouri

Metropolitan Community College-Business & Technology College, A
St. Louis Community College at Forest Park, A

Montana

Montana Tech of The University of Montana, B

New Hampshire

New Hampshire Community Technical College, Nashua/Claremont, A

New Jersey

Camden County College, A
Cumberland County College, A

Raritan Valley Community College, A

New York

Cornell University, MD
Dutchess Community College, A

North Carolina

Wake Technical Community College, A

Ohio

James A. Rhodes State College, A
Lorain County Community College, A
Ohio University, D
Sinclair Community College, A
University of Cincinnati, A

Oklahoma

Oklahoma State University, Okmulgee, A
Tulsa Community College, A

Oregon

Portland State University, O

Pennsylvania

Carnegie Mellon University, MD
Villanova University, O
Westmoreland County Community College, A
York Technical Institute, A

South Dakota

Southeast Technical Institute, A

Tennessee

Chattanooga State Technical Community College, A
The University of Tennessee, M

Texas

Hill College of the Hill Junior College District, A
Lamar University, A
Mountain View College, A
Richland College, A

Washington

South Seattle Community College, A
Spokane Community College, A

Wisconsin

Gateway Technical College, A

Ontario

University of Windsor, B

Quebec

Universite du Quebec, Ecole de technologie superieure, B
Université du Québec àTrois-Rivières, B

ARTS MANAGEMENT

Alabama

Spring Hill College, B

Arizona

Northern Arizona University, B

California

California State University, East Bay, B
Cuesta College, A
Palomar College, A
University of San Francisco, B

University of Southern California, M

Colorado

Fort Lewis College, B

Delaware

Delaware State University, B

District of Columbia

American University, MO

Florida

Florida State University, M

Georgia

Brenau University, B

Illinois

Benedictine University, B
Columbia College Chicago, BM
DePaul University, B
Millikin University, B
Quincy University, B
School of the Art Institute of Chicago, M

Indiana

Butler University, B
Indiana University Bloomington, M

Iowa

Buena Vista University, B
Luther College, B
The University of Iowa, B
Upper Iowa University, B
Wartburg College, B

Kansas

Benedictine College, B
Bethany College, B
Kansas Wesleyan University, B

Kentucky

Bellarmine University, B
University of Kentucky, B

Louisiana

Southeastern Louisiana University, B
University of New Orleans, M

Maryland

Goucher College, M

Massachusetts

Boston University, M
Simmons College, B

Michigan

Adrian College, B
Aquinas College, B
Eastern Michigan University, BM

Minnesota

Saint Mary's University of Minnesota, M

Missouri

Culver-Stockton College, B
Drury University, B
Fontbonne University, B
Webster University, M

New Jersey

Seton Hall University, M

New Mexico

College of Santa Fe, B

New York

Bernard M. Baruch College of the City University of New York, B
Concordia College, B
Fashion Institute of Technology, BM
Ithaca College, B
Long Island University, C.W. Post Campus, B

New York University, M
Pratt Institute, M
State University of New York, Fredonia, B
Wagner College, B

North Carolina

Appalachian State University, B
Bennett College For Women, B
North Carolina State University, B
Pfeiffer University, B
Salem College, B
The University of North Carolina at Charlotte, M

Ohio

The Ohio State University, M
Tiffin University, B
The University of Akron, M
University of Cincinnati, MO
Wright State University, B

Oklahoma

Oklahoma City University, BM
University of Tulsa, B

Oregon

University of Oregon, M
University of Portland, B

Pennsylvania

Carnegie Mellon University, M
Chatham College, B
Drexel University, M
Marywood University, B
Mercyhurst College, B
Point Park University, B
Seton Hill University, B
Temple University, MD
Waynesburg College, B

Rhode Island

Rhode Island College, M

South Carolina

College of Charleston, B
Winthrop University, M

Vermont

Green Mountain College, B

Virginia

Hollins University, B
Mary Baldwin College, B
Randolph-Macon College, B
Shenandoah University, BM
Virginia Polytechnic Institute and State University, M

Washington

Whitworth College, B

Wisconsin

University of Wisconsin-Madison, M
University of Wisconsin-Stevens Point, B
Viterbo University, B

Ontario

Ryerson University, M
University of Toronto, B
University of Waterloo, B
University of Windsor, B

Quebec

Bishop's University, B
HEC Montreal, O

ASIAN-AMERICAN STUDIES

California

California State University, East Bay, B
California State University, Fullerton, B
California State University, Long Beach, BMO
California State University, Los Angeles, B
California State University, Northridge, B

Claremont McKenna College, B
Loyola Marymount University, B
Pitzer College, B
Scripps College, B
Southwestern College, A
University of California, Berkeley, B
University of California, Davis, B
University of California, Irvine, B
University of California, Los Angeles, BM
University of California, Riverside, B
University of California, Santa Barbara, B
University of Southern California, B

Colorado

Colorado State University, B
University of Denver, B

Georgia

Emory University, B

Massachusetts

Hampshire College, B

New York

Columbia College, B
State University of New York at Binghamton, B
Stony Brook University, State University of New York, B

Ohio

The Ohio State University, B

ASIAN HISTORY

California

University of the West, B

New York

Bard College, B
Cornell University, B
Sarah Lawrence College, B

Pennsylvania

Gettysburg College, B

Saskatchewan

University of Regina, B

ASIAN LANGUAGES

California

University of California, Berkeley, MD
University of California, Irvine, MD
University of California, Los Angeles, MD
University of California, Santa Barbara, D
University of Southern California, MDO

Colorado

Naropa University, M

Connecticut

Yale University, D

Hawaii

University of Hawaii at Manoa, MD

Illinois

University of Chicago, MD
University of Illinois at Urbana-Champaign, MD

Indiana

Indiana University Bloomington, MDO

Kansas

University of Kansas, M

Massachusetts

Harvard University, MD

Michigan

University of Michigan, MD

Missouri

Washington University in St. Louis, MDO

New Mexico

St. John's College, M

New York

Cornell University, MD

Ohio

Kent State University, M
The Ohio State University, MD

Oregon

University of Oregon, MD

Texas

The University of Texas at Austin, MD

Utah

Brigham Young University, M

Washington

University of Washington, MD

Wisconsin

University of Wisconsin-Madison, MD

ASIAN STUDIES/CIVILIZATION

Alabama

Birmingham-Southern College, B
Samford University, B
The University of Alabama, B

California

California State University, Chico, B
California State University, Long Beach, BMO
California State University, Los Angeles, B
California State University, Sacramento, B
City College of San Francisco, A
Claremont McKenna College, B
East Los Angeles College, A
El Camino College, A
Laney College, A
Occidental College, B
Pitzer College, B
Pomona College, B
San Diego State University, BM
Scripps College, B
Stanford University, BM
University of California, Berkeley, BMDO
University of California, Los Angeles, B
University of California, Riverside, B
University of California, Santa Barbara, B
University of California, Santa Cruz, B
University of Redlands, B
University of San Francisco, BM

Colorado

The Colorado College, B
Colorado State University, B
Fort Lewis College, B
University of Colorado at Boulder, B

District of Columbia

The George Washington University, BMO

Florida

Florida International University, B
Florida State University, BM
Manatee Community College, A
Miami Dade College, A

University of Florida, B

Georgia

Emory University, B

Hawaii

University of Hawaii at Manoa, BMO

Illinois

Augustana College, B
Illinois Wesleyan University, B
Lake Forest College, B
Northwestern University, B
University of Chicago, B

Indiana

Indiana University Bloomington, BMD

Iowa

Coe College, B
Maharishi University of Management, MD
The University of Iowa, BM
University of Northern Iowa, B

Louisiana

Tulane University, B

Maine

Bowdoin College, B

Massachusetts

Amherst College, B
Clark University, B
College of the Holy Cross, B
Hampshire College, B
Harvard University, BMD
Mount Holyoke College, B
Simon's Rock College of Bard, B
Tufts University, B
Wheaton College, B
Williams College, B

Michigan

Calvin College, B
University of Michigan, BMDO
Wayne State University, B
Western Michigan University, B

Minnesota

Carleton College, B
Hamline University, B
Macalester College, B
St. Olaf College, B

Missouri

Washington University in St. Louis, BMDO

Montana

The University of Montana-Missoula, B

New Hampshire

Dartmouth College, B

New Jersey

Princeton University, D
Seton Hall University, BM

New Mexico

St. John's College, M
University of New Mexico, B

New York

Bard College, B
Barnard College, B
City College of the City University of New York, B
Colgate University, B
Cornell University, BMD
Hamilton College, B
Hobart and William Smith Colleges, B
Hofstra University, B
Manhattanville College, B
St. John's University, BMO
St. Lawrence University, B

Sarah Lawrence College, B
Skidmore College, B
State University of New York at Buffalo, B
State University of New York College at
  Brockport, B
State University of New York at New Paltz, B
University at Albany, State University of New York, B
Vassar College, B

North Carolina

Duke University, B
The University of North Carolina at Chapel Hill, B
Warren Wilson College, B

Ohio

Bowling Green State University, B
Case Western Reserve University, B
John Carroll University, B
Kenyon College, B
Mount Union College, B
Ohio University, B
University of Cincinnati, B
The University of Toledo, B

Oregon

University of Oregon, BM
Willamette University, B

Pennsylvania

Lehigh University, B
Swarthmore College, B
Temple University, B

South Carolina

Furman University, B

Tennessee

Sewanee: The University of the South, B

Texas

Baylor University, B
Rice University, B
Texas State University-San Marcos, B
Trinity University, B
The University of Texas at Austin, BMDO

Utah

Brigham Young University, B
University of Utah, B
Utah State University, B

Vermont

Bennington College, B
Marlboro College, B
University of Vermont, B

Virginia

Mary Baldwin College, B
Old Dominion University, B

Washington

Central Washington University, B
Gonzaga University, B
University of Puget Sound, B
University of Washington, BM
Washington State University, B
Western Washington University, B
Whitman College, B

West Virginia

American Public University System, B
Salem International University, B

Wisconsin

Beloit College, B
University of Wisconsin-Madison, BMD

British Columbia

The University of British Columbia, BMD
University of Victoria, BM

Nova Scotia

Saint Mary's University, B

Ontario

Carleton University, B
University of Toronto, B

ASTRONOMY

Arizona

Arizona State University, MD
Northern Arizona University, B
The University of Arizona, BMD

California

California Institute of Technology, BD
Crafton Hills College, A
El Camino College, A
Fullerton College, A
Palomar College, A
Pasadena City College, A
Pomona College, B
Saddleback College, A
San Bernardino Valley College, A
San Diego State University, BM
San Francisco State University, B
Santa Monica College, A
Santa Rosa Junior College, A
Southwestern College, A
University of California, Los Angeles, BMD
University of California, Santa Cruz, D
University of Southern California, B

Colorado

University of Colorado at Boulder, B

Connecticut

Wesleyan University, BM
Yale University, BMD

Delaware

University of Delaware, BMD

Florida

Daytona Beach Community College, A
Manatee Community College, A
University of Florida, BMD

Georgia

Georgia State University, D
University of Georgia, MD
Valdosta State University, B

Hawaii

University of Hawaii at Manoa, MD

Idaho

North Idaho College, A

Illinois

Northwestern University, BMD
University of Chicago, MD
University of Illinois at Urbana-Champaign, BMD

Indiana

Indiana University Bloomington, BMD
Valparaiso University, B

Iowa

Drake University, B
Iowa Lakes Community College, A
Iowa State University of Science and
  Technology, MD

The University of Iowa, BM

Kansas

Benedictine College, B
University of Kansas, BMD

Kentucky

University of Kentucky, MD

Louisiana

Louisiana State University and Agricultural and
  Mechanical College, MD

Maryland

Anne Arundel Community College, A
The Johns Hopkins University, D
University of Maryland, College Park, BMD

Massachusetts

Amherst College, B
Boston University, BMD
Harvard University, BMD
Mount Holyoke College, B
Smith College, B
Tufts University, B
University of Massachusetts Amherst, BMD
Wellesley College, B
Wheaton College, B
Williams College, B

Michigan

Central Michigan University, B
Michigan State University, MD
University of Michigan, BMD

Minnesota

Minnesota State University Mankato, BM
University of Minnesota, Twin Cities Campus, BMD

Missouri

University of Missouri-Columbia, MD

Montana

The University of Montana-Missoula, B

Nebraska

University of Nebraska-Lincoln, MD

New Hampshire

Dartmouth College, BMD

New Mexico

New Mexico State University, MD

New York

Barnard College, B
Colgate University, B
Columbia College, B
Columbia University, School of General Studies, B
Cornell University, BD
Sarah Lawrence College, B
State University of New York College at
  Brockport, B
Stony Brook University, State University of New
  York, B
Union College, B
University of Rochester, MD
Vassar College, B

North Carolina

The University of North Carolina at Chapel Hill, MD

Ohio

Bowling Green State University, M
Case Western Reserve University, BMD
Mount Union College, B
The Ohio State University, BMD
Ohio University, MD
Ohio Wesleyan University, B
The University of Toledo, B

Youngstown State University, B

Oklahoma

Tulsa Community College, A
University of Oklahoma, B

Pennsylvania

Bryn Mawr College, B
Eastern University, B
Franklin and Marshall College, B
Haverford College, B
Lehigh University, B
Lycoming College, B
The Pennsylvania State University Abington
  College, B
The Pennsylvania State University Altoona
  College, B
The Pennsylvania State University Beaver Campus
  of the Commonwealth College, B
The Pennsylvania State University Berks Campus of
  the Berks-Lehigh Valley College, B
The Pennsylvania State University Delaware County
  Campus of the Commonwealth College, B
The Pennsylvania State University DuBois Campus
  of the Commonwealth College, B
The Pennsylvania State University at Erie, The
  Behrend College, B
The Pennsylvania State University Fayette Campus
  of the Commonwealth College, B
The Pennsylvania State University Hazleton
  Campus of the Commonwealth College, B
The Pennsylvania State University, Lehigh Valley
  Campus of the Berks-Lehigh Valley College, B
The Pennsylvania State University McKeesport
  Campus of the Commonwealth College, B
The Pennsylvania State University Mont Alto
  Campus of the Commonwealth College, B
The Pennsylvania State University New Kensington
  Campus of the Commonwealth College, B
The Pennsylvania State University Schuylkill
  Campus of the Capital College, B
The Pennsylvania State University Shenango
  Campus of the Commonwealth College, B
The Pennsylvania State University University Park
  Campus, BMD
The Pennsylvania State University Wilkes-Barre
  Campus of the Commonwealth College, B
The Pennsylvania State University Worthington
  Scranton Campus of the Commonwealth
  College, B
The Pennsylvania State University York Campus of
  the Commonwealth College, B
Swarthmore College, B
Villanova University, B
West Chester University of Pennsylvania, M

South Carolina

Clemson University, MD
University of South Carolina, MD

Tennessee

Vanderbilt University, BM

Texas

Austin Community College, A
Rice University, BMD
Texas Christian University, MD
The University of Texas at Austin, BMD

Utah

Brigham Young University, BMD

Vermont

Bennington College, B
Marlboro College, B

Virginia

University of Virginia, BMD

Washington

University of Washington, BMD
Whitman College, B

Wisconsin

University of Wisconsin-Madison, BD

Alberta

University of Calgary, MD

British Columbia

The University of British Columbia, BMD
University of Victoria, BMD

Manitoba

University of Manitoba, B

New Brunswick

Université de Moncton, M

Nova Scotia

Saint Mary's University, BM

Ontario

Laurentian University, B
Royal Military College of Canada, B
University of Toronto, BMD
The University of Western Ontario, BMD
York University, BMD

Saskatchewan

University of Saskatchewan, B

ASTRONOMY AND ASTROPHYSICS

New York

Stony Brook University, State University of New
  York, B

Texas

Texas Christian University, B

Wyoming

University of Wyoming, B

ASTROPHYSICS

Alaska

University of Alaska Fairbanks, MD

California

San Francisco State University, BM
University of California, Berkeley, BD
University of California, Los Angeles, BMD
University of California, Santa Cruz, BD

Colorado

University of Colorado at Boulder, MD

Connecticut

Connecticut College, B
Yale University, B

Delaware

University of Delaware, B

Florida

Florida Institute of Technology, B

Georgia

Agnes Scott College, B

Illinois

Northwestern University, D
University of Chicago, MD

Indiana

Indiana University Bloomington, BD

Iowa

Iowa State University of Science and
  Technology, MD

Louisiana

Louisiana State University and Agricultural and
Mechanical College, D

Massachusetts

Boston University, B
Harvard University, BMD
Wellesley College, B
Williams College, B

Michigan

Michigan State University, BM

Minnesota

Augsburg College, B
University of Minnesota, Twin Cities Campus, BMD

Missouri

University of Missouri-St. Louis, M

New Jersey

Princeton University, BD
Rutgers, The State University of New Jersey, New
Brunswick/Piscataway, B

New Mexico

New Mexico Institute of Mining and Technology, MD
University of New Mexico, B

New York

Barnard College, B
Colgate University, B
Columbia College, B
Cornell University, D
Rensselaer Polytechnic Institute, MD

North Carolina

The University of North Carolina at Chapel Hill, MD

Ohio

Ohio University, B
Ohio Wesleyan University, B

Oklahoma

University of Oklahoma, BMD

Pennsylvania

Carnegie Mellon University, B
Franklin and Marshall College, B
Lehigh University, B
The Pennsylvania State University University Park
Campus, MD
Swarthmore College, B
University of Pennsylvania, MD
Villanova University, B

South Carolina

Clemson University, MD

Texas

Rice University, B

Vermont

Marlboro College, B

Alberta

University of Alberta, MD
University of Calgary, B

British Columbia

University of Victoria, MD

Nova Scotia

Saint Mary's University, B

Ontario

McMaster University, BD
The University of Western Ontario, B

ATHLETIC TRAINING AND SPORTS MEDICINE

Alabama

Faulkner University, B
Huntingdon College, B

Samford University, B
Troy University, B
The University of Alabama, B
University of Mobile, B
The University of West Alabama, BM

Arizona

Grand Canyon University, B

Arkansas

Arkansas State University, B
Harding University, B
Henderson State University, B
John Brown University, B
Ouachita Baptist University, B
University of Central Arkansas, B

California

Azusa Pacific University, B
California Lutheran University, B
California State University, East Bay, B
California State University, Long Beach, B
Chapman University, B
College of the Sequoias, A
Foothill College, A
Fresno Pacific University, B
Hope International University, B
Humboldt State University, M
Orange Coast College, A
Pepperdine University, B
Point Loma Nazarene University, B
San Diego Christian College, B
Santa Barbara City College, A
Santa Monica College, A
Santa Rosa Junior College, A
Vanguard University of Southern California, B

Colorado

Colorado State University, B
Colorado State University-Pueblo, B
Fort Lewis College, B
Western State College of Colorado, B

Connecticut

Central Connecticut State University, B
Mitchell College, A
Quinnipiac University, B
Sacred Heart University, B

Delaware

University of Delaware, B

Florida

Barry University, M
Florida Gulf Coast University, B
Florida Southern College, B
Florida State University, B
Nova Southeastern University, B
University of Florida, MD
University of Miami, B
University of North Florida, M
University of South Florida, B

Georgia

Andrew College, A
Columbus State University, B
Georgia Southern University, B
University of Georgia, B
Valdosta State University, B

Idaho

Boise State University, B
Brigham Young University -Idaho, A
North Idaho College, A
Northwest Nazarene University, B
University of Idaho, B

Illinois

Eureka College, B
Illinois State University, B
McKendree College, B
Millikin University, B
North Central College, B
North Park University, B

Olivet Nazarene University, B
Sauk Valley Community College, A
Trinity International University, B
University of Illinois at Urbana-Champaign, B

Indiana

Anderson University, B
Ball State University, B
DePauw University, B
Franklin College, B
Indiana State University, BM
Indiana University Bloomington, BM
Indiana Wesleyan University, B
Manchester College, B
Taylor University, B
University of Evansville, B
University of Indianapolis, B
Vincennes University, A

Iowa

Ashford University, B
Buena Vista University, B
Clarke College, B
Coe College, B
Graceland University, B
Iowa Lakes Community College, A
Loras College, B
Luther College, B
Northwestern College, B
Simpson College, B
The University of Iowa, B
University of Northern Iowa, B
Upper Iowa University, B

Kansas

Allen County Community College, A
Barton County Community College, A
Benedictine College, A
Bethany College, B
Bethel College, B
Central Christian College of Kansas, A
Coffeyville Community College, A
Dodge City Community College, A
Emporia State University, B
Fort Scott Community College, A
Garden City Community College, A
Highland Community College, A
Independence Community College, A
Kansas State University, B
MidAmerica Nazarene University, B
Neosho County Community College, A
Pratt Community College, A
Seward County Community College, A
Southwestern College, B
Sterling College, B
Tabor College, B
Washburn University, B

Kentucky

Campbellsville University, B
Georgetown College, B

Louisiana

Louisiana College, B
Southeastern Louisiana University, B
University of Louisiana at Lafayette, B

Maine

University of Maine at Presque Isle, B
University of New England, B
University of Southern Maine, B

Maryland

Salisbury University, B
Towson University, B

Massachusetts

Boston University, B
Bridgewater State College, B
Dean College, A
Endicott College, B
Massachusetts College of Liberal Arts, B
Northeastern University, B

Springfield College, B

Michigan

Aquinas College, B
Central Michigan University, B
Eastern Michigan University, B
Grand Valley State University, B
Hope College, B
Lake Superior State University, B
Northern Michigan University, B
Saginaw Valley State University, B
University of Michigan, B
Western Michigan University, BM

Minnesota

Augsburg College, B
Bethel University, B
Gustavus Adolphus College, B
Hamline University, B
Minnesota State University Mankato, B
Northland Community and Technical College-Thief
    River Falls, A
Winona State University, B

Mississippi

Belhaven College, B
Meridian Community College, A

Missouri

Central Methodist University, B
Culver-Stockton College, B
Lindenwood University, B
Missouri State University, B
Missouri Valley College, B
Park University, B
Southwest Baptist University, B
William Woods University, B

Montana

Montana State University-Billings, M
Rocky Mountain College, B

Nebraska

Creighton University, B
Midland Lutheran College, B
Nebraska Wesleyan University, B
University of Nebraska-Lincoln, B
Wayne State College, B

Nevada

University of Nevada, Las Vegas, B

New Hampshire

Colby-Sawyer College, B
Keene State College, B
New Hampshire Community Technical College,
    Manchester/Stratham, A
Plymouth State University, BM
University of New Hampshire, B

New Jersey

Montclair State University, B
Seton Hall University, M

New Mexico

New Mexico Junior College, A
New Mexico State University, B

New York

Alfred University, B
Canisius College, B
Dominican College, B
Hofstra University, B
Ithaca College, B
Long Island University, Brooklyn Campus, BM
Marist College, B
Russell Sage College, B
State University of New York College at
    Brockport, B
State University of New York College at Cortland, B

Stony Brook University, State University of New
    York, B

North Carolina

Appalachian State University, B
Barton College, B
Campbell University, B
Catawba College, B
Chowan University, B
East Carolina University, B
Elon University, B
Gardner-Webb University, B
Greensboro College, B
Guilford College, B
High Point University, B
Lees-McRae College, B
Lenoir-Rhyne College, B
Louisburg College, A
Mars Hill College, B
Methodist College, B
Mount Olive College, B
North Carolina Central University, B
Pfeiffer University, B
Shaw University, B
The University of North Carolina at Chapel Hill, M
The University of North Carolina at Charlotte, B
The University of North Carolina at Pembroke, B
The University of North Carolina Wilmington, B
Wingate University, B

North Dakota

North Dakota State University, B
University of Mary, B
University of North Dakota, B

Ohio

Ashland University, B
Baldwin-Wallace College, B
Bowling Green State University, B
Capital University, B
Cedarville University, B
College of Mount St. Joseph, B
Defiance College, B
Heidelberg College, B
Kent State University, B
Lorain County Community College, A
Marietta College, B
Miami University, B
Miami University Hamilton, B
Mount Union College, B
Ohio Northern University, B
The Ohio State University, B
Ohio University, M
Otterbein College, B
Shawnee State University, B
The University of Akron, B
The University of Findlay, BM
Urbana University, B
Walsh University, B
Wilmington College, B
Xavier University, B
Youngstown State University, B

Oklahoma

Oklahoma Baptist University, B
Oklahoma State University, B
Oklahoma Wesleyan University, B
Southern Nazarene University, B
University of Tulsa, B

Oregon

George Fox University, B
Linfield College, B
Oregon State University, B
Pacific University, B
Southwestern Oregon Community College, A

Pennsylvania

California University of Pennsylvania, M
Community College of Allegheny County, A
Duquesne University, B
East Stroudsburg University of Pennsylvania, B
Gannon University, B
King's College, B
Lock Haven University of Pennsylvania, B

Marywood University, B
Mercyhurst College, B
Messiah College, B
Neumann College, B
Slippery Rock University of Pennsylvania, B
University of Pittsburgh at Bradford, B
Waynesburg College, B
West Chester University of Pennsylvania, BM

Puerto Rico

University of Puerto Rico at Ponce, B

South Carolina

Charleston Southern University, B
College of Charleston, B
Erskine College, B
Lander University, B
Limestone College, B
Newberry College, B

South Dakota

Augustana College, B
Dakota Wesleyan University, B
National American University (Rapid City), B
South Dakota State University, B

Tennessee

Bryan College, B
Carson-Newman College, B
Cumberland University, B
Free Will Baptist Bible College, B
Lambuth University, B
Lincoln Memorial University, B
Lipscomb University, B
Middle Tennessee State University, B
Tennessee Wesleyan College, B
Tusculum College, B
Union University, B
The University of Tennessee at Martin, B

Texas

Angelo State University, B
Baylor University, B
East Texas Baptist University, B
Frank Phillips College, A
Hardin-Simmons University, B
Howard Payne University, B
McMurry University, B
Midwestern State University, B
Odessa College, A
Stephen F. Austin State University, M
Texas Lutheran University, B
Texas State University-San Marcos, B
Texas Wesleyan University, B
University of the Incarnate Word, B
University of Mary Hardin-Baylor, B
The University of Texas at Arlington, B
The University of Texas at Austin, B

Utah

Brigham Young University, BM
Weber State University, B

Vermont

Castleton State College, B
Johnson State College, B
Lyndon State College, B
Norwich University, B
University of Vermont, B

Virginia

Averett University, B
Bluefield College, B
Bridgewater College, B
Jefferson College of Health Sciences, B
Liberty University, B
Longwood University, B
Lynchburg College, B
Old Dominion University, M
Radford University, B
Roanoke College, B

Shenandoah University, M

Washington

Eastern Washington University, B
Washington State University, B
Wenatchee Valley College, A
Whitworth College, B

West Virginia

Alderson-Broaddus College, B
Salem International University, B
University of Charleston, B
West Virginia University, M
West Virginia Wesleyan College, B

Wisconsin

Carroll College, B
Carthage College, B
Concordia University Wisconsin, B
Marquette University, B
University of Wisconsin-Eau Claire, B
University of Wisconsin-La Crosse, BM
University of Wisconsin-Stevens Point, B

Alberta

University of Alberta, B

Newfoundland and Labrador

Memorial University of Newfoundland, B

Ontario

Lakehead University, B
University of Windsor, B

Quebec

Concordia University, B
Université de Sherbrooke, B

ATMOSPHERIC SCIENCES AND METEOROLOGY

Alabama

Community College of the Air Force, A
The University of Alabama in Huntsville, MD
University of South Alabama, B

Alaska

University of Alaska Fairbanks, MD

Arizona

Embry-Riddle Aeronautical University, B
The University of Arizona, BMD

California

City College of San Francisco, A
San Francisco State University, B
San Jose State University, B
Santa Rosa Junior College, A
University of California, Berkeley, B
University of California, Davis, BMD
University of California, Los Angeles, BMD

Colorado

Colorado State University, MD
Metropolitan State College of Denver, B
United States Air Force Academy, B
University of Colorado at Boulder, MD

Connecticut

Western Connecticut State University, B

Delaware

University of Delaware, D

District of Columbia

Howard University, MD

Florida

Daytona Beach Community College, A
Embry-Riddle Aeronautical University, B
Florida State University, B
Okaloosa-Walton College, A

University of Miami, BMD

Georgia

Georgia Institute of Technology, MD

Illinois

Northern Illinois University, B
University of Chicago, MD
University of Illinois at Urbana-Champaign, MD

Indiana

Purdue University, MD
Valparaiso University, B

Iowa

Iowa State University of Science and Technology, B

Kansas

University of Kansas, B

Louisiana

University of Louisiana at Monroe, B

Maryland

University of Maryland, Baltimore County, MD

Massachusetts

Harvard University, B
Massachusetts Institute of Technology, MD

Michigan

University of Michigan, BMD

Minnesota

St. Cloud State University, B

Mississippi

Jackson State University, B

Missouri

Saint Louis University, B
University of Missouri-Columbia, BMD

Nebraska

Creighton University, BM
University of Nebraska-Lincoln, B

Nevada

University of Nevada, Reno, MD

New Hampshire

Plymouth State University, B

New Jersey

Princeton University, D
Rutgers, The State University of New Jersey, New
    Brunswick/Piscataway, BMD

New Mexico

New Mexico Institute of Mining and Technology, MD

New York

City College of the City University of New York, MD
Cornell University, BMD
State University of New York College at
    Brockport, B
State University of New York College at Oneonta, B
State University of New York Maritime College, B
State University of New York at Oswego, B
Stony Brook University, State University of New
    York, BMD
University at Albany, State University of New
    York, BMD

North Carolina

North Carolina State University, MD
The University of North Carolina at Asheville, B

The University of North Carolina at Chapel Hill, MD

North Dakota

University of North Dakota, BM

Ohio

The Ohio State University, MD
Ohio University, B

Oklahoma

University of Oklahoma, B

Oregon

Oregon State University, MD

Pennsylvania

Millersville University of Pennsylvania, B
The Pennsylvania State University Abington
    College, B
The Pennsylvania State University Altoona
    College, B
The Pennsylvania State University Beaver Campus
    of the Commonwealth College, B
The Pennsylvania State University Berks Campus of
    the Berks-Lehigh Valley College, B
The Pennsylvania State University Delaware County
    Campus of the Commonwealth College, B
The Pennsylvania State University DuBois Campus
    of the Commonwealth College, B
The Pennsylvania State University at Erie, The
    Behrend College, B
The Pennsylvania State University Fayette Campus
    of the Commonwealth College, B
The Pennsylvania State University Hazleton
    Campus of the Commonwealth College, B
The Pennsylvania State University, Lehigh Valley
    Campus of the Berks-Lehigh Valley College, B
The Pennsylvania State University McKeesport
    Campus of the Commonwealth College, B
The Pennsylvania State University Mont Alto
    Campus of the Commonwealth College, B
The Pennsylvania State University New Kensington
    Campus of the Commonwealth College, B
The Pennsylvania State University Schuylkill
    Campus of the Capital College, B
The Pennsylvania State University Shenango
    Campus of the Commonwealth College, B
The Pennsylvania State University University Park
    Campus, B
The Pennsylvania State University Wilkes-Barre
    Campus of the Commonwealth College, B
The Pennsylvania State University Worthington
    Scranton Campus of the Commonwealth
    College, B
The Pennsylvania State University York Campus of
    the Commonwealth College, B

South Carolina

Clemson University, MD

South Dakota

South Dakota School of Mines and Technology, MD
South Dakota State University, D

Texas

Texas A&M University, B
Texas Tech University, M

Utah

University of Utah, B

Vermont

Lyndon State College, B

Virginia

George Mason University, D

Washington

Everett Community College, A
University of Washington, BMD

Wisconsin

Northland College, B
University of Wisconsin-Madison, MD

University of Wisconsin-Milwaukee, B

Wyoming

University of Wyoming, MD

Alberta

University of Alberta, B

British Columbia

The University of British Columbia, BMD
University of Victoria, B

Nova Scotia

Dalhousie University, B

Ontario

University of Guelph, BMD
University of Waterloo, B
York University, B

Quebec

McGill University, BMD
Université du Québec àMontréal, MDO

ATOMIC/MOLECULAR PHYSICS

California

San Diego State University, B
University of California, San Diego, B

District of Columbia

The Catholic University of America, B

New York

Columbia College, B

Ohio

Ohio University, B
The University of Akron, B

Tennessee

Maryville College, B

Ontario

University of Waterloo, B

AUDIO ENGINEERING

California

Cogswell Polytechnical College, B
Mt. San Jacinto College, A

Connecticut

University of Hartford, B

District of Columbia

American University, B

Maine

New England School of Communications, AB

Maryland

Harford Community College, A
Peabody Conservatory of Music of The Johns
 Hopkins University, B

Massachusetts

Berklee College of Music, B

Michigan

Michigan Technological University, B

Minnesota

Ridgewater College, A

Nebraska

Northeast Community College, A

New Jersey

Brookdale Community College, A

New York

Five Towns College, AB
State University of New York, Fredonia, B

Ohio

Brown Mackie College-Cincinnati, A
Cleveland Institute of Music, B
International College of Broadcasting, A

Texas

South Plains College, A
Texas State Technical College Waco, A

Washington

The Art Institute of Seattle, A
Shoreline Community College, A

AUDIOLOGY/AUDIOLOGIST AND HEARING SCIENCES

Arkansas

Arkansas State University-Mountain Home, A

California

California State University, Long Beach, B

Colorado

University of Northern Colorado, B

Illinois

Northwestern University, B

Indiana

Indiana University Bloomington, B
Indiana University-Purdue University Fort Wayne, B

Iowa

The University of Iowa, B

Massachusetts

Bristol Community College, A

Ohio

Cleveland State University, B
Ohio University, A
The University of Akron, B

Oklahoma

University of Oklahoma Health Sciences Center, B

Tennessee

The University of Tennessee, B

Texas

Stephen F. Austin State University, B
Texas Tech University, B

AUDIOLOGY/AUDIOLOGIST AND SPEECH-LANGUAGE PATHOLOGY/PATHOLOGIST

Alabama

Auburn University, B
The University of Alabama, B
University of Montevallo, B
University of South Alabama, B

Arkansas

Arkansas State University, B
University of Arkansas at Little Rock, B
University of Central Arkansas, B

California

California State University, East Bay, B
California State University, Fresno, B
California State University, Fullerton, B
California State University, Long Beach, B
California State University, Sacramento, B
Loma Linda University, B
San Francisco State University, B
University of the Pacific, B
University of Redlands, B

District of Columbia

The George Washington University, B
University of the District of Columbia, B

Florida

Miami Dade College, A
University of Central Florida, B
University of Florida, B
University of South Florida, B

Idaho

Idaho State University, B

Illinois

Elmhurst College, B
Governors State University, B
Illinois State University, B
Northwestern University, B
Southern Illinois University Edwardsville, B
University of Illinois at Urbana-Champaign, B

Indiana

Ball State University, B
Butler University, B
Indiana State University, B
Indiana University Bloomington, B
Purdue University, B

Iowa

The University of Iowa, B

Kansas

Fort Hays State University, B
Wichita State University, B

Kentucky

Brescia University, B
Eastern Kentucky University, B
Murray State University, B
University of Kentucky, B

Louisiana

Louisiana State University and Agricultural and
 Mechanical College, B
Louisiana State University in Shreveport, B
Louisiana Tech University, B
Southern University and Agricultural and Mechanical
 College, B
Southern University at New Orleans, B
University of Louisiana at Lafayette, B
University of Louisiana at Monroe, B

Massachusetts

Elms College, B
Emerson College, B
Northeastern University, B

Michigan

Andrews University, B
Calvin College, B
Central Michigan University, B
Michigan State University, B
Northern Michigan University, B
Western Michigan University, B

Minnesota

Minnesota State University Mankato, B
Minnesota State University Moorhead, B
St. Cloud State University, B
University of Minnesota, Duluth, B
University of Minnesota, Twin Cities Campus, B

Mississippi

Delta State University, B
Jackson State University, B
Mississippi University for Women, B
University of Mississippi, B

University of Southern Mississippi, B

Missouri

Fontbonne University, B
Missouri State University, B

Montana

The University of Montana-Missoula, B

New Hampshire

University of New Hampshire, B

New Jersey

The Richard Stockton College of New Jersey, B

New Mexico

Eastern New Mexico University, B
University of New Mexico, B

New York

Adelphi University, B
Brooklyn College of the City University of New
  York, B
Buffalo State College, State University of New
  York, B
The College of Saint Rose, B
Elmira College, B
Hofstra University, B
Hunter College of the City University of New York, B
Iona College, B
Ithaca College, B
Lehman College of the City University of New
  York, B
Marymount Manhattan College, B
Molloy College, B
Nazareth College of Rochester, B
St. John's University, B
State University of New York at Buffalo, B
State University of New York College at Cortland, B
State University of New York, Fredonia, B
State University of New York at New Paltz, B
State University of New York at Plattsburgh, B
Syracuse University, B
Touro College, B
Yeshiva University, B

North Carolina

Appalachian State University, B
East Carolina University, B
Shaw University, B
The University of North Carolina at Greensboro, B

North Dakota

University of North Dakota, B

Ohio

Kent State University, B
Miami University, B
Miami University Hamilton, B
The Ohio State University, B
Ohio University, B
Otterbein College, B
The University of Akron, B
University of Cincinnati, B
The University of Toledo, B

Oklahoma

Northeastern State University, B
University of Central Oklahoma, B
University of Oklahoma Health Sciences Center, B
University of Tulsa, B

Oregon

University of Oregon, B

Pennsylvania

Bloomsburg University of Pennsylvania, B
Clarion University of Pennsylvania, B
East Stroudsburg University of Pennsylvania, B
Geneva College, B
La Salle University, B
Marywood University, B
Temple University, B
Thiel College, B

University of Pittsburgh, B
West Chester University of Pennsylvania, B

Puerto Rico

University of Puerto Rico, Medical Sciences
  Campus, B

South Carolina

South Carolina State University, B

South Dakota

Augustana College, B
Northern State University, B

Tennessee

Lambuth University, B
Tennessee State University, B

Texas

Hardin-Simmons University, B
Lamar University, B
Our Lady of the Lake University of San Antonio, B
Southern Methodist University, B
Stephen F. Austin State University, B
Texas State University-San Marcos, B
Texas Woman's University, B
University of Houston, B
University of North Texas, B
The University of Texas at Dallas, B
The University of Texas at El Paso, B
The University of Texas-Pan American, B

Utah

Brigham Young University, B
University of Utah, B
Utah State University, B

Virginia

Hampton University, B
Old Dominion University, B
University of Virginia, B

Washington

Eastern Washington University, B
University of Washington, B
Western Washington University, B

West Virginia

West Virginia University, B

Wisconsin

Marquette University, B
University of Wisconsin-Milwaukee, B
University of Wisconsin-Oshkosh, B
University of Wisconsin-Stevens Point, B

Wyoming

University of Wyoming, B

Quebec

Université de Montréal, B

AUDIOVISUAL COMMUNICATIONS TECHNOLOGIES/TECHNICIANS

Illinois

Greenville College, B

Nevada

Nevada State College at Henderson, B

Washington

Edmonds Community College, A
Olympic College, A

AUDITING

Massachusetts

Babson College, B

Pennsylvania

Carlow University, B

AUTOBODY/COLLISION AND REPAIR TECHNOLOGY/TECHNICIAN

California

Antelope Valley College, A
Cypress College, A
Fresno City College, A
Modesto Junior College, A
Riverside Community College District, A

Colorado

Pikes Peak Community College, A
Pueblo Community College, A

Florida

Florida Community College at Jacksonville, A

Georgia

Georgia Southwestern State University, A

Hawaii

Kauai Community College, A

Idaho

College of Southern Idaho, A
Idaho State University, A
Lewis-Clark State College, AB

Illinois

Black Hawk College, A
Illinois Eastern Community Colleges, Olney Central
  College, A
Kaskaskia College, A
Kishwaukee College, A
Parkland College, A
Prairie State College, A
Southwestern Illinois College, A
Waubonsee Community College, A

Iowa

Hawkeye Community College, A
Iowa Lakes Community College, A
Northwest Iowa Community College, A
Scott Community College, A
Southwestern Community College, A
Western Iowa Tech Community College, A

Kansas

Hutchinson Community College and Area Vocational
  School, A
Manhattan Area Technical College, A

Kentucky

Somerset Community College, A

Michigan

Mott Community College, A

Minnesota

Century College, A
Dakota County Technical College, A
Dunwoody College of Technology, A
Northwest Technical College, A
Riverland Community College, A
St. Cloud Technical College, A
South Central Technical College, A

Mississippi

Coahoma Community College, A

Missouri

Linn State Technical College, A
Ozarks Technical Community College, A

Ranken Technical College, A

Montana

Montana State University-Billings, A
Montana State University-Great Falls College of
  Technology, A
Montana Tech of The University of Montana, A

Nebraska

Central Community College-Hastings Campus, A
Mid-Plains Community College, A
Northeast Community College, A

New Hampshire

New Hampshire Community Technical College,
  Nashua/Claremont, A

New Mexico

San Juan College, A

New York

Erie Community College, South Campus, A
State University of New York College of Technology
  at Alfred, A

North Carolina

Stanly Community College, A

North Dakota

Bismarck State College, A
North Dakota State College of Science, A

Oregon

Clackamas Community College, A

Pennsylvania

Pennco Tech, A
Pennsylvania College of Technology, A

South Dakota

Southeast Technical Institute, A

Tennessee

Nashville Auto Diesel College, A

Texas

Eastfield College, A
Grayson County College, A
Hill College of the Hill Junior College District, A
St. Philip's College, A
Texas State Technical College Harlingen, A
Texas State Technical College Waco, A

Utah

Dixie State College of Utah, A
Salt Lake Community College, A
Utah Valley State College, A
Weber State University, A

Washington

Bates Technical College, A
Green River Community College, A
Lake Washington Technical College, A
Walla Walla Community College, A

Wisconsin

Northeast Wisconsin Technical College, A
Southwest Wisconsin Technical College, A
Waukesha County Technical College, A

Wyoming

Laramie County Community College, A

British Columbia

British Columbia Institute of Technology, A

AUTOMOBILE/AUTOMOTIVE MECHANICS TECHNOLOGY/TECHNICIAN

Alabama

Community College of the Air Force, A
Enterprise-Ozark Community College, A

George C. Wallace Community College, A
H. Councill Trenholm State Technical College, A
Wallace State Community College, A

Alaska

University of Alaska Anchorage, A

Arizona

Arizona Automotive Institute, A
Arizona Western College, A
Central Arizona College, A
Eastern Arizona College, A
GateWay Community College, A
Glendale Community College, A
Mesa Community College, A
Mohave Community College, A
Pima Community College, A
Yavapai College, A

Arkansas

Arkansas State University, A
Cossatot Community College of the University of
  Arkansas, A
North Arkansas College, A
Ouachita Technical College, A
Ozarka College, A
Phillips Community College of the University of
  Arkansas, A
Southeast Arkansas College, A
University of Arkansas Community College at
  Morrilton, A
University of Arkansas at Pine Bluff, B

California

Allan Hancock College, A
American River College, A
Antelope Valley College, A
Bakersfield College, A
Barstow College, A
Butte College, A
Cerritos College, A
Cerro Coso Community College, A
Chabot College, A
Chaffey College, A
Citrus College, A
City College of San Francisco, A
College of Alameda, A
College of the Desert, A
College of Marin, A
College of the Redwoods, A
College of the Sequoias, A
Columbia College, A
Compton Community College, A
Contra Costa College, A
Cosumnes River College (Sacramento), A
Cuesta College, A
Cuyamaca College, A
Cypress College, A
De Anza College, A
Don Bosco Technical Institute, A
East Los Angeles College, A
El Camino College, A
Evergreen Valley College, A
Fresno City College, A
Fullerton College, A
Golden West College, A
Hartnell College, A
Imperial Valley College, A
Las Positas College, A
Lassen Community College District, A
Long Beach City College, A
Los Angeles Harbor College, A
Los Angeles Pierce College, A
Los Angeles Trade-Technical College, A
Los Medanos College, A
Mendocino College, A
Merced College, A
MiraCosta College, A
Modesto Junior College, A
Monterey Peninsula College, A
Mt. San Jacinto College, A
Oxnard College, A
Palo Verde College, A
Palomar College, A
Pasadena City College, A
Porterville College, A

Reedley College, A
Riverside Community College District, A
Saddleback College, A
San Bernardino Valley College, A
San Diego City College, A
San Diego Miramar College, A
San Joaquin Delta College, A
Santa Ana College, A
Santa Barbara City College, A
Santa Monica College, A
Shasta College, A
Sierra College, A
Skyline College, A
Solano Community College, A
Southwestern College, A
Taft College, A
Ventura College, A
Victor Valley College, A
West Hills Community College, A
WyoTech (Fremont), A
Yuba College, A

Colorado

Aims Community College, A
Arapahoe Community College, A
Colorado State University-Pueblo, B
Denver Automotive and Diesel College, A
Mesa State College, A
Morgan Community College, A
Northeastern Junior College, A
Otero Junior College, A
Pikes Peak Community College, A
Pueblo Community College, A
Trinidad State Junior College, A
Westwood College-Denver North, A

Connecticut

Gateway Community College, A
Naugatuck Valley Community College, A

Delaware

Delaware Technical & Community College, Jack F.
  Owens Campus, A

Florida

Broward Community College, A
Central Florida Community College, A
Daytona Beach Community College, A
Florida Community College at Jacksonville, A
Indian River Community College, A
New England Institute of Technology at Palm
  Beach, A
Okaloosa-Walton College, A
Pensacola Junior College, A
Santa Fe Community College, A
Seminole Community College, A

Georgia

Bainbridge College, A
Chattahoochee Technical College, A
Columbus Technical College, A
DeKalb Technical College, A
Georgia Highlands College, A
Georgia Southwestern State University, A
Griffin Technical College, A
Gwinnett Technical College, A
Northwestern Technical College, A
Ogeechee Technical College, A
Savannah Technical College, A
Waycross College, A
West Georgia Technical College, A

Guam

Guam Community College, A

Hawaii

Hawaii Community College, A
Honolulu Community College, A
Kauai Community College, A
Leeward Community College, A
Maui Community College, A

Idaho

Boise State University, A
Brigham Young University -Idaho, A

College of Southern Idaho, A
Eastern Idaho Technical College, A
Idaho State University, A
Lewis-Clark State College, AB
North Idaho College, A

Illinois

Carl Sandburg College, A
City Colleges of Chicago, Kennedy-King College, A
College of DuPage, A
College of Lake County, A
Danville Area Community College, A
Elgin Community College, A
Highland Community College, A
Illinois Central College, A
Illinois Eastern Community Colleges, Olney Central
   College, A
Illinois Valley Community College, A
John A. Logan College, A
Joliet Junior College, A
Kankakee Community College, A
Kaskaskia College, A
Kishwaukee College, A
Lake Land College, A
Lewis and Clark Community College, A
Lincoln Land Community College, A
McHenry County College, A
Moraine Valley Community College, A
Morton College, A
Oakton Community College, A
Parkland College, A
Prairie State College, A
Rend Lake College, A
Richland Community College, A
Rock Valley College, A
Shawnee Community College, A
Southeastern Illinois College, A
Spoon River College, A
Triton College, A
Waubonsee Community College, A

Indiana

Ivy Tech Community College-Central Indiana, A
Ivy Tech Community College-Columbus, A
Ivy Tech Community College-East Central, A
Ivy Tech Community College-Kokomo, A
Ivy Tech Community College-Lafayette, A
Ivy Tech Community College-North Central, A
Ivy Tech Community College-Northeast, A
Ivy Tech Community College-Northwest, A
Ivy Tech Community College-Southern Indiana, A
Ivy Tech Community College-Southwest, A
Ivy Tech Community College-Wabash Valley, A
Ivy Tech Community College-Whitewater, A
Lincoln Technical Institute, A
Oakland City University, A
Vincennes University, A

Iowa

Des Moines Area Community College, A
Hawkeye Community College, A
Indian Hills Community College, A
Iowa Central Community College, A
Iowa Lakes Community College, A
Iowa Western Community College, A
Kirkwood Community College, A
North Iowa Area Community College, A
Northwest Iowa Community College, A
Scott Community College, A
Southeastern Community College, North Campus, A
Southwestern Community College, A
Western Iowa Tech Community College, A

Kansas

Barton County Community College, A
Butler Community College, A
Coffeyville Community College, A
Cowley County Community College and Area
   Vocational-Technical School, A
Dodge City Community College, A
Garden City Community College, A
Highland Community College, A
Hutchinson Community College and Area Vocational
   School, A
Johnson County Community College, A
Manhattan Area Technical College, A

McPherson College, A
Pittsburg State University, AB
Pratt Community College, A
Wichita Area Technical College, A

Kentucky

Somerset Community College, A

Louisiana

Delgado Community College, A
Louisiana Technical College, A

Maine

Central Maine Community College, A
Eastern Maine Community College, A
Northern Maine Community College, A
Southern Maine Community College, A
Washington County Community College, A

Maryland

Allegany College of Maryland, A
Montgomery College, A

Massachusetts

Benjamin Franklin Institute of Technology, AB
Middlesex Community College, A
Mount Wachusett Community College, A
Quinsigamond Community College, A

Michigan

Alpena Community College, A
Baker College of Flint, A
Bay de Noc Community College, A
Delta College, A
Ferris State University, AB
Glen Oaks Community College, A
Gogebic Community College, A
Grand Rapids Community College, A
Henry Ford Community College, A
Jackson Community College, A
Kalamazoo Valley Community College, A
Kirtland Community College, A
Lansing Community College, A
Macomb Community College, A
Mid Michigan Community College, A
Mott Community College, A
Muskegon Community College, A
Northern Michigan University, A
Northwestern Michigan College, A
Oakland Community College, A
Southwestern Michigan College, A
Washtenaw Community College, A
Wayne County Community College District, A

Minnesota

Anoka Technical College, A
Century College, A
Dakota County Technical College, A
Dunwoody College of Technology, A
Hennepin Technical College, A
Lake Superior College, A
Minneapolis Community and Technical College, A
Minnesota State College-Southeast Technical, A
Normandale Community College, A
Northland Community and Technical College-Thief
   River Falls, A
Northwest Technical College, A
Pine Technical College, A
St. Cloud Technical College, A
South Central Technical College, A

Mississippi

East Mississippi Community College, A
Mississippi Gulf Coast Community College, A
Southwest Mississippi Community College, A

Missouri

East Central College, A
Jefferson College, A
Linn State Technical College, A
Longview Community College, A
North Central Missouri College, A
Ozarks Technical Community College, A
Ranken Technical College, A
St. Louis Community College at Forest Park, A

State Fair Community College, A

Montana

Dawson Community College, A
Fort Peck Community College, A
Miles Community College, A
Montana State University-Billings, A
Montana State University-Northern, AB
Montana Tech of The University of Montana, A
The University of Montana-Helena College of
   Technology, A

Nebraska

Central Community College-Columbus Campus, A
Central Community College-Grand Island
   Campus, A
Central Community College-Hastings Campus, A
Metropolitan Community College, A
Mid-Plains Community College, A
Northeast Community College, A
Southeast Community College, Lincoln Campus, A
Southeast Community College, Milford Campus, A

Nevada

Community College of Southern Nevada, A
Truckee Meadows Community College, A
Western Nevada Community College, A

New Hampshire

New Hampshire Community Technical College,
   Berlin/Laconia, A
New Hampshire Community Technical College,
   Manchester/Stratham, A
New Hampshire Community Technical College,
   Nashua/Claremont, A

New Jersey

Bergen Community College, A
Brookdale Community College, A
Burlington County College, A
Camden County College, A
Gloucester County College, A
Middlesex County College, A
Raritan Valley Community College, A

New Mexico

Clovis Community College, A
Doña Ana Branch Community College, A
Eastern New Mexico University-Roswell, A
Mesalands Community College, A
New Mexico Junior College, A
San Juan College, A
University of New Mexico-Gallup, A
Western New Mexico University, A

New York

Columbia-Greene Community College, A
Corning Community College, A
Erie Community College, South Campus, A
Fulton-Montgomery Community College, A
Hudson Valley Community College, A
Monroe Community College, A
Onondaga Community College, A
Rockland Community College, A
State University of New York College of Agriculture
   and Technology at Morrisville, A
State University of New York College of Technology
   at Alfred, A
State University of New York College of Technology
   at Canton, A
Suffolk County Community College, A
Westchester Community College, A

North Carolina

Alamance Community College, A
Asheville-Buncombe Technical Community
   College, A
Beaufort County Community College, A
Cape Fear Community College, A
Catawba Valley Community College, A
Central Carolina Community College, A
Central Piedmont Community College, A
Craven Community College, A
Durham Technical Community College, A
Fayetteville Technical Community College, A

Forsyth Technical Community College, A
Gaston College, A
Guilford Technical Community College, A
Isothermal Community College, A
Martin Community College, A
McDowell Technical Community College, A
Pamlico Community College, A
Randolph Community College, A
Roanoke-Chowan Community College, A
Rowan-Cabarrus Community College, A
Sandhills Community College, A
South Piedmont Community College, A
Southwestern Community College, A
Surry Community College, A
Tri-County Community College, A
Vance-Granville Community College, A
Wayne Community College, A
Wilkes Community College, A

North Dakota

Bismarck State College, A
Lake Region State College, A
North Dakota State College of Science, A
United Tribes Technical College, A
Williston State College, A

Ohio

Columbus State Community College, A
Cuyahoga Community College, A
Kent State University, Trumbull Campus, A
Sinclair Community College, A
Stark State College of Technology, A
Terra State Community College, A
University of Cincinnati Raymond Walters College, A
University of Northwestern Ohio, A
Washington State Community College, A

Oklahoma

Oklahoma City Community College, A
Oklahoma State University, Okmulgee, A
Tulsa Community College, A

Oregon

Blue Mountain Community College, A
Central Oregon Community College, A
Chemeketa Community College, A
Clackamas Community College, A
Lane Community College, A
Linn-Benton Community College, A
Mt. Hood Community College, A
Portland Community College, A
Rogue Community College, A
Umpqua Community College, A

Pennsylvania

Community College of Philadelphia, A
Delaware County Community College, A
Harrisburg Area Community College, A
Johnson College, A
Lincoln Technical Institute (Philadelphia), A
Luzerne County Community College, A
Northampton County Area Community College, A
Pennco Tech, A
Rosedale Technical Institute, A
Thaddeus Stevens College of Technology, A

Puerto Rico

University of Puerto Rico at Carolina, A

Rhode Island

New England Institute of Technology, A

South Carolina

Denmark Technical College, A
Florence-Darlington Technical College, A
Greenville Technical College, A
Midlands Technical College, A
Orangeburg-Calhoun Technical College, A
Piedmont Technical College, A
Spartanburg Technical College, A
Technical College of the Lowcountry, A
Trident Technical College, A

York Technical College, A

South Dakota

Lake Area Technical Institute, A
Southeast Technical Institute, A
Western Dakota Technical Institute, A

Tennessee

Chattanooga State Technical Community College, A
Nashville Auto Diesel College, A
Nashville State Technical Community College, A
Northeast State Technical Community College, A
Pellissippi State Technical Community College, A
Southern Adventist University, A
Southwest Tennessee Community College, A

Texas

Amarillo College, A
Angelina College, A
Austin Community College, A
Brazosport College, A
Brookhaven College, A
Cedar Valley College, A
Central Texas College, A
Cisco Junior College, A
Coastal Bend College, A
Del Mar College, A
Eastfield College, A
El Paso Community College, A
Hill College of the Hill Junior College District, A
Houston Community College System, A
Howard College, A
Kilgore College, A
Lamar State College-Port Arthur, A
Lamar University, A
Midland College, A
North Central Texas College, A
North Harris College, A
Northeast Texas Community College, A
Odessa College, A
Ranger College, A
St. Philip's College, A
South Plains College, A
South Texas College, A
Southwest Texas Junior College, A
Tarrant County College District, A
Temple College, A
Texarkana College, A
Texas Southmost College, A
Texas State Technical College Waco, A
Texas State Technical College West Texas, A
Trinity Valley Community College, A
Universal Technical Institute, A
Vernon College, A
Western Technical College, A
Western Texas College, A
Wharton County Junior College, A

Utah

College of Eastern Utah, A
Dixie State College of Utah, A
Snow College, A
Southern Utah University, A
Utah Valley State College, A
Weber State University, AB

Virginia

New River Community College, A
Northern Virginia Community College, A
Thomas Nelson Community College, A
Tidewater Community College, A
Virginia Western Community College, A

Washington

Bates Technical College, A
Big Bend Community College, A
Clark College, A
Clover Park Technical College, A
Columbia Basin College, A
Grays Harbor College, A
Green River Community College, A
Lake Washington Technical College, A
Lower Columbia College, A
Olympic College, A
Peninsula College, A

Renton Technical College, A
Shoreline Community College, A
Skagit Valley College, A
South Puget Sound Community College, A
South Seattle Community College, A
Spokane Community College, A
Walla Walla College, AB
Walla Walla Community College, A
Wenatchee Valley College, A
Yakima Valley Community College, A

West Virginia

Community and Technical College of Shepherd, A
Community & Technical College at West Virginia
    University Institute of Technology, A
Southern West Virginia Community and Technical
    College, A
West Virginia University at Parkersburg, A

Wisconsin

Chippewa Valley Technical College, A
Fox Valley Technical College, A
Gateway Technical College, A
Madison Area Technical College, A
Milwaukee Area Technical College, A
Moraine Park Technical College, A
Nicolet Area Technical College, A
Northcentral Technical College, A
Northeast Wisconsin Technical College, A
Southwest Wisconsin Technical College, A
Waukesha County Technical College, A
Western Technical College, A

Wyoming

Casper College, A
Central Wyoming College, A
Laramie County Community College, A
Western Wyoming Community College, A
WyoTech, A

British Columbia

British Columbia Institute of Technology, A

AUTOMOTIVE ENGINEERING TECHNOLOGY/TECHNICIAN

Alabama

H. Councill Trenholm State Technical College, A

Arizona

Arizona Automotive Institute, A

California

WyoTech (Fremont), A

Colorado

Front Range Community College, A

Illinois

Rend Lake College, A
Southern Illinois University Carbondale, B

Indiana

Indiana State University, B

Massachusetts

Benjamin Franklin Institute of Technology, AB
Massachusetts Bay Community College, A
Springfield Technical Community College, A

Michigan

Central Michigan University, BMO
Kettering University, M
Lawrence Technological University, M
Macomb Community College, A
University of Detroit Mercy, D
University of Michigan, M
University of Michigan-Dearborn, M

Minnesota

Minnesota State Community and Technical
    College-Fergus Falls, A

Minnesota State University Mankato, BM

New Jersey

Mercer County Community College, A
Sussex County Community College, A

New York

Corning Community College, A
Farmingdale State University of New York, AB

Ohio

Cincinnati State Technical and Community
   College, A
Owens Community College, A
Terra State Community College, A
The University of Akron, A

Pennsylvania

Community College of Allegheny County, A
Harrisburg Area Community College, A
Montgomery County Community College, A
New Castle School of Trades, A
Pennsylvania College of Technology, AB

Utah

Weber State University, B

Vermont

Vermont Technical College, A

West Virginia

Community & Technical College at West Virginia
   University Institute of Technology, A

Wisconsin

Northeast Wisconsin Technical College, A

AVIATION

Connecticut

University of New Haven, M

Florida

Everglades University (Boca Raton), M

Missouri

Central Missouri State University, M
Saint Louis University, M

North Dakota

University of North Dakota, M

Oklahoma

Southeastern Oklahoma State University, M

Tennessee

Middle Tennessee State University, M
The University of Tennessee, M

AVIATION/AIRWAY MANAGEMENT AND OPERATIONS

Alabama

Auburn University, B

Alaska

University of Alaska Anchorage, A
University of Alaska Fairbanks, A

California

California State University, Los Angeles, B
Cypress College, A
Glendale Community College, A
Long Beach City College, A
Palomar College, A

Pasadena City College, A

Colorado

Metropolitan State College of Denver, B

Delaware

Delaware State University, B
Delaware Technical & Community College, Terry
   Campus, A
Wilmington College, B

District of Columbia

University of the District of Columbia, A

Florida

Broward Community College, A
Embry-Riddle Aeronautical University, BM
Embry-Riddle Aeronautical University, Extended
   Campus, BM
Everglades University (Boca Raton), B
Everglades University (Sarasota), B
Florida Community College at Jacksonville, A
Florida Institute of Technology, B
Florida Memorial College, B
Jacksonville University, B
Lynn University, BM
Miami Dade College, A
St. Petersburg College, A

Georgia

Clayton State University, A
Georgia Aviation & Technical College, A

Illinois

Lewis University, B
Quincy University, B
Southern Illinois University Carbondale, B
University of Illinois at Urbana-Champaign, B

Indiana

Indiana State University, B

Iowa

Iowa Central Community College, A
Iowa Lakes Community College, A
University of Dubuque, AB

Kentucky

Northern Kentucky University, A

Louisiana

Louisiana Tech University, B

Massachusetts

Bridgewater State College, B
Salem State College, B

Michigan

Baker College of Muskegon, B
Eastern Michigan University, B
Oakland Community College, A
Western Michigan University, B

Minnesota

Academy College, A
Anoka Technical College, A
Inver Hills Community College, A
Minnesota State University Mankato, B
Northland Community and Technical College-Thief
   River Falls, A
St. Cloud State University, B
University of Minnesota, Crookston, AB
Vermilion Community College, A

Winona State University, B

Mississippi

Delta State University, M

Missouri

Park University, AB
Saint Louis University, B

Montana

Rocky Mountain College, B

Nebraska

University of Nebraska at Kearney, B

New Hampshire

Daniel Webster College, AB

New Jersey

Mercer County Community College, A

New York

Dowling College, MO
Farmingdale State University of New York, B
Schenectady County Community College, A
Vaughn College of Aeronautics and Technology, B

North Carolina

Guilford Technical Community College, A
Lenoir Community College, A

North Dakota

University of North Dakota, B

Ohio

Bowling Green State University, B
Kent State University, B
The Ohio State University, B
Ohio University, B
Sinclair Community College, A
The University of Akron, A

Oklahoma

Southeastern Oklahoma State University, BM
Southern Nazarene University, B
Western Oklahoma State College, A

Pennsylvania

Community College of Allegheny County, A
Geneva College, B
Lehigh Carbon Community College, A
Luzerne County Community College, A
Marywood University, B

Puerto Rico

Inter American University of Puerto Rico, Bayamón
   Campus, B
Inter American University of Puerto Rico, Fajardo
   Campus, B

South Carolina

Bob Jones University, B

Tennessee

Chattanooga State Technical Community College, A

Texas

Mountain View College, A
Palo Alto College, A
Tarleton State University, B
Texas Southern University, B

Utah

Dixie State College of Utah, A
Westminster College, B

Virginia

Averett University, B
Hampton University, B

West Virginia

Fairmont State University, AB
Mountain State University, AB

British Columbia

University College of the Fraser Valley, B

Quebec

Concordia University, O

AVIONICS MAINTENANCE TECHNOLOGY/TECHNICIAN

Alabama

Community College of the Air Force, A
Enterprise-Ozark Community College, A
Wallace State Community College, A

Alaska

University of Alaska Anchorage, A

Arizona

Chandler-Gilbert Community College, A
Cochise College (Douglas), A

Arkansas

Black River Technical College, A

California

Antelope Valley College, A
City College of San Francisco, A
College of Alameda, A
College of San Mateo, A
Foothill College, A
Gavilan College, A
Glendale Community College, A
Long Beach City College, A
Los Angeles Mission College, A
Mt. San Antonio College, A
Orange Coast College, A
Palomar College, A
Pasadena City College, A
Reedley College, A
Sacramento City College, A
San Diego Miramar College, A
Shasta College, A
Solano Community College, A
West Los Angeles College, A

Colorado

Aims Community College, A

Connecticut

Gateway Community College, A
Housatonic Community College, A
Quinebaug Valley Community College, A
Three Rivers Community College, A

Delaware

Delaware Technical & Community College, Terry
    Campus, A
Wilmington College, B

District of Columbia

University of the District of Columbia, A

Florida

Broward Community College, A
Okaloosa-Walton College, A

Georgia

Clayton State University, A
Georgia Southwestern State University, A

Hawaii

Honolulu Community College, A

Illinois

City Colleges of Chicago, Richard J. Daley
    College, A
Kankakee Community College, A
Lewis University, AB
Moody Bible Institute, B
Rock Valley College, A
Southern Illinois University Carbondale, B

Southwestern Illinois College, A

Indiana

Vincennes University, A

Iowa

Hawkeye Community College, A
Indian Hills Community College, A
Iowa Western Community College, A

Kansas

Cloud County Community College, A

Kentucky

Somerset Community College, A

Louisiana

Southern University at Shreveport, A

Massachusetts

Wentworth Institute of Technology, A

Michigan

Andrews University, AB
Baker College of Flint, A
Delta College, A
Lansing Community College, A
Northern Michigan University, A
Wayne County Community College District, A
Western Michigan University, B

Minnesota

Minneapolis Community and Technical College, A
Minnesota State College-Southeast Technical, A
Northland Community and Technical College-Thief
    River Falls, A
University of Minnesota, Crookston, A

Mississippi

Hinds Community College, A

Missouri

College of the Ozarks, B
Maple Woods Community College, A

Nebraska

Grace University, B

New Hampshire

New Hampshire Community Technical College,
    Nashua/Claremont, A

New Jersey

Cumberland County College, A

New York

Excelsior College, A
Mohawk Valley Community College, A
Vaughn College of Aeronautics and Technology, AB

North Carolina

Elizabeth City State University, B
Guilford Technical Community College, A
Lenoir Community College, A
Piedmont Baptist College, AB
Wayne Community College, A

North Dakota

Lake Region State College, A

Ohio

Columbus State Community College, A
Cuyahoga Community College, A
The Ohio State University, B
University of Cincinnati Clermont College, A

Oklahoma

Oklahoma City Community College, A
Oklahoma State University, Okmulgee, A
Rose State College, A
Spartan College of Aeronautics and Technology, A

Tulsa Community College, A

Oregon

Lane Community College, A
Mt. Hood Community College, A
Portland Community College, A

Pennsylvania

Community College of Beaver County, A
Lehigh Carbon Community College, A
Pennsylvania College of Technology, AB
Pittsburgh Institute of Aeronautics, A

Puerto Rico

Inter American University of Puerto Rico, Fajardo
    Campus, B

South Carolina

Greenville Technical College, A

South Dakota

Lake Area Technical Institute, A

Tennessee

Chattanooga State Technical Community College, A

Texas

LeTourneau University, B
Mountain View College, A
Navarro College, A
Palo Alto College, A
Southwest Texas Junior College, A
Tarrant County College District, A
Texas State Technical College Waco, A

Utah

Salt Lake Community College, A

Virginia

Averett University, B
Hampton University, AB
Northern Virginia Community College, A

Washington

Big Bend Community College, A
Clover Park Technical College, A
Everett Community College, A
South Seattle Community College, A
Spokane Community College, A
Walla Walla College, AB

West Virginia

Fairmont State University, AB

Wisconsin

Blackhawk Technical College, A

British Columbia

British Columbia Institute of Technology, A

AYURVEDIC MEDICINE/AYURVEDA

Iowa

Maharishi University of Management, B

BACTERIOLOGY

Iowa

The University of Iowa, MD

Texas

The University of Texas Medical Branch, DO

Washington

University of Washington, MD

West Virginia

West Virginia University, MD

Wisconsin

University of Wisconsin-Madison, M

Prince Edward Island

University of Prince Edward Island, MD

BAKING AND PASTRY ARTS/BAKER/PASTRY CHEF

Alabama

Virginia College at Birmingham, A

California

The Art Institute of California-San Diego, AB

Colorado

Johnson & Wales University, A

Florida

Florida Culinary Institute, A
Johnson & Wales University, A

Illinois

College of DuPage, A
The Cooking and Hospitality Institute of Chicago, A
Kendall College, A
Triton College, A

Indiana

Vincennes University, A

Maryland

Baltimore International College, A

New Hampshire

Southern New Hampshire University, A

New York

The Culinary Institute of America, AB
Sullivan County Community College, A

North Carolina

Johnson & Wales University, A

Pennsylvania

The Art Institute of Pittsburgh, AB
Luzerne County Community College, A
Montgomery County Community College, A
Pennsylvania College of Technology, A

Rhode Island

Johnson & Wales University, AB

Texas

The Art Institute of Houston, A
El Centro College, A

Vermont

New England Culinary Institute, A
New England Culinary Institute at Essex, A

Washington

Clark College, A

Wisconsin

Milwaukee Area Technical College, A

BALLET

Texas

Texas Christian University, B

Utah

Brigham Young University, B
University of Utah, B

BANKING AND FINANCIAL SUPPORT SERVICES

Alabama

Jefferson State Community College, A

Arkansas

Ozarka College, A

California

Modesto Junior College, A
National University, B

Connecticut

Asnuntuck Community College, A

Delaware

Delaware State University, B
Delaware Technical & Community College, Stanton/Wilmington Campus, A

District of Columbia

Southeastern University, B

Florida

Florida Community College at Jacksonville, A
Indian River Community College, A
Northwood University, Florida Campus, AB
Seminole Community College, A
University of North Florida, B

Georgia

Central Georgia Technical College, A
Emory University, B
Lanier Technical College, A
Ogeechee Technical College, A
Valdosta Technical College, A

Illinois

Black Hawk College, A
Southwestern Illinois College, A
University of Illinois at Urbana-Champaign, B
Waubonsee Community College, A

Indiana

University of Indianapolis, AB

Iowa

Buena Vista University, B

Kansas

Allen County Community College, A
Barton County Community College, A
Pittsburg State University, B
Washburn University, A

Kentucky

Madisonville Community College, A

Louisiana

Southern University at Shreveport, A

Maine

Eastern Maine Community College, A
Husson College, B
Saint Joseph's College of Maine, B

Massachusetts

Berkshire Community College, A

Michigan

Central Michigan University, B
Northwood University, AB

Minnesota

Alexandria Technical College, A
Northwest Technical College, A

St. Cloud Technical College, A

Mississippi

East Mississippi Community College, A

Missouri

Mineral Area College, A

Nebraska

University of Nebraska at Omaha, B

New Jersey

Saint Peter's College, B

New Mexico

Central New Mexico Community College, A
Eastern New Mexico University-Roswell, A
San Juan College, A

New York

Adirondack Community College, A
Finger Lakes Community College, A
Globe Institute of Technology, A
Hilbert College, A
Mercy College, A
Mohawk Valley Community College, A
State University of New York College of Technology at Canton, B
Touro College, A

North Carolina

Alamance Community College, A
Catawba Valley Community College, A
Fayetteville Technical Community College, A

North Dakota

University of North Dakota, B

Ohio

Terra State Community College, A
The University of Akron, A

Pennsylvania

Community College of Allegheny County, A
Harrisburg Area Community College, A
Lackawanna College, A
Laurel Business Institute, A
Luzerne County Community College, A
Pennsylvania College of Technology, A
Pennsylvania Highland Community College, A

Rhode Island

Community College of Rhode Island, A

Texas

Northwood University, Texas Campus, AB
Texas Southern University, B
University of North Texas, B
The University of Texas at Arlington, B

Utah

Utah Valley State College, A

West Virginia

Mountain State University, A
West Liberty State College, B
West Virginia Northern Community College, A
West Virginia State Community and Technical College, A

Wisconsin

Gateway Technical College, A

BARBERING/BARBER

Mississippi

Coahoma Community College, A

Washington

Olympic College, A

Wisconsin

Milwaukee Area Technical College, A

BEHAVIORAL GENETICS

Colorado

University of Colorado at Boulder, MD

BEHAVIORAL SCIENCES

Alabama

Athens State University, B
Miles College, B
University of Mobile, B

Arizona

Cochise College (Sierra Vista), A
Phoenix College, A
Western International University, B

California

California Baptist University, B
California State Polytechnic University, Pomona, B
California State University, Dominguez Hills, B
California State University, Monterey Bay, B
Chabot College, A
Citrus College, A
College of Marin, A
Compton Community College, A
Concordia University, B
De Anza College, A
Hartnell College, A
Imperial Valley College, A
Irvine Valley College, A
Los Angeles Southwest College, A
Los Medanos College, A
MiraCosta College, A
Modesto Junior College, A
Moorpark College, A
Mt. San Jacinto College, A
Napa Valley College, A
National University, B
Notre Dame de Namur University, B
Orange Coast College, A
Oxnard College, A
Pacific Union College, B
Palo Verde College, A
San Diego City College, A
San Joaquin Delta College, A
San Jose State University, B
Santa Rosa Junior College, A
University of La Verne, B

Colorado

Colorado Mountain College, A
Colorado Mountain College, Alpine Campus, A
Lamar Community College, A
Mesa State College, B
Metropolitan State College of Denver, B
United States Air Force Academy, B

Connecticut

Northwestern Connecticut Community College, A

Delaware

Wilmington College, B

Florida

Daytona Beach Community College, A
Miami Dade College, A

Georgia

Gordon College, A

Hawaii

Chaminade University of Honolulu, B
Hawaii Pacific University, B

Idaho

Lewis-Clark State College, A

Illinois

East-West University, B
Lincoln College, A

Lincoln College-Normal, A
National-Louis University, B
University of Chicago, B

Indiana

Ancilla College, A
Indiana University Kokomo, B
Purdue University Calumet, B
Vincennes University, A
Vincennes University Jasper Campus, A

Iowa

Iowa Lakes Community College, A

Kansas

Cloud County Community College, A
Coffeyville Community College, A
Colby Community College, A
Dodge City Community College, A
Labette Community College, A
McPherson College, B
Sterling College, B
University of Kansas, B

Louisiana

Louisiana State University at Alexandria, A
Loyola University New Orleans, B
Our Lady of Holy Cross College, B

Maine

University of Maine at Fort Kent, B
University of Maine at Machias, B
University of Maine at Presque Isle, B

Maryland

Anne Arundel Community College, A
Garrett College, A
The Johns Hopkins University, B
Morgan State University, B
Sojourner-Douglass College, B

Massachusetts

Anna Maria College, B
Greenfield Community College, A
Harvard University, B
Northeastern University, B
Quincy College, A
Tufts University, B

Michigan

Andrews University, B
Grand Valley State University, B
Northern Michigan University, B
Rochester College, B
University of Detroit Mercy, B

Minnesota

Augsburg College, B
Bemidji State University, B
Minnesota State University Mankato, B
St. Cloud State University, B

Mississippi

East Central Community College, A
Mississippi Delta Community College, A

Missouri

Evangel University, B
Northwest Missouri State University, B
University of Missouri-Columbia, B

Nebraska

Concordia University, B
Midland Lutheran College, B

Nevada

Community College of Southern Nevada, A

New Hampshire

Granite State College, AB

New Jersey

Drew University, B
Felician College, AB

William Paterson University of New Jersey, B

New York

Adirondack Community College, A
Fulton-Montgomery Community College, A
John Jay College of Criminal Justice of the City
    University of New York, B
Mercy College, B
Monroe Community College, A
St. Joseph's College, Suffolk Campus, B
United States Military Academy, B

North Carolina

Mars Hill College, B
Methodist College, AB

Ohio

Antioch College, B
Circleville Bible College, AB
Ohio University-Eastern, B
The University of Akron, B
Ursuline College, B
Walsh University, B

Oklahoma

Mid-America Christian University, B
Oklahoma Wesleyan University, AB
Seminole State College, A
Southwestern Christian University, B
Tulsa Community College, A

Oregon

George Fox University, B
Umpqua Community College, A

Pennsylvania

Carnegie Mellon University, B
Cedar Crest College, B
Mount Aloysius College, AB
Point Park University, B
Reading Area Community College, A
Westminster College, B
Widener University, B
Wilson College, B
York College of Pennsylvania, B

Puerto Rico

Inter American University of Puerto Rico,
    Metropolitan Campus, B
Inter American University of Puerto Rico, San
    Germán Campus, B

Rhode Island

Brown University, B

South Carolina

Erskine College, B

South Dakota

Dakota Wesleyan University, B
University of Sioux Falls, B

Tennessee

Freed-Hardeman University, B
Martin Methodist College, B
Tennessee Wesleyan College, B
Trevecca Nazarene University, B

Texas

Amarillo College, A
Clarendon College, A
Galveston College, A
Hill College of the Hill Junior College District, A
Howard College, A
Howard Payne University, B
Midland College, A
South Texas College, A
Texas Wesleyan University, B
Tyler Junior College, A
University of Houston-Clear Lake, B
University of North Texas, B

Wharton County Junior College, A

Utah

University of Utah, B
Utah Valley State College, AB

Vermont

Marlboro College, B

Washington

Highline Community College, A
Tacoma Community College, A

West Virginia

Glenville State College, B
Mountain State University, B
West Virginia State Community and Technical
  College, A

Wisconsin

Mount Mary College, B

Ontario

Laurentian University, B
University of Ottawa, B
York University, B

Quebec

Concordia University, B
Université du Québec en Abitibi-Témiscamingue, B

BENGALI LANGUAGE AND LITERATURE

Illinois

University of Chicago, B

BIBLE/BIBLICAL STUDIES

Alabama

Faulkner University, AB
Heritage Christian University, AB
Oakwood College, A
Southeastern Bible College, AB
Southern Christian University, B
University of Mobile, B

Alaska

Alaska Bible College, AB

Arizona

Grand Canyon University, B
International Baptist College, AB
Southwestern College, B

Arkansas

Central Baptist College, B
Crowley's Ridge College, A
John Brown University, AB
Ouachita Baptist University, AB

California

Azusa Pacific University, B
Bethany University, B
Bethesda Christian University, B
Biola University, B
California Baptist University, B
California Christian College, AB
Emmanuel Bible College, AB
Fresno Pacific University, AB
Hope International University, B
Life Pacific College, AB
The Master's College and Seminary, B
Pacific Union College, A
Patten University, AB
Point Loma Nazarene University, B
San Diego Christian College, B
Shasta Bible College, AB
Simpson University, AB

Vanguard University of Southern California, B

Colorado

Colorado Christian University, B
Nazarene Bible College, AB

Connecticut

Holy Apostles College and Seminary, B

Florida

The Baptist College of Florida, B
Clearwater Christian College, B
Florida Christian College, AB
Florida College, B
Hobe Sound Bible College, AB
Palm Beach Atlantic University, B
Southeastern University, B
Talmudic College of Florida, B
Trinity Baptist College, B
Trinity College of Florida, AB
Warner Southern College, B

Georgia

Atlanta Christian College, B
Beacon University, AB
Beulah Heights Bible College, AB
Covenant College, AB
Luther Rice University, B
Toccoa Falls College, B

Idaho

Boise Bible College, AB

Illinois

Judson College, B
Lincoln Christian College, AB
Moody Bible Institute, B
North Park University, B
Olivet Nazarene University, B
Trinity International University, B
Wheaton College, B

Indiana

Anderson University, B
Bethel College, AB
Crossroads Bible College, B
Goshen College, B
Grace College, AB
Huntington University, B
Indiana Wesleyan University, B
Oakland City University, B
Taylor University, B
University of Evansville, B

Iowa

Emmaus Bible College, AB
Faith Baptist Bible College and Theological
  Seminary, AB
Vennard College, B

Kansas

Barclay College, AB
Central Christian College of Kansas, B
Friends University, B
Hesston College, A
Manhattan Christian College, AB
Tabor College, AB

Kentucky

Asbury College, B
Campbellsville University, B
Clear Creek Baptist Bible College, AB
Mid-Continent University, B
St. Catharine College, A

Maryland

Baltimore Hebrew University, AB
Maple Springs Baptist Bible College and
  Seminary, AB
Ner Israel Rabbinical College, B

Washington Bible College, AB

Massachusetts

Boston Baptist College, AB
Harvard University, B

Michigan

Andrews University, B
Calvin College, B
Cornerstone University, B
Grace Bible College, B
Great Lakes Christian College, B
Kuyper College, AB
Rochester College, B

Minnesota

Bethel University, B
Crossroads College, B
Crown College, AB
North Central University, AB
Northwestern College, B
Oak Hills Christian College, AB
Pillsbury Baptist Bible College, B

Mississippi

Belhaven College, B
Blue Mountain College, B
Magnolia Bible College, B
Northeast Mississippi Community College, A
Southeastern Baptist College, AB
Wesley College, B

Missouri

Calvary Bible College and Theological Seminary, AB
Central Bible College, AB
Central Christian College of the Bible, AB
Evangel University, B
Global University of the Assemblies of God, B
Hannibal-LaGrange College, B
Messenger College, B
Ozark Christian College, B
St. Louis Christian College, B
Southwest Baptist University, B

Nebraska

Grace University, AB
York College, B

New Jersey

Somerset Christian College, A

New York

Davis College, AB
Houghton College, AB
The Jewish Theological Seminary, B
Nyack College, B
Rabbinical Academy Mesivta Rabbi Chaim Berlin, B
Touro College, B
Yeshiva Karlin Stolin Rabbinical Institute, B
Yeshivat Mikdash Melech, B

North Carolina

John Wesley College, B
Methodist College, B
Montreat College, B
Piedmont Baptist College, AB
Roanoke Bible College, AB

North Dakota

Trinity Bible College, AB

Ohio

Cedarville University, B
Cincinnati Christian University, AB
Circleville Bible College, AB
God's Bible School and College, A
Laura and Alvin Siegal College of Judaic Studies, B
Malone College, B
Mount Vernon Nazarene University, B

Oklahoma

Hillsdale Free Will Baptist College, A
Mid-America Christian University, B
Oklahoma Baptist University, B

Oklahoma Christian University, B
Oral Roberts University, B
Southwestern Christian University, B

Oregon

Cascade College, B
Corban College, AB
Eugene Bible College, B
George Fox University, B
Multnomah Bible College and Biblical Seminary, B
Northwest Christian College, B
Warner Pacific College, AB

Pennsylvania

Baptist Bible College of Pennsylvania, B
Eastern University, B
Geneva College, AB
Lancaster Bible College, AB
Messiah College, B
Philadelphia Biblical University, B
Valley Forge Christian College, AB

Puerto Rico

Colegio Biblico Pentecostal, B
Universidad Adventista de las Antillas, AB

South Carolina

Bob Jones University, B
Columbia International University, AB
Erskine College, B
North Greenville College, B
Southern Methodist College, AB

Tennessee

American Baptist College of American Baptist
  Theological Seminary, AB
Belmont University, B
Bryan College, B
Carson-Newman College, B
Crichton College, B
Free Will Baptist Bible College, B
Freed-Hardeman University, B
Johnson Bible College, B
King College, B
Lee University, B
Lipscomb University, B
Milligan College, B
Tennessee Temple University, B
Union University, B
Williamson Christian College, B

Texas

Abilene Christian University, B
Amarillo College, A
Arlington Baptist College, B
Austin Graduate School of Theology, B
Baptist University of the Americas, B
College of Biblical Studies-Houston, AB
The Criswell College, AB
Dallas Baptist University, AB
Dallas Christian College, B
East Texas Baptist University, B
Hardin-Simmons University, B
Houston Baptist University, B
Howard Payne University, AB
LeTourneau University, B
Lon Morris College, A
Lubbock Christian University, B
Southwestern Assemblies of God University, AB
Southwestern Christian College, AB
University of Mary Hardin-Baylor, B

Vermont

Marlboro College, B

Virginia

Bluefield College, B
Eastern Mennonite University, AB

Washington

Northwest University, B
Puget Sound Christian College, B

Trinity Lutheran College, AB

West Virginia

Appalachian Bible College, AB
Ohio Valley University, AB

Wisconsin

Maranatha Baptist Bible College, B

Alberta

Alliance University College, B
Prairie Bible Institute, AB
Rocky Mountain College, B
Taylor University College and Seminary, B
Vanguard College, B

British Columbia

Columbia Bible College, B
Summit Pacific College, B
Trinity Western University, B

Manitoba

Canadian Mennonite University, B
Providence College and Theological Seminary, B
Steinbach Bible College, B
William and Catherine Booth College, B

New Brunswick

Atlantic Baptist University, B
Bethany Bible College, B

Ontario

Heritage Baptist College and Heritage Theological
  Seminary, B
Master's College and Seminary, B
Redeemer University College, B
Saint Paul University, B
Tyndale University College & Seminary, B
The University of Western Ontario, B

Quebec

Université de Montréal, B

Saskatchewan

Briercrest College, B
Central Pentecostal College, B

BILINGUAL AND MULTILINGUAL EDUCATION

Arizona

Prescott College, B

California

Biola University, B
California State Polytechnic University, Pomona, B
California State University, Dominguez Hills, B
Fresno Pacific University, B
University of San Francisco, B

Delaware

University of Delaware, B

Florida

Florida State University, B

Idaho

Boise State University, B

Illinois

Chicago State University, B
Northeastern Illinois University, B

Western Illinois University, B

Indiana

Goshen College, B
Indiana University Bloomington, B

Maine

University of Maine at Fort Kent, B

Massachusetts

Boston University, B
Elms College, B

Michigan

Adrian College, B
Calvin College, B

Montana

Blackfeet Community College, A

Nevada

Nevada State College at Henderson, B

New Jersey

Rider University, B

New Mexico

Clovis Community College, A
College of the Southwest, B
New Mexico Highlands University, B

New York

Boricua College, B
Brooklyn College of the City University of New
  York, B
Fordham University, B
Long Island University, Brooklyn Campus, B
State University of New York College at Old
  Westbury, B

Ohio

The University of Akron, B
The University of Findlay, B

Puerto Rico

Universidad Metropolitana, B
University of the Sacred Heart, B

South Dakota

Oglala Lakota College, B

Tennessee

Belmont University, B

Texas

Houston Baptist University, B
Texas A&M International University, B
Texas A&M University-Kingsville, B
Texas Christian University, B
Texas Southern University, B
Texas Wesleyan University, B
University of Houston, B
The University of Texas at Brownsville, B

Utah

Weber State University, B

Washington

Heritage University, B
University of Washington, B
Washington State University, B

Wisconsin

Mount Mary College, B
University of Wisconsin-Milwaukee, B

Alberta

University of Alberta, B

Ontario

University of Ottawa, B
York University, B

Saskatchewan

University of Regina, B

BILINGUAL, MULTILINGUAL, AND MULTICULTURAL EDUCATION

Florida

Florida State University, B

New York

St. John's University, B
State University of New York College at
Brockport, B

BIOCHEMICAL ENGINEERING

California

California Polytechnic State University, San Luis
Obispo, M
University of California, Irvine, MD

Iowa

The University of Iowa, MD

Maryland

University of Maryland, Baltimore County, MDO

Massachusetts

University of Massachusetts Dartmouth, D

Minnesota

Bethel University, M

New Hampshire

Dartmouth College, MD

New Jersey

Rutgers, The State University of New Jersey, New
Brunswick/Piscataway, MD

New York

Cornell University, MD

Pennsylvania

Drexel University, M

BIOCHEMISTRY

Alabama

Auburn University, B
Oakwood College, B
Samford University, B
Spring Hill College, B
The University of Alabama at Birmingham, D
University of South Alabama, D

Alaska

University of Alaska Fairbanks, MD

Arizona

Arizona State University, BMD
Northern Arizona University, M
The University of Arizona, BMD

Arkansas

Harding University, B
John Brown University, B
University of Arkansas for Medical Sciences, MDO

California

Azusa Pacific University, B
Biola University, B
California Institute of Technology, BD
California Lutheran University, B
California Polytechnic State University, San Luis
Obispo, B
California State University, Chico, B

California State University, Dominguez Hills, B
California State University, East Bay, BM
California State University, Fullerton, BM
California State University, Long Beach, BM
California State University, Los Angeles, BM
California State University, Northridge, B
California State University, San Bernardino, B
California State University, San Marcos, B
Chapman University, B
Claremont McKenna College, B
Humboldt State University, B
La Sierra University, B
Loma Linda University, MD
Loyola Marymount University, B
Mills College, B
Mount St. Mary's College, B
Notre Dame de Namur University, B
Occidental College, B
Pacific Union College, B
Pitzer College, B
Point Loma Nazarene University, B
Pomona College, B
Saint Mary's College of California, B
San Francisco State University, BM
San Jose State University, B
Scripps College, B
Stanford University, D
University of California, Berkeley, MD
University of California, Davis, MD
University of California, Irvine, MDO
University of California, Los Angeles, BMD
University of California, Riverside, BMD
University of California, San Diego, BMD
University of California, Santa Barbara, BMDO
University of California, Santa Cruz, B
University of the Pacific, B
University of Southern California, BMD
Whittier College, B

Colorado

The Colorado College, B
Colorado State University, BMD
Fort Lewis College, B
Regis University, B
United States Air Force Academy, B
University of Colorado at Boulder, BMD
University of Denver, B
Western State College of Colorado, B

Connecticut

Central Connecticut State University, B
Connecticut College, B
Eastern Connecticut State University, B
Quinnipiac University, B
Sacred Heart University, B
Saint Joseph College, B
Trinity College, B
University of Connecticut, MD
Wesleyan University, BMD
Yale University, MDO

Delaware

University of Delaware, BMD

District of Columbia

American University, B
The Catholic University of America, B
The George Washington University, MD
Georgetown University, BMDO
Howard University, MD
Trinity (Washington) University, B

Florida

Florida Atlantic University, MD
Florida Institute of Technology, B
Florida State University, BMD
Rollins College, B
Stetson University, B
University of Florida, MD
University of Miami, BDO
University of South Florida, MD

The University of Tampa, B

Georgia

Agnes Scott College, B
Berry College, B
Emory University, D
Georgia Institute of Technology, MD
Georgia State University, MD
Kennesaw State University, B
LaGrange College, B
Medical College of Georgia, D
Mercer University, B
Spelman College, B
University of Georgia, BMD

Hawaii

Brigham Young University-Hawaii, B

Idaho

Idaho State University, B
Northwest Nazarene University, B
University of Idaho, MD

Illinois

Benedictine University, B
Bradley University, B
Chicago State University, B
DePaul University, BM
Dominican University, B
Illinois Institute of Technology, M
Illinois State University, B
Knox College, B
Lewis University, B
Loyola University Chicago, BMDO
Monmouth College, B
North Central College, B
Northern Illinois University, MD
Northwestern University, BD
Olivet Nazarene University, B
Rockford College, B
Rush University, DO
Southern Illinois University Carbondale, MD
University of Chicago, BDO
University of Illinois at Chicago, BMD
University of Illinois at Urbana-Champaign, BMD

Indiana

DePauw University, B
Indiana University Bloomington, BMD
Indiana University-Purdue University
Indianapolis, MDO
Purdue University, BMD
Saint Joseph's College, AB
University of Evansville, B
University of Notre Dame, BMD
Valparaiso University, B

Iowa

Coe College, B
Cornell College, B
Drake University, B
Grinnell College, B
Iowa State University of Science and
Technology, BMD
Loras College, B
Simpson College, B
The University of Iowa, BMDO
University of Northern Iowa, B
Wartburg College, B

Kansas

Benedictine College, B
Kansas State University, BMD
Southwestern College, B
University of Kansas, MDO

Kentucky

Asbury College, B
Centre College, B
University of Kentucky, DO
University of Louisville, MDO

Western Kentucky University, B

Louisiana

Louisiana State University and Agricultural and
  Mechanical College, BMD
Louisiana State University Health Sciences
  Center, MD
Southern University and Agricultural and Mechanical
  College, M
Tulane University, BMDO
Xavier University of Louisiana, B

Maine

Bates College, B
Bowdoin College, B
Colby College, B
University of Maine, BMD
University of New England, B

Maryland

Columbia Union College, B
Hood College, B
The Johns Hopkins University, MD
McDaniel College, B
Mount St. Mary's University, B
St. Mary's College of Maryland, B
University of Maryland, Baltimore County, D
University of Maryland, College Park, BMD

Massachusetts

American International College, B
Atlantic Union College, B
Boston College, BMDO
Boston University, BMDO
Brandeis University, BMD
Bridgewater State College, B
Clark University, B
Emmanuel College, B
Harvard University, BMD
Massachusetts Institute of Technology, D
Merrimack College, B
Mount Holyoke College, B
Northeastern University, BMD
Regis College, B
Simmons College, B
Smith College, B
Stonehill College, B
Suffolk University, B
Tufts University, D
University of Massachusetts Amherst, MD
University of Massachusetts Boston, B
University of Massachusetts Lowell, D
Wellesley College, B
Wheaton College, B
Worcester Polytechnic Institute, BMD

Michigan

Alma College, B
Andrews University, B
Calvin College, B
Eastern Michigan University, B
Grand Valley State University, B
Kettering University, B
Lawrence Technological University, B
Madonna University, B
Michigan State University, BMD
Michigan Technological University, B
Northern Michigan University, BM
Oakland University, B
Olivet College, B
Saginaw Valley State University, B
Spring Arbor University, B
University of Detroit Mercy, BM
University of Michigan, BD
University of Michigan-Dearborn, B
Wayne State University, MD
Western Michigan University, B

Minnesota

College of Saint Benedict, B
College of St. Catherine, B
The College of St. Scholastica, B
Gustavus Adolphus College, B
Hamline University, B
Minnesota State University Mankato, B

Saint John's University, B
Saint Mary's University of Minnesota, B
University of Minnesota, Duluth, BMD
University of Minnesota, Twin Cities Campus, BD
University of St. Thomas, B

Mississippi

Mississippi College, B
Mississippi State University, BMD
University of Mississippi Medical Center, MDO
University of Southern Mississippi, MD

Missouri

Missouri Western State University, B
Rockhurst University, B
Saint Louis University, BD
University of Missouri-Columbia, BMD
University of Missouri-Kansas City, D
University of Missouri-St. Louis, MD
Washington University in St. Louis, BD
William Jewell College, B

Montana

Montana State University, MD
The University of Montana-Missoula, BMD

Nebraska

Nebraska Wesleyan University, B
Union College, B
University of Nebraska-Lincoln, BMD
University of Nebraska Medical Center, MD

Nevada

University of Nevada, Las Vegas, BM
University of Nevada, Reno, BMD

New Hampshire

Dartmouth College, BDO
Saint Anselm College, B
University of New Hampshire, BMD

New Jersey

Bloomfield College, B
College of Saint Elizabeth, B
Drew University, B
Fairleigh Dickinson University, Metropolitan
  Campus, B
Felician College, B
Georgian Court University, B
Montclair State University, BM
The Richard Stockton College of New Jersey, B
Rider University, B
Rowan University, B
Rutgers, The State University of New Jersey, New
  Brunswick/Piscataway, BMD
Rutgers, The State University of New Jersey,
  Newark, MD
Saint Peter's College, B
Seton Hall University, BMD
Stevens Institute of Technology, B

New Mexico

New Mexico Institute of Mining and Technology, M
New Mexico State University, BMD
University of New Mexico, BMD

New York

Adelphi University, B
Bard College, B
Barnard College, B
Canisius College, B
City College of the City University of New
  York, BMD
Clarkson University, B
Colgate University, B
College of Mount Saint Vincent, B
The College of Saint Rose, B
College of Staten Island of the City University of
  New York, B
Columbia College, B
Cornell University, BD
Daemen College, B
Elmira College, B
Hamilton College, B
Hartwick College, B

Hobart and William Smith Colleges, B
Hofstra University, B
Hunter College of the City University of New
  York, M
Iona College, B
Ithaca College, B
Keuka College, B
Le Moyne College, B
Lehman College of the City University of New
  York, B
Manhattan College, B
Manhattanville College, B
Marist College, B
Nazareth College of Rochester, B
New York University, BMDO
Niagara University, B
Pace University, B
Queens College of the City University of New
  York, M
Rensselaer Polytechnic Institute, BMD
Roberts Wesleyan College, B
Rochester Institute of Technology, B
Russell Sage College, B
St. Bonaventure University, B
St. John Fisher College, B
St. Lawrence University, B
State University of New York at Binghamton, B
State University of New York at Buffalo, BMD
State University of New York College at
  Brockport, B
State University of New York College of
  Environmental Science and Forestry, BMD
State University of New York College at Geneseo, B
State University of New York College at Old
  Westbury, B
State University of New York College at Oneonta, B
State University of New York, Fredonia, B
State University of New York at New Paltz, B
State University of New York at Plattsburgh, B
State University of New York Upstate Medical
  University, MDO
Stony Brook University, State University of New
  York, BD
Syracuse University, BD
Union College, B
University at Albany, State University of New
  York, BMD
University of Rochester, MD
Vassar College, B
Wells College, B

North Carolina

Campbell University, B
Duke University, DO
East Carolina University, BD
North Carolina State University, BMD
Queens University of Charlotte, B
The University of North Carolina at Chapel Hill, MD
The University of North Carolina at Greensboro, B
Wake Forest University, D

North Dakota

Jamestown College, B
North Dakota State University, MD
University of North Dakota, MD

Ohio

Capital University, B
Case Western Reserve University, BMDO
College of Mount St. Joseph, B
The College of Wooster, B
Denison University, B
Kent State University, MD
Kenyon College, B
Marietta College, B
Miami University, BMD
Miami University Hamilton, B
Notre Dame College, B
Oberlin College, B
Ohio Northern University, B
The Ohio State University, BMD
Ohio University, MD
Otterbein College, B
University of Cincinnati, BMD
University of Dayton, B
The University of Toledo, MD

Wright State University, BM

Oklahoma

Oklahoma Christian University, B
Oklahoma City University, B
Oklahoma State University, BMD
Oral Roberts University, B
Southern Nazarene University, B
University of Oklahoma, MD
University of Oklahoma Health Sciences Center, MD
University of Tulsa, B

Oregon

Lewis & Clark College, B
Oregon Health & Science University, DO
Oregon State University, BMD
Portland State University, B
Reed College, B
Southern Oregon University, B
University of Oregon, BMD

Pennsylvania

Albright College, B
Allegheny College, B
Alvernia College, B
Carnegie Mellon University, D
Cedar Crest College, B
Chatham College, B
Chestnut Hill College, B
College Misericordia, B
Dickinson College, B
Drexel University, MDO
Duquesne University, BMD
East Stroudsburg University of Pennsylvania, B
Eastern University, B
Edinboro University of Pennsylvania, B
Elizabethtown College, B
Franklin and Marshall College, B
Gettysburg College, B
Grove City College, B
Haverford College, B
Holy Family University, B
Immaculata University, B
Indiana University of Pennsylvania, B
Juniata College, B
La Salle University, B
Lafayette College, B
Lebanon Valley College, B
Lehigh University, BD
Mansfield University of Pennsylvania, B
Mercyhurst College, B
Messiah College, B
Moravian College, B
Muhlenberg College, B
The Pennsylvania State University Abington
    College, B
The Pennsylvania State University Altoona
    College, B
The Pennsylvania State University Beaver Campus
    of the Commonwealth College, B
The Pennsylvania State University Berks Campus of
    the Berks-Lehigh Valley College, B
The Pennsylvania State University Delaware County
    Campus of the Commonwealth College, B
The Pennsylvania State University DuBois Campus
    of the Commonwealth College, B
The Pennsylvania State University at Erie, The
    Behrend College, B
The Pennsylvania State University Fayette Campus
    of the Commonwealth College, B
The Pennsylvania State University Hazleton
    Campus of the Commonwealth College, B
The Pennsylvania State University, Lehigh Valley
    Campus of the Berks-Lehigh Valley College, B
The Pennsylvania State University McKeesport
    Campus of the Commonwealth College, B
The Pennsylvania State University Mont Alto
    Campus of the Commonwealth College, B
The Pennsylvania State University New Kensington
    Campus of the Commonwealth College, B
The Pennsylvania State University Schuylkill
    Campus of the Capital College, B
The Pennsylvania State University Shenango
    Campus of the Commonwealth College, B
The Pennsylvania State University University Park
    Campus, BMD

The Pennsylvania State University Wilkes-Barre
    Campus of the Commonwealth College, B
The Pennsylvania State University Worthington
    Scranton Campus of the Commonwealth
    College, B
The Pennsylvania State University York Campus of
    the Commonwealth College, B
Philadelphia University, B
Rosemont College, B
Saint Joseph's University, B
Saint Vincent College, B
Seton Hill University, B
Susquehanna University, B
Swarthmore College, B
Temple University, BMD
Thomas Jefferson University, MD
University of Pennsylvania, BDO
University of Pittsburgh, MD
University of the Sciences in Philadelphia, BMD
The University of Scranton, M
Washington & Jefferson College, B
West Chester University of Pennsylvania, B
Widener University, B
Wilkes University, B

Puerto Rico

Inter American University of Puerto Rico, Bayamón
    Campus, B
University of Puerto Rico, Medical Sciences
    Campus, MD

Rhode Island

Brown University, BMDO
Providence College, B
University of Rhode Island, MD

South Carolina

Charleston Southern University, B
Claflin University, B
Clemson University, BMD
College of Charleston, B
Converse College, B
Furman University, B
Medical University of South Carolina, DO
University of South Carolina, MD

South Dakota

Dakota Wesleyan University, B
South Dakota State University, BMD

Tennessee

Belmont University, B
East Tennessee State University, MD
Freed-Hardeman University, B
King College, B
Lipscomb University, B
Maryville College, B
Rhodes College, B
Southern Adventist University, B
Tennessee Technological University, B
The University of Tennessee, BMD
Vanderbilt University, MDO

Texas

Abilene Christian University, B
Angelo State University, B
Austin College, B
Baylor University, B
McMurry University, B
Rice University, BMD
St. Edward's University, B
St. Mary's University of San Antonio, B
Schreiner University, B
Southern Methodist University, B
Southwestern University, B
Texas A&M University, BMD
Texas A&M University System Health Science
    Center, D
Texas Christian University, B
Texas State University-San Marcos, BM
Texas Tech University, B
Texas Wesleyan University, B
Trinity University, B
University of Dallas, B
University of Houston, BMD

University of North Texas, BMD
The University of Texas at Arlington, B
The University of Texas at Austin, BMD
The University of Texas at Dallas, B
The University of Texas Health Science Center at
    Houston, MDO
The University of Texas Health Science Center at
    San Antonio, MD
The University of Texas Medical Branch, MD
The University of Texas Southwestern Medical
    Center at Dallas, D

Utah

Brigham Young University, BMD
University of Utah, MD
Utah State University, MD

Vermont

Bennington College, B
Marlboro College, B
Middlebury College, B
Saint Michael's College, B
University of Vermont, BMDO

Virginia

Eastern Mennonite University, B
Hampden-Sydney College, B
Mary Baldwin College, B
Old Dominion University, BM
Roanoke College, B
University of Virginia, DO
Virginia Commonwealth University, MDO
Virginia Polytechnic Institute and State
    University, BMD
Washington and Lee University, B

Washington

Eastern Washington University, B
Gonzaga University, B
Pacific Lutheran University, B
Seattle Pacific University, B
Seattle University, B
University of Washington, BD
Washington State University, BMD
Western Washington University, B
Whitman College, B

West Virginia

West Virginia University, MD

Wisconsin

Beloit College, B
Carroll College, B
Lakeland College, B
Lawrence University, B
Marquette University, B
Ripon College, B
University of Wisconsin-Madison, BMD
University of Wisconsin-Milwaukee, B
University of Wisconsin-River Falls, B
Viterbo University, B
Wisconsin Lutheran College, B

Alberta

University of Alberta, BMD
University of Calgary, BMD
University of Lethbridge, BM

British Columbia

Simon Fraser University, BMD
Thompson Rivers University, B
The University of British Columbia, BMD
University of Victoria, BMD

Manitoba

University of Manitoba, MD
The University of Winnipeg, B

New Brunswick

Mount Allison University, B
Université de Moncton, BM

University of New Brunswick Fredericton, B

Newfoundland and Labrador

Memorial University of Newfoundland, BMD

Nova Scotia

Dalhousie University, MDO
University of King's College, B

Ontario

Brock University, B
Carleton University, B
Laurentian University, BM
McMaster University, BMD
Queen's University at Kingston, BMD
Trent University, B
University of Guelph, BMD
University of Ottawa, BMD
University of Toronto, BMD
University of Waterloo, B
The University of Western Ontario, BMD
University of Windsor, BMD

Quebec

Bishop's University, B
Concordia University, B
McGill University, BMD
Université Laval, BMDO
Université de Montréal, BMDO
Université du Québec àMontréal, B
Université du Québec àTrois-Rivières, B
Université de Sherbrooke, BMD

Saskatchewan

University of Regina, BMD
University of Saskatchewan, BMDO

BIOCHEMISTRY, BIOPHYSICS AND MOLECULAR BIOLOGY

California

California State University, Long Beach, B

Illinois

Illinois Institute of Technology, B
Monmouth College, B

Kansas

University of Kansas, B

Maryland

University of Maryland, Baltimore County, B

Massachusetts

University of Massachusetts Amherst, B

Michigan

Michigan State University, B

Nebraska

Nebraska Wesleyan University, B

New Jersey

Ramapo College of New Jersey, B

New York

Cornell University, B

North Dakota

North Dakota State University, B

Ohio

Mount Union College, B
Wittenberg University, B

Oklahoma

Oklahoma State University, B

Pennsylvania

Lebanon Valley College, B

Tennessee

University of Memphis, B

Texas

Hardin-Simmons University, B

Virginia

Liberty University, B
Sweet Briar College, B

Washington

Washington State University, B

British Columbia

The University of British Columbia, B
University of Northern British Columbia, B

Nova Scotia

Dalhousie University, B

Ontario

University of Waterloo, B

BIOENGINEERING

Arizona

Arizona State University, MD

Arkansas

University of Arkansas, MD

California

California Institute of Technology, MD
Stanford University, MD
University of California, Berkeley, D
University of California, Davis, MDO
University of California, San Diego, MD
University of California, Santa Barbara, MD

Colorado

Colorado State University, MD

Florida

University of Florida, MDO

Georgia

Georgia Institute of Technology, MDO
University of Georgia, MD

Hawaii

University of Hawaii at Manoa, MD

Illinois

University of Illinois at Chicago, MDO
University of Illinois at Urbana-Champaign, D

Indiana

Purdue University, MD
University of Notre Dame, M

Kansas

Kansas State University, MD

Louisiana

Louisiana State University and Agricultural and
  Mechanical College, MD

Maine

University of Maine, M

Maryland

The Johns Hopkins University, MD
University of Maryland, College Park, MD

Massachusetts

Massachusetts Institute of Technology, MD
Tufts University, O

Mississippi

Mississippi State University, MD

Missouri

University of Missouri-Columbia, MD

Nebraska

University of Nebraska-Lincoln, M

New Jersey

Rutgers, The State University of New Jersey, New
  Brunswick/Piscataway, M

New York

Alfred University, M
Cornell University, MD
State University of New York at Buffalo, MD
Syracuse University, MD

North Carolina

North Carolina State University, MD

Ohio

The Ohio State University, MD
The University of Toledo, MD

Oklahoma

Oklahoma State University, MD
University of Oklahoma, MD

Oregon

Oregon State University, MD

Pennsylvania

Carnegie Mellon University, MD
The Pennsylvania State University University Park
  Campus, MD
University of Pennsylvania, MDO
University of Pittsburgh, MDO

South Carolina

Clemson University, MD
Medical University of South Carolina, MD

Texas

Rice University, MDO
Texas A&M University, MD

Utah

University of Utah, MD

Virginia

Virginia Commonwealth University, D
Virginia Polytechnic Institute and State
  University, MD

Washington

University of Washington, MD
Washington State University, MD

Wisconsin

University of Wisconsin-Madison, MD

Nova Scotia

Dalhousie University, MD

Ontario

University of Guelph, MD

Quebec

McGill University, MD

BIOETHICS/MEDICAL ETHICS

Arizona

Midwestern University, Glendale Campus, MO

California

Loma Linda University, M
Loyola Marymount University, M

Illinois

Rush University, M
Trinity International University, MD

Massachusetts

Boston University, M

Michigan

Michigan State University, M

Missouri

Saint Louis University, D

New Jersey

Drew University, MDO

Ohio

Case Western Reserve University, MDO
Cleveland State University, BMO

Pennsylvania

Duquesne University, MDO
University of Pennsylvania, MO
University of Pittsburgh, M

Tennessee

The University of Tennessee, MD

Virginia

University of Virginia, M

Quebec

McGill University, M
Université de Montréal, MO

BIOINFORMATICS

Arkansas

University of Arkansas at Little Rock, MD

California

California State University, Dominguez Hills, MO
University of California, San Diego, D
University of California, Santa Cruz, MD

Colorado

University of Denver, B

Connecticut

Yale University, DO

District of Columbia

The George Washington University, M

Georgia

Georgia Institute of Technology, MD

Idaho

University of Idaho, MD

Illinois

Northwestern University, M

Indiana

Indiana University Bloomington, M

Iowa

Iowa State University of Science and
Technology, MD
University of Northern Iowa, B

Maryland

The Johns Hopkins University, M
Morgan State University, M

University of Maryland, Baltimore County, B

Massachusetts

Boston University, MD
Northeastern University, M

Michigan

Michigan Technological University, B
University of Michigan, MD

Missouri

Rockhurst University, B

New Jersey

Ramapo College of New Jersey, B

New York

Canisius College, B
Polytechnic University, Brooklyn Campus, BM
Rensselaer Polytechnic Institute, B
Rochester Institute of Technology, BM
State University of New York at Buffalo, B

North Carolina

Duke University, D
North Carolina State University, MD

Ohio

University of Cincinnati, MD

Oregon

Oregon Health & Science University, MDO

Pennsylvania

Chatham College, B
Gannon University, B
Saint Vincent College, B
University of Pennsylvania, B
University of Pittsburgh, MDO
University of the Sciences in Philadelphia, BM

South Carolina

Claflin University, B

Tennessee

Vanderbilt University, MD

Texas

Baylor University, B
St. Edward's University, B
Texas Tech University, M
The University of Texas at El Paso, M

Utah

Brigham Young University, B

Virginia

George Mason University, MD
Virginia Commonwealth University, B
Virginia Polytechnic Institute and State University, D

Washington

University of Washington, M

Wisconsin

Marquette University, M

Alberta

University of Alberta, B

Nova Scotia

Dalhousie University, B

Ontario

University of Waterloo, B
The University of Western Ontario, B

University of Windsor, B

Saskatchewan

University of Saskatchewan, B

BIOLOGICAL AND BIOMEDICAL SCIENCES

Alabama

Alabama Agricultural and Mechanical University, M
Alabama State University, MO
Auburn University, MD
Jacksonville State University, M
Tuskegee University, M
The University of Alabama, MD
The University of Alabama at Birmingham, MD
The University of Alabama in Huntsville, M
University of North Alabama, B
University of South Alabama, MD

Alaska

University of Alaska Anchorage, M
University of Alaska Fairbanks, MD

Arizona

Arizona State University, BMD
Arizona State University at the Polytechnic
Campus, M
Midwestern University, Glendale Campus, M
Northern Arizona University, MD
The University of Arizona, MDO

Arkansas

Arkansas State University, MO
University of Arkansas, MD
University of Arkansas at Little Rock, M
University of Arkansas for Medical Sciences, MDO
University of Central Arkansas, M

California

California Institute of Technology, D
California Polytechnic State University, San Luis
Obispo, M
California State Polytechnic University, Pomona, M
California State University, Chico, M
California State University, Dominguez Hills, MO
California State University, East Bay, M
California State University, Fresno, M
California State University, Fullerton, M
California State University, Long Beach, M
California State University, Los Angeles, M
California State University, Northridge, M
California State University, Sacramento, M
California State University, San Bernardino, M
California State University, San Marcos, M
Holy Names University, B
Humboldt State University, M
Loma Linda University, MDO
Mills College, O
Notre Dame de Namur University, O
Occidental College, M
Saint Mary's College of California, B
San Diego State University, MD
San Francisco State University, M
San Jose State University, M
Sonoma State University, M
Stanford University, MD
University of California, Berkeley, D
University of California, Irvine, MDO
University of California, Los Angeles, MDO
University of California, Riverside, MDO
University of California, San Diego, MDO
University of California, Santa Cruz, MD
University of the Pacific, M
University of San Francisco, M
University of Southern California, MDO

Colorado

Colorado State University, MD
University of Colorado at Denver and Health
Sciences Center - Downtown Denver Campus, M
University of Denver, MD

University of Northern Colorado, MD

Connecticut

Central Connecticut State University, MO
Quinnipiac University, M
Saint Joseph College, M
Southern Connecticut State University, M
University of Connecticut, MD
University of Hartford, M
Wesleyan University, D
Western Connecticut State University, M
Yale University, DO

Delaware

Delaware State University, M
University of Delaware, MD

District of Columbia

American University, M
The Catholic University of America, MDO
The George Washington University, MD
Georgetown University, MDO
Howard University, MD

Florida

Barry University, M
Florida Agricultural and Mechanical University, M
Florida Atlantic University, MD
Florida Institute of Technology, MD
Florida International University, MD
Florida State University, MD
Nova Southeastern University, M
University of Central Florida, MDO
University of Florida, DO
University of Miami, MDO
University of North Florida, M
University of South Florida, MD
University of West Florida, M

Georgia

Clark Atlanta University, MD
Emory University, D
Georgia College & State University, M
Georgia Institute of Technology, MD
Georgia Southern University, M
Georgia State University, MD
Medical College of Georgia, MD
University of West Georgia, M

Guam

University of Guam, M

Hawaii

University of Hawaii at Manoa, MD

Idaho

Boise State University, M
Idaho State University, MD
University of Idaho, MD

Illinois

Bradley University, M
Chicago State University, M
DePaul University, M
Eastern Illinois University, M
Illinois Institute of Technology, MD
Illinois State University, MD
Loyola University Chicago, M
Monmouth College, B
Northeastern Illinois University, M
Northern Illinois University, MD
Northwestern University, DO
Southern Illinois University Carbondale, MD
Southern Illinois University Edwardsville, M
University of Chicago, MDPO
University of Illinois at Chicago, MDO
University of Illinois at Springfield, M
University of Illinois at Urbana-Champaign, BMD
Western Illinois University, MO

Indiana

Ball State University, MD
Indiana State University, MD
Indiana University Bloomington, MDO

Indiana University-Purdue University Fort Wayne, M
Indiana University-Purdue University Indianapolis, MD
Purdue University, MD
Purdue University Calumet, M
University of Indianapolis, M
University of Notre Dame, MD

Iowa

Iowa State University of Science and Technology, MD
The University of Iowa, MDO
University of Northern Iowa, M

Kansas

Emporia State University, M
Fort Hays State University, M
Kansas State University, MD
Pittsburg State University, M
University of Kansas, BMDO
Wichita State University, M

Kentucky

Eastern Kentucky University, M
Morehead State University, M
Murray State University, MD
University of Kentucky, MDO
University of Louisville, M
Western Kentucky University, M

Louisiana

Louisiana State University and Agricultural and Mechanical College, MD
Louisiana State University Health Sciences Center, MDO
Louisiana State University in Shreveport, B
Louisiana Tech University, M
McNeese State University, M
Our Lady of the Lake College, B
Southeastern Louisiana University, M
Southern University and Agricultural and Mechanical College, M
Tulane University, MDO
University of Louisiana at Lafayette, MD
University of Louisiana at Monroe, M
University of New Orleans, MD

Maine

University of Maine, D
University of Southern Maine, M

Maryland

Frostburg State University, M
Goucher College, O
Hood College, MO
The Johns Hopkins University, MDO
Towson University, M
University of Maryland, Baltimore County, MD
University of Maryland, College Park, MD

Massachusetts

Boston College, MDO
Boston University, BMDO
Brandeis University, BMDO
Clark University, MD
Harvard University, MDO
Massachusetts Institute of Technology, MDPO
Northeastern University, MD
Smith College, MD
Tufts University, MDO
University of Massachusetts Amherst, MD
University of Massachusetts Boston, M
University of Massachusetts Dartmouth, M
University of Massachusetts Lowell, MD
Worcester Polytechnic Institute, MDO

Michigan

Andrews University, M
Central Michigan University, M
Eastern Michigan University, M
Grand Valley State University, M
Michigan State University, MD
Michigan Technological University, MD
Northern Michigan University, M
Oakland University, M

University of Michigan, MDO
University of Michigan-Flint, M
Wayne State University, MD
Western Michigan University, MD

Minnesota

Bemidji State University, M
Minnesota State University Mankato, M
St. Cloud State University, M
University of Minnesota, Duluth, M
University of Minnesota, Twin Cities Campus, MD

Mississippi

Alcorn State University, M
Delta State University, M
Jackson State University, MD
Mississippi College, M
Mississippi State University, MD
University of Mississippi, MD
University of Mississippi Medical Center, MDO
University of Southern Mississippi, MD

Missouri

Central Missouri State University, M
Missouri State University, M
Northwest Missouri State University, M
Park University, B
Saint Louis University, MD
Southeast Missouri State University, M
Truman State University, M
University of Missouri-Columbia, MDO
University of Missouri-Kansas City, M
University of Missouri-Rolla, M
University of Missouri-St. Louis, MDO
Washington University in St. Louis, BDO

Montana

Montana State University, MD
The University of Montana-Missoula, MD

Nebraska

Creighton University, MDO
University of Nebraska at Kearney, M
University of Nebraska-Lincoln, MD
University of Nebraska Medical Center, MD
University of Nebraska at Omaha, M

Nevada

University of Nevada, Las Vegas, MD
University of Nevada, Reno, MD

New Hampshire

Dartmouth College, D

New Jersey

Fairleigh Dickinson University, College at Florham, BM
Fairleigh Dickinson University, Metropolitan Campus, BM
Georgian Court University, M
Montclair State University, MO
New Jersey Institute of Technology, MD
Princeton University, D
Ramapo College of New Jersey, B
Rutgers, The State University of New Jersey, Camden, M
Rutgers, The State University of New Jersey, Newark, BMD
Seton Hall University, MD
William Paterson University of New Jersey, M

New Mexico

Eastern New Mexico University, M
New Mexico Highlands University, M
New Mexico Institute of Mining and Technology, M
New Mexico State University, MD
University of New Mexico, MD

New York

Adelphi University, M
Brooklyn College of the City University of New York, MD
Buffalo State College, State University of New York, M

City College of the City University of New York, MD
College of Staten Island of the City University of New York, M
Cornell University, MD
Farmingdale State University of New York, B
Fordham University, MD
Hofstra University, M
Hunter College of the City University of New York, MD
Lehman College of the City University of New York, M
Long Island University, Brooklyn Campus, M
Long Island University, C.W. Post Campus, M
New York University, MDO
Queens College of the City University of New York, M
Rensselaer Polytechnic Institute, BMD
Rochester Institute of Technology, BM
Sage College of Albany, B
St. John's University, MD
Skidmore College, B
State University of New York at Binghamton, MD
State University of New York at Buffalo, MDO
State University of New York College at Brockport, M
State University of New York College at Oneonta, M
State University of New York Downstate Medical Center, MDO
State University of New York, Fredonia, M
State University of New York at New Paltz, M
State University of New York Upstate Medical University, MDO
Stony Brook University, State University of New York, DO
Syracuse University, MD
Touro College, MO
Union College, B
University at Albany, State University of New York, MD
University of Rochester, MDO
Vassar College, M
Wagner College, M

North Carolina

Appalachian State University, M
Duke University, DO
East Carolina University, MD
Fayetteville State University, M
Guilford College, B
North Carolina Agricultural and Technical State University, M
North Carolina Central University, M
North Carolina State University, MD
The University of North Carolina at Chapel Hill, MDO
The University of North Carolina at Charlotte, MD
The University of North Carolina at Greensboro, M
The University of North Carolina Wilmington, MD
Wake Forest University, MDO
Western Carolina University, M

North Dakota

North Dakota State University, MD
University of North Dakota, BMDO

Ohio

Bowling Green State University, MDO
Capital University, B
Case Western Reserve University, MDO
Cleveland State University, MD
Hiram College, B
John Carroll University, M
Kent State University, BMD
The Ohio State University, MD
Ohio University, MD
The University of Akron, M
University of Cincinnati, MDO
University of Dayton, MD
The University of Toledo, MD
Ursuline College, B
Wright State University, MD

Youngstown State University, M

Oklahoma

University of Central Oklahoma, M
University of Oklahoma Health Sciences Center, MDO
University of Tulsa, MDO

Oregon

Oregon Health & Science University, MDO
Portland State University, MD
University of Oregon, MD

Pennsylvania

Bloomsburg University of Pennsylvania, M
Bucknell University, M
California University of Pennsylvania, M
Carnegie Mellon University, BMD
Clarion University of Pennsylvania, M
Drexel University, MDO
Duquesne University, MDO
East Stroudsburg University of Pennsylvania, M
Edinboro University of Pennsylvania, M
Gwynedd-Mercy College, A
Indiana University of Pennsylvania, M
Lehigh University, BD
Millersville University of Pennsylvania, M
The Pennsylvania State University Abington College, B
The Pennsylvania State University Altoona College, B
The Pennsylvania State University Beaver Campus of the Commonwealth College, B
The Pennsylvania State University Berks Campus of the Berks-Lehigh Valley College, B
The Pennsylvania State University Delaware County Campus of the Commonwealth College, B
The Pennsylvania State University DuBois Campus of the Commonwealth College, B
The Pennsylvania State University at Erie, The Behrend College, B
The Pennsylvania State University Fayette Campus of the Commonwealth College, B
The Pennsylvania State University Hazleton Campus of the Commonwealth College, B
The Pennsylvania State University, Lehigh Valley Campus of the Berks-Lehigh Valley College, B
The Pennsylvania State University McKeesport Campus of the Commonwealth College, B
The Pennsylvania State University Mont Alto Campus of the Commonwealth College, B
The Pennsylvania State University New Kensington Campus of the Commonwealth College, B
The Pennsylvania State University Schuylkill Campus of the Capital College, B
The Pennsylvania State University Shenango Campus of the Commonwealth College, B
The Pennsylvania State University University Park Campus, BMD
The Pennsylvania State University Wilkes-Barre Campus of the Commonwealth College, B
The Pennsylvania State University Worthington Scranton Campus of the Commonwealth College, B
The Pennsylvania State University York Campus of the Commonwealth College, B
Saint Francis University, M
Saint Joseph's University, M
Shippensburg University of Pennsylvania, M
Swarthmore College, B
Temple University, MDO
Thomas Jefferson University, MDO
University of Pennsylvania, MDO
University of Pittsburgh, MD
Villanova University, M
West Chester University of Pennsylvania, M

Puerto Rico

Inter American University of Puerto Rico, Bayamón Campus, B
University of Puerto Rico, Mayagüez Campus, M
University of Puerto Rico, Medical Sciences Campus, MD

University of Puerto Rico, Río Piedras, MD

Rhode Island

Brown University, MDO
Rhode Island College, M
University of Rhode Island, MD

South Carolina

Charleston Southern University, B
Clemson University, MD
Medical University of South Carolina, MDO
University of South Carolina, MD
Winthrop University, M

South Dakota

South Dakota State University, MD
The University of South Dakota, MD

Tennessee

Austin Peay State University, M
East Tennessee State University, MD
Fisk University, M
Middle Tennessee State University, M
Tennessee State University, MD
Tennessee Technological University, M
University of Memphis, MD
The University of Tennessee, MD
Vanderbilt University, MDO

Texas

Angelo State University, M
Baylor University, MD
Lamar University, M
Midwestern State University, M
Prairie View A&M University, M
Sam Houston State University, M
Southern Methodist University, MD
Stephen F. Austin State University, M
Sul Ross State University, M
Tarleton State University, M
Texas A&M International University, M
Texas A&M University, MD
Texas A&M University-Commerce, M
Texas A&M University-Corpus Christi, M
Texas A&M University-Kingsville, M
Texas A&M University System Health Science Center, MDO
Texas Christian University, MO
Texas Southern University, M
Texas State University-San Marcos, M
Texas Tech University, MD
Texas Wesleyan University, B
Texas Woman's University, MD
University of Houston, MD
University of Houston-Clear Lake, M
University of the Incarnate Word, M
University of North Texas, MD
The University of Texas at Arlington, MD
The University of Texas at Austin, MD
The University of Texas at Brownsville, M
The University of Texas at El Paso, MD
The University of Texas Health Science Center at Houston, MDO
The University of Texas Health Science Center at San Antonio, MDPO
The University of Texas Medical Branch, MDO
The University of Texas-Pan American, M
The University of Texas of the Permian Basin, M
The University of Texas at San Antonio, MD
The University of Texas Southwestern Medical Center at Dallas, DO
The University of Texas at Tyler, M
West Texas A&M University, M

Utah

Brigham Young University, MD
University of Utah, MD
Utah State University, MD

Vermont

University of Vermont, MDO

Virginia

The College of William and Mary, M
George Mason University, MD

Hampton University, M
James Madison University, M
Lynchburg College, B
Old Dominion University, MD
University of Richmond, MO
University of Virginia, MD
Virginia Commonwealth University, MDO
Virginia Polytechnic Institute and State
  University, MD
Virginia State University, M

Washington

Central Washington University, M
Eastern Washington University, M
Heritage University, M
University of Washington, MD
Walla Walla College, M
Washington State University, MD
Western Washington University, M

West Virginia

Marshall University, MD
Salem International University, M
West Virginia University, MDO

Wisconsin

Marquette University, MD
University of Wisconsin-Eau Claire, M
University of Wisconsin-La Crosse, M
University of Wisconsin-Madison, MDO
University of Wisconsin-Milwaukee, MD
University of Wisconsin-Oshkosh, M
University of Wisconsin-Parkside, B

Alberta

University of Alberta, MDO
University of Calgary, MD
University of Lethbridge, M

British Columbia

Open Learning Agency, B
Simon Fraser University, MDO
The University of British Columbia, MDO
University of Victoria, MD

Manitoba

University of Manitoba, MDO

New Brunswick

Mount Allison University, M
Université de Moncton, M
University of New Brunswick Fredericton, MD
University of New Brunswick Saint John, MD

Newfoundland and Labrador

Memorial University of Newfoundland, MDO

Nova Scotia

Acadia University, M
Dalhousie University, MDO
St. Francis Xavier University, M

Ontario

Brock University, M
Carleton University, MD
Lakehead University, M
Laurentian University, M
McMaster University, MD
Queen's University at Kingston, MD
Trent University, MD
University of Guelph, MD
University of Ottawa, MD
University of Toronto, MDO
University of Waterloo, MD
The University of Western Ontario, MDO
University of Windsor, MD
York University, MD

Prince Edward Island

University of Prince Edward Island, M

Quebec

Concordia University, MDO
McGill University, MD

Université Laval, MDO
Université de Montréal, MDO
Université du Québec àMontréal, MD
Université de Sherbrooke, MD

Saskatchewan

University of Regina, MD
University of Saskatchewan, MDO

BIOLOGICAL AND PHYSICAL SCIENCES

Alabama

Enterprise-Ozark Community College, A
Jefferson Davis Community College, A
Marion Military Institute, A
Northeast Alabama Community College, A
The University of Alabama, B
The University of Alabama at Birmingham, B
University of Mobile, B

Alaska

University of Alaska Anchorage, B
University of Alaska Fairbanks, B

Arizona

Arizona Western College, A
Coconino Community College, A
Northland Pioneer College, A

Arkansas

Philander Smith College, B
Phillips Community College of the University of
  Arkansas, A
Southern Arkansas University-Magnolia, B
University of Central Arkansas, B

California

American River College, A
Cabrillo College, A
California State University, Fresno, B
Cañada College, A
Chabot College, A
College of Alameda, A
College of the Canyons, A
College of the Sequoias, A
Compton Community College, A
Cosumnes River College (Sacramento), A
Crafton Hills College, A
Cuyamaca College, A
Cypress College, A
Gavilan College, A
Glendale Community College, A
Golden West College, A
Imperial Valley College, A
Irvine Valley College, A
Lake Tahoe Community College, A
Laney College, A
Lassen Community College District, A
Los Angeles City College, A
The Master's College and Seminary, B
Merced College, A
Merritt College, A
Mt. San Jacinto College, A
Napa Valley College, A
Pasadena City College, A
Porterville College, A
Sacramento City College, A
San Francisco State University, B
Santa Ana College, A
Santa Clara University, B
Skyline College, A
Solano Community College, A
Southwestern College, A
Vanguard University of Southern California, B
Victor Valley College, A
Yuba College, A

Colorado

Adams State College, B
Arapahoe Community College, A
Colorado Christian University, B
Colorado Mountain College, A

Colorado Mountain College, Alpine Campus, A
Community College of Aurora, A
Lamar Community College, A
Morgan Community College, A
Northeastern Junior College, A
Otero Junior College, A
Red Rocks Community College, A
Trinidad State Junior College, A
United States Air Force Academy, B
University of Denver, B

Connecticut

Middlesex Community College, A
Mitchell College, A
Naugatuck Valley Community College, A
Quinnipiac University, B
Sacred Heart University, A

Florida

Chipola College, A
Daytona Beach Community College, A
Florida Institute of Technology, B
Okaloosa-Walton College, A
University of North Florida, B
University of South Florida, B
University of West Florida, B

Georgia

Abraham Baldwin Agricultural College, A
Andrew College, A
Clayton State University, A
Dalton State College, A
Georgia Highlands College, A
Georgia Military College, A
Georgia Perimeter College, A
Gordon College, A
South Georgia College, A
University of Georgia, B
Young Harris College, A

Guam

University of Guam, B

Idaho

North Idaho College, A

Illinois

City Colleges of Chicago, Wilbur Wright College, A
College of DuPage, A
College of Lake County, A
Concordia University, B
Danville Area Community College, A
Elgin Community College, A
Eureka College, B
Heartland Community College, A
Highland Community College, A
Illinois Central College, A
Illinois Eastern Community Colleges, Frontier
  Community College, A
Illinois Eastern Community Colleges, Lincoln Trail
  College, A
Illinois Eastern Community Colleges, Olney Central
  College, A
Illinois Eastern Community Colleges, Wabash Valley
  College, A
John Wood Community College, A
Judson College, B
Kankakee Community College, A
Kaskaskia College, A
Lake Land College, A
Lewis and Clark Community College, A
Lincoln College, A
Lincoln Land Community College, A
McHenry County College, A
Moraine Valley Community College, A
Morton College, A
National-Louis University, B
North Central College, B
North Park University, B
Northwestern University, B
Oakton Community College, A
Olivet Nazarene University, B
Parkland College, A
Rend Lake College, A
Richland Community College, A

Rockford College, B
Saint Xavier University, B
Shawnee Community College, A
Spoon River College, A
Waubonsee Community College, A
William Rainey Harper College, A

Indiana

Ancilla College, A
Huntington University, B
Indiana University East, A
Indiana University Kokomo, B
Oakland City University, B
Purdue University, B
Purdue University Calumet, B
Saint Mary-of-the-Woods College, B
Tri-State University, A
University of Saint Francis, B
University of Southern Indiana, B
Valparaiso University, A

Iowa

Buena Vista University, B
Coe College, B
Ellsworth Community College, A
Iowa Central Community College, A
Iowa Lakes Community College, A
Iowa Wesleyan College, B
Kirkwood Community College, A
Marshalltown Community College, A
Palmer College of Chiropractic, B
Simpson College, B
University of Dubuque, B
University of Northern Iowa, B
Upper Iowa University, B

Kansas

Central Christian College of Kansas, A
Cloud County Community College, A
Coffeyville Community College, A
Colby Community College, A
Dodge City Community College, A
Donnelly College, A
Fort Hays State University, B
Garden City Community College, A
Independence Community College, A
Neosho County Community College, A
Pratt Community College, A
Seward County Community College, A
Tabor College, B

Kentucky

Alice Lloyd College, B
Brescia University, B
Elizabethtown Community and Technical College, A
St. Catharine College, A

Louisiana

Delgado Community College, A
Louisiana State University in Shreveport, B

Maine

College of the Atlantic, B

Maryland

Anne Arundel Community College, A
Baltimore City Community College, A
Chesapeake College, A
Howard Community College, A
The Johns Hopkins University, B
St. Mary's College of Maryland, B
Villa Julie College, AB

Massachusetts

Atlantic Union College, B
Cape Cod Community College, A
Eastern Nazarene College, B
Greenfield Community College, A
Harvard University, B
Massachusetts Bay Community College, A
Massachusetts College of Liberal Arts, B
Northern Essex Community College, A
University of Massachusetts Amherst, B

Worcester State College, B

Michigan

Alma College, B
Calvin College, B
Concordia University, B
Eastern Michigan University, B
Glen Oaks Community College, A
Grand Valley State University, B
Kirtland Community College, A
Lansing Community College, A
Madonna University, AB
Marygrove College, B
Michigan State University, B
Mid Michigan Community College, A
Rochester College, B
St. Clair County Community College, A

Minnesota

Augsburg College, B
Bemidji State University, B
College of Saint Benedict, B
Concordia University, St. Paul, B
Crown College, A
Minnesota State Community and Technical College-Fergus Falls, A
Minnesota State University Mankato, B
Rainy River Community College, A
Ridgewater College, A
Vermilion Community College, A
Winona State University, B

Mississippi

Copiah-Lincoln Community College, A
Delta State University, B
East Central Community College, A
East Mississippi Community College, A
Itawamba Community College, A
Jones County Junior College, A
Mississippi Gulf Coast Community College, A
Mississippi State University, B
Mississippi University for Women, B
Northeast Mississippi Community College, A
Southwest Mississippi Community College, A

Missouri

Avila University, B
Cottey College, A
Jefferson College, A
Longview Community College, A
Maple Woods Community College, A
Maryville University of Saint Louis, B
Northwest Missouri State University, B
Penn Valley Community College, A
St. Louis Community College at Meramec, A
Washington University in St. Louis, B

Montana

Little Big Horn College, A
Montana State University-Northern, B
Montana Tech of The University of Montana, AB

Nebraska

Midland Lutheran College, B
Northeast Community College, A
Peru State College, B
Southeast Community College, Beatrice Campus, A
York College, B

Nevada

Community College of Southern Nevada, A
Sierra Nevada College, B

New Hampshire

Saint Anselm College, B
University of New Hampshire, B

New Jersey

Brookdale Community College, A
Burlington County College, A
Cumberland County College, A
Fairleigh Dickinson University, Metropolitan Campus, A
Middlesex County College, A
Passaic County Community College, A

Saint Peter's College, B
Salem Community College, A
Sussex County Community College, A

New Mexico

New Mexico Junior College, A
New Mexico Military Institute, A
University of New Mexico-Los Alamos Branch, A
Western New Mexico University, B

New York

Adirondack Community College, A
Alfred University, B
Bard College, B
Borough of Manhattan Community College of the City University of New York, A
Canisius College, B
Clinton Community College, A
Columbia-Greene Community College, A
Corning Community College, A
Dowling College, B
Dutchess Community College, A
Finger Lakes Community College, A
Fordham University, B
Fulton-Montgomery Community College, A
Houghton College, B
Le Moyne College, B
Medgar Evers College of the City University of New York, A
Monroe Community College, A
Niagara County Community College, A
North Country Community College, A
Onondaga Community College, A
Orange County Community College, A
Rensselaer Polytechnic Institute, B
Roberts Wesleyan College, B
Rockland Community College, A
Sarah Lawrence College, B
Schenectady County Community College, A
State University of New York College of Agriculture and Technology at Cobleskill, A
State University of New York College of Environmental Science and Forestry, B
State University of New York College of Technology at Alfred, A
State University of New York College of Technology at Canton, A
State University of New York Empire State College, AB
State University of New York, Fredonia, B
Suffolk County Community College, A
Tompkins Cortland Community College, A
Ulster County Community College, A
Union College, B
United States Military Academy, B
University of Rochester, B
Westchester Community College, A

North Carolina

Caldwell Community College and Technical Institute, A
Chowan University, B
Cleveland Community College, A
Guilford Technical Community College, A
Isothermal Community College, A
Johnson C. Smith University, B
Lees-McRae College, B
Louisburg College, A
Mars Hill College, B
Methodist College, B
Mitchell Community College, A
Mount Olive College, A
Rockingham Community College, A
Sandhills Community College, A
Southeastern Community College, A
Wayne Community College, A

North Dakota

Fort Berthold Community College, A
Turtle Mountain Community College, A

Ohio

Antioch College, B
Bowling Green State University-Firelands College, A
Cedarville University, B

John Carroll University, B
Kent State University, Stark Campus, A
Lakeland Community College, A
Lorain County Community College, A
Miami University-Middletown Campus, A
Mount Vernon Nazarene University, B
Ohio University, A
Ohio University-Chillicothe, A
Ohio University-Eastern, B
Ohio University-Lancaster, A
Ohio University-Southern Campus, A
Ohio University-Zanesville, A
Shawnee State University, B
The University of Akron, B
University of Cincinnati, A
The University of Findlay, B
The University of Toledo, B
Walsh University, B
Washington State Community College, A
Wilmington College, B
Wright State University, B
Xavier University, B

Oklahoma

Murray State College, A
Northern Oklahoma College, A
Oklahoma Baptist University, B
Oklahoma City University, B
Oklahoma Panhandle State University, B
Oklahoma Wesleyan University, B
Redlands Community College, A

Oregon

Central Oregon Community College, A
Concordia University, B
Eastern Oregon University, B
Linn-Benton Community College, A
Marylhurst University, B
Oregon State University, B
Portland Community College, A
Portland State University, B
Treasure Valley Community College, A
Umpqua Community College, A
University of Oregon, B
Warner Pacific College, B

Pennsylvania

Alvernia College, B
Bloomsburg University of Pennsylvania, B
California University of Pennsylvania, B
Cedar Crest College, B
Cheyney University of Pennsylvania, B
Clarion University of Pennsylvania, B
Community College of Philadelphia, A
Delaware County Community College, A
Drexel University, B
East Stroudsburg University of Pennsylvania, B
Edinboro University of Pennsylvania, B
Gannon University, B
Gettysburg College, B
Indiana University of Pennsylvania, B
Keystone College, B
King's College, B
Kutztown University of Pennsylvania, B
Lehigh University, B
Lock Haven University of Pennsylvania, B
Luzerne County Community College, A
Manor College, A
Mansfield University of Pennsylvania, B
The Pennsylvania State University Abington
    College, B
The Pennsylvania State University Altoona
    College, AB
The Pennsylvania State University Beaver Campus
    of the Commonwealth College, AB
The Pennsylvania State University Berks Campus of
    the Berks-Lehigh Valley College, B
The Pennsylvania State University Delaware County
    Campus of the Commonwealth College, B
The Pennsylvania State University DuBois Campus
    of the Commonwealth College, AB
The Pennsylvania State University at Erie, The
    Behrend College, B
The Pennsylvania State University Fayette Campus
    of the Commonwealth College, AB

The Pennsylvania State University Hazleton
    Campus of the Commonwealth College, B
The Pennsylvania State University, Lehigh Valley
    Campus of the Berks-Lehigh Valley College, B
The Pennsylvania State University McKeesport
    Campus of the Commonwealth College, AB
The Pennsylvania State University Mont Alto
    Campus of the Commonwealth College, B
The Pennsylvania State University New Kensington
    Campus of the Commonwealth College, AB
The Pennsylvania State University Schuylkill
    Campus of the Capital College, AB
The Pennsylvania State University Shenango
    Campus of the Commonwealth College, AB
The Pennsylvania State University University Park
    Campus, B
The Pennsylvania State University Wilkes-Barre
    Campus of the Commonwealth College, B
The Pennsylvania State University Worthington
    Scranton Campus of the Commonwealth
    College, B
The Pennsylvania State University York Campus of
    the Commonwealth College, B
University of Pittsburgh, B
Ursinus College, B
Valley Forge Military College, A

Puerto Rico

Bayamon Central University, B
Pontifical Catholic University of Puerto Rico, B
Universidad del Este, A
University of Puerto Rico, Aguadilla University
    College, A
University of Puerto Rico at Bayamón, A
University of Puerto Rico, Río Piedras, B

Rhode Island

Community College of Rhode Island, A

South Carolina

Aiken Technical College, A
Charleston Southern University, B
Erskine College, B
Florence-Darlington Technical College, A
Piedmont Technical College, A
Spartanburg Technical College, A
Technical College of the Lowcountry, A
Trident Technical College, A
University of South Carolina Lancaster, A
University of South Carolina Salkehatchie, A
University of South Carolina Union, A

South Dakota

Northern State University, B

Tennessee

Belmont University, B
Freed-Hardeman University, B
King College, B
Lee University, B
Martin Methodist College, A
Middle Tennessee State University, B
Tennessee Temple University, B
Trevecca Nazarene University, B
Union University, B

Texas

Angelina College, A
Angelo State University, B
Coastal Bend College, A
Frank Phillips College, A
Galveston College, A
Hill College of the Hill Junior College District, A
Jacksonville College, A
Kilgore College, A
McMurry University, B
Navarro College, A
North Central Texas College, A
North Harris College, A
Paris Junior College, A
Sam Houston State University, B
San Antonio College, A
South Plains College, A
Southwest Texas Junior College, A
Texas A&M University at Galveston, B

Texas Southern University, B
Texas Tech University, B
University of Houston-Downtown, B
The University of Texas at San Antonio, B
Weatherford College, A

Utah

Brigham Young University, B

Vermont

Castleton State College, B
Lyndon State College, B
Sterling College, AB

Virginia

Averett University, B
Central Virginia Community College, A
Dabney S. Lancaster Community College, A
Danville Community College, A
Eastern Shore Community College, A
Germanna Community College, A
J. Sargeant Reynolds Community College, A
Lord Fairfax Community College, A
Mountain Empire Community College, A
New River Community College, A
Northern Virginia Community College, A
Patrick Henry Community College, A
Piedmont Virginia Community College, A
Rappahannock Community College, A
Southside Virginia Community College, A
Southwest Virginia Community College, A
Thomas Nelson Community College, A
Tidewater Community College, A
Virginia Commonwealth University, B
Virginia Highlands Community College, A
Virginia Western Community College, A
Wytheville Community College, A

Washington

Centralia College, A
Eastern Washington University, B
The Evergreen State College, B
Heritage University, AB
Highline Community College, A
Peninsula College, A
Seattle Central Community College, A
Seattle University, B
Skagit Valley College, A
South Seattle Community College, A
Tacoma Community College, A
Western Washington University, B

West Virginia

Bluefield State College, AB
New River Community and Technical College, A
Potomac State College of West Virginia
    University, A

Wisconsin

Marian College of Fond du Lac, B
Northland College, B
St. Norbert College, B
University of Wisconsin-Platteville, B
University of Wisconsin-Richland, A
University of Wisconsin-Superior, B
University of Wisconsin-Whitewater, B

Wyoming

Laramie County Community College, A
Northwest College, A
Sheridan College-Sheridan and Gillette, A
Western Wyoming Community College, A

Alberta

Athabasca University, B
University of Alberta, B
University of Lethbridge, B

British Columbia

Simon Fraser University, B
Trinity Western University, B

University of Northern British Columbia, B

New Brunswick

Mount Allison University, B
Université de Moncton, B
University of New Brunswick Fredericton, B

Newfoundland and Labrador

Memorial University of Newfoundland, B

Nova Scotia

Cape Breton University, B
Mount Saint Vincent University, B
St. Francis Xavier University, B

Ontario

Brock University, B
Carleton University, B
Lakehead University, B
McMaster University, B
Redeemer University College, B
Trent University, B
University of Ottawa, B
University of Toronto, B
University of Waterloo, B
The University of Western Ontario, B
University of Windsor, B
York University, B

Quebec

Bishop's University, B

Saskatchewan

University of Regina, B

BIOLOGICAL ANTHROPOLOGY

Alabama

Alabama State University, D

District of Columbia

The George Washington University, MD

Georgia

Georgia State University, MDO

Hawaii

University of Hawaii at Manoa, D

Illinois

Illinois State University, D
Loyola University Chicago, MD
University of Illinois at Chicago, D
University of Illinois at Urbana-Champaign, MDO

Indiana

Indiana University Bloomington, MDO

Iowa

The University of Iowa, MDO

Kansas

University of Kansas, D

Kentucky

University of Kentucky, MD

Massachusetts

Harvard University, MD

Michigan

Michigan State University, D
Wayne State University, D

Minnesota

University of Minnesota, Twin Cities Campus, MDO

Missouri

University of Missouri-St. Louis, D

New Jersey

Rutgers, The State University of New Jersey, New
   Brunswick/Piscataway, D

North Carolina

Duke University, D

Ohio

Kent State University, D
The Ohio State University, MD

Oregon

Portland State University, MD

Pennsylvania

DeSales University, O
Mercyhurst College, M
University of Pennsylvania, MD

Tennessee

Vanderbilt University, D

Virginia

The College of William and Mary, D
University of Virginia, MD

Washington

University of Washington, MD

Wisconsin

University of Wisconsin-Madison, MD
University of Wisconsin-Milwaukee, M

Alberta

University of Alberta, MDO

British Columbia

The University of British Columbia, D

Ontario

The University of Western Ontario, M

BIOLOGY/BIOLOGICAL SCIENCES

Alabama

Alabama Agricultural and Mechanical University, B
Alabama Southern Community College, A
Alabama State University, B
Athens State University, B
Auburn University, B
Auburn University Montgomery, B
Birmingham-Southern College, B
Calhoun Community College, A
Chattahoochee Valley Community College, A
Faulkner University, B
Huntingdon College, B
Jacksonville State University, B
Jefferson Davis Community College, A
Judson College, B
Lawson State Community College, A
Miles College, B
Oakwood College, B
Samford University, B
Spring Hill College, B
Stillman College, B
Talladega College, B
Troy University, B
Tuskegee University, B
The University of Alabama, B
The University of Alabama at Birmingham, B
The University of Alabama in Huntsville, B
University of Mobile, B
University of Montevallo, B
University of North Alabama, B
University of South Alabama, B

The University of West Alabama, B

Alaska

University of Alaska Fairbanks, B
University of Alaska Southeast, B

Arizona

Arizona State University, B
Arizona State University at the Polytechnic
   Campus, B
Arizona State University West, B
Arizona Western College, A
Cochise College (Douglas), A
Cochise College (Sierra Vista), A
Eastern Arizona College, A
Grand Canyon University, B
Mesa Community College, A
Northern Arizona University, B
Prescott College, B
South Mountain Community College, A
The University of Arizona, B

Arkansas

Arkansas State University, B
Arkansas Tech University, B
Harding University, B
Henderson State University, B
Hendrix College, B
John Brown University, B
Lyon College, B
Ouachita Baptist University, B
Philander Smith College, B
Phillips Community College of the University of
   Arkansas, A
Southern Arkansas University-Magnolia, B
University of Arkansas, B
University of Arkansas at Little Rock, B
University of Arkansas at Monticello, B
University of Arkansas at Pine Bluff, B
University of Central Arkansas, B
University of the Ozarks, B
Williams Baptist College, B

California

Allan Hancock College, A
Antelope Valley College, A
Azusa Pacific University, B
Bakersfield College, A
Biola University, B
Butte College, A
California Baptist University, B
California Institute of Technology, B
California Lutheran University, B
California Polytechnic State University, San Luis
   Obispo, B
California State Polytechnic University, Pomona, B
California State University, Bakersfield, B
California State University Channel Islands, B
California State University, Chico, B
California State University, Dominguez Hills, B
California State University, East Bay, B
California State University, Fresno, B
California State University, Fullerton, B
California State University, Long Beach, B
California State University, Los Angeles, B
California State University, Northridge, B
California State University, Sacramento, B
California State University, San Bernardino, B
California State University, San Marcos, B
California State University, Stanislaus, B
Cañada College, A
Cerritos College, A
Chabot College, A
Chaffey College, A
Chapman University, B
Citrus College, A
Claremont McKenna College, B
Cleveland Chiropractic College-Los Angeles
   Campus, AB
College of Alameda, A
College of the Canyons, A
College of the Desert, A
College of Marin, A
College of San Mateo, A
College of the Sequoias, A
College of the Siskiyous, A

Columbia College, A
Compton Community College, A
Concordia University, B
Contra Costa College, A
Cosumnes River College (Sacramento), A
Crafton Hills College, A
Cuesta College, A
Cypress College, A
De Anza College, A
Dominican University of California, B
East Los Angeles College, A
El Camino College, A
Evergreen Valley College, A
Feather River College, A
Folsom Lake College, A
Foothill College, A
Fresno Pacific University, AB
Fullerton College, A
Gavilan College, A
Golden West College, A
Grossmont College, A
Harvey Mudd College, B
Holy Names University, B
Humboldt State University, B
Irvine Valley College, A
Lassen Community College District, A
Long Beach City College, A
Los Angeles City College, A
Los Angeles Harbor College, A
Los Angeles Mission College, A
Los Angeles Southwest College, A
Los Angeles Valley College, A
Los Medanos College, A
Loyola Marymount University, B
The Master's College and Seminary, B
Mendocino College, A
Mills College, B
MiraCosta College, A
Modesto Junior College, A
Monterey Peninsula College, A
Moorpark College, A
Mount St. Mary's College, B
National University, B
Notre Dame de Namur University, B
Occidental College, B
Ohlone College, A
Orange Coast College, A
Oxnard College, A
Pacific Union College, B
Palo Verde College, A
Palomar College, A
Pasadena City College, A
Pepperdine University, B
Pitzer College, B
Point Loma Nazarene University, B
Pomona College, B
Porterville College, A
Reedley College, A
Saddleback College, A
Saint Mary's College of California, B
San Bernardino Valley College, A
San Diego Christian College, B
San Diego City College, A
San Diego Mesa College, A
San Diego Miramar College, A
San Diego State University, B
San Francisco State University, B
San Joaquin Delta College, A
San Jose State University, B
Santa Ana College, A
Santa Barbara City College, A
Santa Clara University, B
Santa Monica College, A
Santa Rosa Junior College, A
Santiago Canyon College, A
Scripps College, B
Sierra College, A
Skyline College, A
Solano Community College, A
Sonoma State University, B
Southwestern College, A
Stanford University, B
Taft College, A
University of California, Berkeley, B
University of California, Davis, B
University of California, Irvine, B

University of California, Los Angeles, B
University of California, Riverside, B
University of California, San Diego, B
University of California, Santa Barbara, B
University of California, Santa Cruz, B
University of La Verne, B
University of the Pacific, B
University of Redlands, B
University of San Diego, B
University of San Francisco, B
University of Southern California, B
Vanguard University of Southern California, B
Ventura College, A
Victor Valley College, A
West Hills Community College, A
West Los Angeles College, A
West Valley College, A
Westmont College, B
Whittier College, B
Yuba College, A

Colorado

Adams State College, B
Colorado Christian University, B
The Colorado College, B
Colorado Mountain College, A
Colorado Mountain College, Alpine Campus, A
Colorado State University, B
Colorado State University-Pueblo, B
Fort Lewis College, B
Lamar Community College, A
Mesa State College, AB
Metropolitan State College of Denver, B
Northeastern Junior College, A
Otero Junior College, A
Red Rocks Community College, A
Regis University, B
Trinidad State Junior College, A
United States Air Force Academy, B
University of Colorado at Colorado Springs, B
University of Colorado at Denver and Health
  Sciences Center - Downtown Denver Campus, B
University of Denver, B
University of Northern Colorado, B
Western State College of Colorado, B

Connecticut

Albertus Magnus College, B
Central Connecticut State University, B
Connecticut College, B
Eastern Connecticut State University, B
Fairfield University, B
Northwestern Connecticut Community College, A
Post University, B
Quinnipiac University, B
Sacred Heart University, AB
Saint Joseph College, B
Southern Connecticut State University, B
Trinity College, B
University of Bridgeport, B
University of Connecticut, B
University of Hartford, B
University of New Haven, B
Wesleyan University, B
Western Connecticut State University, B
Yale University, B

Delaware

Delaware State University, B
University of Delaware, B
Wesley College, B

District of Columbia

American University, B
The Catholic University of America, B
Gallaudet University, B
The George Washington University, B
Georgetown University, B
Howard University, B
Trinity (Washington) University, B
University of the District of Columbia, B

Florida

Ave Maria University, B
Barry University, B

Bethune-Cookman College, B
Clearwater Christian College, B
Daytona Beach Community College, A
Eckerd College, B
Edward Waters College, B
Florida Agricultural and Mechanical University, B
Florida Atlantic University, B
Florida Institute of Technology, B
Florida International University, B
Florida Memorial College, B
Florida Southern College, B
Florida State University, B
Gulf Coast Community College, A
Indian River Community College, A
Jacksonville University, B
Manatee Community College, A
Miami Dade College, A
New College of Florida, B
Nova Southeastern University, B
Okaloosa-Walton College, A
Palm Beach Atlantic University, B
Palm Beach Community College, A
Pensacola Junior College, A
Rollins College, B
Saint Leo University, B
St. Thomas University, B
Southeastern University, B
Stetson University, B
University of Central Florida, B
University of Miami, B
University of North Florida, B
University of South Florida, B
The University of Tampa, AB
University of West Florida, B
Warner Southern College, B

Georgia

Abraham Baldwin Agricultural College, A
Agnes Scott College, B
Albany State University, B
Andrew College, A
Armstrong Atlantic State University, B
Atlanta Metropolitan College, A
Augusta State University, B
Bainbridge College, A
Berry College, B
Brenau University, B
Brewton-Parker College, AB
Clark Atlanta University, B
Clayton State University, B
Coastal Georgia Community College, A
Columbus State University, B
Covenant College, B
Dalton State College, A
Darton College, A
East Georgia College, A
Emmanuel College, B
Emory University, B
Fort Valley State University, B
Gainesville College, A
Georgia College & State University, B
Georgia Institute of Technology, B
Georgia Perimeter College, A
Georgia Southern University, B
Georgia Southwestern State University, B
Georgia State University, B
Gordon College, A
Kennesaw State University, B
LaGrange College, B
Life University, B
Macon State College, A
Mercer University, B
Morehouse College, B
North Georgia College & State University, B
Oglethorpe University, B
Paine College, B
Piedmont College, B
Reinhardt College, B
Savannah State University, B
Shorter College, B
South Georgia College, A
Southern Polytechnic State University, B
Spelman College, B
Thomas University, B
Toccoa Falls College, B
University of Georgia, B

University of West Georgia, B
Valdosta State University, B
Waycross College, A
Wesleyan College, B
Young Harris College, A

Guam

University of Guam, B

Hawaii

Brigham Young University-Hawaii, B
Chaminade University of Honolulu, B
Hawaii Pacific University, B
University of Hawaii at Hilo, B
University of Hawaii at Manoa, B

Idaho

Albertson College of Idaho, B
Boise State University, B
Brigham Young University -Idaho, A
College of Southern Idaho, A
Idaho State University, AB
Lewis-Clark State College, B
North Idaho College, A
Northwest Nazarene University, B
University of Idaho, B

Illinois

Augustana College, B
Aurora University, B
Benedictine University, B
Blackburn College, B
Bradley University, B
Chicago State University, B
City Colleges of Chicago, Harold Washington
    College, A
City Colleges of Chicago, Kennedy-King College, A
City Colleges of Chicago, Olive-Harvey College, A
Concordia University, B
Danville Area Community College, A
DePaul University, B
Dominican University, B
East-West University, B
Eastern Illinois University, B
Elmhurst College, B
Eureka College, B
Governors State University, B
Greenville College, B
Illinois College, B
Illinois Institute of Technology, B
Illinois State University, B
Illinois Wesleyan University, B
John A. Logan College, A
Joliet Junior College, A
Judson College, B
Knox College, B
Lake Forest College, B
Lewis and Clark Community College, A
Lewis University, B
Lincoln College, A
Loyola University Chicago, B
MacMurray College, B
McKendree College, B
Millikin University, B
Monmouth College, B
National-Louis University, B
North Central College, B
North Park University, B
Northeastern Illinois University, B
Northern Illinois University, B
Northwestern University, B
Olivet Nazarene University, B
Principia College, B
Quincy University, B
Rockford College, B
Roosevelt University, B
Saint Xavier University, B
Sauk Valley Community College, A
Southern Illinois University Carbondale, B
Southern Illinois University Edwardsville, B
Spoon River College, A
Trinity Christian College, B
Trinity International University, B
University of Chicago, B
University of Illinois at Chicago, B
University of Illinois at Springfield, B

University of Illinois at Urbana-Champaign, B
University of St. Francis, B
Western Illinois University, B
Wheaton College, B
William Rainey Harper College, A

Indiana

Ancilla College, A
Anderson University, B
Ball State University, B
Bethel College, B
Butler University, B
DePauw University, B
Earlham College, B
Franklin College, B
Goshen College, B
Grace College, B
Hanover College, B
Huntington University, B
Indiana State University, B
Indiana University Bloomington, B
Indiana University East, B
Indiana University Kokomo, B
Indiana University Northwest, B
Indiana University-Purdue University Fort
    Wayne, AB
Indiana University-Purdue University Indianapolis, B
Indiana University South Bend, AB
Indiana University Southeast, B
Indiana Wesleyan University, AB
Manchester College, B
Marian College, B
Martin University, B
Oakland City University, B
Purdue University, B
Purdue University Calumet, B
Purdue University North Central, B
Rose-Hulman Institute of Technology, B
Saint Joseph's College, B
Saint Mary-of-the-Woods College, B
Saint Mary's College, B
Taylor University, B
Tri-State University, B
University of Evansville, B
University of Indianapolis, B
University of Notre Dame, B
University of Saint Francis, B
University of Southern Indiana, B
Valparaiso University, B
Vincennes University, A
Wabash College, B

Iowa

Ashford University, B
Briar Cliff University, B
Buena Vista University, B
Central College, B
Clarke College, B
Coe College, B
Cornell College, B
Dordt College, B
Drake University, B
Ellsworth Community College, A
Graceland University, B
Grand View College, B
Grinnell College, B
Hawkeye Community College, A
Iowa Lakes Community College, A
Iowa State University of Science and Technology, B
Iowa Wesleyan College, B
Kirkwood Community College, A
Loras College, B
Luther College, B
Morningside College, B
Mount Mercy College, B
Northwestern College, B
St. Ambrose University, B
Simpson College, B
University of Dubuque, AB
The University of Iowa, B
University of Northern Iowa, B
Upper Iowa University, B
Wartburg College, B

William Penn University, B

Kansas

Allen County Community College, A
Baker University, B
Barton County Community College, A
Benedictine College, B
Bethany College, B
Bethel College, B
Butler Community College, A
Cloud County Community College, A
Coffeyville Community College, A
Colby Community College, A
Dodge City Community College, A
Emporia State University, B
Fort Hays State University, B
Friends University, B
Highland Community College, A
Hutchinson Community College and Area Vocational
    School, A
Independence Community College, A
Kansas State University, B
Kansas Wesleyan University, B
Labette Community College, A
McPherson College, B
MidAmerica Nazarene University, B
Newman University, B
Ottawa University, B
Pittsburg State University, B
Pratt Community College, A
Seward County Community College, A
Southwestern College, B
Sterling College, B
Tabor College, B
University of Kansas, B
University of Saint Mary, B
Washburn University, B
Wichita State University, B

Kentucky

Alice Lloyd College, B
Asbury College, B
Bellarmine University, B
Berea College, B
Brescia University, B
Campbellsville University, B
Centre College, B
Eastern Kentucky University, B
Georgetown College, B
Kentucky State University, B
Kentucky Wesleyan College, B
Lindsey Wilson College, B
Midway College, B
Morehead State University, B
Murray State University, B
Northern Kentucky University, B
Pikeville College, B
St. Catharine College, A
Thomas More College, AB
Transylvania University, B
Union College, B
University of the Cumberlands, B
University of Kentucky, B
University of Louisville, B
Western Kentucky University, B

Louisiana

Centenary College of Louisiana, B
Dillard University, B
Grambling State University, B
Louisiana College, B
Louisiana State University and Agricultural and
    Mechanical College, B
Louisiana State University at Alexandria, AB
Louisiana State University in Shreveport, B
Louisiana Tech University, B
Loyola University New Orleans, B
McNeese State University, B
Nicholls State University, B
Northwestern State University of Louisiana, B
Our Lady of Holy Cross College, B
Our Lady of the Lake College, B
Southeastern Louisiana University, B
Southern University and Agricultural and Mechanical
    College, B
Southern University at New Orleans, B

Southern University at Shreveport, A
Tulane University, B
University of Louisiana at Lafayette, B
University of Louisiana at Monroe, B
University of New Orleans, B
Xavier University of Louisiana, B

Maine

Bates College, B
Bowdoin College, B
Colby College, B
College of the Atlantic, B
Husson College, B
Kennebec Valley Community College, A
Saint Joseph's College of Maine, B
University of Maine, B
The University of Maine at Augusta, A
University of Maine at Farmington, B
University of Maine at Fort Kent, B
University of Maine at Machias, B
University of Maine at Presque Isle, B
University of New England, B
University of Southern Maine, B

Maryland

Anne Arundel Community College, A
Bowie State University, B
Cecil Community College, A
College of Notre Dame of Maryland, B
College of Southern Maryland, A
Columbia Union College, B
Coppin State University, B
Frederick Community College, A
Frostburg State University, B
Garrett College, A
Goucher College, B
Hood College, B
The Johns Hopkins University, B
Loyola College in Maryland, B
McDaniel College, B
Morgan State University, B
Mount St. Mary's University, B
St. Mary's College of Maryland, B
Salisbury University, B
Towson University, B
University of Maryland, Baltimore County, B
University of Maryland, College Park, B
University of Maryland Eastern Shore, B
Villa Julie College, AB
Washington College, B

Massachusetts

American International College, B
Amherst College, B
Anna Maria College, B
Assumption College, B
Atlantic Union College, B
Bay Path College, B
Berkshire Community College, A
Boston College, B
Boston University, B
Brandeis University, B
Bridgewater State College, B
Clark University, B
College of the Holy Cross, B
Curry College, B
Eastern Nazarene College, B
Elms College, B
Emmanuel College, B
Fitchburg State College, B
Framingham State College, B
Gordon College, B
Hampshire College, B
Harvard University, B
Holyoke Community College, A
Massachusetts College of Liberal Arts, B
Massachusetts Institute of Technology, B
Merrimack College, B
Mount Holyoke College, B
Northeastern University, B
Pine Manor College, AB
Regis College, B
Roxbury Community College, A
Salem State College, B
Simmons College, B
Simon's Rock College of Bard, B

Smith College, B
Springfield College, B
Springfield Technical Community College, A
Stonehill College, B
Suffolk University, B
Tufts University, B
University of Massachusetts Amherst, B
University of Massachusetts Boston, B
University of Massachusetts Dartmouth, B
University of Massachusetts Lowell, B
Wellesley College, B
Western New England College, B
Westfield State College, B
Wheaton College, B
Williams College, B
Worcester Polytechnic Institute, B
Worcester State College, B

Michigan

Adrian College, AB
Albion College, B
Alma College, B
Alpena Community College, A
Andrews University, B
Aquinas College, B
Calvin College, B
Central Michigan University, B
Concordia University, B
Cornerstone University, B
Eastern Michigan University, B
Ferris State University, B
Gogebic Community College, A
Grand Valley State University, B
Hillsdale College, B
Hope College, B
Kalamazoo College, B
Kellogg Community College, A
Lansing Community College, A
Macomb Community College, A
Madonna University, B
Marygrove College, B
Michigan State University, B
Michigan Technological University, B
Mid Michigan Community College, A
Monroe County Community College, A
Northern Michigan University, B
Northwestern Michigan College, A
Oakland University, B
Olivet College, B
Saginaw Valley State University, B
Siena Heights University, B
Spring Arbor University, B
University of Detroit Mercy, B
University of Michigan, B
University of Michigan-Dearborn, B
University of Michigan-Flint, B
Washtenaw Community College, A
Wayne State University, B
Western Michigan University, B

Minnesota

Augsburg College, B
Bemidji State University, B
Bethany Lutheran College, B
Bethel University, B
Carleton College, B
College of Saint Benedict, B
College of St. Catherine, B
The College of St. Scholastica, B
Concordia College, B
Concordia University, St. Paul, B
Crown College, AB
Gustavus Adolphus College, B
Hamline University, B
Macalester College, B
Metropolitan State University, B
Minnesota State University Mankato, B
Minnesota State University Moorhead, B
North Hennepin Community College, A
Northwestern College, B
St. Cloud State University, B
Saint John's University, B
Saint Mary's University of Minnesota, B
St. Olaf College, B
Southwest Minnesota State University, B
University of Minnesota, Duluth, B

University of Minnesota, Morris, B
University of Minnesota, Twin Cities Campus, B
University of St. Thomas, B
Vermilion Community College, A
Winona State University, B

Mississippi

Alcorn State University, B
Belhaven College, B
Blue Mountain College, B
Coahoma Community College, A
Copiah-Lincoln Community College, A
Delta State University, B
East Central Community College, A
Hinds Community College, A
Holmes Community College, A
Itawamba Community College, A
Jackson State University, B
Jones County Junior College, A
Millsaps College, B
Mississippi College, B
Mississippi Delta Community College, A
Mississippi State University, B
Mississippi University for Women, B
Mississippi Valley State University, B
Northeast Mississippi Community College, A
Rust College, B
Southwest Mississippi Community College, A
Tougaloo College, B
University of Mississippi, B
University of Southern Mississippi, B
William Carey College, B

Missouri

Avila University, B
Central Methodist University, B
Central Missouri State University, B
Cleveland Chiropractic College-Kansas City
   Campus, AB
College of the Ozarks, B
Columbia College, B
Crowder College, A
Culver-Stockton College, B
Drury University, B
East Central College, A
Evangel University, B
Fontbonne University, B
Hannibal-LaGrange College, B
Lincoln University, B
Lindenwood University, B
Logan University-College of Chiropractic, B
Longview Community College, A
Maple Woods Community College, A
Maryville University of Saint Louis, B
Missouri Baptist University, B
Missouri Southern State University, B
Missouri State University, B
Missouri Valley College, B
Missouri Western State University, B
Northwest Missouri State University, B
Park University, B
Penn Valley Community College, A
Rockhurst University, B
St. Louis Community College at Forest Park, A
Saint Louis University, B
Southeast Missouri State University, B
Southwest Baptist University, B
Stephens College, B
Truman State University, B
University of Missouri-Columbia, B
University of Missouri-Kansas City, B
University of Missouri-Rolla, B
University of Missouri-St. Louis, B
Washington University in St. Louis, B
Webster University, B
Westminster College, B
William Jewell College, B
William Woods University, B

Montana

Carroll College, B
Montana State University, B
Montana State University-Billings, B
Montana State University-Northern, B
Montana Tech of The University of Montana, AB
Rocky Mountain College, B

University of Great Falls, B
The University of Montana-Missoula, B

Nebraska

Chadron State College, B
College of Saint Mary, B
Concordia University, B
Creighton University, B
Dana College, B
Doane College, B
Hastings College, B
Midland Lutheran College, B
Nebraska Wesleyan University, B
Northeast Community College, A
Peru State College, B
Southeast Community College, Beatrice Campus, A
Union College, B
University of Nebraska at Kearney, B
University of Nebraska-Lincoln, B
University of Nebraska at Omaha, B
Wayne State College, B
Western Nebraska Community College, A
York College, B

Nevada

Community College of Southern Nevada, A
Nevada State College at Henderson, B
University of Nevada, Las Vegas, B
University of Nevada, Reno, B
Western Nevada Community College, A

New Hampshire

Colby-Sawyer College, B
Dartmouth College, B
Franklin Pierce College, B
Keene State College, B
New England College, B
Plymouth State University, B
Rivier College, B
Saint Anselm College, B
Thomas More College of Liberal Arts, B
University of New Hampshire, B
University of New Hampshire at Manchester, A

New Jersey

Atlantic Cape Community College, A
Bergen Community College, A
Bloomfield College, B
Burlington County College, A
Caldwell College, B
Centenary College, B
The College of New Jersey, B
College of Saint Elizabeth, B
Drew University, B
Essex County College, A
Fairleigh Dickinson University, College at Florham, B
Fairleigh Dickinson University, Metropolitan Campus, B
Felician College, AB
Georgian Court University, B
Gloucester County College, A
Kean University, B
Mercer County Community College, A
Middlesex County College, A
Monmouth University, B
Montclair State University, B
New Jersey City University, B
New Jersey Institute of Technology, B
Ramapo College of New Jersey, B
Raritan Valley Community College, A
The Richard Stockton College of New Jersey, B
Rider University, B
Rowan University, B
Rutgers, The State University of New Jersey, Camden, B
Rutgers, The State University of New Jersey, New Brunswick/Piscataway, B
Rutgers, The State University of New Jersey, Newark, B
Saint Peter's College, B
Salem Community College, A
Seton Hall University, B
Union County College, A
Warren County Community College, A

William Paterson University of New Jersey, B

New Mexico

College of the Southwest, B
Eastern New Mexico University, B
New Mexico Highlands University, B
New Mexico Institute of Mining and Technology, B
New Mexico Junior College, A
New Mexico Military Institute, A
New Mexico State University, B
San Juan College, A
Santa Fe Community College, A
University of New Mexico, B
Western New Mexico University, B

New York

Adelphi University, B
Adirondack Community College, A
Alfred University, B
Bard College, B
Barnard College, B
Bronx Community College of the City University of New York, A
Brooklyn College of the City University of New York, B
Buffalo State College, State University of New York, B
City College of the City University of New York, B
Clarkson University, B
Colgate University, B
College of Mount Saint Vincent, B
The College of New Rochelle, B
The College of Saint Rose, B
College of Staten Island of the City University of New York, B
Columbia College, B
Columbia University, School of General Studies, B
Concordia College, B
Cornell University, B
Daemen College, B
Dominican College, B
Dowling College, B
D'Youville College, B
Elmira College, B
Excelsior College, B
Finger Lakes Community College, A
Fordham University, B
Fulton-Montgomery Community College, A
Hamilton College, B
Hartwick College, B
Hobart and William Smith Colleges, B
Hofstra University, B
Houghton College, B
Hunter College of the City University of New York, B
Iona College, B
Ithaca College, B
Keuka College, B
Kingsborough Community College of the City University of New York, A
Le Moyne College, B
Lehman College of the City University of New York, B
Long Island University, Brooklyn Campus, B
Long Island University, C.W. Post Campus, B
Manhattan College, B
Manhattanville College, B
Marist College, B
Marymount Manhattan College, B
Medaille College, B
Medgar Evers College of the City University of New York, B
Mercy College, B
Molloy College, B
Monroe Community College, A
Mount Saint Mary College, B
Nazareth College of Rochester, B
New York Institute of Technology, B
New York University, B
Niagara University, B
Orange County Community College, A
Pace University, B
Purchase College, State University of New York, B
Queens College of the City University of New York, B
Rensselaer Polytechnic Institute, B
Roberts Wesleyan College, B

Rochester Institute of Technology, AB
Russell Sage College, B
St. Bonaventure University, B
St. Francis College, B
St. John Fisher College, B
St. John's University, B
St. Joseph's College, New York, B
St. Joseph's College, Suffolk Campus, B
St. Lawrence University, B
St. Thomas Aquinas College, B
Sarah Lawrence College, B
Siena College, B
Skidmore College, B
State University of New York at Binghamton, B
State University of New York at Buffalo, B
State University of New York College of Agriculture and Technology at Morrisville, A
State University of New York College at Brockport, B
State University of New York College at Cortland, B
State University of New York College of Environmental Science and Forestry, B
State University of New York College at Geneseo, B
State University of New York College at Old Westbury, B
State University of New York College at Oneonta, B
State University of New York College at Potsdam, B
State University of New York, Fredonia, B
State University of New York at New Paltz, B
State University of New York at Oswego, B
State University of New York at Plattsburgh, B
Stony Brook University, State University of New York, B
Suffolk County Community College, A
Syracuse University, B
Touro College, B
Union College, B
United States Military Academy, B
University at Albany, State University of New York, B
University of Rochester, B
Utica College, B
Vassar College, B
Wagner College, B
Wells College, B
Yeshiva University, B
York College of the City University of New York, B

North Carolina

Appalachian State University, B
Barber-Scotia College, B
Barton College, B
Belmont Abbey College, B
Bennett College For Women, B
Campbell University, B
Catawba College, B
Central Piedmont Community College, A
Chowan University, B
Davidson College, B
Duke University, B
East Carolina University, B
Elizabeth City State University, B
Elon University, B
Fayetteville State University, B
Gardner-Webb University, B
Greensboro College, B
Guilford College, B
High Point University, B
Johnson C. Smith University, B
Lees-McRae College, B
Lenoir-Rhyne College, B
Livingstone College, B
Louisburg College, A
Mars Hill College, B
Meredith College, B
Methodist College, AB
Montreat College, B
Mount Olive College, AB
North Carolina Agricultural and Technical State University, B
North Carolina Central University, B
North Carolina State University, B
North Carolina Wesleyan College, B
Peace College, B
Pfeiffer University, B
Queens University of Charlotte, B
St. Andrews Presbyterian College, B

Saint Augustine's College, B
Salem College, B
Shaw University, B
The University of North Carolina at Asheville, B
The University of North Carolina at Chapel Hill, B
The University of North Carolina at Charlotte, B
The University of North Carolina at Greensboro, B
The University of North Carolina at Pembroke, B
The University of North Carolina Wilmington, B
Wake Forest University, B
Warren Wilson College, B
Western Carolina University, B
Wingate University, B
Winston-Salem State University, B

North Dakota

Dickinson State University, B
Jamestown College, B
Mayville State University, B
Minot State University, B
North Dakota State University, B
Turtle Mountain Community College, A
University of Mary, B
University of North Dakota, B
Valley City State University, B

Ohio

Antioch College, B
Ashland University, B
Baldwin-Wallace College, B
Bluffton University, B
Bowling Green State University, B
Capital University, B
Case Western Reserve University, B
Cedarville University, B
Central State University, B
Cleveland State University, B
College of Mount St. Joseph, B
The College of Wooster, B
Defiance College, B
Denison University, B
Franciscan University of Steubenville, B
Heidelberg College, B
Hiram College, B
John Carroll University, B
Kent State University, B
Kenyon College, B
Lake Erie College, B
Lorain County Community College, A
Lourdes College, AB
Malone College, B
Marietta College, B
Miami University, B
Mount Union College, B
Mount Vernon Nazarene University, B
Muskingum College, B
Notre Dame College, B
Oberlin College, B
Ohio Dominican University, B
Ohio Northern University, B
The Ohio State University, B
The Ohio State University at Lima, B
Ohio University, B
Ohio Wesleyan University, B
Otterbein College, B
Shawnee State University, AB
The University of Akron, B
University of Cincinnati, B
University of Cincinnati Raymond Walters College, A
University of Dayton, B
The University of Findlay, B
University of Rio Grande, AB
The University of Toledo, AB
Urbana University, B
Ursuline College, B
Walsh University, B
Washington State Community College, A
Wilberforce University, B
Wilmington College, B
Wittenberg University, B
Wright State University, AB
Wright State University, Lake Campus, A
Xavier University, B

Youngstown State University, B

Oklahoma

Cameron University, B
Carl Albert State College, A
Connors State College, A
East Central University, B
Eastern Oklahoma State College, A
Langston University, B
Northeastern Oklahoma Agricultural and Mechanical College, A
Northeastern State University, B
Northwestern Oklahoma State University, B
Oklahoma Baptist University, B
Oklahoma Christian University, B
Oklahoma City Community College, A
Oklahoma City University, B
Oklahoma Panhandle State University, B
Oklahoma State University, B
Oklahoma Wesleyan University, AB
Oral Roberts University, B
Redlands Community College, A
Rogers State University, AB
Rose State College, A
St. Gregory's University, B
Seminole State College, A
Southeastern Oklahoma State University, B
Southern Nazarene University, B
Southwestern Oklahoma State University, B
Tulsa Community College, A
University of Central Oklahoma, B
University of Science and Arts of Oklahoma, B
University of Tulsa, B

Oregon

Concordia University, B
Eastern Oregon University, B
George Fox University, B
Lewis & Clark College, B
Linfield College, B
Linn-Benton Community College, A
Oregon State University, B
Pacific University, B
Portland State University, B
Reed College, B
Southern Oregon University, B
Treasure Valley Community College, A
Umpqua Community College, A
University of Oregon, B
University of Portland, B
Warner Pacific College, B
Western Oregon University, B
Willamette University, B

Pennsylvania

Albright College, B
Allegheny College, B
Alvernia College, B
Arcadia University, B
Bloomsburg University of Pennsylvania, B
Bryn Athyn College of the New Church, B
Bryn Mawr College, B
Bucknell University, B
Bucks County Community College, A
Butler County Community College, A
Cabrini College, B
California University of Pennsylvania, B
Carlow University, B
Carnegie Mellon University, B
Cedar Crest College, B
Chatham College, B
Chestnut Hill College, AB
Cheyney University of Pennsylvania, B
Clarion University of Pennsylvania, B
College Misericordia, B
Community College of Allegheny County, A
Community College of Beaver County, A
Delaware Valley College, B
DeSales University, B
Dickinson College, B
Drexel University, B
Duquesne University, B
East Stroudsburg University of Pennsylvania, B
Eastern University, B
Edinboro University of Pennsylvania, B
Elizabethtown College, B

Franklin and Marshall College, B
Gannon University, B
Geneva College, B
Gettysburg College, B
Grove City College, B
Gwynedd-Mercy College, B
Harrisburg Area Community College, A
Haverford College, B
Holy Family University, B
Immaculata University, B
Indiana University of Pennsylvania, B
Juniata College, B
Keystone College, AB
King's College, B
Kutztown University of Pennsylvania, B
La Roche College, B
La Salle University, B
Lafayette College, B
Lebanon Valley College, B
Lehigh Carbon Community College, A
Lehigh University, B
Lincoln University, B
Lock Haven University of Pennsylvania, B
Lycoming College, B
Mansfield University of Pennsylvania, B
Marywood University, B
Mercyhurst College, B
Messiah College, B
Millersville University of Pennsylvania, B
Montgomery County Community College, A
Moravian College, B
Muhlenberg College, B
Neumann College, B
Northampton County Area Community College, A
Pennsylvania College of Technology, B
The Pennsylvania State University Abington College, B
The Pennsylvania State University Altoona College, B
The Pennsylvania State University Beaver Campus of the Commonwealth College, B
The Pennsylvania State University Berks Campus of the Berks-Lehigh Valley College, B
The Pennsylvania State University Delaware County Campus of the Commonwealth College, B
The Pennsylvania State University DuBois Campus of the Commonwealth College, B
The Pennsylvania State University at Erie, The Behrend College, B
The Pennsylvania State University Fayette Campus of the Commonwealth College, B
The Pennsylvania State University Hazleton Campus of the Commonwealth College, B
The Pennsylvania State University, Lehigh Valley Campus of the Berks-Lehigh Valley College, B
The Pennsylvania State University McKeesport Campus of the Commonwealth College, B
The Pennsylvania State University Mont Alto Campus of the Commonwealth College, B
The Pennsylvania State University New Kensington Campus of the Commonwealth College, B
The Pennsylvania State University Schuylkill Campus of the Capital College, B
The Pennsylvania State University Shenango Campus of the Commonwealth College, B
The Pennsylvania State University University Park Campus, B
The Pennsylvania State University Wilkes-Barre Campus of the Commonwealth College, B
The Pennsylvania State University Worthington Scranton Campus of the Commonwealth College, B
The Pennsylvania State University York Campus of the Commonwealth College, B
Philadelphia University, B
Point Park University, B
Reading Area Community College, A
Rosemont College, B
Saint Francis University, B
Saint Joseph's University, AB
Saint Vincent College, B
Seton Hill University, B
Shippensburg University of Pennsylvania, B
Slippery Rock University of Pennsylvania, B
Susquehanna University, B
Swarthmore College, B

Temple University, B
Thiel College, B
University of Pennsylvania, B
University of Pittsburgh, B
University of Pittsburgh at Bradford, B
University of Pittsburgh at Greensburg, B
University of Pittsburgh at Johnstown, B
University of the Sciences in Philadelphia, B
The University of Scranton, B
Ursinus College, B
Villanova University, B
Washington & Jefferson College, B
Waynesburg College, B
West Chester University of Pennsylvania, B
Westminster College, B
Widener University, B
Wilkes University, B
Wilson College, B
York College of Pennsylvania, AB

Puerto Rico

Bayamon Central University, B
Inter American University of Puerto Rico, Aguadilla
    Campus, B
Inter American University of Puerto Rico, Arecibo
    Campus, B
Inter American University of Puerto Rico,
    Barranquitas Campus, AB
Inter American University of Puerto Rico, Bayamón
    Campus, B
Inter American University of Puerto Rico, Fajardo
    Campus, B
Inter American University of Puerto Rico,
    Metropolitan Campus, B
Inter American University of Puerto Rico, Ponce
    Campus, B
Inter American University of Puerto Rico, San
    Germán Campus, B
Pontifical Catholic University of Puerto Rico, B
Universidad Adventista de las Antillas, B
Universidad Metropolitana, B
Universidad del Turabo, B
University of Puerto Rico, Cayey University
    College, B
University of Puerto Rico at Humacao, B
University of Puerto Rico, Mayagüez Campus, B
University of Puerto Rico, Río Piedras, B
University of the Sacred Heart, B

Rhode Island

Brown University, B
Providence College, B
Rhode Island College, B
Roger Williams University, B
Salve Regina University, B
University of Rhode Island, B

South Carolina

Allen University, B
Anderson University, B
Benedict College, B
Bob Jones University, B
Charleston Southern University, B
The Citadel, The Military College of South
    Carolina, B
Claflin University, B
Clemson University, B
Coastal Carolina University, B
Coker College, B
College of Charleston, B
Columbia College, B
Converse College, B
Erskine College, B
Francis Marion University, B
Furman University, B
Lander University, B
Limestone College, B
Morris College, B
Newberry College, B
North Greenville College, B
Presbyterian College, B
South Carolina State University, B
Southern Wesleyan University, B
University of South Carolina, B
University of South Carolina Aiken, B
University of South Carolina Beaufort, B

University of South Carolina Upstate, B
Voorhees College, B
Winthrop University, B
Wofford College, B

South Dakota

Augustana College, B
Black Hills State University, B
Dakota State University, B
Dakota Wesleyan University, B
Mount Marty College, B
Northern State University, B
Presentation College, AB
South Dakota State University, B
University of Sioux Falls, B
The University of South Dakota, B

Tennessee

Austin Peay State University, B
Belmont University, B
Bethel College, B
Bryan College, B
Carson-Newman College, B
Chattanooga State Technical Community College, A
Christian Brothers University, B
Columbia State Community College, A
Crichton College, B
Cumberland University, AB
East Tennessee State University, B
Fisk University, B
Freed-Hardeman University, B
King College, B
Lambuth University, B
Lane College, B
Lee University, B
LeMoyne-Owen College, B
Lincoln Memorial University, B
Lipscomb University, B
Martin Methodist College, A
Maryville College, B
Middle Tennessee State University, B
Milligan College, B
Rhodes College, B
Roane State Community College, A
Sewanee: The University of the South, B
Southern Adventist University, B
Tennessee State University, B
Tennessee Technological University, B
Tennessee Temple University, B
Tennessee Wesleyan College, B
Trevecca Nazarene University, B
Tusculum College, B
Union University, B
University of Memphis, B
The University of Tennessee, B
The University of Tennessee at Chattanooga, B
The University of Tennessee at Martin, B
Vanderbilt University, B

Texas

Abilene Christian University, B
Alvin Community College, A
Amarillo College, A
Angelina College, A
Angelo State University, B
Austin College, B
Austin Community College, A
Baylor University, B
Blinn College, A
Brazosport College, A
Central Texas College, A
Cisco Junior College, A
Clarendon College, A
Coastal Bend College, A
Concordia University at Austin, B
Dallas Baptist University, B
Del Mar College, A
East Texas Baptist University, B
El Paso Community College, A
Frank Phillips College, A
Grayson County College, A
Hardin-Simmons University, B
Hill College of the Hill Junior College District, A
Houston Baptist University, B
Howard College, A
Howard Payne University, B

Huston-Tillotson University, B
Jarvis Christian College, B
Kingwood College, A
Lamar University, B
Lee College, A
LeTourneau University, B
Lon Morris College, A
Lubbock Christian University, B
McMurry University, B
Midland College, A
Midwestern State University, B
Navarro College, A
Odessa College, A
Our Lady of the Lake University of San Antonio, B
Palo Alto College, A
Paul Quinn College, B
Prairie View A&M University, B
Rice University, B
St. Edward's University, B
St. Mary's University of San Antonio, B
St. Philip's College, A
Sam Houston State University, B
Schreiner University, B
South Plains College, A
Southern Methodist University, B
Southwestern Adventist University, B
Southwestern University, B
Stephen F. Austin State University, B
Sul Ross State University, B
Tarleton State University, B
Texarkana College, A
Texas A&M International University, B
Texas A&M University, B
Texas A&M University-Commerce, B
Texas A&M University-Corpus Christi, B
Texas A&M University-Kingsville, B
Texas A&M University-Texarkana, B
Texas Chiropractic College, B
Texas Christian University, B
Texas College, B
Texas Lutheran University, B
Texas Southern University, B
Texas State University-San Marcos, B
Texas Tech University, B
Texas Wesleyan University, B
Texas Woman's University, B
Trinity University, B
Trinity Valley Community College, A
University of Dallas, B
University of Houston, B
University of Houston-Clear Lake, B
University of Houston-Downtown, B
University of Houston-Victoria, B
University of the Incarnate Word, B
University of Mary Hardin-Baylor, B
University of North Texas, B
University of St. Thomas, B
The University of Texas at Arlington, B
The University of Texas at Austin, B
The University of Texas at Brownsville, B
The University of Texas at Dallas, B
The University of Texas at El Paso, B
The University of Texas-Pan American, B
The University of Texas of the Permian Basin, B
The University of Texas at San Antonio, B
The University of Texas at Tyler, B
Wayland Baptist University, B
West Texas A&M University, B
Wharton County Junior College, A
Wiley College, B

United States Virgin Islands

University of the Virgin Islands, B

Utah

Brigham Young University, B
Dixie State College of Utah, A
Salt Lake Community College, A
Snow College, A
Southern Utah University, B
University of Utah, B
Utah State University, B
Utah Valley State College, AB

Westminster College, B

Vermont

Bennington College, B
Castleton State College, B
Green Mountain College, B
Johnson State College, B
Marlboro College, B
Middlebury College, B
Norwich University, B
Saint Michael's College, B
University of Vermont, B

Virginia

Averett University, B
Bluefield College, B
Bridgewater College, B
Christopher Newport University, B
The College of William and Mary, B
Eastern Mennonite University, B
Emory & Henry College, B
Ferrum College, B
George Mason University, B
Hampden-Sydney College, B
Hampton University, B
Hollins University, B
James Madison University, B
Liberty University, B
Longwood University, B
Lynchburg College, B
Mary Baldwin College, B
Marymount University, B
Mountain Empire Community College, A
Norfolk State University, B
Old Dominion University, B
Radford University, B
Randolph-Macon College, B
Randolph-Macon Woman's College, B
Roanoke College, B
Saint Paul's College, B
Shenandoah University, B
Southern Virginia University, B
Sweet Briar College, B
University of Mary Washington, B
University of Richmond, B
University of Virginia, B
The University of Virginia's College at Wise, B
Virginia Commonwealth University, B
Virginia Intermont College, B
Virginia Military Institute, B
Virginia Polytechnic Institute and State University, B
Virginia State University, B
Virginia Union University, B
Virginia Wesleyan College, B
Washington and Lee University, B

Washington

Central Washington University, B
Centralia College, A
Eastern Washington University, B
Everett Community College, A
The Evergreen State College, B
Gonzaga University, B
Heritage University, B
Lower Columbia College, A
Northwest Indian College, A
Pacific Lutheran University, B
Saint Martin's University, B
Seattle Pacific University, B
Seattle University, B
Skagit Valley College, A
Tacoma Community College, A
University of Puget Sound, B
University of Washington, B
Walla Walla College, B
Washington State University, B
Wenatchee Valley College, A
Western Washington University, B
Whitman College, B
Whitworth College, B

West Virginia

Alderson-Broaddus College, B
Bethany College, B
Concord University, B
Davis & Elkins College, B

Fairmont State University, B
Glenville State College, B
Marshall University, B
Potomac State College of West Virginia
   University, A
Salem International University, B
Shepherd University, B
University of Charleston, B
West Liberty State College, B
West Virginia State University, B
West Virginia University, B
West Virginia University Institute of Technology, B
West Virginia Wesleyan College, B
Wheeling Jesuit University, B

Wisconsin

Alverno College, B
Beloit College, B
Cardinal Stritch University, B
Carroll College, B
Carthage College, B
Concordia University Wisconsin, B
Edgewood College, B
Lakeland College, B
Lawrence University, B
Marian College of Fond du Lac, B
Marquette University, B
Mount Mary College, B
Northland College, B
Ripon College, B
St. Norbert College, B
Silver Lake College, B
University of Wisconsin-Green Bay, AB
University of Wisconsin-La Crosse, B
University of Wisconsin-Madison, B
University of Wisconsin-Milwaukee, B
University of Wisconsin-Oshkosh, B
University of Wisconsin-Platteville, B
University of Wisconsin-River Falls, B
University of Wisconsin-Stevens Point, B
University of Wisconsin-Superior, B
University of Wisconsin-Whitewater, B
Viterbo University, B
Wisconsin Lutheran College, B

Wyoming

Casper College, A
Central Wyoming College, A
Eastern Wyoming College, A
Laramie County Community College, A
Northwest College, A
Sheridan College-Sheridan and Gillette, A
University of Wyoming, B
Western Wyoming Community College, A

Alberta

Concordia University College of Alberta, B
The King's University College, B
University of Alberta, B
University of Calgary, B
University of Lethbridge, B

British Columbia

Malaspina University-College, B
Simon Fraser University, B
Thompson Rivers University, B
Trinity Western University, B
The University of British Columbia, B
University College of the Fraser Valley, B
University of Northern British Columbia, B
University of Victoria, B

Manitoba

Brandon University, B
Canadian Mennonite University, A
University of Manitoba, B
The University of Winnipeg, B

New Brunswick

Atlantic Baptist University, B
Mount Allison University, B
Université de Moncton, B
University of New Brunswick Fredericton, B

University of New Brunswick Saint John, B

Newfoundland and Labrador

Memorial University of Newfoundland, B

Nova Scotia

Acadia University, B
Cape Breton University, B
Dalhousie University, B
Mount Saint Vincent University, B
St. Francis Xavier University, B
Saint Mary's University, B
Université Sainte-Anne, B
University of King's College, B

Ontario

Brock University, B
Carleton University, B
Lakehead University, B
Laurentian University, B
McMaster University, B
Nipissing University, B
Queen's University at Kingston, B
Redeemer University College, B
Ryerson University, B
Trent University, B
University of Guelph, B
University of Ottawa, B
University of Toronto, B
University of Waterloo, B
The University of Western Ontario, B
University of Windsor, B
Wilfrid Laurier University, B
York University, B

Prince Edward Island

University of Prince Edward Island, B

Quebec

Bishop's University, B
Concordia University, B
McGill University, B
Université Laval, B
Université de Montréal, B
Université du Québec àChicoutimi, B
Université du Québec àMontréal, B
Université du Québec àRimouski, B
Université du Québec àTrois-Rivières, B
Université de Sherbrooke, B

Saskatchewan

University of Regina, B
University of Saskatchewan, B

BIOLOGY TEACHER EDUCATION

Alabama

Samford University, B
Talladega College, B

Arizona

Northern Arizona University, B
The University of Arizona, B

Arkansas

Arkansas State University, B
Arkansas Tech University, B
Harding University, B
John Brown University, B
Southern Arkansas University-Magnolia, B
University of Arkansas at Fort Smith, B
University of the Ozarks, B

California

California State University, Chico, B
California State University, Long Beach, B

College of the Siskiyous, A

Colorado

Colorado State University, B
Fort Lewis College, B

Connecticut

Sacred Heart University, B

Delaware

Delaware State University, B
University of Delaware, B

District of Columbia

The Catholic University of America, B

Florida

Bethune-Cookman College, B
Clearwater Christian College, B
Florida Institute of Technology, B
Manatee Community College, A
Miami Dade College, B
St. Petersburg College, B

Georgia

Brewton-Parker College, B
Columbus State University, B
Georgia Southern University, B
Kennesaw State University, B
Paine College, B
University of West Georgia, B

Hawaii

Brigham Young University-Hawaii, B

Idaho

Northwest Nazarene University, B

Illinois

Chicago State University, B
Concordia University, B
Elmhurst College, B
Greenville College, B
Illinois Wesleyan University, B
McKendree College, B
Saint Xavier University, B
Trinity Christian College, B
University of Illinois at Chicago, B

Indiana

Ancilla College, A
Franklin College, B
Indiana University Bloomington, B
Indiana University Northwest, B
Indiana University-Purdue University Fort Wayne, B
Indiana University South Bend, B
Indiana University Southeast, B
Oakland City University, B
Taylor University, B
University of Evansville, B
University of Saint Francis, B
Valparaiso University, B

Iowa

Buena Vista University, B
Dordt College, B
Northwestern College, B
St. Ambrose University, B
University of Dubuque, B
The University of Iowa, B

Kansas

Bethany College, B
Central Christian College of Kansas, A
Pittsburg State University, B

Kentucky

Berea College, B
Campbellsville University, B
Kentucky Wesleyan College, B
Lindsey Wilson College, B
Murray State University, B

Pikeville College, B

Louisiana

Centenary College of Louisiana, B
Dillard University, B
Louisiana State University in Shreveport, B
Louisiana Tech University, B
McNeese State University, B
Northwestern State University of Louisiana, B
Southern University and Agricultural and Mechanical
   College, B
University of Louisiana at Lafayette, B
University of Louisiana at Monroe, B
Xavier University of Louisiana, B

Maine

Husson College, B
Saint Joseph's College of Maine, B
University of Maine, B
University of Maine at Farmington, B
University of Maine at Machias, B

Massachusetts

Bridgewater State College, B
Fitchburg State College, B
Framingham State College, B

Michigan

Alma College, B
Central Michigan University, B
Concordia University, B
Cornerstone University, B
Eastern Michigan University, B
Hope College, B
Michigan Technological University, B
Rochester College, B
University of Michigan-Flint, B

Minnesota

Bethel University, B
College of St. Catherine, B
Concordia College, B
Concordia University, St. Paul, B
Gustavus Adolphus College, B
Minnesota State University Moorhead, B
Saint Mary's University of Minnesota, B
Southwest Minnesota State University, B
University of St. Thomas, B

Mississippi

Blue Mountain College, B
Delta State University, B
Rust College, B
William Carey College, B

Missouri

Central Methodist University, B
College of the Ozarks, B
Evangel University, B
Lincoln University, B
Lindenwood University, B
Maryville University of Saint Louis, B
Missouri State University, B
University of Missouri-Columbia, B
University of Missouri-St. Louis, B
Washington University in St. Louis, B

Montana

Carroll College, B
Montana State University-Billings, B
Rocky Mountain College, B
University of Great Falls, B
The University of Montana-Western, B

Nebraska

Chadron State College, B
Concordia University, B
Hastings College, B
Union College, B
University of Nebraska-Lincoln, B
Wayne State College, B

York College, B

Nevada

Nevada State College at Henderson, B

New Hampshire

Keene State College, B
Rivier College, B

New Jersey

Bloomfield College, B
The College of New Jersey, B

New York

Brooklyn College of the City University of New
   York, B
City College of the City University of New York, B
The College of Saint Rose, B
Daemen College, B
Dominican College, B
Dowling College, B
Elmira College, B
Hofstra University, B
Hunter College of the City University of New York, B
Iona College, B
Ithaca College, B
Keuka College, B
Le Moyne College, B
Long Island University, C.W. Post Campus, B
Manhattanville College, B
Marist College, B
Molloy College, B
Nazareth College of Rochester, B
New York Institute of Technology, B
New York University, B
Niagara University, B
Pace University, B
Roberts Wesleyan College, B
St. Bonaventure University, B
St. Francis College, B
St. John's University, B
State University of New York College at
   Brockport, B
State University of New York College at Cortland, B
State University of New York College of
   Environmental Science and Forestry, B
State University of New York College at Old
   Westbury, B
State University of New York College at Oneonta, B
State University of New York College at Potsdam, B
Syracuse University, B
University at Albany, State University of New York, B
Utica College, B

North Carolina

Appalachian State University, B
Campbell University, B
Elizabeth City State University, B
Fayetteville State University, B
Greensboro College, B
Louisburg College, A
North Carolina Central University, B
North Carolina State University, B
Saint Augustine's College, B
The University of North Carolina at Greensboro, B
The University of North Carolina at Pembroke, B
The University of North Carolina Wilmington, B
Wingate University, B

North Dakota

Jamestown College, B
Mayville State University, B
Minot State University, B
North Dakota State University, B
University of Mary, B
Valley City State University, B

Ohio

Bowling Green State University, B
Capital University, B
Cedarville University, B
Miami University, B
Ohio Northern University, B
Ohio University, B
Ohio Wesleyan University, B

The University of Akron, B
University of Rio Grande, B
Xavier University, B
Youngstown State University, B

Oklahoma

East Central University, B
Oklahoma Baptist University, B
St. Gregory's University, B

Oregon

Corban College, B

Pennsylvania

Alvernia College, B
Cabrini College, B
Juniata College, B
La Roche College, B
Lebanon Valley College, B
Mansfield University of Pennsylvania, B
Marywood University, B
Mercyhurst College, B
Messiah College, B
Moravian College, B
Point Park University, B
Saint Francis University, B
Seton Hill University, B
University of Pittsburgh at Johnstown, B
Waynesburg College, B
West Chester University of Pennsylvania, B
Widener University, B

Puerto Rico

Caribbean University, B
Inter American University of Puerto Rico, Aguadilla
    Campus, B
Inter American University of Puerto Rico,
    Metropolitan Campus, B
Pontifical Catholic University of Puerto Rico, B
Universidad Adventista de las Antillas, B
University of Puerto Rico, Cayey University
    College, B

Rhode Island

Rhode Island College, B
Salve Regina University, B

South Carolina

Anderson University, B
Charleston Southern University, B
The Citadel, The Military College of South
    Carolina, B
Coker College, B
Limestone College, B
Morris College, B

South Dakota

Dakota State University, B
Dakota Wesleyan University, B
The University of South Dakota, B

Tennessee

Bethel College, B
Christian Brothers University, B
Cumberland University, B
Freed-Hardeman University, B
King College, B
Lambuth University, B
Lincoln Memorial University, B
Lipscomb University, B
Maryville College, B
Tennessee Temple University, B
Tennessee Wesleyan College, B
Trevecca Nazarene University, B
The University of Tennessee at Martin, B

Texas

Abilene Christian University, B
Baylor University, B
East Texas Baptist University, B
Houston Baptist University, B
Howard Payne University, B
St. Edward's University, B
Texas A&M International University, B

Texas Wesleyan University, B

Utah

University of Utah, B
Utah State University, B
Utah Valley State College, B
Weber State University, B
Westminster College, B

Vermont

Johnson State College, B

Virginia

Averett University, B
Bluefield College, B
Eastern Mennonite University, B
Liberty University, B
Old Dominion University, B
Virginia Intermont College, B

Washington

Central Washington University, B
Northwest University, B
Seattle Pacific University, B
University of Washington, B
Washington State University, B

West Virginia

Glenville State College, B
University of Charleston, B
Wheeling Jesuit University, B

Wisconsin

Carroll College, B
Marian College of Fond du Lac, B
Mount Mary College, B
University of Wisconsin-River Falls, B
University of Wisconsin-Superior, B
Viterbo University, B

Ontario

University of Waterloo, B
University of Windsor, B
York University, B

Quebec

Bishop's University, B
McGill University, B

Saskatchewan

University of Regina, B

BIOLOGY TECHNICIAN/BIOTECHNOLOGY LABORATORY TECHNICIAN

Arkansas

Southeast Arkansas College, A

California

Berkeley City College, A
California State Polytechnic University, Pomona, B
California State University, Sacramento, B
College of San Mateo, A
Contra Costa College, A
Foothill College, A

Connecticut

Middlesex Community College, A
University of New Haven, B

Delaware

University of Delaware, B

District of Columbia

University of the District of Columbia, A

Georgia

Athens Technical College, A

Indiana

Purdue University Calumet, B

Iowa

Des Moines Area Community College, A
Ellsworth Community College, A

Indian Hills Community College, A
Kirkwood Community College, A

Maryland

Villa Julie College, AB

Massachusetts

Harvard University, B
Massachusetts Bay Community College, A
North Shore Community College, A
Northeastern University, B
Suffolk University, B
Worcester Polytechnic Institute, B

Michigan

Ferris State University, A
Lansing Community College, A
Michigan Technological University, B
Mid Michigan Community College, A
Muskegon Community College, A

Minnesota

Minnesota State University Mankato, B
St. Cloud State University, B

Montana

Montana State University-Great Falls College of
    Technology, A

Nebraska

Southeast Community College, Beatrice Campus, A

New Jersey

County College of Morris, A
Mercer County Community College, A
Middlesex County College, A

New York

Finger Lakes Community College, A
Hudson Valley Community College, A
Jefferson Community College, A
Monroe Community College, A
Niagara University, B
State University of New York College of Agriculture
    and Technology at Cobleskill, A
State University of New York College of Agriculture
    and Technology at Morrisville, A
State University of New York College at
    Brockport, B
State University of New York College at Oneonta, B
State University of New York College of Technology
    at Alfred, A
State University of New York, Fredonia, B
York College of the City University of New York, B

North Carolina

Elizabeth City State University, B
Fayetteville Technical Community College, A
Guilford Technical Community College, A

Ohio

Cleveland State University, B
The Ohio State University Agricultural Technical
    Institute, A

Oregon

Portland Community College, A

Pennsylvania

Gannon University, B
Marywood University, B
The Pennsylvania State University Abington
    College, B
The Pennsylvania State University Altoona
    College, B
The Pennsylvania State University Beaver Campus
    of the Commonwealth College, B
The Pennsylvania State University Berks Campus of
    the Berks-Lehigh Valley College, B
The Pennsylvania State University Delaware County
    Campus of the Commonwealth College, B
The Pennsylvania State University DuBois Campus
    of the Commonwealth College, B

The Pennsylvania State University at Erie, The Behrend College, B
The Pennsylvania State University Fayette Campus of the Commonwealth College, B
The Pennsylvania State University Hazleton Campus of the Commonwealth College, B
The Pennsylvania State University, Lehigh Valley Campus of the Berks-Lehigh Valley College, B
The Pennsylvania State University McKeesport Campus of the Commonwealth College, B
The Pennsylvania State University Mont Alto Campus of the Commonwealth College, B
The Pennsylvania State University New Kensington Campus of the Commonwealth College, B
The Pennsylvania State University Schuylkill Campus of the Capital College, B
The Pennsylvania State University Shenango Campus of the Commonwealth College, B
The Pennsylvania State University University Park Campus, B
The Pennsylvania State University Wilkes-Barre Campus of the Commonwealth College, B
The Pennsylvania State University Worthington Scranton Campus of the Commonwealth College, B
The Pennsylvania State University York Campus of the Commonwealth College, B
Point Park University, B
Westminster College, B

Puerto Rico

University of Puerto Rico, Mayagüez Campus, B

South Dakota

Lake Area Technical Institute, A

Texas

Collin County Community College District, A
Northwest Vista College, A

Utah

Salt Lake Community College, A
Weber State University, A

Virginia

John Tyler Community College, A

Washington

Bates Technical College, A
Seattle Central Community College, A
Shoreline Community College, A

West Virginia

Salem International University, B

Wisconsin

Madison Area Technical College, A

Alberta

University of Alberta, B

British Columbia

British Columbia Institute of Technology, A

Ontario

Carleton University, B
McMaster University, B
University of Ottawa, B

Quebec

Université de Sherbrooke, B

BIOMATHEMATICS AND BIOINFORMATICS

California

University of California, Los Angeles, B

Florida

Florida State University, B

Pennsylvania

The University of Scranton, B

BIOMEDICAL ENGINEERING

Alabama

The University of Alabama at Birmingham, MD

California

California State University, Northridge, M
Stanford University, M
University of California, Davis, MD
University of California, Irvine, MD
University of California, Los Angeles, MD
University of Southern California, MD

Colorado

Colorado State University, MD

Connecticut

University of Connecticut, MD

District of Columbia

The Catholic University of America, MD

Florida

Florida Agricultural and Mechanical University, MD
Florida International University, M
Florida State University, MD
University of Florida, MDO
University of Miami, MD
University of South Florida, MD

Georgia

Georgia Institute of Technology, MDO
Mercer University, M

Illinois

Illinois Institute of Technology, D
Northwestern University, MD

Indiana

Indiana University-Purdue University Indianapolis, MD
Purdue University, MD
Rose-Hulman Institute of Technology, MO

Iowa

The University of Iowa, MD

Kentucky

University of Kentucky, MD

Louisiana

Louisiana Tech University, MD
Tulane University, MD

Maryland

The Johns Hopkins University, MD

Massachusetts

Boston University, MDO
Harvard University, MD
Massachusetts Institute of Technology, MD
Tufts University, MD
Worcester Polytechnic Institute, MDO

Michigan

Michigan Technological University, D
University of Michigan, MD

Wayne State University, MD

Minnesota

University of Minnesota, Twin Cities Campus, MDO

Mississippi

Mississippi State University, MD

Missouri

Saint Louis University, MD
Washington University in St. Louis, MDO

Nevada

University of Nevada, Reno, MD

New Hampshire

Dartmouth College, MDO

New Jersey

New Jersey Institute of Technology, MD
Rutgers, The State University of New Jersey, New Brunswick/Piscataway, MD

New York

City College of the City University of New York, MD
Cornell University, MD
Polytechnic University, Brooklyn Campus, M
Rensselaer Polytechnic Institute, MD
State University of New York Downstate Medical Center, MDO
Stony Brook University, State University of New York, MDO
Syracuse University, MD
University of Rochester, MD

North Carolina

Duke University, MD
North Carolina State University, MD
The University of North Carolina at Chapel Hill, MD
Wake Forest University, MDO

Ohio

Case Western Reserve University, MDO
Cleveland State University, D
The Ohio State University, MD
The University of Akron, MD
University of Cincinnati, MD
Wright State University, M

Pennsylvania

Carnegie Mellon University, MD
Drexel University, MD
The Pennsylvania State University University Park Campus, MD
Thomas Jefferson University, D

Rhode Island

Brown University, MD

Tennessee

University of Memphis, MD
The University of Tennessee, MD
Vanderbilt University, MDO

Texas

Baylor University, M
Rice University, MD
Texas A&M University, MD
University of Houston, M
The University of Texas at Arlington, MD
The University of Texas at Austin, MDO
The University of Texas at San Antonio, D
The University of Texas Southwestern Medical Center at Dallas, MD

Vermont

University of Vermont, M

Virginia

University of Virginia, MD
Virginia Commonwealth University, MDO

Virginia Polytechnic Institute and State University, MDO

Wisconsin

Marquette University, MD
Milwaukee School of Engineering, M
University of Wisconsin-Madison, MD

Alberta

University of Alberta, MD
University of Calgary, MD

Nova Scotia

Dalhousie University, M

Ontario

University of Toronto, MD

Quebec

McGill University, MD
Université de Montréal, MDO

Saskatchewan

University of Saskatchewan, MD

BIOMEDICAL/MEDICAL ENGINEERING

Alabama

The University of Alabama at Birmingham, B

Arizona

Arizona State University, B

California

California Lutheran University, B
California State University, Long Beach, B
University of California, Berkeley, B
University of California, Davis, B
University of California, Irvine, B
University of California, Los Angeles, B
University of California, San Diego, B
University of the Pacific, B
University of Southern California, B

Connecticut

Trinity College, B
University of Connecticut, B
University of Hartford, B
Yale University, B

District of Columbia

The Catholic University of America, B
Trinity (Washington) University, B

Florida

Florida International University, B
Florida State University, B
University of Miami, B

Georgia

DeVry University (Decatur), B
Georgia Institute of Technology, B

Idaho

University of Idaho, B

Illinois

Illinois Institute of Technology, B
Northwestern University, B
University of Illinois at Chicago, B

University of Illinois at Urbana-Champaign, B

Indiana

Indiana University-Purdue University Indianapolis, B
Rose-Hulman Institute of Technology, B

Iowa

The University of Iowa, B

Louisiana

Louisiana State University and Agricultural and Mechanical College, B
Louisiana Tech University, B
Tulane University, B

Maryland

The Johns Hopkins University, B

Massachusetts

Boston University, B
Eastern Nazarene College, B
Harvard University, B
Western New England College, B
Worcester Polytechnic Institute, B

Michigan

Kettering University, B
Lawrence Technological University, B
Michigan State University, B
Michigan Technological University, B

Mississippi

Mississippi State University, B

Missouri

Saint Louis University, B
Washington University in St. Louis, B

Nebraska

University of Nebraska-Lincoln, B

New Jersey

The College of New Jersey, B
New Jersey Institute of Technology, B
Rutgers, The State University of New Jersey, New Brunswick/Piscataway, B
Stevens Institute of Technology, B

New York

City College of the City University of New York, B
Columbia University, The Fu Foundation School of Engineering and Applied Science, B
Hofstra University, B
Rensselaer Polytechnic Institute, B
Rochester Institute of Technology, B
State University of New York at Binghamton, B
Stony Brook University, State University of New York, B
Syracuse University, B
University of Rochester, B

North Carolina

Duke University, B
North Carolina State University, B

Ohio

Case Western Reserve University, B
The University of Akron, B
The University of Toledo, B
Wright State University, B

Oklahoma

Oklahoma State University, B
Oral Roberts University, B
University of Central Oklahoma, B
University of Oklahoma, B

Pennsylvania

Bucknell University, B
Carnegie Mellon University, B
Cedar Crest College, B
Drexel University, B
Lehigh University, B

The Pennsylvania State University Abington College, B
The Pennsylvania State University Altoona College, B
The Pennsylvania State University Beaver Campus of the Commonwealth College, B
The Pennsylvania State University Berks Campus of the Berks-Lehigh Valley College, B
The Pennsylvania State University Delaware County Campus of the Commonwealth College, B
The Pennsylvania State University DuBois Campus of the Commonwealth College, B
The Pennsylvania State University at Erie, The Behrend College, B
The Pennsylvania State University Fayette Campus of the Commonwealth College, B
The Pennsylvania State University Hazleton Campus of the Commonwealth College, B
The Pennsylvania State University, Lehigh Valley Campus of the Berks-Lehigh Valley College, B
The Pennsylvania State University McKeesport Campus of the Commonwealth College, B
The Pennsylvania State University Mont Alto Campus of the Commonwealth College, B
The Pennsylvania State University New Kensington Campus of the Commonwealth College, B
The Pennsylvania State University Schuylkill Campus of the Capital College, B
The Pennsylvania State University Shenango Campus of the Commonwealth College, B
The Pennsylvania State University University Park Campus, B
The Pennsylvania State University Wilkes-Barre Campus of the Commonwealth College, B
The Pennsylvania State University Worthington Scranton Campus of the Commonwealth College, B
The Pennsylvania State University York Campus of the Commonwealth College, B
University of Pennsylvania, B
University of Pittsburgh, B

Rhode Island

Brown University, B
University of Rhode Island, B

South Carolina

Clemson University, B

Tennessee

University of Memphis, B
Vanderbilt University, B

Texas

LeTourneau University, B
Rice University, B
Texas A&M University, B
University of Houston, B
The University of Texas at Austin, B

Utah

University of Utah, B

Virginia

University of Virginia, B
Virginia Commonwealth University, B

Washington

DeVry University (Federal Way), B
Walla Walla College, B

Wisconsin

Marquette University, B
Milwaukee School of Engineering, B

University of Wisconsin-Madison, B

British Columbia

The University of British Columbia, B

Nova Scotia

Dalhousie University, B

Ontario

University of Guelph, B
University of Toronto, B

BIOMEDICAL SCIENCES

Alabama

Auburn University, B
University of South Alabama, B

Arizona

Midwestern University, Glendale Campus, B

California

Charles R. Drew University of Medicine and
  Science, B
University of California, Riverside, B

Colorado

University of Colorado at Denver and Health
  Sciences Center - Downtown Denver Campus, B

Florida

Florida Institute of Technology, B

Georgia

Emory University, B

Louisiana

Our Lady of the Lake College, B

Maine

University of Maine, B
University of New England, B

Massachusetts

Bridgewater State College, B
Framingham State College, B
Harvard University, B
Suffolk University, B
Worcester Polytechnic Institute, B

Michigan

Grand Valley State University, B
University of Michigan, B
Western Michigan University, B

Minnesota

Anoka-Ramsey Community College, A
Anoka-Ramsey Community College, Cambridge
  Campus, A
St. Cloud State University, B

Mississippi

University of Mississippi, B

Missouri

Maryville University of Saint Louis, B
Stephens College, B

New Jersey

Rutgers, The State University of New Jersey, New
  Brunswick/Piscataway, B

New York

Albany College of Pharmacy of Union University, B
City College of the City University of New York, B
Keuka College, B
Marist College, B
St. Francis College, B

State University of New York, Fredonia, B

Ohio

Antioch College, B

Oklahoma

St. Gregory's University, B

Pennsylvania

Cedar Crest College, B
University of Pennsylvania, B

Puerto Rico

Inter American University of Puerto Rico,
  Metropolitan Campus, B
Inter American University of Puerto Rico, San
  Germán Campus, B

Rhode Island

Brown University, B

Texas

Texas A&M University, B

Utah

Brigham Young University, B
University of Utah, B

Virginia

Jefferson College of Health Sciences, B

Wisconsin

Marquette University, B
University of Wisconsin-Eau Claire, B
University of Wisconsin-Green Bay, B

Alberta

University of Calgary, B

Ontario

Brock University, B
University of Guelph, B
University of Ottawa, B

Quebec

Université de Montréal, B
Université du Québec àTrois-Rivières, B

BIOMEDICAL TECHNOLOGY/TECHNICIAN

Alabama

Alabama Southern Community College, A
Community College of the Air Force, A
Faulkner University, A
George Corley Wallace State Community College, A
Jefferson State Community College, A

Arizona

DeVry University (Phoenix), B

Arkansas

North Arkansas College, A
University of Arkansas for Medical Sciences, A

California

California State University, East Bay, B
Cerritos College, A
DeVry University (Pomona), B
DeVry University (West Hills), B
Napa Valley College, A

Santa Barbara City College, A

Colorado

Colorado State University-Pueblo, B
DeVry University (Westminster), B

Connecticut

Gateway Community College, A

Delaware

Delaware Technical & Community College,
  Stanton/Wilmington Campus, A

Florida

DeVry University (Miramar), B
DeVry University (Orlando), B
Florida Community College at Jacksonville, A
Hillsborough Community College, A
Miami Dade College, A
Santa Fe Community College, A

Georgia

Chattahoochee Technical College, A

Illinois

Parkland College, A
South Suburban College, A

Indiana

Indiana University-Purdue University Indianapolis, A

Iowa

Southeastern Community College, North Campus, A
Western Iowa Tech Community College, A

Kansas

Washburn University, B

Kentucky

Madisonville Community College, A

Louisiana

Delgado Community College, A

Maryland

Howard Community College, A

Massachusetts

Middlesex Community College, A
Suffolk University, A
Wentworth Institute of Technology, A

Michigan

Andrews University, B
Baker College of Flint, A
Muskegon Community College, A
Schoolcraft College, A

Minnesota

Dakota County Technical College, A
Northwest Technical College, A

Missouri

DeVry University (Kansas City), B
Northwest Missouri State University, B
St. Louis Community College at Forest Park, A

New Hampshire

University of New Hampshire, B

New Jersey

DeVry University, AB
Rutgers, The State University of New Jersey,
  Camden, B

New York

DeVry Institute of Technology, B
Erie Community College, South Campus, A
New York Institute of Technology, B

North Carolina

Caldwell Community College and Technical
  Institute, A

Rowan-Cabarrus Community College, A
Stanly Community College, A

Ohio

Cincinnati State Technical and Community
College, A
DeVry University (Columbus), B
Stark State College of Technology, A
Wright State University, B

Oklahoma

Oklahoma City Community College, A
Oral Roberts University, B
Tulsa Community College, A

Pennsylvania

Alvernia College, B
Cedar Crest College, B
Community College of Philadelphia, A
Delaware County Community College, A
DeVry University (Fort Washington), B
Johnson College, A
Lehigh Carbon Community College, A
Pennsylvania College of Technology, A
The Pennsylvania State University Altoona
College, A
The Pennsylvania State University Berks Campus of
the Berks-Lehigh Valley College, A
The Pennsylvania State University DuBois Campus
of the Commonwealth College, A
The Pennsylvania State University at Erie, The
Behrend College, A
The Pennsylvania State University Fayette Campus
of the Commonwealth College, A
The Pennsylvania State University Hazleton
Campus of the Commonwealth College, A
The Pennsylvania State University New Kensington
Campus of the Commonwealth College, A
The Pennsylvania State University Schuylkill
Campus of the Capital College, A
The Pennsylvania State University Shenango
Campus of the Commonwealth College, A
The Pennsylvania State University York Campus of
the Commonwealth College, A

South Dakota

Southeast Technical Institute, A

Tennessee

Southwest Tennessee Community College, A

Texas

DeVry University (Houston), B
DeVry University (Irving), B
St. Philip's College, A
Texas Southern University, B
Texas State Technical College Harlingen, A
Texas State Technical College Waco, A

Virginia

ECPI College of Technology (Virginia Beach), A

Washington

Bates Technical College, A
North Seattle Community College, A
Spokane Community College, A
Walla Walla College, B

Wisconsin

Milwaukee Area Technical College, A

BIOMETRY/BIOMETRICS

Alabama

The University of Alabama at Birmingham, MD

California

San Diego State University, D
University of California, Los Angeles, MD

University of Southern California, M

Louisiana

Louisiana State University Health Sciences
Center, M

Massachusetts

Harvard University, B

Nebraska

University of Nebraska-Lincoln, M

New Jersey

Rutgers, The State University of New Jersey, New
Brunswick/Piscataway, B

New York

Cornell University, BMD

North Carolina

North Carolina State University, MD

Oregon

Oregon State University, MD

South Carolina

Medical University of South Carolina, MDO

Texas

The University of Texas Health Science Center at
Houston, MDO

Wisconsin

University of Wisconsin-Madison, M

BIOPHYSICS

Alabama

The University of Alabama at Birmingham, MD

Arkansas

University of Arkansas for Medical Sciences, MDO

California

California Institute of Technology, D
Claremont McKenna College, B
La Sierra University, B
Pacific Union College, B
Stanford University, D
University of California, Berkeley, D
University of California, Davis, MD
University of California, Irvine, DO
University of California, Los Angeles, B
University of California, San Diego, BMD
University of California, Santa Barbara, MD
University of Southern California, BMDO

Connecticut

University of Connecticut, BMD
Yale University, MD

District of Columbia

Georgetown University, MDO
Howard University, D

Florida

University of Miami, BDO
University of South Florida, D

Illinois

Illinois Institute of Technology, B
Northwestern University, D
University of Illinois at Chicago, MD
University of Illinois at Urbana-Champaign, BD

Indiana

Indiana University-Purdue University
Indianapolis, MDO
Purdue University, D

University of Southern Indiana, B

Iowa

Iowa State University of Science and
Technology, BMD
The University of Iowa, MD

Kansas

University of Kansas, MD

Kentucky

University of Louisville, MD

Louisiana

Centenary College of Louisiana, B

Maryland

The Johns Hopkins University, BMD
University of Maryland, College Park, D

Massachusetts

Boston University, MDO
Brandeis University, BMD
Harvard University, BD
Massachusetts Institute of Technology, D
Suffolk University, B

Michigan

Andrews University, B
University of Michigan, BD

Minnesota

Saint Mary's University of Minnesota, B
University of Minnesota, Twin Cities Campus, MD

Mississippi

University of Mississippi Medical Center, MDO

Missouri

University of Missouri-Kansas City, D
Washington University in St. Louis, B

New Jersey

Princeton University, D

New York

Barnard College, B
Clarkson University, B
Columbia College, B
Cornell University, BD
Rensselaer Polytechnic Institute, BMD
St. Bonaventure University, B
St. Lawrence University, B
State University of New York at Buffalo, BMD
State University of New York College at Geneseo, B
Stony Brook University, State University of New
York, D
Syracuse University, BD
University of Rochester, MD

North Carolina

East Carolina University, M
The University of North Carolina at Chapel Hill, MD

Ohio

Case Western Reserve University, MDO
The Ohio State University, MD
University of Cincinnati, D
Wright State University, M

Oklahoma

Oklahoma City University, B
Southwestern Oklahoma State University, B

Oregon

Oregon State University, BMD

Pennsylvania

Carnegie Mellon University, BD
Haverford College, B
Temple University, B
University of Pennsylvania, B

The University of Scranton, B

Rhode Island

Brown University, B

South Carolina

Bob Jones University, B
Clemson University, MD

Tennessee

East Tennessee State University, MD
Freed-Hardeman University, B
King College, B
Vanderbilt University, DO

Texas

Texas A&M University, MD
The University of Texas Health Science Center at
Houston, MDO

Utah

Brigham Young University, B

Vermont

University of Vermont, MDO

Virginia

Hampden-Sydney College, B
Longwood University, B
University of Virginia, MDO

Washington

University of Washington, D
Walla Walla College, B
Washington State University, BMD
Whitman College, B

Wisconsin

University of Wisconsin-Madison, D

British Columbia

Simon Fraser University, MD
The University of British Columbia, B

New Brunswick

University of New Brunswick Fredericton, B

Nova Scotia

Dalhousie University, MDO

Ontario

Laurentian University, B
University of Guelph, BMD
University of Toronto, BMD
The University of Western Ontario, BMD
University of Windsor, B

Quebec

Université de Montréal, MD
Université du Québec àTrois-Rivières, BMD
Université de Sherbrooke, MD

BIOPSYCHOLOGY

California

Chapman University, B
University of California, Santa Barbara, B

Colorado

University of Denver, B
Western State College of Colorado, B

District of Columbia

American University, M
Howard University, D

Georgia

Emory University, D

Illinois

Northwestern University, D

University of Illinois at Urbana-Champaign, MD

Indiana

Indiana University-Purdue University Indianapolis, D

Iowa

Morningside College, B

Louisiana

Louisiana State University and Agricultural and
Mechanical College, MD

Massachusetts

Boston University, M

Michigan

University of Michigan, D
Wayne State University, M

Minnesota

University of Minnesota, Twin Cities Campus, D

Missouri

University of Missouri-Columbia, MD
Washington University in St. Louis, B

Nebraska

Hastings College, B
Nebraska Wesleyan University, B

New Jersey

Rider University, B
Rutgers, The State University of New Jersey, New
Brunswick/Piscataway, D
Rutgers, The State University of New Jersey,
Newark, D

New York

Barnard College, B
Columbia College, B
Cornell University, D
Hunter College of the City University of New
York, M
Rochester Institute of Technology, B
Russell Sage College, B
State University of New York at Binghamton, MD
Stony Brook University, State University of New
York, D
University at Albany, State University of New
York, D

North Carolina

Duke University, D

Ohio

The Ohio State University, D

Oklahoma

University of Oklahoma Health Sciences Center, MD

Oregon

Oregon Health & Science University, MDO
University of Oregon, MD

Pennsylvania

Bucknell University, B
Carnegie Mellon University, BD
Drexel University, MDO
Immaculata University, B
Lehigh University, B
Messiah College, B
The Pennsylvania State University University Park
Campus, MD
Philadelphia University, B

University of Pittsburgh at Johnstown, B

Texas

Texas A&M University, MD
The University of Texas at Austin, MDO

Virginia

The College of William and Mary, B

Wisconsin

University of Wisconsin-Madison, D

New Brunswick

Mount Allison University, B

Newfoundland and Labrador

Memorial University of Newfoundland, MD

Ontario

University of Windsor, BM

BIOSTATISTICS

Alabama

The University of Alabama at Birmingham, MD

Arizona

Arizona State University, MD

California

Loma Linda University, M
San Diego State University, D
University of California, Berkeley, MD
University of California, Davis, MD
University of California, Los Angeles, BMD
University of Southern California, MD

Connecticut

Yale University, MD

District of Columbia

The George Washington University, MD
Georgetown University, M

Florida

Florida State University, M
University of Florida, M
University of South Florida, MD

Georgia

Emory University, MD

Illinois

University of Illinois at Chicago, MD

Iowa

Iowa State University of Science and
Technology, MD
The University of Iowa, MD

Kentucky

University of Louisville, MD

Louisiana

Tulane University, BMD

Maryland

The Johns Hopkins University, MD

Massachusetts

Boston University, MD
Emmanuel College, B
Harvard University, MD

Tufts University, MD

Michigan

University of Michigan, MD
Western Michigan University, M

Minnesota

University of Minnesota, Twin Cities Campus, MD

New York

State University of New York at Buffalo, BMD
University at Albany, State University of New
  York, MD
University of Rochester, MD

North Carolina

The University of North Carolina at Chapel
  Hill, BMD

Ohio

Case Western Reserve University, MD
The Ohio State University, D
University of Cincinnati, MD

Oklahoma

University of Oklahoma Health Sciences Center, MD

Oregon

Oregon Health & Science University, MO

Pennsylvania

Drexel University, M
University of Pennsylvania, MD
University of Pittsburgh, MD

Puerto Rico

University of Puerto Rico, Medical Sciences
  Campus, M

Rhode Island

Brown University, MDO

South Carolina

Medical University of South Carolina, MD
University of South Carolina, MD

Texas

Rice University, D

Utah

Brigham Young University, B
University of Utah, M

Vermont

University of Vermont, M

Virginia

Virginia Commonwealth University, MDO

Washington

University of Washington, BMD

Alberta

University of Alberta, M

Ontario

University of Waterloo, M
The University of Western Ontario, MD

Quebec

McGill University, MDO

BIOSYSTEMS ENGINEERING

Arizona

The University of Arizona, MD

Iowa

Iowa State University of Science and
  Technology, MD

Michigan

Michigan State University, MD

North Dakota

North Dakota State University, MD

South Carolina

Clemson University, MD

Tennessee

The University of Tennessee, MD

Manitoba

University of Manitoba, MD

BIOTECHNOLOGY

Alabama

The University of Alabama in Huntsville, D

California

Santa Barbara City College, A
University of California, Davis, B
University of California, Irvine, M
University of California, Los Angeles, B
University of California, San Diego, B

Connecticut

Briarwood College, A
University of Connecticut, MD

Delaware

Delaware State University, B
University of Delaware, BMD

District of Columbia

Howard University, M

Florida

Florida Gulf Coast University, B
Florida Institute of Technology, M

Georgia

Augusta Technical College, A
Kennesaw State University, B

Illinois

Illinois Institute of Technology, M
Illinois State University, M
Northwestern University, D
Roosevelt University, BM
Southern Illinois University Edwardsville, M
University of Illinois at Chicago, MD
University of Illinois at Urbana-Champaign, B

Indiana

Ivy Tech Community College-Central Indiana, A
Ivy Tech Community College-Lafayette, A
Ivy Tech Community College-North Central, A
Purdue University Calumet, M

Iowa

University of Northern Iowa, B

Louisiana

Louisiana State University and Agricultural and
  Mechanical College, B

Maine

University of Southern Maine, B

Maryland

College of Southern Maryland, A
Howard Community College, A
The Johns Hopkins University, M
University of Maryland University College, MO

Massachusetts

Assumption College, B
Bay Path College, B
Fitchburg State College, B

Framingham State College, B
Harvard University, M
Northeastern University, M
Springfield Technical Community College, A
Tufts University, O
University of Massachusetts Amherst, MD
University of Massachusetts Boston, M
University of Massachusetts Dartmouth, D
University of Massachusetts Lowell, M
Worcester Polytechnic Institute, MDO
Worcester State College, BM

Michigan

Calvin College, B

Minnesota

University of Minnesota, Twin Cities Campus, M

Missouri

Missouri Southern State University, B
Missouri Western State University, B
University of Missouri-St. Louis, O

Montana

Montana State University, B

Nebraska

University of Nebraska at Omaha, B

Nevada

University of Nevada, Reno, BM

New Hampshire

Dartmouth College, MD
Plymouth State University, B

New Jersey

Burlington County College, A
Kean University, M
Rutgers, The State University of New Jersey, New
  Brunswick/Piscataway, B
William Paterson University of New Jersey, M

New Mexico

Central New Mexico Community College, A
Northern New Mexico Community College, A

New York

Clarkson University, B
Hunter College of the City University of New York, B
Manhattan College, B
Rochester Institute of Technology, B
State University of New York at Buffalo, BM
State University of New York College at
  Brockport, B
State University of New York College of
  Environmental Science and Forestry, B
State University of New York at New Paltz, B
University at Albany, State University of New
  York, MD

North Carolina

Alamance Community College, A
Bladen Community College, A
College of The Albemarle, A
East Carolina University, M
North Carolina State University, M
Southeastern Community College, A

North Dakota

North Dakota State University, B

Ohio

Kent State University, B
Lakeland Community College, A
The Ohio State University, B
Sinclair Community College, A

Ursuline College, B

Oklahoma

Southeastern Oklahoma State University, B

Pennsylvania

East Stroudsburg University of Pennsylvania, B
Elizabethtown College, B
Lackawanna College, A
Lehigh Carbon Community College, A
Montgomery County Community College, A
Northampton County Area Community College, A
The Pennsylvania State University University Park
  Campus, M
Point Park University, B
Thomas Jefferson University, BD
University of Pennsylvania, M
University of the Sciences in Philadelphia, M

Rhode Island

Brown University, MD

Texas

El Centro College, A
Stephen F. Austin State University, M
Texas A&M University, M
Texas Tech University, M
The University of Texas at Dallas, M
The University of Texas at San Antonio, M
West Texas A&M University, B

Utah

Brigham Young University, B
Dixie State College of Utah, A

Virginia

James Madison University, B
Piedmont Virginia Community College, A

Washington

Eastern Washington University, B
University of Washington, D
Washington State University, B

West Virginia

Salem International University, M
West Virginia State University, M

Wisconsin

University of Wisconsin-River Falls, B

Alberta

University of Alberta, MD
University of Calgary, M
University of Lethbridge, B

British Columbia

British Columbia Institute of Technology, AB
The University of British Columbia, B

Ontario

Brock University, BMD
University of Guelph, MD
University of Waterloo, B
The University of Western Ontario, M
University of Windsor, B
Wilfrid Laurier University, B
York University, B

Quebec

Concordia University, O
McGill University, MO

Université de Sherbrooke, P

Saskatchewan

University of Saskatchewan, BM

BOILERMAKING/BOILERMAKER

Indiana

Ivy Tech Community College-Southwest, A

BOTANY/PLANT BIOLOGY

Alabama

Auburn University, BMD

Arizona

Arizona State University, B
Northern Arizona University, B

California

California State Polytechnic University, Pomona, B
California State University, Chico, M
California State University, Fullerton, M
California State University, Long Beach, B
Cerritos College, A
City College of San Francisco, A
El Camino College, A
Humboldt State University, B
Lassen Community College District, A
San Bernardino Valley College, A
San Francisco State University, B
San Joaquin Delta College, A
Santa Rosa Junior College, A
Sonoma State University, B
University of California, Berkeley, B
University of California, Davis, B
University of California, Los Angeles, B
University of California, Riverside, BMD
University of California, Santa Cruz, B

Colorado

Colorado State University, BMD

Connecticut

Connecticut College, BM
University of Connecticut, MD

Delaware

University of Delaware, B

Florida

Palm Beach Community College, A
University of Florida, BMD
University of South Florida, M

Georgia

Fort Valley State University, B
University of Georgia, B

Hawaii

University of Hawaii at Manoa, BMD

Idaho

Brigham Young University -Idaho, A
College of Southern Idaho, A
Idaho State University, B
North Idaho College, A
University of Idaho, B

Illinois

Illinois State University, D
Lincoln College, A
Saint Xavier University, B
Southern Illinois University Carbondale, B
Spoon River College, A
University of Illinois at Urbana-Champaign, B

William Rainey Harper College, A

Indiana

Ball State University, B
Purdue University, BMD

Iowa

Iowa Lakes Community College, A
Iowa State University of Science and Technology, B

Kansas

Coffeyville Community College, A
Emporia State University, M
University of Kansas, MD

Maine

College of the Atlantic, B
Southern Maine Community College, A
University of Maine, BM

Maryland

Anne Arundel Community College, A

Michigan

Andrews University, B
Michigan State University, B
Northern Michigan University, B
University of Michigan, B

Minnesota

Minnesota State University Mankato, B
St. Cloud State University, B
University of Minnesota, Twin Cities Campus, B

Missouri

East Central College, A
Northwest Missouri State University, B

Montana

University of Great Falls, B
The University of Montana-Missoula, B

New Hampshire

University of New Hampshire, B

New Jersey

Rutgers, The State University of New Jersey,
  Newark, B

New Mexico

Western New Mexico University, B

New York

Cornell University, B
State University of New York College of
  Environmental Science and Forestry, B

North Carolina

Mars Hill College, B
North Carolina State University, BMD
The University of North Carolina at Chapel Hill, MD

North Dakota

North Dakota State University, BMD
University of North Dakota, MD

Ohio

Kent State University, BM
Miami University, BMD
Miami University Hamilton, B
Miami University-Middletown Campus, A
The Ohio State University, B
Ohio University, B
Ohio University-Eastern, B
Ohio Wesleyan University, B
The University of Akron, B

Oklahoma

Northeastern Oklahoma Agricultural and Mechanical
  College, A
Oklahoma State University, BMD
Southeastern Oklahoma State University, B
Tulsa Community College, A

University of Oklahoma, BMD

Oregon

Oregon State University, BMD

Pennsylvania

Juniata College, B

Tennessee

The University of Tennessee, B

Texas

Frank Phillips College, A
Hill College of the Hill Junior College District, A
Lon Morris College, A
Texas A&M University, BMD
Texas State University-San Marcos, B
The University of Texas at Austin, B
The University of Texas at El Paso, B

Utah

Brigham Young University, B
Dixie State College of Utah, A
Snow College, A
Southern Utah University, B
Utah State University, B
Weber State University, B

Vermont

Goddard College, B
Marlboro College, B
University of Vermont, BMD

Virginia

Virginia Polytechnic Institute and State
    University, MD

Washington

Centralia College, A
Everett Community College, A
Tacoma Community College, A
University of Washington, BMD
Washington State University, MD

Wisconsin

University of Wisconsin-Madison, BMD

Wyoming

Northwest College, A
University of Wyoming, BMD

Alberta

University of Alberta, B
University of Calgary, B

British Columbia

The University of British Columbia, MD
University of Northern British Columbia, B
University of Victoria, B

Manitoba

Brandon University, B
University of Manitoba, BMD

New Brunswick

University of New Brunswick Fredericton, B

Ontario

Carleton University, B
University of Toronto, BMD

Quebec

McGill University, B

BROADCAST JOURNALISM

Alabama

Auburn University, B
Troy University, B

University of Montevallo, B

Alaska

University of Alaska, Prince William Sound
    Community College, A

Arizona

Arizona Western College, A

Arkansas

Harding University, B
John Brown University, AB
Southern Arkansas University-Magnolia, B

California

Bakersfield College, A
California State University, East Bay, B
California State University, Long Beach, B
Chabot College, A
Chaffey College, A
Chapman University, B
City College of San Francisco, A
College of San Mateo, A
Columbia College Hollywood, B
Cosumnes River College (Sacramento), A
Humboldt State University, B
Laney College, A
Los Angeles City College, A
Los Angeles Valley College, A
Moorpark College, A
Ohlone College, A
Pasadena City College, A
Point Loma Nazarene University, B
San Joaquin Delta College, A
Santa Monica College, A
University of La Verne, B
University of Southern California, B

Colorado

Colorado State University-Pueblo, B
Mesa State College, B
University of Colorado at Boulder, B

Connecticut

Middlesex Community College, A
Quinnipiac University, B

Delaware

Delaware State University, B

District of Columbia

Howard University, B

Florida

Barry University, B
Florida International University, B
Florida Southern College, B
Palm Beach Atlantic University, B
University of Miami, B

Georgia

Paine College, B
University of Georgia, B

Idaho

Brigham Young University -Idaho, A

Illinois

Bradley University, B
City Colleges of Chicago, Kennedy-King College, A
Columbia College Chicago, B
Lewis University, B
Lincoln College, A
Olivet Nazarene University, B
University of Illinois at Urbana-Champaign, B

Indiana

Goshen College, B
Huntington University, B
Indiana University Bloomington, B
Manchester College, A

Vincennes University, A

Iowa

Drake University, B
Iowa Central Community College, A
Iowa Lakes Community College, A
Kirkwood Community College, A
University of Northern Iowa, B
Waldorf College, B
Wartburg College, B

Kansas

Cloud County Community College, A
Coffeyville Community College, A
Colby Community College, A
Dodge City Community College, A
Pratt Community College, A

Kentucky

Eastern Kentucky University, B

Louisiana

Louisiana College, B

Maine

New England School of Communications, AB

Maryland

Anne Arundel Community College, A
Bowie State University, B
Columbia Union College, B

Massachusetts

Emerson College, B
Massachusetts College of Liberal Arts, B
Suffolk University, B

Michigan

Adrian College, B
Cornerstone University, A
Grand Valley State University, B
Kuyper College, B
Lansing Community College, A
Northern Michigan University, B
St. Clair County Community College, A
University of Detroit Mercy, B

Minnesota

Bemidji State University, B
Concordia College, B
Minnesota State University Moorhead, B
North Central University, AB
Northland Community and Technical College-Thief
    River Falls, A
Ridgewater College, A
St. Cloud State University, B
University of St. Thomas, B
Winona State University, B

Mississippi

Meridian Community College, A
Northeast Mississippi Community College, A
Rust College, B

Missouri

Calvary Bible College and Theological Seminary, B
College of the Ozarks, B
Drury University, B
Evangel University, AB
Fontbonne University, B
Lindenwood University, B
Northwest Missouri State University, B
St. Louis Community College at Florissant Valley, A
St. Louis Community College at Meramec, A
Stephens College, B
University of Missouri-Columbia, B
Webster University, B
William Woods University, B

Nebraska

Grace University, B
Hastings College, B
Midland Lutheran College, B
Northeast Community College, A

Southeast Community College, Beatrice Campus, A
University of Nebraska-Lincoln, B
University of Nebraska at Omaha, B

Nevada

University of Nevada, Reno, B

New Jersey

Bergen Community College, A
Cumberland County College, A
Montclair State University, B
Sussex County Community College, A

New York

Adirondack Community College, A
Brooklyn College of the City University of New
    York, B
Buffalo State College, State University of New
    York, B
The College of New Rochelle, B
Finger Lakes Community College, A
Five Towns College, A
Fordham University, B
Herkimer County Community College, A
Hofstra University, B
Ithaca College, B
Kingsborough Community College of the City
    University of New York, A
Long Island University, C.W. Post Campus, B
Marist College, B
State University of New York College at
    Brockport, B
State University of New York, Fredonia, B
State University of New York at New Paltz, B
State University of New York at Plattsburgh, B
Syracuse University, B

North Carolina

Campbell University, B
East Carolina University, B
Elon University, B
Isothermal Community College, A

Ohio

Baldwin-Wallace College, B
Bowling Green State University, B
Cedarville University, B
Mount Vernon Nazarene University, B
Muskingum College, B
Ohio University, B
Ohio University-Zanesville, A
Ohio Wesleyan University, B
The University of Akron, B
University of Cincinnati, B
University of Dayton, B
The University of Findlay, B

Oklahoma

Langston University, B
Northeastern Oklahoma Agricultural and Mechanical
    College, A
Northern Oklahoma College, A
Oklahoma Baptist University, B
Oklahoma Christian University, B
Oklahoma City Community College, A
Oklahoma City University, B
Oklahoma State University, B
Rogers State University, A
Rose State College, A
St. Gregory's University, B
Southern Nazarene University, B
University of Central Oklahoma, B
University of Oklahoma, B

Oregon

George Fox University, B
Lane Community College, A
Mt. Hood Community College, A
Pacific University, B
University of Oregon, B

Pennsylvania

Edinboro University of Pennsylvania, B
Gettysburg College, B
La Salle University, B

Mansfield University of Pennsylvania, B
Marywood University, B
Mercyhurst College, B
Pennsylvania College of Technology, A
Point Park University, B
Susquehanna University, B
Westminster College, B

South Carolina

Benedict College, B
Bob Jones University, B
Morris College, B
Trident Technical College, A
University of South Carolina, B

Tennessee

Belmont University, B
Carson-Newman College, B
Chattanooga State Technical Community College, A
Draughons Junior College (Nashville), A
Martin Methodist College, A
Southern Adventist University, B
Trevecca Nazarene University, A
Union University, B
The University of Tennessee at Martin, B

Texas

Amarillo College, A
El Paso Community College, A
Hardin-Simmons University, B
Lamar University, B
Navarro College, A
Southern Methodist University, B
Southwestern Adventist University, B
Texas Christian University, B
University of North Texas, B
The University of Texas at El Paso, B
West Texas A&M University, B

Utah

Brigham Young University, B
Dixie State College of Utah, A
University of Utah, B

Virginia

Hampton University, B

Washington

Centralia College, A
Gonzaga University, B
Pacific Lutheran University, B
Yakima Valley Community College, A

Wisconsin

Marquette University, B
University of Wisconsin-Madison, B
University of Wisconsin-Milwaukee, B
University of Wisconsin-Oshkosh, B
University of Wisconsin-Platteville, B
University of Wisconsin-River Falls, B
University of Wisconsin-Superior, B

Ontario

University of Windsor, B

BUDDHIST STUDIES

California

University of the West, B

North Carolina

Heritage Bible College, AB

BUILDING/CONSTRUCTION
FINISHING, MANAGEMENT,
AND INSPECTION

Arizona

Pima Community College, A

Arkansas

John Brown University, AB

California

Cabrillo College, A
California State University, Long Beach, B
City College of San Francisco, A
College of the Desert, A
Cosumnes River College (Sacramento), A
Fresno City College, A
Laney College, A
Modesto Junior College, A
Mt. San Antonio College, A
San Joaquin Valley College, A
Santa Rosa Junior College, A
Sierra College, A
Victor Valley College, A

Colorado

Arapahoe Community College, A
Pikes Peak Community College, A
University of Denver, B

Connecticut

Central Connecticut State University, B

Delaware

Delaware Technical & Community College, Jack F.
    Owens Campus, A
Delaware Technical & Community College, Terry
    Campus, A

District of Columbia

University of the District of Columbia, B

Florida

Broward Community College, A
Palm Beach Community College, A
Seminole Community College, A

Georgia

Gwinnett Technical College, A

Idaho

Boise State University, B

Illinois

Oakton Community College, A
Parkland College, A
Southwestern Illinois College, A
Triton College, A

Indiana

Ivy Tech Community College-Northwest, A

Kansas

Manhattan Area Technical College, A
Pittsburg State University, B

Louisiana

Delgado Community College, A

Maryland

Frederick Community College, A
Montgomery College, A
University of Maryland Eastern Shore, B

Massachusetts

Wentworth Institute of Technology, AB

Michigan

Baker College of Flint, A
Delta College, A
Ferris State University, B
Gogebic Community College, A
Washtenaw Community College, A
Western Michigan University, B

Minnesota

Inver Hills Community College, A
Minnesota State University Mankato, B
Northwest Technical College, A

University of Minnesota, Twin Cities Campus, B

Mississippi

Mississippi State University, B

Nebraska

Mid-Plains Community College, A

Nevada

Community College of Southern Nevada, A
Western Nevada Community College, A

New Hampshire

University of New Hampshire, A

New Mexico

Central New Mexico Community College, A
University of New Mexico-Valencia Campus, A

New York

Farmingdale State University of New York, B
Polytechnic University, Brooklyn Campus, B
Pratt Institute, AB
Rensselaer Polytechnic Institute, B
State University of New York College of Technology
at Delhi, A

North Carolina

Fayetteville Technical Community College, A
Guilford Technical Community College, A
North Carolina Agricultural and Technical State
University, B
Wilkes Community College, A

Ohio

Columbus State Community College, A
University of Cincinnati, B

Oregon

Oregon State University, B

Rhode Island

Roger Williams University, B

South Carolina

Piedmont Technical College, A

Texas

El Paso Community College, A
St. Philip's College, A
Sam Houston State University, B

Utah

Salt Lake Community College, A
Snow College, A

Virginia

Hampton University, B

Washington

University of Washington, B

Wisconsin

University of Wisconsin-Madison, B
University of Wisconsin-Platteville, B

British Columbia

British Columbia Institute of Technology, A

BUILDING/CONSTRUCTION SITE MANAGEMENT/MANAGER

Missouri

Metropolitan Community College-Business &
Technology College, A

Ohio

The Ohio State University Agricultural Technical
Institute, A

South Carolina

Bob Jones University, B

BUILDING/HOME/CONSTRUCTION INSPECTION/INSPECTOR

Alabama

Tuskegee University, B

California

Modesto Junior College, A
Orange Coast College, A

Colorado

Arapahoe Community College, A

Illinois

McHenry County College, A

Indiana

Vincennes University, A

Iowa

Iowa Western Community College, A

Pennsylvania

Johnson College, A

Utah

Utah Valley State College, A

Washington

Edmonds Community College, A

BUILDING/PROPERTY MAINTENANCE AND MANAGEMENT

Arizona

Northland Pioneer College, A
Pima Community College, A

Colorado

Pikes Peak Community College, A

Illinois

College of DuPage, A
Illinois Eastern Community Colleges, Lincoln Trail
College, A

Indiana

Ivy Tech Community College-Bloomington, A
Ivy Tech Community College-Central Indiana, A
Ivy Tech Community College-Columbus, A
Ivy Tech Community College-East Central, A
Ivy Tech Community College-Kokomo, A
Ivy Tech Community College-Lafayette, A
Ivy Tech Community College-North Central, A
Ivy Tech Community College-Northeast, A
Ivy Tech Community College-Northwest, A
Ivy Tech Community College-Southern Indiana, A
Ivy Tech Community College-Southwest, A
Ivy Tech Community College-Wabash Valley, A
Ivy Tech Community College-Whitewater, A

Louisiana

Delgado Community College, A

Missouri

Park University, A

Montana

Miles Community College, A

New York

Erie Community College, A
Mohawk Valley Community College, A

Pennsylvania

Community College of Allegheny County, A
Delaware County Community College, A

Luzerne County Community College, A

Texas

Del Mar College, A

Washington

Bates Technical College, A

BUILDING SCIENCE

Alabama

Auburn University, M

Arizona

Arizona State University, M

California

University of California, Berkeley, D
University of Southern California, MO

Colorado

Colorado State University, M

Florida

University of Florida, MD

Georgia

Georgia Institute of Technology, MD

New York

Cornell University, M
Rensselaer Polytechnic Institute, M

Pennsylvania

Carnegie Mellon University, MD

BUSINESS ADMINISTRATION AND MANAGEMENT

Alabama

Alabama Agricultural and Mechanical University, B
Alabama Southern Community College, A
Alabama State University, AB
American College of Computer & Information
Sciences, B
Athens State University, B
Auburn University, B
Auburn University Montgomery, B
Bevill State Community College, A
Birmingham-Southern College, B
Calhoun Community College, A
Central Alabama Community College, A
Chattahoochee Valley Community College, A
Columbia Southern University, B
Concordia College, B
Enterprise-Ozark Community College, A
Faulkner University, AB
George C. Wallace Community College, A
George Corley Wallace State Community College, A
Huntingdon College, B
Jacksonville State University, B
James H. Faulkner State Community College, A
Jefferson Davis Community College, A
Lawson State Community College, A
Miles College, B
Northeast Alabama Community College, A
Northwest-Shoals Community College, A
Oakwood College, B
Samford University, B
Snead State Community College, A
South University, AB
Southern Union State Community College, A
Spring Hill College, AB
Stillman College, B
Talladega College, B
Troy University, B
Tuskegee University, B
The University of Alabama, B
The University of Alabama at Birmingham, B
The University of Alabama in Huntsville, B
University of Mobile, B

University of Montevallo, B
University of North Alabama, B
University of South Alabama, B
The University of West Alabama, B
Virginia College at Birmingham, B
Wallace State Community College, A

Alaska

Alaska Pacific University, AB
Charter College, A
Sheldon Jackson College, AB
University of Alaska Anchorage, AB
University of Alaska Anchorage, Kenai Peninsula
   College, A
University of Alaska Anchorage, Kodiak College, A
University of Alaska Anchorage, Matanuska-Susitna
   College, A
University of Alaska Fairbanks, AB
University of Alaska, Prince William Sound
   Community College, A
University of Alaska Southeast, AB
University of Alaska Southeast, Ketchikan
   Campus, A
University of Alaska Southeast, Sitka Campus, A

Arizona

American Indian College of the Assemblies of God,
   Inc., A
Arizona State University, B
Arizona State University at the Polytechnic
   Campus, B
Arizona Western College, A
Central Arizona College, A
Chandler-Gilbert Community College, A
Chaparral College, AB
Cochise College (Douglas), A
Cochise College (Sierra Vista), A
Coconino Community College, A
Diné College, A
Eastern Arizona College, A
Glendale Community College, A
Grand Canyon University, B
International Institute of the Americas (Mesa), AB
International Institute of the Americas (Phoenix), AB
International Institute of the Americas (Tucson), AB
International Institute of the Americas (West Valley)
   , AB
ITT Technical Institute (Tempe), B
ITT Technical Institute (Tucson), B
Lamson College, A
Mesa Community College, A
Mohave Community College, A
Northcentral University, B
Northern Arizona University, B
Northland Pioneer College, A
Paradise Valley Community College, A
Phoenix College, A
Pima Community College, A
Rio Salado College, A
Scottsdale Community College, A
South Mountain Community College, A
Southwestern College, B
University of Phoenix Online Campus, B
University of Phoenix-Phoenix Campus, B
University of Phoenix-Southern Arizona Campus, B
Western International University, B
Yavapai College, A

Arkansas

Arkansas Baptist College, B
Arkansas State University, B
Arkansas State University-Beebe, A
Arkansas Tech University, B
Black River Technical College, A
Central Baptist College, AB
Cossatot Community College of the University of
   Arkansas, A
East Arkansas Community College, A
Harding University, B
ITT Technical Institute, B
John Brown University, B
Lyon College, B
National Park Community College, A
NorthWest Arkansas Community College, A
Ouachita Baptist University, B
Ouachita Technical College, A

Ozarka College, A
Philander Smith College, B
Phillips Community College of the University of
   Arkansas, A
Southeast Arkansas College, A
Southern Arkansas University Tech, A
University of Arkansas, B
University of Arkansas Community College at
   Hope, A
University of Arkansas at Fort Smith, AB
University of Arkansas at Little Rock, B
University of Arkansas at Monticello, B
University of Arkansas at Pine Bluff, B
University of Central Arkansas, B
University of the Ozarks, B
University of Phoenix-Little Rock Campus, B
Williams Baptist College, AB

California

Allan Hancock College, A
Alliant International University, B
American InterContinental University, AB
American River College, A
Antelope Valley College, A
Azusa Pacific University, B
Bakersfield College, A
Barstow College, A
Berkeley City College, A
Biola University, B
Cabrillo College, A
California Baptist University, B
California Coast University, AB
California Lutheran University, B
California Maritime Academy, B
California National University for Advanced
   Studies, B
California Polytechnic State University, San Luis
   Obispo, B
California State Polytechnic University, Pomona, B
California State University, Bakersfield, B
California State University Channel Islands, B
California State University, Chico, B
California State University, Dominguez Hills, B
California State University, East Bay, B
California State University, Fresno, B
California State University, Fullerton, B
California State University, Long Beach, B
California State University, Los Angeles, B
California State University, Monterey Bay, B
California State University, Northridge, B
California State University, Sacramento, B
California State University, San Bernardino, B
California State University, San Marcos, B
California State University, Stanislaus, B
Cañada College, A
Cerritos College, A
Cerro Coso Community College, A
Chabot College, A
Chaffey College, A
Chapman University, B
Citrus College, A
City College of San Francisco, A
College of Alameda, A
College of the Canyons, A
College of the Desert, A
College of Marin, A
College of the Redwoods, A
College of San Mateo, A
College of the Sequoias, A
College of the Siskiyous, A
Columbia College, A
Compton Community College, A
Concordia University, B
Contra Costa College, A
Cosumnes River College (Sacramento), A
Crafton Hills College, A
Cuesta College, A
Cuyamaca College, A
Cypress College, A
De Anza College, A
DeVry University (West Hills), B
Dominican University of California, B
East Los Angeles College, A
El Camino College, A
Evergreen Valley College, A

FIDM/The Fashion Institute of Design &
   Merchandising, Los Angeles Campus, B
Folsom Lake College, A
Foothill College, A
Fresno City College, A
Fresno Pacific University, AB
Fullerton College, A
Gavilan College, A
Glendale Community College, A
Golden Gate University, B
Golden West College, A
Grossmont College, A
Hartnell College, A
Heald College-Fresno, A
Heald College-Rancho Cordova, A
Heald College-Roseville, A
Heald College-Salinas, A
Holy Names University, B
Hope International University, B
Humboldt State University, B
Humphreys College, AB
Imperial Valley College, A
Institute of Computer Technology, AB
Irvine Valley College, A
ITT Technical Institute (Anaheim), B
ITT Technical Institute (Lathrop), B
ITT Technical Institute (Oxnard), B
ITT Technical Institute (Rancho Cordova), B
ITT Technical Institute (San Bernardino), B
ITT Technical Institute (San Diego), B
ITT Technical Institute (Sylmar), B
ITT Technical Institute (Torrance), B
ITT Technical Institute (West Covina), B
John F. Kennedy University, B
La Sierra University, B
Lake Tahoe Community College, A
Laney College, A
Las Positas College, A
Lassen Community College District, A
Lincoln University, B
Long Beach City College, A
Los Angeles City College, A
Los Angeles Harbor College, A
Los Angeles Mission College, A
Los Angeles Southwest College, A
Los Angeles Trade-Technical College, A
Los Angeles Valley College, A
Los Medanos College, A
Loyola Marymount University, B
The Master's College and Seminary, B
Mendocino College, A
Menlo College, B
Merced College, A
Merritt College, A
MiraCosta College, A
Mission College, A
Modesto Junior College, A
Monterey Peninsula College, A
Moorpark College, A
Mount St. Mary's College, AB
Mt. San Antonio College, A
Mt. San Jacinto College, A
Mt. Sierra College, B
MTI College of Business and Technology, A
Napa Valley College, A
The National Hispanic University, AB
National University, B
Northwestern Polytechnic University, B
Notre Dame de Namur University, B
Ohlone College, A
Orange Coast College, A
Oxnard College, A
Pacific States University, B
Pacific Union College, B
Palo Verde College, A
Palomar College, A
Pasadena City College, A
Patten University, B
Pepperdine University, B
Point Loma Nazarene University, B
Porterville College, A
Riverside Community College District, A
Sacramento City College, A
Saddleback College, A
Saint Mary's College of California, B
San Bernardino Valley College, A

San Diego Christian College, B
San Diego City College, A
San Diego Mesa College, A
San Diego Miramar College, A
San Diego State University, B
San Francisco State University, B
San Joaquin Delta College, A
San Jose City College, A
San Jose State University, B
Santa Ana College, A
Santa Barbara City College, A
Santa Monica College, A
Santa Rosa Junior College, A
Santiago Canyon College, A
Shasta College, A
Sierra College, A
Simpson University, B
Skyline College, A
Solano Community College, A
Sonoma State University, B
Southern California Institute of Technology, A
Southwestern College, A
Taft College, A
University of California, Berkeley, B
University of California, Los Angeles, B
University of California, Riverside, B
University of La Verne, B
University of the Pacific, B
University of Phoenix-Bay Area Campus, B
University of Phoenix-Central Valley Campus, B
University of Phoenix-Sacramento Valley Campus, B
University of Phoenix-San Diego Campus, B
University of Phoenix-Southern California
  Campus, B
University of Redlands, B
University of San Diego, B
University of San Francisco, B
University of Southern California, B
University of the West, B
Vanguard University of Southern California, B
Ventura College, A
Victor Valley College, A
West Hills Community College, A
West Los Angeles College, A
West Valley College, A
Whittier College, B
Woodbury University, B
Yuba College, A

Colorado

Adams State College, B
Arapahoe Community College, A
Blair College, A
CollegeAmerica-Fort Collins, AB
Colorado Christian University, B
Colorado Mountain College, A
Colorado Mountain College, Alpine Campus, A
Colorado Northwestern Community College, A
Colorado State University, B
Colorado State University-Pueblo, B
Colorado Technical University, B
Colorado Technical University Denver Campus, B
Community College of Aurora, A
Community College of Denver, A
DeVry University (Colorado Springs), B
DeVry University (Westminster), B
Fort Lewis College, B
Front Range Community College, A
Institute of Business & Medical Careers, A
ITT Technical Institute, B
Johnson & Wales University, A
Lamar Community College, A
Mesa State College, AB
Morgan Community College, A
National American University (Colorado Springs)
  , AB
National American University (Denver), AB
Northeastern Junior College, A
Otero Junior College, A
Parks College (Denver), A
Pikes Peak Community College, A
Pueblo Community College, A
Red Rocks Community College, A
Regis University, B
Remington College-Denver Campus, AB
Trinidad State Junior College, A

United States Air Force Academy, B
University of Colorado at Colorado Springs, B
University of Denver, B
University of Northern Colorado, B
University of Phoenix-Denver Campus, B
University of Phoenix-Southern Colorado
  Campus, B
Western State College of Colorado, B

Connecticut

Asnuntuck Community College, A
Briarwood College, A
Capital Community College, A
Central Connecticut State University, B
Eastern Connecticut State University, B
Fairfield University, B
Gateway Community College, A
Goodwin College, A
Housatonic Community College, A
Manchester Community College, A
Middlesex Community College, A
Mitchell College, AB
Naugatuck Valley Community College, A
Northwestern Connecticut Community College, A
Norwalk Community College, A
Post University, AB
Quinebaug Valley Community College, A
Quinnipiac University, B
Sacred Heart University, AB
Saint Joseph College, B
Southern Connecticut State University, B
Three Rivers Community College, A
Tunxis Community College, A
University of Bridgeport, AB
University of Hartford, B
University of New Haven, B
Western Connecticut State University, B

Delaware

Delaware State University, B
Delaware Technical & Community College, Jack F.
  Owens Campus, A
Delaware Technical & Community College,
  Stanton/Wilmington Campus, A
Delaware Technical & Community College, Terry
  Campus, A
Goldey-Beacom College, AB
University of Delaware, B
Wesley College, B
Wilmington College, B

District of Columbia

American University, B
The Catholic University of America, B
Gallaudet University, B
The George Washington University, B
Georgetown University, B
Howard University, B
Potomac College, B
Southeastern University, AB
Strayer University, AB
Trinity (Washington) University, B
University of the District of Columbia, B

Florida

Argosy University/Sarasota, B
Argosy University/Tampa, B
Barry University, B
Bethune-Cookman College, B
Brevard Community College, A
Broward Community College, A
Brown Mackie College-Miami, A
Carlos Albizu University, Miami Campus, B
Chipola College, A
Clearwater Christian College, B
College of Business and Technology, A
Daytona Beach Community College, A
DeVry University (Miramar), B
Eckerd College, B
Edison College, A
Edward Waters College, B
Everglades University (Boca Raton), B
Flagler College, B
Florida Agricultural and Mechanical University, B
Florida Atlantic University, B
Florida Community College at Jacksonville, A

Florida Gulf Coast University, B
Florida Institute of Technology, B
Florida International University, B
Florida Keys Community College, A
Florida Memorial College, B
Florida Metropolitan University-Brandon
  Campus, AB
Florida Metropolitan University-Jacksonville
  Campus, AB
Florida Metropolitan University-Lakeland
  Campus, AB
Florida Metropolitan University-Melbourne
  Campus, AB
Florida Metropolitan University-North Orlando
  Campus, AB
Florida Metropolitan University-Pompano Beach
  Campus, AB
Florida Metropolitan University-South Orlando
  Campus, AB
Florida Metropolitan University-Tampa Campus, AB
Florida National College, A
Florida Southern College, B
Florida State University, B
Gulf Coast Community College, A
Herzing College, A
Hillsborough Community College, A
Indian River Community College, A
International College, AB
ITT Technical Institute (Fort Lauderdale), B
ITT Technical Institute (Jacksonville), B
ITT Technical Institute (Lake Mary), B
ITT Technical Institute (Miami), B
ITT Technical Institute (Tampa), B
Jacksonville University, B
Johnson & Wales University, AB
Jones College (Jacksonville), AB
Jones College (Miami), AB
Keiser College (Daytona Beach), A
Keiser College (Fort Lauderdale), AB
Keiser College (Melbourne), A
Keiser College (Miami), A
Keiser College (Sarasota), A
Keiser College (Tallahassee), A
Lake City Community College, A
Lake-Sumter Community College, A
Lynn University, B
Manatee Community College, A
Miami Dade College, A
North Florida Community College, A
Northwood University, Florida Campus, AB
Nova Southeastern University, B
Okaloosa-Walton College, A
Palm Beach Atlantic University, B
Palm Beach Community College, A
Pasco-Hernando Community College, A
Pensacola Junior College, A
Polk Community College, A
Remington College-Pinellas Campus, B
Remington College-Tampa Campus, A
St. Johns River Community College, A
Saint Leo University, B
St. Petersburg College, A
St. Thomas University, B
Santa Fe Community College, A
Seminole Community College, A
South Florida Community College, A
South University (West Palm Beach), AB
Southwest Florida College (Fort Myers), A
Stetson University, B
Tallahassee Community College, A
University of Central Florida, B
University of Florida, B
University of Miami, B
University of North Florida, B
University of Phoenix-Central Florida Campus, B
University of Phoenix-North Florida Campus, B
University of Phoenix-South Florida Campus, B
University of Phoenix-West Florida Campus, B
University of South Florida, B
The University of Tampa, B
University of West Florida, B
Valencia Community College, A
Warner Southern College, B
Webber International University, AB
Webster College (Holiday), A

Webster College (Ocala), A

Georgia

Abraham Baldwin Agricultural College, A
Albany State University, B
Andrew College, A
Appalachian Technical College, A
Atlanta Christian College, B
Atlanta Metropolitan College, A
Augusta State University, B
Augusta Technical College, A
Bainbridge College, A
Bauder College, A
Beacon University, B
Berry College, B
Brenau University, B
Brewton-Parker College, B
Brown Mackie College-Atlanta, A
Central Georgia Technical College, A
Chattahoochee Technical College, A
Clark Atlanta University, B
Clayton State University, B
Coastal Georgia Community College, A
Columbus State University, B
Covenant College, AB
Dalton State College, A
Darton College, A
East Georgia College, A
Emmanuel College, AB
Emory University, B
Fort Valley State University, B
Gainesville College, A
Georgia College & State University, B
Georgia Highlands College, A
Georgia Institute of Technology, B
Georgia Military College, A
Georgia Perimeter College, A
Georgia Southern University, B
Georgia Southwestern State University, B
Georgia State University, B
Gordon College, A
Griffin Technical College, A
Gwinnett Technical College, A
Herzing College, AB
ITT Technical Institute (Duluth), B
ITT Technical Institute (Kennesaw), B
Kennesaw State University, B
LaGrange College, B
Life University, B
Macon State College, AB
Middle Georgia College, A
Morehouse College, B
North Georgia College & State University, B
Oglethorpe University, B
Paine College, B
Piedmont College, B
Reinhardt College, AB
Savannah State University, B
Shorter College, B
South Georgia College, A
South University, AB
Thomas University, B
Toccoa Falls College, B
University of Phoenix-Atlanta Campus, B
University of Phoenix-Columbus Georgia
 Campus, B
University of West Georgia, B
Valdosta State University, B
Waycross College, A
Wesleyan College, B
West Central Technical College, A
Young Harris College, A

Guam

Guam Community College, A
University of Guam, B

Hawaii

Brigham Young University-Hawaii, B
Chaminade University of Honolulu, AB
Hawaii Business College, A
Hawaii Pacific University, AB
Heald College-Honolulu, A
Leeward Community College, A
University of Hawaii at Hilo, B

University of Hawaii-West Oahu, B

Idaho

Albertson College of Idaho, B
Boise State University, B
Brigham Young University -Idaho, A
College of Southern Idaho, A
Idaho State University, B
ITT Technical Institute, B
Lewis-Clark State College, B
North Idaho College, A
Northwest Nazarene University, B

Illinois

Argosy University/Chicago, B
Augustana College, B
Benedictine University, A
Black Hawk College, A
Blackburn College, B
Bradley University, B
Carl Sandburg College, A
Chicago State University, B
City Colleges of Chicago, Harold Washington
 College, A
City Colleges of Chicago, Harry S. Truman
 College, A
City Colleges of Chicago, Kennedy-King College, A
City Colleges of Chicago, Olive-Harvey College, A
City Colleges of Chicago, Richard J. Daley
 College, A
City Colleges of Chicago, Wilbur Wright College, A
College of DuPage, A
College of Lake County, A
Columbia College Chicago, B
Concordia University, B
Danville Area Community College, A
DePaul University, B
DeVry University (Chicago), B
Dominican University, B
East-West University, AB
Eastern Illinois University, B
Elgin Community College, A
Elmhurst College, B
Eureka College, B
Gem City College, A
Governors State University, B
Greenville College, B
Heartland Community College, A
Highland Community College, A
Illinois Central College, A
Illinois College, B
Illinois Eastern Community Colleges, Wabash Valley
 College, A
Illinois State University, B
Illinois Valley Community College, A
Illinois Wesleyan University, B
John A. Logan College, A
John Wood Community College, A
Joliet Junior College, A
Judson College, B
Kaskaskia College, A
Kendall College, B
Kishwaukee College, A
Lake Land College, A
Lewis and Clark Community College, A
Lewis University, B
Lincoln Christian College, B
Lincoln College, A
Lincoln College-Normal, AB
Lincoln Land Community College, A
Loyola University Chicago, B
MacCormac College, A
MacMurray College, AB
McHenry County College, A
McKendree College, B
Midstate College, AB
Monmouth College, B
Moraine Valley Community College, A
Morton College, A
National-Louis University, B
North Central College, B
North Park University, B
Northeastern Illinois University, B
Northern Illinois University, B
Northwestern Business College, A
Oakton Community College, A

Olivet Nazarene University, B
Parkland College, A
Principia College, B
Quincy University, B
Rend Lake College, A
Richland Community College, A
Robert Morris College, AB
Rock Valley College, A
Rockford Business College, A
Rockford College, B
Roosevelt University, B
St. Augustine College, A
Sauk Valley Community College, A
Shawnee Community College, A
Southeastern Illinois College, A
Southern Illinois University Carbondale, B
Southern Illinois University Edwardsville, B
Southwestern Illinois College, A
Spoon River College, A
Springfield College in Illinois, A
Trinity Christian College, B
Trinity International University, B
Triton College, A
University of Illinois at Chicago, B
University of Illinois at Springfield, B
University of Illinois at Urbana-Champaign, B
University of Phoenix-Chicago Campus, B
University of St. Francis, B
Waubonsee Community College, A
Western Illinois University, B
William Rainey Harper College, A

Indiana

Ancilla College, A
Anderson University, B
Ball State University, AB
Bethel College, AB
Brown Mackie College-Fort Wayne, A
Brown Mackie College-Merrillville, A
Brown Mackie College-Michigan City, A
Brown Mackie College-South Bend, A
Butler University, B
Calumet College of Saint Joseph, AB
DeVry University (Indianapolis), B
Earlham College, B
Goshen College, B
Grace College, B
Hanover College, B
Huntington University, B
Indiana Business College (Anderson), A
Indiana Business College (Columbus), A
Indiana Business College (Evansville), A
Indiana Business College (Fort Wayne), A
Indiana Business College (Indianapolis), A
Indiana Business College (Indianapolis), A
Indiana Business College (Lafayette), A
Indiana Business College (Marion), A
Indiana Business College (Muncie), A
Indiana Business College (Terre Haute), A
Indiana State University, B
Indiana Tech, AB
Indiana University Bloomington, B
Indiana University Northwest, AB
Indiana University-Purdue University Fort
 Wayne, AB
Indiana Wesleyan University, AB
International Business College (Fort Wayne), AB
ITT Technical Institute (Fort Wayne), B
ITT Technical Institute (Indianapolis), B
ITT Technical Institute (Newburgh), B
Ivy Tech Community College-Bloomington, A
Ivy Tech Community College-Central Indiana, A
Ivy Tech Community College-Columbus, A
Ivy Tech Community College-East Central, A
Ivy Tech Community College-Kokomo, A
Ivy Tech Community College-Lafayette, A
Ivy Tech Community College-North Central, A
Ivy Tech Community College-Northeast, A
Ivy Tech Community College-Northwest, A
Ivy Tech Community College-Southeast, A
Ivy Tech Community College-Southern Indiana, A
Ivy Tech Community College-Southwest, A
Ivy Tech Community College-Wabash Valley, A
Ivy Tech Community College-Whitewater, A
Manchester College, AB
Marian College, AB

Martin University, B
Oakland City University, AB
Purdue University, B
Purdue University Calumet, B
Purdue University North Central, AB
Saint Mary-of-the-Woods College, B
Saint Mary's College, B
Taylor University, AB
Tri-State University, AB
University of Evansville, B
University of Indianapolis, AB
University of Phoenix-Indianapolis Campus, B
University of Saint Francis, AB
University of Southern Indiana, B
Vincennes University, A
Vincennes University Jasper Campus, A

Iowa

AIB College of Business, A
Ashford University, B
Briar Cliff University, B
Central College, B
Clarke College, B
Clinton Community College, A
Coe College, B
Des Moines Area Community College, A
Dordt College, B
Drake University, B
Ellsworth Community College, A
Graceland University, B
Grand View College, B
Hamilton College (Cedar Rapids), AB
Hawkeye Community College, A
Indian Hills Community College, A
Iowa Central Community College, A
Iowa Lakes Community College, A
Iowa State University of Science and Technology, B
Iowa Wesleyan College, B
Iowa Western Community College, A
Kaplan University, AB
Kirkwood Community College, A
Loras College, B
Luther College, B
Maharishi University of Management, B
Marshalltown Community College, A
Morningside College, B
Mount Mercy College, B
Muscatine Community College, A
North Iowa Area Community College, A
Northwest Iowa Community College, A
Northwestern College, B
St. Ambrose University, B
Scott Community College, A
Simpson College, B
Southeastern Community College, North Campus, A
Southeastern Community College, South
   Campus, A
Southwestern Community College, A
University of Dubuque, AB
The University of Iowa, B
University of Northern Iowa, B
Upper Iowa University, AB
Vennard College, B
Waldorf College, B
Wartburg College, B
Western Iowa Tech Community College, A
William Penn University, B

Kansas

Allen County Community College, A
Barclay College, B
Barton County Community College, A
Benedictine College, B
Bethany College, B
Brown Mackie College-Kansas City, A
Brown Mackie College-Salina, A
Butler Community College, A
Central Christian College of Kansas, AB
Cloud County Community College, A
Coffeyville Community College, A
Colby Community College, A
Cowley County Community College and Area
   Vocational-Technical School, A
Dodge City Community College, A
Donnelly College, A
Emporia State University, B

Fort Hays State University, B
Fort Scott Community College, A
Friends University, AB
Garden City Community College, A
Haskell Indian Nations University, AB
Hesston College, A
Highland Community College, A
Independence Community College, A
Johnson County Community College, A
Kansas City Kansas Community College, A
Kansas State University, B
Kansas Wesleyan University, AB
Labette Community College, A
Manhattan Christian College, B
McPherson College, B
MidAmerica Nazarene University, AB
Neosho County Community College, A
Newman University, AB
Ottawa University, B
Pittsburg State University, B
Pratt Community College, A
Seward County Community College, A
Southwestern College, B
Sterling College, B
Tabor College, B
University of Phoenix-Wichita Campus, B
University of Saint Mary, B
Washburn University, B
Wichita State University, B

Kentucky

Alice Lloyd College, B
Ashland Community and Technical College, A
Beckfield College, AB
Bellarmine University, B
Berea College, B
Big Sandy Community and Technical College, A
Brown Mackie College-Hopkinsville, A
Brown Mackie College-Louisville, A
Brown Mackie College-Northern Kentucky, A
Campbellsville University, AB
Daymar College (Owensboro), A
Draughons Junior College, A
Eastern Kentucky University, B
Elizabethtown Community and Technical College, A
Georgetown College, B
Hazard Community and Technical College, A
Henderson Community College, A
Hopkinsville Community College, A
ITT Technical Institute (Lexington), B
ITT Technical Institute (Louisville), B
Jefferson Community and Technical College, A
Kentucky Christian University, B
Kentucky State University, B
Kentucky Wesleyan College, B
Lexington Community College, A
Lindsey Wilson College, AB
Madisonville Community College, A
Maysville Community and Technical College, A
Mid-Continent University, B
Midway College, AB
Morehead State University, B
Murray State University, B
National College of Business & Technology
   (Danville), A
National College of Business & Technology
   (Florence), A
National College of Business & Technology
   (Lexington), A
National College of Business & Technology
   (Louisville), A
National College of Business & Technology
   (Pikeville), A
National College of Business & Technology
   (Richmond), A
Northern Kentucky University, AB
Owensboro Community and Technical College, A
Pikeville College, AB
St. Catharine College, A
Southeast Kentucky Community and Technical
   College, A
Southwestern College of Business, A
Spalding University, AB
Spencerian College, A
Sullivan University, AB
Transylvania University, B

Union College, B
University of Louisville, B
West Kentucky Community and Technical College, A
Western Kentucky University, AB

Louisiana

Bossier Parish Community College, A
Centenary College of Louisiana, B
Delgado Community College, A
Dillard University, B
Grambling State University, B
ITT Technical Institute, B
Louisiana College, B
Louisiana State University and Agricultural and
   Mechanical College, B
Louisiana State University at Alexandria, AB
Louisiana State University at Eunice, A
Louisiana State University in Shreveport, B
Louisiana Tech University, B
Loyola University New Orleans, B
McNeese State University, B
Nicholls State University, B
Northwestern State University of Louisiana, AB
Our Lady of Holy Cross College, B
Remington College-Lafayette Campus, A
Southeastern Louisiana University, B
Southern University and Agricultural and Mechanical
   College, B
Southern University at New Orleans, B
Southern University at Shreveport, A
Tulane University, AB
University of Louisiana at Lafayette, B
University of Louisiana at Monroe, B
University of New Orleans, B
University of Phoenix-Louisiana Campus, B
Xavier University of Louisiana, B

Maine

Andover College, A
Beal College, A
Central Maine Community College, A
Eastern Maine Community College, A
Husson College, AB
Kennebec Valley Community College, A
Maine Maritime Academy, B
Northern Maine Community College, A
Saint Joseph's College of Maine, B
Southern Maine Community College, A
Thomas College, AB
University of Maine, B
The University of Maine at Augusta, AB
University of Maine at Fort Kent, AB
University of Maine at Machias, B
University of Maine at Presque Isle, B
University of New England, B
University of Southern Maine, B
York County Community College, A

Maryland

Allegany College of Maryland, A
Anne Arundel Community College, A
Baltimore City Community College, A
Bowie State University, B
Carroll Community College, A
Cecil Community College, A
Chesapeake College, A
College of Notre Dame of Maryland, B
College of Southern Maryland, A
Columbia Union College, B
Coppin State University, B
DeVry University, B
Frederick Community College, A
Frostburg State University, B
Garrett College, A
Goucher College, B
Griggs University, B
Hagerstown Business College, A
Hagerstown Community College, A
Harford Community College, A
Hood College, B
Howard Community College, A
McDaniel College, B
Montgomery College, A
Morgan State University, B
Prince George's Community College, A
Salisbury University, B

Sojourner-Douglass College, B
Towson University, B
University of Baltimore, B
University of Maryland, Baltimore County, B
University of Maryland, College Park, B
University of Maryland Eastern Shore, B
University of Maryland University College, B
University of Phoenix-Maryland Campus, B
Villa Julie College, AB
Washington College, B
Wor-Wic Community College, A

Massachusetts

American International College, AB
Anna Maria College, AB
Assumption College, B
Atlantic Union College, B
Babson College, B
Bay State College, AB
Becker College, AB
Bentley College, AB
Berkshire Community College, A
Boston College, B
Boston University, B
Bridgewater State College, B
Bristol Community College, A
Bunker Hill Community College, A
Cape Cod Community College, A
Clark University, B
Curry College, B
Dean College, A
Eastern Nazarene College, B
Elms College, B
Emmanuel College, B
Endicott College, B
Fisher College, AB
Fitchburg State College, B
Framingham State College, B
Gibbs College, A
Gordon College, B
Greenfield Community College, A
Hellenic College, B
Holyoke Community College, A
Lasell College, B
Lesley University, B
Marian Court College, A
Massachusetts Bay Community College, A
Massachusetts College of Liberal Arts, B
Massasoit Community College, A
Merrimack College, AB
Middlesex Community College, A
Mount Ida College, AB
Mount Wachusett Community College, A
New England College of Finance, A
Newbury College, AB
Nichols College, AB
North Shore Community College, A
Northeastern University, B
Northern Essex Community College, A
Pine Manor College, AB
Quincy College, A
Quinsigamond Community College, A
Roxbury Community College, A
Salem State College, B
Simmons College, B
Springfield College, B
Springfield Technical Community College, A
Stonehill College, B
Suffolk University, B
University of Massachusetts Amherst, B
University of Massachusetts Boston, B
University of Massachusetts Dartmouth, B
University of Massachusetts Lowell, B
University of Phoenix-Boston Campus, B
University of Phoenix-Central Massachusetts
  Campus, B
Wentworth Institute of Technology, AB
Western New England College, B
Westfield State College, B
Worcester Polytechnic Institute, B
Worcester State College, B

Michigan

Adrian College, AB
Albion College, B
Alma College, B

Alpena Community College, A
Andrews University, AB
Aquinas College, B
Baker College of Allen Park, A
Baker College of Auburn Hills, AB
Baker College of Cadillac, AB
Baker College of Clinton Township, AB
Baker College of Flint, AB
Baker College of Jackson, AB
Baker College of Muskegon, AB
Baker College of Owosso, AB
Baker College of Port Huron, AB
Bay Mills Community College, A
Bay de Noc Community College, A
Calvin College, B
Central Michigan University, B
Cleary University, AB
Concordia University, B
Cornerstone University, B
Davenport University (Dearborn), AB
Davenport University (Midland), A
Delta College, A
Eastern Michigan University, B
Ferris State University, B
Finlandia University, B
Glen Oaks Community College, A
Gogebic Community College, A
Grace Bible College, AB
Grand Rapids Community College, A
Grand Valley State University, B
Henry Ford Community College, A
Hillsdale College, B
Hope College, B
ITT Technical Institute (Canton), A
ITT Technical Institute (Grand Rapids), A
ITT Technical Institute (Troy), A
Jackson Community College, A
Kalamazoo Valley Community College, A
Kellogg Community College, A
Kettering University, B
Kirtland Community College, A
Kuyper College, B
Lake Michigan College, A
Lake Superior State University, AB
Lansing Community College, A
Lawrence Technological University, B
Lewis College of Business, A
Macomb Community College, A
Madonna University, AB
Marygrove College, B
Michigan State University, B
Michigan Technological University, B
Mid Michigan Community College, A
Monroe County Community College, A
Montcalm Community College, A
Mott Community College, A
Muskegon Community College, A
North Central Michigan College, A
Northern Michigan University, AB
Northwestern Michigan College, A
Northwood University, AB
Oakland Community College, A
Olivet College, B
Rochester College, B
Saginaw Valley State University, B
St. Clair County Community College, A
Schoolcraft College, A
Siena Heights University, AB
Southwestern Michigan College, A
Spring Arbor University, B
University of Detroit Mercy, B
University of Michigan, B
University of Michigan-Dearborn, B
University of Michigan-Flint, B
University of Phoenix-Metro Detroit Campus, B
University of Phoenix-West Michigan Campus, B
Walsh College of Accountancy and Business
  Administration, B
Washtenaw Community College, A
Wayne County Community College District, A
Western Michigan University, B

Minnesota

Academy College, AB
Alexandria Technical College, A
Anoka-Ramsey Community College, A

Anoka-Ramsey Community College, Cambridge
  Campus, A
Anoka Technical College, A
Augsburg College, B
Bemidji State University, B
Bethany Lutheran College, B
Bethel University, B
Brown College, B
Central Lakes College, A
Century College, A
College of Saint Benedict, B
College of St. Catherine, B
The College of St. Scholastica, B
Concordia College, B
Concordia University, St. Paul, B
Crown College, AB
DeVry University, B
Duluth Business University, A
Globe College, AB
Gustavus Adolphus College, B
Hamline University, B
Hibbing Community College, A
Inver Hills Community College, A
Itasca Community College, A
Lake Superior College, A
Metropolitan State University, B
Minneapolis Community and Technical College, A
Minnesota School of Business, AB
Minnesota School of Business-Brooklyn Center, AB
Minnesota School of Business-Plymouth, AB
Minnesota School of Business-Richfield, AB
Minnesota School of Business-St. Cloud, AB
Minnesota School of Business-Shakopee, AB
Minnesota State Community and Technical
  College-Fergus Falls, A
Minnesota State University Mankato, B
Minnesota State University Moorhead, B
National American University (Roseville), AB
Normandale Community College, A
North Central University, AB
Northland Community and Technical College-Thief
  River Falls, A
Northwestern College, B
Pillsbury Baptist Bible College, B
Rainy River Community College, A
Rasmussen College Eagan, A
Rasmussen College Eden Prairie, A
Rasmussen College Mankato, A
Rasmussen College St. Cloud, A
Ridgewater College, A
Riverland Community College, A
Rochester Community and Technical College, A
St. Cloud State University, B
St. Cloud Technical College, A
Saint John's University, B
Saint Mary's University of Minnesota, B
South Central Technical College, A
Southwest Minnesota State University, AB
University of Minnesota, Crookston, AB
University of Minnesota, Duluth, B
University of Minnesota, Morris, B
University of St. Thomas, B
Vermilion Community College, A
Winona State University, B

Mississippi

Alcorn State University, B
Belhaven College, B
Blue Mountain College, B
Coahoma Community College, A
Copiah-Lincoln Community College, A
Delta State University, B
East Central Community College, A
East Mississippi Community College, A
Hinds Community College, A
Holmes Community College, A
Itawamba Community College, A
Jackson State University, B
Jones County Junior College, A
Millsaps College, B
Mississippi College, B
Mississippi Gulf Coast Community College, A
Mississippi State University, B
Mississippi University for Women, B
Mississippi Valley State University, B
Northeast Mississippi Community College, A

Northwest Mississippi Community College, A
Pearl River Community College, A
Rust College, AB
Southeastern Baptist College, A
Southwest Mississippi Community College, A
Tougaloo College, B
University of Mississippi, B
University of Southern Mississippi, B
William Carey College, B

Missouri

Baptist Bible College, AB
Blue River Community College, A
Central Methodist University, B
Central Missouri State University, B
College of the Ozarks, B
Columbia College, AB
Crowder College, A
Culver-Stockton College, B
Drury University, B
East Central College, A
Evangel University, B
Fontbonne University, B
Grantham University, AB
Hannibal-LaGrange College, B
Harris-Stowe State University, B
Hickey College, B
ITT Technical Institute (Arnold), B
ITT Technical Institute (Earth City), B
ITT Technical Institute (Kansas City), B
Jefferson College, A
Lincoln University, B
Lindenwood University, B
Longview Community College, A
Maple Woods Community College, A
Maryville University of Saint Louis, B
Messenger College, B
Metro Business College (Cape Girardeau), A
Metropolitan Community College-Business &
    Technology College, A
Mineral Area College, A
Missouri Baptist University, AB
Missouri State University, B
Missouri State University-West Plains, A
Missouri Valley College, AB
Missouri Western State University, AB
National American University, AB
North Central Missouri College, A
Northwest Missouri State University, B
Ozarks Technical Community College, A
Park University, AB
Penn Valley Community College, A
Rockhurst University, B
Saint Charles Community College, A
St. Louis Community College at Florissant Valley, A
St. Louis Community College at Forest Park, A
St. Louis Community College at Meramec, A
Saint Louis University, B
Sanford-Brown College (Hazelwood), A
Sanford-Brown College (St. Charles), A
Southeast Missouri State University, B
Springfield College, A
State Fair Community College, A
Stephens College, B
Three Rivers Community College, A
Truman State University, B
University of Missouri-Columbia, B
University of Missouri-Kansas City, B
University of Missouri-Rolla, B
University of Missouri-St. Louis, B
University of Phoenix-Kansas City Campus, B
University of Phoenix-St. Louis Campus, B
University of Phoenix-Springfield Campus, B
Washington University in St. Louis, B
Webster University, B
Westminster College, B
William Jewell College, B
William Woods University, B

Montana

Blackfeet Community College, A
Carroll College, AB
Chief Dull Knife College, A
Flathead Valley Community College, A
Fort Peck Community College, A
Little Big Horn College, A

Miles Community College, A
Montana State University-Billings, AB
Montana State University-Northern, AB
Montana Tech of The University of Montana, B
Rocky Mountain College, B
Stone Child College, A
University of Great Falls, B
The University of Montana-Western, A

Nebraska

Bellevue University, B
Central Community College-Columbus Campus, A
Central Community College-Grand Island
    Campus, A
Central Community College-Hastings Campus, A
Chadron State College, B
Clarkson College, B
College of Saint Mary, AB
Concordia University, B
Dana College, B
Doane College, B
Grace University, B
Hamilton College-Lincoln, A
Hamilton College-Omaha, A
Hastings College, B
ITT Technical Institute, B
Metropolitan Community College, A
Mid-Plains Community College, A
Midland Lutheran College, B
Nebraska Indian Community College, A
Nebraska Wesleyan University, B
Northeast Community College, A
Peru State College, B
Southeast Community College, Beatrice Campus, A
Southeast Community College, Lincoln Campus, A
Union College, AB
University of Nebraska at Kearney, B
University of Nebraska-Lincoln, B
University of Nebraska at Omaha, B
Wayne State College, B
Western Nebraska Community College, A
York College, B

Nevada

Career College of Northern Nevada, A
Community College of Southern Nevada, A
DeVry University, B
Great Basin College, A
ITT Technical Institute, B
Las Vegas College, A
Morrison University, AB
Nevada State College at Henderson, B
Sierra Nevada College, B
Truckee Meadows Community College, A
University of Nevada, Las Vegas, B
University of Phoenix-Nevada Campus, B
Western Nevada Community College, A

New Hampshire

Colby-Sawyer College, B
Daniel Webster College, AB
Franklin Pierce College, B
Granite State College, AB
Hesser College, AB
Keene State College, B
McIntosh College, A
New England College, B
New Hampshire Community Technical College,
    Berlin/Laconia, A
New Hampshire Community Technical College,
    Manchester/Stratham, A
New Hampshire Community Technical College,
    Nashua/Claremont, A
New Hampshire Technical Institute, A
Plymouth State University, B
Rivier College, AB
Southern New Hampshire University, AB
University of New Hampshire, AB
University of New Hampshire at Manchester, AB

New Jersey

Atlantic Cape Community College, A
Bergen Community College, A
Berkeley College, AB
Bloomfield College, B
Brookdale Community College, A

Burlington County College, A
Caldwell College, B
Camden County College, A
Centenary College, B
The College of New Jersey, B
College of Saint Elizabeth, B
County College of Morris, A
Cumberland County College, A
DeVry University, AB
Essex County College, A
Fairleigh Dickinson University, College at
    Florham, B
Fairleigh Dickinson University, Metropolitan
    Campus, B
Felician College, AB
Georgian Court University, B
Gloucester County College, A
Hudson County Community College, A
Kean University, B
Mercer County Community College, A
Middlesex County College, A
Monmouth University, B
Montclair State University, B
New Jersey City University, B
New Jersey Institute of Technology, B
Ocean County College, A
Passaic County Community College, A
Ramapo College of New Jersey, B
Raritan Valley Community College, A
The Richard Stockton College of New Jersey, B
Rider University, AB
Rowan University, B
Rutgers, The State University of New Jersey,
    Camden, B
Rutgers, The State University of New Jersey, New
    Brunswick/Piscataway, B
Rutgers, The State University of New Jersey,
    Newark, B
Saint Peter's College, AB
Salem Community College, A
Seton Hall University, B
Stevens Institute of Technology, B
Sussex County Community College, A
Union County College, A
Warren County Community College, A
William Paterson University of New Jersey, B

New Mexico

Central New Mexico Community College, A
Clovis Community College, A
College of Santa Fe, AB
College of the Southwest, B
Doña Ana Branch Community College, A
Eastern New Mexico University, B
Eastern New Mexico University-Roswell, A
International Institute of the Americas, AB
ITT Technical Institute, B
Luna Community College, A
Mesalands Community College, A
National American University (Albuquerque), AB
New Mexico Highlands University, B
New Mexico Institute of Mining and Technology, AB
New Mexico Junior College, A
New Mexico Military Institute, A
New Mexico State University, B
New Mexico State University-Carlsbad, A
New Mexico State University-Grants, A
San Juan College, A
Santa Fe Community College, A
Southwestern Indian Polytechnic Institute, A
University of New Mexico, B
University of New Mexico-Gallup, A
University of New Mexico-Los Alamos Branch, A
University of New Mexico-Valencia Campus, A
University of Phoenix-New Mexico Campus, B
Western New Mexico University, B

New York

Adelphi University, B
Adirondack Community College, A
Alfred University, B
Berkeley College-New York City Campus, AB
Berkeley College-Westchester Campus, AB
Bernard M. Baruch College of the City University of
    New York, B
Boricua College, B

Borough of Manhattan Community College of the City University of New York, A
Bramson ORT College, A
Briarcliffe College, A
Bronx Community College of the City University of New York, A
Broome Community College, A
Bryant and Stratton College, North Campus, A
Bryant and Stratton College (Rochester-Henrietta Campus), A
Buffalo State College, State University of New York, B
Canisius College, B
Cayuga County Community College, A
Cazenovia College, AB
City College of the City University of New York, B
Clarkson University, B
Clinton Community College, A
College of Mount Saint Vincent, AB
The College of New Rochelle, B
The College of Saint Rose, B
The College of Westchester, A
Columbia-Greene Community College, A
Concordia College, AB
Cornell University, B
Corning Community College, A
Daemen College, B
Dominican College, B
Dowling College, B
Dutchess Community College, A
D'Youville College, B
Elmira College, B
Erie Community College, A
Erie Community College, North Campus, A
Erie Community College, South Campus, A
Eugenio María de Hostos Community College of the City University of New York, A
Excelsior College, AB
Farmingdale State University of New York, A
Finger Lakes Community College, A
Fiorello H. LaGuardia Community College of the City University of New York, A
Five Towns College, AB
Fordham University, B
Fulton-Montgomery Community College, A
Genesee Community College, A
Globe Institute of Technology, AB
Hartwick College, B
Herkimer County Community College, A
Hilbert College, AB
Hofstra University, B
Houghton College, B
Hudson Valley Community College, A
Interboro Institute, A
Iona College, B
Ithaca College, B
Jamestown Business College, A
Jamestown Community College, A
Jefferson Community College, A
Keuka College, B
The King's College, B
Kingsborough Community College of the City University of New York, A
Le Moyne College, B
Lehman College of the City University of New York, B
Long Island Business Institute, A
Long Island University, Brentwood Campus, B
Long Island University, Brooklyn Campus, AB
Long Island University, C.W. Post Campus, B
Manhattanville College, B
Maria College, A
Marist College, B
Marymount Manhattan College, B
Medaille College, AB
Medgar Evers College of the City University of New York, AB
Mercy College, AB
Metropolitan College of New York, B
Mildred Elley, A
Mohawk Valley Community College, A
Molloy College, B
Monroe College (Bronx), AB
Monroe College (New Rochelle), AB
Monroe Community College, A
Mount Saint Mary College, B

Nassau Community College, A
Nazareth College of Rochester, B
New York Institute of Technology, AB
New York University, B
Niagara County Community College, A
Niagara University, AB
North Country Community College, A
Nyack College, AB
Olean Business Institute, A
Onondaga Community College, A
Orange County Community College, A
Pace University, B
Paul Smith's College of Arts and Sciences, A
Plaza College, A
Queensborough Community College of the City University of New York, A
Rensselaer Polytechnic Institute, B
Roberts Wesleyan College, B
Rochester Business Institute, A
Rochester Institute of Technology, AB
Rockland Community College, A
Russell Sage College, B
Sage College of Albany, AB
St. Bonaventure University, B
St. Francis College, AB
St. John Fisher College, B
St. John's University, B
St. Joseph's College, New York, B
St. Joseph's College, Suffolk Campus, B
St. Thomas Aquinas College, B
Schenectady County Community College, A
State University of New York at Buffalo, B
State University of New York College of Agriculture and Technology at Cobleskill, A
State University of New York College of Agriculture and Technology at Morrisville, A
State University of New York College at Brockport, B
State University of New York College at Geneseo, B
State University of New York College at Old Westbury, B
State University of New York College at Potsdam, B
State University of New York College of Technology at Alfred, A
State University of New York College of Technology at Canton, A
State University of New York College of Technology at Delhi, A
State University of New York Empire State College, AB
State University of New York, Fredonia, B
State University of New York Institute of Technology, B
State University of New York Maritime College, B
State University of New York at New Paltz, B
State University of New York at Oswego, B
State University of New York at Plattsburgh, B
Stony Brook University, State University of New York, B
Suffolk County Community College, A
Sullivan County Community College, A
Syracuse University, B
Taylor Business Institute, A
Tompkins Cortland Community College, A
Touro College, B
Trocaire College, A
Ulster County Community College, A
United States Military Academy, B
University at Albany, State University of New York, B
Utica College, B
Utica School of Commerce, A
Villa Maria College of Buffalo, A
Wagner College, B
Wells College, B
Westchester Community College, A
Yeshiva University, B
York College of the City University of New York, B

North Carolina

Alamance Community College, A
Appalachian State University, B
Asheville-Buncombe Technical Community College, A
Barber-Scotia College, B
Barton College, B
Beaufort County Community College, A

Belmont Abbey College, B
Bennett College For Women, B
Bladen Community College, A
Blue Ridge Community College, A
Brevard College, B
Brunswick Community College, A
Caldwell Community College and Technical Institute, A
Campbell University, B
Cape Fear Community College, A
Carteret Community College, A
Catawba College, B
Catawba Valley Community College, A
Central Carolina Community College, A
Central Piedmont Community College, A
Chowan University, B
Cleveland Community College, A
Coastal Carolina Community College, A
College of The Albemarle, A
Craven Community College, A
Davidson County Community College, A
DeVry University, B
Durham Technical Community College, A
East Carolina University, B
Edgecombe Community College, A
Elizabeth City State University, B
Elon University, B
Fayetteville State University, B
Fayetteville Technical Community College, A
Forsyth Technical Community College, A
Gardner-Webb University, B
Gaston College, A
Greensboro College, B
Guilford College, B
Guilford Technical Community College, A
Halifax Community College, A
Haywood Community College, A
High Point University, B
Isothermal Community College, A
James Sprunt Community College, A
John Wesley College, B
Johnson C. Smith University, B
Johnson & Wales University, A
Johnston Community College, A
Lees-McRae College, B
Lenoir Community College, A
Lenoir-Rhyne College, B
Livingstone College, B
Louisburg College, A
Mars Hill College, B
Martin Community College, A
Mayland Community College, A
McDowell Technical Community College, A
Meredith College, B
Methodist College, AB
Mitchell Community College, A
Montgomery Community College, A
Montreat College, AB
Mount Olive College, AB
Nash Community College, A
North Carolina Agricultural and Technical State University, B
North Carolina Central University, B
North Carolina State University, B
North Carolina Wesleyan College, B
Pamlico Community College, A
Peace College, B
Pfeiffer University, B
Piedmont Community College, A
Pitt Community College, A
Queens University of Charlotte, B
Randolph Community College, A
Richmond Community College, A
Roanoke-Chowan Community College, A
Robeson Community College, A
Rockingham Community College, A
Rowan-Cabarrus Community College, A
St. Andrews Presbyterian College, B
Saint Augustine's College, B
Salem College, B
Sampson Community College, A
Sandhills Community College, A
Shaw University, AB
South College-Asheville, A
South Piedmont Community College, A
Southeastern Community College, A

Southwestern Community College, A
Stanly Community College, A
Surry Community College, A
Tri-County Community College, A
The University of North Carolina at Asheville, B
The University of North Carolina at Chapel Hill, B
The University of North Carolina at Charlotte, B
The University of North Carolina at Greensboro, B
The University of North Carolina at Pembroke, B
The University of North Carolina Wilmington, B
University of Phoenix-Raleigh Campus, B
Vance-Granville Community College, A
Wake Technical Community College, A
Warren Wilson College, B
Wayne Community College, A
Western Carolina University, B
Western Piedmont Community College, A
Wilkes Community College, A
Wilson Technical Community College, A
Wingate University, B
Winston-Salem State University, B

North Dakota

Aakers Business College, AB
Cankdeska Cikana Community College, A
Dickinson State University, B
Fort Berthold Community College, A
Jamestown College, B
Lake Region State College, A
Mayville State University, AB
Minot State University, B
Minot State University-Bottineau Campus, A
North Dakota State University, B
Sitting Bull College, A
Trinity Bible College, AB
Turtle Mountain Community College, A
United Tribes Technical College, A
University of Mary, AB
Valley City State University, B

Ohio

Antioch College, B
Antioch University McGregor, B
Ashland University, B
Baldwin-Wallace College, B
Belmont Technical College, A
Bluffton University, B
Brown Mackie College-Akron, A
Brown Mackie College-Cincinnati, A
Brown Mackie College-Findlay, A
Brown Mackie College-North Canton, A
Bryant and Stratton College (Cleveland), B
Bryant and Stratton College (Parma), B
Bryant and Stratton College (Willoughby Hills), A
Capital University, B
Case Western Reserve University, B
Cedarville University, B
Central Ohio Technical College, A
Central State University, B
Chatfield College, A
Cincinnati State Technical and Community
    College, A
Clark State Community College, A
Cleveland State University, B
College of Mount St. Joseph, AB
Columbus State Community College, A
Cuyahoga Community College, A
David N. Myers University, AB
Davis College, A
Defiance College, AB
DeVry University (Columbus), B
Edison State Community College, A
Franciscan University of Steubenville, AB
Franklin University, AB
Gallipolis Career College, A
Heidelberg College, B
Hiram College, B
Hocking College, A
ITT Technical Institute (Dayton), A
ITT Technical Institute (Hilliard), A
ITT Technical Institute (Norwood), A
ITT Technical Institute (Strongsville), A
ITT Technical Institute (Warrensville Heights), A
James A. Rhodes State College, A
Jefferson Community College, A
John Carroll University, B

Kent State University, AB
Kent State University, Ashtabula Campus, A
Kent State University, East Liverpool Campus, A
Kent State University, Geauga Campus, AB
Kent State University, Salem Campus, AB
Kent State University, Stark Campus, A
Kent State University, Trumbull Campus, AB
Kent State University, Tuscarawas Campus, AB
Lake Erie College, B
Lakeland Community College, A
Lorain County Community College, A
Lourdes College, AB
Malone College, B
Marietta College, AB
Marion Technical College, A
Miami University, B
Miami University Hamilton, A
Miami University-Middletown Campus, A
Mount Union College, B
Muskingum College, B
North Central State College, A
Northwest State Community College, A
Notre Dame College, AB
Ohio Business College (Lorain), A
Ohio Business College (Sandusky), A
Ohio Dominican University, AB
Ohio Northern University, B
The Ohio State University, B
The Ohio State University at Lima, B
The Ohio State University-Mansfield Campus, B
The Ohio State University at Marion, B
The Ohio State University-Newark Campus, B
Ohio University, AB
Ohio University-Chillicothe, AB
Ohio University-Eastern, B
Ohio University-Lancaster, AB
Ohio University-Southern Campus, B
Ohio Wesleyan University, B
Otterbein College, B
Remington College-Cleveland West Campus, A
Shawnee State University, AB
Sinclair Community College, A
Southwestern College of Business (Cincinnati), A
Southwestern College of Business (Cincinnati), A
Southwestern College of Business (Dayton), A
Southwestern College of Business (Franklin), A
Stark State College of Technology, A
Terra State Community College, A
Tiffin University, AB
The University of Akron, B
The University of Akron-Wayne College, A
University of Cincinnati, AB
University of Cincinnati Clermont College, A
University of Cincinnati Raymond Walters College, A
University of Dayton, B
The University of Findlay, AB
University of Northwestern Ohio, AB
University of Phoenix-Cincinnati Campus, B
University of Phoenix-Cleveland Campus, B
University of Rio Grande, AB
The University of Toledo, AB
Urbana University, AB
Ursuline College, B
Walsh University, AB
Washington State Community College, A
Wilberforce University, B
Wilmington College, B
Wittenberg University, B
Wright State University, B
Wright State University, Lake Campus, A
Xavier University, AB
Youngstown State University, AB
Zane State College, A

Oklahoma

Bacone College, AB
Cameron University, AB
Carl Albert State College, A
Connors State College, A
East Central University, B
Eastern Oklahoma State College, A
ITT Technical Institute, B
Langston University, B
Mid-America Christian University, B
Murray State College, A

Northeastern Oklahoma Agricultural and Mechanical
    College, A
Northeastern State University, B
Northern Oklahoma College, A
Northwestern Oklahoma State University, B
Oklahoma Baptist University, B
Oklahoma Christian University, B
Oklahoma City Community College, A
Oklahoma City University, B
Oklahoma Panhandle State University, AB
Oklahoma State University, Oklahoma City, A
Oklahoma State University, Okmulgee, A
Oklahoma Wesleyan University, AB
Oral Roberts University, B
Redlands Community College, A
Rogers State University, A
Rose State College, A
St. Gregory's University, AB
Seminole State College, A
Southeastern Oklahoma State University, B
Southern Nazarene University, B
Southwestern Oklahoma State University, B
Southwestern Oklahoma State University at
    Sayre, A
Tulsa Community College, A
University of Central Oklahoma, B
University of Oklahoma, B
University of Phoenix-Oklahoma City Campus, B
University of Phoenix-Tulsa Campus, B
University of Tulsa, B

Oregon

Blue Mountain Community College, A
Cascade College, B
Central Oregon Community College, A
Chemeketa Community College, A
Clatsop Community College, A
Concordia University, AB
Corban College, AB
DeVry University, B
George Fox University, B
Heald College-Portland, A
ITT Technical Institute, B
Lane Community College, A
Linn-Benton Community College, A
Marylhurst University, B
Mt. Hood Community College, A
Oregon Institute of Technology, B
Oregon State University, B
Pacific University, B
Pioneer Pacific College, AB
Portland Community College, A
Portland State University, B
Rogue Community College, A
Southern Oregon University, B
Southwestern Oregon Community College, A
Treasure Valley Community College, A
Umpqua Community College, A
University of Oregon, B
University of Phoenix-Oregon Campus, B
University of Portland, B
Warner Pacific College, B

Pennsylvania

Albright College, B
Alvernia College, AB
Arcadia University, B
Bloomsburg University of Pennsylvania, B
Bucknell University, B
Bucks County Community College, A
Business Institute of Pennsylvania (Sharon), A
Butler County Community College, A
Cabrini College, B
California University of Pennsylvania, AB
Cambria-Rowe Business College (Johnstown), A
Carnegie Mellon University, B
Cedar Crest College, B
Central Pennsylvania College, AB
Chatham College, B
Chestnut Hill College, AB
Cheyney University of Pennsylvania, B
Clarion University of Pennsylvania, AB
College Misericordia, B
Community College of Allegheny County, A
Community College of Beaver County, A
Community College of Philadelphia, A

Consolidated School of Business (Lancaster), A
Consolidated School of Business (York), A
Delaware County Community College, A
Delaware Valley College, B
DeSales University, B
DeVry University (Fort Washington), B
Douglas Education Center, A
Duff's Business Institute, A
East Stroudsburg University of Pennsylvania, B
Edinboro University of Pennsylvania, AB
Elizabethtown College, B
Erie Business Center South, A
Franklin and Marshall College, B
Gannon University, B
Geneva College, AB
Gettysburg College, B
Grove City College, B
Gwynedd-Mercy College, AB
Harcum College, A
Harrisburg Area Community College, A
Holy Family University, B
ICM School of Business & Medical Careers, A
Immaculata University, AB
Indiana University of Pennsylvania, AB
Juniata College, B
Keystone College, AB
King's College, AB
Kutztown University of Pennsylvania, B
La Roche College, B
La Salle University, B
Lackawanna College, A
Laurel Business Institute, A
Lebanon Valley College, AB
Lehigh Carbon Community College, A
Lehigh University, B
Lehigh Valley College, A
Lincoln University, B
Lock Haven University of Pennsylvania, B
Luzerne County Community College, A
Lycoming College, B
Manor College, A
Mansfield University of Pennsylvania, B
Marywood University, B
McCann School of Business & Technology, A
Mercyhurst College, AB
Messiah College, B
Millersville University of Pennsylvania, B
Montgomery County Community College, A
Moravian College, B
Mount Aloysius College, AB
Muhlenberg College, B
Neumann College, B
Newport Business Institute (Lower Burrell), A
Newport Business Institute (Williamsport), A
Northampton County Area Community College, A
Pace Institute, A
Peirce College, AB
Penn Commercial Business and Technical School, A
Pennsylvania College of Technology, AB
Pennsylvania Institute of Technology, A
The Pennsylvania State University Altoona
    College, B
The Pennsylvania State University Beaver Campus
    of the Commonwealth College, B
The Pennsylvania State University Berks Campus of
    the Berks-Lehigh Valley College, B
The Pennsylvania State University Delaware County
    Campus of the Commonwealth College, B
The Pennsylvania State University DuBois Campus
    of the Commonwealth College, B
The Pennsylvania State University at Erie, The
    Behrend College, B
The Pennsylvania State University Fayette Campus
    of the Commonwealth College, B
The Pennsylvania State University Harrisburg
    Campus, B
The Pennsylvania State University Hazleton
    Campus of the Commonwealth College, B
The Pennsylvania State University McKeesport
    Campus of the Commonwealth College, B
The Pennsylvania State University Mont Alto
    Campus of the Commonwealth College, B
The Pennsylvania State University New Kensington
    Campus of the Commonwealth College, B
The Pennsylvania State University Shenango
    Campus of the Commonwealth College, B

The Pennsylvania State University Wilkes-Barre
    Campus of the Commonwealth College, B
The Pennsylvania State University Worthington
    Scranton Campus of the Commonwealth
    College, B
The Pennsylvania State University York Campus of
    the Commonwealth College, B
Philadelphia Biblical University, B
Philadelphia University, B
Point Park University, AB
Reading Area Community College, A
Robert Morris University, B
Rosemont College, B
Saint Francis University, AB
Saint Joseph's University, AB
Saint Vincent College, B
Schuylkill Institute of Business and Technology, A
Seton Hill University, B
Shippensburg University of Pennsylvania, B
Slippery Rock University of Pennsylvania, B
South Hills School of Business & Technology (State
    College), A
Susquehanna University, B
Temple University, B
Thiel College, B
Thompson Institute, A
University of Pennsylvania, B
University of Phoenix-Philadelphia Campus, B
University of Phoenix-Pittsburgh Campus, B
University of Pittsburgh at Bradford, B
University of Pittsburgh at Greensburg, B
University of Pittsburgh at Johnstown, B
The University of Scranton, AB
Ursinus College, B
Valley Forge Military College, A
Villanova University, B
Waynesburg College, AB
West Chester University of Pennsylvania, B
Westminster College, B
Westmoreland County Community College, A
Widener University, B
Wilkes University, B
Wilson College, AB
York College of Pennsylvania, AB

Puerto Rico

American University of Puerto Rico, AB
Bayamon Central University, B
Caribbean University, AB
Columbia College (Caguas), A
Electronic Data Processing College of Puerto
    Rico, AB
Huertas Junior College, A
Instituto Comercial de Puerto Rico Junior College, A
Inter American University of Puerto Rico, Aguadilla
    Campus, AB
Inter American University of Puerto Rico, Arecibo
    Campus, AB
Inter American University of Puerto Rico,
    Barranquitas Campus, AB
Inter American University of Puerto Rico, Bayamón
    Campus, AB
Inter American University of Puerto Rico, Fajardo
    Campus, AB
Inter American University of Puerto Rico, Guayama
    Campus, AB
Inter American University of Puerto Rico,
    Metropolitan Campus, AB
Inter American University of Puerto Rico, Ponce
    Campus, AB
Inter American University of Puerto Rico, San
    Germán Campus, AB
Polytechnic University of Puerto Rico, B
Pontifical Catholic University of Puerto Rico, AB
Ramírez College of Business and Technology, A
Universidad Adventista de las Antillas, AB
Universidad del Este, A
Universidad Metropolitana, B
Universidad del Turabo, B
University of Phoenix-Puerto Rico Campus, B
University of Puerto Rico, Aguadilla University
    College, AB
University of Puerto Rico at Arecibo, AB
University of Puerto Rico at Bayamón, AB
University of Puerto Rico, Cayey University
    College, B

University of Puerto Rico at Humacao, AB
University of Puerto Rico, Mayagüez Campus, B
University of Puerto Rico at Ponce, AB
University of Puerto Rico, Río Piedras, B
University of Puerto Rico at Utuado, A
University of the Sacred Heart, B

Rhode Island

Bryant University, B
Community College of Rhode Island, A
Johnson & Wales University, AB
New England Institute of Technology, AB
Providence College, B
Rhode Island College, B
Roger Williams University, AB
Salve Regina University, AB
University of Rhode Island, B

South Carolina

Aiken Technical College, A
Allen University, B
Anderson University, B
Benedict College, B
Bob Jones University, B
Central Carolina Technical College, A
Charleston Southern University, AB
The Citadel, The Military College of South
    Carolina, B
Claflin University, B
Clemson University, B
Coastal Carolina University, B
Coker College, B
College of Charleston, B
Columbia College, B
Converse College, B
Denmark Technical College, A
Erskine College, B
Florence-Darlington Technical College, A
Forrest Junior College, A
Francis Marion University, B
Furman University, B
Greenville Technical College, A
Horry-Georgetown Technical College, A
Lander University, B
Limestone College, AB
Midlands Technical College, A
Morris College, B
Newberry College, B
North Greenville College, B
Northeastern Technical College, A
Piedmont Technical College, A
Presbyterian College, B
South Carolina State University, B
South University, AB
Southern Wesleyan University, AB
Spartanburg Technical College, A
Technical College of the Lowcountry, A
Tri-County Technical College, A
Trident Technical College, A
University of South Carolina, B
University of South Carolina Aiken, B
University of South Carolina Beaufort, B
University of South Carolina Lancaster, A
University of South Carolina Upstate, B
Voorhees College, B
Winthrop University, B
York Technical College, A

South Dakota

Augustana College, B
Black Hills State University, B
Colorado Technical University Sioux Falls
    Campus, AB
Dakota State University, AB
Dakota Wesleyan University, AB
Kilian Community College, A
Mount Marty College, AB
National American University (Rapid City), AB
National American University-Sioux Falls
    Branch, AB
Northern State University, AB
Oglala Lakota College, AB
Presentation College, AB
Sinte Gleska University, AB
Sisseton-Wahpeton Community College, A
Southeast Technical Institute, A

University of Sioux Falls, AB
The University of South Dakota, B
Western Dakota Technical Institute, A

Tennessee

Austin Peay State University, AB
Belmont University, B
Bethel College, B
Bryan College, AB
Carson-Newman College, B
Chattanooga State Technical Community College, A
Christian Brothers University, B
Cleveland State Community College, A
Crichton College, B
Draughons Junior College (Clarksville), A
Draughons Junior College (Nashville), A
Dyersburg State Community College, A
East Tennessee State University, B
Fisk University, B
Free Will Baptist Bible College, AB
Freed-Hardeman University, B
ITT Technical Institute (Knoxville), B
ITT Technical Institute (Memphis), B
ITT Technical Institute (Nashville), B
Jackson State Community College, A
King College, B
Lambuth University, B
Lane College, B
Lee University, B
LeMoyne-Owen College, B
Lincoln Memorial University, AB
Lipscomb University, B
Martin Methodist College, AB
Maryville College, B
Middle Tennessee State University, B
Milligan College, B
Motlow State Community College, A
Nashville State Technical Community College, A
National College of Business & Technology (Bristol)
   , A
National College of Business & Technology
   (Nashville), A
Northeast State Technical Community College, A
Pellissippi State Technical Community College, A
Remington College-Memphis Campus, A
Rhodes College, B
Roane State Community College, A
South College, A
Southern Adventist University, B
Southwest Tennessee Community College, A
Tennessee State University, B
Tennessee Technological University, B
Tennessee Temple University, B
Tennessee Wesleyan College, B
Trevecca Nazarene University, B
Tusculum College, B
Union University, B
University of Phoenix-Nashville Campus, B
The University of Tennessee, B
The University of Tennessee at Chattanooga, B
The University of Tennessee at Martin, B
Volunteer State Community College, A
Walters State Community College, A
Williamson Christian College, AB

Texas

Alvin Community College, A
Amarillo College, A
Amberton University, B
American InterContinental University, AB
Angelina College, A
Angelo State University, B
Austin College, B
Austin Community College, A
Baylor University, B
Blinn College, A
Brazosport College, A
Brookhaven College, A
Brown Mackie College-Dallas, A
Brown Mackie College-Fort Worth, A
Cedar Valley College, A
Central Texas College, A
Cisco Junior College, A
Clarendon College, A
Coastal Bend College, A
College of the Mainland, A

Collin County Community College District, A
Concordia University at Austin, B
Dallas Baptist University, AB
Dallas Christian College, B
Del Mar College, A
DeVry University (Houston), B
East Texas Baptist University, B
Eastfield College, A
El Centro College, A
El Paso Community College, A
Frank Phillips College, A
Galveston College, A
Grayson County College, A
Hardin-Simmons University, B
Hill College of the Hill Junior College District, A
Houston Baptist University, B
Houston Community College System, A
Howard College, A
Howard Payne University, B
Huston-Tillotson University, B
Jarvis Christian College, B
Kilgore College, A
Kingwood College, A
Lamar State College-Orange, A
Lamar State College-Port Arthur, A
Lamar University, B
Lee College, A
LeTourneau University, B
Lon Morris College, A
Lubbock Christian University, B
McLennan Community College, A
McMurry University, B
Midwestern State University, B
Montgomery College, A
Navarro College, A
North Central Texas College, A
North Lake College, A
Northwood University, Texas Campus, AB
Odessa College, A
Our Lady of the Lake University of San Antonio, B
Palo Alto College, A
Paris Junior College, A
Paul Quinn College, B
Prairie View A&M University, B
Rice University, B
Richland College, A
St. Edward's University, B
St. Mary's University of San Antonio, B
St. Philip's College, A
Sam Houston State University, B
San Antonio College, A
South Plains College, A
South Texas College, A
Southern Methodist University, B
Southwest Texas Junior College, A
Southwestern Adventist University, B
Southwestern Assemblies of God University, AB
Southwestern Christian College, A
Southwestern University, B
Stephen F. Austin State University, B
Sul Ross State University, B
Tarleton State University, B
Tarrant County College District, A
Temple College, A
Texarkana College, A
Texas A&M International University, B
Texas A&M University, B
Texas A&M University-Commerce, B
Texas A&M University-Corpus Christi, B
Texas A&M University at Galveston, B
Texas A&M University-Kingsville, B
Texas A&M University-Texarkana, B
Texas College, B
Texas Lutheran University, B
Texas Southern University, B
Texas Southmost College, A
Texas State University-San Marcos, B
Texas Tech University, B
Texas Wesleyan University, B
Texas Woman's University, B
Tomball College, A
Trinity University, B
Trinity Valley Community College, A
Tyler Junior College, A
University of Houston, B
University of Houston-Clear Lake, B

University of Houston-Downtown, B
University of Houston-Victoria, B
University of the Incarnate Word, B
University of Mary Hardin-Baylor, B
University of Phoenix-Houston Campus, B
University of St. Thomas, B
The University of Texas at Arlington, B
The University of Texas at Austin, B
The University of Texas at Brownsville, B
The University of Texas at El Paso, B
The University of Texas-Pan American, B
The University of Texas of the Permian Basin, B
The University of Texas at San Antonio, B
The University of Texas at Tyler, B
Vernon College, A
Victoria College, A
Wayland Baptist University, AB
Weatherford College, A
West Texas A&M University, B
Western Texas College, A
Wharton County Junior College, A
Wiley College, B

United States Virgin Islands

University of the Virgin Islands, AB

Utah

Brigham Young University, B
College of Eastern Utah, A
Dixie State College of Utah, AB
Mountain West College, A
Salt Lake Community College, A
Snow College, A
Southern Utah University, B
University of Phoenix-Utah Campus, B
University of Utah, B
Utah Career College, A
Utah State University, B
Utah Valley State College, AB
Weber State University, B
Westminster College, B

Vermont

Castleton State College, B
Champlain College, AB
College of St. Joseph, AB
Community College of Vermont, A
Johnson State College, AB
Lyndon State College, AB
Norwich University, B
Saint Michael's College, B
Southern Vermont College, AB
University of Vermont, B
Vermont Technical College, AB

Virginia

Averett University, AB
Blue Ridge Community College, A
Bluefield College, B
Bridgewater College, B
Bryant and Stratton College, Richmond, B
Bryant and Stratton College, Virginia Beach, AB
Central Virginia Community College, A
Christopher Newport University, B
The College of William and Mary, B
Dabney S. Lancaster Community College, A
Danville Community College, A
DeVry University (Arlington), B
Eastern Mennonite University, B
Eastern Shore Community College, A
Emory & Henry College, B
Ferrum College, B
George Mason University, B
Germanna Community College, A
Hampton University, B
ITT Technical Institute (Chantilly), B
ITT Technical Institute (Norfolk), B
ITT Technical Institute (Richmond), B
ITT Technical Institute (Springfield), B
J. Sargeant Reynolds Community College, A
James Madison University, B
Liberty University, B
Longwood University, B
Lord Fairfax Community College, A
Lynchburg College, B
Mary Baldwin College, B

Marymount University, B
Mountain Empire Community College, A
National College of Business & Technology
    (Bluefield), A
National College of Business & Technology
    (Danville), A
National College of Business & Technology
    (Harrisonburg), A
National College of Business & Technology
    (Lynchburg), A
National College of Business & Technology
    (Martinsville), A
New River Community College, A
Northern Virginia Community College, A
Old Dominion University, B
Patrick Henry Community College, A
Paul D. Camp Community College, A
Piedmont Virginia Community College, A
Rappahannock Community College, A
Roanoke College, B
Saint Paul's College, B
Shenandoah University, B
Southern Virginia University, B
Southside Virginia Community College, A
Southwest Virginia Community College, A
Stratford University, AB
Thomas Nelson Community College, A
Tidewater Community College, A
University of Management and Technology, AB
University of Mary Washington, B
University of Phoenix-Northern Virginia Campus, B
University of Phoenix-Richmond Campus, B
University of Richmond, B
The University of Virginia's College at Wise, B
Virginia Commonwealth University, B
Virginia Highlands Community College, A
Virginia Intermont College, B
Virginia Polytechnic Institute and State University, B
Virginia State University, B
Virginia Union University, B
Virginia Wesleyan College, B
Virginia Western Community College, A
Washington and Lee University, B
Wytheville Community College, A

Washington

Bellevue Community College, A
Central Washington University, B
Centralia College, A
City University, B
Clark College, A
Eastern Washington University, B
Edmonds Community College, A
Everett Community College, A
The Evergreen State College, B
Gonzaga University, B
Grays Harbor College, A
Henry Cogswell College, B
Heritage University, AB
Highline Community College, A
ITT Technical Institute (Bothell), B
ITT Technical Institute (Seattle), B
Lower Columbia College, A
Northwest University, B
Olympic College, A
Pacific Lutheran University, B
Peninsula College, A
Pierce College, A
Renton Technical College, A
Saint Martin's University, B
Seattle Pacific University, B
Seattle University, B
Shoreline Community College, A
Skagit Valley College, A
South Puget Sound Community College, A
South Seattle Community College, A
Spokane Community College, A
Spokane Falls Community College, A
Tacoma Community College, A
University of Phoenix-Spokane Campus, B
University of Phoenix-Washington Campus, B
University of Washington, B
University of Washington, Bothell, B
University of Washington, Tacoma, B
Walla Walla College, AB
Walla Walla Community College, A

Washington State University, B
Wenatchee Valley College, A
Western Washington University, B
Whatcom Community College, A
Whitworth College, B
Yakima Valley Community College, A

West Virginia

Alderson-Broaddus College, AB
American Public University System, B
Bluefield State College, B
Community & Technical College at West Virginia
    University Institute of Technology, A
Concord University, AB
Davis & Elkins College, B
Fairmont State University, AB
Glenville State College, B
Huntington Junior College, A
Marshall University, B
Mountain State University, A
Ohio Valley University, B
Potomac State College of West Virginia
    University, A
Salem International University, AB
Shepherd University, B
Southern West Virginia Community and Technical
    College, A
University of Charleston, AB
Valley College, A
West Liberty State College, B
West Virginia Business College (Wheeling), A
West Virginia Junior College (Bridgeport), A
West Virginia Junior College (Charleston), A
West Virginia Junior College (Morgantown), A
West Virginia Northern Community College, A
West Virginia State University, AB
West Virginia University, B
West Virginia University Institute of Technology, B
West Virginia University at Parkersburg, AB
West Virginia Wesleyan College, B
Wheeling Jesuit University, B

Wisconsin

Alverno College, B
Beloit College, B
Bryant and Stratton College, Wauwatosa
    Campus, B
Cardinal Stritch University, AB
Carroll College, B
Carthage College, B
College of Menominee Nation, A
Concordia University Wisconsin, B
DeVry University (Milwaukee), B
Edgewood College, B
Fox Valley Technical College, A
ITT Technical Institute (Green Bay), B
ITT Technical Institute (Greenfield), B
Lac Courte Oreilles Ojibwa Community College, A
Lakeland College, B
Madison Area Technical College, A
Maranatha Baptist Bible College, B
Marian College of Fond du Lac, B
Marquette University, B
Mid-State Technical College, A
Milwaukee Area Technical College, A
Milwaukee School of Engineering, B
Mount Mary College, B
Nicolet Area Technical College, A
Northcentral Technical College, A
Northeast Wisconsin Technical College, A
Northland College, B
Ripon College, B
St. Norbert College, B
Silver Lake College, B
University of Phoenix-Wisconsin Campus, B
University of Wisconsin-Eau Claire, B
University of Wisconsin-Green Bay, AB
University of Wisconsin-La Crosse, B
University of Wisconsin-Madison, B
University of Wisconsin-Milwaukee, B
University of Wisconsin-Oshkosh, B
University of Wisconsin-Parkside, B
University of Wisconsin-Platteville, B
University of Wisconsin-River Falls, B
University of Wisconsin-Stevens Point, B
University of Wisconsin-Stout, B

University of Wisconsin-Superior, B
University of Wisconsin-Whitewater, B
Viterbo University, B
Western Technical College, A

Wyoming

Casper College, A
Central Wyoming College, A
Eastern Wyoming College, A
Laramie County Community College, A
Northwest College, A
Sheridan College-Sheridan and Gillette, A
University of Wyoming, B
Western Wyoming Community College, A

Alberta

Athabasca University, B
Concordia University College of Alberta, B
The King's University College, B
Southern Alberta Institute of Technology, B
University of Alberta, B
University of Calgary, B
University of Lethbridge, B

British Columbia

British Columbia Institute of Technology, AB
Open Learning Agency, B
Royal Roads University, B
Simon Fraser University, B
Thompson Rivers University, B
Trinity Western University, B
The University of British Columbia, B
University College of the Fraser Valley, B
University of Northern British Columbia, B
University of Phoenix-Vancouver Campus, B

Manitoba

Brandon University, B
Providence College and Theological Seminary, B
University of Manitoba, B
The University of Winnipeg, B

New Brunswick

Atlantic Baptist University, B
Mount Allison University, B
Université de Moncton, B
University of New Brunswick Fredericton, B
University of New Brunswick Saint John, B

Newfoundland and Labrador

Memorial University of Newfoundland, B

Nova Scotia

Acadia University, B
Cape Breton University, B
Dalhousie University, B
Mount Saint Vincent University, B
St. Francis Xavier University, B
Saint Mary's University, B
Université Sainte-Anne, B

Ontario

Brock University, B
Carleton University, B
Lakehead University, B
Laurentian University, B
McMaster University, B
Nipissing University, B
Redeemer University College, B
Royal Military College of Canada, B
Ryerson University, B
Trent University, B
University of Ottawa, B
University of Toronto, B
University of Waterloo, B
The University of Western Ontario, B
University of Windsor, B
Wilfrid Laurier University, B

York University, B

Prince Edward Island

University of Prince Edward Island, B

Quebec

Bishop's University, B
Concordia University, B
HEC Montreal, B
McGill University, B
Télé-université, B
Université Laval, B
Université du Québec en Abitibi-Témiscamingue, B
Université du Québec àChicoutimi, B
Université du Québec àMontréal, B
Université du Québec en Outaouais, B
Université du Québec àRimouski, B
Université du Québec àTrois-Rivières, B
Université de Sherbrooke, B

Saskatchewan

Briercrest College, B
University of Regina, AB

BUSINESS ADMINISTRATION, MANAGEMENT AND OPERATIONS

Alabama

Alabama Agricultural and Mechanical University, M
Alabama State University, M
Andrew Jackson University, M
Auburn University, M
Auburn University Montgomery, M
Columbia Southern University, M
Jacksonville State University, M
Samford University, MO
Spring Hill College, M
Troy University, M
The University of Alabama at Birmingham, MD
University of Mobile, M
University of North Alabama, M
University of South Alabama, M
Virginia College at Birmingham, M

Alaska

Alaska Pacific University, M
University of Alaska Anchorage, M
University of Alaska Fairbanks, M
University of Alaska Southeast, M

Arizona

Argosy University/Phoenix, MD
Arizona State University, MDO
Arizona State University West, M
DeVry University (Mesa), M
DeVry University (Phoenix), BM
Embry-Riddle Aeronautical University, B
Grand Canyon University, M
Northern Arizona University, M
The University of Arizona, MDO
University of Phoenix Online Campus, MD
University of Phoenix-Phoenix Campus, M
University of Phoenix-Southern Arizona Campus, M
Western International University, M

Arkansas

Arkansas State University, MO
Harding University, M
Henderson State University, M
John Brown University, M
University of Arkansas, MD
University of Arkansas at Little Rock, MO
University of Central Arkansas, M
University of Phoenix-Little Rock Campus, M

California

American InterContinental University, M
Argosy University/Orange County, AMD
Argosy University/San Diego, M
Argosy University/San Francisco Bay Area, MD
Argosy University/Santa Monica, A
Azusa Pacific University, M

Biola University, M
California Baptist University, M
California Lutheran University, M
California National University for Advanced
   Studies, M
California Polytechnic State University, San Luis
   Obispo, MO
California State Polytechnic University, Pomona, M
California State University, Bakersfield, M
California State University, Chico, BM
California State University, Dominguez Hills, M
California State University, East Bay, M
California State University, Fresno, M
California State University, Fullerton, M
California State University, Long Beach, M
California State University, Los Angeles, M
California State University, Sacramento, M
California State University, San Bernardino, M
California State University, San Marcos, M
California State University, Stanislaus, M
Chapman University, MO
Coleman College (La Mesa), AB
Concordia University, M
DeVry University (Elk Grove), M
DeVry University (Fremont), BM
DeVry University (Irvine), M
DeVry University (Long Beach), BM
DeVry University (Pomona), BM
DeVry University (San Diego), M
DeVry University (San Francisco), M
DeVry University (West Hills), BM
Dominican University of California, M
Fresno Pacific University, M
Golden Gate University, MDO
Humboldt State University, M
International Technological University, M
John F. Kennedy University, MO
La Sierra University, MO
Lincoln University, M
Loyola Marymount University, MO
National University, M
Northwestern Polytechnic University, M
Notre Dame de Namur University, M
Pacific States University, M
Pepperdine University, MO
Point Loma Nazarene University, M
Saint Mary's College of California, M
San Diego State University, M
San Francisco State University, M
San Jose State University, BM
Santa Clara University, MO
Santiago Canyon College, A
Sonoma State University, M
Stanford University, MDO
Touro University International, MD
University of California, Berkeley, MDO
University of California, Davis, M
University of California, Irvine, MD
University of California, Los Angeles, MDO
University of California, Riverside, M
University of California, San Diego, M
University of Judaism, M
University of La Verne, M
University of the Pacific, MO
University of Phoenix-Bay Area Campus, M
University of Phoenix-Sacramento Valley
   Campus, M
University of Phoenix-San Diego Campus, M
University of Phoenix-Southern California
   Campus, M
University of Redlands, MO
University of San Diego, MO
University of San Francisco, MO
University of Southern California, BMDO
University of the West, M
Vanguard University of Southern California, M
William Jessup University, B
Woodbury University, BM

Colorado

Argosy University/Denver, A
Aspen University, MO
Colorado Christian University, M
Colorado State University, M
Colorado State University-Pueblo, M
Colorado Technical University, MD

Colorado Technical University Denver Campus, M
DeVry University (Colorado Springs), BM
Jones International University, M
Mesa State College, M
Regis University, MO
University of Colorado at Boulder, MDO
University of Colorado at Colorado Springs, M
University of Colorado at Denver and Health
   Sciences Center - Downtown Denver Campus, M
University of Denver, M
University of Phoenix-Denver Campus, M
University of Phoenix-Southern Colorado
   Campus, M

Connecticut

Central Connecticut State University, M
Fairfield University, MO
Post University, B
Quinnipiac University, MO
Sacred Heart University, MO
Southern Connecticut State University, M
University of Bridgeport, M
University of Connecticut, MDO
University of Hartford, MO
University of New Haven, MO
Western Connecticut State University, M
Yale University, MDO

Delaware

Delaware State University, M
Goldey-Beacom College, M
University of Delaware, MO
Wesley College, M
Wilmington College, M

District of Columbia

American University, MO
The Catholic University of America, MO
Georgetown University, MO
Howard University, MO
Southeastern University, M
Strayer University, M
Trinity (Washington) University, M
University of the District of Columbia, M

Florida

Argosy University/Sarasota, BMD
Argosy University/Tampa, M
Barry University, MO
Carlos Albizu University, Miami Campus, BMD
DeVry University (Miami), M
DeVry University (Miramar), BM
DeVry University (Orlando), BM
DeVry University (Tampa), M
Embry-Riddle Aeronautical University, BM
Embry-Riddle Aeronautical University, Extended
   Campus, AB
Everglades University (Boca Raton), M
Florida Agricultural and Mechanical University, M
Florida Atlantic University, MD
Florida Gulf Coast University, M
Florida Institute of Technology, BM
Florida International University, MD
Florida Metropolitan University-Brandon Campus, M
Florida Metropolitan University-Melbourne
   Campus, M
Florida Metropolitan University-North Orlando
   Campus, M
Florida Metropolitan University-Pinellas Campus, M
Florida Metropolitan University-Pompano Beach
   Campus, M
Florida Metropolitan University-South Orlando
   Campus, M
Florida Metropolitan University-Tampa Campus, M
Florida Southern College, M
Florida State University, MDO
International College, B
Jacksonville University, M
Lynn University, MD
Nova Southeastern University, MDO
Palm Beach Atlantic University, BM
Rollins College, M
Saint Leo University, M
St. Thomas University, MO
Schiller International University, M
Stetson University, MO

University of Central Florida, MD
University of Florida, MO
University of Miami, BMO
University of North Florida, M
University of Phoenix-Central Florida Campus, M
University of Phoenix-North Florida Campus, M
University of Phoenix-South Florida Campus, M
University of Phoenix-West Florida Campus, M
University of South Florida, MD
The University of Tampa, M
University of West Florida, M
Warner Southern College, M
Webber International University, M

Georgia

Albany State University, M
American InterContinental University (Atlanta), M
Argosy University/Atlanta, M
Augusta State University, M
Berry College, M
Brenau University, M
Clark Atlanta University, M
Columbus State University, M
DeVry University (Alpharetta), BM
DeVry University (Atlanta), M
DeVry University (Decatur), BM
DeVry University (Duluth), M
Emory University, MDO
Georgia College & State University, M
Georgia Institute of Technology, MO
Georgia Southern University, M
Georgia Southwestern State University, M
Georgia State University, M
Kennesaw State University, M
Mercer University, BMO
Oglethorpe University, M
Piedmont College, M
Shorter College, M
Southern Polytechnic State University, M
Thomas University, M
University of Georgia, MDO
University of Phoenix-Atlanta Campus, M
University of Phoenix-Columbus Georgia
  Campus, M
University of West Georgia, M
Valdosta State University, M
Wesleyan College, M

Guam

University of Guam, M

Hawaii

Argosy University/Hawaii, M
Chaminade University of Honolulu, M
Hawaii Pacific University, M
University of Hawaii at Manoa, M
University of Phoenix-Hawaii Campus, M

Idaho

Boise State University, M
Idaho State University, MO
Northwest Nazarene University, M
University of Idaho, M
University of Phoenix-Idaho Campus, BM

Illinois

American InterContinental University Online, ABM
Argosy University/Chicago, MD
Argosy University/Schaumburg, MD
Aurora University, M
Benedictine University, MO
Bradley University, M
DePaul University, BMO
DeVry University (Addison), B
DeVry University (Chicago), B
DeVry University (Elgin), M
DeVry University (Gurnee), M
DeVry University (Naperville), M
DeVry University (Oakbrook Terrace), M
DeVry University (Tinley Park), BM
Dominican University, MO
Eastern Illinois University, MO
Elmhurst College, M
Governors State University, M
Illinois Institute of Technology, MO

Illinois State University, M
Lewis University, M
Loyola University Chicago, MO
Millikin University, M
National-Louis University, M
North Central College, M
North Park University, MO
Northeastern Illinois University, M
Northern Illinois University, M
Northwestern University, MO
Olivet Nazarene University, M
Quincy University, M
Rockford College, M
Roosevelt University, M
St. Augustine College, A
Saint Xavier University, MO
Southern Illinois University Carbondale, MDO
Southern Illinois University Edwardsville, M
Trinity Christian College, B
University of Chicago, MD
University of Illinois at Chicago, MDO
University of Illinois at Springfield, BM
University of Illinois at Urbana-Champaign, MDO
University of Phoenix-Chicago Campus, M
University of St. Francis, M
Western Illinois University, M

Indiana

Anderson University, MD
Ball State University, M
Bethel College, M
Butler University, M
DeVry University (Indianapolis), BM
DeVry University (Merrillville), M
Indiana Business College (Anderson), A
Indiana Business College (Columbus), A
Indiana Business College (Indianapolis), A
Indiana Business College (Lafayette), A
Indiana Business College (Muncie), A
Indiana Business College (Terre Haute), A
Indiana State University, M
Indiana Tech, M
Indiana University Bloomington, MDO
Indiana University Kokomo, MO
Indiana University Northwest, MO
Indiana University-Purdue University Fort Wayne, M
Indiana University-Purdue University
  Indianapolis, MO
Indiana University South Bend, M
Indiana University Southeast, MO
Indiana Wesleyan University, M
ITT Technical Institute (Indianapolis), M
Oakland City University, B
Purdue University, MD
Purdue University Calumet, M
Saint Mary-of-the-Woods College, B
Taylor University Fort Wayne, M
University of Indianapolis, M
University of Notre Dame, BMO
University of Phoenix-Indianapolis Campus, M
University of Saint Francis, M
University of Southern Indiana, M
Valparaiso University, MO

Iowa

Drake University, MO
Iowa State University of Science and
  Technology, MO
Maharishi University of Management, MD
St. Ambrose University, MD
University of Dubuque, M
The University of Iowa, MDO
University of Northern Iowa, M
Upper Iowa University, M

Kansas

Baker University, M
Benedictine College, M
Emporia State University, M
Fort Hays State University, M
Friends University, M
Kansas State University, M
Kansas Wesleyan University, M
MidAmerica Nazarene University, M
Newman University, M
Ottawa University, M

Pittsburg State University, M
University of Kansas, MDO
University of Phoenix-Wichita Campus, M
University of Saint Mary, M
Washburn University, M
Wichita State University, MO

Kentucky

Bellarmine University, M
Campbellsville University, M
Eastern Kentucky University, M
Morehead State University, M
Murray State University, M
Northern Kentucky University, MO
Spalding University, M
Sullivan University, M
Thomas More College, M
University of Kentucky, MD
University of Louisville, BM
Western Kentucky University, M

Louisiana

Centenary College of Louisiana, M
Louisiana State University and Agricultural and
  Mechanical College, MD
Louisiana State University in Shreveport, M
Louisiana Tech University, MD
Loyola University New Orleans, MO
McNeese State University, M
Nicholls State University, M
Southeastern Louisiana University, M
Southern University and Agricultural and Mechanical
  College, BM
Tulane University, MDO
University of Louisiana at Lafayette, M
University of Louisiana at Monroe, M
University of New Orleans, M
University of Phoenix-Louisiana Campus, M

Maine

Husson College, M
Saint Joseph's College of Maine, M
Thomas College, M
University of Maine, M
University of Southern Maine, MO

Maryland

Bowie State University, M
Capitol College, M
DeVry University, BM
Frostburg State University, M
Hood College, M
The Johns Hopkins University, MO
Loyola College in Maryland, M
Morgan State University, MD
Mount St. Mary's University, M
Salisbury University, M
Towson University, BM
University of Baltimore, MO
University of Maryland, College Park, MO
University of Maryland University College, M
University of Phoenix-Maryland Campus, M

Massachusetts

American International College, M
Anna Maria College, MO
Assumption College, MO
Babson College, BM
Becker College, B
Bentley College, MO
Boston College, MO
Boston University, M
Brandeis University, MO
Clark University, M
Endicott College, M
Fitchburg State College, M
Framingham State College, M
Harvard University, MDO
Lasell College, M
Massasoit Community College, A
Nichols College, M
Northeastern University, MO
Regis College, M
Salem State College, MO
Simmons College, M

Suffolk University, MO
University of Massachusetts Amherst, M
University of Massachusetts Boston, MO
University of Massachusetts Dartmouth, MO
University of Massachusetts Lowell, M
University of Phoenix-Boston Campus, M
University of Phoenix-Central Massachusetts
　Campus, M
Western New England College, M
Worcester Polytechnic Institute, MO

Michigan

Central Michigan University, BM
Cleary University, M
Cornerstone University, B
Davenport University (Dearborn), M
Eastern Michigan University, M
Ferris State University, M
Grand Valley State University, MO
Lawrence Technological University, MD
Madonna University, M
Michigan State University, MD
Michigan Technological University, M
Northwood University, M
Oakland University, MO
Saginaw Valley State University, M
University of Detroit Mercy, MO
University of Michigan, MD
University of Michigan-Dearborn, BMO
University of Michigan-Flint, M
University of Phoenix-Metro Detroit Campus, M
University of Phoenix-West Michigan Campus, M
Walsh College of Accountancy and Business
　Administration, M
Wayne State University, MDO
Western Michigan University, M

Minnesota

Augsburg College, M
Bethel University, M
Capella University, MD
Metropolitan State University, M
St. Cloud State University, M
Saint Mary's University of Minnesota, M
Southwest Minnesota State University, M
University of Minnesota, Duluth, M
University of Minnesota, Twin Cities Campus, MDO
University of St. Thomas, BM

Mississippi

Alcorn State University, M
Belhaven College, M
Delta State University, M
Jackson State University, MD
Millsaps College, M
Mississippi College, MO
Mississippi State University, MD
University of Mississippi, MDO
University of Southern Mississippi, M
William Carey College, M

Missouri

Avila University, M
Central Missouri State University, M
Columbia College, M
DeVry University (Kansas City), B
DeVry University (Kansas City), M
DeVry University (St. Louis), M
Drury University, MO
Fontbonne University, M
Grantham University, M
Lincoln University, M
Lindenwood University, M
Maryville University of Saint Louis, MO
Missouri Baptist University, B
Missouri State University, M
Northwest Missouri State University, M
Park University, M
Saint Louis University, M
Southeast Missouri State University, M
Southwest Baptist University, M
Stephens College, M
University of Missouri-Columbia, MD
University of Missouri-Kansas City, MDO
University of Missouri-St. Louis, MO
University of Phoenix-Kansas City Campus, M

University of Phoenix-St. Louis Campus, M
Washington University in St. Louis, BMDO
Webster University, M
William Woods University, M

Montana

The University of Montana-Missoula, MO

Nebraska

Bellevue University, M
Chadron State College, M
Creighton University, MO
Doane College, M
University of Nebraska at Kearney, M
University of Nebraska-Lincoln, MDO
University of Nebraska at Omaha, M
Wayne State College, M

Nevada

DeVry University, M
Morrison University, M
University of Nevada, Las Vegas, M
University of Nevada, Reno, M
University of Phoenix-Nevada Campus, M

New Hampshire

Dartmouth College, MO
Franklin Pierce College, M
Plymouth State University, M
Rivier College, M
Southern New Hampshire University, MDO
University of New Hampshire, M

New Jersey

Caldwell College, M
Centenary College, M
College of Saint Elizabeth, M
DeVry University, AB
Fairleigh Dickinson University, College at
　Florham, MO
Fairleigh Dickinson University, Metropolitan
　Campus, MO
Georgian Court University, M
Kean University, MO
Monmouth University, MO
Montclair State University, M
New Jersey Institute of Technology, M
The Richard Stockton College of New Jersey, M
Rider University, M
Rowan University, M
Rutgers, The State University of New Jersey,
　Camden, M
Rutgers, The State University of New Jersey,
　Newark, MDO
Saint Peter's College, MO
Seton Hall University, MO
Stevens Institute of Technology, MDO
William Paterson University of New Jersey, M

New Mexico

College of Santa Fe, M
Eastern New Mexico University, M
New Mexico Highlands University, M
New Mexico State University, MD
University of New Mexico, MO
University of Phoenix-New Mexico Campus, M
Western New Mexico University, M

New York

Adelphi University, M
Alfred University, M
Bernard M. Baruch College of the City University of
　New York, MDO
Briarcliffe College, A
Bryant and Stratton College, Amherst Campus, B
Canisius College, BM
Clarkson University, M
The College of Saint Rose, MO
Cornell University, MDO
DeVry Institute of Technology, B
Dowling College, MO
Excelsior College, M
Fordham University, MO
Hofstra University, BMO
Iona College, MO

Le Moyne College, M
Long Island University, Brentwood Campus, M
Long Island University, Brooklyn Campus, M
Long Island University, C.W. Post Campus, MO
Marist College, MO
Medaille College, M
Mount Saint Mary College, M
New York Institute of Technology, MO
New York University, MDO
Niagara University, M
Nyack College, M
Pace University, MDO
Polytechnic University, Brooklyn Campus, M
Rensselaer Polytechnic Institute, MDO
Rochester Institute of Technology, M
St. Bonaventure University, MO
St. John Fisher College, M
St. John's University, MO
St. Thomas Aquinas College, M
State University of New York at Binghamton, MD
State University of New York at Buffalo, MDO
State University of New York Empire State
　College, M
State University of New York Institute of
　Technology, M
State University of New York at New Paltz, M
State University of New York at Oswego, M
Stony Brook University, State University of New
　York, MO
Syracuse University, MDO
University at Albany, State University of New
　York, MD
University of Rochester, MD
Wagner College, M

North Carolina

Appalachian State University, M
Campbell University, M
DeVry University, BM
Duke University, MDO
East Carolina University, M
Elon University, M
Fayetteville State University, M
Fayetteville Technical Community College, A
Gardner-Webb University, M
High Point University, M
Lenoir-Rhyne College, M
Meredith College, M
Montreat College, M
North Carolina Central University, MO
North Carolina State University, M
Pfeiffer University, MO
Queens University of Charlotte, M
The University of North Carolina at Chapel
　Hill, MDO
The University of North Carolina at Charlotte, M
The University of North Carolina at Greensboro, MO
The University of North Carolina at Pembroke, M
The University of North Carolina Wilmington, M
University of Phoenix-Charlotte Campus, M
Wake Forest University, MO
Western Carolina University, M
Wingate University, M

North Dakota

Mayville State University, B
North Dakota State University, M
University of Mary, M
University of North Dakota, M

Ohio

Ashland University, M
Baldwin-Wallace College, M
Bowling Green State University, M
Capital University, BMO
Case Western Reserve University, MDO
Cleveland State University, BMDO
David N. Myers University, M
Defiance College, M
DeVry University (Cleveland), M
DeVry University (Columbus), BM
DeVry University (Seven Hills), M
Franciscan University of Steubenville, M
Franklin University, M
Heidelberg College, M
John Carroll University, M

Kent State University, M
Lake Erie College, M
Malone College, BM
Miami University, M
Miami University Hamilton, B
The Ohio State University, MD
Ohio University, M
Otterbein College, M
Tiffin University, M
University of Cincinnati, MDO
University of Dayton, MO
The University of Findlay, M
University of Phoenix-Cincinnati Campus, M
University of Phoenix-Cleveland Campus, M
University of Phoenix-Columbus Ohio Campus, M
The University of Toledo, BMD
Urbana University, M
Ursuline College, B
Walsh University, M
Wright State University, MO
Xavier University, MO
Youngstown State University, M

Oklahoma

Cameron University, M
Community Care College, A
Northeastern State University, M
Oklahoma City University, MO
Oklahoma State University, M
Oral Roberts University, M
Southeastern Oklahoma State University, M
Southern Nazarene University, M
Southwestern Oklahoma State University, M
University of Central Oklahoma, M
University of Oklahoma, MDO
University of Phoenix-Oklahoma City Campus, M
University of Phoenix-Tulsa Campus, M
University of Tulsa, MO

Oregon

DeVry University, BM
George Fox University, M
Marylhurst University, M
Northwest Christian College, BM
Oregon State University, MO
Portland State University, MD
Southern Oregon University, M
University of Oregon, M
University of Phoenix-Oregon Campus, M
University of Portland, M
Willamette University, MO

Pennsylvania

Alvernia College, M
Bloomsburg University of Pennsylvania, M
California University of Pennsylvania, M
Chatham College, M
Clarion University of Pennsylvania, M
Delaware County Community College, A
DeSales University, M
DeVry University (Chesterbrook), M
DeVry University (Fort Washington), M
DeVry University (Pittsburgh), M
Drexel University, MDO
Duquesne University, BMO
Eastern University, MO
Gannon University, M
Geneva College, M
Gettysburg College, B
Holy Family University, M
Indiana University of Pennsylvania, M
King's College, M
Kutztown University of Pennsylvania, M
La Salle University, MO
Lebanon Valley College, M
Lehigh University, MDO
Marywood University, M
Millersville University of Pennsylvania, M
Moravian College, M
Peirce College, A
Pennsylvania College of Technology, B
The Pennsylvania State University at Erie, The
  Behrend College, M
The Pennsylvania State University Harrisburg
  Campus, MO

The Pennsylvania State University University Park
  Campus, MD
Philadelphia University, MO
Point Park University, BM
Robert Morris University, M
Rosemont College, M
Saint Francis University, M
Saint Joseph's University, MO
Seton Hill University, M
Shippensburg University of Pennsylvania, M
Slippery Rock University of Pennsylvania, M
Temple University, MDO
University of Pennsylvania, BMDO
University of Phoenix-Philadelphia Campus, M
University of Phoenix-Pittsburgh Campus, M
University of Pittsburgh, MDO
The University of Scranton, BM
Villanova University, MO
Waynesburg College, MO
West Chester University of Pennsylvania, M
Widener University, BMO
Wilkes University, M
York College of Pennsylvania, M

Puerto Rico

Bayamon Central University, M
Inter American University of Puerto Rico, San
  Germán Campus, MD
Polytechnic University of Puerto Rico, M
Pontifical Catholic University of Puerto Rico, MDO
Universidad Metropolitana, MO
Universidad del Turabo, M
University of Phoenix-Puerto Rico Campus, M
University of Puerto Rico, Mayagüez Campus, M
University of Puerto Rico, Río Piedras, MD
University of the Sacred Heart, M

Rhode Island

Bryant University, MO
Providence College, M
Salve Regina University, MO
University of Rhode Island, MD

South Carolina

Charleston Southern University, BM
The Citadel, The Military College of South
  Carolina, M
Clemson University, M
College of Charleston, M
Francis Marion University, M
Morris College, B
Southern Wesleyan University, M
University of South Carolina, MDO
Winthrop University, M

South Dakota

Black Hills State University, M
Colorado Technical University Sioux Falls
  Campus, M
National American University (Rapid City), M
University of Sioux Falls, M
The University of South Dakota, MO

Tennessee

Austin Peay State University, M
Belmont University, M
Christian Brothers University, M
Cumberland University, M
East Tennessee State University, MO
Freed-Hardeman University, M
King College, M
Lincoln Memorial University, M
Lipscomb University, M
Southern Adventist University, M
Tennessee State University, M
Tennessee Technological University, M
Trevecca Nazarene University, M
Union University, M
University of Memphis, MDO
University of Phoenix-Nashville Campus, M
The University of Tennessee, MDO
The University of Tennessee at Chattanooga, M
The University of Tennessee at Martin, M

Vanderbilt University, MO

Texas

Amberton University, M
Argosy University/Dallas, M
Baylor University, MO
Dallas Baptist University, M
DeVry University (Houston), BM
DeVry University (Irving), BM
DeVry University (Plano), M
Hardin-Simmons University, M
Lamar University, M
LeTourneau University, M
Midwestern State University, M
Northwest Vista College, A
Our Lady of the Lake University of San Antonio, M
Prairie View A&M University, M
Rice University, MO
St. Mary's University of San Antonio, MO
Sam Houston State University, M
Southern Methodist University, M
Southwestern Adventist University, M
Stephen F. Austin State University, M
Sul Ross State University, M
Tarleton State University, M
Texas A&M International University, M
Texas A&M University, M
Texas A&M University-Commerce, M
Texas A&M University-Corpus Christi, M
Texas A&M University-Kingsville, M
Texas A&M University-Texarkana, M
Texas Christian University, M
Texas Southern University, M
Texas State University-San Marcos, M
Texas Tech University, BMDO
Texas Wesleyan University, M
Texas Woman's University, M
Trinity University, M
University of Dallas, M
University of Houston, MDO
University of Houston-Clear Lake, BMO
University of Houston-Victoria, M
University of the Incarnate Word, MO
University of Mary Hardin-Baylor, M
University of North Texas, MD
University of Phoenix-Dallas Campus, M
University of Phoenix-Houston Campus, M
University of St. Thomas, M
The University of Texas at Arlington, MD
The University of Texas at Austin, BMO
The University of Texas at Brownsville, M
The University of Texas at Dallas, M
The University of Texas at El Paso, M
The University of Texas-Pan American, MD
The University of Texas of the Permian Basin, M
The University of Texas at San Antonio, D
The University of Texas at Tyler, M
Wayland Baptist University, M
West Texas A&M University, M

United States Virgin Islands

University of the Virgin Islands, M

Utah

Brigham Young University, MO
Southern Utah University, M
University of Phoenix-Utah Campus, M
University of Utah, MDO
Utah State University, M
Weber State University, M
Westminster College, MO

Vermont

College of St. Joseph, M
Norwich University, M
Saint Michael's College, MO
University of Vermont, M

Virginia

Argosy University/Washington D.C., MD
Averett University, M
The College of William and Mary, MO
DeVry University (Arlington), BM
DeVry University (McLean), M
Eastern Mennonite University, M

George Mason University, M
Hampton University, M
James Madison University, M
Liberty University, M
Lynchburg College, M
Marymount University, BMO
Old Dominion University, MD
Radford University, M
Regent University, MO
Shenandoah University, MO
Stratford University, M
University of Management and Technology, ABMO
University of Mary Washington, M
University of Northern Virginia, D
University of Richmond, M
University of Virginia, MDO
Virginia Commonwealth University, MDO
Virginia Polytechnic Institute and State University, MD
Virginia State University, M

Washington

Argosy University/Seattle, MD
City University, MO
DeVry University (Bellevue), M
DeVry University (Federal Way), BM
Eastern Washington University, MO
Gonzaga University, MO
Pacific Lutheran University, M
Saint Martin's University, M
Seattle Pacific University, M
Seattle University, MO
University of Phoenix-Spokane Campus, M
University of Phoenix-Washington Campus, M
University of Washington, MDO
Washington State University, MDO
Western Washington University, M
Whitworth College, M

West Virginia

American Public University System, M
Marshall University, M
University of Charleston, BM
West Virginia State Community and Technical College, A
West Virginia University, MO
West Virginia Wesleyan College, M
Wheeling Jesuit University, M

Wisconsin

Alverno College, B
Cardinal Stritch University, M
Concordia University Wisconsin, M
DeVry University (Milwaukee), BM
DeVry University (Waukesha), M
Edgewood College, M
Lakeland College, M
Marian College of Fond du Lac, M
Marquette University, MO
Milwaukee School of Engineering, M
Northeast Wisconsin Technical College, A
University of Phoenix-Wisconsin Campus, M
University of Wisconsin-Eau Claire, M
University of Wisconsin-La Crosse, M
University of Wisconsin-Madison, MD
University of Wisconsin-Milwaukee, MDO
University of Wisconsin-Oshkosh, M
University of Wisconsin-Parkside, M
University of Wisconsin-Stevens Point, M
University of Wisconsin-Whitewater, M
Viterbo University, B
Western Technical College, A

Wyoming

University of Wyoming, M

Alberta

Athabasca University, MO
Southern Alberta Institute of Technology, B
University of Alberta, MDO
University of Calgary, MO

British Columbia

Malaspina University-College, M
Open Learning Agency, B

Royal Roads University, M
Simon Fraser University, MO
The University of British Columbia, MD
University of Phoenix-Vancouver Campus, M
University of Victoria, MO

Manitoba

University of Manitoba, MD

New Brunswick

Université de Moncton, MO
University of New Brunswick Fredericton, M
University of New Brunswick Saint John, M

Newfoundland and Labrador

Memorial University of Newfoundland, M

Nova Scotia

Cape Breton University, M
Dalhousie University, MO
Saint Mary's University, MD

Ontario

Carleton University, MD
Laurentian University, M
McMaster University, MD
Queen's University at Kingston, M
Royal Military College of Canada, M
University of Guelph, M
University of Ottawa, M
University of Toronto, MDO
University of Waterloo, BM
The University of Western Ontario, MDO
University of Windsor, MO
Wilfrid Laurier University, M
York University, MDO

Quebec

Concordia University, MDO
HEC Montreal, MD
McGill University, MDO
Université Laval, MO
Université du Québec en Abitibi-Témiscamingue, M
Université du Québec àChicoutimi, M
Université du Québec àMontréal, MDO
Université du Québec àTrois-Rivières, MD
Université de Sherbrooke, MDO

Saskatchewan

University of Regina, M
University of Saskatchewan, M

BUSINESS AND PERSONAL/FINANCIAL SERVICES MARKETING OPERATIONS

Arizona

Northland Pioneer College, A

Florida

North Florida Community College, A

Illinois

Heartland Community College, A

Kansas

Hutchinson Community College and Area Vocational School, A

Michigan

Northwestern Michigan College, A

New Hampshire

Hesser College, A
Southern New Hampshire University, AB

New Jersey

Union County College, A

New York

Mohawk Valley Community College, A

Oklahoma

Tulsa Community College, A

Puerto Rico

Caribbean University, B

Texas

North Central Texas College, A

Washington

Centralia College, A
Spokane Falls Community College, A

West Virginia

American Public University System, B

Wisconsin

Moraine Park Technical College, A
Wisconsin Indianhead Technical College, A

Ontario

Nipissing University, B

BUSINESS/COMMERCE

Alabama

Alabama Agricultural and Mechanical University, B
American College of Computer & Information Sciences, B
Andrew Jackson University, AB
Auburn University Montgomery, B
Jefferson State Community College, A
Judson College, B
Troy University, AB
University of South Alabama, B

Alaska

Ilisagvik College, A

Arizona

Everest College, A
GateWay Community College, A
Glendale Community College, A
Northern Arizona University, B
Northland Pioneer College, A
The University of Arizona, B

Arkansas

Arkansas Northeastern College, A
Henderson State University, B
North Arkansas College, A
South Arkansas Community College, A
Southeast Arkansas College, A
Southern Arkansas University-Magnolia, B
University of Arkansas, B
University of Arkansas Community College at Batesville, A
University of Arkansas at Little Rock, B
University of Central Arkansas, B

California

Antelope Valley College, A
Berkeley City College, A
Cuyamaca College, A
Evergreen Valley College, A
Feather River College, A
Mt. Sierra College, A
Reedley College, A
Saint Mary's College of California, B
San Diego State University, B
San Joaquin Valley College, A
Touro University International, B
University of Phoenix-San Diego Campus, B
University of Redlands, B
University of San Francisco, B
Victor Valley College, A

Westmont College, B

Colorado

Colorado Mountain College, Timberline Campus, A
University of Colorado at Denver and Health
   Sciences Center - Downtown Denver Campus, B
University of Denver, B
Westwood College-Denver North, B

Connecticut

Eastern Connecticut State University, B
Goodwin College, A
University of Connecticut, B

District of Columbia

The Catholic University of America, B

Florida

American InterContinental University, B
Central Florida Community College, A
Everglades University (Sarasota), B
Florida Metropolitan University-Pinellas Campus, AB
Florida Southern College, B
Florida State University, B
Jacksonville University, B
Manatee Community College, A
Pensacola Junior College, A
South Florida Community College, A
Trinity College of Florida, B
University of Central Florida, B
University of South Florida, B
Warner Southern College, B
Webber International University, AB

Georgia

Atlanta Christian College, A
Columbus State University, B
Dalton State College, A
DeKalb Technical College, A
LaGrange College, B
Macon State College, AB
Mercer University, B
Reinhardt College, B
Thomas University, A
Truett-McConnell College, AB

Hawaii

University of Hawaii at Manoa, B

Idaho

College of Southern Idaho, A
Idaho State University, AB

Illinois

Argosy University/Schaumburg, B
Aurora University, B
Benedictine University, B
DePaul University, B
Illinois Institute of Technology, B
John Wood Community College, A
Kankakee Community College, A
Moraine Valley Community College, A
Northeastern Illinois University, B
Northern Illinois University, B
Roosevelt University, B
Saint Xavier University, B
Trinity Christian College, B
University of Illinois at Urbana-Champaign, B

Indiana

Ancilla College, A
Anderson University, A
Franklin College, B
Grace College, B
Indiana University Bloomington, B
Indiana University East, AB
Indiana University Kokomo, AB
Indiana University-Purdue University Indianapolis, B
Indiana University South Bend, AB
Indiana University Southeast, AB
Manchester College, B
Saint Joseph's College, B
University of Evansville, B
University of Notre Dame, B

University of Southern Indiana, B

Iowa

Drake University, B
Hawkeye Community College, A
Kaplan University, B
Loras College, B
St. Ambrose University, B

Kansas

Allen County Community College, A
Baker University, B
Bethel College, B
Central Christian College of Kansas, B
Hutchinson Community College and Area Vocational
   School, A
University of Kansas, B

Kentucky

Asbury College, B
Brescia University, AB
Eastern Kentucky University, B
Murray State University, B
Northern Kentucky University, A
Somerset Community College, A
Spalding University, AB
Thomas More College, AB
University of the Cumberlands, B
University of Kentucky, B

Louisiana

Nicholls State University, A
Tulane University, A
University of Louisiana at Lafayette, B

Maine

University of Maine, B

Maryland

Hagerstown Community College, A
Harford Community College, A
The Johns Hopkins University, B
Loyola College in Maryland, B
Montgomery College, A
Mount St. Mary's University, B
University of Maryland, College Park, B
Wor-Wic Community College, A

Massachusetts

Bay Path College, B
Berkshire Community College, A
Eastern Nazarene College, A
Massachusetts Bay Community College, A
Massachusetts Institute of Technology, B
Nichols College, B
Northeastern University, B
Regis College, B
Springfield Technical Community College, A
Western New England College, B

Michigan

Baker College of Flint, A
Baker College of Jackson, B
Bay de Noc Community College, A
Central Michigan University, B
Davenport University (Dearborn), B
Eastern Michigan University, B
Macomb Community College, A
Marygrove College, AB
Mott Community College, A
Northern Michigan University, A
Saginaw Chippewa Tribal College, A
Western Michigan University, B

Minnesota

Academy College, A
Capella University, B
Concordia College, B
Crown College, A
Fond du Lac Tribal and Community College, A
Mesabi Range Community and Technical College, A
Minneapolis Community and Technical College, A

Saint Mary's University of Minnesota, B

Mississippi

Delta State University, B
University of Mississippi, B

Missouri

Avila University, B
Harris-Stowe State University, B
Jefferson College, A
Maryville University of Saint Louis, B
Metropolitan Community College-Business &
   Technology College, A
Missouri College, A
Missouri State University, B
Missouri State University-West Plains, A
Patricia Stevens College, A
Southwest Baptist University, A
University of Missouri-Rolla, B
University of Missouri-St. Louis, B
Washington University in St. Louis, B
Webster University, B

Montana

Dawson Community College, A
Fort Belknap College, A
Montana State University, B
Montana State University-Billings, AB
Montana State University-Great Falls College of
   Technology, A
Montana Tech of The University of Montana, B
The University of Montana-Missoula, B
The University of Montana-Western, AB

Nebraska

Concordia University, B
University of Nebraska at Omaha, B

Nevada

Great Basin College, A
University of Nevada, Reno, B
Western Nevada Community College, A

New Hampshire

Plymouth State University, B
Saint Anselm College, B
Southern New Hampshire University, B

New Jersey

Berkeley College, A
Ocean County College, A
Union County College, A

New Mexico

New Mexico State University, AB
New Mexico State University-Alamogordo, A
Northern New Mexico Community College, A

New York

Berkeley College-New York City Campus, B
Berkeley College-Westchester Campus, B
Bryant and Stratton College (Albany), A
Bryant and Stratton College, Amherst Campus, A
Bryant and Stratton College, Buffalo Campus, A
Bryant and Stratton College, Lackawanna
   Campus, A
Bryant and Stratton College (Rochester-Greece
   Campus), A
Bryant and Stratton College (Rochester-Henrietta
   Campus), A
Bryant and Stratton College (Syracuse), A
College of Staten Island of the City University of
   New York, AB
Cornell University, B
Hofstra University, B
Ithaca College, B
Le Moyne College, B
Metropolitan College of New York, A
Niagara University, B
Pace University, B
St. Bonaventure University, B

Skidmore College, B

North Carolina

Campbell University, B
Louisburg College, A
University of Phoenix-Raleigh Campus, B
Wake Forest University, B

North Dakota

Bismarck State College, A
North Dakota State College of Science, A
University of North Dakota, B

Ohio

Bowling Green State University, B
Bryant and Stratton College (Cleveland), A
Bryant and Stratton College (Parma), A
Capital University, B
Circleville Bible College, B
Gallipolis Career College, A
God's Bible School and College, A
Miami University, B
Miami University Hamilton, B
Miami University-Middletown Campus, A
Mount Vernon Nazarene University, AB
Northwest State Community College, A
Ohio Northern University, B
Ohio University, B
Owens Community College, A
Southern State Community College, A
Union Institute & University, B
The University of Akron, B
The University of Toledo, AB
Wright State University, B
Youngstown State University, AB

Oklahoma

Hillsdale Free Will Baptist College, AB
Oklahoma Christian University, B
Oklahoma City University, B
Oklahoma State University, B
Rose State College, A
Southern Nazarene University, A
University of Central Oklahoma, B
University of Science and Arts of Oklahoma, B

Oregon

Linfield College, B
Western Oregon University, B

Pennsylvania

Bloomsburg University of Pennsylvania, B
California University of Pennsylvania, A
Carlow University, B
Delaware Valley College, A
Drexel University, B
Duquesne University, B
Gannon University, A
Harrisburg Area Community College, A
Juniata College, B
Keystone College, AB
Lackawanna College, A
Lehigh University, B
Montgomery County Community College, A
Northampton County Area Community College, A
Peirce College, A
Penn Foster Career School, A
The Pennsylvania State University Abington
  College, AB
The Pennsylvania State University Altoona
  College, AB
The Pennsylvania State University Beaver Campus
  of the Commonwealth College, A
The Pennsylvania State University Berks Campus of
  the Berks-Lehigh Valley College, AB
The Pennsylvania State University Delaware County
  Campus of the Commonwealth College, A
The Pennsylvania State University DuBois Campus
  of the Commonwealth College, A
The Pennsylvania State University at Erie, The
  Behrend College, A
The Pennsylvania State University Fayette Campus
  of the Commonwealth College, A
The Pennsylvania State University Harrisburg
  Campus, A

The Pennsylvania State University Hazleton
  Campus of the Commonwealth College, A
The Pennsylvania State University, Lehigh Valley
  Campus of the Berks-Lehigh Valley College, AB
The Pennsylvania State University McKeesport
  Campus of the Commonwealth College, A
The Pennsylvania State University Mont Alto
  Campus of the Commonwealth College, A
The Pennsylvania State University New Kensington
  Campus of the Commonwealth College, A
The Pennsylvania State University Schuylkill
  Campus of the Capital College, AB
The Pennsylvania State University Shenango
  Campus of the Commonwealth College, A
The Pennsylvania State University University Park
  Campus, A
The Pennsylvania State University Wilkes-Barre
  Campus of the Commonwealth College, A
The Pennsylvania State University Worthington
  Scranton Campus of the Commonwealth
  College, A
The Pennsylvania State University York Campus of
  the Commonwealth College, A
Shippensburg University of Pennsylvania, B
Temple University, B
University of Pittsburgh, B
University of Pittsburgh at Titusville, A
Washington & Jefferson College, B
Yorktowne Business Institute, A

Puerto Rico

Bayamon Central University, AB
Columbia College (Caguas), B
University of Puerto Rico at Humacao, B
University of Puerto Rico, Río Piedras, B

Rhode Island

Community College of Rhode Island, A

South Carolina

Limestone College, AB
Midlands Technical College, A
Orangeburg-Calhoun Technical College, A
Piedmont Technical College, A
Southern Wesleyan University, AB
Williamsburg Technical College, A
York Technical College, A

Tennessee

Austin Peay State University, B
Columbia State Community College, A
Cumberland University, AB
Southwest Tennessee Community College, A
The University of Tennessee, B

Texas

Baylor University, B
Brazosport College, A
Concordia University at Austin, B
Del Mar College, A
East Texas Baptist University, B
Houston Baptist University, B
Howard Payne University, B
Kilgore College, A
Lamar State College-Port Arthur, A
McMurry University, B
Midland College, A
Midwestern State University, B
Panola College, A
Sam Houston State University, B
Schreiner University, B
Southern Methodist University, B
Southwestern Assemblies of God University, A
Stephen F. Austin State University, B
Tarleton State University, B
Texas A&M University-Texarkana, B
Texas College, B
Texas Tech University, B
University of Houston-Clear Lake, B
University of Houston-Downtown, B
University of the Incarnate Word, B
University of Mary Hardin-Baylor, B
University of North Texas, B
The University of Texas at Austin, B
The University of Texas at Dallas, B

The University of Texas at San Antonio, B
West Texas A&M University, B

Utah

Brigham Young University, B
California College for Health Sciences, AB
University of Utah, B
Utah State University, B
Utah Valley State College, AB
Western Governors University, AB
Westminster College, B

Vermont

Castleton State College, A
Champlain College, AB
Johnson State College, B

Virginia

Bryant and Stratton College, Richmond, A
Hollins University, B
John Tyler Community College, A
Liberty University, B
National College of Business & Technology
  (Charlottesville), A
National College of Business & Technology (Salem)
  , AB
Norfolk State University, B
University of Management and Technology, AB
University of Virginia, B

Washington

Argosy University/Seattle, B
Centralia College, A
Lower Columbia College, A
University of Puget Sound, B
University of Washington, B
Washington State University, B

West Virginia

Bluefield State College, A
Fairmont State Community & Technical College, A
Glenville State College, AB
Marshall Community and Technical College, A
Mountain State University, AB
New River Community and Technical College, A

Wisconsin

Bryant and Stratton College, A
Bryant and Stratton College, Wauwatosa Campus, A
Milwaukee School of Engineering, B
University of Wisconsin-Whitewater, B

Wyoming

Laramie County Community College, A
Sheridan College-Sheridan and Gillette, A

British Columbia

Malaspina University-College, B
Thompson Rivers University, B
The University of British Columbia, B
University of Northern British Columbia, B
University of Victoria, B

New Brunswick

Mount Allison University, B

Nova Scotia

Cape Breton University, B
Dalhousie University, B

Ontario

Brock University, B
Queen's University at Kingston, B
Tyndale University College & Seminary, B
University of Windsor, B

York University, B

Quebec

HEC Montreal, B

Saskatchewan

University of Saskatchewan, B

BUSINESS/CORPORATE COMMUNICATIONS

Alabama

Southern Christian University, B

Arkansas

Harding University, B

California

Holy Names University, B
Point Loma Nazarene University, B

Colorado

Jones International University, B

Georgia

Brenau University, B

Hawaii

Hawaii Pacific University, B

Iowa

Morningside College, B
Simpson College, B

Kansas

Central Christian College of Kansas, A
Southwestern College, B

Massachusetts

Babson College, B
Bentley College, B
Framingham State College, B
Middlesex Community College, A

Michigan

Aquinas College, B
Calvin College, B
Rochester College, B

Minnesota

University of St. Thomas, B

Missouri

Rockhurst University, B

Montana

The University of Montana-Western, B

New York

Mercy College, B
State University of New York College of Agriculture
and Technology at Cobleskill, B

North Carolina

Elon University, B
University of Phoenix-Raleigh Campus, B

North Dakota

University of Mary, B

Ohio

Marietta College, B
Ohio Dominican University, B
The University of Findlay, B
University of Rio Grande, B

Pennsylvania

Chestnut Hill College, AB
Duquesne University, B
Montgomery County Community College, A

The Pennsylvania State University Abington
College, B
Point Park University, B

South Dakota

Augustana College, B

Tennessee

Bryan College, B

Texas

Houston Community College System, A
University of Houston, B

Washington

North Seattle Community College, A

Ontario

Brock University, B

BUSINESS EDUCATION

Alabama

Auburn University, MD
University of South Alabama, M

Arkansas

Arkansas State University, MO

Connecticut

Central Connecticut State University, M

Delaware

University of Delaware, M

Florida

Florida Agricultural and Mechanical University, M

Georgia

Albany State University, M
Georgia Southern University, M
University of West Georgia, MO
Valdosta State University, MDO

Idaho

University of Idaho, MD

Indiana

Ball State University, M

Iowa

Drake University, M

Kansas

Emporia State University, M

Kentucky

Eastern Kentucky University, M
Western Kentucky University, M

Louisiana

Louisiana State University and Agricultural and
Mechanical College, M
Northwestern State University of Louisiana, M

Maryland

Salisbury University, M

Michigan

Central Michigan University, M
Wayne State University, M

Minnesota

University of Minnesota, Twin Cities Campus, MD

Mississippi

Jackson State University, M
Mississippi College, M

Missouri

Maryville University of Saint Louis, O
Southeast Missouri State University, M

University of Missouri-Columbia, MDO

Nebraska

Chadron State College, M

New Hampshire

Southern New Hampshire University, M

New Jersey

Rider University, O

New York

Buffalo State College, State University of New
York, M
Canisius College, M
The College of Saint Rose, MO
Hofstra University, M
Iona College, M
Lehman College of the City University of New
York, M
Nazareth College of Rochester, M
New York University, MO

Ohio

Ashland University, M
Bowling Green State University, M
The University of Toledo, MDO
Wright State University, M

Pennsylvania

Bloomsburg University of Pennsylvania, M
Robert Morris University, M

Puerto Rico

Inter American University of Puerto Rico,
Metropolitan Campus, M
Inter American University of Puerto Rico, San
Germán Campus, M

South Carolina

University of South Carolina, M

Tennessee

Middle Tennessee State University, M

Texas

Texas Southern University, M

Utah

Utah State University, MD

Virginia

Old Dominion University, M

Washington

Central Washington University, M

Wisconsin

University of Wisconsin-Whitewater, M

BUSINESS FAMILY AND CONSUMER SCIENCES/HUMAN SCIENCES

New York

Cornell University, B

Ohio

The Ohio State University, B

Texas

University of Houston, B

Utah

Brigham Young University, B

Virginia

Virginia Polytechnic Institute and State University, B

BUSINESS MACHINE REPAIRER

Alabama

Herzing College, A

Alaska

University of Alaska Anchorage, A

California

Cabrillo College, A
Cañada College, A
Chabot College, A
De Anza College, A
Hartnell College, A
Irvine Valley College, A
Lassen Community College District, A
Los Angeles Valley College, A
Moorpark College, A
Palomar College, A
Solano Community College, A

Idaho

Boise State University, A
Idaho State University, A

Iowa

Iowa Lakes Community College, A

Kansas

Coffeyville Community College, A
Neosho County Community College, A

Kentucky

St. Catharine College, A

Maine

Southern Maine Community College, A

Michigan

Henry Ford Community College, A
Muskegon Community College, A
Washtenaw Community College, A

Minnesota

Minnesota State College-Southeast Technical, A

Mississippi

Coahoma Community College, A
Mississippi Delta Community College, A

Missouri

Ozarks Technical Community College, A

New York

Bramson ORT College, A
Dutchess Community College, A

North Carolina

Central Piedmont Community College, A
Rockingham Community College, A

Pennsylvania

Community College of Allegheny County, A

Tennessee

Pellissippi State Technical Community College, A

Texas

Del Mar College, A
Frank Phillips College, A
Lamar University, A

San Antonio College, A

Utah

Stevens-Henager College, A

Virginia

ECPI College of Technology (Virginia Beach), A
ECPI Technical College (Richmond), A

Washington

Clover Park Technical College, A

BUSINESS, MANAGEMENT, MARKETING, AND RELATED SUPPORT SERVICES

Alabama

Athens State University, B
Herzing College, B

Arizona

Eastern Arizona College, A

California

The Art Institute of California-San Francisco, AB
California State University, Sacramento, B
California State University, Stanislaus, B
University of Southern California, B

Colorado

University of Denver, B

Florida

Argosy University/Sarasota, B
Full Sail Real World Education, B
Southeastern University, B

Georgia

Heart of Georgia Technical College, A
University of Georgia, B

Illinois

Benedictine University, B

Indiana

Taylor University Fort Wayne, AB
University of Southern Indiana, A

Iowa

Hamilton College (Cedar Falls), AB
Iowa State University of Science and Technology, B

Maryland

University of Maryland, College Park, B
University of Phoenix-Maryland Campus, B

Massachusetts

Bridgewater State College, B

Michigan

Central Michigan University, B
Northwestern Michigan College, A
Southwestern Michigan College, A

Missouri

Park University, B
University of Phoenix-Kansas City Campus, B

Nebraska

Nebraska Wesleyan University, B

Nevada

University of Phoenix-Nevada Campus, B

New York

Adelphi University, B
Dowling College, B
New York University, B
Queensborough Community College of the City
University of New York, A
Skidmore College, B

Utica College, B

North Carolina

Catawba Valley Community College, A
Sandhills Community College, A

Ohio

Bowling Green State University, B
Cincinnati State Technical and Community
College, A
College of Mount St. Joseph, B
Northwest State Community College, A
Ohio University, B
Stautzenberger College, A
The University of Akron, A
The University of Toledo, B

Oregon

Corban College, B

Pennsylvania

Cabrini College, B
Drexel University, B
Duquesne University, B
Harrisburg Area Community College, A
Mercyhurst College, B
Messiah College, B
Saint Vincent College, B
York College of Pennsylvania, B

Puerto Rico

Inter American University of Puerto Rico, Bayamón
Campus, B

South Carolina

Claflin University, B
Clemson University, B

Tennessee

University of Phoenix-Nashville Campus, B

Texas

Baylor University, B
Texas Wesleyan University, B

Utah

University of Utah, B

Virginia

George Mason University, B
Sweet Briar College, B
University of Phoenix-Northern Virginia Campus, B

West Virginia

Community and Technical College of Shepherd, A

Wisconsin

Milwaukee Area Technical College, A
Northeast Wisconsin Technical College, A
University of Wisconsin-Stout, B

BUSINESS/MANAGERIAL ECONOMICS

Alabama

Alabama Agricultural and Mechanical University, B
Auburn University, B
Auburn University Montgomery, B
Huntingdon College, B
The University of Alabama, B
The University of Alabama at Birmingham, B
University of North Alabama, B

Alaska

University of Alaska Anchorage, B

Arizona

Grand Canyon University, B
Northern Arizona University, B

The University of Arizona, B

Arkansas

Arkansas State University, B
Hendrix College, B
University of Arkansas, B
University of Arkansas at Pine Bluff, B

California

California Institute of Technology, B
California State University, East Bay, B
California State University, Fullerton, B
California State University, Long Beach, B
California State University, San Bernardino, B
Chabot College, A
Chapman University, B
College of the Desert, A
Los Medanos College, A
Mills College, B
Notre Dame de Namur University, B
Occidental College, B
San Joaquin Delta College, A
Sonoma State University, B
University of California, Los Angeles, B
University of California, Riverside, B
University of California, Santa Barbara, B
University of California, Santa Cruz, B
University of Judaism, B
University of San Diego, B
Westmont College, B

Colorado

Fort Lewis College, B
Mesa State College, B
Morgan Community College, A
University of Denver, B

Connecticut

Albertus Magnus College, B
Quinnipiac University, B
Sacred Heart University, B
Southern Connecticut State University, B
University of Hartford, B
University of New Haven, B

Delaware

Delaware State University, B
University of Delaware, B

District of Columbia

The George Washington University, B

Florida

Manatee Community College, A
Stetson University, B
University of Central Florida, B
University of Miami, B
University of North Florida, B
University of South Florida, B
University of West Florida, B

Georgia

Columbus State University, B
Emory University, B
Georgia College & State University, B
Georgia Institute of Technology, B
Georgia Southern University, B
Georgia State University, B
North Georgia College & State University, B
Oglethorpe University, B
Shorter College, B
South Georgia College, A
University of West Georgia, B

Valdosta State University, B

Hawaii

Hawaii Pacific University, AB
University of Hawaii at Manoa, B

Idaho

Boise State University, B

Illinois

Aurora University, B
Benedictine University, B
Bradley University, B
DePaul University, B
Illinois College, B
Joliet Junior College, A
Lake Forest College, B
Lewis University, B
Lincoln College, A
Loyola University Chicago, B
Olivet Nazarene University, B
Roosevelt University, B
Southern Illinois University Carbondale, B
Southern Illinois University Edwardsville, B
Western Illinois University, B
Wheaton College, B

Indiana

Anderson University, B
Ball State University, B
Butler University, B
Huntington University, B
Indiana University Bloomington, B
Indiana University-Purdue University Fort Wayne, B
Indiana University Southeast, B
University of Evansville, B
University of Indianapolis, B

Iowa

Buena Vista University, B
The University of Iowa, B

Kansas

Bethany College, B
Central Christian College of Kansas, A
Colby Community College, A
Fort Hays State University, B

Kentucky

Bellarmine University, B
Campbellsville University, B
Eastern Kentucky University, B
Morehead State University, B
St. Catharine College, A
University of Kentucky, B
University of Louisville, B
Western Kentucky University, B

Louisiana

Centenary College of Louisiana, B
Grambling State University, B
Louisiana State University and Agricultural and
    Mechanical College, B
Louisiana State University in Shreveport, B
Louisiana Tech University, B
Loyola University New Orleans, B
Southern University and Agricultural and Mechanical
    College, B
University of Louisiana at Lafayette, B
University of Louisiana at Monroe, B
University of New Orleans, B

Maine

University of Maine at Farmington, B

Maryland

Anne Arundel Community College, A
Morgan State University, B

Massachusetts

American International College, B
Bentley College, B
Emmanuel College, B
Framingham State College, B

Merrimack College, B
Salem State College, B

Michigan

Andrews University, B
Eastern Michigan University, B
Ferris State University, B
Hope College, B
Kalamazoo College, B
Lake Superior State University, B
Michigan Technological University, B
Northwood University, AB
Saginaw Valley State University, B
Western Michigan University, B

Minnesota

Augsburg College, B
Gustavus Adolphus College, B
Vermilion Community College, A
Winona State University, B

Mississippi

Jackson State University, B
Mississippi State University, B
Northeast Mississippi Community College, A
University of Mississippi, B
University of Southern Mississippi, B

Missouri

College of the Ozarks, B
Northwest Missouri State University, B
Park University, B
Southeast Missouri State University, B
University of Missouri-Columbia, B
Washington University in St. Louis, B
William Woods University, B

Montana

Carroll College, B
Montana State University-Billings, B

Nebraska

University of Nebraska-Lincoln, B
University of Nebraska at Omaha, B
Wayne State College, B

Nevada

University of Nevada, Reno, B

New Hampshire

Southern New Hampshire University, B

New Jersey

The College of New Jersey, B
Fairleigh Dickinson University, College at
    Florham, B
Fairleigh Dickinson University, Metropolitan
    Campus, B
Rider University, B
Saint Peter's College, AB
Seton Hall University, B
William Paterson University of New Jersey, B

New York

Bernard M. Baruch College of the City University of
    New York, B
College of Mount Saint Vincent, B
Elmira College, B
Fordham University, B
Hofstra University, B
Ithaca College, B
Mercy College, B
New York University, B
Niagara University, B
St. Bonaventure University, B
St. John's University, B
State University of New York College at Oneonta, B
State University of New York College at Potsdam, B
State University of New York College of Technology
    at Canton, A
State University of New York at New Paltz, B
State University of New York at Plattsburgh, B

Utica College, B

North Carolina

Catawba College, B
Fayetteville State University, B
Greensboro College, B
Mars Hill College, B
Meredith College, B
Pfeiffer University, B
The University of North Carolina at Charlotte, B
The University of North Carolina Wilmington, B

North Dakota

Jamestown College, B
University of North Dakota, B

Ohio

Bowling Green State University, B
Capital University, B
Cleveland State University, B
The College of Wooster, B
Kent State University, B
Miami University, B
Miami University Hamilton, B
Miami University-Middletown Campus, A
The Ohio State University, B
Ohio Wesleyan University, B
Otterbein College, B
University of Dayton, B
The University of Toledo, B
Urbana University, AB
Wilberforce University, B
Wilmington College, B
Wittenberg University, B
Wright State University, B
Xavier University, B
Youngstown State University, B

Oklahoma

East Central University, B
Oklahoma City University, B
Oklahoma State University, B
University of Central Oklahoma, B
University of Oklahoma, B

Oregon

Eastern Oregon University, B

Pennsylvania

Allegheny College, B
Bloomsburg University of Pennsylvania, B
Carnegie Mellon University, B
Cedar Crest College, B
Clarion University of Pennsylvania, B
Drexel University, B
Duquesne University, B
Grove City College, B
Kutztown University of Pennsylvania, B
La Salle University, B
Lafayette College, B
Lehigh University, B
Lock Haven University of Pennsylvania, B
Messiah College, B
The Pennsylvania State University Abington
　College, B
The Pennsylvania State University Altoona
　College, B
The Pennsylvania State University Beaver Campus
　of the Commonwealth College, B
The Pennsylvania State University Berks Campus of
　the Berks-Lehigh Valley College, B
The Pennsylvania State University Delaware County
　Campus of the Commonwealth College, B
The Pennsylvania State University DuBois Campus
　of the Commonwealth College, B
The Pennsylvania State University at Erie, The
　Behrend College, B
The Pennsylvania State University Fayette Campus
　of the Commonwealth College, B
The Pennsylvania State University Hazleton
　Campus of the Commonwealth College, B
The Pennsylvania State University Lehigh Valley
　Campus of the Berks-Lehigh Valley College, B
The Pennsylvania State University McKeesport
　Campus of the Commonwealth College, B

The Pennsylvania State University Mont Alto
　Campus of the Commonwealth College, B
The Pennsylvania State University New Kensington
　Campus of the Commonwealth College, B
The Pennsylvania State University Schuylkill
　Campus of the Capital College, B
The Pennsylvania State University Shenango
　Campus of the Commonwealth College, B
The Pennsylvania State University University Park
　Campus, B
The Pennsylvania State University Wilkes-Barre
　Campus of the Commonwealth College, B
The Pennsylvania State University Worthington
　Scranton Campus of the Commonwealth
　College, B
The Pennsylvania State University York Campus of
　the Commonwealth College, B
Robert Morris University, B
Seton Hill University, B
Susquehanna University, B
University of Pittsburgh at Johnstown, B
Villanova University, B
West Chester University of Pennsylvania, B
Widener University, B
York College of Pennsylvania, B

Puerto Rico

Inter American University of Puerto Rico, Bayamón
　Campus, B
Inter American University of Puerto Rico,
　Metropolitan Campus, B
Inter American University of Puerto Rico, San
　Germán Campus, B
University of Puerto Rico, Río Piedras, B

Rhode Island

Providence College, B

South Carolina

Charleston Southern University, B
Limestone College, B
North Greenville College, B
South Carolina State University, B
University of South Carolina, B
Wofford College, B

South Dakota

Northern State University, B
The University of South Dakota, B

Tennessee

Belmont University, B
Carson-Newman College, B
East Tennessee State University, B
Freed-Hardeman University, B
Lincoln Memorial University, B
Lipscomb University, B
Middle Tennessee State University, B
Tennessee State University, B
Union University, B
University of Memphis, B
The University of Tennessee, B
The University of Tennessee at Martin, B

Texas

Baylor University, B
Dallas Baptist University, B
Frank Phillips College, A
Hill College of the Hill Junior College District, A
Houston Baptist University, B
McMurry University, B
Midwestern State University, B
Sam Houston State University, B
Stephen F. Austin State University, B
Texas A&M International University, B
Texas A&M University-Kingsville, B
Texas State University-San Marcos, B
Texas Wesleyan University, B
University of North Texas, B
The University of Texas at Arlington, B
The University of Texas at San Antonio, B

West Texas A&M University, B

Utah

Weber State University, B
Westminster College, B

Vermont

Green Mountain College, B

Virginia

Christopher Newport University, B
Hampden-Sydney College, B
James Madison University, B
Longwood University, B
Old Dominion University, B
Randolph-Macon College, B
University of Richmond, B
Virginia Commonwealth University, B
Virginia Polytechnic Institute and State University, B
Virginia State University, B

Washington

Eastern Washington University, B
Gonzaga University, B
Seattle University, B
Tacoma Community College, A
Washington State University, B

West Virginia

Bethany College, B
Marshall University, B
Potomac State College of West Virginia
　University, A
West Liberty State College, B
West Virginia University, B
West Virginia Wesleyan College, B

Wisconsin

Beloit College, B
Cardinal Stritch University, B
Marian College of Fond du Lac, B
Marquette University, B
Northland College, B
University of Wisconsin-Platteville, B
University of Wisconsin-Superior, B
University of Wisconsin-Whitewater, B
Wisconsin Lutheran College, B

Wyoming

University of Wyoming, B

Manitoba

University of Manitoba, B

New Brunswick

Mount Allison University, B
University of New Brunswick Fredericton, B

Nova Scotia

Cape Breton University, B
Saint Mary's University, B

Ontario

Brock University, B
University of Ottawa, B
University of Windsor, B
York University, B

Quebec

Bishop's University, B
Concordia University, B
HEC Montreal, B
McGill University, B

Université du Québec àTrois-Rivières, B

Saskatchewan

University of Saskatchewan, B

BUSINESS/OFFICE AUTOMATION/TECHNOLOGY/ DATA ENTRY

Arizona

Northland Pioneer College, A

Arkansas

Arkansas State University-Mountain Home, A

California

Santiago Canyon College, A

Colorado

Front Range Community College, A

Connecticut

Asnuntuck Community College, A

Illinois

College of Lake County, A
Illinois Eastern Community Colleges, Frontier
  Community College, A
Illinois Eastern Community Colleges, Lincoln Trail
  College, A
Illinois Eastern Community Colleges, Olney Central
  College, A
Illinois Eastern Community Colleges, Wabash Valley
  College, A
Joliet Junior College, A
Kaskaskia College, A
Lincoln Land Community College, A
Parkland College, A
Waubonsee Community College, A

Indiana

Ivy Tech Community College-East Central, A
Ivy Tech Community College-Kokomo, A
Ivy Tech Community College-North Central, A
Ivy Tech Community College-Northeast, A
Ivy Tech Community College-Southern Indiana, A

Iowa

Iowa Lakes Community College, A

Kansas

Central Christian College of Kansas, A

Massachusetts

Berkshire Community College, A
Bristol Community College, A

Michigan

Alpena Community College, A
Baker College of Clinton Township, A
Davenport University (Midland), A
Gogebic Community College, A
Macomb Community College, A
Northwestern Michigan College, A
Oakland Community College, A

Minnesota

Normandale Community College, A

Missouri

Crowder College, A
Metro Business College (Cape Girardeau), A

Montana

Montana State University-Billings, A
Montana Tech of The University of Montana, A
The University of Montana-Helena College of
  Technology, A

The University of Montana-Western, A

Nevada

Western Nevada Community College, A

New Mexico

Clovis Community College, A

New York

Adirondack Community College, A

North Carolina

East Carolina University, B

North Dakota

Bismarck State College, A
United Tribes Technical College, A

Ohio

The University of Akron, A
The University of Akron-Wayne College, A
University of Rio Grande, A
The University of Toledo, A

Oklahoma

East Central University, B
Oklahoma State University, Oklahoma City, A

Oregon

Clatsop Community College, A
Tillamook Bay Community College, A

Pennsylvania

Business Institute of Pennsylvania (Sharon), A
Community College of Allegheny County, A
DuBois Business College, A
Laurel Business Institute, A
Pennsylvania College of Technology, A

Puerto Rico

Inter American University of Puerto Rico, Bayamón
  Campus, B

Tennessee

Austin Peay State University, A
Electronic Computer Programming College, A

Texas

Collin County Community College District, A
El Centro College, A
Midland College, A
MTI College of Business and Technology (Houston)
  , A

Utah

Utah Valley State College, A

Washington

Clark College, A

Wyoming

Central Wyoming College, A

BUSINESS OPERATIONS SUPPORT AND SECRETARIAL SERVICES

Arizona

Eastern Arizona College, A

Florida

Hillsborough Community College, A

Indiana

Ancilla College, A

Mississippi

Virginia College at Jackson, A

Missouri

East Central College, A

North Carolina

Guilford Technical Community College, A

Ohio

Bowling Green State University-Firelands College, A
The University of Akron, A

Pennsylvania

Business Institute of Pennsylvania (Meadville), A

Texas

MTI College of Business and Technology (Houston)
  , A

Wisconsin

Wisconsin Indianhead Technical College, A

Wyoming

Laramie County Community College, A

BUSINESS STATISTICS

Alabama

Alabama Agricultural and Mechanical University, B

Michigan

Western Michigan University, B

Missouri

Central Missouri State University, B

Ohio

Cleveland State University, B

Oregon

Southern Oregon University, B

Puerto Rico

University of Puerto Rico, Río Piedras, B

Texas

Baylor University, B
University of Houston, B

Utah

Brigham Young University, B

Ontario

York University, B

Quebec

HEC Montreal, B

BUSINESS TEACHER EDUCATION

Alabama

Alabama Southern Community College, A
Alabama State University, B
Auburn University, B
Faulkner University, A
George Corley Wallace State Community College, A
Lawson State Community College, A
Oakwood College, B
Troy University, B
Wallace State Community College, A

Arizona

Eastern Arizona College, A
Grand Canyon University, B

Arkansas

Arkansas State University, B
Arkansas Tech University, B
Henderson State University, B
John Brown University, B
Phillips Community College of the University of
  Arkansas, A
Southern Arkansas University-Magnolia, B

University of Arkansas at Monticello, B
University of Arkansas at Pine Bluff, B
University of Central Arkansas, B
University of the Ozarks, B

California

Butte College, A
Chabot College, A
Chaffey College, A
College of Alameda, A
Merritt College, A
Mount St. Mary's College, B
Mt. San Antonio College, A
Pacific Union College, B
Palomar College, A
Pasadena City College, A
Porterville College, A
Rio Hondo College, A

Colorado

Colorado State University, B
Johnson & Wales University, B
Lamar Community College, A
Morgan Community College, A
Northeastern Junior College, A

Delaware

Delaware State University, B

District of Columbia

University of the District of Columbia, AB

Florida

Bethune-Cookman College, B
Florida Agricultural and Mechanical University, B
St. Petersburg College, B
University of Central Florida, B
University of South Florida, B

Georgia

Albany State University, B
Armstrong Atlantic State University, B
Bainbridge College, A
Clark Atlanta University, B
Clayton State University, A
Darton College, A
East Georgia College, A
Emmanuel College, B
Georgia Southern University, B
Macon State College, A
South Georgia College, A
University of West Georgia, B
Valdosta State University, B
Waycross College, A

Hawaii

Brigham Young University-Hawaii, B

Idaho

Boise State University, B
Brigham Young University -Idaho, A
North Idaho College, A
University of Idaho, B

Illinois

Chicago State University, B
Illinois State University, B
John A. Logan College, A
Lincoln College, A
Lincoln College-Normal, A
McKendree College, B
Spoon River College, A
Trinity Christian College, B
University of Illinois at Urbana-Champaign, B

Indiana

Ball State University, B
Bethel College, B
Calumet College of Saint Joseph, B
Goshen College, B
Huntington University, B
Indiana State University, B
Oakland City University, B
Saint Mary's College, B

University of Indianapolis, B
University of Saint Francis, B
University of Southern Indiana, B
Vincennes University, A
Vincennes University Jasper Campus, A

Iowa

Ashford University, B
Buena Vista University, B
Dordt College, B
Iowa Central Community College, A
Iowa Lakes Community College, A
Kirkwood Community College, A
Morningside College, B
Northwestern College, B
St. Ambrose University, B
University of Northern Iowa, B
Upper Iowa University, B
William Penn University, B

Kansas

Allen County Community College, A
Bethany College, B
Central Christian College of Kansas, A
Coffeyville Community College, A
Colby Community College, A
Fort Hays State University, B
Friends University, B
Highland Community College, A
Independence Community College, A
McPherson College, B
MidAmerica Nazarene University, B
Pratt Community College, A
Tabor College, B
Washburn University, B

Kentucky

Campbellsville University, B
Eastern Kentucky University, B
Morehead State University, B
Murray State University, B
Northern Kentucky University, B
St. Catharine College, A
Thomas More College, B
Union College, B
University of the Cumberlands, B
Western Kentucky University, B

Louisiana

Centenary College of Louisiana, B
Grambling State University, B
Louisiana College, B
Louisiana Tech University, B
McNeese State University, B
Nicholls State University, B
Northwestern State University of Louisiana, B
Our Lady of Holy Cross College, B

Maine

University of Maine at Fort Kent, B
University of Maine at Machias, B

Maryland

Morgan State University, B
Prince George's Community College, A
University of Maryland Eastern Shore, B

Massachusetts

American International College, B
Atlantic Union College, B
Holyoke Community College, A
Northern Essex Community College, A
Salem State College, B
Suffolk University, B
Westfield State College, B

Michigan

Adrian College, B
Central Michigan University, B
Eastern Michigan University, B
Ferris State University, B
Michigan Technological University, B
Northern Michigan University, B
Siena Heights University, B

Western Michigan University, B

Minnesota

Concordia College, B
Pillsbury Baptist Bible College, B
Pine Technical College, A
University of Minnesota, Twin Cities Campus, B
Winona State University, B

Mississippi

Delta State University, B
East Mississippi Community College, A
Holmes Community College, A
Jackson State University, B
Mississippi College, B
Mississippi Gulf Coast Community College, A
Mississippi State University, B
Northeast Mississippi Community College, A
Rust College, B
Southwest Mississippi Community College, A
University of Southern Mississippi, B

Missouri

Central Missouri State University, B
College of the Ozarks, B
Evangel University, B
Hannibal-LaGrange College, B
Jefferson College, A
Lincoln University, B
Lindenwood University, B
Missouri Baptist University, B
Missouri State University, B
Northwest Missouri State University, B
Southeast Missouri State University, B
University of Missouri-Columbia, B
University of Missouri-St. Louis, B

Montana

Montana State University-Northern, B
The University of Montana-Missoula, B
The University of Montana-Western, B

Nebraska

Chadron State College, B
Concordia University, B
Dana College, B
Doane College, B
Grace University, B
Hastings College, B
Midland Lutheran College, B
Northeast Community College, A
Union College, B
University of Nebraska at Kearney, B
University of Nebraska-Lincoln, B
Wayne State College, B
York College, B

Nevada

University of Nevada, Reno, B

New Hampshire

Southern New Hampshire University, B

New Jersey

Essex County College, A
Rider University, B

New Mexico

College of Santa Fe, B
College of the Southwest, B
Eastern New Mexico University, B
New Mexico Junior College, A
Western New Mexico University, B

New York

Alfred University, B
Bramson ORT College, A
Bronx Community College of the City University of
New York, A
Buffalo State College, State University of New
York, B
Concordia College, B
Dowling College, B
D'Youville College, B

Hofstra University, B
Lehman College of the City University of New York, B
Nazareth College of Rochester, B
New York Institute of Technology, B
Niagara University, B
Pace University, B
St. Francis College, B
Utica College, B

North Carolina

Appalachian State University, B
East Carolina University, B
Elizabeth City State University, B
Fayetteville State University, B
Halifax Community College, A
Isothermal Community College, A
Lenoir-Rhyne College, B
Louisburg College, A
North Carolina Agricultural and Technical State University, B
Saint Augustine's College, B
The University of North Carolina at Greensboro, B

North Dakota

Cankdeska Cikana Community College, A
Dickinson State University, B
Mayville State University, B
Minot State University, B
University of North Dakota, B
Valley City State University, B

Ohio

Bowling Green State University, B
Defiance College, B
Kent State University, B
Mount Vernon Nazarene University, B
Muskingum College, B
Ohio University-Lancaster, B
Ohio Wesleyan University, B
The University of Akron, B
The University of Findlay, B
University of Rio Grande, B
The University of Toledo, B
Wilmington College, B
Wright State University, B
Youngstown State University, B

Oklahoma

Carl Albert State College, A
East Central University, B
Eastern Oklahoma State College, A
Murray State College, A
Northeastern State University, B
Northwestern Oklahoma State University, B
Oklahoma Panhandle State University, B
Oklahoma Wesleyan University, B
Tulsa Community College, A
University of Central Oklahoma, B

Oregon

Corban College, B
Mt. Hood Community College, A

Pennsylvania

Community College of Philadelphia, A
Gannon University, B
Geneva College, B
Gwynedd-Mercy College, B
Harrisburg Area Community College, A
Indiana University of Pennsylvania, B
La Salle University, B
Mercyhurst College, B
Reading Area Community College, A
Robert Morris University, B
Saint Vincent College, B
Temple University, B

Puerto Rico

Inter American University of Puerto Rico, Fajardo Campus, AB

Pontifical Catholic University of Puerto Rico, B

South Carolina

South Carolina State University, B
Winthrop University, B

South Dakota

Black Hills State University, B
Dakota State University, B
Dakota Wesleyan University, B
Northern State University, B
Sinte Gleska University, A

Tennessee

Belmont University, B
Carson-Newman College, B
Lambuth University, B
Lee University, B
Martin Methodist College, A
Middle Tennessee State University, B
Roane State Community College, A
Tennessee State University, B
Union University, B
The University of Tennessee, B
The University of Tennessee at Martin, B

Texas

Amarillo College, A
Baylor University, B
Cisco Junior College, A
Frank Phillips College, A
Hardin-Simmons University, B
Howard Payne University, B
Jarvis Christian College, B
Paris Junior College, A
St. Mary's University of San Antonio, B
Sam Houston State University, B
Texas A&M University-Commerce, B
Texas Southern University, B
Texas Wesleyan University, B
Trinity Valley Community College, A
Wiley College, B

Utah

Snow College, A
Southern Utah University, B
Utah State University, B
Utah Valley State College, B
Weber State University, B

Virginia

Bluefield College, B
Hampton University, B
James Madison University, B
Liberty University, B
Mountain Empire Community College, A
Norfolk State University, B
Virginia State University, B
Virginia Union University, B

Washington

Central Washington University, B
Eastern Washington University, B
Walla Walla College, B

West Virginia

Concord University, B
Davis & Elkins College, B
Fairmont State University, B
Glenville State College, B
West Virginia State University, B

Wisconsin

Concordia University Wisconsin, B
Lakeland College, B
Madison Area Technical College, A
Maranatha Baptist Bible College, B
Mount Mary College, B
University of Wisconsin-Superior, B
University of Wisconsin-Whitewater, B

Viterbo University, B

Wyoming

Eastern Wyoming College, A
Northwest College, A

Alberta

University of Alberta, B
University of Lethbridge, B

British Columbia

The University of British Columbia, B

New Brunswick

University of New Brunswick Fredericton, B

Ontario

The University of Western Ontario, B

Quebec

McGill University, B
Université du Québec en Abitibi-Témiscamingue, B
Université du Québec àChicoutimi, B
Université du Québec àRimouski, B

Saskatchewan

University of Regina, B

CABINETMAKING AND MILLWORK/MILLWRIGHT

Georgia

Central Georgia Technical College, A

Idaho

College of Southern Idaho, A

Illinois

Illinois Eastern Community Colleges, Olney Central College, A

Indiana

Ivy Tech Community College-Bloomington, A
Ivy Tech Community College-Central Indiana, A
Ivy Tech Community College-Columbus, A
Ivy Tech Community College-East Central, A
Ivy Tech Community College-Kokomo, A
Ivy Tech Community College-Lafayette, A
Ivy Tech Community College-North Central, A
Ivy Tech Community College-Northeast, A
Ivy Tech Community College-Northwest, A
Ivy Tech Community College-Southern Indiana, A
Ivy Tech Community College-Southwest, A
Ivy Tech Community College-Wabash Valley, A
Ivy Tech Community College-Whitewater, A

Michigan

Macomb Community College, A
Oakland Community College, A

Pennsylvania

Johnson College, A
Pennsylvania College of Technology, A

Utah

Utah Valley State College, A

British Columbia

British Columbia Institute of Technology, A

CAD/CADD DRAFTING AND/OR DESIGN TECHNOLOGY/TECHNICIAN

Arizona

ITT Technical Institute (Tempe), A
ITT Technical Institute (Tucson), A

Arkansas

ITT Technical Institute, A

California

ITT Technical Institute (Anaheim), A
ITT Technical Institute (Lathrop), A

ITT Technical Institute (Oxnard), A
ITT Technical Institute (Rancho Cordova), A
ITT Technical Institute (San Bernardino), A
ITT Technical Institute (San Diego), A
ITT Technical Institute (Sylmar), A
ITT Technical Institute (Torrance), A
ITT Technical Institute (West Covina), A
Western Career College (Walnut Creek), A

Colorado

ITT Technical Institute, A

Florida

Florida Technical College (DeLand), A
ITT Technical Institute (Fort Lauderdale), A
ITT Technical Institute (Jacksonville), A
ITT Technical Institute (Lake Mary), A
ITT Technical Institute (Tampa), A

Georgia

ITT Technical Institute (Duluth), A
ITT Technical Institute (Kennesaw), A

Idaho

ITT Technical Institute, A

Illinois

Black Hawk College, A
ITT Technical Institute (Matteson), A
ITT Technical Institute (Mount Prospect), A
Morrison Institute of Technology, A
Oakton Community College, A
Waubonsee Community College, A

Indiana

ITT Technical Institute (Fort Wayne), A
ITT Technical Institute (Indianapolis), A
ITT Technical Institute (Newburgh), A

Iowa

Vatterott College, A

Kentucky

Brown Mackie College-Northern Kentucky, A
ITT Technical Institute (Lexington), A
ITT Technical Institute (Louisville), A
Louisville Technical Institute, A
Somerset Community College, A

Louisiana

ITT Technical Institute, A

Maryland

ITT Technical Institute, A
TESST College of Technology (Towson), A

Massachusetts

ITT Technical Institute (Norwood), A
ITT Technical Institute (Woburn), A
Springfield Technical Community College, A

Michigan

Eastern Michigan University, B
ITT Technical Institute (Canton), A
ITT Technical Institute (Grand Rapids), A
ITT Technical Institute (Troy), A

Minnesota

Alexandria Technical College, A
ITT Technical Institute, A

Missouri

ITT Technical Institute (Arnold), A
ITT Technical Institute (Earth City), A
Jefferson College, A
Vatterott College (St. Ann), A

Vatterott College (Springfield), A

Nebraska

ITT Technical Institute, A

Nevada

The Art Institute of Las Vegas, A
ITT Technical Institute, A

New York

ITT Technical Institute (Getzville), A

Ohio

Brown Mackie College-North Canton, A
ITT Technical Institute (Dayton), A
ITT Technical Institute (Hilliard), A
ITT Technical Institute (Norwood), A
ITT Technical Institute (Strongsville), A
ITT Technical Institute (Warrensville Heights), A
ITT Technical Institute (Youngstown), A
Owens Community College, A
Shawnee State University, A

Oklahoma

ITT Technical Institute, A

Oregon

ITT Technical Institute, A

Pennsylvania

The Art Institute of Pittsburgh, B
Northampton County Area Community College, A

Rhode Island

Johnson & Wales University, A

South Carolina

ITT Technical Institute, A

Tennessee

ITT Technical Institute (Knoxville), A
ITT Technical Institute (Memphis), A
ITT Technical Institute (Nashville), A

Texas

ITT Technical Institute (Arlington), A
ITT Technical Institute (Austin), A
ITT Technical Institute (Houston), A
ITT Technical Institute (Houston), A
ITT Technical Institute (Houston), A
ITT Technical Institute (Richardson), A
ITT Technical Institute (San Antonio), A
Montgomery College, A
St. Philip's College, A

Utah

ITT Technical Institute, A

Virginia

ITT Technical Institute (Chantilly), A
ITT Technical Institute (Norfolk), A
ITT Technical Institute (Richmond), A
ITT Technical Institute (Springfield), A

Washington

ITT Technical Institute (Bothell), A
ITT Technical Institute (Seattle), A
ITT Technical Institute (Spokane), A
Lower Columbia College, A

West Virginia

West Virginia State Community and Technical
  College, A

Wisconsin

ITT Technical Institute (Green Bay), A
ITT Technical Institute (Greenfield), A

CANADIAN GOVERNMENT AND POLITICS

British Columbia

The University of British Columbia, B

CANADIAN HISTORY

Saskatchewan

University of Regina, B

CANADIAN STUDIES

Indiana

Franklin College, B

New York

St. Lawrence University, B
State University of New York at Plattsburgh, B

North Carolina

Duke University, B

Vermont

Sterling College, B
University of Vermont, B

Washington

University of Washington, B
Western Washington University, B

Alberta

Athabasca University, BM
Concordia University College of Alberta, B
University of Alberta, B
University of Calgary, B
University of Lethbridge, BM

British Columbia

Simon Fraser University, B
Thompson Rivers University, B
The University of British Columbia, B
University of Northern British Columbia, B

Manitoba

Brandon University, B
Collège universitaire de Saint-Boniface, M
University of Manitoba, BM
The University of Winnipeg, B

New Brunswick

Mount Allison University, B
University of New Brunswick Fredericton, B

Newfoundland and Labrador

Memorial University of Newfoundland, B

Nova Scotia

Acadia University, B
Dalhousie University, B
St. Francis Xavier University, B
Saint Mary's University, BM
Université Sainte-Anne, B

Ontario

Brock University, B
Carleton University, BMD
Queen's University at Kingston, B
Trent University, BM
University of Ottawa, BD
University of Toronto, B
University of Waterloo, B
Wilfrid Laurier University, B

York University, B

Prince Edward Island

University of Prince Edward Island, B

Quebec

Bishop's University, B
McGill University, B
Université du Québec àChicoutimi, M
Université du Québec àTrois-Rivières, MD
Université de Sherbrooke, MD

Saskatchewan

University of Regina, BMD
University of Saskatchewan, MD

CANCER BIOLOGY/ONCOLOGY

Arizona

The University of Arizona, D

California

Stanford University, D
University of California, San Diego, D

Connecticut

Yale University, DO

District of Columbia

The George Washington University, D

Florida

University of South Florida, D

Illinois

Northwestern University, D
University of Chicago, D

Kansas

Kansas State University, MD

Massachusetts

Harvard University, D

Michigan

Wayne State University, MD

Nebraska

University of Nebraska Medical Center, MD

New York

New York University, DO
State University of New York at Buffalo, D

North Carolina

Duke University, D
Wake Forest University, D

Pennsylvania

Drexel University, MD
University of Pennsylvania, DO

Rhode Island

Brown University, D

Tennessee

Vanderbilt University, MD

Texas

The University of Texas Health Science Center at Houston, MDO

Utah

University of Utah, MD

West Virginia

West Virginia University, MDO

Wisconsin

University of Wisconsin-Madison, D

Alberta

University of Alberta, MD

Ontario

McMaster University, MD

Quebec

Université Laval, O

CARDIOPULMONARY TECHNOLOGY/TECHNOLOGIST

Kentucky

Bellarmine University, B

Louisiana

Nicholls State University, A

Oklahoma

Bacone College, A

CARDIOVASCULAR SCIENCES

Arizona

Midwestern University, Glendale Campus, M

California

University of California, San Diego, D

Georgia

Medical College of Georgia, MD

Massachusetts

Northeastern University, M

New York

Long Island University, C.W. Post Campus, MO

South Dakota

The University of South Dakota, MD

Texas

Texas A&M University System Health Science Center, D

Wisconsin

Milwaukee School of Engineering, M

Alberta

University of Calgary, MD

Ontario

McMaster University, MD

Quebec

Université Laval, O

CARDIOVASCULAR TECHNOLOGY/TECHNOLOGIST

Alabama

Community College of the Air Force, A

California

Orange Coast College, A

Florida

Valencia Community College, A

Georgia

Augusta Technical College, A
Central Georgia Technical College, A
Darton College, A

Northwestern Technical College, A

Louisiana

Louisiana State University Health Sciences Center, B
Southern University at Shreveport, A

Maine

Southern Maine Community College, A

Maryland

Howard Community College, A

Massachusetts

Bunker Hill Community College, A

Minnesota

Northwest Technical College, A
St. Cloud Technical College, A

Nebraska

Nebraska Methodist College, AB

New Jersey

Bloomfield College, B

New York

Molloy College, A
State University of New York Upstate Medical University, B

North Carolina

Caldwell Community College and Technical Institute, A

Ohio

The University of Toledo, A

Pennsylvania

Gwynedd-Mercy College, AB
Harrisburg Area Community College, A
Pennsylvania College of Technology, B
Thomas Jefferson University, B

South Dakota

Southeast Technical Institute, A

Tennessee

Northeast State Technical Community College, A

Texas

El Centro College, A

Wisconsin

Milwaukee Area Technical College, A

British Columbia

British Columbia Institute of Technology, A
Thompson Rivers University, A

CARIBBEAN STUDIES

Florida

Florida State University, B
University of Miami, B

Illinois

Northwestern University, B

New York

Brooklyn College of the City University of New York, B
Hofstra University, B

CARPENTRY/CARPENTER

Alabama

George C. Wallace Community College, A
H. Councill Trenholm State Technical College, A
Lawson State Community College, A

Wallace State Community College, A

Arizona

GateWay Community College, A
Northland Pioneer College, A

Arkansas

Cossatot Community College of the University of
   Arkansas, A

California

American River College, A
Bakersfield College, A
College of the Sequoias, A
Fresno City College, A
Fullerton College, A
Hartnell College, A
Laney College, A
Lassen Community College District, A
Long Beach City College, A
Los Angeles Trade-Technical College, A
Merced College, A
Palomar College, A
Pasadena City College, A
Porterville College, A
Saddleback College, A
San Diego City College, A
San Joaquin Delta College, A
Santiago Canyon College, A
Sierra College, A

Colorado

Red Rocks Community College, A
Trinidad State Junior College, A

Delaware

Delaware Technical & Community College, Jack F.
   Owens Campus, A

Florida

Indian River Community College, A

Georgia

Central Georgia Technical College, A

Hawaii

Hawaii Community College, A
Honolulu Community College, A
Kauai Community College, A
Maui Community College, A

Idaho

Brigham Young University -Idaho, A
Idaho State University, A
North Idaho College, A

Illinois

Black Hawk College, A
Illinois Valley Community College, A
Kaskaskia College, A
Southwestern Illinois College, A

Indiana

Ivy Tech Community College-Central Indiana, A
Ivy Tech Community College-East Central, A
Ivy Tech Community College-Lafayette, A
Ivy Tech Community College-North Central, A
Ivy Tech Community College-Northwest, A
Ivy Tech Community College-Southern Indiana, A
Ivy Tech Community College-Southwest, A
Ivy Tech Community College-Wabash Valley, A

Iowa

Des Moines Area Community College, A
Iowa Central Community College, A
Iowa Lakes Community College, A
North Iowa Area Community College, A
Southwestern Community College, A

Kansas

Coffeyville Community College, A
Highland Community College, A
Hutchinson Community College and Area Vocational
   School, A

Neosho County Community College, A

Kentucky

Somerset Community College, A

Maine

Eastern Maine Community College, A
Northern Maine Community College, A
Southern Maine Community College, A

Maryland

Cecil Community College, A

Michigan

Davenport University (Midland), A
Delta College, A
Gogebic Community College, A
Lansing Community College, A
Oakland Community College, A

Minnesota

Alexandria Technical College, A
Hennepin Technical College, A
Lake Superior College, A
Minnesota State College-Southeast Technical, A
Northwest Technical College, A
St. Cloud Technical College, A

Mississippi

Coahoma Community College, A
East Central Community College, A
Hinds Community College, A
Northeast Mississippi Community College, A
Southwest Mississippi Community College, A

Missouri

Metropolitan Community College-Business &
   Technology College, A
North Central Missouri College, A
Ranken Technical College, A

Montana

Little Big Horn College, A
Miles Community College, A
Salish Kootenai College, A
The University of Montana-Helena College of
   Technology, A

Nebraska

Nebraska Indian Community College, A
Northeast Community College, A
Southeast Community College, Milford Campus, A

Nevada

Truckee Meadows Community College, A
Western Nevada Community College, A

New Mexico

New Mexico Junior College, A
San Juan College, A

New York

Fulton-Montgomery Community College, A
Mohawk Valley Community College, A
State University of New York College of Technology
   at Alfred, A
State University of New York College of Technology
   at Canton, A

North Carolina

Alamance Community College, A
Forsyth Technical Community College, A
Mayland Community College, A
Rockingham Community College, A
Vance-Granville Community College, A

North Dakota

Bismarck State College, A
Cankdeska Cikana Community College, A
Sitting Bull College, A

Turtle Mountain Community College, A

Oregon

Portland Community College, A

Pennsylvania

Community College of Allegheny County, A
Johnson College, A
Pennsylvania College of Technology, A
Thaddeus Stevens College of Technology, A
Triangle Tech, Inc.-DuBois School, A
Triangle Tech, Inc.-Greensburg School, A
Triangle Tech, Inc.-Pittsburgh School, A
The Williamson Free School of Mechanical
   Trades, A

South Carolina

Bob Jones University, A
Piedmont Technical College, A
Technical College of the Lowcountry, A

South Dakota

Lake Area Technical Institute, A
Mitchell Technical Institute, A
Oglala Lakota College, A

Texas

North Lake College, A
South Plains College, A

Utah

College of Eastern Utah, A
Snow College, A
Southern Utah University, A

Virginia

Piedmont Virginia Community College, A

Washington

Bates Technical College, A
Columbia Basin College, A
Grays Harbor College, A
Green River Community College, A
Seattle Central Community College, A
Spokane Community College, A
Walla Walla Community College, A
Wenatchee Valley College, A

Wisconsin

Northeast Wisconsin Technical College, A

Wyoming

Casper College, A
Laramie County Community College, A

British Columbia

British Columbia Institute of Technology, A
Thompson Rivers University, A

CARTOGRAPHY

Alabama

Samford University, B

California

Cabrillo College, A
Santiago Canyon College, A

Georgia

Kennesaw State University, B

Idaho

University of Idaho, B

Indiana

Ball State University, B

Massachusetts

Salem State College, B

Minnesota

Alexandria Technical College, A
Anoka-Ramsey Community College, A

Anoka-Ramsey Community College, Cambridge Campus, A

Missouri

Missouri State University, B

New Hampshire

New Hampshire Community Technical College, Berlin/Laconia, A

New York

State University of New York College at Oneonta, B

Ohio

The University of Akron, B

Oklahoma

East Central University, B

Oregon

Central Oregon Community College, A

Pennsylvania

Mansfield University of Pennsylvania, B

South Carolina

Midlands Technical College, A

Tennessee

Southwest Tennessee Community College, A

Texas

Houston Community College System, A
Texas A&M University, B
Texas A&M University-Corpus Christi, B
Texas State University-San Marcos, B

Utah

Brigham Young University, B
Dixie State College of Utah, A

Wisconsin

University of Wisconsin-Madison, B
University of Wisconsin-Platteville, B

Alberta

University of Alberta, B

Newfoundland and Labrador

Memorial University of Newfoundland, B

Ontario

Queen's University at Kingston, B

CELL BIOLOGY AND ANATOMY

Alabama

The University of Alabama at Birmingham, D
University of South Alabama, D

Arizona

Arizona State University, MD
The University of Arizona, MD

Arkansas

University of Arkansas, MD

California

California Institute of Technology, D
San Diego State University, D
San Francisco State University, M
University of California, Berkeley, D
University of California, Davis, MD
University of California, Irvine, MD
University of California, Los Angeles, MD
University of California, Riverside, MD
University of California, San Diego, D
University of California, Santa Barbara, MDO
University of California, Santa Cruz, MD

University of Southern California, MD

Colorado

Colorado State University, MD
University of Colorado at Boulder, MD

Connecticut

Central Connecticut State University, O
Quinnipiac University, M
University of Connecticut, MD
University of New Haven, M
Wesleyan University, D
Yale University, DO

Delaware

University of Delaware, MD

District of Columbia

The Catholic University of America, MD
Georgetown University, DO

Florida

Florida Institute of Technology, D
Florida State University, MD
University of Florida, MD
University of Miami, DO

Georgia

Emory University, D
Georgia State University, MD
Medical College of Georgia, D
University of Georgia, MD

Hawaii

University of Hawaii at Manoa, MD

Illinois

Illinois Institute of Technology, M
Loyola University Chicago, MDO
Northwestern University, D
Rush University, MDO
University of Chicago, D
University of Illinois at Chicago, MDO
University of Illinois at Urbana-Champaign, D

Indiana

Indiana University Bloomington, MD
Indiana University-Purdue University Indianapolis, MDO
Purdue University, D
University of Notre Dame, MD

Iowa

Iowa State University of Science and Technology, MD
The University of Iowa, D

Kansas

Emporia State University, M
Kansas State University, MD
University of Kansas, MDO

Louisiana

Louisiana State University Health Sciences Center, MDO
Tulane University, MDO

Maryland

The Johns Hopkins University, D
University of Maryland, Baltimore County, D
University of Maryland, College Park, MD

Massachusetts

Boston University, MDO
Brandeis University, MD
Harvard University, D
Massachusetts Institute of Technology, D
Tufts University, D
University of Massachusetts Amherst, D
University of Massachusetts Boston, D

Michigan

Michigan State University, MD
Oakland University, M

University of Michigan, MD

Minnesota

University of Minnesota, Duluth, MD
University of Minnesota, Twin Cities Campus, MD

Missouri

Missouri State University, M
University of Missouri-Columbia, MD
University of Missouri-Kansas City, MD
Washington University in St. Louis, D

Montana

Montana State University, B

Nebraska

University of Nebraska Medical Center, MD

Nevada

University of Nevada, Reno, MD

New Jersey

Rutgers, The State University of New Jersey, New Brunswick/Piscataway, MD

New Mexico

University of New Mexico, MD

New York

Cornell University, MD
New York University, MDO
Rensselaer Polytechnic Institute, MD
State University of New York at Buffalo, D
State University of New York Downstate Medical Center, DO
State University of New York Upstate Medical University, MDO
Stony Brook University, State University of New York, MD
University at Albany, State University of New York, MD

North Carolina

Duke University, DO
East Carolina University, D
North Carolina State University, MD
The University of North Carolina at Chapel Hill, MD

North Dakota

North Dakota State University, D

Ohio

Case Western Reserve University, MD
Kent State University, MD
The Ohio State University, MD
Ohio University, MD
University of Cincinnati, D

Oklahoma

University of Oklahoma Health Sciences Center, MD

Oregon

Oregon Health & Science University, DO
Oregon State University, MD

Pennsylvania

Carnegie Mellon University, D
Drexel University, MDO
The Pennsylvania State University University Park Campus, D
Temple University, D
Thomas Jefferson University, D
University of Pennsylvania, DO
University of Pittsburgh, MD

University of the Sciences in Philadelphia, M

Rhode Island

Brown University, MDO
University of Rhode Island, MD

South Carolina

Medical University of South Carolina, DO
University of South Carolina, MD

South Dakota

The University of South Dakota, MD

Tennessee

Vanderbilt University, MDO

Texas

Rice University, MD
Texas A&M University, D
The University of Texas at Austin, D
The University of Texas at Dallas, MD
The University of Texas Health Science Center at
    Houston, MDO
The University of Texas Health Science Center at
    San Antonio, D
The University of Texas Medical Branch, MD
The University of Texas at San Antonio, D
The University of Texas Southwestern Medical
    Center at Dallas, D

Vermont

University of Vermont, MD

Virginia

George Mason University, M
University of Virginia, DO

Washington

University of Washington, D
Washington State University, MD

West Virginia

West Virginia University, MD

Wisconsin

Marquette University, MD
University of Wisconsin-La Crosse, M
University of Wisconsin-Madison, MD

Alberta

University of Alberta, MD

British Columbia

The University of British Columbia, MD
University of Victoria, MD

Ontario

Brock University, M
McMaster University, MD
Queen's University at Kingston, MD
University of Ottawa, MD
The University of Western Ontario, MD

Quebec

McGill University, MD
Université Laval, MD
Université de Montréal, MD
Université de Sherbrooke, MD

Saskatchewan

University of Saskatchewan, MD

CELL/CELLULAR AND MOLECULAR BIOLOGY

California

California State University Channel Islands, B
University of California, Berkeley, B

University of California, Los Angeles, B

Colorado

Fort Lewis College, B
University of Colorado at Boulder, B

Connecticut

Connecticut College, B

Florida

Florida State University, B

Illinois

University of Illinois at Urbana-Champaign, B

Massachusetts

Bridgewater State College, B

Michigan

Grand Valley State University, B

Missouri

Missouri State University, B

New York

State University of New York College at
    Brockport, B

Oklahoma

Oklahoma State University, B

Tennessee

The University of Tennessee at Martin, B

Texas

Texas A&M University, B
Texas Tech University, B

Vermont

Bennington College, B

Virginia

Marymount University, B

Washington

Western Washington University, B

British Columbia

Thompson Rivers University, B

CELL/CELLULAR BIOLOGY AND ANATOMICAL SCIENCES

Alabama

Huntingdon College, B

Arizona

Northern Arizona University, B

Arkansas

University of Arkansas, B

Connecticut

University of Connecticut, B
Yale University, B

Kentucky

University of Kentucky, B

Louisiana

Tulane University, B

Massachusetts

Brandeis University, B

New Jersey

Rutgers, The State University of New Jersey, New
    Brunswick/Piscataway, B

Pennsylvania

Washington & Jefferson College, B

CELL/CELLULAR BIOLOGY AND HISTOLOGY

Arizona

The University of Arizona, B

California

California State University, Fresno, B
California State University, Long Beach, B
California State University, San Marcos, B
Humboldt State University, B
Pomona College, B
San Francisco State University, B
Sonoma State University, B
University of California, Davis, B
University of California, San Diego, B
University of California, Santa Barbara, B
University of California, Santa Cruz, B

Colorado

Western State College of Colorado, B

Georgia

University of Georgia, B

Illinois

Northwestern University, B
University of Illinois at Urbana-Champaign, B

Indiana

Ball State University, B

Louisiana

Tulane University, B

Maine

Colby College, B
University of Maine, B

Massachusetts

Harvard University, B
Worcester Polytechnic Institute, B

Michigan

University of Michigan, B

Minnesota

University of Minnesota, Duluth, B
University of Minnesota, Twin Cities Campus, B

Missouri

Lindenwood University, B
William Jewell College, B

New Hampshire

University of New Hampshire, B

New Jersey

Rutgers, The State University of New Jersey, New
    Brunswick/Piscataway, B

New York

Clarkson University, B
The College of Saint Rose, B
Cornell University, B
State University of New York College at
    Brockport, B

Ohio

Ohio University, B

Oklahoma

Northeastern State University, B

Oregon

Oregon State University, B

Pennsylvania

Juniata College, B
Mansfield University of Pennsylvania, B

Texas

Texas Tech University, B

Utah

University of Utah, B

Vermont

Marlboro College, B

Washington

University of Washington, B
Western Washington University, B

Wisconsin

Beloit College, B
University of Wisconsin-Madison, B

Alberta

University of Alberta, B
University of Calgary, B

British Columbia

Thompson Rivers University, B
The University of British Columbia, B

Newfoundland and Labrador

Memorial University of Newfoundland, B

Ontario

The University of Western Ontario, B

Quebec

Concordia University, B

CELTIC LANGUAGES, LITERATURES, AND LINGUISTICS

California

University of California, Berkeley, B

Connecticut

Sacred Heart University, A

Massachusetts

Harvard University, MD

CENTRAL/MIDDLE AND EASTERN EUROPEAN STUDIES

California

San Diego State University, B

Connecticut

Connecticut College, B
Wesleyan University, B

Florida

Florida State University, B
Manatee Community College, A

Illinois

University of Chicago, B

Indiana

Indiana University Bloomington, B

Maine

Bowdoin College, B

Maryland

Baltimore Hebrew University, AB

Massachusetts

Harvard University, B
Salem State College, B

Minnesota

Hamline University, B

Missouri

University of Missouri-Columbia, B

New Jersey

Rutgers, The State University of New Jersey, New Brunswick/Piscataway, B

New York

Bard College, B
Fordham University, B
Sarah Lawrence College, B
United States Military Academy, B
University at Albany, State University of New York, B

Ohio

Kent State University, B

Oregon

Portland State University, B
University of Oregon, B

Utah

Brigham Young University, B

Vermont

Marlboro College, B
Middlebury College, B

Virginia

University of Richmond, B

Alberta

University of Alberta, B

British Columbia

The University of British Columbia, B
University of Victoria, B

Ontario

Carleton University, B
University of Toronto, B

Quebec

McGill University, B

CERAMIC ARTS AND CERAMICS

Alabama

University of Montevallo, B

Arizona

Mohave Community College, A

California

Cabrillo College, A
California College of the Arts, BM
California State University, East Bay, B
California State University, Fullerton, B
California State University, Long Beach, B
Chaffey College, A
De Anza College, A
Glendale Community College, A
Grossmont College, A
Laney College, A
Lassen Community College District, A
Los Angeles City College, A
Los Angeles Valley College, A
Mills College, M
Monterey Peninsula College, A
Palomar College, A
Pasadena City College, A
San Francisco Art Institute, MO

Ventura College, A

Colorado

Colorado State University, B
University of Colorado at Boulder, M

Connecticut

University of Hartford, B

District of Columbia

Corcoran College of Art and Design, B
The George Washington University, M
Howard University, BM
University of the District of Columbia, B

Florida

Florida Atlantic University, M
Palm Beach Community College, A
University of Miami, BM

Guam

University of Guam, M

Idaho

Northwest Nazarene University, B

Illinois

Bradley University, M
Illinois State University, M
Lincoln College, A
School of the Art Institute of Chicago, BM
Southern Illinois University Carbondale, M
Trinity Christian College, B

Indiana

Ball State University, B
Indiana State University, M
Indiana University Bloomington, BM
Indiana Wesleyan University, B

Iowa

Coe College, B
Iowa Lakes Community College, A
Kirkwood Community College, A
The University of Iowa, B

Kansas

Bethany College, B
Friends University, AB
Garden City Community College, A
University of Kansas, B

Kentucky

St. Catharine College, A

Louisiana

Louisiana State University and Agricultural and Mechanical College, M
McNeese State University, B

Maine

College of the Atlantic, B
Maine College of Art, B

Maryland

Hood College, O
Maryland Institute College of Art, B

Massachusetts

Massachusetts College of Art, BM
Massachusetts Institute of Technology, D
School of the Museum of Fine Arts, Boston, B
Simon's Rock College of Bard, B
University of Massachusetts Dartmouth, B

Michigan

Aquinas College, B
Finlandia University, B
Grand Valley State University, B
Henry Ford Community College, A
Oakland Community College, A
University of Michigan, B

University of Michigan-Flint, B

Minnesota

Minnesota State University Mankato, B
Minnesota State University Moorhead, B
St. Cloud State University, B

Missouri

Kansas City Art Institute, B
Washington University in St. Louis, BM

New Hampshire

Franklin Pierce College, B

New Jersey

Mercer County Community College, A
Rutgers, The State University of New Jersey, New
　Brunswick/Piscataway, B

New Mexico

Institute of American Indian Arts, A

New York

Alfred University, BM
City College of the City University of New York, M
Hofstra University, B
Nazareth College of Rochester, B
Pratt Institute, BM
Rochester Institute of Technology, ABM
State University of New York College at
　Brockport, B
State University of New York at New Paltz, BM
Syracuse University, BM

North Carolina

Haywood Community College, A
Montgomery Community College, A

Ohio

The Cleveland Institute of Art, B
Kent State University, B
Ohio Northern University, B
The Ohio State University, B
Ohio University, BM
Shawnee State University, B
The University of Akron, B

Oklahoma

University of Oklahoma, M

Oregon

University of Oregon, B

Pennsylvania

Arcadia University, B
Seton Hill University, B
Temple University, BM
The University of the Arts, M

Puerto Rico

Inter American University of Puerto Rico, San
　Germán Campus, BM

Rhode Island

Rhode Island School of Design, BM
Salve Regina University, B

South Carolina

Anderson University, B

Tennessee

Memphis College of Art, B
University of Memphis, M
The University of Tennessee, M

Texas

Hill College of the Hill Junior College District, A
McMurry University, B
University of Dallas, B
University of North Texas, BM

The University of Texas at El Paso, B

Utah

Brigham Young University, B
Dixie State College of Utah, A
University of Utah, M

Vermont

Bennington College, B
Marlboro College, B

Virginia

Hampton University, B
James Madison University, M
Virginia Commonwealth University, M

Washington

University of Washington, B
Washington State University, M
Western Washington University, B

West Virginia

Concord University, B
West Virginia University, M
West Virginia Wesleyan College, B

Wisconsin

University of Wisconsin-Milwaukee, B

Wyoming

Casper College, A

Alberta

Alberta College of Art & Design, B

Nova Scotia

NSCAD University, B

Quebec

Concordia University, B

Saskatchewan

University of Regina, B

CERAMIC SCIENCES AND ENGINEERING

California

Pasadena City College, A
University of California, Berkeley, MD
University of California, Los Angeles, MD

Georgia

University of Georgia, B

Missouri

University of Missouri-Rolla, BMD

New Jersey

Rutgers, The State University of New Jersey, New
　Brunswick/Piscataway, BMD

New York

Alfred University, BMD
Rensselaer Polytechnic Institute, MD

Ohio

Case Western Reserve University, M
Hocking College, A
The Ohio State University, B

University of Cincinnati, MD

Pennsylvania

The Pennsylvania State University University Park
　Campus, MD

South Carolina

Clemson University, B

Washington

University of Washington, B

CHEMICAL ENGINEERING

Alabama

Auburn University, BMD
Tuskegee University, B
The University of Alabama, BMD
The University of Alabama in Huntsville, BMD
University of South Alabama, BM

Arizona

Arizona State University, BMD
The University of Arizona, BMD

Arkansas

University of Arkansas, BMD

California

California Institute of Technology, BMD
California State Polytechnic University, Pomona, B
California State University, Long Beach, B
City College of San Francisco, A
Los Angeles Trade-Technical College, A
Saddleback College, A
San Bernardino Valley College, A
San Jose State University, BM
Stanford University, BMDO
University of California, Berkeley, BMD
University of California, Davis, BMD
University of California, Irvine, BMD
University of California, Los Angeles, BMD
University of California, Riverside, BMD
University of California, San Diego, BMD
University of California, Santa Barbara, BMD
University of Southern California, BMDO

Colorado

Colorado School of Mines, BMD
Colorado State University, BMD
University of Colorado at Boulder, BMD

Connecticut

Naugatuck Valley Community College, A
University of Connecticut, BMD
University of New Haven, AB
Yale University, BMD

Delaware

Delaware Technical & Community College, Jack F.
　Owens Campus, A
Delaware Technical & Community College,
　Stanton/Wilmington Campus, A
University of Delaware, BMD

District of Columbia

Gallaudet University, B
Howard University, BM
University of the District of Columbia, A

Florida

Brevard Community College, A
Florida Agricultural and Mechanical University, BMD
Florida Institute of Technology, BMD
Florida International University, B
Florida State University, BMD
University of Florida, BMD

University of South Florida, BMD

Georgia

Georgia Institute of Technology, BMD
Savannah State University, B

Idaho

Brigham Young University -Idaho, A
University of Idaho, BMD

Illinois

City Colleges of Chicago, Harry S. Truman
College, A
Illinois Institute of Technology, BMD
Northwestern University, BMD
University of Illinois at Chicago, BMD
University of Illinois at Urbana-Champaign, BMD

Indiana

Ball State University, A
Bethel College, B
Purdue University, BMD
Rose-Hulman Institute of Technology, BM
Tri-State University, B
University of Notre Dame, BMD

Iowa

Iowa State University of Science and
Technology, BMD
The University of Iowa, BMD
Waldorf College, B

Kansas

Kansas State University, BMD
University of Kansas, BMD

Kentucky

Murray State University, B
University of Kentucky, BMD
University of Louisville, BMD

Louisiana

Louisiana State University and Agricultural and
Mechanical College, BMD
Louisiana Tech University, BMD
McNeese State University, M
Tulane University, BMD
University of Louisiana at Lafayette, BM

Maine

University of Maine, BMD

Maryland

The Johns Hopkins University, BMD
University of Maryland, Baltimore County, BMDO
University of Maryland, College Park, BMD

Massachusetts

Harvard University, B
Massachusetts Institute of Technology, BMDO
Northeastern University, BMD
Tufts University, BMD
University of Massachusetts Amherst, BMD
University of Massachusetts Lowell, BM
Worcester Polytechnic Institute, BMD

Michigan

Alpena Community College, A
Calvin College, B
Delta College, A
Ferris State University, A
Lansing Community College, A
Michigan State University, BMD
Michigan Technological University, BMD
Muskegon Community College, A
University of Detroit Mercy, MD
University of Michigan, BMDO
Wayne State University, BMD
Western Michigan University, BMD

Minnesota

Itasca Community College, A
University of Minnesota, Duluth, B
University of Minnesota, Twin Cities Campus, BMD

Walden University, M
Winona State University, B

Mississippi

Mississippi Gulf Coast Community College, A
Mississippi State University, BMD
University of Mississippi, B

Missouri

St. Louis Community College at Florissant Valley, A
University of Missouri-Columbia, BMD
University of Missouri-Rolla, BMD
Washington University in St. Louis, BMD

Montana

Montana State University, BMD

Nebraska

University of Nebraska-Lincoln, BMD

Nevada

University of Nevada, Reno, BMD

New Hampshire

University of New Hampshire, BMD

New Jersey

Burlington County College, A
Fairleigh Dickinson University, College at
Florham, MO
Gloucester County College, A
New Jersey Institute of Technology, BMD
Princeton University, BMD
Rowan University, B
Rutgers, The State University of New Jersey, New
Brunswick/Piscataway, BMD
Stevens Institute of Technology, BMDO

New Mexico

New Mexico Institute of Mining and Technology, B
New Mexico State University, BMD
University of New Mexico, BMD

New York

City College of the City University of New
York, BMD
Clarkson University, BMD
Columbia University, The Fu Foundation School of
Engineering and Applied Science, B
Cooper Union for the Advancement of Science and
Art, B
Cornell University, BMD
Excelsior College, AB
Manhattan College, BM
Monroe Community College, A
Onondaga Community College, A
Polytechnic University, Brooklyn Campus, MD
Rensselaer Polytechnic Institute, BMD
State University of New York at Buffalo, BMD
State University of New York College of
Environmental Science and Forestry, B
Syracuse University, BMD
United States Military Academy, B
University of Rochester, BMD
Westchester Community College, A

North Carolina

North Carolina Agricultural and Technical State
University, BM
North Carolina State University, BMD

North Dakota

University of North Dakota, BM

Ohio

Case Western Reserve University, BMD
Cleveland State University, BMD
Miami University, B
Miami University-Middletown Campus, A
The Ohio State University, BMD
Ohio University, BMD
Ohio University-Eastern, B
The University of Akron, BMD
University of Cincinnati, BMD

University of Dayton, BM
The University of Toledo, BMD
Washington State Community College, A
Xavier University, B
Youngstown State University, BM

Oklahoma

Oklahoma State University, BMD
University of Oklahoma, BMD
University of Tulsa, BMD

Oregon

Oregon State University, BMD

Pennsylvania

Bucknell University, BM
Carlow University, B
Carnegie Mellon University, BMD
Community College of Philadelphia, A
Drexel University, BMD
Geneva College, B
Lafayette College, B
Lehigh University, BMDO
The Pennsylvania State University Abington
College, B
The Pennsylvania State University Altoona
College, B
The Pennsylvania State University Beaver Campus
of the Commonwealth College, B
The Pennsylvania State University Berks Campus of
the Berks-Lehigh Valley College, B
The Pennsylvania State University Delaware County
Campus of the Commonwealth College, B
The Pennsylvania State University DuBois Campus
of the Commonwealth College, B
The Pennsylvania State University at Erie, The
Behrend College, B
The Pennsylvania State University Fayette Campus
of the Commonwealth College, B
The Pennsylvania State University Hazleton
Campus of the Commonwealth College, B
The Pennsylvania State University, Lehigh Valley
Campus of the Berks-Lehigh Valley College, B
The Pennsylvania State University McKeesport
Campus of the Commonwealth College, B
The Pennsylvania State University Mont Alto
Campus of the Commonwealth College, B
The Pennsylvania State University New Kensington
Campus of the Commonwealth College, B
The Pennsylvania State University Schuylkill
Campus of the Capital College, B
The Pennsylvania State University Shenango
Campus of the Commonwealth College, B
The Pennsylvania State University University Park
Campus, BMD
The Pennsylvania State University Wilkes-Barre
Campus of the Commonwealth College, B
The Pennsylvania State University Worthington
Scranton Campus of the Commonwealth
College, B
The Pennsylvania State University York Campus of
the Commonwealth College, B
Thiel College, B
University of Pennsylvania, BMDO
University of Pittsburgh, BMDO
Villanova University, BM
Widener University, BM

Puerto Rico

Inter American University of Puerto Rico, Guayama
Campus, B
Polytechnic University of Puerto Rico, B
University of Puerto Rico, Mayagüez Campus, BMD

Rhode Island

Brown University, BMD
University of Rhode Island, BMD

South Carolina

Clemson University, BMD
Florence-Darlington Technical College, A

University of South Carolina, BMD

South Dakota

South Dakota School of Mines and
Technology, BMD

Tennessee

Chattanooga State Technical Community College, A
Christian Brothers University, B
Pellissippi State Technical Community College, A
Tennessee Technological University, BMD
The University of Tennessee, BMDO
Vanderbilt University, BMD

Texas

Lamar University, BMD
Prairie View A&M University, B
Rice University, BMD
Texas A&M University, BMD
Texas A&M University-Kingsville, BM
Texas State Technical College Harlingen, A
Texas State Technical College Waco, A
Texas Tech University, BMD
University of Houston, BMD
The University of Texas at Austin, BMD

Utah

Brigham Young University, BMD
University of Utah, BMD

Virginia

Hampton University, B
University of Virginia, BMD
Virginia Commonwealth University, B
Virginia Polytechnic Institute and State
University, BMD
Washington and Lee University, B

Washington

Shoreline Community College, A
University of Washington, BMD
Washington State University, BMD

West Virginia

West Virginia State University, A
West Virginia University, BMD
West Virginia University Institute of Technology, B
West Virginia University at Parkersburg, A

Wisconsin

Milwaukee Area Technical College, A
University of Wisconsin-Madison, BMD

Wyoming

University of Wyoming, BMD

Alberta

University of Alberta, BMD
University of Calgary, BMD

British Columbia

The University of British Columbia, BMD

New Brunswick

University of New Brunswick Fredericton, BMD
University of New Brunswick Saint John, B

Newfoundland and Labrador

Memorial University of Newfoundland, B

Nova Scotia

Dalhousie University, BMD

Ontario

Lakehead University, B
McMaster University, BMD
Queen's University at Kingston, BMD
Royal Military College of Canada, BMD
Ryerson University, B
University of Guelph, B
University of Ottawa, BMD
University of Toronto, BMD
University of Waterloo, BMD

The University of Western Ontario, B

Quebec

McGill University, BMD
Université Laval, BMD
Université de Montréal, B
Université du Québec àTrois-Rivières, B
Université de Sherbrooke, BMD

Saskatchewan

University of Saskatchewan, BMD

CHEMICAL PHYSICS

California

California Institute of Technology, B

Maine

Bowdoin College, B

Michigan

Michigan State University, B
Michigan Technological University, B
Saginaw Valley State University, B

New York

Barnard College, B

Pennsylvania

Carnegie Mellon University, B
Swarthmore College, B

British Columbia

Simon Fraser University, B

Ontario

University of Waterloo, B

CHEMICAL TECHNOLOGY/TECHNICIAN

Florida

Pensacola Junior College, A
St. Johns River Community College, A

Illinois

College of Lake County, A

Indiana

Indiana University-Purdue University Fort Wayne, A

Kansas

Johnson County Community College, A

Kentucky

Murray State University, B

Louisiana

Nicholls State University, A
River Parishes Community College, A

Massachusetts

Massachusetts Bay Community College, A

Michigan

Kalamazoo Valley Community College, A
Kellogg Community College, A
Lawrence Technological University, A
Mid Michigan Community College, A

New Jersey

Burlington County College, A
County College of Morris, A
Essex County College, A

New York

Corning Community College, A
Hudson Valley Community College, A
Jefferson Community College, A
Mohawk Valley Community College, A

New York City College of Technology of the City
University of New York, A
Niagara County Community College, A
State University of New York at Buffalo, B
State University of New York College of Agriculture
and Technology at Cobleskill, A

North Carolina

Cape Fear Community College, A

Ohio

Cincinnati State Technical and Community
College, A
The University of Akron, A
University of Cincinnati Raymond Walters College, A
The University of Toledo, A

Pennsylvania

Community College of Allegheny County, A
Lehigh Carbon Community College, A
Millersville University of Pennsylvania, A
Northampton County Area Community College, A

Puerto Rico

Inter American University of Puerto Rico, Bayamón
Campus, B
University of Puerto Rico at Humacao, A

Rhode Island

Community College of Rhode Island, A

South Carolina

Midlands Technical College, A

South Dakota

Dakota State University, B

Tennessee

Pellissippi State Technical Community College, A

Texas

Alvin Community College, A
Amarillo College, A
Brazosport College, A
College of the Mainland, A
Del Mar College, A
Texas State Technical College Waco, A

Utah

Weber State University, A

Vermont

Norwich University, B

West Virginia

West Virginia State Community and Technical
College, A

British Columbia

British Columbia Institute of Technology, A

Nova Scotia

Cape Breton University, B

Ontario

University of Windsor, B

Saskatchewan

University of Regina, B

CHEMISTRY

Alabama

Alabama Agricultural and Mechanical University, B
Alabama Southern Community College, A
Alabama State University, B
Athens State University, B
Auburn University, BMD
Birmingham-Southern College, B
Chattahoochee Valley Community College, A
Huntingdon College, B
Jacksonville State University, B

Judson College, B
Lawson State Community College, A
Miles College, B
Oakwood College, B
Samford University, B
Spring Hill College, B
Stillman College, B
Talladega College, B
Troy University, B
Tuskegee University, BM
The University of Alabama, BMD
The University of Alabama at Birmingham, BMD
The University of Alabama in Huntsville, BM
University of Montevallo, B
University of North Alabama, B
University of South Alabama, B
The University of West Alabama, B

Alaska

University of Alaska Anchorage, B
University of Alaska Fairbanks, BMD

Arizona

Arizona State University, BMD
Arizona Western College, A
Cochise College (Douglas), A
Cochise College (Sierra Vista), A
Eastern Arizona College, A
Grand Canyon University, B
Northern Arizona University, BM
South Mountain Community College, A
The University of Arizona, BMD

Arkansas

Arkansas State University, BMO
Arkansas Tech University, B
Harding University, B
Henderson State University, B
Hendrix College, B
John Brown University, B
Lyon College, B
Ouachita Baptist University, B
Philander Smith College, B
Phillips Community College of the University of Arkansas, A
Southern Arkansas University-Magnolia, B
University of Arkansas, BMD
University of Arkansas at Little Rock, BM
University of Arkansas at Monticello, B
University of Arkansas at Pine Bluff, B
University of Central Arkansas, B
University of the Ozarks, B

California

Allan Hancock College, A
Azusa Pacific University, B
Bakersfield College, A
California Institute of Technology, BMD
California Lutheran University, B
California Polytechnic State University, San Luis Obispo, B
California State Polytechnic University, Pomona, BM
California State University, Bakersfield, B
California State University Channel Islands, B
California State University, Chico, B
California State University, Dominguez Hills, B
California State University, East Bay, BM
California State University, Fresno, BM
California State University, Fullerton, BM
California State University, Long Beach, BM
California State University, Los Angeles, BM
California State University, Northridge, BM
California State University, Sacramento, BM
California State University, San Bernardino, B
California State University, San Marcos, B
California State University, Stanislaus, B
Cañada College, A
Cerritos College, A
Chabot College, A
Chaffey College, A
Chapman University, B
City College of San Francisco, A
Claremont McKenna College, B
College of the Canyons, A
College of the Desert, A
College of Marin, A

College of San Mateo, A
College of the Sequoias, A
College of the Siskiyous, A
Columbia College, A
Compton Community College, A
Concordia University, B
Contra Costa College, A
Crafton Hills College, A
Cuesta College, A
Cuyamaca College, A
Cypress College, A
East Los Angeles College, A
El Camino College, A
Foothill College, A
Fresno Pacific University, B
Fullerton College, A
Gavilan College, A
Grossmont College, A
Harvey Mudd College, B
Humboldt State University, B
La Sierra University, B
Lassen Community College District, A
Los Angeles City College, A
Los Angeles Mission College, A
Los Medanos College, A
Loyola Marymount University, B
Mendocino College, A
Mills College, B
MiraCosta College, A
Monterey Peninsula College, A
Moorpark College, A
Mount St. Mary's College, B
Occidental College, B
Orange Coast College, A
Pacific Union College, B
Palomar College, A
Pasadena City College, A
Pepperdine University, B
Pitzer College, B
Point Loma Nazarene University, B
Pomona College, B
Saddleback College, A
Saint Mary's College of California, B
San Bernardino Valley College, A
San Diego Mesa College, A
San Diego Miramar College, A
San Diego State University, BMD
San Francisco State University, BM
San Joaquin Delta College, A
San Jose State University, BM
Santa Ana College, A
Santa Barbara City College, A
Santa Clara University, B
Santa Monica College, A
Santa Rosa Junior College, A
Santiago Canyon College, A
Scripps College, B
Sierra College, A
Skyline College, A
Solano Community College, A
Sonoma State University, B
Southwestern College, A
Stanford University, BD
University of California, Berkeley, BMD
University of California, Davis, BMD
University of California, Irvine, BMD
University of California, Los Angeles, BMD
University of California, Riverside, BMD
University of California, San Diego, BMD
University of California, Santa Barbara, BMD
University of California, Santa Cruz, BMD
University of La Verne, B
University of the Pacific, B
University of Redlands, B
University of San Diego, B
University of San Francisco, BM
University of Southern California, BMD
Vanguard University of Southern California, B
West Hills Community College, A
West Los Angeles College, A
West Valley College, A
Westmont College, B
Whittier College, B

Yuba College, A

Colorado

Adams State College, B
The Colorado College, B
Colorado School of Mines, BMD
Colorado State University, BMD
Colorado State University-Pueblo, B
Fort Lewis College, B
Mesa State College, B
Metropolitan State College of Denver, B
Red Rocks Community College, A
Regis University, B
Trinidad State Junior College, A
United States Air Force Academy, B
University of Colorado at Boulder, BMD
University of Colorado at Colorado Springs, B
University of Colorado at Denver and Health Sciences Center - Downtown Denver Campus, BM
University of Denver, BMD
University of Northern Colorado, BMD
Western State College of Colorado, B

Connecticut

Albertus Magnus College, B
Central Connecticut State University, BM
Connecticut College, B
Fairfield University, B
Quinnipiac University, B
Sacred Heart University, ABM
Saint Joseph College, BM
Southern Connecticut State University, BMO
Trinity College, B
University of Connecticut, BMD
University of Hartford, B
University of New Haven, B
Wesleyan University, BMD
Western Connecticut State University, B
Yale University, BD

Delaware

Delaware State University, BM
University of Delaware, BMD

District of Columbia

American University, BM
The Catholic University of America, BM
Gallaudet University, B
The George Washington University, BMD
Georgetown University, BMD
Howard University, BMD
Trinity (Washington) University, B
University of the District of Columbia, B

Florida

Barry University, B
Bethune-Cookman College, B
Daytona Beach Community College, A
Eckerd College, B
Edward Waters College, B
Florida Agricultural and Mechanical University, BM
Florida Atlantic University, BMD
Florida Institute of Technology, BMD
Florida International University, BMD
Florida Southern College, B
Florida State University, BMD
Indian River Community College, A
Jacksonville University, B
Manatee Community College, A
Miami Dade College, A
New College of Florida, B
Okaloosa-Walton College, A
Palm Beach Community College, A
Pensacola Junior College, A
Rollins College, B
St. Thomas University, B
Stetson University, B
University of Central Florida, BMD
University of Florida, BMD
University of Miami, BMD
University of North Florida, B
University of South Florida, BMD
The University of Tampa, AB

University of West Florida, B

Georgia

Abraham Baldwin Agricultural College, A
Agnes Scott College, B
Albany State University, B
Armstrong Atlantic State University, B
Atlanta Metropolitan College, A
Augusta State University, B
Bainbridge College, A
Berry College, B
Clark Atlanta University, BMD
Clayton State University, A
Coastal Georgia Community College, A
Columbus State University, B
Covenant College, B
Dalton State College, A
Darton College, A
East Georgia College, A
Emory University, BD
Fort Valley State University, B
Gainesville College, A
Georgia College & State University, B
Georgia Institute of Technology, BMD
Georgia Perimeter College, A
Georgia Southern University, B
Georgia Southwestern State University, B
Georgia State University, BMD
Kennesaw State University, B
LaGrange College, B
Macon State College, A
Mercer University, B
Morehouse College, B
North Georgia College & State University, B
Oglethorpe University, B
Paine College, B
Piedmont College, B
Savannah State University, B
Shorter College, B
South Georgia College, A
Spelman College, B
University of Georgia, BMD
University of West Georgia, B
Valdosta State University, B
Waycross College, A
Wesleyan College, B
Young Harris College, A

Guam

University of Guam, B

Hawaii

Brigham Young University-Hawaii, B
University of Hawaii at Hilo, B
University of Hawaii at Manoa, BMD

Idaho

Albertson College of Idaho, B
Boise State University, B
Brigham Young University -Idaho, A
College of Southern Idaho, A
Idaho State University, ABM
Lewis-Clark State College, B
North Idaho College, A
Northwest Nazarene University, B
University of Idaho, BMD

Illinois

Augustana College, B
Aurora University, B
Benedictine University, B
Blackburn College, B
Bradley University, BM
Chicago State University, B
City Colleges of Chicago, Harold Washington College, A
City Colleges of Chicago, Kennedy-King College, A
City Colleges of Chicago, Olive-Harvey College, A
Concordia University, B
DePaul University, BM
Dominican University, B
Eastern Illinois University, BM
Elmhurst College, B
Eureka College, B
Governors State University, B

Greenville College, B
Highland Community College, A
Illinois College, B
Illinois Institute of Technology, BMD
Illinois State University, BM
Illinois Wesleyan University, B
John A. Logan College, A
Joliet Junior College, A
Judson College, B
Knox College, B
Lake Forest College, B
Lewis University, B
Lincoln College, A
Loyola University Chicago, BMD
MacMurray College, B
McKendree College, B
Millikin University, B
Monmouth College, B
North Central College, B
North Park University, B
Northeastern Illinois University, BM
Northern Illinois University, BMD
Northwestern University, BD
Olivet Nazarene University, B
Principia College, B
Quincy University, B
Rend Lake College, A
Rockford College, B
Roosevelt University, BM
Saint Xavier University, B
Sauk Valley Community College, A
South Suburban College, A
Southern Illinois University Carbondale, BMD
Southern Illinois University Edwardsville, BM
Spoon River College, A
Trinity Christian College, B
Trinity International University, B
University of Chicago, BD
University of Illinois at Chicago, BMD
University of Illinois at Springfield, B
University of Illinois at Urbana-Champaign, BMD
Western Illinois University, BM
Wheaton College, B

Indiana

Ancilla College, A
Anderson University, B
Ball State University, BM
Bethel College, AB
Butler University, B
DePauw University, B
Earlham College, B
Franklin College, B
Goshen College, B
Hanover College, B
Huntington University, B
Indiana State University, B
Indiana University Bloomington, BMD
Indiana University Northwest, B
Indiana University-Purdue University Fort Wayne, B
Indiana University-Purdue University Indianapolis, BMDO
Indiana University South Bend, AB
Indiana University Southeast, B
Indiana Wesleyan University, AB
Manchester College, B
Marian College, B
Martin University, B
Oakland City University, B
Purdue University, BMD
Purdue University Calumet, B
Purdue University North Central, B
Rose-Hulman Institute of Technology, B
Saint Joseph's College, B
Saint Mary's College, B
Taylor University, B
Tri-State University, B
University of Evansville, B
University of Indianapolis, AB
University of Notre Dame, BMD
University of Saint Francis, B
University of Southern Indiana, B
Valparaiso University, B
Vincennes University, A

Wabash College, B

Iowa

Briar Cliff University, B
Buena Vista University, B
Central College, B
Clarke College, B
Coe College, B
Cornell College, B
Dordt College, B
Drake University, B
Graceland University, B
Grinnell College, B
Iowa Lakes Community College, A
Iowa State University of Science and Technology, BMD
Iowa Wesleyan College, B
Loras College, B
Luther College, B
Morningside College, B
Northwestern College, B
St. Ambrose University, B
Simpson College, B
The University of Iowa, BMDO
University of Northern Iowa, BM
Upper Iowa University, B
Wartburg College, B

Kansas

Allen County Community College, A
Baker University, B
Barton County Community College, A
Benedictine College, B
Bethany College, B
Bethel College, B
Butler Community College, A
Coffeyville Community College, A
Colby Community College, A
Cowley County Community College and Area Vocational-Technical School, A
Dodge City Community College, A
Emporia State University, BM
Fort Hays State University, B
Friends University, B
Highland Community College, A
Independence Community College, A
Kansas State University, BMD
Kansas Wesleyan University, B
Labette Community College, A
McPherson College, B
MidAmerica Nazarene University, B
Newman University, B
Pittsburg State University, BM
Pratt Community College, A
Seward County Community College, A
Southwestern College, B
Tabor College, B
University of Kansas, BMD
University of Saint Mary, B
Washburn University, B
Wichita State University, BMD

Kentucky

Asbury College, B
Bellarmine University, B
Berea College, B
Brescia University, B
Campbellsville University, B
Centre College, B
Eastern Kentucky University, BM
Georgetown College, B
Kentucky State University, B
Kentucky Wesleyan College, B
Lindsey Wilson College, A
Midway College, B
Morehead State University, B
Murray State University, BM
Northern Kentucky University, B
Pikeville College, B
St. Catharine College, A
Thomas More College, AB
Transylvania University, B
Union College, B
University of the Cumberlands, B
University of Kentucky, BMD
University of Louisville, BMD

Western Kentucky University, BM

Louisiana

Centenary College of Louisiana, B
Dillard University, B
Grambling State University, B
Louisiana College, B
Louisiana State University and Agricultural and
  Mechanical College, BMD
Louisiana State University in Shreveport, B
Louisiana Tech University, BM
Loyola University New Orleans, B
McNeese State University, BM
Nicholls State University, B
Northwestern State University of Louisiana, B
Southeastern Louisiana University, B
Southern University and Agricultural and Mechanical
  College, BM
Southern University at Shreveport, A
Tulane University, BMD
University of Louisiana at Lafayette, B
University of Louisiana at Monroe, B
University of New Orleans, BMD
Xavier University of Louisiana, B

Maine

Bates College, B
Bowdoin College, B
Colby College, B
Saint Joseph's College of Maine, B
University of Maine, BMD
University of New England, B
University of Southern Maine, B

Maryland

Anne Arundel Community College, A
College of Notre Dame of Maryland, B
Columbia Union College, B
Coppin State University, B
Frederick Community College, A
Frostburg State University, B
Goucher College, B
Hood College, B
The Johns Hopkins University, BMD
Loyola College in Maryland, B
McDaniel College, B
Morgan State University, B
Mount St. Mary's University, B
St. Mary's College of Maryland, B
Salisbury University, B
Towson University, B
United States Naval Academy, B
University of Maryland, Baltimore County, BMD
University of Maryland, College Park, BMD
University of Maryland Eastern Shore, B
Villa Julie College, AB
Washington College, B

Massachusetts

American International College, B
Amherst College, B
Assumption College, B
Atlantic Union College, B
Boston College, BMD
Boston University, BMD
Brandeis University, BMD
Bridgewater State College, B
Bunker Hill Community College, A
Clark University, BMD
College of the Holy Cross, B
Eastern Nazarene College, B
Elms College, B
Emmanuel College, B
Framingham State College, B
Gordon College, B
Hampshire College, B
Harvard University, BMD
Holyoke Community College, A
Massachusetts College of Liberal Arts, B
Massachusetts College of Pharmacy and Health
  Sciences, BMD
Massachusetts Institute of Technology, BD
Merrimack College, B
Mount Holyoke College, B
Northeastern University, BMD
Salem State College, B

Simmons College, B
Simon's Rock College of Bard, B
Smith College, BM
Springfield Technical Community College, A
Stonehill College, B
Suffolk University, B
Tufts University, BMD
University of Massachusetts Amherst, BMD
University of Massachusetts Boston, BM
University of Massachusetts Dartmouth, BM
University of Massachusetts Lowell, BMD
Wellesley College, B
Western New England College, B
Wheaton College, B
Williams College, B
Worcester Polytechnic Institute, BMD
Worcester State College, B

Michigan

Adrian College, AB
Albion College, B
Alma College, B
Alpena Community College, A
Andrews University, B
Aquinas College, B
Calvin College, B
Central Michigan University, BM
Eastern Michigan University, BMO
Ferris State University, B
Grand Valley State University, B
Hillsdale College, B
Hope College, B
Kalamazoo College, B
Kellogg Community College, A
Kettering University, B
Lake Superior State University, A
Lansing Community College, A
Lawrence Technological University, B
Macomb Community College, A
Madonna University, AB
Marygrove College, B
Michigan State University, BMD
Michigan Technological University, BMD
Mid Michigan Community College, A
Northern Michigan University, BM
Oakland University, BMD
Olivet College, B
Saginaw Valley State University, B
Siena Heights University, AB
Spring Arbor University, B
University of Detroit Mercy, BM
University of Michigan, BD
University of Michigan-Dearborn, B
University of Michigan-Flint, B
Wayne State University, BMD
Western Michigan University, BMD

Minnesota

Augsburg College, B
Bemidji State University, B
Bethany Lutheran College, B
Bethel University, B
Carleton College, B
College of Saint Benedict, B
College of St. Catherine, B
The College of St. Scholastica, B
Concordia College, B
Gustavus Adolphus College, B
Hamline University, B
Macalester College, B
Minnesota State University Mankato, BM
Minnesota State University Moorhead, B
North Hennepin Community College, A
St. Cloud State University, B
Saint John's University, B
Saint Mary's University of Minnesota, B
St. Olaf College, B
Southwest Minnesota State University, B
University of Minnesota, Duluth, BM
University of Minnesota, Morris, B
University of Minnesota, Twin Cities Campus, BMD
University of St. Thomas, B
Vermilion Community College, A

Winona State University, B

Mississippi

Alcorn State University, B
Belhaven College, B
Blue Mountain College, B
Coahoma Community College, A
Copiah-Lincoln Community College, A
Delta State University, B
East Central Community College, A
Itawamba Community College, A
Jackson State University, BMD
Jones County Junior College, A
Millsaps College, B
Mississippi College, BM
Mississippi State University, BMD
Mississippi University for Women, B
Mississippi Valley State University, B
Northeast Mississippi Community College, A
Rust College, B
Southwest Mississippi Community College, A
Tougaloo College, B
University of Mississippi, BMD
University of Southern Mississippi, BMD
William Carey College, B

Missouri

Avila University, B
Central Methodist University, AB
Central Missouri State University, B
College of the Ozarks, B
Columbia College, B
Drury University, B
East Central College, A
Evangel University, B
Hannibal-LaGrange College, A
Lincoln University, B
Lindenwood University, B
Longview Community College, A
Maple Woods Community College, A
Maryville University of Saint Louis, B
Missouri Baptist University, B
Missouri Southern State University, B
Missouri State University, BM
Missouri Western State University, B
Northwest Missouri State University, B
Park University, B
Penn Valley Community College, A
Rockhurst University, B
Saint Louis University, BM
Southeast Missouri State University, BM
Southwest Baptist University, B
Truman State University, B
University of Missouri-Columbia, BMD
University of Missouri-Kansas City, BMD
University of Missouri-Rolla, BMD
University of Missouri-St. Louis, BMD
Washington University in St. Louis, BMD
Westminster College, B
William Jewell College, B

Montana

Carroll College, B
Montana State University, BMD
Montana State University-Billings, B
Montana Tech of The University of Montana, B
Rocky Mountain College, B
University of Great Falls, B
The University of Montana-Missoula, BMD

Nebraska

Chadron State College, B
College of Saint Mary, B
Concordia University, B
Creighton University, B
Dana College, B
Doane College, B
Hastings College, B
Midland Lutheran College, B
Nebraska Wesleyan University, B
Northeast Community College, A
Peru State College, B
Union College, B
University of Nebraska at Kearney, B
University of Nebraska-Lincoln, BMD
University of Nebraska at Omaha, B

Wayne State College, B
Western Nebraska Community College, A

Nevada

Community College of Southern Nevada, A
Great Basin College, A
University of Nevada, Las Vegas, BMD
University of Nevada, Reno, BMD

New Hampshire

Dartmouth College, BD
Keene State College, AB
Plymouth State University, B
Rivier College, B
Saint Anselm College, B
University of New Hampshire, BMD

New Jersey

Atlantic Cape Community College, A
Bergen Community College, A
Bloomfield College, B
Brookdale Community College, A
Burlington County College, A
Caldwell College, B
The College of New Jersey, B
College of Saint Elizabeth, B
Drew University, B
Essex County College, A
Fairleigh Dickinson University, College at
  Florham, BM
Fairleigh Dickinson University, Metropolitan
  Campus, B
Georgian Court University, B
Gloucester County College, A
Kean University, B
Mercer County Community College, A
Middlesex County College, A
Monmouth University, B
Montclair State University, BM
New Jersey City University, B
New Jersey Institute of Technology, BMD
Princeton University, BMD
Ramapo College of New Jersey, B
Raritan Valley Community College, A
The Richard Stockton College of New Jersey, B
Rider University, B
Rowan University, B
Rutgers, The State University of New Jersey,
  Camden, BM
Rutgers, The State University of New Jersey, New
  Brunswick/Piscataway, BMD
Rutgers, The State University of New Jersey,
  Newark, BMD
Saint Peter's College, B
Salem Community College, A
Seton Hall University, BMD
Stevens Institute of Technology, BMDO
Union County College, A

New Mexico

Eastern New Mexico University, BM
New Mexico Highlands University, BM
New Mexico Institute of Mining and
  Technology, BMD
New Mexico Junior College, A
New Mexico Military Institute, A
New Mexico State University, BMD
San Juan College, A
University of New Mexico, BMD
Western New Mexico University, B

New York

Adelphi University, B
Alfred University, B
Bard College, B
Barnard College, B
Bronx Community College of the City University of
  New York, A
Brooklyn College of the City University of New
  York, BMD
Buffalo State College, State University of New
  York, BM
Canisius College, B
City College of the City University of New
  York, BMD

Clarkson University, BMD
Colgate University, B
College of Mount Saint Vincent, B
The College of New Rochelle, B
The College of Saint Rose, B
College of Staten Island of the City University of
  New York, BD
Columbia College, B
Columbia University, School of General Studies, B
Cornell University, BD
Elmira College, B
Excelsior College, B
Finger Lakes Community College, A
Fordham University, B
Hamilton College, B
Hartwick College, B
Hobart and William Smith Colleges, B
Hofstra University, B
Houghton College, B
Hunter College of the City University of New York, B
Iona College, B
Ithaca College, B
Kingsborough Community College of the City
  University of New York, A
Le Moyne College, B
Lehman College of the City University of New
  York, B
Long Island University, Brooklyn Campus, BM
Long Island University, C.W. Post Campus, B
Manhattan College, B
Manhattanville College, B
Marist College, B
Monroe Community College, A
Mount Saint Mary College, B
Nazareth College of Rochester, B
New York Institute of Technology, B
New York University, BMD
Niagara University, B
Pace University, B
Polytechnic University, Brooklyn Campus, BMD
Purchase College, State University of New York, B
Queens College of the City University of New
  York, BM
Rensselaer Polytechnic Institute, BMD
Roberts Wesleyan College, B
Rochester Institute of Technology, ABM
Russell Sage College, B
St. Bonaventure University, B
St. Francis College, B
St. John Fisher College, B
St. John's University, BM
St. Joseph's College, New York, B
St. Lawrence University, B
Sarah Lawrence College, B
Siena College, B
Skidmore College, B
State University of New York at Binghamton, BMD
State University of New York at Buffalo, BMD
State University of New York College of Agriculture
  and Technology at Morrisville, A
State University of New York College at
  Brockport, B
State University of New York College at Cortland, B
State University of New York College of
  Environmental Science and Forestry, BMD
State University of New York College at Geneseo, B
State University of New York College at Old
  Westbury, B
State University of New York College at Oneonta, B
State University of New York College at Potsdam, B
State University of New York, Fredonia, BM
State University of New York at New Paltz, BM
State University of New York at Oswego, BM
State University of New York at Plattsburgh, B
Stony Brook University, State University of New
  York, BMD
Suffolk County Community College, A
Syracuse University, BMD
Touro College, B
Union College, B
United States Military Academy, B
University at Albany, State University of New
  York, BMD
University of Rochester, BMD
Utica College, B
Vassar College, BM

Wagner College, B
Wells College, B
Yeshiva University, B
York College of the City University of New York, B

North Carolina

Appalachian State University, B
Barton College, B
Bennett College For Women, B
Campbell University, B
Catawba College, B
Davidson College, B
Duke University, BD
East Carolina University, BM
Elizabeth City State University, B
Elon University, B
Fayetteville State University, B
Gardner-Webb University, B
Greensboro College, B
Guilford College, B
Guilford Technical Community College, A
High Point University, B
Johnson C. Smith University, B
Lenoir-Rhyne College, B
Livingstone College, B
Louisburg College, A
Mars Hill College, B
Meredith College, B
Methodist College, AB
North Carolina Agricultural and Technical State
  University, BM
North Carolina Central University, BM
North Carolina State University, BMD
North Carolina Wesleyan College, B
Pfeiffer University, B
St. Andrews Presbyterian College, B
Saint Augustine's College, B
Salem College, B
Shaw University, B
The University of North Carolina at Asheville, B
The University of North Carolina at Chapel
  Hill, BMD
The University of North Carolina at Charlotte, BM
The University of North Carolina at Greensboro, BM
The University of North Carolina at Pembroke, B
The University of North Carolina Wilmington, BM
Wake Forest University, BMD
Warren Wilson College, B
Western Carolina University, BM
Wingate University, B
Winston-Salem State University, B

North Dakota

Cankdeska Cikana Community College, A
Dickinson State University, B
Jamestown College, B
Mayville State University, B
Minot State University, B
North Dakota State University, BMD
University of North Dakota, BMD
Valley City State University, B

Ohio

Antioch College, B
Ashland University, B
Baldwin-Wallace College, B
Bluffton University, B
Bowling Green State University, BMD
Capital University, B
Case Western Reserve University, BMD
Cedarville University, B
Central State University, B
Cleveland State University, BMD
College of Mount St. Joseph, B
The College of Wooster, B
Denison University, B
Franciscan University of Steubenville, B
Heidelberg College, B
Hiram College, B
John Carroll University, BM
Kent State University, BMD
Kenyon College, B
Lake Erie College, B
Lorain County Community College, A
Lourdes College, AB
Malone College, B

Marietta College, B
Miami University, BMD
Miami University Hamilton, B
Miami University-Middletown Campus, A
Mount Union College, B
Mount Vernon Nazarene University, B
Muskingum College, B
Notre Dame College, B
Oberlin College, B
Ohio Dominican University, AB
Ohio Northern University, B
The Ohio State University, BMD
Ohio University, B
Ohio University-Eastern, B
Ohio Wesleyan University, B
Otterbein College, B
Shawnee State University, B
Terra State Community College, A
The University of Akron, BMD
University of Cincinnati, BMD
University of Cincinnati Raymond Walters College, A
University of Dayton, BM
University of Rio Grande, AB
The University of Toledo, BMD
Urbana University, B
Walsh University, B
Wilberforce University, B
Wilmington College, B
Wittenberg University, B
Wright State University, ABM
Wright State University, Lake Campus, A
Xavier University, B
Youngstown State University, BM

Oklahoma

Cameron University, B
Connors State College, A
East Central University, B
Eastern Oklahoma State College, A
Langston University, B
Murray State College, A
Northeastern Oklahoma Agricultural and Mechanical College, A
Northeastern State University, B
Northwestern Oklahoma State University, B
Oklahoma Baptist University, B
Oklahoma Christian University, B
Oklahoma City Community College, A
Oklahoma City University, B
Oklahoma Panhandle State University, B
Oklahoma State University, BMD
Oklahoma Wesleyan University, AB
Oral Roberts University, B
Rogers State University, A
Rose State College, A
St. Gregory's University, B
Southeastern Oklahoma State University, B
Southern Nazarene University, B
Southwestern Oklahoma State University, B
Tulsa Community College, A
University of Central Oklahoma, BM
University of Oklahoma, BMD
University of Science and Arts of Oklahoma, B
University of Tulsa, BM

Oregon

Concordia University, B
Eastern Oregon University, B
George Fox University, B
Lewis & Clark College, B
Linfield College, B
Linn-Benton Community College, A
Oregon State University, BMD
Pacific University, B
Portland State University, BMD
Reed College, B
Southern Oregon University, B
Treasure Valley Community College, A
Umpqua Community College, A
University of Oregon, BMD
University of Portland, B
Western Oregon University, B

Willamette University, B

Pennsylvania

Albright College, B
Allegheny College, B
Alvernia College, B
Arcadia University, B
Bloomsburg University of Pennsylvania, B
Bryn Mawr College, BMD
Bucknell University, BM
Bucks County Community College, A
Cabrini College, B
California University of Pennsylvania, B
Carlow University, B
Carnegie Mellon University, BMD
Cedar Crest College, B
Chatham College, B
Chestnut Hill College, AB
Cheyney University of Pennsylvania, B
Clarion University of Pennsylvania, B
College Misericordia, B
Community College of Allegheny County, A
Delaware Valley College, B
DeSales University, B
Dickinson College, B
Drexel University, BMD
Duquesne University, BMD
East Stroudsburg University of Pennsylvania, B
Eastern University, B
Edinboro University of Pennsylvania, B
Elizabethtown College, B
Franklin and Marshall College, B
Gannon University, B
Geneva College, B
Gettysburg College, B
Grove City College, B
Harrisburg Area Community College, A
Haverford College, B
Holy Family University, B
Immaculata University, B
Indiana University of Pennsylvania, BM
Juniata College, B
King's College, B
Kutztown University of Pennsylvania, B
La Roche College, B
La Salle University, B
Lafayette College, B
Lebanon Valley College, B
Lehigh University, BMD
Lincoln University, B
Lock Haven University of Pennsylvania, B
Lycoming College, B
Mansfield University of Pennsylvania, B
Mercyhurst College, B
Messiah College, B
Millersville University of Pennsylvania, B
Moravian College, B
Muhlenberg College, B
Northampton County Area Community College, A
The Pennsylvania State University Abington College, B
The Pennsylvania State University Altoona College, B
The Pennsylvania State University Beaver Campus of the Commonwealth College, B
The Pennsylvania State University Berks Campus of the Berks-Lehigh Valley College, B
The Pennsylvania State University Delaware County Campus of the Commonwealth College, B
The Pennsylvania State University DuBois Campus of the Commonwealth College, B
The Pennsylvania State University at Erie, The Behrend College, B
The Pennsylvania State University Fayette Campus of the Commonwealth College, B
The Pennsylvania State University Hazleton Campus of the Commonwealth College, B
The Pennsylvania State University, Lehigh Valley Campus of the Berks-Lehigh Valley College, B
The Pennsylvania State University McKeesport Campus of the Commonwealth College, B
The Pennsylvania State University Mont Alto Campus of the Commonwealth College, B
The Pennsylvania State University New Kensington Campus of the Commonwealth College, B

The Pennsylvania State University Schuylkill Campus of the Capital College, B
The Pennsylvania State University Shenango Campus of the Commonwealth College, B
The Pennsylvania State University University Park Campus, BMD
The Pennsylvania State University Wilkes-Barre Campus of the Commonwealth College, B
The Pennsylvania State University Worthington Scranton Campus of the Commonwealth College, B
The Pennsylvania State University York Campus of the Commonwealth College, B
Philadelphia University, B
Reading Area Community College, A
Rosemont College, B
Saint Francis University, B
Saint Joseph's University, AB
Saint Vincent College, B
Seton Hill University, B
Shippensburg University of Pennsylvania, B
Slippery Rock University of Pennsylvania, B
Susquehanna University, B
Swarthmore College, B
Temple University, BMD
Thiel College, B
University of Pennsylvania, BMD
University of Pittsburgh, BMD
University of Pittsburgh at Bradford, B
University of Pittsburgh at Johnstown, B
University of the Sciences in Philadelphia, BMD
The University of Scranton, BM
Ursinus College, B
Villanova University, BM
Washington & Jefferson College, B
Waynesburg College, B
West Chester University of Pennsylvania, BM
Westminster College, B
Widener University, B
Wilkes University, B
Wilson College, B
York College of Pennsylvania, AB

Puerto Rico

Bayamon Central University, B
Inter American University of Puerto Rico, Arecibo Campus, AB
Inter American University of Puerto Rico, Bayamón Campus, B
Inter American University of Puerto Rico, Guayama Campus, AB
Inter American University of Puerto Rico, Metropolitan Campus, B
Inter American University of Puerto Rico, San Germán Campus, B
Pontifical Catholic University of Puerto Rico, BM
Universidad Adventista de las Antillas, B
Universidad del Turabo, B
University of Puerto Rico, Cayey University College, B
University of Puerto Rico at Humacao, B
University of Puerto Rico, Mayagüez Campus, BM
University of Puerto Rico, Río Piedras, BMD
University of the Sacred Heart, B

Rhode Island

Brown University, BMD
Providence College, B
Rhode Island College, B
Roger Williams University, B
Salve Regina University, B
University of Rhode Island, BMD

South Carolina

Allen University, B
Benedict College, B
Bob Jones University, B
Charleston Southern University, B
The Citadel, The Military College of South Carolina, B
Claflin University, B
Clemson University, BMD
Coastal Carolina University, B
Coker College, B
College of Charleston, B
Columbia College, B

Converse College, B
Erskine College, B
Francis Marion University, B
Furman University, BM
Lander University, B
Limestone College, B
Newberry College, B
Presbyterian College, B
South Carolina State University, B
Southern Wesleyan University, B
University of South Carolina, BMD
University of South Carolina Aiken, B
University of South Carolina Upstate, B
Voorhees College, B
Winthrop University, B
Wofford College, B

South Dakota

Augustana College, B
Black Hills State University, B
Mount Marty College, B
Northern State University, B
Presentation College, A
South Dakota School of Mines and
    Technology, BMD
South Dakota State University, BMD
University of Sioux Falls, B
The University of South Dakota, BM

Tennessee

Austin Peay State University, B
Belmont University, B
Bethel College, B
Carson-Newman College, B
Chattanooga State Technical Community College, A
Christian Brothers University, B
Columbia State Community College, A
Crichton College, B
East Tennessee State University, BM
Fisk University, BM
Freed-Hardeman University, B
King College, B
Lambuth University, B
Lane College, B
Lee University, B
LeMoyne-Owen College, B
Lincoln Memorial University, B
Lipscomb University, B
Martin Methodist College, A
Maryville College, B
Middle Tennessee State University, BMD
Milligan College, B
Northeast State Technical Community College, A
Rhodes College, B
Roane State Community College, A
Sewanee: The University of the South, B
Southern Adventist University, B
Tennessee State University, BM
Tennessee Technological University, BM
Tennessee Wesleyan College, B
Trevecca Nazarene University, B
Union University, B
University of Memphis, BMD
The University of Tennessee, BMD
The University of Tennessee at Chattanooga, B
The University of Tennessee at Martin, B
Vanderbilt University, BMD

Texas

Abilene Christian University, B
Amarillo College, A
Angelo State University, B
Austin College, B
Austin Community College, A
Baylor University, BMD
Blinn College, A
Brazosport College, A
Central Texas College, A
Cisco Junior College, A
Clarendon College, A
Coastal Bend College, A
Del Mar College, A
East Texas Baptist University, B
El Paso Community College, A
Frank Phillips College, A
Grayson County College, A

Hardin-Simmons University, B
Hill College of the Hill Junior College District, A
Houston Baptist University, B
Howard College, A
Howard Payne University, B
Huston-Tillotson University, B
Jarvis Christian College, B
Kilgore College, A
Lamar University, BM
Lee College, A
LeTourneau University, B
Lon Morris College, A
Lubbock Christian University, B
McMurry University, B
Midland College, A
Midwestern State University, B
Navarro College, A
Odessa College, A
Our Lady of the Lake University of San Antonio, B
Palo Alto College, A
Prairie View A&M University, BM
Rice University, BMD
St. Edward's University, B
St. Mary's University of San Antonio, B
St. Philip's College, A
Sam Houston State University, BM
Schreiner University, B
South Plains College, A
Southern Methodist University, BMD
Southwestern Adventist University, B
Southwestern University, B
Stephen F. Austin State University, BM
Sul Ross State University, BM
Tarleton State University, B
Texarkana College, A
Texas A&M International University, B
Texas A&M University, BMD
Texas A&M University-Commerce, BM
Texas A&M University-Corpus Christi, B
Texas A&M University-Kingsville, BM
Texas Christian University, BMD
Texas Lutheran University, B
Texas Southern University, BM
Texas State University-San Marcos, BM
Texas Tech University, BMD
Texas Wesleyan University, B
Texas Woman's University, BM
Trinity University, B
Trinity Valley Community College, A
University of Dallas, B
University of Houston, BMD
University of Houston-Clear Lake, BM
University of Houston-Downtown, B
University of the Incarnate Word, AB
University of Mary Hardin-Baylor, B
University of North Texas, BMD
University of St. Thomas, B
The University of Texas at Arlington, BMD
The University of Texas at Austin, BMD
The University of Texas at Brownsville, B
The University of Texas at Dallas, BMD
The University of Texas at El Paso, BM
The University of Texas-Pan American, B
The University of Texas of the Permian Basin, B
The University of Texas at San Antonio, BM
The University of Texas at Tyler, B
Wayland Baptist University, B
West Texas A&M University, BM
Wharton County Junior College, A
Wiley College, B

United States Virgin Islands

University of the Virgin Islands, B

Utah

Brigham Young University, BMD
Dixie State College of Utah, A
Salt Lake Community College, A
Snow College, A
Southern Utah University, B
University of Utah, BMD
Utah State University, BMD
Utah Valley State College, AB
Weber State University, B

Westminster College, B

Vermont

Bennington College, B
Castleton State College, A
Marlboro College, B
Middlebury College, B
Norwich University, B
Saint Michael's College, B
University of Vermont, BMD

Virginia

Averett University, B
Bluefield College, B
Bridgewater College, B
Christopher Newport University, B
The College of William and Mary, BM
Eastern Mennonite University, B
Emory & Henry College, B
Ferrum College, B
George Mason University, BM
Hampden-Sydney College, B
Hampton University, BM
Hollins University, B
James Madison University, B
Longwood University, B
Lynchburg College, B
Mary Baldwin College, B
Mountain Empire Community College, A
Norfolk State University, B
Old Dominion University, BMD
Radford University, B
Randolph-Macon College, B
Randolph-Macon Woman's College, B
Roanoke College, B
Shenandoah University, B
Sweet Briar College, B
University of Mary Washington, B
University of Richmond, B
University of Virginia, BMD
The University of Virginia's College at Wise, B
Virginia Commonwealth University, BMD
Virginia Military Institute, B
Virginia Polytechnic Institute and State
    University, BMD
Virginia State University, B
Virginia Union University, B
Virginia Wesleyan College, B
Washington and Lee University, B

Washington

Central Washington University, BM
Centralia College, A
Eastern Washington University, B
Everett Community College, A
Gonzaga University, B
Pacific Lutheran University, B
Saint Martin's University, B
Seattle Pacific University, B
Seattle University, B
Skagit Valley College, A
Tacoma Community College, A
University of Puget Sound, B
University of Washington, BMD
Walla Walla College, B
Washington State University, BMD
Wenatchee Valley College, A
Western Washington University, BM
Whitman College, B
Whitworth College, B

West Virginia

Bethany College, B
Concord University, B
Davis & Elkins College, B
Fairmont State University, B
Glenville State College, B
Marshall University, BM
Potomac State College of West Virginia
    University, A
Shepherd University, B
University of Charleston, B
West Liberty State College, B
West Virginia State University, B
West Virginia University, BMD
West Virginia University Institute of Technology, B

West Virginia Wesleyan College, B
Wheeling Jesuit University, B

Wisconsin

Alverno College, B
Beloit College, B
Cardinal Stritch University, B
Carroll College, B
Carthage College, B
Edgewood College, B
Lakeland College, B
Lawrence University, B
Marian College of Fond du Lac, B
Marquette University, BMD
Mount Mary College, B
Northland College, B
Ripon College, B
St. Norbert College, B
University of Wisconsin-Eau Claire, B
University of Wisconsin-Green Bay, AB
University of Wisconsin-La Crosse, B
University of Wisconsin-Madison, BMD
University of Wisconsin-Milwaukee, BMD
University of Wisconsin-Oshkosh, B
University of Wisconsin-Parkside, B
University of Wisconsin-River Falls, B
University of Wisconsin-Stevens Point, B
University of Wisconsin-Superior, B
University of Wisconsin-Whitewater, B
Viterbo University, B
Wisconsin Lutheran College, B

Wyoming

Casper College, A
Laramie County Community College, A
Northwest College, A
University of Wyoming, BMD
Western Wyoming Community College, A

Alberta

Concordia University College of Alberta, B
The King's University College, B
University of Alberta, BMD
University of Calgary, BMD
University of Lethbridge, BM

British Columbia

Simon Fraser University, BMD
Thompson Rivers University, B
Trinity Western University, B
The University of British Columbia, BMD
University College of the Fraser Valley, B
University of Northern British Columbia, B
University of Victoria, BMD

Manitoba

Brandon University, B
University of Manitoba, BMD
The University of Winnipeg, B

New Brunswick

Mount Allison University, BM
Université de Moncton, BM
University of New Brunswick Fredericton, BMD

Newfoundland and Labrador

Memorial University of Newfoundland, BMD

Nova Scotia

Acadia University, BM
Cape Breton University, B
Dalhousie University, BMD
Mount Saint Vincent University, B
St. Francis Xavier University, BM
Saint Mary's University, B
Université Sainte-Anne, B
University of King's College, B

Ontario

Brock University, BM
Carleton University, BMD
Lakehead University, BM
Laurentian University, BM
McMaster University, BMD
Queen's University at Kingston, BMD

Royal Military College of Canada, BMD
Ryerson University, B
Trent University, BM
University of Guelph, BMD
University of Ottawa, BMD
University of Toronto, BMD
University of Waterloo, BMD
The University of Western Ontario, BMD
University of Windsor, BMD
Wilfrid Laurier University, B
York University, BMD

Prince Edward Island

University of Prince Edward Island, BM

Quebec

Bishop's University, B
Concordia University, BMD
McGill University, BMD
Université Laval, BMD
Université de Montréal, BMD
Université du Québec àChicoutimi, B
Université du Québec àMontréal, BM
Université du Québec àRimouski, B
Université du Québec àTrois-Rivières, BM
Université de Sherbrooke, BMD

Saskatchewan

University of Regina, BMD
University of Saskatchewan, BMD

CHEMISTRY TEACHER EDUCATION

Alabama

Huntingdon College, B
Talladega College, B

Arizona

The University of Arizona, B

Arkansas

Arkansas State University, B
Arkansas Tech University, B
John Brown University, B
Southern Arkansas University-Magnolia, B

California

California State University, Chico, B
College of the Siskiyous, A
University of California, San Diego, B

Colorado

Colorado State University, B
Fort Lewis College, B

Connecticut

Sacred Heart University, B

Delaware

Delaware State University, B
University of Delaware, B

District of Columbia

The Catholic University of America, B

Florida

Bethune-Cookman College, B
Florida Institute of Technology, B
Manatee Community College, A
Miami Dade College, B

Georgia

Columbus State University, B
Georgia Southern University, B
Kennesaw State University, B

University of West Georgia, B

Hawaii

Brigham Young University-Hawaii, B

Idaho

Northwest Nazarene University, B

Illinois

Elmhurst College, B
Greenville College, B
Illinois Wesleyan University, B
Millikin University, B
Trinity Christian College, B
University of Illinois at Chicago, B
University of Illinois at Urbana-Champaign, B

Indiana

Ancilla College, A
Franklin College, B
Indiana University Bloomington, B
Indiana University Northwest, B
Indiana University-Purdue University Fort Wayne, B
Indiana University South Bend, B
Taylor University, B
University of Evansville, B
University of Saint Francis, B
Valparaiso University, B

Iowa

Buena Vista University, B
Dordt College, B
St. Ambrose University, B
The University of Iowa, B

Kansas

Bethany College, B
Central Christian College of Kansas, A
Pittsburg State University, B

Kentucky

Campbellsville University, B
Kentucky Wesleyan College, B
Murray State University, B
Pikeville College, B

Louisiana

Centenary College of Louisiana, B
Louisiana State University in Shreveport, B
Louisiana Tech University, B
McNeese State University, B
Northwestern State University of Louisiana, B
Southern University and Agricultural and Mechanical
   College, B
University of Louisiana at Lafayette, B
University of Louisiana at Monroe, B
Xavier University of Louisiana, B

Maine

Saint Joseph's College of Maine, B
University of Maine, B

Massachusetts

Boston University, B
Framingham State College, B

Michigan

Alma College, B
Central Michigan University, B
Eastern Michigan University, B
Hope College, B
Michigan State University, B
University of Michigan-Dearborn, B
University of Michigan-Flint, B
Western Michigan University, B

Minnesota

Bethel University, B
College of St. Catherine, B
Concordia College, B
Concordia University, St. Paul, B
Gustavus Adolphus College, B
Minnesota State University Moorhead, B
Saint Mary's University of Minnesota, B

Southwest Minnesota State University, B
University of St. Thomas, B

Mississippi

Blue Mountain College, B
Delta State University, B

Missouri

Central Methodist University, B
College of the Ozarks, B
Evangel University, B
Lincoln University, B
Lindenwood University, B
Maryville University of Saint Louis, B
Missouri State University, B
Southwest Baptist University, B
University of Missouri-Columbia, B
University of Missouri-St. Louis, B
Washington University in St. Louis, B

Montana

Montana State University-Billings, B
Rocky Mountain College, B
University of Great Falls, B

Nebraska

Chadron State College, B
Concordia University, B
Hastings College, B
Union College, B
University of Nebraska-Lincoln, B
Wayne State College, B

New Hampshire

Keene State College, B
Rivier College, B
University of New Hampshire, B

New Jersey

Bloomfield College, B
The College of New Jersey, B

New York

Brooklyn College of the City University of New
    York, B
City College of the City University of New York, B
The College of Saint Rose, B
Elmira College, B
Hofstra University, B
Ithaca College, B
Le Moyne College, B
Long Island University, Brooklyn Campus, B
Long Island University, C.W. Post Campus, B
Manhattanville College, B
Marist College, B
Nazareth College of Rochester, B
New York Institute of Technology, B
New York University, B
Niagara University, B
Pace University, B
Roberts Wesleyan College, B
St. Bonaventure University, B
St. Francis College, B
St. John's University, B
State University of New York College at
    Brockport, B
State University of New York College at Cortland, B
State University of New York College of
    Environmental Science and Forestry, B
State University of New York College at Old
    Westbury, B
State University of New York College at Oneonta, B
State University of New York College at Potsdam, B
Syracuse University, B
University at Albany, State University of New York, B
Utica College, B

North Carolina

Appalachian State University, B
Elizabeth City State University, B
Louisburg College, A
North Carolina Central University, B
North Carolina State University, B
The University of North Carolina at Charlotte, B

The University of North Carolina Wilmington, B

North Dakota

Mayville State University, B
Minot State University, B
North Dakota State University, B
Valley City State University, B

Ohio

Capital University, B
Kent State University, B
Miami University Hamilton, B
Ohio Dominican University, B
Ohio Northern University, B
Ohio Wesleyan University, B
The University of Akron, B
Xavier University, B

Oklahoma

East Central University, B
Oklahoma Baptist University, B

Pennsylvania

Alvernia College, B
Cabrini College, B
Chatham College, B
Juniata College, B
La Roche College, B
Lebanon Valley College, B
Mansfield University of Pennsylvania, B
Mercyhurst College, B
Messiah College, B
Moravian College, B
Saint Francis University, B
Seton Hill University, B
University of Pittsburgh at Johnstown, B
Waynesburg College, B
West Chester University of Pennsylvania, B
Widener University, B

Puerto Rico

Inter American University of Puerto Rico,
    Metropolitan Campus, B
University of Puerto Rico, Cayey University
    College, B

Rhode Island

Rhode Island College, B

South Carolina

Coker College, B

South Dakota

Mount Marty College, B

Tennessee

Christian Brothers University, B
Crichton College, B
King College, B
Lambuth University, B
Lincoln Memorial University, B
Maryville College, B
Tennessee Wesleyan College, B
Trevecca Nazarene University, B
The University of Tennessee at Martin, B

Texas

Baylor University, B
East Texas Baptist University, B
University of Mary Hardin-Baylor, B

Utah

Brigham Young University, B
Utah State University, B
Utah Valley State College, B
Weber State University, B
Westminster College, B

Virginia

Averett University, B
Bluefield College, B
Eastern Mennonite University, B

Old Dominion University, B

Washington

Central Washington University, B
Eastern Washington University, B
Washington State University, B
Western Washington University, B

West Virginia

Glenville State College, B
Wheeling Jesuit University, B

Wisconsin

Carroll College, B
Marian College of Fond du Lac, B
Mount Mary College, B
University of Wisconsin-River Falls, B
University of Wisconsin-Superior, B
Viterbo University, B

Ontario

University of Waterloo, B
University of Windsor, B
York University, B

Quebec

Bishop's University, B
McGill University, B

Saskatchewan

University of Regina, B

CHILD AND FAMILY STUDIES

Alabama

Auburn University, MD
The University of Alabama, M

Arizona

Arizona State University, D
The University of Arizona, MD

California

California State University, Los Angeles, M
Loma Linda University, MO
San Diego State University, M
San Jose State University, M
Stanford University, D
University of California, Davis, M
University of La Verne, M

Colorado

Colorado State University, M

Connecticut

University of Connecticut, MD

Delaware

University of Delaware, MD

Florida

Florida State University, MD
Nova Southeastern University, MD

Georgia

University of Georgia, MD

Illinois

Northern Illinois University, M
University of Illinois at Springfield, M

Indiana

Indiana State University, M
Purdue University, MD

Iowa

Iowa State University of Science and
    Technology, MD

Kansas

Kansas State University, MD

Kentucky

University of Kentucky, MD

Maryland

University of Maryland, College Park, MD

Massachusetts

Brandeis University, M
Fitchburg State College, O
Springfield College, O
Tufts University, MDO
Wheelock College, M

Michigan

Central Michigan University, M
Michigan State University, MD
Spring Arbor University, M
Wayne State University, O

Minnesota

Concordia University, St. Paul, M
St. Cloud State University, M
University of Minnesota, Twin Cities Campus, MD

Mississippi

University of Southern Mississippi, M

Missouri

University of Missouri-Columbia, MD

Montana

University of Great Falls, M

Nebraska

University of Nebraska-Lincoln, MD

Nevada

University of Nevada, Reno, M

New Hampshire

University of New Hampshire, M

New Jersey

Montclair State University, M

New Mexico

University of New Mexico, MD

New York

Cornell University, D
Roberts Wesleyan College, M
Syracuse University, MD

North Carolina

East Carolina University, M
The University of North Carolina at Greensboro, MD

North Dakota

North Dakota State University, MD

Ohio

Bowling Green State University, MD
Miami University, M
The Ohio State University, MD
Ohio University, M
The University of Akron, M

Oklahoma

Oklahoma State University, MD

Oregon

Oregon State University, MD

Pennsylvania

The Pennsylvania State University University Park
    Campus, MD

Rhode Island

University of Rhode Island, M

South Carolina

South Carolina State University, M

Tennessee

Middle Tennessee State University, M
Tennessee State University, MD

The University of Tennessee, MD
The University of Tennessee at Martin, M
Vanderbilt University, M

Texas

Texas State University-San Marcos, M
Texas Tech University, MD
Texas Woman's University, MD
University of North Texas, MD
The University of Texas at Austin, MD
The University of Texas at Dallas, M

Utah

Brigham Young University, MD
University of Utah, M
Utah State University, MD

Vermont

University of Vermont, M

Virginia

Virginia Polytechnic Institute and State
    University, MD

Washington

Central Washington University, M

West Virginia

West Virginia University, M

Wisconsin

Concordia University Wisconsin, M
University of Wisconsin-Madison, MD
University of Wisconsin-Stout, M

British Columbia

The University of British Columbia, MD
University of Victoria, M

Manitoba

University of Manitoba, M

Nova Scotia

Mount Saint Vincent University, M

Ontario

Brock University, M
University of Guelph, MD

Quebec

Concordia University, M

CHILD CARE AND SUPPORT SERVICES MANAGEMENT

Alabama

Calhoun Community College, A
Gadsden State Community College, A
H. Councill Trenholm State Technical College, A
Jefferson State Community College, A
Snead State Community College, A

Arizona

Northland Pioneer College, A
Pima Community College, A

Arkansas

Henderson State University, A
Ouachita Technical College, A
University of Central Arkansas, A

California

Antelope Valley College, A
Cerro Coso Community College, A
Feather River College, A
MiraCosta College, A
Modesto Junior College, A
Orange Coast College, A
Pacific Union College, B
Reedley College, A
Santa Barbara City College, A

Victor Valley College, A

Colorado

Arapahoe Community College, A
Colorado Northwestern Community College, A

Connecticut

Post University, A

Florida

The Baptist College of Florida, A
Florida Community College at Jacksonville, A

Georgia

Central Georgia Technical College, A
Georgia Southwestern State University, A

Idaho

Idaho State University, A

Illinois

College of DuPage, A
Highland Community College, A
Kishwaukee College, A
Lake Land College, A
McHenry County College, A
St. Augustine College, A

Indiana

Ivy Tech Community College-Bloomington, A
Ivy Tech Community College-Central Indiana, A
Ivy Tech Community College-Columbus, A
Ivy Tech Community College-East Central, A
Ivy Tech Community College-Kokomo, A
Ivy Tech Community College-Lafayette, A
Ivy Tech Community College-North Central, A
Ivy Tech Community College-Northeast, A
Ivy Tech Community College-Northwest, A
Ivy Tech Community College-Southeast, A
Ivy Tech Community College-Southern Indiana, A
Ivy Tech Community College-Southwest, A
Ivy Tech Community College-Wabash Valley, A
Ivy Tech Community College-Whitewater, A
Saint Mary-of-the-Woods College, B
Vincennes University, A

Iowa

Iowa Western Community College, A
Muscatine Community College, A
Scott Community College, A
Western Iowa Tech Community College, A

Kansas

Barton County Community College, A
Hutchinson Community College and Area Vocational
    School, A
Kansas City Kansas Community College, A

Kentucky

Eastern Kentucky University, A
Hopkinsville Community College, A

Louisiana

Nicholls State University, A
University of Louisiana at Monroe, A

Maine

Kennebec Valley Community College, A

Maryland

Hagerstown Community College, A
Harford Community College, A
Montgomery College, A
Wor-Wic Community College, A

Massachusetts

Bristol Community College, A
Massachusetts Bay Community College, A
Massasoit Community College, A

Michigan

Bay de Noc Community College, A
Central Michigan University, B
Gogebic Community College, A

Macomb Community College, A
Montcalm Community College, A
Northwestern Michigan College, A
Oakland Community College, A
Schoolcraft College, A
Southwestern Michigan College, A

Minnesota

Alexandria Technical College, A
Anoka Technical College, A
Concordia University, St. Paul, B
Dakota County Technical College, A
Normandale Community College, A
Northwest Technical College, A
Rasmussen College Mankato, A
St. Cloud Technical College, A

Missouri

College of the Ozarks, B
Jefferson College, A
Southeast Missouri State University, A

Montana

Dawson Community College, A

Nevada

Western Nevada Community College, A

New Hampshire

Hesser College, A

New Jersey

Ocean County College, A

New Mexico

Central New Mexico Community College, A
Eastern New Mexico University, A
Eastern New Mexico University-Roswell, A

New York

Broome Community College, A
Erie Community College, A
State University of New York College of Agriculture
   and Technology at Cobleskill, B

North Carolina

Asheville-Buncombe Technical Community
   College, A
Caldwell Community College and Technical
   Institute, A
Cape Fear Community College, A
Craven Community College, A
Montgomery Community College, A
Pitt Community College, A
Richmond Community College, A
Stanly Community College, A
Wilkes Community College, A

North Dakota

Lake Region State College, A
Mayville State University, B
Sitting Bull College, A

Ohio

Jefferson Community College, A
Mount Vernon Nazarene University, A
Youngstown State University, A

Oklahoma

Cameron University, A
Tulsa Community College, A

Oregon

Linn-Benton Community College, A

Pennsylvania

Academy of Medical Arts and Business, A
Chestnut Hill College, AB
Montgomery County Community College, A
Mount Aloysius College, A
Penn Foster Career School, A
Pennsylvania College of Technology, A
Seton Hill University, B

Western School of Health and Business Careers
   (Pittsburgh), A

South Carolina

Bob Jones University, AB
Central Carolina Technical College, A
York Technical College, A

Texas

Angelina College, A
Brazosport College, A
Central Texas College, A
Eastfield College, A
Houston Community College System, A
Kilgore College, A
San Antonio College, A
University of the Incarnate Word, B
Vernon College, A

Utah

Brigham Young University, B
Dixie State College of Utah, A
Weber State University, A

Virginia

J. Sargeant Reynolds Community College, A

Washington

Centralia College, A
Eastern Washington University, B
Grays Harbor College, A
Green River Community College, A
Olympic College, A
Peninsula College, A
Spokane Falls Community College, A
Walla Walla Community College, A

Wisconsin

Northeast Wisconsin Technical College, A
Wisconsin Indianhead Technical College, A

Wyoming

Central Wyoming College, A

British Columbia

Malaspina University-College, B
Thompson Rivers University, A
University College of the Fraser Valley, B

Ontario

Ryerson University, B

CHILD CARE PROVIDER/ASSISTANT

Alabama

Gadsden State Community College-Ayers
   Campus, A

Alaska

University of Alaska Fairbanks, A

Arizona

Eastern Arizona College, A
Northland Pioneer College, A
Pima Community College, A

Arkansas

University of Arkansas Community College at
   Hope, A

California

Cerro Coso Community College, A
College of the Redwoods, A
Crafton Hills College, A
Modesto Junior College, A
Orange Coast College, A
Pacific Union College, A

San Diego Mesa College, A

Colorado

Arapahoe Community College, A

Florida

Florida Community College at Jacksonville, A
Gulf Coast Community College, A

Illinois

City Colleges of Chicago, Malcolm X College, A
College of DuPage, A
College of Lake County, A
Heartland Community College, A
Highland Community College, A
Lincoln Land Community College, A
McHenry County College, A
Moraine Valley Community College, A
Parkland College, A
Triton College, A
Waubonsee Community College, A

Indiana

Saint Mary-of-the-Woods College, A
Vincennes University, A

Iowa

Iowa Lakes Community College, A
Iowa Western Community College, A

Kentucky

Eastern Kentucky University, A
Murray State University, A

Louisiana

Louisiana Technical College, A

Maine

Kennebec Valley Community College, A

Massachusetts

Massasoit Community College, A

Michigan

Mid Michigan Community College, A
Montcalm Community College, A

Minnesota

Alexandria Technical College, A
Dakota County Technical College, A
Northland Community and Technical College-Thief
   River Falls, A
Rasmussen College Mankato, A

Missouri

Mineral Area College, A
Penn Valley Community College, A

Nebraska

Wayne State College, B

New York

Corning Community College, A
Tompkins Cortland Community College, A
Westchester Community College, A

North Carolina

Bladen Community College, A
Brunswick Community College, A
Coastal Carolina Community College, A
Surry Community College, A

North Dakota

Lake Region State College, A
Mayville State University, A
United Tribes Technical College, A

Ohio

Cincinnati State Technical and Community
   College, A

Zane State College, A

Oregon

Southwestern Oregon Community College, A

Pennsylvania

Academy of Medical Arts and Business, A
Community College of Allegheny County, A
Lehigh Carbon Community College, A
Luzerne County Community College, A
Northampton County Area Community College, A
Pennsylvania College of Technology, A

South Carolina

Midlands Technical College, A
Trident Technical College, A
York Technical College, A

Texas

Angelina College, A
Hill College of the Hill Junior College District, A
Midland College, A
San Antonio College, A

Utah

Brigham Young University, B

Washington

Bates Technical College, A

West Virginia

Eastern West Virginia Community and Technical
College, A

Wisconsin

Moraine Park Technical College, A
Western Technical College, A

CHILD DEVELOPMENT

Alabama

Alabama State University, A
Auburn University, B
Enterprise-Ozark Community College, A
Northwest-Shoals Community College, A
Wallace State Community College, A

Arizona

Central Arizona College, A
Mesa Community College, A
Northland Pioneer College, A

Arkansas

Arkansas Tech University, A
National Park Community College, A
University of Arkansas Community College at
Morrilton, A
University of Arkansas at Fort Smith, A

California

American River College, A
Antelope Valley College, A
Bakersfield College, A
Barstow College, A
Cabrillo College, A
California State University, Dominguez Hills, B
California State University, East Bay, B
California State University, Fresno, B
California State University, Long Beach, B
California State University, Los Angeles, B
California State University, Northridge, B
Chaffey College, A
College of the Canyons, A
Compton Community College, A
Cosumnes River College (Sacramento), A
Crafton Hills College, A
Cuesta College, A
Cuyamaca College, A
De Anza College, A
East Los Angeles College, A
Foothill College, A
Gavilan College, A
Glendale Community College, A

Grossmont College, A
Hartnell College, A
Hope International University, B
Humboldt State University, B
Los Angeles City College, A
Los Angeles Southwest College, A
Los Angeles Valley College, A
Mendocino College, A
Merritt College, A
Modesto Junior College, A
Monterey Peninsula College, A
Mt. San Antonio College, A
Napa Valley College, A
National University, B
Ohlone College, A
Oxnard College, A
Pacific Oaks College, B
Palo Verde College, A
Point Loma Nazarene University, B
Porterville College, A
Saddleback College, A
San Diego State University, B
San Joaquin Delta College, A
San Jose City College, A
Santa Rosa Junior College, A
University of La Verne, B
Victor Valley College, A
West Hills Community College, A
Yuba College, A

Colorado

Aims Community College, A
Northeastern Junior College, A
Otero Junior College, A
Pikes Peak Community College, A

Connecticut

Albertus Magnus College, B
Briarwood College, A
Housatonic Community College, A
Mitchell College, AB
Northwestern Connecticut Community College, A
Quinnipiac University, B
Saint Joseph College, B

Delaware

Delaware Technical & Community College, Jack F.
Owens Campus, A
University of Delaware, B

District of Columbia

Gallaudet University, B
University of the District of Columbia, A

Florida

Broward Community College, A
Daytona Beach Community College, A
Florida State University, B
Gulf Coast Community College, A
Hillsborough Community College, A
Indian River Community College, A
Manatee Community College, A
Miami Dade College, A
Okaloosa-Walton College, A
Pensacola Junior College, A
Polk Community College, A
Santa Fe Community College, A
Seminole Community College, A
South Florida Community College, A

Georgia

Abraham Baldwin Agricultural College, A
Albany Technical College, A
Altamaha Technical College, A
Appalachian Technical College, A
Athens Technical College, A
Atlanta Metropolitan College, A
Atlanta Technical College, A
Augusta Technical College, A
Central Georgia Technical College, A
Chattahoochee Technical College, A
Columbus Technical College, A
Coosa Valley Technical College, A
East Central Technical College, A
Flint River Technical College, A

Griffin Technical College, A
Heart of Georgia Technical College, A
Lanier Technical College, A
Middle Georgia Technical College, A
Moultrie Technical College, A
North Metro Technical College, A
Northwestern Technical College, A
Ogeechee Technical College, A
Okefenokee Technical College, A
Sandersville Technical College, A
Savannah Technical College, A
South Georgia Technical College, A
Southeastern Technical College, A
Southwest Georgia Technical College, A
Swainsboro Technical College, A
University of Georgia, B
Valdosta Technical College, A
West Central Technical College, A
West Georgia Technical College, A

Guam

Guam Community College, A

Idaho

Boise State University, A
Brigham Young University -Idaho, A
College of Southern Idaho, A
Lewis-Clark State College, AB
University of Idaho, B

Illinois

Black Hawk College, A
City Colleges of Chicago, Harold Washington
College, A
City Colleges of Chicago, Kennedy-King College, A
City Colleges of Chicago, Richard J. Daley
College, A
College of DuPage, A
Danville Area Community College, A
Heartland Community College, A
Highland Community College, A
Illinois Eastern Community Colleges, Wabash Valley
College, A
Illinois Valley Community College, A
John Wood Community College, A
Kankakee Community College, A
Lewis and Clark Community College, A
Lincoln Christian College, B
Lincoln Land Community College, A
Olivet Nazarene University, B
Prairie State College, A
Rend Lake College, A
Richland Community College, A
Rock Valley College, A
Shawnee Community College, A
South Suburban College, A
Southeastern Illinois College, A
Southwestern Illinois College, A
Spoon River College, A
University of Illinois at Urbana-Champaign, B
William Rainey Harper College, A

Indiana

Goshen College, B
Indiana University Bloomington, B
Ivy Tech Community College-Central Indiana, A
Purdue University Calumet, A
Vincennes University, A

Iowa

Des Moines Area Community College, A
Ellsworth Community College, A
Hawkeye Community College, A
Indian Hills Community College, A
Iowa Lakes Community College, A
Iowa Western Community College, A
Kirkwood Community College, A
Marshalltown Community College, A
Southeastern Community College, North Campus, A

Kansas

Allen County Community College, A
Butler Community College, A
Cloud County Community College, A
Colby Community College, A

Cowley County Community College and Area
 Vocational-Technical School, A
Dodge City Community College, A
Friends University, AB
Garden City Community College, A
Independence Community College, A
Kansas State University, B
Labette Community College, A
Pittsburg State University, B
Pratt Community College, A
Seward County Community College, A
University of Saint Mary, B

Kentucky

Berea College, B
Eastern Kentucky University, AB
Elizabethtown Community and Technical College, A
Jefferson Community and Technical College, A

Louisiana

Grambling State University, A
Louisiana Tech University, B

Maine

Southern Maine Community College, A
University of Maine, B

Maryland

Frederick Community College, A
Howard Community College, A
University of Maryland Eastern Shore, B
Villa Julie College, A

Massachusetts

Lasell College, B
Lesley University, B
Mount Ida College, B
Mount Wachusett Community College, A
North Shore Community College, A
Tufts University, B
Wheelock College, B

Michigan

Delta College, A
Gogebic Community College, A
Kuyper College, AB
Lansing Community College, A
Madonna University, AB
Michigan State University, B
Mid Michigan Community College, A
Monroe County Community College, A
Muskegon Community College, A
North Central Michigan College, A
Northern Michigan University, AB
St. Clair County Community College, A
Siena Heights University, AB
Washtenaw Community College, A
Wayne County Community College District, A
Western Michigan University, B

Minnesota

Concordia College, B
Hennepin Technical College, A
Minneapolis Community and Technical College, A
Minnesota State College-Southeast Technical, A
Minnesota State University Mankato, B
Northland Community and Technical College-Thief
 River Falls, A
Rasmussen College Eagan, A
Rasmussen College Eden Prairie, A
Rasmussen College Mankato, A
Ridgewater College, A
Rochester Community and Technical College, A
St. Cloud State University, B
St. Cloud Technical College, A
Saint Paul College-A Community & Technical
 College, A

Mississippi

Alcorn State University, B
Copiah-Lincoln Community College, A
Hinds Community College, A
Holmes Community College, A
Jackson State University, B
Jones County Junior College, A

Northeast Mississippi Community College, A
Tougaloo College, AB

Missouri

College of the Ozarks, B
Evangel University, A
Missouri Baptist University, B
Moberly Area Community College, A
Northwest Missouri State University, B
Saint Charles Community College, A
St. Louis Community College at Florissant Valley, A
St. Louis Community College at Forest Park, A
St. Louis Community College at Meramec, A
Stephens College, B

Montana

Salish Kootenai College, A

Nebraska

Central Community College-Grand Island
 Campus, A
Central Community College-Hastings Campus, A
Metropolitan Community College, A
Southeast Community College, Lincoln Campus, A

Nevada

Community College of Southern Nevada, A
Truckee Meadows Community College, A
University of Nevada, Reno, B

New Hampshire

New Hampshire Community Technical College,
 Manchester/Stratham, A
New Hampshire Community Technical College,
 Nashua/Claremont, A
Southern New Hampshire University, B
University of New Hampshire, B

New Jersey

Atlantic Cape Community College, A
Hudson County Community College, A
Middlesex County College, A

New York

Borough of Manhattan Community College of the
 City University of New York, A
Bronx Community College of the City University of
 New York, A
Dutchess Community College, A
Orange County Community College, A
Pace University, B
St. Joseph's College, New York, B
State University of New York College at Oneonta, B
State University of New York at Plattsburgh, B
Suffolk County Community College, A
Syracuse University, B
Tompkins Cortland Community College, A
Westchester Community College, A

North Carolina

Appalachian State University, B
Campbell University, B
Central Piedmont Community College, A
Durham Technical Community College, A
East Carolina University, B
Forsyth Technical Community College, A
McDowell Technical Community College, A
Meredith College, B
Mitchell Community College, A
North Carolina Agricultural and Technical State
 University, B
Piedmont Baptist College, A
Rockingham Community College, A
Sandhills Community College, A
Southwestern Community College, A
The University of North Carolina at Charlotte, B
Vance-Granville Community College, A

Ohio

Ashland University, B
Bowling Green State University, B
Columbus State Community College, A
Franciscan University of Steubenville, A
Hocking College, A
James A. Rhodes State College, A

Miami University, B
Northwest State Community College, A
Ohio University, AB
Ohio University-Lancaster, A
Sinclair Community College, A
Stark State College of Technology, A
The University of Akron, B
University of Cincinnati, A
Youngstown State University, AB

Oklahoma

Connors State College, A
Murray State College, A
Northeastern Oklahoma Agricultural and Mechanical
 College, A
Oklahoma Baptist University, B
Oklahoma Christian University, B
Oklahoma City Community College, A
Redlands Community College, A
Tulsa Community College, A
University of Central Oklahoma, B
Western Oklahoma State College, A

Oregon

Lane Community College, A
Portland Community College, A
Portland State University, B
Rogue Community College, A
Umpqua Community College, A

Pennsylvania

Central Pennsylvania College, A
Community College of Allegheny County, A
Harcum College, A
Laurel Business Institute, A
Manor College, A
Reading Area Community College, A
Seton Hill University, B
University of Pittsburgh, B
Westmoreland County Community College, A

Puerto Rico

University of Puerto Rico, Río Piedras, B

South Carolina

Benedict College, B
Piedmont Technical College, A

South Dakota

South Dakota State University, B

Tennessee

Carson-Newman College, B
Chattanooga State Technical Community College, A
Cleveland State Community College, A
Dyersburg State Community College, A
East Tennessee State University, B
Freed-Hardeman University, B
Jackson State Community College, A
Tennessee Technological University, B
Trevecca Nazarene University, A
The University of Tennessee at Martin, B
Walters State Community College, A

Texas

Alvin Community College, A
Amarillo College, A
Angelina College, A
Blinn College, A
Brazosport College, A
Brookhaven College, A
Cisco Junior College, A
Coastal Bend College, A
College of the Mainland, A
Del Mar College, A
El Paso Community College, A
Hill College of the Hill Junior College District, A
Houston Baptist University, B
Houston Community College System, A
Howard College, A
Lamar State College-Port Arthur, A
Lamar University, A
Laredo Community College, A
North Harris College, A
Odessa College, A

San Antonio College, A
South Plains College, A
Texas A&M University-Kingsville, B
Texas Southern University, B
Texas Southmost College, A
Texas Tech University, B
Texas Woman's University, B
Trinity Valley Community College, A
University of North Texas, B
The University of Texas at Arlington, B

Utah

Brigham Young University, B
College of Eastern Utah, A
Snow College, A
Southern Utah University, A
University of Utah, B
Weber State University, AB

Vermont

Community College of Vermont, A
Southern Vermont College, A

Virginia

Hampton University, B
New River Community College, A
Virginia Western Community College, A

Washington

Centralia College, A
Eastern Washington University, B
Lake Washington Technical College, A
Peninsula College, A
Shoreline Community College, A
Skagit Valley College, A
Yakima Valley Community College, A

West Virginia

Fairmont State Community & Technical College, A
Fairmont State University, A

Wisconsin

Chippewa Valley Technical College, A
Fox Valley Technical College, A
Gateway Technical College, A
Madison Area Technical College, A
Milwaukee Area Technical College, A
Nicolet Area Technical College, A
Southwest Wisconsin Technical College, A
University of Wisconsin-Madison, B
Western Technical College, A

Alberta

University of Alberta, B

British Columbia

University of Victoria, B

Manitoba

University of Manitoba, B

New Brunswick

Université de Moncton, B

Nova Scotia

Mount Saint Vincent University, B

Ontario

Carleton University, B
University of Guelph, B

Saskatchewan

Briercrest College, B

CHINESE LANGUAGE AND LITERATURE

California

California State University, Long Beach, B
California State University, Los Angeles, B
Claremont McKenna College, B
Pomona College, B

San Francisco State University, B
San Jose State University, B
Scripps College, B
Stanford University, B
University of California, Berkeley, B
University of California, Davis, B
University of California, Irvine, B
University of California, Los Angeles, B
University of California, Riverside, B
University of California, San Diego, B
University of California, Santa Barbara, B
University of California, Santa Cruz, B

Colorado

University of Colorado at Boulder, B

Connecticut

Connecticut College, B
Yale University, B

District of Columbia

The George Washington University, B
Georgetown University, B

Georgia

Emory University, B

Hawaii

University of Hawaii at Manoa, B

Idaho

Brigham Young University -Idaho, A

Illinois

Augustana College, B
University of Chicago, B

Indiana

Indiana University Bloomington, B
University of Notre Dame, B

Iowa

Grinnell College, B
The University of Iowa, B

Maine

Bates College, B

Maryland

University of Maryland, College Park, B

Massachusetts

Harvard University, B
Simon's Rock College of Bard, B
Tufts University, B
University of Massachusetts Amherst, B
Wellesley College, B
Williams College, B

Michigan

University of Michigan, B

Minnesota

University of Minnesota, Twin Cities Campus, B

Missouri

Washington University in St. Louis, B

Montana

The University of Montana-Missoula, B

New Hampshire

Dartmouth College, B

New Jersey

Rutgers, The State University of New Jersey, New
  Brunswick/Piscataway, B

New York

Bard College, B
Brooklyn College of the City University of New
  York, B
Colgate University, B

Cornell University, B
Hobart and William Smith Colleges, B
Hunter College of the City University of New York, B
United States Military Academy, B
University at Albany, State University of New York, B
Vassar College, B

Ohio

The Ohio State University, B

Oklahoma

University of Oklahoma, B

Oregon

Pacific University, B
Portland State University, B
Reed College, B
University of Oregon, B

Pennsylvania

Carnegie Mellon University, B
Lincoln University, B
Swarthmore College, B
University of Pittsburgh, B

Texas

Trinity University, B

Utah

Brigham Young University, B
University of Utah, B

Vermont

Bennington College, B
Middlebury College, B

Washington

Pacific Lutheran University, B
University of Washington, B

Wisconsin

Lawrence University, B
University of Wisconsin-Madison, B

Alberta

University of Alberta, B

British Columbia

The University of British Columbia, B
University of Victoria, B

Saskatchewan

University of Regina, B

CHINESE STUDIES

California

Claremont McKenna College, B
San Francisco State University, M
Stanford University, MD
University of California, Berkeley, MD
University of California, Irvine, MD
University of the West, B

Colorado

University of Colorado at Boulder, M

Indiana

Indiana University Bloomington, MD

Kansas

University of Kansas, M

Massachusetts

Harvard University, MD
Simon's Rock College of Bard, B

University of Massachusetts Amherst, M

Missouri

Washington University in St. Louis, MD

New Jersey

Drew University, B

New York

Cornell University, MD
Sarah Lawrence College, B

Oregon

University of Oregon, MD

Washington

University of Washington, MD

Wisconsin

University of Wisconsin-Madison, MD

Alberta

University of Alberta, M

CHIROPRACTIC

California

Cleveland Chiropractic College-Los Angeles
   Campus, P

Connecticut

University of Bridgeport, P

Georgia

Life University, P

Illinois

Sauk Valley Community College, A

Iowa

Iowa Lakes Community College, A
Palmer College of Chiropractic, P

Kansas

Barton County Community College, A

Missouri

Cleveland Chiropractic College-Kansas City
   Campus, P
Logan University-College of Chiropractic, P

New York

D'Youville College, P

Texas

Texas Chiropractic College, P

Wisconsin

Moraine Park Technical College, A

CHRISTIAN STUDIES

Arkansas

Harding University, B

California

California Baptist University, B

Georgia

Mercer University, B
Truett-McConnell College, AB

Indiana

Bethel College, B

Iowa

Vennard College, AB

Kansas

Bethany College, B

Massachusetts

Gordon College, B

Michigan

Hillsdale College, B

Minnesota

Crown College, B

Mississippi

Mississippi College, B

Missouri

Lindenwood University, B

New Jersey

Seton Hall University, B

North Carolina

Heritage Bible College, AB

Ohio

God's Bible School and College, AB
Ursuline College, B

Tennessee

Bryan College, B

Texas

College of Biblical Studies-Houston, AB
Dallas Baptist University, B
Houston Baptist University, B
University of Mary Hardin-Baylor, B
Wayland Baptist University, AB

Ontario

University of Ottawa, B

Saskatchewan

Central Pentecostal College, B

CINEMATOGRAPHY AND FILM/VIDEO PRODUCTION

Arizona

Collins College: A School of Design and
   Technology, A
Glendale Community College, A
University of Advancing Technology, B

California

Academy of Art University, AB
American InterContinental University, B
Antelope Valley College, A
Art Center College of Design, B
The Art Institute of California-Los Angeles, AB
Brooks Institute of Photography, B
California State University, Long Beach, B
California State University, Northridge, B
Chapman University, B
City College of San Francisco, A
College of the Canyons, A
College of San Mateo, A
Columbia College Hollywood, B
Loyola Marymount University, B
Orange Coast College, A
Riverside Community College District, A
Saddleback College, A
San Francisco Art Institute, B
University of California, Santa Cruz, B
University of Southern California, B

Vanguard University of Southern California, B

Colorado

The Art Institute of Colorado, A
Colorado State University-Pueblo, B

Connecticut

Quinnipiac University, B
Sacred Heart University, B
University of Hartford, B

District of Columbia

American University, B

Florida

The Art Institute of Fort Lauderdale, A
Daytona Beach Community College, A
Florida Metropolitan University-Melbourne
   Campus, A
Florida Metropolitan University-North Orlando
   Campus, A
Florida State University, B
Keiser College (Daytona Beach), A
Miami Dade College, A
Miami International University of Art & Design, B
University of Central Florida, B
University of Miami, B
Valencia Community College, A

Georgia

American InterContinental University (Atlanta), AB
The Art Institute of Atlanta, AB
Savannah College of Art and Design, B

Illinois

College of DuPage, A
Columbia College Chicago, B
The Illinois Institute of Art-Chicago, B
School of the Art Institute of Chicago, B
Southern Illinois University Carbondale, B
University of Illinois at Chicago, B

Iowa

Maharishi University of Management, B
The University of Iowa, B
Waldorf College, B

Maine

New England School of Communications, AB
Southern Maine Community College, A

Maryland

Anne Arundel Community College, A

Massachusetts

Boston University, B
Emerson College, B
Fitchburg State College, B
Holyoke Community College, A
Massachusetts College of Art, B
School of the Museum of Fine Arts, Boston, B

Michigan

Grand Valley State University, B
Lansing Community College, A
Wayne State University, B

Minnesota

Brown College, A
Minneapolis College of Art and Design, B
Minneapolis Community and Technical College, A

Missouri

St. Louis Community College at Florissant Valley, A
St. Louis Community College at Meramec, A

Webster University, B

Montana

Montana State University, B

New Hampshire

Keene State College, B

New Jersey

Cumberland County College, A

New York

The Art Institute of New York City, A
Bard College, B
Brooklyn College of the City University of New
    York, B
City College of the City University of New York, B
College of Staten Island of the City University of
    New York, B
Five Towns College, AB
Hunter College of the City University of New York, B
Ithaca College, B
Long Island University, C.W. Post Campus, B
New York University, B
Pratt Institute, B
Purchase College, State University of New York, B
Rochester Institute of Technology, AB
Sarah Lawrence College, B
School of Visual Arts, B
Syracuse University, B

North Carolina

Guilford Technical Community College, A
North Carolina School of the Arts, B
Piedmont Community College, A
The University of North Carolina Wilmington, B

Ohio

Antioch College, B
Bowling Green State University, B
Cincinnati State Technical and Community
    College, A
Ohio University, B

Oklahoma

Oklahoma City University, B
University of Oklahoma, B

Oregon

George Fox University, B
Lane Community College, A

Pennsylvania

The Art Institute of Philadelphia, A
The Art Institute of Pittsburgh, AB
Bucks County Community College, A
DeSales University, B
Drexel University, B
Point Park University, B
The University of the Arts, B

South Carolina

Bob Jones University, B

Tennessee

Pellissippi State Technical Community College, A
Southern Adventist University, AB

Texas

The Art Institute of Dallas, A

Utah

Brigham Young University, B

Vermont

Bennington College, B
Burlington College, AB
Middlebury College, B

Washington

The Art Institute of Seattle, A
Everett Community College, A
The Evergreen State College, B
Seattle Central Community College, A

Shoreline Community College, A

Ontario

Ryerson University, B
York University, B

Quebec

Concordia University, B

Saskatchewan

University of Regina, B

CITY/URBAN, COMMUNITY AND REGIONAL PLANNING

Alabama

Alabama Agricultural and Mechanical University, B

Arizona

Arizona State University, B
The University of Arizona, B

California

California Polytechnic State University, San Luis
    Obispo, B
California State Polytechnic University, Pomona, B
California State University, Chico, B
University of California, Davis, B
University of California, Los Angeles, B
University of San Francisco, B
University of Southern California, B

District of Columbia

University of the District of Columbia, AB

Florida

Florida Atlantic University, B

Illinois

DePaul University, B
University of Illinois at Urbana-Champaign, B

Indiana

Ball State University, B
Indiana University Bloomington, B

Iowa

Iowa State University of Science and Technology, B

Maryland

Frostburg State University, B
Sojourner-Douglass College, B

Massachusetts

Bridgewater State College, B
Framingham State College, B
Harvard University, B
Massachusetts Institute of Technology, B
Salem State College, B
Westfield State College, B

Michigan

Eastern Michigan University, B
Michigan State University, B

Minnesota

Minnesota State University Mankato, B
St. Cloud State University, B

Mississippi

University of Southern Mississippi, B

Missouri

Missouri State University, B
Saint Louis University, B

Montana

The University of Montana-Missoula, B

Nevada

University of Nevada, Las Vegas, B

New Hampshire

Plymouth State University, B
University of New Hampshire, B

New Mexico

New Mexico State University, B

New York

Buffalo State College, State University of New
    York, B
Cornell University, B
New York University, B
State University of New York College of
    Environmental Science and Forestry, B
State University of New York at New Paltz, B

North Carolina

Appalachian State University, B
East Carolina University, B

Ohio

Miami University, B
Miami University Hamilton, B
The Ohio State University, B
University of Cincinnati, B
Wright State University, B

Oregon

Eastern Oregon University, B
Portland State University, B
University of Oregon, B

Pennsylvania

Indiana University of Pennsylvania, B
Mansfield University of Pennsylvania, B
Temple University, B
West Chester University of Pennsylvania, B

Texas

Texas State University-San Marcos, B
University of North Texas, B

Vermont

Burlington College, B

Virginia

University of Virginia, B

Washington

Eastern Washington University, B
University of Washington, B

West Virginia

West Virginia University Institute of Technology, B

Nova Scotia

Dalhousie University, B

Ontario

Carleton University, B
Ryerson University, B
University of Waterloo, B
The University of Western Ontario, B
University of Windsor, B

CIVIL DRAFTING AND CIVIL ENGINEERING CAD/CADD

Florida

Florida Technical College (Orlando), A

Montana

Montana Tech of The University of Montana, A

New Mexico

Luna Community College, A

Oregon

Blue Mountain Community College, A

Pennsylvania

Community College of Allegheny County, A

Washington

North Seattle Community College, A

British Columbia

British Columbia Institute of Technology, A

CIVIL ENGINEERING

Alabama

Alabama Agricultural and Mechanical University, B
Auburn University, BMD
The University of Alabama, BMD
The University of Alabama at Birmingham, BMD
The University of Alabama in Huntsville, BMD
University of South Alabama, B

Alaska

University of Alaska Anchorage, BM
University of Alaska Fairbanks, BMD

Arizona

Arizona State University, BMD
Northern Arizona University, B
The University of Arizona, BMD

Arkansas

University of Arkansas, BMD

California

California Institute of Technology, BMD
California Polytechnic State University, San Luis
  Obispo, BMO
California State Polytechnic University, Pomona, B
California State University, Chico, B
California State University, Fresno, BM
California State University, Fullerton, BM
California State University, Long Beach, BMDO
California State University, Los Angeles, BM
California State University, Northridge, M
California State University, Sacramento, BM
Loyola Marymount University, BM
San Diego State University, BM
San Francisco State University, B
San Jose State University, BM
Santa Clara University, M
Santa Rosa Junior College, A
Stanford University, BMDO
University of California, Berkeley, BMDO
University of California, Davis, BMDO
University of California, Irvine, BMD
University of California, Los Angeles, BMD
University of the Pacific, B
University of Southern California, BMDO

Colorado

Colorado School of Mines, B
Colorado State University, BMD
United States Air Force Academy, B
University of Colorado at Boulder, BMD
University of Colorado at Denver and Health
  Sciences Center - Downtown Denver
  Campus, BMD

Connecticut

Central Connecticut State University, M
United States Coast Guard Academy, B
University of Connecticut, BMD
University of Hartford, B
University of New Haven, B

Delaware

Delaware State University, B
University of Delaware, BMD

District of Columbia

The Catholic University of America, BMD
Gallaudet University, B
The George Washington University, BMDO
Howard University, BM

University of the District of Columbia, B

Florida

Embry-Riddle Aeronautical University, B
Florida Agricultural and Mechanical University, BMD
Florida Atlantic University, BM
Florida Institute of Technology, BMD
Florida International University, BMD
Florida State University, BMD
University of Central Florida, BMDO
University of Florida, BMDO
University of Miami, BMD
University of North Florida, B
University of South Florida, BMD

Georgia

Georgia Institute of Technology, BMDO
Macon State College, A
Savannah State University, B

Hawaii

University of Hawaii at Manoa, BMD

Idaho

Boise State University, BM
Idaho State University, BM
University of Idaho, BMD

Illinois

Bradley University, BM
Illinois Institute of Technology, BMD
Northwestern University, BMD
Southern Illinois University Carbondale, BM
Southern Illinois University Edwardsville, BM
University of Illinois at Chicago, BMD
University of Illinois at Urbana-Champaign, BMDO

Indiana

Purdue University, BMD
Rose-Hulman Institute of Technology, B
Tri-State University, B
University of Evansville, B
University of Notre Dame, BMD
Valparaiso University, B

Iowa

Dordt College, B
Iowa State University of Science and
  Technology, BMD
The University of Iowa, BMD

Kansas

Kansas State University, BMD
University of Kansas, BMD

Kentucky

University of Kentucky, BMD
University of Louisville, BMD
Western Kentucky University, B

Louisiana

Louisiana State University and Agricultural and
  Mechanical College, BMD
Louisiana Tech University, BMD
McNeese State University, M
Southern University and Agricultural and Mechanical
  College, B
Tulane University, BMD
University of Louisiana at Lafayette, BM
University of New Orleans, B

Maine

University of Maine, BMD

Maryland

The Johns Hopkins University, BMD
Morgan State University, BMD
University of Maryland, Baltimore County, MD
University of Maryland, College Park, BMD

Massachusetts

Bristol Community College, A
Harvard University, B
Massachusetts Institute of Technology, BMDO

Merrimack College, B
Northeastern University, BMD
Tufts University, BMD
University of Massachusetts Amherst, BMD
University of Massachusetts Dartmouth, BM
University of Massachusetts Lowell, BM
Worcester Polytechnic Institute, BMDO

Michigan

Calvin College, B
Lawrence Technological University, BM
Michigan State University, BMD
Michigan Technological University, BMD
University of Detroit Mercy, BM
University of Michigan, BMDO
Wayne State University, BMD
Western Michigan University, B

Minnesota

Itasca Community College, A
Minnesota State University Mankato, B
University of Minnesota, Twin Cities Campus, BMD

Mississippi

Jackson State University, B
Mississippi State University, BMD
University of Mississippi, B

Missouri

Lincoln University, B
University of Missouri-Columbia, BMD
University of Missouri-Kansas City, BM
University of Missouri-Rolla, BMD
University of Missouri-St. Louis, B
Washington University in St. Louis, BMDO

Montana

Carroll College, B
Montana State University, BMD
Montana Tech of The University of Montana, B

Nebraska

University of Nebraska-Lincoln, BMDO
University of Nebraska at Omaha, B

Nevada

University of Nevada, Las Vegas, BMD
University of Nevada, Reno, BMD

New Hampshire

University of New Hampshire, BMD

New Jersey

New Jersey Institute of Technology, BMD
Princeton University, BMD
Rowan University, B
Rutgers, The State University of New Jersey, New
  Brunswick/Piscataway, BMD
Stevens Institute of Technology, BMDO

New Mexico

New Mexico Institute of Mining and Technology, B
New Mexico State University, BMD
University of New Mexico, BMD

New York

City College of the City University of New
  York, BMD
Clarkson University, BMD
Columbia University, The Fu Foundation School of
  Engineering and Applied Science, B
Cooper Union for the Advancement of Science and
  Art, B
Cornell University, BMD
Hofstra University, B
Manhattan College, BM
Polytechnic University, Brooklyn Campus, BMD
Rensselaer Polytechnic Institute, BMDO
State University of New York at Buffalo, BMD
Syracuse University, BMD

United States Military Academy, B

North Carolina

Duke University, BMD
North Carolina Agricultural and Technical State University, BM
North Carolina State University, BMD
The University of North Carolina at Charlotte, BM

North Dakota

North Dakota State University, BMD
University of North Dakota, BM

Ohio

Case Western Reserve University, BMD
Cleveland State University, BMD
Ohio Northern University, B
The Ohio State University, BMD
Ohio University, BMD
Ohio University-Eastern, B
The University of Akron, BMD
University of Cincinnati, BMD
University of Dayton, BM
The University of Toledo, BMD
Youngstown State University, BM

Oklahoma

Oklahoma State University, BMD
University of Oklahoma, BMD

Oregon

Oregon Institute of Technology, B
Oregon State University, BMD
Portland State University, BMD
University of Portland, B

Pennsylvania

Bucknell University, BM
Carnegie Mellon University, BMDO
Drexel University, BMD
Lafayette College, B
Lehigh University, BMD
Messiah College, B
The Pennsylvania State University Abington College, B
The Pennsylvania State University Altoona College, B
The Pennsylvania State University Beaver Campus of the Commonwealth College, B
The Pennsylvania State University Berks Campus of the Berks-Lehigh Valley College, B
The Pennsylvania State University Delaware County Campus of the Commonwealth College, B
The Pennsylvania State University DuBois Campus of the Commonwealth College, B
The Pennsylvania State University at Erie, The Behrend College, B
The Pennsylvania State University Fayette Campus of the Commonwealth College, B
The Pennsylvania State University Hazleton Campus of the Commonwealth College, B
The Pennsylvania State University, Lehigh Valley Campus of the Berks-Lehigh Valley College, B
The Pennsylvania State University McKeesport Campus of the Commonwealth College, B
The Pennsylvania State University Mont Alto Campus of the Commonwealth College, B
The Pennsylvania State University New Kensington Campus of the Commonwealth College, B
The Pennsylvania State University Schuylkill Campus of the Capital College, B
The Pennsylvania State University Shenango Campus of the Commonwealth College, B
The Pennsylvania State University University Park Campus, BMD
The Pennsylvania State University Wilkes-Barre Campus of the Commonwealth College, B
The Pennsylvania State University Worthington Scranton Campus of the Commonwealth College, B
The Pennsylvania State University York Campus of the Commonwealth College, B
Temple University, BM
University of Pittsburgh, BMD
Ursinus College, B

Villanova University, BM
Widener University, BM

Puerto Rico

Caribbean University, B
Polytechnic University of Puerto Rico, BM
University of Puerto Rico, Mayagüez Campus, BMD

Rhode Island

Brown University, B
University of Rhode Island, BMD

South Carolina

The Citadel, The Military College of South Carolina, B
Clemson University, BMD
University of South Carolina, BMD

South Dakota

South Dakota School of Mines and Technology, BMD
South Dakota State University, BM

Tennessee

Christian Brothers University, B
Tennessee State University, B
Tennessee Technological University, BMD
University of Memphis, BMD
The University of Tennessee, BMD
Vanderbilt University, BMD

Texas

Lamar University, BMD
Prairie View A&M University, B
Rice University, BMD
Southern Methodist University, BMD
Texas A&M University, BMD
Texas A&M University-Kingsville, BM
Texas Tech University, BMD
University of Houston, BMD
The University of Texas at Arlington, BMD
The University of Texas at Austin, BMD
The University of Texas at El Paso, BMD
The University of Texas at San Antonio, BM
The University of Texas at Tyler, B

Utah

Brigham Young University, BMD
University of Utah, BMD
Utah State University, BMDO

Vermont

Norwich University, B
University of Vermont, BMD

Virginia

George Mason University, BM
Old Dominion University, BMD
Tidewater Community College, A
University of Virginia, BMD
Virginia Military Institute, B
Virginia Polytechnic Institute and State University, BMD

Washington

Gonzaga University, B
Saint Martin's University, BM
Seattle University, B
University of Washington, BMD
Walla Walla College, B
Washington State University, BMD

West Virginia

West Virginia University, BMD
West Virginia University Institute of Technology, B

Wisconsin

Marquette University, BMD
University of Wisconsin-Madison, BMD
University of Wisconsin-Milwaukee, B

University of Wisconsin-Platteville, B

Wyoming

University of Wyoming, BMD

Alberta

University of Alberta, BMD
University of Calgary, BMD

British Columbia

The University of British Columbia, BMD

Manitoba

University of Manitoba, BMD

New Brunswick

Université de Moncton, BM
University of New Brunswick Fredericton, BMD
University of New Brunswick Saint John, B

Newfoundland and Labrador

Memorial University of Newfoundland, BMD

Nova Scotia

Dalhousie University, BMD

Ontario

Carleton University, BMD
Lakehead University, B
McMaster University, BMD
Queen's University at Kingston, BMD
Royal Military College of Canada, BMD
Ryerson University, B
University of Ottawa, BMD
University of Toronto, BMD
University of Waterloo, BMD
The University of Western Ontario, B
University of Windsor, BMD

Quebec

Concordia University, BMDO
McGill University, MD
Université Laval, BMDO
Université de Sherbrooke, BMD

Saskatchewan

University of Saskatchewan, BMD

CIVIL ENGINEERING TECHNOLOGY/TECHNICIAN

Alabama

Alabama Agricultural and Mechanical University, B
Bishop State Community College, A
Gadsden State Community College, A

Arizona

Central Arizona College, A
Eastern Arizona College, A
Phoenix College, A

California

Allan Hancock College, A
Butte College, A
Chabot College, A
City College of San Francisco, A
Compton Community College, A
East Los Angeles College, A
Fullerton College, A
Los Angeles Valley College, A
Mt. San Antonio College, A
Pasadena City College, A
San Bernardino Valley College, A
San Joaquin Delta College, A
Shasta College, A

Colorado

Colorado State University-Pueblo, B
Metropolitan State College of Denver, B
Pueblo Community College, A

Trinidad State Junior College, A

Connecticut

Central Connecticut State University, B
Three Rivers Community College, A

Delaware

Delaware Technical & Community College, Jack F. Owens Campus, A
Delaware Technical & Community College, Stanton/Wilmington Campus, A
Delaware Technical & Community College, Terry Campus, A

District of Columbia

University of the District of Columbia, A

Florida

Broward Community College, A
Daytona Beach Community College, A
Florida Agricultural and Mechanical University, B
Florida Community College at Jacksonville, A
Gulf Coast Community College, A
Indian River Community College, A
Manatee Community College, A
Miami Dade College, A
Pensacola Junior College, A
Seminole Community College, A
Tallahassee Community College, A
Valencia Community College, A

Georgia

Chattahoochee Technical College, A
Georgia Southern University, B
Moultrie Technical College, A
Savannah State University, B
Southern Polytechnic State University, B

Guam

Guam Community College, A

Idaho

Brigham Young University -Idaho, A
Idaho State University, A

Illinois

Black Hawk College, A
College of Lake County, A
Lake Land College, A

Indiana

Indiana University-Purdue University Fort Wayne, A
Indiana University-Purdue University Indianapolis, A
Purdue University Calumet, A
Purdue University North Central, A
Vincennes University, A

Iowa

Des Moines Area Community College, A
Hawkeye Community College, A
Iowa Western Community College, A

Kansas

Independence Community College, A
Johnson County Community College, A

Kentucky

Lexington Community College, A
Murray State University, AB

Louisiana

Delgado Community College, A

Maine

Central Maine Community College, A

Maryland

Montgomery College, A

Massachusetts

Bristol Community College, A
Northern Essex Community College, A
Springfield Technical Community College, A

University of Massachusetts Lowell, AB
Wentworth Institute of Technology, AB

Michigan

Ferris State University, A
Lansing Community College, A
Macomb Community College, A
Michigan Technological University, A

Minnesota

Lake Superior College, A
Northwest Technical College, A
Rochester Community and Technical College, A
St. Cloud Technical College, A
Saint Paul College-A Community & Technical College, A

Mississippi

Copiah-Lincoln Community College, A
Hinds Community College, A
Itawamba Community College, A
Mississippi Delta Community College, A
Northeast Mississippi Community College, A
Northwest Mississippi Community College, A

Missouri

Fontbonne University, B
Jefferson College, A
Linn State Technical College, A
Missouri Western State University, AB
St. Louis Community College at Florissant Valley, A
Washington University in St. Louis, B

Montana

Montana State University-Northern, AB

Nebraska

Metropolitan Community College, A
Southeast Community College, Milford Campus, A

New Hampshire

University of New Hampshire, A

New Jersey

Burlington County College, A
Essex County College, A
Fairleigh Dickinson University, Metropolitan Campus, B
Gloucester County College, A
Mercer County Community College, A
Middlesex County College, A
Ocean County College, A
Union County College, A

New Mexico

New Mexico Military Institute, A
Southwestern Indian Polytechnic Institute, A

New York

Broome Community College, A
Erie Community College, North Campus, A
Hudson Valley Community College, A
Mohawk Valley Community College, A
Monroe Community College, A
Nassau Community College, A
New York City College of Technology of the City University of New York, A
Rochester Institute of Technology, B
State University of New York College of Technology at Alfred, A
State University of New York College of Technology at Canton, A
State University of New York Institute of Technology, B
Suffolk County Community College, A
Westchester Community College, A

North Carolina

Asheville-Buncombe Technical Community College, A
Central Piedmont Community College, A
Fayetteville Technical Community College, A
Gaston College, A
Guilford Technical Community College, A

Sandhills Community College, A
The University of North Carolina at Charlotte, B
Wake Technical Community College, A
Western Piedmont Community College, A

North Dakota

North Dakota State College of Science, A

Ohio

Belmont Technical College, A
Cincinnati State Technical and Community College, A
Clark State Community College, A
Columbus State Community College, A
James A. Rhodes State College, A
Lakeland Community College, A
Lorain County Community College, A
Sinclair Community College, A
Stark State College of Technology, A
University of Cincinnati, AB
The University of Toledo, AB
Youngstown State University, AB

Oklahoma

Oklahoma State University, Oklahoma City, A
Tulsa Community College, A

Oregon

Blue Mountain Community College, A
Chemeketa Community College, A
Linn-Benton Community College, A
Mt. Hood Community College, A
Portland Community College, A
Umpqua Community College, A

Pennsylvania

Butler County Community College, A
Community College of Allegheny County, A
Harrisburg Area Community College, A
Penn Foster Career School, A
Pennsylvania College of Technology, AB
Point Park University, AB
Temple University, B
University of Pittsburgh at Johnstown, B

Puerto Rico

Caribbean University, A
University of Puerto Rico at Bayamón, A
University of Puerto Rico at Ponce, A

South Carolina

Central Carolina Technical College, A
Florence-Darlington Technical College, A
Horry-Georgetown Technical College, A
Midlands Technical College, A
South Carolina State University, B
Spartanburg Technical College, A
Trident Technical College, A

South Dakota

Southeast Technical Institute, A

Tennessee

Chattanooga State Technical Community College, A
Nashville State Technical Community College, A
Pellissippi State Technical Community College, A

Texas

Hill College of the Hill Junior College District, A
Houston Community College System, A
San Antonio College, A
Texas Southern University, B
University of Houston, B
University of Houston-Downtown, B
University of North Texas, B

Vermont

Vermont Technical College, A

Virginia

Central Virginia Community College, A
J. Sargeant Reynolds Community College, A
Lord Fairfax Community College, A
Northern Virginia Community College, A

Old Dominion University, B
Virginia Western Community College, A
Wytheville Community College, A

Washington

Bates Technical College, A
Big Bend Community College, A
Centralia College, A
Everett Community College, A
Peninsula College, A
Renton Technical College, A
Shoreline Community College, A
Spokane Community College, A
Walla Walla Community College, A
Yakima Valley Community College, A

West Virginia

Bluefield State College, AB
Community & Technical College at West Virginia
   University Institute of Technology, A
Fairmont State Community & Technical College, A
Fairmont State University, AB
Potomac State College of West Virginia
   University, A
West Virginia University Institute of Technology, B

Wisconsin

Chippewa Valley Technical College, A
Gateway Technical College, A
Madison Area Technical College, A
Mid-State Technical College, A
Milwaukee Area Technical College, A
Moraine Park Technical College, A
Northeast Wisconsin Technical College, A

Wyoming

Laramie County Community College, A

British Columbia

British Columbia Institute of Technology, A

Ontario

Lakehead University, B

CLASSICAL, ANCIENT MEDITERRANEAN AND NEAR EASTERN STUDIES AND ARCHAEOLOGY

Alabama

Samford University, B

California

University of California, Berkeley, B
University of California, Davis, B
University of California, Irvine, B
University of California, Los Angeles, B

Maine

Bates College, B

Nebraska

Creighton University, B

New York

Columbia College, B

Utah

Brigham Young University, B

Ontario

University of Toronto, B

CLASSICS AND CLASSICAL LANGUAGES, LITERATURES, AND LINGUISTICS

Alabama

Samford University, B
The University of Alabama, B

Arizona

The University of Arizona, BM

Arkansas

University of Arkansas, B

California

California State University, Long Beach, B
Claremont McKenna College, B
Foothill College, A
Loyola Marymount University, B
Pitzer College, B
Pomona College, B
San Diego State University, B
San Francisco State University, BM
Santa Clara University, B
Scripps College, B
Stanford University, BMD
University of California, Berkeley, BMD
University of California, Irvine, BMD
University of California, Los Angeles, BMD
University of California, Riverside, BMD
University of California, San Diego, B
University of California, Santa Barbara, BMD
University of California, Santa Cruz, B
University of the Pacific, B
University of Southern California, BMD

Colorado

The Colorado College, B
University of Colorado at Boulder, BMD

Connecticut

Albertus Magnus College, B
Connecticut College, BM
Trinity College, B
University of Connecticut, B
Wesleyan University, B
Yale University, BD

Delaware

University of Delaware, B

District of Columbia

The Catholic University of America, BMDO
The George Washington University, B
Georgetown University, B
Howard University, B

Florida

Ave Maria University, B
Florida State University, BMD
New College of Florida, B
Rollins College, B
University of Florida, BMD
University of South Florida, B

Georgia

Agnes Scott College, B
Emory University, B
Mercer University, B
University of Georgia, BM

Hawaii

University of Hawaii at Manoa, BM

Idaho

University of Idaho, B

Illinois

Augustana College, B
Illinois Wesleyan University, B
Knox College, B
Loyola University Chicago, B
Monmouth College, B
North Central College, B
Northwestern University, B
Rockford College, B
Southern Illinois University Carbondale, B
University of Chicago, BMD
University of Illinois at Chicago, B

University of Illinois at Urbana-Champaign, BMD

Indiana

Ball State University, B
DePauw University, B
Earlham College, B
Hanover College, B
Indiana University Bloomington, BMD
University of Evansville, B
University of Notre Dame, B
Valparaiso University, B
Wabash College, B

Iowa

Coe College, B
Cornell College, B
Grinnell College, B
Luther College, B
The University of Iowa, BMD

Kansas

University of Kansas, BM

Kentucky

Asbury College, B
Berea College, B
Centre College, B
University of Kentucky, BM

Louisiana

Loyola University New Orleans, B
Tulane University, BM

Maine

Bowdoin College, B
Colby College, B
Saint Joseph's College of Maine, B
University of Maine, B
University of Southern Maine, B

Maryland

College of Notre Dame of Maryland, B
The Johns Hopkins University, BMD
Loyola College in Maryland, B
University of Maryland, Baltimore County, B
University of Maryland, College Park, BM

Massachusetts

Amherst College, B
Assumption College, B
Boston College, BM
Boston University, BMDO
Brandeis University, B
Clark University, B
College of the Holy Cross, B
Harvard University, BMD
Hellenic College, B
Mount Holyoke College, B
Smith College, B
Tufts University, BM
University of Massachusetts Amherst, BM
University of Massachusetts Boston, B
Wellesley College, B
Wheaton College, B
Williams College, B

Michigan

Ave Maria College, B
Calvin College, B
Grand Valley State University, B
Hillsdale College, B
Hope College, B
Kalamazoo College, B
University of Michigan, BMDO
Wayne State University, BM

Minnesota

Carleton College, B
College of Saint Benedict, B
Concordia College, B
Gustavus Adolphus College, B
Macalester College, B
Saint John's University, B
St. Olaf College, B

University of Minnesota, Twin Cities Campus, MD
University of St. Thomas, B

Mississippi

Millsaps College, B
University of Mississippi, BM

Missouri

Saint Louis University, B
Truman State University, B
University of Missouri-Columbia, BMD
Washington University in St. Louis, BM

Montana

The University of Montana-Missoula, B

Nebraska

University of Nebraska-Lincoln, BM

New Hampshire

Dartmouth College, B
Saint Anselm College, B
University of New Hampshire, B

New Jersey

Drew University, B
Montclair State University, B
Princeton University, BD
Rutgers, The State University of New Jersey, New
  Brunswick/Piscataway, BMD
Rutgers, The State University of New Jersey,
  Newark, B
Saint Peter's College, B
Seton Hall University, B

New Mexico

St. John's College, B
University of New Mexico, B

New York

Bard College, B
Barnard College, B
Brooklyn College of the City University of New
  York, B
Colgate University, B
The College of New Rochelle, B
Columbia College, B
Columbia University, School of General Studies, B
Cornell University, BD
Elmira College, B
Fordham University, BMD
Hamilton College, B
Hobart and William Smith Colleges, B
Hofstra University, B
Hunter College of the City University of New
  York, BM
Lehman College of the City University of New
  York, B
Manhattan College, B
Manhattanville College, B
New York University, BMDO
St. Bonaventure University, B
Sarah Lawrence College, B
Siena College, B
Skidmore College, B
State University of New York at Binghamton, B
State University of New York at Buffalo, BMD
Syracuse University, B
Union College, B
University at Albany, State University of New York, B
University of Rochester, B
Vassar College, B
Yeshiva University, B

North Carolina

Davidson College, B
Duke University, BD
Lenoir-Rhyne College, B
The University of North Carolina at Asheville, B
The University of North Carolina at Chapel
  Hill, BMD
The University of North Carolina at Greensboro, BM

Wake Forest University, B

North Dakota

North Dakota State University, B
University of North Dakota, B

Ohio

Bowling Green State University, B
Case Western Reserve University, B
The College of Wooster, B
Denison University, B
Franciscan University of Steubenville, B
Hiram College, B
John Carroll University, B
Kent State University, BM
Kenyon College, B
Miami University, B
Miami University Hamilton, B
Oberlin College, B
The Ohio State University, BMD
Ohio University, B
Ohio Wesleyan University, B
Pontifical College Josephinum, B
The University of Akron, B
University of Cincinnati, BMD
The University of Toledo, B
Wright State University, B
Xavier University, B

Oklahoma

University of Oklahoma, B

Oregon

Reed College, B
University of Oregon, BM
Willamette University, B

Pennsylvania

Bryn Mawr College, BMD
Bucknell University, B
Dickinson College, B
Duquesne University, B
Franklin and Marshall College, B
Gettysburg College, B
Haverford College, B
La Salle University, B
Lehigh University, B
Moravian College, B
The Pennsylvania State University Abington
  College, B
The Pennsylvania State University Altoona
  College, B
The Pennsylvania State University Beaver Campus
  of the Commonwealth College, B
The Pennsylvania State University Berks Campus of
  the Berks-Lehigh Valley College, B
The Pennsylvania State University Delaware County
  Campus of the Commonwealth College, B
The Pennsylvania State University DuBois Campus
  of the Commonwealth College, B
The Pennsylvania State University at Erie, The
  Behrend College, B
The Pennsylvania State University Fayette Campus
  of the Commonwealth College, B
The Pennsylvania State University Hazleton
  Campus of the Commonwealth College, B
The Pennsylvania State University, Lehigh Valley
  Campus of the Berks-Lehigh Valley College, B
The Pennsylvania State University McKeesport
  Campus of the Commonwealth College, B
The Pennsylvania State University Mont Alto
  Campus of the Commonwealth College, B
The Pennsylvania State University New Kensington
  Campus of the Commonwealth College, B
The Pennsylvania State University Schuylkill
  Campus of the Capital College, B
The Pennsylvania State University Shenango
  Campus of the Commonwealth College, B
The Pennsylvania State University University Park
  Campus, B
The Pennsylvania State University Wilkes-Barre
  Campus of the Commonwealth College, B
The Pennsylvania State University Worthington
  Scranton Campus of the Commonwealth
  College, B

The Pennsylvania State University York Campus of
  the Commonwealth College, B
Swarthmore College, B
Temple University, B
University of Pennsylvania, BMD
University of Pittsburgh, BMD
Ursinus College, B
Villanova University, BM
West Chester University of Pennsylvania, M
Westminster College, B

Rhode Island

Brown University, BMD
University of Rhode Island, B

South Carolina

College of Charleston, B
Furman University, B
University of South Carolina, B

South Dakota

The University of South Dakota, B

Tennessee

Rhodes College, B
Sewanee: The University of the South, B
The University of Tennessee, B
Vanderbilt University, BMD

Texas

Austin College, B
Baylor University, B
Rice University, B
Southwestern University, B
Texas Tech University, BM
Trinity University, B
University of Dallas, B
University of Houston, B
The University of Texas at Arlington, B
The University of Texas at Austin, BMD
The University of Texas at San Antonio, B

Utah

Brigham Young University, B
University of Utah, B

Vermont

Marlboro College, B
Middlebury College, B
Saint Michael's College, B
University of Vermont, BM

Virginia

Christendom College, B
The College of William and Mary, B
Hampden-Sydney College, B
Hollins University, B
Randolph-Macon College, B
Randolph-Macon Woman's College, B
Sweet Briar College, B
University of Mary Washington, B
University of Richmond, B
University of Virginia, BMD
Virginia Wesleyan College, B
Washington and Lee University, B

Washington

The Evergreen State College, B
Pacific Lutheran University, B
Seattle Pacific University, B
University of Puget Sound, B
University of Washington, BMD
Western Washington University, B
Whitman College, B

Wisconsin

Beloit College, B
Carthage College, B
Lawrence University, B
Marquette University, B
University of Wisconsin-Madison, BMD

University of Wisconsin-Milwaukee, BM

Alberta

University of Alberta, BMD
University of Calgary, BMD

British Columbia

The University of British Columbia, BMD
University of Victoria, BM

Manitoba

University of Manitoba, BM
The University of Winnipeg, B

New Brunswick

Mount Allison University, B
University of New Brunswick Fredericton, BM

Newfoundland and Labrador

Memorial University of Newfoundland, BM

Nova Scotia

Acadia University, B
Dalhousie University, BMD
St. Francis Xavier University, B
Saint Mary's University, B
University of King's College, B

Ontario

Brock University, B
Carleton University, B
Laurentian University, B
McMaster University, BMD
Nipissing University, B
Queen's University at Kingston, M
Trent University, B
University of Guelph, B
University of Ottawa, BMD
University of Toronto, BMD
University of Waterloo, B
The University of Western Ontario, BM
University of Windsor, B
Wilfrid Laurier University, B
York University, B

Quebec

Bishop's University, B
Concordia University, B
McGill University, B
Université Laval, B
Université de Montréal, B

Saskatchewan

University of Regina, B
University of Saskatchewan, B

CLINICAL CHILD PSYCHOLOGY

New York

St. John's University, B

Ontario

University of Windsor, B

CLINICAL LABORATORY SCIENCE/MEDICAL TECHNOLOGY/TECHNOLOGIST

Alabama

Auburn University, B
Chattahoochee Valley Community College, A
Faulkner University, A
Lawson State Community College, A
Northwest-Shoals Community College, A
Oakwood College, A
Tuskegee University, B
The University of Alabama at Birmingham, B

University of South Alabama, B

Arizona

Arizona State University, B
Phoenix College, A
The University of Arizona, B

Arkansas

Arkansas State University, AB
Arkansas Tech University, B
Harding University, B
Henderson State University, B
National Park Community College, A
Southern Arkansas University-Magnolia, B
University of Arkansas for Medical Sciences, B
University of Central Arkansas, B

California

Butte College, A
California State University, Chico, B
California State University, Dominguez Hills, B
Grossmont College, A
Humboldt State University, B
Loma Linda University, B
Orange Coast College, A
Pacific Union College, B

Colorado

Arapahoe Community College, A
Northeastern Junior College, A

Connecticut

University of Connecticut, B
University of Hartford, B
Western Connecticut State University, B

Delaware

University of Delaware, B
Wesley College, B

District of Columbia

The Catholic University of America, B
The George Washington University, B
Howard University, B
University of the District of Columbia, B

Florida

Barry University, B
Bethune-Cookman College, B
Broward Community College, A
Chipola College, A
Edison College, A
Florida Atlantic University, B
Florida Memorial University, B
Okaloosa-Walton College, A
Pensacola Junior College, A
Saint Leo University, B
Stetson University, B
University of Central Florida, B
University of South Florida, B
University of West Florida, B

Georgia

Andrew College, A
Armstrong Atlantic State University, B
Athens Technical College, A
Augusta State University, B
Clayton State University, A
Dalton State College, A
Darton College, A
Georgia Highlands College, A
Georgia Southern University, B
Medical College of Georgia, B
Waycross College, A
Young Harris College, A

Idaho

Boise State University, B
College of Southern Idaho, A
Idaho State University, B
North Idaho College, A

University of Idaho, B

Illinois

Aurora University, B
Benedictine University, B
Blackburn College, B
Bradley University, B
City Colleges of Chicago, Harry S. Truman College, A
City Colleges of Chicago, Kennedy-King College, A
City Colleges of Chicago, Richard J. Daley College, A
DePaul University, B
Dominican University, B
Eastern Illinois University, B
Elmhurst College, B
Eureka College, B
Illinois College, B
Illinois State University, B
Joliet Junior College, A
Lewis University, B
McKendree College, B
National-Louis University, B
North Park University, B
Northern Illinois University, B
Olivet Nazarene University, B
Quincy University, B
Roosevelt University, B
Rush University, B
University of St. Francis, B
Western Illinois University, B

Indiana

Anderson University, B
Ball State University, B
Indiana State University, B
Indiana University East, AB
Indiana University Kokomo, B
Indiana University-Purdue University Fort Wayne, B
Indiana University-Purdue University Indianapolis, B
Indiana University Southeast, B
Indiana Wesleyan University, B
Manchester College, B
Purdue University, B
Purdue University Calumet, B
Saint Joseph's College, B
Saint Mary-of-the-Woods College, B
Saint Mary's College, B
Taylor University, B
University of Indianapolis, B
University of Saint Francis, B
Vincennes University, A

Iowa

Dordt College, B
Ellsworth Community College, A
Graceland University, B
Loras College, B
Morningside College, B
Mount Mercy College, B
Northwestern College, B
Simpson College, B
The University of Iowa, B
Wartburg College, B

Kansas

Dodge City Community College, A
Fort Hays State University, B
Fort Scott Community College, A
Highland Community College, A
Kansas State University, B
Tabor College, B
University of Kansas, B
Wichita State University, B

Kentucky

Bellarmine University, B
Brescia University, B
Campbellsville University, B
Eastern Kentucky University, B
Henderson Community College, A
Kentucky State University, B
Kentucky Wesleyan College, B
Murray State University, B
Thomas More College, B

University of the Cumberlands, B
University of Kentucky, B
Western Kentucky University, B

Louisiana

Louisiana College, B
Louisiana State University at Alexandria, A
Louisiana State University Health Sciences
   Center, B
Louisiana Tech University, B
McNeese State University, B
Northwestern State University of Louisiana, B
Our Lady of Holy Cross College, B
Our Lady of the Lake College, B
University of Louisiana at Monroe, B
University of New Orleans, B

Maine

University of Maine, B
University of New England, B

Maryland

Anne Arundel Community College, A
Howard Community College, A
Morgan State University, B
Salisbury University, B
University of Maryland Eastern Shore, B
Villa Julie College, A

Massachusetts

American International College, B
Atlantic Union College, B
Boston University, B
Holyoke Community College, A
Labouré College, A
Marian Court College, A
Massachusetts College of Liberal Arts, B
Salem State College, B
Suffolk University, B
University of Massachusetts Boston, B
University of Massachusetts Dartmouth, B
University of Massachusetts Lowell, B
Westfield State College, B

Michigan

Andrews University, B
Aquinas College, B
Central Michigan University, B
Eastern Michigan University, B
Ferris State University, B
Grand Valley State University, B
Lake Superior State University, B
Lansing Community College, A
Madonna University, B
Michigan State University, B
Michigan Technological University, B
Monroe County Community College, A
Saginaw Valley State University, B
University of Michigan, B
University of Michigan-Flint, B
Wayne State University, B

Minnesota

Anoka-Ramsey Community College, A
Bemidji State University, B
College of St. Catherine, B
College of St. Catherine-Minneapolis, A
Concordia College, B
Globe College, A
Minnesota State University Mankato, B
Minnesota State University Moorhead, B
St. Cloud State University, B
Saint Mary's University of Minnesota, B
University of Minnesota, Twin Cities Campus, B
Winona State University, B

Mississippi

Alcorn State University, B
Blue Mountain College, B
Coahoma Community College, A
Delta State University, B
Holmes Community College, A
Jackson State University, B
Mississippi State University, B
Northeast Mississippi Community College, A

University of Mississippi, B
University of Mississippi Medical Center, B
University of Southern Mississippi, B

Missouri

Barnes-Jewish College of Nursing and Allied
   Health, B
Central Missouri State University, B
College of the Ozarks, B
Evangel University, B
Lincoln University, B
Lindenwood University, B
Maryville University of Saint Louis, B
Mineral Area College, A
Missouri Southern State University, B
Missouri State University, B
Missouri Western State University, B
Northwest Missouri State University, B
Saint Louis University, B
Southeast Missouri State University, B
Southwest Baptist University, B
University of Missouri-St. Louis, B
William Jewell College, B

Montana

Carroll College, B
The University of Montana-Missoula, B

Nebraska

College of Saint Mary, B
Peru State College, B
Union College, B
University of Nebraska Medical Center, B
Wayne State College, B
Western Nebraska Community College, A

Nevada

Community College of Southern Nevada, A
University of Nevada, Las Vegas, B

New Jersey

Bloomfield College, B
Caldwell College, B
Fairleigh Dickinson University, College at
   Florham, B
Fairleigh Dickinson University, Metropolitan
   Campus, B
Felician College, B
Kean University, B
Monmouth University, B
Ramapo College of New Jersey, B
Rutgers, The State University of New Jersey,
   Camden, B
Rutgers, The State University of New Jersey, New
   Brunswick/Piscataway, B
Rutgers, The State University of New Jersey,
   Newark, B

New Mexico

Eastern New Mexico University, B
Western New Mexico University, B

New York

The College of Saint Rose, B
College of Staten Island of the City University of
   New York, B
Elmira College, B
Hartwick College, B
Houghton College, B
Iona College, B
Keuka College, B
Long Island University, Brooklyn Campus, B
Long Island University, C.W. Post Campus, B
Marist College, B
Mount Saint Mary College, B
Pace University, B
Roberts Wesleyan College, B
Rochester Institute of Technology, B
Sage College of Albany, B
St. Francis College, B
St. John's University, B
St. Thomas Aquinas College, B
State University of New York at Buffalo, B
State University of New York College at
   Brockport, B

State University of New York, Fredonia, B
State University of New York at Plattsburgh, B
State University of New York Upstate Medical
   University, B
Stony Brook University, State University of New
   York, B
Suffolk County Community College, A
Westchester Community College, A
York College of the City University of New York, B

North Carolina

Appalachian State University, B
Belmont Abbey College, B
Catawba College, B
Central Piedmont Community College, A
East Carolina University, B
Elon University, B
Gardner-Webb University, B
Greensboro College, B
High Point University, B
Lenoir-Rhyne College, B
Louisburg College, A
Salem College, B
The University of North Carolina at Chapel Hill, B
The University of North Carolina at Charlotte, B
The University of North Carolina at Greensboro, B
The University of North Carolina Wilmington, B
Wake Forest University, B
Western Carolina University, B
Winston-Salem State University, B

North Dakota

Jamestown College, B
Minot State University, B
North Dakota State University, B
Turtle Mountain Community College, A
University of Mary, B
University of North Dakota, B

Ohio

Bowling Green State University, B
Cedarville University, B
College of Mount St. Joseph, B
Columbus State Community College, A
Cuyahoga Community College, A
Defiance College, B
Kent State University, B
Malone College, B
Miami University, B
Miami University Hamilton, B
Mount Vernon Nazarene University, B
Muskingum College, B
Ohio Northern University, B
The Ohio State University, B
Ohio University-Eastern, B
University of Cincinnati, B
University of Cincinnati Raymond Walters College, A
The University of Findlay, B
University of Rio Grande, B
The University of Toledo, AB
Wright State University, B
Xavier University, B
Youngstown State University, B

Oklahoma

Cameron University, B
Eastern Oklahoma State College, A
Langston University, B
Northeastern State University, B
Oklahoma Christian University, B
Oklahoma Panhandle State University, B
Southwestern Oklahoma State University, B
University of Central Oklahoma, B

Oregon

Oregon State University, B

Pennsylvania

Alvernia College, B
Bloomsburg University of Pennsylvania, B
Cedar Crest College, B
Cheyney University of Pennsylvania, B
CHI Institute, A
Clarion University of Pennsylvania, B
College Misericordia, B

DeSales University, B
East Stroudsburg University of Pennsylvania, B
Gannon University, B
Gwynedd-Mercy College, B
Indiana University of Pennsylvania, B
King's College, B
Kutztown University of Pennsylvania, B
Lycoming College, B
Mansfield University of Pennsylvania, B
Marywood University, B
Mercyhurst College, B
Moravian College, B
Reading Area Community College, A
Saint Francis University, B
Seton Hill University, B
Thiel College, B
Thomas Jefferson University, B
University of Pittsburgh, B
University of the Sciences in Philadelphia, B
The University of Scranton, B
Wilkes University, B
York College of Pennsylvania, B

Puerto Rico

Inter American University of Puerto Rico, Fajardo
    Campus, B
Inter American University of Puerto Rico,
    Metropolitan Campus, B
Inter American University of Puerto Rico, San
    Germán Campus, B
Pontifical Catholic University of Puerto Rico, B
University of Puerto Rico, Mayagüez Campus, B
University of the Sacred Heart, B

Rhode Island

Rhode Island College, B
Salve Regina University, B
University of Rhode Island, B

South Carolina

Coker College, B
Erskine College, B
Southern Wesleyan University, B
Winthrop University, B

South Dakota

Augustana College, B
Mount Marty College, B
Northern State University, B
South Dakota State University, B
University of Sioux Falls, B

Tennessee

Austin Peay State University, B
Belmont University, B
Carson-Newman College, B
King College, B
Lee University, B
Lincoln Memorial University, B
Southern Adventist University, B
Tennessee State University, B
Trevecca Nazarene University, B
Tusculum College, B
Union University, B
The University of Tennessee, B
The University of Tennessee at Chattanooga, B

Texas

Abilene Christian University, B
Amarillo College, A
Angelina College, A
Angelo State University, B
Baylor University, B
Cisco Junior College, A
Del Mar College, A
East Texas Baptist University, B
El Centro College, A
Grayson County College, A
Kilgore College, A
Lamar University, B
Lubbock Christian University, B
Midwestern State University, B
Prairie View A&M University, B
Sam Houston State University, B
South Texas College, A

Southwestern Adventist University, B
Stephen F. Austin State University, B
Tarleton State University, B
Tarrant County College District, A
Temple College, A
Texas A&M University-Corpus Christi, B
Texas Southern University, B
Texas State University-San Marcos, B
Texas Woman's University, B
University of Houston, B
University of the Incarnate Word, B
University of Mary Hardin-Baylor, B
University of North Texas, B
The University of Texas at Arlington, B
The University of Texas at Austin, B
The University of Texas at El Paso, B
The University of Texas Health Science Center at
    San Antonio, B
The University of Texas Medical Branch, B
The University of Texas-Pan American, B
The University of Texas at San Antonio, B
The University of Texas Southwestern Medical
    Center at Dallas, B
The University of Texas at Tyler, B
West Texas A&M University, B

Utah

Brigham Young University, B
University of Utah, B
Utah State University, B
Weber State University, AB

Vermont

University of Vermont, B

Virginia

Averett University, B
Bridgewater College, B
Eastern Mennonite University, B
Emory & Henry College, B
Ferrum College, B
George Mason University, B
Longwood University, B
Mary Baldwin College, B
Norfolk State University, B
Old Dominion University, B
Radford University, B
Roanoke College, B
The University of Virginia's College at Wise, B
Virginia Commonwealth University, B

Washington

Renton Technical College, A
Seattle University, B
University of Washington, B
Walla Walla College, B

West Virginia

Concord University, B
Marshall University, B
West Liberty State College, B
West Virginia University, B

Wisconsin

Carroll College, B
Edgewood College, B
Marian College of Fond du Lac, B
University of Wisconsin-La Crosse, B
University of Wisconsin-Madison, B
University of Wisconsin-Milwaukee, B
University of Wisconsin-Oshkosh, B

University of Wisconsin-Stevens Point, B

Wyoming

Casper College, A

CLINICAL LABORATORY SCIENCES

Alabama

The University of Alabama at Birmingham, M

California

California State University, Dominguez Hills, MO
San Francisco State University, M

Connecticut

Quinnipiac University, M

District of Columbia

The Catholic University of America, MD

Illinois

Rush University, M

Iowa

The University of Iowa, MD

Kentucky

University of Kentucky, MD

Massachusetts

University of Massachusetts Lowell, M

Michigan

Michigan State University, M
Wayne State University, MO

Minnesota

University of Minnesota, Twin Cities Campus, M

Mississippi

University of Mississippi Medical Center, MD

Nebraska

University of Nebraska Medical Center, M

New York

Long Island University, C.W. Post Campus, M
Rochester Institute of Technology, M
State University of New York at Buffalo, M

North Carolina

Duke University, M

North Dakota

University of North Dakota, M

Pennsylvania

Thomas Jefferson University, M

Puerto Rico

University of Puerto Rico, Medical Sciences
    Campus, M

Rhode Island

University of Rhode Island, M

Texas

The University of Texas Health Science Center at
    San Antonio, M

Virginia

Virginia Commonwealth University, M

Washington

University of Washington, M

Wisconsin

Milwaukee School of Engineering, M
University of Wisconsin-Milwaukee, M

Alberta

University of Alberta, MD

Quebec

Université de Sherbrooke, MD

CLINICAL/MEDICAL LABORATORY ASSISTANT

Arkansas

North Arkansas College, A

Colorado

IntelliTec College (Grand Junction), A
Westwood College-Denver South, A

Florida

Jones College (Miami), A

Kentucky

Somerset Community College, A

Louisiana

Louisiana Technical College, A

Maine

The University of Maine at Augusta, A

Maryland

Allegany College of Maryland, A

Michigan

Northern Michigan University, A

Minnesota

Minnesota State Community and Technical
College-Fergus Falls, A

Ohio

Columbus State Community College, A
Zane State College, A

Pennsylvania

Harrisburg Area Community College, A

Washington

Clover Park Technical College, A
Edmonds Community College, A

Wisconsin

Moraine Park Technical College, A

CLINICAL/MEDICAL LABORATORY SCIENCE AND ALLIED PROFESSIONS

Illinois

Roosevelt University, B

Kentucky

Bellarmine University, B

Michigan

Oakland Community College, A

Missouri

Saint Louis University, B

New York

Hunter College of the City University of New York, B

North Dakota

University of North Dakota, B

Ohio

The University of Akron, A

Pennsylvania

Lebanon Valley College, B

Washington

Highline Community College, A

CLINICAL/MEDICAL LABORATORY TECHNICIAN

Alabama

Alabama Southern Community College, A
Alabama State University, B
Auburn University, B
Bevill State Community College, A
Community College of the Air Force, A
Faulkner University, A
Gadsden State Community College, A
George C. Wallace Community College, A
George Corley Wallace State Community College, A
Jefferson State Community College, A
Wallace State Community College, A

Alaska

University of Alaska Anchorage, A

Arizona

Apollo College-Phoenix, Inc., A
Apollo College-Tucson, Inc., A
Phoenix College, A

Arkansas

Arkansas State University-Beebe, A
National Park Community College, A
North Arkansas College, A
Phillips Community College of the University of
Arkansas, A
South Arkansas Community College, A

California

California State University, Dominguez Hills, B
California State University, East Bay, B
San Bernardino Valley College, A
San Diego Mesa College, A
Sonoma State University, B

Colorado

Arapahoe Community College, A
IntelliTec Medical Institute, A

Connecticut

Housatonic Community College, A
Manchester Community College, A

Delaware

Delaware Technical & Community College, Jack F.
Owens Campus, A

District of Columbia

The George Washington University, A
University of the District of Columbia, A

Florida

Barry University, B
Brevard Community College, A
Broward Community College, A
Indian River Community College, A
Keiser College (Fort Lauderdale), A
Lake City Community College, A
Miami Dade College, A
St. Petersburg College, A

Georgia

Central Georgia Technical College, A
Clayton State University, A
Coastal Georgia Community College, A
Dalton State College, A
DeKalb Technical College, A
Macon State College, A
Okefenokee Technical College, A

Waycross College, A

Hawaii

Kapiolani Community College, A

Idaho

Brigham Young University -Idaho, A

Illinois

City Colleges of Chicago, Malcolm X College, A
DePaul University, B
Elgin Community College, A
Illinois Central College, A
John A. Logan College, A
John Wood Community College, A
Kankakee Community College, A
Oakton Community College, A
Rend Lake College, A
Southeastern Illinois College, A
Southwestern Illinois College, A

Indiana

Indiana Business College-Medical, A
Indiana University Northwest, A
Ivy Tech Community College-North Central, A
Ivy Tech Community College-Wabash Valley, A
Purdue University Calumet, B
Vincennes University, A

Iowa

Des Moines Area Community College, A
Hawkeye Community College, A
Iowa Central Community College, A
North Iowa Area Community College, A
Northeast Iowa Community College, A
Scott Community College, A
Western Iowa Tech Community College, A

Kansas

Barton County Community College, A
Friends University, A
Pittsburg State University, B
Seward County Community College, A
Wichita Area Technical College, A

Kentucky

Eastern Kentucky University, A
Hazard Community and Technical College, A
Southeast Kentucky Community and Technical
College, A

Louisiana

Delgado Community College, A
MedVance Institute, A
Our Lady of the Lake College, AB
Southern University at Shreveport, A

Maine

Central Maine Community College, A
University of Maine at Presque Isle, A

Maryland

Allegany College of Maryland, A
Morgan State University, B
University of Maryland Eastern Shore, B
Villa Julie College, A

Massachusetts

Bristol Community College, A
Massachusetts College of Liberal Arts, B
Northeastern University, B
Springfield Technical Community College, A

Michigan

Baker College of Owosso, A
Ferris State University, AB
Kellogg Community College, A
Madonna University, AB
Northern Michigan University, B
Wayne County Community College District, A

Minnesota

Alexandria Technical College, A
Hibbing Community College, A

Lake Superior College, A
Minnesota State Community and Technical
  College-Fergus Falls, A
Minnesota West Community and Technical
  College, A
Northwest Technical College, A
Rochester Community and Technical College, A
Saint Paul College-A Community & Technical
  College, A
Winona State University, B

Mississippi

Copiah-Lincoln Community College, A
Hinds Community College, A
Meridian Community College, A
Mississippi Delta Community College, A
Mississippi Gulf Coast Community College, A
Northeast Mississippi Community College, A

Missouri

Mineral Area College, A
Moberly Area Community College, A
Northwest Missouri State University, B
St. Louis Community College at Forest Park, A
Three Rivers Community College, A
University of Missouri-Kansas City, B

Montana

The University of Montana-Missoula, B

Nebraska

Mid-Plains Community College, A
Southeast Community College, Lincoln Campus, A

Nevada

Community College of Southern Nevada, A
Western Nevada Community College, A

New Hampshire

University of New Hampshire, B

New Jersey

Bergen Community College, A
Brookdale Community College, A
Camden County College, A
County College of Morris, A
Felician College, A
Mercer County Community College, A
Middlesex County College, A
Ocean County College, A
Union County College, A

New Mexico

Central New Mexico Community College, A
New Mexico Junior College, A
New Mexico State University-Alamogordo, A
University of New Mexico, B
University of New Mexico-Gallup, A

New York

Bronx Community College of the City University of
  New York, A
Broome Community College, A
Clinton Community College, A
College of Staten Island of the City University of
  New York, A
Dutchess Community College, A
Erie Community College, North Campus, A
Eugenio María de Hostos Community College of the
  City University of New York, A
Farmingdale State University of New York, A
Genesee Community College, A
Jamestown Community College, A
Long Island University, C.W. Post Campus, B
Mount Saint Mary College, B
Nassau Community College, A
Orange County Community College, A
Queensborough Community College of the City
  University of New York, A
St. Thomas Aquinas College, B
State University of New York College of Agriculture
  and Technology at Cobleskill, A
State University of New York College of Agriculture
  and Technology at Morrisville, A

State University of New York College of Technology
  at Canton, A
Westchester Community College, A

North Carolina

Alamance Community College, A
Asheville-Buncombe Technical Community
  College, A
Beaufort County Community College, A
Central Piedmont Community College, A
Coastal Carolina Community College, A
Davidson County Community College, A
Gardner-Webb University, B
Guilford Technical Community College, A
Halifax Community College, A
Pamlico Community College, A
Sandhills Community College, A
Southeastern Community College, A
Southwestern Community College, A
Wake Technical Community College, A
Western Piedmont Community College, A

North Dakota

Bismarck State College, A
Turtle Mountain Community College, A

Ohio

Cincinnati State Technical and Community
  College, A
Clark State Community College, A
Columbus State Community College, A
Lakeland Community College, A
Lorain County Community College, A
Marion Technical College, A
The Ohio State University Agricultural Technical
  Institute, A
Shawnee State University, A
Southwestern College of Business (Cincinnati), A
Stark State College of Technology, A
University of Cincinnati, A
University of Rio Grande, A
Washington State Community College, A
Youngstown State University, A

Oklahoma

Cameron University, B
East Central University, B
Eastern Oklahoma State College, A
Oral Roberts University, B
Rose State College, A
Seminole State College, A
Southwestern Oklahoma State University at
  Sayre, A
Tulsa Community College, A
University of Oklahoma, B
University of Science and Arts of Oklahoma, B

Oregon

Portland Community College, A

Pennsylvania

Bloomsburg University of Pennsylvania, B
California University of Pennsylvania, B
Community College of Allegheny County, A
Community College of Beaver County, A
Community College of Philadelphia, A
Edinboro University of Pennsylvania, B
Harcum College, A
Harrisburg Area Community College, A
Holy Family University, B
Lehigh Carbon Community College, A
Manor College, A
Montgomery County Community College, A
The Pennsylvania State University DuBois Campus
  of the Commonwealth College, B
The Pennsylvania State University Hazleton
  Campus of the Commonwealth College, A
The Pennsylvania State University Schuylkill
  Campus of the Capital College, A
Reading Area Community College, A
Slippery Rock University of Pennsylvania, B

Western School of Health and Business Careers
  (Pittsburgh), A

Rhode Island

Community College of Rhode Island, A

South Carolina

Florence-Darlington Technical College, A
Greenville Technical College, A
Midlands Technical College, A
Orangeburg-Calhoun Technical College, A
Spartanburg Technical College, A
Tri-County Technical College, A
Trident Technical College, A
York Technical College, A

South Dakota

Lake Area Technical Institute, A
Mitchell Technical Institute, A
Northern State University, B
Presentation College, A
Southeast Technical Institute, A

Tennessee

Columbia State Community College, A
Jackson State Community College, A
Martin Methodist College, A
MedVance Institute, A
Roane State Community College, A
Southwest Tennessee Community College, A
Walters State Community College, A

Texas

Angelina College, A
Austin Community College, A
Central Texas College, A
Del Mar College, A
El Centro College, A
El Paso Community College, A
Grayson County College, A
Houston Community College System, A
Kilgore College, A
Lamar State College-Orange, A
Laredo Community College, A
McLennan Community College, A
Navarro College, A
Odessa College, A
St. Philip's College, A
Tarrant County College District, A
Temple College, A
Texas Southmost College, A
Tyler Junior College, A
Victoria College, A
Wharton County Junior College, A

Utah

Salt Lake Community College, A
University of Utah, B
Weber State University, AB

Virginia

Central Virginia Community College, A
J. Sargeant Reynolds Community College, A
Longwood University, B
Northern Virginia Community College, A
Piedmont Virginia Community College, A
Thomas Nelson Community College, A
Wytheville Community College, A

Washington

Pierce College, A
Shoreline Community College, A
Wenatchee Valley College, A

West Virginia

Fairmont State University, A
Marshall University, A
Southern West Virginia Community and Technical
  College, A

Wisconsin

Chippewa Valley Technical College, A
Madison Area Technical College, A
Marquette University, B

Milwaukee Area Technical College, A
Northeast Wisconsin Technical College, A
Western Technical College, A

Alberta

University of Alberta, B

British Columbia

British Columbia Institute of Technology, A
The University of British Columbia, B

CLINICAL/MEDICAL SOCIAL WORK

Arkansas

Arkansas Tech University, B

Minnesota

University of St. Thomas, B

Montana

Dawson Community College, A

Nebraska

Central Community College-Grand Island
   Campus, A
Central Community College-Hastings Campus, A

North Carolina

Wayne Community College, A

Pennsylvania

Slippery Rock University of Pennsylvania, B

CLINICAL MICROBIOLOGY

Idaho

Idaho State University, M

New Jersey

Rutgers, The State University of New Jersey, New
   Brunswick/Piscataway, MD

Wisconsin

University of Wisconsin-La Crosse, M

CLINICAL NUTRITION/NUTRITIONIST

Massachusetts

Framingham State College, B

Pennsylvania

Messiah College, B
West Chester University of Pennsylvania, B

CLINICAL PSYCHOLOGY

Alabama

Troy University, M
The University of Alabama, D
The University of Alabama at Birmingham, D

Alaska

University of Alaska Anchorage, M
University of Alaska Fairbanks, D

Arizona

Argosy University/Phoenix, MDO
Arizona State University, D

California

Antioch University Los Angeles, M
Antioch University Santa Barbara, MD
Argosy University/Orange County, MD
Argosy University/San Francisco Bay Area, MD
Azusa Pacific University, MD

Biola University, B
California Institute of Integral Studies, D
California Lutheran University, M
California State University, Dominguez Hills, M
California State University, Fullerton, BM
California State University, San Bernardino, M
Loma Linda University, D
New College of California, M
San Diego State University, MD
San Jose State University, M
University of California, San Diego, D
University of California, Santa Barbara, D
University of La Verne, D
University of Southern California, D
Vanguard University of Southern California, M

Colorado

Colorado State University-Pueblo, B
University of Denver, MD
Western State College of Colorado, B

Connecticut

Fairfield University, B
University of Connecticut, MD
University of Hartford, MD

Delaware

University of Delaware, D

District of Columbia

American University, D
The Catholic University of America, D
Gallaudet University, D
The George Washington University, D
Howard University, D
University of the District of Columbia, M

Florida

Argosy University/Sarasota, D
Argosy University/Tampa, MD
Barry University, M
Carlos Albizu University, Miami Campus, D
Florida Institute of Technology, D
Florida State University, D
Nova Southeastern University, DO
University of Central Florida, MD
University of Florida, D
University of Miami, D
University of South Florida, D

Georgia

Argosy University/Atlanta, MD
Emory University, D
Valdosta State University, M

Hawaii

Argosy University/Hawaii, MD
University of Hawaii at Manoa, D

Idaho

Idaho State University, D

Illinois

Argosy University/Chicago, MD
Argosy University/Schaumburg, MD
Benedictine University, M
Blackburn College, B
DePaul University, MD
Eastern Illinois University, M
Illinois Institute of Technology, D
Loyola University Chicago, MD
Northwestern University, D
Roosevelt University, MD
Southern Illinois University Carbondale, MD
University of Illinois at Urbana-Champaign, MD
Western Illinois University, M
Wheaton College, MD

Indiana

Ball State University, M
Indiana State University, D
Indiana University-Purdue University
   Indianapolis, MD

Valparaiso University, M

Iowa

Loras College, M

Kansas

Emporia State University, M
University of Kansas, MD
Washburn University, M
Wichita State University, D

Kentucky

Eastern Kentucky University, M
Morehead State University, M
Murray State University, M
Spalding University, MD
University of Louisville, D

Louisiana

Louisiana State University and Agricultural and
   Mechanical College, MD
Northwestern State University of Louisiana, M

Maine

Husson College, B
University of Maine, D

Maryland

Loyola College in Maryland, MDO
Towson University, M
University of Maryland, College Park, D

Massachusetts

American International College, M
Clark University, D
Eastern Nazarene College, B
Lesley University, M
Suffolk University, D
University of Massachusetts Amherst, MD
University of Massachusetts Boston, D
University of Massachusetts Dartmouth, M
Westfield State College, M

Michigan

Central Michigan University, D
Eastern Michigan University, MD
Madonna University, M
University of Detroit Mercy, MD
University of Michigan, D
University of Michigan-Flint, B
Wayne State University, DO
Western Michigan University, MD

Minnesota

Minnesota State University Mankato, M
University of Minnesota, Twin Cities Campus, D

Mississippi

Jackson State University, D
Mississippi State University, M
University of Mississippi, D

Missouri

Evangel University, M
Saint Louis University, MD
University of Missouri-St. Louis, DO
Washington University in St. Louis, D

Montana

The University of Montana-Missoula, D

Nevada

University of Nevada, Las Vegas, D

New Hampshire

Franklin Pierce College, B
Southern New Hampshire University, O

New Jersey

Fairleigh Dickinson University, College at
   Florham, M
Fairleigh Dickinson University, Metropolitan
   Campus, MD
Montclair State University, M

Rutgers, The State University of New Jersey, New
    Brunswick/Piscataway, MD
William Paterson University of New Jersey, M

New Mexico

University of New Mexico, MD

New York

Adelphi University, DO
City College of the City University of New York, D
Fordham University, D
Hofstra University, DO
Long Island University, Brooklyn Campus, D
Long Island University, C.W. Post Campus, D
New York University, D
Pace University, D
Queens College of the City University of New
    York, M
St. John's University, MD
State University of New York at Binghamton, MD
State University of New York at Buffalo, D
Stony Brook University, State University of New
    York, D
Syracuse University, D
University at Albany, State University of New
    York, D
University of Rochester, D
Yeshiva University, D

North Carolina

Appalachian State University, M
Duke University, D
East Carolina University, M
The University of North Carolina at Chapel Hill, D
The University of North Carolina at Charlotte, M
The University of North Carolina at Greensboro, MD
Western Carolina University, M

North Dakota

North Dakota State University, MD
University of North Dakota, D

Ohio

Bowling Green State University, MD
Case Western Reserve University, D
Cleveland State University, M
Kent State University, MD
Miami University, D
The Ohio State University, D
Ohio University, D
University of Cincinnati, D
University of Dayton, M
The University of Toledo, D
Wright State University, D
Xavier University, D

Oklahoma

Oklahoma State University, D
University of Tulsa, MDO

Oregon

George Fox University, BMD
University of Oregon, D

Pennsylvania

Bryn Mawr College, D
Chestnut Hill College, DO
Drexel University, MDO
Duquesne University, D
Edinboro University of Pennsylvania, M
Immaculata University, D
Indiana University of Pennsylvania, D
La Salle University, MD
Mansfield University of Pennsylvania, B
Marywood University, MD
Millersville University of Pennsylvania, M
Moravian College, B
The Pennsylvania State University Harrisburg
    Campus, BM
The Pennsylvania State University University Park
    Campus, MD
Temple University, D
University of Pennsylvania, D
West Chester University of Pennsylvania, M

Widener University, DO

Puerto Rico

Carlos Albizu University, D
Pontifical Catholic University of Puerto Rico, M

Rhode Island

University of Rhode Island, D

South Carolina

Francis Marion University, M
University of South Carolina, MD
University of South Carolina Aiken, M

South Dakota

The University of South Dakota, MD

Tennessee

Austin Peay State University, M
East Tennessee State University, M
Fisk University, M
Tennessee State University, B
University of Memphis, D
The University of Tennessee, D

Texas

Abilene Christian University, M
Argosy University/Dallas, MD
Baylor University, MD
Lamar University, BM
Prairie View A&M University, D
St. Mary's University of San Antonio, M
Sam Houston State University, BMD
Southern Methodist University, MD
Texas A&M University, MD
Texas Tech University, D
University of Houston, D
University of Houston-Clear Lake, BM
University of North Texas, D
The University of Texas at El Paso, M
The University of Texas of the Permian Basin, M
The University of Texas Southwestern Medical
    Center at Dallas, D
The University of Texas at Tyler, M

Utah

Brigham Young University, D
Utah State University, D

Vermont

College of St. Joseph, M
Saint Michael's College, M
University of Vermont, D

Virginia

Argosy University/Washington D.C., MD
Averett University, B
The College of William and Mary, D
George Mason University, D
Norfolk State University, M
Old Dominion University, D
Radford University, M
University of Virginia, D
Virginia Commonwealth University, D
Virginia Polytechnic Institute and State University, D

Washington

Argosy University/Seattle, MD
Seattle Pacific University, D
University of Washington, D
Washington State University, D

West Virginia

Marshall University, M
West Virginia University, MD

Wisconsin

Cardinal Stritch University, M
Marquette University, M
University of Wisconsin-Madison, D

University of Wisconsin-Milwaukee, MD

Alberta

University of Alberta, B
University of Calgary, MD

British Columbia

Simon Fraser University, B
The University of British Columbia, BMD
University of Victoria, MD

Manitoba

University of Manitoba, D

New Brunswick

University of New Brunswick Fredericton, B

Nova Scotia

Acadia University, M
Dalhousie University, D

Ontario

Lakehead University, BMD
Queen's University at Kingston, MD
University of Windsor, BD

Quebec

Concordia University, MDO
McGill University, D
Université Laval, D

CLINICAL RESEARCH

California

Touro University International, M
University of California, Los Angeles, M
University of California, San Diego, M

Florida

University of Florida, M

Georgia

Emory University, M

Illinois

Northwestern University, MO

Iowa

Palmer College of Chiropractic, M
The University of Iowa, O

Kentucky

University of Louisville, O

Maryland

The Johns Hopkins University, MD

Massachusetts

Boston University, M
Tufts University, MD

Michigan

University of Michigan, M

Minnesota

University of Minnesota, Twin Cities Campus, M

New York

New York University, M

North Carolina

Duke University, M

Ohio

Case Western Reserve University, M

Pennsylvania

Thomas Jefferson University, O
University of Pittsburgh, MO

South Carolina

Medical University of South Carolina, M

Tennessee

Vanderbilt University, M

Virginia

University of Virginia, M

CLOTHING AND TEXTILES

Alabama

Auburn University, M
The University of Alabama, M

California

Academy of Art University, M
University of California, Davis, M

Florida

Florida State University, MD

Georgia

University of Georgia, MD

Indiana

Indiana State University, M
Indiana University Bloomington, M
Purdue University, MD

Iowa

Iowa State University of Science and
    Technology, MD

Kansas

Kansas State University, MD

Kentucky

University of Kentucky, M

Minnesota

University of Minnesota, Twin Cities Campus, MD

Missouri

University of Missouri-Columbia, M

Nebraska

University of Nebraska-Lincoln, M

New York

Cornell University, MD
Fashion Institute of Technology, M

North Carolina

North Carolina State University, D

Ohio

The Ohio State University, MD
The University of Akron, M

Oklahoma

Oklahoma State University, MD

Oregon

Oregon State University, MD

Pennsylvania

Philadelphia University, M

Rhode Island

University of Rhode Island, M

Tennessee

The University of Tennessee, MD

Texas

University of North Texas, M

Virginia

Virginia Polytechnic Institute and State
    University, MD

Washington

Washington State University, M

Alberta

University of Alberta, MD

Manitoba

University of Manitoba, M

COGNITIVE PSYCHOLOGY AND PSYCHOLINGUISTICS

California

California State University, Stanislaus, B
Occidental College, B
University of California, San Diego, B
University of California, Santa Cruz, B

Connecticut

Yale University, B

Georgia

University of Georgia, B

Illinois

Northwestern University, B

Indiana

Indiana University Bloomington, B

Kansas

University of Kansas, B

Louisiana

Tulane University, B

Maryland

The Johns Hopkins University, B

Massachusetts

Harvard University, B
Massachusetts Institute of Technology, B
Simon's Rock College of Bard, B
Wellesley College, B

Missouri

Washington University in St. Louis, B

New Hampshire

Dartmouth College, B

New York

State University of New York at Oswego, B
Vassar College, B

Oregon

George Fox University, B

Rhode Island

Brown University, B

Tennessee

Vanderbilt University, B

Texas

The University of Texas at Dallas, B

Virginia

Averett University, B

Wisconsin

Lawrence University, B

Ontario

Carleton University, B
Wilfrid Laurier University, B

COGNITIVE SCIENCES

Alabama

The University of Alabama, D

Arizona

Arizona State University, D

California

University of California, Berkeley, B
University of California, Los Angeles, B
University of California, San Diego, D

Colorado

Colorado State University, M
University of Colorado at Colorado Springs, D

Connecticut

University of Connecticut, BMD

Delaware

University of Delaware, D

District of Columbia

The George Washington University, D

Florida

Florida State University, D

Georgia

Emory University, D

Illinois

Northwestern University, D
University of Illinois at Urbana-Champaign, MD

Indiana

Ball State University, M
Indiana University Bloomington, D
University of Evansville, B
University of Notre Dame, D

Iowa

Iowa State University of Science and Technology, D

Louisiana

Louisiana State University and Agricultural and
    Mechanical College, MD
University of Louisiana at Lafayette, D

Maryland

The Johns Hopkins University, D
University of Maryland, Baltimore County, D
University of Maryland, College Park, D

Massachusetts

Boston University, MD
Brandeis University, D
Hampshire College, B
Harvard University, BM
Massachusetts Institute of Technology, D

Michigan

Wayne State University, D

Minnesota

University of Minnesota, Twin Cities Campus, D

Mississippi

Mississippi State University, D

New Hampshire

Dartmouth College, D

New Jersey

Rutgers, The State University of New Jersey, New
    Brunswick/Piscataway, D

Rutgers, The State University of New Jersey, Newark, D

New Mexico

New Mexico Highlands University, M

New York

Cornell University, D
Hunter College of the City University of New York, M
New York University, D
Rensselaer Polytechnic Institute, D
State University of New York at Binghamton, MD
State University of New York at Buffalo, D
State University of New York at Oswego, B
University of Rochester, BMD

North Carolina

Duke University, D
The University of North Carolina at Chapel Hill, D
The University of North Carolina at Greensboro, MD

Ohio

Case Western Reserve University, B
The Ohio State University, D
The University of Akron, MD

Oregon

George Fox University, B
University of Oregon, MD

Pennsylvania

Carnegie Mellon University, BD
The Pennsylvania State University University Park Campus, MD
Temple University, D
University of Pennsylvania, B
University of Pittsburgh, D

Rhode Island

Brown University, MD

Texas

Rice University, MD
Texas A&M University, MD
The University of Texas at Austin, D
The University of Texas at Dallas, MD

Wisconsin

Lawrence University, B
University of Wisconsin-Madison, D

British Columbia

Simon Fraser University, B
The University of British Columbia, BMD

Ontario

Carleton University, D
Queen's University at Kingston, BMD
University of Guelph, M

COLLEGE STUDENT COUNSELING AND PERSONNEL SERVICES

Pennsylvania

Kutztown University of Pennsylvania, B

COMMERCIAL AND ADVERTISING ART

Alabama

Auburn University, B
Community College of the Air Force, A
George C. Wallace Community College, A
J. F. Drake State Technical College, A
James H. Faulkner State Community College, A
Oakwood College, A
Samford University, B
University of Montevallo, B

Virginia College at Huntsville, A

Arizona

The Art Center Design College, A
Collins College: A School of Design and Technology, A
Eastern Arizona College, A
Glendale Community College, A
Grand Canyon University, B
University of Advancing Technology, B
Yavapai College, A

Arkansas

Arkansas State University, B
National Park Community College, A
University of Arkansas Community College at Morrilton, A

California

Academy of Art University, AB
Allan Hancock College, A
American InterContinental University, AB
Art Center College of Design, B
The Art Institute of California-San Diego, AB
The Art Institute of California-San Francisco, AB
Biola University, B
Brooks College (Long Beach), A
Butte College, A
California College of the Arts, B
California Institute of the Arts, B
California Polytechnic State University, San Luis Obispo, B
California State Polytechnic University, Pomona, B
California State University, Dominguez Hills, B
California State University, East Bay, B
California State University, Fresno, B
California State University, Fullerton, B
California State University, Long Beach, B
Chabot College, A
College of the Redwoods, A
College of San Mateo, A
College of the Sequoias, A
Compton Community College, A
Cuyamaca College, A
De Anza College, A
Don Bosco Technical Institute, A
FIDM/The Fashion Institute of Design & Merchandising, Los Angeles Campus, A
FIDM/The Fashion Institute of Design & Merchandising, Orange County Campus, A
FIDM/The Fashion Institute of Design & Merchandising, San Diego Campus, A
FIDM/The Fashion Institute of Design & Merchandising, San Francisco Campus, A
Fresno City College, A
Glendale Community College, A
Golden West College, A
Hartnell College, A
Laguna College of Art & Design, B
Laney College, A
Lassen Community College District, A
Los Angeles Trade-Technical College, A
Los Angeles Valley College, A
Los Medanos College, A
Mission College, A
Modesto Junior College, A
Monterey Peninsula College, A
Moorpark College, A
Mt. San Antonio College, A
Mt. Sierra College, B
Newschool of Architecture & Design, A
Notre Dame de Namur University, B
Ohlone College, A
Orange Coast College, A
Otis College of Art and Design, B
Palomar College, A
Platt College (Cerritos), A
Platt College-Los Angeles, Inc, A
Platt College (Newport Beach), A
Platt College (Ontario), A
Platt College San Diego, A
Porterville College, A
Reedley College, A
Saddleback College, A
San Bernardino Valley College, A
San Diego City College, A

San Joaquin Delta College, A
Santa Ana College, A
Santa Barbara City College, A
Santa Monica College, A
Solano Community College, A
Southwestern College, A
University of the Pacific, B
Ventura College, A
Westwood College-Inland Empire, A
Woodbury University, B

Colorado

Aims Community College, A
Arapahoe Community College, A
The Art Institute of Colorado, AB
Colorado Mountain College, A
Colorado State University, B
Community College of Aurora, A
Mesa State College, A
Platt College, AB
Trinidad State Junior College, A
University of Denver, B
Western State College of Colorado, B

Connecticut

Albertus Magnus College, B
Housatonic Community College, A
Manchester Community College, A
Middlesex Community College, A
Mitchell College, A
Northwestern Connecticut Community College, A
Norwalk Community College, A
Paier College of Art, Inc., B
Sacred Heart University, AB
Tunxis Community College, A
University of New Haven, AB
Western Connecticut State University, B

Delaware

University of Delaware, B

District of Columbia

Gallaudet University, B
University of the District of Columbia, A

Florida

The Art Institute of Fort Lauderdale, A
Daytona Beach Community College, A
Florida Agricultural and Mechanical University, B
Florida Community College at Jacksonville, A
Florida Keys Community College, A
Florida Metropolitan University-North Orlando Campus, A
Florida Metropolitan University-Tampa Campus, A
Florida Southern College, B
Florida State University, B
Hillsborough Community College, A
International Academy of Design & Technology, AB
Lake-Sumter Community College, A
Lynn University, B
Manatee Community College, A
Miami Dade College, A
Miami International University of Art & Design, A
Okaloosa-Walton College, A
Palm Beach Community College, A
Pensacola Junior College, A
St. Johns River Community College, A
St. Petersburg College, A
Santa Fe Community College, A
University of Miami, B
Valencia Community College, A

Georgia

The Art Institute of Atlanta, AB
Brenau University, B

Hawaii

Honolulu Community College, A
Leeward Community College, A

Idaho

Boise State University, B
Brigham Young University -Idaho, B
College of Southern Idaho, A
North Idaho College, A

Northwest Nazarene University, B

Illinois

American Academy of Art, B
City Colleges of Chicago, Harold Washington College, A
City Colleges of Chicago, Kennedy-King College, A
College of DuPage, A
Columbia College Chicago, B
Concordia University, B
DePaul University, B
Dominican University, B
Elgin Community College, A
Highland Community College, A
Illinois Central College, A
The Illinois Institute of Art-Chicago, AB
International Academy of Design & Technology, AB
Judson College, B
Lewis University, B
Lincoln College, A
Lincoln College-Normal, A
Millikin University, B
Olivet Nazarene University, B
Rend Lake College, A
Robert Morris College, A
School of the Art Institute of Chicago, B
South Suburban College, A
Trinity Christian College, B
Triton College, A
University of Illinois at Chicago, B
Westwood College-Chicago Du Page, AB
Westwood College-Chicago O'Hare Airport, AB

Indiana

Anderson University, B
Ball State University, B
Grace College, B
Huntington University, B
Indiana University Bloomington, B
Indiana University-Purdue University Fort Wayne, AB
International Business College (Fort Wayne), AB
Taylor University, B
University of Indianapolis, B
University of Saint Francis, AB
Vincennes University, A

Iowa

Buena Vista University, B
Des Moines Area Community College, A
Dordt College, B
Drake University, B
Graceland University, B
Hawkeye Community College, A
Iowa Lakes Community College, A
Iowa State University of Science and Technology, B
Iowa Western Community College, A
Morningside College, B
Simpson College, B
Upper Iowa University, B
Wartburg College, B

Kansas

Colby Community College, A
Fort Hays State University, B
Fort Scott Community College, A
Friends University, A
Garden City Community College, A
Highland Community College, A
Johnson County Community College, A
Labette Community College, A
Pratt Community College, A
Wichita State University, B

Kentucky

Brescia University, B
Eastern Kentucky University, B
Jefferson Community and Technical College, A
Northern Kentucky University, B
Western Kentucky University, B

Louisiana

Delgado Community College, A
Delta College of Arts and Technology, A
Louisiana College, B

Louisiana Tech University, B
Loyola University New Orleans, B

Maine

Central Maine Community College, A

Maryland

Baltimore City Community College, A
Hagerstown Community College, A
Harford Community College, A
Montgomery College, A
Villa Julie College, A

Massachusetts

Becker College, AB
Boston University, B
Clark University, B
Curry College, B
Emmanuel College, B
Greenfield Community College, A
Holyoke Community College, A
Lasell College, B
Massachusetts College of Art, B
Middlesex Community College, A
Mount Ida College, AB
The New England Institute of Art, B
Newbury College, A
Northeastern University, B
Northern Essex Community College, A
Quinsigamond Community College, A
Salem State College, B
Simmons College, B
Springfield Technical Community College, A
Suffolk University, AB
University of Massachusetts Dartmouth, B
Westfield State College, B

Michigan

Andrews University, AB
Baker College of Auburn Hills, A
Baker College of Clinton Township, A
Baker College of Flint, AB
Baker College of Muskegon, A
Baker College of Owosso, AB
Baker College of Port Huron, A
Central Michigan University, B
Ferris State University, A
Gogebic Community College, A
Grand Valley State University, B
Henry Ford Community College, A
Kalamazoo Valley Community College, A
Kellogg Community College, A
Lansing Community College, A
Macomb Community College, A
Mid Michigan Community College, A
Muskegon Community College, A
Northern Michigan University, AB
Northwestern Michigan College, A
Olivet College, B
St. Clair County Community College, A
Schoolcraft College, A
University of Michigan, B
Washtenaw Community College, A
Western Michigan University, B

Minnesota

Academy College, A
Alexandria Technical College, A
The Art Institutes International Minnesota, AB
Bemidji State University, B
Dakota County Technical College, A
Globe College, A
Minneapolis College of Art and Design, B
Minneapolis Community and Technical College, A
Minnesota State University Mankato, B
Minnesota State University Moorhead, B
Northwest Technical College, A
University of Minnesota, Duluth, B
University of Minnesota, Twin Cities Campus, B
Winona State University, B

Mississippi

Hinds Community College, A
Northeast Mississippi Community College, A

Northwest Mississippi Community College, A

Missouri

Central Missouri State University, B
East Central College, A
Fontbonne University, B
Kansas City Art Institute, B
Mineral Area College, A
Missouri Southern State University, B
Northwest Missouri State University, B
Penn Valley Community College, A
Saint Charles Community College, A
St. Louis Community College at Florissant Valley, A
St. Louis Community College at Forest Park, A
St. Louis Community College at Meramec, A
Southwest Baptist University, B
Truman State University, B
Washington University in St. Louis, B
William Woods University, B

Montana

Miles Community College, A
Montana State University-Northern, AB

Nebraska

Central Community College-Columbus Campus, A
Central Community College-Hastings Campus, A
Concordia University, B
Metropolitan Community College, A
Peru State College, B
Southeast Community College, Milford Campus, A
Union College, B
Vatterott College (Omaha), A

Nevada

Community College of Southern Nevada, A
Truckee Meadows Community College, A

New Hampshire

Franklin Pierce College, B
Hesser College, A
Keene State College, B
New Hampshire Community Technical College, Manchester/Stratham, A
Rivier College, B

New Jersey

Bergen Community College, A
Brookdale Community College, A
Burlington County College, A
Centenary College, B
The College of New Jersey, B
County College of Morris, A
Felician College, AB
Mercer County Community College, A
Middlesex County College, A
Ocean County College, A
Raritan Valley Community College, A
Rutgers, The State University of New Jersey, New Brunswick/Piscataway, B
Seton Hall University, B
Sussex County Community College, A
William Paterson University of New Jersey, B

New Mexico

Clovis Community College, A
New Mexico Highlands University, B
New Mexico Junior College, A
New Mexico State University-Alamogordo, A
San Juan College, A
Southwestern Indian Polytechnic Institute, A

New York

Briarcliffe College, A
Buffalo State College, State University of New York, B
The College of Saint Rose, B
Dowling College, B
Dutchess Community College, A
Fashion Institute of Technology, AB
Finger Lakes Community College, A
Fordham University, B
Fulton-Montgomery Community College, A
Genesee Community College, A
Katharine Gibbs School (Melville), A

Kingsborough Community College of the City
  University of New York, A
Mercy College, AB
Mohawk Valley Community College, A
Monroe Community College, A
Nassau Community College, A
Nazareth College of Rochester, B
New York City College of Technology of the City
  University of New York, AB
New York Institute of Technology, B
Onondaga Community College, A
Pace University, A
Parsons The New School for Design, AB
Pratt Institute, AB
Rockland Community College, A
St. John's University, B
St. Thomas Aquinas College, B
State University of New York, Fredonia, B
State University of New York at New Paltz, B
State University of New York at Oswego, B
Suffolk County Community College, A
Sullivan County Community College, A
Syracuse University, B
Tompkins Cortland Community College, A
Ulster County Community College, A

North Carolina

Alamance Community College, A
Campbell University, B
Catawba Valley Community College, A
Central Piedmont Community College, A
Chowan University, B
Fayetteville Technical Community College, A
Forsyth Technical Community College, A
Guilford Technical Community College, A
Halifax Community College, A
Isothermal Community College, A
James Sprunt Community College, A
Johnston Community College, A
Lenoir Community College, A
McDowell Technical Community College, A
Mount Olive College, B
Pitt Community College, A
Randolph Community College, A
South Piedmont Community College, A
Southwestern Community College, A
Surry Community College, A

North Dakota

Bismarck State College, A

Ohio

Antonelli College, A
Ashland University, B
Cincinnati State Technical and Community
  College, A
Clark State Community College, A
The Cleveland Institute of Art, B
Columbus State Community College, A
Cuyahoga Community College, A
Davis College, A
Edison State Community College, A
Kent State University, B
Lakeland Community College, A
Marietta College, B
Ohio Northern University, B
The Ohio State University, B
Ohio University, B
Ohio University-Eastern, B
Owens Community College, A
School of Advertising Art, A
Sinclair Community College, A
Terra State Community College, A
The University of Akron, B
University of Cincinnati, B
University of Cincinnati Raymond Walters College, A
University of Dayton, B
Virginia Marti College of Art and Design, A

Oklahoma

Northeastern State University, B
Northern Oklahoma College, A
Oklahoma Christian University, B
Oklahoma City Community College, A
Oklahoma City University, B
Oklahoma State University, Okmulgee, A

Oral Roberts University, B
Redlands Community College, A
Rogers State University, A
Southwestern Oklahoma State University, B
University of Central Oklahoma, B

Oregon

Lane Community College, A
Linn-Benton Community College, A
Mt. Hood Community College, A
Portland Community College, A
Portland State University, B
Treasure Valley Community College, A
University of Oregon, B

Pennsylvania

Antonelli Institute, A
Arcadia University, B
The Art Institute of Pittsburgh, AB
Bradley Academy for the Visual Arts, A
Bucks County Community College, A
Butler County Community College, A
CHI Institute, A
Community College of Allegheny County, A
Delaware County Community College, A
Drexel University, B
Harrisburg Area Community College, A
Hussian School of Art, A
Kutztown University of Pennsylvania, B
Lehigh Carbon Community College, A
Luzerne County Community College, A
Lycoming College, B
Montgomery County Community College, A
Oakbridge Academy of Arts, A
Pennsylvania College of Technology, AB
Philadelphia University, B
Schuylkill Institute of Business and Technology, A
Seton Hill University, B
Waynesburg College, B
Westmoreland County Community College, A

Puerto Rico

Escuela de Artes Plasticas de Puerto Rico, B
University of Puerto Rico at Carolina, A

South Carolina

Anderson University, B
Benedict College, B
Bob Jones University, B
Midlands Technical College, A
Piedmont Technical College, A
Trident Technical College, A
York Technical College, A

South Dakota

Black Hills State University, B
Northern State University, A
Southeast Technical Institute, A
University of Sioux Falls, B

Tennessee

Carson-Newman College, B
Chattanooga State Technical Community College, A
Freed-Hardeman University, B
Jackson State Community College, A
Lipscomb University, B
Memphis College of Art, B
Nashville State Technical Community College, A
Nossi College of Art, A
O'More College of Design, B
Pellissippi State Technical Community College, A
Southwest Tennessee Community College, A
The University of Tennessee, B
The University of Tennessee at Martin, B

Texas

Abilene Christian University, B
Amarillo College, A
American InterContinental University, AB
The Art Institute of Dallas, B
Austin Community College, A
Central Texas College, A
Coastal Bend College, A
Collin County Community College District, A
El Paso Community College, A

Hill College of the Hill Junior College District, A
Houston Community College System, A
Kilgore College, A
Lamar University, B
Lon Morris College, A
Midland College, A
Navarro College, A
Sam Houston State University, B
San Antonio College, A
South Plains College, A
Texas A&M University-Commerce, B
Texas State Technical College Harlingen, A
Texas State Technical College Waco, A
Texas Tech University, B
Tyler Junior College, A
University of the Incarnate Word, B
The University of Texas at El Paso, B
The University of Texas-Pan American, B
West Texas A&M University, B

Utah

Dixie State College of Utah, A
Utah Valley State College, A
Weber State University, B

Vermont

Champlain College, AB
Lyndon State College, B

Virginia

The Art Institute of Washington, AB
Central Virginia Community College, A
Hampton University, B
Longwood University, B
Lord Fairfax Community College, A
Northern Virginia Community College, A
Thomas Nelson Community College, A
Tidewater Community College, A
Virginia Intermont College, A
Virginia Western Community College, A

Washington

Centralia College, A
Everett Community College, A
Northwest College of Art, B
Seattle Central Community College, A
Shoreline Community College, A
Skagit Valley College, A
Spokane Falls Community College, A
University of Washington, B
Walla Walla College, AB
Wenatchee Valley College, A
Whatcom Community College, A

West Virginia

Concord University, B
Fairmont State University, AB
West Liberty State College, B
West Virginia Wesleyan College, B

Wisconsin

Cardinal Stritch University, B
Carroll College, B
Concordia University Wisconsin, B
Edgewood College, B
Fox Valley Technical College, A
Madison Area Technical College, A
Milwaukee Area Technical College, A
Milwaukee Institute of Art and Design, B
Mount Mary College, B
St. Norbert College, B
Silver Lake College, A
University of Wisconsin-Platteville, B
University of Wisconsin-Stevens Point, B

Western Technical College, A

Wyoming

Casper College, A
Northwest College, A

Alberta

Alberta College of Art & Design, B

British Columbia

British Columbia Institute of Technology, A

Nova Scotia

NSCAD University, B

Ontario

York University, B

Quebec

Concordia University, B
Université Laval, B
Université du Québec àMontréal, B

COMMERCIAL FISHING

Washington

Peninsula College, A

COMMERCIAL PHOTOGRAPHY

California

Art Center College of Design, B

Connecticut

Paier College of Art, Inc., A

Georgia

The Art Institute of Atlanta, AB

Illinois

Harrington College of Design, A

Maryland

Montgomery College, A

Minnesota

Dakota County Technical College, A
Minnesota State University Moorhead, B
Normandale Community College, A

New York

Fashion Institute of Technology, AB
Mohawk Valley Community College, A
Rochester Institute of Technology, B

North Carolina

Randolph Community College, A

Ohio

The University of Akron, A

Pennsylvania

The Art Institute of Pittsburgh, AB
Luzerne County Community College, A
Oakbridge Academy of Arts, A

Tennessee

Memphis College of Art, B

Texas

Houston Community College System, A
Kilgore College, A

Washington

Spokane Falls Community College, A

COMMUNICATION AND MEDIA STUDIES

Alabama

Auburn University, M
Miles College, B

Troy University, M
The University of Alabama, MD
The University of Alabama at Birmingham, M
University of South Alabama, M

Alaska

University of Alaska Fairbanks, M

Arizona

Arizona State University, MD
Arizona State University West, MO
Northern Arizona University, M
The University of Arizona, MD

Arkansas

Arkansas State University, MO
Harding University, B
University of Arkansas, M

California

California State University, Chico, M
California State University, East Bay, M
California State University, Fresno, M
California State University, Fullerton, M
California State University, Long Beach, M
California State University, Los Angeles, M
California State University, Northridge, M
California State University, Sacramento, M
California State University, San Bernardino, M
Loyola Marymount University, M
National University, M
Pepperdine University, M
San Diego State University, M
San Jose State University, M
Stanford University, MD
University of California, San Diego, MD
University of California, Santa Barbara, DO
University of California, Santa Cruz, O
University of the Pacific, M
University of Southern California, MDO

Colorado

Regis University, MO
University of Colorado at Boulder, MD
University of Colorado at Colorado Springs, M
University of Colorado at Denver and Health
   Sciences Center - Downtown Denver Campus, M
University of Denver, MD
University of Northern Colorado, M

Connecticut

Asnuntuck Community College, A
Central Connecticut State University, M
Quinnipiac University, M
University of Connecticut, M
University of Hartford, M

Delaware

University of Delaware, M
Wilmington College, B

District of Columbia

American University, M
Georgetown University, M
Howard University, MD
Trinity (Washington) University, M

Florida

Barry University, MO
Florida Atlantic University, M
Florida Institute of Technology, M
Florida State University, BMD
St. Thomas University, MO
University of Central Florida, M
University of Florida, MDO
University of Miami, MD
University of South Florida, MD
University of West Florida, M

Georgia

Clayton State University, B
Georgia State University, MD
Macon State College, B

University of Georgia, MD

Hawaii

Hawaii Pacific University, M
University of Hawaii at Manoa, M

Idaho

Boise State University, M
University of Idaho, M

Illinois

DePaul University, M
DeVry University (Oakbrook Terrace), M
Governors State University, M
Greenville College, B
Illinois Institute of Technology, MD
Illinois State University, M
Northern Illinois University, M
Northwestern University, BMD
Roosevelt University, M
Southern Illinois University Carbondale, MDO
Trinity International University, BM
University of Illinois at Chicago, BM
University of Illinois at Springfield, BM
University of Illinois at Urbana-Champaign, D
Western Illinois University, M

Indiana

Ball State University, M
Calumet College of Saint Joseph, B
Indiana State University, M
Indiana University Bloomington, MD
Indiana University-Purdue University Fort
   Wayne, BM
Purdue University, MD
Purdue University Calumet, M

Iowa

University of Dubuque, M
The University of Iowa, MD
University of Northern Iowa, M

Kansas

Fort Hays State University, M
Pittsburg State University, M
Southwestern College, B
University of Kansas, MD
Wichita State University, M

Kentucky

Morehead State University, M
Somerset Community College, A
Spalding University, M
University of Kentucky, MD
University of Louisville, M
Western Kentucky University, M

Louisiana

Centenary College of Louisiana, B
Louisiana State University and Agricultural and
   Mechanical College, MD
Loyola University New Orleans, MO
Southeastern Louisiana University, M
University of Louisiana at Lafayette, M
University of Louisiana at Monroe, M

Maine

University of Maine, M

Maryland

College of Notre Dame of Maryland, M
Hood College, B
The Johns Hopkins University, M
Towson University, MO
University of Baltimore, MD
University of Maryland, Baltimore County, M
University of Maryland, College Park, MD

Massachusetts

Boston University, MO
Clark University, M
Emerson College, M
Fitchburg State College, BMO
Framingham State College, B

Harvard University, O
Suffolk University, M
University of Massachusetts Amherst, MD

Michigan

Alma College, B
Andrews University, M
Central Michigan University, M
Eastern Michigan University, M
Grand Valley State University, M
Michigan State University, MD
Saginaw Valley State University, M
Spring Arbor University, M
University of Michigan, D
Wayne State University, MD
Western Michigan University, BM

Minnesota

Bethel University, MO
Brown College, B
Crown College, B
University of Minnesota, Twin Cities Campus, MD

Mississippi

Mississippi College, M

Missouri

Central Missouri State University, BM
Drury University, M
Missouri State University, M
Saint Louis University, M
University of Missouri-Columbia, MD
University of Missouri-St. Louis, M
Webster University, M

Montana

Montana State University-Billings, M
The University of Montana-Missoula, M

Nebraska

Bellevue University, BM
University of Nebraska-Lincoln, MD
University of Nebraska at Omaha, M
Wayne State College, M

Nevada

University of Nevada, Las Vegas, M

New Jersey

Fairleigh Dickinson University, Metropolitan
  Campus, M
Kean University, MO
Monmouth University, MO
Montclair State University, M
Rutgers, The State University of New Jersey, New
  Brunswick/Piscataway, MD
Seton Hall University, M
William Paterson University of New Jersey, M

New Mexico

Eastern New Mexico University, M
New Mexico State University, M
University of New Mexico, MD

New York

Canisius College, B
The College of New Rochelle, MO
Cornell University, MD
Fordham University, M
Hofstra University, B
Iona College, MO
Ithaca College, M
New York Institute of Technology, M
New York University, MDO
Polytechnic University, Brooklyn Campus, MO
Rensselaer Polytechnic Institute, MD
Rochester Institute of Technology, BM
State University of New York at Buffalo, MD
State University of New York College at
  Brockport, BM
State University of New York College of
  Environmental Science and Forestry, MD
Syracuse University, MDO

University at Albany, State University of New
  York, MD

North Carolina

Campbell University, B
North Carolina State University, M
The University of North Carolina at Chapel Hill, MD
The University of North Carolina at Charlotte, M
The University of North Carolina at Greensboro, M
Wake Forest University, M

North Dakota

North Dakota State University, MD
University of North Dakota, MD

Ohio

Bowling Green State University, MD
Cleveland State University, M
Kent State University, MD
Miami University, M
The Ohio State University, MD
Ohio University, MD
The University of Akron, M
University of Cincinnati, M
University of Dayton, M
Walsh University, B

Oklahoma

Northeastern State University, M
St. Gregory's University, B
University of Oklahoma, MD

Oregon

Cascade College, B
University of Oregon, MD
University of Portland, M

Pennsylvania

California University of Pennsylvania, M
Carnegie Mellon University, BM
Clarion University of Pennsylvania, M
Drexel University, M
Duquesne University, MD
Edinboro University of Pennsylvania, M
Keystone College, A
King's College, B
Marywood University, M
The Pennsylvania State University at Erie, The
  Behrend College, B
The Pennsylvania State University University Park
  Campus, MD
Point Park University, BM
Shippensburg University of Pennsylvania, M
Temple University, MD
The University of the Arts, B
University of Pennsylvania, D
University of Pittsburgh, MD
West Chester University of Pennsylvania, M

Puerto Rico

University of the Sacred Heart, M

Rhode Island

Roger Williams University, B

South Carolina

Clemson University, MD

South Dakota

South Dakota State University, M

Tennessee

Austin Peay State University, M
East Tennessee State University, M
Lane College, B
Milligan College, B
University of Memphis, MD
The University of Tennessee, MD

Texas

Abilene Christian University, M
Angelo State University, M
Baylor University, M
Houston Baptist University, B

St. Edward's University, B
St. Mary's University of San Antonio, M
Stephen F. Austin State University, M
Texas A&M University, MD
Texas Southern University, M
Texas State University-San Marcos, M
Texas Tech University, M
University of Houston, M
University of the Incarnate Word, M
University of North Texas, M
The University of Texas at Arlington, M
The University of Texas at Austin, MDO
The University of Texas at Dallas, D
The University of Texas at El Paso, M
The University of Texas-Pan American, M
The University of Texas at Tyler, M
West Texas A&M University, M

Utah

Brigham Young University, M
University of Utah, MD
Utah State University, M
Westminster College, M

Vermont

Champlain College, AB
University of Vermont, M

Virginia

George Mason University, M
Liberty University, M
Norfolk State University, M
Virginia Wesleyan College, B

Washington

Eastern Washington University, M
University of Washington, MD
Washington State University, MD

West Virginia

Marshall University, M
West Virginia University, M

Wisconsin

Marquette University, M
University of Wisconsin-Madison, MD
University of Wisconsin-Milwaukee, MO
University of Wisconsin-Stevens Point, M
University of Wisconsin-Superior, M
University of Wisconsin-Whitewater, M

Wyoming

University of Wyoming, M

Alberta

Athabasca University, B
University of Alberta, M
University of Calgary, MD

British Columbia

Simon Fraser University, MD

Manitoba

Providence College and Theological Seminary, B

Ontario

Carleton University, MD
University of Ottawa, BM
University of Windsor, M
York University, MD

Quebec

Concordia University, MDO
McGill University, MD
Université de Montréal, MD
Université du Québec àMontréal, MD
Université de Sherbrooke, B

COMMUNICATION DISORDERS

Alabama

Alabama Agricultural and Mechanical University, M
Auburn University, BM

The University of Alabama, M
University of Montevallo, M
University of South Alabama, MD

Arizona

Arizona State University, BMD
Northern Arizona University, M
The University of Arizona, BMD

Arkansas

Arkansas State University, M
Harding University, B
University of Arkansas, M
University of Arkansas for Medical Sciences, M
University of Central Arkansas, M

California

Biola University, B
California State University, Chico, BM
California State University, East Bay, M
California State University, Fresno, BM
California State University, Fullerton, BM
California State University, Long Beach, BM
California State University, Los Angeles, BM
California State University, Northridge, BM
California State University, Sacramento, M
Loma Linda University, M
San Diego State University, BMD
San Francisco State University, M
San Jose State University, BM
University of California, San Diego, D
University of the Pacific, M
University of Redlands, BM

Colorado

University of Colorado at Boulder, MD
University of Northern Colorado, M

Connecticut

Southern Connecticut State University, M
University of Connecticut, MDO

District of Columbia

Gallaudet University, MD
The George Washington University, M
Howard University, MD
University of the District of Columbia, M

Florida

Florida Atlantic University, M
Florida International University, M
Florida State University, MD
Nova Southeastern University, MD
University of Central Florida, M
University of Florida, MD
University of South Florida, D

Georgia

Georgia State University, M
University of Georgia, BMDO
University of West Georgia, M
Valdosta State University, M

Hawaii

University of Hawaii at Manoa, M

Idaho

Brigham Young University -Idaho, A
Idaho State University, MD

Illinois

Augustana College, B
Eastern Illinois University, BM
Governors State University, M
Illinois State University, M
Northern Illinois University, BMD
Northwestern University, BMD
Rush University, MD
Saint Xavier University, M
Southern Illinois University Carbondale, BM
Southern Illinois University Edwardsville, M
University of Illinois at Urbana-Champaign, MD

Western Illinois University, BM

Indiana

Ball State University, MD
Indiana State University, M
Indiana University Bloomington, BMD
Purdue University, MD

Iowa

The University of Iowa, MD
University of Northern Iowa, M

Kansas

Fort Hays State University, M
Kansas State University, B
University of Kansas, BMD
Wichita State University, MD

Kentucky

Eastern Kentucky University, BM
Murray State University, BM
University of Kentucky, M
University of Louisville, MD
Western Kentucky University, M

Louisiana

Louisiana State University and Agricultural and
    Mechanical College, MD
Louisiana State University Health Sciences
    Center, M
Louisiana Tech University, M
Southeastern Louisiana University, M
University of Louisiana at Lafayette, MD
University of Louisiana at Monroe, M
Xavier University of Louisiana, B

Maine

University of Maine, BM

Maryland

Loyola College in Maryland, MO
Towson University, MD
University of Maryland, College Park, MD

Massachusetts

Boston University, BMDO
Bridgewater State College, B
Elms College, BO
Emerson College, BM
Harvard University, D
Massachusetts Institute of Technology, D
Mount Wachusett Community College, A
Northeastern University, MD
Springfield College, B
University of Massachusetts Amherst, BMD
Worcester State College, BM

Michigan

Central Michigan University, MD
Eastern Michigan University, M
Michigan State University, M
Northern Michigan University, M
Wayne State University, MD
Western Michigan University, M

Minnesota

Minnesota State University Mankato, BM
Minnesota State University Moorhead, M
St. Cloud State University, BM
University of Minnesota, Duluth, M
University of Minnesota, Twin Cities Campus, MD

Mississippi

Jackson State University, M
Mississippi University for Women, M
Northeast Mississippi Community College, A
University of Mississippi, M
University of Southern Mississippi, MD

Missouri

Central Missouri State University, M
Fontbonne University, BM
Missouri State University, D
Rockhurst University, M

Saint Louis University, M
Southeast Missouri State University, BM
Truman State University, BM
University of Missouri-Columbia, M
Washington University in St. Louis, MD

Nebraska

University of Nebraska at Kearney, BM
University of Nebraska-Lincoln, M
University of Nebraska at Omaha, M

Nevada

University of Nevada, Reno, MD

New Hampshire

University of New Hampshire, BM

New Jersey

The College of New Jersey, M
Kean University, M
Montclair State University, M
Seton Hall University, M
William Paterson University of New Jersey, M

New Mexico

Eastern New Mexico University, M
New Mexico State University, M
University of New Mexico, M

New York

Adelphi University, MD
Brooklyn College of the City University of New
    York, MD
Buffalo State College, State University of New
    York, M
Canisius College, M
The College of New Rochelle, M
The College of Saint Rose, BM
Hofstra University, MDO
Hunter College of the City University of New
    York, M
Ithaca College, M
Lehman College of the City University of New
    York, M
Long Island University, Brooklyn Campus, M
Long Island University, C.W. Post Campus, M
Mercy College, BM
Nazareth College of Rochester, M
New York University, MD
Pace University, B
Queens College of the City University of New
    York, BM
St. John's University, M
State University of New York at Buffalo, MD
State University of New York College at
    Geneseo, BM
State University of New York, Fredonia, BM
State University of New York at New Paltz, BM
State University of New York at Plattsburgh, BM
Syracuse University, MD

North Carolina

Appalachian State University, BM
East Carolina University, MD
North Carolina Central University, M
The University of North Carolina at Chapel Hill, MD
The University of North Carolina at Greensboro, M
Western Carolina University, BM

North Dakota

Minot State University, BM
University of North Dakota, BMD

Ohio

Baldwin-Wallace College, B
Bowling Green State University, BMD
Case Western Reserve University, BMDO
Cleveland State University, M
Kent State University, MD
Miami University, M
The Ohio State University, MD
Ohio University, MD
The University of Akron, BMD
University of Cincinnati, MD

The University of Toledo, BM

Oklahoma

Northeastern State University, BM
Oklahoma State University, BM
University of Central Oklahoma, M
University of Oklahoma Health Sciences
   Center, BMDO
University of Tulsa, M

Oregon

Lewis & Clark College, M
Portland State University, M
University of Oregon, B

Pennsylvania

Bloomsburg University of Pennsylvania, MD
California University of Pennsylvania, M
Clarion University of Pennsylvania, M
College Misericordia, M
Duquesne University, M
East Stroudsburg University of Pennsylvania, M
Edinboro University of Pennsylvania, BM
Indiana University of Pennsylvania, M
La Salle University, M
Marywood University, M
Northampton County Area Community College, A
The Pennsylvania State University Abington
   College, B
The Pennsylvania State University Altoona
   College, B
The Pennsylvania State University Beaver Campus
   of the Commonwealth College, B
The Pennsylvania State University Berks Campus of
   the Berks-Lehigh Valley College, B
The Pennsylvania State University Delaware County
   Campus of the Commonwealth College, B
The Pennsylvania State University DuBois Campus
   of the Commonwealth College, B
The Pennsylvania State University at Erie, The
   Behrend College, B
The Pennsylvania State University Fayette Campus
   of the Commonwealth College, B
The Pennsylvania State University Hazleton
   Campus of the Commonwealth College, B
The Pennsylvania State University, Lehigh Valley
   Campus of the Berks-Lehigh Valley College, B
The Pennsylvania State University McKeesport
   Campus of the Commonwealth College, B
The Pennsylvania State University Mont Alto
   Campus of the Commonwealth College, B
The Pennsylvania State University New Kensington
   Campus of the Commonwealth College, B
The Pennsylvania State University Schuylkill
   Campus of the Capital College, B
The Pennsylvania State University Shenango
   Campus of the Commonwealth College, B
The Pennsylvania State University University Park
   Campus, BMD
The Pennsylvania State University Wilkes-Barre
   Campus of the Commonwealth College, B
The Pennsylvania State University Worthington
   Scranton Campus of the Commonwealth
   College, B
The Pennsylvania State University York Campus of
   the Commonwealth College, B
Temple University, M
University of Pittsburgh, MD
West Chester University of Pennsylvania, M

Puerto Rico

University of Puerto Rico, Medical Sciences
   Campus, M

Rhode Island

University of Rhode Island, BM

South Carolina

Bob Jones University, B
Medical University of South Carolina, M
South Carolina State University, M
University of South Carolina, MD

Winthrop University, B

South Dakota

The University of South Dakota, BM

Tennessee

East Tennessee State University, MD
University of Memphis, MD
The University of Tennessee, MD
Vanderbilt University, MD

Texas

Abilene Christian University, M
Baylor University, BM
Lamar University, BM
Our Lady of the Lake University of San Antonio, M
Stephen F. Austin State University, M
Texas A&M University-Kingsville, BM
Texas Christian University, M
Texas Southern University, B
Texas State University-San Marcos, M
Texas Woman's University, M
University of Houston, BM
University of North Texas, MD
The University of Texas at Austin, BMD
The University of Texas at Dallas, MD
The University of Texas at El Paso, M
The University of Texas-Pan American, BM
West Texas A&M University, BM

Utah

Brigham Young University, M
University of Utah, MD
Utah State University, MDO

Vermont

University of Vermont, B

Virginia

Hampton University, BM
James Madison University, MD
Longwood University, BM
Old Dominion University, M
Radford University, M
University of Virginia, BM

Washington

Eastern Washington University, BM
University of Washington, MD
Western Washington University, M

West Virginia

Marshall University, BM
West Virginia University, M

Wisconsin

Marquette University, M
University of Wisconsin-Eau Claire, BM
University of Wisconsin-Madison, BMD
University of Wisconsin-Milwaukee, M
University of Wisconsin-River Falls, BM
University of Wisconsin-Stevens Point, M
University of Wisconsin-Whitewater, M

Wyoming

University of Wyoming, M

Alberta

University of Alberta, M

British Columbia

The University of British Columbia, BMD

Nova Scotia

Dalhousie University, M

Ontario

Brock University, B
University of Ottawa, M
University of Toronto, MD

The University of Western Ontario, M

Quebec

McGill University, MD
Université Laval, M
Université de Montréal, M

COMMUNICATION DISORDERS SCIENCES AND SERVICES

Arkansas

Ouachita Baptist University, B

Minnesota

St. Cloud State University, B

Missouri

University of Missouri-Columbia, B

New York

Long Island University, Brooklyn Campus, B

Ohio

Ohio University, B

Oklahoma

University of Oklahoma Health Sciences Center, B

Virginia

Radford University, B

COMMUNICATION, JOURNALISM AND RELATED PROGRAMS

Alabama

Auburn University, B
Spring Hill College, B

Arizona

Arizona State University at the Polytechnic
   Campus, B
Northern Arizona University, B

Arkansas

Arkansas State University, B

California

The Art Institute of California-San Diego, B
California Baptist University, B
Folsom Lake College, A
Notre Dame de Namur University, B
Saint Mary's College of California, B
San Diego State University, B

Connecticut

Quinnipiac University, B

Florida

Flagler College, B
University of Miami, B

Georgia

Berry College, B
Mercer University, B

Hawaii

Brigham Young University-Hawaii, B
Hawaii Pacific University, B

Illinois

Bradley University, B
Illinois Institute of Technology, B
Loyola University Chicago, B
University of Illinois at Urbana-Champaign, B

Indiana

Indiana State University, B
Taylor University Fort Wayne, B

Valparaiso University, B

Iowa

Ashford University, B
Iowa Lakes Community College, A
Luther College, B

Kansas

Sterling College, B

Kentucky

Western Kentucky University, B

Louisiana

Centenary College of Louisiana, B
Delgado Community College, A
Tulane University, A

Maine

New England School of Communications, AB

Massachusetts

Framingham State College, B
Springfield College, B

Mississippi

Mississippi College, B
University of Southern Mississippi, B

Missouri

College of the Ozarks, B
Hannibal-LaGrange College, B
Saint Louis University, B
Washington University in St. Louis, B
Webster University, B

New York

Alfred University, B
Ithaca College, B
Lehman College of the City University of New York, B
Mercy College, B
Pace University, B
Queensborough Community College of the City University of New York, A
State University of New York College at Brockport, B
State University of New York Institute of Technology, B
Syracuse University, B

North Carolina

Campbell University, B

Ohio

Bowling Green State University, B
Malone College, B
Ohio Northern University, B
The Ohio State University, B
Ohio University, B
The University of Akron, B

Oklahoma

Southeastern Oklahoma State University, B
University of Oklahoma, B

Pennsylvania

Chestnut Hill College, B
Delaware County Community College, A
Drexel University, B
Juniata College, B
Keystone College, A
Lehigh University, B
The Pennsylvania State University Abington College, B
The Pennsylvania State University Altoona College, B
The Pennsylvania State University Beaver Campus of the Commonwealth College, B
The Pennsylvania State University Berks Campus of the Berks-Lehigh Valley College, B
The Pennsylvania State University Delaware County Campus of the Commonwealth College, B

The Pennsylvania State University DuBois Campus of the Commonwealth College, B
The Pennsylvania State University at Erie, The Behrend College, B
The Pennsylvania State University Fayette Campus of the Commonwealth College, B
The Pennsylvania State University Hazleton Campus of the Commonwealth College, B
The Pennsylvania State University, Lehigh Valley Campus of the Berks-Lehigh Valley College, B
The Pennsylvania State University McKeesport Campus of the Commonwealth College, B
The Pennsylvania State University Mont Alto Campus of the Commonwealth College, B
The Pennsylvania State University New Kensington Campus of the Commonwealth College, B
The Pennsylvania State University Schuylkill Campus of the Capital College, B
The Pennsylvania State University Shenango Campus of the Commonwealth College, B
The Pennsylvania State University University Park Campus, B
The Pennsylvania State University Wilkes-Barre Campus of the Commonwealth College, B
The Pennsylvania State University Worthington Scranton Campus of the Commonwealth College, B
The Pennsylvania State University York Campus of the Commonwealth College, B
The University of the Arts, B

Puerto Rico

Inter American University of Puerto Rico, Ponce Campus, B

South Carolina

Clemson University, B
Columbia College, B

Tennessee

Bryan College, B

Texas

Abilene Christian University, B

Utah

Brigham Young University, B

Vermont

Champlain College, AB

Virginia

Mary Baldwin College, B
Norfolk State University, B
Old Dominion University, B
Radford University, B

Washington

Eastern Washington University, B

West Virginia

West Virginia University, B
Wheeling Jesuit University, B

Wisconsin

Marquette University, B
Milwaukee School of Engineering, B
University of Wisconsin-Green Bay, B
Wisconsin Lutheran College, B

Nova Scotia

Dalhousie University, B

Ontario

McMaster University, B

COMMUNICATION STUDIES/SPEECH COMMUNICATION AND RHETORIC

Alabama

Andrew Jackson University, AB
Auburn University Montgomery, B

Jacksonville State University, B
The University of Alabama, B
The University of Alabama at Birmingham, B
University of South Alabama, B

Alaska

University of Alaska Fairbanks, B

Arizona

Arizona State University, B
Arizona State University West, B
Cochise College (Douglas), A
Northern Arizona University, B
Prescott College, B
The University of Arizona, B

Arkansas

Harding University, B
Ouachita Baptist University, B
University of Arkansas, B
University of the Ozarks, B

California

Azusa Pacific University, B
California Baptist University, B
California State University, Fresno, B
California State University, Fullerton, B
California State University, Los Angeles, B
California State University, Monterey Bay, B
California State University, Sacramento, B
California State University, San Marcos, B
California State University, Stanislaus, B
Chapman University, B
Concordia University, B
Dominican University of California, B
Humboldt State University, B
La Sierra University, B
Notre Dame de Namur University, B
Pepperdine University, B
Point Loma Nazarene University, B
Saint Mary's College of California, B
San Diego Christian College, B
Santa Ana College, A
Santa Barbara City College, A
Santa Clara University, B
Santa Rosa Junior College, A
Santiago Canyon College, A
Simpson University, B
Sonoma State University, B
Stanford University, B
University of California, Davis, B
University of California, Los Angeles, B
University of California, Santa Barbara, B
University of La Verne, B
University of the Pacific, B
University of San Francisco, B
University of Southern California, B
Vanguard University of Southern California, B
Westmont College, B
Woodbury University, B
Yuba College, A

Colorado

Adams State College, B
Colorado Christian University, B
Colorado State University, B
Regis University, B
University of Colorado at Boulder, B
University of Colorado at Colorado Springs, B
University of Colorado at Denver and Health Sciences Center - Downtown Denver Campus, B
University of Denver, B
University of Northern Colorado, B

Connecticut

Briarwood College, A
Central Connecticut State University, B
Eastern Connecticut State University, B
Manchester Community College, A
Southern Connecticut State University, B
University of Connecticut, B
University of Hartford, B

University of New Haven, AB

Delaware

University of Delaware, B

District of Columbia

The Catholic University of America, B
Gallaudet University, B

Florida

Barry University, B
Clearwater Christian College, B
Eckerd College, B
Embry-Riddle Aeronautical University, B
Florida Institute of Technology, B
Florida International University, B
Florida Southern College, B
Florida State University, B
Jacksonville University, B
Palm Beach Atlantic University, B
Southeastern University, B
Stetson University, B
University of Miami, B
University of North Florida, B
University of South Florida, B
University of West Florida, B
Warner Southern College, B

Georgia

Atlanta Metropolitan College, A
Augusta State University, B
Brewton-Parker College, B
Georgia Southern University, B
Kennesaw State University, B
Oglethorpe University, B
Thomas University, B
Valdosta State University, B
Wesleyan College, B

Hawaii

Brigham Young University-Hawaii, A
Hawaii Pacific University, B
University of Hawaii at Manoa, B

Idaho

College of Southern Idaho, A
Idaho State University, AB
Lewis-Clark State College, B
Northwest Nazarene University, B
University of Idaho, B

Illinois

Aurora University, B
Benedictine University, B
Blackburn College, B
Bradley University, B
Concordia University, B
DePaul University, B
Elmhurst College, B
Governors State University, B
Lake Forest College, B
Loyola University Chicago, B
Millikin University, B
Moody Bible Institute, B
Northern Illinois University, B
Northwestern University, B
Quincy University, B
Roosevelt University, B
Saint Xavier University, B
Sauk Valley Community College, A
Trinity Christian College, B
Waubonsee Community College, A
Western Illinois University, B
Wheaton College, B

Indiana

Bethel College, B
Calumet College of Saint Joseph, B
Huntington University, B
Indiana State University, B
Indiana University Bloomington, B
Indiana University East, B
Indiana University Kokomo, B
Indiana University-Purdue University Indianapolis, B
Indiana University Southeast, B

Indiana Wesleyan University, AB
Martin University, B
Purdue University, B
Saint Mary's College, B
Taylor University, B
Tri-State University, AB
University of Evansville, B
University of Indianapolis, B
University of Saint Francis, B
University of Southern Indiana, B
Vincennes University, A

Iowa

Buena Vista University, B
Central College, B
Mount Mercy College, B
The University of Iowa, B
University of Northern Iowa, B
William Penn University, B

Kansas

Baker University, B
Barton County Community College, A
Bethany College, B
Central Christian College of Kansas, AB
Emporia State University, B
Friends University, B
Hutchinson Community College and Area Vocational
    School, A
Kansas State University, B
Pittsburg State University, B
Tabor College, B
Washburn University, B
Wichita State University, B

Kentucky

Bellarmine University, B
Kentucky Wesleyan College, B
Morehead State University, B
Pikeville College, B
Thomas More College, AB
Union College, B
University of the Cumberlands, B
University of Kentucky, B
University of Louisville, B
Western Kentucky University, B

Louisiana

Louisiana State University at Alexandria, B
Loyola University New Orleans, B
Southeastern Louisiana University, B
Southern University and Agricultural and Mechanical
    College, B
Tulane University, A
University of Louisiana at Lafayette, B
University of New Orleans, B

Maine

University of Maine, B
University of Southern Maine, B

Maryland

College of Southern Maryland, A
Frostburg State University, B
Loyola College in Maryland, B
McDaniel College, B
Mount St. Mary's University, B
Salisbury University, B
Towson University, B
University of Maryland, College Park, B
University of Maryland University College, B

Massachusetts

Boston University, B
Bridgewater State College, B
Bristol Community College, A
Bunker Hill Community College, A
Dean College, A
Emerson College, B
Emmanuel College, B
Framingham State College, B
Gordon College, B
Lasell College, B
Massachusetts Bay Community College, A
Merrimack College, B

The New England Institute of Art, A
Northeastern University, B
Pine Manor College, B
Regis College, B
Stonehill College, B
University of Massachusetts Amherst, B
Western New England College, B

Michigan

Aquinas College, B
Baker College of Jackson, A
Calvin College, B
Concordia University, B
Hope College, B
Kellogg Community College, A
Kuyper College, B
Macomb Community College, A
Michigan State University, B
Michigan Technological University, B
Northern Michigan University, B
Northwestern Michigan College, A
Oakland University, B
Rochester College, B
Saginaw Valley State University, B
Spring Arbor University, B
University of Michigan-Dearborn, B
University of Michigan-Flint, B
Wayne State University, B
Western Michigan University, B

Minnesota

Bethany Lutheran College, B
Bethel University, B
The College of St. Scholastica, B
Concordia College, B
Macalester College, B
Metropolitan State University, B
Northwestern College, B
Southwest Minnesota State University, B
University of St. Thomas, B

Mississippi

Belhaven College, B
Mississippi College, B
Mississippi State University, B
Mississippi University for Women, B
University of Southern Mississippi, B
William Carey College, B

Missouri

Avila University, B
Central Methodist University, B
Drury University, B
Fontbonne University, B
Hannibal-LaGrange College, B
Missouri Baptist University, B
Missouri Southern State University, B
Missouri State University, B
Park University, B
Rockhurst University, B
Saint Louis University, B
Southeast Missouri State University, B
Southwest Baptist University, B
Truman State University, B
University of Missouri-Columbia, B
University of Missouri-Kansas City, B
University of Missouri-St. Louis, B
Washington University in St. Louis, B
William Woods University, B

Montana

Carroll College, B
Montana Tech of The University of Montana, B
Rocky Mountain College, B
The University of Montana-Missoula, B

Nebraska

Concordia University, B
Creighton University, B
Dana College, B
Doane College, B
Grace University, B
Hastings College, B
Nebraska Wesleyan University, B
University of Nebraska-Lincoln, B

University of Nebraska at Omaha, B

Nevada

University of Nevada, Las Vegas, B
University of Nevada, Reno, B

New Hampshire

Keene State College, B
Plymouth State University, B
Rivier College, B

New Jersey

Bloomfield College, B
Caldwell College, B
College of Saint Elizabeth, B
Fairleigh Dickinson University, College at
  Florham, B
Fairleigh Dickinson University, Metropolitan
  Campus, B
Georgian Court University, B
Gloucester County College, A
Kean University, B
Monmouth University, B
Montclair State University, B
New Jersey City University, B
Ramapo College of New Jersey, B
The Richard Stockton College of New Jersey, B
Rowan University, B
Rutgers, The State University of New Jersey, New
  Brunswick/Piscataway, B
Saint Peter's College, B
Seton Hall University, B
Union County College, A

New Mexico

Eastern New Mexico University, B
Mesalands Community College, A
San Juan College, A
University of New Mexico-Gallup, A

New York

Brooklyn College of the City University of New
  York, B
Broome Community College, A
Buffalo State College, State University of New
  York, B
Clarkson University, B
The College of Saint Rose, B
College of Staten Island of the City University of
  New York, B
Cornell University, B
Dowling College, B
Dutchess Community College, A
Erie Community College, South Campus, A
Hofstra University, B
Iona College, B
Jamestown Community College, A
Keuka College, B
Le Moyne College, B
Long Island University, Brooklyn Campus, B
Long Island University, C.W. Post Campus, B
Molloy College, B
Nassau Community College, A
Nazareth College of Rochester, B
New York University, B
Nyack College, B
Pace University, B
Purchase College, State University of New York, B
Rensselaer Polytechnic Institute, B
Roberts Wesleyan College, B
St. Francis College, B
St. John's University, B
State University of New York at Buffalo, B
State University of New York College at
  Brockport, B
State University of New York College at Cortland, B
State University of New York College at Geneseo, B
State University of New York College at Old
  Westbury, B
State University of New York at Plattsburgh, B
Syracuse University, B

Utica College, B

North Carolina

Campbell University, B
East Carolina University, B
Elon University, B
Greensboro College, B
Meredith College, B
North Carolina State University, B
Peace College, B
Pfeiffer University, B
Saint Augustine's College, B
The University of North Carolina at Chapel Hill, B
The University of North Carolina at Charlotte, B
Wake Forest University, B
Western Carolina University, B

North Dakota

Jamestown College, B
University of North Dakota, B

Ohio

Antioch College, B
Baldwin-Wallace College, B
Bluffton University, B
Bowling Green State University, B
Capital University, B
Cedarville University, B
Cleveland State University, B
College of Mount St. Joseph, AB
The College of Wooster, B
Franciscan University of Steubenville, B
Marietta College, B
Miami University Hamilton, B
Miami University-Middletown Campus, A
Mount Union College, B
Mount Vernon Nazarene University, B
Notre Dame College, B
Ohio Dominican University, B
Ohio Northern University, B
The Ohio State University, B
Ohio University, B
Tiffin University, B
Union Institute & University, B
The University of Akron, B
University of Rio Grande, AB
The University of Toledo, B
Wittenberg University, B
Wright State University, AB

Oklahoma

Cameron University, AB
Oral Roberts University, B
Southeastern Oklahoma State University, B
Southern Nazarene University, A
University of Central Oklahoma, B
University of Oklahoma, B
University of Science and Arts of Oklahoma, B
University of Tulsa, B

Oregon

Corban College, B
George Fox University, B
Lewis & Clark College, B
Linfield College, B
Multnomah Bible College and Biblical Seminary, B
Northwest Christian College, B
Oregon Institute of Technology, B
Southern Oregon University, B

Pennsylvania

Albright College, B
Allegheny College, B
Alvernia College, B
Bloomsburg University of Pennsylvania, B
Cabrini College, B
California University of Pennsylvania, B
Carlow University, B
Cedar Crest College, B
Chatham College, B
Clarion University of Pennsylvania, B
College Misericordia, B
Delaware County Community College, A
Duquesne University, B
East Stroudsburg University of Pennsylvania, B

Eastern University, B
Edinboro University of Pennsylvania, B
Elizabethtown College, B
Geneva College, B
Holy Family University, B
Immaculata University, B
Indiana University of Pennsylvania, B
Juniata College, B
Keystone College, AB
La Roche College, B
Lackawanna College, A
Lehigh Carbon Community College, A
Lincoln University, B
Messiah College, B
Millersville University of Pennsylvania, B
Montgomery County Community College, A
Neumann College, B
Northampton County Area Community College, A
The Pennsylvania State University Abington
  College, B
The Pennsylvania State University Altoona
  College, B
The Pennsylvania State University Beaver Campus
  of the Commonwealth College, B
The Pennsylvania State University Berks Campus of
  the Berks-Lehigh Valley College, B
The Pennsylvania State University Delaware County
  Campus of the Commonwealth College, B
The Pennsylvania State University DuBois Campus
  of the Commonwealth College, B
The Pennsylvania State University at Erie, The
  Behrend College, B
The Pennsylvania State University Fayette Campus
  of the Commonwealth College, B
The Pennsylvania State University Harrisburg
  Campus, B
The Pennsylvania State University Hazleton
  Campus of the Commonwealth College, B
The Pennsylvania State University, Lehigh Valley
  Campus of the Berks-Lehigh Valley College, B
The Pennsylvania State University McKeesport
  Campus of the Commonwealth College, B
The Pennsylvania State University Mont Alto
  Campus of the Commonwealth College, B
The Pennsylvania State University New Kensington
  Campus of the Commonwealth College, B
The Pennsylvania State University Schuylkill
  Campus of the Capital College, B
The Pennsylvania State University Shenango
  Campus of the Commonwealth College, B
The Pennsylvania State University University Park
  Campus, B
The Pennsylvania State University Wilkes-Barre
  Campus of the Commonwealth College, B
The Pennsylvania State University Worthington
  Scranton Campus of the Commonwealth
  College, B
The Pennsylvania State University York Campus of
  the Commonwealth College, B
Rosemont College, B
Saint Joseph's University, B
Saint Vincent College, B
Seton Hill University, B
Slippery Rock University of Pennsylvania, B
Susquehanna University, B
Thiel College, B
The University of the Arts, B
University of Pennsylvania, B
University of Pittsburgh, B
The University of Scranton, B
Waynesburg College, B
West Chester University of Pennsylvania, B
Wilkes University, B

Puerto Rico

Inter American University of Puerto Rico, Bayamón
  Campus, B
University of the Sacred Heart, B

Rhode Island

Bryant University, B
Rhode Island College, B

University of Rhode Island, B

South Carolina

Bob Jones University, B
College of Charleston, B
Columbia College, B
Columbia International University, B
Furman University, B
University of South Carolina Aiken, B
University of South Carolina Upstate, B

South Dakota

Augustana College, B
Presentation College, AB

Tennessee

Tennessee Temple University, B
Trevecca Nazarene University, B
University of Memphis, B

Texas

Angelo State University, B
Austin College, B
Baylor University, B
Dallas Baptist University, B
Hardin-Simmons University, B
Houston Baptist University, B
Howard Payne University, B
Lee College, A
McMurry University, B
Our Lady of the Lake University of San Antonio, B
St. Mary's University of San Antonio, B
Southwestern Assemblies of God University, A
Southwestern University, B
Stephen F. Austin State University, B
Texas A&M International University, B
Texas A&M University-Corpus Christi, B
Texas Christian University, B
Texas Lutheran University, B
Texas Southern University, B
Trinity University, B
University of Houston, B
University of Houston-Clear Lake, B
University of the Incarnate Word, B
University of Mary Hardin-Baylor, B
University of North Texas, B
University of St. Thomas, B
The University of Texas at Austin, B
The University of Texas at Brownsville, B
The University of Texas-Pan American, B
The University of Texas at San Antonio, B

Utah

Dixie State College of Utah, A
University of Utah, B
Utah Valley State College, A
Westminster College, B

Vermont

College of St. Joseph, B
Green Mountain College, B
Lyndon State College, A
Norwich University, B
Southern Vermont College, B

Virginia

Christopher Newport University, B
Eastern Mennonite University, B
James Madison University, B
Liberty University, B
Longwood University, B
Lord Fairfax Community College, A
Lynchburg College, B
Mary Baldwin College, B
Marymount University, B
Randolph-Macon Woman's College, B
Regent University, B
Shenandoah University, B
The University of Virginia's College at Wise, B
Virginia Polytechnic Institute and State University, B

Washington

Eastern Washington University, B
Seattle Pacific University, B
University of Puget Sound, B

University of Washington, B
Washington State University, B
Western Washington University, B

West Virginia

Bethany College, B
Davis & Elkins College, B
Shepherd University, B
West Virginia State University, AB
West Virginia Wesleyan College, B

Wisconsin

Alverno College, B
Cardinal Stritch University, B
Carroll College, B
Carthage College, B
Marian College of Fond du Lac, B
Marquette University, B
Mount Mary College, B
Ripon College, B
St. Norbert College, B
University of Wisconsin-Eau Claire, B
University of Wisconsin-La Crosse, B
University of Wisconsin-Parkside, B
University of Wisconsin-Stevens Point, B
University of Wisconsin-Whitewater, B
Wisconsin Lutheran College, B

Wyoming

Eastern Wyoming College, A
Laramie County Community College, A
University of Wyoming, B
Western Wyoming Community College, A

Alberta

University of Calgary, B

British Columbia

Simon Fraser University, B
Trinity Western University, B

New Brunswick

University of New Brunswick Saint John, B

Nova Scotia

Cape Breton University, B

Ontario

Brock University, B
University of Waterloo, B
University of Windsor, B
York University, B

Quebec

Concordia University, B

COMMUNICATION THEORY

California

Stanford University, D
University of Southern California, D

Colorado

Colorado State University, M

Iowa

The University of Iowa, MD

New York

Syracuse University, M

Ohio

Kent State University, MD

West Virginia

West Virginia University, M

COMMUNICATIONS SYSTEMS INSTALLATION AND REPAIR TECHNOLOGY

California

Modesto Junior College, A

Colorado

Arapahoe Community College, A

Idaho

Idaho State University, A

Illinois

College of DuPage, A

Kentucky

Daymar College (Owensboro), A

Louisiana

Louisiana Technical College, A

Maine

Kennebec Valley Community College, A

Minnesota

Anoka Technical College, A
Dakota County Technical College, A

New York

Broome Community College, A
Erie Community College, South Campus, A
Mohawk Valley Community College, A
Suffolk County Community College, A

Washington

North Seattle Community College, A

Wisconsin

Wisconsin Indianhead Technical College, A

British Columbia

Thompson Rivers University, A

COMMUNICATIONS TECHNOLOGIES/TECHNICIANS AND SUPPORT SERVICES

Indiana

Saint Mary-of-the-Woods College, B

Maine

New England School of Communications, AB

Maryland

Harford Community College, A

Massachusetts

Lesley University, B
Springfield Technical Community College, A

Ohio

Bowling Green State University-Firelands College, A

Pennsylvania

Chestnut Hill College, B
Community College of Allegheny County, A
Montgomery County Community College, A
The University of Scranton, B

South Dakota

Mitchell Technical Institute, A

Wisconsin

Alverno College, B
Northeast Wisconsin Technical College, A

Western Technical College, A

Ontario

University of Windsor, B

COMMUNICATIONS TECHNOLOGY/TECHNICIAN

Alabama

Community College of the Air Force, A

California

Lassen Community College District, A
Napa Valley College, A
Orange Coast College, A
Pasadena City College, A

Colorado

Arapahoe Community College, A

Connecticut

Northwestern Connecticut Community College, A

Florida

Santa Fe Community College, A

Georgia

Athens Technical College, A

Illinois

Black Hawk College, A
College of DuPage, A

Indiana

Saint Mary-of-the-Woods College, B
Vincennes University, A

Iowa

Kirkwood Community College, A
Vennard College, A

Kansas

Coffeyville Community College, A
Dodge City Community College, A
Hutchinson Community College and Area Vocational
    School, A

Kentucky

Paducah Technical College, A

Maine

Southern Maine Community College, A

Maryland

Allegany College of Maryland, A
Anne Arundel Community College, A

Michigan

Eastern Michigan University, B
Ferris State University, A
Lawrence Technological University, B
Mott Community College, A

Minnesota

Northwest Technical College, A

Nebraska

Hastings College, B

New Jersey

Burlington County College, A
Essex County College, A

Ocean County College, A

New York

The College of Saint Rose, B

North Carolina

Cleveland Community College, A

Ohio

Cedarville University, B
Kent State University, Tuscarawas Campus, A

Oklahoma

Spartan College of Aeronautics and Technology, A

Pennsylvania

Cheyney University of Pennsylvania, B
Community College of Beaver County, A
Community College of Philadelphia, A
East Stroudsburg University of Pennsylvania, AB
Lackawanna College, A
Reading Area Community College, A

Puerto Rico

Inter American University of Puerto Rico, Bayamón
    Campus, B

Rhode Island

Salve Regina University, B

Tennessee

Bryan College, B
Fountainhead College of Technology, A

Texas

North Lake College, A
St. Philip's College, A

Virginia

ECPI College of Technology (Newport News), A
ECPI College of Technology (Virginia Beach), A
ECPI Technical College (Richmond), A
ECPI Technical College (Roanoke), A

Washington

Renton Technical College, A
South Puget Sound Community College, A

West Virginia

Bluefield State College, A
Fairmont State Community & Technical College, A
New River Community and Technical College, A
Southern West Virginia Community and Technical
    College, A

Wisconsin

Gateway Technical College, A
Madison Area Technical College, A
Milwaukee Area Technical College, A

COMMUNITY COLLEGE EDUCATION

Arizona

Northern Arizona University, M

Florida

University of Central Florida, O
University of South Florida, MDO

Kansas

Pittsburg State University, O

Maryland

Morgan State University, D

New Jersey

Princeton University, D

North Carolina

North Carolina State University, MD

Western Carolina University, M

South Carolina

Clemson University, M

Virginia

George Mason University, DO
Old Dominion University, MD

Washington

Eastern Washington University, M

COMMUNITY HEALTH AND PREVENTIVE MEDICINE

California

University of California, Los Angeles, BMD

Colorado

University of Northern Colorado, M

District of Columbia

The George Washington University, MO

Florida

University of Florida, M
University of Miami, M
University of North Florida, M
University of South Florida, MD

Georgia

Emory University, MD

Idaho

Idaho State University, O

Illinois

University of Illinois at Chicago, MD
University of Illinois at Urbana-Champaign, BMD

Indiana

Indiana State University, M

Iowa

The University of Iowa, MD

Kentucky

Eastern Kentucky University, M

Louisiana

University of New Orleans, O

Massachusetts

Harvard University, M
Tufts University, B
University of Massachusetts Lowell, B

Michigan

Wayne State University, MO

Minnesota

Minnesota State University Mankato, M
University of Minnesota, Twin Cities Campus, M

Missouri

Saint Louis University, M
University of Missouri-Columbia, MO

New Hampshire

Southern New Hampshire University, M

New Jersey

New Jersey City University, M

New York

Brooklyn College of the City University of New
    York, M
Hofstra University, B
Long Island University, Brooklyn Campus, M
New York University, MD
State University of New York at Buffalo, D

State University of New York Downstate Medical Center, M
Stony Brook University, State University of New York, MO

North Carolina

The University of North Carolina at Greensboro, M

North Dakota

United Tribes Technical College, A

Pennsylvania

Arcadia University, MO
University of Pittsburgh, MDO

Rhode Island

Brown University, MDO

Tennessee

East Tennessee State University, M
The University of Tennessee, MD

Texas

Northwest Vista College, A
University of North Texas, M
The University of Texas Medical Branch, MD

Utah

California College for Health Sciences, M
Utah Valley State College, A

Virginia

Old Dominion University, M

West Virginia

West Virginia University, M

Wisconsin

University of Wisconsin-La Crosse, M
University of Wisconsin-Madison, MD

Alberta

University of Calgary, MDO

British Columbia

The University of British Columbia, M
University of Northern British Columbia, M

Manitoba

University of Manitoba, MD

Newfoundland and Labrador

Memorial University of Newfoundland, MDO

Nova Scotia

Dalhousie University, M

Ontario

University of Ottawa, MO

Quebec

McGill University, M
Université Laval, MDO
Université de Montréal, MDO

Saskatchewan

University of Saskatchewan, MD

COMMUNITY HEALTH NURSING

Alabama

University of South Alabama, M

California

Holy Names University, M

Connecticut

University of Hartford, M

Georgia

Georgia Southern University, MO
Medical College of Georgia, M

Valdosta State University, M

Hawaii

Hawaii Pacific University, M

Illinois

Rush University, MD
Saint Xavier University, M
Southern Illinois University Edwardsville, MO
University of Illinois at Chicago, M

Indiana

Indiana Wesleyan University, M

Kentucky

Bellarmine University, M

Louisiana

Louisiana State University Health Sciences Center, MD

Maryland

The Johns Hopkins University, MO

Massachusetts

Boston College, M
Northeastern University, MO
University of Massachusetts Dartmouth, MO
University of Massachusetts Lowell, M
Worcester State College, M

Michigan

University of Michigan, M
Wayne State University, M

Minnesota

Augsburg College, M
University of Minnesota, Twin Cities Campus, M

Mississippi

University of Southern Mississippi, M

New Jersey

Kean University, M

New York

Hunter College of the City University of New York, MO

North Carolina

The University of North Carolina at Chapel Hill, M
The University of North Carolina at Charlotte, MO

Ohio

Capital University, M
Cleveland State University, M
Wright State University, M

Oregon

Oregon Health & Science University, MO

Pennsylvania

La Roche College, M
La Salle University, M

South Carolina

University of South Carolina, MO

South Dakota

Augustana College, M

Texas

The University of Texas at Brownsville, M
The University of Texas at El Paso, M

Washington

Seattle University, M

COMMUNITY HEALTH SERVICES/LIAISON/COUNSELING

California

California State University, Sacramento, B

Delaware

Delaware State University, B

Florida

Florida State University, B
Manatee Community College, A
University of Florida, B
University of West Florida, B

Illinois

Northeastern Illinois University, B

Indiana

Indiana State University, B
Indiana University-Purdue University Fort Wayne, B

Iowa

University of Northern Iowa, B

Kansas

University of Kansas, B

Kentucky

Eastern Kentucky University, B
University of the Cumberlands, B
Western Kentucky University, B

Michigan

Bay de Noc Community College, A
Mott Community College, A

Minnesota

Bethel University, B
Minnesota State University Moorhead, B

Nebraska

University of Nebraska-Lincoln, B
University of Nebraska at Omaha, B

New York

Erie Community College, A
Kingsborough Community College of the City University of New York, A

Ohio

Cleveland State University, B
Youngstown State University, B

Pennsylvania

Community College of Allegheny County, A
Seton Hill University, B
University of Pennsylvania, B

South Carolina

Morris College, B

Texas

Prairie View A&M University, B
Sam Houston State University, B
Stephen F. Austin State University, B
Texas A&M University, B
Texas State University-San Marcos, B
Texas Tech University, B
Texas Woman's University, B

University of Houston, B

Virginia

James Madison University, B
Longwood University, B

Washington

Central Washington University, B
Western Washington University, B

COMMUNITY ORGANIZATION AND ADVOCACY

Alabama

Alabama State University, A
Samford University, AB

Alaska

University of Alaska Fairbanks, B

Arkansas

Southern Arkansas University-Magnolia, B

California

College of the Sequoias, A
Crafton Hills College, A
Humphreys College, B
Merritt College, A

Colorado

Lamar Community College, A

Delaware

University of Delaware, B

Florida

Saint Leo University, B

Georgia

Mercer University, B

Hawaii

Honolulu Community College, A

Illinois

North Park University, B
Northwestern University, B
Roosevelt University, B

Iowa

Iowa Central Community College, A
Marshalltown Community College, A

Kansas

University of Saint Mary, B

Kentucky

Bellarmine University, B

Maryland

University of Baltimore, B

Massachusetts

University of Massachusetts Boston, B

Michigan

Central Michigan University, B
Eastern Michigan University, B
Siena Heights University, B

Minnesota

Bemidji State University, B
Ridgewater College, A

Missouri

Rockhurst University, B

Montana

Montana State University-Northern, AB

Nebraska

Midland Lutheran College, A

New Hampshire

New Hampshire Community Technical College,
Manchester/Stratham, A

University of New Hampshire, A

New Jersey

Cumberland County College, A
Mercer County Community College, A

New Mexico

New Mexico State University, B
University of New Mexico, A
University of New Mexico-Gallup, A

New York

Clinton Community College, A
Cornell University, B
Mohawk Valley Community College, A
State University of New York Empire State
College, AB
Suffolk County Community College, A
Touro College, AB
Ulster County Community College, A

North Carolina

High Point University, B

Ohio

Cleveland State University, B
The University of Akron, AB
The University of Findlay, A
The University of Toledo, B

Oregon

Clackamas Community College, A
Corban College, B
Lane Community College, A
University of Oregon, B

Pennsylvania

Community College of Philadelphia, A
Marywood University, B

South Dakota

Northern State University, B

Tennessee

Cleveland State Community College, A
Martin Methodist College, A

Texas

Del Mar College, A
The University of Texas at El Paso, B

Vermont

Community College of Vermont, A

Virginia

Emory & Henry College, B
J. Sargeant Reynolds Community College, A
New River Community College, A

Washington

Saint Martin's University, B

West Virginia

Fairmont State University, A
West Virginia University Institute of Technology, B

Wisconsin

Alverno College, B

Nova Scotia

Cape Breton University, B

COMMUNITY PSYCHOLOGY

Alabama

Auburn University, MDO

Alaska

University of Alaska Fairbanks, D

Arizona

University of Phoenix-Phoenix Campus, M
University of Phoenix-Southern Arizona Campus, M

Arkansas

Henderson State University, M
University of Central Arkansas, M

California

Azusa Pacific University, M
California State University, Fullerton, M
University of La Verne, D

Colorado

University of Phoenix-Denver Campus, M
University of Phoenix-Southern Colorado
Campus, M

Connecticut

Central Connecticut State University, M
Saint Joseph College, M
University of New Haven, MO
Western Connecticut State University, M

Delaware

Wilmington College, M

Florida

Florida Agricultural and Mechanical University, M

Georgia

North Georgia College & State University, M

Illinois

DePaul University, MDO
Eastern Illinois University, M
Northwestern University, B
Western Illinois University, M

Indiana

Indiana Wesleyan University, M
Martin University, M

Kansas

University of Saint Mary, B
Wichita State University, D

Kentucky

Pikeville College, B

Michigan

Andrews University, M

Minnesota

St. Cloud State University, M

Missouri

Southeast Missouri State University, M

Montana

Montana State University-Billings, B

Nebraska

Western Nebraska Community College, A

New York

The College of New Rochelle, M
Hofstra University, DO
New York Institute of Technology, B
New York University, D
Pace University, MD

North Carolina

Appalachian State University, M
North Carolina State University, M
The University of North Carolina at Charlotte, M
Western Carolina University, M

Ohio

Malone College, M
University of Dayton, M
The University of Toledo, M

Wright State University, B

Oklahoma

University of Oklahoma, M

Pennsylvania

Chatham College, M
The Pennsylvania State University Harrisburg
 Campus, M
Seton Hill University, B
University of Pennsylvania, D
The University of Scranton, M

South Carolina

Francis Marion University, M
University of South Carolina, MD

Texas

Lamar University, M
St. Mary's University of San Antonio, M

Vermont

College of St. Joseph, M
Woodbury College, AB

Virginia

Norfolk State University, M

Washington

Saint Martin's University, M

Wisconsin

University of Wisconsin-Superior, M
University of Wisconsin-Whitewater, M

British Columbia

Kwantlen University College, AB

Ontario

Wilfrid Laurier University, BM

Quebec

Université Laval, D

COMPARATIVE AND INTERDISCIPLINARY ARTS

California

John F. Kennedy University, M

Florida

Florida Atlantic University, D

Illinois

Bradley University, M
Columbia College Chicago, M

Ohio

Ohio University, D

Utah

Brigham Young University, M

Vermont

Goddard College, M

British Columbia

Simon Fraser University, M

COMPARATIVE LITERATURE

Arizona

Grand Canyon University, B
Prescott College, B

The University of Arizona, MD

Arkansas

University of Arkansas, MD

California

California Institute of Technology, B
California State University, Dominguez Hills, B
California State University, Fullerton, B
California State University, Long Beach, B
Chabot College, A
Chapman University, B
Claremont McKenna College, B
Compton Community College, A
Foothill College, A
Fresno Pacific University, B
Irvine Valley College, A
Mills College, B
New College of California, B
Occidental College, B
Pitzer College, B
Sacramento City College, A
Saddleback College, A
Saint Mary's College of California, B
San Diego State University, B
San Francisco State University, BM
San Joaquin Delta College, A
San Jose State University, MO
Skyline College, A
Sonoma State University, B
Southwestern College, A
Stanford University, BD
University of California, Berkeley, BD
University of California, Davis, BD
University of California, Irvine, BMD
University of California, Los Angeles, BMD
University of California, Riverside, BMD
University of California, San Diego, BMD
University of California, Santa Barbara, BDO
University of California, Santa Cruz, BMD
University of Judaism, B
University of La Verne, B
University of Redlands, B
University of Southern California, BMD

Colorado

The Colorado College, B
Lamar Community College, A
Otero Junior College, A
University of Colorado at Boulder, MD

Connecticut

Quinnipiac University, B
Sacred Heart University, AB
Southern Connecticut State University, B
Trinity College, B
University of Connecticut, MD
Yale University, BD

Delaware

University of Delaware, B

District of Columbia

American University, BM
The Catholic University of America, MD
Georgetown University, B

Florida

Barry University, B
Eckerd College, B
Florida Atlantic University, M
Florida State University, B
Miami Dade College, A
New College of Florida, B
Palm Beach Community College, A
Warner Southern College, B

Georgia

Agnes Scott College, B
Andrew College, A
Columbus State University, B
Emory University, BDO

University of Georgia, BMD

Hawaii

Hawaii Pacific University, B

Idaho

Boise State University, B

Illinois

Augustana College, B
Benedictine University, B
Blackburn College, B
Chicago State University, B
DePaul University, B
Eureka College, B
Judson College, B
Lincoln Land Community College, A
North Park University, B
Northwestern University, BMD
Olivet Nazarene University, B
Rockford College, B
Roosevelt University, B
Shimer College, B
University of Chicago, BMD
University of Illinois at Urbana-Champaign, BMD

Indiana

Indiana University Bloomington, BMDO
Manchester College, A
Purdue University, MD
Purdue University Calumet, B
Taylor University, B
University of Notre Dame, D

Iowa

Coe College, B
Graceland University, B
Iowa Lakes Community College, A
Morningside College, B
The University of Iowa, BMD

Kansas

Friends University, AB
Kansas Wesleyan University, B
Pratt Community College, A
Seward County Community College, A

Kentucky

Western Kentucky University, M

Louisiana

Louisiana State University and Agricultural and
 Mechanical College, MD

Maine

College of the Atlantic, B

Maryland

The Johns Hopkins University, BD
University of Baltimore, B
University of Maryland, College Park, MD

Massachusetts

Brandeis University, B
Clark University, B
College of the Holy Cross, B
Fitchburg State College, B
Hampshire College, B
Harvard University, BD
Massachusetts College of Liberal Arts, B
Salem State College, B
Simmons College, B
Simon's Rock College of Bard, B
Smith College, B
University of Massachusetts Amherst, BMD
Wellesley College, B
Westfield State College, B
Wheaton College, B
Williams College, B

Michigan

Ave Maria College, B
Grand Valley State University, B
Hillsdale College, B

Lake Superior State University, B
Oakland University, B
Rochester College, B
University of Michigan, BD
Wayne State University, M

Minnesota

College of St. Catherine, B
Minnesota State University Mankato, B
North Central University, A
St. Cloud State University, B
Southwest Minnesota State University, B
University of Minnesota, Twin Cities Campus, BD

Mississippi

East Central Community College, A

Missouri

Northwest Missouri State University, B
St. Louis Community College at Meramec, A
University of Missouri-Columbia, M
University of Missouri-St. Louis, B
Washington University in St. Louis, BMD
Webster University, B
William Woods University, B

Montana

The University of Montana-Western, B

Nebraska

Hastings College, B
Wayne State College, B

Nevada

Community College of Southern Nevada, A
University of Nevada, Las Vegas, B

New Hampshire

Dartmouth College, BM
Franklin Pierce College, B
Thomas More College of Liberal Arts, B
University of New Hampshire, BM

New Jersey

Atlantic Cape Community College, A
Bergen Community College, A
Fairleigh Dickinson University, Metropolitan
    Campus, M
Princeton University, BD
Ramapo College of New Jersey, B
Rutgers, The State University of New Jersey, New
    Brunswick/Piscataway, BMD
William Paterson University of New Jersey, B

New Mexico

St. John's College, B
University of New Mexico, BMD

New York

Alfred University, B
Bard College, B
Barnard College, B
Bernard M. Baruch College of the City University of
    New York, B
Brooklyn College of the City University of New
    York, B
Cazenovia College, B
City College of the City University of New York, B
Columbia College, B
Columbia University, School of General Studies, B
Cornell University, BD
Elmira College, B
Eugene Lang College The New School for Liberal
    Arts, B
Excelsior College, B
Fordham University, B
Hamilton College, B
Hobart and William Smith Colleges, B
Hofstra University, BM
Houghton College, B
Hunter College of the City University of New York, B
The Jewish Theological Seminary, B
Long Island University, Brooklyn Campus, M
Marist College, B

Nazareth College of Rochester, B
New York University, BMD
Pace University, B
Purchase College, State University of New York, B
Queens College of the City University of New
    York, B
Sarah Lawrence College, B
State University of New York at Binghamton, BMD
State University of New York at Buffalo, MD
State University of New York College at
    Brockport, B
State University of New York College at Geneseo, B
State University of New York College at Old
    Westbury, B
Stony Brook University, State University of New
    York, BMD
Syracuse University, B
Touro College, B
United States Military Academy, B
University of Rochester, B

North Carolina

Duke University, BD
High Point University, B
The University of North Carolina at Chapel
    Hill, BMD

Ohio

Antioch College, B
Capital University, B
Case Western Reserve University, BM
The College of Wooster, B
John Carroll University, B
Kent State University, M
Kenyon College, B
Oberlin College, B
The Ohio State University, B
Ohio University-Eastern, B
Ohio Wesleyan University, B
Otterbein College, B
The University of Akron, B
University of Cincinnati, B
The University of Toledo, B
Wilberforce University, B

Oklahoma

East Central University, B
Oklahoma City Community College, A
Oklahoma City University, M

Oregon

Mount Angel Seminary, B
Oregon State University, B
Pacific University, B
Reed College, B
University of Oregon, BMD
Willamette University, B

Pennsylvania

Arcadia University, B
Bryn Mawr College, B
Carnegie Mellon University, MD
Gettysburg College, B
Grove City College, B
Haverford College, B
Holy Family University, B
Lycoming College, B
The Pennsylvania State University Abington
    College, B
The Pennsylvania State University Altoona
    College, B
The Pennsylvania State University Beaver Campus
    of the Commonwealth College, B
The Pennsylvania State University Berks Campus of
    the Berks-Lehigh Valley College, B
The Pennsylvania State University Delaware County
    Campus of the Commonwealth College, B
The Pennsylvania State University DuBois Campus
    of the Commonwealth College, B
The Pennsylvania State University at Erie, The
    Behrend College, B
The Pennsylvania State University Fayette Campus
    of the Commonwealth College, B
The Pennsylvania State University Hazleton
    Campus of the Commonwealth College, B

The Pennsylvania State University, Lehigh Valley
    Campus of the Berks-Lehigh Valley College, B
The Pennsylvania State University McKeesport
    Campus of the Commonwealth College, B
The Pennsylvania State University Mont Alto
    Campus of the Commonwealth College, B
The Pennsylvania State University New Kensington
    Campus of the Commonwealth College, B
The Pennsylvania State University Schuylkill
    Campus of the Capital College, B
The Pennsylvania State University Shenango
    Campus of the Commonwealth College, B
The Pennsylvania State University University Park
    Campus, BMD
The Pennsylvania State University Wilkes-Barre
    Campus of the Commonwealth College, B
The Pennsylvania State University Worthington
    Scranton Campus of the Commonwealth
    College, B
The Pennsylvania State University York Campus of
    the Commonwealth College, B
Saint Francis University, B
Swarthmore College, B
University of Pennsylvania, BMD
University of Pittsburgh at Greensburg, B
University of Pittsburgh at Johnstown, B
West Chester University of Pennsylvania, B

Puerto Rico

Inter American University of Puerto Rico,
    Metropolitan Campus, B
Inter American University of Puerto Rico, San
    Germán Campus, B
University of Puerto Rico, Mayagüez Campus, B
University of Puerto Rico, Río Piedras, BM
University of the Sacred Heart, B

Rhode Island

Brown University, BMD
University of Rhode Island, B

South Carolina

University of South Carolina, MD

Tennessee

Bryan College, B
Carson-Newman College, B
Sewanee: The University of the South, B
Vanderbilt University, MD

Texas

Blinn College, A
Lamar State College-Orange, A
Lon Morris College, A
Midland College, A
Schreiner University, B
Southwestern University, B
University of Dallas, D
The University of Texas at Austin, MD
The University of Texas at Dallas, B

Utah

Brigham Young University, BM
University of Utah, MD

Vermont

Burlington College, B
Castleton State College, B
Johnson State College, B
Marlboro College, B
Southern Vermont College, B

Virginia

Christendom College, B
Christopher Newport University, B
University of Virginia, B

Washington

Eastern Washington University, B
Gonzaga University, B
Northwest University, B
Pacific Lutheran University, B
Skagit Valley College, A
Tacoma Community College, A
University of Washington, BMD

Western Washington University, B

West Virginia

Alderson-Broaddus College, B
Davis & Elkins College, B
West Virginia University, M
West Virginia Wesleyan College, B

Wisconsin

Beloit College, B
University of Wisconsin-Madison, BMD
University of Wisconsin-Milwaukee, BMDO

Alberta

University of Alberta, B

British Columbia

The University of British Columbia, MD
University of Victoria, B

New Brunswick

Mount Allison University, B
Université de Moncton, B
University of New Brunswick Fredericton, B

Newfoundland and Labrador

Memorial University of Newfoundland, B

Nova Scotia

Dalhousie University, B
Mount Saint Vincent University, B

Ontario

Brock University, B
Carleton University, BD
McMaster University, B
Trent University, B
University of Guelph, D
University of Ottawa, B
University of Toronto, BMD
The University of Western Ontario, BMD
University of Windsor, B
York University, B

Quebec

Bishop's University, B
Concordia University, B
Université Laval, ABMD
Université de Montréal, BMD
Université du Québec àChicoutimi, BM
Université du Québec àMontréal, BMD
Université du Québec àRimouski, BM
Université du Québec àTrois-Rivières, M
Université de Sherbrooke, MD

COMPOSITION

Arizona

Northern Arizona University, M
The University of Arizona, MD

California

California Institute of the Arts, MO
California State University, Fullerton, M
California State University, Los Angeles, M
California State University, Northridge, M
San Diego State University, M
San Francisco Conservatory of Music, M
San Francisco State University, M
Stanford University, MD
University of California, Davis, MD
University of California, Santa Barbara, MD
University of Southern California, MD

Colorado

Colorado State University, M
University of Colorado at Boulder, MD

University of Denver, M

Connecticut

University of Connecticut, M
University of Hartford, MDO

Delaware

University of Delaware, M

District of Columbia

The Catholic University of America, MD

Florida

Florida State University, MD
University of Miami, MD
University of South Florida, M

Illinois

DePaul University, M
Northwestern University, MD
Southern Illinois University Carbondale, M

Indiana

Butler University, M

Iowa

University of Northern Iowa, M

Kansas

Kansas State University, M
University of Kansas, MD

Kentucky

Eastern Kentucky University, M
University of Louisville, M

Maryland

Towson University, M

Massachusetts

The Boston Conservatory, M
Boston University, MD
Brandeis University, MD
Harvard University, MD
Tufts University, M

Michigan

Michigan State University, MD
Wayne State University, M

Mississippi

University of Southern Mississippi, M

Missouri

University of Missouri-Kansas City, MD
Webster University, M

Nevada

University of Nevada, Las Vegas, M

New Jersey

Montclair State University, M
Princeton University, D
Rider University, M
Rutgers, The State University of New Jersey, New
    Brunswick/Piscataway, MD

New York

Brooklyn College of the City University of New
    York, M
Cornell University, D
Ithaca College, M
Manhattan School of Music, MD
Mannes College The New School for Music, MO
New York University, M
Purchase College, State University of New York, M
State University of New York at Buffalo, MD
State University of New York College at Potsdam, M
Syracuse University, M

University of Rochester, MD

North Carolina

Duke University, MD
East Carolina University, M
North Carolina School of the Arts, M
The University of North Carolina at Greensboro, M

Ohio

Bowling Green State University, M
Cleveland State University, M
Kent State University, MD
Ohio University, M
The University of Akron, M
University of Cincinnati, MD
Youngstown State University, M

Oklahoma

Oklahoma City University, M
University of Oklahoma, MD

Pennsylvania

Carnegie Mellon University, M
Duquesne University, M
Indiana University of Pennsylvania, M
The Pennsylvania State University University Park
    Campus, M
Temple University, MD
University of Pittsburgh, MD

South Carolina

University of South Carolina, MD

Tennessee

Belmont University, M
University of Memphis, MD
The University of Tennessee, M

Texas

Baylor University, M
Hardin-Simmons University, M
Rice University, MD
Southern Methodist University, M
Texas A&M University-Commerce, M
Texas Christian University, M
Texas Tech University, M
University of Houston, MD
University of North Texas, MD

Utah

Brigham Young University, M

Virginia

James Madison University, M
Norfolk State University, M
Shenandoah University, M
Virginia Commonwealth University, M

Washington

Eastern Washington University, M

West Virginia

West Virginia University, MD

Wisconsin

University of Wisconsin-Madison, MD

Alberta

University of Alberta, M

British Columbia

University of Victoria, M

Ontario

York University, M

Quebec

McGill University, MD
Université Laval, M

Université de Montréal, MD

COMPUTATIONAL BIOLOGY

Arizona
Arizona State University, M

California
University of Southern California, D

Connecticut
Yale University, DO

Florida
Florida State University, D

Idaho
University of Idaho, MD

Illinois
Northwestern University, M
University of Illinois at Urbana-Champaign, D

Iowa
Iowa State University of Science and
   Technology, MD

Massachusetts
Massachusetts Institute of Technology, D

Missouri
Washington University in St. Louis, D

New Jersey
New Jersey Institute of Technology, M
Rutgers, The State University of New Jersey,
   Newark, M

New York
New York University, D
University of Rochester, MD

Pennsylvania
Carnegie Mellon University, MD
University of Pennsylvania, DO

Virginia
Virginia Polytechnic Institute and State University, D

COMPUTATIONAL MATHEMATICS

California
University of California, Davis, B
University of California, Los Angeles, B

Illinois
Northern Illinois University, B

Indiana
Indiana University-Purdue University Fort Wayne, B

Michigan
Michigan State University, B
Michigan Technological University, B

New Jersey
Stevens Institute of Technology, B

New York
Brooklyn College of the City University of New
   York, B

Marist College, B

Pennsylvania
Carnegie Mellon University, B

Texas
Southwestern University, B

Wisconsin
Marquette University, B

Ontario
University of Waterloo, B

COMPUTATIONAL SCIENCES

Arizona
Arizona State University, MD

California
California Institute of Technology, MD
San Diego State University, MD
Stanford University, MD
University of California, Santa Barbara, MD

Colorado
University of Colorado at Denver and Health
   Sciences Center - Downtown Denver Campus, D

Illinois
Northwestern University, M

Iowa
The University of Iowa, D

Louisiana
Louisiana Tech University, D

Massachusetts
Massachusetts Institute of Technology, M
University of Massachusetts Lowell, D

Michigan
Michigan Technological University, D
University of Michigan-Dearborn, M
Western Michigan University, M

Minnesota
University of Minnesota, Duluth, M
University of Minnesota, Twin Cities Campus, MD

Mississippi
University of Mississippi, MD
University of Southern Mississippi, D

New Jersey
Kean University, M
Princeton University, D

New York
Cornell University, MD
State University of New York College at
   Brockport, M

Pennsylvania
Carnegie Mellon University, MD
Temple University, MD

Puerto Rico
University of Puerto Rico, Mayagüez Campus, M

South Carolina
Clemson University, MD

Texas
Rice University, MD
Sam Houston State University, M
Southern Methodist University, MD

The University of Texas at Austin, MD

Virginia
The College of William and Mary, M
George Mason University, MDO

Alberta
University of Lethbridge, D

Manitoba
University of Manitoba, M

Newfoundland and Labrador
Memorial University of Newfoundland, M

Quebec
McGill University, M

COMPUTER AND INFORMATION SCIENCES

Alabama
Alabama Agricultural and Mechanical University, B
American College of Computer & Information
   Sciences, B
Auburn University, B
Bevill State Community College, A
Bishop State Community College, A
Calhoun Community College, A
Gadsden State Community College, A
H. Councill Trenholm State Technical College, A
Herzing College, A
Huntingdon College, B
Jacksonville State University, B
James H. Faulkner State Community College, A
Jefferson State Community College, A
Lawson State Community College, A
Miles College, B
Northwest-Shoals Community College, A
Remington College-Mobile Campus, A
Snead State Community College, A
Spring Hill College, AB
Troy University, AB
The University of Alabama, B
The University of Alabama at Birmingham, B
The University of Alabama in Huntsville, B
University of North Alabama, B
University of South Alabama, B
Virginia College at Huntsville, A

Alaska
University of Alaska Anchorage, A
University of Alaska Fairbanks, B
University of Alaska Southeast, Sitka Campus, A

Arizona
Arizona State University West, B
Central Arizona College, A
DeVry University (Phoenix), B
GateWay Community College, A
Mohave Community College, A
Northern Arizona University, A
Northland Pioneer College, A
Phoenix College, A
Pima Community College, A
Prescott College, B
Rio Salado College, A
The University of Arizona, B

Arkansas
Arkansas State University, B
Arkansas Tech University, B
Harding University, B
Henderson State University, B
Mid-South Community College, A
North Arkansas College, A
Ouachita Technical College, A
Southern Arkansas University-Magnolia, B
Southern Arkansas University Tech, A
University of Arkansas, B
University of Arkansas at Fort Smith, B
University of Central Arkansas, B

Williams Baptist College, B

California

American River College, A
Antelope Valley College, A
Berkeley City College, A
Biola University, B
California Lutheran University, B
California State Polytechnic University, Pomona, B
California State University, Los Angeles, B
California State University, Sacramento, B
California State University, San Bernardino, B
California State University, Stanislaus, B
Cerro Coso Community College, A
Chabot College, A
Chapman University, B
Citrus College, A
Claremont McKenna College, B
Coleman College (La Mesa), AB
College of the Canyons, A
College of the Desert, A
College of the Redwoods, A
Cypress College, A
Empire College, A
Evergreen Valley College, A
Folsom Lake College, A
Fresno Pacific University, B
Gavilan College, A
Glendale Community College, A
Heald College-Hayward, A
Los Angeles City College, A
Los Angeles Valley College, A
The Master's College and Seminary, B
Mt. Sierra College, B
Pacific Union College, B
Palo Verde College, A
Platt College-Los Angeles, Inc, A
Reedley College, A
Saddleback College, A
San Diego Mesa College, A
Santa Ana College, A
Santa Monica College, A
Santiago Canyon College, A
Southwestern College, A
University of California, Irvine, B
University of San Francisco, B
University of Southern California, B
Ventura College, A
Victor Valley College, A
Yuba College, A

Colorado

CollegeAmerica-Fort Collins, B
Colorado Christian University, B
Colorado State University, B
Colorado State University-Pueblo, B
Colorado Technical University Denver Campus, AB
Community College of Denver, A
DeVry University (Colorado Springs), B
DeVry University (Westminster), B
Front Range Community College, A
IntelliTec College (Grand Junction), A
Metropolitan State College of Denver, B
National American University (Denver), AB
Trinidad State Junior College, A
University of Colorado at Colorado Springs, B
University of Colorado at Denver and Health
   Sciences Center - Downtown Denver Campus, B
University of Denver, B

Connecticut

Asnuntuck Community College, A
Capital Community College, A
Central Connecticut State University, B
Connecticut College, B
Eastern Connecticut State University, B
Gateway Community College, A
Goodwin College, A
Norwalk Community College, A
Quinebaug Valley Community College, A
Sacred Heart University, AB
University of Hartford, B
University of New Haven, B

Yale University, B

Delaware

Delaware State University, B
University of Delaware, B

District of Columbia

Gallaudet University, B
The George Washington University, B

Florida

Bethune-Cookman College, B
Chipola College, A
Daytona Beach Community College, A
DeVry University (Miramar), B
DeVry University (Orlando), B
Florida Agricultural and Mechanical University, B
Florida Atlantic University, B
Florida Community College at Jacksonville, A
Florida Gulf Coast University, B
Florida International University, B
Florida Metropolitan University-Brandon
   Campus, AB
Florida Metropolitan University-North Orlando
   Campus, B
Florida Metropolitan University-Pinellas Campus, AB
Florida Metropolitan University-South Orlando
   Campus, AB
Herzing College, A
Jacksonville University, B
Jones College (Miami), AB
Lake-Sumter Community College, A
Manatee Community College, A
Northwood University, Florida Campus, B
Nova Southeastern University, B
Palm Beach Atlantic University, B
Remington College-Pinellas Campus, A
St. Johns River Community College, A
Seminole Community College, A
Tallahassee Community College, A
University of Central Florida, B
University of Florida, B
University of Miami, B
University of North Florida, B
University of Phoenix-West Florida Campus, B
University of South Florida, B
University of West Florida, B
Webber International University, B

Georgia

Albany State University, B
Albany Technical College, A
Andrew College, A
Atlanta Metropolitan College, A
Augusta State University, B
Brewton-Parker College, B
Clark Atlanta University, B
Dalton State College, A
Darton College, A
DeVry University (Decatur), B
Emmanuel College, B
Georgia College & State University, B
Georgia Institute of Technology, B
Georgia Southern University, B
Georgia Southwestern State University, B
Georgia State University, B
Gordon College, A
Herzing College, AB
Kennesaw State University, B
LaGrange College, B
Middle Georgia College, A
Morehouse College, B
North Georgia College & State University, B
Shorter College, B
South Georgia College, A
Southern Polytechnic State University, B
University of Georgia, B
University of Phoenix-Columbus Georgia
   Campus, B
University of West Georgia, B
Valdosta State University, B
Waycross College, A
Wesleyan College, B

West Central Technical College, A

Hawaii

Chaminade University of Honolulu, AB
Hawaii Pacific University, B
University of Hawaii at Manoa, B

Idaho

Boise State University, B
Idaho State University, B
Lewis-Clark State College, AB
North Idaho College, A
University of Phoenix-Idaho Campus, B

Illinois

Aurora University, B
Bradley University, B
City Colleges of Chicago, Wilbur Wright College, A
DePaul University, B
DeVry University (Chicago), B
DeVry University (Tinley Park), B
Eastern Illinois University, B
Heartland Community College, A
Highland Community College, A
Joliet Junior College, A
Kishwaukee College, A
Knox College, B
MacCormac College, A
Midstate College, A
Millikin University, B
Northeastern Illinois University, B
Northwestern University, B
Oakton Community College, A
Parkland College, A
Prairie State College, A
Principia College, B
Quincy University, B
Rend Lake College, A
Richland Community College, A
Rockford Business College, A
St. Augustine College, A
Saint Xavier University, B
Sauk Valley Community College, A
University of Illinois at Chicago, B
Waubonsee Community College, A
Western Illinois University, B
William Rainey Harper College, A

Indiana

Bethel College, B
DeVry University (Indianapolis), B
Franklin College, B
Indiana Business College (Indianapolis), A
Indiana State University, B
Indiana University Bloomington, B
Indiana University-Purdue University Indianapolis, B
Indiana Wesleyan University, AB
Ivy Tech Community College-Bloomington, A
Ivy Tech Community College-Central Indiana, A
Ivy Tech Community College-Columbus, A
Ivy Tech Community College-East Central, A
Ivy Tech Community College-Kokomo, A
Ivy Tech Community College-Lafayette, A
Ivy Tech Community College-North Central, A
Ivy Tech Community College-Northeast, A
Ivy Tech Community College-Northwest, A
Ivy Tech Community College-Southeast, A
Ivy Tech Community College-Southern Indiana, A
Ivy Tech Community College-Southwest, A
Ivy Tech Community College-Wabash Valley, A
Ivy Tech Community College-Whitewater, A
Purdue University, B
Purdue University Calumet, B
Saint Joseph's College, B
Saint Mary-of-the-Woods College, B
Tri-State University, B
University of Evansville, B
University of Notre Dame, B
University of Southern Indiana, B
Vincennes University, A

Iowa

Ashford University, B
Ellsworth Community College, A
Emmaus Bible College, B

Iowa Lakes Community College, A
Iowa State University of Science and Technology, B
Kaplan University, AB
Mount Mercy College, B
North Iowa Area Community College, A
Scott Community College, A
University of Dubuque, B
The University of Iowa, B
University of Northern Iowa, B

Kansas

Brown Mackie College-Salina, A
Butler Community College, A
Coffeyville Community College, A
Colby Community College, A
Donnelly College, A
Emporia State University, B
Friends University, B
Haskell Indian Nations University, AB
Hutchinson Community College and Area Vocational
   School, A
Kansas State University, B
Sterling College, B
University of Kansas, B
University of Saint Mary, B
Washburn University, AB
Wichita State University, B

Kentucky

Bellarmine University, B
Eastern Kentucky University, B
Georgetown College, B
Henderson Community College, A
Kentucky State University, AB
Kentucky Wesleyan College, B
Lindsey Wilson College, A
Louisville Technical Institute, A
Midway College, AB
Morehead State University, B
Murray State University, B
National College of Business & Technology
   (Danville), A
National College of Business & Technology
   (Florence), A
National College of Business & Technology
   (Lexington), A
National College of Business & Technology
   (Louisville), A
National College of Business & Technology
   (Pikeville), A
National College of Business & Technology
   (Richmond), A
Northern Kentucky University, B
Owensboro Community and Technical College, A
Pikeville College, B
Thomas More College, AB
University of the Cumberlands, B
University of Kentucky, B
Western Kentucky University, B

Louisiana

Elaine P. Nunez Community College, A
Loyola University New Orleans, B
Remington College-New Orleans Campus, A
Tulane University, AB
University of Louisiana at Lafayette, B
University of Phoenix-Louisiana Campus, B
Xavier University of Louisiana, B

Maine

Beal College, A
Saint Joseph's College of Maine, B
Thomas College, AB
The University of Maine at Augusta, AB

Maryland

Anne Arundel Community College, A
Bowie State University, B
Carroll Community College, A
DeVry University, B
Frostburg State University, B
Hagerstown Community College, A
Harford Community College, A
Hood College, B
Howard Community College, A

The Johns Hopkins University, B
Loyola College in Maryland, B
McDaniel College, B
Montgomery College, A
Mount St. Mary's University, B
St. Mary's College of Maryland, B
Salisbury University, B
United States Naval Academy, B
University of Baltimore, B
University of Maryland, College Park, B
University of Maryland University College, B
University of Phoenix-Maryland Campus, B
Villa Julie College, AB
Wor-Wic Community College, A

Massachusetts

Bentley College, B
Berkshire Community College, A
Bristol Community College, A
Cape Cod Community College, A
Harvard University, B
Massachusetts Bay Community College, A
Massachusetts College of Liberal Arts, B
Massasoit Community College, A
North Shore Community College, A
Northern Essex Community College, A
Regis College, B
Simon's Rock College of Bard, B
Suffolk University, B
University of Massachusetts Dartmouth, B
Worcester Polytechnic Institute, B
Worcester State College, B

Michigan

Alpena Community College, A
Andrews University, B
Aquinas College, B
Baker College of Allen Park, A
Baker College of Muskegon, B
Central Michigan University, B
Concordia University, B
Davenport University (Dearborn), AB
Eastern Michigan University, B
Grace Bible College, B
Grand Valley State University, B
Henry Ford Community College, A
Kuyper College, B
Lake Michigan College, A
Madonna University, AB
Marygrove College, B
Michigan State University, B
Monroe County Community College, A
North Central Michigan College, A
Northern Michigan University, B
Northwood University, B
Oakland Community College, A
Olivet College, B
Saginaw Valley State University, B
Southwestern Michigan College, A
University of Detroit Mercy, B
University of Michigan-Dearborn, B
Walsh College of Accountancy and Business
   Administration, B
Wayne State University, B
Western Michigan University, B

Minnesota

Academy College, A
Alexandria Technical College, A
Bethel University, B
College of St. Catherine, B
The College of St. Scholastica, B
Dunwoody College of Technology, A
Herzing College, A
Hibbing Community College, A
Minneapolis Community and Technical College, A
Minnesota State University Moorhead, B
Normandale Community College, A
Northland Community and Technical College-Thief
   River Falls, A
Ridgewater College, A
University of St. Thomas, B

Winona State University, B

Mississippi

Alcorn State University, B
Hinds Community College, A
Holmes Community College, A
Itawamba Community College, A
Jackson State University, B
Mississippi College, B
Mississippi Gulf Coast Community College, A
Mississippi State University, B
Northwest Mississippi Community College, A
University of Mississippi, B
University of Southern Mississippi, B

Missouri

Avila University, B
Blue River Community College, A
Central Missouri State University, B
College of the Ozarks, B
Columbia College, AB
Drury University, B
Hannibal-LaGrange College, B
Longview Community College, A
Maple Woods Community College, A
Metro Business College (Jefferson City), A
Metropolitan Community College-Business &
   Technology College, A
Missouri Baptist University, B
Missouri Southern State University, B
Missouri State University-West Plains, A
Missouri Western State University, B
Moberly Area Community College, A
Park University, B
Penn Valley Community College, A
Ranken Technical College, A
St. Louis Community College at Forest Park, A
Saint Louis University, B
Southeast Missouri State University, B
State Fair Community College, A
Three Rivers Community College, A
University of Missouri-Columbia, B
University of Missouri-St. Louis, B
University of Phoenix-Kansas City Campus, B
Washington University in St. Louis, B
William Woods University, B

Montana

Dawson Community College, A
Montana State University-Billings, A
Montana State University-Great Falls College of
   Technology, A
Montana Tech of The University of Montana, B
University of Great Falls, B
The University of Montana-Missoula, B
The University of Montana-Western, A

Nebraska

Bellevue University, B
Central Community College-Columbus Campus, A
Central Community College-Grand Island
   Campus, A
Central Community College-Hastings Campus, A
Concordia University, B
Doane College, B
Grace University, B
Hastings College, B
Mid-Plains Community College, A
Northeast Community College, A
Southeast Community College, Lincoln Campus, A
Southeast Community College, Milford Campus, A
University of Nebraska at Kearney, B
University of Nebraska-Lincoln, B
Wayne State College, B
Western Nebraska Community College, A

Nevada

Career College of Northern Nevada, A
Sierra Nevada College, B
University of Nevada, Reno, B
University of Phoenix-Nevada Campus, B

Western Nevada Community College, A

New Hampshire

Hesser College, A
Keene State College, AB
McIntosh College, A
New Hampshire Community Technical College,
   Berlin/Laconia, A
New Hampshire Community Technical College,
   Nashua/Claremont, A
New Hampshire Technical Institute, A

New Jersey

Caldwell College, B
Camden County College, A
The College of New Jersey, B
DeVry University, B
Fairleigh Dickinson University, College at
   Florham, B
Fairleigh Dickinson University, Metropolitan
   Campus, B
Georgian Court University, B
Kean University, B
Monmouth University, B
New Jersey City University, B
New Jersey Institute of Technology, B
Ocean County College, A
Ramapo College of New Jersey, B
The Richard Stockton College of New Jersey, B
Rowan University, B
Rutgers, The State University of New Jersey,
   Camden, B
Rutgers, The State University of New Jersey,
   Newark, B
Saint Peter's College, B
Salem Community College, A
Seton Hall University, B
Sussex County Community College, A

New Mexico

Clovis Community College, A
Eastern New Mexico University, B
Eastern New Mexico University-Roswell, A
Luna Community College, A
New Mexico State University, B
Northern New Mexico Community College, A
Santa Fe Community College, A
University of New Mexico, B

New York

Adelphi University, B
Adirondack Community College, A
Barnard College, B
Brooklyn College of the City University of New
   York, B
Broome Community College, A
Cayuga County Community College, A
Clarkson University, B
The College of Saint Rose, B
College of Staten Island of the City University of
   New York, B
The College of Westchester, A
Columbia-Greene Community College, A
Cornell University, B
Corning Community College, A
DeVry Institute of Technology, B
Dominican College, B
Dowling College, B
Dutchess Community College, A
Erie Community College, North Campus, A
Finger Lakes Community College, A
Fiorello H. LaGuardia Community College of the
   City University of New York, A
Fordham University, B
Genesee Community College, A
Globe Institute of Technology, AB
Hartwick College, B
Herkimer County Community College, A
Ithaca College, B
Jamestown Business College, A
Jamestown Community College, A
Kingsborough Community College of the City
   University of New York, A
Lehman College of the City University of New
   York, B
Long Island University, C.W. Post Campus, B

Medaille College, B
Mohawk Valley Community College, A
Monroe Community College, A
Mount Saint Mary College, B
Nassau Community College, A
New York Institute of Technology, B
New York University, B
Onondaga Community College, A
Orange County Community College, A
Pace University, B
Rensselaer Polytechnic Institute, B
Rochester Institute of Technology, B
Rockland Community College, A
Sage College of Albany, AB
St. John's University, B
Schenectady County Community College, A
Siena College, B
Skidmore College, B
State University of New York College at Old
   Westbury, B
State University of New York College at Potsdam, B
State University of New York College of Technology
   at Alfred, AB
State University of New York Institute of
   Technology, B
Syracuse University, B
Tompkins Cortland Community College, A
Union College, B
University at Albany, State University of New York, B
Utica College, B
Vassar College, B
Wagner College, B
Westchester Community College, A

North Carolina

Barton College, B
Campbell University, B
DeVry University, B
ECPI Technical College, A
Guilford College, B
High Point University, B
Mars Hill College, B
Meredith College, B
Montreat College, B
Robeson Community College, A
Saint Augustine's College, B
Sampson Community College, A
Shaw University, B
South College-Asheville, A
The University of North Carolina at Greensboro, B
Wake Forest University, B
Wake Technical Community College, A

North Dakota

Lake Region State College, A
Mayville State University, B
University of Mary, B
University of North Dakota, B
Valley City State University, B

Ohio

Antonelli College, A
Baldwin-Wallace College, B
Bowling Green State University, B
Brown Mackie College-Cincinnati, A
Central State University, B
Cincinnati State Technical and Community
   College, A
Cleveland State University, B
DeVry University (Columbus), B
Franciscan University of Steubenville, B
Franklin University, AB
Kent State University, East Liverpool Campus, A
Kent State University, Salem Campus, A
Lorain County Community College, A
Miami University, B
Miami University Hamilton, B
Miami University-Middletown Campus, B
Mount Vernon Nazarene University, B
Ohio Business College (Lorain), A
Ohio Dominican University, B
The Ohio State University, B
Sinclair Community College, A
Stark State College of Technology, A
Terra State Community College, A
University of Cincinnati, AB

University of Cincinnati Clermont College, A
Wright State University, B

Oklahoma

Cameron University, B
Oklahoma Baptist University, B
Oklahoma Panhandle State University, B
Oklahoma State University, Oklahoma City, A
Southeastern Oklahoma State University, B
Southwestern Oklahoma State University, B
Tulsa Community College, A
University of Oklahoma, B
University of Phoenix-Tulsa Campus, B
University of Science and Arts of Oklahoma, B

Oregon

Central Oregon Community College, A
DeVry University, B
George Fox University, B
Linn-Benton Community College, A
Northwest Christian College, B
Oregon Institute of Technology, B
Portland State University, B
University of Oregon, B

Pennsylvania

Arcadia University, B
Berks Technical Institute, A
Bloomsburg University of Pennsylvania, B
Bucknell University, B
Bucks County Community College, A
Butler County Community College, A
Cabrini College, B
Cedar Crest College, B
Chatham College, B
Chestnut Hill College, B
Clarion University of Pennsylvania, B
Community College of Beaver County, A
Delaware County Community College, A
Delaware Valley College, A
DeVry University (Fort Washington), B
East Stroudsburg University of Pennsylvania, B
Edinboro University of Pennsylvania, AB
Erie Business Center, Main, A
Gannon University, B
Grove City College, B
Gwynedd-Mercy College, B
Harrisburg Area Community College, A
Holy Family University, B
Indiana University of Pennsylvania, B
Juniata College, B
King's College, AB
La Roche College, B
La Salle University, B
Lackawanna College, A
Lancaster Bible College, B
Laurel Business Institute, A
Lehigh Valley College, A
Lincoln University, B
Lock Haven University of Pennsylvania, B
Luzerne County Community College, A
Manor College, A
Mansfield University of Pennsylvania, B
Marywood University, B
McCann School of Business & Technology, A
Mercyhurst College, B
Millersville University of Pennsylvania, AB
Montgomery County Community College, A
Neumann College, B
Pennsylvania College of Technology, A
Pennsylvania Highland Community College, A
The Pennsylvania State University Abington
   College, A
The Pennsylvania State University Altoona
   College, B
The Pennsylvania State University Beaver Campus
   of the Commonwealth College, B
The Pennsylvania State University Berks Campus of
   the Berks-Lehigh Valley College, B
The Pennsylvania State University Delaware County
   Campus of the Commonwealth College, B
The Pennsylvania State University DuBois Campus
   of the Commonwealth College, B
The Pennsylvania State University at Erie, The
   Behrend College, B

The Pennsylvania State University Fayette Campus
of the Commonwealth College, B
The Pennsylvania State University Harrisburg
Campus, B
The Pennsylvania State University Hazleton
Campus of the Commonwealth College, B
The Pennsylvania State University, Lehigh Valley
Campus of the Berks-Lehigh Valley College, B
The Pennsylvania State University McKeesport
Campus of the Commonwealth College, B
The Pennsylvania State University Mont Alto
Campus of the Commonwealth College, B
The Pennsylvania State University New Kensington
Campus of the Commonwealth College, B
The Pennsylvania State University Schuylkill
Campus of the Capital College, AB
The Pennsylvania State University Shenango
Campus of the Commonwealth College, B
The Pennsylvania State University University Park
Campus, B
The Pennsylvania State University Wilkes-Barre
Campus of the Commonwealth College, B
The Pennsylvania State University Worthington
Scranton Campus of the Commonwealth
College, B
The Pennsylvania State University York Campus of
the Commonwealth College, B
Philadelphia University, B
Saint Joseph's University, B
Saint Vincent College, B
Shippensburg University of Pennsylvania, B
Slippery Rock University of Pennsylvania, B
South Hills School of Business & Technology (State
College), A
Swarthmore College, B
Temple University, B
University of Pittsburgh at Greensburg, B
Waynesburg College, B
West Chester University of Pennsylvania, B
Westmoreland County Community College, A
Widener University, B
Wilkes University, B
York College of Pennsylvania, B
York Technical Institute, A

Puerto Rico

Inter American University of Puerto Rico,
Barranquitas Campus, AB
Technological College of San Juan, A
University of Puerto Rico, Río Piedras, B

Rhode Island

Bryant University, B
Johnson & Wales University, B
New England Institute of Technology, AB
Rhode Island College, B
University of Rhode Island, B

South Carolina

Benedict College, B
Bob Jones University, B
Clemson University, B
Coastal Carolina University, B
College of Charleston, B
Denmark Technical College, A
Francis Marion University, B
Lander University, B
Southern Wesleyan University, B
Spartanburg Technical College, A
University of South Carolina, B
University of South Carolina Upstate, B

South Dakota

Black Hills State University, A
Dakota State University, B
Mitchell Technical Institute, A
South Dakota State University, B
Southeast Technical Institute, A
The University of South Dakota, B

Tennessee

Austin Peay State University, B
East Tennessee State University, B
Freed-Hardeman University, B
Lambuth University, B

Lane College, B
Lincoln Memorial University, B
Maryville College, B
Milligan College, B
National College of Business & Technology (Bristol)
, A
National College of Business & Technology
(Nashville), A
Pellissippi State Technical Community College, A
University of Phoenix-Nashville Campus, B
Walters State Community College, A

Texas

Amberton University, B
Angelo State University, B
Austin Community College, A
Brazosport College, A
Central Texas College, A
Clarendon College, A
Coastal Bend College, A
Collin County Community College District, A
Computer Career Center, A
Dallas Baptist University, B
Del Mar College, A
DeVry University (Houston), B
Eastfield College, A
El Paso Community College, A
Frank Phillips College, A
Galveston College, A
Houston Baptist University, B
Houston Community College System, A
Howard College, A
Kilgore College, A
Kingwood College, A
Lubbock Christian University, B
McMurry University, B
North Harris College, A
Northwest Vista College, A
Northwood University, Texas Campus, B
Odessa College, A
Palo Alto College, A
Rice University, B
St. Edward's University, B
Sam Houston State University, B
Stephen F. Austin State University, B
Tarleton State University, B
Texas Christian University, B
Texas Southern University, B
Texas State Technical College Harlingen, A
Texas State Technical College Waco, A
Texas State University-San Marcos, B
Texas Tech University, B
Texas Wesleyan University, B
Texas Woman's University, B
Trinity University, B
Tyler Junior College, A
University of Houston, B
University of Houston-Clear Lake, B
University of Houston-Downtown, B
University of Mary Hardin-Baylor, B
University of North Texas, B
University of Phoenix-Houston Campus, B
The University of Texas at Arlington, B
The University of Texas at Austin, B
The University of Texas at Brownsville, B
The University of Texas at Dallas, B
The University of Texas at Tyler, B
West Texas A&M University, B
Wiley College, AB

Utah

Neumont University, B
Salt Lake Community College, A
Utah State University, B
Utah Valley State College, A
Weber State University, AB

Vermont

Castleton State College, B
Champlain College, AB
Lyndon State College, AB
University of Vermont, B

Virginia

Christopher Newport University, B
The College of William and Mary, B

DeVry University (Arlington), B
ECPI College of Technology (Newport News), A
ECPI College of Technology (Virginia Beach), A
ECPI Technical College (Richmond), A
ECPI Technical College (Roanoke), A
George Mason University, B
J. Sargeant Reynolds Community College, A
James Madison University, B
Liberty University, B
Lord Fairfax Community College, A
Mary Baldwin College, B
Marymount University, B
National College of Business & Technology
(Bluefield), A
National College of Business & Technology
(Charlottesville), A
National College of Business & Technology
(Danville), A
National College of Business & Technology
(Harrisonburg), A
National College of Business & Technology
(Lynchburg), A
National College of Business & Technology
(Martinsville), A
National College of Business & Technology (Salem)
, A
Norfolk State University, B
Old Dominion University, B
Southern Virginia University, B
University of Phoenix-Northern Virginia Campus, B
University of Virginia, B
The University of Virginia's College at Wise, B
Virginia Commonwealth University, B
Virginia Intermont College, B
Virginia Polytechnic Institute and State University, B
Washington and Lee University, B

Washington

Central Washington University, B
Centralia College, A
Columbia Basin College, A
DeVry University (Federal Way), B
Eastern Washington University, B
The Evergreen State College, B
Lower Columbia College, A
Olympic College, A
Shoreline Community College, A
Skagit Valley College, A
South Puget Sound Community College, A
Tacoma Community College, A
University of Washington, B
University of Washington, Bothell, B
University of Washington, Tacoma, B

West Virginia

Bluefield State College, AB
Marshall University, B
Mountain State College, A
New River Community and Technical College, A
Potomac State College of West Virginia
University, A
Shepherd University, B
University of Charleston, AB
West Virginia University, B
West Virginia Wesleyan College, B

Wisconsin

Alverno College, B
Blackhawk Technical College, A
Carroll College, B
Chippewa Valley Technical College, A
DeVry University (Milwaukee), B
Herzing College, AB
Lakeshore Technical College, A
Mid-State Technical College, A
Milwaukee Area Technical College, A
Nicolet Area Technical College, A
St. Norbert College, B
Silver Lake College, B
University of Wisconsin-Eau Claire, B
University of Wisconsin-La Crosse, B
University of Wisconsin-River Falls, B
University of Wisconsin-Stevens Point, B
University of Wisconsin-Superior, B
University of Wisconsin-Whitewater, B

Viterbo University, B

Wyoming

Laramie County Community College, A
Western Wyoming Community College, A

Alberta

Athabasca University, B
University of Lethbridge, B

British Columbia

Malaspina University-College, B
Thompson Rivers University, B
University College of the Fraser Valley, B
University of Northern British Columbia, B

Nova Scotia

Cape Breton University, B
Mount Saint Vincent University, B
St. Francis Xavier University, B

Ontario

University of Guelph, B
University of Ottawa, B
The University of Western Ontario, B
University of Windsor, B
Wilfrid Laurier University, B
York University, B

Quebec

Bishop's University, B
McGill University, B
Université de Sherbrooke, B

COMPUTER AND INFORMATION SCIENCES AND SUPPORT SERVICES

Arkansas

Southern Arkansas University Tech, A
University of Arkansas at Fort Smith, AB

California

California State University, Chico, B
California State University, Los Angeles, B
Mt. Sierra College, B
University of California, Irvine, B

District of Columbia

Strayer University, AB

Florida

Florida Metropolitan University-Brandon Campus, A

Georgia

Southern Polytechnic State University, B

Illinois

Columbia College Chicago, B
International Academy of Design & Technology, B

Indiana

Indiana Business College (Indianapolis), A
Indiana Business College (Lafayette), A
Indiana Business College (Muncie), A
Purdue University, B
University of Evansville, B
University of Notre Dame, B

Iowa

University of Northern Iowa, B

Kentucky

Louisville Technical Institute, A

Massachusetts

Anna Maria College, B
Becker College, AB
Bunker Hill Community College, A
Massasoit Community College, A

Springfield Technical Community College, A

Michigan

Cleary University, A
Jackson Community College, A
Mott Community College, A

Minnesota

Academy College, A

Missouri

Metropolitan Community College-Business & Technology College, A
Park University, B
Ranken Technical College, A
Saint Louis University, B
University of Missouri-Rolla, B
Washington University in St. Louis, B

Montana

Blackfeet Community College, A
Montana State University-Billings, A
University of Great Falls, B

New Jersey

Atlantic Cape Community College, A
Fairleigh Dickinson University, Metropolitan Campus, B
New Jersey Institute of Technology, B

New York

College of Staten Island of the City University of New York, B
Dowling College, B
Herkimer County Community College, A
Long Island University, C.W. Post Campus, B
Mohawk Valley Community College, A
Roberts Wesleyan College, B
Utica School of Commerce, A

North Carolina

Robeson Community College, A

North Dakota

Mayville State University, B
Valley City State University, B
Williston State College, A

Ohio

College of Mount St. Joseph, B
Tiffin University, B

Pennsylvania

Cabrini College, B
Delaware Valley College, B
Harrisburg Area Community College, A
Lehigh University, B
Penn Foster Career School, A
Pennsylvania College of Technology, A
Schuylkill Institute of Business and Technology, A
University of Pittsburgh, B
The University of Scranton, B
York College of Pennsylvania, B

Puerto Rico

Inter American University of Puerto Rico, Bayamón Campus, B

South Carolina

Columbia College, B
Midlands Technical College, A
York Technical College, A

South Dakota

Mitchell Technical Institute, A

Utah

LDS Business College, A
Utah State University, B

Washington

City University, B
Clover Park Technical College, A

Edmonds Community College, A

West Virginia

West Virginia University, B

Wisconsin

Northeast Wisconsin Technical College, A
Waukesha County Technical College, A

Wyoming

Laramie County Community College, A

COMPUTER AND INFORMATION SYSTEMS SECURITY

Arizona

Cochise College (Douglas), A
ITT Technical Institute (Phoenix), B
ITT Technical Institute (Tempe), A

Arkansas

ITT Technical Institute, B

California

American River College, A
Berkeley City College, A
ITT Technical Institute (Anaheim), A
ITT Technical Institute (Lathrop), B
ITT Technical Institute (Oxnard), B
ITT Technical Institute (Rancho Cordova), B
ITT Technical Institute (San Bernardino), B
ITT Technical Institute (San Diego), B
ITT Technical Institute (Sylmar), B
ITT Technical Institute (Torrance), B
ITT Technical Institute (West Covina), B
Los Angeles City College, A
Mt. Sierra College, B
Southwestern College, A
Westwood College-Anaheim, B
Westwood College-Inland Empire, B
Westwood College-Long Beach, B

Colorado

ITT Technical Institute, B
Westwood College-Denver North, B
Westwood College-Denver South, B

Florida

Florida Community College at Jacksonville, A
Florida National College, A
ITT Technical Institute (Fort Lauderdale), B
ITT Technical Institute (Jacksonville), B
ITT Technical Institute (Lake Mary), B
ITT Technical Institute (Miami), B
ITT Technical Institute (Tampa), B
Seminole Community College, A

Georgia

Chattahoochee Technical College, A
Flint River Technical College, A
Griffin Technical College, A
ITT Technical Institute (Duluth), B
Lanier Technical College, A
Valdosta Technical College, A

Idaho

ITT Technical Institute, B

Illinois

City Colleges of Chicago, Wilbur Wright College, A
ITT Technical Institute (Burr Ridge), B
ITT Technical Institute (Mount Prospect), B
Northwestern Business College, A
Triton College, A
Westwood College-Chicago Du Page, B
Westwood College-Chicago Loop Campus, B
Westwood College-Chicago O'Hare Airport, B

Westwood College-Chicago River Oaks, B

Indiana

ITT Technical Institute (Fort Wayne), B
ITT Technical Institute (Indianapolis), B
ITT Technical Institute (Newburgh), B

Kentucky

Daymar College (Owensboro), A
ITT Technical Institute (Lexington), B
ITT Technical Institute (Louisville), B
Louisville Technical Institute, A

Louisiana

ITT Technical Institute, B

Maryland

Hagerstown Business College, A
ITT Technical Institute, B

Michigan

Davenport University (Dearborn), B
Delta College, A

Minnesota

Academy College, A
Dakota County Technical College, A
ITT Technical Institute, B
Minnesota State Community and Technical
    College-Fergus Falls, A
Riverland Community College, A

Missouri

ITT Technical Institute (Arnold), B
ITT Technical Institute (Earth City), B
ITT Technical Institute (Kansas City), B
Metropolitan Community College-Business &
    Technology College, A

Montana

University of Great Falls, B

Nebraska

ITT Technical Institute, B

Nevada

ITT Technical Institute, B

New Mexico

ITT Technical Institute, B

New York

Island Drafting and Technical Institute, A
ITT Technical Institute (Getzville), A
Jamestown Community College, A
Rochester Institute of Technology, B
Tompkins Cortland Community College, A

North Carolina

Fayetteville Technical Community College, A

Ohio

ITT Technical Institute (Youngstown), A

Oklahoma

ITT Technical Institute, B
Tulsa Community College, A

Oregon

ITT Technical Institute, B

Pennsylvania

East Stroudsburg University of Pennsylvania, B
Laurel Business Institute, A
Northampton County Area Community College, A

York Technical Institute, A

South Carolina

ITT Technical Institute, B

South Dakota

Dakota State University, B

Tennessee

Fountainhead College of Technology, B
ITT Technical Institute (Knoxville), B
ITT Technical Institute (Memphis), B
ITT Technical Institute (Nashville), B

Texas

Montgomery College, A
MTI College of Business and Technology (Houston)
    , A
Northwest Vista College, A
St. Philip's College, A

Utah

ITT Technical Institute, A

Vermont

Champlain College, AB

Virginia

ECPI Technical College (Glen Allen), A
ECPI Technical College (Richmond), A
ECPI Technical College (Roanoke), A
ITT Technical Institute (Chantilly), A
ITT Technical Institute (Richmond), B
ITT Technical Institute (Springfield), B

Washington

Clover Park Technical College, A
Edmonds Community College, A
ITT Technical Institute (Bothell), B
ITT Technical Institute (Seattle), B
ITT Technical Institute (Spokane), B
North Seattle Community College, A

Wisconsin

ITT Technical Institute (Green Bay), B
ITT Technical Institute (Greenfield), B

COMPUTER ART AND DESIGN

California

Academy of Art University, M
Art Center College of Design, M
University of California, Santa Cruz, M

Florida

Miami International University of Art & Design, M
University of Central Florida, MD
University of Florida, M

Georgia

Savannah College of Art and Design, M

Illinois

American Academy of Art, M
DePaul University, M

Indiana

Indiana University Bloomington, M

Maryland

Maryland Institute College of Art, M
University of Baltimore, M

Minnesota

Minneapolis College of Art and Design, O

Mississippi

Mississippi State University, M

Missouri

University of Missouri-Columbia, M

New Mexico

New Mexico Highlands University, M

New York

Alfred University, M
Cornell University, M

Long Island University, Brooklyn Campus, M
Long Island University, C.W. Post Campus, M
New York University, M
Rensselaer Polytechnic Institute, M
Rochester Institute of Technology, M
School of Visual Arts, M
State University of New York at New Paltz, M
Syracuse University, M

Pennsylvania

Carnegie Mellon University, M
Philadelphia University, M
University of Pennsylvania, M

Rhode Island

Rhode Island School of Design, M

South Carolina

Clemson University, M

Tennessee

East Tennessee State University, M
Memphis College of Art, M

Texas

St. Edward's University, M

Washington

Washington State University, M

British Columbia

University of Victoria, M

Quebec

Concordia University, O

COMPUTER EDUCATION

California

California State University, Dominguez Hills, MO
California State University, Los Angeles, M
Stanford University, MD

Connecticut

University of Bridgeport, MO

Florida

Florida Institute of Technology, M
Jacksonville University, M
Nova Southeastern University, MD

Iowa

Morningside College, M

Maine

Thomas College, M

Maryland

Maple Springs Baptist Bible College and
    Seminary, M
University of Maryland, Baltimore County, O

Massachusetts

Lesley University, MO

Michigan

University of Michigan, M

Mississippi

Mississippi College, M

Missouri

Fontbonne University, M

New Jersey

Kean University, M

New York

Long Island University, C.W. Post Campus, M
Stony Brook University, State University of New
    York, MO

North Carolina

The University of North Carolina Wilmington, M

Ohio

Ashland University, M
Ohio University, M

Wright State University, M

Pennsylvania

Arcadia University, MO
California University of Pennsylvania, M
DeSales University, M
Wilkes University, M

Rhode Island

Providence College, M

Texas

University of North Texas, MD

Vermont

Marlboro College, MO

Washington

Eastern Washington University, M

Wisconsin

Cardinal Stritch University, M

Nova Scotia

Dalhousie University, M

COMPUTER ENGINEERING

Alabama

Auburn University, BMD
The University of Alabama at Birmingham, MD
The University of Alabama in Huntsville, BMD
University of South Alabama, B

Alaska

University of Alaska Fairbanks, MD

Arizona

Arizona State University, B
Arizona State University at the Polytechnic
  Campus, M
Embry-Riddle Aeronautical University, B
The University of Arizona, BMD

Arkansas

Harding University, B
University of Arkansas, BMD

California

California Institute of Technology, B
California Polytechnic State University, San Luis
  Obispo, B
California State Polytechnic University, Pomona, B
California State University, Chico, BM
California State University, Fresno, B
California State University, Long Beach, BM
California State University, Northridge, M
California State University, Sacramento, B
College of the Canyons, A
Glendale Community College, A
International Technological University, M
Loyola Marymount University, B
Northwestern Polytechnic University, BM
San Diego State University, B
San Jose State University, BM
Santa Barbara City College, A
Santa Clara University, BMDO
Stanford University, B
University of California, Davis, MD
University of California, Irvine, BMD
University of California, Los Angeles, B
University of California, San Diego, BMD
University of California, Santa Barbara, BMDO
University of California, Santa Cruz, BMD
University of La Verne, B
University of the Pacific, B
University of Southern California, BMD

Colorado

Colorado State University, BMD
Colorado Technical University, BM
University of Colorado at Boulder, BMD
University of Colorado at Colorado Springs, B

University of Colorado at Denver and Health
  Sciences Center - Downtown Denver Campus, M
University of Denver, BM

Connecticut

Fairfield University, M
Gateway Community College, A
Trinity College, B
University of Bridgeport, BM
University of Connecticut, B
University of Hartford, B
University of New Haven, B

Delaware

University of Delaware, B

District of Columbia

The Catholic University of America, B
Gallaudet University, B
The George Washington University, BMDO

Florida

Bethune-Cookman College, B
Daytona Beach Community College, A
Embry-Riddle Aeronautical University, B
Florida Agricultural and Mechanical University, B
Florida Atlantic University, BMD
Florida Career College, A
Florida Institute of Technology, BMD
Florida International University, BM
Florida State University, BMD
Okaloosa-Walton College, A
Seminole Community College, A
University of Central Florida, BMD
University of Florida, BMDO
University of Miami, BMD
University of South Florida, BMD
University of West Florida, B

Georgia

Columbus Technical College, A
Georgia Institute of Technology, BMD
Mercer University, M
Middle Georgia College, A
Savannah State University, B
Southern Polytechnic State University, M

Idaho

Boise State University, M
University of Idaho, BM

Illinois

Dominican University, B
Illinois Institute of Technology, BMD
Northwestern University, BMDO
Southern Illinois University Carbondale, B
Southern Illinois University Edwardsville, B
University of Illinois at Chicago, BMD
University of Illinois at Urbana-Champaign, BMD

Indiana

Indiana State University, M
Indiana Tech, B
Indiana University-Purdue University Fort Wayne, B
Indiana University-Purdue University
  Indianapolis, BMD
Purdue University, BMD
Purdue University Calumet, B
Rose-Hulman Institute of Technology, B
Taylor University, B
Tri-State University, B
University of Evansville, B
University of Indianapolis, B
University of Notre Dame, BMD
Valparaiso University, B
Vincennes University, A

Iowa

Dordt College, B
Iowa State University of Science and
  Technology, BMD

The University of Iowa, MD

Kansas

Kansas State University, BMD
University of Kansas, BM
Wichita State University, B

Kentucky

Bellarmine University, B
Daymar College (Owensboro), A
University of Louisville, BMD

Louisiana

Louisiana State University and Agricultural and
  Mechanical College, BMD
Tulane University, B
University of Louisiana at Lafayette, BMD
Xavier University of Louisiana, B

Maine

University of Maine, BMD

Maryland

Capitol College, B
The Johns Hopkins University, BMD
University of Maryland, Baltimore County, BMD
University of Maryland, College Park, BMD

Massachusetts

Boston University, BMD
Eastern Nazarene College, B
Harvard University, B
Massachusetts Institute of Technology, D
Merrimack College, B
Northeastern University, BMD
Stonehill College, B
Tufts University, B
University of Massachusetts Amherst, BMD
University of Massachusetts Dartmouth, BMDO
University of Massachusetts Lowell, BM
Western New England College, M
Worcester Polytechnic Institute, BMDO

Michigan

Grand Valley State University, BM
Kettering University, B
Lawrence Technological University, BM
Michigan State University, B
Michigan Technological University, BD
Oakland University, BM
University of Detroit Mercy, B
University of Michigan, BMD
University of Michigan-Dearborn, M
Wayne State University, MD
Western Michigan University, BMD

Minnesota

Itasca Community College, A
Minnesota State University Mankato, B
St. Cloud State University, B
Saint Mary's University of Minnesota, B
University of Minnesota, Duluth, BM
University of Minnesota, Twin Cities Campus, MD
Walden University, M

Mississippi

Jackson State University, B
Mississippi State University, BMD

Missouri

Missouri Tech, B
Missouri Western State University, AB
University of Missouri-Columbia, B
University of Missouri-Kansas City, D
University of Missouri-Rolla, BMD
Vatterott College (St. Ann), A

Washington University in St. Louis, BMD

Montana

Montana State University, B
Montana Tech of The University of Montana, B

Nebraska

University of Nebraska-Lincoln, BMD
University of Nebraska at Omaha, B

Nevada

University of Nevada, Las Vegas, BMD
University of Nevada, Reno, BMD

New Hampshire

Dartmouth College, MD
University of New Hampshire, B

New Jersey

The College of New Jersey, B
Fairleigh Dickinson University, Metropolitan
    Campus, M
New Jersey Institute of Technology, BMD
Princeton University, B
Rutgers, The State University of New Jersey, New
    Brunswick/Piscataway, BMD
Stevens Institute of Technology, BMDO

New Mexico

New Mexico State University, MD
University of New Mexico, BMD

New York

Clarkson University, BMD
Columbia University, The Fu Foundation School of
    Engineering and Applied Science, B
Cornell University, MD
Hofstra University, B
Manhattan College, BM
Monroe Community College, A
New York Institute of Technology, M
Onondaga Community College, A
Orange County Community College, A
Polytechnic University, Brooklyn Campus, BMO
Rensselaer Polytechnic Institute, BMDO
Rochester Institute of Technology, BM
State University of New York at Binghamton, B
State University of New York at Buffalo, B
State University of New York at New Paltz, BM
Stony Brook University, State University of New
    York, MD
Syracuse University, BMDO
United States Military Academy, B
University of Rochester, MD

North Carolina

Catawba Valley Community College, A
Duke University, MD
Johnson C. Smith University, B
North Carolina State University, BMD
Sandhills Community College, A
Surry Community College, A
The University of North Carolina at Charlotte, BMD

North Dakota

Minot State University-Bottineau Campus, A
North Dakota State University, B

Ohio

Capital University, B
Case Western Reserve University, BMD
Cedarville University, B
Cleveland State University, BMD
Jefferson Community College, A
Miami University Hamilton, B
Ohio Northern University, B
The Ohio State University, B
Ohio University, B
Sinclair Community College, A
Stark State College of Technology, A
The University of Akron, B
University of Cincinnati, BMD
University of Dayton, BMD
The University of Toledo, B

Wilberforce University, B
Wright State University, BMD

Oklahoma

Oklahoma Christian University, B
Oklahoma State University, MD
Oral Roberts University, B
University of Oklahoma, BMD

Oregon

Oregon State University, B
Portland State University, BMD
University of Portland, B

Pennsylvania

Bucknell University, B
Carnegie Mellon University, BMD
Drexel University, BM
Elizabethtown College, B
Lehigh University, BMD
The Pennsylvania State University Abington
    College, B
The Pennsylvania State University Altoona
    College, B
The Pennsylvania State University Beaver Campus
    of the Commonwealth College, B
The Pennsylvania State University Berks Campus of
    the Berks-Lehigh Valley College, B
The Pennsylvania State University Delaware County
    Campus of the Commonwealth College, B
The Pennsylvania State University DuBois Campus
    of the Commonwealth College, B
The Pennsylvania State University at Erie, The
    Behrend College, B
The Pennsylvania State University Fayette Campus
    of the Commonwealth College, B
The Pennsylvania State University Hazleton
    Campus of the Commonwealth College, B
The Pennsylvania State University, Lehigh Valley
    Campus of the Berks-Lehigh Valley College, B
The Pennsylvania State University McKeesport
    Campus of the Commonwealth College, B
The Pennsylvania State University Mont Alto
    Campus of the Commonwealth College, B
The Pennsylvania State University New Kensington
    Campus of the Commonwealth College, B
The Pennsylvania State University Schuylkill
    Campus of the Capital College, B
The Pennsylvania State University Shenango
    Campus of the Commonwealth College, B
The Pennsylvania State University University Park
    Campus, BMD
The Pennsylvania State University Wilkes-Barre
    Campus of the Commonwealth College, B
The Pennsylvania State University Worthington
    Scranton Campus of the Commonwealth
    College, B
The Pennsylvania State University York Campus of
    the Commonwealth College, B
Robert Morris University, B
Temple University, M
University of Pennsylvania, B
University of Pittsburgh, B
The University of Scranton, AB
Villanova University, BMO
Widener University, M

Puerto Rico

Polytechnic University of Puerto Rico, BM
University of Puerto Rico, Mayagüez Campus, BM

Rhode Island

Brown University, B
Johnson & Wales University, B
University of Rhode Island, BMD

South Carolina

Bob Jones University, B
Clemson University, BMD

University of South Carolina, BMD

South Dakota

South Dakota School of Mines and Technology, B

Tennessee

Tennessee Technological University, B
University of Memphis, BMD
The University of Tennessee, B
Vanderbilt University, B

Texas

Baylor University, M
LeTourneau University, B
Midwestern State University, B
Rice University, BMD
St. Mary's University of San Antonio, BM
Southern Methodist University, BMD
Texas A&M University, BMD
Texas Tech University, B
University of Houston, BMD
University of Houston-Clear Lake, BM
University of North Texas, B
The University of Texas at Arlington, BMD
The University of Texas at Austin, MD
The University of Texas at Dallas, BMD
The University of Texas at El Paso, MD
The University of Texas at San Antonio, B

Utah

Brigham Young University, B
University of Utah, BM
Utah State University, B
Western Governors University, A

Virginia

Christopher Newport University, B
George Mason University, BMD
Norfolk State University, M
Old Dominion University, BMD
University of Virginia, BMD
Virginia Commonwealth University, B
Virginia Polytechnic Institute and State
    University, BMD
Virginia State University, B

Washington

DigiPen Institute of Technology, B
Gonzaga University, B
Pacific Lutheran University, B
University of Washington, B
Washington State University, B

West Virginia

West Virginia University, BD

Wisconsin

Marquette University, BMD
Milwaukee School of Engineering, B
University of Wisconsin-Madison, B

Wyoming

University of Wyoming, B

Alberta

University of Alberta, BMD
University of Calgary, BMD

British Columbia

Thompson Rivers University, A
The University of British Columbia, BMD

University of Victoria, B

Manitoba

University of Manitoba, BMD

New Brunswick

University of New Brunswick Fredericton, BMD

Newfoundland and Labrador

Memorial University of Newfoundland, MD

Nova Scotia

Dalhousie University, BMD

Ontario

Carleton University, B
Lakehead University, B
McMaster University, B
Queen's University at Kingston, BMD
Royal Military College of Canada, BMD
Ryerson University, B
University of Ottawa, BMD
University of Toronto, BMD
University of Waterloo, BMD
University of Windsor, B
York University, B

Quebec

Concordia University, BMD
McGill University, BMD
Université Laval, B
Université du Québec àChicoutimi, B
Université du Québec en Outaouais, B
Université du Québec àTrois-Rivières, B
Université de Sherbrooke, B

Saskatchewan

University of Regina, MD

COMPUTER ENGINEERING TECHNOLOGIES/TECHNICIANS

New York

ITT Technical Institute (Albany), A

Virginia

Old Dominion University, B

COMPUTER ENGINEERING TECHNOLOGY/TECHNICIAN

Alabama

Alabama Southern Community College, A
Northwest-Shoals Community College, A
Remington College-Mobile Campus, A

Alaska

University of Alaska Southeast, Sitka Campus, A

Arizona

Arizona State University at the Polytechnic
  Campus, B
Chandler-Gilbert Community College, A
DeVry University (Phoenix), B
High-Tech Institute, A
Pima Community College, A

Arkansas

East Arkansas Community College, A
Pulaski Technical College, A
University of Arkansas at Little Rock, B

California

Allan Hancock College, A
American River College, A
California State University, Long Beach, B
Cañada College, A
Cerro Coso Community College, A
Chabot College, A
College of the Redwoods, A

College of the Sequoias, A
Compton Community College, A
Cuesta College, A
DeVry University (Fremont), B
DeVry University (Long Beach), B
DeVry University (Pomona), AB
DeVry University (West Hills), B
East Los Angeles College, A
Foundation College, A
Glendale Community College, A
Heald College-Concord, A
Heald College-Fresno, A
Heald College-Roseville, A
Heald College-San Francisco, A
Heald College-San Jose, A
Irvine Valley College, A
Los Angeles City College, A
Los Angeles Harbor College, A
Los Angeles Pierce College, A
Los Angeles Trade-Technical College, A
Merced College, A
Merritt College, A
MiraCosta College, A
Mission College, A
Monterey Peninsula College, A
Mt. San Antonio College, A
Orange Coast College, A
Pasadena City College, A
San Bernardino Valley College, A
San Diego City College, A
San Joaquin Delta College, A
San Jose City College, A
Sierra College, A

Colorado

Colorado Mountain College, A
Colorado Mountain College, Alpine Campus, A
Colorado State University-Pueblo, B
DeVry University (Westminster), B
Lamar Community College, A
Northeastern Junior College, A
Red Rocks Community College, A
Westwood College-Denver North, A

Connecticut

Capital Community College, A
Gateway Community College, A
Northwestern Connecticut Community College, A
Three Rivers Community College, A
University of Hartford, A

Delaware

Delaware Technical & Community College, Terry
  Campus, A

District of Columbia

University of the District of Columbia, A

Florida

Brevard Community College, A
Broward Community College, A
DeVry University (Miramar), B
DeVry University (Orlando), B
Florida Community College at Jacksonville, A
Gulf Coast Community College, A
Hillsborough Community College, A
Indian River Community College, A
Keiser College (Fort Lauderdale), A
Manatee Community College, A
Miami Dade College, A
St. Johns River Community College, A
St. Petersburg College, A
Santa Fe Community College, A
Seminole Community College, A

Georgia

Abraham Baldwin Agricultural College, A
Clayton State University, A
Dalton State College, A
DeKalb Technical College, A
DeVry University (Alpharetta), B
DeVry University (Decatur), B
Georgia Southwestern State University, B
Savannah State University, B

Southern Polytechnic State University, B

Illinois

City Colleges of Chicago, Olive-Harvey College, A
DeVry University (Addison), B
DeVry University (Chicago), B
DeVry University (Tinley Park), B
East-West University, B
Heartland Community College, A
Rend Lake College, A
Rock Valley College, A
Triton College, A
William Rainey Harper College, A

Indiana

Indiana State University, B
Indiana University-Purdue University Fort Wayne, B
International Business College (Fort Wayne), AB
Martin University, B
Oakland City University, A
Purdue University Calumet, AB
Purdue University North Central, AB
Vincennes University, A

Iowa

Des Moines Area Community College, A
Hawkeye Community College, A
Indian Hills Community College, A
Iowa Central Community College, A
Northeast Iowa Community College, A

Kansas

Garden City Community College, A
Kansas City Kansas Community College, A

Kentucky

Eastern Kentucky University, A
Louisville Technical Institute, A
Murray State University, B
Paducah Technical College, A
St. Catharine College, A
Southeast Kentucky Community and Technical
  College, A

Louisiana

Delgado Community College, A
Elaine P. Nunez Community College, A

Maine

Northern Maine Community College, A
Southern Maine Community College, A
York County Community College, A

Maryland

Allegany College of Maryland, A
Anne Arundel Community College, A
Capitol College, AB
Cecil Community College, A
Chesapeake College, A
Frederick Community College, A
Prince George's Community College, A

Massachusetts

Benjamin Franklin Institute of Technology, A
Harvard University, B
Massachusetts Bay Community College, A
Middlesex Community College, A
North Shore Community College, A
Northeastern University, B
Northern Essex Community College, A
Springfield Technical Community College, A
Wentworth Institute of Technology, AB

Michigan

Andrews University, AB
Baker College of Owosso, A
Central Michigan University, B
Davenport University (Midland), A
Eastern Michigan University, B
Gogebic Community College, A
Grand Rapids Community College, A
Kellogg Community College, A
Lake Superior State University, AB
Lansing Community College, A

Madonna University, A
Monroe County Community College, A
Washtenaw Community College, A

Minnesota

Century College, A
Minnesota State College-Southeast Technical, A
Minnesota State University Mankato, B
Ridgewater College, A
Vermilion Community College, A

Mississippi

Meridian Community College, A
Mississippi Delta Community College, A
Mississippi Gulf Coast Community College, A
University of Southern Mississippi, B

Missouri

DeVry University (Kansas City), B
Grantham University, AB
Missouri Tech, A
National American University, B
North Central Missouri College, A
Ranken Technical College, A
St. Louis Community College at Florissant Valley, A
State Fair Community College, A
Three Rivers Community College, A

Montana

Flathead Valley Community College, A
Miles Community College, A

Nebraska

Southeast Community College, Milford Campus, A

Nevada

Community College of Southern Nevada, A
Truckee Meadows Community College, A

New Hampshire

Hesser College, A
New Hampshire Community Technical College,
 Berlin/Laconia, A
New Hampshire Community Technical College,
 Nashua/Claremont, A
New Hampshire Technical Institute, A

New Jersey

Bergen Community College, A
Brookdale Community College, A
Camden County College, A
Hudson County Community College, A
Middlesex County College, A

New Mexico

Doña Ana Branch Community College, A
University of New Mexico-Los Alamos Branch, A

New York

Bramson ORT College, A
Broome Community College, A
DeVry Institute of Technology, B
Excelsior College, AB
Farmingdale State University of New York, B
Fiorello H. LaGuardia Community College of the
 City University of New York, A
Fulton-Montgomery Community College, A
Genesee Community College, A
Jamestown Community College, A
Monroe Community College, A
Onondaga Community College, A
Orange County Community College, A
Queensborough Community College of the City
 University of New York, A
Rochester Institute of Technology, B
State University of New York College of Agriculture
 and Technology at Morrisville, A
State University of New York College of Technology
 at Alfred, AB
State University of New York Institute of
 Technology, B
Suffolk County Community College, A

TCI-The College of Technology, A

North Carolina

Carteret Community College, A
Catawba Valley Community College, A
Central Piedmont Community College, A
Cleveland Community College, A
College of The Albemarle, A
Davidson County Community College, A
East Carolina University, B
ECPI Technical College, A
Forsyth Technical Community College, A
Pamlico Community College, A
Piedmont Community College, A
Richmond Community College, A
Sandhills Community College, A
Southeastern Community College, A
Southwestern Community College, A
Surry Community College, A
Vance-Granville Community College, A
Wake Technical Community College, A
Western Piedmont Community College, A

North Dakota

Minot State University-Bottineau Campus, A

Ohio

Belmont Technical College, A
Bowling Green State University-Firelands College, A
Cincinnati State Technical and Community
 College, A
Columbus State Community College, A
Cuyahoga Community College, A
DeVry University (Columbus), B
Edison State Community College, A
Hocking College, A
Kent State University, Ashtabula Campus, A
Kent State University, East Liverpool Campus, A
Kent State University, Trumbull Campus, A
Kent State University, Tuscarawas Campus, A
Lorain County Community College, A
Miami University-Middletown Campus, A
Ohio University-Lancaster, A
RETS Tech Center, A
Shawnee State University, B
University of Cincinnati, A
University of Cincinnati Raymond Walters College, A
University of Dayton, B
Washington State Community College, A

Oklahoma

Eastern Oklahoma State College, A
Oklahoma City Community College, A
Rogers State University, A

Oregon

Chemeketa Community College, A
Clatsop Community College, A
Lane Community College, A
Mt. Hood Community College, A
Oregon Institute of Technology, AB
Portland Community College, A
Umpqua Community College, A

Pennsylvania

Bucks County Community College, A
CHI Institute, A
Community College of Allegheny County, A
Community College of Philadelphia, A
DeVry University (Fort Washington), AB
ICM School of Business & Medical Careers, A
Lansdale School of Business, A
Lehigh Carbon Community College, A
Montgomery County Community College, A
Peirce College, A
The Pennsylvania State University New Kensington
 Campus of the Commonwealth College, A

Westmoreland County Community College, A

Puerto Rico

Inter American University of Puerto Rico,
 Metropolitan Campus, B

Rhode Island

Community College of Rhode Island, A
Johnson & Wales University, A

South Carolina

Aiken Technical College, A
Florence-Darlington Technical College, A
Horry-Georgetown Technical College, A
Technical College of the Lowcountry, A
Trident Technical College, A
York Technical College, A

South Dakota

National American University (Rapid City), A

Tennessee

Chattanooga State Technical Community College, A
Fountainhead College of Technology, A
Nashville State Technical Community College, A
Pellissippi State Technical Community College, A
Roane State Community College, A
Southwest Tennessee Community College, A
University of Memphis, B

Texas

Alvin Community College, A
Amarillo College, A
Angelina College, A
Coastal Bend College, A
Collin County Community College District, A
DeVry University (Houston), B
DeVry University (Irving), B
Eastfield College, A
Frank Phillips College, A
Grayson County College, A
Houston Community College System, A
Kingwood College, A
LeTourneau University, B
McLennan Community College, A
North Central Texas College, A
Palo Alto College, A
Paris Junior College, A
Ranger College, A
San Antonio College, A
South Plains College, A
Southwest Texas Junior College, A
Texas Southern University, B
Texas State Technical College Waco, A
Texas State Technical College West Texas, A
Tyler Junior College, A
University of Houston, B
University of Houston-Downtown, B
Western Technical College, A
Western Texas College, A

Utah

Utah State University, B
Weber State University, A

Vermont

Vermont Technical College, AB

Virginia

DeVry University (Arlington), B
ECPI College of Technology (Newport News), A
ECPI College of Technology (Virginia Beach), A
ECPI Technical College (Roanoke), A
J. Sargeant Reynolds Community College, A
New River Community College, A
Norfolk State University, B
Piedmont Virginia Community College, A

Washington

DeVry University (Federal Way), B
Eastern Washington University, B
Highline Community College, A
Lake Washington Technical College, A
Lower Columbia College, A

Skagit Valley College, A
South Seattle Community College, A
Whatcom Community College, A
Yakima Valley Community College, A

West Virginia

Marshall Community and Technical College, A
Marshall University, B
Potomac State College of West Virginia
  University, A

Wisconsin

Madison Area Technical College, A
Mid-State Technical College, A

New Brunswick

University of New Brunswick Saint John, B

Ontario

Brock University, B

COMPUTER GRAPHICS

Alabama

Calhoun Community College, A
Huntingdon College, B
Northeast Alabama Community College, A

Arizona

Northland Pioneer College, A
Phoenix College, A
University of Advancing Technology, AB

Arkansas

John Brown University, B
National Park Community College, A

California

Academy of Art University, AB
American River College, A
Antelope Valley College, A
The Art Institute of California-Orange County, AB
The Art Institute of California-San Francisco, AB
Berkeley City College, A
California Institute of the Arts, B
California State University, Chico, B
California State University, East Bay, B
Cerro Coso Community College, A
Cogswell Polytechnical College, B
Coleman College (La Mesa), A
College of the Desert, A
College of the Sequoias, A
College of the Siskiyous, A
Cypress College, A
De Anza College, A
Dominican University of California, B
Evergreen Valley College, A
Gavilan College, A
Hartnell College, A
Modesto Junior College, A
Mt. San Antonio College, A
Newschool of Architecture & Design, AB
Orange Coast College, A
Platt College-Los Angeles, Inc, A
Platt College (Newport Beach), AB
Platt College (Ontario), A
Platt College San Diego, A
Southwestern College, A
Western Career College (San Jose), AB

Colorado

Arapahoe Community College, A
The Art Institute of Colorado, AB
CollegeAmerica-Fort Collins, A
Platt College, A
Pueblo Community College, A

Connecticut

Gateway Community College, A
Northwestern Connecticut Community College, A

Quinebaug Valley Community College, A

Florida

The Art Institute of Fort Lauderdale, B
College of Business and Technology, A
Daytona Beach Community College, A
Florida Community College at Jacksonville, A
Florida National College, A
Full Sail Real World Education, B
International Academy of Design & Technology, A
Keiser College (Daytona Beach), A
Keiser College (Fort Lauderdale), A
Keiser College (Melbourne), A
Keiser College (Sarasota), A
Keiser College (Tallahassee), A
Manatee Community College, A
Miami Dade College, A
Miami International University of Art & Design, A
Seminole Community College, A
Tallahassee Community College, A
The University of Tampa, B

Georgia

Savannah College of Art and Design, B

Illinois

American Academy of Art, B
DePaul University, B
Elgin Community College, A
The Illinois Institute of Art-Chicago, B
International Academy of Design & Technology, A
Judson College, B
Lincoln College-Normal, A
Oakton Community College, A
Parkland College, A
Prairie State College, A
Richland Community College, A
School of the Art Institute of Chicago, B
Triton College, A

Indiana

Indiana Wesleyan University, B
Oakland City University, B
Taylor University, B
Vincennes University, A

Iowa

Iowa Lakes Community College, A
University of Dubuque, B

Kansas

Cowley County Community College and Area
  Vocational-Technical School, A
Garden City Community College, A

Kentucky

Daymar College (Owensboro), A
Louisville Technical Institute, A
Spencerian College-Lexington, A

Louisiana

Remington College-New Orleans Campus, A

Maine

College of the Atlantic, B
New England School of Communications, AB

Maryland

Baltimore City Community College, A
Bowie State University, B
Carroll Community College, A
Cecil Community College, A
Howard Community College, A
Villa Julie College, A

Massachusetts

Cape Cod Community College, A
Hampshire College, B
Harvard University, B
Mount Wachusett Community College, A
The New England Institute of Art, B
North Shore Community College, A
Northern Essex Community College, A
School of the Museum of Fine Arts, Boston, B

Simon's Rock College of Bard, B
Springfield College, B

Michigan

Baker College of Cadillac, A
Baker College of Flint, B
Gogebic Community College, A
Kellogg Community College, A
Lansing Community College, A
Mid Michigan Community College, A
Monroe County Community College, A
Washtenaw Community College, A

Minnesota

Academy College, A
The Art Institutes International Minnesota, B
Capella University, B
Dakota County Technical College, A
Globe College, A
Mesabi Range Community and Technical College, A
Northland Community and Technical College-Thief
  River Falls, A
Rasmussen College Mankato, A
Ridgewater College, A

Mississippi

Hinds Community College, A
Meridian Community College, A
Mississippi Gulf Coast Community College, A

Missouri

Metropolitan Community College-Business &
  Technology College, A
Missouri State University-West Plains, A

Montana

Miles Community College, A
University of Great Falls, B

Nebraska

The Creative Center, A

New Jersey

Bloomfield College, B
Burlington County College, A
Camden County College, A
Gloucester County College, A
Mercer County Community College, A
Middlesex County College, A

New Mexico

New Mexico Junior College, A

New York

Adirondack Community College, A
Brooklyn College of the City University of New
  York, B
The College of Westchester, A
Columbia-Greene Community College, A
Corning Community College, A
Genesee Community College, A
Nassau Community College, A
North Country Community College, A
Pratt Institute, B
Rochester Institute of Technology, B
Rockland Community College, A
School of Visual Arts, B
State University of New York College at Oneonta, B
State University of New York College of Technology
  at Alfred, A
State University of New York, Fredonia, B
Sullivan County Community College, A
Syracuse University, B
Tompkins Cortland Community College, A
Vaughn College of Aeronautics and Technology, AB

North Carolina

Wake Technical Community College, A
Wingate University, B

Ohio

Brown Mackie College-Cincinnati, A
Edison State Community College, A
James A. Rhodes State College, A

Lakeland Community College, A
Sinclair Community College, A
University of Cincinnati Clermont College, A

Oklahoma

Oklahoma State University, Okmulgee, A
Tulsa Community College, A

Pennsylvania

The Art Institute of Pittsburgh, AB
Berks Technical Institute, A
Bradley Academy for the Visual Arts, A
CHI Institute, A
Luzerne County Community College, A
Oakbridge Academy of Arts, A
University of Pennsylvania, B
Westmoreland County Community College, A

Rhode Island

Johnson & Wales University, AB

South Carolina

Trident Technical College, A

South Dakota

Dakota State University, B
South Dakota State University, B
Southeast Technical Institute, A

Tennessee

Memphis College of Art, B
Pellissippi State Technical Community College, A
Southern Adventist University, B

Texas

The Art Institute of Dallas, A
El Paso Community College, A
Kingwood College, A
Navarro College, A
North Central Texas College, A
San Antonio College, A
Texas State Technical College Harlingen, A
Tyler Junior College, A
University of the Incarnate Word, B
University of Mary Hardin-Baylor, B
Wade College, A
Weatherford College, A

Utah

College of Eastern Utah, A
Utah Career College, A

Vermont

Champlain College, AB

Virginia

The Art Institute of Washington, A
New River Community College, A
Northern Virginia Community College, A

Washington

Olympic College, A
Shoreline Community College, A
Yakima Valley Community College, A

Wisconsin

Gateway Technical College, A
Milwaukee Area Technical College, A

Alberta

Alberta College of Art & Design, B

British Columbia

Thompson Rivers University, A

COMPUTER HARDWARE ENGINEERING

Alabama

Auburn University, B

California

Cuesta College, A

Florida

Florida Community College at Jacksonville, A
Lake City Community College, A

Seminole Community College, A

Indiana

Vincennes University, A

Kentucky

Daymar College (Owensboro), A
Louisville Technical Institute, A

Louisiana

Remington College-New Orleans Campus, A

New York

State University of New York College of Technology
  at Alfred, B
Stony Brook University, State University of New
  York, B
Tompkins Cortland Community College, A

North Carolina

Stanly Community College, A

Ohio

Sinclair Community College, A
Stark State College of Technology, A

Oklahoma

Tulsa Community College, A

Texas

Abilene Christian University, B
Eastfield College, A

Ontario

York University, B

COMPUTER HARDWARE TECHNOLOGY/TECHNICIAN

Kentucky

Louisville Technical Institute, A

Puerto Rico

Inter American University of Puerto Rico, Aguadilla
  Campus, A

Texas

Brazosport College, A

Wyoming

Laramie County Community College, A

COMPUTER/INFORMATION TECHNOLOGY SERVICES ADMINISTRATION AND MANAGEMENT

California

Cypress College, A
Heald College-Hayward, A
Holy Names University, B
Los Angeles City College, A
Modesto Junior College, A
Mt. Sierra College, B

Colorado

Arapahoe Community College, A
National American University (Denver), AB
Platt College, A
Westwood College-Denver North, B

Connecticut

Naugatuck Valley Community College, A

Florida

Brevard Community College, A
Daytona Beach Community College, A
Florida Community College at Jacksonville, A
International College, B

St. Petersburg College, A
Seminole Community College, A
University of South Florida, B

Georgia

Atlanta Metropolitan College, A
Clayton State University, B
Dalton State College, A
Georgia Perimeter College, A
Middle Georgia College, A

Illinois

Black Hawk College, A
Eastern Illinois University, B
Parkland College, A

Indiana

University of Phoenix-Indianapolis Campus, B
Vincennes University, A

Iowa

Clinton Community College, A
Dordt College, B
Hawkeye Community College, A
Iowa Lakes Community College, A
Muscatine Community College, A
Vennard College, A

Kansas

Barton County Community College, A
Hesston College, A

Kentucky

Daymar College (Owensboro), A
Henderson Community College, A
Owensboro Community and Technical College, A
Southeast Kentucky Community and Technical
  College, A

Louisiana

Elaine P. Nunez Community College, A

Maine

Andover College, A
Kennebec Valley Community College, A
York County Community College, A

Maryland

Howard Community College, A

Michigan

Alpena Community College, A
Gogebic Community College, A
Kettering University, B

Minnesota

Capella University, B
Mesabi Range Community and Technical College, A
Ridgewater College, A
St. Cloud Technical College, A
Saint Mary's University of Minnesota, B

Missouri

Lindenwood University, B
Metropolitan Community College-Business &
  Technology College, A
Washington University in St. Louis, B

Montana

Flathead Valley Community College, A
University of Great Falls, B

Nebraska

Bellevue University, B

New Jersey

Camden County College, A

New York

Cayuga County Community College, A
Clinton Community College, A
The College of Westchester, A
Corning Community College, A

Maria College, A
Medgar Evers College of the City University of New York, A
Mercy College, A
Onondaga Community College, A
Rockland Community College, A
Schenectady County Community College, A
State University of New York College of Technology at Alfred, B
State University of New York College of Technology at Canton, AB
State University of New York College of Technology at Delhi, B
Tompkins Cortland Community College, A

North Carolina

Brunswick Community College, A
Central Carolina Community College, A
Coastal Carolina Community College, A
Guilford Technical Community College, A
Queens University of Charlotte, B
Saint Augustine's College, B
Sandhills Community College, A
Stanly Community College, A

Ohio

ETI Technical College of Niles, A
Sinclair Community College, A
Stark State College of Technology, A
Trumbull Business College, A
The University of Akron, A

Oklahoma

Tulsa Community College, A
Western Oklahoma State College, A

Pennsylvania

Bucks County Community College, A
Chestnut Hill College, B
CHI Institute, A
Keystone College, A
Laurel Business Institute, A
Pennsylvania College of Technology, A
Pennsylvania Highland Community College, A
Point Park University, B
Robert Morris University, B
York Technical Institute, A

Rhode Island

Johnson & Wales University, AB

South Carolina

Horry-Georgetown Technical College, A
Trident Technical College, A

South Dakota

Mitchell Technical Institute, A
Southeast Technical Institute, A

Tennessee

Dyersburg State Community College, A

Texas

Eastfield College, A
El Centro College, A
North Central Texas College, A
Northwest Vista College, A
San Antonio College, A
Texas State Technical College Harlingen, A

Vermont

Champlain College, AB

Virginia

Eastern Shore Community College, A

Washington

Seattle Pacific University, B

Wisconsin

Milwaukee Area Technical College, A

Nova Scotia

Dalhousie University, B

COMPUTER INSTALLATION AND REPAIR TECHNOLOGY/TECHNICIAN

Arizona

Northland Pioneer College, A

California

Modesto Junior College, A

Colorado

CollegeAmerica-Fort Collins, A

Georgia

Dalton State College, A

Illinois

Black Hawk College, A
College of DuPage, A
College of Lake County, A

Kentucky

Daymar College (Louisville), A
Daymar College (Owensboro), A
Louisville Technical Institute, A

Louisiana

Delgado Community College, A
Louisiana Technical College, A

Maine

Kennebec Valley Community College, A

Michigan

Montcalm Community College, A

Minnesota

Hibbing Community College, A
Ridgewater College, A
Riverland Community College, A

Mississippi

Coahoma Community College, A

New York

State University of New York College of Technology at Alfred, A

Pennsylvania

Harrisburg Area Community College, A
Northampton County Area Community College, A

Puerto Rico

Inter American University of Puerto Rico, Bayamón Campus, AB

South Carolina

Midlands Technical College, A

South Dakota

Western Dakota Technical Institute, A

Wisconsin

Waukesha County Technical College, A

British Columbia

Thompson Rivers University, A

COMPUTER PROGRAMMING

Arizona

Rio Salado College, A

California

American River College, A
College of the Desert, A
Cypress College, A
Glendale Community College, A
Los Angeles City College, A
Riverside Community College District, A

San Diego Mesa College, A
Santa Ana College, A

Colorado

Arapahoe Community College, A
National American University (Denver), AB

Connecticut

Norwalk Community College, A

Florida

Florida Community College at Jacksonville, A
Florida National College, A
Key College, A
Manatee Community College, A
Pasco-Hernando Community College, A
Seminole Community College, A
Valencia Community College, A

Illinois

Kishwaukee College, A
Triton College, A

Indiana

Vincennes University, A
Vincennes University Jasper Campus, A

Iowa

Iowa Western Community College, A
Northwest Iowa Community College, A

Kansas

Brown Mackie College-Kansas City, A
Donnelly College, A

Kentucky

Daymar College (Owensboro), A
Henderson Community College, A

Louisiana

Remington College-Lafayette Campus, A
Remington College-New Orleans Campus, A

Maine

Kennebec Valley Community College, A

Massachusetts

Northern Essex Community College, A

Minnesota

Dakota County Technical College, A
Mesabi Range Community and Technical College, A
St. Cloud Technical College, A

Mississippi

Hinds Community College, A
Mississippi Gulf Coast Community College, A
Southwest Mississippi Community College, A

Missouri

Metropolitan Community College-Business & Technology College, A
Saint Charles Community College, A
St. Louis Community College at Forest Park, A

Nebraska

Hamilton College-Lincoln, A

Nevada

Truckee Meadows Community College, A

New Jersey

Camden County College, A

New York

The College of Westchester, A
Corning Community College, A
Farmingdale State University of New York, B
Fiorello H. LaGuardia Community College of the City University of New York, A
Rockland Community College, A
Schenectady County Community College, A

Tompkins Cortland Community College, A

North Carolina

Blue Ridge Community College, A
Brunswick Community College, A
Durham Technical Community College, A
Stanly Community College, A
Surry Community College, A

Ohio

Clark State Community College, A
Lakeland Community College, A
Lorain County Community College, A
Sinclair Community College, A
Stark State College of Technology, A

Oklahoma

Tulsa Community College, A

Pennsylvania

Academy of Medical Arts and Business, A
Berks Technical Institute, A
Bucks County Community College, A
Central Pennsylvania College, A
Erie Business Center, Main, A
Luzerne County Community College, A
Pennsylvania Highland Community College, A

Puerto Rico

Caribbean University, B
Inter American University of Puerto Rico,
Barranquitas Campus, AB

South Carolina

Orangeburg-Calhoun Technical College, A

South Dakota

Lake Area Technical Institute, A
Southeast Technical Institute, A

Tennessee

Northeast State Technical Community College, A

Texas

Austin Community College, A
Brazosport College, A
Central Texas College, A
Coastal Bend College, A
Del Mar College, A
Eastfield College, A
El Paso Community College, A
Hill College of the Hill Junior College District, A
Laredo Community College, A
North Central Texas College, A
San Antonio College, A
Texas State Technical College Harlingen, A
Tyler Junior College, A

Utah

Neumont University, B

Virginia

J. Sargeant Reynolds Community College, A
Patrick Henry Community College, A
Stratford University, A

Washington

Centralia College, A
Columbia Basin College, A
Olympic College, A

Wisconsin

Herzing College, A
Lakeshore Technical College, A
Mid-State Technical College, A

Milwaukee Area Technical College, A

COMPUTER PROGRAMMING/PROGRAMMER

Alabama

Alabama Southern Community College, A
Central Alabama Community College, A
George Corley Wallace State Community College, A
Herzing College, A
Northwest-Shoals Community College, A
Wallace State Community College, A

Arizona

Cochise College (Douglas), A
Cochise College (Sierra Vista), A
ITT Technical Institute (Phoenix), A
ITT Technical Institute (Tempe), A
ITT Technical Institute (Tucson), A
University of Advancing Technology, AB
University of Phoenix Online Campus, B

Arkansas

ITT Technical Institute, A
NorthWest Arkansas Community College, A
Phillips Community College of the University of
Arkansas, A
University of Arkansas at Little Rock, A

California

American River College, A
Antelope Valley College, A
Cabrillo College, A
Cañada College, A
Cerritos College, A
City College of San Francisco, A
College of the Redwoods, A
College of the Sequoias, A
College of the Siskiyous, A
Compton Community College, A
Contra Costa College, A
Cosumnes River College (Sacramento), A
De Anza College, A
East Los Angeles College, A
Foundation College, A
Gavilan College, A
Grossmont College, A
Humphreys College, AB
ITT Technical Institute (Lathrop), A
ITT Technical Institute (Rancho Cordova), A
ITT Technical Institute (San Bernardino), A
ITT Technical Institute (San Diego), A
ITT Technical Institute (Sylmar), A
Laney College, A
Long Beach City College, A
Los Angeles City College, A
Los Angeles Mission College, A
Los Angeles Pierce College, A
Los Angeles Trade-Technical College, A
Los Angeles Valley College, A
Merritt College, A
Mission College, A
Mt. Sierra College, B
The National Hispanic University, AB
Ohlone College, A
Orange Coast College, A
Pacific Union College, B
Pasadena City College, A
Riverside Community College District, A
Saddleback College, A
San Joaquin Delta College, A
Santa Monica College, A
Skyline College, A
Solano Community College, A
Southwestern College, A
West Los Angeles College, A
Westwood College-Inland Empire, A
Westwood College-Los Angeles, A

Colorado

Arapahoe Community College, A
Blair College, A
CollegeAmerica-Fort Collins, A
ITT Technical Institute, A

Lamar Community College, A
National American University (Denver), AB
Parks College (Denver), A
Red Rocks Community College, A
Westwood College-Denver South, A

Connecticut

Middlesex Community College, A
Naugatuck Valley Community College, A
Northwestern Connecticut Community College, A
Three Rivers Community College, A

Delaware

Delaware Technical & Community College, Jack F.
Owens Campus, A
Delaware Technical & Community College, Terry
Campus, A

Florida

Brevard Community College, A
Broward Community College, A
Daytona Beach Community College, A
Edison College, A
Florida Career College, A
Florida Community College at Jacksonville, A
Florida Keys Community College, A
Florida Metropolitan University-Lakeland
Campus, AB
Florida Metropolitan University-North Orlando
Campus, AB
Florida Metropolitan University-Pompano Beach
Campus, AB
Florida Metropolitan University-Tampa Campus, AB
Florida National College, A
Florida State University, B
Florida Technical College (Jacksonville), A
Florida Technical College (Orlando), A
Gulf Coast Community College, A
Hillsborough Community College, A
Indian River Community College, A
ITT Technical Institute (Fort Lauderdale), A
ITT Technical Institute (Jacksonville), A
ITT Technical Institute (Lake Mary), A
ITT Technical Institute (Miami), A
ITT Technical Institute (Tampa), A
Keiser College (Daytona Beach), A
Keiser College (Fort Lauderdale), A
Keiser College (Melbourne), A
Keiser College (Sarasota), A
Keiser College (Tallahassee), A
Lake City Community College, A
Manatee Community College, A
Miami Dade College, A
Okaloosa-Walton College, A
Palm Beach Community College, A
St. Johns River Community College, A
Santa Fe Community College, A
Seminole Community College, A
South Florida Community College, A
Tallahassee Community College, A
The University of Tampa, B
Valencia Community College, A

Georgia

Abraham Baldwin Agricultural College, A
Altamaha Technical College, A
Athens Technical College, A
Atlanta Technical College, A
Augusta Technical College, A
Central Georgia Technical College, A
Chattahoochee Technical College, A
Coosa Valley Technical College, A
Darton College, A
DeKalb Technical College, A
Georgia Highlands College, A
Griffin Technical College, A
Gwinnett Technical College, A
Lanier Technical College, A
Macon State College, A
South Georgia College, A

Valdosta Technical College, A

Hawaii

Brigham Young University-Hawaii, B

Idaho

Brigham Young University -Idaho, A
ITT Technical Institute, A
North Idaho College, A

Illinois

American InterContinental University Online, B
Black Hawk College, A
Danville Area Community College, A
DePaul University, B
East-West University, B
Heartland Community College, A
Illinois Valley Community College, A
ITT Technical Institute (Burr Ridge), A
ITT Technical Institute (Matteson), A
ITT Technical Institute (Mount Prospect), A
Joliet Junior College, A
Lewis and Clark Community College, A
Lincoln College, A
Lincoln College-Normal, A
Northwestern Business College, A
Oakton Community College, A
Parkland College, A
Westwood College-Chicago Du Page, A
Westwood College-Chicago Loop Campus, A
Westwood College-Chicago O'Hare Airport, A
Westwood College-Chicago River Oaks, A
William Rainey Harper College, A

Indiana

Ancilla College, A
Indiana Business College (Indianapolis), A
Indiana University East, A
International Business College (Fort Wayne), AB
International Business College (Indianapolis), A
ITT Technical Institute (Fort Wayne), A
ITT Technical Institute (Indianapolis), A
ITT Technical Institute (Newburgh), A
Oakland City University, A
Purdue University Calumet, A
Purdue University North Central, A
Sawyer College (Hammond), A
Taylor University, B
Vincennes University, A
Vincennes University Jasper Campus, A

Iowa

Des Moines Area Community College, A
Dordt College, B
Hamilton College (Cedar Falls), A
Indian Hills Community College, A
Iowa Lakes Community College, A
Iowa Wesleyan College, B
Iowa Western Community College, A
Kirkwood Community College, A
Northwest Iowa Community College, A
Southeastern Community College, North Campus, A
Southwestern Community College, A

Kansas

Coffeyville Community College, A
Dodge City Community College, A
Friends University, A
Garden City Community College, A
McPherson College, B
Seward County Community College, A
Southwestern College, B

Kentucky

Brown Mackie College-Hopkinsville, A
Daymar College (Louisville), A
ITT Technical Institute (Louisville), A
Lindsey Wilson College, A

Louisiana

ITT Technical Institute, A
Louisiana State University at Eunice, A

Remington College-Lafayette Campus, A

Maine

Andover College, A
Husson College, B
Northern Maine Community College, A

Maryland

Anne Arundel Community College, A
Cecil Community College, A
Chesapeake College, A
College of Southern Maryland, A
ITT Technical Institute, A
Prince George's Community College, A
Villa Julie College, A

Massachusetts

Atlantic Union College, A
Bristol Community College, A
Bunker Hill Community College, A
Framingham State College, B
Greenfield Community College, A
Harvard University, B
ITT Technical Institute (Norwood), A
ITT Technical Institute (Woburn), A
Massasoit Community College, A
Newbury College, AB
North Shore Community College, A
Northern Essex Community College, A
Quinsigamond Community College, A

Michigan

Andrews University, B
Baker College of Flint, AB
Baker College of Muskegon, A
Baker College of Owosso, AB
Baker College of Port Huron, A
Davenport University (Midland), A
Ferris State University, B
Grand Rapids Community College, A
Grand Valley State University, B
ITT Technical Institute (Canton), A
ITT Technical Institute (Grand Rapids), A
ITT Technical Institute (Troy), A
Kalamazoo Valley Community College, A
Kellogg Community College, A
Lansing Community College, A
Lewis College of Business, A
Macomb Community College, A
Michigan Technological University, B
North Central Michigan College, A
Oakland Community College, A
Schoolcraft College, A
Southwestern Michigan College, A
University of Detroit Mercy, B
University of Michigan-Dearborn, B
Washtenaw Community College, A

Minnesota

Academy College, A
Hennepin Technical College, A
ITT Technical Institute, A
Minneapolis Business College, A
Minneapolis Community and Technical College, A
Minnesota State College-Southeast Technical, A
Minnesota State Community and Technical
    College-Fergus Falls, A
Minnesota State University Mankato, B
Northwest Technical College, A
St. Cloud Technical College, A
Saint Paul College-A Community & Technical
    College, A
South Central Technical College, A
Winona State University, B

Mississippi

Copiah-Lincoln Community College, A
East Mississippi Community College, A
Hinds Community College, A
Northeast Mississippi Community College, A
Northwest Mississippi Community College, A

Missouri

Hickey College, A
ITT Technical Institute (Arnold), A

ITT Technical Institute (Earth City), A
Linn State Technical College, A
Longview Community College, A
Maple Woods Community College, A
Metropolitan Community College-Business &
    Technology College, A
Mineral Area College, A
Northwest Missouri State University, B
Pinnacle Career Institute, A
Rockhurst University, B
St. Louis Community College at Florissant Valley, A
St. Louis Community College at Meramec, A
Sanford-Brown College (Hazelwood), A
Sanford-Brown College (St. Charles), A
Southeast Missouri State University, B
Vatterott College (St. Ann), A
Vatterott College (Springfield), A

Montana

Montana Tech of The University of Montana, B
University of Great Falls, B
The University of Montana-Helena College of
    Technology, A

Nebraska

Grace University, B
Hamilton College-Lincoln, A
Hamilton College-Omaha, A
ITT Technical Institute, A
Metropolitan Community College, A
Midland Lutheran College, AB
Northeast Community College, A
Southeast Community College, Milford Campus, A

Nevada

Community College of Southern Nevada, A
ITT Technical Institute, A
Nevada State College at Henderson, B
Truckee Meadows Community College, A
Western Nevada Community College, A

New Hampshire

Daniel Webster College, AB
Franklin Pierce College, B
Granite State College, B
Hesser College, A

New Jersey

Atlantic Cape Community College, A
Bergen Community College, A
Brookdale Community College, A
Camden County College, A
Essex County College, A
Middlesex County College, A
Ocean County College, A
Raritan Valley Community College, A
Saint Peter's College, B

New Mexico

ITT Technical Institute, A
New Mexico Highlands University, B
New Mexico Junior College, A
New Mexico Military Institute, A
University of New Mexico-Los Alamos Branch, A

New York

Borough of Manhattan Community College of the
    City University of New York, A
Bramson ORT College, A
Briarcliffe College, A
Cayuga County Community College, A
College of Staten Island of the City University of
    New York, A
The College of Westchester, A
Corning Community College, A
Farmingdale State University of New York, AB
Fiorello H. LaGuardia Community College of the
    City University of New York, A
Globe Institute of Technology, B
ITT Technical Institute (Albany), A
ITT Technical Institute (Getzville), A
ITT Technical Institute (Liverpool), A
Medaille College, B
Mohawk Valley Community College, A
New York University, A

Orange County Community College, A
Rochester Business Institute, A
Rockland Community College, A
State University of New York College of Agriculture
  and Technology at Cobleskill, A
State University of New York College of Agriculture
  and Technology at Morrisville, A
Suffolk County Community College, A

North Carolina

Alamance Community College, A
Asheville-Buncombe Technical Community
  College, A
Beaufort County Community College, A
Bladen Community College, A
Blue Ridge Community College, A
Brunswick Community College, A
Catawba Valley Community College, A
Central Carolina Community College, A
Central Piedmont Community College, A
College of The Albemarle, A
Davidson County Community College, A
Durham Technical Community College, A
Fayetteville Technical Community College, A
Gaston College, A
Guilford Technical Community College, A
Isothermal Community College, A
Johnston Community College, A
Lenoir Community College, A
Mayland Community College, A
McDowell Technical Community College, A
Roanoke-Chowan Community College, A
Sampson Community College, A
Sandhills Community College, A
Surry Community College, A
Wake Technical Community College, A
Western Piedmont Community College, A
Wilson Technical Community College, A

Ohio

Belmont Technical College, A
Bowling Green State University-Firelands College, A
Bradford School, A
Central Ohio Technical College, A
Cincinnati State Technical and Community
  College, A
Clark State Community College, A
Columbus State Community College, A
Edison State Community College, A
Hocking College, A
ITT Technical Institute (Dayton), A
ITT Technical Institute (Norwood), A
ITT Technical Institute (Strongsville), A
ITT Technical Institute (Youngstown), A
James A. Rhodes State College, A
Kent State University, AB
Lorain County Community College, A
Miami-Jacobs College, A
Northwest State Community College, A
Ohio Business College (Sandusky), A
RETS Tech Center, A
Southwestern College of Business (Cincinnati), A
Stark State College of Technology, A
Tiffin University, A
University of Cincinnati, AB
University of Cincinnati Clermont College, A
University of Cincinnati Raymond Walters College, A
University of Northwestern Ohio, A
The University of Toledo, AB
Youngstown State University, AB

Oklahoma

Northeastern Oklahoma Agricultural and Mechanical
  College, A
Redlands Community College, A
Rogers State University, A
Vatterott College (Oklahoma City), A
Vatterott College (Tulsa), A

Oregon

Chemeketa Community College, A
ITT Technical Institute, A
Lane Community College, A
Oregon Institute of Technology, AB

Portland Community College, A

Pennsylvania

Arcadia University, B
Berks Technical Institute, A
Bucks County Community College, A
Business Institute of Pennsylvania (Sharon), A
Butler County Community College, A
California University of Pennsylvania, A
CHI Institute, A
Community College of Beaver County, A
Delaware Valley College, A
Duff's Business Institute, A
Gannon University, B
Gwynedd-Mercy College, A
ICM School of Business & Medical Careers, A
Keystone College, A
La Salle University, B
Lehigh Valley College, A
Montgomery County Community College, A
Newport Business Institute (Lower Burrell), A
Northampton County Area Community College, A
Pace Institute, A
Pennco Tech, A
Pennsylvania Highland Community College, A
Reading Area Community College, A
Saint Francis University, AB
Thompson Institute, A

Puerto Rico

Caribbean University, AB
Electronic Data Processing College of Puerto
  Rico, AB
Humacao Community College, A
Inter American University of Puerto Rico, Bayamón
  Campus, B
Inter American University of Puerto Rico,
  Metropolitan Campus, B
Inter American University of Puerto Rico, San
  Germán Campus, B
Pontifical Catholic University of Puerto Rico, A
Technological College of San Juan, A
Universidad del Este, A
University of Puerto Rico, Aguadilla University
  College, A

Rhode Island

Community College of Rhode Island, A
Johnson & Wales University, A

South Carolina

Charleston Southern University, AB
Clemson University, B
Greenville Technical College, A
ITT Technical Institute, A
Limestone College, AB
Northeastern Technical College, A
Piedmont Technical College, A
Tri-County Technical College, A

South Dakota

Black Hills State University, A
Dakota State University, A
Lake Area Technical Institute, A
National American University (Rapid City), AB
National American University-Sioux Falls
  Branch, AB
Southeast Technical Institute, A

Tennessee

Belmont University, B
Chattanooga State Technical Community College, A
Draughons Junior College (Clarksville), A
Draughons Junior College (Nashville), A
ITT Technical Institute (Knoxville), A
ITT Technical Institute (Memphis), A
ITT Technical Institute (Nashville), A
Martin Methodist College, A
Northeast State Technical Community College, A
Pellissippi State Technical Community College, A

Texas

Alvin Community College, A
Amarillo College, A
Angelina College, A

Austin Community College, A
Brazosport College, A
Cedar Valley College, A
Central Texas College, A
Cisco Junior College, A
College of the Mainland, A
Collin County Community College District, A
Del Mar College, A
Eastfield College, A
El Centro College, A
El Paso Community College, A
Hardin-Simmons University, B
Hill College of the Hill Junior College District, A
Howard College, A
ITT Technical Institute (Arlington), A
ITT Technical Institute (Austin), A
ITT Technical Institute (Houston), A
ITT Technical Institute (Houston), A
ITT Technical Institute (Houston), A
ITT Technical Institute (Richardson), A
ITT Technical Institute (San Antonio), A
Kilgore College, A
Lamar University, B
Laredo Community College, A
Lee College, A
Montgomery College, A
Mountain View College, A
Navarro College, A
North Central Texas College, A
North Lake College, A
Northwest Vista College, A
Richland College, A
San Antonio College, A
South Plains College, A
Tarrant County College District, A
Temple College, A
Texarkana College, A
Texas Southern University, B
Texas State Technical College Harlingen, A
Texas State Technical College Waco, A
Texas State Technical College West Texas, A
Tomball College, A
Victoria College, A
Weatherford College, A

Utah

ITT Technical Institute, A
Neumont University, B

Vermont

Castleton State College, A

Virginia

Dabney S. Lancaster Community College, A
Danville Community College, A
ECPI College of Technology (Virginia Beach), A
ECPI Technical College (Glen Allen), A
ECPI Technical College (Richmond), A
ITT Technical Institute (Chantilly), A
ITT Technical Institute (Norfolk), A
ITT Technical Institute (Richmond), A
ITT Technical Institute (Springfield), A
J. Sargeant Reynolds Community College, A
Lord Fairfax Community College, A
Patrick Henry Community College, A
Piedmont Virginia Community College, A
Stratford University, A
Tidewater Community College, A

Washington

Bates Technical College, A
Bellevue Community College, A
City University, B
Clark College, A
Clover Park Technical College, A
Edmonds Community College, A
Highline Community College, A
ITT Technical Institute (Bothell), A
ITT Technical Institute (Seattle), A
ITT Technical Institute (Spokane), A
Lower Columbia College, A
Olympic College, A
Pierce College, A
South Puget Sound Community College, A
South Seattle Community College, A
Spokane Community College, A

Walla Walla College, A

West Virginia

Huntington Junior College, A
Potomac State College of West Virginia
University, A
West Virginia Northern Community College, A
West Virginia State University, A
West Virginia University Institute of Technology, B
Wheeling Jesuit University, B

Wisconsin

Fox Valley Technical College, A
ITT Technical Institute (Green Bay), A
ITT Technical Institute (Greenfield), A
Lakeshore Technical College, A
Madison Area Technical College, A
Northeast Wisconsin Technical College, A
Southwest Wisconsin Technical College, A
Waukesha County Technical College, A
Western Technical College, A

Wyoming

Casper College, A
Laramie County Community College, A

British Columbia

Thompson Rivers University, B

Newfoundland and Labrador

Memorial University of Newfoundland, B

Ontario

Brock University, B
Carleton University, B
Wilfrid Laurier University, B
York University, B

Quebec

Bishop's University, B
Université du Québec àTrois-Rivières, B
Université de Sherbrooke, B

COMPUTER PROGRAMMING, SPECIFIC APPLICATIONS

Arizona

DeVry University (Phoenix), B
GateWay Community College, A
Mohave Community College, A

California

American River College, A
The Art Institute of California-San Francisco, B
Chabot College, A
Cypress College, A
DeVry University (Fremont), B
DeVry University (Long Beach), B
DeVry University (Pomona), B
DeVry University (West Hills), B
Glendale Community College, A
Los Angeles City College, A
Orange Coast College, A
San Diego Mesa College, A
Santa Monica College, A
Victor Valley College, A
Westwood College-Inland Empire, B

Colorado

Arapahoe Community College, A
CollegeAmerica-Fort Collins, A
National American University (Denver), AB
Westwood College-Denver North, B
Westwood College-Denver South, B

Connecticut

Naugatuck Valley Community College, A

Florida

Brevard Community College, A
Daytona Beach Community College, A
DeVry University (Orlando), B

Edison College, A
Florida Career College, A
Florida Community College at Jacksonville, A
Florida National College, A
Gulf Coast Community College, A
Lake City Community College, A
Okaloosa-Walton College, A
Palm Beach Community College, A
Pasco-Hernando Community College, A
Seminole Community College, A
Tallahassee Community College, A
Valencia Community College, A

Georgia

DeVry University (Alpharetta), B
DeVry University (Decatur), B
Georgia Southwestern State University, AB
Macon State College, A
West Central Technical College, A

Idaho

Idaho State University, A

Illinois

City Colleges of Chicago, Malcolm X College, A
College of DuPage, A
College of Lake County, A
DePaul University, B
DeVry University (Tinley Park), B
Elgin Community College, A
Heartland Community College, A
Highland Community College, A
John Wood Community College, A
Joliet Junior College, A
Kaskaskia College, A
Kishwaukee College, A
Lake Land College, A
Lincoln Land Community College, A
McHenry County College, A
Moraine Valley Community College, A
Oakton Community College, A
Parkland College, A
Rend Lake College, A
Richland Community College, A
Robert Morris College, A
Waubonsee Community College, A
Westwood College-Chicago Du Page, B
Westwood College-Chicago Loop Campus, B
Westwood College-Chicago River Oaks, B

Indiana

Indiana Business College (Indianapolis), A
Indiana Business College (Muncie), A
Professional Careers Institute, A
Vincennes University, A

Iowa

AIB College of Business, A
Des Moines Area Community College, A
Iowa Western Community College, A
Western Iowa Tech Community College, A

Kansas

Barton County Community College, A
Johnson County Community College, A

Kentucky

Brown Mackie College-Hopkinsville, A
Brown Mackie College-Northern Kentucky, A
Daymar College (Owensboro), A
Henderson Community College, A

Louisiana

Louisiana Technical College, A

Maine

Husson College, B

Massachusetts

Bunker Hill Community College, A
North Shore Community College, A

Northern Essex Community College, A

Michigan

Gogebic Community College, A
Kellogg Community College, A
Macomb Community College, A
Monroe County Community College, A

Minnesota

Alexandria Technical College, A
Dakota County Technical College, A
Dunwoody College of Technology, A
Inver Hills Community College, A
Lake Superior College, A
Mesabi Range Community and Technical College, A
Ridgewater College, A
Riverland Community College, A
St. Cloud Technical College, A

Mississippi

Northwest Mississippi Community College, A

Missouri

Metropolitan Community College-Business &
Technology College, A
Missouri State University-West Plains, A
Saint Charles Community College, A
St. Louis Community College at Forest Park, A
Sanford-Brown College (Fenton), A
State Fair Community College, A

Nebraska

Central Community College-Columbus Campus, A
Central Community College-Grand Island
Campus, A
Central Community College-Hastings Campus, A
Hamilton College-Omaha, A
Northeast Community College, A

New Hampshire

New Hampshire Technical Institute, A

New Jersey

Camden County College, A
Essex County College, A

New York

The College of Westchester, A
Fiorello H. LaGuardia Community College of the
City University of New York, A
Hudson Valley Community College, A
ITT Technical Institute (Albany), A
Onondaga Community College, A
Rockland Community College, A
Sullivan County Community College, A

North Carolina

Bladen Community College, A
Caldwell Community College and Technical
Institute, A
Catawba Valley Community College, A
Central Carolina Community College, A
Central Piedmont Community College, A
Cleveland Community College, A
Coastal Carolina Community College, A
College of The Albemarle, A
Craven Community College, A
Pitt Community College, A
Sandhills Community College, A
South Piedmont Community College, A
Stanly Community College, A
Wake Technical Community College, A
Wilkes Community College, A

North Dakota

Lake Region State College, A
North Dakota State College of Science, A

Ohio

Bradford School, A
Cincinnati State Technical and Community
College, A
ETI Technical College of Niles, A
Kent State University, AB

Lakeland Community College, A
Lorain County Community College, A
Sinclair Community College, A
Southern State Community College, A
Stark State College of Technology, A
The University of Toledo, A
Zane State College, A

Oklahoma

Oklahoma Baptist University, B
Tulsa Community College, A

Oregon

Linn-Benton Community College, A

Pennsylvania

Academy of Medical Arts and Business, A
Bucks County Community College, A
CHI Institute, A
Delaware County Community College, A
McCann School of Business & Technology, A
Peirce College, A
Pennsylvania College of Technology, A
Pennsylvania Highland Community College, A
South Hills School of Business & Technology (State College), A

South Carolina

Horry-Georgetown Technical College, A
Trident Technical College, A
Williamsburg Technical College, A

South Dakota

Lake Area Technical Institute, A
Southeast Technical Institute, A

Texas

Brazosport College, A
Cedar Valley College, A
Central Texas College, A
Coastal Bend College, A
Del Mar College, A
El Paso Community College, A
Midland College, A
North Central Texas College, A
San Antonio College, A
Texas State Technical College Harlingen, A

Utah

Neumont University, B

Virginia

DeVry University (Arlington), B
Piedmont Virginia Community College, A

Washington

DeVry University (Federal Way), B
Edmonds Community College, A
Tacoma Community College, A
University of Puget Sound, B

West Virginia

Potomac State College of West Virginia University, A
Southern West Virginia Community and Technical College, A

Wisconsin

Gateway Technical College, A
Mid-State Technical College, A
Milwaukee Area Technical College, A
Moraine Park Technical College, A

Wisconsin Indianhead Technical College, A

Wyoming

Sheridan College-Sheridan and Gillette, A
Western Wyoming Community College, A

Ontario

University of Windsor, B

COMPUTER PROGRAMMING, VENDOR/PRODUCT CERTIFICATION

Arizona

GateWay Community College, A

Arkansas

Arkansas State University-Beebe, A

California

American River College, A
Heald College-Hayward, A
Los Angeles City College, A

Florida

Florida Community College at Jacksonville, A
Lake City Community College, A
Seminole Community College, A

Guam

Guam Community College, A

Illinois

Heartland Community College, A
Parkland College, A

Indiana

Vincennes University, A

Kentucky

Daymar College (Owensboro), A
Henderson Community College, A
Louisville Technical Institute, A

Michigan

Davenport University (Dearborn), B
Washtenaw Community College, A

Minnesota

Dakota County Technical College, A
Inver Hills Community College, A
Riverland Community College, A

Missouri

Metropolitan Community College-Business & Technology College, A
St. Louis Community College at Forest Park, A
Sanford-Brown College (Fenton), A

New York

The College of Westchester, A
Fiorello H. LaGuardia Community College of the City University of New York, A

North Dakota

Lake Region State College, A

Ohio

ETI Technical College of Niles, A
Lorain County Community College, A
Marion Technical College, A
Sinclair Community College, A

Stark State College of Technology, A

Oklahoma

Tulsa Community College, A

Pennsylvania

Academy of Medical Arts and Business, A
Thaddeus Stevens College of Technology, A

South Dakota

National American University-Sioux Falls Branch, B
Southeast Technical Institute, A

Texas

Central Texas College, A
Coastal Bend College, A
Del Mar College, A
North Central Texas College, A
San Antonio College, A
Texas State Technical College Harlingen, A

Utah

Neumont University, B

Washington

Edmonds Community College, A
Peninsula College, A

Wisconsin

Milwaukee Area Technical College, A

COMPUTER SCIENCE

Alabama

Alabama Agricultural and Mechanical University, M
Alabama Southern Community College, A
Alabama State University, B
American College of Computer & Information Sciences, BM
Athens State University, B
Auburn University, MD
Birmingham-Southern College, B
Central Alabama Community College, A
Enterprise-Ozark Community College, A
Gadsden State Community College-Ayers Campus, A
George C. Wallace Community College, A
George Corley Wallace State Community College, A
Herzing College, A
Huntingdon College, B
Jacksonville State University, M
Northeast Alabama Community College, A
Northwest-Shoals Community College, A
Oakwood College, B
Samford University, B
Stillman College, B
Talladega College, B
Tuskegee University, B
The University of Alabama, MD
The University of Alabama at Birmingham, MD
The University of Alabama in Huntsville, MDO
University of Mobile, B
University of South Alabama, M
Wallace State Community College, A

Alaska

Charter College, A
University of Alaska Anchorage, B
University of Alaska Fairbanks, BM

Arizona

Arizona State University, BMD
Arizona State University at the Polytechnic Campus, M
Arizona Western College, A
Central Arizona College, A
Cochise College (Douglas), A
Cochise College (Sierra Vista), A
Diné College, A
Mohave Community College, A
Rio Salado College, A
The University of Arizona, MD

University of Phoenix-Phoenix Campus, M

Arkansas

Arkansas Baptist College, AB
Arkansas State University, BM
Harding University, B
Hendrix College, B
Lyon College, B
Ouachita Baptist University, B
Philander Smith College, B
University of Arkansas, MD
University of Arkansas at Little Rock, BM
University of Arkansas at Pine Bluff, B
University of Central Arkansas, M

California

Allan Hancock College, A
Azusa Pacific University, BMO
Bakersfield College, A
Barstow College, A
Cabrillo College, A
California Institute of Technology, BMD
California Lutheran University, B
California National University for Advanced
  Studies, B
California Polytechnic State University, San Luis
  Obispo, BM
California State Polytechnic University, Pomona, BM
California State University, Bakersfield, B
California State University Channel Islands, B
California State University, Chico, BM
California State University, Dominguez Hills, B
California State University, East Bay, BM
California State University, Fresno, BM
California State University, Fullerton, BM
California State University, Long Beach, BM
California State University, Los Angeles, B
California State University, Northridge, BM
California State University, Sacramento, M
California State University, San Bernardino, BM
California State University, San Marcos, BM
Cañada College, A
Cerritos College, A
Chabot College, A
Chapman University, B
Citrus College, A
City College of San Francisco, A
Claremont McKenna College, B
College of the Canyons, A
College of the Desert, A
College of Marin, A
College of San Mateo, A
College of the Sequoias, A
College of the Siskiyous, A
Columbia College, A
Contra Costa College, A
Crafton Hills College, A
Cuesta College, A
Cypress College, A
De Anza College, A
Foundation College, A
Fullerton College, A
Gavilan College, A
Glendale Community College, A
Grossmont College, A
Hartnell College, A
Harvey Mudd College, B
Heald College-Hayward, A
Heald College-San Jose, A
Humboldt State University, B
Humphreys College, AB
Institute of Computer Technology, AB
La Sierra University, B
Lake Tahoe Community College, A
Las Positas College, A
Lassen Community College District, A
Lincoln University, B
Los Angeles Pierce College, A
Los Angeles Southwest College, A
Loyola Marymount University, BM
Merced College, A
Mills College, BMO
Modesto Junior College, A
Monterey Peninsula College, A
Moorpark College, A
Mt. San Antonio College, A

Mt. San Jacinto College, A
Mt. Sierra College, B
Napa Valley College, A
National University, BM
Northwestern Polytechnic University, BM
Notre Dame de Namur University, B
Ohlone College, A
Pacific States University, BM
Pacific Union College, B
Palomar College, A
Pasadena City College, A
Pepperdine University, B
Point Loma Nazarene University, B
Pomona College, B
Porterville College, A
Sacramento City College, A
Saddleback College, A
San Bernardino Valley College, A
San Diego Mesa College, A
San Diego State University, BM
San Francisco State University, BM
San Joaquin Delta College, A
San Jose City College, A
San Jose State University, BMO
Santa Ana College, A
Santa Barbara City College, A
Santa Clara University, BMDO
Santa Rosa Junior College, A
Santiago Canyon College, A
Scripps College, B
Sierra College, A
Skyline College, A
Sonoma State University, B
Southern California Institute of Technology, AB
Southwestern College, A
Stanford University, BMD
Taft College, A
University of California, Berkeley, BMD
University of California, Davis, MD
University of California, Irvine, BMD
University of California, Los Angeles, BMDO
University of California, Riverside, BMD
University of California, San Diego, BMD
University of California, Santa Barbara, BD
University of California, Santa Cruz, BMD
University of La Verne, B
University of the Pacific, B
University of Redlands, B
University of San Diego, B
University of San Francisco, BM
University of Southern California, BMD
Victor Valley College, A
Westmont College, B
Yuba College, A

Colorado

Arapahoe Community College, A
Blair College, A
Colorado School of Mines, BMD
Colorado State University, BMD
Colorado Technical University, BMD
Colorado Technical University Denver Campus, BM
Fort Lewis College, B
Lamar Community College, A
Mesa State College, AB
Metropolitan State College of Denver, B
Northeastern Junior College, A
Parks College (Denver), A
Red Rocks Community College, A
Regis University, BMO
Trinidad State Junior College, A
United States Air Force Academy, B
University of Colorado at Boulder, BMD
University of Colorado at Colorado Springs, BMD
University of Colorado at Denver and Health
  Sciences Center - Downtown Denver
  Campus, MD
University of Denver, MD
Western State College of Colorado, B

Connecticut

Central Connecticut State University, M
Fairfield University, B
Northwestern Connecticut Community College, A
Quinnipiac University, B
Sacred Heart University, ABMO

Southern Connecticut State University, BM
Trinity College, B
University of Bridgeport, BM
University of Connecticut, BMD
University of New Haven, AM
Wesleyan University, B
Western Connecticut State University, BM
Yale University, D

Delaware

Delaware State University, B
University of Delaware, BMD

District of Columbia

American University, BMO
The Catholic University of America, BMD
Gallaudet University, B
The George Washington University, BMDO
Georgetown University, B
Howard University, M
Southeastern University, ABM
University of the District of Columbia, B

Florida

Barry University, B
Bethune-Cookman College, B
Broward Community College, A
Chipola College, A
Daytona Beach Community College, A
Eckerd College, B
Edison College, A
Florida Atlantic University, MD
Florida Career College, A
Florida Gulf Coast University, M
Florida Institute of Technology, BMD
Florida International University, BMD
Florida Memorial College, B
Florida Metropolitan University-Jacksonville
  Campus, AB
Florida Metropolitan University-Lakeland
  Campus, AB
Florida Metropolitan University-Tampa Campus, AB
Florida National College, A
Florida Southern College, B
Florida State University, BMD
Florida Technical College (DeLand), A
Gulf Coast College, A
Indian River Community College, A
Lake-Sumter Community College, A
Miami Dade College, A
Nova Southeastern University, BMDO
Okaloosa-Walton College, A
Palm Beach Community College, A
Pensacola Junior College, A
Rollins College, B
St. Thomas University, B
Stetson University, B
University of Central Florida, MD
University of Florida, MDO
University of Miami, BM
University of North Florida, M
University of South Florida, MD
University of West Florida, M
Webster College (Holiday), A

Georgia

Abraham Baldwin Agricultural College, A
Armstrong Atlantic State University, BM
Atlanta Metropolitan College, A
Berry College, B
Clark Atlanta University, BM
Clayton State University, A
Coastal Georgia Community College, A
Columbus State University, ABM
Covenant College, B
Dalton State College, A
Darton College, A
Emory University, BMD
Fort Valley State University, B
Gainesville College, A
Georgia Institute of Technology, MD
Georgia Perimeter College, A
Georgia Southwestern State University, BM
Georgia State University, MD
Gordon College, A
Gwinnett Technical College, A

Kennesaw State University, BM
LaGrange College, B
Lanier Technical College, A
Macon State College, A
Mercer University, B
Middle Georgia College, A
North Georgia College & State University, B
Oglethorpe University, B
Piedmont College, B
South Georgia College, A
Southern Polytechnic State University, M
Spelman College, B
University of Georgia, MD
University of West Georgia, M
Valdosta State University, B
Waycross College, A
Young Harris College, A

Guam

Guam Community College, A
University of Guam, B

Hawaii

Brigham Young University-Hawaii, B
Chaminade University of Honolulu, B
Hawaii Business College, A
Hawaii Pacific University, B
Leeward Community College, A
University of Hawaii at Hilo, B
University of Hawaii at Manoa, BMDO

Idaho

Boise State University, BM
Brigham Young University -Idaho, A
College of Southern Idaho, A
Lewis-Clark State College, B
North Idaho College, A
Northwest Nazarene University, B
University of Idaho, BMD

Illinois

Augustana College, B
Benedictine University, B
Blackburn College, B
Bradley University, M
Career Colleges of Chicago, A
Chicago State University, BM
Concordia University, B
DePaul University, BMD
Dominican University, B
East-West University, AB
Eastern Illinois University, MO
Elmhurst College, BM
Eureka College, B
Gem City College, A
Governors State University, BM
Greenville College, B
Heartland Community College, A
Highland Community College, A
Illinois College, B
Illinois Institute of Technology, BMDO
Illinois Wesleyan University, B
John A. Logan College, A
Judson College, B
Lake Forest College, B
Lewis University, B
Lincoln College, A
Lincoln College-Normal, A
Loyola University Chicago, BM
McKendree College, B
Monmouth College, B
North Central College, BM
Northeastern Illinois University, BM
Northern Illinois University, BM
Northwestern Business College, A
Northwestern University, BMD
Oakton Community College, A
Olivet Nazarene University, B
Parkland College, A
Quincy University, B
Rend Lake College, A
Rock Valley College, A
Rockford College, B
Roosevelt University, BM
Saint Xavier University, BMO
Southern Illinois University Carbondale, BM

Southern Illinois University Edwardsville, BM
Springfield College in Illinois, A
Trinity Christian College, B
Trinity International University, B
Triton College, A
University of Chicago, BM
University of Illinois at Chicago, MD
University of Illinois at Springfield, BM
University of Illinois at Urbana-Champaign, BMD
University of St. Francis, B
Western Illinois University, M
Wheaton College, B
William Rainey Harper College, A

Indiana

Anderson University, B
Ball State University, BM
Bethel College, AB
Butler University, B
Calumet College of Saint Joseph, AB
DePauw University, B
Earlham College, B
Franklin College, B
Goshen College, B
Hanover College, B
Huntington University, B
Indiana State University, M
Indiana Tech, B
Indiana University Bloomington, MD
Indiana University-Purdue University Fort
    Wayne, ABM
Indiana University-Purdue University Indianapolis, M
Indiana University South Bend, ABM
Indiana University Southeast, AB
Manchester College, AB
Oakland City University, A
Purdue University, MD
Purdue University Calumet, B
Rose-Hulman Institute of Technology, B
Taylor University, B
Tri-State University, B
University of Evansville, M
University of Indianapolis, B
University of Notre Dame, MD
Valparaiso University, B
Vincennes University, A

Iowa

Buena Vista University, B
Central College, B
Clarke College, B
Coe College, B
Cornell College, B
Dordt College, B
Drake University, B
Graceland University, B
Grand View College, B
Grinnell College, B
Iowa Lakes Community College, A
Iowa State University of Science and
    Technology, MD
Iowa Wesleyan College, B
Kirkwood Community College, A
Loras College, B
Luther College, B
Maharishi University of Management, BM
Marshalltown Community College, A
Morningside College, B
Mount Mercy College, B
Northwestern College, B
St. Ambrose University, B
Simpson College, B
University of Dubuque, AB
The University of Iowa, BMD
University of Northern Iowa, BM
Wartburg College, B
William Penn University, B

Kansas

Allen County Community College, A
Baker University, B
Barton County Community College, A
Benedictine College, B
Bethel College, B
Butler Community College, A
Central Christian College of Kansas, A

Coffeyville Community College, A
Colby Community College, A
Dodge City Community College, A
Donnelly College, A
Emporia State University, M
Fort Scott Community College, A
Friends University, AB
Garden City Community College, A
Highland Community College, A
Kansas State University, MD
Kansas Wesleyan University, AB
Labette Community College, A
McPherson College, B
MidAmerica Nazarene University, B
Neosho County Community College, A
Pittsburg State University, B
Seward County Community College, A
Southwestern College, B
Tabor College, AB
University of Kansas, MD
Wichita State University, M

Kentucky

Bellarmine University, B
Centre College, B
Daymar College (Owensboro), A
Eastern Kentucky University, B
Kentucky State University, M
Kentucky Wesleyan College, B
Northern Kentucky University, BM
Southwestern College of Business, A
Sullivan University, AB
Transylvania University, B
University of Kentucky, MD
University of Louisville, MD
Western Kentucky University, M

Louisiana

Dillard University, B
Elaine P. Nunez Community College, A
Grambling State University, B
Louisiana State University and Agricultural and
    Mechanical University, BMD
Louisiana State University in Shreveport, B
Louisiana Tech University, BM
McNeese State University, M
Nicholls State University, B
Southeastern Louisiana University, B
Southern University and Agricultural and Mechanical
    College, BM
Southern University at New Orleans, A
Southern University at Shreveport, A
Tulane University, BMD
University of Louisiana at Lafayette, BMD
University of Louisiana at Monroe, B
University of New Orleans, BM
Xavier University of Louisiana, B

Maine

Andover College, A
Bowdoin College, B
Central Maine Community College, A
Colby College, B
Thomas College, B
University of Maine, BMD
University of Maine at Farmington, B
University of Maine at Fort Kent, AB
University of Southern Maine, BM

Maryland

Anne Arundel Community College, A
Baltimore City Community College, A
Bowie State University, M
Capitol College, M
Chesapeake College, A
College of Notre Dame of Maryland, B
Columbia Union College, AB
Coppin State University, B
Frederick Community College, A
Frostburg State University, M
Goucher College, B
Hood College, M
Howard Community College, A
The Johns Hopkins University, MD
Morgan State University, B
Prince George's Community College, A

Towson University, M
United States Naval Academy, B
University of Maryland, Baltimore County, BMD
University of Maryland, College Park, MD
University of Maryland Eastern Shore, BM
University of Maryland University College, B
Washington College, B

Massachusetts

Amherst College, B
Assumption College, B
Atlantic Union College, B
Benjamin Franklin Institute of Technology, A
Boston College, B
Boston University, BMD
Brandeis University, BMDO
Bridgewater State College, BM
Bristol Community College, A
Bunker Hill Community College, A
Cape Cod Community College, A
Clark University, B
College of the Holy Cross, B
Eastern Nazarene College, B
Elms College, B
Fitchburg State College, BM
Framingham State College, B
Gordon College, B
Hampshire College, B
Harvard University, BMD
Massachusetts Bay Community College, A
Massachusetts College of Liberal Arts, B
Massachusetts Institute of Technology, BMDO
Merrimack College, AB
Middlesex Community College, A
Mount Holyoke College, B
New England College of Finance, A
Newbury College, AB
North Shore Community College, A
Northeastern University, BMD
Northern Essex Community College, A
Salem State College, B
Simmons College, B
Simon's Rock College of Bard, B
Smith College, B
Springfield College, B
Springfield Technical Community College, A
Stonehill College, B
Suffolk University, BM
Tufts University, BMDO
University of Massachusetts Amherst, BMD
University of Massachusetts Boston, BMD
University of Massachusetts Dartmouth, MO
University of Massachusetts Lowell, BMD
Wellesley College, B
Wentworth Institute of Technology, AB
Western New England College, B
Westfield State College, B
Wheaton College, B
Williams College, B
Worcester Polytechnic Institute, BMDO

Michigan

Albion College, B
Alma College, B
Andrews University, B
Aquinas College, B
Baker College of Allen Park, A
Baker College of Muskegon, B
Baker College of Owosso, AB
Calvin College, B
Central Michigan University, M
Delta College, A
Eastern Michigan University, BM
Ferris State University, M
Gogebic Community College, A
Grand Rapids Community College, A
Grand Valley State University, B
Henry Ford Community College, A
Hillsdale College, B
Hope College, B
Kalamazoo College, B
Kettering University, B
Lake Superior State University, B
Lawrence Technological University, BM
Lewis College of Business, A
Madonna University, AB

Michigan State University, MD
Michigan Technological University, B
Mid Michigan Community College, A
Northern Michigan University, B
Oakland University, BM
Olivet College, B
Spring Arbor University, B
University of Detroit Mercy, BM
University of Michigan, BMD
University of Michigan-Dearborn, M
University of Michigan-Flint, BM
Washtenaw Community College, A
Wayne County Community College District, A
Wayne State University, MDO
Western Michigan University, BMD

Minnesota

Academy College, B
Anoka-Ramsey Community College, A
Anoka-Ramsey Community College, Cambridge
    Campus, A
Augsburg College, B
Bemidji State University, B
Carleton College, B
College of Saint Benedict, B
Concordia College, B
Gustavus Adolphus College, B
Macalester College, B
Metropolitan State University, B
Minnesota State University Mankato, BM
Minnesota State University Moorhead, B
Normandale Community College, A
North Hennepin Community College, A
Northland Community and Technical College-Thief
    River Falls, A
Rochester Community and Technical College, A
St. Cloud State University, BM
Saint John's University, B
Saint Mary's University of Minnesota, B
St. Olaf College, B
Southwest Minnesota State University, B
University of Minnesota, Duluth, BM
University of Minnesota, Morris, B
University of Minnesota, Twin Cities Campus, BMD
Vermilion Community College, A
Walden University, M
Winona State University, B

Mississippi

Alcorn State University, M
Belhaven College, B
Coahoma Community College, A
East Central Community College, A
East Mississippi Community College, A
Hinds Community College, A
Holmes Community College, A
Itawamba Community College, A
Jackson State University, M
Millsaps College, B
Mississippi College, BM
Mississippi Gulf Coast Community College, A
Mississippi State University, MD
Mississippi Valley State University, B
Northeast Mississippi Community College, A
Rust College, B
Southwest Mississippi Community College, A
Tougaloo College, B
University of Southern Mississippi, M

Missouri

Blue River Community College, A
Central Methodist University, AB
College of the Ozarks, B
Columbia College, B
Drury University, B
Evangel University, B
Fontbonne University, B
Grantham University, AB
Lincoln University, A
Lindenwood University, B
Longview Community College, A
Maple Woods Community College, A
Maryville University of Saint Louis, B
Metropolitan Community College-Business &
    Technology College, A
Missouri Southern State University, AB

Missouri State University, B
Missouri Valley College, B
Northwest Missouri State University, BM
Park University, AB
Penn Valley Community College, A
Rockhurst University, B
Saint Charles Community College, A
St. Louis Community College at Florissant Valley, A
St. Louis Community College at Forest Park, A
St. Louis Community College at Meramec, A
Sanford-Brown College (Fenton), A
Southwest Baptist University, AB
Truman State University, B
University of Missouri-Columbia, BMD
University of Missouri-Kansas City, BMD
University of Missouri-Rolla, BMD
University of Missouri-St. Louis, BMDO
Washington University in St. Louis, BMD
Webster University, BMO
Westminster College, B
William Jewell College, B

Montana

Carroll College, AB
Fort Peck Community College, A
Little Big Horn College, A
Montana State University, BMD
Montana Tech of The University of Montana, AB
Rocky Mountain College, B
Salish Kootenai College, A
Stone Child College, A
University of Great Falls, B
The University of Montana-Missoula, BM

Nebraska

Concordia University, B
Creighton University, AB
Dana College, B
Doane College, B
Grace University, B
Hastings College, B
Midland Lutheran College, B
Nebraska Wesleyan University, B
Northeast Community College, A
Southeast Community College, Beatrice Campus, A
Union College, B
University of Nebraska-Lincoln, MD
University of Nebraska at Omaha, BM

Nevada

Community College of Southern Nevada, A
Morrison University, A
University of Nevada, Las Vegas, BMD
University of Nevada, Reno, BMD

New Hampshire

Daniel Webster College, B
Dartmouth College, BMD
Franklin Pierce College, B
Hesser College, A
Keene State College, AB
New Hampshire Community Technical College,
    Nashua/Claremont, A
Plymouth State University, B
Rivier College, ABM
Saint Anselm College, B
University of New Hampshire, BMD

New Jersey

Bergen Community College, A
Burlington County College, A
Caldwell College, B
College of Saint Elizabeth, B
Cumberland County College, A
Drew University, B
Essex County College, A
Fairleigh Dickinson University, Metropolitan
    Campus, M
Felician College, AB
Gloucester County College, A
Hudson County Community College, A
Mercer County Community College, A
Middlesex County College, A
Monmouth University, M
Montclair State University, BMO

New Jersey Institute of Technology, MD
Princeton University, MD
Raritan Valley Community College, A
The Richard Stockton College of New Jersey, B
Rider University, B
Rowan University, B
Rutgers, The State University of New Jersey, New
  Brunswick/Piscataway, BMD
Stevens Institute of Technology, BMDO
William Paterson University of New Jersey, B

New Mexico

College of Santa Fe, B
College of the Southwest, B
New Mexico Highlands University, BM
New Mexico Institute of Mining and
  Technology, BMD
New Mexico Junior College, A
New Mexico Military Institute, A
New Mexico State University, MD
New Mexico State University-Carlsbad, A
San Juan College, A
Southwestern Indian Polytechnic Institute, A
University of New Mexico, MD
University of New Mexico-Los Alamos Branch, A
University of New Mexico-Valencia Campus, A
Western New Mexico University, B

New York

Adirondack Community College, A
Bard College, B
Bramson ORT College, A
Bronx Community College of the City University of
  New York, A
Brooklyn College of the City University of New
  York, MD
Canisius College, B
Cayuga County Community College, A
City College of the City University of New
  York, BMD
Clarkson University, BMD
Colgate University, B
College of Mount Saint Vincent, B
The College of Saint Rose, M
College of Staten Island of the City University of
  New York, MD
Columbia College, B
Columbia-Greene Community College, A
Columbia University, School of General Studies, B
Columbia University, The Fu Foundation School of
  Engineering and Applied Science, B
Cornell University, BMD
Corning Community College, A
Dutchess Community College, A
Excelsior College, AB
Farmingdale State University of New York, A
Finger Lakes Community College, A
Fiorello H. LaGuardia Community College of the
  City University of New York, A
Fordham University, BM
Fulton-Montgomery Community College, A
Hamilton College, B
Hartwick College, B
Hobart and William Smith Colleges, B
Hofstra University, BM
Houghton College, B
Hunter College of the City University of New York, B
Iona College, BM
Ithaca College, B
Jamestown Community College, A
Jefferson Community College, A
Kingsborough Community College of the City
  University of New York, A
Lehman College of the City University of New
  York, BM
Long Island University, Brooklyn Campus, BM
Long Island University, C.W. Post Campus, BM
Manhattan College, B
Manhattanville College, B
Marist College, BMO
Medgar Evers College of the City University of New
  York, A
Mercy College, B
Molloy College, B
Monroe College (Bronx), A
Monroe College (New Rochelle), A

Monroe Community College, A
Mount Saint Mary College, B
Nassau Community College, A
New York City College of Technology of the City
  University of New York, A
New York Institute of Technology, M
New York University, BMD
Niagara County Community College, A
Niagara University, B
Nyack College, B
Onondaga Community College, A
Orange County Community College, A
Pace University, BMDO
Plaza College, A
Polytechnic University, Brooklyn Campus, BMD
Queens College of the City University of New
  York, BM
Rensselaer Polytechnic Institute, BMD
Roberts Wesleyan College, B
Rochester Institute of Technology, ABM
Sage College of Albany, A
St. Bonaventure University, B
St. John Fisher College, B
St. John's University, M
St. Joseph's College, Suffolk Campus, B
St. Lawrence University, B
Sarah Lawrence College, B
Schenectady County Community College, A
State University of New York at Binghamton, BMD
State University of New York at Buffalo, BMD
State University of New York College of Agriculture
  and Technology at Cobleskill, A
State University of New York College of Agriculture
  and Technology at Morrisville, A
State University of New York College at
  Brockport, B
State University of New York College at Geneseo, B
State University of New York College at Old
  Westbury, B
State University of New York College at Oneonta, B
State University of New York College of Technology
  at Alfred, A
State University of New York, Fredonia, B
State University of New York Institute of
  Technology, BM
State University of New York at New Paltz, BM
State University of New York at Oswego, B
State University of New York at Plattsburgh, B
Stony Brook University, State University of New
  York, BMDO
Suffolk County Community College, A
Syracuse University, MDO
Tompkins Cortland Community College, A
Touro College, B
Ulster County Community College, A
United States Military Academy, B
University at Albany, State University of New
  York, BMD
University of Rochester, BMD
Wagner College, B
Wells College, B
Westchester Community College, A
Yeshiva University, B

North Carolina

Appalachian State University, BM
Barber-Scotia College, B
Bennett College For Women, B
Catawba College, B
Catawba Valley Community College, A
Central Piedmont Community College, A
Duke University, BMD
East Carolina University, BMO
ECPI Technical College, A
Elizabeth City State University, B
Elon University, B
Fayetteville State University, B
Forsyth Technical Community College, A
Gardner-Webb University, B
High Point University, B
Isothermal Community College, A
Johnson C. Smith University, B
Lenoir-Rhyne College, B
Livingstone College, B
Louisburg College, A
Mars Hill College, B

Meredith College, B
Methodist College, AB
Mitchell Community College, A
North Carolina Agricultural and Technical State
  University, BM
North Carolina Central University, B
North Carolina State University, BMD
Saint Augustine's College, B
Shaw University, B
The University of North Carolina at Asheville, B
The University of North Carolina at Chapel
  Hill, BMD
The University of North Carolina at Charlotte, BM
The University of North Carolina at Greensboro, BM
The University of North Carolina at Pembroke, B
The University of North Carolina Wilmington, BM
Wake Forest University, M
Western Carolina University, BM
Winston-Salem State University, B

North Dakota

Cankdeska Cikana Community College, A
Dickinson State University, B
Jamestown College, B
Lake Region State College, A
Minot State University, B
North Dakota State University, BMDO
Turtle Mountain Community College, A
University of North Dakota, BM

Ohio

Antioch College, B
Ashland University, B
Baldwin-Wallace College, B
Bluffton University, B
Bowling Green State University, M
Brown Mackie College-Cincinnati, A
Capital University, B
Case Western Reserve University, BMD
Cedarville University, B
Cleveland State University, BM
College of Mount St. Joseph, B
The College of Wooster, B
Defiance College, AB
Denison University, B
Edison State Community College, A
Franciscan University of Steubenville, B
Franklin University, M
Gallipolis Career College, A
Heidelberg College, B
Hiram College, B
Hocking College, A
John Carroll University, B
Kent State University, BMD
Lorain County Community College, A
Malone College, B
Marietta College, B
Miami University Hamilton, B
Miami University-Middletown Campus, A
Mount Union College, B
Muskingum College, B
Oberlin College, B
Ohio Dominican University, B
Ohio Northern University, B
The Ohio State University, BMD
Ohio University, BMD
Ohio University-Eastern, B
Ohio University-Lancaster, A
Ohio University-Southern Campus, A
Ohio Wesleyan University, B
Otterbein College, B
RETS Tech Center, A
Southwestern College of Business (Cincinnati), A
Southwestern College of Business (Cincinnati), A
Southwestern College of Business (Dayton), A
Southwestern College of Business (Franklin), A
The University of Akron, BM
The University of Akron-Wayne College, A
University of Cincinnati, BMD
University of Cincinnati Raymond Walters College, A
University of Dayton, BM
The University of Findlay, AB
University of Rio Grande, AB
The University of Toledo, BMD
Walsh University, B
Wilberforce University, B

Wilmington College, B
Wittenberg University, B
Wright State University, BMD
Xavier University, B
Youngstown State University, B

Oklahoma

Bacone College, A
Carl Albert State College, A
Connors State College, A
East Central University, B
Eastern Oklahoma State College, A
Langston University, B
Murray State College, A
Northeastern Oklahoma Agricultural and Mechanical
    College, A
Northeastern State University, B
Northern Oklahoma College, A
Northwestern Oklahoma State University, B
Oklahoma Baptist University, B
Oklahoma Christian University, B
Oklahoma City Community College, A
Oklahoma City University, BM
Oklahoma State University, BMD
Oral Roberts University, B
Redlands Community College, A
Rogers State University, A
Seminole State College, A
Southwestern Oklahoma State University, B
Southwestern Oklahoma State University at
    Sayre, A
Tulsa Community College, A
University of Central Oklahoma, B
University of Oklahoma, MD
University of Tulsa, BMD

Oregon

Central Oregon Community College, A
Chemeketa Community College, A
Corban College, B
Eastern Oregon University, B
Lewis & Clark College, B
Linfield College, B
Oregon State University, BMD
Pacific University, B
Portland State University, BMD
Rogue Community College, A
Southern Oregon University, BM
Treasure Valley Community College, A
Umpqua Community College, A
University of Oregon, BMD
University of Portland, B
Western Oregon University, B
Willamette University, B

Pennsylvania

Albright College, B
Allegheny College, B
Arcadia University, B
Berean Institute, A
Bloomsburg University of Pennsylvania, B
Bucks County Community College, A
Carlow University, B
Carnegie Mellon University, BMD
Chestnut Hill College, B
Cheyney University of Pennsylvania, B
College Misericordia, B
Commonwealth Technical Institute, A
Community College of Philadelphia, A
DeSales University, B
Dickinson College, B
Drexel University, BMD
Duquesne University, B
East Stroudsburg University of Pennsylvania, M
Elizabethtown College, B
Erie Business Center, Main, A
Erie Business Center South, A
Gannon University, M
Geneva College, B
Gettysburg College, B
Haverford College, B
ICM School of Business & Medical Careers, A
Immaculata University, B
King's College, B
Kutztown University of Pennsylvania, M
La Salle University, BM

Lafayette College, B
Lebanon Valley College, B
Lehigh University, BMD
Lock Haven University of Pennsylvania, B
Luzerne County Community College, A
Lycoming College, B
Manor College, A
Mansfield University of Pennsylvania, B
McCann School of Business & Technology, A
Mercyhurst College, B
Messiah College, B
Millersville University of Pennsylvania, AB
Moravian College, B
Mount Aloysius College, A
Muhlenberg College, B
Northampton County Area Community College, A
Penn Foster Career School, A
The Pennsylvania State University at Erie, The
    Behrend College, B
The Pennsylvania State University Harrisburg
    Campus, M
The Pennsylvania State University University Park
    Campus, MD
Philadelphia University, B
Reading Area Community College, A
Saint Francis University, B
Saint Joseph's University, ABM
Seton Hill University, B
Shippensburg University of Pennsylvania, M
Susquehanna University, B
Temple University, MD
Thiel College, B
University of Pennsylvania, MD
University of Pittsburgh, BMD
University of Pittsburgh at Bradford, B
University of Pittsburgh at Johnstown, B
University of the Sciences in Philadelphia, B
The University of Scranton, B
Ursinus College, B
Villanova University, BMO
Waynesburg College, B
West Chester University of Pennsylvania, MO
Westminster College, B
Westmoreland County Community College, A
Widener University, B
York College of Pennsylvania, B

Puerto Rico

Bayamon Central University, A
Caribbean University, B
Huertas Junior College, A
Inter American University of Puerto Rico, Aguadilla
    Campus, AB
Inter American University of Puerto Rico, Arecibo
    Campus, AB
Inter American University of Puerto Rico,
    Barranquitas Campus, A
Inter American University of Puerto Rico, Bayamón
    Campus, AB
Inter American University of Puerto Rico, Fajardo
    Campus, AB
Inter American University of Puerto Rico, Guayama
    Campus, A
Inter American University of Puerto Rico,
    Metropolitan Campus, BM
Inter American University of Puerto Rico, Ponce
    Campus, AB
Inter American University of Puerto Rico, San
    Germán Campus, B
Pontifical Catholic University of Puerto Rico, B
Universidad Adventista de las Antillas, AB
Universidad Metropolitana, B
Universidad del Turabo, A
University of Puerto Rico at Arecibo, AB
University of Puerto Rico at Bayamón, AB
University of Puerto Rico, Mayagüez Campus, B
University of Puerto Rico at Ponce, AB
University of Puerto Rico, Río Piedras, B
University of the Sacred Heart, B

Rhode Island

Brown University, BMD
Providence College, B
Roger Williams University, B

University of Rhode Island, MD

South Carolina

Benedict College, B
Charleston Southern University, B
The Citadel, The Military College of South
    Carolina, BM
Claflin University, B
Clemson University, BMD
Coker College, B
College of Charleston, M
Converse College, B
Furman University, B
Limestone College, AB
Newberry College, B
Northeastern Technical College, A
Presbyterian College, B
South Carolina State University, B
University of South Carolina, MD
University of South Carolina Aiken, B
Voorhees College, B
Winthrop University, B
Wofford College, B

South Dakota

Augustana College, B
Black Hills State University, A
Colorado Technical University Sioux Falls
    Campus, B
Dakota State University, M
Kilian Community College, A
Mount Marty College, B
Oglala Lakota College, A
South Dakota School of Mines and Technology, BM
South Dakota State University, M
University of Sioux Falls, B
The University of South Dakota, M

Tennessee

Belmont University, B
Bryan College, B
Carson-Newman College, B
Chattanooga State Technical Community College, A
Christian Brothers University, B
Draughons Junior College (Clarksville), A
Draughons Junior College (Nashville), A
East Tennessee State University, M
Fisk University, B
Freed-Hardeman University, B
Jackson State Community College, A
King College, B
LeMoyne-Owen College, B
Lipscomb University, B
Martin Methodist College, A
Maryville College, B
Middle Tennessee State University, BM
Milligan College, B
Pellissippi State Technical Community College, A
Rhodes College, B
Roane State Community College, A
Sewanee: The University of the South, B
South College, A
Southern Adventist University, AB
Tennessee State University, B
Tennessee Technological University, BM
Tusculum College, B
Union University, B
University of Memphis, BMD
The University of Tennessee, BMD
The University of Tennessee at Chattanooga, BM
The University of Tennessee at Martin, B
Vanderbilt University, BMD
Walters State Community College, A

Texas

Abilene Christian University, B
Amarillo College, A
Angelina College, A
Austin College, B
Austin Community College, A
Baylor University, BM
Blinn College, A
Cisco Junior College, A
Coastal Bend College, A
Concordia University at Austin, B
Dallas Baptist University, B

Del Mar College, A
El Centro College, A
Frank Phillips College, A
Galveston College, A
Grayson County College, A
Hill College of the Hill Junior College District, A
Houston Baptist University, B
Houston Community College System, A
Howard College, A
Howard Payne University, B
Huston-Tillotson University, B
Jarvis Christian College, A
Lamar State College-Orange, A
Lamar University, BM
LeTourneau University, B
Lon Morris College, A
Lubbock Christian University, B
Midwestern State University, M
Navarro College, A
North Central Texas College, A
North Harris College, A
Northeast Texas Community College, A
Northwest Vista College, A
Odessa College, A
Palo Alto College, A
Paul Quinn College, B
Prairie View A&M University, BM
Rice University, MD
St. Edward's University, B
St. Mary's University of San Antonio, BMO
Sam Houston State University, M
South Plains College, A
South Texas College, A
Southern Methodist University, BMD
Southwestern Adventist University, B
Southwestern Christian College, A
Southwestern University, B
Stephen F. Austin State University, M
Tarrant County College District, A
Temple College, A
Texarkana College, A
Texas A&M University, BMD
Texas A&M University-Commerce, BM
Texas A&M University-Corpus Christi, BM
Texas A&M University-Kingsville, BM
Texas College, B
Texas Lutheran University, B
Texas Southern University, B
Texas State Technical College Harlingen, A
Texas State Technical College Waco, A
Texas State University-San Marcos, M
Texas Tech University, MD
Trinity Valley Community College, A
Tyler Junior College, A
University of Houston, MD
University of Houston-Clear Lake, M
University of Houston-Victoria, B
University of Mary Hardin-Baylor, B
University of North Texas, MD
The University of Texas at Arlington, BMD
The University of Texas at Austin, MD
The University of Texas at Dallas, BMD
The University of Texas at El Paso, BM
The University of Texas-Pan American, BM
The University of Texas of the Permian Basin, B
The University of Texas at San Antonio, MD
The University of Texas at Tyler, BM
Western Texas College, A
Wharton County Junior College, A
Wiley College, AB

United States Virgin Islands

University of the Virgin Islands, A

Utah

Brigham Young University, BMD
Dixie State College of Utah, AB
Neumont University, B
Salt Lake Community College, A
Snow College, A
Southern Utah University, B
University of Utah, BMD
Utah State University, MD
Utah Valley State College, AB
Weber State University, AB

Westminster College, B

Vermont

Bennington College, B
Community College of Vermont, A
Lyndon State College, A
Marlboro College, BM
Middlebury College, B
Norwich University, B
Saint Michael's College, B
University of Vermont, BMD

Virginia

Averett University, BM
Bluefield College, B
Bridgewater College, B
Christopher Newport University, BM
The College of William and Mary, MD
Eastern Mennonite University, B
ECPI College of Technology (Newport News), A
ECPI College of Technology (Virginia Beach), A
ECPI Technical College (Richmond), A
ECPI Technical College (Roanoke), A
Emory & Henry College, B
Ferrum College, B
George Mason University, MD
Hampden-Sydney College, B
Hampton University, BM
Hollins University, O
James Madison University, M
Longwood University, B
Lynchburg College, B
Marymount University, BMO
Norfolk State University, M
Northern Virginia Community College, A
Old Dominion University, MD
Piedmont Virginia Community College, A
Radford University, B
Randolph-Macon College, B
Roanoke College, B
Saint Paul's College, B
Sweet Briar College, B
Thomas Nelson Community College, A
University of Management and Technology, M
University of Mary Washington, B
University of Northern Virginia, M
University of Richmond, B
University of Virginia, MD
Virginia Commonwealth University, M
Virginia Military Institute, B
Virginia Polytechnic Institute and State
    University, BMD
Virginia State University, B
Virginia Wesleyan College, B
Virginia Western Community College, A
Washington and Lee University, B

Washington

City University, MO
Columbia Basin College, A
Eastern Washington University, M
Everett Community College, A
Gonzaga University, B
Henry Cogswell College, B
Heritage University, AB
Lake Washington Technical College, A
Lower Columbia College, A
Pacific Lutheran University, B
Renton Technical College, A
Saint Martin's University, B
Seattle Pacific University, B
Seattle University, B
Skagit Valley College, A
Tacoma Community College, A
University of Puget Sound, B
University of Washington, BMD
Walla Walla College, B
Washington State University, BMD
Western Washington University, BM
Whatcom Community College, A
Whitworth College, B
Yakima Valley Community College, A

West Virginia

Alderson-Broaddus College, AB
American Public University System, B

Bethany College, B
Concord University, B
Davis & Elkins College, B
Fairmont State University, B
Glenville State College, B
Huntington Junior College, A
Mountain State University, AB
Potomac State College of West Virginia
    University, A
Salem International University, B
West Virginia State Community and Technical
    College, A
West Virginia State University, A
West Virginia University, BMD
West Virginia University Institute of Technology, B
West Virginia Wesleyan College, B
Wheeling Jesuit University, B

Wisconsin

Alverno College, B
Beloit College, B
Cardinal Stritch University, B
Carroll College, B
Carthage College, B
College of Menominee Nation, A
Concordia University Wisconsin, B
Lakeland College, B
Lawrence University, B
Marquette University, BM
Milwaukee Area Technical College, A
Mount Mary College, B
Nicolet Area Technical College, A
Ripon College, B
University of Wisconsin-Green Bay, B
University of Wisconsin-Madison, BMD
University of Wisconsin-Milwaukee, BMD
University of Wisconsin-Oshkosh, B
University of Wisconsin-Parkside, BM
University of Wisconsin-Platteville, BM
University of Wisconsin-River Falls, B
University of Wisconsin-Superior, B

Wyoming

Casper College, A
Central Wyoming College, A
Laramie County Community College, A
University of Wyoming, BMD
Western Wyoming Community College, A

Alberta

The King's University College, B
University of Alberta, BMD
University of Calgary, BMD
University of Lethbridge, BM

British Columbia

British Columbia Institute of Technology, AB
Simon Fraser University, BMD
Thompson Rivers University, B
Trinity Western University, B
The University of British Columbia, BMD
University of Northern British Columbia, BM
University of Victoria, BMD

Manitoba

Brandon University, B
Canadian Mennonite University, B
University of Manitoba, BMD

New Brunswick

Mount Allison University, B
Université de Moncton, BMO
University of New Brunswick Fredericton, BMD
University of New Brunswick Saint John, B

Newfoundland and Labrador

Memorial University of Newfoundland, BMD

Nova Scotia

Acadia University, BM
Cape Breton University, B
Dalhousie University, BMD
Saint Mary's University, B

University of King's College, B

Ontario

Brock University, B
Carleton University, BMD
Lakehead University, BM
Laurentian University, B
McMaster University, BMD
Nipissing University, B
Queen's University at Kingston, BMD
Redeemer University College, B
Royal Military College of Canada, BM
Ryerson University, B
Trent University, BM
University of Guelph, BMD
University of Ottawa, BMD
University of Toronto, BMD
University of Waterloo, BMD
The University of Western Ontario, BMD
University of Windsor, BMD
Wilfrid Laurier University, B
York University, BMD

Prince Edward Island

University of Prince Edward Island, B

Quebec

Bishop's University, B
Concordia University, BMDO
McGill University, BMD
Télé-université, D
Université Laval, BMD
Université de Montréal, BMDO
Université du Québec àChicoutimi, B
Université du Québec en Outaouais, BMO
Université du Québec àRimouski, B
Université du Québec àTrois-Rivières, BM
Université de Sherbrooke, B

Saskatchewan

University of Regina, BMD
University of Saskatchewan, BMD

COMPUTER SOFTWARE AND MEDIA APPLICATIONS

California

American River College, A
Berkeley City College, A
Cerro Coso Community College, A
College of the Sequoias, A
Cypress College, A
Glendale Community College, A
Holy Names University, B
Los Angeles City College, A
Platt College San Diego, A
San Diego Mesa College, A
Westwood College-Inland Empire, B

Colorado

Arapahoe Community College, A

Florida

Brevard Community College, A
Florida Community College at Jacksonville, A
Florida State University, B
Seminole Community College, A

Illinois

Parkland College, A
Triton College, A
Westwood College-Chicago Loop Campus, B

Indiana

Ancilla College, A
Indiana University-Purdue University Fort
  Wayne, AB
Professional Careers Institute, A

Vincennes University, A

Iowa

AIB College of Business, A

Kentucky

Daymar College (Owensboro), A

Maine

Kennebec Valley Community College, A
New England School of Communications, AB

Michigan

Kellogg Community College, A

Minnesota

Dakota County Technical College, A
Mesabi Range Community and Technical College, A
Northland Community and Technical College-Thief
  River Falls, A
Rasmussen College Mankato, A
Riverland Community College, A

Missouri

Metropolitan Community College-Business &
  Technology College, A

Montana

University of Great Falls, B

New York

The College of Westchester, A
Genesee Community College, A

North Carolina

Carteret Community College, A

Ohio

ETI Technical College of Niles, A
Gallipolis Career College, A
Marion Technical College, A
Stark State College of Technology, A

Oklahoma

Tulsa Community College, A

Pennsylvania

Duquesne University, B
Laurel Business Institute, A

South Dakota

Dakota Wesleyan University, B
Kilian Community College, A
Mitchell Technical Institute, A
Southeast Technical Institute, A

Tennessee

Pellissippi State Technical Community College, A

Texas

El Paso Community College, A
Laredo Community College, A
McMurry University, B
Texas State Technical College Harlingen, A

Utah

Neumont University, B

Vermont

Champlain College, B

Washington

Columbia Basin College, A
Eastern Washington University, B

Olympic College, A

Wyoming

Sheridan College-Sheridan and Gillette, A

Ontario

Carleton University, B
University of Windsor, B

COMPUTER SOFTWARE ENGINEERING

Alabama

Auburn University, B

Arizona

Embry-Riddle Aeronautical University, B

California

Mt. San Jacinto College, A
National University, B
Notre Dame de Namur University, B

Connecticut

Fairfield University, B

Florida

Embry-Riddle Aeronautical University, B
Florida Community College at Jacksonville, A
Florida Institute of Technology, B
Florida State University, B
Lake City Community College, A
Seminole Community College, A

Illinois

Westwood College-Chicago Du Page, A
Westwood College-Chicago O'Hare Airport, A

Indiana

Rose-Hulman Institute of Technology, B
Vincennes University, A

Kentucky

Daymar College (Owensboro), A

Michigan

Michigan Technological University, B

Mississippi

Mississippi State University, B

Missouri

Grantham University, AB

New Jersey

Monmouth University, B

New York

Clarkson University, B
Rochester Institute of Technology, B
Tompkins Cortland Community College, A

Ohio

ETI Technical College of Niles, A
Sinclair Community College, A
Stark State College of Technology, A

Oklahoma

Tulsa Community College, A

Pennsylvania

Allegheny College, B
The Pennsylvania State University at Erie, The
  Behrend College, B

Robert Morris University, B

South Carolina

Claflin University, B

South Dakota

South Dakota State University, B
Southeast Technical Institute, A

Texas

University of Houston-Clear Lake, B
The University of Texas at Arlington, B
The University of Texas at Dallas, B

Vermont

Champlain College, B
Vermont Technical College, AB

Wisconsin

Carroll College, B
Milwaukee School of Engineering, B
University of Wisconsin-Platteville, B

British Columbia

University of Victoria, B

Nova Scotia

Dalhousie University, B

Ontario

Brock University, B
University of Toronto, B
University of Waterloo, B
The University of Western Ontario, B
York University, B

Quebec

Université Laval, B

Saskatchewan

University of Regina, B

COMPUTER SOFTWARE TECHNOLOGY/TECHNICIAN

Arizona

ITT Technical Institute (Tempe), B
ITT Technical Institute (Tucson), B

Arkansas

ITT Technical Institute, B

California

ITT Technical Institute (Lathrop), A
ITT Technical Institute (Torrance), B

Colorado

Westwood College-Denver North, A

Florida

Brown Mackie College-Miami, A
Miami Dade College, A

Georgia

Brown Mackie College-Atlanta, A

Idaho

ITT Technical Institute, B

Indiana

Brown Mackie College-Fort Wayne, A
Brown Mackie College-Merrillville, A
Brown Mackie College-Michigan City, A
ITT Technical Institute (Indianapolis), B

ITT Technical Institute (Newburgh), B

Iowa

Iowa Lakes Community College, A

Kentucky

Brown Mackie College-Hopkinsville, A
Brown Mackie College-Northern Kentucky, A

Massachusetts

Middlesex Community College, A

Minnesota

Brown College, A
ITT Technical Institute, B

Missouri

ITT Technical Institute (Arnold), B

Nebraska

ITT Technical Institute, B

New Hampshire

University of New Hampshire, A

Ohio

Brown Mackie College-Akron, A
Brown Mackie College-Findlay, A

Tennessee

ITT Technical Institute (Knoxville), B
ITT Technical Institute (Nashville), B

Texas

Montgomery College, A

Utah

ITT Technical Institute, B

Virginia

ITT Technical Institute (Chantilly), B
ITT Technical Institute (Springfield), B

Wisconsin

ITT Technical Institute (Green Bay), B

COMPUTER SYSTEMS ANALYSIS/ANALYST

Alaska

University of Alaska Southeast, Sitka Campus, A

Arizona

Arizona State University at the Polytechnic
   Campus, B
Pima Community College, A
University of Advancing Technology, B

Arkansas

Arkansas Tech University, B

California

DeVry University (Fremont), B
DeVry University (Long Beach), B
DeVry University (Pomona), B
DeVry University (West Hills), B
Heald College-Stockton, A

Colorado

DeVry University (Colorado Springs), B
University of Denver, B

Florida

Brevard Community College, A
DeVry University (Orlando), B
Florida Community College at Jacksonville, A
Gulf Coast College, A
Keiser College (Tallahassee), A

University of Miami, B

Georgia

DeVry University (Alpharetta), B
DeVry University (Decatur), B

Illinois

DeVry University (Addison), B
DeVry University (Chicago), B
DeVry University (Tinley Park), B

Iowa

St. Ambrose University, B

Louisiana

Louisiana Technical College, A
Remington College-Lafayette Campus, A
University of Louisiana at Lafayette, B
University of Louisiana at Monroe, B

Maryland

Wor-Wic Community College, A

Michigan

Baker College of Flint, AB
Davenport University (Dearborn), AB

Minnesota

Metropolitan State University, B

Missouri

DeVry University (Kansas City), B
Linn State Technical College, A
Metropolitan Community College-Business &
   Technology College, A

Montana

Montana Tech of The University of Montana, B
University of Great Falls, B

New Hampshire

Granite State College, B
Hesser College, A

New Mexico

Central New Mexico Community College, A

New York

DeVry Institute of Technology, B
Pace University, B
Rochester Institute of Technology, B

North Carolina

Cape Fear Community College, A
Coastal Carolina Community College, A
James Sprunt Community College, A
Pitt Community College, A
Randolph Community College, A
Richmond Community College, A
South Piedmont Community College, A
Wayne Community College, A
Wilkes Community College, A

North Dakota

United Tribes Technical College, A
University of North Dakota, B

Ohio

Baldwin-Wallace College, B
DeVry University (Columbus), B
Kent State University, B
Miami University, B
Miami University Hamilton, B
The University of Akron, A

The University of Toledo, A

Oklahoma

Oklahoma Baptist University, B

Oregon

Southwestern Oregon Community College, A

Pennsylvania

Pennsylvania College of Technology, B
Shippensburg University of Pennsylvania, B

Puerto Rico

Inter American University of Puerto Rico, Bayamón
   Campus, B

Texas

Amarillo College, A
DeVry University (Irving), B
Lee College, A
University of Houston, B

Vermont

University of Vermont, B

Virginia

DeVry University (Arlington), B
Eastern Mennonite University, B

Washington

DeVry University (Federal Way), B
Lower Columbia College, A
Seattle Pacific University, B

Wisconsin

Lakeshore Technical College, A
Milwaukee Area Technical College, A
Waukesha County Technical College, A

Wyoming

Laramie County Community College, A

British Columbia

British Columbia Institute of Technology, AB
Thompson Rivers University, B
University College of the Fraser Valley, B

Nova Scotia

Mount Saint Vincent University, B

Quebec

HEC Montreal, B
Université du Québec àTrois-Rivières, B

COMPUTER SYSTEMS NETWORKING AND TELECOMMUNICATIONS

Alabama

Remington College-Mobile Campus, A
Virginia College at Huntsville, A

Alaska

Charter College, A

Arizona

Chaparral College, AB
Cochise College (Douglas), A
DeVry University (Phoenix), B
Glendale Community College, A
High-Tech Institute, A
ITT Technical Institute (Phoenix), B
ITT Technical Institute (Tempe), B
ITT Technical Institute (Tucson), B
Northland Pioneer College, A
Pima Community College, A

Arkansas

Arkansas State University-Beebe, A
ITT Technical Institute, B

University of Arkansas Community College at
   Batesville, A
University of Arkansas Community College at
   Morrilton, A

California

American River College, A
California State University, East Bay, B
Coleman College (La Mesa), AB
Cuesta College, A
Cypress College, A
DeVry University (Fremont), AB
DeVry University (Long Beach), AB
DeVry University (Pomona), AB
DeVry University (West Hills), AB
Foundation College, A
Heald College-San Francisco, A
ITT Technical Institute (Anaheim), B
ITT Technical Institute (Lathrop), B
ITT Technical Institute (Rancho Cordova), B
ITT Technical Institute (Sylmar), B
ITT Technical Institute (Torrance), B
Los Angeles City College, A
Mt. Sierra College, B
Platt College (Ontario), A
San Joaquin Valley College, A
Westwood College-Anaheim, AB
Westwood College-Inland Empire, AB
Westwood College-Long Beach, AB
Westwood College-Los Angeles, AB

Colorado

Arapahoe Community College, A
CollegeAmerica-Fort Collins, A
Colorado Mountain College, A
DeVry University (Colorado Springs), AB
DeVry University (Westminster), AB
IntelliTec College (Grand Junction), A
National American University (Denver), AB
Remington College-Colorado Springs Campus, A
Trinidad State Junior College, A
Westwood College-Denver North, AB
Westwood College-Denver South, AB

Connecticut

Quinebaug Valley Community College, A

District of Columbia

Strayer University, AB

Florida

Brevard Community College, A
College of Business and Technology, A
Daytona Beach Community College, A
DeVry University (Miramar), AB
DeVry University (Orlando), AB
Florida Community College at Jacksonville, A
Florida National College, A
Florida Technical College (Orlando), A
Hillsborough Community College, A
ITT Technical Institute (Lake Mary), B
ITT Technical Institute (Miami), B
Keiser College (Miami), A
New England Institute of Technology at Palm
   Beach, A
Okaloosa-Walton College, A
Pasco-Hernando Community College, A
St. Petersburg College, A
Seminole Community College, A
Tallahassee Community College, A

Georgia

Altamaha Technical College, A
Appalachian Technical College, A
Athens Technical College, A
Augusta Technical College, A
Central Georgia Technical College, A
Chattahoochee Technical College, A
Columbus Technical College, A
DeKalb Technical College, A
DeVry University (Alpharetta), AB
DeVry University (Decatur), AB
East Central Technical College, A
Flint River Technical College, A
Griffin Technical College, A

Gwinnett Technical College, A
Lanier Technical College, A
Middle Georgia Technical College, A
Moultrie Technical College, A
North Georgia Technical College, A
North Metro Technical College, A
Northwestern Technical College, A
Ogeechee Technical College, A
Okefenokee Technical College, A
Sandersville Technical College, A
Savannah Technical College, A
South Georgia Technical College, A
Southeastern Technical College, A
Southwest Georgia Technical College, A
Swainsboro Technical College, A
Valdosta Technical College, A
West Central Technical College, A
West Georgia Technical College, A
Westwood College-Atlanta Midtown, AB
Westwood College-Atlanta Northlake, AB

Idaho

Boise State University, B
Eastern Idaho Technical College, A
ITT Technical Institute, B

Illinois

Aurora University, B
Black Hawk College, A
College of Lake County, A
DePaul University, B
DeVry University (Addison), AB
DeVry University (Chicago), AB
DeVry University (Tinley Park), AB
Heartland Community College, A
Illinois Valley Community College, A
Joliet Junior College, A
Lake Land College, A
Lincoln Land Community College, A
Moraine Valley Community College, A
Parkland College, A
Robert Morris College, A
Roosevelt University, B
Triton College, A
Westwood College-Chicago Du Page, AB
Westwood College-Chicago Loop Campus, AB
Westwood College-Chicago O'Hare Airport, AB
Westwood College-Chicago River Oaks, AB

Indiana

Ancilla College, A
ITT Technical Institute (Fort Wayne), B
ITT Technical Institute (Indianapolis), B
ITT Technical Institute (Newburgh), B
Vincennes University, A
Vincennes University Jasper Campus, A

Iowa

AIB College of Business, A
Ellsworth Community College, A
Hamilton College (Cedar Falls), A
Hawkeye Community College, A
Iowa Lakes Community College, A
Northwest Iowa Community College, A
St. Ambrose University, B

Kansas

Allen County Community College, A
Barton County Community College, A
Garden City Community College, A
Johnson County Community College, A
Manhattan Area Technical College, A
Pratt Community College, A

Kentucky

Brown Mackie College-Louisville, A
Daymar College (Louisville), A
Daymar College (Owensboro), A
Henderson Community College, A
Lexington Community College, A
Louisville Technical Institute, A

Louisiana

Louisiana Technical College, A
Remington College-Lafayette Campus, A

Remington College-New Orleans Campus, A

Maine

Kennebec Valley Community College, A
York County Community College, A

Maryland

Howard Community College, A
ITT Technical Institute, B
TESST College of Technology (Towson), A

Massachusetts

Bunker Hill Community College, A
Cape Cod Community College, A
Northern Essex Community College, A

Michigan

Alpena Community College, A
Baker College of Allen Park, A
Baker College of Flint, A
Michigan Technological University, B
Mott Community College, A
North Central Michigan College, A
Northern Michigan University, B

Minnesota

Academy College, A
Alexandria Technical College, A
Anoka-Ramsey Community College, A
Anoka-Ramsey Community College, Cambridge
   Campus, A
Brown College, A
Capella University, B
Dakota County Technical College, A
Duluth Business University, A
Globe College, A
Hennepin Technical College, A
Herzing College, A
Hibbing Community College, A
Mesabi Range Community and Technical College, A
Minnesota School of Business, A
Minnesota School of Business-Brooklyn Center, A
Minnesota School of Business-Plymouth, A
Minnesota School of Business-Richfield, A
Minnesota School of Business-St. Cloud, A
Minnesota School of Business-Shakopee, A
Minnesota State Community and Technical
   College-Fergus Falls, A
Normandale Community College, A
Northland Community and Technical College-Thief
   River Falls, A
Northwest Technical College, A
Rasmussen College Mankato, A
Ridgewater College, A
Riverland Community College, A
St. Cloud Technical College, A

Mississippi

Mississippi Gulf Coast Community College, A
Virginia College at Jackson, A

Missouri

Crowder College, A
DeVry University (Kansas City), B
East Central College, A
ITT Technical Institute (Arnold), B
Jefferson College, A
Metropolitan Community College-Business &
   Technology College, A
Ozarks Technical Community College, A
Saint Charles Community College, A
St. Louis Community College at Forest Park, A
State Fair Community College, A
Vatterott College (St. Joseph), A

Montana

Montana State University-Great Falls College of
   Technology, A

University of Great Falls, B

Nebraska

ITT Technical Institute, B

New Hampshire

New Hampshire Technical Institute, A

New Jersey

Cumberland County College, A
DeVry University, AB
Gibbs College (Montclair), A
Kean University, B
Mercer County Community College, A
Middlesex County College, A
Salem Community College, A

New York

Adirondack Community College, A
The College of Westchester, A
Columbia-Greene Community College, A
Corning Community College, A
DeVry Institute of Technology, AB
Fiorello H. LaGuardia Community College of the
   City University of New York, A
Herkimer County Community College, A
Iona College, B
Island Drafting and Technical Institute, A
Jefferson Community College, A
Katharine Gibbs School (Melville), A
Nassau Community College, A
Onondaga Community College, A
Rochester Institute of Technology, B
Rockland Community College, A
Westchester Community College, A

North Carolina

Asheville-Buncombe Technical Community
   College, A
Beaufort County Community College, A
Caldwell Community College and Technical
   Institute, A
Cape Fear Community College, A
Carteret Community College, A
Catawba Valley Community College, A
Central Carolina Community College, A
Coastal Carolina Community College, A
Craven Community College, A
Guilford Technical Community College, A
Pitt Community College, A
Robeson Community College, A
South Piedmont Community College, A
Stanly Community College, A
Surry Community College, A
Wake Technical Community College, A
Wilkes Community College, A

North Dakota

Aakers Business College, A
Bismarck State College, A
Lake Region State College, A
Minot State University-Bottineau Campus, A

Ohio

Antonelli College, A
Baldwin-Wallace College, B
Bowling Green State University-Firelands College, A
Brown Mackie College-Akron, A
Brown Mackie College-North Canton, A
Clark State Community College, A
Davis College, A
DeVry University (Columbus), AB
Lakeland Community College, A
Lorain County Community College, A
Marion Technical College, A
North Central State College, A
Remington College-Cleveland West Campus, A
Sinclair Community College, A
Stark State College of Technology, A
Stautzenberger College, A
The University of Akron-Wayne College, A

The University of Findlay, B

Oklahoma

Northwestern Oklahoma State University, B
Tulsa Community College, A

Oregon

Clatsop Community College, A
ITT Technical Institute, B
Southwestern Oregon Community College, A

Pennsylvania

CHI Institute, A
Community College of Allegheny County, A
Delaware County Community College, A
Erie Business Center, Main, A
Harrisburg Area Community College, A
Laurel Business Institute, A
Luzerne County Community College, A
Montgomery County Community College, A
Northampton County Area Community College, A
Pace Institute, A
Pennsylvania College of Technology, AB
Thompson Institute, A
University of Pennsylvania, B
York Technical Institute, A

South Carolina

Midlands Technical College, A
Trident Technical College, A

South Dakota

Lake Area Technical Institute, A
Mitchell Technical Institute, A
Southeast Technical Institute, A

Tennessee

ITT Technical Institute (Knoxville), B
ITT Technical Institute (Memphis), B
ITT Technical Institute (Nashville), B
Nashville State Technical Community College, A
Northeast State Technical Community College, A
Pellissippi State Technical Community College, A
Remington College-Memphis Campus, A

Texas

Austin Community College, A
Blinn College, A
Coastal Bend College, A
College of the Mainland, A
Collin County Community College District, A
Del Mar College, A
DeVry University (Houston), B
DeVry University (Irving), AB
Eastfield College, A
El Paso Community College, A
Kilgore College, A
Lamar State College-Port Arthur, A
Laredo Community College, A
Montgomery College, A
Odessa College, A
Our Lady of the Lake University of San Antonio, B
St. Philip's College, A
Texas State Technical College Harlingen, A
Texas State Technical College West Texas, A
Tyler Junior College, A
University of Houston-Clear Lake, B
Victoria College, A
Westwood College-Dallas, A
Westwood College-Fort Worth, A
Westwood College-Houston South Campus, A

Utah

ITT Technical Institute, B
Mountain West College, A
Weber State University, B

Vermont

Champlain College, AB

Virginia

Blue Ridge Community College, A
DeVry University (Arlington), AB
ITT Technical Institute (Chantilly), B

Mountain Empire Community College, A
Patrick Henry Community College, A
Piedmont Virginia Community College, A
Stratford University, A

Washington

Bates Technical College, A
Centralia College, A
Clark College, A
Clover Park Technical College, A
Columbia Basin College, A
DeVry University (Federal Way), AB
Edmonds Community College, A
Highline Community College, A
ITT Technical Institute (Bothell), B
Lower Columbia College, A
North Seattle Community College, A
Olympic College, A
Tacoma Community College, A

West Virginia

Mountain State University, B
Potomac State College of West Virginia
    University, A

Wisconsin

Gateway Technical College, A
Herzing College, A
ITT Technical Institute (Green Bay), B
Moraine Park Technical College, A
University of Wisconsin-Stout, B
Waukesha County Technical College, A
Wisconsin Indianhead Technical College, A

Wyoming

Central Wyoming College, A
Sheridan College-Sheridan and Gillette, A

Ontario

University of Toronto, B
University of Windsor, B

COMPUTER TEACHER EDUCATION

Florida

Florida Institute of Technology, B

Illinois

Concordia University, B

Iowa

Buena Vista University, B
Dordt College, B

Kansas

Central Christian College of Kansas, A

Louisiana

Southern University and Agricultural and Mechanical
    College, B

Michigan

Alma College, B
Baker College of Flint, A
Central Michigan University, B
Eastern Michigan University, B
Michigan Technological University, B

Minnesota

Pillsbury Baptist Bible College, B

Nebraska

Concordia University, B
Union College, B

University of Nebraska-Lincoln, B

New Hampshire

Keene State College, B

New York

Long Island University, Brooklyn Campus, B
Utica College, B

Ohio

Capital University, B
The University of Akron, B
Wright State University, B

Pennsylvania

Immaculata University, B

Puerto Rico

Pontifical Catholic University of Puerto Rico, B

South Dakota

Dakota State University, B
South Dakota State University, B

Texas

Baylor University, B
Hardin-Simmons University, B
University of North Texas, B

Virginia

Liberty University, B

Washington

Eastern Washington University, B

Wisconsin

University of Wisconsin-River Falls, B
Viterbo University, B

Quebec

Bishop's University, B

COMPUTER TECHNOLOGY/COMPUTER SYSTEMS TECHNOLOGY

Alaska

Charter College, A

Arizona

Collins College: A School of Design and
    Technology, A
High-Tech Institute, A
Pima Community College, A

Arkansas

Arkansas State University-Beebe, A

California

Foundation College, A
MTI College of Business and Technology, A

Colorado

DeVry University (Westminster), AB

Florida

Miami Dade College, A
Pasco-Hernando Community College, A
Remington College-Tampa Campus, A
University of Central Florida, B

Georgia

Dalton State College, A
Okefenokee Technical College, A

Iowa

Vatterott College, AB

Kansas

Manhattan Area Technical College, A
Southwestern College, B

Kentucky

Eastern Kentucky University, A
Louisville Technical Institute, A

Madisonville Community College, A

Louisiana

ITI Technical College, A

Maine

Eastern Maine Community College, A

Maryland

Montgomery College, A
TESST College of Technology (Towson), A

Massachusetts

Mount Wachusett Community College, A
Quinsigamond Community College, A

Michigan

Oakland Community College, A
Schoolcraft College, A
Wayne State University, B

Minnesota

Alexandria Technical College, A
Anoka Technical College, A
Lake Superior College, A

Missouri

Southeast Missouri State University, A
Vatterott College (St. Joseph), A

Nevada

DeVry University, A

New York

Corning Community College, A
Erie Community College, South Campus, A
Island Drafting and Technical Institute, A
State University of New York College of Agriculture
    and Technology at Cobleskill, A

North Carolina

Cape Fear Community College, A
ECPI Technical College, A
Stanly Community College, A

Ohio

Lorain County Community College, A
Miami University Hamilton, A

Oregon

Clackamas Community College, A

Pennsylvania

Community College of Allegheny County, A
Delaware County Community College, A
Lehigh Carbon Community College, A
Luzerne County Community College, A
Peirce College, A
Pennsylvania College of Technology, A

Rhode Island

New England Institute of Technology, A

South Carolina

Bob Jones University, B

South Dakota

Mitchell Technical Institute, A
Southeast Technical Institute, A

Tennessee

Electronic Computer Programming College, A

Texas

Brazosport College, A
MTI College of Business and Technology (Houston)
    , A
Prairie View A&M University, B
St. Philip's College, A
Texas State Technical College Harlingen, A

Texas State Technical College Waco, A

Virginia

ECPI Technical College (Glen Allen), A
ECPI Technical College (Richmond), A
ECPI Technical College (Roanoke), A

Washington

Bates Technical College, A
Edmonds Community College, A
Lower Columbia College, A
Skagit Valley College, A
Walla Walla Community College, A

Wyoming

Central Wyoming College, A

British Columbia

Thompson Rivers University, A

COMPUTER TYPOGRAPHY AND COMPOSITION EQUIPMENT OPERATOR

Alabama

Faulkner University, A
Northeast Alabama Community College, A
Northwest-Shoals Community College, A

Arizona

Paradise Valley Community College, A
South Mountain Community College, A

Arkansas

University of Arkansas Community College at
    Morrilton, A

California

Chabot College, A
Chaffey College, A
College of the Desert, A
College of the Redwoods, A
College of the Sequoias, A
Fresno City College, A
Laney College, A
Long Beach City College, A
Merritt College, A
Monterey Peninsula College, A
Ohlone College, A
Orange Coast College, A
Pasadena City College, A
Saddleback College, A

Colorado

Lamar Community College, A

Connecticut

Gateway Community College, A
Housatonic Community College, A
Three Rivers Community College, A

Florida

Daytona Beach Community College, A
Indian River Community College, A
St. Johns River Community College, A

Georgia

Abraham Baldwin Agricultural College, A

Illinois

College of DuPage, A
Elgin Community College, A
Lincoln College, A
Lincoln College-Normal, A
MacCormac College, A
Triton College, A

William Rainey Harper College, A

Indiana

Calumet College of Saint Joseph, A

Iowa

Western Iowa Tech Community College, A

Kansas

Brown Mackie College-Kansas City, A
Pratt Community College, A

Kentucky

Hazard Community and Technical College, A

Louisiana

McNeese State University, A

Maryland

Baltimore Hebrew University, AB
Prince George's Community College, A

Massachusetts

Holyoke Community College, A
Northern Essex Community College, A

Michigan

Baker College of Auburn Hills, A
Baker College of Cadillac, A
Baker College of Clinton Township, A
Baker College of Flint, A
Baker College of Jackson, A
Davenport University (Midland), A
Gogebic Community College, A
Lansing Community College, A
St. Clair County Community College, A
Washtenaw Community College, A

Minnesota

Minnesota State College-Southeast Technical, A
Rasmussen College Eagan, A
Rasmussen College Mankato, A

Missouri

Longview Community College, A

Montana

Flathead Valley Community College, A

Nevada

Community College of Southern Nevada, A

New Jersey

Bergen Community College, A
Camden County College, A
Cumberland County College, A

New Mexico

Clovis Community College, A
Doña Ana Branch Community College, A
New Mexico Junior College, A
University of New Mexico-Valencia Campus, A

New York

The College of Westchester, A
Fulton-Montgomery Community College, A
Jefferson Community College, A
Onondaga Community College, A
State University of New York College of Agriculture
    and Technology at Morrisville, A
State University of New York College of Technology
    at Alfred, A

North Carolina

Durham Technical Community College, A

Ohio

Cuyahoga Community College, A
David N. Myers University, B
The University of Toledo, A

Wright State University, Lake Campus, A

Oklahoma

Northeastern Oklahoma Agricultural and Mechanical
    College, A

Pennsylvania

CHI Institute, A
Community College of Beaver County, A

South Carolina

Technical College of the Lowcountry, A

Texas

Del Mar College, A
Hill College of the Hill Junior College District, A
Kingwood College, A
Paris Junior College, A
South Texas College, A
Texas Southmost College, A

Virginia

ECPI College of Technology (Newport News), A
ECPI College of Technology (Virginia Beach), A
ECPI Technical College (Richmond), A
ECPI Technical College (Roanoke), A
New River Community College, A

Washington

Highline Community College, A
Pierce College, A
Seattle Central Community College, A
Spokane Community College, A

West Virginia

West Virginia Junior College (Charleston), A

Wisconsin

Fox Valley Technical College, A
Madison Area Technical College, A

CONCRETE FINISHING/CONCRETE FINISHER

Minnesota

Dakota County Technical College, A

CONDENSED MATTER PHYSICS

Iowa

Iowa State University of Science and
    Technology, MD

New Jersey

Rutgers, The State University of New Jersey, New
    Brunswick/Piscataway, MD

Ohio

Cleveland State University, M

West Virginia

West Virginia University, MD

Alberta

University of Alberta, MD

British Columbia

University of Victoria, MD

Newfoundland and Labrador

Memorial University of Newfoundland, M

CONDUCTING

California

Bethesda Christian University, B

Loyola Marymount University, B

Florida
University of Miami, B

Michigan
Calvin College, B

New Jersey
Westminster Choir College of Rider University, B

New York
Mannes College The New School for Music, B

Ohio
Ohio University, B

Pennsylvania
Temple University, B

Texas
Sam Houston State University, B

Manitoba
Canadian Mennonite University, B

CONFLICT RESOLUTION AND MEDIATION/PEACE STUDIES

California
California State University, Dominguez Hills, MO
Fresno Pacific University, M
John F. Kennedy University, O
Pepperdine University, M
Touro University International, M
University of San Diego, M

Colorado
Jones International University, M
Regis University, O

District of Columbia
American University, M

Florida
Nova Southeastern University, MDO

Georgia
Brenau University, O
Kennesaw State University, M

Hawaii
Chaminade University of Honolulu, M

Indiana
University of Notre Dame, M

Kentucky
Sullivan University, M

Maryland
University of Baltimore, M

Massachusetts
Brandeis University, M
Lesley University, M
Tufts University, MDO
University of Massachusetts Boston, MO

Michigan
Wayne State University, MO

Missouri
University of Missouri-Columbia, M
University of Missouri-St. Louis, M

New Jersey
Montclair State University, M

New York
Cornell University, MD

Ohio
Antioch University McGregor, M

Oregon
Portland State University, M

Pennsylvania
Arcadia University, M
Duquesne University, O

South Carolina
Columbia College, MO

Texas
Abilene Christian University, O
Dallas Baptist University, M
St. Edward's University, O

Virginia
Eastern Mennonite University, MO
George Mason University, MD

British Columbia
Royal Roads University, M
University of Victoria, M

Quebec
Université de Sherbrooke, MO

CONSERVATION BIOLOGY

Arizona
Arizona State University, BMD

California
California State University, Sacramento, B
San Francisco State University, M

Florida
University of Central Florida, DO

Hawaii
University of Hawaii at Manoa, MD

Maine
University of Maine at Machias, B

Maryland
Frostburg State University, M
University of Maryland, College Park, M

Michigan
Central Michigan University, M

Minnesota
University of Minnesota, Twin Cities Campus, MD

Missouri
University of Missouri-St. Louis, O

Nevada
University of Nevada, Reno, D

New York
State University of New York College of
    Environmental Science and Forestry, MD
University at Albany, State University of New
    York, M

North Dakota
North Dakota State University, MD

Oklahoma
St. Gregory's University, B

Pennsylvania
Philadelphia University, B

Utah
Brigham Young University, B

Vermont
Sterling College, B

Wisconsin
University of Wisconsin-Madison, M

Alberta
University of Alberta, MD

CONSTRUCTION ENGINEERING

Arizona
Arizona State University, B

Arkansas
John Brown University, B

California
California State University, Long Beach, B
National University, B
University of Southern California, B

Illinois
Bradley University, B

Indiana
Purdue University, B

Michigan
Andrews University, B
Michigan Technological University, B
Western Michigan University, B

Nevada
University of Nevada, Las Vegas, B

New York
Clarkson University, B
State University of New York College of
    Environmental Science and Forestry, B
State University of New York College of Technology
    at Alfred, AB

North Carolina
North Carolina State University, B

North Dakota
North Dakota State University, B

Ohio
University of Cincinnati, B

Oregon
Oregon State University, B

Texas
Texas A&M University-Commerce, B

Alberta
University of Alberta, B

New Brunswick
University of New Brunswick Fredericton, B

Quebec
Universite du Quebec, Ecole de technologie
    superieure, B

CONSTRUCTION ENGINEERING AND MANAGEMENT

Alabama
Auburn University, MD

Arizona
Arizona State University, M

California
University of Southern California, M

Colorado
Colorado State University, M
University of Colorado at Boulder, MD

University of Denver, M

Connecticut

Central Connecticut State University, M

District of Columbia

The Catholic University of America, MD

Florida

Florida International University, M
University of Central Florida, O
University of Florida, MD

Georgia

Georgia Institute of Technology, MD
Southern Polytechnic State University, M

Illinois

Bradley University, M
Illinois Institute of Technology, M

Kansas

University of Kansas, M

Massachusetts

Massachusetts Institute of Technology, D

Michigan

Lawrence Technological University, M
Michigan State University, MD
University of Michigan, M
Western Michigan University, M

Missouri

University of Missouri-Rolla, MD
Washington University in St. Louis, MO

Nevada

University of Nevada, Las Vegas, M

New Jersey

Stevens Institute of Technology, M

New York

New York University, MO
Polytechnic University, Brooklyn Campus, M
State University of New York College of
    Environmental Science and Forestry, MD

North Carolina

Western Carolina University, M

Ohio

Ohio University, M
University of Cincinnati, M

Oregon

Oregon State University, MD

Pennsylvania

Carnegie Mellon University, M

South Carolina

Clemson University, M

Texas

Texas A&M University, MD

Utah

Brigham Young University, M

Washington

University of Washington, MD
Washington State University, M

Wisconsin

Marquette University, MD

Alberta

University of Alberta, MD

New Brunswick

University of New Brunswick Fredericton, MD

Quebec

Concordia University, MDO

CONSTRUCTION ENGINEERING TECHNOLOGY/TECHNICIAN

Alabama

Community College of the Air Force, A
H. Councill Trenholm State Technical College, A
Jefferson State Community College, A
Tuskegee University, B
Wallace State Community College, A

Arizona

GateWay Community College, A
Northern Arizona University, B
Phoenix College, A
Pima Community College, A
Yavapai College, A

Arkansas

University of Arkansas at Little Rock, B

California

American River College, A
Antelope Valley College, A
Butte College, A
California State Polytechnic University, Pomona, B
California State University, Chico, B
California State University, Fresno, B
California State University, Long Beach, B
California State University, Sacramento, B
College of the Redwoods, A
College of San Mateo, A
College of the Sequoias, A
Compton Community College, A
Cosumnes River College (Sacramento), A
Cuesta College, A
De Anza College, A
Don Bosco Technical Institute, A
El Camino College, A
Feather River College, A
Fresno City College, A
Fullerton College, A
Hartnell College, A
Lassen Community College District, A
Los Angeles Pierce College, A
Los Angeles Trade-Technical College, A
Merced College, A
Orange Coast College, A
Palomar College, A
Pasadena City College, A
Riverside Community College District, A
Saddleback College, A
San Diego Mesa College, A
San Joaquin Delta College, A
San Jose City College, A
Santa Monica College, A
Shasta College, A
Sierra College, A
Southwestern College, A
Ventura College, A
Victor Valley College, A

Colorado

Colorado State University-Pueblo, B
Trinidad State Junior College, A

Connecticut

Norwalk Community College, A

Delaware

Delaware Technical & Community College, Terry
    Campus, A

Florida

Daytona Beach Community College, A
Florida Agricultural and Mechanical University, B

Florida Community College at Jacksonville, A
Florida International University, B
Gulf Coast Community College, A
Hillsborough Community College, A
Manatee Community College, A
Miami Dade College, A
Okaloosa-Walton College, A
Pensacola Junior College, A
St. Petersburg College, A
Santa Fe Community College, A
Seminole Community College, A
South Florida Community College, A
Tallahassee Community College, A
University of Florida, B
University of North Florida, B
Valencia Community College, A

Georgia

Georgia Southern University, B
Southern Polytechnic State University, B

Hawaii

Maui Community College, A

Idaho

Brigham Young University -Idaho, A

Illinois

College of Lake County, A
Joliet Junior College, A
Morrison Institute of Technology, A
Richland Community College, A
Rock Valley College, A
South Suburban College, A
Southern Illinois University Carbondale, B
Southern Illinois University Edwardsville, B
Southwestern Illinois College, A
Triton College, A

Indiana

Indiana University-Purdue University Fort Wayne, B
Purdue University Calumet, AB
Purdue University North Central, A
Vincennes University, A

Iowa

Iowa Lakes Community College, A
Kirkwood Community College, A
Northeast Iowa Community College, A
Southeastern Community College, North Campus, A

Kansas

Coffeyville Community College, A
Dodge City Community College, A
Highland Community College, A
Neosho County Community College, A
Pittsburg State University, B

Kentucky

Eastern Kentucky University, B

Louisiana

Louisiana Tech University, B
University of Louisiana at Monroe, B

Maine

Central Maine Community College, A
Eastern Maine Community College, A
Southern Maine Community College, A
University of Maine, B
Washington County Community College, A

Maryland

Cecil Community College, A
University of Maryland Eastern Shore, B

Massachusetts

Fitchburg State College, B
Wentworth Institute of Technology, AB

Michigan

Baker College of Owosso, A
Central Michigan University, B
Delta College, A

Eastern Michigan University, B
Ferris State University, A
Gogebic Community College, A
Henry Ford Community College, A
Lake Superior State University, A
Lansing Community College, A
Lawrence Technological University, A
Macomb Community College, A
Western Michigan University, B

Minnesota

Bemidji State University, B
Inver Hills Community College, A
Minnesota State University Moorhead, B
St. Cloud Technical College, A

Mississippi

Itawamba Community College, A
Southwest Mississippi Community College, A

Missouri

Crowder College, A
East Central College, A
Mineral Area College, A
North Central Missouri College, A
Ozarks Technical Community College, A
St. Louis Community College at Florissant Valley, A
Southeast Missouri State University, B
State Fair Community College, A
Three Rivers Community College, A

Montana

Blackfeet Community College, A
Flathead Valley Community College, A
Fort Peck Community College, A
Miles Community College, A
Montana State University, B

Nebraska

Central Community College-Hastings Campus, A
Metropolitan Community College, A
Mid-Plains Community College, A
Southeast Community College, Milford Campus, A
University of Nebraska-Lincoln, B
University of Nebraska at Omaha, B

Nevada

Community College of Southern Nevada, A
Truckee Meadows Community College, A
University of Nevada, Reno, B

New Hampshire

New Hampshire Community Technical College,
    Manchester/Stratham, A
University of New Hampshire, A

New Jersey

Fairleigh Dickinson University, Metropolitan
    Campus, B
Middlesex County College, A
Ocean County College, A
Raritan Valley Community College, A

New Mexico

New Mexico Junior College, A
Santa Fe Community College, A
University of New Mexico-Gallup, A
University of New Mexico-Valencia Campus, A
Western New Mexico University, A

New York

College of Staten Island of the City University of
    New York, A
Dutchess Community College, A
Farmingdale State University of New York, B
Fulton-Montgomery Community College, A
Hudson Valley Community College, A
Institute of Design and Construction, A
Monroe Community College, A
New York City College of Technology of the City
    University of New York, A
Onondaga Community College, A
Orange County Community College, A

State University of New York College of Agriculture
    and Technology at Morrisville, A
State University of New York College of Technology
    at Alfred, A
State University of New York College of Technology
    at Canton, A
State University of New York College of Technology
    at Delhi, A
Suffolk County Community College, A
TCI-The College of Technology, A
Tompkins Cortland Community College, A

North Carolina

Forsyth Technical Community College, A
McDowell Technical Community College, A
Roanoke-Chowan Community College, A
Rockingham Community College, A
Surry Community College, A
Vance-Granville Community College, A

North Dakota

Bismarck State College, A
Fort Berthold Community College, A
North Dakota State College of Science, A

Ohio

Bowling Green State University, B
The Ohio State University Agricultural Technical
    Institute, A
The University of Akron, A
University of Cincinnati, AB
The University of Toledo, AB
Wright State University, A

Oklahoma

Northeastern Oklahoma Agricultural and Mechanical
    College, A
Northern Oklahoma College, A
Oklahoma State University, Oklahoma City, A
Oklahoma State University, Okmulgee, A
Redlands Community College, A
Tulsa Community College, A

Oregon

Chemeketa Community College, A
Lane Community College, A
Portland Community College, A

Pennsylvania

Community College of Allegheny County, A
Community College of Philadelphia, A
Delaware County Community College, A
Harrisburg Area Community College, A
Lehigh Carbon Community College, A
New Castle School of Trades, A
Pennsylvania College of Technology, AB
Pennsylvania Highland Community College, A
Thaddeus Stevens College of Technology, A
The Williamson Free School of Mechanical
    Trades, A

Puerto Rico

University of Puerto Rico at Bayamón, A

Rhode Island

New England Institute of Technology, A

South Carolina

Greenville Technical College, A
Midlands Technical College, A
Piedmont Technical College, A
Technical College of the Lowcountry, A

South Dakota

South Dakota State University, B

Tennessee

Pellissippi State Technical Community College, A

Texas

Austin Community College, A
Brazosport College, A
Cisco Junior College, A
Houston Community College System, A

Laredo Community College, A
North Lake College, A
Odessa College, A
St. Philip's College, A
Sam Houston State University, B
Tarrant County College District, A
Texas A&M University, B
Texas Southern University, B
Texas Southmost College, A
Texas State Technical College Harlingen, A
Texas State University-San Marcos, B
University of Houston, B
University of North Texas, B

Utah

College of Eastern Utah, A
Snow College, A
Southern Utah University, B

Vermont

Vermont Technical College, A

Virginia

Hampton University, B
J. Sargeant Reynolds Community College, A
Norfolk State University, B

Washington

Clark College, A
Eastern Washington University, B
Edmonds Community College, A
Northwest Indian College, A
Spokane Community College, A

West Virginia

Fairmont State University, A

Wisconsin

Chippewa Valley Technical College, A
Milwaukee Area Technical College, A
University of Wisconsin-Stout, B

Wyoming

Casper College, A
Laramie County Community College, A

British Columbia

British Columbia Institute of Technology, A

CONSTRUCTION/HEAVY EQUIPMENT/EARTHMOVING EQUIPMENT OPERATION

Indiana

Ivy Tech Community College-Southwest, A
Ivy Tech Community College-Wabash Valley, A

Iowa

Northwest Iowa Community College, A

Texas

Brazosport College, A

CONSTRUCTION MANAGEMENT

California

California State University, Fresno, B

Florida

Everglades University (Boca Raton), B
Everglades University (Sarasota), B

Iowa

Iowa Lakes Community College, A
University of Northern Iowa, B

Louisiana

Louisiana State University and Agricultural and
    Mechanical College, B

Michigan

Eastern Michigan University, B
Lawrence Technological University, B

Michigan State University, B
Northern Michigan University, B
Oakland Community College, A

Minnesota

North Hennepin Community College, A

New York

Erie Community College, North Campus, A

North Carolina

North Carolina State University, B
Western Carolina University, B

North Dakota

North Dakota State University, B

Ohio

Columbus State Community College, A
The Ohio State University Agricultural Technical
    Institute, A

Oklahoma

Oklahoma State University, B

Oregon

Rogue Community College, A

South Carolina

Clemson University, B

Vermont

Vermont Technical College, A

Virginia

Virginia Polytechnic Institute and State University, B

Wisconsin

Milwaukee School of Engineering, B

CONSTRUCTION TRADES

Alaska

Ilisagvik College, A
University of Alaska Southeast, A

California

Palo Verde College, A

Colorado

Front Range Community College, A

Georgia

Ogeechee Technical College, A

Indiana

Ivy Tech Community College-East Central, A
Ivy Tech Community College-Kokomo, A
Ivy Tech Community College-Northeast, A
Ivy Tech Community College-Northwest, A
Ivy Tech Community College-Whitewater, A

Iowa

Iowa Lakes Community College, A

Michigan

Delta College, A
Hope College, B
Jackson Community College, A
Northern Michigan University, A

Missouri

East Central College, A

New Mexico

Central New Mexico Community College, A

New York

Erie Community College, North Campus, A

North Carolina

College of The Albemarle, A
Pitt Community College, A

North Dakota

United Tribes Technical College, A

Pennsylvania

Community College of Allegheny County, A
Triangle Tech, Inc.-Greensburg School, A

South Dakota

Mitchell Technical Institute, A

Utah

Utah Valley State College, A

Wisconsin

Moraine Park Technical College, A

Wyoming

Laramie County Community College, A

British Columbia

British Columbia Institute of Technology, A

CONSUMER ECONOMICS

Alabama

The University of Alabama, BM

Alaska

University of Alaska Southeast, A

Arizona

The University of Arizona, BMD

Colorado

Colorado State University, M

Delaware

University of Delaware, B

Florida

Florida State University, MD
University of Florida, M

Georgia

University of Georgia, BMD

Illinois

Eastern Illinois University, M
University of Illinois at Urbana-Champaign, MD

Indiana

Indiana State University, M
Purdue University, MD

Iowa

Iowa State University of Science and
    Technology, MD

Louisiana

Louisiana Tech University, B

Minnesota

Minnesota State University Mankato, M

Missouri

University of Missouri-Columbia, M

Nebraska

University of Nebraska-Lincoln, MD

New Jersey

Montclair State University, M

New York

Cornell University, BD

Ohio

The Ohio State University, MD

Pennsylvania

Indiana University of Pennsylvania, B

Rhode Island

University of Rhode Island, B

South Carolina

University of South Carolina, M

Tennessee

The University of Tennessee, BMD

Texas

Texas Tech University, MD

Utah

University of Utah, M
Utah State University, M

Vermont

University of Vermont, M

Virginia

Virginia Polytechnic Institute and State
    University, MD

Wisconsin

University of Wisconsin-Madison, MD

Wyoming

University of Wyoming, M

Ontario

University of Guelph, M

Quebec

Université Laval, O

CONSUMER MERCHANDISING/RETAILING MANAGEMENT

Alabama

Enterprise-Ozark Community College, A
University of Montevallo, B

Arizona

Glendale Community College, A

California

American River College, A
Cabrillo College, A
Chabot College, A
College of Marin, A
College of San Mateo, A
FIDM/The Fashion Institute of Design &
    Merchandising, Los Angeles Campus, A
FIDM/The Fashion Institute of Design &
    Merchandising, Orange County Campus, A
FIDM/The Fashion Institute of Design &
    Merchandising, San Diego Campus, A
FIDM/The Fashion Institute of Design &
    Merchandising, San Francisco Campus, A
Golden West College, A
Grossmont College, A
John F. Kennedy University, B
Long Beach City College, A
Los Angeles City College, A
Los Angeles Valley College, A
Merced College, A
Riverside Community College District, A
Saddleback College, A
San Francisco State University, B
West Los Angeles College, A

Colorado

Arapahoe Community College, A
Colorado Mountain College, Alpine Campus, A

Parks College (Denver), A

Connecticut

Gateway Community College, A
Three Rivers Community College, A

Delaware

Delaware Technical & Community College, Jack F. Owens Campus, A

Florida

Indian River Community College, A

Hawaii

Leeward Community College, A

Illinois

Elgin Community College, A
Governors State University, B
John A. Logan College, A
MacCormac College, A
Parkland College, A
South Suburban College, A
Triton College, A

Indiana

Indiana University Bloomington, B
International Business College (Fort Wayne), AB

Iowa

Des Moines Area Community College, A
Ellsworth Community College, A
Iowa Lakes Community College, A
Iowa Western Community College, A
Kirkwood Community College, A
Southwestern Community College, A

Kansas

Coffeyville Community College, A
Cowley County Community College and Area Vocational-Technical School, A
Fort Scott Community College, A
Garden City Community College, A

Kentucky

Eastern Kentucky University, B
Madisonville Community College, A
Sullivan University, A
West Kentucky Community and Technical College, A

Maryland

Anne Arundel Community College, A
Howard Community College, A

Massachusetts

Bay State College, A
Bristol Community College, A
Holyoke Community College, A
Lasell College, B
Middlesex Community College, A
Mount Ida College, AB
Newbury College, A
Quinsigamond Community College, A
Salem State College, B
Simmons College, B

Michigan

Baker College of Owosso, A
Delta College, A
Ferris State University, B
Lansing Community College, A
Madonna University, AB
Oakland Community College, A

Minnesota

Minnesota State College-Southeast Technical, A
Northland Community and Technical College-Thief River Falls, A
Ridgewater College, A
St. Cloud Technical College, A

Winona State University, B

Missouri

Fontbonne University, B
Jefferson College, A
Lindenwood University, B
Northwest Missouri State University, B

Montana

Miles Community College, A

Nevada

Community College of Southern Nevada, A

New Jersey

Bergen Community College, A
Gloucester County College, A
Middlesex County College, A
Passaic County Community College, A
Raritan Valley Community College, A
Sussex County Community College, A

New Mexico

Doña Ana Branch Community College, A

New York

Cayuga County Community College, A
Clinton Community College, A
Dutchess Community College, A
Finger Lakes Community College, A
Genesee Community College, A
Jefferson Community College, A
Monroe Community College, A
Niagara County Community College, A
North Country Community College, A
Orange County Community College, A
Suffolk County Community College, A
Sullivan County Community College, A
Syracuse University, B
Ulster County Community College, A
Westchester Community College, A

North Carolina

Central Piedmont Community College, A
Lenoir Community College, A

Ohio

Columbus State Community College, A
David N. Myers University, B
Edison State Community College, A
Hocking College, A
James A. Rhodes State College, A
Jefferson Community College, A
Lorain County Community College, A
Ohio University-Eastern, B
Sinclair Community College, A
Stark State College of Technology, A
The University of Toledo, A
Wright State University, Lake Campus, A

Oklahoma

East Central University, B
University of Central Oklahoma, B

Pennsylvania

Bucks County Community College, A
Central Pennsylvania College, A
Community College of Philadelphia, A
Harcum College, A
Harrisburg Area Community College, A
Laurel Business Institute, A
Newport Business Institute (Lower Burrell), A
Pennsylvania Highland Community College, A
Reading Area Community College, A
Westmoreland County Community College, A

Rhode Island

Johnson & Wales University, AB

Tennessee

Belmont University, B
Chattanooga State Technical Community College, A

University of Memphis, B

Texas

Austin Community College, A
Cisco Junior College, A
Del Mar College, A
Navarro College, A
South Plains College, A
Tarrant County College District, A
Texarkana College, A
Texas Southmost College, A

Virginia

Bryant and Stratton College, Virginia Beach, A
Central Virginia Community College, A

Washington

Centralia College, A
Everett Community College, A
Shoreline Community College, A
Spokane Falls Community College, A

West Virginia

Fairmont State University, A

Wisconsin

Fox Valley Technical College, A
Milwaukee Area Technical College, A
Western Technical College, A

Wyoming

Casper College, A

Quebec

HEC Montreal, B

CONSUMER SERVICES AND ADVOCACY

Arizona

Rio Salado College, A

California

City College of San Francisco, A
Los Angeles Mission College, A
Ohlone College, A
Saddleback College, A
San Diego City College, A

Missouri

College of the Ozarks, B

New York

State University of New York College at Oneonta, B
Syracuse University, B

North Carolina

Rockingham Community College, A

South Dakota

South Dakota State University, B

Tennessee

Carson-Newman College, B
Tennessee State University, B

Wisconsin

University of Wisconsin-Madison, B

Quebec

Université Laval, B

COOKING AND RELATED CULINARY ARTS

Alabama

Virginia College at Birmingham, A

California

The Art Institute of California-Los Angeles, AB
The Art Institute of California-Orange County, A

The Art Institute of California-San Diego, AB

Colorado

Pikes Peak Community College, A

Illinois

Kendall College, AB
Lexington College, AB

Iowa

Iowa Lakes Community College, A

Pennsylvania

The Art Institute of Pittsburgh, AB

Wisconsin

Milwaukee Area Technical College, A

CORPORATE AND ORGANIZATIONAL COMMUNICATION

Alaska

University of Alaska Fairbanks, M

Arkansas

University of Arkansas at Little Rock, M

California

University of Southern California, O

Colorado

Jones International University, M
University of Colorado at Boulder, M

Connecticut

Central Connecticut State University, M
University of Connecticut, D

District of Columbia

Howard University, MD

Florida

Barry University, M
Florida State University, M
Rollins College, M

Illinois

DePaul University, M
Illinois Institute of Technology, M
Loyola University Chicago, M
Northwestern University, M
Roosevelt University, M
Southern Illinois University Edwardsville, O

Iowa

Iowa State University of Science and Technology, D

Kentucky

Murray State University, M
Spalding University, M

Maryland

Bowie State University, MO
Towson University, M

Massachusetts

Emerson College, M
Regis College, M
Simmons College, M

Michigan

Central Michigan University, M
Wayne State University, M

Western Michigan University, M

Minnesota

University of St. Thomas, M

Missouri

Lindenwood University, M

New Jersey

Fairleigh Dickinson University, College at
   Florham, MO
Monmouth University, MO
Montclair State University, M
Seton Hall University, M

New York

Bernard M. Baruch College of the City University of
   New York, M
Canisius College, M
Fordham University, M
Manhattanville College, M
Marist College, M
Metropolitan College of New York, M
Syracuse University, M

North Carolina

North Carolina State University, M
Queens University of Charlotte, M

Ohio

Franklin University, M
John Carroll University, M
Marietta College, M

Oklahoma

Oklahoma City University, M

Oregon

Marylhurst University, M
University of Portland, M

Pennsylvania

La Salle University, M

South Carolina

College of Charleston, O

Virginia

Radford University, M

West Virginia

West Virginia University, M

Wisconsin

Concordia University Wisconsin, M
University of Wisconsin-Stevens Point, M
University of Wisconsin-Whitewater, M

British Columbia

Royal Roads University, M

Quebec

HEC Montreal, O

CORRECTIONS

Alabama

Jacksonville State University, B
Troy University, B

Arizona

Central Arizona College, A
Eastern Arizona College, A
Northland Pioneer College, A

Phoenix College, A

Arkansas

University of Arkansas at Pine Bluff, B

California

Antelope Valley College, A
Bakersfield College, A
California State University, East Bay, B
Chabot College, A
Chaffey College, A
College of Marin, A
College of the Sequoias, A
De Anza College, A
Fresno City College, A
Gavilan College, A
Grossmont College, A
Hartnell College, A
Los Angeles City College, A
Modesto Junior College, A
Moorpark College, A
Mt. San Antonio College, A
Napa Valley College, A
San Bernardino Valley College, A
San Diego Miramar College, A
San Joaquin Delta College, A
San Joaquin Valley College, A
Sierra College, A
Southwestern College, A
Yuba College, A

Colorado

Colorado Mountain College, Timberline Campus, A
Colorado State University-Pueblo, B
Northeastern Junior College, A
Pueblo Community College, A
Trinidad State Junior College, A

Connecticut

Three Rivers Community College, A
Tunxis Community College, A
University of New Haven, M

Delaware

Delaware Technical & Community College,
   Stanton/Wilmington Campus, A
Delaware Technical & Community College, Terry
   Campus, A

District of Columbia

University of the District of Columbia, A

Florida

Brevard Community College, A
Broward Community College, A
Daytona Beach Community College, A
Hillsborough Community College, A
Indian River Community College, A
Polk Community College, A
St. Petersburg College, A
Santa Fe Community College, A

Georgia

Macon State College, A

Guam

Guam Community College, A

Idaho

Lewis-Clark State College, B

Illinois

City Colleges of Chicago, Harold Washington
   College, A
College of DuPage, A
Elgin Community College, A
Heartland Community College, A
Illinois Eastern Community Colleges, Frontier
   Community College, A
Illinois Eastern Community Colleges, Lincoln Trail
   College, A
Illinois Eastern Community Colleges, Olney Central
   College, A

Illinois Eastern Community Colleges, Wabash Valley
  College, A
Joliet Junior College, A
Lake Land College, A
Lincoln College, A
Lincoln College-Normal, A
Moraine Valley Community College, A
Rend Lake College, A
Sauk Valley Community College, A
Southeastern Illinois College, A

Indiana

University of Indianapolis, AB
Vincennes University, A

Iowa

Des Moines Area Community College, A
Ellsworth Community College, A
Hawkeye Community College, A
Iowa Lakes Community College, A
Kirkwood Community College, A

Kansas

Cowley County Community College and Area
  Vocational-Technical School, A
Washburn University, AB

Kentucky

Eastern Kentucky University, ABM

Louisiana

Bossier Parish Community College, A
Tulane University, B

Maryland

Anne Arundel Community College, A
Baltimore City Community College, A
Chesapeake College, A

Massachusetts

Northeastern University, B
Westfield State College, B

Michigan

Alpena Community College, A
Baker College of Muskegon, A
Delta College, A
Gogebic Community College, A
Grand Rapids Community College, A
Henry Ford Community College, A
Jackson Community College, A
Kellogg Community College, A
Kirtland Community College, A
Lake Superior State University, AB
Lansing Community College, A
Marygrove College, A
Mid Michigan Community College, A
Montcalm Community College, A
Northern Michigan University, A
St. Clair County Community College, A
Schoolcraft College, A
Washtenaw Community College, A
West Shore Community College, A

Minnesota

Fond du Lac Tribal and Community College, A
Minnesota State Community and Technical
  College-Fergus Falls, A
Minnesota State University Mankato, B
Riverland Community College, A
Saint Mary's University of Minnesota, B
Winona State University, B

Mississippi

University of Southern Mississippi, M

Missouri

College of the Ozarks, B
Longview Community College, A
Mineral Area College, A
Penn Valley Community College, A
St. Louis Community College at Florissant Valley, A
St. Louis Community College at Meramec, A
Saint Louis University, B

Southeast Missouri State University, B

Montana

University of Great Falls, B

Nebraska

Northeast Community College, A

Nevada

Community College of Southern Nevada, A
Truckee Meadows Community College, A
Western Nevada Community College, A

New Hampshire

Hesser College, A

New Jersey

Atlantic Cape Community College, A
Cumberland County College, A
Mercer County Community College, A
Middlesex County College, A

New Mexico

Clovis Community College, A
University of New Mexico, B
University of New Mexico-Gallup, A

New York

Adirondack Community College, A
Broome Community College, A
Cayuga County Community College, A
Herkimer County Community College, A
John Jay College of Criminal Justice of the City
  University of New York, AB
Monroe Community College, A
State University of New York College at
  Brockport, B
State University of New York College of Technology
  at Canton, A
Sullivan County Community College, A
Westchester Community College, A

North Carolina

Halifax Community College, A
Vance-Granville Community College, A

Ohio

Belmont Technical College, A
Central Ohio Technical College, A
Clark State Community College, A
Columbus State Community College, A
Hocking College, A
James A. Rhodes State College, A
Jefferson Community College, A
Lakeland Community College, A
Lorain County Community College, A
Northwest State Community College, A
Sinclair Community College, A
Southern State Community College, A
Tiffin University, B
The University of Akron, B
The University of Toledo, A
Xavier University, A

Oklahoma

East Central University, B
Eastern Oklahoma State College, A
Langston University, B
Oklahoma City University, B
Oklahoma State University, M
Redlands Community College, A
Southwestern Oklahoma State University at
  Sayre, A
Tulsa Community College, A

Oregon

Clackamas Community College, A
Southwestern Oregon Community College, A
Western Oregon University, BM

Pennsylvania

Bucks County Community College, A
Community College of Allegheny County, A
Lehigh Carbon Community College, A

Mercyhurst College, B
Mount Aloysius College, M
University of Pittsburgh, B
York College of Pennsylvania, B

South Carolina

Coker College, B
Limestone College, B

Tennessee

Roane State Community College, A

Texas

Alvin Community College, A
Amarillo College, A
El Paso Community College, A
Hardin-Simmons University, B
Kilgore College, A
Lamar University, AB
Navarro College, A
Sam Houston State University, B
San Antonio College, A
Stephen F. Austin State University, B
Texas State University-San Marcos, B
Trinity Valley Community College, A
The University of Texas at Brownsville, B
The University of Texas-Pan American, B
Weatherford College, A
Western Texas College, A

Utah

Weber State University, AB

Virginia

Mountain Empire Community College, A
Wytheville Community College, A

Washington

Centralia College, A
Eastern Washington University, B
Grays Harbor College, A
Lower Columbia College, A
Spokane Community College, A
Walla Walla Community College, A

West Virginia

Bluefield State College, AB
Community & Technical College at West Virginia
  University Institute of Technology, A
New River Community and Technical College, A

Wisconsin

Gateway Technical College, A
Mid-State Technical College, A
Northeast Wisconsin Technical College, A

Wyoming

Casper College, A
Laramie County Community College, A

CORRECTIONS ADMINISTRATION

Florida

St. Petersburg College, A

Montana

University of Great Falls, B

CORRECTIONS AND CRIMINAL JUSTICE

Alabama

The University of Alabama at Birmingham, B

Alaska

University of Alaska Fairbanks, B

Arizona

University of Phoenix Online Campus, B

University of Phoenix-Southern Arizona Campus, B

Arkansas

Harding University, B

California

Reedley College, A
University of Phoenix-Bay Area Campus, B
University of Phoenix-Central Valley Campus, B
University of Phoenix-Sacramento Valley Campus, B
University of Phoenix-San Diego Campus, B
University of Phoenix-Southern California
  Campus, B
Westwood College-Anaheim, B
Westwood College-Inland Empire, B
Westwood College-Long Beach, B
Westwood College-Los Angeles, B

Colorado

University of Phoenix-Southern Colorado
  Campus, B
Westwood College-Denver North, B
Westwood College-Denver South, B

Florida

Bethune-Cookman College, B
Keiser College (Fort Lauderdale), A
Remington College-Pinellas Campus, A
University of Phoenix-Central Florida Campus, B
University of Phoenix-West Florida Campus, B

Georgia

Albany Technical College, A

Illinois

American InterContinental University Online, B
Westwood College-Chicago Du Page, B
Westwood College-Chicago O'Hare Airport, B
Westwood College-Chicago River Oaks, B

Michigan

Northwestern Michigan College, A
Oakland Community College, A
University of Michigan-Flint, B
University of Phoenix-West Michigan Campus, B

Missouri

University of Phoenix-St. Louis Campus, B

Montana

University of Great Falls, B

Nebraska

Chadron State College, B
Hastings College, B
Nebraska Indian Community College, A

New Hampshire

Granite State College, B

New York

Corning Community College, A
John Jay College of Criminal Justice of the City
  University of New York, B
Monroe College (New Rochelle), AB
Russell Sage College, B
State University of New York College at
  Brockport, B

North Carolina

Fayetteville Technical Community College, A

North Dakota

North Dakota State University, B

Oklahoma

University of Phoenix-Tulsa Campus, B

Pennsylvania

Mercyhurst College, B
University of Phoenix-Pittsburgh Campus, B

South Carolina

Bob Jones University, B
Limestone College, B

Texas

Brazosport College, A
Sam Houston State University, B

Utah

University of Phoenix-Utah Campus, B

Virginia

Averett University, B

Wisconsin

Moraine Park Technical College, A
Mount Mary College, B
Wisconsin Indianhead Technical College, A

COSMETOLOGY AND RELATED PERSONAL GROOMING ARTS

Maryland

Allegany College of Maryland, A

Ohio

Lorain County Community College, A

Pennsylvania

Community College of Allegheny County, A

Wisconsin

Milwaukee Area Technical College, A

COSMETOLOGY, BARBER/STYLING, AND NAIL INSTRUCTOR

Washington

Olympic College, A

Wisconsin

Moraine Park Technical College, A

COSMETOLOGY/ COSMETOLOGIST

Alabama

H. Councill Trenholm State Technical College, A
Lawson State Community College, A
Wallace State Community College, A

Arizona

Northland Pioneer College, A

Arkansas

Phillips Community College of the University of
  Arkansas, A

California

Allan Hancock College, A
Bakersfield College, A
Barstow College, A
Butte College, A
Cerritos College, A
Citrus College, A
College of San Mateo, A
College of the Sequoias, A
El Camino College, A
Fullerton College, A
Gavilan College, A
Glendale Community College, A
Golden West College, A
Laney College, A
Lassen Community College District, A
Los Angeles Trade-Technical College, A
MiraCosta College, A
Napa Valley College, A
Pasadena City College, A

Riverside Community College District, A
Sacramento City College, A
Saddleback College, A
San Diego City College, A
San Jose City College, A
Santa Ana College, A
Santa Barbara City College, A
Santa Monica College, A
Santiago Canyon College, A
Skyline College, A
Solano Community College, A
Yuba College, A

Colorado

Lamar Community College, A
Northeastern Junior College, A
Trinidad State Junior College, A

Florida

Daytona Beach Community College, A
Indian River Community College, A

Georgia

Georgia Southwestern State University, A
Waycross College, A

Hawaii

Honolulu Community College, A

Illinois

Carl Sandburg College, A
Gem City College, A
John A. Logan College, A
Lincoln College, A
Shawnee Community College, A

Indiana

Vincennes University, A

Iowa

Southeastern Community College, North Campus, A
Southeastern Community College, South
  Campus, A

Kansas

Cowley County Community College and Area
  Vocational-Technical School, A
Dodge City Community College, A
Fort Scott Community College, A
Garden City Community College, A
Independence Community College, A
Johnson County Community College, A

Kentucky

Somerset Community College, A

Massachusetts

Springfield Technical Community College, A

Michigan

Delta College, A
Kirtland Community College, A
Montcalm Community College, A
Oakland Community College, A

Minnesota

Century College, A
Minnesota State College-Southeast Technical, A
Minnesota State Community and Technical
  College-Fergus Falls, A
Northland Community and Technical College-Thief
  River Falls, A

Mississippi

Coahoma Community College, A
Copiah-Lincoln Community College, A
East Central Community College, A
East Mississippi Community College, A
Southwest Mississippi Community College, A

New Mexico

Central New Mexico Community College, A
Clovis Community College, A
New Mexico Junior College, A

University of New Mexico-Gallup, A

North Carolina

Bladen Community College, A
Blue Ridge Community College, A
Caldwell Community College and Technical Institute, A
Guilford Technical Community College, A
Haywood Community College, A
Isothermal Community College, A
James Sprunt Community College, A
Lenoir Community College, A
Martin Community College, A
McDowell Technical Community College, A
Nash Community College, A
Roanoke-Chowan Community College, A
Rockingham Community College, A
Sandhills Community College, A
Southeastern Community College, A
Southwestern Community College, A
Stanly Community College, A
Surry Community College, A
Vance-Granville Community College, A

Ohio

Lorain County Community College, A

Oregon

Mt. Hood Community College, A
Umpqua Community College, A

South Carolina

Bob Jones University, A

South Dakota

Lake Area Technical Institute, A

Texas

Central Texas College, A
Cisco Junior College, A
Coastal Bend College, A
Del Mar College, A
Frank Phillips College, A
Grayson County College, A
Hill College of the Hill Junior College District, A
Howard College, A
Lamar State College-Port Arthur, A
Lamar University, A
North Harris College, A
Northeast Texas Community College, A
Odessa College, A
Paris Junior College, A
South Plains College, A
Southwest Texas Junior College, A
Texarkana College, A
Trinity Valley Community College, A
Vernon College, A
Weatherford College, A

Utah

College of Eastern Utah, A
Salt Lake Community College, A

Washington

Everett Community College, A
Olympic College, A
Seattle Central Community College, A
Shoreline Community College, A
South Seattle Community College, A
Spokane Community College, A

Walla Walla Community College, A

Wisconsin

Milwaukee Area Technical College, A
Southwest Wisconsin Technical College, A

Wyoming

Eastern Wyoming College, A

COUNSELING PSYCHOLOGY

Alabama

Auburn University, MDO
Huntingdon College, B
Samford University, B
Southern Christian University, MP
University of North Alabama, B

Alaska

Alaska Pacific University, M

Arizona

Argosy University/Phoenix, M
Arizona State University, D
Northern Arizona University, D
Prescott College, M
Southwestern College, B

Arkansas

Central Baptist College, B
University of Central Arkansas, M

California

Antioch University Santa Barbara, M
Argosy University/Orange County, MD
Argosy University/San Francisco Bay Area, MD
California Baptist University, M
California Institute of Integral Studies, M
California State University, Bakersfield, M
California State University, Sacramento, M
California State University, San Bernardino, M
California State University, Stanislaus, M
Dominican University of California, M
Holy Names University, M
Hope International University, M
John F. Kennedy University, M
Mount St. Mary's College, M
National University, M
Notre Dame de Namur University, M
San Diego Christian College, B
San Francisco State University, M
San Jose State University, M
Santa Clara University, MO
Southern California Seminary, M
Stanford University, D
University of California, Santa Barbara, D
University of La Verne, M
University of San Francisco, MD
University of Southern California, MDO

Colorado

Colorado Christian University, M
Colorado State University, M
Naropa University, M
Regis University, M
University of Colorado at Denver and Health Sciences Center - Downtown Denver Campus, MO
University of Denver, MD
University of Northern Colorado, MD
Western State College of Colorado, B

Connecticut

University of Connecticut, MD

District of Columbia

Gallaudet University, M
Howard University, MDO
University of the District of Columbia, M

Florida

Argosy University/Sarasota, D
Carlos Albizu University, Miami Campus, M

Florida Atlantic University, MO
Florida State University, D
Nova Southeastern University, M
Palm Beach Atlantic University, M
Saint Leo University, M
St. Thomas University, M
Trinity College of Florida, B
University of Miami, D
University of North Florida, M

Georgia

Argosy University/Atlanta, M
Atlanta Christian College, B
Columbus State University, M
Fort Valley State University, M
Georgia State University, MDO
Paine College, B
Toccoa Falls College, B
University of Georgia, D
Valdosta State University, M

Hawaii

Chaminade University of Honolulu, M

Idaho

Idaho State University, O

Illinois

Argosy University/Chicago, MD
Argosy University/Schaumburg, MD
Concordia University, M
Governors State University, M
Lewis University, M
Loyola University Chicago, D
Northwestern University, BM
Saint Xavier University, BMO
Southern Illinois University Carbondale, MD
Trinity International University, M

Indiana

Ball State University, MD
Bethel College, M
Grace College, BM
Indiana State University, MD
Indiana Wesleyan University, M
Taylor University Fort Wayne, B
University of Notre Dame, D
University of Saint Francis, M
Valparaiso University, M

Iowa

Iowa State University of Science and Technology, D
Morningside College, B
The University of Iowa, D

Kansas

MidAmerica Nazarene University, M
Newman University, B
Ottawa University, M
University of Kansas, MD

Kentucky

Mid-Continent University, B
Morehead State University, M
University of Kentucky, MDO
University of Louisville, MD

Louisiana

Louisiana State University in Shreveport, M
Louisiana Tech University, D
Nicholls State University, M

Maryland

Bowie State University, M
Columbia Union College, B
Frostburg State University, M
Loyola College in Maryland, MO
University of Maryland, College Park, D

Massachusetts

Anna Maria College, M
Assumption College, MO
Boston College, MDO
Boston University, MD

Cambridge College, M
Eastern Nazarene College, M
Fitchburg State College, MO
Framingham State College, M
Lesley University, BMO
Northeastern University, MDO
Springfield College, MO
University of Massachusetts Boston, MO
Westfield State College, M

Michigan

Andrews University, D
Rochester College, B
Spring Arbor University, M
Western Michigan University, MD

Minnesota

Bethel University, MO
Crossroads College, B
Oak Hills Christian College, B
Saint Mary's University of Minnesota, MO
University of Minnesota, Twin Cities Campus, D
University of St. Thomas, MD

Mississippi

Mississippi College, M
William Carey College, M

Missouri

Avila University, M
Lindenwood University, M
Northwest Missouri State University, M
University of Missouri-Columbia, MDO
University of Missouri-Kansas City, MDO
Webster University, M

Montana

University of Great Falls, BM

Nebraska

Grace University, M
Wayne State College, B

Nevada

University of Nevada, Las Vegas, M

New Hampshire

New England College, M
Rivier College, M

New Jersey

Caldwell College, M
Centenary College, M
College of Saint Elizabeth, M
Georgian Court University, MO
Kean University, MO
Monmouth University, MO
New Jersey City University, M
Rowan University, M
Rutgers, The State University of New Jersey, New Brunswick/Piscataway, M
Seton Hall University, D

New Mexico

College of Santa Fe, B
New Mexico State University, MDO
University of Phoenix-New Mexico Campus, M

New York

Adelphi University, M
College of Mount Saint Vincent, O
The College of New Rochelle, M
Fordham University, D
Marist College, M
Medaille College, M
Mercy College, MO
New York Institute of Technology, M
New York University, D
St. John Fisher College, M
Schenectady County Community College, A
State University of New York at Oswego, MO

University at Albany, State University of New York, MDO

North Carolina

Gardner-Webb University, M
The University of North Carolina at Greensboro, MD

North Dakota

Jamestown College, B
University of North Dakota, MD

Ohio

Cleveland State University, M
Franciscan University of Steubenville, M
Heidelberg College, M
John Carroll University, MO
Kent State University, M
The Ohio State University, D
The University of Akron, MD
Walsh University, M

Oklahoma

Northeastern State University, M
Northwestern Oklahoma State University, M
Southern Nazarene University, M
University of Central Oklahoma, M
University of Oklahoma, D

Oregon

George Fox University, M
Lewis & Clark College, MO
Marylhurst University, O
Oregon Institute of Technology, B

Pennsylvania

Arcadia University, M
Carlow University, M
Chatham College, BM
Chestnut Hill College, MO
Eastern University, M
Gannon University, D
Geneva College, M
Holy Family University, M
Immaculata University, MO
Kutztown University of Pennsylvania, BM
La Salle University, M
Lehigh University, MDO
Marywood University, BM
Millersville University of Pennsylvania, M
The Pennsylvania State University University Park Campus, D
Rosemont College, M
Temple University, MD
University of Pennsylvania, M
The University of Scranton, O

Puerto Rico

Inter American University of Puerto Rico, San Germán Campus, MD

Rhode Island

Salve Regina University, MO
University of Rhode Island, M

South Carolina

Bob Jones University, B
Coker College, B

South Dakota

Kilian Community College, A

Tennessee

Argosy University/Nashville, M
Lee University, M
Tennessee State University, D
Tennessee Temple University, B
Trevecca Nazarene University, M
University of Memphis, D
The University of Tennessee, M

Texas

Abilene Christian University, M
Amberton University, M
Argosy University/Dallas, M

Dallas Baptist University, M
Houston Baptist University, M
Our Lady of the Lake University of San Antonio, MD
St. Edward's University, M
St. Mary's University of San Antonio, DO
Sam Houston State University, B
Southern Methodist University, M
Southwestern Assemblies of God University, MO
Tarleton State University, B
Texas A&M International University, M
Texas A&M University, D
Texas A&M University-Commerce, MD
Texas A&M University-Texarkana, M
Texas Tech University, MD
Texas Wesleyan University, B
Texas Woman's University, MD
University of Houston, MD
University of Mary Hardin-Baylor, M
University of North Texas, MD
The University of Texas at Austin, D
The University of Texas at Tyler, M

Utah

Brigham Young University, MDO
University of Phoenix-Utah Campus, M
Utah State University, D

Vermont

College of St. Joseph, M
Goddard College, M
University of Vermont, M

Virginia

Argosy University/Washington D.C., MD
James Madison University, MO
Liberty University, MD
Marymount University, MO
Radford University, M
Regent University, MDO
Virginia Commonwealth University, MDO

Washington

Argosy University/Seattle, M
Central Washington University, M
City University, M
Eastern Washington University, M
Gonzaga University, M
Saint Martin's University, M
Walla Walla College, M
Washington State University, MD
Western Washington University, M

West Virginia

West Virginia University, MD

Wisconsin

University of Wisconsin-Madison, D
University of Wisconsin-Stout, M

Alberta

Rocky Mountain College, B
University of Alberta, MD
University of Calgary, MD
University of Lethbridge, BM

British Columbia

Trinity Western University, M
The University of British Columbia, MD

Quebec

McGill University, MD

COUNSELOR EDUCATION/SCHOOL COUNSELING AND GUIDANCE SERVICES

Alabama

Alabama State University, MO
Auburn University, MDO
Auburn University Montgomery, MO
Jacksonville State University, M

Troy University, MO
The University of Alabama, MDO
The University of Alabama at Birmingham, M
University of Montevallo, M
University of North Alabama, M
University of South Alabama, MO
The University of West Alabama, M

Alaska

University of Alaska Anchorage, M
University of Alaska Fairbanks, M

Arizona

Arizona State University, M
Northern Arizona University, BM
University of Phoenix-Phoenix Campus, MO
University of Phoenix-Southern Arizona Campus, M

Arkansas

Arkansas State University, MO
Harding University, BM
Henderson State University, M
John Brown University, M
Southern Arkansas University-Magnolia, M
University of Arkansas, MDO
University of Arkansas at Little Rock, M
University of Central Arkansas, M

California

Azusa Pacific University, M
California Lutheran University, M
California Polytechnic State University, San Luis
   Obispo, M
California State Polytechnic University, Pomona, B
California State University, Bakersfield, M
California State University, Dominguez Hills, M
California State University, East Bay, M
California State University, Fresno, M
California State University, Fullerton, M
California State University, Long Beach, MO
California State University, Los Angeles, M
California State University, Northridge, MO
California State University, Sacramento, M
California State University, San Bernardino, M
California State University, Stanislaus, M
Chapman University, M
East Los Angeles College, A
Fresno Pacific University, M
La Sierra University, MO
Loyola Marymount University, M
National University, M
Saint Mary's College of California, M
San Diego State University, M
San Jose State University, M
Santa Clara University, M
Sonoma State University, M
University of La Verne, MO
University of San Diego, M
University of San Francisco, M

Colorado

Adams State College, M
Mesa State College, B
University of Colorado at Colorado Springs, M
University of Colorado at Denver and Health
   Sciences Center - Downtown Denver
   Campus, MO
University of Northern Colorado, MD
University of Phoenix-Denver Campus, M
University of Phoenix-Southern Colorado
   Campus, M

Connecticut

Central Connecticut State University, MO
Fairfield University, MO
Saint Joseph College, MO
Southern Connecticut State University, MO
University of Hartford, MO

Western Connecticut State University, M

Delaware

University of Delaware, M
Wilmington College, M

District of Columbia

The Catholic University of America, M
Gallaudet University, M
The George Washington University, MDO
Howard University, BMO
Trinity (Washington) University, M
University of the District of Columbia, M

Florida

Argosy University/Sarasota, M
Barry University, MDO
Florida Agricultural and Mechanical University, M
Florida Atlantic University, MO
Florida Gulf Coast University, M
Florida International University, M
Florida State University, MDO
Rollins College, M
St. Thomas University, MO
Stetson University, M
University of Central Florida, MD
University of Florida, MDO
University of Miami, MO
University of North Florida, M
University of South Florida, M
University of West Florida, M

Georgia

Albany State University, M
Augusta State University, MO
Clark Atlanta University, MD
Columbus State University, MO
Fort Valley State University, MO
Georgia Southern University, MO
Georgia State University, MDO
University of Georgia, MD
University of West Georgia, MO
Valdosta State University, MO

Guam

University of Guam, M

Hawaii

University of Hawaii at Manoa, BM
University of Phoenix-Hawaii Campus, M

Idaho

Boise State University, M
Idaho State University, MDO
Northwest Nazarene University, M
University of Idaho, MDO

Illinois

Chicago State University, M
Concordia University, MO
DePaul University, BM
Eastern Illinois University, M
Illinois State University, M
Lewis University, M
Loyola University Chicago, M
Northeastern Illinois University, M
Northern Illinois University, MD
Roosevelt University, M
Saint Xavier University, M
Southern Illinois University Carbondale, MD
University of Illinois at Urbana-Champaign, MDO
Western Illinois University, M

Indiana

Butler University, M
Indiana State University, MD
Indiana University Bloomington, MD
Indiana University-Purdue University Fort Wayne, M
Indiana University South Bend, M
Indiana University Southeast, M
Indiana Wesleyan University, M
Martin University, B
Purdue University, MD
Purdue University Calumet, M

University of Saint Francis, M

Iowa

Buena Vista University, BM
Drake University, M
Iowa State University of Science and Technology, M
The University of Iowa, MD
University of Northern Iowa, MD

Kansas

Emporia State University, M
Fort Hays State University, M
Kansas State University, MD
Pittsburg State University, M
Pratt Community College, A
Wichita State University, M

Kentucky

Eastern Kentucky University, M
Morehead State University, MO
Murray State University, MO
University of Louisville, MD
Western Kentucky University, MO

Louisiana

Louisiana State University and Agricultural and
   Mechanical College, MDO
Louisiana Tech University, M
Loyola University New Orleans, M
McNeese State University, M
Nicholls State University, M
Northwestern State University of Louisiana, MO
Our Lady of Holy Cross College, AM
Southeastern Louisiana University, M
Southern University and Agricultural and Mechanical
   College, M
University of Louisiana at Lafayette, M
University of Louisiana at Monroe, M
University of New Orleans, MDO
Xavier University of Louisiana, M

Maine

University of Maine, MDO
University of Southern Maine, MO

Maryland

Bowie State University, M
Frostburg State University, M
The Johns Hopkins University, MDO
Loyola College in Maryland, MO
McDaniel College, M
University of Maryland, College Park, MDO
University of Maryland Eastern Shore, M

Massachusetts

Boston University, MO
Bridgewater State College, MO
Fitchburg State College, MO
Northeastern University, M
Salem State College, M
Springfield College, MO
Suffolk University, MO
University of Massachusetts Amherst, MDO
University of Massachusetts Boston, MO
Westfield State College, B

Michigan

Central Michigan University, M
Eastern Michigan University, MO
Michigan State University, MD
Oakland University, MDO
Siena Heights University, MO
University of Detroit Mercy, M
Wayne State University, MDO
Western Michigan University, MD

Minnesota

Minnesota State University Mankato, M
Minnesota State University Moorhead, M
St. Cloud State University, BM
University of Minnesota, Twin Cities Campus, MDO

Winona State University, M

Mississippi

Alcorn State University, M
Delta State University, M
Jackson State University, MO
Mississippi College, MO
Mississippi State University, MDO
University of Mississippi, MDO

Missouri

Central Missouri State University, M
Lincoln University, M
Missouri State University, M
Northwest Missouri State University, BM
Saint Louis University, MDO
Southeast Missouri State University, MO
Stephens College, M
Truman State University, M
University of Missouri-St. Louis, MD

Montana

Montana State University-Billings, M
Montana State University-Northern, M
University of Great Falls, M
The University of Montana-Missoula, MDO

Nebraska

Chadron State College, M
Creighton University, M
Doane College, M
University of Nebraska at Kearney, MO
University of Nebraska at Omaha, M
Wayne State College, M

Nevada

University of Nevada, Reno, MDO
University of Phoenix-Nevada Campus, M

New Hampshire

Franklin Pierce College, B
Keene State College, BMO
Plymouth State University, M
Rivier College, M
University of New Hampshire, M

New Jersey

Caldwell College, M
The College of New Jersey, M
Kean University, MO
Montclair State University, M
Rider University, MO
Seton Hall University, M
William Paterson University of New Jersey, M

New Mexico

College of the Southwest, M
Eastern New Mexico University, M
New Mexico Highlands University, M
New Mexico State University, MDO
University of New Mexico, MD
Western New Mexico University, M

New York

Alfred University, M
Brooklyn College of the City University of New
  York, MO
Canisius College, M
The College of Saint Rose, M
Fordham University, MO
Hofstra University, MO
Hunter College of the City University of New
  York, M
Iona College, M
Lehman College of the City University of New
  York, M
Long Island University, Brentwood Campus, M
Long Island University, Brooklyn Campus, MO
Long Island University, C.W. Post Campus, M
Manhattan College, MO
Mercy College, M
New York Institute of Technology, M
New York University, MDO
Niagara University, MO

Queens College of the City University of New
  York, M
St. Bonaventure University, MO
St. John's University, BMO
St. Lawrence University, MO
State University of New York at Buffalo, MDO
State University of New York College at
  Brockport, MO
State University of New York College at
  Oneonta, MO
State University of New York at Plattsburgh, MO
Syracuse University, MDO
University at Albany, State University of New
  York, O

North Carolina

Appalachian State University, MO
Campbell University, M
East Carolina University, MO
Lenoir-Rhyne College, M
North Carolina Agricultural and Technical State
  University, M
North Carolina Central University, M
North Carolina State University, MD
The University of North Carolina at Chapel Hill, M
The University of North Carolina at Charlotte, MD
The University of North Carolina at
  Greensboro, MDO
The University of North Carolina at Pembroke, M
Wake Forest University, M
Western Carolina University, M

North Dakota

North Dakota State University, MD

Ohio

Bowling Green State University, M
Circleville Bible College, B
Cleveland State University, MDO
John Carroll University, MO
Kent State University, MDO
Malone College, M
Ohio University, MD
Ohio University-Eastern, B
The University of Akron, MD
University of Cincinnati, MDO
University of Dayton, M
The University of Toledo, MDO
Walsh University, M
Wright State University, BM
Xavier University, M
Youngstown State University, M

Oklahoma

East Central University, BM
Northeastern State University, M
Northwestern Oklahoma State University, M
Oklahoma State University, MD
Southeastern Oklahoma State University, M
Southwestern Oklahoma State University, M
University of Central Oklahoma, BM
University of Oklahoma, M

Oregon

George Fox University, M
Northwest Christian College, M
Oregon State University, MD
Portland State University, MD

Pennsylvania

Baptist Bible College of Pennsylvania, M
Bucknell University, M
California University of Pennsylvania, M
Duquesne University, MD
Eastern University, M
Edinboro University of Pennsylvania, MO
Gannon University, MO
Geneva College, M
Gwynedd-Mercy College, M
Indiana University of Pennsylvania, M
Kutztown University of Pennsylvania, BM
Lancaster Bible College, BM
Lehigh University, MO
Marywood University, M

The Pennsylvania State University University Park
  Campus, MD
Rosemont College, M
Shippensburg University of Pennsylvania, MO
Slippery Rock University of Pennsylvania, M
The University of Scranton, M
Villanova University, M
West Chester University of Pennsylvania, M
Westminster College, MO
Widener University, M

Puerto Rico

Bayamon Central University, M
Inter American University of Puerto Rico, Arecibo
  Campus, M
Inter American University of Puerto Rico,
  Metropolitan Campus, M
Inter American University of Puerto Rico, San
  Germán Campus, M
University of Puerto Rico, Río Piedras, MD

Rhode Island

Providence College, M
Rhode Island College, MO

South Carolina

The Citadel, The Military College of South
  Carolina, M
Clemson University, BM
Columbia International University, M
South Carolina State University, MDO
University of South Carolina, DO
Winthrop University, M

South Dakota

Northern State University, M
Oglala Lakota College, AB
South Dakota State University, M
The University of South Dakota, MDO

Tennessee

Austin Peay State University, O
Belmont University, B
Carson-Newman College, M
East Tennessee State University, M
Freed-Hardeman University, M
Lee University, M
Lincoln Memorial University, M
Martin Methodist College, A
Middle Tennessee State University, MO
Southern Adventist University, M
Tennessee State University, M
Trevecca Nazarene University, M
University of Memphis, MD
The University of Tennessee, MDO
The University of Tennessee at Chattanooga, M
The University of Tennessee at Martin, M
Vanderbilt University, M

Texas

Amberton University, B
Angelo State University, M
Dallas Baptist University, M
Hardin-Simmons University, M
Houston Baptist University, BM
Lamar University, BMO
Midwestern State University, M
Our Lady of the Lake University of San Antonio, M
Prairie View A&M University, MD
St. Mary's University of San Antonio, MD
Sam Houston State University, BMD
Stephen F. Austin State University, M
Sul Ross State University, M
Tarleton State University, BM
Texas A&M University, M
Texas A&M University-Commerce, BMD
Texas A&M University-Corpus Christi, MD
Texas A&M University-Kingsville, M
Texas Christian University, BMO
Texas Southern University, BMD
Texas State University-San Marcos, M
Texas Tech University, MDO
Texas Woman's University, M
University of Houston-Clear Lake, BM
University of North Texas, MD

The University of Texas at Austin, M
The University of Texas at Brownsville, M
The University of Texas-Pan American, M
The University of Texas of the Permian Basin, M
The University of Texas at San Antonio, M
West Texas A&M University, M

Utah

University of Phoenix-Utah Campus, M
Utah State University, M

Vermont

College of St. Joseph, M
Johnson State College, M
Lyndon State College, M
University of Vermont, M

Virginia

The College of William and Mary, MD
George Mason University, M
Hampton University, M
Liberty University, M
Longwood University, M
Lynchburg College, M
Marymount University, M
Old Dominion University, MO
Radford University, M
Regent University, MDO
University of Northern Virginia, M
University of Virginia, MDO
Virginia Commonwealth University, M
Virginia Polytechnic Institute and State
    University, MDO
Virginia State University, M

Washington

Central Washington University, M
Eastern Washington University, M
Heritage University, M
Seattle Pacific University, M
Seattle University, MO
University of Puget Sound, M
University of Washington, MD
Western Washington University, BM
Whitworth College, M

West Virginia

Marshall University, BMO

Wisconsin

Carthage College, M
Concordia University Wisconsin, M
Mount Mary College, M
University of Wisconsin-Madison, M
University of Wisconsin-Oshkosh, M
University of Wisconsin-Platteville, M
University of Wisconsin-River Falls, MO
University of Wisconsin-Stevens Point, M
University of Wisconsin-Superior, M
University of Wisconsin-Whitewater, M

Wyoming

University of Wyoming, MD

Alberta

University of Alberta, M

British Columbia

Simon Fraser University, M
The University of British Columbia, B

University of Victoria, M

Manitoba

Brandon University, BMO
University of Manitoba, M

New Brunswick

Université de Moncton, M
University of New Brunswick Fredericton, BM

Newfoundland and Labrador

Memorial University of Newfoundland, B

Nova Scotia

Acadia University, M
Cape Breton University, O

Ontario

The University of Western Ontario, M
University of Windsor, B

Quebec

Université Laval, BMD
Université du Québec àMontréal, B
Université de Sherbrooke, B

COURT REPORTING/COURT REPORTER

Alabama

Gadsden State Community College, A
Prince Institute of Professional Studies, A

Arizona

GateWay Community College, A
Northland Pioneer College, A

California

Butte College, A
Cerritos College, A
Chaffey College, A
City College of San Francisco, A
College of Marin, A
Cypress College, A
Humphreys College, A
San Diego City College, A
West Valley College, A

Colorado

Denver Academy of Court Reporting, A

Florida

Daytona Beach Community College, A
Key College, A
Miami Dade College, A
Pensacola Junior College, A
Southwest Florida College (Fort Myers), A

Illinois

Career Colleges of Chicago, A
Illinois Central College, A
Illinois Eastern Community Colleges, Wabash Valley
    College, A
MacCormac College, A
Midstate College, A
South Suburban College, A
Triton College, A

Indiana

College of Court Reporting, A

Iowa

AIB College of Business, A
Kaplan University, A

Maryland

Villa Julie College, A

Michigan

Lansing Community College, A
Oakland Community College, A

Wayne County Community College District, A

Minnesota

Anoka Technical College, A
Rasmussen College Eagan, A
Rasmussen College Eden Prairie, A
Rasmussen College St. Cloud, A

Mississippi

Mississippi Gulf Coast Community College, A
Northwest Mississippi Community College, A
University of Mississippi, B

Missouri

Kansas City College, B
Metro Business College (Cape Girardeau), A
St. Louis Community College at Meramec, A
State Fair Community College, A

Nevada

Las Vegas College, A

New Mexico

Central New Mexico Community College, A

New York

Long Island Business Institute, A
New York Career Institute, A
State University of New York College of Technology
    at Alfred, A

North Carolina

Lenoir Community College, A

Ohio

Clark State Community College, A
Cuyahoga Community College, A
Stark State College of Technology, A
University of Cincinnati, A
University of Cincinnati Clermont College, A

Oklahoma

Metropolitan College (Tulsa), AB
Rose State College, A

Pennsylvania

Berean Institute, A
Community College of Allegheny County, A
Duff's Business Institute, A
Luzerne County Community College, A
Pennsylvania Highland Community College, A

South Carolina

Midlands Technical College, A

Tennessee

Southwest Tennessee Community College, A

Texas

Alvin Community College, A
Court Reporting Institute of Dallas, A
Del Mar College, A
El Paso Community College, A
Houston Community College System, A
San Antonio College, A

Washington

Bates Technical College, A
Green River Community College, A

West Virginia

Huntington Junior College, A

Wisconsin

Gateway Technical College, A
Lakeshore Technical College, A
Madison Area Technical College, A

Wisconsin Indianhead Technical College, A

CRAFTS

California
California College of the Arts, M
California State University, Long Beach, M

Illinois
Southern Illinois University Carbondale, M

New York
City College of the City University of New York, M
Rochester Institute of Technology, M

Ohio
Kent State University, M

Pennsylvania
Temple University, M

Nova Scotia
NSCAD University, M

CRAFTS/CRAFT DESIGN, FOLK ART AND ARTISANRY

Alabama
Lawson State Community College, A

Georgia
North Georgia College & State University, B

Illinois
School of the Art Institute of Chicago, B
University of Illinois at Urbana-Champaign, B

Indiana
Indiana University-Purdue University Fort Wayne, B

Massachusetts
Bridgewater State College, B

New York
Rochester Institute of Technology, B

North Carolina
College of The Albemarle, A
Haywood Community College, A

Ohio
Bowling Green State University, B
The Cleveland Institute of Art, B
Kent State University, B
The University of Akron, B

Oregon
Oregon College of Art & Craft, B

Pennsylvania
Kutztown University of Pennsylvania, B
The University of the Arts, B

Utah
Brigham Young University, B

Virginia
Virginia Commonwealth University, B

Nova Scotia
NSCAD University, B

CREATIVE WRITING

Alabama
Huntingdon College, B

Arizona
The University of Arizona, B

Arkansas
Arkansas Tech University, B

California
Berkeley City College, A
California State University, East Bay, B
California State University, Long Beach, B
California State University, San Bernardino, B
Chapman University, B
Dominican University of California, B
Foothill College, A
Grossmont College, A
Irvine Valley College, A
Mills College, B
New College of California, B
Pitzer College, B
San Diego State University, B
San Francisco State University, B
University of California, Riverside, B
University of California, San Diego, B
University of California, Santa Cruz, B
University of Redlands, B
University of Southern California, B

Colorado
The Colorado College, B
Colorado State University, B
University of Denver, B
Western State College of Colorado, B

Connecticut
Trinity College, B

Florida
Eckerd College, B
Florida State University, B
University of Miami, B
The University of Tampa, AB

Georgia
Agnes Scott College, B
Columbus State University, B
Emory University, B
Georgia College & State University, B
South Georgia College, A

Idaho
Albertson College of Idaho, B
Lewis-Clark State College, B

Illinois
Augustana College, B
Columbia College Chicago, B
DePaul University, B
Knox College, B
Lincoln College, A
Millikin University, B
North Central College, B
School of the Art Institute of Chicago, B
University of Chicago, B

Indiana
Bethel College, A
Indiana University-Purdue University Fort Wayne, B
Indiana Wesleyan University, B
Manchester College, A
Saint Joseph's College, B
Saint Mary's College, B
Taylor University, B
University of Evansville, B

Iowa
Briar Cliff University, B
Coe College, B
Loras College, B

Waldorf College, B

Kansas
Haskell Indian Nations University, A

Louisiana
Loyola University New Orleans, B

Maine
Colby College, B
University of Maine at Farmington, B
University of Maine at Machias, B
University of Maine at Presque Isle, A

Maryland
Bowie State University, B
The Johns Hopkins University, B
Loyola College in Maryland, B

Massachusetts
Bridgewater State College, B
Emerson College, B
Framingham State College, B
Harvard University, B
Massachusetts College of Liberal Arts, B
Massachusetts Institute of Technology, B
Pine Manor College, B
Simon's Rock College of Bard, B
Western New England College, B

Michigan
Central Michigan University, B
Cornerstone University, B
Eastern Michigan University, B
Grand Valley State University, B
Kirtland Community College, A
Northern Michigan University, B
University of Michigan, B
Western Michigan University, B

Minnesota
College of St. Catherine, B
Concordia College, B
Minnesota State University Mankato, B
Northwestern College, B
St. Cloud State University, B
Southwest Minnesota State University, B
University of St. Thomas, B

Mississippi
Belhaven College, B

Missouri
Drury University, B
Kansas City Art Institute, B
Rockhurst University, B
St. Louis Community College at Meramec, A
Stephens College, B
Washington University in St. Louis, B

Montana
University of Great Falls, B
The University of Montana-Missoula, B

Nebraska
Hastings College, B
University of Nebraska at Omaha, B
Wayne State College, B

New Hampshire
Chester College of New England, B
Dartmouth College, B
Franklin Pierce College, B

Southern New Hampshire University, B

New Jersey

Bloomfield College, B
Fairleigh Dickinson University, College at
    Florham, B

New Mexico

College of Santa Fe, B
Institute of American Indian Arts, A

New York

Bard College, B
Bernard M. Baruch College of the City University of
    New York, B
Brooklyn College of the City University of New
    York, B
Canisius College, B
City College of the City University of New York, B
Columbia College, B
Cornell University, B
Eugene Lang College The New School for Liberal
    Arts, B
Fordham University, B
Hamilton College, B
Hofstra University, B
Houghton College, B
Ithaca College, B
Le Moyne College, B
Lehman College of the City University of New
    York, B
Medaille College, B
Nazareth College of Rochester, B
Pratt Institute, B
Purchase College, State University of New York, B
St. Lawrence University, B
Sarah Lawrence College, B
State University of New York College at
    Brockport, B
State University of New York at New Paltz, B
State University of New York at Oswego, B
Wells College, B

North Carolina

High Point University, B
Methodist College, B
North Carolina State University, B
St. Andrews Presbyterian College, B
The University of North Carolina Wilmington, B
Warren Wilson College, B

Ohio

Antioch College, B
Ashland University, B
Bluffton University, B
Bowling Green State University, B
Capital University, B
Denison University, B
Kenyon College, B
Miami University, B
Miami University Hamilton, B
Oberlin College, B
Ohio Northern University, B
The Ohio State University, B
Ohio University, B
Ohio University-Eastern, B
Ohio Wesleyan University, B
The University of Findlay, B

Oklahoma

Oklahoma Christian University, B
Tulsa Community College, A

Oregon

Linfield College, B
Marylhurst University, B
Pacific University, B

Pennsylvania

Allegheny College, B
Carlow University, B
Carnegie Mellon University, B
Chatham College, B
Eastern University, B
Franklin and Marshall College, B

Geneva College, B
Gettysburg College, B
Lycoming College, B
Mercyhurst College, B
Moravian College, B
The Pennsylvania State University at Erie, The
    Behrend College, B
Seton Hill University, B
Susquehanna University, B
University of Pittsburgh, B
University of Pittsburgh at Bradford, B
University of Pittsburgh at Greensburg, B
University of Pittsburgh at Johnstown, B
Waynesburg College, B
Westminster College, B

Rhode Island

Brown University, B
Roger Williams University, B

South Carolina

Anderson University, B
Bob Jones University, B
Wofford College, B

Tennessee

Carson-Newman College, B

Texas

Lon Morris College, A
McMurry University, B
University of Houston, B
The University of Texas at El Paso, B

Vermont

Bennington College, B
Champlain College, B
Green Mountain College, B
Johnson State College, B
Marlboro College, B
Southern Vermont College, B

Virginia

Emory & Henry College, B
Hollins University, B
Lynchburg College, B
Randolph-Macon Woman's College, B
Sweet Briar College, B

Washington

Eastern Washington University, B
Seattle University, B
University of Puget Sound, B
University of Washington, B
Western Washington University, B

West Virginia

Alderson-Broaddus College, B
West Virginia Wesleyan College, B

Wisconsin

Beloit College, B
Cardinal Stritch University, B
Carroll College, B
Marquette University, B
Northland College, B
University of Wisconsin-Parkside, B

British Columbia

Malaspina University-College, B
The University of British Columbia, B

University of Victoria, B

Ontario

University of Windsor, B
York University, B

Quebec

Concordia University, B

CRIMINAL JUSTICE/LAW ENFORCEMENT ADMINISTRATION

Alabama

Alabama State University, B
Athens State University, B
Chattahoochee Valley Community College, A
Community College of the Air Force, A
Enterprise-Ozark Community College, A
Faulkner University, AB
George Corley Wallace State Community College, A
Jacksonville State University, B
James H. Faulkner State Community College, A
Judson College, B
Lawson State Community College, A
Miles College, B
Northwest-Shoals Community College, A
Samford University, B
South University, B
University of North Alabama, B
University of South Alabama, B
Wallace State Community College, A

Alaska

University of Alaska Anchorage, B

Arizona

Arizona State University West, B
Arizona Western College, A
Central Arizona College, A
Cochise College (Sierra Vista), A
Coconino Community College, A
Eastern Arizona College, A
Glendale Community College, A
Grand Canyon University, B
International Institute of the Americas (Mesa), A
International Institute of the Americas (Tucson), A
International Institute of the Americas (West Valley)
    , A
ITT Technical Institute (Tempe), B
ITT Technical Institute (Tucson), B
Mesa Community College, A
Northern Arizona University, B
The Paralegal Institute, Inc., A
Scottsdale Community College, A
The University of Arizona, B
University of Phoenix-Phoenix Campus, B
Western International University, B

Arkansas

Arkansas State University, A
Arkansas State University-Mountain Home, A
East Arkansas Community College, A
ITT Technical Institute, B
National Park Community College, A
North Arkansas College, A
NorthWest Arkansas Community College, A
Ozarka College, A
University of Arkansas Community College at
    Hope, A
University of Arkansas at Fort Smith, AB
University of Arkansas at Little Rock, B
University of Arkansas at Pine Bluff, B
University of Phoenix-Little Rock Campus, B

California

American InterContinental University, AB
Antelope Valley College, A
Argosy University/Orange County, A
Argosy University/San Diego, A
Argosy University/Santa Monica, A
Bakersfield College, A
Butte College, A

California Baptist University, B
California Lutheran University, B
California State University, Bakersfield, B
California State University, Dominguez Hills, B
California State University, East Bay, B
California State University, Fullerton, B
California State University, Long Beach, B
California State University, Sacramento, B
California State University, San Bernardino, B
California State University, Stanislaus, B
Cerro Coso Community College, A
Chabot College, A
Citrus College, A
City College of San Francisco, A
College of the Canyons, A
College of the Desert, A
College of the Redwoods, A
College of the Sequoias, A
College of the Siskiyous, A
Compton Community College, A
Contra Costa College, A
Cosumnes River College (Sacramento), A
Crafton Hills College, A
De Anza College, A
East Los Angeles College, A
Evergreen Valley College, A
Feather River College, A
Folsom Lake College, A
Fresno City College, A
Gavilan College, A
Golden West College, A
Grossmont College, A
Hartnell College, A
Imperial Valley College, A
Irvine Valley College, A
ITT Technical Institute (Anaheim), B
ITT Technical Institute (Lathrop), B
ITT Technical Institute (Oxnard), B
ITT Technical Institute (Rancho Cordova), B
ITT Technical Institute (San Bernardino), B
ITT Technical Institute (San Diego), B
ITT Technical Institute (Sylmar), B
ITT Technical Institute (Torrance), B
ITT Technical Institute (West Covina), B
Lake Tahoe Community College, A
Long Beach City College, A
Los Angeles City College, A
Los Angeles Southwest College, A
Los Angeles Valley College, A
Mendocino College, A
MiraCosta College, A
Modesto Junior College, A
Monterey Peninsula College, A
Moorpark College, A
Napa Valley College, A
National University, B
Ohlone College, A
Palo Verde College, A
Palomar College, A
Pasadena City College, A
Porterville College, A
Rio Hondo College, A
Riverside Community College District, A
Sacramento City College, A
San Diego Miramar College, A
San Diego State University, B
San Francisco State University, B
San Jose City College, A
Santa Ana College, A
Santa Barbara City College, A
Santa Monica College, A
Santa Rosa Junior College, A
Shasta College, A
Sierra College, A
Skyline College, A
Solano Community College, A
Sonoma State University, B
Southwestern College, A
Taft College, A
Ventura College, A
West Hills Community College, A
West Los Angeles College, A
West Valley College, A

Yuba College, A

Colorado

Aims Community College, A
Arapahoe Community College, A
Argosy University/Denver, A
Colorado Mountain College, A
Colorado Mountain College, Timberline Campus, A
Colorado Northwestern Community College, A
Community College of Aurora, A
ITT Technical Institute, B
Johnson & Wales University, A
Mesa State College, A
Metropolitan State College of Denver, B
Pikes Peak Community College, A
Pueblo Community College, A
Red Rocks Community College, A
Regis University, B
Remington College-Colorado Springs Campus, AB
University of Phoenix-Denver Campus, B
Western State College of Colorado, B

Connecticut

Albertus Magnus College, B
Briarwood College, AB
Housatonic Community College, A
Manchester Community College, A
Mitchell College, AB
Naugatuck Valley Community College, A
Northwestern Connecticut Community College, A
Norwalk Community College, A
Post University, B
Sacred Heart University, B
Three Rivers Community College, A
Tunxis Community College, A
University of New Haven, B

Delaware

Delaware State University, B
Delaware Technical & Community College, Jack F.
   Owens Campus, A
Delaware Technical & Community College,
   Stanton/Wilmington Campus, A
Delaware Technical & Community College, Terry
   Campus, A
University of Delaware, B
Wilmington College, B

District of Columbia

The George Washington University, B
University of the District of Columbia, AB

Florida

Brevard Community College, A
Broward Community College, A
Daytona Beach Community College, A
Edison College, A
Edward Waters College, B
Florida Agricultural and Mechanical University, B
Florida Community College at Jacksonville, A
Florida Memorial College, B
Florida Metropolitan University-Melbourne
   Campus, AB
Florida Metropolitan University-Tampa Campus, AB
Gulf Coast Community College, A
Hillsborough Community College, A
Indian River Community College, A
ITT Technical Institute (Fort Lauderdale), AB
ITT Technical Institute (Jacksonville), AB
ITT Technical Institute (Lake Mary), AB
ITT Technical Institute (Miami), B
ITT Technical Institute (Tampa), A
Johnson & Wales University, AB
Keiser College (Miami), A
Lake City Community College, A
Lake-Sumter Community College, A
Miami Dade College, A
Okaloosa-Walton College, A
Palm Beach Community College, A
Pasco-Hernando Community College, A
Polk Community College, A
St. Johns River Community College, A
St. Petersburg College, A
St. Thomas University, B
Santa Fe Community College, A

Seminole Community College, A
South Florida Community College, A
Tallahassee Community College, A
Valencia Community College, A

Georgia

Abraham Baldwin Agricultural College, A
Athens Technical College, A
Atlanta Metropolitan College, A
Bainbridge College, A
Clark Atlanta University, B
Clayton State University, A
Coastal Georgia Community College, A
Columbus State University, AB
Dalton State College, A
Darton College, A
East Georgia College, A
Fort Valley State University, AB
Gainesville College, A
Georgia College & State University, B
Georgia Military College, A
Georgia Southwestern State University, A
ITT Technical Institute (Duluth), B
ITT Technical Institute (Kennesaw), B
Macon State College, A
North Georgia College & State University, B
Piedmont College, B
Savannah State University, B
South Georgia College, A
South University, B
Thomas University, AB
Waycross College, A
Young Harris College, A

Guam

Guam Community College, A
University of Guam, B

Hawaii

Hawaii Community College, A
Hawaii Pacific University, B
Maui Community College, A
University of Hawaii-West Oahu, B

Idaho

Boise State University, AB
Brigham Young University -Idaho, A
College of Southern Idaho, A
ITT Technical Institute, B
North Idaho College, A

Illinois

Aurora University, B
Black Hawk College, A
Blackburn College, B
Bradley University, B
Carl Sandburg College, A
Chicago State University, B
City Colleges of Chicago, Harold Washington
   College, A
College of DuPage, A
Danville Area Community College, A
Elgin Community College, A
Governors State University, B
Greenville College, B
Illinois Valley Community College, A
John A. Logan College, A
Joliet Junior College, A
Kankakee Community College, A
Lewis and Clark Community College, A
Lewis University, B
Lincoln College, A
MacMurray College, AB
McKendree College, B
Northwestern Business College, A
Olivet Nazarene University, B
Prairie State College, A
Rock Valley College, A
Sauk Valley Community College, A
South Suburban College, A
Southern Illinois University Carbondale, B
Southwestern Illinois College, A
Spoon River College, A
Triton College, A
University of Phoenix-Chicago Campus, B

Western Illinois University, B
William Rainey Harper College, A

Indiana

Ancilla College, A
Anderson University, AB
Ball State University, AB
Calumet College of Saint Joseph, AB
Grace College, B
Indiana Tech, AB
Indiana University Northwest, AB
Indiana University South Bend, AB
ITT Technical Institute (Fort Wayne), B
ITT Technical Institute (Indianapolis), B
ITT Technical Institute (Newburgh), B
Martin University, B
Oakland City University, B
Purdue University Calumet, B
Taylor University Fort Wayne, B
Tri-State University, AB
University of Indianapolis, AB
Vincennes University, A

Iowa

Briar Cliff University, B
Des Moines Area Community College, A
Dordt College, B
Ellsworth Community College, A
Graceland University, B
Grand View College, B
Hamilton College (Cedar Rapids), A
Hawkeye Community College, A
Indian Hills Community College, A
Iowa Lakes Community College, A
Iowa Wesleyan College, B
Iowa Western Community College, A
Kirkwood Community College, A
Simpson College, B
Southeastern Community College, North Campus, A
University of Dubuque, B
Western Iowa Tech Community College, A

Kansas

Allen County Community College, A
Brown Mackie College-Salina, A
Central Christian College of Kansas, A
Cloud County Community College, A
Colby Community College, A
Cowley County Community College and Area
  Vocational-Technical School, A
Dodge City Community College, A
Fort Scott Community College, A
Garden City Community College, A
Highland Community College, A
Kansas Wesleyan University, AB
Labette Community College, A
MidAmerica Nazarene University, B
Neosho County Community College, A
Newman University, B
Southwestern College, B
Washburn University, AB

Kentucky

Big Sandy Community and Technical College, A
Brown Mackie College-Northern Kentucky, A
Campbellsville University, AB
Eastern Kentucky University, AB
ITT Technical Institute (Lexington), B
ITT Technical Institute (Louisville), B
Lindsey Wilson College, B
Northern Kentucky University, B
St. Catharine College, A
Thomas More College, AB
Union College, B
University of Louisville, B

Louisiana

Grambling State University, AB
ITT Technical Institute, B
Louisiana College, AB
Southern University at New Orleans, B

Southern University at Shreveport, A

Maine

Andover College, A
Beal College, A
Southern Maine Community College, A
Thomas College, B
The University of Maine at Augusta, B
University of Maine at Fort Kent, A
University of Maine at Presque Isle, AB

Maryland

Anne Arundel Community College, A
Bowie State University, B
Cecil Community College, A
Chesapeake College, A
Coppin State University, B
Frederick Community College, A
Frostburg State University, B
Hagerstown Business College, A
Howard Community College, A
Prince George's Community College, A
Sojourner-Douglass College, B
University of Baltimore, B
University of Maryland Eastern Shore, B
University of Maryland University College, B

Massachusetts

American International College, B
Anna Maria College, B
Bay Path College, B
Bay State College, A
Becker College, AB
Bunker Hill Community College, A
Cape Cod Community College, A
Curry College, B
Dean College, A
Fitchburg State College, B
Greenfield Community College, A
Massachusetts Bay Community College, A
Middlesex Community College, A
Mount Ida College, AB
Mount Wachusett Community College, A
Newbury College, AB
North Shore Community College, A
Northern Essex Community College, A
Quincy College, A
Quinsigamond Community College, A
Roxbury Community College, A
Salem State College, B
Suffolk University, AB
University of Massachusetts Lowell, B
Western New England College, B
Westfield State College, B

Michigan

Adrian College, AB
Bay de Noc Community College, A
Concordia University, B
Delta College, A
Finlandia University, A
Gogebic Community College, A
Grand Rapids Community College, A
Grand Valley State University, B
Henry Ford Community College, A
ITT Technical Institute (Canton), A
ITT Technical Institute (Grand Rapids), A
ITT Technical Institute (Troy), A
Jackson Community College, A
Kirtland Community College, A
Lake Superior State University, AB
Lansing Community College, A
Macomb Community College, A
Michigan State University, B
Mid Michigan Community College, A
Montcalm Community College, A
Muskegon Community College, A
North Central Michigan College, A
Northern Michigan University, AB
Oakland Community College, A
St. Clair County Community College, A
Siena Heights University, AB
University of Detroit Mercy, B
Washtenaw Community College, A

Wayne County Community College District, A

Minnesota

Bemidji State University, AB
Brown College, AB
Gustavus Adolphus College, B
Hamline University, B
Metropolitan State University, B
North Hennepin Community College, A
Northland Community and Technical College-Thief
  River Falls, A
Ridgewater College, A
St. Cloud State University, B
Saint Mary's University of Minnesota, B
Vermilion Community College, A
Winona State University, B

Mississippi

Coahoma Community College, A
East Mississippi Community College, A
Hinds Community College, A
Mississippi College, B
Mississippi Delta Community College, A
Mississippi Gulf Coast Community College, A
Mississippi Valley State University, B
Northeast Mississippi Community College, A

Missouri

Central Missouri State University, B
College of the Ozarks, B
Columbia College, AB
Culver-Stockton College, B
East Central College, A
Evangel University, B
Grantham University, AB
Hannibal-LaGrange College, AB
Harris-Stowe State University, B
ITT Technical Institute (Arnold), B
ITT Technical Institute (Earth City), B
ITT Technical Institute (Kansas City), B
Jefferson College, A
Lincoln University, AB
Lindenwood University, B
Longview Community College, A
Maple Woods Community College, A
Missouri Southern State University, B
Missouri State University-West Plains, A
Missouri Valley College, B
North Central Missouri College, A
Park University, AB
Penn Valley Community College, A
Saint Charles Community College, A
St. Louis Community College at Florissant Valley, A
St. Louis Community College at Forest Park, A
St. Louis Community College at Meramec, A
Saint Louis University, B
State Fair Community College, A
Three Rivers Community College, A
Truman State University, B
University of Missouri-Kansas City, B

Montana

Flathead Valley Community College, A
Fort Peck Community College, A
University of Great Falls, B

Nebraska

Bellevue University, B
Dana College, B
ITT Technical Institute, A
Midland Lutheran College, B
Northeast Community College, A
Peru State College, B
Wayne State College, B

Nevada

Community College of Southern Nevada, A
ITT Technical Institute, B
Nevada State College at Henderson, B
Truckee Meadows Community College, A
University of Nevada, Las Vegas, B

Western Nevada Community College, A

New Hampshire

Franklin Pierce College, B
Granite State College, B
Hesser College, AB
McIntosh College, A
New England College, B
New Hampshire Technical Institute, A
University of New Hampshire, B

New Jersey

Bergen Community College, A
Bloomfield College, B
Brookdale Community College, A
Camden County College, A
The College of New Jersey, B
Essex County College, A
Georgian Court University, B
Kean University, B
Middlesex County College, A
Passaic County Community College, A
Raritan Valley Community College, A
Rutgers, The State University of New Jersey, New
  Brunswick/Piscataway, B
Salem Community College, A
Warren County Community College, A

New Mexico

College of Santa Fe, B
International Institute of the Americas, A
ITT Technical Institute, B
New Mexico Military Institute, A
New Mexico State University-Carlsbad, A
New Mexico State University-Grants, A
University of New Mexico-Gallup, A
University of New Mexico-Valencia Campus, A
University of Phoenix-New Mexico Campus, B
Western New Mexico University, AB

New York

Adelphi University, B
Adirondack Community College, A
Alfred University, B
Bryant and Stratton College (Albany), A
Bryant and Stratton College, Buffalo Campus, A
Bryant and Stratton College, Lackawanna
  Campus, A
Bryant and Stratton College (Rochester-Henrietta
  Campus), A
Buffalo State College, State University of New
  York, B
Canisius College, B
Cayuga County Community College, A
Clinton Community College, A
The College of Saint Rose, B
Columbia-Greene Community College, A
Corning Community College, A
Dutchess Community College, A
Elmira College, B
Erie Community College, A
Erie Community College, North Campus, A
Excelsior College, B
Farmingdale State University of New York, A
Finger Lakes Community College, A
Fordham University, B
Fulton-Montgomery Community College, A
Genesee Community College, A
Herkimer County Community College, A
Hilbert College, AB
Hudson Valley Community College, A
Iona College, B
Jefferson Community College, A
John Jay College of Criminal Justice of the City
  University of New York, B
Keuka College, B
Marist College, B
Mercy College, B
Mohawk Valley Community College, A
Monroe College (Bronx), AB
Monroe Community College, A
Nassau Community College, A
New York Institute of Technology, B
Niagara County Community College, A
Niagara University, B
Onondaga Community College, A

Orange County Community College, A
Pace University, B
Roberts Wesleyan College, B
Rochester Institute of Technology, B
Rockland Community College, A
St. John's University, AB
St. Thomas Aquinas College, B
Schenectady County Community College, A
State University of New York College at
  Brockport, B
State University of New York College of Technology
  at Canton, A
State University of New York, Fredonia, B
State University of New York at Oswego, B
Suffolk County Community College, A
Tompkins Cortland Community College, A
Ulster County Community College, A
University at Albany, State University of New York, B
Utica College, B
Westchester Community College, A

North Carolina

Barber-Scotia College, B
Barton College, B
Campbell University, B
Carteret Community College, A
Central Carolina Community College, A
Central Piedmont Community College, A
Cleveland Community College, A
Coastal Carolina Community College, A
College of The Albemarle, A
Craven Community College, A
Davidson County Community College, A
Durham Technical Community College, A
ECPI Technical College, A
Edgecombe Community College, A
Elizabeth City State University, B
Fayetteville State University, B
Forsyth Technical Community College, A
Gaston College, A
Guilford Technical Community College, A
Haywood Community College, A
Isothermal Community College, A
Johnson C. Smith University, B
Lees-McRae College, B
Lenoir Community College, A
Mars Hill College, B
Mayland Community College, A
McDowell Technical Community College, A
Methodist College, AB
Mitchell Community College, A
Mount Olive College, B
North Carolina Central University, B
North Carolina Wesleyan College, B
Pfeiffer University, B
Piedmont Community College, A
Richmond Community College, A
Roanoke-Chowan Community College, A
Robeson Community College, A
Rockingham Community College, A
Rowan-Cabarrus Community College, A
Saint Augustine's College, B
Sampson Community College, A
Sandhills Community College, A
Southeastern Community College, A
Surry Community College, A
University of Phoenix-Raleigh Campus, B
Vance-Granville Community College, A
Wake Technical Community College, A
Western Piedmont Community College, A
Wilson Technical Community College, A

North Dakota

Aakers Business College, A
United Tribes Technical College, A

Ohio

Ashland University, AB
Baldwin-Wallace College, B
Bryant and Stratton College (Cleveland), A
Bryant and Stratton College (Parma), A
Cedarville University, B
Central Ohio Technical College, A
Clark State Community College, A
Defiance College, AB
Edison State Community College, A

Hocking College, A
ITT Technical Institute (Dayton), A
ITT Technical Institute (Hilliard), A
ITT Technical Institute (Norwood), A
ITT Technical Institute (Strongsville), A
ITT Technical Institute (Warrensville Heights), A
Kent State University, East Liverpool Campus, A
Kent State University, Trumbull Campus, AB
Lakeland Community College, A
Lourdes College, AB
Mount Vernon Nazarene University, B
Muskingum College, B
North Central State College, A
Northwest State Community College, A
Ohio Dominican University, B
Ohio Institute of Photography and Technology, A
Ohio Northern University, B
Ohio University, B
Ohio University-Chillicothe, B
Ohio University-Eastern, B
Ohio University-Lancaster, B
Ohio University-Southern Campus, AB
Ohio University-Zanesville, B
Owens Community College, A
Remington College-Cleveland West Campus, A
Sinclair Community College, A
Southern State Community College, A
Tiffin University, B
Union Institute & University, B
The University of Akron, B
University of Cincinnati, AB
University of Cincinnati Clermont College, A
University of Dayton, B
The University of Findlay, AB
Urbana University, AB
Wilmington College, B
Youngstown State University, B
Zane State College, A

Oklahoma

East Central University, B
Eastern Oklahoma State College, A
ITT Technical Institute, B
Langston University, B
Northeastern Oklahoma Agricultural and Mechanical
  College, A
Northeastern State University, B
Northern Oklahoma College, A
Oklahoma City University, B
Redlands Community College, A
Rogers State University, A
Rose State College, A
Southwestern Oklahoma State University, B
Tulsa Community College, A
University of Central Oklahoma, B

Oregon

Central Oregon Community College, A
Chemeketa Community College, A
Clatsop Community College, A
ITT Technical Institute, B
Lane Community College, A
Portland Community College, A
Portland State University, B
Rogue Community College, A
Tillamook Bay Community College, A
Treasure Valley Community College, A
Umpqua Community College, A
Western Oregon University, B

Pennsylvania

Alvernia College, B
Arcadia University, B
Bucks County Community College, A
Central Pennsylvania College, AB
Chestnut Hill College, AB
Community College of Beaver County, A
Community College of Philadelphia, A
Delaware Valley College, B
DeSales University, B
Harrisburg Area Community College, A
Holy Family University, B
ICM School of Business & Medical Careers, A
Keystone College, B
Lehigh Carbon Community College, A
Lehigh Valley College, A

Lock Haven University of Pennsylvania, B
Luzerne County Community College, A
Lycoming College, B
Mansfield University of Pennsylvania, AB
Marywood University, B
Mercyhurst College, AB
Moravian College, B
The Pennsylvania State University Abington
  College, B
The Pennsylvania State University Altoona
  College, B
The Pennsylvania State University Beaver Campus
  of the Commonwealth College, B
The Pennsylvania State University Berks Campus of
  the Berks-Lehigh Valley College, B
The Pennsylvania State University Delaware County
  Campus of the Commonwealth College, B
The Pennsylvania State University DuBois Campus
  of the Commonwealth College, B
The Pennsylvania State University at Erie, The
  Behrend College, B
The Pennsylvania State University Fayette Campus
  of the Commonwealth College, B
The Pennsylvania State University Hazleton
  Campus of the Commonwealth College, B
The Pennsylvania State University, Lehigh Valley
  Campus of the Berks-Lehigh Valley College, B
The Pennsylvania State University McKeesport
  Campus of the Commonwealth College, B
The Pennsylvania State University Mont Alto
  Campus of the Commonwealth College, B
The Pennsylvania State University New Kensington
  Campus of the Commonwealth College, B
The Pennsylvania State University Schuylkill
  Campus of the Capital College, B
The Pennsylvania State University Shenango
  Campus of the Commonwealth College, B
The Pennsylvania State University University Park
  Campus, B
The Pennsylvania State University Wilkes-Barre
  Campus of the Commonwealth College, B
The Pennsylvania State University Worthington
  Scranton Campus of the Commonwealth
  College, B
The Pennsylvania State University York Campus of
  the Commonwealth College, B
Point Park University, B
Saint Francis University, B
Saint Joseph's University, AB
Seton Hill University, B
University of Phoenix-Philadelphia Campus, B
University of Pittsburgh at Bradford, B
University of Pittsburgh at Greensburg, B
Valley Forge Military College, A
Villanova University, B
Waynesburg College, B
Westminster College, B
Westmoreland County Community College, A
Widener University, B

Puerto Rico

Caribbean University, B
Inter American University of Puerto Rico, Arecibo
  Campus, B
Inter American University of Puerto Rico,
  Barranquitas Campus, B
Inter American University of Puerto Rico, Fajardo
  Campus, B
Inter American University of Puerto Rico, Guayama
  Campus, B
Inter American University of Puerto Rico,
  Metropolitan Campus, B
Inter American University of Puerto Rico, Ponce
  Campus, B
Pontifical Catholic University of Puerto Rico, B

Rhode Island

Johnson & Wales University, AB
Roger Williams University, AB
Salve Regina University, B

South Carolina

Anderson University, B
Benedict College, B
Charleston Southern University, B

The Citadel, The Military College of South
  Carolina, B
Claflin University, B
Coker College, B
Denmark Technical College, A
Florence-Darlington Technical College, A
Greenville Technical College, A
Horry-Georgetown Technical College, A
Morris College, A
Piedmont Technical College, A
South Carolina State University, B
South University, B
Spartanburg Methodist College, A
Technical College of the Lowcountry, A
Tri-County Technical College, A
Trident Technical College, A
University of South Carolina, B
University of South Carolina Lancaster, A
University of South Carolina Upstate, B
Voorhees College, B

South Dakota

Dakota Wesleyan University, AB
Kilian Community College, A
Oglala Lakota College, AB
Sinte Gleska University, B
The University of South Dakota, B

Tennessee

Austin Peay State University, B
Chattanooga State Technical Community College, A
Cumberland University, B
East Tennessee State University, B
ITT Technical Institute (Knoxville), B
ITT Technical Institute (Memphis), B
ITT Technical Institute (Nashville), B
Lambuth University, B
Lincoln Memorial University, B
Martin Methodist College, A
Middle Tennessee State University, B
Roane State Community College, A
Tennessee State University, B
University of Memphis, B
The University of Tennessee at Chattanooga, B
The University of Tennessee at Martin, B
Walters State Community College, A

Texas

Amarillo College, A
Angelina College, A
Austin Community College, A
Blinn College, A
Cedar Valley College, A
Coastal Bend College, A
College of the Mainland, A
Concordia University at Austin, B
Dallas Baptist University, B
Del Mar College, A
Frank Phillips College, A
Grayson County College, A
Hill College of the Hill Junior College District, A
Kilgore College, A
Lamar University, B
McLennan Community College, A
Midwestern State University, B
Montgomery College, A
Mountain View College, A
Navarro College, A
North Central Texas College, A
North Harris College, A
Northeast Texas Community College, A
Odessa College, A
Paul Quinn College, B
St. Mary's University of San Antonio, B
St. Philip's College, A
Sam Houston State University, B
San Antonio College, A
South Plains College, A
Southwest Texas Junior College, A
Southwestern Adventist University, B
Sul Ross State University, B
Tarrant County College District, A
Temple College, A
Texarkana College, A
Texas A&M University-Commerce, B
Texas A&M University-Corpus Christi, B

Texas Southern University, B
Texas Southmost College, A
Trinity Valley Community College, A
Tyler Junior College, A
University of Mary Hardin-Baylor, B
The University of Texas at Brownsville, B
The University of Texas at El Paso, B
The University of Texas-Pan American, B
Vernon College, A
Weatherford College, A
West Texas A&M University, B
Western Texas College, A
Wharton County Junior College, A

Utah

ITT Technical Institute, B
Salt Lake Community College, A
Snow College, A
Southern Utah University, A
Utah Valley State College, AB

Vermont

Castleton State College, AB
Champlain College, AB
Norwich University, B
Southern Vermont College, AB

Virginia

Averett University, B
Bluefield College, B
Bryant and Stratton College, Richmond, A
Central Virginia Community College, A
Dabney S. Lancaster Community College, A
Hampton University, B
ITT Technical Institute (Chantilly), B
ITT Technical Institute (Norfolk), B
ITT Technical Institute (Richmond), B
ITT Technical Institute (Springfield), B
Liberty University, B
Longwood University, B
Mountain Empire Community College, A
New River Community College, A
Northern Virginia Community College, A
Paul D. Camp Community College, A
Radford University, B
Saint Paul's College, B
Shenandoah University, B
Southside Virginia Community College, A
University of Richmond, B
Virginia Commonwealth University, B
Virginia Intermont College, B
Virginia Western Community College, A
Wytheville Community College, A

Washington

Bellevue Community College, A
Central Washington University, B
Centralia College, A
Eastern Washington University, B
Everett Community College, A
Gonzaga University, B
Highline Community College, A
ITT Technical Institute (Bothell), B
ITT Technical Institute (Seattle), B
ITT Technical Institute (Spokane), B
Lower Columbia College, A
Olympic College, A
Peninsula College, A
Pierce College, A
Saint Martin's University, B
Seattle University, B
Tacoma Community College, A
University of Phoenix-Spokane Campus, B
University of Phoenix-Washington Campus, B
University of Washington, B
Washington State University, B
Yakima Valley Community College, A

West Virginia

Glenville State College, A
Mountain State University, B
Salem International University, B
Southern West Virginia Community and Technical
  College, A
West Liberty State College, B

West Virginia State University, AB
West Virginia University at Parkersburg, A
West Virginia Wesleyan College, B
Wheeling Jesuit University, B

Wisconsin

Bryant and Stratton College, A
Bryant and Stratton College, Wauwatosa Campus, A
Carroll College, B
Carthage College, B
Concordia University Wisconsin, B
Edgewood College, B
Fox Valley Technical College, A
ITT Technical Institute (Green Bay), B
ITT Technical Institute (Greenfield), B
Marian College of Fond du Lac, B
Milwaukee Area Technical College, A
University of Wisconsin-Milwaukee, B
University of Wisconsin-Oshkosh, B
University of Wisconsin-Parkside, B
University of Wisconsin-Platteville, B

Wyoming

Casper College, A
Central Wyoming College, A
Laramie County Community College, A
Sheridan College-Sheridan and Gillette, A
Western Wyoming Community College, A

Alberta

University of Alberta, B

Ontario

Carleton University, B
University of Guelph, B
University of Ottawa, B

Saskatchewan

University of Regina, B

CRIMINAL JUSTICE/POLICE SCIENCE

Alabama

Calhoun Community College, A
Enterprise-Ozark Community College, A
Gadsden State Community College, A
George C. Wallace Community College, A
George Corley Wallace State Community College, A
Jacksonville State University, B
Jefferson Davis Community College, A
Jefferson State Community College, A
Lawson State Community College, A
Northwest-Shoals Community College, A
Wallace State Community College, A

Arizona

Arizona Western College, A
Cochise College (Douglas), A
Cochise College (Sierra Vista), A
Eastern Arizona College, A
Everest College, AB
Glendale Community College, A
Mohave Community College, A
Phoenix College, A
Pima Community College, A
Yavapai College, A

Arkansas

Arkansas Northeastern College, A
Arkansas State University, A
East Arkansas Community College, A
North Arkansas College, A
South Arkansas Community College, A
University of Arkansas at Little Rock, A
University of Arkansas at Pine Bluff, A

California

Allan Hancock College, A
Antelope Valley College, A
Bakersfield College, A
Butte College, A
California State University, East Bay, B

Cerritos College, A
Chabot College, A
Citrus College, A
City College of San Francisco, A
College of the Canyons, A
College of the Desert, A
College of Marin, A
College of San Mateo, A
College of the Sequoias, A
Compton Community College, A
Contra Costa College, A
De Anza College, A
East Los Angeles College, A
El Camino College, A
Fresno City College, A
Fullerton College, A
Gavilan College, A
Glendale Community College, A
Golden West College, A
Grossmont College, A
Lake Tahoe Community College, A
Las Positas College, A
Lassen Community College District, A
Los Angeles City College, A
Los Angeles Harbor College, A
Los Angeles Mission College, A
Los Angeles Southwest College, A
Los Angeles Valley College, A
Mendocino College, A
Merced College, A
MiraCosta College, A
Modesto Junior College, A
Monterey Peninsula College, A
Moorpark College, A
Mt. San Antonio College, A
Mt. San Jacinto College, A
Napa Valley College, A
Ohlone College, A
Palo Verde College, A
Palomar College, A
Porterville College, A
Reedley College, A
San Bernardino Valley College, A
San Diego Miramar College, A
San Joaquin Delta College, A
Santa Ana College, A
Santa Monica College, A
Sierra College, A
Skyline College, A
Victor Valley College, A
West Los Angeles College, A
West Valley College, A
Yuba College, A

Colorado

Aims Community College, A
Arapahoe Community College, A
Northeastern Junior College, A
Pueblo Community College, A
Trinidad State Junior College, A

Connecticut

Northwestern Connecticut Community College, A
University of Hartford, B
University of New Haven, A
Western Connecticut State University, B

Delaware

Delaware Technical & Community College,
  Stanton/Wilmington Campus, A

District of Columbia

Howard University, B
University of the District of Columbia, A

Florida

Brevard Community College, A
Broward Community College, A
Daytona Beach Community College, A
Florida Community College at Jacksonville, A
Florida Metropolitan University-Pompano Beach
  Campus, B
Hillsborough Community College, A
Indian River Community College, A
Miami Dade College, A

Okaloosa-Walton College, A
Palm Beach Community College, A
St. Petersburg College, A
Santa Fe Community College, A

Georgia

Abraham Baldwin Agricultural College, A
Armstrong Atlantic State University, A
Dalton State College, A
Georgia Highlands College, A
Macon State College, A
Middle Georgia College, A
Okefenokee Technical College, A

Guam

Guam Community College, A
University of Guam, B

Hawaii

Honolulu Community College, A

Idaho

Brigham Young University -Idaho, A
College of Southern Idaho, A
Idaho State University, A
North Idaho College, A

Illinois

Carl Sandburg College, A
Chicago State University, B
City Colleges of Chicago, Harold Washington
  College, A
City Colleges of Chicago, Harry S. Truman
  College, A
City Colleges of Chicago, Richard J. Daley
  College, A
City Colleges of Chicago, Wilbur Wright College, A
College of DuPage, A
College of Lake County, A
Danville Area Community College, A
Elgin Community College, A
Illinois Central College, A
Illinois Eastern Community Colleges, Olney Central
  College, A
Illinois Valley Community College, A
John Wood Community College, A
Joliet Junior College, A
Kankakee Community College, A
Kaskaskia College, A
Kishwaukee College, A
Lake Land College, A
Lincoln College, A
Lincoln Land Community College, A
MacMurray College, AB
McHenry County College, A
Moraine Valley Community College, A
Morton College, A
Oakton Community College, A
Rend Lake College, A
Richland Community College, A
Sauk Valley Community College, A
Shawnee Community College, A
South Suburban College, A
Southeastern Illinois College, A
Spoon River College, A
Triton College, A
Waubonsee Community College, A
William Rainey Harper College, A

Indiana

Brown Mackie College-Fort Wayne, A
Purdue University Calumet, B
Vincennes University, A
Vincennes University Jasper Campus, A

Iowa

Des Moines Area Community College, A
Hawkeye Community College, A
Iowa Central Community College, A
Iowa Lakes Community College, A
Iowa Western Community College, A
Kirkwood Community College, A
North Iowa Area Community College, A

Scott Community College, A

Kansas

Barton County Community College, A
Butler Community College, A
Cowley County Community College and Area
  Vocational-Technical School, A
Garden City Community College, A
Highland Community College, A
Hutchinson Community College and Area Vocational
  School, A
Johnson County Community College, A
Kansas City Kansas Community College, A
Labette Community College, A
Neosho County Community College, A
Seward County Community College, A
Washburn University, AB

Kentucky

Ashland Community and Technical College, A
Eastern Kentucky University, AB
Elizabethtown Community and Technical College, A
Hopkinsville Community College, A
Madisonville Community College, A
Northern Kentucky University, A
Owensboro Community and Technical College, A
Somerset Community College, A
Southeast Kentucky Community and Technical
  College, A

Louisiana

Bossier Parish Community College, A
Delgado Community College, A
Grambling State University, B
Louisiana College, B
Louisiana State University at Alexandria, A
Louisiana State University at Eunice, A
Nicholls State University, A
Northwestern State University of Louisiana, A
Southeastern Louisiana University, A
Southern University and Agricultural and Mechanical
  College, A
University of Louisiana at Monroe, A

Maine

Husson College, AB
Southern Maine Community College, A

Maryland

Allegany College of Maryland, A
Anne Arundel Community College, A
Baltimore City Community College, A
Frostburg State University, B
Hagerstown Community College, A
Montgomery College, A
Wor-Wic Community College, A

Massachusetts

American International College, B
Becker College, AB
Dean College, A
Holyoke Community College, A
Massasoit Community College, A
Northeastern University, B
Quincy College, A
Springfield Technical Community College, A

Michigan

Alpena Community College, A
Bay de Noc Community College, A
Delta College, A
Ferris State University, B
Grand Rapids Community College, A
Grand Valley State University, B
Henry Ford Community College, A
Kalamazoo Valley Community College, A
Kellogg Community College, A
Lake Michigan College, A
Lake Superior State University, AB
Lansing Community College, A
Macomb Community College, A
Monroe County Community College, A
Mott Community College, A
North Central Michigan College, A
Northern Michigan University, AB

Oakland Community College, A
Schoolcraft College, A
Washtenaw Community College, A
Wayne County Community College District, A
West Shore Community College, A

Minnesota

Alexandria Technical College, A
Bemidji State University, B
Century College, A
Fond du Lac Tribal and Community College, A
Hibbing Community College, A
Inver Hills Community College, A
Metropolitan State University, B
Minneapolis Community and Technical College, A
Minnesota State Community and Technical
  College-Fergus Falls, A
Minnesota State University Mankato, B
Normandale Community College, A
Northland Community and Technical College-Thief
  River Falls, A
Ridgewater College, A
Riverland Community College, A
Rochester Community and Technical College, A
Saint Mary's University of Minnesota, B
Vermilion Community College, A
Winona State University, B

Mississippi

Copiah-Lincoln Community College, A
Hinds Community College, A
Itawamba Community College, A
Jones County Junior College, A
Mississippi Gulf Coast Community College, A
Northeast Mississippi Community College, A

Missouri

Blue River Community College, A
College of the Ozarks, B
East Central College, A
Grantham University, AB
Jefferson College, A
Longview Community College, A
Maple Woods Community College, A
Mineral Area College, A
Missouri Southern State University, A
Missouri State University-West Plains, A
Moberly Area Community College, A
Penn Valley Community College, A
Saint Charles Community College, A
St. Louis Community College at Florissant Valley, A
St. Louis Community College at Meramec, A
Saint Louis University, B
Three Rivers Community College, A
Truman State University, B

Montana

Dawson Community College, A
University of Great Falls, B

Nebraska

Metropolitan Community College, A
Northeast Community College, A
Wayne State College, B

Nevada

Community College of Southern Nevada, A
Truckee Meadows Community College, A
Western Nevada Community College, A

New Hampshire

Hesser College, AB

New Jersey

County College of Morris, A
Cumberland County College, A
Essex County College, A
Gloucester County College, A
Mercer County Community College, A
Middlesex County College, A
Ocean County College, A
Rowan University, B

Union County College, A

New Mexico

Clovis Community College, A
Luna Community College, A
New Mexico Junior College, A
New Mexico Military Institute, A
San Juan College, A
Western New Mexico University, AB

New York

Adirondack Community College, A
Broome Community College, A
Cayuga County Community College, A
Clinton Community College, A
Erie Community College, A
Erie Community College, North Campus, A
Finger Lakes Community College, A
Herkimer County Community College, A
Hilbert College, B
Jamestown Community College, A
John Jay College of Criminal Justice of the City
  University of New York, AB
Monroe College (Bronx), AB
Monroe Community College, A
Orange County Community College, A
State University of New York College at
  Brockport, B
State University of New York College of Technology
  at Canton, AB
Suffolk County Community College, A
Westchester Community College, A

North Carolina

Asheville-Buncombe Technical Community
  College, A
Beaufort County Community College, A
Bladen Community College, A
Cape Fear Community College, A
Catawba Valley Community College, A
Central Piedmont Community College, A
Davidson County Community College, A
Durham Technical Community College, A
Forsyth Technical Community College, A
Guilford Technical Community College, A
Halifax Community College, A
Isothermal Community College, A
James Sprunt Community College, A
Johnston Community College, A
Lenoir Community College, A
Mayland Community College, A
Montgomery Community College, A
Nash Community College, A
Pitt Community College, A
Randolph Community College, A
Rockingham Community College, A
Sandhills Community College, A
South Piedmont Community College, A
Southwestern Community College, A
Stanly Community College, A
Vance-Granville Community College, A
Wake Technical Community College, A
Wayne Community College, A
Western Piedmont Community College, A
Wilkes Community College, A

North Dakota

Lake Region State College, A
University of Mary, B

Ohio

Central Ohio Technical College, A
Cincinnati State Technical and Community
  College, A
Clark State Community College, A
Columbus State Community College, A
Cuyahoga Community College, A
Defiance College, AB
Edison State Community College, A
Hocking College, A
James A. Rhodes State College, A
Jefferson Community College, A
Kent State University, Ashtabula Campus, A
Kent State University, Tuscarawas Campus, AB
Lakeland Community College, A

Lorain County Community College, A
Northwest State Community College, A
Ohio Northern University, B
Ohio University, A
Ohio University-Chillicothe, A
Ohio University-Lancaster, A
Owens Community College, A
Sinclair Community College, A
Terra State Community College, A
Tiffin University, AB
The University of Akron, A
University of Cincinnati, AB
The University of Toledo, A
Wright State University, B

Oklahoma

Cameron University, AB
Connors State College, A
East Central University, B
Langston University, B
Northeastern State University, B
Northwestern Oklahoma State University, B
Oklahoma City University, B
Oklahoma State University, Oklahoma City, A
Redlands Community College, A
Rogers State University, A
St. Gregory's University, B
Seminole State College, A
Tulsa Community College, A
Western Oklahoma State College, A

Oregon

Clackamas Community College, A
Linn-Benton Community College, A
Pioneer Pacific College, AB
Southwestern Oregon Community College, A
Treasure Valley Community College, A
Western Oregon University, B

Pennsylvania

Bucks County Community College, A
Butler County Community College, A
Community College of Allegheny County, A
Community College of Beaver County, A
Delaware County Community College, A
Edinboro University of Pennsylvania, A
Harrisburg Area Community College, A
Lehigh Carbon Community College, A
Mercyhurst College, AB
Montgomery County Community College, A
Penn Foster Career School, A
University of Pittsburgh at Greensburg, B
Westmoreland County Community College, A
York College of Pennsylvania, AB

Puerto Rico

Caribbean University, A
Inter American University of Puerto Rico, Fajardo
  Campus, A
University of Puerto Rico at Carolina, A

Rhode Island

Community College of Rhode Island, A

South Carolina

Greenville Technical College, A

South Dakota

Northern State University, B
Western Dakota Technical Institute, A

Tennessee

Dyersburg State Community College, A
Martin Methodist College, A
Middle Tennessee State University, A
Nashville State Technical Community College, A
Roane State Community College, A
The University of Tennessee at Chattanooga, B

Texas

Alvin Community College, A
Amarillo College, A
Austin Community College, A
Brazosport College, A
Central Texas College, A

Cisco Junior College, A
Coastal Bend College, A
Del Mar College, A
El Centro College, A
El Paso Community College, A
Frank Phillips College, A
Galveston College, A
Grayson County College, A
Hardin-Simmons University, B
Hill College of the Hill Junior College District, A
Houston Community College System, A
Howard College, A
Kilgore College, A
Lamar University, B
Laredo Community College, A
Lee College, A
McLennan Community College, A
Midland College, A
Navarro College, A
North Central Texas College, A
North Harris College, A
Odessa College, A
Sam Houston State University, B
San Antonio College, A
South Plains College, A
Stephen F. Austin State University, B
Temple College, A
Texarkana College, A
Texas A&M University-Commerce, B
Texas Southmost College, A
Texas State University-San Marcos, B
Trinity Valley Community College, A
Tyler Junior College, A
The University of Texas at Brownsville, B
The University of Texas-Pan American, B
Victoria College, A
Western Texas College, A

United States Virgin Islands

University of the Virgin Islands, A

Utah

Weber State University, AB

Virginia

George Mason University, B
Germanna Community College, A
Mountain Empire Community College, A
New River Community College, A
Northern Virginia Community College, A
Piedmont Virginia Community College, A
Rappahannock Community College, A
Southwest Virginia Community College, A
Thomas Nelson Community College, A
Virginia Highlands Community College, A
Wytheville Community College, A

Washington

Bellevue Community College, A
Columbia Basin College, A
Everett Community College, A
Grays Harbor College, A
Green River Community College, A
Highline Community College, A
Lower Columbia College, A
Olympic College, A
Skagit Valley College, A
Spokane Community College, A
Tacoma Community College, A
Whatcom Community College, A
Yakima Valley Community College, A

West Virginia

Bluefield State College, A
Davis & Elkins College, A
Fairmont State University, AB
Marshall Community and Technical College, A
New River Community and Technical College, A
West Virginia Northern Community College, A

Wisconsin

Blackhawk Technical College, A
Chippewa Valley Technical College, A
Fox Valley Technical College, A
Gateway Technical College, A

Lakeshore Technical College, A
Madison Area Technical College, A
Mid-State Technical College, A
Milwaukee Area Technical College, A
Nicolet Area Technical College, A
Northcentral Technical College, A
Northeast Wisconsin Technical College, A
University of Wisconsin-Milwaukee, B
Waukesha County Technical College, A
Western Technical College, A
Wisconsin Indianhead Technical College, A

Wyoming

Casper College, A
Eastern Wyoming College, A
Sheridan College-Sheridan and Gillette, A

Alberta

Athabasca University, B

Manitoba

The University of Winnipeg, B

Newfoundland and Labrador

Memorial University of Newfoundland, B

Ontario

Carleton University, B
University of Toronto, B

Saskatchewan

University of Regina, B

CRIMINAL JUSTICE/SAFETY STUDIES

Alabama

Andrew Jackson University, AB
Auburn University Montgomery, B
Columbia Southern University, B
The University of Alabama, B

Arizona

Arizona State University, B
Chaparral College, AB
Phoenix College, A
Pima Community College, A
Prescott College, B

Arkansas

Arkansas State University-Mountain Home, A
Arkansas Tech University, A
Harding University, B
Southern Arkansas University-Magnolia, B
University of Arkansas, B
University of Arkansas Community College at
  Batesville, A
University of Arkansas at Monticello, B

California

California State University, Chico, B
California State University, Los Angeles, B
San Jose State University, B

Colorado

Colorado State University, B
Lamar Community College, A
Remington College-Denver Campus, AB
University of Northern Colorado, B

Connecticut

Asnuntuck Community College, A
Quinnipiac University, B

Florida

Brown Mackie College-Miami, A
Florida Atlantic University, B
Florida Gulf Coast University, B
Florida International University, B
Florida Metropolitan University-Brandon
  Campus, AB

Florida Metropolitan University-Jacksonville
  Campus, AB
Florida Metropolitan University-Lakeland
  Campus, AB
Florida Metropolitan University-North Orlando
  Campus, AB
Florida Metropolitan University-Pinellas Campus, AB
Florida Metropolitan University-South Orlando
  Campus, AB
Florida Southern College, B
Florida State University, B
Florida Technical College (DeLand), A
International College, AB
Manatee Community College, A
North Florida Community College, A
Pensacola Junior College, A
Remington College-Tampa Campus, A
Saint Leo University, B
University of Central Florida, B
University of North Florida, B
University of South Florida, B
University of West Florida, B

Georgia

Albany State University, B
Altamaha Technical College, A
Andrew College, A
Appalachian Technical College, A
Augusta State University, AB
Augusta Technical College, A
Brown Mackie College-Atlanta, A
Central Georgia Technical College, A
Chattahoochee Technical College, A
Coosa Valley Technical College, A
DeKalb Technical College, A
East Central Technical College, A
Flint River Technical College, A
Georgia Highlands College, A
Georgia Southern University, B
Georgia Southwestern State University, A
Georgia State University, B
Griffin Technical College, A
Heart of Georgia Technical College, A
Kennesaw State University, B
Lanier Technical College, A
Mercer University, B
Moultrie Technical College, A
North Georgia College & State University, B
North Georgia Technical College, A
Northwestern Technical College, A
Savannah Technical College, A
South Georgia Technical College, A
Southeastern Technical College, A
Southwest Georgia Technical College, A
Swainsboro Technical College, A
University of Georgia, B
Valdosta State University, B
Valdosta Technical College, A
West Central Technical College, A
West Georgia Technical College, A

Idaho

Idaho State University, A
University of Idaho, B

Illinois

Aurora University, B
Illinois State University, B
Judson College, B
Loyola University Chicago, B
Northeastern Illinois University, B
Parkland College, A
Quincy University, B
Saint Xavier University, B
Southern Illinois University Edwardsville, B
University of Illinois at Chicago, B

Indiana

Ancilla College, A
Bethel College, AB
Brown Mackie College-Merrillville, A
Brown Mackie College-Michigan City, A
Butler University, B
Indiana Business College (Anderson), A
Indiana Business College (Columbus), A
Indiana Business College (Muncie), A

Indiana Business College (Terre Haute), A
Indiana University Bloomington, B
Indiana University East, A
Indiana University Kokomo, AB
Indiana University-Purdue University Fort
  Wayne, AB
Indiana University-Purdue University
  Indianapolis, AB
Indiana Wesleyan University, AB
Ivy Tech Community College-Bloomington, A
Ivy Tech Community College-Central Indiana, A
Ivy Tech Community College-East Central, A
Ivy Tech Community College-Kokomo, A
Ivy Tech Community College-North Central, A
Ivy Tech Community College-Northwest, A
Ivy Tech Community College-Southwest, A
Ivy Tech Community College-Wabash Valley, A
Manchester College, A
Saint Joseph's College, B

Iowa

Ashford University, B
Buena Vista University, B
Hamilton College (Cedar Falls), AB
Kaplan University, AB
Loras College, B
St. Ambrose University, B
Southeastern Community College, South
  Campus, A

Kansas

Bethany College, B
Central Christian College of Kansas, A
Fort Hays State University, B
Wichita State University, B

Kentucky

Bellarmine University, B
Brown Mackie College-Hopkinsville, A
Brown Mackie College-Louisville, A
Kentucky State University, B
Kentucky Wesleyan College, B
Murray State University, AB
Northern Kentucky University, B
Pikeville College, AB
Sullivan University, A

Louisiana

Louisiana State University at Eunice, A
Louisiana State University in Shreveport, B
Louisiana Technical College, A
Loyola University New Orleans, B
McNeese State University, B
Northwestern State University of Louisiana, B
Southeastern Louisiana University, B
Southern University and Agricultural and Mechanical
  College, B
Tulane University, B
University of Louisiana at Lafayette, B
University of Louisiana at Monroe, B

Maine

Husson College, AB
Saint Joseph's College of Maine, B
The University of Maine at Augusta, A

Maryland

Garrett College, A
Mount St. Mary's University, B
TESST College of Technology (Towson), A

Massachusetts

Berkshire Community College, A
Bridgewater State College, B
Bristol Community College, A
Endicott College, B
Lasell College, B
Marian Court College, A
Northeastern University, B
Stonehill College, B
University of Massachusetts Boston, B

Worcester State College, B

Michigan

Kellogg Community College, A
Madonna University, AB
Michigan State University, B
Monroe County Community College, A
Olivet College, B
Saginaw Valley State University, B
University of Michigan-Dearborn, B
Wayne State University, B
Western Michigan University, B

Minnesota

Augsburg College, B
Concordia University, St. Paul, B
Inver Hills Community College, A
Metropolitan State University, B
Minneapolis Community and Technical College, A
Minnesota State University Moorhead, B
Normandale Community College, A
North Hennepin Community College, A
Northwestern College, B
Southwest Minnesota State University, B
Vermilion Community College, A

Mississippi

Alcorn State University, B
Delta State University, B
Jackson State University, B
University of Southern Mississippi, B

Missouri

Central Methodist University, B
Grantham University, AB
Missouri Baptist University, B
Missouri State University, B
Missouri Western State University, AB

Montana

University of Great Falls, B

Nebraska

Central Community College-Grand Island
  Campus, A
University of Nebraska at Kearney, B
University of Nebraska at Omaha, B
Wayne State College, B
Western Nebraska Community College, A

Nevada

Great Basin College, A

New Hampshire

Hesser College, B
Plymouth State University, B
Saint Anselm College, B

New Jersey

Caldwell College, B
Fairleigh Dickinson University, Metropolitan
  Campus, B
Hudson County Community College, A
Monmouth University, B
New Jersey City University, B
Rutgers, The State University of New Jersey,
  Camden, B
Rutgers, The State University of New Jersey,
  Newark, B
Saint Peter's College, B
Seton Hall University, B

New Mexico

Central New Mexico Community College, A
College of the Southwest, B
Eastern New Mexico University, B
Eastern New Mexico University-Roswell, A
New Mexico Highlands University, B
New Mexico State University, AB
New Mexico State University-Alamogordo, A
Northern New Mexico Community College, A
San Juan College, A

Santa Fe Community College, A

New York

Cazenovia College, AB
Dutchess Community College, A
Jamestown Community College, A
Long Island University, Brentwood Campus, B
Long Island University, C.W. Post Campus, B
Medaille College, B
Molloy College, B
Mount Saint Mary College, B
Nassau Community College, A
North Country Community College, A
Rochester Institute of Technology, B
St. Francis College, AB
State University of New York College at Oneonta, B

North Carolina

Alamance Community College, A
Appalachian State University, B
Chowan University, B
Cleveland Community College, A
East Carolina University, B
Elizabeth City State University, B
Fayetteville Technical Community College, A
Guilford College, B
High Point University, B
Shaw University, AB
The University of North Carolina at Charlotte, B
The University of North Carolina at Pembroke, B
The University of North Carolina Wilmington, B
Western Carolina University, B

North Dakota

Jamestown College, B
Minot State University, B
University of North Dakota, B

Ohio

Bluffton University, B
Bowling Green State University, B
Bowling Green State University-Firelands
    College, AB
Brown Mackie College-Akron, A
Brown Mackie College-Findlay, A
Brown Mackie College-North Canton, A
Capital University, B
North Central State College, A
Northwest State Community College, A
Ohio Northern University, B
The Ohio State University, B
Ohio University, B
Tiffin University, B
The University of Akron, B
The University of Toledo, B
Xavier University, AB
Youngstown State University, AB

Oklahoma

St. Gregory's University, A
Southeastern Oklahoma State University, B
Southwestern Oklahoma State University at
    Sayre, A
University of Central Oklahoma, B

Oregon

Linn-Benton Community College, A
Southwestern Oregon Community College, A
University of Portland, B

Pennsylvania

Bloomsburg University of Pennsylvania, B
DeSales University, B
Edinboro University of Pennsylvania, B
Elizabethtown College, B
Gannon University, AB
Juniata College, B
Keystone College, A
King's College, AB
Kutztown University of Pennsylvania, B
La Roche College, B
La Salle University, B
Lackawanna College, A
Lincoln University, B
Marywood University, B

Mercyhurst College, B
Messiah College, B
Mount Aloysius College, AB
Neumann College, B
Northampton County Area Community College, A
The Pennsylvania State University Abington
    College, B
The Pennsylvania State University Altoona
    College, AB
The Pennsylvania State University Fayette Campus
    of the Commonwealth College, B
The Pennsylvania State University Harrisburg
    Campus, B
The Pennsylvania State University Schuylkill
    Campus of the Capital College, B
The Pennsylvania State University Wilkes-Barre
    Campus of the Commonwealth College, B
Point Park University, B
Shippensburg University of Pennsylvania, B
Temple University, B
Thiel College, B
The University of Scranton, AB
West Chester University of Pennsylvania, B
Wilkes University, B

Puerto Rico

Inter American University of Puerto Rico, Aguadilla
    Campus, B
Universidad Metropolitana, B
University of the Sacred Heart, B

Rhode Island

Rhode Island College, B

South Carolina

Central Carolina Technical College, A
Charleston Southern University, B
Limestone College, B
Midlands Technical College, A
Orangeburg-Calhoun Technical College, A
Piedmont Technical College, A

South Dakota

Colorado Technical University Sioux Falls
    Campus, AB
Mount Marty College, B

Tennessee

Draughons Junior College (Clarksville), A
Lane College, B
Southwest Tennessee Community College, A

Texas

Angelo State University, B
Central Texas College, A
College of the Mainland, A
Eastfield College, A
El Centro College, A
Kilgore College, A
Lamar State College-Port Arthur, A
Lubbock Christian University, B
Northwest Vista College, A
Prairie View A&M University, B
St. Edward's University, B
Sam Houston State University, B
Stephen F. Austin State University, B
Tarleton State University, B
Texas A&M International University, B
Texas A&M University-Texarkana, B
Texas Christian University, B
Texas State University-San Marcos, B
Texas Wesleyan University, B
Texas Woman's University, B
University of Houston-Downtown, B
University of North Texas, B
The University of Texas at Arlington, B
The University of Texas at San Antonio, B
The University of Texas at Tyler, B

Wayland Baptist University, B

Utah

Dixie State College of Utah, A
Weber State University, AB

Vermont

Champlain College, AB

Virginia

Ferrum College, B
J. Sargeant Reynolds Community College, A
Marymount University, B
Roanoke College, B
The University of Virginia's College at Wise, B
Virginia State University, B

Washington

Columbia Basin College, A
Crown College, A
Lower Columbia College, A
Walla Walla Community College, A

West Virginia

American Public University System, B
Bluefield State College, B
Community and Technical College of Shepherd, A
Marshall University, B
Mountain State University, AB
Potomac State College of West Virginia
    University, A
West Virginia State Community and Technical
    College, A

Wisconsin

Lakeland College, B
University of Wisconsin-Eau Claire, B
University of Wisconsin-Superior, B
Viterbo University, B

Wyoming

Eastern Wyoming College, A
University of Wyoming, B

British Columbia

University College of the Fraser Valley, B

Ontario

Ryerson University, B
University of Windsor, B

Saskatchewan

University of Regina, B

CRIMINALISTICS AND CRIMINAL SCIENCE

Florida

St. Petersburg College, A

West Virginia

West Virginia University, B

CRIMINOLOGY

Alabama

Andrew Jackson University, M
Auburn University, B
Auburn University Montgomery, M
Faulkner University, A
Jacksonville State University, M
Troy University, M
The University of Alabama, M
The University of Alabama at Birmingham, M

University of North Alabama, M

Alaska

University of Alaska Fairbanks, M

Arizona

Arizona State University West, M
Northern Arizona University, MO

Arkansas

Arkansas State University, B
Southeast Arkansas College, A
University of Arkansas at Little Rock, M

California

California State University, Fresno, BM
California State University, Long Beach, M
California State University, Los Angeles, M
California State University, Sacramento, M
California State University, San Bernardino, M
California State University, Stanislaus, M
Hartnell College, A
San Diego State University, M
San Jose State University, M
Touro University International, M
University of California, Irvine, BMD
University of La Verne, B

Colorado

Colorado State University-Pueblo, B
Mesa State College, B
University of Colorado at Colorado Springs, M
University of Colorado at Denver and Health
  Sciences Center - Downtown Denver Campus, M
University of Denver, BM

Connecticut

Central Connecticut State University, BM
University of New Haven, M
Western Connecticut State University, M

Delaware

University of Delaware, MD
Wilmington College, M

District of Columbia

American University, MDO
Gallaudet University, B
The George Washington University, M
University of the District of Columbia, A

Florida

Barry University, B
Daytona Beach Community College, A
Florida Agricultural and Mechanical University, M
Florida Atlantic University, M
Florida Gulf Coast University, M
Florida International University, M
Florida Metropolitan University-Brandon Campus, M
Florida Metropolitan University-Pinellas Campus, M
Florida State University, BMDO
Lynn University, M
Nova Southeastern University, M
Pensacola Junior College, A
Saint Leo University, M
St. Thomas University, MO
University of Central Florida, MO
University of Florida, BMDO
University of Miami, B
University of North Florida, M
University of South Florida, MD
The University of Tampa, B

Georgia

Albany State University, M
Armstrong Atlantic State University, M
Clark Atlanta University, M
Dalton State College, A
Georgia College & State University, M
Georgia State University, M
Paine College, B
South Georgia College, A
Thomas University, B

Valdosta State University, M

Hawaii

Chaminade University of Honolulu, ABM

Idaho

Boise State University, M

Illinois

Chicago State University, M
Dominican University, B
Illinois State University, M
Lewis University, M
Lincoln College, A
Loyola University Chicago, M
Southern Illinois University Carbondale, M
University of Illinois at Chicago, M

Indiana

Ball State University, AB
Indiana State University, ABM
Indiana University Bloomington, MD
Indiana University Northwest, M
Valparaiso University, B

Iowa

St. Ambrose University, M
University of Northern Iowa, B
Upper Iowa University, BM
William Penn University, B

Kansas

Bethel College, B
Washburn University, M
Wichita State University, M

Kentucky

Eastern Kentucky University, M
Morehead State University, M
University of Louisville, M

Louisiana

Grambling State University, M
Loyola University New Orleans, M
University of Louisiana at Monroe, M

Maine

Husson College, B
University of Southern Maine, B

Maryland

Coppin State University, M
University of Baltimore, MO
University of Maryland, College Park, BMDO
University of Maryland Eastern Shore, M

Massachusetts

American International College, M
Anna Maria College, M
Boston University, M
Bridgewater State College, M
Fitchburg State College, M
Northeastern University, M
Stonehill College, B
Suffolk University, O
University of Massachusetts Lowell, M
Western New England College, M
Westfield State College, M

Michigan

Central Michigan University, BM
Eastern Michigan University, BM
Ferris State University, M
Grand Valley State University, MO
Madonna University, M
Michigan State University, MD
Northern Michigan University, M
University of Detroit Mercy, M
Wayne State University, M

Western Michigan University, B

Minnesota

Concordia University, St. Paul, M
Northland Community and Technical College-Thief
  River Falls, A
St. Cloud State University, BM
Saint Mary's University of Minnesota, M
University of Minnesota, Duluth, BM
University of St. Thomas, B

Mississippi

Delta State University, M
Jackson State University, M
Mississippi College, M
Mississippi Valley State University, M
University of Southern Mississippi, MD

Missouri

Central Missouri State University, M
College of the Ozarks, B
Columbia College, M
Drury University, BM
Lincoln University, M
Lindenwood University, BM
Maryville University of Saint Louis, B
Saint Louis University, M
Southeast Missouri State University, M
University of Missouri-Kansas City, BMD
University of Missouri-St. Louis, BMD

Montana

University of Great Falls, M
The University of Montana-Missoula, M

Nebraska

Midland Lutheran College, B
University of Nebraska at Omaha, MD

Nevada

University of Nevada, Las Vegas, M
University of Nevada, Reno, B

New Hampshire

Rivier College, B

New Jersey

Centenary College, B
Monmouth University, MO
New Jersey City University, M
The Richard Stockton College of New Jersey, B
Rutgers, The State University of New Jersey,
  Camden, M
Rutgers, The State University of New Jersey,
  Newark, MD

New Mexico

New Mexico Highlands University, B
New Mexico State University, M

New York

Buffalo State College, State University of New
  York, M
Iona College, M
John Jay College of Criminal Justice of the City
  University of New York, MD
Le Moyne College, B
Long Island University, Brentwood Campus, M
Long Island University, C.W. Post Campus, M
Niagara University, BM
Sage College of Albany, B
St. John's University, BM
State University of New York College at
  Brockport, B
State University of New York College at Cortland, B
State University of New York College at Old
  Westbury, B
State University of New York at New Paltz, B
State University of New York at Plattsburgh, B
University at Albany, State University of New
  York, MDO

Utica College, M

North Carolina

Catawba Valley Community College, A
East Carolina University, M
North Carolina Central University, M
North Carolina State University, B
The University of North Carolina at Charlotte, M

North Dakota

Minot State University, M
North Dakota State University, MD
University of North Dakota, D

Ohio

Bowling Green State University, MD
Capital University, B
College of Mount St. Joseph, B
Kent State University, M
The Ohio State University, B
Ohio University, B
Tiffin University, M
University of Cincinnati, MD
The University of Toledo, M
Wright State University, BM
Xavier University, M
Youngstown State University, M

Oklahoma

East Central University, M
Northeastern State University, M
Oklahoma City University, M
University of Central Oklahoma, M
University of Oklahoma, B

Oregon

Portland State University, MD
Southern Oregon University, B

Pennsylvania

Albright College, B
Butler County Community College, A
Cabrini College, B
DeSales University, M
Immaculata University, B
Indiana University of Pennsylvania, ABMD
Juniata College, B
Marywood University, BM
Mercyhurst College, M
Mount Aloysius College, B
The Pennsylvania State University Harrisburg
    Campus, M
The Pennsylvania State University University Park
    Campus, MD
Point Park University, M
Rosemont College, M
Saint Francis University, B
Saint Joseph's University, BMO
Shippensburg University of Pennsylvania, M
Temple University, MD
University of Pennsylvania, MD
University of Pittsburgh, M
Villanova University, M
West Chester University of Pennsylvania, M
Widener University, MO

Puerto Rico

Caribbean University, B
Inter American University of Puerto Rico,
    Metropolitan Campus, M
Pontifical Catholic University of Puerto Rico, BM
Universidad del Turabo, BM

Rhode Island

Roger Williams University, M

South Carolina

Charleston Southern University, M
Coker College, B
University of South Carolina, MO

Tennessee

East Tennessee State University, M
Middle Tennessee State University, M

Tennessee State University, M
University of Memphis, BM
The University of Tennessee, MD
The University of Tennessee at Chattanooga, M

Texas

College of the Mainland, A
Dallas Baptist University, M
Lamar University, M
Midwestern State University, M
St. Edward's University, B
St. Mary's University of San Antonio, B
Sam Houston State University, MD
Sul Ross State University, M
Tarleton State University, M
Texas A&M International University, M
Texas A&M University-Kingsville, B
Texas State University-San Marcos, M
University of Houston-Clear Lake, M
University of North Texas, M
The University of Texas at Arlington, M
The University of Texas at Dallas, B
The University of Texas-Pan American, M
The University of Texas of the Permian Basin, BM
The University of Texas at San Antonio, M
The University of Texas at Tyler, M
West Texas A&M University, M

Vermont

Castleton State College, B
Norwich University, M

Virginia

Longwood University, M
Marymount University, B
Norfolk State University, M
Old Dominion University, B
Radford University, M
Virginia Commonwealth University, MO
Virginia Union University, B
Virginia Wesleyan College, B

Washington

Washington State University, MD

West Virginia

American Public University System, M
Davis & Elkins College, B
Marshall University, M
Mountain State University, M

Wisconsin

Marquette University, AB
University of Wisconsin-Milwaukee, M
University of Wisconsin-Platteville, M

Wyoming

Western Wyoming Community College, A

Alberta

University of Alberta, BM

British Columbia

Kwantlen University College, AB
Simon Fraser University, BMD

New Brunswick

St. Thomas University, B

Newfoundland and Labrador

Memorial University of Newfoundland, B

Nova Scotia

Saint Mary's University, BM

Ontario

Carleton University, B
University of Ottawa, BMD
University of Toronto, BMDO
The University of Western Ontario, B

University of Windsor, B

Quebec

Université de Montréal, BMD

CRITICAL CARE NURSING

New York

State University of New York at Buffalo, B

British Columbia

British Columbia Institute of Technology, B

CROP PRODUCTION

Arkansas

University of Arkansas, B

Colorado

Colorado State University, B

Iowa

Iowa Lakes Community College, A

Kansas

Barton County Community College, A

Massachusetts

University of Massachusetts Amherst, A

Michigan

Northwestern Michigan College, A

Nebraska

Northeast Community College, A

New York

Cornell University, B

North Dakota

North Dakota State University, B

Ohio

The Ohio State University Agricultural Technical
    Institute, A

Pennsylvania

Delaware Valley College, B

Vermont

Sterling College, AB

Washington

Washington State University, B

CULINARY ARTS AND RELATED SERVICES

California

Santa Barbara City College, A

Florida

Hillsborough Community College, A

Illinois

Lexington College, AB

Iowa

Iowa Lakes Community College, A

Massachusetts

Newbury College, B

New York

New York Institute of Technology, A

Oregon

Linn-Benton Community College, A

Pennsylvania

The Art Institute of Pittsburgh, AB
Delaware Valley College, A

Keystone College, A

Washington

Olympic College, A

CULINARY ARTS/CHEF TRAINING

Alabama

H. Councill Trenholm State Technical College, A
Shelton State Community College, A
Virginia College at Birmingham, A

Alaska

University of Alaska Anchorage, A
University of Alaska Fairbanks, A

Arizona

The Art Institute of Phoenix, AB
Cochise College (Douglas), A
Scottsdale Community College, A

Arkansas

Ozarka College, A

California

American River College, A
The Art Institute of California-San Diego, A
Bakersfield College, A
California Culinary Academy, A
College of the Desert, A
College of the Sequoias, A
Columbia College, A
Contra Costa College, A
Cypress College, A
El Camino College, A
Glendale Community College, A
Laney College, A
Long Beach City College, A
Los Angeles Mission College, A
Los Angeles Trade-Technical College, A
Orange Coast College, A
Oxnard College, A
Riverside Community College District, A
San Joaquin Delta College, A
Santa Rosa Junior College, A
Shasta College, A

Colorado

The Art Institute of Colorado, AB
Johnson & Wales University, AB
Mesa State College, A
Pueblo Community College, A

Connecticut

International College of Hospitality Management, A

Delaware

Delaware Technical & Community College,
Stanton/Wilmington Campus, A

Florida

The Art Institute of Fort Lauderdale, A
The Art Institute of Tampa, A
Brevard Community College, A
Daytona Beach Community College, A
Florida Community College at Jacksonville, A
Florida Culinary Institute, A
Gulf Coast Community College, A
Hillsborough Community College, A
Indian River Community College, A
Johnson & Wales University, AB
Keiser College (Fort Lauderdale), A
Keiser College (Melbourne), A
Keiser College (Tallahassee), A
Pensacola Junior College, A
Valencia Community College, A

Georgia

Albany Technical College, A
The Art Institute of Atlanta, A
Atlanta Technical College, A
Augusta Technical College, A

Chattahoochee Technical College, A
Georgia Southwestern State University, A
North Georgia Technical College, A
Ogeechee Technical College, A
Savannah Technical College, A
South Georgia Technical College, A

Hawaii

Kapiolani Community College, A
Kauai Community College, A

Idaho

Boise State University, A
College of Southern Idaho, A
Idaho State University, A
North Idaho College, A

Illinois

Black Hawk College, A
College of DuPage, A
The Cooking and Hospitality Institute of Chicago, A
Elgin Community College, A
Illinois Eastern Community Colleges, Lincoln Trail
College, A
The Illinois Institute of Art-Chicago, A
Joliet Junior College, A
Kaskaskia College, A
Kendall College, AB
Lexington College, AB
Rend Lake College, A
Robert Morris College, A
St. Augustine College, A
Triton College, A
William Rainey Harper College, A

Indiana

Oakland City University, A
Purdue University Calumet, A
Vincennes University, A

Iowa

Des Moines Area Community College, A
Iowa Western Community College, A
Kirkwood Community College, A
Scott Community College, A

Kentucky

Jefferson Community and Technical College, A
Sullivan University, AB

Louisiana

Louisiana Technical College, A
Nicholls State University, AB

Maine

Eastern Maine Community College, A
Southern Maine Community College, A
York County Community College, A

Maryland

Allegany College of Maryland, A
Baltimore International College, A

Massachusetts

Bristol Community College, A
Bunker Hill Community College, A
Massasoit Community College, A
Middlesex Community College, A
Newbury College, A
North Shore Community College, A

Michigan

Baker College of Muskegon, A
Grand Rapids Community College, A
Henry Ford Community College, A
Macomb Community College, A
Monroe County Community College, A
Mott Community College, A
Northwestern Michigan College, A
Oakland Community College, A
Schoolcraft College, A
Washtenaw Community College, A

Wayne County Community College District, A

Minnesota

The Art Institutes International Minnesota, AB
Hibbing Community College, A
Metropolitan State University, B
Minneapolis Community and Technical College, A
South Central Technical College, A

Mississippi

Mississippi University for Women, B

Missouri

East Central College, A
Jefferson College, A
Ozarks Technical Community College, A
St. Louis Community College at Forest Park, A

Montana

The University of Montana-Missoula, A

Nebraska

Metropolitan Community College, A
Southeast Community College, Lincoln Campus, A

Nevada

Community College of Southern Nevada, A
Truckee Meadows Community College, A
University of Nevada, Las Vegas, B

New Hampshire

McIntosh College, A
New Hampshire Community Technical College,
Berlin/Laconia, A
Southern New Hampshire University, A
University of New Hampshire, A

New Jersey

Atlantic Cape Community College, A
Brookdale Community College, A
Hudson County Community College, A
Mercer County Community College, A
Middlesex County College, A

New Mexico

Central New Mexico Community College, A
Santa Fe Community College, A
Southwestern Indian Polytechnic Institute, A

New York

Adirondack Community College, A
The Culinary Institute of America, AB
Erie Community College, A
Erie Community College, North Campus, A
Mohawk Valley Community College, A
Niagara County Community College, A
Onondaga Community College, A
Paul Smith's College of Arts and Sciences, AB
Rockland Community College, A
Schenectady County Community College, A
State University of New York College of Agriculture
and Technology at Cobleskill, A
State University of New York College of Technology
at Alfred, A
State University of New York College of Technology
at Delhi, A
Suffolk County Community College, A
Sullivan County Community College, A
Westchester Community College, A

North Carolina

Alamance Community College, A
Asheville-Buncombe Technical Community
College, A
Central Piedmont Community College, A
College of The Albemarle, A
Fayetteville Technical Community College, A
Guilford Technical Community College, A
Johnson & Wales University, A
Sandhills Community College, A
Southwestern Community College, A

Wake Technical Community College, A

Ohio

Cincinnati State Technical and Community
  College, A
Columbus State Community College, A
Hocking College, A
Sinclair Community College, A
The University of Akron, A
Zane State College, A

Oklahoma

Oklahoma State University, Okmulgee, A

Oregon

Central Oregon Community College, A
Lane Community College, A
Linn-Benton Community College, A

Pennsylvania

The Art Institute of Philadelphia, A
The Art Institute of Pittsburgh, AB
Bucks County Community College, A
Commonwealth Technical Institute, A
Community College of Allegheny County, A
Community College of Beaver County, A
Community College of Philadelphia, A
Drexel University, B
Harrisburg Area Community College, A
International Academy of Design & Technology, A
Keystone College, A
Lehigh Carbon Community College, A
Luzerne County Community College, A
Mercyhurst College, AB
Montgomery County Community College, A
Pennsylvania College of Technology, AB
Pennsylvania Culinary Institute, A
Reading Area Community College, A
The Restaurant School at Walnut Hill College, A
Saint Francis University, A
Westmoreland County Community College, A
Yorktowne Business Institute, A

Rhode Island

Johnson & Wales University, AB

South Carolina

Horry-Georgetown Technical College, A
Trident Technical College, A

South Dakota

Mitchell Technical Institute, A

Tennessee

Nashville State Technical Community College, A

Texas

The Art Institute of Dallas, A
The Art Institute of Houston, A
Del Mar College, A
El Centro College, A
Galveston College, A
Odessa College, A
St. Philip's College, A
Texas Culinary Academy, A
Texas State Technical College Waco, A

Utah

Utah Valley State College, A

Vermont

New England Culinary Institute, A
New England Culinary Institute at Essex, A

Virginia

The Art Institute of Washington, A
J. Sargeant Reynolds Community College, A
Stratford University, A
Virginia Intermont College, AB

Washington

The Art Institute of Seattle, A
Bates Technical College, A
Clark College, A

Edmonds Community College, A
Lake Washington Technical College, A
Olympic College, A
Renton Technical College, A
Seattle Central Community College, A
Skagit Valley College, A
South Puget Sound Community College, A
South Seattle Community College, A
Spokane Community College, A

West Virginia

Community and Technical College of Shepherd, A
Community & Technical College at West Virginia
  University Institute of Technology, A
Mountain State University, AB

Wisconsin

Blackhawk Technical College, A
Chippewa Valley Technical College, A
Fox Valley Technical College, A
Madison Area Technical College, A
Milwaukee Area Technical College, A
Moraine Park Technical College, A
Nicolet Area Technical College, A
Southwest Wisconsin Technical College, A

CULTURAL RESOURCE MANAGEMENT AND POLICY ANALYSIS

Louisiana

Northwestern State University of Louisiana, B

Vermont

Sterling College, B

Ontario

University of Waterloo, B

CULTURAL STUDIES

Alaska

University of Alaska Fairbanks, M

California

Biola University, MDO
University of California, Davis, MD

Illinois

Southern Illinois University Carbondale, M
University of Chicago, MD
Wheaton College, MO

Indiana

Valparaiso University, M

Massachusetts

Simmons College, M

Michigan

Cornerstone University, P

Minnesota

University of Minnesota, Twin Cities Campus, D

Missouri

Baptist Bible College, M

New York

Cornell University, D
Stony Brook University, State University of New
  York, O

Oregon

Lewis & Clark College, M

Pennsylvania

University of Pittsburgh, D

Puerto Rico

University of the Sacred Heart, M

South Carolina

Columbia International University, MPO

Tennessee

Union University, M

Texas

University of Houston-Clear Lake, M
The University of Texas at San Antonio, D

Virginia

George Mason University, D

Alberta

Athabasca University, M
Taylor University College and Seminary, M

Nova Scotia

St. Francis Xavier University, M

Ontario

Brock University, M
McMaster University, MD

CURRICULUM AND INSTRUCTION

Alabama

Auburn University, MDO
The University of Alabama, MDO

Alaska

University of Alaska Fairbanks, M

Arizona

Argosy University/Phoenix, DO
Arizona State University, MD
Northern Arizona University, D
University of Phoenix Online Campus, M
University of Phoenix-Phoenix Campus, M
University of Phoenix-Southern Arizona Campus, M

Arkansas

Arkansas State University, MDO
Arkansas Tech University, M
Henderson State University, M
University of Arkansas, D

California

Argosy University/Orange County, MD
Argosy University/San Francisco Bay Area, MD
Azusa Pacific University, M
California Baptist University, M
California Polytechnic State University, San Luis
  Obispo, M
California State University, Bakersfield, M
California State University, Chico, M
California State University, Dominguez Hills, M
California State University, Fresno, M
California State University, Sacramento, M
California State University, San Bernardino, M
California State University, Stanislaus, M
Chapman University, M
Concordia University, M
Dominican University of California, M
Fresno Pacific University, M
Holy Names University, M
La Sierra University, MDO
Notre Dame de Namur University, M
San Diego State University, M
Sonoma State University, M
Stanford University, MD
University of California, Davis, D
University of the Pacific, MD
University of Phoenix-Bay Area Campus, M
University of Phoenix-Sacramento Valley
  Campus, M
University of Phoenix-San Diego Campus, M

University of Phoenix-Southern California
  Campus, M
University of San Diego, MD
University of San Francisco, MD
University of Southern California, MD

Colorado

Colorado Christian University, M
Jones International University, M
University of Colorado at Boulder, MD
University of Colorado at Colorado Springs, M
University of Denver, MD
University of Phoenix-Denver Campus, M
University of Phoenix-Southern Colorado
  Campus, M

Connecticut

Albertus Magnus College, B
University of Connecticut, MD
Western Connecticut State University, M

Delaware

Delaware State University, M
University of Delaware, M

District of Columbia

The Catholic University of America, M
The George Washington University, MDO

Florida

Argosy University/Sarasota, MDO
Argosy University/Tampa, MDO
Florida Atlantic University, MDO
Florida Gulf Coast University, M
Florida International University, MDO
Saint Leo University, M
Stetson University, O
University of Central Florida, DO
University of Florida, MDO
University of Phoenix-Central Florida Campus, M
University of Phoenix-North Florida Campus, M
University of Phoenix-South Florida Campus, M
University of Phoenix-West Florida Campus, M
University of West Florida, MDO

Georgia

Argosy University/Atlanta, MD
Berry College, O
Clark Atlanta University, MO
Georgia Southern University, D
LaGrange College, M
Piedmont College, O

Hawaii

Argosy University/Hawaii, MD
University of Hawaii at Manoa, MD
University of Phoenix-Hawaii Campus, M

Idaho

Boise State University, MD
Idaho State University, M
Northwest Nazarene University, M

Illinois

American InterContinental University Online, M
Argosy University/Schaumburg, MDO
Aurora University, D
Benedictine University, M
Bradley University, M
Concordia University, M
DePaul University, MD
Dominican University, M
Illinois State University, MD
Lewis University, M
Loyola University Chicago, MD
National-Louis University, MDO
Northern Illinois University, MD
Olivet Nazarene University, M
Saint Xavier University, M
Southern Illinois University Carbondale, MD
University of Illinois at Chicago, MD
University of Illinois at Urbana-Champaign, MDO
University of St. Francis, M

Western Illinois University, M

Indiana

Ball State University, MO
Indiana State University, MD
Indiana University Bloomington, MDO
Indiana Wesleyan University, M
Purdue University, MDO
Purdue University Calumet, M
Valparaiso University, M

Iowa

Iowa State University of Science and
  Technology, MD
The University of Iowa, MD
University of Northern Iowa, MD

Kansas

Emporia State University, M
Kansas State University, MD
MidAmerica Nazarene University, M
Newman University, M
University of Kansas, MD
University of Saint Mary, BM
Washburn University, BM
Wichita State University, M

Kentucky

Brescia University, M
Campbellsville University, M
Eastern Kentucky University, M
Morehead State University, O
University of Kentucky, MD
University of Louisville, D

Louisiana

Centenary College of Louisiana, M
Grambling State University, D
Louisiana State University and Agricultural and
  Mechanical College, MDO
Louisiana Tech University, MD
Nicholls State University, M
Our Lady of Holy Cross College, M
Southeastern Louisiana University, M
University of Louisiana at Lafayette, M
University of Louisiana at Monroe, DO
University of New Orleans, MDO
Xavier University of Louisiana, M

Maryland

Coppin State University, M
Frostburg State College, M
Hood College, M
The Johns Hopkins University, M
Loyola College in Maryland, MO
McDaniel College, M
University of Maryland, College Park, MDO

Massachusetts

Boston College, MDO
Boston University, MDO
Framingham State College, M
Harvard University, M
Lesley University, MO
Massachusetts College of Liberal Arts, M
Suffolk University, O
University of Massachusetts Amherst, MDO
University of Massachusetts Boston, M
University of Massachusetts Lowell, MO

Michigan

Andrews University, MDO
Calvin College, M
Eastern Michigan University, M
Ferris State University, M
Michigan State University, MDO
Siena Heights University, M
University of Detroit Mercy, M
University of Michigan, M
University of Michigan-Dearborn, MO
University of Phoenix-Metro Detroit Campus, M
University of Phoenix-West Michigan Campus, M

Wayne State University, MDO

Minnesota

The College of St. Scholastica, M
Minnesota State University Moorhead, M
St. Cloud State University, M
Saint Mary's University of Minnesota, MO
University of Minnesota, Twin Cities Campus, MDO
University of St. Thomas, MDO

Mississippi

Delta State University, D
Mississippi State University, MDO
University of Mississippi, MDO
University of Southern Mississippi, MDO

Missouri

Central Missouri State University, MO
Missouri State University, M
Saint Louis University, MD
University of Missouri-Columbia, MDO
University of Missouri-Kansas City, MO
University of Missouri-St. Louis, M
William Woods University, M

Montana

Montana State University-Billings, M
University of Great Falls, M
The University of Montana-Missoula, BMD

Nebraska

Concordia University, M
Doane College, M
University of Nebraska at Kearney, M
University of Nebraska-Lincoln, MDO

Nevada

University of Nevada, Las Vegas, MDO
University of Nevada, Reno, MDO
University of Phoenix-Nevada Campus, M

New Hampshire

Keene State College, BM
Rivier College, M
Southern New Hampshire University, M

New Jersey

Caldwell College, M
Fairleigh Dickinson University, Metropolitan
  Campus, M
Kean University, MO
Montclair State University, MD
Rider University, BM
Rowan University, M
Saint Peter's College, MO

New Mexico

College of Santa Fe, M
College of the Southwest, M
New Mexico Highlands University, M
New Mexico State University, MDO
University of Phoenix-New Mexico Campus, M

New York

Cornell University, MD
Fordham University, MD
Medaille College, M
Pace University, M
St. John's University, B
State University of New York College at
  Brockport, M
State University of New York at Plattsburgh, M
Syracuse University, MDO
University at Albany, State University of New
  York, MDO

North Carolina

Appalachian State University, M
East Carolina University, M
North Carolina State University, MD
Shaw University, M
The University of North Carolina at Chapel Hill, MD
The University of North Carolina at Charlotte, MD
The University of North Carolina at Greensboro, D

The University of North Carolina Wilmington, M

Ohio

Ashland University, M
Bowling Green State University, M
Cleveland State University, M
Franciscan University of Steubenville, M
Kent State University, MDO
Malone College, M
Miami University, M
Ohio University, BMD
University of Cincinnati, MD
The University of Toledo, MDO
Wright State University, BMO

Oklahoma

Oklahoma City University, M
Oklahoma State University, MD
Oral Roberts University, M
University of Oklahoma, MD

Oregon

Concordia University, M
Portland State University, MD

Pennsylvania

Bloomsburg University of Pennsylvania, M
Bucknell University, M
College Misericordia, M
Drexel University, M
Duquesne University, D
Gannon University, M
Indiana University of Pennsylvania, MD
Kutztown University of Pennsylvania, M
Lock Haven University of Pennsylvania, B
Moravian College, M
The Pennsylvania State University Harrisburg
   Campus, BM
The Pennsylvania State University University Park
   Campus, MD
Philadelphia Biblical University, M
Point Park University, M
Rosemont College, M
Saint Vincent College, M
Shippensburg University of Pennsylvania, M
The University of Scranton, M

Puerto Rico

Pontifical Catholic University of Puerto Rico, M
Universidad Metropolitana, M
University of Phoenix-Puerto Rico Campus, M
University of Puerto Rico, Río Piedras, MD

South Carolina

Clemson University, D
Columbia International University, M
Converse College, O
Lander University, M
University of South Carolina, D

South Dakota

Black Hills State University, M
South Dakota State University, M
The University of South Dakota, BMDO

Tennessee

Austin Peay State University, M
Carson-Newman College, M
East Tennessee State University, M
Freed-Hardeman University, M
Lincoln Memorial University, MO
Middle Tennessee State University, MO
Southern Adventist University, M
Tennessee State University, MD
Tennessee Technological University, MO
Tennessee Temple University, M
Trevecca Nazarene University, M
University of Memphis, MD
The University of Tennessee, MDO
The University of Tennessee at Martin, M
Vanderbilt University, M

Texas

Angelo State University, M
Baylor University, MDO

Houston Baptist University, M
Midwestern State University, M
Our Lady of the Lake University of San Antonio, M
Prairie View A&M University, M
Sam Houston State University, M
Southwestern Assemblies of God University, M
Tarleton State University, BM
Texas A&M International University, M
Texas A&M University, BMD
Texas A&M University-Commerce, D
Texas A&M University-Corpus Christi, M
Texas Southern University, BMD
Texas Tech University, MDO
University of Houston, MD
University of Houston-Clear Lake, BM
University of North Texas, D
The University of Texas at Arlington, M
The University of Texas at Austin, MD
The University of Texas at Brownsville, M
The University of Texas at El Paso, M
The University of Texas at San Antonio, M
The University of Texas at Tyler, M
West Texas A&M University, M

Utah

University of Phoenix-Utah Campus, M
Utah State University, BD
Weber State University, M

Vermont

Castleton State College, M
Johnson State College, M
Lyndon State College, M
Saint Michael's College, MO
Sterling College, B
University of Vermont, M

Virginia

Argosy University/Washington D.C., MD
Averett University, M
The College of William and Mary, MD
Liberty University, M
Old Dominion University, M
University of Virginia, MDO
Virginia Commonwealth University, MO
Virginia Polytechnic Institute and State
   University, MDO

Washington

Argosy University/Seattle, MD
Central Washington University, M
City University, M
Eastern Washington University, M
Gonzaga University, M
Pacific Lutheran University, M
Seattle University, MO
University of Washington, MD
Walla Walla College, M
Washington State University, D

West Virginia

Shepherd University, M
West Virginia University, MD

Wisconsin

Concordia University Wisconsin, M
University of Wisconsin-Madison, MD
University of Wisconsin-Milwaukee, M
University of Wisconsin-Oshkosh, M
University of Wisconsin-Superior, M
University of Wisconsin-Whitewater, M

Wyoming

University of Wyoming, MD

Alberta

University of Calgary, MDO

British Columbia

Simon Fraser University, MD
The University of British Columbia, MD
University of Phoenix-Vancouver Campus, M

University of Victoria, M

Manitoba

Brandon University, MO
University of Manitoba, M

New Brunswick

University of New Brunswick Fredericton, M

Newfoundland and Labrador

Memorial University of Newfoundland, M

Nova Scotia

Acadia University, M
Mount Saint Vincent University, M

Ontario

Brock University, M
Lakehead University, M
The University of Western Ontario, M
York University, B

Quebec

McGill University, M
Université Laval, MD
Université de Montréal, MDO

Saskatchewan

University of Regina, M
University of Saskatchewan, MDO

CUSTOMER SERVICE MANAGEMENT

Wisconsin

University of Wisconsin-Stout, B

CUSTOMER SERVICE SUPPORT/CALL CENTER/TELESERVICE OPERATION

South Dakota

National American University-Sioux Falls
   Branch, AB

Wyoming

Laramie County Community College, A

CYTOGENETICS/GENETICS/CLINICAL GENETICS TECHNOLOGY/TECHNOLOGIST

Minnesota

Saint Mary's University of Minnesota, B

CYTOTECHNOLOGY/CYTOTECHNOLO

Alabama

The University of Alabama at Birmingham, B

Arkansas

University of Arkansas for Medical Sciences, B

California

California State University, Dominguez Hills, B
Loma Linda University, B

Connecticut

University of Connecticut, B

Florida

Barry University, B

Illinois

Elmhurst College, B
Illinois College, B

Indiana

Indiana University-Purdue University
   Indianapolis, AB

Indiana University Southeast, AB
Saint Mary's College, B

Iowa

Ashford University, B

Kansas

Barton County Community College, A
Highland Community College, A
University of Kansas, B

Kentucky

Bellarmine University, B

Louisiana

Louisiana State University Health Sciences
Center, B

Michigan

Michigan Technological University, B
Northern Michigan University, B

Minnesota

Minnesota State University Moorhead, B
Saint Mary's University of Minnesota, B
Winona State University, B

Mississippi

University of Mississippi Medical Center, B

Missouri

Barnes-Jewish College of Nursing and Allied
Health, B

New Jersey

Bloomfield College, B
Felician College, B

New York

The College of Saint Rose, B
Long Island University, Brooklyn Campus, B
Long Island University, C.W. Post Campus, B
St. John's University, B
State University of New York Upstate Medical
University, B
Stony Brook University, State University of New
York, B

North Dakota

University of North Dakota, B

Pennsylvania

Manor College, A
Slippery Rock University of Pennsylvania, B
Thiel College, B
Thomas Jefferson University, B

Rhode Island

Salve Regina University, B

South Carolina

Anderson University, B

Texas

University of North Texas, B

Virginia

Old Dominion University, B

West Virginia

Alderson-Broaddus College, B
Marshall University, B

Wisconsin

Edgewood College, B
Marian College of Fond du Lac, B

CZECH LANGUAGE AND LITERATURE

Texas

The University of Texas at Austin, B

DAIRY HUSBANDRY AND PRODUCTION

Ohio

The Ohio State University Agricultural Technical
Institute, A

Oregon

Linn-Benton Community College, A

Vermont

Sterling College, AB
University of Vermont, B

DAIRY SCIENCE

Alabama

Auburn University, B

California

California Polytechnic State University, San Luis
Obispo, B
College of the Sequoias, A
Modesto Junior College, A
Mt. San Antonio College, A

Florida

University of Florida, B

Georgia

University of Georgia, BM

Idaho

Brigham Young University -Idaho, A

Iowa

Iowa State University of Science and Technology, B
Northeast Iowa Community College, A

Kansas

Highland Community College, A

Louisiana

Louisiana State University and Agricultural and
Mechanical College, MD

Mississippi

Northeast Mississippi Community College, A
Northwest Mississippi Community College, A

New Hampshire

University of New Hampshire, AB

New York

Cornell University, B
State University of New York College of Agriculture
and Technology at Cobleskill, AB
State University of New York College of Agriculture
and Technology at Morrisville, A

Ohio

The Ohio State University Agricultural Technical
Institute, A

Oklahoma

Northeastern Oklahoma Agricultural and Mechanical
College, A

Pennsylvania

Delaware Valley College, B

South Dakota

South Dakota State University, BMD

Texas

Cisco Junior College, A
Hill College of the Hill Junior College District, A

Northeast Texas Community College, A
Texas A&M University, BM

Utah

Utah State University, BM

Vermont

Sterling College, B
Vermont Technical College, A

Virginia

Virginia Polytechnic Institute and State
University, BMD

Wisconsin

Chippewa Valley Technical College, A
Southwest Wisconsin Technical College, A
University of Wisconsin-Madison, BMD
University of Wisconsin-River Falls, B

Alberta

University of Alberta, B

DANCE

Alabama

Birmingham-Southern College, B
The University of Alabama, B

Arizona

Arizona State University, BM
Prescott College, B
The University of Arizona, B

California

Allan Hancock College, A
California Institute of the Arts, BMO
California State University, East Bay, B
California State University, Fresno, B
California State University, Fullerton, BM
California State University, Long Beach, BM
California State University, Los Angeles, B
California State University, Sacramento, BM
Cañada College, A
Chaffey College, A
Chapman University, B
Citrus College, A
Claremont McKenna College, B
College of Marin, A
Compton Community College, A
Cypress College, A
Fullerton College, A
Glendale Community College, A
Grossmont College, A
Lake Tahoe Community College, A
Laney College, A
Long Beach City College, A
Loyola Marymount University, B
Mills College, BM
MiraCosta College, A
Monterey Peninsula College, A
Mt. San Jacinto College, A
Orange Coast College, A
Palomar College, A
Pitzer College, B
Pomona College, B
Saint Mary's College of California, B
San Diego State University, B
San Francisco State University, B
San Joaquin Delta College, A
San Jose State University, B
Santa Ana College, A
Santa Monica College, A
Santa Rosa Junior College, A
Scripps College, B
Southwestern College, A
University of California, Berkeley, B
University of California, Irvine, BM
University of California, Los Angeles, BMD
University of California, Riverside, BMD
University of California, San Diego, B
University of California, Santa Barbara, B
University of California, Santa Cruz, B

Westmont College, B

Colorado

The Colorado College, B
Colorado State University, B
University of Colorado at Boulder, BMD

Connecticut

Connecticut College, BM
Trinity College, B
University of Hartford, B
Wesleyan University, B

District of Columbia

American University, MO
The George Washington University, B

Florida

Daytona Beach Community College, A
Florida International University, B
Florida State University, BM
Hillsborough Community College, A
Jacksonville University, B
Miami Dade College, A
New World School of the Arts, AB
Palm Beach Atlantic University, B
St. Johns River Community College, A
University of Florida, B
University of Miami, B
University of South Florida, B

Georgia

Brenau University, B
Emory University, B
University of Georgia, B

Hawaii

University of Hawaii at Manoa, BMD

Idaho

Brigham Young University -Idaho, A
Idaho State University, M
University of Idaho, B

Illinois

Columbia College Chicago, B
Lincoln College, A
Northern Illinois University, M
Northwestern University, B
University of Illinois at Urbana-Champaign, BM

Indiana

Ball State University, B
Butler University, B
Indiana University Bloomington, B

Iowa

Luther College, B
The University of Iowa, BM

Kansas

Barton County Community College, A
Friends University, B
University of Kansas, B

Kentucky

St. Catharine College, A

Louisiana

Centenary College of Louisiana, B
Tulane University, M

Maryland

Frostburg State University, B
Goucher College, B
Towson University, B
University of Maryland, Baltimore County, B
University of Maryland, College Park, BM

Massachusetts

Amherst College, B
The Boston Conservatory, B
Dean College, AB
Hampshire College, B

Mount Holyoke College, B
Northern Essex Community College, A
Simon's Rock College of Bard, B
Smith College, BM
Tufts University, MD
University of Massachusetts Amherst, B

Michigan

Alma College, B
Eastern Michigan University, B
Henry Ford Community College, A
Hope College, B
Lansing Community College, A
Marygrove College, B
Oakland University, B
University of Michigan, BM
Wayne State University, B
Western Michigan University, B

Minnesota

Gustavus Adolphus College, B
St. Olaf College, B
University of Minnesota, Twin Cities Campus, BMD

Mississippi

Belhaven College, B
University of Southern Mississippi, B

Missouri

Lindenwood University, B
Missouri State University, B
Stephens College, B
University of Missouri-Kansas City, B
Washington University in St. Louis, B
Webster University, B

Montana

The University of Montana-Missoula, B

Nebraska

University of Nebraska-Lincoln, B

Nevada

University of Nevada, Las Vegas, BM

New Jersey

Bergen Community College, A
Mercer County Community College, A
Middlesex County College, A
Montclair State University, B
Rutgers, The State University of New Jersey, New
  Brunswick/Piscataway, B

New Mexico

New Mexico State University, B
Santa Fe Community College, A
University of New Mexico, BM

New York

Adelphi University, B
Bard College, B
Barnard College, B
Columbia College, B
Columbia University, School of General Studies, B
Cornell University, B
Fordham University, B
Hamilton College, B
Hobart and William Smith Colleges, B
Hofstra University, B
Hunter College of the City University of New York, B
Ithaca College, B
The Juilliard School, B
Lehman College of the City University of New
  York, B
Long Island University, Brooklyn Campus, B
Long Island University, C.W. Post Campus, B
Manhattanville College, B
Marymount Manhattan College, B
Nassau Community College, A
New York University, BMD
Purchase College, State University of New York, BM
Queens College of the City University of New
  York, B
Sarah Lawrence College, BM

Skidmore College, B
State University of New York at Buffalo, B
State University of New York College at
  Brockport, BM
State University of New York College at Potsdam, B
State University of New York, Fredonia, B
Wells College, B
Westchester Community College, A

North Carolina

Central Piedmont Community College, A
East Carolina University, B
Elon University, B
Louisburg College, A
Meredith College, B
North Carolina School of the Arts, B
The University of North Carolina at Charlotte, B
The University of North Carolina at Greensboro, BM

Ohio

Antioch College, B
Bowling Green State University, B
Case Western Reserve University, M
Cleveland State University, B
Denison University, B
Kent State University, B
Kenyon College, B
Lake Erie College, B
Oberlin College, B
The Ohio State University, BM
Ohio University, B
Sinclair Community College, A
The University of Akron, B
University of Cincinnati, B
Wittenberg University, B
Wright State University, B

Oklahoma

Oklahoma City University, B
St. Gregory's University, B
University of Central Oklahoma, B
University of Oklahoma, BM

Oregon

Reed College, B
University of Oregon, BM
Western Oregon University, B

Pennsylvania

Cedar Crest College, B
DeSales University, B
Dickinson College, B
Franklin and Marshall College, B
La Roche College, B
Mercyhurst College, B
Muhlenberg College, B
Point Park University, B
Slippery Rock University of Pennsylvania, B
Swarthmore College, B
Temple University, BMD
The University of the Arts, B

Rhode Island

Rhode Island College, B
Roger Williams University, B

South Carolina

Coker College, B
Columbia College, B
Winthrop University, B

Tennessee

The University of Tennessee at Martin, B

Texas

Kilgore College, A
Lamar University, B
Lon Morris College, A
Navarro College, A
Sam Houston State University, BM
Southern Methodist University, BM
Stephen F. Austin State University, B
Texas State University-San Marcos, B
Texas Tech University, BMD
Texas Woman's University, BMD

Trinity Valley Community College, A
University of North Texas, B
The University of Texas at Austin, B
West Texas A&M University, B

Utah

Brigham Young University, B
Dixie State College of Utah, A
Snow College, A
Southern Utah University, B
University of Utah, BM
Utah State University, B
Utah Valley State College, A
Weber State University, B

Vermont

Bennington College, BM
Johnson State College, B
Marlboro College, B
Middlebury College, B

Virginia

George Mason University, BM
Hollins University, BM
Old Dominion University, B
Radford University, B
Randolph-Macon Woman's College, B
Shenandoah University, BM
Sweet Briar College, B
Virginia Commonwealth University, B
Virginia Intermont College, B

Washington

Cornish College of the Arts, B
University of Washington, BM

Wisconsin

University of Wisconsin-Milwaukee, BM
University of Wisconsin-Stevens Point, B

Wyoming

Casper College, A
Western Wyoming Community College, A

Alberta

University of Alberta, B
University of Calgary, B

British Columbia

Simon Fraser University, B

Ontario

Ryerson University, B
York University, BM

Quebec

Concordia University, B
Université du Québec àMontréal, BM

DANCE THERAPY/THERAPIST

Colorado

Naropa University, M

Illinois

Columbia College Chicago, BMO

New York

Pratt Institute, M

Pennsylvania

Drexel University, M

DATA ENTRY/MICROCOMPUTER APPLICATIONS

Arizona

Eastern Arizona College, A
Rio Salado College, A

Arkansas

University of Arkansas Community College at
  Batesville, A

California

American River College, A
Berkeley City College, A
Cypress College, A
Glendale Community College, A
Los Angeles City College, A
Modesto Junior College, A
Orange Coast College, A
San Diego Mesa College, A
Santa Ana College, A

Colorado

Colorado Mountain College, A
Colorado Mountain College, Alpine Campus, A
IntelliTec College (Grand Junction), A
National American University (Denver), AB

Connecticut

Capital Community College, A
Gateway Community College, A
Quinebaug Valley Community College, A

Florida

Florida Community College at Jacksonville, A
Florida National College, A
Okaloosa-Walton College, A
Seminole Community College, A
Valencia Community College, A

Georgia

West Central Technical College, A

Illinois

College of DuPage, A
Heartland Community College, A
Parkland College, A
Richland Community College, A

Indiana

Vincennes University, A

Iowa

AIB College of Business, A
Ellsworth Community College, A
Hawkeye Community College, A
Iowa Lakes Community College, A
Iowa Western Community College, A

Kansas

Brown Mackie College-Kansas City, A
Donnelly College, A
Pratt Community College, A

Kentucky

Daymar College (Owensboro), A
Henderson Community College, A
Owensboro Community and Technical College, A

Louisiana

Remington College-Lafayette Campus, A
Remington College-New Orleans Campus, A

Maryland

Anne Arundel Community College, A
Howard Community College, A
TESST College of Technology (Towson), A

Massachusetts

Bunker Hill Community College, A
North Shore Community College, A
Roxbury Community College, A

Michigan

Baker College of Allen Park, A
Kellogg Community College, A
Southwestern Michigan College, A

West Shore Community College, A

Minnesota

Dakota County Technical College, A
Northland Community and Technical College-Thief
  River Falls, A
Rasmussen College Mankato, A
Riverland Community College, A

Mississippi

Hinds Community College, A
Mississippi Gulf Coast Community College, A

Missouri

Metropolitan Community College-Business &
  Technology College, A
St. Louis Community College at Forest Park, A
Three Rivers Community College, A

Montana

Flathead Valley Community College, A
Montana State University-Great Falls College of
  Technology, A

Nebraska

Nebraska Indian Community College, A

New Jersey

Atlantic Cape Community College, A
Camden County College, A

New York

The College of Westchester, A
Eugenio María de Hostos Community College of the
  City University of New York, A
Fiorello H. LaGuardia Community College of the
  City University of New York, A
Herkimer County Community College, A
Onondaga Community College, A
Orange County Community College, A
Sullivan County Community College, A
Tompkins Cortland Community College, A

North Carolina

Cleveland Community College, A
College of The Albemarle, A
Edgecombe Community College, A

Ohio

ETI Technical College of Niles, A
Gallipolis Career College, A
Lorain County Community College, A
Marion Technical College, A
Ohio Business College (Sandusky), A
Sinclair Community College, A
Stark State College of Technology, A
Zane State College, A

Oklahoma

Oklahoma State University, Oklahoma City, A
Tulsa Community College, A

Pennsylvania

Academy of Medical Arts and Business, A
Business Institute of Pennsylvania (Meadville), A
Laurel Business Institute, A
Luzerne County Community College, A
Newport Business Institute (Lower Burrell), A
Thaddeus Stevens College of Technology, A

South Carolina

Horry-Georgetown Technical College, A
Williamsburg Technical College, A

South Dakota

Lake Area Technical Institute, A
Mitchell Technical Institute, A

Tennessee

Pellissippi State Technical Community College, A

Texas

Austin Business College, A
Austin Community College, A

Coastal Bend College, A
Del Mar College, A
Eastfield College, A
El Paso Community College, A
Galveston College, A
Laredo Community College, A
St. Philip's College, A
San Antonio College, A
Texarkana College, A
Tyler Junior College, A

Vermont

Community College of Vermont, A

Virginia

ECPI Technical College (Glen Allen), A
ECPI Technical College (Richmond), A
ECPI Technical College (Roanoke), A
Mountain Empire Community College, A
Patrick Henry Community College, A

Washington

Bellingham Technical College, A
Clark College, A
Edmonds Community College, A
Highline Community College, A
Lower Columbia College, A
Peninsula College, A
Walla Walla Community College, A

Wisconsin

Mid-State Technical College, A
Milwaukee Area Technical College, A

Wyoming

Sheridan College-Sheridan and Gillette, A
Western Wyoming Community College, A

DATA MODELING/WAREHOUSING AND DATABASE ADMINISTRATION

Arizona

Northland Pioneer College, A

California

College of the Sequoias, A
National University, B

Colorado

Arapahoe Community College, A

Florida

Florida Community College at Jacksonville, A
St. Petersburg College, A
Seminole Community College, A

Kentucky

Daymar College (Owensboro), A

Maine

Kennebec Valley Community College, A

Massachusetts

Middlesex Community College, A

Michigan

Davenport University (Dearborn), B

Minnesota

Dakota County Technical College, A
Northland Community and Technical College-Thief
River Falls, A

Missouri

Metropolitan Community College-Business &
Technology College, A

New York

Rochester Institute of Technology, B

Oklahoma

Tulsa Community College, A

Texas

El Paso Community College, A
Midland College, A

Utah

Neumont University, B

Washington

Bates Technical College, A
Edmonds Community College, A

Wyoming

Laramie County Community College, A

DATA PROCESSING AND DATA PROCESSING TECHNOLOGY/TECHNICIAN

Alabama

Chattahoochee Valley Community College, A
George C. Wallace Community College, A
Herzing College, A
Snead State Community College, A

Arizona

Cochise College (Douglas), A
Mesa Community College, A
Phoenix College, A
University of Advancing Technology, B

Arkansas

Arkansas State University, B
Black River Technical College, A
Central Baptist College, B
National Park Community College, A
NorthWest Arkansas Community College, A
Phillips Community College of the University of
Arkansas, A

California

American River College, A
Antelope Valley College, A
Bakersfield College, A
Butte College, A
Cabrillo College, A
Cañada College, A
Cerritos College, A
Cerro Coso Community College, A
Chabot College, A
Citrus College, A
College of Marin, A
Compton Community College, A
Cuesta College, A
East Los Angeles College, A
El Camino College, A
Evergreen Valley College, A
Foundation College, A
Fullerton College, A
Glendale Community College, A
Hartnell College, A
Heald College-Stockton, A
Humphreys College, A
Irvine Valley College, A
Long Beach City College, A
Los Angeles City College, A
Los Angeles Harbor College, A
Los Angeles Pierce College, A
Los Angeles Southwest College, A
Los Angeles Trade-Technical College, A
Los Angeles Valley College, A
Mendocino College, A
Merced College, A
Mission College, A
Monterey Peninsula College, A
Moorpark College, A
Mt. San Antonio College, A
Napa Valley College, A
Orange Coast College, A
Pacific Union College, B

Pasadena City College, A
Sacramento City College, A
San Bernardino Valley College, A
San Diego City College, A
San Jose City College, A
Santa Monica College, A
Skyline College, A
Taft College, A
West Los Angeles College, A
West Valley College, A

Colorado

Lamar Community College, A
Northeastern Junior College, A
Otero Junior College, A
Parks College (Denver), A
Trinidad State Junior College, A

Connecticut

Gateway Community College, A
Housatonic Community College, A
Norwalk Community College, A
Sacred Heart University, A
Three Rivers Community College, A
Tunxis Community College, A

Delaware

Delaware Technical & Community College, Jack F.
Owens Campus, A
Delaware Technical & Community College,
Stanton/Wilmington Campus, A
Delaware Technical & Community College, Terry
Campus, A

Florida

Broward Community College, A
Florida Memorial College, B
Florida Metropolitan University-Lakeland Campus, A
Florida Metropolitan University-North Orlando
Campus, AB
Florida Metropolitan University-Tampa Campus, AB
Florida National College, A
Miami Dade College, A
Palm Beach Community College, A
Polk Community College, A
Santa Fe Community College, A
Seminole Community College, A
Tallahassee Community College, A
Webster College (Ocala), A

Georgia

Abraham Baldwin Agricultural College, A
Bainbridge College, A
Clayton State University, A
Macon State College, A
Middle Georgia College, A

Hawaii

Hawaii Pacific University, A
Kapiolani Community College, A

Idaho

Brigham Young University -Idaho, A

Illinois

American InterContinental University Online, A
Black Hawk College, A
Carl Sandburg College, A
City Colleges of Chicago, Harold Washington
College, A
City Colleges of Chicago, Kennedy-King College, A
City Colleges of Chicago, Richard J. Daley
College, A
City Colleges of Chicago, Wilbur Wright College, A
Danville Area Community College, A
Highland Community College, A
Illinois Central College, A
Illinois Valley Community College, A
John A. Logan College, A
Lewis and Clark Community College, A
Lincoln College, A
Lincoln College-Normal, A
Morton College, A
South Suburban College, A
Southwestern Illinois College, A

Triton College, A
William Rainey Harper College, A

Indiana

Indiana University Kokomo, B
Indiana University Northwest, B
University of Southern Indiana, B

Iowa

Des Moines Area Community College, A
Dordt College, A
Ellsworth Community College, A
Iowa Central Community College, A
Iowa Lakes Community College, A
Kirkwood Community College, A

Kansas

Allen County Community College, A
Butler Community College, A
Dodge City Community College, A
Donnelly College, A
Highland Community College, A
Independence Community College, A
Kansas City Kansas Community College, A
Labette Community College, A
Seward County Community College, A

Kentucky

Campbellsville University, A
Hazard Community and Technical College, A
Henderson Community College, A
Jefferson Community and Technical College, A
Southeast Kentucky Community and Technical
    College, A
Thomas More College, A
Western Kentucky University, A

Louisiana

Delgado Community College, A
Louisiana Technical College, A

Maine

Northern Maine Community College, A

Maryland

Anne Arundel Community College, A
Baltimore City Community College, A
Carroll Community College, A
Cecil Community College, A
Chesapeake College, A
Frederick Community College, A
Hagerstown Business College, A

Massachusetts

Bristol Community College, A
Marian Court College, A
Northern Essex Community College, A
Quinsigamond Community College, A

Michigan

Alpena Community College, A
Baker College of Auburn Hills, A
Baker College of Cadillac, A
Baker College of Clinton Township, A
Baker College of Flint, A
Baker College of Jackson, A
Baker College of Muskegon, A
Baker College of Owosso, A
Baker College of Port Huron, A
Davenport University (Midland), A
Gogebic Community College, A
Henry Ford Community College, A
Jackson Community College, A
Lake Michigan College, A
Lewis College of Business, A
Monroe County Community College, A
Montcalm Community College, A
Muskegon Community College, A
North Central Michigan College, A
Schoolcraft College, A
Washtenaw Community College, A
Wayne County Community College District, A

West Shore Community College, A

Minnesota

Academy College, A
Bemidji State University, B
Minnesota State University Mankato, B
Rasmussen College Mankato, A
Ridgewater College, A
Vermilion Community College, A

Mississippi

Copiah-Lincoln Community College, A
East Central Community College, A
Hinds Community College, A
Holmes Community College, A
Itawamba Community College, A
Jones County Junior College, A
Northeast Mississippi Community College, A
Northwest Mississippi Community College, A
University of Southern Mississippi, B

Missouri

Longview Community College, A
Maple Woods Community College, A
Metropolitan Community College-Business &
    Technology College, A
Missouri Southern State University, A
North Central Missouri College, A
Northwest Missouri State University, B
Penn Valley Community College, A
St. Louis Community College at Florissant Valley, A
St. Louis Community College at Forest Park, A
Sanford-Brown College (St. Charles), A
Springfield College, A

Montana

Fort Belknap College, A
Montana State University-Billings, A
Montana Tech of The University of Montana, A
The University of Montana-Western, A

Nebraska

Central Community College-Grand Island
    Campus, A
Southeast Community College, Milford Campus, A

Nevada

Career College of Northern Nevada, A
Community College of Southern Nevada, A
Great Basin College, A
Truckee Meadows Community College, A

New Hampshire

New Hampshire Community Technical College,
    Nashua/Claremont, A

New Jersey

Camden County College, A
Essex County College, A
Gloucester County College, A
Hudson County Community College, A
Raritan Valley Community College, A
Saint Peter's College, A
Warren County Community College, A

New Mexico

Central New Mexico Community College, A
New Mexico Junior College, A
New Mexico State University-Alamogordo, A
New Mexico State University-Grants, A
Southwestern Indian Polytechnic Institute, A

New York

Adirondack Community College, A
Borough of Manhattan Community College of the
    City University of New York, A
Bronx Community College of the City University of
    New York, A
Broome Community College, A
Cayuga County Community College, A
The College of Westchester, A
Columbia-Greene Community College, A
Eugenio María de Hostos Community College of the
    City University of New York, A

Farmingdale State University of New York, A
Finger Lakes Community College, A
Five Towns College, A
Fulton-Montgomery Community College, A
Kingsborough Community College of the City
    University of New York, A
Monroe Community College, A
Nassau Community College, A
New York City College of Technology of the City
    University of New York, A
New York Institute of Technology, A
Onondaga Community College, A
Orange County Community College, A
Pace University, B
Rochester Business Institute, A
Rockland Community College, A
St. Francis College, A
St. John's University, A
State University of New York College of Agriculture
    and Technology at Cobleskill, A
State University of New York College of Agriculture
    and Technology at Morrisville, A
Suffolk County Community College, A
Ulster County Community College, A
Westchester Community College, A

North Carolina

Catawba Valley Community College, A
Central Piedmont Community College, A
Davidson County Community College, A
Durham Technical Community College, A
Forsyth Technical Community College, A
Gaston College, A
Mitchell Community College, A
Vance-Granville Community College, A

North Dakota

Williston State College, A

Ohio

Davis College, A
Edison State Community College, A
Jefferson Community College, A
Marion Technical College, A
Mount Vernon Nazarene University, B
Ohio Valley College of Technology, A
The University of Akron, A
The University of Akron-Wayne College, A
University of Cincinnati, A
The University of Toledo, A
Washington State Community College, A
Wright State University, A
Youngstown State University, A

Pennsylvania

Academy of Medical Arts and Business, A
Bucks County Community College, A
Community College of Beaver County, A
Community College of Philadelphia, A
Keystone College, A
Luzerne County Community College, A
Reading Area Community College, A
Saint Francis University, A
Westmoreland County Community College, A

South Carolina

Central Carolina Technical College, A
Midlands Technical College, A
Northeastern Technical College, A
Piedmont Technical College, A
Technical College of the Lowcountry, A
Tri-County Technical College, A
York Technical College, A

South Dakota

Northern State University, A
Sinte Gleska University, A

Tennessee

Austin Peay State University, A
Chattanooga State Technical Community College, A
Northeast State Technical Community College, A

Pellissippi State Technical Community College, A

Texas

Angelina College, A
Brazosport College, A
Cedar Valley College, A
Central Texas College, A
Cisco Junior College, A
Coastal Bend College, A
Eastfield College, A
El Centro College, A
Frank Phillips College, A
Hill College of the Hill Junior College District, A
Kilgore College, A
Lamar State College-Orange, A
Lamar State College-Port Arthur, A
Lamar University, A
Laredo Community College, A
Lee College, A
Navarro College, A
North Central Texas College, A
North Lake College, A
Odessa College, A
Richland College, A
San Antonio College, A
South Plains College, A
Southwest Texas Junior College, A
Stephen F. Austin State University, B
Temple College, A
Texarkana College, A
Texas Southmost College, A
Texas State Technical College Harlingen, A
Texas State University-San Marcos, B
Trinity Valley Community College, A
Vernon College, A
Wharton County Junior College, A

United States Virgin Islands

University of the Virgin Islands, A

Utah

Dixie State College of Utah, A
Utah Valley State College, AB

Virginia

Dabney S. Lancaster Community College, A
ECPI College of Technology (Virginia Beach), A
ECPI Technical College (Richmond), A
J. Sargeant Reynolds Community College, A
Patrick Henry Community College, A
Paul D. Camp Community College, A
Piedmont Virginia Community College, A
Virginia Highlands Community College, A
Virginia Western Community College, A

Washington

Bates Technical College, A
Bellevue Community College, A
Edmonds Community College, A
Everett Community College, A
Lower Columbia College, A
South Puget Sound Community College, A
Spokane Community College, A
Tacoma Community College, A
University of Washington, B

West Virginia

Community & Technical College at West Virginia
   University Institute of Technology, A
Potomac State College of West Virginia
   University, A
West Virginia Junior College (Charleston), A
West Virginia University Institute of Technology, B
West Virginia University at Parkersburg, A

Wisconsin

Chippewa Valley Technical College, A
Madison Area Technical College, A
Milwaukee Area Technical College, A
Nicolet Area Technical College, A
Northeast Wisconsin Technical College, A
Southwest Wisconsin Technical College, A

Western Technical College, A

Wyoming

Casper College, A
Western Wyoming Community College, A

British Columbia

British Columbia Institute of Technology, A

Manitoba

The University of Winnipeg, B

New Brunswick

University of New Brunswick Fredericton, B

Nova Scotia

Saint Mary's University, B

DEMOGRAPHY

California

University of California, Berkeley, MD

District of Columbia

Georgetown University, M

Illinois

University of Illinois at Urbana-Champaign, MD

New York

University at Albany, State University of New
   York, O

North Carolina

Duke University, D

Puerto Rico

University of Puerto Rico, Medical Sciences
   Campus, M

DEMOGRAPHY AND POPULATION STUDIES

Arizona

Arizona State University, MD

California

University of California, Irvine, M

Florida

Florida State University, MO

Massachusetts

Hampshire College, B

New Jersey

Princeton University, DO

Ohio

Bowling Green State University, MD

Rhode Island

Brown University, D

Alberta

University of Alberta, MD

Ontario

The University of Western Ontario, B

DENTAL AND ORAL SURGERY

California

Loma Linda University, MO
University of the Pacific, O

District of Columbia

Howard University, O

Iowa

The University of Iowa, MO

Massachusetts

Boston University, MDO
Harvard University, O

Missouri

University of Missouri-Kansas City, O

New York

New York University, O

Ohio

Case Western Reserve University, O

Pennsylvania

Temple University, O
University of Pittsburgh, O

Puerto Rico

University of Puerto Rico, Medical Sciences
   Campus, M

Texas

Texas A&M University System Health Science
   Center, PO

Manitoba

University of Manitoba, M

Nova Scotia

Dalhousie University, O

Ontario

University of Toronto, M

Quebec

McGill University, MD

DENTAL ASSISTING/ASSISTANT

Alabama

Calhoun Community College, A
Community College of the Air Force, A
H. Councill Trenholm State Technical College, A
James H. Faulkner State Community College, A
Wallace State Community College, A

Alaska

University of Alaska Anchorage, A

Arizona

The Bryman School, A

California

Allan Hancock College, A
Citrus College, A
College of the Redwoods, A
Cypress College, A
Foothill College, A
Modesto Junior College, A
Oxnard College, A
Reedley College, A
Sacramento City College, A
San Diego Mesa College, A
San Joaquin Valley College, A

Colorado

Pikes Peak Community College, A
Pueblo Community College, A

Connecticut

Briarwood College, A

Florida

New England Institute of Technology at Palm
   Beach, A

Georgia

Athens Technical College, A
Georgia Southwestern State University, A

Idaho

College of Southern Idaho, A

Illinois

Black Hawk College, A
Robert Morris College, A

Indiana

University of Southern Indiana, A

Iowa

Marshalltown Community College, A
Vatterott College, A

Louisiana

Louisiana State University Health Sciences
    Center, AB

Maine

The University of Maine at Augusta, A

Massachusetts

Massasoit Community College, A
Middlesex Community College, A
Northern Essex Community College, A

Michigan

Delta College, A
Lake Michigan College, A
Mott Community College, A
Northwestern Michigan College, A
Washtenaw Community College, A

Minnesota

Century College, A
Duluth Business University, A
Hennepin Technical College, A
Herzing College, A
Hibbing Community College, A
Normandale Community College, A
St. Cloud Technical College, A
South Central Technical College, A

Montana

Montana State University-Great Falls College of
    Technology, A

Nebraska

Central Community College-Hastings Campus, A
Mid-Plains Community College, A

Nevada

Truckee Meadows Community College, A

New Hampshire

New Hampshire Technical Institute, A

New Jersey

Essex County College, A

Ohio

Jefferson Community College, A
Ohio Valley College of Technology, A

Oklahoma

Community Care College, A
Rose State College, A
Tulsa Community College, A

Oregon

Blue Mountain Community College, A
Central Oregon Community College, A

Pennsylvania

Academy of Medical Arts and Business, A
Harcum College, A

Luzerne County Community College, A

Puerto Rico

University of Puerto Rico, Medical Sciences
    Campus, A

South Carolina

Midlands Technical College, A
York Technical College, A

South Dakota

Lake Area Technical Institute, A

Texas

Texas State Technical College Harlingen, A
Texas State Technical College Waco, A

Washington

Lake Washington Technical College, A

West Virginia

Huntington Junior College, A

Wisconsin

Milwaukee Area Technical College, A
Northeast Wisconsin Technical College, A
Southwest Wisconsin Technical College, A

Wyoming

Laramie County Community College, A

DENTAL HYGIENE/HYGIENIST

Alabama

Wallace State Community College, A

Alaska

University of Alaska Anchorage, A

Arizona

Northern Arizona University, B
Phoenix College, A
Pima Community College, A
Rio Salado College, A

Arkansas

University of Arkansas at Fort Smith, A
University of Arkansas for Medical Sciences, AB

California

Bakersfield College, A
Cabrillo College, A
Cerritos College, A
Chabot College, A
City College of San Francisco, A
College of Alameda, A
College of Marin, A
College of San Mateo, A
Contra Costa College, A
Cypress College, A
Foothill College, A
Fresno City College, A
Loma Linda University, B
Los Angeles City College, A
Merced College, A
Monterey Peninsula College, A
Orange Coast College, A
Oxnard College, A
Palomar College, A
Pasadena City College, A
Sacramento City College, A
San Bernardino Valley College, A
San Joaquin Valley College, A
San Jose City College, A
Santa Monica College, A
Santa Rosa Junior College, A
Shasta College, A
Southwestern College, A
Taft College, A
University of Southern California, B

West Los Angeles College, A

Colorado

Colorado Northwestern Community College, A
Community College of Denver, A
Pueblo Community College, A
University of Colorado at Denver and Health
    Sciences Center - Downtown Denver Campus, B

Connecticut

Tunxis Community College, A
University of Bridgeport, AB
University of New Haven, AB

Delaware

Delaware Technical & Community College,
    Stanton/Wilmington Campus, A

District of Columbia

Howard University, B

Florida

Brevard Community College, A
Broward Community College, A
Edison College, A
Florida Community College at Jacksonville, A
Florida National College, A
Gulf Coast Community College, A
Hillsborough Community College, A
Indian River Community College, A
Miami Dade College, A
Palm Beach Community College, A
Pasco-Hernando Community College, A
Pensacola Junior College, A
St. Petersburg College, A
Santa Fe Community College, A
Tallahassee Community College, A
Valencia Community College, A

Georgia

Andrew College, A
Armstrong Atlantic State University, AB
Athens Technical College, A
Atlanta Technical College, A
Central Georgia Technical College, A
Clayton State University, AB
Coastal Georgia Community College, A
Columbus Technical College, A
Dalton State College, A
Georgia Highlands College, A
Georgia Perimeter College, A
Medical College of Georgia, BM
Middle Georgia Technical College, A
Ogeechee Technical College, A
Southeastern Technical College, A
West Central Technical College, A

Hawaii

University of Hawaii at Manoa, B

Idaho

Apollo College, A
Brigham Young University -Idaho, A
College of Southern Idaho, A
Idaho State University, BM

Illinois

City Colleges of Chicago, Richard J. Daley
    College, A
College of DuPage, A
College of Lake County, A
Illinois Central College, A
John A. Logan College, A
Lake Land College, A
Lewis and Clark Community College, A
Parkland College, A
Prairie State College, A
Southern Illinois University Carbondale, B
William Rainey Harper College, A

Indiana

Indiana University Northwest, A
Indiana University-Purdue University Fort Wayne, A

Indiana University-Purdue University
 Indianapolis, AB
Indiana University South Bend, A
University of Southern Indiana, AB
Vincennes University, A

Iowa

Des Moines Area Community College, A
Hawkeye Community College, A
Iowa Western Community College, A

Kansas

Barton County Community College, A
Brown Mackie College-Kansas City, A
Colby Community College, A
Highland Community College, A
Johnson County Community College, A
Wichita State University, AB

Kentucky

Big Sandy Community and Technical College, A
Elizabethtown Community and Technical College, A
Lexington Community College, A
University of Louisville, AB
Western Kentucky University, AB

Louisiana

Delgado Community College, A
Louisiana State University Health Sciences
 Center, AB
Southern University at Shreveport, A
University of Louisiana at Lafayette, B
University of Louisiana at Monroe, B

Maine

The University of Maine at Augusta, AB
University of New England, AB

Maryland

Allegany College of Maryland, A
Baltimore City Community College, A

Massachusetts

Boston University, M
Bristol Community College, A
Cape Cod Community College, A
Massachusetts College of Pharmacy and Health
 Sciences, B
Middlesex Community College, A
Mount Ida College, A
Mount Wachusett Community College, A
Northeastern University, B
Quinsigamond Community College, A
Springfield Technical Community College, A

Michigan

Baker College of Port Huron, A
Delta College, A
Ferris State University, A
Grand Rapids Community College, A
Kalamazoo Valley Community College, A
Kellogg Community College, A
Lansing Community College, A
Mott Community College, A
Oakland Community College, A
University of Detroit Mercy, B
University of Michigan, B
Wayne County Community College District, A

Minnesota

Century College, A
Herzing College, A
Lake Superior College, A
Minnesota State Community and Technical
 College-Fergus Falls, A
Minnesota State University Mankato, AB
Normandale Community College, A
Northwest Technical College, A
Rochester Community and Technical College, A
St. Cloud Technical College, A

University of Minnesota, Twin Cities Campus, B

Mississippi

Hinds Community College, A
Meridian Community College, A
Mississippi Delta Community College, A
Northeast Mississippi Community College, A
University of Mississippi Medical Center, B

Missouri

Missouri Southern State University, A
St. Louis Community College at Forest Park, A
University of Missouri-Kansas City, BM

Montana

Montana State University-Billings, A
Montana State University-Great Falls College of
 Technology, A
Salish Kootenai College, A

Nebraska

Central Community College-Hastings Campus, A
University of Nebraska Medical Center, B

Nevada

Community College of Southern Nevada, A
Truckee Meadows Community College, A

New Hampshire

New Hampshire Technical Institute, A

New Jersey

Bergen Community College, A
Camden County College, A
Essex County College, A
Middlesex County College, A
Union County College, A

New Mexico

University of New Mexico, ABM

New York

Broome Community College, A
Erie Community College, North Campus, A
Eugenio María de Hostos Community College of the
 City University of New York, A
Farmingdale State University of New York, AB
Hudson Valley Community College, A
Monroe Community College, A
New York City College of Technology of the City
 University of New York, A
New York University, AB
Onondaga Community College, A
Orange County Community College, A

North Carolina

Asheville-Buncombe Technical Community
 College, A
Cape Fear Community College, A
Catawba Valley Community College, A
Central Piedmont Community College, A
Coastal Carolina Community College, A
Durham Technical Community College, A
Fayetteville Technical Community College, A
Guilford Technical Community College, A
The University of North Carolina at Chapel Hill, B
Wayne Community College, A

North Dakota

North Dakota State College of Science, A

Ohio

Columbus State Community College, A
James A. Rhodes State College, A
Lakeland Community College, A
The Ohio State University, B
Shawnee State University, A
Sinclair Community College, A
Stark State College of Technology, A
University of Cincinnati Raymond Walters College, A

Youngstown State University, A

Oklahoma

Rose State College, A
Tulsa Community College, A
University of Oklahoma Health Sciences Center, B

Oregon

Chemeketa Community College, A
Lane Community College, A
Mt. Hood Community College, A
Oregon Institute of Technology, B
Portland Community College, A

Pennsylvania

Community College of Philadelphia, A
Harcum College, A
Harrisburg Area Community College, A
Luzerne County Community College, A
Manor College, A
Montgomery County Community College, A
Northampton County Area Community College, A
Pennsylvania College of Technology, AB
University of Pittsburgh, B
Westmoreland County Community College, A

Puerto Rico

Huertas Junior College, A
Ramírez College of Business and Technology, A
University of Puerto Rico, Medical Sciences
 Campus, A

Rhode Island

Community College of Rhode Island, A
University of Rhode Island, B

South Carolina

Florence-Darlington Technical College, A
Greenville Technical College, A
Midlands Technical College, A
Trident Technical College, A
York Technical College, A

South Dakota

The University of South Dakota, AB

Tennessee

Chattanooga State Technical Community College, A
Columbia State Community College, A
East Tennessee State University, B
Roane State Community College, A
Southern Adventist University, A
Tennessee State University, AB

Texas

Amarillo College, A
Blinn College, A
Coastal Bend College, A
Collin County Community College District, A
Del Mar College, A
El Paso Community College, A
Howard College, A
Lamar University, A
Midwestern State University, B
Navarro College, A
Northeast Texas Community College, A
San Antonio College, A
Tarrant County College District, A
Temple College, A
Texas A&M University System Health Science
 Center, BM
Texas State Technical College Harlingen, A
Texas Woman's University, B
Tyler Junior College, A
The University of Texas Health Science Center at
 Houston, B
The University of Texas Health Science Center at
 San Antonio, BM
Wharton County Junior College, A

Utah

Dixie State College of Utah, A
Salt Lake Community College, A
Utah Valley State College, A

Weber State University, AB

Vermont

Vermont Technical College, A

Virginia

Germanna Community College, A
Lord Fairfax Community College, A
Northern Virginia Community College, A
Old Dominion University, BM
Virginia Commonwealth University, B
Virginia Western Community College, A
Wytheville Community College, A

Washington

Clark College, A
Eastern Washington University, B
Everett Community College, A
Highline Community College, A
Lake Washington Technical College, A
Pierce College, A
Shoreline Community College, A
South Puget Sound Community College, A
Spokane Community College, A
University of Washington, B
Yakima Valley Community College, A

West Virginia

Community & Technical College at West Virginia
    University Institute of Technology, A
West Liberty State College, AB
West Virginia University, B

Wisconsin

Blackhawk Technical College, A
Chippewa Valley Technical College, A
Gateway Technical College, A
Lakeshore Technical College, A
Madison Area Technical College, A
Marquette University, B
Milwaukee Area Technical College, A
Northcentral Technical College, A
Northeast Wisconsin Technical College, A
Waukesha County Technical College, A
Western Technical College, A

Wyoming

Laramie County Community College, A
Sheridan College-Sheridan and Gillette, A
University of Wyoming, B

Alberta

University of Alberta, BO

British Columbia

The University of British Columbia, B

Manitoba

University of Manitoba, B

Nova Scotia

Dalhousie University, BO

Quebec

Université de Montréal, O

DENTAL LABORATORY TECHNOLOGY/TECHNICIAN

Alabama

Community College of the Air Force, A
H. Councill Trenholm State Technical College, A

Arizona

Pima Community College, A

Idaho

Idaho State University, A

Illinois

Southern Illinois University Carbondale, A

Indiana

Indiana University-Purdue University Fort Wayne, A

Kentucky

Lexington Community College, A

Louisiana

Delgado Community College, A
Louisiana State University Health Sciences
    Center, AB

Massachusetts

Boston University, B
Middlesex Community College, A

Minnesota

Century College, A

New York

Erie Community College, South Campus, A
New York City College of Technology of the City
    University of New York, A

Ohio

Columbus State Community College, A

Pennsylvania

Commonwealth Technical Institute, A

Texas

Texas State Technical College Harlingen, A

Virginia

J. Sargeant Reynolds Community College, A

Washington

Bates Technical College, A

West Virginia

Marshall Community and Technical College, A

DENTISTRY

Alabama

The University of Alabama at Birmingham, P

California

Loma Linda University, MPO
University of California, Los Angeles, PO
University of the Pacific, MPO
University of Southern California, PO

District of Columbia

Howard University, PO

Florida

Nova Southeastern University, MP
University of Florida, PO

Georgia

Medical College of Georgia, PO

Idaho

Idaho State University, O

Illinois

Southern Illinois University Edwardsville, P
University of Illinois at Chicago, PO

Indiana

Indiana University-Purdue University
    Indianapolis, MDP

Iowa

The University of Iowa, MDPO

Kentucky

University of Kentucky, MP
University of Louisville, P

Louisiana

Louisiana State University Health Sciences
    Center, P

Massachusetts

Boston University, O
Harvard University, PO

Tufts University, PO

Michigan

University of Detroit Mercy, P
University of Michigan, P

Minnesota

University of Minnesota, Twin Cities Campus, P

Mississippi

University of Mississippi Medical Center, MDP

Missouri

University of Missouri-Kansas City, MDPO

Nebraska

Creighton University, P
University of Nebraska Medical Center, PO

New York

New York University, P
State University of New York at Buffalo, PO
Stony Brook University, State University of New
    York, PO

North Carolina

The University of North Carolina at Chapel Hill, PO

Ohio

Case Western Reserve University, P
The Ohio State University, PO

Oklahoma

University of Oklahoma Health Sciences Center, P

Oregon

Oregon Health & Science University, PO

Pennsylvania

Temple University, PO
University of Pennsylvania, PO
University of Pittsburgh, MPO

Puerto Rico

University of Puerto Rico, Medical Sciences
    Campus, P

South Carolina

Medical University of South Carolina, PO

Texas

Texas A&M University System Health Science
    Center, P
The University of Texas Health Science Center at
    Houston, P
The University of Texas Health Science Center at
    San Antonio, MPO

Virginia

Virginia Commonwealth University, PO

Washington

University of Washington, PO

West Virginia

West Virginia University, P

Wisconsin

Marquette University, P

Alberta

University of Alberta, P

British Columbia

The University of British Columbia, P

Manitoba

University of Manitoba, P

Nova Scotia

Dalhousie University, P

Ontario

University of Toronto, P
The University of Western Ontario, P

Quebec

McGill University, MDPO
Université Laval, P

Saskatchewan

University of Saskatchewan, P

DESIGN AND APPLIED ARTS

Arizona

Arizona State University, M

Arkansas

Harding University, B

California

Art Center College of Design, BM
The Art Institute of California-San Diego, B
California College of the Arts, M
California State University, Chico, M
California State University, Fresno, M
California State University, Fullerton, M
Laguna College of Art & Design, B
Mt. Sierra College, B
Platt College (Newport Beach), B
University of California, Berkeley, M
University of California, Los Angeles, BM
Westwood College-Anaheim, B
Westwood College-Inland Empire, B

Delaware

University of Delaware, M

District of Columbia

The George Washington University, M
Howard University, M

Florida

Florida State University, M
Full Sail Real World Education, B
Ringling School of Art and Design, B

Georgia

Savannah College of Art and Design, B

Idaho

University of Idaho, M

Illinois

Bradley University, M
The Illinois Institute of Art-Chicago, B
Robert Morris College, B
School of the Art Institute of Chicago, B
Westwood College-Chicago Du Page, B
Westwood College-Chicago O'Hare Airport, B

Indiana

Purdue University, M
University of Notre Dame, M
University of Saint Francis, B

Kansas

University of Kansas, M

Kentucky

University of Kentucky, M

Louisiana

Louisiana State University and Agricultural and
　　Mechanical College, M

Massachusetts

Massachusetts College of Art, M
The New England Institute of Art, B

University of Massachusetts Dartmouth, BM

Michigan

Ferris State University, M
University of Michigan, M
Wayne State University, M

Minnesota

St. Cloud State University, B
University of Minnesota, Twin Cities Campus, MDO

New Jersey

Rutgers, The State University of New Jersey, New
　　Brunswick/Piscataway, M

New York

Daemen College, B
Hofstra University, B
Mohawk Valley Community College, A
New York Institute of Technology, B
New York University, M
Niagara County Community College, A
Pratt Institute, B
School of Visual Arts, M

North Carolina

North Carolina State University, BD

Ohio

Ohio University, B
The University of Akron, B

Oklahoma

Oklahoma State University, MD
University of Central Oklahoma, M
University of Oklahoma, M

Pennsylvania

Carnegie Mellon University, D
Drexel University, B
Lehigh University, B
Point Park University, B

Texas

Lamar University, M
Stephen F. Austin State University, M
The University of Texas at Austin, M

Virginia

Virginia Polytechnic Institute and State University, M

Wisconsin

University of Wisconsin-Madison, MD
University of Wisconsin-Stout, B

Alberta

University of Alberta, M

British Columbia

Open Learning Agency, B

Nova Scotia

NSCAD University, BM

Ontario

York University, M

Quebec

Concordia University, O

DESIGN AND VISUAL COMMUNICATIONS

Alabama

Auburn University, B

Arizona

Collins College: A School of Design and
　　Technology, AB
Pima Community College, A

University of Advancing Technology, B

California

Bethesda Christian University, B
California State University, Chico, B
FIDM/The Fashion Institute of Design &
　　Merchandising, Los Angeles Campus, A
FIDM/The Fashion Institute of Design &
　　Merchandising, San Diego Campus, A
FIDM/The Fashion Institute of Design &
　　Merchandising, San Francisco Campus, A
Fresno City College, A
Laguna College of Art & Design, B
Platt College-Los Angeles, Inc, A
San Diego State University, B
San Francisco Art Institute, B
Shasta College, A
Western Career College (Walnut Creek), B
Westwood College-Anaheim, B
Westwood College-Inland Empire, B
Westwood College-Long Beach, B
Westwood College-Los Angeles, B

Colorado

Pueblo Community College, A
Trinidad State Junior College, A
Westwood College-Denver North, B
Westwood College-Denver South, B

Connecticut

Central Connecticut State University, B
Gibbs College, A
Paier College of Art, Inc., B

Delaware

Wilmington College, AB

District of Columbia

American University, B

Florida

American InterContinental University, B
Florida Community College at Jacksonville, A
International Academy of Design & Technology, AB
Jacksonville University, B
Pensacola Junior College, A

Georgia

American InterContinental University (Atlanta), B
American InterContinental University (Dunwoody
　　Campus), AB
North Metro Technical College, A
Savannah College of Art and Design, B
Southeastern Technical College, A
Westwood College-Atlanta Midtown, B
Westwood College-Atlanta Northlake, B

Illinois

American Academy of Art, B
American InterContinental University Online, B
Black Hawk College, A
College of DuPage, A
Columbia College Chicago, B
Elgin Community College, A
The Illinois Institute of Art-Chicago, B
The Illinois Institute of Art-Schaumburg, B
Illinois Institute of Technology, B
International Academy of Design & Technology, B
Moraine Valley Community College, A
Parkland College, A
School of the Art Institute of Chicago, B
Southern Illinois University Carbondale, B
Waubonsee Community College, A
Westwood College-Chicago Du Page, AB
Westwood College-Chicago Loop Campus, B
Westwood College-Chicago O'Hare Airport, AB
Westwood College-Chicago River Oaks, B

Indiana

Bethel College, B
Ivy Tech Community College-Central Indiana, A
Ivy Tech Community College-Columbus, A
Ivy Tech Community College-North Central, A
Ivy Tech Community College-Southern Indiana, A
Ivy Tech Community College-Southwest, A

Ivy Tech Community College-Wabash Valley, A
Purdue University, B
Saint Mary-of-the-Woods College, B
University of Evansville, B
University of Notre Dame, B

Iowa

Iowa State University of Science and Technology, B
St. Ambrose University, B

Kansas

University of Kansas, B

Maryland

Villa Julie College, B

Massachusetts

Bunker Hill Community College, A
Endicott College, B
Framingham State College, B
University of Massachusetts Dartmouth, B

Michigan

Alma College, B
Saginaw Valley State University, B
University of Michigan, B

Minnesota

Academy College, A
Brown College, AB
Duluth Business University, A

Missouri

Drury University, B
East Central College, A
Missouri State University, B
Truman State University, B
Washington University in St. Louis, B
William Woods University, B

Montana

Montana State University, B

Nebraska

The Creative Center, A

New Jersey

Brookdale Community College, A
Kean University, B

New Mexico

Santa Fe Community College, A

New York

Buffalo State College, State University of New
  York, B
Cazenovia College, B
Farmingdale State University of New York, B
Nassau Community College, A
Pace University, A
Rochester Institute of Technology, B
Syracuse University, B

North Carolina

Duke University, B
North Carolina State University, B
Peace College, B

Ohio

Bowling Green State University, B
Bowling Green State University-Firelands College, B
Mount Union College, B
Northwest State Community College, A
Ohio Northern University, B
The Ohio State University, B

Ohio University, B

Oklahoma

University of Oklahoma, B

Oregon

Pacific Northwest College of Art, B

Pennsylvania

Albright College, B
The Art Institute of Pittsburgh, AB
Bradley Academy for the Visual Arts, A
Carlow University, B
Douglas Education Center, A
Harrisburg Area Community College, A
Lehigh University, B
Lehigh Valley College, A
Marywood University, B
Robert Morris University, B

Tennessee

Lambuth University, B
Memphis College of Art, B
The University of Tennessee at Martin, B

Texas

Kilgore College, A
Lubbock Christian University, B
The University of Texas at Austin, B
Wade College, A

Utah

Brigham Young University, B
Weber State University, B

Vermont

Bennington College, B
Champlain College, AB

Virginia

The Art Institute of Washington, B
Virginia Commonwealth University, B

Washington

Henry Cogswell College, B
Western Washington University, B

West Virginia

Community and Technical College of Shepherd, A

Wisconsin

Viterbo University, B

Alberta

Alberta College of Art & Design, B

Nova Scotia

NSCAD University, B

Ontario

York University, B

Quebec

Université du Québec en Outaouais, B

DEVELOPMENT ECONOMICS AND INTERNATIONAL DEVELOPMENT

California

Point Loma Nazarene University, B
University of California, Los Angeles, B

Georgia

Georgia Southern University, B

Massachusetts

Clark University, B
Fitchburg State College, B

Michigan

Calvin College, B

Ohio

The Ohio State University, B

Rhode Island

Brown University, B

Vermont

University of Vermont, B

Virginia

Eastern Mennonite University, B

Manitoba

Canadian Mennonite University, B
The University of Winnipeg, B

Nova Scotia

Dalhousie University, B
University of King's College, B

Ontario

University of Windsor, B
York University, B

DEVELOPMENTAL AND CHILD PSYCHOLOGY

Arizona

Arizona Western College, A

California

Bakersfield College, A
California Polytechnic State University, San Luis
  Obispo, B
California State University, Bakersfield, B
California State University, East Bay, B
California State University, San Bernardino, B
Chaffey College, A
City College of San Francisco, A
College of the Canyons, A
College of the Sequoias, A
Columbia College, A
Compton Community College, A
De Anza College, A
East Los Angeles College, A
Fresno Pacific University, AB
Fullerton College, A
Gavilan College, A
Grossmont College, A
Hartnell College, A
Humboldt State University, B
Long Beach City College, A
Los Angeles City College, A
Los Angeles Harbor College, A
Los Angeles Mission College, A
Los Angeles Southwest College, A
Los Angeles Valley College, A
Los Medanos College, A
Mendocino College, A
Merced College, A
Mills College, B
MiraCosta College, A
Mount St. Mary's College, B
Palo Verde College, A
Palomar College, A
Pasadena City College, A
Saddleback College, A
San Bernardino Valley College, A
San Diego City College, A
San Diego Miramar College, A
San Joaquin Delta College, A
Santa Monica College, A
Sonoma State University, B
University of California, Santa Cruz, B
West Los Angeles College, A

Whittier College, B

Colorado

Colorado State University-Pueblo, B

Connecticut

Eastern Connecticut State University, B
Mitchell College, A
Quinnipiac University, B

Delaware

University of Delaware, B

District of Columbia

University of the District of Columbia, B

Georgia

Clark Atlanta University, B
Fort Valley State University, B
Spelman College, B
Waycross College, A

Idaho

North Idaho College, A

Illinois

Carl Sandburg College, A
City Colleges of Chicago, Harold Washington
  College, A
City Colleges of Chicago, Harry S. Truman
  College, A
City Colleges of Chicago, Olive-Harvey College, A
City Colleges of Chicago, Richard J. Daley
  College, A
Illinois Central College, A
Lincoln College, A
Olivet Nazarene University, B

Iowa

Ellsworth Community College, A
Iowa Lakes Community College, A
Kirkwood Community College, A

Kansas

Garden City Community College, A

Kentucky

Berea College, B

Maryland

Villa Julie College, AB

Massachusetts

Bridgewater State College, B
Emmanuel College, B
Fitchburg State College, B
Framingham State College, B
Mount Ida College, B
Simon's Rock College of Bard, B
Suffolk University, B
Tufts University, B

Michigan

Lansing Community College, A
Muskegon Community College, A
Northern Michigan University, B
University of Detroit Mercy, B

Minnesota

Central Lakes College, A
Metropolitan State University, B
Minnesota State University Mankato, B
Ridgewater College, A
Rochester Community and Technical College, A
University of Minnesota, Twin Cities Campus, B

Mississippi

Hinds Community College, A
Itawamba Community College, A
Mississippi Delta Community College, A

Northeast Mississippi Community College, A

Missouri

Northwest Missouri State University, B
St. Louis Community College at Forest Park, A

Montana

Flathead Valley Community College, A

New Hampshire

Colby-Sawyer College, B

New York

Brooklyn College of the City University of New
  York, B
Fulton-Montgomery Community College, A
Rockland Community College, A
St. Joseph's College, New York, B
St. Joseph's College, Suffolk Campus, B
Sarah Lawrence College, B
Utica College, B

North Dakota

Cankdeska Cikana Community College, A

Ohio

Jefferson Community College, A
Ohio University-Eastern, B
The University of Akron, B
The University of Toledo, B

Oklahoma

Langston University, B
Oklahoma Baptist University, B
Rose State College, A

Pennsylvania

Marywood University, B

South Dakota

University of Sioux Falls, A

Tennessee

Belmont University, B
Carson-Newman College, B
Maryville College, B

Texas

Angelina College, A
Austin Community College, A
Cisco Junior College, A
Coastal Bend College, A
Frank Phillips College, A
Hill College of the Hill Junior College District, A
Houston Baptist University, B
McLennan Community College, A
Midland College, A
Navarro College, A
San Antonio College, A
South Plains College, A
South Texas College, A
Southwestern Christian College, A
Tarrant County College District, A
Trinity Valley Community College, A
Tyler Junior College, A
University of the Incarnate Word, B

Utah

University of Utah, B

Vermont

Castleton State College, B
Community College of Vermont, A
Marlboro College, B

Virginia

Hampton University, B
Liberty University, B

Longwood University, B

Washington

Eastern Washington University, B
Western Washington University, B

Wisconsin

Edgewood College, B
University of Wisconsin-Green Bay, B
University of Wisconsin-Madison, B

Alberta

University of Alberta, B

British Columbia

The University of British Columbia, B

Manitoba

The University of Winnipeg, B

New Brunswick

University of New Brunswick Fredericton, B

Nova Scotia

Mount Saint Vincent University, B

Ontario

University of Ottawa, B
University of Windsor, B
Wilfrid Laurier University, B

Quebec

Concordia University, B
Université de Montréal, B

DEVELOPMENTAL BIOLOGY AND EMBRYOLOGY

Arizona

Arizona State University, MD

California

California Institute of Technology, D
Stanford University, D
University of California, Davis, MD
University of California, Irvine, MD
University of California, Los Angeles, MD
University of California, Riverside, MD
University of California, San Diego, D
University of California, Santa Barbara, MDO

Colorado

University of Colorado at Boulder, BMD

Connecticut

University of Connecticut, MD
Wesleyan University, D
Yale University, D

Florida

Florida State University, MD
University of Miami, DO

Georgia

Emory University, D

Illinois

Northwestern University, D
University of Chicago, D
University of Illinois at Chicago, D

Indiana

Indiana University Bloomington, D
Purdue University, D

Iowa

Iowa State University of Science and
  Technology, MD

Kansas

Kansas State University, MD

University of Kansas, MD

Maryland

The Johns Hopkins University, D

Massachusetts

Massachusetts Institute of Technology, D
Tufts University, D
University of Massachusetts Amherst, D

Michigan

University of Michigan, MD

Minnesota

University of Minnesota, Twin Cities Campus, MD

Missouri

Washington University in St. Louis, D

New Jersey

Rutgers, The State University of New Jersey, New
   Brunswick/Piscataway, MD

New York

Cornell University, MD
Rensselaer Polytechnic Institute, MD
State University of New York Upstate Medical
   University, DO
Stony Brook University, State University of New
   York, D
University at Albany, State University of New
   York, MD

North Carolina

Duke University, DO
The University of North Carolina at Chapel Hill, MD

Ohio

Case Western Reserve University, D
The Ohio State University, MD
University of Cincinnati, MD

Oregon

Oregon Health & Science University, DO

Pennsylvania

Carnegie Mellon University, D
The Pennsylvania State University University Park
   Campus, D
Thomas Jefferson University, MD
University of Pennsylvania, DO
University of Pittsburgh, D

Rhode Island

Brown University, MD

South Carolina

University of South Carolina, MD

Texas

The University of Texas at Austin, D
The University of Texas Health Science Center at
   Houston, MDO
The University of Texas Southwestern Medical
   Center at Dallas, D

Utah

Brigham Young University, MD

Virginia

Virginia Polytechnic Institute and State
   University, MD

West Virginia

West Virginia University, MD

Wisconsin

Marquette University, MD

British Columbia

University of Victoria, MD

DEVELOPMENTAL EDUCATION

California

University of California, Berkeley, M

Illinois

National-Louis University, MO

Iowa

The University of Iowa, M

Louisiana

Grambling State University, MD

Michigan

Ferris State University, M

New Jersey

Rutgers, The State University of New Jersey, New
   Brunswick/Piscataway, M

North Carolina

North Carolina State University, M

Pennsylvania

Edinboro University of Pennsylvania, O

Texas

Texas State University-San Marcos, M

DEVELOPMENTAL PSYCHOLOGY

Alabama

The University of Alabama at Birmingham, D

Arizona

Arizona State University, D

California

California State University, San Bernardino, M
Stanford University, D
University of California, Santa Cruz, D

Connecticut

University of Connecticut, MD

District of Columbia

Gallaudet University, M
Howard University, D

Florida

Florida International University, D
Florida State University, D
University of Miami, D

Georgia

Emory University, D

Illinois

Loyola University Chicago, D
University of Illinois at Urbana-Champaign, MD

Indiana

Indiana University Bloomington, D
University of Notre Dame, D

Kansas

University of Kansas, MD

Louisiana

Louisiana State University and Agricultural and
   Mechanical College, MD

Maine

University of Maine, M

Maryland

University of Maryland, Baltimore County, D
University of Maryland, College Park, D

Massachusetts

Boston College, MD
Brandeis University, D

Clark University, D
Suffolk University, D
Tufts University, D

Michigan

Andrews University, MD
University of Michigan, D
Wayne State University, D

Nebraska

University of Nebraska at Omaha, D

New Jersey

Rutgers, The State University of New Jersey, New
   Brunswick/Piscataway, D

New York

Cornell University, D
Fordham University, D
New York University, D
University of Rochester, D
Yeshiva University, D

North Carolina

Duke University, D
North Carolina State University, D
The University of North Carolina at Chapel Hill, D
The University of North Carolina at Greensboro, MD

Ohio

Bowling Green State University, MD
The Ohio State University, D

Oregon

University of Oregon, MD

Pennsylvania

Bryn Mawr College, D
Carnegie Mellon University, D
The Pennsylvania State University University Park
   Campus, MD
Temple University, D
University of Pittsburgh, MD

Texas

Texas A&M University, MD

Virginia

George Mason University, MD
Virginia Polytechnic Institute and State University, D

West Virginia

West Virginia University, D

Wisconsin

University of Wisconsin-Madison, D

British Columbia

The University of British Columbia, MD
University of Victoria, MD

Ontario

Queen's University at Kingston, MD
University of Guelph, D

Quebec

McGill University, MDO
Université de Montréal, M

DIAGNOSTIC MEDICAL SONOGRAPHY/SONOGRAPHER AND ULTRASOUND TECHNICIAN

Alabama

Virginia College at Birmingham, A

Arizona

GateWay Community College, A

Arkansas

University of Arkansas at Fort Smith, B

California

Charles R. Drew University of Medicine and
   Science, B

Foothill College, A

Delaware

Delaware Technical & Community College,
Stanton/Wilmington Campus, A

Florida

ATI Health Education Center, A
Florida Community College at Jacksonville, A
Florida Hospital College of Health Sciences, A
Florida National College, A
Hillsborough Community College, A
Keiser College (Melbourne), A
Miami Dade College, A
Valencia Community College, A

Georgia

Athens Technical College, A
Columbus Technical College, A
Darton College, A
Medical College of Georgia, B

Maryland

Montgomery College, A

Massachusetts

Middlesex Community College, A
Springfield Technical Community College, A

Michigan

Baker College of Auburn Hills, A
Baker College of Owosso, A
Baker College of Port Huron, A
Delta College, A
Ferris State University, A
Jackson Community College, A
Lansing Community College, A
Oakland Community College, A

Minnesota

College of St. Catherine, A
College of St. Catherine-Minneapolis, A
St. Cloud Technical College, A

Missouri

University of Missouri-Columbia, B

Nebraska

Nebraska Methodist College, AB
University of Nebraska Medical Center, B

New Hampshire

New Hampshire Technical Institute, A

New Jersey

Gloucester County College, A

New Mexico

Central New Mexico Community College, A

New York

New York University, A
Rochester Institute of Technology, B
State University of New York Downstate Medical
Center, B

North Carolina

Caldwell Community College and Technical
Institute, A
Cape Fear Community College, A
Pitt Community College, A

Ohio

Central Ohio Technical College, A
Cincinnati State Technical and Community
College, A
Lorain County Community College, A

Pennsylvania

Community College of Allegheny County, A
Keystone College, A
Lackawanna College, A
Northampton County Area Community College, A

South Hills School of Business & Technology (State
College), A
Western School of Health and Business Careers
(Pittsburgh), A

Tennessee

Baptist College of Health Sciences, B

Texas

Del Mar College, A
El Centro College, A

Utah

Weber State University, B

Washington

Seattle University, B

West Virginia

Mountain State University, AB

Wisconsin

Chippewa Valley Technical College, A

Wyoming

Laramie County Community College, A

Nova Scotia

Dalhousie University, B

DIESEL MECHANICS TECHNOLOGY/TECHNICIAN

Alabama

Shelton State Community College, A

Alaska

University of Alaska Anchorage, A

Arizona

Arizona Automotive Institute, A

California

College of the Redwoods, A
Santa Ana College, A
Shasta College, A

Georgia

Georgia Southwestern State University, A

Idaho

College of Southern Idaho, A
Eastern Idaho Technical College, A
Idaho State University, A
Lewis-Clark State College, AB

Illinois

Black Hawk College, A
Illinois Eastern Community Colleges, Wabash Valley
College, A
Rend Lake College, A

Indiana

Lincoln Technical Institute, A

Iowa

Northwest Iowa Community College, A
Scott Community College, A
Western Iowa Tech Community College, A

Kentucky

Somerset Community College, A

Massachusetts

Massasoit Community College, A

Minnesota

Alexandria Technical College, A
Century College, A
Dakota County Technical College, A
Northwest Technical College, A

Riverland Community College, A
St. Cloud Technical College, A

Missouri

Ozarks Technical Community College, A

Montana

Montana State University-Billings, A
The University of Montana-Helena College of
Technology, A

Nebraska

Central Community College-Hastings Campus, A
Mid-Plains Community College, A
Northeast Community College, A

Nevada

Great Basin College, A

New Hampshire

New Hampshire Community Technical College,
Berlin/Laconia, A

New Jersey

Raritan Valley Community College, A

New Mexico

Mesalands Community College, A
San Juan College, A

North Carolina

Johnston Community College, A
Wilkes Community College, A

North Dakota

Lake Region State College, A
North Dakota State College of Science, A
Williston State College, A

Ohio

University of Northwestern Ohio, A

Oregon

Blue Mountain Community College, A
Linn-Benton Community College, A

Pennsylvania

Johnson College, A
Pennsylvania College of Technology, A
Rosedale Technical Institute, A

South Dakota

Southeast Technical Institute, A

Tennessee

Nashville Auto Diesel College, A

Texas

Kilgore College, A
St. Philip's College, A
Texas State Technical College Waco, A
Texas State Technical College West Texas, A
Universal Technical Institute, A

Utah

Dixie State College of Utah, A
Salt Lake Community College, A
Utah Valley State College, A
Weber State University, A

Washington

Bates Technical College, A
Centralia College, A
Clark College, A
Grays Harbor College, A
Lake Washington Technical College, A
Lower Columbia College, A
Peninsula College, A

Skagit Valley College, A

Wisconsin

Northeast Wisconsin Technical College, A

Wyoming

Laramie County Community College, A
Sheridan College-Sheridan and Gillette, A
Western Wyoming Community College, A

British Columbia

British Columbia Institute of Technology, A

DIETETIC TECHNICIAN (DTR)

Colorado

Front Range Community College, A

Florida

Miami Dade College, A

New Hampshire

University of New Hampshire, A

Ohio

Columbus State Community College, A

Wisconsin

Milwaukee Area Technical College, A

DIETETICS AND CLINICAL NUTRITION SERVICES

Michigan

Madonna University, B

Texas

Texas Christian University, B

DIETETICS/DIETICIANS

Alabama

Community College of the Air Force, A
Faulkner University, A
Jacksonville State University, B
Lawson State Community College, A
Oakwood College, AB
Tuskegee University, B
University of Montevallo, B

Arizona

Central Arizona College, A

Arkansas

Black River Technical College, A
Harding University, B
Ouachita Baptist University, B
University of Arkansas at Pine Bluff, B

California

Allan Hancock College, A
Bakersfield College, A
California State Polytechnic University, Pomona, B
California State University, Chico, B
California State University, Fresno, B
California State University, Long Beach, B
California State University, Los Angeles, B
California State University, San Bernardino, B
Chaffey College, A
City College of San Francisco, A
Fresno City College, A
Grossmont College, A
Loma Linda University, AB
Long Beach City College, A
Los Angeles City College, A
Merced College, A
Orange Coast College, A
Point Loma Nazarene University, B
San Francisco State University, B

San Jose State University, B
Santa Rosa Junior College, A

Colorado

Colorado State University, B
University of Northern Colorado, B

Connecticut

Briarwood College, A
Gateway Community College, A
Saint Joseph College, B
University of Connecticut, B
University of New Haven, B

Delaware

Delaware State University, B
University of Delaware, B

Florida

Florida Community College at Jacksonville, A
Florida International University, B
Florida State University, B
Manatee Community College, A
Miami Dade College, A
Okaloosa-Walton College, A
Pensacola Junior College, A

Georgia

Life University, B
University of Georgia, B

Hawaii

University of Hawaii at Manoa, B

Idaho

Brigham Young University -Idaho, A
College of Southern Idaho, A
Idaho State University, B

Illinois

Dominican University, B
Olivet Nazarene University, B
University of Illinois at Chicago, B
University of Illinois at Urbana-Champaign, B
William Rainey Harper College, A

Indiana

Ball State University, AB
Indiana University Bloomington, B
Vincennes University, A

Iowa

Iowa State University of Science and Technology, B

Kansas

Kansas State University, B

Kentucky

Berea College, B
Eastern Kentucky University, B

Louisiana

Delgado Community College, A
Louisiana Tech University, B
Nicholls State University, B
University of Louisiana at Lafayette, B

Maine

Southern Maine Community College, A

Maryland

Baltimore City Community College, A
Morgan State University, B
University of Maryland, College Park, B
University of Maryland Eastern Shore, B

Massachusetts

Framingham State College, B
Labouré College, A

Simmons College, B

Michigan

Andrews University, B
Central Michigan University, B
Eastern Michigan University, B
Michigan State University, B
Wayne County Community College District, A
Wayne State University, B
Western Michigan University, B

Minnesota

College of Saint Benedict, B
College of St. Catherine, B
Concordia College, B
Minnesota State University Mankato, B
Normandale Community College, A
Saint John's University, B
University of Minnesota, Crookston, A

Mississippi

Hinds Community College, A
University of Southern Mississippi, B

Missouri

Central Missouri State University, B
College of the Ozarks, B
Fontbonne University, B
Missouri State University, B
Northwest Missouri State University, B
St. Louis Community College at Florissant Valley, A
University of Missouri-Columbia, B

Nebraska

Southeast Community College, Lincoln Campus, A
University of Nebraska at Kearney, B
Western Nebraska Community College, A

New Hampshire

Keene State College, B
University of New Hampshire, AB

New Jersey

Camden County College, A
College of Saint Elizabeth, B
Middlesex County College, A

New York

Buffalo State College, State University of New York, B
Dutchess Community College, A
D'Youville College, B
Fiorello H. LaGuardia Community College of the City University of New York, A
Lehman College of the City University of New York, B
Rochester Institute of Technology, AB
Rockland Community College, A
State University of New York College of Agriculture and Technology at Morrisville, A
State University of New York College at Oneonta, B
Suffolk County Community College, A
Syracuse University, B
Westchester Community College, A

North Carolina

East Carolina University, B
Gaston College, A
Meredith College, B
North Carolina Agricultural and Technical State University, B
Western Carolina University, B

North Dakota

North Dakota State University, B
University of North Dakota, B

Ohio

Ashland University, B
Bowling Green State University, B
Case Western Reserve University, B
Cincinnati State Technical and Community College, A
Columbus State Community College, A

Hocking College, A
Miami University, B
Miami University Hamilton, B
The Ohio State University, B
Sinclair Community College, A
The University of Akron, B
University of Cincinnati Raymond Walters College, A
University of Dayton, B
Youngstown State University, AB

Oklahoma

Langston University, B
Oklahoma State University, Okmulgee, A
University of Central Oklahoma, B
University of Oklahoma Health Sciences Center, B

Oregon

Portland Community College, A

Pennsylvania

Butler County Community College, A
Community College of Philadelphia, A
Gannon University, B
Harrisburg Area Community College, A
Immaculata University, B
Indiana University of Pennsylvania, B
Mansfield University of Pennsylvania, B
Marywood University, B
Mercyhurst College, B
Seton Hill University, B
University of Pittsburgh, B
West Chester University of Pennsylvania, B
Westmoreland County Community College, A

Puerto Rico

University of Puerto Rico, Río Piedras, B

Rhode Island

University of Rhode Island, B

South Dakota

South Dakota State University, B

Tennessee

Carson-Newman College, B
Lipscomb University, B
Tennessee Technological University, B
The University of Tennessee at Martin, B

Texas

Abilene Christian University, B
El Paso Community College, A
Lamar University, B
South Plains College, A
Tarrant County College District, A
Texas A&M University-Kingsville, B
Texas Christian University, B
Texas Southern University, B
Texas Tech University, B
The University of Texas-Pan American, B
The University of Texas Southwestern Medical
    Center at Dallas, B

Utah

Brigham Young University, B

Vermont

University of Vermont, B

Virginia

J. Sargeant Reynolds Community College, A
James Madison University, B
Northern Virginia Community College, A

Washington

Bastyr University, B
Shoreline Community College, A

Spokane Community College, A

West Virginia

Marshall University, B

Wisconsin

Madison Area Technical College, A
Milwaukee Area Technical College, A
Mount Mary College, B
University of Wisconsin-Madison, B
University of Wisconsin-Stevens Point, B
University of Wisconsin-Stout, B
Viterbo University, B

British Columbia

The University of British Columbia, B

Newfoundland and Labrador

Memorial University of Newfoundland, B

Nova Scotia

Acadia University, B
Mount Saint Vincent University, B

Ontario

University of Ottawa, A
The University of Western Ontario, B

Quebec

McGill University, B

DIETICIAN ASSISTANT

Florida

Florida Community College at Jacksonville, A

Illinois

City Colleges of Chicago, Malcolm X College, A

Kansas

Barton County Community College, A

Kentucky

Eastern Kentucky University, A

Nevada

Truckee Meadows Community College, A

New York

Erie Community College, North Campus, A

North Carolina

Martin Community College, A

Ohio

Youngstown State University, A

Pennsylvania

Community College of Allegheny County, A
Pennsylvania College of Technology, A
The Pennsylvania State University University Park
    Campus, A

Tennessee

Southwest Tennessee Community College, A

DIGITAL COMMUNICATION AND MEDIA/MULTIMEDIA

Arkansas

Harding University, B

California

Academy of Art University, AB
The Art Institute of California-San Diego, B
California Lutheran University, B
California State University, Sacramento, B
Cogswell Polytechnical College, B
Gavilan College, A

Platt College San Diego, A

Colorado

Trinidad State Junior College, A

District of Columbia

Corcoran College of Art and Design, AB

Florida

Brevard Community College, A
Florida Atlantic University, B
Hillsborough Community College, A

Georgia

Georgia Institute of Technology, B
Savannah College of Art and Design, B
University of Georgia, B

Illinois

The Illinois Institute of Art-Schaumburg, B
School of the Art Institute of Chicago, B

Indiana

Huntington University, B

Iowa

University of Northern Iowa, B

Kentucky

Louisville Technical Institute, A

Maine

Saint Joseph's College of Maine, B

Maryland

University of Baltimore, B

Massachusetts

The New England Institute of Art, B

Michigan

Calvin College, B
Grace Bible College, B
Michigan Technological University, B

Minnesota

The Art Institutes International Minnesota, AB
Globe College, A
Northwestern College, B

Missouri

Lindenwood University, B

New Hampshire

Southern New Hampshire University, B

New York

Canisius College, B
Clarkson University, B
Fashion Institute of Technology, B
Marist College, B
New York University, B

North Dakota

Minot State University, B

Ohio

Kent State University, B

Oklahoma

Cameron University, A

Pennsylvania

The Art Institute of Pittsburgh, AB
Kutztown University of Pennsylvania, B
Lebanon Valley College, B
Lehigh Carbon Community College, A
The University of the Arts, B

Texas

Abilene Christian University, B
Sam Houston State University, B

Texas A&M University, B
The University of Texas at Arlington, B

Utah

Utah Valley State College, AB

Vermont

Champlain College, AB

Virginia

The Art Institute of Washington, B

Washington

Eastern Washington University, B
Olympic College, A
Washington State University, B

West Virginia

Wheeling Jesuit University, B

Wyoming

Central Wyoming College, A
Laramie County Community College, A

Alberta

University of Lethbridge, B

Ontario

University of Toronto, B
University of Waterloo, B

DIRECT ENTRY MIDWIFERY (LM, CPM)

Florida

The Florida School of Midwifery, A

Utah

Midwives College of Utah, B

DIRECTING AND THEATRICAL PRODUCTION

California

California State University, Long Beach, B
University of Southern California, B

Iowa

Coe College, B
Drake University, B

Michigan

Oakland University, B
Western Michigan University, B

New York

Sarah Lawrence College, B

North Carolina

Campbell University, B

Ohio

Ohio University, B

Oregon

George Fox University, B

Pennsylvania

Elizabethtown College, B
Marywood University, B

Utah

Brigham Young University, B

Vermont

Bennington College, B

Washington

Cornish College of the Arts, B

DISABILITY STUDIES

Illinois

University of Illinois at Chicago, MD

Maryland

The Johns Hopkins University, O

Massachusetts

Suffolk University, M

New York

Syracuse University, O

British Columbia

University of Northern British Columbia, M

Manitoba

University of Manitoba, M

Ontario

York University, M

DISTANCE EDUCATION DEVELOPMENT

Arizona

University of Phoenix-Phoenix Campus, M

California

University of Phoenix-Sacramento Valley Campus, M

Colorado

Jones International University, M
University of Phoenix-Denver Campus, M

Florida

Florida State University, M
Nova Southeastern University, MD

Illinois

Western Illinois University, O

Maryland

University of Maryland, Baltimore County, O
University of Maryland University College, MO

Michigan

University of Phoenix-Metro Detroit Campus, M

New York

New York Institute of Technology, O
New York University, M

Wyoming

University of Wyoming, D

Alberta

Athabasca University, MO

Quebec

Télé-université, M

DIVINITY/MINISTRY (BD, MDIV.)

Alabama

Faulkner University, AB

Arizona

Grand Canyon University, B

Arkansas

Harding University, B
John Brown University, B

Williams Baptist College, B

California

Azusa Pacific University, B
Bethany University, B
Bethesda Christian University, B
Biola University, B
Concordia University, B
Fresno Pacific University, B
The Master's College and Seminary, B
Patten University, B
The Salvation Army College for Officer Training at Crestmont, A
San Diego Christian College, B

Florida

Florida Christian College, AB
Okaloosa-Walton College, A
Warner Southern College, AB

Georgia

Shorter College, B

Idaho

Boise Bible College, AB
Northwest Nazarene University, B

Illinois

Lincoln Christian College, B
North Park University, B

Indiana

Bethel College, B
Grace College, B
Huntington University, B
Oakland City University, B

Iowa

Faith Baptist Bible College and Theological Seminary, AB

Kansas

Barclay College, B
Central Christian College of Kansas, B
Friends University, B
Manhattan Christian College, AB
Tabor College, B

Kentucky

Campbellsville University, B
Clear Creek Baptist Bible College, AB

Massachusetts

Atlantic Union College, AB

Michigan

Great Lakes Christian College, B
Kuyper College, B

Minnesota

North Central University, AB
Oak Hills Christian College, B

Missouri

Baptist Bible College, B
Central Christian College of the Bible, B
Global University of the Assemblies of God, B
Messenger College, B
St. Louis Christian College, AB

Nebraska

Grace University, B
Nebraska Christian College, AB

New York

Roberts Wesleyan College, B
St. John's University, B
Yeshivat Mikdash Melech, B

North Carolina

Campbell University, B
John Wesley College, B
Mount Olive College, AB

Southeastern Baptist Theological Seminary, A

North Dakota

University of Mary, B

Ohio

Cincinnati Christian University, B

Oklahoma

Mid-America Christian University, B
Oklahoma Baptist University, B
Oklahoma Wesleyan University, B
Southwestern Christian University, B

Oregon

Corban College, B
Eugene Bible College, B
Marylhurst University, B
Warner Pacific College, AB

Pennsylvania

Baptist Bible College of Pennsylvania, B
Grove City College, B

South Carolina

Southern Wesleyan University, B

Tennessee

Belmont University, B
Carson-Newman College, A
Lipscomb University, B
Martin Methodist College, B

Texas

College of Biblical Studies-Houston, AB
Dallas Baptist University, B
Lon Morris College, A
Southwestern Assemblies of God University, B

Virginia

Bluefield College, B
Regent University, B

Washington

Northwest University, B
Puget Sound Christian College, B

Wisconsin

Cardinal Stritch University, B
Viterbo University, B

Alberta

Taylor University College and Seminary, B

British Columbia

Trinity Western University, B

Manitoba

Canadian Mennonite University, B
Providence College and Theological Seminary, B

New Brunswick

Bethany Bible College, B

Ontario

Emmanuel Bible College, B
Master's College and Seminary, B
Saint Paul University, B
Tyndale University College & Seminary, B

Saskatchewan

Briercrest College, B

DOG/PET/ANIMAL GROOMING

Massachusetts

Becker College, A

DRAFTING AND DESIGN TECHNOLOGY/TECHNICIAN

Alabama

Bevill State Community College, A
Bishop State Community College, A

Calhoun Community College, A
Central Alabama Community College, A
Gadsden State Community College-Ayers Campus, A
George C. Wallace Community College, A
George Corley Wallace State Community College, A
H. Councill Trenholm State Technical College, A
J. F. Drake State Technical College, A
Lawson State Community College, A
Northwest-Shoals Community College, A
Remington College-Mobile Campus, A
Shelton State Community College, A
Virginia College at Birmingham, A
Wallace State Community College, A

Alaska

University of Alaska Anchorage, A

Arizona

Arizona Western College, A
Cochise College (Sierra Vista), A
Eastern Arizona College, A
High-Tech Institute, A
Mesa Community College, A
Northland Pioneer College, A
Phoenix College, A

Arkansas

Arkansas State University-Beebe, A
East Arkansas Community College, A
North Arkansas College, A
NorthWest Arkansas Community College, A
Phillips Community College of the University of Arkansas, A
Pulaski Technical College, A
Southeast Arkansas College, A
University of Arkansas Community College at Morrilton, A
University of Arkansas at Fort Smith, A

California

American River College, A
Antelope Valley College, A
Bakersfield College, A
Barstow College, A
Cabrillo College, A
Cerritos College, A
Cerro Coso Community College, A
Chaffey College, A
Citrus College, A
College of the Canyons, A
College of the Desert, A
College of the Redwoods, A
College of San Mateo, A
College of the Sequoias, A
Compton Community College, A
Contra Costa College, A
Cosumnes River College (Sacramento), A
Cuyamaca College, A
Don Bosco Technical Institute, A
East Los Angeles College, A
El Camino College, A
Evergreen Valley College, A
Fresno City College, A
Fullerton College, A
Gavilan College, A
Glendale Community College, A
Golden West College, A
Hartnell College, A
Las Positas College, A
Lassen Community College District, A
Long Beach City College, A
Los Angeles City College, A
Los Angeles Harbor College, A
Los Angeles Pierce College, A
Los Angeles Southwest College, A
Los Angeles Trade-Technical College, A
Los Angeles Valley College, A
Los Medanos College, A
MiraCosta College, A
Mission College, A
Modesto Junior College, A
Mt. San Antonio College, A
Napa Valley College, A
Ohlone College, A

Orange Coast College, A
Pacific Union College, B
Palomar College, A
Pasadena City College, A
Porterville College, A
Sacramento City College, A
Saddleback College, A
San Bernardino Valley College, A
San Diego City College, A
San Joaquin Delta College, A
San Jose City College, A
Santa Ana College, A
Santa Barbara City College, A
Santa Monica College, A
Shasta College, A
Sierra College, A
Solano Community College, A
Taft College, A
West Los Angeles College, A
West Valley College, A
Western Career College (Walnut Creek), A

Colorado

Arapahoe Community College, A
Community College of Denver, A
IntelliTec College (Colorado Springs), A
Red Rocks Community College, A
Trinidad State Junior College, A

Connecticut

Naugatuck Valley Community College, A
Three Rivers Community College, A

Delaware

Delaware Technical & Community College, Jack F. Owens Campus, A
Delaware Technical & Community College, Stanton/Wilmington Campus, A
Delaware Technical & Community College, Terry Campus, A

Florida

ATI Career Training Center (Fort Lauderdale), A
Brevard Community College, A
Central Florida Community College, A
Daytona Beach Community College, A
Edison College, A
Florida Community College at Jacksonville, A
Gulf Coast Community College, A
Indian River Community College, A
Keiser College (Melbourne), A
Lynn University, B
Manatee Community College, A
Miami Dade College, A
New England Institute of Technology at Palm Beach, A
Okaloosa-Walton College, A
Palm Beach Community College, A
Pasco-Hernando Community College, A
Pensacola Junior College, A
St. Petersburg College, A
Santa Fe Community College, A
Seminole Community College, A
South Florida Community College, A
Valencia Community College, A

Georgia

Albany Technical College, A
Bainbridge College, A
Central Georgia Technical College, A
Chattahoochee Technical College, A
Clayton State University, A
Columbus Technical College, A
Dalton State College, A
DeKalb Technical College, A
Georgia Southwestern State University, A
Griffin Technical College, A
Gwinnett Technical College, A
Lanier Technical College, A
Middle Georgia Technical College, A
Northwestern Technical College, A
South Georgia Technical College, A
Swainsboro Technical College, A
Valdosta Technical College, A

Waycross College, A

Hawaii

Hawaii Community College, A
Honolulu Community College, A
Leeward Community College, A

Idaho

Boise State University, A
Brigham Young University -Idaho, A
College of Southern Idaho, A
Idaho State University, A
Lewis-Clark State College, AB
North Idaho College, A

Illinois

Carl Sandburg College, A
City Colleges of Chicago, Harry S. Truman
    College, A
City Colleges of Chicago, Richard J. Daley
    College, A
College of DuPage, A
Danville Area Community College, A
Elgin Community College, A
Heartland Community College, A
Highland Community College, A
Illinois Valley Community College, A
John A. Logan College, A
Kankakee Community College, A
Lake Land College, A
Lewis and Clark Community College, A
Morrison Institute of Technology, A
Morton College, A
Richland Community College, A
Robert Morris College, A
South Suburban College, A
Southwestern Illinois College, A
Triton College, A
William Rainey Harper College, A

Indiana

Ivy Tech Community College-Central Indiana, A
Ivy Tech Community College-Columbus, A
Ivy Tech Community College-Kokomo, A
Ivy Tech Community College-Lafayette, A
Ivy Tech Community College-Northeast, A
Ivy Tech Community College-Northwest, A
Lincoln Technical Institute, A
Tri-State University, AB
Vincennes University, A
Vincennes University Jasper Campus, A

Iowa

Des Moines Area Community College, A
Hamilton Technical College, A
Hawkeye Community College, A
Indian Hills Community College, A
Iowa Central Community College, A
Iowa Lakes Community College, A
Kirkwood Community College, A
Marshalltown Community College, A
Southeastern Community College, North Campus, A
Southwestern Community College, A

Kansas

Allen County Community College, A
Butler Community College, A
Cloud County Community College, A
Coffeyville Community College, A
Cowley County Community College and Area
    Vocational-Technical School, A
Donnelly College, A
Fort Scott Community College, A
Garden City Community College, A
Highland Community College, A
Hutchinson Community College and Area Vocational
    School, A
Independence Community College, A
Johnson County Community College, A
Kansas City Kansas Community College, A
Labette Community College, A
Manhattan Area Technical College, A

Washburn University, A

Kentucky

Eastern Kentucky University, A
Kentucky State University, A
Louisville Technical Institute, A
Murray State University, A

Louisiana

Bossier Parish Community College, A
Delgado Community College, A
Elaine P. Nunez Community College, A
Grambling State University, B
ITI Technical College, A
Louisiana Technical College, A

Maine

Eastern Maine Community College, A
Kennebec Valley Community College, A
Northern Maine Community College, A
Southern Maine Community College, A
York County Community College, A

Maryland

Baltimore City Community College, A
Frederick Community College, A
Prince George's Community College, A

Massachusetts

Benjamin Franklin Institute of Technology, A
Massachusetts Bay Community College, A
Middlesex Community College, A

Michigan

Alpena Community College, A
Baker College of Auburn Hills, A
Baker College of Cadillac, A
Baker College of Clinton Township, A
Baker College of Flint, AB
Baker College of Muskegon, A
Baker College of Owosso, AB
Baker College of Port Huron, A
Bay de Noc Community College, A
Delta College, A
Ferris State University, A
Gogebic Community College, A
Grand Rapids Community College, A
Henry Ford Community College, A
Hillsdale College, B
Kalamazoo Valley Community College, A
Kellogg Community College, A
Kirtland Community College, A
Lake Michigan College, A
Lansing Community College, A
Macomb Community College, A
Mid Michigan Community College, A
Monroe County Community College, A
Montcalm Community College, A
Mott Community College, A
Muskegon Community College, A
North Central Michigan College, A
Northern Michigan University, AB
Northwestern Michigan College, A
St. Clair County Community College, A
Schoolcraft College, A
Southwestern Michigan College, A
Washtenaw Community College, A
Wayne County Community College District, A

Minnesota

Dakota County Technical College, A
Hibbing Community College, A
Minnesota State College-Southeast Technical, A
Northland Community and Technical College-Thief
    River Falls, A
Ridgewater College, A

Mississippi

Copiah-Lincoln Community College, A
East Central Community College, A
East Mississippi Community College, A
Hinds Community College, A
Holmes Community College, A
Itawamba Community College, A
Jones County Junior College, A

Meridian Community College, A
Mississippi Gulf Coast Community College, A
Northeast Mississippi Community College, A
Northwest Mississippi Community College, A
Pearl River Community College, A

Missouri

Central Missouri State University, AB
Crowder College, A
East Central College, A
Lincoln University, A
Linn State Technical College, A
Metropolitan Community College-Business &
    Technology College, A
Mineral Area College, A
Missouri Southern State University, A
Moberly Area Community College, A
North Central Missouri College, A
Saint Charles Community College, A

Montana

Montana State University-Billings, A
Montana State University-Great Falls College of
    Technology, A
Montana State University-Northern, AB
Montana Tech of The University of Montana, A

Nebraska

Central Community College-Columbus Campus, A
Central Community College-Grand Island
    Campus, A
Central Community College-Hastings Campus, A
Metropolitan Community College, A
Northeast Community College, A
Southeast Community College, Lincoln Campus, A
Southeast Community College, Milford Campus, A

Nevada

Community College of Southern Nevada, A
Truckee Meadows Community College, A
Western Nevada Community College, A

New Hampshire

Keene State College, AB
New Hampshire Community Technical College,
    Manchester/Stratham, A
New Hampshire Community Technical College,
    Nashua/Claremont, A

New Jersey

Bergen Community College, A
Brookdale Community College, A
Burlington County College, A
Cumberland County College, A
Gloucester County College, A
Middlesex County College, A

New Mexico

Doña Ana Branch Community College, A
Eastern New Mexico University-Roswell, A
New Mexico Junior College, A
San Juan College, A
Santa Fe Community College, A
Southwestern Indian Polytechnic Institute, A
Western New Mexico University, A

New York

Adirondack Community College, A
Cayuga County Community College, A
Corning Community College, A
Finger Lakes Community College, A
Genesee Community College, A
Institute of Design and Construction, A
Mohawk Valley Community College, A
New York City College of Technology of the City
    University of New York, A
Niagara County Community College, A
Onondaga Community College, A
Orange County Community College, A
Rockland Community College, A
State University of New York College of Agriculture
    and Technology at Morrisville, A
State University of New York College of Technology
    at Alfred, A
Suffolk County Community College, A

Ulster County Community College, A

North Carolina

Beaufort County Community College, A
Blue Ridge Community College, A
Caldwell Community College and Technical
   Institute, A
Central Carolina Community College, A
Central Piedmont Community College, A
Forsyth Technical Community College, A
Guilford Technical Community College, A
Isothermal Community College, A
Lenoir Community College, A
Mitchell Community College, A
South Piedmont Community College, A
Surry Community College, A
Western Piedmont Community College, A

Ohio

Central Ohio Technical College, A
Clark State Community College, A
Edison State Community College, A
Hocking College, A
James A. Rhodes State College, A
Jefferson Community College, A
Lorain County Community College, A
Marion Technical College, A
North Central State College, A
Ohio University-Lancaster, A
Sinclair Community College, A
Southern State Community College, A
Stark State College of Technology, A
The University of Akron, A
University of Cincinnati, A
University of Rio Grande, AB
The University of Toledo, A
Washington State Community College, A
Wright State University, A
Wright State University, Lake Campus, A
Youngstown State University, A
Zane State College, A

Oklahoma

Cameron University, B
East Central University, B
Langston University, A
Murray State College, A
Northeastern Oklahoma Agricultural and Mechanical
   College, A
Northern Oklahoma College, A
Oklahoma City Community College, A
Oklahoma State University, Okmulgee, A
Redlands Community College, A
Rose State College, A
Tulsa Community College, A

Oregon

Chemeketa Community College, A
Clackamas Community College, A
Lane Community College, A
Linn-Benton Community College, A
Portland Community College, A
Treasure Valley Community College, A

Pennsylvania

Berks Technical Institute, A
Butler County Community College, A
California University of Pennsylvania, A
Community College of Allegheny County, A
Community College of Beaver County, A
Community College of Philadelphia, A
Delaware County Community College, A
Lehigh Carbon Community College, A
Lincoln Technical Institute (Allentown), A
Lincoln Technical Institute (Philadelphia), A
Luzerne County Community College, A
Penn Commercial Business and Technical School, A
Pennco Tech, A
Pennsylvania College of Technology, A
Saint Francis University, A
Schuylkill Institute of Business and Technology, A
Thaddeus Stevens College of Technology, A
Thompson Institute, A
Triangle Tech, Inc.-DuBois School, A
Triangle Tech, Inc.-Erie School, A

Triangle Tech, Inc.-Greensburg School, A
Triangle Tech, Inc.-Pittsburgh School, A
Westmoreland County Community College, A

Puerto Rico

Caribbean University, B
University of Puerto Rico at Ponce, A

South Carolina

Florence-Darlington Technical College, A
Greenville Technical College, A
Piedmont Technical College, A
Spartanburg Technical College, A
Tri-County Technical College, A
Williamsburg Technical College, A

South Dakota

Black Hills State University, A
Lake Area Technical Institute, A
Mitchell Technical Institute, A
Southeast Technical Institute, A
Western Dakota Technical Institute, A

Tennessee

Chattanooga State Technical Community College, A
Northeast State Technical Community College, A
Pellissippi State Technical Community College, A

Texas

Alvin Community College, A
Amarillo College, A
Austin Community College, A
Brazosport College, A
Central Texas College, A
Cisco Junior College, A
Coastal Bend College, A
Collin County Community College District, A
Del Mar College, A
Eastfield College, A
El Centro College, A
El Paso Community College, A
Grayson County College, A
Hill College of the Hill Junior College District, A
Houston Community College System, A
Howard College, A
Kilgore College, A
Lamar University, A
Lee College, A
LeTourneau University, A
Midland College, A
Mountain View College, A
Navarro College, A
North Central Texas College, A
North Harris College, A
Odessa College, A
Paris Junior College, A
Prairie View A&M University, B
Sam Houston State University, B
San Antonio College, A
South Plains College, A
Tarrant County College District, A
Temple College, A
Texarkana College, A
Texas Southern University, B
Texas Southmost College, A
Texas State Technical College Harlingen, A
Texas State Technical College Waco, A
Texas State Technical College West Texas, A
Trinity Valley Community College, A
Tyler Junior College, A
University of Houston, B
Vernon College, A
Victoria College, A
Wharton County Junior College, A

Utah

Salt Lake Community College, A
Southern Utah University, A
Utah State University, A
Utah Valley State College, A
Weber State University, A

Virginia

Central Virginia Community College, A
Dabney S. Lancaster Community College, A

Mountain Empire Community College, A
New River Community College, A
Norfolk State University, B
Southside Virginia Community College, A
Southwest Virginia Community College, A
Thomas Nelson Community College, A
Tidewater Community College, A
Virginia Highlands Community College, A
Wytheville Community College, A

Washington

Everett Community College, A
Green River Community College, A
Highline Community College, A
Lake Washington Technical College, A
Olympic College, A
Seattle Central Community College, A
Shoreline Community College, A
South Puget Sound Community College, A
South Seattle Community College, A
Spokane Community College, A

West Virginia

Community & Technical College at West Virginia
   University Institute of Technology, A
Fairmont State University, A
Southern West Virginia Community and Technical
   College, A
West Virginia State University, A
West Virginia University at Parkersburg, A

Wisconsin

Chippewa Valley Technical College, A
Fox Valley Technical College, A
Herzing College, AB
Milwaukee Area Technical College, A
Northcentral Technical College, A
Northeast Wisconsin Technical College, A
Southwest Wisconsin Technical College, A

Wyoming

Casper College, A
Northwest College, A
Sheridan College-Sheridan and Gillette, A

British Columbia

British Columbia Institute of Technology, A
Thompson Rivers University, A

DRAFTING/DESIGN ENGINEERING TECHNOLOGIES/TECHNICIANS

Arizona

Phoenix College, A

California

Cuyamaca College, A
De Anza College, A
Hartnell College, A
Los Angeles Valley College, A
Mt. San Antonio College, A
National University, B

Colorado

Arapahoe Community College, A
Front Range Community College, A

Georgia

Clayton State University, A

Idaho

Brigham Young University -Idaho, A
Idaho State University, A

Illinois

College of DuPage, A
Heartland Community College, A
Illinois Central College, A
Illinois Valley Community College, A
Joliet Junior College, A
Oakton Community College, A

Prairie State College, A
Rock Valley College, A
South Suburban College, A
William Rainey Harper College, A

Iowa

Hawkeye Community College, A
Iowa Western Community College, A
Kirkwood Community College, A
Northeast Iowa Community College, A
Northwest Iowa Community College, A

Kansas

Garden City Community College, A

Kentucky

Louisville Technical Institute, A

Maine

Central Maine Community College, A

Maryland

Carroll Community College, A

Michigan

Delta College, A
Ferris State University, A
Lansing Community College, A
Macomb Community College, A

Minnesota

Hennepin Technical College, A
Minnesota State College-Southeast Technical, A
Northwest Technical College, A
St. Cloud Technical College, A

Missouri

Jefferson College, A
Lincoln University, B

Nebraska

Southeast Community College, Milford Campus, A

Nevada

Community College of Southern Nevada, A

New Hampshire

New Hampshire Community Technical College,
  Manchester/Stratham, A

New Jersey

Raritan Valley Community College, A

New York

Adirondack Community College, A
Cayuga County Community College, A
Mohawk Valley Community College, A
Niagara County Community College, A
State University of New York College of Technology
  at Alfred, A

North Carolina

Asheville-Buncombe Technical Community
  College, A
College of The Albemarle, A
Forsyth Technical Community College, A
Isothermal Community College, A
Lenoir Community College, A

Ohio

Bowling Green State University, B
Bowling Green State University-Firelands College, A
Edison State Community College, A
James A. Rhodes State College, A
Lorain County Community College, A
Owens Community College, A

The University of Akron, A

Oregon

Chemeketa Community College, A

Pennsylvania

Butler County Community College, A
Community College of Allegheny County, A
Luzerne County Community College, A
Pennsylvania College of Technology, A
Thaddeus Stevens College of Technology, A
Triangle Tech, Inc.-Erie School, A
Triangle Tech, Inc.-Pittsburgh School, A
Westmoreland County Community College, A

South Carolina

Northeastern Technical College, A

Tennessee

Chattanooga State Technical Community College, A

Texas

Montgomery College, A
Richland College, A

Virginia

Blue Ridge Community College, A
Dabney S. Lancaster Community College, A

Washington

Eastern Washington University, B
Spokane Community College, A

West Virginia

Fairmont State Community & Technical College, A

Wisconsin

Blackhawk Technical College, A
Chippewa Valley Technical College, A
Fox Valley Technical College, A
Gateway Technical College, A
Lakeshore Technical College, A
Madison Area Technical College, A
Mid-State Technical College, A
Moraine Park Technical College, A
Northcentral Technical College, A
Northeast Wisconsin Technical College, A
Southwest Wisconsin Technical College, A
Western Technical College, A

DRAMA AND DANCE TEACHER EDUCATION

Arizona

Northern Arizona University, B
The University of Arizona, B

District of Columbia

The Catholic University of America, B

Florida

Jacksonville University, B
University of South Florida, B

Georgia

Brenau University, B
Columbus State University, B
University of Georgia, B

Indiana

Huntington University, B
Indiana University-Purdue University Fort Wayne, B
University of Evansville, B
Valparaiso University, B

Iowa

Dordt College, B
The University of Iowa, B

Waldorf College, B

Kansas

Central Christian College of Kansas, A

Louisiana

Centenary College of Louisiana, B

Massachusetts

Boston University, B
Bridgewater State College, B
Emerson College, B

Michigan

Hope College, B

Minnesota

College of St. Catherine, B
Minnesota State University Moorhead, B
Southwest Minnesota State University, B
University of St. Thomas, B

Mississippi

William Carey College, B

Missouri

Washington University in St. Louis, B
William Jewell College, B

Nebraska

Chadron State College, B
Concordia University, B
Dana College, B
Hastings College, B
Wayne State College, B
Western Nebraska Community College, A

North Carolina

Appalachian State University, B
East Carolina University, B
Greensboro College, B
Meredith College, B
The University of North Carolina at Charlotte, B
The University of North Carolina at Greensboro, B

Ohio

Bowling Green State University, B
Capital University, B
The Ohio State University, B
Ohio Wesleyan University, B
The University of Akron, B
Youngstown State University, B

Oklahoma

Oklahoma Baptist University, B

Pennsylvania

Point Park University, B
The University of the Arts, B

Rhode Island

Salve Regina University, B

South Carolina

Columbia College, B

South Dakota

The University of South Dakota, B

Texas

Baylor University, B
East Texas Baptist University, B
Hardin-Simmons University, B
Howard Payne University, B
St. Edward's University, B
Texas Wesleyan University, B

Utah

Brigham Young University, B
University of Utah, B
Utah Valley State College, B

Weber State University, B

Vermont

Johnson State College, B

Virginia

Old Dominion University, B

Washington

Central Washington University, B
Eastern Washington University, B

Wisconsin

Viterbo University, B

Alberta

University of Calgary, B
University of Lethbridge, B

Ontario

University of Windsor, B
York University, B

Quebec

Bishop's University, B
Concordia University, B

DRAMA AND DRAMATICS/THEATRE ARTS

Alabama

Alabama State University, B
Auburn University, B
Birmingham-Southern College, B
Calhoun Community College, A
Chattahoochee Valley Community College, A
Faulkner University, B
Huntingdon College, B
Jacksonville State University, B
Jefferson Davis Community College, A
Samford University, B
Spring Hill College, B
Troy University, B
The University of Alabama, B
University of Mobile, B
University of Montevallo, B
University of South Alabama, B

Alaska

University of Alaska Anchorage, B
University of Alaska Fairbanks, B

Arizona

Arizona State University, B
Arizona Western College, A
Eastern Arizona College, A
Grand Canyon University, B
Northern Arizona University, B
Pima Community College, A
Prescott College, B
Scottsdale Community College, A
The University of Arizona, B

Arkansas

Arkansas State University, B
Harding University, B
Henderson State University, B
Hendrix College, B
Lyon College, B
Ouachita Baptist University, B
Phillips Community College of the University of
    Arkansas, A
Southern Arkansas University-Magnolia, B
University of Arkansas, B
University of Arkansas at Little Rock, B
University of Arkansas at Pine Bluff, B
University of the Ozarks, B

California

American Academy of Dramatic Arts/Hollywood, A
American River College, A
Bakersfield College, A

Bethany University, B
California Baptist University, B
California Institute of the Arts, B
California Lutheran University, B
California State Polytechnic University, Pomona, B
California State University, Bakersfield, B
California State University, Chico, B
California State University, Dominguez Hills, B
California State University, East Bay, B
California State University, Fresno, B
California State University, Fullerton, B
California State University, Long Beach, B
California State University, Los Angeles, B
California State University, Monterey Bay, B
California State University, Northridge, B
California State University, Sacramento, B
California State University, San Bernardino, B
California State University, Stanislaus, B
Cañada College, A
Cerritos College, A
Chaffey College, A
Chapman University, B
Citrus College, A
Claremont McKenna College, B
College of the Desert, A
College of Marin, A
College of the Sequoias, A
Columbia College, A
Compton Community College, A
Concordia University, B
Cosumnes River College (Sacramento), A
Crafton Hills College, A
Cypress College, A
De Anza College, A
East Los Angeles College, A
El Camino College, A
Fresno City College, A
Fullerton College, A
Glendale Community College, A
Grossmont College, A
Humboldt State University, B
Lake Tahoe Community College, A
Laney College, A
Long Beach City College, A
Los Angeles City College, A
Los Angeles Mission College, A
Los Angeles Pierce College, A
Los Angeles Southwest College, A
Los Angeles Valley College, A
Loyola Marymount University, B
Mendocino College, A
Merced College, A
MiraCosta College, A
Modesto Junior College, A
Monterey Peninsula College, A
Moorpark College, A
Notre Dame de Namur University, B
Occidental College, B
Orange Coast College, A
Oxnard College, A
Palomar College, A
Pasadena City College, A
Pepperdine University, B
Pitzer College, B
Point Loma Nazarene University, B
Pomona College, B
Sacramento City College, A
Saddleback College, A
Saint Mary's College of California, B
San Diego City College, A
San Diego State University, B
San Francisco State University, B
San Joaquin Delta College, A
San Jose State University, B
Santa Ana College, A
Santa Barbara City College, A
Santa Clara University, B
Santa Monica College, A
Santa Rosa Junior College, A
Santiago Canyon College, A
Scripps College, B
Shasta College, A
Sonoma State University, B
Southwestern College, A
Stanford University, B
University of California, Berkeley, B

University of California, Irvine, B
University of California, Los Angeles, B
University of California, Riverside, B
University of California, San Diego, B
University of California, Santa Barbara, B
University of California, Santa Cruz, B
University of La Verne, B
University of the Pacific, B
University of San Diego, B
University of Southern California, B
Vanguard University of Southern California, B
Ventura College, A
Victor Valley College, A
West Valley College, A
Westmont College, B
Whittier College, B
Yuba College, A

Colorado

Adams State College, B
Colorado Christian University, B
The Colorado College, B
Colorado Mountain College, A
Colorado State University, B
Fort Lewis College, B
Mesa State College, AB
Naropa University, B
Northeastern Junior College, A
Otero Junior College, A
Trinidad State Junior College, A
University of Colorado at Boulder, B
University of Colorado at Denver and Health
    Sciences Center - Downtown Denver Campus, B
University of Denver, B
University of Northern Colorado, B
Western State College of Colorado, B

Connecticut

Albertus Magnus College, B
Central Connecticut State University, B
Connecticut College, B
Manchester Community College, A
Sacred Heart University, B
Southern Connecticut State University, B
Three Rivers Community College, A
Trinity College, B
University of Connecticut, B
University of Hartford, B
Wesleyan University, B
Western Connecticut State University, B
Yale University, B

District of Columbia

American University, B
The Catholic University of America, B
Gallaudet University, B
The George Washington University, B
Howard University, B
University of the District of Columbia, B

Florida

Barry University, B
Daytona Beach Community College, A
Eckerd College, B
Flagler College, B
Florida Agricultural and Mechanical University, B
Florida Atlantic University, B
Florida International University, B
Florida Southern College, B
Florida State University, B
Hillsborough Community College, A
Indian River Community College, A
Jacksonville University, B
Manatee Community College, A
Miami Dade College, A
New World School of the Arts, AB
Nova Southeastern University, B
Palm Beach Atlantic University, B
Palm Beach Community College, A
Pensacola Junior College, A
Rollins College, B
St. Johns River Community College, A
Southeastern University, B
Stetson University, B
University of Central Florida, B
University of Florida, B

University of Miami, B
University of South Florida, B
The University of Tampa, B
University of West Florida, B
Valencia Community College, A

Georgia

Agnes Scott College, B
Armstrong Atlantic State University, B
Bainbridge College, A
Brenau University, B
Clark Atlanta University, B
Clayton State University, A
Columbus State University, B
Darton College, A
Emory University, B
Gainesville College, A
Georgia College & State University, B
Georgia Perimeter College, A
Georgia Southern University, B
Georgia Southwestern State University, B
Gordon College, A
Kennesaw State University, B
LaGrange College, B
Macon State College, A
Mercer University, B
Morehouse College, B
Paine College, B
Piedmont College, B
Savannah College of Art and Design, B
Shorter College, B
South Georgia College, A
Spelman College, B
University of Georgia, B
University of West Georgia, B
Valdosta State University, B
Young Harris College, A

Hawaii

Brigham Young University-Hawaii, A
University of Hawaii at Manoa, B

Idaho

Albertson College of Idaho, B
Boise State University, B
Brigham Young University -Idaho, A
College of Southern Idaho, A
Idaho State University, B
North Idaho College, A
University of Idaho, B

Illinois

Augustana College, B
Bradley University, B
City Colleges of Chicago, Harold Washington
    College, A
City Colleges of Chicago, Richard J. Daley
    College, A
Columbia College Chicago, B
Concordia University, B
DePaul University, B
Dominican University, B
Eastern Illinois University, B
Elmhurst College, B
Eureka College, B
Greenville College, B
Highland Community College, A
Illinois College, B
Illinois State University, B
Illinois Wesleyan University, B
Judson College, B
Knox College, B
Lewis University, B
Lincoln College, A
Loyola University Chicago, B
MacMurray College, B
Millikin University, B
Monmouth College, B
National-Louis University, B
North Central College, B
North Park University, B
Northern Illinois University, B
Northwestern University, B
Principia College, B
Rockford College, B
Roosevelt University, B

Sauk Valley Community College, A
Southern Illinois University Carbondale, B
Southern Illinois University Edwardsville, B
Spoon River College, A
Triton College, A
University of Illinois at Chicago, B
University of Illinois at Urbana-Champaign, B
Western Illinois University, B

Indiana

Anderson University, B
Ball State University, B
Bethel College, B
Butler University, B
DePauw University, B
Earlham College, B
Franklin College, B
Goshen College, B
Hanover College, B
Huntington University, B
Indiana State University, B
Indiana University Bloomington, AB
Indiana University Northwest, B
Indiana University-Purdue University Fort Wayne, B
Indiana University South Bend, B
Manchester College, B
Purdue University, B
Saint Joseph's College, B
Saint Mary-of-the-Woods College, B
Saint Mary's College, B
Taylor University, B
University of Evansville, B
University of Indianapolis, B
University of Notre Dame, B
University of Southern Indiana, B
Valparaiso University, B
Vincennes University, A
Wabash College, B

Iowa

Briar Cliff University, B
Central College, B
Clarke College, B
Coe College, B
Cornell College, B
Dordt College, B
Drake University, B
Graceland University, B
Grand View College, B
Grinnell College, B
Iowa State University of Science and Technology, B
Kirkwood Community College, A
Luther College, B
Morningside College, B
Mount Mercy College, B
Northwestern College, B
St. Ambrose University, B
Simpson College, B
The University of Iowa, B
University of Northern Iowa, B
Waldorf College, B

Kansas

Allen County Community College, A
Baker University, B
Barton County Community College, A
Benedictine College, B
Bethel College, B
Butler Community College, A
Coffeyville Community College, A
Colby Community College, A
Cowley County Community College and Area
    Vocational-Technical School, A
Dodge City Community College, A
Emporia State University, B
Garden City Community College, A
Highland Community College, A
Kansas State University, B
Kansas Wesleyan University, B
McPherson College, B
Ottawa University, B
Seward County Community College, A
Sterling College, B
University of Kansas, B
University of Saint Mary, B
Washburn University, B

Wichita State University, B

Kentucky

Berea College, B
Centre College, B
Eastern Kentucky University, B
Georgetown College, B
Morehead State University, B
Murray State University, B
Northern Kentucky University, B
Thomas More College, AB
Transylvania University, B
University of the Cumberlands, B
University of Kentucky, B
University of Louisville, B
Western Kentucky University, B

Louisiana

Centenary College of Louisiana, B
Dillard University, B
Grambling State University, B
Louisiana College, B
Louisiana State University and Agricultural and
    Mechanical College, B
Loyola University New Orleans, B
McNeese State University, B
Northwestern State University of Louisiana, B
Southern University and Agricultural and Mechanical
    College, A
Tulane University, B
University of Louisiana at Lafayette, B

Maine

Bates College, B
Colby College, B
University of Maine, B
University of Maine at Farmington, B
University of Maine at Machias, B
University of Southern Maine, B

Maryland

College of Southern Maryland, A
Frostburg State University, B
Goucher College, B
Howard Community College, A
McDaniel College, B
Morgan State University, B
St. Mary's College of Maryland, B
Salisbury University, B
Towson University, B
University of Maryland, Baltimore County, B
University of Maryland, College Park, B
Villa Julie College, A
Washington College, B

Massachusetts

Amherst College, B
Berkshire Community College, A
Boston College, B
The Boston Conservatory, B
Brandeis University, B
Bridgewater State College, B
Bunker Hill Community College, A
Cape Cod Community College, A
Clark University, B
College of the Holy Cross, B
Dean College, A
Eastern Nazarene College, B
Emerson College, B
Fitchburg State College, B
Hampshire College, B
Harvard University, B
Holyoke Community College, A
Massachusetts College of Liberal Arts, B
Massasoit Community College, A
Middlesex Community College, A
Mount Holyoke College, B
Northeastern University, B
Northern Essex Community College, A
Quincy College, A
Regis College, B
Salem State College, B
Simon's Rock College of Bard, B
Smith College, B
Suffolk University, B

Tufts University, B
University of Massachusetts Amherst, B
University of Massachusetts Boston, B
Wellesley College, B
Wheaton College, B
Williams College, B

Michigan

Adrian College, AB
Albion College, B
Alma College, B
Aquinas College, B
Calvin College, B
Central Michigan University, B
Concordia University, B
Eastern Michigan University, B
Grand Valley State University, B
Henry Ford Community College, A
Hillsdale College, B
Hope College, B
Kalamazoo College, B
Kellogg Community College, A
Lansing Community College, A
Michigan State University, B
Mid Michigan Community College, A
Northern Michigan University, B
Northwestern Michigan College, A
Saginaw Valley State University, B
Siena Heights University, B
University of Detroit Mercy, B
University of Michigan, B
University of Michigan-Flint, B
Wayne State University, B
Western Michigan University, B

Minnesota

Augsburg College, B
Bemidji State University, B
Bethany Lutheran College, B
Bethel University, B
College of Saint Benedict, B
College of St. Catherine, B
Concordia College, B
Concordia University, St. Paul, B
Gustavus Adolphus College, B
Hamline University, B
Macalester College, B
Metropolitan State University, B
Minnesota State University Mankato, B
Minnesota State University Moorhead, B
North Central University, AB
Northwestern College, B
Ridgewater College, A
St. Cloud State University, B
Saint John's University, B
Saint Mary's University of Minnesota, B
St. Olaf College, B
Southwest Minnesota State University, B
University of Minnesota, Duluth, B
University of Minnesota, Morris, B
University of Minnesota, Twin Cities Campus, B
University of St. Thomas, B
Vermilion Community College, A
Winona State University, B

Mississippi

Belhaven College, B
Hinds Community College, A
Millsaps College, B
Mississippi Delta Community College, A
Mississippi University for Women, B
Northeast Mississippi Community College, A
University of Mississippi, B
University of Southern Mississippi, B
William Carey College, B

Missouri

Avila University, B
Central Methodist University, B
Central Missouri State University, B
College of the Ozarks, B
Crowder College, A
Culver-Stockton College, B
Drury University, B
Fontbonne University, B
Hannibal-LaGrange College, B

Jefferson College, A
Lindenwood University, B
Missouri Southern State University, B
Missouri State University, B
Missouri Valley College, B
Northwest Missouri State University, B
Park University, B
St. Louis Community College at Florissant Valley, A
St. Louis Community College at Meramec, A
Saint Louis University, B
Southeast Missouri State University, B
Southwest Baptist University, B
Stephens College, B
Truman State University, B
University of Missouri-Columbia, B
University of Missouri-Kansas City, B
Washington University in St. Louis, B
Webster University, B
William Jewell College, B
William Woods University, B

Montana

Carroll College, B
Montana State University, B
Montana State University-Billings, B
Rocky Mountain College, B
The University of Montana-Missoula, B
The University of Montana-Western, B

Nebraska

Chadron State College, B
Concordia University, B
Creighton University, B
Doane College, B
Hastings College, B
Midland Lutheran College, B
Nebraska Wesleyan University, B
Northeast Community College, A
University of Nebraska at Kearney, B
University of Nebraska-Lincoln, B
University of Nebraska at Omaha, B
Wayne State College, B

Nevada

Community College of Southern Nevada, A
University of Nevada, Las Vegas, B
University of Nevada, Reno, B

New Hampshire

Dartmouth College, B
Franklin Pierce College, B
Keene State College, B
New England College, B
Plymouth State University, B
University of New Hampshire, B

New Jersey

Bergen Community College, A
Bloomfield College, B
Brookdale Community College, A
Burlington County College, A
Camden County College, A
Cumberland County College, A
Drew University, B
Fairleigh Dickinson University, College at Florham, B
Fairleigh Dickinson University, Metropolitan Campus, B
Gloucester County College, A
Kean University, B
Mercer County Community College, A
Middlesex County College, A
Montclair State University, B
Raritan Valley Community College, A
Rowan University, B
Rutgers, The State University of New Jersey, Camden, B
Rutgers, The State University of New Jersey, New Brunswick/Piscataway, B
Rutgers, The State University of New Jersey, Newark, B

William Paterson University of New Jersey, B

New Mexico

College of Santa Fe, B
College of the Southwest, B
Eastern New Mexico University, B
New Mexico Junior College, A
New Mexico State University, B
San Juan College, A
University of New Mexico, B

New York

Adelphi University, B
Alfred University, B
American Academy of Dramatic Arts, A
Bard College, B
Barnard College, B
Buffalo State College, State University of New York, B
Canisius College, B
City College of the City University of New York, B
Colgate University, B
College of Staten Island of the City University of New York, B
Columbia College, B
Columbia University, School of General Studies, B
Cornell University, B
Elmira College, B
Eugene Lang College The New School for Liberal Arts, B
Finger Lakes Community College, A
Five Towns College, AB
Fordham University, B
Fulton-Montgomery Community College, A
Genesee Community College, A
Hamilton College, B
Hartwick College, B
Hobart and William Smith Colleges, B
Hofstra University, B
Hunter College of the City University of New York, B
Iona College, B
Ithaca College, B
The Juilliard School, B
Kingsborough Community College of the City University of New York, A
Le Moyne College, B
Lehman College of the City University of New York, B
Long Island University, C.W. Post Campus, B
Marist College, B
Marymount Manhattan College, B
Mohawk Valley Community College, A
Nassau Community College, A
Nazareth College of Rochester, B
New York University, B
Niagara County Community College, A
Niagara University, B
Pace University, B
Purchase College, State University of New York, B
Queens College of the City University of New York, B
Rockland Community College, A
Russell Sage College, B
St. Lawrence University, B
Sarah Lawrence College, B
Schenectady County Community College, A
Skidmore College, B
State University of New York at Binghamton, B
State University of New York at Buffalo, B
State University of New York College at Brockport, B
State University of New York College at Geneseo, B
State University of New York College at Oneonta, B
State University of New York College at Potsdam, B
State University of New York, Fredonia, B
State University of New York at New Paltz, B
State University of New York at Oswego, B
State University of New York at Plattsburgh, B
Stony Brook University, State University of New York, B
Suffolk County Community College, A
Syracuse University, B
University at Albany, State University of New York, B
Vassar College, B
Wagner College, B
Wells College, B

Yeshiva University, B
York College of the City University of New York, B

North Carolina

Appalachian State University, B
Barton College, B
Campbell University, B
Catawba College, B
College of The Albemarle, A
Davidson College, B
Duke University, B
East Carolina University, B
Elon University, B
Gardner-Webb University, B
Greensboro College, B
Guilford College, B
Guilford Technical Community College, A
High Point University, B
Lees-McRae College, B
Lenoir-Rhyne College, B
Mars Hill College, B
Meredith College, B
Methodist College, AB
North Carolina Agricultural and Technical State
    University, B
North Carolina Central University, B
North Carolina School of the Arts, B
North Carolina Wesleyan College, B
Queens University of Charlotte, B
Shaw University, B
The University of North Carolina at Asheville, B
The University of North Carolina at Chapel Hill, B
The University of North Carolina at Charlotte, B
The University of North Carolina at Greensboro, B
The University of North Carolina at Pembroke, B
The University of North Carolina Wilmington, B
Wake Forest University, B
Western Carolina University, B

North Dakota

Dickinson State University, B
Jamestown College, B
North Dakota State University, B
University of North Dakota, B

Ohio

Antioch College, B
Ashland University, B
Bowling Green State University, B
Capital University, B
Case Western Reserve University, B
Cedarville University, B
Clark State Community College, A
Cleveland State University, B
The College of Wooster, B
Denison University, B
Franciscan University of Steubenville, B
Heidelberg College, B
Hiram College, B
Kent State University, B
Kenyon College, B
Lake Erie College, B
Lorain County Community College, A
Marietta College, B
Miami University, B
Mount Union College, B
Mount Vernon Nazarene University, B
Muskingum College, B
Oberlin College, B
Ohio Northern University, B
The Ohio State University, B
Ohio University, B
Ohio University-Eastern, B
Ohio Wesleyan University, B
Otterbein College, B
Shawnee State University, B
Sinclair Community College, A
The University of Akron, B
University of Cincinnati, B
University of Dayton, B
The University of Findlay, B
The University of Toledo, B
Wilmington College, B
Wittenberg University, B

Wright State University, B

Oklahoma

Bacone College, A
Eastern Oklahoma State College, A
Langston University, B
Northeastern Oklahoma Agricultural and Mechanical
    College, A
Northeastern State University, B
Oklahoma Baptist University, B
Oklahoma Christian University, B
Oklahoma City Community College, A
Oklahoma City University, B
Oklahoma State University, B
Oral Roberts University, B
Rose State College, A
Southeastern Oklahoma State University, B
Tulsa Community College, A
University of Central Oklahoma, B
University of Oklahoma, B
University of Science and Arts of Oklahoma, B
University of Tulsa, B

Oregon

Concordia University, B
Eastern Oregon University, B
George Fox University, B
Lewis & Clark College, B
Linfield College, B
Linn-Benton Community College, A
Pacific University, B
Portland State University, B
Reed College, B
Southern Oregon University, B
Treasure Valley Community College, A
Umpqua Community College, A
University of Oregon, B
University of Portland, B
Western Oregon University, B
Willamette University, B

Pennsylvania

Albright College, B
Allegheny College, B
Arcadia University, B
Bloomsburg University of Pennsylvania, B
Bucknell University, B
Bucks County Community College, A
California University of Pennsylvania, B
Carnegie Mellon University, B
Cedar Crest College, B
Chatham College, B
Cheyney University of Pennsylvania, B
Clarion University of Pennsylvania, B
Community College of Allegheny County, A
DeSales University, B
Dickinson College, B
Duquesne University, B
East Stroudsburg University of Pennsylvania, B
Edinboro University of Pennsylvania, B
Franklin and Marshall College, B
Gannon University, B
Gettysburg College, B
Harrisburg Area Community College, A
Indiana University of Pennsylvania, B
King's College, B
Kutztown University of Pennsylvania, B
Lehigh University, B
Lock Haven University of Pennsylvania, B
Lycoming College, B
Marywood University, B
Messiah College, B
Moravian College, B
Muhlenberg College, B
Point Park University, B
Saint Vincent College, B
Seton Hill University, B
Slippery Rock University of Pennsylvania, B
Susquehanna University, B
Swarthmore College, B
Temple University, B
The University of the Arts, B
University of Pennsylvania, B
University of Pittsburgh, B
University of Pittsburgh at Johnstown, B
The University of Scranton, B

West Chester University of Pennsylvania, B
Westminster College, B
Wilkes University, B

Puerto Rico

University of Puerto Rico, Río Piedras, B
University of the Sacred Heart, B

Rhode Island

Brown University, B
Community College of Rhode Island, A
Rhode Island College, B
Roger Williams University, B
Salve Regina University, B

South Carolina

Anderson University, B
Bob Jones University, B
Coastal Carolina University, B
Coker College, B
College of Charleston, B
Converse College, B
Francis Marion University, B
Furman University, B
Limestone College, B
Newberry College, B
North Greenville College, A
Presbyterian College, B
South Carolina State University, B
University of South Carolina, B
Winthrop University, B
Wofford College, B

South Dakota

Augustana College, B
Dakota Wesleyan University, B
Northern State University, B
South Dakota State University, B
University of Sioux Falls, AB
The University of South Dakota, B

Tennessee

Belmont University, B
Bethel College, B
Carson-Newman College, B
Cumberland University, B
Fisk University, B
Freed-Hardeman University, B
Lambuth University, B
Martin Methodist College, A
Maryville College, B
Middle Tennessee State University, B
Rhodes College, B
Sewanee: The University of the South, B
Trevecca Nazarene University, B
Union University, B
University of Memphis, B
The University of Tennessee, B
The University of Tennessee at Chattanooga, B
The University of Tennessee at Martin, B
Vanderbilt University, B

Texas

Abilene Christian University, B
Alvin Community College, A
Amarillo College, A
Angelo State University, B
Baylor University, B
Blinn College, A
Brazosport College, A
Clarendon College, A
Coastal Bend College, A
College of the Mainland, A
Del Mar College, A
East Texas Baptist University, B
El Paso Community College, A
Galveston College, A
Grayson County College, A
Hardin-Simmons University, B
Hill College of the Hill Junior College District, A
Houston Community College System, A
Howard College, A
Howard Payne University, B
Kilgore College, A
Lamar University, B

Lee College, A
Lon Morris College, A
McMurry University, B
Midwestern State University, B
Navarro College, A
North Harris College, A
Our Lady of the Lake University of San Antonio, B
Prairie View A&M University, B
St. Edward's University, B
St. Philip's College, A
Sam Houston State University, B
Schreiner University, B
Southern Methodist University, B
Southwestern University, B
Stephen F. Austin State University, B
Sul Ross State University, B
Tarleton State University, B
Texarkana College, A
Texas A&M University, B
Texas A&M University-Commerce, B
Texas A&M University-Kingsville, B
Texas Christian University, B
Texas Lutheran University, B
Texas Southern University, B
Texas State University-San Marcos, B
Texas Tech University, B
Texas Wesleyan University, B
Texas Woman's University, B
Trinity University, B
Trinity Valley Community College, A
University of Dallas, B
University of Houston, B
University of the Incarnate Word, B
University of Mary Hardin-Baylor, B
University of North Texas, B
University of St. Thomas, B
The University of Texas at Arlington, B
The University of Texas at Austin, B
The University of Texas at El Paso, B
The University of Texas-Pan American, B
The University of Texas at Tyler, B
Wayland Baptist University, B
West Texas A&M University, B
Wharton County Junior College, A

United States Virgin Islands

University of the Virgin Islands, B

Utah

Brigham Young University, B
Dixie State College of Utah, A
Snow College, A
Southern Utah University, B
University of Utah, B
Utah State University, B
Utah Valley State College, A
Weber State University, B

Vermont

Bennington College, B
Castleton State College, B
Johnson State College, B
Marlboro College, B
Middlebury College, B
Saint Michael's College, B
University of Vermont, B

Virginia

Averett University, B
Bluefield College, B
Christopher Newport University, B
The College of William and Mary, B
Eastern Mennonite University, B
Emory & Henry College, B
Ferrum College, B
George Mason University, B
Hampton University, B
Hollins University, B
James Madison University, B
Longwood University, B
Lynchburg College, B
Mary Baldwin College, B
Old Dominion University, B
Radford University, B
Randolph-Macon College, B
Randolph-Macon Woman's College, B

Roanoke College, B
Shenandoah University, B
Southern Virginia University, B
Sweet Briar College, B
University of Mary Washington, B
University of Richmond, B
University of Virginia, B
The University of Virginia's College at Wise, B
Virginia Commonwealth University, B
Virginia Highlands Community College, A
Virginia Intermont College, B
Virginia Polytechnic Institute and State University, B
Virginia Wesleyan College, B
Washington and Lee University, B

Washington

Central Washington University, B
Centralia College, A
Cornish College of the Arts, B
Eastern Washington University, B
Everett Community College, A
The Evergreen State College, B
Gonzaga University, B
Lower Columbia College, A
Northwest University, B
Pacific Lutheran University, B
Saint Martin's University, B
Seattle Pacific University, B
Seattle University, B
University of Puget Sound, B
University of Washington, B
Washington State University, B
Western Washington University, B
Whitman College, B
Whitworth College, B

West Virginia

Alderson-Broaddus College, B
Bethany College, B
Davis & Elkins College, B
Fairmont State University, B
West Virginia University, B
West Virginia Wesleyan College, B

Wisconsin

Beloit College, B
Cardinal Stritch University, B
Carroll College, B
Carthage College, B
Edgewood College, B
Lawrence University, B
Marquette University, B
Ripon College, B
University of Wisconsin-Eau Claire, B
University of Wisconsin-Green Bay, AB
University of Wisconsin-La Crosse, B
University of Wisconsin-Madison, B
University of Wisconsin-Milwaukee, B
University of Wisconsin-Oshkosh, B
University of Wisconsin-Parkside, B
University of Wisconsin-River Falls, B
University of Wisconsin-Stevens Point, B
University of Wisconsin-Superior, B
University of Wisconsin-Whitewater, B
Viterbo University, B
Wisconsin Lutheran College, B

Wyoming

Casper College, A
Central Wyoming College, A
Laramie County Community College, A
University of Wyoming, B
Western Wyoming Community College, A

Alberta

Prairie Bible Institute, AB
University of Alberta, B
University of Calgary, B
University of Lethbridge, B

British Columbia

Simon Fraser University, B
Thompson Rivers University, B
Trinity Western University, B
The University of British Columbia, B

University College of the Fraser Valley, A
University of Victoria, B

Manitoba

Providence College and Theological Seminary, B
University of Manitoba, B
The University of Winnipeg, B

New Brunswick

Mount Allison University, B
Université de Moncton, B
University of New Brunswick Fredericton, B

Newfoundland and Labrador

Memorial University of Newfoundland, B

Nova Scotia

Acadia University, B
Dalhousie University, B
Université Sainte-Anne, B
University of King's College, B

Ontario

Brock University, B
Carleton University, B
Laurentian University, B
McMaster University, B
Queen's University at Kingston, B
Redeemer University College, B
University of Guelph, B
University of Ottawa, B
University of Toronto, B
University of Waterloo, B
University of Windsor, B
Wilfrid Laurier University, B
York University, B

Quebec

Bishop's University, B
Concordia University, B
McGill University, B
Université Laval, AB
Université du Québec àMontréal, B

Saskatchewan

University of Regina, B
University of Saskatchewan, B

DRAMA THERAPY

California

California Institute of Integral Studies, M

District of Columbia

Howard University, B

New York

New York University, M

Virginia

Virginia Union University, B

DRAMATIC/THEATRE ARTS AND STAGECRAFT

California

California Institute of the Arts, B
California State University, Chico, B

Colorado

University of Northern Colorado, B

Connecticut

University of Connecticut, B

Florida

Full Sail Real World Education, A

Illinois

DePaul University, B

Iowa

Drake University, B

Maine

Bowdoin College, B

Massachusetts

Bristol Community College, A

Minnesota

St. Cloud State University, B

Nebraska

Nebraska Wesleyan University, B

Nevada

University of Nevada, Las Vegas, B

New Mexico

College of Santa Fe, B

New York

State University of New York at Buffalo, B

North Carolina

Brevard College, B
Fayetteville State University, B
Saint Augustine's College, B

Ohio

Baldwin-Wallace College, B
Bowling Green State University, B
Ohio University, B
The University of Akron, B

Pennsylvania

Lehigh University, B
Seton Hill University, B
The University of the Arts, B

South Carolina

Charleston Southern University, B
Coastal Carolina University, B
Coker College, B

Texas

St. Philip's College, A

Utah

Brigham Young University, B

Virginia

Shenandoah University, B

British Columbia

Thompson Rivers University, B

Nova Scotia

Dalhousie University, B

Saskatchewan

University of Regina, B

DRAWING

Alabama

Birmingham-Southern College, B
University of Montevallo, B

California

Academy of Art University, AB
Biola University, B
California College of the Arts, B
California State University, East Bay, B
California State University, Fullerton, B
California State University, Long Beach, B
Cañada College, A
Chabot College, A
College of San Mateo, A
Cuyamaca College, A
De Anza College, A

Grossmont College, A
Laguna College of Art & Design, B
Lassen Community College District, A
Monterey Peninsula College, A
Otis College of Art and Design, B
Palomar College, A
Pasadena City College, A
San Joaquin Delta College, A
Sonoma State University, B
University of California, Santa Cruz, B
University of San Francisco, B

Colorado

Colorado State University, B
Northeastern Junior College, A

Connecticut

Lyme Academy College of Fine Arts, B
Sacred Heart University, AB
University of Hartford, B

District of Columbia

Corcoran College of Art and Design, B

Florida

New World School of the Arts, AB

Georgia

North Georgia College & State University, B
University of Georgia, B

Idaho

Boise State University, B

Illinois

American Academy of Art, B
DePaul University, B
Governors State University, B
Judson College, B
Lewis University, B
Lincoln College, A
Lincoln College-Normal, A
School of the Art Institute of Chicago, B
Trinity Christian College, B

Indiana

Ball State University, B
Grace College, B
Indiana University Bloomington, B
Indiana University-Purdue University Fort Wayne, B

Iowa

Drake University, B
Iowa Lakes Community College, A
The University of Iowa, B

Kansas

Bethany College, B
Coffeyville Community College, A
Seward County Community College, A

Louisiana

McNeese State University, B

Maine

College of the Atlantic, B

Maryland

Maryland Institute College of Art, B

Massachusetts

Boston University, B
Montserrat College of Art, B
Salem State College, B
School of the Museum of Fine Arts, Boston, B
Simon's Rock College of Bard, B

Michigan

Aquinas College, B
Grand Valley State University, B
Henry Ford Community College, A

University of Michigan, B

Minnesota

College of Visual Arts, B
Minneapolis College of Art and Design, B
Minnesota State University Mankato, B
St. Cloud State University, B
Vermilion Community College, A
Winona State University, B

Mississippi

East Central Community College, A
Mississippi University for Women, B
Northeast Mississippi Community College, A

Missouri

Columbia College, B
Lindenwood University, B
Northwest Missouri State University, B
University of Missouri-St. Louis, B
Washington University in St. Louis, B

Montana

The University of Montana-Missoula, B

New Hampshire

New England College, B
Rivier College, B

New Jersey

Rutgers, The State University of New Jersey, New Brunswick/Piscataway, B

New Mexico

Institute of American Indian Arts, A

New York

Bard College, B
Buffalo State College, State University of New York, B
Nazareth College of Rochester, B
Parsons The New School for Design, AB
Pratt Institute, AB
Sarah Lawrence College, B
School of Visual Arts, B
State University of New York at Binghamton, B
State University of New York College at Brockport, B
State University of New York, Fredonia, B

Ohio

Antioch College, B
Art Academy of Cincinnati, B
The Cleveland Institute of Art, B
The Ohio State University, B
Ohio University, B
Shawnee State University, B
The University of Akron, B
The University of Toledo, B
Wright State University, B

Oregon

Portland State University, B
University of Oregon, B

Pennsylvania

Arcadia University, B
Keystone College, A
Luzerne County Community College, A
Seton Hill University, B

Puerto Rico

Inter American University of Puerto Rico, San Germán Campus, B
University of Puerto Rico, Río Piedras, B

South Carolina

Anderson University, B

Tennessee

Carson-Newman College, B
Memphis College of Art, B

Sewanee: The University of the South, B

Texas

Lon Morris College, A
Midland College, A
Texas A&M University-Commerce, B
University of North Texas, B
The University of Texas at El Paso, B

Utah

Brigham Young University, B
Dixie State College of Utah, A

Vermont

Bennington College, B
Marlboro College, B

Virginia

Hampton University, B
Longwood University, B

Washington

Everett Community College, A
Western Washington University, B

West Virginia

West Virginia Wesleyan College, B

Wisconsin

Milwaukee Institute of Art and Design, B

Alberta

Alberta College of Art & Design, B
University of Alberta, B

New Brunswick

Mount Allison University, B

Newfoundland and Labrador

Memorial University of Newfoundland, B

Nova Scotia

NSCAD University, B

Ontario

Brock University, B
University of Windsor, B
York University, B

Quebec

Concordia University, B

Saskatchewan

University of Regina, B

DRIVER AND SAFETY TEACHER EDUCATION

Iowa

University of Northern Iowa, B
William Penn University, B

DUTCH/FLEMISH LANGUAGE AND LITERATURE

California

University of California, Berkeley, B

E-COMMERCE/ELECTRONIC COMMERCE

Alabama

University of South Alabama, B

Arizona

ITT Technical Institute (Tempe), B
ITT Technical Institute (Tucson), B

Arkansas

ITT Technical Institute, B

California

Dominican University of California, B
ITT Technical Institute (Anaheim), B

ITT Technical Institute (Lathrop), B
ITT Technical Institute (Oxnard), B
ITT Technical Institute (Rancho Cordova), B
ITT Technical Institute (San Bernardino), B
ITT Technical Institute (San Diego), B
ITT Technical Institute (Sylmar), B
ITT Technical Institute (Torrance), B
ITT Technical Institute (West Covina), B
Mt. Sierra College, B
National University, B
University of La Verne, B
Westwood College-Anaheim, B
Westwood College-Inland Empire, B
Westwood College-Los Angeles, B

Colorado

Colorado Northwestern Community College, A
Westwood College-Denver North, B
Westwood College-Denver South, B

Delaware

Delaware State University, B

Florida

Argosy University/Sarasota, B
Argosy University/Tampa, B
ITT Technical Institute (Jacksonville), B
ITT Technical Institute (Tampa), B
Pasco-Hernando Community College, B
Stetson University, B
University of Phoenix-Central Florida Campus, B
University of Phoenix-North Florida Campus, B

Georgia

Augusta Technical College, A
Central Georgia Technical College, A
ITT Technical Institute (Duluth), B
Valdosta Technical College, A
Westwood College-Atlanta Midtown, B
Westwood College-Atlanta Northlake, B

Hawaii

University of Phoenix-Hawaii Campus, B

Idaho

ITT Technical Institute, B
University of Phoenix-Idaho Campus, B

Illinois

ITT Technical Institute (Burr Ridge), B
ITT Technical Institute (Matteson), B
ITT Technical Institute (Mount Prospect), B
University of Phoenix-Chicago Campus, B
Westwood College-Chicago Du Page, B
Westwood College-Chicago O'Hare Airport, B
Westwood College-Chicago River Oaks, B

Indiana

ITT Technical Institute (Fort Wayne), B
ITT Technical Institute (Indianapolis), B
ITT Technical Institute (Newburgh), B
University of Southern Indiana, B

Kentucky

ITT Technical Institute (Louisville), B

Louisiana

Southern University and Agricultural and Mechanical College, B

Maryland

ITT Technical Institute, B

Massachusetts

University of Phoenix-Central Massachusetts Campus, B

Michigan

Davenport University (Dearborn), B
Western Michigan University, B

Missouri

ITT Technical Institute (Arnold), B
ITT Technical Institute (Earth City), B

Maryville University of Saint Louis, B
North Central Missouri College, A

Nebraska

ITT Technical Institute, B

New Mexico

ITT Technical Institute, B

New York

Clarkson University, B
Hudson Valley Community College, A

North Carolina

Fayetteville Technical Community College, A

Oregon

ITT Technical Institute, B

Pennsylvania

DeSales University, B
Messiah College, B
Philadelphia University, B
Temple University, B
Thiel College, B
University of Pennsylvania, B

South Carolina

ITT Technical Institute, B

Tennessee

ITT Technical Institute (Knoxville), B
ITT Technical Institute (Memphis), B
ITT Technical Institute (Nashville), B

Texas

Del Mar College, A
Montgomery College, A
St. Philip's College, A
Texas Christian University, B
University of Phoenix-Dallas Campus, B

Utah

ITT Technical Institute, B

Vermont

Champlain College, AB

Virginia

ITT Technical Institute (Norfolk), B

Washington

Edmonds Community College, A
ITT Technical Institute (Bothell), B
ITT Technical Institute (Spokane), B
Washington State University, B

West Virginia

Mountain State University, B

Wisconsin

ITT Technical Institute (Green Bay), B
ITT Technical Institute (Greenfield), B
Milwaukee Area Technical College, A

Ontario

University of Toronto, B

EARLY CHILDHOOD EDUCATION AND TEACHING

Alabama

Alabama Agricultural and Mechanical University, MO
Alabama State University, MO
Auburn University, BMDO
Auburn University Montgomery, MO
Concordia College, B
Jacksonville State University, M
Miles College, B
Samford University, MO
Spring Hill College, BM

The University of Alabama, B
The University of Alabama at Birmingham, MD
University of Montevallo, M
University of South Alabama, BMO
The University of West Alabama, BM

Alaska

University of Alaska Southeast, M

Arizona

Cochise College (Douglas), A
Northern Arizona University, M
Northland Pioneer College, A
University of Phoenix Online Campus, M

Arkansas

Arkansas State University, BM
Harding University, BM
Henderson State University, BM
Lyon College, B
Ouachita Baptist University, B
University of Arkansas, BM
University of Arkansas at Little Rock, M
University of Central Arkansas, M

California

Bethesda Christian University, B
California State University, Chico, B
California State University, Fullerton, B
California State University, Los Angeles, B
California State University, Sacramento, M
Cerro Coso Community College, A
Folsom Lake College, A
Mills College, M
Saint Mary's College of California, M
San Diego State University, B
San Francisco State University, M
San Jose State University, B

Colorado

Colorado Mountain College, Timberline Campus, A
Colorado Northwestern Community College, A
Fort Lewis College, B
Front Range Community College, A
Naropa University, B
Regis University, M
University of Colorado at Denver and Health
   Sciences Center - Downtown Denver Campus, M
University of Northern Colorado, M

Connecticut

Central Connecticut State University, M
Eastern Connecticut State University, BM
Goodwin College, A
Saint Joseph College, M
University of Bridgeport, MO
University of Hartford, BM

Delaware

Delaware State University, B
Wilmington College, AB

District of Columbia

Gallaudet University, MO
The George Washington University, M
Howard University, MO
Trinity (Washington) University, M
University of the District of Columbia, M

Florida

Barry University, M
Brevard Community College, A
Central Florida Community College, A
Florida Agricultural and Mechanical University, M
Florida Gulf Coast University, B
Florida International University, M
Florida State University, BMDO
Jacksonville University, O
Nova Southeastern University, MO
St. Petersburg College, A
University of Central Florida, BM
University of Florida, D
University of Miami, MO
University of South Florida, MDO

University of West Florida, BM

Georgia

Albany State University, M
Armstrong Atlantic State University, M
Augusta State University, MO
Berry College, BM
Brenau University, MO
Brewton-Parker College, B
Clark Atlanta University, B
Columbus State University, BMO
Fort Valley State University, M
Gainesville College, AB
Georgia College & State University, BMO
Georgia Southern University, M
Georgia Southwestern State University, MO
Georgia State University, BMDO
Kennesaw State University, BM
LaGrange College, B
Mercer University, MO
North Georgia College & State University, M
Oglethorpe University, M
Piedmont College, M
Thomas University, B
Toccoa Falls College, B
University of Georgia, BMDO
University of West Georgia, MO
Valdosta State University, BMO
Wesleyan College, BM

Hawaii

Chaminade University of Honolulu, B
University of Hawaii at Manoa, M
University of Phoenix-Hawaii Campus, M

Idaho

Boise State University, M

Illinois

Chicago State University, BM
Columbia College Chicago, B
Concordia University, MD
Dominican University, M
Eastern Illinois University, M
Governors State University, BM
Greenville College, B
Illinois College, B
Illinois State University, B
John Wood Community College, A
Kendall College, B
National-Louis University, MO
Northeastern Illinois University, B
Northern Illinois University, M
Oakton Community College, A
Rend Lake College, A
Roosevelt University, M
St. Augustine College, A
Saint Xavier University, M
Sauk Valley Community College, A
Southern Illinois University Carbondale, B
Southern Illinois University Edwardsville, B

Indiana

Ancilla College, A
Bethel College, A
Indiana State University, BM
Indiana University-Purdue University Fort Wayne, A
Ivy Tech Community College-East Central, A
Ivy Tech Community College-Kokomo, A
Ivy Tech Community College-North Central, A
Ivy Tech Community College-Northeast, A
Ivy Tech Community College-Northwest, B
Oakland City University, A
Purdue University, B
Taylor University Fort Wayne, A

Iowa

Clarke College, M
Iowa Lakes Community College, A
Iowa State University of Science and Technology, B
St. Ambrose University, B
The University of Iowa, MD
University of Northern Iowa, M

Waldorf College, B

Kansas

Barton County Community College, A
Emporia State University, M
Pittsburg State University, M
Southwestern College, B
Washburn University, AB

Kentucky

Bellarmine University, M
Hopkinsville Community College, A
Lindsey Wilson College, A
Murray State University, BM
Somerset Community College, A
University of the Cumberlands, M
University of Louisville, M
Western Kentucky University, M

Louisiana

Grambling State University, M
Louisiana State University and Agricultural and
   Mechanical College, B
Louisiana State University at Alexandria, A
Louisiana Tech University, B
McNeese State University, BM
Nicholls State University, B
Northwestern State University of Louisiana, BM
Southern University and Agricultural and Mechanical
   College, B
University of New Orleans, B
Xavier University of Louisiana, B

Maine

Beal College, A

Maryland

Columbia Union College, A
Hagerstown Community College, A
Loyola College in Maryland, MO
Salisbury University, M
Towson University, BM
University of Maryland, Baltimore County, M
University of Maryland, College Park, MD
Villa Julie College, B

Massachusetts

Anna Maria College, M
Bay State College, A
Becker College, B
Berkshire Community College, A
Boston College, M
Boston University, MDO
Bridgewater State College, BM
Bristol Community College, A
Bunker Hill Community College, A
Dean College, A
Eastern Nazarene College, MO
Elms College, M
Endicott College, B
Fitchburg State College, BM
Framingham State College, B
Hebrew College, O
Lesley University, M
Quincy College, A
Salem State College, M
Tufts University, M
University of Massachusetts Amherst, MDO
Westfield State College, M
Wheelock College, AM

Michigan

Alma College, B
Baker College of Allen Park, A
Baker College of Jackson, A
Cornerstone University, B
Eastern Michigan University, M
Grace Bible College, B
Grand Valley State University, M
Hillsdale College, B
Jackson Community College, A
Lake Michigan College, A
Lake Superior State University, AB
Mott Community College, A
Northern Michigan University, B

Oakland University, MDO
Rochester College, B
Saginaw Valley State University, M
Siena Heights University, M
University of Detroit Mercy, M
University of Michigan, MD
University of Michigan-Dearborn, B
University of Michigan-Flint, BM
Wayne State University, M
Western Michigan University, M

Minnesota

Bethel University, B
Concordia University, St. Paul, BM
Crown College, AB
Minnesota State University Mankato, M
Northwestern College, B
University of Minnesota, Crookston, B
University of Minnesota, Twin Cities Campus, MD

Mississippi

Jackson State University, MDO
Rust College, A
University of Southern Mississippi, MO

Missouri

Central Methodist University, B
Evangel University, B
Hannibal-LaGrange College, B
Harris-Stowe State University, B
Lincoln University, AB
Maryville University of Saint Louis, M
Missouri State University, BM
North Central Missouri College, A
Northwest Missouri State University, M
Park University, B
Stephens College, B
University of Missouri-Columbia, BMDO
University of Missouri-Kansas City, B
University of Missouri-St. Louis, B
Webster University, M

Montana

Montana State University-Billings, M
University of Great Falls, A

Nebraska

College of Saint Mary, AB
Concordia University, BM
Hastings College, B
Nebraska Indian Community College, A
Wayne State College, B

New Hampshire

Colby-Sawyer College, B
Granite State College, AB
Keene State College, A
Plymouth State University, B
Rivier College, M
Southern New Hampshire University, B
University of New Hampshire, M

New Jersey

Bloomfield College, B
The College of New Jersey, M
Kean University, MO
Montclair State University, M
New Jersey City University, M
Rutgers, The State University of New Jersey, New Brunswick/Piscataway, MD
Salem Community College, A

New Mexico

College of Santa Fe, B
Luna Community College, A
New Mexico State University, B
University of New Mexico, B

New York

Brooklyn College of the City University of New York, BM
Buffalo State College, State University of New York, M
Canisius College, BM
Cazenovia College, B

City College of the City University of New York, BM
The College of New Rochelle, M
The College of Saint Rose, M
Daemen College, BM
Five Towns College, M
Fordham University, M
Hofstra University, BMO
Hudson Valley Community College, A
Hunter College of the City University of New York, M
Iona College, B
Keuka College, M
Kingsborough Community College of the City University of New York, A
Lehman College of the City University of New York, M
Long Island University, C.W. Post Campus, M
Manhattan College, O
Manhattanville College, M
Mount Saint Mary College, M
Nazareth College of Rochester, M
New York University, MDO
Queens College of the City University of New York, M
St. Bonaventure University, B
St. John's University, BM
St. Joseph's College, Suffolk Campus, BM
Sarah Lawrence College, B
State University of New York at Binghamton, M
State University of New York at Buffalo, M
State University of New York College at Brockport, B
State University of New York College at Cortland, M
State University of New York College at Geneseo, B
State University of New York College at Old Westbury, B
State University of New York at New Paltz, M
Syracuse University, M
Wagner College, M

North Carolina

Appalachian State University, M
Fayetteville Technical Community College, A
Gardner-Webb University, B
Greensboro College, B
Johnson C. Smith University, B
Lenoir-Rhyne College, B
North Carolina Agricultural and Technical State University, M
Robeson Community College, A
Saint Augustine's College, B
Salem College, M
Tri-County Community College, A
The University of North Carolina at Chapel Hill, BMD
The University of North Carolina at Greensboro, M
Western Carolina University, B

North Dakota

United Tribes Technical College, A
University of Mary, BM
University of North Dakota, BM

Ohio

Ashland University, M
Baldwin-Wallace College, B
Capital University, B
Cedarville University, B
Cleveland State University, B
College of Mount St. Joseph, M
John Carroll University, M
Kent State University, M
Kent State University, Tuscarawas Campus, A
Malone College, B
Miami University, M
Miami University Hamilton, B
Mount Union College, B
Mount Vernon Nazarene University, B
Muskingum College, B
Notre Dame College, B
Ohio Dominican University, B
Ohio Northern University, B
The Ohio State University at Lima, M
The Ohio State University-Mansfield Campus, BM
The Ohio State University at Marion, M
The Ohio State University-Newark Campus, M

Ohio University, B
Ohio University-Southern Campus, AB
Ohio Wesleyan University, B
Owens Community College, A
Shawnee State University, B
University of Cincinnati, M
University of Dayton, M
The University of Findlay, M
The University of Toledo, MDO
Ursuline College, B
Wright State University, M
Xavier University, M
Youngstown State University, BM

Oklahoma

Bacone College, B
East Central University, B
Northeastern State University, M
Oklahoma Christian University, B
Oklahoma City University, M
Oklahoma State University, Oklahoma City, A
Oral Roberts University, BM
Southern Nazarene University, B
Southwestern Oklahoma State University, M
University of Central Oklahoma, M
University of Oklahoma, B
University of Science and Arts of Oklahoma, B

Oregon

Cascade College, B
Central Oregon Community College, A
Pacific University, M
Portland State University, M
Tillamook Bay Community College, A
University of Portland, M
Western Oregon University, M

Pennsylvania

Albright College, M
Arcadia University, BMO
Bloomsburg University of Pennsylvania, BM
Carlow University, M
Chestnut Hill College, BM
Cheyney University of Pennsylvania, O
Duquesne University, BM
East Stroudsburg University of Pennsylvania, B
Edinboro University of Pennsylvania, M
Gannon University, ABMO
Indiana University of Pennsylvania, M
Juniata College, B
Keystone College, AB
King's College, B
Kutztown University of Pennsylvania, O
Lackawanna College, A
Lancaster Bible College, AB
Luzerne County Community College, A
Marywood University, M
Mercyhurst College, AB
Messiah College, B
Millersville University of Pennsylvania, BM
The Pennsylvania State University University Park Campus, MD
Point Park University, AB
Slippery Rock University of Pennsylvania, M
Temple University, M
University of Pennsylvania, M
University of Pittsburgh, M
The University of Scranton, BM
Widener University, BM

Puerto Rico

Bayamon Central University, M
Inter American University of Puerto Rico, Aguadilla Campus, B
Universidad Metropolitana, M
University of Phoenix-Puerto Rico Campus, M
University of Puerto Rico, Río Piedras, M

Rhode Island

Rhode Island College, BM
Salve Regina University, B

South Carolina

Bob Jones University, B
Charleston Southern University, B

Claflin University, B
Clemson University, B
Coastal Carolina University, BM
Coker College, B
College of Charleston, BM
Columbia International University, M
Converse College, M
Francis Marion University, BM
Furman University, M
Lander University, B
Morris College, B
South Carolina State University, M
University of South Carolina, MD
University of South Carolina Aiken, B
University of South Carolina Upstate, M

Tennessee

East Tennessee State University, M
Middle Tennessee State University, M
Milligan College, B
Tennessee Technological University, MO
University of Memphis, MD
The University of Tennessee, MD
Vanderbilt University, M

Texas

Arlington Baptist College, B
Dallas Baptist University, M
Hardin-Simmons University, B
Houston Baptist University, B
Lubbock Christian University, B
Midwestern State University, B
St. Philip's College, A
Sam Houston State University, M
Schreiner University, B
Stephen F. Austin State University, M
Texas A&M International University, M
Texas A&M University-Commerce, M
Texas A&M University-Corpus Christi, M
Texas A&M University-Kingsville, M
Texas Christian University, BM
Texas Southern University, M
Texas State University-San Marcos, M
Texas Woman's University, MD
University of Houston, M
University of Houston-Clear Lake, BM
University of the Incarnate Word, M
University of North Texas, MD
The University of Texas at Brownsville, M
The University of Texas-Pan American, M
The University of Texas of the Permian Basin, M
The University of Texas at San Antonio, M
The University of Texas at Tyler, M

Utah

Brigham Young University, B
Utah Valley State College, AB

Vermont

Bennington College, BM
Champlain College, A
University of Vermont, B

Virginia

George Mason University, M
James Madison University, M
Liberty University, M
Norfolk State University, M
Old Dominion University, M
University of Northern Virginia, M
Virginia Commonwealth University, M

Washington

Central Washington University, B
Clark College, A
Clover Park Technical College, A
Eastern Washington University, BM
Edmonds Community College, A
Lower Columbia College, A
North Seattle Community College, A

Olympic College, A

West Virginia

Marshall University, M

Wisconsin

Carroll College, B
Concordia University Wisconsin, M
Moraine Park Technical College, A
Ripon College, B
University of Wisconsin-Milwaukee, M
University of Wisconsin-Oshkosh, M
University of Wisconsin-Stout, B
University of Wisconsin-Whitewater, B
Waukesha County Technical College, A

Wyoming

Laramie County Community College, A
Northwest College, A
Western Wyoming Community College, A

British Columbia

Thompson Rivers University, A
The University of British Columbia, M

Ontario

Ryerson University, B
Wilfrid Laurier University, B

Quebec

McGill University, B

Saskatchewan

University of Regina, B

EAST ASIAN LANGUAGES, LITERATURES, AND LINGUISTICS

Arizona

Arizona State University, B

California

Claremont McKenna College, B
University of California, Los Angeles, B
University of Southern California, B

Florida

Eckerd College, B
University of Florida, B

Illinois

Northwestern University, B

Kansas

University of Kansas, B

Massachusetts

Smith College, B

Michigan

Michigan State University, B

Missouri

Washington University in St. Louis, B

New Hampshire

Dartmouth College, B

New York

Columbia College, B
Cornell University, B

Oregon

University of Oregon, B

Pennsylvania

University of Pennsylvania, B

Texas

The University of Texas at Austin, B

EAST ASIAN STUDIES

Arizona

The University of Arizona, BMD

California

Pomona College, B
Scripps College, B
Stanford University, B
University of California, Berkeley, M
University of California, Davis, B
University of California, Irvine, B
University of California, Los Angeles, BMD
University of California, Santa Barbara, M
University of California, Santa Cruz, B
University of Southern California, BMDO

Colorado

University of Colorado at Boulder, M

Connecticut

Connecticut College, B
Wesleyan University, B
Yale University, BM

Delaware

University of Delaware, B

District of Columbia

The George Washington University, BMO

Guam

University of Guam, B

Illinois

DePaul University, B
North Central College, B
University of Chicago, BMD
University of Illinois at Urbana-Champaign, BMD

Indiana

DePauw University, B
Indiana University Bloomington, BMDO
Valparaiso University, B

Kansas

University of Kansas, M

Maine

Bates College, B
Colby College, B

Maryland

The Johns Hopkins University, B

Massachusetts

Boston University, B
Brandeis University, B
Harvard University, BM
Simmons College, B
Smith College, B
Wellesley College, B

Michigan

Oakland University, B
University of Michigan, MO
Wayne State University, B

Minnesota

Augsburg College, B
Hamline University, B
Minnesota State University Moorhead, B
University of Minnesota, Twin Cities Campus, B

University of St. Thomas, B

Missouri

University of Missouri-Columbia, B
Washington University in St. Louis, B

Montana

The University of Montana-Missoula, B

New Jersey

Princeton University, B
Rutgers, The State University of New Jersey, New
    Brunswick/Piscataway, B

New York

Colgate University, B
Columbia College, B
Columbia University, School of General Studies, B
Cornell University, BMD
Hamilton College, B
New York University, B
Queens College of the City University of New
    York, B
St. John's University, BMO
Sarah Lawrence College, B
United States Military Academy, B
University at Albany, State University of New York, B

North Carolina

Duke University, MO

Ohio

Denison University, B
John Carroll University, B
Oberlin College, B
The Ohio State University, B
Ohio Wesleyan University, B
Wittenberg University, B

Oregon

Lewis & Clark College, B
Portland State University, B
University of Oregon, B

Pennsylvania

Bryn Mawr College, B
Bucknell University, B
Dickinson College, B
Gettysburg College, B
Haverford College, B
The Pennsylvania State University Abington
    College, B
The Pennsylvania State University Altoona
    College, B
The Pennsylvania State University Beaver Campus
    of the Commonwealth College, B
The Pennsylvania State University Berks Campus of
    the Berks-Lehigh Valley College, B
The Pennsylvania State University Delaware County
    Campus of the Commonwealth College, B
The Pennsylvania State University DuBois Campus
    of the Commonwealth College, B
The Pennsylvania State University at Erie, The
    Behrend College, B
The Pennsylvania State University Fayette Campus
    of the Commonwealth College, B
The Pennsylvania State University Hazleton
    Campus of the Commonwealth College, B
The Pennsylvania State University, Lehigh Valley
    Campus of the Berks-Lehigh Valley College, B
The Pennsylvania State University McKeesport
    Campus of the Commonwealth College, B
The Pennsylvania State University Mont Alto
    Campus of the Commonwealth College, B
The Pennsylvania State University New Kensington
    Campus of the Commonwealth College, B
The Pennsylvania State University Schuylkill
    Campus of the Capital College, B
The Pennsylvania State University Shenango
    Campus of the Commonwealth College, B
The Pennsylvania State University University Park
    Campus, B
The Pennsylvania State University Worthington
    Scranton Campus of the Commonwealth
    College, B

The Pennsylvania State University York Campus of
    the Commonwealth College, B
University of Pennsylvania, BMD
University of Pittsburgh, M
Ursinus College, B

Rhode Island

Brown University, B

Tennessee

Vanderbilt University, B

Vermont

Marlboro College, B
Middlebury College, B

Virginia

The College of William and Mary, B
Emory & Henry College, B
University of Virginia, MO
Washington and Lee University, B

Washington

Seattle University, B
University of Washington, B
Western Washington University, B

West Virginia

West Virginia University, MD

Wisconsin

Lawrence University, B

Alberta

University of Alberta, BM
University of Calgary, B

Ontario

Carleton University, B
University of Toronto, BMD
The University of Western Ontario, B
York University, B

Quebec

McGill University, BMD
Université de Montréal, B

EAST EUROPEAN AND RUSSIAN STUDIES

California

Stanford University, M

Connecticut

Yale University, M

District of Columbia

The George Washington University, MO
Georgetown University, MO

Florida

Florida State University, M

Illinois

University of Illinois at Chicago, MD
University of Illinois at Urbana-Champaign, M

Indiana

Indiana University Bloomington, MO

Kansas

University of Kansas, MO

Massachusetts

Boston College, MO
Harvard University, M

Michigan

University of Michigan, MO

Minnesota

University of Minnesota, Twin Cities Campus, M

New York

Cornell University, MD

North Carolina

The University of North Carolina at Chapel Hill, M

Ohio

The Ohio State University, M

Pennsylvania

La Salle University, M

Texas

The University of Texas at Austin, MO

Washington

University of Washington, M

Alberta

University of Alberta, MD

British Columbia

The University of British Columbia, MD

Ontario

Carleton University, M
University of Toronto, MO

Saskatchewan

University of Saskatchewan, M

ECOLOGY

Alabama

Jacksonville State University, B

Arizona

Arizona State University, MD
Northern Arizona University, BO
Prescott College, BM
The University of Arizona, MD

California

California State University, Chico, B
California State University, East Bay, B
California State University, Fresno, BM
California State University, Long Beach, B
California State University, San Marcos, B
Chabot College, A
College of Marin, A
New College of California, B
Pitzer College, B
Pomona College, B
San Diego State University, MD
San Francisco State University, BM
Sonoma State University, B
University of California, Davis, MD
University of California, Irvine, BMD
University of California, Los Angeles, B
University of California, San Diego, BD
University of California, Santa Barbara, BMD
University of California, Santa Cruz, BMD

Colorado

Colorado State University, MD
University of Colorado at Boulder, MD
University of Colorado at Colorado Springs, B
Western State College of Colorado, B

Connecticut

University of Connecticut, BMD
University of New Haven, B

Yale University, BD

Delaware

University of Delaware, BMD

Florida

Barry University, B
Florida Institute of Technology, BM
Florida State University, BMD
University of Florida, MD
University of Miami, BMD
University of South Florida, D

Georgia

Abraham Baldwin Agricultural College, A
Emory University, D
University of Georgia, BMD

Hawaii

University of Hawaii at Manoa, MD

Idaho

Brigham Young University -Idaho, A
Idaho State University, B

Illinois

Bradley University, B
Illinois State University, D
Joliet Junior College, A
Northwestern University, B
University of Chicago, D
University of Illinois at Chicago, MD
University of Illinois at Urbana-Champaign, BD

Indiana

Ball State University, B
Indiana State University, D
Indiana University Bloomington, MD
Manchester College, B
Purdue University, MD
University of Notre Dame, MD

Iowa

Iowa Lakes Community College, A
Iowa State University of Science and
    Technology, BMD
University of Northern Iowa, B

Kansas

Friends University, B
Kansas State University, MD
University of Kansas, MD

Kentucky

Eastern Kentucky University, BM
Georgetown College, B
Morehead State University, B

Louisiana

Tulane University, B

Maine

Unity College, B
University of Maine, BMD
University of Maine at Machias, B

Maryland

Frostburg State University, M
University of Maryland, College Park, BMD
University of Maryland Eastern Shore, B
Washington College, B

Massachusetts

Boston University, B
Clark University, B
Harvard University, B
Lesley University, M
Simon's Rock College of Bard, B
Tufts University, B

Michigan

Michigan Technological University, BM
Northern Michigan University, B
University of Michigan, MD

University of Michigan-Flint, B

Minnesota

Bemidji State University, B
Minnesota State University Mankato, BM
St. Cloud State University, B
University of Minnesota, Twin Cities Campus, BMD
Vermilion Community College, A
Winona State University, B

Missouri

East Central College, A
Missouri Southern State University, B
Northwest Missouri State University, B
University of Missouri-Columbia, MD
Washington University in St. Louis, D

Montana

Montana State University, MD
The University of Montana-Missoula, MD

Nebraska

Western Nebraska Community College, A

Nevada

Sierra Nevada College, B
University of Nevada, Reno, D

New Hampshire

Dartmouth College, B
Franklin Pierce College, B
Keene State College, B
University of New Hampshire, B

New Jersey

Princeton University, BD
Rutgers, The State University of New Jersey, New
    Brunswick/Piscataway, BMD
William Paterson University of New Jersey, BM

New York

Bard College, B
Clarkson University, B
Columbia University, School of General Studies, B
Concordia College, B
Cornell University, MD
Pace University, B
Paul Smith's College of Arts and Sciences, A
St. John's University, B
Sarah Lawrence College, B
Siena College, B
State University of New York College of
    Environmental Science and Forestry, BMD
Stony Brook University, State University of New
    York, D
University at Albany, State University of New
    York, MD

North Carolina

Appalachian State University, B
Brevard College, B
Duke University, MDO
Lenoir-Rhyne College, B
Mars Hill College, B
North Carolina State University, BD
The University of North Carolina at Chapel Hill, MD

North Dakota

North Dakota State University, MD
University of North Dakota, MD

Ohio

Defiance College, B
Hocking College, A
Kent State University, BMD
Oberlin College, B
The Ohio State University, MD
Ohio University, MD
The University of Akron, B
University of Rio Grande, B

The University of Toledo, MD

Oklahoma

East Central University, B
Oklahoma State University, MD
Tulsa Community College, A

Oregon

University of Oregon, MD

Pennsylvania

Juniata College, B
Lehigh University, B
The Pennsylvania State University University Park
    Campus, MD
Susquehanna University, B
University of Pennsylvania, D
University of Pittsburgh, BMD
University of Pittsburgh at Johnstown, B
West Chester University of Pennsylvania, B

Rhode Island

Brown University, D

South Carolina

University of South Carolina, MD

Tennessee

The University of Tennessee, BMD
Vanderbilt University, B

Texas

Rice University, BMD
Texas A&M University, B
Texas Christian University, M
The University of Texas at Austin, BD

Utah

Dixie State College of Utah, A
University of Utah, MD
Utah State University, BMD

Vermont

Bennington College, B
Marlboro College, B
Sterling College, AB

Virginia

Averett University, B
George Mason University, M
Old Dominion University, D
Virginia Polytechnic Institute and State
    University, MD

Washington

Everett Community College, A
Washington State University, B

Wisconsin

Lawrence University, B
Marquette University, MD
Northland College, B
University of Wisconsin-Madison, MD
University of Wisconsin-Milwaukee, B

Wyoming

Northwest College, A

Alberta

University of Alberta, MD
University of Calgary, B

British Columbia

Thompson Rivers University, B
University of Victoria, BMD

Manitoba

University of Manitoba, B
The University of Winnipeg, B

New Brunswick

University of New Brunswick Fredericton, B

Newfoundland and Labrador

Memorial University of Newfoundland, B

Ontario

Brock University, M
Carleton University, B

University of Guelph, BMD
University of Toronto, B
University of Waterloo, B
The University of Western Ontario, B
York University, B

Quebec

Concordia University, B
McGill University, B
Université de Montréal, B
Université de Sherbrooke, B

ECOLOGY, EVOLUTION, SYSTEMATICS AND POPULATION BIOLOGY

California

University of California, Davis, B

Colorado

University of Colorado at Boulder, B

New York

Cornell University, B

Pennsylvania

Marywood University, B

Utah

Brigham Young University, B

Vermont

Sterling College, B

ECONOMETRICS AND QUANTITATIVE ECONOMICS

California

University of California, San Diego, B

Colorado

The Colorado College, B

Maryland

United States Naval Academy, B

Minnesota

University of St. Thomas, B

New York

Hofstra University, B
State University of New York at Oswego, B

North Carolina

Wake Forest University, B

Ohio

Baldwin-Wallace College, B
Miami University Hamilton, B

Pennsylvania

Haverford College, B

Rhode Island

Providence College, B
University of Rhode Island, B

Texas

Southern Methodist University, B

Virginia

Hampden-Sydney College, B
James Madison University, B

Ontario

University of Guelph, B

Quebec

Université Laval, B

ECONOMICS

Alabama

Alabama Agricultural and Mechanical University, BM
Alabama Southern Community College, A
Alabama State University, B
Auburn University, BMD
Birmingham-Southern College, B
Jacksonville State University, B
Oakwood College, B
Talladega College, B
Tuskegee University, B
The University of Alabama, MD
University of Mobile, B

Alaska

University of Alaska Anchorage, B
University of Alaska Fairbanks, BM

Arizona

Arizona State University, BMDO
Cochise College (Douglas), A
GateWay Community College, A
Grand Canyon University, B
Northern Arizona University, B
The University of Arizona, BMDO

Arkansas

Arkansas State University, B
Arkansas Tech University, B
Harding University, B
Hendrix College, B
Lyon College, B
University of Arkansas, BMD
University of Arkansas at Little Rock, B
University of Arkansas at Pine Bluff, B
University of Central Arkansas, BM

California

Bakersfield College, A
California Institute of Technology, BD
California Lutheran University, B
California Polytechnic State University, San Luis Obispo, B
California State Polytechnic University, Pomona, BM
California State University, Bakersfield, B
California State University Channel Islands, B
California State University, Chico, B
California State University, Dominguez Hills, B
California State University, East Bay, BM
California State University, Fresno, B
California State University, Fullerton, BM
California State University, Long Beach, BM
California State University, Los Angeles, BM
California State University, Northridge, B
California State University, Sacramento, B
California State University, San Bernardino, B
California State University, San Marcos, B
California State University, Stanislaus, B
Cañada College, A
Cerritos College, A
Chabot College, A
Chaffey College, A
Claremont McKenna College, B
College of the Desert, A
Compton Community College, A
Crafton Hills College, A
Cypress College, A
De Anza College, A
El Camino College, A
Foothill College, A
Fullerton College, A
Grossmont College, A
Hartnell College, A
Humboldt State University, B
Lincoln University, B
Los Angeles Mission College, A
Los Angeles Southwest College, A
Los Angeles Valley College, A
Loyola Marymount University, B
Merritt College, A
Mills College, B
MiraCosta College, A
Monterey Peninsula College, A
National University, BM

Occidental College, B
Orange Coast College, A
Oxnard College, A
Palo Verde College, A
Palomar College, A
Pasadena City College, A
Pepperdine University, B
Pitzer College, B
Pomona College, B
Saddleback College, A
Saint Mary's College of California, B
San Bernardino Valley College, A
San Diego State University, BM
San Francisco State University, BM
San Joaquin Delta College, A
San Jose State University, BM
Santa Ana College, A
Santa Barbara City College, A
Santa Clara University, B
Santa Monica College, A
Santa Rosa Junior College, A
Santiago Canyon College, A
Scripps College, B
Skyline College, A
Sonoma State University, B
Southwestern College, A
Stanford University, BD
University of California, Berkeley, BDO
University of California, Davis, BMD
University of California, Irvine, BMD
University of California, Los Angeles, BMD
University of California, Riverside, BMD
University of California, San Diego, BD
University of California, Santa Barbara, BMD
University of California, Santa Cruz, BMD
University of La Verne, B
University of the Pacific, B
University of Redlands, B
University of San Diego, B
University of San Francisco, BM
University of Southern California, BMDO
West Los Angeles College, A
West Valley College, A
Westmont College, B
Whittier College, B

Colorado

The Colorado College, B
Colorado School of Mines, B
Colorado State University, MD
Fort Lewis College, B
Metropolitan State College of Denver, B
Northeastern Junior College, A
Parks College (Denver), A
Red Rocks Community College, A
Regis University, B
United States Air Force Academy, B
University of Colorado at Boulder, BMD
University of Colorado at Colorado Springs, B
University of Colorado at Denver and Health Sciences Center - Downtown Denver Campus, BM
University of Denver, BM
University of Northern Colorado, B
Western State College of Colorado, B

Connecticut

Albertus Magnus College, B
Central Connecticut State University, B
Connecticut College, B
Eastern Connecticut State University, B
Fairfield University, B
Quinnipiac University, BM
Sacred Heart University, AB
Saint Joseph College, B
Southern Connecticut State University, B
Trinity College, BM
University of Connecticut, BMD
University of Hartford, B
Wesleyan University, B
Western Connecticut State University, B

Yale University, BMD

Delaware

University of Delaware, BMDO

District of Columbia

American University, BMDO
The Catholic University of America, BM
Gallaudet University, B
The George Washington University, BMD
Georgetown University, BDO
Howard University, BMD
Strayer University, AB
Trinity (Washington) University, B
University of the District of Columbia, B

Florida

Barry University, B
Daytona Beach Community College, A
Eckerd College, B
Florida Agricultural and Mechanical University, BM
Florida Atlantic University, BM
Florida International University, BMD
Florida Southern College, B
Florida State University, BMDO
Gulf Coast Community College, A
Indian River Community College, A
Jacksonville University, B
Manatee Community College, A
Miami Dade College, A
New College of Florida, B
Palm Beach Community College, A
Rollins College, B
Stetson University, B
University of Central Florida, BM
University of Florida, BMD
University of Miami, BMD
University of North Florida, B
University of South Florida, BMD
The University of Tampa, AB
University of West Florida, B

Georgia

Agnes Scott College, B
Albany State University, M
Armstrong Atlantic State University, B
Berry College, B
Clark Atlanta University, BM
Clayton State University, A
Dalton State College, A
Darton College, A
Emory University, BD
Fort Valley State University, B
Georgia Highlands College, A
Georgia Institute of Technology, M
Georgia Southern University, B
Georgia State University, BMD
Kennesaw State University, B
LaGrange College, B
Macon State College, A
Mercer University, B
Morehouse College, B
Oglethorpe University, B
Shorter College, B
South Georgia College, A
Spelman College, B
University of Georgia, BMD
University of West Georgia, B
Wesleyan College, B

Guam

University of Guam, B

Hawaii

Hawaii Pacific University, BM
University of Hawaii at Hilo, B
University of Hawaii at Manoa, BMD
University of Hawaii-West Oahu, B

Idaho

Albertson College of Idaho, B
Boise State University, B
Brigham Young University -Idaho, A
Idaho State University, B

University of Idaho, B

Illinois

Augustana College, B
Aurora University, B
Benedictine University, B
Bradley University, B
Chicago State University, B
DePaul University, BM
Dominican University, B
Eastern Illinois University, BM
Elmhurst College, B
Eureka College, B
Illinois College, B
Illinois State University, BM
Illinois Wesleyan University, B
Knox College, B
Lake Forest College, B
Lewis University, B
Lincoln College, A
Lincoln College-Normal, A
Loyola University Chicago, B
McKendree College, B
Monmouth College, B
North Central College, B
North Park University, B
Northeastern Illinois University, B
Northern Illinois University, BMD
Northwestern University, BMDO
Olivet Nazarene University, B
Principia College, B
Rockford College, B
Roosevelt University, BM
Sauk Valley Community College, A
Southern Illinois University Carbondale, BMD
Southern Illinois University Edwardsville, BM
University of Chicago, BD
University of Illinois at Chicago, BMDO
University of Illinois at Springfield, B
University of Illinois at Urbana-Champaign, BMD
Western Illinois University, BM
Wheaton College, B

Indiana

Ball State University, B
Butler University, B
DePauw University, B
Earlham College, B
Franklin College, B
Goshen College, B
Hanover College, B
Huntington University, B
Indiana State University, B
Indiana University Bloomington, BMD
Indiana University Northwest, B
Indiana University-Purdue University Fort Wayne, B
Indiana University-Purdue University
  Indianapolis, BMO
Indiana University South Bend, B
Indiana University Southeast, BO
Indiana Wesleyan University, B
Manchester College, B
Purdue University, BD
Purdue University Calumet, B
Rose-Hulman Institute of Technology, B
Saint Joseph's College, B
Saint Mary's College, B
Taylor University, B
University of Evansville, B
University of Notre Dame, B
University of Southern Indiana, B
Valparaiso University, B
Wabash College, B

Iowa

Central College, B
Clarke College, B
Coe College, B
Cornell College, B
Ellsworth Community College, A
Graceland University, B
Iowa Lakes Community College, A
Iowa State University of Science and
  Technology, BMDO
Loras College, B
Luther College, B

Marshalltown Community College, A
Northwestern College, B
St. Ambrose University, B
Simpson College, B
The University of Iowa, BD
University of Northern Iowa, B
Wartburg College, B

Kansas

Allen County Community College, A
Baker University, B
Barton County Community College, A
Benedictine College, B
Central Christian College of Kansas, A
Coffeyville Community College, A
Emporia State University, B
Fort Hays State University, B
Kansas State University, BMD
Pittsburg State University, B
Seward County Community College, A
University of Kansas, BMDO
Washburn University, B
Wichita State University, BM

Kentucky

Bellarmine University, B
Berea College, B
Campbellsville University, B
Centre College, B
Eastern Kentucky University, B
Georgetown College, B
Murray State University, BM
Northern Kentucky University, B
Thomas More College, AB
Transylvania University, B
University of Kentucky, BMD
University of Louisville, B
Western Kentucky University, B

Louisiana

Centenary College of Louisiana, B
Dillard University, B
Louisiana College, B
Louisiana State University and Agricultural and
  Mechanical College, BMD
Louisiana Tech University, MD
Loyola University New Orleans, B
Tulane University, BMD
University of New Orleans, BD

Maine

Bates College, B
Bowdoin College, B
Colby College, B
College of the Atlantic, B
University of Maine, BM
University of Southern Maine, B

Maryland

Anne Arundel Community College, A
Bowie State University, B
College of Notre Dame of Maryland, B
Frostburg State University, B
Goucher College, B
Hood College, B
The Johns Hopkins University, BD
Loyola College in Maryland, BM
McDaniel College, B
Morgan State University, BM
Mount St. Mary's University, B
St. Mary's College of Maryland, B
Salisbury University, B
Sojourner-Douglass College, B
Towson University, B
United States Naval Academy, B
University of Baltimore, B
University of Maryland, Baltimore County, BM
University of Maryland, College Park, MD
Washington College, B

Massachusetts

American International College, B
Amherst College, B
Assumption College, B
Babson College, B

Boston College, BD
Boston University, BMDO
Brandeis University, BMD
Bridgewater State College, B
Clark University, BD
College of the Holy Cross, B
Emmanuel College, B
Fitchburg State College, B
Framingham State College, B
Gordon College, B
Hampshire College, B
Harvard University, BMD
Massachusetts College of Liberal Arts, B
Massachusetts Institute of Technology, BMD
Merrimack College, B
Mount Holyoke College, B
Nichols College, B
Northeastern University, BMD
Salem State College, B
Simmons College, B
Simon's Rock College of Bard, B
Smith College, B
Stonehill College, B
Suffolk University, BMDO
Tufts University, BM
University of Massachusetts Amherst, BMD
University of Massachusetts Boston, B
University of Massachusetts Dartmouth, B
University of Massachusetts Lowell, BM
Wellesley College, B
Western New England College, B
Westfield State College, B
Wheaton College, B
Williams College, B
Worcester Polytechnic Institute, B
Worcester State College, B

Michigan

Adrian College, AB
Albion College, B
Alma College, B
Andrews University, BM
Aquinas College, B
Ave Maria College, B
Calvin College, B
Central Michigan University, BM
Eastern Michigan University, BM
Grand Valley State University, B
Hillsdale College, B
Hope College, B
Michigan State University, BMD
Michigan Technological University, B
Muskegon Community College, A
Northern Michigan University, B
Oakland University, BO
Olivet College, B
Saginaw Valley State University, B
University of Detroit Mercy, B
University of Michigan, BMDO
University of Michigan-Dearborn, B
University of Michigan-Flint, B
Walsh College of Accountancy and Business
    Administration, M
Wayne State University, BMDO
Western Michigan University, BMD

Minnesota

Augsburg College, B
Bemidji State University, B
Bethel University, B
Carleton College, B
College of Saint Benedict, B
College of St. Catherine, B
Concordia College, B
Gustavus Adolphus College, B
Hamline University, B
Macalester College, B
Metropolitan State University, B
Minnesota State University Mankato, B
Minnesota State University Moorhead, B
St. Cloud State University, BM
Saint John's University, B
St. Olaf College, B
University of Minnesota, Duluth, B
University of Minnesota, Morris, B
University of Minnesota, Twin Cities Campus, BD

University of St. Thomas, B
Vermilion Community College, A
Winona State University, B

Mississippi

Alcorn State University, B
Copiah-Lincoln Community College, A
East Central Community College, A
East Mississippi Community College, A
Hinds Community College, A
Itawamba Community College, A
Jackson State University, B
Jones County Junior College, A
Millsaps College, B
Mississippi Delta Community College, A
Mississippi State University, BMD
Northeast Mississippi Community College, A
Tougaloo College, B
University of Mississippi, BMD
University of Southern Mississippi, MD

Missouri

Central Methodist University, B
Central Missouri State University, BM
Drury University, B
East Central College, A
Lincoln University, B
Lindenwood University, B
Missouri State University, B
Missouri Valley College, B
Missouri Western State University, B
Northwest Missouri State University, B
Park University, B
Rockhurst University, B
Saint Louis University, BM
Southeast Missouri State University, B
Truman State University, B
University of Missouri-Columbia, BMDO
University of Missouri-Kansas City, BMD
University of Missouri-Rolla, B
University of Missouri-St. Louis, BMO
Washington University in St. Louis, BMDO
Webster University, B
Westminster College, B
William Jewell College, B

Montana

Montana State University, B
Rocky Mountain College, B
The University of Montana-Missoula, BM

Nebraska

Creighton University, B
Doane College, B
Hastings College, B
Midland Lutheran College, B
Nebraska Wesleyan University, B
University of Nebraska at Kearney, B
University of Nebraska-Lincoln, BMDO
University of Nebraska at Omaha, M
Western Nebraska Community College, A

Nevada

Community College of Southern Nevada, A
Nevada State College at Henderson, B
University of Nevada, Las Vegas, BM
University of Nevada, Reno, M

New Hampshire

Dartmouth College, B
Franklin Pierce College, B
Keene State College, B
Saint Anselm College, B
Southern New Hampshire University, BMDO
University of New Hampshire, BMD

New Jersey

Bergen Community College, A
Bloomfield College, B
The College of New Jersey, B
Drew University, B
Fairleigh Dickinson University, College at
    Florham, B
Kean University, B
Montclair State University, BM

New Jersey City University, B
Princeton University, BD
Ramapo College of New Jersey, B
The Richard Stockton College of New Jersey, B
Rider University, B
Rowan University, B
Rutgers, The State University of New Jersey,
    Camden, B
Rutgers, The State University of New Jersey, New
    Brunswick/Piscataway, BMD
Rutgers, The State University of New Jersey,
    Newark, BM
Saint Peter's College, B
Seton Hall University, B

New Mexico

New Mexico Military Institute, A
New Mexico State University, BM
San Juan College, A
University of New Mexico, BMD

New York

Adelphi University, B
Alfred University, B
Bard College, B
Barnard College, B
Bernard M. Baruch College of the City University of
    New York, B
Brooklyn College of the City University of New
    York, BM
Buffalo State College, State University of New
    York, BM
Canisius College, B
City College of the City University of New York, BM
Colgate University, B
College of Mount Saint Vincent, B
The College of New Rochelle, B
College of Staten Island of the City University of
    New York, B
Columbia College, B
Columbia University, School of General Studies, B
Cornell University, BMD
Dominican College, B
Dowling College, B
Elmira College, B
Eugene Lang College The New School for Liberal
    Arts, B
Excelsior College, B
Fordham University, BMDO
Hamilton College, B
Hartwick College, B
Hobart and William Smith Colleges, B
Hofstra University, B
Hunter College of the City University of New
    York, BM
Iona College, B
Ithaca College, B
Le Moyne College, B
Lehman College of the City University of New
    York, B
Long Island University, Brooklyn Campus, BM
Long Island University, C.W. Post Campus, B
Manhattan College, B
Manhattanville College, B
Marist College, B
Nazareth College of Rochester, B
New York Institute of Technology, BM
New York University, BMDO
Niagara University, B
Pace University, BM
Purchase College, State University of New York, B
Queens College of the City University of New
    York, B
Rensselaer Polytechnic Institute, BM
Rochester Institute of Technology, B
St. Francis College, B
St. John Fisher College, B
St. John's University, B
St. Joseph's College, Suffolk Campus, B
St. Lawrence University, B
Sarah Lawrence College, B
Siena College, B,
Skidmore College, B
State University of New York at Binghamton, BMD
State University of New York at Buffalo, BMDO

State University of New York College at
  Brockport, B
State University of New York College at Cortland, B
State University of New York College at Geneseo, B
State University of New York College at Old
  Westbury, B
State University of New York College at Oneonta, B
State University of New York College at Potsdam, B
State University of New York Empire State
  College, AB
State University of New York, Fredonia, B
State University of New York at New Paltz, B
State University of New York at Oswego, B
State University of New York at Plattsburgh, B
Stony Brook University, State University of New
  York, BMD
Syracuse University, BMD
Touro College, B
Union College, B
United States Military Academy, B
University at Albany, State University of New
  York, BMDO
University of Rochester, BMD
Utica College, B
Vassar College, B
Wagner College, B
Wells College, B
Yeshiva University, B
York College of the City University of New York, B

North Carolina

Appalachian State University, B
Barton College, B
Belmont Abbey College, B
Campbell University, B
Davidson College, B
Duke University, BMDO
East Carolina University, BM
Elon University, B
Guilford College, B
Johnson C. Smith University, B
Lenoir-Rhyne College, B
Louisburg College, A
Mars Hill College, B
Meredith College, B
Methodist College, AB
North Carolina Agricultural and Technical State
  University, B
North Carolina State University, BMD
Pfeiffer University, B
Salem College, B
The University of North Carolina at Asheville, B
The University of North Carolina at Chapel
  Hill, BMD
The University of North Carolina at Charlotte, BM
The University of North Carolina at Greensboro, BD
The University of North Carolina Wilmington, B
Wake Forest University, B
Warren Wilson College, B
Wingate University, B
Winston-Salem State University, B

North Dakota

Minot State University, B
University of North Dakota, B

Ohio

Antioch College, B
Ashland University, B
Baldwin-Wallace College, B
Bluffton University, B
Bowling Green State University, BM
Capital University, B
Case Western Reserve University, BM
Central State University, B
Cleveland State University, BMO
The College of Wooster, B
David N. Myers University, B
Denison University, B
Franciscan University of Steubenville, B
Heidelberg College, B
Hiram College, B
John Carroll University, B
Kent State University, BM
Kenyon College, B
Marietta College, B

Miami University, BM
Miami University Hamilton, B
Miami University-Middletown Campus, A
Mount Union College, B
Muskingum College, B
Oberlin College, B
Ohio Dominican University, B
The Ohio State University, BMD
Ohio University, BM
Ohio University-Eastern, B
Ohio Wesleyan University, B
Otterbein College, B
The University of Akron, BM
University of Cincinnati, BM
University of Cincinnati Raymond Walters College, A
University of Dayton, B
The University of Findlay, B
University of Rio Grande, B
The University of Toledo, BM
Wilberforce University, B
Wilmington College, B
Wittenberg University, B
Wright State University, BMO
Xavier University, B
Youngstown State University, BM

Oklahoma

Eastern Oklahoma State College, A
Langston University, B
Northeastern Oklahoma Agricultural and Mechanical
  College, A
Oklahoma State University, BMD
Southeastern Oklahoma State University, B
Tulsa Community College, A
University of Central Oklahoma, B
University of Oklahoma, BMD
University of Science and Arts of Oklahoma, B
University of Tulsa, B

Oregon

Chemeketa Community College, A
Eastern Oregon University, B
George Fox University, B
Lewis & Clark College, B
Linfield College, B
Linn-Benton Community College, A
Oregon State University, BMD
Pacific University, B
Portland State University, BMD
Reed College, B
Southern Oregon University, B
Treasure Valley Community College, A
Umpqua Community College, A
University of Oregon, BMD
Western Oregon University, B
Willamette University, B

Pennsylvania

Albright College, B
Allegheny College, B
Bloomsburg University of Pennsylvania, B
Bryn Mawr College, B
Bucknell University, B
California University of Pennsylvania, B
Carnegie Mellon University, BMD
Chatham College, B
Cheyney University of Pennsylvania, B
Clarion University of Pennsylvania, B
Dickinson College, B
Duquesne University, B
East Stroudsburg University of Pennsylvania, B
Eastern University, M
Edinboro University of Pennsylvania, B
Elizabethtown College, B
Franklin and Marshall College, B
Gettysburg College, B
Grove City College, B
Haverford College, B
Holy Family University, B
Immaculata University, B
Indiana University of Pennsylvania, B
Juniata College, B
King's College, B
Kutztown University of Pennsylvania, B
La Salle University, B
Lafayette College, B

Lebanon Valley College, B
Lehigh University, MD
Lincoln University, B
Lock Haven University of Pennsylvania, B
Lycoming College, B
Mansfield University of Pennsylvania, B
Messiah College, B
Millersville University of Pennsylvania, B
Moravian College, B
Muhlenberg College, B
The Pennsylvania State University Abington
  College, B
The Pennsylvania State University Altoona
  College, B
The Pennsylvania State University Beaver Campus
  of the Commonwealth College, B
The Pennsylvania State University Berks Campus of
  the Berks-Lehigh Valley College, B
The Pennsylvania State University Delaware County
  Campus of the Commonwealth College, B
The Pennsylvania State University DuBois Campus
  of the Commonwealth College, B
The Pennsylvania State University at Erie, The
  Behrend College, B
The Pennsylvania State University Fayette Campus
  of the Commonwealth College, B
The Pennsylvania State University Hazleton
  Campus of the Commonwealth College, B
The Pennsylvania State University, Lehigh Valley
  Campus of the Berks-Lehigh Valley College, B
The Pennsylvania State University McKeesport
  Campus of the Commonwealth College, B
The Pennsylvania State University Mont Alto
  Campus of the Commonwealth College, B
The Pennsylvania State University New Kensington
  Campus of the Commonwealth College, B
The Pennsylvania State University Schuylkill
  Campus of the Capital College, B
The Pennsylvania State University Shenango
  Campus of the Commonwealth College, B
The Pennsylvania State University University Park
  Campus, BMD
The Pennsylvania State University Wilkes-Barre
  Campus of the Commonwealth College, B
The Pennsylvania State University Worthington
  Scranton Campus of the Commonwealth
  College, B
The Pennsylvania State University York Campus of
  the Commonwealth College, B
Robert Morris University, B
Rosemont College, B
Saint Francis University, B
Saint Joseph's University, B
Saint Vincent College, B
Seton Hill University, B
Shippensburg University of Pennsylvania, B
Slippery Rock University of Pennsylvania, B
Susquehanna University, B
Swarthmore College, B
Temple University, BMD
University of Pennsylvania, BMDO
University of Pittsburgh, BMDO
University of Pittsburgh at Bradford, B
University of Pittsburgh at Johnstown, B
The University of Scranton, B
Ursinus College, B
Villanova University, B
Washington & Jefferson College, B
West Chester University of Pennsylvania, M
Westminster College, B
Widener University, B

Puerto Rico

Inter American University of Puerto Rico, Fajardo
  Campus, B
Inter American University of Puerto Rico,
  Metropolitan Campus, B
Inter American University of Puerto Rico, San
  Germán Campus, B
Pontifical Catholic University of Puerto Rico, B
Universidad Metropolitana, B
University of Puerto Rico, Cayey University
  College, B
University of Puerto Rico, Mayagüez Campus, B

University of Puerto Rico, Río Piedras, BM

Rhode Island

Brown University, BMD
Bryant University, B
Providence College, B
Rhode Island College, B
Salve Regina University, B
University of Rhode Island, BMD

South Carolina

Charleston Southern University, B
Clemson University, BMD
Coastal Carolina University, B
College of Charleston, B
Converse College, B
Francis Marion University, B
Furman University, B
Presbyterian College, B
South Carolina State University, B
University of South Carolina, BMDO
Wofford College, B

South Dakota

Augustana College, B
Northern State University, B
South Dakota State University, BM
University of Sioux Falls, AB
The University of South Dakota, B

Tennessee

Belmont University, B
Carson-Newman College, B
Columbia State Community College, A
East Tennessee State University, BM
Fisk University, B
King College, B
Lambuth University, B
Lincoln Memorial University, B
Martin Methodist College, A
Maryville College, B
Middle Tennessee State University, BMD
Rhodes College, B
Sewanee: The University of the South, B
Tennessee Technological University, B
Union University, B
University of Memphis, BMD
The University of Tennessee, BMD
The University of Tennessee at Chattanooga, B
The University of Tennessee at Martin, B
Vanderbilt University, BMD

Texas

Austin College, B
Austin Community College, A
Baylor University, BM
Brazosport College, A
Clarendon College, A
Coastal Bend College, A
Frank Phillips College, A
Hardin-Simmons University, B
Hill College of the Hill Junior College District, A
Houston Baptist University, B
Jarvis Christian College, B
Lamar University, B
Lee College, A
Lon Morris College, A
Midland College, A
Midwestern State University, B
Palo Alto College, A
Rice University, BMD
St. Edward's University, B
St. Mary's University of San Antonio, B
St. Philip's College, A
Southern Methodist University, BMDO
Southwestern University, B
Stephen F. Austin State University, B
Tarleton State University, BM
Texas A&M University, BMD
Texas A&M University-Commerce, BM
Texas A&M University-Kingsville, B
Texas Christian University, B
Texas Lutheran University, B
Texas Southern University, B
Texas State University-San Marcos, B

Texas Tech University, BMD
Texas Wesleyan University, B
Trinity University, B
University of Dallas, B
University of Houston, BMD
University of Mary Hardin-Baylor, B
University of North Texas, BM
University of St. Thomas, B
The University of Texas at Arlington, BM
The University of Texas at Austin, BMD
The University of Texas at Dallas, BMD
The University of Texas at El Paso, BM
The University of Texas-Pan American, B
The University of Texas of the Permian Basin, B
The University of Texas at San Antonio, M
The University of Texas at Tyler, B
West Texas A&M University, BM

Utah

Brigham Young University, B
Dixie State College of Utah, A
Salt Lake Community College, A
Snow College, A
Southern Utah University, B
University of Utah, BMD
Utah State University, BMD
Weber State University, B

Vermont

Marlboro College, B
Middlebury College, B
Norwich University, B
Saint Michael's College, B
University of Vermont, B

Virginia

Bridgewater College, B
Christopher Newport University, B
The College of William and Mary, B
Eastern Mennonite University, B
Emory & Henry College, B
George Mason University, BMD
Hampden-Sydney College, B
Hampton University, B
Hollins University, B
James Madison University, B
Liberty University, B
Longwood University, B
Lynchburg College, B
Mary Baldwin College, B
Marymount University, B
Old Dominion University, BM
Radford University, B
Randolph-Macon College, B
Randolph-Macon Woman's College, B
Roanoke College, B
Sweet Briar College, B
University of Mary Washington, B
University of Richmond, B
University of Virginia, BMDO
The University of Virginia's College at Wise, B
Virginia Commonwealth University, M
Virginia Military Institute, B
Virginia Polytechnic Institute and State
 University, BMD
Virginia State University, M
Washington and Lee University, B

Washington

Central Washington University, B
Eastern Washington University, B
Everett Community College, A
Gonzaga University, B
Lower Columbia College, A
Pacific Lutheran University, B
Saint Martin's University, B
Seattle Pacific University, BM
Seattle University, B
Skagit Valley College, A
Tacoma Community College, A
University of Puget Sound, B
University of Washington, BMD
Walla Walla College, B
Washington State University, BMDO
Wenatchee Valley College, A
Western Washington University, B

Whitman College, B
Whitworth College, B

West Virginia

Bethany College, B
Davis & Elkins College, B
Fairmont State University, B
Marshall University, B
Potomac State College of West Virginia
 University, A
Shepherd University, B
West Virginia State University, B
West Virginia University, MD
West Virginia Wesleyan College, B

Wisconsin

Beloit College, B
Carthage College, B
Concordia University Wisconsin, B
Edgewood College, B
Lawrence University, B
Marquette University, BM
Northland College, B
Ripon College, B
St. Norbert College, B
University of Wisconsin-Eau Claire, B
University of Wisconsin-Green Bay, AB
University of Wisconsin-La Crosse, B
University of Wisconsin-Madison, D
University of Wisconsin-Milwaukee, BMD
University of Wisconsin-Oshkosh, B
University of Wisconsin-Parkside, B
University of Wisconsin-Platteville, B
University of Wisconsin-River Falls, B
University of Wisconsin-Stevens Point, B
University of Wisconsin-Superior, B
University of Wisconsin-Whitewater, B

Wyoming

Casper College, A
Eastern Wyoming College, A
Laramie County Community College, A
Northwest College, A
University of Wyoming, MD
Western Wyoming Community College, A

Alberta

University of Alberta, BMD
University of Calgary, BMD
University of Lethbridge, BM

British Columbia

Simon Fraser University, BMD
Thompson Rivers University, B
The University of British Columbia, BMD
University of Northern British Columbia, B
University of Victoria, BMD

Manitoba

Brandon University, B
Canadian Mennonite University, B
University of Manitoba, BMD
The University of Winnipeg, B

New Brunswick

Mount Allison University, B
St. Thomas University, B
Université de Moncton, BM
University of New Brunswick Fredericton, BM
University of New Brunswick Saint John, B

Newfoundland and Labrador

Memorial University of Newfoundland, BM

Nova Scotia

Acadia University, B
Cape Breton University, B
Dalhousie University, BMD
Mount Saint Vincent University, B
St. Francis Xavier University, B
Saint Mary's University, B

University of King's College, B

Ontario

Brock University, B
Carleton University, BMD
Lakehead University, BM
Laurentian University, B
McMaster University, BMD
Nipissing University, B
Queen's University at Kingston, B
Trent University, B
University of Guelph, BMD
University of Ottawa, BMD
University of Toronto, BMDO
University of Waterloo, BMD
The University of Western Ontario, BMD
University of Windsor, BM
Wilfrid Laurier University, BM
York University, BMD

Prince Edward Island

University of Prince Edward Island, B

Quebec

Bishop's University, B
Concordia University, BMDO
McGill University, BMD
Université Laval, BMD
Université de Montréal, BMD
Université du Québec àMontréal, BMD
Université du Québec àTrois-Rivières, B
Université de Sherbrooke, BM

Saskatchewan

University of Regina, BM
University of Saskatchewan, M

EDUCATION

Alabama

Alabama Agricultural and Mechanical University, MO
Alabama Southern Community College, A
Alabama State University, ABMDO
Auburn University, MDO
Auburn University Montgomery, MO
Birmingham-Southern College, B
Calhoun Community College, A
Enterprise-Ozark Community College, A
Faulkner University, B
Huntingdon College, B
Jacksonville State University, BMO
Jefferson Davis Community College, A
Judson College, B
Lawson State Community College, A
Miles College, B
Northwest-Shoals Community College, A
Samford University, MDO
Southeastern Bible College, B
Spring Hill College, AM
Stillman College, B
Talladega College, B
Troy University, BMO
Tuskegee University, M
The University of Alabama at Birmingham, MDO
University of Mobile, M
University of Montevallo, MO
University of North Alabama, MO
University of South Alabama, MDO
The University of West Alabama, M
Wallace State Community College, A

Alaska

Alaska Pacific University, M
University of Alaska Anchorage, BM
University of Alaska Fairbanks, BM
University of Alaska Southeast, BM

Arizona

Argosy University/Phoenix, DO
Arizona State University, MD
Arizona State University West, MO
Arizona Western College, A
Cochise College (Douglas), A
Cochise College (Sierra Vista), A

GateWay Community College, A
Grand Canyon University, M
Northern Arizona University, BMDO
Prescott College, BM
The University of Arizona, MDO
University of Phoenix Online Campus, MDO
University of Phoenix-Phoenix Campus, MO
University of Phoenix-Southern Arizona
    Campus, MO
Yavapai College, A

Arkansas

Arkansas State University, MDO
Arkansas Tech University, BM
Central Baptist College, A
Harding University, MO
Henderson State University, MO
John Brown University, B
National Park Community College, A
NorthWest Arkansas Community College, A
Ouachita Baptist University, B
Phillips Community College of the University of
    Arkansas, A
Southern Arkansas University-Magnolia, M
University of Arkansas, MDO
University of Arkansas Community College at
    Batesville, A
University of Arkansas at Little Rock, BMDO
University of Arkansas at Monticello, BM
University of Arkansas at Pine Bluff, M
University of Central Arkansas, MD
Williams Baptist College, B

California

Alliant International University, B
Antioch University Los Angeles, M
Antioch University Santa Barbara, M
Argosy University/Orange County, MD
Argosy University/San Francisco Bay Area, MD
Azusa Pacific University, MD
Barstow College, A
Bethany University, BM
Biola University, BM
California Baptist University, M
California Lutheran University, MO
California Polytechnic State University, San Luis
    Obispo, M
California State Polytechnic University, Pomona, M
California State University, Bakersfield, M
California State University Channel Islands, B
California State University, Chico, M
California State University, Dominguez Hills, MO
California State University, East Bay, M
California State University, Fresno, MD
California State University, Fullerton, M
California State University, Long Beach, MDO
California State University, Los Angeles, MD
California State University, Monterey Bay, M
California State University, Northridge, M
California State University, Sacramento, M
California State University, San Bernardino, M
California State University, San Marcos, M
California State University, Stanislaus, M
Chabot College, A
Chapman University, MO
College of the Desert, A
Concordia University, M
Dominican University of California, BMO
Folsom Lake College, A
Fresno Pacific University, BM
Glendale Community College, A
Holy Names University, MO
Hope International University, M
Humboldt State University, B
John F. Kennedy University, M
La Sierra University, MDO
Las Positas College, A
Los Angeles Southwest College, A
Loyola Marymount University, MD
The Master's College and Seminary, B
Mills College, MD
Mount St. Mary's College, BM
The National Hispanic University, AB
National University, AM
New College of California, B
Notre Dame de Namur University, BM

Occidental College, M
Pacific Union College, BM
Palo Verde College, A
Pepperdine University, B
Point Loma Nazarene University, MO
Porterville College, A
Saint Mary's College of California, MD
San Diego Christian College, B
San Diego State University, MD
San Francisco State University, MDO
San Jose State University, MO
Santa Clara University, MO
Santa Rosa Junior College, A
Shasta Bible College, B
Simpson University, M
Sonoma State University, M
Stanford University, MD
Touro University International, MDO
University of California, Berkeley, MDO
University of California, Davis, MD
University of California, Irvine, MD
University of California, Los Angeles, BMDO
University of California, Riverside, MD
University of California, San Diego, MD
University of California, Santa Barbara, MD
University of California, Santa Cruz, MO
University of Judaism, M
University of La Verne, BMO
University of the Pacific, BMDO
University of Phoenix-Bay Area Campus, M
University of Phoenix-Sacramento Valley
    Campus, MO
University of Phoenix-San Diego Campus, M
University of Phoenix-Southern California
    Campus, MO
University of Redlands, BM
University of San Diego, MDO
University of San Francisco, BMD
University of Southern California, BMDO
Vanguard University of Southern California, BM
West Los Angeles College, A
Westmont College, B
Whittier College, M
William Jessup University, B
Yuba College, A

Colorado

Adams State College, M
Colorado Christian University, M
The Colorado College, M
Colorado Northwestern Community College, A
Colorado State University-Pueblo, B
Jones International University, M
Mesa State College, B
Naropa University, M
Northeastern Junior College, A
Regis University, BMO
Trinidad State Junior College, A
University of Colorado at Boulder, MD
University of Colorado at Colorado Springs, M
University of Colorado at Denver and Health
    Sciences Center - Downtown Denver
    Campus, MDO
University of Denver, MDO
University of Northern Colorado, MDO
University of Phoenix-Denver Campus, M
University of Phoenix-Southern Colorado
    Campus, MO
Western State College of Colorado, B

Connecticut

Albertus Magnus College, B
Central Connecticut State University, MDO
Connecticut College, M
Eastern Connecticut State University, M
Fairfield University, MO
Quinnipiac University, BM
Sacred Heart University, BMO
Saint Joseph College, BM
Southern Connecticut State University, MDO
Trinity College, B
University of Bridgeport, MDO
University of Connecticut, MD
University of Hartford, MDO
University of New Haven, M

Western Connecticut State University, BM

Delaware

Delaware State University, M
University of Delaware, BMD
Wesley College, BM
Wilmington College, M

District of Columbia

American University, MDO
The Catholic University of America, BMD
Gallaudet University, BMDO
The George Washington University, MDO
Howard University, BMDO
Trinity (Washington) University, BM
University of the District of Columbia, M

Florida

Argosy University/Sarasota, MDO
Argosy University/Tampa, MDO
The Baptist College of Florida, B
Barry University, BMDO
Chipola College, A
Daytona Beach Community College, A
Edward Waters College, B
Florida Agricultural and Mechanical University, BMD
Florida Atlantic University, MDO
Florida Gulf Coast University, M
Florida International University, MDO
Florida National College, A
Florida Southern College, BM
Florida State University, MDO
Hillsborough Community College, A
Indian River Community College, A
Jacksonville University, MO
Lynn University, B
Miami Dade College, A
Nova Southeastern University, MDO
Okaloosa-Walton College, A
Palm Beach Atlantic University, BM
Palm Beach Community College, A
Pensacola Junior College, A
Rollins College, BM
Saint Leo University, M
St. Petersburg College, B
St. Thomas University, MDO
Santa Fe Community College, A
South Florida Community College, A
Stetson University, BMO
University of Central Florida, MDO
University of Florida, MDO
University of Miami, BMDO
University of North Florida, MD
University of Phoenix-Central Florida Campus, M
University of Phoenix-North Florida Campus, M
University of Phoenix-South Florida Campus, M
University of Phoenix-West Florida Campus, M
University of South Florida, BMDO

Georgia

Abraham Baldwin Agricultural College, A
Albany State University, BMO
Andrew College, A
Argosy University/Atlanta, MD
Armstrong Atlantic State University, M
Augusta State University, MO
Bainbridge College, A
Berry College, MO
Brenau University, BMO
Brewton-Parker College, B
Clark Atlanta University, BMDO
Clayton State University, A
Columbus State University, MO
Covenant College, M
Dalton State College, A
Darton College, A
East Georgia College, A
Emory University, BMDO
Georgia College & State University, MO
Georgia Perimeter College, A
Georgia Southern University, BMDO
Georgia Southwestern State University, BMO
Georgia State University, MDO
Gordon College, A
Kennesaw State University, M
LaGrange College, BM

Macon State College, A
Mercer University, BMO
North Georgia College & State University, BMO
Oglethorpe University, M
Piedmont College, MO
Reinhardt College, A
South Georgia College, A
Truett-McConnell College, A
University of Georgia, MDO
University of West Georgia, MDO
Valdosta State University, MDO
Waycross College, A
Wesleyan College, BM
Young Harris College, A

Guam

Guam Community College, A
University of Guam, BM

Hawaii

Argosy University/Hawaii, MD
Brigham Young University-Hawaii, B
Chaminade University of Honolulu, M
University of Hawaii at Manoa, BMD
University of Phoenix-Hawaii Campus, MO

Idaho

Albertson College of Idaho, M
Boise State University, BMD
Brigham Young University -Idaho, A
College of Southern Idaho, A
Idaho State University, MDO
North Idaho College, A
Northwest Nazarene University, M
University of Idaho, MDO

Illinois

Argosy University/Chicago, MDO
Argosy University/Schaumburg, MDO
Augustana College, B
Aurora University, MD
Benedictine University, BM
Bradley University, MD
Chicago State University, BM
City Colleges of Chicago, Harry S. Truman
    College, A
City Colleges of Chicago, Kennedy-King College, A
City Colleges of Chicago, Richard J. Daley
    College, A
Columbia College Chicago, M
Concordia University, BM
Danville Area Community College, A
DePaul University, BM
Dominican University, M
Eastern Illinois University, MO
Elmhurst College, B
Eureka College, B
Greenville College, M
Highland Community College, A
Illinois College, B
Illinois State University, MD
Illinois Valley Community College, A
Illinois Wesleyan University, B
John A. Logan College, A
Joliet Junior College, A
Judson College, B
Kendall College, B
Knox College, B
Lake Forest College, B
Lewis University, BMO
Lincoln College, A
Lincoln College-Normal, A
Loyola University Chicago, MDO
Monmouth College, B
National-Louis University, MDO
North Central College, BM
North Park University, BM
Northeastern Illinois University, M
Northern Illinois University, BMDO
Northwestern University, BMD
Olivet Nazarene University, BM
Quincy University, M
Rockford College, BM
Roosevelt University, BMD
Saint Xavier University, MO
Sauk Valley Community College, A

Southern Illinois University Carbondale, MDO
Southern Illinois University Edwardsville, MO
Spoon River College, A
Springfield College in Illinois, A
Trinity Christian College, B
Trinity International University, BM
University of Illinois at Chicago, MD
University of Illinois at Urbana-Champaign, MDO
University of St. Francis, M
Western Illinois University, MO
Wheaton College, M

Indiana

Anderson University, B
Ball State University, BMDO
Bethel College, B
Butler University, M
Goshen College, B
Huntington University, B
Indiana State University, MDO
Indiana University Bloomington, BMDO
Indiana University East, B
Indiana University Kokomo, M
Indiana University Northwest, BM
Indiana University-Purdue University Fort
    Wayne, BM
Indiana University-Purdue University
    Indianapolis, BM
Indiana University South Bend, BM
Indiana University Southeast, BM
Indiana Wesleyan University, BM
Manchester College, B
Marian College, BM
Martin University, B
Oakland City University, BMD
Purdue University, BMDO
Purdue University Calumet, BM
Purdue University North Central, M
Saint Mary-of-the-Woods College, B
Saint Mary's College, B
Taylor University, B
Taylor University Fort Wayne, B
Tri-State University, B
University of Evansville, BM
University of Indianapolis, BM
University of Notre Dame, M
University of Saint Francis, BM
University of Southern Indiana, AM
Valparaiso University, MO
Vincennes University, A
Vincennes University Jasper Campus, A

Iowa

Ashford University, B
Briar Cliff University, B
Buena Vista University, M
Clarke College, BM
Coe College, BM
Des Moines Area Community College, A
Dordt College, BM
Drake University, MDO
Ellsworth Community College, A
Graceland University, BM
Hawkeye Community College, A
Iowa Central Community College, A
Iowa Lakes Community College, A
Iowa State University of Science and
    Technology, BMD
Iowa Wesleyan College, B
Kirkwood Community College, A
Loras College, B
Maharishi University of Management, M
Morningside College, BM
Mount Mercy College, B
St. Ambrose University, B
Simpson College, B
The University of Iowa, MDO
University of Northern Iowa, MDO
Upper Iowa University, B
Waldorf College, B
William Penn University, B

Kansas

Baker University, M
Bethany College, B
Cloud County Community College, A

Coffeyville Community College, A
Colby Community College, A
Cowley County Community College and Area
　Vocational-Technical School, A
Dodge City Community College, A
Donnelly College, A
Emporia State University, MO
Fort Hays State University, MO
Fort Scott Community College, A
Friends University, ABM
Garden City Community College, A
Highland Community College, A
Hutchinson Community College and Area Vocational
　School, A
Johnson County Community College, A
Kansas State University, MD
Kansas Wesleyan University, B
Labette Community College, A
McPherson College, B
MidAmerica Nazarene University, M
Newman University, BM
Ottawa University, M
Pittsburg State University, MO
Seward County Community College, A
Southwestern College, M
Tabor College, B
University of Kansas, MDO
University of Saint Mary, BM
Washburn University, BM
Wichita State University, MDO

Kentucky

Bellarmine University, BM
Berea College, B
Brescia University, B
Campbellsville University, M
Eastern Kentucky University, BM
Georgetown College, M
Lindsey Wilson College, B
Midway College, B
Morehead State University, MO
Murray State University, MDO
Northern Kentucky University, BMO
St. Catharine College, A
Spalding University, BMD
Union College, BM
University of the Cumberlands, MO
University of Kentucky, MDO
University of Louisville, MDO
Western Kentucky University, MO

Louisiana

Centenary College of Louisiana, BM
Dillard University, B
Grambling State University, MD
Louisiana State University and Agricultural and
　Mechanical College, MDO
Louisiana State University in Shreveport, MO
Louisiana Tech University, MD
Loyola University New Orleans, BM
McNeese State University, BM
Nicholls State University, BM
Northwestern State University of Louisiana, MO
Our Lady of Holy Cross College, BM
Southeastern Louisiana University, M
Southern University and Agricultural and Mechanical
　College, M
University of Louisiana at Lafayette, BM
University of Louisiana at Monroe, MDO
University of New Orleans, MDO
Xavier University of Louisiana, BM

Maine

College of the Atlantic, B
Kennebec Valley Community College, A
Saint Joseph's College of Maine, BM
University of Maine, BMDO
University of Maine at Fort Kent, B
University of Maine at Machias, B
University of Maine at Presque Isle, B
University of New England, M
University of Southern Maine, MDO

Maryland

Anne Arundel Community College, A
Baltimore Hebrew University, AB

Bowie State University, BM
Cecil Community College, A
College of Notre Dame of Maryland, BM
College of Southern Maryland, A
Coppin State University, BM
Frederick Community College, A
Frostburg State University, M
Garrett College, A
Goucher College, BM
Hagerstown Community College, A
Harford Community College, A
Hood College, MO
The Johns Hopkins University, MDO
Loyola College in Maryland, BMO
Montgomery College, A
Morgan State University, BMD
Mount St. Mary's University, M
Prince George's Community College, A
Salisbury University, BM
Towson University, BM
University of Maryland, Baltimore County, MO
University of Maryland, College Park, BMDO
University of Maryland Eastern Shore, BM
University of Maryland University College, M

Massachusetts

American International College, BMDO
Anna Maria College, MO
Atlantic Union College, BM
Becker College, B
Boston College, MDO
Boston University, BMDO
Bridgewater State College, MO
Bunker Hill Community College, A
Cambridge College, M
Cape Cod Community College, A
Clark University, BM
Curry College, BMO
Eastern Nazarene College, BMO
Elms College, BM
Emmanuel College, BMO
Endicott College, M
Fitchburg State College, B
Framingham State College, B
Gordon College, M
Greenfield Community College, A
Hampshire College, B
Harvard University, MD
Hebrew College, BMO
Lasell College, B
Lesley University, BMDO
Massachusetts College of Liberal Arts, BM
Merrimack College, M
Mount Holyoke College, B
Northeastern University, BM
Northern Essex Community College, A
Regis College, M
Salem State College, BMO
Simmons College, BMO
Smith College, BM
Springfield College, BM
Suffolk University, BMO
Tufts University, MO
University of Massachusetts Amherst, MDO
University of Massachusetts Boston, MDO
University of Massachusetts Dartmouth, MO
University of Massachusetts Lowell, MDO
Westfield State College, BMO
Wheelock College, BM
Worcester State College, M

Michigan

Adrian College, B
Albion College, B
Alma College, B
Andrews University, BMDO
Aquinas College, BM
Baker College of Auburn Hills, A
Baker College of Cadillac, A
Calvin College, M
Central Michigan University, MDO
Cornerstone University, B
Eastern Michigan University, MDO
Ferris State University, M
Finlandia University, B
Gogebic Community College, A

Grand Valley State University, BM
Great Lakes Christian College, B
Hillsdale College, B
Lake Superior State University, B
Lansing Community College, A
Lawrence Technological University, M
Madonna University, BM
Marygrove College, BM
Michigan State University, BMDO
Muskegon Community College, A
Northern Michigan University, BMO
Northwestern Michigan College, A
Oakland University, MDO
Olivet College, BM
Saginaw Valley State University, MO
Schoolcraft College, A
Siena Heights University, M
Spring Arbor University, M
University of Detroit Mercy, BM
University of Michigan, BMDO
University of Michigan-Dearborn, BM
University of Michigan-Flint, BM
University of Phoenix-Metro Detroit Campus, M
University of Phoenix-West Michigan Campus, M
Wayne County Community College District, A
Wayne State University, MDO
Western Michigan University, MDO

Minnesota

Augsburg College, BM
Bemidji State University, BM
Bethel University, MDO
Capella University, MD
College of Saint Benedict, B
College of St. Catherine, BM
The College of St. Scholastica, M
Concordia College, B
Concordia University, St. Paul, BM
Gustavus Adolphus College, B
Hamline University, BMD
Itasca Community College, A
Minnesota State University Mankato, BMO
Minnesota State University Moorhead, MO
Pillsbury Baptist Bible College, B
St. Cloud State University, BMO
Saint John's University, B
Saint Mary's University of Minnesota, M
Southwest Minnesota State University, BM
University of Minnesota, Duluth, B
University of Minnesota, Morris, B
University of Minnesota, Twin Cities
　Campus, BMDO
University of St. Thomas, M
Vermilion Community College, A
Walden University, MD
Winona State University, BM

Mississippi

Alcorn State University, MO
Belhaven College, M
Copiah-Lincoln Community College, A
Delta State University, BMDO
East Central Community College, A
East Mississippi Community College, A
Itawamba Community College, A
Jackson State University, BMDO
Jones County Junior College, A
Millsaps College, B
Mississippi College, BMO
Mississippi Delta Community College, A
Mississippi Gulf Coast Community College, A
Mississippi State University, MDO
Mississippi University for Women, BM
Mississippi Valley State University, BM
Northeast Mississippi Community College, A
Northwest Mississippi Community College, A
Southwest Mississippi Community College, A
Tougaloo College, B
University of Mississippi, MDO
University of Southern Mississippi, MDO
William Carey College, MO

Missouri

Avila University, M
Central Methodist University, BM
Central Missouri State University, BMO

College of the Ozarks, B
Columbia College, BM
Crowder College, A
Drury University, BM
East Central College, A
Evangel University, ABM
Fontbonne University, BM
Hannibal-LaGrange College, B
Jefferson College, A
Lincoln University, MO
Lindenwood University, BMO
Maryville University of Saint Louis, M
Messenger College, B
Missouri Southern State University, B
Missouri State University, M
Missouri Valley College, B
National American University, B
Northwest Missouri State University, BMO
Park University, BM
Rockhurst University, BM
St. Louis Community College at Meramec, A
Saint Louis University, BMD
Southwest Baptist University, MO
Three Rivers Community College, A
Truman State University, M
University of Missouri-Columbia, BMDO
University of Missouri-Kansas City, MDO
University of Missouri-St. Louis, BMDO
Washington University in St. Louis, BMD
Webster University, BMO
William Jewell College, B
William Woods University, BMO

Montana

Carroll College, B
Montana State University, MDO
Montana State University-Billings, ABMO
Montana State University-Northern, BM
Rocky Mountain College, B
University of Great Falls, M
The University of Montana-Missoula, BMDO
The University of Montana-Western, B

Nebraska

Chadron State College, MO
College of Saint Mary, B
Concordia University, BM
Creighton University, M
Dana College, B
Doane College, M
Hastings College, BM
Midland Lutheran College, B
Northeast Community College, A
Peru State College, BM
Southeast Community College, Beatrice Campus, A
Union College, B
University of Nebraska at Kearney, MO
University of Nebraska-Lincoln, MDO
University of Nebraska at Omaha, MDO
Wayne State College, BMO
York College, B

Nevada

Nevada State College at Henderson, B
Sierra Nevada College, O
University of Nevada, Las Vegas, BMDO
University of Nevada, Reno, MDO
University of Phoenix-Nevada Campus, M

New Hampshire

Franklin Pierce College, B
Keene State College, BMO
New England College, BM
Plymouth State University, MO
Rivier College, BMO
Southern New Hampshire University, MO
University of New Hampshire, MDO

New Jersey

Atlantic Cape Community College, A
Bergen Community College, A
Brookdale Community College, A
Burlington County College, A
Centenary College, BM
The College of New Jersey, BMO

College of Saint Elizabeth, O
Cumberland County College, A
Fairleigh Dickinson University, College at
  Florham, MO
Fairleigh Dickinson University, Metropolitan
  Campus, BMO
Felician College, BM
Georgian Court University, MO
Gloucester County College, A
Kean University, MO
Middlesex County College, A
Monmouth University, BMO
Montclair State University, MDO
Raritan Valley Community College, A
Rider University, BMO
Rowan University, MDO
Rutgers, The State University of New Jersey, New
  Brunswick/Piscataway, MD
Saint Peter's College, MO
Salem Community College, A
Seton Hall University, MDO
Warren County Community College, A
William Paterson University of New Jersey, BM

New Mexico

College of Santa Fe, M
College of the Southwest, BM
Eastern New Mexico University, M
New Mexico Highlands University, BM
New Mexico Junior College, A
New Mexico State University, MDO
New Mexico State University-Alamogordo, A
New Mexico State University-Carlsbad, A
New Mexico State University-Grants, A
San Juan College, A
University of New Mexico, MDO
University of New Mexico-Gallup, A
University of New Mexico-Valencia Campus, A
University of Phoenix-New Mexico Campus, M
Western New Mexico University, BM

New York

Adelphi University, BMDO
Alfred University, M
Bard College, M
Bernard M. Baruch College of the City University of
  New York, B
Brooklyn College of the City University of New
  York, BMO
Canisius College, BM
City College of the City University of New
  York, BMO
Colgate University, B
College of Mount Saint Vincent, BMO
The College of New Rochelle, BMO
The College of Saint Rose, MO
College of Staten Island of the City University of
  New York, MO
Concordia College, B
Cornell University, BMD
Corning Community College, A
Daemen College, M
Dominican College, BM
Dowling College, BMDO
D'Youville College, BMO
Elmira College, B
Eugene Lang College The New School for Liberal
  Arts, B
Fiorello H. LaGuardia Community College of the
  City University of New York, A
Fordham University, BMDO
Genesee Community College, A
Hofstra University, BMDO
Hunter College of the City University of New
  York, MO
Iona College, B
The King's College, B
Kingsborough Community College of the City
  University of New York, A
Le Moyne College, M
Lehman College of the City University of New
  York, M
Long Island University, Brentwood Campus, M
Long Island University, Brooklyn Campus, BMO
Long Island University, C.W. Post Campus, BMO
Manhattan College, BMO

Manhattanville College, BM
Medaille College, BM
Medgar Evers College of the City University of New
  York, AB
Mercy College, MO
Molloy College, B
Mount Saint Mary College, BM
Nazareth College of Rochester, BM
New York Institute of Technology, BMO
New York University, BMDO
Niagara University, BMO
Nyack College, M
Pace University, BMO
Queens College of the City University of New
  York, MO
Roberts Wesleyan College, BMO
St. Bonaventure University, MO
St. John Fisher College, MO
St. John's University, MDO
St. Joseph's College, New York, B
St. Joseph's College, Suffolk Campus, B
St. Lawrence University, MO
St. Thomas Aquinas College, BMO
Sarah Lawrence College, BM
Schenectady County Community College, A
State University of New York at Binghamton, MDO
State University of New York at Buffalo, MDO
State University of New York College at
  Brockport, BM
State University of New York College at
  Cortland, MO
State University of New York College at
  Geneseo, BM
State University of New York College at
  Oneonta, BMO
State University of New York College at Potsdam, M
State University of New York Empire State
  College, ABM
State University of New York, Fredonia, BMO
State University of New York at New Paltz, BMO
State University of New York at Oswego, BMO
State University of New York at Plattsburgh, B
Syracuse University, BMDO
Touro College, B
University at Albany, State University of New
  York, MDO
University of Rochester, MDO
Villa Maria College of Buffalo, A
Wagner College, BM
Wells College, B
Yeshiva University, B

North Carolina

Appalachian State University, MDO
Belmont Abbey College, B
Brevard College, B
Campbell University, BM
Catawba College, BM
College of The Albemarle, A
Duke University, MO
East Carolina University, MDO
Elizabeth City State University, B
Elon University, BM
Fayetteville State University, B
Gardner-Webb University, BM
Greensboro College, B
Guilford Technical Community College, A
Halifax Community College, A
Haywood Community College, A
High Point University, BM
Isothermal Community College, A
Johnson C. Smith University, B
Lees-McRae College, B
Lenoir-Rhyne College, BM
Livingstone College, B
Mars Hill College, B
Meredith College, M
Methodist College, B
Montreat College, A
North Carolina Agricultural and Technical State
  University, BM
North Carolina Central University, M
North Carolina State University, BMDO
North Carolina Wesleyan College, B
Pfeiffer University, BM
Piedmont Baptist College, AB

Queens University of Charlotte, BM
Roanoke-Chowan Community College, A
Salem College, BM
The University of North Carolina at Chapel Hill, MD
The University of North Carolina at Charlotte, M
The University of North Carolina at Greensboro, MDO
The University of North Carolina at Pembroke, M
The University of North Carolina Wilmington, M
Vance-Granville Community College, A
Wake Forest University, M
Warren Wilson College, B
Western Carolina University, MDO
Winston-Salem State University, B

North Dakota

Dickinson State University, B
Mayville State University, B
North Dakota State University, MDO
Sitting Bull College, A
United Tribes Technical College, A
University of Mary, M
University of North Dakota, MDO
Valley City State University, B

Ohio

Antioch College, B
Antioch University McGregor, M
Ashland University, BMD
Baldwin-Wallace College, M
Bluffton University, M
Bowling Green State University, BMDO
Bowling Green State University-Firelands College, A
Capital University, B
Cedarville University, M
Central State University, M
Cincinnati Christian University, AB
Circleville Bible College, AB
Cleveland State University, BMDO
College of Mount St. Joseph, M
Defiance College, BM
Franciscan University of Steubenville, M
Heidelberg College, BM
John Carroll University, BM
Kent State University, ABMDO
Kent State University, Salem Campus, AB
Kent State University, Stark Campus, A
Lake Erie College, M
Lorain County Community College, A
Lourdes College, M
Malone College, M
Marietta College, BM
Miami University, MDO
Miami University-Middletown Campus, A
Mount Vernon Nazarene University, BM
Muskingum College, BM
Northwest State Community College, A
Notre Dame College, O
Ohio Northern University, B
The Ohio State University, MD
The Ohio State University at Lima, M
The Ohio State University at Marion, M
The Ohio State University-Newark Campus, M
Ohio University, BMD
Ohio University-Eastern, B
Ohio University-Lancaster, B
Ohio University-Southern Campus, B
Ohio Wesleyan University, B
Otterbein College, BM
Shawnee State University, B
Sinclair Community College, A
Union Institute & University, BMO
The University of Akron, ABMD
University of Cincinnati, BMDO
University of Cincinnati Raymond Walters College, A
University of Dayton, BMDO
The University of Findlay, BM
University of Rio Grande, BM
The University of Toledo, BMDO
Urbana University, BM
Ursuline College, M
Walsh University, BM
Washington State Community College, A
Wilmington College, BM
Wittenberg University, B
Wright State University, BMO

Xavier University, BM
Youngstown State University, BMD

Oklahoma

Bacone College, AB
Cameron University, BM
Connors State College, A
East Central University, BM
Eastern Oklahoma State College, A
Langston University, BM
Northeastern State University, BM
Northwestern Oklahoma State University, M
Oklahoma Baptist University, BM
Oklahoma City University, BM
Oklahoma State University, BMDO
Oklahoma State University, Oklahoma City, A
Oklahoma Wesleyan University, B
Oral Roberts University, BMD
Redlands Community College, A
Southeastern Oklahoma State University, BM
Southern Nazarene University, B
Southwestern Oklahoma State University, BM
Tulsa Community College, A
University of Central Oklahoma, M
University of Oklahoma, MDO
University of Tulsa, BM

Oregon

Central Oregon Community College, A
Chemeketa Community College, A
Concordia University, BM
Corban College, B
Eastern Oregon University, BM
George Fox University, MD
Lewis & Clark College, MDO
Linn-Benton Community College, A
Marylhurst University, B
Oregon State University, MD
Pacific University, BM
Portland State University, MD
Rogue Community College, A
Southern Oregon University, M
Treasure Valley Community College, A
Umpqua Community College, A
University of Oregon, BMD
University of Phoenix-Oregon Campus, M
University of Portland, BM
Warner Pacific College, B
Western Oregon University, M
Willamette University, M

Pennsylvania

Albright College, M
Allegheny College, B
Alvernia College, BM
Arcadia University, BMDO
Baptist Bible College of Pennsylvania, B
Bloomsburg University of Pennsylvania, M
Bryn Athyn College of the New Church, B
Bucknell University, BM
Bucks County Community College, A
Butler County Community College, A
Cabrini College, BM
California University of Pennsylvania, BM
Carlow University, M
Carnegie Mellon University, MD
Cedar Crest College, BM
Chatham College, M
Chestnut Hill College, M
Cheyney University of Pennsylvania, BMO
Clarion University of Pennsylvania, BMO
College Misericordia, M
Community College of Beaver County, A
Community College of Philadelphia, A
DeSales University, MO
Drexel University, MDO
Duquesne University, BMDO
East Stroudsburg University of Pennsylvania, M
Eastern University, MO
Edinboro University of Pennsylvania, MDO
Elizabethtown College, B
Gannon University, MO
Geneva College, M
Gettysburg College, B
Gratz College, M
Gwynedd-Mercy College, BM

Harrisburg Area Community College, A
Haverford College, B
Holy Family University, BM
Indiana University of Pennsylvania, MDO
Juniata College, B
Kutztown University of Pennsylvania, BMO
La Salle University, BM
Lackawanna College, A
Lancaster Bible College, B
Lehigh Carbon Community College, A
Lehigh University, BMDO
Lincoln University, B
Lock Haven University of Pennsylvania, BM
Luzerne County Community College, A
Lycoming College, B
Manor College, A
Mansfield University of Pennsylvania, BM
Marywood University, BM
Mercyhurst College, B
Millersville University of Pennsylvania, M
Moravian College, BM
Neumann College, M
Northampton County Area Community College, A
The Pennsylvania State University Harrisburg Campus, MD
The Pennsylvania State University University Park Campus, MD
Philadelphia Biblical University, M
Point Park University, BM
Reading Area Community College, A
Robert Morris University, MDO
Saint Francis University, ABM
Saint Joseph's University, BMD
Saint Vincent College, M
Shippensburg University of Pennsylvania, MO
Slippery Rock University of Pennsylvania, M
Swarthmore College, B
Temple University, MD
University of Pennsylvania, MDO
University of Pittsburgh, MD
University of Pittsburgh at Greensburg, B
University of Pittsburgh at Johnstown, B
The University of Scranton, M
Villanova University, BM
Washington & Jefferson College, B
West Chester University of Pennsylvania, MO
Westminster College, BMO
Widener University, MD
Wilkes University, BM
York College of Pennsylvania, M

Puerto Rico

American University of Puerto Rico, B
Bayamon Central University, M
Caribbean University, AB
Inter American University of Puerto Rico, Arecibo Campus, BM
Inter American University of Puerto Rico, Barranquitas Campus, AB
Inter American University of Puerto Rico, Fajardo Campus, B
Inter American University of Puerto Rico, Metropolitan Campus, BMD
Inter American University of Puerto Rico, Ponce Campus, B
Inter American University of Puerto Rico, San Germán Campus, B
Pontifical Catholic University of Puerto Rico, ABMD
Universidad Metropolitana, M
Universidad del Turabo, BM
University of Phoenix-Puerto Rico Campus, M
University of Puerto Rico at Bayamón, A
University of Puerto Rico at Carolina, A
University of Puerto Rico, Río Piedras, MD
University of Puerto Rico at Utuado, A
University of the Sacred Heart, BM

Rhode Island

Brown University, BM
Johnson & Wales University, M
Providence College, M
Rhode Island College, BD
Roger Williams University, M

University of Rhode Island, M

South Carolina

Allen University, B
Anderson University, B
Charleston Southern University, BM
The Citadel, The Military College of South
  Carolina, MO
Clemson University, MDO
Coastal Carolina University, M
Coker College, B
College of Charleston, MO
Columbia College, M
Columbia International University, MDO
Converse College, BMO
Francis Marion University, M
Furman University, BM
Lander University, M
Limestone College, B
Newberry College, B
Presbyterian College, B
South Carolina State University, BMDO
Southern Wesleyan University, BM
University of South Carolina, MDO
University of South Carolina Aiken, M
University of South Carolina Beaufort, B
University of South Carolina Upstate, M
Voorhees College, B
Winthrop University, M

South Dakota

Augustana College, M
Black Hills State University, M
Dakota State University, M
Dakota Wesleyan University, B
Mount Marty College, B
Northern State University, BM
Sinte Gleska University, AM
South Dakota State University, BM
University of Sioux Falls, BM
The University of South Dakota, BMDO

Tennessee

Austin Peay State University, MO
Belmont University, BM
Bethel College, BM
Bryan College, B
Carson-Newman College, BM
Christian Brothers University, B
Cumberland University, ABM
East Tennessee State University, MDO
Free Will Baptist Bible College, B
Freed-Hardeman University, BMO
Johnson Bible College, M
King College, B
Lambuth University, B
Lee University, BM
LeMoyne-Owen College, B
Lincoln Memorial University, BMO
Lipscomb University, BM
Martin Methodist College, A
Maryville College, B
Middle Tennessee State University, MDO
Milligan College, BM
Roane State Community College, A
Southern Adventist University, M
Tennessee State University, BMD
Tennessee Technological University, BMDO
Tennessee Temple University, M
Tennessee Wesleyan College, B
Trevecca Nazarene University, MD
Tusculum College, BM
Union University, BMDO
University of Memphis, MDO
The University of Tennessee, MDO
The University of Tennessee at Chattanooga, MDO
The University of Tennessee at Martin, M
Vanderbilt University, BMD
Walters State Community College, A

Texas

Abilene Christian University, MO
Angelo State University, M
Arlington Baptist College, B
Austin College, M
Baylor University, BMDO

Brazosport College, A
Cisco Junior College, A
Clarendon College, A
Coastal Bend College, A
Concordia University at Austin, M
Dallas Baptist University, BM
Dallas Christian College, B
Del Mar College, A
East Texas Baptist University, B
El Paso Community College, A
Frank Phillips College, A
Galveston College, A
Grayson County College, A
Hardin-Simmons University, BM
Hill College of the Hill Junior College District, A
Houston Baptist University, BM
Howard Payne University, B
Huston-Tillotson University, B
Kingwood College, A
Lamar University, ABMDO
Lee College, A
Lon Morris College, A
Lubbock Christian University, B
Midwestern State University, M
Navarro College, A
North Harris College, A
Northeast Texas Community College, A
Odessa College, A
Our Lady of the Lake University of San Antonio, MD
Palo Alto College, A
Paris Junior College, A
Paul Quinn College, B
Prairie View A&M University, MD
Rice University, M
St. Mary's University of San Antonio, BMO
St. Philip's College, A
Sam Houston State University, B
Schreiner University, BM
South Plains College, A
South Texas College, A
Southern Methodist University, M
Southwest Texas Junior College, A
Southwestern Adventist University, M
Southwestern Assemblies of God University, AMO
Stephen F. Austin State University, MD
Sul Ross State University, M
Tarleton State University, BMDO
Texas A&M International University, M
Texas A&M University, MD
Texas A&M University-Commerce, BMD
Texas A&M University-Corpus Christi, MD
Texas A&M University-Kingsville, BMD
Texas A&M University-Texarkana, M
Texas Christian University, MO
Texas Lutheran University, B
Texas Southern University, BMD
Texas State University-San Marcos, M
Texas Tech University, MDO
Texas Wesleyan University, BM
Texas Woman's University, MD
Trinity University, M
Trinity Valley Community College, A
University of Dallas, B
University of Houston, BMD
University of Houston-Clear Lake, M
University of Houston-Victoria, BM
University of the Incarnate Word, BM
University of Mary Hardin-Baylor, BM
University of North Texas, MDO
University of St. Thomas, BM
The University of Texas at Arlington, M
The University of Texas at Austin, MD
The University of Texas at Brownsville, M
The University of Texas at El Paso, MD
The University of Texas-Pan American, MD
The University of Texas of the Permian Basin, M
The University of Texas at San Antonio, M
The University of Texas at Tyler, M
Wayland Baptist University, ABM
West Texas A&M University, M

Western Texas College, A

United States Virgin Islands

University of the Virgin Islands, MO

Utah

Brigham Young University, BMDO
Snow College, A
Southern Utah University, BM
University of Phoenix-Utah Campus, M
University of Utah, BMDO
Utah State University, MDO
Weber State University, M
Western Governors University, MO
Westminster College, M

Vermont

Bennington College, BM
Castleton State College, MO
College of St. Joseph, BM
Community College of Vermont, A
Goddard College, M
Johnson State College, BM
Lyndon State College, M
Marlboro College, M
Saint Michael's College, BMO
Sterling College, B
University of Vermont, BMD

Virginia

Argosy University/Washington D.C., MD
Averett University, M
Bluefield College, B
Central Virginia Community College, A
Christopher Newport University, BM
The College of William and Mary, MDO
Dabney S. Lancaster Community College, A
Danville Community College, A
Eastern Mennonite University, M
Eastern Shore Community College, A
Ferrum College, B
George Mason University, MD
Germanna Community College, A
Hampton University, BM
Hollins University, BM
James Madison University, M
Liberty University, MDO
Longwood University, BM
Lord Fairfax Community College, A
Lynchburg College, BM
Mary Baldwin College, M
Marymount University, MO
Mountain Empire Community College, A
New River Community College, A
Norfolk State University, M
Old Dominion University, MDO
Paul D. Camp Community College, A
Piedmont Virginia Community College, A
Radford University, M
Regent University, MDO
Shenandoah University, M
Southside Virginia Community College, A
Southwest Virginia Community College, A
Tidewater Community College, A
University of Mary Washington, M
University of Virginia, MDO
Virginia Commonwealth University, MDO
Virginia Highlands Community College, A
Virginia Intermont College, B
Virginia State University, MO
Virginia Western Community College, A
Wytheville Community College, A

Washington

Antioch University Seattle, M
Argosy University/Seattle, MD
Central Washington University, M
City University, MO
Eastern Washington University, BM
Everett Community College, A
The Evergreen State College, M
Gonzaga University, MD
Heritage University, BM
Highline Community College, A
Northwest Indian College, A

Northwest University, B
Pacific Lutheran University, BM
Puget Sound Christian College, A
Saint Martin's University, BM
Seattle Pacific University, MD
Seattle University, MDO
Shoreline Community College, A
Tacoma Community College, A
University of Puget Sound, M
University of Washington, BMDO
University of Washington, Tacoma, B
Walla Walla College, M
Washington State University, BMD
Wenatchee Valley College, A
Western Washington University, BM
Whitworth College, M

West Virginia

Alderson-Broaddus College, B
Bethany College, B
Concord University, B
Fairmont State University, B
Glenville State College, B
Marshall University, MDO
Ohio Valley University, B
Potomac State College of West Virginia
    University, A
Salem International University, BM
University of Charleston, B
West Liberty State College, B
West Virginia State University, B
West Virginia University, MD
West Virginia University at Parkersburg, A
West Virginia Wesleyan College, B
Wheeling Jesuit University, B

Wisconsin

Alverno College, BM
Beloit College, B
Cardinal Stritch University, BMD
Carroll College, BM
Carthage College, MO
College of Menominee Nation, A
Concordia University Wisconsin, BM
Edgewood College, BMDO
Lakeland College, M
Maranatha Baptist Bible College, B
Marian College of Fond du Lac, BMD
Marquette University, BMDO
Mount Mary College, BM
Northland College, B
Ripon College, B
St. Norbert College, M
Silver Lake College, M
University of Wisconsin-Eau Claire, M
University of Wisconsin-Green Bay, M
University of Wisconsin-La Crosse, M
University of Wisconsin-Madison, MDO
University of Wisconsin-Milwaukee, BMDO
University of Wisconsin-Oshkosh, BM
University of Wisconsin-Platteville, BM
University of Wisconsin-River Falls, BM
University of Wisconsin-Stevens Point, BM
University of Wisconsin-Stout, M
University of Wisconsin-Superior, BM
University of Wisconsin-Whitewater, BM
Viterbo University, M

Wyoming

Casper College, A
Laramie County Community College, A
Northwest College, A
Sheridan College-Sheridan and Gillette, A
University of Wyoming, O
Western Wyoming Community College, A

Alberta

Athabasca University, MO
Concordia University College of Alberta, B
Prairie Bible Institute, B
Rocky Mountain College, B
Taylor University College and Seminary, A
University of Alberta, B
University of Calgary, B

University of Lethbridge, BMO

British Columbia

Malaspina University-College, B
Simon Fraser University, BMD
Trinity Western University, B
The University of British Columbia, BMDO
University of Northern British Columbia, M
University of Phoenix-Vancouver Campus, M
University of Victoria, BMD

Manitoba

Brandon University, BMO
Collège universitaire de Saint-Boniface, M
Providence College and Theological Seminary, B
University of Manitoba, BMD
The University of Winnipeg, B

New Brunswick

Atlantic Baptist University, B
St. Thomas University, B
Université de Moncton, BM
University of New Brunswick Fredericton, BM
University of New Brunswick Saint John, B

Newfoundland and Labrador

Memorial University of Newfoundland, BMDO

Nova Scotia

Acadia University, BM
Cape Breton University, O
Mount Saint Vincent University, BM
St. Francis Xavier University, BMO
Université Sainte-Anne, B

Ontario

Brock University, BMD
Lakehead University, BMD
Laurentian University, B
Nipissing University, BMO
Queen's University at Kingston, BMD
Redeemer University College, B
Trent University, B
University of Ottawa, BMDO
University of Toronto, BMD
University of Waterloo, M
The University of Western Ontario, BM
University of Windsor, BMD
York University, BMD

Prince Edward Island

University of Prince Edward Island, BM

Quebec

Bishop's University, BMO
Concordia University, MDO
McGill University, BMDO
Télé-université, B
Université Laval, MDO
Université de Montréal, BMDO
Université du Québec en
    Abitibi-Témiscamingue, BMD
Université du Québec àChicoutimi, MD
Université du Québec àMontréal, BMDO
Université du Québec en Outaouais, BMDO
Université du Québec àRimouski, MD
Université du Québec àTrois-Rivières, BMO
Université de Sherbrooke, BMO

Saskatchewan

University of Regina, BMDO
University of Saskatchewan, BMDO

EDUCATION/TEACHING OF INDIVIDUALS IN EARLY CHILDHOOD SPECIAL EDUCATION PROGRAMS

Alabama

Calhoun Community College, A

Arizona

Northland Pioneer College, A

Arkansas

Harding University, B

Delaware

Delaware State University, B

Iowa

University of Northern Iowa, B

Minnesota

Itasca Community College, A

New York

Canisius College, B
Cazenovia College, B
Keuka College, B
State University of New York College at Geneseo, B

Pennsylvania

Juniata College, B

Tennessee

Motlow State Community College, A

Texas

Northeast Texas Community College, A

Vermont

University of Vermont, B

Washington

Eastern Washington University, B
Olympic College, A

EDUCATION/TEACHING OF INDIVIDUALS WITH EMOTIONAL DISTURBANCES

Florida

Florida International University, B
Florida State University, B
University of South Florida, B

Illinois

Bradley University, B
Trinity Christian College, B

Iowa

Loras College, B

Maine

University of Maine at Farmington, B

Michigan

Central Michigan University, B
Eastern Michigan University, B
Hope College, B
Marygrove College, B
University of Detroit Mercy, B

Minnesota

Augsburg College, B
Minnesota State University Moorhead, B

North Carolina

East Carolina University, B
Greensboro College, B

The University of North Carolina Wilmington, B

Ohio

The University of Toledo, B
Wright State University, B

Oklahoma

Oklahoma Baptist University, B

South Carolina

Bob Jones University, B
Southern Wesleyan University, B

Virginia

Eastern Mennonite University, B

EDUCATION/TEACHING OF INDIVIDUALS WITH HEARING IMPAIRMENTS, INCLUDING DEAFNESS

Alabama

Bishop State Community College, A

Arkansas

University of Arkansas at Little Rock, B

Florida

Flagler College, B
North Florida Community College, A

Illinois

MacMurray College, B

Kentucky

Eastern Kentucky University, B

Massachusetts

Boston University, B

Michigan

Eastern Michigan University, B
Michigan State University, B

Mississippi

University of Southern Mississippi, B

Nebraska

University of Nebraska-Lincoln, B

New Jersey

The College of New Jersey, B

North Carolina

Barton College, B
The University of North Carolina at Greensboro, B

North Dakota

Minot State University, B

Ohio

Bowling Green State University, B
Ohio University-Chillicothe, A
The University of Toledo, B

Oklahoma

University of Science and Arts of Oklahoma, B

Pennsylvania

Indiana University of Pennsylvania, B

South Dakota

Augustana College, B

Tennessee

Lambuth University, B

Texas

Texas Christian University, B

EDUCATION/TEACHING OF INDIVIDUALS WITH MENTAL RETARDATION

Florida

Florida International University, B
Florida State University, B
University of South Florida, B
University of West Florida, B

Georgia

Augusta State University, B
University of West Georgia, B

Illinois

Bradley University, B
Trinity Christian College, B

Indiana

Oakland City University, B

Iowa

Loras College, B
University of Northern Iowa, B

Maine

University of Maine at Farmington, B

Michigan

Central Michigan University, B
Eastern Michigan University, B
Northern Michigan University, B
Western Michigan University, B

Minnesota

Minnesota State University Moorhead, B

North Carolina

East Carolina University, B
Greensboro College, B
Shaw University, B
The University of North Carolina at Charlotte, B
The University of North Carolina at Pembroke, B
The University of North Carolina Wilmington, B

North Dakota

Minot State University, B
University of Mary, B

Ohio

The University of Akron, B
University of Rio Grande, B
Wright State University, B

Oklahoma

Oklahoma Baptist University, B

South Carolina

Southern Wesleyan University, B

Virginia

Eastern Mennonite University, B

Wisconsin

Silver Lake College, B

Quebec

Université du Québec àTrois-Rivières, B

EDUCATION/TEACHING OF INDIVIDUALS WITH MULTIPLE DISABILITIES

Alabama

University of South Alabama, M

Arkansas

University of Arkansas at Little Rock, M

California

Fresno Pacific University, M

District of Columbia

Gallaudet University, MO

Georgia

Georgia State University, M

Illinois

University of Illinois at Urbana-Champaign, MDO

Iowa

University of Northern Iowa, B

Massachusetts

Boston College, M

Michigan

University of Detroit Mercy, B

Minnesota

Minnesota State University Mankato, M

New Jersey

Montclair State University, M

New York

Dominican College, B
Hunter College of the City University of New York, M

North Carolina

The University of North Carolina Wilmington, B

Ohio

Ohio University, B
The University of Akron, B
The University of Toledo, B
Wright State University, B

Oregon

Western Oregon University, M

Puerto Rico

Inter American University of Puerto Rico, Barranquitas Campus, AB

Virginia

Norfolk State University, M

West Virginia

West Virginia University, M

EDUCATION/TEACHING OF INDIVIDUALS WITH ORTHOPEDIC AND OTHER PHYSICAL HEALTH IMPAIRMENTS

Michigan

Eastern Michigan University, B

Ohio

Wright State University, B

Pennsylvania

Indiana University of Pennsylvania, B

EDUCATION/TEACHING OF INDIVIDUALS WITH SPECIFIC LEARNING DISABILITIES

Arkansas

Harding University, B

Florida

Bethune-Cookman College, B
Flagler College, B

Florida International University, B
Florida Southern College, B
Florida State University, B
University of South Florida, B

Illinois

Bradley University, B
Northwestern University, B
Trinity Christian College, B

Maine

University of Maine at Farmington, B

Michigan

Aquinas College, B
Eastern Michigan University, B
Hope College, B
Michigan State University, B
University of Detroit Mercy, B

Minnesota

Minnesota State University Moorhead, B

North Carolina

Appalachian State University, B
East Carolina University, B
Elizabeth City State University, B
Greensboro College, B
The University of North Carolina at Pembroke, B
The University of North Carolina Wilmington, B
Winston-Salem State University, B

Ohio

Baldwin-Wallace College, B
Malone College, B
Notre Dame College, B
The University of Akron, B
University of Rio Grande, B
The University of Toledo, B
Wright State University, B

Oklahoma

Oklahoma Baptist University, B

South Carolina

Bob Jones University, B
Southern Wesleyan University, B

Virginia

Eastern Mennonite University, B

West Virginia

West Virginia Wesleyan College, B
Wheeling Jesuit University, B

Wisconsin

Silver Lake College, B

EDUCATION/TEACHING OF INDIVIDUALS WITH SPEECH OR LANGUAGE IMPAIRMENTS

Alabama

Alabama Agricultural and Mechanical University, B

Arizona

Northern Arizona University, B

Kentucky

Eastern Kentucky University, B
Western Kentucky University, B

Louisiana

Louisiana Tech University, B
Southeastern Louisiana University, B

Massachusetts

Emerson College, B

Michigan

Eastern Michigan University, B

Wayne State University, B

Nebraska

University of Nebraska at Omaha, A

New Mexico

New Mexico State University, B

New York

Brooklyn College of the City University of New York, B
Buffalo State College, State University of New York, B
Ithaca College, B
Long Island University, Brooklyn Campus, B
New York University, B
Pace University, B
State University of New York College at Cortland, B

North Dakota

Minot State University, B

Ohio

The University of Akron, B
The University of Toledo, B

Pennsylvania

Bloomsburg University of Pennsylvania, B
Indiana University of Pennsylvania, B
Kutztown University of Pennsylvania, B

Texas

Baylor University, B

EDUCATION/TEACHING OF INDIVIDUALS WITH VISION IMPAIRMENTS, INCLUDING BLINDNESS

Alabama

Auburn University, B

Florida

Florida State University, B

Michigan

Eastern Michigan University, B
Western Michigan University, B

New York

St. Francis College, B

Ohio

The University of Toledo, B

Pennsylvania

Kutztown University of Pennsylvania, B

EDUCATION/TEACHING OF THE GIFTED AND TALENTED

Alabama

University of South Alabama, M

Arkansas

Arkansas Tech University, M
University of Arkansas at Little Rock, M

California

California State University, Northridge, M

Colorado

University of Northern Colorado, M

Connecticut

University of Connecticut, MD

Delaware

Wilmington College, M

Florida

Barry University, MDO
Carlos Albizu University, Miami Campus, M

Flagler College, B
Lynn University, M
Nova Southeastern University, M
Saint Leo University, M
University of South Florida, M
Warner Southern College, B

Georgia

Clark Atlanta University, MO
University of Georgia, D

Illinois

Northeastern Illinois University, M

Indiana

Purdue University, M

Kansas

Emporia State University, M

Louisiana

University of Louisiana at Lafayette, M

Maryland

The Johns Hopkins University, O

Michigan

Grand Valley State University, M

Minnesota

Minnesota State University Mankato, M
University of Minnesota, Twin Cities Campus, O

Mississippi

Mississippi University for Women, M
University of Southern Mississippi, MDO

Missouri

Drury University, M
Maryville University of Saint Louis, M
University of Missouri-Columbia, MD

Montana

University of Great Falls, B

New York

The College of New Rochelle, MO
Hofstra University, O

Ohio

Ashland University, M
Kent State University, M
Wright State University, BM
Youngstown State University, M

South Carolina

Converse College, M

Tennessee

Tennessee Technological University, D

Texas

Hardin-Simmons University, M
Texas A&M University, MD
Texas Christian University, B
University of Houston, M
The University of Texas-Pan American, M

Vermont

Johnson State College, M

Virginia

The College of William and Mary, M
Liberty University, M

Washington

Western Washington University, M
Whitworth College, M

West Virginia

West Virginia University, M

Wisconsin

Carthage College, M

Alberta

University of Calgary, MDO

EDUCATIONAL ADMINISTRATION AND SUPERVISION

Alabama

Alabama Agricultural and Mechanical University, M
Alabama State University, MDO
Auburn University, MDO
Auburn University Montgomery, MO
Jacksonville State University, MO
Samford University, MO
Troy University, MO
The University of Alabama, MD
University of Montevallo, MO
University of North Alabama, M
University of South Alabama, MO
The University of West Alabama, M

Arizona

Arizona State University, MD
Arizona State University West, M
Northern Arizona University, M
The University of Arizona, D
University of Phoenix Online Campus, M
University of Phoenix-Phoenix Campus, M

Arkansas

Arkansas State University, MO
Henderson State University, M
Philander Smith College, B
University of Arkansas, MDO
University of Arkansas at Little Rock, MDO

California

Azusa Pacific University, MD
California Lutheran University, M
California Polytechnic State University, San Luis
  Obispo, M
California State University, Bakersfield, M
California State University, Chico, M
California State University, Dominguez Hills, M
California State University, Fresno, M
California State University, Long Beach, M
California State University, Los Angeles, M
California State University, Northridge, M
California State University, Sacramento, M
California State University, San Bernardino, M
California State University, Stanislaus, M
Chapman University, M
Fresno Pacific University, M
La Sierra University, MDO
Loyola Marymount University, M
Mills College, D
Mount St. Mary's College, M
National University, M
Notre Dame de Namur University, MO
Saint Mary's College of California, MD
San Francisco State University, MO
San Jose State University, MO
Santa Clara University, M
Shasta Bible College, M
Simpson University, M
Sonoma State University, M
Stanford University, MD
University of California, Berkeley, MD
University of California, Irvine, D
University of La Verne, MO
University of the Pacific, MD
University of San Francisco, MD
University of Southern California, MD
Whittier College, M

Colorado

University of Colorado at Colorado Springs, M
University of Colorado at Denver and Health
  Sciences Center - Downtown Denver
  Campus, MO

University of Denver, D
University of Phoenix-Denver Campus, M
University of Phoenix-Southern Colorado
  Campus, MO

Connecticut

Sacred Heart University, O
University of Bridgeport, DO
University of Connecticut, MD

Delaware

Wilmington College, M

District of Columbia

American University, D
The Catholic University of America, MD
Gallaudet University, MDO
The George Washington University, MDO
Howard University, MDO
Trinity (Washington) University, M

Florida

Barry University, MD
Florida Agricultural and Mechanical University, MD
Florida Atlantic University, D
Florida International University, MD
Florida State University, MDO
Nova Southeastern University, M
St. Thomas University, MO
University of Florida, MDO
University of Miami, M
University of North Florida, M

Georgia

Albany State University, MO
Georgia College & State University, MO
Georgia Southern University, D
Georgia State University, MDO
North Georgia College & State University, O
University of Georgia, MO
University of West Georgia, MO

Guam

University of Guam, M

Hawaii

University of Hawaii at Manoa, MD
University of Phoenix-Hawaii Campus, M

Idaho

Idaho State University, MO
University of Idaho, MDO

Illinois

Aurora University, D
Benedictine University, M
Chicago State University, M
Concordia University, MO
DePaul University, M
Dominican University, M
Eastern Illinois University, MO
Governors State University, M
Illinois State University, MD
Kendall College, B
Lewis University, M
Loyola University Chicago, MD
National-Louis University, MO
Northeastern Illinois University, M
Northern Illinois University, MDO
Saint Xavier University, M
Southern Illinois University Carbondale, MD
Southern Illinois University Edwardsville, MO
University of Illinois at Chicago, MD
University of Illinois at Springfield, M
University of Illinois at Urbana-Champaign, MDO

Indiana

Ball State University, MDO
Butler University, M
Indiana State University, MDO
Indiana University Bloomington, MDO
Indiana University-Purdue University Fort Wayne, M
Indiana University South Bend, M
Purdue University, MDO

Purdue University Calumet, M

Iowa

Clarke College, M
Iowa State University of Science and Technology, M
Loras College, M
The University of Iowa, MDO
University of Northern Iowa, MD

Kansas

Benedictine College, M
Emporia State University, M
Fort Hays State University, MO
Kansas State University, M
University of Kansas, MD
Washburn University, M
Wichita State University, MDO

Kentucky

Eastern Kentucky University, M
Morehead State University, MO
Murray State University, MO
Spalding University, M
Union College, M
University of the Cumberlands, O
University of Kentucky, MDO
University of Louisville, MDO
Western Kentucky University, MO

Louisiana

Centenary College of Louisiana, M
Louisiana State University and Agricultural and
  Mechanical College, MDO
McNeese State University, MO
Nicholls State University, M
Northwestern State University of Louisiana, MO
Our Lady of Holy Cross College, M
Southeastern Louisiana University, M
Southern University and Agricultural and Mechanical
  College, M
University of Louisiana at Lafayette, M
University of Louisiana at Monroe, M
Xavier University of Louisiana, M

Maine

University of Southern Maine, O

Maryland

Bowie State University, M
Frostburg State University, M
The Johns Hopkins University, MO
Loyola College in Maryland, MO
McDaniel College, M
Morgan State University, MD
Salisbury University, M
University of Maryland, College Park, MD

Massachusetts

American International College, MO
Boston College, MDO
Boston University, MO
Bridgewater State College, MO
Eastern Nazarene College, MO
Emmanuel College, M
Fitchburg State College, MO
Lesley University, MO
Massachusetts College of Liberal Arts, M
Salem State College, M
Suffolk University, MO
University of Massachusetts Amherst, MDO
University of Massachusetts Boston, MDO
University of Massachusetts Lowell, MO
Westfield State College, MO
Worcester State College, M

Michigan

Andrews University, MDO
Central Michigan University, MDO
Ferris State University, M
Grand Valley State University, M
Michigan State University, MDO
Northern Michigan University, MO
Oakland University, O
Saginaw Valley State University, M
University of Detroit Mercy, M

University of Michigan, MDO
University of Michigan-Dearborn, O
University of Phoenix-Metro Detroit Campus, M
University of Phoenix-West Michigan Campus, M
Wayne State University, MDO

Minnesota

Bethel University, D
Minnesota State University Mankato, MO
Minnesota State University Moorhead, O
St. Cloud State University, M
Saint Mary's University of Minnesota, MO
University of Minnesota, Twin Cities Campus, MD
University of St. Thomas, MDO
Winona State University, M

Mississippi

Delta State University, MDO
Jackson State University, MDO
University of Southern Mississippi, MDO

Missouri

Central Missouri State University, MO
Lincoln University, M
Lindenwood University, M
Missouri State University, MO
Park University, M
Saint Louis University, M
Southeast Missouri State University, MO
Southwest Baptist University, MO
University of Missouri-Columbia, MDO
University of Missouri-Kansas City, D
University of Missouri-St. Louis, MDO
William Woods University, M

Montana

University of Great Falls, M
The University of Montana-Missoula, MDO

Nebraska

Chadron State College, MO
Concordia University, M
Creighton University, M
University of Nebraska at Kearney, MO
University of Nebraska-Lincoln, MDO
University of Nebraska at Omaha, MDO
Wayne State College, MO

Nevada

University of Nevada, Las Vegas, MDO
University of Phoenix-Nevada Campus, M

New Hampshire

Keene State College, MO
Plymouth State University, M
Rivier College, M
University of New Hampshire, MO

New Jersey

Caldwell College, M
The College of New Jersey, M
Georgian Court University, M
Kean University, MO
Monmouth University, MO
Montclair State University, M
New Jersey City University, M
Rider University, MO
Rowan University, M
Rutgers, The State University of New Jersey, New
  Brunswick/Piscataway, MD
Saint Peter's College, MO
Seton Hall University, MDO

New Mexico

College of the Southwest, M
New Mexico Highlands University, M
New Mexico State University, MD
University of New Mexico, MDO
University of Phoenix-New Mexico Campus, M
Western New Mexico University, M

New York

Bernard M. Baruch College of the City University of
  New York, MO

Canisius College, M
Cazenovia College, B
City College of the City University of New York, MO
The College of New Rochelle, MO
The College of Saint Rose, MO
Dowling College, DO
Fordham University, MDO
Hofstra University, MO
Hunter College of the City University of New
  York, O
Iona College, M
Le Moyne College, B
Long Island University, Brentwood Campus, M
Long Island University, C.W. Post Campus, MO
Manhattan College, MO
Mercy College, MO
New York University, M
Niagara University, MO
Pace University, MO
Queens College of the City University of New
  York, O
St. John Fisher College, M
St. John's University, MDO
St. Lawrence University, MO
State University of New York at Buffalo, MDO
State University of New York College at
  Brockport, MO
State University of New York, Fredonia, O
State University of New York at New Paltz, MO
State University of New York at Oswego, MO
State University of New York at Plattsburgh, O
Stony Brook University, State University of New
  York, O
University at Albany, State University of New
  York, MDO
Yeshiva University, MDO

North Carolina

Appalachian State University, M
Campbell University, M
East Carolina University, MDO
Fayetteville State University, M
Gardner-Webb University, M
North Carolina Agricultural and Technical State
  University, M
North Carolina State University, MD
The University of North Carolina at Chapel Hill, MD
The University of North Carolina at Charlotte, MO
The University of North Carolina at Greensboro, M
The University of North Carolina at Pembroke, M
The University of North Carolina Wilmington, M
Western Carolina University, M

North Dakota

North Dakota State University, MDO
University of Mary, M

Ohio

Antioch University McGregor, M
Ashland University, M
Baldwin-Wallace College, M
Bowling Green State University, MDO
Cleveland State University, MDO
Franciscan University of Steubenville, M
John Carroll University, M
Kent State University, MDO
Miami University, D
Ohio University, MD
The University of Akron, MD
University of Cincinnati, MO
University of Dayton, M
The University of Findlay, M
The University of Toledo, MDO
Ursuline College, M
Wright State University, MO
Xavier University, M
Youngstown State University, MD

Oklahoma

Northeastern State University, M
Oklahoma State University, M
Oral Roberts University, MD
Southeastern Oklahoma State University, M
Southwestern Oklahoma State University, M
University of Central Oklahoma, M

University of Oklahoma, MD

Oregon

Concordia University, M
Lewis & Clark College, MD
Portland State University, MD

Pennsylvania

Bucknell University, M
California University of Pennsylvania, M
Cheyney University of Pennsylvania, MO
Drexel University, O
Duquesne University, M
Edinboro University of Pennsylvania, MO
Gannon University, O
Geneva College, M
Gwynedd-Mercy College, M
Immaculata University, MDO
Indiana University of Pennsylvania, MDO
Kutztown University of Pennsylvania, M
Philadelphia Biblical University, M
Point Park University, M
Shippensburg University of Pennsylvania, M
Slippery Rock University of Pennsylvania, M
Temple University, MD
University of Pennsylvania, MD
The University of Scranton, M
Westminster College, MO
Widener University, MD

Puerto Rico

Bayamon Central University, M
Inter American University of Puerto Rico, Arecibo
  Campus, M
Inter American University of Puerto Rico,
  Metropolitan Campus, M
Inter American University of Puerto Rico, San
  Germán Campus, M
Universidad Metropolitana, M
Universidad del Turabo, M
University of Phoenix-Puerto Rico Campus, M
University of Puerto Rico, Río Piedras, MD

Rhode Island

Providence College, M
Rhode Island College, MO

South Carolina

Charleston Southern University, M
The Citadel, The Military College of South
  Carolina, MO
Clemson University, MO
Columbia International University, MD
Converse College, O
Furman University, M
South Carolina State University, MDO
University of South Carolina, MDO

South Dakota

Northern State University, M
Oglala Lakota College, M
South Dakota State University, M
The University of South Dakota, MDO

Tennessee

Austin Peay State University, O
Bethel College, M
Lincoln Memorial University, MO
Middle Tennessee State University, MO
Southern Adventist University, M
Tennessee State University, MD
Tennessee Temple University, M
Union University, O
University of Memphis, MDO
The University of Tennessee, MDO
The University of Tennessee at Chattanooga, M
The University of Tennessee at Martin, M
Vanderbilt University, MD

Texas

Abilene Christian University, MO
Angelo State University, M
Baylor University, MO
Houston Baptist University, M
Lamar University, MO

Midwestern State University, M
Our Lady of the Lake University of San Antonio, M
Prairie View A&M University, M
Sam Houston State University, M
Southwestern Assemblies of God University, M
Sul Ross State University, M
Tarleton State University, MO
Texas A&M International University, M
Texas A&M University, MD
Texas A&M University-Commerce, MD
Texas A&M University-Corpus Christi, M
Texas A&M University-Kingsville, MD
Texas A&M University-Texarkana, M
Texas Christian University, M
Texas Southern University, MD
Texas State University-San Marcos, M
Texas Tech University, O
Texas Woman's University, M
Trinity University, M
University of Houston, MD
University of Houston-Clear Lake, M
University of Mary Hardin-Baylor, M
University of North Texas, MD
The University of Texas at Arlington, M
The University of Texas at Austin, MD
The University of Texas at Brownsville, M
The University of Texas of the Permian Basin, M
West Texas A&M University, M

Utah

Western Governors University, O

Vermont

Saint Michael's College, MO
University of Vermont, M

Virginia

Liberty University, M
Longwood University, M
Norfolk State University, M
Old Dominion University, O
Shenandoah University, D
University of Virginia, MDO
Virginia Commonwealth University, MO
Virginia Polytechnic Institute and State
  University, DO
Virginia State University, M

Washington

Central Washington University, M
City University, MO
Eastern Washington University, M
Gonzaga University, M
Heritage University, M
Pacific Lutheran University, M
Seattle University, MO
University of Puget Sound, M
University of Washington, O
Western Washington University, M
Whitworth College, M

West Virginia

West Virginia University, MD

Wisconsin

Alverno College, M
Concordia University Wisconsin, M
Edgewood College, MO
Silver Lake College, M
University of Wisconsin-Madison, O
University of Wisconsin-Milwaukee, MO
University of Wisconsin-Stevens Point, M
University of Wisconsin-Superior, MO
University of Wisconsin-Whitewater, M

Alberta

Newman Theological College, O
University of Alberta, MDO
University of Calgary, D

British Columbia

Simon Fraser University, M
The University of British Columbia, M

University of Phoenix-Vancouver Campus, M

Manitoba

Brandon University, MO
University of Manitoba, M

New Brunswick

Université de Moncton, M
University of New Brunswick Fredericton, M

Ontario

Brock University, M
Lakehead University, M

Quebec

McGill University, M
Université Laval, MD
Université de Montréal, MDO
Université du Québec àTrois-Rivières, D
Université de Sherbrooke, M

Saskatchewan

University of Regina, MO
University of Saskatchewan, MDO

EDUCATIONAL, INSTRUCTIONAL, AND CURRICULUM SUPERVISION

Ohio

Wright State University, B

Vermont

Sterling College, B

EDUCATIONAL/INSTRUCTIONAL MEDIA DESIGN

Alabama

Community College of the Air Force, A
Jacksonville State University, B

California

California State University, Chico, B
City College of San Francisco, A

Illinois

Western Illinois University, B

Indiana

Ball State University, B
Indiana State University, B
Ivy Tech Community College-North Central, A

Kansas

Hutchinson Community College and Area Vocational
  School, A

Maine

University of Maine, B

Minnesota

Century College, A
Hibbing Community College, A
St. Cloud State University, B

Mississippi

Jackson State University, B
Virginia College at Jackson, A

Missouri

Lindenwood University, B

New Jersey

Brookdale Community College, A
County College of Morris, A

New York

Ithaca College, B

Ohio

Capital University, B
The University of Toledo, B

Oklahoma

University of Central Oklahoma, B

Oregon

Portland Community College, A
Western Oregon University, B

Pennsylvania

Kutztown University of Pennsylvania, B
Seton Hill University, B
Widener University, B

Puerto Rico

Bayamon Central University, AB

Texas

Collin County Community College District, A
Tarrant County College District, A
Texas State Technical College Waco, A
University of Houston-Clear Lake, B

Vermont

Norwich University, B

Washington

Bellevue Community College, A

Wisconsin

Milwaukee Area Technical College, A

EDUCATIONAL LEADERSHIP AND ADMINISTRATION

Alabama

Alabama State University, MDO
Community College of the Air Force, A
Samford University, D
The University of Alabama, MDO
The University of Alabama at Birmingham, MDO
University of Montevallo, O
University of North Alabama, O

Alaska

University of Alaska Anchorage, M

Arizona

Argosy University/Phoenix, DO
Arizona State University, D
Northern Arizona University, BMD

Arkansas

Arkansas State University, MDO
Arkansas Tech University, M
Harding University, BMO
Henderson State University, MO
University of Arkansas at Monticello, M
University of Central Arkansas, O

California

Argosy University/Orange County, MD
Argosy University/San Francisco Bay Area, MD
Azusa Pacific University, M
Bethany University, M
California Baptist University, M
California State University, East Bay, M
California State University, Fresno, D
California State University, Fullerton, M
Chapman University, M
Loyola Marymount University, D
San Diego State University, M
Shasta Bible College, A
Touro University International, MD
University of California, Berkeley, D
University of California, Los Angeles, B
University of California, Santa Barbara, D
University of La Verne, D
University of San Diego, MDO
University of San Francisco, B

University of Southern California, M

Colorado

Jones International University, M
University of Colorado at Colorado Springs, M
University of Colorado at Denver and Health
  Sciences Center - Downtown Denver Campus, D
University of Northern Colorado, MDO

Connecticut

Central Connecticut State University, MDO
Southern Connecticut State University, DO
University of Hartford, MDO
Western Connecticut State University, D

Delaware

University of Delaware, MD
Wilmington College, MD

District of Columbia

American University, M
The Catholic University of America, M
Gallaudet University, M
The George Washington University, MO

Florida

Argosy University/Sarasota, MDO
Argosy University/Tampa, MDO
Barry University, MDO
Florida Agricultural and Mechanical University, D
Florida Atlantic University, MDO
Florida Gulf Coast University, M
Florida International University, MO
Lynn University, MD
Nova Southeastern University, MDO
Saint Leo University, M
St. Thomas University, D
Stetson University, MO
University of Central Florida, MDO
University of North Florida, MD
University of South Florida, MDO
University of West Florida, MO

Georgia

Argosy University/Atlanta, D
Augusta State University, MO
Clark Atlanta University, MDO
Columbus State University, MO
Georgia Southern University, MO
Kennesaw State University, M
Mercer University, M
North Georgia College & State University, B
University of West Georgia, MO
Valdosta State University, MDO

Guam

University of Guam, M

Hawaii

Argosy University/Hawaii, MD

Idaho

Idaho State University, DO
Northwest Nazarene University, M

Illinois

Argosy University/Schaumburg, MDO
Aurora University, M
Benedictine University, M
Bradley University, M
Concordia University, D
DePaul University, MD
Elmhurst College, M
Eureka College, B
Kendall College, B
Lewis University, M
Loyola University Chicago, M
National-Louis University, MD
North Central College, M
Northeastern Illinois University, M
Roosevelt University, MD
Trinity International University, M
University of St. Francis, M

Western Illinois University, MO

Indiana

Indiana University Bloomington, D
Oakland City University, D

Iowa

Drake University, MDO
Iowa State University of Science and
  Technology, MD

Kansas

Friends University, M
Newman University, M
Pittsburg State University, M
University of Kansas, D

Kentucky

Eastern Kentucky University, M
Northern Kentucky University, M
Spalding University, D
Union College, O
University of Louisville, D

Louisiana

Grambling State University, D
Louisiana State University and Agricultural and
  Mechanical College, MDO
Louisiana Tech University, D
McNeese State University, B
University of Louisiana at Monroe, D
University of New Orleans, MDO

Maine

University of Maine, MDO
University of New England, O
University of Southern Maine, MO

Maryland

Bowie State University, D
College of Notre Dame of Maryland, M
Hood College, M
The Johns Hopkins University, MDO
Morgan State University, D
Towson University, O
University of Maryland, College Park, MDO
University of Maryland Eastern Shore, D

Massachusetts

Emmanuel College, O
Framingham State College, M
Harvard University, MD
Simmons College, MO
Suffolk University, O
University of Massachusetts Boston, D
University of Massachusetts Lowell, D
Wheelock College, M

Michigan

Andrews University, MDO
Central Michigan University, D
Eastern Michigan University, MDO
Ferris State University, M
Grand Valley State University, M
Madonna University, M
Marygrove College, M
Oakland University, MDO
Saginaw Valley State University, MO
Wayne State University, MDO
Western Michigan University, MDO

Minnesota

Minnesota State University Mankato, MO
Minnesota State University Moorhead, MO
St. Cloud State University, B
Saint Mary's University of Minnesota, D
Southwest Minnesota State University, M
University of Minnesota, Twin Cities Campus, M
Winona State University, MO

Mississippi

Mississippi College, M
Mississippi State University, M

University of Mississippi, MDO

Missouri

Evangel University, M
Lincoln University, O
Lindenwood University, B
Northwest Missouri State University, BMO
Saint Louis University, MDO
University of Missouri-St. Louis, D
Webster University, O

Nebraska

Doane College, M

Nevada

University of Nevada, Las Vegas, M
University of Nevada, Reno, MDO

New Hampshire

Keene State College, BO
New England College, M
Plymouth State University, M
Rivier College, O
University of New Hampshire, M

New Jersey

Centenary College, M
The College of New Jersey, M
College of Saint Elizabeth, M
Fairleigh Dickinson University, College at
  Florham, M
Fairleigh Dickinson University, Metropolitan
  Campus, M
Kean University, M
Rider University, BO
Rowan University, D
Seton Hall University, DO
William Paterson University of New Jersey, M

New Mexico

New Mexico Highlands University, M

New York

Adelphi University, MO
Brooklyn College of the City University of New
  York, O
Buffalo State College, State University of New
  York, O
College of Staten Island of the City University of
  New York, O
Hofstra University, DO
Long Island University, Brooklyn Campus, M
Manhattanville College, M
New York Institute of Technology, O
New York University, MDO
St. Bonaventure University, MO
St. John's University, BDO
State University of New York College at Cortland, O
Syracuse University, MDO

North Carolina

Appalachian State University, D
Campbell University, B
East Carolina University, MDO
Fayetteville State University, D
High Point University, M
North Carolina Central University, M
The University of North Carolina at Chapel Hill, D
The University of North Carolina at Charlotte, MDO
The University of North Carolina at
  Greensboro, MDO
Western Carolina University, DO

North Dakota

Jamestown College, B
University of North Dakota, MDO

Ohio

Ashland University, MD
Baldwin-Wallace College, B
Bowling Green State University, D
Central State University, M
Cleveland State University, BD
Kent State University, MDO

Miami University, M
The Ohio State University, MD
Ohio University, B
Ohio University-Eastern, B
University of Cincinnati, D
University of Dayton, MD
The University of Findlay, M
Wright State University, BMO
Youngstown State University, D

Oklahoma

Cameron University, M
Oklahoma State University, MD
Oral Roberts University, B
Southeastern Oklahoma State University, M
University of Central Oklahoma, B

Oregon

George Fox University, MD
University of Oregon, B

Pennsylvania

Arcadia University, MO
Cabrini College, O
Carlow University, M
Chestnut Hill College, M
Delaware Valley College, M
Drexel University, D
Duquesne University, D
Edinboro University of Pennsylvania, M
Gannon University, MO
Geneva College, M
Lehigh University, MDO
Marywood University, M
Mercyhurst College, O
The Pennsylvania State University University Park
    Campus, MD
Robert Morris University, MD
Saint Francis University, M
Saint Joseph's University, D
University of Pennsylvania, MD
University of Pittsburgh, MD
Villanova University, M
Widener University, MD
Wilkes University, M

Puerto Rico

Caribbean University, B

Rhode Island

Johnson & Wales University, D

South Carolina

Charleston Southern University, B
Clemson University, D
Converse College, M
Winthrop University, M

South Dakota

University of Sioux Falls, M

Tennessee

Austin Peay State University, M
East Tennessee State University, MDO
Freed-Hardeman University, O
Lee University, M
Tennessee State University, B
Tennessee Technological University, MO
Trevecca Nazarene University, M
Union University, DO
University of Memphis, MD
The University of Tennessee, D
The University of Tennessee at Chattanooga, D
Vanderbilt University, D

Texas

Dallas Baptist University, M
Lamar University, BD
Our Lady of the Lake University of San Antonio, D
Prairie View A&M University, MD
St. Mary's University of San Antonio, MO
Sam Houston State University, D
Stephen F. Austin State University, MD
Tarleton State University, BD
Texas A&M University-Corpus Christi, D

Texas Christian University, BO
Texas Southern University, B
Texas Tech University, MDO
University of Houston-Clear Lake, B
The University of Texas at El Paso, MD
The University of Texas-Pan American, MD
The University of Texas at San Antonio, MD
The University of Texas at Tyler, M

Utah

Brigham Young University, MDO
University of Utah, MDO

Vermont

Castleton State College, MO
Sterling College, B
University of Vermont, MD

Virginia

Argosy University/Washington D.C., MD
The College of William and Mary, MD
George Mason University, M
James Madison University, M
Liberty University, D
Lynchburg College, M
Marymount University, MO
Norfolk State University, M
Old Dominion University, MDO
Radford University, M
Shenandoah University, D
University of Northern Virginia, M
Virginia Polytechnic Institute and State
    University, MDO

Washington

Argosy University/Seattle, MD
City University, M
Eastern Washington University, M
Gonzaga University, D
Seattle Pacific University, MD
Seattle University, D
University of Washington, MD
Walla Walla College, M
Washington State University, MD
Western Washington University, B

West Virginia

Marshall University, MDO
West Virginia University, MD

Wisconsin

Alverno College, M
Cardinal Stritch University, MD
Carthage College, M
Edgewood College, D
Marian College of Fond du Lac, MD
Silver Lake College, M
University of Wisconsin-Madison, MDO
University of Wisconsin-Oshkosh, M
University of Wisconsin-Superior, B

Wyoming

University of Wyoming, MDO

Alberta

University of Alberta, MDO
University of Calgary, MDO
University of Lethbridge, B

British Columbia

Royal Roads University, M
Trinity Western University, M
The University of British Columbia, BD

University of Victoria, M

Newfoundland and Labrador

Memorial University of Newfoundland, M

Nova Scotia

Acadia University, M

Ontario

University of Windsor, B

Prince Edward Island

University of Prince Edward Island, M

Quebec

McGill University, O
Université Laval, O

EDUCATIONAL MEASUREMENT AND EVALUATION

California

Stanford University, M
University of California, Berkeley, MD

Colorado

University of Colorado at Boulder, D
University of Northern Colorado, MD

Connecticut

Southern Connecticut State University, M
University of Connecticut, MD

District of Columbia

Gallaudet University, O

Florida

Florida State University, MD
University of Florida, MDO
University of Miami, MD
University of South Florida, MDO

Georgia

Georgia State University, MD
University of West Georgia, D

Illinois

Loyola University Chicago, MD
Southern Illinois University Carbondale, D

Iowa

Iowa State University of Science and Technology, M
The University of Iowa, MD

Kansas

University of Kansas, MD

Kentucky

University of Kentucky, MD
University of Louisville, M

Louisiana

Louisiana State University and Agricultural and
    Mechanical College, D

Maryland

University of Maryland, College Park, MD

Massachusetts

Boston College, MD
University of Massachusetts Amherst, MDO

Michigan

Michigan State University, D
University of Michigan, D
Wayne State University, MD

Western Michigan University, MD

Minnesota

University of Minnesota, Twin Cities Campus, MDO

Mississippi

Mississippi College, M

Missouri

University of Missouri-St. Louis, DO
Washington University in St. Louis, D

Nevada

University of Nevada, Las Vegas, D

New Jersey

Rutgers, The State University of New Jersey, New
Brunswick/Piscataway, M

New Mexico

College of the Southwest, M

New York

Hofstra University, M
Syracuse University, MDO
University at Albany, State University of New
York, D

North Carolina

North Carolina State University, D
The University of North Carolina at Chapel Hill, MD
The University of North Carolina at Greensboro, MD

North Dakota

University of North Dakota, D

Ohio

Kent State University, MD
Ohio University, MD
The University of Toledo, D

Oklahoma

Southwestern Oklahoma State University, M

Pennsylvania

Bucknell University, M
University of Pennsylvania, MD
University of Pittsburgh, MD
West Chester University of Pennsylvania, M
Wilkes University, M

Puerto Rico

University of Puerto Rico, Río Piedras, M

South Carolina

University of South Carolina, MD

Tennessee

University of Memphis, MD
The University of Tennessee, D
Vanderbilt University, MD

Texas

Abilene Christian University, M
Angelo State University, M
Houston Baptist University, M
Sul Ross State University, M
Texas A&M University, MD
Texas Christian University, M
Texas Southern University, D
University of North Texas, D
The University of Texas-Pan American, M
West Texas A&M University, M

Utah

Utah State University, D

Virginia

George Mason University, M
University of Virginia, MD

Virginia Polytechnic Institute and State University, D

Washington

Seattle University, O
University of Washington, MD

Alberta

University of Calgary, MDO

British Columbia

The University of British Columbia, MD

Quebec

Université Laval, MD

EDUCATIONAL MEDIA/INSTRUCTIONAL TECHNOLOGY

Alabama

Alabama State University, MO
Auburn University, M
Jacksonville State University, M
University of South Alabama, MD
The University of West Alabama, M

Alaska

University of Alaska Southeast, M

Arizona

Arizona State University, MD
Northern Arizona University, MO
University of Phoenix Online Campus, M
University of Phoenix-Phoenix Campus, M

Arkansas

University of Arkansas, M
University of Arkansas at Little Rock, M
University of Central Arkansas, M

California

Argosy University/San Francisco Bay Area, M
Azusa Pacific University, M
California Baptist University, M
California State University, Chico, M
California State University, Fullerton, M
California State University, Los Angeles, M
California State University, San Bernardino, M
California State University, Stanislaus, M
Fresno Pacific University, M
National University, M
Notre Dame de Namur University, MO
San Diego State University, MD
San Francisco State University, MO
San Jose State University, MO
Touro University International, D
University of Phoenix-Sacramento Valley
Campus, M
University of Phoenix-San Diego Campus, M
University of Phoenix-Southern California
Campus, M
University of San Francisco, M
University of Southern California, M

Colorado

Jones International University, M
Regis University, O
University of Colorado at Denver and Health
Sciences Center - Downtown Denver Campus, M
University of Northern Colorado, MD
University of Phoenix-Denver Campus, M

Connecticut

Central Connecticut State University, M
Eastern Connecticut State University, M
Fairfield University, MO
Southern Connecticut State University, M
University of Connecticut, MD
University of Hartford, M

Western Connecticut State University, M

Delaware

Wilmington College, M

District of Columbia

American University, M
Gallaudet University, O
The George Washington University, M

Florida

American InterContinental University, M
Barry University, MDO
Florida Atlantic University, M
Florida Gulf Coast University, M
Florida State University, MDO
Jacksonville University, M
Nova Southeastern University, MDO
University of Central Florida, MDO
University of Florida, MD
University of Phoenix-Central Florida Campus, M
University of Phoenix-South Florida Campus, M
University of Phoenix-West Florida Campus, M
University of South Florida, MD
University of West Florida, M

Georgia

Georgia College & State University, M
Georgia Southern University, MO
Georgia State University, MDO
University of Georgia, MDO
University of West Georgia, MO

Hawaii

University of Hawaii at Manoa, M
University of Phoenix-Hawaii Campus, M

Idaho

Boise State University, M
Idaho State University, M

Illinois

American InterContinental University Online, M
Chicago State University, M
DePaul University, MD
Governors State University, M
National-Louis University, MO
Northern Illinois University, MD
Northwestern University, MD
Southern Illinois University Edwardsville, M
Western Illinois University, MO

Indiana

Indiana State University, MD
Indiana University Bloomington, MDO
Purdue University, MDO
Purdue University Calumet, M

Iowa

Clarke College, M
Iowa State University of Science and
Technology, MD
University of Northern Iowa, M

Kansas

Emporia State University, M
Fort Hays State University, M
MidAmerica Nazarene University, M
Pittsburg State University, M

Kentucky

University of Louisville, M
Western Kentucky University, M

Louisiana

Louisiana State University and Agricultural and
Mechanical College, M
McNeese State University, M
Northwestern State University of Louisiana, MO

Southern University and Agricultural and Mechanical College, M

Maine

University of Maine, M

Maryland

Frostburg State University, M
The Johns Hopkins University, MO
Loyola College in Maryland, M
McDaniel College, M
Salisbury University, M
Towson University, MD
University of Maryland, Baltimore County, MO
University of Maryland, College Park, MD

Massachusetts

Boston University, MDO
Bridgewater State College, M
Framingham State College, M
Harvard University, M
Salem State College, M
Simmons College, MO
University of Massachusetts Amherst, MDO
Westfield State College, M

Michigan

Central Michigan University, M
Ferris State University, M
Grand Valley State University, M
Michigan State University, MD
Oakland University, O
Saginaw Valley State University, M
University of Michigan, D
Wayne State University, MDO

Minnesota

The College of St. Scholastica, M
Minnesota State University Mankato, MO
St. Cloud State University, M
University of Minnesota, Twin Cities Campus, MDO

Mississippi

Mississippi State University, MDO
Mississippi University for Women, M

Missouri

Central Missouri State University, M
Lindenwood University, M
Missouri State University, M
Northwest Missouri State University, M
University of Missouri-Columbia, MDO
Webster University, M

Montana

Montana State University-Billings, M

Nebraska

University of Nebraska at Kearney, M
University of Nebraska at Omaha, O
Wayne State College, M

Nevada

University of Nevada, Las Vegas, M

New Jersey

The College of New Jersey, MO
College of Saint Elizabeth, M
Fairleigh Dickinson University, College at Florham, O
Fairleigh Dickinson University, Metropolitan Campus, O
Georgian Court University, MO
Kean University, M
New Jersey City University, M
The Richard Stockton College of New Jersey, M
Rowan University, M

Seton Hall University, MO

New Mexico

University of New Mexico, MDO

New York

Adelphi University, MO
Buffalo State College, State University of New York, M
College of Mount Saint Vincent, O
The College of Saint Rose, MO
Hofstra University, M
Iona College, MO
Long Island University, Brooklyn Campus, M
Long Island University, C.W. Post Campus, M
Mercy College, M
Nazareth College of Rochester, M
New York Institute of Technology, MO
New York University, MDO
Rochester Institute of Technology, M
State University of New York College at Potsdam, M
Stony Brook University, State University of New York, MO
Syracuse University, MO
University at Albany, State University of New York, MO

North Carolina

Appalachian State University, MO
East Carolina University, MO
North Carolina Agricultural and Technical State University, M
North Carolina Central University, M
North Carolina State University, MD
The University of North Carolina at Charlotte, M
The University of North Carolina Wilmington, M

North Dakota

University of North Dakota, M

Ohio

Baldwin-Wallace College, M
Bowling Green State University, M
Central State University, M
Kent State University, M
Lourdes College, M
Malone College, M
Ohio University, D
The University of Akron, M
University of Dayton, M
The University of Findlay, M
The University of Toledo, DO

Oklahoma

Southeastern Oklahoma State University, M
University of Central Oklahoma, M

Oregon

Portland State University, M
Western Oregon University, M

Pennsylvania

Arcadia University, M
Bloomsburg University of Pennsylvania, M
Cabrini College, M
Chestnut Hill College, MO
DeSales University, O
Drexel University, DO
Duquesne University, MD
East Stroudsburg University of Pennsylvania, M
Gannon University, MO
Indiana University of Pennsylvania, M
Kutztown University of Pennsylvania, MO
Lehigh University, MD
Marywood University, M
The Pennsylvania State University University Park Campus, MD
Philadelphia University, M
Robert Morris University, DO
Rosemont College, M
Saint Joseph's University, M
Saint Vincent College, M
Seton Hill University, M
West Chester University of Pennsylvania, O
Widener University, M

Wilkes University, M

Puerto Rico

Inter American University of Puerto Rico, Metropolitan Campus, M
Pontifical Catholic University of Puerto Rico, M
University of the Sacred Heart, M

South Carolina

Coastal Carolina University, M
University of South Carolina, M
University of South Carolina Aiken, M

South Dakota

Dakota State University, M
Northern State University, M
University of Sioux Falls, M
The University of South Dakota, MO

Tennessee

Belmont University, M
East Tennessee State University, M
Johnson Bible College, M
University of Memphis, MD
The University of Tennessee, MDO
The University of Tennessee at Chattanooga, O

Texas

Lamar University, O
Our Lady of the Lake University of San Antonio, M
Texas A&M University, M
Texas A&M University-Commerce, M
Texas A&M University-Corpus Christi, M
Texas Southern University, M
Texas Tech University, MD
University of Houston-Clear Lake, M
University of the Incarnate Word, M
The University of Texas at Brownsville, M
The University of Texas at San Antonio, M
West Texas A&M University, M

Utah

Brigham Young University, MD
University of Phoenix-Utah Campus, M
Utah State University, MDO
Western Governors University, MO

Vermont

Saint Michael's College, MO

Virginia

The College of William and Mary, D
George Mason University, M
Longwood University, M
Old Dominion University, MD
Radford University, M
University of Northern Virginia, M
Virginia Polytechnic Institute and State University, MDO

Washington

City University, M
Eastern Washington University, M

Wisconsin

Alverno College, M

Wyoming

University of Wyoming, MDO

Alberta

University of Alberta, M
University of Calgary, MDO

British Columbia

Royal Roads University, M

Newfoundland and Labrador

Memorial University of Newfoundland, M

Nova Scotia

Acadia University, M
Cape Breton University, O

Quebec

Concordia University, MDO
Université Laval, MD

EDUCATIONAL PSYCHOLOGY

Alabama

Auburn University, D
Jacksonville State University, B

Arizona

Arizona State University, MD
Northern Arizona University, D
The University of Arizona, MD
University of Phoenix-Southern Arizona Campus, M

California

California State University, Long Beach, M
California State University, Northridge, MO
California State University, San Bernardino, M
Chapman University, MO
Holy Names University, M
La Sierra University, MO
Loyola Marymount University, M
Stanford University, D
University of California, Berkeley, D
University of California, Davis, D
University of the Pacific, MDO
University of Southern California, D

Colorado

University of Colorado at Boulder, MD
University of Colorado at Denver and Health
    Sciences Center - Downtown Denver Campus, M
University of Denver, MDO
University of Northern Colorado, MD

Connecticut

University of Connecticut, MD

District of Columbia

The Catholic University of America, BD
Howard University, MDO

Florida

Florida Atlantic University, M
Florida State University, MD
University of Florida, MDO

Georgia

Clark Atlanta University, MD
Georgia State University, MD
University of Georgia, MDO

Hawaii

University of Hawaii at Manoa, MD

Illinois

Loyola University Chicago, MD
National-Louis University, MDO
Northern Illinois University, MDO
Southern Illinois University Carbondale, MD
University of Illinois at Chicago, D
University of Illinois at Urbana-Champaign, MDO

Indiana

Ball State University, MDO
Indiana State University, MDO
Indiana University Bloomington, MD
Purdue University, MD

Iowa

The University of Iowa, MD
University of Northern Iowa, MO

Kansas

Kansas State University, MD
University of Kansas, MD

Wichita State University, M

Kentucky

Lindsey Wilson College, M
University of Kentucky, MDO
University of Louisville, MD

Maryland

University of Maryland, College Park, MD

Massachusetts

American International College, MD
Boston College, MD
Harvard University, M
Northeastern University, M

Michigan

Andrews University, MD
Eastern Michigan University, M
Wayne State University, MDO

Minnesota

University of Minnesota, Twin Cities Campus, MDO

Mississippi

Alcorn State University, B
Mississippi State University, BMDO

Missouri

University of Missouri-Columbia, MDO
University of Missouri-St. Louis, DO

Nebraska

University of Nebraska-Lincoln, MO
University of Nebraska at Omaha, M

Nevada

University of Nevada, Las Vegas, MD
University of Nevada, Reno, MDO

New Jersey

Georgian Court University, O
Kean University, M
Montclair State University, M
New Jersey City University, MO
Rutgers, The State University of New Jersey, New
    Brunswick/Piscataway, MD

New Mexico

University of New Mexico, MD

New York

The College of Saint Rose, M
Cornell University, B
Fordham University, MDO
Marist College, M
New York University, MDO
State University of New York at Buffalo, MDO
State University of New York College at
    Oneonta, MO
University at Albany, State University of New
    York, MDO

North Carolina

The University of North Carolina at Chapel Hill, MD

Ohio

John Carroll University, M
Kent State University, MD
Miami University, MO
The University of Toledo, MD

Oklahoma

Oklahoma State University, MD
University of Oklahoma, MD

Pennsylvania

Arcadia University, O
Eastern University, M
Edinboro University of Pennsylvania, M
Indiana University of Pennsylvania, MO
The Pennsylvania State University University Park
    Campus, MD

Temple University, MD
University of Pennsylvania, MD
University of Pittsburgh, B
Widener University, M

South Carolina

University of South Carolina, MD

South Dakota

The University of South Dakota, MDO

Tennessee

Tennessee Technological University, MO
University of Memphis, MD
The University of Tennessee, MD

Texas

Baylor University, MDO
Texas A&M University, MD
Texas A&M University-Commerce, D
Texas Christian University, O
Texas Tech University, MDO
University of Houston, MD
University of Mary Hardin-Baylor, M
The University of Texas at Austin, MD
The University of Texas-Pan American, M
The University of Texas at San Antonio, M

Utah

Brigham Young University, MD
University of Utah, MD

Vermont

Johnson State College, M

Virginia

Marymount University, B
Shenandoah University, B
University of Virginia, MDO

Washington

University of Washington, MD

West Virginia

West Virginia University, MD

Wisconsin

University of Wisconsin-Madison, MD
University of Wisconsin-Milwaukee, MO

Alberta

University of Alberta, MD
University of Calgary, MD

British Columbia

Simon Fraser University, MD
University of Victoria, MD

Manitoba

University of Manitoba, M

New Brunswick

Université de Moncton, M
University of New Brunswick Fredericton, M

Newfoundland and Labrador

Memorial University of Newfoundland, M

Nova Scotia

Mount Saint Vincent University, M

Ontario

The University of Western Ontario, M

Quebec

McGill University, MD
Université Laval, MD
Université de Montréal, MDO
Université du Québec en Outaouais, M

Université du Québec àTrois-Rivières, M

Saskatchewan

University of Regina, BMDO
University of Saskatchewan, MDO

EDUCATIONAL STATISTICS AND RESEARCH METHODS

Pennsylvania

Bucknell University, B

ELECTRICAL AND ELECTRONIC ENGINEERING TECHNOLOGIES/TECHNICIANS

Florida

Embry-Riddle Aeronautical University, B
Miami Dade College, A

Georgia

Albany Technical College, A
Southern Polytechnic State University, B

Idaho

Boise State University, A

Illinois

Southern Illinois University Carbondale, B

Kentucky

Louisville Technical Institute, A

Massachusetts

Fitchburg State College, B
Massasoit Community College, A
Springfield Technical Community College, A

Michigan

Lawrence Technological University, A
Southwestern Michigan College, A

Minnesota

Minnesota State Community and Technical
College-Fergus Falls, A

Missouri

Pinnacle Career Institute, A

New York

Eugenio María de Hostos Community College of the
City University of New York, A
Mohawk Valley Community College, A
New York Institute of Technology, AB

North Carolina

Western Carolina University, B

Ohio

Cincinnati State Technical and Community
College, A
Columbus State Community College, A
Miami University Hamilton, A

Oklahoma

Vatterott College (Oklahoma City), A

Pennsylvania

Grove City College, B
Pennsylvania College of Technology, AB

Puerto Rico

Caribbean University, B

South Carolina

York Technical College, A

South Dakota

Mitchell Technical Institute, A

Texas

Lamar State College-Port Arthur, A

Virginia

Old Dominion University, B

West Virginia

Fairmont State Community & Technical College, A
West Virginia State Community and Technical
College, A

British Columbia

Open Learning Agency, B

ELECTRICAL AND POWER TRANSMISSION INSTALLATION/INSTALLER

California

Orange Coast College, A

Indiana

Ivy Tech Community College-Columbus, A

Kansas

Johnson County Community College, A

Massachusetts

Benjamin Franklin Institute of Technology, A

Minnesota

Dunwoody College of Technology, A
St. Cloud Technical College, A

Nevada

Western Nevada Community College, A

New York

State University of New York College of Technology
at Delhi, A

North Carolina

Wake Technical Community College, A

Oklahoma

Oklahoma State University, Oklahoma City, A

South Dakota

Mitchell Technical Institute, A

Washington

Bates Technical College, A

Wisconsin

Moraine Park Technical College, A

British Columbia

British Columbia Institute of Technology, A

ELECTRICAL AND POWER TRANSMISSION INSTALLERS

Alabama

Calhoun Community College, A

Kansas

Manhattan Area Technical College, A

Missouri

Vatterott College (St. Ann), A

North Carolina

Martin Community College, A

ELECTRICAL, ELECTRONIC AND COMMUNICATIONS ENGINEERING TECHNOLOGY/TECHNICIAN

Alabama

Bishop State Community College, A
Calhoun Community College, A

Central Alabama Community College, A
Community College of the Air Force, A
Gadsden State Community College-Ayers
Campus, A
George C. Wallace Community College, A
George Corley Wallace State Community College, A
H. Councill Trenholm State Technical College, A
Herzing College, AB
J. F. Drake State Technical College, A
Jacksonville State University, B
Lawson State Community College, A
Northeast Alabama Community College, A
Northwest-Shoals Community College, A
Reid State Technical College, A
Shelton State Community College, A
Wallace State Community College, A

Alaska

University of Alaska Anchorage, A
University of Alaska Anchorage, Kenai Peninsula
College, A
University of Alaska Anchorage, Matanuska-Susitna
College, A

Arizona

Arizona Western College, A
Cochise College (Douglas), A
Cochise College (Sierra Vista), A
DeVry University (Phoenix), AB
Glendale Community College, A
ITT Technical Institute (Phoenix), AB
ITT Technical Institute (Tempe), AB
ITT Technical Institute (Tucson), AB
Mesa Community College, A
Northland Pioneer College, A
Pima Community College, A
Scottsdale Community College, A

Arkansas

Arkansas State University, A
Arkansas State University-Beebe, A
ITT Technical Institute, A
National Park Community College, A
North Arkansas College, A
NorthWest Arkansas Community College, A
Southeast Arkansas College, A
University of Arkansas at Little Rock, AB

California

Allan Hancock College, A
American River College, A
Antelope Valley College, A
Bakersfield College, A
Barstow College, A
Butte College, A
Cabrillo College, A
California State Polytechnic University, Pomona, B
California State University, Long Beach, B
Cerritos College, A
Chabot College, A
Chaffey College, A
Citrus College, A
City College of San Francisco, A
Cogswell Polytechnical College, B
College of the Canyons, A
College of Marin, A
College of the Redwoods, A
College of San Mateo, A
College of the Sequoias, A
Compton Community College, A
Contra Costa College, A
Cosumnes River College (Sacramento), A
Cuesta College, A
DeVry University (Fremont), AB
DeVry University (Long Beach), AB
DeVry University (Pomona), AB
DeVry University (West Hills), AB
Don Bosco Technical Institute, A
East Los Angeles College, A
El Camino College, A
Evergreen Valley College, A
Foothill College, A
Golden West College, A
Hartnell College, A
Heald College-Concord, A
Heald College-Fresno, A

Heald College-Roseville, A
Heald College-San Francisco, A
Heald College-San Jose, A
ITT Technical Institute (Anaheim), AB
ITT Technical Institute (Lathrop), AB
ITT Technical Institute (Oxnard), AB
ITT Technical Institute (Rancho Cordova), AB
ITT Technical Institute (San Bernardino), AB
ITT Technical Institute (San Diego), AB
ITT Technical Institute (Sylmar), AB
ITT Technical Institute (Torrance), AB
ITT Technical Institute (West Covina), AB
Las Positas College, A
Long Beach City College, A
Los Angeles City College, A
Los Angeles Harbor College, A
Los Angeles Pierce College, A
Los Angeles Southwest College, A
Los Angeles Trade-Technical College, A
Los Angeles Valley College, A
Los Medanos College, A
Mendocino College, A
Merced College, A
Mission College, A
Modesto Junior College, A
Moorpark College, A
Mt. San Antonio College, A
Napa Valley College, A
Ohlone College, A
Orange Coast College, A
Oxnard College, A
Pacific Union College, B
Palomar College, A
Pasadena City College, A
Sacramento City College, A
Saddleback College, A
San Bernardino Valley College, A
San Diego City College, A
San Joaquin Delta College, A
San Jose City College, A
Santa Ana College, A
Santa Barbara City College, A
Santa Monica College, A
Santa Rosa Junior College, A
Shasta College, A
Sierra College, A
Solano Community College, A
Southern California Institute of Technology, AB
Southwestern College, A
Taft College, A
University of California, Santa Barbara, B
Victor Valley College, A
West Los Angeles College, A
Yuba College, A

Colorado

Aims Community College, A
Arapahoe Community College, A
Colorado Technical University, AB
DeVry University (Colorado Springs), A
DeVry University (Westminster), AB
IntelliTec College (Colorado Springs), A
IntelliTec College (Grand Junction), A
ITT Technical Institute, AB
Mesa State College, A
Metropolitan State College of Denver, B
Pikes Peak Community College, A
Pueblo Community College, A
Red Rocks Community College, A
Westwood College-Denver North, AB
Westwood College-Denver South, B

Connecticut

Capital Community College, A
Gateway Community College, A
Naugatuck Valley Community College, A
Northwestern Connecticut Community College, A
Norwalk Community College, A
Three Rivers Community College, A
University of Hartford, AB

Delaware

Delaware State University, B
Delaware Technical & Community College, Jack F. Owens Campus, A

Delaware Technical & Community College, Stanton/Wilmington Campus, A
Delaware Technical & Community College, Terry Campus, A

District of Columbia

University of the District of Columbia, A

Florida

ATI Career Training Center (Fort Lauderdale), A
Brevard Community College, A
Broward Community College, A
Daytona Beach Community College, A
DeVry University (Miramar), AB
DeVry University (Orlando), AB
Edison College, A
Florida Agricultural and Mechanical University, B
Florida Community College at Jacksonville, A
Florida Technical College (Jacksonville), A
Florida Technical College (Orlando), A
Gulf Coast Community College, A
Hillsborough Community College, A
Indian River Community College, A
ITT Technical Institute (Fort Lauderdale), AB
ITT Technical Institute (Jacksonville), AB
ITT Technical Institute (Lake Mary), AB
ITT Technical Institute (Miami), AB
ITT Technical Institute (Tampa), AB
Lake City Community College, A
Manatee Community College, A
Miami Dade College, A
New England Institute of Technology at Palm Beach, A
Okaloosa-Walton College, A
Palm Beach Community College, A
Pensacola Junior College, A
Remington College-Tampa Campus, A
St. Johns River Community College, A
St. Petersburg College, A
Santa Fe Community College, A
Seminole Community College, A
South Florida Community College, A
University of Central Florida, B
Valencia Community College, A

Georgia

Athens Technical College, A
Augusta Technical College, A
Bainbridge College, A
Central Georgia Technical College, A
Chattahoochee Technical College, A
Clayton State University, A
Columbus Technical College, A
Dalton State College, A
DeKalb Technical College, A
DeVry University (Alpharetta), AB
DeVry University (Decatur), AB
Flint River Technical College, A
Fort Valley State University, AB
Georgia Highlands College, A
Georgia Southern University, B
Griffin Technical College, A
Gwinnett Technical College, A
Heart of Georgia Technical College, A
Herzing College, AB
ITT Technical Institute (Duluth), AB
ITT Technical Institute (Kennesaw), A
Lanier Technical College, A
Moultrie Technical College, A
North Metro Technical College, A
Northwestern Technical College, A
Savannah State University, B
Savannah Technical College, A
South Georgia Technical College, A
Southeastern Technical College, A
Southern Polytechnic State University, B
Swainsboro Technical College, A
Waycross College, A
West Central Technical College, A

West Georgia Technical College, A

Guam

Guam Community College, A

Hawaii

Hawaii Community College, A
Heald College-Honolulu, A
Honolulu Community College, A
Kauai Community College, A

Idaho

Boise State University, A
Brigham Young University -Idaho, A
College of Southern Idaho, A
Eastern Idaho Technical College, A
Idaho State University, A
ITT Technical Institute, AB
North Idaho College, A

Illinois

Bradley University, B
Carl Sandburg College, A
City Colleges of Chicago, Olive-Harvey College, A
City Colleges of Chicago, Richard J. Daley College, A
College of DuPage, A
College of Lake County, A
Danville Area Community College, A
DeVry University (Addison), AB
DeVry University (Chicago), AB
DeVry University (Tinley Park), AB
East-West University, B
Elgin Community College, A
Heartland Community College, A
Highland Community College, A
Illinois Central College, A
Illinois Eastern Community Colleges, Wabash Valley College, A
Illinois Valley Community College, A
ITT Technical Institute (Burr Ridge), A
ITT Technical Institute (Matteson), A
ITT Technical Institute (Mount Prospect), AB
John A. Logan College, A
John Wood Community College, A
Joliet Junior College, A
Kankakee Community College, A
Kaskaskia College, A
Lake Land College, A
Lincoln Land Community College, A
McHenry County College, A
Oakton Community College, A
Prairie State College, A
Richland Community College, A
Rock Valley College, A
Roosevelt University, B
Sauk Valley Community College, A
Shawnee Community College, A
South Suburban College, A
Southeastern Illinois College, A
Southwestern Illinois College, A
Spoon River College, A
Triton College, A
Waubonsee Community College, A
William Rainey Harper College, A

Indiana

DeVry University (Indianapolis), A
Indiana State University, AB
Indiana University-Purdue University Fort Wayne, AB
Indiana University-Purdue University Indianapolis, AB
ITT Technical Institute (Fort Wayne), AB
ITT Technical Institute (Indianapolis), AB
ITT Technical Institute (Newburgh), AB
Ivy Tech Community College-Bloomington, A
Ivy Tech Community College-Central Indiana, A
Ivy Tech Community College-Columbus, A
Ivy Tech Community College-East Central, A
Ivy Tech Community College-Kokomo, A
Ivy Tech Community College-Lafayette, A
Ivy Tech Community College-North Central, A
Ivy Tech Community College-Northeast, A
Ivy Tech Community College-Northwest, A

Ivy Tech Community College-Southeast, A
Ivy Tech Community College-Southern Indiana, A
Ivy Tech Community College-Southwest, A
Ivy Tech Community College-Wabash Valley, A
Ivy Tech Community College-Whitewater, A
Purdue University, AB
Purdue University Calumet, AB
Purdue University North Central, A
Vincennes University, A

Iowa

Clinton Community College, A
Des Moines Area Community College, A
Hamilton Technical College, AB
Indian Hills Community College, A
Iowa Central Community College, A
Iowa Western Community College, A
Kirkwood Community College, A
Marshalltown Community College, A
North Iowa Area Community College, A
Northeast Iowa Community College, A
Northwest Iowa Community College, A
Southeastern Community College, North Campus, A
Western Iowa Tech Community College, A

Kansas

Allen County Community College, A
Butler Community College, A
Dodge City Community College, A
Fort Scott Community College, A
Garden City Community College, A
Independence Community College, A
Neosho County Community College, A
Pittsburg State University, AB

Kentucky

Eastern Kentucky University, A
Henderson Community College, A
Hopkinsville Community College, A
ITT Technical Institute (Lexington), AB
ITT Technical Institute (Louisville), A
Jefferson Community and Technical College, A
Kentucky State University, A
Lexington Community College, A
Louisville Technical Institute, A
Madisonville Community College, A
Maysville Community and Technical College, A
Northern Kentucky University, B
Owensboro Community and Technical College, A
Paducah Technical College, A
Somerset Community College, A
Spencerian College-Lexington, A
West Kentucky Community and Technical College, A

Louisiana

Bossier Parish Community College, A
Delgado Community College, A
Elaine P. Nunez Community College, A
Grambling State University, B
ITI Technical College, A
ITT Technical Institute, AB
Louisiana Tech University, B
McNeese State University, AB
Northwestern State University of Louisiana, AB
Remington College-Lafayette Campus, A
Southern University and Agricultural and Mechanical College, B
Southern University at Shreveport, A

Maine

Eastern Maine Community College, A
Northern Maine Community College, A
Southern Maine Community College, A
University of Maine, B

Maryland

Anne Arundel Community College, A
Baltimore City Community College, A
Capitol College, AB
Cecil Community College, A
Chesapeake College, A
College of Southern Maryland, A
Frederick Community College, A
Howard Community College, A
ITT Technical Institute, AB

Montgomery College, A
Prince George's Community College, A
University of Maryland Eastern Shore, B
Wor-Wic Community College, A

Massachusetts

Benjamin Franklin Institute of Technology, A
Berkshire Community College, A
Bristol Community College, A
ITT Technical Institute (Norwood), A
ITT Technical Institute (Woburn), A
Massasoit Community College, A
Merrimack College, A
Middlesex Community College, A
Mount Wachusett Community College, A
Northern Essex Community College, A
Quinsigamond Community College, A
Springfield Technical Community College, A
University of Massachusetts Dartmouth, B
University of Massachusetts Lowell, AB
Wentworth Institute of Technology, AB

Michigan

Andrews University, AB
Baker College of Cadillac, A
Baker College of Muskegon, AB
Baker College of Owosso, AB
Bay de Noc Community College, A
Central Michigan University, B
Davenport University (Dearborn), A
Davenport University (Midland), A
Eastern Michigan University, B
Ferris State University, B
Grand Rapids Community College, A
Henry Ford Community College, A
ITT Technical Institute (Canton), A
ITT Technical Institute (Grand Rapids), A
ITT Technical Institute (Troy), A
Jackson Community College, A
Kalamazoo Valley Community College, A
Lake Michigan College, A
Lake Superior State University, AB
Lansing Community College, A
Lawrence Technological University, A
Macomb Community College, A
Michigan Technological University, AB
Monroe County Community College, A
Montcalm Community College, A
Mott Community College, A
Muskegon Community College, A
Northern Michigan University, AB
Northwestern Michigan College, A
Oakland Community College, A
St. Clair County Community College, A
Schoolcraft College, A
Washtenaw Community College, A
Wayne County Community College District, A
Wayne State University, B
West Shore Community College, A

Minnesota

Anoka Technical College, A
Brown College, A
Dunwoody College of Technology, A
Hennepin Technical College, A
ITT Technical Institute, AB
Lake Superior College, A
Minnesota State College-Southeast Technical, A
Minnesota State Community and Technical College-Fergus Falls, A
Minnesota State University Mankato, B
Normandale Community College, A
Northland Community and Technical College-Thief River Falls, A
Northwest Technical College, A
Ridgewater College, A
Rochester Community and Technical College, A
St. Cloud State University, B
St. Cloud Technical College, A
Saint Paul College-A Community & Technical College, A

Mississippi

Copiah-Lincoln Community College, A
East Central Community College, A
East Mississippi Community College, A

Hinds Community College, A
Itawamba Community College, A
Jones County Junior College, A
Meridian Community College, A
Mississippi Delta Community College, A
Mississippi Gulf Coast Community College, A
Northeast Mississippi Community College, A
Northwest Mississippi Community College, A
Pearl River Community College, A
Southwest Mississippi Community College, A
University of Southern Mississippi, B

Missouri

Central Missouri State University, B
Crowder College, A
DeVry University (Kansas City), AB
East Central College, A
Grantham University, AB
ITT Technical Institute (Arnold), AB
ITT Technical Institute (Earth City), AB
ITT Technical Institute (Kansas City), A
Jefferson College, A
Linn State Technical College, A
Metropolitan Community College-Business & Technology College, A
Mineral Area College, A
Missouri Tech, A
Missouri Western State University, AB
Moberly Area Community College, A
North Central Missouri College, A
Ozarks Technical Community College, A
Ranken Technical College, A
St. Louis Community College at Florissant Valley, A
St. Louis Community College at Forest Park, A
St. Louis Community College at Meramec, A
State Fair Community College, A
Vatterott College (St. Ann), A

Montana

Fort Peck Community College, A
Miles Community College, A
Montana State University-Northern, AB
The University of Montana-Helena College of Technology, A
The University of Montana-Missoula, A

Nebraska

Central Community College-Columbus Campus, A
Central Community College-Grand Island Campus, A
Central Community College-Hastings Campus, A
ITT Technical Institute, AB
Metropolitan Community College, A
Mid-Plains Community College, A
Northeast Community College, A
Southeast Community College, Lincoln Campus, A
Southeast Community College, Milford Campus, A
University of Nebraska-Lincoln, B

Nevada

Career College of Northern Nevada, A
Community College of Southern Nevada, A
DeVry University, A
Great Basin College, A
ITT Technical Institute, AB
Truckee Meadows Community College, A
Western Nevada Community College, A

New Hampshire

Keene State College, AB
New Hampshire Community Technical College, Nashua/Claremont, A
New Hampshire Technical Institute, A
University of New Hampshire at Manchester, B

New Jersey

Bergen Community College, A
Brookdale Community College, A
Burlington County College, A
Camden County College, A
County College of Morris, A
DeVry University, AB
Essex County College, A
Fairleigh Dickinson University, Metropolitan Campus, B

Hudson County Community College, A
Mercer County Community College, A
Middlesex County College, A
Ocean County College, A
Passaic County Community College, A
Raritan Valley Community College, A

New Mexico

Central New Mexico Community College, A
Doña Ana Branch Community College, A
ITT Technical Institute, AB
Luna Community College, A
New Mexico State University-Alamogordo, A
New Mexico State University-Carlsbad, A
New Mexico State University-Grants, A
Northern New Mexico Community College, A
Santa Fe Community College, A
Southwestern Indian Polytechnic Institute, A
University of New Mexico-Los Alamos Branch, A

New York

Adirondack Community College, A
Bramson ORT College, A
Briarcliffe College, A
Bronx Community College of the City University of
   New York, A
Broome Community College, A
Bryant and Stratton College, North Campus, A
Buffalo State College, State University of New
   York, B
Cayuga County Community College, A
Clinton Community College, A
Corning Community College, A
DeVry Institute of Technology, AB
Dutchess Community College, A
Erie Community College, North Campus, A
Excelsior College, AB
Farmingdale State University of New York, B
Fulton-Montgomery Community College, A
Genesee Community College, A
Hudson Valley Community College, A
Island Drafting and Technical Institute, A
ITT Technical Institute (Albany), A
ITT Technical Institute (Getzville), A
Jamestown Community College, A
Mohawk Valley Community College, A
Monroe Community College, A
New York City College of Technology of the City
   University of New York, A
New York Institute of Technology, B
Niagara County Community College, A
Onondaga Community College, A
Orange County Community College, A
Queensborough Community College of the City
   University of New York, A
Rochester Institute of Technology, AB
Rockland Community College, A
Schenectady County Community College, A
State University of New York College of Agriculture
   and Technology at Morrisville, A
State University of New York College of Technology
   at Alfred, AB
State University of New York College of Technology
   at Canton, A
State University of New York Institute of
   Technology, B
Suffolk County Community College, A
Sullivan County Community College, A
TCI-The College of Technology, A
Tompkins Cortland Community College, A
Westchester Community College, A

North Carolina

Alamance Community College, A
Appalachian State University, B
Beaufort County Community College, A
Bladen Community College, A
Blue Ridge Community College, A
Brunswick Community College, A
Caldwell Community College and Technical
   Institute, A
Cape Fear Community College, A
Catawba Valley Community College, A
Central Carolina Community College, A
Central Piedmont Community College, A
Cleveland Community College, A

Craven Community College, A
Davidson County Community College, A
Durham Technical Community College, A
East Carolina University, B
Edgecombe Community College, A
Fayetteville Technical Community College, A
Forsyth Technical Community College, A
Gaston College, A
Guilford Technical Community College, A
Isothermal Community College, A
Johnston Community College, A
Lenoir Community College, A
Mayland Community College, A
McDowell Technical Community College, A
Mitchell Community College, A
Nash Community College, A
Pamlico Community College, A
Piedmont Community College, A
Pitt Community College, A
Richmond Community College, A
Roanoke-Chowan Community College, A
Robeson Community College, A
Rowan-Cabarrus Community College, A
South Piedmont Community College, A
Southeastern Community College, A
Southwestern Community College, A
Stanly Community College, A
Surry Community College, A
Tri-County Community College, A
The University of North Carolina at Charlotte, B
Vance-Granville Community College, A
Wake Technical Community College, A
Wayne Community College, A
Western Carolina University, B
Western Piedmont Community College, A
Wilkes Community College, A
Wilson Technical Community College, A

North Dakota

North Dakota State College of Science, A

Ohio

Belmont Technical College, A
Bowling Green State University, B
Bowling Green State University-Firelands College, A
Bryant and Stratton College (Cleveland), AB
Central Ohio Technical College, A
Cincinnati State Technical and Community
   College, A
Clark State Community College, A
Cleveland State University, B
Columbus State Community College, A
DeVry University (Columbus), AB
Edison State Community College, A
ETI Technical College of Niles, A
Hocking College, A
ITT Technical Institute (Dayton), A
ITT Technical Institute (Hilliard), A
ITT Technical Institute (Norwood), A
ITT Technical Institute (Strongsville), A
ITT Technical Institute (Warrensville Heights), A
James A. Rhodes State College, A
Jefferson Community College, A
Kent State University, Ashtabula Campus, A
Kent State University, Trumbull Campus, A
Kent State University, Tuscarawas Campus, A
Lakeland Community College, A
Lorain County Community College, A
Marion Technical College, A
Miami University-Middletown Campus, A
North Central State College, A
Northwest State Community College, A
Ohio University, A
Ohio University-Lancaster, A
Owens Community College, A
RETS Tech Center, A
Sinclair Community College, A
The University of Akron, AB
University of Cincinnati, AB
University of Cincinnati Clermont College, A
University of Dayton, B
The University of Toledo, AB
Washington State Community College, A
Wright State University, A
Wright State University, Lake Campus, A
Youngstown State University, AB

Zane State College, A

Oklahoma

Cameron University, AB
East Central University, B
Eastern Oklahoma State College, A
ITT Technical Institute, AB
Langston University, A
Murray State College, A
Northeastern Oklahoma Agricultural and Mechanical
   College, A
Northeastern State University, B
Oklahoma City Community College, A
Oklahoma State University, B
Oklahoma State University, Oklahoma City, A
Oklahoma State University, Okmulgee, A
Redlands Community College, A
Rose State College, A
Spartan College of Aeronautics and Technology, A
Tulsa Community College, A
Vatterott College (Tulsa), A

Oregon

Blue Mountain Community College, A
Chemeketa Community College, A
ITT Technical Institute, AB
Lane Community College, A
Mt. Hood Community College, A
Oregon Institute of Technology, AB
Portland Community College, A
Rogue Community College, A
Umpqua Community College, A

Pennsylvania

Berean Institute, A
Butler County Community College, A
California University of Pennsylvania, B
CHI Institute, A
CHI Institute, RETS Campus, A
Community College of Allegheny County, A
Community College of Beaver County, A
Community College of Philadelphia, A
Delaware County Community College, A
DeVry University (Fort Washington), B
Edinboro University of Pennsylvania, B
Erie Institute of Technology, A
Harrisburg Area Community College, A
Johnson College, A
Lehigh Carbon Community College, A
Lincoln Technical Institute (Allentown), A
Luzerne County Community College, A
Montgomery County Community College, A
New Castle School of Trades, A
Northampton County Area Community College, A
Penn Foster Career School, A
Pennco Tech, A
Pennsylvania College of Technology, A
Pennsylvania Highland Community College, A
Pennsylvania Institute of Technology, A
The Pennsylvania State University Abington
   College, A
The Pennsylvania State University Altoona
   College, A
The Pennsylvania State University Berks Campus of
   the Berks-Lehigh Valley College, A
The Pennsylvania State University Delaware County
   Campus of the Commonwealth College, A
The Pennsylvania State University DuBois Campus
   of the Commonwealth College, A
The Pennsylvania State University at Erie, The
   Behrend College, AB
The Pennsylvania State University Fayette Campus
   of the Commonwealth College, A
The Pennsylvania State University Hazleton
   Campus of the Commonwealth College, A
The Pennsylvania State University New Kensington
   Campus of the Commonwealth College, A
The Pennsylvania State University Schuylkill
   Campus of the Capital College, A
The Pennsylvania State University Shenango
   Campus of the Commonwealth College, A
The Pennsylvania State University Wilkes-Barre
   Campus of the Commonwealth College, A
The Pennsylvania State University Worthington
   Scranton Campus of the Commonwealth
   College, A

The Pennsylvania State University York Campus of
the Commonwealth College, A
Pittsburgh Institute of Aeronautics, A
Point Park University, AB
Reading Area Community College, A
Schuylkill Institute of Business and Technology, A
Thaddeus Stevens College of Technology, A
Thompson Institute, A
Triangle Tech, Inc.-DuBois School, A
Triangle Tech, Inc.-Erie School, A
Triangle Tech, Inc.-Pittsburgh School, A
University of Pittsburgh at Johnstown, B
Westmoreland County Community College, A
The Williamson Free School of Mechanical
Trades, A

Puerto Rico

Columbia College (Caguas), A
Electronic Data Processing College of Puerto
Rico, A
Inter American University of Puerto Rico, Aguadilla
Campus, B
Inter American University of Puerto Rico, Bayamón
Campus, B
Inter American University of Puerto Rico, San
Germán Campus, B
Technological College of San Juan, A
University of Puerto Rico, Aguadilla University
College, AB
University of Puerto Rico at Bayamón, AB
University of Puerto Rico at Humacao, A

Rhode Island

Community College of Rhode Island, A
Johnson & Wales University, AB
New England Institute of Technology, AB

South Carolina

Aiken Technical College, A
Florence-Darlington Technical College, A
Greenville Technical College, A
Horry-Georgetown Technical College, A
ITT Technical Institute, AB
Midlands Technical College, A
Northeastern Technical College, A
Orangeburg-Calhoun Technical College, A
Piedmont Technical College, A
South Carolina State University, B
Spartanburg Technical College, A
Technical College of the Lowcountry, A
Tri-County Technical College, A
Trident Technical College, A
York Technical College, A

South Dakota

Lake Area Technical Institute, A
Mitchell Technical Institute, A
Northern State University, AB
Oglala Lakota College, A
Sisseton-Wahpeton Community College, A
South Dakota State University, B
Southeast Technical Institute, A
Western Dakota Technical Institute, A

Tennessee

Chattanooga State Technical Community College, A
Columbia State Community College, A
Dyersburg State Community College, A
Fountainhead College of Technology, A
ITT Technical Institute (Knoxville), AB
ITT Technical Institute (Memphis), AB
ITT Technical Institute (Nashville), AB
Nashville State Technical Community College, A
Northeast State Technical Community College, A
Pellissippi State Technical Community College, A
Remington College-Memphis Campus, A
Southwest Tennessee Community College, A
University of Memphis, B

Texas

Alvin Community College, A
Amarillo College, A
Angelina College, A
Austin Community College, A
Brazosport College, A

Central Texas College, A
Cisco Junior College, A
Collin County Community College District, A
Del Mar College, A
DeVry University (Houston), AB
DeVry University (Irving), AB
Eastfield College, A
El Paso Community College, A
Frank Phillips College, A
Grayson County College, A
Hallmark Institute of Technology, A
Hill College of the Hill Junior College District, A
Houston Community College System, A
ITT Technical Institute (Arlington), A
ITT Technical Institute (Austin), A
ITT Technical Institute (Houston), A
ITT Technical Institute (Houston), A
ITT Technical Institute (Houston), A
ITT Technical Institute (Richardson), A
ITT Technical Institute (San Antonio), A
Kilgore College, A
Lamar State College-Port Arthur, A
Lamar University, A
Laredo Community College, A
Lee College, A
LeTourneau University, B
Midland College, A
Montgomery College, A
Mountain View College, A
North Central Texas College, A
North Harris College, A
North Lake College, A
Odessa College, A
Paris Junior College, A
Prairie View A&M University, B
Richland College, A
Sam Houston State University, B
San Antonio College, A
South Plains College, A
Tarrant County College District, A
Temple College, A
Texarkana College, A
Texas A&M University, B
Texas Southern University, B
Texas Southmost College, A
Texas State Technical College Harlingen, A
Texas State Technical College Waco, A
Texas State Technical College West Texas, A
Texas Tech University, B
Tomball College, A
Tyler Junior College, A
University of North Texas, B
The University of Texas at Brownsville, B
Victoria College, A
Wharton County Junior College, A

Utah

ITT Technical Institute, AB
Salt Lake Community College, A
Snow College, A
Southern Utah University, AB
Utah Valley State College, A
Weber State University, AB

Vermont

Vermont Technical College, A

Virginia

Blue Ridge Community College, A
Central Virginia Community College, A
Dabney S. Lancaster Community College, A
DeVry University (Arlington), AB
Eastern Shore Community College, A
ECPI College of Technology (Newport News), A
ECPI College of Technology (Virginia Beach), A
ECPI Technical College (Richmond), A
ECPI Technical College (Roanoke), A
Hampton University, B
ITT Technical Institute (Chantilly), AB
ITT Technical Institute (Norfolk), AB
ITT Technical Institute (Richmond), AB
ITT Technical Institute (Springfield), AB
J. Sargeant Reynolds Community College, A
Mountain Empire Community College, A
New River Community College, A
Norfolk State University, B

Northern Virginia Community College, A
Patrick Henry Community College, A
Southside Virginia Community College, A
Southwest Virginia Community College, A
Thomas Nelson Community College, A
Tidewater Community College, A
Virginia Highlands Community College, A
Virginia Western Community College, A
World College, B
Wytheville Community College, A

Washington

Bates Technical College, A
Central Washington University, B
Centralia College, A
Clark College, A
Columbia Basin College, A
DeVry University (Federal Way), AB
Eastern Washington University, B
Edmonds Community College, A
ITT Technical Institute (Bothell), AB
ITT Technical Institute (Seattle), AB
ITT Technical Institute (Spokane), AB
Lake Washington Technical College, A
Lower Columbia College, A
North Seattle Community College, A
Olympic College, A
Peninsula College, A
Pierce College, A
Renton Technical College, A
Skagit Valley College, A
South Puget Sound Community College, A
Spokane Community College, A
Western Washington University, B
Yakima Valley Community College, A

West Virginia

Bluefield State College, AB
Community & Technical College at West Virginia
University Institute of Technology, A
Fairmont State Community & Technical College, A
Fairmont State University, AB
Marshall Community and Technical College, A
National Institute of Technology, A
Potomac State College of West Virginia
University, A
West Virginia Northern Community College, A
West Virginia State University, A
West Virginia University at Parkersburg, A

Wisconsin

Blackhawk Technical College, A
Chippewa Valley Technical College, A
Fox Valley Technical College, A
Gateway Technical College, A
Herzing College, AB
ITT Technical Institute (Green Bay), AB
ITT Technical Institute (Greenfield), AB
Lakeshore Technical College, A
Madison Area Technical College, A
Mid-State Technical College, A
Milwaukee Area Technical College, A
Northcentral Technical College, A
Northeast Wisconsin Technical College, A
Southwest Wisconsin Technical College, A
Waukesha County Technical College, A
Western Technical College, A

Wyoming

Casper College, A
Western Wyoming Community College, A

British Columbia

British Columbia Institute of Technology, AB

Ontario

Lakehead University, B

Saskatchewan

University of Regina, B

ELECTRICAL, ELECTRONICS AND COMMUNICATIONS ENGINEERING

Alabama

Alabama Agricultural and Mechanical University, B
Auburn University, B
Tuskegee University, B
The University of Alabama, B
The University of Alabama at Birmingham, B
The University of Alabama in Huntsville, B
University of South Alabama, B

Alaska

University of Alaska Fairbanks, B

Arizona

Arizona State University, B
Embry-Riddle Aeronautical University, B
Northern Arizona University, B
The University of Arizona, B

Arkansas

John Brown University, B
University of Arkansas, B

California

California Institute of Technology, B
California Polytechnic State University, San Luis Obispo, B
California State Polytechnic University, Pomona, B
California State University, Chico, B
California State University, Fresno, B
California State University, Fullerton, B
California State University, Long Beach, B
California State University, Los Angeles, B
California State University, Sacramento, B
Cogswell Polytechnical College, B
Loyola Marymount University, B
Northwestern Polytechnic University, B
Pacific States University, B
San Diego State University, B
San Francisco State University, B
San Jose State University, B
Santa Clara University, B
Southern California Institute of Technology, AB
Stanford University, B
University of California, Berkeley, B
University of California, Davis, B
University of California, Irvine, B
University of California, Los Angeles, B
University of California, Riverside, B
University of California, San Diego, B
University of California, Santa Barbara, B
University of California, Santa Cruz, B
University of the Pacific, B
University of San Diego, B
University of Southern California, B

Colorado

Colorado School of Mines, B
Colorado State University, B
Colorado Technical University, B
United States Air Force Academy, B
University of Colorado at Boulder, B
University of Colorado at Colorado Springs, B
University of Colorado at Denver and Health Sciences Center - Downtown Denver Campus, B
University of Denver, B

Connecticut

Central Connecticut State University, B
Fairfield University, AB
Trinity College, B
United States Coast Guard Academy, B
University of Connecticut, B
University of Hartford, B
University of New Haven, B

Yale University, B

Delaware

University of Delaware, B

District of Columbia

The Catholic University of America, B
Gallaudet University, B
The George Washington University, B
Howard University, B
University of the District of Columbia, B

Florida

Embry-Riddle Aeronautical University, B
Florida Agricultural and Mechanical University, B
Florida Atlantic University, B
Florida Institute of Technology, B
Florida International University, B
Florida State University, B
Jacksonville University, B
University of Central Florida, B
University of Florida, B
University of Miami, B
University of North Florida, B
University of South Florida, B
University of West Florida, B

Georgia

Georgia Institute of Technology, B
Macon State College, A

Hawaii

University of Hawaii at Manoa, B

Idaho

Boise State University, B
Idaho State University, B
University of Idaho, B

Illinois

Black Hawk College, A
Bradley University, B
Dominican University, B
East-West University, B
Illinois Institute of Technology, B
Northern Illinois University, B
Northwestern University, B
Southern Illinois University Carbondale, B
Southern Illinois University Edwardsville, B
University of Illinois at Chicago, B
University of Illinois at Urbana-Champaign, B

Indiana

Indiana Tech, B
Indiana University-Purdue University Fort Wayne, B
Indiana University-Purdue University Indianapolis, B
Purdue University, B
Purdue University Calumet, B
Rose-Hulman Institute of Technology, B
Tri-State University, B
University of Evansville, B
University of Notre Dame, B
Valparaiso University, B

Iowa

Dordt College, B
Iowa State University of Science and Technology, B
The University of Iowa, B

Kansas

Allen County Community College, A
Kansas State University, B
University of Kansas, B
Wichita State University, B

Kentucky

University of Kentucky, B
University of Louisville, B
Western Kentucky University, B

Louisiana

Louisiana State University and Agricultural and Mechanical College, B
Louisiana Tech University, B

Southern University and Agricultural and Mechanical College, B
Tulane University, B
University of Louisiana at Lafayette, B
University of New Orleans, B

Maine

University of Maine, B
University of Southern Maine, B

Maryland

Capitol College, B
Frostburg State University, B
The Johns Hopkins University, B
Loyola College in Maryland, B
Morgan State University, B
United States Naval Academy, B
University of Maryland, College Park, B

Massachusetts

Boston University, B
Eastern Nazarene College, B
Harvard University, B
Massachusetts Institute of Technology, B
Merrimack College, B
Northeastern University, B
Suffolk University, B
Tufts University, B
University of Massachusetts Amherst, B
University of Massachusetts Dartmouth, B
University of Massachusetts Lowell, B
Wentworth Institute of Technology, B
Western New England College, B
Worcester Polytechnic Institute, B

Michigan

Calvin College, B
Grand Valley State University, B
Kettering University, B
Lake Superior State University, B
Lawrence Technological University, B
Michigan State University, B
Michigan Technological University, B
Oakland University, B
Saginaw Valley State University, B
University of Detroit Mercy, B
University of Michigan, B
University of Michigan-Dearborn, B
Wayne State University, B
Western Michigan University, B

Minnesota

Minnesota State University Mankato, B
St. Cloud State University, B
University of Minnesota, Duluth, B
University of Minnesota, Twin Cities Campus, B
University of St. Thomas, B

Mississippi

Jackson State University, B
Mississippi State University, B
University of Mississippi, B

Missouri

Missouri Tech, AB
Saint Louis University, B
University of Missouri-Columbia, B
University of Missouri-Kansas City, B
University of Missouri-Rolla, B
University of Missouri-St. Louis, B

Washington University in St. Louis, B

Montana

Montana State University, B

Nebraska

University of Nebraska-Lincoln, B
University of Nebraska at Omaha, B

Nevada

University of Nevada, Las Vegas, B
University of Nevada, Reno, B

New Hampshire

University of New Hampshire, B

New Jersey

The College of New Jersey, B
Fairleigh Dickinson University, Metropolitan
  Campus, B
New Jersey Institute of Technology, B
Princeton University, B
Rowan University, B
Rutgers, The State University of New Jersey, New
  Brunswick/Piscataway, B
Stevens Institute of Technology, B

New Mexico

New Mexico Institute of Mining and Technology, B
New Mexico State University, B
University of New Mexico, B

New York

Alfred University, B
City College of the City University of New York, B
Clarkson University, B
Columbia University, The Fu Foundation School of
  Engineering and Applied Science, B
Cooper Union for the Advancement of Science and
  Art, B
Cornell University, B
Dutchess Community College, A
Hofstra University, B
Jamestown Community College, A
Manhattan College, B
New York Institute of Technology, B
Polytechnic University, Brooklyn Campus, B
Rensselaer Polytechnic Institute, B
Rochester Institute of Technology, B
State University of New York at Binghamton, B
State University of New York at Buffalo, B
State University of New York Maritime College, B
State University of New York at New Paltz, B
Stony Brook University, State University of New
  York, B
Syracuse University, B
Union College, B
United States Military Academy, B
University of Rochester, B

North Carolina

Duke University, B
Mayland Community College, A
North Carolina Agricultural and Technical State
  University, B
North Carolina State University, B
The University of North Carolina at Charlotte, B
Western Carolina University, B

North Dakota

Lake Region State College, A
North Dakota State University, B
University of North Dakota, B

Ohio

Case Western Reserve University, B
Cedarville University, B
Cleveland State University, B
Miami University, B
Ohio Northern University, B
The Ohio State University, B
Ohio University, B
Ohio University-Eastern, B
The University of Akron, B

University of Cincinnati, B
University of Dayton, B
The University of Toledo, B
Wilberforce University, B
Wright State University, B
Youngstown State University, B

Oklahoma

Oklahoma Christian University, B
Oklahoma State University, B
Oral Roberts University, B
University of Oklahoma, B
University of Tulsa, B

Oregon

George Fox University, B
Oregon State University, B
Portland State University, B
University of Portland, B

Pennsylvania

Bloomsburg University of Pennsylvania, B
Bucknell University, B
Drexel University, B
Gannon University, B
Grove City College, B
Lafayette College, B
Lehigh Carbon Community College, A
Lehigh University, B
The Pennsylvania State University Abington
  College, B
The Pennsylvania State University Altoona
  College, B
The Pennsylvania State University Beaver Campus
  of the Commonwealth College, B
The Pennsylvania State University Berks Campus of
  the Berks-Lehigh Valley College, B
The Pennsylvania State University Delaware County
  Campus of the Commonwealth College, B
The Pennsylvania State University DuBois Campus
  of the Commonwealth College, B
The Pennsylvania State University at Erie, The
  Behrend College, B
The Pennsylvania State University Fayette Campus
  of the Commonwealth College, B
The Pennsylvania State University Harrisburg
  Campus, B
The Pennsylvania State University Hazleton
  Campus of the Commonwealth College, B
The Pennsylvania State University, Lehigh Valley
  Campus of the Berks-Lehigh Valley College, B
The Pennsylvania State University McKeesport
  Campus of the Commonwealth College, B
The Pennsylvania State University Mont Alto
  Campus of the Commonwealth College, B
The Pennsylvania State University New Kensington
  Campus of the Commonwealth College, B
The Pennsylvania State University Schuylkill
  Campus of the Capital College, B
The Pennsylvania State University Shenango
  Campus of the Commonwealth College, B
The Pennsylvania State University University Park
  Campus, B
The Pennsylvania State University Wilkes-Barre
  Campus of the Commonwealth College, B
The Pennsylvania State University Worthington
  Scranton Campus of the Commonwealth
  College, B
The Pennsylvania State University York Campus of
  the Commonwealth College, B
Temple University, B
University of Pennsylvania, B
University of Pittsburgh, B
The University of Scranton, B
Ursinus College, B
Villanova University, B
Widener University, B
Wilkes University, B

Puerto Rico

Inter American University of Puerto Rico, Bayamón
  Campus, B
Inter American University of Puerto Rico, Fajardo
  Campus, B
Polytechnic University of Puerto Rico, B
Universidad del Turabo, B

University of Puerto Rico, Mayagüez Campus, B

Rhode Island

Brown University, B
Johnson & Wales University, B
New England Institute of Technology, B
University of Rhode Island, B

South Carolina

Bob Jones University, B
The Citadel, The Military College of South
  Carolina, B
Clemson University, B
University of South Carolina, B

South Dakota

South Dakota School of Mines and Technology, B
South Dakota State University, B

Tennessee

Christian Brothers University, B
Tennessee State University, B
Tennessee Technological University, B
University of Memphis, B
The University of Tennessee, B
Vanderbilt University, B

Texas

Baylor University, B
Lamar University, B
LeTourneau University, B
Prairie View A&M University, B
Rice University, B
St. Mary's University of San Antonio, B
Southern Methodist University, B
Texas A&M University, B
Texas A&M University-Kingsville, B
Texas Tech University, B
University of Houston, B
The University of Texas at Arlington, B
The University of Texas at Austin, B
The University of Texas at Dallas, B
The University of Texas at El Paso, B
The University of Texas-Pan American, B
The University of Texas at San Antonio, B
The University of Texas at Tyler, B

Utah

Brigham Young University, B
University of Utah, B
Utah State University, B

Vermont

Norwich University, B
University of Vermont, B

Virginia

George Mason University, B
Hampton University, B
John Tyler Community College, A
Norfolk State University, B
Old Dominion University, B
University of Virginia, B
Virginia Commonwealth University, B
Virginia Military Institute, B
Virginia Polytechnic Institute and State University, B

Washington

Gonzaga University, B
Henry Cogswell College, B
Pacific Lutheran University, B
Seattle Pacific University, B
Seattle University, B
University of Washington, B
Walla Walla College, B
Washington State University, B

West Virginia

West Virginia University, B
West Virginia University Institute of Technology, B

Wisconsin

Marquette University, B
Milwaukee School of Engineering, B

University of Wisconsin-Madison, B
University of Wisconsin-Milwaukee, B
University of Wisconsin-Platteville, B

Wyoming

University of Wyoming, B

Alberta

University of Alberta, B
University of Calgary, B

British Columbia

Thompson Rivers University, A
The University of British Columbia, B
University of Victoria, B

Manitoba

University of Manitoba, B

New Brunswick

Université de Moncton, B
University of New Brunswick Fredericton, B
University of New Brunswick Saint John, B

Newfoundland and Labrador

Memorial University of Newfoundland, B

Nova Scotia

Dalhousie University, B

Ontario

Carleton University, B
Lakehead University, B
McMaster University, B
Queen's University at Kingston, B
Royal Military College of Canada, B
Ryerson University, B
University of Ottawa, B
University of Toronto, B
University of Waterloo, B
The University of Western Ontario, B
University of Windsor, B

Quebec

Concordia University, B
McGill University, B
Université Laval, B
Université du Québec en Abitibi-Témiscamingue, B
Université du Quebec, Ecole de technologie
superieure, B
Université du Québec àTrois-Rivières, B
Université de Sherbrooke, B

Saskatchewan

University of Regina, B

ELECTRICAL/ELECTRONICS DRAFTING AND ELECTRICAL/ELECTRONICS CAD/CADD

California

Mission College, A

Florida

Brevard Community College, A
Florida Technical College (Orlando), A

Illinois

Joliet Junior College, A

Minnesota

Anoka Technical College, A

New Mexico

Central New Mexico Community College, A

Texas

Collin County Community College District, A
Eastfield College, A

Texas State Technical College Waco, A

Washington

North Seattle Community College, A

Wisconsin

Waukesha County Technical College, A

ELECTRICAL/ELECTRONICS EQUIPMENT INSTALLATION AND REPAIR

Alabama

Gadsden State Community College-Ayers
Campus, A

Arizona

Arizona State University at the Polytechnic
Campus, B

Arkansas

University of Arkansas at Fort Smith, A

California

Modesto Junior College, A
Orange Coast College, A
Santa Barbara City College, A

Georgia

Georgia Southwestern State University, A

Idaho

Idaho State University, A
Lewis-Clark State College, AB

Illinois

College of DuPage, A

Iowa

Iowa Western Community College, A

Kansas

Hutchinson Community College and Area Vocational
School, A

Kentucky

Louisville Technical Institute, A

Louisiana

Delgado Community College, A

Maine

Kennebec Valley Community College, A

Michigan

Macomb Community College, A

Minnesota

Dakota County Technical College, A
Mesabi Range Community and Technical College, A
Ridgewater College, A
Riverland Community College, A

Montana

Miles Community College, A

New York

State University of New York College of Technology
at Alfred, A

North Carolina

Cape Fear Community College, A
Guilford Technical Community College, A

North Dakota

Lake Region State College, A

Pennsylvania

Triangle Tech, Inc.-Greensburg School, A

South Carolina

York Technical College, A

South Dakota

Western Dakota Technical Institute, A

Tennessee

Southwest Tennessee Community College, A

Texas

Angelina College, A
Collin County Community College District, A
St. Philip's College, A

Washington

Bates Technical College, A

Wisconsin

Milwaukee Area Technical College, A

Wyoming

Western Wyoming Community College, A

British Columbia

Thompson Rivers University, A

Nova Scotia

Cape Breton University, B

ELECTRICAL/ELECTRONICS MAINTENANCE AND REPAIR TECHNOLOGY

Colorado

Front Range Community College, A

Kentucky

Louisville Technical Institute, A

Massachusetts

Bunker Hill Community College, A

New York

Hudson Valley Community College, A
Mohawk Valley Community College, A

Pennsylvania

Triangle Tech, Inc.-Greensburg School, A

West Virginia

West Virginia State Community and Technical
College, A

ELECTRICAL ENGINEERING

Alabama

Auburn University, MD
Tuskegee University, M
The University of Alabama, MD
The University of Alabama at Birmingham, MD
The University of Alabama in Huntsville, MD
University of South Alabama, M

Alaska

University of Alaska Fairbanks, MD

Arizona

Arizona State University, MD
Arizona State University at the Polytechnic
Campus, M
The University of Arizona, MD

Arkansas

University of Arkansas, MD

California

California Institute of Technology, MD
California Polytechnic State University, San Luis
Obispo, M

California State Polytechnic University, Pomona, M
California State University, Chico, M
California State University, Fresno, M
California State University, Fullerton, M
California State University, Long Beach, M
California State University, Los Angeles, M
California State University, Northridge, M
California State University, Sacramento, M
International Technological University, M
Loyola Marymount University, M
Northwestern Polytechnic University, M
San Diego State University, M
San Jose State University, M
Santa Clara University, MDO
Stanford University, MDO
University of California, Berkeley, MD
University of California, Davis, MD
University of California, Irvine, MD
University of California, Los Angeles, MD
University of California, Riverside, MD
University of California, San Diego, MD
University of California, Santa Barbara, MDO
University of California, Santa Cruz, MD
University of Southern California, MDO

Colorado

Colorado State University, MD
Colorado Technical University, M
University of Colorado at Boulder, MD
University of Colorado at Colorado Springs, MD
University of Colorado at Denver and Health
   Sciences Center - Downtown Denver Campus, M
University of Denver, M

Connecticut

Fairfield University, M
University of Bridgeport, M
University of Connecticut, MD
University of New Haven, M
Yale University, MD

Delaware

University of Delaware, MD

District of Columbia

The Catholic University of America, MD
The George Washington University, MDO
Howard University, MD

Florida

Florida Agricultural and Mechanical University, MD
Florida Atlantic University, MD
Florida Institute of Technology, MD
Florida International University, MD
Florida State University, MD
University of Central Florida, MDO
University of Florida, MDO
University of Miami, MD
University of South Florida, MD

Georgia

Georgia Institute of Technology, MD
Mercer University, M
Southern Polytechnic State University, M

Hawaii

University of Hawaii at Manoa, MD

Idaho

Boise State University, M
University of Idaho, MD

Illinois

Bradley University, M
Illinois Institute of Technology, MD
Northern Illinois University, M
Northwestern University, MDO
Southern Illinois University Carbondale, MD
Southern Illinois University Edwardsville, M
University of Illinois at Chicago, MD

University of Illinois at Urbana-Champaign, MD

Indiana

Indiana University-Purdue University
   Indianapolis, MD
Purdue University, MD
Rose-Hulman Institute of Technology, M
University of Evansville, M
University of Notre Dame, MD

Iowa

Iowa State University of Science and
   Technology, MD
The University of Iowa, MD

Kansas

Kansas State University, MD
University of Kansas, MD
Wichita State University, MD

Kentucky

University of Kentucky, MD
University of Louisville, M

Louisiana

Louisiana State University and Agricultural and
   Mechanical College, MD
Louisiana Tech University, MD
McNeese State University, M
Tulane University, MD

Maine

University of Maine, MD

Maryland

Capitol College, M
The Johns Hopkins University, MD
Morgan State University, MD
University of Maryland, Baltimore County, MD
University of Maryland, College Park, MD

Massachusetts

Boston University, MD
Massachusetts Institute of Technology, MDO
Northeastern University, MD
Tufts University, MDO
University of Massachusetts Amherst, MD
University of Massachusetts Dartmouth, MDO
University of Massachusetts Lowell, MD
Western New England College, M
Worcester Polytechnic Institute, MDO

Michigan

Grand Valley State University, M
Lawrence Technological University, M
Michigan State University, MD
Michigan Technological University, MD
Oakland University, M
University of Detroit Mercy, MD
University of Michigan, MD
University of Michigan-Dearborn, M
Wayne State University, MD
Western Michigan University, MD

Minnesota

Minnesota State University Mankato, M
St. Cloud State University, M
University of Minnesota, Duluth, M
University of Minnesota, Twin Cities Campus, MD
Walden University, M

Mississippi

Mississippi State University, MD

Missouri

University of Missouri-Columbia, MD
University of Missouri-Kansas City, MD
University of Missouri-Rolla, MD

Washington University in St. Louis, MD

Montana

Montana State University, MD

Nebraska

University of Nebraska-Lincoln, MD

Nevada

University of Nevada, Las Vegas, MD
University of Nevada, Reno, MD

New Hampshire

Dartmouth College, MD
University of New Hampshire, MD

New Jersey

Fairleigh Dickinson University, Metropolitan
   Campus, M
New Jersey Institute of Technology, MD
Princeton University, MD
Rutgers, The State University of New Jersey, New
   Brunswick/Piscataway, MD
Stevens Institute of Technology, MDO

New Mexico

New Mexico Institute of Mining and Technology, M
New Mexico State University, MD
University of New Mexico, MD

New York

Alfred University, M
City College of the City University of New York, MD
Clarkson University, MD
Cornell University, MD
Manhattan College, M
New York Institute of Technology, M
Polytechnic University, Brooklyn Campus, MD
Rensselaer Polytechnic Institute, MDO
Rochester Institute of Technology, M
State University of New York at Binghamton, MD
State University of New York at Buffalo, MD
State University of New York at New Paltz, M
Stony Brook University, State University of New
   York, MD
Syracuse University, MDO
University of Rochester, MD

North Carolina

Duke University, MD
North Carolina Agricultural and Technical State
   University, MD
North Carolina State University, MD
The University of North Carolina at Charlotte, MD

North Dakota

North Dakota State University, MD
University of North Dakota, M

Ohio

Case Western Reserve University, MD
Cleveland State University, MD
The Ohio State University, MD
Ohio University, MD
The University of Akron, MD
University of Cincinnati, MD
University of Dayton, MD
The University of Toledo, MD
Wright State University, M
Youngstown State University, M

Oklahoma

Oklahoma State University, MD
University of Oklahoma, MD
University of Tulsa, M

Oregon

Oregon State University, MD
Portland State University, MD

Pennsylvania

Bucknell University, M
Carnegie Mellon University, MD
Drexel University, MD

Gannon University, M
Lehigh University, MD
The Pennsylvania State University Harrisburg
    Campus, M
The Pennsylvania State University University Park
    Campus, MD
Temple University, M
University of Pennsylvania, MD
University of Pittsburgh, MD
Villanova University, MO
Wilkes University, M

Puerto Rico

Polytechnic University of Puerto Rico, M
University of Puerto Rico, Mayagüez Campus, M

Rhode Island

Brown University, MD
University of Rhode Island, MD

South Carolina

Clemson University, MD
University of South Carolina, MD

South Dakota

South Dakota School of Mines and Technology, MD
South Dakota State University, M

Tennessee

Tennessee Technological University, MD
University of Memphis, MD
The University of Tennessee, MDO
Vanderbilt University, MD

Texas

Baylor University, M
Lamar University, MD
Prairie View A&M University, MD
Rice University, MD
St. Mary's University of San Antonio, M
Southern Methodist University, MD
Texas A&M University, MD
Texas A&M University-Kingsville, M
Texas Tech University, MD
University of Houston, MD
The University of Texas at Arlington, MD
The University of Texas at Austin, MD
The University of Texas at Dallas, MD
The University of Texas at El Paso, MD
The University of Texas at San Antonio, MD

Utah

Brigham Young University, MD
University of Utah, MDO
Utah State University, MDO

Vermont

University of Vermont, MD

Virginia

George Mason University, MD
Norfolk State University, M
Old Dominion University, MD
University of Virginia, MD
Virginia Polytechnic Institute and State
    University, MD

Washington

University of Washington, MD
Washington State University, MD

West Virginia

West Virginia University, MD

Wisconsin

Marquette University, MD
University of Wisconsin-Madison, MD

Wyoming

University of Wyoming, MD

Alberta

University of Alberta, MD
University of Calgary, MD

British Columbia

The University of British Columbia, MD
University of Victoria, MD

Manitoba

University of Manitoba, MD

New Brunswick

Université de Moncton, M
University of New Brunswick Fredericton, MD

Newfoundland and Labrador

Memorial University of Newfoundland, MD

Nova Scotia

Dalhousie University, MD

Ontario

Carleton University, MD
McMaster University, MD
Queen's University at Kingston, MD
Royal Military College of Canada, MD
University of Ottawa, MD
University of Toronto, MD
University of Waterloo, MD
University of Windsor, MD

Quebec

Concordia University, MD
McGill University, MD
Université Laval, MD
Université du Québec àTrois-Rivières, MD
Université de Sherbrooke, MD

Saskatchewan

University of Saskatchewan, MD

ELECTRICIAN

Alabama

H. Councill Trenholm State Technical College, A

Arizona

Northland Pioneer College, A

California

Santiago Canyon College, A

Georgia

Georgia Southwestern State University, A

Illinois

Black Hawk College, A
College of Lake County, A
John Wood Community College, A
Rend Lake College, A

Indiana

Ivy Tech Community College-Bloomington, A
Ivy Tech Community College-Central Indiana, A
Ivy Tech Community College-East Central, A
Ivy Tech Community College-Kokomo, A
Ivy Tech Community College-Lafayette, A
Ivy Tech Community College-North Central, A
Ivy Tech Community College-Northeast, A
Ivy Tech Community College-Northwest, A
Ivy Tech Community College-Southern Indiana, A
Ivy Tech Community College-Southwest, A
Ivy Tech Community College-Wabash Valley, A

Ivy Tech Community College-Whitewater, A

Maryland

TESST College of Technology (Towson), A

Michigan

Delta College, A

Minnesota

Dakota County Technical College, A
Lake Superior College, A

Missouri

Linn State Technical College, A

Nebraska

Northeast Community College, A

North Carolina

Cleveland Community College, A
Fayetteville Technical Community College, A

Pennsylvania

Johnson College, A
Luzerne County Community College, A
Northampton County Area Community College, A
Pennsylvania College of Technology, A
Rosedale Technical Institute, A

South Dakota

Mitchell Technical Institute, A

Texas

Brazosport College, A

Virginia

Piedmont Virginia Community College, A

Washington

Bates Technical College, A
Lower Columbia College, A

Wyoming

Western Wyoming Community College, A

British Columbia

Thompson Rivers University, A

ELECTROCARDIOGRAPH TECHNOLOGY/TECHNICIAN

Minnesota

St. Cloud Technical College, A

Washington

Edmonds Community College, A

Wisconsin

Milwaukee Area Technical College, A

ELECTROMECHANICAL AND INSTRUMENTATION AND MAINTENANCE TECHNOLOGIES/TECHNICIANS

Alabama

Calhoun Community College, A

Arkansas

North Arkansas College, A

Florida

Gulf Coast Community College, A
St. Petersburg College, A

Georgia

Georgia Southwestern State University, A

Kentucky

Louisville Technical Institute, A

Michigan

Northwestern Michigan College, A

New Hampshire

Keene State College, B

Wisconsin

Waukesha County Technical College, A

ELECTROMECHANICAL TECHNOLOGY/ ELECTROMECHANICAL ENGINEERING TECHNOLOGY

Arizona

GateWay Community College, A

Arkansas

North Arkansas College, A
Pulaski Technical College, A

California

Chabot College, A
Glendale Community College, A
Irvine Valley College, A
Los Angeles Harbor College, A

Delaware

Delaware Technical & Community College, Terry Campus, A

District of Columbia

University of the District of Columbia, AB

Georgia

Clayton State University, A
DeKalb Technical College, A

Idaho

Idaho State University, A

Illinois

Black Hawk College, A
College of DuPage, A
Lake Land College, A

Iowa

Kirkwood Community College, A
Southwestern Community College, A
University of Northern Iowa, B

Kentucky

Maysville Community and Technical College, A
Murray State University, B

Maine

Central Maine Community College, A

Maryland

Hagerstown Community College, A
Montgomery College, A

Massachusetts

Springfield Technical Community College, A

Michigan

Lake Michigan College, A
Lansing Community College, A
Macomb Community College, A
Michigan Technological University, A
Muskegon Community College, A
Northern Michigan University, A
Oakland Community College, A
Schoolcraft College, A
Washtenaw Community College, A

Wayne State University, B

Nebraska

Central Community College-Columbus Campus, A
Northeast Community College, A
Southeast Community College, Milford Campus, A

New Hampshire

New Hampshire Community Technical College, Nashua/Claremont, A

New Jersey

Raritan Valley Community College, A
Union County College, A

New Mexico

Clovis Community College, A
Eastern New Mexico University-Roswell, A

New York

Bramson ORT College, A
Buffalo State College, State University of New York, B
Dutchess Community College, A
Excelsior College, AB
New York City College of Technology of the City University of New York, AB
Rochester Institute of Technology, B
State University of New York College of Technology at Alfred, AB

North Carolina

Alamance Community College, A
Central Piedmont Community College, A
Craven Community College, A
Forsyth Technical Community College, A
Martin Community College, A
Pitt Community College, A
Randolph Community College, A
Rockingham Community College, A
South Piedmont Community College, A
Wake Technical Community College, A
Wayne Community College, A
Wilkes Community College, A

Ohio

Belmont Technical College, A
Central Ohio Technical College, A
Cincinnati State Technical and Community College, A
Columbus State Community College, A
Miami University Hamilton, B
Miami University-Middletown Campus, A
Shawnee State University, A
Sinclair Community College, A
Terra State Community College, A
The University of Akron, A
The University of Toledo, B
Wright State University, A

Pennsylvania

Dean Institute of Technology, A
Montgomery County Community College, A
Northampton County Area Community College, A

South Carolina

Aiken Technical College, A
Florence-Darlington Technical College, A
Tri-County Technical College, A

South Dakota

Mitchell Technical Institute, A
Southeast Technical Institute, A

Tennessee

Jackson State Community College, A

Texas

Angelina College, A
Mountain View College, A
St. Philip's College, A
Tarrant County College District, A
Texas State Technical College Harlingen, A

University of Houston, B

Utah

Utah Valley State College, A

Vermont

Vermont Technical College, B

Virginia

ECPI College of Technology (Newport News), A
ECPI College of Technology (Virginia Beach), A
ECPI Technical College (Richmond), A
ECPI Technical College (Roanoke), A

Washington

Walla Walla College, A

West Virginia

Community and Technical College of Shepherd, A
West Virginia University at Parkersburg, A

Wisconsin

Blackhawk Technical College, A
Chippewa Valley Technical College, A
Gateway Technical College, A
Lakeshore Technical College, A
Milwaukee Area Technical College, A
Moraine Park Technical College, A
Northcentral Technical College, A
Northeast Wisconsin Technical College, A
Southwest Wisconsin Technical College, A
Western Technical College, A
Wisconsin Indianhead Technical College, A

Quebec

Université du Québec en Abitibi-Témiscamingue, B

ELECTRONEURODIAGNOSTIC/ ELECTROENCEPHALOGRAPHIC TECHNOLOGY/TECHNOLOGIST

Colorado

Community College of Denver, A

Illinois

Black Hawk College, A
Parkland College, A

Iowa

Scott Community College, A

Louisiana

Louisiana State University Health Sciences Center, B

Maryland

Harford Community College, A
The Johns Hopkins University, B

Michigan

Oakland Community College, A

New York

Niagara County Community College, A

Pennsylvania

Community College of Allegheny County, A

Wisconsin

Western Technical College, A

ELECTRONIC COMMERCE

Alabama

Columbia Southern University, M

Arizona

University of Phoenix Online Campus, M
University of Phoenix-Phoenix Campus, M

University of Phoenix-Southern Arizona Campus, M

Arkansas

Arkansas State University, M

California

California State University, East Bay, M
National University, M
University of Phoenix-Bay Area Campus, M
University of Phoenix-Sacramento Valley
  Campus, M
University of Phoenix-Southern California
  Campus, M
University of San Francisco, M

Colorado

Regis University, MO
University of Denver, M
University of Phoenix-Denver Campus, M
University of Phoenix-Southern Colorado
  Campus, M

Connecticut

Sacred Heart University, O

District of Columbia

American University, M

Florida

Florida Atlantic University, M
Florida Institute of Technology, M
Lynn University, M
University of Phoenix-North Florida Campus, M

Georgia

Georgia Institute of Technology, O

Hawaii

Hawaii Pacific University, M
University of Phoenix-Hawaii Campus, M

Illinois

DePaul University, M
Illinois Institute of Technology, M
Northwestern University, M
Saint Xavier University, M
University of Phoenix-Chicago Campus, M

Indiana

Indiana Tech, M

Kentucky

Morehead State University, M

Louisiana

University of Phoenix-Louisiana Campus, M

Maryland

The Johns Hopkins University, O
University of Maryland University College, MO
University of Phoenix-Maryland Campus, M
Villa Julie College, M

Massachusetts

Boston University, M
Cambridge College, M

Michigan

Davenport University (Dearborn), M
Eastern Michigan University, M
Ferris State University, M
University of Phoenix-West Michigan Campus, M

Missouri

Maryville University of Saint Louis, MO
University of Missouri-St. Louis, O
University of Phoenix-Kansas City Campus, M

University of Phoenix-St. Louis Campus, M

Nebraska

Creighton University, M

Nevada

University of Phoenix-Nevada Campus, M

New Jersey

Fairleigh Dickinson University, Metropolitan
  Campus, M
Stevens Institute of Technology, MO

New Mexico

University of Phoenix-New Mexico Campus, M

New York

Adelphi University, M
Mercy College, M
Metropolitan College of New York, M
New York Institute of Technology, M
Rensselaer Polytechnic Institute, MD
State University of New York at Buffalo, O

North Carolina

University of Phoenix-Charlotte Campus, M

Ohio

The University of Akron, M
University of Cincinnati, M
University of Phoenix-Cincinnati Campus, M
University of Phoenix-Cleveland Campus, M
Xavier University, M

Oklahoma

University of Phoenix-Oklahoma City Campus, M
University of Phoenix-Tulsa Campus, M

Pennsylvania

Carnegie Mellon University, M
Marywood University, M
Temple University, M
West Chester University of Pennsylvania, M

Puerto Rico

University of Phoenix-Puerto Rico Campus, M

Rhode Island

Bryant University, MO

South Carolina

Clemson University, M

Tennessee

University of Phoenix-Nashville Campus, M

Texas

Dallas Baptist University, M
Texas Tech University, M
University of Phoenix-Dallas Campus, M
University of Phoenix-Houston Campus, M

Utah

University of Phoenix-Utah Campus, M

Washington

City University, MO

Wisconsin

University of Phoenix-Wisconsin Campus, M

New Brunswick

University of New Brunswick Saint John, M

Nova Scotia

Dalhousie University, M

Ontario

University of Ottawa, O

Quebec

Concordia University, O
HEC Montreal, MO

Université Laval, MO

ELECTRONIC MATERIALS

Arkansas

University of Arkansas, MD

Colorado

Colorado School of Mines, M

Illinois

Northwestern University, MDO

Massachusetts

Massachusetts Institute of Technology, D

New Jersey

Princeton University, D

ELEMENTARY AND MIDDLE SCHOOL ADMINISTRATION/PRINCIPALSHIP

Arkansas

Philander Smith College, B
University of Central Arkansas, B

Georgia

Piedmont College, B

New Jersey

Bloomfield College, B
Cumberland County College, A

New York

Le Moyne College, B

North Carolina

Campbell University, B

Ohio

Ohio University, B

Oklahoma

Tulsa Community College, A

Puerto Rico

Caribbean University, B
Inter American University of Puerto Rico,
  Barranquitas Campus, AB

South Carolina

Charleston Southern University, B

ELEMENTARY EDUCATION AND TEACHING

Alabama

Alabama Agricultural and Mechanical
  University, BMO
Alabama Southern Community College, A
Alabama State University, BMO
Athens State University, B
Auburn University, BMDO
Auburn University Montgomery, BMO
Birmingham-Southern College, B
Calhoun Community College, A
Chattahoochee Valley Community College, A
Concordia College, B
Faulkner University, B
Jacksonville State University, BM
Jefferson Davis Community College, A
Judson College, B
Miles College, B
Northwest-Shoals Community College, A
Oakwood College, B
Samford University, MO
Spring Hill College, BM
Troy University, BMO

Tuskegee University, B
The University of Alabama, BMDO
The University of Alabama at Birmingham, BM
The University of Alabama in Huntsville, B
University of Mobile, B
University of Montevallo, BM
University of North Alabama, BMO
University of South Alabama, BMO
The University of West Alabama, BM
Wallace State Community College, A

Alaska

Alaska Pacific University, ABM
Sheldon Jackson College, B
University of Alaska Anchorage, B
University of Alaska Fairbanks, B
University of Alaska Southeast, M

Arizona

American Indian College of the Assemblies of God,
   Inc., B
Arizona State University, B
Arizona State University at the Polytechnic
   Campus, B
Arizona State University West, BMO
Diné College, A
Eastern Arizona College, A
Grand Canyon University, BM
Northern Arizona University, BM
Northland Pioneer College, A
Pima Community College, A
Prescott College, B
Southwestern College, B
The University of Arizona, BMD
University of Phoenix Online Campus, M
University of Phoenix-Phoenix Campus, M
University of Phoenix-Southern Arizona Campus, M

Arkansas

Arkansas Baptist College, B
Arkansas State University, MO
Arkansas Tech University, B
Harding University, BM
Henderson State University, B
Hendrix College, B
John Brown University, B
National Park Community College, A
Southern Arkansas University-Magnolia, B
University of Arkansas, BMO
University of Arkansas at Little Rock, B
University of Arkansas at Monticello, B
University of Arkansas at Pine Bluff, BM
University of Central Arkansas, B
Williams Baptist College, B

California

Bethany University, B
Biola University, B
California State University, Fullerton, M
California State University, Long Beach, M
California State University, Los Angeles, M
California State University, Northridge, M
California State University, San Bernardino, M
California State University, Stanislaus, M
Chapman University, M
Cuyamaca College, A
Fresno Pacific University, B
Hope International University, B
Humboldt State University, B
La Sierra University, B
Loyola Marymount University, M
The Master's College and Seminary, B
Mount St. Mary's College, BM
Notre Dame de Namur University, B
Occidental College, M
Pacific Oaks College, B
Pacific Union College, B
Pepperdine University, B
San Diego Christian College, B
San Diego State University, M
San Francisco State University, M
San Jose State University, MO
Simpson University, B
Sonoma State University, M
Southwestern College, A
University of California, Irvine, M

University of La Verne, B
University of Phoenix-Sacramento Valley
   Campus, M
University of Phoenix-San Diego Campus, M
University of Phoenix-Southern California
   Campus, M
University of Redlands, B
University of San Francisco, B
Westmont College, B
Whittier College, M
Yuba College, A

Colorado

Adams State College, B
The Colorado College, M
Colorado State University-Pueblo, B
Fort Lewis College, B
Mesa State College, B
Northeastern Junior College, A
Otero Junior College, A
Regis University, BM
University of Northern Colorado, MD
University of Phoenix-Denver Campus, M
University of Phoenix-Southern Colorado
   Campus, M
Western State College of Colorado, B

Connecticut

Albertus Magnus College, B
Central Connecticut State University, BMO
Connecticut College, BM
Eastern Connecticut State University, BM
Fairfield University, M
Quinnipiac University, M
Sacred Heart University, BM
Saint Joseph College, B
Southern Connecticut State University, BMO
University of Bridgeport, MO
University of Connecticut, BMD
University of Hartford, BM
Western Connecticut State University, B

Delaware

Delaware State University, B
University of Delaware, B
Wilmington College, BM

District of Columbia

American University, BMO
The Catholic University of America, B
Gallaudet University, BMO
The George Washington University, M
Howard University, M
Trinity (Washington) University, BM
University of the District of Columbia, B

Florida

The Baptist College of Florida, B
Barry University, BMQ
Bethune-Cookman College, B
Broward Community College, A
Carlos Albizu University, Miami Campus, B
Clearwater Christian College, B
Edward Waters College, B
Flagler College, B
Florida Agricultural and Mechanical University, BM
Florida Atlantic University, BM
Florida College, B
Florida Gulf Coast University, BM
Florida International University, BM
Florida Memorial College, B
Florida Southern College, B
Florida State University, BMDO
Gulf Coast Community College, A
Hillsborough Community College, A
Hobe Sound Bible College, B
Jacksonville University, BM
Lynn University, B
Miami Dade College, A
Nova Southeastern University, BMO
Okaloosa-Walton College, A
Palm Beach Atlantic University, BM
Palm Beach Community College, A
Rollins College, M
Saint Leo University, B

St. Petersburg College, B
St. Thomas University, BM
Southeastern University, B
Stetson University, B
Trinity Baptist College, B
Trinity College of Florida, B
University of Central Florida, BMD
University of Florida, BM
University of Miami, BMO
University of North Florida, BM
University of Phoenix-North Florida Campus, M
University of South Florida, BMDO
The University of Tampa, B
University of West Florida, BM
Warner Southern College, B

Georgia

Abraham Baldwin Agricultural College, A
Armstrong Atlantic State University, M
Augusta State University, B
Bainbridge College, A
Clark Atlanta University, B
Clayton State University, A
Covenant College, B
Dalton State College, A
East Georgia College, A
Emmanuel College, B
Gainesville College, A
Georgia Perimeter College, A
Georgia Southwestern State University, B
Georgia State University, B
Kennesaw State University, B
LaGrange College, B
Macon State College, A
Mercer University, B
Morehouse College, B
North Georgia College & State University, B
Paine College, B
Shorter College, B
South Georgia College, A
University of Georgia, MDO
University of West Georgia, B
Waycross College, A

Guam

University of Guam, B

Hawaii

Brigham Young University-Hawaii, B
Chaminade University of Honolulu, B
University of Hawaii at Hilo, B
University of Hawaii at Manoa, B
University of Phoenix-Hawaii Campus, MO

Idaho

Boise State University, B
Brigham Young University -Idaho, A
College of Southern Idaho, A
Idaho State University, B
Lewis-Clark State College, B
North Idaho College, A
Northwest Nazarene University, B
University of Idaho, BM

Illinois

Augustana College, B
Aurora University, B
Benedictine University, BM
Blackburn College, B
Bradley University, B
Chicago State University, BM
City Colleges of Chicago, Harold Washington
   College, A
City Colleges of Chicago, Harry S. Truman
   College, A
City Colleges of Chicago, Malcolm X College, A
City Colleges of Chicago, Richard J. Daley
   College, A
City Colleges of Chicago, Wilbur Wright College, A
Columbia College Chicago, M
Concordia University, B
Danville Area Community College, A
DePaul University, BM
Dominican University, B
Eastern Illinois University, BM

Elmhurst College, B
Eureka College, B
Governors State University, B
Greenville College, BM
Illinois College, B
Illinois State University, B
Illinois Valley Community College, A
Illinois Wesleyan University, B
John A. Logan College, A
Judson College, B
Kankakee Community College, A
Kendall College, B
Lake Forest College, B
Lewis University, B
Lincoln Christian College, B
Lincoln College, A
Loyola University Chicago, B
MacMurray College, B
McKendree College, B
Millikin University, B
Monmouth College, B
National-Louis University, BM
North Central College, B
North Park University, B
Northeastern Illinois University, B
Northern Illinois University, BM
Northwestern University, M
Olivet Nazarene University, BM
Parkland College, A
Principia College, B
Quincy University, B
Rend Lake College, A
Rockford College, BM
Roosevelt University, BM
Saint Xavier University, BM
Sauk Valley Community College, A
South Suburban College, A
Southern Illinois University Carbondale, B
Southern Illinois University Edwardsville, BM
Southwestern Illinois College, A
Trinity Christian College, B
Trinity International University, B
University of Illinois at Chicago, B
University of Illinois at Urbana-Champaign, B
University of St. Francis, BM
Western Illinois University, BM
Wheaton College, B

Indiana

Ancilla College, A
Anderson University, B
Ball State University, BMD
Bethel College, B
Butler University, BM
Calumet College of Saint Joseph, B
Crossroads Bible College, B
DePauw University, B
Franklin College, B
Goshen College, B
Grace College, B
Huntington University, B
Indiana State University, BM
Indiana University Bloomington, BMO
Indiana University East, B
Indiana University Kokomo, BM
Indiana University Northwest, BM
Indiana University-Purdue University Fort
    Wayne, BM
Indiana University-Purdue University Indianapolis, B
Indiana University South Bend, BM
Indiana University Southeast, BM
Indiana Wesleyan University, B
Manchester College, B
Marian College, B
Martin University, B
Oakland City University, B
Purdue University, BM
Purdue University Calumet, BM
Purdue University North Central, BM
Saint Joseph's College, B
Saint Mary-of-the-Woods College, B
Saint Mary's College, B
Taylor University, B
Tri-State University, B
University of Evansville, B
University of Indianapolis, BM

University of Saint Francis, B
University of Southern Indiana, BM
Valparaiso University, B
Vincennes University, A
Vincennes University Jasper Campus, A

Iowa

Ashford University, B
Briar Cliff University, B
Buena Vista University, B
Central College, B
Clarke College, B
Coe College, B
Cornell College, B
Dordt College, B
Drake University, BM
Emmaus Bible College, B
Faith Baptist Bible College and Theological
    Seminary, B
Graceland University, B
Grand View College, B
Iowa Lakes Community College, A
Iowa State University of Science and
    Technology, BM
Iowa Wesleyan College, B
Kirkwood Community College, A
Loras College, B
Luther College, B
Maharishi University of Management, BM
Morningside College, BM
Mount Mercy College, B
Northwestern College, B
St. Ambrose University, B
Simpson College, B
University of Dubuque, B
The University of Iowa, BMD
University of Northern Iowa, BM
Upper Iowa University, B
Vennard College, AB
Waldorf College, B
Wartburg College, B
William Penn University, B

Kansas

Allen County Community College, A
Baker University, B
Barclay College, B
Barton County Community College, A
Benedictine College, B
Bethany College, B
Bethel College, B
Central Christian College of Kansas, A
Cloud County Community College, A
Coffeyville Community College, A
Cowley County Community College and Area
    Vocational-Technical School, A
Dodge City Community College, A
Emporia State University, BM
Fort Hays State University, BM
Friends University, BM
Garden City Community College, A
Haskell Indian Nations University, B
Independence Community College, A
Kansas State University, BMD
Kansas Wesleyan University, B
Labette Community College, A
McPherson College, B
MidAmerica Nazarene University, B
Newman University, BM
Ottawa University, B
Pittsburg State University, BM
Pratt Community College, A
Seward County Community College, A
Southwestern College, B
Sterling College, B
Tabor College, B
University of Kansas, B
University of Saint Mary, B
Washburn University, B
Wichita State University, B

Kentucky

Alice Lloyd College, B
Asbury College, B
Bellarmine University, BM
Berea College, B

Brescia University, B
Campbellsville University, B
Centre College, B
Eastern Kentucky University, BM
Georgetown College, B
Kentucky Christian University, B
Kentucky State University, B
Kentucky Wesleyan College, B
Lindsey Wilson College, B
Mid-Continent University, B
Midway College, B
Morehead State University, BM
Murray State University, BMO
Northern Kentucky University, B
Pikeville College, B
St. Catharine College, A
Spalding University, BM
Thomas More College, B
Transylvania University, B
Union College, BM
University of the Cumberlands, BMO
University of Kentucky, B
University of Louisville, BM
Western Kentucky University, BMO

Louisiana

Centenary College of Louisiana, BM
Dillard University, B
Grambling State University, BM
Louisiana College, B
Louisiana State University and Agricultural and
    Mechanical College, BM
Louisiana State University at Alexandria, B
Louisiana State University in Shreveport, B
Louisiana Tech University, B
Loyola University New Orleans, BM
McNeese State University, BM
Nicholls State University, B
Northwestern State University of Louisiana, BMO
Our Lady of Holy Cross College, B
Southeastern Louisiana University, BM
Southern University and Agricultural and Mechanical
    College, BM
Southern University at New Orleans, B
University of Louisiana at Lafayette, B
University of Louisiana at Monroe, BM
University of New Orleans, B
Xavier University of Louisiana, BM

Maine

College of the Atlantic, B
Husson College, B
Saint Joseph's College of Maine, B
Thomas College, B
University of Maine, BMO
University of Maine at Farmington, B
University of Maine at Fort Kent, B
University of Maine at Machias, B
University of Maine at Presque Isle, B
University of New England, B

Maryland

Anne Arundel Community College, A
Bowie State University, BM
Cecil Community College, A
Chesapeake College, A
College of Notre Dame of Maryland, B
College of Southern Maryland, A
Columbia Union College, B
Coppin State University, B
Frederick Community College, A
Frostburg State University, BM
Garrett College, A
Goucher College, B
Hagerstown Community College, A
Harford Community College, A
Howard Community College, A
The Johns Hopkins University, M
Loyola College in Maryland, B
McDaniel College, M
Morgan State University, BM
Mount St. Mary's University, B
Prince George's Community College, A
Salisbury University, BM
Towson University, BM
University of Maryland, Baltimore County, M

University of Maryland, College Park, B
University of Maryland Eastern Shore, B
Villa Julie College, AB
Washington Bible College, B
Wor-Wic Community College, A

Massachusetts

American International College, BMO
Anna Maria College, BM
Assumption College, B
Atlantic Union College, B
Bay Path College, B
Becker College, B
Boston College, BM
Boston University, BM
Brandeis University, M
Bridgewater State College, BM
Bristol Community College, A
Clark University, B
Curry College, B
Eastern Nazarene College, BMO
Elms College, BM
Emmanuel College, BM
Endicott College, B
Fitchburg State College, BM
Framingham State College, B
Gordon College, B
Hellenic College, B
Holyoke Community College, A
Lasell College, B
Lesley University, BM
Massachusetts College of Liberal Arts, B
Merrimack College, B
Middlesex Community College, A
Northeastern University, BM
Northern Essex Community College, A
Pine Manor College, B
Quincy College, A
Salem State College, BM
Simmons College, BMO
Smith College, M
Springfield College, B
Springfield Technical Community College, A
Stonehill College, B
Suffolk University, B
Tufts University, BM
University of Massachusetts Amherst, MDO
University of Massachusetts Boston, M
Western New England College, BM
Westfield State College, BM
Wheelock College, BM
Worcester State College, BM

Michigan

Adrian College, B
Albion College, B
Alma College, B
Alpena Community College, A
Andrews University, BM
Aquinas College, B
Calvin College, B
Central Michigan University, BM
Concordia University, B
Cornerstone University, B
Eastern Michigan University, BM
Ferris State University, B
Grace Bible College, B
Grand Valley State University, BM
Hillsdale College, B
Hope College, B
Kalamazoo Valley Community College, A
Kellogg Community College, A
Kuyper College, B
Lake Superior State University, B
Lansing Community College, A
Madonna University, B
Marygrove College, M
Michigan State University, B
Mid Michigan Community College, A
Monroe County Community College, A
Muskegon Community College, A
Northern Michigan University, BM
Oakland University, B
Olivet College, B
Rochester College, B
Saginaw Valley State University, BM

Siena Heights University, BM
Spring Arbor University, B
University of Detroit Mercy, B
University of Michigan, BO
University of Michigan-Dearborn, B
University of Michigan-Flint, BM
University of Phoenix-Metro Detroit Campus, M
Wayne State University, BMDO
Western Michigan University, BM

Minnesota

Augsburg College, B
Bemidji State University, B
Bethany Lutheran College, B
Bethel University, B
College of Saint Benedict, B
College of St. Catherine, B
The College of St. Scholastica, B
Concordia College, B
Concordia University, St. Paul, B
Crown College, B
Gustavus Adolphus College, B
Hamline University, B
Martin Luther College, B
Minnesota State University Mankato, BM
Minnesota State University Moorhead, B
North Central University, B
Northwestern College, B
Pillsbury Baptist Bible College, B
St. Cloud State University, B
Saint John's University, B
Saint Mary's University of Minnesota, B
Southwest Minnesota State University, B
University of Minnesota, Duluth, B
University of Minnesota, Morris, B
University of Minnesota, Twin Cities Campus, BMD
University of St. Thomas, B
Vermilion Community College, A
Winona State University, B

Mississippi

Alcorn State University, BMO
Belhaven College, BM
Blue Mountain College, B
Coahoma Community College, A
Copiah-Lincoln Community College, A
Copiah-Lincoln Community College-Natchez
    Campus, A
Delta State University, BMO
East Central Community College, A
East Mississippi Community College, A
Holmes Community College, A
Itawamba Community College, A
Jackson State University, BMDO
Mississippi College, BM
Mississippi Delta Community College, A
Mississippi Gulf Coast Community College, A
Mississippi State University, BMDO
Mississippi University for Women, B
Mississippi Valley State University, BM
Northeast Mississippi Community College, A
Northwest Mississippi Community College, A
Rust College, B
Southwest Mississippi Community College, A
Tougaloo College, B
University of Mississippi, B
University of Southern Mississippi, BMDO
William Carey College, BO

Missouri

Avila University, B
Baptist Bible College, B
Calvary Bible College and Theological Seminary, B
Central Methodist University, B
Central Missouri State University, BM
College of the Ozarks, B
Crowder College, A
Culver-Stockton College, B
Drury University, BM
Evangel University, B
Fontbonne University, B
Hannibal-LaGrange College, B
Harris-Stowe State University, B
Jefferson College, A
Lincoln University, BM
Lindenwood University, B

Maryville University of Saint Louis, BM
Missouri Baptist University, B
Missouri Southern State University, B
Missouri State University, BMO
Missouri Valley College, B
Missouri Western State University, B
Northwest Missouri State University, BMO
Ozark Christian College, A
Park University, B
Rockhurst University, B
St. Louis Community College at Florissant Valley, A
St. Louis Community College at Meramec, A
Southeast Missouri State University, B
Southwest Baptist University, B
Stephens College, B
Three Rivers Community College, A
University of Missouri-Columbia, BMDO
University of Missouri-Kansas City, B
University of Missouri-St. Louis, BM
Washington University in St. Louis, BM
Webster University, B
Westminster College, B
William Jewell College, B
William Woods University, B

Montana

Blackfeet Community College, A
Carroll College, B
Fort Belknap College, A
Little Big Horn College, A
Montana State University, B
Montana State University-Billings, B
Montana State University-Great Falls College of
    Technology, A
Montana State University-Northern, B
Rocky Mountain College, B
University of Great Falls, B
The University of Montana-Missoula, B
The University of Montana-Western, B

Nebraska

Chadron State College, BM
College of Saint Mary, B
Concordia University, B
Creighton University, B
Dana College, B
Doane College, B
Grace University, B
Hastings College, B
Midland Lutheran College, B
Nebraska Christian College, B
Nebraska Wesleyan University, B
Northeast Community College, A
Peru State College, B
Southeast Community College, Beatrice Campus, A
Union College, B
University of Nebraska at Kearney, B
University of Nebraska-Lincoln, B
University of Nebraska at Omaha, BM
Wayne State College, BM
Western Nebraska Community College, A
York College, B

Nevada

Great Basin College, AB
Sierra Nevada College, O
Truckee Meadows Community College, A
University of Nevada, Las Vegas, BM
University of Nevada, Reno, BMO
University of Phoenix-Nevada Campus, M

New Hampshire

Franklin Pierce College, B
Keene State College, B
New England College, B
Plymouth State University, BM
Rivier College, BM
Southern New Hampshire University, M
University of New Hampshire, BM

New Jersey

Caldwell College, B
Centenary College, B
The College of New Jersey, BM
Essex County College, A

Felician College, B
Georgian Court University, B
Kean University, BMO
Monmouth University, M
Montclair State University, M
New Jersey City University, BM
Raritan Valley Community College, A
Rider University, BO
Rowan University, BM
Rutgers, The State University of New Jersey, New
 Brunswick/Piscataway, MD
Saint Peter's College, BO
Seton Hall University, BM
William Paterson University of New Jersey, BM

New Mexico

Central New Mexico Community College, A
College of Santa Fe, B
College of the Southwest, B
Eastern New Mexico University, B
Mesalands Community College, A
New Mexico Highlands University, AB
New Mexico Junior College, A
New Mexico State University, B
Northern New Mexico Community College, A
University of New Mexico, BM
University of New Mexico-Gallup, AB
Western New Mexico University, BM

New York

Adelphi University, MO
Alfred University, B
Boricua College, B
Brooklyn College of the City University of New
 York, BM
Buffalo State College, State University of New
 York, BM
City College of the City University of New York, BM
College of Mount Saint Vincent, B
The College of New Rochelle, B
The College of Saint Rose, BM
College of Staten Island of the City University of
 New York, M
Concordia College, B
Corning Community College, A
Daemen College, B
Dominican College, B
Dowling College, B
Dutchess Community College, A
D'Youville College, BMO
Elmira College, B
Five Towns College, B
Fordham University, BM
Fulton-Montgomery Community College, A
Genesee Community College, A
Hofstra University, BM
Houghton College, B
Hunter College of the City University of New
 York, BM
Iona College, BM
Keuka College, B
The King's College, B
Kingsborough Community College of the City
 University of New York, A
Le Moyne College, B
Lehman College of the City University of New
 York, M
Long Island University, Brentwood Campus, M
Long Island University, Brooklyn Campus, BM
Long Island University, C.W. Post Campus, BM
Manhattan College, B
Manhattanville College, BM
Marist College, B
Medaille College, BM
Mercy College, B
Mohawk Valley Community College, A
Molloy College, B
Mount Saint Mary College, BM
Nazareth College of Rochester, BM
New York Institute of Technology, BMO
New York University, BMDO
Niagara University, BM
Nyack College, B
Orange County Community College, A
Pace University, B

Queens College of the City University of New
 York, BMO
Roberts Wesleyan College, B
Russell Sage College, B
St. Bonaventure University, B
St. John Fisher College, BM
St. John's University, BM
St. Joseph's College, Suffolk Campus, B
St. Thomas Aquinas College, BM
Sarah Lawrence College, B
Skidmore College, B
State University of New York at Binghamton, M
State University of New York at Buffalo, MD
State University of New York College at
 Brockport, B
State University of New York College at Cortland, B
State University of New York College at
 Geneseo, BM
State University of New York College at Old
 Westbury, B
State University of New York College at
 Oneonta, BM
State University of New York College at
 Potsdam, BM
State University of New York, Fredonia, BM
State University of New York at New Paltz, BM
State University of New York at Oswego, BM
State University of New York at Plattsburgh, BM
Sullivan County Community College, A
Syracuse University, O
Ulster County Community College, A
Utica College, B
Wagner College, BM
Wells College, B
Yeshiva University, B

North Carolina

Appalachian State University, BM
Barber-Scotia College, B
Barton College, B
Belmont Abbey College, B
Bennett College For Women, B
Brevard College, B
Campbell University, BM
Catawba College, BM
Chowan University, B
East Carolina University, BM
Elizabeth City State University, BM
Elon University, BM
Fayetteville State University, BM
Fayetteville Technical Community College, A
Gardner-Webb University, BM
Greensboro College, B
Guilford College, B
High Point University, BM
Isothermal Community College, A
John Wesley College, B
Johnson C. Smith University, B
Lees-McRae College, B
Lenoir Community College, A
Lenoir-Rhyne College, B
Livingstone College, B
Louisburg College, A
Mars Hill College, B
Methodist College, B
Mitchell Community College, A
Montreat College, B
North Carolina Agricultural and Technical State
 University, BM
North Carolina Central University, BM
North Carolina Wesleyan College, B
Pfeiffer University, BM
Piedmont Baptist College, B
Queens University of Charlotte, BM
St. Andrews Presbyterian College, B
Saint Augustine's College, B
Salem College, M
Shaw University, B
The University of North Carolina at Chapel Hill, B
The University of North Carolina at Charlotte, BM
The University of North Carolina at Greensboro, B
The University of North Carolina at Pembroke, BM
The University of North Carolina Wilmington, BM
Vance-Granville Community College, A
Warren Wilson College, B
Western Carolina University, BM

Wingate University, BM
Winston-Salem State University, BM

North Dakota

Dickinson State University, B
Jamestown College, B
Mayville State University, B
Minot State University, BM
North Dakota State University, B
Trinity Bible College, B
Turtle Mountain Community College, A
University of Mary, BM
University of North Dakota, BMD
Valley City State University, B

Ohio

Ashland University, B
Baldwin-Wallace College, B
Bluffton University, B
Bowling Green State University, B
Capital University, B
Circleville Bible College, B
Cleveland State University, B
Defiance College, B
Edison State Community College, A
Franciscan University of Steubenville, B
God's Bible School and College, AB
Heidelberg College, B
Hiram College, B
John Carroll University, B
Lake Erie College, B
Lorain County Community College, A
Marietta College, B
Miami University, BM
Miami University-Middletown Campus, A
Mount Vernon Nazarene University, B
Muskingum College, B
Notre Dame College, B
Ohio Northern University, B
The Ohio State University at Lima, B
The Ohio State University-Mansfield Campus, B
The Ohio State University at Marion, B
The Ohio State University-Newark Campus, B
Ohio University, B
Ohio University-Chillicothe, B
Ohio University-Eastern, B
Ohio University-Lancaster, B
Ohio University-Zanesville, B
Ohio Wesleyan University, B
Otterbein College, B
Shawnee State University, B
The University of Akron, BMD
University of Cincinnati, BM
University of Cincinnati Clermont College, A
University of Dayton, B
The University of Findlay, BM
University of Rio Grande, B
The University of Toledo, BDO
Urbana University, B
Walsh University, B
Wilmington College, B
Wright State University, BM
Wright State University, Lake Campus, A
Xavier University, BM
Youngstown State University, BM

Oklahoma

Bacone College, B
Cameron University, B
Carl Albert State College, A
East Central University, B
Eastern Oklahoma State College, A
Hillsdale Free Will Baptist College, A
Langston University, BM
Mid-America Christian University, B
Murray State College, A
Northeastern Oklahoma Agricultural and Mechanical
 College, A
Northeastern State University, B
Northern Oklahoma College, A
Northwestern Oklahoma State University, BM
Oklahoma Baptist University, B
Oklahoma Christian University, B
Oklahoma City University, BM
Oklahoma Panhandle State University, B
Oklahoma State University, B

Oklahoma Wesleyan University, B
Oral Roberts University, B
Redlands Community College, A
Rogers State University, A
Rose State College, A
Seminole State College, A
Southeastern Oklahoma State University, BM
Southern Nazarene University, B
Southwestern Oklahoma State University, BM
Tulsa Community College, A
University of Central Oklahoma, BM
University of Oklahoma, B
University of Science and Arts of Oklahoma, B
University of Tulsa, B

Oregon

Cascade College, B
Concordia University, BM
Corban College, B
Eastern Oregon University, M
George Fox University, B
Lewis & Clark College, M
Linfield College, B
Linn-Benton Community College, A
Oregon State University, M
Pacific University, BM
Portland Community College, A
Portland State University, M
Southern Oregon University, M
Umpqua Community College, A
University of Portland, B
Warner Pacific College, B

Pennsylvania

Albright College, BM
Alvernia College, B
Arcadia University, BMO
Baptist Bible College of Pennsylvania, B
Bloomsburg University of Pennsylvania, BM
Bucknell University, B
Butler County Community College, A
Cabrini College, B
California University of Pennsylvania, BM
Carlow University, B
Cedar Crest College, B
Chatham College, BM
Chestnut Hill College, BM
Cheyney University of Pennsylvania, BM
Clarion University of Pennsylvania, BM
College Misericordia, B
DeSales University, B
Duquesne University, BM
East Stroudsburg University of Pennsylvania, BM
Eastern University, B
Edinboro University of Pennsylvania, BM
Elizabethtown College, B
Gannon University, B
Geneva College, B
Gettysburg College, B
Grove City College, B
Gwynedd-Mercy College, B
Harrisburg Area Community College, A
Holy Family University, BM
Immaculata University, BO
Indiana University of Pennsylvania, B
Juniata College, B
Keystone College, B
King's College, B
Kutztown University of Pennsylvania, BMO
La Roche College, B
La Salle University, B
Lancaster Bible College, B
Lebanon Valley College, B
Lehigh University, MO
Lincoln University, B
Lock Haven University of Pennsylvania, BM
Lycoming College, B
Manor College, A
Mansfield University of Pennsylvania, BM
Marywood University, BM
Mercyhurst College, B
Messiah College, B
Millersville University of Pennsylvania, BM
Montgomery County Community College, A
Moravian College, B
Neumann College, B

The Pennsylvania State University Abington
College, B
The Pennsylvania State University Altoona
College, B
The Pennsylvania State University Beaver Campus
of the Commonwealth College, B
The Pennsylvania State University Berks Campus of
the Berks-Lehigh Valley College, B
The Pennsylvania State University Delaware County
Campus of the Commonwealth College, B
The Pennsylvania State University DuBois Campus
of the Commonwealth College, B
The Pennsylvania State University at Erie, The
Behrend College, B
The Pennsylvania State University Fayette Campus
of the Commonwealth College, B
The Pennsylvania State University Harrisburg
Campus, B
The Pennsylvania State University Hazleton
Campus of the Commonwealth College, B
The Pennsylvania State University Lehigh Valley
Campus of the Berks-Lehigh Valley College, B
The Pennsylvania State University McKeesport
Campus of the Commonwealth College, B
The Pennsylvania State University Mont Alto
Campus of the Commonwealth College, B
The Pennsylvania State University New Kensington
Campus of the Commonwealth College, B
The Pennsylvania State University Schuylkill
Campus of the Capital College, B
The Pennsylvania State University Shenango
Campus of the Commonwealth College, B
The Pennsylvania State University University Park
Campus, BMD
The Pennsylvania State University Wilkes-Barre
Campus of the Commonwealth College, B
The Pennsylvania State University Worthington
Scranton Campus of the Commonwealth
College, B
The Pennsylvania State University York Campus of
the Commonwealth College, B
Philadelphia Biblical University, B
Point Park University, B
Reading Area Community College, A
Robert Morris University, B
Rosemont College, M
Saint Francis University, B
Saint Joseph's University, BM
Seton Hill University, BMO
Shippensburg University of Pennsylvania, B
Slippery Rock University of Pennsylvania, BM
Susquehanna University, B
Temple University, BM
Thiel College, B
University of Pennsylvania, BM
University of Pittsburgh, M
University of Pittsburgh at Johnstown, B
The University of Scranton, BM
Valley Forge Christian College, B
Villanova University, BM
Waynesburg College, B
West Chester University of Pennsylvania, BM
Westminster College, B
Widener University, BM
Wilkes University, BM
Wilson College, AB
York College of Pennsylvania, B

Puerto Rico

American University of Puerto Rico, B
Bayamon Central University, BM
Caribbean University, B
Inter American University of Puerto Rico, Aguadilla
Campus, B
Inter American University of Puerto Rico, Arecibo
Campus, AB
Inter American University of Puerto Rico,
Barranquitas Campus, AB
Inter American University of Puerto Rico, Fajardo
Campus, AB
Inter American University of Puerto Rico, Guayama
Campus, AB
Inter American University of Puerto Rico,
Metropolitan Campus, BM
Inter American University of Puerto Rico, Ponce
Campus, B

Inter American University of Puerto Rico, San
Germán Campus, B
Pontifical Catholic University of Puerto Rico, B
Universidad Adventista de las Antillas, B
Universidad Metropolitana, B
Universidad del Turabo, B
University of Puerto Rico at Arecibo, AB
University of Puerto Rico, Cayey University
College, B
University of Puerto Rico at Humacao, B
University of Puerto Rico at Ponce, B
University of Puerto Rico, Río Piedras, B
University of Puerto Rico at Utuado, B
University of the Sacred Heart, B

Rhode Island

Brown University, M
Rhode Island College, BM
Roger Williams University, BM
Salve Regina University, B
University of Rhode Island, BM

South Carolina

Allen University, B
Anderson University, B
Benedict College, B
Bob Jones University, B
Charleston Southern University, BM
Claflin University, B
Clemson University, BM
Coastal Carolina University, BM
Coker College, B
College of Charleston, BM
Columbia College, BM
Columbia International University, M
Converse College, BM
Erskine College, B
Francis Marion University, BM
Furman University, BM
Lander University, BM
Limestone College, B
Morris College, B
Newberry College, B
North Greenville College, B
South Carolina State University, BM
Southern Wesleyan University, B
University of South Carolina, MD
University of South Carolina Aiken, BM
University of South Carolina Upstate, BM
Voorhees College, B
Winthrop University, B

South Dakota

Augustana College, BM
Black Hills State University, B
Dakota State University, B
Dakota Wesleyan University, B
Mount Marty College, B
Northern State University, BM
Oglala Lakota College, AB
Sinte Gleska University, BM
University of Sioux Falls, B
The University of South Dakota, BM

Tennessee

Aquinas College, B
Austin Peay State University, O
Belmont University, BM
Bethel College, BM
Bryan College, B
Carson-Newman College, BM
Christian Brothers University, B
Columbia State Community College, A
Crichton College, B
Cumberland University, B
East Tennessee State University, M
Free Will Baptist Bible College, B
Freed-Hardeman University, B
Johnson Bible College, B
King College, B
Lambuth University, B
Lee University, BM
LeMoyne-Owen College, B
Lincoln Memorial University, B
Lipscomb University, B
Martin Methodist College, B

Middle Tennessee State University, MO
Roane State Community College, A
South College, A
Southern Adventist University, B
Tennessee State University, BMD
Tennessee Technological University, BMO
Tennessee Temple University, B
Tennessee Wesleyan College, B
Trevecca Nazarene University, M
Tusculum College, B
Union University, B
University of Memphis, M
The University of Tennessee, MO
The University of Tennessee at Chattanooga, M
The University of Tennessee at Martin, BM
Vanderbilt University, BM

Texas

Abilene Christian University, BMO
Amarillo College, A
Angelina College, A
Arlington Baptist College, B
Austin College, M
Baylor University, B
Brazosport College, A
Clarendon College, A
Coastal Bend College, A
Concordia University at Austin, B
Dallas Baptist University, BM
Del Mar College, A
East Texas Baptist University, B
El Paso Community College, A
Frank Phillips College, A
Grayson County College, A
Hill College of the Hill Junior College District, A
Houston Baptist University, B
Howard Payne University, B
Huston-Tillotson University, B
Jarvis Christian College, B
Kilgore College, A
Lamar University, B
LeTourneau University, B
Lon Morris College, A
Lubbock Christian University, B
McMurry University, B
Navarro College, A
Northeast Texas Community College, A
Paris Junior College, A
Paul Quinn College, B
Sam Houston State University, M
Schreiner University, B
Southern Methodist University, B
Southwestern Adventist University, BM
Southwestern Assemblies of God University, B
Stephen F. Austin State University, M
Sul Ross State University, BM
Tarleton State University, B
Texas A&M University-Commerce, BMD
Texas A&M University-Corpus Christi, M
Texas A&M University-Kingsville, BM
Texas A&M University-Texarkana, M
Texas Christian University, BMO
Texas College, B
Texas Lutheran University, B
Texas Southern University, BM
Texas State University-San Marcos, M
Texas Tech University, M
Texas Wesleyan University, B
Texas Woman's University, M
Trinity Valley Community College, A
University of Dallas, B
University of Houston, M
University of the Incarnate Word, B
University of Mary Hardin-Baylor, B
University of North Texas, M
University of St. Thomas, B
The University of Texas at Brownsville, M
The University of Texas-Pan American, BM
The University of Texas at San Antonio, M
Wayland Baptist University, B

Wiley College, B

United States Virgin Islands

University of the Virgin Islands, B

Utah

Brigham Young University, B
Dixie State College of Utah, AB
Snow College, A
Southern Utah University, B
University of Phoenix-Utah Campus, M
University of Utah, B
Utah State University, BM
Weber State University, B
Westminster College, B

Vermont

Bennington College, BM
Champlain College, B
College of St. Joseph, BM
Green Mountain College, B
Johnson State College, B
Lyndon State College, B
Saint Michael's College, B
University of Vermont, B

Virginia

Averett University, M
Bluefield College, B
Christopher Newport University, M
The College of William and Mary, M
Eastern Mennonite University, B
Hampton University, BM
Liberty University, BM
Longwood University, BM
Lynchburg College, BM
Mary Baldwin College, M
Marymount University, M
Mountain Empire Community College, A
Old Dominion University, M
Randolph-Macon Woman's College, B
Saint Paul's College, B
Shenandoah University, O
University of Mary Washington, B
Virginia Intermont College, B
Virginia Union University, B
Virginia Wesleyan College, B

Washington

Central Washington University, BM
City University, B
Eastern Washington University, BM
Everett Community College, A
Gonzaga University, B
Heritage University, B
Northwest University, B
Pacific Lutheran University, BM
Saint Martin's University, B
University of Puget Sound, M
University of Washington, B
Walla Walla College, B
Washington State University, BM
Western Washington University, BM
Whitworth College, BM

West Virginia

Alderson-Broaddus College, B
Bluefield State College, B
Concord University, B
Davis & Elkins College, B
Fairmont State University, B
Glenville State College, B
Marshall University, BM
Mountain State University, A
Ohio Valley University, B
Potomac State College of West Virginia
 University, A
Salem International University, BM
Shepherd University, B
University of Charleston, B
West Liberty State College, B
West Virginia State College, B
West Virginia University, BM
West Virginia University at Parkersburg, B
West Virginia Wesleyan College, B

Wheeling Jesuit University, B

Wisconsin

Alverno College, B
Beloit College, B
Cardinal Stritch University, B
Carroll College, B
Carthage College, B
Concordia University Wisconsin, B
Edgewood College, B
Lakeland College, B
Maranatha Baptist Bible College, B
Marian College of Fond du Lac, B
Marquette University, B
Mount Mary College, B
Northland College, B
Ripon College, B
St. Norbert College, B
Silver Lake College, B
University of Wisconsin-Eau Claire, BM
University of Wisconsin-Green Bay, B
University of Wisconsin-La Crosse, BM
University of Wisconsin-Madison, B
University of Wisconsin-Milwaukee, BM
University of Wisconsin-Oshkosh, B
University of Wisconsin-Platteville, BM
University of Wisconsin-River Falls, BM
University of Wisconsin-Stevens Point, BM
University of Wisconsin-Superior, B
University of Wisconsin-Whitewater, B
Viterbo University, B
Wisconsin Lutheran College, B

Wyoming

Casper College, A
Central Wyoming College, A
Eastern Wyoming College, A
Northwest College, A
Sheridan College-Sheridan and Gillette, A
University of Wyoming, B
Western Wyoming Community College, A

Alberta

Concordia University College of Alberta, B
The King's University College, B
University of Alberta, BMD
University of Calgary, B

British Columbia

Thompson Rivers University, B
Trinity Western University, B
The University of British Columbia, B
University of Northern British Columbia, B
University of Victoria, B

Manitoba

Brandon University, B
University of Manitoba, B
The University of Winnipeg, B

New Brunswick

Bethany Bible College, B
Université de Moncton, B
University of New Brunswick Fredericton, B
University of New Brunswick Saint John, B

Newfoundland and Labrador

Memorial University of Newfoundland, B

Nova Scotia

Acadia University, B
Mount Saint Vincent University, BM
St. Francis Xavier University, B
Université Sainte-Anne, B

Ontario

Brock University, B
Lakehead University, B
Queen's University at Kingston, B
Redeemer University College, B
Trent University, B
University of Ottawa, B
The University of Western Ontario, B
University of Windsor, B

York University, B

Prince Edward Island

University of Prince Edward Island, B

Quebec

Bishop's University, B
Concordia University, B
McGill University, B
Université Laval, B
Université de Montréal, B
Université du Québec en Abitibi-Témiscamingue, B
Université du Québec àChicoutimi, B
Université du Québec àMontréal, B
Université du Québec en Outaouais, B
Université du Québec àRimouski, B
Université du Québec àTrois-Rivières, B
Université de Sherbrooke, BMO

Saskatchewan

University of Regina, B
University of Saskatchewan, B

EMERGENCY CARE ATTENDANT (EMT AMBULANCE)

Illinois

Trinity College of Nursing and Health Sciences, A

Iowa

Iowa Lakes Community College, A

Ohio

Columbus State Community College, A

EMERGENCY MEDICAL SERVICES

California

California State University, Long Beach, M
San Diego State University, M
Touro University International, MO

District of Columbia

The George Washington University, O

Florida

Lynn University, MO

Oklahoma

Oklahoma State University, M

Pennsylvania

Drexel University, M

West Virginia

Alderson-Broaddus College, M

Quebec

Université Laval, O
Université de Montréal, O

EMERGENCY MEDICAL TECHNOLOGY/TECHNICIAN (EMT PARAMEDIC)

Alabama

Bevill State Community College, A
Calhoun Community College, A
Faulkner University, A
Gadsden State Community College, A
George C. Wallace Community College, A
H. Councill Trenholm State Technical College, A
Lurleen B. Wallace Community College, A
Northeast Alabama Community College, A
Shelton State Community College, A

Wallace State Community College, A

Alaska

University of Alaska Anchorage, A

Arizona

Central Arizona College, A
Cochise College (Douglas), A
Eastern Arizona College, A
Glendale Community College, A
Northland Pioneer College, A
Phoenix College, A
Pima Community College, A
Scottsdale Community College, A

Arkansas

Arkansas State University, A
Arkansas State University-Mountain Home, A
Black River Technical College, A
Cossatot Community College of the University of
　　Arkansas, A
National Park Community College, A
North Arkansas College, A
NorthWest Arkansas Community College, A
South Arkansas Community College, A
Southeast Arkansas College, A
Southern Arkansas University Tech, A
University of Arkansas Community College at
　　Batesville, A
University of Arkansas for Medical Sciences, A

California

Bakersfield College, A
Cerro Coso Community College, A
Chabot College, A
Compton Community College, A
Contra Costa College, A
Cosumnes River College (Sacramento), A
Crafton Hills College, A
East Los Angeles College, A
Foothill College, A
Loma Linda University, B
Los Medanos College, A
Modesto Junior College, A
Mt. San Antonio College, A
Napa Valley College, A
National Polytechnic College of Engineering and
　　Oceaneering, A
Orange Coast College, A
Palomar College, A
Saddleback College, A
San Diego City College, A
San Diego Miramar College, A
San Joaquin Delta College, A
Santa Rosa Junior College, A
Skyline College, A
Southwestern College, A

Colorado

Arapahoe Community College, A
Colorado Northwestern Community College, A
Community College of Aurora, A
Lamar Community College, A
Northeastern Junior College, A
Pikes Peak Community College, A

Connecticut

Capital Community College, A
Goodwin College, A

Delaware

Delaware Technical & Community College, Jack F.
　　Owens Campus, A
Delaware Technical & Community College,
　　Stanton/Wilmington Campus, A

District of Columbia

The George Washington University, B
University of the District of Columbia, AB

Florida

Brevard Community College, A
Broward Community College, A
Central Florida Community College, A
Daytona Beach Community College, A

Edison College, A
Florida Community College at Jacksonville, A
Gulf Coast Community College, A
Hillsborough Community College, A
Indian River Community College, A
Keiser College (Fort Lauderdale), A
Lake City Community College, A
Lake-Sumter Community College, A
Miami Dade College, A
Pasco-Hernando Community College, A
Pensacola Junior College, A
Polk Community College, A
St. Johns River Community College, A
St. Petersburg College, A
Santa Fe Community College, A
Seminole Community College, A
Tallahassee Community College, A
Valencia Community College, A

Georgia

Athens Technical College, A
Augusta Technical College, A
Clayton State University, A
Columbus Technical College, A
Georgia Highlands College, A
Griffin Technical College, A
Gwinnett Technical College, A
Waycross College, A

Idaho

Brigham Young University -Idaho, A
Idaho State University, A

Illinois

City Colleges of Chicago, Harold Washington
　　College, A
City Colleges of Chicago, Malcolm X College, A
College of DuPage, A
Elgin Community College, A
John A. Logan College, A
John Wood Community College, A
Joliet Junior College, A
Kankakee Community College, A
Kishwaukee College, A
McHenry County College, A
Rend Lake College, A
Southeastern Illinois College, A

Indiana

Ball State University, A
Indiana University-Purdue University Indianapolis, A
Ivy Tech Community College-Bloomington, A
Ivy Tech Community College-Kokomo, A
Ivy Tech Community College-North Central, A
Ivy Tech Community College-Southwest, A
Ivy Tech Community College-Wabash Valley, A
University of Saint Francis, A

Iowa

Clinton Community College, A
Iowa Lakes Community College, A
Muscatine Community College, A
North Iowa Area Community College, A
Northwest Iowa Community College, A
Scott Community College, A
Southeastern Community College, North Campus, A
Southeastern Community College, South
　　Campus, A
Western Iowa Tech Community College, A

Kansas

Allen County Community College, A
Barton County Community College, A
Coffeyville Community College, A
Cowley County Community College and Area
　　Vocational-Technical School, A
Fort Scott Community College, A
Garden City Community College, A
Highland Community College, A
Hutchinson Community College and Area Vocational
　　School, A
Independence Community College, A
Johnson County Community College, A

Kansas City Kansas Community College, A

Kentucky

Eastern Kentucky University, AB
Spalding University, A
Western Kentucky University, A

Louisiana

Bossier Parish Community College, A
Delgado Community College, A
Elaine P. Nunez Community College, A
Nicholls State University, A
Our Lady of the Lake College, A

Maine

Kennebec Valley Community College, A
Northern Maine Community College, A

Maryland

Anne Arundel Community College, A
Baltimore City Community College, A
College of Southern Maryland, A
Frederick Community College, A
Hagerstown Community College, A
Howard Community College, A
Prince George's Community College, A
University of Maryland, Baltimore County, B
Wor-Wic Community College, A

Massachusetts

Quincy College, A
Quinsigamond Community College, A
Springfield College, B

Michigan

Baker College of Cadillac, A
Baker College of Clinton Township, A
Baker College of Muskegon, A
Davenport University (Midland), A
Delta College, A
Henry Ford Community College, A
Jackson Community College, A
Kalamazoo Valley Community College, A
Kellogg Community College, A
Lansing Community College, A
Macomb Community College, A
Mid Michigan Community College, A
Montcalm Community College, A
Mott Community College, A
Muskegon Community College, A
North Central Michigan College, A
Oakland Community College, A
Schoolcraft College, A
Wayne County Community College District, A
West Shore Community College, A

Minnesota

Century College, A
Inver Hills Community College, A
Lake Superior College, A
Minnesota State College-Southeast Technical, A
Northwest Technical College, A
St. Cloud Technical College, A
South Central Technical College, A
University of Minnesota, Twin Cities Campus, B

Mississippi

Hinds Community College, A
Jones County Junior College, A
Meridian Community College, A
Mississippi Gulf Coast Community College, A
Southwest Mississippi Community College, A

Missouri

East Central College, A
Hannibal-LaGrange College, A
IHM Health Studies Center, A
Jefferson College, A
Missouri Western State University, A
North Central Missouri College, A
Ozarks Technical Community College, A
Penn Valley Community College, A
St. Louis Community College at Florissant Valley, A
St. Louis Community College at Meramec, A

Southwest Baptist University, A

Montana

Montana State University-Billings, A
Montana State University-Great Falls College of
  Technology, A

Nebraska

Creighton University, AB
Nebraska Methodist College, AB
Northeast Community College, A

Nevada

Community College of Southern Nevada, A

New Hampshire

New Hampshire Technical Institute, A

New Jersey

Essex County College, A

New Mexico

Doña Ana Branch Community College, A
Eastern New Mexico University-Roswell, A
New Mexico Junior College, A

New York

Borough of Manhattan Community College of the
  City University of New York, A
Broome Community College, A
Corning Community College, A
Dutchess Community College, A
Fiorello H. LaGuardia Community College of the
  City University of New York, A
Herkimer County Community College, A
Hudson Valley Community College, A
Mohawk Valley Community College, A
Rockland Community College, A
Westchester Community College, A

North Carolina

Asheville-Buncombe Technical Community
  College, A
Catawba Valley Community College, A
Coastal Carolina Community College, A
Davidson County Community College, A
Fayetteville Technical Community College, A
Guilford Technical Community College, A
Montgomery Community College, A
Southwestern Community College, A
Wake Technical Community College, A
Western Carolina University, B

North Dakota

Bismarck State College, A
Turtle Mountain Community College, A

Ohio

Belmont Technical College, A
Cincinnati State Technical and Community
  College, A
Clark State Community College, A
Columbus State Community College, A
Hocking College, A
James A. Rhodes State College, A
Jefferson Community College, A
Kent State University, Geauga Campus, A
Shawnee State University, A
Sinclair Community College, A
Southern State Community College, A
University of Cincinnati Raymond Walters College, A
The University of Toledo, A
Youngstown State University, A

Oklahoma

Oklahoma City Community College, A
Redlands Community College, A
Rogers State University, A
Tulsa Community College, A
Western Oklahoma State College, A

Oregon

Central Oregon Community College, A
Chemeketa Community College, A

Tillamook Bay Community College, A
Umpqua Community College, A

Pennsylvania

Butler County Community College, A
Harrisburg Area Community College, A
Lackawanna College, A
Luzerne County Community College, A
Pennsylvania College of Technology, A
Saint Francis University, A
University of Pittsburgh at Johnstown, A

Puerto Rico

Inter American University of Puerto Rico,
  Metropolitan Campus, A

South Carolina

Greenville Technical College, A

Tennessee

Chattanooga State Technical Community College, A
Northeast State Technical Community College, A
Roane State Community College, A

Texas

Alvin Community College, A
Amarillo College, A
Angelina College, A
Austin Community College, A
Brazosport College, A
Brookhaven College, A
Central Texas College, A
College of the Mainland, A
Collin County Community College District, A
Del Mar College, A
El Centro College, A
Galveston College, A
Houston Community College System, A
Kilgore College, A
Laredo Community College, A
Lee College, A
Midland College, A
North Central Texas College, A
North Harris College, A
Odessa College, A
South Texas College, A
Tarrant County College District, A
Texarkana College, A
Texas Southmost College, A
Texas State Technical College West Texas, A
Trinity Valley Community College, A
Victoria College, A
Weatherford College, A

Utah

Dixie State College of Utah, A
Weber State University, A

Virginia

Jefferson College of Health Sciences, A
Northern Virginia Community College, A
Piedmont Virginia Community College, A

Washington

Central Washington University, B
Clark College, A
Tacoma Community College, A

West Virginia

Community and Technical College of Shepherd, A
Fairmont State Community & Technical College, A
Marshall Community and Technical College, A
Mountain State University, A

Wisconsin

Madison Area Technical College, A
Northeast Wisconsin Technical College, A

Wisconsin Indianhead Technical College, A

Wyoming

Casper College, A

ENERGY AND POWER ENGINEERING

Illinois

Southern Illinois University Carbondale, D

Massachusetts

University of Massachusetts Lowell, MD

New York

New York Institute of Technology, O
Rensselaer Polytechnic Institute, MDO

Tennessee

University of Memphis, M

Wisconsin

University of Wisconsin-Madison, M

Alberta

University of Alberta, MD

ENERGY MANAGEMENT AND POLICY

California

University of California, Berkeley, MD

Massachusetts

Boston University, M

New York

New York Institute of Technology, MO

Quebec

Université du Québec àTrois-Rivières, MD

ENERGY MANAGEMENT AND SYSTEMS TECHNOLOGY/TECHNICIAN

California

Cabrillo College, A
Lassen Community College District, A

Iowa

Iowa Lakes Community College, A

Kansas

Pratt Community College, A

Massachusetts

Fitchburg State College, B

Michigan

Baker College of Flint, A
Henry Ford Community College, A
Macomb Community College, A

Montana

Miles Community College, A

North Dakota

Bismarck State College, A

Ohio

University of Cincinnati, A
University of Rio Grande, A

Oregon

Lane Community College, A

Pennsylvania

Community College of Allegheny County, A
Delaware County Community College, A

The Williamson Free School of Mechanical Trades, A

Tennessee

Chattanooga State Technical Community College, A

Texas

Lamar University, B

Vermont

Sterling College, B

ENGINE MACHINIST

Illinois

Black Hawk College, A

ENGINEERING

Alabama

Alabama Southern Community College, A
Auburn University, B
Marion Military Institute, A
Oakwood College, B
Samford University, B
Spring Hill College, B
The University of Alabama in Huntsville, B
Wallace State Community College, A

Arizona

Arizona State University at the Polytechnic Campus, B
Central Arizona College, A
Northern Arizona University, B
The University of Arizona, B

Arkansas

Arkansas State University, B
Arkansas Tech University, B
John Brown University, B

California

Allan Hancock College, A
Antelope Valley College, A
Bakersfield College, A
California Institute of Technology, B
California National University for Advanced Studies, B
California State University, Chico, B
California State University, Fullerton, B
California State University, Long Beach, B
California State University, Los Angeles, B
California State University, Northridge, B
Cañada College, A
Chabot College, A
Chaffey College, A
Citrus College, A
Claremont McKenna College, B
College of Marin, A
College of San Mateo, A
College of the Sequoias, A
Compton Community College, A
Contra Costa College, A
Cuesta College, A
Cypress College, A
De Anza College, A
East Los Angeles College, A
El Camino College, A
Evergreen Valley College, A
Fresno City College, A
Harvey Mudd College, B
Laney College, A
Long Beach City College, A
Los Angeles City College, A
Los Angeles Southwest College, A
Los Angeles Trade-Technical College, A
Los Angeles Valley College, A
Mills College, B
Modesto Junior College, A
Monterey Peninsula College, A
Moorpark College, A
Mt. San Jacinto College, A

Napa Valley College, A
Orange Coast College, A
Pacific Union College, B
Palomar College, A
Pasadena City College, A
Pitzer College, B
Sacramento City College, A
Saddleback College, A
Saint Mary's College of California, B
San Diego Mesa College, A
San Diego State University, B
San Joaquin Delta College, A
San Jose City College, A
San Jose State University, B
Santa Ana College, A
Santa Barbara City College, A
Santa Clara University, B
Santa Rosa Junior College, A
Sierra College, A
Southwestern College, A
Stanford University, B
University of California, Davis, B
University of California, Los Angeles, B
University of California, San Diego, B
University of Southern California, B
Ventura College, A
West Los Angeles College, A

Colorado

Colorado School of Mines, B
Lamar Community College, A
Mesa State College, A
Trinidad State Junior College, A
United States Air Force Academy, B
University of Denver, B

Connecticut

Fairfield University, B
Mitchell College, A
Northwestern Connecticut Community College, A
Three Rivers Community College, A
Trinity College, B
Tunxis Community College, A
University of Connecticut, B
University of Hartford, B
University of New Haven, B

Delaware

Delaware Technical & Community College, Jack F. Owens Campus, A
Delaware Technical & Community College, Stanton/Wilmington Campus, A
University of Delaware, B

District of Columbia

The Catholic University of America, B
Gallaudet University, B
The George Washington University, B

Florida

Barry University, B
Daytona Beach Community College, A
Edison College, A
Hillsborough Community College, A
Indian River Community College, A
Manatee Community College, A
Miami Dade College, A
Okaloosa-Walton College, A
Palm Beach Atlantic University, A
Santa Fe Community College, A
Tallahassee Community College, A
University of South Florida, B

Georgia

Clark Atlanta University, B
Clayton State University, A
Columbus State University, A
Georgia Military College, A
Macon State College, A
Mercer University, B
Morehouse College, B

Spelman College, B

Hawaii

Hawaii Pacific University, B

Idaho

Brigham Young University -Idaho, A
College of Southern Idaho, A
Idaho State University, B
North Idaho College, A
University of Idaho, B

Illinois

Augustana College, B
City Colleges of Chicago, Harold Washington
  College, A
City Colleges of Chicago, Kennedy-King College, A
City Colleges of Chicago, Olive-Harvey College, A
City Colleges of Chicago, Wilbur Wright College, A
College of DuPage, A
College of Lake County, A
Danville Area Community College, A
Eastern Illinois University, B
Heartland Community College, A
Highland Community College, A
Kankakee Community College, A
Kishwaukee College, A
McHenry County College, A
Northwestern University, B
Oakton Community College, A
Olivet Nazarene University, B
Principia College, B
Rend Lake College, A
University of Illinois at Urbana-Champaign, B
Waubonsee Community College, A
Wheaton College, B
William Rainey Harper College, A

Indiana

Bethel College, B
Indiana University-Purdue University Indianapolis, B
Purdue University, B
Purdue University Calumet, B
Rose-Hulman Institute of Technology, B
University of Southern Indiana, B
Vincennes University, A

Iowa

Dordt College, B
Iowa Lakes Community College, A
Iowa State University of Science and Technology, B
Kirkwood Community College, A
Loras College, B
Southeastern Community College, North Campus, A
The University of Iowa, B
Wartburg College, B

Kansas

Allen County Community College, A
Central Christian College of Kansas, A
Coffeyville Community College, A
Dodge City Community College, A
Donnelly College, A
Garden City Community College, A
Hutchinson Community College and Area Vocational
  School, A
Independence Community College, A
Kansas Wesleyan University, B

Kentucky

Brescia University, A
Eastern Kentucky University, A
Kentucky Wesleyan College, B
University of Louisville, B

Louisiana

McNeese State University, B
University of Louisiana at Lafayette, B

Maine

Bates College, B
Maine Maritime Academy, B

Southern Maine Community College, A

Maryland

Baltimore City Community College, A
Columbia Union College, A
Frederick Community College, A
Hagerstown Community College, A
Harford Community College, A
Hood College, B
Howard Community College, A
The Johns Hopkins University, B
Loyola College in Maryland, B
Montgomery College, A
Morgan State University, B
Prince George's Community College, A
United States Naval Academy, B
University of Maryland, College Park, B

Massachusetts

Berkshire Community College, A
Boston University, B
Bristol Community College, A
Clark University, B
Harvard University, B
Massachusetts Maritime Academy, B
Northeastern University, B
Springfield Technical Community College, A
Tufts University, B
University of Massachusetts Amherst, B
Worcester Polytechnic Institute, B

Michigan

Calvin College, B
Gogebic Community College, A
Grand Valley State University, B
Hope College, B
Kellogg Community College, A
Lake Superior State University, A
Lansing Community College, A
Macomb Community College, A
Madonna University, B
Michigan State University, B
Michigan Technological University, B
Northwestern Michigan College, A
Oakland Community College, A
Oakland University, B
Schoolcraft College, A
University of Detroit Mercy, B
University of Michigan, B
University of Michigan-Dearborn, B
Wayne State University, B
Western Michigan University, B

Minnesota

Bethany Lutheran College, B
Dunwoody College of Technology, A
Itasca Community College, A
Ridgewater College, A
St. Cloud State University, B
Vermilion Community College, A
Winona State University, B

Mississippi

Copiah-Lincoln Community College, A
East Central Community College, A
Holmes Community College, A
Northeast Mississippi Community College, A
Southwest Mississippi Community College, A
University of Mississippi, B

Missouri

College of the Ozarks, B
Drury University, B
East Central College, A
Fontbonne University, B
Jefferson College, A
Longview Community College, A
Metropolitan Community College-Business &
  Technology College, A
Missouri State University-West Plains, A
Park University, B
Penn Valley Community College, A
St. Louis Community College at Florissant Valley, A
St. Louis Community College at Forest Park, A

Washington University in St. Louis, B

Montana

Carroll College, B
Montana State University-Billings, A
Montana Tech of The University of Montana, AB

Nebraska

Northeast Community College, A
Union College, A
University of Nebraska-Lincoln, B

Nevada

Western Nevada Community College, A

New Hampshire

Daniel Webster College, A
Dartmouth College, B
Saint Anselm College, B

New Jersey

Brookdale Community College, A
Burlington County College, A
Cumberland County College, A
Middlesex County College, A
Ocean County College, A
Raritan Valley Community College, A
Rutgers, The State University of New Jersey,
  Camden, B
Rutgers, The State University of New Jersey,
  Newark, B
Union County College, A

New Mexico

Central New Mexico Community College, A
National American University (Albuquerque), B
New Mexico Highlands University, B
New Mexico Junior College, A
New Mexico Military Institute, A
New Mexico State University-Alamogordo, A
San Juan College, A
Santa Fe Community College, A
University of New Mexico-Los Alamos Branch, A

New York

Adirondack Community College, A
Buffalo State College, State University of New
  York, B
Canisius College, B
Clarkson University, B
College of Staten Island of the City University of
  New York, AB
Cooper Union for the Advancement of Science and
  Art, B
Dowling College, B
Erie Community College, North Campus, A
Jamestown Community College, A
Manhattan College, B
Mohawk Valley Community College, A
Nassau Community College, A
New York University, B
Rensselaer Polytechnic Institute, B
Rochester Institute of Technology, B
Russell Sage College, B
State University of New York College of Agriculture
  and Technology at Morrisville, A
State University of New York Maritime College, B
Stony Brook University, State University of New
  York, B
Suffolk County Community College, A
Syracuse University, B
Ulster County Community College, A
United States Military Academy, B
Wells College, B

North Carolina

Campbell University, A
Elon University, B
Johnson C. Smith University, B
Mitchell Community College, A
North Carolina State University, B
Pfeiffer University, B

Wake Forest University, B

North Dakota

North Dakota State University, B

Ohio

Case Western Reserve University, B
Cleveland State University, B
Edison State Community College, A
Lorain County Community College, A
Miami University-Middletown Campus, A
Northwest State Community College, A
Ohio Northern University, B
Ohio University, B
Ohio University-Eastern, B
Ohio Wesleyan University, B
Sinclair Community College, A
Terra State Community College, A
The University of Akron, B
The University of Akron-Wayne College, A
University of Cincinnati, B
The University of Toledo, B
Washington State Community College, A
Wright State University, B
Wright State University, Lake Campus, A
Youngstown State University, B

Oklahoma

Connors State College, A
Murray State College, A
Northern Oklahoma College, A
Oklahoma Christian University, B
Oklahoma State University, B
Oklahoma State University, Oklahoma City, A
Tulsa Community College, A
University of Oklahoma, B

Oregon

Chemeketa Community College, A
George Fox University, B
Linn-Benton Community College, A
Oregon State University, B
Portland Community College, A
Southwestern Oregon Community College, A
Treasure Valley Community College, A
Umpqua Community College, A
University of Portland, B

Pennsylvania

Bucks County Community College, A
Carnegie Mellon University, B
Chatham College, B
Community College of Philadelphia, A
Delaware County Community College, A
Dickinson College, B
Drexel University, B
Elizabethtown College, B
Geneva College, AB
Gettysburg College, B
Harrisburg Area Community College, A
Juniata College, B
Lafayette College, B
Lehigh Carbon Community College, A
Lehigh University, B
Lock Haven University of Pennsylvania, B
Messiah College, B
Northampton County Area Community College, A
Reading Area Community College, A
Robert Morris University, B
Saint Francis University, B
Saint Vincent College, B
Seton Hill University, B
Swarthmore College, B
University of Pennsylvania, B
University of Pittsburgh, B
Valley Forge Military College, A
Waynesburg College, B
Westmoreland County Community College, A
Widener University, B
Wilkes University, B

York College of Pennsylvania, A

Puerto Rico

Inter American University of Puerto Rico, Bayamón
Campus, B

Rhode Island

Brown University, B
Community College of Rhode Island, A

South Carolina

Charleston Southern University, B
Piedmont Technical College, A

Tennessee

Chattanooga State Technical Community College, A
Lipscomb University, B
Maryville College, B
Roane State Community College, A
Southern Adventist University, A
Tennessee State University, B
The University of Tennessee at Chattanooga, B
The University of Tennessee at Martin, B
Vanderbilt University, B

Texas

Abilene Christian University, B
Amarillo College, A
Angelina College, A
Baylor University, B
Brazosport College, A
Central Texas College, A
Clarendon College, A
Coastal Bend College, A
Frank Phillips College, A
Hill College of the Hill Junior College District, A
LeTourneau University, B
Lon Morris College, A
Lubbock Christian University, B
Navarro College, A
Palo Alto College, A
Paris Junior College, A
Richland College, A
St. Mary's University of San Antonio, B
Schreiner University, B
South Plains College, A
Southwest Texas Junior College, A
Texarkana College, A
Texas Christian University, B
Texas Tech University, B
Texas Wesleyan University, B
University of Houston-Downtown, B
University of the Incarnate Word, B
The University of Texas-Pan American, B

Utah

Dixie State College of Utah, A
Salt Lake Community College, A
Snow College, A
University of Utah, B

Virginia

J. Sargeant Reynolds Community College, A
New River Community College, A
Northern Virginia Community College, A
Piedmont Virginia Community College, A
Southwest Virginia Community College, A
Thomas Nelson Community College, A
Tidewater Community College, A
University of Virginia, B
Virginia Western Community College, A

Washington

Centralia College, A
Columbia Basin College, A
Everett Community College, A
Gonzaga University, B
Highline Community College, A
Lower Columbia College, A
Olympic College, A
South Seattle Community College, A
Tacoma Community College, A
University of Washington, B
Walla Walla College, B

Western Washington University, B

West Virginia

Mountain State University, A
Potomac State College of West Virginia
University, A
West Virginia University Institute of Technology, B

Wisconsin

Beloit College, B
Carthage College, B
Marquette University, B
University of Wisconsin-Madison, B
University of Wisconsin-Milwaukee, B

Wyoming

Casper College, A
Laramie County Community College, A
Northwest College, A
Sheridan College-Sheridan and Gillette, A

Alberta

University of Alberta, B

British Columbia

British Columbia Institute of Technology, A
Thompson Rivers University, A

New Brunswick

Université de Moncton, B
University of New Brunswick Fredericton, B

Newfoundland and Labrador

Memorial University of Newfoundland, B

Nova Scotia

Cape Breton University, B
Dalhousie University, B
Nova Scotia Agricultural College, B
Saint Mary's University, B

Ontario

Carleton University, B
Lakehead University, B
Queen's University at Kingston, B
University of Ottawa, B
University of Toronto, B
University of Waterloo, B
University of Windsor, B
York University, B

Quebec

McGill University, B
Université Laval, B
Université du Québec en Abitibi-Témiscamingue, B
Université du Québec àChicoutimi, B
Universite du Quebec, Ecole de technologie
superieure, B
Université du Québec àRimouski, B
Université de Sherbrooke, B

Saskatchewan

University of Regina, B
University of Saskatchewan, B

ENGINEERING AND APPLIED SCIENCES

Alabama

Alabama Agricultural and Mechanical University, M
Auburn University, MD
Tuskegee University, MD
The University of Alabama, MD
The University of Alabama at Birmingham, MD
The University of Alabama in Huntsville, MD

University of South Alabama, M

Alaska

University of Alaska Anchorage, M
University of Alaska Fairbanks, D

Arizona

Arizona State University, MDO
Arizona State University at the Polytechnic
    Campus, M
Northern Arizona University, MDO
The University of Arizona, MD

Arkansas

University of Arkansas, MD

California

California Institute of Technology, MDO
California National University for Advanced
    Studies, M
California Polytechnic State University, San Luis
    Obispo, MO
California State Polytechnic University, Pomona, M
California State University, Chico, M
California State University, Fresno, M
California State University, Fullerton, M
California State University, Los Angeles, M
California State University, Northridge, M
California State University, Sacramento, M
Golden Gate University, MO
Loyola Marymount University, MO
National University, M
Northwestern Polytechnic University, M
San Diego State University, MD
San Francisco State University, M
San Jose State University, M
Santa Clara University, MDO
Stanford University, MDO
University of California, Berkeley, MDO
University of California, Davis, MDO
University of California, Irvine, MD
University of California, Los Angeles, MDO
University of California, Santa Barbara, MDO
University of California, Santa Cruz, MD
University of Southern California, MDO

Colorado

Colorado School of Mines, MDO
Colorado State University, MD
Colorado State University-Pueblo, M
University of Colorado at Boulder, MDO
University of Colorado at Colorado Springs, MD
University of Colorado at Denver and Health
    Sciences Center - Downtown Denver Campus, M
University of Denver, MD

Connecticut

Central Connecticut State University, M
Fairfield University, M
University of Bridgeport, M
University of Connecticut, MD
University of Hartford, M
University of New Haven, MO
Yale University, MD

Delaware

University of Delaware, MD

District of Columbia

The Catholic University of America, MD
The George Washington University, MDO
Howard University, MD

Florida

Florida Agricultural and Mechanical University, MD
Florida Atlantic University, MD
Florida Institute of Technology, MD
Florida International University, MD
Florida State University, MD
University of Central Florida, MDO
University of Florida, MDO
University of Miami, MDO

University of South Florida, MD

Georgia

Georgia Institute of Technology, MDO
Georgia Southern University, M
Mercer University, M
Southern Polytechnic State University, M

Hawaii

University of Hawaii at Manoa, MD

Idaho

Idaho State University, MDO
University of Idaho, MDO

Illinois

Bradley University, M
Eastern Illinois University, MO
Illinois Institute of Technology, MDO
Northern Illinois University, M
Northwestern University, MDO
Southern Illinois University Carbondale, MD
Southern Illinois University Edwardsville, M
University of Illinois at Chicago, MDO
University of Illinois at Urbana-Champaign, MDO

Indiana

Indiana State University, MD
Indiana University-Purdue University Fort Wayne, M
Purdue University, MD
Purdue University Calumet, M
Rose-Hulman Institute of Technology, MO
Tri-State University, M
University of Evansville, M
University of Notre Dame, MD
University of Southern Indiana, M

Iowa

Iowa State University of Science and
    Technology, MD
The University of Iowa, MD

Kansas

Kansas State University, MD
Pittsburg State University, M
University of Kansas, MD
Wichita State University, MD

Kentucky

University of Kentucky, MD
University of Louisville, MDO

Louisiana

Louisiana State University and Agricultural and
    Mechanical College, MD
Louisiana Tech University, MD
McNeese State University, M
University of New Orleans, MDO

Maine

University of Maine, MD

Maryland

The Johns Hopkins University, MD
Loyola College in Maryland, M
Morgan State University, MD
University of Maryland, Baltimore County, MDO
University of Maryland, College Park, MDO

Massachusetts

Boston University, MDO
Harvard University, MD
Massachusetts Institute of Technology, MDO
Northeastern University, MD
Tufts University, MD
University of Massachusetts Amherst, MD
University of Massachusetts Dartmouth, MDO
University of Massachusetts Lowell, MDO
Western New England College, M
Worcester Polytechnic Institute, MDO

Michigan

Andrews University, M
Grand Valley State University, M

Kettering University, M
Lawrence Technological University, MD
Michigan State University, MD
Michigan Technological University, MD
Oakland University, MD
Saginaw Valley State University, M
University of Detroit Mercy, MD
University of Michigan, MDO
University of Michigan-Dearborn, MDO
Wayne State University, MDO
Western Michigan University, MD

Minnesota

St. Cloud State University, M
University of Minnesota, Twin Cities Campus, MDO
University of St. Thomas, MO
Walden University, M

Mississippi

Mississippi State University, MD
University of Mississippi, MD
University of Southern Mississippi, M

Missouri

Central Missouri State University, MO
University of Missouri-Columbia, MD
University of Missouri-Kansas City, MD
University of Missouri-Rolla, MD
Washington University in St. Louis, MDO

Montana

Montana State University, MD
Montana Tech of The University of Montana, M

Nebraska

University of Nebraska-Lincoln, MDO

Nevada

University of Nevada, Las Vegas, MD
University of Nevada, Reno, MDO

New Hampshire

Dartmouth College, MDO

New Jersey

Fairleigh Dickinson University, Metropolitan
    Campus, M
New Jersey Institute of Technology, MDO
Rowan University, M
Rutgers, The State University of New Jersey, New
    Brunswick/Piscataway, MD
Stevens Institute of Technology, MDO

New Mexico

New Mexico State University, MD
University of New Mexico, MD

New York

City College of the City University of New York, MD
Clarkson University, MD
Cornell University, MDO
Manhattan College, M
New York Institute of Technology, MO
Rensselaer Polytechnic Institute, MDO
Rochester Institute of Technology, MDO
State University of New York at Binghamton, MD
State University of New York at Buffalo, MD
State University of New York Institute of
    Technology, M
Stony Brook University, State University of New
    York, MDO
Syracuse University, MDO
University of Rochester, MD

North Carolina

Duke University, MDO
North Carolina Agricultural and Technical State
    University, MD
North Carolina State University, MD

The University of North Carolina at Charlotte, MD

North Dakota

North Dakota State University, MD
University of North Dakota, D

Ohio

Case Western Reserve University, MDO
Cleveland State University, MD
Kent State University, M
Miami University, MO
The Ohio State University, MD
Ohio University, MD
The University of Akron, MDO
University of Cincinnati, MDO
University of Dayton, MD
The University of Toledo, M
Wright State University, MD
Youngstown State University, M

Oklahoma

Oklahoma State University, MD
University of Oklahoma, MD
University of Tulsa, MDO

Oregon

Oregon State University, MD
Portland State University, MDO
University of Portland, M

Pennsylvania

Bucknell University, M
Carnegie Mellon University, MD
Drexel University, MD
Lehigh University, MDO
The Pennsylvania State University Harrisburg
   Campus, M
The Pennsylvania State University University Park
   Campus, MD
Temple University, MD
University of Pennsylvania, MDO
University of Pittsburgh, MDO
Villanova University, MDO
Widener University, MO
Wilkes University, M

Puerto Rico

University of Puerto Rico, Mayagüez Campus, MD

Rhode Island

Brown University, MD
University of Rhode Island, MD

South Carolina

Clemson University, MD
University of South Carolina, MD

South Dakota

South Dakota School of Mines and Technology, MD
South Dakota State University, MD

Tennessee

Christian Brothers University, M
Tennessee State University, MD
Tennessee Technological University, MD
University of Memphis, MD
The University of Tennessee, MDO
The University of Tennessee at Chattanooga, M
Vanderbilt University, MDO

Texas

Baylor University, M
Lamar University, MD
Prairie View A&M University, MD
Rice University, MDO
St. Mary's University of San Antonio, MO
Southern Methodist University, MD
Texas A&M University, MD
Texas A&M University-Kingsville, MD
Texas Tech University, MD
University of Houston, MDO
University of North Texas, M
The University of Texas at Arlington, MD
The University of Texas at Austin, MDO

The University of Texas at Dallas, MD
The University of Texas at El Paso, MD
The University of Texas at San Antonio, MD
The University of Texas at Tyler, M
West Texas A&M University, M

Utah

Brigham Young University, MDO
University of Utah, MDO
Utah State University, MDO

Vermont

University of Vermont, MD

Virginia

George Mason University, MDO
Old Dominion University, MD
University of Virginia, MDO
Virginia Commonwealth University, MDO
Virginia Polytechnic Institute and State
   University, MD

Washington

Central Washington University, M
Seattle University, M
University of Washington, MD
Washington State University, MD

West Virginia

Marshall University, M
West Virginia University, MD
West Virginia University Institute of Technology, M

Wisconsin

Marquette University, MD
Milwaukee School of Engineering, M
University of Wisconsin-Madison, MDO
University of Wisconsin-Milwaukee, MDO
University of Wisconsin-Platteville, M

Wyoming

University of Wyoming, MD

Alberta

University of Calgary, MD

British Columbia

Simon Fraser University, MD
The University of British Columbia, MD
University of Victoria, MD

Manitoba

University of Manitoba, MD

New Brunswick

Université de Moncton, M
University of New Brunswick Fredericton, MDO

Newfoundland and Labrador

Memorial University of Newfoundland, MD

Nova Scotia

Dalhousie University, MDO

Ontario

Carleton University, MD
Lakehead University, M
Laurentian University, M
McMaster University, MD
Queen's University at Kingston, MD
Royal Military College of Canada, MD
University of Guelph, MD
University of Ottawa, MDO
University of Toronto, MD
University of Waterloo, MD
The University of Western Ontario, MD
University of Windsor, MD

Quebec

Concordia University, MDO
McGill University, MDO
Université Laval, MDO
Université du Québec àChicoutimi, MD

Universite du Quebec, Ecole de technologie
   superieure, MDO
Université de Sherbrooke, MDO

Saskatchewan

University of Regina, MD
University of Saskatchewan, MDO

ENGINEERING DESIGN

California

San Diego State University, M
Santa Clara University, O
Stanford University, M

Connecticut

University of New Haven, O

District of Columbia

The Catholic University of America, D

Florida

University of Central Florida, O

Illinois

University of Illinois at Urbana-Champaign, MO

Michigan

Kettering University, M

New York

Rochester Institute of Technology, M

ENGINEERING/INDUSTRIAL MANAGEMENT

Arizona

The University of Arizona, B

Arkansas

John Brown University, B

California

California State University, Long Beach, B
Claremont McKenna College, B
University of the Pacific, B

Colorado

Fort Lewis College, B

Florida

St. Petersburg College, A

Illinois

Illinois Institute of Technology, B
University of Illinois at Chicago, B

Indiana

International Business College (Fort Wayne), AB
Tri-State University, B
University of Evansville, B

Massachusetts

University of Massachusetts Lowell, B
Worcester Polytechnic Institute, B

Michigan

Grand Valley State University, B
Kettering University, B
Lake Superior State University, B
Lawrence Technological University, B
Saginaw Valley State University, B
Western Michigan University, B

Missouri

Grantham University, AB
Missouri Tech, B
Saint Louis University, B

University of Missouri-Rolla, B

New Jersey

Stevens Institute of Technology, B

New York

Columbia University, The Fu Foundation School of
   Engineering and Applied Science, B
Farmingdale State University of New York, B
United States Merchant Marine Academy, B
United States Military Academy, B

North Carolina

Cape Fear Community College, A
Pitt Community College, A

Ohio

Miami University, B
Miami University Hamilton, B

Oregon

University of Portland, B

Pennsylvania

Robert Morris University, B
Widener University, B
Wilkes University, B
York College of Pennsylvania, B

Puerto Rico

Caribbean University, B

South Carolina

Clemson University, B

South Dakota

South Dakota State University, B

Tennessee

Middle Tennessee State University, B
The University of Tennessee at Chattanooga, B

Vermont

University of Vermont, B

Wisconsin

University of Wisconsin-Stout, B

Ontario

McMaster University, B
University of Ottawa, B

Quebec

Université du Québec àTrois-Rivières, B

ENGINEERING MANAGEMENT

Alaska

University of Alaska Anchorage, M
University of Alaska Fairbanks, M

California

California State University, Long Beach, M
California State University, Northridge, M
Loyola Marymount University, MO
National University, M
Santa Clara University, M
Stanford University, MD
University of California, Berkeley, MD
University of Southern California, M

Colorado

Colorado School of Mines, M
Colorado State University, M
University of Colorado at Boulder, M

University of Colorado at Colorado Springs, M

Connecticut

University of New Haven, M

District of Columbia

The Catholic University of America, M
The George Washington University, MDO

Florida

Florida Institute of Technology, M
University of Central Florida, M
University of South Florida, MD

Georgia

Mercer University, M

Illinois

Northwestern University, MD

Indiana

Rose-Hulman Institute of Technology, M

Kansas

Kansas State University, M
University of Kansas, M

Kentucky

University of Louisville, M

Louisiana

McNeese State University, M
University of Louisiana at Lafayette, M
University of New Orleans, MO

Maryland

University of Maryland, Baltimore County, M

Massachusetts

Massachusetts Institute of Technology, M
Northeastern University, M
Tufts University, M
University of Massachusetts Amherst, M

Michigan

Kettering University, M
Lawrence Technological University, M
Michigan State University, M
Oakland University, M
University of Detroit Mercy, M
University of Michigan-Dearborn, M
Wayne State University, M
Western Michigan University, M

Minnesota

St. Cloud State University, M
University of Minnesota, Duluth, M
University of St. Thomas, MO
Walden University, M

Missouri

University of Missouri-Rolla, MD

New Hampshire

Dartmouth College, MO

New Jersey

New Jersey Institute of Technology, M

New Mexico

New Mexico Institute of Mining and Technology, M

New York

Clarkson University, M
Cornell University, MD
Hofstra University, M
Long Island University, C.W. Post Campus, M
Rensselaer Polytechnic Institute, MDO
Rochester Institute of Technology, M

Syracuse University, M

North Carolina

Duke University, M
The University of North Carolina at Charlotte, M

Ohio

Case Western Reserve University, M
The University of Akron, M
University of Dayton, M

Oklahoma

Oklahoma State University, M
University of Tulsa, M

Oregon

Portland State University, MDO

Pennsylvania

Drexel University, MD
Gannon University, M
The Pennsylvania State University University Park
   Campus, M
Point Park University, M
Robert Morris University, MD
Widener University, M

Puerto Rico

Polytechnic University of Puerto Rico, M

Tennessee

The University of Tennessee, M
The University of Tennessee at Chattanooga, M

Texas

Dallas Baptist University, M
Lamar University, M
St. Mary's University of San Antonio, M
Southern Methodist University, MD
Texas Tech University, M

Virginia

Old Dominion University, MD
Virginia Polytechnic Institute and State University, M

Washington

Saint Martin's University, M

Wisconsin

Marquette University, M
Milwaukee School of Engineering, M

Alberta

University of Alberta, M

Ontario

University of Ottawa, MO
University of Waterloo, MD

Quebec

Université de Sherbrooke, MO

ENGINEERING MECHANICS

Colorado

United States Air Force Academy, B

Illinois

University of Illinois at Urbana-Champaign, B

Iowa

Dordt College, B

Maryland

The Johns Hopkins University, B

Massachusetts

Wentworth Institute of Technology, B
Worcester Polytechnic Institute, B

Michigan

Michigan Technological University, B

New Mexico

New Mexico Institute of Mining and Technology, B

New York

Columbia University, The Fu Foundation School of
  Engineering and Applied Science, B

Ohio

Cleveland State University, B
University of Cincinnati, B

Oklahoma

Oral Roberts University, B

Pennsylvania

Lehigh University, B

Puerto Rico

Universidad del Turabo, B

South Carolina

Clemson University, B

Virginia

Virginia Polytechnic Institute and State University, B

West Virginia

West Virginia Wesleyan College, B

Wisconsin

University of Wisconsin-Madison, B

Ontario

University of Windsor, B

Quebec

Université du Québec en Abitibi-Témiscamingue, B
Université du Québec àTrois-Rivières, B

ENGINEERING PHYSICS

Alabama

Samford University, B

Arizona

Northern Arizona University, B
The University of Arizona, B

Arkansas

Arkansas Tech University, B
Southern Arkansas University-Magnolia, B

California

California Institute of Technology, B
Loyola Marymount University, B
Point Loma Nazarene University, B
Santa Clara University, B
University of California, Berkeley, B
University of California, San Diego, BMD
University of the Pacific, B
Westmont College, B

Colorado

Colorado School of Mines, B
Colorado State University, B
Fort Lewis College, B
University of Colorado at Boulder, B

Connecticut

Connecticut College, B
University of Connecticut, B

Yale University, BMD

Delaware

Delaware State University, B

Florida

Embry-Riddle Aeronautical University, B
Jacksonville University, B

Idaho

Northwest Nazarene University, B

Illinois

Augustana College, B
Aurora University, B
Bradley University, B
Rend Lake College, A
University of Illinois at Chicago, B
University of Illinois at Urbana-Champaign, B

Indiana

Rose-Hulman Institute of Technology, B
Taylor University, B

Iowa

Loras College, B
Morningside College, B
St. Ambrose University, B
University of Northern Iowa, B

Kansas

Southwestern College, B
University of Kansas, B

Kentucky

Murray State University, B

Maine

University of Maine, BM

Maryland

Morgan State University, B

Massachusetts

Brandeis University, B
Eastern Nazarene College, B
Harvard University, B
Merrimack College, B
Tufts University, B
University of Massachusetts Boston, B
Worcester Polytechnic Institute, B

Michigan

Hope College, B
Michigan Technological University, BD
University of Michigan, B

Minnesota

Bemidji State University, B
Saint Mary's University of Minnesota, B

Mississippi

Mississippi State University, D

Missouri

Missouri State University, B
Southeast Missouri State University, B
Washington University in St. Louis, B

Nebraska

University of Nebraska at Omaha, B

Nevada

University of Nevada, Reno, B

New Hampshire

Dartmouth College, BMD

New Jersey

Stevens Institute of Technology, BMDO

New Mexico

New Mexico State University, B

New York

Columbia University, The Fu Foundation School of
  Engineering and Applied Science, B

Cornell University, BMD
Polytechnic University, Brooklyn Campus, M
Rensselaer Polytechnic Institute, BMD
St. Bonaventure University, B
State University of New York at Buffalo, B
State University of New York at New Paltz, B
Syracuse University, B
United States Military Academy, B

North Carolina

North Carolina Agricultural and Technical State
  University, B

Ohio

Case Western Reserve University, B
John Carroll University, B
Miami University, B
Miami University Hamilton, B
The Ohio State University, B
The University of Akron, B
The University of Toledo, B
Wilberforce University, B
Wright State University, B

Oklahoma

Northeastern State University, B
Southwestern Oklahoma State University, B
University of Oklahoma, BMD
University of Tulsa, B

Oregon

Oregon State University, B

Pennsylvania

Elizabethtown College, B
Juniata College, B
Lehigh University, B
Thiel College, B
University of Pittsburgh, B

Rhode Island

Brown University, B

South Dakota

Augustana College, B
South Dakota State University, B

Tennessee

Christian Brothers University, B
The University of Tennessee, B

Texas

Abilene Christian University, B
Tarleton State University, B
Texas Tech University, B
The University of Texas at Brownsville, B

Virginia

George Mason University, M
Randolph-Macon Woman's College, B
University of Virginia, MD
Washington and Lee University, B

Washington

Pacific Lutheran University, B

West Virginia

West Virginia University Institute of Technology, B
West Virginia Wesleyan College, B

Wisconsin

University of Wisconsin-Madison, BMD

Alberta

University of Alberta, B

British Columbia

The University of British Columbia, BM

Ontario

McMaster University, BMD
Queen's University at Kingston, B

York University, B

Quebec

Université Laval, B

Saskatchewan

University of Saskatchewan, BMD

ENGINEERING-RELATED TECHNOLOGIES

Alaska

University of Alaska Southeast, A

Missouri

Metropolitan Community College-Business & Technology College, A

New York

Rochester Institute of Technology, B
United States Merchant Marine Academy, B

ENGINEERING SCIENCE

California

California Polytechnic State University, San Luis Obispo, B
California State University, Fullerton, B
Claremont McKenna College, B
Sonoma State University, B
University of California, Berkeley, B
University of California, San Diego, B

Colorado

Colorado School of Mines, B
Colorado State University, B
United States Air Force Academy, B

Connecticut

Asnuntuck Community College, A
Manchester Community College, A
Middlesex Community College, A
Norwalk Community College, A
Three Rivers Community College, A
Yale University, B

District of Columbia

Gallaudet University, B

Florida

Broward Community College, A
University of Florida, B
University of Miami, B

Illinois

Benedictine University, B
Highland Community College, A
Northwestern University, B
Parkland College, A
Rend Lake College, A

Indiana

Manchester College, B

Iowa

Iowa State University of Science and Technology, B

Louisiana

Tulane University, B
University of New Orleans, B

Maryland

College of Notre Dame of Maryland, B
University of Maryland, Baltimore County, B

Massachusetts

Bristol Community College, A
Greenfield Community College, A
Harvard University, B
Holyoke Community College, A

Merrimack College, A
North Shore Community College, A
Northern Essex Community College, A
Smith College, B
Tufts University, B

Michigan

University of Michigan, B
University of Michigan-Flint, B

Minnesota

Bethel University, B
Itasca Community College, A

Mississippi

Jones County Junior College, A

Missouri

St. Louis Community College at Florissant Valley, A
St. Louis Community College at Forest Park, A
St. Louis Community College at Meramec, A
Washington University in St. Louis, B

Montana

Montana Tech of The University of Montana, B

New Hampshire

Daniel Webster College, A

New Jersey

Bergen Community College, A
Camden County College, A
The College of New Jersey, B
County College of Morris, A
Gloucester County College, A
Hudson County Community College, A
Mercer County Community College, A
Middlesex County College, A
New Jersey Institute of Technology, B
Rutgers, The State University of New Jersey, New Brunswick/Piscataway, B

New Mexico

University of New Mexico, B

New York

Adirondack Community College, A
Borough of Manhattan Community College of the City University of New York, A
Broome Community College, A
Dutchess Community College, A
Finger Lakes Community College, A
Fulton-Montgomery Community College, A
Genesee Community College, A
Hofstra University, B
Hudson Valley Community College, A
Jefferson Community College, A
Kingsborough Community College of the City University of New York, A
Monroe Community College, A
Onondaga Community College, A
Orange County Community College, A
Queensborough Community College of the City University of New York, A
Rensselaer Polytechnic Institute, B
Rochester Institute of Technology, A
St. Thomas Aquinas College, B
State University of New York at Buffalo, B
State University of New York College of Agriculture and Technology at Morrisville, A
State University of New York College at Oneonta, B
State University of New York College of Technology at Alfred, A
State University of New York College of Technology at Canton, A
State University of New York College of Technology at Delhi, A
Suffolk County Community College, A
Sullivan County Community College, A
Tompkins Cortland Community College, A
University of Rochester, B

Westchester Community College, A

North Dakota

University of Mary, B

Ohio

Case Western Reserve University, B
Cleveland State University, B
Ohio Wesleyan University, B
University of Cincinnati, AB
Wright State University, B

Oregon

University of Portland, B

Pennsylvania

Montgomery County Community College, A
Pennsylvania College of Technology, A
The Pennsylvania State University Abington College, B
The Pennsylvania State University Altoona College, B
The Pennsylvania State University Beaver Campus of the Commonwealth College, B
The Pennsylvania State University Berks Campus of the Berks-Lehigh Valley College, B
The Pennsylvania State University Delaware County Campus of the Commonwealth College, B
The Pennsylvania State University DuBois Campus of the Commonwealth College, B
The Pennsylvania State University at Erie, The Behrend College, B
The Pennsylvania State University Fayette Campus of the Commonwealth College, B
The Pennsylvania State University Hazleton Campus of the Commonwealth College, B
The Pennsylvania State University, Lehigh Valley Campus of the Berks-Lehigh Valley College, B
The Pennsylvania State University McKeesport Campus of the Commonwealth College, B
The Pennsylvania State University Mont Alto Campus of the Commonwealth College, B
The Pennsylvania State University New Kensington Campus of the Commonwealth College, B
The Pennsylvania State University Schuylkill Campus of the Capital College, B
The Pennsylvania State University Shenango Campus of the Commonwealth College, B
The Pennsylvania State University University Park Campus, B
The Pennsylvania State University Wilkes-Barre Campus of the Commonwealth College, B
The Pennsylvania State University Worthington Scranton Campus of the Commonwealth College, B
The Pennsylvania State University York Campus of the Commonwealth College, B
Reading Area Community College, A

South Carolina

Bob Jones University, B

Tennessee

Belmont University, B
Lipscomb University, B
The University of Tennessee, B
Vanderbilt University, B

Texas

Abilene Christian University, B
Hill College of the Hill Junior College District, A
Houston Baptist University, B
Lamar University, B
St. Mary's University of San Antonio, B
Trinity University, B

Virginia

Sweet Briar College, B

Washington

Everett Community College, A
Pacific Lutheran University, B

Seattle Pacific University, B

British Columbia

Simon Fraser University, B

Manitoba

University of Manitoba, B

Ontario

University of Ottawa, B
University of Toronto, B
The University of Western Ontario, B

ENGINEERING TECHNOLOGIES/TECHNICIANS

Arkansas

Southern Arkansas University Tech, A

California

California Maritime Academy, B
California State Polytechnic University, Pomona, B

Connecticut

University of Hartford, B

Indiana

University of Southern Indiana, B

Kentucky

Louisville Technical Institute, A
Western Kentucky University, A

Louisiana

McNeese State University, A

Maryland

Harford Community College, A
Wor-Wic Community College, A

Massachusetts

Bristol Community College, A
Massasoit Community College, A

Michigan

Mid Michigan Community College, A
Mott Community College, A
Western Michigan University, B

Minnesota

McNally Smith College of Music, A
St. Cloud State University, B

New Hampshire

Keene State College, A

New Jersey

New Jersey Institute of Technology, B

New Mexico

Central New Mexico Community College, A

North Carolina

Catawba Valley Community College, A
Cleveland Community College, A
East Carolina University, B

Ohio

Bowling Green State University, B
Bowling Green State University-Firelands College, A
Ohio University, B
The University of Akron, A

Oklahoma

Cameron University, AB
Rogers State University, AB

Pennsylvania

Community College of Allegheny County, A
Harrisburg Area Community College, A
Montgomery County Community College, A

Pennsylvania College of Technology, B

South Dakota

Mitchell Technical Institute, A

Virginia

Old Dominion University, B

Wisconsin

Wisconsin Indianhead Technical College, A

British Columbia

The University of British Columbia, B

ENGINEERING TECHNOLOGY

Alabama

Bishop State Community College, A
Snead State Community College, A
Tuskegee University, B
The University of West Alabama, B

Alaska

University of Alaska Anchorage, A

Arizona

Arizona Western College, A
Glendale Community College, A
Mesa Community College, A

Arkansas

Arkansas State University, AB
John Brown University, A

California

Allan Hancock College, A
American River College, A
Antelope Valley College, A
California State Polytechnic University, Pomona, B
California State University, Long Beach, B
Cerro Coso Community College, A
Chabot College, A
Citrus College, A
College of the Desert, A
College of Marin, A
College of San Mateo, A
De Anza College, A
Golden West College, A
Laney College, A
Los Angeles Harbor College, A
Moorpark College, A
Mt. San Antonio College, A
Pacific Union College, AB
Pasadena City College, A
San Diego City College, A
San Joaquin Delta College, A
Santa Ana College, A
Santa Barbara City College, A
Santa Rosa Junior College, A

Colorado

Aims Community College, A
Colorado State University-Pueblo, B
Pueblo Community College, A

Connecticut

Central Connecticut State University, B
Gateway Community College, A
Middlesex Community College, A
Naugatuck Valley Community College, A
Norwalk Community College, A
Quinebaug Valley Community College, A
Three Rivers Community College, A
Tunxis Community College, A
University of Hartford, B

Delaware

Delaware Technical & Community College, Jack F. Owens Campus, A

Delaware Technical & Community College, Terry Campus, A

District of Columbia

Gallaudet University, B
University of the District of Columbia, AB

Florida

Edison College, A
Florida Community College at Jacksonville, A
Gulf Coast Community College, A
Indian River Community College, A
Keiser College (Fort Lauderdale), A
Miami Dade College, A
University of Central Florida, B
University of West Florida, B

Georgia

Atlanta Metropolitan College, A
Berry College, B
Clayton State University, A
Darton College, A
DeKalb Technical College, A
Gainesville College, A
Macon State College, A
Waycross College, A

Hawaii

Honolulu Community College, A

Idaho

Brigham Young University -Idaho, A

Illinois

City Colleges of Chicago, Harold Washington College, A
Highland Community College, A
Illinois Central College, A
Morrison Institute of Technology, A
Northern Illinois University, B
Rend Lake College, A
Southern Illinois University Carbondale, B
Southwestern Illinois College, A
Triton College, A

Indiana

Purdue University Calumet, B
Tri-State University, A
Vincennes University, A

Iowa

Dordt College, B
Hawkeye Community College, A
Iowa Western Community College, A
William Penn University, B

Kansas

Allen County Community College, A
Barton County Community College, A
Cowley County Community College and Area Vocational-Technical School, A
Dodge City Community College, A
Garden City Community College, A
Independence Community College, A
Pittsburg State University, B

Kentucky

Ashland Community and Technical College, A
Henderson Community College, A
Louisville Technical Institute, A
Murray State University, B

Louisiana

McNeese State University, AB
Remington College-New Orleans Campus, A

Maine

Maine Maritime Academy, B
University of Maine, B

Washington County Community College, A

Maryland

Anne Arundel Community College, A
University of Maryland Eastern Shore, B

Massachusetts

Benjamin Franklin Institute of Technology, A
Berkshire Community College, A
Massachusetts Bay Community College, A
Massachusetts Maritime Academy, B
Wentworth Institute of Technology, AB

Michigan

Andrews University, AB
Delta College, A
Eastern Michigan University, B
Lake Superior State University, A
Lansing Community College, A
Lawrence Technological University, B
Michigan Technological University, A
Mid Michigan Community College, A
Muskegon Community College, A
North Central Michigan College, A
Southwestern Michigan College, A
Washtenaw Community College, A
Wayne County Community College District, A

Minnesota

Dakota County Technical College, A
Itasca Community College, A
St. Cloud State University, B

Mississippi

Jackson State University, B
Northeast Mississippi Community College, A

Missouri

Missouri Tech, AB
St. Louis Community College at Florissant Valley, A
St. Louis Community College at Forest Park, A
Three Rivers Community College, A

Montana

Montana Tech of The University of Montana, A

Nevada

Truckee Meadows Community College, A

New Hampshire

New Hampshire Community Technical College,
    Nashua/Claremont, A
New Hampshire Technical Institute, A

New Jersey

County College of Morris, A
Middlesex County College, A
New Jersey Institute of Technology, B

New Mexico

Eastern New Mexico University, B
New Mexico State University, AB
New Mexico State University-Carlsbad, A
Southwestern Indian Polytechnic Institute, A

New York

Buffalo State College, State University of New
    York, B
Rochester Institute of Technology, B
State University of New York College of Agriculture
    and Technology at Cobleskill, A
State University of New York College of Agriculture
    and Technology at Morrisville, A
State University of New York College of Technology
    at Canton, A
State University of New York College of Technology
    at Delhi, A
Ulster County Community College, A
Vaughn College of Aeronautics and Technology, A
Westchester Community College, A

North Carolina

Brunswick Community College, A
Central Piedmont Community College, A

Davidson County Community College, A
Forsyth Technical Community College, A

Ohio

Cleveland State University, B
Cuyahoga Community College, A
Edison State Community College, A
James A. Rhodes State College, A
Kent State University, Ashtabula Campus, A
Kent State University, Tuscarawas Campus, A
Lakeland Community College, A
Lorain County Community College, A
Marion Technical College, A
Miami University, B
Miami University Hamilton, B
Miami University-Middletown Campus, AB
Terra State Community College, A
The University of Akron, B
Wright State University, Lake Campus, A
Youngstown State University, B

Oklahoma

Murray State College, A
Oklahoma State University, B
Southwestern Oklahoma State University, B

Oregon

Portland Community College, A

Pennsylvania

Community College of Philadelphia, A
Harrisburg Area Community College, A
Luzerne County Community College, A
Pennsylvania Institute of Technology, A
Reading Area Community College, A
South Hills School of Business & Technology (State
    College), A
Temple University, B
University of Pittsburgh at Johnstown, B

South Carolina

Aiken Technical College, A
Charleston Southern University, B
Denmark Technical College, A
Florence-Darlington Technical College, A
Midlands Technical College, A
Piedmont Technical College, A
Spartanburg Technical College, A
Trident Technical College, A

South Dakota

Southeast Technical Institute, A

Tennessee

Austin Peay State University, B
East Tennessee State University, B
Middle Tennessee State University, B
Northeast State Technical Community College, A

Texas

Angelina College, A
Frank Phillips College, A
Houston Community College System, A
LeTourneau University, B
Midwestern State University, B
Mountain View College, A
North Central Texas College, A
Prairie View A&M University, B
San Antonio College, A
Texas A&M University, B
Texas A&M University-Corpus Christi, B
Texas Southern University, B
Texas State University-San Marcos, B
Texas Tech University, B
University of North Texas, B
The University of Texas at Tyler, B

Utah

Brigham Young University, B
Salt Lake Community College, A

Virginia

Central Virginia Community College, A
Danville Community College, A

ECPI College of Technology (Newport News), A
ECPI College of Technology (Virginia Beach), A
ECPI Technical College (Richmond), A
ECPI Technical College (Roanoke), A
Mountain Empire Community College, A
Patrick Henry Community College, A
Rappahannock Community College, A
Virginia Highlands Community College, A
Virginia State University, B

Washington

Eastern Washington University, B
Everett Community College, A
Highline Community College, A
Lower Columbia College, A
Peninsula College, A
Shoreline Community College, A
South Seattle Community College, A
Walla Walla College, B
Western Washington University, B

West Virginia

Fairmont State University, AB
Southern West Virginia Community and Technical
    College, A
West Virginia University Institute of Technology, B

Wisconsin

Moraine Park Technical College, A
University of Wisconsin-River Falls, B
University of Wisconsin-Stout, B

Wyoming

Laramie County Community College, A
Sheridan College-Sheridan and Gillette, A
Western Wyoming Community College, A

ENGLISH

Alabama

Auburn University, MD
Jacksonville State University, M
The University of Alabama, MD
The University of Alabama at Birmingham, M
The University of Alabama in Huntsville, MO
University of Montevallo, M
University of North Alabama, M
University of South Alabama, M

Alaska

University of Alaska Anchorage, M
University of Alaska Fairbanks, M

Arizona

Arizona State University, MD
Northern Arizona University, M
The University of Arizona, MD

Arkansas

Arkansas State University, MO
Arkansas Tech University, M
University of Arkansas, MD
University of Central Arkansas, M

California

California Baptist University, M
California Polytechnic State University, San Luis
    Obispo, M
California State Polytechnic University, Pomona, M
California State University, Bakersfield, M
California State University, Chico, M
California State University, Dominguez Hills, MO
California State University, East Bay, M
California State University, Fresno, M
California State University, Fullerton, M
California State University, Long Beach, M
California State University, Los Angeles, M
California State University, Northridge, M
California State University, Sacramento, M
California State University, San Bernardino, M
California State University, San Marcos, M
California State University, Stanislaus, M
Chapman University, M

Humboldt State University, M
La Sierra University, M
Loyola Marymount University, M
Mills College, M
National University, M
Notre Dame de Namur University, M
San Diego State University, M
San Francisco State University, MO
San Jose State University, MO
Sonoma State University, M
Stanford University, MD
University of California, Berkeley, D
University of California, Davis, MD
University of California, Irvine, MD
University of California, Los Angeles, MD
University of California, Riverside, MD
University of California, San Diego, M
University of California, Santa Barbara, DO

Colorado

Colorado State University, M
University of Colorado at Boulder, MD
University of Colorado at Denver and Health
   Sciences Center - Downtown Denver Campus, M
University of Denver, MD
University of Northern Colorado, M

Connecticut

Central Connecticut State University, M
Connecticut College, M
Southern Connecticut State University, MO
Trinity College, M
University of Connecticut, MD
Western Connecticut State University, M
Yale University, MD

Delaware

University of Delaware, MDO

District of Columbia

The Catholic University of America, MDO
The George Washington University, MD
Georgetown University, M
Howard University, MD
University of the District of Columbia, M

Florida

Florida Atlantic University, M
Florida International University, M
Florida State University, MD
Stetson University, M
University of Central Florida, MDO
University of Florida, MD
University of Miami, MD
University of North Florida, M
University of South Florida, MD
University of West Florida, M

Georgia

Clark Atlanta University, M
Emory University, DO
Georgia College & State University, M
Georgia Southern University, M
Georgia State University, MD
University of Georgia, MD
University of West Georgia, M
Valdosta State University, M

Hawaii

University of Hawaii at Manoa, MD

Idaho

Boise State University, M
Idaho State University, MD
University of Idaho, M

Illinois

Bradley University, M
Chicago State University, M
DePaul University, M
Eastern Illinois University, M
Elmhurst College, M
Governors State University, M
Illinois State University, MD
Loyola University Chicago, MD

Northeastern Illinois University, M
Northern Illinois University, MD
Northwestern University, MD
Roosevelt University, M
Saint Xavier University, MO
Southern Illinois University Carbondale, MD
Southern Illinois University Edwardsville, MO
University of Chicago, MD
University of Illinois at Chicago, MD
University of Illinois at Springfield, M
University of Illinois at Urbana-Champaign, MD
Western Illinois University, M

Indiana

Ball State University, MD
Butler University, M
Indiana State University, M
Indiana University Bloomington, MD
Indiana University-Purdue University Fort Wayne, M
Indiana University-Purdue University Indianapolis, M
Purdue University, MD
Purdue University Calumet, M
University of Indianapolis, M
University of Notre Dame, MD
Valparaiso University, MO

Iowa

Iowa State University of Science and
   Technology, MD
The University of Iowa, MDO
University of Northern Iowa, M

Kansas

Emporia State University, M
Fort Hays State University, M
Kansas State University, M
Pittsburg State University, M
University of Kansas, MD
Wichita State University, M

Kentucky

Eastern Kentucky University, M
Morehead State University, M
Murray State University, M
University of Kentucky, MD
University of Louisville, MD
Western Kentucky University, M

Louisiana

Louisiana State University and Agricultural and
   Mechanical College, MD
Louisiana Tech University, M
McNeese State University, M
Northwestern State University of Louisiana, M
Southeastern Louisiana University, M
Tulane University, MD
University of Louisiana at Lafayette, MD
University of Louisiana at Monroe, M
University of New Orleans, M

Maine

University of Maine, M

Maryland

The Johns Hopkins University, D
Morgan State University, MD
Salisbury University, M
University of Maryland, College Park, MD
Washington College, M

Massachusetts

Boston College, MD
Boston University, MD
Brandeis University, MD
Bridgewater State College, M
Clark University, M
Harvard University, MDO
Northeastern University, MDO
Salem State College, M
Simmons College, MO
Tufts University, MD
University of Massachusetts Amherst, MD
University of Massachusetts Boston, M

Westfield State College, M

Michigan

Andrews University, M
Central Michigan University, M
Eastern Michigan University, M
Grand Valley State University, M
Michigan State University, MD
Northern Michigan University, M
Oakland University, M
University of Michigan, MD
Wayne State University, MD
Western Michigan University, MD

Minnesota

Bemidji State University, M
Minnesota State University Mankato, M
St. Cloud State University, M
University of Minnesota, Duluth, M
University of Minnesota, Twin Cities Campus, MD
University of St. Thomas, M
Winona State University, M

Mississippi

Jackson State University, M
Mississippi College, M
Mississippi State University, M
University of Mississippi, MD
University of Southern Mississippi, MD

Missouri

Central Missouri State University, M
Missouri State University, M
Northwest Missouri State University, M
Saint Louis University, MD
Southeast Missouri State University, M
Truman State University, M
University of Missouri-Columbia, MD
University of Missouri-Kansas City, MD
University of Missouri-St. Louis, M
Washington University in St. Louis, MD

Montana

Montana State University, M
The University of Montana-Missoula, M

Nebraska

University of Nebraska at Kearney, M
University of Nebraska-Lincoln, MD
University of Nebraska at Omaha, MO

Nevada

University of Nevada, Las Vegas, MD
University of Nevada, Reno, MD

New Hampshire

Rivier College, MO
University of New Hampshire, MD

New Jersey

The College of New Jersey, M
Drew University, MD
Fairleigh Dickinson University, Metropolitan
   Campus, M
Kean University, M
Montclair State University, M
Princeton University, D
Rutgers, The State University of New Jersey,
   Camden, M
Rutgers, The State University of New Jersey, New
   Brunswick/Piscataway, D
Rutgers, The State University of New Jersey,
   Newark, M
Seton Hall University, M
William Paterson University of New Jersey, M

New Mexico

Eastern New Mexico University, M
New Mexico Highlands University, M
New Mexico State University, MD

University of New Mexico, MD

New York

Brooklyn College of the City University of New York, MD
Buffalo State College, State University of New York, M
City College of the City University of New York, M
The College of Saint Rose, M
College of Staten Island of the City University of New York, M
Cornell University, MDO
Fordham University, MD
Hofstra University, M
Hunter College of the City University of New York, M
Iona College, M
Lehman College of the City University of New York, M
Long Island University, Brooklyn Campus, M
Long Island University, C.W. Post Campus, M
Mercy College, M
New York University, MD
Queens College of the City University of New York, M
St. Bonaventure University, M
St. John's University, MD
State University of New York at Binghamton, MD
State University of New York at Buffalo, MD
State University of New York College at Brockport, M
State University of New York College at Cortland, M
State University of New York College at Potsdam, M
State University of New York, Fredonia, M
State University of New York at New Paltz, M
State University of New York at Oswego, M
Stony Brook University, State University of New York, MDO
Syracuse University, MD
University at Albany, State University of New York, MDO
University of Rochester, MD

North Carolina

Appalachian State University, M
Duke University, DO
East Carolina University, M
Fayetteville State University, M
Gardner-Webb University, M
North Carolina Agricultural and Technical State University, M
North Carolina Central University, M
North Carolina State University, M
The University of North Carolina at Chapel Hill, MD
The University of North Carolina at Charlotte, M
The University of North Carolina at Greensboro, MDO
The University of North Carolina Wilmington, M
Wake Forest University, M
Western Carolina University, M

North Dakota

North Dakota State University, M
University of North Dakota, MD

Ohio

Bowling Green State University, MD
Case Western Reserve University, MD
Cleveland State University, M
John Carroll University, M
Kent State University, MD
Miami University, MD
The Ohio State University, MD
Ohio University, MD
The University of Akron, M
University of Cincinnati, MD
University of Dayton, M
The University of Toledo, M
Wright State University, M
Xavier University, M
Youngstown State University, M

Oklahoma

Northeastern State University, M
Oklahoma State University, MD

University of Central Oklahoma, M
University of Oklahoma, MD
University of Tulsa, MDO

Oregon

Oregon State University, M
Portland State University, MO
University of Oregon, MD

Pennsylvania

Arcadia University, M
Bucknell University, M
Carnegie Mellon University, MD
Clarion University of Pennsylvania, M
Duquesne University, MD
Gannon University, M
Indiana University of Pennsylvania, MD
Kutztown University of Pennsylvania, M
Lehigh University, MD
Millersville University of Pennsylvania, M
The Pennsylvania State University University Park Campus, MD
Rosemont College, M
Slippery Rock University of Pennsylvania, M
Temple University, MD
University of Pennsylvania, MD
University of Pittsburgh, MD
Villanova University, M
West Chester University of Pennsylvania, M

Puerto Rico

University of Puerto Rico, Mayagüez Campus, M
University of Puerto Rico, Río Piedras, MD

Rhode Island

Brown University, MD
Rhode Island College, M
University of Rhode Island, MD

South Carolina

The Citadel, The Military College of South Carolina, M
Clemson University, M
College of Charleston, M
Converse College, M
University of South Carolina, MDO
Winthrop University, M

South Dakota

South Dakota State University, M
The University of South Dakota, MD

Tennessee

Austin Peay State University, M
Belmont University, M
East Tennessee State University, M
Middle Tennessee State University, MD
Tennessee State University, M
Tennessee Technological University, M
University of Memphis, MD
The University of Tennessee, MD
The University of Tennessee at Chattanooga, M
Vanderbilt University, MD

Texas

Abilene Christian University, M
Angelo State University, M
Baylor University, MD
Hardin-Simmons University, M
Lamar University, M
Midwestern State University, M
Our Lady of the Lake University of San Antonio, M
Prairie View A&M University, M
Rice University, MD
St. Mary's University of San Antonio, M
Sam Houston State University, M
Southern Methodist University, M
Stephen F. Austin State University, M
Sul Ross State University, M
Tarleton State University, M
Texas A&M International University, M
Texas A&M University, MD
Texas A&M University-Commerce, MD
Texas A&M University-Corpus Christi, M
Texas A&M University-Kingsville, M

Texas Christian University, MD
Texas Southern University, M
Texas State University-San Marcos, M
Texas Tech University, MD
Texas Woman's University, MD
University of Dallas, M
University of Houston, MD
University of Houston-Clear Lake, M
University of the Incarnate Word, M
University of North Texas, MD
The University of Texas at Arlington, MD
The University of Texas at Austin, MD
The University of Texas at Brownsville, M
The University of Texas at El Paso, M
The University of Texas-Pan American, M
The University of Texas of the Permian Basin, M
The University of Texas at San Antonio, MD
The University of Texas at Tyler, M
West Texas A&M University, M

Utah

Brigham Young University, M
University of Utah, MD
Utah State University, M

Vermont

Bennington College, M
Middlebury College, M
University of Vermont, M

Virginia

George Mason University, M
Hollins University, M
James Madison University, M
Longwood University, M
Marymount University, M
Old Dominion University, M
Radford University, M
University of Richmond, M
University of Virginia, MD
Virginia Commonwealth University, M
Virginia Polytechnic Institute and State University, M
Virginia State University, M

Washington

Central Washington University, M
Eastern Washington University, M
Heritage University, M
University of Washington, MD
Washington State University, MD
Western Washington University, M

West Virginia

Marshall University, M
West Virginia University, MD

Wisconsin

Marquette University, MD
University of Wisconsin-Eau Claire, M
University of Wisconsin-Madison, MD
University of Wisconsin-Milwaukee, MDO
University of Wisconsin-Oshkosh, M
University of Wisconsin-Stevens Point, M

Wyoming

University of Wyoming, M

Alberta

University of Alberta, MD
University of Calgary, MD
University of Lethbridge, M

British Columbia

Simon Fraser University, MD
The University of British Columbia, MD

University of Victoria, MD

Manitoba

University of Manitoba, MD

New Brunswick

University of New Brunswick Fredericton, MD

Newfoundland and Labrador

Memorial University of Newfoundland, MD

Nova Scotia

Acadia University, M
Dalhousie University, MD

Ontario

Carleton University, M
Lakehead University, M
McMaster University, MD
Queen's University at Kingston, MD
University of Guelph, M
University of Ottawa, MD
University of Toronto, MD
University of Waterloo, MD
The University of Western Ontario, MD
University of Windsor, M
Wilfrid Laurier University, MD
York University, MD

Quebec

Concordia University, M
McGill University, MD
Université Laval, MD
Université de Montréal, MD

Saskatchewan

University of Regina, MD
University of Saskatchewan, MD

ENGLISH AS A SECOND LANGUAGE

Alabama

The University of Alabama, M
The University of Alabama in Huntsville, O

Arizona

Arizona State University, M
Grand Canyon University, M
Northern Arizona University, MDO
The University of Arizona, MD
University of Phoenix-Phoenix Campus, M

Arkansas

Arkansas Tech University, M
Henderson State University, M

California

Azusa Pacific University, M
Biola University, MO
California State University, Dominguez Hills, O
California State University, Fullerton, M
California State University, Los Angeles, M
California State University, Sacramento, M
California State University, San Bernardino, M
Fresno Pacific University, M
Holy Names University, MO
San Diego State University, MO
San Francisco State University, M
San Jose State University, M
University of California, Los Angeles, M
University of San Francisco, M
University of Southern California, M

Colorado

Regis University, M
University of Colorado at Denver and Health
  Sciences Center - Downtown Denver Campus, M

University of Phoenix-Denver Campus, M

Connecticut

Central Connecticut State University, M
Fairfield University, MO
Southern Connecticut State University, M

Delaware

University of Delaware, M

District of Columbia

American University, MO
The Catholic University of America, M
Georgetown University, MO
Trinity (Washington) University, M

Florida

Florida International University, M
Nova Southeastern University, MO
University of Central Florida, MO
University of Florida, MDO
University of Miami, MDO

Georgia

Georgia State University, MD

Guam

University of Guam, M

Hawaii

Hawaii Pacific University, M
University of Hawaii at Manoa, MD
University of Phoenix-Hawaii Campus, M

Idaho

University of Idaho, M

Illinois

Moody Bible Institute, O
Southern Illinois University Carbondale, M
Southern Illinois University Edwardsville, MO
University of Illinois at Chicago, M
University of Illinois at Urbana-Champaign, M
Wheaton College, MO

Indiana

Ball State University, M
Indiana State University, MO
Indiana University Bloomington, MDO

Iowa

University of Northern Iowa, M

Kansas

Newman University, M

Kentucky

Asbury College, M
Murray State University, M
Western Kentucky University, M

Maine

University of Southern Maine, MO

Maryland

College of Notre Dame of Maryland, M
Salisbury University, M
University of Maryland, College Park, M

Massachusetts

Boston University, MO
Eastern Nazarene College, MO
Elms College, M
Framingham State College, M
Salem State College, M
Simmons College, M
University of Massachusetts Boston, M

Michigan

Central Michigan University, M
Eastern Michigan University, MO
Grand Valley State University, M
Madonna University, M

Michigan State University, M

Minnesota

St. Cloud State University, M
University of Minnesota, Twin Cities Campus, M

Missouri

Central Missouri State University, M
Southeast Missouri State University, M

Nebraska

University of Nebraska at Omaha, O
Wayne State College, M

Nevada

University of Nevada, Las Vegas, M

New Hampshire

Southern New Hampshire University, M

New Jersey

The College of New Jersey, MO
Kean University, MO
Montclair State University, M
New Jersey City University, M
Rider University, O
Rutgers, The State University of New Jersey, New
  Brunswick/Piscataway, M
Seton Hall University, MO

New York

Adelphi University, MO
The College of New Rochelle, MO
Fordham University, M
Hofstra University, MO
Hunter College of the City University of New
  York, M
Lehman College of the City University of New
  York, M
Long Island University, Brooklyn Campus, M
Long Island University, C.W. Post Campus, M
Manhattanville College, M
Mercy College, M
Nazareth College of Rochester, M
New York University, MDO
Queens College of the City University of New
  York, M
St. John's University, M
State University of New York at Buffalo, MD
State University of New York College at Cortland, M
State University of New York at New Paltz, M
Stony Brook University, State University of New
  York, MD

North Carolina

Greensboro College, M
Salem College, M

Ohio

Bowling Green State University, M
Kent State University, M
Ohio University, M
University of Cincinnati, MDO
The University of Findlay, M
The University of Toledo, M
Wright State University, M

Oklahoma

Langston University, M
Oklahoma City University, M
Oral Roberts University, M
University of Central Oklahoma, M

Oregon

Portland State University, M

Pennsylvania

Albright College, M
Chatham College, M
DeSales University, O
Drexel University, O
Duquesne University, M
Eastern University, O
Gannon University, O

Indiana University of Pennsylvania, MD
The Pennsylvania State University University Park
    Campus, M
University of Pennsylvania, MD
University of Pittsburgh, O
West Chester University of Pennsylvania, M

Puerto Rico

Inter American University of Puerto Rico,
    Metropolitan Campus, M
Inter American University of Puerto Rico, San
    Germán Campus, M
Pontifical Catholic University of Puerto Rico, M
Universidad del Turabo, M
University of Puerto Rico, Río Piedras, M

Rhode Island

Rhode Island College, M

South Carolina

College of Charleston, O
Columbia International University, MO
University of South Carolina, O

Tennessee

Carson-Newman College, M
Middle Tennessee State University, M
The University of Tennessee, MDO

Texas

Houston Baptist University, M
Texas A&M University, MD
Texas A&M University-Kingsville, M
University of Houston, M
The University of Texas at Arlington, M
The University of Texas at Brownsville, M
The University of Texas-Pan American, M
The University of Texas of the Permian Basin, M
The University of Texas at San Antonio, M

Utah

Brigham Young University, MO

Vermont

Saint Michael's College, MO

Virginia

George Mason University, M
Marymount University, M
Shenandoah University, O
University of Northern Virginia, M

Washington

Central Washington University, M
City University, M
Gonzaga University, M
Heritage University, M
Seattle Pacific University, M
Seattle University, MO
University of Washington, M

West Virginia

West Virginia University, M

Alberta

University of Alberta, M
University of Calgary, MDO

British Columbia

Trinity Western University, M
The University of British Columbia, MD

Manitoba

Providence College and Theological Seminary, O
University of Manitoba, M

Nova Scotia

Mount Saint Vincent University, M

Quebec

Bishop's University, O

ENGLISH COMPOSITION

Arkansas

University of Central Arkansas, B

California

Berkeley City College, A

Colorado

University of Colorado at Denver and Health
    Sciences Center - Downtown Denver Campus, B

District of Columbia

Gallaudet University, B

Florida

Florida Southern College, B

Illinois

Aurora University, B
University of Illinois at Urbana-Champaign, B

Indiana

DePauw University, B
University of Evansville, B

Iowa

Graceland University, B
Wartburg College, B

Kansas

Allen County Community College, A

Louisiana

Dillard University, B

Massachusetts

Simon's Rock College of Bard, B

Michigan

Eastern Michigan University, B
University of Michigan-Flint, B
Western Michigan University, B

Minnesota

Bethel University, B
Metropolitan State University, B

Mississippi

Rust College, B

Missouri

William Woods University, B

Montana

University of Great Falls, B

Nevada

University of Nevada, Reno, B

New York

Columbia University, School of General Studies, B

North Dakota

Jamestown College, B

Ohio

Miami University Hamilton, B
Mount Union College, B

Oklahoma

Oklahoma Baptist University, B

Pennsylvania

Gettysburg College, B

Texas

Baylor University, B
St. Edward's University, B

University of North Texas, B

Utah

Brigham Young University, B

Vermont

Bennington College, B

Washington

Northwest University, B

Wisconsin

Lakeland College, B

British Columbia

Kwantlen University College, A

ENGLISH EDUCATION

Alabama

Alabama State University, M
The University of West Alabama, M

Alaska

University of Alaska Fairbanks, M

Arizona

Northern Arizona University, M
The University of Arizona, MD

Arkansas

Arkansas State University, MO
Arkansas Tech University, M
Henderson State University, M

California

California State University, San Bernardino, M
Occidental College, M
San Francisco State University, MO
Stanford University, MD

Colorado

The Colorado College, M
Colorado State University, M
University of Colorado at Denver and Health
    Sciences Center - Downtown Denver Campus, M

Connecticut

Connecticut College, M
Quinnipiac University, M
University of Connecticut, MD
Western Connecticut State University, M

Florida

Florida Agricultural and Mechanical University, M
Florida Gulf Coast University, M
Florida International University, MD
Florida State University, MDO
Nova Southeastern University, MO
University of Central Florida, M
University of Florida, MD
University of South Florida, MD

Georgia

Agnes Scott College, M
Albany State University, M
Georgia College & State University, M
Georgia Southern University, M
Georgia State University, MDO
University of Georgia, MO
University of West Georgia, MO

Idaho

University of Idaho, M

Illinois

Columbia College Chicago, M
National-Louis University, MO
Northeastern Illinois University, M
Rockford College, M

Southern Illinois University Edwardsville, MO

Indiana

Indiana University Bloomington, M
Indiana University-Purdue University Fort Wayne, M
Indiana University-Purdue University Indianapolis, M
Purdue University, MDO
University of Indianapolis, M

Iowa

Drake University, M
The University of Iowa, MD

Kentucky

Eastern Kentucky University, M
Western Kentucky University, M

Maryland

Salisbury University, M

Massachusetts

Boston College, M
Boston University, MDO
Fitchburg State College, M
Framingham State College, M
Salem State College, M
Smith College, M
Western New England College, M
Worcester State College, M

Michigan

Andrews University, M
University of Michigan, MD
Wayne State University, MO
Western Michigan University, MD

Minnesota

Minnesota State University Mankato, M
University of Minnesota, Twin Cities Campus, MD

Mississippi

Delta State University, M
Jackson State University, M
William Carey College, M

Missouri

Maryville University of Saint Louis, M
Northwest Missouri State University, M
University of Missouri-Columbia, MDO

Montana

The University of Montana-Missoula, M

Nebraska

Chadron State College, M
Wayne State College, M

Nevada

University of Nevada, Las Vegas, M

New Hampshire

Plymouth State University, M
University of New Hampshire, M

New Jersey

Montclair State University, M
Rider University, O
Rutgers, The State University of New Jersey, New
    Brunswick/Piscataway, M

New York

Brooklyn College of the City University of New
    York, M
City College of the City University of New York, M
The College of Saint Rose, M
Hofstra University, M
Hunter College of the City University of New
    York, M
Iona College, M
Lehman College of the City University of New
    York, M
Long Island University, Brooklyn Campus, M
Long Island University, C.W. Post Campus, M
Manhattanville College, M

New York University, MDO
Queens College of the City University of New
    York, MO
St. John Fisher College, M
State University of New York at Binghamton, M
State University of New York at Buffalo, MD
State University of New York College at
    Brockport, M
State University of New York College at Cortland, M
State University of New York at Plattsburgh, M
Stony Brook University, State University of New
    York, M
Syracuse University, MDO

North Carolina

Appalachian State University, M
Campbell University, M
East Carolina University, M
Gardner-Webb University, M
North Carolina Agricultural and Technical State
    University, M
The University of North Carolina at Chapel Hill, M
The University of North Carolina at Charlotte, M
The University of North Carolina at Greensboro, M
The University of North Carolina at Pembroke, M
Western Carolina University, M

Ohio

Kent State University, M
Miami University, M
The University of Toledo, M

Oklahoma

Southwestern Oklahoma State University, M

Pennsylvania

Arcadia University, MO
Chatham College, M
DeSales University, M
Edinboro University of Pennsylvania, M
Indiana University of Pennsylvania, M
Kutztown University of Pennsylvania, M
Millersville University of Pennsylvania, M
University of Pittsburgh, MD
Widener University, M

Puerto Rico

University of Puerto Rico, Río Piedras, M

Rhode Island

Brown University, M

South Carolina

Charleston Southern University, M
Clemson University, M
Converse College, M
University of South Carolina, M

South Dakota

Northern State University, M

Tennessee

Austin Peay State University, M
Belmont University, M
Bethel College, M
The University of Tennessee, MO
Vanderbilt University, M

Texas

Texas A&M University, MD
Texas A&M University-Commerce, D
Texas Tech University, M
The University of Texas at El Paso, M
The University of Texas at Tyler, M

Vermont

Bennington College, M
College of St. Joseph, M

Virginia

Averett University, M
Christopher Newport University, M
Emory & Henry College, M
Longwood University, M

Lynchburg College, M

Washington

University of Washington, M
Washington State University, M

Wisconsin

Carthage College, M
University of Wisconsin-Eau Claire, M
University of Wisconsin-Madison, M

British Columbia

University of Victoria, MD

Manitoba

University of Manitoba, M

ENGLISH LANGUAGE AND LITERATURE

Alabama

Alabama Agricultural and Mechanical University, B
Alabama Southern Community College, A
Alabama State University, B
Athens State University, B
Auburn University, B
Auburn University Montgomery, B
Birmingham-Southern College, B
Calhoun Community College, A
Faulkner University, B
Huntingdon College, B
Jacksonville State University, B
Judson College, B
Lawson State Community College, A
Miles College, B
Oakwood College, B
Samford University, B
Spring Hill College, B
Stillman College, B
Talladega College, B
Troy University, B
Tuskegee University, B
The University of Alabama, B
The University of Alabama at Birmingham, B
The University of Alabama in Huntsville, B
University of Mobile, B
University of Montevallo, B
University of North Alabama, B
University of South Alabama, B
The University of West Alabama, B

Alaska

University of Alaska Anchorage, B
University of Alaska Fairbanks, B
University of Alaska Southeast, B

Arizona

Arizona State University, B
Arizona State University West, B
Arizona Western College, A
Cochise College (Douglas), A
Cochise College (Sierra Vista), A
Eastern Arizona College, A
Grand Canyon University, B
Mohave Community College, A
Northern Arizona University, B
The University of Arizona, B

Arkansas

Arkansas State University, B
Arkansas Tech University, B
Harding University, B
Henderson State University, B
Hendrix College, B
John Brown University, B
Lyon College, B
Ouachita Baptist University, B
Philander Smith College, B
Phillips Community College of the University of
    Arkansas, A
Southern Arkansas University-Magnolia, B
University of Arkansas, B
University of Arkansas at Little Rock, B

University of Arkansas at Monticello, B
University of Arkansas at Pine Bluff, B
University of Central Arkansas, B
University of the Ozarks, B
Williams Baptist College, B

California

Allan Hancock College, A
Azusa Pacific University, B
Bakersfield College, A
Berkeley City College, A
Bethany University, B
Biola University, B
California Baptist University, B
California Lutheran University, B
California Polytechnic State University, San Luis
  Obispo, B
California State Polytechnic University, Pomona, B
California State University, Bakersfield, B
California State University Channel Islands, B
California State University, Chico, B
California State University, Dominguez Hills, B
California State University, East Bay, B
California State University, Fresno, B
California State University, Fullerton, B
California State University, Long Beach, B
California State University, Los Angeles, B
California State University, Northridge, B
California State University, Sacramento, B
California State University, San Bernardino, B
California State University, San Marcos, B
California State University, Stanislaus, B
Cañada College, A
Cerritos College, A
Chabot College, A
Chaffey College, A
Chapman University, B
Citrus College, A
City College of San Francisco, A
Claremont McKenna College, B
College of Alameda, A
College of the Canyons, A
College of the Desert, A
College of San Mateo, A
College of the Sequoias, A
College of the Siskiyous, A
Columbia College, A
Compton Community College, A
Concordia University, B
Contra Costa College, A
Crafton Hills College, A
Cuyamaca College, A
Cypress College, A
De Anza College, A
Dominican University of California, B
East Los Angeles College, A
El Camino College, A
Evergreen Valley College, A
Feather River College, A
Folsom Lake College, A
Foothill College, A
Fresno Pacific University, AB
Fullerton College, A
Gavilan College, A
Glendale Community College, A
Grossmont College, A
Hartnell College, A
Holy Names University, B
Humboldt State University, B
Imperial Valley College, A
Irvine Valley College, A
La Sierra University, B
Long Beach City College, A
Los Angeles City College, A
Los Angeles Mission College, A
Los Angeles Southwest College, A
Loyola Marymount University, B
The Master's College and Seminary, B
Mendocino College, A
Mills College, B
MiraCosta College, A
Modesto Junior College, A
Monterey Peninsula College, A
Mount St. Mary's College, B
National University, B
Notre Dame de Namur University, B

Orange Coast College, A
Oxnard College, A
Pacific Union College, B
Palo Verde College, A
Pasadena City College, A
Pepperdine University, B
Pitzer College, B
Point Loma Nazarene University, B
Pomona College, B
Porterville College, A
Reedley College, A
Saint Mary's College of California, B
San Bernardino Valley College, A
San Diego Christian College, B
San Diego City College, A
San Diego Mesa College, A
San Diego Miramar College, A
San Diego State University, B
San Francisco State University, B
San Joaquin Delta College, A
San Jose State University, B
Santa Ana College, A
Santa Barbara City College, A
Santa Clara University, B
Santa Monica College, A
Santa Rosa Junior College, A
Santiago Canyon College, A
Scripps College, B
Simpson University, B
Skyline College, A
Solano Community College, A
Sonoma State University, B
Southwestern College, A
Stanford University, B
Taft College, A
University of California, Berkeley, B
University of California, Davis, B
University of California, Irvine, B
University of California, Los Angeles, B
University of California, Riverside, B
University of California, San Diego, B
University of California, Santa Barbara, B
University of California, Santa Cruz, B
University of La Verne, B
University of the Pacific, B
University of Redlands, B
University of San Diego, B
University of San Francisco, B
University of Southern California, B
University of the West, B
Vanguard University of Southern California, B
West Los Angeles College, A
West Valley College, A
Westmont College, B
Whittier College, B
Yuba College, A

Colorado

Adams State College, B
Colorado Christian University, B
The Colorado College, B
Colorado Mountain College, A
Colorado Mountain College, Alpine Campus, A
Colorado Northwestern Community College, A
Colorado State University, B
Colorado State University-Pueblo, B
Fort Lewis College, B
Lamar Community College, A
Mesa State College, AB
Metropolitan State College of Denver, B
Naropa University, B
Northeastern Junior College, A
Parks College (Denver), A
Red Rocks Community College, A
Regis University, B
Trinidad State Junior College, A
United States Air Force Academy, B
University of Colorado at Boulder, B
University of Colorado at Colorado Springs, B
University of Colorado at Denver and Health
  Sciences Center - Downtown Denver Campus, B
University of Denver, B
University of Northern Colorado, B

Western State College of Colorado, B

Connecticut

Albertus Magnus College, B
Central Connecticut State University, B
Connecticut College, B
Eastern Connecticut State University, B
Fairfield University, B
Northwestern Connecticut Community College, A
Post University, B
Quinnipiac University, B
Sacred Heart University, AB
Saint Joseph College, B
Southern Connecticut State University, B
Trinity College, B
University of Bridgeport, B
University of Connecticut, B
University of Hartford, B
University of New Haven, B
Wesleyan University, B
Western Connecticut State University, B
Yale University, B

Delaware

Delaware State University, B
University of Delaware, B
Wesley College, B

District of Columbia

The Catholic University of America, B
Gallaudet University, B
The George Washington University, B
Georgetown University, B
Howard University, B
Trinity (Washington) University, B
University of the District of Columbia, AB

Florida

Ave Maria University, B
Barry University, B
Bethune-Cookman College, B
Clearwater Christian College, B
Daytona Beach Community College, A
Edward Waters College, B
Flagler College, B
Florida Agricultural and Mechanical University, B
Florida Atlantic University, B
Florida International University, B
Florida Memorial College, B
Florida Southern College, B
Florida State University, B
Gulf Coast Community College, A
Indian River Community College, A
Jacksonville University, B
Lynn University, B
Manatee Community College, A
Miami Dade College, A
New College of Florida, B
Nova Southeastern University, B
Palm Beach Atlantic University, B
Palm Beach Community College, A
Rollins College, B
Saint Leo University, B
St. Thomas University, B
Southeastern University, B
Stetson University, B
University of Central Florida, B
University of Florida, B
University of Miami, B
University of North Florida, B
University of South Florida, B
The University of Tampa, AB
University of West Florida, B
Warner Southern College, B

Georgia

Abraham Baldwin Agricultural College, A
Agnes Scott College, B
Albany State University, B
Andrew College, A
Armstrong Atlantic State University, B
Atlanta Metropolitan College, A
Augusta State University, B
Bainbridge College, A
Berry College, B

Brenau University, B
Brewton-Parker College, B
Clark Atlanta University, B
Clayton State University, A
Coastal Georgia Community College, A
Columbus State University, B
Covenant College, B
Dalton State College, A
Darton College, A
East Georgia College, A
Emmanuel College, B
Emory University, B
Gainesville College, A
Georgia College & State University, B
Georgia Highlands College, A
Georgia Perimeter College, A
Georgia Southern University, B
Georgia Southwestern State University, B
Georgia State University, B
Gordon College, A
Kennesaw State University, B
LaGrange College, B
Macon State College, A
Mercer University, B
Morehouse College, B
North Georgia College & State University, B
Oglethorpe University, B
Paine College, B
Piedmont College, B
Reinhardt College, B
Savannah State University, B
Shorter College, B
South Georgia College, A
Spelman College, B
Thomas University, B
Toccoa Falls College, B
University of Georgia, B
University of West Georgia, B
Valdosta State University, B
Waycross College, A
Wesleyan College, B
Young Harris College, A

Guam

University of Guam, B

Hawaii

Brigham Young University-Hawaii, B
Chaminade University of Honolulu, B
Hawaii Pacific University, B
University of Hawaii at Hilo, B
University of Hawaii at Manoa, B
University of Hawaii-West Oahu, B

Idaho

Albertson College of Idaho, B
Boise State University, B
Brigham Young University -Idaho, A
College of Southern Idaho, A
Idaho State University, AB
Lewis-Clark State College, B
North Idaho College, A
Northwest Nazarene University, B
University of Idaho, B

Illinois

Augustana College, B
Aurora University, B
Benedictine University, B
Blackburn College, B
Bradley University, B
Chicago State University, B
City Colleges of Chicago, Harold Washington College, A
City Colleges of Chicago, Wilbur Wright College, A
Concordia University, B
Danville Area Community College, A
DePaul University, B
Dominican University, B
East-West University, B
Eastern Illinois University, B
Elmhurst College, B
Eureka College, B
Governors State University, B
Greenville College, B
Illinois College, B

Illinois State University, B
Illinois Valley Community College, A
Illinois Wesleyan University, B
John A. Logan College, A
Judson College, B
Knox College, B
Lake Forest College, B
Lewis University, B
Lincoln College, A
Loyola University Chicago, B
MacMurray College, B
McKendree College, B
Millikin University, B
Monmouth College, B
National-Louis University, B
North Central College, B
North Park University, B
Northeastern Illinois University, B
Northern Illinois University, B
Northwestern University, B
Olivet Nazarene University, B
Parkland College, A
Principia College, B
Quincy University, B
Rend Lake College, A
Rockford College, B
Roosevelt University, B
Saint Xavier University, B
Sauk Valley Community College, A
Southern Illinois University Carbondale, B
Southern Illinois University Edwardsville, B
Spoon River College, A
Trinity Christian College, B
Trinity International University, B
University of Chicago, B
University of Illinois at Chicago, B
University of Illinois at Springfield, B
University of Illinois at Urbana-Champaign, B
University of St. Francis, B
Western Illinois University, B
Wheaton College, B

Indiana

Ancilla College, A
Anderson University, B
Ball State University, B
Bethel College, B
Butler University, B
Calumet College of Saint Joseph, AB
DePauw University, B
Earlham College, B
Franklin College, B
Goshen College, B
Grace College, B
Hanover College, B
Huntington University, B
Indiana State University, B
Indiana University Bloomington, B
Indiana University East, B
Indiana University Kokomo, B
Indiana University Northwest, B
Indiana University-Purdue University Fort Wayne, AB
Indiana University-Purdue University Indianapolis, B
Indiana University South Bend, B
Indiana University Southeast, B
Indiana Wesleyan University, AB
Manchester College, AB
Marian College, B
Martin University, B
Oakland City University, B
Purdue University, B
Purdue University Calumet, B
Purdue University North Central, B
Saint Joseph's College, B
Saint Mary-of-the-Woods College, B
Taylor University, B
Taylor University Fort Wayne, B
Tri-State University, B
University of Evansville, B
University of Indianapolis, B
University of Notre Dame, B
University of Saint Francis, B
University of Southern Indiana, B
Valparaiso University, B
Vincennes University, A

Wabash College, B

Iowa

Ashford University, B
Briar Cliff University, B
Buena Vista University, B
Central College, B
Clarke College, B
Coe College, B
Cornell College, B
Dordt College, B
Drake University, B
Graceland University, B
Grand View College, B
Grinnell College, B
Iowa Lakes Community College, A
Iowa State University of Science and Technology, B
Iowa Wesleyan College, B
Kirkwood Community College, A
Loras College, B
Luther College, B
Maharishi University of Management, B
Morningside College, B
Mount Mercy College, B
Northwestern College, B
St. Ambrose University, B
Simpson College, B
University of Dubuque, AB
The University of Iowa, B
University of Northern Iowa, B
Upper Iowa University, B
Waldorf College, B
Wartburg College, B

Kansas

Baker University, B
Barton County Community College, A
Benedictine College, B
Bethany College, B
Bethel College, B
Butler Community College, A
Coffeyville Community College, A
Colby Community College, A
Dodge City Community College, A
Donnelly College, A
Emporia State University, B
Fort Hays State University, B
Friends University, B
Garden City Community College, A
Highland Community College, A
Hutchinson Community College and Area Vocational School, A
Independence Community College, A
Kansas State University, B
Kansas Wesleyan University, B
Labette Community College, A
McPherson College, B
MidAmerica Nazarene University, B
Newman University, B
Ottawa University, B
Pittsburg State University, B
Pratt Community College, A
Seward County Community College, A
Southwestern College, B
Sterling College, B
Tabor College, B
University of Kansas, B
University of Saint Mary, B
Washburn University, B
Wichita State University, B

Kentucky

Alice Lloyd College, B
Asbury College, B
Bellarmine University, B
Berea College, B
Brescia University, B
Campbellsville University, B
Centre College, B
Eastern Kentucky University, B
Georgetown College, B
Kentucky State University, B
Kentucky Wesleyan College, B
Lindsey Wilson College, B
Mid-Continent University, B
Midway College, B

Morehead State University, B
Murray State University, B
Northern Kentucky University, B
Pikeville College, B
Spalding University, B
Thomas More College, AB
Transylvania University, B
University of the Cumberlands, B
University of Kentucky, B
University of Louisville, B
Western Kentucky University, B

Louisiana

Centenary College of Louisiana, B
Dillard University, B
Grambling State University, B
Louisiana College, B
Louisiana State University and Agricultural and
   Mechanical College, B
Louisiana State University at Alexandria, B
Louisiana State University in Shreveport, B
Louisiana Tech University, B
Loyola University New Orleans, B
McNeese State University, B
Nicholls State University, B
Northwestern State University of Louisiana, B
Our Lady of Holy Cross College, B
Southeastern Louisiana University, B
Southern University and Agricultural and Mechanical
   College, B
Southern University at New Orleans, B
Tulane University, B
University of Louisiana at Lafayette, B
University of Louisiana at Monroe, B
University of New Orleans, B
Xavier University of Louisiana, B

Maine

Bates College, B
Bowdoin College, B
Colby College, B
College of the Atlantic, B
Saint Joseph's College of Maine, B
University of Maine, B
The University of Maine at Augusta, B
University of Maine at Farmington, B
University of Maine at Fort Kent, B
University of Maine at Machias, B
University of Maine at Presque Isle, B
University of New England, B
University of Southern Maine, B

Maryland

Anne Arundel Community College, A
Bowie State University, B
College of Notre Dame of Maryland, B
College of Southern Maryland, A
Columbia Union College, B
Coppin State University, B
Frederick Community College, A
Frostburg State University, B
Goucher College, B
Hood College, B
The Johns Hopkins University, B
Loyola College in Maryland, B
McDaniel College, B
Morgan State University, B
Mount St. Mary's University, B
St. Mary's College of Maryland, B
Salisbury University, B
Towson University, B
United States Naval Academy, B
University of Baltimore, B
University of Maryland, Baltimore County, B
University of Maryland, College Park, B
University of Maryland Eastern Shore, B
University of Maryland University College, B
Villa Julie College, B
Washington College, B

Massachusetts

American International College, B
Amherst College, B
Anna Maria College, B
Assumption College, B
Atlantic Union College, B

Bentley College, B
Boston College, B
Boston University, B
Brandeis University, B
Bridgewater State College, B
Bunker Hill Community College, A
Clark University, B
College of the Holy Cross, B
Curry College, B
Eastern Nazarene College, B
Elms College, B
Emmanuel College, B
Endicott College, B
Fitchburg State College, B
Framingham State College, B
Gordon College, B
Hampshire College, B
Harvard University, B
Lesley University, B
Massachusetts College of Liberal Arts, B
Massachusetts Institute of Technology, B
Merrimack College, B
Mount Holyoke College, B
Nichols College, B
Northeastern University, B
Pine Manor College, AB
Quincy College, A
Regis College, B
Roxbury Community College, A
Salem State College, B
Simmons College, B
Smith College, B
Springfield College, B
Stonehill College, B
Suffolk University, B
Tufts University, B
University of Massachusetts Amherst, B
University of Massachusetts Boston, B
University of Massachusetts Dartmouth, B
University of Massachusetts Lowell, B
Wellesley College, B
Western New England College, B
Westfield State College, B
Wheaton College, B
Williams College, B
Worcester State College, B

Michigan

Adrian College, AB
Albion College, B
Alma College, B
Alpena Community College, A
Andrews University, B
Aquinas College, B
Calvin College, B
Central Michigan University, B
Concordia University, B
Cornerstone University, B
Eastern Michigan University, B
Grand Valley State University, B
Hillsdale College, B
Hope College, B
Kalamazoo College, B
Kellogg Community College, A
Lake Superior State University, B
Lansing Community College, A
Madonna University, AB
Marygrove College, B
Michigan State University, B
Michigan Technological University, B
Monroe County Community College, A
Northern Michigan University, B
Northwestern Michigan College, A
Oakland University, B
Olivet College, B
Rochester College, B
Saginaw Valley State University, B
Siena Heights University, AB
Spring Arbor University, B
University of Detroit Mercy, B
University of Michigan, B
University of Michigan-Dearborn, B
University of Michigan-Flint, B
Wayne State University, B

Western Michigan University, B

Minnesota

Augsburg College, B
Bemidji State University, B
Bethany Lutheran College, B
Bethel University, B
Carleton College, B
College of Saint Benedict, B
College of St. Catherine, B
The College of St. Scholastica, B
Concordia College, B
Concordia University, St. Paul, B
Crown College, B
Gustavus Adolphus College, B
Hamline University, B
Macalester College, B
Metropolitan State University, B
Minnesota State University Mankato, B
Minnesota State University Moorhead, B
North Central University, B
Northwestern College, B
St. Cloud State University, B
Saint John's University, B
Saint Mary's University of Minnesota, B
St. Olaf College, B
Southwest Minnesota State University, B
University of Minnesota, Duluth, B
University of Minnesota, Morris, B
University of Minnesota, Twin Cities Campus, B
University of St. Thomas, B
Winona State University, B

Mississippi

Alcorn State University, B
Belhaven College, B
Blue Mountain College, B
Coahoma Community College, A
Copiah-Lincoln Community College, A
Delta State University, B
East Central Community College, A
East Mississippi Community College, A
Hinds Community College, A
Itawamba Community College, A
Jackson State University, B
Jones County Junior College, A
Millsaps College, B
Mississippi College, B
Mississippi Delta Community College, A
Mississippi State University, B
Mississippi University for Women, B
Mississippi Valley State University, B
Northeast Mississippi Community College, A
Southwest Mississippi Community College, A
Tougaloo College, B
University of Mississippi, B
University of Southern Mississippi, B
William Carey College, B

Missouri

Avila University, B
Central Methodist University, AB
Central Missouri State University, B
College of the Ozarks, B
Columbia College, B
Culver-Stockton College, B
Drury University, B
East Central College, A
Evangel University, B
Fontbonne University, B
Hannibal-LaGrange College, AB
Jefferson College, A
Lincoln University, B
Lindenwood University, B
Maryville University of Saint Louis, B
Missouri Baptist University, B
Missouri Southern State University, B
Missouri State University, B
Missouri Valley College, B
Missouri Western State University, B
Northwest Missouri State University, B
Park University, B
Rockhurst University, B
Saint Louis University, B
Southeast Missouri State University, B
Southwest Baptist University, B

Stephens College, B
Truman State University, B
University of Missouri-Columbia, B
University of Missouri-Kansas City, B
University of Missouri-Rolla, B
University of Missouri-St. Louis, B
Washington University in St. Louis, B
Webster University, B
Westminster College, B
William Jewell College, B
William Woods University, B

Montana

Carroll College, AB
Montana State University, B
Montana State University-Billings, B
Rocky Mountain College, B
University of Great Falls, B
The University of Montana-Missoula, B
The University of Montana-Western, B

Nebraska

Chadron State College, B
College of Saint Mary, B
Concordia University, B
Creighton University, B
Dana College, B
Doane College, B
Hastings College, B
Midland Lutheran College, B
Nebraska Wesleyan University, B
Northeast Community College, A
Peru State College, B
Union College, B
University of Nebraska at Kearney, B
University of Nebraska-Lincoln, B
University of Nebraska at Omaha, B
Wayne State College, B
Western Nebraska Community College, A
York College, B

Nevada

Community College of Southern Nevada, A
Great Basin College, A
Nevada State College at Henderson, B
University of Nevada, Las Vegas, B
University of Nevada, Reno, B

New Hampshire

Colby-Sawyer College, B
Dartmouth College, B
Franklin Pierce College, B
Keene State College, B
New England College, B
Plymouth State University, B
Rivier College, B
Saint Anselm College, B
Southern New Hampshire University, B
University of New Hampshire, B
University of New Hampshire at Manchester, B

New Jersey

Bloomfield College, B
Brookdale Community College, A
Burlington County College, A
Caldwell College, B
Centenary College, B
The College of New Jersey, B
College of Saint Elizabeth, B
Drew University, B
Fairleigh Dickinson University, College at
    Florham, B
Fairleigh Dickinson University, Metropolitan
    Campus, B
Felician College, AB
Georgian Court University, B
Gloucester County College, A
Kean University, B
Middlesex County College, A
Monmouth University, B
Montclair State University, B
New Jersey City University, B
Passaic County Community College, A
Princeton University, B
The Richard Stockton College of New Jersey, B

Rider University, B
Rowan University, B
Rutgers, The State University of New Jersey,
    Camden, B
Rutgers, The State University of New Jersey, New
    Brunswick/Piscataway, B
Rutgers, The State University of New Jersey,
    Newark, B
Saint Peter's College, B
Salem Community College, A
Seton Hall University, B
Stevens Institute of Technology, B
Sussex County Community College, A
William Paterson University of New Jersey, B

New Mexico

College of Santa Fe, AB
College of the Southwest, B
Eastern New Mexico University, B
New Mexico Highlands University, B
New Mexico Junior College, A
New Mexico Military Institute, A
New Mexico State University, B
St. John's College, B
San Juan College, A
University of New Mexico, B
Western New Mexico University, B

New York

Adelphi University, B
Alfred University, B
Bard College, B
Barnard College, B
Bernard M. Baruch College of the City University of
    New York, B
Brooklyn College of the City University of New
    York, B
Buffalo State College, State University of New
    York, B
Canisius College, B
Cazenovia College, B
City College of the City University of New York, B
Colgate University, B
College of Mount Saint Vincent, B
The College of New Rochelle, B
The College of Saint Rose, B
College of Staten Island of the City University of
    New York, B
Columbia College, B
Columbia University, School of General Studies, B
Concordia College, B
Cornell University, B
Daemen College, B
Dominican College, B
Dowling College, B
D'Youville College, B
Elmira College, B
Eugene Lang College The New School for Liberal
    Arts, B
Fordham University, B
Fulton-Montgomery Community College, A
Hamilton College, B
Hartwick College, B
Herkimer County Community College, A
Hilbert College, B
Hobart and William Smith Colleges, B
Hofstra University, B
Houghton College, B
Hunter College of the City University of New York, B
Iona College, B
Ithaca College, B
Keuka College, B
Le Moyne College, B
Lehman College of the City University of New
    York, B
Long Island University, Brooklyn Campus, B
Long Island University, C.W. Post Campus, B
Manhattan College, B
Manhattanville College, B
Marist College, B
Marymount Manhattan College, B
Medaille College, B
Mercy College, B
Mohawk Valley Community College, A
Molloy College, B
Mount Saint Mary College, B

Nazareth College of Rochester, B
New York Institute of Technology, B
New York University, B
Niagara University, B
Nyack College, B
Pace University, B
Queens College of the City University of New
    York, B
Roberts Wesleyan College, B
Russell Sage College, B
St. Bonaventure University, B
St. Francis College, B
St. John Fisher College, B
St. John's University, B
St. Joseph's College, New York, B
St. Joseph's College, Suffolk Campus, B
St. Lawrence University, B
St. Thomas Aquinas College, B
Sarah Lawrence College, B
Siena College, B
Skidmore College, B
State University of New York at Binghamton, B
State University of New York at Buffalo, B
State University of New York College at
    Brockport, B
State University of New York College at Cortland, B
State University of New York College at Geneseo, B
State University of New York College at Oneonta, B
State University of New York College at Potsdam, B
State University of New York, Fredonia, B
State University of New York at New Paltz, B
State University of New York at Oswego, B
State University of New York at Plattsburgh, B
Stony Brook University, State University of New
    York, B
Suffolk County Community College, A
Syracuse University, B
Touro College, B
Union College, B
University at Albany, State University of New York, B
University of Rochester, B
Utica College, B
Vassar College, B
Wagner College, B
Wells College, B
Yeshiva University, B
York College of the City University of New York, B

North Carolina

Appalachian State University, B
Barber-Scotia College, B
Barton College, B
Belmont Abbey College, B
Bennett College For Women, B
Brevard College, B
Campbell University, B
Catawba College, B
Chowan University, B
Davidson College, B
Duke University, B
East Carolina University, B
Elizabeth City State University, B
Elon University, B
Fayetteville State University, B
Gardner-Webb University, B
Greensboro College, B
Guilford College, B
High Point University, B
Johnson C. Smith University, B
Lees-McRae College, B
Lenoir-Rhyne College, B
Livingstone College, B
Louisburg College, A
Mars Hill College, B
Meredith College, B
Methodist College, AB
Montreat College, B
Mount Olive College, B
North Carolina Agricultural and Technical State
    University, B
North Carolina Central University, B
North Carolina State University, B
North Carolina Wesleyan College, B
Peace College, B
Pfeiffer University, B
Piedmont Baptist College, B

Queens University of Charlotte, B
St. Andrews Presbyterian College, B
Saint Augustine's College, B
Salem College, B
Shaw University, B
The University of North Carolina at Asheville, B
The University of North Carolina at Chapel Hill, B
The University of North Carolina at Charlotte, B
The University of North Carolina at Greensboro, B
The University of North Carolina at Pembroke, B
The University of North Carolina Wilmington, B
Wake Forest University, B
Warren Wilson College, B
Western Carolina University, B
Wingate University, B
Winston-Salem State University, B

North Dakota

Cankdeska Cikana Community College, A
Dickinson State University, B
Jamestown College, B
Mayville State University, B
Minot State University, B
North Dakota State University, B
Turtle Mountain Community College, A
University of Mary, B
University of North Dakota, B
Valley City State University, B

Ohio

Antioch College, B
Ashland University, B
Baldwin-Wallace College, B
Bluffton University, B
Bowling Green State University, B
Capital University, B
Case Western Reserve University, B
Cedarville University, B
Central State University, B
Cleveland State University, B
College of Mount St. Joseph, B
The College of Wooster, B
Defiance College, B
Denison University, B
Edison State Community College, A
Franciscan University of Steubenville, B
Heidelberg College, B
Hiram College, B
John Carroll University, B
Kent State University, B
Kent State University, Trumbull Campus, B
Kenyon College, B
Lake Erie College, B
Lourdes College, AB
Malone College, B
Marietta College, B
Miami University, B
Miami University Hamilton, B
Miami University-Middletown Campus, A
Mount Union College, B
Mount Vernon Nazarene University, B
Muskingum College, B
Notre Dame College, B
Oberlin College, B
Ohio Dominican University, B
Ohio Northern University, B
The Ohio State University, B
The Ohio State University at Lima, B
The Ohio State University-Mansfield Campus, B
The Ohio State University at Marion, B
The Ohio State University-Newark Campus, B
Ohio University, B
Ohio University-Eastern, B
Ohio Wesleyan University, B
Otterbein College, B
Pontifical College Josephinum, B
Shawnee State University, B
Terra State Community College, A
Tiffin University, B
The University of Akron, B
University of Cincinnati, B
University of Dayton, B
The University of Findlay, B
University of Rio Grande, AB
The University of Toledo, B
Urbana University, B

Ursuline College, B
Walsh University, B
Wilmington College, B
Wittenberg University, B
Wright State University, B
Wright State University, Lake Campus, A
Xavier University, AB
Youngstown State University, B

Oklahoma

Cameron University, B
Carl Albert State College, A
East Central University, B
Eastern Oklahoma State College, A
Hillsdale Free Will Baptist College, A
Langston University, B
Mid-America Christian University, B
Murray State College, A
Northeastern State University, B
Northwestern Oklahoma State University, B
Oklahoma Baptist University, B
Oklahoma Christian University, B
Oklahoma City University, B
Oklahoma Panhandle State University, B
Oklahoma State University, B
Oklahoma Wesleyan University, B
Oral Roberts University, B
Redlands Community College, A
Rose State College, A
St. Gregory's University, B
Seminole State College, A
Southeastern Oklahoma State University, B
Southern Nazarene University, B
Southwestern Oklahoma State University, B
Tulsa Community College, A
University of Central Oklahoma, B
University of Oklahoma, B
University of Science and Arts of Oklahoma, B
University of Tulsa, B

Oregon

Cascade College, B
Chemeketa Community College, A
Concordia University, B
Corban College, B
Eastern Oregon University, B
George Fox University, B
Lewis & Clark College, B
Linfield College, B
Linn-Benton Community College, A
Oregon State University, B
Pacific University, B
Portland State University, B
Reed College, B
Southern Oregon University, B
Treasure Valley Community College, A
Umpqua Community College, A
University of Oregon, B
University of Portland, B
Warner Pacific College, B
Western Oregon University, B
Willamette University, B

Pennsylvania

Albright College, B
Allegheny College, B
Alvernia College, B
Arcadia University, B
Bloomsburg University of Pennsylvania, B
Bryn Athyn College of the New Church, B
Bryn Mawr College, B
Bucknell University, B
Butler County Community College, A
Cabrini College, B
California University of Pennsylvania, B
Carlow University, B
Carnegie Mellon University, B
Cedar Crest College, B
Chatham College, B
Chestnut Hill College, B
Cheyney University of Pennsylvania, B
Clarion University of Pennsylvania, B
College Misericordia, B
Community College of Allegheny County, A
Delaware Valley College, B
DeSales University, B

Dickinson College, B
Drexel University, B
Duquesne University, B
East Stroudsburg University of Pennsylvania, B
Eastern University, B
Edinboro University of Pennsylvania, B
Elizabethtown College, B
Franklin and Marshall College, B
Geneva College, B
Gettysburg College, B
Grove City College, B
Gwynedd-Mercy College, B
Haverford College, B
Holy Family University, B
Immaculata University, B
Indiana University of Pennsylvania, B
Juniata College, B
King's College, B
Kutztown University of Pennsylvania, B
La Roche College, B
La Salle University, B
Lafayette College, B
Lebanon Valley College, B
Lehigh University, B
Lincoln University, B
Lock Haven University of Pennsylvania, B
Lycoming College, B
Mansfield University of Pennsylvania, B
Marywood University, B
Mercyhurst College, B
Messiah College, B
Millersville University of Pennsylvania, B
Moravian College, B
Mount Aloysius College, B
Muhlenberg College, B
Neumann College, B
The Pennsylvania State University Abington
  College, B
The Pennsylvania State University Altoona
  College, B
The Pennsylvania State University Beaver Campus
  of the Commonwealth College, B
The Pennsylvania State University Berks Campus of
  the Berks-Lehigh Valley College, B
The Pennsylvania State University Delaware County
  Campus of the Commonwealth College, B
The Pennsylvania State University DuBois Campus
  of the Commonwealth College, B
The Pennsylvania State University at Erie, The
  Behrend College, B
The Pennsylvania State University Fayette Campus
  of the Commonwealth College, B
The Pennsylvania State University Harrisburg
  Campus, B
The Pennsylvania State University Hazleton
  Campus of the Commonwealth College, B
The Pennsylvania State University, Lehigh Valley
  Campus of the Berks-Lehigh Valley College, B
The Pennsylvania State University McKeesport
  Campus of the Commonwealth College, B
The Pennsylvania State University Mont Alto
  Campus of the Commonwealth College, B
The Pennsylvania State University New Kensington
  Campus of the Commonwealth College, B
The Pennsylvania State University Schuylkill
  Campus of the Capital College, B
The Pennsylvania State University Shenango
  Campus of the Commonwealth College, B
The Pennsylvania State University University Park
  Campus, B
The Pennsylvania State University Wilkes-Barre
  Campus of the Commonwealth College, B
The Pennsylvania State University Worthington
  Scranton Campus of the Commonwealth
  College, B
The Pennsylvania State University York Campus of
  the Commonwealth College, B
Point Park University, B
Robert Morris University, B
Rosemont College, B
Saint Francis University, B
Saint Joseph's University, B
Saint Vincent College, B
Seton Hill University, B
Shippensburg University of Pennsylvania, B
Slippery Rock University of Pennsylvania, B

Susquehanna University, B
Swarthmore College, B
Temple University, B
Thiel College, B
University of Pennsylvania, B
University of Pittsburgh, B
University of Pittsburgh at Bradford, B
University of Pittsburgh at Greensburg, B
University of Pittsburgh at Johnstown, B
The University of Scranton, B
Ursinus College, B
Villanova University, B
Washington & Jefferson College, B
Waynesburg College, B
West Chester University of Pennsylvania, B
Westminster College, B
Widener University, B
Wilkes University, B
Wilson College, B
York College of Pennsylvania, B

Puerto Rico

Inter American University of Puerto Rico,
   Metropolitan Campus, B
Inter American University of Puerto Rico, San
   Germán Campus, B
Pontifical Catholic University of Puerto Rico, B
Universidad del Turabo, B
University of Puerto Rico, Cayey University
   College, B
University of Puerto Rico, Mayagüez Campus, B
University of Puerto Rico, Río Piedras, B

Rhode Island

Brown University, B
Bryant University, B
Providence College, B
Rhode Island College, B
Roger Williams University, B
Salve Regina University, B
University of Rhode Island, B

South Carolina

Allen University, B
Anderson University, B
Benedict College, B
Bob Jones University, B
Charleston Southern University, B
The Citadel, The Military College of South
   Carolina, B
Claflin University, B
Clemson University, B
Coastal Carolina University, B
Coker College, B
College of Charleston, B
Columbia College, B
Converse College, B
Erskine College, B
Francis Marion University, B
Furman University, B
Lander University, B
Limestone College, B
Morris College, B
Newberry College, B
North Greenville College, B
Presbyterian College, B
South Carolina State University, B
Southern Wesleyan University, B
University of South Carolina, B
University of South Carolina Aiken, B
University of South Carolina Beaufort, B
University of South Carolina Upstate, B
Voorhees College, B
Winthrop University, B
Wofford College, B

South Dakota

Augustana College, B
Black Hills State University, B
Dakota State University, B
Dakota Wesleyan University, B
Mount Marty College, B
Northern State University, B
Presentation College, A
South Dakota State University, B
University of Sioux Falls, B

The University of South Dakota, B

Tennessee

Aquinas College, B
Austin Peay State University, B
Belmont University, B
Bethel College, B
Bryan College, B
Carson-Newman College, B
Christian Brothers University, B
Crichton College, B
Cumberland University, B
East Tennessee State University, B
Fisk University, B
Free Will Baptist Bible College, B
Freed-Hardeman University, B
King College, B
Lambuth University, B
Lane College, B
Lee University, B
LeMoyne-Owen College, B
Lincoln Memorial University, B
Lipscomb University, B
Martin Methodist College, AB
Maryville College, B
Middle Tennessee State University, B
Milligan College, B
Rhodes College, B
Sewanee: The University of the South, B
Southern Adventist University, B
Tennessee State University, B
Tennessee Technological University, B
Tennessee Temple University, B
Tennessee Wesleyan College, B
Trevecca Nazarene University, B
Tusculum College, B
Union University, B
University of Memphis, B
The University of Tennessee, B
The University of Tennessee at Chattanooga, B
The University of Tennessee at Martin, B
Vanderbilt University, B

Texas

Abilene Christian University, B
Amarillo College, A
Angelina College, A
Angelo State University, B
Austin College, B
Austin Community College, A
Baylor University, B
Blinn College, A
Brazosport College, A
Clarendon College, A
Coastal Bend College, A
Concordia University at Austin, B
Dallas Baptist University, B
Del Mar College, A
East Texas Baptist University, B
El Paso Community College, A
Frank Phillips College, A
Galveston College, A
Hardin-Simmons University, B
Hill College of the Hill Junior College District, A
Houston Baptist University, B
Howard College, A
Howard Payne University, B
Huston-Tillotson University, B
Jarvis Christian College, B
Kilgore College, A
Kingwood College, A
Lamar University, B
Lee College, A
LeTourneau University, B
Lon Morris College, A
McMurry University, B
Midland College, A
Midwestern State University, B
Navarro College, A
Odessa College, A
Our Lady of the Lake University of San Antonio, B
Palo Alto College, A
Paul Quinn College, B
Prairie View A&M University, B
Rice University, B
St. Edward's University, B

St. Mary's University of San Antonio, B
St. Philip's College, A
Sam Houston State University, B
Schreiner University, B
Southern Methodist University, B
Southwestern Adventist University, B
Southwestern University, B
Stephen F. Austin State University, B
Sul Ross State University, B
Tarleton State University, B
Texas A&M International University, B
Texas A&M University, B
Texas A&M University-Commerce, B
Texas A&M University-Corpus Christi, B
Texas A&M University-Kingsville, B
Texas A&M University-Texarkana, B
Texas Christian University, B
Texas College, B
Texas Lutheran University, B
Texas Southern University, B
Texas State University-San Marcos, B
Texas Tech University, B
Texas Wesleyan University, B
Texas Woman's University, B
Trinity University, B
Trinity Valley Community College, A
University of Dallas, B
University of Houston, B
University of Houston-Clear Lake, B
University of Houston-Downtown, B
University of the Incarnate Word, B
University of Mary Hardin-Baylor, B
University of North Texas, B
University of St. Thomas, B
The University of Texas at Arlington, B
The University of Texas at Austin, B
The University of Texas at Brownsville, B
The University of Texas at El Paso, B
The University of Texas-Pan American, B
The University of Texas of the Permian Basin, B
The University of Texas at San Antonio, B
The University of Texas at Tyler, B
Wayland Baptist University, B
West Texas A&M University, B
Wharton County Junior College, A
Wiley College, B

United States Virgin Islands

University of the Virgin Islands, B

Utah

Brigham Young University, B
Dixie State College of Utah, A
Salt Lake Community College, A
Southern Utah University, B
University of Utah, B
Utah State University, B
Utah Valley State College, AB
Weber State University, B
Westminster College, B

Vermont

Bennington College, B
College of St. Joseph, B
Green Mountain College, B
Johnson State College, B
Lyndon State College, B
Marlboro College, B
Middlebury College, B
Norwich University, B
Saint Michael's College, B
Southern Vermont College, B
University of Vermont, B

Virginia

Averett University, B
Bluefield College, B
Bridgewater College, B
Christopher Newport University, B
The College of William and Mary, B
Eastern Mennonite University, B
Emory & Henry College, B
Ferrum College, B
George Mason University, B
Hampden-Sydney College, B
Hampton University, B

Hollins University, B
James Madison University, B
Liberty University, B
Longwood University, B
Lynchburg College, B
Mary Baldwin College, B
Marymount University, B
Mountain Empire Community College, A
Norfolk State University, B
Old Dominion University, B
Patrick Henry College, B
Radford University, B
Randolph-Macon College, B
Randolph-Macon Woman's College, B
Roanoke College, B
Saint Paul's College, B
Shenandoah University, B
Southern Virginia University, B
Sweet Briar College, B
University of Mary Washington, B
University of Richmond, B
University of Virginia, B
The University of Virginia's College at Wise, B
Virginia Commonwealth University, B
Virginia Intermont College, B
Virginia Military Institute, B
Virginia Polytechnic Institute and State University, B
Virginia State University, B
Virginia Union University, B
Virginia Wesleyan College, B
Washington and Lee University, B

Washington

Central Washington University, B
Centralia College, A
Eastern Washington University, B
Everett Community College, A
Gonzaga University, B
Heritage University, B
Highline Community College, A
Lower Columbia College, A
Northwest University, B
Pacific Lutheran University, B
Saint Martin's University, B
Seattle Pacific University, B
Seattle University, B
Skagit Valley College, A
Tacoma Community College, A
University of Puget Sound, B
University of Washington, B
Walla Walla College, B
Washington State University, B
Western Washington University, B
Whitman College, B
Whitworth College, B

West Virginia

American Public University System, B
Bethany College, B
Concord University, B
Davis & Elkins College, B
Fairmont State University, B
Glenville State College, B
Marshall University, B
Mountain State University, B
Potomac State College of West Virginia
   University, A
Shepherd University, B
West Liberty State College, B
West Virginia State University, B
West Virginia University, B
West Virginia Wesleyan College, B
Wheeling Jesuit University, B

Wisconsin

Alverno College, B
Beloit College, B
Cardinal Stritch University, B
Carroll College, B
Carthage College, B
Concordia University Wisconsin, B
Edgewood College, B
Lakeland College, B
Lawrence University, B
Marian College of Fond du Lac, B
Marquette University, B

Mount Mary College, B
Northland College, B
Ripon College, B
St. Norbert College, B
Silver Lake College, B
University of Wisconsin-Eau Claire, B
University of Wisconsin-Green Bay, AB
University of Wisconsin-La Crosse, B
University of Wisconsin-Madison, B
University of Wisconsin-Milwaukee, B
University of Wisconsin-Oshkosh, B
University of Wisconsin-Parkside, B
University of Wisconsin-Platteville, B
University of Wisconsin-River Falls, B
University of Wisconsin-Stevens Point, B
University of Wisconsin-Superior, B
University of Wisconsin-Whitewater, B
Viterbo University, B
Wisconsin Lutheran College, B

Wyoming

Casper College, A
Central Wyoming College, A
Eastern Wyoming College, A
Laramie County Community College, A
Northwest College, A
Sheridan College-Sheridan and Gillette, A
University of Wyoming, B
Western Wyoming Community College, A

Alberta

Athabasca University, B
Concordia University College of Alberta, B
The King's University College, B
Taylor University College and Seminary, B
University of Alberta, B
University of Calgary, B
University of Lethbridge, B

British Columbia

Kwantlen University College, A
Simon Fraser University, B
Thompson Rivers University, B
Trinity Western University, B
The University of British Columbia, B
University College of the Fraser Valley, B
University of Northern British Columbia, B
University of Victoria, B

Manitoba

Brandon University, B
Canadian Mennonite University, B
University of Manitoba, B
The University of Winnipeg, B

New Brunswick

Atlantic Baptist University, B
Mount Allison University, B
St. Thomas University, B
Université de Moncton, B
University of New Brunswick Fredericton, B
University of New Brunswick Saint John, B

Newfoundland and Labrador

Memorial University of Newfoundland, B

Nova Scotia

Acadia University, B
Cape Breton University, B
Dalhousie University, B
Mount Saint Vincent University, B
St. Francis Xavier University, B
Saint Mary's University, B
Université Sainte-Anne, B
University of King's College, B

Ontario

Brock University, B
Carleton University, B
Lakehead University, B
Laurentian University, B
McMaster University, B
Nipissing University, B
Queen's University at Kingston, B
Redeemer University College, B

Royal Military College of Canada, B
Trent University, B
Tyndale University College & Seminary, B
University of Guelph, B
University of Ottawa, B
University of Toronto, B
University of Waterloo, B
The University of Western Ontario, B
University of Windsor, B
Wilfrid Laurier University, B
York University, B

Prince Edward Island

University of Prince Edward Island, B

Quebec

Bishop's University, B
Concordia University, B
McGill University, B
Université Laval, AB
Université de Montréal, B
Université du Québec àChicoutimi, B
Université de Sherbrooke, B

Saskatchewan

University of Regina, B
University of Saskatchewan, B

ENGLISH/LANGUAGE ARTS TEACHER EDUCATION

Alabama

Auburn University, B
Huntingdon College, B
Judson College, B
Miles College, B
Samford University, B
Talladega College, B

Arizona

Northern Arizona University, B
Prescott College, B
The University of Arizona, B

Arkansas

Arkansas State University, B
Arkansas Tech University, B
Harding University, B
John Brown University, B
Southern Arkansas University-Magnolia, B
University of Arkansas at Fort Smith, B
University of Central Arkansas, B
University of the Ozarks, B

California

California State University, Chico, B
California State University, Long Beach, B
College of the Siskiyous, A
Hope International University, B
Simpson University, B
Westmont College, B

Colorado

Colorado State University, B
Fort Lewis College, B

Connecticut

Sacred Heart University, B

Delaware

Delaware State University, B
University of Delaware, B

District of Columbia

The Catholic University of America, B
Gallaudet University, B

Florida

Barry University, B
Bethune-Cookman College, B
Clearwater Christian College, B
Florida Atlantic University, B

Florida International University, B
Florida State University, B
Manatee Community College, A
Southeastern University, B
University of Central Florida, B
University of South Florida, B
University of West Florida, B

Georgia

Brewton-Parker College, B
Columbus State University, B
Emmanuel College, B
Georgia Southern University, B
Kennesaw State University, B
North Georgia College & State University, B
Paine College, B
Toccoa Falls College, B
University of Georgia, B

Hawaii

Brigham Young University-Hawaii, B

Idaho

Lewis-Clark State College, B
Northwest Nazarene University, B

Illinois

Chicago State University, B
Concordia University, B
Elmhurst College, B
Greenville College, B
Illinois Wesleyan University, B
McKendree College, B
Saint Xavier University, B
Trinity Christian College, B
University of Illinois at Chicago, B
University of Illinois at Urbana-Champaign, B
University of St. Francis, B

Indiana

Ancilla College, A
Anderson University, B
Bethel College, B
Calumet College of Saint Joseph, B
Franklin College, B
Grace College, B
Indiana University Bloomington, B
Indiana University Northwest, B
Indiana University-Purdue University Fort Wayne, B
Indiana University-Purdue University Indianapolis, B
Indiana University South Bend, B
Indiana University Southeast, B
Indiana Wesleyan University, B
Oakland City University, B
Tri-State University, B
University of Evansville, B
University of Indianapolis, B
University of Saint Francis, B
Valparaiso University, B

Iowa

Buena Vista University, B
Faith Baptist Bible College and Theological
    Seminary, B
St. Ambrose University, B
University of Dubuque, B
Waldorf College, B
William Penn University, B

Kansas

Bethany College, B
MidAmerica Nazarene University, B
Pittsburg State University, B

Kentucky

Berea College, B
Campbellsville University, B
Kentucky Wesleyan College, B
Murray State University, B
Pikeville College, B

Louisiana

Centenary College of Louisiana, B
Grambling State University, B
Louisiana State University in Shreveport, B

Louisiana Tech University, B
McNeese State University, B
Northwestern State University of Louisiana, B
Southeastern Louisiana University, B
Southern University and Agricultural and Mechanical
    College, B
University of Louisiana at Monroe, B
University of New Orleans, B

Maine

Saint Joseph's College of Maine, B
University of Maine, B
University of Maine at Farmington, B
University of Maine at Fort Kent, B
University of Maine at Machias, B

Maryland

Columbia Union College, B
University of Maryland, College Park, B

Massachusetts

Boston University, B
Bridgewater State College, B
Elms College, B
Fitchburg State College, B
Framingham State College, B

Michigan

Alma College, B
Aquinas College, B
Central Michigan University, B
Concordia University, B
Cornerstone University, B
Eastern Michigan University, B
Hope College, B
Michigan Technological University, B
Northern Michigan University, B
Rochester College, B
Saginaw Valley State University, B
Wayne State University, B
Western Michigan University, B

Minnesota

Bethel University, B
College of St. Catherine, B
Concordia College, B
Crown College, B
Minnesota State University Moorhead, B
Northwestern College, B
Pillsbury Baptist Bible College, B
Saint Mary's University of Minnesota, B
Southwest Minnesota State University, B
University of Minnesota, Twin Cities Campus, B
University of St. Thomas, B

Mississippi

Blue Mountain College, B
Delta State University, B
Mississippi Valley State University, B
Rust College, B
University of Mississippi, B
William Carey College, B

Missouri

College of the Ozarks, B
Culver-Stockton College, B
Hannibal-LaGrange College, B
Lincoln University, B
Maryville University of Saint Louis, B
Missouri State University, B
Missouri Western State University, B
Southeast Missouri State University, B
Southwest Baptist University, B
University of Missouri-St. Louis, B
Washington University in St. Louis, B
William Woods University, B

Montana

Carroll College, B
Montana State University-Billings, B
Rocky Mountain College, B
University of Great Falls, B

The University of Montana-Western, B

Nebraska

Chadron State College, B
Concordia University, B
Dana College, B
Hastings College, B
Nebraska Wesleyan University, B
Union College, B
University of Nebraska-Lincoln, B
Wayne State College, B
York College, B

Nevada

Nevada State College at Henderson, B
University of Nevada, Reno, B

New Hampshire

Colby-Sawyer College, B
Keene State College, B
Rivier College, B
Southern New Hampshire University, B
University of New Hampshire, B

New Jersey

Bloomfield College, B
The College of New Jersey, B

New Mexico

College of Santa Fe, B

New York

Brooklyn College of the City University of New
    York, B
Buffalo State College, State University of New
    York, B
The College of Saint Rose, B
Daemen College, B
Dominican College, B
Dowling College, B
Elmira College, B
Hofstra University, B
Iona College, B
Ithaca College, B
Keuka College, B
Le Moyne College, B
Long Island University, Brooklyn Campus, B
Long Island University, C.W. Post Campus, B
Manhattanville College, B
Marist College, B
Mercy College, B
Molloy College, B
Nazareth College of Rochester, B
New York Institute of Technology, B
New York University, B
Pace University, B
Roberts Wesleyan College, B
St. Bonaventure University, B
St. Francis College, B
St. John's University, B
State University of New York College at
    Brockport, B
State University of New York College at Oneonta, B
State University of New York College at Potsdam, B
Syracuse University, B
University at Albany, State University of New York, B
Utica College, B

North Carolina

Appalachian State University, B
Chowan University, B
East Carolina University, B
Elizabeth City State University, B
Fayetteville State University, B
Gardner-Webb University, B
Greensboro College, B
Louisburg College, A
North Carolina Central University, B
North Carolina State University, B
Queens University of Charlotte, B
Saint Augustine's College, B
Shaw University, B
The University of North Carolina at Charlotte, B
The University of North Carolina at Greensboro, B
The University of North Carolina at Pembroke, B

The University of North Carolina Wilmington, B
Western Carolina University, B
Winston-Salem State University, B

North Dakota

Jamestown College, B
Mayville State University, B
Minot State University, B
North Dakota State University, B
University of Mary, B
Valley City State University, B

Ohio

Bowling Green State University, B
Capital University, B
Cedarville University, B
Central State University, B
Kent State University, B
Malone College, B
Miami University, B
Miami University Hamilton, B
Mount Vernon Nazarene University, B
Ohio Northern University, B
Shawnee State University, B
The University of Akron, B
University of Rio Grande, B
The University of Toledo, B
Ursuline College, B
Wright State University, B
Youngstown State University, B

Oklahoma

East Central University, B
Oklahoma Baptist University, B
Oklahoma Christian University, B
Oral Roberts University, B
St. Gregory's University, B
Southeastern Oklahoma State University, B
Southern Nazarene University, B
Southwestern Oklahoma State University, B
University of Central Oklahoma, B
University of Oklahoma, B

Oregon

Concordia University, B
Corban College, B

Pennsylvania

Alvernia College, B
Cabrini College, B
Chatham College, B
Duquesne University, B
Eastern University, B
Indiana University of Pennsylvania, B
Juniata College, B
La Roche College, B
Lebanon Valley College, B
Lincoln University, B
Mansfield University of Pennsylvania, B
Marywood University, B
Mercyhurst College, B
Messiah College, B
Millersville University of Pennsylvania, B
Philadelphia Biblical University, B
Point Park University, B
Saint Francis University, B
Seton Hill University, B
Temple University, B
University of Pittsburgh at Johnstown, B
Waynesburg College, B
West Chester University of Pennsylvania, B
Widener University, B
York College of Pennsylvania, B

Puerto Rico

Bayamon Central University, B
Caribbean University, B
Pontifical Catholic University of Puerto Rico, B

University of Puerto Rico, Cayey University
College, B

Rhode Island

Rhode Island College, B
Salve Regina University, B

South Carolina

Anderson University, B
Bob Jones University, B
Charleston Southern University, B
The Citadel, The Military College of South
Carolina, B
Coker College, B
Limestone College, B
Morris College, B

South Dakota

Dakota State University, B
Dakota Wesleyan University, B
Mount Marty College, B
The University of South Dakota, B

Tennessee

Bethel College, B
Christian Brothers University, B
Crichton College, B
Freed-Hardeman University, B
King College, B
Lambuth University, B
Maryville College, B
Southern Adventist University, B
Tennessee Temple University, B
Tennessee Wesleyan College, B
Trevecca Nazarene University, B
The University of Tennessee at Martin, B

Texas

Abilene Christian University, B
Arlington Baptist College, B
Baylor University, B
East Texas Baptist University, B
Hardin-Simmons University, B
Houston Baptist University, B
Howard Payne University, B
Sam Houston State University, B
Schreiner University, B
Texas A&M International University, B
Texas Christian University, B
Texas Wesleyan University, B

Utah

Brigham Young University, B
Utah Valley State College, B
Weber State University, B

Vermont

Johnson State College, B
Lyndon State College, A
University of Vermont, B

Virginia

Averett University, B
Bluefield College, B
Eastern Mennonite University, B
Liberty University, B
Old Dominion University, B
Virginia Intermont College, B

Washington

Central Washington University, B
Eastern Washington University, B
Northwest University, B
Seattle Pacific University, B
Washington State University, B

West Virginia

Glenville State College, B
Ohio Valley University, B
West Virginia Wesleyan College, B

Wheeling Jesuit University, B

Wisconsin

Alverno College, B
Carroll College, B
Marian College of Fond du Lac, B
Marquette University, B
Mount Mary College, B
University of Wisconsin-River Falls, B
University of Wisconsin-Superior, B
Viterbo University, B

Ontario

The University of Western Ontario, B
University of Windsor, B
York University, B

Quebec

Bishop's University, B
McGill University, B
Université du Québec àTrois-Rivières, B

Saskatchewan

University of Regina, B

ENGLISH LITERATURE (BRITISH AND COMMONWEALTH)

California

University of Southern California, B

Florida

University of Miami, B

Indiana

Indiana University-Purdue University Fort Wayne, B
Saint Mary's College, B

Missouri

Washington University in St. Louis, B

New Hampshire

University of New Hampshire, B

New York

Hofstra University, B
Hunter College of the City University of New York, B
St. Lawrence University, B
Sarah Lawrence College, B
Syracuse University, B

Oklahoma

Oral Roberts University, B

Oregon

Marylhurst University, B

Pennsylvania

Gannon University, B
University of Pittsburgh, B

Vermont

Bennington College, B

ENTOMOLOGY

Alabama

Auburn University, MD

Arizona

The University of Arizona, MD

Arkansas

University of Arkansas, MD

California

University of California, Davis, BMD
University of California, Riverside, BMD

Colorado

Colorado State University, BMD

Connecticut

University of Connecticut, MD

Delaware

University of Delaware, BMD

Florida

Florida Agricultural and Mechanical University, BM
University of Florida, BMD

Georgia

University of Georgia, BMD

Hawaii

University of Hawaii at Manoa, BMD

Idaho

University of Idaho, BMD

Illinois

University of Illinois at Urbana-Champaign, BMD

Indiana

Purdue University, BMD

Iowa

Iowa State University of Science and
Technology, BMD

Kansas

Kansas State University, MD
University of Kansas, MD

Kentucky

University of Kentucky, MD

Louisiana

Louisiana State University and Agricultural and
Mechanical College, MD

Maine

University of Maine, M

Maryland

University of Maryland, College Park, MD

Massachusetts

Harvard University, B
University of Massachusetts Amherst, MD

Michigan

Michigan State University, BMD

Minnesota

University of Minnesota, Twin Cities Campus, MD

Mississippi

Mississippi State University, MD
Northeast Mississippi Community College, A

Missouri

University of Missouri-Columbia, MD

Montana

Montana State University, M

Nebraska

University of Nebraska-Lincoln, MD

New Jersey

Rutgers, The State University of New Jersey, New
Brunswick/Piscataway, MD

New Mexico

New Mexico State University, M

New York

Cornell University, BMD

State University of New York College of
Environmental Science and Forestry, BMD

North Carolina

North Carolina State University, MD

North Dakota

North Dakota State University, MD
University of North Dakota, MD

Ohio

The Ohio State University, BMD

Oklahoma

Oklahoma State University, BMD

Oregon

Oregon State University, B

Pennsylvania

The Pennsylvania State University University Park
Campus, MD

Rhode Island

University of Rhode Island, MD

South Carolina

Clemson University, MD

South Dakota

South Dakota State University, M

Tennessee

The University of Tennessee, MD

Texas

Texas A&M University, BMD
Texas Tech University, M

Utah

Snow College, A
Utah State University, B

Virginia

Virginia Polytechnic Institute and State
University, MD

Washington

Washington State University, BMD

West Virginia

West Virginia University, M

Wisconsin

University of Wisconsin-Madison, BMD

Wyoming

University of Wyoming, MD

Alberta

University of Alberta, B

British Columbia

Simon Fraser University, M

Manitoba

University of Manitoba, BMD

New Brunswick

University of New Brunswick Fredericton, B

Newfoundland and Labrador

Memorial University of Newfoundland, B

Ontario

University of Guelph, MD

Quebec

McGill University, MD

ENTREPRENEURIAL AND SMALL BUSINESS OPERATIONS

Arizona

Northland Pioneer College, A

Florida

Florida State University, B
Stetson University, B
University of Miami, B

Illinois

Kendall College, B

Kansas

Haskell Indian Nations University, A

Massachusetts

Babson College, B

Minnesota

Dakota County Technical College, A

New York

Herkimer County Community College, A

North Carolina

Warren Wilson College, B

North Dakota

Williston State College, A

Alberta

University of Alberta, B

ENTREPRENEURSHIP/ ENTREPRENEURIAL STUDIES

Alabama

Andrew Jackson University, M
Calhoun Community College, A

Arizona

Eastern Arizona College, A
The University of Arizona, B

California

California Lutheran University, M
California State University, East Bay, M
California State University, Fullerton, B
Cuyamaca College, A
National University, B
Palo Verde College, A
Reedley College, A
San Diego State University, M

Colorado

Colorado Northwestern Community College, A
Johnson & Wales University, AB
Jones International University, M
University of Colorado at Boulder, M

Connecticut

Goodwin College, A

Delaware

University of Delaware, M

District of Columbia

American University, M
University of the District of Columbia, A

Florida

Carlos Albizu University, Miami Campus, M
Florida Atlantic University, M
Palm Beach Atlantic University, B
University of Miami, B
University of Phoenix-North Florida Campus, B

The University of Tampa, M

Georgia

Georgia Institute of Technology, MO
Georgia State University, M
Reinhardt College, B
Southern Polytechnic State University, B

Hawaii

Hawaii Pacific University, B
University of Hawaii at Manoa, M

Illinois

Bradley University, B
DePaul University, M
Illinois Institute of Technology, M
Kendall College, B
Millikin University, B
Moraine Valley Community College, A
University of Illinois at Chicago, B
Waubonsee Community College, A

Indiana

Indiana Tech, M
Indiana University Bloomington, M
University of Indianapolis, B
University of Southern Indiana, B

Iowa

Buena Vista University, B
Iowa State University of Science and Technology, B
North Iowa Area Community College, A
The University of Iowa, BM

Kansas

Newman University, M
Wichita State University, B

Kentucky

University of Louisville, D

Louisiana

University of Phoenix-Louisiana Campus, B

Maine

University of Maine at Machias, B

Massachusetts

Babson College, B
Bay Path College, M
Northeastern University, B
Springfield Technical Community College, A

Michigan

Baker College of Flint, A
Davenport University (Dearborn), AB
Delta College, A
Eastern Michigan University, B
Montcalm Community College, A
Mott Community College, A
Northern Michigan University, B
Northwood University, AB
Oakland Community College, A
Schoolcraft College, A
University of Phoenix-Metro Detroit Campus, B

Minnesota

Dakota County Technical College, A
University of Minnesota, Twin Cities Campus, M
University of St. Thomas, B

Missouri

Missouri State University-West Plains, A
Park University, M
University of Phoenix-Kansas City Campus, B

Washington University in St. Louis, B

Montana

Blackfeet Community College, A

Nebraska

Northeast Community College, A
Union College, B

Nevada

University of Nevada, Reno, B

New Jersey

Fairleigh Dickinson University, College at Florham, MO
Fairleigh Dickinson University, Metropolitan Campus, MO

New Mexico

Santa Fe Community College, A
University of New Mexico-Gallup, A

New York

Bernard M. Baruch College of the City University of New York, M
Canisius College, B
Fordham University, B
Hofstra University, B
Mohawk Valley Community College, A
Nassau Community College, A
Pace University, B
Rensselaer Polytechnic Institute, M
Syracuse University, B

North Carolina

Mars Hill College, B
Western Carolina University, M

North Dakota

United Tribes Technical College, A
University of North Dakota, B

Ohio

Baldwin-Wallace College, M
Cincinnati State Technical and Community College, A
Terra State Community College, A
The University of Akron, AM
The University of Toledo, B
Xavier University, BM

Oklahoma

Bacone College, B
East Central University, B
University of Oklahoma, B

Pennsylvania

Bucks County Community College, A
Community College of Allegheny County, A
Delaware County Community College, A
Duquesne University, B
Grove City College, B
Messiah College, B
Robert Morris University, B
Seton Hill University, B
Susquehanna University, B
Temple University, B
University of Pittsburgh at Bradford, B
The University of Scranton, B
Wilkes University, B

Puerto Rico

Inter American University of Puerto Rico, Bayamón Campus, B
Inter American University of Puerto Rico, San Germán Campus, D
University of Puerto Rico, Río Piedras, B

Texas

Baylor University, B
Dallas Baptist University, M
Houston Baptist University, B
Northwood University, Texas Campus, B
St. Edward's University, BMO

Texas Tech University, M
University of Dallas, M
University of Houston, D
University of the Incarnate Word, D
The University of Texas at San Antonio, B

Utah

Brigham Young University, B
LDS Business College, A

Vermont

Lyndon State College, AB

Virginia

Stratford University, M

Washington

Edmonds Community College, A
Washington State University, B

West Virginia

Mountain State University, A

Wisconsin

University of Wisconsin-Madison, M

Wyoming

Laramie County Community College, A

British Columbia

British Columbia Institute of Technology, A
Kwantlen University College, B

Nova Scotia

Dalhousie University, B

Ontario

University of Waterloo, M
The University of Western Ontario, M
York University, B

Quebec

Concordia University, B
HEC Montreal, B
McGill University, BM
Université Laval, O
Université du Québec àTrois-Rivières, BM

ENVIRONMENTAL AND OCCUPATIONAL HEALTH

Alabama

Columbia Southern University, M
The University of Alabama at Birmingham, D
University of South Alabama, M

Arkansas

University of Arkansas for Medical Sciences, M

California

California State University, Fresno, M
California State University, Northridge, M
Loma Linda University, M
San Diego State University, M
University of California, Berkeley, MD
University of California, Los Angeles, MD

Colorado

Colorado State University, MD

Connecticut

University of Connecticut, M
University of New Haven, M
Yale University, MD

District of Columbia

The George Washington University, MD

Florida

University of Florida, M
University of Miami, M

University of South Florida, MD

Georgia

Emory University, M
Fort Valley State University, M
University of Georgia, MD

Illinois

Illinois State University, M
Loyola University Chicago, M
University of Illinois at Chicago, MD

Indiana

Indiana State University, M
Purdue University, MD

Iowa

The University of Iowa, MDO

Kentucky

Eastern Kentucky University, M
Murray State University, M
Western Kentucky University, M

Louisiana

Tulane University, MDO

Maryland

The Johns Hopkins University, D
Towson University, D

Massachusetts

Anna Maria College, M
Boston University, MD
Harvard University, MD

Michigan

University of Michigan, MD
Wayne State University, MO

Minnesota

University of Minnesota, Twin Cities Campus, MDO

Mississippi

Mississippi Valley State University, M
University of Southern Mississippi, M

Missouri

Central Missouri State University, MO

Nevada

University of Nevada, Reno, MD

New Jersey

New Jersey Institute of Technology, M

New York

Hunter College of the City University of New
York, M
New York University, MD
Stony Brook University, State University of New
York, O
University at Albany, State University of New
York, MD

North Carolina

Duke University, M
East Carolina University, M
The University of North Carolina at Chapel Hill, MD

Ohio

University of Cincinnati, MD

Oklahoma

University of Oklahoma, M
University of Oklahoma Health Sciences
Center, MDO

Oregon

Oregon State University, M

Pennsylvania

Gannon University, MO
Indiana University of Pennsylvania, M

The Pennsylvania State University University Park
Campus, M
Saint Joseph's University, MO
Temple University, M
University of Pittsburgh, M
West Chester University of Pennsylvania, M

Puerto Rico

University of Puerto Rico, Medical Sciences
Campus, MD
University of the Sacred Heart, M

South Carolina

Clemson University, D
University of South Carolina, MD

Tennessee

East Tennessee State University, M

Texas

Texas A&M University System Health Science
Center, M

Virginia

Old Dominion University, M
Virginia Commonwealth University, M

Washington

University of Washington, MD

West Virginia

West Virginia University, D

Wisconsin

University of Wisconsin-Eau Claire, M
University of Wisconsin-Whitewater, M

Alberta

University of Alberta, MD

British Columbia

The University of British Columbia, MD

Quebec

McGill University, MDO
Université Laval, O
Université de Montréal, MO
Université du Québec àMontréal, O

ENVIRONMENTAL BIOLOGY

Alabama

Jacksonville State University, B
Northwest-Shoals Community College, A

Arizona

Grand Canyon University, B

Arkansas

University of Arkansas at Pine Bluff, B

California

California Polytechnic State University, San Luis
Obispo, B
California State University, Monterey Bay, B
Humboldt State University, B
The Master's College and Seminary, B
Sonoma State University, M
University of California, Santa Cruz, MD
University of La Verne, B

Colorado

Colorado State University-Pueblo, B
Fort Lewis College, B

Connecticut

Sacred Heart University, B

Florida

Florida State University, B
The University of Tampa, B

Georgia

Georgia State University, MD

Illinois

Chicago State University, B
Governors State University, M

Greenville College, B

Indiana

Bethel College, B
Taylor University, B

Iowa

Iowa Wesleyan College, B
Simpson College, B
University of Dubuque, B
William Penn University, B

Kansas

Emporia State University, M
Tabor College, B

Kentucky

Midway College, B
University of Louisville, D

Louisiana

Nicholls State University, BM
Tulane University, B
University of Louisiana at Lafayette, D

Maine

College of the Atlantic, B
Unity College, B

Maryland

Hood College, M
Morgan State University, D

Massachusetts

Bridgewater State College, B
Framingham State College, B
Harvard University, B
Massachusetts Institute of Technology, D
Suffolk University, B
University of Massachusetts Amherst, MD
University of Massachusetts Boston, D
Westfield State College, B

Michigan

Cornerstone University, B
Marygrove College, B
Michigan State University, B

Minnesota

Minnesota State University Mankato, B
St. Cloud State University, B
Saint Mary's University of Minnesota, B
Winona State University, B

Mississippi

University of Southern Mississippi, MD

Missouri

Central Methodist University, B
University of Missouri-Rolla, B
Washington University in St. Louis, D

Montana

Montana State University, M

Nevada

Truckee Meadows Community College, A

New Hampshire

Franklin Pierce College, B
Plymouth State University, B

New Jersey

Bloomfield College, B
Monmouth University, B
Rutgers, The State University of New Jersey, New
Brunswick/Piscataway, MD

New York

Bard College, B
Barnard College, B
Colgate University, B
Columbia College, B

Columbia University, School of General Studies, B
Houghton College, B
Iona College, B
Queens College of the City University of New
   York, B
State University of New York College at
   Brockport, B
State University of New York College at Cortland, B
State University of New York College of
   Environmental Science and Forestry, BMD

North Carolina

Chowan University, B
Queens University of Charlotte, B
Wingate University, B

North Dakota

University of North Dakota, MD

Ohio

Antioch College, B
Cedarville University, B
Heidelberg College, B
Mount Union College, B
Ohio University, BMD
Otterbein College, B
University of Dayton, B
Ursuline College, B

Oregon

Oregon State University, B

Pennsylvania

Arcadia University, B
Carlow University, B
Cedar Crest College, B
East Stroudsburg University of Pennsylvania, B
Keystone College, B
Mansfield University of Pennsylvania, B
Philadelphia University, B
University of Pittsburgh at Greensburg, B
University of Pittsburgh at Johnstown, B

Puerto Rico

Inter American University of Puerto Rico, Bayamón
   Campus, B

Tennessee

Tennessee Technological University, M
The University of Tennessee at Martin, B

Texas

Baylor University, M

Vermont

Bennington College, B
Marlboro College, B
Sterling College, B

Virginia

Averett University, B

Washington

Eastern Washington University, B
Western Washington University, B

West Virginia

University of Charleston, B
West Virginia University, MD

Wisconsin

Beloit College, B
Northland College, B

University of Wisconsin-Madison, MD

Wyoming

Eastern Wyoming College, A

Alberta

Concordia University College of Alberta, B
University of Alberta, BMD

British Columbia

Thompson Rivers University, B
Trinity Western University, B
The University of British Columbia, B

Newfoundland and Labrador

Memorial University of Newfoundland, B

Ontario

Lakehead University, B
Nipissing University, B
University of Guelph, BMD
University of Windsor, B
York University, B

Quebec

Concordia University, B
McGill University, B

Saskatchewan

University of Regina, B

ENVIRONMENTAL CONTROL TECHNOLOGIES/TECHNICIANS

Florida

Florida International University, B

Illinois

Black Hawk College, A

Michigan

Oakland Community College, A

New York

New York Institute of Technology, B

North Carolina

Pitt Community College, A

Pennsylvania

Pennsylvania College of Technology, A

Puerto Rico

Inter American University of Puerto Rico, Bayamón
   Campus, B

South Carolina

Central Carolina Technical College, A

ENVIRONMENTAL DESIGN/ARCHITECTURE

Alabama

Auburn University, B

Arizona

Arizona State University, D
Prescott College, B
Scottsdale Community College, A

California

Art Center College of Design, BM
Cosumnes River College (Sacramento), A
Otis College of Art and Design, B
University of California, Berkeley, M

University of California, Irvine, BMD

Colorado

University of Colorado at Boulder, B

Connecticut

Yale University, MO

Florida

Florida International University, B

Georgia

Abraham Baldwin Agricultural College, A
Gainesville College, B

Indiana

Ball State University, B

Iowa

Iowa Lakes Community College, A

Maine

College of the Atlantic, B

Massachusetts

Hampshire College, B
Harvard University, B
University of Massachusetts Amherst, B

Michigan

Lawrence Technological University, B
Michigan State University, M

Missouri

University of Missouri-Columbia, M

Montana

Montana State University, B

New Jersey

Rutgers, The State University of New Jersey, New
   Brunswick/Piscataway, B

New Mexico

University of New Mexico, B

New York

Cornell University, BM
Parsons The New School for Design, B
Queensborough Community College of the City
   University of New York, A
State University of New York at Buffalo, B
State University of New York College of
   Environmental Science and Forestry, B

North Carolina

North Carolina State University, B

North Dakota

North Dakota State University, B

Ohio

Bowling Green State University, B
Kent State University, BO
Miami University, B

Oklahoma

University of Oklahoma, B

Pennsylvania

University of Pennsylvania, B

Puerto Rico

University of Puerto Rico, Río Piedras, B

South Carolina

Clemson University, D

Texas

Texas A&M University, B
Texas Tech University, MD

University of Houston, B

Vermont

Sterling College, B

Virginia

Virginia Polytechnic Institute and State University, D

Alberta

University of Calgary, MD

Manitoba

University of Manitoba, B

Nova Scotia

Dalhousie University, B

Quebec

Université de Montréal, MDO
Université du Québec àMontréal, B

ENVIRONMENTAL EDUCATION

Arizona

Prescott College, BM

California

California State University, Fullerton, M
California State University, San Bernardino, M
Sonoma State University, B

Connecticut

Southern Connecticut State University, MO

Florida

Florida Institute of Technology, M

Indiana

Indiana University Bloomington, D

Iowa

Iowa Lakes Community College, A

Maine

College of the Atlantic, B
Unity College, B
University of Maine at Machias, B

Massachusetts

Lesley University, M

Minnesota

University of Minnesota, Twin Cities Campus, M
Vermilion Community College, A

Missouri

Maryville University of Saint Louis, M

Montana

The University of Montana-Missoula, B

New Hampshire

University of New Hampshire, M

New Jersey

Rowan University, M

New Mexico

New Mexico Junior College, A

New York

Brooklyn College of the City University of New
   York, M
New York University, M
State University of New York College of
   Environmental Science and Forestry, B

State University of New York at New Paltz, M

Ohio

The Ohio State University, B

Oregon

Southern Oregon University, M

Pennsylvania

Arcadia University, MO
Chatham College, M
Gannon University, MO
Saint Vincent College, M
Slippery Rock University of Pennsylvania, M

Puerto Rico

Universidad Metropolitana, M

Vermont

Johnson State College, B

Washington

Western Washington University, BM

West Virginia

West Virginia University, M

Wisconsin

Northland College, B

Ontario

York University, B

Quebec

Université du Québec àMontréal, O

ENVIRONMENTAL ENGINEERING TECHNOLOGY/ENVIRONMENTAL TECHNOLOGY

Alabama

Auburn University, MD
Central Alabama Community College, A
James H. Faulkner State Community College, A
The University of Alabama, MD
The University of Alabama at Birmingham, MD
The University of Alabama in Huntsville, MD

Alaska

University of Alaska Fairbanks, MD
University of Alaska Southeast, Sitka Campus, A

Arizona

Pima Community College, A
The University of Arizona, MD

Arkansas

Southern Arkansas University Tech, A
University of Arkansas, M

California

Allan Hancock College, A
Bakersfield College, A
California Institute of Technology, MD
California Polytechnic State University, San Luis
   Obispo, MO
California State University, Long Beach, B
Chaffey College, A
Cosumnes River College (Sacramento), A
Cuyamaca College, A
Merced College, A
Napa Valley College, A
National University, M
San Diego City College, A
San Jose State University, M
Stanford University, MDO
University of California, Berkeley, MDO
University of California, Davis, MDO
University of California, Irvine, MD
University of California, Los Angeles, MD

University of California, Riverside, MD
University of Southern California, MD

Colorado

Arapahoe Community College, A
Colorado School of Mines, MD
Colorado State University, MD
IntelliTec College (Colorado Springs), A
Mesa State College, A
University of Colorado at Boulder, MD

Connecticut

Three Rivers Community College, A
University of Connecticut, MD
University of New Haven, MO

Delaware

Delaware Technical & Community College, Jack F.
   Owens Campus, A
University of Delaware, BMD

District of Columbia

The Catholic University of America, MD
The George Washington University, MDO
University of the District of Columbia, A

Florida

Broward Community College, A
Florida Agricultural and Mechanical University, MD
Florida International University, M
Florida State University, MD
Miami Dade College, A
University of Central Florida, MDO
University of Florida, MDO
University of South Florida, MD
Valencia Community College, A

Georgia

Coosa Valley Technical College, A
Georgia Institute of Technology, MD

Hawaii

University of Hawaii at Manoa, MD

Idaho

Idaho State University, M
University of Idaho, MDO

Illinois

City Colleges of Chicago, Wilbur Wright College, A
Illinois Institute of Technology, MD
Northwestern University, MD
University of Illinois at Urbana-Champaign, MDO

Indiana

Rose-Hulman Institute of Technology, M
University of Notre Dame, M

Iowa

Clinton Community College, A
Ellsworth Community College, A
Iowa Lakes Community College, A
Muscatine Community College, A
Scott Community College, A
The University of Iowa, MD

Kansas

University of Kansas, MD

Kentucky

Eastern Kentucky University, B
Murray State University, B
University of Louisville, MD
Western Kentucky University, B

Louisiana

Elaine P. Nunez Community College, A
Louisiana State University and Agricultural and
   Mechanical College, MD

Tulane University, MD

Maine

Southern Maine Community College, A
Unity College, B

Maryland

Harford Community College, A
The Johns Hopkins University, MD
University of Maryland, Baltimore County, MD
University of Maryland, College Park, MD

Massachusetts

Bristol Community College, A
Cape Cod Community College, A
Harvard University, MD
Massachusetts Bay Community College, A
Massachusetts Institute of Technology, MDO
Northeastern University, MD
Roxbury Community College, A
Tufts University, MD
University of Massachusetts Amherst, M
University of Massachusetts Lowell, M
Wentworth Institute of Technology, A
Worcester Polytechnic Institute, MDO

Michigan

Baker College of Flint, A
Baker College of Owosso, A
Baker College of Port Huron, A
Bay de Noc Community College, A
Delta College, A
Lake Superior State University, B
Michigan State University, MD
Michigan Technological University, MD
Schoolcraft College, A
University of Detroit Mercy, M
University of Michigan, MDO
Wayne County Community College District, A

Minnesota

Vermilion Community College, A

Missouri

Crowder College, A
Metropolitan Community College-Business &
  Technology College, A
University of Missouri-Columbia, MD
University of Missouri-Rolla, MD

Montana

Montana State University, M
Montana Tech of The University of Montana, M

Nebraska

University of Nebraska-Lincoln, MD

New Jersey

Gloucester County College, A
New Jersey Institute of Technology, MD
Princeton University, D
Rutgers, The State University of New Jersey, New
  Brunswick/Piscataway, MD
Stevens Institute of Technology, MDO

New Mexico

New Mexico Institute of Mining and Technology, M
New Mexico State University, M
New Mexico State University-Carlsbad, A

New York

Clarkson University, MD
Cornell University, BMD
Manhattan College, M
New York Institute of Technology, ABM
Polytechnic University, Brooklyn Campus, M
Rensselaer Polytechnic Institute, MD
State University of New York at Buffalo, MD
State University of New York College of
  Environmental Science and Forestry, MD
Syracuse University, MD
Ulster County Community College, A

Westchester Community College, A

North Carolina

Blue Ridge Community College, A
Central Piedmont Community College, A
Duke University, MD
East Carolina University, B
North Carolina Agricultural and Technical State
  University, M
Roanoke-Chowan Community College, A
The University of North Carolina at Chapel Hill, MD
The University of North Carolina at Charlotte, D
Wake Technical Community College, A

North Dakota

Minot State University-Bottineau Campus, A
North Dakota State University, MD
University of North Dakota, M

Ohio

Cincinnati State Technical and Community
  College, A
Cleveland State University, MD
Columbus State Community College, A
Kent State University, Trumbull Campus, A
Ohio University, AMD
Shawnee State University, B
University of Cincinnati, AMD
University of Dayton, M
The University of Toledo, A
Wright State University, B
Youngstown State University, M

Oklahoma

Oklahoma State University, MD
Rose State College, A
Tulsa Community College, A
University of Oklahoma, M

Oregon

Oregon State University, MD
Portland State University, MD

Pennsylvania

Carnegie Mellon University, MDO
Community College of Allegheny County, A
Community College of Philadelphia, A
Drexel University, MD
Gannon University, M
Lehigh University, MD
Pennsylvania College of Technology, AB
Pennsylvania Highland Community College, A
The Pennsylvania State University Harrisburg
  Campus, M
The Pennsylvania State University University Park
  Campus, MD
Temple University, BM
University of Pittsburgh, MD
Villanova University, M
Westmoreland County Community College, A

Rhode Island

University of Rhode Island, MD

South Carolina

Clemson University, MD

South Dakota

South Dakota State University, M

Tennessee

Chattanooga State Technical Community College, A
Middle Tennessee State University, B
Pellissippi State Technical Community College, A
University of Memphis, M
The University of Tennessee, M
Vanderbilt University, MD

Texas

Angelina College, A
Coastal Bend College, A
Collin County Community College District, A
Lamar University, M
Rice University, MD

Southern Methodist University, MD
Texas A&M University, MD
Texas A&M University-Kingsville, MD
Texas Southern University, B
Texas State Technical College Harlingen, A
Texas State Technical College West Texas, A
Texas Tech University, M
Tyler Junior College, A
University of Houston, MD
The University of Texas at Arlington, MD
The University of Texas at Austin, M
The University of Texas at El Paso, MD
The University of Texas at San Antonio, D

Utah

Salt Lake Community College, A
University of Utah, MD
Utah State University, MDO
Utah Valley State College, A

Vermont

Sterling College, B
University of Vermont, MD

Virginia

John Tyler Community College, A
Lord Fairfax Community College, A
Old Dominion University, MD
Virginia Polytechnic Institute and State University, M

Washington

Clover Park Technical College, A
Columbia Basin College, A
Shoreline Community College, A
Skagit Valley College, A
University of Washington, MD
Washington State University, M

West Virginia

West Virginia University, MD
West Virginia University at Parkersburg, A

Wisconsin

Marquette University, MD
Milwaukee Area Technical College, A
Milwaukee School of Engineering, M
University of Wisconsin-Madison, MD
University of Wisconsin-Whitewater, B

Wyoming

University of Wyoming, M

Alberta

University of Alberta, MD

British Columbia

British Columbia Institute of Technology, B
The University of British Columbia, B

New Brunswick

University of New Brunswick Fredericton, MD

Newfoundland and Labrador

Memorial University of Newfoundland, M

Nova Scotia

Cape Breton University, B

Ontario

Carleton University, MD
Royal Military College of Canada, MD
University of Guelph, BMD
University of Windsor, MD

Quebec

Concordia University, O
McGill University, MD
Université Laval, M

Université de Sherbrooke, M

Saskatchewan

University of Regina, MD
University of Saskatchewan, MDO

ENVIRONMENTAL/ ENVIRONMENTAL HEALTH ENGINEERING

Arizona

Arizona State University at the Polytechnic Campus, B
Northern Arizona University, B

California

California Institute of Technology, B
California Polytechnic State University, San Luis Obispo, B
Humboldt State University, B
Santa Barbara City College, A
Stanford University, B
University of California, Berkeley, B
University of California, Irvine, B
University of California, Riverside, B
University of Southern California, B

Colorado

Colorado School of Mines, B
Colorado State University, B
United States Air Force Academy, B
University of Colorado at Boulder, B

Connecticut

University of Connecticut, B
University of Hartford, B
Yale University, B

Delaware

University of Delaware, B

District of Columbia

The George Washington University, B

Florida

Florida State University, B
University of Central Florida, B
University of Florida, B
University of Miami, B

Illinois

Bradley University, B
Illinois Institute of Technology, B
Northwestern University, B

Indiana

University of Notre Dame, B

Louisiana

Louisiana State University and Agricultural and Mechanical College, B
Tulane University, B

Maryland

The Johns Hopkins University, B

Massachusetts

Bristol Community College, A
Harvard University, B
Massachusetts Institute of Technology, B
Massachusetts Maritime Academy, B
Tufts University, B
Wentworth Institute of Technology, B

Michigan

Michigan Technological University, B
University of Michigan, B

Missouri

University of Missouri-Rolla, B

Montana

Montana Tech of The University of Montana, B

Nevada

University of Nevada, Reno, B

New Hampshire

University of New Hampshire, B

New Jersey

New Jersey Institute of Technology, B
Stevens Institute of Technology, B

New Mexico

Central New Mexico Community College, A
New Mexico Institute of Mining and Technology, B

New York

Clarkson University, B
Columbia University, The Fu Foundation School of Engineering and Applied Science, B
Cornell University, B
Hofstra University, B
Manhattan College, B
Rensselaer Polytechnic Institute, B
State University of New York at Buffalo, B
State University of New York College of Environmental Science and Forestry, B
Syracuse University, B
United States Military Academy, B

North Carolina

North Carolina State University, B

North Dakota

University of North Dakota, B

Ohio

Ohio University, A
Ohio University-Chillicothe, A

Oklahoma

University of Oklahoma, B

Oregon

Oregon State University, B

Pennsylvania

Drexel University, B
Gannon University, B
Lafayette College, B
Lehigh University, B
The Pennsylvania State University Abington College, B
The Pennsylvania State University Altoona College, B
The Pennsylvania State University Beaver Campus of the Commonwealth College, B
The Pennsylvania State University Berks Campus of the Berks-Lehigh Valley College, B
The Pennsylvania State University Delaware County Campus of the Commonwealth College, B
The Pennsylvania State University DuBois Campus of the Commonwealth College, B
The Pennsylvania State University at Erie, The Behrend College, B
The Pennsylvania State University Fayette Campus of the Commonwealth College, B
The Pennsylvania State University Harrisburg Campus, B
The Pennsylvania State University Hazleton Campus of the Commonwealth College, B
The Pennsylvania State University, Lehigh Valley Campus of the Berks-Lehigh Valley College, B

The Pennsylvania State University McKeesport Campus of the Commonwealth College, B
The Pennsylvania State University Mont Alto Campus of the Commonwealth College, B
The Pennsylvania State University New Kensington Campus of the Commonwealth College, B
The Pennsylvania State University Schuylkill Campus of the Capital College, B
The Pennsylvania State University Shenango Campus of the Commonwealth College, B
The Pennsylvania State University University Park Campus, B
The Pennsylvania State University Wilkes-Barre Campus of the Commonwealth College, B
The Pennsylvania State University Worthington Scranton Campus of the Commonwealth College, B
The Pennsylvania State University York Campus of the Commonwealth College, B
University of Pennsylvania, B
Wilkes University, B

Puerto Rico

Polytechnic University of Puerto Rico, B

South Dakota

South Dakota School of Mines and Technology, B
South Dakota State University, B

Tennessee

Christian Brothers University, B

Texas

Rice University, B
Southern Methodist University, B
Texas A&M University-Kingsville, B
Texas Tech University, B

Utah

University of Utah, B
Utah State University, B

Vermont

University of Vermont, B

Virginia

Old Dominion University, B

Washington

Seattle University, B

Wisconsin

Marquette University, B
University of Wisconsin-Madison, B
University of Wisconsin-Platteville, B

Alberta

University of Alberta, B

British Columbia

British Columbia Institute of Technology, A
University of Northern British Columbia, B

Nova Scotia

Dalhousie University, B

Ontario

Carleton University, B
University of Waterloo, B
The University of Western Ontario, B
University of Windsor, B

Quebec

Concordia University, B
Université Laval, B

Saskatchewan

University of Regina, B

ENVIRONMENTAL HEALTH

Alabama
Community College of the Air Force, A

Arkansas
University of Arkansas at Little Rock, B

California
California State University, Northridge, B
University of California, Los Angeles, B

Colorado
Colorado State University, B
Colorado State University-Pueblo, B

Georgia
University of Georgia, B

Idaho
Boise State University, B
North Idaho College, A

Illinois
Black Hawk College, A
Illinois State University, B

Indiana
Indiana State University, B
Vincennes University, A

Iowa
Iowa Wesleyan College, B

Kentucky
Eastern Kentucky University, B

Maine
University of Southern Maine, B

Maryland
Salisbury University, B

Michigan
Ferris State University, B
Oakland University, B
University of Michigan-Flint, B

Missouri
Crowder College, A
Missouri Southern State University, B

New Mexico
New Mexico State University, B

New York
Clarkson University, B
Queensborough Community College of the City University of New York, A
York College of the City University of New York, B

North Carolina
East Carolina University, B
The University of North Carolina at Chapel Hill, B
Western Carolina University, B

Ohio
Bowling Green State University, B
The University of Akron, A
The University of Akron-Wayne College, A

Wright State University, B

Oklahoma
East Central University, B

Oregon
Mt. Hood Community College, A
Oregon State University, B

Pennsylvania
Indiana University of Pennsylvania, B
West Chester University of Pennsylvania, B

South Carolina
Benedict College, B

Tennessee
East Tennessee State University, B
Roane State Community College, A

Texas
Amarillo College, A
Brazosport College, A
Texas Southern University, B

Utah
University of Utah, B

Virginia
Old Dominion University, B

Washington
University of Washington, B

Wisconsin
Milwaukee Area Technical College, A
University of Wisconsin-Eau Claire, B

Alberta
Concordia University College of Alberta, B

British Columbia
British Columbia Institute of Technology, AB

Nova Scotia
Cape Breton University, B

ENVIRONMENTAL POLICY

Arizona
Northern Arizona University, MO

Colorado
Colorado State University, D

Delaware
University of Delaware, M

District of Columbia
American University, M

Florida
Florida Gulf Coast University, M

Georgia
Georgia Institute of Technology, M

Maryland
The Johns Hopkins University, M

Massachusetts
University of Massachusetts Lowell, MD

Michigan
Michigan Technological University, M

New York
Bard College, MO
State University of New York College of Environmental Science and Forestry, MD

North Carolina
Duke University, MD

Pennsylvania
Drexel University, M
University of Pittsburgh, M

Wisconsin
University of Wisconsin-Green Bay, M

ENVIRONMENTAL POLICY AND RESOURCE MANAGEMENT

Alabama
Troy University, M

Arizona
Arizona State University at the Polytechnic Campus, M
The University of Arizona, M

California
California State University, Fullerton, M
Stanford University, M
University of California, Berkeley, MD
University of California, Irvine, MD
University of California, Santa Barbara, MD

Colorado
Naropa University, M
University of Denver, M

Connecticut
Yale University, MDO

Delaware
University of Delaware, MD

District of Columbia
American University, M
The George Washington University, M

Florida
Florida Institute of Technology, M
University of Miami, D
University of South Florida, M

Hawaii
University of Hawaii at Manoa, MD

Idaho
Boise State University, M

Illinois
Illinois Institute of Technology, MO
Southern Illinois University Edwardsville, M
University of Chicago, M

Indiana
Purdue University, MD

Kansas
Kansas State University, M

Louisiana
Louisiana State University and Agricultural and Mechanical College, M

Maryland
University of Maryland University College, MO

Massachusetts
Boston University, M
Clark University, M
Harvard University, MO

Tufts University, MO

Michigan

University of Michigan, MDO

Minnesota

Saint Mary's University of Minnesota, M
University of Minnesota, Twin Cities Campus, MO
University of St. Thomas, M
Walden University, M

Missouri

Missouri State University, M
Southeast Missouri State University, M
Webster University, M

Nevada

University of Nevada, Reno, M

New Hampshire

University of New Hampshire, M

New Jersey

Kean University, M
Montclair State University, MD
New Jersey Institute of Technology, MD

New Mexico

New Mexico Highlands University, M

New York

Cornell University, MD
Long Island University, C.W. Post Campus, M
New York Institute of Technology, O
Rensselaer Polytechnic Institute, MD
Rochester Institute of Technology, M
State University of New York College of
    Environmental Science and Forestry, MD
Stony Brook University, State University of New
    York, MO
University at Albany, State University of New
    York, M

North Carolina

Duke University, MO
The University of North Carolina at Chapel Hill, MD

Ohio

The University of Findlay, M

Oregon

Oregon State University, M
Portland State University, M

Pennsylvania

Duquesne University, MO
The Pennsylvania State University University Park
    Campus, M
Saint Joseph's University, MO
Slippery Rock University of Pennsylvania, M

Puerto Rico

Polytechnic University of Puerto Rico, M
Universidad Metropolitana, M

Rhode Island

University of Rhode Island, MD

South Carolina

University of South Carolina, MO

Tennessee

The University of Tennessee, MD
Vanderbilt University, MD

Texas

Hardin-Simmons University, M
Rice University, M
Texas Tech University, D

University of Houston-Clear Lake, M

Utah

Utah State University, MD

Virginia

Virginia Commonwealth University, M

Washington

Antioch University Seattle, M
University of Washington, MD

West Virginia

West Virginia University, M

Wisconsin

University of Wisconsin-Madison, MD

Alberta

University of Alberta, D
University of Calgary, MD

British Columbia

Royal Roads University, M
Simon Fraser University, MD

Ontario

Trent University, MD
University of Guelph, MD
University of Waterloo, M
York University, MDO

Quebec

Université de Montréal, O
Université du Québec àChicoutimi, M

ENVIRONMENTAL PSYCHOLOGY

Florida

Embry-Riddle Aeronautical University, B

ENVIRONMENTAL SCIENCES

Alabama

Alabama Agricultural and Mechanical University, M
Auburn University, B
Miles College, B
Northwest-Shoals Community College, A
Samford University, B
Troy University, B
Tuskegee University, M
The University of Alabama in Huntsville, MD

Alaska

Alaska Pacific University, BM
Sheldon Jackson College, B
University of Alaska Anchorage, M
University of Alaska Fairbanks, M

Arizona

Northern Arizona University, MO
The University of Arizona, MD

Arkansas

Arkansas State University, D
John Brown University, B
University of Arkansas, B

California

California State Polytechnic University, Pomona, M
California State University Channel Islands, B
California State University, Chico, M
California State University, Fresno, B
California State University, Fullerton, M
California State University, Long Beach, B
Humboldt State University, M
Loyola Marymount University, M
Mills College, B
National University, B
Pitzer College, B

Santa Clara University, B
Scripps College, B
Stanford University, MDO
University of California, Berkeley, BMD
University of California, Davis, MD
University of California, Los Angeles, BD
University of California, Riverside, MD
University of California, Santa Barbara, MD
University of San Francisco, B

Colorado

The Colorado College, B
Colorado Northwestern Community College, A
Colorado School of Mines, MD
University of Colorado at Colorado Springs, M
University of Colorado at Denver and Health
    Sciences Center - Downtown Denver Campus, M
Western State College of Colorado, B

Connecticut

Eastern Connecticut State University, B
Post University, B
Sacred Heart University, B
Trinity College, B
University of New Haven, M
Western Connecticut State University, M
Yale University, MDO

Delaware

Delaware State University, B

District of Columbia

American University, M
Howard University, MD

Florida

Florida Agricultural and Mechanical University, BMD
Florida Atlantic University, M
Florida Gulf Coast University, BM
Florida Institute of Technology, BMD
Florida International University, M
Nova Southeastern University, BM
University of Florida, B
University of South Florida, M
University of West Florida, M

Georgia

Andrew College, A
Berry College, B
Columbus State University, M
Georgia Institute of Technology, MD
Mercer University, B
Paine College, B
Piedmont College, B
University of West Georgia, B
Wesleyan College, B

Guam

University of Guam, M

Hawaii

Hawaii Pacific University, B
University of Hawaii at Manoa, B

Idaho

Idaho State University, M
University of Idaho, M

Illinois

Blackburn College, B
City Colleges of Chicago, Wilbur Wright College, A
Monmouth College, B
Northwestern University, B
Southern Illinois University Carbondale, D
Southern Illinois University Edwardsville, M
University of Chicago, M
University of Illinois at Springfield, M
University of Illinois at Urbana-Champaign, BMD
University of St. Francis, B

Indiana

Indiana University Bloomington, MDO
Taylor University, M
University of Evansville, B

Valparaiso University, B

Iowa

Briar Cliff University, B
Drake University, B
Iowa State University of Science and
  Technology, MD
Northwestern College, B
University of Dubuque, B
The University of Iowa, B
University of Northern Iowa, BM
Upper Iowa University, B

Kansas

Haskell Indian Nations University, B
University of Kansas, MD
Wichita State University, M

Louisiana

Louisiana State University and Agricultural and
  Mechanical College, BD
McNeese State University, BM
Southern University and Agricultural and Mechanical
  College, M

Maine

Colby College, B
Saint Joseph's College of Maine, B
University of Maine, BMD
University of New England, B

Maryland

The Johns Hopkins University, M
McDaniel College, B
Towson University, MO
University of Maryland, Baltimore County, BMD
University of Maryland, College Park, MD
University of Maryland Eastern Shore, MD

Massachusetts

Assumption College, B
Bristol Community College, A
Fitchburg State College, B
Framingham State College, B
Harvard University, MD
Massachusetts Institute of Technology, D
University of Massachusetts Amherst, B
University of Massachusetts Boston, MD
University of Massachusetts Lowell, BMD

Michigan

Aquinas College, B
Michigan State University, BMD
Michigan Technological University, B
Oakland University, D
University of Michigan-Dearborn, BM
Wayne State University, B
Western Michigan University, B

Minnesota

Bethel University, B
Concordia University, St. Paul, B
Minnesota State University Mankato, M

Mississippi

Jackson State University, MD

Missouri

Central Methodist University, B
Lindenwood University, B
Maryville University of Saint Louis, B
Saint Louis University, B
Westminster College, B

Montana

Montana State University, BMD
Rocky Mountain College, B
The University of Montana-Missoula, MO

Nevada

Nevada State College at Henderson, B
University of Nevada, Las Vegas, MD

University of Nevada, Reno, MD

New Hampshire

Keene State College, B
University of New Hampshire, B

New Jersey

New Jersey Institute of Technology, MD
Ramapo College of New Jersey, B
Rutgers, The State University of New Jersey, New
  Brunswick/Piscataway, MD
Rutgers, The State University of New Jersey,
  Newark, MD

New Mexico

College of Santa Fe, B
New Mexico Institute of Mining and Technology, D
University of New Mexico, B

New York

Barnard College, B
Canisius College, B
City College of the City University of New York, D
Clarkson University, MD
College of Staten Island of the City University of
  New York, M
Cornell University, MD
Hartwick College, B
Hunter College of the City University of New
  York, BM
Keuka College, B
Long Island University, C.W. Post Campus, BM
Nazareth College of Rochester, B
Polytechnic University, Brooklyn Campus, M
Queens College of the City University of New
  York, BM
Rensselaer Polytechnic Institute, MD
Rochester Institute of Technology, BM
Skidmore College, B
State University of New York College at Cortland, B
State University of New York College of
  Environmental Science and Forestry, MD
University at Albany, State University of New
  York, BM
University of Rochester, B
Vassar College, B

North Carolina

Duke University, MDO
Meredith College, B
North Carolina Agricultural and Technical State
  University, M
North Carolina Central University, B
North Carolina State University, B
Pfeiffer University, B
The University of North Carolina at Chapel
  Hill, BMD
The University of North Carolina Wilmington, B
Western Carolina University, B

North Dakota

North Dakota State University, MD
United Tribes Technical College, A

Ohio

Capital University, B
Cleveland State University, MD
Heidelberg College, B
Marietta College, B
Miami University, M
Miami University Hamilton, B
Muskingum College, B
Notre Dame College, B
The Ohio State University, MD
The Ohio State University Agricultural Technical
  Institute, A
Otterbein College, B
University of Cincinnati, MD
Wright State University, BMD

Oklahoma

East Central University, B
Oklahoma State University, MD
Southeastern Oklahoma State University, B

University of Oklahoma, BMD

Oregon

Oregon State University, MD
Portland State University, MD
University of Oregon, B
Willamette University, B

Pennsylvania

Albright College, B
Allegheny College, B
DeSales University, B
Dickinson College, B
Drexel University, MD
Duquesne University, BMO
Franklin and Marshall College, B
Gannon University, BO
Gettysburg College, B
Juniata College, B
King's College, B
Kutztown University of Pennsylvania, B
Lehigh University, BMD
Marywood University, B
Messiah College, B
Muhlenberg College, B
The Pennsylvania State University Harrisburg
  Campus, M
The Pennsylvania State University University Park
  Campus, M
Point Park University, B
Saint Francis University, B
Saint Joseph's University, B
Saint Vincent College, B
Slippery Rock University of Pennsylvania, B
Temple University, B
University of the Sciences in Philadelphia, B

Puerto Rico

Inter American University of Puerto Rico, Ponce
  Campus, B
Inter American University of Puerto Rico, San
  Germán Campus, M

Rhode Island

Brown University, B
Roger Williams University, B

South Carolina

Claflin University, B
Clemson University, MD
College of Charleston, M
Lander University, B
University of South Carolina, M

South Dakota

South Dakota School of Mines and Technology, D
South Dakota State University, D

Tennessee

Lambuth University, B
Tennessee Technological University, D
The University of Tennessee at Chattanooga, M
Vanderbilt University, M

Texas

Abilene Christian University, B
Clarendon College, A
Hardin-Simmons University, B
McMurry University, B
Midwestern State University, B
Rice University, MD
St. Philip's College, A
Southern Methodist University, M
Stephen F. Austin State University, M
Tarleton State University, M
Texas A&M University, B
Texas A&M University-Corpus Christi, M
Texas Christian University, BMO
Texas Southern University, B
Texas State University-San Marcos, B
Texas Tech University, MD
University of Houston-Clear Lake, BM
University of North Texas, MD
The University of Texas at Arlington, MD
The University of Texas at Brownsville, B

The University of Texas at El Paso, D
The University of Texas at San Antonio, BMD
West Texas A&M University, BM

Utah

Brigham Young University, B

Vermont

University of Vermont, B

Virginia

Averett University, B
Bridgewater College, B
Christopher Newport University, M
Eastern Mennonite University, B
George Mason University, MD
Marymount University, B
Roanoke College, B
Sweet Briar College, B
University of Virginia, BMD
Virginia Commonwealth University, M
Virginia Polytechnic Institute and State University, M

Washington

Eastern Washington University, B
Northwest University, B
University of Washington, Bothell, B
University of Washington, Tacoma, B
Washington State University, BMD
Western Washington University, BM

West Virginia

Davis & Elkins College, B
Marshall University, BM
University of Charleston, B
West Virginia Wesleyan College, B

Wisconsin

Carroll College, B
Carthage College, B
St. Norbert College, B
University of Wisconsin-Green Bay, ABM
University of Wisconsin-Madison, MD

Wyoming

Central Wyoming College, A
Western Wyoming Community College, A

Alberta

Concordia University College of Alberta, B
University of Alberta, BMD
University of Lethbridge, BM

British Columbia

Simon Fraser University, B
Trinity Western University, B
University of Northern British Columbia, B

Newfoundland and Labrador

Memorial University of Newfoundland, M

Nova Scotia

Dalhousie University, B

Ontario

Queen's University at Kingston, B
Royal Military College of Canada, MD
University of Guelph, MD
University of Ottawa, B
University of Waterloo, B
The University of Western Ontario, MD
University of Windsor, BMD
York University, B

Quebec

Université Laval, M
Université du Québec àMontréal, MD
Université du Québec àTrois-Rivières, MD

Université de Sherbrooke, MO

ENVIRONMENTAL STUDIES

Alabama

Auburn University, B
Columbia Southern University, B
Community College of the Air Force, A
Samford University, AB
Tuskegee University, B
University of Mobile, B

Arizona

Arizona Western College, A
Northern Arizona University, B
Prescott College, BM
The University of Arizona, B

Arkansas

Cossatot Community College of the University of
   Arkansas, A
John Brown University, B
Lyon College, B
University of Central Arkansas, B
University of the Ozarks, B

California

California State University, East Bay, B
California State University, Fullerton, M
California State University, Monterey Bay, B
California State University, Sacramento, B
California State University, San Bernardino, B
Cañada College, A
Claremont McKenna College, B
College of the Desert, A
College of San Mateo, A
Columbia College, A
Cosumnes River College (Sacramento), A
De Anza College, A
Dominican University of California, B
East Los Angeles College, A
Fullerton College, A
Humboldt State University, B
Las Positas College, A
Mills College, B
Napa Valley College, A
Pitzer College, B
Pomona College, B
Saddleback College, A
San Bernardino Valley College, A
San Diego State University, B
San Jose State University, BM
Santa Ana College, A
Santa Barbara City College, A
Santa Monica College, A
Santa Rosa Junior College, A
Scripps College, B
Sonoma State University, B
Stanford University, B
University of California, Berkeley, B
University of California, Davis, B
University of California, Riverside, B
University of California, San Diego, B
University of California, Santa Barbara, B
University of California, Santa Cruz, BD
University of the Pacific, B
University of Redlands, B
University of San Diego, B
University of San Francisco, B
University of Southern California, B

Colorado

Colorado Mountain College, Timberline Campus, A
Metropolitan State College of Denver, B
Naropa University, B
Regis University, B
University of Colorado at Boulder, BMD
University of Denver, B
Western State College of Colorado, B

Connecticut

Connecticut College, B
Housatonic Community College, A
Middlesex Community College, A

Naugatuck Valley Community College, A
Post University, B
Saint Joseph College, B
University of Connecticut, B
Wesleyan University, B
Western Connecticut State University, B
Yale University, B

Delaware

University of Delaware, B
Wesley College, BM

District of Columbia

American University, B
The George Washington University, BMD
Trinity (Washington) University, B
University of the District of Columbia, B

Florida

Eckerd College, B
Florida International University, BM
Florida Southern College, B
Florida State University, B
Hillsborough Community College, A
Jacksonville University, B
Lynn University, B
New College of Florida, B
Nova Southeastern University, B
Pensacola Junior College, A
Rollins College, B
Santa Fe Community College, A
Stetson University, B
University of Miami, B
University of South Florida, B
The University of Tampa, B
University of West Florida, B

Georgia

Brenau University, B
Darton College, A
Georgia College & State University, B
Macon State College, A
Mercer University, B
Piedmont College, B
Savannah State University, B
Shorter College, B
Spelman College, B
University of Georgia, B
University of West Georgia, B

Hawaii

Chaminade University of Honolulu, B
Hawaii Pacific University, B
University of Hawaii at Manoa, B

Idaho

Boise State University, B
College of Southern Idaho, A
University of Idaho, B

Illinois

Augustana College, B
Aurora University, B
Benedictine University, B
Concordia University, B
DePaul University, B
Dominican University, B
Elmhurst College, B
Illinois College, B
Illinois Wesleyan University, B
Knox College, B
Lake Forest College, B
Lewis University, B
Loyola University Chicago, B
Northeastern Illinois University, BM
Northwestern University, B
Olivet Nazarene University, B
Principia College, B
University of Chicago, B
University of Illinois at Springfield, M
Wheaton College, B

Indiana

Ball State University, B
DePauw University, B

Earlham College, B
Goshen College, B
Indiana University Bloomington, B
Manchester College, B
Saint Mary-of-the-Woods College, M
Taylor University, B
Tri-State University, B
University of Evansville, B
University of Indianapolis, B
University of Saint Francis, B
Vincennes University, A

Iowa

Central College, B
Coe College, B
Cornell College, B
Dordt College, B
Drake University, B
Iowa Lakes Community College, A
Iowa State University of Science and Technology, B
Maharishi University of Management, B
University of Dubuque, AB
The University of Iowa, B

Kansas

Central Christian College of Kansas, A
Friends University, M
McPherson College, B
Pittsburg State University, B
University of Kansas, B

Kentucky

Eastern Kentucky University, B
Kentucky Wesleyan College, B
Northern Kentucky University, B
St. Catharine College, A

Louisiana

Centenary College of Louisiana, B
Louisiana State University and Agricultural and
  Mechanical College, M
Louisiana State University in Shreveport, B
Louisiana Tech University, B
Tulane University, B
University of New Orleans, B
Xavier University of Louisiana, B

Maine

Bates College, B
Bowdoin College, B
Colby College, B
College of the Atlantic, BM
Saint Joseph's College of Maine, B
Unity College, B
University of Maine at Farmington, B
University of Maine at Fort Kent, B
University of Maine at Machias, B
University of Maine at Presque Isle, B
University of New England, B
University of Southern Maine, B

Maryland

Anne Arundel Community College, A
Frostburg State University, B
Hood College, B
Howard Community College, A
The Johns Hopkins University, B
Towson University, M
University of Maryland, Baltimore County, B
University of Maryland Eastern Shore, B
University of Maryland University College, B
Villa Julie College, B
Washington College, B

Massachusetts

Berkshire Community College, A
Boston College, B
Boston University, B
Cape Cod Community College, A
Clark University, M
College of the Holy Cross, B
Curry College, B
Emmanuel College, B
Endicott College, B
Framingham State College, B

Hampshire College, B
Harvard University, B
Holyoke Community College, A
Lesley University, B
Massachusetts College of Liberal Arts, B
Massachusetts Maritime Academy, B
Merrimack College, B
Mount Holyoke College, B
Mount Wachusett Community College, A
Northeastern University, B
Simmons College, B
Simon's Rock College of Bard, B
Suffolk University, B
Tufts University, BO
University of Massachusetts Lowell, O
Wellesley College, B
Wheaton College, B
Worcester Polytechnic Institute, B

Michigan

Adrian College, B
Albion College, B
Aquinas College, B
Calvin College, B
Central Michigan University, B
Hope College, B
Lake Superior State University, B
Marygrove College, B
Michigan State University, B
Mid Michigan Community College, A
Northern Michigan University, B
Olivet College, B
University of Michigan, B
University of Michigan-Dearborn, B
Western Michigan University, B

Minnesota

Bemidji State University, BM
Century College, A
College of Saint Benedict, B
Concordia College, B
Fond du Lac Tribal and Community College, A
Gustavus Adolphus College, B
Hamline University, B
Itasca Community College, A
Macalester College, B
Minnesota State University Mankato, B
St. Cloud State University, M
Saint John's University, B
St. Olaf College, B
Southwest Minnesota State University, B
University of Minnesota, Crookston, B
University of Minnesota, Duluth, B
University of Minnesota, Twin Cities Campus, B
Vermilion Community College, A

Missouri

Columbia College, B
Drury University, B
Maryville University of Saint Louis, B
Southeast Missouri State University, M
Stephens College, B
University of Missouri-Columbia, B
Washington University in St. Louis, B
Webster University, B
Westminster College, B

Montana

Carroll College, B
Montana State University, B
Montana State University-Billings, B
Rocky Mountain College, B
Salish Kootenai College, AB
The University of Montana-Missoula, BMO
The University of Montana-Western, B

Nebraska

Creighton University, B
Dana College, B
Doane College, B
Midland Lutheran College, B
Southeast Community College, Lincoln Campus, A
University of Nebraska-Lincoln, B

University of Nebraska at Omaha, B

Nevada

Community College of Southern Nevada, A
Great Basin College, A
Sierra Nevada College, B
Truckee Meadows Community College, A
University of Nevada, Las Vegas, B
Western Nevada Community College, A

New Hampshire

Colby-Sawyer College, B
Dartmouth College, B
Franklin Pierce College, B
Keene State College, B
New England College, B
New Hampshire Community Technical College,
  Berlin/Laconia, A
Saint Anselm College, B
Southern New Hampshire University, B
University of New Hampshire, B

New Jersey

Burlington County College, A
Camden County College, A
Fairleigh Dickinson University, Metropolitan
  Campus, B
Felician College, B
Montclair State University, M
Princeton University, MD
Ramapo College of New Jersey, B
Raritan Valley Community College, A
The Richard Stockton College of New Jersey, B
Rider University, B
Rowan University, B
Rutgers, The State University of New Jersey, New
  Brunswick/Piscataway, B
Rutgers, The State University of New Jersey,
  Newark, B
Sussex County Community College, A
Warren County Community College, A
William Paterson University of New Jersey, B

New Mexico

College of the Southwest, B
New Mexico Highlands University, B
New Mexico Institute of Mining and Technology, B
New Mexico Junior College, A
New Mexico State University, B
Northern New Mexico Community College, A
University of New Mexico-Los Alamos Branch, A

New York

Adelphi University, M
Alfred University, B
Bard College, B
Barnard College, B
Brooklyn College of the City University of New
  York, B
Cazenovia College, B
Clarkson University, B
Colgate University, B
The College of New Rochelle, B
The College of Saint Rose, B
Columbia College, B
Cornell University, BMD
Elmira College, B
Finger Lakes Community College, A
Fulton-Montgomery Community College, A
Hobart and William Smith Colleges, B
Hofstra University, B
Hudson Valley Community College, A
Ithaca College, B
Long Island University, C.W. Post Campus, BM
Marist College, B
Medgar Evers College of the City University of New
  York, B
Molloy College, B
Monroe Community College, A
Nazareth College of Rochester, B
Pace University, B
Paul Smith's College of Arts and Sciences, AB
Purchase College, State University of New York, B
Queens College of the City University of New
  York, B

St. Bonaventure University, B
St. John's University, B
St. Lawrence University, B
Sarah Lawrence College, B
Skidmore College, B
State University of New York at Binghamton, B
State University of New York College of Agriculture and Technology at Cobleskill, AB
State University of New York College of Agriculture and Technology at Morrisville, A
State University of New York College at Brockport, B
State University of New York College at Cortland, B
State University of New York College of Environmental Science and Forestry, BMD
State University of New York College at Oneonta, B
State University of New York College of Technology at Alfred, A
State University of New York College of Technology at Canton, A
State University of New York, Fredonia, B
State University of New York Maritime College, B
State University of New York at New Paltz, B
State University of New York at Plattsburgh, B
Stony Brook University, State University of New York, B
Sullivan County Community College, A
Tompkins Cortland Community College, A
Trocaire College, A
United States Military Academy, B
University of Rochester, B
Vassar College, B
Wells College, B

North Carolina

Barton College, B
Brevard College, B
Cape Fear Community College, A
Catawba College, B
Duke University, B
Elon University, B
Guilford College, B
Lees-McRae College, B
Lenoir-Rhyne College, B
Meredith College, B
Montreat College, B
Mount Olive College, B
North Carolina State University, B
North Carolina Wesleyan College, B
Pamlico Community College, A
Pfeiffer University, B
Shaw University, B
Southeastern Community College, A
Southwestern Community College, A
The University of North Carolina at Asheville, B
The University of North Carolina at Chapel Hill, B
The University of North Carolina at Pembroke, B
The University of North Carolina Wilmington, B
Warren Wilson College, B

North Dakota

Dickinson State University, AB
Fort Berthold Community College, A
Sitting Bull College, A
Turtle Mountain Community College, A

Ohio

Antioch College, B
Ashland University, B
Case Western Reserve University, B
Cleveland State University, BMO
Defiance College, AB
Denison University, B
Heidelberg College, B
Hiram College, B
John Carroll University, B
Kent State University, Ashtabula Campus, A
Kent State University, Salem Campus, A
Kent State University, Tuscarawas Campus, A
Kenyon College, B
Lake Erie College, B
Marietta College, B
Miami University Hamilton, B
Muskingum College, B
Oberlin College, B
Ohio Northern University, B

The Ohio State University, B
Ohio University, M
Ohio University-Chillicothe, A
Ohio Wesleyan University, B
Stark State College of Technology, A
University of Cincinnati, A
University of Cincinnati Raymond Walters College, A
University of Dayton, B
The University of Findlay, AB
The University of Toledo, AB
Wittenberg University, B
Wright State University, M
Youngstown State University, MO
Zane State College, A

Oklahoma

East Central University, B
Eastern Oklahoma State College, A
Oklahoma State University, B
Southern Nazarene University, B
University of Tulsa, B

Oregon

Concordia University, B
Lewis & Clark College, B
Linfield College, B
Marylhurst University, B
Oregon Institute of Technology, B
Oregon State University, B
Pacific University, B
Portland State University, BM
Southern Oregon University, B
Southwestern Oregon Community College, A
University of Oregon, BMD
University of Portland, B

Pennsylvania

Allegheny College, B
Bucknell University, B
Bucks County Community College, A
California University of Pennsylvania, B
Cedar Crest College, B
Chatham College, B
Chestnut Hill College, B
Clarion University of Pennsylvania, B
DeSales University, B
Dickinson College, B
Drexel University, B
Eastern University, B
Edinboro University of Pennsylvania, B
Elizabethtown College, B
Franklin and Marshall College, B
Gannon University, M
Gettysburg College, B
Harrisburg Area Community College, A
Immaculata University, B
Indiana University of Pennsylvania, B
Juniata College, B
Keystone College, AB
King's College, B
Kutztown University of Pennsylvania, B
La Salle University, B
Lehigh University, B
Lincoln University, B
Mansfield University of Pennsylvania, B
Messiah College, B
Moravian College, B
Neumann College, B
The Pennsylvania State University Altoona College, B
Robert Morris University, B
Saint Francis University, B
Saint Vincent College, B
Shippensburg University of Pennsylvania, BM
Slippery Rock University of Pennsylvania, B
Temple University, B
Thiel College, B
University of Pennsylvania, BM
University of Pittsburgh at Bradford, B
University of Pittsburgh at Johnstown, B
Ursinus College, B
Waynesburg College, B
West Chester University of Pennsylvania, B
Westminster College, B
Widener University, B

Wilson College, B

Puerto Rico

Bayamon Central University, B
Inter American University of Puerto Rico, Metropolitan Campus, B
Inter American University of Puerto Rico, San Germán Campus, B
Pontifical Catholic University of Puerto Rico, B
Universidad Metropolitana, B
Universidad del Turabo, M
University of Puerto Rico, Aguadilla University College, A
University of Puerto Rico, Río Piedras, B

Rhode Island

Brown University, BM
University of Rhode Island, B

South Carolina

Charleston Southern University, B
Clemson University, MD
Furman University, B
Technical College of the Lowcountry, A

South Dakota

Black Hills State University, B
Northern State University, B

Tennessee

Austin Peay State University, B
Lambuth University, B
Lincoln Memorial University, B
Lipscomb University, B
Maryville College, B
Sewanee: The University of the South, B
Tusculum College, B
The University of Tennessee at Chattanooga, B
The University of Tennessee at Martin, B

Texas

Austin College, B
Baylor University, BM
Central Texas College, A
Concordia University at Austin, B
Lamar State College-Orange, A
Lamar University, BM
Lee College, A
Sam Houston State University, B
Southern Methodist University, B
Southwestern University, B
Stephen F. Austin State University, B
Sul Ross State University, B
Tarleton State University, B
Texas A&M University, B
Texas A&M University-Corpus Christi, B
Texas State University-San Marcos, M
University of Houston, B
University of the Incarnate Word, B
University of St. Thomas, B
The University of Texas of the Permian Basin, B

Utah

Dixie State College of Utah, A
University of Utah, B
Westminster College, B

Vermont

Bennington College, B
Castleton State College, B
Goddard College, M
Green Mountain College, B
Johnson State College, B
Marlboro College, B
Middlebury College, B
Norwich University, B
Southern Vermont College, AB
Sterling College, AB
University of Vermont, B

Virginia

Christopher Newport University, B
The College of William and Mary, B
Emory & Henry College, B
Ferrum College, B

Hampton University, B
Longwood University, B
Lynchburg College, B
Mountain Empire Community College, A
Randolph-Macon College, B
Randolph-Macon Woman's College, B
Roanoke College, B
Saint Paul's College, B
Shenandoah University, B
Sweet Briar College, B
University of Mary Washington, B
University of Richmond, B
The University of Virginia's College at Wise, B
Virginia Commonwealth University, BM
Virginia Intermont College, B
Virginia Polytechnic Institute and State University, B
Virginia Wesleyan College, B

Washington

Everett Community College, A
The Evergreen State College, BM
Heritage University, B
Lake Washington Technical College, A
Lower Columbia College, A
Pacific Lutheran University, B
Seattle University, B
Tacoma Community College, A
University of Washington, B
Walla Walla College, B
Western Washington University, B

West Virginia

Alderson-Broaddus College, B
American Public University System, B
Bethany College, B
Mountain State University, AB
Salem International University, B
Shepherd University, B
West Virginia University, B
Wheeling Jesuit University, B

Wisconsin

Alverno College, B
Beloit College, B
Carthage College, B
Lawrence University, B
Northeast Wisconsin Technical College, A
Northland College, B
Ripon College, B
St. Norbert College, B
University of Wisconsin-Green Bay, AB
University of Wisconsin-River Falls, B

Wyoming

Northwest College, A
University of Wyoming, B

Alberta

Concordia University College of Alberta, B
The King's University College, B
University of Alberta, B
University of Calgary, B

British Columbia

Royal Roads University, B
Trinity Western University, B
The University of British Columbia, B
University of Northern British Columbia, BMD
University of Victoria, B

Manitoba

University of Manitoba, B
The University of Winnipeg, B

New Brunswick

Mount Allison University, B

Newfoundland and Labrador

Memorial University of Newfoundland, B

Nova Scotia

Acadia University, B
Cape Breton University, B
Dalhousie University, BM

Nova Scotia Agricultural College, B
St. Francis Xavier University, B

Ontario

Carleton University, B
Lakehead University, B
McMaster University, B
Nipissing University, B
Trent University, B
University of Guelph, B
University of Ottawa, AB
University of Toronto, B
University of Waterloo, B
The University of Western Ontario, B
University of Windsor, B
York University, B

Quebec

Bishop's University, B
Concordia University, BO
McGill University, B
Université Laval, BM

Saskatchewan

University of Regina, B
University of Saskatchewan, B

ENVIRONMENTAL TOXICOLOGY

California

University of California, Davis, B

New York

Cornell University, B

Ontario

University of Guelph, B

EPIDEMIOLOGY

Alabama

The University of Alabama at Birmingham, D

Arizona

The University of Arizona, MD

California

California State University, Long Beach, M
Loma Linda University, MD
San Diego State University, MD
Stanford University, MD
University of California, Berkeley, MD
University of California, Davis, MD
University of California, Los Angeles, BMD
University of California, San Diego, D
University of Southern California, MD

Connecticut

Yale University, MD

District of Columbia

The George Washington University, MD
Georgetown University, M

Florida

University of Florida, M
University of Miami, D
University of South Florida, MD

Georgia

Emory University, MD

Hawaii

University of Hawaii at Manoa, MD

Illinois

University of Illinois at Chicago, MD

Indiana

Purdue University, MD

Iowa

The University of Iowa, MDO

Kentucky

University of Louisville, MD

Louisiana

Tulane University, MD

Maryland

The Johns Hopkins University, MD
University of Maryland, Baltimore County, M

Massachusetts

Boston University, MD
Harvard University, MD
Tufts University, MDO
University of Massachusetts Lowell, MD

Michigan

Michigan State University, MD
University of Michigan, MD

Minnesota

University of Minnesota, Twin Cities Campus, MD

New York

Cornell University, MD
State University of New York at Buffalo, MD
University at Albany, State University of New York, MD
University of Rochester, MD

North Carolina

North Carolina State University, MD
The University of North Carolina at Chapel Hill, MD

Ohio

Case Western Reserve University, MD
University of Cincinnati, MD

Oklahoma

University of Oklahoma Health Sciences Center, MD

Oregon

Oregon Health & Science University, MO

Pennsylvania

University of Pennsylvania, MD
University of Pittsburgh, MD

Puerto Rico

University of Puerto Rico, Medical Sciences Campus, M

Rhode Island

Brown University, MDO

South Carolina

Medical University of South Carolina, MDO
University of South Carolina, MD

Tennessee

East Tennessee State University, O

Texas

Texas A&M University, M
Texas A&M University System Health Science Center, M

Virginia

Virginia Commonwealth University, D

Washington

University of Washington, MD

Alberta

University of Alberta, MD
University of Calgary, MD

British Columbia

The University of British Columbia, MD

Newfoundland and Labrador

Memorial University of Newfoundland, MDO

Nova Scotia

Dalhousie University, M

Ontario

Queen's University at Kingston, M
University of Guelph, MD
University of Ottawa, M
The University of Western Ontario, MD

Prince Edward Island

University of Prince Edward Island, MD

Quebec

McGill University, MDO
Université Laval, MD

Saskatchewan

University of Saskatchewan, MD

EQUESTRIAN/EQUINE STUDIES

Arizona

Scottsdale Community College, A
Yavapai College, A

California

Los Angeles Pierce College, A
Sierra College, A
West Hills Community College, A

Colorado

Colorado State University, B
Lamar Community College, A
Northeastern Junior College, A

Connecticut

Post University, AB

Idaho

College of Southern Idaho, A

Illinois

Black Hawk College, A

Indiana

Saint Mary-of-the-Woods College, AB

Iowa

Ellsworth Community College, A
Kirkwood Community College, A
Scott Community College, A

Kansas

Allen County Community College, A
Dodge City Community College, A

Kentucky

Midway College, AB

Massachusetts

Mount Ida College, B
University of Massachusetts Amherst, A

Minnesota

University of Minnesota, Crookston, AB

Missouri

Stephens College, B
Truman State University, B

William Woods University, B

Montana

Rocky Mountain College, B
The University of Montana-Western, A

New Hampshire

University of New Hampshire, AB

New Jersey

Centenary College, AB
Rutgers, The State University of New Jersey, New Brunswick/Piscataway, B

New York

Cazenovia College, B
State University of New York College of Agriculture and Technology at Cobleskill, A
State University of New York College of Agriculture and Technology at Morrisville, AB

North Carolina

Martin Community College, A
St. Andrews Presbyterian College, B

North Dakota

North Dakota State University, B

Ohio

Hocking College, A
Lake Erie College, B
The Ohio State University Agricultural Technical Institute, A
Ohio University, A
Otterbein College, B
The University of Findlay, AB

Oklahoma

Murray State College, A
Redlands Community College, A
Rogers State University, A

Pennsylvania

Wilson College, B

Rhode Island

Johnson & Wales University, AB

South Dakota

National American University (Rapid City), AB

Texas

Central Texas College, A
North Central Texas College, A
Sul Ross State University, B
West Texas A&M University, B

Vermont

Sterling College, B

Virginia

Averett University, B
Virginia Intermont College, B

West Virginia

Salem International University, B

Wisconsin

University of Wisconsin-River Falls, B

Wyoming

Central Wyoming College, A
Laramie County Community College, A

Northwest College, A

ERGONOMICS AND HUMAN FACTORS

California

San Jose State University, M

District of Columbia

The Catholic University of America, M

Florida

Embry-Riddle Aeronautical University, M
Florida Institute of Technology, M
University of Central Florida, O
University of Miami, D

Indiana

Purdue University, MD

Iowa

The University of Iowa, MD

Massachusetts

Bentley College, M
Tufts University, M
University of Massachusetts Lowell, MDO

New York

Cornell University, M

North Carolina

North Carolina State University, D

Ohio

University of Cincinnati, MD
Wright State University, MD

South Carolina

Clemson University, D

Tennessee

The University of Tennessee, M

Virginia

Old Dominion University, D

Washington

University of Washington, M

Quebec

Université de Montréal, O
Université du Québec àMontréal, O

ETHICS

California

Azusa Pacific University, M
Biola University, M

District of Columbia

American University, M

Florida

University of North Florida, M

Indiana

Valparaiso University, MO

Iowa

Drake University, B

Maryland

University of Baltimore, M

Massachusetts

Bridgewater State College, B

Michigan

University of Michigan-Flint, B

Nevada

University of Nevada, Las Vegas, M

New Jersey

Drew University, MD

New Mexico

St. John's College, B

New York

Fordham University, O

North Carolina

Southeastern Baptist Theological Seminary, D

Pennsylvania

Carnegie Mellon University, B

Texas

St. Edward's University, M

Wisconsin

Marquette University, MD

Ontario

Wilfrid Laurier University, M

Quebec

Université Laval, O
Université du Québec àChicoutimi, O
Université du Québec àRimouski, M
Université de Sherbrooke, O

ETHNIC AND CULTURAL STUDIES

California

Azusa Pacific University, B
California State Polytechnic University, Pomona, B
California State University, East Bay, B
California State University, Fullerton, B
California State University, Sacramento, B
College of Marin, A
College of San Mateo, A
College of the Sequoias, A
Compton Community College, A
Cosumnes River College (Sacramento), A
De Anza College, A
Foothill College, A
Fresno City College, A
Fullerton College, A
Grossmont College, A
Laney College, A
Mendocino College, A
Mills College, B
Monterey Peninsula College, A
New College of California, B
Orange Coast College, A
Pasadena City College, A
Sacramento City College, A
San Francisco State University, M
Santa Ana College, A
Santa Barbara City College, A
Santa Monica College, A
Santa Rosa Junior College, A
Santiago Canyon College, A
Solano Community College, A
Sonoma State University, B
University of California, Berkeley, D
University of California, Irvine, B
University of California, Riverside, B
University of California, San Diego, BMD
University of Southern California, B

Yuba College, A

Colorado

Fort Lewis College, B
University of Colorado at Boulder, B

Connecticut

Yale University, B

Hawaii

Brigham Young University-Hawaii, B

Idaho

Boise State University, B

Indiana

Indiana Wesleyan University, AB
Saint Mary-of-the-Woods College, B

Iowa

Cornell College, B

Maryland

Baltimore Hebrew University, AB

Massachusetts

Clark University, B
Harvard University, B
Simon's Rock College of Bard, B

Michigan

Bay Mills Community College, A

Minnesota

Minnesota State University Mankato, B
St. Olaf College, B

Missouri

Washington University in St. Louis, B

Nevada

University of Nevada, Las Vegas, B

New Jersey

Rutgers, The State University of New Jersey, New
  Brunswick/Piscataway, B
Rutgers, The State University of New Jersey,
  Newark, B

New York

Bard College, B
Cornell University, MD
Houghton College, B
The Jewish Theological Seminary, B

Ohio

Kent State University, B
The Ohio State University, B
Ohio Wesleyan University, B

Oregon

Oregon State University, B
University of Oregon, B

Tennessee

The University of Tennessee, B

Texas

Baptist University of the Americas, A

Vermont

Marlboro College, B

Virginia

The College of William and Mary, B
University of Virginia, B

Washington

Highline Community College, A
Skagit Valley College, A
University of Washington, B

Western Washington University, B

Wisconsin

University of Wisconsin-Milwaukee, B

British Columbia

The University of British Columbia, B

Nova Scotia

St. Francis Xavier University, B

Ontario

University of Ottawa, B
University of Toronto, B
York University, B

Quebec

Concordia University, B
Université Laval, MD

Saskatchewan

Briercrest College, B

ETHNIC, CULTURAL MINORITY, AND GENDER STUDIES

California

California State Polytechnic University, Pomona, B
California State University, Chico, B
California State University, Sacramento, B
Claremont McKenna College, B
Dominican University of California, B
Santa Rosa Junior College, A
University of California, Berkeley, B

Colorado

The Colorado College, B

Connecticut

Connecticut College, B
Yale University, B

Hawaii

University of Hawaii at Manoa, B

Indiana

Indiana University Bloomington, B

Iowa

Cornell College, B

Massachusetts

Boston University, B
Harvard University, B
Simon's Rock College of Bard, B
Stonehill College, B
Wellesley College, B
Williams College, B

Minnesota

Metropolitan State University, B
St. Olaf College, B

Missouri

Washington University in St. Louis, B

New York

St. Francis College, B

Ohio

Bowling Green State University, B
Kenyon College, B
Miami University Hamilton, B

The Ohio State University, B

Oregon

Marylhurst University, B
University of Oregon, B

Pennsylvania

Carnegie Mellon University, B
University of Pittsburgh, B

Texas

Brazosport College, A
The University of Texas at Austin, B
The University of Texas at Dallas, B

Vermont

Marlboro College, B
Sterling College, B

Washington

Washington State University, B

Wisconsin

Lawrence University, B

Alberta

University of Alberta, B

Newfoundland and Labrador

Memorial University of Newfoundland, B

Ontario

Laurentian University, B
The University of Western Ontario, B

Quebec

Université Laval, A

Saskatchewan

University of Regina, B

ETHNOMUSICOLOGY

Alaska

University of Alaska Fairbanks, M

California

San Diego State University, M
University of California, Los Angeles, MD
University of California, Santa Barbara, MD

Connecticut

Wesleyan University, D

Florida

Florida State University, M

Indiana

Indiana University Bloomington, MD

Maryland

University of Maryland, College Park, M

Massachusetts

Harvard University, MD
Tufts University, M

New York

New York University, MD

Ohio

Kent State University, MD

Pennsylvania

University of Pittsburgh, MD

Texas

The University of Texas-Pan American, M

Wisconsin

University of Wisconsin-Madison, MD

Ontario

York University, MD

Quebec

Université de Montréal, MD

EUROPEAN HISTORY

California

Chapman University, B
University of California, Santa Cruz, B

Florida

Ave Maria University, B

Massachusetts

Framingham State College, B

New York

Bard College, B
Cornell University, B
Sarah Lawrence College, B

Pennsylvania

Carnegie Mellon University, B
Gettysburg College, B

Puerto Rico

University of Puerto Rico, Río Piedras, B

South Carolina

Charleston Southern University, B

Vermont

Bennington College, B

Saskatchewan

University of Regina, B

EUROPEAN STUDIES/CIVILIZATION

Alabama

Huntingdon College, B

California

Claremont McKenna College, B
Loyola Marymount University, B
Pitzer College, B
Saint Mary's College of California, B
San Diego State University, B
Scripps College, B
Thomas Aquinas College, B
University of California, Irvine, B
University of California, Los Angeles, B

Colorado

Fort Lewis College, B
Lamar Community College, A

Connecticut

Sacred Heart University, A

District of Columbia

American University, B
The George Washington University, B

Florida

Rollins College, B

Illinois

Lincoln College, A

Iowa

University of Northern Iowa, B

Kansas

University of Kansas, B

Kentucky

Georgetown College, B

Maryland

Anne Arundel Community College, A
St. John's College, B

Massachusetts

Amherst College, B
Brandeis University, B
Harvard University, B
Mount Holyoke College, B
Salem State College, B
Simon's Rock College of Bard, B

Michigan

Central Michigan University, B
Grand Valley State University, B
Hillsdale College, B
University of Michigan, B

Minnesota

Hamline University, B
University of Minnesota, Morris, B
University of Minnesota, Twin Cities Campus, B

Mississippi

Millsaps College, B

Missouri

University of Missouri-Columbia, B
Washington University in St. Louis, B

New Hampshire

University of New Hampshire, B

New Mexico

St. John's College, B
University of New Mexico, B

New York

Bard College, B
Barnard College, B
Canisius College, B
Elmira College, B
Hobart and William Smith Colleges, B
New York University, B
Sarah Lawrence College, B
State University of New York College at Brockport, B
United States Military Academy, B

North Carolina

The University of North Carolina at Chapel Hill, B

Ohio

Antioch College, B
Ohio University, B
Ohio University-Eastern, B
The University of Toledo, B

Pennsylvania

Carnegie Mellon University, B
Gettysburg College, B

Puerto Rico

University of Puerto Rico at Bayamón, A

South Carolina

University of South Carolina, B

Tennessee

Belmont University, B
Sewanee: The University of the South, B
Vanderbilt University, B

Texas

Howard Payne University, B
Lon Morris College, A
Southern Methodist University, B
Texas State University-San Marcos, B

Trinity University, B

Vermont

Bennington College, B
Marlboro College, B
Middlebury College, B
University of Vermont, B

Virginia

The College of William and Mary, B
Emory & Henry College, B
University of Richmond, B

Washington

Seattle Pacific University, B
University of Washington, B

Wisconsin

Beloit College, B

British Columbia

The University of British Columbia, B

Nova Scotia

Dalhousie University, B
Université Sainte-Anne, B
University of King's College, B

Ontario

Brock University, B
Carleton University, B
University of Guelph, B
University of Toronto, B
The University of Western Ontario, B
York University, B

Quebec

Concordia University, B

EVOLUTIONARY BIOLOGY

Arizona

Arizona State University, MD
The University of Arizona, MD

California

University of California, Irvine, MD
University of California, Riverside, MD
University of California, San Diego, D
University of California, Santa Barbara, MD
University of California, Santa Cruz, MD

Colorado

University of Colorado at Boulder, BMD

Connecticut

Yale University, BD

Delaware

University of Delaware, MD

Florida

Florida State University, BMD
University of Miami, MD

Georgia

Emory University, D

Hawaii

University of Hawaii at Manoa, MD

Illinois

Northwestern University, D
University of Chicago, D
University of Illinois at Chicago, MD
University of Illinois at Urbana-Champaign, D

Indiana

Indiana University Bloomington, MD
Purdue University, MD

University of Notre Dame, MD

Iowa

Iowa State University of Science and
Technology, MD

Kansas

University of Kansas, MD

Louisiana

Tulane University, B
University of Louisiana at Lafayette, D

Maine

College of the Atlantic, B

Maryland

The Johns Hopkins University, D
University of Maryland, College Park, MD

Massachusetts

Harvard University, BD
University of Massachusetts Amherst, MD

Michigan

University of Michigan, MD

Minnesota

University of Minnesota, Twin Cities Campus, MD

Missouri

University of Missouri-Columbia, MD
Washington University in St. Louis, D

Nevada

University of Nevada, Reno, D

New Hampshire

Dartmouth College, B
University of New Hampshire, B

New Jersey

Princeton University, D
Rutgers, The State University of New Jersey, New
Brunswick/Piscataway, BMD

New York

Columbia University, School of General Studies, B
Cornell University, D
Stony Brook University, State University of New
York, D
University at Albany, State University of New
York, MD

North Carolina

The University of North Carolina at Chapel Hill, MD

Ohio

Case Western Reserve University, B
The Ohio State University, MD
Ohio University, MD

Oregon

Oregon State University, B
University of Oregon, MD

Pennsylvania

The Pennsylvania State University University Park
Campus, MD
University of Pennsylvania, D
University of Pittsburgh, MD

Rhode Island

Brown University, D

South Carolina

University of South Carolina, MD

Tennessee

The University of Tennessee, MD

Texas

Rice University, BMD
The University of Texas at Austin, D

Utah

University of Utah, MD

Vermont

Bennington College, B

Virginia

George Mason University, M
Virginia Polytechnic Institute and State
University, MD

West Virginia

West Virginia University, MD

Wisconsin

Marquette University, MD

Alberta

University of Alberta, MD

Ontario

University of Guelph, MD

EXECUTIVE ASSISTANT/EXECUTIVE SECRETARY

Illinois

Elgin Community College, A
John Wood Community College, A
Kaskaskia College, A
Lake Land College, A
Prairie State College, A
Robert Morris College, A
Rockford Business College, A
Waubonsee Community College, A

Indiana

Ivy Tech Community College-Bloomington, A
Ivy Tech Community College-Central Indiana, A
Ivy Tech Community College-Columbus, A
Ivy Tech Community College-East Central, A
Ivy Tech Community College-Kokomo, A
Ivy Tech Community College-Lafayette, A
Ivy Tech Community College-North Central, A
Ivy Tech Community College-Northeast, A
Ivy Tech Community College-Northwest, A
Ivy Tech Community College-Southeast, A
Ivy Tech Community College-Southern Indiana, A
Ivy Tech Community College-Southwest, A
Ivy Tech Community College-Wabash Valley, A
Ivy Tech Community College-Whitewater, A

Iowa

Hamilton College (Cedar Falls), A
Western Iowa Tech Community College, A

Kentucky

Kentucky State University, A
Murray State University, A
Owensboro Community and Technical College, A
University of the Cumberlands, B
Western Kentucky University, A

Maine

Kennebec Valley Community College, A

Massachusetts

Cape Cod Community College, A

Michigan

Baker College of Allen Park, A
Baker College of Flint, A
Delta College, A
Jackson Community College, A
Kalamazoo Valley Community College, A
Kellogg Community College, A

Montcalm Community College, A
Northwestern Michigan College, A

Minnesota

Dakota County Technical College, A
Lake Superior College, A

Missouri

Crowder College, A
Hickey College, A

Montana

Montana Tech of The University of Montana, A
The University of Montana-Helena College of
Technology, A
The University of Montana-Missoula, A

New Jersey

Gibbs College (Montclair), A

New Mexico

Clovis Community College, A

New York

Adirondack Community College, A
Broome Community College, A

North Carolina

Alamance Community College, A
Asheville-Buncombe Technical Community
College, A
Cape Fear Community College, A
Cleveland Community College, A
Coastal Carolina Community College, A
Craven Community College, A
Randolph Community College, A
South Piedmont Community College, A
Stanly Community College, A
Wayne Community College, A
Wilkes Community College, A

North Dakota

Lake Region State College, A
Minot State University-Bottineau Campus, A

Ohio

Cincinnati State Technical and Community
College, A
Northwest State Community College, A
Ohio Valley College of Technology, A
Southern State Community College, A
The University of Akron, A
The University of Akron-Wayne College, A

Pennsylvania

Business Institute of Pennsylvania (Meadville), A
Business Institute of Pennsylvania (Sharon), A
Butler County Community College, A
Central Pennsylvania College, A
Laurel Business Institute, A
Lehigh Carbon Community College, A
Luzerne County Community College, A
Newport Business Institute (Lower Burrell), A
Yorktowne Business Institute, A

Puerto Rico

Caribbean University, B
Inter American University of Puerto Rico, Bayamón
Campus, B

Texas

Eastfield College, A
Kilgore College, A

Lee College, A

Utah

LDS Business College, A
Utah Valley State College, A

Virginia

J. Sargeant Reynolds Community College, A
National College of Business & Technology (Salem)
, A

Washington

Clark College, A

British Columbia

Thompson Rivers University, A

EXERCISE AND SPORTS SCIENCE

Alabama

University of South Alabama, M

Arizona

Arizona State University, D
Arizona State University at the Polytechnic
Campus, M
Northern Arizona University, M

Arkansas

Arkansas State University, M

California

California State University, Fresno, M
Humboldt State University, M
San Diego State University, M
University of California, Davis, M
University of the Pacific, M

Colorado

Colorado State University, M
University of Northern Colorado, MD

Connecticut

Central Connecticut State University, MO
Southern Connecticut State University, M
University of Connecticut, MD

Delaware

University of Delaware, M

District of Columbia

American University, M
The George Washington University, M
Howard University, M

Florida

Barry University, M
Florida Atlantic University, M
Florida State University, MD
University of Central Florida, MD
University of Florida, MD
University of Miami, MD
University of West Florida, M

Georgia

Armstrong Atlantic State University, M
Georgia State University, MD
Life University, M
University of Georgia, MDO

Idaho

Boise State University, M

Illinois

Benedictine University, M

Indiana

Ball State University, D
Indiana State University, M
Indiana University Bloomington, MD

Purdue University, MD

Iowa

Iowa State University of Science and Technology, M
The University of Iowa, MD

Kansas

Wichita State University, M

Kentucky

Morehead State University, M
University of Kentucky, D
University of Louisville, M

Louisiana

Louisiana Tech University, M
University of Louisiana at Monroe, M
University of New Orleans, M

Massachusetts

Northeastern University, M
Smith College, M
Springfield College, MD
University of Massachusetts Amherst, MD

Michigan

Central Michigan University, M
Eastern Michigan University, M
Northern Michigan University, M
Oakland University, MO
Western Michigan University, M

Minnesota

The College of St. Scholastica, M
St. Cloud State University, M
University of Minnesota, Twin Cities Campus, MD

Mississippi

Mississippi State University, M
University of Mississippi, MD

Missouri

Central Missouri State University, M
Southeast Missouri State University, M
University of Missouri-Columbia, MD

Montana

The University of Montana-Missoula, M

Nebraska

University of Nebraska at Kearney, M
Wayne State College, M

Nevada

University of Nevada, Las Vegas, M

New Jersey

Kean University, M
Montclair State University, MO

New Mexico

New Mexico Highlands University, M

New York

Brooklyn College of the City University of New
York, M
Ithaca College, M
Long Island University, Brooklyn Campus, M
Queens College of the City University of New
York, M
State University of New York at Buffalo, MD
State University of New York College at Cortland, M
Syracuse University, M

North Carolina

Appalachian State University, M
East Carolina University, MD
Gardner-Webb University, M
High Point University, M
The University of North Carolina at Chapel Hill, M
The University of North Carolina at Greensboro, MD

Wake Forest University, M

North Dakota

North Dakota State University, M

Ohio

Ashland University, M
Cleveland State University, M
Kent State University, MD
Miami University, M
Ohio University, MD
The University of Akron, M
University of Dayton, M
The University of Toledo, MD

Oklahoma

University of Oklahoma, MD

Oregon

Oregon State University, MD

Pennsylvania

Bloomsburg University of Pennsylvania, M
California University of Pennsylvania, M
East Stroudsburg University of Pennsylvania, M
Indiana University of Pennsylvania, M
Slippery Rock University of Pennsylvania, M
University of Pittsburgh, MD
West Chester University of Pennsylvania, M

South Carolina

University of South Carolina, MD

Tennessee

Austin Peay State University, M
East Tennessee State University, M
Middle Tennessee State University, D
Tennessee State University, M
University of Memphis, M
The University of Tennessee, MD

Texas

Baylor University, D
Texas Tech University, M
Texas Woman's University, M
University of Houston, M
University of Houston-Clear Lake, M
The University of Texas at Arlington, M
The University of Texas at El Paso, M
The University of Texas at Tyler, M
West Texas A&M University, M

Utah

Brigham Young University, MD
University of Utah, MD

Virginia

George Mason University, M
Old Dominion University, M

West Virginia

Marshall University, M
West Virginia University, MD

Wisconsin

University of Wisconsin-La Crosse, M

Alberta

University of Alberta, MD
University of Lethbridge, M

British Columbia

University of Victoria, M

New Brunswick

University of New Brunswick Fredericton, M

Ontario

Lakehead University, M
Queen's University at Kingston, MD

Quebec

Concordia University, M

EXERCISE PHYSIOLOGY

California

Chapman University, B
University of California, Davis, B

Minnesota

The College of St. Scholastica, B

New York

State University of New York College at
   Brockport, B

North Carolina

Pfeiffer University, B

Ohio

Miami University Hamilton, B

West Virginia

West Virginia University, B

Wisconsin

Concordia University Wisconsin, B

EXPERIMENTAL PSYCHOLOGY

Alabama

Huntingdon College, B

California

California State University, San Bernardino, M
La Sierra University, B
University of California, Santa Cruz, D

Colorado

Colorado State University-Pueblo, B

Connecticut

University of Connecticut, MD
University of Hartford, M

District of Columbia

American University, M
The Catholic University of America, MD
Howard University, D

Florida

University of Central Florida, D
University of South Florida, D

Georgia

Paine College, B

Illinois

Blackburn College, B
DePaul University, MD
Southern Illinois University Carbondale, MD

Kentucky

Morehead State University, M
University of Louisville, D

Maine

University of Maine, MD

Maryland

The Johns Hopkins University, D
Towson University, M
University of Maryland, College Park, D

Massachusetts

Northeastern University, MD
Tufts University, B

Michigan

Central Michigan University, MD
University of Michigan, D

Western Michigan University, MD

Mississippi

Mississippi State University, M
University of Mississippi, D

Missouri

Saint Louis University, MD
University of Missouri-St. Louis, D
Washington University in St. Louis, MD

Montana

The University of Montana-Missoula, D

Nebraska

University of Nebraska at Omaha, D

Nevada

University of Nevada, Las Vegas, D

New Jersey

Fairleigh Dickinson University, Metropolitan
   Campus, MO
Seton Hall University, M

New York

Brooklyn College of the City University of New
   York, M
City College of the City University of New York, D
Cornell University, D
Long Island University, C.W. Post Campus, MO
St. John's University, BM
Stony Brook University, State University of New
   York, D
Syracuse University, D
University at Albany, State University of New
   York, D

North Carolina

Appalachian State University, M
Duke University, D
North Carolina State University, D
The University of North Carolina at Chapel Hill, D

North Dakota

University of North Dakota, D

Ohio

Bowling Green State University, MD
Case Western Reserve University, D
Cleveland State University, M
Kent State University, MD
Miami University, D
The Ohio State University, D
Ohio University, D
University of Cincinnati, D
University of Dayton, M
The University of Toledo, BMD

Oklahoma

Oklahoma State University, D

Pennsylvania

Cedar Crest College, B
Moravian College, B
Temple University, D

Rhode Island

University of Rhode Island, D

South Carolina

University of South Carolina, BMD

Tennessee

University of Memphis, D
The University of Tennessee, MD
The University of Tennessee at Chattanooga, M

Texas

Dallas Baptist University, M
Texas Tech University, MD
University of North Texas, MD
The University of Texas at Arlington, D

The University of Texas at El Paso, M

Vermont

Marlboro College, B

Virginia

The College of William and Mary, M
George Mason University, M
Longwood University, B
Old Dominion University, D
Radford University, M

Washington

Central Washington University, M
Western Washington University, M

Wisconsin

University of Wisconsin-Madison, B
University of Wisconsin-Oshkosh, M

Alberta

University of Alberta, B

British Columbia

The University of British Columbia, B
University of Victoria, MD

Newfoundland and Labrador

Memorial University of Newfoundland, MD

Ontario

Lakehead University, M
University of Guelph, M
Wilfrid Laurier University, BM

Quebec

McGill University, MD

FACILITIES PLANNING AND MANAGEMENT

Georgia

Georgia State University, B

Michigan

Eastern Michigan University, B

New York

Cornell University, M
Pratt Institute, M

North Dakota

North Dakota State University, B

Pennsylvania

Indiana University of Pennsylvania, M

Texas

Southern Methodist University, M
University of North Texas, M

Quebec

Université Laval, M

FAMILY AND COMMUNITY SERVICES

California

Oxnard College, A
Point Loma Nazarene University, B
Saddleback College, A
San Jose City College, A

University of California, Santa Cruz, B

Delaware

University of Delaware, B

Florida

University of Florida, B
University of Miami, B

Idaho

Brigham Young University -Idaho, A

Illinois

Olivet Nazarene University, B

Indiana

Goshen College, B

Iowa

Iowa State University of Science and Technology, B
University of Northern Iowa, B

Kansas

Central Christian College of Kansas, A
Garden City Community College, A

Kentucky

Eastern Kentucky University, B

Maine

University of Maine at Machias, B

Maryland

University of Maryland, College Park, B
Villa Julie College, B

Massachusetts

Curry College, B

Michigan

Andrews University, B
Baker College of Flint, A
Michigan State University, B

Minnesota

Ridgewater College, A
St. Olaf College, B
University of Minnesota, Twin Cities Campus, B

Missouri

College of the Ozarks, B

New Jersey

Salem Community College, A

New York

State University of New York College of Agriculture
and Technology at Cobleskill, A
Syracuse University, B

Ohio

Bowling Green State University-Firelands College, A
God's Bible School and College, B
Youngstown State University, B

Oklahoma

Oklahoma Christian University, B

Oregon

Oregon State University, B

Pennsylvania

Keystone College, B
Messiah College, B

Tennessee

Union University, B

Texas

Collin County Community College District, A
Lubbock Christian University, B
Our Lady of the Lake University of San Antonio, B

Prairie View A&M University, B

Utah

Snow College, A
Southern Utah University, B
University of Utah, B

Washington

Skagit Valley College, A

West Virginia

Alderson-Broaddus College, B

Ontario

Saint Paul University, B

FAMILY AND CONSUMER ECONOMICS AND RELATED SERVICES

Alabama

Alabama Agricultural and Mechanical University, B
University of Montevallo, B

Arizona

Arizona Western College, A

California

Allan Hancock College, A
Bakersfield College, A
Butte College, A
California State University, Fresno, B
California State University, Sacramento, B
Cosumnes River College (Sacramento), A
Cuesta College, A
Evergreen Valley College, A
Grossmont College, A
Hartnell College, A
Long Beach City College, A
Los Angeles City College, A
Los Angeles Mission College, A
Los Angeles Southwest College, A
Los Angeles Valley College, A
Modesto Junior College, A
Monterey Peninsula College, A
Orange Coast College, A
Palomar College, A
Sacramento City College, A
San Bernardino Valley College, A
Santa Ana College, A
West Los Angeles College, A
Yuba College, A

Connecticut

Saint Joseph College, B

Delaware

University of Delaware, B

District of Columbia

Howard University, B

Florida

Florida State University, B

Georgia

Dalton State College, A

Indiana

Ball State University, B
Indiana University Bloomington, B

Vincennes University, A

Iowa

Iowa State University of Science and Technology, B
University of Northern Iowa, B

Kansas

Cowley County Community College and Area
  Vocational-Technical School, A

Kentucky

Berea College, B
Murray State University, B

Louisiana

Louisiana College, B

Maryland

University of Maryland Eastern Shore, B

Massachusetts

Framingham State College, B

Michigan

Andrews University, B

Minnesota

Minnesota State University Mankato, B

Missouri

Northwest Missouri State University, B
University of Missouri-Columbia, B

Nebraska

Chadron State College, B
University of Nebraska at Kearney, B
University of Nebraska-Lincoln, B

New Hampshire

University of New Hampshire, B

North Carolina

North Carolina Central University, B

Ohio

Ashland University, B
Miami University, B
The University of Akron, B

Oregon

Oregon State University, B
Portland Community College, A

South Carolina

Bob Jones University, B

Tennessee

Carson-Newman College, B
Lipscomb University, B
Tennessee State University, B

Utah

Brigham Young University, B
University of Utah, B
Utah State University, B

Virginia

Virginia State University, B

Washington

Seattle Pacific University, B
Yakima Valley Community College, A

West Virginia

Fairmont State University, AB

Wisconsin

University of Wisconsin-Madison, B
University of Wisconsin-Stevens Point, B

Alberta

University of Alberta, B

New Brunswick

Université de Moncton, B

Nova Scotia

Mount Saint Vincent University, B

Ontario

University of Windsor, B

Prince Edward Island

University of Prince Edward Island, B

FAMILY AND CONSUMER SCIENCES/HOME ECONOMICS TEACHER EDUCATION

Alabama

Jacksonville State University, B
Oakwood College, B
University of Montevallo, B

Arizona

The University of Arizona, B

Arkansas

Harding University, B
Henderson State University, B
University of Arkansas at Pine Bluff, B
University of Central Arkansas, B

California

American River College, A
Antelope Valley College, A
College of the Sequoias, A
Los Angeles Mission College, A
MiraCosta College, A

Colorado

Colorado State University, B
Johnson & Wales University, B

Connecticut

Saint Joseph College, B

District of Columbia

University of the District of Columbia, B

Florida

Florida International University, B
Florida State University, B
Manatee Community College, A
Okaloosa-Walton College, A

Georgia

East Georgia College, A
Fort Valley State University, B
Georgia Southern University, B
University of Georgia, B

Guam

University of Guam, B

Idaho

Brigham Young University -Idaho, A
University of Idaho, B

Illinois

Northern Illinois University, B
Olivet Nazarene University, B

Indiana

Ball State University, B

Iowa

Iowa State University of Science and Technology, B

Kansas

Cloud County Community College, A
Pittsburg State University, B

Kentucky

Berea College, B
Eastern Kentucky University, B

Murray State University, B
Western Kentucky University, B

Louisiana

Grambling State University, B
Louisiana Tech University, B
McNeese State University, B
Northwestern State University of Louisiana, B
University of Louisiana at Monroe, B

Maryland

University of Maryland Eastern Shore, B

Massachusetts

Framingham State College, B

Michigan

Ferris State University, B
Madonna University, B
Michigan State University, B
Western Michigan University, B

Minnesota

College of St. Catherine, B
Minnesota State University Mankato, B
University of Minnesota, Twin Cities Campus, B

Mississippi

Copiah-Lincoln Community College, A
Delta State University, B
Itawamba Community College, A
Jones County Junior College, A
Northeast Mississippi Community College, A
Northwest Mississippi Community College, A

Missouri

College of the Ozarks, B
Fontbonne University, B
Missouri State University, B
Northwest Missouri State University, B
Southeast Missouri State University, B

Nebraska

Chadron State College, B
Concordia University, B
Wayne State College, B

Nevada

University of Nevada, Reno, B

New Hampshire

Keene State College, B

New Mexico

New Mexico State University, B

New York

Cornell University, B
Queens College of the City University of New
  York, B
State University of New York College at Oneonta, B
Syracuse University, B

North Carolina

Appalachian State University, B
Campbell University, B
East Carolina University, B
North Carolina Agricultural and Technical State
  University, B
North Carolina Central University, B

North Dakota

North Dakota State University, B

Ohio

Ashland University, B
Bluffton University, B
Kent State University, B
Miami University, B
Mount Vernon Nazarene University, B
The University of Akron, B

Youngstown State University, B

Oklahoma

East Central University, B
Langston University, B
Northeastern State University, B
University of Central Oklahoma, B

Pennsylvania

Cheyney University of Pennsylvania, B
Immaculata University, B
Indiana University of Pennsylvania, B
Marywood University, B
Mercyhurst College, B
Seton Hill University, B

Puerto Rico

Pontifical Catholic University of Puerto Rico, B

South Carolina

South Carolina State University, B
Winthrop University, B

South Dakota

South Dakota State University, B

Tennessee

Carson-Newman College, B
Tennessee Technological University, B
The University of Tennessee, B
The University of Tennessee at Martin, B

Texas

Lamar University, B
Sam Houston State University, B
Texas A&M University-Kingsville, B

Utah

Brigham Young University, B
Southern Utah University, B
University of Utah, B
Utah State University, B

Vermont

University of Vermont, B

Virginia

Hampton University, B
Liberty University, B
Virginia Polytechnic Institute and State University, B

Washington

Seattle Pacific University, B
Washington State University, B

West Virginia

Fairmont State University, B

Wisconsin

University of Wisconsin-Madison, B
University of Wisconsin-Stevens Point, B
University of Wisconsin-Stout, B

Alberta

University of Alberta, B

British Columbia

The University of British Columbia, B

New Brunswick

University of New Brunswick Fredericton, B

Saskatchewan

University of Saskatchewan, B

FAMILY AND CONSUMER SCIENCES/HUMAN SCIENCES

Alabama

Auburn University, B
Jacksonville State University, B

Oakwood College, B
The University of Alabama, B
University of Montevallo, B
University of North Alabama, B

Alaska

University of Alaska Anchorage, A

Arizona

Mesa Community College, A
Phoenix College, A
Prescott College, B
South Mountain Community College, A

Arkansas

Harding University, B
Henderson State University, B
University of Arkansas, M
University of Arkansas at Pine Bluff, B
University of Central Arkansas, B

California

Butte College, A
California State Polytechnic University, Pomona, B
California State University, East Bay, B
California State University, Fresno, M
California State University, Long Beach, B
California State University, Northridge, BM
Cerritos College, A
Chaffey College, A
College of the Sequoias, A
Compton Community College, A
Contra Costa College, A
East Los Angeles College, A
El Camino College, A
Fresno City College, A
Fullerton College, A
Long Beach City College, A
Los Angeles City College, A
Los Angeles Valley College, A
The Master's College and Seminary, B
Merced College, A
Mt. San Antonio College, A
Ohlone College, A
Orange Coast College, A
Oxnard College, A
Point Loma Nazarene University, B
Saddleback College, A
San Francisco State University, B
San Joaquin Delta College, A
Santa Monica College, A
Santa Rosa Junior College, A
Shasta College, A
Sierra College, A
Skyline College, A
Solano Community College, A
University of California, Irvine, B
University of California, San Diego, B
Yuba College, A

Colorado

Colorado State University, B
Northeastern Junior College, A
Regis University, B

Connecticut

Connecticut College, B
Saint Joseph College, B

Delaware

Delaware State University, B

District of Columbia

University of the District of Columbia, B

Florida

Florida State University, BMD
Indian River Community College, A
Palm Beach Community College, A
University of Florida, M

Georgia

Abraham Baldwin Agricultural College, A
Bainbridge College, A

Clayton State University, A
Kennesaw State University, B
University of Georgia, MD

Hawaii

University of Hawaii at Manoa, B

Idaho

Brigham Young University -Idaho, A
Idaho State University, B

Illinois

City Colleges of Chicago, Kennedy-King College, A
Eastern Illinois University, B
Illinois State University, BM
Olivet Nazarene University, B
Western Illinois University, B

Indiana

Ball State University, BM
Indiana State University, B
Purdue University, B
Vincennes University, A

Iowa

Iowa Lakes Community College, A
Iowa State University of Science and
   Technology, BM

Kansas

Allen County Community College, A
Cloud County Community College, A
Coffeyville Community College, A
Colby Community College, A
Garden City Community College, A
Highland Community College, A
Hutchinson Community College and Area Vocational
   School, A
Kansas State University, BMD
Pittsburg State University, B
Pratt Community College, A

Kentucky

Eastern Kentucky University, B
Morehead State University, AB
University of Kentucky, BMD

Louisiana

Louisiana State University and Agricultural and
   Mechanical College, BMD
Louisiana Tech University, M
McNeese State University, B
Nicholls State University, B
Northwestern State University of Louisiana, B
Southeastern Louisiana University, B
Southern University and Agricultural and Mechanical
   College, A
University of Louisiana at Lafayette, M
University of Louisiana at Monroe, B

Maine

College of the Atlantic, B

Maryland

Morgan State University, B
University of Maryland Eastern Shore, B

Massachusetts

Framingham State College, B
Greenfield Community College, A
Holyoke Community College, A

Michigan

Delta College, A
Hope College, B
Madonna University, B
Michigan State University, B
Western Michigan University, M

Minnesota

College of St. Catherine, B
Minnesota State University Mankato, B
University of Minnesota, Twin Cities Campus, D

Vermilion Community College, A

Mississippi

Alcorn State University, B
Copiah-Lincoln Community College-Natchez
  Campus, A
Delta State University, B
Hinds Community College, A
Itawamba Community College, A
Jones County Junior College, A
Mississippi Delta Community College, A
Mississippi State University, B
Northeast Mississippi Community College, A
University of Mississippi, B
University of Southern Mississippi, B

Missouri

Central Missouri State University, B
College of the Ozarks, B
East Central College, A
Fontbonne University, BM
Missouri State University, M
Northwest Missouri State University, B
Penn Valley Community College, A
Southeast Missouri State University, B

Montana

Montana State University, B

Nebraska

Central Community College-Columbus Campus, A
University of Nebraska-Lincoln, MD
University of Nebraska at Omaha, B
Wayne State College, B

New Hampshire

University of New Hampshire, B

New Jersey

Rutgers, The State University of New Jersey, New
  Brunswick/Piscataway, B

New Mexico

Eastern New Mexico University, B
New Mexico State University, M
University of New Mexico, B

New York

Cornell University, B
Monroe Community College, A
Queens College of the City University of New
  York, BM
State University of New York College at
  Oneonta, BM

North Carolina

Appalachian State University, M
Bennett College For Women, B
Campbell University, B
Meredith College, B
North Carolina Agricultural and Technical State
  University, B
North Carolina Central University, BM
The University of North Carolina at Greensboro, B

North Dakota

North Dakota State University, M

Ohio

Ashland University, B
Bluffton University, B
Bowling Green State University, M
Kent State University, BMO
Kent State University, Salem Campus, AB
Miami University, B
Mount Vernon Nazarene University, AB
Ohio University, BM
The University of Akron, B
Youngstown State University, B

Oklahoma

Cameron University, B
Connors State College, A
East Central University, B

Langston University, B
Northeastern State University, B
Oklahoma State University, MD
Rose State College, A
University of Central Oklahoma, B

Oregon

George Fox University, B
Linn-Benton Community College, A
Oregon State University, BM
Portland Community College, A
University of Oregon, B

Pennsylvania

Marywood University, B
Mercyhurst College, B
Seton Hill University, B

Puerto Rico

Pontifical Catholic University of Puerto Rico, B
University of Puerto Rico, Río Piedras, BM

South Carolina

South Carolina State University, BM

South Dakota

Oglala Lakota College, A

Tennessee

Carson-Newman College, B
East Tennessee State University, B
Freed-Hardeman University, B
Lambuth University, B
Lipscomb University, B
Tennessee Technological University, B
University of Memphis, M
The University of Tennessee at Chattanooga, B
The University of Tennessee at Martin, BM

Texas

Abilene Christian University, B
Baylor University, B
Brazosport College, A
Hill College of the Hill Junior College District, A
Houston Community College System, A
Lamar State College-Port Arthur, A
Lamar University, BMO
Prairie View A&M University, M
Sam Houston State University, BM
Stephen F. Austin State University, B
Tarleton State University, B
Texas A&M University-Kingsville, B
Texas Southern University, BM
Texas State University-San Marcos, B
Texas Tech University, B
Texas Woman's University, B
University of Houston, BM
The University of Texas at Austin, BMD

Utah

Brigham Young University, B
Snow College, A
Southern Utah University, B
University of Utah, B

Vermont

Sterling College, AB

Virginia

Bridgewater College, B
Liberty University, B
Norfolk State University, B
Regent University, B
Southern Virginia University, B

Washington

Central Washington University, B
Washington State University, B

West Virginia

Fairmont State University, B
Marshall University, BM
Shepherd University, B

West Virginia University, B

Wisconsin

University of Wisconsin-Madison, BMD
University of Wisconsin-Stevens Point, M

Wyoming

University of Wyoming, B

Alberta

University of Alberta, BMD

British Columbia

The University of British Columbia, B

Manitoba

University of Manitoba, B

Nova Scotia

Mount Saint Vincent University, B

Ontario

The University of Western Ontario, B

FAMILY AND CONSUMER SCIENCES/HUMAN SCIENCES BUSINESS SERVICES

Utah

Brigham Young University, B

FAMILY AND CONSUMER SCIENCES/HUMAN SCIENCES COMMUNICATION

Indiana

Vincennes University, A

Massachusetts

Framingham State College, B

Nebraska

University of Nebraska at Omaha, B

FAMILY PRACTICE NURSE/NURSE PRACTITIONER

Georgia

North Georgia College & State University, B

New York

State University of New York at Buffalo, B

Virginia

The University of Virginia's College at Wise, B

Ontario

Ryerson University, B
University of Windsor, B

Quebec

Université du Québec àTrois-Rivières, B

FAMILY PSYCHOLOGY

Arizona

Cochise College (Douglas), A

Oregon

Corban College, B

FAMILY RESOURCE MANAGEMENT STUDIES

Alabama
Calhoun Community College, A

Arizona
Arizona State University, B

Illinois
Bradley University, B

Iowa
Iowa State University of Science and Technology, B

Nebraska
University of Nebraska at Omaha, B

New York
Cornell University, B

Ohio
The Ohio State University, B
Ohio University, B

Tennessee
Middle Tennessee State University, B

Texas
Texas Tech University, B

Utah
Brigham Young University, B
University of Utah, B

FAMILY SYSTEMS

District of Columbia
Gallaudet University, B

Indiana
Anderson University, B

Maryland
Towson University, B

Michigan
Central Michigan University, B
Spring Arbor University, B
Western Michigan University, B

Mississippi
University of Southern Mississippi, B

New York
Syracuse University, B

Ohio
The University of Akron, B

Tennessee
Southern Adventist University, B
The University of Tennessee, B

Texas
Texas Tech University, B

Utah
Brigham Young University, B
Weber State University, B

FARM/FARM AND RANCH MANAGEMENT

Alabama
Wallace State Community College, A

California
California Polytechnic State University, San Luis Obispo, B

California State Polytechnic University, Pomona, B
Cosumnes River College (Sacramento), A
Lassen Community College District, A

Colorado
Colorado State University, B
Lamar Community College, A
Northeastern Junior College, A
Trinidad State Junior College, A

Georgia
Abraham Baldwin Agricultural College, A

Idaho
Brigham Young University -Idaho, A
Idaho State University, AB

Iowa
Hawkeye Community College, A
Iowa Lakes Community College, A
Iowa State University of Science and Technology, B
Iowa Western Community College, A
Kirkwood Community College, A

Kansas
Allen County Community College, A
Butler Community College, A
Cloud County Community College, A
Colby Community College, A
Cowley County Community College and Area
   Vocational-Technical School, A
Dodge City Community College, A
Garden City Community College, A
Highland Community College, A
Hutchinson Community College and Area Vocational
   School, A
Pratt Community College, A
Seward County Community College, A

Kentucky
Eastern Kentucky University, B
St. Catharine College, A

Minnesota
Alexandria Technical College, A
Northland Community and Technical College-Thief
   River Falls, A
Ridgewater College, A
University of Minnesota, Crookston, B

Mississippi
Copiah-Lincoln Community College, A

Missouri
Crowder College, A
North Central Missouri College, A
Northwest Missouri State University, B

Nebraska
Northeast Community College, A

North Dakota
Fort Berthold Community College, A
Sitting Bull College, A

Ohio
The University of Findlay, B

Oklahoma
Eastern Oklahoma State College, A
Oklahoma Panhandle State University, A
Rogers State University, A

Rhode Island
Johnson & Wales University, AB

South Dakota
Mitchell Technical Institute, A
Western Dakota Technical Institute, A

Texas
Central Texas College, A
Clarendon College, A

Frank Phillips College, A
Hill College of the Hill Junior College District, A
North Central Texas College, A
Southwest Texas Junior College, A
Tarleton State University, B
Texas A&M University, B
Texas State Technical College Harlingen, A
Trinity Valley Community College, A
Tyler Junior College, A
Vernon College, A
Wharton County Junior College, A

Utah
Snow College, A

Vermont
Sterling College, B

Wisconsin
Northeast Wisconsin Technical College, A
University of Wisconsin-Madison, B

Wyoming
Eastern Wyoming College, A
Northwest College, A

Alberta
University of Alberta, B

FASHION AND FABRIC CONSULTANT

Georgia
University of Georgia, B

Illinois
College of DuPage, A

FASHION/APPAREL DESIGN

Arizona
Phoenix College, A

California
Academy of Art University, AB
Allan Hancock College, A
American InterContinental University, AB
American River College, A
The Art Institute of California-San Francisco, AB
Brooks College (Long Beach), A
Butte College, A
California College of the Arts, B
California Design College, A
Cañada College, A
Cerritos College, A
Chabot College, A
Chaffey College, A
College of Alameda, A
College of the Sequoias, A
East Los Angeles College, A
El Camino College, A
Fashion Careers College, A
FIDM/The Fashion Institute of Design &
   Merchandising, Los Angeles Campus, A
FIDM/The Fashion Institute of Design &
   Merchandising, Orange County Campus, A
FIDM/The Fashion Institute of Design &
   Merchandising, San Diego Campus, A
FIDM/The Fashion Institute of Design &
   Merchandising, San Francisco Campus, A
Fullerton College, A
Glendale Community College, A
Long Beach City College, A
Los Angeles Trade-Technical College, A
Merced College, A
Moorpark College, A
Otis College of Art and Design, B
Palomar College, A
Saddleback College, A
San Diego Mesa College, A
Santa Ana College, A
Ventura College, A

West Valley College, A
Woodbury University, B

Delaware

University of Delaware, B

District of Columbia

Howard University, B

Florida

American InterContinental University, B
The Art Institute of Fort Lauderdale, A
Daytona Beach Community College, A
Florida State University, B
International Academy of Design & Technology, AB
Lynn University, B
Miami International University of Art & Design, A
Palm Beach Community College, A

Georgia

American InterContinental University (Atlanta), AB
Bauder College, A
Clark Atlanta University, B
Savannah College of Art and Design, B

Hawaii

Honolulu Community College, A
Maui Community College, A
University of Hawaii at Manoa, B

Idaho

Brigham Young University -Idaho, A

Illinois

College of DuPage, A
Columbia College Chicago, B
Dominican University, B
The Illinois Institute of Art-Chicago, B
International Academy of Design & Technology, AB
School of the Art Institute of Chicago, B
William Rainey Harper College, A

Indiana

Indiana University Bloomington, AB
Vincennes University, A

Iowa

Iowa State University of Science and Technology, B
Kirkwood Community College, A

Kansas

Cloud County Community College, A
Garden City Community College, A
Highland Community College, A

Louisiana

University of Louisiana at Lafayette, B

Maryland

Baltimore City Community College, A
University of Maryland Eastern Shore, B

Massachusetts

Bay State College, A
Fisher College, A
Framingham State College, B
Lasell College, B
Massachusetts College of Art, B
Mount Ida College, AB

Michigan

Michigan State University, B

Minnesota

College of St. Catherine, B
Minnesota State University Mankato, B

Mississippi

Hinds Community College, A
Itawamba Community College, A

Northeast Mississippi Community College, A

Missouri

Lindenwood University, B
Northwest Missouri State University, B
Penn Valley Community College, A
Stephens College, B
Washington University in St. Louis, B

New Jersey

Burlington County College, A
Centenary College, B
Middlesex County College, A
Montclair State University, B

New York

The Art Institute of New York City, A
Buffalo State College, State University of New
   York, B
Cazenovia College, B
Fashion Institute of Technology, AB
Marist College, B
Monroe Community College, A
Nassau Community College, A
Parsons The New School for Design, AB
Pratt Institute, B
Syracuse University, B
Wood Tobe-Coburn School, A

North Carolina

Meredith College, B

Ohio

Columbus College of Art & Design, B
Kent State University, B
University of Cincinnati, B
Ursuline College, B
Virginia Marti College of Art and Design, A

Oklahoma

Tulsa Community College, A

Oregon

The Art Institute of Portland, AB
Oregon State University, B

Pennsylvania

The Art Institute of Philadelphia, AB
Drexel University, B
Harcum College, A
Moore College of Art & Design, B
Philadelphia University, B
Westmoreland County Community College, A

Puerto Rico

Pontifical Catholic University of Puerto Rico, B

Rhode Island

Rhode Island School of Design, B

Tennessee

O'More College of Design, B

Texas

The Art Institute of Dallas, A
Baylor University, B
El Centro College, A
El Paso Community College, A
Houston Community College System, A
Lamar University, B
Texas Southern University, B
Texas Tech University, B
Texas Woman's University, B
University of the Incarnate Word, AB
University of North Texas, B
Wade College, A

Virginia

Hampton University, B
Marymount University, B

Virginia Commonwealth University, B

Washington

The Art Institute of Seattle, A
Seattle Central Community College, A

Wisconsin

Mount Mary College, B

British Columbia

Kwantlen University College, B

Nova Scotia

Dalhousie University, B

Ontario

Ryerson University, B

Quebec

Université du Québec àMontréal, B

FASHION MERCHANDISING

Alabama

University of Montevallo, B
Wallace State Community College, A

Arizona

The Art Institute of Phoenix, B
Mesa Community College, A
Scottsdale Community College, A

Arkansas

Harding University, B
University of Arkansas at Pine Bluff, B

California

Academy of Art University, AB
American InterContinental University, AB
American River College, A
Brooks College (Long Beach), A
Butte College, A
California Design College, A
California State University, Long Beach, B
Chabot College, A
City College of San Francisco, A
College of Alameda, A
College of the Sequoias, A
Cuesta College, A
Evergreen Valley College, A
Fashion Careers College, A
FIDM/The Fashion Institute of Design &
   Merchandising, Los Angeles Campus, A
FIDM/The Fashion Institute of Design &
   Merchandising, Orange County Campus, A
FIDM/The Fashion Institute of Design &
   Merchandising, San Diego Campus, A
FIDM/The Fashion Institute of Design &
   Merchandising, San Francisco Campus, A
Fresno City College, A
Fullerton College, A
Las Positas College, A
Long Beach City College, A
Los Angeles Trade-Technical College, A
Merced College, A
Modesto Junior College, A
Monterey Peninsula College, A
Mt. San Antonio College, A
Ohlone College, A
Orange Coast College, A
Oxnard College, A
Palomar College, A
Pasadena City College, A
Saddleback College, A
San Diego City College, A
San Diego Mesa College, A
San Joaquin Delta College, A
Santa Ana College, A
Santa Monica College, A
Sierra College, A
Skyline College, A
Solano Community College, A
Westwood College-Inland Empire, B

Westwood College-Long Beach, B
Westwood College-Los Angeles, A
Woodbury University, B

Colorado

Johnson & Wales University, A
Northeastern Junior College, A
Parks College (Denver), A
Westwood College-Denver North, B
Westwood College-Denver South, B

Connecticut

Briarwood College, A
Gateway Community College, A
Tunxis Community College, A
University of Bridgeport, AB

Delaware

Delaware State University, B
University of Delaware, B

District of Columbia

University of the District of Columbia, A

Florida

Florida Community College at Jacksonville, A
Florida State University, B
Indian River Community College, A
Johnson & Wales University, A
Lynn University, AB
Miami International University of Art & Design, AB
Okaloosa-Walton College, A
Palm Beach Community College, A
Santa Fe Community College, A

Georgia

Abraham Baldwin Agricultural College, A
American InterContinental University (Atlanta), AB
Bauder College, A
Brenau University, B
Clayton State University, A
Middle Georgia College, A
University of Georgia, B

Idaho

Brigham Young University -Idaho, A

Illinois

Carl Sandburg College, A
College of DuPage, A
Dominican University, B
The Illinois Institute of Art-Chicago, B
International Academy of Design & Technology, AB
John A. Logan College, A
Joliet Junior College, A
Olivet Nazarene University, B
South Suburban College, A
Triton College, A
University of Illinois at Urbana-Champaign, B
William Rainey Harper College, A

Indiana

Ball State University, B
Indiana Business College (Indianapolis), A
Indiana University Bloomington, B
Vincennes University, A

Iowa

Des Moines Area Community College, A
Ellsworth Community College, A
Iowa Lakes Community College, A
Iowa Western Community College, A
Kirkwood Community College, A

Kansas

Garden City Community College, A

Kentucky

Eastern Kentucky University, B

Louisiana

Louisiana State University and Agricultural and
  Mechanical College, B

University of Louisiana at Lafayette, B

Maryland

Baltimore City Community College, A
Howard Community College, A
University of Maryland Eastern Shore, B

Massachusetts

Bay State College, AB
Fisher College, A
Framingham State College, B
Lasell College, B
Middlesex Community College, A
Mount Ida College, AB
Newbury College, A

Michigan

Central Michigan University, B
Eastern Michigan University, B
Grand Rapids Community College, A
Northwood University, AB
Oakland Community College, A

Minnesota

Alexandria Technical College, A
Century College, A
College of St. Catherine, B
Northwest Technical College, A
Rochester Community and Technical College, A

Mississippi

Delta State University, B
Mississippi Gulf Coast Community College, A
Northeast Mississippi Community College, A
Northwest Mississippi Community College, A
Southwest Mississippi Community College, A

Missouri

Fontbonne University, B
Lindenwood University, B
Northwest Missouri State University, B
Patricia Stevens College, A
Penn Valley Community College, A
St. Louis Community College at Florissant Valley, A
Stephens College, B

Montana

The University of Montana-Missoula, B

Nebraska

Wayne State College, B

New Hampshire

Southern New Hampshire University, A

New Jersey

Berkeley College, A
Brookdale Community College, A
Middlesex County College, A

New Mexico

Doña Ana Branch Community College, A

New York

Berkeley College-New York City Campus, A
Berkeley College-Westchester Campus, A
Buffalo State College, State University of New
  York, B
Fashion Institute of Technology, AB
Genesee Community College, A
Herkimer County Community College, A
Kingsborough Community College of the City
  University of New York, A
Laboratory Institute of Merchandising, AB
Marist College, A
Monroe Community College, A
Nassau Community College, A
New York City College of Technology of the City
  University of New York, A
Parsons The New School for Design, AB
State University of New York College at Oneonta, B

Wood Tobe-Coburn School, A

North Carolina

Central Piedmont Community College, A
Cleveland Community College, A
Johnson & Wales University, A
Mars Hill College, B
Meredith College, B

North Dakota

Lake Region State College, A

Ohio

Ashland University, B
Bowling Green State University, B
Davis College, A
James A. Rhodes State College, A
Kent State University, B
Owens Community College, A
The University of Akron, AB
Ursuline College, B
Virginia Marti College of Art and Design, A
Youngstown State University, B

Oklahoma

East Central University, B
Eastern Oklahoma State College, A
Northeastern State University, B
University of Central Oklahoma, B

Oregon

George Fox University, B
Oregon State University, B

Pennsylvania

The Art Institute of Philadelphia, AB
Bradley Academy for the Visual Arts, A
Community College of Philadelphia, A
Duff's Business Institute, A
Harcum College, A
ICM School of Business & Medical Careers, A
Immaculata University, B
Indiana University of Pennsylvania, B
Mercyhurst College, B
Pace Institute, A
Philadelphia University, B
Westmoreland County Community College, A

Rhode Island

Community College of Rhode Island, A
Johnson & Wales University, A

South Carolina

Midlands Technical College, A
South Carolina State University, B
Technical College of the Lowcountry, A

South Dakota

South Dakota State University, B

Tennessee

Carson-Newman College, B
Draughons Junior College (Clarksville), A
Draughons Junior College (Nashville), A
Freed-Hardeman University, B
Lambuth University, B
Lipscomb University, B
O'More College of Design, B
Tennessee Technological University, B
The University of Tennessee at Martin, B

Texas

Austin Community College, A
Baylor University, B
Brookhaven College, A
El Paso Community College, A
Houston Community College System, A
Kilgore College, A
Lamar University, B
Laredo Community College, A
Lee College, A
Northwood University, Texas Campus, AB
Odessa College, A
Our Lady of the Lake University of San Antonio, B

Sam Houston State University, B
South Plains College, A
Stephen F. Austin State University, B
Tarrant County College District, A
Texas A&M University-Kingsville, B
Texas Christian University, B
Texas Southern University, B
Texas State University-San Marcos, B
Texas Tech University, B
Texas Woman's University, B
Trinity Valley Community College, A
Tyler Junior College, A
University of the Incarnate Word, AB
University of North Texas, B
Wade College, A

Utah

Utah State University, B
Weber State University, A

Virginia

Hampton University, B
J. Sargeant Reynolds Community College, A
Liberty University, B
Marymount University, B

Washington

The Art Institute of Seattle, A
Bellevue Community College, A
Central Washington University, B
Edmonds Community College, A
Spokane Falls Community College, A

West Virginia

Community and Technical College of Shepherd, A
Fairmont State University, A
Huntington Junior College, A
West Virginia State University, A

Wisconsin

Madison Area Technical College, A
Milwaukee Area Technical College, A
Mount Mary College, B
Northeast Wisconsin Technical College, A
University of Wisconsin-Madison, B
Western Technical College, A

FASHION MODELING

New York

Fashion Institute of Technology, A

FIBER, TEXTILE AND WEAVING ARTS

California

Academy of Art University, AB
Antelope Valley College, A
California College of the Arts, B
California State University, Long Beach, B
Compton Community College, A
FIDM/The Fashion Institute of Design &
  Merchandising, Orange County Campus, A
Mendocino College, A
Monterey Peninsula College, A
Pasadena City College, A

Colorado

Colorado State University, B

Georgia

Savannah College of Art and Design, B

Illinois

School of the Art Institute of Chicago, B

Kansas

Highland Community College, A
University of Kansas, B

Maryland

Maryland Institute College of Art, B

Massachusetts

Massachusetts College of Art, B
University of Massachusetts Dartmouth, B

Michigan

Finlandia University, B
University of Michigan, B

Missouri

Kansas City Art Institute, B
Northwest Missouri State University, B

New Mexico

Institute of American Indian Arts, A

New York

Syracuse University, B

North Carolina

Haywood Community College, A

Ohio

The Cleveland Institute of Art, B

Oregon

University of Oregon, B

Pennsylvania

Mercyhurst College, B
Moore College of Art & Design, B
Philadelphia University, B
Temple University, B

Rhode Island

Rhode Island School of Design, B

Texas

University of North Texas, B

Washington

University of Washington, B
Western Washington University, B

Wisconsin

University of Wisconsin-Milwaukee, B

Alberta

Alberta College of Art & Design, B

Nova Scotia

NSCAD University, B

Quebec

Concordia University, B

FILIPINO/TAGALOG LANGUAGE AND LITERATURE

Hawaii

University of Hawaii at Manoa, B

FILM/CINEMA STUDIES

Arizona

Arizona State University, B
Cochise College (Sierra Vista), A
Prescott College, B
Yavapai College, A

California

Academy of Art University, AB
Allan Hancock College, A
Art Center College of Design, B
California College of the Arts, B
California Institute of the Arts, B
California State University, Long Beach, B

California State University, Northridge, B
Chapman University, B
Claremont McKenna College, B
Columbia College Hollywood, B
De Anza College, A
Long Beach City College, A
Los Angeles Valley College, A
Moorpark College, A
Orange Coast College, A
Palomar College, A
Pitzer College, B
Pomona College, B
San Francisco State University, B
Santa Barbara City College, A
Santa Rosa Junior College, A
Stanford University, B
University of California, Berkeley, B
University of California, Davis, B
University of California, Irvine, B
University of California, Los Angeles, B
University of California, San Diego, B
University of California, Santa Barbara, B
University of California, Santa Cruz, B
University of Southern California, B

Colorado

The Colorado College, B
University of Colorado at Boulder, B

Connecticut

Connecticut College, B
Quinnipiac University, B
Sacred Heart University, B
University of Hartford, B
Wesleyan University, B
Yale University, B

Delaware

University of Delaware, B

District of Columbia

Howard University, B

Florida

Florida State University, B
Tallahassee Community College, A
University of Miami, B

Georgia

Emory University, B
Georgia State University, B
University of Georgia, B

Illinois

Columbia College Chicago, B
Northwestern University, B
Olivet Nazarene University, B
School of the Art Institute of Chicago, B
University of Chicago, B

Indiana

Huntington University, B
Indiana University South Bend, A

Iowa

The University of Iowa, B

Louisiana

Centenary College of Louisiana, B

Maryland

The Johns Hopkins University, B
University of Maryland, Baltimore County, B

Massachusetts

Clark University, B
Curry College, B
Emerson College, B
Framingham State College, B
Harvard University, B
Mount Holyoke College, B
School of the Museum of Fine Arts, Boston, B

Wellesley College, B

Michigan

Calvin College, B
Eastern Michigan University, B
Grand Valley State University, B
Lansing Community College, A
Northern Michigan University, B
University of Michigan, B
Wayne State University, B

Minnesota

St. Cloud State University, B
University of Minnesota, Twin Cities Campus, B

Missouri

Washington University in St. Louis, B
Webster University, B

Nebraska

University of Nebraska-Lincoln, B

Nevada

University of Nevada, Las Vegas, B

New Hampshire

Dartmouth College, B

New Jersey

Rutgers, The State University of New Jersey, New
    Brunswick/Piscataway, B

New Mexico

College of Santa Fe, B
University of New Mexico, B

New York

Bard College, B
Barnard College, B
Brooklyn College of the City University of New
    York, B
Columbia College, B
Columbia University, School of General Studies, B
Cornell University, B
Fordham University, B
Hofstra University, B
Hunter College of the City University of New York, B
Ithaca College, B
New York University, B
Purchase College, State University of New York, B
Queens College of the City University of New
    York, B
Sarah Lawrence College, B
State University of New York at Binghamton, B
State University of New York at Buffalo, B
State University of New York, Fredonia, B
University of Rochester, B
Vassar College, B

North Carolina

North Carolina School of the Arts, B
North Carolina State University, B
Saint Augustine's College, B

Ohio

Baldwin-Wallace College, B
Bowling Green State University, B
Denison University, B
Ohio University, B
The University of Toledo, B
Wright State University, B

Oklahoma

Oral Roberts University, B
University of Tulsa, B

Oregon

George Fox University, B

Pennsylvania

La Salle University, B
The Pennsylvania State University Abington
    College, B

The Pennsylvania State University Altoona
    College, B
The Pennsylvania State University Beaver Campus
    of the Commonwealth College, B
The Pennsylvania State University Berks Campus of
    the Berks-Lehigh Valley College, B
The Pennsylvania State University Delaware County
    Campus of the Commonwealth College, B
The Pennsylvania State University DuBois Campus
    of the Commonwealth College, B
The Pennsylvania State University at Erie, The
    Behrend College, B
The Pennsylvania State University Fayette Campus
    of the Commonwealth College, B
The Pennsylvania State University Hazleton
    Campus of the Commonwealth College, B
The Pennsylvania State University, Lehigh Valley
    Campus of the Berks-Lehigh Valley College, B
The Pennsylvania State University McKeesport
    Campus of the Commonwealth College, B
The Pennsylvania State University Mont Alto
    Campus of the Commonwealth College, B
The Pennsylvania State University New Kensington
    Campus of the Commonwealth College, B
The Pennsylvania State University Schuylkill
    Campus of the Capital College, B
The Pennsylvania State University Shenango
    Campus of the Commonwealth College, B
The Pennsylvania State University University Park
    Campus, B
The Pennsylvania State University Wilkes-Barre
    Campus of the Commonwealth College, B
The Pennsylvania State University Worthington
    Scranton Campus of the Commonwealth
    College, B
The Pennsylvania State University York Campus of
    the Commonwealth College, B
Temple University, B
University of Pennsylvania, B
University of Pittsburgh, B

Rhode Island

Brown University, B
Rhode Island College, B
Rhode Island School of Design, B

Tennessee

Carson-Newman College, B
Watkins College of Art and Design, B

Texas

Southern Methodist University, B

Utah

Brigham Young University, B
University of Utah, B

Vermont

Bennington College, B
Burlington College, AB
Marlboro College, B
University of Vermont, B

Washington

Whitman College, B

Wisconsin

Milwaukee Area Technical College, A
University of Wisconsin-Milwaukee, B

Alberta

University of Alberta, B

British Columbia

Simon Fraser University, B
The University of British Columbia, B

Manitoba

University of Manitoba, B

Nova Scotia

NSCAD University, B

Ontario

Brock University, B
Carleton University, B

Laurentian University, B
Queen's University at Kingston, B
University of Toronto, B
University of Waterloo, B
The University of Western Ontario, B
University of Windsor, B
Wilfrid Laurier University, B
York University, B

Quebec

Bishop's University, B
Concordia University, B
Université de Montréal, B

Saskatchewan

University of Regina, B

FILM, TELEVISION, AND VIDEO PRODUCTION

Alabama

The University of Alabama, M

California

Academy of Art University, M
Art Center College of Design, M
California College of the Arts, M
California Institute of the Arts, MO
California State University, Fullerton, M
Chapman University, M
Loyola Marymount University, M
National University, M
San Diego State University, M
San Francisco Art Institute, MO
San Francisco State University, M
San Jose State University, M
Stanford University, M
University of California, Los Angeles, MDO
University of California, Santa Barbara, DO
University of Southern California, M

Colorado

University of Denver, M

District of Columbia

American University, M
Howard University, M

Florida

Florida State University, M
Miami International University of Art & Design, M
University of Central Florida, M
University of Miami, M

Georgia

Savannah College of Art and Design, M

Idaho

University of Idaho, M

Illinois

Columbia College Chicago, M
Northwestern University, MD
School of the Art Institute of Chicago, M

Iowa

The University of Iowa, M

Louisiana

University of New Orleans, M

Massachusetts

Boston University, MO
Emerson College, M

Massachusetts College of Art, M

Michigan

Central Michigan University, M
University of Michigan, O

Minnesota

Minneapolis College of Art and Design, M

Montana

Montana State University, M

Nevada

University of Nevada, Las Vegas, M

New Mexico

New Mexico Highlands University, M

New York

Brooklyn College of the City University of New
  York, M
New York University, M
Rochester Institute of Technology, M
Syracuse University, M

North Carolina

North Carolina School of the Arts, M
The University of North Carolina at Greensboro, M

Ohio

Ohio University, M

Oklahoma

University of Oklahoma, M

Pennsylvania

Carnegie Mellon University, M
Chestnut Hill College, O
Marywood University, M
Temple University, M

Tennessee

University of Memphis, M

Texas

Southern Methodist University, M
University of North Texas, M
The University of Texas at Austin, M

Utah

Brigham Young University, MD
University of Utah, M

Virginia

Hollins University, M

Wisconsin

University of Wisconsin-Milwaukee, M

British Columbia

The University of British Columbia, M

Ontario

Carleton University, M
York University, M

Quebec

Concordia University, M

FILM, TELEVISION, AND VIDEO THEORY AND CRITICISM

California

California College of the Arts, M
San Francisco State University, M

University of Southern California, MD

Florida

University of Miami, M

Georgia

Emory University, MO

Illinois

University of Chicago, MD

Iowa

The University of Iowa, MD

Kansas

University of Kansas, MD

Massachusetts

Boston University, M

New York

College of Staten Island of the City University of
  New York, M
New York University, MD

Ohio

Ohio University, M

Virginia

Hollins University, M

British Columbia

The University of British Columbia, M

Quebec

Concordia University, M
Université Laval, MD
Université de Montréal, M

FILM/VIDEO AND PHOTOGRAPHIC ARTS

California

Art Center College of Design, B
California Institute of the Arts, B
Scripps College, B
Woodbury University, B

Colorado

Rocky Mountain College of Art & Design, B

Florida

Full Sail Real World Education, B

Illinois

The Illinois Institute of Art-Chicago, B
School of the Art Institute of Chicago, B

Iowa

The University of Iowa, B

Kansas

Haskell Indian Nations University, A

Maine

New England School of Communications, AB

Maryland

Maryland Institute College of Art, B
Villa Julie College, B

Massachusetts

Hampshire College, B
School of the Museum of Fine Arts, Boston, B

New Jersey

Bloomfield College, B

New York

Pratt Institute, B
Syracuse University, B

Pennsylvania

The Art Institute of Philadelphia, B
The Art Institute of Pittsburgh, AB

Swarthmore College, B
The University of the Arts, B

Texas

Southern Methodist University, B

Utah

Brigham Young University, B

Virginia

Hollins University, B

Ontario

Ryerson University, B

FINANCE

Alabama

Alabama Agricultural and Mechanical University, B
Alabama Southern Community College, A
Alabama State University, B
Auburn University, B
Auburn University Montgomery, B
Community College of the Air Force, A
Enterprise-Ozark Community College, A
Jacksonville State University, B
Jefferson Davis Community College, A
Northeast Alabama Community College, A
Southern Union State Community College, A
Spring Hill College, B
Talladega College, B
Troy University, B
Tuskegee University, B
The University of Alabama, B
The University of Alabama at Birmingham, B
The University of Alabama in Huntsville, B
University of North Alabama, B
University of South Alabama, B
Wallace State Community College, A

Alaska

University of Alaska Anchorage, B

Arizona

Arizona State University, B
GateWay Community College, A
Grand Canyon University, B
Mesa Community College, A
Northern Arizona University, B
Phoenix College, A
Scottsdale Community College, A
The University of Arizona, B
University of Phoenix Online Campus, B
University of Phoenix-Southern Arizona Campus, B
Western International University, B

Arkansas

Arkansas State University, B
National Park Community College, A
NorthWest Arkansas Community College, A
University of Arkansas, B
University of Arkansas at Little Rock, B
University of Central Arkansas, B

California

American River College, A
Bakersfield College, A
Butte College, A
California State Polytechnic University, Pomona, B
California State University, Bakersfield, B
California State University, Chico, B
California State University, Dominguez Hills, B
California State University, East Bay, B
California State University, Fresno, B
California State University, Fullerton, B
California State University, Long Beach, B
California State University, Sacramento, B
California State University, San Bernardino, B
Chabot College, A
City College of San Francisco, A
Cosumnes River College (Sacramento), A
East Los Angeles College, A
El Camino College, A

Folsom Lake College, A
Fresno Pacific University, B
Glendale Community College, A
Golden Gate University, B
Lake Tahoe Community College, A
Laney College, A
Los Angeles City College, A
Los Angeles Mission College, A
Los Angeles Southwest College, A
The Master's College and Seminary, B
Mendocino College, A
Merced College, A
Modesto Junior College, A
Mt. San Antonio College, A
National University, B
Notre Dame de Namur University, B
Pacific Union College, B
Pasadena City College, A
Porterville College, A
San Bernardino Valley College, A
San Diego City College, A
San Diego State University, B
San Francisco State University, B
San Jose State University, B
Santa Barbara City College, A
Santa Clara University, B
Skyline College, A
Solano Community College, A
Southwestern College, A
University of San Francisco, B
Vanguard University of Southern California, B

Colorado

Arapahoe Community College, A
Colorado State University, B
Colorado State University-Pueblo, B
Community College of Aurora, A
Fort Lewis College, B
Jones International University, B
Mesa State College, B
Metropolitan State College of Denver, B
University of Colorado at Boulder, B
University of Colorado at Colorado Springs, B
University of Denver, B
Western State College of Colorado, B

Connecticut

Albertus Magnus College, B
Central Connecticut State University, B
Fairfield University, B
Naugatuck Valley Community College, A
Norwalk Community College, A
Post University, B
Quinnipiac University, B
Sacred Heart University, AB
Southern Connecticut State University, B
University of Bridgeport, B
University of Connecticut, B
University of Hartford, B
University of New Haven, B
Western Connecticut State University, B

Delaware

Delaware State University, B
Goldey-Beacom College, B
University of Delaware, B
Wilmington College, B

District of Columbia

The Catholic University of America, B
The George Washington University, B
Georgetown University, B
Howard University, B
University of the District of Columbia, B

Florida

Barry University, B
Broward Community College, A
Chipola College, A
Daytona Beach Community College, A
Edison College, A
Florida Agricultural and Mechanical University, B
Florida Atlantic University, B
Florida Gulf Coast University, B
Florida International University, B

Florida Southern College, B
Florida State University, B
Hillsborough Community College, A
Indian River Community College, A
Jacksonville University, B
Manatee Community College, A
Miami Dade College, A
Nova Southeastern University, B
Okaloosa-Walton College, A
Palm Beach Community College, A
Polk Community College, A
St. Thomas University, B
Santa Fe Community College, A
Seminole Community College, A
South Florida Community College, A
Stetson University, B
Tallahassee Community College, A
University of Central Florida, B
University of Florida, B
University of Miami, B
University of North Florida, B
University of South Florida, B
The University of Tampa, B
University of West Florida, B
Webber International University, AB

Georgia

Augusta State University, B
Berry College, B
Clayton State University, A
Columbus State University, B
Emory University, B
Georgia Southern University, B
Georgia State University, B
Kennesaw State University, B
Morehouse College, B
North Georgia College & State University, B
South Georgia College, A
University of Georgia, B
University of West Georgia, B
Valdosta State University, B

Guam

University of Guam, B

Hawaii

Hawaii Pacific University, AB
University of Hawaii at Manoa, B
University of Phoenix-Hawaii Campus, B

Idaho

Boise State University, B
Brigham Young University -Idaho, A
College of Southern Idaho, A
Idaho State University, B
Northwest Nazarene University, B
University of Idaho, B

Illinois

Augustana College, B
Aurora University, B
Benedictine University, B
Black Hawk College, A
Bradley University, B
Chicago State University, B
City Colleges of Chicago, Harold Washington
  College, A
DePaul University, B
East-West University, B
Eastern Illinois University, B
Elmhurst College, B
Eureka College, B
Governors State University, B
Illinois Central College, A
Illinois College, B
Illinois State University, B
John A. Logan College, A
Lewis University, B
Loyola University Chicago, B
MacMurray College, B
McKendree College, B
Millikin University, B
Morton College, A
North Central College, B
North Park University, B

Northeastern Illinois University, B
Northern Illinois University, B
Oakton Community College, A
Olivet Nazarene University, B
Prairie State College, A
Quincy University, B
Rockford College, B
Roosevelt University, B
South Suburban College, A
Southern Illinois University Carbondale, B
Spoon River College, A
University of Illinois at Chicago, B
University of Illinois at Urbana-Champaign, B
University of St. Francis, B
Western Illinois University, B
William Rainey Harper College, A

Indiana

Anderson University, B
Ball State University, B
Butler University, B
Indiana State University, B
Indiana University Bloomington, B
Indiana University-Purdue University Fort Wayne, B
Indiana University South Bend, B
Indiana Wesleyan University, AB
International Business College (Fort Wayne), AB
Manchester College, B
Marian College, AB
Saint Mary's College, B
Taylor University, B
University of Evansville, B
University of Notre Dame, B
University of Southern Indiana, B
Valparaiso University, B
Vincennes University Jasper Campus, A

Iowa

AIB College of Business, A
Drake University, B
Iowa Lakes Community College, A
Iowa State University of Science and Technology, B
Kirkwood Community College, A
Loras College, B
St. Ambrose University, B
The University of Iowa, B
University of Northern Iowa, B
Waldorf College, B
Wartburg College, B

Kansas

Central Christian College of Kansas, A
Dodge City Community College, A
Fort Hays State University, B
Independence Community College, A
Kansas State University, B
McPherson College, B
Neosho County Community College, A
Newman University, B
Pittsburg State University, B
Seward County Community College, A
University of Kansas, B
Washburn University, B
Wichita State University, B

Kentucky

Brescia University, B
Eastern Kentucky University, B
Elizabethtown Community and Technical College, A
Hopkinsville Community College, A
Morehead State University, B
Murray State University, B
Northern Kentucky University, B
University of Kentucky, B
University of Louisville, B
Western Kentucky University, B

Louisiana

Centenary College of Louisiana, B
Louisiana College, B
Louisiana State University and Agricultural and
  Mechanical College, B
Louisiana State University in Shreveport, B
Louisiana Tech University, B
Loyola University New Orleans, B

McNeese State University, B
Nicholls State University, B
Southeastern Louisiana University, B
Southern University and Agricultural and Mechanical
    College, B
Tulane University, B
University of Louisiana at Lafayette, B
University of Louisiana at Monroe, B
University of New Orleans, B

Maine

Husson College, B
Saint Joseph's College of Maine, B
Thomas College, B
University of Maine, B

Maryland

Frederick Community College, A
Loyola College in Maryland, B
Morgan State University, B
Salisbury University, B
University of Baltimore, B
University of Maryland, College Park, B

Massachusetts

American International College, B
Babson College, B
Bentley College, B
Boston College, B
Boston University, B
Bridgewater State College, B
Bunker Hill Community College, A
Framingham State College, B
Lasell College, B
Massachusetts College of Liberal Arts, B
Merrimack College, B
New England College of Finance, A
Newbury College, AB
Nichols College, B
Northeastern University, B
Northern Essex Community College, A
Salem State College, B
Simmons College, B
Springfield Technical Community College, A
Stonehill College, B
Suffolk University, B
University of Massachusetts Amherst, B
University of Massachusetts Dartmouth, B
Western New England College, B
Westfield State College, B

Michigan

Central Michigan University, B
Cleary University, B
Davenport University (Dearborn), AB
Davenport University (Midland), A
Eastern Michigan University, B
Ferris State University, B
Grand Valley State University, B
Hillsdale College, B
Kettering University, B
Lake Superior State University, B
Lansing Community College, A
Macomb Community College, A
Michigan State University, B
Michigan Technological University, B
Monroe County Community College, A
Muskegon Community College, A
North Central Michigan College, A
Northern Michigan University, B
Oakland University, B
Olivet College, B
Saginaw Valley State University, B
University of Detroit Mercy, B
University of Michigan-Dearborn, B
University of Michigan-Flint, B
Walsh College of Accountancy and Business
    Administration, B
Wayne County Community College District, A
Wayne State University, B
Western Michigan University, B

Minnesota

Academy College, A
Augsburg College, B

Concordia University, St. Paul, B
Fond du Lac Tribal and Community College, A
Metropolitan State University, B
Minnesota State University Mankato, B
Minnesota State University Moorhead, B
North Hennepin Community College, A
Northwestern College, B
St. Cloud State University, B
St. Cloud Technical College, A
University of Minnesota, Duluth, B
University of Minnesota, Twin Cities Campus, B
University of St. Thomas, B
Vermilion Community College, A
Winona State University, B

Mississippi

Delta State University, B
Hinds Community College, A
Holmes Community College, A
Jackson State University, B
Mississippi Gulf Coast Community College, A
Mississippi State University, B
Southwest Mississippi Community College, A
University of Mississippi, B
University of Southern Mississippi, B

Missouri

Avila University, B
Central Missouri State University, B
Columbia College, B
Culver-Stockton College, B
Drury University, B
Fontbonne University, B
Lindenwood University, B
Missouri Southern State University, B
Missouri State University, B
Missouri Western State University, B
National American University, B
Northwest Missouri State University, B
St. Louis Community College at Florissant Valley, A
St. Louis Community College at Forest Park, A
St. Louis Community College at Meramec, A
Southeast Missouri State University, B
State Fair Community College, A
Truman State University, B
University of Missouri-Columbia, B
University of Missouri-St. Louis, B
Washington University in St. Louis, B

Montana

Carroll College, B
Montana State University-Billings, B
Montana Tech of The University of Montana, B
The University of Montana-Missoula, B

Nebraska

Creighton University, B
Southeast Community College, Beatrice Campus, A
University of Nebraska-Lincoln, B
University of Nebraska at Omaha, B
Wayne State College, B

Nevada

Community College of Southern Nevada, A
University of Nevada, Las Vegas, B
University of Nevada, Reno, B

New Hampshire

Franklin Pierce College, B
Granite State College, B
Saint Anselm College, B
Southern New Hampshire University, B
University of New Hampshire, B

New Jersey

Bergen Community College, A
Bloomfield College, B
Camden County College, A
The College of New Jersey, B
Fairleigh Dickinson University, College at
    Florham, B
Fairleigh Dickinson University, Metropolitan
    Campus, B
Gloucester County College, A
Kean University, B

Passaic County Community College, A
Rider University, B
Rutgers, The State University of New Jersey,
    Camden, B
Rutgers, The State University of New Jersey, New
    Brunswick/Piscataway, B
Rutgers, The State University of New Jersey,
    Newark, B
Saint Peter's College, A
Seton Hall University, B

New Mexico

Clovis Community College, A
Doña Ana Branch Community College, A
Eastern New Mexico University, B
New Mexico Junior College, A
New Mexico Military Institute, A
New Mexico State University, B

New York

Adelphi University, B
Adirondack Community College, A
Bernard M. Baruch College of the City University of
    New York, B
Canisius College, B
Clarkson University, B
Dominican College, B
Dowling College, B
Excelsior College, B
Fordham University, B
Fulton-Montgomery Community College, A
Globe Institute of Technology, B
Hilbert College, B
Hofstra University, B
Hudson Valley Community College, A
Iona College, B
Ithaca College, B
The King's College, B
Long Island University, Brentwood Campus, B
Long Island University, Brooklyn Campus, B
Long Island University, C.W. Post Campus, B
Manhattan College, B
Manhattanville College, B
New York Institute of Technology, B
New York University, B
Onondaga Community College, A
Orange County Community College, A
Pace University, B
Queens College of the City University of New
    York, B
Rensselaer Polytechnic Institute, B
Rochester Institute of Technology, B
Rockland Community College, A
St. Bonaventure University, B
St. John Fisher College, B
St. John's University, B
St. Thomas Aquinas College, B
Siena College, B
State University of New York College at
    Brockport, B
State University of New York College at Old
    Westbury, B
State University of New York College of Technology
    at Alfred, A
State University of New York, Fredonia, B
State University of New York Institute of
    Technology, B
State University of New York at New Paltz, B
State University of New York at Oswego, B
Syracuse University, B
Touro College, B
Wagner College, B
Westchester Community College, A
Yeshiva University, B

North Carolina

Appalachian State University, B
Barber-Scotia College, B
Campbell University, B
Central Piedmont Community College, A
East Carolina University, B
Fayetteville State University, B
Forsyth Technical Community College, A
Lenoir Community College, A
Mars Hill College, B
Mayland Community College, A

Methodist College, AB
North Carolina State University, B
Pfeiffer University, B
The University of North Carolina at Charlotte, B
The University of North Carolina at Greensboro, B
The University of North Carolina Wilmington, B
Wake Forest University, B
Western Carolina University, B
Western Piedmont Community College, A
Wingate University, B

North Dakota

Dickinson State University, B
Minot State University, B
Trinity Bible College, B
University of North Dakota, B

Ohio

Ashland University, B
Baldwin-Wallace College, B
Bowling Green State University, B
Capital University, B
Cedarville University, B
Central State University, B
Cleveland State University, B
Columbus State Community College, A
Cuyahoga Community College, A
David N. Myers University, B
Edison State Community College, A
Franklin University, B
James A. Rhodes State College, A
Jefferson Community College, A
John Carroll University, B
Kent State University, B
Kent State University, Ashtabula Campus, A
Lorain County Community College, A
Marion Technical College, A
Miami University, B
Miami University Hamilton, B
North Central State College, A
Ohio Dominican University, B
The Ohio State University, B
Otterbein College, B
Sinclair Community College, A
Stark State College of Technology, A
Terra State Community College, A
Tiffin University, B
The University of Akron, B
University of Cincinnati, AB
University of Dayton, B
The University of Toledo, B
Walsh University, AB
Wilberforce University, B
Wright State University, B
Wright State University, Lake Campus, A
Xavier University, B
Youngstown State University, AB

Oklahoma

Bacone College, B
East Central University, B
Northeastern State University, B
Oklahoma Baptist University, B
Oklahoma City Community College, A
Oklahoma City University, B
Oklahoma State University, B
Oral Roberts University, B
Southeastern Oklahoma State University, B
Southern Nazarene University, B
Southwestern Oklahoma State University, B
University of Central Oklahoma, B
University of Oklahoma, B
University of Tulsa, B

Oregon

Chemeketa Community College, A
Corban College, B
George Fox University, B
Linfield College, B
Oregon State University, B
Pacific University, B
Portland State University, B
University of Oregon, B

University of Portland, B

Pennsylvania

Albright College, B
Arcadia University, B
Cabrini College, B
Central Pennsylvania College, A
Clarion University of Pennsylvania, B
Community College of Philadelphia, A
DeSales University, B
Drexel University, B
Duquesne University, B
Eastern University, B
Gannon University, B
Grove City College, B
Immaculata University, B
Indiana University of Pennsylvania, B
Juniata College, B
King's College, B
Kutztown University of Pennsylvania, B
La Roche College, B
La Salle University, B
Lehigh University, B
Lincoln University, B
Lycoming College, B
Mercyhurst College, B
The Pennsylvania State University Abington
    College, B
The Pennsylvania State University Altoona
    College, B
The Pennsylvania State University Beaver Campus
    of the Commonwealth College, B
The Pennsylvania State University Berks Campus of
    the Berks-Lehigh Valley College, B
The Pennsylvania State University Delaware County
    Campus of the Commonwealth College, B
The Pennsylvania State University DuBois Campus
    of the Commonwealth College, B
The Pennsylvania State University at Erie, The
    Behrend College, B
The Pennsylvania State University Fayette Campus
    of the Commonwealth College, B
The Pennsylvania State University Harrisburg
    Campus, B
The Pennsylvania State University Hazleton
    Campus of the Commonwealth College, B
The Pennsylvania State University, Lehigh Valley
    Campus of the Berks-Lehigh Valley College, B
The Pennsylvania State University McKeesport
    Campus of the Commonwealth College, B
The Pennsylvania State University Mont Alto
    Campus of the Commonwealth College, B
The Pennsylvania State University New Kensington
    Campus of the Commonwealth College, B
The Pennsylvania State University Schuylkill
    Campus of the Capital College, B
The Pennsylvania State University Shenango
    Campus of the Commonwealth College, B
The Pennsylvania State University University Park
    Campus, B
The Pennsylvania State University Wilkes-Barre
    Campus of the Commonwealth College, B
The Pennsylvania State University Worthington
    Scranton Campus of the Commonwealth
    College, B
The Pennsylvania State University York Campus of
    the Commonwealth College, B
Philadelphia University, B
Reading Area Community College, A
Robert Morris University, B
Saint Francis University, B
Saint Joseph's University, AB
Saint Vincent College, B
Seton Hill University, B
Shippensburg University of Pennsylvania, B
Susquehanna University, B
Temple University, B
University of Pennsylvania, B
University of Pittsburgh, B
University of Pittsburgh at Johnstown, B
The University of Scranton, B
Villanova University, B
Waynesburg College, B
West Chester University of Pennsylvania, B
Westmoreland County Community College, A

York College of Pennsylvania, B

Puerto Rico

Caribbean University, A
Inter American University of Puerto Rico, Bayamón
    Campus, B
Inter American University of Puerto Rico,
    Metropolitan Campus, B
Inter American University of Puerto Rico, Ponce
    Campus, B
Inter American University of Puerto Rico, San
    Germán Campus, B
Polytechnic University of Puerto Rico, B
Pontifical Catholic University of Puerto Rico, B
University of Puerto Rico at Arecibo, B
University of Puerto Rico at Bayamón, AB
University of Puerto Rico at Carolina, A
University of Puerto Rico, Mayagüez Campus, B
University of Puerto Rico, Río Piedras, B

Rhode Island

Bryant University, B
Johnson & Wales University, B
Providence College, B
Rhode Island College, B
Roger Williams University, B
Salve Regina University, B
University of Rhode Island, B

South Carolina

Anderson University, B
Benedict College, B
Bob Jones University, B
Charleston Southern University, B
Clemson University, B
Coastal Carolina University, B
Francis Marion University, B
University of South Carolina, B
Wofford College, B

South Dakota

Colorado Technical University Sioux Falls
    Campus, B
Dakota State University, B
Dakota Wesleyan University, B
Lake Area Technical Institute, A
National American University (Rapid City), B
Northern State University, B
Southeast Technical Institute, A
The University of South Dakota, B

Tennessee

Belmont University, B
Chattanooga State Technical Community College, A
East Tennessee State University, B
Fisk University, B
Freed-Hardeman University, B
King College, B
Lincoln Memorial University, B
Lipscomb University, B
Middle Tennessee State University, B
Pellissippi State Technical Community College, A
Tennessee Technological University, B
Tennessee Wesleyan College, B
Union University, B
University of Memphis, B
The University of Tennessee, B
The University of Tennessee at Martin, B

Texas

Abilene Christian University, B
Angelo State University, B
Austin Community College, A
Baylor University, B
Brazosport College, A
Cisco Junior College, A
Clarendon College, A
Coastal Bend College, A
Dallas Baptist University, B
Del Mar College, A
El Paso Community College, A
Frank Phillips College, A
Hardin-Simmons University, B
Hill College of the Hill Junior College District, A
Houston Baptist University, B

Houston Community College System, A
Howard College, A
Howard Payne University, B
Kilgore College, A
Lamar University, B
LeTourneau University, B
Lubbock Christian University, B
McLennan Community College, A
McMurry University, B
Midwestern State University, B
North Harris College, A
Northeast Texas Community College, A
Palo Alto College, A
Prairie View A&M University, B
St. Edward's University, B
St. Mary's University of San Antonio, B
Sam Houston State University, B
Southern Methodist University, B
Stephen F. Austin State University, B
Tarleton State University, B
Texarkana College, A
Texas A&M International University, B
Texas A&M University, B
Texas A&M University-Commerce, B
Texas A&M University-Corpus Christi, B
Texas A&M University-Kingsville, B
Texas A&M University-Texarkana, B
Texas Christian University, B
Texas Lutheran University, B
Texas Southern University, B
Texas Southmost College, A
Texas State University-San Marcos, B
Texas Tech University, B
Trinity University, B
Trinity Valley Community College, A
Tyler Junior College, A
University of Houston, B
University of Houston-Clear Lake, B
University of Houston-Downtown, B
University of the Incarnate Word, B
University of Mary Hardin-Baylor, B
University of North Texas, B
University of St. Thomas, B
The University of Texas at Austin, B
The University of Texas at Brownsville, B
The University of Texas at Dallas, B
The University of Texas at El Paso, B
The University of Texas-Pan American, B
The University of Texas of the Permian Basin, B
The University of Texas at San Antonio, B
The University of Texas at Tyler, B
West Texas A&M University, B

Utah

California College for Health Sciences, AB
University of Phoenix-Utah Campus, B
University of Utah, B
Utah State University, B
Weber State University, B
Westminster College, B

Vermont

Castleton State College, B
College of St. Joseph, B

Virginia

Averett University, B
Central Virginia Community College, A
Christopher Newport University, B
George Mason University, B
Hampton University, B
James Madison University, B
Longwood University, B
Marymount University, B
Old Dominion University, B
Radford University, B
Tidewater Community College, A
University of Richmond, B
Virginia Polytechnic Institute and State University, B

Washington

Eastern Washington University, B
Gonzaga University, B
Pacific Lutheran University, B
Saint Martin's University, B
Seattle University, B

Washington State University, B
Western Washington University, B

West Virginia

Alderson-Broaddus College, B
Fairmont State Community & Technical College, A
Fairmont State University, AB
Marshall Community and Technical College, A
Marshall University, B
Southern West Virginia Community and Technical
    College, A
University of Charleston, B
West Virginia State University, A
West Virginia University, B
West Virginia University at Parkersburg, A
West Virginia Wesleyan College, B

Wisconsin

Carroll College, B
Fox Valley Technical College, A
Lakeshore Technical College, A
Madison Area Technical College, A
Marian College of Fond du Lac, B
Marquette University, B
Milwaukee Area Technical College, A
Northeast Wisconsin Technical College, A
Southwest Wisconsin Technical College, A
University of Wisconsin-Eau Claire, B
University of Wisconsin-La Crosse, B
University of Wisconsin-Madison, B
University of Wisconsin-Milwaukee, B
University of Wisconsin-Oshkosh, B
University of Wisconsin-Parkside, B
University of Wisconsin-River Falls, B
University of Wisconsin-Superior, B
University of Wisconsin-Whitewater, B
Western Technical College, A
Wisconsin Indianhead Technical College, A

Wyoming

University of Wyoming, B

Alberta

University of Alberta, B
University of Calgary, B
University of Lethbridge, B

British Columbia

British Columbia Institute of Technology, A
Thompson Rivers University, B
The University of British Columbia, B
University of Northern British Columbia, B

Manitoba

University of Manitoba, B

New Brunswick

Université de Moncton, B
University of New Brunswick Fredericton, B

Newfoundland and Labrador

Memorial University of Newfoundland, B

Nova Scotia

Cape Breton University, B
Dalhousie University, B
Saint Mary's University, B

Ontario

Brock University, B
Carleton University, B
Lakehead University, B
Ryerson University, B
University of Ottawa, B
University of Toronto, B
University of Windsor, B
York University, B

Quebec

Bishop's University, B
Concordia University, B
HEC Montreal, B
McGill University, B

Université de Sherbrooke, B

Saskatchewan

University of Regina, B
University of Saskatchewan, B

FINANCE AND BANKING

Alabama

Alabama Agricultural and Mechanical University, M
Andrew Jackson University, M
Auburn University, M
Troy University, M
The University of Alabama, MD

Alaska

Alaska Pacific University, M
University of Alaska Fairbanks, M

Arizona

Arizona State University, D
The University of Arizona, MD
Western International University, M

California

Argosy University/Orange County, M
California Lutheran University, M
California State University, East Bay, M
California State University, Fullerton, M
California State University, Los Angeles, M
California State University, Stanislaus, M
Golden Gate University, MO
National University, M
Pacific States University, M
San Diego State University, M
Touro University International, M
University of California, Berkeley, D
University of La Verne, M
University of Redlands, O
University of San Diego, M
University of San Francisco, M
University of Southern California, M
University of the West, M

Colorado

Jones International University, M
Regis University, M
University of Colorado at Boulder, MD
University of Colorado at Colorado Springs, M
University of Colorado at Denver and Health
    Sciences Center - Downtown Denver Campus, M
University of Denver, M

Connecticut

Fairfield University, MO
Quinnipiac University, M
University of Connecticut, D
University of New Haven, M
Yale University, D

Delaware

Goldey-Beacom College, M

District of Columbia

American University, MO
The Catholic University of America, M
The George Washington University, MD
Howard University, M
Southeastern University, M

Florida

Argosy University/Sarasota, M
Argosy University/Tampa, M
Florida Agricultural and Mechanical University, M
Florida Atlantic University, M
Florida International University, M
University of Central Florida, D
University of Florida, MDO
University of Miami, M

Georgia

Clark Atlanta University, M
Emory University, D

Georgia Institute of Technology, MD
Georgia State University, MD

Hawaii

Hawaii Pacific University, M
University of Hawaii at Manoa, MD

Illinois

American InterContinental University Online, M
Argosy University/Schaumburg, M
DePaul University, MO
DeVry University (Oakbrook Terrace), M
Illinois Institute of Technology, MO
Northeastern Illinois University, M
Northwestern University, D
Saint Xavier University, MO
Southern Illinois University Edwardsville, M
University of Illinois at Urbana-Champaign, MD

Indiana

Indiana University Bloomington, MD
Indiana University Southeast, MO
Purdue University, MD

Iowa

The University of Iowa, MD
Upper Iowa University, M

Louisiana

Louisiana State University and Agricultural and
   Mechanical College, MD
Louisiana Tech University, MD

Maryland

The Johns Hopkins University, M
Loyola College in Maryland, M
University of Baltimore, M
University of Maryland University College, MO

Massachusetts

Bentley College, MO
Boston College, MDO
Boston University, M
Brandeis University, MD
Bridgewater State College, M
Clark University, M
Nichols College, M
Northeastern University, M
Suffolk University, MO

Michigan

Andrews University, M
Central Michigan University, M
Davenport University (Dearborn), M
Michigan State University, MD
Oakland University, O
University of Michigan-Dearborn, M
Walsh College of Accountancy and Business
   Administration, M

Minnesota

Metropolitan State University, M
St. Cloud State University, M
University of Minnesota, Twin Cities Campus, MD
University of St. Thomas, M

Mississippi

Mississippi State University, MD
University of Southern Mississippi, MD

Missouri

Lindenwood University, M
Saint Louis University, M
Southeast Missouri State University, M
University of Missouri-St. Louis, M

Webster University, M

Nebraska

University of Nebraska-Lincoln, MD

New Hampshire

Southern New Hampshire University, M

New Jersey

Fairleigh Dickinson University, College at
   Florham, MO
Fairleigh Dickinson University, Metropolitan
   Campus, MO
Montclair State University, M
Princeton University, M
Rutgers, The State University of New Jersey,
   Newark, MDO
Saint Peter's College, M
Seton Hall University, MO

New Mexico

University of New Mexico, M

New York

Adelphi University, M
Bernard M. Baruch College of the City University of
   New York, MD
Cornell University, D
Dowling College, MO
Fordham University, M
Hofstra University, MO
Iona College, MO
Long Island University, C.W. Post Campus, MO
Mercy College, M
Mount Saint Mary College, M
New York Institute of Technology, MO
New York University, D
Pace University, M
Rensselaer Polytechnic Institute, M
Rochester Institute of Technology, M
St. Bonaventure University, MO
St. John's University, MO
St. Thomas Aquinas College, M
State University of New York at Binghamton, MD
State University of New York at Buffalo, M
State University of New York at New Paltz, M
Syracuse University, D
University at Albany, State University of New
   York, M
Wagner College, M

North Carolina

The University of North Carolina at Chapel Hill, D

Ohio

Case Western Reserve University, MD
Cleveland State University, O
Kent State University, D
Miami University, M
Notre Dame College, O
Ohio University, M
The University of Akron, MO
University of Cincinnati, MD
The University of Findlay, M
The University of Toledo, M
Wright State University, MO
Xavier University, M
Youngstown State University, M

Oklahoma

Northeastern State University, M
Oklahoma City University, M
Oklahoma State University, MD
Oral Roberts University, M
University of Tulsa, M

Oregon

Portland State University, M
University of Oregon, D

Pennsylvania

Carnegie Mellon University, D
Drexel University, M
Gannon University, O

Lehigh University, M
Marywood University, M
The Pennsylvania State University University Park
   Campus, D
Philadelphia University, M
Robert Morris University, M
Saint Joseph's University, M
Temple University, MD
University of Pennsylvania, MD
The University of Scranton, M
West Chester University of Pennsylvania, M
Wilkes University, M

Puerto Rico

Inter American University of Puerto Rico,
   Metropolitan Campus, M
Inter American University of Puerto Rico, San
   Germán Campus, M
Pontifical Catholic University of Puerto Rico, M
University of Puerto Rico, Mayagüez Campus, M

Rhode Island

Bryant University, MO
Johnson & Wales University, M
University of Rhode Island, M

South Carolina

Charleston Southern University, M

Tennessee

East Tennessee State University, M
Lipscomb University, M
Middle Tennessee State University, MD
Southern Adventist University, M
University of Memphis, MD
The University of Tennessee, MD
Vanderbilt University, D

Texas

Dallas Baptist University, M
St. Edward's University, MO
St. Mary's University of San Antonio, M
Sam Houston State University, M
Tarleton State University, M
Texas A&M International University, M
Texas A&M University, MD
Texas Tech University, MD
University of Dallas, M
University of Houston, MD
University of Houston-Clear Lake, M
University of North Texas, MD
The University of Texas at Arlington, M
The University of Texas at Austin, D
The University of Texas at San Antonio, MD
West Texas A&M University, M

Utah

University of Utah, MD

Virginia

University of Northern Virginia, M
Virginia Commonwealth University, M
Virginia Polytechnic Institute and State
   University, MD
Virginia State University, M

Washington

City University, MO
Seattle University, MO

Wisconsin

Cardinal Stritch University, M
Concordia University Wisconsin, M
University of Wisconsin-Madison, MD

University of Wisconsin-Whitewater, M

Wyoming

University of Wyoming, M

Alberta

University of Alberta, MD
University of Lethbridge, M

British Columbia

The University of British Columbia, D
University of Victoria, M

Ontario

University of Ottawa, O
University of Waterloo, M
The University of Western Ontario, M

Quebec

HEC Montreal, M
McGill University, M
Télé-université, M
Université Laval, M
Université du Québec àMontréal, O
Université du Québec en Outaouais, M
Université du Québec àTrois-Rivières, O
Université de Sherbrooke, M

Saskatchewan

University of Saskatchewan, M

FINANCE AND FINANCIAL MANAGEMENT SERVICES

California

Saint Mary's College of California, B
San Diego State University, B
San Jose State University, B

Colorado

Johnson & Wales University, B

Florida

Florida Agricultural and Mechanical University, B

Illinois

Black Hawk College, A

Massachusetts

Babson College, B
Bristol Community College, A

Michigan

Grace Bible College, B

Missouri

Park University, B

Ohio

The University of Akron, B

Rhode Island

Bryant University, B

Utah

Salt Lake Community College, A

Virginia

Virginia Commonwealth University, B

Wisconsin

Northeast Wisconsin Technical College, A

British Columbia

British Columbia Institute of Technology, A

FINANCIAL ENGINEERING

California

University of California, Berkeley, M

Michigan

University of Michigan, M

New Jersey

Princeton University, MD

New York

Polytechnic University, Brooklyn Campus, M

Ohio

Kent State University, M

Oklahoma

University of Tulsa, M

Quebec

HEC Montreal, M

FINANCIAL PLANNING AND SERVICES

Illinois

Trinity Christian College, B

Kansas

Bethany College, B

Maine

The University of Maine at Augusta, AB

Maryland

Howard Community College, A

Michigan

Central Michigan University, B
Cleary University, B
Northern Michigan University, B
Western Michigan University, B

Minnesota

Minnesota State Community and Technical College-Fergus Falls, A

New York

Broome Community College, A
Medaille College, B

North Dakota

Jamestown College, B

Ohio

The Ohio State University at Lima, B

Pennsylvania

Marywood University, B
Widener University, B

Rhode Island

Roger Williams University, B

Texas

Baylor University, B
Southern Methodist University, B
University of North Texas, B

Utah

Brigham Young University, B

Wisconsin

Waukesha County Technical College, A

British Columbia

British Columbia Institute of Technology, A

FINE ARTS AND ART STUDIES

Alabama

Auburn University, MD
Troy University, M

The University of Alabama, M
University of North Alabama, B

Alaska

University of Alaska Fairbanks, M

Arizona

Arizona State University, M
The University of Arizona, M
Yavapai College, A

Arkansas

Arkansas State University, M
University of Arkansas, M
University of Arkansas at Little Rock, M

California

Academy of Art University, M
Art Center College of Design, BM
California College of the Arts, M
California Institute of the Arts, MO
California State University, Chico, M
California State University, Fresno, M
California State University, Fullerton, MO
California State University, Long Beach, BM
California State University, Los Angeles, M
California State University, Northridge, M
California State University, Sacramento, M
California State University, San Bernardino, M
John F. Kennedy University, M
Mills College, M
Otis College of Art and Design, M
Point Loma Nazarene University, B
Reedley College, A
San Diego State University, M
San Francisco State University, M
San Jose State University, M
Stanford University, MDO
University of California, Berkeley, M
University of California, Davis, M
University of California, Irvine, M
University of California, Los Angeles, BM
University of California, Riverside, M
University of California, San Diego, MD
University of California, Santa Barbara, M
University of California, Santa Cruz, M
University of Southern California, M

Colorado

Adams State College, M
Colorado Northwestern Community College, A
Colorado State University, M
Regis University, M
University of Colorado at Boulder, M
University of Denver, M
University of Northern Colorado, M

Connecticut

University of Connecticut, M
University of Hartford, BM
Western Connecticut State University, M
Yale University, M

Delaware

University of Delaware, M

District of Columbia

The Catholic University of America, B
Howard University, M

Florida

Barry University, MO
Florida International University, M
Florida State University, M
Miami International University of Art & Design, M
University of Central Florida, M
University of Florida, MD
University of Miami, M
University of South Florida, M

Georgia

Georgia Southern University, M
Georgia State University, M
Savannah College of Art and Design, M

University of Georgia, MD

Guam

University of Guam, M

Hawaii

University of Hawaii at Manoa, M

Idaho

Boise State University, M
Idaho State University, M
University of Idaho, M

Illinois

Bradley University, M
Eastern Illinois University, M
Governors State University, M
Illinois State University, M
Loyola University Chicago, B
Northern Illinois University, M
Northwestern University, M
School of the Art Institute of Chicago, BM
Southern Illinois University Carbondale, M
Southern Illinois University Edwardsville, M
University of Chicago, MD
University of Illinois at Chicago, M

Indiana

Ancilla College, A
Ball State University, M
Indiana State University, BM
Indiana University Bloomington, M
Purdue University, M
University of Indianapolis, M
University of Notre Dame, M
University of Saint Francis, BM

Iowa

Drake University, M
The University of Iowa, M
University of Northern Iowa, M

Kansas

Fort Hays State University, M
Kansas State University, M
Pittsburg State University, M
University of Kansas, M
Wichita State University, M

Kentucky

Kentucky Wesleyan College, B
Morehead State University, M
University of Kentucky, M
University of Louisville, M

Louisiana

Louisiana State University and Agricultural and
   Mechanical College, M
Louisiana Tech University, M
Northwestern State University of Louisiana, M
Tulane University, M
University of New Orleans, M

Maine

Maine College of Art, M

Maryland

Maryland Institute College of Art, MO
Salisbury University, B
Towson University, M
University of Maryland, Baltimore County, M
University of Maryland, College Park, M

Massachusetts

Anna Maria College, M
The Art Institute of Boston at Lesley University, M
Boston University, M
Brandeis University, O
Framingham State College, M
Lesley University, M
Massachusetts College of Art, M
Montserrat College of Art, B
School of the Museum of Fine Arts, Boston, BM
Tufts University, MO

University of Massachusetts Amherst, M
University of Massachusetts Dartmouth, BMO

Michigan

Central Michigan University, M
Eastern Michigan University, M
Ferris State University, M
Madonna University, B
Michigan State University, M
Oakland Community College, A
University of Michigan, M
Wayne State University, M

Minnesota

Minneapolis College of Art and Design, MO
Minnesota State University Mankato, M
St. Cloud State University, M
University of Minnesota, Duluth, M
University of Minnesota, Twin Cities Campus, M

Mississippi

Mississippi College, M
Mississippi State University, M
University of Mississippi, M

Missouri

Fontbonne University, M
University of Missouri-Columbia, M
University of Missouri-Kansas City, MD
Washington University in St. Louis, M
Webster University, M

Montana

Montana State University, M
The University of Montana-Missoula, M

Nebraska

University of Nebraska-Lincoln, M

Nevada

University of Nevada, Las Vegas, M

New Jersey

Monmouth University, B
Montclair State University, M
New Jersey City University, M
Rutgers, The State University of New Jersey, New
   Brunswick/Piscataway, M
Rutgers, The State University of New Jersey,
   Newark, B
Seton Hall University, M
William Paterson University of New Jersey, M

New Mexico

New Mexico State University, M
University of New Mexico, M

New York

Adelphi University, BM
Bard College, M
Brooklyn College of the City University of New
   York, MD
City College of the City University of New York, M
The College of New Rochelle, M
College of Staten Island of the City University of
   New York, B
Cornell University, M
Dowling College, B
Hofstra University, M
Hunter College of the City University of New
   York, M
Lehman College of the City University of New
   York, M
Long Island University, Brooklyn Campus, B
Long Island University, C.W. Post Campus, BM
New York University, MDO
Pratt Institute, BMO
Purchase College, State University of New York, M
Queens College of the City University of New
   York, M
Rensselaer Polytechnic Institute, M
Rochester Institute of Technology, M
St. John's University, B
School of Visual Arts, M

Skidmore College, B
State University of New York at Buffalo, M
State University of New York College at
   Brockport, M
State University of New York at New Paltz, M
State University of New York at Oswego, M
Stony Brook University, State University of New
   York, M
Syracuse University, BM
University at Albany, State University of New
   York, M
University of Rochester, MD

North Carolina

East Carolina University, M
The University of North Carolina at Chapel Hill, M
The University of North Carolina at Greensboro, M
Western Carolina University, M

North Dakota

United Tribes Technical College, A
University of North Dakota, M

Ohio

Bowling Green State University, BM
Kent State University, M
Miami University, M
Mount Vernon Nazarene University, B
The Ohio State University, M
Ohio University, M
Union Institute & University, M
The University of Akron, B
University of Cincinnati, M

Oklahoma

Oklahoma City University, M
University of Oklahoma, M
University of Tulsa, M

Oregon

Oregon College of Art & Craft, B
Portland State University, M
University of Oregon, M

Pennsylvania

Allegheny College, B
Carnegie Mellon University, M
Edinboro University of Pennsylvania, M
Indiana University of Pennsylvania, M
Marywood University, M
The Pennsylvania State University University Park
   Campus, M
Saint Francis University, A
Temple University, M
University of Pennsylvania, M
Ursinus College, B
Widener University, B
York College of Pennsylvania, AB

Puerto Rico

Inter American University of Puerto Rico, San
   Germán Campus, M

Rhode Island

Rhode Island College, M
Rhode Island School of Design, B

South Carolina

Clemson University, M
University of South Carolina, M
Winthrop University, M

South Dakota

The University of South Dakota, M

Tennessee

East Tennessee State University, M
Memphis College of Art, BM
University of Memphis, M
The University of Tennessee, M

Vanderbilt University, M

Texas

Abilene Christian University, B
Lamar University, M
Our Lady of the Lake University of San Antonio, B
Sam Houston State University, M
Southern Methodist University, M
Stephen F. Austin State University, M
Sul Ross State University, M
Texas A&M University-Commerce, M
Texas A&M University-Corpus Christi, M
Texas A&M University-Kingsville, M
Texas Christian University, M
Texas Tech University, MD
Texas Woman's University, M
University of Dallas, M
University of Houston, M
University of North Texas, MD
The University of Texas at Austin, M
The University of Texas at El Paso, M
The University of Texas-Pan American, M
The University of Texas at San Antonio, M
The University of Texas at Tyler, M
West Texas A&M University, M

Utah

Brigham Young University, M
Southern Utah University, M
University of Utah, M
Utah State University, M

Vermont

Johnson State College, M

Virginia

Hollins University, M
James Madison University, M
Norfolk State University, M
Old Dominion University, M
Radford University, M
University of Virginia, MD
Virginia Commonwealth University, M

Washington

Central Washington University, M
Cornish College of the Arts, B
University of Washington, M
Washington State University, M

West Virginia

Marshall University, M
West Virginia University, M

Wisconsin

University of Wisconsin-Madison, M
University of Wisconsin-Milwaukee, M
University of Wisconsin-Superior, M

Alberta

University of Alberta, M
University of Calgary, M
University of Lethbridge, M

British Columbia

The University of British Columbia, MDO
University of Victoria, M

Nova Scotia

NSCAD University, M

Ontario

University of Guelph, M
University of Waterloo, M
University of Windsor, M
York University, M

Quebec

Concordia University, M
Université Laval, M
Université du Québec àChicoutimi, M

Université du Québec àMontréal, M

Saskatchewan

University of Regina, BM
University of Saskatchewan, M

FINE/STUDIO ARTS

Alabama

Alabama Southern Community College, A
Auburn University, B
Birmingham-Southern College, B
Spring Hill College, B
Talladega College, B
Troy University, B
The University of Alabama, B
The University of Alabama at Birmingham, B
University of Montevallo, B
University of North Alabama, B

Arizona

The Art Center Design College, B
Grand Canyon University, B
The University of Arizona, B

Arkansas

Harding University, B
Ouachita Baptist University, B
Williams Baptist College, B

California

Academy of Art University, AB
Art Center College of Design, B
Berkeley City College, A
Biola University, B
California College of the Arts, B
California Institute of the Arts, B
California State University, Chico, B
California State University, Dominguez Hills, B
California State University, East Bay, B
California State University, Fullerton, B
California State University, Long Beach, B
California State University, Stanislaus, B
Cerro Coso Community College, A
Chabot College, A
Chapman University, B
Claremont McKenna College, B
Foothill College, A
Humboldt State University, B
La Sierra University, B
Laguna College of Art & Design, B
Loyola Marymount University, B
Mills College, B
Monterey Peninsula College, A
Notre Dame de Namur University, B
Occidental College, B
Otis College of Art and Design, B
Pacific Union College, B
Pitzer College, B
Pomona College, B
San Diego Miramar College, A
San Diego State University, B
San Jose State University, B
Santa Barbara City College, A
Scripps College, B
Skyline College, A
Sonoma State University, B
Stanford University, B
University of California, Davis, B
University of California, Irvine, B
University of California, Riverside, B
University of California, San Diego, B
University of California, Santa Barbara, B
University of the Pacific, B
University of Redlands, B
University of San Francisco, B
University of Southern California, B
Ventura College, A

Colorado

Colorado Christian University, B
The Colorado College, B
Colorado Mountain College, Alpine Campus, A
Colorado State University, B

Naropa University, B
Northeastern Junior College, A
University of Colorado at Boulder, B
University of Colorado at Colorado Springs, B
University of Colorado at Denver and Health
  Sciences Center - Downtown Denver Campus, B
University of Denver, B
University of Northern Colorado, B
Western State College of Colorado, B

Connecticut

Albertus Magnus College, B
Asnuntuck Community College, A
Manchester Community College, A
Middlesex Community College, A
Norwalk Community College, A
Paier College of Art, Inc., B
Southern Connecticut State University, B
Trinity College, B
University of Connecticut, B
University of New Haven, B
Wesleyan University, B

Delaware

Delaware College of Art and Design, A

District of Columbia

American University, B
The Catholic University of America, B
Corcoran College of Art and Design, AB
Gallaudet University, B
The George Washington University, B
Georgetown University, B
University of the District of Columbia, B

Florida

Flagler College, B
Florida International University, B
Florida Southern College, B
Florida State University, B
Jacksonville University, B
Manatee Community College, A
New College of Florida, B
Palm Beach Atlantic University, B
Ringling School of Art and Design, B
Rollins College, B
University of Central Florida, B
University of Florida, B
University of Miami, B
University of North Florida, B
University of West Florida, B

Georgia

Brenau University, B
Emory University, B
Georgia State University, B
Piedmont College, B
Shorter College, B
Wesleyan College, B

Idaho

University of Idaho, B

Illinois

American Academy of Art, B
Augustana College, B
Benedictine University, B
Bradley University, B
Chicago State University, B
Columbia College Chicago, B
DePaul University, B
Governors State University, B
Illinois State University, B
Judson College, B
Kankakee Community College, A
Lake Forest College, B
Lewis University, B
Lincoln College, A
MacMurray College, B
Millikin University, B
Morton College, A
North Park University, B
Northern Illinois University, B
Principia College, B
School of the Art Institute of Chicago, B

South Suburban College, A
Southern Illinois University Carbondale, B
Southern Illinois University Edwardsville, B
Southwestern Illinois College, A
University of Chicago, B
University of Illinois at Chicago, B
Western Illinois University, B

Indiana

Ancilla College, A
Anderson University, B
Ball State University, B
DePauw University, B
Indiana University Bloomington, B
Indiana University-Purdue University Fort Wayne, B
Indiana University-Purdue University Indianapolis, B
Indiana University South Bend, B
Indiana University Southeast, B
Manchester College, AB
Marian College, B
Martin University, B
Saint Joseph's College, B
Saint Mary-of-the-Woods College, B
University of Indianapolis, B
University of Notre Dame, B
Valparaiso University, B

Iowa

Clarke College, B
Coe College, B
Drake University, B
Graceland University, B
Grand View College, B
Iowa Lakes Community College, A
Iowa Wesleyan College, B
Loras College, B
Maharishi University of Management, B
Morningside College, B
St. Ambrose University, B
The University of Iowa, B
University of Northern Iowa, B

Kansas

Baker University, B
Bethel College, B
Garden City Community College, A
Pratt Community College, A
University of Kansas, B

Kentucky

Asbury College, B
Berea College, B
Eastern Kentucky University, B
Georgetown College, B
Kentucky State University, B
Morehead State University, B
Murray State University, B
Northern Kentucky University, B
Thomas More College, A
Transylvania University, B
University of the Cumberlands, B
University of Kentucky, B
University of Louisville, B
Western Kentucky University, B

Louisiana

Centenary College of Louisiana, B
Delgado Community College, A
Louisiana College, B
Louisiana State University and Agricultural and
    Mechanical College, B
Northwestern State University of Louisiana, B
Southern University and Agricultural and Mechanical
    College, B
Tulane University, B
University of New Orleans, B

Maine

Bowdoin College, B
Colby College, B
University of Maine, B
The University of Maine at Augusta, AB

University of Maine at Presque Isle, B

Maryland

Maryland Institute College of Art, B

Massachusetts

Amherst College, B
Anna Maria College, B
The Art Institute of Boston at Lesley University, B
Boston College, B
Brandeis University, B
Bridgewater State College, B
Bristol Community College, A
Clark University, B
College of the Holy Cross, B
Emmanuel College, B
Endicott College, B
Framingham State College, B
Hampshire College, B
Harvard University, B
Holyoke Community College, A
Massachusetts College of Art, B
Massasoit Community College, A
Merrimack College, B
Montserrat College of Art, B
Mount Holyoke College, B
Mount Wachusett Community College, A
Pine Manor College, AB
School of the Museum of Fine Arts, Boston, B
Simon's Rock College of Bard, B
Smith College, B
Springfield Technical Community College, A
Stonehill College, B
University of Massachusetts Amherst, B
University of Massachusetts Lowell, B
Wellesley College, B
Wheaton College, B
Williams College, B

Michigan

Alma College, B
Aquinas College, B
Calvin College, B
Ferris State University, B
Finlandia University, B
Grand Valley State University, B
Hope College, B
Lansing Community College, A
Marygrove College, B
Olivet College, B
Saginaw Valley State University, B
University of Michigan-Flint, B

Minnesota

Augsburg College, B
Bemidji State University, B
Carleton College, B
College of Saint Benedict, B
College of St. Catherine, B
College of Visual Arts, B
Concordia College, B
Concordia University, St. Paul, B
Hamline University, B
Macalester College, B
Minneapolis College of Art and Design, B
Minnesota State University Mankato, B
Minnesota State University Moorhead, B
North Hennepin Community College, A
Northwestern College, B
St. Cloud State University, B
Saint John's University, B
Saint Mary's University of Minnesota, B
Southwest Minnesota State University, B
University of Minnesota, Duluth, B
University of Minnesota, Morris, B
Winona State University, B

Mississippi

William Carey College, B

Missouri

Central Missouri State University, B
College of the Ozarks, B
Drury University, B
Fontbonne University, B

Lincoln University, B
Lindenwood University, B
Maryville University of Saint Louis, B
Missouri State University, B
Northwest Missouri State University, B
Park University, B
Saint Louis University, B
Truman State University, B
University of Missouri-Kansas City, B
University of Missouri-St. Louis, B
Washington University in St. Louis, B
Webster University, B
William Woods University, B

Montana

Montana State University, B
University of.Great Falls, B

Nebraska

Concordia University, B
Union College, B
University of Nebraska-Lincoln, B
University of Nebraska at Omaha, B

Nevada

Sierra Nevada College, B

New Hampshire

Chester College of New England, B
Colby-Sawyer College, B
Dartmouth College, B
Franklin Pierce College, B
Keene State College, B
New England College, B
New Hampshire Institute of Art, B
Plymouth State University, B
Rivier College, B
University of New Hampshire, B
University of New Hampshire at Manchester, A

New Jersey

Atlantic Cape Community College, A
Bloomfield College, B
The College of New Jersey, B
Cumberland County College, A
Felician College, B
Georgian Court University, B
Gloucester County College, A
Kean University, B
Middlesex County College, A
Montclair State University, B
Ramapo College of New Jersey, B
Rider University, B
Rowan University, B
Saint Peter's College, B
Sussex County Community College, A
Warren County Community College, A
William Paterson University of New Jersey, B

New Mexico

Clovis Community College, A
College of Santa Fe, B
Institute of American Indian Arts, A
New Mexico State University, B
Northern New Mexico Community College, A
University of New Mexico-Los Alamos Branch, A

New York

Alfred University, B
Bard College, B
Brooklyn College of the City University of New
    York, B
Buffalo State College, State University of New
    York, B
Canisius College, B
Cazenovia College, B
The College of New Rochelle, B
The College of Saint Rose, B
Cooper Union for the Advancement of Science and
    Art, B
Cornell University, B
Daemen College, B
Dowling College, B
Elmira College, B
Fashion Institute of Technology, AB

Finger Lakes Community College, A
Fiorello H. LaGuardia Community College of the
City University of New York, A
Fordham University, B
Fulton-Montgomery Community College, A
Hamilton College, B
Herkimer County Community College, A
Hobart and William Smith Colleges, B
Hofstra University, B
Hudson Valley Community College, A
Hunter College of the City University of New York, B
Ithaca College, B
Jamestown Community College, A
Long Island University, C.W. Post Campus, B
Manhattanville College, B
Marist College, B
Marymount Manhattan College, B
Nazareth College of Rochester, B
New York Institute of Technology, B
New York University, B
Niagara County Community College, A
Pace University, A
Pratt Institute, AB
Queens College of the City University of New
York, B
Queensborough Community College of the City
University of New York, A
Roberts Wesleyan College, B
Rochester Institute of Technology, AB
Rockland Community College, A
Sage College of Albany, A
St. John's University, B
St. Lawrence University, B
St. Thomas Aquinas College, B
Sarah Lawrence College, B
School of Visual Arts, B
Siena College, B
State University of New York at Binghamton, B
State University of New York at Buffalo, B
State University of New York College at
Brockport, B
State University of New York College at Cortland, B
State University of New York College at Geneseo, B
State University of New York College at Oneonta, B
State University of New York, Fredonia, B
State University of New York at New Paltz, B
State University of New York at Plattsburgh, B
Stony Brook University, State University of New
York, B
Syracuse University, B
Union College, B
University of Rochester, B
Vassar College, B
Villa Maria College of Buffalo, A
Wells College, B
Westchester Community College, A

North Carolina

Appalachian State University, B
Barton College, B
Campbell University, B
Chowan University, B
East Carolina University, B
Elizabeth City State University, B
Gardner-Webb University, B
High Point University, B
Mars Hill College, B
Meredith College, B
North Carolina Central University, B
Queens University of Charlotte, B
Randolph Community College, A
St. Andrews Presbyterian College, B
Salem College, B
Sandhills Community College, A
The University of North Carolina at Asheville, B
The University of North Carolina at Chapel Hill, B
The University of North Carolina at Charlotte, B
The University of North Carolina at Greensboro, B
The University of North Carolina at Pembroke, B
The University of North Carolina Wilmington, B
Wake Forest University, B
Western Carolina University, B

Wingate University, B

North Dakota

Jamestown College, B

Ohio

Art Academy of Cincinnati, B
Ashland University, B
Baldwin-Wallace College, B
Bowling Green State University, B
Capital University, B
Cedarville University, B
College of Mount St. Joseph, B
The College of Wooster, B
Columbus College of Art & Design, B
Denison University, B
Hiram College, B
Kent State University, B
Kenyon College, B
Lake Erie College, B
Malone College, B
Marietta College, B
Miami University, B
Notre Dame College, B
Oberlin College, B
Ohio Dominican University, B
Ohio Northern University, B
The Ohio State University, B
Ohio University, B
Ohio Wesleyan University, B
Shawnee State University, B
Sinclair Community College, A
The University of Akron, B
University of Dayton, B
The University of Toledo, B
Ursuline College, B
Wilberforce University, B
Xavier University, B
Youngstown State University, B

Oklahoma

Northeastern State University, B
Oklahoma Baptist University, B
Oklahoma City Community College, A
Oklahoma City University, B
Oral Roberts University, B
St. Gregory's University, AB
University of Oklahoma, B
University of Science and Arts of Oklahoma, B
University of Tulsa, B

Oregon

George Fox University, B
Pacific Northwest College of Art, B
Reed College, B
University of Oregon, B
Willamette University, B

Pennsylvania

Allegheny College, B
Arcadia University, B
Bloomsburg University of Pennsylvania, B
Bucknell University, B
Cabrini College, B
Cedar Crest College, B
Chatham College, B
Dickinson College, B
Duquesne University, B
Edinboro University of Pennsylvania, B
Franklin and Marshall College, B
Gettysburg College, B
Juniata College, B
Keystone College, B
Kutztown University of Pennsylvania, B
Lafayette College, B
Lebanon Valley College, B
Lycoming College, B
Marywood University, B
Mercyhurst College, B
Messiah College, B
Moore College of Art & Design, B
Moravian College, B
Northampton County Area Community College, A
Pennsylvania College of Art & Design, B
Rosemont College, B

Saint Vincent College, B
Seton Hill University, B
Swarthmore College, B
University of Pennsylvania, B
University of Pittsburgh, B
West Chester University of Pennsylvania, B

Rhode Island

Brown University, B
Providence College, B
Rhode Island College, B
Salve Regina University, B

South Carolina

Anderson University, B
Coastal Carolina University, B
Coker College, B
College of Charleston, B
Columbia College, B
Converse College, B
Furman University, B
Limestone College, B
University of South Carolina, B
University of South Carolina Aiken, B

Tennessee

Belmont University, B
Cumberland University, B
Lambuth University, B
Lipscomb University, B
Maryville College, B
Memphis College of Art, B
Milligan College, B
Rhodes College, B
Sewanee: The University of the South, B
The University of Tennessee, B
The University of Tennessee at Chattanooga, B
Watkins College of Art and Design, B

Texas

Abilene Christian University, B
Amarillo College, A
Angelo State University, B
Baylor University, B
Brazosport College, A
Coastal Bend College, A
College of the Mainland, A
Del Mar College, A
Hardin-Simmons University, B
Houston Baptist University, B
Howard Payne University, B
Lamar University, B
Lon Morris College, A
Midland College, A
Rice University, B
Sam Houston State University, B
Southern Methodist University, B
Southwestern University, B
Tarleton State University, B
Texas A&M University-Corpus Christi, B
Texas Christian University, B
Texas Southern University, B
Texas State University-San Marcos, B
Texas Tech University, B
University of Dallas, B
University of Houston, B
University of Mary Hardin-Baylor, B
University of St. Thomas, B
The University of Texas at Arlington, B
The University of Texas at Austin, B
The University of Texas at El Paso, B
The University of Texas-Pan American, B
West Texas A&M University, B

Utah

Brigham Young University, B

Vermont

Bennington College, B
Green Mountain College, B
Johnson State College, B
Marlboro College, B
Middlebury College, B

University of Vermont, B

Virginia

Bridgewater College, B
Christopher Newport University, B
Ferrum College, B
George Mason University, B
Hampden-Sydney College, B
Longwood University, B
Marymount University, B
Old Dominion University, B
Randolph-Macon College, B
Randolph-Macon Woman's College, B
Sweet Briar College, B
Tidewater Community College, A
University of Mary Washington, B
University of Richmond, B
Washington and Lee University, B

Washington

Cornish College of the Arts, B
Eastern Washington University, B
The Evergreen State College, B
Pacific Lutheran University, B
Seattle University, B
Tacoma Community College, A
Washington State University, B
Western Washington University, B
Whitworth College, B

West Virginia

Bethany College, B
West Virginia Wesleyan College, B

Wisconsin

Beloit College, B
Cardinal Stritch University, B
Carroll College, B
Carthage College, B
Lawrence University, B
Marian College of Fond du Lac, B
Milwaukee Institute of Art and Design, B
Northland College, B
University of Wisconsin-Milwaukee, B
University of Wisconsin-Oshkosh, B
University of Wisconsin-Stevens Point, B
University of Wisconsin-Superior, B
Viterbo University, B

Alberta

Alberta College of Art & Design, B
University of Alberta, B

British Columbia

Open Learning Agency, B
Thompson Rivers University, B
The University of British Columbia, B
University of Victoria, B

New Brunswick

Mount Allison University, B
Université de Moncton, B

Nova Scotia

Mount Saint Vincent University, B
NSCAD University, B

Ontario

Brock University, B
University of Guelph, B
University of Ottawa, B
University of Toronto, B
University of Waterloo, B
The University of Western Ontario, B
University of Windsor, B
York University, B

Quebec

Bishop's University, B
Concordia University, B
Université Laval, B

Université du Québec en Outaouais, B

Saskatchewan

University of Saskatchewan, B

FIRE PROTECTION

Connecticut

University of New Haven, B

New Jersey

Sussex County Community College, A

North Carolina

Fayetteville Technical Community College, A

Ohio

The University of Akron, B

Oklahoma

Western Oklahoma State College, A

FIRE PROTECTION AND SAFETY TECHNOLOGY/TECHNICIAN

Alabama

Columbia Southern University, B

California

Antelope Valley College, A
Victor Valley College, A

Colorado

Pikes Peak Community College, A

Connecticut

Capital Community College, A
University of New Haven, AB

Florida

Florida Community College at Jacksonville, A
St. Petersburg College, AB

Illinois

College of Lake County, A
Elgin Community College, A
John Wood Community College, A
Lincoln Land Community College, A
Moraine Valley Community College, A
Waubonsee Community College, A

Kentucky

Eastern Kentucky University, AB

Louisiana

Delgado Community College, A

Maryland

College of Southern Maryland, A
Montgomery College, A

Massachusetts

Bunker Hill Community College, A

Michigan

Kellogg Community College, A
Macomb Community College, A
Mott Community College, A

Missouri

Jefferson College, A

Montana

Montana State University-Billings, A

Nebraska

University of Nebraska-Lincoln, A

Nevada

Western Nevada Community College, A

New Jersey

Ocean County College, A
Union County College, A

New Mexico

Central New Mexico Community College, A
San Juan College, A

North Carolina

Catawba Valley Community College, A
Cleveland Community College, A
Fayetteville Technical Community College, A

Ohio

Owens Community College, A
The University of Akron, A
University of Cincinnati, B
The University of Toledo, A

Oklahoma

Oklahoma State University, B
Tulsa Community College, A

Pennsylvania

Community College of Allegheny County, A
Delaware County Community College, A
Montgomery County Community College, A

Texas

College of the Mainland, A
Collin County Community College District, A
Del Mar College, A

Virginia

Jefferson College of Health Sciences, A

Wisconsin

Waukesha County Technical College, A
Western Technical College, A

British Columbia

British Columbia Institute of Technology, A

FIRE PROTECTION ENGINEERING

Connecticut

University of New Haven, M

Maryland

University of Maryland, College Park, M

Massachusetts

Anna Maria College, M
Worcester Polytechnic Institute, MDO

Missouri

Central Missouri State University, M

Oklahoma

Oklahoma State University, M

FIRE SCIENCE/FIREFIGHTING

Alabama

Alabama Southern Community College, A
Chattahoochee Valley Community College, A
Community College of the Air Force, A
George Corley Wallace State Community College, A
Lawson State Community College, A
Northwest-Shoals Community College, A
Wallace State Community College, A

Alaska

University of Alaska Anchorage, A
University of Alaska Anchorage, Matanuska-Susitna College, A

University of Alaska Fairbanks, A

Arizona

Arizona Western College, A
Cochise College (Douglas), A
Cochise College (Sierra Vista), A
Coconino Community College, A
Glendale Community College, A
Mesa Community College, A
Mohave Community College, A
Northland Pioneer College, A
Phoenix College, A
Pima Community College, A
Scottsdale Community College, A
Yavapai College, A

Arkansas

Black River Technical College, A
National Park Community College, A
Southern Arkansas University Tech, A

California

Allan Hancock College, A
American River College, A
Bakersfield College, A
Butte College, A
Cabrillo College, A
Cerro Coso Community College, A
Chabot College, A
City College of San Francisco, A
Cogswell Polytechnical College, B
College of the Desert, A
College of Marin, A
College of San Mateo, A
College of the Sequoias, A
College of the Siskiyous, A
Columbia College, A
Compton Community College, A
Cosumnes River College (Sacramento), A
Crafton Hills College, A
East Los Angeles College, A
El Camino College, A
Fresno City College, A
Glendale Community College, A
Hartnell College, A
Imperial Valley College, A
Lake Tahoe Community College, A
Las Positas College, A
Long Beach City College, A
Los Angeles Harbor College, A
Los Angeles Valley College, A
Los Medanos College, A
Merced College, A
Mission College, A
Modesto Junior College, A
Monterey Peninsula College, A
Mt. San Antonio College, A
Mt. San Jacinto College, A
Oxnard College, A
Palomar College, A
Pasadena City College, A
Porterville College, A
Riverside Community College District, A
San Diego Miramar College, A
San Joaquin Delta College, A
Santa Ana College, A
Santa Monica College, A
Santa Rosa Junior College, A
Shasta College, A
Sierra College, A
Solano Community College, A
Southwestern College, A
Victor Valley College, A
Yuba College, A

Colorado

Aims Community College, A
Colorado Northwestern Community College, A
Red Rocks Community College, A

Connecticut

Gateway Community College, A
Naugatuck Valley Community College, A
Norwalk Community College, A

Three Rivers Community College, A

Delaware

Delaware Technical & Community College,
Stanton/Wilmington Campus, A

District of Columbia

University of the District of Columbia, AB

Florida

Brevard Community College, A
Broward Community College, A
Central Florida Community College, A
Daytona Beach Community College, A
Edison College, A
Florida Community College at Jacksonville, A
Gulf Coast Community College, A
Hillsborough Community College, A
Indian River Community College, A
Keiser College (Fort Lauderdale), A
Lake-Sumter Community College, A
Manatee Community College, A
Miami Dade College, A
Palm Beach Community College, A
Pensacola Junior College, A
Polk Community College, A
St. Johns River Community College, A
St. Petersburg College, A
Santa Fe Community College, A
Seminole Community College, A
University of Florida, B
Valencia Community College, A

Georgia

Augusta Technical College, A
Chattahoochee Technical College, A
Coosa Valley Technical College, A
Georgia Military College, A
Georgia Perimeter College, A
Lanier Technical College, A
Savannah Technical College, A
Valdosta Technical College, A
West Georgia Technical College, A

Guam

Guam Community College, A

Hawaii

Hawaii Community College, A
Honolulu Community College, A
Maui Community College, A

Idaho

Idaho State University, A
Lewis-Clark State College, AB

Illinois

City Colleges of Chicago, Harold Washington
College, A
City Colleges of Chicago, Richard J. Daley
College, A
College of DuPage, A
Elgin Community College, A
Illinois Central College, A
Joliet Junior College, A
Lewis and Clark Community College, A
McHenry County College, A
Oakton Community College, A
Prairie State College, A
Richland Community College, A
Rock Valley College, A
South Suburban College, A
Southeastern Illinois College, A
Southwestern Illinois College, A
Triton College, A
William Rainey Harper College, A

Indiana

Vincennes University, A

Iowa

Des Moines Area Community College, A
Hawkeye Community College, A
Iowa Western Community College, A

Kirkwood Community College, A

Kansas

Barton County Community College, A
Butler Community College, A
Dodge City Community College, A
Hutchinson Community College and Area Vocational
School, A
Kansas City Kansas Community College, A
Labette Community College, A

Louisiana

Louisiana State University at Eunice, A

Maine

Southern Maine Community College, A

Maryland

Frederick Community College, A
University of Maryland University College, B

Massachusetts

Anna Maria College, B
Berkshire Community College, A
Bristol Community College, A
Cape Cod Community College, A
Greenfield Community College, A
Massasoit Community College, A
Middlesex Community College, A
Mount Wachusett Community College, A
North Shore Community College, A
Quincy College, A
Quinsigamond Community College, A
Springfield Technical Community College, A

Michigan

Delta College, A
Henry Ford Community College, A
Kalamazoo Valley Community College, A
Lake Superior State University, AB
Lansing Community College, A
Madonna University, AB
Mid Michigan Community College, A
Oakland Community College, A
St. Clair County Community College, A
Schoolcraft College, A

Minnesota

Hennepin Technical College, A

Mississippi

East Mississippi Community College, A
Jackson State University, B
Meridian Community College, A

Missouri

Blue River Community College, A
Crowder College, A
East Central College, A
Mineral Area College, A
Missouri State University-West Plains, A
Ozarks Technical Community College, A
St. Louis Community College at Florissant Valley, A
St. Louis Community College at Forest Park, A

Montana

Miles Community College, A
Montana State University-Great Falls College of
Technology, A
The University of Montana-Helena College of
Technology, A

Nebraska

Mid-Plains Community College, A
Southeast Community College, Lincoln Campus, A

Nevada

Community College of Southern Nevada, A
Truckee Meadows Community College, A

New Jersey

Burlington County College, A
Camden County College, A
Essex County College, A

Mercer County Community College, A
Middlesex County College, A
Passaic County Community College, A

New Mexico

Doña Ana Branch Community College, A
Eastern New Mexico University-Roswell, A
New Mexico Junior College, A
New Mexico State University-Alamogordo, A
New Mexico State University-Carlsbad, A

New York

Broome Community College, A
Corning Community College, A
John Jay College of Criminal Justice of the City
    University of New York, B
Monroe Community College, A
Onondaga Community College, A
Rockland Community College, A
Schenectady County Community College, A

North Carolina

Central Piedmont Community College, A
Coastal Carolina Community College, A
Davidson County Community College, A
Durham Technical Community College, A
Gaston College, A
Guilford Technical Community College, A
Lenoir Community College, A
Wilson Technical Community College, A

Ohio

Cincinnati State Technical and Community
    College, A
Cuyahoga Community College, A
Hocking College, A
Lakeland Community College, A
Lorain County Community College, A
Sinclair Community College, A
Stark State College of Technology, A
University of Cincinnati, A

Oklahoma

Oklahoma State University, Oklahoma City, A
Tulsa Community College, A

Oregon

Central Oregon Community College, A
Chemeketa Community College, A
Clatsop Community College, A
Eastern Oregon University, B
Mt. Hood Community College, A
Portland Community College, A
Rogue Community College, A
Southwestern Oregon Community College, A
Umpqua Community College, A

Pennsylvania

Community College of Philadelphia, A
Harrisburg Area Community College, A
Holy Family University, B
Luzerne County Community College, A
Westmoreland County Community College, A

Rhode Island

Community College of Rhode Island, A

South Carolina

Greenville Technical College, A

Tennessee

Chattanooga State Technical Community College, A
Southwest Tennessee Community College, A
Volunteer State Community College, A

Texas

Amarillo College, A
Austin Community College, A
Blinn College, A
Cisco Junior College, A
Del Mar College, A
El Paso Community College, A
Frank Phillips College, A
Hill College of the Hill Junior College District, A

Houston Community College System, A
Kilgore College, A
Lamar University, A
Laredo Community College, A
Midland College, A
Navarro College, A
Odessa College, A
San Antonio College, A
South Plains College, A
Tarrant County College District, A
Texas Southmost College, A
Tyler Junior College, A
Weatherford College, A

Utah

Utah Valley State College, A

Virginia

Hampton University, B
J. Sargeant Reynolds Community College, A
Northern Virginia Community College, A
Thomas Nelson Community College, A

Washington

Bates Technical College, A
Bellevue Community College, A
Columbia Basin College, A
Everett Community College, A
Lower Columbia College, A
Olympic College, A
Pierce College, A
Skagit Valley College, A
South Puget Sound Community College, A
Spokane Community College, A
Wenatchee Valley College, A
Yakima Valley Community College, A

West Virginia

Community and Technical College of Shepherd, A
Mountain State University, A

Wisconsin

Blackhawk Technical College, A
Chippewa Valley Technical College, A
Fox Valley Technical College, A
Gateway Technical College, A
Madison Area Technical College, A
Milwaukee Area Technical College, A
Northeast Wisconsin Technical College, A

Wyoming

Casper College, A

New Brunswick

University of New Brunswick Fredericton, B

FIRE SERVICES ADMINISTRATION

Alabama

Calhoun Community College, A
Columbia Southern University, B
Jefferson State Community College, A

California

California State University, Los Angeles, B

Colorado

Community College of Aurora, A

Connecticut

Capital Community College, A

Illinois

Black Hawk College, A
Southern Illinois University Carbondale, B

Iowa

North Iowa Area Community College, A

Kansas

Johnson County Community College, A

Michigan

Concordia University, B

Minnesota

Lake Superior College, A
Minnesota State Community and Technical
    College-Fergus Falls, A

New York

Erie Community College, South Campus, A
John Jay College of Criminal Justice of the City
    University of New York, B

Oregon

Western Oregon University, B

Pennsylvania

Northampton County Area Community College, A

Texas

Midland College, A

Utah

Utah Valley State College, B

Washington

Edmonds Community College, A
Lower Columbia College, A
Olympic College, A
Walla Walla Community College, A

Wisconsin

Northeast Wisconsin Technical College, A

FISH, GAME AND WILDLIFE MANAGEMENT

Alabama

Auburn University, MD

Alaska

University of Alaska Fairbanks, MD

Arizona

The University of Arizona, MD

Arkansas

Arkansas Tech University, M

Colorado

Colorado State University, MD

Florida

University of Florida, MD
University of Miami, MD

Idaho

University of Idaho, MD

Indiana

Purdue University, MD

Louisiana

Louisiana State University and Agricultural and
    Mechanical College, MD

Maine

University of Maine, MD

Maryland

Frostburg State University, M

Massachusetts

University of Massachusetts Amherst, MD

Michigan

Michigan State University, MD

Minnesota

University of Minnesota, Twin Cities Campus, MD

Mississippi

Mississippi State University, M

Missouri

University of Missouri-Columbia, MD

Montana

Montana State University, M
The University of Montana-Missoula, MD

New Hampshire

University of New Hampshire, M

New Mexico

New Mexico State University, M

New York

Cornell University, MD
State University of New York College of
  Environmental Science and Forestry, MD

North Carolina

North Carolina State University, M

North Dakota

University of North Dakota, MD

Oregon

Oregon State University, MD

Pennsylvania

The Pennsylvania State University University Park
  Campus, MD

Rhode Island

University of Rhode Island, MD

South Carolina

Clemson University, MD

South Dakota

South Dakota State University, MD

Tennessee

Tennessee Technological University, M
The University of Tennessee, M

Texas

Sul Ross State University, M
Texas A&M University, MD
Texas A&M University-Kingsville, MD
Texas State University-San Marcos, M
Texas Tech University, MD

Utah

Brigham Young University, MD
Utah State University, MD

Virginia

Virginia Polytechnic Institute and State
  University, MD

Washington

University of Washington, MD

West Virginia

West Virginia University, M

Newfoundland and Labrador

Memorial University of Newfoundland, M

Quebec

McGill University, MD
Université du Québec àRimouski, MO

FISHING AND FISHERIES SCIENCES AND MANAGEMENT

Alaska

University of Alaska Fairbanks, B

California

Humboldt State University, B
Santa Rosa Junior College, A

Colorado

Colorado State University, B

Georgia

University of Georgia, B

Iowa

Iowa Lakes Community College, A

Kentucky

Murray State University, B

Maine

Unity College, B

Missouri

University of Missouri-Columbia, B

New York

State University of New York College of Agriculture
  and Technology at Cobleskill, B
State University of New York College of
  Environmental Science and Forestry, B

North Carolina

Brunswick Community College, A
North Carolina State University, B

Ohio

Hocking College, A
The Ohio State University, B

Oregon

Oregon State University, B

Pennsylvania

Mansfield University of Pennsylvania, B

Rhode Island

University of Rhode Island, B

South Carolina

Clemson University, B

Tennessee

The University of Tennessee at Martin, B

Texas

Texas A&M University, B
Texas Tech University, B

Vermont

Sterling College, AB

Washington

Peninsula College, A
University of Washington, B

British Columbia

Malaspina University-College, B
University of Northern British Columbia, B

FLIGHT INSTRUCTOR

Iowa

Iowa Lakes Community College, A

FLORICULTURE/FLORISTRY OPERATIONS AND MANAGEMENT

California

Santa Rosa Junior College, A

New York

Cornell University, B

Ohio

The Ohio State University Agricultural Technical
  Institute, A

Puerto Rico

Inter American University of Puerto Rico,
  Barranquitas Campus, A

FLUID AND THERMAL SCIENCES

Massachusetts

Harvard University, B
Worcester Polytechnic Institute, B

FOLKLORE

California

University of California, Berkeley, M

District of Columbia

The George Washington University, M

Indiana

Indiana University Bloomington, MD

Kentucky

Western Kentucky University, M

North Carolina

The University of North Carolina at Chapel Hill, M

Oregon

University of Oregon, M

Pennsylvania

University of Pennsylvania, MD

Texas

The University of Texas at Austin, MD

Utah

Utah State University, M

Alberta

University of Alberta, MD

Newfoundland and Labrador

Memorial University of Newfoundland, MD

FOOD ENGINEERING

Illinois

Illinois Institute of Technology, M

Kansas

Kansas State University, MD

Ohio

The Ohio State University, MD

Oklahoma

Oklahoma State University, MD

Quebec

McGill University, MD

FOOD PREPARATION/PROFESSIONAL COOKING/KITCHEN ASSISTANT

Illinois

Lexington College, AB

Iowa

Iowa Lakes Community College, A

Pennsylvania

The Art Institute of Pittsburgh, AB
Keystone College, A
Northampton County Area Community College, A

FOOD SCIENCE

Alabama

Alabama Agricultural and Mechanical University, B
Auburn University, B
Tuskegee University, B

Arkansas

University of Arkansas, B

California

Cabrillo College, A
California Polytechnic State University, San Luis Obispo, B
Los Angeles City College, A
Modesto Junior College, A
Ohlone College, A
Orange Coast College, A
Saddleback College, A
San Jose State University, B
University of California, Davis, B

Delaware

University of Delaware, B

District of Columbia

University of the District of Columbia, B

Florida

Miami Dade College, A
University of Florida, B

Georgia

Macon State College, A
University of Georgia, B

Idaho

University of Idaho, B

Illinois

Dominican University, B
Olivet Nazarene University, B
University of Illinois at Urbana-Champaign, B

Indiana

Purdue University, B
Vincennes University, A

Iowa

Hawkeye Community College, A

Kansas

Highland Community College, A
Kansas State University, B

Kentucky

University of Kentucky, B

Louisiana

Louisiana State University and Agricultural and Mechanical College, B

Maine

University of Maine, B

Maryland

University of Maryland, College Park, B

Massachusetts

Framingham State College, B
Greenfield Community College, A
University of Massachusetts Amherst, B

Michigan

Michigan State University, B

Mississippi

Mississippi State University, B
Northeast Mississippi Community College, A

Missouri

Northwest Missouri State University, B
St. Louis Community College at Florissant Valley, A
University of Missouri-Columbia, B

Nebraska

University of Nebraska-Lincoln, B

New Jersey

Rutgers, The State University of New Jersey, New Brunswick/Piscataway, B

New York

Cornell University, B

North Carolina

Central Piedmont Community College, A
North Carolina Agricultural and Technical State University, B
North Carolina State University, B

North Dakota

North Dakota State University, B

Ohio

Hocking College, A
The Ohio State University, B
The University of Akron, B

Oregon

Mt. Hood Community College, A
Oregon State University, B

Pennsylvania

Delaware Valley College, B
The Pennsylvania State University Abington College, B
The Pennsylvania State University Altoona College, B
The Pennsylvania State University Beaver Campus of the Commonwealth College, B
The Pennsylvania State University Berks Campus of the Berks-Lehigh Valley College, B
The Pennsylvania State University Delaware County Campus of the Commonwealth College, B
The Pennsylvania State University DuBois Campus of the Commonwealth College, B
The Pennsylvania State University at Erie, The Behrend College, B
The Pennsylvania State University Fayette Campus of the Commonwealth College, B
The Pennsylvania State University Hazleton Campus of the Commonwealth College, B
The Pennsylvania State University, Lehigh Valley Campus of the Berks-Lehigh Valley College, B
The Pennsylvania State University McKeesport Campus of the Commonwealth College, B
The Pennsylvania State University Mont Alto Campus of the Commonwealth College, B
The Pennsylvania State University New Kensington Campus of the Commonwealth College, B
The Pennsylvania State University Schuylkill Campus of the Capital College, B
The Pennsylvania State University Shenango Campus of the Commonwealth College, B
The Pennsylvania State University University Park Campus, B
The Pennsylvania State University Wilkes-Barre Campus of the Commonwealth College, B

The Pennsylvania State University Worthington Scranton Campus of the Commonwealth College, B
The Pennsylvania State University York Campus of the Commonwealth College, B

Puerto Rico

University of Puerto Rico at Utuado, A

South Carolina

Clemson University, B

South Dakota

South Dakota State University, B

Tennessee

The University of Tennessee, B

Texas

El Centro College, A
Lamar University, AB
Texas A&M University, B
Texas A&M University-Kingsville, B
Texas Tech University, B

Utah

Brigham Young University, B
University of Utah, B

Virginia

Virginia Polytechnic Institute and State University, B

Washington

South Seattle Community College, A
Washington State University, B

Wisconsin

University of Wisconsin-Madison, B
University of Wisconsin-River Falls, B

Alberta

University of Alberta, B

British Columbia

The University of British Columbia, B

Manitoba

University of Manitoba, B

Newfoundland and Labrador

Memorial University of Newfoundland, B

Nova Scotia

Acadia University, B
Dalhousie University, B

Ontario

University of Guelph, B

Quebec

McGill University, B
Université Laval, B

Saskatchewan

University of Saskatchewan, B

FOOD SCIENCE AND TECHNOLOGY

Alabama

Alabama Agricultural and Mechanical University, MD
Auburn University, MD
Tuskegee University, M

Arkansas

University of Arkansas, MD

California

California State Polytechnic University, Pomona, M
California State University, Fresno, M
Chapman University, M

University of California, Davis, MD

Colorado

Colorado State University, MD

Delaware

University of Delaware, MD

Florida

Florida Agricultural and Mechanical University, M
Florida State University, MD
University of Florida, MD

Georgia

University of Georgia, MD

Hawaii

University of Hawaii at Manoa, M

Idaho

University of Idaho, M

Illinois

Illinois Institute of Technology, M
University of Illinois at Urbana-Champaign, MDO

Indiana

Purdue University, MD

Iowa

Iowa State University of Science and
Technology, MD

Kansas

Kansas State University, MD

Louisiana

Louisiana State University and Agricultural and
Mechanical College, MD

Maine

University of Maine, MD

Maryland

University of Maryland, College Park, MD
University of Maryland Eastern Shore, MD

Massachusetts

Framingham State College, BM
University of Massachusetts Amherst, MD

Michigan

Michigan State University, MD
Wayne State University, MD

Minnesota

University of Minnesota, Twin Cities Campus, MD

Mississippi

Mississippi State University, MD
University of Southern Mississippi, MD

Missouri

University of Missouri-Columbia, MD

Nebraska

University of Nebraska-Lincoln, MD

New Jersey

Rutgers, The State University of New Jersey, New
Brunswick/Piscataway, MD

New York

Cornell University, MD

North Carolina

North Carolina State University, MD

North Dakota

North Dakota State University, MD

Ohio

The Ohio State University, MD
The University of Akron, M

Oklahoma

Oklahoma State University, MD

Oregon

Oregon State University, MD

Pennsylvania

Drexel University, MD
Marywood University, M
The Pennsylvania State University University Park
Campus, MD

Puerto Rico

University of Puerto Rico, Mayagüez Campus, M

Rhode Island

University of Rhode Island, MD

South Carolina

Clemson University, MD

Tennessee

The University of Tennessee, MD
The University of Tennessee at Martin, M

Texas

Texas A&M University, MD
Texas Tech University, MD
Texas Woman's University, MD

Utah

Brigham Young University, M
Utah State University, MD

Virginia

Virginia Polytechnic Institute and State
University, MD

Washington

Washington State University, MD

West Virginia

West Virginia University, MD

Wisconsin

University of Wisconsin-Madison, MD
University of Wisconsin-Stout, M

Wyoming

University of Wyoming, M

British Columbia

The University of British Columbia, BMD

Manitoba

University of Manitoba, M

New Brunswick

Université de Moncton, M

Newfoundland and Labrador

Memorial University of Newfoundland, MD

Nova Scotia

Dalhousie University, MD

Ontario

University of Guelph, MD

Quebec

McGill University, MD
Université Laval, MD

Saskatchewan

University of Saskatchewan, MD

FOOD SERVICE, WAITER/WAITRESS, AND DINING ROOM MANAGEMENT/MANAGER

Colorado

Johnson & Wales University, B

Florida

Johnson & Wales University, AB

Illinois

Lexington College, AB

Iowa

Iowa Lakes Community College, A

North Carolina

Johnson & Wales University, AB

Pennsylvania

The Art Institute of Pittsburgh, B

West Virginia

Fairmont State Community & Technical College, A

FOOD SERVICES MANAGEMENT

Michigan

Michigan State University, M

New York

New York University, MD
Rochester Institute of Technology, M

Ohio

The Ohio State University, MD

FOOD TECHNOLOGY AND PROCESSING

California

Cabrillo College, A
Cerritos College, A
Columbia College, A
Fresno City College, A
Long Beach City College, A
Los Angeles City College, A
Mission College, A
Modesto Junior College, A
Orange Coast College, A
Palomar College, A
Saddleback College, A
San Joaquin Delta College, A
Sierra College, A
Victor Valley College, A

Colorado

Arapahoe Community College, A

Delaware

Delaware Technical & Community College,
Stanton/Wilmington Campus, A

District of Columbia

University of the District of Columbia, A

Hawaii

Hawaii Community College, A
Honolulu Community College, A
Leeward Community College, A

Maui Community College, A

Illinois

Richland Community College, A
Shawnee Community College, A

Indiana

Purdue University Calumet, A

Iowa

Indian Hills Community College, A
Iowa State University of Science and Technology, B
Iowa Western Community College, A
Kirkwood Community College, A

Kansas

Washburn University, A

Maine

Southern Maine Community College, A

Maryland

Anne Arundel Community College, A

Michigan

Henry Ford Community College, A
Madonna University, B
Washtenaw Community College, A

Mississippi

Copiah-Lincoln Community College, A
Hinds Community College, A

Missouri

St. Louis Community College at Florissant Valley, A

Nebraska

Southeast Community College, Lincoln Campus, A

Nevada

Community College of Southern Nevada, A

New York

Adirondack Community College, A
Mohawk Valley Community College, A
Monroe Community College, A
State University of New York College of Agriculture
    and Technology at Cobleskill, A
State University of New York College of Agriculture
    and Technology at Morrisville, A
Westchester Community College, A

North Carolina

Central Piedmont Community College, A
Lenoir Community College, A
Robeson Community College, A

Ohio

Columbus State Community College, A
Owens Community College, A
Stark State College of Technology, A

Oklahoma

Oklahoma State University, Okmulgee, A

Oregon

Lane Community College, A

Pennsylvania

Butler County Community College, A
Luzerne County Community College, A
Mansfield University of Pennsylvania, B

Rhode Island

Johnson & Wales University, B

Tennessee

Chattanooga State Technical Community College, A
Tennessee State University, B

Texas

El Centro College, A
Tarrant County College District, A

Texas State Technical College Harlingen, A
Texas State Technical College Waco, A

Utah

Brigham Young University, B

Washington

Skagit Valley College, A
South Puget Sound Community College, A
South Seattle Community College, A
Spokane Community College, A

Wisconsin

Milwaukee Area Technical College, A
Southwest Wisconsin Technical College, A
Western Technical College, A

New Brunswick

Université de Moncton, B

FOODS, NUTRITION, AND RELATED SERVICES

California

California State University, Long Beach, B
San Diego Mesa College, A

Iowa

Iowa Lakes Community College, A

Massachusetts

Framingham State College, B

New York

Schenectady County Community College, A

Ohio

Kent State University, B

Pennsylvania

Marywood University, B

Utah

Utah State University, B

Wisconsin

University of Wisconsin-Stout, B

British Columbia

The University of British Columbia, B

FOODS, NUTRITION, AND WELLNESS STUDIES

Alabama

Auburn University, B
Jacksonville State University, B
Tuskegee University, B
The University of Alabama, B

Arizona

Arizona State University at the Polytechnic
    Campus, B

Arkansas

University of Arkansas, B

California

Antelope Valley College, A
Bakersfield College, A
California Polytechnic State University, San Luis
    Obispo, B
California State Polytechnic University, Pomona, B
California State University, Fresno, B
California State University, Los Angeles, B
California State University, San Bernardino, B
Compton Community College, A
Cuesta College, A
The Master's College and Seminary, B
Ohlone College, A

Orange Coast College, A
Pepperdine University, B
Point Loma Nazarene University, B
Saddleback College, A
San Diego Mesa College, A
Santa Ana College, A

Colorado

Colorado State University, B

Connecticut

Saint Joseph College, B

Delaware

Delaware State University, B
University of Delaware, B

District of Columbia

Gallaudet University, B
Howard University, B

Florida

Daytona Beach Community College, A
Florida State University, B
Indian River Community College, A
Okaloosa-Walton College, A
Palm Beach Community College, A

Georgia

Fort Valley State University, B
Georgia Southern University, B
Georgia State University, B

Idaho

Brigham Young University -Idaho, A
Idaho State University, B
University of Idaho, B

Illinois

Dominican University, B
Lincoln College, A
Loyola University Chicago, B
Northern Illinois University, B
Southern Illinois University Carbondale, B

Indiana

Indiana State University, B
Indiana University Bloomington, B
Purdue University, B

Iowa

Iowa State University of Science and Technology, B
University of Northern Iowa, B

Kansas

Colby Community College, A
Kansas State University, B

Kentucky

Eastern Kentucky University, A
Murray State University, B
University of Kentucky, B
Western Kentucky University, B

Louisiana

McNeese State University, B

Maine

University of Maine, B
University of Maine at Presque Isle, A

Maryland

Morgan State University, B
University of Maryland, College Park, B

Massachusetts

Framingham State College, B
Holyoke Community College, A
North Shore Community College, A

Simmons College, B

Michigan

Andrews University, B
Madonna University, AB
Wayne State University, B

Minnesota

College of Saint Benedict, B
College of St. Catherine, B
Concordia College, B
Minnesota State University Mankato, B
Saint John's University, B
University of Minnesota, Twin Cities Campus, B

Mississippi

Alcorn State University, B
Northwest Mississippi Community College, A

Missouri

College of the Ozarks, B
Northwest Missouri State University, B
Saint Louis University, B
University of Missouri-Columbia, B

Nebraska

University of Nebraska-Lincoln, B

Nevada

University of Nevada, Reno, B

New Hampshire

Keene State College, B
University of New Hampshire, AB

New Jersey

Camden County College, A
Montclair State University, B

New Mexico

New Mexico State University, B
University of New Mexico, B

New York

Brooklyn College of the City University of New
 York, B
Dutchess Community College, A
Hunter College of the City University of New York, B
Ithaca College, B
Lehman College of the City University of New
 York, B
New York University, B
State University of New York College of Agriculture
 and Technology at Morrisville, A
State University of New York at Plattsburgh, B
Syracuse University, B

North Carolina

Appalachian State University, B
North Carolina Agricultural and Technical State
 University, B
The University of North Carolina at Chapel Hill, B

North Dakota

United Tribes Technical College, A

Ohio

Ashland University, B
Bluffton University, B
Bowling Green State University, B
Kent State University, B
The Ohio State University, B
Ohio University, B
Sinclair Community College, A
The University of Akron, B
University of Cincinnati, B
University of Dayton, B
Youngstown State University, B

Oklahoma

Langston University, B
Northeastern State University, B

University of Central Oklahoma, B

Oregon

George Fox University, B
Oregon State University, B

Pennsylvania

Cedar Crest College, AB
Community College of Philadelphia, A
Harrisburg Area Community College, A
Immaculata University, B
Indiana University of Pennsylvania, B

Puerto Rico

University of Puerto Rico, Río Piedras, B

Rhode Island

University of Rhode Island, B

South Carolina

Bob Jones University, B
South Carolina State University, B
Winthrop University, B

South Dakota

Mount Marty College, B
South Dakota State University, B

Tennessee

American Academy of Nutrition, College of
 Nutrition, A
Carson-Newman College, B
Lambuth University, B
Middle Tennessee State University, B
Southern Adventist University, A
Tennessee Technological University, B
The University of Tennessee, B

Texas

Prairie View A&M University, B
Sam Houston State University, B
Stephen F. Austin State University, B
Texas A&M University, B
Texas A&M University-Kingsville, B
Texas Southern University, B
Texas State University-San Marcos, B
Texas Tech University, B
Texas Woman's University, B
University of Houston, B
University of the Incarnate Word, B
The University of Texas at Austin, B

Utah

Snow College, A

Vermont

Goddard College, B

Virginia

Bridgewater College, B
James Madison University, B
Radford University, B
Virginia Polytechnic Institute and State University, B

Washington

Bastyr University, B
Central Washington University, B
Seattle Pacific University, B
Washington State University, B

Wisconsin

University of Wisconsin-Madison, B

Alberta

University of Alberta, B

British Columbia

The University of British Columbia, B

Manitoba

University of Manitoba, B

New Brunswick

Université de Moncton, B

Newfoundland and Labrador

Memorial University of Newfoundland, B

Nova Scotia

Acadia University, B
Mount Saint Vincent University, B
St. Francis Xavier University, B

Ontario

University of Ottawa, A
University of Toronto, B
The University of Western Ontario, B

Prince Edward Island

University of Prince Edward Island, B

Quebec

McGill University, B
Université Laval, B
Université de Montréal, B

FOODSERVICE SYSTEMS ADMINISTRATION/MANAGEMENT

California

Santa Barbara City College, A

Connecticut

University of New Haven, A

Florida

Florida Community College at Jacksonville, A

Illinois

Dominican University, B

Kentucky

Murray State University, A

Michigan

Central Michigan University, B
Mott Community College, A
Oakland Community College, A
Western Michigan University, B

Minnesota

Hibbing Community College, A

New Jersey

Atlantic Cape Community College, A
Burlington County College, A

New York

Mohawk Valley Community College, A
Rochester Institute of Technology, B
State University of New York College at Oneonta, B

North Carolina

The University of North Carolina at Greensboro, B

North Dakota

North Dakota State College of Science, A

Pennsylvania

Community College of Allegheny County, A

Rhode Island

Johnson & Wales University, B

Wisconsin

University of Wisconsin-Stout, B

FOREIGN LANGUAGE TEACHER EDUCATION

Alabama

Auburn University, M

Arizona

Northern Arizona University, M
The University of Arizona, BM

Arkansas

Arkansas Tech University, B
University of Central Arkansas, M

California

California State University, Chico, M
Occidental College, M
Stanford University, M
University of California, Irvine, M

Colorado

The Colorado College, M

Connecticut

Central Connecticut State University, M
Connecticut College, M
Fairfield University, MO
Quinnipiac University, M
University of Connecticut, MD

Delaware

University of Delaware, BM

District of Columbia

The Catholic University of America, B

Florida

Florida Atlantic University, M
Florida International University, BMD
Florida State University, B
Manatee Community College, A
University of Central Florida, BO
University of Florida, M
University of South Florida, BM
University of West Florida, B

Georgia

Georgia Southern University, M
Georgia State University, O
University of Georgia, BMDO
University of West Georgia, M

Hawaii

University of Hawaii at Manoa, D

Idaho

University of Idaho, M

Illinois

Southern Illinois University Edwardsville, M
University of Illinois at Chicago, B
University of Illinois at Urbana-Champaign, BM

Indiana

Indiana University Bloomington, M
Purdue University, MDO
University of Indianapolis, M
Valparaiso University, B

Iowa

The University of Iowa, MD
University of Northern Iowa, B

Kentucky

Berea College, B
Murray State University, B

University of Louisville, M

Louisiana

McNeese State University, B
University of New Orleans, B

Maine

University of Maine, BM

Maryland

Hood College, O
Salisbury University, M
University of Maryland, College Park, BM

Massachusetts

Boston College, M
Boston University, BM
Framingham State College, BM
Smith College, M
University of Massachusetts Amherst, M
University of Massachusetts Boston, M
Worcester State College, M

Michigan

Andrews University, M
Eastern Michigan University, B
University of Michigan, M
Wayne State University, MD
Western Michigan University, B

Minnesota

University of Minnesota, Twin Cities Campus, BM
University of St. Thomas, B

Mississippi

Delta State University, B
Mississippi State University, M
University of Southern Mississippi, M

Missouri

Central Methodist University, B
Missouri State University, M
Southeast Missouri State University, B
University of Missouri-Columbia, MDO

Nebraska

Dana College, B
Hastings College, B
University of Nebraska at Kearney, M
University of Nebraska-Lincoln, B
Wayne State College, B

Nevada

University of Nevada, Reno, BM

New Hampshire

Rivier College, BM

New Jersey

The College of New Jersey, M
Rider University, O
Rutgers, The State University of New Jersey, New Brunswick/Piscataway, MD

New York

Brooklyn College of the City University of New York, M
Buffalo State College, State University of New York, B
The College of Saint Rose, M
Cornell University, MD
Elmira College, B
Hofstra University, BM
Hunter College of the City University of New York, M
Iona College, M
Le Moyne College, B
Long Island University, C.W. Post Campus, BM
Manhattanville College, M
Nazareth College of Rochester, B
New York University, BMO
Queens College of the City University of New York, MO
St. Bonaventure University, B

St. John Fisher College, M
St. John's University, B
State University of New York at Binghamton, M
State University of New York at Buffalo, MD
State University of New York College at Brockport, B
State University of New York College at Cortland, M
State University of New York College at Old Westbury, B
Stony Brook University, State University of New York, M
University at Albany, State University of New York, B

North Carolina

Gardner-Webb University, B
Greensboro College, B
North Carolina State University, B
The University of North Carolina at Chapel Hill, M

Ohio

Bowling Green State University, BM
Kent State University, B
Ohio Dominican University, B
Ohio Northern University, B
Ohio Wesleyan University, B
The University of Akron, B
The University of Toledo, M
Wright State University, B
Youngstown State University, B

Oklahoma

Oral Roberts University, B
University of Oklahoma, B

Oregon

Portland State University, M

Pennsylvania

Gannon University, B
Juniata College, B
Lincoln University, B
Mercyhurst College, B
Millersville University of Pennsylvania, B
Moravian College, B
The Pennsylvania State University Abington College, B
The Pennsylvania State University Altoona College, B
The Pennsylvania State University Beaver Campus of the Commonwealth College, B
The Pennsylvania State University Berks Campus of the Berks-Lehigh Valley College, B
The Pennsylvania State University Delaware County Campus of the Commonwealth College, B
The Pennsylvania State University DuBois Campus of the Commonwealth College, B
The Pennsylvania State University at Erie, The Behrend College, B
The Pennsylvania State University Fayette Campus of the Commonwealth College, B
The Pennsylvania State University McKeesport Campus of the Commonwealth College, B
The Pennsylvania State University Mont Alto Campus of the Commonwealth College, B
The Pennsylvania State University Shenango Campus of the Commonwealth College, B
The Pennsylvania State University University Park Campus, B
The Pennsylvania State University Worthington Scranton Campus of the Commonwealth College, B
The Pennsylvania State University York Campus of the Commonwealth College, B
Saint Francis University, B
Seton Hill University, B
Temple University, B
University of Pittsburgh, MD

West Chester University of Pennsylvania, BM

Puerto Rico

University of Puerto Rico, Río Piedras, M

Rhode Island

Rhode Island College, M

South Carolina

College of Charleston, M
University of South Carolina, MD

South Dakota

The University of South Dakota, B

Tennessee

Middle Tennessee State University, M
The University of Tennessee, MO
Vanderbilt University, M

Texas

Baylor University, B
Sam Houston State University, B
Texas A&M University-Kingsville, M
Texas Wesleyan University, B
The University of Texas at Austin, MD

Utah

Brigham Young University, BM
University of Utah, M

Vermont

Bennington College, BM
University of Vermont, BM

Virginia

Christopher Newport University, M
George Mason University, M
Old Dominion University, B
Virginia Wesleyan College, B

Washington

Eastern Washington University, M
Washington State University, B

West Virginia

Wheeling Jesuit University, B

Wisconsin

Carroll College, B
Marquette University, BM
University of Wisconsin-Madison, M

Alberta

University of Lethbridge, B

British Columbia

University of Victoria, M

Ontario

University of Windsor, B

Quebec

McGill University, MD

FOREIGN LANGUAGES AND LITERATURES

Alabama

Auburn University, B
Auburn University Montgomery, B
Samford University, B
The University of Alabama in Huntsville, B
University of North Alabama, B

University of South Alabama, B

Alaska

University of Alaska Anchorage, B
University of Alaska Fairbanks, B

Arizona

Cochise College (Douglas), A
Eastern Arizona College, A

Arkansas

Arkansas Tech University, B

California

California State University, Monterey Bay, B
Dominican University of California, B
Glendale Community College, A
Modesto Junior College, A
Pitzer College, B
Reedley College, A
Scripps College, B
University of California, San Diego, B
University of California, Santa Cruz, B

Colorado

Colorado State University, B
Metropolitan State College of Denver, B
University of Northern Colorado, B

Connecticut

University of Hartford, B

Delaware

University of Delaware, B

District of Columbia

American University, B

Florida

Eckerd College, B
Gulf Coast Community College, A
New College of Florida, B
University of Central Florida, B

Georgia

Atlanta Metropolitan College, A
Coastal Georgia Community College, A
Covenant College, B
Dalton State College, A
Darton College, A
Gainesville College, A
Georgia Highlands College, A
Georgia Perimeter College, A
University of Georgia, B

Idaho

College of Southern Idaho, A
University of Idaho, B

Illinois

Eastern Illinois University, B
Knox College, B
Millikin University, B
Principia College, B
Roosevelt University, B
Southern Illinois University Edwardsville, B

Indiana

Indiana State University, B
Purdue University, B

Iowa

Graceland University, B
Iowa Lakes Community College, A
University of Northern Iowa, B

Kansas

Emporia State University, B
Hutchinson Community College and Area Vocational
    School, A

Kansas State University, B

Louisiana

Centenary College of Louisiana, B
Tulane University, B

Maine

University of Maine, B

Maryland

Frostburg State University, B
St. Mary's College of Maryland, B
University of Maryland, College Park, B
Washington College, B

Massachusetts

Assumption College, B
Boston University, B
Framingham State College, B
Gordon College, B
Massachusetts Institute of Technology, B
Simon's Rock College of Bard, B
Stonehill College, B
University of Massachusetts Lowell, B

Michigan

Wayne State University, B

Minnesota

Minnesota State University Moorhead, B

Mississippi

Delta State University, B
Jackson State University, B
Mississippi College, B
Mississippi State University, B
University of Southern Mississippi, B

Missouri

Central Methodist University, B
Saint Louis University, B

Montana

Montana State University, B
The University of Montana-Missoula, B

Nebraska

Hastings College, B

New Jersey

Monmouth University, B
The Richard Stockton College of New Jersey, B
Rutgers, The State University of New Jersey, New
    Brunswick/Piscataway, B
Saint Peter's College, B
Seton Hall University, B

New Mexico

New Mexico State University, B
St. John's College, B
San Juan College, A
University of New Mexico, B

New York

Dowling College, B
Elmira College, B
Excelsior College, B
Long Island University, Brooklyn Campus, B
Long Island University, C.W. Post Campus, B
Pace University, B
St. Lawrence University, B
Sarah Lawrence College, B
State University of New York College at Old
    Westbury, B
Syracuse University, B
Union College, B

North Carolina

Campbell University, B
Elon University, B

Queens University of Charlotte, B

North Dakota

University of North Dakota, B

Ohio

Kenyon College, B
Wright State University, B
Youngstown State University, B

Oregon

Lewis & Clark College, B
Linn-Benton Community College, A

Pennsylvania

Carnegie Mellon University, B
Community College of Allegheny County, A
Duquesne University, B
Gannon University, B
Juniata College, B
Mercyhurst College, B
The Pennsylvania State University Berks Campus of
   the Berks-Lehigh Valley College, B
The Pennsylvania State University, Lehigh Valley
   Campus of the Berks-Lehigh Valley College, B
The University of Scranton, B
Widener University, B

Puerto Rico

University of Puerto Rico, Río Piedras, B

Rhode Island

Rhode Island College, B
Roger Williams University, B

South Carolina

Francis Marion University, B
University of South Carolina Beaufort, B

South Dakota

Augustana College, B

Tennessee

Austin Peay State University, B
East Tennessee State University, B
Lambuth University, B
Middle Tennessee State University, B
Southern Adventist University, B
Union University, B
University of Memphis, B

Texas

Brazosport College, A
Kingwood College, A
Midland College, A
Southern Methodist University, B
Texas Southern University, B
The University of Texas at Arlington, B
The University of Texas at Austin, B
The University of Texas at Tyler, B

Utah

Dixie State College of Utah, A
University of Utah, B

Vermont

Bennington College, B

Virginia

George Mason University, B
James Madison University, B
Old Dominion University, B
Radford University, B
Sweet Briar College, B
The University of Virginia's College at Wise, B
Virginia Commonwealth University, B
Virginia Wesleyan College, B
Washington and Lee University, B

Washington

Central Washington University, B
Lower Columbia College, A
Skagit Valley College, A

Washington State University, B

West Virginia

Marshall University, B
West Virginia University, B

Wisconsin

Marian College of Fond du Lac, B

Wyoming

Eastern Wyoming College, A
Sheridan College-Sheridan and Gillette, A

Alberta

Concordia University College of Alberta, B

Quebec

McGill University, B

FOREIGN LANGUAGES, LITERATURES, AND LINGUISTICS

Alaska

University of Alaska Fairbanks, A

California

Saint Mary's College of California, B
University of California, Berkeley, B
University of California, Los Angeles, B

Connecticut

Yale University, B

Georgia

Georgia Perimeter College, A

Illinois

Southern Illinois University Carbondale, B

Iowa

University of Northern Iowa, B

Michigan

University of Michigan-Flint, B

Minnesota

University of St. Thomas, B

Mississippi

Mississippi College, B

New York

The College of New Rochelle, B
Hofstra University, B

Pennsylvania

Edinboro University of Pennsylvania, B

Puerto Rico

University of the Sacred Heart, B

Texas

Houston Baptist University, B

Wisconsin

Marquette University, B

FORENSIC NURSING

Connecticut

Quinnipiac University, M

Massachusetts

Fitchburg State College, MO

Ohio

Cleveland State University, M

Pennsylvania

Duquesne University, O

FORENSIC PSYCHOLOGY

Arizona

Argosy University/Phoenix, M

Florida

Florida Institute of Technology, B

Illinois

Argosy University/Chicago, D

Iowa

St. Ambrose University, B

Massachusetts

American International College, M
University of Massachusetts Boston, MO

New York

John Jay College of Criminal Justice of the City
   University of New York, BMD

Ohio

Tiffin University, BM

Pennsylvania

Drexel University, D
Gwynedd-Mercy College, B

Rhode Island

Roger Williams University, M

Texas

Argosy University/Dallas, M
Prairie View A&M University, MD
Sam Houston State University, B

Vermont

Castleton State College, M

Virginia

Argosy University/Washington D.C., M
Marymount University, M

British Columbia

The University of British Columbia, MD

FORENSIC SCIENCE AND TECHNOLOGY

Alabama

Jacksonville State University, B
The University of Alabama at Birmingham, M

Arkansas

Arkansas State University, AB
Arkansas State University-Mountain Home, A
North Arkansas College, A
University of Arkansas at Fort Smith, A

California

National University, M
University of California, Davis, M

Connecticut

Tunxis Community College, A
University of New Haven, BM

District of Columbia

The George Washington University, MO

Florida

Florida Atlantic University, M
Florida International University, M

University of Central Florida, BO

Georgia

Appalachian Technical College, A
Darton College, A

Hawaii

Chaminade University of Honolulu, B

Idaho

Northwest Nazarene University, B

Illinois

Springfield College in Illinois, A
University of Illinois at Chicago, M

Indiana

Indiana University Bloomington, B
Tri-State University, B

Kansas

Washburn University, B

Kentucky

Eastern Kentucky University, B
Thomas More College, B

Louisiana

Loyola University New Orleans, B
Our Lady of the Lake College, B

Maryland

Prince George's Community College, A
Towson University, B
University of Baltimore, B

Massachusetts

Massachusetts Bay Community College, A

Michigan

Macomb Community College, A
Michigan State University, M
Northern Michigan University, B
Oakland Community College, A

Minnesota

Minnesota State Community and Technical
    College-Fergus Falls, A

Mississippi

University of Mississippi, B

Missouri

College of the Ozarks, B
Columbia College, B

Montana

University of Great Falls, B

Nebraska

Nebraska Wesleyan University, M

New York

Buffalo State College, State University of New
    York, B
Hudson Valley Community College, A
John Jay College of Criminal Justice of the City
    University of New York, BMD
Long Island University, C.W. Post Campus, B
Mohawk Valley Community College, A
Pace University, BM
Russell Sage College, B

University at Albany, State University of New
    York, M

North Carolina

Fayetteville Technical Community College, A
Saint Augustine's College, B

North Dakota

University of North Dakota, B

Ohio

Defiance College, B
Tiffin University, B
Youngstown State University, B

Oklahoma

University of Central Oklahoma, B

Pennsylvania

Alvernia College, B
Cedar Crest College, B
Chestnut Hill College, B
Keystone College, B
Lehigh Carbon Community College, A
Mercyhurst College, BM
Saint Francis University, B
Seton Hill University, B
Waynesburg College, B

Puerto Rico

Inter American University of Puerto Rico, Bayamón
    Campus, B

Texas

Baylor University, B
St. Edward's University, B
Sam Houston State University, BM

Vermont

Champlain College, B

Virginia

New River Community College, A
Virginia Commonwealth University, BM

Washington

Seattle University, B

West Virginia

Marshall University, M
Mountain State University, B
West Virginia University, B

Wisconsin

Carroll College, B

British Columbia

British Columbia Institute of Technology, A

Ontario

University of Toronto, B
University of Windsor, B

Quebec

McGill University, O

FOREST ENGINEERING

Georgia

Columbus State University, A

Maine

University of Maine, B

New York

State University of New York College of
    Environmental Science and Forestry, B

Oregon

Oregon State University, B

Washington

University of Washington, B

New Brunswick

Université de Moncton, B
University of New Brunswick Fredericton, B

University of New Brunswick Saint John, B

FOREST MANAGEMENT/FOREST RESOURCES MANAGEMENT

California

University of California, Berkeley, B

Florida

Lake City Community College, A

Louisiana

Louisiana State University and Agricultural and
    Mechanical College, B

Maryland

Allegany College of Maryland, A

Michigan

Northwestern Michigan College, A

Minnesota

University of Minnesota, Twin Cities Campus, B
Vermilion Community College, A

Montana

The University of Montana-Missoula, B

Nebraska

Western Nebraska Community College, A

New York

State University of New York College of
    Environmental Science and Forestry, B

North Carolina

North Carolina State University, B

Oregon

Oregon State University, B

South Carolina

Clemson University, B

Texas

Stephen F. Austin State University, B
Texas A&M University, B

Vermont

Sterling College, AB

Washington

University of Washington, B

West Virginia

West Virginia University, B

Alberta

University of Alberta, B

British Columbia

British Columbia Institute of Technology, A
The University of British Columbia, B

Ontario

University of Toronto, B

Quebec

Université Laval, B

FOREST RESOURCES PRODUCTION AND MANAGEMENT

Oregon

Oregon State University, B

Vermont

Sterling College, AB

FOREST SCIENCES AND BIOLOGY

Alabama

Auburn University, B

Arizona

Northern Arizona University, B

Colorado

Colorado State University, B

Georgia

University of Georgia, B

Illinois

University of Illinois at Urbana-Champaign, B

Kentucky

University of Kentucky, B

Michigan

Gogebic Community College, A

Minnesota

Vermilion Community College, A

New York

Canisius College, B

Pennsylvania

The Pennsylvania State University Abington College, B

The Pennsylvania State University Altoona College, B

The Pennsylvania State University Beaver Campus of the Commonwealth College, B

The Pennsylvania State University Berks Campus of the Berks-Lehigh Valley College, B

The Pennsylvania State University Delaware County Campus of the Commonwealth College, B

The Pennsylvania State University DuBois Campus of the Commonwealth College, B

The Pennsylvania State University at Erie, The Behrend College, B

The Pennsylvania State University Fayette Campus of the Commonwealth College, B

The Pennsylvania State University Hazleton Campus of the Commonwealth College, B

The Pennsylvania State University, Lehigh Valley Campus of the Berks-Lehigh Valley College, B

The Pennsylvania State University McKeesport Campus of the Commonwealth College, B

The Pennsylvania State University Mont Alto Campus of the Commonwealth College, B

The Pennsylvania State University New Kensington Campus of the Commonwealth College, B

The Pennsylvania State University Schuylkill Campus of the Capital College, B

The Pennsylvania State University Shenango Campus of the Commonwealth College, B

The Pennsylvania State University University Park Campus, B

The Pennsylvania State University Wilkes-Barre Campus of the Commonwealth College, B

The Pennsylvania State University Worthington Scranton Campus of the Commonwealth College, B

The Pennsylvania State University York Campus of the Commonwealth College, B

Vermont

Sterling College, AB

Washington

University of Washington, B

British Columbia

University of Northern British Columbia, B

Newfoundland and Labrador

Memorial University of Newfoundland, B

FORESTRY

Alabama

Auburn University, MD

Chattahoochee Valley Community College, A

Northwest-Shoals Community College, A

Arizona

Eastern Arizona College, A

Northern Arizona University, MD

The University of Arizona, MD

Arkansas

University of Arkansas at Monticello, BM

California

Bakersfield College, A

California Polytechnic State University, San Luis Obispo, BM

Cerritos College, A

City College of San Francisco, A

College of the Redwoods, A

Feather River College, A

Fullerton College, A

Humboldt State University, B

Modesto Junior College, A

Palo Verde College, A

Sierra College, A

University of California, Berkeley, BMD

Colorado

Colorado State University, MD

Northeastern Junior College, A

Trinidad State Junior College, A

Connecticut

Yale University, MDO

Delaware

Delaware State University, B

District of Columbia

University of the District of Columbia, B

Florida

Daytona Beach Community College, A

Indian River Community College, A

Miami Dade College, A

University of Florida, BMDO

Georgia

Abraham Baldwin Agricultural College, A

Bainbridge College, A

Clayton State University, A

Coastal Georgia Community College, A

Columbus State University, A

Dalton State College, A

Darton College, A

Gainesville College, A

Georgia Highlands College, A

University of Georgia, BMD

Waycross College, A

Idaho

Brigham Young University -Idaho, A

College of Southern Idaho, A

North Idaho College, A

University of Idaho, BMD

Illinois

Southern Illinois University Carbondale, BM

University of Illinois at Urbana-Champaign, B

Indiana

Purdue University, BMD

Vincennes University, A

Iowa

Iowa Lakes Community College, A

Iowa State University of Science and Technology, BMD

Kirkwood Community College, A

Kansas

Allen County Community College, A

Barton County Community College, A

Colby Community College, A

Dodge City Community College, A

Highland Community College, A

Kentucky

University of Kentucky, M

Louisiana

Louisiana State University and Agricultural and Mechanical College, MD

Louisiana Tech University, B

Southern University and Agricultural and Mechanical College, M

Maine

Unity College, B

University of Maine, BMD

University of Maine at Fort Kent, A

Massachusetts

Harvard University, M

North Shore Community College, A

University of Massachusetts Amherst, BMD

Michigan

Grand Rapids Community College, A

Michigan State University, BMD

Michigan Technological University, BMD

University of Michigan, MDO

Minnesota

College of Saint Benedict, B

Itasca Community College, A

Saint John's University, B

University of Minnesota, Twin Cities Campus, BMD

Vermilion Community College, A

Mississippi

Copiah-Lincoln Community College, A

Copiah-Lincoln Community College-Natchez Campus, A

Holmes Community College, A

Mississippi State University, BM

Northeast Mississippi Community College, A

Missouri

East Central College, A

Jefferson College, A

Northwest Missouri State University, B

University of Missouri-Columbia, BMD

Montana

Salish Kootenai College, A

The University of Montana-Missoula, BMD

Nevada

University of Nevada, Reno, B

New Hampshire

New Hampshire Community Technical College, Berlin/Laconia, A

University of New Hampshire, BM

New Jersey

Camden County College, A

New York

Cornell University, MD
Monroe Community College, A
Paul Smith's College of Arts and Sciences, A
State University of New York College of Agriculture
and Technology at Morrisville, A
State University of New York College of
Environmental Science and Forestry, BMD

North Carolina

Duke University, M
North Carolina State University, MD

North Dakota

Minot State University-Bottineau Campus, A

Ohio

Hocking College, A
The Ohio State University, B
Ohio University-Eastern, B

Oklahoma

Eastern Oklahoma State College, A
Northeastern Oklahoma Agricultural and Mechanical
College, A
Oklahoma State University, BM
Tulsa Community College, A

Oregon

Central Oregon Community College, A
Chemeketa Community College, A
Oregon State University, BMD
Southwestern Oregon Community College, A
Treasure Valley Community College, A
Umpqua Community College, A

Pennsylvania

Albright College, B
Keystone College, A
The Pennsylvania State University University Park
Campus, MD

South Carolina

Clemson University, MD

Tennessee

Chattanooga State Technical Community College, A
Sewanee: The University of the South, B
The University of Tennessee, BM
The University of Tennessee at Martin, B

Texas

Baylor University, B
Kilgore College, A
Stephen F. Austin State University, BMD
Texas A&M University, BMD

Utah

Dixie State College of Utah, A
Snow College, A
Utah State University, BMD

Vermont

Sterling College, AB
University of Vermont, B

Virginia

Mountain Empire Community College, A
Virginia Polytechnic Institute and State
University, BMD

Washington

Spokane Community College, A
Tacoma Community College, A
University of Washington, BMDO

Washington State University, B

West Virginia

Davis & Elkins College, B
Potomac State College of West Virginia
University, A
West Virginia University, BMD

Wisconsin

Northland College, B
University of Wisconsin-Madison, BMD
University of Wisconsin-Milwaukee, B
University of Wisconsin-Stevens Point, B

Wyoming

Northwest College, A
Western Wyoming Community College, A

Alberta

University of Alberta, BMD

British Columbia

The University of British Columbia, BMD

New Brunswick

University of New Brunswick Fredericton, BMD
University of New Brunswick Saint John, B

Ontario

Lakehead University, BM
University of Toronto, BMD

Quebec

McGill University, MD
Université Laval, BMD

FORESTRY TECHNOLOGY/TECHNICIAN

Alabama

Alabama Southern Community College, A
Lurleen B. Wallace Community College, A

California

American River College, A
Columbia College, A
El Camino College, A
Hartnell College, A
Modesto Junior College, A
Mt. San Antonio College, A
Pasadena City College, A
Sierra College, A

Florida

Lake City Community College, A
Pensacola Junior College, A

Georgia

Abraham Baldwin Agricultural College, A
Albany Technical College, A
Georgia Southwestern State University, A
Ogeechee Technical College, A
Okefenokee Technical College, A
Swainsboro Technical College, A
Waycross College, A

Illinois

Southeastern Illinois College, A

Kansas

Pittsburg State University, A

Kentucky

Hazard Community and Technical College, A

Louisiana

Louisiana Technical College, A

Maine

University of Maine at Fort Kent, A

Michigan

Michigan Technological University, A

Minnesota

Itasca Community College, A
Vermilion Community College, A

Mississippi

East Mississippi Community College, A
Itawamba Community College, A
Jones County Junior College, A
Northeast Mississippi Community College, A

Montana

Flathead Valley Community College, A
Salish Kootenai College, A

New Hampshire

University of New Hampshire, A

New York

Jefferson Community College, A
Paul Smith's College of Arts and Sciences, A
State University of New York College of Agriculture
and Technology at Morrisville, A
State University of New York College of
Environmental Science & Forestry, Ranger
School, A
State University of New York College of Technology
at Canton, A

North Carolina

Haywood Community College, A
Montgomery Community College, A
Southeastern Community College, A
Wayne Community College, A

Ohio

Hocking College, A

Oklahoma

Eastern Oklahoma State College, A

Oregon

Central Oregon Community College, A
Chemeketa Community College, A
Mt. Hood Community College, A
Treasure Valley Community College, A

Pennsylvania

Keystone College, A
Pennsylvania College of Technology, A
The Pennsylvania State University Abington
College, B
The Pennsylvania State University Altoona
College, B
The Pennsylvania State University Beaver Campus
of the Commonwealth College, B
The Pennsylvania State University Berks Campus of
the Berks-Lehigh Valley College, B
The Pennsylvania State University Delaware County
Campus of the Commonwealth College, B
The Pennsylvania State University DuBois Campus
of the Commonwealth College, B
The Pennsylvania State University at Erie, The
Behrend College, B
The Pennsylvania State University Fayette Campus
of the Commonwealth College, B
The Pennsylvania State University Hazleton
Campus of the Commonwealth College, B
The Pennsylvania State University, Lehigh Valley
Campus of the Berks-Lehigh Valley College, B
The Pennsylvania State University McKeesport
Campus of the Commonwealth College, B
The Pennsylvania State University Mont Alto
Campus of the Commonwealth College, AB
The Pennsylvania State University New Kensington
Campus of the Commonwealth College, B
The Pennsylvania State University Schuylkill
Campus of the Capital College, B
The Pennsylvania State University Shenango
Campus of the Commonwealth College, B
The Pennsylvania State University University Park
Campus, B

The Pennsylvania State University Wilkes-Barre
Campus of the Commonwealth College, B
The Pennsylvania State University Worthington
Scranton Campus of the Commonwealth
College, B
The Pennsylvania State University York Campus of
the Commonwealth College, B

South Carolina

Horry-Georgetown Technical College, A

Tennessee

Chattanooga State Technical Community College, A

Virginia

Dabney S. Lancaster Community College, A

Washington

Green River Community College, A

West Virginia

Glenville State College, A
Potomac State College of West Virginia
University, A

Wisconsin

Fox Valley Technical College, A

British Columbia

British Columbia Institute of Technology, A

FOUNDATIONS AND PHILOSOPHY OF EDUCATION

Alabama

Troy University, M
The University of West Alabama, M

Arizona

Arizona State University, M

California

California State University, Long Beach, M
California State University, Los Angeles, M
California State University, Northridge, M
Stanford University, D
University of California, Berkeley, MD

Connecticut

Central Connecticut State University, M
Fairfield University, MO
Southern Connecticut State University, O
University of Connecticut, MD

Florida

Florida Atlantic University, M
Florida State University, MDO

Georgia

Georgia State University, MD
University of Georgia, D

Hawaii

University of Hawaii at Manoa, MD

Illinois

DePaul University, M
Loyola University Chicago, MD
Northern Illinois University, M
Western Illinois University, M

Indiana

Indiana University Bloomington, MD
Purdue University, MD

Iowa

Iowa State University of Science and Technology, M
The University of Iowa, MDO

Kansas

University of Kansas, D

Louisiana

University of New Orleans, MDO

Maryland

Loyola College in Maryland, MO
University of Maryland, College Park, MDO

Massachusetts

Harvard University, O
Suffolk University, MO

Michigan

Eastern Michigan University, M
Oakland University, M
University of Michigan, D
Wayne State University, MDO

Minnesota

University of Minnesota, Twin Cities Campus, MDO

Missouri

Saint Louis University, MD
Southeast Missouri State University, M

New Jersey

Rutgers, The State University of New Jersey, New
Brunswick/Piscataway, MD

New Mexico

University of New Mexico, MD

New York

Hofstra University, MO
New York University, MD
Niagara University, M
State University of New York at Binghamton, D
Syracuse University, MDO

Ohio

Ashland University, M
Kent State University, MD
University of Cincinnati, MD
The University of Toledo, MDO
Youngstown State University, MD

Oklahoma

University of Oklahoma, MD

Oregon

George Fox University, MD

Pennsylvania

Duquesne University, M
Millersville University of Pennsylvania, M
The Pennsylvania State University University Park
Campus, MD
University of Pittsburgh, MD
Widener University, M

South Carolina

University of South Carolina, D

Tennessee

The University of Tennessee, MD

Texas

Texas A&M University, MD
University of Houston, MD
University of Houston-Clear Lake, M
The University of Texas of the Permian Basin, M

Utah

Brigham Young University, MDO
University of Utah, MD

Washington

Eastern Washington University, M

Wisconsin

University of Wisconsin-Milwaukee, M

Alberta

University of Calgary, MDO

British Columbia

The University of British Columbia, MD

Manitoba

University of Manitoba, M

Nova Scotia

Mount Saint Vincent University, M

Quebec

McGill University, MD

Saskatchewan

University of Saskatchewan, MDO

FRENCH LANGUAGE AND LITERATURE

Alabama

Alabama State University, B
Auburn University, BM
Birmingham-Southern College, B
Jacksonville State University, B
Oakwood College, B
Samford University, B
Talladega College, B
The University of Alabama, BMD
The University of Alabama at Birmingham, B
University of Montevallo, B

Arizona

Arizona State University, BM
Northern Arizona University, B
The University of Arizona, BMD

Arkansas

Arkansas State University, B
Harding University, B
Hendrix College, B
Ouachita Baptist University, B
University of Arkansas, BM
University of Arkansas at Little Rock, B
University of Central Arkansas, B

California

Bakersfield College, A
California Lutheran University, B
California State University, Chico, B
California State University, Dominguez Hills, B
California State University, East Bay, B
California State University, Fresno, B
California State University, Fullerton, BM
California State University, Long Beach, BM
California State University, Los Angeles, BM
California State University, Northridge, B
California State University, Sacramento, BM
California State University, San Bernardino, B
California State University, Stanislaus, B
Cañada College, A
Cerritos College, A
Chaffey College, A
Chapman University, B
Citrus College, A
Claremont McKenna College, B
College of the Canyons, A
College of the Desert, A
College of Marin, A
College of San Mateo, A
College of the Sequoias, A
Compton Community College, A
Contra Costa College, A
Crafton Hills College, A
East Los Angeles College, A
Grossmont College, A
Humboldt State University, B
Imperial Valley College, A
Long Beach City College, A
Los Angeles City College, A
Los Angeles Mission College, A

Los Angeles Valley College, A
Loyola Marymount University, B
Mendocino College, A
Merritt College, A
Mills College, B
MiraCosta College, A
Monterey Peninsula College, A
Mount St. Mary's College, B
Occidental College, B
Orange Coast College, A
Pasadena City College, A
Pepperdine University, B
Pitzer College, B
Pomona College, B
Saint Mary's College of California, B
San Bernardino Valley College, A
San Diego Mesa College, A
San Diego State University, B
San Francisco State University, BM
San Joaquin Delta College, A
San Jose State University, BM
Santa Barbara City College, A
Santa Clara University, B
Santa Monica College, A
Scripps College, B
Skyline College, A
Solano Community College, A
Sonoma State University, B
Southwestern College, A
Stanford University, BMD
University of California, Berkeley, BD
University of California, Davis, BD
University of California, Irvine, BMD
University of California, Los Angeles, BMD
University of California, Riverside, B
University of California, San Diego, BM
University of California, Santa Barbara, BMD
University of California, Santa Cruz, B
University of La Verne, B
University of the Pacific, B
University of Redlands, B
University of San Diego, B
University of San Francisco, B
University of Southern California, BMD
West Los Angeles College, A
West Valley College, A
Westmont College, B
Whittier College, B

Colorado

The Colorado College, B
Colorado State University, BM
Red Rocks Community College, A
Regis University, B
University of Colorado at Boulder, BMD
University of Colorado at Denver and Health
    Sciences Center - Downtown Denver Campus, B
University of Denver, BM
University of Northern Colorado, B
Western State College of Colorado, B

Connecticut

Albertus Magnus College, B
Central Connecticut State University, BM
Connecticut College, BM
Fairfield University, B
Southern Connecticut State University, BMO
Trinity College, B
University of Connecticut, BMD
Wesleyan University, B
Yale University, BMD

Delaware

Delaware State University, B
University of Delaware, B

District of Columbia

American University, BO
The Catholic University of America, BMD
Gallaudet University, B
The George Washington University, B
Georgetown University, B
Howard University, BM
Trinity (Washington) University, B

University of the District of Columbia, B

Florida

Barry University, B
Eckerd College, B
Florida Agricultural and Mechanical University, B
Florida Atlantic University, BM
Florida International University, B
Florida State University, BMD
Indian River Community College, A
Jacksonville University, B
Manatee Community College, A
Miami Dade College, A
New College of Florida, B
Rollins College, B
Stetson University, B
University of Central Florida, B
University of Florida, BMD
University of Miami, BD
University of South Florida, BM

Georgia

Agnes Scott College, B
Albany State University, B
Augusta State University, B
Berry College, B
Clark Atlanta University, B
Clayton State University, A
Emory University, BDO
Fort Valley State University, B
Georgia College & State University, B
Georgia Southern University, B
Georgia State University, BM
Kennesaw State University, B
Mercer University, B
Morehouse College, B
North Georgia College & State University, B
Oglethorpe University, B
Shorter College, B
South Georgia College, A
Spelman College, B
University of Georgia, BM
University of West Georgia, B
Valdosta State University, B
Wesleyan College, B
Young Harris College, A

Hawaii

University of Hawaii at Manoa, BM

Idaho

Boise State University, B
Brigham Young University -Idaho, A
Idaho State University, AB
North Idaho College, A
University of Idaho, BM

Illinois

Augustana College, B
Bradley University, B
City Colleges of Chicago, Harold Washington
    College, A
DePaul University, B
Dominican University, B
Elmhurst College, B
Illinois College, B
Illinois State University, BM
Illinois Wesleyan University, B
Knox College, B
Lake Forest College, B
Loyola University Chicago, B
Millikin University, B
Monmouth College, B
North Central College, B
North Park University, B
Northeastern Illinois University, B
Northern Illinois University, BM
Northwestern University, BDO
Principia College, B
Rockford College, B
Sauk Valley Community College, A
Southern Illinois University Carbondale, B
University of Chicago, BMD
University of Illinois at Chicago, BM
University of Illinois at Urbana-Champaign, BMD

Western Illinois University, B
Wheaton College, B

Indiana

Anderson University, B
Ball State University, B
Butler University, B
DePauw University, B
Earlham College, B
Franklin College, B
Grace College, B
Hanover College, B
Indiana State University, BM
Indiana University Bloomington, BMD
Indiana University Northwest, B
Indiana University-Purdue University Fort
    Wayne, AB
Indiana University-Purdue University Indianapolis, B
Indiana University South Bend, B
Indiana University Southeast, B
Manchester College, B
Marian College, B
Purdue University, MD
Purdue University Calumet, B
Saint Mary-of-the-Woods College, B
Saint Mary's College, B
Taylor University, B
University of Evansville, B
University of Indianapolis, B
University of Notre Dame, BM
University of Southern Indiana, B
Valparaiso University, B
Vincennes University, A
Wabash College, B

Iowa

Central College, B
Clarke College, B
Coe College, B
Cornell College, B
Grinnell College, B
Iowa State University of Science and Technology, B
Kirkwood Community College, A
Loras College, B
Luther College, B
St. Ambrose University, B
Simpson College, B
The University of Iowa, BMD
University of Northern Iowa, BM
Wartburg College, B

Kansas

Baker University, B
Benedictine College, B
Fort Hays State University, B
Independence Community College, A
Kansas State University, M
Pittsburg State University, B
University of Kansas, BMD
Washburn University, B
Wichita State University, B

Kentucky

Asbury College, B
Bellarmine University, B
Berea College, B
Centre College, B
Eastern Kentucky University, B
Georgetown College, B
Morehead State University, B
Murray State University, B
Northern Kentucky University, B
Transylvania University, B
University of Kentucky, BM
University of Louisville, BM
Western Kentucky University, B

Louisiana

Centenary College of Louisiana, B
Dillard University, B
Grambling State University, B
Louisiana College, B
Louisiana State University and Agricultural and
    Mechanical College, BMD
Louisiana State University in Shreveport, B

Louisiana Tech University, B
Loyola University New Orleans, B
McNeese State University, B
Nicholls State University, B
Southeastern Louisiana University, B
Southern University and Agricultural and Mechanical
  College, B
Southern University at New Orleans, B
Tulane University, BMD
University of Louisiana at Lafayette, BMD
University of Louisiana at Monroe, B
University of New Orleans, B
Xavier University of Louisiana, B

Maine

Bates College, B
Bowdoin College, B
Colby College, B
University of Maine, BM
University of Maine at Fort Kent, B
University of Southern Maine, B

Maryland

Goucher College, B
Hood College, B
The Johns Hopkins University, BD
Loyola College in Maryland, B
McDaniel College, B
Mount St. Mary's University, B
Salisbury University, B
Towson University, B
University of Maryland, Baltimore County, BM
University of Maryland, College Park, BMD
Washington College, B

Massachusetts

Amherst College, B
Assumption College, B
Atlantic Union College, B
Boston College, BMD
Boston University, BMD
Brandeis University, B
Clark University, B
College of the Holy Cross, B
Elms College, B
Framingham State College, B
Gordon College, B
Harvard University, BMD
Merrimack College, B
Mount Holyoke College, B
Northeastern University, B
Simmons College, B
Simon's Rock College of Bard, B
Smith College, BM
Suffolk University, B
Tufts University, BM
University of Massachusetts Amherst, BM
University of Massachusetts Boston, B
University of Massachusetts Dartmouth, B
Wellesley College, B
Wheaton College, B
Williams College, B

Michigan

Adrian College, AB
Albion College, B
Alma College, B
Andrews University, B
Aquinas College, B
Calvin College, B
Central Michigan University, B
Eastern Michigan University, BM
Grand Valley State University, B
Hillsdale College, B
Hope College, B
Kalamazoo College, B
Madonna University, B
Michigan State University, BMD
Northern Michigan University, B
Oakland University, B
Saginaw Valley State University, B
University of Michigan, BD
University of Michigan-Dearborn, B
University of Michigan-Flint, B
Wayne State University, M

Western Michigan University, B

Minnesota

Augsburg College, B
Bethel University, B
Carleton College, B
College of Saint Benedict, B
College of St. Catherine, B
Concordia College, B
Gustavus Adolphus College, B
Hamline University, B
Macalester College, B
Minnesota State University Mankato, BM
St. Cloud State University, B
Saint John's University, B
Saint Mary's University of Minnesota, B
St. Olaf College, B
University of Minnesota, Morris, B
University of Minnesota, Twin Cities Campus, BMD
University of St. Thomas, B
Winona State University, B

Mississippi

Copiah-Lincoln Community College, A
Millsaps College, B
Mississippi College, B
Mississippi State University, M
University of Mississippi, BM

Missouri

Central Methodist University, B
Central Missouri State University, B
College of the Ozarks, B
Drury University, B
Lindenwood University, B
Missouri Southern State University, B
Missouri State University, B
Missouri Western State University, B
Northwest Missouri State University, B
Rockhurst University, B
Saint Louis University, BM
Southeast Missouri State University, B
Truman State University, B
University of Missouri-Columbia, BMD
University of Missouri-Kansas City, B
University of Missouri-St. Louis, B
Washington University in St. Louis, BMD
Webster University, B
Westminster College, B
William Jewell College, B

Montana

Carroll College, B
The University of Montana-Missoula, BM

Nebraska

Creighton University, B
Doane College, B
Nebraska Wesleyan University, B
Union College, B
University of Nebraska at Kearney, B
University of Nebraska-Lincoln, BMD
University of Nebraska at Omaha, B
Wayne State College, B
Western Nebraska Community College, A

Nevada

University of Nevada, Las Vegas, BM
University of Nevada, Reno, BM

New Hampshire

Dartmouth College, B
Keene State College, B
Plymouth State University, B
Rivier College, B
Saint Anselm College, B
University of New Hampshire, B

New Jersey

Caldwell College, B
Drew University, B
Fairleigh Dickinson University, College at
  Florham, B
Fairleigh Dickinson University, Metropolitan
  Campus, B

Montclair State University, BM
Princeton University, BD
Rider University, B
Rutgers, The State University of New Jersey,
  Camden, B
Rutgers, The State University of New Jersey, New
  Brunswick/Piscataway, BMD
Rutgers, The State University of New Jersey,
  Newark, B
Seton Hall University, B

New Mexico

New Mexico Military Institute, A
St. John's College, B
University of New Mexico, BMD

New York

Adelphi University, B
Alfred University, B
Bard College, B
Barnard College, B
Brooklyn College of the City University of New
  York, BMD
Buffalo State College, State University of New
  York, B
Canisius College, B
City College of the City University of New York, B
Colgate University, B
College of Mount Saint Vincent, B
The College of New Rochelle, B
Columbia College, B
Columbia University, School of General Studies, B
Cornell University, BD
Daemen College, B
Elmira College, B
Fordham University, B
Hamilton College, B
Hartwick College, B
Hobart and William Smith Colleges, B
Hofstra University, BM
Houghton College, B
Hunter College of the City University of New
  York, BM
Iona College, B
Ithaca College, B
Le Moyne College, B
Lehman College of the City University of New
  York, B
Long Island University, C.W. Post Campus, B
Manhattan College, B
Manhattanville College, B
Marist College, B
Molloy College, B
Nazareth College of Rochester, B
New York University, BMDO
Niagara University, B
Pace University, B
Purchase College, State University of New York, B
Queens College of the City University of New
  York, BM
St. Bonaventure University, B
St. John Fisher College, B
St. John's University, B
St. Lawrence University, B
Sarah Lawrence College, B
Siena College, B
Skidmore College, B
State University of New York at Binghamton, BM
State University of New York at Buffalo, BMD
State University of New York College at
  Brockport, B
State University of New York College at Cortland, B
State University of New York College at Geneseo, B
State University of New York College at Oneonta, B
State University of New York College at Potsdam, B
State University of New York, Fredonia, B
State University of New York at New Paltz, B
State University of New York at Oswego, B
State University of New York at Plattsburgh, B
Stony Brook University, State University of New
  York, BMD
Syracuse University, BM
United States Military Academy, B
University at Albany, State University of New
  York, BMD
University of Rochester, B

Vassar College, B
Wells College, B
Yeshiva University, B
York College of the City University of New York, B

North Carolina

Appalachian State University, B
Campbell University, B
Catawba College, B
Davidson College, B
Duke University, BDO
East Carolina University, B
Elon University, B
Gardner-Webb University, B
Greensboro College, B
Guilford College, B
High Point University, B
Johnson C. Smith University, B
Lenoir-Rhyne College, B
Meredith College, B
Methodist College, AB
North Carolina Agricultural and Technical State
   University, B
North Carolina Central University, B
North Carolina State University, BM
Salem College, B
The University of North Carolina at Asheville, B
The University of North Carolina at Chapel Hill, MD
The University of North Carolina at Charlotte, B
The University of North Carolina at Greensboro, BM
The University of North Carolina Wilmington, B
Wake Forest University, B

North Dakota

Minot State University, B
North Dakota State University, B
University of North Dakota, B

Ohio

Antioch College, B
Ashland University, B
Baldwin-Wallace College, B
Bowling Green State University, BM
Capital University, B
Case Western Reserve University, BMD
Cleveland State University, B
The College of Wooster, B
Denison University, B
Franciscan University of Steubenville, B
Hiram College, B
John Carroll University, B
Kent State University, BM
Kenyon College, B
Lake Erie College, B
Miami University, BM
Miami University Hamilton, B
Mount Union College, B
Muskingum College, B
Oberlin College, B
Ohio Northern University, B
The Ohio State University, BMD
Ohio University, BM
Ohio Wesleyan University, B
Otterbein College, B
The University of Akron, B
University of Cincinnati, BMD
University of Dayton, B
The University of Toledo, BM
Walsh University, B
Wittenberg University, B
Wright State University, B
Xavier University, AB
Youngstown State University, B

Oklahoma

Oklahoma Baptist University, B
Oklahoma City University, B
Oklahoma State University, B
Oral Roberts University, B
Tulsa Community College, A
University of Central Oklahoma, B
University of Oklahoma, BMDO

University of Tulsa, B

Oregon

Lewis & Clark College, B
Linfield College, B
Oregon State University, B
Pacific University, B
Portland State University, BM
Reed College, B
Southern Oregon University, B
University of Oregon, BM
Willamette University, B

Pennsylvania

Albright College, B
Allegheny College, B
Bloomsburg University of Pennsylvania, B
Bryn Mawr College, BMD
Bucknell University, B
Cabrini College, B
California University of Pennsylvania, B
Carnegie Mellon University, B
Chatham College, BM
Chestnut Hill College, AB
Cheyney University of Pennsylvania, B
Clarion University of Pennsylvania, B
Dickinson College, B
East Stroudsburg University of Pennsylvania, B
Eastern University, B
Elizabethtown College, B
Franklin and Marshall College, B
Gettysburg College, B
Grove City College, B
Haverford College, B
Holy Family University, B
Immaculata University, B
Indiana University of Pennsylvania, B
Juniata College, B
King's College, B
Kutztown University of Pennsylvania, B
La Salle University, B
Lafayette College, B
Lebanon Valley College, B
Lehigh University, B
Lincoln University, B
Lock Haven University of Pennsylvania, B
Lycoming College, B
Mansfield University of Pennsylvania, B
Marywood University, B
Mercyhurst College, B
Messiah College, B
Millersville University of Pennsylvania, BM
Moravian College, B
Muhlenberg College, B
The Pennsylvania State University Abington
   College, B
The Pennsylvania State University Altoona
   College, B
The Pennsylvania State University Beaver Campus
   of the Commonwealth College, B
The Pennsylvania State University Berks Campus of
   the Berks-Lehigh Valley College, B
The Pennsylvania State University Delaware County
   Campus of the Commonwealth College, B
The Pennsylvania State University DuBois Campus
   of the Commonwealth College, B
The Pennsylvania State University at Erie, The
   Behrend College, B
The Pennsylvania State University Fayette Campus
   of the Commonwealth College, B
The Pennsylvania State University Hazleton
   Campus of the Commonwealth College, B
The Pennsylvania State University, Lehigh Valley
   Campus of the Berks-Lehigh Valley College, B
The Pennsylvania State University McKeesport
   Campus of the Commonwealth College, B
The Pennsylvania State University Mont Alto
   Campus of the Commonwealth College, B
The Pennsylvania State University New Kensington
   Campus of the Commonwealth College, B
The Pennsylvania State University Schuylkill
   Campus of the Capital College, B
The Pennsylvania State University Shenango
   Campus of the Commonwealth College, B
The Pennsylvania State University University Park
   Campus, BMD

The Pennsylvania State University Wilkes-Barre
   Campus of the Commonwealth College, B
The Pennsylvania State University Worthington
   Scranton Campus of the Commonwealth
   College, B
The Pennsylvania State University York Campus of
   the Commonwealth College, B
Rosemont College, B
Saint Francis University, B
Saint Joseph's University, B
Saint Vincent College, B
Shippensburg University of Pennsylvania, B
Slippery Rock University of Pennsylvania, B
Susquehanna University, B
Swarthmore College, B
Temple University, B
University of Pennsylvania, BMD
University of Pittsburgh, BMD
The University of Scranton, B
Ursinus College, B
Villanova University, B
Washington & Jefferson College, B
West Chester University of Pennsylvania, BM
Westminster College, B
Widener University, B
Wilkes University, B
Wilson College, B

Puerto Rico

Pontifical Catholic University of Puerto Rico, B
University of Puerto Rico, Mayagüez Campus, B
University of Puerto Rico, Río Piedras, B

Rhode Island

Brown University, BMD
Providence College, B
Rhode Island College, BM
Salve Regina University, B
University of Rhode Island, BM

South Carolina

Bob Jones University, B
The Citadel, The Military College of South
   Carolina, B
Coker College, B
College of Charleston, B
Columbia College, B
Converse College, B
Erskine College, B
Francis Marion University, B
Furman University, B
Newberry College, B
Presbyterian College, B
South Carolina State University, B
University of South Carolina, BM
University of South Carolina Upstate, B
Wofford College, B

South Dakota

Augustana College, B
Northern State University, B
South Dakota State University, B
The University of South Dakota, B

Tennessee

Carson-Newman College, B
Fisk University, B
King College, B
Lambuth University, B
Lane College, B
Lipscomb University, B
Rhodes College, B
Sewanee: The University of the South, B
Southern Adventist University, B
Tennessee State University, B
Tennessee Technological University, B
Union University, B
University of Memphis, M
The University of Tennessee, BMD
The University of Tennessee at Chattanooga, B
The University of Tennessee at Martin, B

Vanderbilt University, BMD

Texas

Angelo State University, B
Austin College, B
Austin Community College, A
Baylor University, B
Blinn College, A
Cisco Junior College, A
Coastal Bend College, A
Houston Baptist University, B
Lamar University, B
Lee College, A
Midland College, A
Rice University, BMD
St. Mary's University of San Antonio, B
Sam Houston State University, B
Southern Methodist University, B
Southwestern University, B
Stephen F. Austin State University, B
Texas A&M University, B
Texas A&M University-Commerce, B
Texas Christian University, B
Texas Southern University, B
Texas State University-San Marcos, B
Texas Tech University, BM
Trinity University, B
University of Dallas, B
University of Houston, BMDO
University of North Texas, BM
University of St. Thomas, B
The University of Texas at Arlington, BM
The University of Texas at Austin, BMD
The University of Texas at El Paso, B
The University of Texas at San Antonio, B

Utah

Brigham Young University, BM
Snow College, A
Southern Utah University, B
University of Utah, BM
Utah State University, B
Weber State University, B

Vermont

Bennington College, BM
Marlboro College, B
Middlebury College, BMD
Saint Michael's College, B
University of Vermont, BM

Virginia

Bridgewater College, B
Christendom College, B
Christopher Newport University, BM
The College of William and Mary, B
Eastern Mennonite University, B
Emory & Henry College, B
Hampden-Sydney College, B
Hollins University, B
Longwood University, B
Lynchburg College, B
Mary Baldwin College, B
Old Dominion University, B
Randolph-Macon College, B
Randolph-Macon Woman's College, B
Roanoke College, B
Sweet Briar College, B
University of Mary Washington, B
University of Richmond, B
University of Virginia, BMD
The University of Virginia's College at Wise, B
Virginia Polytechnic Institute and State University, B
Virginia Wesleyan College, B
Washington and Lee University, B

Washington

Centralia College, A
Eastern Washington University, B
Gonzaga University, B
Pacific Lutheran University, B
Seattle Pacific University, B
Seattle University, B
University of Puget Sound, B
University of Washington, BMD

Walla Walla College, B
Washington State University, B
Western Washington University, B
Whitman College, B
Whitworth College, B

West Virginia

Bethany College, B
Fairmont State University, B
West Virginia University, M
Wheeling Jesuit University, B

Wisconsin

Beloit College, B
Cardinal Stritch University, B
Carthage College, B
Edgewood College, B
Lawrence University, B
Marquette University, B
Mount Mary College, B
Ripon College, B
St. Norbert College, B
University of Wisconsin-Eau Claire, B
University of Wisconsin-Green Bay, AB
University of Wisconsin-La Crosse, B
University of Wisconsin-Madison, BMDO
University of Wisconsin-Milwaukee, BM
University of Wisconsin-Oshkosh, B
University of Wisconsin-Parkside, B
University of Wisconsin-River Falls, B
University of Wisconsin-Stevens Point, B
University of Wisconsin-Whitewater, B

Wyoming

Casper College, A
University of Wyoming, BM

Alberta

Athabasca University, B
Concordia University College of Alberta, B
University of Alberta, BMD
University of Calgary, BMD
University of Lethbridge, BM

British Columbia

Simon Fraser University, BM
The University of British Columbia, BMD
University of Victoria, BM

Manitoba

Brandon University, B
University of Manitoba, BMD
The University of Winnipeg, B

New Brunswick

Mount Allison University, B
St. Thomas University, B
Université de Moncton, BMD
University of New Brunswick Fredericton, BM
University of New Brunswick Saint John, B

Newfoundland and Labrador

Memorial University of Newfoundland, BM

Nova Scotia

Acadia University, B
Cape Breton University, B
Dalhousie University, BMD
Mount Saint Vincent University, B
St. Francis Xavier University, B
Saint Mary's University, B
Université Sainte-Anne, B
University of King's College, B

Ontario

Brock University, B
Carleton University, BM
Lakehead University, B
Laurentian University, B
McMaster University, BM
Queen's University at Kingston, BMD
Redeemer University College, B
Royal Military College of Canada, B
Trent University, B

University of Ottawa, BMD
University of Toronto, BMD
University of Waterloo, BM
The University of Western Ontario, BMD
University of Windsor, B
Wilfrid Laurier University, B
York University, BM

Prince Edward Island

University of Prince Edward Island, B

Quebec

Bishop's University, B
Concordia University, BMO
McGill University, BMD
Université Laval, ABM
Université de Montréal, BMD
Université du Québec àChicoutimi, BO
Université du Québec àRimouski, B
Université du Québec àTrois-Rivières, B
Université de Sherbrooke, BMD

Saskatchewan

University of Regina, BM
University of Saskatchewan, BM

FRENCH LANGUAGE TEACHER EDUCATION

Alabama

Auburn University, B
Talladega College, B

Arizona

The University of Arizona, B

Arkansas

Arkansas State University, B

California

California Lutheran University, B
California State University, Chico, B

Colorado

Colorado State University, B

Delaware

Delaware State University, B

District of Columbia

The Catholic University of America, B

Georgia

Columbus State University, B
Georgia Southern University, B

Illinois

Elmhurst College, B
Illinois Wesleyan University, B
University of Illinois at Chicago, B
University of Illinois at Urbana-Champaign, B

Indiana

Anderson University, B
Franklin College, B
Grace College, B
Indiana University Bloomington, B
Indiana University Northwest, B
Indiana University-Purdue University Fort Wayne, B
Indiana University-Purdue University Indianapolis, B
Indiana University South Bend, B
University of Evansville, B
University of Indianapolis, B

Valparaiso University, B

Iowa

St. Ambrose University, B
The University of Iowa, B

Kansas

Pittsburg State University, B

Kentucky

Berea College, B
Murray State University, B

Louisiana

Centenary College of Louisiana, B
Grambling State University, B
Louisiana State University in Shreveport, B
Louisiana Tech University, B
Southeastern Louisiana University, B
Southern University and Agricultural and Mechanical
  College, B
University of Louisiana at Lafayette, B
University of Louisiana at Monroe, B
Xavier University of Louisiana, B

Maine

University of Maine, B
University of Maine at Fort Kent, B

Michigan

Alma College, B
Central Michigan University, B
Eastern Michigan University, B
Hope College, B
Northern Michigan University, B
University of Michigan-Flint, B
Western Michigan University, B

Minnesota

Bethel University, B
College of St. Catherine, B
Concordia College, B
Saint Mary's University of Minnesota, B
University of Minnesota, Duluth, B

Missouri

College of the Ozarks, B
Lindenwood University, B
Missouri State University, B
Missouri Western State University, B
University of Missouri-St. Louis, B
Washington University in St. Louis, B
William Woods University, B

Nebraska

University of Nebraska-Lincoln, B

New Hampshire

Keene State College, B

New York

Brooklyn College of the City University of New
  York, B
Daemen College, B
Elmira College, B
Hofstra University, B
Iona College, B
Ithaca College, B
Le Moyne College, B
Long Island University, C.W. Post Campus, B
Manhattanville College, B
Marist College, B
Molloy College, B
New York University, B
Niagara University, B
Pace University, B
St. Bonaventure University, B
St. John's University, B
State University of New York College at
  Brockport, B
State University of New York College at Cortland, B
State University of New York College at Oneonta, B
State University of New York College at Potsdam, B

University at Albany, State University of New York, B

North Carolina

Appalachian State University, B
East Carolina University, B
Gardner-Webb University, B
North Carolina Central University, B
North Carolina State University, B
The University of North Carolina at Charlotte, B
The University of North Carolina at Greensboro, B
The University of North Carolina Wilmington, B
Western Carolina University, B

North Dakota

Minot State University, B
North Dakota State University, B

Ohio

Kent State University, B
Miami University Hamilton, B
Ohio Northern University, B
Ohio University, B
Ohio Wesleyan University, B
The University of Akron, B
The University of Toledo, B
Youngstown State University, B

Oklahoma

Oklahoma Baptist University, B
Oral Roberts University, B

Pennsylvania

Duquesne University, B
Juniata College, B
Lebanon Valley College, B
Mansfield University of Pennsylvania, B
Marywood University, B
Messiah College, B
Moravian College, B
Saint Francis University, B
Seton Hill University, B
West Chester University of Pennsylvania, B
Widener University, B

Rhode Island

Rhode Island College, B
Salve Regina University, B

South Dakota

The University of South Dakota, B

Tennessee

King College, B
Lipscomb University, B
The University of Tennessee at Martin, B

Texas

Baylor University, B

Utah

Brigham Young University, B
University of Utah, B
Weber State University, B

Virginia

Eastern Mennonite University, B
Old Dominion University, B

Washington

Central Washington University, B
Eastern Washington University, B
Washington State University, B

West Virginia

Wheeling Jesuit University, B

Wisconsin

Carroll College, B
Mount Mary College, B

University of Wisconsin-River Falls, B

Nova Scotia

Université Sainte-Anne, B

Ontario

University of Toronto, B
University of Waterloo, B
University of Windsor, B

Quebec

Bishop's University, B
McGill University, B
Université Laval, B

Saskatchewan

University of Regina, B

FRENCH STUDIES

Alabama

The University of Alabama, B

California

Claremont McKenna College, B
Mills College, B
Santa Clara University, B

Colorado

The Colorado College, B

Florida

New College of Florida, B

Iowa

Coe College, B

Massachusetts

Simon's Rock College of Bard, B
Smith College, B

Michigan

Lake Superior State University, B

Minnesota

Carleton College, B

New York

Barnard College, B
Columbia College, B
Fordham University, B

Ohio

Case Western Reserve University, B

Pennsylvania

Saint Joseph's University, B

Rhode Island

Brown University, B

Alberta

Concordia University College of Alberta, B

British Columbia

University of Victoria, B

Manitoba

The University of Winnipeg, B

Ontario

Brock University, B
University of Guelph, B
University of Waterloo, B
University of Windsor, B
Wilfrid Laurier University, B

York University, B

FUNERAL SERVICE AND MORTUARY SCIENCE

Alabama

Bishop State Community College, A
Jefferson State Community College, A

Arkansas

Arkansas State University-Mountain Home, A
University of Arkansas Community College at Hope, A

California

Cypress College, A

Colorado

Arapahoe Community College, A

Connecticut

Briarwood College, AB

District of Columbia

University of the District of Columbia, B

Florida

Lynn University, A
Miami Dade College, A
St. Petersburg College, A

Georgia

Gupton-Jones College of Funeral Service, A
Ogeechee Technical College, A

Illinois

Carl Sandburg College, A
City Colleges of Chicago, Malcolm X College, A
Southern Illinois University Carbondale, B
Worsham College of Mortuary Science, A

Indiana

Ivy Tech Community College-Northwest, A
Mid-America College of Funeral Service, A
Vincennes University, A

Kansas

Allen County Community College, A
Barton County Community College, A
Highland Community College, A
Kansas City Kansas Community College, A

Louisiana

Delgado Community College, A

Massachusetts

Mount Ida College, AB

Michigan

Monroe County Community College, A
Wayne State University, B

Minnesota

University of Minnesota, Twin Cities Campus, B

Mississippi

East Mississippi Community College, A

Missouri

Lindenwood University, B
St. Louis Community College at Forest Park, A

New Jersey

Mercer County Community College, A

New York

American Academy McAllister Institute of Funeral Service, A
Fiorello H. LaGuardia Community College of the City University of New York, A
Hudson Valley Community College, A

Nassau Community College, A
St. John's University, B
Simmons Institute of Funeral Service, A
State University of New York College of Technology at Canton, A

North Carolina

Catawba Valley Community College, A
Fayetteville Technical Community College, A
Forsyth Technical Community College, A

Ohio

Cincinnati College of Mortuary Science, AB

Oklahoma

University of Central Oklahoma, B

Oregon

Mt. Hood Community College, A

Pennsylvania

Gannon University, B
Luzerne County Community College, A
Northampton County Area Community College, A
Pittsburgh Institute of Mortuary Science, Incorporated, A
Point Park University, AB
Thiel College, B

South Carolina

Florence-Darlington Technical College, A
Piedmont Technical College, A

Tennessee

John A. Gupton College, A

Texas

Amarillo College, A
Commonwealth Institute of Funeral Service, A
Dallas Institute of Funeral Service, A
San Antonio College, A

Virginia

John Tyler Community College, A

Washington

Everett Community College, A

Wisconsin

Milwaukee Area Technical College, A

FURNITURE DESIGN AND MANUFACTURING

Indiana

Vincennes University Jasper Campus, A

Michigan

Ferris State University, B

Minnesota

Dakota County Technical College, A

New York

Rochester Institute of Technology, AB

North Carolina

Catawba Valley Community College, A

Rhode Island

Rhode Island School of Design, B

Wisconsin

Milwaukee Area Technical College, A

GAY/LESBIAN STUDIES

New York

Cornell University, B
Hobart and William Smith Colleges, B

Sarah Lawrence College, B

Vermont

Bennington College, B

GENDER STUDIES

Florida

University of Central Florida, O
University of Florida, MDO

Illinois

Northwestern University, O
Roosevelt University, M

Massachusetts

Simmons College, M

New Jersey

Rutgers, The State University of New Jersey, New Brunswick/Piscataway, MD

New York

Cornell University, MD

Alberta

Athabasca University, M

British Columbia

University of Northern British Columbia, M

Newfoundland and Labrador

Memorial University of Newfoundland, D

Saskatchewan

University of Saskatchewan, MD

GENERAL MERCHANDISING, SALES, AND RELATED MARKETING OPERATIONS

Georgia

Clayton State University, A

Iowa

Iowa Lakes Community College, A

Michigan

Eastern Michigan University, B
Southwestern Michigan College, A

Minnesota

Minnesota State Community and Technical College-Fergus Falls, A

Missouri

Washington University in St. Louis, B

New York

Broome Community College, A

Ohio

The University of Akron, B

Oregon

Oregon State University, B

Puerto Rico

Caribbean University, B

Utah

Brigham Young University, B

Wisconsin

Northeast Wisconsin Technical College, A
Wisconsin Indianhead Technical College, A

Nova Scotia

Dalhousie University, B

GENERAL OFFICE OCCUPATIONS AND CLERICAL SERVICES

Alaska

University of Alaska Fairbanks, A

Arizona

GateWay Community College, A

California

Modesto Junior College, A
Reedley College, A

Colorado

Institute of Business & Medical Careers, A

Florida

Florida Community College at Jacksonville, A
Hillsborough Community College, A

Georgia

Darton College, A
Georgia Southwestern State University, A

Iowa

Iowa Lakes Community College, A

Kentucky

Big Sandy Community and Technical College, A

Louisiana

ITI Technical College, A

Michigan

Delta College, A

Minnesota

Alexandria Technical College, A

Mississippi

East Mississippi Community College, A

Montana

The University of Montana-Helena College of Technology, A

New Mexico

New Mexico State University-Alamogordo, A

New York

Mohawk Valley Community College, A
North Country Community College, A

North Carolina

Alamance Community College, A

North Dakota

Lake Region State College, A
Minot State University-Bottineau Campus, A
Sitting Bull College, A
United Tribes Technical College, A

Ohio

Ohio University-Southern Campus, A
Terra State Community College, A
Wright State University, A

Pennsylvania

Butler County Community College, A
Laurel Business Institute, A
Lehigh Carbon Community College, A
Pennsylvania College of Technology, A

Pennsylvania Institute of Technology, A

Puerto Rico

University of Puerto Rico at Utuado, A

South Carolina

Bob Jones University, A
York Technical College, A

Tennessee

The University of Tennessee at Martin, B

Texas

Del Mar College, A
El Centro College, A

Washington

Spokane Falls Community College, A
Walla Walla Community College, A

West Virginia

Community and Technical College of Shepherd, A
West Virginia State Community and Technical College, A

Wisconsin

Northeast Wisconsin Technical College, A

GENERAL STUDIES

Alabama

Bevill State Community College, A
Bishop State Community College, A
Calhoun Community College, A
Concordia College, A
Gadsden State Community College, A
James H. Faulkner State Community College, A
Jefferson State Community College, A
Northwest-Shoals Community College, A
Samford University, B
Snead State Community College, A
Spring Hill College, B
University of Mobile, AB
University of North Alabama, B

Alaska

Ilisagvik College, A
Sheldon Jackson College, A
University of Alaska Southeast, AB

Arizona

Arizona State University at the Polytechnic Campus, B
Cochise College (Douglas), A
Estrella Mountain Community College, A
GateWay Community College, A
Northcentral University, B
Northern Arizona University, B
Northland Pioneer College, A
Pima Community College, A
University of Phoenix Online Campus, B
University of Phoenix-Phoenix Campus, A

Arkansas

Arkansas Northeastern College, A
Arkansas State University, AB
Arkansas State University-Beebe, A
Arkansas Tech University, AB
Central Baptist College, A
Crowley's Ridge College, A
Harding University, B
South Arkansas Community College, A
Southeast Arkansas College, A
Southern Arkansas University-Magnolia, A
Southern Arkansas University Tech, A
University of Arkansas at Fort Smith, A
University of Arkansas at Little Rock, A
University of Central Arkansas, A
University of the Ozarks, B

California

Antioch University Santa Barbara, B
Berkeley City College, A

California Institute of Technology, B
College of Alameda, A
Cuyamaca College, A
Evergreen Valley College, A
Hope International University, A
Merritt College, A
MiraCosta College, A
Modesto Junior College, A
National University, B
Palo Verde College, A
Reedley College, A
Simpson University, A
Southwestern College, A
Taft College, A
University of Southern California, B

Colorado

Colorado Mountain College, Timberline Campus, A
Colorado Northwestern Community College, A
Community College of Denver, A
Front Range Community College, A
Pikes Peak Community College, A
Pueblo Community College, A

Connecticut

Albertus Magnus College, B
Asnuntuck Community College, A
Briarwood College, A
Eastern Connecticut State University, AB
Manchester Community College, A
Norwalk Community College, A
University of Connecticut, B
University of Hartford, A
University of New Haven, A

Delaware

Wilmington College, AB

District of Columbia

The Catholic University of America, B

Florida

Clearwater Christian College, AB
Florida Gulf Coast University, B
Florida Hospital College of Health Sciences, AB
Miami Dade College, A
New College of Florida, B
Palm Beach Atlantic University, AB
Pensacola Junior College, A
University of Miami, B
University of North Florida, A
University of South Florida, B
Warner Southern College, A

Georgia

Atlanta Metropolitan College, A
Brenau University, B
Brewton-Parker College, AB
Dalton State College, A
Darton College, A
Gainesville College, A
Georgia Perimeter College, A
Georgia Southern University, B
Gordon College, A
Macon State College, A
Shorter College, B
Toccoa Falls College, A
Truett-McConnell College, A
Valdosta State University, B

Hawaii

Chaminade University of Honolulu, A
University of Phoenix-Hawaii Campus, A

Idaho

Idaho State University, AB
University of Idaho, B

Illinois

Chicago State University, B
City Colleges of Chicago, Malcolm X College, A
City Colleges of Chicago, Wilbur Wright College, A
DePaul University, B
Illinois Eastern Community Colleges, Frontier Community College, A

Illinois Eastern Community Colleges, Lincoln Trail College, A
Illinois Eastern Community Colleges, Olney Central College, A
Illinois Eastern Community Colleges, Wabash Valley College, A
John Wood Community College, A
Kaskaskia College, A
Lake Land College, A
Lincoln Land Community College, A
Loyola University Chicago, B
McHenry County College, A
Northwestern University, B
Parkland College, A
St. Augustine College, A
Shimer College, B
Springfield College in Illinois, A
University of Illinois at Urbana-Champaign, B
Waubonsee Community College, A

Indiana

Anderson University, A
Calumet College of Saint Joseph, AB
Indiana University Bloomington, AB
Indiana University East, AB
Indiana University Kokomo, AB
Indiana University Northwest, AB
Indiana University-Purdue University Fort Wayne, AB
Indiana University-Purdue University Indianapolis, AB
Indiana University South Bend, AB
Indiana University Southeast, AB
Indiana Wesleyan University, AB
Ivy Tech Community College-East Central, A
Ivy Tech Community College-Kokomo, A
Ivy Tech Community College-North Central, A
Ivy Tech Community College-Northeast, A
Ivy Tech Community College-Northwest, A
Oakland City University, AB
Taylor University Fort Wayne, A

Iowa

Ashford University, B
Central College, B
Dordt College, B
Hamilton College (Cedar Rapids), A
Iowa Lakes Community College, A
Vennard College, A

Kansas

Allen County Community College, A
Barclay College, A
Barton County Community College, A
Emporia State University, B
Pittsburg State University, B
Southwestern College, B

Kentucky

Eastern Kentucky University, B
Mid-Continent University, B
Morehead State University, AB
Murray State University, B
University of the Cumberlands, B
Western Kentucky University, AB

Louisiana

Delgado Community College, A
Louisiana State University and Agricultural and Mechanical College, B
Louisiana State University at Alexandria, B
Louisiana State University at Eunice, A
Louisiana State University in Shreveport, B
Louisiana Tech University, AB
Loyola University New Orleans, B
McNeese State University, AB
Nicholls State University, AB
Northwestern State University of Louisiana, AB
Our Lady of Holy Cross College, B
Our Lady of the Lake College, A
Southeastern Louisiana University, AB
Southern University at Shreveport, A
University of Louisiana at Lafayette, B
University of Louisiana at Monroe, AB
University of New Orleans, B

University of Phoenix-Louisiana Campus, A

Maine

Central Maine Community College, A
Kennebec Valley Community College, A
Southern Maine Community College, A
The University of Maine at Augusta, B
University of Maine at Farmington, B
University of Maine at Fort Kent, A
University of Maine at Machias, B
York County Community College, A

Maryland

Carroll Community College, A
Cecil Community College, A
Columbia Union College, AB
Frederick Community College, A
Garrett College, A
Howard Community College, A
Montgomery College, A

Massachusetts

Bay State College, A
Bristol Community College, A
Bunker Hill Community College, A
Eastern Nazarene College, A
Fitchburg State College, BM
Massachusetts Bay Community College, A
Middlesex Community College, A
Mount Wachusett Community College, A
Northern Essex Community College, A
Quincy College, A
Quinsigamond Community College, A
Roxbury Community College, A
Springfield College, B
Springfield Technical Community College, A
University of Massachusetts Amherst, B

Michigan

Alpena Community College, A
Aquinas College, B
Concordia University, A
Finlandia University, A
Hope College, B
Jackson Community College, A
Kellogg Community College, A
Lawrence Technological University, A
Macomb Community College, A
Madonna University, B
Marygrove College, B
Michigan Technological University, B
Mid Michigan Community College, A
Mott Community College, A
Northern Michigan University, A
Oakland Community College, A
Saginaw Valley State University, B
Siena Heights University, AB
Southwestern Michigan College, A
University of Michigan, B
University of Michigan-Dearborn, B
Western Michigan University, B

Minnesota

Concordia University, St. Paul, AB
Crown College, AB
Itasca Community College, A
Metropolitan State University, B
Oak Hills Christian College, A
Rochester Community and Technical College, A

Mississippi

Copiah-Lincoln Community College-Natchez Campus, A
William Carey College, B

Missouri

Avila University, AB
Crowder College, A
East Central College, A
Grantham University, AB
Messenger College, A
Missouri State University-West Plains, A
Southeast Missouri State University, B
Southwest Baptist University, A
University of Missouri-Columbia, B

University of Missouri-St. Louis, B

Montana

Blackfeet Community College, A
Carroll College, B
Montana State University-Billings, A
Montana State University-Great Falls College of Technology, A
The University of Montana-Helena College of Technology, A

Nebraska

College of Saint Mary, AB
Northeast Community College, A
University of Nebraska at Kearney, B
University of Nebraska at Omaha, B
Western Nebraska Community College, A
York College, B

Nevada

University of Nevada, Reno, B
Western Nevada Community College, A

New Hampshire

Granite State College, A
Keene State College, B
New Hampshire Community Technical College, Berlin/Laconia, A
New Hampshire Community Technical College, Nashua/Claremont, A
New Hampshire Technical Institute, A
University of New Hampshire, A

New Jersey

Atlantic Cape Community College, A
Fairleigh Dickinson University, Metropolitan Campus, B
Middlesex County College, A
Monmouth University, A
Ocean County College, A
Rider University, AB

New Mexico

Eastern New Mexico University, A
New Mexico Institute of Mining and Technology, A
New Mexico State University, B
St. John's College, B
San Juan College, A
Santa Fe Community College, A
University of New Mexico, B
University of New Mexico-Gallup, AB

New York

Adirondack Community College, A
Alfred University, B
Buffalo State College, State University of New York, B
Canisius College, B
Corning Community College, A
Herkimer County Community College, A
Mohawk Valley Community College, A
Nassau Community College, A
New York University, A
Niagara County Community College, A
Nyack College, A
Rochester Institute of Technology, AB
St. Joseph's College, New York, B
State University of New York College of Technology at Delhi, A
State University of New York Institute of Technology, B

North Carolina

Bladen Community College, A
Brevard College, B
Campbell University, B
Durham Technical Community College, A
Fayetteville Technical Community College, A
Johnson C. Smith University, B
Martin Community College, A
Wake Technical Community College, A
Wilson Technical Community College, A

Winston-Salem State University, B

North Dakota

Mayville State University, B
Minot State University, B
University of Mary, B
University of North Dakota, B

Ohio

Cincinnati State Technical and Community
    College, A
Cleveland State University, B
Franciscan University of Steubenville, A
God's Bible School and College, B
Kent State University, B
Kent State University, Trumbull Campus, B
Kettering College of Medical Arts, A
Mercy College of Northwest Ohio, A
Miami University Hamilton, A
Mount Vernon Nazarene University, A
Ohio Dominican University, AB
Ohio Northern University, B
Ohio University, B
Ohio Wesleyan University, B
Owens Community College, A
Shawnee State University, AB
Terra State Community College, A
The University of Akron-Wayne College, A
University of Dayton, B
University of Rio Grande, A
The University of Toledo, AB
Youngstown State University, B

Oklahoma

Bacone College, A
Connors State College, A
East Central University, B
Hillsdale Free Will Baptist College, A
Oklahoma Panhandle State University, A
Southeastern Oklahoma State University, B
Southwestern Oklahoma State University at
    Sayre, A
Western Oklahoma State College, A

Oregon

Clackamas Community College, A
Oregon Coast Community College, A
Tillamook Bay Community College, A

Pennsylvania

Butler County Community College, A
Community College of Allegheny County, A
Delaware County Community College, A
Drexel University, B
Duquesne University, B
Indiana University of Pennsylvania, AB
Kutztown University of Pennsylvania, B
La Roche College, B
Lackawanna College, A
Lebanon Valley College, A
Lehigh Carbon Community College, A
Luzerne County Community College, A
Mount Aloysius College, A
Northampton County Area Community College, A
Pennsylvania College of Technology, A
Point Park University, B
Seton Hill University, B
Temple University, AB

Puerto Rico

University of Puerto Rico, Río Piedras, B

Rhode Island

Community College of Rhode Island, A
Providence College, B

South Carolina

Columbia International University, B

South Dakota

Black Hills State University, A
Dakota State University, A
Mount Marty College, AB
Presentation College, A
South Dakota School of Mines and Technology, A

The University of South Dakota, A

Tennessee

Cleveland State Community College, A
Crichton College, B
East Tennessee State University, B
Southern Adventist University, A
Southwest Tennessee Community College, A
Trevecca Nazarene University, A
University of Memphis, B

Texas

Amarillo College, A
Angelo State University, B
Brazosport College, A
Clarendon College, A
College of the Mainland, A
Concordia University at Austin, A
Dallas Baptist University, B
Howard Payne University, B
Kilgore College, A
Lamar State College-Port Arthur, A
Southwestern Assemblies of God University, AB
Texas A&M University-Texarkana, B
Texas Christian University, B
Texas Southern University, B
Texas Tech University, B
University of Mary Hardin-Baylor, B
University of North Texas, B
University of St. Thomas, B
The University of Texas-Pan American, B
The University of Texas at Tyler, B
West Texas A&M University, B

Utah

Salt Lake Community College, A
Utah State University, A
Utah Valley State College, A

Vermont

Castleton State College, A
Johnson State College, A
Woodbury College, A

Virginia

Averett University, A
Central Virginia Community College, A
Eastern Mennonite University, A
Germanna Community College, A
Hampton University, B
Liberty University, AB
New River Community College, A
Piedmont Virginia Community College, A
Radford University, B
Southside Virginia Community College, A
Virginia Commonwealth University, B
Virginia Intermont College, A

Washington

City University, AB
Grays Harbor College, A
Northwest Indian College, A
Northwest University, A
Seattle Pacific University, B
Tacoma Community College, A
University of Washington, B
Western Washington University, B

West Virginia

Alderson-Broaddus College, A
American Public University System, A
Bluefield State College, B
Community and Technical College of Shepherd, A
Eastern West Virginia Community and Technical
    College, A
Fairmont State Community & Technical College, A
Marshall University, B
Shepherd University, B
University of Charleston, B
West Virginia State Community and Technical
    College, A

West Virginia University, B

Wisconsin

Alverno College, B
Cardinal Stritch University, M
Concordia University Wisconsin, B
Silver Lake College, A
University of Wisconsin-Green Bay, B
University of Wisconsin-La Crosse, B
University of Wisconsin-Stevens Point, B
University of Wisconsin-Superior, A

Wyoming

Central Wyoming College, A
Eastern Wyoming College, A
Sheridan College-Sheridan and Gillette, A
Western Wyoming Community College, A

Alberta

Athabasca University, B
University of Calgary, B

British Columbia

Open Learning Agency, B
Simon Fraser University, B
Trinity Western University, B
University of Northern British Columbia, B

Manitoba

Brandon University, B

Ontario

Ryerson University, B
University of Windsor, B

GENETIC COUNSELING/COUNSELOR

California

California State University, Northridge, M
University of California, Berkeley, MO
University of California, Irvine, M

Illinois

Northwestern University, M

Maryland

The Johns Hopkins University, M

Massachusetts

Boston University, M
Brandeis University, M

Minnesota

University of Minnesota, Twin Cities Campus, M

New York

Sarah Lawrence College, M

Ohio

Case Western Reserve University, M
University of Cincinnati, M

Oklahoma

University of Oklahoma Health Sciences Center, M

Pennsylvania

Arcadia University, M
University of Pittsburgh, M

South Carolina

University of South Carolina, M

Texas

The University of Texas Health Science Center at
    Houston, M

Virginia

Virginia Commonwealth University, M

Ontario

University of Toronto, M

Quebec

McGill University, M

GENETICS

Alabama

The University of Alabama at Birmingham, D

Arizona

Arizona State University, MD
The University of Arizona, MD

California

California Institute of Technology, D
Stanford University, D
University of California, Davis, BMD
University of California, Irvine, D
University of California, Riverside, D
University of California, San Diego, D
University of Southern California, D

Colorado

Colorado State University, MD
University of Colorado at Boulder, MD

Connecticut

University of Connecticut, MD
Wesleyan University, D
Yale University, DO

Delaware

University of Delaware, MD

District of Columbia

The George Washington University, MD
Howard University, MD

Florida

Florida State University, MD
University of Florida, D
University of Miami, MD

Georgia

Emory University, D
University of Georgia, BMD

Hawaii

University of Hawaii at Manoa, MD

Illinois

Illinois State University, D
Northwestern University, D
University of Chicago, D
University of Illinois at Chicago, D

Indiana

Indiana University Bloomington, D
Purdue University, MD
University of Notre Dame, MD

Iowa

Iowa State University of Science and
  Technology, BMD
The University of Iowa, MDO

Kansas

Kansas State University, MD

Maryland

The Johns Hopkins University, MD

Massachusetts

Brandeis University, D
Harvard University, D
Massachusetts Institute of Technology, D

Tufts University, D

Michigan

Michigan State University, MD
Wayne State University, MD

Minnesota

University of Minnesota, Twin Cities Campus, MD

Missouri

University of Missouri-Columbia, D
Washington University in St. Louis, MDO

New Hampshire

Dartmouth College, D
University of New Hampshire, MD

New Jersey

Rutgers, The State University of New Jersey, New
  Brunswick/Piscataway, MD

New Mexico

University of New Mexico, MD

New York

Cornell University, BD
State University of New York Downstate Medical
  Center, D
Stony Brook University, State University of New
  York, D
University at Albany, State University of New
  York, MD
University of Rochester, MD

North Carolina

Duke University, D
North Carolina State University, MD
The University of North Carolina at Chapel Hill, MD

North Dakota

University of North Dakota, MD

Ohio

Case Western Reserve University, DO
The Ohio State University, MD
Ohio Wesleyan University, B

Oregon

Oregon Health & Science University, D
Oregon State University, MD
University of Oregon, D

Pennsylvania

Carnegie Mellon University, D
Drexel University, MDO
The Pennsylvania State University University Park
  Campus, MD
Temple University, DO
Thomas Jefferson University, D
University of Pennsylvania, DO

South Carolina

Clemson University, BMD

Tennessee

The University of Tennessee, MD

Texas

Texas A&M University, MD
Texas A&M University System Health Science
  Center, D
The University of Texas at Austin, D
The University of Texas Health Science Center at
  Houston, MDO
The University of Texas Medical Branch, MD

The University of Texas Southwestern Medical
  Center at Dallas, D

Utah

University of Utah, MD

Virginia

Virginia Commonwealth University, D
Virginia Polytechnic Institute and State
  University, MD

Washington

University of Washington, MD
Washington State University, BMD

West Virginia

West Virginia University, MD

Wisconsin

Marquette University, MD
University of Wisconsin-Madison, MD

Alberta

University of Alberta, MD

British Columbia

The University of British Columbia, MD

Ontario

McMaster University, MD
University of Toronto, MD

Quebec

Université du Québec àChicoutimi, M

GENOMIC SCIENCES

Connecticut

University of Connecticut, M
Yale University, DO

District of Columbia

The George Washington University, M

Florida

University of Florida, D

Massachusetts

Harvard University, D

North Carolina

Duke University, D
North Carolina State University, MD
Wake Forest University, D

North Dakota

North Dakota State University, MD

Ohio

Case Western Reserve University, DO
University of Cincinnati, MD

Pennsylvania

University of Pennsylvania, DO

Tennessee

The University of Tennessee, MD

Texas

Texas A&M University, D

Washington

University of Washington, D

Quebec

Concordia University, O

GEOCHEMISTRY

Arizona

Northern Arizona University, B

California

California Institute of Technology, BMD
California State University, Fullerton, M

Pomona College, B
University of California, Los Angeles, BMD

Colorado

Colorado School of Mines, MD

Connecticut

Yale University, D

Georgia

Georgia Institute of Technology, MD

Hawaii

University of Hawaii at Manoa, MD

Illinois

University of Illinois at Chicago, MD
University of Illinois at Urbana-Champaign, MD

Indiana

Indiana University Bloomington, MD

Maine

Bowdoin College, B

Maryland

The Johns Hopkins University, MD

Massachusetts

Bridgewater State College, B
Harvard University, B
Massachusetts Institute of Technology, D

Michigan

University of Michigan, MD
Western Michigan University, B

Missouri

University of Missouri-Rolla, MD
Washington University in St. Louis, D

Montana

Montana Tech of The University of Montana, M

Nevada

University of Nevada, Reno, MD

New Mexico

New Mexico Institute of Mining and Technology, MD

New York

Columbia College, B
Cornell University, MD
Rensselaer Polytechnic Institute, MD
State University of New York College at Cortland, B
State University of New York College at Geneseo, B
State University of New York, Fredonia, B
State University of New York at Oswego, B

Ohio

Ohio University, M
Wright State University, M

Rhode Island

Brown University, B

British Columbia

University of Victoria, MD

New Brunswick

University of New Brunswick Fredericton, B

Ontario

McMaster University, D
University of Waterloo, B

GEODETIC SCIENCES

Ohio

The Ohio State University, MD

Virginia

George Mason University, O

New Brunswick

University of New Brunswick Fredericton, MDO

Quebec

Université Laval, MD

GEOGRAPHIC INFORMATION SYSTEMS

Arizona

Northern Arizona University, MO

Arkansas

University of Central Arkansas, O

California

University of Redlands, MO

Colorado

University of Denver, M

Florida

Florida State University, M

Georgia

Georgia Institute of Technology, M

Idaho

Idaho State University, M

Massachusetts

Boston University, M
Clark University, M

Minnesota

Saint Mary's University of Minnesota, MO
University of Minnesota, Twin Cities Campus, M

Missouri

Northwest Missouri State University, M

New York

Hunter College of the City University of New York, MO
State University of New York at Buffalo, O
University at Albany, State University of New York, O

North Carolina

North Carolina State University, M

Ohio

The University of Akron, M

Pennsylvania

The Pennsylvania State University University Park Campus, M
University of Pittsburgh, M

Texas

Texas State University-San Marcos, MD
The University of Texas at Dallas, MD

Virginia

George Mason University, MD

West Virginia

West Virginia University, MD

Wisconsin

University of Wisconsin-Madison, MO

Quebec

Université du Québec àMontréal, O

GEOGRAPHY

Alabama

Auburn University, BM
Jacksonville State University, B

Samford University, B
The University of Alabama, BM
University of North Alabama, B
University of South Alabama, B

Alaska

University of Alaska Fairbanks, B

Arizona

Arizona State University, BMD
Northern Arizona University, BMO
The University of Arizona, BMD

Arkansas

Arkansas State University, B
University of Arkansas, BM
University of Central Arkansas, BO

California

Bakersfield College, A
California State Polytechnic University, Pomona, B
California State University, Chico, BM
California State University, Dominguez Hills, B
California State University, East Bay, BM
California State University, Fresno, B
California State University, Fullerton, BM
California State University, Long Beach, BM
California State University, Los Angeles, BM
California State University, Northridge, BM
California State University, Sacramento, B
California State University, San Bernardino, B
California State University, Stanislaus, B
Cañada College, A
Cerritos College, A
College of Alameda, A
College of the Canyons, A
College of the Desert, A
Contra Costa College, A
Cypress College, A
East Los Angeles College, A
El Camino College, A
Grossmont College, A
Humboldt State University, B
Los Angeles Mission College, A
Los Angeles Valley College, A
Orange Coast College, A
Pasadena City College, A
Saddleback College, A
San Bernardino Valley College, A
San Diego Mesa College, A
San Diego Miramar College, A
San Diego State University, BMD
San Francisco State University, BM
San Jose State University, BMO
Santa Ana College, A
Santa Barbara City College, A
Santa Monica College, A
Santa Rosa Junior College, A
Santiago Canyon College, A
Sonoma State University, B
Southwestern College, A
University of California, Berkeley, BD
University of California, Davis, MD
University of California, Los Angeles, BMD
University of California, Santa Barbara, BMD
University of Southern California, BMD
West Hills Community College, A
West Los Angeles College, A

Colorado

Parks College (Denver), A
United States Air Force Academy, B
University of Colorado at Boulder, BMD
University of Colorado at Colorado Springs, BM
University of Colorado at Denver and Health Sciences Center - Downtown Denver Campus, B
University of Denver, BMD
University of Northern Colorado, B

Connecticut

Central Connecticut State University, BM
Southern Connecticut State University, B

University of Connecticut, BMD

Delaware

University of Delaware, BMD

District of Columbia

The George Washington University, BM
University of the District of Columbia, B

Florida

Florida Agricultural and Mechanical University, B
Florida Atlantic University, BM
Florida International University, B
Florida State University, BMD
Jacksonville University, B
Stetson University, B
University of Florida, BMD
University of Miami, B
University of South Florida, BM
The University of Tampa, A

Georgia

Dalton State College, A
Darton College, A
Gainesville College, A
Georgia Southern University, B
Georgia State University, BM
University of Georgia, BMD
University of West Georgia, B

Hawaii

University of Hawaii at Hilo, B
University of Hawaii at Manoa, BMD

Idaho

Brigham Young University -Idaho, A
College of Southern Idaho, A
University of Idaho, BMD

Illinois

Augustana College, B
Chicago State University, BM
Concordia University, B
DePaul University, B
Eastern Illinois University, B
Elmhurst College, B
Illinois State University, B
Joliet Junior College, A
Lincoln College, A
Northeastern Illinois University, BM
Northern Illinois University, BM
Northwestern University, B
Roosevelt University, B
Southern Illinois University Carbondale, BMD
Southern Illinois University Edwardsville, BM
University of Chicago, B
University of Illinois at Chicago, M
University of Illinois at Urbana-Champaign, BMD
Western Illinois University, BMO

Indiana

Ball State University, B
Indiana State University, BMD
Indiana University Bloomington, BMD
Indiana University-Purdue University Indianapolis, B
Indiana University Southeast, B
Valparaiso University, B
Vincennes University, A

Iowa

The University of Iowa, BMD
University of Northern Iowa, BM

Kansas

Allen County Community College, A
Kansas State University, BMD
Pittsburg State University, B
University of Kansas, BMD

Kentucky

Eastern Kentucky University, B
Morehead State University, B
Murray State University, B
Northern Kentucky University, B

University of Kentucky, BMD
University of Louisville, B
Western Kentucky University, BM

Louisiana

Louisiana State University and Agricultural and
  Mechanical College, BMD
Louisiana State University in Shreveport, B
Louisiana Tech University, B
University of New Orleans, BM

Maine

University of Maine at Farmington, B
University of Southern Maine, B

Maryland

Frostburg State University, B
The Johns Hopkins University, BMD
Salisbury University, B
Towson University, BM
University of Maryland, Baltimore County, B
University of Maryland, College Park, BMDO

Massachusetts

Boston University, BMD
Bridgewater State College, B
Clark University, BD
Fitchburg State College, B
Framingham State College, B
Mount Holyoke College, B
Salem State College, BM
Simon's Rock College of Bard, B
University of Massachusetts Amherst, BM
University of Massachusetts Boston, B
Westfield State College, B
Worcester State College, B

Michigan

Aquinas College, B
Calvin College, B
Central Michigan University, B
Eastern Michigan University, BM
Lansing Community College, A
Michigan State University, BMD
Northern Michigan University, B
Wayne State University, BM
Western Michigan University, BM

Minnesota

Bemidji State University, B
Gustavus Adolphus College, B
Itasca Community College, A
Macalester College, B
Minnesota State University Mankato, BM
St. Cloud State University, BM
University of Minnesota, Duluth, B
University of Minnesota, Twin Cities Campus, BMD
University of St. Thomas, B
Vermilion Community College, A

Mississippi

Mississippi Delta Community College, A
University of Southern Mississippi, BM

Missouri

Central Missouri State University, B
East Central College, A
Jefferson College, A
Missouri State University, BM
Northwest Missouri State University, BM
Park University, B
Southeast Missouri State University, B
University of Missouri-Columbia, BM
University of Missouri-Kansas City, B

Montana

The University of Montana-Missoula, BM

Nebraska

Concordia University, B
University of Nebraska at Kearney, B
University of Nebraska-Lincoln, BMD
University of Nebraska at Omaha, BMO
Wayne State College, B

Western Nebraska Community College, A

Nevada

University of Nevada, Reno, BM

New Hampshire

Dartmouth College, B
Keene State College, B
Plymouth State University, B
University of New Hampshire, B

New Jersey

Montclair State University, B
Rowan University, B
Rutgers, The State University of New Jersey, New
  Brunswick/Piscataway, BMD
William Paterson University of New Jersey, B

New Mexico

New Mexico State University, BM
University of New Mexico, BM

New York

Barnard College, B
Buffalo State College, State University of New
  York, B
City College of the City University of New York, B
Colgate University, B
Excelsior College, B
Hofstra University, B
Hunter College of the City University of New
  York, BMO
Lehman College of the City University of New
  York, B
Long Island University, C.W. Post Campus, B
State University of New York at Binghamton, BM
State University of New York at Buffalo, BMDO
State University of New York College at Cortland, B
State University of New York College at Geneseo, B
State University of New York College at Oneonta, B
State University of New York at New Paltz, B
State University of New York at Plattsburgh, B
Syracuse University, BMD
United States Military Academy, B
University at Albany, State University of New
  York, BMO
Vassar College, B

North Carolina

Appalachian State University, BM
East Carolina University, BM
Fayetteville State University, B
North Carolina Central University, B
The University of North Carolina at Chapel
  Hill, BMD
The University of North Carolina at Charlotte, BM
The University of North Carolina at Greensboro, BM
The University of North Carolina Wilmington, B
Western Carolina University, B

North Dakota

Cankdeska Cikana Community College, A
Dickinson State University, B
University of North Dakota, BM

Ohio

Bowling Green State University, B
Kent State University, BMD
Miami University, BM
Miami University Hamilton, B
Miami University-Middletown Campus, A
The Ohio State University, BMD
Ohio University, BM
Ohio University-Eastern, B
Ohio Wesleyan University, B
The University of Akron, BM
University of Cincinnati, BMD
The University of Toledo, BM
Wittenberg University, B
Wright State University, AB
Wright State University, Lake Campus, A

Youngstown State University, B

Oklahoma

Northeastern State University, B
Oklahoma State University, BM
Tulsa Community College, A
University of Central Oklahoma, B
University of Oklahoma, BMD

Oregon

Oregon State University, BMD
Portland State University, BMD
Southern Oregon University, B
University of Oregon, BMD
Western Oregon University, B

Pennsylvania

Bloomsburg University of Pennsylvania, B
Bucknell University, B
California University of Pennsylvania, BM
Cheyney University of Pennsylvania, B
Clarion University of Pennsylvania, B
East Stroudsburg University of Pennsylvania, B
Edinboro University of Pennsylvania, B
Indiana University of Pennsylvania, BM
Kutztown University of Pennsylvania, B
Lock Haven University of Pennsylvania, B
Mansfield University of Pennsylvania, B
Millersville University of Pennsylvania, B
Pennsylvania Highland Community College, A
The Pennsylvania State University Abington
    College, B
The Pennsylvania State University Altoona
    College, B
The Pennsylvania State University Beaver Campus
    of the Commonwealth College, B
The Pennsylvania State University Berks Campus of
    the Berks-Lehigh Valley College, B
The Pennsylvania State University Delaware County
    Campus of the Commonwealth College, B
The Pennsylvania State University DuBois Campus
    of the Commonwealth College, B
The Pennsylvania State University at Erie, The
    Behrend College, B
The Pennsylvania State University Fayette Campus
    of the Commonwealth College, B
The Pennsylvania State University Hazleton
    Campus of the Commonwealth College, B
The Pennsylvania State University, Lehigh Valley
    Campus of the Berks-Lehigh Valley College, B
The Pennsylvania State University McKeesport
    Campus of the Commonwealth College, B
The Pennsylvania State University Mont Alto
    Campus of the Commonwealth College, B
The Pennsylvania State University New Kensington
    Campus of the Commonwealth College, B
The Pennsylvania State University Schuylkill
    Campus of the Capital College, B
The Pennsylvania State University Shenango
    Campus of the Commonwealth College, B
The Pennsylvania State University University Park
    Campus, BMD
The Pennsylvania State University Wilkes-Barre
    Campus of the Commonwealth College, B
The Pennsylvania State University Worthington
    Scranton Campus of the Commonwealth
    College, B
The Pennsylvania State University York Campus of
    the Commonwealth College, B
Shippensburg University of Pennsylvania, B
Slippery Rock University of Pennsylvania, B
Temple University, BM
University of Pittsburgh at Johnstown, B
Villanova University, B

West Chester University of Pennsylvania, BM

Puerto Rico

University of Puerto Rico, Río Piedras, B

Rhode Island

Rhode Island College, B

South Carolina

Francis Marion University, B
University of South Carolina, BMD

South Dakota

South Dakota State University, BM

Tennessee

Columbia State Community College, A
East Tennessee State University, B
Pellissippi State Technical Community College, A
University of Memphis, BM
The University of Tennessee, BMD
The University of Tennessee at Martin, B

Texas

Del Mar College, A
Hill College of the Hill Junior College District, A
Sam Houston State University, B
Stephen F. Austin State University, B
Texas A&M University, BMD
Texas A&M University-Commerce, B
Texas A&M University-Kingsville, B
Texas State University-San Marcos, BMD
Texas Tech University, B
University of Houston-Clear Lake, B
University of North Texas, BM
The University of Texas at Austin, BMDO
The University of Texas at Dallas, B
The University of Texas at El Paso, B
The University of Texas at San Antonio, B
West Texas A&M University, B

Utah

Brigham Young University, BM
Snow College, A
University of Utah, BMD
Utah State University, BMD
Weber State University, B

Vermont

Middlebury College, B
University of Vermont, B

Virginia

Emory & Henry College, B
George Mason University, BM
James Madison University, B
Longwood University, B
Old Dominion University, B
Radford University, B
University of Mary Washington, B
Virginia Polytechnic Institute and State
    University, BM

Washington

Central Washington University, B
Eastern Washington University, B
Lower Columbia College, A
Skagit Valley College, A
University of Washington, BMD
Western Washington University, BM

West Virginia

Concord University, B
Marshall University, BM
West Virginia University, BMD

Wisconsin

Carthage College, B
University of Wisconsin-Eau Claire, B
University of Wisconsin-La Crosse, B
University of Wisconsin-Madison, BMDO
University of Wisconsin-Milwaukee, BMDO
University of Wisconsin-Oshkosh, B
University of Wisconsin-Parkside, B

University of Wisconsin-River Falls, B
University of Wisconsin-Stevens Point, B
University of Wisconsin-Whitewater, B

Wyoming

University of Wyoming, BM
Western Wyoming Community College, A

Alberta

Southern Alberta Institute of Technology, B
University of Alberta, B
University of Calgary, BMD
University of Lethbridge, BM

British Columbia

Kwantlen University College, A
Simon Fraser University, BMD
Thompson Rivers University, B
Trinity Western University, B
The University of British Columbia, BMD
University College of the Fraser Valley, B
University of Northern British Columbia, B
University of Victoria, BMD

Manitoba

Brandon University, B
Canadian Mennonite University, B
University of Manitoba, BMD
The University of Winnipeg, B

New Brunswick

Mount Allison University, B
Université de Moncton, B

Newfoundland and Labrador

Memorial University of Newfoundland, BMD

Nova Scotia

Saint Mary's University, B

Ontario

Brock University, B
Carleton University, BMD
Lakehead University, B
Laurentian University, B
McMaster University, BMD
Nipissing University, B
Queen's University at Kingston, BMD
Ryerson University, B
Trent University, BMD
University of Guelph, BMD
University of Ottawa, BMD
University of Toronto, BMD
University of Waterloo, BMD
The University of Western Ontario, BMD
Wilfrid Laurier University, BMD
York University, BMD

Prince Edward Island

University of Prince Edward Island, M

Quebec

Bishop's University, B
Concordia University, BO
McGill University, BMD
Université Laval, ABMD
Université de Montréal, BMDO
Université du Québec àChicoutimi, B
Université du Québec àMontréal, BM
Université du Québec àRimouski, B
Université du Québec àTrois-Rivières, B

Université de Sherbrooke, BMD

Saskatchewan

University of Regina, BM
University of Saskatchewan, BMD

GEOGRAPHY TEACHER EDUCATION

Illinois

Chicago State University, B

Indiana

University of Evansville, B
Valparaiso University, B

Iowa

The University of Iowa, B

Massachusetts

Fitchburg State College, B
Framingham State College, B

Michigan

Northern Michigan University, B
Western Michigan University, B

Nebraska

Concordia University, B
Wayne State College, B

New Hampshire

Keene State College, B

North Dakota

Mayville State University, B

Ohio

Shawnee State University, B

Tennessee

Cumberland University, B
The University of Tennessee at Martin, B

Ontario

University of Windsor, B

Quebec

Bishop's University, B
Université Laval, B

GEOLOGICAL AND EARTH SCIENCES/GEOSCIENCES

Arkansas

University of Arkansas, B

California

California State University, Chico, B
San Jose State University, B
University of California, Los Angeles, B

Connecticut

Yale University, B

Florida

University of Miami, B

Georgia

Georgia Institute of Technology, B
University of West Georgia, B

Illinois

University of Illinois at Urbana-Champaign, B

Iowa

University of Northern Iowa, B

Massachusetts

Bridgewater State College, B

Michigan

Western Michigan University, B

Missouri

Southeast Missouri State University, B

Nevada

University of Nevada, Las Vegas, B

New Jersey

Montclair State University, B
Princeton University, B

New York

Queens College of the City University of New York, B
State University of New York College at Brockport, B

North Carolina

The University of North Carolina at Charlotte, B

Ohio

Ohio University, B
The University of Akron, B

Oklahoma

University of Oklahoma, B

Pennsylvania

Bucknell University, B
Lehigh University, B
The Pennsylvania State University Abington College, B
The Pennsylvania State University Altoona College, B
The Pennsylvania State University Beaver Campus of the Commonwealth College, B
The Pennsylvania State University Berks Campus of the Berks-Lehigh Valley College, B
The Pennsylvania State University Delaware County Campus of the Commonwealth College, B
The Pennsylvania State University DuBois Campus of the Commonwealth College, B
The Pennsylvania State University at Erie, The Behrend College, B
The Pennsylvania State University Fayette Campus of the Commonwealth College, B
The Pennsylvania State University Hazleton Campus of the Commonwealth College, B
The Pennsylvania State University, Lehigh Valley Campus of the Berks-Lehigh Valley College, B
The Pennsylvania State University McKeesport Campus of the Commonwealth College, B
The Pennsylvania State University Mont Alto Campus of the Commonwealth College, B
The Pennsylvania State University New Kensington Campus of the Commonwealth College, B
The Pennsylvania State University Schuylkill Campus of the Capital College, B
The Pennsylvania State University Shenango Campus of the Commonwealth College, B
The Pennsylvania State University University Park Campus, B
The Pennsylvania State University Wilkes-Barre Campus of the Commonwealth College, B
The Pennsylvania State University Worthington Scranton Campus of the Commonwealth College, B
The Pennsylvania State University York Campus of the Commonwealth College, B
University of Pittsburgh, B

Texas

Baylor University, B
Texas A&M University, B

The University of Texas at Austin, B

Utah

Brigham Young University, B
University of Utah, B

Virginia

Washington and Lee University, B

Wyoming

University of Wyoming, B

British Columbia

Kwantlen University College, A

GEOLOGICAL ENGINEERING

Alaska

University of Alaska Fairbanks, MO

Arizona

Arizona State University, MD

California

University of California, Berkeley, MD

Colorado

Colorado School of Mines, MDO

Idaho

University of Idaho, M

Michigan

Michigan Technological University, MD

Minnesota

University of Minnesota, Twin Cities Campus, MD

Missouri

University of Missouri-Rolla, MD

Montana

Montana Tech of The University of Montana, M

Nevada

University of Nevada, Reno, MO

North Dakota

University of North Dakota, M

Oklahoma

University of Oklahoma, MD

Pennsylvania

Drexel University, M

South Dakota

South Dakota School of Mines and Technology, MD

Utah

University of Utah, MD

Wisconsin

University of Wisconsin-Madison, MD

British Columbia

The University of British Columbia, MD

GEOLOGICAL/GEOPHYSICAL ENGINEERING

Alabama

Auburn University, B

Alaska

University of Alaska Fairbanks, B

Arizona

The University of Arizona, B

California

University of California, Berkeley, B
University of California, Los Angeles, B

Colorado

Colorado School of Mines, B

Idaho

University of Idaho, B

Massachusetts

Harvard University, B
Tufts University, B

Michigan

Michigan Technological University, B

Minnesota

University of Minnesota, Twin Cities Campus, B

Mississippi

University of Mississippi, B

Missouri

University of Missouri-Rolla, B

Montana

Montana Tech of The University of Montana, B

Nevada

University of Nevada, Reno, B

New Jersey

New Jersey Institute of Technology, B
Rutgers, The State University of New Jersey, Newark, B

New York

Cornell University, B
University of Rochester, B

North Dakota

University of North Dakota, B

Ohio

The University of Akron, B

Oregon

Oregon State University, B

South Dakota

South Dakota School of Mines and Technology, B

Utah

University of Utah, B

Alberta

University of Calgary, B

British Columbia

The University of British Columbia, B

Manitoba

University of Manitoba, B

New Brunswick

University of New Brunswick Fredericton, B
University of New Brunswick Saint John, B

Newfoundland and Labrador

Memorial University of Newfoundland, B

Ontario

Laurentian University, B
Queen's University at Kingston, B
University of Toronto, B

University of Waterloo, B

Quebec

Université Laval, B
Université du Québec àChicoutimi, B

Saskatchewan

University of Saskatchewan, B

GEOLOGY/EARTH SCIENCE

Alabama

Auburn University, BM
Jacksonville State University, B
The University of Alabama, BMD
University of North Alabama, B
University of South Alabama, B

Alaska

University of Alaska Fairbanks, BMD

Arizona

Arizona State University, B
Arizona Western College, A
Diné College, A
Eastern Arizona College, A
Northern Arizona University, BM
The University of Arizona, B

Arkansas

Arkansas Tech University, B
University of Arkansas, BM
University of Arkansas at Little Rock, B

California

Bakersfield College, A
California Institute of Technology, BMD
California Lutheran University, B
California State Polytechnic University, Pomona, B
California State University, Bakersfield, BM
California State University, Chico, BM
California State University, Dominguez Hills, B
California State University, East Bay, BM
California State University, Fresno, BM
California State University, Fullerton, BM
California State University, Long Beach, BM
California State University, Los Angeles, BM
California State University, Monterey Bay, B
California State University, Northridge, BM
California State University, Sacramento, B
California State University, San Bernardino, B
California State University, Stanislaus, B
Cañada College, A
Cerritos College, A
Chaffey College, A
City College of San Francisco, A
College of the Canyons, A
College of the Desert, A
College of Marin, A
College of San Mateo, A
College of the Siskiyous, A
Columbia College, A
Contra Costa College, A
Cosumnes River College (Sacramento), A
Crafton Hills College, A
Cuesta College, A
Cypress College, A
East Los Angeles College, A
El Camino College, A
Folsom Lake College, A
Fullerton College, A
Grossmont College, A
Humboldt State University, B
Loma Linda University, M
Los Angeles Valley College, A
Monterey Peninsula College, A
Moorpark College, A
National University, B
Occidental College, B
Orange Coast College, A
Palomar College, A
Pasadena City College, A
Pomona College, B
Saddleback College, A

San Bernardino Valley College, A
San Diego State University, BM
San Francisco State University, B
San Joaquin Delta College, A
San Jose State University, BM
Santa Ana College, A
Santa Barbara City College, A
Santa Monica College, A
Santa Rosa Junior College, A
Santiago Canyon College, A
Scripps College, B
Sierra College, A
Sonoma State University, B
Southwestern College, A
Stanford University, B
University of California, Berkeley, BMD
University of California, Davis, BMD
University of California, Irvine, B
University of California, Los Angeles, BMD
University of California, Riverside, BMD
University of California, San Diego, B
University of California, Santa Barbara, BMD
University of California, Santa Cruz, B
University of the Pacific, B
University of Southern California, B
West Hills Community College, A
West Los Angeles College, A

Colorado

Adams State College, B
The Colorado College, B
Colorado Mountain College, Alpine Campus, A
Colorado Northwestern Community College, A
Colorado School of Mines, MDO
Colorado State University, BM
Fort Lewis College, B
Mesa State College, AB
Red Rocks Community College, A
University of Colorado at Boulder, BMD
University of Northern Colorado, B
Western State College of Colorado, B

Connecticut

Central Connecticut State University, B
Southern Connecticut State University, B
University of Connecticut, BMD
Wesleyan University, B
Western Connecticut State University, B
Yale University, D

Delaware

University of Delaware, BMD

District of Columbia

The George Washington University, BMD

Florida

Daytona Beach Community College, A
Florida Atlantic University, BM
Florida International University, B
Florida State University, BMD
Miami Dade College, A
Pensacola Junior College, A
University of Florida, BMD
University of Miami, B
University of South Florida, BMD

Georgia

Clayton State University, A
Coastal Georgia Community College, A
Columbus State University, B
Dalton State College, A
East Georgia College, A
Gainesville College, A
Georgia Highlands College, A
Georgia Perimeter College, A
Georgia Southern University, B
Georgia Southwestern State University, B
Georgia State University, BM
Piedmont College, B
University of Georgia, BMD
University of West Georgia, B

Young Harris College, A

Hawaii

University of Hawaii at Hilo, B
University of Hawaii at Manoa, BMD

Idaho

Boise State University, BM
Brigham Young University -Idaho, A
College of Southern Idaho, A
Idaho State University, ABMO
North Idaho College, A
University of Idaho, BMD

Illinois

Augustana College, B
Bradley University, B
City Colleges of Chicago, Olive-Harvey College, A
Eastern Illinois University, B
Highland Community College, A
Illinois State University, B
Lincoln College, A
Northeastern Illinois University, B
Northern Illinois University, BMD
Northwestern University, BMD
Olivet Nazarene University, B
Southern Illinois University Carbondale, BMD
University of Illinois at Chicago, BMD
University of Illinois at Urbana-Champaign, BMD
Western Illinois University, B
Wheaton College, B

Indiana

Ball State University, BM
DePauw University, B
Earlham College, B
Hanover College, B
Indiana State University, B
Indiana University Bloomington, BMDO
Indiana University East, A
Indiana University Northwest, B
Indiana University-Purdue University Fort Wayne, B
Indiana University-Purdue University
   Indianapolis, BM
Purdue University, B
University of Indianapolis, B
University of Notre Dame, B
University of Southern Indiana, B
Valparaiso University, B
Vincennes University, A

Iowa

Cornell College, B
Iowa Lakes Community College, A
Iowa State University of Science and
   Technology, BMD
The University of Iowa, B
University of Northern Iowa, B

Kansas

Barton County Community College, A
Colby Community College, A
Emporia State University, B
Fort Hays State University, BM
Highland Community College, A
Kansas State University, BM
University of Kansas, BMD
Wichita State University, BM

Kentucky

Eastern Kentucky University, BMD
Morehead State University, B
Murray State University, B
Northern Kentucky University, B
University of Kentucky, BMD
Western Kentucky University, BM

Louisiana

Centenary College of Louisiana, B
Louisiana State University and Agricultural and
   Mechanical College, BMD
Louisiana Tech University, B
McNeese State University, B
Tulane University, BMD
University of Louisiana at Lafayette, BM

University of New Orleans, BM

Maine

Bates College, B
Bowdoin College, B
Colby College, B
University of Maine, BMD
University of Maine at Farmington, B
University of Maine at Presque Isle, B
University of Southern Maine, B

Maryland

The Johns Hopkins University, BMD
Towson University, B
University of Maryland, College Park, BMD

Massachusetts

Amherst College, B
Boston College, BMO
Boston University, B
Bridgewater State College, B
Clark University, B
Fitchburg State College, B
Framingham State College, B
Hampshire College, B
Harvard University, B
Massachusetts Institute of Technology, BD
Mount Holyoke College, B
Northeastern University, B
Salem State College, B
Simon's Rock College of Bard, B
Smith College, B
Tufts University, B
University of Massachusetts Amherst, B
University of Massachusetts Boston, B
Wellesley College, B
Williams College, B

Michigan

Adrian College, AB
Albion College, B
Calvin College, B
Central Michigan University, B
Eastern Michigan University, B
Grand Rapids Community College, A
Grand Valley State University, B
Hope College, B
Lake Superior State University, B
Lansing Community College, A
Michigan State University, BMD
Michigan Technological University, BMD
Northern Michigan University, B
University of Michigan, BMD
University of Michigan-Dearborn, B
Wayne State University, BM
Western Michigan University, BMD

Minnesota

Bemidji State University, B
Carleton College, B
Gustavus Adolphus College, B
Macalester College, B
Minnesota State University Mankato, B
St. Cloud State University, B
University of Minnesota, Duluth, BMD
University of Minnesota, Morris, B
University of Minnesota, Twin Cities Campus, BMD
University of St. Thomas, B
Vermilion Community College, A
Winona State University, B

Mississippi

Millsaps College, B
Mississippi State University, B
University of Mississippi, B
University of Southern Mississippi, BM

Missouri

Central Missouri State University, B
East Central College, A
Missouri State University, BM
Northwest Missouri State University, B
Saint Louis University, BM
University of Missouri-Columbia, BMD
University of Missouri-Kansas City, BM

University of Missouri-Rolla, BMD
Washington University in St. Louis, BMD

Montana

Montana State University, B
Montana Tech of The University of Montana, M
Rocky Mountain College, B
The University of Montana-Missoula, BMD

Nebraska

University of Nebraska-Lincoln, B
University of Nebraska at Omaha, B

Nevada

Great Basin College, A
University of Nevada, Las Vegas, B
University of Nevada, Reno, BMDO

New Hampshire

Dartmouth College, B
Keene State College, B
University of New Hampshire, B

New Jersey

Kean University, B
New Jersey City University, B
Princeton University, D
The Richard Stockton College of New Jersey, B
Rider University, B
Rutgers, The State University of New Jersey, New
   Brunswick/Piscataway, BMD
Rutgers, The State University of New Jersey,
   Newark, BM

New Mexico

Eastern New Mexico University, B
Mesalands Community College, A
New Mexico Institute of Mining and
   Technology, BMD
New Mexico State University, BM
San Juan College, A
University of New Mexico, B
Western New Mexico University, B

New York

Alfred University, B
Barnard College, B
Brooklyn College of the City University of New
   York, BMD
Buffalo State College, State University of New
   York, B
City College of the City University of New York, B
Colgate University, B
Columbia College, B
Columbia University, School of General Studies, B
Cornell University, BMD
Excelsior College, B
Hamilton College, B
Hartwick College, B
Hobart and William Smith Colleges, B
Hofstra University, B
Lehman College of the City University of New
   York, B
Long Island University, C.W. Post Campus, B
Pace University, B
Queens College of the City University of New
   York, BM
Rensselaer Polytechnic Institute, BMD
St. Lawrence University, B
Sarah Lawrence College, B
Skidmore College, B
State University of New York at Binghamton, BMD
State University of New York at Buffalo, BMD
State University of New York College at
   Brockport, B
State University of New York College at Cortland, B
State University of New York College at Geneseo, B
State University of New York College at Oneonta, B
State University of New York College at Potsdam, B
State University of New York, Fredonia, B
State University of New York at New Paltz, BM
State University of New York at Oswego, B
State University of New York at Plattsburgh, B
Stony Brook University, State University of New
   York, B

Syracuse University, BMD
Union College, B
University at Albany, State University of New
York, BMD
University of Rochester, BMD
Vassar College, B
York College of the City University of New York, B

North Carolina

Appalachian State University, B
Duke University, BMD
East Carolina University, BM
Elizabeth City State University, B
Guilford College, B
North Carolina State University, B
The University of North Carolina at Chapel
Hill, BMD
The University of North Carolina at Charlotte, B
The University of North Carolina Wilmington, BM
Western Carolina University, B

North Dakota

Dickinson State University, B
Minot State University, B
North Dakota State University, B
University of North Dakota, BMD

Ohio

Antioch College, B
Ashland University, B
Bowling Green State University, BM
Case Western Reserve University, BMD
Cleveland State University, BMD
The College of Wooster, B
Denison University, B
Kent State University, BMD
Marietta College, B
Miami University, BMD
Miami University Hamilton, B
Mount Union College, B
Muskingum College, B
Oberlin College, B
The Ohio State University, BMD
Ohio University, BM
Ohio University-Eastern, B
Ohio Wesleyan University, B
The University of Akron, BM
University of Cincinnati, BMD
University of Dayton, B
The University of Toledo, BMD
Wittenberg University, B
Wright State University, BM
Youngstown State University, B

Oklahoma

Oklahoma State University, BM
Tulsa Community College, A
University of Oklahoma, BMD
University of Tulsa, BM

Oregon

Oregon State University, BMD
Portland State University, BMD
Southern Oregon University, B
University of Oregon, BMD

Pennsylvania

Allegheny College, B
Bloomsburg University of Pennsylvania, B
Bryn Mawr College, B
Bucknell University, B
California University of Pennsylvania, B
Clarion University of Pennsylvania, B
Dickinson College, B
East Stroudsburg University of Pennsylvania, B
Edinboro University of Pennsylvania, B
Franklin and Marshall College, B
Haverford College, B
Indiana University of Pennsylvania, B
Juniata College, B
Kutztown University of Pennsylvania, B
La Salle University, B
Lafayette College, B
Lehigh University, MD
Lock Haven University of Pennsylvania, B

Mansfield University of Pennsylvania, B
Mercyhurst College, B
Millersville University of Pennsylvania, B
Moravian College, B
The Pennsylvania State University Abington
College, B
The Pennsylvania State University Altoona
College, B
The Pennsylvania State University Beaver Campus
of the Commonwealth College, B
The Pennsylvania State University Berks Campus of
the Berks-Lehigh Valley College, B
The Pennsylvania State University Delaware County
Campus of the Commonwealth College, B
The Pennsylvania State University DuBois Campus
of the Commonwealth College, B
The Pennsylvania State University at Erie, The
Behrend College, B
The Pennsylvania State University Fayette Campus
of the Commonwealth College, B
The Pennsylvania State University Hazleton
Campus of the Commonwealth College, B
The Pennsylvania State University, Lehigh Valley
Campus of the Berks-Lehigh Valley College, B
The Pennsylvania State University McKeesport
Campus of the Commonwealth College, B
The Pennsylvania State University Mont Alto
Campus of the Commonwealth College, B
The Pennsylvania State University New Kensington
Campus of the Commonwealth College, B
The Pennsylvania State University Schuylkill
Campus of the Capital College, B
The Pennsylvania State University Shenango
Campus of the Commonwealth College, B
The Pennsylvania State University University Park
Campus, B
The Pennsylvania State University Wilkes-Barre
Campus of the Commonwealth College, B
The Pennsylvania State University Worthington
Scranton Campus of the Commonwealth
College, B
The Pennsylvania State University York Campus of
the Commonwealth College, B
Shippensburg University of Pennsylvania, B
Slippery Rock University of Pennsylvania, B
Susquehanna University, B
Temple University, BM
University of Pennsylvania, BMD
University of Pittsburgh, BMD
University of Pittsburgh at Johnstown, B
West Chester University of Pennsylvania, BM
Wilkes University, B

Puerto Rico

University of Puerto Rico, Mayagüez Campus, BM

Rhode Island

Brown University, B
University of Rhode Island, B

South Carolina

Clemson University, BM
College of Charleston, B
Furman University, B
University of South Carolina, BMD

South Dakota

South Dakota School of Mines and
Technology, BMD
The University of South Dakota, B

Tennessee

Austin Peay State University, B
Middle Tennessee State University, B
Sewanee: The University of the South, B
Tennessee Technological University, B
Tennessee Temple University, B
University of Memphis, BMD
The University of Tennessee, BMD
The University of Tennessee at Chattanooga, B
The University of Tennessee at Martin, B

Vanderbilt University, B

Texas

Amarillo College, A
Austin Community College, A
Baylor University, BMD
Brazosport College, A
Central Texas College, A
Coastal Bend College, A
Del Mar College, A
El Paso Community College, A
Grayson County College, A
Hardin-Simmons University, B
Hill College of the Hill Junior College District, A
Kilgore College, A
Lamar University, B
Lee College, A
Midland College, A
Midwestern State University, B
Odessa College, A
Palo Alto College, A
Rice University, B
St. Mary's University of San Antonio, B
St. Philip's College, A
Sam Houston State University, B
Southern Methodist University, BMD
Stephen F. Austin State University, BM
Sul Ross State University, BM
Tarleton State University, B
Texas A&M University, BMD
Texas A&M University-Commerce, B
Texas A&M University-Corpus Christi, B
Texas A&M University-Kingsville, BM
Texas Christian University, BM
Texas Tech University, B
Trinity University, B
Trinity Valley Community College, A
University of Houston, BMD
University of North Texas, B
The University of Texas at Arlington, BMD
The University of Texas at Austin, BMD
The University of Texas at Dallas, B
The University of Texas at El Paso, BMD
The University of Texas of the Permian Basin, BM
The University of Texas at San Antonio, BMD
West Texas A&M University, B

Utah

Brigham Young University, BM
Dixie State College of Utah, A
Snow College, A
Southern Utah University, B
University of Utah, BMD
Utah State University, BM
Utah Valley State College, AB
Weber State University, B

Vermont

Castleton State College, B
Middlebury College, B
Norwich University, B
University of Vermont, BM

Virginia

The College of William and Mary, B
George Mason University, B
James Madison University, B
Longwood University, B
Old Dominion University, B
Radford University, B
University of Mary Washington, B
Virginia Polytechnic Institute and State
University, BMD
Virginia Wesleyan College, B
Washington and Lee University, B

Washington

Central Washington University, BM
Centralia College, A
Eastern Washington University, B
Everett Community College, A
Lower Columbia College, A
Pacific Lutheran University, B
Skagit Valley College, A
Tacoma Community College, A

University of Puget Sound, B
University of Washington, BMD
Washington State University, BMD
Western Washington University, BM
Whitman College, B

West Virginia

Marshall University, B
Potomac State College of West Virginia
University, A
West Virginia University, BMD

Wisconsin

Beloit College, B
Lawrence University, B
Northland College, B
St. Norbert College, B
University of Wisconsin-Eau Claire, B
University of Wisconsin-Green Bay, AB
University of Wisconsin-Madison, BMD
University of Wisconsin-Milwaukee, BMD
University of Wisconsin-Oshkosh, B
University of Wisconsin-Parkside, B
University of Wisconsin-Platteville, B
University of Wisconsin-River Falls, B

Wyoming

Casper College, A
University of Wyoming, BMD
Western Wyoming Community College, A

Alberta

University of Alberta, B
University of Calgary, BMD

British Columbia

Simon Fraser University, B
The University of British Columbia, BMD
University of Victoria, B

Manitoba

Brandon University, B
University of Manitoba, BMD

New Brunswick

Mount Allison University, B
University of New Brunswick Fredericton, BMD

Newfoundland and Labrador

Memorial University of Newfoundland, BMD

Nova Scotia

Acadia University, BM
Dalhousie University, B
St. Francis Xavier University, BM
Saint Mary's University, B
University of King's College, B

Ontario

Brock University, B
Carleton University, B
Lakehead University, BM
Laurentian University, BM
McMaster University, BMD
Queen's University at Kingston, BMD
University of Ottawa, B
University of Toronto, BMD
University of Waterloo, B
The University of Western Ontario, BMD
University of Windsor, B
York University, B

Quebec

McGill University, B
Université Laval, BMD
Université de Montréal, B
Université du Québec àChicoutimi, B

Université du Québec àMontréal, BM

Saskatchewan

University of Regina, BMD
University of Saskatchewan, BMDO

GEOPHYSICS AND SEISMOLOGY

Alaska

University of Alaska Fairbanks, MD

California

California Institute of Technology, BMD
Occidental College, B
Stanford University, BMD
University of California, Berkeley, MD
University of California, Los Angeles, BMD
University of California, Riverside, B
University of California, Santa Barbara, BM
University of California, Santa Cruz, B

Colorado

Colorado School of Mines, MDO
University of Colorado at Boulder, D

Connecticut

Yale University, D

Delaware

University of Delaware, B

Florida

Florida State University, D
University of Miami, MD

Georgia

Georgia Institute of Technology, MD

Hawaii

University of Hawaii at Manoa, MD

Idaho

Boise State University, BMD
Idaho State University, M
University of Idaho, M

Illinois

University of Chicago, BMD
University of Illinois at Chicago, MD
University of Illinois at Urbana-Champaign, MD

Indiana

Indiana University Bloomington, MD

Louisiana

Louisiana State University and Agricultural and
Mechanical College, MD
University of New Orleans, BM

Maine

Bowdoin College, B

Maryland

The Johns Hopkins University, MD

Massachusetts

Boston College, BMO
Harvard University, B
Massachusetts Institute of Technology, MD

Michigan

Eastern Michigan University, B
Hope College, B
Michigan State University, B
Michigan Technological University, BM

Western Michigan University, B

Minnesota

University of Minnesota, Twin Cities Campus, BMD

Missouri

Saint Louis University, BD
University of Missouri-Rolla, BMD
Washington University in St. Louis, D

Nevada

University of Nevada, Reno, BMD

New Jersey

Princeton University, D

New Mexico

New Mexico Institute of Mining and
Technology, BMD

New York

Cornell University, MD
Rensselaer Polytechnic Institute, MD
St. Lawrence University, B
State University of New York College at Geneseo, B
State University of New York, Fredonia, B

Ohio

Ohio University, M
The University of Akron, BM
Wright State University, BM

Oklahoma

University of Oklahoma, BM
University of Tulsa, B

Oregon

Oregon State University, BMD

Rhode Island

Brown University, B

South Carolina

University of South Carolina, B

Tennessee

University of Memphis, M

Texas

Baylor University, B
Rice University, BM
Southern Methodist University, BMD
Texas A&M University, BMD
Texas Tech University, B
University of Houston, BMD
The University of Texas at Austin, B
The University of Texas at El Paso, BM

Utah

University of Utah, BMD

Virginia

Virginia Polytechnic Institute and State
University, MD

Washington

University of Washington, BMD
Western Washington University, B

West Virginia

West Virginia University, MD

Wisconsin

University of Wisconsin-Madison, BMD

Wyoming

University of Wyoming, MD

Alberta

University of Alberta, BMD
University of Calgary, BMD

British Columbia

The University of British Columbia, BMD
University of Victoria, BMD

Manitoba

University of Manitoba, MD

New Brunswick

University of New Brunswick Fredericton, B

Newfoundland and Labrador

Memorial University of Newfoundland, BMD

Ontario

University of Ottawa, A
University of Toronto, B
University of Waterloo, B
The University of Western Ontario, BMD

Quebec

McGill University, B

Saskatchewan

University of Saskatchewan, B

GEOPHYSICS ENGINEERING

Colorado

Colorado School of Mines, MD

Connecticut

University of Connecticut, D

Montana

Montana Tech of The University of Montana, M

GEOSCIENCES

Arizona

Arizona State University, MD
Northern Arizona University, M
The University of Arizona, MD

California

San Francisco State University, M
Stanford University, MDO
University of California, Irvine, MD
University of California, Los Angeles, MD
University of California, Santa Cruz, MD
University of San Diego, M
University of Southern California, MD

Colorado

Colorado School of Mines, O
Colorado State University, MD
University of Northern Colorado, M

Connecticut

Central Connecticut State University, M
Wesleyan University, M
Western Connecticut State University, M
Yale University, D

District of Columbia

The George Washington University, MD

Florida

Florida International University, MD
University of Florida, MD

Georgia

Georgia Institute of Technology, MD

Idaho

Boise State University, M
Idaho State University, MO

Illinois

Northeastern Illinois University, M
Northwestern University, MD

University of Chicago, MD
University of Illinois at Chicago, MD
University of Illinois at Urbana-Champaign, MD

Indiana

Ball State University, M
Indiana State University, M
Indiana University Bloomington, MDO
Purdue University, MD
University of Notre Dame, MD

Iowa

Iowa State University of Science and
    Technology, MD
The University of Iowa, MD

Kansas

Emporia State University, M

Kentucky

Murray State University, M

Louisiana

University of Louisiana at Monroe, M

Maine

University of Maine, MD

Massachusetts

Boston University, MD
Harvard University, MD
Massachusetts Institute of Technology, MD
University of Massachusetts Amherst, MD

Michigan

Michigan State University, MD
Western Michigan University, M

Mississippi

Mississippi State University, M

Missouri

Missouri State University, M
Saint Louis University, MD
University of Missouri-Kansas City, MD
Washington University in St. Louis, MD

Montana

Montana State University, MD
Montana Tech of The University of Montana, M

Nebraska

University of Nebraska-Lincoln, MD

Nevada

University of Nevada, Las Vegas, MD

New Hampshire

Dartmouth College, MD
University of New Hampshire, M

New Jersey

Montclair State University, MO
Princeton University, D

New Mexico

New Mexico Institute of Mining and Technology, MD
University of New Mexico, MD

New York

City College of the City University of New York, MD
Cornell University, MD
Hunter College of the City University of New
    York, M
Rensselaer Polytechnic Institute, MD
State University of New York College at Oneonta, M
Stony Brook University, State University of New
    York, MD
University at Albany, State University of New
    York, MD

University of Rochester, MD

North Carolina

North Carolina Central University, M
North Carolina State University, MD
The University of North Carolina at Charlotte, M
The University of North Carolina Wilmington, M

North Dakota

University of North Dakota, MD

Ohio

Case Western Reserve University, MD
The University of Akron, M

Oklahoma

University of Tulsa, MD

Oregon

Oregon State University, MD

Pennsylvania

California University of Pennsylvania, M
Lehigh University, MD
Millersville University of Pennsylvania, M
The Pennsylvania State University University Park
    Campus, MD

Rhode Island

Brown University, MD
University of Rhode Island, M

South Carolina

University of South Carolina, MD

Tennessee

Middle Tennessee State University, O
University of Memphis, D

Texas

Baylor University, M
Rice University, MD
Texas A&M University-Commerce, M
Texas Christian University, M
Texas Tech University, MD
The University of Texas at Arlington, D
The University of Texas at Austin, MD
The University of Texas at Dallas, MD

Alberta

University of Alberta, MD

British Columbia

Simon Fraser University, M
University of Victoria, MD

Newfoundland and Labrador

Memorial University of Newfoundland, MD

Nova Scotia

Dalhousie University, MD
St. Francis Xavier University, M

Ontario

Brock University, M
Carleton University, MD
McMaster University, MD
University of Ottawa, MD
University of Waterloo, MD
The University of Western Ontario, MD
University of Windsor, MD
York University, MD

Quebec

McGill University, MD
Université Laval, MD
Université du Québec àChicoutimi, M

Université du Québec àMontréal, MDO

GEOTECHNICAL ENGINEERING

Alabama

Auburn University, MD

California

University of California, Berkeley, MD
University of California, Los Angeles, MD
University of Southern California, M

Colorado

Colorado State University, MD
University of Colorado at Boulder, MD

Delaware

University of Delaware, MD

District of Columbia

The Catholic University of America, M

Illinois

Illinois Institute of Technology, M
Northwestern University, MD
University of Illinois at Chicago, D

Louisiana

Louisiana State University and Agricultural and
   Mechanical College, MD

Massachusetts

Massachusetts Institute of Technology, D

Missouri

University of Missouri-Columbia, MD
University of Missouri-Rolla, MD

Montana

Montana Tech of The University of Montana, B

New York

Cornell University, MD
Rensselaer Polytechnic Institute, MD

Ohio

Ohio University, MD

Oklahoma

University of Oklahoma, M

Rhode Island

University of Rhode Island, MD

Texas

Texas A&M University, MD
The University of Texas at Austin, MD

Washington

University of Washington, MD

Wisconsin

Marquette University, MD

Alberta

University of Alberta, MD
University of Calgary, MD

New Brunswick

University of New Brunswick Fredericton, MD

Ontario

York University, B

Quebec

McGill University, MD

GERMAN LANGUAGE AND LITERATURE

Alabama

Auburn University, B
Birmingham-Southern College, B

Jacksonville State University, B
Samford University, B
The University of Alabama, BM

Arizona

Arizona State University, BM
Northern Arizona University, B
The University of Arizona, BM

Arkansas

Hendrix College, B
University of Arkansas, BM

California

Bakersfield College, A
California Lutheran University, B
California State University, Chico, B
California State University, Fullerton, BM
California State University, Long Beach, BM
California State University, Northridge, B
California State University, Sacramento, M
Cañada College, A
Cerritos College, A
Chaffey College, A
Citrus College, A
Claremont McKenna College, B
College of the Canyons, A
College of Marin, A
College of San Mateo, A
Compton Community College, A
Contra Costa College, A
El Camino College, A
Grossmont College, A
Humboldt State University, B
Long Beach City College, A
Los Angeles City College, A
Monterey Peninsula College, A
Orange Coast College, A
Pasadena City College, A
Pepperdine University, B
Pitzer College, B
Pomona College, B
Saint Mary's College of California, B
San Bernardino Valley College, A
San Diego State University, B
San Francisco State University, BM
San Joaquin Delta College, A
San Jose State University, B
Santa Monica College, A
Scripps College, B
Solano Community College, A
Stanford University, BMD
University of California, Berkeley, BMD
University of California, Davis, BMD
University of California, Irvine, BMD
University of California, Los Angeles, BMD
University of California, Riverside, B
University of California, San Diego, BM
University of California, Santa Barbara, BMD
University of California, Santa Cruz, B
University of La Verne, B
University of the Pacific, B
University of Redlands, B
University of Southern California, B
West Valley College, A

Colorado

The Colorado College, B
Colorado State University, BM
Red Rocks Community College, A
University of Colorado at Boulder, M
University of Denver, BM
University of Northern Colorado, B

Connecticut

Central Connecticut State University, B
Fairfield University, B
Southern Connecticut State University, B
Trinity College, B
University of Connecticut, BMD
Wesleyan University, B

Yale University, BMD

Delaware

University of Delaware, B

District of Columbia

American University, B
The Catholic University of America, B
The George Washington University, B
Georgetown University, BMDO
Howard University, B

Florida

Eckerd College, B
Florida Atlantic University, BM
Florida International University, B
Florida State University, BM
Manatee Community College, A
Miami Dade College, A
New College of Florida, B
Stetson University, B
University of Florida, BMD
University of Miami, B
University of South Florida, B

Georgia

Agnes Scott College, B
Berry College, B
Emory University, B
Georgia Southern University, B
Georgia State University, BM
Mercer University, B
Morehouse College, B
South Georgia College, A
University of Georgia, BM
University of West Georgia, B

Hawaii

University of Hawaii at Manoa, BM

Idaho

Boise State University, B
Brigham Young University -Idaho, A
Idaho State University, AB
North Idaho College, A
University of Idaho, B

Illinois

Augustana College, B
Bradley University, B
City Colleges of Chicago, Harold Washington
   College, A
DePaul University, B
Elmhurst College, B
Illinois College, B
Illinois State University, BM
Illinois Wesleyan University, B
Knox College, B
Loyola University Chicago, B
Millikin University, B
North Central College, B
Northern Illinois University, B
Northwestern University, BD
Principia College, B
Southern Illinois University Carbondale, B
University of Chicago, BMD
University of Illinois at Chicago, BMD
University of Illinois at Urbana-Champaign, BMD
Wheaton College, B

Indiana

Ball State University, B
Butler University, B
DePauw University, B
Earlham College, B
Grace College, B
Hanover College, B
Indiana State University, B
Indiana University Bloomington, BMD
Indiana University-Purdue University Fort
   Wayne, AB
Indiana University-Purdue University Indianapolis, B
Indiana University South Bend, B
Indiana University Southeast, B
Manchester College, B

Purdue University, MD
Purdue University Calumet, B
University of Evansville, B
University of Indianapolis, B
University of Notre Dame, BM
University of Southern Indiana, B
Valparaiso University, B
Vincennes University, A
Wabash College, B

Iowa

Coe College, B
Cornell College, B
Dordt College, B
Graceland University, B
Grinnell College, B
Iowa State University of Science and Technology, B
Luther College, B
St. Ambrose University, B
Simpson College, B
The University of Iowa, BMD
University of Northern Iowa, BM
Wartburg College, B

Kansas

Baker University, B
Fort Hays State University, B
Kansas State University, M
University of Kansas, MD
Washburn University, B

Kentucky

Bellarmine University, B
Berea College, B
Centre College, B
Georgetown College, B
Murray State University, B
University of Kentucky, BM
Western Kentucky University, B

Louisiana

Centenary College of Louisiana, B
Dillard University, B
Louisiana State University and Agricultural and
    Mechanical College, B
Loyola University New Orleans, B
Tulane University, B

Maine

Bates College, B
Bowdoin College, B
Colby College, B
University of Maine, B

Maryland

Hood College, B
The Johns Hopkins University, BD
Loyola College in Maryland, B
McDaniel College, B
Mount St. Mary's University, B
Towson University, B
University of Maryland, Baltimore County, BM
University of Maryland, College Park, BMD
Washington College, B

Massachusetts

Amherst College, B
Boston College, B
Boston University, B
Brandeis University, B
College of the Holy Cross, B
Gordon College, B
Harvard University, BMD
Mount Holyoke College, B
Northeastern University, B
Simon's Rock College of Bard, B
Smith College, B
Tufts University, BM
University of Massachusetts Amherst, BMD
University of Massachusetts Boston, B
Wellesley College, B
Wheaton College, B

Williams College, B

Michigan

Adrian College, AB
Albion College, B
Alma College, B
Aquinas College, B
Calvin College, B
Central Michigan University, B
Eastern Michigan University, BMO
Grand Valley State University, B
Hillsdale College, B
Hope College, B
Kalamazoo College, B
Michigan State University, BM
Oakland University, B
University of Michigan, BMD
Wayne State University, BMD
Western Michigan University, B

Minnesota

Augsburg College, B
Bemidji State University, B
Carleton College, B
College of Saint Benedict, B
Concordia College, B
Gustavus Adolphus College, B
Hamline University, B
Minnesota State University Mankato, BM
St. Cloud State University, B
Saint John's University, B
St. Olaf College, B
University of Minnesota, Morris, B
University of Minnesota, Twin Cities Campus, BMD
University of St. Thomas, B
Winona State University, B

Mississippi

Millsaps College, B
Mississippi State University, M
University of Mississippi, BM

Missouri

Central Missouri State University, B
College of the Ozarks, B
Drury University, B
Missouri Southern State University, B
Missouri State University, B
Saint Louis University, B
Southeast Missouri State University, B
Truman State University, B
University of Missouri-Columbia, BM
University of Missouri-Kansas City, B
University of Missouri-St. Louis, B
Washington University in St. Louis, BMD
Webster University, B

Montana

The University of Montana-Missoula, BM

Nebraska

Creighton University, B
Dana College, B
Doane College, B
Hastings College, B
Nebraska Wesleyan University, B
Union College, B
University of Nebraska at Kearney, B
University of Nebraska-Lincoln, BMD
University of Nebraska at Omaha, B
Wayne State College, B
Western Nebraska Community College, A

Nevada

University of Nevada, Las Vegas, B
University of Nevada, Reno, BM

New Hampshire

Dartmouth College, B
University of New Hampshire, B

New Jersey

Drew University, B
Princeton University, BD
Rider University, B

Rutgers, The State University of New Jersey,
    Camden, B
Rutgers, The State University of New Jersey, New
    Brunswick/Piscataway, BMD
Rutgers, The State University of New Jersey,
    Newark, B

New Mexico

New Mexico Military Institute, A
University of New Mexico, BM

New York

Alfred University, B
Bard College, B
Barnard College, B
Brooklyn College of the City University of New
    York, B
Canisius College, B
Colgate University, B
Columbia College, B
Columbia University, School of General Studies, B
Cornell University, BMD
Fordham University, B
Hamilton College, B
Hartwick College, B
Hofstra University, BM
Hunter College of the City University of New York, B
Ithaca College, B
Nazareth College of Rochester, B
New York University, BMD
Queens College of the City University of New
    York, B
St. John Fisher College, B
St. Lawrence University, B
Sarah Lawrence College, B
Skidmore College, B
State University of New York at Binghamton, B
State University of New York at Buffalo, B
State University of New York College at Cortland, B
State University of New York at New Paltz, B
State University of New York at Oswego, B
Stony Brook University, State University of New
    York, BMD
Syracuse University, B
United States Military Academy, B
University of Rochester, B
Vassar College, B

North Carolina

Davidson College, B
Duke University, BD
East Carolina University, B
Guilford College, B
Lenoir-Rhyne College, B
Mars Hill College, B
Methodist College, A
Salem College, B
The University of North Carolina at Asheville, B
The University of North Carolina at Chapel
    Hill, BMD
The University of North Carolina at Charlotte, B
The University of North Carolina at Greensboro, B
The University of North Carolina Wilmington, B
Wake Forest University, B
Western Carolina University, B

North Dakota

Minot State University, B
University of North Dakota, B

Ohio

Antioch College, B
Baldwin-Wallace College, B
Bowling Green State University, BMO
Case Western Reserve University, B
The College of Wooster, B
Denison University, B
Franciscan University of Steubenville, B
Heidelberg College, B
Hiram College, B
John Carroll University, B
Kent State University, BM
Kenyon College, B
Lake Erie College, B
Miami University, B

Miami University Hamilton, B
Mount Union College, B
Muskingum College, B
Oberlin College, B
The Ohio State University, BMD
Ohio University, B
Ohio Wesleyan University, B
The University of Akron, B
University of Cincinnati, BMD
University of Dayton, B
The University of Toledo, BM
Wittenberg University, B
Wright State University, B
Xavier University, AB

Oklahoma

Oklahoma Baptist University, B
Oklahoma City University, B
Oklahoma State University, B
Oral Roberts University, B
Tulsa Community College, A
University of Central Oklahoma, B
University of Oklahoma, BMO
University of Tulsa, B

Oregon

Lewis & Clark College, B
Linfield College, B
Oregon State University, B
Pacific University, B
Portland State University, BM
Reed College, B
Southern Oregon University, B
University of Oregon, BMD
Western Oregon University, B
Willamette University, B

Pennsylvania

Allegheny College, B
Bloomsburg University of Pennsylvania, B
Bryn Mawr College, B
Bucknell University, B
California University of Pennsylvania, B
Carnegie Mellon University, B
Dickinson College, B
Edinboro University of Pennsylvania, B
Elizabethtown College, B
Franklin and Marshall College, B
Gettysburg College, B
Haverford College, B
Indiana University of Pennsylvania, B
Juniata College, B
Kutztown University of Pennsylvania, B
La Salle University, B
Lafayette College, B
Lebanon Valley College, B
Lehigh University, B
Lock Haven University of Pennsylvania, B
Lycoming College, B
Mansfield University of Pennsylvania, B
Mercyhurst College, B
Messiah College, B
Millersville University of Pennsylvania, BM
Moravian College, B
Muhlenberg College, B
The Pennsylvania State University Abington
   College, B
The Pennsylvania State University Altoona
   College, B
The Pennsylvania State University Beaver Campus
   of the Commonwealth College, B
The Pennsylvania State University Berks Campus of
   the Berks-Lehigh Valley College, B
The Pennsylvania State University Delaware County
   Campus of the Commonwealth College, B
The Pennsylvania State University DuBois Campus
   of the Commonwealth College, B
The Pennsylvania State University at Erie, The
   Behrend College, B
The Pennsylvania State University Fayette Campus
   of the Commonwealth College, B
The Pennsylvania State University Hazleton
   Campus of the Commonwealth College, B
The Pennsylvania State University, Lehigh Valley
   Campus of the Berks-Lehigh Valley College, B

The Pennsylvania State University McKeesport
   Campus of the Commonwealth College, B
The Pennsylvania State University Mont Alto
   Campus of the Commonwealth College, B
The Pennsylvania State University New Kensington
   Campus of the Commonwealth College, B
The Pennsylvania State University Schuylkill
   Campus of the Capital College, B
The Pennsylvania State University Shenango
   Campus of the Commonwealth College, B
The Pennsylvania State University University Park
   Campus, BMD
The Pennsylvania State University Wilkes-Barre
   Campus of the Commonwealth College, B
The Pennsylvania State University Worthington
   Scranton Campus of the Commonwealth
   College, B
The Pennsylvania State University York Campus of
   the Commonwealth College, B
Rosemont College, B
Saint Joseph's University, B
Susquehanna University, B
Swarthmore College, B
Temple University, B
University of Pennsylvania, BMD
University of Pittsburgh, BMD
The University of Scranton, B
Ursinus College, B
Villanova University, B
Washington & Jefferson College, B
West Chester University of Pennsylvania, BM
Westminster College, B

Rhode Island

Brown University, BMD
University of Rhode Island, B

South Carolina

Bob Jones University, B
The Citadel, The Military College of South
   Carolina, B
College of Charleston, B
Furman University, B
Newberry College, B
Presbyterian College, B
University of South Carolina, BM
Wofford College, B

South Dakota

Augustana College, B
Northern State University, B
South Dakota State University, B
The University of South Dakota, B

Tennessee

Lambuth University, B
Lipscomb University, B
Rhodes College, B
Sewanee: The University of the South, B
Tennessee Technological University, B
The University of Tennessee, BMD
Vanderbilt University, BMD

Texas

Angelo State University, B
Austin College, B
Austin Community College, A
Baylor University, B
Blinn College, A
Coastal Bend College, A
Lee College, A
Midland College, A
Rice University, B
Sam Houston State University, B
Southern Methodist University, B
Southwestern University, B
Texas A&M University, B
Texas Southern University, B
Texas State University-San Marcos, B
Texas Tech University, BM
Trinity University, B
University of Dallas, B
University of Houston, B
University of North Texas, B
The University of Texas at Arlington, B

The University of Texas at Austin, BMD
The University of Texas at El Paso, B

Utah

Brigham Young University, BM
Southern Utah University, B
University of Utah, BMD
Utah State University, B
Weber State University, B

Vermont

Marlboro College, B
Middlebury College, BMD
University of Vermont, BM

Virginia

Christopher Newport University, B
The College of William and Mary, B
Eastern Mennonite University, B
Hampden-Sydney College, B
Hollins University, B
Longwood University, B
Mary Baldwin College, B
Old Dominion University, B
Randolph-Macon College, B
Randolph-Macon Woman's College, B
Sweet Briar College, B
University of Mary Washington, B
University of Richmond, B
University of Virginia, BMD
Virginia Polytechnic Institute and State University, B
Virginia Wesleyan College, B
Washington and Lee University, B

Washington

Centralia College, A
Everett Community College, A
Gonzaga University, B
Pacific Lutheran University, B
Seattle Pacific University, B
Seattle University, B
University of Puget Sound, B
University of Washington, BMD
Walla Walla College, B
Washington State University, B
Western Washington University, B
Whitman College, B

West Virginia

Bethany College, B
West Virginia University, M

Wisconsin

Beloit College, B
Carthage College, B
Concordia University Wisconsin, B
Lakeland College, B
Lawrence University, B
Marquette University, B
Ripon College, B
St. Norbert College, B
University of Wisconsin-La Crosse, B
University of Wisconsin-Madison, BMD
University of Wisconsin-Milwaukee, BM
University of Wisconsin-Oshkosh, B
University of Wisconsin-Parkside, B
University of Wisconsin-Platteville, B
University of Wisconsin-River Falls, B
University of Wisconsin-Stevens Point, B
University of Wisconsin-Whitewater, B

Wyoming

Casper College, A
University of Wyoming, BM

Alberta

University of Alberta, BMD
University of Calgary, BM

University of Lethbridge, BM

British Columbia

The University of British Columbia, B
University of Victoria, BM

Manitoba

University of Manitoba, BM
The University of Winnipeg, B

New Brunswick

Mount Allison University, B
University of New Brunswick Fredericton, BM

Newfoundland and Labrador

Memorial University of Newfoundland, BM

Nova Scotia

Dalhousie University, BM
Mount Saint Vincent University, B
Saint Mary's University, B
University of King's College, B

Ontario

Brock University, B
Carleton University, B
McMaster University, B
Queen's University at Kingston, BMD
Trent University, B
University of Ottawa, B
University of Toronto, BMD
University of Waterloo, BMD
The University of Western Ontario, B
University of Windsor, B
Wilfrid Laurier University, B
York University, B

Prince Edward Island

University of Prince Edward Island, B

Quebec

Bishop's University, B
Concordia University, B
McGill University, BMD
Université de Montréal, BMD

Saskatchewan

University of Regina, B
University of Saskatchewan, BM

GERMAN LANGUAGE TEACHER EDUCATION

Alabama

Auburn University, B

Arizona

The University of Arizona, B

California

California Lutheran University, B
California State University, Chico, B

Colorado

Colorado State University, B

District of Columbia

The Catholic University of America, B

Georgia

Georgia Southern University, B

Illinois

Elmhurst College, B
University of Illinois at Chicago, B
University of Illinois at Urbana-Champaign, B

Indiana

Grace College, B
Indiana University Bloomington, B
Indiana University-Purdue University Fort Wayne, B

Indiana University-Purdue University Indianapolis, B
Indiana University South Bend, B
University of Evansville, B
Valparaiso University, B

Iowa

St. Ambrose University, B
The University of Iowa, B

Kentucky

Berea College, B
Murray State University, B

Louisiana

Centenary College of Louisiana, B
University of Louisiana at Lafayette, B

Michigan

Alma College, B
Central Michigan University, B
Eastern Michigan University, B
Hope College, B
Western Michigan University, B

Minnesota

Concordia College, B
University of Minnesota, Duluth, B

Missouri

Missouri State University, B
University of Missouri-St. Louis, B
Washington University in St. Louis, B

Nebraska

Hastings College, B
University of Nebraska-Lincoln, B

New York

Hofstra University, B
Hunter College of the City University of New York, B
Ithaca College, B
St. Bonaventure University, B

North Carolina

East Carolina University, B
The University of North Carolina at Charlotte, B
The University of North Carolina at Greensboro, B
Western Carolina University, B

North Dakota

Minot State University, B

Ohio

Miami University Hamilton, B
Ohio Northern University, B
Ohio University, B
Ohio Wesleyan University, B
The University of Akron, B
The University of Toledo, B

Oklahoma

Oklahoma Baptist University, B
Oral Roberts University, B

Pennsylvania

Juniata College, B
Lebanon Valley College, B
Mansfield University of Pennsylvania, B
Messiah College, B
Moravian College, B

South Dakota

The University of South Dakota, B

Tennessee

The University of Tennessee at Martin, B

Texas

Baylor University, B

Utah

Brigham Young University, B
University of Utah, B

Weber State University, B

Virginia

Eastern Mennonite University, B
Old Dominion University, B

Washington

Central Washington University, B
Eastern Washington University, B
Washington State University, B

Wisconsin

Carroll College, B
Concordia University Wisconsin, B
University of Wisconsin-River Falls, B

Ontario

University of Windsor, B

GERMAN STUDIES

Alabama

The University of Alabama, B

California

Claremont McKenna College, B
Santa Clara University, B
Stanford University, B
University of California, Irvine, B

Connecticut

Connecticut College, B

Iowa

Central College, B
Coe College, B

Massachusetts

College of the Holy Cross, B
Simon's Rock College of Bard, B
Smith College, B
Wheaton College, B

New York

Barnard College, B
Columbia College, B
Cornell University, B
Fordham University, B
Ithaca College, B
Manhattanville College, B

Ohio

Case Western Reserve University, B
The College of Wooster, B

Pennsylvania

Franklin and Marshall College, B
Moravian College, B
Swarthmore College, B

Rhode Island

Brown University, B

Texas

Southern Methodist University, B
University of Houston, B

British Columbia

University of Victoria, B

Manitoba

The University of Winnipeg, B

Ontario

Brock University, B
Queen's University at Kingston, B
University of Windsor, B
Wilfrid Laurier University, B

York University, B

GERMANIC LANGUAGES, LITERATURES, AND LINGUISTICS

California

Claremont McKenna College, B
University of California, Los Angeles, B

Colorado

University of Colorado at Boulder, B

Florida

New College of Florida, B

Georgia

University of Georgia, B

Kansas

Bethel College, B
University of Kansas, B

Michigan

Calvin College, B
Eastern Michigan University, B

Missouri

Washington University in St. Louis, B

New York

Canisius College, B

Ohio

Cleveland State University, B
Ohio Northern University, B

Texas

The University of Texas at San Antonio, B

Wisconsin

University of Wisconsin-Eau Claire, B
University of Wisconsin-Green Bay, AB

GERONTOLOGICAL NURSING

Arkansas

Arkansas State University, O

California

Loma Linda University, M
San Jose State University, M

Colorado

University of Colorado at Colorado Springs, M

Delaware

University of Delaware, MO

Illinois

Rush University, MDO

Massachusetts

Boston College, M
University of Massachusetts Lowell, M

Michigan

Oakland University, M
University of Michigan, M

Minnesota

University of Minnesota, Twin Cities Campus, M

Missouri

Barnes-Jewish College of Nursing and Allied
Health, M

Nevada

University of Nevada, Las Vegas, M

New Jersey

Seton Hall University, M

New York

College of Mount Saint Vincent, M
College of Staten Island of the City University of
New York, MO
Hunter College of the City University of New
York, M
Lehman College of the City University of New
York, M
Nazareth College of Rochester, M
New York University, MO
State University of New York at Buffalo, M
State University of New York at New Paltz, M
Stony Brook University, State University of New
York, M

North Carolina

Duke University, O
The University of North Carolina at Greensboro, O

Ohio

Case Western Reserve University, M

Oregon

Oregon Health & Science University, MDO

Pennsylvania

Villanova University, MO

South Carolina

Medical University of South Carolina, MO

Tennessee

Vanderbilt University, M

Texas

Abilene Christian University, O
Texas Wesleyan University, M

Utah

University of Utah, MO

Wisconsin

Concordia University Wisconsin, M
Marquette University, O

GERONTOLOGY

Alabama

University of South Alabama, O

Arizona

Arizona State University West, O
The University of Arizona, MO

Arkansas

University of Arkansas at Little Rock, MO
University of Arkansas at Pine Bluff, B

California

American River College, A
California State University, Chico, B
California State University, Dominguez Hills, B
California State University, East Bay, B
California State University, Fullerton, M
California State University, Long Beach, M
California State University, Sacramento, B
Chaffey College, A
Cosumnes River College (Sacramento), A
El Camino College, A
Mount St. Mary's College, B
Mt. San Jacinto College, A
Notre Dame de Namur University, MO
Saddleback College, A
San Diego State University, BM
San Francisco State University, M
San Jose State University, O
University of La Verne, M

University of Southern California, BMDO

Colorado

Naropa University, M
University of Northern Colorado, M

Connecticut

Gateway Community College, A
Naugatuck Valley Community College, A
Quinnipiac University, B
Sacred Heart University, M
Saint Joseph College, O

Delaware

Delaware Technical & Community College,
Stanton/Wilmington Campus, A
Wilmington College, M

Florida

Bethune-Cookman College, B
Florida State University, M
Lynn University, B
University of Central Florida, O
University of North Florida, MO
University of South Florida, BMD

Georgia

University of West Georgia, M

Illinois

City Colleges of Chicago, Wilbur Wright College, A
Concordia University, M
Dominican University, B
Eastern Illinois University, M
Elgin Community College, A
National-Louis University, BMO
Northeastern Illinois University, M
Roosevelt University, BM
University of Illinois at Springfield, M

Indiana

Ball State University, M
Brown Mackie College-Merrillville, A
Manchester College, A
Saint Mary-of-the-Woods College, B
University of Indianapolis, M
Valparaiso University, MO

Iowa

University of Northern Iowa, B

Kansas

University of Kansas, MD
Washburn University, AB
Wichita State University, BM

Kentucky

Brown Mackie College-Louisville, A
Morehead State University, M
Thomas More College, A
University of Kentucky, D
Western Kentucky University, M

Louisiana

University of Louisiana at Monroe, MO
University of New Orleans, O

Maine

University of New England, O

Maryland

Baltimore City Community College, A
College of Notre Dame of Maryland, M
Sojourner-Douglass College, B
Towson University, BMO
University of Maryland, Baltimore County, MD

Massachusetts

North Shore Community College, A
University of Massachusetts Boston, BMDO

Michigan

Alma College, B
Eastern Michigan University, O

Lansing Community College, A
Madonna University, AB
Oakland Community College, A
Siena Heights University, A
Wayne State University, O

Minnesota

Bethel University, M
Minnesota State University Mankato, M
Minnesota State University Moorhead, B
Ridgewater College, A
St. Cloud State University, BM

Missouri

Central Missouri State University, M
College of the Ozarks, B
Lindenwood University, BM
Missouri State University, B
University of Missouri-St. Louis, MO
Webster University, M

Nebraska

University of Nebraska at Omaha, BMO

Nevada

University of Nevada, Las Vegas, B

New Jersey

Camden County College, A
Felician College, B
Union County College, A

New York

Alfred University, B
The College of New Rochelle, MO
Eugenio María de Hostos Community College of the
    City University of New York, A
Fiorello H. LaGuardia Community College of the
    City University of New York, A
Genesee Community College, A
Hofstra University, MO
Ithaca College, B
Long Island University, C.W. Post Campus, MO
Nazareth College of Rochester, B
Rochester Institute of Technology, O
State University of New York College at Oneonta, B
State University of New York, Fredonia, B
York College of the City University of New York, B

North Carolina

Appalachian State University, BM
Sandhills Community College, A
The University of North Carolina at Charlotte, M
Winston-Salem State University, B

North Dakota

North Dakota State University, D

Ohio

Bowling Green State University, B
Case Western Reserve University, BO
Cleveland State University, B
Columbus State Community College, A
John Carroll University, B
Kent State University, MO
Miami University, M
Miami University Hamilton, B
Ohio Dominican University, A
Sinclair Community College, A
The University of Akron, B
The University of Toledo, A

Oklahoma

Langston University, B
Oklahoma City Community College, A
Oklahoma State University, M
Southern Nazarene University, B
University of Central Oklahoma, M

Oregon

Marylhurst University, M
Oregon State University, M
Portland Community College, A

Portland State University, O

Pennsylvania

California University of Pennsylvania, B
Cedar Crest College, B
Chestnut Hill College, O
Community College of Philadelphia, A
Gannon University, O
Gwynedd-Mercy College, B
Mercyhurst College, B
Millersville University of Pennsylvania, A
Saint Joseph's University, MO
Shippensburg University of Pennsylvania, MO
University of Pittsburgh, O
The University of Scranton, B
West Chester University of Pennsylvania, MO

Puerto Rico

Pontifical Catholic University of Puerto Rico, AB
University of Puerto Rico, Medical Sciences
    Campus, MO

South Carolina

Midlands Technical College, A
University of South Carolina, O

Tennessee

East Tennessee State University, O
Middle Tennessee State University, O
The University of Tennessee, M

Texas

Abilene Christian University, MO
Stephen F. Austin State University, B
Texas A&M University-Kingsville, M
Texas Tech University, M
University of North Texas, BMO

Utah

University of Utah, MO
Weber State University, B

Virginia

New River Community College, A
Northern Virginia Community College, A
Virginia Commonwealth University, MO
Virginia Polytechnic Institute and State
    University, MD

Washington

Central Washington University, B
Spokane Falls Community College, A

West Virginia

West Virginia State Community and Technical
    College, A
West Virginia State University, A

Wisconsin

Mount Mary College, M

British Columbia

Simon Fraser University, M

New Brunswick

St. Thomas University, B

Nova Scotia

Mount Saint Vincent University, BM

Ontario

Lakehead University, BM
McMaster University, B
University of Guelph, B
York University, B

Quebec

Bishop's University, B
Université Laval, O

Université de Sherbrooke, M

GLAZIER

Missouri

Metropolitan Community College-Business &
    Technology College, A

GRAPHIC AND PRINTING EQUIPMENT OPERATOR PRODUCTION

Alabama

Bishop State Community College, A
H. Councill Trenholm State Technical College, A

Arkansas

Phillips Community College of the University of
    Arkansas, A

California

California Polytechnic State University, San Luis
    Obispo, B
City College of San Francisco, A
Compton Community College, A
Don Bosco Technical Institute, A
Fresno City College, A
Fullerton College, A
Golden West College, A
Laney College, A
Los Angeles Trade-Technical College, A
Mission College, A
Modesto Junior College, A
Moorpark College, A
Palomar College, A
Riverside Community College District, A
Sacramento City College, A
San Diego City College, A
San Joaquin Delta College, A
Santa Monica College, A
Western Career College (Walnut Creek), A

District of Columbia

University of the District of Columbia, AB

Florida

Florida Agricultural and Mechanical University, B

Georgia

Georgia Southern University, B
Georgia Southwestern State University, A

Idaho

Idaho State University, A
Lewis-Clark State College, AB

Illinois

City Colleges of Chicago, Kennedy-King College, A
College of DuPage, A
Lake Land College, A
South Suburban College, A
Triton College, A
Western Illinois University, B

Indiana

Ball State University, A
Vincennes University, A

Iowa

Clinton Community College, A
Des Moines Area Community College, A
Iowa Lakes Community College, A
Kirkwood Community College, A

Kansas

Pittsburg State University, B

Kentucky

Eastern Kentucky University, AB
Louisville Technical Institute, A

Murray State University, B

Maine

Central Maine Community College, A

Maryland

Montgomery College, A

Michigan

Gogebic Community College, A
Macomb Community College, A
Southwestern Michigan College, A
Washtenaw Community College, A

Minnesota

Dunwoody College of Technology, A

Mississippi

Hinds Community College, A
Mississippi Delta Community College, A

Missouri

College of the Ozarks, B
Moberly Area Community College, A
Ozarks Technical Community College, A

Nebraska

Central Community College-Hastings Campus, A
Metropolitan Community College, A

Nevada

Community College of Southern Nevada, A

New Jersey

Burlington County College, A

New Mexico

University of New Mexico-Gallup, A

New York

Erie Community College, South Campus, A
Fulton-Montgomery Community College, A
Monroe Community College, A

North Carolina

Appalachian State University, B
Central Piedmont Community College, A
Chowan University, AB
Forsyth Technical Community College, A
Lenoir Community College, A
Randolph Community College, A

Ohio

Sinclair Community College, A

Oklahoma

Northeastern Oklahoma Agricultural and Mechanical
  College, A
Northern Oklahoma College, A
Oklahoma State University, Okmulgee, A

Oregon

Chemeketa Community College, A

Pennsylvania

Luzerne County Community College, A
Pennsylvania College of Technology, AB
Thaddeus Stevens College of Technology, A
Westmoreland County Community College, A

South Carolina

Midlands Technical College, A

South Dakota

Southeast Technical Institute, A

Tennessee

Chattanooga State Technical Community College, A

Texas

Austin Community College, A
Central Texas College, A
Eastfield College, A

Houston Community College System, A
Kilgore College, A
Tarrant County College District, A
Texas A&M University-Commerce, B
Texas State Technical College Waco, A
Tyler Junior College, A

Washington

Clover Park Technical College, A
Highline Community College, A
Seattle Central Community College, A
Shoreline Community College, A

West Virginia

Community & Technical College at West Virginia
  University Institute of Technology, A
Fairmont State University, AB
West Virginia University Institute of Technology, B

Wisconsin

Fox Valley Technical College, A
Madison Area Technical College, A
Milwaukee Area Technical College, A
Moraine Park Technical College, A
Northcentral Technical College, A

Wyoming

Northwest College, A

GRAPHIC COMMUNICATIONS

Alabama

H. Councill Trenholm State Technical College, A

Arizona

Arizona State University at the Polytechnic
  Campus, B

Arkansas

Arkansas State University, B

California

Academy of Art University, AB
Point Loma Nazarene University, B
Western Career College (Walnut Creek), AB

Colorado

Pikes Peak Community College, A

District of Columbia

University of the District of Columbia, B

Illinois

Robert Morris College, A
School of the Art Institute of Chicago, B

Indiana

Indiana Tech, A

Iowa

Grand View College, B
Iowa Lakes Community College, A
University of Northern Iowa, B

Kansas

Pittsburg State University, B

Kentucky

Louisville Technical Institute, A

Maine

New England School of Communications, AB

Minnesota

The Art Institutes International Minnesota, AB
Minnesota State University Moorhead, B

Missouri

Drury University, B

New York

New York University, B
Rochester Institute of Technology, B

Ohio

Notre Dame College, B

Oregon

Linn-Benton Community College, A

South Carolina

Clemson University, B

Tennessee

Memphis College of Art, B

Texas

University of Houston, B

Washington

Clark College, A

West Virginia

Fairmont State Community & Technical College, A

Wisconsin

Carroll College, B
Waukesha County Technical College, A

Ontario

Ryerson University, B

GRAPHIC DESIGN

Alabama

Auburn University, B
Calhoun Community College, A
Spring Hill College, B

Arizona

Arizona State University, B
The Art Center Design College, B
The Art Institute of Phoenix, AB
Collins College: A School of Design and
  Technology, B
Yavapai College, A

Arkansas

Harding University, B
Ouachita Baptist University, B
University of Arkansas at Fort Smith, AB

California

Academy of Art University, ABM
Art Center College of Design, B
The Art Institute of California-Inland Empire, AB
The Art Institute of California-Los Angeles, AB
The Art Institute of California-Orange County, AB
The Art Institute of California-San Diego, AB
The Art Institute of California-San Francisco, B
California Institute of the Arts, BMO
California State University, Chico, B
California State University, Fullerton, B
California State University, Long Beach, B
California State University, Sacramento, B
Chapman University, B
Laguna College of Art & Design, B
Mt. Sierra College, B
Platt College San Diego, A
Point Loma Nazarene University, B
San Diego State University, B
San Jose State University, B
Santa Rosa Junior College, A
University of San Francisco, B
Westwood College-Anaheim, A
Westwood College-Inland Empire, A
Westwood College-Long Beach, A
Westwood College-Los Angeles, AB

Colorado

Colorado State University, M
Community College of Denver, A

Rocky Mountain College of Art & Design, B
Western State College of Colorado, B
Westwood College-Denver North, A
Westwood College-Denver South, A

Connecticut

Albertus Magnus College, B
University of Bridgeport, B
Yale University, M

Delaware

Delaware College of Art and Design, A

District of Columbia

American University, B
Corcoran College of Art and Design, AB

Florida

The Art Institute of Tampa, AB
Flagler College, B
Florida State University, B
Miami International University of Art & Design, M
New World School of the Arts, AB
Palm Beach Atlantic University, B
Ringling School of Art and Design, B
St. Petersburg College, A
University of Florida, B
University of Miami, BM

Georgia

Savannah College of Art and Design, BM
University of Georgia, B
Westwood College-Atlanta Midtown, A
Westwood College-Atlanta Northlake, A

Guam

University of Guam, M

Idaho

Northwest Nazarene University, B

Illinois

Illinois Institute of Technology, MD
Illinois State University, M
North Central College, B
Parkland College, A
Quincy University, B
School of the Art Institute of Chicago, BM
University of Illinois at Chicago, BM
University of Illinois at Urbana-Champaign, BM
Waubonsee Community College, A
Western Illinois University, O
Westwood College-Chicago Du Page, A
Westwood College-Chicago Loop Campus, AB
Westwood College-Chicago O'Hare Airport, A
Westwood College-Chicago River Oaks, A

Indiana

Ancilla College, A
Huntington University, B
Indiana State University, M
Indiana University Bloomington, M
Indiana University-Purdue University Fort Wayne, B
International Business College (Indianapolis), A
Ivy Tech Community College-Southwest, A
University of Evansville, B

Iowa

Briar Cliff University, B
Dordt College, B
Drake University, B
Grand View College, B
Iowa Lakes Community College, A
Iowa State University of Science and
  Technology, BM
Iowa Wesleyan College, B
St. Ambrose University, B

Kansas

Barton County Community College, A
MidAmerica Nazarene University, B
Pittsburg State University, M

University of Kansas, B

Kentucky

Brown Mackie College-Louisville, A
Louisville Technical Institute, A

Louisiana

Louisiana State University and Agricultural and
  Mechanical College, M
Louisiana Tech University, M

Maine

Maine College of Art, B

Maryland

Maryland Institute College of Art, BM
TESST College of Technology (Towson), A
University of Baltimore, M

Massachusetts

The Art Institute of Boston at Lesley University, B
Becker College, AB
Boston University, M
Bridgewater State College, B
Bristol Community College, A
Emmanuel College, B
Fitchburg State College, B
Framingham State College, B
Lasell College, B
Massasoit Community College, A
Montserrat College of Art, B
The New England Institute of Art, B
Regis College, B
School of the Museum of Fine Arts, Boston, B
Springfield Technical Community College, A

Michigan

Alma College, B
Jackson Community College, A
Lake Michigan College, A
Mott Community College, A
Oakland Community College, A
University of Michigan-Flint, B
Western Michigan University, M

Minnesota

Academy College, A
The Art Institutes International Minnesota, AB
College of Visual Arts, B
Dakota County Technical College, A
Minneapolis College of Art and Design, M
North Hennepin Community College, A
Northwestern College, B
Saint Mary's University of Minnesota, B
University of Minnesota, Duluth, M

Mississippi

Mississippi College, B

Missouri

Columbia College, B
Drury University, B
Hickey College, A
Kansas City Art Institute, B
Maryville University of Saint Louis, B
Missouri Western State University, B
Park University, B
University of Missouri-St. Louis, B
Washington University in St. Louis, B

Nebraska

Creighton University, B
Union College, AB
Wayne State College, B

New Hampshire

Chester College of New England, B
Colby-Sawyer College, B
Keene State College, B

Southern New Hampshire University, B

New Jersey

Kean University, M

New York

The Art Institute of New York City, A
Bryant and Stratton College, Amherst Campus, A
Bryant and Stratton College (Rochester-Henrietta
  Campus), A
City College of the City University of New York, BM
The College of New Rochelle, M
Daemen College, B
Fashion Institute of Technology, B
Pratt Institute, ABM
Rochester Institute of Technology, ABM
Sage College of Albany, A
St. John's University, B
Syracuse University, M
Villa Maria College of Buffalo, A
Wood Tobe-Coburn School, A

North Carolina

Appalachian State University, B
Campbell University, B
Mars Hill College, B
Meredith College, B
North Carolina State University, BM
Peace College, B

North Dakota

University of North Dakota, B

Ohio

Antonelli College, A
Art Academy of Cincinnati, AB
The Art Institute of Ohio-Cincinnati, A
Bradford School, A
Cedarville University, B
The Cleveland Institute of Art, B
College of Mount St. Joseph, AB
Columbus College of Art & Design, B
Kent State University, M
Marietta College, B
Miami University, B
Miami University Hamilton, B
Mount Vernon Nazarene University, B
Ohio Dominican University, B
Ohio Institute of Photography and Technology, A
Ohio Northern University, B
Shawnee State University, B
University of Cincinnati, M
University of Rio Grande, B
Ursuline College, B
Youngstown State University, B

Oregon

The Art Institute of Portland, AB
George Fox University, B
Pacific Northwest College of Art, B

Pennsylvania

The Art Institute of Philadelphia, AB
The Art Institute of Pittsburgh, AB
Cabrini College, B
East Stroudsburg University of Pennsylvania, B
Keystone College, A
La Roche College, B
Luzerne County Community College, A
Marywood University, BM
Moore College of Art & Design, B
Moravian College, B
Northampton County Area Community College, A
Pennsylvania College of Art & Design, B
The Pennsylvania State University Abington
  College, B
The Pennsylvania State University Altoona
  College, B
The Pennsylvania State University Beaver Campus
  of the Commonwealth College, B
The Pennsylvania State University Berks Campus of
  the Berks-Lehigh Valley College, B
The Pennsylvania State University Delaware County
  Campus of the Commonwealth College, B

The Pennsylvania State University DuBois Campus of the Commonwealth College, B
The Pennsylvania State University at Erie, The Behrend College, B
The Pennsylvania State University Fayette Campus of the Commonwealth College, B
The Pennsylvania State University Hazleton Campus of the Commonwealth College, B
The Pennsylvania State University, Lehigh Valley Campus of the Berks-Lehigh Valley College, B
The Pennsylvania State University McKeesport Campus of the Commonwealth College, B
The Pennsylvania State University Mont Alto Campus of the Commonwealth College, B
The Pennsylvania State University New Kensington Campus of the Commonwealth College, B
The Pennsylvania State University Schuylkill Campus of the Capital College, B
The Pennsylvania State University Shenango Campus of the Commonwealth College, B
The Pennsylvania State University University Park Campus, B
The Pennsylvania State University Wilkes-Barre Campus of the Commonwealth College, B
The Pennsylvania State University Worthington Scranton Campus of the Commonwealth College, B
The Pennsylvania State University York Campus of the Commonwealth College, B
Philadelphia University, B
Susquehanna University, B
Temple University, BM
The University of the Arts, B
Waynesburg College, B

Rhode Island

Rhode Island School of Design, BM
Roger Williams University, B
Salve Regina University, B

South Carolina

Coker College, B
Limestone College, B

Tennessee

Memphis College of Art, B
Southern Adventist University, B
University of Memphis, M
The University of Tennessee, M
The University of Tennessee at Martin, B
Watkins College of Art and Design, B

Texas

The Art Institute of Dallas, AB
The Art Institute of Houston, AB
Hardin-Simmons University, B
McMurry University, B
St. Edward's University, B
Schreiner University, B
Texas State University-San Marcos, B
Texas Tech University, B
University of Houston, M
University of North Texas, M
Westwood College-Dallas, A
Westwood College-Fort Worth, A
Westwood College-Houston South Campus, A

Utah

Brigham Young University, B
Salt Lake Community College, A
University of Utah, M

Vermont

Champlain College, AB

Virginia

George Mason University, M
Marymount University, B
Old Dominion University, B
Tidewater Community College, A
Westwood College-Annandale Campus, A

Washington

The Art Institute of Seattle, AB
Cornish College of the Arts, B

Western Washington University, B

West Virginia

West Virginia University, M

Wisconsin

Bryant and Stratton College, Wauwatosa Campus, A
Cardinal Stritch University, M
Carthage College, B
Concordia University Wisconsin, B
Mount Mary College, B
Viterbo University, B
Waukesha County Technical College, A

Alberta

Alberta College of Art & Design, B

British Columbia

Kwantlen University College, B
Thompson Rivers University, A

Nova Scotia

NSCAD University, B

Quebec

Université Laval, M

GREENHOUSE OPERATIONS AND MANAGEMENT

Illinois

Joliet Junior College, A
Kishwaukee College, A

Minnesota

Rochester Community and Technical College, A

North Dakota

Minot State University-Bottineau Campus, A

Ohio

Kent State University, Salem Campus, A
The Ohio State University Agricultural Technical Institute, A

Pennsylvania

Community College of Allegheny County, A

Vermont

Sterling College, AB

GUNSMITHING/GUNSMITH

Arizona

Yavapai College, A

Colorado

Colorado School of Trades, A
Trinidad State Junior College, A

HAIR STYLING/STYLIST AND HAIR DESIGN

Colorado

Colorado Northwestern Community College, A

Wisconsin

Milwaukee Area Technical College, A

HAZARDOUS MATERIALS INFORMATION SYSTEMS TECHNOLOGY/TECHNICIAN

Ohio

Ohio University, A

HAZARDOUS MATERIALS MANAGEMENT AND WASTE TECHNOLOGY/TECHNICIAN

California

California State University, Long Beach, O

Florida

University of Central Florida, O

Idaho

Idaho State University, M
University of Idaho, M

Kansas

Barton County Community College, A
Kansas City Kansas Community College, A

Michigan

Wayne State University, MO

New Jersey

Rutgers, The State University of New Jersey, New Brunswick/Piscataway, MD

New York

Rochester Institute of Technology, B
Stony Brook University, State University of New York, O

Ohio

Ohio University, A

Oklahoma

University of Oklahoma, M

South Carolina

University of South Carolina, MD

Texas

Odessa College, A

HEALTH AIDE

Arizona

Central Arizona College, A

Kansas

Allen County Community College, A

Massachusetts

Springfield Technical Community College, A

Missouri

Jefferson College, A

Washington

Edmonds Community College, A

HEALTH AND MEDICAL ADMINISTRATIVE SERVICES

California

Western Career College (Walnut Creek), A

Florida

Keiser College (Miami), A
University of Miami, B

Hawaii

Hawaii Business College, A

Maryland

University of Baltimore, B

Michigan

University of Michigan-Flint, B

North Carolina

Catawba Valley Community College, A

Ohio

Kent State University, AB
The University of Akron, A

Ursuline College, B

Pennsylvania

Pennsylvania College of Technology, B
Robert Morris University, B

British Columbia

British Columbia Institute of Technology, A

HEALTH AND MEDICAL LABORATORY TECHNOLOGIES

Alabama

Auburn University, B
Northwest-Shoals Community College, A

Arizona

Phoenix College, A

Connecticut

Quinnipiac University, B

Delaware

Delaware Technical & Community College, Jack F.
    Owens Campus, A

District of Columbia

The George Washington University, B

Florida

Florida Community College at Jacksonville, A

Georgia

Athens Technical College, A
Central Georgia Technical College, A
Chattahoochee Technical College, A
DeKalb Technical College, A
Flint River Technical College, A
Lanier Technical College, A
North Georgia Technical College, A
Southeastern Technical College, A
Southwest Georgia Technical College, A
Valdosta Technical College, A
West Central Technical College, A

Illinois

Roosevelt University, B

Indiana

Indiana Business College (Indianapolis-Northwest
    Campus), A
Vincennes University, A

Iowa

Ellsworth Community College, A
Iowa Lakes Community College, A

Maine

Central Maine Community College, A
University of New England, B

Maryland

Cecil Community College, A
Frederick Community College, A
Harford Community College, A
Villa Julie College, A

Michigan

Oakland University, B
Schoolcraft College, A

Minnesota

Minnesota State Community and Technical
    College-Fergus Falls, A

North Hennepin Community College, A

Missouri

Evangel University, A
Rockhurst University, B

Nevada

University of Nevada, Las Vegas, B

New Jersey

Camden County College, A
Felician College, B

New York

Jefferson Community College, A
Mohawk Valley Community College, A

North Carolina

Rowan-Cabarrus Community College, A

Ohio

The Ohio State University Agricultural Technical
    Institute, A
University of Cincinnati, B
University of Cincinnati Raymond Walters College, A

Oklahoma

Rose State College, A
Southeastern Oklahoma State University, B
University of Oklahoma, B

Oregon

Portland Community College, A

Pennsylvania

Reading Area Community College, A

Puerto Rico

University of Puerto Rico, Medical Sciences
    Campus, B

Texas

Abilene Christian University, B

Washington

Shoreline Community College, A

Wisconsin

Chippewa Valley Technical College, A
Madison Area Technical College, A

British Columbia

British Columbia Institute of Technology, A

Ontario

University of Windsor, B

HEALTH AND PHYSICAL EDUCATION

Alabama

Jacksonville State University, B
Lawson State Community College, A
Samford University, B
University of Montevallo, B

Arizona

Cochise College (Douglas), A
Eastern Arizona College, A

Arkansas

Arkansas State University, B
Philander Smith College, B
University of Arkansas, B

California

Antelope Valley College, A
California State University, Chico, B
California State University, Fullerton, B
California State University, Sacramento, B
Cerro Coso Community College, A

Citrus College, A
La Sierra University, B
The Master's College and Seminary, B
Point Loma Nazarene University, B
Reedley College, A
Saint Mary's College of California, B
San Diego State University, B
San Jose State University, B
University of San Francisco, B
Vanguard University of Southern California, B

Colorado

Colorado Christian University, B

Connecticut

Wesleyan University, B

Delaware

University of Delaware, B

Florida

Florida Agricultural and Mechanical University, B
Pensacola Junior College, A
University of West Florida, B

Georgia

Andrew College, A
Atlanta Metropolitan College, A
Coastal Georgia Community College, A
Darton College, A
Georgia Perimeter College, A
Georgia Southern University, B
University of Georgia, B

Hawaii

Brigham Young University-Hawaii, B
University of Hawaii at Manoa, B

Idaho

Northwest Nazarene University, B

Illinois

Elmhurst College, B
John Wood Community College, A
Robert Morris College, A
Southern Illinois University Edwardsville, B

Indiana

Anderson University, B
Bethel College, AB
University of Evansville, B
Valparaiso University, B

Iowa

Dordt College, B
Iowa Lakes Community College, A
Iowa State University of Science and Technology, B
Loras College, B
Luther College, B
St. Ambrose University, B
University of Northern Iowa, B
William Penn University, B

Kansas

Allen County Community College, A
Baker University, B
Bethel College, B
Central Christian College of Kansas, A
Haskell Indian Nations University, A
Pittsburg State University, B
Southwestern College, B
Sterling College, B
University of Kansas, B

Kentucky

Asbury College, B
Kentucky State University, B
University of the Cumberlands, B

University of Louisville, B

Louisiana

Louisiana Tech University, B

Maryland

Columbia Union College, B
Salisbury University, B

Michigan

Concordia University, B
Eastern Michigan University, B
Olivet College, B

Minnesota

Alexandria Technical College, A
Bethel University, B
College of St. Catherine, B
Concordia College, B
Hamline University, B
Minnesota State University Moorhead, B
Northwestern College, B
Southwest Minnesota State University, B
University of St. Thomas, B

Mississippi

Mississippi College, B
University of Southern Mississippi, B
William Carey College, B

Missouri

College of the Ozarks, B
Evangel University, B
Lindenwood University, B
Missouri Western State University, B
Southeast Missouri State University, B

Montana

Montana State University, B
Montana State University-Billings, B
University of Great Falls, B

Nebraska

Concordia University, B
Dana College, B
Doane College, B
Hastings College, B
Nebraska Wesleyan University, B
Northeast Community College, A
University of Nebraska at Omaha, B
Western Nebraska Community College, A

New Hampshire

Keene State College, B
New England College, B
Plymouth State University, B

New Jersey

Gloucester County College, A
Salem Community College, A

New Mexico

Clovis Community College, A
Santa Fe Community College, A

New York

Corning Community College, A
Houghton College, B
Ithaca College, B
Sage College of Albany, B
State University of New York College at
   Brockport, B
State University of New York College of Technology
   at Delhi, A

North Carolina

Campbell University, B
Gardner-Webb University, B
Guilford College, B
Johnson C. Smith University, B
Louisburg College, A
North Carolina Central University, B
The University of North Carolina at Chapel Hill, B
The University of North Carolina at Charlotte, B

The University of North Carolina at Pembroke, B
The University of North Carolina Wilmington, B
Wingate University, B

North Dakota

Mayville State University, B
University of Mary, B

Ohio

Bluffton University, B
Capital University, B
Cedarville University, B
Malone College, B
Miami University, B
Mount Vernon Nazarene University, A
Ohio Northern University, B
Ohio University, B
University of Rio Grande, B
Youngstown State University, B

Oklahoma

Cameron University, B
Oklahoma Baptist University, B
University of Oklahoma, B
University of Science and Arts of Oklahoma, B

Oregon

Blue Mountain Community College, A
George Fox University, B
Linfield College, B
Southwestern Oregon Community College, A

Pennsylvania

Community College of Allegheny County, A
Eastern University, B
Edinboro University of Pennsylvania, B
Indiana University of Pennsylvania, B
Lincoln University, B
Luzerne County Community College, A
Slippery Rock University of Pennsylvania, B
Ursinus College, B
West Chester University of Pennsylvania, B

Puerto Rico

Inter American University of Puerto Rico,
   Metropolitan Campus, B

South Carolina

Bob Jones University, B
Claflin University, B
Coker College, B
Southern Wesleyan University, B

South Dakota

Black Hills State University, B
South Dakota State University, B

Tennessee

Austin Peay State University, B
Belmont University, B
Bethel College, B
Bryan College, B
East Tennessee State University, B
Freed-Hardeman University, B
Lincoln Memorial University, B
Maryville College, B
Middle Tennessee State University, B
Milligan College, B
Tennessee Wesleyan College, B
The University of Tennessee at Martin, B

Texas

Abilene Christian University, B
Angelo State University, B
Baylor University, B
Brazosport College, A
East Texas Baptist University, B
Hardin-Simmons University, B
Houston Baptist University, B
Howard Payne University, B
Jarvis Christian College, B
Lubbock Christian University, B
St. Mary's University of San Antonio, B
Southwestern Adventist University, B

Stephen F. Austin State University, B
Texas A&M International University, B
Texas A&M University, B
Texas Christian University, B
Texas College, B
Texas Southern University, B
Texas State University-San Marcos, B
Texas Tech University, B
Texas Wesleyan University, B
University of Houston, B
University of Houston-Clear Lake, B
University of North Texas, B
The University of Texas at Arlington, B
The University of Texas at Austin, B
The University of Texas-Pan American, B
The University of Texas at San Antonio, B
The University of Texas at Tyler, B
West Texas A&M University, B

Utah

Brigham Young University, B
University of Utah, B
Utah Valley State College, A
Weber State University, B

Vermont

Castleton State College, B
Johnson State College, B
Lyndon State College, B

Virginia

Averett University, B
Bridgewater College, B
Emory & Henry College, B
James Madison University, B
Liberty University, B
Radford University, B
Roanoke College, B
Southern Virginia University, B
Virginia Intermont College, B

Washington

Eastern Washington University, B
Walla Walla College, B
Washington State University, B

West Virginia

West Virginia University, B
West Virginia Wesleyan College, B

Wisconsin

Carroll College, B
Concordia University Wisconsin, B
University of Wisconsin-Stevens Point, B
University of Wisconsin-Superior, B

Wyoming

Sheridan College-Sheridan and Gillette, A

British Columbia

Trinity Western University, B

Ontario

Queen's University at Kingston, B
Redeemer University College, B
University of Toronto, B
University of Windsor, B
York University, B

Quebec

Université du Québec àTrois-Rivières, B

HEALTH AND PHYSICAL EDUCATION/FITNESS

Arizona

Arizona State University at the Polytechnic
   Campus, B

California

California Baptist University, B
California State University, Long Beach, B

California State University, Sacramento, B
Saint Mary's College of California, B
Santa Rosa Junior College, A

Colorado

Naropa University, B

Georgia

Brewton-Parker College, B
Reinhardt College, B
University of Georgia, B

Iowa

Coe College, B
Cornell College, B

Kansas

Garden City Community College, A

Maine

University of New England, B

Maryland

Towson University, B

Massachusetts

Bridgewater State College, B

Michigan

Oakland Community College, A

Minnesota

Gustavus Adolphus College, B
University of Minnesota, Twin Cities Campus, B

Missouri

Avila University, B

Montana

Rocky Mountain College, B

New York

Hudson Valley Community College, A
Ithaca College, B
Kingsborough Community College of the City
   University of New York, A
St. John Fisher College, B
State University of New York College at
   Brockport, B

North Carolina

Campbell University, B
East Carolina University, B
Greensboro College, B
Saint Augustine's College, B

North Dakota

Mayville State University, B

Ohio

Bowling Green State University, B
Capital University, B
Ohio Northern University, B
The University of Akron, B

Oklahoma

University of Central Oklahoma, B

Pennsylvania

Bloomsburg University of Pennsylvania, B
East Stroudsburg University of Pennsylvania, B
Lincoln University, B

Pennsylvania College of Technology, A

South Carolina

Coker College, B
Limestone College, B

Tennessee

Lambuth University, B

Texas

Midwestern State University, B
Sam Houston State University, B
Texas Christian University, B
Texas Lutheran University, B

Utah

Brigham Young University, B
Utah Valley State College, AB

Virginia

Averett University, B

Wisconsin

Concordia University Wisconsin, B
University of Wisconsin-Superior, B

British Columbia

University of Victoria, B

HEALTH COMMUNICATION

Pennsylvania

Juniata College, B

HEALTH EDUCATION

Alabama

Alabama State University, M
Auburn University, MDO
Jacksonville State University, M
The University of Alabama, MD
The University of Alabama at Birmingham, MD
University of South Alabama, M

Arizona

Midwestern University, Glendale Campus, M
Northern Arizona University, M

Arkansas

Arkansas State University, O
University of Arkansas, MD
University of Central Arkansas, M

California

California State University, Dominguez Hills, M
California State University, Long Beach, M
California State University, Los Angeles, M
California State University, Northridge, M
California State University, San Bernardino, M
John F. Kennedy University, M
Loma Linda University, MD
Mills College, M
Touro University International, M
University of California, Berkeley, M

Colorado

Adams State College, M
University of Colorado at Denver and Health
   Sciences Center - Downtown Denver Campus, D

Connecticut

Southern Connecticut State University, M

District of Columbia

Howard University, M

Florida

Florida Agricultural and Mechanical University, M
Florida International University, M
Florida State University, M
Nova Southeastern University, D

University of Florida, MD
University of West Florida, M

Georgia

Albany State University, M
Georgia College & State University, MO
Georgia Southern University, M
Georgia Southwestern State University, M
University of Georgia, MDO
Valdosta State University, M

Idaho

Idaho State University, M

Illinois

Illinois State University, M
Southern Illinois University Carbondale, MD
Southern Illinois University Edwardsville, MO
University of Illinois at Chicago, M
Western Illinois University, MO

Indiana

Ball State University, M
Indiana State University, M
Indiana University-Purdue University Indianapolis, M

Iowa

Allen College, M
Iowa State University of Science and
   Technology, MD
University of Northern Iowa, M

Kansas

Fort Hays State University, M

Kentucky

Eastern Kentucky University, M
Morehead State University, M
Union College, M

Louisiana

Louisiana Tech University, M
McNeese State University, M
Northwestern State University of Louisiana, M
Southeastern Louisiana University, M
Tulane University, M
University of New Orleans, MO

Maryland

University of Maryland, Baltimore County, M
University of Maryland, College Park, MD

Massachusetts

Boston University, MO
Lesley University, M
Springfield College, M
Worcester State College, M

Michigan

University of Michigan-Flint, M
Wayne State University, M

Minnesota

Minnesota State University Mankato, M

Mississippi

Jackson State University, M
Mississippi State University, M
Mississippi University for Women, M
University of Southern Mississippi, M

Missouri

Northwest Missouri State University, M
University of Missouri-Columbia, MD

Montana

Montana State University, M
The University of Montana-Missoula, M

Nebraska

University of Nebraska-Lincoln, M
University of Nebraska at Omaha, M

Wayne State College, M

New Hampshire

Plymouth State University, M

New Jersey

The College of New Jersey, M
Montclair State University, MO
New Jersey City University, M

New Mexico

University of New Mexico, M

New York

Adelphi University, MO
Brooklyn College of the City University of New York, M
Hofstra University, M
Lehman College of the City University of New York, M
Long Island University, Brooklyn Campus, M
New York University, D
State University of New York College at Brockport, M
State University of New York College at Cortland, M

North Carolina

East Carolina University, M
North Carolina Agricultural and Technical State University, M
The University of North Carolina at Chapel Hill, MD

Ohio

Cleveland State University, M
Kent State University, MD
University of Cincinnati, M
The University of Toledo, D
Wright State University, M

Oklahoma

Oklahoma State University, MD
University of Central Oklahoma, M
University of Oklahoma Health Sciences Center, D

Oregon

Oregon State University, M
Portland State University, M
Western Oregon University, M

Pennsylvania

Arcadia University, M
East Stroudsburg University of Pennsylvania, M
Eastern University, M
Indiana University of Pennsylvania, M
The Pennsylvania State University Harrisburg Campus, M
Saint Francis University, M
Saint Joseph's University, M
Temple University, M
University of Pennsylvania, MD
University of Pittsburgh, MO
West Chester University of Pennsylvania, M
Widener University, M

Puerto Rico

Inter American University of Puerto Rico, Metropolitan Campus, M
University of Puerto Rico, Medical Sciences Campus, M

Rhode Island

Rhode Island College, M
University of Rhode Island, M

South Carolina

The Citadel, The Military College of South Carolina, M
University of South Carolina, MDO

South Dakota

Northern State University, M
South Dakota State University, M

The University of South Dakota, M

Tennessee

Austin Peay State University, M
Middle Tennessee State University, MD
Tennessee Technological University, M
The University of Tennessee, M

Texas

Baylor University, MD
Prairie View A&M University, M
Tarleton State University, MO
Texas A&M University, MD
Texas A&M University-Commerce, MD
Texas A&M University-Kingsville, M
Texas A&M University System Health Science Center, M
Texas Southern University, M
Texas State University-San Marcos, M
Texas Woman's University, M
University of Houston, MD
The University of Texas at Austin, MD
The University of Texas at El Paso, M
The University of Texas at Tyler, M

Utah

Brigham Young University, M
University of Utah, MD
Utah State University, M

Virginia

James Madison University, M
University of Virginia, MD
Virginia Polytechnic Institute and State University, M

Washington

Central Washington University, M

West Virginia

Marshall University, M

Wisconsin

Mount Mary College, M
University of Wisconsin-La Crosse, M

Wyoming

University of Wyoming, M

Nova Scotia

Dalhousie University, M

Ontario

University of Waterloo, MD

HEALTH/HEALTH CARE ADMINISTRATION/MANAGEMENT

Alabama

Auburn University, B
Columbia Southern University, B
Community College of the Air Force, A

Alaska

Alaska Pacific University, B
University of Alaska Southeast, Sitka Campus, A

Arizona

GateWay Community College, A
International Institute of the Americas (Mesa), A
International Institute of the Americas (Phoenix), A
International Institute of the Americas (Tucson), A
International Institute of the Americas (West Valley), A
The University of Arizona, B
University of Phoenix Online Campus, B
University of Phoenix-Phoenix Campus, B
University of Phoenix-Southern Arizona Campus, B

Western International University, B

Arkansas

Harding University, B
National Park Community College, A

California

California Coast University, B
California State University, Dominguez Hills, B
California State University, Long Beach, B
California State University, Sacramento, B
California State University, San Bernardino, B
Mount St. Mary's College, B
San Jose State University, B
Touro University International, B
University of La Verne, B
University of Phoenix-Bay Area Campus, B
University of Phoenix-Central Valley Campus, B
University of Phoenix-Sacramento Valley Campus, B
University of Phoenix-San Diego Campus, B

Colorado

Metropolitan State College of Denver, B
National American University (Colorado Springs), B
National American University (Denver), AB

Connecticut

Albertus Magnus College, B
St. Vincent's College, A
University of Connecticut, B

District of Columbia

Southeastern University, AB

Florida

Florida Agricultural and Mechanical University, B
Florida Atlantic University, B
Florida International University, B
Florida Metropolitan University-North Orlando Campus, B
Florida Metropolitan University-South Orlando Campus, B
International College, B
Keiser College (Daytona Beach), A
Keiser College (Fort Lauderdale), A
Keiser College (Melbourne), A
Keiser College (Tallahassee), A
Lynn University, B
Manatee Community College, A
Pensacola Junior College, A
St. Petersburg College, A
South University (West Palm Beach), B
University of Central Florida, B
University of Phoenix-North Florida Campus, B
University of Phoenix-South Florida Campus, B
University of Phoenix-West Florida Campus, B

Georgia

Clayton State University, B
Macon State College, B
South University, B
University of Phoenix-Columbus Georgia Campus, B

Hawaii

University of Phoenix-Hawaii Campus, B

Idaho

College of Southern Idaho, A
Idaho State University, B
North Idaho College, A
University of Phoenix-Idaho Campus, B

Illinois

American InterContinental University Online, B
Benedictine University, B
College of DuPage, A
Governors State University, B
Illinois Central College, A
Lewis University, B
National-Louis University, B
Roosevelt University, B
Southern Illinois University Carbondale, B
University of St. Francis, B

Western Illinois University, B

Indiana

Calumet College of Saint Joseph, B
Indiana University Northwest, B
Indiana University-Purdue University Indianapolis, B
Indiana University South Bend, B
University of Evansville, B
University of Phoenix-Indianapolis Campus, B

Iowa

Ashford University, B
Des Moines Area Community College, A
Indian Hills Community College, A
Iowa Lakes Community College, A
Mercy College of Health Sciences, B
Upper Iowa University, B

Kansas

Friends University, B
Wichita State University, B

Kentucky

Brown Mackie College-Louisville, A
Eastern Kentucky University, B
Midway College, B
National College of Business & Technology
(Louisville), A
University of Kentucky, B
Western Kentucky University, B

Louisiana

Dillard University, B
Our Lady of the Lake College, B

Maine

University of New England, B

Maryland

Columbia Union College, B
Sojourner-Douglass College, B
Towson University, B
University of Maryland, Baltimore County, B

Massachusetts

Newbury College, B
Northeastern University, B
Springfield College, B
Stonehill College, B

Michigan

Baker College of Auburn Hills, AB
Baker College of Flint, AB
Baker College of Muskegon, AB
Baker College of Owosso, B
Baker College of Port Huron, B
Davenport University (Dearborn), B
Eastern Michigan University, B
Ferris State University, B
Madonna University, AB
Oakland Community College, A
Spring Arbor University, B
University of Detroit Mercy, B
University of Michigan-Dearborn, B
University of Michigan-Flint, B
University of Phoenix-West Michigan Campus, B
Western Michigan University, B

Minnesota

Concordia College, B
Inver Hills Community College, A
Minnesota State University Moorhead, B
University of Minnesota, Crookston, B
Winona State University, B

Mississippi

Belhaven College, B
Jackson State University, B

Missouri

Harris-Stowe State University, B
Lindenwood University, B
Mineral Area College, A
Saint Louis University, B

University of Phoenix-Kansas City Campus, B

Montana

Montana State University, B
Montana State University-Billings, B
University of Great Falls, B

Nebraska

Bellevue University, B
Creighton University, B
Hastings College, B

Nevada

University of Nevada, Las Vegas, B

New Hampshire

Granite State College, B
University of New Hampshire, B

New Jersey

Essex County College, A
Saint Peter's College, B

New Mexico

International Institute of the Americas, A
New Mexico Highlands University, B
University of Phoenix-New Mexico Campus, B

New York

Dominican College, B
D'Youville College, B
Globe Institute of Technology, B
Herkimer County Community College, A
Iona College, B
Ithaca College, B
Lehman College of the City University of New
York, B
New York University, AB
St. John's University, B
St. Joseph's College, New York, B
St. Joseph's College, Suffolk Campus, B
State University of New York College at
Brockport, B
State University of New York College of Technology
at Canton, B
State University of New York, Fredonia, B
State University of New York Institute of
Technology, B

North Carolina

Appalachian State University, B
Cabarrus College of Health Sciences, A
Caldwell Community College and Technical
Institute, A
Central Piedmont Community College, A
Methodist College, AB
The University of North Carolina at Chapel Hill, B

Ohio

Bowling Green State University, B
Brown Mackie College-Akron, A
Brown Mackie College-Findlay, A
Brown Mackie College-North Canton, A
David N. Myers University, B
Franklin University, B
Heidelberg College, B
Mercy College of Northwest Ohio, B
Ohio University-Eastern, B
Ohio University-Southern Campus, B
University of Cincinnati, B
University of Northwestern Ohio, B
University of Phoenix-Cleveland Campus, B
Ursuline College, B
Wilberforce University, B
Wright State University, B

Oklahoma

Community Care College, A
Langston University, B
Northeastern State University, B
Southwestern Oklahoma State University, B
University of Phoenix-Oklahoma City Campus, B

University of Phoenix-Tulsa Campus, B

Oregon

Chemeketa Community College, A
Concordia University, B
Oregon State University, B
Pioneer Pacific College, AB

Pennsylvania

Alvernia College, B
Arcadia University, B
Cedar Crest College, B
Chestnut Hill College, AB
Consolidated School of Business (Lancaster), A
Consolidated School of Business (York), A
Drexel University, B
Duquesne University, B
Immaculata University, B
Lebanon Valley College, B
Luzerne County Community College, A
Marywood University, B
Pennsylvania Highland Community College, A
The Pennsylvania State University Abington
College, B
The Pennsylvania State University Altoona
College, B
The Pennsylvania State University Beaver Campus
of the Commonwealth College, B
The Pennsylvania State University Berks Campus of
the Berks-Lehigh Valley College, B
The Pennsylvania State University Delaware County
Campus of the Commonwealth College, B
The Pennsylvania State University DuBois Campus
of the Commonwealth College, B
The Pennsylvania State University at Erie, The
Behrend College, B
The Pennsylvania State University Fayette Campus
of the Commonwealth College, B
The Pennsylvania State University Harrisburg
Campus, B
The Pennsylvania State University Hazleton
Campus of the Commonwealth College, B
The Pennsylvania State University, Lehigh Valley
Campus of the Berks-Lehigh Valley College, B
The Pennsylvania State University McKeesport
Campus of the Commonwealth College, B
The Pennsylvania State University Mont Alto
Campus of the Commonwealth College, B
The Pennsylvania State University New Kensington
Campus of the Commonwealth College, B
The Pennsylvania State University Schuylkill
Campus of the Capital College, B
The Pennsylvania State University Shenango
Campus of the Commonwealth College, B
The Pennsylvania State University University Park
Campus, B
The Pennsylvania State University Wilkes-Barre
Campus of the Commonwealth College, B
The Pennsylvania State University Worthington
Scranton Campus of the Commonwealth
College, B
The Pennsylvania State University York Campus of
the Commonwealth College, B
Point Park University, AB
Robert Morris University, B
Saint Joseph's University, AB
Shippensburg University of Pennsylvania, B
University of Pennsylvania, B
The University of Scranton, AB
Waynesburg College, B
West Chester University of Pennsylvania, B
York College of Pennsylvania, B

Rhode Island

Providence College, B
Roger Williams University, B

University of Rhode Island, B

South Carolina

South University, B

South Dakota

Augustana College, B
Black Hills State University, B

Tennessee

Baptist College of Health Sciences, B
Belmont University, B
Fisk University, B
Martin Methodist College, AB
Southern Adventist University, B
Tennessee State University, B
University of Phoenix-Nashville Campus, B

Texas

Dallas Baptist University, B
Houston Community College System, A
Howard Payne University, B
South Plains College, A
Southwestern Adventist University, B
Texas Southern University, B
Texas State University-San Marcos, B
Tyler Junior College, A
University of Houston-Clear Lake, B
The University of Texas at El Paso, B

Utah

California College for Health Sciences, B
University of Phoenix-Utah Campus, B
Weber State University, B

Virginia

ECPI College of Technology (Newport News), A
ECPI College of Technology (Virginia Beach), A
ECPI Technical College (Richmond), A
ECPI Technical College (Roanoke), A
Jefferson College of Health Sciences, B
Mary Baldwin College, B
Norfolk State University, B

Washington

Eastern Washington University, B
University of Phoenix-Spokane Campus, B
University of Phoenix-Washington Campus, B

West Virginia

Community & Technical College at West Virginia
   University Institute of Technology, A
Mountain State University, B
West Virginia University Institute of Technology, B
Wheeling Jesuit University, B

Wisconsin

Concordia University Wisconsin, B
University of Wisconsin-Eau Claire, B
University of Wisconsin-Milwaukee, B

British Columbia

British Columbia Institute of Technology, AB
University of Victoria, B

Ontario

Brock University, B

HEALTH INFORMATICS

Alabama

The University of Alabama at Birmingham, M

California

Loma Linda University, M
Touro University International, O

University of La Verne, M

District of Columbia

The George Washington University, M

Florida

University of Central Florida, O

Georgia

Emory University, M
Medical College of Georgia, M

Minnesota

The College of St. Scholastica, M
University of Minnesota, Twin Cities Campus, MDO

Missouri

University of Missouri-Columbia, M

New York

Molloy College, O
New York University, MO
Touro College, O

North Carolina

Duke University, O

Ohio

Case Western Reserve University, M

Pennsylvania

La Salle University, O

Puerto Rico

University of Puerto Rico, Medical Sciences
   Campus, M

Texas

University of the Incarnate Word, M
The University of Texas Health Science Center at
   Houston, MD

Virginia

University of Virginia, M

Washington

University of Washington, M

Wisconsin

University of Wisconsin-Milwaukee, M

HEALTH INFORMATION/MEDICAL RECORDS ADMINISTRATION/ ADMINISTRATOR

Alabama

Alabama Southern Community College, A
Alabama State University, B
Enterprise-Ozark Community College, A
Faulkner University, A
George Corley Wallace State Community College, A
The University of Alabama at Birmingham, B
Wallace State Community College, A

Arizona

Northland Pioneer College, A
Phoenix College, A

Arkansas

Arkansas Tech University, B
National Park Community College, A

California

Cabrillo College, A
Chabot College, A
Charles R. Drew University of Medicine and
   Science, A
City College of San Francisco, A
Cosumnes River College (Sacramento), A
Cypress College, A

East Los Angeles College, A
Fresno City College, A
Glendale Community College, A
Loma Linda University, B
San Diego Mesa College, A
West Valley College, A

Colorado

Arapahoe Community College, A
Pueblo Community College, A
Regis University, B

Connecticut

Briarwood College, A

Florida

Daytona Beach Community College, A
Florida Agricultural and Mechanical University, B
Florida Community College at Jacksonville, A
Florida International University, B
Indian River Community College, A
Lake-Sumter Community College, A
Miami Dade College, A
Pensacola Junior College, A
Polk Community College, A
St. Johns River Community College, A
St. Petersburg College, A
Santa Fe Community College, A
University of Central Florida, B

Georgia

Clark Atlanta University, B
Clayton State University, A
Dalton State College, A
Darton College, A
Macon State College, B
Medical College of Georgia, B

Idaho

Boise State University, A

Illinois

Black Hawk College, A
Chicago State University, B
City Colleges of Chicago, Harry S. Truman
   College, A
College of DuPage, A
Elgin Community College, A
Illinois Central College, A
Illinois State University, B
John A. Logan College, A
Oakton Community College, A
Southeastern Illinois College, A
Southwestern Illinois College, A
University of Illinois at Chicago, B

Indiana

Indiana University Northwest, AB
Indiana University-Purdue University Indianapolis, B
Vincennes University, A

Iowa

Indian Hills Community College, A
Kirkwood Community College, A
Northeast Iowa Community College, A

Kansas

Barton County Community College, A
Brown Mackie College-Kansas City, A
Butler Community College, A
Dodge City Community College, A
Highland Community College, A
University of Kansas, B

Kentucky

Draughons Junior College, A
Eastern Kentucky University, AB

Louisiana

Elaine P. Nunez Community College, A
Louisiana Tech University, B
Southern University at Shreveport, A

University of Louisiana at Lafayette, B

Maine

Andover College, A
Kennebec Valley Community College, A

Maryland

Baltimore City Community College, A
Hagerstown Business College, A
Hagerstown Community College, A
Prince George's Community College, A

Massachusetts

Bunker Hill Community College, A
Holyoke Community College, A
Labouré College, A
Northern Essex Community College, A

Michigan

Baker College of Auburn Hills, AB
Baker College of Cadillac, A
Baker College of Clinton Township, A
Baker College of Flint, AB
Baker College of Jackson, A
Baker College of Port Huron, A
Ferris State University, AB
Gogebic Community College, A
Henry Ford Community College, A
Northern Michigan University, A

Minnesota

College of St. Catherine-Minneapolis, A
The College of St. Scholastica, B
Rasmussen College Eagan, A
Rasmussen College Mankato, A
Rasmussen College St. Cloud, A
Ridgewater College, A
Vermilion Community College, A

Mississippi

East Central Community College, A
Hinds Community College, A
Holmes Community College, A
Itawamba Community College, A
Jackson State University, B
Meridian Community College, A
Mississippi Delta Community College, A
University of Mississippi Medical Center, B
Virginia College at Jackson, A

Missouri

Park University, A
Penn Valley Community College, A
Saint Charles Community College, A
Saint Louis University, B
State Fair Community College, A

Montana

Carroll College, B
Montana State University-Billings, A
Montana State University-Great Falls College of
Technology, A

Nebraska

College of Saint Mary, AB

Nevada

Community College of Southern Nevada, A

New Jersey

Kean University, B
Passaic County Community College, A

New Mexico

Central New Mexico Community College, A

New York

Adirondack Community College, A
Long Island University, C.W. Post Campus, B
Monroe Community College, A
Onondaga Community College, A
Rockland Community College, A
State University of New York College of Technology
at Alfred, A

State University of New York Downstate Medical
Center, B
State University of New York Institute of
Technology, B
Touro College, B
Trocaire College, A

North Carolina

Brunswick Community College, A
Central Piedmont Community College, A
Davidson County Community College, A
Durham Technical Community College, A
East Carolina University, B
Edgecombe Community College, A
Southwestern Community College, A
Western Carolina University, B

North Dakota

Fort Berthold Community College, A
Turtle Mountain Community College, A

Ohio

Bowling Green State University-Firelands College, A
Columbus State Community College, A
Edison State Community College, A
Hocking College, A
The Ohio State University, B
Sinclair Community College, A
Stark State College of Technology, A
The University of Toledo, B

Oklahoma

East Central University, B
Oklahoma City Community College, A
Southwestern Oklahoma State University, B
Tulsa Community College, A

Oregon

Chemeketa Community College, A
Portland Community College, A

Pennsylvania

Business Institute of Pennsylvania (Sharon), A
CHI Institute, A
Community College of Philadelphia, A
Erie Business Center South, A
Gwynedd-Mercy College, AB
Harrisburg Area Community College, A
Pennsylvania College of Technology, A
Reading Area Community College, A
Temple University, B
Thompson Institute, A
University of Pittsburgh, B
Westmoreland County Community College, A

Puerto Rico

Inter American University of Puerto Rico, San
Germán Campus, A
Universidad Adventista de las Antillas, A
Universidad del Este, A

South Carolina

Florence-Darlington Technical College, A

South Dakota

Dakota State University, B

Tennessee

Chattanooga State Technical Community College, A
Draughons Junior College (Clarksville), A
Draughons Junior College (Nashville), A
Roane State Community College, A
Tennessee State University, B

Texas

Amarillo College, A
El Centro College, A
El Paso Community College, A
Houston Community College System, A
Howard College, A
McLennan Community College, A
North Central Texas College, A
South Plains College, A
Tarrant County College District, A

Texas Southern University, B
Texas State Technical College Harlingen, A
Texas State University-San Marcos, B
Wharton County Junior College, A

Utah

California College for Health Sciences, A
LDS Business College, A

Virginia

ECPI College of Technology (Newport News), A
ECPI College of Technology (Virginia Beach), A
ECPI Technical College (Richmond), A
ECPI Technical College (Roanoke), A
Norfolk State University, B
Northern Virginia Community College, A

Washington

Shoreline Community College, A
Spokane Community College, A
Tacoma Community College, A

West Virginia

Fairmont State University, A

Wisconsin

Chippewa Valley Technical College, A
Gateway Technical College, A
University of Wisconsin-Milwaukee, B

Nova Scotia

Dalhousie University, B

Ontario

Ryerson University, B

HEALTH INFORMATION/MEDICAL RECORDS TECHNOLOGY/TECHNICIAN

Alabama

Bishop State Community College, A

Arkansas

Ozarka College, A

California

Charles R. Drew University of Medicine and
Science, A
DeVry University (Fremont), A
DeVry University (Long Beach), A
DeVry University (Pomona), A
DeVry University (West Hills), A
Santa Barbara City College, A

Colorado

DeVry University (Westminster), A

Florida

Central Florida Community College, A
DeVry University (Miramar), A
DeVry University (Orlando), A
International College, A
Tallahassee Community College, A

Georgia

Andrew College, A
Atlanta Technical College, A
Columbus Technical College, A
Darton College, A
DeVry University (Alpharetta), A
DeVry University (Decatur), A
Heart of Georgia Technical College, A
Macon State College, A
Northwestern Technical College, A
Ogeechee Technical College, A

West Georgia Technical College, A

Idaho

Idaho State University, A

Illinois

College of DuPage, A
DeVry University (Chicago), A
Moraine Valley Community College, A
Northwestern Business College, A
Rend Lake College, A
Robert Morris College, A

Indiana

Indiana Business College (Anderson), A
Indiana Business College (Muncie), A

Iowa

Northwest Iowa Community College, A

Kansas

Hutchinson Community College and Area Vocational
  School, A
Johnson County Community College, A
Washburn University, A

Kentucky

Eastern Kentucky University, A
Jefferson Community and Technical College, A
Western Kentucky University, A

Louisiana

Delgado Community College, A
Louisiana Tech University, A

Maryland

Montgomery College, A

Massachusetts

Bristol Community College, A

Michigan

Baker College of Flint, A
Baker College of Jackson, A
Davenport University (Dearborn), A
Schoolcraft College, A

Minnesota

Anoka Technical College, A
College of St. Catherine, A
Northwest Technical College, A

Missouri

Missouri Western State University, A
Ozarks Technical Community College, A

Montana

Montana State University-Great Falls College of
  Technology, A

Nebraska

Central Community College-Hastings Campus, A

New Jersey

Burlington County College, A
DeVry University, A
Hudson County Community College, A

New Mexico

San Juan College, A

New York

Broome Community College, A
Erie Community College, North Campus, A
Hudson Valley Community College, A
Mohawk Valley Community College, A
Molloy College, A
New York University, A

North Carolina

Catawba Valley Community College, A
Fayetteville Technical Community College, A
Pitt Community College, A

Rowan-Cabarrus Community College, A
South Piedmont Community College, A
Southwestern Community College, A

North Dakota

North Dakota State College of Science, A
United Tribes Technical College, A
Williston State College, A

Ohio

Cincinnati State Technical and Community
  College, A
Columbus State Community College, A
DeVry University (Columbus), A
Mercy College of Northwest Ohio, A
Owens Community College, A

Oregon

Blue Mountain Community College, A
Central Oregon Community College, A

Pennsylvania

Business Institute of Pennsylvania (Meadville), A
Community College of Allegheny County, A
DeVry University (Fort Washington), A
Gwynedd-Mercy College, AB
Lehigh Carbon Community College, A
Mercyhurst College, B
South Hills School of Business & Technology (State
  College), A

South Carolina

Midlands Technical College, A

South Dakota

Dakota State University, A

Tennessee

Dyersburg State Community College, A
Electronic Computer Programming College, A
Volunteer State Community College, A

Texas

Blinn College, A
Del Mar College, A
DeVry University (Houston), A
DeVry University (Irving), A
Houston Community College System, A
Lee College, A
Midland College, A
Mountain View College, A
Panola College, A
St. Philip's College, A
Texas State Technical College West Texas, A
Vernon College, A

Utah

Weber State University, A

Washington

Edmonds Community College, A

West Virginia

Marshall Community and Technical College, A
West Virginia Northern Community College, A

Wisconsin

Moraine Park Technical College, A
Northeast Wisconsin Technical College, A

HEALTH/MEDICAL CLAIMS EXAMINER

Ohio

Ohio Business College (Sandusky), A

HEALTH/MEDICAL PHYSICS

California

California State University, Northridge, B

Nevada

University of Nevada, Las Vegas, B

Pennsylvania

Bloomsburg University of Pennsylvania, B

Ontario

Ryerson University, B

HEALTH/MEDICAL PREPARATORY PROGRAMS

Alabama

University of South Alabama, B

Arizona

Eastern Arizona College, A

Arkansas

Arkansas State University-Beebe, A

California

Charles R. Drew University of Medicine and
  Science, B

Florida

International College, B
Miami Dade College, A
University of Miami, B

Georgia

Emmanuel College, AB
Mercer University, B

Illinois

Aurora University, B
Roosevelt University, B
Wheaton College, B

Indiana

Ancilla College, A
University of Evansville, B

Kentucky

Asbury College, B
University of Louisville, B

Louisiana

University of Louisiana at Monroe, B

Maryland

Salisbury University, B

Michigan

Madonna University, B

Minnesota

St. Cloud State University, B

Missouri

Avila University, B
College of the Ozarks, B
Maryville University of Saint Louis, B
University of Missouri-Columbia, B

Montana

Blackfeet Community College, A

Nebraska

Chadron State College, B
Concordia University, B
Union College, A

Nevada

University of Nevada, Reno, B

New York

Fordham University, B
Ithaca College, B

Utica College, B

North Carolina

Guilford College, B
Meredith College, B

Ohio

Wright State University, B

Pennsylvania

Allegheny College, B
DeSales University, B
Gannon University, B
Juniata College, B
Mercyhurst College, B

South Carolina

Bob Jones University, B
Charleston Southern University, B

Tennessee

Cumberland University, B

Texas

Abilene Christian University, B
Baylor University, B

Wyoming

Eastern Wyoming College, A
Laramie County Community College, A
Western Wyoming Community College, A

Ontario

University of Waterloo, B

HEALTH/MEDICAL PSYCHOLOGY

Massachusetts

Bridgewater State College, B
Massachusetts College of Pharmacy and Health
  Sciences, B

New York

Iona College, B

Pennsylvania

University of the Sciences in Philadelphia, B

HEALTH OCCUPATIONS TEACHER EDUCATION

Georgia

University of Georgia, B

Maine

University of Maine at Farmington, B

New York

New York Institute of Technology, B

North Carolina

North Carolina State University, B

Oklahoma

University of Central Oklahoma, B

Texas

Baylor University, B

HEALTH PHYSICS/RADIOLOGICAL HEALTH

California

San Diego State University, M

District of Columbia

Georgetown University, M

Georgia

Georgia Institute of Technology, MD
Medical College of Georgia, M

Illinois

Illinois Institute of Technology, M
University of Illinois at Urbana-Champaign, MD

Indiana

Purdue University, MDO

Kentucky

University of Kentucky, M

Massachusetts

University of Massachusetts Lowell, MD

Michigan

University of Michigan, MD
Wayne State University, MD

Missouri

University of Missouri-Columbia, M

Nevada

University of Nevada, Las Vegas, M

Ohio

University of Cincinnati, M

Oklahoma

University of Oklahoma Health Sciences Center, MD

Oregon

Oregon State University, MD

Pennsylvania

Bloomsburg University of Pennsylvania, M
Drexel University, MD

South Carolina

Clemson University, D

Texas

Midwestern State University, M
Texas A&M University, M

Virginia

Virginia Commonwealth University, D

Alberta

University of Alberta, MD

Ontario

McMaster University, MD

Quebec

McGill University, MD
Université Laval, O

HEALTH PROFESSIONS AND RELATED CLINICAL SCIENCES

Alabama

The University of Alabama, B

Alaska

University of Alaska Southeast, A

Arizona

Arizona State University at the Polytechnic
  Campus, B

Arkansas

Arkansas Tech University, B

California

California State University, Fullerton, B
California State University, Los Angeles, B

California State University, Sacramento, B
Saint Mary's College of California, B
San Diego State University, B

Florida

Miami Dade College, A
University of Miami, B

Georgia

Albany State University, B
Armstrong Atlantic State University, B
Lanier Technical College, A

Illinois

Bradley University, B

Indiana

Purdue University, B
University of Saint Francis, B
University of Southern Indiana, B

Iowa

University of Northern Iowa, B

Louisiana

University of Louisiana at Lafayette, B

Maine

University of New England, B

Maryland

Allegany College of Maryland, A
Towson University, B

Massachusetts

Berkshire Community College, A
Massachusetts College of Pharmacy and Health
  Sciences, B
Worcester State College, B

Michigan

Northwestern Michigan College, A
Oakland Community College, A
Southwestern Michigan College, A

Mississippi

Alcorn State University, B
William Carey College, B

Missouri

Washington University in St. Louis, B

Nevada

University of Nevada, Reno, B

New Jersey

Essex County College, A

New York

Albany College of Pharmacy of Union University, B
Dowling College, B
D'Youville College, B
Hofstra University, B
Long Island University, Brooklyn Campus, B
Long Island University, C.W. Post Campus, B
Mercy College, B
Phillips Beth Israel School of Nursing, A
Sage College of Albany, B
St. Francis College, B
Stony Brook University, State University of New
  York, B
Touro College, B

North Carolina

East Carolina University, B
Pitt Community College, A

Ohio

Bowling Green State University, B
Bowling Green State University-Firelands College, A
Cincinnati State Technical and Community
  College, A
Cleveland State University, B

Northwest State Community College, A
The Ohio State University, B

Pennsylvania

Chatham College, B
Community College of Allegheny County, A
Gannon University, B
King's College, B
Lebanon Valley College, B
Lock Haven University of Pennsylvania, A
Marywood University, B
Pennsylvania College of Technology, B
Saint Joseph's University, B
University of Pennsylvania, B
University of Pittsburgh, B

South Carolina

Clemson University, B
Midlands Technical College, A

Tennessee

East Tennessee State University, AB
King College, B
Southwest Tennessee Community College, A
Volunteer State Community College, A

Texas

Brazosport College, A
Howard Payne University, A
The University of Texas at Tyler, B

Utah

Dixie State College of Utah, A
University of Utah, B

Virginia

George Mason University, B
Randolph-Macon Woman's College, B

Washington

Edmonds Community College, A

British Columbia

British Columbia Institute of Technology, A

Nova Scotia

Dalhousie University, B

HEALTH PROMOTION

Alabama

The University of Alabama, MD
The University of Alabama at Birmingham, D

Arizona

Northern Arizona University, M

California

California State University, Fresno, M
Loma Linda University, MD
San Diego State University, M
University of Southern California, M

Delaware

University of Delaware, M

District of Columbia

The George Washington University, M
Georgetown University, M

Florida

University of Central Florida, O
University of Florida, M

Georgia

Emory University, M
Georgia State University, D

University of Georgia, MDO

Illinois

Benedictine University, M
University of Chicago, M

Indiana

Ball State University, M
Indiana State University, M
Purdue University, MD

Kentucky

University of Kentucky, MD

Louisiana

Northwestern State University of Louisiana, M

Massachusetts

Boston University, MD
Bridgewater State College, M
Emerson College, M
Harvard University, MD
Simmons College, MO
University of Massachusetts Lowell, D

Michigan

Central Michigan University, M
Eastern Michigan University, M
University of Michigan, MDO

Missouri

Barnes-Jewish College of Nursing and Allied
    Health, M
Missouri State University, M

Montana

The University of Montana-Missoula, M

Nebraska

Nebraska Methodist College, M

Nevada

University of Nevada, Las Vegas, M

New York

Canisius College, M
Lehman College of the City University of New
    York, M

North Carolina

The University of North Carolina at Chapel Hill, M
The University of North Carolina at Charlotte, M

Ohio

Wright State University, M

Oklahoma

University of Oklahoma Health Sciences Center, MD

Oregon

Portland State University, M

Pennsylvania

Marywood University, MD

South Carolina

University of South Carolina, MDO

Tennessee

University of Memphis, M
The University of Tennessee, M

Texas

University of North Texas, M

Utah

Brigham Young University, MD
California College for Health Sciences, M

University of Utah, MD

Vermont

Goddard College, M

Virginia

Marymount University, M
Old Dominion University, M

West Virginia

West Virginia University, M

Wisconsin

University of Wisconsin-Stevens Point, M

Alberta

University of Alberta, MO

Quebec

Université de Montréal, O

HEALTH PSYCHOLOGY

Arizona

Northern Arizona University, M

California

California Institute of Integral Studies, M
San Diego State University, D

Connecticut

Central Connecticut State University, M

District of Columbia

The George Washington University, D

Florida

University of Florida, D

Illinois

Argosy University/Chicago, D
National-Louis University, M

Kansas

Emporia State University, M

Michigan

University of Michigan-Dearborn, M

Montana

The University of Montana-Missoula, M

New Jersey

Rutgers, The State University of New Jersey, New
    Brunswick/Piscataway, D

New York

Stony Brook University, State University of New
    York, D
Yeshiva University, D

North Carolina

Appalachian State University, M
Duke University, D

Pennsylvania

Drexel University, DO
University of the Sciences in Philadelphia, M
West Chester University of Pennsylvania, O

Texas

Texas State University-San Marcos, M
University of North Texas, D

Virginia

Shenandoah University, O

Washington

Bastyr University, M

HEALTH SERVICES ADMINISTRATION

Alabama

Andrew Jackson University, M
Columbia Southern University, M

The University of Alabama at Birmingham, MD

Alaska

Alaska Pacific University, M

Arizona

Arizona State University, MO
University of Phoenix Online Campus, MD
University of Phoenix-Phoenix Campus, M
University of Phoenix-Southern Arizona Campus, M

Arkansas

University of Arkansas at Little Rock, M

California

Argosy University/Orange County, M
California Lutheran University, M
California State University, Bakersfield, M
California State University, Chico, M
California State University, Fresno, M
California State University, Long Beach, MO
California State University, Los Angeles, M
California State University, Northridge, M
California State University, San Bernardino, M
Loma Linda University, M
National University, M
San Diego State University, M
Touro University International, MO
University of California, Berkeley, MDO
University of California, Los Angeles, BMD
University of California, San Diego, M
University of La Verne, M
University of Phoenix-Sacramento Valley
    Campus, M
University of Phoenix-San Diego Campus, MO
University of Phoenix-Southern California
    Campus, M
University of San Francisco, M
University of Southern California, MO

Colorado

Jones International University, M
Regis University, M
University of Colorado at Colorado Springs, M
University of Colorado at Denver and Health
    Sciences Center - Downtown Denver Campus, M
University of Phoenix-Southern Colorado
    Campus, M

Connecticut

Quinnipiac University, M
University of Connecticut, M
University of New Haven, M
Western Connecticut State University, M
Yale University, MD

Delaware

Wilmington College, M

District of Columbia

The George Washington University, MDO
Southeastern University, M

Florida

Argosy University/Sarasota, M
Argosy University/Tampa, M
Barry University, M
Florida International University, M
Lynn University, M
Nova Southeastern University, M
St. Thomas University, MO
University of Central Florida, MO
University of Florida, MD
University of North Florida, M
University of Phoenix-Central Florida Campus, M
University of Phoenix-North Florida Campus, M
University of Phoenix-South Florida Campus, M
University of Phoenix-West Florida Campus, M
University of South Florida, MD

Georgia

Albany State University, M
Armstrong Atlantic State University, M
Brenau University, M

Emory University, MD
Georgia Institute of Technology, M
Georgia Southern University, M
Georgia State University, M

Hawaii

University of Phoenix-Hawaii Campus, M

Illinois

American InterContinental University Online, M
Argosy University/Schaumburg, M
DePaul University, M
Governors State University, M
Loyola University Chicago, MO
Rush University, MD
Saint Xavier University, MO
University of Illinois at Chicago, MD
University of St. Francis, M
Western Illinois University, O

Indiana

Indiana University Northwest, M
Indiana University-Purdue University Fort Wayne, B
Indiana University-Purdue University
    Indianapolis, MO
Indiana University South Bend, MO
University of Evansville, M
University of Southern Indiana, M

Iowa

St. Ambrose University, M
The University of Iowa, MDO

Kansas

University of Kansas, MO
Washburn University, B

Kentucky

Eastern Kentucky University, M
University of Kentucky, M
Western Kentucky University, M

Louisiana

Louisiana State University in Shreveport, M
Loyola University New Orleans, M
Tulane University, MDO
University of Louisiana at Lafayette, M
University of New Orleans, M
University of Phoenix-Louisiana Campus, M

Maine

Saint Joseph's College of Maine, M
University of Southern Maine, MO

Maryland

The Johns Hopkins University, MDO
Towson University, O
University of Baltimore, M
University of Maryland, Baltimore County, M
University of Maryland University College, MO

Massachusetts

Boston University, MDO
Brandeis University, M
Clark University, M
Framingham State College, M
Harvard University, MD
Massachusetts College of Pharmacy and Health
    Sciences, M
Northeastern University, M
Simmons College, MO
Springfield College, M
Suffolk University, M
University of Massachusetts Boston, M
University of Massachusetts Lowell, M
Worcester State College, M

Michigan

Central Michigan University, MDO
Davenport University (Dearborn), M
Grand Valley State University, M
Madonna University, M
University of Detroit Mercy, M
University of Michigan, MDO

University of Phoenix-Metro Detroit Campus, M
University of Phoenix-West Michigan Campus, M

Minnesota

Saint Mary's University of Minnesota, M
University of Minnesota, Twin Cities Campus, MDO
University of St. Thomas, M
Walden University, D

Mississippi

Mississippi College, M
University of Southern Mississippi, M

Missouri

Barnes-Jewish College of Nursing and Allied
    Health, M
Lindenwood University, M
Maryville University of Saint Louis, M
Missouri State University, M
Northwest Missouri State University, M
Park University, M
Saint Louis University, MD
Southwest Baptist University, M
Stephens College, O
University of Missouri-Columbia, M
University of Missouri-St. Louis, M
University of Phoenix-St. Louis Campus, M
Washington University in St. Louis, MO
Webster University, M
William Woods University, M

Montana

Montana State University-Billings, M

Nebraska

Bellevue University, M

Nevada

University of Phoenix-Nevada Campus, M

New Hampshire

University of New Hampshire, M

New Jersey

College of Saint Elizabeth, M
Fairleigh Dickinson University, College at
    Florham, MO
Kean University, M
Monmouth University, MO
New Jersey City University, M
Rutgers, The State University of New Jersey,
    Camden, M
Rutgers, The State University of New Jersey,
    Newark, M
Seton Hall University, MO

New Mexico

University of Phoenix-New Mexico Campus, M

New York

Bernard M. Baruch College of the City University of
    New York, M
Brooklyn College of the City University of New
    York, M
College of Mount Saint Vincent, O
Cornell University, MD
D'Youville College, MO
Hofstra University, MO
Iona College, MO
Long Island University, Brooklyn Campus, M
Long Island University, C.W. Post Campus, MO
Mercy College, M
New York Institute of Technology, M
New York University, MO
Pace University, M
Rochester Institute of Technology, MO
State University of New York at Binghamton, M
State University of New York Institute of
    Technology, M
Stony Brook University, State University of New
    York, MDO
Syracuse University, O
Touro College, O

University at Albany, State University of New York, M
Utica School of Commerce, A
Wagner College, M

North Carolina

Duke University, M
Pfeiffer University, MO
The University of North Carolina at Chapel Hill, MDO
The University of North Carolina at Charlotte, MO
University of Phoenix-Charlotte Campus, M
Western Carolina University, M

Ohio

Baldwin-Wallace College, M
Cleveland State University, M
Lake Erie College, M
The Ohio State University, M
Ohio University, M
Ohio University-Southern Campus, B
Ursuline College, B
Wright State University, M
Xavier University, MO
Youngstown State University, M

Oklahoma

Oklahoma City University, M
Oklahoma State University, M
University of Oklahoma Health Sciences Center, MDO
University of Phoenix-Oklahoma City Campus, M
University of Phoenix-Tulsa Campus, M

Oregon

Northwest Christian College, B
Oregon State University, M
Portland State University, M

Pennsylvania

Carlow University, M
Carnegie Mellon University, M
Duquesne University, M
East Stroudsburg University of Pennsylvania, B
King's College, M
Marywood University, BM
Mount Aloysius College, M
The Pennsylvania State University Harrisburg Campus, M
The Pennsylvania State University University Park Campus, MD
Philadelphia University, M
Robert Morris University, B
Saint Joseph's University, MO
Temple University, MD
University of Pennsylvania, MD
University of Pittsburgh, MDO
University of the Sciences in Philadelphia, MD
The University of Scranton, M
Villanova University, M
West Chester University of Pennsylvania, MO
Widener University, MO
Wilkes University, M

Puerto Rico

University of Phoenix-Puerto Rico Campus, M
University of Puerto Rico, Medical Sciences Campus, M

Rhode Island

Salve Regina University, MO

South Carolina

Charleston Southern University, M
Clemson University, M
Francis Marion University, M
Medical University of South Carolina, BMDO

University of South Carolina, MDO

South Dakota

Colorado Technical University Sioux Falls Campus, M

Tennessee

East Tennessee State University, MO
Freed-Hardeman University, B
Lipscomb University, M
Middle Tennessee State University, O
Southern Adventist University, M
University of Memphis, M
University of Phoenix-Nashville Campus, M
The University of Tennessee, M

Texas

Baylor University, M
Dallas Baptist University, M
Houston Baptist University, M
Midwestern State University, M
Our Lady of the Lake University of San Antonio, M
Texas A&M University System Health Science Center, M
Texas State University-San Marcos, M
Texas Tech University, MO
Texas Wesleyan University, M
Texas Woman's University, M
Trinity University, M
University of Dallas, M
University of Houston-Clear Lake, M
University of North Texas, M
University of Phoenix-Houston Campus, M
The University of Texas at Arlington, M
The University of Texas at Dallas, M
The University of Texas at Tyler, M
Wayland Baptist University, M

Utah

California College for Health Sciences, M
University of Phoenix-Utah Campus, M
Utah Valley State College, B

Vermont

Norwich University, M

Virginia

Marymount University, M
Old Dominion University, M
Shenandoah University, O
University of Virginia, M
Virginia Commonwealth University, MDO

Washington

University of Phoenix-Washington Campus, M
University of Washington, MO

West Virginia

Marshall University, M

Wisconsin

Cardinal Stritch University, M
Concordia University Wisconsin, M
University of Phoenix-Wisconsin Campus, M
University of Wisconsin-Oshkosh, M

Alberta

University of Alberta, MDO

British Columbia

The University of British Columbia, M

Nova Scotia

Dalhousie University, MO

Ontario

University of Ottawa, M

Quebec

Concordia University, O
McGill University, M

Université de Montréal, MO

Saskatchewan

University of Saskatchewan, M

HEALTH SERVICES/ALLIED HEALTH/HEALTH SCIENCES

Arizona

Cochise College (Douglas), A

California

California State University, Chico, B
California State University, Sacramento, B
National University, B
San Diego State University, B
San Jose State University, B

Colorado

Colorado Northwestern Community College, A
National American University (Denver), A

Florida

Florida Atlantic University, B
Florida Gulf Coast University, B
Florida International University, B
Florida National College, A
Jones College (Miami), B
Keiser College (Miami), A
Nova Southeastern University, B
South University (West Palm Beach), A
Stetson University, B
University of Central Florida, B
University of Florida, B
University of North Florida, B

Georgia

Atlanta Metropolitan College, A
Columbus State University, B

Idaho

Idaho State University, B

Illinois

Rend Lake College, A

Indiana

Ancilla College, A

Kentucky

Bellarmine University, B
Lindsey Wilson College, A

Louisiana

Louisiana State University at Alexandria, A
Nicholls State University, B

Massachusetts

Emmanuel College, B

Minnesota

The College of St. Scholastica, B
St. Cloud State University, B
University of Minnesota, Crookston, B

Missouri

Missouri Southern State University, B

New Jersey

Atlantic Cape Community College, A
Montclair State University, B

New York

Daemen College, B
D'Youville College, B

New York College of Health Professions, AB

North Carolina

Brevard College, B

North Dakota

Aakers Business College, A

Ohio

Kent State University, B
The Ohio State University at Lima, B
Ursuline College, B

Oklahoma

Connors State College, A

Oregon

Corban College, B

Pennsylvania

Gwynedd-Mercy College, B
Immaculata University, A
Lebanon Valley College, B
Marywood University, B
Mount Aloysius College, B
University of the Sciences in Philadelphia, B
Widener University, B

Tennessee

Baptist College of Health Sciences, B

Texas

Clarendon College, A
Texas State University-San Marcos, B
Texas Tech University, B
The University of Texas at Austin, B
The University of Texas at Brownsville, B
The University of Texas at San Antonio, B

Utah

University of Utah, B

Virginia

Liberty University, B
Old Dominion University, B

West Virginia

West Virginia State Community and Technical
College, A

Wyoming

University of Wyoming, B
Western Wyoming Community College, A

British Columbia

Thompson Rivers University, B

Nova Scotia

Dalhousie University, B

Ontario

University of Ottawa, B
York University, B

HEALTH SERVICES RESEARCH

Arizona

Arizona State University, D

California

Stanford University, M
University of Southern California, MD

Florida

Florida State University, MO
University of Florida, D

Georgia

Emory University, D

Indiana

Indiana University-Purdue University Indianapolis, M

Maryland

The Johns Hopkins University, M

Minnesota

University of Minnesota, Twin Cities Campus, MDO

New Hampshire

Dartmouth College, MD

New York

Clarkson University, M
University of Rochester, DO

North Carolina

Wake Forest University, M

Pennsylvania

Lehigh University, M
Thomas Jefferson University, O

Puerto Rico

University of Puerto Rico, Medical Sciences
Campus, M

Rhode Island

Brown University, MD

Texas

Texas State University-San Marcos, M

Virginia

Old Dominion University, D
University of Virginia, M
Virginia Commonwealth University, D

Washington

University of Washington, MD

Alberta

University of Alberta, M

British Columbia

The University of British Columbia, MD

Ontario

McMaster University, MD
University of Ottawa, O

HEALTH TEACHER EDUCATION

Alabama

Auburn University, B
Jacksonville State University, B
Troy University, B
The University of Alabama at Birmingham, B

Arizona

Northern Arizona University, B
The University of Arizona, B

Arkansas

Arkansas State University, B
Harding University, B
John Brown University, B
University of Arkansas at Little Rock, B

California

California State University, Chico, B
California State University, San Bernardino, B
Cañada College, A
Chabot College, A
College of the Sequoias, A
Columbia College, A
Hartnell College, A
Los Angeles Mission College, A
San Francisco State University, B
Touro University International, B

Yuba College, A

Connecticut

Western Connecticut State University, B

Delaware

University of Delaware, B

District of Columbia

University of the District of Columbia, B

Florida

Daytona Beach Community College, A
Florida Agricultural and Mechanical University, B
Florida International University, B
Florida State University, B
Manatee Community College, A
Palm Beach Community College, A
University of Florida, B

Georgia

Armstrong Atlantic State University, B
Bainbridge College, A
Clark Atlanta University, B
Clayton State University, A
Columbus State University, B
East Georgia College, A
Fort Valley State University, B
Georgia College & State University, B
South Georgia College, A
University of Georgia, B
Waycross College, A
Young Harris College, A

Idaho

Idaho State University, B

Illinois

Chicago State University, B
DePaul University, B
Eastern Illinois University, B
Illinois State University, B
Northern Illinois University, B
Southern Illinois University Carbondale, B
Southern Illinois University Edwardsville, B
Western Illinois University, B
William Rainey Harper College, A

Indiana

Ball State University, B
Indiana State University, B
Indiana University-Purdue University Indianapolis, B
Manchester College, B
University of Saint Francis, B

Iowa

Graceland University, B
Iowa State University of Science and Technology, B
St. Ambrose University, B
University of Northern Iowa, B
Waldorf College, B
William Penn University, B

Kansas

Central Christian College of Kansas, A
Donnelly College, A
Friends University, B
Highland Community College, A
Kansas Wesleyan University, B
Pittsburg State University, B
Pratt Community College, A
Tabor College, B

Kentucky

Campbellsville University, B
Eastern Kentucky University, B
Morehead State University, B
Murray State University, B
St. Catharine College, A
Union College, B
University of the Cumberlands, B

University of Kentucky, B

Louisiana

Dillard University, B
Louisiana College, B
Nicholls State University, B
Xavier University of Louisiana, B

Maine

University of Maine, B
University of Maine at Farmington, B
University of Maine at Presque Isle, B

Maryland

Anne Arundel Community College, A
Chesapeake College, A
Howard Community College, A
Morgan State University, B
Prince George's Community College, A
Salisbury University, B
University of Maryland, College Park, B

Massachusetts

Bridgewater State College, B
Curry College, B
Framingham State College, B
Salem State College, B
Springfield College, B

Michigan

Alma College, B
Aquinas College, B
Central Michigan University, B
Northern Michigan University, B
Wayne State University, B
Western Michigan University, B

Minnesota

Augsburg College, B
Bemidji State University, B
Bethel University, B
Concordia College, B
Concordia University, St. Paul, B
Gustavus Adolphus College, B
Hamline University, B
Minnesota State University Mankato, B
Minnesota State University Moorhead, B
St. Cloud State University, B
Southwest Minnesota State University, B
University of Minnesota, Duluth, B
University of St. Thomas, B
Vermilion Community College, A
Winona State University, B

Mississippi

Coahoma Community College, A
Copiah-Lincoln Community College, A
East Central Community College, A
East Mississippi Community College, A
Jackson State University, B
Mississippi Delta Community College, A
Northeast Mississippi Community College, A

Missouri

Missouri Baptist University, B
Missouri Valley College, B
Northwest Missouri State University, B
Sanford-Brown College (Hazelwood), A

Montana

Montana State University-Billings, B
Rocky Mountain College, B
University of Great Falls, B
The University of Montana-Missoula, B
The University of Montana-Western, B

Nebraska

Concordia University, B
Peru State College, B

University of Nebraska-Lincoln, B

Nevada

University of Nevada, Las Vegas, B
University of Nevada, Reno, B

New Hampshire

Keene State College, B

New Jersey

Montclair State University, B
William Paterson University of New Jersey, B

New Mexico

New Mexico Highlands University, B
University of New Mexico, B
University of New Mexico-Gallup, A

New York

Brooklyn College of the City University of New
  York, B
Fulton-Montgomery Community College, A
Hofstra University, B
Hunter College of the City University of New York, B
Ithaca College, B
Lehman College of the City University of New
  York, B
Long Island University, C.W. Post Campus, B
State University of New York College at
  Brockport, B
State University of New York College at Cortland, B
State University of New York at Oswego, B
York College of the City University of New York, B

North Carolina

Appalachian State University, B
East Carolina University, B
Elon University, B
Fayetteville State University, B
Gardner-Webb University, B
Johnson C. Smith University, B
North Carolina Agricultural and Technical State
  University, B
North Carolina Central University, B

North Dakota

Cankdeska Cikana Community College, A
Mayville State University, B
North Dakota State University, B
Valley City State University, B

Ohio

Ashland University, B
Baldwin-Wallace College, B
Bowling Green State University, B
Capital University, B
Cedarville University, B
Central State University, B
Defiance College, B
Heidelberg College, B
Kent State University, B
Malone College, B
Miami University, B
Miami University Hamilton, B
Mount Vernon Nazarene University, B
Muskingum College, B
Ohio Northern University, B
Ohio University-Eastern, B
Ohio Wesleyan University, B
Otterbein College, B
The University of Akron, B
University of Cincinnati, B
University of Dayton, B
University of Rio Grande, B
The University of Toledo, B
Urbana University, B
Wilmington College, B
Wright State University, B
Youngstown State University, B

Oklahoma

East Central University, B
Northeastern State University, B
Northwestern Oklahoma State University, B
Southeastern Oklahoma State University, B

Tulsa Community College, A

Oregon

Chemeketa Community College, A
George Fox University, B
Portland State University, B
Southern Oregon University, B
Umpqua Community College, A

Pennsylvania

Bucks County Community College, A
East Stroudsburg University of Pennsylvania, B
The Pennsylvania State University Harrisburg
  Campus, B
Temple University, B
West Chester University of Pennsylvania, B
Westmoreland County Community College, A

Puerto Rico

Pontifical Catholic University of Puerto Rico, B
University of Puerto Rico, Medical Sciences
  Campus, B

Rhode Island

Rhode Island College, B

South Carolina

South Carolina State University, B

South Dakota

Northern State University, B
University of Sioux Falls, B
The University of South Dakota, B

Tennessee

Belmont University, B
Freed-Hardeman University, B
Lambuth University, B
Lee University, B
Lincoln Memorial University, B
Lipscomb University, B
Martin Methodist College, A
Maryville College, B
Middle Tennessee State University, B
Tennessee State University, B
Tennessee Technological University, B
The University of Tennessee, B

Texas

Angelina College, A
Baylor University, B
Coastal Bend College, A
Del Mar College, A
El Paso Community College, A
Hill College of the Hill Junior College District, A
Kilgore College, A
Lamar University, B
Sam Houston State University, B
Texas A&M University-Commerce, B
Texas A&M University-Kingsville, B
Texas Southern University, B

Utah

University of Utah, B
Utah State University, B
Utah Valley State College, B

Virginia

Averett University, B
Bluefield College, B
Eastern Mennonite University, B
George Mason University, B
Hampton University, B
Liberty University, B
Longwood University, B
Lynchburg College, B
University of Richmond, B
Virginia Commonwealth University, B

Washington

Central Washington University, B
Eastern Washington University, B
Washington State University, B

Western Washington University, B

West Virginia

Concord University, B
University of Charleston, B
West Liberty State College, B
West Virginia State University, B
West Virginia University Institute of Technology, B
West Virginia Wesleyan College, B

Wisconsin

Carroll College, B
University of Wisconsin-La Crosse, B

Wyoming

Northwest College, A
University of Wyoming, B

Alberta

University of Lethbridge, B

New Brunswick

University of New Brunswick Fredericton, B

Ontario

University of Toronto, B
University of Windsor, B

Saskatchewan

University of Regina, B

HEALTH UNIT COORDINATOR/WARD CLERK

Kansas

Brown Mackie College-Kansas City, A

Minnesota

Rasmussen College Mankato, A
Riverland Community College, A

Missouri

Jefferson College, A

Pennsylvania

Community College of Allegheny County, A

South Dakota

Southeast Technical Institute, A

Wisconsin

Milwaukee Area Technical College, A

HEALTH UNIT MANAGER/WARD SUPERVISOR

Kansas

Brown Mackie College-Kansas City, A

Minnesota

Ridgewater College, A

Pennsylvania

Delaware County Community College, A

Ontario

Ryerson University, B

HEATING, AIR CONDITIONING AND REFRIGERATION TECHNOLOGY/TECHNICIAN

Alabama

Bevill State Community College, A
Calhoun Community College, A

Gadsden State Community College, A

Arizona

GateWay Community College, A

California

Riverside Community College District, A

Colorado

Front Range Community College, A

Florida

Miami Dade College, A

Georgia

DeKalb Technical College, A
Griffin Technical College, A
North Georgia Technical College, A
Savannah Technical College, A
South Georgia Technical College, A

Illinois

Oakton Community College, A

Indiana

Oakland City University, A

Kansas

Johnson County Community College, A
Manhattan Area Technical College, A

Maryland

TESST College of Technology (Towson), A

Massachusetts

Benjamin Franklin Institute of Technology, A
Massasoit Community College, A
Springfield Technical Community College, A

Michigan

Delta College, A
Jackson Community College, A
Kalamazoo Valley Community College, A
Macomb Community College, A
Mott Community College, A
Oakland Community College, A

Minnesota

Dunwoody College of Technology, A
Minnesota State Community and Technical
   College-Fergus Falls, A
Northwest Technical College, A
St. Cloud Technical College, A

Mississippi

Northwest Mississippi Community College, A

Missouri

Vatterott College (St. Ann), A

New Jersey

Mercer County Community College, A

New York

Mohawk Valley Community College, A
State University of New York College of Technology
   at Alfred, A
State University of New York College of Technology
   at Delhi, A
TCI-The College of Technology, A

North Carolina

Alamance Community College, A
Martin Community College, A
South Piedmont Community College, A

North Dakota

North Dakota State College of Science, A

Ohio

Cincinnati State Technical and Community
   College, A

Terra State Community College, A

Oklahoma

Vatterott College (Oklahoma City), A
Vatterott College (Tulsa), A

Pennsylvania

Dean Institute of Technology, A
Delaware County Community College, A
Harrisburg Area Community College, A
New Castle School of Trades, A
Pennsylvania College of Technology, AB
Pennsylvania Highland Community College, A
Triangle Tech, Inc.-Greensburg School, A

South Dakota

Mitchell Technical Institute, A

Texas

Texas State Technical College Waco, A

Virginia

Piedmont Virginia Community College, A

Wisconsin

Gateway Technical College, A
Milwaukee Area Technical College, A
Moraine Park Technical College, A
Northeast Wisconsin Technical College, A
Wisconsin Indianhead Technical College, A

HEATING, AIR CONDITIONING, VENTILATION AND REFRIGERATION MAINTENANCE TECHNOLOGY/TECHNICIAN

Alabama

Calhoun Community College, A
Gadsden State Community College-Ayers
   Campus, A
George C. Wallace Community College, A
H. Councill Trenholm State Technical College, A
Shelton State Community College, A
Wallace State Community College, A

Alaska

University of Alaska Anchorage, A
University of Alaska Anchorage, Matanuska-Susitna
   College, A

Arizona

Arizona Western College, A
GateWay Community College, A

Arkansas

Phillips Community College of the University of
   Arkansas, A
University of Arkansas Community College at
   Morrilton, A

California

Antelope Valley College, A
College of the Desert, A
College of the Sequoias, A
Cypress College, A
El Camino College, A
Fresno City College, A
Laney College, A
Long Beach City College, A
Los Angeles Trade-Technical College, A
Los Medanos College, A
Modesto Junior College, A
Mt. San Antonio College, A
Orange Coast College, A
Oxnard College, A
San Bernardino Valley College, A
San Joaquin Delta College, A
San Joaquin Valley College, A
San Jose City College, A

WyoTech (Fremont), A

Colorado

IntelliTec College (Grand Junction), A

Florida

College of Business and Technology, A
Daytona Beach Community College, A
Indian River Community College, A
Miami Dade College, A
New England Institute of Technology at Palm
   Beach, A
Okaloosa-Walton College, A

Hawaii

Honolulu Community College, A

Idaho

Boise State University, A
College of Southern Idaho, A
Lewis-Clark State College, AB
North Idaho College, A

Illinois

Black Hawk College, A
City Colleges of Chicago, Kennedy-King College, A
College of DuPage, A
College of Lake County, A
Elgin Community College, A
Heartland Community College, A
Illinois Eastern Community Colleges, Lincoln Trail
   College, A
John A. Logan College, A
Kankakee Community College, A
Morton College, A
Sauk Valley Community College, A
Southwestern Illinois College, A
Triton College, A
Waubonsee Community College, A
William Rainey Harper College, A

Indiana

Ivy Tech Community College-Bloomington, A
Ivy Tech Community College-Central Indiana, A
Ivy Tech Community College-Columbus, A
Ivy Tech Community College-East Central, A
Ivy Tech Community College-Kokomo, A
Ivy Tech Community College-Lafayette, A
Ivy Tech Community College-North Central, A
Ivy Tech Community College-Northeast, A
Ivy Tech Community College-Northwest, A
Ivy Tech Community College-Southern Indiana, A
Ivy Tech Community College-Southwest, A
Ivy Tech Community College-Wabash Valley, A
Ivy Tech Community College-Whitewater, A
Oakland City University, A

Iowa

Des Moines Area Community College, A
Kirkwood Community College, A
North Iowa Area Community College, A
Scott Community College, A
Western Iowa Tech Community College, A

Kansas

Labette Community College, A

Kentucky

Somerset Community College, A

Louisiana

Elaine P. Nunez Community College, A

Maine

Eastern Maine Community College, A
Northern Maine Community College, A
Southern Maine Community College, A

Michigan

Delta College, A
Ferris State University, AB
Grand Rapids Community College, A
Henry Ford Community College, A
Kellogg Community College, A

Lansing Community College, A
Macomb Community College, A
Mid Michigan Community College, A
Northern Michigan University, A
Washtenaw Community College, A

Minnesota

Century College, A
Dunwoody College of Technology, A
Minnesota State College-Southeast Technical, A
Minnesota West Community and Technical
   College, A
St. Cloud Technical College, A
South Central Technical College, A

Mississippi

Northeast Mississippi Community College, A
Northwest Mississippi Community College, A

Missouri

East Central College, A
Jefferson College, A
Linn State Technical College, A
Ozarks Technical Community College, A
Ranken Technical College, A

Montana

Montana State University-Billings, A

Nebraska

Central Community College-Grand Island
   Campus, A
Central Community College-Hastings Campus, A
Metropolitan Community College, A
Mid-Plains Community College, A
Northeast Community College, A
Southeast Community College, Milford Campus, A
Vatterott College (Omaha), A

Nevada

Community College of Southern Nevada, A
Truckee Meadows Community College, A
Western Nevada Community College, A

New Hampshire

New Hampshire Community Technical College,
   Manchester/Stratham, A

New Jersey

Raritan Valley Community College, A

New Mexico

Clovis Community College, A
Doña Ana Branch Community College, A

New York

Hudson Valley Community College, A
Mohawk Valley Community College, A
Monroe Community College, A
New York City College of Technology of the City
   University of New York, A
State University of New York College of Technology
   at Alfred, A
State University of New York College of Technology
   at Canton, A
State University of New York College of Technology
   at Delhi, A

North Carolina

Asheville-Buncombe Technical Community
   College, A
Craven Community College, A
Fayetteville Technical Community College, A
Forsyth Technical Community College, A
Guilford Technical Community College, A
Johnston Community College, A
Martin Community College, A
Roanoke-Chowan Community College, A
Rockingham Community College, A
Surry Community College, A

Vance-Granville Community College, A

North Dakota

Bismarck State College, A
North Dakota State College of Science, A

Ohio

Belmont Technical College, A
Columbus State Community College, A
North Central State College, A
Terra State Community College, A
University of Cincinnati, A
University of Northwestern Ohio, A
Washington State Community College, A

Oklahoma

Oklahoma State University, Okmulgee, A
Tulsa Community College, A

Oregon

Lane Community College, A

Pennsylvania

CHI Institute, A
Community College of Allegheny County, A
Delaware County Community College, A
Lehigh Carbon Community College, A
Luzerne County Community College, A
Northampton County Area Community College, A
Thaddeus Stevens College of Technology, A
Triangle Tech, Inc.-Greensburg School, A
Triangle Tech, Inc.-Pittsburgh School, A
Westmoreland County Community College, A

Rhode Island

New England Institute of Technology, A

South Carolina

Florence-Darlington Technical College, A
Greenville Technical College, A
Horry-Georgetown Technical College, A
Midlands Technical College, A
Piedmont Technical College, A
Spartanburg Technical College, A
Technical College of the Lowcountry, A
Tri-County Technical College, A
Williamsburg Technical College, A
York Technical College, A

South Dakota

Mitchell Technical Institute, A
Southeast Technical Institute, A

Tennessee

Chattanooga State Technical Community College, A

Texas

Amarillo College, A
Austin Community College, A
Brazosport College, A
Cedar Valley College, A
Central Texas College, A
Eastfield College, A
El Paso Community College, A
Frank Phillips College, A
Grayson County College, A
Hill College of the Hill Junior College District, A
Kilgore College, A
Lamar State College-Port Arthur, A
Lamar University, A
Lee College, A
Midland College, A
North Harris College, A
North Lake College, A
Odessa College, A
Paris Junior College, A
St. Philip's College, A
South Plains College, A
South Texas College, A
Tarrant County College District, A
Texarkana College, A
Texas State Technical College Harlingen, A
Texas State Technical College Waco, A
Trinity Valley Community College, A

Tyler Junior College, A
Western Technical College, A

Utah

Salt Lake Community College, A
Utah Valley State College, A

Virginia

Northern Virginia Community College, A
Virginia Highlands Community College, A

Washington

Bates Technical College, A
Clover Park Technical College, A
North Seattle Community College, A
Renton Technical College, A
Spokane Community College, A
Walla Walla Community College, A
Wenatchee Valley College, A

West Virginia

Community and Technical College of Shepherd, A
West Virginia Northern Community College, A
West Virginia State Community and Technical
  College, A

Wisconsin

Chippewa Valley Technical College, A
Milwaukee Area Technical College, A
Northeast Wisconsin Technical College, A
Western Technical College, A

British Columbia

British Columbia Institute of Technology, A

HEAVY EQUIPMENT MAINTENANCE TECHNOLOGY/TECHNICIAN

Alabama

H. Councill Trenholm State Technical College, A
Lawson State Community College, A

Alaska

University of Alaska Anchorage, A

Arizona

Mesa Community College, A

California

Allan Hancock College, A
Long Beach City College, A
Los Angeles Trade-Technical College, A

Colorado

Mesa State College, A
Pueblo Community College, A
Red Rocks Community College, A
Trinidad State Junior College, A

Delaware

Delaware Technical & Community College, Jack F.
  Owens Campus, A

Georgia

Georgia Southwestern State University, A
Waycross College, A
West Central Technical College, A

Idaho

North Idaho College, A

Illinois

Illinois Eastern Community Colleges, Olney Central
  College, A

Rend Lake College, A

Indiana

Vincennes University, A

Iowa

Des Moines Area Community College, A
Hawkeye Community College, A
Indian Hills Community College, A
Marshalltown Community College, A

Maine

Eastern Maine Community College, A
Northern Maine Community College, A

Michigan

Ferris State University, AB
Lansing Community College, A

Missouri

Linn State Technical College, A
Longview Community College, A
Ozarks Technical Community College, A

Montana

Montana State University-Northern, A
The University of Montana-Missoula, A

Nebraska

Metropolitan Community College, A
Nebraska College of Technical Agriculture, A

Nevada

Community College of Southern Nevada, A

New Hampshire

New Hampshire Community Technical College,
  Nashua/Claremont, A

New York

Mohawk Valley Community College, A
State University of New York College of Technology
  at Alfred, A

North Carolina

Beaufort County Community College, A
Guilford Technical Community College, A
Lenoir Community College, A
McDowell Technical Community College, A
Wake Technical Community College, A

Ohio

The Ohio State University Agricultural Technical
  Institute, A

Oklahoma

Oklahoma State University, Okmulgee, A

Oregon

Lane Community College, A
Rogue Community College, A

Pennsylvania

Pennsylvania College of Technology, A

Tennessee

Southwest Tennessee Community College, A

Texas

Amarillo College, A
Del Mar College, A
South Texas College, A
Texas State Technical College Waco, A

Utah

Salt Lake Community College, A

Washington

Centralia College, A
Clover Park Technical College, A
Lower Columbia College, A
Skagit Valley College, A
South Seattle Community College, A

Spokane Community College, A
Spokane Falls Community College, A

Wyoming

Sheridan College-Sheridan and Gillette, A
Western Wyoming Community College, A

British Columbia

British Columbia Institute of Technology, A

HEAVY/INDUSTRIAL EQUIPMENT MAINTENANCE TECHNOLOGIES

Michigan

Southwestern Michigan College, A

Pennsylvania

Pennsylvania College of Technology, A

Washington

Big Bend Community College, A

West Virginia

Eastern West Virginia Community and Technical
  College, A

Wisconsin

Northeast Wisconsin Technical College, A

HEBREW LANGUAGE AND LITERATURE

California

Los Angeles Valley College, A
University of California, Los Angeles, B

Illinois

Hebrew Theological College, B
University of Illinois at Urbana-Champaign, B

Maryland

Baltimore Hebrew University, AB

Massachusetts

Brandeis University, M
Harvard University, BMD

Michigan

University of Michigan, BMD

Minnesota

North Central University, A
University of Minnesota, Twin Cities Campus, B

Missouri

Washington University in St. Louis, B

New Hampshire

Dartmouth College, B

New York

Bard College, B
Brooklyn College of the City University of New
  York, B
Hofstra University, B
Hunter College of the City University of New York, B
The Jewish Theological Seminary, B
Lehman College of the City University of New
  York, B
Machzikei Hadath Rabbinical College, B
New York University, B
Queens College of the City University of New
  York, B
Sh'or Yoshuv Rabbinical College, B
State University of New York at Binghamton, B
Touro College, B
Yeshiva University, B

Yeshivat Mikdash Melech, B

Ohio

Laura and Alvin Siegal College of Judaic Studies, B
The Ohio State University, B

Oregon

Multnomah Bible College and Biblical Seminary, B
University of Oregon, B

Pennsylvania

Temple University, B

Texas

The University of Texas at Austin, BMD

Utah

Brigham Young University, B

Wisconsin

Concordia University Wisconsin, B
University of Wisconsin-Madison, BMD
University of Wisconsin-Milwaukee, B

Alberta

University of Alberta, B

Ontario

York University, B

Saskatchewan

University of Saskatchewan, B

HEBREW STUDIES

Maryland

Baltimore Hebrew University, MD

New York

Brooklyn College of the City University of New
   York, M

Rhode Island

Brown University, MD

Wisconsin

University of Wisconsin-Madison, MD
University of Wisconsin-Milwaukee, M

HEMATOLOGY TECHNOLOGY/TECHNICIAN

Alabama

Community College of the Air Force, A

HERBALISM/HERBALIST

Washington

Bastyr University, B

HIGHER EDUCATION/HIGHER EDUCATION ADMINISTRATION

Alabama

Auburn University, MDO
The University of Alabama, MD

Arizona

Arizona State University, MD
The University of Arizona, MD

Arkansas

University of Arkansas, MDO
University of Arkansas at Little Rock, D

California

Azusa Pacific University, M
San Diego State University, M

San Jose State University, MO
Stanford University, D
Touro University International, D

Colorado

University of Denver, MD
University of Northern Colorado, D

Connecticut

University of Connecticut, MD

Delaware

University of Delaware, M

District of Columbia

The George Washington University, MDO

Florida

Barry University, MD
Florida Atlantic University, MD
Florida International University, D
Florida State University, MDO
Nova Southeastern University, D
University of Florida, DO
University of Miami, M
University of South Florida, MDO

Georgia

Georgia Southern University, M
Georgia State University, D
University of Georgia, D

Illinois

DePaul University, M
Illinois State University, D
Loyola University Chicago, MD
Northern Illinois University, MD
Northwestern University, M
Southern Illinois University Carbondale, M
University of Illinois at Urbana-Champaign, MDO

Indiana

Ball State University, MD
Indiana University Bloomington, MD
Purdue University, MD

Iowa

Iowa State University of Science and Technology, M
The University of Iowa, MDO
University of Northern Iowa, M

Kansas

Pittsburg State University, O
University of Kansas, MD

Kentucky

Eastern Kentucky University, M
Morehead State University, MO
University of Kentucky, M
University of Louisville, MO

Louisiana

Louisiana State University and Agricultural and
   Mechanical College, D

Maine

University of Maine, MDO

Maryland

Morgan State University, D

Massachusetts

Boston College, MDO
University of Massachusetts Amherst, MDO
University of Massachusetts Boston, D

Michigan

Grand Valley State University, M
Michigan State University, MD
Oakland University, O
University of Michigan, M

Wayne State University, DO

Minnesota

Bethel University, O
Minnesota State University Mankato, M
University of Minnesota, Twin Cities Campus, MD

Mississippi

University of Mississippi, M

Missouri

Saint Louis University, MDO
University of Missouri-Columbia, MDO
University of Missouri-St. Louis, DO

Nevada

University of Nevada, Las Vegas, M

New Hampshire

University of New Hampshire, M

New Jersey

Rowan University, M
Seton Hall University, D

New York

Bernard M. Baruch College of the City University of
   New York, M
New York University, MD
St. John's University, O
State University of New York at Buffalo, D
Syracuse University, MD

North Carolina

Appalachian State University, MO
North Carolina State University, MD
The University of North Carolina at Greensboro, MO

North Dakota

University of Mary, M

Ohio

Bowling Green State University, D
Kent State University, MDO
Ohio University, MD
The University of Akron, MD
The University of Toledo, MD
Wright State University, BMO

Oklahoma

Northeastern State University, M
Oklahoma State University, MD
University of Central Oklahoma, M
University of Oklahoma, MD

Oregon

Portland State University, D

Pennsylvania

Drexel University, M
Geneva College, M
Indiana University of Pennsylvania, M
The Pennsylvania State University University Park
   Campus, MD
University of Pittsburgh, MD

Puerto Rico

Inter American University of Puerto Rico,
   Metropolitan Campus, M

South Carolina

University of South Carolina, M

Tennessee

University of Memphis, D
Vanderbilt University, MD

Texas

Dallas Baptist University, M
Texas A&M University-Commerce, MD
Texas A&M University-Kingsville, D
Texas Southern University, MD
Texas Tech University, MD

University of Houston, M
University of North Texas, D
The University of Texas at San Antonio, M

Virginia

Old Dominion University, MDO
University of Virginia, DO

Washington

Eastern Washington University, M
Western Washington University, M

West Virginia

West Virginia University, M

Wisconsin

University of Wisconsin-Whitewater, M

Alberta

University of Calgary, D

British Columbia

The University of British Columbia, M

Quebec

Université de Sherbrooke, MO

HINDI LANGUAGE AND LITERATURE

Illinois

University of Chicago, B

HISPANIC-AMERICAN, PUERTO RICAN, AND MEXICAN-AMERICAN/CHICANO STUDIES

Arizona

Arizona State University, B
The University of Arizona, B

California

California State University, Dominguez Hills, B
California State University, East Bay, B
California State University, Fresno, B
California State University, Fullerton, B
California State University, Long Beach, B
California State University, Los Angeles, B
California State University, Northridge, B
Cerritos College, A
Claremont McKenna College, B
College of Alameda, A
Compton Community College, A
Contra Costa College, A
East Los Angeles College, A
Fresno City College, A
Laney College, A
Los Angeles City College, A
Loyola Marymount University, B
Mills College, B
Pasadena City College, A
Pitzer College, B
Pomona College, B
San Diego City College, A
San Diego Mesa College, A
San Diego State University, B
San Francisco State University, B
Santa Ana College, A
Santa Barbara City College, A
Scripps College, B
Solano Community College, A
Sonoma State University, B
Southwestern College, A
Stanford University, B
University of California, Berkeley, B
University of California, Davis, B
University of California, Irvine, B
University of California, Los Angeles, B
University of California, Riverside, B
University of California, Santa Barbara, B
University of California, Santa Cruz, B

University of San Diego, B
University of Southern California, B
Yuba College, A

Colorado

The Colorado College, B
Metropolitan State College of Denver, B
University of Northern Colorado, B

Connecticut

Connecticut College, B

Illinois

City Colleges of Chicago, Wilbur Wright College, A

Louisiana

Tulane University, B

Maine

University of Southern Maine, B

Massachusetts

Boston College, B
Hampshire College, B
Harvard University, B
Wheaton College, B

Minnesota

St. Olaf College, B
University of Minnesota, Twin Cities Campus, B

New Hampshire

Dartmouth College, B

New Jersey

Rutgers, The State University of New Jersey, New
    Brunswick/Piscataway, B
Rutgers, The State University of New Jersey,
    Newark, B

New Mexico

Western New Mexico University, B

New York

Brooklyn College of the City University of New
    York, B
Columbia College, B
Columbia University, School of General Studies, B
Cornell University, B
Fordham University, B
Hofstra University, B
Hunter College of the City University of New York, B
State University of New York College at Oneonta, B
University at Albany, State University of New York, B

Oregon

Lewis & Clark College, B

Pennsylvania

Gettysburg College, B

Puerto Rico

Pontifical Catholic University of Puerto Rico, B
University of Puerto Rico, Mayagüez Campus, B

Rhode Island

Brown University, B

Texas

Our Lady of the Lake University of San Antonio, B
Southern Methodist University, B
Sul Ross State University, B
The University of Texas at El Paso, B
The University of Texas-Pan American, B

The University of Texas at San Antonio, B

Washington

University of Washington, B

Wisconsin

University of Wisconsin-Madison, B

Ontario

McMaster University, B
Trent University, B
University of Windsor, B

Quebec

Université de Montréal, B

HISPANIC STUDIES

California

California State University, Los Angeles, M
California State University, Northridge, M
San Jose State University, M
University of California, Berkeley, MD
University of California, Los Angeles, D
University of California, Riverside, MD
University of California, Santa Barbara, DO

Connecticut

Connecticut College, M

Florida

St. Thomas University, MO

Illinois

University of Illinois at Chicago, MD

Michigan

Eastern Michigan University, O
Michigan State University, MD

New Mexico

New Mexico Highlands University, M

New York

Stony Brook University, State University of New
    York, MD

Pennsylvania

La Salle University, M
University of Pittsburgh, MD
Villanova University, M

Puerto Rico

Pontifical Catholic University of Puerto Rico, M
University of Puerto Rico, Mayagüez Campus, M
University of Puerto Rico, Río Piedras, MD

Rhode Island

Brown University, MD

Washington

University of Washington, M

Alberta

University of Alberta, MD

British Columbia

The University of British Columbia, MD
University of Victoria, M

Quebec

McGill University, MD

HISTOLOGIC TECHNICIAN

Connecticut

Goodwin College, A

Florida

Miami Dade College, A

Georgia

Darton College, A

Michigan

Mott Community College, A
Oakland Community College, A

Ohio

Columbus State Community College, A

HISTOLOGIC TECHNOLOGY/ HISTOTECHNOLOGIST

Michigan

Michigan Technological University, B
Northern Michigan University, B

Minnesota

North Hennepin Community College, A

Texas

Tarleton State University, A

HISTORIC PRESERVATION AND CONSERVATION

California

Saint Mary's College of California, B
University of California, Riverside, M
University of Southern California, O

Colorado

Colorado Mountain College, Timberline Campus, A
Colorado State University, M

Delaware

University of Delaware, BM

District of Columbia

The George Washington University, M

Georgia

Georgia State University, M
Savannah College of Art and Design, BM
University of Georgia, M

Illinois

School of the Art Institute of Chicago, M

Indiana

Ball State University, M

Kentucky

University of Kentucky, M
Western Kentucky University, M

Maryland

Goucher College, BM
University of Maryland, College Park, MO

Massachusetts

Boston University, MO

Michigan

Eastern Michigan University, M
Michigan Technological University, D

New Jersey

Rutgers, The State University of New Jersey, New Brunswick/Piscataway, D

New York

Buffalo State College, State University of New York, MO
Cornell University, BM
New York University, O

Rensselaer Polytechnic Institute, M

North Carolina

Randolph Community College, A

Ohio

Belmont Technical College, A
Ursuline College, B

Oregon

University of Oregon, M

Pennsylvania

Bucks County Community College, A
University of Pennsylvania, MO

Rhode Island

Roger Williams University, B
Salve Regina University, B

South Carolina

Clemson University, M
College of Charleston, B
University of South Carolina, M

Tennessee

Middle Tennessee State University, D

Texas

Texas Tech University, M

Vermont

University of Vermont, M

Virginia

University of Mary Washington, B

Washington

University of Washington, O

HISTORY

Alabama

Alabama Southern Community College, A
Alabama State University, B
Athens State University, B
Auburn University, BMD
Auburn University Montgomery, B
Birmingham-Southern College, B
Faulkner University, B
Huntingdon College, B
Jacksonville State University, BM
Jefferson Davis Community College, A
Judson College, B
Lawson State Community College, A
Miles College, B
Oakwood College, B
Samford University, B
Spring Hill College, B
Stillman College, B
Talladega College, B
Troy University, B
Tuskegee University, B
The University of Alabama, BMD
The University of Alabama at Birmingham, BM
The University of Alabama in Huntsville, BM
University of Mobile, B
University of Montevallo, B
University of North Alabama, B
University of South Alabama, BM
The University of West Alabama, B

Alaska

University of Alaska Anchorage, B
University of Alaska Fairbanks, B
University of Alaska Southeast, B

Arizona

Arizona State University, BMD
Arizona State University West, B
Cochise College (Douglas), A
Cochise College (Sierra Vista), A

Eastern Arizona College, A
Grand Canyon University, B
Mohave Community College, A
Northern Arizona University, BMD
Prescott College, BM
South Mountain Community College, A
The University of Arizona, BMD

Arkansas

Arkansas State University, BMDO
Arkansas Tech University, M
Harding University, B
Henderson State University, B
Hendrix College, B
John Brown University, B
Lyon College, B
Ouachita Baptist University, B
Southern Arkansas University-Magnolia, B
University of Arkansas, BMD
University of Arkansas at Fort Smith, B
University of Arkansas at Little Rock, B
University of Arkansas at Monticello, B
University of Arkansas at Pine Bluff, B
University of Central Arkansas, BM
University of the Ozarks, B
Williams Baptist College, B

California

Azusa Pacific University, B
Bakersfield College, A
Biola University, B
California Baptist University, B
California Institute of Technology, B
California Lutheran University, B
California Polytechnic State University, San Luis Obispo, B
California State Polytechnic University, Pomona, BM
California State University, Bakersfield, BM
California State University Channel Islands, B
California State University, Chico, BM
California State University, Dominguez Hills, B
California State University, East Bay, BM
California State University, Fresno, BM
California State University, Fullerton, BM
California State University, Long Beach, BM
California State University, Los Angeles, BM
California State University, Northridge, BM
California State University, Sacramento, B
California State University, San Bernardino, B
California State University, San Marcos, B
California State University, Stanislaus, BM
Cañada College, A
Cerritos College, A
Cerro Coso Community College, A
Chabot College, A
Chaffey College, A
Claremont McKenna College, B
College of Alameda, A
College of the Canyons, A
College of the Desert, A
College of Marin, A
College of the Sequoias, A
College of the Siskiyous, A
Columbia College, A
Compton Community College, A
Concordia University, B
Contra Costa College, A
Crafton Hills College, A
Cuyamaca College, A
Cypress College, A
De Anza College, A
Dominican University of California, B
East Los Angeles College, A
El Camino College, A
Feather River College, A
Foothill College, A
Fresno Pacific University, AB
Fullerton College, A
Gavilan College, A
Grossmont College, A
Hartnell College, A
Holy Names University, B
Humboldt State University, B
Irvine Valley College, A
La Sierra University, B
Lassen Community College District, A

Los Angeles City College, A
Los Angeles Mission College, A
Los Angeles Valley College, A
Loyola Marymount University, B
The Master's College and Seminary, B
Mills College, B
MiraCosta College, A
Monterey Peninsula College, A
Mount St. Mary's College, B
National University, B
Notre Dame de Namur University, B
Occidental College, B
Orange Coast College, A
Oxnard College, A
Pacific Union College, B
Palo Verde College, A
Pasadena City College, A
Pepperdine University, BM
Pitzer College, B
Point Loma Nazarene University, B
Pomona College, B
Porterville College, A
Saddleback College, A
Saint Mary's College of California, B
San Bernardino Valley College, A
San Diego Christian College, B
San Diego State University, BM
San Francisco State University, BM
San Joaquin Delta College, A
San Jose City College, A
San Jose State University, BM
Santa Ana College, A
Santa Barbara City College, A
Santa Clara University, B
Santa Monica College, A
Santa Rosa Junior College, A
Santiago Canyon College, A
Scripps College, B
Simpson University, B
Skyline College, A
Solano Community College, A
Sonoma State University, BM
Southwestern College, A
Stanford University, BMD
University of California, Berkeley, BMDO
University of California, Davis, BMD
University of California, Irvine, BMD
University of California, Los Angeles, BMDO
University of California, Riverside, BMD
University of California, San Diego, BMD
University of California, Santa Barbara, BMD
University of California, Santa Cruz, BD
University of La Verne, B
University of the Pacific, B
University of Redlands, B
University of San Diego, BM
University of San Francisco, B
University of Southern California, BMD
University of the West, B
Vanguard University of Southern California, B
West Los Angeles College, A
West Valley College, A
Westmont College, B
Whittier College, B
Woodbury University, B
Yuba College, A

Colorado

Adams State College, B
Colorado Christian University, B
The Colorado College, B
Colorado Northwestern Community College, A
Colorado State University, BM
Colorado State University-Pueblo, B
Fort Lewis College, B
Lamar Community College, A
Mesa State College, B
Metropolitan State College of Denver, B
Northeastern Junior College, A
Otero Junior College, A
Red Rocks Community College, A
Regis University, B
United States Air Force Academy, B
University of Colorado at Boulder, BMD
University of Colorado at Colorado Springs, BM

University of Colorado at Denver and Health
  Sciences Center - Downtown Denver
  Campus, BM
University of Denver, BM
University of Northern Colorado, BM
Western State College of Colorado, B

Connecticut

Albertus Magnus College, B
Central Connecticut State University, BM
Connecticut College, B
Eastern Connecticut State University, B
Fairfield University, B
Naugatuck Valley Community College, A
Post University, B
Quinnipiac University, B
Sacred Heart University, AB
Saint Joseph College, B
Southern Connecticut State University, BMO
Trinity College, BM
University of Connecticut, BMD
University of Hartford, B
University of New Haven, B
Wesleyan University, B
Western Connecticut State University, BM
Yale University, BMD

Delaware

Delaware State University, B
University of Delaware, BMD
Wesley College, B

District of Columbia

American University, BMD
The Catholic University of America, BMDO
Gallaudet University, B
The George Washington University, BMD
Georgetown University, BMDO
Howard University, BMD
Trinity (Washington) University, B
University of the District of Columbia, AB

Florida

Barry University, B
Bethune-Cookman College, B
Clearwater Christian College, B
Daytona Beach Community College, A
Eckerd College, B
Edward Waters College, B
Flagler College, B
Florida Agricultural and Mechanical University, BM
Florida Atlantic University, BM
Florida International University, BMD
Florida Southern College, B
Florida State University, BMD
Gulf Coast Community College, A
Indian River Community College, A
Jacksonville University, B
Lynn University, B
Manatee Community College, A
Miami Dade College, A
New College of Florida, B
Nova Southeastern University, B
Palm Beach Atlantic University, B
Palm Beach Community College, A
Pensacola Junior College, A
Rollins College, B
Saint Leo University, B
St. Thomas University, B
Stetson University, B
University of Central Florida, BM
University of Florida, BMDO
University of Miami, BMD
University of North Florida, BM
University of South Florida, BM
The University of Tampa, AB
University of West Florida, BM
Warner Southern College, B

Georgia

Abraham Baldwin Agricultural College, A
Agnes Scott College, B
Albany State University, B
Andrew College, A
Armstrong Atlantic State University, BM

Atlanta Metropolitan College, A
Augusta State University, B
Bainbridge College, A
Berry College, B
Brenau University, B
Brewton-Parker College, B
Clark Atlanta University, BM
Clayton State University, B
Coastal Georgia Community College, A
Columbus State University, B
Covenant College, B
Dalton State College, A
Darton College, A
East Georgia College, A
Emory University, BD
Gainesville College, A
Georgia College & State University, BM
Georgia Highlands College, A
Georgia Perimeter College, A
Georgia Southern University, BM
Georgia Southwestern State University, B
Georgia State University, BMD
Gordon College, A
Kennesaw State University, B
LaGrange College, B
Macon State College, A
Mercer University, B
Morehouse College, B
North Georgia College & State University, B
Oglethorpe University, B
Paine College, B
Piedmont College, B
Reinhardt College, B
Savannah State University, B
Shorter College, B
South Georgia College, A
Spelman College, B
University of Georgia, BMD
University of West Georgia, BM
Valdosta State University, BM
Waycross College, A
Wesleyan College, B
Young Harris College, A

Guam

University of Guam, B

Hawaii

Brigham Young University-Hawaii, B
Chaminade University of Honolulu, B
Hawaii Pacific University, B
University of Hawaii at Hilo, B
University of Hawaii at Manoa, BMD
University of Hawaii-West Oahu, B

Idaho

Albertson College of Idaho, B
Boise State University, BM
Brigham Young University -Idaho, A
College of Southern Idaho, A
Idaho State University, AB
North Idaho College, A
Northwest Nazarene University, B
University of Idaho, BMD

Illinois

Augustana College, B
Aurora University, B
Benedictine University, B
Blackburn College, B
Bradley University, B
Chicago State University, BM
Concordia University, B
Danville Area Community College, A
DePaul University, BM
Dominican University, B
Eastern Illinois University, BM
Elmhurst College, B
Eureka College, B
Highland Community College, A
Illinois College, B
Illinois State University, BM
Illinois Wesleyan University, B
John A. Logan College, A
Judson College, B
Knox College, B

Lake Forest College, B
Lewis University, B
Lincoln College, A
Loyola University Chicago, BMD
MacMurray College, B
McKendree College, B
Millikin University, B
Monmouth College, B
North Central College, B
North Park University, B
Northeastern Illinois University, BM
Northern Illinois University, BMD
Northwestern University, BDO
Olivet Nazarene University, B
Parkland College, A
Principia College, B
Quincy University, B
Rend Lake College, A
Rockford College, B
Roosevelt University, BM
Saint Xavier University, B
Sauk Valley Community College, A
Southern Illinois University Carbondale, BMD
Southern Illinois University Edwardsville, BM
Spoon River College, A
Trinity Christian College, B
Trinity International University, B
University of Chicago, BMD
University of Illinois at Chicago, BMD
University of Illinois at Springfield, B
University of Illinois at Urbana-Champaign, BMD
University of St. Francis, B
Western Illinois University, BM
Wheaton College, B

Indiana

Ancilla College, A
Anderson University, B
Ball State University, BM
Bethel College, B
Butler University, BM
DePauw University, B
Earlham College, B
Franklin College, B
Goshen College, B
Hanover College, B
Huntington University, B
Indiana State University, BM
Indiana University Bloomington, BMDO
Indiana University East, A
Indiana University Northwest, B
Indiana University-Purdue University Fort
  Wayne, AB
Indiana University-Purdue University
  Indianapolis, BM
Indiana University South Bend, B
Indiana University Southeast, B
Indiana Wesleyan University, AB
Manchester College, B
Marian College, AB
Martin University, B
Purdue University, BMD
Purdue University Calumet, BM
Saint Joseph's College, B
Saint Mary-of-the-Woods College, B
Saint Mary's College, B
Taylor University, B
University of Evansville, B
University of Indianapolis, BM
University of Notre Dame, BMD
University of Saint Francis, B
University of Southern Indiana, B
Valparaiso University, BMO
Vincennes University, A
Wabash College, B

Iowa

Ashford University, B
Briar Cliff University, B
Buena Vista University, B
Central College, B
Clarke College, B
Coe College, B
Cornell College, B
Dordt College, B
Drake University, BM

Ellsworth Community College, A
Graceland University, B
Grand View College, B
Grinnell College, A
Iowa Lakes Community College, A
Iowa State University of Science and
  Technology, BMD
Iowa Wesleyan College, B
Kirkwood Community College, A
Loras College, B
Luther College, B
Morningside College, B
Mount Mercy College, B
Northwestern College, B
St. Ambrose University, B
Simpson College, B
The University of Iowa, BMD
University of Northern Iowa, BM
Waldorf College, B
Wartburg College, B
William Penn University, B

Kansas

Allen County Community College, A
Baker University, B
Barton County Community College, A
Benedictine College, B
Bethany College, B
Bethel College, B
Butler Community College, A
Central Christian College of Kansas, A
Cloud County Community College, A
Coffeyville Community College, A
Colby Community College, A
Dodge City Community College, A
Donnelly College, A
Emporia State University, BM
Fort Hays State University, BM
Friends University, B
Highland Community College, A
Independence Community College, A
Kansas State University, BMD
Kansas Wesleyan University, B
Labette Community College, A
McPherson College, B
MidAmerica Nazarene University, B
Newman University, B
Ottawa University, B
Pittsburg State University, BM
Pratt Community College, A
Seward County Community College, A
Southwestern College, B
Sterling College, B
Tabor College, B
University of Kansas, BMD
University of Saint Mary, B
Washburn University, B
Wichita State University, BM

Kentucky

Alice Lloyd College, B
Asbury College, B
Bellarmine University, B
Berea College, B
Brescia University, B
Campbellsville University, B
Centre College, B
Eastern Kentucky University, BM
Georgetown College, B
Kentucky Christian University, B
Kentucky State University, B
Kentucky Wesleyan College, B
Lindsey Wilson College, AB
Morehead State University, B
Murray State University, BM
Northern Kentucky University, B
Pikeville College, B
St. Catharine College, A
Spalding University, B
Thomas More College, AB
Transylvania University, B
Union College, B
University of the Cumberlands, B
University of Kentucky, BMD
University of Louisville, BM

Western Kentucky University, BM

Louisiana

Centenary College of Louisiana, B
Dillard University, B
Grambling State University, B
Louisiana College, B
Louisiana State University and Agricultural and
  Mechanical College, BMD
Louisiana State University at Alexandria, B
Louisiana State University in Shreveport, B
Louisiana Tech University, BM
Loyola University New Orleans, B
McNeese State University, B
Nicholls State University, B
Northwestern State University of Louisiana, B
Our Lady of Holy Cross College, B
Southeastern Louisiana University, BM
Southern University and Agricultural and Mechanical
  College, BM
Southern University at New Orleans, B
Tulane University, BMD
University of Louisiana at Lafayette, BM
University of Louisiana at Monroe, BM
University of New Orleans, BM
Xavier University of Louisiana, B

Maine

Bates College, B
Bowdoin College, B
Colby College, B
Saint Joseph's College of Maine, B
University of Maine, BMD
University of Maine at Farmington, B
University of Maine at Machias, B
University of New England, B
University of Southern Maine, B

Maryland

Bowie State University, B
College of Notre Dame of Maryland, B
College of Southern Maryland, A
Columbia Union College, B
Coppin State University, B
Frostburg State University, B
Goucher College, B
Hood College, B
The Johns Hopkins University, BD
Loyola College in Maryland, B
McDaniel College, B
Morgan State University, BMD
Mount St. Mary's University, B
St. Mary's College of Maryland, B
Salisbury University, BM
Towson University, B
United States Naval Academy, B
University of Baltimore, B
University of Maryland, Baltimore County, BM
University of Maryland, College Park, BMDO
University of Maryland Eastern Shore, B
University of Maryland University College, B
Villa Julie College, A
Washington College, BM

Massachusetts

American International College, B
Amherst College, B
Anna Maria College, B
Assumption College, B
Atlantic Union College, B
Bentley College, B
Boston College, BMD
Boston University, BMD
Brandeis University, BMD
Bridgewater State College, B
Bunker Hill Community College, A
Cape Cod Community College, A
Clark University, BMDO
College of the Holy Cross, B
Curry College, B
Eastern Nazarene College, B
Elms College, B
Emmanuel College, B
Fitchburg State College, B
Framingham State College, B
Gordon College, B

Michigan

Hampshire College, B
Harvard University, BD
Lasell College, B
Massachusetts College of Liberal Arts, B
Massachusetts Institute of Technology, B
Merrimack College, B
Mount Holyoke College, B
Nichols College, B
Northeastern University, BMD
Northern Essex Community College, A
Pine Manor College, AB
Quincy College, A
Regis College, B
Salem State College, BM
Simmons College, B
Smith College, BM
Springfield College, B
Stonehill College, B
Suffolk University, B
Tufts University, BMD
University of Massachusetts Amherst, BMD
University of Massachusetts Boston, BM
University of Massachusetts Dartmouth, B
University of Massachusetts Lowell, B
Wellesley College, B
Western New England College, B
Westfield State College, BM
Wheaton College, B
Williams College, B
Worcester Polytechnic Institute, B
Worcester State College, B

Michigan

Adrian College, AB
Albion College, B
Alma College, B
Andrews University, BM
Aquinas College, B
Ave Maria College, B
Calvin College, B
Central Michigan University, BMD
Concordia University, B
Cornerstone University, B
Eastern Michigan University, BM
Grand Valley State University, B
Hillsdale College, B
Hope College, B
Kalamazoo College, B
Kellogg Community College, A
Lake Superior State University, B
Madonna University, B
Marygrove College, B
Michigan State University, BMD
Michigan Technological University, B
Northern Michigan University, B
Oakland University, BM
Olivet College, B
Rochester College, B
Saginaw Valley State University, B
Siena Heights University, B
Spring Arbor University, B
University of Detroit Mercy, B
University of Michigan, BDO
University of Michigan-Dearborn, B
University of Michigan-Flint, B
Wayne State University, BMDO
Western Michigan University, BMD

Minnesota

Augsburg College, B
Bemidji State University, B
Bethany Lutheran College, B
Bethel University, B
Carleton College, B
College of Saint Benedict, B
College of St. Catherine, B
The College of St. Scholastica, B
Concordia College, B
Concordia University, St. Paul, B
Crown College, B
Gustavus Adolphus College, B
Hamline University, B
Macalester College, B
Metropolitan State University, B
Minnesota State University Mankato, BM
Minnesota State University Moorhead, B

North Central University, A
Northwestern College, B
Ridgewater College, A
St. Cloud State University, BM
Saint John's University, B
Saint Mary's University of Minnesota, B
St. Olaf College, B
Southwest Minnesota State University, B
University of Minnesota, Duluth, B
University of Minnesota, Morris, B
University of Minnesota, Twin Cities Campus, BMD
University of St. Thomas, B
Vermilion Community College, A
Winona State University, B

Mississippi

Alcorn State University, B
Belhaven College, B
Blue Mountain College, B
Copiah-Lincoln Community College, A
Delta State University, B
East Central Community College, A
East Mississippi Community College, A
Itawamba Community College, A
Jackson State University, BM
Millsaps College, B
Mississippi College, BM
Mississippi Delta Community College, A
Mississippi State University, BMD
Mississippi University for Women, B
Mississippi Valley State University, B
Northeast Mississippi Community College, A
Southwest Mississippi Community College, A
Tougaloo College, B
University of Mississippi, BMD
University of Southern Mississippi, BMD
William Carey College, B

Missouri

Avila University, B
Central Methodist University, B
Central Missouri State University, BM
College of the Ozarks, B
Columbia College, B
Culver-Stockton College, B
Drury University, B
East Central College, A
Evangel University, B
Fontbonne University, B
Hannibal-LaGrange College, B
Jefferson College, A
Lincoln University, BM
Lindenwood University, B
Maryville University of Saint Louis, B
Missouri Baptist University, B
Missouri Southern State University, B
Missouri State University, BM
Missouri Valley College, B
Missouri Western State University, B
Northwest Missouri State University, BM
Park University, B
Rockhurst University, B
Saint Louis University, BMD
Southeast Missouri State University, BM
Southwest Baptist University, B
Truman State University, B
University of Missouri-Columbia, BMD
University of Missouri-Kansas City, BMD
University of Missouri-Rolla, B
University of Missouri-St. Louis, BM
Washington University in St. Louis, BMD
Webster University, B
Westminster College, B
William Jewell College, B
William Woods University, B

Montana

Carroll College, B
Montana State University, BMD
Montana State University-Billings, B
Rocky Mountain College, B
University of Great Falls, B

The University of Montana-Missoula, BMD

Nebraska

Chadron State College, B
Concordia University, B
Creighton University, B
Dana College, B
Doane College, B
Hastings College, B
Midland Lutheran College, B
Nebraska Wesleyan University, B
Peru State College, B
Union College, B
University of Nebraska at Kearney, BM
University of Nebraska-Lincoln, BMD
University of Nebraska at Omaha, BM
Wayne State College, B
Western Nebraska Community College, A
York College, B

Nevada

Community College of Southern Nevada, A
Great Basin College, A
Nevada State College at Henderson, B
University of Nevada, Las Vegas, BMD
University of Nevada, Reno, BMD

New Hampshire

Dartmouth College, B
Franklin Pierce College, B
Keene State College, B
New England College, B
Plymouth State University, B
Rivier College, B
Saint Anselm College, B
Southern New Hampshire University, B
University of New Hampshire, BMD
University of New Hampshire at Manchester, B

New Jersey

Atlantic Cape Community College, A
Bergen Community College, A
Bloomfield College, B
Burlington County College, A
Caldwell College, B
Centenary College, B
The College of New Jersey, B
College of Saint Elizabeth, B
Drew University, BMD
Fairleigh Dickinson University, College at
    Florham, B
Fairleigh Dickinson University, Metropolitan
    Campus, BM
Felician College, AB
Georgian Court University, B
Gloucester County College, A
Kean University, B
Middlesex County College, A
Monmouth University, BM
Montclair State University, BM
New Jersey City University, B
New Jersey Institute of Technology, BM
Princeton University, BD
Ramapo College of New Jersey, B
The Richard Stockton College of New Jersey, B
Rider University, B
Rowan University, B
Rutgers, The State University of New Jersey,
    Camden, BM
Rutgers, The State University of New Jersey, New
    Brunswick/Piscataway, BD
Rutgers, The State University of New Jersey,
    Newark, BM
Saint Peter's College, B
Salem Community College, A
Seton Hall University, B
Stevens Institute of Technology, B
William Paterson University of New Jersey, BM

New Mexico

College of the Southwest, B
Eastern New Mexico University, B
Mesalands Community College, A
New Mexico Highlands University, BM
New Mexico Junior College, A

New Mexico Military Institute, A
New Mexico State University, BM
St. John's College, B
San Juan College, A
University of New Mexico, BMD
Western New Mexico University, B

New York

Adelphi University, B
Adirondack Community College, A
Alfred University, B
Bard College, B
Barnard College, B
Bernard M. Baruch College of the City University of
    New York, B
Bronx Community College of the City University of
    New York, A
Brooklyn College of the City University of New
    York, BMD
Buffalo State College, State University of New
    York, BM
Canisius College, B
City College of the City University of New York, BM
Clarkson University, B
Colgate University, B
College of Mount Saint Vincent, B
The College of New Rochelle, B
The College of Saint Rose, BM
College of Staten Island of the City University of
    New York, BM
Columbia College, B
Columbia University, School of General Studies, B
Concordia College, B
Cornell University, BMD
Daemen College, B
Dominican College, B
Dowling College, B
D'Youville College, B
Elmira College, B
Eugene Lang College The New School for Liberal
    Arts, B
Excelsior College, B
Fordham University, BMD
Fulton-Montgomery Community College, A
Hamilton College, B
Hartwick College, B
Hobart and William Smith Colleges, B
Hofstra University, B
Houghton College, B
Hunter College of the City University of New
    York, BM
Iona College, BM
Ithaca College, B
The Jewish Theological Seminary, B
Keuka College, B
Le Moyne College, B
Lehman College of the City University of New
    York, BM
Long Island University, Brooklyn Campus, BM
Long Island University, C.W. Post Campus, BM
Manhattan College, B
Manhattanville College, B
Marist College, B
Marymount Manhattan College, B
Mercy College, B
Molloy College, B
Monroe Community College, A
Mount Saint Mary College, B
Nazareth College of Rochester, B
New York University, BMDO
Niagara University, B
Nyack College, B
Pace University, B
Purchase College, State University of New York, B
Queens College of the City University of New
    York, BM
Roberts Wesleyan College, B
Russell Sage College, B
St. Bonaventure University, B
St. Francis College, B
St. John Fisher College, B
St. John's University, BMD
St. Joseph's College, New York, B
St. Joseph's College, Suffolk Campus, B
St. Lawrence University, B
St. Thomas Aquinas College, B

Sarah Lawrence College, BM
Siena College, B
Skidmore College, B
State University of New York at Binghamton, BMD
State University of New York at Buffalo, BMD
State University of New York College at
    Brockport, BM
State University of New York College at
    Cortland, BM
State University of New York College at Geneseo, B
State University of New York College at Oneonta, B
State University of New York Empire State
    College, AB
State University of New York, Fredonia, B
State University of New York at New Paltz, B
State University of New York at Oswego, BM
State University of New York at Plattsburgh, B
Stony Brook University, State University of New
    York, BMD
Syracuse University, BMD
Touro College, B
Union College, B
United States Military Academy, B
University at Albany, State University of New
    York, BMDO
University of Rochester, BMD
Utica College, B
Vassar College, B
Wagner College, B
Wells College, B
Yeshiva University, B
York College of the City University of New York, B

North Carolina

Appalachian State University, BM
Barton College, B
Belmont Abbey College, B
Brevard College, B
Campbell University, B
Catawba College, B
Chowan University, B
Davidson College, B
Duke University, BMDO
East Carolina University, BM
Elizabeth City State University, B
Elon University, B
Fayetteville State University, BM
Gardner-Webb University, B
Greensboro College, B
Guilford College, B
High Point University, B
Johnson C. Smith University, B
Lees-McRae College, B
Lenoir-Rhyne College, B
Livingstone College, B
Louisburg College, A
Mars Hill College, B
Meredith College, B
Methodist College, AB
Montreat College, B
Mount Olive College, B
North Carolina Agricultural and Technical State
    University, B
North Carolina Central University, BM
North Carolina State University, BM
North Carolina Wesleyan College, B
Pfeiffer University, B
Queens University of Charlotte, B
St. Andrews Presbyterian College, B
Saint Augustine's College, B
Salem College, B
The University of North Carolina at Asheville, B
The University of North Carolina at Chapel
    Hill, BMD
The University of North Carolina at Charlotte, BM
The University of North Carolina at
    Greensboro, BMO
The University of North Carolina at Pembroke, B
The University of North Carolina Wilmington, BM
Wake Forest University, B
Warren Wilson College, B
Western Carolina University, BM
Wingate University, B

Winston-Salem State University, B

North Dakota

Cankdeska Cikana Community College, A
Dickinson State University, B
Jamestown College, B
Minot State University, B
North Dakota State University, BMD
Turtle Mountain Community College, A
University of North Dakota, BMD
Valley City State University, B

Ohio

Antioch College, B
Ashland University, B
Baldwin-Wallace College, B
Bluffton University, B
Bowling Green State University, BMDO
Capital University, B
Case Western Reserve University, BMD
Cedarville University, B
Central State University, B
Cleveland State University, M
College of Mount St. Joseph, B
The College of Wooster, B
Defiance College, B
Denison University, B
Franciscan University of Steubenville, B
Heidelberg College, B
Hiram College, B
John Carroll University, BM
Kent State University, BMD
Kenyon College, B
Laura and Alvin Siegal College of Judaic Studies, B
Lorain County Community College, A
Lourdes College, AB
Malone College, B
Marietta College, B
Miami University, BMD
Miami University Hamilton, B
Miami University-Middletown Campus, A
Mount Union College, B
Mount Vernon Nazarene University, B
Muskingum College, B
Notre Dame College, B
Oberlin College, B
Ohio Dominican University, B
Ohio Northern University, B
The Ohio State University, BMD
The Ohio State University at Lima, B
The Ohio State University-Mansfield Campus, B
The Ohio State University at Marion, B
The Ohio State University-Newark Campus, B
Ohio University, MD
Ohio University-Eastern, B
Ohio Wesleyan University, B
Otterbein College, B
Pontifical College Josephinum, B
Shawnee State University, B
Tiffin University, B
Union Institute & University, B
The University of Akron, BMD
University of Cincinnati, BMD
University of Dayton, B
The University of Findlay, B
University of Rio Grande, AB
The University of Toledo, BMD
Urbana University, B
Ursuline College, B
Walsh University, B
Wilmington College, B
Wittenberg University, B
Wright State University, ABM
Wright State University, Lake Campus, A
Xavier University, AB
Youngstown State University, BM

Oklahoma

Bacone College, A
Cameron University, B
Connors State College, A
East Central University, B
Eastern Oklahoma State College, A
Langston University, B
Murray State College, A
Northeastern State University, B

Northwestern Oklahoma State University, B
Oklahoma Baptist University, B
Oklahoma Christian University, B
Oklahoma City Community College, A
Oklahoma City University, B
Oklahoma Panhandle State University, B
Oklahoma State University, BMD
Oklahoma Wesleyan University, B
Oral Roberts University, B
Rogers State University, A
Rose State College, A
St. Gregory's University, B
Southeastern Oklahoma State University, B
Southern Nazarene University, B
Southwestern Oklahoma State University, B
Tulsa Community College, A
University of Central Oklahoma, BM
University of Oklahoma, BMD
University of Science and Arts of Oklahoma, B
University of Tulsa, BMO

Oregon

Eastern Oregon University, B
George Fox University, B
Lewis & Clark College, B
Linfield College, B
Marylhurst University, B
Multnomah Bible College and Biblical Seminary, B
Oregon State University, BMD
Pacific University, B
Portland State University, BM
Reed College, B
Southern Oregon University, B
Treasure Valley Community College, A
Umpqua Community College, A
University of Oregon, BMD
University of Portland, B
Warner Pacific College, B
Western Oregon University, B
Willamette University, B

Pennsylvania

Albright College, B
Allegheny College, B
Alvernia College, B
Arcadia University, B
Bloomsburg University of Pennsylvania, B
Bryn Athyn College of the New Church, B
Bryn Mawr College, B
Bucknell University, B
Cabrini College, B
California University of Pennsylvania, B
Carlow University, B
Carnegie Mellon University, BMD
Cedar Crest College, B
Chatham College, B
Chestnut Hill College, B
Clarion University of Pennsylvania, B
College Misericordia, B
DeSales University, B
Dickinson College, B
Drexel University, B
Duquesne University, BM
East Stroudsburg University of Pennsylvania, BM
Eastern University, B
Edinboro University of Pennsylvania, B
Elizabethtown College, B
Franklin and Marshall College, B
Gannon University, B
Geneva College, B
Gettysburg College, B
Grove City College, B
Gwynedd-Mercy College, B
Haverford College, B
Holy Family University, B
Immaculata University, B
Indiana University of Pennsylvania, BM
Juniata College, B
King's College, B
Kutztown University of Pennsylvania, B
La Roche College, B
La Salle University, BM
Lafayette College, B
Lebanon Valley College, B
Lehigh University, BMD
Lincoln University, B

Lock Haven University of Pennsylvania, B
Lycoming College, B
Mansfield University of Pennsylvania, B
Marywood University, B
Mercyhurst College, B
Messiah College, B
Millersville University of Pennsylvania, ABM
Moravian College, B
Mount Aloysius College, B
Muhlenberg College, B
The Pennsylvania State University Abington College, B
The Pennsylvania State University Altoona College, B
The Pennsylvania State University Beaver Campus of the Commonwealth College, B
The Pennsylvania State University Berks Campus of the Berks-Lehigh Valley College, B
The Pennsylvania State University Delaware County Campus of the Commonwealth College, B
The Pennsylvania State University DuBois Campus of the Commonwealth College, B
The Pennsylvania State University at Erie, The Behrend College, B
The Pennsylvania State University Fayette Campus of the Commonwealth College, B
The Pennsylvania State University Hazleton Campus of the Commonwealth College, B
The Pennsylvania State University, Lehigh Valley Campus of the Berks-Lehigh Valley College, B
The Pennsylvania State University McKeesport Campus of the Commonwealth College, B
The Pennsylvania State University Mont Alto Campus of the Commonwealth College, B
The Pennsylvania State University New Kensington Campus of the Commonwealth College, B
The Pennsylvania State University Schuylkill Campus of the Capital College, B
The Pennsylvania State University Shenango Campus of the Commonwealth College, B
The Pennsylvania State University University Park Campus, BMD
The Pennsylvania State University Wilkes-Barre Campus of the Commonwealth College, B
The Pennsylvania State University Worthington Scranton Campus of the Commonwealth College, B
The Pennsylvania State University York Campus of the Commonwealth College, B
Point Park University, B
Rosemont College, B
Saint Francis University, B
Saint Joseph's University, B
Saint Vincent College, B
Seton Hill University, B
Shippensburg University of Pennsylvania, BMO
Slippery Rock University of Pennsylvania, BM
Susquehanna University, B
Swarthmore College, B
Temple University, BMD
Thiel College, B
University of Pennsylvania, BMD
University of Pittsburgh, BMD
University of Pittsburgh at Bradford, B
University of Pittsburgh at Johnstown, B
The University of Scranton, BM
Ursinus College, B
Villanova University, BM
Washington & Jefferson College, B
Waynesburg College, B
West Chester University of Pennsylvania, BM
Westminster College, B
Widener University, B
Wilkes University, B
York College of Pennsylvania, B

Puerto Rico

Inter American University of Puerto Rico, Fajardo Campus, B
Inter American University of Puerto Rico, Metropolitan Campus, B
Pontifical Catholic University of Puerto Rico, BM
Universidad Adventista de las Antillas, B
Universidad del Turabo, B
University of Puerto Rico, Cayey University College, B

University of Puerto Rico, Mayagüez Campus, B
University of Puerto Rico, Río Piedras, MD

Rhode Island

Brown University, BMD
Bryant University, B
Providence College, BM
Rhode Island College, BM
Roger Williams University, B
Salve Regina University, B
University of Rhode Island, BM

South Carolina

Anderson University, B
Benedict College, B
Bob Jones University, B
Charleston Southern University, B
The Citadel, The Military College of South Carolina, BM
Claflin University, B
Clemson University, BM
Coastal Carolina University, B
Coker College, B
College of Charleston, BM
Columbia College, B
Converse College, BM
Erskine College, B
Francis Marion University, B
Furman University, B
Lander University, B
Limestone College, B
Morris College, B
Newberry College, B
Presbyterian College, B
South Carolina State University, B
Southern Wesleyan University, B
University of South Carolina, BMDO
University of South Carolina Aiken, B
University of South Carolina Beaufort, B
University of South Carolina Upstate, B
Winthrop University, BM
Wofford College, B

South Dakota

Augustana College, B
Black Hills State University, B
Dakota Wesleyan University, B
Mount Marty College, B
Northern State University, B
Oglala Lakota College, B
South Dakota State University, B
University of Sioux Falls, B
The University of South Dakota, BMO

Tennessee

Austin Peay State University, B
Belmont University, B
Bethel College, B
Bryan College, B
Carson-Newman College, B
Christian Brothers University, B
Columbia State Community College, A
Crichton College, B
Cumberland University, B
East Tennessee State University, BM
Fisk University, B
Freed-Hardeman University, B
King College, B
Lambuth University, B
Lane College, B
Lee University, B
LeMoyne-Owen College, B
Lincoln Memorial University, B
Lipscomb University, B
Martin Methodist College, A
Maryville College, B
Middle Tennessee State University, BMD
Milligan College, B
Rhodes College, B
Sewanee: The University of the South, B
Southern Adventist University, B
Tennessee State University, B
Tennessee Technological University, B
Tennessee Temple University, B
Tennessee Wesleyan College, B
Trevecca Nazarene University, B

Tusculum College, B
Union University, B
University of Memphis, BMD
The University of Tennessee, BMD
The University of Tennessee at Chattanooga, B
The University of Tennessee at Martin, B
Vanderbilt University, BMD

Texas

Abilene Christian University, B
Amarillo College, A
Angelina College, A
Angelo State University, BM
Austin College, B
Austin Community College, A
Baylor University, BM
Blinn College, A
Brazosport College, A
Cisco Junior College, A
Clarendon College, A
Coastal Bend College, A
Concordia University at Austin, B
Dallas Baptist University, B
Del Mar College, A
East Texas Baptist University, B
El Paso Community College, A
Frank Phillips College, A
Galveston College, A
Hardin-Simmons University, BM
Hill College of the Hill Junior College District, A
Houston Baptist University, B
Howard Payne University, B
Jarvis Christian College, B
Lamar University, BM
Lee College, A
LeTourneau University, B
Lon Morris College, A
McMurry University, B
Midland College, A
Midwestern State University, BM
Odessa College, A
Our Lady of the Lake University of San Antonio, B
Palo Alto College, A
Paul Quinn College, B
Prairie View A&M University, B
Rice University, BMD
St. Edward's University, B
St. Mary's University of San Antonio, B
St. Philip's College, A
Sam Houston State University, BM
Schreiner University, B
Southern Methodist University, BMD
Southwestern Adventist University, B
Southwestern University, B
Stephen F. Austin State University, BM
Sul Ross State University, BM
Tarleton State University, BM
Texas A&M International University, BM
Texas A&M University, BMD
Texas A&M University-Commerce, BM
Texas A&M University-Corpus Christi, BM
Texas A&M University-Kingsville, BM
Texas A&M University-Texarkana, B
Texas Christian University, BMD
Texas College, B
Texas Lutheran University, B
Texas Southern University, BMO
Texas State University-San Marcos, BM
Texas Tech University, BMD
Texas Wesleyan University, B
Texas Woman's University, BM
Trinity University, B
Trinity Valley Community College, A
University of Dallas, B
University of Houston, BMD
University of Houston-Clear Lake, BM
University of Houston-Victoria, B
University of the Incarnate Word, B
University of Mary Hardin-Baylor, B
University of North Texas, BMD
University of St. Thomas, B
The University of Texas at Arlington, BMD
The University of Texas at Austin, BMD
The University of Texas at Brownsville, BM
The University of Texas at Dallas, B
The University of Texas at El Paso, BMD

The University of Texas-Pan American, BM
The University of Texas of the Permian Basin, BM
The University of Texas at San Antonio, BM
The University of Texas at Tyler, BM
Wayland Baptist University, B
West Texas A&M University, BM
Wiley College, B

Utah

Brigham Young University, BM
Dixie State College of Utah, A
Salt Lake Community College, A
Snow College, A
Southern Utah University, B
University of Utah, BMD
Utah State University, BM
Utah Valley State College, B
Weber State University, B
Westminster College, B

Vermont

Bennington College, B
Castleton State College, B
College of St. Joseph, B
Green Mountain College, B
Johnson State College, B
Marlboro College, B
Middlebury College, B
Norwich University, B
Saint Michael's College, B
University of Vermont, BM

Virginia

Averett University, B
Bluefield College, B
Bridgewater College, B
Christendom College, B
Christopher Newport University, BM
The College of William and Mary, BMD
Eastern Mennonite University, B
Emory & Henry College, B
Ferrum College, B
George Mason University, BMD
Hampden-Sydney College, B
Hampton University, B
Hollins University, B
James Madison University, BM
Liberty University, B
Longwood University, B
Lynchburg College, B
Mary Baldwin College, B
Marymount University, B
Norfolk State University, B
Old Dominion University, BM
Patrick Henry College, B
Radford University, B
Randolph-Macon College, B
Randolph-Macon Woman's College, B
Roanoke College, B
Shenandoah University, B
Southern Virginia University, B
Sweet Briar College, B
University of Mary Washington, B
University of Richmond, BMO
University of Virginia, BMDO
The University of Virginia's College at Wise, B
Virginia Commonwealth University, BM
Virginia Intermont College, B
Virginia Military Institute, B
Virginia Polytechnic Institute and State
    University, BM
Virginia State University, BM
Virginia Union University, B
Virginia Wesleyan College, B
Washington and Lee University, B

Washington

Central Washington University, BM
Centralia College, A
Eastern Washington University, BM
Everett Community College, A
Gonzaga University, B
Heritage University, B
Lower Columbia College, A
Northwest University, B
Pacific Lutheran University, B

Saint Martin's University, B
Seattle Pacific University, B
Seattle University, B
Skagit Valley College, A
Tacoma Community College, A
University of Puget Sound, B
University of Washington, BMD
Walla Walla College, B
Washington State University, BMD
Wenatchee Valley College, A
Western Washington University, BM
Whitman College, B
Whitworth College, B

West Virginia

Alderson-Broaddus College, B
American Public University System, B
Bethany College, B
Concord University, B
Davis & Elkins College, B
Fairmont State University, B
Glenville State College, B
Marshall University, BM
Potomac State College of West Virginia
    University, A
Shepherd University, B
University of Charleston, B
West Liberty State College, B
West Virginia State University, B
West Virginia University, BMD
West Virginia University Institute of Technology, B
West Virginia Wesleyan College, B
Wheeling Jesuit University, B

Wisconsin

Alverno College, B
Beloit College, B
Cardinal Stritch University, B
Carroll College, B
Carthage College, B
Concordia University Wisconsin, B
Edgewood College, B
Lakeland College, B
Lawrence University, B
Marian College of Fond du Lac, B
Marquette University, BMD
Mount Mary College, B
Northland College, B
Ripon College, B
St. Norbert College, B
Silver Lake College, B
University of Wisconsin-Eau Claire, BM
University of Wisconsin-Green Bay, AB
University of Wisconsin-La Crosse, B
University of Wisconsin-Madison, BMD
University of Wisconsin-Milwaukee, BMDO
University of Wisconsin-Oshkosh, B
University of Wisconsin-Parkside, B
University of Wisconsin-Platteville, B
University of Wisconsin-River Falls, B
University of Wisconsin-Stevens Point, BM
University of Wisconsin-Superior, B
University of Wisconsin-Whitewater, B
Wisconsin Lutheran College, B

Wyoming

Casper College, A
Eastern Wyoming College, A
Laramie County Community College, A
Northwest College, A
Sheridan College-Sheridan and Gillette, A
University of Wyoming, BM
Western Wyoming Community College, A

Alberta

Athabasca University, BM
Concordia University College of Alberta, B
The King's University College, B
University of Alberta, BMD
University of Calgary, BMD
University of Lethbridge, BM

British Columbia

Kwantlen University College, A
Malaspina University-College, B

Simon Fraser University, BMD
Thompson Rivers University, B
Trinity Western University, B
The University of British Columbia, BMD
University College of the Fraser Valley, B
University of Northern British Columbia, BM
University of Victoria, BMD

Manitoba

Brandon University, B
Canadian Mennonite University, B
Providence College and Theological Seminary, B
University of Manitoba, BMD
The University of Winnipeg, BM

New Brunswick

Atlantic Baptist University, B
Mount Allison University, B
St. Thomas University, B
Université de Moncton, BM
University of New Brunswick Fredericton, BMD
University of New Brunswick Saint John, B

Newfoundland and Labrador

Memorial University of Newfoundland, BMD

Nova Scotia

Acadia University, B
Cape Breton University, B
Dalhousie University, BMD
Mount Saint Vincent University, B
St. Francis Xavier University, B
Saint Mary's University, BM
Université Sainte-Anne, B
University of King's College, B

Ontario

Brock University, B
Carleton University, BMD
Lakehead University, BM
Laurentian University, BM
McMaster University, BMD
Nipissing University, B
Queen's University at Kingston, B
Redeemer University College, B
Royal Military College of Canada, B
Trent University, BM
Tyndale University College & Seminary, B
University of Guelph, BMD
University of Ottawa, BMD
University of Toronto, BMD
University of Waterloo, BMD
The University of Western Ontario, BMD
University of Windsor, BM
Wilfrid Laurier University, BMD
York University, BMD

Prince Edward Island

University of Prince Edward Island, B

Quebec

Bishop's University, B
Concordia University, BMD
McGill University, BMD
Université Laval, BMD
Université de Montréal, BMD
Université du Québec àChicoutimi, B
Université du Québec àMontréal, BMD
Université du Québec àRimouski, B
Université du Québec àTrois-Rivières, B

Université de Sherbrooke, BM

Saskatchewan

University of Regina, BM
University of Saskatchewan, BMD

HISTORY AND PHILOSOPHY OF SCIENCE AND TECHNOLOGY

Georgia

Georgia Institute of Technology, B

Maryland

The Johns Hopkins University, B

Massachusetts

Harvard University, B
Worcester Polytechnic Institute, B

New Jersey

Stevens Institute of Technology, B

New York

Bard College, B
Farmingdale State University of New York, B
Sarah Lawrence College, B

Ohio

Case Western Reserve University, B

Oregon

Oregon State University, B

Pennsylvania

University of Pennsylvania, B
University of Pittsburgh, B

Washington

University of Washington, B

Wisconsin

University of Wisconsin-Madison, B

Nova Scotia

Dalhousie University, B

Ontario

University of Toronto, B

HISTORY OF MEDICINE

Connecticut

Yale University, MD

Minnesota

University of Minnesota, Twin Cities Campus, MD

New Jersey

New Jersey Institute of Technology, M
Rutgers, The State University of New Jersey, New Brunswick/Piscataway, D

North Carolina

Duke University, O

Quebec

McGill University, MD

HISTORY OF SCIENCE AND TECHNOLOGY

Arizona

Arizona State University, MD

California

University of California, Berkeley, D
University of California, San Diego, D

Connecticut

Yale University, MD

Georgia

Georgia Institute of Technology, MD

Illinois

University of Chicago, MD

Indiana

Indiana University Bloomington, MDO
University of Notre Dame, MD

Iowa

Iowa State University of Science and Technology, MD

Maryland

The Johns Hopkins University, D

Massachusetts

Harvard University, MD
Massachusetts Institute of Technology, D
University of Massachusetts Amherst, M

Minnesota

University of Minnesota, Twin Cities Campus, MD

New Jersey

New Jersey Institute of Technology, M
Princeton University, D
Rutgers, The State University of New Jersey, New Brunswick/Piscataway, D

New York

Cornell University, MD
Polytechnic University, Brooklyn Campus, M
Rensselaer Polytechnic Institute, MD

Oklahoma

University of Oklahoma, MD

Pennsylvania

Drexel University, M
University of Pennsylvania, MD
University of Pittsburgh, MD

Rhode Island

Brown University, MD

Virginia

Virginia Polytechnic Institute and State University, MD

West Virginia

West Virginia University, MD

Wisconsin

University of Wisconsin-Madison, MD

Ontario

University of Toronto, MD

HISTORY TEACHER EDUCATION

Alabama

Auburn University, B
Huntingdon College, B
Samford University, B

Talladega College, B

Arizona

Northern Arizona University, B
The University of Arizona, B

Arkansas

University of Arkansas at Fort Smith, B

Connecticut

Sacred Heart University, B

Delaware

University of Delaware, B

District of Columbia

The Catholic University of America, B

Georgia

Brewton-Parker College, B
Clark Atlanta University, B
Columbus State University, B
Georgia Southern University, B
Paine College, B
Toccoa Falls College, B

Idaho

Northwest Nazarene University, B

Illinois

Concordia University, B
Elmhurst College, B
Greenville College, B
Illinois Wesleyan University, B
McKendree College, B
Saint Xavier University, B
Trinity Christian College, B
University of Illinois at Chicago, B

Indiana

Ancilla College, A
Taylor University, B
Valparaiso University, B

Iowa

Buena Vista University, B
Dordt College, B
St. Ambrose University, B
The University of Iowa, B
Wartburg College, B

Kansas

Central Christian College of Kansas, A
Pittsburg State University, B

Kentucky

Campbellsville University, B
Murray State University, B

Louisiana

Xavier University of Louisiana, B

Maine

Saint Joseph's College of Maine, B
University of Maine, B
University of Maine at Machias, B

Massachusetts

Fitchburg State College, B
Framingham State College, B

Michigan

Alma College, B
Central Michigan University, B
Concordia University, B
Cornerstone University, B
Eastern Michigan University, B
Hope College, B
Northern Michigan University, B
Rochester College, B
University of Michigan-Flint, B

Western Michigan University, B

Minnesota

Crown College, B

Missouri

College of the Ozarks, B
Culver-Stockton College, B
Evangel University, B
Hannibal-LaGrange College, B
Lindenwood University, B
Maryville University of Saint Louis, B
Missouri State University, B
Washington University in St. Louis, B

Montana

Carroll College, B
Montana State University-Billings, B
Rocky Mountain College, B
University of Great Falls, B
The University of Montana-Western, B

Nebraska

Chadron State College, B
Concordia University, B
Dana College, B
Hastings College, B
Union College, B
University of Nebraska-Lincoln, B
Wayne State College, B
York College, B

Nevada

Nevada State College at Henderson, B

New Hampshire

Keene State College, B

New Jersey

Bloomfield College, B
The College of New Jersey, B

New York

Dominican College, B
Elmira College, B
Ithaca College, B
Marist College, B
Nazareth College of Rochester, B
Pace University, B
State University of New York College at
    Brockport, B
Utica College, B

North Carolina

Appalachian State University, B
Campbell University, B
Chowan University, B
Elizabeth City State University, B
North Carolina Central University, B
North Carolina State University, B
The University of North Carolina at Charlotte, B
The University of North Carolina Wilmington, B

North Dakota

Jamestown College, B
Mayville State University, B
Minot State University, B
North Dakota State University, B
University of Mary, B
Valley City State University, B

Ohio

Ohio Northern University, B
Ohio Wesleyan University, B
Shawnee State University, B
The University of Akron, B
University of Rio Grande, B

Oklahoma

East Central University, B
Oklahoma Baptist University, B
Southwestern Oklahoma State University, B

University of Central Oklahoma, B

Pennsylvania

Gwynedd-Mercy College, B
Marywood University, B
Moravian College, B
Saint Francis University, B
University of Pittsburgh at Johnstown, B
West Chester University of Pennsylvania, B
Widener University, B

Puerto Rico

Inter American University of Puerto Rico,
    Metropolitan Campus, B
Pontifical Catholic University of Puerto Rico, B
Universidad Adventista de las Antillas, B
University of Puerto Rico, Cayey University
    College, B

Rhode Island

Rhode Island College, B
Salve Regina University, B

South Carolina

Anderson University, B
Charleston Southern University, B
The Citadel, The Military College of South
    Carolina, B
Coker College, B

South Dakota

Dakota Wesleyan University, B
Mount Marty College, B
The University of South Dakota, B

Tennessee

Bethel College, B
Christian Brothers University, B
Cumberland University, B
King College, B
Lambuth University, B
Lincoln Memorial University, B
Maryville College, B
Tennessee Temple University, B
Tennessee Wesleyan College, B
Trevecca Nazarene University, B
The University of Tennessee at Martin, B

Texas

Abilene Christian University, B
East Texas Baptist University, B
Hardin-Simmons University, B
Howard Payne University, B
St. Edward's University, B
Schreiner University, B
Texas A&M International University, B
Texas Lutheran University, B
Texas Wesleyan University, B

Utah

Brigham Young University, B
University of Utah, B
Weber State University, B

Vermont

Johnson State College, B

Virginia

Averett University, B
Bluefield College, B
Liberty University, B
Old Dominion University, B

Washington

Central Washington University, B
Washington State University, B

West Virginia

Wheeling Jesuit University, B

Wisconsin

Carroll College, B
Concordia University Wisconsin, B
Marian College of Fond du Lac, B

Mount Mary College, B
University of Wisconsin-River Falls, B
University of Wisconsin-Superior, B

Ontario

University of Windsor, B
York University, B

Quebec

Bishop's University, B
McGill University, B
Université Laval, B

HIV/AIDS NURSING

Delaware

University of Delaware, MO

North Carolina

Duke University, O

HOLOCAUST STUDIES

Massachusetts

Clark University, D

New Jersey

Drew University, O
The Richard Stockton College of New Jersey, M

HOME ECONOMICS

Alabama

Alabama Agricultural and Mechanical University, M
The University of Alabama, MD

Arizona

The University of Arizona, MD

Arkansas

University of Central Arkansas, M

California

California State University, Long Beach, M
San Francisco State University, M

Idaho

University of Idaho, M

Illinois

Eastern Illinois University, M

Indiana

Indiana State University, M
Purdue University, MD

Iowa

Iowa State University of Science and
Technology, MD

Michigan

Central Michigan University, M
Michigan State University, D

Missouri

Southeast Missouri State University, M
University of Missouri-Columbia, MD

New Jersey

Montclair State University, M

New York

Cornell University, MD

North Carolina

Appalachian State University, M
The University of North Carolina at Greensboro, MD

Ohio

The Ohio State University, MD
The University of Akron, M

Oklahoma

Oklahoma State University, MD
University of Central Oklahoma, M

South Dakota

South Dakota State University, M

Tennessee

The University of Tennessee, D

Texas

Lamar University, O
Prairie View A&M University, M
Stephen F. Austin State University, M
Texas A&M University-Kingsville, M
Texas Tech University, MD

Washington

Central Washington University, M

Manitoba

University of Manitoba, M

HOME ECONOMICS EDUCATION

Florida

Florida International University, M

Indiana

Indiana State University, M
Purdue University, MDO

Iowa

Iowa State University of Science and
Technology, MD

Kentucky

Eastern Kentucky University, M

Louisiana

Louisiana State University and Agricultural and
Mechanical College, M
Northwestern State University of Louisiana, M

Nebraska

Wayne State College, M

New Jersey

Montclair State University, M

New York

Brooklyn College of the City University of New
York, M
Queens College of the City University of New
York, M
State University of New York College at Oneonta, M

North Carolina

Western Carolina University, M

Ohio

The Ohio State University, MD

Oklahoma

University of Central Oklahoma, M

Rhode Island

University of Rhode Island, M

Texas

Texas Tech University, MD

Utah

Utah State University, M

Washington

Central Washington University, M

British Columbia

The University of British Columbia, M

HOME FURNISHINGS AND EQUIPMENT INSTALLERS

Alabama

Jefferson State Community College, A

Kentucky

Eastern Kentucky University, A

Texas

St. Philip's College, A

Utah

Brigham Young University, B

HOME HEALTH AIDE/HOME ATTENDANT

California

Mt. San Jacinto College, A

Kansas

Allen County Community College, A
Barton County Community College, A

Pennsylvania

Laurel Business Institute, A

HORSE HUSBANDRY/EQUINE SCIENCE AND MANAGEMENT

Arizona

Yavapai College, A

California

Santa Rosa Junior College, A

Illinois

Black Hawk College, A

Kentucky

Midway College, B

Massachusetts

Becker College, B
Mount Ida College, B

Missouri

Stephens College, B

Ohio

The Ohio State University Agricultural Technical
Institute, A

Oregon

Linn-Benton Community College, A

Texas

Clarendon College, A

Vermont

Sterling College, B

West Virginia

Bethany College, B

Wyoming

Central Wyoming College, A

HORTICULTURAL SCIENCE

Alabama

Auburn University, BMD
Wallace State Community College, A

Arizona

Mesa Community College, A

Arkansas

University of Arkansas, BM
University of Arkansas Community College at
    Morrilton, A

California

American River College, A
Bakersfield College, A
Butte College, A
Cabrillo College, A
California Polytechnic State University, San Luis
    Obispo, B
California State Polytechnic University, Pomona, B
Chabot College, A
City College of San Francisco, A
College of the Desert, A
College of San Mateo, A
College of the Sequoias, A
Cosumnes River College (Sacramento), A
El Camino College, A
Fullerton College, A
Hartnell College, A
Las Positas College, A
Long Beach City College, A
Los Angeles Pierce College, A
Merritt College, A
MiraCosta College, A
Mt. San Antonio College, A
Orange Coast College, A
Reedley College, A
Saddleback College, A
Shasta College, A
Sierra College, A
University of California, Davis, M
Victor Valley College, A

Colorado

Colorado State University, BMD
Northeastern Junior College, A

Connecticut

Naugatuck Valley Community College, A
University of Connecticut, AB

Delaware

University of Delaware, BM

Florida

Edison College, A
Florida Agricultural and Mechanical University, B
Florida Southern College, B
Miami Dade College, A
Pensacola Junior College, A
University of Florida, BMD

Georgia

Abraham Baldwin Agricultural College, A
Chattahoochee Technical College, A
Columbus Technical College, A
Georgia Highlands College, A
Griffin Technical College, A
Gwinnett Technical College, A
North Georgia Technical College, A
North Metro Technical College, A
South Georgia Technical College, A
University of Georgia, BMD

Hawaii

Maui Community College, A
University of Hawaii at Hilo, B
University of Hawaii at Manoa, MD

Idaho

Boise State University, A
Brigham Young University -Idaho, A

University of Idaho, BMD

Illinois

Black Hawk College, A
City Colleges of Chicago, Richard J. Daley
    College, A
Danville Area Community College, A
Illinois Central College, A
Joliet Junior College, A
Shawnee Community College, A
Southern Illinois University Carbondale, M
Southwestern Illinois College, A
University of Illinois at Urbana-Champaign, B
William Rainey Harper College, A

Indiana

Purdue University, BMD
Vincennes University, A

Iowa

Des Moines Area Community College, A
Hawkeye Community College, A
Indian Hills Community College, A
Iowa State University of Science and
    Technology, BMD
Kirkwood Community College, A

Kansas

Coffeyville Community College, A
Kansas State University, BMD

Kentucky

Eastern Kentucky University, AB
St. Catharine College, A

Louisiana

Louisiana State University and Agricultural and
    Mechanical College, MD
Southeastern Louisiana University, B
University of Louisiana at Lafayette, B

Maine

Southern Maine Community College, A
University of Maine, M

Maryland

Anne Arundel Community College, A
University of Maryland, College Park, BD

Michigan

Andrews University, A
Lansing Community College, A
Michigan State University, BMD
St. Clair County Community College, A

Minnesota

Central Lakes College, A
University of Minnesota, Crookston, AB

Mississippi

Jones County Junior College, A
Meridian Community College, A
Mississippi Delta Community College, A
Mississippi Gulf Coast Community College, A
Mississippi State University, B
Northeast Mississippi Community College, A

Missouri

College of the Ozarks, B
East Central College, A
Missouri State University, B
Northwest Missouri State University, B
St. Louis Community College at Meramec, A
State Fair Community College, A
Truman State University, B
University of Missouri-Columbia, MD

Montana

Montana State University, B

Nebraska

Nebraska College of Technical Agriculture, A
Northeast Community College, A

University of Nebraska-Lincoln, BMD

Nevada

Community College of Southern Nevada, A

New Hampshire

University of New Hampshire, AB

New Jersey

Cumberland County College, A
Rutgers, The State University of New Jersey, New
    Brunswick/Piscataway, MD

New Mexico

New Mexico State University, BMD

New York

Cornell University, BMD
State University of New York College of Agriculture
    and Technology at Cobleskill, AB
State University of New York College of Agriculture
    and Technology at Morrisville, A
State University of New York College of Technology
    at Delhi, A
Suffolk County Community College, A

North Carolina

Blue Ridge Community College, A
Central Piedmont Community College, A
Forsyth Technical Community College, A
Haywood Community College, A
Lenoir Community College, A
Mayland Community College, A
North Carolina State University, BMD
Rockingham Community College, A
Sampson Community College, A
Surry Community College, A
Western Piedmont Community College, A

North Dakota

Minot State University-Bottineau Campus, A
North Dakota State University, B

Ohio

Clark State Community College, A
Kent State University, Salem Campus, A
The Ohio State University, BMD
The Ohio State University Agricultural Technical
    Institute, A

Oklahoma

Bacone College, A
Connors State College, A
Eastern Oklahoma State College, A
Northeastern Oklahoma Agricultural and Mechanical
    College, A
Oklahoma State University, BMD
Oklahoma State University, Oklahoma City, A
Tulsa Community College, A

Oregon

Linn-Benton Community College, A
Mt. Hood Community College, A
Oregon State University, BMD

Pennsylvania

Delaware Valley College, B
Lehigh Carbon Community College, A
Luzerne County Community College, A
The Pennsylvania State University Abington
    College, B
The Pennsylvania State University Altoona
    College, B
The Pennsylvania State University Beaver Campus
    of the Commonwealth College, B
The Pennsylvania State University Berks Campus of
    the Berks-Lehigh Valley College, B
The Pennsylvania State University Delaware County
    Campus of the Commonwealth College, B
The Pennsylvania State University DuBois Campus
    of the Commonwealth College, B
The Pennsylvania State University at Erie, The
    Behrend College, B

The Pennsylvania State University Fayette Campus
of the Commonwealth College, B
The Pennsylvania State University Hazleton
Campus of the Commonwealth College, B
The Pennsylvania State University, Lehigh Valley
Campus of the Berks-Lehigh Valley College, B
The Pennsylvania State University McKeesport
Campus of the Commonwealth College, B
The Pennsylvania State University Mont Alto
Campus of the Commonwealth College, B
The Pennsylvania State University New Kensington
Campus of the Commonwealth College, B
The Pennsylvania State University Schuylkill
Campus of the Capital College, B
The Pennsylvania State University Shenango
Campus of the Commonwealth College, B
The Pennsylvania State University University Park
Campus, BMD
The Pennsylvania State University Wilkes-Barre
Campus of the Commonwealth College, B
The Pennsylvania State University Worthington
Scranton Campus of the Commonwealth
College, B
The Pennsylvania State University York Campus of
the Commonwealth College, B
Temple University, B
Westmoreland County Community College, A
The Williamson Free School of Mechanical
Trades, A

Puerto Rico

University of Puerto Rico, Mayagüez Campus, BM
University of Puerto Rico at Utuado, A

South Carolina

Clemson University, B
Spartanburg Technical College, A
Technical College of the Lowcountry, A
Trident Technical College, A

South Dakota

Southeast Technical Institute, A

Tennessee

Tennessee Technological University, B

Texas

Frank Phillips College, A
Hill College of the Hill Junior College District, A
Houston Community College System, A
Palo Alto College, A
Richland College, A
Sam Houston State University, B
Stephen F. Austin State University, B
Tarleton State University, B
Tarrant County College District, A
Texas A&M University, BMD
Texas A&M University-Kingsville, B
Texas Tech University, BM
Trinity Valley Community College, A
Tyler Junior College, A

Utah

Brigham Young University, M
Utah State University, B

Vermont

Sterling College, B
University of Vermont, MD

Virginia

Christopher Newport University, B
Ferrum College, B
Northern Virginia Community College, A
Tidewater Community College, A
Virginia Polytechnic Institute and State
University, BMD

Washington

Lake Washington Technical College, A
South Puget Sound Community College, A
South Seattle Community College, A
University of Washington, MD

Washington State University, BMD

West Virginia

Potomac State College of West Virginia
University, A
West Virginia University, M

Wisconsin

University of Wisconsin-Madison, BMD
University of Wisconsin-River Falls, B

British Columbia

The University of British Columbia, B

Manitoba

University of Manitoba, MD

Ontario

University of Guelph, BMD

Saskatchewan

University of Saskatchewan, B

HOSPICE NURSING

Michigan

Madonna University, M

New York

D'Youville College, O

HOSPITAL AND HEALTH CARE FACILITIES ADMINISTRATION/MANAGEMENT

Alabama

The University of Alabama, B

Arizona

Apollo College-Westside, Inc., A
The Bryman School, A

Florida

Manatee Community College, A
Saint Leo University, B

Illinois

City Colleges of Chicago, Malcolm X College, A
College of DuPage, A

Kansas

Allen County Community College, A

Michigan

Central Michigan University, B

Missouri

Avila University, B

Nebraska

Central Community College-Hastings Campus, A

New York

Ithaca College, B
St. John's University, B

Ohio

The University of Toledo, B
Ursuline College, B
Youngstown State University, B

Pennsylvania

Eastern University, B
Gwynedd-Mercy College, B
Harrisburg Area Community College, A
Marywood University, B

Saint Joseph's University, B

South Dakota

Black Hills State University, B
The University of South Dakota, B

Tennessee

Carson-Newman College, B

Texas

Texas State University-San Marcos, B

Wisconsin

Western Technical College, A

Ontario

York University, B

HOSPITALITY ADMINISTRATION/MANAGEMENT

Alabama

Andrew Jackson University, M
Auburn University, B
James H. Faulkner State Community College, A
Jefferson State Community College, A
Tuskegee University, B
The University of Alabama, M

Arizona

Arizona Western College, A
Cochise College (Douglas), A
Pima Community College, A
Scottsdale Community College, A

Arkansas

Arkansas Tech University, B
Philander Smith College, B

California

Heald College-Salinas, A
Heald College-San Francisco, A
Monterey Peninsula College, A
National University, B
Reedley College, A
San Diego City College, A
San Diego State University, B
San Francisco State University, B
San Jose State University, B
Touro University International, B

Colorado

Colorado Mountain College, Alpine Campus, A
Metropolitan State College of Denver, B
Parks College (Denver), A
University of Denver, BM

Connecticut

International College of Hospitality Management, A
Naugatuck Valley Community College, A
Three Rivers Community College, A
University of New Haven, BM

Delaware

Delaware State University, B
Delaware Technical & Community College, Jack F.
Owens Campus, A
University of Delaware, M

District of Columbia

The George Washington University, M
University of the District of Columbia, AB

Florida

Daytona Beach Community College, A
Edison College, A
Florida Atlantic University, B
Florida Community College at Jacksonville, A
Florida International University, BM
Florida National College, A
Florida State University, B
Gulf Coast Community College, A

Hillsborough Community College, A
Johnson & Wales University, AB
Keiser College (Fort Lauderdale), A
Keiser College (Melbourne), A
Lynn University, M
Miami Dade College, A
Saint Leo University, B
St. Petersburg College, A
Schiller International University, M
South Florida Community College, A
University of Central Florida, BM
University of South Florida, B
University of West Florida, B
Valencia Community College, A

Georgia

Abraham Baldwin Agricultural College, A
Young Harris College, A

Guam

Guam Community College, A

Hawaii

Kauai Community College, A

Idaho

Lewis-Clark State College, AB
North Idaho College, A

Illinois

City Colleges of Chicago, Harold Washington
  College, A
College of DuPage, A
Joliet Junior College, A
Kendall College, AB
Lexington College, AB
Midstate College, A
Northwestern Business College, A
Rend Lake College, A
Roosevelt University, BM
Southwestern Illinois College, A
Triton College, A
University of Illinois at Urbana-Champaign, B
William Rainey Harper College, A

Indiana

Indiana University-Purdue University Fort
  Wayne, AB
Indiana University-Purdue University Indianapolis, B
International Business College (Fort Wayne), AB
Ivy Tech Community College-Central Indiana, A
Ivy Tech Community College-East Central, A
Ivy Tech Community College-North Central, A
Ivy Tech Community College-Northeast, A
Ivy Tech Community College-Northwest, A
Purdue University, AMD

Iowa

Des Moines Area Community College, A
Iowa Lakes Community College, A
Iowa State University of Science and
  Technology, MD

Kansas

Johnson County Community College, A
Kansas State University, MD

Kentucky

University of Kentucky, BM

Louisiana

Delgado Community College, A
Northwestern State University of Louisiana, B
Southern University at Shreveport, A
University of Louisiana at Lafayette, B
University of New Orleans, BM

Maine

Central Maine Community College, A
Husson College, B

Southern Maine Community College, A

Maryland

Allegany College of Maryland, A
Baltimore City Community College, A
Baltimore International College, AB
Morgan State University, B
Sojourner-Douglass College, B
Wor-Wic Community College, A

Massachusetts

Bay State College, A
Becker College, B
Berkshire Community College, A
Boston University, B
Bunker Hill Community College, A
Endicott College, BM
Fisher College, A
Gibbs College, A
Holyoke Community College, A
Marian Court College, A
Massachusetts Bay Community College, A
North Shore Community College, A
University of Massachusetts Amherst, BM

Michigan

Baker College of Flint, A
Baker College of Owosso, A
Central Michigan University, BMO
Concordia University, B
Davenport University (Midland), A
Eastern Michigan University, B
Ferris State University, B
Henry Ford Community College, A
Lake Michigan College, A
Lansing Community College, A
Madonna University, B
Michigan State University, BM
Mid Michigan Community College, A
Muskegon Community College, A
Northern Michigan University, B
Siena Heights University, AB

Minnesota

Alexandria Technical College, A
Metropolitan State University, B
National American University (Roseville), B
Normandale Community College, A
Rasmussen College Mankato, A
University of Minnesota, Crookston, A

Mississippi

Delta State University, B

Missouri

East Central College, A
Jefferson College, A
Mineral Area College, A
Missouri State University, B
Springfield College, A

Montana

Blackfeet Community College, A

Nebraska

Central Community College-Hastings Campus, A

Nevada

Community College of Southern Nevada, A
Truckee Meadows Community College, A
University of Nevada, Las Vegas, BMD
University of Nevada, Reno, B

New Hampshire

Southern New Hampshire University, B
University of New Hampshire, B

New Jersey

Atlantic Cape Community College, A
Fairleigh Dickinson University, College at
  Florham, M
Fairleigh Dickinson University, Metropolitan
  Campus, M
Gibbs College (Montclair), A

Middlesex County College, A
Montclair State University, B
Rutgers, The State University of New Jersey,
  Camden, B

New Mexico

Central New Mexico Community College, A
Doña Ana Branch Community College, A
National American University (Albuquerque), AB

New York

Adirondack Community College, A
Buffalo State College, State University of New
  York, B
Cornell University, MD
Globe Institute of Technology, B
Jefferson Community College, A
Katharine Gibbs School (Melville), A
Monroe College (Bronx), A
Monroe College (New Rochelle), A
New York City College of Technology of the City
  University of New York, AB
New York University, BMO
Niagara County Community College, A
Niagara University, B
Paul Smith's College of Arts and Sciences, A
Rochester Institute of Technology, BM
Rockland Community College, A
St. John's University, B
State University of New York College of Agriculture
  and Technology at Morrisville, A
Sullivan County Community College, A
Syracuse University, B

North Carolina

Appalachian State University, B
Central Piedmont Community College, A
North Carolina Central University, B
The University of North Carolina at Greensboro, B
Western Carolina University, B

North Dakota

North Dakota State University, B
United Tribes Technical College, A

Ohio

Bowling Green State University, B
Hocking College, A
Kent State University, B
Lakeland Community College, A
The Ohio State University, B
The Ohio State University at Lima, B
The University of Akron, A
University of Cincinnati Clermont College, A
Youngstown State University, AB

Oklahoma

Oklahoma State University, MD
Oklahoma State University, Okmulgee, A

Oregon

Central Oregon Community College, A
Chemeketa Community College, A
Lane Community College, A
Mt. Hood Community College, A

Pennsylvania

The Art Institute of Pittsburgh, AB
Bucks County Community College, A
Butler County Community College, A
Drexel University, B
East Stroudsburg University of Pennsylvania, BM
Lehigh Valley College, A
Mercyhurst College, B
Pennsylvania Highland Community College, A
The Pennsylvania State University Abington
  College, B
The Pennsylvania State University Altoona
  College, B
The Pennsylvania State University Beaver Campus
  of the Commonwealth College, AB
The Pennsylvania State University Berks Campus of
  the Berks-Lehigh Valley College, AB
The Pennsylvania State University Delaware County
  Campus of the Commonwealth College, B

The Pennsylvania State University DuBois Campus
of the Commonwealth College, B
The Pennsylvania State University at Erie, The
Behrend College, B
The Pennsylvania State University Fayette Campus
of the Commonwealth College, B
The Pennsylvania State University Hazleton
Campus of the Commonwealth College, B
The Pennsylvania State University, Lehigh Valley
Campus of the Berks-Lehigh Valley College, B
The Pennsylvania State University McKeesport
Campus of the Commonwealth College, B
The Pennsylvania State University Mont Alto
Campus of the Commonwealth College, B
The Pennsylvania State University New Kensington
Campus of the Commonwealth College, B
The Pennsylvania State University Schuylkill
Campus of the Capital College, B
The Pennsylvania State University Shenango
Campus of the Commonwealth College, B
The Pennsylvania State University University Park
Campus, ABMD
The Pennsylvania State University Wilkes-Barre
Campus of the Commonwealth College, B
The Pennsylvania State University Worthington
Scranton Campus of the Commonwealth
College, B
The Pennsylvania State University York Campus of
the Commonwealth College, B
Robert Morris University, B
Seton Hill University, B
Temple University, BM
Westmoreland County Community College, A
Widener University, B
Yorktowne Business Institute, A

Rhode Island

Johnson & Wales University, BM

South Carolina

Bob Jones University, AB
College of Charleston, B
Greenville Technical College, A
University of South Carolina, BM
University of South Carolina Beaufort, B

South Dakota

Sisseton-Wahpeton Community College, A

Tennessee

Pellissippi State Technical Community College, A
University of Memphis, B
The University of Tennessee, M

Texas

Collin County Community College District, A
El Centro College, A
South Texas College, A
Stephen F. Austin State University, B
Texas Tech University, MD
Texas Woman's University, M
University of Houston, M
University of North Texas, BM

Utah

Utah Valley State College, AB

Vermont

Champlain College, AB
Green Mountain College, B
Johnson State College, B

Virginia

J. Sargeant Reynolds Community College, A
James Madison University, B
National College of Business & Technology (Salem)
, A
Stratford University, B
Virginia Polytechnic Institute and State
University, MD
Virginia State University, B

Washington

Seattle Central Community College, A
South Seattle Community College, A

Washington State University, B

West Virginia

Concord University, B
Davis & Elkins College, AB
Marshall Community and Technical College, A
Mountain State University, AB
West Virginia Northern Community College, A

Wisconsin

Chippewa Valley Technical College, A
Fox Valley Technical College, A
Madison Area Technical College, A
University of Wisconsin-Stout, BM
Waukesha County Technical College, A

Wyoming

Casper College, A
Sheridan College-Sheridan and Gillette, A

British Columbia

Thompson Rivers University, B

New Brunswick

University of New Brunswick Saint John, B

Nova Scotia

Cape Breton University, B
Mount Saint Vincent University, B

Ontario

Ryerson University, B
University of Guelph, M

Prince Edward Island

University of Prince Edward Island, B

HOSPITALITY AND RECREATION MARKETING OPERATIONS

Alabama

Tuskegee University, B

Arkansas

University of Arkansas, B

California

American River College, A
San Diego Mesa College, A

Delaware

University of Delaware, B

Florida

Florida Community College at Jacksonville, A

Guam

Guam Community College, A

Illinois

Kendall College, B

Indiana

Vincennes University, A

Iowa

AIB College of Business, A
Iowa Central Community College, A
Iowa Western Community College, A
Kirkwood Community College, A

Massachusetts

Middlesex Community College, A

Michigan

Mid Michigan Community College, A
Muskegon Community College, A

Northern Michigan University, B

Minnesota

Rasmussen College Mankato, A

Mississippi

Northeast Mississippi Community College, A

Missouri

Northwest Missouri State University, B

Montana

Flathead Valley Community College, A

New Jersey

Cumberland County College, A
Gloucester County College, A
Raritan Valley Community College, A

New York

Rochester Institute of Technology, B
State University of New York College of Technology
at Delhi, A

North Carolina

Methodist College, B

Ohio

The University of Akron, A

Oklahoma

Oral Roberts University, B

Oregon

Central Oregon Community College, A

Pennsylvania

Luzerne County Community College, A
Montgomery County Community College, A

Rhode Island

Johnson & Wales University, AB

Texas

Austin Community College, A

Vermont

Champlain College, AB

West Virginia

Mountain State University, B

Wisconsin

Milwaukee Area Technical College, A

British Columbia

Thompson Rivers University, A

Nova Scotia

Cape Breton University, B

Ontario

Tyndale University College & Seminary, B

HOTEL/MOTEL ADMINISTRATION/MANAGEMENT

Alabama

Auburn University, B
Community College of the Air Force, A

Arizona

Central Arizona College, A
Cochise College (Sierra Vista), A
Northern Arizona University, B

Scottsdale Community College, A

Arkansas

University of Arkansas at Pine Bluff, B

California

Alliant International University, B
American River College, A
Bakersfield College, A
California State Polytechnic University, Pomona, B
California State University, Long Beach, B
Chaffey College, A
City College of San Francisco, A
College of the Canyons, A
Columbia College, A
Cypress College, A
Glendale Community College, A
Lake Tahoe Community College, A
Long Beach City College, A
Los Angeles Valley College, A
MiraCosta College, A
Monterey Peninsula College, A
Mt. San Antonio College, A
Orange Coast College, A
Oxnard College, A
San Bernardino Valley College, A
San Diego Mesa College, A
San Diego State University, B
Santa Barbara City College, A
Santa Rosa Junior College, A
Skyline College, A
University of San Francisco, B

Colorado

Colorado Mountain College, Alpine Campus, A
Colorado State University, B
Johnson & Wales University, B
Mesa State College, A
National American University (Colorado Springs), A
Parks College (Denver), A
University of Denver, B
Westwood College-Denver North, A

Connecticut

Briarwood College, A
Gateway Community College, A
Manchester Community College, A
Naugatuck Valley Community College, A
Norwalk Community College, A
Three Rivers Community College, A
University of New Haven, B

Delaware

Delaware Technical & Community College, Jack F.
  Owens Campus, A
Delaware Technical & Community College,
  Stanton/Wilmington Campus, A
University of Delaware, B

District of Columbia

Howard University, B

Florida

Bethune-Cookman College, B
Broward Community College, A
Daytona Beach Community College, A
Florida Community College at Jacksonville, A
Florida Metropolitan University-Pompano Beach
  Campus, AB
Florida Southern College, B
Hillsborough Community College, A
Indian River Community College, A
Johnson & Wales University, AB
Lynn University, B
Northwood University, Florida Campus, AB
Okaloosa-Walton College, A
Palm Beach Community College, A
Pensacola Junior College, A
St. Thomas University, B
Schiller International University, B
Webber International University, AB

Georgia

Albany Technical College, A
Athens Technical College, A

Atlanta Technical College, A
Central Georgia Technical College, A
Georgia Highlands College, A
Georgia Southern University, B
Georgia Southwestern State University, A
Gwinnett Technical College, A
Ogeechee Technical College, A
Savannah Technical College, A

Guam

Guam Community College, A

Hawaii

Brigham Young University-Hawaii, B
Hawaii Community College, A
Kapiolani Community College, A
Maui Community College, A

Idaho

College of Southern Idaho, A

Illinois

City Colleges of Chicago, Harold Washington
  College, A
College of DuPage, A
Elgin Community College, A
John Wood Community College, A
Kendall College, AB
Lexington College, AB
Lincoln Land Community College, A
MacCormac College, A
Triton College, A
William Rainey Harper College, A

Indiana

Indiana University-Purdue University Indianapolis, A
Purdue University, B
Purdue University Calumet, AB
Vincennes University, A

Iowa

Des Moines Area Community College, A
Iowa Lakes Community College, A
Iowa State University of Science and Technology, B
Iowa Western Community College, A
Kirkwood Community College, A

Kansas

Butler Community College, A
Cowley County Community College and Area
  Vocational-Technical School, A
Johnson County Community College, A
Kansas State University, B

Kentucky

Sullivan University, AB
Western Kentucky University, B

Louisiana

Grambling State University, B
Louisiana Technical College, A
Southern University at Shreveport, A

Maine

Southern Maine Community College, A
Thomas College, B
University of Maine at Machias, B
York County Community College, A

Maryland

Anne Arundel Community College, A
Garrett College, A
Montgomery College, A
Morgan State University, B
University of Maryland Eastern Shore, B

Massachusetts

Becker College, B
Boston University, B
Bunker Hill Community College, A
Cape Cod Community College, A
Holyoke Community College, A
Lasell College, B
Massasoit Community College, A

Middlesex Community College, A
Mount Ida College, AB
Newbury College, AB
Northern Essex Community College, A
Quinsigamond Community College, A

Michigan

Baker College of Muskegon, A
Baker College of Owosso, A
Baker College of Port Huron, A
Bay Mills Community College, A
Grand Valley State University, B
Henry Ford Community College, A
Lansing Community College, A
Michigan State University, B
Muskegon Community College, A
Northwood University, AB
Oakland Community College, A
Washtenaw Community College, A

Minnesota

Alexandria Technical College, A
Rasmussen College Eagan, A
Rasmussen College Mankato, A
University of Minnesota, Crookston, AB

Mississippi

Copiah-Lincoln Community College-Natchez
  Campus, A
East Mississippi Community College, A
Hinds Community College, A
Meridian Community College, A
Mississippi Gulf Coast Community College, A
Northeast Mississippi Community College, A
Northwest Mississippi Community College, A
University of Southern Mississippi, B

Missouri

Central Missouri State University, B
College of the Ozarks, B
East Central College, A
Ozarks Technical Community College, A
St. Louis Community College at Forest Park, A
University of Missouri-Columbia, B

Montana

Flathead Valley Community College, A

Nebraska

Central Community College-Hastings Campus, A

Nevada

Community College of Southern Nevada, A
Sierra Nevada College, B

New Hampshire

New Hampshire Technical Institute, A
University of New Hampshire, B

New Jersey

Bergen Community College, A
Burlington County College, A
County College of Morris, A
Essex County College, A
Fairleigh Dickinson University, College at
  Florham, B
Fairleigh Dickinson University, Metropolitan
  Campus, B
Mercer County Community College, A
Middlesex County College, A
Passaic County Community College, A
Raritan Valley Community College, A
Union County College, A

New Mexico

National American University (Albuquerque), AB
Santa Fe Community College, A

New York

Broome Community College, A
Bryant and Stratton College (Syracuse), A
Buffalo State College, State University of New
  York, B
Cornell University, B

Finger Lakes Community College, A
Genesee Community College, A
Jefferson Community College, A
Katharine Gibbs School (New York), A
Keuka College, B
Mohawk Valley Community College, A
Monroe Community College, A
Nassau Community College, A
New York Institute of Technology, B
New York University, B
Niagara University, B
Onondaga Community College, A
Pace University, B
Paul Smith's College of Arts and Sciences, AB
Rochester Institute of Technology, AB
St. John's University, B
Schenectady County Community College, A
State University of New York College of Agriculture
    and Technology at Cobleskill, A
State University of New York College of Agriculture
    and Technology at Morrisville, A
State University of New York College of Technology
    at Delhi, AB
State University of New York at Plattsburgh, B
Tompkins Cortland Community College, A
Trocaire College, A
Westchester Community College, A

North Carolina

Asheville-Buncombe Technical Community
    College, A
Barber-Scotia College, B
Cape Fear Community College, A
Central Piedmont Community College, A
East Carolina University, B
Fayetteville Technical Community College, A
Johnson & Wales University, AB
North Carolina Wesleyan College, B
Sandhills Community College, A
Wake Technical Community College, A
Wilkes Community College, A

North Dakota

Bismarck State College, A

Ohio

Ashland University, B
Central State University, B
Cincinnati State Technical and Community
    College, A
Columbus State Community College, A
Hocking College, A
Sinclair Community College, A
The University of Akron, A
The University of Findlay, B

Oklahoma

Carl Albert State College, A
Langston University, B
Northeastern Oklahoma Agricultural and Mechanical
    College, A
Oklahoma State University, B
Tulsa Community College, A
University of Central Oklahoma, B

Oregon

Central Oregon Community College, A
Chemeketa Community College, A
Lane Community College, A
Southern Oregon University, B

Pennsylvania

The Art Institute of Pittsburgh, AB
Bucks County Community College, A
Central Pennsylvania College, A
Cheyney University of Pennsylvania, B
Community College of Allegheny County, A
Community College of Philadelphia, A
Delaware County Community College, A
Harrisburg Area Community College, A
Indiana University of Pennsylvania, B
Keystone College, A
Lehigh Carbon Community College, A
Luzerne County Community College, A
Marywood University, B

Mercyhurst College, AB
Northampton County Area Community College, A
Penn Foster Career School, A
Pennsylvania Culinary Institute, A
The Restaurant School at Walnut Hill College, A
Westmoreland County Community College, A
Widener University, B

Puerto Rico

Instituto Comercial de Puerto Rico Junior College, A
Inter American University of Puerto Rico, Aguadilla
    Campus, B
Inter American University of Puerto Rico, Fajardo
    Campus, B
Inter American University of Puerto Rico, Ponce
    Campus, B
University of Puerto Rico at Carolina, AB

Rhode Island

Johnson & Wales University, AB

South Carolina

Horry-Georgetown Technical College, A
Trident Technical College, A

South Dakota

South Dakota State University, B

Tennessee

Chattanooga State Technical Community College, A
Pellissippi State Technical Community College, A
South College, A
The University of Tennessee, B

Texas

Austin Community College, A
Central Texas College, A
Del Mar College, A
El Centro College, A
Galveston College, A
Houston Community College System, A
Laredo Community College, A
Northwood University, Texas Campus, AB
St. Philip's College, A
South Texas College, A
Texas A&M University-Kingsville, B
Texas Southmost College, A
Texas Tech University, B
University of Houston, B
Wiley College, B

United States Virgin Islands

University of the Virgin Islands, A

Vermont

Champlain College, AB
New England Culinary Institute, B
New England Culinary Institute at Essex, AB

Virginia

Bryant and Stratton College, Virginia Beach, A
Hampton University, B
J. Sargeant Reynolds Community College, A
National College of Business & Technology (Salem)
    , A
Northern Virginia Community College, A
Stratford University, A
Virginia Polytechnic Institute and State University, B

Washington

Highline Community College, A
Lake Washington Technical College, A
Seattle Central Community College, A
Skagit Valley College, A
Spokane Community College, A
Yakima Valley Community College, A

West Virginia

Bluefield State College, A
Concord University, B
New River Community and Technical College, A

West Virginia State University, A

Wisconsin

Mid-State Technical College, A
Milwaukee Area Technical College, A
Nicolet Area Technical College, A

Alberta

University of Calgary, B

British Columbia

Thompson Rivers University, A
University of Victoria, B

Nova Scotia

Mount Saint Vincent University, B

Ontario

Ryerson University, B
University of Guelph, B

Quebec

Université du Québec àMontréal, B

HOUSING AND HUMAN ENVIRONMENTS

California

Modesto Junior College, A
Orange Coast College, A

Florida

Florida State University, B

Georgia

University of Georgia, B

Indiana

Vincennes University, A

Iowa

University of Northern Iowa, B

Kentucky

Eastern Kentucky University, B
Louisville Technical Institute, A
Western Kentucky University, B

Minnesota

Dakota County Technical College, A

Missouri

Missouri State University, B
University of Missouri-Columbia, B

Nebraska

University of Nebraska-Lincoln, B

Nevada

University of Nevada, Reno, B

New York

Cornell University, B
Syracuse University, B

Ohio

Ohio University, B
The University of Akron, B

Pennsylvania

Community College of Allegheny County, A

South Carolina

Bob Jones University, B

Texas

University of the Incarnate Word, B

Utah

Utah State University, B

HUMAN-COMPUTER INTERACTION

Georgia
Georgia Institute of Technology, M

Illinois
DePaul University, M

Indiana
Indiana University Bloomington, M

Iowa
Iowa State University of Science and
  Technology, MD

Maryland
University of Baltimore, M

Massachusetts
Tufts University, O

Michigan
University of Michigan, M

New York
Cornell University, D
State University of New York at Oswego, M

Pennsylvania
Carnegie Mellon University, MD

Nova Scotia
Dalhousie University, M

HUMAN DEVELOPMENT

Alabama
Auburn University, MD
The University of Alabama, M

Arizona
Arizona State University, MD
The University of Arizona, MD

Arkansas
University of Central Arkansas, M

California
Pacific Oaks College, M
University of California, Berkeley, MD
University of California, Davis, D

Colorado
Colorado State University, M

Connecticut
Saint Joseph College, O
University of Connecticut, MD

Delaware
University of Delaware, MD

District of Columbia
The Catholic University of America, D
The George Washington University, MD
Howard University, M

Hawaii
Argosy University/Hawaii, MD

Illinois
Argosy University/Chicago, D
Bradley University, M
National-Louis University, MDO
Northwestern University, D
Southern Illinois University Carbondale, M
University of Chicago, D
University of Illinois at Chicago, MD
University of Illinois at Springfield, M

University of Illinois at Urbana-Champaign, MD

Indiana
Purdue University, MD

Iowa
Iowa State University of Science and
  Technology, MD

Kansas
Kansas State University, D
University of Kansas, M

Kentucky
Lindsey Wilson College, M

Maine
University of Maine, M

Maryland
Hood College, M
University of Maryland, College Park, MD

Massachusetts
Boston University, MDO
Harvard University, MD
Wheelock College, M

Michigan
Central Michigan University, M
Wayne State University, M

Minnesota
Saint Mary's University of Minnesota, M
University of St. Thomas, MDO

Missouri
Saint Louis University, M
University of Missouri-Columbia, MD

Montana
Montana State University, M

Nevada
University of Nevada, Reno, M

New York
Cornell University, D
Dowling College, M
New York Institute of Technology, M
St. Lawrence University, MO
Sarah Lawrence College, M

North Carolina
Appalachian State University, M
Duke University, D
The University of North Carolina at Greensboro, MD

North Dakota
North Dakota State University, D

Ohio
Bowling Green State University, M
Kent State University, D
The Ohio State University, MD
University of Dayton, M

Oklahoma
University of Central Oklahoma, M

Oregon
Oregon State University, MD

Pennsylvania
Lehigh University, MD
Marywood University, D
The Pennsylvania State University University Park
  Campus, MD

University of Pennsylvania, MD

Puerto Rico
University of Puerto Rico, Medical Sciences
  Campus, MO

South Carolina
Clemson University, M

Tennessee
East Tennessee State University, M
Vanderbilt University, M

Texas
Our Lady of the Lake University of San Antonio, M
Texas A&M University, MD
Texas Tech University, MD
University of Houston, M
University of North Texas, MD
The University of Texas at Austin, D

Utah
Brigham Young University, MD
Utah State University, MD

Virginia
Virginia Polytechnic Institute and State University, M

Washington
University of Washington, MD
Washington State University, M

Wisconsin
University of Wisconsin-Madison, MD
University of Wisconsin-Stevens Point, M
University of Wisconsin-Stout, M

Alberta
University of Calgary, MD

British Columbia
University of Victoria, M

Ontario
Brock University, M
Laurentian University, M
University of Guelph, MD

HUMAN DEVELOPMENT AND FAMILY STUDIES

Alabama
Auburn University, B
Samford University, B
The University of Alabama, B

Arizona
Prescott College, B
The University of Arizona, B

Arkansas
Harding University, B
University of Arkansas, B

California
California State University, East Bay, B
California State University, Long Beach, B
California State University, San Bernardino, B
College of Alameda, A
Cuesta College, A
Hope International University, B
Imperial Valley College, A
Orange Coast College, A
Pacific Oaks College, B
Saddleback College, A
San Diego Christian College, B
Santiago Canyon College, A
University of California, Davis, B

University of California, Riverside, B

Colorado

Colorado State University, B

Connecticut

Mitchell College, AB
University of Connecticut, B

Delaware

University of Delaware, B

District of Columbia

Trinity (Washington) University, B

Florida

Eckerd College, B
Florida State University, B

Georgia

Albany Technical College, A
Georgia Southern University, B
University of Georgia, B

Hawaii

Hawaii Pacific University, B
University of Hawaii at Manoa, B

Illinois

Lincoln College, A
National-Louis University, B
Northern Illinois University, B
University of Chicago, B
University of Illinois at Urbana-Champaign, B

Indiana

Indiana State University, B
Indiana University Bloomington, B
Purdue University, B

Kansas

Kansas State University, B

Kentucky

Eastern Kentucky University, B
Kentucky State University, B
Murray State University, B

Louisiana

Southern University and Agricultural and Mechanical
College, B
University of Louisiana at Lafayette, B

Maine

Saint Joseph's College of Maine, B
University of Maine, B

Maryland

Sojourner-Douglass College, B

Massachusetts

Boston College, B
Harvard University, B
Hellenic College, B
Lesley University, B
Wheelock College, B

Michigan

Concordia University, B
Wayne State University, B

Minnesota

St. Olaf College, B

Mississippi

Mississippi University for Women, B

Missouri

Missouri State University, B
Park University, B

University of Missouri-Columbia, B

Montana

Montana State University, B

Nevada

University of Nevada, Reno, B

New Jersey

Gloucester County College, A

New Mexico

New Mexico State University, B
University of New Mexico, B

New York

Cornell University, B
Sarah Lawrence College, B
State University of New York at Binghamton, B
State University of New York Empire State
College, AB
State University of New York at Oswego, B
Syracuse University, B

North Carolina

East Carolina University, B
The University of North Carolina at Charlotte, B
The University of North Carolina at Greensboro, B

North Dakota

North Dakota State University, B

Ohio

Antioch College, B
Antioch University McGregor, B
Ashland University, B
Kent State University, B
Miami University, B
Northwest State Community College, A
The Ohio State University, B
Ohio University, B
The University of Toledo, A
Youngstown State University, B

Oklahoma

Oklahoma State University, B
Southern Nazarene University, B

Oregon

Oregon State University, B
Warner Pacific College, B

Pennsylvania

Community College of Allegheny County, A
Geneva College, B
Indiana University of Pennsylvania, B
Mercyhurst College, B
The Pennsylvania State University Abington
College, B
The Pennsylvania State University Altoona
College, AB
The Pennsylvania State University Beaver Campus
of the Commonwealth College, B
The Pennsylvania State University Berks Campus of
the Berks-Lehigh Valley College, B
The Pennsylvania State University Delaware County
Campus of the Commonwealth College, AB
The Pennsylvania State University DuBois Campus
of the Commonwealth College, AB
The Pennsylvania State University at Erie, The
Behrend College, B
The Pennsylvania State University Fayette Campus
of the Commonwealth College, AB
The Pennsylvania State University Hazleton
Campus of the Commonwealth College, B
The Pennsylvania State University, Lehigh Valley
Campus of the Berks-Lehigh Valley College, B
The Pennsylvania State University McKeesport
Campus of the Commonwealth College, B
The Pennsylvania State University Mont Alto
Campus of the Commonwealth College, AB
The Pennsylvania State University New Kensington
Campus of the Commonwealth College, AB

The Pennsylvania State University Schuylkill
Campus of the Capital College, AB
The Pennsylvania State University Shenango
Campus of the Commonwealth College, AB
The Pennsylvania State University University Park
Campus, AB
The Pennsylvania State University Wilkes-Barre
Campus of the Commonwealth College, B
The Pennsylvania State University Worthington
Scranton Campus of the Commonwealth
College, AB
The Pennsylvania State University York Campus of
the Commonwealth College, AB

Rhode Island

University of Rhode Island, B

South Carolina

Columbia College, B

South Dakota

South Dakota State University, B

Tennessee

Lee University, B
University of Memphis, B
The University of Tennessee, B
Vanderbilt University, B

Texas

Abilene Christian University, B
Amberton University, B
Baylor University, B
Stephen F. Austin State University, B
Texas State University-San Marcos, B
Texas Tech University, B
Texas Woman's University, B
University of Houston, B
University of North Texas, B
The University of Texas at Austin, B

Utah

Brigham Young University, B
Salt Lake Community College, A
University of Utah, B
Utah State University, AB

Virginia

Liberty University, B
Virginia Polytechnic Institute and State University, B

Washington

Shoreline Community College, A
Washington State University, B

Wisconsin

University of Wisconsin-Stout, B

Ontario

University of Waterloo, B

HUMAN GENETICS

California

University of California, Los Angeles, MD

District of Columbia

Howard University, MD

Illinois

University of Chicago, D

Louisiana

Louisiana State University Health Sciences
Center, MDO

Tulane University, MDO

Maryland

The Johns Hopkins University, DO

Michigan

University of Michigan, MD

New York

Sarah Lawrence College, M

North Carolina

Wake Forest University, D

Ohio

Case Western Reserve University, DO

Pennsylvania

Drexel University, MDO
University of Pittsburgh, MD

Texas

The University of Texas Health Science Center at
   Houston, MDO

Utah

University of Utah, MD

Virginia

Virginia Commonwealth University, DO

West Virginia

West Virginia University, MD

Manitoba

University of Manitoba, MD

Newfoundland and Labrador

Memorial University of Newfoundland, MDO

Quebec

McGill University, MD

HUMAN/MEDICAL GENETICS

California

University of California, Los Angeles, B

Michigan

Northern Michigan University, B

New York

Sarah Lawrence College, B

HUMAN NUTRITION

Alabama

Samford University, B

Georgia

Life University, B

Massachusetts

Framingham State College, B
University of Massachusetts Amherst, B

Missouri

University of Missouri-Columbia, B

New York

Cornell University, B
Rochester Institute of Technology, B

Ohio

Case Western Reserve University, B
Kent State University, B

Pennsylvania

The Pennsylvania State University Abington
   College, B

The Pennsylvania State University Altoona
   College, B
The Pennsylvania State University Beaver Campus
   of the Commonwealth College, B
The Pennsylvania State University Berks Campus of
   the Berks-Lehigh Valley College, B
The Pennsylvania State University Delaware County
   Campus of the Commonwealth College, B
The Pennsylvania State University DuBois Campus
   of the Commonwealth College, B
The Pennsylvania State University at Erie, The
   Behrend College, B
The Pennsylvania State University Fayette Campus
   of the Commonwealth College, B
The Pennsylvania State University Hazleton
   Campus of the Commonwealth College, B
The Pennsylvania State University, Lehigh Valley
   Campus of the Berks-Lehigh Valley College, B
The Pennsylvania State University McKeesport
   Campus of the Commonwealth College, B
The Pennsylvania State University Mont Alto
   Campus of the Commonwealth College, B
The Pennsylvania State University New Kensington
   Campus of the Commonwealth College, B
The Pennsylvania State University Schuylkill
   Campus of the Capital College, B
The Pennsylvania State University Shenango
   Campus of the Commonwealth College, B
The Pennsylvania State University University Park
   Campus, B
The Pennsylvania State University Wilkes-Barre
   Campus of the Commonwealth College, B
The Pennsylvania State University Worthington
   Scranton Campus of the Commonwealth
   College, B
The Pennsylvania State University York Campus of
   the Commonwealth College, B

Texas

Baylor University, B
Tarleton State University, B
University of Houston, B

Washington

Washington State University, B

British Columbia

The University of British Columbia, B

Ontario

Ryerson University, B
University of Guelph, B

HUMAN RESOURCES DEVELOPMENT

California

Antioch University Los Angeles, M
Azusa Pacific University, M
California State University, Sacramento, M
John F. Kennedy University, MO

Connecticut

University of Bridgeport, M
University of Connecticut, M

District of Columbia

The George Washington University, MDO

Florida

Argosy University/Tampa, M
Barry University, MD
Florida International University, M
Florida State University, MDO
Palm Beach Atlantic University, M
Rollins College, M

Georgia

Georgia Southwestern State University, A
Georgia State University, B

University of Georgia, M

Illinois

Illinois Institute of Technology, M
National-Louis University, M
Northeastern Illinois University, M
Trinity International University, B
University of Illinois at Urbana-Champaign, MDO

Indiana

Indiana State University, M
Indiana Tech, M
Indiana University Bloomington, M

Iowa

Iowa State University of Science and Technology, M

Kansas

Friends University, M
Ottawa University, M
Pittsburg State University, MO

Kentucky

University of Louisville, M

Maryland

Bowie State University, M
The Johns Hopkins University, M
McDaniel College, M
Towson University, MO

Massachusetts

American International College, MO
Suffolk University, MO

Michigan

Oakland University, M
Siena Heights University, M
Western Michigan University, M

Minnesota

University of Minnesota, Twin Cities Campus, MDO

Mississippi

Mississippi State University, MDO
University of Southern Mississippi, M

Missouri

Webster University, M
William Woods University, M

New York

The College of New Rochelle, MO
Manhattanville College, M
New York University, M
Rochester Institute of Technology, MO
St. John Fisher College, M
Syracuse University, D

North Carolina

North Carolina Agricultural and Technical State
   University, M
Western Carolina University, M

Ohio

Xavier University, M

Pennsylvania

Carlow University, M
Indiana University of Pennsylvania, M
The Pennsylvania State University University Park
   Campus, M
University of Pittsburgh, M
The University of Scranton, M
Villanova University, M

Puerto Rico

Inter American University of Puerto Rico,
   Metropolitan Campus, M
Inter American University of Puerto Rico, San
   Germán Campus, M

Universidad del Turabo, M

Rhode Island

Salve Regina University, O

South Carolina

Clemson University, BM
Limestone College, B

Tennessee

The University of Tennessee, M
Vanderbilt University, M

Texas

Abilene Christian University, M
Amberton University, M
Concordia University at Austin, B
Midwestern State University, M
Texas A&M University, MD
University of Houston-Clear Lake, B
The University of Texas at Austin, M
The University of Texas at Tyler, BM

Utah

Brigham Young University, B

Virginia

Virginia Polytechnic Institute and State
University, MD

Wisconsin

Marquette University, M
University of Wisconsin-Milwaukee, MO
University of Wisconsin-Stout, M

Saskatchewan

University of Regina, M

HUMAN RESOURCES MANAGEMENT AND SERVICES

Alabama

Andrew Jackson University, M
Auburn University, D
Columbia Southern University, BM
Troy University, M
The University of Alabama in Huntsville, O

Arizona

University of Phoenix Online Campus, M
University of Phoenix-Phoenix Campus, M

California

Argosy University/Orange County, M
California State University, East Bay, M
California State University, Sacramento, M
Chapman University, MO
Golden Gate University, MO
San Diego State University, M
Touro University International, M
University of Phoenix-Bay Area Campus, M
University of Phoenix-Sacramento Valley
Campus, M
University of Phoenix-Southern California
Campus, M

Colorado

Colorado Technical University, M
Regis University, MO
University of Denver, M
University of Phoenix-Southern Colorado
Campus, M

Connecticut

Albertus Magnus College, B
Fairfield University, MO
University of Connecticut, M

University of New Haven, M

Delaware

Goldey-Beacom College, M
Wilmington College, M

District of Columbia

American University, M
The Catholic University of America, M
The George Washington University, M
University of the District of Columbia, B

Florida

Argosy University/Sarasota, M
Florida Institute of Technology, M
Florida Metropolitan University-South Orlando
Campus, M
Florida Metropolitan University-Tampa Campus, M
Nova Southeastern University, M
Rollins College, M
St. Thomas University, MO
University of Phoenix-South Florida Campus, M

Georgia

Albany State University, M
Georgia State University, MD
University of Phoenix-Columbus Georgia
Campus, M
Valdosta State University, M

Hawaii

Hawaii Pacific University, M
University of Hawaii at Manoa, M

Idaho

University of Phoenix-Idaho Campus, M

Illinois

American InterContinental University Online, M
Argosy University/Schaumburg, M
DePaul University, M
DeVry University (Oakbrook Terrace), M
Loyola University Chicago, MO
National-Louis University, M
Roosevelt University, M
University of Illinois at Urbana-Champaign, MD
University of Phoenix-Chicago Campus, M

Indiana

Indiana Tech, M
Indiana University Bloomington, M
Purdue University, MD

Iowa

Briar Cliff University, M
Iowa Lakes Community College, A
Upper Iowa University, M

Kansas

Barton County Community College, A
Ottawa University, M

Louisiana

University of Phoenix-Louisiana Campus, M

Maine

Thomas College, M

Massachusetts

Becker College, AB
Boston University, MO
Emmanuel College, MO
Fitchburg State College, M
Framingham State College, M
Lesley University, M
Suffolk University, M

Michigan

Central Michigan University, MO
Davenport University (Dearborn), M
Eastern Michigan University, M
Marygrove College, M
Michigan State University, MD
Oakland University, O

University of Phoenix-Metro Detroit Campus, M
University of Phoenix-West Michigan Campus, M

Minnesota

Capella University, B
Concordia University, St. Paul, M
Lake Superior College, A
Metropolitan State University, M
Saint Mary's University of Minnesota, M
University of Minnesota, Twin Cities Campus, MD
University of St. Thomas, M

Missouri

Lindenwood University, M
Park University, B
University of Missouri-St. Louis, MO
Webster University, M

Nevada

University of Phoenix-Nevada Campus, M

New Hampshire

Rivier College, M

New Jersey

Bloomfield College, B
Fairleigh Dickinson University, College at
Florham, MO
Fairleigh Dickinson University, Metropolitan
Campus, MO
Rutgers, The State University of New Jersey, New
Brunswick/Piscataway, MD
Rutgers, The State University of New Jersey,
Newark, M
Thomas Edison State College, M

New Mexico

University of New Mexico, M
University of Phoenix-New Mexico Campus, M

New York

Adelphi University, MO
Bernard M. Baruch College of the City University of
New York, M
Bryant and Stratton College (Albany), A
Bryant and Stratton College, Amherst Campus, A
Bryant and Stratton College, Buffalo Campus, A
Bryant and Stratton College, Lackawanna
Campus, A
Bryant and Stratton College (Rochester-Greece
Campus), A
Bryant and Stratton College (Rochester-Henrietta
Campus), A
Bryant and Stratton College (Syracuse), A
Buffalo State College, State University of New
York, O
Clarkson University, M
Cornell University, MD
Fordham University, M
Herkimer County Community College, A
Hofstra University, MO
Iona College, MO
Long Island University, Brooklyn Campus, M
Manhattanville College, M
Mercy College, M
New York Institute of Technology, MO
New York University, M
Niagara University, B
State University of New York at Buffalo, O
Stony Brook University, State University of New
York, O
University at Albany, State University of New
York, M

North Carolina

North Carolina Agricultural and Technical State
University, M

North Dakota

Aakers Business College, A

Ohio

Baldwin-Wallace College, M
Bryant and Stratton College (Cleveland), A

Bryant and Stratton College (Parma), A
Case Western Reserve University, MD
Cleveland State University, M
Miami University Hamilton, B
The Ohio State University, MD
The University of Akron, M
The University of Findlay, M

Oklahoma

East Central University, M
Oral Roberts University, M
University of Oklahoma, B
University of Phoenix-Oklahoma City Campus, M
University of Phoenix-Tulsa Campus, M

Pennsylvania

Gannon University, O
Holy Family University, M
La Roche College, M
Saint Francis University, M
Saint Joseph's University, M
Temple University, MD
University of Pittsburgh, O
The University of Scranton, M
Widener University, BMO
Wilkes University, M

Puerto Rico

Inter American University of Puerto Rico,
    Metropolitan Campus, M
Inter American University of Puerto Rico, San
    Germán Campus, MD
Pontifical Catholic University of Puerto Rico, M
Universidad Metropolitana, M
Universidad del Turabo, M
University of Phoenix-Puerto Rico Campus, M
University of Puerto Rico, Mayagüez Campus, M
University of the Sacred Heart, M

Rhode Island

Salve Regina University, O

South Carolina

University of South Carolina, MO

South Dakota

Colorado Technical University Sioux Falls
    Campus, M

Tennessee

Cumberland University, M
Southern Adventist University, M

Texas

Amberton University, M
Dallas Baptist University, M
Houston Baptist University, M
St. Edward's University, MO
Texas A&M University, M
University of Dallas, M
University of Houston-Clear Lake, M
University of Phoenix-Houston Campus, M
The University of Texas at Arlington, M
Wayland Baptist University, M

Utah

Utah State University, M

Virginia

Bryant and Stratton College, Richmond, A
George Mason University, M
Marymount University, MO

Virginia Commonwealth University, M

Washington

City University, M
University of Phoenix-Washington Campus, M

West Virginia

Marshall University, M
Mountain State University, B

Wisconsin

Bryant and Stratton College, A
Bryant and Stratton College, Wauwatosa Campus, A
Concordia University Wisconsin, M
Marquette University, M
University of Wisconsin-Madison, MD
University of Wisconsin-Whitewater, M

Alberta

Concordia University College of Alberta, A
University of Lethbridge, M

British Columbia

Royal Roads University, M
Thompson Rivers University, B
The University of British Columbia, B
University of Phoenix-Vancouver Campus, M
University of Victoria, M

Ontario

McMaster University, MD
York University, M

Quebec

HEC Montreal, M
Université du Québec en Outaouais, B

Saskatchewan

University of Regina, M

HUMAN RESOURCES MANAGEMENT/PERSONNEL ADMINISTRATION

Alabama

Athens State University, B
Auburn University, B
Auburn University Montgomery, B
Birmingham-Southern College, B
Community College of the Air Force, A
Faulkner University, B
Samford University, B
Southern Christian University, B
Troy University, B

Alaska

University of Alaska Fairbanks, B

Arizona

Grand Canyon University, B
The University of Arizona, B

Arkansas

Harding University, B

California

California Polytechnic State University, San Luis
    Obispo, B
California State Polytechnic University, Pomona, B
California State University, Chico, B
California State University, Dominguez Hills, B
California State University, East Bay, B
California State University, Fresno, B
California State University, Long Beach, B
California State University, Sacramento, B
Dominican University of California, B
Golden Gate University, B
Holy Names University, B
National University, B
San Jose State University, B

Simpson University, B

Colorado

Colorado Technical University, B
Mesa State College, B
Western State College of Colorado, B

Connecticut

Quinnipiac University, B

Delaware

Delaware State University, B
Wilmington College, B

District of Columbia

The Catholic University of America, B
The George Washington University, B

Florida

Eckerd College, B
Florida Atlantic University, B
Florida International University, B
Florida Southern College, B
Florida State University, B
Okaloosa-Walton College, A
Palm Beach Atlantic University, B
Saint Leo University, B
University of Miami, B
Valencia Community College, A
Warner Southern College, B

Georgia

Georgia Southwestern State University, B

Hawaii

Hawaii Pacific University, B
University of Hawaii at Manoa, B

Idaho

Boise State University, B
Idaho State University, B
University of Idaho, B

Illinois

American InterContinental University Online, B
DePaul University, B
Governors State University, B
Judson College, B
Lewis University, B
Loyola University Chicago, B
Millikin University, B
Moraine Valley Community College, A
North Central College, B
Northeastern Illinois University, B
Olivet Nazarene University, B
Prairie State College, A
Roosevelt University, B
Trinity Christian College, B
Trinity International University, B
University of Illinois at Urbana-Champaign, B
University of St. Francis, B
Western Illinois University, B
William Rainey Harper College, A

Indiana

Ball State University, B
Indiana Business College (Anderson), A
Indiana Business College (Columbus), A
Indiana Business College (Indianapolis), A
Indiana Business College (Terre Haute), A
Indiana State University, B
Indiana Tech, B
Martin University, B
Oakland City University, B
Purdue University Calumet, B
Saint Mary-of-the-Woods College, B
Taylor University, B
University of Saint Francis, AB

Iowa

Briar Cliff University, B
Buena Vista University, B
Loras College, B

The University of Iowa, B

Kansas

Central Christian College of Kansas, A
Friends University, B
MidAmerica Nazarene University, B
Southwestern College, B
Wichita State University, B

Kentucky

Bellarmine University, B
Brescia University, B
Midway College, B

Louisiana

Louisiana Tech University, B

Maine

Thomas College, B

Maryland

Sojourner-Douglass College, B
University of Baltimore, B
University of Maryland, College Park, B
University of Maryland University College, B

Massachusetts

American International College, B
Boston College, B
Marian Court College, A
Newbury College, B
Nichols College, B
Northeastern University, B

Michigan

Baker College of Owosso, AB
Central Michigan University, B
Cleary University, B
Grand Valley State University, B
Lansing Community College, A
Madonna University, B
Michigan State University, B
Oakland University, B
Spring Arbor University, B
University of Detroit Mercy, B
University of Michigan-Dearborn, B
University of Michigan-Flint, B
Western Michigan University, B

Minnesota

Metropolitan State University, B
Minnesota State Community and Technical
   College-Fergus Falls, A
Northwest Technical College, A
St. Cloud State University, B
Saint Mary's University of Minnesota, B
Saint Paul College-A Community & Technical
   College, A
University of Minnesota, Duluth, B
University of St. Thomas, B
Winona State University, B

Mississippi

Virginia College at Jackson, A

Missouri

Central Missouri State University, B
Lindenwood University, B
Saint Louis University, B
Washington University in St. Louis, B
Webster University, B

Montana

Montana State University-Billings, A
Montana Tech of The University of Montana, A
The University of Montana-Western, A

Nebraska

Grace University, B
Hastings College, B
University of Nebraska at Omaha, B

York College, B

Nevada

University of Nevada, Las Vegas, B
University of Nevada, Reno, B

New Hampshire

Granite State College, B
New Hampshire Technical Institute, A

New Jersey

Bloomfield College, B
College of Saint Elizabeth, B
Cumberland County College, A
Rider University, B
Salem Community College, A

New Mexico

Eastern New Mexico University, B
Mesalands Community College, A

New York

Bernard M. Baruch College of the City University of
   New York, B
Clarkson University, B
Dominican College, B
Excelsior College, B
Fordham University, B
Herkimer County Community College, A
Medaille College, B
Nazareth College of Rochester, B
New York Institute of Technology, B
Niagara University, B
Pace University, B
Roberts Wesleyan College, B
St. John Fisher College, B
St. Joseph's College, New York, B
St. Joseph's College, Suffolk Campus, B
State University of New York at Oswego, B

North Carolina

Barton College, B
Beaufort County Community College, A
Fayetteville Technical Community College, A
North Carolina State University, B
Peace College, B
Rockingham Community College, A
The University of North Carolina at Chapel Hill, B
Wake Technical Community College, A

North Dakota

Valley City State University, B

Ohio

Antioch University McGregor, B
Baldwin-Wallace College, B
Bowling Green State University, B
Capital University, B
Columbus State Community College, A
Edison State Community College, A
Franklin University, B
Marietta College, B
Miami University, B
Notre Dame College, B
The Ohio State University, B
The University of Akron, B
The University of Findlay, AB
The University of Toledo, B
Urbana University, AB
Ursuline College, B
Wright State University, B
Xavier University, B
Zane State College, A

Oklahoma

East Central University, B
Northeastern State University, B
Oklahoma Baptist University, B
Tulsa Community College, A

University of Central Oklahoma, B

Oregon

Portland State University, B
Umpqua Community College, A

Pennsylvania

Arcadia University, B
Cabrini College, B
Carlow University, B
Chestnut Hill College, AB
Community College of Allegheny County, A
DeSales University, B
Drexel University, B
Immaculata University, B
Indiana University of Pennsylvania, B
Juniata College, B
Keystone College, A
King's College, AB
Kutztown University of Pennsylvania, B
La Salle University, B
Lehigh Carbon Community College, A
Mansfield University of Pennsylvania, B
Mercyhurst College, B
Messiah College, B
Point Park University, B
Reading Area Community College, A
Robert Morris University, B
Saint Francis University, B
Seton Hill University, B
Susquehanna University, B
University of Pennsylvania, B
The University of Scranton, B

Puerto Rico

Bayamon Central University, B
Caribbean University, B
Inter American University of Puerto Rico, Bayamón
   Campus, B
Inter American University of Puerto Rico, Guayama
   Campus, B
Inter American University of Puerto Rico, Ponce
   Campus, B
Inter American University of Puerto Rico, San
   Germán Campus, B
Pontifical Catholic University of Puerto Rico, B
Universidad Metropolitana, B
University of Puerto Rico at Humacao, B
University of Puerto Rico, Mayagüez Campus, B
University of Puerto Rico, Río Piedras, B

South Carolina

Anderson University, B
Bob Jones University, B
Southern Wesleyan University, B

South Dakota

Black Hills State University, B
Colorado Technical University Sioux Falls
   Campus, B

Tennessee

Freed-Hardeman University, B
Tennessee Wesleyan College, B
The University of Tennessee at Martin, B
Vanderbilt University, B

Texas

Amberton University, B
Baylor University, B
Houston Community College System, A
Our Lady of the Lake University of San Antonio, B
St. Mary's University of San Antonio, B
Sam Houston State University, B
Tarleton State University, B
Texas A&M University-Commerce, B
Texas A&M University-Texarkana, B
Tyler Junior College, A
University of the Incarnate Word, B
The University of Texas at San Antonio, B

Utah

Brigham Young University, B
Utah State University, B
Weber State University, B

Westminster College, B

Virginia

University of Richmond, A

Washington

Clark College, A
Eastern Washington University, B
Edmonds Community College, A
Washington State University, B
Western Washington University, B

West Virginia

Ohio Valley University, B

Wisconsin

Marquette University, B
Silver Lake College, B
University of Wisconsin-Milwaukee, B
University of Wisconsin-Whitewater, B
Western Technical College, A

Alberta

Athabasca University, B
University of Alberta, B
University of Lethbridge, B

British Columbia

British Columbia Institute of Technology, A
Thompson Rivers University, B

New Brunswick

University of New Brunswick Fredericton, B
University of New Brunswick Saint John, B

Nova Scotia

Saint Mary's University, B

Ontario

Brock University, B
Carleton University, B
Lakehead University, B
Redeemer University College, B
University of Guelph, B
University of Ottawa, B
University of Waterloo, B
University of Windsor, B
York University, B

Quebec

Bishop's University, B
Concordia University, B
HEC Montreal, B
McGill University, B
Université de Montréal, B
Université du Québec àTrois-Rivières, B

Saskatchewan

University of Saskatchewan, B

HUMAN SERVICES

Alaska

Alaska Pacific University, B
Sheldon Jackson College, AB
University of Alaska Anchorage, A
University of Alaska Anchorage, Matanuska-Susitna
   College, A

Arizona

Arizona Western College, A
Cochise College (Douglas), A
Glendale Community College, A

Arkansas

Central Baptist College, B
University of Arkansas Community College at
   Hope, A

California

Allan Hancock College, A
American River College, A

Bakersfield College, A
California State University, Dominguez Hills, B
California State University, Monterey Bay, B
California State University, Sacramento, M
California State University, San Bernardino, B
Chabot College, A
Compton Community College, A
Cosumnes River College (Sacramento), A
Crafton Hills College, A
Cuesta College, A
Cypress College, A
Folsom Lake College, A
Fresno City College, A
Hartnell College, A
Holy Names University, B
Long Beach City College, A
Los Angeles City College, A
Mendocino College, A
Merced College, A
Modesto Junior College, A
Notre Dame de Namur University, B
Pacific Oaks College, B
Pasadena City College, A
Porterville College, A
Sacramento City College, A
Saddleback College, A
San Bernardino Valley College, A
San Jose City College, A
Santa Rosa Junior College, A
University of Phoenix-Sacramento Valley Campus, B
Yuba College, A

Colorado

Colorado Northwestern Community College, A
Community College of Denver, A
Mesa State College, B
Metropolitan State College of Denver, B
University of Colorado at Colorado Springs, M
University of Northern Colorado, B

Connecticut

Albertus Magnus College, B
Asnuntuck Community College, A
Gateway Community College, A
Goodwin College, A
Housatonic Community College, A
Manchester Community College, A
Middlesex Community College, A
Mitchell College, A
Naugatuck Valley Community College, A
Northwestern Connecticut Community College, A
Norwalk Community College, A
Post University, B
Quinebaug Valley Community College, A
Quinnipiac University, B
Three Rivers Community College, A
Tunxis Community College, A
University of Bridgeport, BM

Delaware

Delaware Technical & Community College, Jack F.
   Owens Campus, A
Delaware Technical & Community College,
   Stanton/Wilmington Campus, A
Delaware Technical & Community College, Terry
   Campus, A

District of Columbia

The George Washington University, B

Florida

Beacon College, AB
Central Florida Community College, A
Daytona Beach Community College, A
Edison College, A
Florida Community College at Jacksonville, A
Florida Gulf Coast University, B
Gulf Coast Community College, A
Hillsborough Community College, A
Indian River Community College, A
Miami Dade College, A
Pasco-Hernando Community College, A
Saint Leo University, B

St. Petersburg College, A

Georgia

Atlanta Metropolitan College, A
Clayton State University, B
Georgia Highlands College, A
Georgia State University, M
LaGrange College, B
Mercer University, B

Hawaii

Hawaii Pacific University, B
Honolulu Community College, A
Leeward Community College, A
Maui Community College, A

Idaho

College of Southern Idaho, A
North Idaho College, A

Illinois

College of DuPage, A
Concordia University, M
Danville Area Community College, A
DePaul University, M
Elgin Community College, A
Highland Community College, A
Judson College, B
Kendall College, AB
Lake Land College, A
National-Louis University, BMO
Parkland College, A
Rock Valley College, A
Roosevelt University, B
Sauk Valley Community College, A
Shawnee Community College, A
South Suburban College, A
Southeastern Illinois College, A
University of Illinois at Springfield, M

Indiana

Bethel College, B
Calumet College of Saint Joseph, B
Indiana Tech, B
Indiana University East, A
Indiana University Northwest, M
Indiana University-Purdue University Fort
   Wayne, AB
Ivy Tech Community College-East Central, A
Ivy Tech Community College-Kokomo, A
Ivy Tech Community College-North Central, A
Ivy Tech Community College-Northeast, A
Saint Mary-of-the-Woods College, B
University of Saint Francis, A

Iowa

Ashford University, B
Des Moines Area Community College, A
Ellsworth Community College, A
Graceland University, B
Grand View College, B
Iowa Western Community College, A
Kirkwood Community College, A
Upper Iowa University, BM
William Penn University, B

Kansas

Friends University, B
Kansas State University, M
Ottawa University, B
Pratt Community College, A
Washburn University, AB
Wichita State University, M

Kentucky

Big Sandy Community and Technical College, A
Henderson Community College, A
Hopkinsville Community College, A
Kentucky Wesleyan College, B
Lindsey Wilson College, BM
Murray State University, M
Northern Kentucky University, AB

Owensboro Community and Technical College, A

Louisiana

Louisiana State University in Shreveport, M
Southern University at Shreveport, A

Maine

The University of Maine at Augusta, A
University of Maine at Fort Kent, A
University of Maine at Machias, B

Maryland

Anne Arundel Community College, A
Baltimore City Community College, A
Carroll Community College, A
Chesapeake College, A
College of Notre Dame of Maryland, B
College of Southern Maryland, A
Coppin State University, M
Frederick Community College, A
McDaniel College, M
Sojourner-Douglass College, B
University of Baltimore, BM
University of Maryland, Baltimore County, MD

Massachusetts

American International College, B
Anna Maria College, M
Berkshire Community College, A
Brandeis University, M
Bristol Community College, A
Bunker Hill Community College, A
Cambridge College, B
Endicott College, B
Fitchburg State College, B
Framingham State College, B
Greenfield Community College, A
Holyoke Community College, A
Lasell College, B
Lesley University, BM
Massachusetts Bay Community College, A
Massasoit Community College, A
Merrimack College, AB
Middlesex Community College, A
Mount Ida College, B
Mount Wachusett Community College, A
Northeastern University, B
Northern Essex Community College, A
Quincy College, A
Quinsigamond Community College, A
Simmons College, B
Springfield College, M
Suffolk University, B
University of Massachusetts Boston, BM
Urban College of Boston, A

Michigan

Adrian College, AB
Albion College, B
Andrews University, M
Baker College of Clinton Township, A
Baker College of Flint, A
Baker College of Muskegon, A
Bay Mills Community College, A
Bay de Noc Community College, A
Ferris State University, M
Finlandia University, B
Grace Bible College, B
Kellogg Community College, A
Lake Superior State University, B
Lansing Community College, A
Siena Heights University, B
University of Detroit Mercy, B
Wayne State University, O

Minnesota

Alexandria Technical College, A
Anoka Technical College, A
Capella University, MD
Concordia University, St. Paul, B
Fond du Lac Tribal and Community College, A
Inver Hills Community College, A
Itasca Community College, A
Mesabi Range Community and Technical College, A
Metropolitan State University, B

Minneapolis Community and Technical College, A
Minnesota State University Moorhead, MO
Pine Technical College, A
Ridgewater College, A
Riverland Community College, A
Rochester Community and Technical College, A
Saint Mary's University of Minnesota, B
University of Minnesota, Morris, B
Walden University, D

Mississippi

Itawamba Community College, A
Mississippi Gulf Coast Community College, A

Missouri

Central Missouri State University, O
Drury University, M
Fontbonne University, B
Hannibal-LaGrange College, B
Lindenwood University, BM
Longview Community College, A
Missouri Baptist University, B
Missouri Valley College, B
North Central Missouri College, A
Park University, B
Saint Charles Community College, A
St. Louis Community College at Florissant Valley, A
St. Louis Community College at Forest Park, A
St. Louis Community College at Meramec, A
Southwest Baptist University, B

Montana

Blackfeet Community College, A
Flathead Valley Community College, A
Fort Peck Community College, A
Miles Community College, A
Salish Kootenai College, AB
Stone Child College, A
University of Great Falls, ABM

Nebraska

Bellevue University, M
Doane College, B
Hastings College, B
Metropolitan Community College, A
Midland Lutheran College, B
Nebraska Indian Community College, A
Southeast Community College, Lincoln Campus, A

Nevada

University of Nevada, Las Vegas, B
University of Phoenix-Nevada Campus, M

New Hampshire

Hesser College, A
New Hampshire Community Technical College,
    Berlin/Laconia, A
New Hampshire Community Technical College,
    Manchester/Stratham, A
New Hampshire Community Technical College,
    Nashua/Claremont, A
New Hampshire Technical Institute, A

New Jersey

Brookdale Community College, A
Burlington County College, A
Camden County College, A
Essex County College, A
Hudson County Community College, A
Montclair State University, M
Passaic County Community College, A
Raritan Valley Community College, A
Sussex County Community College, A

New Mexico

Eastern New Mexico University-Roswell, A
Northern New Mexico Community College, A
San Juan College, A
University of New Mexico-Valencia Campus, A

New York

Boricua College, BM
Borough of Manhattan Community College of the
    City University of New York, A

Bronx Community College of the City University of
    New York, A
Cazenovia College, AB
Columbia-Greene Community College, A
Cornell University, B
Corning Community College, A
Elmira College, B
Finger Lakes Community College, A
Fiorello H. LaGuardia Community College of the
    City University of New York, A
Fulton-Montgomery Community College, A
Genesee Community College, A
Herkimer County Community College, A
Hilbert College, AB
Hudson Valley Community College, A
Jamestown Community College, A
Jefferson Community College, A
Kingsborough Community College of the City
    University of New York, A
Medaille College, B
Mercy College, A
Metropolitan College of New York, AB
Mohawk Valley Community College, A
Monroe Community College, A
Mount Saint Mary College, B
New York City College of Technology of the City
    University of New York, AB
New York University, A
Niagara County Community College, A
Onondaga Community College, A
Roberts Wesleyan College, M
Rockland Community College, A
St. John Fisher College, M
St. John's University, B
St. Joseph's College, New York, B
Schenectady County Community College, A
State University of New York College at Cortland, B
State University of New York College of Technology
    at Alfred, A
State University of New York Empire State
    College, AB
State University of New York at Oswego, M
Suffolk County Community College, A
Sullivan County Community College, A
Tompkins Cortland Community College, A
Touro College, B
Ulster County Community College, A
Westchester Community College, A

North Carolina

Central Piedmont Community College, A
Edgecombe Community College, A
Elon College, B
Guilford Technical Community College, A
High Point University, B
Lenoir-Rhyne College, B
Livingstone College, B
Mitchell Community College, A
Montreat College, B
Mount Olive College, B
Pfeiffer University, B
Richmond Community College, A
Sandhills Community College, A
Stanly Community College, A
Vance-Granville Community College, A
Wingate University, B

North Dakota

Fort Berthold Community College, A
Sitting Bull College, A
Turtle Mountain Community College, A
University of North Dakota, B

Ohio

Antioch University McGregor, B
Bowling Green State University-Firelands College, A
Central Ohio Technical College, A
Chatfield College, A
Clark State Community College, A
Edison State Community College, A
James A. Rhodes State College, A
Kent State University, Ashtabula Campus, A
Kent State University, Salem Campus, A
Lakeland Community College, A
Lorain County Community College, A
Marion Technical College, A

Mount Vernon Nazarene University, A
North Central State College, A
Ohio University, A
Ohio University-Chillicothe, A
Ohio University-Southern Campus, A
Sinclair Community College, A
Southern State Community College, A
Stark State College of Technology, A
Tiffin University, B
University of Cincinnati, A
The University of Toledo, MDO
Walsh University, AB
Youngstown State University, M

Oklahoma

East Central University, B
Tulsa Community College, A
University of Oklahoma, M

Oregon

Chemeketa Community College, A
Northwest Christian College, B
Rogue Community College, A
Southern Oregon University, M
University of Oregon, B

Pennsylvania

Arcadia University, B
Chestnut Hill College, ABMO
Geneva College, B
Harrisburg Area Community College, A
La Roche College, B
Lehigh University, M
Lincoln University, BM
Luzerne County Community College, A
Manor College, A
Mansfield University of Pennsylvania, B
Marywood University, B
Pennsylvania Highland Community College, A
Reading Area Community College, A
Rosemont College, M
Saint Joseph's University, BM
Seton Hill University, B
University of Pittsburgh at Titusville, A
The University of Scranton, AB
Villanova University, B
Westmoreland County Community College, A

Puerto Rico

Caribbean University, B
Pontifical Catholic University of Puerto Rico, MD
Universidad del Turabo, M

Rhode Island

Providence College, B
University of Rhode Island, B

South Carolina

Aiken Technical College, A
Anderson University, B
Denmark Technical College, A
Florence-Darlington Technical College, A
Piedmont Technical College, A
Technical College of the Lowcountry, A
Trident Technical College, A

South Dakota

Black Hills State University, B
Dakota Wesleyan University, B
Mount Marty College, B
Oglala Lakota College, AB
Sinte Gleska University, AB

Tennessee

Bethel College, B
Carson-Newman College, B
Martin Methodist College, AB
Tennessee Wesleyan College, B
The University of Tennessee at Chattanooga, B

Texas

Abilene Christian University, MO
Angelina College, A
Austin Community College, A
Cisco Junior College, A

El Paso Community College, A
Montgomery College, A
North Harris College, A
Odessa College, A
St. Edward's University, MO
St. Mary's University of San Antonio, MDO
South Texas College, A
Texas A&M University-Kingsville, B
Texas Southern University, M
Tomball College, A
The University of Texas-Pan American, B
Wayland Baptist University, B

Vermont

Burlington College, B
Champlain College, AB
College of St. Joseph, B
Community College of Vermont, A
Southern Vermont College, B

Virginia

John Tyler Community College, A
Northern Virginia Community College, A
Southside Virginia Community College, A
Southwest Virginia Community College, A
Virginia Highlands Community College, A
Virginia Wesleyan College, B

Washington

Everett Community College, A
Grays Harbor College, A
Highline Community College, A
Northwest Indian College, A
Seattle Central Community College, A
Skagit Valley College, A
Tacoma Community College, A
Western Washington University, B

West Virginia

Fairmont State University, B
Salem International University, B
West Virginia University, M

Wisconsin

Gateway Technical College, A
Madison Area Technical College, A
Milwaukee Area Technical College, A
Northcentral Technical College, A
Southwest Wisconsin Technical College, A
University of Wisconsin-Oshkosh, B

Wyoming

Central Wyoming College, A
Western Wyoming Community College, A

British Columbia

Trinity Western University, B

Ontario

Tyndale University College & Seminary, B

Quebec

Université de Montréal, D

HUMANITIES/HUMANISTIC STUDIES

Alabama

Athens State University, B
Faulkner University, AB
Spring Hill College, B
University of Mobile, B

Alaska

University of Alaska Southeast, AB

Arizona

Arizona State University, M
Cochise College (Douglas), A
Northern Arizona University, B

Prescott College, BM

Arkansas

Arkansas Tech University, B
Harding University, B

California

Barstow College, A
Biola University, B
California Institute of Integral Studies, MD
California State Polytechnic University, Pomona, B
California State University, Chico, B
California State University, Dominguez Hills, BM
California State University, Monterey Bay, B
California State University, Northridge, B
California State University, Sacramento, B
California State University, San Bernardino, B
Cañada College, A
Cerro Coso Community College, A
Chabot College, A
Chaffey College, A
College of Alameda, A
College of the Canyons, A
College of Marin, A
College of San Mateo, A
College of the Sequoias, A
Columbia College, A
Concordia University, B
Contra Costa College, A
Cosumnes River College (Sacramento), A
Crafton Hills College, A
De Anza College, A
Dominican University of California, BM
Fresno City College, A
Fresno Pacific University, B
Glendale Community College, A
Golden West College, A
Holy Names University, B
Imperial Valley College, A
Irvine Valley College, A
John F. Kennedy University, B
Lake Tahoe Community College, A
Laney College, A
Lassen Community College District, A
Los Angeles Mission College, A
Los Angeles Southwest College, A
Loyola Marymount University, B
Merced College, A
Merritt College, A
MiraCosta College, A
Modesto Junior College, A
Mount St. Mary's College, M
Mt. San Jacinto College, A
Napa Valley College, A
New College of California, BMO
Orange Coast College, A
Pepperdine University, BM
Pomona College, B
Sacramento City College, A
Saddleback College, A
San Diego Miramar College, A
San Diego State University, B
San Francisco State University, BM
San Joaquin Delta College, A
San Jose State University, B
Stanford University, BM
University of California, Irvine, B
University of California, Riverside, B
University of California, Santa Cruz, D
University of San Diego, B
Victor Valley College, A
West Hills Community College, A

Colorado

Colorado Mountain College, A
Colorado Mountain College, Alpine Campus, A
Colorado State University, B
Fort Lewis College, B
Lamar Community College, A
Mesa State College, AB
Northeastern Junior College, A
Otero Junior College, A
Red Rocks Community College, A
Regis University, B
United States Air Force Academy, B
University of Colorado at Boulder, B

University of Colorado at Denver and Health
   Sciences Center - Downtown Denver Campus, M

Connecticut

Albertus Magnus College, B
Holy Apostles College and Seminary, B
Housatonic Community College, A
University of Bridgeport, B
Wesleyan University, B
Yale University, B

District of Columbia

The George Washington University, B

Florida

Clearwater Christian College, B
Daytona Beach Community College, A
Eckerd College, B
Florida Institute of Technology, B
Florida International University, B
Florida Southern College, B
Florida State University, BMD
Indian River Community College, A
Jacksonville University, B
Lynn University, B
Manatee Community College, A
Miami Dade College, A
New College of Florida, B
Nova Southeastern University, B
Okaloosa-Walton College, A
Stetson University, B
University of Central Florida, B
University of South Florida, B
University of West Florida, BM

Georgia

Abraham Baldwin Agricultural College, A
Andrew College, A
Atlanta Christian College, B
Clark Atlanta University, D
Macon State College, A
South Georgia College, A
Thomas University, B
Truett-McConnell College, B
Wesleyan College, B

Hawaii

Brigham Young University-Hawaii, B
Chaminade University of Honolulu, B
Hawaii Pacific University, B
University of Hawaii-West Oahu, B

Idaho

Brigham Young University -Idaho, A

Illinois

Aurora University, B
City Colleges of Chicago, Harold Washington
   College, A
City Colleges of Chicago, Richard J. Daley
   College, A
Danville Area Community College, A
John A. Logan College, A
Lincoln College, A
Lincoln College-Normal, A
Monmouth College, B
North Central College, B
Northwestern University, B
Principia College, B
Quincy University, B
Rockford College, B
Shimer College, B
Trinity International University, B
University of Chicago, BM
University of Illinois at Urbana-Champaign, B
William Rainey Harper College, A

Indiana

Ancilla College, A
Indiana University Kokomo, B
Martin University, B
Oakland City University, B
Purdue University, B
Saint Mary-of-the-Woods College, B
Saint Mary's College, B

Taylor University Fort Wayne, A
Valparaiso University, B

Iowa

Ashford University, B
Iowa Lakes Community College, A
Kirkwood Community College, A
Northwestern College, B
University of Northern Iowa, B
Waldorf College, B

Kansas

Allen County Community College, A
Cloud County Community College, A
Coffeyville Community College, A
Colby Community College, A
Dodge City Community College, A
Garden City Community College, A
Independence Community College, A
Kansas State University, B
Pratt Community College, A
Tabor College, B
University of Kansas, B
Washburn University, A

Kentucky

Lindsey Wilson College, B
St. Catharine College, A
Spalding University, B
Thomas More College, B
University of Louisville, MD

Louisiana

Grambling State University, M
Loyola University New Orleans, B
Our Lady of the Lake College, B

Maryland

Anne Arundel Community College, A
Chesapeake College, A
Hood College, M
Towson University, M
University of Maryland University College, B
Villa Julie College, B
Washington College, B

Massachusetts

Bristol Community College, A
Fisher College, A
Fitchburg State College, B
Framingham State College, B
Greenfield Community College, A
Harvard University, B
Lesley University, B
Massachusetts Institute of Technology, M
Newbury College, A
Quincy College, A
Roxbury Community College, A
Suffolk University, B
University of Massachusetts Amherst, B
Worcester Polytechnic Institute, B

Michigan

Alma College, B
Central Michigan University, M
Gogebic Community College, A
Grand Valley State University, B
Hope College, B
Lawrence Technological University, B
Michigan State University, BM
Michigan Technological University, A
Siena Heights University, B
University of Detroit Mercy, B
University of Michigan, B
University of Michigan-Dearborn, B

Minnesota

Augsburg College, B
Bemidji State University, B
College of Saint Benedict, B
The College of St. Scholastica, B
Concordia College, B
Macalester College, B
Minnesota State University Mankato, B
Ridgewater College, A

Saint John's University, B

Mississippi

Belhaven College, B
Hinds Community College, A
Southwest Mississippi Community College, A

Missouri

Northwest Missouri State University, B
Saint Louis University, B
Southeast Missouri State University, B
Washington University in St. Louis, B

Montana

Montana State University-Northern, AB

Nebraska

College of Saint Mary, B
Grace University, B
Midland Lutheran College, B

Nevada

Sierra Nevada College, B

New Hampshire

Plymouth State University, B
University of New Hampshire, B
University of New Hampshire at Manchester, B

New Jersey

Atlantic Cape Community College, A
Brookdale Community College, A
Drew University, MDO
Fairleigh Dickinson University, College at
   Florham, B
Fairleigh Dickinson University, Metropolitan
   Campus, B
Felician College, AB
Georgian Court University, B
Mercer County Community College, A
Montclair State University, B
Passaic County Community College, A
Rider University, A
Saint Peter's College, AB
Salem Community College, A
Seton Hall University, B
Stevens Institute of Technology, B
William Paterson University of New Jersey, B

New Mexico

College of Santa Fe, B
New Mexico Military Institute, A
St. John's College, B
University of New Mexico, B
Western New Mexico University, B

New York

Adelphi University, B
Adirondack Community College, A
Bard College, B
Buffalo State College, State University of New
   York, B
Cayuga County Community College, A
Clarkson University, B
Clinton Community College, A
Colgate University, B
Columbia-Greene Community College, A
Cornell University, B
Corning Community College, A
Dominican College, B
Dowling College, B
Dutchess Community College, A
Elmira College, B
Erie Community College, A
Erie Community College, North Campus, A
Erie Community College, South Campus, A
Eugene Lang College The New School for Liberal
   Arts, B
Finger Lakes Community College, A
Fulton-Montgomery Community College, A
Herkimer County Community College, A
Hofstra University, BM
Houghton College, B
Hunter College of the City University of New York, B
Jamestown Community College, A

Jefferson Community College, A
Long Island University, Brooklyn Campus, B
Mohawk Valley Community College, A
New York University, BMO
Niagara County Community College, A
Onondaga Community College, A
Orange County Community College, A
Polytechnic University, Brooklyn Campus, M
Roberts Wesleyan College, B
Sage College of Albany, A
St. Thomas Aquinas College, B
Sarah Lawrence College, B
Schenectady County Community College, A
State University of New York at Buffalo, M
State University of New York College of Agriculture
    and Technology at Morrisville, A
State University of New York College at Old
    Westbury, B
State University of New York College of Technology
    at Alfred, A
State University of New York College of Technology
    at Canton, A
State University of New York College of Technology
    at Delhi, A
State University of New York Empire State
    College, AB
State University of New York Maritime College, B
Stony Brook University, State University of New
    York, B
Suffolk County Community College, A
Syracuse University, B
Tompkins Cortland Community College, A
Touro College, B
Ulster County Community College, A
Union College, B
United States Military Academy, B
Westchester Community College, A

North Carolina

Catawba College, B
Duke University, MO
Lees-McRae College, B
Warren Wilson College, B

North Dakota

North Dakota State University, B

Ohio

Antioch College, B
Antioch University McGregor, B
Bowling Green State University-Firelands College, A
Franciscan University of Steubenville, B
John Carroll University, BM
Kenyon College, B
Laura and Alvin Siegal College of Judaic Studies, M
Muskingum College, B
The Ohio State University, B
Ohio University, A
Ohio University-Eastern, B
Ohio Wesleyan University, B
Pontifical College Josephinum, B
Shawnee State University, A
Union Institute & University, B
The University of Akron, B
University of Cincinnati, AB
The University of Findlay, A
University of Rio Grande, B
The University of Toledo, B
Ursuline College, B
Wright State University, BM

Oklahoma

Bacone College, A
Oklahoma Baptist University, B
Oklahoma City Community College, A
Oklahoma City University, B
Oklahoma Panhandle State University, B
St. Gregory's University, AB
Tulsa Community College, A

Oregon

Central Oregon Community College, A
Chemeketa Community College, A
Concordia University, B
Corban College, B

Pacific University, B
Portland State University, B
Rogue Community College, A
Treasure Valley Community College, A
Umpqua Community College, A
University of Oregon, B
Western Oregon University, B
Willamette University, B

Pennsylvania

Arcadia University, M
Bucknell University, B
Bucks County Community College, A
Butler County Community College, A
Clarion University of Pennsylvania, B
Community College of Allegheny County, A
Drexel University, B
East Stroudsburg University of Pennsylvania, B
Edinboro University of Pennsylvania, B
Holy Family University, B
Juniata College, B
Lackawanna College, A
Lehigh Carbon Community College, A
Lock Haven University of Pennsylvania, B
Luzerne County Community College, A
Mercyhurst College, B
Messiah College, B
Montgomery County Community College, A
Mount Aloysius College, B
The Pennsylvania State University Harrisburg
    Campus, BM
Reading Area Community College, A
Rosemont College, B
Saint Joseph's University, B
University of Pittsburgh, B
University of Pittsburgh at Greensburg, B
University of Pittsburgh at Johnstown, B
Widener University, B

Puerto Rico

Universidad del Turabo, B
University of Puerto Rico at Arecibo, A
University of Puerto Rico at Bayamón, A
University of Puerto Rico at Carolina, A
University of Puerto Rico, Cayey University
    College, B
University of Puerto Rico, Mayagüez Campus, B
University of Puerto Rico, Río Piedras, B
University of the Sacred Heart, B

Rhode Island

Providence College, B
Salve Regina University, MDO

South Carolina

Allen University, B
Bob Jones University, B
Charleston Southern University, B
Columbia International University, B
North Greenville College, B
Wofford College, B

South Dakota

University of Sioux Falls, A

Tennessee

Freed-Hardeman University, B
LeMoyne-Owen College, B
Lincoln Memorial University, B
Martin Methodist College, A
Milligan College, B
Tennessee State University, B
The University of Tennessee at Chattanooga, B

Texas

Angelina College, A
Baylor University, B
Galveston College, A
Hill College of the Hill Junior College District, A
Lee College, A
Lon Morris College, A
Lubbock Christian University, B
Midwestern State University, B
Sam Houston State University, MD
Schreiner University, B

Southern Methodist University, B
Southwestern Christian College, A
Stephen F. Austin State University, B
Texas Tech University, M
Texas Wesleyan University, B
Trinity University, B
University of Dallas, M
University of Houston-Clear Lake, BM
University of Houston-Downtown, B
University of Houston-Victoria, B
The University of Texas at Arlington, M
The University of Texas at Austin, B
The University of Texas at Dallas, BMD
The University of Texas Medical Branch, MDO
The University of Texas of the Permian Basin, B
The University of Texas at San Antonio, B

United States Virgin Islands

University of the Virgin Islands, B

Utah

Brigham Young University, BM
Dixie State College of Utah, A
Salt Lake Community College, A
Snow College, A
University of Utah, B
Utah Valley State College, A

Vermont

Bennington College, B
Burlington College, AB
Johnson State College, B
Marlboro College, B

Virginia

Hampden-Sydney College, B
Hollins University, M
Marymount University, M
Old Dominion University, M
Virginia Wesleyan College, B

Washington

Centralia College, A
Eastern Washington University, B
The Evergreen State College, B
Highline Community College, A
Saint Martin's University, B
Seattle University, B
Skagit Valley College, A
Tacoma Community College, A
University of Washington, B
Walla Walla College, B
Washington State University, B
Western Washington University, B

West Virginia

Bluefield State College, B
Marshall University, BM
Mountain State University, B

Wisconsin

Concordia University Wisconsin, B
Maranatha Baptist Bible College, B
St. Norbert College, B
University of Wisconsin-Green Bay, AB
University of Wisconsin-Parkside, B

Wyoming

Laramie County Community College, A
Northwest College, A
Sheridan College-Sheridan and Gillette, A
University of Wyoming, B
Western Wyoming Community College, A

Alberta

University of Alberta, B
University of Calgary, B

University of Lethbridge, B

British Columbia

Simon Fraser University, B
Trinity Western University, B

Manitoba

Providence College and Theological Seminary, B

New Brunswick

Mount Allison University, B

Newfoundland and Labrador

Memorial University of Newfoundland, BM

Nova Scotia

Mount Saint Vincent University, B

Ontario

Brock University, B
Carleton University, B
Laurentian University, M
Redeemer University College, B
Ryerson University, B
Trent University, B
University of Ottawa, B
University of Toronto, B
University of Windsor, B
York University, BMD

Quebec

Bishop's University, B
Concordia University, D
McGill University, B

Saskatchewan

University of Regina, B

HYDRAULICS AND FLUID POWER TECHNOLOGY

Alabama

Auburn University, MD

Colorado

Colorado State University, MD

Massachusetts

Massachusetts Institute of Technology, D

Minnesota

Alexandria Technical College, A
Hennepin Technical College, A
Normandale Community College, A

Missouri

University of Missouri-Rolla, MD

Ohio

The Ohio State University Agricultural Technical
  Institute, A

Texas

Texas A&M University, MD

Washington

University of Washington, MD

Wisconsin

Gateway Technical College, A

Quebec

McGill University, MD

HYDROLOGY AND WATER RESOURCES SCIENCE

Alabama

Auburn University, MD
Lawson State Community College, A

Northeast Alabama Community College, A

Arizona

The University of Arizona, MD

California

California State University, Bakersfield, M
California State University, Chico, BM
Citrus College, A
College of the Canyons, A
Hartnell College, A
Humboldt State University, B
Imperial Valley College, A
Los Angeles Trade-Technical College, A
Palomar College, A
University of California, Davis, BMD
University of California, Los Angeles, M
University of California, Santa Barbara, B
Ventura College, A

Colorado

Colorado School of Mines, O
Colorado State University, MD
Red Rocks Community College, A

Connecticut

Three Rivers Community College, A

District of Columbia

University of the District of Columbia, A

Florida

Florida Institute of Technology, B
Indian River Community College, A
St. Petersburg College, A

Georgia

Georgia Institute of Technology, MD

Hawaii

University of Hawaii at Manoa, MD

Idaho

College of Southern Idaho, A
Idaho State University, M
University of Idaho, M

Illinois

Illinois State University, M
Southeastern Illinois College, A
University of Illinois at Chicago, MD

Iowa

Iowa Lakes Community College, A
Kirkwood Community College, A

Kansas

Dodge City Community College, A
Fort Scott Community College, A

Maryland

Cecil Community College, A

Massachusetts

Massachusetts Institute of Technology, D

Michigan

Bay de Noc Community College, A
Grand Valley State University, B
Lake Superior State University, A
Northern Michigan University, B

Western Michigan University, B

Minnesota

Vermilion Community College, A

Mississippi

University of Southern Mississippi, M

Missouri

University of Missouri-Rolla, MD

Montana

Montana State University-Northern, AB
Montana Tech of The University of Montana, M

Nevada

University of Nevada, Reno, MD

New Hampshire

University of New Hampshire, BM

New Mexico

Doña Ana Branch Community College, A
New Mexico Institute of Mining and Technology, MD

New York

Cornell University, BMD
Rensselaer Polytechnic Institute, B
State University of New York College at
  Brockport, B
State University of New York College of
  Environmental Science and Forestry, BMD
State University of New York College at Oneonta, B

North Carolina

Lenoir Community College, A
North Carolina State University, B

Ohio

Heidelberg College, B
Ohio University, M
Wright State University, BM

Oklahoma

East Central University, B

South Carolina

Clemson University, M

Texas

Tarleton State University, B
Texas A&M University, MD
The University of Texas at Austin, B

Virginia

Mountain Empire Community College, A

Washington

Spokane Community College, A
University of Washington, MD

West Virginia

West Virginia University, MD

Wisconsin

Milwaukee Area Technical College, A
Northland College, B
University of Wisconsin-Madison, B
University of Wisconsin-Stevens Point, B

New Brunswick

University of New Brunswick Fredericton, MD

Nova Scotia

St. Francis Xavier University, B

Ontario

Lakehead University, B
University of Toronto, B

ILLUSTRATION

Arizona

The Art Center Design College, B

California

Academy of Art University, ABM
Art Center College of Design, B

California State University, Fullerton, B
California State University, Long Beach, BM
Laguna College of Art & Design, B
Mt. Sierra College, B
University of San Francisco, B

Colorado

Rocky Mountain College of Art & Design, B

Connecticut

University of Bridgeport, B
Western Connecticut State University, M

Delaware

Delaware College of Art and Design, A

Florida

Ringling School of Art and Design, B
University of Miami, B

Georgia

Savannah College of Art and Design, BM

Illinois

Bradley University, M
School of the Art Institute of Chicago, B

Kansas

University of Kansas, B

Maryland

Maryland Institute College of Art, B

Massachusetts

The Art Institute of Boston at Lesley University, B
Montserrat College of Art, B
School of the Museum of Fine Arts, Boston, B

Michigan

Lawrence Technological University, B

Minnesota

Minneapolis College of Art and Design, M

Missouri

Columbia College, B
Kansas City Art Institute, B
Washington University in St. Louis, B

Nebraska

The Creative Center, A

New York

Fashion Institute of Technology, ABM
Pratt Institute, AB
Rochester Institute of Technology, B
St. John's University, B
School of Visual Arts, BM
Syracuse University, BM

Ohio

Art Academy of Cincinnati, B
The Cleveland Institute of Art, B
Columbus College of Art & Design, B
Kent State University, M

Oregon

Pacific Northwest College of Art, B

Pennsylvania

The Art Institute of Pittsburgh, AB
Keystone College, A
Moore College of Art & Design, B
Pennsylvania College of Art & Design, B

The University of the Arts, B

Rhode Island

Rhode Island School of Design, B

Tennessee

Memphis College of Art, B

Utah

Brigham Young University, B
University of Utah, M

Washington

Cornish College of the Arts, B

Alberta

Alberta College of Art & Design, B

IMMUNOLOGY

Alabama

University of South Alabama, D

Arizona

The University of Arizona, MD

Arkansas

University of Arkansas for Medical Sciences, MDO

California

California Institute of Technology, D
Stanford University, D
University of California, Berkeley, D
University of California, Davis, MD
University of California, Los Angeles, MD
University of California, San Diego, D
University of Southern California, MD

Colorado

Colorado State University, MD

Connecticut

Yale University, DO

District of Columbia

The George Washington University, D
Georgetown University, MD

Florida

Florida State University, MD
University of Florida, D
University of Miami, DO
University of South Florida, D

Georgia

Emory University, D

Illinois

Loyola University Chicago, MDO
Northwestern University, D
Rush University, MD
University of Chicago, D
University of Illinois at Chicago, DO

Indiana

Indiana University-Purdue University
    Indianapolis, MDO
Purdue University, MD

Iowa

Iowa State University of Science and
    Technology, MD

The University of Iowa, MDO

Kansas

Kansas State University, MD
University of Kansas, DO

Kentucky

University of Kentucky, D
University of Louisville, MD

Louisiana

Louisiana State University Health Sciences
    Center, MD
Tulane University, MDO

Maine

University of Southern Maine, M

Maryland

The Johns Hopkins University, MD

Massachusetts

Boston University, DO
Harvard University, D
Massachusetts Institute of Technology, D
Tufts University, D

Michigan

University of Michigan, D
Wayne State University, MDO

Minnesota

University of Minnesota, Duluth, MD

Missouri

Saint Louis University, D
University of Missouri-Columbia, MD
Washington University in St. Louis, D

Nebraska

Creighton University, MD

New Jersey

Rutgers, The State University of New Jersey, New
    Brunswick/Piscataway, MD

New York

Cornell University, MD
Long Island University, C.W. Post Campus, M
New York University, DO
State University of New York at Buffalo, MD
State University of New York Upstate Medical
    University, MDO
Stony Brook University, State University of New
    York, D
University at Albany, State University of New
    York, MD
University of Rochester, MDO

North Carolina

Duke University, D
East Carolina University, D
North Carolina State University, MD
The University of North Carolina at Chapel Hill, MD
Wake Forest University, D

North Dakota

University of North Dakota, MD

Ohio

Case Western Reserve University, MDO
The Ohio State University, MD
University of Cincinnati, MD

Wright State University, M

Oklahoma

University of Oklahoma Health Sciences Center, MD

Oregon

Oregon Health & Science University, D

Pennsylvania

Drexel University, MD
Temple University, MDO
Thomas Jefferson University, D
University of Pennsylvania, DO
University of Pittsburgh, MD

Rhode Island

Brown University, MD

South Carolina

Medical University of South Carolina, MDO

South Dakota

The University of South Dakota, MD

Tennessee

Vanderbilt University, MDO

Texas

Texas A&M University System Health Science
Center, D
The University of Texas at Austin, D
The University of Texas Health Science Center at
Houston, MDO
The University of Texas Health Science Center at
San Antonio, MD
The University of Texas Medical Branch, MD
The University of Texas Southwestern Medical
Center at Dallas, D

Virginia

University of Virginia, DO
Virginia Commonwealth University, MO

Washington

University of Washington, D

West Virginia

West Virginia University, MD

Alberta

University of Alberta, BMD

British Columbia

The University of British Columbia, MD

Manitoba

University of Manitoba, MD

Nova Scotia

Dalhousie University, MDO

Ontario

McMaster University, MD
Queen's University at Kingston, MD
University of Guelph, MD
University of Ottawa, MD
University of Toronto, MD
The University of Western Ontario, BMD

Prince Edward Island

University of Prince Edward Island, MD

Quebec

McGill University, MD
Université Laval, MD
Université de Montréal, MD

Université de Sherbrooke, MD

INDIAN/NATIVE AMERICAN EDUCATION

Massachusetts

Simon's Rock College of Bard, B

Minnesota

The College of St. Scholastica, B

Alberta

University of Lethbridge, B

Ontario

Queen's University at Kingston, B

Saskatchewan

University of Regina, B

INDUSTRIAL AND LABOR RELATIONS

California

University of California, Berkeley, D

Connecticut

University of New Haven, M

Georgia

Georgia State University, MD

Illinois

Loyola University Chicago, MO
University of Illinois at Urbana-Champaign, MD

Kentucky

University of Louisville, M

Massachusetts

University of Massachusetts Amherst, M

Michigan

Michigan State University, MD
Wayne State University, M

Minnesota

University of Minnesota, Twin Cities Campus, MD

New Jersey

Rutgers, The State University of New Jersey, New
Brunswick/Piscataway, MD

New York

Bernard M. Baruch College of the City University of
New York, M
Cornell University, MD
New York Institute of Technology, MO
State University of New York Empire State
College, M

Ohio

Case Western Reserve University, MD
Cleveland State University, M
The Ohio State University, MD
The University of Akron, M
University of Cincinnati, M

Pennsylvania

Indiana University of Pennsylvania, M
The Pennsylvania State University University Park
Campus, M

Puerto Rico

Inter American University of Puerto Rico,
Metropolitan Campus, M

Inter American University of Puerto Rico, San
Germán Campus, MD

Rhode Island

University of Rhode Island, M

Tennessee

Middle Tennessee State University, M

Texas

University of North Texas, MD

Virginia

Virginia Commonwealth University, M

West Virginia

West Virginia University, M

Wisconsin

University of Wisconsin-Madison, MD
University of Wisconsin-Milwaukee, MO

Alberta

University of Alberta, D

Newfoundland and Labrador

Memorial University of Newfoundland, M

Ontario

McMaster University, M
Queen's University at Kingston, M
University of Toronto, MD

Quebec

Université Laval, MD
Université de Montréal, MD
Université du Québec en Outaouais, MO
Université du Québec àTrois-Rivières, O

Saskatchewan

University of Saskatchewan, M

INDUSTRIAL AND MANUFACTURING MANAGEMENT

Arkansas

University of Arkansas, M

California

California Polytechnic State University, San Luis
Obispo, M
San Diego State University, M
San Jose State University, M

Colorado

Regis University, M
University of Colorado at Boulder, M

District of Columbia

The George Washington University, M

Georgia

Georgia State University, D

Illinois

American InterContinental University Online, M
DePaul University, M
Illinois Institute of Technology, M
Northern Illinois University, M

Indiana

Indiana University Southeast, O
Purdue University, MD

University of Southern Indiana, M

Iowa

The University of Iowa, M

Kansas

Friends University, M

Massachusetts

Boston University, D
University of Massachusetts Lowell, M

Michigan

Central Michigan University, M
Eastern Michigan University, M
Lawrence Technological University, M
Oakland University, O

Minnesota

University of Minnesota, Twin Cities Campus, MD
University of St. Thomas, M

Missouri

Central Missouri State University, M
Southeast Missouri State University, M

New Jersey

Stevens Institute of Technology, MO

New York

Clarkson University, M
Marist College, O
Rensselaer Polytechnic Institute, M
Rochester Institute of Technology, M
Stony Brook University, State University of New
  York, MO
Syracuse University, D

North Dakota

University of North Dakota, M

Ohio

Case Western Reserve University, MD
University of Cincinnati, MD
The University of Toledo, D

Oklahoma

Northeastern State University, M
Oklahoma State University, D
Southeastern Oklahoma State University, M

Oregon

Portland State University, M

Pennsylvania

Carnegie Mellon University, MD
The Pennsylvania State University University Park
  Campus, MD

Puerto Rico

Inter American University of Puerto Rico,
  Metropolitan Campus, M
Polytechnic University of Puerto Rico, M
University of Puerto Rico, Mayagüez Campus, M

Rhode Island

Bryant University, M

South Carolina

Clemson University, MD

Tennessee

The University of Tennessee, M

Texas

Texas A&M University, D
Texas Tech University, MD
University of North Texas, MD

The University of Texas at Tyler, M

Wisconsin

University of Wisconsin-Madison, MD

Quebec

HEC Montreal, M
McGill University, M

INDUSTRIAL AND ORGANIZATIONAL PSYCHOLOGY

California

California State University, East Bay, B
California State University, Sacramento, B
California State University, San Bernardino, M
John F. Kennedy University, MO
National University, M
Point Loma Nazarene University, B
Saint Mary's College of California, B
San Diego State University, M
San Jose State University, M

Colorado

Colorado State University, M

Connecticut

Eastern Connecticut State University, B
University of Connecticut, MD
University of New Haven, MO

District of Columbia

The George Washington University, D

Florida

Carlos Albizu University, Miami Campus, M
Florida Institute of Technology, MD
University of Central Florida, MD
University of South Florida, D

Georgia

Georgia Institute of Technology, B
Valdosta State University, M

Illinois

American InterContinental University Online, M
DePaul University, MD
Elmhurst College, M
Illinois Institute of Technology, D
National-Louis University, M
Roosevelt University, M
Saint Xavier University, B
University of Illinois at Urbana-Champaign, BMD

Indiana

Indiana University-Purdue University Indianapolis, M

Kansas

Emporia State University, M

Kentucky

Eastern Kentucky University, M
Northern Kentucky University, M

Louisiana

Louisiana State University and Agricultural and
  Mechanical College, MD
Louisiana Tech University, M

Maryland

University of Maryland, College Park, MD

Massachusetts

Bridgewater State College, B
Fitchburg State College, B
Springfield College, MO

Michigan

Central Michigan University, MD
Madonna University, B

University of Detroit Mercy, M
University of Michigan, D
Wayne State University, D
Western Michigan University, M

Minnesota

Minnesota State University Mankato, M
St. Cloud State University, M
University of Minnesota, Twin Cities Campus, D

Mississippi

William Carey College, M

Missouri

Maryville University of Saint Louis, B
University of Missouri-St. Louis, D
Washington University in St. Louis, B

Nebraska

Nebraska Wesleyan University, B
University of Nebraska at Omaha, MD

New Jersey

Fairleigh Dickinson University, College at
  Florham, MO
Kean University, M
Montclair State University, M
Rutgers, The State University of New Jersey, New
  Brunswick/Piscataway, MD

New Mexico

College of Santa Fe, B

New York

Bernard M. Baruch College of the City University of
  New York, MDO
Brooklyn College of the City University of New
  York, BM
Clarkson University, B
Hofstra University, MD
Ithaca College, B
New York University, MD
State University of New York at New Paltz, B
University at Albany, State University of New
  York, D

North Carolina

Appalachian State University, M
North Carolina State University, D
The University of North Carolina at Charlotte, M

Ohio

Bowling Green State University, MD
Cleveland State University, M
Ohio University, D
The University of Akron, MD
Wright State University, BMD

Oklahoma

University of Tulsa, MDO

Oregon

Corban College, B

Pennsylvania

Albright College, B
Chatham College, M
Holy Family University, B
Lincoln University, B
Marywood University, B
Moravian College, B
The Pennsylvania State University University Park
  Campus, MD
Saint Joseph's University, B
Temple University, M

West Chester University of Pennsylvania, M

Puerto Rico

Carlos Albizu University, MD
Pontifical Catholic University of Puerto Rico, M

South Carolina

Clemson University, D

Tennessee

Middle Tennessee State University, BM
The University of Tennessee, D
The University of Tennessee at Chattanooga, M
The University of Tennessee at Martin, B

Texas

Abilene Christian University, B
Lamar University, M
Rice University, MD
St. Mary's University of San Antonio, M
Texas A&M University, MD
Texas Wesleyan University, B
University of Houston, D
University of North Texas, M

Vermont

Goddard College, M

Virginia

Averett University, B
George Mason University, MD
Old Dominion University, D
Radford University, M
Virginia Polytechnic Institute and State University, D

Washington

Antioch University Seattle, M
Central Washington University, M

West Virginia

Marshall University, M

Wisconsin

University of Wisconsin-Oshkosh, M

Ontario

University of Guelph, MD

INDUSTRIAL DESIGN

Alabama

Auburn University, BM

Arizona

Arizona State University, B

California

Academy of Art University, ABM
Art Center College of Design, BM
The Art Institute of California-Orange County, B
Cabrillo College, A
California College of the Arts, B
California State University, Long Beach, B
Chaffey College, A
Las Positas College, A
Mt. San Antonio College, A
Orange Coast College, A
San Francisco State University, BM
San Jose State University, B
Santa Rosa Junior College, A

Colorado

The Art Institute of Colorado, B
Metropolitan State College of Denver, B

Connecticut

University of Bridgeport, B

Florida

The Art Institute of Fort Lauderdale, B

Georgia

Georgia Institute of Technology, B
Savannah College of Art and Design, BM

Idaho

Brigham Young University -Idaho, A

Illinois

Columbia College Chicago, B
Illinois Institute of Technology, MD
Kishwaukee College, A
Rock Valley College, A
University of Illinois at Chicago, BM
University of Illinois at Urbana-Champaign, BM

Indiana

Oakland City University, A
Vincennes University, A

Iowa

Iowa Western Community College, A

Kansas

University of Kansas, B

Louisiana

University of Louisiana at Lafayette, B

Massachusetts

Massachusetts College of Art, B
Wentworth Institute of Technology, AB

Michigan

Ferris State University, A
Finlandia University, B
University of Michigan, B
Washtenaw Community College, A
Western Michigan University, B

Nebraska

Southeast Community College, Milford Campus, A

New Jersey

Kean University, B

New York

Fashion Institute of Technology, B
Parsons The New School for Design, B
Pratt Institute, BM
Rochester Institute of Technology, ABM
Syracuse University, B

North Carolina

Appalachian State University, B
North Carolina State University, BM

Ohio

The Cleveland Institute of Art, B
Columbus College of Art & Design, B
The Ohio State University, BM
Ohio University-Lancaster, A
University of Cincinnati, BM

Oklahoma

Oklahoma State University, Oklahoma City, A

Oregon

George Fox University, B
Portland Community College, A

Pennsylvania

The Art Institute of Philadelphia, B
The Art Institute of Pittsburgh, AB
Carnegie Mellon University, B
Luzerne County Community College, A
Philadelphia University, B

The University of the Arts, BM

Puerto Rico

Escuela de Artes Plasticas de Puerto Rico, B

Rhode Island

Rhode Island School of Design, BM

South Carolina

Clemson University, B

Texas

Navarro College, A

Utah

Brigham Young University, BM

Virginia

Virginia Polytechnic Institute and State University, B

Washington

The Art Institute of Seattle, A
University of Washington, B
Western Washington University, B

Wisconsin

Milwaukee Area Technical College, A
Milwaukee Institute of Art and Design, B
Northeast Wisconsin Technical College, A
University of Wisconsin-Platteville, B

Alberta

University of Alberta, B
University of Calgary, M

Ontario

Carleton University, B

Quebec

Université de Montréal, B

INDUSTRIAL EDUCATION

Alabama

Alabama Agricultural and Mechanical University, M

Florida

Florida Agricultural and Mechanical University, M
University of South Florida, M

Idaho

Idaho State University, M
University of Idaho, MD

Indiana

Indiana State University, M
Purdue University, M

Iowa

Drake University, M
University of Northern Iowa, MD

Kentucky

Eastern Kentucky University, M
University of Louisville, M

Louisiana

Louisiana State University and Agricultural and
  Mechanical College, M

Maine

University of Southern Maine, M

Michigan

Central Michigan University, M
Wayne State University, M

Minnesota

Bemidji State University, M

Mississippi

Alcorn State University, M
Jackson State University, M

Missouri

Central Missouri State University, MO

New York

Buffalo State College, State University of New York, M

North Carolina

Appalachian State University, M
North Carolina Agricultural and Technical State University, M

Oklahoma

Oklahoma State University, MD

South Carolina

Clemson University, M

Tennessee

Middle Tennessee State University, M

Texas

Sam Houston State University, M
Sul Ross State University, M
The University of Texas at Tyler, M

Utah

Utah State University, M

British Columbia

The University of British Columbia, M

INDUSTRIAL ELECTRONICS TECHNOLOGY/TECHNICIAN

Alabama

H. Councill Trenholm State Technical College, A
Northwest-Shoals Community College, A
Shelton State Community College, A

California

Modesto Junior College, A

Georgia

Dalton State College, A

Idaho

Lewis-Clark State College, AB

Illinois

College of DuPage, A
John Wood Community College, A
Rend Lake College, A

Indiana

Vincennes University, A

Iowa

North Iowa Area Community College, A
Northwest Iowa Community College, A

Kentucky

Brown Mackie College-Louisville, A
Louisville Technical Institute, A

Louisiana

Louisiana Technical College, A

Maine

Kennebec Valley Community College, A

Michigan

Oakland Community College, A

Minnesota

Northland Community and Technical College-Thief River Falls, A

New York

State University of New York College of Technology at Alfred, A

North Dakota

North Dakota State College of Science, A

Ohio

Brown Mackie College-North Canton, A

Pennsylvania

Johnson College, A
Northampton County Area Community College, A
Pennsylvania College of Technology, A

South Carolina

Central Carolina Technical College, A
Midlands Technical College, A
York Technical College, A

South Dakota

Mitchell Technical Institute, A
Western Dakota Technical Institute, A

Washington

Bates Technical College, A
Big Bend Community College, A

Wyoming

Western Wyoming Community College, A

British Columbia

Thompson Rivers University, A

INDUSTRIAL ENGINEERING

Alabama

Auburn University, B
The University of Alabama, B
The University of Alabama in Huntsville, B

Alaska

University of Alaska Fairbanks, B

Arizona

Arizona State University, B
The University of Arizona, B

Arkansas

University of Arkansas, B

California

California Polytechnic State University, San Luis Obispo, B
California State Polytechnic University, Pomona, B
California State University, East Bay, B
California State University, Long Beach, B
San Jose State University, B
Santa Barbara City College, A
Stanford University, B
University of San Diego, B

Colorado

Colorado State University-Pueblo, B

Connecticut

Manchester Community College, A
University of Connecticut, B

Florida

Florida Agricultural and Mechanical University, B
Florida State University, B
University of Central Florida, B
University of Florida, B
University of Miami, B

University of South Florida, B

Georgia

Georgia Institute of Technology, B

Idaho

University of Idaho, B

Illinois

Bradley University, B
Northern Illinois University, B
Northwestern University, B
Southern Illinois University Edwardsville, B
University of Illinois at Chicago, B
University of Illinois at Urbana-Champaign, B

Indiana

Indiana Tech, B
Purdue University, B

Iowa

Iowa State University of Science and Technology, B
St. Ambrose University, B
The University of Iowa, B

Kansas

Kansas State University, B
Wichita State University, B

Kentucky

Northern Kentucky University, B
University of Louisville, B

Louisiana

Louisiana State University and Agricultural and Mechanical College, B
Louisiana Tech University, B

Maryland

The Johns Hopkins University, B
Morgan State University, B

Massachusetts

Boston University, B
Eastern Nazarene College, B
Mount Wachusett Community College, A
Northeastern University, B
Tufts University, B
University of Massachusetts Amherst, B
Western New England College, B
Worcester Polytechnic Institute, B

Michigan

Central Michigan University, B
Ferris State University, B
Grand Valley State University, B
Kettering University, B
Michigan Technological University, B
University of Michigan, B
University of Michigan-Dearborn, B
Wayne State University, B
Western Michigan University, B

Minnesota

St. Cloud State University, B
University of Minnesota, Duluth, B
University of Minnesota, Twin Cities Campus, B

Mississippi

Mississippi State University, B

Missouri

University of Missouri-Columbia, B
University of Missouri-Rolla, B

Montana

Montana State University, B

Nebraska

University of Nebraska-Lincoln, B

New Jersey

New Jersey Institute of Technology, B

Rutgers, The State University of New Jersey, New Brunswick/Piscataway, B

New Mexico

New Mexico State University, B
Northern New Mexico Community College, A

New York

Columbia University, The Fu Foundation School of Engineering and Applied Science, B
Hofstra University, B
New York Institute of Technology, B
Rensselaer Polytechnic Institute, B
Rochester Institute of Technology, B
State University of New York at Binghamton, B
State University of New York at Buffalo, B

North Carolina

North Carolina Agricultural and Technical State University, B
North Carolina State University, B

North Dakota

North Dakota State University, B

Ohio

Central State University, B
Cleveland State University, B
Kent State University, B
Miami University, B
The Ohio State University, B
Ohio University, B
Ohio University-Eastern, B
University of Cincinnati, B
The University of Toledo, AB
Youngstown State University, B

Oklahoma

Oklahoma State University, B
University of Oklahoma, B

Oregon

Oregon State University, B

Pennsylvania

Drexel University, B
Elizabethtown College, B
Gannon University, B
Lehigh University, B
Penn Foster Career School, A
The Pennsylvania State University Abington College, B
The Pennsylvania State University Altoona College, B
The Pennsylvania State University Beaver Campus of the Commonwealth College, B
The Pennsylvania State University Berks Campus of the Berks-Lehigh Valley College, B
The Pennsylvania State University Delaware County Campus of the Commonwealth College, B
The Pennsylvania State University DuBois Campus of the Commonwealth College, B
The Pennsylvania State University at Erie, The Behrend College, B
The Pennsylvania State University Fayette Campus of the Commonwealth College, B
The Pennsylvania State University Hazleton Campus of the Commonwealth College, B
The Pennsylvania State University, Lehigh Valley Campus of the Berks-Lehigh Valley College, B
The Pennsylvania State University McKeesport Campus of the Commonwealth College, B
The Pennsylvania State University Mont Alto Campus of the Commonwealth College, B
The Pennsylvania State University New Kensington Campus of the Commonwealth College, B
The Pennsylvania State University Schuylkill Campus of the Capital College, B
The Pennsylvania State University Shenango Campus of the Commonwealth College, B
The Pennsylvania State University University Park Campus, B
The Pennsylvania State University Wilkes-Barre Campus of the Commonwealth College, B

The Pennsylvania State University Worthington Scranton Campus of the Commonwealth College, B
The Pennsylvania State University York Campus of the Commonwealth College, B
Robert Morris University, B
University of Pittsburgh, B

Puerto Rico

Caribbean University, B
Inter American University of Puerto Rico, Bayamón Campus, B
Polytechnic University of Puerto Rico, B
Universidad del Turabo, B
University of Puerto Rico, Mayagüez Campus, B

Rhode Island

University of Rhode Island, B

South Carolina

Clemson University, B

South Dakota

South Dakota School of Mines and Technology, B

Tennessee

Nashville State Technical Community College, A
Tennessee State University, B
Tennessee Technological University, B
The University of Tennessee, B

Texas

Lamar University, B
St. Mary's University of San Antonio, B
Texas A&M University, B
Texas A&M University-Commerce, B
Texas A&M University-Kingsville, B
Texas State University-San Marcos, B
Texas Tech University, B
University of Houston, B
The University of Texas at Arlington, B
The University of Texas at El Paso, B

Vermont

University of Vermont, B

Virginia

Virginia Polytechnic Institute and State University, B

Washington

Seattle University, B
University of Washington, B

West Virginia

West Virginia University, B

Wisconsin

Marquette University, B
Milwaukee School of Engineering, B
University of Wisconsin-Madison, B
University of Wisconsin-Milwaukee, B
University of Wisconsin-Platteville, B

Alberta

University of Calgary, B

Manitoba

University of Manitoba, B

New Brunswick

Université de Moncton, B

Newfoundland and Labrador

Memorial University of Newfoundland, B

Nova Scotia

Dalhousie University, B

Ontario

McMaster University, B
Ryerson University, B
University of Toronto, B

University of Windsor, B

Quebec

Concordia University, B
Université du Québec àTrois-Rivières, B

Saskatchewan

University of Regina, B

INDUSTRIAL HYGIENE

Alabama

The University of Alabama at Birmingham, D

California

San Diego State University, M

Connecticut

University of New Haven, M

Indiana

Purdue University, MD

Massachusetts

University of Massachusetts Lowell, MD

Michigan

University of Michigan, MD

Minnesota

University of Minnesota, Twin Cities Campus, MD

Missouri

Central Missouri State University, M

Montana

Montana Tech of The University of Montana, M

New Jersey

New Jersey Institute of Technology, M

North Carolina

The University of North Carolina at Chapel Hill, MD

Ohio

University of Cincinnati, MD

Puerto Rico

University of Puerto Rico, Medical Sciences Campus, M

South Carolina

University of South Carolina, MD

Washington

University of Washington, M

West Virginia

West Virginia University, M

INDUSTRIAL/MANAGEMENT ENGINEERING

Alabama

Auburn University, MD
The University of Alabama, M
The University of Alabama in Huntsville, MD

Arizona

Arizona State University, MDO
The University of Arizona, MD

Arkansas

University of Arkansas, MD

California

California Polytechnic State University, San Luis Obispo, MO
California State University, Fresno, M

California State University, Northridge, M
Loyola Marymount University, M
San Jose State University, M
Stanford University, MD
University of California, Berkeley, MD
University of Southern California, MDO

Colorado

Colorado State University, MD
Colorado State University-Pueblo, M

Connecticut

University of New Haven, MO

Florida

Florida Agricultural and Mechanical University, MD
Florida International University, M
Florida State University, MD
University of Central Florida, MDO
University of Florida, MDO
University of Miami, MDO
University of South Florida, MD

Georgia

Georgia Institute of Technology, MD
Southern Polytechnic State University, M

Illinois

Bradley University, M
Illinois State University, M
Northern Illinois University, M
Northwestern University, MD
University of Illinois at Chicago, MD
University of Illinois at Urbana-Champaign, MD

Indiana

Indiana State University, M
Purdue University, MD

Iowa

Iowa State University of Science and
    Technology, MD
The University of Iowa, MD

Kansas

Kansas State University, MD
Wichita State University, MD

Kentucky

Eastern Kentucky University, M
University of Louisville, MD

Louisiana

Louisiana State University and Agricultural and
    Mechanical College, MD
Louisiana Tech University, MD

Maryland

Morgan State University, MD

Massachusetts

Northeastern University, MD
University of Massachusetts Amherst, MD
University of Massachusetts Lowell, MDO
Western New England College, M

Michigan

University of Michigan, MDO
University of Michigan-Dearborn, MO
Wayne State University, MD
Western Michigan University, M

Minnesota

University of Minnesota, Twin Cities Campus, MD

Mississippi

Mississippi State University, MD

Missouri

Central Missouri State University, M
University of Missouri-Columbia, MD

Montana

Montana State University, MD
Montana Tech of The University of Montana, M

Nebraska

University of Nebraska-Lincoln, MD

New Jersey

New Jersey Institute of Technology, MD
Rutgers, The State University of New Jersey, New
    Brunswick/Piscataway, MD

New Mexico

New Mexico State University, MD

New York

Buffalo State College, State University of New
    York, M
Cornell University, MD
Polytechnic University, Brooklyn Campus, M
Rensselaer Polytechnic Institute, MO
Rochester Institute of Technology, M
State University of New York at Binghamton, MD
State University of New York at Buffalo, MD

North Carolina

East Carolina University, M
North Carolina Agricultural and Technical State
    University, MD
North Carolina State University, MD
Western Carolina University, M

North Dakota

North Dakota State University, MD

Ohio

Cleveland State University, MD
The Ohio State University, MD
Ohio University, M
University of Cincinnati, MDO
University of Dayton, M
The University of Toledo, MD
Youngstown State University, M

Oklahoma

Oklahoma State University, MD
University of Oklahoma, MD

Oregon

Oregon State University, MD

Pennsylvania

Lehigh University, MD
The Pennsylvania State University University Park
    Campus, MD
University of Pittsburgh, MD

Puerto Rico

University of Puerto Rico, Mayagüez Campus, M

Rhode Island

University of Rhode Island, M

South Carolina

Clemson University, MD

South Dakota

South Dakota State University, M

Tennessee

Tennessee Technological University, MD
University of Memphis, M
The University of Tennessee, MDO

Texas

Lamar University, MD
St. Mary's University of San Antonio, MO
Sam Houston State University, M
Texas A&M University, MD
Texas A&M University-Commerce, M
Texas A&M University-Kingsville, M
Texas State University-San Marcos, M
Texas Tech University, MD

University of Houston, MDO
The University of Texas at Arlington, MD
The University of Texas at Austin, MD
The University of Texas at El Paso, M

Virginia

Virginia Polytechnic Institute and State
    University, MD

Washington

Central Washington University, M
University of Washington, MD

West Virginia

West Virginia University, MD

Wisconsin

University of Wisconsin-Madison, MD

Manitoba

University of Manitoba, MD

New Brunswick

Université de Moncton, M

Nova Scotia

Dalhousie University, MD

Ontario

University of Toronto, MD
University of Windsor, MD

Quebec

Concordia University, MDO
Université Laval, O
Université du Québec àTrois-Rivières, MO

Saskatchewan

University of Regina, MD

INDUSTRIAL MECHANICS AND MAINTENANCE TECHNOLOGY

Alabama

Calhoun Community College, A
George C. Wallace Community College, A
H. Councill Trenholm State Technical College, A
Northwest-Shoals Community College, A

Arizona

Northland Pioneer College, A

Arkansas

Arkansas Northeastern College, A
Arkansas State University-Beebe, A
Arkansas Tech University, A
Southern Arkansas University Tech, A
University of Arkansas Community College at
    Hope, A

California

San Joaquin Valley College, A

Georgia

Dalton State College, A

Illinois

College of Lake County, A
Heartland Community College, A
Illinois Eastern Community Colleges, Olney Central
    College, A
John Wood Community College, A
Kaskaskia College, A
Rend Lake College, A

Waubonsee Community College, A

Indiana

Ivy Tech Community College-East Central, A
Vincennes University, A

Kentucky

Louisville Technical Institute, A

Maine

Kennebec Valley Community College, A

Michigan

Macomb Community College, A
Southwestern Michigan College, A

Minnesota

Dakota County Technical College, A
Riverland Community College, A

Mississippi

Coahoma Community College, A

Missouri

Jefferson College, A

North Carolina

Guilford Technical Community College, A

Pennsylvania

Harrisburg Area Community College, A
Johnson College, A
Pennsylvania College of Technology, A

South Carolina

Midlands Technical College, A
York Technical College, A

Texas

North Central Texas College, A

Washington

Lower Columbia College, A

Wyoming

Western Wyoming Community College, A

British Columbia

British Columbia Institute of Technology, A

INDUSTRIAL PRODUCTION TECHNOLOGIES/TECHNICIANS

Arkansas

Arkansas Northeastern College, A

Connecticut

Central Connecticut State University, B

Georgia

Georgia Southern University, B
Southern Polytechnic State University, B

Indiana

Ivy Tech Community College-Central Indiana, A
Ivy Tech Community College-East Central, A
Ivy Tech Community College-Lafayette, A
Ivy Tech Community College-North Central, A
Ivy Tech Community College-Northeast, A
Ivy Tech Community College-Southwest, A
Ivy Tech Community College-Wabash Valley, A

Ivy Tech Community College-Whitewater, A

Kansas

Southwestern College, B

Kentucky

Western Kentucky University, B

Louisiana

Louisiana Technical College, A

Michigan

Central Michigan University, B
Ferris State University, A
Wayne State University, B

Nebraska

Chadron State College, B
University of Nebraska-Lincoln, AB
Wayne State College, B

New Jersey

Essex County College, A

New York

Broome Community College, A
Erie Community College, A
Mohawk Valley Community College, A

North Carolina

Appalachian State University, B
Cape Fear Community College, A
East Carolina University, B
Richmond Community College, A

Ohio

The University of Akron, B

Pennsylvania

Millersville University of Pennsylvania, B
Pennsylvania College of Technology, AB

Texas

Tarleton State University, B

Utah

Utah State University, B

Wisconsin

University of Wisconsin-Stout, B

INDUSTRIAL RADIOLOGIC TECHNOLOGY/TECHNICIAN

Alabama

Chattahoochee Valley Community College, A
Faulkner University, A
George Corley Wallace State Community College, A
Wallace State Community College, A

Arkansas

National Park Community College, A
NorthWest Arkansas Community College, A
Phillips Community College of the University of
  Arkansas, A
University of Arkansas for Medical Sciences, AB

California

Bakersfield College, A
Cañada College, A
City College of San Francisco, A
Compton Community College, A
Crafton Hills College, A
Cypress College, A
Fresno City College, A
Las Positas College, A
Long Beach City College, A
Los Angeles City College, A
Merced College, A
Merritt College, A
Mt. San Antonio College, A
Orange Coast College, A

Pasadena City College, A
San Diego Mesa College, A
San Joaquin Delta College, A
Yuba College, A

Colorado

Aims Community College, A
Mesa State College, A

Connecticut

Gateway Community College, A
Middlesex Community College, A
Naugatuck Valley Community College, A

Delaware

Delaware Technical & Community College,
  Stanton/Wilmington Campus, A

District of Columbia

The George Washington University, A
Howard University, B
University of the District of Columbia, A

Florida

Broward Community College, A
Daytona Beach Community College, A
Gulf Coast Community College, A
Hillsborough Community College, A
Indian River Community College, A
Keiser College (Fort Lauderdale), A
Palm Beach Community College, A
St. Petersburg College, A
Santa Fe Community College, A

Georgia

West Central Technical College, A

Hawaii

Kapiolani Community College, A

Idaho

Boise State University, AB

Illinois

Carl Sandburg College, A
Danville Area Community College, A
Illinois Central College, A
Kankakee Community College, A
National-Louis University, B
Sauk Valley Community College, A
South Suburban College, A
Southwestern Illinois College, A

Indiana

Ball State University, A

Iowa

Briar Cliff University, B
Indian Hills Community College, A
Iowa Central Community College, A
Marshalltown Community College, A
Southeastern Community College, North Campus, A

Kansas

Cowley County Community College and Area
  Vocational-Technical School, A
Fort Hays State University, A
Friends University, B
Highland Community College, A
Labette Community College, A

Kentucky

Northern Kentucky University, A
West Kentucky Community and Technical College, A

Louisiana

Our Lady of the Lake College, A

Maine

Central Maine Community College, A
Southern Maine Community College, A

Maryland

Anne Arundel Community College, A
University of Maryland Eastern Shore, B

Massachusetts

Labouré College, A
Northern Essex Community College, A

Michigan

Baker College of Owosso, AB
Delta College, A
Ferris State University, A
Henry Ford Community College, A
Madonna University, B
Mid Michigan Community College, A
Montcalm Community College, A

Minnesota

Ridgewater College, A

Mississippi

Copiah-Lincoln Community College, A
Hinds Community College, A
Mississippi Gulf Coast Community College, A
Northeast Mississippi Community College, A

Missouri

St. Louis Community College at Forest Park, A

Nevada

Community College of Southern Nevada, A
Truckee Meadows Community College, A

New Jersey

Bergen Community College, A
Cumberland County College, A
Passaic County Community College, A

New Mexico

Doña Ana Branch Community College, A
Northern New Mexico Community College, A

New York

Monroe Community College, A
Orange County Community College, A
Trocaire College, A
Westchester Community College, A

North Carolina

Carteret Community College, A
Cleveland Community College, A
Forsyth Technical Community College, A
Vance-Granville Community College, A

North Dakota

Jamestown College, B

Ohio

Columbus State Community College, A
Cuyahoga Community College, A
James A. Rhodes State College, A
Jefferson Community College, A
Lorain County Community College, A
Marion Technical College, A
Sinclair Community College, A
University of Cincinnati, A
University of Cincinnati Raymond Walters College, A
Zane State College, A

Oklahoma

Rose State College, A
Tulsa Community College, A

Oregon

Oregon Institute of Technology, B
Portland Community College, A

Pennsylvania

Community College of Philadelphia, A
Reading Area Community College, A
Thomas Jefferson University, B

Widener University, A

Puerto Rico

Inter American University of Puerto Rico, San
Germán Campus, A
Universidad del Este, A

South Carolina

Florence-Darlington Technical College, A
Greenville Technical College, A
Horry-Georgetown Technical College, A

South Dakota

University of Sioux Falls, B

Tennessee

Chattanooga State Technical Community College, A
Columbia State Community College, A
Roane State Community College, A
Walters State Community College, A

Texas

Amarillo College, A
Angelina College, A
Austin Community College, A
Blinn College, A
Del Mar College, A
El Paso Community College, A
Houston Community College System, A
Lamar University, A
Laredo Community College, A
McLennan Community College, A
Odessa College, A
South Plains College, A
South Texas College, A
Tarrant County College District, A
Texas Southmost College, A
Tyler Junior College, A
Wharton County Junior College, A

Utah

Salt Lake Community College, A

Virginia

Northern Virginia Community College, A
Southwest Virginia Community College, A
Virginia Highlands Community College, A
Virginia Western Community College, A

Washington

Bellevue Community College, A
Wenatchee Valley College, A
Yakima Valley Community College, A

West Virginia

Southern West Virginia Community and Technical
College, A

Wisconsin

Concordia University Wisconsin, B
Madison Area Technical College, A
Milwaukee Area Technical College, A
Northcentral Technical College, A

Wyoming

Laramie County Community College, A

INDUSTRIAL SAFETY TECHNOLOGY/TECHNICIAN

New York

Rochester Institute of Technology, B

South Dakota

South Dakota State University, B

INDUSTRIAL TECHNOLOGY/TECHNICIAN

Alabama

Community College of the Air Force, A
Jacksonville State University, B

The University of West Alabama, B

Alaska

University of Alaska Fairbanks, A

Arizona

Arizona State University at the Polytechnic
Campus, B
Central Arizona College, A
GateWay Community College, A
Glendale Community College, A
Mesa Community College, A
Northland Pioneer College, A

Arkansas

Arkansas Northeastern College, A
Black River Technical College, A
Cossatot Community College of the University of
Arkansas, A
North Arkansas College, A
Ouachita Technical College, A
Pulaski Technical College, A
South Arkansas Community College, A
Southeast Arkansas College, A
Southern Arkansas University-Magnolia, AB
Southern Arkansas University Tech, A
University of Arkansas Community College at
Batesville, A
University of Arkansas at Pine Bluff, AB

California

Bakersfield College, A
California Polytechnic State University, San Luis
Obispo, B
California State University, Fresno, B
California State University, Long Beach, B
California State University, Los Angeles, B
Cerritos College, A
Chabot College, A
City College of San Francisco, A
Cuesta College, A
De Anza College, A
Don Bosco Technical Institute, A
Evergreen Valley College, A
FIDM/The Fashion Institute of Design &
Merchandising, Orange County Campus, A
Fresno City College, A
Fullerton College, A
Glendale Community College, A
Hartnell College, A
Long Beach City College, A
Los Angeles Pierce College, A
Los Angeles Trade-Technical College, A
MiraCosta College, A
San Diego City College, A
Santa Ana College, A
Santa Barbara City College, A
Sierra College, A
Yuba College, A

Colorado

Mesa State College, A
Metropolitan State College of Denver, B
Trinidad State Junior College, A

Connecticut

Asnuntuck Community College, A
Gateway Community College, A
Manchester Community College, A
Naugatuck Valley Community College, A
Three Rivers Community College, A

Delaware

Delaware Technical & Community College,
Stanton/Wilmington Campus, A
Delaware Technical & Community College, Terry
Campus, A

Florida

Miami Dade College, A
North Florida Community College, A
Pensacola Junior College, A
St. Petersburg College, A
Seminole Community College, A

Valencia Community College, A

Georgia

Albany Technical College, A
Central Georgia Technical College, A
Columbus Technical College, A
Dalton State College, A
DeKalb Technical College, A
Georgia Southern University, B
Griffin Technical College, A
Lanier Technical College, A
North Georgia Technical College, A
Savannah Technical College, A
South Georgia Technical College, A
Southern Polytechnic State University, B
West Georgia Technical College, A

Idaho

Boise State University, B
Brigham Young University -Idaho, A
University of Idaho, B

Illinois

Bradley University, B
College of DuPage, A
Danville Area Community College, A
Eastern Illinois University, B
Elgin Community College, A
Heartland Community College, A
Illinois Central College, A
Illinois Eastern Community Colleges, Wabash Valley
  College, A
Illinois Institute of Technology, B
Illinois State University, B
Illinois Valley Community College, A
Joliet Junior College, A
Lake Land College, A
Northern Illinois University, B
Parkland College, A
Prairie State College, A
Rend Lake College, A
Richland Community College, A
Rock Valley College, A
South Suburban College, A
Southern Illinois University Carbondale, B
Spoon River College, A
Triton College, A
Waubonsee Community College, A
Western Illinois University, B
William Rainey Harper College, A

Indiana

Ball State University, AB
Indiana State University, B
Indiana University-Purdue University Fort
  Wayne, AB
Ivy Tech Community College-Bloomington, A
Ivy Tech Community College-Central Indiana, A
Ivy Tech Community College-Columbus, A
Ivy Tech Community College-East Central, A
Ivy Tech Community College-Kokomo, A
Ivy Tech Community College-Lafayette, A
Ivy Tech Community College-North Central, A
Ivy Tech Community College-Northeast, A
Ivy Tech Community College-Northwest, A
Ivy Tech Community College-Southeast, A
Ivy Tech Community College-Southern Indiana, A
Ivy Tech Community College-Southwest, A
Ivy Tech Community College-Wabash Valley, A
Ivy Tech Community College-Whitewater, A
Purdue University Calumet, AB
Purdue University North Central, A
Tri-State University, A
Vincennes University Jasper Campus, A

Iowa

Kirkwood Community College, A
University of Northern Iowa, B
William Penn University, B

Kansas

Allen County Community College, A
Coffeyville Community College, A
Dodge City Community College, A
Garden City Community College, A

Labette Community College, A
Pittsburg State University, B
Washburn University, A

Kentucky

Berea College, B
Eastern Kentucky University, AB
Hopkinsville Community College, A
Morehead State University, AB
Murray State University, AB
Northern Kentucky University, B
Paducah Technical College, A
Somerset Community College, A
Western Kentucky University, B

Louisiana

Grambling State University, B
Northwestern State University of Louisiana, B
Southeastern Louisiana University, AB
University of Louisiana at Lafayette, B

Maryland

Anne Arundel Community College, A
Hagerstown Community College, A

Massachusetts

Fitchburg State College, B
Greenfield Community College, A
Mount Wachusett Community College, A
University of Massachusetts Lowell, B
Wentworth Institute of Technology, A

Michigan

Baker College of Flint, B
Baker College of Muskegon, A
Eastern Michigan University, B
Ferris State University, AB
Grand Rapids Community College, A
Henry Ford Community College, A
Kellogg Community College, A
Kirtland Community College, A
Lake Michigan College, A
Lake Superior State University, B
Lansing Community College, A
Lawrence Technological University, B
Macomb Community College, A
Monroe County Community College, A
Montcalm Community College, A
Muskegon Community College, A
Northwestern Michigan College, A
Oakland Community College, A
St. Clair County Community College, A
Schoolcraft College, A
Washtenaw Community College, A
Wayne County Community College District, A
Wayne State University, B

Minnesota

Alexandria Technical College, A
Bemidji State University, B
Century College, A
Dunwoody College of Technology, A
Minnesota State College-Southeast Technical, A
Minnesota State Community and Technical
  College-Fergus Falls, A
Minnesota State University Mankato, B
Minnesota State University Moorhead, B
Northwest Technical College, A
Saint Mary's University of Minnesota, B
Saint Paul College-A Community & Technical
  College, A
Vermilion Community College, A

Mississippi

Alcorn State University, B
Jackson State University, B
Mississippi State University, B
Mississippi Valley State University, B
Northeast Mississippi Community College, A
University of Southern Mississippi, B

Missouri

Central Missouri State University, AB
Crowder College, A
East Central College, A

Mineral Area College, A
Missouri Southern State University, B
Missouri State University-West Plains, A
Moberly Area Community College, A
Ozarks Technical Community College, A
St. Louis Community College at Forest Park, A
Southeast Missouri State University, B
State Fair Community College, A
Three Rivers Community College, A

Montana

Montana State University-Northern, AB

Nebraska

Central Community College-Columbus Campus, A
Central Community College-Grand Island
  Campus, A
Central Community College-Hastings Campus, A
Southeast Community College, Milford Campus, A
University of Nebraska-Lincoln, B
University of Nebraska at Omaha, B

Nevada

Great Basin College, A
Western Nevada Community College, A

New Hampshire

Keene State College, AB
New Hampshire Community Technical College,
  Berlin/Laconia, A
New Hampshire Community Technical College,
  Nashua/Claremont, A

New Jersey

Bergen Community College, A
Cumberland County College, A
Passaic County Community College, A
Raritan Valley Community College, A
Union County College, A

New Mexico

Central New Mexico Community College, A
Eastern New Mexico University-Roswell, A
New Mexico State University-Carlsbad, A

New York

Buffalo State College, State University of New
  York, B
Clinton Community College, A
Corning Community College, A
Erie Community College, South Campus, A
Excelsior College, AB
Hudson Valley Community College, A
Monroe Community College, A
State University of New York College of Technology
  at Canton, A
State University of New York Institute of
  Technology, B
Suffolk County Community College, A
Ulster County Community College, A

North Carolina

Appalachian State University, B
Bladen Community College, A
Blue Ridge Community College, A
Brunswick Community College, A
Catawba Valley Community College, A
Central Piedmont Community College, A
East Carolina University, B
Elizabeth City State University, B
Forsyth Technical Community College, A
Guilford Technical Community College, A
Halifax Community College, A
Haywood Community College, A
Lenoir Community College, A
Mitchell Community College, A
North Carolina Agricultural and Technical State
  University, A
Pitt Community College, A
Robeson Community College, A
Rowan-Cabarrus Community College, A
Sampson Community College, A
Southeastern Community College, A
Stanly Community College, A
The University of North Carolina at Charlotte, B

Vance-Granville Community College, A
Wake Technical Community College, A
Western Piedmont Community College, A
Wilson Technical Community College, A

North Dakota

Bismarck State College, A
North Dakota State College of Science, A
University of North Dakota, B

Ohio

Bowling Green State University, B
Bowling Green State University-Firelands
  College, AB
Central Ohio Technical College, A
Central State University, B
Clark State Community College, A
Cleveland State University, B
Edison State Community College, A
Hocking College, A
James A. Rhodes State College, A
Jefferson Community College, A
Kent State University, AB
Kent State University, Ashtabula Campus, A
Kent State University, Geauga Campus, A
Kent State University, Salem Campus, A
Kent State University, Trumbull Campus, AB
Kent State University, Tuscarawas Campus, AB
Lakeland Community College, A
Lorain County Community College, A
Marion Technical College, A
Miami University-Middletown Campus, A
North Central State College, A
Ohio Northern University, B
The Ohio State University Agricultural Technical
  Institute, A
Ohio University, B
Ohio University-Lancaster, A
Sinclair Community College, A
Stark State College of Technology, A
Terra State Community College, A
The University of Akron, AB
University of Cincinnati, A
University of Cincinnati Raymond Walters College, A
University of Dayton, B
University of Rio Grande, AB
The University of Toledo, AB
Washington State Community College, A
Wright State University, A
Wright State University, Lake Campus, A
Zane State College, A

Oklahoma

Cameron University, A
Langston University, B
Northeastern State University, B
Oklahoma Panhandle State University, AB
Oklahoma State University, Okmulgee, A
Southeastern Oklahoma State University, B
Southwestern Oklahoma State University, B
Tulsa Community College, A

Oregon

Blue Mountain Community College, A
Central Oregon Community College, A
Chemeketa Community College, A
Lane Community College, A
Linn-Benton Community College, A
Mt. Hood Community College, A
Rogue Community College, A
Southwestern Oregon Community College, A

Pennsylvania

California University of Pennsylvania, B
Cheyney University of Pennsylvania, B
Community College of Allegheny County, A
Edinboro University of Pennsylvania, A
Lackawanna College, A
Lehigh Carbon Community College, A
Millersville University of Pennsylvania, AB
Pennsylvania College of Technology, AB
Pennsylvania Highland Community College, A
The Pennsylvania State University York Campus of
  the Commonwealth College, A

Reading Area Community College, A

Puerto Rico

University of Puerto Rico at Arecibo, B
University of Puerto Rico at Bayamón, A
University of Puerto Rico at Ponce, A

Rhode Island

New England Institute of Technology, AB
Rhode Island College, B

South Carolina

Aiken Technical College, A
Greenville Technical College, A
South Carolina State University, B
Trident Technical College, A

South Dakota

Black Hills State University, B
South Dakota State University, B
Southeast Technical Institute, A

Tennessee

Cleveland State Community College, A
Fountainhead College of Technology, A
Jackson State Community College, A
Middle Tennessee State University, B
Nashville State Technical Community College, A
Northeast State Technical Community College, A
Pellissippi State Technical Community College, A
Southwest Tennessee Community College, A
Tennessee State University, B
Tennessee Technological University, B

Texas

Austin Community College, A
Houston Community College System, A
Kilgore College, A
Lamar University, B
Navarro College, A
Panola College, A
Prairie View A&M University, B
Richland College, A
Sam Houston State University, B
San Antonio College, A
South Texas College, A
Temple College, A
Texas A&M University-Kingsville, B
Texas Southern University, B
Texas State Technical College Harlingen, A
Texas State Technical College Waco, A
Texas State University-San Marcos, B
University of Houston, B
The University of Texas at Tyler, B
Victoria College, A
West Texas A&M University, B

Utah

Weber State University, AB

Vermont

Community College of Vermont, A

Virginia

Mountain Empire Community College, A
Patrick Henry Community College, A

Washington

Central Washington University, B
Everett Community College, A
Grays Harbor College, A
Highline Community College, A
Lower Columbia College, A
North Seattle Community College, A
Olympic College, A
Pierce College, A
Shoreline Community College, A
Spokane Community College, A
Western Washington University, B
Yakima Valley Community College, A

West Virginia

Fairmont State University, AB
West Virginia Northern Community College, A

West Virginia University Institute of Technology, B

Wisconsin

Blackhawk Technical College, A
Fox Valley Technical College, A
Gateway Technical College, A
Mid-State Technical College, A
Milwaukee Area Technical College, A
Northcentral Technical College, A
Northeast Wisconsin Technical College, A
University of Wisconsin-Platteville, B

British Columbia

British Columbia Institute of Technology, A

INFECTIOUS DISEASES

California

University of California, Berkeley, MD

Connecticut

Yale University, DO

District of Columbia

The George Washington University, M
Georgetown University, M

Georgia

University of Georgia, MD

Illinois

Loyola University Chicago, M

Indiana

Purdue University, MD

Maryland

The Johns Hopkins University, MD

Massachusetts

Harvard University, D

Minnesota

University of Minnesota, Twin Cities Campus, MD

New York

Cornell University, MD

Pennsylvania

University of Pittsburgh, MD

Texas

The University of Texas Medical Branch, DO

Alberta

University of Calgary, MD

Ontario

University of Guelph, MD

Quebec

Université Laval, O
Université de Montréal, O

INFORMATION RESOURCES MANAGEMENT/CIO TRAINING

Maryland

Mount St. Mary's University, B

Michigan

Mott Community College, A

New York

Clarkson University, B

Pennsylvania

Juniata College, B

Wisconsin

University of Wisconsin-Eau Claire, B

INFORMATION SCIENCE/STUDIES

Alabama

Alabama State University, B
American College of Computer & Information
    Sciences, BM
Athens State University, B
Central Alabama Community College, A
Chattahoochee Valley Community College, A
Faulkner University, AB
H. Councill Trenholm State Technical College, A
Herzing College, AB
J. F. Drake State Technical College, A
Lawson State Community College, A
Northeast Alabama Community College, A
Northwest-Shoals Community College, A
Oakwood College, AB
Remington College-Mobile Campus, A
South University, AB
Southern Union State Community College, A
The University of Alabama, MD
The University of Alabama at Birmingham, MD
University of Mobile, B
University of South Alabama, M

Alaska

University of Alaska Anchorage, A

Arizona

Arizona State University at the Polytechnic
    Campus, M
Arizona Western College, A
Cochise College (Douglas), A
Cochise College (Sierra Vista), A
Coconino Community College, A
DeVry University (Phoenix), B
Diné College, A
Eastern Arizona College, A
Lamson College, A
Northland Pioneer College, A
Phoenix College, A
Rio Salado College, A
Scottsdale Community College, A
South Mountain Community College, A
The University of Arizona, MD
University of Phoenix-Phoenix Campus, M
Western International University, B
Yavapai College, A

Arkansas

Arkansas State University-Mountain Home, A
Arkansas Tech University, AM
Black River Technical College, A
National Park Community College, A
Ozarka College, A
Pulaski Technical College, A
University of Arkansas Community College at
    Morrilton, A
University of Arkansas at Little Rock, B

California

Allan Hancock College, A
Bakersfield College, A
California Baptist University, B
California Lutheran University, B
California State Polytechnic University, Pomona, B
California State University, Dominguez Hills, B
California State University, East Bay, B
California State University, Fullerton, BM
California State University, Northridge, B
California State University, Stanislaus, B
Cañada College, A
Chabot College, A
Chaffey College, A
Coleman College (La Mesa), M
College of Alameda, A
College of the Canyons, A
College of Marin, A
College of San Mateo, A

College of the Sequoias, A
Compton Community College, A
Cosumnes River College (Sacramento), A
Cuyamaca College, A
Cypress College, A
De Anza College, A
DeVry University (Fremont), B
DeVry University (Long Beach), B
DeVry University (Pomona), B
DeVry University (West Hills), B
Evergreen Valley College, A
Fullerton College, A
Gavilan College, A
Grossmont College, A
Heald College-Fresno, A
Humboldt State University, B
Humphreys College, AB
Imperial Valley College, A
La Sierra University, B
Laney College, A
Las Positas College, A
Los Angeles Harbor College, A
Los Angeles Trade-Technical College, A
Los Angeles Valley College, A
Mendocino College, A
Merritt College, A
MiraCosta College, A
Mission College, A
Monterey Peninsula College, A
Moorpark College, A
Mt. Sierra College, B
The National Hispanic University, AB
National University, BM
Orange Coast College, A
Oxnard College, A
Pacific Union College, AB
Palomar College, A
Pasadena City College, A
Platt College-Los Angeles, Inc, A
Platt College (Newport Beach), A
Reedley College, A
Saddleback College, A
San Diego Miramar College, A
San Diego State University, B
San Francisco State University, B
San Jose State University, M
Santa Ana College, A
Santa Barbara City College, A
Santa Monica College, A
Sierra College, A
Southwestern College, A
University of California, Berkeley, MD
University of California, Irvine, MD
University of California, Los Angeles, BMDO
University of California, Santa Cruz, B
University of the Pacific, B
University of Phoenix-Southern California
    Campus, M
University of San Francisco, B
Victor Valley College, A
West Hills Community College, A
West Valley College, A
Woodbury University, B

Colorado

Aims Community College, A
Arapahoe Community College, A
Aspen University, M
Colorado State University, B
Colorado Technical University, BM
Colorado Technical University Denver Campus, AB
Community College of Aurora, A
DeVry University (Colorado Springs), AB
Fort Lewis College, B
Lamar Community College, A
Mesa State College, B
National American University (Colorado Springs)
    , AB
National American University (Denver), AB
Pueblo Community College, A
Regis University, MO
Trinidad State Junior College, A
University of Colorado at Colorado Springs, M
University of Colorado at Denver and Health
    Sciences Center - Downtown Denver Campus, D
University of Denver, M

University of Phoenix-Southern Colorado
    Campus, M

Connecticut

Albertus Magnus College, AB
Central Connecticut State University, M
Fairfield University, B
Gibbs College, A
Manchester Community College, A
Naugatuck Valley Community College, A
Northwestern Connecticut Community College, A
Norwalk Community College, A
Quinnipiac University, B
Sacred Heart University, MO
Southern Connecticut State University, O
Tunxis Community College, A
University of Bridgeport, B
University of New Haven, BM

Delaware

Delaware State University, B
Delaware Technical & Community College,
    Stanton/Wilmington Campus, A
Goldey-Beacom College, AB
University of Delaware, MD

District of Columbia

The Catholic University of America, MO
Gallaudet University, B
Howard University, B
Southeastern University, AB
Strayer University, ABM
University of the District of Columbia, B

Florida

American InterContinental University, M
Barry University, BM
Beacon College, AB
Bethune-Cookman College, B
Broward Community College, A
Daytona Beach Community College, A
DeVry University (Orlando), B
Edward Waters College, B
Everglades University (Boca Raton), M
Florida Agricultural and Mechanical University, B
Florida Community College at Jacksonville, A
Florida Gulf Coast University, M
Florida Institute of Technology, BM
Florida Metropolitan University-Melbourne
    Campus, AB
Florida State University, BMDO
Hillsborough Community College, A
Indian River Community College, A
Jones College (Jacksonville), AB
Keiser College (Sarasota), A
Manatee Community College, A
Miami Dade College, A
Nova Southeastern University, MDO
Pensacola Junior College, A
Polk Community College, A
Remington College-Tampa Campus, A
St. Thomas University, B
Santa Fe Community College, A
Seminole Community College, A
South University (West Palm Beach), A
Southwest Florida College (Fort Myers), A
University of Florida, MDO
University of Miami, B
University of North Florida, M
University of Phoenix-Central Florida Campus, M
University of Phoenix-North Florida Campus, B
University of South Florida, BM
The University of Tampa, AB

Georgia

Altamaha Technical College, A
American InterContinental University (Dunwoody
    Campus), M
Appalachian Technical College, A
Armstrong Atlantic State University, B
Athens Technical College, A
Atlanta Metropolitan College, A
Augusta Technical College, A
Bainbridge College, A
Brewton-Parker College, B

Central Georgia Technical College, A
Chattahoochee Technical College, A
Clark Atlanta University, BMO
Clayton State University, AB
Columbus State University, A
Columbus Technical College, A
Coosa Valley Technical College, A
Dalton State College, A
DeKalb Technical College, A
DeVry University (Alpharetta), B
DeVry University (Decatur), B
East Central Technical College, A
Flint River Technical College, A
Georgia Highlands College, A
Georgia Southwestern State University, M
Gwinnett Technical College, A
Herzing College, AB
Kennesaw State University, M
Lanier Technical College, A
Macon State College, AB
Mercer University, B
Middle Georgia College, A
Middle Georgia Technical College, A
Moultrie Technical College, A
North Georgia College & State University, B
Northwestern Technical College, A
Ogeechee Technical College, A
Okefenokee Technical College, A
Reinhardt College, B
Sandersville Technical College, A
South Georgia College, A
South Georgia Technical College, A
Southeastern Technical College, A
Southern Polytechnic State University, BM
Southwest Georgia Technical College, A
Swainsboro Technical College, A
Valdosta State University, BM
West Central Technical College, A
West Georgia Technical College, A

Hawaii

Brigham Young University-Hawaii, B
Hawaii Pacific University, B
Heald College-Honolulu, A
University of Hawaii at Manoa, MDO

Idaho

Boise State University, B
Brigham Young University -Idaho, A
Idaho State University, B

Illinois

American InterContinental University Online, M
Benedictine University, B
Bradley University, BM
Chicago State University, B
City Colleges of Chicago, Harold Washington
    College, A
City Colleges of Chicago, Harry S. Truman
    College, A
Concordia University, B
Danville Area Community College, A
DePaul University, BM
DeVry University (Addison), B
DeVry University (Chicago), B
DeVry University (Tinley Park), B
Dominican University, BMO
Elgin Community College, A
Gem City College, A
Heartland Community College, A
Illinois College, B
Illinois Institute of Technology, B
Illinois State University, B
John A. Logan College, A
Judson College, B
Kankakee Community College, A
Lincoln College-Normal, A
Loyola University Chicago, M
MacMurray College, B
McKendree College, B
Midstate College, A
National-Louis University, B
Northwestern University, BM
Oakton Community College, A
Olivet Nazarene University, B
Parkland College, A

Quincy University, B
Richland Community College, A
Saint Xavier University, M
Shawnee Community College, A
South Suburban College, A
Southeastern Illinois College, A
Southern Illinois University Carbondale, B
Southwestern Illinois College, A
Spoon River College, A
Trinity Christian College, B
Triton College, A
University of Illinois at Urbana-Champaign, MDO
William Rainey Harper College, A

Indiana

Anderson University, B
Ball State University, ABM
Butler University, B
Calumet College of Saint Joseph, AB
Goshen College, B
Indiana Tech, AB
Indiana University Bloomington, MDO
Indiana University-Purdue University
    Indianapolis, MO
Oakland City University, AB
Purdue University Calumet, B
Purdue University North Central, A
Saint Mary-of-the-Woods College, B
Taylor University, B
Vincennes University, A

Iowa

Central College, B
Clarke College, B
Grand View College, B
Iowa State University of Science and Technology, M
Iowa Wesleyan College, B
St. Ambrose University, B
Simpson College, B
Southeastern Community College, North Campus, A
Southeastern Community College, South
    Campus, A
The University of Iowa, MO
Waldorf College, B
Wartburg College, B

Kansas

Allen County Community College, A
Baker University, B
Barton County Community College, A
Coffeyville Community College, A
Dodge City Community College, A
Emporia State University, BMD
Fort Hays State University, B
Garden City Community College, A
Highland Community College, A
Kansas State University, BMD
Kansas Wesleyan University, B
Neosho County Community College, A
Newman University, AB
Ottawa University, B
University of Saint Mary, B

Kentucky

Ashland Community and Technical College, A
Campbellsville University, AB
Draughons Junior College, A
Eastern Kentucky University, B
Elizabethtown Community and Technical College, A
Hazard Community and Technical College, A
Lexington Community College, A
Madisonville Community College, A
Murray State University, AB
Northern Kentucky University, BM
St. Catharine College, A
West Kentucky Community and Technical College, A

Louisiana

Bossier Parish Community College, A
Dillard University, B
Elaine P. Nunez Community College, A
Grambling State University, B
Louisiana State University and Agricultural and
    Mechanical College, MO
Louisiana State University in Shreveport, B

Loyola University New Orleans, B
Northwestern State University of Louisiana, B
Tulane University, AB

Maine

Husson College, AB
Southern Maine Community College, A

Maryland

Anne Arundel Community College, A
Baltimore City Community College, A
Capitol College, M
Cecil Community College, A
College of Notre Dame of Maryland, B
College of Southern Maryland, A
Columbia Union College, B
Frostburg State University, B
Hagerstown Business College, A
Hood College, M
Howard Community College, A
The Johns Hopkins University, M
Morgan State University, B
Prince George's Community College, A
Towson University, BO
University of Baltimore, BMD
University of Maryland, Baltimore County, BMDO
University of Maryland, College Park, BMDO
University of Maryland University College, BMO
University of Phoenix-Maryland Campus, M
Villa Julie College, ABM

Massachusetts

American International College, B
Atlantic Union College, B
Bentley College, M
Boston University, B
Bristol Community College, A
Cape Cod Community College, A
Clark University, M
Fitchburg State College, B
Greenfield Community College, A
Harvard University, BM
Holyoke Community College, A
Lasell College, B
Massachusetts Bay Community College, A
Massachusetts Institute of Technology, D
Mount Wachusett Community College, A
North Shore Community College, A
Northeastern University, BM
Quinsigamond Community College, A
Roxbury Community College, A
Simmons College, MDO
Suffolk University, B
Westfield State College, B
Worcester Polytechnic Institute, B

Michigan

Alpena Community College, A
Andrews University, B
Baker College of Cadillac, AB
Baker College of Clinton Township, A
Baker College of Flint, AB
Baker College of Jackson, AB
Baker College of Muskegon, AB
Baker College of Owosso, AB
Baker College of Port Huron, AB
Bay Mills Community College, A
Bay de Noc Community College, A
Cleary University, B
Cornerstone University, B
Eastern Michigan University, B
Ferris State University, B
Grand Valley State University, BM
Henry Ford Community College, A
Kettering University, BM
Kirtland Community College, A
Lansing Community College, A
Lewis College of Business, A
Madonna University, B
Michigan Technological University, B
Mid Michigan Community College, A
Muskegon Community College, A
Northern Michigan University, B
St. Clair County Community College, A
Siena Heights University, AB
University of Detroit Mercy, B

University of Michigan, MD
University of Michigan-Dearborn, M
University of Michigan-Flint, B
Washtenaw Community College, A
Wayne State University, BMO

Minnesota

Bemidji State University, B
Brown College, A
Capella University, M
College of St. Catherine, M
DeVry University, B
Metropolitan State University, BM
Minneapolis Community and Technical College, A
Minnesota State University Mankato, B
National American University (Roseville), AB
Ridgewater College, A
St. Cloud State University, B
Saint Mary's University of Minnesota, B
University of Minnesota, Crookston, AB
University of Minnesota, Twin Cities Campus, MD
Winona State University, B

Mississippi

Alcorn State University, M
Belhaven College, B
Mississippi University for Women, B
Northeast Mississippi Community College, A

Missouri

Blue River Community College, A
Central Missouri State University, MO
Culver-Stockton College, B
DeVry University (Kansas City), B
Harris-Stowe State University, B
Lincoln University, B
Metropolitan Community College-Business &
   Technology College, A
Missouri Southern State University, AB
Missouri Western State University, B
National American University, AB
Northwest Missouri State University, B
Ozarks Technical Community College, A
St. Louis Community College at Florissant Valley, A
St. Louis Community College at Meramec, A
State Fair Community College, A
University of Missouri-Columbia, MDO
University of Missouri-Rolla, BM
Washington University in St. Louis, B
Webster University, B
William Jewell College, B

Montana

Montana State University-Northern, AB
Montana Tech of The University of Montana, B
University of Great Falls, BM
The University of Montana-Missoula, B
The University of Montana-Western, A

Nebraska

Bellevue University, BM
Chadron State College, B
Nebraska Wesleyan University, B
Union College, AB
University of Nebraska at Omaha, D
Wayne State College, B

Nevada

Community College of Southern Nevada, A
Morrison University, A
Truckee Meadows Community College, A

New Hampshire

Daniel Webster College, AB
Hesser College, A
McIntosh College, A
New Hampshire Community Technical College,
   Manchester/Stratham, A
New Hampshire Community Technical College,
   Nashua/Claremont, A
Rivier College, AB

New Jersey

Bloomfield College, B
Centenary College, B

Cumberland County College, A
DeVry University, A
Essex County College, A
Gloucester County College, A
Middlesex County College, A
Montclair State University, M
New Jersey Institute of Technology, BMD
Ocean County College, A
Passaic County Community College, A
Ramapo College of New Jersey, B
Raritan Valley Community College, A
The Richard Stockton College of New Jersey, B
Rider University, B
Rutgers, The State University of New Jersey, New
   Brunswick/Piscataway, BMD
Rutgers, The State University of New Jersey,
   Newark, B
Saint Peter's College, AB
Stevens Institute of Technology, MO
Union County College, A
Warren County Community College, A

New Mexico

Central New Mexico Community College, A
Mesalands Community College, A
National American University (Albuquerque), AB
New Mexico Highlands University, B
New Mexico State University, B
New Mexico State University-Carlsbad, A
San Juan College, A
University of New Mexico-Valencia Campus, A
University of Phoenix-New Mexico Campus, M

New York

Adirondack Community College, A
Bernard M. Baruch College of the City University of
   New York, B
Bramson ORT College, A
Briarcliffe College, A
Brooklyn College of the City University of New
   York, BMD
Broome Community College, A
Bryant and Stratton College, North Campus, A
Buffalo State College, State University of New
   York, B
Cayuga County Community College, A
Clarkson University, M
The College of Saint Rose, BM
College of Staten Island of the City University of
   New York, B
The College of Westchester, A
Columbia-Greene Community College, A
Cornell University, BD
DeVry Institute of Technology, B
Dutchess Community College, A
Elmira College, B
Erie Community College, A
Erie Community College, North Campus, A
Erie Community College, South Campus, A
Excelsior College, B
Farmingdale State University of New York, A
Fiorello H. LaGuardia Community College of the
   City University of New York, A
Fordham University, B
Fulton-Montgomery Community College, A
Genesee Community College, A
Hofstra University, B
Jefferson Community College, A
John Jay College of Criminal Justice of the City
   University of New York, B
Le Moyne College, B
Long Island University, C.W. Post Campus, BMDO
Marist College, B
Medgar Evers College of the City University of New
   York, B
Mercy College, B
Monroe College (Bronx), AB
Monroe College (New Rochelle), AB
Monroe Community College, A
Nazareth College of Rochester, B
New York City College of Technology of the City
   University of New York, A
New York Institute of Technology, B
New York University, B
Niagara County Community College, A
Niagara University, B

Onondaga Community College, A
Orange County Community College, A
Pace University, BMDO
Pratt Institute, MO
Queens College of the City University of New
   York, MO
Queensborough Community College of the City
   University of New York, A
Rensselaer Polytechnic Institute, M
Rochester Institute of Technology, M
Sage College of Albany, A
St. John's University, BMO
St. Thomas Aquinas College, B
State University of New York at Binghamton, B
State University of New York at Buffalo, MDO
State University of New York College of Agriculture
   and Technology at Cobleskill, A
State University of New York College of Agriculture
   and Technology at Morrisville, A
State University of New York College at Old
   Westbury, B
State University of New York College of Technology
   at Canton, A
State University of New York, Fredonia, B
State University of New York Institute of
   Technology, BM
State University of New York at Oswego, B
Stony Brook University, State University of New
   York, B
Suffolk County Community College, A
Sullivan County Community College, A
Syracuse University, BMDO
Tompkins Cortland Community College, A
Touro College, A
Ulster County Community College, A
United States Military Academy, B
University at Albany, State University of New
   York, BMDO
Westchester Community College, A
York College of the City University of New York, B

North Carolina

Alamance Community College, A
Beaufort County Community College, A
Belmont Abbey College, B
Blue Ridge Community College, A
Catawba College, B
Central Carolina Community College, A
Chowan University, B
Cleveland Community College, A
College of The Albemarle, A
Durham Technical Community College, A
East Carolina University, M
Fayetteville Technical Community College, A
Gaston College, A
Guilford College, B
Guilford Technical Community College, A
Haywood Community College, A
High Point University, B
Johnson C. Smith University, B
Lees-McRae College, B
Livingstone College, B
Louisburg College, A
Martin Community College, A
Mount Olive College, AB
North Carolina Central University, BM
North Carolina Wesleyan College, B
Queens University of Charlotte, B
Rockingham Community College, A
Rowan-Cabarrus Community College, A
Sandhills Community College, A
Southwestern Community College, A
Stanly Community College, A
Surry Community College, A
The University of North Carolina at Chapel
   Hill, BMDO
The University of North Carolina at Charlotte, MD
The University of North Carolina at Greensboro, M
Wilson Technical Community College, A

North Dakota

Fort Berthold Community College, A
Minot State University-Bottineau Campus, A

University of North Dakota, B

Ohio

Ashland University, B
Baldwin-Wallace College, B
Bluffton University, B
Case Western Reserve University, MD
Cincinnati State Technical and Community
  College, A
Clark State Community College, A
Cleveland State University, B
DeVry University (Columbus), B
Heidelberg College, B
James A. Rhodes State College, A
Kent State University, M
Lakeland Community College, A
Lorain County Community College, A
Marietta College, B
Miami-Jacobs College, A
Miami University-Middletown Campus, A
Mount Union College, B
North Central State College, A
Notre Dame College, B
Ohio Dominican University, B
The Ohio State University, BMD
Ohio University-Eastern, B
Sinclair Community College, A
Southwestern College of Business (Cincinnati), A
Terra State Community College, A
Tiffin University, B
University of Cincinnati, AB
University of Cincinnati Clermont College, A
University of Cincinnati Raymond Walters College, A
University of Dayton, B
University of Phoenix-Cincinnati Campus, M
The University of Toledo, AB
Wilberforce University, B
Wright State University, B

Oklahoma

Murray State College, A
Northern Oklahoma College, A
Northwestern Oklahoma State University, B
Oklahoma Baptist University, B
Oklahoma Christian University, B
Oklahoma Panhandle State University, AB
Oklahoma State University, Okmulgee, A
Oklahoma Wesleyan University, AB
Rogers State University, A
Rose State College, A
Southeastern Oklahoma State University, B
Tulsa Community College, A
University of Oklahoma, MO
University of Phoenix-Oklahoma City Campus, M
University of Tulsa, B

Oregon

Blue Mountain Community College, A
George Fox University, B
Heald College-Portland, A
Oregon State University, B
Pioneer Pacific College, A
Portland Community College, A
University of Oregon, MD

Pennsylvania

Albright College, B
Alvernia College, AB
Bucks County Community College, A
Carlow University, B
Carnegie Mellon University, BMD
Cedar Crest College, B
Central Pennsylvania College, AB
Clarion University of Pennsylvania, B
College Misericordia, B
Community College of Beaver County, A
Delaware County Community College, A
DeSales University, B
Drexel University, BMDO
Erie Business Center, Main, A
Gannon University, M
Harcum College, A
Immaculata University, AB
La Salle University, B
Lehigh Carbon Community College, A

Lehigh University, BM
Lehigh Valley College, A
Mansfield University of Pennsylvania, ABM
Marywood University, M
Mercyhurst College, B
Messiah College, B
Montgomery County Community College, A
Mount Aloysius College, B
Peirce College, B
The Pennsylvania State University Abington
  College, B
The Pennsylvania State University Altoona
  College, AB
The Pennsylvania State University Beaver Campus
  of the Commonwealth College, B
The Pennsylvania State University Berks Campus of
  the Berks-Lehigh Valley College, AB
The Pennsylvania State University Delaware County
  Campus of the Commonwealth College, B
The Pennsylvania State University DuBois Campus
  of the Commonwealth College, AB
The Pennsylvania State University at Erie, The
  Behrend College, B
The Pennsylvania State University Fayette Campus
  of the Commonwealth College, B
The Pennsylvania State University Harrisburg
  Campus, B
The Pennsylvania State University Hazleton
  Campus of the Commonwealth College, A
The Pennsylvania State University, Lehigh Valley
  Campus of the Berks-Lehigh Valley College, AB
The Pennsylvania State University McKeesport
  Campus of the Commonwealth College, B
The Pennsylvania State University Mont Alto
  Campus of the Commonwealth College, B
The Pennsylvania State University New Kensington
  Campus of the Commonwealth College, AB
The Pennsylvania State University Schuylkill
  Campus of the Capital College, AB
The Pennsylvania State University Shenango
  Campus of the Commonwealth College, B
The Pennsylvania State University University Park
  Campus, BMD
The Pennsylvania State University Wilkes-Barre
  Campus of the Commonwealth College, B
The Pennsylvania State University Worthington
  Scranton Campus of the Commonwealth
  College, B
The Pennsylvania State University York Campus of
  the Commonwealth College, B
Philadelphia University, B
Reading Area Community College, A
Robert Morris University, BMD
Saint Joseph's University, B
Shippensburg University of Pennsylvania, M
Susquehanna University, B
Temple University, MD
Thaddeus Stevens College of Technology, A
Thiel College, B
University of Pennsylvania, MD
University of Pittsburgh, BMDO
University of Pittsburgh at Bradford, A
The University of Scranton, AB
Villanova University, B
Westminster College, B
Westmoreland County Community College, A
Widener University, B
Wilkes University, B

Puerto Rico

Caribbean University, B
Instituto Comercial de Puerto Rico Junior College, A
Inter American University of Puerto Rico,
  Metropolitan Campus, B
Inter American University of Puerto Rico, Ponce
  Campus, B
Inter American University of Puerto Rico, San
  Germán Campus, B
Universidad Metropolitana, B
University of Puerto Rico, Mayagüez Campus, BD
University of Puerto Rico, Río Piedras, M
University of the Sacred Heart, B

Rhode Island

Bryant University, M
Johnson & Wales University, B

Salve Regina University, B
University of Rhode Island, M

South Carolina

The Citadel, The Military College of South
  Carolina, M
Clemson University, B
College of Charleston, B
Limestone College, AB
University of South Carolina, MO

South Dakota

Colorado Technical University Sioux Falls
  Campus, AB
Dakota State University, ABM
Mitchell Technical Institute, A
National American University (Rapid City), AB
National American University-Sioux Falls
  Branch, AB
Sisseton-Wahpeton Community College, A
South Dakota State University, B
Southeast Technical Institute, A
University of Sioux Falls, B

Tennessee

Belmont University, B
Carson-Newman College, B
Chattanooga State Technical Community College, A
Columbia State Community College, A
Draughons Junior College (Clarksville), A
Draughons Junior College (Nashville), A
East Tennessee State University, M
Fountainhead College of Technology, A
Freed-Hardeman University, B
King College, B
Lee University, B
Lipscomb University, B
Nashville State Technical Community College, A
Remington College-Memphis Campus, A
South College, A
Tennessee Technological University, B
Tennessee Temple University, B
Trevecca Nazarene University, ABM
Tusculum College, B
Union University, B
The University of Tennessee, MD

Texas

Amarillo College, A
Austin Community College, A
Del Mar College, A
DeVry University (Irving), B
El Centro College, A
Frank Phillips College, A
Hill College of the Hill Junior College District, A
Houston Baptist University, B
Howard Payne University, B
Kingwood College, A
Lamar State College-Orange, A
Lamar University, BM
Laredo Community College, A
Lee College, A
LeTourneau University, B
McLennan Community College, A
McMurry University, B
Midwestern State University, B
Mountain View College, A
North Central Texas College, A
North Harris College, A
North Lake College, A
Northeast Texas Community College, A
Odessa College, A
Palo Alto College, A
Panola College, A
Paris Junior College, A
St. Mary's University of San Antonio, BM
Sam Houston State University, M
South Texas College, A
Southern Methodist University, MD
Southwestern Adventist University, AB
Texas A&M International University, B
Texas A&M University-Commerce, B
Texas A&M University-Corpus Christi, B
Texas A&M University-Kingsville, B
Texas Lutheran University, B
Texas State Technical College Waco, A

University of Houston, BMD
University of Houston-Clear Lake, BM
University of Mary Hardin-Baylor, B
University of North Texas, BMD
The University of Texas at Austin, MD
The University of Texas at Brownsville, B
The University of Texas at El Paso, BM
The University of Texas at San Antonio, MD
The University of Texas at Tyler, M
Victoria College, A
Weatherford College, A

Utah

Brigham Young University, M
Mountain West College, A
Salt Lake Community College, A
Snow College, A
Southern Utah University, A
Utah State University, B
Weber State University, AB
Western Governors University, AB

Vermont

Champlain College, AB
College of St. Joseph, AB
Johnson State College, AB
Marlboro College, M
Norwich University, B
Saint Michael's College, B
University of Vermont, B

Virginia

Averett University, B
Blue Ridge Community College, A
Bryant and Stratton College, Virginia Beach, A
Central Virginia Community College, A
Christopher Newport University, B
Dabney S. Lancaster Community College, A
DeVry University (Arlington), B
ECPI College of Technology (Newport News), A
ECPI College of Technology (Virginia Beach), A
ECPI Technical College (Richmond), A
ECPI Technical College (Roanoke), A
Ferrum College, B
George Mason University, MDO
Hampton University, B
James Madison University, B
Lord Fairfax Community College, A
Marymount University, B
Mountain Empire Community College, A
New River Community College, A
Northern Virginia Community College, A
Radford University, B
Rappahannock Community College, A
Roanoke College, B
Southside Virginia Community College, A
Southwest Virginia Community College, A
Thomas Nelson Community College, A
University of Management and Technology, M
Virginia Commonwealth University, B
Virginia Highlands Community College, A
Virginia Polytechnic Institute and State
    University, BM
Wytheville Community College, A

Washington

Bates Technical College, A
Bellevue Community College, A
Big Bend Community College, A
Central Washington University, M
DeVry University (Federal Way), B
Gonzaga University, B
Grays Harbor College, A
Green River Community College, A
Lower Columbia College, A
Olympic College, A
Pierce College, A
Saint Martin's University, B
South Puget Sound Community College, A
Spokane Falls Community College, A
Tacoma Community College, A
University of Washington, BMD

Walla Walla Community College, A

West Virginia

Concord University, B
Davis & Elkins College, B
Fairmont State University, A
Glenville State College, B
Marshall University, M
Mountain State University, AB
Southern West Virginia Community and Technical
    College, A
University of Charleston, B
West Liberty State College, B
West Virginia Wesleyan College, B

Wisconsin

Carroll College, B
Edgewood College, B
Marquette University, B
Mid-State Technical College, A
Northcentral Technical College, A
Northland College, B
Silver Lake College, B
University of Wisconsin-Green Bay, AB
University of Wisconsin-Madison, MDO
University of Wisconsin-Milwaukee, MO
University of Wisconsin-Parkside, M
University of Wisconsin-River Falls, B
University of Wisconsin-Superior, B

Wyoming

Northwest College, A
Sheridan College-Sheridan and Gillette, A
Western Wyoming Community College, A

Alberta

Athabasca University, BM
Southern Alberta Institute of Technology, B
University of Alberta, BM

British Columbia

British Columbia Institute of Technology, A
Simon Fraser University, M
The University of British Columbia, MDO

Manitoba

The University of Winnipeg, B

New Brunswick

University of New Brunswick Fredericton, B

Newfoundland and Labrador

Memorial University of Newfoundland, B

Nova Scotia

Cape Breton University, B
Dalhousie University, MO
Mount Saint Vincent University, B
St. Francis Xavier University, B

Ontario

Brock University, B
Carleton University, BMD
Lakehead University, B
University of Guelph, B
University of Ottawa, BO
University of Toronto, MDO
University of Waterloo, MD
The University of Western Ontario, BMD
University of Windsor, B

Quebec

Concordia University, M
HEC Montreal, B
McGill University, BMDO
Université de Montréal, MD
Université du Québec àChicoutimi, B
Université du Québec àTrois-Rivières, B

Université de Sherbrooke, B

Saskatchewan

University of Saskatchewan, B

INFORMATION TECHNOLOGY

Alabama

American College of Computer & Information
    Sciences, B
Virginia College at Birmingham, B

Arizona

GateWay Community College, A
ITT Technical Institute (Phoenix), B
Mohave Community College, A
Rio Salado College, A
University of Phoenix-Phoenix Campus, B
University of Phoenix-Southern Arizona Campus, B

Arkansas

Arkansas State University-Beebe, A
Harding University, B
University of Arkansas, B
University of Arkansas Community College at
    Batesville, A
University of Phoenix-Little Rock Campus, B

California

California State University Channel Islands, B
California State University, Chico, B
California State University, Los Angeles, B
College of the Siskiyous, A
Concordia University, B
Cuesta College, A
Golden Gate University, B
Los Angeles City College, A
National University, B
Platt College-Los Angeles, Inc, A
Platt College (Newport Beach), A
Platt College (Ontario), A
San Diego State University, B
San Jose State University, B
Santa Ana College, A
Santa Barbara City College, A
Southwestern College, A
University of Phoenix-Bay Area Campus, B
University of Phoenix-Sacramento Valley Campus, B
University of Phoenix-San Diego Campus, B
University of Phoenix-Southern California
    Campus, B
Western Career College (Walnut Creek), A

Colorado

National American University (Denver), AB
Trinidad State Junior College, A
University of Phoenix-Denver Campus, B
University of Phoenix-Southern Colorado
    Campus, B

Connecticut

Capital Community College, A
Naugatuck Valley Community College, A
Sacred Heart University, B

Delaware

Wilmington College, B

Florida

American InterContinental University, B
Central Florida Community College, A
Daytona Beach Community College, A
Edison College, A
Everglades University (Boca Raton), B
Everglades University (Sarasota), B
Florida Community College at Jacksonville, A
Florida International University, B
Gulf Coast College, A
International College, AB
Okaloosa-Walton College, A
Pasco-Hernando Community College, A
St. Petersburg College, A
Seminole Community College, A

South University (West Palm Beach), AB
University of Central Florida, B
University of Phoenix-Central Florida Campus, B
University of Phoenix-South Florida Campus, B
Valencia Community College, A

Georgia

American InterContinental University (Dunwoody
   Campus), B
Armstrong Atlantic State University, B
Atlanta Metropolitan College, A
Atlanta Technical College, A
Bauder College, A
Gainesville College, B
Gordon College, A
Savannah Technical College, A
South University, AB
University of Phoenix-Atlanta Campus, B

Hawaii

University of Phoenix-Hawaii Campus, B

Illinois

American InterContinental University Online, B
Black Hawk College, A
Heartland Community College, A
Illinois Institute of Technology, B
Illinois State University, B
International Academy of Design & Technology, A
Lake Land College, A
Robert Morris College, B
University of St. Francis, B

Indiana

Indiana Business College (Evansville), A
Indiana Business College (Indianapolis), A
Indiana Business College (Lafayette), A
Indiana Business College (Muncie), A
Indiana Tech, A
ITT Technical Institute (Indianapolis), B
University of Phoenix-Indianapolis Campus, B
Vincennes University, A

Iowa

Hawkeye Community College, A
Iowa Lakes Community College, A
Kaplan University, AB

Kansas

Brown Mackie College-Kansas City, A
University of Phoenix-Wichita Campus, B

Kentucky

Big Sandy Community and Technical College, A
Draughons Junior College, A
Henderson Community College, A
Louisville Technical Institute, A
Northern Kentucky University, B
Owensboro Community and Technical College, A
Somerset Community College, A
Southeast Kentucky Community and Technical
   College, A

Louisiana

ITI Technical College, A
Louisiana State University at Alexandria, A
McNeese State University, A

Maryland

Cecil Community College, A
Frederick Community College, A
Howard Community College, A

Massachusetts

Bristol Community College, A
Cape Cod Community College, A
Curry College, B
Endicott College, B
Framingham State College, B
Simmons College, B
University of Massachusetts Lowell, AB

University of Phoenix-Central Massachusetts
   Campus, B

Michigan

Davenport University (Dearborn), AB
Delta College, A
Gogebic Community College, A
Lawrence Technological University, B
Monroe County Community College, A
North Central Michigan College, A
University of Michigan-Flint, B
University of Phoenix-Metro Detroit Campus, B
University of Phoenix-West Michigan Campus, B
West Shore Community College, A

Minnesota

Brown College, B
Capella University, B
Globe College, B
Mesabi Range Community and Technical College, A
Minnesota School of Business, AB
Minnesota School of Business-Brooklyn Center, AB
Minnesota School of Business-Plymouth, AB
Minnesota School of Business-Richfield, AB
Minnesota School of Business-St. Cloud, AB
Minnesota School of Business-Shakopee, AB
Northland Community and Technical College-Thief
   River Falls, A
St. Cloud Technical College, A

Mississippi

Hinds Community College, A
Mississippi Gulf Coast Community College, A
Southwest Mississippi Community College, A

Missouri

College of the Ozarks, B
Grantham University, AB
Metropolitan Community College-Business &
   Technology College, A
Missouri State University-West Plains, A
St. Louis Community College at Forest Park, A
Three Rivers Community College, A
University of Missouri-Kansas City, B
University of Phoenix-St. Louis Campus, B
University of Phoenix-Springfield Campus, B

Montana

Miles Community College, A
Rocky Mountain College, B
University of Great Falls, B
The University of Montana-Missoula, B

Nebraska

Bellevue University, B
Central Community College-Columbus Campus, A
Central Community College-Grand Island
   Campus, A
Central Community College-Hastings Campus, A
Hamilton College-Lincoln, A
Nebraska Indian Community College, A
Western Nebraska Community College, A

New Hampshire

Plymouth State University, B
Southern New Hampshire University, AB

New Jersey

Burlington County College, A
Camden County College, A
Montclair State University, B

New Mexico

New Mexico Institute of Mining and Technology, B
New Mexico State University, B
University of Phoenix-New Mexico Campus, B

New York

Adirondack Community College, A
Bryant and Stratton College (Albany), A
Bryant and Stratton College, Amherst Campus, A
Bryant and Stratton College, Buffalo Campus, A
Bryant and Stratton College, Lackawanna
   Campus, A

Bryant and Stratton College, North Campus, A
Bryant and Stratton College (Rochester-Greece
   Campus), A
Bryant and Stratton College (Rochester-Henrietta
   Campus), A
Bryant and Stratton College (Syracuse), A
Canisius College, B
The College of Westchester, A
Corning Community College, A
D'Youville College, B
Houghton College, B
Hudson Valley Community College, A
Long Island University, C.W. Post Campus, B
Marist College, B
Mildred Elley, A
Monroe Community College, A
Mount Saint Mary College, B
Nazareth College of Rochester, B
Onondaga Community College, A
Orange County Community College, A
Queensborough Community College of the City
   University of New York, A
Rensselaer Polytechnic Institute, B
Rochester Institute of Technology, B
St. Francis College, B
Schenectady County Community College, A
State University of New York College of Agriculture
   and Technology at Cobleskill, B
Suffolk County Community College, A

North Carolina

Bladen Community College, A
Caldwell Community College and Technical
   Institute, A
Carteret Community College, A
Catawba Valley Community College, A
Central Carolina Community College, A
Cleveland Community College, A
College of The Albemarle, A
Durham Technical Community College, A
Edgecombe Community College, A
Fayetteville Technical Community College, A
Mayland Community College, A
Nash Community College, A
North Carolina State University, B
Randolph Community College, A
Sampson Community College, A
Surry Community College, A
Tri-County Community College, A
University of Phoenix-Raleigh Campus, B

North Dakota

Lake Region State College, A
Minot State University-Bottineau Campus, A

Ohio

Bluffton University, B
Bryant and Stratton College (Cleveland), A
Bryant and Stratton College (Parma), A
Bryant and Stratton College (Willoughby Hills), A
Clark State Community College, A
Davis College, A
James A. Rhodes State College, A
Kent State University, Geauga Campus, A
Lorain County Community College, A
Marion Technical College, A
Miami-Jacobs College, A
Ohio Valley College of Technology, A
Sinclair Community College, A
Stark State College of Technology, A
University of Phoenix-Cincinnati Campus, B
University of Phoenix-Cleveland Campus, B
University of Rio Grande, B

Oklahoma

Tulsa Community College, A
University of Phoenix-Oklahoma City Campus, B

Vatterott College (Oklahoma City), A

Oregon

Pioneer Pacific College, B
University of Phoenix-Oregon Campus, B

Pennsylvania

Berks Technical Institute, A
Bucks County Community College, A
Cabrini College, B
Harrisburg Area Community College, A
Johnson College, A
Juniata College, B
Keystone College, AB
Kutztown University of Pennsylvania, B
Laurel Business Institute, A
Pennsylvania College of Technology, A
Point Park University, AB
Slippery Rock University of Pennsylvania, B
Temple University, B
University of Phoenix-Philadelphia Campus, B
University of Phoenix-Pittsburgh Campus, B
Washington & Jefferson College, B
York Technical Institute, A

Rhode Island

Bryant University, B

South Carolina

Furman University, B
South University, AB
Spartanburg Methodist College, A
Williamsburg Technical College, A

South Dakota

Dakota State University, B
Kilian Community College, A
Lake Area Technical Institute, A
Mount Marty College, B
National American University-Sioux Falls
    Branch, AB
Southeast Technical Institute, A

Tennessee

Walters State Community College, A

Texas

American InterContinental University, B
Austin Community College, A
Brazosport College, A
Coastal Bend College, A
Del Mar College, A
El Centro College, A
El Paso Community College, A
Galveston College, A
Laredo Community College, A
Montgomery College, A
Palo Alto College, A
Texarkana College, A
Texas State Technical College Harlingen, A
Tyler Junior College, A
University of Houston, B
University of the Incarnate Word, B

Utah

Brigham Young University, B
LDS Business College, A
Neumont University, B
Salt Lake Community College, A
University of Phoenix-Utah Campus, B
Utah Valley State College, AB
Western Governors University, A

Vermont

Community College of Vermont, A
Vermont Technical College, B

Virginia

Blue Ridge Community College, A
Bryant and Stratton College, Richmond, A
Germanna Community College, A
ITT Technical Institute (Norfolk), B
J. Sargeant Reynolds Community College, A
Mountain Empires Community College, A

Patrick Henry Community College, A
Southside Virginia Community College, A
Stratford University, B
Tidewater Community College, A
University of Phoenix-Richmond Campus, B

Washington

Bellingham Technical College, A
Lower Columbia College, A
Olympic College, A
Tacoma Community College, A
University of Phoenix-Spokane Campus, B
University of Phoenix-Washington Campus, B

West Virginia

American Public University System, B
Community and Technical College of Shepherd, A
Mountain State University, A
Potomac State College of West Virginia
    University, A
West Virginia Northern Community College, A

Wisconsin

Bryant and Stratton College, A
Marian College of Fond du Lac, B
Milwaukee Area Technical College, A
University of Phoenix-Wisconsin Campus, B
University of Wisconsin-Whitewater, B

Wyoming

Laramie County Community College, A
Western Wyoming Community College, A

British Columbia

Kwantlen University College, B

Ontario

Ryerson University, B
University of Windsor, B
York University, B

Quebec

Université de Sherbrooke, B

INORGANIC CHEMISTRY

California

California Institute of Technology, B
California State University, Fullerton, M
California State University, Los Angeles, M

Connecticut

Wesleyan University, MD
Yale University, D

District of Columbia

The George Washington University, MD
Georgetown University, MD
Howard University, MD

Florida

Florida State University, MD
University of Miami, D
University of South Florida, MD

Georgia

Clark Atlanta University, MD
University of Georgia, MD

Illinois

Illinois Institute of Technology, MD

Indiana

Indiana University Bloomington, D
Purdue University, MD

University of Notre Dame, MD

Kansas

Kansas State University, M

Kentucky

University of Louisville, MD

Louisiana

Southern University and Agricultural and Mechanical
    College, M

Maryland

University of Maryland, College Park, MD

Massachusetts

Boston College, D
Brandeis University, MD
Harvard University, MD
Massachusetts Institute of Technology, D
Northeastern University, D
Tufts University, MD

Michigan

University of Michigan, D

Mississippi

University of Southern Mississippi, MD

Missouri

University of Missouri-Columbia, MD
University of Missouri-Kansas City, MD

Nebraska

University of Nebraska-Lincoln, D

New Jersey

Rutgers, The State University of New Jersey, New
    Brunswick/Piscataway, MD
Rutgers, The State University of New Jersey,
    Newark, MD
Seton Hall University, MD

New York

Clarkson University, MD
Cornell University, D
Rensselaer Polytechnic Institute, MD
State University of New York at Binghamton, D

North Carolina

Wake Forest University, MD

Ohio

Case Western Reserve University, MD
Cleveland State University, M
Kent State University, MD
Miami University, MD
University of Cincinnati, MD
The University of Toledo, MD

Oregon

Oregon State University, MD

South Dakota

South Dakota State University, MD

Tennessee

The University of Tennessee, MD
Vanderbilt University, MD

Texas

Rice University, D
The University of Texas at Austin, MD

Utah

Brigham Young University, MD

Washington

Washington State University, MD

West Virginia

West Virginia University, MD

Wisconsin

Marquette University, MD

Alberta

University of Calgary, MD

Ontario

McMaster University, MD

Saskatchewan

University of Regina, MD

INSTITUTIONAL FOOD WORKERS

Arkansas

North Arkansas College, A

California

MiraCosta College, A
Santa Barbara City College, A

Illinois

Kendall College, AB
Lexington College, AB

Iowa

Iowa Lakes Community College, A

Louisiana

Delgado Community College, A
Elaine P. Nunez Community College, A
Grambling State University, B

Missouri

Jefferson College, A

New York

State University of New York College of Agriculture
and Technology at Cobleskill, A

North Carolina

Asheville-Buncombe Technical Community
College, A
Cape Fear Community College, A
Wilkes Community College, A

Pennsylvania

The Art Institute of Pittsburgh, AB
Harrisburg Area Community College, A
Pennsylvania College of Technology, A

Texas

Texas State Technical College Harlingen, A
Texas State Technical College Waco, A
Texas Woman's University, B

West Virginia

Fairmont State University, A
West Virginia Northern Community College, A

INSTRUMENTATION TECHNOLOGY/TECHNICIAN

Alabama

Bishop State Community College, A
H. Councill Trenholm State Technical College, A

Alaska

University of Alaska Anchorage, Kenai Peninsula
College, A

Arkansas

Phillips Community College of the University of
Arkansas, A

California

Chabot College, A

Colorado

Colorado Northwestern Community College, A
Colorado State University-Pueblo, B

Delaware

Delaware Technical & Community College,
Stanton/Wilmington Campus, A

Florida

Florida Community College at Jacksonville, A

Georgia

Clayton State University, A
DeKalb Technical College, A

Idaho

Idaho State University, A

Illinois

Moraine Valley Community College, A
Southwestern Illinois College, A

Louisiana

ITI Technical College, A
Louisiana Technical College, A
McNeese State University, A

Maine

Northern Maine Community College, A

Michigan

Henry Ford Community College, A

Minnesota

Mesabi Range Community and Technical College, A
Ridgewater College, A
St. Cloud Technical College, A

Mississippi

Copiah-Lincoln Community College-Natchez
Campus, A
East Mississippi Community College, A

Missouri

Ozarks Technical Community College, A

New Mexico

San Juan College, A

New York

Excelsior College, AB
Monroe Community College, A
Nassau Community College, A

North Carolina

Cape Fear Community College, A
Central Carolina Community College, A
Lenoir Community College, A
Wake Technical Community College, A

Oklahoma

Spartan College of Aeronautics and Technology, A

Pennsylvania

Butler County Community College, A
Pennsylvania College of Technology, A

Puerto Rico

University of Puerto Rico at Bayamón, A

Rhode Island

Community College of Rhode Island, A

South Carolina

Orangeburg-Calhoun Technical College, A

Tennessee

Chattanooga State Technical Community College, A
Northeast State Technical Community College, A

Texas

Amarillo College, A
Brazosport College, A

Lee College, A
Texas State Technical College Harlingen, A
Texas State Technical College Waco, A

Utah

Salt Lake Community College, A

Virginia

New River Community College, A

Washington

Lower Columbia College, A
Yakima Valley Community College, A

Wisconsin

Mid-State Technical College, A
Northeast Wisconsin Technical College, A

Wyoming

Western Wyoming Community College, A

INSURANCE

Alabama

Alabama Southern Community College, A
Enterprise-Ozark Community College, A

Arizona

Mesa Community College, A

Arkansas

University of Central Arkansas, B

California

California State Polytechnic University, Pomona, B
California State University, Sacramento, B
City College of San Francisco, A
Merced College, A
San Diego City College, A

Connecticut

University of Connecticut, B
University of Hartford, B

District of Columbia

Howard University, B

Florida

Broward Community College, A
Daytona Beach Community College, A
Florida Community College at Jacksonville, A
Florida International University, B
Florida State University, M
University of Florida, B

Georgia

Georgia State University, BMD
University of Georgia, B

Illinois

Bradley University, B
Illinois State University, B
Illinois Wesleyan University, B
Richland Community College, A
Roosevelt University, B
William Rainey Harper College, A

Indiana

Ball State University, B
Indiana State University, B

Martin University, B

Kentucky

Eastern Kentucky University, B
St. Catharine College, A

Louisiana

University of Louisiana at Lafayette, B
University of Louisiana at Monroe, B

Michigan

Ferris State University, B
Olivet College, B

Minnesota

Fond du Lac Tribal and Community College, A
Minnesota State University Mankato, B
St. Cloud State University, B
University of Minnesota, Twin Cities Campus, B
University of St. Thomas, M

Mississippi

Delta State University, B
Mississippi State University, B
Northeast Mississippi Community College, A
University of Mississippi, B

Missouri

Missouri State University, B

New Jersey

Thomas Edison State College, M

New York

Excelsior College, B
Nassau Community College, A
Onondaga Community College, A
St. John's University, BM
Suffolk County Community College, A

North Carolina

Appalachian State University, B
Central Piedmont Community College, A
Isothermal Community College, A
Lenoir Community College, A

Ohio

Hondros College, A
The Ohio State University, B
University of Cincinnati, AB

Oklahoma

Oklahoma City Community College, A
Tulsa Community College, A

Pennsylvania

Community College of Allegheny County, A
Gannon University, B
Laurel Business Institute, A
Mercyhurst College, A
Temple University, BMD
University of Pennsylvania, BMD

South Carolina

University of South Carolina, B

Tennessee

University of Memphis, B

Texas

Austin Community College, A
Baylor University, B
Houston Community College System, A
Texas Southern University, B
Trinity Valley Community College, A

University of North Texas, BMD

Virginia

Virginia Commonwealth University, M

Washington

Seattle University, B
Washington State University, B

Wisconsin

Fox Valley Technical College, A
Madison Area Technical College, A
University of Wisconsin-Madison, BMD

Alberta

University of Calgary, B

Quebec

Université Laval, A

INTERCULTURAL/ MULTICULTURAL AND DIVERSITY STUDIES

California

William Jessup University, B

Indiana

Taylor University Fort Wayne, B

Minnesota

College of St. Catherine, B
St. Olaf College, B

Missouri

Evangel University, B

Oregon

Western Oregon University, B

Pennsylvania

Immaculata University, A

South Carolina

Columbia International University, B

Texas

University of Houston-Clear Lake, B

Vermont

Sterling College, B

Washington

The Evergreen State College, B
Northwest University, B

Wisconsin

Marquette University, B

British Columbia

Columbia Bible College, B

INTERDISCIPLINARY STUDIES

Alabama

Birmingham-Southern College, B
Huntingdon College, B
Judson College, B
Oakwood College, B
Stillman College, B
The University of Alabama, B

Alaska

Alaska Pacific University, M
University of Alaska Anchorage, BM
University of Alaska Fairbanks, MD

Arizona

Arizona State University, B
Arizona State University at the Polytechnic Campus, B

Arizona State University West, BM
Prescott College, B
The University of Arizona, MDO

Arkansas

Hendrix College, B
John Brown University, B
University of Arkansas, D

California

Bethany University, B
California Baptist University, B
California Lutheran University, B
California State University, Bakersfield, BM
California State University, Chico, M
California State University, Dominguez Hills, B
California State University, East Bay, BMO
California State University, Long Beach, BM
California State University, Los Angeles, B
California State University, Monterey Bay, B
California State University, Northridge, M
California State University, Sacramento, M
California State University, San Bernardino, BM
California State University, Stanislaus, M
Chabot College, A
Evergreen Valley College, A
Folsom Lake College, A
Fresno Pacific University, M
Hope International University, B
John F. Kennedy University, M
Mills College, B
Mt. San Jacinto College, A
National University, B
New College of California, B
Pacific Union College, B
Pasadena City College, A
Pepperdine University, B
Pitzer College, B
Pomona College, B
Saint Mary's College of California, B
San Diego Christian College, B
San Diego State University, M
San Jose State University, M
Santa Clara University, B
Sonoma State University, BM
Stanford University, BD
Thomas Aquinas College, B
University of California, San Diego, B
University of California, Santa Barbara, B
University of Judaism, B
University of the Pacific, B
University of Redlands, B
University of San Francisco, B
University of Southern California, B
Vanguard University of Southern California, B
Woodbury University, B

Colorado

United States Air Force Academy, B
University of Northern Colorado, BMDO
Western State College of Colorado, B

Connecticut

Albertus Magnus College, B
Central Connecticut State University, B
Connecticut College, B
Trinity College, B
University of Bridgeport, B
University of Hartford, B
Wesleyan University, B

District of Columbia

American University, BM
The Catholic University of America, B
The George Washington University, B
Georgetown University, B
Trinity (Washington) University, B

Florida

Eckerd College, B
Florida Institute of Technology, B
Jacksonville University, B
Jones College (Jacksonville), B
Jones College (Miami), B
Nova Southeastern University, BM

Schiller International University, B
Southeastern University, B

Georgia

Agnes Scott College, B
Clark Atlanta University, B
Covenant College, B
Emory University, BD
Morehouse College, B
Oglethorpe University, B
Piedmont College, B
University of Georgia, B
Wesleyan College, B

Hawaii

Brigham Young University-Hawaii, B
Hawaii Pacific University, B
University of Hawaii at Hilo, B
University of Hawaii at Manoa, B

Idaho

Boise State University, BM
Idaho State University, M
Lewis-Clark State College, B
University of Idaho, M

Illinois

Blackburn College, B
Columbia College Chicago, B
DePaul University, BM
Elmhurst College, B
Illinois College, B
Illinois State University, B
Illinois Wesleyan University, B
Millikin University, B
Northwestern University, B
Olivet Nazarene University, B
Triton College, A
University of Chicago, B
University of Illinois at Springfield, M
Wheaton College, M

Indiana

DePauw University, B
Earlham College, B
Manchester College, BM
Oakland City University, B
Purdue University, B
Saint Mary's College, B

Iowa

Central College, B
Coe College, B
Cornell College, B
Grinnell College, B
Hawkeye Community College, A
Iowa State University of Science and
  Technology, BM
Luther College, B
Morningside College, B
The University of Iowa, B

Kansas

Friends University, AB
Kansas State University, A
McPherson College, B
Sterling College, B
Tabor College, AB
University of Kansas, MDO
University of Saint Mary, B

Kentucky

Alice Lloyd College, B
Kentucky Christian University, B
Kentucky Wesleyan College, B
University of Kentucky, B

University of Louisville, M

Louisiana

Centenary College of Louisiana, B
Louisiana College, B

Maine

Bowdoin College, B
College of the Atlantic, B
Unity College, AB
University of Maine, D
University of Maine at Farmington, B

Maryland

College of Notre Dame of Maryland, B
Frostburg State University, M
Goucher College, B
The Johns Hopkins University, B
Loyola College in Maryland, BM
St. John's College, B
Towson University, B
University of Baltimore, B
University of Maryland, Baltimore County, B
University of Maryland, College Park, DO
Villa Julie College, AB

Massachusetts

Amherst College, B
Anna Maria College, B
Bentley College, B
Boston College, B
Boston University, BMD
Clark University, B
Elms College, B
Emerson College, B
Emmanuel College, B
Fitchburg State College, O
Harvard University, B
Lasell College, B
Lesley University, AM
Massachusetts College of Liberal Arts, B
Merrimack College, B
Mount Holyoke College, B
North Shore Community College, A
Simon's Rock College of Bard, B
Smith College, B
Suffolk University, AB
University of Massachusetts Boston, B
University of Massachusetts Dartmouth, B
Wheaton College, B
Worcester Polytechnic Institute, BMD

Michigan

Calvin College, B
Cornerstone University, BM
Grand Valley State University, B
Hillsdale College, B
Hope College, B
Kalamazoo College, B
Lake Superior State University, B
Rochester College, B
University of Michigan, B
Wayne State University, BMD

Minnesota

Augsburg College, B
Carleton College, B
Gustavus Adolphus College, B
Macalester College, B
Martin Luther College, B
Minneapolis College of Art and Design, B
Minnesota State University Mankato, M
Minnesota State University Moorhead, B
North Central University, AB
Ridgewater College, A
St. Cloud State University, B
Southwest Minnesota State University, B
University of Minnesota, Crookston, B
University of Minnesota, Duluth, B
University of Minnesota, Twin Cities Campus, D
University of St. Thomas, B

Vermilion Community College, A

Mississippi

Tougaloo College, B
University of Southern Mississippi, B

Missouri

Central Methodist University, AB
College of the Ozarks, B
Grantham University, AB
Harris-Stowe State University, B
Jefferson College, A
Maryville University of Saint Louis, B
Southeast Missouri State University, B
Stephens College, B
University of Missouri-Columbia, B
University of Missouri-Kansas City, BD
Washington University in St. Louis, B
Webster University, B
William Jewell College, B
William Woods University, B

Montana

Montana State University-Billings, M
Montana State University-Northern, AB
Rocky Mountain College, B
The University of Montana-Missoula, BMD

Nebraska

Chadron State College, B
Dana College, B
Nebraska Wesleyan University, B
Wayne State College, BM
Western Nebraska Community College, A

Nevada

Great Basin College, A
University of Nevada, Las Vegas, B

New Hampshire

Chester College of New England, B
Keene State College, B
University of New Hampshire, B

New Jersey

County College of Morris, A
Drew University, MDO
Felician College, B
Ramapo College of New Jersey, B
The Richard Stockton College of New Jersey, B
Rutgers, The State University of New Jersey, New
  Brunswick/Piscataway, BD

New Mexico

New Mexico State University, BMD
Western New Mexico University, BM

New York

Alfred University, B
Bard College, B
Bernard M. Baruch College of the City University of
  New York, B
Buffalo State College, State University of New
  York, M
Clarkson University, BMD
College of Mount Saint Vincent, AB
The College of Saint Rose, B
Columbia-Greene Community College, A
Cornell University, B
Dowling College, B
D'Youville College, B
Elmira College, B
Eugene Lang College The New School for Liberal
  Arts, B
Fordham University, B
Hobart and William Smith Colleges, B
Hofstra University, M
Hudson Valley Community College, A
Iona College, B
Ithaca College, B
Jefferson Community College, A
Keuka College, B
Lehman College of the City University of New
  York, B
Long Island University, Brooklyn Campus, B

Long Island University, C.W. Post Campus, BM
Long Island University, Friends World Program, B
Molloy College, B
Mount Saint Mary College, B
Nazareth College of Rochester, B
New York University, BM
North Country Community College, A
Nyack College, B
Queens College of the City University of New
  York, B
Rensselaer Polytechnic Institute, B
Rochester Institute of Technology, BM
Russell Sage College, B
St. Bonaventure University, B
Sarah Lawrence College, BM
State University of New York at Binghamton, B
State University of New York College at
  Brockport, B
State University of New York College at Oneonta, B
State University of New York College of Technology
  at Canton, A
State University of New York Empire State
  College, AB
State University of New York, Fredonia, B
State University of New York at Plattsburgh, B
Syracuse University, B
Touro College, B
United States Military Academy, B
University at Albany, State University of New York, B
Vassar College, B
Yeshiva University, B

North Carolina

Bennett College For Women, B
Brevard College, B
Campbell University, M
Catawba College, B
Chowan University, B
Greensboro College, B
Guilford College, B
Lees-McRae College, B
Mars Hill College, B
St. Andrews Presbyterian College, B
Salem College, B
The University of North Carolina at Greensboro, B
Warren Wilson College, B

North Dakota

University of North Dakota, B

Ohio

Antioch College, B
Bowling Green State University, MD
Bowling Green State University-Firelands College, A
Capital University, B
Cedarville University, B
Cleveland State University, B
The College of Wooster, B
Franklin University, B
Hiram College, B
John Carroll University, B
Kent State University, Stark Campus, B
Kenyon College, B
Miami University, B
Miami University-Middletown Campus, A
Mount Union College, B
Muskingum College, B
Oberlin College, B
Ohio Dominican University, AB
The Ohio State University, MD
Ohio University, BD
Ohio University-Southern Campus, A
Union Institute & University, MD
The University of Akron, AB
The University of Akron-Wayne College, A
University of Cincinnati, D
Wright State University, M

Oklahoma

Hillsdale Free Will Baptist College, AB
Oklahoma Baptist University, B
Southwestern Christian University, A

University of Oklahoma, MD

Oregon

Concordia University, B
Corban College, B
George Fox University, B
Marylhurst University, BM
Oregon State University, BM
Southern Oregon University, B
University of Oregon, M
University of Portland, B
Western Oregon University, B

Pennsylvania

Albright College, B
Bryn Athyn College of the New Church, B
Bucknell University, B
College Misericordia, B
Gettysburg College, B
Harcum College, A
Lycoming College, B
Marywood University, BM
Saint Joseph's University, B
Temple University, B
University of Pittsburgh, B
Villanova University, D
Westminster College, B

Puerto Rico

University of Puerto Rico, Río Piedras, B
University of the Sacred Heart, B

Rhode Island

Providence College, B
University of Rhode Island, B

South Carolina

Aiken Technical College, A
Lander University, B
North Greenville College, B
University of South Carolina Sumter, A
University of South Carolina Upstate, B

South Dakota

South Dakota School of Mines and Technology, B
University of Sioux Falls, AB
The University of South Dakota, MO

Tennessee

Austin Peay State University, B
Bethel College, B
Carson-Newman College, B
Freed-Hardeman University, B
Lane College, B
Lee University, B
Middle Tennessee State University, B
Rhodes College, B
Tennessee Temple University, B
Tennessee Wesleyan College, B
University of Memphis, B
The University of Tennessee at Martin, B
Vanderbilt University, B
Walters State Community College, A

Texas

Abilene Christian University, B
Amberton University, BM
Angelo State University, BM
Baylor University, MD
Central Texas College, A
Dallas Baptist University, BM
Del Mar College, A
Houston Baptist University, B
Lamar University, B
LeTourneau University, B
Midwestern State University, B
Prairie View A&M University, B
South Texas College, A
Southern Methodist University, M
Stephen F. Austin State University, BM
Tarleton State University, B
Texas A&M International University, M
Texas A&M University, B
Texas A&M University-Commerce, B
Texas A&M University-Corpus Christi, B

Texas A&M University-Texarkana, BM
Texas Southern University, B
Texas State University-San Marcos, M
Texas Tech University, BMD
Texas Woman's University, B
University of Houston, B
University of Houston-Downtown, B
University of Houston-Victoria, M
University of the Incarnate Word, BM
University of North Texas, BM
The University of Texas at Arlington, BM
The University of Texas at Brownsville, M
The University of Texas at Dallas, BM
The University of Texas at El Paso, BM
The University of Texas-Pan American, BM
The University of Texas of the Permian Basin, B
The University of Texas at San Antonio, M
The University of Texas at Tyler, BM
Wayland Baptist University, M
West Texas A&M University, BM

Vermont

Bennington College, B
Burlington College, AB
Goddard College, BM
Marlboro College, B
University of Vermont, B

Virginia

Averett University, B
Bluefield College, B
Christopher Newport University, B
The College of William and Mary, B
Emory & Henry College, B
George Mason University, BM
Hollins University, BM
Liberty University, B
Radford University, B
University of Mary Washington, B
University of Richmond, B
The University of Virginia's College at Wise, B
Virginia Commonwealth University, M
Virginia Intermont College, B
Virginia Polytechnic Institute and State University, B
Virginia State University, BM
Virginia Wesleyan College, B

Washington

Central Washington University, M
Eastern Washington University, BM
Heritage University, AB
Northwest University, B
University of Puget Sound, B
University of Washington, B
Western Washington University, B

West Virginia

Alderson-Broaddus College, B
Bethany College, B
Bluefield State College, A
Mountain State University, AM
New River Community and Technical College, A
West Liberty State College, B
West Virginia University, B

Wisconsin

Beloit College, B
Cardinal Stritch University, A
Marquette University, BD
Northland College, B
Ripon College, B
Silver Lake College, B
University of Wisconsin-Green Bay, AB
University of Wisconsin-Milwaukee, BD
University of Wisconsin-Parkside, B
Wisconsin Lutheran College, B

Alberta

Athabasca University, M
University of Alberta, B

British Columbia

Simon Fraser University, D
The University of British Columbia, B
University College of the Fraser Valley, B

University of Northern British Columbia, M

Manitoba

University of Manitoba, MD
The University of Winnipeg, B

New Brunswick

Atlantic Baptist University, B
Mount Allison University, B
St. Thomas University, B

Nova Scotia

Dalhousie University, D
Mount Saint Vincent University, B
Saint Mary's University, B

Ontario

Brock University, B
Carleton University, B
Trent University, B
University of Ottawa, BDO
University of Waterloo, B
The University of Western Ontario, BMD
York University, BM

Quebec

Concordia University, B
Université Laval, B
Université de Montréal, B
Université de Sherbrooke, B

INTERIOR ARCHITECTURE

Alabama

Auburn University, B

Arizona

Arizona State University, B

California

The Art Institute of California-San Diego, B
California College of the Arts, B
Woodbury University, B

Connecticut

University of New Haven, AB

Idaho

University of Idaho, B

Illinois

School of the Art Institute of Chicago, B

Indiana

Indiana State University, B

Kansas

Kansas State University, B

Louisiana

Delgado Community College, A
Louisiana State University and Agricultural and
   Mechanical College, B
Louisiana Tech University, B
University of Louisiana at Lafayette, B

Michigan

Central Michigan University, B
Lawrence Technological University, B

Mississippi

University of Southern Mississippi, B

Missouri

Central Missouri State University, B
University of Missouri-Columbia, B

Nebraska

University of Nebraska-Lincoln, B

Nevada

University of Nevada, Las Vegas, B

New York

Institute of Design and Construction, A
Syracuse University, B

Ohio

Bowling Green State University, B

Oregon

University of Oregon, B

Pennsylvania

Indiana University of Pennsylvania, B
Lehigh Carbon Community College, A
Philadelphia University, B

Rhode Island

Rhode Island School of Design, B

Texas

St. Philip's College, A
Stephen F. Austin State University, B
Texas Tech University, B
University of Houston, B
The University of Texas at Arlington, B
The University of Texas at San Antonio, B

Washington

University of Washington, B

INTERIOR DESIGN

Alabama

Samford University, B
The University of Alabama, BM
University of Montevallo, B
Virginia College at Birmingham, AB
Virginia College at Huntsville, A
Wallace State Community College, A

Arizona

The Art Center Design College, AB
The Art Institute of Phoenix, B
Collins College: A School of Design and
   Technology, B
Mesa Community College, A
Northern Arizona University, B
Phoenix College, A
Scottsdale Community College, A

Arkansas

Harding University, B
University of Arkansas, B

California

Academy of Art University, ABM
Allan Hancock College, A
American InterContinental University, AB
American River College, A
Antelope Valley College, A
Art Center College of Design, B
The Art Institute of California-Inland Empire, B
The Art Institute of California-Los Angeles, B
The Art Institute of California-Orange County, B
The Art Institute of California-San Diego, B
The Art Institute of California-San Francisco, B
Bakersfield College, A
Brooks College (Long Beach), A
California State University, Chico, B
California State University, Fresno, B
California State University, Long Beach, B
California State University, Sacramento, B
Cañada College, A
Chaffey College, A
City College of San Francisco, A
College of the Canyons, A
College of the Desert, A
College of Marin, A
College of the Sequoias, A
Cosumnes River College (Sacramento), A

Cuesta College, A
Design Institute of San Diego, B
El Camino College, A
FIDM/The Fashion Institute of Design &
   Merchandising, Los Angeles Campus, A
FIDM/The Fashion Institute of Design &
   Merchandising, Orange County Campus, A
FIDM/The Fashion Institute of Design &
   Merchandising, San Diego Campus, A
FIDM/The Fashion Institute of Design &
   Merchandising, San Francisco Campus, A
Fullerton College, A
Las Positas College, A
Long Beach City College, A
Los Angeles Valley College, A
Modesto Junior College, A
Monterey Peninsula College, A
Mt. San Antonio College, A
Ohlone College, A
Orange Coast College, A
Otis College of Art and Design, B
Palo Verde College, A
Palomar College, A
Pasadena City College, A
Saddleback College, A
San Bernardino Valley College, A
San Diego City College, A
San Diego Mesa College, A
San Diego State University, B
San Francisco State University, B
San Joaquin Delta College, A
San Jose State University, B
Santa Barbara City College, A
Santa Monica College, A
Santa Rosa Junior College, A
Sierra College, A
West Valley College, A
Westwood College-Anaheim, B
Westwood College-Inland Empire, B
Westwood College-Los Angeles, B

Colorado

The Art Institute of Colorado, B
Colorado State University, B
IntelliTec College (Colorado Springs), A
Pikes Peak Community College, A
Rocky Mountain College of Art & Design, B
Westwood College-Denver North, B
Westwood College-Denver South, B

Connecticut

Paier College of Art, Inc., B
University of Bridgeport, B

Delaware

Delaware College of Art and Design, A

District of Columbia

The George Washington University, M
Howard University, B

Florida

American InterContinental University, B
The Art Institute of Fort Lauderdale, B
The Art Institute of Tampa, B
Broward Community College, A
Daytona Beach Community College, A
Florida Community College at Jacksonville, A
Florida International University, B
Florida State University, BM
Hillsborough Community College, A
Indian River Community College, A
International Academy of Design & Technology, AB
Miami Dade College, A
Miami International University of Art & Design, ABM
Okaloosa-Walton College, A
Palm Beach Community College, A
Ringling School of Art and Design, A
Seminole Community College, A
University of Florida, BMD

Georgia

American InterContinental University (Atlanta), AB
The Art Institute of Atlanta, B
Bauder College, A

Brenau University, B
Georgia Southern University, B
Gwinnett Technical College, A
Lanier Technical College, A
Ogeechee Technical College, A
Savannah College of Art and Design, BM
University of Georgia, BMD
Valdosta State University, B
Westwood College-Atlanta Midtown, B
Westwood College-Atlanta Northlake, B

Hawaii

Chaminade University of Honolulu, AB

Idaho

Brigham Young University -Idaho, A
University of Idaho, B

Illinois

Black Hawk College, A
College of DuPage, A
Columbia College Chicago, BM
Harrington College of Design, AB
Illinois Central College, A
The Illinois Institute of Art-Chicago, AB
The Illinois Institute of Art-Schaumburg, B
International Academy of Design & Technology, AB
Joliet Junior College, A
Prairie State College, A
Robert Morris College, A
School of the Art Institute of Chicago, BM
Southern Illinois University Carbondale, B
Triton College, A
Westwood College-Chicago Du Page, B
Westwood College-Chicago Loop Campus, B
Westwood College-Chicago O'Hare Airport, B
Westwood College-Chicago River Oaks, B
William Rainey Harper College, A

Indiana

Indiana University Bloomington, BM
Indiana University-Purdue University Fort Wayne, A
Indiana University-Purdue University Indianapolis, B
Ivy Tech Community College-North Central, A
Ivy Tech Community College-Southwest, A
Marian College, A
Vincennes University, A

Iowa

Ellsworth Community College, A
Hawkeye Community College, A
Iowa State University of Science and
   Technology, BM
Kirkwood Community College, A
Scott Community College, A
University of Northern Iowa, B

Kansas

Garden City Community College, A
Kansas State University, B
University of Kansas, B
Wichita Area Technical College, A

Kentucky

Eastern Kentucky University, AB
Louisville Technical Institute, A
University of Kentucky, BM

Louisiana

Louisiana Tech University, M

Maryland

Harford Community College, A
Maryland Institute College of Art, B

Massachusetts

Atlantic Union College, B
Boston Architectural College, BM
Mount Ida College, B
The New England Institute of Art, B
Newbury College, AB
Suffolk University, BM
University of Massachusetts Amherst, BM

Wentworth Institute of Technology, AB

Michigan

Adrian College, B
Baker College of Allen Park, A
Baker College of Auburn Hills, A
Baker College of Clinton Township, A
Baker College of Flint, AB
Baker College of Muskegon, A
Baker College of Owosso, A
Baker College of Port Huron, A
Delta College, A
Eastern Michigan University, B
Ferris State University, B
Henry Ford Community College, A
Lawrence Technological University, M
Michigan State University, BM
Oakland Community College, A
Western Michigan University, B

Minnesota

Alexandria Technical College, A
The Art Institutes International Minnesota, AB
Brown College, B
Century College, A
Dakota County Technical College, A
Minnesota State University Mankato, B
University of Minnesota, Twin Cities
   Campus, BMDO

Mississippi

Mississippi College, B
Northeast Mississippi Community College, A

Missouri

Central Missouri State University, B
East Central College, A
Maryville University of Saint Louis, B
Northwest Missouri State University, B
Park University, B
Patricia Stevens College, A
St. Louis Community College at Meramec, A
William Woods University, B

Montana

Montana State University-Great Falls College of
   Technology, A

Nebraska

Metropolitan Community College, A
Wayne State College, B

Nevada

The Art Institute of Las Vegas, AB

New Hampshire

Hesser College, A

New Jersey

Berkeley College, A
Brookdale Community College, A
Kean University, B

New Mexico

Santa Fe Community College, A

New York

Cazenovia College, B
Cornell University, M
Fashion Institute of Technology, AB
Monroe Community College, A
Nassau Community College, A
New York Institute of Technology, B
New York School of Interior Design, ABM
Onondaga Community College, A
Parsons The New School for Design, AB
Pratt Institute, BM
Rochester Institute of Technology, AB
Sage College of Albany, AB
School of Visual Arts, B
Suffolk County Community College, A
Syracuse University, B

Villa Maria College of Buffalo, AB

North Carolina

Cape Fear Community College, A
Carteret Community College, A
Central Piedmont Community College, A
East Carolina University, B
Halifax Community College, A
High Point University, B
Meredith College, B
Randolph Community College, A
Salem College, B
The University of North Carolina at Greensboro, BM
Western Carolina University, B
Western Piedmont Community College, A

North Dakota

North Dakota State University, B

Ohio

Antonelli College, A
The Art Institute of Ohio-Cincinnati, A
The Cleveland Institute of Art, B
College of Mount St. Joseph, AB
Columbus College of Art & Design, B
Davis College, A
Kent State University, B
Miami University, B
Miami University Hamilton, B
The Ohio State University, BM
Sinclair Community College, A
The University of Akron, B
University of Cincinnati, BM
Ursuline College, B
Virginia Marti College of Art and Design, A

Oklahoma

Oklahoma Christian University, B
Tulsa Community College, A
University of Central Oklahoma, BM
University of Oklahoma, B

Oregon

The Art Institute of Portland, AB
Marylhurst University, B
Oregon State University, B
University of Oregon, M

Pennsylvania

Arcadia University, B
The Art Institute of Philadelphia, AB
The Art Institute of Pittsburgh, AB
Bradley Academy for the Visual Arts, A
Drexel University, BM
Harcum College, A
La Roche College, B
Mercyhurst College, B
Moore College of Art & Design, B
Northampton County Area Community College, A
Philadelphia University, B

Puerto Rico

University of Puerto Rico at Carolina, A

Rhode Island

New England Institute of Technology, A
Rhode Island School of Design, M

South Carolina

Anderson University, B
Converse College, B

South Dakota

South Dakota State University, B

Tennessee

Carson-Newman College, B
Lambuth University, B
Martin Methodist College, A
Middle Tennessee State University, B
O'More College of Design, B
Pellissippi State Technical Community College, A
University of Memphis, M
The University of Tennessee, B

The University of Tennessee at Martin, B
Watkins College of Art and Design, AB

Texas

Abilene Christian University, B
Amarillo College, A
The Art Institute of Dallas, AB
The Art Institute of Houston, B
Baylor University, B
Collin County Community College District, A
El Centro College, A
El Paso Community College, A
Houston Community College System, A
Lamar University, B
North Harris College, A
St. Philip's College, A
Sam Houston State University, B
Texas A&M University-Kingsville, B
Texas Christian University, B
Texas State University-San Marcos, B
University of Houston, BM
University of the Incarnate Word, AB
University of North Texas, M
The University of Texas at Austin, B
The University of Texas at San Antonio, B
Wade College, A

Utah

Brigham Young University, B
Dixie State College of Utah, A
LDS Business College, A
Southern Utah University, A
Utah State University, BM
Weber State University, A

Virginia

The Art Institute of Washington, B
Hampton University, B
Longwood University, B
Marymount University, BM
Northern Virginia Community College, A
Radford University, B
Tidewater Community College, A
Virginia Commonwealth University, BM
Virginia Polytechnic Institute and State
    University, BMD
Westwood College-Annandale Campus, B

Washington

The Art Institute of Seattle, AB
Bellevue Community College, A
Clover Park Technical College, A
Cornish College of the Arts, B
Highline Community College, A
Spokane Falls Community College, A
Washington State University, BM

West Virginia

Fairmont State University, A
Marshall Community and Technical College, A

Wisconsin

Concordia University Wisconsin, B
Fox Valley Technical College, A
Gateway Technical College, A
Madison Area Technical College, A
Milwaukee Institute of Art and Design, B
Mount Mary College, B
University of Wisconsin-Madison, B
University of Wisconsin-Stevens Point, B
Waukesha County Technical College, A

Western Technical College, A

British Columbia

British Columbia Institute of Technology, A
Kwantlen University College, B

Manitoba

University of Manitoba, BM

Ontario

Ryerson University, B

INTERMEDIA/MULTIMEDIA

California

Art Center College of Design, B
The Art Institute of California-San Diego, B
College of the Siskiyous, A
Laguna College of Art & Design, B
Mills College, B
Mt. Sierra College, B
National University, B
Platt College (Cerritos), A
Platt College (Newport Beach), B
Platt College San Diego, A
San Diego Mesa College, A
University of California, San Diego, B
Westwood College-Anaheim, AB
Westwood College-Inland Empire, AB
Westwood College-Los Angeles, A

Colorado

The Art Institute of Colorado, A
Front Range Community College, A
Platt College, AB
Westwood College-Denver South, AB

Connecticut

Middlesex Community College, A

District of Columbia

American University, B

Florida

Hillsborough Community College, A
International Academy of Design & Technology, A
New World School of the Arts, AB
University of Central Florida, B
University of Florida, B

Georgia

The Art Institute of Atlanta, A
Augusta State University, B

Illinois

Columbia College Chicago, B
International Academy of Design & Technology, A
Lewis University, B
Robert Morris College, A
School of the Art Institute of Chicago, B
Westwood College-Chicago Du Page, AB
Westwood College-Chicago Loop Campus, AB
Westwood College-Chicago O'Hare Airport, AB
Westwood College-Chicago River Oaks, AB

Indiana

Calumet College of Saint Joseph, B

Maine

Maine College of Art, B
New England School of Communications, AB

Maryland

Maryland Institute College of Art, B

Massachusetts

Emerson College, B
Fitchburg State College, B
Massachusetts College of Art, B
The New England Institute of Art, B
School of the Museum of Fine Arts, Boston, B

University of Massachusetts Dartmouth, B

Michigan

Northern Michigan University, B
University of Michigan, B

Minnesota

Academy College, A
The Art Institutes International Minnesota, AB
Minneapolis College of Art and Design, B
Minnesota School of Business, A
Minnesota School of Business-Brooklyn Center, A
Minnesota School of Business-Plymouth, A
Minnesota School of Business-Richfield, A
Minnesota School of Business-St. Cloud, A
Minnesota School of Business-Shakopee, A

Missouri

Kansas City Art Institute, B

New Jersey

The College of New Jersey, B
Ramapo College of New Jersey, B
Raritan Valley Community College, A

New Mexico

College of Santa Fe, B

New York

City College of the City University of New York, B
Long Island University, C.W. Post Campus, B
State University of New York, Fredonia, B

Ohio

Art Academy of Cincinnati, B
The Cleveland Institute of Art, B

Oregon

The Art Institute of Portland, AB
George Fox University, B
Pacific Northwest College of Art, B
University of Oregon, B

Pennsylvania

The Art Institute of Philadelphia, AB
The Art Institute of Pittsburgh, AB
Eastern University, B
Indiana University of Pennsylvania, B

Puerto Rico

University of Puerto Rico, Río Piedras, B

Tennessee

Memphis College of Art, B

Texas

Westwood College-Fort Worth, A

Vermont

Bennington College, B
Champlain College, AB

Virginia

The Art Institute of Washington, AB
Radford University, B
Westwood College-Annandale Campus, A

Washington

The Art Institute of Seattle, AB
DigiPen Institute of Technology, AB
The Evergreen State College, B

Western Washington University, B

Alberta

Alberta College of Art & Design, B

Ontario

McMaster University, B
University of Windsor, B

Saskatchewan

University of Regina, B

INTERNATIONAL AFFAIRS

Alabama

Troy University, M

California

California State University, Fresno, M
California State University, Sacramento, M
San Francisco State University, M
Stanford University, M
University of California, Berkeley, MO
University of California, San Diego, MD
University of California, Santa Cruz, MD
University of the Pacific, M
University of San Diego, MO
University of Southern California, MDO

Colorado

University of Colorado at Boulder, M
University of Denver, MD

Connecticut

Central Connecticut State University, M
University of Connecticut, M
Yale University, MO

Delaware

University of Delaware, MD

District of Columbia

American University, MDO
The Catholic University of America, M
The George Washington University, MO
Georgetown University, MDO

Florida

Florida Agricultural and Mechanical University, M
Florida International University, MD
Florida State University, MO
University of Florida, MD
University of Miami, MD
University of South Florida, M

Georgia

Clark Atlanta University, MD
Georgia Institute of Technology, M

Illinois

DePaul University, MO
Loyola University Chicago, MD
Northwestern University, O
University of Chicago, MO

Kansas

Kansas State University, M
University of Kansas, M

Kentucky

University of Kentucky, M

Maryland

The Johns Hopkins University, MDO
Morgan State University, M

Massachusetts

Boston University, MO
Brandeis University, MD
Lesley University, MO
Northeastern University, M

Tufts University, MDO

Michigan

Central Michigan University, MO
Michigan State University, M

Missouri

Missouri State University, M
Webster University, M

Nebraska

Creighton University, M

New Jersey

Fairleigh Dickinson University, Metropolitan
    Campus, M
Princeton University, MDO
Rutgers, The State University of New Jersey,
    Camden, M
Rutgers, The State University of New Jersey, New
    Brunswick/Piscataway, D
Rutgers, The State University of New Jersey,
    Newark, MD
Seton Hall University, MO

New York

City College of the City University of New York, M
Cornell University, D
Fordham University, MO
Long Island University, Brooklyn Campus, O
Long Island University, C.W. Post Campus, M
New York University, M
St. John Fisher College, M
Syracuse University, M

North Carolina

East Carolina University, M
North Carolina State University, M

Ohio

Ohio University, M

Oklahoma

Oklahoma City University, M
Oklahoma State University, M
University of Central Oklahoma, M
University of Oklahoma, M

Oregon

University of Oregon, M

Pennsylvania

University of Pennsylvania, M
University of Pittsburgh, MDO

Rhode Island

Salve Regina University, MO

South Carolina

University of South Carolina, MD

Texas

Baylor University, M
St. Mary's University of San Antonio, MO
Texas A&M University, M
Texas State University-San Marcos, M

Vermont

Norwich University, M

Virginia

George Mason University, M
Old Dominion University, MD
University of Virginia, MD

Virginia Polytechnic Institute and State University, M

Washington

University of Washington, MO

West Virginia

West Virginia University, M

Wisconsin

Marquette University, MO

Wyoming

University of Wyoming, M

British Columbia

The University of British Columbia, M
University of Northern British Columbia, M

Ontario

Brock University, M
Carleton University, M
McMaster University, D

Quebec

Université Laval, M

INTERNATIONAL AGRICULTURE

California

University of California, Davis, B

Iowa

Iowa State University of Science and Technology, B

Missouri

University of Missouri-Columbia, B

New York

Cornell University, B

Texas

Tarleton State University, B

Utah

Utah State University, B

Vermont

Sterling College, B

Virginia

Eastern Mennonite University, B

Quebec

McGill University, B

INTERNATIONAL AND COMPARATIVE EDUCATION

California

Stanford University, MD
University of San Francisco, MD
University of Southern California, M

Connecticut

University of Bridgeport, MO

District of Columbia

American University, M
The George Washington University, M

Florida

Florida International University, MDO
Florida State University, MDO

Lynn University, D

Illinois

Loyola University Chicago, MD

Indiana

Indiana University Bloomington, M

Kentucky

Morehead State University, M

Louisiana

Louisiana State University and Agricultural and
   Mechanical College, MD

Massachusetts

Boston University, M
Endicott College, M
Harvard University, M
Lesley University, M
Tufts University, MDO
University of Massachusetts Amherst, MDO

Minnesota

University of Minnesota, Twin Cities Campus, MD

New Jersey

The College of New Jersey, M

New York

New York University, MDO

Ohio

Wright State University, M

Pennsylvania

University of Pennsylvania, MD
University of Pittsburgh, MD

Tennessee

Vanderbilt University, M

Texas

University of the Incarnate Word, MD

Vermont

Sterling College, B

INTERNATIONAL BUSINESS/TRADE/COMMERCE

Alabama

Andrew Jackson University, M
Auburn University, B
Birmingham-Southern College, B
Columbia Southern University, BM
Huntingdon College, B
Samford University, B
Spring Hill College, B

Arizona

Argosy University/Phoenix, D
Arizona State University West, B
GateWay Community College, A
Grand Canyon University, B
Paradise Valley Community College, A
Pima Community College, A
University of Phoenix-Phoenix Campus, M
University of Phoenix-Southern Arizona Campus, M
Western International University, BM

Arkansas

Arkansas State University, B
Harding University, B
John Brown University, B
University of Arkansas, B
University of Arkansas at Little Rock, B

University of Central Arkansas, M

California

Alliant International University, B
Argosy University/Orange County, D
Azusa Pacific University, M
California Lutheran University, M
California State Polytechnic University, Pomona, B
California State University, Dominguez Hills, B
California State University, East Bay, M
California State University, Fresno, B
California State University, Fullerton, M
California State University, Long Beach, BM
California State University, Los Angeles, M
California State University, Monterey Bay, B
California State University, Sacramento, B
Chapman University, B
Claremont McKenna College, B
Concordia University, B
Dominican University of California, BM
Foothill College, A
Fresno Pacific University, B
Fullerton College, A
Golden Gate University, BM
Grossmont College, A
Hope International University, M
Lincoln University, B
Long Beach City College, A
Monterey Peninsula College, A
Mount St. Mary's College, B
Notre Dame de Namur University, B
Pacific States University, M
Pacific Union College, B
Palomar College, A
Pepperdine University, BM
Saint Mary's College of California, B
San Diego State University, BM
San Francisco State University, B
San Jose State University, B
Touro University International, M
University of La Verne, BM
University of Phoenix-Bay Area Campus, M
University of Phoenix-Sacramento Valley
   Campus, M
University of Phoenix-San Diego Campus, M
University of Phoenix-Southern California
   Campus, M
University of Redlands, O
University of San Francisco, BM
University of Southern California, BM
University of the West, M
Vanguard University of Southern California, B

Colorado

Fort Lewis College, B
Johnson & Wales University, B
Regis University, MO
University of Colorado at Colorado Springs, M
University of Colorado at Denver and Health
   Sciences Center - Downtown Denver Campus, M
University of Denver, BM
University of Phoenix-Southern Colorado
   Campus, M
Western State College of Colorado, B

Connecticut

Albertus Magnus College, B
Central Connecticut State University, BM
Fairfield University, MO
Post University, B
Quinnipiac University, BM
Sacred Heart University, B
University of Bridgeport, B
University of New Haven, BM

Delaware

Goldey-Beacom College, B

District of Columbia

American University, M
The George Washington University, BMDO
Georgetown University, B
Howard University, BM
Potomac College, AB
Southeastern University, M

Strayer University, B

Florida

American InterContinental University, M
Argosy University/Sarasota, MD
Barry University, B
Bethune-Cookman College, B
Brevard Community College, A
Eckerd College, B
Florida Atlantic University, BM
Florida International University, BM
Florida Metropolitan University-Pompano Beach
   Campus, AB
Florida Metropolitan University-South Orlando
   Campus, M
Florida Metropolitan University-Tampa Campus, M
Florida Southern College, BM
Florida State University, B
Jacksonville University, B
Lynn University, BM
Northwood University, Florida Campus, AB
Nova Southeastern University, MD
Palm Beach Atlantic University, B
Rollins College, B
St. Petersburg College, B
St. Thomas University, BMO
Schiller International University, ABM
Stetson University, B
University of Florida, M
University of Miami, BM
University of North Florida, B
University of Phoenix-Central Florida Campus, M
University of Phoenix-South Florida Campus, M
University of South Florida, B
The University of Tampa, BM
Webber International University, AB

Georgia

American InterContinental University (Atlanta), B
American InterContinental University (Dunwoody
   Campus), BM
Clark Atlanta University, M
Georgia College & State University, B
Georgia Institute of Technology, MO
Georgia Southern University, B
Georgia State University, MO
Paine College, B
Savannah State University, B
University of Georgia, B
University of Phoenix-Columbus Georgia
   Campus, M
Wesleyan College, B
Young Harris College, A

Guam

University of Guam, B

Hawaii

Argosy University/Hawaii, M
Brigham Young University-Hawaii, B
Hawaii Pacific University, BM
University of Hawaii at Manoa, BMD
University of Phoenix-Hawaii Campus, M

Idaho

Albertson College of Idaho, B
Boise State University, B
Northwest Nazarene University, B

Illinois

Argosy University/Schaumburg, D
Benedictine University, B
Black Hawk College, A
Bradley University, B
City Colleges of Chicago, Harold Washington
   College, A
DePaul University, BM
Dominican University, B
Elmhurst College, B
Illinois Institute of Technology, M
Illinois State University, B
Illinois Wesleyan University, B
Judson College, B
Lewis University, B
MacCormac College, A

Millikin University, B
National-Louis University, B
North Central College, B
North Park University, B
Oakton Community College, A
Roosevelt University, BM
Saint Xavier University, B
Trinity International University, B
Triton College, A
University of Chicago, M
University of Phoenix-Chicago Campus, M
William Rainey Harper College, A

Indiana

Bethel College, B
Butler University, B
Grace College, B
Indiana University Bloomington, M
Saint Mary's College, B
Taylor University, B
University of Evansville, B
University of Indianapolis, B
Valparaiso University, BM
Vincennes University, A

Iowa

Buena Vista University, B
Central College, B
Clarke College, B
Cornell College, B
Drake University, B
Graceland University, B
Iowa State University of Science and Technology, B
Iowa Western Community College, A
Kirkwood Community College, A
Loras College, B
St. Ambrose University, B
Simpson College, B
Upper Iowa University, M
Wartburg College, B

Kansas

Baker University, B
Bethany College, B
Friends University, B
Kansas City Kansas Community College, A
McPherson College, B
MidAmerica Nazarene University, B
Newman University, M
Pittsburg State University, B
Wichita State University, B

Kentucky

Bellarmine University, B
Murray State University, B
University of Kentucky, M

Louisiana

Dillard University, B
Louisiana State University and Agricultural and
    Mechanical College, B
Loyola University New Orleans, B

Maine

Husson College, B
Maine Maritime Academy, BMO
Saint Joseph's College of Maine, B
Thomas College, B

Maryland

College of Notre Dame of Maryland, B
Frederick Community College, A
The Johns Hopkins University, O
Loyola College in Maryland, BM
University of Baltimore, B
University of Maryland University College, MO
University of Phoenix-Maryland Campus, M

Massachusetts

American International College, B
Assumption College, B
Babson College, BM
Bay Path College, B
Boston University, BM
Brandeis University, MD

Bridgewater State College, B
Bunker Hill Community College, A
Clark University, M
Emerson College, M
Framingham State College, B
Lasell College, B
Massachusetts Maritime Academy, B
Merrimack College, B
Newbury College, B
Nichols College, M
Northeastern University, B
Roxbury Community College, A
Suffolk University, MDO
Tufts University, MDO
University of Phoenix-Boston Campus, M

Michigan

Adrian College, B
Alma College, B
Aquinas College, B
Central Michigan University, BM
Davenport University (Dearborn), BM
Eastern Michigan University, BM
Ferris State University, B
Finlandia University, B
Grand Valley State University, B
Lansing Community College, A
Madonna University, BM
Marygrove College, B
Mott Community College, A
Northwood University, AB
Oakland Community College, A
Oakland University, O
Saginaw Valley State University, B
University of Detroit Mercy, B
University of Phoenix-Metro Detroit Campus, M
University of Phoenix-West Michigan Campus, M

Minnesota

Augsburg College, B
College of St. Catherine, B
The College of St. Scholastica, B
Concordia College, B
Gustavus Adolphus College, B
Hamline University, B
Metropolitan State University, BM
Minnesota State University Mankato, B
Minnesota State University Moorhead, B
Northland Community and Technical College-Thief
    River Falls, A
Northwestern College, B
St. Cloud State University, B
Saint Mary's University of Minnesota, BM
Saint Paul College-A Community & Technical
    College, A
University of Minnesota, Twin Cities Campus, BM
University of St. Thomas, B
Walden University, M

Mississippi

University of Mississippi, B
University of Southern Mississippi, BMD

Missouri

Avila University, B
College of the Ozarks, B
Columbia College, B
Drury University, BMO
Lindenwood University, M
Maryville University of Saint Louis, MO
Missouri Southern State University, B
Northwest Missouri State University, B
Park University, M
St. Louis Community College at Forest Park, A
Saint Louis University, BMD
Southeast Missouri State University, M
University of Missouri-Columbia, B
University of Missouri-St. Louis, B
Washington University in St. Louis, B
Webster University, BM
Westminster College, B
William Jewell College, B

William Woods University, B

Montana

The University of Montana-Missoula, B

Nebraska

Creighton University, B
Nebraska Wesleyan University, B
University of Nebraska-Lincoln, B

Nevada

University of Nevada, Las Vegas, B
University of Nevada, Reno, B

New Hampshire

Southern New Hampshire University, ABMD

New Jersey

Berkeley College, AB
Caldwell College, B
The College of New Jersey, B
Fairleigh Dickinson University, College at
    Florham, MO
Fairleigh Dickinson University, Metropolitan
    Campus, M
Montclair State University, M
Ramapo College of New Jersey, B
Raritan Valley Community College, A
Rider University, B
Rutgers, The State University of New Jersey,
    Newark, MD
Saint Peter's College, ABM
Seton Hall University, MO
William Paterson University of New Jersey, B

New Mexico

College of Santa Fe, B
New Mexico State University, B
University of New Mexico, M
University of Phoenix-New Mexico Campus, M
Western New Mexico University, B

New York

Berkeley College-New York City Campus, AB
Berkeley College-Westchester Campus, AB
Bernard M. Baruch College of the City University of
    New York, BM
Canisius College, B
Clarkson University, B
Daemen College, M
Dominican College, B
Dowling College, B
D'Youville College, BM
Elmira College, B
Excelsior College, B
Fordham University, B
Herkimer County Community College, A
Hofstra University, BMO
Iona College, BO
Ithaca College, B
Long Island University, C.W. Post Campus, MO
Mercy College, M
Monroe Community College, A
Mount Saint Mary College, B
New York Institute of Technology, BMO
New York University, BM
Niagara University, B
Pace University, BM
Queens College of the City University of New
    York, B
Rochester Institute of Technology, BM
St. Bonaventure University, B
St. John Fisher College, B
St. John's University, BMO
State University of New York College of Agriculture
    and Technology at Cobleskill, A
State University of New York College at
    Brockport, B
State University of New York at New Paltz, BM
State University of New York at Plattsburgh, B
Tompkins Cortland Community College, A
Touro College, B
Utica College, B
Wagner College, M

Westchester Community College, A

North Carolina

Appalachian State University, B
Belmont Abbey College, B
Campbell University, B
High Point University, B
Lenoir-Rhyne College, B
Mars Hill College, B
Pfeiffer University, B
Saint Augustine's College, B
Salem College, B
Shaw University, B
The University of North Carolina at Charlotte, B
The University of North Carolina at Greensboro, O
University of Phoenix-Charlotte Campus, M
Warren Wilson College, B
Western Carolina University, B

North Dakota

Dickinson State University, B
Jamestown College, B
Minot State University, B

Ohio

Baldwin-Wallace College, M
Bowling Green State University, B
Cedarville University, B
Cincinnati State Technical and Community
   College, A
Hiram College, B
Lake Erie College, B
Marietta College, B
Mount Union College, B
Muskingum College, B
Ohio Dominican University, B
Ohio Northern University, B
The Ohio State University, B
Ohio University-Eastern, B
Ohio Wesleyan University, B
Otterbein College, B
Stark State College of Technology, A
The University of Akron, BMO
University of Cincinnati, M
University of Dayton, B
The University of Findlay, BM
University of Phoenix-Cincinnati Campus, M
University of Phoenix-Cleveland Campus, M
University of Rio Grande, B
The University of Toledo, B
Wright State University, M
Xavier University, BM

Oklahoma

Oklahoma Baptist University, B
Oklahoma City University, BM
Oral Roberts University, B
Tulsa Community College, A
University of Oklahoma, B
University of Tulsa, BM

Oregon

George Fox University, B
Linfield College, B
Oregon State University, B
Portland State University, M
University of Oregon, B
University of Portland, B

Pennsylvania

Albright College, B
Arcadia University, B
Carlow University, B
Chatham College, B
Chestnut Hill College, B
Clarion University of Pennsylvania, B
Community College of Philadelphia, A
Dickinson College, B
Drexel University, B
Duquesne University, B
Elizabethtown College, B
Gannon University, B
Gettysburg College, B
Grove City College, B
Holy Family University, B

Immaculata University, B
Indiana University of Pennsylvania, B
Juniata College, B
King's College, B
Kutztown University of Pennsylvania, B
La Roche College, B
Luzerne County Community College, A
Lycoming College, B
Manor College, A
Mansfield University of Pennsylvania, B
Marywood University, B
Messiah College, B
Moravian College, B
Neumann College, B
The Pennsylvania State University DuBois Campus
   of the Commonwealth College, B
The Pennsylvania State University at Erie, The
   Behrend College, B
The Pennsylvania State University Harrisburg
   Campus, B
The Pennsylvania State University, Lehigh Valley
   Campus of the Berks-Lehigh Valley College, B
The Pennsylvania State University Schuylkill
   Campus of the Capital College, B
The Pennsylvania State University University Park
   Campus, B
Philadelphia University, BM
Saint Francis University, B
Saint Joseph's University, BM
Saint Vincent College, B
Seton Hill University, B
Temple University, BMD
Thiel College, B
University of Pennsylvania, BMO
University of Phoenix-Philadelphia Campus, M
University of Pittsburgh, MO
The University of Scranton, BM
Villanova University, B
Washington & Jefferson College, B
Waynesburg College, B
Westminster College, B
Widener University, B
Wilkes University, M
York College of Pennsylvania, B

Puerto Rico

Inter American University of Puerto Rico,
   Metropolitan Campus, M
Inter American University of Puerto Rico, Ponce
   Campus, B
Inter American University of Puerto Rico, San
   Germán Campus, D
Pontifical Catholic University of Puerto Rico, B
University of Phoenix-Puerto Rico Campus, M

Rhode Island

Bryant University, B
Johnson & Wales University, M
Roger Williams University, B
University of Rhode Island, BM

South Carolina

Bob Jones University, AB
Clemson University, B
College of Charleston, B
Converse College, B
University of South Carolina, M
Wofford College, B

South Dakota

National American University (Rapid City), B
Northern State University, B

Tennessee

Belmont University, B
King College, B
Maryville College, B
Rhodes College, B
Southern Adventist University, B
Tennessee Technological University, B
University of Memphis, BM

The University of Tennessee at Martin, B

Texas

Baylor University, BM
Dallas Baptist University, M
El Paso Community College, A
Houston Baptist University, B
Laredo Community College, A
Lee College, A
LeTourneau University, B
Midwestern State University, B
Northwood University, Texas Campus, B
Richland College, A
St. Edward's University, BMO
St. Mary's University of San Antonio, BM
Sam Houston State University, B
Southwestern Adventist University, B
Stephen F. Austin State University, B
Tarleton State University, B
Texas A&M University-Kingsville, B
Texas A&M University-Texarkana, B
Texas Christian University, BM
Texas Tech University, BM
Texas Wesleyan University, B
Trinity University, B
University of Dallas, M
University of the Incarnate Word, BM
University of Phoenix-Houston Campus, M
The University of Texas at Arlington, B
The University of Texas at Dallas, BMD
The University of Texas-Pan American, B
The University of Texas at San Antonio, B
Wayland Baptist University, M

Utah

University of Phoenix-Utah Campus, M
Utah Valley State College, B
Westminster College, B

Vermont

Champlain College, AB
Norwich University, M

Virginia

Christopher Newport University, B
Eastern Mennonite University, B
James Madison University, B
Marymount University, BO
Northern Virginia Community College, A
Old Dominion University, B
Regent University, B
University of Richmond, B
Virginia Intermont College, B

Washington

City University, BM
Edmonds Community College, A
Gonzaga University, B
Highline Community College, A
Pacific Lutheran University, B
Seattle University, BMO
Shoreline Community College, A
Spokane Falls Community College, A
Tacoma Community College, A
University of Puget Sound, B
University of Washington, B
Washington State University, BO
Western Washington University, B
Whitworth College, BM

West Virginia

Davis & Elkins College, B
Salem International University, B
Wheeling Jesuit University, B

Wisconsin

Alverno College, B
Cardinal Stritch University, B
Concordia University Wisconsin, M
Lakeland College, B
Marquette University, B
Milwaukee School of Engineering, B
St. Norbert College, B
University of Wisconsin-La Crosse, B
University of Wisconsin-Madison, M

University of Wisconsin-Whitewater, M

Alberta

University of Alberta, BM
University of Lethbridge, BM

British Columbia

British Columbia Institute of Technology, A
Simon Fraser University, M
The University of British Columbia, BD
University of Northern British Columbia, B
University of Phoenix-Vancouver Campus, M
University of Victoria, B

New Brunswick

Mount Allison University, B
University of New Brunswick Fredericton, B
University of New Brunswick Saint John, M

Nova Scotia

Dalhousie University, B

Ontario

Brock University, B
Carleton University, B
University of Ottawa, B
University of Waterloo, B
York University, B

Quebec

Bishop's University, B
Concordia University, B
HEC Montreal, BM
McGill University, BM
Université Laval, M
Université du Québec en Outaouais, B
Université de Sherbrooke, M

Saskatchewan

University of Saskatchewan, M

INTERNATIONAL DEVELOPMENT

California

Hope International University, M

District of Columbia

American University, MO
The George Washington University, MO

Florida

University of Florida, MO

Georgia

Clark Atlanta University, MD

Iowa

The University of Iowa, M

Louisiana

Tulane University, MD

Massachusetts

Brandeis University, M
Clark University, M
Harvard University, M
Tufts University, MDO

Michigan

Andrews University, M

New Jersey

Rutgers, The State University of New Jersey,
  Camden, M

New York

Cornell University, M
Fordham University, MO

North Carolina

Duke University, MO

Ohio

Ohio University, M

Pennsylvania

University of Pittsburgh, M

Rhode Island

University of Rhode Island, O

Virginia

Old Dominion University, M

Alberta

Athabasca University, M

Nova Scotia

Dalhousie University, M
Saint Mary's University, M

Ontario

University of Guelph, M

Quebec

McGill University, M

INTERNATIONAL ECONOMICS

California

California State University, Chico, B
Claremont McKenna College, B
Loyola Marymount University, B
University of California, Los Angeles, B
University of California, Santa Cruz, B

Colorado

The Colorado College, B

Connecticut

Albertus Magnus College, B

District of Columbia

The Catholic University of America, B
Georgetown University, B
Howard University, B

Georgia

University of West Georgia, B

Idaho

Albertson College of Idaho, B

Illinois

Rockford College, B

Indiana

Taylor University, B
Valparaiso University, B

Massachusetts

Harvard University, B
Suffolk University, B

Michigan

Eastern Michigan University, B

Minnesota

College of St. Catherine, B
Hamline University, B
University of St. Thomas, B

Missouri

University of Missouri-Columbia, B
Washington University in St. Louis, B

New York

Bard College, B
Fordham University, B

State University of New York at New Paltz, B
State University of New York at Oswego, B

Ohio

Hiram College, B
John Carroll University, B
Ohio University, B

Pennsylvania

Gettysburg College, B
Westminster College, B

Tennessee

Carson-Newman College, B
Rhodes College, B

Texas

Austin College, B
Texas Christian University, B

Vermont

Marlboro College, B

Virginia

Longwood University, B
University of Richmond, B

Washington

Seattle University, B
University of Puget Sound, B

Wisconsin

Carthage College, B
Lawrence University, B

Ontario

Brock University, B
Ryerson University, B

Quebec

HEC Montreal, B

INTERNATIONAL FINANCE

District of Columbia

The Catholic University of America, B

Massachusetts

Babson College, B
Boston University, B

Missouri

Washington University in St. Louis, B

New York

Broome Community College, A

Ohio

The University of Akron, B

Texas

Texas Christian University, B

Utah

Brigham Young University, B

Quebec

HEC Montreal, B

INTERNATIONAL/GLOBAL STUDIES

Arizona

Arizona State University, B

Arkansas

Harding University, B

California

Concordia University, B
Dominican University of California, B

National University, B
Pitzer College, B
Point Loma Nazarene University, B
University of California, Irvine, B

Colorado

Colorado Christian University, B
University of Colorado at Boulder, B
University of Colorado at Denver and Health
   Sciences Center - Downtown Denver Campus, B

Florida

New College of Florida, B

Georgia

Andrew College, A
Georgia Institute of Technology, B

Illinois

Illinois Wesleyan University, B
Lewis University, B
Rockford College, B
University of Chicago, B

Indiana

Hanover College, B

Iowa

Central College, B
The University of Iowa, B

Kansas

Baker University, B
Pittsburg State University, B

Louisiana

Louisiana State University and Agricultural and
   Mechanical College, B
University of New Orleans, B

Massachusetts

Assumption College, B
Berkshire Community College, A
Endicott College, B
Framingham State College, B
Hampshire College, B

Michigan

Hope College, B
Macomb Community College, A
Michigan State University, B
Northern Michigan University, B
Western Michigan University, B

Minnesota

The College of St. Scholastica, B
Concordia College, B
Minnesota State University Moorhead, B
Saint Mary's University of Minnesota, B

Mississippi

Belhaven College, B

Nebraska

Nebraska Wesleyan University, B
University of Nebraska at Omaha, B

New Hampshire

University of New Hampshire, B

New Jersey

Ramapo College of New Jersey, B

New York

Adelphi University, B
City College of the City University of New York, B
The College of New Rochelle, B
Iona College, B
Russell Sage College, B
St. Lawrence University, B
State University of New York at Binghamton, B

State University of New York College at Cortland, B

North Carolina

Warren Wilson College, B

North Dakota

North Dakota State University, B
University of North Dakota, B

Ohio

Baldwin-Wallace College, B
Case Western Reserve University, B
Kenyon College, B
Miami University Hamilton, B

Oklahoma

Oral Roberts University, B

Oregon

George Fox University, B
Oregon State University, B
Willamette University, B

Pennsylvania

Allegheny College, B
Arcadia University, B
Chatham College, B
University of Pennsylvania, B

Rhode Island

Providence College, B

Texas

Abilene Christian University, B
Midwestern State University, B
Northwest Vista College, A
Southern Methodist University, B
Texas A&M University, B
Texas State University-San Marcos, B
University of North Texas, B

Utah

Salt Lake Community College, A
University of Utah, B

Vermont

Bennington College, B
Sterling College, B

Virginia

Randolph-Macon College, B
Virginia Commonwealth University, B

Washington

The Evergreen State College, B

Wisconsin

Alverno College, B
Marquette University, B
University of Wisconsin-Whitewater, B

British Columbia

University of Northern British Columbia, B

Ontario

University of Waterloo, B
The University of Western Ontario, B

INTERNATIONAL MARKETING

New York

Fashion Institute of Technology, B
Pace University, B

Ohio

The University of Akron, B

Oklahoma

Oklahoma Baptist University, B

Texas

Texas Christian University, B

Utah

Brigham Young University, B

Virginia

Averett University, B

West Virginia

Davis & Elkins College, B

Ontario

York University, B

INTERNATIONAL PUBLIC HEALTH/INTERNATIONAL HEALTH

California

Loma Linda University, M
Touro University International, M

Connecticut

Yale University, M

District of Columbia

The George Washington University, M

Florida

University of South Florida, MD

Georgia

Emory University, MD

Louisiana

Tulane University, MDO

Maryland

The Johns Hopkins University, MD

Massachusetts

Boston University, MDO
Brandeis University, M
Harvard University, MD
Tufts University, MDO

Michigan

University of Michigan, M

New York

New York University, M

South Carolina

Clemson University, B

Washington

University of Washington, M

INTERNATIONAL RELATIONS AND AFFAIRS

Alabama

Huntingdon College, B
Samford University, B
Spring Hill College, B
Stillman College, B
The University of Alabama, B

Arizona

Cochise College (Sierra Vista), A
Embry-Riddle Aeronautical University, B
Grand Canyon University, B
Northern Arizona University, B
Western International University, B

Arkansas

Harding University, B
Hendrix College, B

John Brown University, B
University of Arkansas, B
University of Arkansas at Little Rock, B

California

Allan Hancock College, A
Alliant International University, B
Azusa Pacific University, B
Bethany University, B
California Lutheran University, B
California State University, Chico, B
California State University, East Bay, B
California State University, Long Beach, B
California State University, Monterey Bay, B
Chapman University, B
Claremont McKenna College, B
De Anza College, A
Holy Names University, B
Mills College, B
Occidental College, B
Pepperdine University, B
Pitzer College, B
Pomona College, B
Saint Mary's College of California, B
San Diego State University, B
San Francisco State University, B
Santa Barbara City College, A
Scripps College, B
Sonoma State University, B
Stanford University, B
University of California, Davis, B
University of La Verne, B
University of the Pacific, B
University of Redlands, B
University of San Diego, B
University of Southern California, B
Whittier College, B

Colorado

University of Denver, B

Connecticut

Connecticut College, B
Fairfield University, B
Naugatuck Valley Community College, A
Quinnipiac University, B
Sacred Heart University, B
Trinity College, B
University of Bridgeport, B

Delaware

University of Delaware, B

District of Columbia

American University, B
The Catholic University of America, B
Gallaudet University, B
The George Washington University, B
Georgetown University, B
Trinity (Washington) University, B

Florida

Barry University, B
Bethune-Cookman College, B
Eckerd College, B
Florida International University, B
Florida State University, B
Jacksonville University, B
Miami Dade College, A
Rollins College, B
Saint Leo University, B
Schiller International University, B
Stetson University, B
University of Miami, B
University of North Florida, B
University of South Florida, B
The University of Tampa, B
University of West Florida, B

Georgia

Agnes Scott College, B
Berry College, B
Brenau University, B
Emory University, B
Georgia Institute of Technology, B

Georgia Southern University, B
Kennesaw State University, B
Mercer University, B
Morehouse College, B
Oglethorpe University, B
Southern Polytechnic State University, B
University of Georgia, B
University of West Georgia, B
Wesleyan College, B

Hawaii

Chaminade University of Honolulu, B
Hawaii Pacific University, B

Idaho

Northwest Nazarene University, B
University of Idaho, B

Illinois

Benedictine University, B
Bradley University, B
DePaul University, B
Illinois College, B
Knox College, B
Lake Forest College, B
Loyola University Chicago, B
McKendree College, B
Millikin University, B
North Central College, B
North Park University, B
Northwestern University, B
Roosevelt University, B
Saint Xavier University, B
Wheaton College, B

Indiana

Butler University, B
Earlham College, B
Saint Joseph's College, B
Taylor University, B
University of Evansville, B
University of Indianapolis, B
University of Southern Indiana, B
Valparaiso University, B

Iowa

Cornell College, B
Drake University, B
Graceland University, B
Iowa State University of Science and Technology, B
Loras College, B
Luther College, B
Mount Mercy College, B
Simpson College, B
Wartburg College, B

Kansas

Tabor College, B
University of Kansas, B

Kentucky

Bellarmine University, B
Centre College, B
Murray State University, B
Northern Kentucky University, B
Thomas More College, AB

Louisiana

Tulane University, B

Maine

Colby College, B
University of Maine, B
University of Maine at Farmington, B
University of Maine at Presque Isle, B
University of Southern Maine, B

Maryland

College of Notre Dame of Maryland, B
Frostburg State University, B
Goucher College, B
The Johns Hopkins University, B
Mount St. Mary's University, B
Towson University, B

Washington College, B

Massachusetts

American International College, B
Boston University, B
Bridgewater State College, B
Clark University, B
Elms College, B
Gordon College, B
Harvard University, B
Massachusetts Bay Community College, A
Mount Holyoke College, B
Northeastern University, B
Northern Essex Community College, A
Regis College, B
Simmons College, B
Stonehill College, B
Tufts University, B
Wellesley College, B
Western New England College, B
Wheaton College, B

Michigan

Adrian College, B
Albion College, B
Aquinas College, B
Calvin College, B
Central Michigan University, B
Grand Valley State University, B
Hillsdale College, B
Kellogg Community College, A
Michigan State University, B
Saginaw Valley State University, B
University of Michigan, B

Minnesota

Augsburg College, B
Bethel University, B
Carleton College, B
College of St. Catherine, B
Hamline University, B
Macalester College, B
Minnesota State University Mankato, B
St. Cloud State University, B
University of Minnesota, Duluth, B
University of Minnesota, Twin Cities Campus, B
University of St. Thomas, B
Winona State University, B

Mississippi

University of Mississippi, B
University of Southern Mississippi, B

Missouri

Lindenwood University, B
Missouri Southern State University, B
Rockhurst University, B
Saint Louis University, B
Stephens College, B
Washington University in St. Louis, B
Webster University, B
Westminster College, B
William Jewell College, B
William Woods University, B

Montana

Carroll College, B

Nebraska

Creighton University, B
Doane College, B
Hastings College, B
Union College, B
University of Nebraska at Kearney, B

University of Nebraska-Lincoln, B

Nevada

University of Nevada, Reno, B

New Hampshire

University of New Hampshire, B

New Jersey

Brookdale Community College, A
Centenary College, B
The College of New Jersey, B
College of Saint Elizabeth, B
Fairleigh Dickinson University, Metropolitan
   Campus, B
Seton Hall University, B

New York

Bard College, B
Bronx Community College of the City University of
   New York, A
Canisius College, B
City College of the City University of New York, B
Colgate University, B
College of Staten Island of the City University of
   New York, B
Concordia College, B
Elmira College, B
Eugene Lang College The New School for Liberal
   Arts, B
Fordham University, B
Hamilton College, B
Hobart and William Smith Colleges, B
Houghton College, B
Le Moyne College, B
Long Island University, C.W. Post Campus, B
Manhattan College, B
Manhattanville College, B
Marymount Manhattan College, B
Mount Saint Mary College, B
Nazareth College of Rochester, B
New York University, B
Niagara University, B
Pace University, B
Rochester Institute of Technology, B
St. John Fisher College, B
St. John's University, B
Sarah Lawrence College, B
Skidmore College, B
State University of New York College at
   Brockport, B
State University of New York College at Cortland, B
State University of New York College at Geneseo, B
State University of New York College at Oneonta, B
State University of New York at New Paltz, B
State University of New York at Oswego, B
Syracuse University, B
Utica College, B
Vassar College, B
Wagner College, B
Wells College, B

North Carolina

Campbell University, B
Catawba College, B
Duke University, B
Elon University, B
Guilford College, B
High Point University, B
Lees-McRae College, B
Lenoir-Rhyne College, B
Mars Hill College, B
Meredith College, B
Methodist College, B
Queens University of Charlotte, B
Saint Augustine's College, B
Salem College, B
Shaw University, B

Ohio

Antioch College, B
Ashland University, B
Bowling Green State University, B
Capital University, B
Case Western Reserve University, B

Cedarville University, B
Cleveland State University, B
The College of Wooster, B
Denison University, B
Heidelberg College, B
John Carroll University, B
Kent State University, B
Kenyon College, B
Miami University, B
Muskingum College, B
Ohio Northern University, B
The Ohio State University, B
Ohio University, B
Ohio University-Eastern, B
Ohio Wesleyan University, B
Otterbein College, B
Shawnee State University, B
Tiffin University, B
University of Cincinnati, B
University of Dayton, B
The University of Toledo, B
Wright State University, B
Xavier University, B

Oklahoma

Oral Roberts University, B
Southern Nazarene University, B
Tulsa Community College, A

Oregon

Lewis & Clark College, B
Oregon State University, B
Pacific University, B
Portland State University, B
Reed College, B
Southern Oregon University, B
University of Oregon, B
Western Oregon University, B

Pennsylvania

Allegheny College, B
Bucknell University, B
Carnegie Mellon University, B
Cedar Crest College, B
Chatham College, B
Dickinson College, B
Duquesne University, B
Gettysburg College, B
Harrisburg Area Community College, A
Immaculata University, B
Indiana University of Pennsylvania, B
Juniata College, B
La Roche College, B
Lafayette College, B
Lehigh University, B
Lincoln University, B
Lock Haven University of Pennsylvania, B
Lycoming College, B
Mansfield University of Pennsylvania, B
Muhlenberg College, B
The Pennsylvania State University Abington
   College, B
The Pennsylvania State University Altoona
   College, B
The Pennsylvania State University Beaver Campus
   of the Commonwealth College, B
The Pennsylvania State University Berks Campus of
   the Berks-Lehigh Valley College, B
The Pennsylvania State University Delaware County
   Campus of the Commonwealth College, B
The Pennsylvania State University DuBois Campus
   of the Commonwealth College, B
The Pennsylvania State University at Erie, The
   Behrend College, B
The Pennsylvania State University Fayette Campus
   of the Commonwealth College, B
The Pennsylvania State University Hazleton
   Campus of the Commonwealth College, B
The Pennsylvania State University, Lehigh Valley
   Campus of the Berks-Lehigh Valley College, B
The Pennsylvania State University McKeesport
   Campus of the Commonwealth College, B
The Pennsylvania State University Mont Alto
   Campus of the Commonwealth College, B
The Pennsylvania State University New Kensington
   Campus of the Commonwealth College, B

The Pennsylvania State University Schuylkill
   Campus of the Capital College, B
The Pennsylvania State University Shenango
   Campus of the Commonwealth College, B
The Pennsylvania State University University Park
   Campus, B
The Pennsylvania State University Wilkes-Barre
   Campus of the Commonwealth College, B
The Pennsylvania State University Worthington
   Scranton Campus of the Commonwealth
   College, B
The Pennsylvania State University York Campus of
   the Commonwealth College, B
Saint Francis University, B
Saint Joseph's University, B
Seton Hill University, B
Susquehanna University, B
University of Pennsylvania, B
The University of Scranton, B
Ursinus College, B
West Chester University of Pennsylvania, B
Westminster College, B
Widener University, B
Wilkes University, B
Wilson College, B
York College of Pennsylvania, B

Rhode Island

Brown University, B
Bryant University, B

South Carolina

Bob Jones University, B
Francis Marion University, B
University of South Carolina, B
Wofford College, B

South Dakota

Augustana College, B

Tennessee

Lambuth University, B
Lee University, B
Maryville College, B
Middle Tennessee State University, B
Rhodes College, B
Sewanee: The University of the South, B
University of Memphis, B
The University of Tennessee at Martin, B

Texas

Austin College, B
Baylor University, B
St. Edward's University, B
Southern Methodist University, B
Southwestern Adventist University, B
Southwestern University, B
Texas Christian University, B
Texas Lutheran University, B
Texas State University-San Marcos, B
Texas Wesleyan University, B
University of St. Thomas, B

Utah

Brigham Young University, B
Salt Lake Community College, A

Vermont

Bennington College, B
Marlboro College, B
Middlebury College, B
Norwich University, B

Virginia

Bridgewater College, B
The College of William and Mary, B
Emory & Henry College, B
Ferrum College, B
George Mason University, B
Hampden-Sydney College, B
Hollins University, B
James Madison University, B
Longwood University, B
Lynchburg College, B
Mary Baldwin College, B

Old Dominion University, B
Randolph-Macon College, B
Randolph-Macon Woman's College, B
Roanoke College, B
Sweet Briar College, B
University of Mary Washington, B
University of Richmond, B
University of Virginia, B
Virginia Military Institute, B
Virginia Polytechnic Institute and State University, B
Virginia Wesleyan College, B

Washington

Eastern Washington University, B
Gonzaga University, B
Pacific Lutheran University, B
Seattle University, B
Tacoma Community College, A
University of Puget Sound, B
University of Washington, B
Whitworth College, B

West Virginia

Bethany College, B
Marshall University, B
West Virginia University, B
West Virginia Wesleyan College, B
Wheeling Jesuit University, B

Wisconsin

Alverno College, B
Beloit College, B
Carroll College, B
Edgewood College, B
Lawrence University, B
Marian College of Fond du Lac, B
Marquette University, B
Mount Mary College, B
St. Norbert College, B
University of Wisconsin-Madison, B
University of Wisconsin-Milwaukee, B
University of Wisconsin-Oshkosh, B
University of Wisconsin-Parkside, B
University of Wisconsin-Platteville, B
University of Wisconsin-Stevens Point, B
University of Wisconsin-Superior, B
University of Wisconsin-Whitewater, B

Wyoming

University of Wyoming, B
Western Wyoming Community College, A

Alberta

Prairie Bible Institute, B
University of Alberta, B
University of Calgary, B

British Columbia

Trinity Western University, B
The University of British Columbia, B

Manitoba

Canadian Mennonite University, B

New Brunswick

Mount Allison University, B
University of New Brunswick Fredericton, B
University of New Brunswick Saint John, B

Nova Scotia

Dalhousie University, B
Saint Mary's University, B

Ontario

Carleton University, B
Trent University, B
University of Ottawa, B
University of Toronto, B
University of Waterloo, B
University of Windsor, B
Wilfrid Laurier University, B

York University, B

Quebec

Bishop's University, B

Saskatchewan

University of Saskatchewan, B

INTERNATIONAL TRADE

California

Argosy University/Orange County, M

District of Columbia

The George Washington University, MO

Florida

Argosy University/Tampa, M

Illinois

Argosy University/Schaumburg, M

Michigan

Eastern Michigan University, M

Rhode Island

Johnson & Wales University, M

Texas

Sul Ross State University, M
Texas A&M International University, M

Washington

University of Washington, O

INTERNET AND INTERACTIVE MULTIMEDIA

California

San Diego State University, M
University of San Francisco, M
University of Southern California, M

Connecticut

Quinnipiac University, M
Sacred Heart University, O

District of Columbia

American University, M
Georgetown University, M

Florida

Florida State University, M
University of Central Florida, M
University of Miami, M

Georgia

Georgia Institute of Technology, M
Georgia State University, MD
Savannah College of Art and Design, M
Southern Polytechnic State University, M

Illinois

American Academy of Art, M
DePaul University, M
Western Illinois University, O

Indiana

Indiana University-Purdue University Indianapolis, M

Maryland

Towson University, O

New Jersey

New Jersey Institute of Technology, M

New Mexico

New Mexico Highlands University, M

New York

Alfred University, M
Brooklyn College of the City University of New York, O

Long Island University, C.W. Post Campus, M
Metropolitan College of New York, M
New York University, M
Pratt Institute, M
Rochester Institute of Technology, O
Syracuse University, M

Pennsylvania

Chestnut Hill College, O
Duquesne University, MO
Robert Morris University, M

Vermont

Marlboro College, M

Virginia

Virginia Commonwealth University, M

Washington

City University, MO

British Columbia

Simon Fraser University, M

INVESTMENT MANAGEMENT

District of Columbia

The George Washington University, M

Iowa

The University of Iowa, M

Maryland

The Johns Hopkins University, O

Massachusetts

Boston University, M

Missouri

Lindenwood University, M

New York

Pace University, M

Oklahoma

University of Tulsa, M

Pennsylvania

Marywood University, M

Wisconsin

University of Wisconsin-Madison, MD

Quebec

Concordia University, MO

INVESTMENTS AND SECURITIES

Massachusetts

Babson College, B

Pennsylvania

Duquesne University, B

IRANIAN/PERSIAN LANGUAGES, LITERATURES, AND LINGUISTICS

Texas

The University of Texas at Austin, B

IRONWORKING/IRONWORKER

Indiana

Ivy Tech Community College-Lafayette, A
Ivy Tech Community College-North Central, A

Ivy Tech Community College-Northeast, A
Ivy Tech Community College-Northwest, A
Ivy Tech Community College-Southwest, A
Ivy Tech Community College-Wabash Valley, A

ISLAMIC STUDIES

California

University of California, Los Angeles, B
University of California, Santa Barbara, B

Illinois

East-West University, B

Massachusetts

Brandeis University, B
Harvard University, B
Wellesley College, B

Michigan

University of Michigan, B

Missouri

Washington University in St. Louis, B

Ohio

The Ohio State University, B

Texas

The University of Texas at Austin, B

Ontario

University of Toronto, B

ITALIAN LANGUAGE AND LITERATURE

Arizona

Arizona State University, B
The University of Arizona, B

California

California State University, Long Beach, B
Chabot College, A
Claremont McKenna College, B
College of the Desert, A
Contra Costa College, A
El Camino College, A
Los Angeles Mission College, A
Los Angeles Valley College, A
Saint Mary's College of California, B
San Francisco State University, BM
San Joaquin Delta College, A
Santa Clara University, B
Scripps College, B
Stanford University, BMD
University of California, Berkeley, BD
University of California, Davis, B
University of California, Los Angeles, BMD
University of California, San Diego, B
University of California, Santa Barbara, B
University of California, Santa Cruz, B
University of Southern California, B
West Valley College, A

Colorado

The Colorado College, B
University of Colorado at Boulder, B
University of Denver, B

Connecticut

Albertus Magnus College, B
Central Connecticut State University, B
Connecticut College, BM
Southern Connecticut State University, B
Trinity College, B
University of Connecticut, BMD
Wesleyan Stuiversity, B

Yale University, BD

Delaware

University of Delaware, B

District of Columbia

The Catholic University of America, M
Georgetown University, B

Florida

Florida International University, B
Florida State University, BM
Miami Dade College, A
University of Miami, B
University of South Florida, B

Georgia

Emory University, B
University of Georgia, B

Illinois

City Colleges of Chicago, Harold Washington
    College, A
DePaul University, B
Dominican University, B
Loyola University Chicago, B
Northwestern University, BDO
University of Chicago, BMD
University of Illinois at Chicago, B
University of Illinois at Urbana-Champaign, BMD

Indiana

Indiana University Bloomington, BMD
University of Notre Dame, BM

Iowa

The University of Iowa, B

Louisiana

Tulane University, B

Maryland

The Johns Hopkins University, BD
University of Maryland, College Park, B

Massachusetts

Boston College, BM
Boston University, B
College of the Holy Cross, B
Harvard University, BMD
Mount Holyoke College, B
Northeastern University, B
Smith College, BM
University of Massachusetts Amherst, BM
University of Massachusetts Boston, B
Wellesley College, B

Michigan

Oakland University, B
University of Michigan, B
Wayne State University, M

Minnesota

University of Minnesota, Twin Cities Campus, B

Missouri

Washington University in St. Louis, B

New Hampshire

Dartmouth College, B

New Jersey

Montclair State University, B
Princeton University, D
Rutgers, The State University of New Jersey, New
    Brunswick/Piscataway, BMD
Rutgers, The State University of New Jersey,
    Newark, B
Seton Hall University, B

New York

Bard College, B
Barnard College, B

Brooklyn College of the City University of New
    York, B
Columbia College, B
Columbia University, School of General Studies, B
Cornell University, BD
Fordham University, B
Hofstra University, B
Hunter College of the City University of New
    York, BM
Iona College, B
Lehman College of the City University of New
    York, B
Long Island University, C.W. Post Campus, B
Nazareth College of Rochester, B
New York University, BMD
Queens College of the City University of New
    York, BM
St. John Fisher College, B
St. John's University, B
Sarah Lawrence College, B
State University of New York at Binghamton, BM
State University of New York at Buffalo, B
Stony Brook University, State University of New
    York, BMD
Syracuse University, B
University at Albany, State University of New
    York, BM
Vassar College, B
York College of the City University of New York, B

North Carolina

Duke University, B
The University of North Carolina at Chapel Hill, MD

Ohio

Lake Erie College, B
The Ohio State University, BMD
Youngstown State University, B

Oklahoma

Tulsa Community College, A

Oregon

University of Oregon, BM

Pennsylvania

Bryn Mawr College, B
Dickinson College, B
Gettysburg College, B
Haverford College, B
La Salle University, B
The Pennsylvania State University Abington
    College, B
The Pennsylvania State University Altoona
    College, B
The Pennsylvania State University Beaver Campus
    of the Commonwealth College, B
The Pennsylvania State University Berks Campus of
    the Berks-Lehigh Valley College, B
The Pennsylvania State University Delaware County
    Campus of the Commonwealth College, B
The Pennsylvania State University DuBois Campus
    of the Commonwealth College, B
The Pennsylvania State University at Erie, The
    Behrend College, B
The Pennsylvania State University Fayette Campus
    of the Commonwealth College, B
The Pennsylvania State University Hazleton
    Campus of the Commonwealth College, B
The Pennsylvania State University, Lehigh Valley
    Campus of the Berks-Lehigh Valley College, B
The Pennsylvania State University McKeesport
    Campus of the Commonwealth College, B
The Pennsylvania State University Mont Alto
    Campus of the Commonwealth College, B
The Pennsylvania State University New Kensington
    Campus of the Commonwealth College, B
The Pennsylvania State University Schuylkill
    Campus of the Capital College, B
The Pennsylvania State University Shenango
    Campus of the Commonwealth College, B
The Pennsylvania State University University Park
    Campus, B
The Pennsylvania State University Wilkes-Barre
    Campus of the Commonwealth College, B

The Pennsylvania State University Worthington Scranton Campus of the Commonwealth College, B
The Pennsylvania State University York Campus of the Commonwealth College, B
Rosemont College, B
Saint Joseph's University, B
Temple University, B
University of Pennsylvania, BMD
University of Pittsburgh, BM
The University of Scranton, B
Villanova University, B

Rhode Island

Brown University, BMD
Providence College, B
University of Rhode Island, B

South Carolina

University of South Carolina, B

Tennessee

The University of Tennessee, BD

Texas

University of Houston, B
The University of Texas at Austin, B

Utah

Brigham Young University, B

Vermont

Marlboro College, B
Middlebury College, BMD

Virginia

Sweet Briar College, B
University of Virginia, BM

Washington

Gonzaga University, B
University of Washington, BMD

Wisconsin

University of Wisconsin-Madison, BMD
University of Wisconsin-Milwaukee, BM

Wyoming

Casper College, A

Alberta

University of Alberta, BM

British Columbia

The University of British Columbia, B
University of Victoria, BM

Manitoba

University of Manitoba, MD

Ontario

Brock University, B
Carleton University, B
Laurentian University, B
University of Ottawa, B
University of Toronto, BMD
University of Windsor, B
York University, B

Quebec

Bishop's University, B
Concordia University, B

McGill University, BMD

ITALIAN STUDIES

California

Santa Clara University, B
University of California, Santa Cruz, B

Connecticut

Connecticut College, B

Massachusetts

Wellesley College, B

New York

Columbia College, B
Fordham University, B

Ohio

Miami University, B

Rhode Island

Brown University, B

Texas

Southern Methodist University, B

Vermont

Bennington College, B
University of Vermont, B

British Columbia

University of Victoria, B

Manitoba

The University of Winnipeg, B

Nova Scotia

Dalhousie University, B

Ontario

Brock University, B
University of Windsor, B
York University, B

JAPANESE LANGUAGE AND LITERATURE

Alaska

University of Alaska Fairbanks, B

California

California State University, Fullerton, B
California State University, Long Beach, B
California State University, Los Angeles, B
Citrus College, A
Claremont McKenna College, B
East Los Angeles College, A
El Camino College, A
MiraCosta College, A
Pomona College, B
San Diego State University, B
San Francisco State University, B
San Joaquin Delta College, A
San Jose State University, B
Scripps College, B
Stanford University, B
University of California, Berkeley, B
University of California, Davis, B
University of California, Irvine, B
University of California, Los Angeles, B
University of California, San Diego, B
University of California, Santa Barbara, B
University of California, Santa Cruz, B

University of the Pacific, B

Colorado

University of Colorado at Boulder, B

Connecticut

Connecticut College, B
Yale University, B

District of Columbia

Georgetown University, B

Georgia

Emory University, B
University of Georgia, B

Hawaii

Hawaii Tokai International College, A
University of Hawaii at Hilo, B
University of Hawaii at Manoa, B

Illinois

Augustana College, B
City Colleges of Chicago, Harold Washington College, A
DePaul University, B
North Central College, B
University of Chicago, B

Indiana

Ball State University, B
Indiana University Bloomington, B
University of Notre Dame, B

Iowa

The University of Iowa, B

Kentucky

St. Catharine College, A

Louisiana

Dillard University, B

Maine

Bates College, B

Maryland

University of Maryland, College Park, B

Massachusetts

Harvard University, B
University of Massachusetts Amherst, B
Wellesley College, B
Williams College, B

Michigan

Aquinas College, B
Eastern Michigan University, B
Hope College, B
University of Michigan, B

Minnesota

Gustavus Adolphus College, B
University of Minnesota, Twin Cities Campus, B
University of St. Thomas, B

Missouri

Washington University in St. Louis, B

Montana

The University of Montana-Missoula, B

New Hampshire

Dartmouth College, B

New York

Colgate University, B
Hobart and William Smith Colleges, B
Sarah Lawrence College, B
University of Rochester, B

Vassar College, B

Ohio

Antioch College, B
Mount Union College, B
The Ohio State University, B
The University of Findlay, B

Oklahoma

Tulsa Community College, A

Oregon

Linfield College, B
Pacific University, B
Portland State University, B
University of Oregon, B

Pennsylvania

Carnegie Mellon University, B
Gettysburg College, B
Lincoln University, B
The Pennsylvania State University Abington
 College, B
The Pennsylvania State University Altoona
 College, B
The Pennsylvania State University Beaver Campus
 of the Commonwealth College, B
The Pennsylvania State University Berks Campus of
 the Berks-Lehigh Valley College, B
The Pennsylvania State University Delaware County
 Campus of the Commonwealth College, B
The Pennsylvania State University DuBois Campus
 of the Commonwealth College, B
The Pennsylvania State University at Erie, The
 Behrend College, B
The Pennsylvania State University Fayette Campus
 of the Commonwealth College, B
The Pennsylvania State University Hazleton
 Campus of the Commonwealth College, B
The Pennsylvania State University, Lehigh Valley
 Campus of the Berks-Lehigh Valley College, B
The Pennsylvania State University McKeesport
 Campus of the Commonwealth College, B
The Pennsylvania State University Mont Alto
 Campus of the Commonwealth College, B
The Pennsylvania State University New Kensington
 Campus of the Commonwealth College, B
The Pennsylvania State University Schuylkill
 Campus of the Capital College, B
The Pennsylvania State University Shenango
 Campus of the Commonwealth College, B
The Pennsylvania State University University Park
 Campus, B
The Pennsylvania State University Wilkes-Barre
 Campus of the Commonwealth College, B
The Pennsylvania State University Worthington
 Scranton Campus of the Commonwealth
 College, B
The Pennsylvania State University York Campus of
 the Commonwealth College, B
University of Pittsburgh, B

Texas

Austin Community College, A

Utah

Brigham Young University, B
Snow College, A
University of Utah, B

Vermont

Bennington College, B
Middlebury College, B

Washington

Everett Community College, A
Tacoma Community College, A

University of Washington, B

West Virginia

Salem International University, B

Wisconsin

Lawrence University, B
University of Wisconsin-Madison, B

Alberta

University of Alberta, B

British Columbia

The University of British Columbia, B
University of Victoria, B

Ontario

McMaster University, B
University of Windsor, B
York University, B

Saskatchewan

University of Regina, B

JAPANESE STUDIES

California

Claremont McKenna College, B
San Francisco State University, M
Stanford University, MD
University of California, Berkeley, MD
University of California, Irvine, MD
University of San Francisco, B

Colorado

University of Colorado at Boulder, M

Hawaii

Hawaii Tokai International College, A

Indiana

Earlham College, B
Indiana University Bloomington, MD

Kansas

University of Kansas, M

Massachusetts

Harvard University, MD
University of Massachusetts Amherst, M

Minnesota

Gustavus Adolphus College, B

Missouri

Washington University in St. Louis, MD

New York

Cornell University, MD
State University of New York at Buffalo, M
University at Albany, State University of New York, B

Ohio

Case Western Reserve University, B

Oregon

Portland State University, M
University of Oregon, MD
Willamette University, B

Pennsylvania

Gettysburg College, B

Washington

University of Washington, MD

Wisconsin

University of Wisconsin-Madison, MD

Alberta

University of Alberta, M

JAZZ/JAZZ STUDIES

California

California Institute of the Arts, B
Compton Community College, A

University of Southern California, B

Connecticut

University of Hartford, B

Florida

Florida Agricultural and Mechanical University, B
Florida State University, B
Manatee Community College, A
University of North Florida, B

Illinois

Augustana College, B
DePaul University, B
Lincoln College, A
North Central College, B
Northwestern University, B
Roosevelt University, B

Indiana

Indiana University Bloomington, B
Indiana University South Bend, A

Iowa

Drake University, B
Iowa Lakes Community College, A
Kirkwood Community College, A
The University of Iowa, B

Louisiana

Loyola University New Orleans, B
Southern University and Agricultural and Mechanical
 College, A
University of Louisiana at Lafayette, B

Maryland

Peabody Conservatory of Music of The Johns
 Hopkins University, B

Massachusetts

Berklee College of Music, B
New England Conservatory of Music, B
Simon's Rock College of Bard, B
Westfield State College, B

Michigan

Hope College, B
Michigan State University, B
University of Michigan, B

Minnesota

St. Cloud State University, B
University of Minnesota, Duluth, B

Nevada

University of Nevada, Las Vegas, B

New Jersey

Rowan University, B
Rutgers, The State University of New Jersey, New
 Brunswick/Piscataway, B
William Paterson University of New Jersey, B

New York

Bard College, B
Barnard College, B
City College of the City University of New York, B
Five Towns College, AB
Hofstra University, B
Ithaca College, B
Long Island University, Brooklyn Campus, B
Manhattan School of Music, B
The New School for Jazz and Contemporary
 Music, B
Sarah Lawrence College, B
State University of New York at New Paltz, B
University of Rochester, B

Villa Maria College of Buffalo, A

North Carolina

North Carolina Central University, B

Ohio

Bowling Green State University, B
Capital University, B
Central State University, B
Oberlin College, B
The Ohio State University, B
The University of Akron, B
University of Cincinnati, B

Oregon

University of Oregon, B

Pennsylvania

Temple University, B

South Carolina

Limestone College, B

Texas

Lamar University, B
Texas Southern University, B
Texas State University-San Marcos, B
University of North Texas, B

Utah

Brigham Young University, B

Vermont

Bennington College, B
Johnson State College, B

Virginia

Hampton University, B
Virginia Union University, B

Washington

Cornish College of the Arts, B
Western Washington University, B

British Columbia

Open Learning Agency, B

Nova Scotia

St. Francis Xavier University, B

Quebec

Concordia University, B
McGill University, B
Université Laval, A
Université de Montréal, B

JEWELRY/METALSMITHING

California

California College of the Arts, M

Colorado

Colorado State University, M

Illinois

Illinois State University, M
Southern Illinois University Carbondale, M

Indiana

Indiana University Bloomington, M

Massachusetts

Massachusetts College of Art, M

New York

City College of the City University of New York, M
Pratt Institute, M
Rochester Institute of Technology, M
State University of New York at New Paltz, M

Syracuse University, M

Pennsylvania

Marywood University, M
Temple University, M

Rhode Island

Rhode Island School of Design, M

Texas

University of North Texas, M

Virginia

James Madison University, M
Virginia Commonwealth University, M

JEWISH/JUDAIC STUDIES

Arizona

The University of Arizona, B

California

California State University, Chico, B
San Diego State University, B
Scripps College, B
University of California, Berkeley, D
University of California, Los Angeles, B
University of California, San Diego, BM
University of Judaism, BM
University of Southern California, B
Yeshiva Ohr Elchonon Chabad/West Coast
  Talmudical Seminary, B

Colorado

University of Denver, M
Yeshiva Toras Chaim Talmudical Seminary, B

Connecticut

Trinity College, B
University of Connecticut, M
University of Hartford, B
Yale University, B

District of Columbia

American University, B
The George Washington University, B

Florida

Florida Atlantic University, B
Manatee Community College, A
Talmudic College of Florida, B
University of Florida, B
University of Miami, B

Georgia

Emory University, BM

Illinois

DePaul University, B
Hebrew Theological College, B
University of Chicago, BMD

Indiana

Indiana University Bloomington, B

Louisiana

Tulane University, B

Maryland

Baltimore Hebrew University, AB
Ner Israel Rabbinical College, B
University of Maryland, College Park, B

Massachusetts

Brandeis University, BMDO
Clark University, B
Hampshire College, B
Harvard University, BMD
Hebrew College, BMO
Mount Holyoke College, B
Tufts University, B
University of Massachusetts Amherst, B

Wellesley College, B

Michigan

University of Michigan, B

Minnesota

Hamline University, B
University of Minnesota, Twin Cities Campus, B

Missouri

Washington University in St. Louis, BM

New Jersey

Rutgers, The State University of New Jersey, New
  Brunswick/Piscataway, B
Seton Hall University, M

New York

Bard College, B
Brooklyn College of the City University of New
  York, B
City College of the City University of New York, B
Cornell University, MD
Hofstra University, B
Hunter College of the City University of New York, B
The Jewish Theological Seminary, BMDO
Kol Yaakov Torah Center, B
Lehman College of the City University of New
  York, B
Machzikei Hadath Rabbinical College, B
Mesivta of Eastern Parkway Rabbinical Seminary, B
Mesivta Torah Vodaath Rabbinical Seminary, B
New York University, BMD
Queens College of the City University of New
  York, B
Sh'or Yoshuv Rabbinical College, B
State University of New York at Binghamton, B
Talmudical Institute of Upstate New York, B
Touro College, BM
University at Albany, State University of New York, B
Vassar College, B
Yeshiva University, BMD

Ohio

Laura and Alvin Siegal College of Judaic
  Studies, BM
Oberlin College, B
The Ohio State University, B
University of Cincinnati, B

Oregon

University of Oregon, B

Pennsylvania

Dickinson College, B
Gratz College, BM
The Pennsylvania State University Abington
  College, B
The Pennsylvania State University Altoona
  College, B
The Pennsylvania State University Beaver Campus
  of the Commonwealth College, B
The Pennsylvania State University Berks Campus of
  the Berks-Lehigh Valley College, B
The Pennsylvania State University Delaware County
  Campus of the Commonwealth College, B
The Pennsylvania State University DuBois Campus
  of the Commonwealth College, B
The Pennsylvania State University at Erie, The
  Behrend College, B
The Pennsylvania State University Fayette Campus
  of the Commonwealth College, B
The Pennsylvania State University Hazleton
  Campus of the Commonwealth College, B
The Pennsylvania State University, Lehigh Valley
  Campus of the Berks-Lehigh Valley College, B
The Pennsylvania State University McKeesport
  Campus of the Commonwealth College, B
The Pennsylvania State University Mont Alto
  Campus of the Commonwealth College, B
The Pennsylvania State University New Kensington
  Campus of the Commonwealth College, B
The Pennsylvania State University Schuylkill
  Campus of the Capital College, B

The Pennsylvania State University Shenango
  Campus of the Commonwealth College, B
The Pennsylvania State University University Park
  Campus, B
The Pennsylvania State University Wilkes-Barre
  Campus of the Commonwealth College, B
The Pennsylvania State University Worthington
  Scranton Campus of the Commonwealth
  College, B
The Pennsylvania State University York Campus of
  the Commonwealth College, B
Temple University, B
University of Pennsylvania, B
Yeshiva Beth Moshe, B

Rhode Island

Brown University, B

Texas

The University of Texas at Austin, B

Washington

University of Washington, B

Manitoba

University of Manitoba, B

Ontario

Ner Israel Yeshiva College of Toronto, B
University of Toronto, B
York University, B

Quebec

Concordia University, M
McGill University, BMD

JOURNALISM

Alabama

Alabama State University, B
Auburn University, BM
Enterprise-Ozark Community College, A
Samford University, B
Spring Hill College, B
Talladega College, B
Troy University, B
The University of Alabama, BM

Alaska

University of Alaska Anchorage, B
University of Alaska Fairbanks, BM

Arizona

Arizona State University, BM
Cochise College (Douglas), A
Cochise College (Sierra Vista), A
Northern Arizona University, B
The University of Arizona, BM

Arkansas

Arkansas State University, BM
Arkansas Tech University, BM
Henderson State University, B
John Brown University, AB
Southern Arkansas University-Magnolia, B
University of Arkansas, BM
University of Arkansas at Little Rock, B
University of Central Arkansas, B

California

Alliant International University, B
American River College, A
Bakersfield College, A
California Baptist University, B
California Lutheran University, B
California Polytechnic State University, San Luis
  Obispo, B
California State Polytechnic University, Pomona, B
California State University, Chico, B
California State University, East Bay, B
California State University, Fresno, BM
California State University, Fullerton, BM
California State University, Long Beach, B

California State University, Northridge, BM
California State University, Sacramento, B
Cañada College, A
Cerritos College, A
Chabot College, A
Chaffey College, A
Citrus College, A
City College of San Francisco, A
College of the Canyons, A
College of the Desert, A
College of Marin, A
College of San Mateo, A
College of the Sequoias, A
Compton Community College, A
Contra Costa College, A
Cosumnes River College (Sacramento), A
Cuesta College, A
De Anza College, A
East Los Angeles College, A
El Camino College, A
Fresno City College, A
Fullerton College, A
Gavilan College, A
Glendale Community College, A
Golden West College, A
Humboldt State University, B
Imperial Valley College, A
Laney College, A
Lassen Community College District, A
Long Beach City College, A
Los Angeles City College, A
Los Angeles Mission College, A
Los Angeles Pierce College, A
Los Angeles Trade-Technical College, A
Los Angeles Valley College, A
Los Medanos College, A
MiraCosta College, A
Moorpark College, A
Mt. San Antonio College, A
Ohlone College, A
Orange Coast College, A
Oxnard College, A
Pacific Union College, B
Palomar College, A
Pasadena City College, A
Pepperdine University, B
Point Loma Nazarene University, B
Saddleback College, A
San Bernardino Valley College, A
San Diego City College, A
San Diego State University, B
San Francisco State University, B
San Joaquin Delta College, A
San Jose State University, B
Santa Ana College, A
Santa Monica College, A
Santa Rosa Junior College, A
Shasta College, A
Sierra College, A
Skyline College, A
Solano Community College, A
Southwestern College, A
Stanford University, M
Taft College, A
University of California, Berkeley, MO
University of California, Irvine, B
University of La Verne, B
University of Southern California, BM
Ventura College, A
West Los Angeles College, A

Colorado

Colorado State University, B
Colorado State University-Pueblo, B
Metropolitan State College of Denver, B
Northeastern Junior College, A
University of Colorado at Boulder, BMD
University of Denver, B
University of Northern Colorado, B
Western State College of Colorado, B

Connecticut

Housatonic Community College, A
Manchester Community College, A
Quinnipiac University, BM
Sacred Heart University, B

Southern Connecticut State University, B
University of Bridgeport, B
University of Connecticut, B

Delaware

Delaware State University, B
Delaware Technical & Community College, Jack F.
  Owens Campus, A
University of Delaware, B

District of Columbia

American University, BM
The George Washington University, B
Howard University, B

Florida

Barry University, B
Daytona Beach Community College, A
Edward Waters College, B
Florida Agricultural and Mechanical University, BM
Florida Southern College, B
Indian River Community College, A
Manatee Community College, A
Miami Dade College, A
Palm Beach Atlantic University, B
Palm Beach Community College, A
Pensacola Junior College, A
University of Central Florida, B
University of Florida, BMD
University of Miami, BM

Georgia

Abraham Baldwin Agricultural College, A
Bainbridge College, A
Clayton State University, A
Dalton State College, A
Darton College, A
Emory University, B
Gainesville College, A
Georgia College & State University, B
Georgia Highlands College, A
Georgia Perimeter College, A
Georgia Southern University, B
Georgia State University, B
Gordon College, A
Macon State College, A
Mercer University, B
Paine College, B
South Georgia College, A
University of Georgia, BMD
University of West Georgia, B
Young Harris College, A

Hawaii

Hawaii Pacific University, B
University of Hawaii at Manoa, B

Idaho

Brigham Young University -Idaho, A
North Idaho College, A
University of Idaho, B

Illinois

Bradley University, B
City Colleges of Chicago, Harold Washington
  College, A
City Colleges of Chicago, Harry S. Truman
  College, A
City Colleges of Chicago, Richard J. Daley
  College, A
City Colleges of Chicago, Wilbur Wright College, A
Columbia College Chicago, BM
Danville Area Community College, A
Eastern Illinois University, B
Illinois State University, B
Illinois Valley Community College, A
John A. Logan College, A
Judson College, B
Lewis University, B
Lincoln College, A
Loyola University Chicago, B
North Central College, B
Northern Illinois University, B
Northwestern University, BM
Olivet Nazarene University, B

Quincy University, B
Roosevelt University, BM
Southern Illinois University Carbondale, B
University of Illinois at Springfield, M
University of Illinois at Urbana-Champaign, BM
Western Illinois University, B
William Rainey Harper College, A

Indiana

Ball State University, ABM
Bethel College, A
Butler University, B
Franklin College, B
Goshen College, B
Grace College, B
Huntington University, B
Indiana State University, B
Indiana University Bloomington, BMDO
Indiana University-Purdue University Indianapolis, B
Indiana University Southeast, A
Manchester College, A
Purdue University Calumet, B
Saint Mary-of-the-Woods College, B
University of Southern Indiana, B
Valparaiso University, B
Vincennes University, A

Iowa

Ashford University, B
Dordt College, B
Drake University, BM
Grand View College, B
Iowa Central Community College, A
Iowa Lakes Community College, A
Iowa State University of Science and
   Technology, BM
Iowa Western Community College, A
Kirkwood Community College, A
Loras College, B
St. Ambrose University, B
The University of Iowa, BMO
Waldorf College, B
Wartburg College, B
William Penn University, B

Kansas

Allen County Community College, A
Barton County Community College, A
Butler Community College, A
Cloud County Community College, A
Coffeyville Community College, A
Colby Community College, A
Cowley County Community College and Area
   Vocational-Technical School, A
Dodge City Community College, A
Fort Hays State University, B
Garden City Community College, A
Highland Community College, A
Kansas State University, B
Seward County Community College, A
Tabor College, B
University of Kansas, BM

Kentucky

Asbury College, B
Campbellsville University, B
Eastern Kentucky University, B
Lindsey Wilson College, B
Morehead State University, M
Murray State University, B
Northern Kentucky University, B
St. Catharine College, B
University of Kentucky, B
Western Kentucky University, B

Louisiana

Louisiana College, B
Louisiana Tech University, B

Northwestern State University of Louisiana, B

Maine

Saint Joseph's College of Maine, B
University of Maine, B

Maryland

College of Southern Maryland, A
Columbia Union College, B
University of Baltimore, B
University of Maryland, College Park, BMD
Villa Julie College, A

Massachusetts

Boston University, BM
Curry College, B
Eastern Nazarene College, B
Emerson College, BM
Fitchburg State College, B
Framingham State College, B
Massachusetts College of Liberal Arts, B
Northeastern University, BM
Northern Essex Community College, A
Salem State College, B
Suffolk University, B
University of Massachusetts Amherst, B

Michigan

Andrews University, B
Central Michigan University, B
Concordia University, B
Eastern Michigan University, B
Grand Valley State University, B
Kellogg Community College, A
Lansing Community College, A
Madonna University, AB
Michigan State University, BM
Monroe County Community College, A
Oakland University, B
Olivet College, B
St. Clair County Community College, A
University of Detroit Mercy, B
Wayne State University, B
Western Michigan University, B

Minnesota

Bemidji State University, B
College of St. Catherine, B
Concordia College, B
Minnesota State University Mankato, B
Minnesota State University Moorhead, B
North Central University, AB
Northwestern College, B
Ridgewater College, A
St. Cloud State University, B
University of Minnesota, Twin Cities Campus, B
University of St. Thomas, B
Winona State University, B

Mississippi

Copiah-Lincoln Community College, A
Delta State University, B
East Central Community College, A
Hinds Community College, A
Itawamba Community College, A
Jackson State University, B
Northeast Mississippi Community College, A
Northwest Mississippi Community College, A
Rust College, B
University of Mississippi, BM
University of Southern Mississippi, B
William Carey College, B

Missouri

Central Missouri State University, B
College of the Ozarks, B
Drury University, B
East Central College, A
Evangel University, AB
Jefferson College, A
Lincoln University, B
Lindenwood University, B
Missouri State University, B
Northwest Missouri State University, B
St. Louis Community College at Florissant Valley, A

St. Louis Community College at Meramec, A
Truman State University, B
University of Missouri-Columbia, BMD
Webster University, B

Montana

The University of Montana-Missoula, BM

Nebraska

Creighton University, B
Hastings College, B
Midland Lutheran College, B
Northeast Community College, A
Southeast Community College, Beatrice Campus, A
Union College, B
University of Nebraska at Kearney, B
University of Nebraska-Lincoln, BM
University of Nebraska at Omaha, B
Wayne State College, B
Western Nebraska Community College, A

Nevada

University of Nevada, Reno, BM

New Hampshire

Chester College of New England, B
Franklin Pierce College, B
Keene State College, B
New England College, B
University of New Hampshire, B

New Jersey

Brookdale Community College, A
Burlington County College, A
Middlesex County College, A
Ocean County College, A
Rider University, B
Rutgers, The State University of New Jersey, New
   Brunswick/Piscataway, B
Rutgers, The State University of New Jersey,
   Newark, B
Salem Community College, A
Sussex County Community College, A

New Mexico

New Mexico Highlands University, B
New Mexico State University, B
University of New Mexico, B

New York

Bernard M. Baruch College of the City University of
   New York, BM
Brooklyn College of the City University of New
   York, B
Buffalo State College, State University of New
   York, B
Fordham University, B
Hofstra University, B
Houghton College, B
Iona College, BM
Ithaca College, B
Kingsborough Community College of the City
   University of New York, A
Long Island University, Brooklyn Campus, B
Long Island University, C.W. Post Campus, B
Marist College, B
New York University, BMO
Polytechnic University, Brooklyn Campus, B
Purchase College, State University of New York, B
St. Bonaventure University, B
St. John's University, B
St. Thomas Aquinas College, B
State University of New York College of Agriculture
   and Technology at Morrisville, A
State University of New York College at
   Brockport, B
State University of New York at New Paltz, B
State University of New York at Oswego, B
Suffolk County Community College, A
Syracuse University, BM
Ulster County Community College, A

Utica College, B

North Carolina

Appalachian State University, B
Campbell University, B
Elon University, B
Gardner-Webb University, B
Pfeiffer University, B
Queens University of Charlotte, B
The University of North Carolina at Asheville, B

North Dakota

Turtle Mountain Community College, A

Ohio

Ashland University, B
Bowling Green State University, B
Central State University, B
Cincinnati Christian University, B
Kent State University, BM
Lorain County Community College, A
Marietta College, B
Miami University, B
Miami University Hamilton, B
Mount Vernon Nazarene University, B
Muskingum College, B
Ohio Northern University, B
The Ohio State University, BM
Ohio University, BMD
Ohio University-Eastern, B
Ohio Wesleyan University, B
Otterbein College, B
University of Dayton, B
The University of Findlay, B
The University of Toledo, B
Youngstown State University, B

Oklahoma

Bacone College, A
Carl Albert State College, A
Connors State College, A
Eastern Oklahoma State College, A
Langston University, B
Northeastern Oklahoma Agricultural and Mechanical
    College, A
Northeastern State University, B
Oklahoma Baptist University, B
Oklahoma Christian University, B
Oklahoma City University, B
Oklahoma State University, B
Oral Roberts University, B
Rose State College, A
St. Gregory's University, B
Southern Nazarene University, B
Tulsa Community College, A
University of Central Oklahoma, B
University of Oklahoma, BM

Oregon

Corban College, B
Linn-Benton Community College, A
Mt. Hood Community College, A
Multnomah Bible College and Biblical Seminary, B
Pacific University, B
Umpqua Community College, A
University of Oregon, BMD
University of Portland, B

Pennsylvania

Allegheny College, B
Bucks County Community College, A
Community College of Allegheny County, A
Delaware County Community College, A
Duquesne University, B
Edinboro University of Pennsylvania, B
Gettysburg College, B
Harrisburg Area Community College, A
Indiana University of Pennsylvania, B
Keystone College, A
La Salle University, B
Lehigh University, B
Lincoln University, B
Lock Haven University of Pennsylvania, B
Luzerne County Community College, A
Mansfield University of Pennsylvania, B

Mercyhurst College, B
Messiah College, B
Northampton County Area Community College, A
The Pennsylvania State University Abington
    College, B
The Pennsylvania State University Altoona
    College, B
The Pennsylvania State University Beaver Campus
    of the Commonwealth College, B
The Pennsylvania State University Berks Campus of
    the Berks-Lehigh Valley College, B
The Pennsylvania State University Delaware County
    Campus of the Commonwealth College, B
The Pennsylvania State University DuBois Campus
    of the Commonwealth College, B
The Pennsylvania State University at Erie, The
    Behrend College, B
The Pennsylvania State University Fayette Campus
    of the Commonwealth College, B
The Pennsylvania State University Hazleton
    Campus of the Commonwealth College, B
The Pennsylvania State University, Lehigh Valley
    Campus of the Berks-Lehigh Valley College, B
The Pennsylvania State University McKeesport
    Campus of the Commonwealth College, B
The Pennsylvania State University Mont Alto
    Campus of the Commonwealth College, B
The Pennsylvania State University New Kensington
    Campus of the Commonwealth College, B
The Pennsylvania State University Schuylkill
    Campus of the Capital College, B
The Pennsylvania State University Shenango
    Campus of the Commonwealth College, B
The Pennsylvania State University University Park
    Campus, B
The Pennsylvania State University Wilkes-Barre
    Campus of the Commonwealth College, B
The Pennsylvania State University Worthington
    Scranton Campus of the Commonwealth
    College, B
The Pennsylvania State University York Campus of
    the Commonwealth College, B
Point Park University, BM
Saint Francis University, B
Seton Hill University, B
Shippensburg University of Pennsylvania, B
Susquehanna University, B
Temple University, BM
University of Pittsburgh at Greensburg, B
University of Pittsburgh at Johnstown, B
Waynesburg College, B

Puerto Rico

Bayamon Central University, B
Inter American University of Puerto Rico, Ponce
    Campus, B
University of the Sacred Heart, BM

Rhode Island

University of Rhode Island, B

South Carolina

Anderson University, B
Benedict College, B
Bob Jones University, B
Columbia College, B
Morris College, B
North Greenville College, B
University of South Carolina, BMD

South Dakota

Augustana College, B
South Dakota State University, BM

Tennessee

Belmont University, B
Carson-Newman College, B
Southern Adventist University, B
Tennessee Technological University, B
Union University, B
University of Memphis, BM
The University of Tennessee, BMD

The University of Tennessee at Martin, B

Texas

Abilene Christian University, B
Amarillo College, A
Angelina College, A
Angelo State University, BM
Austin Community College, A
Baylor University, BM
Brazosport College, A
Central Texas College, A
Coastal Bend College, A
Del Mar College, A
Hill College of the Hill Junior College District, A
Kilgore College, A
Lamar University, B
Lee College, A
Midland College, A
Navarro College, A
North Harris College, A
Palo Alto College, A
Sam Houston State University, B
South Plains College, A
Southern Methodist University, B
Southwestern Adventist University, B
Stephen F. Austin State University, B
Texarkana College, A
Texas A&M University, BM
Texas A&M University-Commerce, B
Texas A&M University-Kingsville, B
Texas Christian University, BM
Texas Southern University, BM
Texas State University-San Marcos, B
Texas Tech University, B
Texas Wesleyan University, B
Texas Woman's University, B
Trinity Valley Community College, A
University of Houston, B
University of North Texas, BM
The University of Texas at Arlington, B
The University of Texas at Austin, BMD
The University of Texas at El Paso, B
The University of Texas-Pan American, B
The University of Texas at Tyler, B
West Texas A&M University, B
Western Texas College, A

Utah

Brigham Young University, B
Dixie State College of Utah, A
University of Utah, B
Utah State University, B
Weber State University, B

Vermont

Bennington College, B
Castleton State College, B
Champlain College, B
College of St. Joseph, B
Johnson State College, B
Lyndon State College, B
Saint Michael's College, B

Virginia

Averett University, B
Hampton University, B
Longwood University, B
Lynchburg College, B
Norfolk State University, B
Patrick Henry College, B
University of Richmond, B
Virginia Union University, B
Washington and Lee University, B

Washington

Central Washington University, B
Eastern Washington University, B
Everett Community College, A
Gonzaga University, B
Highline Community College, A
Pacific Lutheran University, B
Seattle University, B
Skagit Valley College, A
Tacoma Community College, A
Walla Walla College, B

Western Washington University, B
Whitworth College, B

West Virginia

Marshall University, BM
Potomac State College of West Virginia
  University, A
West Virginia University, BM
Wheeling Jesuit University, B

Wisconsin

Carroll College, B
Marquette University, BM
University of Wisconsin-Eau Claire, B
University of Wisconsin-Madison, BMD
University of Wisconsin-Milwaukee, BM
University of Wisconsin-Oshkosh, B
University of Wisconsin-River Falls, B
University of Wisconsin-Superior, B
University of Wisconsin-Whitewater, B

Wyoming

Casper College, A
Laramie County Community College, A
Northwest College, A
University of Wyoming, B
Western Wyoming Community College, A

British Columbia

Kwantlen University College, B
Thompson Rivers University, B
The University of British Columbia, M

Manitoba

The University of Winnipeg, B

New Brunswick

St. Thomas University, B

Nova Scotia

University of King's College, B

Ontario

Carleton University, BMD
Ryerson University, B
University of Ottawa, B
The University of Western Ontario, BM
University of Windsor, B

Quebec

Concordia University, BO
Université Laval, O

Saskatchewan

University of Regina, B

JUNIOR HIGH/INTERMEDIATE/MIDDLE SCHOOL EDUCATION AND TEACHING

Alabama

Jacksonville State University, B
Judson College, B

Alaska

Alaska Pacific University, B

Arizona

Prescott College, B

Arkansas

Arkansas Northeastern College, A
Arkansas State University, B
Arkansas State University-Mountain Home, A
Arkansas Tech University, B
Harding University, B
Henderson State University, B
John Brown University, B
North Arkansas College, A
Ouachita Baptist University, B

Ozarka College, A
University of Arkansas, B
University of Arkansas at Fort Smith, AB
University of Central Arkansas, B
University of the Ozarks, B

California

The Master's College and Seminary, B

Colorado

Colorado State University-Pueblo, B
Mesa State College, B

Connecticut

Albertus Magnus College, B
Sacred Heart University, B

Delaware

Delaware State University, B
University of Delaware, B
Wilmington College, B

Florida

Florida State University, B
Lynn University, B
Miami Dade College, A
Saint Leo University, B
University of Florida, B
University of North Florida, B
University of West Florida, B

Georgia

Albany State University, B
Armstrong Atlantic State University, B
Augusta State University, B
Berry College, B
Brenau University, B
Brewton-Parker College, B
Clark Atlanta University, B
Clayton State University, B
Columbus State University, B
Covenant College, B
Dalton State College, A
Emmanuel College, B
Gainesville College, A
Georgia College & State University, B
Georgia Southern University, B
Georgia Southwestern State University, B
Kennesaw State University, B
LaGrange College, B
Mercer University, B
Morehouse College, B
North Georgia College & State University, B
Oglethorpe University, B
Piedmont College, B
Reinhardt College, B
Shorter College, B
South Georgia College, A
Thomas University, B
Toccoa Falls College, B
University of Georgia, B
University of West Georgia, B
Valdosta State University, B
Wesleyan College, B

Illinois

Chicago State University, B
Eastern Illinois University, B
Governors State University, B
Lincoln College, A
McKendree College, B
Trinity Christian College, B

Indiana

Bethel College, B
Huntington University, B
Indiana Wesleyan University, B
Oakland City University, B
Taylor University, B
Valparaiso University, B
Vincennes University, A

Iowa

Ashford University, B
Clarke College, B

Mount Mercy College, B
University of Northern Iowa, B
Waldorf College, B

Kansas

MidAmerica Nazarene University, B
University of Kansas, B

Kentucky

Asbury College, B
Bellarmine University, B
Berea College, B
Brescia University, B
Eastern Kentucky University, B
Georgetown College, B
Kentucky Christian University, B
Kentucky Wesleyan College, B
Lindsey Wilson College, B
Midway College, B
Morehead State University, B
Murray State University, B
Northern Kentucky University, B
Pikeville College, B
Spalding University, B
Thomas More College, B
Transylvania University, B
Union College, B
University of the Cumberlands, B
University of Kentucky, B
Western Kentucky University, B

Louisiana

Louisiana Tech University, B
Nicholls State University, B
Northwestern State University of Louisiana, B
Southeastern Louisiana University, B
Southern University and Agricultural and Mechanical
  College, B
University of New Orleans, B
Xavier University of Louisiana, B

Maine

College of the Atlantic, B

Maryland

Villa Julie College, B

Massachusetts

American International College, B
Clark University, B
Eastern Nazarene College, B
Fitchburg State College, B
Gordon College, B
Lesley University, B
Massachusetts College of Liberal Arts, B
Merrimack College, B
Springfield College, B

Michigan

Lake Superior State University, B

Minnesota

Concordia University, St. Paul, B
Minnesota State University Moorhead, B
St. Cloud State University, B
University of Minnesota, Duluth, B
University of St. Thomas, B
Winona State University, B

Missouri

Avila University, B
Central Methodist University, B
Central Missouri State University, B
College of the Ozarks, B
Evangel University, B
Fontbonne University, B
Harris-Stowe State University, B
Lincoln University, B
Lindenwood University, B
Maryville University of Saint Louis, B
Missouri Baptist University, B
Missouri Southern State University, B
Missouri State University, B
Northwest Missouri State University, B
Southeast Missouri State University, B

Southwest Baptist University, B
University of Missouri-Columbia, B
University of Missouri-Kansas City, B
Washington University in St. Louis, B
Westminster College, B
William Woods University, B

Montana

University of Great Falls, B

Nebraska

Chadron State College, B
Concordia University, B
Grace University, B
Midland Lutheran College, B
Nebraska Wesleyan University, B
Peru State College, B
University of Nebraska-Lincoln, B
Wayne State College, B
York College, B

New Mexico

College of the Southwest, B

New York

Concordia College, B
Elmira College, B
Ithaca College, B
Manhattan College, B
Medaille College, B
Mercy College, B
New York University, B
St. Bonaventure University, B
St. John's University, B
State University of New York College at
   Brockport, B
State University of New York College at Cortland, B
State University of New York College at Old
   Westbury, B
State University of New York College at Oneonta, B

North Carolina

Appalachian State University, B
Barton College, B
Bennett College For Women, B
Brevard College, B
Campbell University, B
Catawba College, B
East Carolina University, B
Elizabeth City State University, B
Elon University, B
Fayetteville State University, B
Greensboro College, B
High Point University, B
Mars Hill College, B
Mount Olive College, B
North Carolina Central University, B
North Carolina State University, B
North Carolina Wesleyan College, B
The University of North Carolina at Chapel Hill, B
The University of North Carolina at Charlotte, B
The University of North Carolina at Greensboro, B
The University of North Carolina at Pembroke, B
The University of North Carolina Wilmington, B
Western Carolina University, B
Wingate University, B
Winston-Salem State University, B

North Dakota

University of North Dakota, B

Ohio

Antioch College, B
Ashland University, B
Baldwin-Wallace College, B
Bluffton University, B
Bowling Green State University, B
Capital University, B
Central State University, B
Cleveland State University, B
College of Mount St. Joseph, B
Kent State University, B
Lourdes College, B
Malone College, B
Miami University, B

Mount Union College, B
Mount Vernon Nazarene University, B
Muskingum College, B
Notre Dame College, B
Ohio Dominican University, B
Ohio Northern University, B
Ohio University, B
Ohio Wesleyan University, B
Otterbein College, B
Shawnee State University, B
The University of Akron, B
Urbana University, B
Ursuline College, B
Wright State University, B
Xavier University, B
Youngstown State University, B

Oklahoma

Southern Nazarene University, B

Oregon

Warner Pacific College, B

Pennsylvania

Cedar Crest College, B
Gettysburg College, B

Puerto Rico

Inter American University of Puerto Rico,
   Metropolitan Campus, B

South Carolina

Bob Jones University, B
Claflin University, B
Coastal Carolina University, B
College of Charleston, B
Presbyterian College, B

South Dakota

Black Hills State University, B
Dakota Wesleyan University, B
University of Sioux Falls, B
The University of South Dakota, B

Tennessee

Bryan College, B
Johnson Bible College, B
King College, B
Lambuth University, B
Lipscomb University, B
Tusculum College, B
The University of Tennessee at Chattanooga, B

Texas

Abilene Christian University, B
Arlington Baptist College, B
Concordia University at Austin, B
Houston Baptist University, B
Lubbock Christian University, B
McMurry University, B
Northeast Texas Community College, A
Tarleton State University, B
Texas Lutheran University, B
University of Mary Hardin-Baylor, B

Vermont

Bennington College, B
Champlain College, B
Johnson State College, B
University of Vermont, B

Virginia

Bluefield College, B
Christopher Newport University, B
Eastern Mennonite University, B
Hampton University, B
University of Richmond, B

Virginia Wesleyan College, B

West Virginia

West Virginia Wesleyan College, B
Wheeling Jesuit University, B

Wisconsin

Alverno College, B
Carroll College, B
Concordia University Wisconsin, B
Lakeland College, B
Marian College of Fond du Lac, B
Marquette University, B
Northland College, B
University of Wisconsin-Platteville, B

Manitoba

Brandon University, B

Newfoundland and Labrador

Memorial University of Newfoundland, B

Ontario

The University of Western Ontario, B
York University, B

Saskatchewan

University of Regina, B

JUVENILE CORRECTIONS

Missouri

Harris-Stowe State University, B

Oklahoma

East Central University, B

Oregon

Linn-Benton Community College, A

KINDERGARTEN/PRESCHOOL EDUCATION AND TEACHING

Alabama

Alabama Agricultural and Mechanical University, B
Alabama Southern Community College, A
Alabama State University, B
Athens State University, B
Auburn University, B
Enterprise-Ozark Community College, A
Faulkner University, B
Jacksonville State University, B
Troy University, B
The University of Alabama, B
The University of Alabama at Birmingham, B
University of Mobile, B
University of Montevallo, B
University of North Alabama, B
Wallace State Community College, A

Alaska

University of Alaska Anchorage, B
University of Alaska Fairbanks, A

Arizona

Arizona State University, B
Central Arizona College, A
Glendale Community College, A
Northland Pioneer College, A
Prescott College, A
Scottsdale Community College, A
The University of Arizona, B

Arkansas

Harding University, B
John Brown University, B
Philander Smith College, B
Southern Arkansas University-Magnolia, B
University of Arkansas Community College at
   Batesville, A
University of Arkansas at Fort Smith, B

University of Arkansas at Little Rock, B
University of Arkansas at Pine Bluff, AB
Williams Baptist College, B

California

Allan Hancock College, A
American River College, A
Barstow College, A
Bethany University, AB
Butte College, A
Cabrillo College, A
California Polytechnic State University, San Luis
   Obispo, B
Cañada College, A
Cerritos College, A
Cerro Coso Community College, A
Chabot College, A
Chaffey College, A
College of the Canyons, A
College of the Desert, A
College of Marin, A
College of the Redwoods, A
College of the Sequoias, A
College of the Siskiyous, A
Compton Community College, A
Contra Costa College, A
Cosumnes River College (Sacramento), A
Cuesta College, A
El Camino College, A
Fullerton College, A
Gavilan College, A
Hartnell College, A
Hope International University, A
Humboldt State University, B
Imperial Valley College, A
Lake Tahoe Community College, A
Las Positas College, A
Lassen Community College District, A
Long Beach City College, A
Los Angeles Southwest College, A
Los Angeles Valley College, A
Mendocino College, A
Merced College, A
Merritt College, A
MiraCosta College, A
Modesto Junior College, A
Monterey Peninsula College, A
Moorpark College, A
Mount St. Mary's College, A
Mt. San Antonio College, A
Mt. San Jacinto College, A
Napa Valley College, A
Ohlone College, A
Orange Coast College, A
Oxnard College, A
Pacific Oaks College, B
Pacific Union College, AB
Palo Verde College, A
Palomar College, A
Pasadena City College, A
Patten University, B
Sacramento City College, A
Saddleback College, A
San Diego State University, B
San Joaquin Delta College, A
San Jose City College, A
Santa Ana College, A
Santa Barbara City College, A
Santa Monica College, A
Shasta College, A
Sierra College, A
Solano Community College, A
Southwestern College, A
Taft College, A
Victor Valley College, A
West Hills Community College, A
West Valley College, A
Whittier College, B
Yuba College, A

Colorado

Aims Community College, A
Community College of Aurora, A
Mesa State College, A
Northeastern Junior College, A
Otero Junior College, A

Pueblo Community College, A
Trinidad State Junior College, A

Connecticut

Asnuntuck Community College, A
Capital Community College, A
Eastern Connecticut State University, B
Gateway Community College, A
Manchester Community College, A
Mitchell College, AB
Naugatuck Valley Community College, A
Northwestern Connecticut Community College, A
Norwalk Community College, A
Sacred Heart University, B
Saint Joseph College, B
Three Rivers Community College, A
Tunxis Community College, A

Delaware

Delaware State University, B
Delaware Technical & Community College,
   Stanton/Wilmington Campus, A
Delaware Technical & Community College, Terry
   Campus, A
University of Delaware, B
Wilmington College, A

District of Columbia

The Catholic University of America, B
Gallaudet University, B
Howard University, B
Trinity (Washington) University, B
University of the District of Columbia, B

Florida

Barry University, B
Broward Community College, A
Daytona Beach Community College, A
Edward Waters College, B
Florida Agricultural and Mechanical University, B
Florida Southern College, B
Florida State University, B
Indian River Community College, A
Lynn University, AB
Manatee Community College, A
Miami Dade College, A
Nova Southeastern University, AB
Okaloosa-Walton College, A
Palm Beach Community College, A
Pensacola Junior College, A
St. Petersburg College, A
Santa Fe Community College, A
Tallahassee Community College, A
University of South Florida, B

Georgia

Abraham Baldwin Agricultural College, A
Albany State University, B
Armstrong Atlantic State University, B
Atlanta Christian College, B
Augusta State University, B
Bainbridge College, A
Brenau University, B
Clark Atlanta University, B
Clayton State University, A
Fort Valley State University, B
Georgia Highlands College, A
Georgia Southern University, B
North Georgia College & State University, B
Oglethorpe University, B
Piedmont College, B
Reinhardt College, B
South Georgia College, A
Thomas University, B

Guam

Guam Community College, A
University of Guam, B

Hawaii

Hawaii Community College, A
Honolulu Community College, A

Kauai Community College, A

Idaho

Boise State University, B
Brigham Young University -Idaho, A

Illinois

Bradley University, B
Chicago State University, B
City Colleges of Chicago, Harold Washington
   College, A
City Colleges of Chicago, Kennedy-King College, A
City Colleges of Chicago, Olive-Harvey College, A
Columbia College Chicago, B
Concordia University, B
Danville Area Community College, A
DePaul University, B
Eastern Illinois University, B
Elgin Community College, A
Elmhurst College, B
Governors State University, B
Heartland Community College, A
Highland Community College, A
John A. Logan College, A
Judson College, B
Kendall College, AB
Lewis and Clark Community College, A
Lincoln Christian College, B
Lincoln College, A
Millikin University, B
National-Louis University, B
North Park University, B
Northeastern Illinois University, B
Northern Illinois University, B
Oakton Community College, A
Olivet Nazarene University, B
Parkland College, A
Roosevelt University, B
Saint Xavier University, B
South Suburban College, A
Spoon River College, A
Triton College, A
University of Illinois at Urbana-Champaign, B
Waubonsee Community College, A
William Rainey Harper College, A

Indiana

Ball State University, B
Goshen College, B
Indiana University Bloomington, B
Indiana University-Purdue University Indianapolis, A
Indiana University South Bend, A
Manchester College, B
Marian College, AB
Martin University, B
Purdue University, B
Purdue University Calumet, A
Saint Mary-of-the-Woods College, B
Taylor University, AB
Vincennes University, A

Iowa

Ashford University, B
Clarke College, B
Ellsworth Community College, A
Iowa Lakes Community College, A
Iowa Wesleyan College, B
Kirkwood Community College, A
Loras College, B
Simpson College, B
University of Northern Iowa, B
Waldorf College, B
Wartburg College, B

Kansas

Butler Community College, A
Central Christian College of Kansas, A
Colby Community College, A
Donnelly College, A
Fort Hays State University, B
Friends University, AB
Hesston College, A
Independence Community College, A
Kansas Wesleyan University, A
Labette Community College, A

McPherson College, B
Pratt Community College, A
Tabor College, B

Kentucky

Berea College, B
Eastern Kentucky University, B
Hazard Community and Technical College, A
Hopkinsville Community College, A
Morehead State University, B
Northern Kentucky University, B
Owensboro Community and Technical College, A
St. Catharine College, A
Spalding University, B
University of Kentucky, B
Western Kentucky University, AB

Louisiana

Delgado Community College, A
Dillard University, B
Elaine P. Nunez Community College, A
Grambling State University, B
Louisiana College, B
Louisiana Tech University, B
McNeese State University, AB
Nicholls State University, B
Southeastern Louisiana University, B
Southern University and Agricultural and Mechanical
   College, B
Southern University at Shreveport, A

Maine

Andover College, A
Central Maine Community College, A
Eastern Maine Community College, A
Northern Maine Community College, A
Southern Maine Community College, A
University of Maine at Farmington, B
York County Community College, A

Maryland

Anne Arundel Community College, A
Baltimore City Community College, A
Bowie State University, B
Carroll Community College, A
Cecil Community College, A
Chesapeake College, A
College of Notre Dame of Maryland, B
College of Southern Maryland, A
Coppin State University, B
Frederick Community College, A
Frostburg State University, B
Howard Community College, A
Prince George's Community College, A
Sojourner-Douglass College, B
University of Maryland, College Park, B
University of Maryland Eastern Shore, B
Villa Julie College, A
Washington Bible College, B

Massachusetts

American International College, B
Anna Maria College, B
Atlantic Union College, AB
Bay Path College, B
Boston College, B
Boston University, B
Cape Cod Community College, A
Curry College, B
Eastern Nazarene College, AB
Elms College, B
Fisher College, A
Greenfield Community College, A
Holyoke Community College, A
Lasell College, B
Lesley University, B
Massachusetts College of Liberal Arts, B
Middlesex Community College, A
Mount Ida College, AB
North Shore Community College, A
Northeastern University, B
Northern Essex Community College, A
Pine Manor College, B
Quinsigamond Community College, A
Roxbury Community College, A

Salem State College, B
Simmons College, B
Springfield College, B
Springfield Technical Community College, A
Stonehill College, B
Tufts University, B
Urban College of Boston, A
Westfield State College, B
Wheelock College, B
Worcester State College, B

Michigan

Alma College, B
Baker College of Clinton Township, A
Baker College of Muskegon, A
Baker College of Owosso, A
Concordia University, B
Gogebic Community College, A
Hillsdale College, B
Kellogg Community College, A
Lansing Community College, A
Marygrove College, AB
Siena Heights University, B
University of Detroit Mercy, B
University of Michigan-Flint, B
Washtenaw Community College, A

Minnesota

Augsburg College, B
College of St. Catherine, B
Concordia College, B
Concordia University, St. Paul, B
Crown College, AB
Martin Luther College, B
Metropolitan State University, B
Minnesota State College-Southeast Technical, A
Minnesota State Community and Technical
   College-Fergus Falls, A
Minnesota State University Mankato, B
Minnesota State University Moorhead, B
St. Cloud State University, B
St. Cloud Technical College, A
Southwest Minnesota State University, B
University of Minnesota, Duluth, B
University of Minnesota, Twin Cities Campus, B
Vermilion Community College, A
Winona State University, B

Mississippi

Coahoma Community College, A
Delta State University, B
East Central Community College, A
Itawamba Community College, A
Jackson State University, B
Mississippi Gulf Coast Community College, A
Mississippi Valley State University, B
Northeast Mississippi Community College, A
Tougaloo College, AB

Missouri

Central Methodist University, B
East Central College, A
Evangel University, B
Fontbonne University, B
Hannibal-LaGrange College, B
Harris-Stowe State University, B
Jefferson College, A
Lindenwood University, B
Maryville University of Saint Louis, B
Missouri Baptist University, B
Missouri Southern State University, B
Northwest Missouri State University, B
Ozarks Technical Community College, A
Penn Valley Community College, A
Southeast Missouri State University, B
Stephens College, B
University of Missouri-Columbia, B

Montana

Blackfeet Community College, A
Fort Belknap College, A
Fort Peck Community College, A
Salish Kootenai College, A
University of Great Falls, AB

The University of Montana-Western, A

Nebraska

Concordia University, B
Metropolitan Community College, A
Midland Lutheran College, AB
Peru State College, B
Western Nebraska Community College, A

Nevada

Community College of Southern Nevada, A
Great Basin College, A
Truckee Meadows Community College, A
University of Nevada, Las Vegas, B

New Hampshire

Franklin Pierce College, B
Hesser College, A
Keene State College, AB
New Hampshire Community Technical College,
   Berlin/Laconia, A
New Hampshire Community Technical College,
   Manchester/Stratham, A
New Hampshire Community Technical College,
   Nashua/Claremont, A
New Hampshire Technical Institute, A
Rivier College, AB
University of New Hampshire, B

New Jersey

Bergen Community College, A
Brookdale Community College, A
Camden County College, A
The College of New Jersey, B
County College of Morris, A
Cumberland County College, A
Essex County College, A
Kean University, B
Middlesex County College, A
New Jersey City University, B
Passaic County Community College, A
Raritan Valley Community College, A
Rider University, B
Rowan University, B

New Mexico

Eastern New Mexico University, B
New Mexico Highlands University, B
New Mexico State University, B
San Juan College, A
Santa Fe Community College, A
University of New Mexico-Gallup, A
Western New Mexico University, B

New York

Boricua College, B
Borough of Manhattan Community College of the
   City University of New York, A
Buffalo State College, State University of New
   York, B
Cayuga County Community College, A
Dutchess Community College, A
Eugenio María de Hostos Community College of the
   City University of New York, A
Finger Lakes Community College, A
Fiorello H. LaGuardia Community College of the
   City University of New York, A
Fulton-Montgomery Community College, A
Genesee Community College, A
Hunter College of the City University of New York, B
Jefferson Community College, A
Long Island University, C.W. Post Campus, B
Maria College, A
Medaille College, B
Mercy College, B
Nassau Community College, A
New York University, B
Onondaga Community College, A
St. Bonaventure University, B
St. Joseph's College, Suffolk Campus, B
St. Thomas Aquinas College, B
Sarah Lawrence College, B
State University of New York College of Agriculture
   and Technology at Cobleskill, A
State University of New York College at Cortland, B

State University of New York College at Oneonta, B
State University of New York College of Technology at Canton, A
State University of New York, Fredonia, B
State University of New York at New Paltz, B
Suffolk County Community College, A
Sullivan County Community College, A
Syracuse University, B
Tompkins Cortland Community College, A
Touro College, B
Trocaire College, A
Villa Maria College of Buffalo, A
Wagner College, B
Yeshiva University, B

North Carolina

Alamance Community College, A
Appalachian State University, B
Beaufort County Community College, A
Bennett College For Women, B
Blue Ridge Community College, A
Central Carolina Community College, A
Central Piedmont Community College, A
Durham Technical Community College, A
East Carolina University, B
Edgecombe Community College, A
Elizabeth City State University, B
Fayetteville State University, B
Forsyth Technical Community College, A
Gardner-Webb University, B
Gaston College, A
Greensboro College, B
Guilford Technical Community College, A
High Point University, B
Isothermal Community College, A
James Sprunt Community College, A
Johnston Community College, A
Lenoir-Rhyne College, B
Livingstone College, B
Mars Hill College, B
Mayland Community College, A
Methodist College, B
Mitchell Community College, A
Nash Community College, A
North Carolina Agricultural and Technical State University, B
North Carolina Central University, B
Piedmont Baptist College, A
Roanoke-Chowan Community College, A
Rowan-Cabarrus Community College, A
Sandhills Community College, A
Shaw University, B
Southeastern Community College, A
The University of North Carolina at Charlotte, B
The University of North Carolina at Greensboro, B
The University of North Carolina at Pembroke, B
The University of North Carolina Wilmington, B
Vance-Granville Community College, A
Wake Technical Community College, A
Wilson Technical Community College, A
Winston-Salem State University, B

North Dakota

Fort Berthold Community College, A
Turtle Mountain Community College, A
University of North Dakota, B

Ohio

Ashland University, B
Bluffton University, B
Bowling Green State University, B
Bowling Green State University-Firelands College, B
Cedarville University, B
Central Ohio Technical College, A
Central State University, B
Chatfield College, A
Cincinnati Christian University, B
Clark State Community College, A
College of Mount St. Joseph, AB
Columbus State Community College, A
Cuyahoga Community College, A
Edison State Community College, A
John Carroll University, B
Kent State University, B
Kent State University, Ashtabula Campus, A
Kent State University, Salem Campus, A

Lakeland Community College, A
Lorain County Community College, A
Lourdes College, AB
Miami University, B
Miami University-Middletown Campus, A
Mount Vernon Nazarene University, B
Muskingum College, B
North Central State College, A
Notre Dame College, B
Ohio Dominican University, B
Ohio Northern University, B
The Ohio State University-Mansfield Campus, B
Ohio University, B
Ohio University-Eastern, B
Ohio University-Southern Campus, A
Ohio Wesleyan University, B
Shawnee State University, B
Sinclair Community College, A
Southern State Community College, A
Terra State Community College, A
The University of Akron, B
University of Cincinnati, B
University of Dayton, B
University of Rio Grande, A
The University of Toledo, B
Walsh University, B
Washington State Community College, A
Wright State University, B

Oklahoma

Carl Albert State College, A
East Central University, B
Langston University, B
Northeastern State University, B
Northwestern Oklahoma State University, B
Oklahoma Baptist University, B
Oklahoma Christian University, B
Oklahoma City University, B
Oral Roberts University, B
Redlands Community College, A
Rose State College, A
Southeastern Oklahoma State University, B
Tulsa Community College, A
University of Central Oklahoma, B

Oregon

Chemeketa Community College, A
Concordia University, B
Lane Community College, A
Mt. Hood Community College, A
Oregon State University, B
Pacific University, B
Umpqua Community College, A
Warner Pacific College, B

Pennsylvania

Albright College, B
Alvernia College, B
Arcadia University, B
Bucknell University, B
Bucks County Community College, A
Butler County Community College, A
Cabrini College, B
California University of Pennsylvania, AB
Carlow University, B
Cheyney University of Pennsylvania, B
Clarion University of Pennsylvania, B
College Misericordia, B
Community College of Philadelphia, A
Edinboro University of Pennsylvania, AB
Elizabethtown College, B
Grove City College, B
Harcum College, A
Harrisburg Area Community College, A
Holy Family University, B
Indiana University of Pennsylvania, B
Juniata College, B
Keystone College, A
Kutztown University of Pennsylvania, B
Lehigh Carbon Community College, A
Lincoln University, B
Lock Haven University of Pennsylvania, B
Manor College, A
Mansfield University of Pennsylvania, B
Mount Aloysius College, AB
Neumann College, B

Philadelphia Biblical University, B
Reading Area Community College, A
Seton Hill University, B
Susquehanna University, B
The University of Scranton, B
Valley Forge Christian College, A
Widener University, B

Puerto Rico

Bayamon Central University, B
Caribbean University, AB
Inter American University of Puerto Rico, Aguadilla Campus, B
Inter American University of Puerto Rico, Arecibo Campus, B
Inter American University of Puerto Rico, Guayama Campus, B
Inter American University of Puerto Rico, Metropolitan Campus, B
Inter American University of Puerto Rico, Ponce Campus, B
Inter American University of Puerto Rico, San Germán Campus, B
Pontifical Catholic University of Puerto Rico, B
Universidad Metropolitana, B
University of Puerto Rico at Bayamón, B

Rhode Island

Community College of Rhode Island, A
Rhode Island College, B

South Carolina

Anderson University, B
Benedict College, B
Charleston Southern University, B
Columbia College, B
Converse College, B
Denmark Technical College, A
Erskine College, B
Furman University, B
Newberry College, B
North Greenville College, B
Orangeburg-Calhoun Technical College, A
Presbyterian College, B
South Carolina State University, B
Southern Wesleyan University, B
Technical College of the Lowcountry, A
University of South Carolina Aiken, B
University of South Carolina Upstate, B
Voorhees College, B
Winthrop University, B

South Dakota

Black Hills State University, B
Oglala Lakota College, AB
Sinte Gleska University, B
Sisseton-Wahpeton Community College, A
South Dakota State University, B
University of Sioux Falls, A

Tennessee

Bryan College, B
Carson-Newman College, B
Chattanooga State Technical Community College, A
Cleveland State Community College, A
Columbia State Community College, A
Johnson Bible College, AB
King College, B
Lincoln Memorial University, B
Martin Methodist College, A
Middle Tennessee State University, B
Nashville State Technical Community College, A
Northeast State Technical Community College, A
Roane State Community College, A
Southern Adventist University, B
Southwest Tennessee Community College, A
Tennessee State University, AB
Tennessee Technological University, B
Tusculum College, B
Union University, B
The University of Tennessee at Martin, B

Vanderbilt University, B

Texas

Baylor University, B
Cisco Junior College, A
Dallas Baptist University, B
Del Mar College, A
Houston Baptist University, B
Howard Payne University, B
Jarvis Christian College, B
Lamar University, B
McLennan Community College, A
Odessa College, A
Our Lady of the Lake University of San Antonio, B
Texas A&M International University, B
Texas A&M University-Commerce, B
Texas A&M University-Kingsville, B
Texas Southern University, B
Trinity Valley Community College, A
University of the Incarnate Word, B
University of Mary Hardin-Baylor, B
The University of Texas at Brownsville, B

Utah

California College for Health Sciences, A
College of Eastern Utah, A
Dixie State College of Utah, A
Snow College, A
University of Utah, B
Utah State University, B
Weber State University, B
Westminster College, B

Vermont

Champlain College, AB
College of St. Joseph, B
University of Vermont, B

Virginia

Bluefield College, B
Eastern Mennonite University, B
Hampton University, B
Longwood University, B
Lynchburg College, B
Norfolk State University, B
Northern Virginia Community College, A
Thomas Nelson Community College, A
Tidewater Community College, A
Virginia Union University, B
Virginia Western Community College, A

Washington

Bellevue Community College, A
Central Washington University, B
Centralia College, A
Columbia Basin College, A
Everett Community College, A
Heritage University, B
Highline Community College, A
Lower Columbia College, A
Northwest Indian College, A
Pacific Lutheran University, B
Pierce College, A
Seattle Central Community College, A
Shoreline Community College, A
Skagit Valley College, A
South Puget Sound Community College, A
Washington State University, B
Wenatchee Valley College, A
Western Washington University, B
Whatcom Community College, A
Yakima Valley Community College, A

West Virginia

Concord University, B
Glenville State College, B
Potomac State College of West Virginia
    University, A
West Liberty State College, B
West Virginia State University, B
West Virginia Wesleyan College, B

Wisconsin

Cardinal Stritch University, B
Carroll College, B

Concordia University Wisconsin, B
Edgewood College, B
Lakeland College, B
Maranatha Baptist Bible College, AB
Marian College of Fond du Lac, B
Mount Mary College, B
Nicolet Area Technical College, A
Northcentral Technical College, A
Silver Lake College, B
University of Wisconsin-Madison, B
University of Wisconsin-Milwaukee, B
University of Wisconsin-Oshkosh, B
University of Wisconsin-Platteville, B
University of Wisconsin-Stevens Point, B

Wyoming

Casper College, A
Northwest College, A

Alberta

University of Alberta, B

British Columbia

Columbia Bible College, B
Summit Pacific College, B
The University of British Columbia, B
University of Victoria, B

Manitoba

Brandon University, B
University of Manitoba, B

New Brunswick

Université de Moncton, B
University of New Brunswick Fredericton, B

Nova Scotia

Mount Saint Vincent University, B

Ontario

University of Ottawa, B
The University of Western Ontario, B
University of Windsor, B
York University, B

Quebec

Concordia University, B
McGill University, B
Université Laval, B
Université de Montréal, B
Université du Québec en Abitibi-Témiscamingue, B
Université du Québec àChicoutimi, B
Université du Québec àMontréal, B
Université du Québec en Outaouais, B
Université du Québec àRimouski, B
Université du Québec àTrois-Rivières, B
Université de Sherbrooke, B

Saskatchewan

University of Regina, B

KINESIOLOGY AND EXERCISE SCIENCE

Alabama

Huntingdon College, B
Jacksonville State University, B
Samford University, B
University of Mobile, B

Arizona

Arizona State University, B
Diné College, A
Grand Canyon University, B
Northern Arizona University, B

Arkansas

Arkansas State University, B
Harding University, B
John Brown University, B
Ouachita Baptist University, B
Southern Arkansas University-Magnolia, B

University of Arkansas, B
University of Central Arkansas, B

California

Biola University, B
California Baptist University, B
California Lutheran University, B
California State University, Chico, B
California State University, East Bay, B
California State University, Long Beach, B
California State University, Los Angeles, B
California State University, Northridge, B
California State University, Sacramento, B
Cañada College, A
Concordia University, B
Humboldt State University, B
La Sierra University, B
The Master's College and Seminary, B
Monterey Peninsula College, A
Occidental College, B
Orange Coast College, A
Pacific Union College, B
Point Loma Nazarene University, B
Saint Mary's College of California, B
San Diego Christian College, B
Santa Ana College, A
Santa Barbara City College, A
Santiago Canyon College, A
Sonoma State University, B
University of California, Los Angeles, B
University of La Verne, B
University of the Pacific, B
University of Southern California, B
Vanguard University of Southern California, B
Westmont College, B

Colorado

Adams State College, B
Colorado State University, B
Colorado State University-Pueblo, B
Fort Lewis College, B
Mesa State College, B
Metropolitan State College of Denver, B
University of Northern Colorado, B
Western State College of Colorado, B

Connecticut

Naugatuck Valley Community College, A
Sacred Heart University, B

Delaware

Delaware Technical & Community College,
    Stanton/Wilmington Campus, A
University of Delaware, B

District of Columbia

The George Washington University, B

Florida

Barry University, B
Clearwater Christian College, B
Florida Atlantic University, B
Florida Gulf Coast University, B
Florida International University, B
Florida State University, B
Jacksonville University, B
Stetson University, B
University of Florida, B
University of Miami, B
The University of Tampa, B
Warner Southern College, B

Georgia

Andrew College, A
Columbus State University, B
Emmanuel College, B
Gainesville College, A
Georgia Southern University, B
Kennesaw State University, B
South Georgia College, A

Valdosta State University, B

Hawaii

Brigham Young University-Hawaii, B
University of Hawaii at Manoa, B

Idaho

Albertson College of Idaho, B
Boise State University, B
Lewis-Clark State College, B
Northwest Nazarene University, B

Illinois

Concordia University, B
Elmhurst College, B
Eureka College, B
Greenville College, B
Illinois State University, B
North Central College, B
North Park University, B
Olivet Nazarene University, B
University of Illinois at Chicago, B
University of Illinois at Urbana-Champaign, B
William Rainey Harper College, A

Indiana

Ball State University, B
Bethel College, B
DePauw University, B
Huntington University, B
Indiana Wesleyan University, B
Manchester College, A
University of Evansville, B
University of Indianapolis, B
University of Southern Indiana, B
Valparaiso University, B
Vincennes University, A

Iowa

Central College, B
Dordt College, B
Iowa Wesleyan College, B
Loras College, B
Northwestern College, B
The University of Iowa, B
Upper Iowa University, B

Kansas

Baker University, B
Barton County Community College, A
Central Christian College of Kansas, B
Kansas State University, B
MidAmerica Nazarene University, B

Kentucky

Georgetown College, B
Morehead State University, B
Murray State University, B
Northern Kentucky University, B
Thomas More College, A
Transylvania University, B

Louisiana

Centenary College of Louisiana, B
Louisiana College, B
McNeese State University, B
Tulane University, B

Maine

Saint Joseph's College of Maine, B
University of New England, B

Maryland

Frostburg State University, B
McDaniel College, B
Towson University, B

Massachusetts

Atlantic Union College, A
Becker College, B
Boston University, B
Bridgewater State College, B
Fitchburg State College, B
Gordon College, B

Lasell College, B
Mount Wachusett Community College, A
Salem State College, B
Springfield College, B
University of Massachusetts Amherst, B
University of Massachusetts Lowell, B

Michigan

Adrian College, B
Alma College, B
Calvin College, B
Cornerstone University, B
Henry Ford Community College, A
Hope College, B
Lake Superior State University, B
Michigan State University, B
Oakland Community College, A
Saginaw Valley State University, B
Spring Arbor University, B
University of Michigan, B
Western Michigan University, B

Minnesota

Bethel University, B
Concordia College, B
Concordia University, St. Paul, B
Globe College, A
Hamline University, B
Minnesota State University Moorhead, B
Northwestern College, B
St. Cloud State University, B
St. Olaf College, B
University of Minnesota, Duluth, B
Winona State University, B

Mississippi

Mississippi College, B
Mississippi University for Women, B
Northeast Mississippi Community College, A
University of Mississippi, B

Missouri

Drury University, B
Missouri Southern State University, B
Saint Louis University, B
Truman State University, B

Montana

Rocky Mountain College, B

Nebraska

Concordia University, B
Creighton University, B
Hastings College, B
Nebraska Wesleyan University, B
Union College, B
University of Nebraska-Lincoln, B
Wayne State College, B

Nevada

University of Nevada, Las Vegas, B

New Hampshire

Colby-Sawyer College, B
New Hampshire Community Technical College, Manchester/Stratham, A
University of New Hampshire, B

New Jersey

Bergen Community College, A
Camden County College, A
County College of Morris, A
Gloucester County College, A
Rutgers, The State University of New Jersey, New Brunswick/Piscataway, B
Salem Community College, A
William Paterson University of New Jersey, B

New York

Buffalo State College, State University of New York, B
College of Mount Saint Vincent, B
Columbia-Greene Community College, A
Hofstra University, B

Ithaca College, B
North Country Community College, A
Orange County Community College, A
Queens College of the City University of New York, B
Skidmore College, B
State University of New York at Buffalo, B
State University of New York College at Brockport, B
State University of New York College at Cortland, B
Syracuse University, B

North Carolina

Appalachian State University, B
Brevard College, B
Campbell University, B
Chowan University, B
East Carolina University, B
Greensboro College, B
High Point University, B
Lenoir-Rhyne College, B
Mars Hill College, B
Meredith College, B
Shaw University, B
The University of North Carolina at Greensboro, B
Wake Forest University, B
Winston-Salem State University, B

North Dakota

Mayville State University, B
University of Mary, B
University of North Dakota, B

Ohio

Baldwin-Wallace College, B
Capital University, B
Cedarville University, B
Clark State Community College, A
Cleveland State University, B
Defiance College, B
Kent State University, B
Malone College, B
Miami University, B
Mount Union College, B
Mount Vernon Nazarene University, B
Ohio Northern University, B
The Ohio State University, B
Ohio University, B
Ohio University-Eastern, B
University of Dayton, B
The University of Toledo, B
Youngstown State University, B

Oklahoma

Oklahoma Baptist University, B
Oklahoma City University, B
Oklahoma Wesleyan University, B
Oral Roberts University, B
Rose State College, A
Southern Nazarene University, B
University of Tulsa, B

Oregon

Central Oregon Community College, A
Linfield College, B
Oregon State University, B
Pacific University, B
Warner Pacific College, B
Willamette University, B

Pennsylvania

Butler County Community College, A
Cabrini College, B
Chatham College, B
DeSales University, B
East Stroudsburg University of Pennsylvania, B
Immaculata University, B
Messiah College, B
The Pennsylvania State University Abington College, B
The Pennsylvania State University Altoona College, B
The Pennsylvania State University Beaver Campus of the Commonwealth College, B

The Pennsylvania State University Berks Campus of the Berks-Lehigh Valley College, B
The Pennsylvania State University Delaware County Campus of the Commonwealth College, B
The Pennsylvania State University DuBois Campus of the Commonwealth College, B
The Pennsylvania State University at Erie, The Behrend College, B
The Pennsylvania State University Fayette Campus of the Commonwealth College, B
The Pennsylvania State University Hazleton Campus of the Commonwealth College, B
The Pennsylvania State University, Lehigh Valley Campus of the Berks-Lehigh Valley College, B
The Pennsylvania State University McKeesport Campus of the Commonwealth College, B
The Pennsylvania State University Mont Alto Campus of the Commonwealth College, B
The Pennsylvania State University New Kensington Campus of the Commonwealth College, B
The Pennsylvania State University Schuylkill Campus of the Capital College, B
The Pennsylvania State University Shenango Campus of the Commonwealth College, B
The Pennsylvania State University University Park Campus, B
The Pennsylvania State University Wilkes-Barre Campus of the Commonwealth College, B
The Pennsylvania State University Worthington Scranton Campus of the Commonwealth College, B
The Pennsylvania State University York Campus of the Commonwealth College, B
Shippensburg University of Pennsylvania, B
The University of Scranton, B
Waynesburg College, B
West Chester University of Pennsylvania, B
Wilson College, B

Puerto Rico

University of the Sacred Heart, B

South Carolina

Coker College, B
Furman University, B
Lander University, B
University of South Carolina, B
University of South Carolina Aiken, B
Voorhees College, B

South Dakota

Augustana College, B
Dakota State University, B
University of Sioux Falls, B

Tennessee

Bryan College, B
Carson-Newman College, B
Lincoln Memorial University, B
Lipscomb University, B
Southern Adventist University, B
Tennessee Wesleyan College, B
Trevecca Nazarene University, B
Union University, B
University of Memphis, B
The University of Tennessee, B
The University of Tennessee at Chattanooga, B

Texas

Clarendon College, A
Concordia University at Austin, B
Hardin-Simmons University, B
Houston Baptist University, B
Houston Community College System, A
Howard Payne University, B
Lee College, A
Lubbock Christian University, B
Midwestern State University, B
North Lake College, A
Rice University, B
St. Edward's University, B
St. Mary's University of San Antonio, B
St. Philip's College, A
Sam Houston State University, B
Schreiner University, B

Southwestern Adventist University, B
Southwestern University, B
Tarleton State University, B
Texas Lutheran University, B
Texas Tech University, B
Texas Woman's University, B
University of Houston, B
University of North Texas, B
The University of Texas at Brownsville, B
The University of Texas of the Permian Basin, B
The University of Texas at Tyler, B

Utah

Brigham Young University, B
Salt Lake Community College, A
University of Utah, B
Utah Career College, A
Weber State University, B

Vermont

Castleton State College, B
Johnson State College, B

Virginia

Bluefield College, B
Bridgewater College, B
Liberty University, B
Longwood University, B
Lynchburg College, B
Marymount University, B
Norfolk State University, B
Old Dominion University, B
Radford University, B
Shenandoah University, B

Washington

Bastyr University, B
Central Washington University, B
Eastern Washington University, B
Gonzaga University, B
Seattle Pacific University, B
University of Puget Sound, B
Walla Walla College, B
Washington State University, B
Western Washington University, B

West Virginia

Davis & Elkins College, B
West Liberty State College, B
West Virginia University, B

Wisconsin

Carroll College, B
Marquette University, B
University of Wisconsin-Eau Claire, B
University of Wisconsin-La Crosse, B
University of Wisconsin-Superior, B

Wyoming

Northwest College, A
University of Wyoming, B
Western Wyoming Community College, A

Alberta

University of Alberta, B
University of Calgary, B
University of Lethbridge, B

British Columbia

Simon Fraser University, B
The University of British Columbia, B
University of Victoria, B

New Brunswick

University of New Brunswick Fredericton, B
University of New Brunswick Saint John, B

Newfoundland and Labrador

Memorial University of Newfoundland, B

Nova Scotia

Acadia University, B
Dalhousie University, B

St. Francis Xavier University, B

Ontario

Brock University, B
Laurentian University, B
McMaster University, B
Redeemer University College, B
University of Waterloo, B
The University of Western Ontario, B
University of Windsor, B
Wilfrid Laurier University, B

Quebec

Concordia University, B
McGill University, B
Université Laval, B
Université de Sherbrooke, B

Saskatchewan

University of Regina, B
University of Saskatchewan, B

KINESIOLOGY AND MOVEMENT STUDIES

Alabama

The University of Alabama, MD

Arizona

Arizona State University, M

Arkansas

University of Arkansas, MD
University of Central Arkansas, M

California

California Baptist University, M
California Polytechnic State University, San Luis Obispo, M
California State Polytechnic University, Pomona, M
California State University, Chico, M
California State University, Fresno, M
California State University, Long Beach, M
California State University, Los Angeles, M
California State University, Northridge, M
California State University, San Bernardino, M
Humboldt State University, M
Saint Mary's College of California, M
San Jose State University, M
Sonoma State University, M
University of Southern California, MD

Colorado

University of Colorado at Boulder, MD

Connecticut

University of Connecticut, MD

Delaware

University of Delaware, MD

Florida

Barry University, M
Florida State University, M
University of Florida, MD

Georgia

Georgia Southern University, M

Hawaii

University of Hawaii at Manoa, M

Illinois

Southern Illinois University Edwardsville, MO
University of Illinois at Chicago, M
University of Illinois at Urbana-Champaign, MD

Western Illinois University, M

Indiana

Indiana University Bloomington, MDO

Kansas

Kansas State University, M

Kentucky

University of Kentucky, MD

Louisiana

Louisiana State University and Agricultural and
    Mechanical College, MD
Southeastern Louisiana University, M

Maine

University of Maine, M

Maryland

University of Maryland, College Park, MD

Massachusetts

Springfield College, M

Michigan

Michigan State University, MD
University of Michigan, MD
Wayne State University, M

Minnesota

University of Minnesota, Twin Cities Campus, MD

Missouri

Washington University in St. Louis, D

Nevada

University of Nevada, Las Vegas, M

New Hampshire

University of New Hampshire, M

New York

New York University, M

North Carolina

The University of North Carolina at Chapel Hill, MD

North Dakota

University of North Dakota, M

Ohio

Bowling Green State University, M
The University of Toledo, MD

Oklahoma

Southwestern Oklahoma State University, M

Oregon

Oregon State University, M

Pennsylvania

The Pennsylvania State University University Park
    Campus, MD
Temple University, MD
West Chester University of Pennsylvania, MO

Puerto Rico

Inter American University of Puerto Rico, San
    Germán Campus, M

Tennessee

The University of Tennessee, MD

Texas

Angelo State University, M
Lamar University, M
Midwestern State University, M
Sam Houston State University, M
Stephen F. Austin State University, M
Texas A&M University, MD
Texas A&M University-Commerce, MD

Texas A&M University-Kingsville, M
Texas Christian University, M
Texas Woman's University, MD
University of Houston, D
University of North Texas, M
The University of Texas at Austin, MD
The University of Texas at El Paso, M
The University of Texas-Pan American, M
The University of Texas of the Permian Basin, M
The University of Texas at Tyler, M

Virginia

James Madison University, M
University of Virginia, MD

Washington

Western Washington University, M

Wisconsin

University of Wisconsin-Madison, MD
University of Wisconsin-Milwaukee, M

Alberta

University of Calgary, MD
University of Lethbridge, M

British Columbia

Simon Fraser University, MD
The University of British Columbia, MD

Newfoundland and Labrador

Memorial University of Newfoundland, M

Nova Scotia

Acadia University, M
Dalhousie University, M

Ontario

McMaster University, MD
University of Ottawa, M
University of Waterloo, MD
The University of Western Ontario, MD
University of Windsor, M
York University, MD

Quebec

McGill University, MDO
Université Laval, MD
Université de Montréal, MDO
Université du Québec àMontréal, M
Université de Sherbrooke, M

Saskatchewan

University of Regina, MD
University of Saskatchewan, MDO

KINESIOTHERAPY/
KINESIOTHERAPIST

California

California State University, Long Beach, B

Massachusetts

Bridgewater State College, B

Saskatchewan

University of Regina, B

KOREAN LANGUAGE AND
LITERATURE

California

University of California, Los Angeles, B

Hawaii

University of Hawaii at Manoa, B

Utah

Brigham Young University, B

KOREAN STUDIES

California

Claremont McKenna College, B

LABOR AND INDUSTRIAL
RELATIONS

Alabama

Wallace State Community College, A

California

California State University, Dominguez Hills, B
City College of San Francisco, A
El Camino College, A
Laney College, A
Los Angeles Trade-Technical College, A
San Diego City College, A
San Francisco State University, B
San Jose City College, A

Illinois

Governors State University, B
Roosevelt University, B

Indiana

Indiana University Bloomington, AB
Indiana University Kokomo, AB
Indiana University Northwest, AB
Indiana University-Purdue University
    Indianapolis, AB
Indiana University South Bend, AB
Indiana University Southeast, AB

Iowa

The University of Iowa, B

Kentucky

Northern Kentucky University, B

Maine

University of Maine, B

Massachusetts

University of Massachusetts Boston, B

Michigan

Ferris State University, B
Grand Valley State University, B
Lansing Community College, A
University of Detroit Mercy, B
Wayne County Community College District, A

Minnesota

Winona State University, B

New Jersey

Rutgers, The State University of New Jersey, New
    Brunswick/Piscataway, B
Seton Hall University, B

New York

Cornell University, B
Ithaca College, B
Kingsborough Community College of the City
    University of New York, A
Le Moyne College, B
Onondaga Community College, A
Queens College of the City University of New
    York, B
State University of New York College at Old
    Westbury, B
State University of New York College at Potsdam, B
State University of New York Empire State
    College, AB

State University of New York, Fredonia, B

North Carolina

Rockingham Community College, A

Ohio

Cleveland State University, B
Sinclair Community College, A
Southwestern College of Business (Cincinnati), A
The University of Akron, A
Youngstown State University, A

Oklahoma

Tulsa Community College, A

Pennsylvania

Clarion University of Pennsylvania, B
The Pennsylvania State University Abington
    College, B
The Pennsylvania State University Altoona
    College, B
The Pennsylvania State University Beaver Campus
    of the Commonwealth College, B
The Pennsylvania State University Berks Campus of
    the Berks-Lehigh Valley College, B
The Pennsylvania State University Delaware County
    Campus of the Commonwealth College, B
The Pennsylvania State University DuBois Campus
    of the Commonwealth College, B
The Pennsylvania State University at Erie, The
    Behrend College, B
The Pennsylvania State University Fayette Campus
    of the Commonwealth College, B
The Pennsylvania State University Hazleton
    Campus of the Commonwealth College, B
The Pennsylvania State University, Lehigh Valley
    Campus of the Berks-Lehigh Valley College, B
The Pennsylvania State University McKeesport
    Campus of the Commonwealth College, B
The Pennsylvania State University Mont Alto
    Campus of the Commonwealth College, B
The Pennsylvania State University New Kensington
    Campus of the Commonwealth College, B
The Pennsylvania State University Schuylkill
    Campus of the Capital College, B
The Pennsylvania State University Shenango
    Campus of the Commonwealth College, B
The Pennsylvania State University University Park
    Campus, B
The Pennsylvania State University Wilkes-Barre
    Campus of the Commonwealth College, B
The Pennsylvania State University Worthington
    Scranton Campus of the Commonwealth
    College, B
The Pennsylvania State University York Campus of
    the Commonwealth College, B
Saint Francis University, B
Temple University, B
Westminster College, B

Puerto Rico

University of Puerto Rico, Río Piedras, B

Rhode Island

Community College of Rhode Island, A
Rhode Island College, B

Tennessee

Tennessee Technological University, B

Texas

Texas A&M University-Commerce, B

West Virginia

West Virginia University Institute of Technology, B

Wisconsin

University of Wisconsin-Madison, B
University of Wisconsin-Milwaukee, B

Alberta

Athabasca University, B
University of Alberta, B

British Columbia

The University of British Columbia, B

Manitoba

University of Manitoba, B

Newfoundland and Labrador

Memorial University of Newfoundland, B

Nova Scotia

Cape Breton University, B

Ontario

Brock University, B
Carleton University, B
Lakehead University, B
McMaster University, B
University of Toronto, B
University of Windsor, B
York University, B

Quebec

McGill University, B
Université Laval, AB
Université de Montréal, B
Université du Québec en Outaouais, B

LABOR STUDIES

Indiana

Indiana University-Purdue University Fort
    Wayne, AB

Michigan

Eastern Michigan University, B
Wayne State University, B

New York

Hofstra University, B

Ontario

University of Windsor, B

LAND USE PLANNING AND MANAGEMENT/DEVELOPMENT

California

California State University, Bakersfield, B
Fullerton College, A
Merritt College, A

Colorado

Colorado Mountain College, Timberline Campus, A
Metropolitan State College of Denver, B

Kentucky

St. Catharine College, A

Michigan

Grand Valley State University, B

Minnesota

Vermilion Community College, A

New York

State University of New York College of
    Environmental Science and Forestry, B

Ohio

Hocking College, A

Texas

Texas State University-San Marcos, B

Vermont

Burlington College, B
Sterling College, B

Virginia

Mountain Empire Community College, A
Southwest Virginia Community College, A

Wisconsin

Northland College, B
University of Wisconsin-Platteville, B

University of Wisconsin-River Falls, B

Alberta

University of Alberta, B

British Columbia

University of Northern British Columbia, B

Saskatchewan

University of Saskatchewan, B

LANDSCAPE ARCHITECTURE

Alabama

Auburn University, BM

Arizona

Arizona State University, BM
The University of Arizona, BM

Arkansas

University of Arkansas, B
University of Arkansas at Little Rock, A

California

American River College, A
Butte College, A
California Polytechnic State University, San Luis
    Obispo, B
California State Polytechnic University, Pomona, BM
City College of San Francisco, A
College of Marin, A
College of San Mateo, A
Foothill College, A
Los Angeles Pierce College, A
Merced College, A
Merritt College, A
Modesto Junior College, A
Mt. San Antonio College, A
Pasadena City College, A
Saddleback College, A
San Diego Mesa College, A
Santa Rosa Junior College, A
Southwestern College, A
University of California, Berkeley, BMO
University of California, Davis, B
University of Southern California, BMO
West Valley College, A

Colorado

Colorado State University, BMD
University of Colorado at Denver and Health
    Sciences Center - Downtown Denver Campus, M

Connecticut

University of Connecticut, B

Florida

Florida Agricultural and Mechanical University, BM
Florida International University, M
University of Florida, BMD

Georgia

University of Georgia, BM

Hawaii

University of Hawaii at Manoa, B

Idaho

Brigham Young University -Idaho, A
University of Idaho, BM

Illinois

Triton College, A
University of Illinois at Urbana-Champaign, BM
William Rainey Harper College, A

Indiana

Ball State University, BM
Purdue University, B

Vincennes University, A

Iowa

Iowa State University of Science and
Technology, BMO
Kirkwood Community College, A

Kansas

Kansas State University, BM

Kentucky

Eastern Kentucky University, AB
St. Catharine College, A
University of Kentucky, B

Louisiana

Louisiana State University and Agricultural and
Mechanical College, BM

Maine

College of the Atlantic, B

Maryland

Anne Arundel Community College, A
Morgan State University, M
University of Maryland, College Park, B

Massachusetts

Harvard University, MD
University of Massachusetts Amherst, BMO

Michigan

Lansing Community College, A
Michigan State University, B
Oakland Community College, A
University of Michigan, BMDO

Minnesota

University of Minnesota, Twin Cities Campus, BM

Mississippi

Mississippi State University, BM
Northeast Mississippi Community College, A

Missouri

Northwest Missouri State University, B

Nevada

Truckee Meadows Community College, A
University of Nevada, Las Vegas, B

New Hampshire

University of New Hampshire, A

New Mexico

University of New Mexico, M

New York

Cornell University, BM
Monroe Community College, A
Onondaga Community College, A
State University of New York College of Agriculture
and Technology at Cobleskill, A
State University of New York College of Agriculture
and Technology at Morrisville, A
State University of New York College of
Environmental Science and Forestry, BM
State University of New York College of Technology
at Delhi, A

North Carolina

Lenoir Community College, A
North Carolina Agricultural and Technical State
University, B
North Carolina State University, BM

Wake Technical Community College, A

North Dakota

North Dakota State University, B

Ohio

Columbus State Community College, A
The Ohio State University, BM

Oklahoma

Oklahoma State University, BMD
Oklahoma State University, Oklahoma City, A
Tulsa Community College, A
University of Oklahoma, MO

Oregon

Portland Community College, A
University of Oregon, BM

Pennsylvania

Chatham College, BM
Keystone College, A
The Pennsylvania State University Berks Campus of
the Berks-Lehigh Valley College, B
The Pennsylvania State University Delaware County
Campus of the Commonwealth College, B
The Pennsylvania State University, Lehigh Valley
Campus of the Berks-Lehigh Valley College, B
The Pennsylvania State University Schuylkill
Campus of the Capital College, B
The Pennsylvania State University University Park
Campus, BM
The Pennsylvania State University Wilkes-Barre
Campus of the Commonwealth College, B
Philadelphia University, B
Temple University, B
University of Pennsylvania, MO

Rhode Island

Rhode Island School of Design, M
University of Rhode Island, B

South Carolina

Clemson University, BM

Texas

Texas A&M University, BMD
Texas Tech University, BM
University of North Texas, B
The University of Texas at Arlington, M
Western Texas College, A

Utah

Utah State University, BM

Virginia

University of Virginia, M
Virginia Polytechnic Institute and State
University, BM

Washington

South Seattle Community College, A
University of Washington, BM
Washington State University, BMD

West Virginia

West Virginia University, B

Wisconsin

University of Wisconsin-Madison, BM

British Columbia

The University of British Columbia, BM

Manitoba

University of Manitoba, M

Ontario

University of Guelph, BM

Quebec

Université de Montréal, B

LANDSCAPING AND GROUNDSKEEPING

Alabama

James H. Faulkner State Community College, A

Arizona

Glendale Community College, A

California

Chabot College, A
College of Marin, A
College of San Mateo, A
Cosumnes River College (Sacramento), A
Cuyamaca College, A
Los Angeles Pierce College, A
Merritt College, A
MiraCosta College, A
Santa Barbara City College, A
Southwestern College, A

Colorado

Colorado State University, B
Front Range Community College, A
Northeastern Junior College, A
Pikes Peak Community College, A

Florida

Central Florida Community College, A
Lake City Community College, A
Miami Dade College, A
Pensacola Junior College, A

Georgia

Abraham Baldwin Agricultural College, A
University of Georgia, B

Illinois

College of DuPage, A
College of Lake County, A
Danville Area Community College, A
Joliet Junior College, A
Kishwaukee College, A
Lincoln Land Community College, A
Parkland College, A
Triton College, A
William Rainey Harper College, A

Iowa

Iowa Lakes Community College, A

Kentucky

St. Catharine College, A

Maine

Southern Maine Community College, A
University of Maine, B

Massachusetts

North Shore Community College, A
Springfield Technical Community College, A
University of Massachusetts Amherst, A

Michigan

Andrews University, B
Northwestern Michigan College, A
Oakland Community College, A

Minnesota

Anoka Technical College, A
Dakota County Technical College, A

Rochester Community and Technical College, A

Mississippi

Hinds Community College, A
Mississippi State University, B

Nebraska

University of Nebraska-Lincoln, B

Nevada

Community College of Southern Nevada, A

New Hampshire

University of New Hampshire, A

New York

Farmingdale State University of New York, A
State University of New York College of Agriculture
and Technology at Cobleskill, A
State University of New York College of Agriculture
and Technology at Morrisville, A
State University of New York College of Technology
at Alfred, A
State University of New York College of Technology
at Delhi, A

North Carolina

Caldwell Community College and Technical
Institute, A
Cape Fear Community College, A
Johnston Community College, A
North Carolina State University, A
Sandhills Community College, A

Ohio

Cincinnati State Technical and Community
College, A
Clark State Community College, A
The Ohio State University Agricultural Technical
Institute, A

Oklahoma

Tulsa Community College, A

Pennsylvania

Community College of Allegheny County, A
The Pennsylvania State University Abington
College, B
The Pennsylvania State University Altoona
College, B
The Pennsylvania State University Beaver Campus
of the Commonwealth College, B
The Pennsylvania State University Berks Campus of
the Berks-Lehigh Valley College, B
The Pennsylvania State University Delaware County
Campus of the Commonwealth College, B
The Pennsylvania State University DuBois Campus
of the Commonwealth College, B
The Pennsylvania State University at Erie, The
Behrend College, B
The Pennsylvania State University Fayette Campus
of the Commonwealth College, B
The Pennsylvania State University Hazleton
Campus of the Commonwealth College, B
The Pennsylvania State University, Lehigh Valley
Campus of the Berks-Lehigh Valley College, B
The Pennsylvania State University McKeesport
Campus of the Commonwealth College, B
The Pennsylvania State University Mont Alto
Campus of the Commonwealth College, B
The Pennsylvania State University New Kensington
Campus of the Commonwealth College, B
The Pennsylvania State University Schuylkill
Campus of the Capital College, B
The Pennsylvania State University Shenango
Campus of the Commonwealth College, B
The Pennsylvania State University University Park
Campus, B
The Pennsylvania State University Wilkes-Barre
Campus of the Commonwealth College, B
The Pennsylvania State University Worthington
Scranton Campus of the Commonwealth
College, B
The Pennsylvania State University York Campus of
the Commonwealth College, B

The Williamson Free School of Mechanical
Trades, A

Puerto Rico

Inter American University of Puerto Rico, Guayama
Campus, A

South Carolina

Bob Jones University, B
Horry-Georgetown Technical College, A

South Dakota

South Dakota State University, B

Tennessee

Tennessee Technological University, B
The University of Tennessee at Martin, B

Texas

Grayson County College, A

Vermont

Vermont Technical College, A

Virginia

J. Sargeant Reynolds Community College, A

Washington

Clark College, A
Clover Park Technical College, A
Edmonds Community College, A
South Puget Sound Community College, A
South Seattle Community College, A
Spokane Community College, A

Wisconsin

Milwaukee Area Technical College, A

LANGUAGE INTERPRETATION AND TRANSLATION

Arizona

Cochise College (Douglas), A

Colorado

Front Range Community College, A

Florida

Indian River Community College, A

Kansas

Allen County Community College, A

Mississippi

Mississippi College, B

New Jersey

Union County College, A

North Carolina

Fayetteville Technical Community College, A
Wilson Technical Community College, A

Utah

Brigham Young University, B

New Brunswick

Université de Moncton, B

Ontario

Laurentian University, B
York University, B

Quebec

Concordia University, B
Université Laval, B

Université du Québec en Outaouais, B

LASER AND OPTICAL TECHNOLOGY/TECHNICIAN

Alabama

George C. Wallace Community College, A

California

Moorpark College, A

Connecticut

Three Rivers Community College, A

Idaho

Idaho State University, A

Indiana

Indiana University Bloomington, A
Vincennes University, A

Iowa

Indian Hills Community College, A

Louisiana

Elaine P. Nunez Community College, A

Maryland

Capitol College, A

Massachusetts

Springfield Technical Community College, A

Michigan

Schoolcraft College, A

Missouri

Jefferson College, A
Linn State Technical College, A

New Jersey

Camden County College, A

New Mexico

Central New Mexico Community College, A
Southwestern Indian Polytechnic Institute, A

New York

Excelsior College, AB
Monroe Community College, A
Queensborough Community College of the City
University of New York, A

North Carolina

Central Carolina Community College, A
Durham Technical Community College, A

Ohio

Brown Mackie College-Cincinnati, A
Cincinnati State Technical and Community
College, A

Oregon

Oregon Institute of Technology, B
Portland Community College, A

Pennsylvania

Pennsylvania College of Technology, A

South Dakota

Southeast Technical Institute, A

Tennessee

Roane State Community College, A

Texas

Amarillo College, A
Texas State Technical College Waco, A

Wisconsin

Northcentral Technical College, A

LATIN AMERICAN STUDIES

Alabama

Samford University, B
The University of Alabama, BMO

Arizona

Arizona State University, MD
Prescott College, B
The University of Arizona, BM

California

Alliant International University, B
California State University, Chico, B
California State University, East Bay, B
California State University, Fullerton, B
California State University, Los Angeles, BM
City College of San Francisco, A
Claremont McKenna College, B
Fullerton College, A
Pasadena City College, A
Pitzer College, B
Saint Mary's College of California, B
San Diego City College, A
San Diego State University, BMO
Santa Rosa Junior College, A
Scripps College, B
University of California, Berkeley, BMDO
University of California, Los Angeles, BMO
University of California, Riverside, B
University of California, San Diego, BM
University of California, Santa Barbara, BMD
University of California, Santa Cruz, B
University of San Francisco, B

Colorado

Colorado State University, B
Fort Lewis College, B
University of Denver, B

Connecticut

Connecticut College, B
University of Connecticut, BM
Wesleyan University, B
Yale University, B

Delaware

University of Delaware, B

District of Columbia

American University, BMO
The George Washington University, BMO
Georgetown University, MO

Florida

Flagler College, B
Florida International University, M
Florida State University, B
Manatee Community College, A
Miami Dade College, A
Rollins College, B
Stetson University, B
University of Central Florida, O
University of Florida, MO
University of Miami, B

Georgia

Emory University, B

Idaho

University of Idaho, B

Illinois

DePaul University, B
Illinois Wesleyan University, B
Lake Forest College, B
University of Chicago, BMO
University of Illinois at Chicago, B
University of Illinois at Urbana-Champaign, BM

Indiana

Ball State University, B
Earlham College, B
Hanover College, B

Indiana University Bloomington, BMO
University of Notre Dame, M

Iowa

Cornell College, B
The University of Iowa, B
University of Northern Iowa, B

Kansas

University of Kansas, BMO

Kentucky

University of Kentucky, B

Louisiana

Tulane University, BMDO

Maine

Bowdoin College, B
Colby College, B

Maryland

Hood College, B
The Johns Hopkins University, B
Washington College, B

Massachusetts

Assumption College, B
Boston University, B
Brandeis University, B
Hampshire College, B
Harvard University, B
Mount Holyoke College, B
Simon's Rock College of Bard, B
Smith College, B
Wellesley College, B

Michigan

Oakland University, B
University of Michigan, B

Minnesota

Carleton College, B
Gustavus Adolphus College, B
Hamline University, B
Macalester College, B
St. Cloud State University, B
St. Olaf College, B
University of Minnesota, Morris, B
University of Minnesota, Twin Cities Campus, B

Missouri

University of Missouri-Columbia, B
Washington University in St. Louis, B

Nebraska

University of Nebraska-Lincoln, B
University of Nebraska at Omaha, B

New Hampshire

Dartmouth College, B

New Jersey

Rutgers, The State University of New Jersey, New
  Brunswick/Piscataway, B

New Mexico

University of New Mexico, BMDO

New York

Adelphi University, B
Bard College, B
Barnard College, B
Boricua College, BM
City College of the City University of New York, B
Colgate University, B
Columbia College, B
Cornell University, BMD
Fordham University, BO
Hobart and William Smith Colleges, B
Hofstra University, B
Hunter College of the City University of New York, B
Lehman College of the City University of New
  York, B

New York University, BMO
Queens College of the City University of New
  York, B
Sarah Lawrence College, B
State University of New York at Binghamton, B
State University of New York College at
  Brockport, B
State University of New York at New Paltz, B
State University of New York at Plattsburgh, B
Syracuse University, B
United States Military Academy, B
University at Albany, State University of New
  York, BMO
Vassar College, B

North Carolina

Duke University, DO
The University of North Carolina at Chapel Hill, BO
The University of North Carolina at Charlotte, B
Warren Wilson College, B

Ohio

Denison University, B
Kent State University, B
Oberlin College, B
The Ohio State University, B
Ohio University, BM
Ohio Wesleyan University, B
Pontifical College Josephinum, B
University of Cincinnati, B
The University of Toledo, B

Oregon

Portland State University, B
Willamette University, B

Pennsylvania

Albright College, B
Bucknell University, B
Carnegie Mellon University, B
Edinboro University of Pennsylvania, B
Gettysburg College, B
Haverford College, B
La Salle University, M
Lock Haven University of Pennsylvania, B
The Pennsylvania State University Abington
  College, B
The Pennsylvania State University Altoona
  College, B
The Pennsylvania State University Beaver Campus
  of the Commonwealth College, B
The Pennsylvania State University Berks Campus of
  the Berks-Lehigh Valley College, B
The Pennsylvania State University Delaware County
  Campus of the Commonwealth College, B
The Pennsylvania State University DuBois Campus
  of the Commonwealth College, B
The Pennsylvania State University at Erie, The
  Behrend College, B
The Pennsylvania State University Fayette Campus
  of the Commonwealth College, B
The Pennsylvania State University Hazleton
  Campus of the Commonwealth College, B
The Pennsylvania State University, Lehigh Valley
  Campus of the Berks-Lehigh Valley College, B
The Pennsylvania State University McKeesport
  Campus of the Commonwealth College, B
The Pennsylvania State University Mont Alto
  Campus of the Commonwealth College, B
The Pennsylvania State University New Kensington
  Campus of the Commonwealth College, B
The Pennsylvania State University Schuylkill
  Campus of the Capital College, B
The Pennsylvania State University Shenango
  Campus of the Commonwealth College, B
The Pennsylvania State University University Park
  Campus, B
The Pennsylvania State University Wilkes-Barre
  Campus of the Commonwealth College, B
The Pennsylvania State University Worthington
  Scranton Campus of the Commonwealth
  College, B
The Pennsylvania State University York Campus of
  the Commonwealth College, B
Temple University, B
University of Pennsylvania, B

University of Pittsburgh, O

Puerto Rico

University of Puerto Rico, Mayagüez Campus, B

Rhode Island

Brown University, BMD
University of Rhode Island, B

South Carolina

College of Charleston, B
University of South Carolina, B

Tennessee

Vanderbilt University, BMO

Texas

Austin College, B
Baylor University, B
Rice University, B
St. Edward's University, B
Southern Methodist University, B
Southwestern University, B
Texas Christian University, B
Texas Tech University, B
Trinity University, B
The University of Texas at Austin, BMDO
The University of Texas at El Paso, B

Utah

Brigham Young University, B

Vermont

Burlington College, B
Marlboro College, B
Middlebury College, B
University of Vermont, B

Virginia

The College of William and Mary, B
University of Richmond, B

Washington

Seattle Pacific University, B
University of Washington, B
Western Washington University, B

West Virginia

American Public University System, B
West Virginia University, M

Wisconsin

Beloit College, B
Ripon College, B
University of Wisconsin-Eau Claire, B
University of Wisconsin-Madison, BM
University of Wisconsin-Milwaukee, B

Alberta

University of Alberta, B
University of Calgary, B

British Columbia

Simon Fraser University, M
The University of British Columbia, B
University College of the Fraser Valley, A

Ontario

Carleton University, B
McMaster University, B
University of Toronto, B

York University, B

Quebec

McGill University, B

LATIN LANGUAGE AND LITERATURE

Alabama

Samford University, B

California

Claremont McKenna College, B
Loyola Marymount University, B
Saint Mary's College of California, B
Santa Clara University, B
Scripps College, B
Stanford University, B
University of California, Berkeley, B
University of California, Los Angeles, B
University of California, Santa Cruz, B

Connecticut

Yale University, B

Delaware

University of Delaware, B

District of Columbia

The Catholic University of America, B

Florida

Ave Maria University, B
Florida State University, B

Georgia

Emory University, B
Mercer University, B
University of Georgia, B

Idaho

Idaho State University, A
University of Idaho, B

Illinois

Augustana College, B
Loyola University Chicago, B
Monmouth College, B
Rockford College, B
University of Chicago, B

Indiana

Ball State University, B
Butler University, B
DePauw University, B
Indiana University Bloomington, B
University of Notre Dame, B
Wabash College, B

Iowa

Cornell College, B
Luther College, B
The University of Iowa, B

Kansas

Wichita State University, B

Kentucky

Asbury College, B

Louisiana

Centenary College of Louisiana, B
Louisiana State University and Agricultural and
Mechanical College, B

Tulane University, B

Maine

University of Maine, B

Maryland

University of Maryland, College Park, B

Massachusetts

Amherst College, B
Boston University, B
Brandeis University, B
Harvard University, B
Simon's Rock College of Bard, B
Smith College, B
Tufts University, B
Wellesley College, B

Michigan

Calvin College, B
Hope College, B
University of Michigan, B
Western Michigan University, B

Minnesota

Carleton College, B
Concordia College, B
Macalester College, B
St. Olaf College, B
University of Minnesota, Twin Cities Campus, B
University of St. Thomas, B

Missouri

Missouri State University, B
Saint Louis University, B
University of Missouri-Columbia, B
Washington University in St. Louis, B

Montana

Carroll College, B
The University of Montana-Missoula, B

Nebraska

Creighton University, B
University of Nebraska-Lincoln, B

New Hampshire

Dartmouth College, B
University of New Hampshire, B

New Jersey

Montclair State University, B
Rutgers, The State University of New Jersey, New
Brunswick/Piscataway, B

New York

Bard College, B
Barnard College, B
Brooklyn College of the City University of New
York, B
Colgate University, B
The College of New Rochelle, B
Fordham University, B
Hamilton College, B
Hobart and William Smith Colleges, B
Hofstra University, B
Hunter College of the City University of New York, B
Lehman College of the City University of New
York, B
New York University, B
Queens College of the City University of New
York, B
Sarah Lawrence College, B
State University of New York at Binghamton, B
University at Albany, State University of New York, B
Vassar College, B

North Carolina

Duke University, B
Lenoir-Rhyne College, B

Wake Forest University, B

Ohio

The College of Wooster, B
John Carroll University, B
Kent State University, B
Kenyon College, B
Miami University, B
Miami University Hamilton, B
Oberlin College, B
Ohio University, B

Oklahoma

Tulsa Community College, A

Oregon

University of Oregon, B

Pennsylvania

Bryn Mawr College, B
Duquesne University, B
Franklin and Marshall College, B
Gettysburg College, B
Haverford College, B
Swarthmore College, B
The University of Scranton, B
West Chester University of Pennsylvania, B
Westminster College, B

South Carolina

Furman University, B

Tennessee

Rhodes College, B
Sewanee: The University of the South, B
The University of Tennessee at Chattanooga, B

Texas

Austin College, B
Baylor University, B
Rice University, B
Southwestern University, B
University of Houston, B
The University of Texas at Austin, B

Utah

Brigham Young University, B

Vermont

Marlboro College, B
University of Vermont, B

Virginia

The College of William and Mary, B
Hampden-Sydney College, B
Randolph-Macon College, B
Randolph-Macon Woman's College, B
University of Mary Washington, B
University of Richmond, B

Washington

Seattle Pacific University, B
University of Washington, B

Wisconsin

Lawrence University, B
University of Wisconsin-Madison, B
University of Wisconsin-Milwaukee, B

Alberta

University of Alberta, B

British Columbia

The University of British Columbia, B
University of Victoria, B

Manitoba

University of Manitoba, B
The University of Winnipeg, B

New Brunswick

Mount Allison University, B
University of New Brunswick Fredericton, B

Newfoundland and Labrador

Memorial University of Newfoundland, B

Nova Scotia

Acadia University, B

Ontario

Carleton University, B
Trent University, B
University of Ottawa, B
University of Toronto, B
The University of Western Ontario, B
University of Windsor, B
Wilfrid Laurier University, B
York University, B

Saskatchewan

University of Saskatchewan, B

LATIN TEACHER EDUCATION

Illinois

University of Illinois at Urbana-Champaign, B

Iowa

The University of Iowa, B

Louisiana

Centenary College of Louisiana, B

Michigan

Hope College, B
Western Michigan University, B

Ohio

Bowling Green State University, B
Kent State University, B
Miami University Hamilton, B
Ohio Wesleyan University, B

Pennsylvania

Duquesne University, B

Texas

Baylor University, B

Utah

Brigham Young University, B

LAW AND LEGAL STUDIES

Alabama

Faulkner University, P
Samford University, MPO
South University, B
The University of Alabama, MPO

Alaska

University of Alaska Southeast, A

Arizona

Arizona State University, PO
The University of Arizona, MPO

Arkansas

Harding University, B
University of Arkansas, MP
University of Arkansas at Little Rock, PO

California

California State University, Chico, B
Chapman University, BMPO
Claremont McKenna College, B
College of the Siskiyous, A
Foothill College, A
Golden Gate University, MDPO
Humphreys College, P
John F. Kennedy University, P
Loyola Marymount University, MPO
National University, B

New College of California, P
Oxnard College, A
Pasadena City College, A
Pepperdine University, PO
Saddleback College, A
Santa Ana College, A
Santa Barbara City College, A
Santa Clara University, MPO
Scripps College, B
Stanford University, MDPO
University of California, Berkeley, BMDPO
University of California, Davis, MPO
University of California, Los Angeles, MPO
University of California, Santa Cruz, B
University of La Verne, P
University of the Pacific, MDPO
University of San Diego, MPO
University of San Francisco, MPO
University of Southern California, MPO
University of West Los Angeles, BP
Whittier College, MP

Colorado

United States Air Force Academy, B
University of Colorado at Boulder, PO
University of Denver, MP

Connecticut

Quinnipiac University, BPO
University of Connecticut, PO
University of Hartford, AB
University of New Haven, AB
Yale University, MDPO

Delaware

Wilmington College, B

District of Columbia

American University, BMPO
The Catholic University of America, PO
The George Washington University, MDPO
Georgetown University, MDPO
Howard University, MPO
Southeastern University, AB
University of the District of Columbia, P

Florida

Barry University, P
Edison College, A
Florida Agricultural and Mechanical University, P
Florida International University, P
Florida National College, A
Florida State University, PO
Hillsborough Community College, A
Nova Southeastern University, MPO
Okaloosa-Walton College, A
St. Thomas University, MPO
Santa Fe Community College, A
South University (West Palm Beach), B
Stetson University, MPO
University of Florida, MDPO
University of Miami, BMPO
Webster College (Holiday), A

Georgia

Clayton State University, A
Emory University, MPO
Georgia State University, PO
Mercer University, PO
South University, B
University of Georgia, MP

Hawaii

University of Hawaii at Manoa, PO

Idaho

University of Idaho, P

Illinois

City Colleges of Chicago, Harold Washington College, A
City Colleges of Chicago, Harry S. Truman College, A
City Colleges of Chicago, Kennedy-King College, A

City Colleges of Chicago, Richard J. Daley
  College, A
Concordia University, B
DePaul University, MPO
Illinois Institute of Technology, MPO
Loyola University Chicago, MDPO
MacCormac College, A
Northern Illinois University, P
Northwestern University, BMPO
Roosevelt University, B
Southern Illinois University Carbondale, PO
Trinity International University, P
University of Chicago, MDPO
University of Illinois at Springfield, B
University of Illinois at Urbana-Champaign, MDPO

Indiana

Indiana University Bloomington, MDPO
Indiana University-Purdue University Fort Wayne, B
University of Notre Dame, MDP
Valparaiso University, MPO

Iowa

Drake University, PO
Iowa Lakes Community College, A
Kirkwood Community College, A
The University of Iowa, MPO

Kansas

Central Christian College of Kansas, A
Friends University, M
Pittsburg State University, B
University of Kansas, PO
Washburn University, BP

Kentucky

Northern Kentucky University, PO
University of Kentucky, PO
University of Louisville, PO

Louisiana

Louisiana State University and Agricultural and
  Mechanical College, MPO
Loyola University New Orleans, PO
Southern University and Agricultural and Mechanical
  College, P
Tulane University, MDPO

Maine

College of the Atlantic, B
University of Southern Maine, PO

Maryland

Hood College, B
University of Baltimore, BMPO
University of Maryland, College Park, O
Villa Julie College, B

Massachusetts

Amherst College, B
Bay Path College, B
Boston College, PO
Boston University, MPO
Bridgewater State College, B
Elms College, B
Hampshire College, B
Harvard University, MDPO
Lasell College, B
Newbury College, B
Northeastern University, PO
Quincy College, A
Regis College, B
Suffolk University, BPO
University of Massachusetts Amherst, B
University of Massachusetts Boston, B
Western New England College, MP

Michigan

Grand Valley State University, B
Hope College, B
Lake Superior State University, AB
Macomb Community College, A
University of Detroit Mercy, ABPO
University of Michigan, MDPO

Wayne State University, MDPO

Minnesota

Hamline University, BMPO
Minnesota State University Moorhead, B
Northland Community and Technical College-Thief
  River Falls, A
Rasmussen College Mankato, A
University of Minnesota, Twin Cities Campus, MPO
University of St. Thomas, PO
Winona State University, B

Mississippi

Mississippi College, PO
University of Mississippi, PO

Missouri

Park University, BM
St. Louis Community College at Florissant Valley, A
Saint Louis University, MP
University of Missouri-Columbia, MPO
University of Missouri-Kansas City, MPO
Washington University in St. Louis, MDPO
Webster University, B

Montana

The University of Montana-Missoula, ABPO

Nebraska

Creighton University, PO
Metropolitan Community College, A
University of Nebraska-Lincoln, MPO

Nevada

University of Nevada, Las Vegas, PO

New Hampshire

New Hampshire Community Technical College,
  Nashua/Claremont, A
Rivier College, B

New Jersey

Gloucester County College, A
Montclair State University, B
Ramapo College of New Jersey, B
Rutgers, The State University of New Jersey,
  Camden, PO
Rutgers, The State University of New Jersey,
  Newark, PO
Seton Hall University, MPO

New Mexico

University of New Mexico, PO

New York

Cornell University, MDPO
Fordham University, MPO
Hilbert College, AB
Hofstra University, MPO
John Jay College of Criminal Justice of the City
  University of New York, B
Manhattanville College, B
Maria College, A
New York University, MDPO
Sage College of Albany, AB
St. John's University, BMPO
State University of New York at Buffalo, MPO
State University of New York, Fredonia, B
Syracuse University, PO
Touro College, MP
Yeshiva University, MP

North Carolina

Campbell University, P
Duke University, MDPO
Methodist College, B
North Carolina Central University, PO
North Carolina Wesleyan College, B
The University of North Carolina at Chapel Hill, PO

Wake Forest University, MPO

North Dakota

Aakers Business College, A
University of North Dakota, P

Ohio

Capital University, MPO
Case Western Reserve University, MPO
Cleveland State University, MPO
Edison State Community College, A
Franciscan University of Steubenville, B
Kenyon College, B
Oberlin College, B
Ohio Dominican University, A
Ohio Northern University, P
The Ohio State University, PO
The University of Akron, PO
University of Cincinnati, PO
University of Dayton, PO
The University of Toledo, PO

Oklahoma

East Central University, B
Oklahoma City University, PO
Tulsa Community College, A
University of Oklahoma, PO
University of Tulsa, MPO

Oregon

Lewis & Clark College, MP
University of Oregon, PO
Willamette University, MPO

Pennsylvania

Dickinson College, B
Duquesne University, PO
Gannon University, B
Pennsylvania College of Technology, B
Point Park University, B
Reading Area Community College, A
Temple University, MPO
University of Pennsylvania, MDPO
University of Pittsburgh, BMPO
Villanova University, PO
Widener University, MDPO

Puerto Rico

Inter American University of Puerto Rico,
  Metropolitan Campus, P
Pontifical Catholic University of Puerto Rico, PO
University of Puerto Rico, Río Piedras, MP

Rhode Island

Roger Williams University, PO

South Carolina

South University, B
Trident Technical College, A
University of South Carolina, PO

South Dakota

The University of South Dakota, PO

Tennessee

Draughons Junior College (Nashville), A
University of Memphis, PO
The University of Tennessee, PO
Vanderbilt University, MPO

Texas

Alvin Community College, A
Baylor University, PO
Del Mar College, A
El Centro College, A
Navarro College, A
North Harris College, A
Palo Alto College, A
St. Mary's University of San Antonio, PO
Schreiner University, B
Southern Methodist University, MDPO
Texas Southern University, PO
Texas Tech University, PO
Texas Wesleyan University, P

University of Houston, MPO
The University of Texas at Austin, MPO
Vernon College, A

Utah

Brigham Young University, MPO
University of Utah, MPO

Vermont

Burlington College, B

Virginia

Christopher Newport University, B
The College of William and Mary, MPO
George Mason University, MPO
Liberty University, P
Regent University, PO
University of Richmond, PO
University of Virginia, MDPO
Virginia Intermont College, B
Washington and Lee University, MP

Washington

Gonzaga University, PO
Seattle University, PO
University of Washington, MDPO

West Virginia

Mountain State University, AB
West Virginia Junior College (Charleston), A
West Virginia University, PO

Wisconsin

Marquette University, PO
University of Wisconsin-Madison, MD
University of Wisconsin-Superior, B

Wyoming

University of Wyoming, PO

Alberta

University of Alberta, BMPO
University of Calgary, BMP

British Columbia

The University of British Columbia, MD
University of Victoria, MDPO

Manitoba

University of Manitoba, M

New Brunswick

Université de Moncton, BMPO
University of New Brunswick Fredericton, BPO

Nova Scotia

Dalhousie University, MDO

Ontario

Laurentian University, B
Queen's University at Kingston, MPO
University of Ottawa, MD
University of Toronto, MDPO
The University of Western Ontario, BMPO
University of Windsor, B
York University, BMDO

Quebec

McGill University, MDO
Université Laval, BMDO
Université de Montréal, BMDPO
Université du Québec àMontréal, BM

Université de Sherbrooke, BMDPO

Saskatchewan

University of Saskatchewan, MP

LAW ENFORCEMENT

Illinois

Western Illinois University, M

Kentucky

Eastern Kentucky University, M

Maryland

The Johns Hopkins University, M

Minnesota

Metropolitan State University, M

Mississippi

University of Southern Mississippi, M

Rhode Island

Salve Regina University, MO

LEATHERWORKING AND UPHOLSTERY

Texas

St. Philip's College, A

Washington

Spokane Falls Community College, A

LEGAL ADMINISTRATIVE ASSISTANT/SECRETARY

Alabama

Chattahoochee Valley Community College, A
Enterprise-Ozark Community College, A
Lawson State Community College, A
Northeast Alabama Community College, A
Virginia College at Huntsville, A
Wallace State Community College, A

Arizona

Central Arizona College, A
Cochise College (Sierra Vista), A
Lamson College, A
Northland Pioneer College, A
Phoenix College, A
Yavapai College, A

Arkansas

Ouachita Technical College, A

California

Allan Hancock College, A
American River College, A
Bakersfield College, A
Butte College, A
Cerritos College, A
Chabot College, A
Chaffey College, A
City College of San Francisco, A
College of the Redwoods, A
Cypress College, A
East Los Angeles College, A
Empire College, A
Fresno City College, A
Fullerton College, A
Glendale Community College, A
Golden West College, A
Grossmont College, A
Heald College-Fresno, A
Heald College-Hayward, A
Heald College-Rancho Cordova, A
Heald College-Salinas, A
Heald College-San Francisco, A

Heald College-San Jose, A
Humphreys College, A
Lassen Community College District, A
Long Beach City College, A
Los Angeles City College, A
Los Angeles Harbor College, A
Merced College, A
Monterey Peninsula College, A
Mt. San Antonio College, A
MTI College of Business and Technology, A
Napa Valley College, A
Orange Coast College, A
Pacific Union College, A
Palomar College, A
Pasadena City College, A
Sacramento City College, A
Saddleback College, A
San Diego City College, A
San Diego Mesa College, A
Shasta College, A
Sierra College, A
Skyline College, A
Solano Community College, A
Southwestern College, A
University of West Los Angeles, B
West Los Angeles College, A
West Valley College, A

Colorado

Arapahoe Community College, A
Institute of Business & Medical Careers, A
Lamar Community College, A
Mesa State College, A
Northeastern Junior College, A
Otero Junior College, A
Pueblo Community College, A

Connecticut

Asnuntuck Community College, A
Briarwood College, A
Gateway Community College, A
Gibbs College, A
Manchester Community College, A
Middlesex Community College, A
Naugatuck Valley Community College, A
Three Rivers Community College, A
Tunxis Community College, A

Delaware

Delaware Technical & Community College, Jack F. Owens Campus, A

District of Columbia

University of the District of Columbia, A

Florida

Broward Community College, A
Daytona Beach Community College, A
Florida National College, A
Hillsborough Community College, A
Miami Dade College, A
Palm Beach Community College, A
Polk Community College, A
St. Petersburg College, A
Santa Fe Community College, A
South University (West Palm Beach), B
Tallahassee Community College, A
Valencia Community College, A
Webster College (Ocala), A

Georgia

Clayton State University, A
DeKalb Technical College, A

Hawaii

Heald College-Honolulu, A
Kapiolani Community College, A

Idaho

Lewis-Clark State College, AB
North Idaho College, A

Illinois

Black Hawk College, A
Career Colleges of Chicago, A

College of DuPage, A
Danville Area Community College, A
Elgin Community College, A
Gem City College, A
John A. Logan College, A
John Wood Community College, A
Lake Land College, A
Lewis and Clark Community College, A
Lincoln College-Normal, A
Lincoln Land Community College, A
MacCormac College, A
Midstate College, A
Morton College, A
Richland Community College, A
Robert Morris College, A
Rockford Business College, A
Sauk Valley Community College, A
Shawnee Community College, A
Southwestern Illinois College, A
Spoon River College, A
Triton College, A
William Rainey Harper College, A

Indiana

Ball State University, AB
Brown Mackie College-Michigan City, A
Indiana Business College (Indianapolis), A
International Business College (Fort Wayne), AB
International Business College (Indianapolis), A
Vincennes University, A
Vincennes University Jasper Campus, A

Iowa

AIB College of Business, A
Des Moines Area Community College, A
Dordt College, A
Ellsworth Community College, A
Iowa Lakes Community College, A
Iowa Western Community College, A
Kirkwood Community College, A
Western Iowa Tech Community College, A

Kansas

Coffeyville Community College, A
Dodge City Community College, A
Fort Scott Community College, A
Garden City Community College, A
Highland Community College, A
Labette Community College, A
Tabor College, B
Washburn University, A

Kentucky

Draughons Junior College, A
St. Catharine College, A
Sullivan University, A

Maine

Andover College, A
Beal College, A
Kennebec Valley Community College, A
Northern Maine Community College, A

Maryland

Baltimore City Community College, A
Chesapeake College, A
Frederick Community College, A
Hagerstown Business College, A
Howard Community College, A

Massachusetts

Bay State College, A
Bristol Community College, A
Cape Cod Community College, A
Gibbs College, A
Holyoke Community College, A
Marian Court College, A
North Shore Community College, A
Roxbury Community College, A

Michigan

Baker College of Auburn Hills, A
Baker College of Clinton Township, A
Baker College of Flint, A
Baker College of Jackson, A

Baker College of Muskegon, A
Baker College of Owosso, A
Baker College of Port Huron, A
Delta College, A
Ferris State University, A
Gogebic Community College, A
Grand Rapids Community College, A
Henry Ford Community College, A
Kalamazoo Valley Community College, A
Kellogg Community College, A
Kirtland Community College, A
Lake Michigan College, A
Lansing Community College, A
Lewis College of Business, A
Mid Michigan Community College, A
Monroe County Community College, A
Mott Community College, A
Muskegon Community College, A
North Central Michigan College, A
Northwestern Michigan College, A
St. Clair County Community College, A
University of Detroit Mercy, AB
Wayne County Community College District, A

Minnesota

Alexandria Technical College, A
Anoka Technical College, A
Central Lakes College, A
Century College, A
Hennepin Technical College, A
Hibbing Community College, A
Inver Hills Community College, A
Lake Superior College, A
Minneapolis Community and Technical College, A
Minnesota School of Business, A
Minnesota School of Business-Brooklyn Center, A
Minnesota State College-Southeast Technical, A
Minnesota State Community and Technical
    College-Fergus Falls, A
Normandale Community College, A
Northland Community and Technical College-Thief
    River Falls, A
Northwest Technical College, A
Rasmussen College Eden Prairie, A
Rasmussen College Mankato, A
Rasmussen College St. Cloud, A
Ridgewater College, A
Riverland Community College, A
Rochester Community and Technical College, A
St. Cloud Technical College, A

Mississippi

Northeast Mississippi Community College, A
Southwest Mississippi Community College, A

Missouri

Crowder College, A
East Central College, A
Hickey College, A
Jefferson College, A
Longview Community College, A
Maple Woods Community College, A
Northwest Missouri State University, B
Penn Valley Community College, A
St. Louis Community College at Meramec, A
State Fair Community College, A

Montana

Montana State University-Billings, A
Montana State University-Great Falls College of
    Technology, A
Montana Tech of The University of Montana, A
The University of Montana-Helena College of
    Technology, A
The University of Montana-Missoula, A

Nebraska

Hamilton College-Lincoln, A
Hamilton College-Omaha, A
Metropolitan Community College, A
Midland Lutheran College, A
Northeast Community College, A

Southeast Community College, Beatrice Campus, A

Nevada

Community College of Southern Nevada, A
Morrison University, A
Truckee Meadows Community College, A

New Hampshire

McIntosh College, A

New Jersey

Bergen Community College, A
Cumberland County College, A
Gibbs College (Montclair), A
Gloucester County College, A
Middlesex County College, A

New Mexico

Clovis Community College, A
New Mexico Junior College, A
Western New Mexico University, A

New York

Bramson ORT College, A
Bryant and Stratton College, North Campus, A
Elmira Business Institute, A
Fiorello H. LaGuardia Community College of the
    City University of New York, A
Fulton-Montgomery Community College, A
Interboro Institute, A
Jamestown Business College, A
Katharine Gibbs School (New York), A
Monroe Community College, A
Nassau Community College, A
Olean Business Institute, A
State University of New York College of Agriculture
    and Technology at Morrisville, A
Trocaire College, A
Westchester Community College, A

North Carolina

Alamance Community College, A
Carteret Community College, A
Central Carolina Community College, A
Central Piedmont Community College, A
Craven Community College, A
Lenoir Community College, A
Nash Community College, A
Rockingham Community College, A
South Piedmont Community College, A
Stanly Community College, A
Vance-Granville Community College, A
Wake Technical Community College, A
Wayne Community College, A
Western Piedmont Community College, A

North Dakota

Bismarck State College, A
Lake Region State College, A

Ohio

Bradford School, A
Bryant and Stratton College (Cleveland), A
Bryant and Stratton College (Parma), A
Columbus State Community College, A
David N. Myers University, A
Davis College, A
James A. Rhodes State College, A
Jefferson Community College, A
Kent State University, Ashtabula Campus, A
Kent State University, East Liverpool Campus, A
Miami-Jacobs College, A
Miami University-Middletown Campus, A
Northwest State Community College, A
Ohio Business College (Lorain), A
Ohio Business College (Sandusky), A
Ohio University-Lancaster, A
Shawnee State University, A
Sinclair Community College, A
Stark State College of Technology, A
Trumbull Business College, A
The University of Akron, A
The University of Akron-Wayne College, A
University of Cincinnati, A
University of Cincinnati Clermont College, A

University of Cincinnati Raymond Walters College, A
University of Northwestern Ohio, A
University of Rio Grande, A
The University of Toledo, A
Wright State University, A
Wright State University, Lake Campus, A
Youngstown State University, A

Oklahoma

Carl Albert State College, A
Eastern Oklahoma State College, A
Northeastern Oklahoma Agricultural and Mechanical
  College, A
Oklahoma State University, Okmulgee, A
Rogers State University, A
Rose State College, A
Tulsa Community College, A

Oregon

Clatsop Community College, A
Linn-Benton Community College, A
Mt. Hood Community College, A
Portland Community College, A
Treasure Valley Community College, A
Umpqua Community College, A

Pennsylvania

Berean Institute, A
Business Institute of Pennsylvania (Meadville), A
Business Institute of Pennsylvania (Sharon), A
Butler County Community College, A
Cambria-Rowe Business College (Johnstown), A
Central Pennsylvania College, A
Clarion University of Pennsylvania, A
Community College of Allegheny County, A
Community College of Philadelphia, A
Consolidated School of Business (Lancaster), A
Consolidated School of Business (York), A
DuBois Business College, A
Duff's Business Institute, A
Erie Business Center, Main, A
Erie Business Center South, A
Harrisburg Area Community College, A
ICM School of Business & Medical Careers, A
Laurel Business Institute, A
Lehigh Carbon Community College, A
Manor College, A
Newport Business Institute (Lower Burrell), A
Newport Business Institute (Williamsport), A
Northampton County Area Community College, A
Peirce College, A
Penn Commercial Business and Technical School, A
Reading Area Community College, A
South Hills School of Business & Technology
  (Altoona), A
South Hills School of Business & Technology (State
  College), A
Thaddeus Stevens College of Technology, A
Westmoreland County Community College, A

Puerto Rico

Caribbean University, A

Rhode Island

Community College of Rhode Island, A

South Carolina

Piedmont Technical College, A
Technical College of the Lowcountry, A
York Technical College, A

Tennessee

Chattanooga State Technical Community College, A
Draughons Junior College (Clarksville), A
Martin Methodist College, A
Pellissippi State Technical Community College, A
Roane State Community College, A
South College, A

Texas

Alvin Community College, A
Amarillo College, A
Austin Community College, A
Blinn College, A
Coastal Bend College, A

Del Mar College, A
Eastfield College, A
El Centro College, A
Frank Phillips College, A
Grayson County College, A
Lamar University, A
McLennan Community College, A
Mountain View College, A
Navarro College, A
North Central Texas College, A
North Harris College, A
North Lake College, A
Northeast Texas Community College, A
Odessa College, A
St. Philip's College, A
San Antonio College, A
South Plains College, A
South Texas College, A
Texas A&M University-Commerce, B
Texas Southmost College, A
Texas State Technical College Harlingen, A
Tomball College, A
Trinity Valley Community College, A
Tyler Junior College, A

Utah

LDS Business College, A
Stevens-Henager College, A

Virginia

Bryant and Stratton College, Richmond, A
Bryant and Stratton College, Virginia Beach, A
Dabney S. Lancaster Community College, A
Mountain Empire Community College, A
University of Richmond, A

Washington

Bates Technical College, A
Centralia College, A
Clover Park Technical College, A
Crown College, A
Edmonds Community College, A
Green River Community College, A
Highline Community College, A
Lake Washington Technical College, A
Lower Columbia College, A
Olympic College, A
Pierce College, A
Renton Technical College, A
South Puget Sound Community College, A
Spokane Community College, A
Walla Walla Community College, A
Wenatchee Valley College, A
Yakima Valley Community College, A

West Virginia

Community & Technical College at West Virginia
  University Institute of Technology, A
Huntington Junior College, A
West Virginia Junior College (Morgantown), A

Wisconsin

Blackhawk Technical College, A
Fox Valley Technical College, A
Gateway Technical College, A
Milwaukee Area Technical College, A
Moraine Park Technical College, A
Northcentral Technical College, A
Northeast Wisconsin Technical College, A
Southwest Wisconsin Technical College, A

Wyoming

Western Wyoming Community College, A

LEGAL AND JUSTICE STUDIES

Arizona

Arizona State University, MDO

California

Golden Gate University, MD
San Francisco State University, O
University of California, Berkeley, D
University of the Pacific, M

University of San Diego, M
Whittier College, M

Colorado

Denver Career College, O
Regis University, O
University of Denver, M

District of Columbia

American University, MDO
The Catholic University of America, DO

Florida

Nova Southeastern University, M

Illinois

DePaul University, M
Governors State University, M
University of Illinois at Springfield, M

Indiana

Indiana University Bloomington, P

Maryland

University of Baltimore, M

Massachusetts

Boston University, M
Northeastern University, MDO

Michigan

Marygrove College, M

Missouri

Webster University, MO

Nebraska

University of Nebraska-Lincoln, M

Nevada

University of Nevada, Reno, M

New Hampshire

University of New Hampshire, M

New Jersey

Montclair State University, MO
Rutgers, The State University of New Jersey, New
  Brunswick/Piscataway, D

New York

Hofstra University, M
John Jay College of Criminal Justice of the City
  University of New York, D
New York University, MDO
St. John's University, M

Ohio

Capital University, M
Case Western Reserve University, M

Pennsylvania

University of Pittsburgh, MO

South Carolina

College of Charleston, MO

Texas

Prairie View A&M University, MD
Texas State University-San Marcos, M

Utah

Weber State University, M

Virginia

Marymount University, MO

Washington

University of Washington, D

West Virginia

West Virginia University, M

Wisconsin

University of Wisconsin-Madison, M

Manitoba

University of Manitoba, M

Ontario

Brock University, M
Carleton University, M
University of Windsor, M

Quebec

Université Laval, O

LEGAL ASSISTANT/PARALEGAL

Alabama

Calhoun Community College, A
Community College of the Air Force, A
Faulkner University, AB
Gadsden State Community College, A
James H. Faulkner State Community College, A
Northeast Alabama Community College, A
South University, A
Virginia College at Birmingham, A
Wallace State Community College, A

Alaska

University of Alaska Anchorage, A
University of Alaska Fairbanks, A

Arizona

Everest College, A
International Institute of the Americas (Mesa), A
International Institute of the Americas (Phoenix), A
International Institute of the Americas (Tucson), A
International Institute of the Americas (West Valley), A
Lamson College, A
Northland Pioneer College, A
The Paralegal Institute, Inc., A
Phoenix College, A
Pima Community College, A
Yavapai College, A

Arkansas

Ouachita Technical College, A
Southeast Arkansas College, A
University of Arkansas at Fort Smith, A

California

American River College, A
Argosy University/Orange County, A
Argosy University/San Diego, A
Argosy University/Santa Monica, A
California State University, Chico, B
Cañada College, A
College of the Redwoods, A
College of the Sequoias, A
College of the Siskiyous, A
Compton Community College, A
Cuyamaca College, A
De Anza College, A
El Camino College, A
Evergreen Valley College, A
Fresno City College, A
Fullerton College, A
Humphreys College, B
Merritt College, A
Mt. San Antonio College, A
Mt. San Jacinto College, A
Napa Valley College, A
Palomar College, A
Platt College (Cerritos), A
Platt College-Los Angeles, Inc, A
Platt College (Newport Beach), A
Platt College (Ontario), A
Riverside Community College District, A
Saddleback College, A
San Diego City College, A
San Diego Miramar College, A
Shasta College, A

Skyline College, A
University of La Verne, B
University of West Los Angeles, B
West Los Angeles College, A

Colorado

Arapahoe Community College, A
Argosy University/Denver, A
Blair College, A
Colorado Northwestern Community College, A
Community College of Aurora, A
Community College of Denver, A
Front Range Community College, A
Institute of Business & Medical Careers, A
Pikes Peak Community College, A
Pueblo Community College, A

Connecticut

Briarwood College, A
Manchester Community College, A
Naugatuck Valley Community College, A
Northwestern Connecticut Community College, A
Norwalk Community College, A
Post University, AB
Quinnipiac University, B

Delaware

Wesley College, B

Florida

Brevard Community College, A
Broward Community College, A
Brown Mackie College-Miami, A
Daytona Beach Community College, A
Florida Community College at Jacksonville, A
Florida Gulf Coast University, B
Florida Metropolitan University-Brandon Campus, AB
Florida Metropolitan University-Lakeland Campus, A
Florida Metropolitan University-North Orlando Campus, AB
Florida Metropolitan University-Pinellas Campus, A
Florida Metropolitan University-Pompano Beach Campus, A
Florida Metropolitan University-South Orlando Campus, AB
Florida Metropolitan University-Tampa Campus, A
Florida National College, A
Florida Technical College (DeLand), A
Florida Technical College (Orlando), A
Gulf Coast Community College, A
Indian River Community College, A
International College, A
Jones College (Jacksonville), AB
Jones College (Miami), AB
Keiser College (Daytona Beach), A
Keiser College (Fort Lauderdale), A
Keiser College (Melbourne), A
Keiser College (Miami), A
Keiser College (Sarasota), A
Keiser College (Tallahassee), A
Key College, A
Lake-Sumter Community College, A
Manatee Community College, A
Miami Dade College, A
Nova Southeastern University, B
Okaloosa-Walton College, A
Pasco-Hernando Community College, A
Pensacola Junior College, A
St. Petersburg College, A
Seminole Community College, A
South University (West Palm Beach), A
Southwest Florida College (Fort Myers), A
Tallahassee Community College, A
University of Central Florida, B
Valencia Community College, A

Georgia

Appalachian Technical College, A
Athens Technical College, A
Atlanta Technical College, A
Brown Mackie College-Atlanta, A
Central Georgia Technical College, A
Clayton State University, A
Coosa Valley Technical College, A

DeKalb Technical College, A
Georgia Highlands College, A
Griffin Technical College, A
Ogeechee Technical College, A
South Georgia Technical College, A
South University, A
Valdosta State University, B

Hawaii

Kapiolani Community College, A

Idaho

Boise State University, A
Eastern Idaho Technical College, A
Lewis-Clark State College, AB
North Idaho College, A

Illinois

Black Hawk College, A
Elgin Community College, A
Gem City College, A
Illinois Central College, A
Lincoln College-Normal, A
MacCormac College, A
Midstate College, A
Northwestern Business College, A
Robert Morris College, A
Rockford Business College, A
Roosevelt University, B
South Suburban College, A
Southern Illinois University Carbondale, B
Southwestern Illinois College, A
William Rainey Harper College, A

Indiana

Ball State University, AB
Brown Mackie College-Fort Wayne, A
Brown Mackie College-Merrillville, A
Brown Mackie College-South Bend, A
Calumet College of Saint Joseph, B
Indiana University South Bend, A
International Business College (Fort Wayne), AB
International Business College (Indianapolis), A
Ivy Tech Community College-Bloomington, A
Ivy Tech Community College-Central Indiana, A
Ivy Tech Community College-Columbus, A
Ivy Tech Community College-East Central, A
Ivy Tech Community College-Kokomo, A
Ivy Tech Community College-Lafayette, A
Ivy Tech Community College-North Central, A
Ivy Tech Community College-Northeast, A
Ivy Tech Community College-Northwest, A
Ivy Tech Community College-Southeast, A
Ivy Tech Community College-Southern Indiana, A
Ivy Tech Community College-Southwest, A
Ivy Tech Community College-Wabash Valley, A
Ivy Tech Community College-Whitewater, A
Saint Mary-of-the-Woods College, AB
Sawyer College (Hammond), A
Vincennes University, A

Iowa

Des Moines Area Community College, A
Hamilton College (Cedar Falls), A
Iowa Lakes Community College, A
Iowa Western Community College, A
Kaplan University, AB
Kirkwood Community College, A

Kansas

Brown Mackie College-Kansas City, A
Brown Mackie College-Salina, A
Hutchinson Community College and Area Vocational School, A
Johnson County Community College, A
Kansas City Kansas Community College, A
Newman University, A

Kentucky

Beckfield College, AB
Brown Mackie College-Hopkinsville, A
Brown Mackie College-Louisville, A
Brown Mackie College-Northern Kentucky, A
Daymar College (Louisville), A
Daymar College (Owensboro), A

Eastern Kentucky University, AB
Morehead State University, B
Sullivan University, AB
University of Louisville, AB
Western Kentucky University, A

Louisiana

Elaine P. Nunez Community College, A
Grambling State University, A
Louisiana State University at Eunice, A
McNeese State University, A
Nicholls State University, A
Remington College-Lafayette Campus, A
Southern University at Shreveport, A
Tulane University, A

Maine

Andover College, A
Husson College, AB

Maryland

Allegany College of Maryland, A
Anne Arundel Community College, A
Baltimore City Community College, A
College of Southern Maryland, A
Frederick Community College, A
Hagerstown Business College, A
Harford Community College, A
Montgomery College, A
Prince George's Community College, A
University of Maryland University College, B
Villa Julie College, AB

Massachusetts

Anna Maria College, AB
Atlantic Union College, A
Becker College, A
Boston University, B
Cape Cod Community College, A
Elms College, AB
Massachusetts Bay Community College, A
Merrimack College, A
Middlesex Community College, A
Mount Wachusett Community College, A
Newbury College, A
North Shore Community College, A
Northern Essex Community College, A
Suffolk University, AB

Michigan

Davenport University (Dearborn), AB
Davenport University (Midland), A
Delta College, A
Eastern Michigan University, B
Ferris State University, A
Grand Valley State University, B
Henry Ford Community College, A
Kellogg Community College, A
Lake Superior State University, AB
Lansing Community College, A
Macomb Community College, A
Madonna University, AB
North Central Michigan College, A
Oakland Community College, A
Southwestern Michigan College, A

Minnesota

Alexandria Technical College, A
Globe College, AB
Hamline University, B
Inver Hills Community College, A
Lake Superior College, A
Minnesota School of Business, AB
Minnesota School of Business-Brooklyn Center, AB
Minnesota School of Business-Plymouth, AB
Minnesota School of Business-Richfield, AB
Minnesota School of Business-St. Cloud, AB
Minnesota School of Business-Shakopee, AB
Minnesota State University Moorhead, B
North Hennepin Community College, A
Northland Community and Technical College-Thief
   River Falls, A
Rasmussen College Mankato, A

Winona State University, B

Mississippi

Hinds Community College, A
Mississippi College, B
Mississippi Gulf Coast Community College, A
Mississippi University for Women, B
Northeast Mississippi Community College, A
Northwest Mississippi Community College, A
University of Southern Mississippi, B

Missouri

Avila University, B
East Central College, A
Hickey College, A
Kansas City College, A
Maryville University of Saint Louis, B
Metro Business College (Cape Girardeau), A
Missouri State University-West Plains, A
Missouri Western State University, A
Patricia Stevens College, A
Penn Valley Community College, A
St. Louis Community College at Meramec, A
Sanford-Brown College (Fenton), A
Sanford-Brown College (Hazelwood), A
Sanford-Brown College (St. Charles), A
Springfield College, A
William Woods University, AB

Montana

University of Great Falls, AB
The University of Montana-Missoula, A

Nebraska

Central Community College-Grand Island
   Campus, A
College of Saint Mary, AB
Hamilton College-Lincoln, A
Hamilton College-Omaha, A
Metropolitan Community College, A
Northeast Community College, A

Nevada

Community College of Southern Nevada, A
Las Vegas College, A
Morrison University, A
Western Nevada Community College, A

New Hampshire

Hesser College, A
McIntosh College, A
New Hampshire Community Technical College,
   Nashua/Claremont, A
New Hampshire Technical Institute, A

New Jersey

Atlantic Cape Community College, A
Bergen Community College, A
Berkeley College, A
Brookdale Community College, A
Burlington County College, A
Essex County College, A
Gloucester County College, A
Hudson County Community College, A
Mercer County Community College, A
Middlesex County College, A
Ocean County College, A
Raritan Valley Community College, A
Sussex County Community College, A
Warren County Community College, A

New Mexico

Central New Mexico Community College, A
Clovis Community College, A
Doña Ana Branch Community College, A
Eastern New Mexico University-Roswell, A
New Mexico State University-Alamogordo, A
New Mexico State University-Carlsbad, A
New Mexico State University-Grants, A
San Juan College, A
Santa Fe Community College, A

University of New Mexico-Gallup, A

New York

Berkeley College-New York City Campus, A
Berkeley College-Westchester Campus, A
Briarcliffe College, A
Bronx Community College of the City University of
   New York, A
Broome Community College, A
Bryant and Stratton College (Albany), A
Bryant and Stratton College, Amherst Campus, A
Bryant and Stratton College, North Campus, A
Bryant and Stratton College (Rochester-Henrietta
   Campus), A
Corning Community College, A
Dutchess Community College, A
Erie Community College, A
Eugenio María de Hostos Community College of the
   City University of New York, A
Finger Lakes Community College, A
Fiorello H. LaGuardia Community College of the
   City University of New York, A
Genesee Community College, A
Herkimer County Community College, A
Hilbert College, AB
Interboro Institute, A
Jefferson Community College, A
Maria College, A
Mildred Elley, A
Nassau Community College, A
New York Career Institute, A
New York City College of Technology of the City
   University of New York, AB
Olean Business Institute, A
St. John's University, AB
Schenectady County Community College, A
Suffolk County Community College, A
Sullivan County Community College, A
Tompkins Cortland Community College, A
Westchester Community College, A

North Carolina

Caldwell Community College and Technical
   Institute, A
Carteret Community College, A
Catawba Valley Community College, A
Central Carolina Community College, A
Central Piedmont Community College, A
Coastal Carolina Community College, A
Davidson County Community College, A
Durham Technical Community College, A
Fayetteville Technical Community College, A
Forsyth Technical Community College, A
Gaston College, A
Guilford Technical Community College, A
Johnston Community College, A
Pitt Community College, A
Rockingham Community College, A
Rowan-Cabarrus Community College, A
South College-Asheville, A
Southwestern Community College, A
Surry Community College, A
Western Piedmont Community College, A
Wilson Technical Community College, A

North Dakota

Lake Region State College, A

Ohio

Bradford School, A
Brown Mackie College-Akron, A
Brown Mackie College-Findlay, A
Brown Mackie College-North Canton, A
Bryant and Stratton College (Cleveland), A
Clark State Community College, A
College of Mount St. Joseph, AB
Columbus State Community College, A
Cuyahoga Community College, A
David N. Myers University, AB
Edison State Community College, A
ETI Technical College of Niles, A
James A. Rhodes State College, A
Lake Erie College, B
Lakeland Community College, A
Marion Technical College, A
North Central State College, A

Northwest State Community College, A
Ohio University-Chillicothe, A
RETS Tech Center, A
Shawnee State University, A
Sinclair Community College, A
Stautzenberger College, A
The University of Akron, A
University of Cincinnati, A
University of Cincinnati Clermont College, A
University of Northwestern Ohio, A
The University of Toledo, A
Ursuline College, B
Zane State College, A

Oklahoma

Metropolitan College (Tulsa), A
Rogers State University, A
Tulsa Community College, A

Oregon

Pioneer Pacific College, A
Portland Community College, A

Pennsylvania

Academy of Medical Arts and Business, A
Bucks County Community College, A
Cedar Crest College, B
Central Pennsylvania College, A
Community College of Allegheny County, A
Community College of Philadelphia, A
Delaware County Community College, A
Duff's Business Institute, A
Erie Business Center, Main, A
Gannon University, AB
Harrisburg Area Community College, A
Lackawanna College, A
Lansdale School of Business, A
Lehigh Carbon Community College, A
Lehigh Valley College, A
Lock Haven University of Pennsylvania, B
Luzerne County Community College, A
Manor College, A
Marywood University, AB
McCann School of Business & Technology, A
Mount Aloysius College, A
Northampton County Area Community College, A
Pace Institute, A
Peirce College, AB
Penn Commercial Business and Technical School, A
Penn Foster Career School, A
Pennsylvania College of Technology, A
Schuylkill Institute of Business and Technology, A
Western School of Health and Business Careers
    (Pittsburgh), A
Westmoreland County Community College, A
Widener University, A

Puerto Rico

Universidad del Este, A

Rhode Island

Community College of Rhode Island, A
Johnson & Wales University, AB
Roger Williams University, B

South Carolina

Central Carolina Technical College, A
Florence-Darlington Technical College, A
Greenville Technical College, A
Horry-Georgetown Technical College, A
Midlands Technical College, A
Orangeburg-Calhoun Technical College, A
South University, A
Technical College of the Lowcountry, A
Trident Technical College, A

South Dakota

National American University (Rapid City), A
National American University-Sioux Falls
    Branch, AB
Oglala Lakota College, AB

Western Dakota Technical Institute, A

Tennessee

Pellissippi State Technical Community College, A
South College, A
Southwest Tennessee Community College, A
University of Memphis, B
The University of Tennessee at Chattanooga, B
Volunteer State Community College, A

Texas

Alvin Community College, A
Angelina College, A
Austin Community College, A
Brazosport College, A
Brown Mackie College-Fort Worth, A
Central Texas College, A
Collin County Community College District, A
El Centro College, A
Houston Community College System, A
Howard Payne University, B
Kilgore College, A
Lamar State College-Port Arthur, A
Lee College, A
McLennan Community College, A
Midland College, A
Navarro College, A
North Central Texas College, A
South Texas College, A
Stephen F. Austin State University, B
Tarrant County College District, A
Texas Woman's University, B
University of Houston-Clear Lake, B
Victoria College, A

Utah

Mountain West College, A
Salt Lake Community College, A
Utah Career College, A
Utah Valley State College, AB

Vermont

Burlington College, A
Champlain College, AB
Woodbury College, AB

Virginia

Bryant and Stratton College, Richmond, A
Bryant and Stratton College, Virginia Beach, A
Hampton University, B
J. Sargeant Reynolds Community College, A
Marymount University, B
New River Community College, A
Northern Virginia Community College, A
Tidewater Community College, A
Virginia Intermont College, B

Washington

Clark College, A
Columbia Basin College, A
Crown College, A
Edmonds Community College, A
Highline Community College, A
Pierce College, A
Skagit Valley College, A
South Puget Sound Community College, A
Spokane Community College, A
Whatcom Community College, A

West Virginia

Bluefield State College, A
Community and Technical College of Shepherd, A
Marshall Community and Technical College, A
Mountain State College, A
Mountain State University, A
New River Community and Technical College, A
West Virginia Business College (Wheeling), A
West Virginia Junior College (Bridgeport), A
West Virginia State Community and Technical
    College, A

Wisconsin

Bryant and Stratton College, Wauwatosa Campus, A
Chippewa Valley Technical College, A
Concordia University Wisconsin, B

Lakeshore Technical College, A
Milwaukee Area Technical College, A
Northeast Wisconsin Technical College, A
Western Technical College, A

Wyoming

Casper College, A

LEGAL PROFESSIONS AND STUDIES

Arizona

Northland Pioneer College, A

Florida

Florida National College, A
International College, B

Georgia

Brenau University, B

Indiana

University of Evansville, B

Kansas

Bethany College, B

Louisiana

Tulane University, B

Nebraska

University of Nebraska-Lincoln, B

New Jersey

Essex County College, A
Ramapo College of New Jersey, B

New York

Mercy College, B

Oklahoma

University of Tulsa, B

Pennsylvania

Peirce College, A
Pennsylvania College of Technology, B
Saint Joseph's University, B
Temple University, B
University of Pennsylvania, B

Rhode Island

Roger Williams University, B

Texas

Texas Wesleyan University, B

Ontario

University of Ottawa, B

LEISURE STUDIES

Alabama

University of South Alabama, M

Arizona

Prescott College, M

California

California State University, Long Beach, M
California State University, Northridge, M

San Francisco State University, M

Connecticut

Southern Connecticut State University, M
University of Connecticut, MD

District of Columbia

Gallaudet University, M
Howard University, M

Florida

University of West Florida, M

Georgia

University of Georgia, MD

Hawaii

University of Hawaii at Manoa, M

Illinois

Aurora University, M
University of Illinois at Urbana-Champaign, MD

Indiana

Indiana University Bloomington, D

Iowa

The University of Iowa, M
University of Northern Iowa, MD

Kentucky

Murray State University, M

Massachusetts

Boston University, M

Michigan

Central Michigan University, M

Minnesota

University of Minnesota, Twin Cities Campus, MD

Mississippi

University of Mississippi, MD

Missouri

Southeast Missouri State University, M

Nevada

University of Nevada, Las Vegas, M

New York

Metropolitan College of New York, M
State University of New York College at
   Brockport, M

North Carolina

East Carolina University, M
The University of North Carolina at Chapel Hill, M

Ohio

Bowling Green State University, M
The University of Toledo, M

Oklahoma

Oklahoma State University, MD

Pennsylvania

The Pennsylvania State University University Park
   Campus, MD
Temple University, M

Puerto Rico

Universidad Metropolitana, M

Tennessee

University of Memphis, M
The University of Tennessee, M

Texas

Texas State University-San Marcos, M
University of North Texas, MO

Utah

University of Utah, MD

British Columbia

University of Victoria, M

Nova Scotia

Dalhousie University, M

Ontario

University of Waterloo, MD

Quebec

Université du Québec àTrois-Rivières, MO

LIBERAL ARTS AND SCIENCES STUDIES AND HUMANITIES

Alabama

Alabama Southern Community College, A
Alabama State University, AB
Auburn University Montgomery, B
Bevill State Community College, A
Bishop State Community College, A
Calhoun Community College, A
Central Alabama Community College, A
Chattahoochee Valley Community College, A
Enterprise-Ozark Community College, A
Faulkner University, AB
Gadsden State Community College, A
George C. Wallace Community College, A
Huntingdon College, B
James H. Faulkner State Community College, A
Jefferson Davis Community College, A
Jefferson State Community College, A
Lawson State Community College, A
Lurleen B. Wallace Community College, A
Marion Military Institute, A
Northeast Alabama Community College, A
Northwest-Shoals Community College, A
Shelton State Community College, A
Snead State Community College, A
Southern Christian University, B
Southern Union State Community College, A
Troy University, A
University of South Alabama, B
Wallace State Community College, A

Alaska

Alaska Pacific University, B
Sheldon Jackson College, B
University of Alaska Anchorage, Kenai Peninsula
   College, A
University of Alaska Anchorage, Kodiak College, A
University of Alaska Anchorage, Matanuska-Susitna
   College, A
University of Alaska Fairbanks, A
University of Alaska, Prince William Sound
   Community College, A
University of Alaska Southeast, AB
University of Alaska Southeast, Ketchikan
   Campus, A
University of Alaska Southeast, Sitka Campus, A

Arizona

Arizona State University, B
Central Arizona College, A
Chandler-Gilbert Community College, A
Cochise College (Douglas), A
Cochise College (Sierra Vista), A
Coconino Community College, A
Diné College, A
Eastern Arizona College, A
Estrella Mountain Community College, A
GateWay Community College, A
Glendale Community College, A
Grand Canyon University, B
Mesa Community College, A
Mohave Community College, A
Northern Arizona University, B
Northland Pioneer College, A
Paradise Valley Community College, A
Phoenix College, A

Pima Community College, A
Prescott College, B
South Mountain Community College, A
The University of Arizona, B
Western International University, AB
Yavapai College, A

Arkansas

Arkansas Baptist College, B
Arkansas State University-Beebe, A
Arkansas State University-Mountain Home, A
Black River Technical College, A
Cossatot Community College of the University of
   Arkansas, A
East Arkansas Community College, A
John Brown University, A
Mid-South Community College, A
National Park Community College, A
North Arkansas College, A
NorthWest Arkansas Community College, A
Ouachita Technical College, A
Ozarka College, A
Phillips Community College of the University of
   Arkansas, A
Rich Mountain Community College, A
University of Arkansas Community College at
   Hope, A
University of Arkansas Community College at
   Morrilton, A
University of Arkansas at Fort Smith, AB
University of Arkansas at Little Rock, B
University of Arkansas at Monticello, A
Williams Baptist College, AB

California

Allan Hancock College, A
American River College, A
Antelope Valley College, A
Antioch University Los Angeles, B
Azusa Pacific University, B
Bakersfield College, A
Barstow College, A
Berkeley City College, A
Bethany University, AB
Butte College, A
Cabrillo College, A
California Baptist University, B
California Lutheran University, B
California Polytechnic State University, San Luis
   Obispo, B
California State Polytechnic University, Pomona, B
California State University, Bakersfield, B
California State University Channel Islands, B
California State University, Chico, B
California State University, Dominguez Hills, B
California State University, East Bay, B
California State University, Fresno, B
California State University, Fullerton, B
California State University, Long Beach, B
California State University, Los Angeles, B
California State University, Monterey Bay, B
California State University, Northridge, B
California State University, Sacramento, B
California State University, San Bernardino, B
California State University, San Marcos, B
California State University, Stanislaus, B
Cañada College, A
Cerritos College, A
Cerro Coso Community College, A
Chabot College, A
Chaffey College, A
Chapman University, B
Citrus College, A
Coastline Community College, A
College of Alameda, A
College of the Canyons, A
College of the Desert, A
College of Marin, A
College of San Mateo, A
College of the Sequoias, A
Columbia College, A
Compton Community College, A
Concordia University, B
Contra Costa College, A
Cosumnes River College (Sacramento), A
Crafton Hills College, A

Cuesta College, A
Cuyamaca College, A
Cypress College, A
De Anza College, A
Diablo Valley College, A
Dominican University of California, B
East Los Angeles College, A
El Camino College, A
Evergreen Valley College, A
Feather River College, A
Folsom Lake College, A
Fresno City College, A
Fresno Pacific University, AB
Fullerton College, A
Gavilan College, A
Glendale Community College, A
Golden West College, A
Grossmont College, A
Hartnell College, A
Holy Names University, B
Humboldt State University, B
Humphreys College, A
Imperial Valley College, A
Irvine Valley College, A
John F. Kennedy University, B
La Sierra University, B
Lake Tahoe Community College, A
Laney College, A
Las Positas College, A
Lassen Community College District, A
Long Beach City College, A
Los Angeles City College, A
Los Angeles Harbor College, A
Los Angeles Mission College, A
Los Angeles Pierce College, A
Los Angeles Trade-Technical College, A
Los Angeles Valley College, A
Los Medanos College, A
Loyola Marymount University, B
Marymount College, Palos Verdes, California, A
The Master's College and Seminary, B
Mendocino College, A
Menlo College, B
Merced College, A
Merritt College, A
Mills College, B
MiraCosta College, A
Mission College, A
Monterey Peninsula College, A
Moorpark College, A
Mount St. Mary's College, A
Mt. San Antonio College, A
The National Hispanic University, AB
Notre Dame de Namur University, B
Ohlone College, A
Orange Coast College, A
Oxnard College, A
Palo Verde College, A
Palomar College, A
Pasadena City College, A
Patten University, AB
Pepperdine University, B
Point Loma Nazarene University, B
Pomona College, B
Porterville College, A
Reedley College, A
Rio Hondo College, A
Riverside Community College District, A
Sacramento City College, A
Saddleback College, A
Saint Mary's College of California, B
San Bernardino Valley College, A
San Diego Christian College, B
San Diego City College, A
San Diego Mesa College, A
San Diego Miramar College, A
San Diego State University, B
San Francisco State University, B
San Joaquin Delta College, A
San Jose City College, A
San Jose State University, B
Santa Ana College, A
Santa Barbara City College, A
Santa Clara University, B
Santa Monica College, A
Santa Rosa Junior College, A

Santiago Canyon College, A
Sierra College, A
Simpson University, B
Skyline College, A
Soka University of America, B
Solano Community College, A
Sonoma State University, B
Southwestern College, A
Taft College, A
Thomas Aquinas College, B
University of California, Los Angeles, B
University of California, Riverside, B
University of Judaism, B
University of La Verne, AB
University of Redlands, B
University of San Diego, B
University of San Francisco, B
Ventura College, A
Victor Valley College, A
West Hills Community College, A
West Los Angeles College, A
West Valley College, A
Westmont College, B
Whittier College, B

Colorado

Adams State College, AB
Aims Community College, A
Arapahoe Community College, A
Colorado Christian University, AB
The Colorado College, B
Colorado Mountain College, A
Colorado Mountain College, Alpine Campus, A
Colorado Mountain College, Timberline Campus, A
Colorado Northwestern Community College, A
Colorado State University, B
Community College of Aurora, A
Fort Lewis College, B
Front Range Community College, A
Lamar Community College, A
Mesa State College, AB
Morgan Community College, A
Northeastern Junior College, A
Otero Junior College, A
Pikes Peak Community College, A
Pueblo Community College, A
Red Rocks Community College, A
Regis University, B
Trinidad State Junior College, A
Western State College of Colorado, B

Connecticut

Albertus Magnus College, AB
Asnuntuck Community College, A
Capital Community College, A
Charter Oak State College, AB
Gateway Community College, A
Housatonic Community College, A
Manchester Community College, A
Middlesex Community College, A
Mitchell College, AB
Naugatuck Valley Community College, A
Northwestern Connecticut Community College, A
Norwalk Community College, A
Post University, AB
Quinebaug Valley Community College, A
Quinnipiac University, B
Sacred Heart University, A
Saint Joseph College, B
Southern Connecticut State University, AB
Three Rivers Community College, A
Tunxis Community College, A
University of Bridgeport, AB
University of Hartford, A
University of New Haven, B
Western Connecticut State University, AB

Delaware

University of Delaware, AB
Wesley College, B

District of Columbia

American University, B
The George Washington University, B
Georgetown University, B
Strayer University, A

Trinity (Washington) University, B

Florida

Barry University, B
Beacon College, AB
Bethune-Cookman College, B
Brevard Community College, A
Broward Community College, A
Central Florida Community College, A
Chipola College, A
Daytona Beach Community College, A
Edison College, A
Flagler College, B
Florida Agricultural and Mechanical University, A
Florida Atlantic University, AB
Florida College, AB
Florida Community College at Jacksonville, A
Florida Gulf Coast University, A
Florida International University, B
Florida Keys Community College, A
Florida National College, A
Florida State University, A
Gulf Coast Community College, A
Hillsborough Community College, A
Indian River Community College, A
Jacksonville University, B
Lake City Community College, A
Lake-Sumter Community College, A
Lynn University, B
Manatee Community College, A
New College of Florida, B
North Florida Community College, A
Nova Southeastern University, B
Okaloosa-Walton College, A
Palm Beach Community College, A
Pasco-Hernando Community College, A
Pensacola Junior College, A
Polk Community College, A
St. Johns River Community College, A
Saint Leo University, A
St. Petersburg College, A
St. Thomas University, B
Santa Fe Community College, A
Schiller International University, A
Seminole Community College, A
South Florida Community College, A
Tallahassee Community College, A
University of Central Florida, AB
University of Miami, B
University of North Florida, B
University of South Florida, AB
The University of Tampa, B
University of West Florida, A
Valencia Community College, A

Georgia

Abraham Baldwin Agricultural College, A
Armstrong Atlantic State University, AB
Augusta State University, A
Bainbridge College, A
Coastal Georgia Community College, A
Columbus State University, A
East Georgia College, A
Emmanuel College, A
Emory University, AB
Emory University, Oxford College, A
Fort Valley State University, B
Georgia Highlands College, A
Georgia Military College, A
LaGrange College, A
Macon State College, A
Mercer University, B
Middle Georgia College, A
Reinhardt College, AB
Shorter College, B
South Georgia College, A
Southern Polytechnic State University, A
Thomas University, AB
Truett-McConnell College, A
Valdosta State University, A
Waycross College, A
Young Harris College, A

Hawaii

Hawaii Community College, A
Hawaii Pacific University, B

Honolulu Community College, A
Kapiolani Community College, A
Kauai Community College, A
Leeward Community College, A
Maui Community College, A
TransPacific Hawaii College, A
Windward Community College, A

Idaho

Boise State University, B
Brigham Young University -Idaho, A
College of Southern Idaho, A
Lewis-Clark State College, A
North Idaho College, A
Northwest Nazarene University, B
University of Idaho, B

Illinois

Augustana College, B
Blackburn College, B
Bradley University, B
Carl Sandburg College, A
Chicago State University, B
City Colleges of Chicago, Harold Washington
   College, A
City Colleges of Chicago, Harry S. Truman
   College, A
City Colleges of Chicago, Kennedy-King College, A
City Colleges of Chicago, Malcolm X College, A
City Colleges of Chicago, Olive-Harvey College, A
City Colleges of Chicago, Richard J. Daley
   College, A
City Colleges of Chicago, Wilbur Wright College, A
College of DuPage, A
College of Lake County, A
Columbia College Chicago, B
Danville Area Community College, A
East-West University, A
Eastern Illinois University, B
Elgin Community College, A
Eureka College, B
Governors State University, B
Greenville College, B
Heartland Community College, A
Highland Community College, A
Illinois Central College, A
Illinois College, B
Illinois Eastern Community Colleges, Frontier
   Community College, A
Illinois Eastern Community Colleges, Lincoln Trail
   College, A
Illinois Eastern Community Colleges, Olney Central
   College, A
Illinois Eastern Community Colleges, Wabash Valley
   College, A
Illinois Valley Community College, A
John A. Logan College, A
John Wood Community College, A
Kankakee Community College, A
Kaskaskia College, A
Kishwaukee College, A
Lake Land College, A
Lewis and Clark Community College, A
Lewis University, B
Lincoln College, A
Lincoln College-Normal, AB
Lincoln Land Community College, A
MacMurray College, B
McHenry County College, A
Monmouth College, B
Moraine Valley Community College, A
Morton College, A
National-Louis University, B
North Central College, B
Northeastern Illinois University, B
Northern Illinois University, B
Northwestern University, B
Oakton Community College, A
Olivet Nazarene University, B
Parkland College, A
Prairie State College, A
Richland Community College, A
Rock Valley College, A
Roosevelt University, B
St. Augustine College, A
Saint Xavier University, B

Sauk Valley Community College, A
Shawnee Community College, A
Shimer College, B
South Suburban College, A
Southern Illinois University Carbondale, B
Southern Illinois University Edwardsville, B
Southwestern Illinois College, A
Spoon River College, A
Springfield College in Illinois, A
Trinity International University, B
Triton College, A
University of Chicago, B
University of Illinois at Springfield, B
University of Illinois at Urbana-Champaign, B
University of St. Francis, A
Waubonsee Community College, A
Western Illinois University, B
William Rainey Harper College, A

Indiana

Ancilla College, A
Ball State University, AB
Bethel College, AB
Butler University, A
Calumet College of Saint Joseph, AB
Goshen College, B
Holy Cross College, AB
Indiana State University, AB
Ivy Tech Community College-Bloomington, A
Ivy Tech Community College-Central Indiana, A
Ivy Tech Community College-Columbus, A
Ivy Tech Community College-East Central, A
Ivy Tech Community College-Kokomo, A
Ivy Tech Community College-Lafayette, A
Ivy Tech Community College-North Central, A
Ivy Tech Community College-Northeast, A
Ivy Tech Community College-Northwest, A
Ivy Tech Community College-Southeast, A
Ivy Tech Community College-Southern Indiana, A
Ivy Tech Community College-Southwest, A
Ivy Tech Community College-Wabash Valley, A
Ivy Tech Community College-Whitewater, A
Marian College, A
Oakland City University, A
Purdue University North Central, B
Saint Mary-of-the-Woods College, AB
Taylor University Fort Wayne, A
Tri-State University, A
University of Evansville, B
University of Indianapolis, AB
University of Notre Dame, B
University of Saint Francis, AB
University of Southern Indiana, B
Vincennes University, A
Vincennes University Jasper Campus, A

Iowa

Ashford University, AB
Briar Cliff University, A
Clarke College, A
Clinton Community College, A
Coe College, B
Cornell College, B
Des Moines Area Community College, A
Ellsworth Community College, A
Graceland University, B
Grand View College, AB
Hawkeye Community College, A
Indian Hills Community College, A
Iowa Central Community College, A
Iowa Lakes Community College, A
Iowa State University of Science and Technology, B
Iowa Wesleyan College, B
Iowa Western Community College, A
Kirkwood Community College, A
Loras College, AB
Marshalltown Community College, A
Muscatine Community College, A
North Iowa Area Community College, A
Northeast Iowa Community College, A
Northwest Iowa Community College, A
Scott Community College, A
Southeastern Community College, North Campus, A
Southeastern Community College, South
   Campus, A
Southwestern Community College, A

The University of Iowa, B
University of Northern Iowa, B
Upper Iowa University, A
Western Iowa Tech Community College, A

Kansas

Barton County Community College, A
Benedictine College, B
Butler Community College, A
Central Christian College of Kansas, B
Cloud County Community College, A
Coffeyville Community College, A
Colby Community College, A
Cowley County Community College and Area
   Vocational-Technical School, A
Dodge City Community College, A
Donnelly College, A
Fort Hays State University, B
Fort Scott Community College, A
Friends University, B
Garden City Community College, A
Haskell Indian Nations University, A
Hesston College, A
Highland Community College, A
Hutchinson Community College and Area Vocational
   School, A
Independence Community College, A
Johnson County Community College, A
Kansas City Kansas Community College, A
Kansas Wesleyan University, B
Labette Community College, A
MidAmerica Nazarene University, A
Neosho County Community College, A
Newman University, AB
Pratt Community College, A
Seward County Community College, A
Southwestern College, B
University of Kansas, B
University of Saint Mary, AB
Washburn University, AB
Wichita State University, AB

Kentucky

Ashland Community and Technical College, A
Bellarmine University, B
Big Sandy Community and Technical College, A
Brescia University, AB
Elizabethtown Community and Technical College, A
Georgetown College, B
Hazard Community and Technical College, A
Hopkinsville Community College, A
Jefferson Community and Technical College, A
Kentucky State University, AB
Lexington Community College, A
Maysville Community and Technical College, A
Midway College, B
Murray State University, AB
Owensboro Community and Technical College, A
St. Catharine College, A
Southeast Kentucky Community and Technical
   College, A
Spalding University, B
Thomas More College, AB
University of Louisville, B

Louisiana

Bossier Parish Community College, A
Centenary College of Louisiana, B
Elaine P. Nunez Community College, A
Louisiana College, B
Louisiana State University and Agricultural and
   Mechanical College, B
Louisiana State University at Alexandria, AB
McNeese State University, B
Nicholls State University, A
Northwestern State University of Louisiana, B
River Parishes Community College, A
Saint Joseph Seminary College, B
Southeastern Louisiana University, B
Tulane University, B

Maine

College of the Atlantic, B
Eastern Maine Community College, A
Husson College, B
Kennebec Valley Community College, A

Saint Joseph's College of Maine, B
Southern Maine Community College, A
Thomas College, A
University of Maine, B
The University of Maine at Augusta, A
University of Maine at Farmington, B
University of Maine at Fort Kent, AB
University of Maine at Presque Isle, AB
University of New England, B

Maryland

Allegany College of Maryland, A
Anne Arundel Community College, A
Baltimore City Community College, A
Carroll Community College, A
Cecil Community College, A
Chesapeake College, A
College of Notre Dame of Maryland, B
College of Southern Maryland, A
Columbia Union College, B
Coppin State University, B
Frederick Community College, A
Frostburg State University, B
Garrett College, A
Hagerstown Community College, A
Harford Community College, A
Howard Community College, A
The Johns Hopkins University, B
Montgomery College, A
Prince George's Community College, A
St. John's College, B
Salisbury University, B
University of Baltimore, B
University of Maryland Eastern Shore, B
Villa Julie College, AB
Washington College, B
Wor-Wic Community College, A

Massachusetts

American International College, AB
Bay Path College, B
Bay State College, A
Becker College, AB
Bentley College, B
Berkshire Community College, A
Bristol Community College, A
Cape Cod Community College, A
Dean College, A
Eastern Nazarene College, B
Elms College, B
Emmanuel College, B
Endicott College, AB
Fisher College, A
Fitchburg State College, B
Framingham State College, B
Greenfield Community College, A
Harvard University, B
Holyoke Community College, A
Lasell College, B
Lesley University, B
Marian Court College, A
Massachusetts Bay Community College, A
Massachusetts Institute of Technology, B
Massasoit Community College, A
Merrimack College, A
Middlesex Community College, A
Mount Ida College, B
Mount Wachusett Community College, A
North Shore Community College, A
Northeastern University, B
Northern Essex Community College, A
Pine Manor College, A
Quincy College, A
Quinsigamond Community College, A
Regis College, B
Salem State College, B
Simon's Rock College of Bard, A
Springfield Technical Community College, A
Suffolk University, B
University of Massachusetts Amherst, B
University of Massachusetts Dartmouth, B
University of Massachusetts Lowell, B
Urban College of Boston, A
Western New England College, AB

Westfield State College, B

Michigan

Alma College, B
Alpena Community College, A
Andrews University, AB
Aquinas College, B
Bay Mills Community College, A
Bay de Noc Community College, A
Delta College, A
Ferris State University, A
Finlandia University, B
Glen Oaks Community College, A
Gogebic Community College, A
Grace Bible College, A
Grand Rapids Community College, A
Grand Valley State University, B
Henry Ford Community College, A
Hope College, B
Jackson Community College, A
Kalamazoo Valley Community College, A
Kellogg Community College, A
Kirtland Community College, A
Kuyper College, A
Lake Michigan College, A
Lake Superior State University, A
Lansing Community College, A
Lewis College of Business, A
Macomb Community College, A
Marygrove College, A
Michigan Technological University, B
Mid Michigan Community College, A
Monroe County Community College, A
Montcalm Community College, A
Mott Community College, A
Muskegon Community College, A
North Central Michigan College, A
Northern Michigan University, A
Northwestern Michigan College, A
Oakland Community College, A
Olivet College, B
Rochester College, A
Sacred Heart Major Seminary, B
Saginaw Chippewa Tribal College, A
St. Clair County Community College, A
Schoolcraft College, A
Southwestern Michigan College, A
Spring Arbor University, A
University of Michigan-Dearborn, B
University of Michigan-Flint, B
Washtenaw Community College, A
Wayne County Community College District, A
West Shore Community College, A

Minnesota

Anoka-Ramsey Community College, A
Anoka-Ramsey Community College, Cambridge
    Campus, A
Augsburg College, B
Bemidji State University, AB
Bethany Lutheran College, AB
Bethel University, A
Central Lakes College, A
Century College, A
College of Saint Benedict, B
College of St. Catherine, A
College of St. Catherine-Minneapolis, A
The College of St. Scholastica, B
Crossroads College, AB
Crown College, AB
Fond du Lac Tribal and Community College, A
Hibbing Community College, A
Inver Hills Community College, A
Itasca Community College, A
Lake Superior College, A
Mesabi Range Community and Technical College, A
Metropolitan State University, B
Minneapolis Community and Technical College, A
Minnesota State Community and Technical
    College-Fergus Falls, A
Minnesota State University Mankato, AB
Minnesota State University Moorhead, A
Minnesota West Community and Technical
    College, A
Normandale Community College, A
North Central University, A

Northland Community and Technical College-Thief
    River Falls, A
Northwestern College, A
Rainy River Community College, A
Ridgewater College, A
Riverland Community College, A
Rochester Community and Technical College, A
St. Cloud State University, AB
St. Olaf College, B
University of Minnesota, Morris, B
Vermilion Community College, A
Winona State University, B

Mississippi

Alcorn State University, B
Coahoma Community College, A
Copiah-Lincoln Community College, A
Copiah-Lincoln Community College-Natchez
    Campus, A
East Central Community College, A
East Mississippi Community College, A
Hinds Community College, A
Holmes Community College, A
Itawamba Community College, A
Mississippi College, B
Mississippi Delta Community College, A
Mississippi Gulf Coast Community College, A
Mississippi State University, B
Northeast Mississippi Community College, A
Northwest Mississippi Community College, A
Pearl River Community College, A
Southwest Mississippi Community College, A
University of Mississippi, B

Missouri

Blue River Community College, A
Columbia College, AB
Conception Seminary College, B
Cottey College, A
Crowder College, A
Fontbonne University, B
Hannibal-LaGrange College, B
Jefferson College, A
Lindenwood University, B
Longview Community College, A
Maple Woods Community College, A
Maryville University of Saint Louis, B
Metropolitan Community College-Business &
    Technology College, A
Mineral Area College, A
Missouri Valley College, AB
Moberly Area Community College, A
North Central Missouri College, A
Ozarks Technical Community College, A
Park University, AB
Penn Valley Community College, A
Saint Charles Community College, A
St. Louis Christian College, A
St. Louis Community College at Florissant Valley, A
St. Louis Community College at Forest Park, A
St. Louis Community College at Meramec, A
State Fair Community College, A
Stephens College, AB
Three Rivers Community College, A
University of Missouri-Kansas City, B
University of Missouri-St. Louis, B
Washington University in St. Louis, B
Webster University, B
Wentworth Military Academy and Junior College, A

Montana

Blackfeet Community College, A
Chief Dull Knife College, A
Dawson Community College, A
Flathead Valley Community College, A
Fort Belknap College, A
Fort Peck Community College, A
Little Big Horn College, A
Miles Community College, A
Montana State University-Billings, AB
Montana Tech of The University of Montana, AB
Rocky Mountain College, A
Salish Kootenai College, A
Stone Child College, A
The University of Montana-Missoula, B

The University of Montana-Western, B

Nebraska

Central Community College-Columbus Campus, A
Central Community College-Grand Island
Campus, A
Central Community College-Hastings Campus, A
Grace University, AB
Hastings College, B
Metropolitan Community College, A
Mid-Plains Community College, A
Midland Lutheran College, B
Nebraska Indian Community College, A
Northeast Community College, A
Southeast Community College, Beatrice Campus, A
Southeast Community College, Lincoln Campus, A
University of Nebraska-Lincoln, B
Western Nebraska Community College, A
York College, AB

Nevada

Community College of Southern Nevada, A
Deep Springs College, A
Nevada State College at Henderson, B
Truckee Meadows Community College, A
Western Nevada Community College, A

New Hampshire

Colby-Sawyer College, A
Daniel Webster College, A
Franklin Pierce College, B
Granite State College, AB
Hesser College, A
Keene State College, AB
Magdalen College, B
New England College, A
New Hampshire Community Technical College,
Berlin/Laconia, A
New Hampshire Community Technical College,
Manchester/Stratham, A
New Hampshire Community Technical College,
Nashua/Claremont, A
New Hampshire Technical Institute, A
Rivier College, AB
Saint Anselm College, B
Southern New Hampshire University, AB
University of New Hampshire, A
University of New Hampshire at Manchester, A

New Jersey

Assumption College for Sisters, A
Atlantic Cape Community College, A
Bergen Community College, A
Brookdale Community College, A
Burlington County College, A
Camden County College, A
Centenary College, A
County College of Morris, A
Cumberland County College, A
Essex County College, A
Fairleigh Dickinson University, Metropolitan
Campus, A
Felician College, A
Georgian Court University, B
Gloucester County College, A
Hudson County Community College, A
Kean University, B
Mercer County Community College, A
Ocean County College, A
Raritan Valley Community College, A
The Richard Stockton College of New Jersey, B
Rider University, AB
Rowan University, B
Rutgers, The State University of New Jersey,
Camden, B
Rutgers, The State University of New Jersey, New
Brunswick/Piscataway, B
Saint Peter's College, B
Salem Community College, A
Seton Hall University, B
Sussex County Community College, A
Union County College, A
Warren County Community College, A

Westminster Choir College of Rider University, B

New Mexico

Central New Mexico Community College, A
Clovis Community College, A
Eastern New Mexico University, B
Eastern New Mexico University-Roswell, A
New Mexico Junior College, A
New Mexico Military Institute, A
New Mexico State University-Alamogordo, A
New Mexico State University-Carlsbad, A
New Mexico State University-Grants, A
St. John's College, B
Southwestern Indian Polytechnic Institute, A
University of New Mexico, B
University of New Mexico-Gallup, A
University of New Mexico-Los Alamos Branch, A
University of New Mexico-Valencia Campus, A

New York

Adelphi University, A
Adirondack Community College, A
Boricua College, AB
Borough of Manhattan Community College of the
City University of New York, A
Bronx Community College of the City University of
New York, A
Broome Community College, A
Buffalo State College, State University of New
York, B
Cayuga County Community College, A
Cazenovia College, AB
Clarkson University, B
Clinton Community College, A
College of Mount Saint Vincent, B
The College of New Rochelle, B
The College of Saint Rose, B
College of Staten Island of the City University of
New York, AB
Columbia-Greene Community College, A
Concordia College, AB
Cornell University, B
Corning Community College, A
Dominican College, A
Dowling College, B
Dutchess Community College, A
D'Youville College, B
Elmira College, B
Erie Community College, A
Erie Community College, North Campus, A
Erie Community College, South Campus, A
Eugene Lang College The New School for Liberal
Arts, B
Eugenio María de Hostos Community College of the
City University of New York, A
Excelsior College, AB
Farmingdale State University of New York, A
Finger Lakes Community College, A
Fiorello H. LaGuardia Community College of the
City University of New York, A
Five Towns College, A
Fordham University, B
Fulton-Montgomery Community College, A
Genesee Community College, A
Herkimer County Community College, A
Hilbert College, A
Hobart and William Smith Colleges, B
Hofstra University, B
Houghton College, AB
Hudson Valley Community College, A
Iona College, B
Ithaca College, B
Jefferson Community College, A
Keuka College, B
Kingsborough Community College of the City
University of New York, A
Long Island University, Brooklyn Campus, AB
Long Island University, C.W. Post Campus, B
Long Island University, Friends World Program, B
Manhattan College, B
Maria College, A
Marymount Manhattan College, B
Medaille College, AB
Medgar Evers College of the City University of New
York, A
Mercy College, A

Mohawk Valley Community College, A
Molloy College, A
Monroe Community College, A
Mount Saint Mary College, B
Nassau Community College, A
The New School for General Studies, B
New York City College of Technology of the City
University of New York, A
New York University, AB
Niagara County Community College, A
Niagara University, AB
North Country Community College, A
Nyack College, AB
Onondaga Community College, A
Orange County Community College, A
Pace University, AB
Paul Smith's College of Arts and Sciences, A
Polytechnic University, Brooklyn Campus, B
Purchase College, State University of New York, B
Queensborough Community College of the City
University of New York, A
Rockland Community College, A
Sage College of Albany, AB
St. Francis College, AB
St. John's University, AB
St. Joseph's College, Suffolk Campus, B
Sarah Lawrence College, B
Schenectady County Community College, A
Skidmore College, B
State University of New York College of Agriculture
and Technology at Cobleskill, A
State University of New York College of Agriculture
and Technology at Morrisville, A
State University of New York College at Oneonta, B
State University of New York College of Technology
at Alfred, A
State University of New York College of Technology
at Canton, A
State University of New York, Fredonia, B
Suffolk County Community College, A
Sullivan County Community College, A
Syracuse University, B
Tompkins Cortland Community College, A
Touro College, AB
Trocaire College, A
Ulster County Community College, A
Union College, B
Utica College, B
Vassar College, B
Villa Maria College of Buffalo, A
Westchester Community College, A
York College of the City University of New York, B

North Carolina

Alamance Community College, A
Appalachian State University, B
Asheville-Buncombe Technical Community
College, A
Barton College, B
Beaufort County Community College, A
Bladen Community College, A
Blue Ridge Community College, A
Brunswick Community College, A
Caldwell Community College and Technical
Institute, A
Campbell University, A
Cape Fear Community College, A
Carteret Community College, A
Catawba Valley Community College, A
Central Carolina Community College, A
Central Piedmont Community College, A
Chowan University, B
Cleveland Community College, A
Coastal Carolina Community College, A
College of The Albemarle, A
Craven Community College, A
Davidson County Community College, A
Durham Technical Community College, A
East Carolina University, B
Edgecombe Community College, A
Fayetteville Technical Community College, A
Guilford Technical Community College, A
Halifax Community College, A
Haywood Community College, A
Isothermal Community College, A
James Sprunt Community College, A

John Wesley College, A
Johnson C. Smith University, B
Johnston Community College, A
Lees-McRae College, B
Lenoir Community College, A
Louisburg College, A
Mars Hill College, B
Martin Community College, A
Mayland Community College, A
McDowell Technical Community College, A
Methodist College, AB
Mitchell Community College, A
Montgomery Community College, A
Mount Olive College, AB
Nash Community College, A
North Carolina State University, B
Pamlico Community College, A
Peace College, AB
Piedmont Community College, A
Pitt Community College, A
Randolph Community College, A
Richmond Community College, A
Roanoke-Chowan Community College, A
Rockingham Community College, A
Rowan-Cabarrus Community College, A
St. Andrews Presbyterian College, B
Sampson Community College, A
Sandhills Community College, A
Shaw University, B
South Piedmont Community College, A
Southeastern Community College, A
Southwestern Community College, A
Surry Community College, A
Tri-County Community College, A
The University of North Carolina at Asheville, B
The University of North Carolina at Chapel Hill, B
The University of North Carolina at Greensboro, B
Vance-Granville Community College, A
Wake Technical Community College, A
Wayne Community College, A
Western Carolina University, B
Western Piedmont Community College, A
Wilkes Community College, A
Wilson Technical Community College, A
Wingate University, B

North Dakota

Bismarck State College, A
Cankdeska Cikana Community College, A
Dickinson State University, AB
Fort Berthold Community College, A
Lake Region State College, A
Minot State University-Bottineau Campus, A
North Dakota State College of Science, A
Sitting Bull College, A
Trinity Bible College, A
Turtle Mountain Community College, A
University of North Dakota, B
Williston State College, A

Ohio

Antioch University McGregor, B
Ashland University, AB
Bowling Green State University, B
Bowling Green State University-Firelands College, A
Capital University, B
Chatfield College, A
Cincinnati State Technical and Community
    College, A
Clark State Community College, A
Cleveland State University, B
College of Mount St. Joseph, B
Columbus State Community College, A
Cuyahoga Community College, A
Defiance College, B
Edison State Community College, A
Kent State University, AB
Kent State University, Ashtabula Campus, A
Kent State University, East Liverpool Campus, A
Kent State University, Geauga Campus, A
Kent State University, Salem Campus, A
Kent State University, Stark Campus, A
Kent State University, Trumbull Campus, A
Kent State University, Tuscarawas Campus, AB
Lakeland Community College, A
Lorain County Community College, A

Lourdes College, AB
Malone College, B
Marietta College, AB
Miami University-Middletown Campus, A
Ohio Dominican University, B
The Ohio State University at Lima, A
The Ohio State University-Mansfield Campus, A
The Ohio State University at Marion, A
The Ohio State University-Newark Campus, A
Ohio University, AB
Ohio University-Chillicothe, AB
Ohio University-Eastern, AB
Ohio University-Lancaster, AB
Ohio University-Southern Campus, A
Ohio University-Zanesville, AB
Sinclair Community College, A
Southern State Community College, A
Union Institute & University, B
The University of Akron, AB
The University of Akron-Wayne College, A
University of Cincinnati, AB
University of Cincinnati Clermont College, A
University of Cincinnati Raymond Walters College, A
The University of Toledo, AB
Urbana University, AB
Walsh University, AB
Washington State Community College, A
Wilberforce University, B
Wilmington College, B
Wittenberg University, B
Wright State University, B
Wright State University, Lake Campus, A
Xavier University, AB
Youngstown State University, AB

Oklahoma

Bacone College, A
Hillsdale Free Will Baptist College, A
Langston University, B
Mid-America Christian University, A
Murray State College, A
Northern Oklahoma College, A
Oklahoma Christian University, B
Oklahoma City Community College, A
Oklahoma City University, B
Oklahoma State University, B
Oklahoma Wesleyan University, A
Oral Roberts University, B
Redlands Community College, A
Rogers State University, AB
Rose State College, A
St. Gregory's University, AB
Seminole State College, A
Southern Nazarene University, B
Tulsa Community College, A
University of Central Oklahoma, B
University of Oklahoma, B
University of Tulsa, B
Western Oklahoma State College, A

Oregon

Blue Mountain Community College, A
Cascade College, B
Central Oregon Community College, A
Chemeketa Community College, A
Clackamas Community College, A
Clatsop Community College, A
Concordia University, AB
Corban College, B
Eastern Oregon University, B
Lane Community College, A
Linn-Benton Community College, A
Mount Angel Seminary, B
Mt. Hood Community College, A
Northwest Christian College, B
Oregon Coast Community College, A
Oregon Institute of Technology, A
Oregon State University, B
Pacific University, B
Portland Community College, A
Portland State University, B
Rogue Community College, A
Southern Oregon University, B
Southwestern Oregon Community College, A
Tillamook Bay Community College, A
Treasure Valley Community College, A

Umpqua Community College, A
University of Oregon, B
Warner Pacific College, A
Western Oregon University, A

Pennsylvania

Alvernia College, AB
Arcadia University, B
Bryn Athyn College of the New Church, A
Bucks County Community College, A
Butler County Community College, A
Cabrini College, B
California University of Pennsylvania, B
Carlow University, B
Carnegie Mellon University, B
Cedar Crest College, B
Chestnut Hill College, B
Clarion University of Pennsylvania, AB
College Misericordia, B
Community College of Allegheny County, A
Community College of Beaver County, A
Community College of Philadelphia, A
Delaware County Community College, A
DeSales University, B
Duquesne University, B
East Stroudsburg University of Pennsylvania, B
Eastern University, B
Edinboro University of Pennsylvania, AB
Gannon University, AB
Geneva College, B
Gettysburg College, B
Gwynedd-Mercy College, A
Harcum College, A
Harrisburg Area Community College, A
Holy Family University, B
Juniata College, B
Keystone College, A
Kutztown University of Pennsylvania, B
La Roche College, B
La Salle University, AB
Lackawanna College, A
Lebanon Valley College, AB
Lehigh Carbon Community College, A
Lock Haven University of Pennsylvania, B
Luzerne County Community College, A
Manor College, A
Mansfield University of Pennsylvania, B
Mercyhurst College, AB
Millersville University of Pennsylvania, A
Montgomery County Community College, A
Mount Aloysius College, AB
Neumann College, AB
Northampton County Area Community College, A
Pennsylvania College of Technology, A
Pennsylvania Highland Community College, A
The Pennsylvania State University Abington
    College, AB
The Pennsylvania State University Altoona
    College, AB
The Pennsylvania State University Beaver Campus
    of the Commonwealth College, AB
The Pennsylvania State University Berks Campus of
    the Berks-Lehigh Valley College, AB
The Pennsylvania State University Delaware County
    Campus of the Commonwealth College, AB
The Pennsylvania State University DuBois Campus
    of the Commonwealth College, AB
The Pennsylvania State University at Erie, The
    Behrend College, AB
The Pennsylvania State University Fayette Campus
    of the Commonwealth College, AB
The Pennsylvania State University Harrisburg
    Campus, A
The Pennsylvania State University Hazleton
    Campus of the Commonwealth College, A
The Pennsylvania State University, Lehigh Valley
    Campus of the Berks-Lehigh Valley College, AB
The Pennsylvania State University McKeesport
    Campus of the Commonwealth College, AB
The Pennsylvania State University Mont Alto
    Campus of the Commonwealth College, AB
The Pennsylvania State University New Kensington
    Campus of the Commonwealth College, AB
The Pennsylvania State University Schuylkill
    Campus of the Capital College, AB

The Pennsylvania State University Shenango
    Campus of the Commonwealth College, AB
The Pennsylvania State University University Park
    Campus, AB
The Pennsylvania State University Wilkes-Barre
    Campus of the Commonwealth College, AB
The Pennsylvania State University Worthington
    Scranton Campus of the Commonwealth
    College, AB
The Pennsylvania State University York Campus of
    the Commonwealth College, AB
Reading Area Community College, A
Saint Joseph's University, AB
Saint Vincent College, B
Thiel College, A
University of Pennsylvania, B
University of Pittsburgh, B
University of Pittsburgh at Bradford, A
University of Pittsburgh at Titusville, A
Valley Forge Military College, A
Villanova University, AB
Washington & Jefferson College, B
Waynesburg College, A
West Chester University of Pennsylvania, B
Westmoreland County Community College, A
Wilkes University, B
Wilson College, A
York College of Pennsylvania, A

Puerto Rico

American University of Puerto Rico, A
Caribbean University, B
Pontifical Catholic University of Puerto Rico, B
Technological College of San Juan, A
Universidad del Este, A
Universidad del Turabo, B
University of Puerto Rico, Aguadilla University
    College, A
University of Puerto Rico at Ponce, A

Rhode Island

Community College of Rhode Island, A
Providence College, B
Rhode Island College, B
Roger Williams University, AB
Salve Regina University, AB
University of Rhode Island, B

South Carolina

Aiken Technical College, A
Anderson University, A
Central Carolina Technical College, A
Charleston Southern University, A
Coastal Carolina University, B
Columbia College, B
Florence-Darlington Technical College, A
Francis Marion University, B
Greenville Technical College, A
Lander University, B
Limestone College, AB
Midlands Technical College, A
Morris College, B
North Greenville College, A
Northeastern Technical College, A
Orangeburg-Calhoun Technical College, A
Piedmont Technical College, A
Spartanburg Methodist College, A
Spartanburg Technical College, A
Technical College of the Lowcountry, A
Tri-County Technical College, A
Trident Technical College, A
University of South Carolina, B
University of South Carolina Aiken, B
University of South Carolina Beaufort, AB
University of South Carolina Lancaster, A
University of South Carolina Salkehatchie, A
University of South Carolina Sumter, A
University of South Carolina Union, A
Williamsburg Technical College, A
York Technical College, A

South Dakota

Augustana College, B
Dakota Wesleyan University, A
Kilian Community College, A
Mount Marty College, AB

National American University (Rapid City), A
Northern State University, A
Oglala Lakota College, A
Sinte Gleska University, A
Sisseton-Wahpeton Community College, A
University of Sioux Falls, B
The University of South Dakota, B

Tennessee

Aquinas College, A
Austin Peay State University, A
Bethel College, B
Bryan College, AB
Carson-Newman College, B
Chattanooga State Technical Community College, A
Cleveland State Community College, A
Columbia State Community College, A
Crichton College, B
Cumberland University, AB
Dyersburg State Community College, A
Freed-Hardeman University, B
Jackson State Community College, A
Lambuth University, B
Lincoln Memorial University, B
Lipscomb University, B
Martin Methodist College, A
Middle Tennessee State University, B
Motlow State Community College, A
Northeast State Technical Community College, A
Pellissippi State Technical Community College, A
Roane State Community College, A
Tennessee State University, B
University of Memphis, B
Volunteer State Community College, A
Walters State Community College, A

Texas

Abilene Christian University, B
Alvin Community College, A
Amarillo College, A
Angelina College, A
Angelo State University, B
Austin Community College, A
Brazosport College, A
Brookhaven College, A
Cedar Valley College, A
Central Texas College, A
Clarendon College, A
Coastal Bend College, A
College of the Mainland, A
The College of Saint Thomas More, AB
Collin County Community College District, A
Concordia University at Austin, AB
Dallas Baptist University, AB
Del Mar College, A
East Texas Baptist University, AB
Eastfield College, A
El Centro College, A
El Paso Community College, A
Frank Phillips College, A
Galveston College, A
Grayson County College, A
Hill College of the Hill Junior College District, A
Houston Baptist University, B
Houston Community College System, A
Howard Payne University, B
Jacksonville College, A
Lamar State College-Orange, A
Lamar State College-Port Arthur, A
Lamar University, B
Laredo Community College, A
Lee College, A
Lon Morris College, A
McLennan Community College, A
Midland College, A
Midwestern State University, AB
Mountain View College, A
North Central Texas College, A
North Harris College, A
North Lake College, A
Northwest Vista College, A
Odessa College, A
Our Lady of the Lake University of San Antonio, B
Palo Alto College, A
Paris Junior College, A
Ranger College, A

Richland College, A
St. Edward's University, B
St. Philip's College, A
San Antonio College, A
Schreiner University, AB
South Plains College, A
South Texas College, A
Southwest Texas Junior College, A
Southwestern Christian College, A
Tarleton State University, B
Tarrant County College District, A
Temple College, A
Texarkana College, A
Texas A&M University-Commerce, B
Texas Christian University, B
Texas Southern University, B
Texas Southmost College, A
Texas Tech University, B
Trinity Valley Community College, A
Tyler Junior College, A
University of Houston-Downtown, B
University of the Incarnate Word, B
University of St. Thomas, B
The University of Texas at Austin, B
The University of Texas at Brownsville, B
The University of Texas at Tyler, B
Vernon College, A
Victoria College, A
Weatherford College, A
Western Texas College, A

Utah

Brigham Young University, B
College of Eastern Utah, A
Dixie State College of Utah, A
LDS Business College, A
Snow College, A
University of Utah, B
Utah State University, B
Weber State University, AB

Vermont

Bennington College, B
Burlington College, AB
Champlain College, A
College of St. Joseph, AB
Community College of Vermont, A
Goddard College, B
Green Mountain College, B
Johnson State College, AB
Landmark College, A
Lyndon State College, AB
Middlebury College, B
Southern Vermont College, AB
Sterling College, AB
University of Vermont, B

Virginia

Averett University, AB
Bluefield College, B
Bridgewater College, B
Central Virginia Community College, A
Christendom College, A
Dabney S. Lancaster Community College, A
Danville Community College, A
Eastern Mennonite University, B
Eastern Shore Community College, A
Ferrum College, B
George Mason University, B
Germanna Community College, A
J. Sargeant Reynolds Community College, A
James Madison University, B
John Tyler Community College, A
Longwood University, B
Lord Fairfax Community College, A
Marymount University, AB
Mountain Empire Community College, A
New River Community College, A
Northern Virginia Community College, A
Patrick Henry College, B
Patrick Henry Community College, A
Paul D. Camp Community College, A
Piedmont Virginia Community College, A
Radford University, B
Randolph-Macon Woman's College, B
Rappahannock Community College, A

Richard Bland College of The College of William
    and Mary, A
Saint Paul's College, B
Shenandoah University, B
Southern Virginia University, B
Southside Virginia Community College, A
Southwest Virginia Community College, A
Sweet Briar College, A
Thomas Nelson Community College, A
Tidewater Community College, A
University of Mary Washington, B
University of Virginia, B
The University of Virginia's College at Wise, B
Virginia Highlands Community College, A
Virginia Intermont College, AB
Virginia State University, B
Virginia Wesleyan College, B
Virginia Western Community College, A
Wytheville Community College, A

Washington

Antioch University Seattle, B
Bellevue Community College, A
Big Bend Community College, A
Cascadia Community College, A
Centralia College, A
Clark College, A
Columbia Basin College, A
Eastern Washington University, B
Edmonds Community College, A
Everett Community College, A
The Evergreen State College, B
Gonzaga University, B
Grays Harbor College, A
Green River Community College, A
Heritage University, A
Lower Columbia College, A
North Seattle Community College, A
Olympic College, A
Pierce College, A
Seattle Central Community College, A
Seattle Pacific University, B
Seattle University, B
Shoreline Community College, A
Skagit Valley College, A
South Puget Sound Community College, A
South Seattle Community College, A
Spokane Community College, A
Spokane Falls Community College, A
Tacoma Community College, A
University of Washington, B
Walla Walla Community College, A
Wenatchee Valley College, A
Western Washington University, B
Whatcom Community College, A
Yakima Valley Community College, A

West Virginia

Alderson-Broaddus College, B
Bluefield State College, A
Community & Technical College at West Virginia
    University Institute of Technology, A
Eastern West Virginia Community and Technical
    College, A
Fairmont State University, A
Glenville State College, A
Marshall Community and Technical College, A
Mountain State University, AB
New River Community and Technical College, A
Ohio Valley University, AB
Potomac State College of West Virginia
    University, A
Salem International University, AB
Southern West Virginia Community and Technical
    College, A
West Virginia Northern Community College, A
West Virginia State University, A
West Virginia University, B
West Virginia University at Parkersburg, A
Wheeling Jesuit University, B

Wisconsin

Alverno College, AB
Cardinal Stritch University, AB
College of Menominee Nation, A
Concordia University Wisconsin, B

Edgewood College, AB
Lac Courte Oreilles Ojibwa Community College, A
Madison Area Technical College, A
Maranatha Baptist Bible College, A
Marian College of Fond du Lac, B
Milwaukee Area Technical College, A
Mount Mary College, B
Nicolet Area Technical College, A
University of Wisconsin-Baraboo/Sauk County, A
University of Wisconsin-Barron County, A
University of Wisconsin-Eau Claire, A
University of Wisconsin-Fond du Lac, A
University of Wisconsin-Fox Valley, A
University of Wisconsin-Manitowoc, A
University of Wisconsin-Marathon County, A
University of Wisconsin-Marinette, A
University of Wisconsin-Marshfield/Wood County, A
University of Wisconsin-Oshkosh, AB
University of Wisconsin-Platteville, AB
University of Wisconsin-Richland, A
University of Wisconsin-River Falls, B
University of Wisconsin-Rock County, A
University of Wisconsin-Sheboygan, A
University of Wisconsin-Stevens Point, A
University of Wisconsin-Washington County, A
University of Wisconsin-Waukesha, A
University of Wisconsin-Whitewater, AB
Viterbo University, B

Wyoming

Casper College, A
Eastern Wyoming College, A
Northwest College, A
Sheridan College-Sheridan and Gillette, A
Western Wyoming Community College, A

Alberta

Athabasca University, B
Taylor University College and Seminary, B
University of Alberta, B
University of Calgary, B

British Columbia

Malaspina University-College, B
Simon Fraser University, B
Trinity Western University, B
The University of British Columbia, B
University of Northern British Columbia, B
University of Victoria, B

Manitoba

Brandon University, B
Providence College and Theological Seminary, B

New Brunswick

Mount Allison University, B
Université de Moncton, B
University of New Brunswick Fredericton, B

Nova Scotia

Cape Breton University, B
Mount Saint Vincent University, B
St. Francis Xavier University, B

Ontario

Brock University, B
Lakehead University, B
Laurentian University, B
Nipissing University, B
Redeemer University College, B
Trent University, B
Tyndale University College & Seminary, B
University of Ottawa, B
University of Waterloo, B

York University, B

Quebec

Bishop's University, B
Télé-université, B

Saskatchewan

University of Regina, B

LIBERAL STUDIES

Alabama

Auburn University Montgomery, M
Jacksonville State University, M
Spring Hill College, M

Arizona

Northern Arizona University, M

Arkansas

Arkansas Tech University, M
Henderson State University, M
University of Arkansas at Little Rock, M

California

California State University, Sacramento, M
Occidental College, M
Saint Mary's College of California, M
San Diego State University, M

Colorado

Regis University, MO
University of Denver, M

Connecticut

Albertus Magnus College, M
Sacred Heart University, M
Wesleyan University, MO

Delaware

University of Delaware, M

District of Columbia

Georgetown University, M

Florida

Florida Atlantic University, M
Rollins College, M
University of Central Florida, M
University of Miami, M
University of South Florida, M

Georgia

Armstrong Atlantic State University, M

Illinois

Bradley University, M
Concordia University, M
DePaul University, M
Lake Forest College, M
North Central College, M
Northwestern University, M

Indiana

Indiana University Kokomo, M
Indiana University-Purdue University Fort Wayne, M
Indiana University Southeast, M
University of Southern Indiana, M
Valparaiso University, MO

Kansas

Baker University, M
Fort Hays State University, M
Washburn University, M
Wichita State University, M

Kentucky

Northern Kentucky University, M

Louisiana

Louisiana State University and Agricultural and
    Mechanical College, M

Louisiana State University in Shreveport, M
Tulane University, M

Maine

University of Maine, M

Maryland

College of Notre Dame of Maryland, M
The Johns Hopkins University, M
McDaniel College, M
St. John's College, M
Towson University, M

Massachusetts

Boston University, M
Clark University, M
Elms College, M
Harvard University, M

Michigan

Madonna University, M
Oakland University, M
University of Detroit Mercy, M
University of Michigan-Dearborn, M

Minnesota

Hamline University, MO
Minnesota State University Moorhead, M
University of Minnesota, Duluth, M

Mississippi

Mississippi College, M

Nebraska

Creighton University, M

New Hampshire

Dartmouth College, M
University of New Hampshire, M

New Jersey

Kean University, M
Monmouth University, M
Ramapo College of New Jersey, M
Rutgers, The State University of New Jersey,
  Camden, M
Rutgers, The State University of New Jersey,
  Newark, M
Thomas Edison State College, M,

New Mexico

St. John's College, M

New York

Brooklyn College of the City University of New
  York, M
College of Staten Island of the City University of
  New York, M
Dowling College, M
Excelsior College, M
Fordham University, M
Manhattanville College, M
Nazareth College of Rochester, M
Queens College of the City University of New
  York, M
Skidmore College, M
State University of New York College at
  Brockport, M
State University of New York Empire State
  College, M
State University of New York at Plattsburgh, M
Stony Brook University, State University of New
  York, M
University at Albany, State University of New
  York, M

North Carolina

Duke University, M
North Carolina State University, M
The University of North Carolina at Asheville, M
The University of North Carolina at Charlotte, M
The University of North Carolina at Greensboro, M
The University of North Carolina Wilmington, M

Wake Forest University, M

Ohio

Antioch University McGregor, M
Kent State University, M
Marietta College, M
The University of Findlay, M
The University of Toledo, M
Ursuline College, M

Oklahoma

Oklahoma City University, M
University of Oklahoma, M

Oregon

Lewis & Clark College, M
Marylhurst University, M
Reed College, M

Pennsylvania

Alvernia College, M
Duquesne University, M
Lock Haven University of Pennsylvania, M
Temple University, M
University of Pennsylvania, M
Villanova University, M
Widener University, M

South Carolina

Converse College, M
Winthrop University, M

Tennessee

Christian Brothers University, M
East Tennessee State University, M
University of Memphis, M
Vanderbilt University, M

Texas

Abilene Christian University, M
Dallas Baptist University, M
Houston Baptist University, M
St. Edward's University, MO
Texas Christian University, M
University of St. Thomas, M

Virginia

George Mason University, M
Hollins University, MO
University of Richmond, M

West Virginia

West Virginia University, M

Wisconsin

University of Wisconsin-Milwaukee, M

British Columbia

Simon Fraser University, M

Ontario

York University, M

LIBRARY ASSISTANT/TECHNICIAN

Arizona

Northland Pioneer College, A

California

Citrus College, A

Illinois

Black Hawk College, A
College of DuPage, A

Indiana

Ivy Tech Community College-Bloomington, A
Ivy Tech Community College-Columbus, A
Ivy Tech Community College-East Central, A
Ivy Tech Community College-Kokomo, A
Ivy Tech Community College-North Central, A

Ivy Tech Community College-Northeast, A
Ivy Tech Community College-Northwest, A
Ivy Tech Community College-Southeast, A
Ivy Tech Community College-Southern Indiana, A
Ivy Tech Community College-Southwest, A
Ivy Tech Community College-Wabash Valley, A
Ivy Tech Community College-Whitewater, A

Maine

The University of Maine at Augusta, A

Michigan

Oakland Community College, A

New Mexico

Clovis Community College, A
Northern New Mexico Community College, A

Ohio

Ohio Dominican University, A

Washington

Spokane Falls Community College, A

LIBRARY SCIENCE

Alabama

Lawson State Community College, A
The University of Alabama, MD
Wallace State Community College, A

Arizona

Mesa Community College, A
The University of Arizona, MD

Arkansas

Southern Arkansas University-Magnolia, M
University of Central Arkansas, M

California

Azusa Pacific University, M
Citrus College, A
City College of San Francisco, A
Cuesta College, A
Fresno City College, A
Fullerton College, A
Hartnell College, A
Los Angeles Valley College, A
Merced College, A
Oxnard College, A
Palomar College, A
Pasadena City College, A
Sacramento City College, A
San Jose State University, M
Santa Ana College, A
University of California, Los Angeles, BMDO

Colorado

University of Denver, M

Connecticut

Southern Connecticut State University, BMO

District of Columbia

The Catholic University of America, MO
University of the District of Columbia, AB

Florida

Florida State University, MDO
Indian River Community College, A

University of South Florida, M

Georgia

Clark Atlanta University, MO
Valdosta State University, M

Hawaii

University of Hawaii at Manoa, MDO

Idaho

College of Southern Idaho, A

Illinois

Chicago State University, M
City Colleges of Chicago, Wilbur Wright College, A
College of DuPage, A
Dominican University, MO
Illinois Central College, A
University of Illinois at Urbana-Champaign, MDO

Indiana

Indiana University Bloomington, MDO
Indiana University-Purdue University
   Indianapolis, MO

Iowa

The University of Iowa, MO

Kansas

Allen County Community College, A
Colby Community College, A
Emporia State University, MD
Highland Community College, A

Kentucky

Murray State University, B
University of Kentucky, M

Louisiana

Louisiana State University and Agricultural and
   Mechanical College, MO

Maine

The University of Maine at Augusta, B

Maryland

McDaniel College, M
University of Maryland, College Park, O

Massachusetts

Simmons College, MDO

Michigan

Hope College, B
University of Michigan, MD
Wayne State University, MO

Minnesota

Bethel University, B
College of St. Catherine, M
Northwest Technical College, A
St. Cloud State University, B

Mississippi

Copiah-Lincoln Community College, A
East Central Community College, A
Itawamba Community College, A
Northeast Mississippi Community College, A
University of Southern Mississippi, BMO

Missouri

Central Missouri State University, MO
East Central College, A

University of Missouri-Columbia, MDO

Montana

University of Great Falls, B

Nebraska

Chadron State College, B
University of Nebraska at Omaha, B

New Jersey

Brookdale Community College, A
Rowan University, M
Rutgers, The State University of New Jersey, New
   Brunswick/Piscataway, M

New Mexico

Doña Ana Branch Community College, A

New York

Long Island University, C.W. Post Campus, MDO
Pratt Institute, MO
Queens College of the City University of New
   York, MO
St. John's University, BMO
State University of New York at Buffalo, MO
Syracuse University, MO
University at Albany, State University of New
   York, MDO

North Carolina

Appalachian State University, BMO
East Carolina University, MO
Lenoir Community College, A
North Carolina Central University, M
The University of North Carolina at Chapel
   Hill, MDO
The University of North Carolina at Greensboro, M

Ohio

Kent State University, M
Ohio University-Eastern, B
University of Cincinnati Raymond Walters College, A
Wright State University, M

Oklahoma

Northeastern State University, B
Rose State College, A
Tulsa Community College, A
University of Oklahoma, BMO

Oregon

Portland Community College, A

Pennsylvania

Clarion University of Pennsylvania, BMO
Community College of Philadelphia, A
Drexel University, MDO
Gratz College, O
Kutztown University of Pennsylvania, BMO
Mansfield University of Pennsylvania, M
Marywood University, M
University of Pittsburgh, MDO

Puerto Rico

Inter American University of Puerto Rico, San
   Germán Campus, M
University of Puerto Rico, Río Piedras, MO

Rhode Island

University of Rhode Island, M

South Carolina

University of South Carolina, MO

Tennessee

Tennessee Technological University, M
Trevecca Nazarene University, M

Texas

Brazosport College, A
Palo Alto College, A
Sam Houston State University, M
Texas Woman's University, MD
University of Houston-Clear Lake, BM

University of North Texas, BMD
The University of Texas at Austin, MD

Virginia

Longwood University, B
Old Dominion University, M

Washington

Highline Community College, A
University of Washington, MD

West Virginia

Concord University, B
Mountain State University, AB

Wisconsin

University of Wisconsin-Madison, MDO
University of Wisconsin-Milwaukee, MO

Alberta

University of Alberta, M

British Columbia

The University of British Columbia, MDO

Nova Scotia

Dalhousie University, MO

Ontario

University of Toronto, MDO
The University of Western Ontario, MD

Quebec

McGill University, MDO
Université de Montréal, MD

LICENSED PRACTICAL/VOCATIONAL NURSE TRAINING

Alabama

Chattahoochee Valley Community College, A
George C. Wallace Community College, A
George Corley Wallace State Community College, A
James H. Faulkner State Community College, A
Northwest-Shoals Community College, A
Wallace State Community College, A

Arizona

Arizona Western College, A
Central Arizona College, A
Northland Pioneer College, A

Arkansas

East Arkansas Community College, A
Ouachita Technical College, A
Phillips Community College of the University of
   Arkansas, A
University of Arkansas Community College at
   Morrilton, A

California

Allan Hancock College, A
Butte College, A
Cerro Coso Community College, A
Citrus College, A
City College of San Francisco, A
College of the Canyons, A
Contra Costa College, A
De Anza College, A
El Camino College, A
Feather River College, A
Fresno City College, A
Gavilan College, A
Glendale Community College, A
Imperial Valley College, A
Lassen Community College District, A
Los Angeles Valley College, A
Merced College, A
Merritt College, A
MiraCosta College, A
Mission College, A

Pasadena City College, A
Porterville College, A
Riverside Community College District, A
Sacramento City College, A
San Diego City College, A
San Joaquin Delta College, A
San Joaquin Valley College, A
Santa Barbara City College, A
Sierra College, A
Yuba College, A

Colorado

Colorado Mountain College, A
Community College of Denver, A
Lamar Community College, A
Northeastern Junior College, A
Trinidad State Junior College, A

Delaware

Delaware Technical & Community College, Jack F.
  Owens Campus, A
Delaware Technical & Community College, Terry
  Campus, A

District of Columbia

University of the District of Columbia, A

Florida

Daytona Beach Community College, A
Gulf Coast College, A
Indian River Community College, A

Georgia

Athens Technical College, A
Atlanta Metropolitan College, A
Bainbridge College, A
Darton College, A
Georgia Southwestern State University, A
Gordon College, A

Hawaii

Hawaii Community College, A

Idaho

Lewis-Clark State College, A
North Idaho College, A

Illinois

Black Hawk College, A
Carl Sandburg College, A
Danville Area Community College, A
Elgin Community College, A
Heartland Community College, A
Illinois Eastern Community Colleges, Olney Central
  College, A
John A. Logan College, A
Lincoln College, A
Lincoln College-Normal, A
Oakton Community College, A
Southeastern Illinois College, A
Triton College, A
William Rainey Harper College, A

Indiana

Ivy Tech Community College-Southeast, A
Vincennes University, A

Iowa

Clinton Community College, A
Des Moines Area Community College, A
Indian Hills Community College, A
Iowa Central Community College, A
Iowa Western Community College, A
Kirkwood Community College, A
Marshalltown Community College, A
Muscatine Community College, A
North Iowa Area Community College, A
Northwest Iowa Community College, A
Scott Community College, A
Southeastern Community College, North Campus, A
Southeastern Community College, South
  Campus, A

Southwestern Community College, A

Kansas

Central Christian College of Kansas, A
Coffeyville Community College, A
Colby Community College, A
Dodge City Community College, A
Johnson County Community College, A
Manhattan Area Technical College, A
Neosho County Community College, A
Seward County Community College, A

Kentucky

Hopkinsville Community College, A

Louisiana

Delta College of Arts and Technology, A
Elaine P. Nunez Community College, A

Maine

Eastern Maine Community College, A
Southern Maine Community College, A

Maryland

College of Southern Maryland, A
Howard Community College, A

Massachusetts

Mount Wachusett Community College, A

Michigan

Alpena Community College, A
Bay de Noc Community College, A
Delta College, A
Gogebic Community College, A
Grand Rapids Community College, A
Jackson Community College, A
Kellogg Community College, A
Kirtland Community College, A
Lansing Community College, A
Mid Michigan Community College, A
Oakland Community College, A
West Shore Community College, A

Minnesota

Alexandria Technical College, A
Dakota County Technical College, A
Itasca Community College, A
Minnesota State College-Southeast Technical, A
Minnesota State Community and Technical
  College-Fergus Falls, A
Northland Community and Technical College-Thief
  River Falls, A
Northwest Technical College, A
Ridgewater College, A
St. Cloud Technical College, A

Mississippi

Coahoma Community College, A
Hinds Community College, A
Jones County Junior College, A
Northwest Mississippi Community College, A

Missouri

Jefferson College, A
Mineral Area College, A
State Fair Community College, A

Montana

Montana State University-Billings, A
Montana State University-Great Falls College of
  Technology, A
The University of Montana-Helena College of
  Technology, A
The University of Montana-Missoula, A

Nebraska

Central Community College-Columbus Campus, A
Central Community College-Grand Island
  Campus, A
Grace University, A
Metropolitan Community College, A
Mid-Plains Community College, A
Northeast Community College, A

Southeast Community College, Beatrice Campus, A

Nevada

Community College of Southern Nevada, A

New Jersey

Union County College, A

New Mexico

Luna Community College, A
New Mexico Junior College, A

New York

Eugenio María de Hostos Community College of the
  City University of New York, A
Maria College, A
Medgar Evers College of the City University of New
  York, A

North Carolina

Carteret Community College, A
Central Piedmont Community College, A
College of The Albemarle, A
Durham Technical Community College, A
ECPI Technical College, A
Edgecombe Community College, A
Isothermal Community College, A
Rockingham Community College, A
Sampson Community College, A
Sandhills Community College, A
Southwestern Community College, A
Surry Community College, A
Vance-Granville Community College, A

North Dakota

Bismarck State College, A
Dickinson State University, A
Fort Berthold Community College, A
Lake Region State College, A
North Dakota State College of Science, A
United Tribes Technical College, A
Williston State College, A

Ohio

Belmont Technical College, A
Clark State Community College, A
Columbus State Community College, A
Hocking College, A
Jefferson Community College, A
Washington State Community College, A

Oregon

Blue Mountain Community College, A
Central Oregon Community College, A
Chemeketa Community College, A

Pennsylvania

Community College of Allegheny County, A
Community College of Beaver County, A
Lehigh Carbon Community College, A
Pennsylvania College of Technology, A
Reading Area Community College, A
Westmoreland County Community College, A

South Carolina

Horry-Georgetown Technical College, A
Midlands Technical College, A
Technical College of the Lowcountry, A
York Technical College, A

South Dakota

Lake Area Technical Institute, A

Texas

Amarillo College, A
Angelina College, A
Central Texas College, A
Coastal Bend College, A
El Centro College, A
Galveston College, A
Hill College of the Hill Junior College District, A
Howard College, A
Kingwood College, A
Lamar State College-Port Arthur, A

Lamar University, A
Lee College, A
Navarro College, A
St. Philip's College, A
South Plains College, A
Temple College, A
Texarkana College, A
Trinity Valley Community College, A
Tyler Junior College, A
Vernon College, A
Western Texas College, A

Vermont

Vermont Technical College, A

Virginia

Jefferson College of Health Sciences, B
New River Community College, A
Virginia State University, A

Washington

Bates Technical College, A
Big Bend Community College, A
Centralia College, A
Everett Community College, A
Green River Community College, A
Lower Columbia College, A
North Seattle Community College, A
Olympic College, A
Skagit Valley College, A
South Puget Sound Community College, A
Spokane Community College, A
Walla Walla Community College, A
Wenatchee Valley College, A

Wisconsin

College of Menominee Nation, A
Milwaukee Area Technical College, A
Moraine Park Technical College, A
Northcentral Technical College, A
Northeast Wisconsin Technical College, A
Southwest Wisconsin Technical College, A

Wyoming

Northwest College, A
Western Wyoming Community College, A

British Columbia

Thompson Rivers University, A

Ontario

The University of Western Ontario, B

LIMNOLOGY

Alaska

University of Alaska Fairbanks, MD

Florida

University of Florida, MD

New Jersey

William Paterson University of New Jersey, M

Texas

Baylor University, M

Wisconsin

University of Wisconsin-Madison, MD

LINEWORKER

Indiana

Ivy Tech Community College-Lafayette, A

Iowa

Northwest Iowa Community College, A

Minnesota

Dakota County Technical College, A

Missouri

Linn State Technical College, A

Nebraska

Northeast Community College, A

North Dakota

Bismarck State College, A

Pennsylvania

Lehigh Carbon Community College, A

South Dakota

Mitchell Technical Institute, A

Utah

Utah Valley State College, A

Washington

Lower Columbia College, A

Wisconsin

Northeast Wisconsin Technical College, A

LINGUISTIC, COMPARATIVE, AND RELATED LANGUAGE STUDIES AND SERVICES

California

University of California, Los Angeles, B

Utah

Brigham Young University, B

LINGUISTICS

Alaska

University of Alaska Fairbanks, BM

Arizona

Northern Arizona University, MDO
The University of Arizona, BMD

California

Biola University, M
California State University, Chico, B
California State University, Dominguez Hills, B
California State University, Fresno, BM
California State University, Fullerton, BM
California State University, Long Beach, M
California State University, Northridge, BM
Foothill College, A
Pitzer College, B
Pomona College, B
San Diego State University, BMO
San Francisco State University, M
San Jose State University, BMO
Scripps College, B
Stanford University, BMD
University of California, Berkeley, BMD
University of California, Davis, BM
University of California, Irvine, B
University of California, Los Angeles, BMD
University of California, Riverside, B
University of California, San Diego, BD
University of California, Santa Barbara, BDO
University of California, Santa Cruz, BMD
University of Southern California, BMD

Colorado

University of Colorado at Boulder, BMD

Connecticut

University of Connecticut, BMD
Yale University, BD

Delaware

University of Delaware, BMD

District of Columbia

Gallaudet University, M
Georgetown University, BMDO

Florida

Florida Atlantic University, B
Florida International University, M
University of Florida, BMDO
University of South Florida, M

Georgia

Georgia State University, MD
University of Georgia, BMD

Hawaii

University of Hawaii at Hilo, B
University of Hawaii at Manoa, BMD

Illinois

Judson College, B
Moody Bible Institute, B
Northeastern Illinois University, BM
Northwestern University, BMDO
Southern Illinois University Carbondale, BM
University of Chicago, BMD
University of Illinois at Chicago, M
University of Illinois at Urbana-Champaign, BMD

Indiana

Ball State University, MD
Indiana State University, M
Indiana University Bloomington, BMDO
Purdue University, MD

Iowa

Central College, B
Iowa State University of Science and Technology, B
The University of Iowa, BMD

Kansas

University of Kansas, BMD

Kentucky

University of Kentucky, B

Louisiana

Louisiana State University and Agricultural and
    Mechanical College, MD
Tulane University, B

Maine

University of Southern Maine, B

Maryland

University of Maryland, Baltimore County, BM
University of Maryland, College Park, BMD

Massachusetts

Boston College, MO
Boston University, BMD
Brandeis University, B
Hampshire College, B
Harvard University, BMD
Massachusetts Institute of Technology, BMD
Northeastern University, B
University of Massachusetts Amherst, BMD
University of Massachusetts Boston, M
Wellesley College, B

Michigan

Eastern Michigan University, BM
Michigan State University, MD
Oakland University, BMO
University of Michigan, BMD
Wayne State University, BM

Minnesota

Crown College, B
Macalester College, B
St. Cloud State University, B

University of Minnesota, Twin Cities Campus, BMD

Mississippi

University of Mississippi, B

Missouri

University of Missouri-Columbia, B
University of Missouri-St. Louis, M

Montana

The University of Montana-Missoula, BM

New Hampshire

Dartmouth College, B
University of New Hampshire, BM

New Jersey

Montclair State University, BM
Rutgers, The State University of New Jersey, New
  Brunswick/Piscataway, BD

New Mexico

University of New Mexico, BMD

New York

Barnard College, B
Brooklyn College of the City University of New
  York, B
City College of the City University of New York, B
Columbia College, B
Cornell University, BMD
Hofstra University, M
Lehman College of the City University of New
  York, B
New York University, BMD
Queens College of the City University of New
  York, BM
State University of New York at Binghamton, B
State University of New York at Buffalo, BMD
State University of New York at Oswego, B
Stony Brook University, State University of New
  York, BMD
Syracuse University, BM
University at Albany, State University of New York, B
University of Rochester, B

North Carolina

Duke University, B
The University of North Carolina at Chapel Hill, MD

North Dakota

University of North Dakota, M

Ohio

Cleveland State University, B
Miami University, B
Miami University Hamilton, B
The Ohio State University, BMD
Ohio University, BM
Ohio University-Eastern, B
University of Cincinnati, B
The University of Toledo, B
Wright State University, B

Oklahoma

Oklahoma Wesleyan University, AB
University of Oklahoma, B

Oregon

Portland State University, B
Reed College, B
University of Oregon, BMD

Pennsylvania

Carnegie Mellon University, MD
Indiana University of Pennsylvania, D
The Pennsylvania State University University Park
  Campus, D
Swarthmore College, B
Temple University, BM
University of Pennsylvania, BMD

University of Pittsburgh, BMD

Puerto Rico

Inter American University of Puerto Rico, San
  Germán Campus, B
University of Puerto Rico, Río Piedras, M

Rhode Island

Brown University, BMD

South Carolina

University of South Carolina, MDO

Tennessee

The University of Tennessee, D

Texas

Baylor University, B
Rice University, BMD
Texas Tech University, M
University of Houston, M
The University of Texas at Arlington, MD
The University of Texas at Austin, BMD
The University of Texas at El Paso, BM

Utah

Brigham Young University, BMO
University of Utah, BM

Vermont

Marlboro College, B

Virginia

The College of William and Mary, B
George Mason University, M
Old Dominion University, M
University of Virginia, M

Washington

University of Washington, BMD
Washington State University, B
Western Washington University, B

West Virginia

West Virginia University, M

Wisconsin

Lawrence University, B
University of Wisconsin-Madison, BMD
University of Wisconsin-Milwaukee, B

Alberta

University of Alberta, BMD
University of Calgary, BMD

British Columbia

Simon Fraser University, BMD
Trinity Western University, B
The University of British Columbia, BMD
University of Victoria, BMD

Manitoba

University of Manitoba, MD

New Brunswick

Université de Moncton, B
University of New Brunswick Fredericton, B

Newfoundland and Labrador

Memorial University of Newfoundland, BMD

Nova Scotia

Dalhousie University, B
Mount Saint Vincent University, B
University of King's College, B

Ontario

Brock University, B
Carleton University, BM
McMaster University, B
Queen's University at Kingston, B
University of Ottawa, BMD
University of Toronto, BMD

The University of Western Ontario, B
University of Windsor, B
York University, B

Quebec

Concordia University, BM
McGill University, BMD
Université Laval, BMD
Université de Montréal, BMDO
Université du Québec àChicoutimi, BM
Université du Québec àMontréal, BMD
Université de Sherbrooke, M

Saskatchewan

University of Regina, BM
University of Saskatchewan, B

LINGUISTICS OF ASL AND OTHER SIGN LANGUAGES

Ohio

Kent State University, B

LIVESTOCK MANAGEMENT

Kansas

Barton County Community College, A

Nebraska

Northeast Community College, A

Ohio

The Ohio State University Agricultural Technical
  Institute, A

Vermont

Sterling College, AB

LOGIC

Pennsylvania

Carnegie Mellon University, B
University of Pennsylvania, B

LOGISTICS AND MATERIALS MANAGEMENT

Alabama

Andrew Jackson University, M
Auburn University, B
Community College of the Air Force, A

Arizona

Arizona State University, D

Arkansas

University of Arkansas, BM

California

California State University, East Bay, M
Loyola Marymount University, M
Touro University International, M

Colorado

Colorado Technical University, M

Connecticut

University of New Haven, O

Delaware

Wilmington College, M

District of Columbia

The George Washington University, M

Florida

Florida Institute of Technology, M
Florida International University, B

Georgia

Athens Technical College, A
Chattahoochee Technical College, A

Georgia College & State University, M
Georgia Southern University, B

Illinois

Elmhurst College, BM
Prairie State College, A
Waubonsee Community College, A

Iowa

Iowa State University of Science and Technology, B

Maine

Maine Maritime Academy, BMO

Massachusetts

Massachusetts Institute of Technology, M
Northeastern University, B
Springfield Technical Community College, A

Michigan

Central Michigan University, B
Eastern Michigan University, M
Michigan State University, BM
Wayne State University, B
Western Michigan University, B

Minnesota

University of Minnesota, Twin Cities Campus, MD

Missouri

Park University, AB
University of Missouri-St. Louis, O

Nevada

University of Nevada, Reno, B

New Hampshire

University of New Hampshire, D

New Jersey

Rutgers, The State University of New Jersey,
Newark, D

New York

Clarkson University, B
Niagara University, B
St. John's University, B
State University of New York at Buffalo, M
Syracuse University, BD

North Dakota

North Dakota State University, D

Ohio

Bowling Green State University, B
Case Western Reserve University, M
Columbus State Community College, A
The Ohio State University, B
Sinclair Community College, A
The University of Akron, A
The University of Findlay, B
The University of Toledo, AB
Wright State University, BM

Oregon

Portland State University, B

Pennsylvania

Duquesne University, B
Lehigh Carbon Community College, A
The Pennsylvania State University Beaver Campus
of the Commonwealth College, B
The Pennsylvania State University Delaware County
Campus of the Commonwealth College, B
The Pennsylvania State University Fayette Campus
of the Commonwealth College, B
The Pennsylvania State University Hazleton
Campus of the Commonwealth College, B
The Pennsylvania State University, Lehigh Valley
Campus of the Berks-Lehigh Valley College, B
The Pennsylvania State University McKeesport
Campus of the Commonwealth College, B
The Pennsylvania State University New Kensington
Campus of the Commonwealth College, B

The Pennsylvania State University Schuylkill
Campus of the Capital College, B
The Pennsylvania State University Shenango
Campus of the Commonwealth College, B
The Pennsylvania State University University Park
Campus, MD
The Pennsylvania State University York Campus of
the Commonwealth College, B
Robert Morris University, B

Puerto Rico

Universidad del Turabo, M

Tennessee

The University of Tennessee, BMD

Texas

Houston Community College System, A
Lee College, A
University of Houston, M
University of North Texas, B
The University of Texas at Arlington, M

Utah

Brigham Young University, B
Weber State University, B

Virginia

George Mason University, M
Virginia Polytechnic Institute and State
University, MD

Washington

University of Washington, O

West Virginia

Mountain State University, B

Wisconsin

Gateway Technical College, A
Northeast Wisconsin Technical College, A
University of Wisconsin-Madison, M

Quebec

HEC Montreal, M

MACHINE SHOP
TECHNOLOGY/ASSISTANT

Alabama

Gadsden State Community College-Ayers
Campus, A

Arizona

Eastern Arizona College, A
Pima Community College, A

Arkansas

University of Arkansas Community College at
Hope, A

California

Modesto Junior College, A
Orange Coast College, A

Colorado

Pikes Peak Community College, A

Florida

Florida Community College at Jacksonville, A

Georgia

Dalton State College, A
Georgia Southwestern State University, A

Illinois

College of Lake County, A
Illinois Eastern Community Colleges, Wabash Valley
College, A

Indiana

Ivy Tech Community College-Central Indiana, A
Vincennes University, A

Iowa

North Iowa Area Community College, A
Northwest Iowa Community College, A

Louisiana

Delgado Community College, A

Michigan

Northwestern Michigan College, A
Southwestern Michigan College, A

Minnesota

Ridgewater College, A
Riverland Community College, A

Missouri

Metropolitan Community College-Business &
Technology College, A

New York

Corning Community College, A
Mohawk Valley Community College, A

North Carolina

Cape Fear Community College, A
Fayetteville Technical Community College, A
Pitt Community College, A

North Dakota

North Dakota State College of Science, A

Pennsylvania

Community College of Allegheny County, A
Johnson College, A
Pennsylvania College of Technology, A

South Dakota

Western Dakota Technical Institute, A

Texas

North Central Texas College, A

Wisconsin

Moraine Park Technical College, A
Northeast Wisconsin Technical College, A

MACHINE TOOL
TECHNOLOGY/MACHINIST

Alabama

Calhoun Community College, A
Gadsden State Community College-Ayers
Campus, A
George C. Wallace Community College, A
George Corley Wallace State Community College, A
H. Councill Trenholm State Technical College, A
J. F. Drake State Technical College, A
Shelton State Community College, A
Wallace State Community College, A

Alaska

University of Alaska Anchorage, Kenai Peninsula
College, A

Arkansas

Ouachita Technical College, A
University of Arkansas Community College at
Morrilton, A

California

Allan Hancock College, A
Bakersfield College, A
Cerritos College, A
Cerro Coso Community College, A
College of Marin, A
College of the Redwoods, A
College of San Mateo, A

Compton Community College, A
De Anza College, A
Fresno City College, A
Glendale Community College, A
Hartnell College, A
Laney College, A
Long Beach City College, A
Los Angeles Pierce College, A
Los Angeles Valley College, A
MiraCosta College, A
Modesto Junior College, A
Mt. San Antonio College, A
Napa Valley College, A
Orange Coast College, A
Oxnard College, A
Pasadena City College, A
Reedley College, A
San Bernardino Valley College, A
San Diego City College, A
San Joaquin Delta College, A
San Jose City College, A
Solano Community College, A
Ventura College, A
Yuba College, A

Colorado

Front Range Community College, A
Mesa State College, A
Pueblo Community College, A

Connecticut

Asnuntuck Community College, A

Georgia

Altamaha Technical College, A
Columbus Technical College, A
DeKalb Technical College, A
Georgia Southwestern State University, A
Gwinnett Technical College, A
Heart of Georgia Technical College, A
Valdosta Technical College, A
Waycross College, A

Idaho

Boise State University, A
Brigham Young University -Idaho, A
Idaho State University, A
North Idaho College, A

Illinois

Black Hawk College, A
City Colleges of Chicago, Richard J. Daley
    College, A
City Colleges of Chicago, Wilbur Wright College, A
College of DuPage, A
Elgin Community College, A
Heartland Community College, A
John A. Logan College, A
Kankakee Community College, A
Lewis and Clark Community College, A
Oakton Community College, A
Shawnee Community College, A
South Suburban College, A
Southwestern Illinois College, A
Triton College, A
Waubonsee Community College, A
William Rainey Harper College, A

Indiana

Ivy Tech Community College-Bloomington, A
Ivy Tech Community College-Central Indiana, A
Ivy Tech Community College-Columbus, A
Ivy Tech Community College-East Central, A
Ivy Tech Community College-Kokomo, A
Ivy Tech Community College-Lafayette, A
Ivy Tech Community College-North Central, A
Ivy Tech Community College-Northeast, A
Ivy Tech Community College-Northwest, A
Ivy Tech Community College-Southern Indiana, A
Ivy Tech Community College-Southwest, A
Ivy Tech Community College-Wabash Valley, A
Ivy Tech Community College-Whitewater, A

Vincennes University, A

Iowa

Clinton Community College, A
Des Moines Area Community College, A
Hawkeye Community College, A
Indian Hills Community College, A
Iowa Central Community College, A
Iowa Western Community College, A
Marshalltown Community College, A
Muscatine Community College, A
North Iowa Area Community College, A
Scott Community College, A
Southeastern Community College, North Campus, A
Western Iowa Tech Community College, A

Kansas

Coffeyville Community College, A
Cowley County Community College and Area
    Vocational-Technical School, A
Hutchinson Community College and Area Vocational
    School, A
Johnson County Community College, A

Kentucky

Somerset Community College, A

Louisiana

Delgado Community College, A

Maine

Central Maine Community College, A
Eastern Maine Community College, A
Kennebec Valley Community College, A
Southern Maine Community College, A

Massachusetts

Northern Essex Community College, A

Michigan

Bay de Noc Community College, A
Delta College, A
Ferris State University, A
Kalamazoo Valley Community College, A
Kellogg Community College, A
Lake Michigan College, A
Lansing Community College, A
Macomb Community College, A
Mid Michigan Community College, A
Muskegon Community College, A
Oakland Community College, A
St. Clair County Community College, A
Washtenaw Community College, A
West Shore Community College, A

Minnesota

Alexandria Technical College, A
Century College, A
Hennepin Technical College, A
Lake Superior College, A
Minnesota State College-Southeast Technical, A
Pine Technical College, A
St. Cloud Technical College, A
South Central Technical College, A

Mississippi

Hinds Community College, A
Meridian Community College, A
Northwest Mississippi Community College, A
Southwest Mississippi Community College, A

Missouri

East Central College, A
Jefferson College, A
Linn State Technical College, A
Missouri Southern State University, A
Ozarks Technical Community College, A
Ranken Technical College, A

State Fair Community College, A

Montana

Montana State University-Northern, A
The University of Montana-Helena College of
    Technology, A

Nebraska

Central Community College-Columbus Campus, A
Central Community College-Hastings Campus, A
Southeast Community College, Lincoln Campus, A
Southeast Community College, Milford Campus, A

Nevada

Western Nevada Community College, A

New Hampshire

New Hampshire Community Technical College,
    Nashua/Claremont, A

New Mexico

New Mexico Junior College, A
Western New Mexico University, A

New York

Corning Community College, A
Onondaga Community College, A
State University of New York College of Technology
    at Alfred, A
Vaughn College of Aeronautics and Technology, A

North Carolina

Alamance Community College, A
Asheville-Buncombe Technical Community
    College, A
Blue Ridge Community College, A
Central Piedmont Community College, A
Durham Technical Community College, A
Forsyth Technical Community College, A
Guilford Technical Community College, A
Haywood Community College, A
Isothermal Community College, A
Johnston Community College, A
McDowell Technical Community College, A
Mitchell Community College, A
Pitt Community College, A
Randolph Community College, A
Richmond Community College, A
South Piedmont Community College, A
Surry Community College, A
Wake Technical Community College, A
Wayne Community College, A

Ohio

Lakeland Community College, A
Lorain County Community College, A
North Central State College, A
Northwest State Community College, A
Sinclair Community College, A

Oklahoma

Oklahoma State University, Okmulgee, A

Oregon

Clackamas Community College, A
Linn-Benton Community College, A
Portland Community College, A
Southwestern Oregon Community College, A

Pennsylvania

Butler County Community College, A
Delaware County Community College, A
Johnson College, A
New Castle School of Trades, A
Reading Area Community College, A
Thaddeus Stevens College of Technology, A
The Williamson Free School of Mechanical
    Trades, A

South Carolina

Aiken Technical College, A
Florence-Darlington Technical College, A
Greenville Technical College, A
Horry-Georgetown Technical College, A

Northeastern Technical College, A
Orangeburg-Calhoun Technical College, A
Piedmont Technical College, A
Spartanburg Technical College, A
Tri-County Technical College, A
Trident Technical College, A
York Technical College, A

South Dakota

Lake Area Technical Institute, A
Southeast Technical Institute, A

Tennessee

Chattanooga State Technical Community College, A
Northeast State Technical Community College, A
Pellissippi State Technical Community College, A

Texas

Amarillo College, A
Brazosport College, A
Del Mar College, A
Grayson County College, A
Hill College of the Hill Junior College District, A
Kilgore College, A
Lamar University, A
Lee College, A
North Central Texas College, A
Odessa College, A
South Plains College, A
South Texas College, A
Tarrant County College District, A
Texas State Technical College Harlingen, A
Texas State Technical College Waco, A
Texas State Technical College West Texas, A
Vernon College, A

Utah

College of Eastern Utah, A
Utah Valley State College, A
Weber State University, A

Virginia

New River Community College, A
Virginia Highlands Community College, A
Wytheville Community College, A

Washington

Clark College, A
Clover Park Technical College, A
Columbia Basin College, A
Grays Harbor College, A
Green River Community College, A
Lake Washington Technical College, A
Lower Columbia College, A
Renton Technical College, A
Shoreline Community College, A
South Seattle Community College, A
Spokane Community College, A
Walla Walla Community College, A

West Virginia

West Virginia University at Parkersburg, A

Wisconsin

Chippewa Valley Technical College, A
Gateway Technical College, A
Milwaukee Area Technical College, A
Nicolet Area Technical College, A
Northcentral Technical College, A
Northeast Wisconsin Technical College, A

Southwest Wisconsin Technical College, A

Wyoming

Casper College, A
Sheridan College-Sheridan and Gillette, A

British Columbia

British Columbia Institute of Technology, A

MANAGEMENT

Alabama

American College of Computer & Information
 Sciences, M
Andrew Jackson University, M
Auburn University, MD
Birmingham-Southern College, M
Columbia Southern University, M
Troy University, M
The University of Alabama, MD
The University of Alabama in Huntsville, MO

Alaska

University of Alaska Fairbanks, M

Arizona

Arizona State University, D
Northern Arizona University, M
University of Phoenix Online Campus, M
University of Phoenix-Phoenix Campus, M
University of Phoenix-Southern Arizona Campus, M

California

Antioch University Los Angeles, M
Argosy University/Orange County, D
California State University, Chico, M
California State University, East Bay, M
California State University, Fullerton, M
California State University, Los Angeles, M
California State University, San Marcos, M
Golden Gate University, M
Holy Names University, M
Mills College, M
Notre Dame de Namur University, M
Saint Mary's College of California, M
San Diego State University, M
University of La Verne, M
University of Phoenix-Bay Area Campus, M
University of Phoenix-Sacramento Valley
 Campus, M
University of Phoenix-San Diego Campus, M
University of Phoenix-Southern California
 Campus, M
University of Redlands, M
University of San Francisco, M

Colorado

Regis University, MO
University of Colorado at Denver and Health
 Sciences Center - Downtown Denver Campus, M
University of Denver, M
University of Phoenix-Denver Campus, M
University of Phoenix-Southern Colorado
 Campus, M

Connecticut

Albertus Magnus College, M
Fairfield University, M
Quinnipiac University, M
Saint Joseph College, M
University of Hartford, M

Delaware

Goldey-Beacom College, M
Wilmington College, M

District of Columbia

The George Washington University, MD
Howard University, M

Florida

Argosy University/Sarasota, MD
Florida Institute of Technology, M

Florida Metropolitan University-South Orlando
 Campus, M
St. Thomas University, MO
University of Central Florida, M
University of Florida, MD
University of Miami, MD
University of Phoenix-Central Florida Campus, M
University of Phoenix-South Florida Campus, M
University of Phoenix-West Florida Campus, M
University of South Florida, M
Webber International University, M

Georgia

Brenau University, M
Georgia Institute of Technology, MD
Georgia State University, MD

Hawaii

Hawaii Pacific University, M
University of Phoenix-Hawaii Campus, M

Illinois

American InterContinental University Online, M
Argosy University/Schaumburg, D
Benedictine University, MO
DePaul University, M
Eastern Illinois University, M
Illinois Institute of Technology, MD
National-Louis University, M
North Central College, M
Northeastern Illinois University, M
Saint Xavier University, M
Trinity International University, D
University of St. Francis, M

Indiana

Indiana Tech, M
Indiana University Bloomington, MD
Indiana Wesleyan University, M
Oakland City University, M
Purdue University Calumet, M

Iowa

Clarke College, M
St. Ambrose University, M
The University of Iowa, D

Kansas

Friends University, M
Newman University, M
University of Saint Mary, M

Kentucky

Brescia University, M

Louisiana

Louisiana State University and Agricultural and
 Mechanical College, D
University of Phoenix-Louisiana Campus, M

Maine

Maine Maritime Academy, MO

Maryland

College of Notre Dame of Maryland, M
The Johns Hopkins University, M
Loyola College in Maryland, M
University of Maryland, College Park, MD
University of Maryland University College, MDO
University of Phoenix-Maryland Campus, M

Massachusetts

Boston University, M
Bridgewater State College, M
Cambridge College, M
Clark University, M
Emmanuel College, M
Lasell College, M
Massachusetts Institute of Technology, MDO
Nichols College, M
University of Massachusetts Amherst, MD
University of Massachusetts Dartmouth, O
University of Phoenix-Central Massachusetts
 Campus, M

Worcester Polytechnic Institute, MO
Worcester State College, M

Michigan

Andrews University, M
Aquinas College, M
Central Michigan University, M
Cleary University, M
Davenport University (Dearborn), M
Eastern Michigan University, M
Spring Arbor University, M
Walsh College of Accountancy and Business
  Administration, M

Minnesota

The College of St. Scholastica, M
Hamline University, MO
Metropolitan State University, M
Saint Mary's University of Minnesota, M
Southwest Minnesota State University, M
University of St. Thomas, M
Walden University, MD

Missouri

Fontbonne University, M
Lindenwood University, M
Maryville University of Saint Louis, MO
Rockhurst University, M
University of Missouri-St. Louis, M
Webster University, MD

Nebraska

Bellevue University, M
University of Nebraska-Lincoln, M

Nevada

University of Phoenix-Nevada Campus, M

New Hampshire

New England College, M

New Jersey

College of Saint Elizabeth, M
Fairleigh Dickinson University, College at
  Florham, M
Fairleigh Dickinson University, Metropolitan
  Campus, MO
Rutgers, The State University of New Jersey,
  Newark, D
Saint Peter's College, M
Thomas Edison State College, M

New York

Adelphi University, O
Daemen College, M
Dowling College, M
Fashion Institute of Technology, M
Ithaca College, M
Keuka College, M
Long Island University, C.W. Post Campus, MO
Marist College, O
Mercy College, M
Metropolitan College of New York, M
Nazareth College of Rochester, M
New York Institute of Technology, M
New York University, MDO
Polytechnic University, Brooklyn Campus, M
Roberts Wesleyan College, M
St. Bonaventure University, MO
St. Thomas Aquinas College, M
State University of New York at Buffalo, D

North Carolina

East Carolina University, O

North Dakota

Minot State University, M
University of Mary, M

Ohio

Antioch University McGregor, M
Baldwin-Wallace College, M
Lake Erie College, M
Miami University, M

Mount Vernon Nazarene University, M
Notre Dame College, O
The University of Akron, MO
The University of Findlay, M
Ursuline College, M

Oklahoma

Oklahoma City University, M
Oklahoma State University, D
University of Oklahoma, M

Oregon

University of Oregon, D
University of Phoenix-Oregon Campus, M

Pennsylvania

Carnegie Mellon University, M
Gannon University, O
Lehigh University, O
Marywood University, M
Rosemont College, M
Saint Joseph's University, M
Temple University, MD
University of Pennsylvania, MD
University of Pittsburgh, M
The University of Scranton, M
West Chester University of Pennsylvania, M

Puerto Rico

Bayamon Central University, M
Inter American University of Puerto Rico, San
  Germán Campus, D
Universidad del Turabo, M

Rhode Island

Bryant University, MO
Salve Regina University, MO
University of Rhode Island, M

South Carolina

Clemson University, MD
Southern Wesleyan University, M

South Dakota

Oglala Lakota College, M

Tennessee

Lipscomb University, M
Middle Tennessee State University, M
Southern Adventist University, M
University of Memphis, MD
The University of Tennessee, MD
Vanderbilt University, D

Texas

Amberton University, M
Angelo State University, M
Dallas Baptist University, M
Houston Baptist University, M
St. Edward's University, MO
Stephen F. Austin State University, M
Sul Ross State University, M
Texas A&M University, MD
Texas A&M University-Corpus Christi, M
University of Dallas, M
University of Phoenix-Dallas Campus, M
The University of Texas at Arlington, M
The University of Texas at Austin, D
The University of Texas at Dallas, MD
The University of Texas at San Antonio, M
The University of Texas at Tyler, M

Utah

University of Phoenix-Utah Campus, M

Vermont

Marlboro College, M

Virginia

Marymount University, MO
Regent University, M
University of Management and Technology, M
University of Northern Virginia, M

Virginia Polytechnic Institute and State University, D

Washington

Antioch University Seattle, M
Central Washington University, M
City University, MO
University of Phoenix-Washington Campus, M

West Virginia

Salem International University, M

Wisconsin

Concordia University Wisconsin, M
Silver Lake College, M
University of Phoenix-Wisconsin Campus, M
University of Wisconsin-Green Bay, M
University of Wisconsin-River Falls, M
University of Wisconsin-Whitewater, M

Alberta

Athabasca University, O
University of Alberta, D
University of Calgary, D
University of Lethbridge, M

British Columbia

Royal Roads University, M
Simon Fraser University, M
The University of British Columbia, D
University of Phoenix-Vancouver Campus, M
University of Victoria, M

Ontario

Carleton University, D
University of Guelph, M

Quebec

Concordia University, O
HEC Montreal, O
McGill University, O
Université Laval, MDO
Université de Sherbrooke, O

MANAGEMENT INFORMATION SYSTEMS AND SERVICES

Alabama

Auburn University, BMD
Auburn University Montgomery, B
Columbia Southern University, B
Community College of the Air Force, A
Troy University, B
The University of Alabama, B
The University of Alabama at Birmingham, B
The University of Alabama in Huntsville, BM
University of Montevallo, B
University of North Alabama, B
The University of West Alabama, B

Alaska

Ilisagvik College, A
University of Alaska Anchorage, B

Arizona

Arizona State University, BMDO
Arizona State University at the Polytechnic
  Campus, M
Chandler-Gilbert Community College, A
Eastern Arizona College, A
Glendale Community College, A
Northern Arizona University, BM
Northland Pioneer College, A
Rio Salado College, A
The University of Arizona, BMD
University of Phoenix Online Campus, M
University of Phoenix-Phoenix Campus, BM
University of Phoenix-Southern Arizona
  Campus, BM
Western International University, M

Arkansas

Arkansas State University, AM
Henderson State University, B

Mid-South Community College, A
Ouachita Technical College, A
South Arkansas Community College, A
University of Arkansas, M
University of Arkansas at Little Rock, M
University of Arkansas at Monticello, B
University of Central Arkansas, B

California

Alliant International University, B
American InterContinental University, BM
American River College, A
Argosy University/Orange County, MD
Azusa Pacific University, B
California Lutheran University, M
California Polytechnic State University, San Luis
    Obispo, B
California State University, Chico, B
California State University, Dominguez Hills, BM
California State University, East Bay, BM
California State University, Fresno, B
California State University, Fullerton, M
California State University, Long Beach, B
California State University, Los Angeles, M
California State University, Monterey Bay, M
California State University, Northridge, M
California State University, Sacramento, BM
California State University, San Bernardino, B
College of the Desert, A
College of San Mateo, A
College of the Siskiyous, A
Cosumnes River College (Sacramento), A
Cuesta College, A
Evergreen Valley College, A
Glendale Community College, A
Laney College, A
Lincoln University, B
Los Angeles City College, A
The Master's College and Seminary, B
Merced College, A
Modesto Junior College, A
Napa Valley College, A
National University, BM
Pacific States University, M
Pacific Union College, B
Point Loma Nazarene University, B
San Diego State University, M
San Joaquin Valley College, A
San Jose State University, M
Santa Clara University, BM
Shasta College, A
Simpson University, B
Touro University International, BM
University of La Verne, M
University of Phoenix-Bay Area Campus, BM
University of Phoenix-Central Valley Campus, B
University of Phoenix-Sacramento Valley
    Campus, BM
University of Phoenix-San Diego Campus, BM
University of Phoenix-Southern California
    Campus, M
University of Redlands, BMO
University of San Francisco, BM
University of Southern California, M
University of the West, M
Victor Valley College, A

Colorado

Arapahoe Community College, A
Aspen University, MO
Colorado Christian University, AB
Colorado Mountain College, A
Colorado State University, M
Colorado Technical University, BM
Colorado Technical University Denver Campus, M
Fort Lewis College, B
Lamar Community College, A
National American University (Denver), B
Pikes Peak Community College, A
Pueblo Community College, A
Regis University, M
Trinidad State Junior College, A
University of Colorado at Colorado Springs, M
University of Colorado at Denver and Health
    Sciences Center - Downtown Denver
    Campus, MD

University of Denver, BM
University of Phoenix-Denver Campus, BM
University of Phoenix-Southern Colorado
    Campus, BM
Western State College of Colorado, B

Connecticut

Albertus Magnus College, B
Central Connecticut State University, B
Eastern Connecticut State University, B
Fairfield University, BMO
Manchester Community College, A
Post University, B
Quinnipiac University, M
Sacred Heart University, MO
University of Connecticut, B
University of Hartford, B
University of New Haven, M
Western Connecticut State University, B

Delaware

Delaware Technical & Community College,
    Stanton/Wilmington Campus, A
Goldey-Beacom College, BM
University of Delaware, M
Wilmington College, M

District of Columbia

American University, MO
The George Washington University, M
Howard University, M
Potomac College, A
Southeastern University, ABM
Strayer University, M

Florida

Argosy University/Sarasota, BMD
Barry University, BO
Florida Agricultural and Mechanical University, BM
Florida Atlantic University, B
Florida Community College at Jacksonville, A
Florida Gulf Coast University, B
Florida Institute of Technology, BM
Florida International University, BD
Florida Metropolitan University-Pompano Beach
    Campus, AB
Florida National College, A
Florida Southern College, B
Florida State University, M
Florida Technical College (Orlando), A
Jacksonville University, B
Keiser College (Daytona Beach), A
Keiser College (Fort Lauderdale), B
Miami Dade College, A
Northwood University, Florida Campus, B
Nova Southeastern University, MD
Palm Beach Community College, A
Saint Leo University, B
Schiller International University, M
Seminole Community College, A
Tallahassee Community College, A
University of Central Florida, BM
University of Florida, MDO
University of Miami, M
University of Phoenix-Central Florida Campus, BM
University of Phoenix-North Florida Campus, BM
University of Phoenix-South Florida Campus, M
University of Phoenix-West Florida Campus, BM
University of South Florida, BM
The University of Tampa, M
University of West Florida, B

Georgia

American InterContinental University (Dunwoody
    Campus), M
Clayton State University, B
Dalton State College, B
Emory University, D
Georgia College & State University, M
Georgia Institute of Technology, MD
Georgia Southern University, B
Georgia Southwestern State University, AB
Georgia State University, MD
Gwinnett Technical College, A
Paine College, B

Savannah State University, B
University of Georgia, B
University of Phoenix-Atlanta Campus, BM
University of West Georgia, B

Hawaii

Hawaii Pacific University, BM
University of Hawaii at Manoa, BMD
University of Phoenix-Hawaii Campus, BM

Idaho

Boise State University, M
Idaho State University, MO
North Idaho College, A
University of Idaho, B

Illinois

Argosy University/Schaumburg, D
Aurora University, B
Benedictine University, MO
Black Hawk College, A
Bradley University, B
Chicago State University, B
DePaul University, BM
DeVry University (Oakbrook Terrace), M
Dominican University, M
Elmhurst College, B
Eureka College, B
Governors State University, BM
Greenville College, B
Heartland Community College, A
Highland Community College, A
Illinois College, B
Illinois Institute of Technology, MD
Illinois State University, M
Joliet Junior College, A
Judson College, B
Lewis University, B
Loyola University Chicago, BM
MacMurray College, B
Millikin University, B
North Central College, BM
Northern Illinois University, BM
Northwestern Business College, A
Northwestern University, M
Oakton Community College, A
Parkland College, A
Robert Morris College, A
Rockford College, B
Roosevelt University, M
St. Augustine College, A
South Suburban College, A
Southern Illinois University Edwardsville, BM
Trinity Christian College, B
Triton College, A
University of Illinois at Chicago, BMD
University of Illinois at Springfield, M
University of Phoenix-Chicago Campus, BM
Western Illinois University, B
William Rainey Harper College, A

Indiana

Ball State University, B
Grace College, B
Indiana Business College (Indianapolis), A
Indiana Business College (Muncie), A
Indiana State University, B
Indiana University Bloomington, BMD
Indiana University South Bend, M
Indiana University Southeast, O
International Business College (Indianapolis), A
Purdue University, ABMD
Saint Joseph's College, AB
Saint Mary's College, B
Taylor University, A
Tri-State University, B
University of Notre Dame, B
University of Southern Indiana, A
Vincennes University, A
Vincennes University Jasper Campus, A

Iowa

Briar Cliff University, B
Buena Vista University, B
Clarke College, B

Dordt College, B
Graceland University, B
Grand View College, B
Hamilton College (Cedar Falls), B
Hamilton College (Cedar Rapids), AB
Hawkeye Community College, A
Iowa State University of Science and
    Technology, BM
Iowa Western Community College, A
Kaplan University, B
Kirkwood Community College, A
Loras College, B
Luther College, B
Morningside College, B
The University of Iowa, BM
University of Northern Iowa, B
Upper Iowa University, B

Kansas

Bethel College, B
Brown Mackie College-Kansas City, A
Friends University, M
Hutchinson Community College and Area Vocational
    School, A
Manhattan Area Technical College, A
Newman University, BM
Pratt Community College, A
Southwestern College, B
University of Kansas, MD
Wichita State University, B

Kentucky

Ashland Community and Technical College, A
Big Sandy Community and Technical College, A
Daymar College (Owensboro), A
Eastern Kentucky University, B
Hopkinsville Community College, A
Lindsey Wilson College, A
Louisville Technical Institute, A
Morehead State University, AB
Murray State University, B
Northern Kentucky University, B
Southeast Kentucky Community and Technical
    College, A
University of Louisville, B
Western Kentucky University, B

Louisiana

Elaine P. Nunez Community College, A
Louisiana State University and Agricultural and
    Mechanical College, MD
Louisiana Tech University, B
Nicholls State University, B
Remington College-Lafayette Campus, A
University of New Orleans, B
University of Phoenix-Louisiana Campus, M

Maine

Husson College, AB
Southern Maine Community College, A
Thomas College, B
University of Maine, BM

Maryland

Allegany College of Maryland, A
Anne Arundel Community College, A
Baltimore City Community College, A
Bowie State University, MO
Capitol College, BM
Hagerstown Community College, A
Harford Community College, A
The Johns Hopkins University, MO
Montgomery College, A
Morgan State University, B
Salisbury University, B
Towson University, MDO
University of Baltimore, BM
University of Maryland, Baltimore County, MD
University of Maryland University College, MO
University of Phoenix-Maryland Campus, M
Villa Julie College, BM

Massachusetts

American International College, B
Babson College, B

Bay Path College, M
Boston College, B
Boston University, BD
Bridgewater State College, B
Bristol Community College, A
Clark University, M
Harvard University, D
Massasoit Community College, A
Mount Wachusett Community College, A
New England College of Finance, A
Nichols College, B
Northeastern University, B
Quincy College, A
Salem State College, B
Simmons College, B
Springfield College, B
Suffolk University, B
University of Massachusetts Dartmouth, B
University of Phoenix-Boston Campus, BM
Western New England College, BM
Westfield State College, B
Worcester Polytechnic Institute, BM

Michigan

Baker College of Flint, B
Calvin College, B
Central Michigan University, BMO
Cleary University, B
Cornerstone University, B
Davenport University (Dearborn), AB
Eastern Michigan University, BMO
Ferris State University, BM
Grand Valley State University, B
Kalamazoo Valley Community College, A
Kettering University, B
Lake Superior State University, A
Lansing Community College, A
Lawrence Technological University, M
Madonna University, B
Michigan State University, MD
Michigan Technological University, B
Montcalm Community College, A
Mott Community College, A
Northern Michigan University, AB
Northwestern Michigan College, A
Northwood University, AB
Oakland Community College, A
Oakland University, BMO
Spring Arbor University, B
University of Detroit Mercy, M
University of Michigan-Dearborn, B
University of Phoenix-Metro Detroit Campus, BM
University of Phoenix-West Michigan Campus, BM
Walsh College of Accountancy and Business
    Administration, M
Washtenaw Community College, A
Wayne State University, B

Minnesota

Academy College, A
Anoka-Ramsey Community College, A
Augsburg College, B
Century College, A
College of St. Catherine, B
The College of St. Scholastica, M
Concordia University, St. Paul, B
Herzing College, B
Inver Hills Community College, A
Lake Superior College, A
Metropolitan State University, BM
National American University (Roseville), AB
Normandale Community College, A
Northland Community and Technical College-Thief
    River Falls, A
Northwestern College, B
Rasmussen College Mankato, A
Riverland Community College, A
St. Cloud Technical College, A
University of Minnesota, Twin Cities Campus, BMD
University of St. Thomas, MO
Winona State University, B

Mississippi

Belhaven College, B
Delta State University, B
Hinds Community College, A

Holmes Community College, A
Mississippi Delta Community College, A
Mississippi State University, BM
University of Mississippi, B
University of Southern Mississippi, BM

Missouri

Central Missouri State University, BM
East Central College, A
Fontbonne University, B
Grantham University, M
Lindenwood University, BM
Maryville University of Saint Louis, BMO
Metropolitan Community College-Business &
    Technology College, A
Missouri State University, BM
National American University, B
Northwest Missouri State University, BM
Ozarks Technical Community College, A
Park University, BM
Saint Louis University, B
Three Rivers Community College, A
University of Missouri-Columbia, B
University of Missouri-St. Louis, BMDO
Webster University, BMO
Westminster College, B
William Woods University, B

Montana

Rocky Mountain College, B

Nebraska

Bellevue University, BM
Concordia University, B
Creighton University, BM
Dana College, B
Midland Lutheran College, B
Peru State College, B
University of Nebraska at Omaha, BMD

Nevada

Career College of Northern Nevada, A
University of Nevada, Las Vegas, BM
University of Phoenix-Nevada Campus, M
Western Nevada Community College, A

New Hampshire

Daniel Webster College, AB
Franklin Pierce College, M
Hesser College, A
New Hampshire Community Technical College,
    Manchester/Stratham, A
Rivier College, M
Southern New Hampshire University, M

New Jersey

Atlantic Cape Community College, A
Burlington County College, A
County College of Morris, A
Fairleigh Dickinson University, Metropolitan
    Campus, MO
Kean University, M
Mercer County Community College, A
Montclair State University, M
Raritan Valley Community College, A
Rutgers, The State University of New Jersey,
    Newark, MD
Saint Peter's College, M
Salem Community College, A
Seton Hall University, BMO
Stevens Institute of Technology, MDO
Union County College, A

New Mexico

Clovis Community College, A
College of Santa Fe, B
Eastern New Mexico University, B
National American University (Albuquerque), AB
New Mexico Highlands University, B
University of New Mexico, M

University of Phoenix-New Mexico Campus, BM

New York

Adelphi University, M
Bernard M. Baruch College of the City University of New York, BMD
Clarkson University, BM
The College of Westchester, A
Dominican College, B
Excelsior College, B
Fordham University, BM
Globe Institute of Technology, A
Hilbert College, A
Hofstra University, BMO
Iona College, B
Island Drafting and Technical Institute, A
Le Moyne College, B
Long Island University, C.W. Post Campus, MO
Marist College, MO
Mohawk Valley Community College, A
Monroe Community College, A
Nassau Community College, A
Nazareth College of Rochester, B
New York Institute of Technology, BMO
New York University, BMO
Onondaga Community College, A
Pace University, M
Polytechnic University, Brooklyn Campus, B
Rensselaer Polytechnic Institute, BM
Roberts Wesleyan College, B
Rochester Business Institute, A
Rochester Institute of Technology, B
St. Bonaventure University, B
St. John Fisher College, B
St. John's University, BMO
State University of New York at Buffalo, M
State University of New York College at Old Westbury, B
State University of New York College of Technology at Alfred, B
Stony Brook University, State University of New York, O
Suffolk County Community College, A
Syracuse University, MDO
Tompkins Cortland Community College, A
University at Albany, State University of New York, M
Yeshiva University, B

North Carolina

Appalachian State University, B
Cleveland Community College, A
Craven Community College, A
East Carolina University, BO
ECPI Technical College, A
Gardner-Webb University, B
Haywood Community College, A
Martin Community College, A
Montgomery Community College, A
Pfeiffer University, B
Stanly Community College, A
The University of North Carolina at Chapel Hill, D
The University of North Carolina at Charlotte, B
The University of North Carolina at Greensboro, BM
The University of North Carolina Wilmington, B
Wake Forest University, B
Wake Technical Community College, A
Western Carolina University, B
Wingate University, B
Winston-Salem State University, B

North Dakota

Jamestown College, B
Lake Region State College, A
Minot State University, BM
University of Mary, B

Ohio

Baldwin-Wallace College, B
Bowling Green State University, B
Bowling Green State University-Firelands College, A
Case Western Reserve University, MDO
Central State University, B
Cincinnati State Technical and Community College, A
Clark State Community College, A

Cleveland State University, MD
College of Mount St. Joseph, AB
Franklin University, B
Gallipolis Career College, A
Miami University, BM
Miami University Hamilton, A
Miami University-Middletown Campus, A
Notre Dame College, O
The Ohio State University, BMD
Ohio University-Eastern, B
Owens Community College, A
Shawnee State University, AB
Stark State College of Technology, A
Trumbull Business College, A
The University of Akron, BM
The University of Akron-Wayne College, A
University of Cincinnati, BMO
University of Cincinnati Raymond Walters College, A
University of Dayton, B
University of Phoenix-Cleveland Campus, M
The University of Toledo, BMD
Ursuline College, B
Wright State University, ABMO
Wright State University, Lake Campus, A
Xavier University, BM
Youngstown State University, B

Oklahoma

Cameron University, A
East Central University, B
Oklahoma Baptist University, B
Oklahoma City University, BM
Oklahoma State University, BMD
Oklahoma State University, Oklahoma City, A
Oral Roberts University, B
Rogers State University, B
Rose State College, A
St. Gregory's University, B
Southeastern Oklahoma State University, B
Southern Nazarene University, B
Tulsa Community College, A
University of Oklahoma, BM
University of Phoenix-Oklahoma City Campus, BM
University of Phoenix-Tulsa Campus, BM
University of Tulsa, B

Oregon

Corban College, B
George Fox University, B
Linn-Benton Community College, A
Northwest Christian College, B
Oregon Institute of Technology, B
Oregon State University, B
Southwestern Oregon Community College, A
University of Oregon, M
University of Phoenix-Oregon Campus, M

Pennsylvania

Arcadia University, B
Carnegie Mellon University, MD
Chatham College, B
College Misericordia, B
Community College of Allegheny County, A
Delaware County Community College, A
Delaware Valley College, B
DeSales University, B
Drexel University, B
Duquesne University, BM
Eastern University, B
Edinboro University of Pennsylvania, MO
Gannon University, B
Harrisburg Area Community College, A
Holy Family University, M
Indiana University of Pennsylvania, B
International Academy of Design & Technology, A
La Salle University, B
Lackawanna College, A
Laurel Business Institute, A
Lehigh University, B
Lock Haven University of Pennsylvania, A
Manor College, A
Marywood University, M
Montgomery County Community College, A
Peirce College, A
Pennsylvania College of Technology, B
Pennsylvania Highland Community College, A

The Pennsylvania State University Abington College, B
The Pennsylvania State University Altoona College, B
The Pennsylvania State University Beaver Campus of the Commonwealth College, B
The Pennsylvania State University Berks Campus of the Berks-Lehigh Valley College, B
The Pennsylvania State University Delaware County Campus of the Commonwealth College, B
The Pennsylvania State University DuBois Campus of the Commonwealth College, B
The Pennsylvania State University at Erie, The Behrend College, B
The Pennsylvania State University Fayette Campus of the Commonwealth College, B
The Pennsylvania State University Harrisburg Campus, BMO
The Pennsylvania State University Hazleton Campus of the Commonwealth College, B
The Pennsylvania State University, Lehigh Valley Campus of the Berks-Lehigh Valley College, B
The Pennsylvania State University McKeesport Campus of the Commonwealth College, B
The Pennsylvania State University Mont Alto Campus of the Commonwealth College, B
The Pennsylvania State University New Kensington Campus of the Commonwealth College, B
The Pennsylvania State University Schuylkill Campus of the Capital College, B
The Pennsylvania State University Shenango Campus of the Commonwealth College, B
The Pennsylvania State University University Park Campus, BMD
The Pennsylvania State University Wilkes-Barre Campus of the Commonwealth College, B
The Pennsylvania State University Worthington Scranton Campus of the Commonwealth College, B
The Pennsylvania State University York Campus of the Commonwealth College, B
Philadelphia University, B
Robert Morris University, BMD
Saint Francis University, B
Saint Joseph's University, ABM
Seton Hill University, B
Temple University, BMD
Thiel College, AB
University of Pennsylvania, BMD
University of Phoenix-Pittsburgh Campus, B
University of Pittsburgh, MO
University of Pittsburgh at Titusville, A
The University of Scranton, M
Villanova University, B
Widener University, B
Wilson College, A
York Technical Institute, A
Yorktowne Business Institute, A

Puerto Rico

Bayamon Central University, AB
Columbia College (Caguas), A
Inter American University of Puerto Rico, Aguadilla Campus, B
Inter American University of Puerto Rico, Bayamón Campus, AB
Inter American University of Puerto Rico, Metropolitan Campus, B
Inter American University of Puerto Rico, San Germán Campus, M
University of the Sacred Heart, M

Rhode Island

Bryant University, MO
Rhode Island College, B
Roger Williams University, B
University of Rhode Island, B

South Carolina

Anderson University, B
Charleston Southern University, BM
Claflin University, B
Clemson University, B

Francis Marion University, B

South Dakota

Augustana College, B
Colorado Technical University Sioux Falls
  Campus, ABM
Dakota State University, M
Mitchell Technical Institute, A
National American University (Rapid City), B
National American University-Sioux Falls
  Branch, AB
Northern State University, B
Southeast Technical Institute, A
University of Sioux Falls, B
Western Dakota Technical Institute, A

Tennessee

Aquinas College, B
Carson-Newman College, B
Crichton College, B
Jackson State Community College, A
Middle Tennessee State University, BM
Southern Adventist University, B
Southwest Tennessee Community College, A
University of Memphis, BMD
University of Phoenix-Nashville Campus, M
The University of Tennessee at Martin, B

Texas

Amberton University, B
Angelo State University, B
Austin Business College, A
Baylor University, BMO
Cedar Valley College, A
Dallas Baptist University, BM
Del Mar College, A
East Texas Baptist University, B
El Paso Community College, A
Galveston College, A
Grayson County College, A
Houston Baptist University, M
Kilgore College, A
LeTourneau University, B
McMurry University, B
Midwestern State University, B
North Central Texas College, A
North Harris College, A
Northwest Vista College, A
Northwood University, Texas Campus, AB
Prairie View A&M University, M
St. Edward's University, MO
Schreiner University, B
Tarleton State University, BM
Texas A&M International University, M
Texas A&M University, MD
Texas A&M University-Commerce, B
Texas A&M University-Texarkana, B
Texas State Technical College Harlingen, A
Texas State University-San Marcos, B
Texas Tech University, BMD
Texas Wesleyan University, B
University of Dallas, M
University of Houston, B
University of Houston-Clear Lake, BM
University of Houston-Downtown, B
University of the Incarnate Word, B
University of Mary Hardin-Baylor, BM
University of North Texas, BMD
University of Phoenix-Dallas Campus, B
University of Phoenix-Houston Campus, B
University of St. Thomas, B
The University of Texas at Arlington, BMD
The University of Texas at Austin, BD
The University of Texas at Dallas, M
The University of Texas-Pan American, BMD
The University of Texas at San Antonio, BM
Wayland Baptist University, B
West Texas A&M University, B

Utah

Brigham Young University, BMO
University of Phoenix-Utah Campus, BM
University of Utah, B
Utah State University, MD
Utah Valley State College, B
Weber State University, AB

Westminster College, B

Vermont

Johnson State College, AB
Norwich University, M

Virginia

Bridgewater College, B
Central Virginia Community College, A
Eastern Shore Community College, A
John Tyler Community College, A
Liberty University, B
Longwood University, B
Marymount University, MO
Mountain Empire Community College, A
Old Dominion University, B
Piedmont Virginia Community College, A
Shenandoah University, O
University of Management and Technology, ABM
University of Northern Virginia, M
University of Richmond, B
University of Virginia, M
Virginia Commonwealth University, MD
Virginia Polytechnic Institute and State
  University, MDO
Virginia Union University, B

Washington

City University, MO
Eastern Washington University, B
Lower Columbia College, A
Northwest Indian College, A
Pacific Lutheran University, B
Saint Martin's University, B
Seattle Pacific University, M
Seattle University, B
Tacoma Community College, A
University of Phoenix-Washington Campus, M
University of Washington, B
Walla Walla College, B
Washington State University, BM
Western Washington University, B
Yakima Valley Community College, A

West Virginia

Alderson-Broaddus College, B
Davis & Elkins College, AB

Wisconsin

Carroll College, B
Concordia University Wisconsin, M
Gateway Technical College, A
Marquette University, B
Milwaukee School of Engineering, B
Moraine Park Technical College, A
University of Phoenix-Wisconsin Campus, M
University of Wisconsin-La Crosse, B
University of Wisconsin-Madison, MD
University of Wisconsin-Milwaukee, B
University of Wisconsin-Oshkosh, BM
University of Wisconsin-River Falls, B
University of Wisconsin-Whitewater, BM
Viterbo University, B
Wisconsin Indianhead Technical College, A

Wyoming

Central Wyoming College, A
Eastern Wyoming College, A
University of Wyoming, B

Alberta

Athabasca University, M
University of Alberta, B
University of Calgary, B
University of Lethbridge, BM

British Columbia

Simon Fraser University, BM
The University of British Columbia, BD
University of Phoenix-Vancouver Campus, M

Nova Scotia

Cape Breton University, B
Dalhousie University, M
Mount Saint Vincent University, B

St. Francis Xavier University, B

Ontario

Carleton University, B
Lakehead University, B
McMaster University, D
University of Ottawa, B
University of Windsor, B
York University, B

Quebec

Bishop's University, B
Concordia University, B
HEC Montreal, BM
McGill University, M
Université Laval, M
Université de Montréal, O
Université du Québec àChicoutimi, B
Université du Québec àMontréal, BM
Université du Québec en Outaouais, B
Université de Sherbrooke, M

MANAGEMENT OF TECHNOLOGY

Arizona

University of Advancing Technology, M
University of Phoenix Online Campus, M
University of Phoenix-Phoenix Campus, M
University of Phoenix-Southern Arizona Campus, M

California

California Polytechnic State University, San Luis
  Obispo, M
Coleman College (La Mesa), M
National University, M
Pacific States University, M
University of Phoenix-Bay Area Campus, M
University of Phoenix-Sacramento Valley
  Campus, M
University of Phoenix-San Diego Campus, M
University of Phoenix-Southern California
  Campus, M

Colorado

Colorado School of Mines, M
Jones International University, M
Regis University, MO
University of Colorado at Boulder, M
University of Colorado at Colorado Springs, M
University of Denver, M
University of Phoenix-Denver Campus, M
University of Phoenix-Southern Colorado
  Campus, M

Connecticut

Central Connecticut State University, M
Fairfield University, M
University of Bridgeport, M
University of New Haven, M

Delaware

University of Delaware, M

District of Columbia

The George Washington University, M

Florida

Embry-Riddle Aeronautical University, Extended
  Campus, M
University of Miami, M
University of Phoenix-Central Florida Campus, M
University of Phoenix-North Florida Campus, M
University of Phoenix-West Florida Campus, M
The University of Tampa, M

Georgia

Georgia Institute of Technology, MO
Mercer University, M
University of Phoenix-Atlanta Campus, M

University of Phoenix-Columbus Georgia
Campus, M

Hawaii

University of Phoenix-Hawaii Campus, M

Idaho

Idaho State University, M
University of Phoenix-Idaho Campus, M

Illinois

Illinois State University, M
University of Illinois at Urbana-Champaign, M
University of Phoenix-Chicago Campus, M

Indiana

Indiana State University, D

Iowa

St. Ambrose University, M

Kansas

University of Phoenix-Wichita Campus, M

Kentucky

Murray State University, M
Northern Kentucky University, M
Sullivan University, M

Louisiana

University of Phoenix-Louisiana Campus, M

Maryland

The Johns Hopkins University, M
University of Maryland University College, MO
University of Phoenix-Maryland Campus, M
Villa Julie College, M

Massachusetts

Boston University, M
University of Phoenix-Boston Campus, M
University of Phoenix-Central Massachusetts
Campus, M

Michigan

Lawrence Technological University, D
Saginaw Valley State University, M
University of Phoenix-Metro Detroit Campus, M
University of Phoenix-West Michigan Campus, M

Minnesota

University of Minnesota, Twin Cities Campus, M
University of St. Thomas, MO

Missouri

Grantham University, M
University of Phoenix-Kansas City Campus, M

Nevada

University of Phoenix-Nevada Campus, M

New Hampshire

University of New Hampshire, M

New Jersey

Fairleigh Dickinson University, College at
Florham, O
Kean University, M
New Jersey Institute of Technology, MD
Stevens Institute of Technology, MDO

New Mexico

University of New Mexico, M
University of Phoenix-New Mexico Campus, M

New York

Iona College, MO
New York Institute of Technology, M
New York University, MDO
Polytechnic University, Brooklyn Campus, M
Rensselaer Polytechnic Institute, MD
State University of New York Institute of
Technology, M

Stony Brook University, State University of New
York, MO

North Carolina

East Carolina University, D
North Carolina Agricultural and Technical State
University, M
North Carolina State University, D
University of Phoenix-Charlotte Campus, M

Ohio

The University of Akron, M
University of Cincinnati, M
University of Phoenix-Cincinnati Campus, M
University of Phoenix-Cleveland Campus, M

Oklahoma

Oklahoma State University, M
University of Phoenix-Oklahoma City Campus, M
University of Phoenix-Tulsa Campus, M
University of Tulsa, M

Oregon

Portland State University, MDO
University of Phoenix-Oregon Campus, M

Pennsylvania

California University of Pennsylvania, M
Carlow University, M
Carnegie Mellon University, M
La Salle University, M
University of Pennsylvania, M
University of Phoenix-Philadelphia Campus, M
University of Phoenix-Pittsburgh Campus, M
The University of Scranton, M
Villanova University, M

Puerto Rico

University of Phoenix-Puerto Rico Campus, M

South Dakota

South Dakota School of Mines and Technology, M

Tennessee

University of Phoenix-Nashville Campus, M
Vanderbilt University, MD

Texas

Dallas Baptist University, M
Texas A&M University-Commerce, M
Texas State University-San Marcos, M
University of Phoenix-Dallas Campus, M
University of Phoenix-Houston Campus, O

Utah

University of Phoenix-Utah Campus, M

Vermont

Champlain College, M

Virginia

George Mason University, MD

Washington

City University, MO
University of Phoenix-Washington Campus, M
Washington State University, M

West Virginia

Marshall University, M

Wisconsin

Marquette University, M
University of Phoenix-Wisconsin Campus, M
University of Wisconsin-Stout, M

University of Wisconsin-Whitewater, M

Alberta

Athabasca University, MO

British Columbia

Simon Fraser University, M
University of Phoenix-Vancouver Campus, M

Ontario

University of Waterloo, MD

Quebec

Université Laval, O

MANAGEMENT SCIENCE

Alabama

Tuskegee University, B
The University of Alabama, B

Arizona

GateWay Community College, A
Phoenix College, A
Prescott College, B
University of Phoenix Online Campus, B
University of Phoenix-Phoenix Campus, B
University of Phoenix-Southern Arizona Campus, B

Arkansas

University of Arkansas, B

California

Reedley College, A
Santa Ana College, A
Santiago Canyon College, A
University of California, San Diego, B
University of Phoenix-Bay Area Campus, B
University of Phoenix-Sacramento Valley Campus, B

Colorado

Colorado Christian University, B
Metropolitan State College of Denver, B
University of Phoenix-Denver Campus, B
University of Phoenix-Southern Colorado
Campus, B

Connecticut

United States Coast Guard Academy, B
University of Connecticut, B

Florida

Everglades University (Boca Raton), B
Nova Southeastern University, B
Stetson University, B
University of Florida, B
University of Phoenix-Central Florida Campus, B
University of Phoenix-North Florida Campus, B
University of Phoenix-South Florida Campus, B
University of Phoenix-West Florida Campus, B
University of South Florida, B

Georgia

University of Phoenix-Atlanta Campus, B

Hawaii

University of Phoenix-Hawaii Campus, B

Illinois

Black Hawk College, A
Oakton Community College, A
Prairie State College, A
Roosevelt University, B
Southern Illinois University Carbondale, B
Trinity International University, B

University of Phoenix-Chicago Campus, B

Indiana

Oakland City University, B
Valparaiso University, B

Iowa

St. Ambrose University, B
The University of Iowa, B

Kansas

Southwestern College, B

Kentucky

Hazard Community and Technical College, A
University of Kentucky, B

Louisiana

Louisiana State University and Agricultural and
    Mechanical College, B
Louisiana Tech University, B

Maryland

Salisbury University, B
University of Maryland, College Park, B
University of Maryland University College, B

Massachusetts

Cambridge College, B
Cape Cod Community College, A
Fitchburg State College, B
Northeastern University, B

Michigan

Grace Bible College, B
Madonna University, B
Oakland Community College, A
University of Phoenix-Metro Detroit Campus, B
University of Phoenix-West Michigan Campus, B

Minnesota

Capella University, B
Minnesota State University Mankato, B
University of Minnesota, Morris, B

Missouri

Central Methodist University, B
Columbia College, B
National American University, AB
University of Missouri-St. Louis, B

Montana

Rocky Mountain College, B
University of Great Falls, B

Nebraska

University of Nebraska-Lincoln, B

Nevada

Western Nevada Community College, A

New Jersey

Caldwell College, B
Rider University, B
Rutgers, The State University of New Jersey, New
    Brunswick/Piscataway, B

New Mexico

New Mexico State University, B
University of Phoenix-New Mexico Campus, B

New York

Le Moyne College, B
Manhattan College, B
Pace University, B
St. Bonaventure University, B
State University of New York at Binghamton, B
State University of New York at New Paltz, B

State University of New York at Oswego, B

North Carolina

Louisburg College, A
Wake Forest University, B

North Dakota

University of Mary, B

Ohio

Franklin University, B
Lourdes College, B
Miami University, B
Ohio Northern University, B
University of Phoenix-Columbus Ohio Campus, B
Wright State University, B

Oklahoma

Oklahoma State University, B
Oral Roberts University, B
St. Gregory's University, B
Southeastern Oklahoma State University, B
Southern Nazarene University, B
Tulsa Community College, A
University of Phoenix-Oklahoma City Campus, B
University of Phoenix-Tulsa Campus, B

Oregon

Tillamook Bay Community College, A
University of Phoenix-Oregon Campus, B

Pennsylvania

Clarion University of Pennsylvania, B
Duquesne University, B
Eastern University, B
Harrisburg Area Community College, A
The Pennsylvania State University Harrisburg
    Campus, B
Saint Joseph's University, B
Shippensburg University of Pennsylvania, B
University of Phoenix-Philadelphia Campus, B
University of Phoenix-Pittsburgh Campus, B
The University of Scranton, B

Puerto Rico

Inter American University of Puerto Rico, Bayamón
    Campus, B

South Carolina

University of South Carolina, B

Tennessee

Southern Adventist University, B
University of Memphis, B
The University of Tennessee at Martin, B

Texas

Hardin-Simmons University, B
Southern Methodist University, B
Texas A&M University, B
Texas Christian University, B
Trinity University, B
University of the Incarnate Word, B
University of Phoenix-Dallas Campus, B
University of Phoenix-Houston Campus, B
The University of Texas at San Antonio, B

Utah

University of Phoenix-Utah Campus, B

Virginia

Averett University, B
Virginia Polytechnic Institute and State University, B
Virginia State University, B

Washington

University of Phoenix-Washington Campus, B
University of Washington, B
Washington State University, B

West Virginia

American Public University System, B
Mountain State University, AB

Wheeling Jesuit University, B

Wisconsin

Lakeshore Technical College, A
University of Phoenix-Wisconsin Campus, B

Wyoming

University of Wyoming, B

British Columbia

British Columbia Institute of Technology, A
Simon Fraser University, B

Nova Scotia

Dalhousie University, B

Ontario

University of Windsor, B

Quebec

HEC Montreal, B
McGill University, B

MANAGEMENT SCIENCES AND QUANTITATIVE METHODS

Indiana

Indiana State University, B
Valparaiso University, B

Iowa

The University of Iowa, B

New Jersey

Rutgers, The State University of New Jersey, New
    Brunswick/Piscataway, B

Ohio

Ohio Northern University, B
The University of Toledo, B

Pennsylvania

Duquesne University, B
The Pennsylvania State University, Lehigh Valley
    Campus of the Berks-Lehigh Valley College, B
The Pennsylvania State University Schuylkill
    Campus of the Capital College, B
The Pennsylvania State University University Park
    Campus, B
University of Pennsylvania, B

MANAGEMENT STRATEGY AND POLICY

Arizona

The University of Arizona, M

California

Azusa Pacific University, M
Dominican University of California, M

Connecticut

University of New Haven, M

District of Columbia

The George Washington University, MD

Georgia

Brenau University, M
Georgia Institute of Technology, MD

Illinois

DePaul University, M
Illinois Institute of Technology, M

Northwestern University, D

Indiana

Purdue University, MD

Iowa

The University of Iowa, M

Massachusetts

Tufts University, O

Minnesota

University of Minnesota, Twin Cities Campus, MD

New Jersey

Rutgers, The State University of New Jersey,
   Newark, M
Stevens Institute of Technology, M

New Mexico

University of New Mexico, M

New York

Bernard M. Baruch College of the City University of
   New York, MD
Manhattanville College, M
New York Institute of Technology, M
New York University, D
Pace University, M
Syracuse University, D

North Carolina

The University of North Carolina at Chapel Hill, D

Ohio

Case Western Reserve University, MD

Pennsylvania

Neumann College, M
Temple University, MD

South Carolina

Clemson University, D

Texas

Lamar University, M
University of Dallas, M
University of Houston-Clear Lake, M
University of North Texas, D

Virginia

Marymount University, O
Regent University, D

West Virginia

Mountain State University, M

Alberta

University of Calgary, MD

British Columbia

The University of British Columbia, D

Quebec

HEC Montreal, M
McGill University, M

MANUFACTURING ENGINEERING

Arizona

Arizona State University at the Polytechnic
   Campus, M
Cochise College (Douglas), A

California

California Polytechnic State University, San Luis
   Obispo, O
University of California, Berkeley, B
University of California, Los Angeles, BM

University of Southern California, M

Colorado

Colorado State University, MD
University of Colorado at Colorado Springs, M

Connecticut

Central Connecticut State University, M
University of Connecticut, B

Florida

Florida State University, MD
University of Central Florida, M

Illinois

Bradley University, M
Illinois Institute of Technology, M
Northwestern University, BM
Southern Illinois University Carbondale, M
Southern Illinois University Edwardsville, B

Indiana

Purdue University, MD

Iowa

The University of Iowa, MD

Kansas

Kansas State University, MD
Wichita State University, BMD

Kentucky

Eastern Kentucky University, M
University of Kentucky, M

Louisiana

Louisiana Tech University, M

Maine

University of Southern Maine, M

Maryland

University of Maryland, College Park, MD

Massachusetts

Boston University, MDO
Northeastern University, MD
Tufts University, O
University of Massachusetts Amherst, M
University of Massachusetts Lowell, O
Western New England College, M
Worcester Polytechnic Institute, MDO

Michigan

Grand Valley State University, M
Kettering University, M
Lawrence Technological University, MD
Michigan State University, MD
University of Detroit Mercy, BD
University of Michigan, MDO
University of Michigan-Dearborn, BMD
Wayne State University, M
Western Michigan University, BM

Minnesota

Minnesota State University Mankato, M
University of St. Thomas, M
Walden University, M

Missouri

University of Missouri-Columbia, MD
University of Missouri-Rolla, BM

Nebraska

University of Nebraska-Lincoln, MD

New Hampshire

Dartmouth College, MD

New Jersey

New Jersey Institute of Technology, BM

New Mexico

University of New Mexico, M

New York

Clarkson University, B
Cornell University, D

Hofstra University, B
Polytechnic University, Brooklyn Campus, M
Rensselaer Polytechnic Institute, BMO
Rochester Institute of Technology, M

North Carolina

North Carolina State University, M

North Dakota

North Dakota State University, BMD

Ohio

Bowling Green State University, M
Kent State University, Salem Campus, A
Ohio University, M

Oklahoma

Oklahoma State University, M

Oregon

Oregon State University, M
Portland State University, M

Pennsylvania

Drexel University, MD
Lehigh University, MO
The Pennsylvania State University Fayette Campus
   of the Commonwealth College, A
The Pennsylvania State University Hazleton
   Campus of the Commonwealth College, A
The Pennsylvania State University McKeesport
   Campus of the Commonwealth College, A
The Pennsylvania State University University Park
   Campus, M
The Pennsylvania State University Wilkes-Barre
   Campus of the Commonwealth College, A
The Pennsylvania State University York Campus of
   the Commonwealth College, A
Robert Morris University, B
Villanova University, O

Puerto Rico

Polytechnic University of Puerto Rico, M

Rhode Island

University of Rhode Island, M

South Carolina

Clemson University, M

Tennessee

East Tennessee State University, M
University of Memphis, M
The University of Tennessee, M

Texas

Southern Methodist University, M
Texas State University-San Marcos, B
Texas Tech University, M
The University of Texas at Austin, MO
The University of Texas-Pan American, B

Utah

Brigham Young University, B

Virginia

Old Dominion University, M
Virginia State University, B

Wisconsin

University of Wisconsin-Madison, M
University of Wisconsin-Stout, B

Alberta

University of Calgary, MD

Ontario

University of Toronto, B
University of Windsor, MD

Saskatchewan

University of Regina, M

MANUFACTURING TECHNOLOGY/TECHNICIAN

Arizona

Arizona State University at the Polytechnic Campus, B

California

California State University, Long Beach, B

Connecticut

Central Connecticut State University, B

Florida

Brevard Community College, A
St. Petersburg College, A

Georgia

Albany Technical College, A
Altamaha Technical College, A
Flint River Technical College, A
Griffin Technical College, A
South Georgia Technical College, A
West Central Technical College, A

Idaho

Lewis-Clark State College, AB

Illinois

Black Hawk College, A
College of DuPage, A
Illinois Eastern Community Colleges, Wabash Valley College, A
Illinois Institute of Technology, B
Rend Lake College, A
Western Illinois University, B

Iowa

University of Northern Iowa, B

Kansas

Hutchinson Community College and Area Vocational School, A
Southwestern College, B

Kentucky

Hopkinsville Community College, A
Murray State University, B

Massachusetts

Fitchburg State College, B
Mount Wachusett Community College, A

Michigan

Alpena Community College, A
Eastern Michigan University, B
Lawrence Technological University, A
Macomb Community College, A
Mott Community College, A
Northern Michigan University, B
Oakland Community College, A

Minnesota

Minnesota State Community and Technical College-Fergus Falls, A

Missouri

East Central College, A
Missouri Western State University, A

Nebraska

University of Nebraska at Omaha, B

New Jersey

Kean University, B

New Mexico

Luna Community College, A

New York

Excelsior College, A
Farmingdale State University of New York, B

Rochester Institute of Technology, B

North Carolina

East Carolina University, B
Western Carolina University, B

Ohio

Owens Community College, A

Oregon

Rogue Community College, A

Pennsylvania

Lehigh Carbon Community College, A
Pennsylvania College of Technology, AB
The Pennsylvania State University at Erie, The Behrend College, A

Rhode Island

Roger Williams University, B

Tennessee

University of Memphis, B

Texas

Midwestern State University, B
Tarleton State University, B
Texas A&M University, B
Texas State University-San Marcos, B
The University of Texas at Brownsville, B

Utah

Utah Valley State College, A

Washington

Bates Technical College, A
Clark College, A
Eastern Washington University, B
Western Washington University, B

West Virginia

Marshall Community and Technical College, A

Wisconsin

Waukesha County Technical College, A

British Columbia

Thompson Rivers University, A

MARINE AFFAIRS

California

University of San Diego, M

Delaware

University of Delaware, MD

Florida

Florida Institute of Technology, M
Nova Southeastern University, M
University of Miami, MO
University of West Florida, M

Louisiana

Louisiana State University and Agricultural and Mechanical College, MD

Maine

University of Maine, M

New Jersey

Stevens Institute of Technology, M

North Carolina

Duke University, M
East Carolina University, D

Oregon

Oregon State University, M

Rhode Island

University of Rhode Island, M

Washington

University of Washington, MO

Newfoundland and Labrador

Memorial University of Newfoundland, MD

Nova Scotia

Dalhousie University, M

Quebec

Université du Québec àRimouski, M

MARINE BIOLOGY AND BIOLOGICAL OCEANOGRAPHY

Alabama

Alabama State University, B
Auburn University, B
Jacksonville State University, B
Samford University, B
Spring Hill College, B
Troy University, B
The University of Alabama, B
University of North Alabama, B
The University of West Alabama, B

Alaska

Alaska Pacific University, B
University of Alaska Fairbanks, MD

Arizona

Northern Arizona University, B

California

California State University, Long Beach, B
California State University, Stanislaus, M
Humboldt State University, B
San Francisco State University, BM
San Jose State University, B
Sonoma State University, B
University of California, Los Angeles, B
University of California, San Diego, MD
University of California, Santa Barbara, BMD
University of California, Santa Cruz, B
University of Southern California, D

Colorado

Colorado Northwestern Community College, A
University of Colorado at Boulder, MD

Connecticut

Mitchell College, A
University of Connecticut, B
University of New Haven, B

District of Columbia

American University, B

Florida

Barry University, B
Daytona Beach Community College, A
Eckerd College, B
Florida Institute of Technology, BM
Florida International University, B
Florida Keys Community College, A
Florida State University, BMD
New College of Florida, B
Nova Southeastern University, BMD
University of Miami, BMD

University of West Florida, B

Georgia

Savannah State University, B

Guam

University of Guam, M

Hawaii

Hawaii Pacific University, B
University of Hawaii at Manoa, BMD

Idaho

Brigham Young University -Idaho, A

Illinois

Lincoln College, A
Western Illinois University, O

Indiana

Ball State University, B

Kansas

Southwestern College, B

Kentucky

Murray State University, M

Louisiana

Nicholls State University, BM

Maine

College of the Atlantic, B
Maine Maritime Academy, B
Saint Joseph's College of Maine, B
Southern Maine Community College, A
Unity College, B
University of Maine, BMD
University of Maine at Machias, B
University of New England, B

Maryland

University of Maryland Eastern Shore, B

Massachusetts

Boston University, B
Harvard University, B
Northeastern University, B
Salem State College, B
Suffolk University, B
University of Massachusetts Dartmouth, M

Michigan

Michigan Technological University, B

Minnesota

Bemidji State University, B

Mississippi

Mississippi State University, B
University of Southern Mississippi, BMD

Missouri

Missouri Southern State University, B

New Hampshire

University of New Hampshire, B

New Jersey

Fairleigh Dickinson University, College at
   Florham, B
Fairleigh Dickinson University, Metropolitan
   Campus, B
Monmouth University, B
The Richard Stockton College of New Jersey, B
Rutgers, The State University of New Jersey, New
   Brunswick/Piscataway, BMD

New York

Cornell University, B
Dowling College, B
Sarah Lawrence College, B

Stony Brook University, State University of New
   York, B

North Carolina

The University of North Carolina Wilmington, BMD

Oregon

Oregon Coast Community College, A
University of Oregon, MD

Pennsylvania

East Stroudsburg University of Pennsylvania, B
Gettysburg College, B
Juniata College, B
Saint Francis University, B
Waynesburg College, B

Puerto Rico

University of Puerto Rico at Humacao, B

Rhode Island

Brown University, B
Roger Williams University, B
University of Rhode Island, B

South Carolina

Coastal Carolina University, B
College of Charleston, BM
University of South Carolina, B

Texas

Texas A&M University at Galveston, B
Texas State University-San Marcos, BM

United States Virgin Islands

University of the Virgin Islands, B

Utah

Dixie State College of Utah, A

Virginia

Hampton University, B
Old Dominion University, B

Washington

Shoreline Community College, A
Western Washington University, B

British Columbia

The University of British Columbia, B
University of Victoria, BMD

New Brunswick

University of New Brunswick Saint John, B

Newfoundland and Labrador

Memorial University of Newfoundland, BM

Nova Scotia

Dalhousie University, B
University of King's College, B

Quebec

McGill University, B

MARINE ENGINEERING

Michigan

University of Michigan, MDO

MARINE GEOLOGY

California

University of California, San Diego, MD

Florida

University of Miami, MD

Hawaii

University of Hawaii at Manoa, MD

Massachusetts

Massachusetts Institute of Technology, M

New York

Cornell University, MD

Washington

University of Washington, MD

British Columbia

University of Victoria, MD

MARINE MAINTENANCE/FITTER AND SHIP REPAIR TECHNOLOGY/TECHNICIAN

Iowa

Iowa Lakes Community College, A

Minnesota

Alexandria Technical College, A

North Carolina

Cape Fear Community College, A

Rhode Island

New England Institute of Technology, A

Washington

Olympic College, A

Wisconsin

Northeast Wisconsin Technical College, A

MARINE SCIENCE/MERCHANT MARINE OFFICER

Arizona

Prescott College, B

California

College of the Redwoods, A
Saddleback College, A
University of San Diego, B

District of Columbia

American University, B
University of the District of Columbia, A

Florida

Indian River Community College, A
Jacksonville University, B
The University of Tampa, B

Maine

Maine Maritime Academy, B

Maryland

Anne Arundel Community College, A

Massachusetts

Massachusetts Maritime Academy, B
Salem State College, B

Michigan

Northwestern Michigan College, A

New Hampshire

University of New Hampshire, B

New Jersey

Rider University, B

New York

State University of New York Maritime College, AB
United States Merchant Marine Academy, B

South Carolina

University of South Carolina, B

Texas

Texas A&M University at Galveston, B

Virginia

Hampton University, B
Saint Paul's College, B

Newfoundland and Labrador

Memorial University of Newfoundland, B

MARINE SCIENCES

Alabama

University of South Alabama, MD

Alaska

University of Alaska Fairbanks, MD

California

California State University, East Bay, M
California State University, Fresno, M
California State University, Monterey Bay, M
California State University, Sacramento, M
San Jose State University, M
University of California, San Diego, MD
University of California, Santa Barbara, MD
University of California, Santa Cruz, MD
University of San Diego, M
University of Southern California, D

Connecticut

University of Connecticut, MD

Delaware

University of Delaware, MD

Florida

Florida Institute of Technology, M
Nova Southeastern University, M
University of Florida, MD
University of Miami, MD
University of South Florida, MD

Georgia

Savannah State University, M
University of Georgia, MD

Kentucky

Murray State University, M

Maine

University of Maine, MD

Maryland

University of Maryland, Baltimore County, MD
University of Maryland, College Park, MD
University of Maryland Eastern Shore, MD

Massachusetts

University of Massachusetts Amherst, M
University of Massachusetts Boston, D
University of Massachusetts Dartmouth, MD

Mississippi

University of Southern Mississippi, MD

New York

Cornell University, MD
Stony Brook University, State University of New York, MD

North Carolina

Duke University, MO
North Carolina State University, MD
The University of North Carolina at Chapel Hill, MD

The University of North Carolina Wilmington, M

Oregon

Oregon State University, M

Puerto Rico

University of Puerto Rico, Mayagüez Campus, MD

South Carolina

Coastal Carolina University, M
University of South Carolina, MD

Texas

Texas A&M University at Galveston, M
The University of Texas at Austin, MD

Virginia

The College of William and Mary, MD

Wisconsin

University of Wisconsin-La Crosse, M
University of Wisconsin-Madison, MD

British Columbia

The University of British Columbia, MD

Newfoundland and Labrador

Memorial University of Newfoundland, M

MARINE TECHNOLOGY

California

California Maritime Academy, B
College of Marin, A
National Polytechnic College of Engineering and Oceaneering, A
Orange Coast College, A
Saddleback College, A
Santa Barbara City College, A

Colorado

Northeastern Junior College, A

Florida

Florida Keys Community College, A

Hawaii

Honolulu Community College, A

Idaho

North Idaho College, A

Kentucky

Louisville Technical Institute, A

Maine

Washington County Community College, A

Minnesota

Northwest Technical College, A

New York

Kingsborough Community College of the City University of New York, A

North Carolina

Cape Fear Community College, A
College of The Albemarle, A

Texas

Lamar University, B

Washington

Highline Community College, A
Seattle Central Community College, A
Shoreline Community College, A

Skagit Valley College, A

MARINE TRANSPORTATION

Michigan

Northwestern Michigan College, A

New York

United States Merchant Marine Academy, B

MARITIME SCIENCE

Maine

College of the Atlantic, B

Massachusetts

Massachusetts Maritime Academy, B

Michigan

Northwestern Michigan College, A

New York

State University of New York Maritime College, B
United States Merchant Marine Academy, B

Tennessee

Martin Methodist College, A

Texas

Texas A&M University at Galveston, B

MARKETING

Alabama

Alabama Agricultural and Mechanical University, M
Andrew Jackson University, M
Columbia Southern University, M
Troy University, B
The University of Alabama, MD

Arizona

Arizona State University, D
The University of Arizona, MD
University of Phoenix Online Campus, M
University of Phoenix-Phoenix Campus, M
Western International University, M

California

Argosy University/Orange County, MD
California Lutheran University, M
California State University, East Bay, M
California State University, Fullerton, M
California State University, Los Angeles, M
Golden Gate University, MO
San Diego State University, M
University of California, Berkeley, D
University of La Verne, M
University of Phoenix-Bay Area Campus, M
University of Phoenix-Sacramento Valley Campus, M
University of San Francisco, M

Colorado

Regis University, M
University of Colorado at Boulder, MD
University of Colorado at Colorado Springs, M
University of Colorado at Denver and Health Sciences Center - Downtown Denver Campus, M
University of Denver, M

Connecticut

Fairfield University, MO
Quinnipiac University, M
University of Connecticut, MD
University of New Haven, M

Yale University, D

Delaware

Goldey-Beacom College, M

District of Columbia

American University, M
The George Washington University, MD
Howard University, M
Southeastern University, M

Florida

Argosy University/Sarasota, MD
Argosy University/Tampa, M
Florida Agricultural and Mechanical University, M
Florida Atlantic University, M
Florida State University, M
Lynn University, M
University of Florida, MD
University of Miami, M
University of Phoenix-Central Florida Campus, M
University of Phoenix-North Florida Campus, M
University of Phoenix-South Florida Campus, M
The University of Tampa, M

Georgia

American InterContinental University (Atlanta), M
Clark Atlanta University, BM
Clayton State University, B
Emory University, D
Georgia Institute of Technology, MD
Georgia State University, MD
Macon State College, B
University of Phoenix-Columbus Georgia
    Campus, M

Hawaii

Hawaii Pacific University, M
University of Hawaii at Manoa, MD
University of Phoenix-Hawaii Campus, M

Illinois

American InterContinental University Online, M
Argosy University/Schaumburg, MD
Black Hawk College, A
DePaul University, M
Illinois Institute of Technology, M
Loyola University Chicago, M
Northeastern Illinois University, M
Northwestern University, MD
Saint Xavier University, M
University of Illinois at Urbana-Champaign, B

Indiana

Indiana Tech, M
Indiana University Bloomington, MD
Indiana University Southeast, O
Purdue University, MD

Iowa

The University of Iowa, BMD

Louisiana

Louisiana State University and Agricultural and
    Mechanical College, MD
Louisiana Tech University, MD

Maryland

The Johns Hopkins University, M
Loyola College in Maryland, M
University of Baltimore, M

Massachusetts

Babson College, B
Bentley College, MO
Boston University, D
Clark University, M
Emerson College, M
Lasell College, M
Nichols College, M
Western New England College, B

Worcester Polytechnic Institute, M

Michigan

Andrews University, M
Central Michigan University, BM
Davenport University (Dearborn), M
Eastern Michigan University, M
Michigan State University, MD
Oakland Community College, A
Oakland University, O
University of Phoenix-Metro Detroit Campus, M
Western Michigan University, B

Minnesota

Capella University, B
Metropolitan State University, M
St. Cloud State University, M
University of Minnesota, Twin Cities Campus, MD
University of St. Thomas, M

Mississippi

Delta State University, M

Missouri

Lindenwood University, M
Maryville University of Saint Louis, MO
University of Missouri-St. Louis, MO
Washington University in St. Louis, B
Webster University, M

Nebraska

Northeast Community College, A
University of Nebraska-Lincoln, MD

Nevada

University of Phoenix-Nevada Campus, M

New Jersey

Fairleigh Dickinson University, College at
    Florham, MO
Fairleigh Dickinson University, Metropolitan
    Campus, MO
Montclair State University, M
Rutgers, The State University of New Jersey,
    Newark, MD
Saint Peter's College, M
Seton Hall University, MO

New Mexico

University of New Mexico, M
University of Phoenix-New Mexico Campus, M

New York

Adelphi University, M
Bernard M. Baruch College of the City University of
    New York, MD
Canisius College, BM
Cornell University, D
Fashion Institute of Technology, AM
Fordham University, M
Hofstra University, MO
Iona College, MO
Long Island University, C.W. Post Campus, MO
Mercy College, M
Mount Saint Mary College, B
New York Institute of Technology, MO
New York University, MD
Pace University, M
Rensselaer Polytechnic Institute, M
St. Bonaventure University, MO
St. John's University, MO
St. Thomas Aquinas College, M
State University of New York at New Paltz, M
Syracuse University, D
University at Albany, State University of New
    York, M
Wagner College, M

North Carolina

The University of North Carolina at Chapel Hill, D
The University of North Carolina at Greensboro, MD

Western Carolina University, B

Ohio

Bowling Green State University, B
Case Western Reserve University, MD
Franklin University, M
Kent State University, D
Miami University, M
Miami University Hamilton, B
The University of Akron, BMO
University of Cincinnati, MD
The University of Findlay, M
The University of Toledo, M
Wright State University, MO
Xavier University, M
Youngstown State University, M

Oklahoma

Oklahoma City University, M
Oklahoma State University, D
Oral Roberts University, M

Oregon

Tillamook Bay Community College, A
University of Oregon, D

Pennsylvania

Carnegie Mellon University, D
DeSales University, B
Drexel University, M
Gannon University, O
La Roche College, B
The Pennsylvania State University University Park
    Campus, D
Philadelphia University, M
Saint Joseph's University, BMO
Temple University, MD
University of Pennsylvania, MD
The University of Scranton, M
Wilkes University, M

Puerto Rico

Bayamon Central University, M
Inter American University of Puerto Rico,
    Metropolitan Campus, M
Inter American University of Puerto Rico, San
    Germán Campus, BM
Pontifical Catholic University of Puerto Rico, M
Universidad Metropolitana, M
Universidad del Turabo, M
University of Phoenix-Puerto Rico Campus, M
University of Puerto Rico, Mayagüez Campus, M
University of the Sacred Heart, M

Rhode Island

Bryant University, MO
Johnson & Wales University, M
University of Rhode Island, M

Tennessee

Middle Tennessee State University, M
Southern Adventist University, M
University of Memphis, MD
The University of Tennessee, MD
Vanderbilt University, D

Texas

Dallas Baptist University, M
St. Edward's University, MO
Stephen F. Austin State University, M
Tarleton State University, M
Texas A&M University, MD
Texas Tech University, MD
University of Dallas, M
University of Houston, D
University of North Texas, MD
University of Phoenix-Dallas Campus, M
The University of Texas at Arlington, MD
The University of Texas at Austin, D

The University of Texas at San Antonio, M

Utah

University of Phoenix-Utah Campus, M
University of Utah, B

Virginia

University of Northern Virginia, M
Virginia Commonwealth University, M
Virginia Polytechnic Institute and State
  University, MD

Washington

City University, MO

West Virginia

West Virginia State Community and Technical
  College, A
West Virginia University, M

Wisconsin

Concordia University Wisconsin, M
University of Wisconsin-Whitewater, M

Alberta

University of Alberta, D

British Columbia

Simon Fraser University, M
The University of British Columbia, D

Quebec

HEC Montreal, M
McGill University, M
Université Laval, M
Université de Sherbrooke, M

Saskatchewan

University of Saskatchewan, M

MARKETING/MARKETING MANAGEMENT

Alabama

Alabama Agricultural and Mechanical University, B
Alabama State University, B
Auburn University, B
Auburn University Montgomery, B
Columbia Southern University, B
Enterprise-Ozark Community College, A
Faulkner University, B
Huntingdon College, B
Jacksonville State University, B
Jefferson Davis Community College, A
Spring Hill College, B
Talladega College, B
Tuskegee University, B
The University of Alabama, B
The University of Alabama at Birmingham, B
The University of Alabama in Huntsville, B
University of Montevallo, B
University of North Alabama, B
University of South Alabama, B
Wallace State Community College, A

Alaska

University of Alaska Anchorage, B

Arizona

Arizona State University, B
Arizona Western College, A
Central Arizona College, A
Grand Canyon University, B
Mesa Community College, A
Mohave Community College, A
Northern Arizona University, B
Phoenix College, A
The University of Arizona, B
University of Phoenix-Phoenix Campus, B
University of Phoenix-Southern Arizona Campus, B

Western International University, B

Arkansas

Arkansas Northeastern College, A
Arkansas State University, B
Harding University, B
John Brown University, B
Ouachita Technical College, A
University of Arkansas, B
University of Arkansas Community College at
  Morrilton, A
University of Arkansas at Little Rock, B
University of Central Arkansas, B
University of the Ozarks, B

California

American InterContinental University, B
American River College, A
Antelope Valley College, A
Azusa Pacific University, B
Bakersfield College, A
Butte College, A
California Lutheran University, B
California State Polytechnic University, Pomona, B
California State University, Chico, B
California State University, Dominguez Hills, B
California State University, East Bay, B
California State University, Fresno, B
California State University, Fullerton, B
California State University, Long Beach, B
California State University, Sacramento, B
California State University, San Bernardino, B
Cerritos College, A
Chaffey College, A
City College of San Francisco, A
College of Alameda, A
College of the Desert, A
College of Marin, A
College of San Mateo, A
College of the Sequoias, A
Cosumnes River College (Sacramento), A
Crafton Hills College, A
Cuesta College, A
Cypress College, A
De Anza College, A
East Los Angeles College, A
El Camino College, A
FIDM/The Fashion Institute of Design &
  Merchandising, Orange County Campus, A
Folsom Lake College, A
Fresno Pacific University, B
Fullerton College, A
Golden Gate University, B
Golden West College, A
Grossmont College, A
Hartnell College, A
Holy Names University, B
Humboldt State University, B
Imperial Valley College, A
Lake Tahoe Community College, A
Laney College, A
Las Positas College, A
Long Beach City College, A
Los Angeles City College, A
Los Angeles Southwest College, A
Los Angeles Valley College, A
Merced College, A
MiraCosta College, A
Mission College, A
Modesto Junior College, A
Monterey Peninsula College, A
Moorpark College, A
Mount St. Mary's College, B
Mt. San Antonio College, A
Napa Valley College, A
National University, B
Notre Dame de Namur University, B
Ohlone College, A
Orange Coast College, A
Oxnard College, A
Pacific Union College, B
Palo Verde College, A
Palomar College, A
Pasadena City College, A
San Bernardino Valley College, A
San Diego City College, A

San Diego Mesa College, A
San Diego State University, B
San Francisco State University, B
San Joaquin Delta College, A
San Jose City College, A
San Jose State University, B
Santa Ana College, A
Santa Barbara City College, A
Santa Clara University, B
Santiago Canyon College, A
Sierra College, A
Solano Community College, A
Southwestern College, A
University of La Verne, B
University of Phoenix-Bay Area Campus, B
University of Phoenix-Central Valley Campus, B
University of Phoenix-Sacramento Valley Campus, B
University of Phoenix-San Diego Campus, B
University of San Francisco, B
Vanguard University of Southern California, B
West Los Angeles College, A
West Valley College, A
Westwood College-Anaheim, B
Westwood College-Inland Empire, B
Westwood College-Los Angeles, B
Woodbury University, B

Colorado

Aims Community College, A
Arapahoe Community College, A
Colorado Mountain College, Alpine Campus, A
Colorado State University, B
Colorado State University-Pueblo, B
Community College of Aurora, A
Fort Lewis College, B
Johnson & Wales University, AB
Jones International University, B
Lamar Community College, A
Mesa State College, B
Northeastern Junior College, A
Red Rocks Community College, A
University of Colorado at Boulder, B
University of Colorado at Colorado Springs, B
University of Denver, B
Western State College of Colorado, B
Westwood College-Denver North, B
Westwood College-Denver South, B

Connecticut

Albertus Magnus College, B
Central Connecticut State University, B
Fairfield University, B
Manchester Community College, A
Middlesex Community College, A
Naugatuck Valley Community College, A
Norwalk Community College, A
Post University, AB
Quinnipiac University, B
Sacred Heart University, B
Three Rivers Community College, A
Tunxis Community College, A
University of Bridgeport, AB
University of Connecticut, B
University of New Haven, B
Western Connecticut State University, B

Delaware

Delaware State University, B
Delaware Technical & Community College, Jack F.
  Owens Campus, A
Delaware Technical & Community College,
  Stanton/Wilmington Campus, A
Goldey-Beacom College, B
University of Delaware, B
Wesley College, B
Wilmington College, B

District of Columbia

The George Washington University, B
Georgetown University, B
Howard University, B
Southeastern University, AB
Strayer University, A

University of the District of Columbia, AB

Florida

Barry University, B
Broward Community College, A
Central Florida Community College, A
Daytona Beach Community College, A
Florida Atlantic University, B
Florida Community College at Jacksonville, A
Florida Gulf Coast University, B
Florida International University, B
Florida Metropolitan University-Brandon
  Campus, AB
Florida Metropolitan University-Lakeland Campus, A
Florida Metropolitan University-North Orlando
  Campus, AB
Florida Metropolitan University-Pinellas Campus, AB
Florida Metropolitan University-Pompano Beach
  Campus, AB
Florida Metropolitan University-Tampa Campus, AB
Florida Southern College, B
Hillsborough Community College, A
Indian River Community College, A
Jacksonville University, B
Johnson & Wales University, AB
Lynn University, B
Miami Dade College, A
Northwood University, Florida Campus, B
Nova Southeastern University, B
Palm Beach Atlantic University, B
Palm Beach Community College, A
Pasco-Hernando Community College, A
Polk Community College, A
St. Johns River Community College, A
St. Petersburg College, A
St. Thomas University, B
Santa Fe Community College, A
Schiller International University, B
Seminole Community College, A
South Florida Community College, A
Southeastern University, B
Stetson University, B
Tallahassee Community College, A
University of Central Florida, B
University of Florida, B
University of Miami, B
University of North Florida, B
University of Phoenix-Central Florida Campus, B
University of Phoenix-North Florida Campus, B
University of Phoenix-South Florida Campus, B
University of Phoenix-West Florida Campus, B
University of South Florida, B
The University of Tampa, B
University of West Florida, B
Valencia Community College, A
Webber International University, AB

Georgia

Abraham Baldwin Agricultural College, A
Albany State University, B
Albany Technical College, A
Altamaha Technical College, A
American InterContinental University (Atlanta), B
American InterContinental University (Dunwoody
  Campus), AB
Athens Technical College, A
Atlanta Technical College, A
Augusta State University, B
Augusta Technical College, A
Bainbridge College, A
Berry College, B
Brenau University, B
Central Georgia Technical College, A
Chattahoochee Technical College, A
Clayton State University, A
Columbus State University, B
Coosa Valley Technical College, A
Dalton State College, AB
DeKalb Technical College, A
Emory University, B
Fort Valley State University, B
Georgia College & State University, B
Georgia Highlands College, A
Georgia Perimeter College, A
Georgia Southern University, B
Georgia Southwestern State University, AB

Georgia State University, B
Griffin Technical College, A
Gwinnett Technical College, A
Heart of Georgia Technical College, A
Kennesaw State University, B
Lanier Technical College, A
Middle Georgia Technical College, A
Morehouse College, B
Moultrie Technical College, A
North Georgia College & State University, B
North Metro Technical College, A
Ogeechee Technical College, A
Savannah State University, B
Savannah Technical College, A
South Georgia Technical College, A
Southeastern Technical College, A
University of Georgia, B
University of Phoenix-Columbus Georgia
  Campus, B
University of West Georgia, B
Valdosta State University, B
Valdosta Technical College, A
West Central Technical College, A
West Georgia Technical College, A

Guam

Guam Community College, A
University of Guam, B

Hawaii

Chaminade University of Honolulu, B
Hawaii Pacific University, AB
Kapiolani Community College, A
Maui Community College, A
University of Hawaii at Manoa, B
University of Phoenix-Hawaii Campus, B

Idaho

Boise State University, AB
Brigham Young University -Idaho, A
College of Southern Idaho, A
Eastern Idaho Technical College, A
Idaho State University, AB
Northwest Nazarene University, B
University of Idaho, B
University of Phoenix-Idaho Campus, B

Illinois

American InterContinental University Online, B
Augustana College, B
Aurora University, B
Benedictine University, B
Blackburn College, B
Bradley University, B
Carl Sandburg College, A
Chicago State University, B
City Colleges of Chicago, Harold Washington
  College, A
City Colleges of Chicago, Harry S. Truman
  College, A
City Colleges of Chicago, Kennedy-King College, A
City Colleges of Chicago, Olive-Harvey College, A
City Colleges of Chicago, Richard J. Daley
  College, A
City Colleges of Chicago, Wilbur Wright College, A
College of DuPage, A
Columbia College Chicago, B
Danville Area Community College, A
DePaul University, B
Eastern Illinois University, B
Elgin Community College, A
Elmhurst College, B
Governors State University, B
Greenville College, B
Highland Community College, A
Illinois Central College, A
Illinois State University, B
Illinois Valley Community College, A
John A. Logan College, A
Joliet Junior College, A
Kankakee Community College, A
Kendall College, B
Lake Land College, A
Lewis University, B
Lincoln College, A
Lincoln College-Normal, A

Loyola University Chicago, B
MacCormac College, A
MacMurray College, B
McKendree College, B
Midstate College, A
Millikin University, B
Morton College, A
North Central College, B
North Park University, B
Northeastern Illinois University, B
Northern Illinois University, B
Oakton Community College, A
Olivet Nazarene University, B
Quincy University, B
Rock Valley College, A
Rockford Business College, A
Rockford College, B
Roosevelt University, B
Sauk Valley Community College, A
South Suburban College, A
Southern Illinois University Carbondale, B
Southwestern Illinois College, A
Trinity Christian College, B
Trinity International University, B
Triton College, A
University of Illinois at Chicago, B
University of Phoenix-Chicago Campus, B
University of St. Francis, B
Western Illinois University, B
Westwood College-Chicago Du Page, B
Westwood College-Chicago Loop Campus, B
Westwood College-Chicago O'Hare Airport, B
Westwood College-Chicago River Oaks, B
William Rainey Harper College, A

Indiana

Anderson University, B
Ball State University, AB
Butler University, B
Indiana State University, B
Indiana Tech, B
Indiana University Bloomington, B
Indiana University-Purdue University Fort Wayne, B
Indiana University South Bend, B
Indiana Wesleyan University, B
Manchester College, B
Martin University, B
Purdue University Calumet, B
Purdue University North Central, A
Saint Mary-of-the-Woods College, B
Saint Mary's College, B
Taylor University, B
Tri-State University, B
University of Evansville, B
University of Indianapolis, B
University of Notre Dame, B
University of Saint Francis, B
University of Southern Indiana, B
Valparaiso University, B
Vincennes University, A

Iowa

AIB College of Business, A
Buena Vista University, B
Clarke College, B
Des Moines Area Community College, A
Drake University, B
Ellsworth Community College, A
Hawkeye Community College, A
Iowa Lakes Community College, A
Iowa State University of Science and Technology, B
Iowa Western Community College, A
Kirkwood Community College, A
Loras College, B
Marshalltown Community College, A
Morningside College, B
Mount Mercy College, B
Northeast Iowa Community College, A
St. Ambrose University, B
Southwestern Community College, A
The University of Iowa, B
University of Northern Iowa, B
Upper Iowa University, B
Waldorf College, B

Wartburg College, B

Kansas

Barton County Community College, A
Butler Community College, A
Central Christian College of Kansas, A
Coffeyville Community College, A
Colby Community College, A
Cowley County Community College and Area
   Vocational-Technical School, A
Dodge City Community College, A
Emporia State University, B
Fort Hays State University, B
Garden City Community College, A
Kansas State University, B
MidAmerica Nazarene University, B
Neosho County Community College, A
Newman University, B
Pittsburg State University, B
Pratt Community College, A
Seward County Community College, A
Tabor College, B
Washburn University, B
Wichita State University, B

Kentucky

Brescia University, B
Campbellsville University, B
Eastern Kentucky University, B
Maysville Community and Technical College, A
Morehead State University, B
Murray State University, B
Northern Kentucky University, B
Sullivan University, AB
University of Kentucky, B
University of Louisville, B
Western Kentucky University, B

Louisiana

Grambling State University, B
Louisiana College, B
Louisiana State University and Agricultural and
   Mechanical College, B
Louisiana State University in Shreveport, B
Louisiana Tech University, B
Loyola University New Orleans, B
McNeese State University, B
Nicholls State University, B
Southeastern Louisiana University, B
Southern University and Agricultural and Mechanical
   College, B
Tulane University, AB
University of Louisiana at Lafayette, B
University of Louisiana at Monroe, B
University of New Orleans, B
Xavier University of Louisiana, B

Maine

Husson College, B
Kennebec Valley Community College, A
New England School of Communications, AB
Saint Joseph's College of Maine, B
Thomas College, B
University of Maine at Machias, B

Maryland

Allegany College of Maryland, A
Anne Arundel Community College, A
Baltimore City Community College, A
Bowie State University, B
Cecil Community College, A
Frederick Community College, A
Hagerstown Business College, A
Morgan State University, B
Prince George's Community College, A
Salisbury University, B
University of Baltimore, B
University of Maryland, College Park, B
University of Maryland University College, B

Massachusetts

American International College, B
Assumption College, B
Babson College, B
Bay State College, B

Becker College, B
Bentley College, B
Boston College, B
Boston University, B
Bridgewater State College, B
Bristol Community College, A
Elms College, B
Emerson College, B
Fitchburg State College, B
Framingham State College, B
Greenfield Community College, A
Lasell College, B
Massachusetts College of Liberal Arts, B
Massasoit Community College, A
Merrimack College, B
Middlesex Community College, A
Mount Ida College, B
New England College of Finance, A
Newbury College, AB
Nichols College, B
North Shore Community College, A
Northeastern University, B
Northern Essex Community College, A
Salem State College, B
Simmons College, B
Springfield Technical Community College, A
Stonehill College, B
Suffolk University, B
University of Massachusetts Amherst, B
University of Massachusetts Dartmouth, B
Western New England College, B
Westfield State College, B

Michigan

Alma College, B
Andrews University, B
Baker College of Allen Park, A
Baker College of Auburn Hills, AB
Baker College of Cadillac, A
Baker College of Clinton Township, A
Baker College of Flint, AB
Baker College of Jackson, AB
Baker College of Muskegon, AB
Baker College of Owosso, AB
Baker College of Port Huron, AB
Bay de Noc Community College, A
Central Michigan University, B
Cleary University, B
Cornerstone University, B
Davenport University (Dearborn), AB
Delta College, A
Eastern Michigan University, B
Ferris State University, B
Grace Bible College, B
Grand Valley State University, B
Henry Ford Community College, A
Hillsdale College, B
Jackson Community College, A
Kalamazoo Valley Community College, A
Kettering University, B
Kirtland Community College, A
Lake Michigan College, A
Lansing Community College, A
Macomb Community College, A
Madonna University, B
Marygrove College, B
Michigan State University, B
Michigan Technological University, B
Mid Michigan Community College, A
Monroe County Community College, A
Mott Community College, A
Muskegon Community College, A
North Central Michigan College, A
Northern Michigan University, B
Northwestern Michigan College, A
Northwood University, B
Oakland University, B
Olivet College, B
Rochester College, B
St. Clair County Community College, A
Schoolcraft College, A
Siena Heights University, AB
University of Detroit Mercy, B
University of Michigan-Dearborn, B
University of Michigan-Flint, B
University of Phoenix-Metro Detroit Campus, B

Walsh College of Accountancy and Business
   Administration, B
Washtenaw Community College, A
Wayne County Community College District, A
Wayne State University, B
West Shore Community College, A
Western Michigan University, B

Minnesota

Alexandria Technical College, A
Anoka-Ramsey Community College, A
Anoka-Ramsey Community College, Cambridge
   Campus, A
Augsburg College, B
Central Lakes College, A
College of St. Catherine, B
The College of St. Scholastica, B
Dakota County Technical College, A
Inver Hills Community College, A
Metropolitan State University, B
Minnesota State College-Southeast Technical, A
Minnesota State Community and Technical
   College-Fergus Falls, A
Minnesota State University Mankato, B
Minnesota State University Moorhead, B
Normandale Community College, A
North Hennepin Community College, A
Northland Community and Technical College-Thief
   River Falls, A
Northwest Technical College, A
Northwestern College, B
Rasmussen College Eden Prairie, A
Rasmussen College Mankato, A
Rasmussen College St. Cloud, A
St. Cloud State University, A
St. Cloud Technical College, A
Saint Mary's University of Minnesota, B
Southwest Minnesota State University, AB
University of Minnesota, Duluth, B
University of Minnesota, Twin Cities Campus, B
University of St. Thomas, B
Winona State University, B

Mississippi

Copiah-Lincoln Community College-Natchez
   Campus, A
Delta State University, B
Hinds Community College, A
Itawamba Community College, A
Jackson State University, B
Meridian Community College, A
Mississippi College, B
Mississippi Gulf Coast Community College, A
Mississippi State University, B
Mississippi University for Women, B
Pearl River Community College, A
Southwest Mississippi Community College, A
University of Mississippi, B
University of Southern Mississippi, B

Missouri

Avila University, B
Central Missouri State University, B
College of the Ozarks, B
Columbia College, B
Drury University, B
East Central College, A
Evangel University, B
Fontbonne University, B
Hannibal-LaGrange College, B
Harris-Stowe State University, B
Lincoln University, B
Lindenwood University, B
Longview Community College, A
Maple Woods Community College, A
Maryville University of Saint Louis, B
Mineral Area College, A
Missouri Baptist University, B
Missouri Southern State University, B
Missouri State University, B
Missouri Valley College, B
Missouri Western State University, B
Moberly Area Community College, A
North Central Missouri College, A
Northwest Missouri State University, B
Park University, B

Penn Valley Community College, A
Saint Charles Community College, A
Saint Louis University, B
Southeast Missouri State University, B
State Fair Community College, A
Stephens College, B
Three Rivers Community College, A
University of Missouri-Columbia, B
University of Missouri-St. Louis, B
Washington University in St. Louis, B
Webster University, B

Montana

Miles Community College, A
Montana State University-Billings, B
University of Great Falls, B
The University of Montana-Missoula, B

Nebraska

Bellevue University, B
Central Community College-Columbus Campus, A
Creighton University, B
Hastings College, B
Midland Lutheran College, B
Northeast Community College, A
Peru State College, B
University of Nebraska-Lincoln, B
University of Nebraska at Omaha, B

Nevada

Community College of Southern Nevada, A
Truckee Meadows Community College, A
University of Nevada, Las Vegas, B
University of Nevada, Reno, B
University of Phoenix-Nevada Campus, B
Western Nevada Community College, A

New Hampshire

Daniel Webster College, A
Franklin Pierce College, B
Hesser College, AB
New England College, B
New Hampshire Community Technical College,
  Manchester/Stratham, A
New Hampshire Technical Institute, A
Plymouth State University, B
Southern New Hampshire University, AB

New Jersey

Berkeley College, A
Bloomfield College, B
Brookdale Community College, A
Caldwell College, B
Camden County College, A
Centenary College, B
Cumberland County College, A
Fairleigh Dickinson University, College at
  Florham, B
Felician College, B
Gloucester County College, A
Kean University, B
Middlesex County College, A
Passaic County Community College, A
Raritan Valley Community College, A
Rider University, B
Rutgers, The State University of New Jersey,
  Camden, B
Rutgers, The State University of New Jersey, New
  Brunswick/Piscataway, B
Rutgers, The State University of New Jersey,
  Newark, B
Saint Peter's College, AB
Salem Community College, A
Seton Hall University, B

New Mexico

College of the Southwest, B
Eastern New Mexico University, B
New Mexico Highlands University, B
New Mexico Junior College, A
New Mexico State University, B
Southwestern Indian Polytechnic Institute, A
University of New Mexico-Gallup, A
University of Phoenix-New Mexico Campus, B

Western New Mexico University, B

New York

Adirondack Community College, A
Berkeley College-New York City Campus, AB
Berkeley College-Westchester Campus, AB
Bernard M. Baruch College of the City University of
  New York, B
Borough of Manhattan Community College of the
  City University of New York, A
Bramson ORT College, A
Bronx Community College of the City University of
  New York, A
Canisius College, B
Cayuga County Community College, A
Clarkson University, B
The College of Westchester, A
Dominican College, A
D'Youville College, B
Elmira College, B
Excelsior College, B
Finger Lakes Community College, A
Five Towns College, A
Fordham University, B
Genesee Community College, A
Herkimer County Community College, A
Hofstra University, B
Hudson Valley Community College, A
Iona College, B
Ithaca College, B
Jamestown Business College, A
Jefferson Community College, A
Katharine Gibbs School (New York), A
Keuka College, B
The King's College, B
Kingsborough Community College of the City
  University of New York, A
Laboratory Institute of Merchandising, B
Le Moyne College, B
Long Island University, Brentwood Campus, B
Long Island University, Brooklyn Campus, B
Long Island University, C.W. Post Campus, B
Manhattan College, B
Medaille College, B
Monroe Community College, A
Nassau Community College, A
Nazareth College of Rochester, B
New York City College of Technology of the City
  University of New York, B
New York Institute of Technology, B
New York University, B
Niagara University, B
Orange County Community College, A
Pace University, B
Rensselaer Polytechnic Institute, B
Roberts Wesleyan College, B
Rochester Institute of Technology, B
Rockland Community College, A
Sage College of Albany, A
St. Bonaventure University, B
St. John Fisher College, B
St. John's University, B
St. Thomas Aquinas College, B
Siena College, B
State University of New York College of Agriculture
  and Technology at Morrisville, A
State University of New York College at
  Brockport, B
State University of New York College at Old
  Westbury, B
State University of New York College of Technology
  at Alfred, A
State University of New York College of Technology
  at Delhi, A
State University of New York, Fredonia, B
State University of New York at New Paltz, B
State University of New York at Oswego, B
State University of New York at Plattsburgh, B
Suffolk County Community College, A
Sullivan County Community College, A
Syracuse University, B
Tompkins Cortland Community College, A
Touro College, A
Trocaire College, A
Ulster County Community College, A
Westchester Community College, A

Wood Tobe-Coburn School, A
Yeshiva University, B
York College of the City University of New York, B

North Carolina

Appalachian State University, B
Barber-Scotia College, B
Barton College, B
Blue Ridge Community College, A
Campbell University, B
Catawba College, B
Catawba Valley Community College, A
Central Carolina Community College, A
Central Piedmont Community College, A
Chowan University, B
East Carolina University, B
Fayetteville State University, B
Forsyth Technical Community College, A
Halifax Community College, A
High Point University, B
Isothermal Community College, A
Lenoir Community College, A
Mars Hill College, B
McDowell Technical Community College, A
Nash Community College, A
North Carolina State University, B
Pfeiffer University, B
Southwestern Community College, A
The University of North Carolina Wilmington, B
Western Carolina University, B
Western Piedmont Community College, A
Wingate University, B

North Dakota

Cankdeska Cikana Community College, A
Dickinson State University, B
Fort Berthold Community College, A
Jamestown College, B
Minot State University, B
Minot State University-Bottineau Campus, A
Sitting Bull College, A
Turtle Mountain Community College, A
University of North Dakota, B
Williston State College, A

Ohio

Ashland University, B
Baldwin-Wallace College, B
Capital University, B
Cedarville University, B
Central State University, B
Cincinnati State Technical and Community
  College, A
Cleveland State University, B
Columbus State Community College, A
Cuyahoga Community College, A
David N. Myers University, AB
Edison State Community College, A
Franklin University, B
Hocking College, A
James A. Rhodes State College, A
John Carroll University, B
Kent State University, B
Kent State University, Ashtabula Campus, A
Lorain County Community College, A
Marietta College, B
Marion Technical College, A
Miami University, B
Miami University Hamilton, A
Miami University-Middletown Campus, A
Mount Vernon Nazarene University, B
Northwest State Community College, A
Notre Dame College, B
The Ohio State University, B
Ohio University-Eastern, B
Otterbein College, B
Owens Community College, A
Sinclair Community College, A
Stark State College of Technology, A
Terra State Community College, A
Tiffin University, B
The University of Akron, B
University of Cincinnati, AB
University of Cincinnati Raymond Walters College, A
University of Dayton, B
The University of Findlay, B

University of Northwestern Ohio, AB
University of Rio Grande, B
The University of Toledo, B
Urbana University, AB
Ursuline College, B
Walsh University, AB
Washington State Community College, A
Wilberforce University, B
Wilmington College, B
Wright State University, AB
Wright State University, Lake Campus, A
Xavier University, B
Youngstown State University, AB
Zane State College, A

Oklahoma

East Central University, B
Eastern Oklahoma State College, A
Northeastern Oklahoma Agricultural and Mechanical
 College, A
Northeastern State University, B
Oklahoma Baptist University, B
Oklahoma Christian University, B
Oklahoma City University, B
Oklahoma State University, B
Oklahoma State University, Okmulgee, A
Oral Roberts University, B
St. Gregory's University, B
Southeastern Oklahoma State University, B
Southern Nazarene University, B
Southwestern Oklahoma State University, B
Tulsa Community College, A
University of Central Oklahoma, B
University of Oklahoma, B
University of Phoenix-Tulsa Campus, B
University of Tulsa, B

Oregon

Blue Mountain Community College, A
Cascade College, B
Central Oregon Community College, A
George Fox University, B
Mt. Hood Community College, A
Oregon State University, B
Pacific University, B
Portland Community College, A
Portland State University, B
Southern Oregon University, B
Southwestern Oregon Community College, A
Umpqua Community College, A
University of Oregon, B
University of Phoenix-Oregon Campus, B
University of Portland, B

Pennsylvania

Albright College, B
Alvernia College, B
Arcadia University, B
Bucks County Community College, A
Butler County Community College, A
Cabrini College, B
Central Pennsylvania College, A
Chatham College, B
Chestnut Hill College, AB
Clarion University of Pennsylvania, B
College Misericordia, B
Community College of Allegheny County, A
Community College of Beaver County, A
Community College of Philadelphia, A
Delaware Valley College, B
DeSales University, B
Drexel University, B
Duquesne University, B
Eastern University, B
Erie Business Center, Main, A
Erie Business Center South, A
Gannon University, B
Grove City College, B
Harrisburg Area Community College, A
Holy Family University, B
Indiana University of Pennsylvania, B
Juniata College, B
King's College, B
Kutztown University of Pennsylvania, B
La Salle University, B
Lehigh University, B

Lehigh Valley College, A
Lycoming College, B
Mansfield University of Pennsylvania, B
Marywood University, B
McCann School of Business & Technology, A
Mercyhurst College, B
Messiah College, B
Neumann College, B
Peirce College, A
The Pennsylvania State University Abington
 College, B
The Pennsylvania State University Altoona
 College, B
The Pennsylvania State University Beaver Campus
 of the Commonwealth College, B
The Pennsylvania State University Berks Campus of
 the Berks-Lehigh Valley College, B
The Pennsylvania State University Delaware County
 Campus of the Commonwealth College, B
The Pennsylvania State University DuBois Campus
 of the Commonwealth College, B
The Pennsylvania State University at Erie, The
 Behrend College, B
The Pennsylvania State University Fayette Campus
 of the Commonwealth College, B
The Pennsylvania State University Harrisburg
 Campus, B
The Pennsylvania State University Hazleton
 Campus of the Commonwealth College, B
The Pennsylvania State University, Lehigh Valley
 Campus of the Berks-Lehigh Valley College, B
The Pennsylvania State University McKeesport
 Campus of the Commonwealth College, B
The Pennsylvania State University Mont Alto
 Campus of the Commonwealth College, B
The Pennsylvania State University New Kensington
 Campus of the Commonwealth College, B
The Pennsylvania State University Schuylkill
 Campus of the Capital College, B
The Pennsylvania State University Shenango
 Campus of the Commonwealth College, B
The Pennsylvania State University University Park
 Campus, B
The Pennsylvania State University Wilkes-Barre
 Campus of the Commonwealth College, B
The Pennsylvania State University Worthington
 Scranton Campus of the Commonwealth
 College, B
The Pennsylvania State University York Campus of
 the Commonwealth College, B
Philadelphia University, B
Reading Area Community College, A
Robert Morris University, B
Saint Francis University, B
Saint Joseph's University, AB
Saint Vincent College, B
Seton Hill University, B
Shippensburg University of Pennsylvania, B
South Hills School of Business & Technology
 (Altoona), A
South Hills School of Business & Technology (State
 College), A
Susquehanna University, B
Temple University, B
University of Pennsylvania, B
University of Pittsburgh, B
University of the Sciences in Philadelphia, B
The University of Scranton, B
Villanova University, B
Waynesburg College, B
Westmoreland County Community College, A
Widener University, B
York College of Pennsylvania, B

Puerto Rico

Bayamon Central University, B
Inter American University of Puerto Rico, Aguadilla
 Campus, B
Inter American University of Puerto Rico, Arecibo
 Campus, B
Inter American University of Puerto Rico, Bayamón
 Campus, B
Inter American University of Puerto Rico, Fajardo
 Campus, A
Inter American University of Puerto Rico,
 Metropolitan Campus, B

Inter American University of Puerto Rico, Ponce
 Campus, B
Inter American University of Puerto Rico, San
 Germán Campus, B
Polytechnic University of Puerto Rico, B
Pontifical Catholic University of Puerto Rico, B
Universidad del Este, A
Universidad Metropolitana, B
University of Phoenix-Puerto Rico Campus, B
University of Puerto Rico at Bayamón, AB
University of Puerto Rico, Mayagüez Campus, B
University of Puerto Rico, Río Piedras, B
University of the Sacred Heart, B

Rhode Island

Bryant University, B
Community College of Rhode Island, A
Johnson & Wales University, AB
Providence College, B
Rhode Island College, B
Roger Williams University, B
University of Rhode Island, B

South Carolina

Aiken Technical College, A
Anderson University, B
Benedict College, B
Bob Jones University, B
Charleston Southern University, B
Claflin University, B
Clemson University, B
Coastal Carolina University, B
Converse College, B
Florence-Darlington Technical College, A
Francis Marion University, B
Greenville Technical College, A
Limestone College, B
Northeastern Technical College, A
Piedmont Technical College, A
South Carolina State University, B
Spartanburg Technical College, A
Technical College of the Lowcountry, A
Trident Technical College, A
University of South Carolina, B

South Dakota

Black Hills State University, B
Colorado Technical University Sioux Falls
 Campus, B
Dakota State University, B
Dakota Wesleyan University, B
Lake Area Technical Institute, A
National American University (Rapid City), B
Northern State University, B
Southeast Technical Institute, A
University of Sioux Falls, AB
The University of South Dakota, B

Tennessee

Belmont University, B
Carson-Newman College, B
East Tennessee State University, B
Freed-Hardeman University, B
Lambuth University, B
Lincoln Memorial University, B
Lipscomb University, B
Martin Methodist College, A
Middle Tennessee State University, B
Pellissippi State Technical Community College, A
Southern Adventist University, B
Tennessee Technological University, B
Tennessee Temple University, B
Trevecca Nazarene University, B
Union University, B
University of Memphis, B
University of Phoenix-Nashville Campus, B
The University of Tennessee, B
The University of Tennessee at Martin, B

Texas

Abilene Christian University, B
Alvin Community College, A
Amberton University, B
Angelo State University, B
Austin Community College, A

Baylor University, B
Brazosport College, A
Brookhaven College, A
Cedar Valley College, A
Central Texas College, A
Cisco Junior College, A
Clarendon College, A
Dallas Baptist University, B
Hardin-Simmons University, B
Houston Baptist University, B
Houston Community College System, A
Howard Payne University, B
Jarvis Christian College, B
Lamar University, B
Laredo Community College, A
LeTourneau University, B
Lubbock Christian University, B
McMurry University, B
Midwestern State University, B
Navarro College, A
North Harris College, A
Northwood University, Texas Campus, B
Our Lady of the Lake University of San Antonio, B
Prairie View A&M University, B
St. Edward's University, B
St. Mary's University of San Antonio, B
Sam Houston State University, B
South Plains College, A
Southern Methodist University, B
Stephen F. Austin State University, B
Tarrant County College District, A
Texas A&M International University, B
Texas A&M University, B
Texas A&M University-Commerce, B
Texas A&M University-Corpus Christi, B
Texas A&M University-Kingsville, B
Texas A&M University-Texarkana, B
Texas Christian University, B
Texas Southern University, B
Texas State University-San Marcos, B
Texas Tech University, B
Texas Wesleyan University, B
Texas Woman's University, B
Trinity University, B
Trinity Valley Community College, A
Tyler Junior College, A
University of Houston, B
University of Houston-Clear Lake, B
University of Houston-Downtown, B
University of Houston-Victoria, B
University of the Incarnate Word, B
University of Mary Hardin-Baylor, B
University of North Texas, B
University of Phoenix-Dallas Campus, B
University of St. Thomas, B
The University of Texas at Arlington, B
The University of Texas at Austin, B
The University of Texas at Brownsville, B
The University of Texas at El Paso, B
The University of Texas-Pan American, B
The University of Texas of the Permian Basin, B
The University of Texas at San Antonio, B
The University of Texas at Tyler, B
West Texas A&M University, B
Western Texas College, A

Utah

Brigham Young University, B
Salt Lake Community College, A
University of Phoenix-Utah Campus, B
University of Utah, B
Utah State University, B
Utah Valley State College, B
Weber State University, AB
Westminster College, B

Vermont

Castleton State College, B
Champlain College, AB
Johnson State College, B

Virginia

Averett University, B
Bridgewater College, B
Central Virginia Community College, A
Christopher Newport University, B

Danville Community College, A
George Mason University, B
Hampton University, B
J. Sargeant Reynolds Community College, A
James Madison University, B
Longwood University, B
Lynchburg College, B
Marymount University, B
Mountain Empire Community College, A
National College of Business & Technology (Salem)
  , A
New River Community College, A
Northern Virginia Community College, A
Old Dominion University, B
Piedmont Virginia Community College, A
Radford University, B
Tidewater Community College, A
University of Management and Technology, AB
University of Richmond, B
Virginia Commonwealth University, B
Virginia Intermont College, B
Virginia Polytechnic Institute and State University, B
Virginia State University, B
Virginia Union University, B

Washington

Bellevue Community College, A
Centralia College, A
Clover Park Technical College, A
Columbia Basin College, A
Eastern Washington University, B
Edmonds Community College, A
Everett Community College, A
Gonzaga University, B
Green River Community College, A
Northwest University, B
Pacific Lutheran University, B
Pierce College, A
Saint Martin's University, B
Seattle University, B
Shoreline Community College, A
Spokane Community College, A
Spokane Falls Community College, A
Walla Walla College, B
Washington State University, B
Western Washington University, B
Yakima Valley Community College, A

West Virginia

Alderson-Broaddus College, B
Bluefield State College, AB
Davis & Elkins College, B
Glenville State College, B
Marshall University, B
Mountain State University, AB
New River Community and Technical College, A
Ohio Valley University, B
University of Charleston, B
West Liberty State College, B
West Virginia State University, A
West Virginia University, B
West Virginia University at Parkersburg, A
West Virginia Wesleyan College, B
Wheeling Jesuit University, B

Wisconsin

Alverno College, B
Blackhawk Technical College, A
Carroll College, B
Carthage College, B
Chippewa Valley Technical College, A
Concordia University Wisconsin, B
Fox Valley Technical College, A
Gateway Technical College, A
Lakeland College, B
Lakeshore Technical College, A
Madison Area Technical College, A
Marian College of Fond du Lac, B
Marquette University, B
Mid-State Technical College, A
Milwaukee Area Technical College, A
Moraine Park Technical College, A
Mount Mary College, B
Nicolet Area Technical College, A
Northcentral Technical College, A
Northeast Wisconsin Technical College, A

Southwest Wisconsin Technical College, A
University of Wisconsin-Eau Claire, A
University of Wisconsin-La Crosse, B
University of Wisconsin-Milwaukee, B
University of Wisconsin-Oshkosh, B
University of Wisconsin-River Falls, B
University of Wisconsin-Superior, B
University of Wisconsin-Whitewater, B
Viterbo University, B
Waukesha County Technical College, A
Western Technical College, A

Wyoming

Casper College, A
Northwest College, A
University of Wyoming, B
Western Wyoming Community College, A

Alberta

Athabasca University, B
University of Alberta, B
University of Calgary, B
University of Lethbridge, B

British Columbia

British Columbia Institute of Technology, A
Thompson Rivers University, B
The University of British Columbia, B
University of Northern British Columbia, B
University of Phoenix-Vancouver Campus, B

New Brunswick

Université de Moncton, B
University of New Brunswick Fredericton, B

Newfoundland and Labrador

Memorial University of Newfoundland, B

Nova Scotia

Cape Breton University, B
Dalhousie University, B
Mount Saint Vincent University, B
Saint Mary's University, B

Ontario

Brock University, B
Carleton University, B
Lakehead University, B
Ryerson University, B
University of Guelph, B
University of Ottawa, B
University of Windsor, B
York University, B

Quebec

Bishop's University, B
Concordia University, B
HEC Montreal, B
Université de Sherbrooke, B

Saskatchewan

University of Regina, B
University of Saskatchewan, B

MARKETING RESEARCH

California

San Diego Mesa College, A

Colorado

Metropolitan State College of Denver, B

Georgia

University of Georgia, M

Guam

Guam Community College, A

Illinois

DePaul University, M
Southern Illinois University Edwardsville, M

Massachusetts

Boston University, B
Newbury College, B

Michigan

Baker College of Jackson, B
Saginaw Valley State University, B

New Jersey

Fairleigh Dickinson University, Metropolitan
 Campus, B

New York

Fashion Institute of Technology, B
Hofstra University, M
Ithaca College, B
Pace University, M

North Carolina

Methodist College, B

North Dakota

Lake Region State College, A

Ohio

Ashland University, B
The University of Toledo, B

Puerto Rico

Inter American University of Puerto Rico, Bayamón
 Campus, B

Texas

The University of Texas at Arlington, M

Wisconsin

University of Wisconsin-Madison, M

Nova Scotia

Mount Saint Vincent University, B

Ontario

University of Windsor, B

Quebec

Concordia University, B
McGill University, B

MARRIAGE AND FAMILY THERAPY/COUNSELING

Alabama

Southern Christian University, BMDP
The University of Alabama at Birmingham, M
University of Mobile, M

Arizona

University of Phoenix-Phoenix Campus, M
University of Phoenix-Southern Arizona Campus, M

Arkansas

Harding University, BM
John Brown University, M

California

Azusa Pacific University, M
California Baptist University, M
California Lutheran University, M
California State University, Bakersfield, O
California State University, Chico, M
California State University, Dominguez Hills, M
California State University, Fresno, M
California State University, Northridge, O
Chapman University, M
Hope International University, M
Loma Linda University, MD
Loyola Marymount University, M
Notre Dame de Namur University, M
Pacific Oaks College, M
Saint Mary's College of California, M
San Francisco State University, M

Sonoma State University, M
University of La Verne, M
University of Phoenix-Sacramento Valley
 Campus, M
University of Phoenix-San Diego Campus, MO
University of San Diego, M
University of Southern California, O

Connecticut

Central Connecticut State University, M
Fairfield University, M
Saint Joseph College, MO
Southern Connecticut State University, M

Florida

Barry University, MO
Carlos Albizu University, Miami Campus, M
Florida Atlantic University, O
Florida State University, D
Nova Southeastern University, MDO
St. Thomas University, MO
Stetson University, M
University of Florida, MDO
University of Miami, M

Georgia

Valdosta State University, M

Hawaii

Argosy University/Hawaii, M
University of Phoenix-Hawaii Campus, M

Illinois

Argosy University/Chicago, D
Northwestern University, M

Indiana

Bethel College, M
Indiana State University, M
Indiana Wesleyan University, M
Purdue University, MD
Purdue University Calumet, M

Iowa

Iowa State University of Science and Technology, D

Kansas

Friends University, BM
Kansas State University, D

Louisiana

Our Lady of Holy Cross College, M
University of Louisiana at Monroe, MD

Maryland

University of Maryland, College Park, M

Massachusetts

Eastern Nazarene College, M
Fitchburg State College, MO
Springfield College, MO
University of Massachusetts Boston, MO

Michigan

Michigan State University, M
Western Michigan University, M

Minnesota

St. Cloud State University, M
Saint Mary's University of Minnesota, O
University of Minnesota, Twin Cities Campus, D

University of St. Thomas, O

Mississippi

University of Southern Mississippi, M

Missouri

Saint Louis University, MDO

Montana

University of Great Falls, M

Nebraska

Grace University, B

Nevada

University of Nevada, Las Vegas, BM
University of Phoenix-Nevada Campus, M

New Hampshire

University of New Hampshire, M

New Jersey

The College of New Jersey, O
Kean University, MO
Montclair State University, M
Seton Hall University, MDO

New Mexico

University of Phoenix-New Mexico Campus, M

New York

Hofstra University, MO
Iona College, MO
Mercy College, MO
Syracuse University, MD
University of Rochester, M

North Carolina

Appalachian State University, M
East Carolina University, M
The University of North Carolina at Greensboro, O

Ohio

The University of Akron, M

Oklahoma

Oklahoma Baptist University, B
Southern Nazarene University, M

Oregon

George Fox University, M
Lewis & Clark College, M

Pennsylvania

Drexel University, MD
Geneva College, M
Kutztown University of Pennsylvania, M
La Salle University, D
Seton Hill University, BM
University of Pittsburgh, O

Puerto Rico

University of Phoenix-Puerto Rico Campus, M

South Carolina

Converse College, O
Limestone College, B

Tennessee

East Tennessee State University, M
Johnson Bible College, M
Martin Methodist College, A
Southern Adventist University, M
Trevecca Nazarene University, M

Texas

Abilene Christian University, M
Hardin-Simmons University, M
Our Lady of the Lake University of San Antonio, M
Prairie View A&M University, M
St. Mary's University of San Antonio, MDO
Texas Tech University, MD
Texas Woman's University, MD

University of Houston-Clear Lake, BM

Utah

Brigham Young University, MD

Virginia

The College of William and Mary, M
Virginia Polytechnic Institute and State
    University, MD

Washington

Pacific Lutheran University, M
Seattle Pacific University, M

Wisconsin

Edgewood College, M
University of Wisconsin-Stout, M

Manitoba

The University of Winnipeg, MO

Ontario

Saint Paul University, BM

MASON/MASONRY

Florida

Florida Community College at Jacksonville, A

Indiana

Ivy Tech Community College-Central Indiana, A
Ivy Tech Community College-Columbus, A
Ivy Tech Community College-East Central, A
Ivy Tech Community College-Lafayette, A
Ivy Tech Community College-North Central, A
Ivy Tech Community College-Northeast, A
Ivy Tech Community College-Northwest, A
Ivy Tech Community College-Southern Indiana, A
Ivy Tech Community College-Southwest, A
Ivy Tech Community College-Wabash Valley, A

Kentucky

Somerset Community College, A

Minnesota

Alexandria Technical College, A
Dakota County Technical College, A

Mississippi

Mississippi Delta Community College, A

Missouri

Metropolitan Community College-Business &
    Technology College, A

Nevada

Western Nevada Community College, A

New York

State University of New York College of Technology
    at Alfred, A

Pennsylvania

Pennsylvania College of Technology, A

Virginia

Piedmont Virginia Community College, A

Wisconsin

Southwest Wisconsin Technical College, A

MASS COMMUNICATION/MEDIA STUDIES

Alabama

Alabama State University, B
Auburn University, BM
Enterprise-Ozark Community College, A
James H. Faulkner State Community College, A

Miles College, B
Oakwood College, B
Stillman College, B
Talladega College, B
University of Mobile, B
University of Montevallo, B

Alaska

University of Alaska Anchorage, B

Arizona

Arizona State University, B
Cochise College (Sierra Vista), A
Grand Canyon University, B
Phoenix College, A
South Mountain Community College, A

Arkansas

John Brown University, B
Ouachita Baptist University, B
Southern Arkansas University-Magnolia, B
University of Arkansas at Little Rock, M

California

California Lutheran University, B
California State Polytechnic University, Pomona, B
California State University, Bakersfield, B
California State University, Dominguez Hills, B
California State University, East Bay, B
California State University, Fresno, BM
California State University, Long Beach, B
California State University, Northridge, M
California State University, Sacramento, B
Chabot College, A
College of the Desert, A
College of Marin, A
College of the Sequoias, A
Cosumnes River College (Sacramento), A
Cuesta College, A
De Anza College, A
Fresno Pacific University, AB
Fullerton College, A
Glendale Community College, A
Lassen Community College District, A
Los Angeles City College, A
Los Angeles Valley College, A
Loyola Marymount University, B
The Master's College and Seminary, B
Menlo College, B
Modesto Junior College, A
Monterey Peninsula College, A
Ohlone College, A
Orange Coast College, A
Pacific Union College, B
Pasadena City College, A
Point Loma Nazarene University, B
Sacramento City College, A
San Diego State University, B
San Jose State University, M
Santa Monica College, A
Sierra College, A
Sonoma State University, B
University of California, Berkeley, B
University of California, San Diego, B
University of San Diego, B
University of San Francisco, B
University of Southern California, B
Yuba College, A

Colorado

Colorado State University-Pueblo, B
Lamar Community College, A
Mesa State College, B
Red Rocks Community College, A
University of Colorado at Boulder, MD
University of Denver, M
Western State College of Colorado, B

Connecticut

Albertus Magnus College, B
Asnuntuck Community College, A
Fairfield University, B
Middlesex Community College, A
Norwalk Community College, A
Quinnipiac University, B

Sacred Heart University, AB
University of Bridgeport, B
Western Connecticut State University, B

Delaware

University of Delaware, B
Wesley College, B

District of Columbia

American University, BM
Gallaudet University, B
The George Washington University, BM
Howard University, BMD
Trinity (Washington) University, B
University of the District of Columbia, B

Florida

Barry University, B
Bethune-Cookman College, B
Chipola College, A
Daytona Beach Community College, A
Florida Agricultural and Mechanical University, B
Florida International University, M
Florida State University, BMD
Hillsborough Community College, A
Lynn University, BM
Manatee Community College, A
Miami Dade College, A
Palm Beach Community College, A
Saint Leo University, B
St. Thomas University, B
University of Central Florida, B
University of Florida, MD
University of Miami, B
University of South Florida, M
The University of Tampa, B

Georgia

Andrew College, A
Brenau University, B
Clark Atlanta University, B
Clayton State University, A
Columbus State University, B
Emmanuel College, B
Fort Valley State University, B
Gainesville College, A
Georgia Military College, A
Macon State College, A
Mercer University, B
Oglethorpe University, B
Piedmont College, B
Reinhardt College, B
Savannah State University, B
South Georgia College, A
Toccoa Falls College, B
University of Georgia, BMD
Valdosta State University, B

Guam

University of Guam, B

Hawaii

Chaminade University of Honolulu, B
Hawaii Pacific University, B

Idaho

Boise State University, B
Brigham Young University -Idaho, A
Idaho State University, B
North Idaho College, A
Northwest Nazarene University, B

Illinois

Augustana College, B
City Colleges of Chicago, Richard J. Daley
    College, A
DePaul University, B
Dominican University, B
Eureka College, B
Governors State University, B
Greenville College, B
Illinois College, B
Illinois State University, B
Judson College, B
Lewis University, B

Lincoln College, A
McKendree College, B
North Park University, B
Olivet Nazarene University, B
Parkland College, A
Principia College, B
Southern Illinois University Edwardsville, BMO
Spoon River College, A
Springfield College in Illinois, A
University of Illinois at Chicago, M
University of Illinois at Urbana-Champaign, B
University of St. Francis, B
Waubonsee Community College, A

Indiana

Anderson University, B
DePauw University, B
Goshen College, B
Grace College, B
Hanover College, B
Huntington University, B
Indiana University Bloomington, BD
Indiana University Northwest, B
Indiana University South Bend, B
Manchester College, B
Marian College, B
Purdue University Calumet, B
Saint Joseph's College, B
Saint Mary-of-the-Woods College, B
Taylor University, B
University of Evansville, B
University of Saint Francis, B
Valparaiso University, B
Vincennes University, A

Iowa

Briar Cliff University, B
Buena Vista University, B
Clarke College, B
Dordt College, B
Drake University, B
Grand View College, B
Iowa Central Community College, A
Iowa Lakes Community College, A
Iowa State University of Science and
    Technology, BM
Iowa Wesleyan College, B
Kirkwood Community College, A
Loras College, B
Morningside College, B
Northwestern College, B
St. Ambrose University, B
Simpson College, B
University of Dubuque, AB
The University of Iowa, BMDO
Upper Iowa University, B
Waldorf College, B
Wartburg College, B
William Penn University, B

Kansas

Baker University, B
Benedictine College, B
Bethel College, B
Butler Community College, A
Coffeyville Community College, A
Colby Community College, A
Dodge City Community College, A
Fort Hays State University, B
Kansas State University, M
Kansas Wesleyan University, B
MidAmerica Nazarene University, B
Newman University, B
Ottawa University, B
Pratt Community College, A
Seward County Community College, A
Tabor College, B
University of Saint Mary, B
Washburn University, B

Kentucky

Berea College, B
Campbellsville University, B
Eastern Kentucky University, B
Georgetown College, B
Henderson Community College, A

Kentucky Mountain Bible College, B
Lindsey Wilson College, B
Murray State University, BM
Spalding University, B
West Kentucky Community and Technical College, A

Louisiana

Dillard University, B
Grambling State University, BM
Louisiana College, B
Louisiana State University and Agricultural and
    Mechanical College, BMD
Louisiana State University in Shreveport, B
Loyola University New Orleans, M
McNeese State University, B
Nicholls State University, B
Southern University and Agricultural and Mechanical
    College, BM
Tulane University, B
University of Louisiana at Lafayette, BM
University of Louisiana at Monroe, B
Xavier University of Louisiana, B

Maine

University of Maine, B
University of Southern Maine, B

Maryland

Anne Arundel Community College, A
Bowie State University, B
College of Notre Dame of Maryland, B
Columbia Union College, B
Frederick Community College, A
Frostburg State University, B
Goucher College, B
Morgan State University, B
Towson University, B
University of Baltimore, B
University of Maryland, College Park, D
University of Maryland Eastern Shore, B
Villa Julie College, A

Massachusetts

American International College, B
Boston College, B
Boston University, BMO
Bunker Hill Community College, A
Cape Cod Community College, A
Clark University, B
Curry College, B
Eastern Nazarene College, B
Emerson College, B
Emmanuel College, B
Endicott College, B
Greenfield Community College, A
Hampshire College, B
Holyoke Community College, A
Massachusetts College of Liberal Arts, B
Massachusetts Institute of Technology, B
Middlesex Community College, A
Newbury College, AB
Northeastern University, B
Pine Manor College, B
Salem State College, B
Simmons College, B
Suffolk University, B
Western New England College, B
Westfield State College, B
Worcester State College, B

Michigan

Adrian College, AB
Albion College, B
Andrews University, B
Calvin College, B
Central Michigan University, M
Cornerstone University, AB
Ferris State University, B
Grand Rapids Community College, A
Grand Valley State University, B
Henry Ford Community College, A
Lansing Community College, A
Madonna University, AB
Michigan State University, B
Monroe County Community College, A

Northern Michigan University, B
Olivet College, B
Rochester College, B
St. Clair County Community College, A
University of Detroit Mercy, B
University of Michigan, D
University of Michigan-Flint, B

Minnesota

Augsburg College, B
Bemidji State University, B
Bethel University, B
College of St. Catherine, B
Concordia College, B
Concordia University, St. Paul, B
Gustavus Adolphus College, B
Hamline University, B
Minnesota State University Mankato, B
Minnesota State University Moorhead, B
North Central University, AB
Northland Community and Technical College-Thief
    River Falls, A
Ridgewater College, A
St. Cloud State University, BM
University of Minnesota, Twin Cities Campus, BMD
Vermilion Community College, A
Winona State University, B

Mississippi

Alcorn State University, B
Hinds Community College, A
Jackson State University, BM
Mississippi College, B
Mississippi Valley State University, B
Northeast Mississippi Community College, A
University of Southern Mississippi, MD

Missouri

Calvary Bible College and Theological Seminary, B
Central Missouri State University, M
College of the Ozarks, B
Crowder College, A
Culver-Stockton College, B
Drury University, B
East Central College, A
Evangel University, AB
Lindenwood University, BM
Maryville University of Saint Louis, B
Mineral Area College, A
Missouri Southern State University, B
Missouri State University, B
Missouri Valley College, B
Northwest Missouri State University, B
St. Louis Community College at Florissant Valley, A
St. Louis Community College at Forest Park, A
State Fair Community College, A
Stephens College, B
Truman State University, B
University of Missouri-Columbia, B
University of Missouri-Kansas City, B
University of Missouri-St. Louis, B

Montana

Montana State University-Billings, B
Montana State University-Northern, B

Nebraska

Central Community College-Hastings Campus, A
Concordia University, B
Doane College, B
Grace University, B
Hastings College, B
Midland Lutheran College, B
Northeast Community College, A
University of Nebraska at Kearney, B
University of Nebraska-Lincoln, M
Wayne State College, B

Nevada

Community College of Southern Nevada, A
University of Nevada, Las Vegas, M

New Hampshire

Colby-Sawyer College, B
Franklin Pierce College, B

Hesser College, A
Keene State College, B
New England College, B
University of New Hampshire, B
University of New Hampshire at Manchester, B

New Jersey

Bergen Community College, A
Brookdale Community College, A
Camden County College, A
Centenary College, B
Felician College, B
Mercer County Community College, A
Rutgers, The State University of New Jersey, New
   Brunswick/Piscataway, B
Seton Hall University, M
William Paterson University of New Jersey, B

New Mexico

New Mexico Highlands University, B

New York

Adirondack Community College, A
Buffalo State College, State University of New
   York, B
City College of the City University of New York, B
College of Mount Saint Vincent, B
The College of New Rochelle, B
The College of Saint Rose, M
Dutchess Community College, A
Excelsior College, B
Finger Lakes Community College, A
Five Towns College, A
Fordham University, BM
Fulton-Montgomery Community College, A
Genesee Community College, A
Hamilton College, B
Hobart and William Smith Colleges, B
Hofstra University, B
Hunter College of the City University of New York, B
Iona College, B
Ithaca College, B
Lehman College of the City University of New
   York, B
Marymount Manhattan College, B
Medaille College, B
Monroe Community College, A
Mount Saint Mary College, B
Nassau Community College, A
New York University, B
Niagara County Community College, A
Niagara University, B
Queens College of the City University of New
   York, B
Rockland Community College, A
Russell Sage College, B
Sage College of Albany, A
St. Bonaventure University, B
St. John Fisher College, B
St. Thomas Aquinas College, B
State University of New York at Buffalo, B
State University of New York College at
   Brockport, B
State University of New York College at Oneonta, B
State University of New York, Fredonia, B
State University of New York at New Paltz, B
State University of New York at Oswego, B
State University of New York at Plattsburgh, B
Syracuse University, MD
Tompkins Cortland Community College, A
Ulster County Community College, A
University at Albany, State University of New York, B
Westchester Community College, A
Yeshiva University, B

North Carolina

Barber-Scotia College, B
Barton College, B
Bennett College For Women, B
Campbell University, B
Catawba College, B
Gardner-Webb University, B
High Point University, B
Johnson C. Smith University, B
Lees-McRae College, B
Lenoir-Rhyne College, B

Mars Hill College, B
Meredith College, B
Methodist College, AB
North Carolina Agricultural and Technical State
   University, B
North Carolina Central University, B
North Carolina State University, B
Queens University of Charlotte, B
St. Andrews Presbyterian College, B
Salem College, B
Shaw University, B
The University of North Carolina at Chapel
   Hill, BMD
The University of North Carolina at Greensboro, B
The University of North Carolina at Pembroke, B
Wingate University, B
Winston-Salem State University, B

North Dakota

North Dakota State University, BM
University of Mary, B
Valley City State University, B

Ohio

Antioch College, B
Ashland University, B
Baldwin-Wallace College, B
The College of Wooster, B
Defiance College, B
Denison University, B
Heidelberg College, B
Hiram College, B
John Carroll University, B
Kent State University, BM
Lorain County Community College, A
Miami University, BM
Miami University Hamilton, B
Miami University-Middletown Campus, A
Mount Union College, B
Muskingum College, B
Ohio Northern University, B
Ohio University-Eastern, B
Sinclair Community College, A
The University of Akron, B
University of Cincinnati, B
University of Dayton, B
University of Rio Grande, AB
The University of Toledo, B
Urbana University, B
Wilberforce University, B
Wilmington College, B
Wright State University, B
Wright State University, Lake Campus, A

Oklahoma

Bacone College, A
East Central University, B
Langston University, B
Northwestern Oklahoma State University, B
Oklahoma Baptist University, B
Oklahoma Christian University, B
Oklahoma City Community College, A
Oklahoma City University, B
Oklahoma State University, M
Oklahoma Wesleyan University, B
Southern Nazarene University, B
Southwestern Oklahoma State University, B
Tulsa Community College, A
University of Oklahoma, M

Oregon

Marylhurst University, B
Pacific University, B
Treasure Valley Community College, A
University of Oregon, B
University of Portland, B

Pennsylvania

Allegheny College, B
Arcadia University, B
Bloomsburg University of Pennsylvania, B
Bucks County Community College, A
Butler County Community College, A
Central Pennsylvania College, AB
Cheyney University of Pennsylvania, B

DeSales University, B
Grove City College, B
Harrisburg Area Community College, A
La Salle University, B
Lackawanna College, A
Lycoming College, B
Mansfield University of Pennsylvania, B
Mercyhurst College, B
Pennsylvania College of Technology, A
The Pennsylvania State University University Park
   Campus, D
Point Park University, BM
Robert Morris University, B
Saint Francis University, B
Susquehanna University, B
Temple University, D
Thiel College, B
University of Pittsburgh at Greensburg, B
University of Pittsburgh at Johnstown, B
Ursinus College, B
Villanova University, B
Westminster College, B
Widener University, B
Wilson College, AB
York College of Pennsylvania, B

Puerto Rico

Inter American University of Puerto Rico, Bayamón
   Campus, AB
Pontifical Catholic University of Puerto Rico, B
Universidad del Turabo, B
University of Puerto Rico, Río Piedras, BM
University of the Sacred Heart, BM

Rhode Island

Johnson & Wales University, B

South Carolina

Anderson University, B
Claflin University, B
Clemson University, B
Coker College, B
Francis Marion University, B
Newberry College, B
North Greenville College, B
Winthrop University, B

South Dakota

Black Hills State University, AB
Oglala Lakota College, A
South Dakota State University, B
University of Sioux Falls, B
The University of South Dakota, BM

Tennessee

Austin Peay State University, B
Belmont University, B
Bryan College, B
Carson-Newman College, B
Chattanooga State Technical Community College, A
Columbia State Community College, A
East Tennessee State University, B
Lambuth University, B
Lee University, B
Lincoln Memorial University, B
Lipscomb University, B
Martin Methodist College, A
Middle Tennessee State University, BM
Southern Adventist University, B
Tennessee State University, B
Trevecca Nazarene University, B
Union University, B
The University of Tennessee at Chattanooga, B
The University of Tennessee at Martin, B
Vanderbilt University, B

Texas

Amarillo College, A
Austin Community College, A
Blinn College, A
Clarendon College, A
Concordia University at Austin, B
East Texas Baptist University, B
El Paso Community College, A
Hill College of the Hill Junior College District, A

Houston Baptist University, B
Houston Community College System, A
Lamar State College-Orange, A
Lamar University, B
Lon Morris College, A
Lubbock Christian University, B
Midland College, A
Midwestern State University, B
Paul Quinn College, B
St. Mary's University of San Antonio, B
South Plains College, A
Southern Methodist University, B
Southwestern Adventist University, B
Southwestern University, B
Stephen F. Austin State University, M
Sul Ross State University, B
Texas A&M University-Kingsville, B
Texas A&M University-Texarkana, B
Texas Christian University, B
Texas Southern University, B
Texas State University-San Marcos, BM
Texas Tech University, MD
Texas Wesleyan University, B
University of Houston, BM
University of the Incarnate Word, B
University of Mary Hardin-Baylor, B
The University of Texas at El Paso, B
The University of Texas-Pan American, B
The University of Texas of the Permian Basin, B
The University of Texas at San Antonio, B
Wayland Baptist University, B
West Texas A&M University, B
Western Texas College, A
Wiley College, B

Utah

Brigham Young University, BM
Salt Lake Community College, A
Snow College, A
Southern Utah University, B
University of Utah, B

Vermont

Champlain College, AB
Southern Vermont College, B

Virginia

Bluefield College, B
Bridgewater College, B
Emory & Henry College, B
Hampton University, B
Hollins University, B
Lynchburg College, B
Virginia Commonwealth University, BM
Virginia State University, B
Wytheville Community College, A

Washington

Central Washington University, B
Centralia College, A
City University, B
Gonzaga University, B
Pacific Lutheran University, B
Seattle University, B
Spokane Falls Community College, A
Walla Walla College, B
Whitworth College, B

West Virginia

Alderson-Broaddus College, B
Concord University, B
Marshall University, M
Mountain State University, B
Salem International University, AB
West Liberty State College, B
West Virginia University, B

Wisconsin

Beloit College, B
Concordia University Wisconsin, B
Edgewood College, B
Marquette University, BM
Northeast Wisconsin Technical College, A
University of Wisconsin-Eau Claire, B
University of Wisconsin-Madison, BMD

University of Wisconsin-Milwaukee, BM
University of Wisconsin-Oshkosh, B
University of Wisconsin-Platteville, B
University of Wisconsin-Stevens Point, M
University of Wisconsin-Superior, BM
University of Wisconsin-Whitewater, M
Western Technical College, A

Wyoming

Casper College, A
Laramie County Community College, A
Northwest College, A

British Columbia

University College of the Fraser Valley, A

New Brunswick

Atlantic Baptist University, B
Université de Moncton, B

Ontario

Brock University, B
Carleton University, B
University of Ottawa, B
University of Toronto, B
The University of Western Ontario, B
University of Windsor, B
Wilfrid Laurier University, B
York University, B

Quebec

Concordia University, B
Télé-université, B
Université Laval, BM
Université de Montréal, B
Université du Québec àMontréal, B
Université du Québec àTrois-Rivières, B

MASSAGE THERAPY/THERAPEUTIC MASSAGE

Alabama

H. Councill Trenholm State Technical College, A
Virginia College at Birmingham, A

Arizona

Arizona Western College, A
Northland Pioneer College, A

Colorado

Colorado School of Healing Arts, A
Institute of Business & Medical Careers, A
IntelliTec College (Grand Junction), A

Florida

National School of Technology, Inc. (North Miami Beach), A

Georgia

Georgia Medical Institute-DeKalb, A

Illinois

College of DuPage, A
Joliet Junior College, A
Northwestern Business College, A
Waubonsee Community College, A

Indiana

Indiana Business College (Indianapolis-Northwest Campus), A
Indiana Business College-Medical, A
Ivy Tech Community College-Northeast, A

Sawyer College (Hammond), A

Iowa

Iowa Lakes Community College, A

Maryland

College of Southern Maryland, A

Massachusetts

Mount Wachusett Community College, A
Springfield Technical Community College, A

Michigan

Oakland Community College, A

Minnesota

Globe College, A
Herzing College, A
Minnesota School of Business, A
Minnesota School of Business-Brooklyn Center, A
Minnesota School of Business-Plymouth, A
Minnesota School of Business-Richfield, A
Minnesota School of Business-St. Cloud, A
Minnesota School of Business-Shakopee, A

New York

New York College of Health Professions, AB

North Carolina

Southwestern Community College, A

Ohio

Columbus State Community College, A
Mercy College of Northwest Ohio, A
Stautzenberger College, A

Oklahoma

Community Care College, A

Pennsylvania

Career Training Academy (New Kensington), A
Lehigh Valley College, A

South Dakota

National American University-Sioux Falls Branch, A

Utah

Utah Career College, A

Washington

Clover Park Technical College, A

MATERIALS ENGINEERING

Alabama

Auburn University, BMD
Tuskegee University, D
The University of Alabama, MD
The University of Alabama at Birmingham, BMD

Arizona

Arizona State University, BMD
The University of Arizona, MD

California

California Polytechnic State University, San Luis Obispo, B
California State Polytechnic University, Pomona, B
California State University, Long Beach, B
California State University, Northridge, M
San Jose State University, BM
Santa Clara University, O
Stanford University, BMDO
University of California, Berkeley, MD
University of California, Davis, BMD
University of California, Irvine, BMD
University of California, Los Angeles, BMD
University of California, Santa Barbara, MDO

University of Southern California, M

Colorado

Colorado School of Mines, MD
Colorado State University, MD

Connecticut

University of Connecticut, BMD

Delaware

University of Delaware, MD

Florida

Florida State University, B
University of Central Florida, MD
University of Florida, BMDO

Georgia

Georgia Institute of Technology, BMD

Idaho

Boise State University, M
University of Idaho, MD

Illinois

Illinois Institute of Technology, BMD
Northwestern University, BMDO
University of Illinois at Chicago, MD
University of Illinois at Urbana-Champaign, MD

Indiana

Purdue University, BMD

Iowa

Iowa State University of Science and
Technology, BMD

Kentucky

University of Kentucky, B

Maryland

The Johns Hopkins University, BMD
University of Maryland, College Park, BMD

Massachusetts

Harvard University, B
Massachusetts Institute of Technology, BMDO
Worcester Polytechnic Institute, BMDO

Michigan

Michigan State University, MD
Michigan Technological University, BMD
University of Michigan, BMD
Wayne State University, MDO
Western Michigan University, M

Minnesota

University of Minnesota, Twin Cities Campus, BMD
Walden University, M
Winona State University, B

Missouri

University of Missouri-Rolla, B

Montana

Montana Tech of The University of Montana, B

New Hampshire

Dartmouth College, MD

New Jersey

New Jersey Institute of Technology, MD
Rutgers, The State University of New Jersey, New
Brunswick/Piscataway, MD
Stevens Institute of Technology, MDO

New Mexico

New Mexico Institute of Mining and
Technology, BMD

New York

Clarkson University, B
Cornell University, BMD

Rensselaer Polytechnic Institute, BMDO
Rochester Institute of Technology, M
Stony Brook University, State University of New
York, MD

North Carolina

North Carolina State University, BMD

Ohio

Case Western Reserve University, BMD
The Ohio State University, BMD
University of Cincinnati, MD
University of Dayton, MD
Wright State University, BM

Pennsylvania

Carnegie Mellon University, MD
Drexel University, BMD
Lehigh University, BMD
The Pennsylvania State University University Park
Campus, MD
University of Pennsylvania, BMDO
University of Pittsburgh, BMD

Rhode Island

Brown University, B

South Carolina

Clemson University, BMD

South Dakota

South Dakota School of Mines and Technology, MD

Tennessee

The University of Tennessee, BMD

Texas

Rice University, B
Texas A&M University, MD
University of Houston, MD
The University of Texas at Arlington, MD
The University of Texas at Austin, MD
The University of Texas at El Paso, D

Utah

University of Utah, BMD

Virginia

Old Dominion University, M
Virginia Polytechnic Institute and State
University, BMD

Washington

University of Washington, BMD
Washington State University, BM

Wisconsin

University of Wisconsin-Milwaukee, B

Alberta

University of Alberta, MD

British Columbia

The University of British Columbia, BMD

Ontario

Carleton University, M
McMaster University, BMD
University of Toronto, BMD
The University of Western Ontario, B
University of Windsor, BMD

Quebec

McGill University, BMD

MATERIALS SCIENCES

Alabama

The University of Alabama, D
The University of Alabama at Birmingham, D

The University of Alabama in Huntsville, MD

Arizona

Arizona State University, MD
Central Arizona College, A
GateWay Community College, A
The University of Arizona, BMD

California

California Institute of Technology, MD
California Polytechnic State University, San Luis
Obispo, M
Contra Costa College, A
Mt. San Antonio College, A
Stanford University, BMDO
University of California, Berkeley, BMD
University of California, Davis, MD
University of California, Irvine, MD
University of California, Los Angeles, BMD
University of California, San Diego, MD
University of California, Santa Barbara, MDO
University of Southern California, MDO

Colorado

Colorado School of Mines, MD
United States Air Force Academy, B
University of Denver, D

Connecticut

University of Connecticut, MD

Delaware

University of Delaware, MD

District of Columbia

The George Washington University, MD

Florida

University of Central Florida, MD
University of Florida, MDO

Idaho

University of Idaho, MD

Illinois

Illinois Institute of Technology, MD
Northwestern University, BMDO
University of Illinois at Urbana-Champaign, BMD
William Rainey Harper College, A

Iowa

Iowa State University of Science and
Technology, MD

Kansas

Neosho County Community College, A

Kentucky

University of Kentucky, MD

Maryland

The Johns Hopkins University, BMD
University of Maryland, College Park, MD

Massachusetts

Harvard University, B
Massachusetts Institute of Technology, MDO
Northern Essex Community College, A
Worcester Polytechnic Institute, BMDO

Michigan

Henry Ford Community College, A
Michigan State University, BMD
University of Michigan, BMD
Wayne State University, MDO

Western Michigan University, M

Minnesota

University of Minnesota, Twin Cities Campus, BMD
Walden University, M

Mississippi

Jackson State University, M

Missouri

Missouri State University, M
St. Louis Community College at Meramec, A

Montana

Montana Tech of The University of Montana, B

New Hampshire

Dartmouth College, MD
University of New Hampshire, AMD

New Jersey

New Jersey Institute of Technology, MD
Rutgers, The State University of New Jersey, New
    Brunswick/Piscataway, MD
Stevens Institute of Technology, MDO

New York

Alfred University, BMD
Clarkson University, B
Columbia University, The Fu Foundation School of
    Engineering and Applied Science, B
Cornell University, BMD
Polytechnic University, Brooklyn Campus, M
Rensselaer Polytechnic Institute, MDO
Rochester Institute of Technology, M
State University of New York at Buffalo, M
Stony Brook University, State University of New
    York, MD
University at Albany, State University of New
    York, MD
University of Rochester, MD

North Carolina

Duke University, BMDO
North Carolina State University, BMD
The University of North Carolina at Chapel Hill, MD

Ohio

Case Western Reserve University, BMD
Kent State University, Ashtabula Campus, A
The Ohio State University, BMD
Ohio University, D
University of Cincinnati, MD
Wright State University, M

Oklahoma

Tulsa Community College, A

Oregon

Oregon State University, MD

Pennsylvania

Carnegie Mellon University, BMD
Lehigh University, MD
The Pennsylvania State University Abington
    College, B
The Pennsylvania State University Altoona
    College, B
The Pennsylvania State University Beaver Campus
    of the Commonwealth College, B
The Pennsylvania State University Berks Campus of
    the Berks-Lehigh Valley College, B
The Pennsylvania State University Delaware County
    Campus of the Commonwealth College, B
The Pennsylvania State University DuBois Campus
    of the Commonwealth College, B
The Pennsylvania State University at Erie, The
    Behrend College, B
The Pennsylvania State University Fayette Campus
    of the Commonwealth College, B
The Pennsylvania State University Hazleton
    Campus of the Commonwealth College, B
The Pennsylvania State University, Lehigh Valley
    Campus of the Berks-Lehigh Valley College, B

The Pennsylvania State University McKeesport
    Campus of the Commonwealth College, B
The Pennsylvania State University Mont Alto
    Campus of the Commonwealth College, B
The Pennsylvania State University New Kensington
    Campus of the Commonwealth College, B
The Pennsylvania State University Schuylkill
    Campus of the Capital College, B
The Pennsylvania State University Shenango
    Campus of the Commonwealth College, B
The Pennsylvania State University University Park
    Campus, BMD
The Pennsylvania State University Wilkes-Barre
    Campus of the Commonwealth College, B
The Pennsylvania State University Worthington
    Scranton Campus of the Commonwealth
    College, B
The Pennsylvania State University York Campus of
    the Commonwealth College, B
University of Pennsylvania, BMDO
University of Pittsburgh, MD

Puerto Rico

University of Puerto Rico at Bayamón, B

Rhode Island

Brown University, MD

South Carolina

Clemson University, MD
Greenville Technical College, A

South Dakota

South Dakota School of Mines and Technology, MD

Tennessee

The University of Tennessee, MD
Vanderbilt University, MD

Texas

Rice University, BMD
University of North Texas, MD
The University of Texas at Arlington, MD
The University of Texas at Austin, MD
The University of Texas at El Paso, D

Utah

University of Utah, BMD

Vermont

University of Vermont, MD

Virginia

Norfolk State University, M
Old Dominion University, M
University of Virginia, MD
Virginia Polytechnic Institute and State
    University, MD

Washington

University of Washington, MD
Washington State University, BMD

Wisconsin

University of Wisconsin-Madison, MD

British Columbia

The University of British Columbia, MD

New Brunswick

University of New Brunswick Fredericton, MD

Ontario

McMaster University, BMD
Royal Military College of Canada, MD

University of Toronto, BMD

MATERNAL AND CHILD HEALTH

Alabama

The University of Alabama at Birmingham, M

California

University of California, Berkeley, M

District of Columbia

The George Washington University, M

Georgia

Emory University, M

Louisiana

Tulane University, MDO

Massachusetts

Boston University, MO
Harvard University, MD

Michigan

Oakland University, O

Minnesota

University of Minnesota, Twin Cities Campus, M

Mississippi

University of Mississippi Medical Center, M

North Carolina

The University of North Carolina at Chapel
    Hill, MDO

Puerto Rico

University of Puerto Rico, Medical Sciences
    Campus, M

Washington

University of Washington, M

MATERNAL/CHILD HEALTH AND NEONATAL NURSE/NURSING

Alabama

The University of Alabama in Huntsville, O
University of South Alabama, M

Colorado

University of Colorado at Colorado Springs, M

Connecticut

Saint Joseph College, M

Delaware

University of Delaware, MO

Georgia

Medical College of Georgia, M

Illinois

Rush University, MDO
University of Illinois at Chicago, M

Indiana

Indiana University-Purdue University Indianapolis, M

Massachusetts

Boston College, M

Michigan

Wayne State University, MO

Mississippi

University of Southern Mississippi, M

Missouri

Barnes-Jewish College of Nursing and Allied
    Health, M

University of Missouri-Kansas City, M

New York

Lehman College of the City University of New York, M
State University of New York at Buffalo, BMO
Stony Brook University, State University of New York, MO

Pennsylvania

University of Pennsylvania, MO

Puerto Rico

Pontifical Catholic University of Puerto Rico, M

South Carolina

Medical University of South Carolina, MO

Texas

Baylor University, M
Hardin-Simmons University, M

Washington

University of Washington, B

Wisconsin

Marquette University, O

Quebec

Université de Montréal, O

MATERNITY NURSING

Colorado

University of Colorado at Colorado Springs, M

Illinois

University of Illinois at Chicago, M

New York

Hunter College of the City University of New York, M
Stony Brook University, State University of New York, MO

North Carolina

Duke University, O

Pennsylvania

University of Pennsylvania, M

South Carolina

Medical University of South Carolina, MO

Tennessee

Vanderbilt University, M

MATHEMATICAL AND COMPUTATIONAL FINANCE

California

Stanford University, M
University of California, Santa Barbara, D

Connecticut

University of Connecticut, M

Florida

Florida State University, MD

Georgia

Georgia Institute of Technology, M

Illinois

University of Chicago, M

Indiana

Purdue University, M

Massachusetts

Boston University, M

New York

Bernard M. Baruch College of the City University of New York, M

New York University, M

North Carolina

North Carolina State University, M
The University of North Carolina at Charlotte, M

Pennsylvania

Carnegie Mellon University, MD
University of Pittsburgh, M

Texas

Rice University, D

Alberta

University of Alberta, MD

MATHEMATICAL PHYSICS

Colorado

University of Colorado at Boulder, D

New Jersey

Princeton University, D

New Mexico

New Mexico Institute of Mining and Technology, D

Virginia

Virginia Polytechnic Institute and State University, MD

Alberta

University of Alberta, MD

MATHEMATICAL STATISTICS AND PROBABILITY

Illinois

Northern Illinois University, B

Pennsylvania

Carnegie Mellon University, B

MATHEMATICS

Alabama

Alabama Agricultural and Mechanical University, B
Alabama Southern Community College, A
Alabama State University, BMO
Athens State University, B
Auburn University, BMD
Auburn University Montgomery, B
Birmingham-Southern College, B
Calhoun Community College, A
Chattahoochee Valley Community College, A
Huntingdon College, B
Jacksonville State University, BM
Judson College, B
Lawson State Community College, A
Miles College, B
Oakwood College, B
Samford University, B
Spring Hill College, B
Stillman College, B
Talladega College, B
Troy University, B
Tuskegee University, B
The University of Alabama, BMD
The University of Alabama at Birmingham, BMD
The University of Alabama in Huntsville, BMD
University of Mobile, B
University of Montevallo, B
University of North Alabama, B
University of South Alabama, M
The University of West Alabama, B

Alaska

University of Alaska Anchorage, B
University of Alaska Fairbanks, BMD

University of Alaska Southeast, B

Arizona

Arizona State University, BMD
Arizona Western College, A
Cochise College (Douglas), A
Eastern Arizona College, A
Grand Canyon University, B
Mesa Community College, A
Mohave Community College, A
Northern Arizona University, BM
Scottsdale Community College, A
South Mountain Community College, A
The University of Arizona, BM

Arkansas

Arkansas State University, BM
Arkansas Tech University, B
Harding University, B
Henderson State University, B
Hendrix College, B
John Brown University, B
Lyon College, B
Ouachita Baptist University, B
Philander Smith College, B
Phillips Community College of the University of Arkansas, A
Southern Arkansas University-Magnolia, B
University of Arkansas, BMD
University of Arkansas at Fort Smith, B
University of Arkansas at Little Rock, BM
University of Arkansas at Monticello, B
University of Arkansas at Pine Bluff, B
University of Central Arkansas, BM
University of the Ozarks, B

California

American River College, A
Antelope Valley College, A
Azusa Pacific University, B
Bakersfield College, A
Barstow College, A
Biola University, B
Butte College, A
California Baptist University, B
California Institute of Technology, BD
California Lutheran University, B
California Polytechnic State University, San Luis Obispo, BM
California State Polytechnic University, Pomona, BM
California State University, Bakersfield, B
California State University Channel Islands, B
California State University, Chico, B
California State University, Dominguez Hills, B
California State University, East Bay, BM
California State University, Fresno, BM
California State University, Fullerton, BM
California State University, Long Beach, BM
California State University, Los Angeles, BM
California State University, Northridge, BM
California State University, Sacramento, BM
California State University, San Bernardino, BM
California State University, San Marcos, BM
California State University, Stanislaus, B
Cañada College, A
Cerritos College, A
Chabot College, A
Chaffey College, A
Chapman University, B
Citrus College, A
City College of San Francisco, A
Claremont McKenna College, B
College of Alameda, A
College of the Canyons, A
College of the Desert, A
College of Marin, A
College of San Mateo, A
College of the Sequoias, A
College of the Siskiyous, A
Columbia College, A
Compton Community College, A
Concordia University, B
Contra Costa College, A
Cosumnes River College (Sacramento), A
Crafton Hills College, A
Cuesta College, A

Cypress College, A
De Anza College, A
East Los Angeles College, A
El Camino College, A
Feather River College, A
Folsom Lake College, A
Foothill College, A
Fresno Pacific University, AB
Fullerton College, A
Gavilan College, A
Glendale Community College, A
Golden West College, A
Grossmont College, A
Hartnell College, A
Harvey Mudd College, B
Humboldt State University, B
Imperial Valley College, A
Irvine Valley College, A
La Sierra University, B
Lake Tahoe Community College, A
Laney College, A
Lassen Community College District, A
Long Beach City College, A
Los Angeles City College, A
Los Angeles Mission College, A
Los Angeles Valley College, A
Los Medanos College, A
Loyola Marymount University, B
The Master's College and Seminary, B
Mendocino College, A
Merced College, A
Merritt College, A
Mills College, B
MiraCosta College, A
Mission College, A
Modesto Junior College, A
Monterey Peninsula College, A
Moorpark College, A
Mount St. Mary's College, B
Mt. San Jacinto College, A
National University, B
Occidental College, B
Orange Coast College, A
Oxnard College, A
Pacific Union College, B
Palomar College, A
Pasadena City College, A
Pepperdine University, B
Pitzer College, B
Point Loma Nazarene University, B
Pomona College, B
Porterville College, A
Reedley College, A
Sacramento City College, A
Saddleback College, A
Saint Mary's College of California, B
San Bernardino Valley College, A
San Diego Christian College, B
San Diego City College, A
San Diego Mesa College, A
San Diego Miramar College, A
San Diego State University, BMD
San Francisco State University, BM
San Joaquin Delta College, A
San Jose State University, BM
Santa Ana College, A
Santa Barbara City College, A
Santa Clara University, B
Santa Monica College, A
Santa Rosa Junior College, A
Santiago Canyon College, A
Scripps College, B
Simpson University, B
Skyline College, A
Solano Community College, A
Sonoma State University, B
Southwestern College, A
Stanford University, BMD
Taft College, A
University of California, Berkeley, BMD
University of California, Davis, BMD
University of California, Irvine, BMD
University of California, Los Angeles, BMD
University of California, Riverside, BMD
University of California, San Diego, BMD
University of California, Santa Barbara, BMD

University of California, Santa Cruz, BMD
University of La Verne, B
University of the Pacific, B
University of Redlands, B
University of San Diego, B
University of San Francisco, B
University of Southern California, BMD
Vanguard University of Southern California, B
Victor Valley College, A
West Hills Community College, A
West Los Angeles College, A
West Valley College, A
Westmont College, B
Whittier College, B
Yuba College, A

Colorado

Adams State College, B
Colorado Christian University, B
The Colorado College, B
Colorado Mountain College, A
Colorado Mountain College, Alpine Campus, A
Colorado School of Mines, BMD
Colorado State University, BMD
Colorado State University-Pueblo, B
Fort Lewis College, B
Lamar Community College, A
Mesa State College, AB
Metropolitan State College of Denver, B
Northeastern Junior College, A
Otero Junior College, A
Red Rocks Community College, A
Regis University, B
United States Air Force Academy, B
University of Colorado at Boulder, BMD
University of Colorado at Colorado Springs, B
University of Colorado at Denver and Health
   Sciences Center - Downtown Denver
   Campus, BM
University of Denver, BMD
University of Northern Colorado, BMD
Western State College of Colorado, B

Connecticut

Albertus Magnus College, B
Central Connecticut State University, BM
Connecticut College, B
Eastern Connecticut State University, B
Fairfield University, BM
Housatonic Community College, A
Naugatuck Valley Community College, A
Northwestern Connecticut Community College, A
Quinnipiac University, B
Sacred Heart University, AB
Saint Joseph College, B
Southern Connecticut State University, BM
Trinity College, B
University of Bridgeport, B
University of Connecticut, BMD
University of Hartford, B
University of New Haven, B
Wesleyan University, BMD
Western Connecticut State University, BM
Yale University, BMD

Delaware

Delaware State University, BM
University of Delaware, BMD

District of Columbia

American University, BM
The Catholic University of America, B
Gallaudet University, B
The George Washington University, BMD
Georgetown University, B
Howard University, BMD
Trinity (Washington) University, B
University of the District of Columbia, BM

Florida

Ave Maria University, B
Barry University, B
Bethune-Cookman College, B
Clearwater Christian College, B
Daytona Beach Community College, A

Eckerd College, B
Edward Waters College, B
Florida Agricultural and Mechanical University, B
Florida Atlantic University, BMD
Florida International University, BM
Florida Memorial College, B
Florida Southern College, B
Florida State University, BMD
Gulf Coast Community College, A
Indian River Community College, A
Jacksonville University, B
Miami Dade College, A
New College of Florida, B
Okaloosa-Walton College, A
Palm Beach Atlantic University, B
Palm Beach Community College, A
Pensacola Junior College, A
Rollins College, B
Saint Leo University, B
Stetson University, B
University of Central Florida, BMDO
University of Florida, BMD
University of Miami, BMD
University of North Florida, BM
University of South Florida, BMD
The University of Tampa, AB
University of West Florida, BM

Georgia

Abraham Baldwin Agricultural College, A
Agnes Scott College, B
Albany State University, B
Andrew College, A
Armstrong Atlantic State University, B
Atlanta Metropolitan College, A
Augusta State University, B
Bainbridge College, A
Berry College, B
Brewton-Parker College, B
Clark Atlanta University, B
Clayton State University, A
Coastal Georgia Community College, A
Columbus State University, B
Covenant College, B
Dalton State College, A
Darton College, A
East Georgia College, A
Emmanuel College, B
Emory University, BMD
Fort Valley State University, B
Gainesville College, A
Georgia College & State University, B
Georgia Institute of Technology, MD
Georgia Perimeter College, A
Georgia Southern University, BM
Georgia Southwestern State University, B
Georgia State University, BM
Gordon College, A
Kennesaw State University, B
LaGrange College, B
Macon State College, A
Mercer University, B
Morehouse College, B
North Georgia College & State University, B
Oglethorpe University, B
Paine College, B
Piedmont College, B
Savannah State University, B
Shorter College, B
South Georgia College, A
Southern Polytechnic State University, B
Spelman College, B
Thomas University, A
University of Georgia, BMD
University of West Georgia, B
Valdosta State University, B
Waycross College, A
Wesleyan College, B
Young Harris College, A

Guam

University of Guam, B

Hawaii

Brigham Young University-Hawaii, B
University of Hawaii at Hilo, B

University of Hawaii at Manoa, BMD

Idaho

Albertson College of Idaho, B
Boise State University, B
Brigham Young University -Idaho, A
College of Southern Idaho, A
Idaho State University, ABMD
Lewis-Clark State College, B
North Idaho College, A
Northwest Nazarene University, B
University of Idaho, BMD

Illinois

Augustana College, B
Aurora University, B
Benedictine University, B
Blackburn College, B
Bradley University, B
Chicago State University, BM
City Colleges of Chicago, Harold Washington
    College, A
City Colleges of Chicago, Kennedy-King College, A
City Colleges of Chicago, Olive-Harvey College, A
Concordia University, B
Danville Area Community College, A
DePaul University, BM
Dominican University, B
East-West University, B
Eastern Illinois University, BM
Elmhurst College, B
Eureka College, B
Greenville College, B
Highland Community College, A
Illinois College, B
Illinois State University, BM
Illinois Wesleyan University, B
John A. Logan College, A
Joliet Junior College, A
Judson College, B
Knox College, B
Lake Forest College, B
Lewis University, B
Lincoln College, A
Loyola University Chicago, BM
MacMurray College, B
McKendree College, B
Millikin University, B
Monmouth College, B
National-Louis University, B
North Central College, B
North Park University, B
Northeastern Illinois University, BM
Northern Illinois University, BMD
Northwestern University, BD
Oakton Community College, A
Olivet Nazarene University, B
Principia College, B
Rend Lake College, A
Rockford College, B
Roosevelt University, BM
Saint Xavier University, BM
Sauk Valley Community College, A
South Suburban College, A
Southern Illinois University Carbondale, BMD
Southern Illinois University Edwardsville, BM
Spoon River College, A
Springfield College in Illinois, A
Trinity Christian College, B
Trinity International University, B
University of Chicago, BMD
University of Illinois at Chicago, BMD
University of Illinois at Springfield, B
University of Illinois at Urbana-Champaign, BMD
University of St. Francis, B
Western Illinois University, BM
Wheaton College, B
William Rainey Harper College, A

Indiana

Ancilla College, A
Anderson University, B
Ball State University, BM
Bethel College, B
Butler University, B
DePauw University, B

Earlham College, B
Franklin College, B
Goshen College, B
Grace College, B
Hanover College, B
Huntington University, B
Indiana State University, BM
Indiana University Bloomington, BMD
Indiana University East, A
Indiana University Kokomo, B
Indiana University Northwest, B
Indiana University-Purdue University Fort
    Wayne, ABM
Indiana University-Purdue University
    Indianapolis, BMD
Indiana University South Bend, B
Indiana University Southeast, B
Indiana Wesleyan University, AB
Manchester College, B
Marian College, B
Martin University, B
Oakland City University, B
Purdue University, BMD
Purdue University Calumet, BM
Purdue University North Central, B
Rose-Hulman Institute of Technology, B
Saint Joseph's College, B
Saint Mary-of-the-Woods College, B
Saint Mary's College, B
Taylor University, B
Tri-State University, AB
University of Evansville, B
University of Indianapolis, B
University of Notre Dame, BMD
University of Saint Francis, B
University of Southern Indiana, B
Valparaiso University, B
Vincennes University, A
Wabash College, B

Iowa

Briar Cliff University, B
Buena Vista University, B
Central College, B
Clarke College, B
Coe College, B
Cornell College, B
Dordt College, B
Drake University, B
Ellsworth Community College, A
Graceland University, B
Grinnell College, B
Iowa Lakes Community College, A
Iowa State University of Science and
    Technology, BMD
Iowa Wesleyan College, B
Kirkwood Community College, A
Loras College, B
Luther College, B
Maharishi University of Management, B
Morningside College, B
Mount Mercy College, B
Northwestern College, B
St. Ambrose University, B
Simpson College, B
The University of Iowa, BMD
University of Northern Iowa, BM
Upper Iowa University, B
Wartburg College, B

Kansas

Allen County Community College, A
Baker University, B
Barton County Community College, A
Benedictine College, B
Bethany College, B
Bethel College, B
Butler Community College, A
Central Christian College of Kansas, A
Coffeyville Community College, A
Colby Community College, A
Dodge City Community College, A
Donnelly College, A
Emporia State University, BM
Fort Hays State University, B
Friends University, B

Garden City Community College, A
Highland Community College, A
Hutchinson Community College and Area Vocational
    School, A
Independence Community College, A
Kansas State University, BMD
Kansas Wesleyan University, B
Labette Community College, A
McPherson College, B
MidAmerica Nazarene University, B
Newman University, B
Ottawa University, B
Pittsburg State University, BM
Pratt Community College, A
Seward County Community College, A
Southwestern College, B
Sterling College, B
Tabor College, B
University of Kansas, BMD
University of Saint Mary, B
Washburn University, B
Wichita State University, BMD

Kentucky

Asbury College, B
Bellarmine University, B
Berea College, B
Campbellsville University, B
Centre College, B
Eastern Kentucky University, BM
Georgetown College, B
Kentucky State University, B
Kentucky Wesleyan College, B
Lindsey Wilson College, AB
Midway College, B
Morehead State University, B
Murray State University, BM
Northern Kentucky University, B
Pikeville College, B
St. Catharine College, A
Thomas More College, AB
Transylvania University, B
Union College, B
University of the Cumberlands, B
University of Kentucky, BMD
University of Louisville, BMD
Western Kentucky University, BM

Louisiana

Centenary College of Louisiana, B
Dillard University, B
Grambling State University, B
Louisiana College, B
Louisiana State University and Agricultural and
    Mechanical College, BMD
Louisiana State University at Alexandria, AB
Louisiana State University in Shreveport, B
Louisiana Tech University, BMD
Loyola University New Orleans, B
McNeese State University, BM
Nicholls State University, BM
Northwestern State University of Louisiana, B
Our Lady of Holy Cross College, B
Southeastern Louisiana University, B
Southern University and Agricultural and Mechanical
    College, BM
Southern University at New Orleans, B
Southern University at Shreveport, A
Tulane University, BMD
University of Louisiana at Lafayette, BMD
University of Louisiana at Monroe, B
University of New Orleans, BM
Xavier University of Louisiana, B

Maine

Bates College, B
Bowdoin College, B
Colby College, B
Saint Joseph's College of Maine, B
University of Maine, BM
University of Maine at Farmington, B
University of New England, B

University of Southern Maine, B

Maryland

Anne Arundel Community College, A
Bowie State University, B
Cecil Community College, A
Chesapeake College, A
College of Notre Dame of Maryland, B
Columbia Union College, B
Coppin State University, B
Frederick Community College, A
Frostburg State University, B
Garrett College, A
Goucher College, B
Hood College, B
The Johns Hopkins University, BD
Loyola College in Maryland, B
McDaniel College, B
Morgan State University, BM
Mount St. Mary's University, B
St. Mary's College of Maryland, B
Salisbury University, B
Towson University, B
United States Naval Academy, B
University of Maryland, Baltimore County, B
University of Maryland, College Park, BMD
University of Maryland Eastern Shore, B
Washington College, B

Massachusetts

American International College, B
Amherst College, B
Assumption College, B
Atlantic Union College, B
Bentley College, B
Boston College, BMO
Boston University, BMD
Brandeis University, BMD
Bridgewater State College, B
Bunker Hill Community College, A
Cape Cod Community College, A
Clark University, B
College of the Holy Cross, B
Eastern Nazarene College, B
Elms College, B
Emmanuel College, B
Fitchburg State College, B
Framingham State College, B
Gordon College, B
Greenfield Community College, A
Hampshire College, B
Harvard University, BMD
Massachusetts College of Liberal Arts, B
Massachusetts Institute of Technology, BD
Merrimack College, B
Mount Holyoke College, B
Nichols College, B
Northeastern University, BMD
Quincy College, A
Regis College, B
Roxbury Community College, A
Salem State College, BM
Simmons College, B
Simon's Rock College of Bard, B
Smith College, B
Springfield College, B
Springfield Technical Community College, A
Stonehill College, B
Suffolk University, B
Tufts University, BMD
University of Massachusetts Amherst, BMD
University of Massachusetts Boston, B
University of Massachusetts Dartmouth, B
University of Massachusetts Lowell, BMD
Wellesley College, B
Western New England College, B
Westfield State College, B
Wheaton College, B
Williams College, B
Worcester Polytechnic Institute, BMDO
Worcester State College, B

Michigan

Adrian College, B
Albion College, B
Alma College, B

Alpena Community College, A
Andrews University, BM
Aquinas College, B
Ave Maria College, B
Calvin College, B
Central Michigan University, BMD
Concordia University, B
Cornerstone University, B
Eastern Michigan University, BM
Ferris State University, B
Gogebic Community College, A
Grand Valley State University, B
Hillsdale College, B
Hope College, B
Kalamazoo College, B
Kellogg Community College, A
Lake Superior State University, B
Lansing Community College, A
Lawrence Technological University, B
Macomb Community College, A
Madonna University, B
Marygrove College, B
Michigan State University, BMD
Michigan Technological University, BMD
Mid Michigan Community College, A
Monroe County Community College, A
Northern Michigan University, B
Northwestern Michigan College, A
Oakland University, BM
Olivet College, B
Saginaw Valley State University, B
Siena Heights University, B
Spring Arbor University, B
University of Detroit Mercy, BM
University of Michigan, BMD
University of Michigan-Dearborn, B
University of Michigan-Flint, B
Wayne State University, BMD
Western Michigan University, BMD

Minnesota

Augsburg College, B
Bemidji State University, B
Bethel University, B
Carleton College, B
College of Saint Benedict, B
College of St. Catherine, B
The College of St. Scholastica, B
Concordia College, B
Concordia University, St. Paul, B
Gustavus Adolphus College, B
Hamline University, B
Macalester College, B
Minnesota State University Mankato, BM
Minnesota State University Moorhead, B
Northwestern College, B
Ridgewater College, A
St. Cloud State University, BM
Saint John's University, B
Saint Mary's University of Minnesota, B
St. Olaf College, B
Southwest Minnesota State University, B
University of Minnesota, Duluth, B
University of Minnesota, Morris, B
University of Minnesota, Twin Cities Campus, BMD
University of St. Thomas, B
Vermilion Community College, A
Winona State University, B

Mississippi

Alcorn State University, B
Belhaven College, B
Blue Mountain College, B
Delta State University, B
East Central Community College, A
East Mississippi Community College, A
Hinds Community College, A
Itawamba Community College, A
Jackson State University, BM
Jones County Junior College, A
Millsaps College, B
Mississippi College, BM
Mississippi Delta Community College, A
Mississippi State University, BMD
Mississippi University for Women, B
Mississippi Valley State University, B

Northeast Mississippi Community College, A
Rust College, B
Tougaloo College, B
University of Mississippi, BMD
University of Southern Mississippi, BM
William Carey College, B

Missouri

Avila University, B
Central Methodist University, B
Central Missouri State University, BM
College of the Ozarks, B
Columbia College, B
Crowder College, A
Culver-Stockton College, B
Drury University, B
East Central College, A
Evangel University, B
Fontbonne University, B
Hannibal-LaGrange College, B
Jefferson College, A
Lincoln University, B
Lindenwood University, B
Maryville University of Saint Louis, B
Missouri Baptist University, B
Missouri Southern State University, B
Missouri State University, BM
Missouri Valley College, B
Missouri Western State University, B
Northwest Missouri State University, B
Park University, B
Rockhurst University, B
St. Louis Community College at Florissant Valley, A
St. Louis Community College at Forest Park, A
St. Louis Community College at Meramec, A
Saint Louis University, BMD
Southeast Missouri State University, BM
Southwest Baptist University, B
Truman State University, B
University of Missouri-Columbia, BMD
University of Missouri-Kansas City, BMD
University of Missouri-Rolla, MD
University of Missouri-St. Louis, BMDO
Washington University in St. Louis, BMD
Webster University, B
Westminster College, B
William Jewell College, B
William Woods University, B

Montana

Carroll College, B
Little Big Horn College, A
Montana State University, BMD
Montana State University-Billings, B
Montana Tech of The University of Montana, B
Rocky Mountain College, B
University of Great Falls, AB
The University of Montana-Missoula, BMD

Nebraska

Chadron State College, B
College of Saint Mary, B
Concordia University, B
Creighton University, AB
Dana College, B
Doane College, B
Hastings College, B
Midland Lutheran College, B
Nebraska Wesleyan University, B
Northeast Community College, A
Peru State College, B
Union College, B
University of Nebraska at Kearney, B
University of Nebraska-Lincoln, BMD
University of Nebraska at Omaha, BM
Wayne State College, B
Western Nebraska Community College, A

Nevada

Community College of Southern Nevada, A
Great Basin College, A
University of Nevada, Las Vegas, BM
University of Nevada, Reno, BM

Western Nevada Community College, A

New Hampshire

Dartmouth College, BD
Franklin Pierce College, B
Keene State College, B
Plymouth State University, B
Rivier College, BM
Saint Anselm College, B
University of New Hampshire, BMD

New Jersey

Atlantic Cape Community College, A
Bergen Community College, A
Brookdale Community College, A
Burlington County College, A
Caldwell College, B
Centenary College, B
The College of New Jersey, B
College of Saint Elizabeth, B
Cumberland County College, A
Drew University, B
Essex County College, A
Fairleigh Dickinson University, College at
  Florham, B
Fairleigh Dickinson University, Metropolitan
  Campus, B
Felician College, AB
Georgian Court University, BM
Gloucester County College, A
Kean University, BM
Mercer County Community College, A
Middlesex County College, A
Monmouth University, B
Montclair State University, BM
New Jersey City University, B
New Jersey Institute of Technology, D
Passaic County Community College, A
Princeton University, BD
Ramapo College of New Jersey, B
Raritan Valley Community College, A
The Richard Stockton College of New Jersey, B
Rider University, B
Rowan University, BM
Rutgers, The State University of New Jersey,
  Camden, BM
Rutgers, The State University of New Jersey, New
  Brunswick/Piscataway, BMD
Rutgers, The State University of New Jersey,
  Newark, BD
Saint Peter's College, B
Salem Community College, A
Seton Hall University, B
Stevens Institute of Technology, BMD
William Paterson University of New Jersey, B

New Mexico

Clovis Community College, A
College of the Southwest, B
Eastern New Mexico University, M
New Mexico Highlands University, B
New Mexico Institute of Mining and
  Technology, BMD
New Mexico Junior College, A
New Mexico Military Institute, A
New Mexico State University, BMD
St. John's College, B
San Juan College, A
University of New Mexico, BMD
Western New Mexico University, B

New York

Adelphi University, B
Adirondack Community College, A
Alfred University, B
Bard College, B
Barnard College, B
Bernard M. Baruch College of the City University of
  New York, B
Borough of Manhattan Community College of the
  City University of New York, A
Bronx Community College of the City University of
  New York, A
Brooklyn College of the City University of New
  York, BMD

Buffalo State College, State University of New
  York, B
Cayuga County Community College, A
City College of the City University of New York, BM
Clarkson University, BMD
Colgate University, B
College of Mount Saint Vincent, B
The College of New Rochelle, B
The College of Saint Rose, B
College of Staten Island of the City University of
  New York, B
Columbia College, B
Columbia-Greene Community College, A
Columbia University, School of General Studies, B
Concordia College, B
Cornell University, BD
Corning Community College, A
Daemen College, B
Dominican College, B
Dowling College, BM
Dutchess Community College, A
Elmira College, B
Excelsior College, B
Finger Lakes Community College, A
Fordham University, B
Fulton-Montgomery Community College, A
Genesee Community College, A
Hamilton College, B
Hartwick College, B
Herkimer County Community College, A
Hobart and William Smith Colleges, B
Hofstra University, BM
Houghton College, B
Hunter College of the City University of New
  York, BM
Iona College, B
Ithaca College, B
Jefferson Community College, A
Keuka College, B
Kingsborough Community College of the City
  University of New York, A
Le Moyne College, B
Lehman College of the City University of New
  York, BM
Long Island University, Brooklyn Campus, B
Long Island University, C.W. Post Campus, BM
Manhattan College, B
Manhattanville College, B
Marist College, B
Mercy College, B
Molloy College, B
Monroe Community College, A
Mount Saint Mary College, B
Nassau Community College, A
Nazareth College of Rochester, B
New York University, BMD
Niagara County Community College, A
Niagara University, B
North Country Community College, A
Nyack College, B
Onondaga Community College, A
Pace University, B
Polytechnic University, Brooklyn Campus, BMD
Purchase College, State University of New York, B
Queens College of the City University of New
  York, BM
Rensselaer Polytechnic Institute, BMD
Roberts Wesleyan College, B
Rochester Institute of Technology, B
Rockland Community College, A
Russell Sage College, B
St. Bonaventure University, B
St. Francis College, B
St. John Fisher College, B
St. John's University, BM
St. Joseph's College, New York, B
St. Joseph's College, Suffolk Campus, B
St. Lawrence University, B
St. Thomas Aquinas College, B
Sarah Lawrence College, B
Schenectady County Community College, A
Siena College, B
Skidmore College, B
State University of New York at Binghamton, BMD
State University of New York at Buffalo, BMD

State University of New York College of Agriculture
  and Technology at Morrisville, A
State University of New York College at
  Brockport, BM
State University of New York College at
  Cortland, BM
State University of New York College at Geneseo, B
State University of New York College at Old
  Westbury, B
State University of New York College at Oneonta, B
State University of New York College at
  Potsdam, BM
State University of New York College of Technology
  at Alfred, A
State University of New York College of Technology
  at Delhi, A
State University of New York Empire State
  College, AB
State University of New York, Fredonia, B
State University of New York at New Paltz, BM
State University of New York at Oswego, B
State University of New York at Plattsburgh, B
Stony Brook University, State University of New
  York, BMD
Suffolk County Community College, A
Sullivan County Community College, A
Syracuse University, BMD
Tompkins Cortland Community College, A
Touro College, B
Ulster County Community College, A
Union College, B
United States Military Academy, B
University at Albany, State University of New
  York, BMD
University of Rochester, BMD
Utica College, B
Vassar College, B
Wagner College, B
Wells College, B
Yeshiva University, B
York College of the City University of New York, B

North Carolina

Appalachian State University, BM
Barber-Scotia College, B
Barton College, B
Bennett College For Women, B
Brevard College, B
Campbell University, B
Catawba College, B
Chowan University, B
Davidson College, B
Duke University, BD
East Carolina University, BM
Elizabeth City State University, B
Elon University, B
Fayetteville State University, BM
Gardner-Webb University, B
Greensboro College, B
Guilford College, B
High Point University, B
Johnson C. Smith University, B
Lees-McRae College, B
Lenoir-Rhyne College, B
Livingstone College, B
Louisburg College, A
Mars Hill College, B
Meredith College, B
Methodist College, AB
Mitchell Community College, A
Mount Olive College, B
North Carolina Agricultural and Technical State
  University, B
North Carolina Central University, BM
North Carolina State University, BMD
North Carolina Wesleyan College, B
Pfeiffer University, B
Queens University of Charlotte, B
St. Andrews Presbyterian College, B
Saint Augustine's College, B
Salem College, B
Sandhills Community College, A
Shaw University, B
The University of North Carolina at Asheville, B
The University of North Carolina at Chapel
  Hill, BMD

The University of North Carolina at Charlotte, BMD
The University of North Carolina at Greensboro, BM
The University of North Carolina at Pembroke, B
The University of North Carolina Wilmington, BM
Wake Forest University, BM
Warren Wilson College, B
Western Carolina University, BM
Wingate University, B
Winston-Salem State University, B

North Dakota

Cankdeska Cikana Community College, A
Dickinson State University, B
Fort Berthold Community College, A
Jamestown College, B
Mayville State University, B
Minot State University, B
North Dakota State University, BMD
Turtle Mountain Community College, A
University of Mary, B
University of North Dakota, BM
Valley City State University, B

Ohio

Antioch College, B
Ashland University, B
Baldwin-Wallace College, B
Bluffton University, B
Bowling Green State University, BMDO
Capital University, B
Case Western Reserve University, BMD
Cedarville University, B
Central State University, B
Cleveland State University, BM
College of Mount St. Joseph, B
The College of Wooster, B
Defiance College, B
Denison University, B
Edison State Community College, A
Franciscan University of Steubenville, B
Heidelberg College, B
Hiram College, B
John Carroll University, BM
Kent State University, BMD
Kenyon College, B
Lake Erie College, B
Lorain County Community College, A
Malone College, B
Marietta College, B
Miami University, BM
Miami University Hamilton, B
Miami University-Middletown Campus, A
Mount Union College, B
Mount Vernon Nazarene University, B
Muskingum College, B
Notre Dame College, B
Oberlin College, B
Ohio Dominican University, B
Ohio Northern University, B
The Ohio State University, BMD
The Ohio State University at Lima, B
Ohio University, BMD
Ohio University-Eastern, B
Ohio Wesleyan University, B
Otterbein College, B
Shawnee State University, B
Terra State Community College, A
The University of Akron, BM
University of Cincinnati, BMD
University of Dayton, B
The University of Findlay, B
University of Rio Grande, AB
The University of Toledo, BMD
Ursuline College, B
Walsh University, B
Washington State Community College, A
Wilberforce University, B
Wilmington College, B
Wittenberg University, B
Wright State University, BM
Xavier University, B
Youngstown State University, BM

Oklahoma

Bacone College, A
Cameron University, B

Carl Albert State College, A
Connors State College, A
East Central University, B
Eastern Oklahoma State College, A
Hillsdale Free Will Baptist College, A
Langston University, B
Murray State College, A
Northeastern Oklahoma Agricultural and Mechanical
College, A
Northeastern State University, B
Northwestern Oklahoma State University, B
Oklahoma Baptist University, B
Oklahoma Christian University, B
Oklahoma City Community College, A
Oklahoma City University, B
Oklahoma Panhandle State University, B
Oklahoma State University, BMD
Oklahoma Wesleyan University, B
Oral Roberts University, B
Redlands Community College, A
Rogers State University, A
Rose State College, A
St. Gregory's University, B
Seminole State College, A
Southeastern Oklahoma State University, B
Southern Nazarene University, B
Southwestern Oklahoma State University, B
Tulsa Community College, A
University of Central Oklahoma, BM
University of Oklahoma, BMDO
University of Science and Arts of Oklahoma, B
University of Tulsa, BM

Oregon

Blue Mountain Community College, A
Central Oregon Community College, A
Chemeketa Community College, A
Corban College, B
Eastern Oregon University, B
George Fox University, B
Lewis & Clark College, B
Linfield College, B
Linn-Benton Community College, A
Oregon State University, BMD
Pacific University, B
Portland State University, BMDO
Reed College, B
Southern Oregon University, BM
Southwestern Oregon Community College, A
Treasure Valley Community College, A
Umpqua Community College, A
University of Oregon, BMD
University of Portland, B
Western Oregon University, B
Willamette University, B

Pennsylvania

Albright College, B
Allegheny College, B
Alvernia College, B
Arcadia University, B
Bloomsburg University of Pennsylvania, B
Bryn Mawr College, BMD
Bucknell University, BM
Bucks County Community College, A
Butler County Community College, A
Cabrini College, B
California University of Pennsylvania, B
Carlow University, B
Carnegie Mellon University, MD
Cedar Crest College, B
Chatham College, B
Cheyney University of Pennsylvania, B
Clarion University of Pennsylvania, B
College Misericordia, B
Community College of Allegheny County, A
Delaware Valley College, B
DeSales University, B
Dickinson College, B
Drexel University, BMD
Duquesne University, BM
East Stroudsburg University of Pennsylvania, B
Eastern University, B
Edinboro University of Pennsylvania, B
Elizabethtown College, B
Franklin and Marshall College, B

Gannon University, B
Gettysburg College, B
Grove City College, B
Gwynedd-Mercy College, B
Harrisburg Area Community College, A
Haverford College, B
Holy Family University, B
Immaculata University, B
Indiana University of Pennsylvania, BM
Juniata College, B
King's College, B
Kutztown University of Pennsylvania, BM
La Roche College, B
La Salle University, B
Lafayette College, B
Lebanon Valley College, B
Lehigh Carbon Community College, A
Lehigh University, BMD
Lincoln University, B
Lock Haven University of Pennsylvania, B
Luzerne County Community College, A
Lycoming College, B
Mansfield University of Pennsylvania, B
Marywood University, B
Mercyhurst College, B
Messiah College, B
Millersville University of Pennsylvania, B
Montgomery County Community College, A
Moravian College, B
Muhlenberg College, B
Northampton County Area Community College, A
The Pennsylvania State University Abington
College, B
The Pennsylvania State University Altoona
College, B
The Pennsylvania State University Beaver Campus
of the Commonwealth College, B
The Pennsylvania State University Berks Campus of
the Berks-Lehigh Valley College, B
The Pennsylvania State University Delaware County
Campus of the Commonwealth College, B
The Pennsylvania State University DuBois Campus
of the Commonwealth College, B
The Pennsylvania State University at Erie, The
Behrend College, B
The Pennsylvania State University Fayette Campus
of the Commonwealth College, B
The Pennsylvania State University Hazleton
Campus of the Commonwealth College, B
The Pennsylvania State University, Lehigh Valley
Campus of the Berks-Lehigh Valley College, B
The Pennsylvania State University McKeesport
Campus of the Commonwealth College, B
The Pennsylvania State University Mont Alto
Campus of the Commonwealth College, B
The Pennsylvania State University New Kensington
Campus of the Commonwealth College, B
The Pennsylvania State University Schuylkill
Campus of the Capital College, B
The Pennsylvania State University Shenango
Campus of the Commonwealth College, B
The Pennsylvania State University University Park
Campus, BMD
The Pennsylvania State University Wilkes-Barre
Campus of the Commonwealth College, B
The Pennsylvania State University Worthington
Scranton Campus of the Commonwealth
College, B
The Pennsylvania State University York Campus of
the Commonwealth College, B
Rosemont College, B
Saint Francis University, B
Saint Joseph's University, B
Saint Vincent College, B
Seton Hill University, B
Shippensburg University of Pennsylvania, B
Slippery Rock University of Pennsylvania, B
Susquehanna University, B
Swarthmore College, B
Temple University, BMD
Thiel College, B
University of Pennsylvania, BMD
University of Pittsburgh, BMD
University of Pittsburgh at Johnstown, B
The University of Scranton, B
Ursinus College, B

Villanova University, BM
Washington & Jefferson College, B
Waynesburg College, B
West Chester University of Pennsylvania, BM
Westminster College, B
Widener University, B
Wilkes University, BM
Wilson College, B
York College of Pennsylvania, AB

Puerto Rico

Inter American University of Puerto Rico, Bayamón
  Campus, B
Inter American University of Puerto Rico,
  Metropolitan Campus, B
Inter American University of Puerto Rico, San
  Germán Campus, B
Pontifical Catholic University of Puerto Rico, B
Universidad del Turabo, B
University of Puerto Rico, Cayey University
  College, B
University of Puerto Rico, Mayagüez Campus, BM
University of Puerto Rico, Río Piedras, BMD

Rhode Island

Brown University, BMD
Providence College, B
Rhode Island College, BMO
Roger Williams University, B
Salve Regina University, B
University of Rhode Island, BMD

South Carolina

Allen University, B
Anderson University, B
Benedict College, B
Bob Jones University, B
Charleston Southern University, B
The Citadel, The Military College of South
  Carolina, B
Claflin University, B
Clemson University, BMD
Coker College, B
College of Charleston, BMO
Columbia College, B
Converse College, B
Erskine College, B
Francis Marion University, B
Furman University, B
Lander University, B
Limestone College, B
Morris College, B
Newberry College, B
Presbyterian College, B
South Carolina State University, B
Southern Wesleyan University, B
University of South Carolina, BMD
University of South Carolina Salkehatchie, A
University of South Carolina Upstate, B
Voorhees College, B
Winthrop University, B
Wofford College, B

South Dakota

Augustana College, B
Black Hills State University, B
Dakota Wesleyan University, B
Mount Marty College, B
Northern State University, B
South Dakota School of Mines and Technology, B
South Dakota State University, BM
University of Sioux Falls, B
The University of South Dakota, BM

Tennessee

Austin Peay State University, B
Belmont University, B
Bethel College, B
Bryan College, B
Carson-Newman College, B
Christian Brothers University, B
Columbia State Community College, A
Cumberland University, B
East Tennessee State University, BM
Fisk University, B

Freed-Hardeman University, B
King College, B
Lambuth University, B
Lane College, B
Lee University, B
LeMoyne-Owen College, B
Lincoln Memorial University, B
Lipscomb University, B
Martin Methodist College, A
Maryville College, B
Middle Tennessee State University, BM
Milligan College, B
Rhodes College, B
Roane State Community College, A
Sewanee: The University of the South, B
Southern Adventist University, B
Tennessee State University, BM
Tennessee Technological University, BM
Tennessee Temple University, B
Tennessee Wesleyan College, B
Trevecca Nazarene University, B
Tusculum College, B
Union University, B
University of Memphis, BMD
The University of Tennessee, BMD
The University of Tennessee at Chattanooga, B
The University of Tennessee at Martin, B
Vanderbilt University, BMD

Texas

Abilene Christian University, B
Alvin Community College, A
Amarillo College, A
Angelina College, A
Angelo State University, B
Austin College, B
Austin Community College, A
Baylor University, BMD
Blinn College, A
Brazosport College, A
Central Texas College, A
Cisco Junior College, A
Clarendon College, A
Coastal Bend College, A
College of the Mainland, A
Concordia University at Austin, B
Dallas Baptist University, B
Del Mar College, A
East Texas Baptist University, B
El Paso Community College, A
Frank Phillips College, A
Galveston College, A
Grayson County College, A
Hardin-Simmons University, BD
Hill College of the Hill Junior College District, A
Houston Baptist University, B
Howard College, A
Howard Payne University, B
Huston-Tillotson University, B
Jarvis Christian College, B
Kilgore College, A
Kingwood College, A
Lamar State College-Orange, A
Lamar University, BM
Lee College, A
LeTourneau University, B
Lon Morris College, A
Lubbock Christian University, B
McMurry University, B
Midland College, A
Midwestern State University, B
Navarro College, A
North Harris College, A
Odessa College, A
Our Lady of the Lake University of San Antonio, B
Palo Alto College, A
Paris Junior College, A
Paul Quinn College, B
Prairie View A&M University, BM
Rice University, BMD
St. Edward's University, B
St. Mary's University of San Antonio, B
St. Philip's College, A
Sam Houston State University, BM
Schreiner University, B
Southern Methodist University, BMD

Southwestern Adventist University, B
Southwestern University, B
Stephen F. Austin State University, BM
Sul Ross State University, B
Tarleton State University, BM
Texarkana College, A
Texas A&M International University, BM
Texas A&M University, BMD
Texas A&M University-Commerce, BM
Texas A&M University-Corpus Christi, B
Texas A&M University-Kingsville, B
Texas A&M University-Texarkana, B
Texas Christian University, BM
Texas College, B
Texas Lutheran University, B
Texas Southern University, BM
Texas State University-San Marcos, BM
Texas Tech University, BMD
Texas Wesleyan University, B
Texas Woman's University, BM
Trinity University, B
Trinity Valley Community College, A
University of Dallas, B
University of Houston, BMD
University of Houston-Clear Lake, BM
University of Houston-Victoria, B
University of the Incarnate Word, BM
University of Mary Hardin-Baylor, B
University of North Texas, BMD
University of St. Thomas, B
The University of Texas at Arlington, BMD
The University of Texas at Austin, BMD
The University of Texas at Brownsville, BM
The University of Texas at Dallas, BMD
The University of Texas at El Paso, BM
The University of Texas-Pan American, BM
The University of Texas of the Permian Basin, B
The University of Texas at San Antonio, B
The University of Texas at Tyler, BM
Wayland Baptist University, B
West Texas A&M University, BM
Wharton County Junior College, A
Wiley College, B

United States Virgin Islands

University of the Virgin Islands, B

Utah

Brigham Young University, BMD
Dixie State College of Utah, A
Snow College, A
Southern Utah University, B
University of Utah, BMD
Utah State University, BMD
Utah Valley State College, AB
Weber State University, B
Westminster College, B

Vermont

Bennington College, B
Castleton State College, B
Johnson State College, B
Lyndon State College, B
Marlboro College, B
Middlebury College, B
Norwich University, B
Saint Michael's College, B
University of Vermont, BMD

Virginia

Averett University, B
Bluefield College, B
Bridgewater College, B
Christopher Newport University, B
The College of William and Mary, B
Eastern Mennonite University, B
Emory & Henry College, B
Ferrum College, B
George Mason University, BM
Hampden-Sydney College, B
Hampton University, B
Hollins University, B
James Madison University, BM
Liberty University, B
Longwood University, B
Lynchburg College, B

Mary Baldwin College, B
Marymount University, B
Mountain Empire Community College, A
Norfolk State University, B
Northern Virginia Community College, A
Old Dominion University, BMD
Radford University, B
Randolph-Macon College, B
Randolph-Macon Woman's College, B
Roanoke College, B
Saint Paul's College, B
Shenandoah University, B
Sweet Briar College, B
University of Mary Washington, B
University of Richmond, B
University of Virginia, BMD
The University of Virginia's College at Wise, B
Virginia Commonwealth University, BMO
Virginia Military Institute, B
Virginia Polytechnic Institute and State
  University, BMD
Virginia State University, BM
Virginia Union University, B
Virginia Wesleyan College, B
Washington and Lee University, B

Washington

Central Washington University, BM
Centralia College, A
Eastern Washington University, BM
Everett Community College, A
Gonzaga University, B
Heritage University, AB
Highline Community College, A
Lower Columbia College, A
Pacific Lutheran University, B
Saint Martin's University, B
Seattle Pacific University, B
Seattle University, B
Skagit Valley College, A
Tacoma Community College, A
University of Puget Sound, B
University of Washington, BMD
Walla Walla College, B
Washington State University, BMD
Wenatchee Valley College, A
Western Washington University, BM
Whitman College, B
Whitworth College, B

West Virginia

Alderson-Broaddus College, B
Bethany College, B
Concord University, B
Davis & Elkins College, B
Fairmont State University, B
Marshall University, BM
Potomac State College of West Virginia
  University, A
Salem International University, B
Shepherd University, B
West Liberty State College, B
West Virginia State University, B
West Virginia University, BMD
West Virginia University Institute of Technology, B
West Virginia Wesleyan College, B
Wheeling Jesuit University, B

Wisconsin

Alverno College, B
Beloit College, B
Cardinal Stritch University, B
Carroll College, B
Carthage College, B
Concordia University Wisconsin, B
Edgewood College, B
Lakeland College, B
Lawrence University, B
Marian College of Fond du Lac, B
Marquette University, BMD
Mount Mary College, B
Northland College, B
Ripon College, B
St. Norbert College, B
Silver Lake College, B
University of Wisconsin-Eau Claire, B

University of Wisconsin-Green Bay, AB
University of Wisconsin-La Crosse, B
University of Wisconsin-Madison, BMD
University of Wisconsin-Milwaukee, BMD
University of Wisconsin-Oshkosh, B
University of Wisconsin-Parkside, B
University of Wisconsin-Platteville, B
University of Wisconsin-River Falls, B
University of Wisconsin-Stevens Point, B
University of Wisconsin-Superior, B
University of Wisconsin-Whitewater, B
Viterbo University, B
Wisconsin Lutheran College, B

Wyoming

Casper College, A
Eastern Wyoming College, A
Laramie County Community College, A
Northwest College, A
Sheridan College-Sheridan and Gillette, A
University of Wyoming, BMD
Western Wyoming Community College, A

Alberta

Concordia University College of Alberta, B
University of Alberta, BMDO
University of Calgary, BMD
University of Lethbridge, BM

British Columbia

Simon Fraser University, BMD
Thompson Rivers University, B
Trinity Western University, B
The University of British Columbia, BMD
University College of the Fraser Valley, B
University of Northern British Columbia, BM
University of Victoria, BMD

Manitoba

Brandon University, B
Canadian Mennonite University, B
University of Manitoba, BMD
The University of Winnipeg, B

New Brunswick

Mount Allison University, B
St. Thomas University, B
Université de Moncton, BM
University of New Brunswick Fredericton, BMD

Newfoundland and Labrador

Memorial University of Newfoundland, BMD

Nova Scotia

Acadia University, B
Cape Breton University, B
Dalhousie University, BMD
Mount Saint Vincent University, B
St. Francis Xavier University, B
Saint Mary's University, B
Université Sainte-Anne, B
University of King's College, B

Ontario

Brock University, B
Carleton University, BMD
Lakehead University, BM
Laurentian University, B
McMaster University, BMD
Nipissing University, B
Queen's University at Kingston, BMD
Redeemer University College, B
Royal Military College of Canada, M
Trent University, B
University of Guelph, BMD
University of Ottawa, BMD
University of Toronto, BMD
University of Waterloo, BMD
The University of Western Ontario, BMD
University of Windsor, BMD
Wilfrid Laurier University, B

York University, BMD

Prince Edward Island

University of Prince Edward Island, B

Quebec

Bishop's University, B
Concordia University, BMD
McGill University, BMD
Université Laval, BMD
Université de Montréal, BMD
Université du Québec àChicoutimi, B
Université du Québec àMontréal, BMD
Université du Québec àRimouski, B
Université du Québec àTrois-Rivières, BM
Université de Sherbrooke, BMD

Saskatchewan

University of Regina, BMD
University of Saskatchewan, BMD

MATHEMATICS AND COMPUTER SCIENCE

California

Fresno City College, A
Saint Mary's College of California, B
Stanford University, B

Colorado

The Colorado College, B

Connecticut

Sacred Heart University, B
Yale University, B

Georgia

Paine College, B
Piedmont College, B

Illinois

Augustana College, B
Eastern Illinois University, B
Loyola University Chicago, B
University of Illinois at Chicago, B
University of Illinois at Urbana-Champaign, B
University of St. Francis, B

Indiana

Anderson University, B
Bethel College, B
Saint Joseph's College, B
Saint Mary's College, B

Iowa

Central College, B

Kentucky

Brescia University, B

Maine

Bowdoin College, B

Massachusetts

Boston University, B
Dean College, A
Harvard University, B
Massachusetts Institute of Technology, B

Michigan

Lake Superior State University, B
Lawrence Technological University, B

Minnesota

Saint John's University, B
Saint Mary's University of Minnesota, B

Missouri

Crowder College, A
Washington University in St. Louis, B

New Hampshire

Keene State College, B

New Jersey

Drew University, B

New York

Adirondack Community College, A
Hofstra University, B
Ithaca College, B
Long Island University, C.W. Post Campus, B
Rochester Institute of Technology, B
St. Joseph's College, New York, B
St. Lawrence University, B
University at Albany, State University of New York, B

North Carolina

Pfeiffer University, B

Ohio

The University of Akron, B

Oklahoma

St. Gregory's University, B

Oregon

Southern Oregon University, B
University of Oregon, B

Pennsylvania

Chestnut Hill College, B
Immaculata University, AB
Saint Francis University, B
Swarthmore College, B

Puerto Rico

University of Puerto Rico at Humacao, B

Rhode Island

Brown University, B

Tennessee

Maryville College, B

Texas

McMurry University, B

Virginia

Averett University, B
Hampden-Sydney College, B

West Virginia

Mountain State University, B

Wisconsin

Cardinal Stritch University, B
Lawrence University, B

British Columbia

Trinity Western University, B
University of Northern British Columbia, B

Manitoba

Brandon University, B

New Brunswick

Mount Allison University, B

Nova Scotia

Mount Saint Vincent University, B

Ontario

University of Waterloo, B
University of Windsor, B

York University, B

Quebec

McGill University, B
Université Laval, B

Saskatchewan

University of Regina, B

MATHEMATICS AND STATISTICS

Alabama

University of South Alabama, B

California

Saint Mary's College of California, B

Connecticut

University of Hartford, B

Florida

University of Miami, B

Illinois

Bradley University, B

Indiana

Anderson University, B

Louisiana

Tulane University, B

Michigan

Ferris State University, B

New York

Barnard College, B
Canisius College, B
Hofstra University, B
New York University, B
University of Rochester, B

Ohio

Miami University Hamilton, B
The Ohio State University, B
The University of Akron, B

Pennsylvania

Carnegie Mellon University, B
University of Pittsburgh, B
The University of Scranton, B

South Dakota

Dakota State University, B

Washington

Seattle Pacific University, B

Saskatchewan

University of Regina, B

MATHEMATICS TEACHER EDUCATION

Alabama

Alabama State University, MO
Auburn University, B
Huntingdon College, B
Judson College, B
Miles College, B
Talladega College, B
The University of West Alabama, M

Arizona

Northern Arizona University, BM
Prescott College, B

The University of Arizona, B

Arkansas

Arkansas State University, B
Arkansas Tech University, B
Harding University, B
Henderson State University, M
Southern Arkansas University-Magnolia, B
University of Arkansas, M
University of Arkansas at Fort Smith, B
University of Central Arkansas, B
University of the Ozarks, B

California

California Lutheran University, B
California State University, Bakersfield, M
California State University, Chico, B
California State University, Dominguez Hills, M
California State University, Fresno, B
California State University, Fullerton, M
California State University, Long Beach, B
Fresno Pacific University, M
Loyola Marymount University, M
Occidental College, M
San Diego State University, BD
San Francisco State University, M
San Jose State University, M
Stanford University, MD
University of California, Berkeley, MD
University of California, San Diego, BD
University of California, Santa Cruz, B
Westmont College, B

Colorado

The Colorado College, M
Colorado State University, B
Colorado State University-Pueblo, B
University of Northern Colorado, MD

Connecticut

Albertus Magnus College, B
Connecticut College, M
Quinnipiac University, M
Sacred Heart University, B
University of Connecticut, MD
Western Connecticut State University, M

Delaware

Delaware State University, B
University of Delaware, B

District of Columbia

The Catholic University of America, B

Florida

Chipola College, B
Clearwater Christian College, B
Florida Agricultural and Mechanical University, M
Florida Atlantic University, B
Florida Gulf Coast University, M
Florida Institute of Technology, BMDO
Florida International University, BM
Florida State University, BMDO
Jacksonville University, M
Manatee Community College, A
Miami Dade College, B
Nova Southeastern University, MO
St. Petersburg College, B
Southeastern University, B
University of Central Florida, BMD
University of Florida, MD
University of Miami, MDO
University of North Florida, B
University of South Florida, BMDO
University of West Florida, BM

Georgia

Albany State University, M
Berry College, B
Brewton-Parker College, B
Columbus State University, B
Emmanuel College, B
Georgia College & State University, M
Georgia Southern University, BM
Georgia State University, MDO

Kennesaw State University, B
North Georgia College & State University, B
Paine College, B
Shorter College, B
University of Georgia, BMDO
University of West Georgia, MO
Wesleyan College, M

Hawaii

Brigham Young University-Hawaii, B

Idaho

Boise State University, M
Lewis-Clark State College, B
Northwest Nazarene University, B
University of Idaho, M

Illinois

Chicago State University, B
Concordia University, B
DePaul University, M
Eastern Illinois University, M
Elmhurst College, B
Greenville College, B
Illinois Institute of Technology, MD
Illinois State University, D
Illinois Wesleyan University, B
McKendree College, B
National-Louis University, MO
Northeastern Illinois University, M
Northwestern University, B
Saint Xavier University, B
Southern Illinois University Edwardsville, M
Trinity Christian College, B
University of Illinois at Chicago, BM
University of Illinois at Urbana-Champaign, M
University of St. Francis, B

Indiana

Ancilla College, A
Anderson University, B
Ball State University, M
Bethel College, B
Franklin College, B
Grace College, B
Indiana University Bloomington, BM
Indiana University Northwest, B
Indiana University-Purdue University Fort Wayne, B
Indiana University South Bend, B
Indiana University Southeast, B
Indiana Wesleyan University, B
Oakland City University, B
Purdue University, MDO
Purdue University Calumet, M
Tri-State University, B
University of Evansville, B
University of Indianapolis, BM
Valparaiso University, B

Iowa

Buena Vista University, B
Drake University, M
Iowa State University of Science and Technology, M
St. Ambrose University, B
The University of Iowa, BMD
University of Northern Iowa, BM
Wartburg College, B
William Penn University, B

Kansas

Bethany College, B
Central Christian College of Kansas, A
MidAmerica Nazarene University, B
Pittsburg State University, B

Kentucky

Asbury College, M
Berea College, B
Campbellsville University, B
Eastern Kentucky University, M
Kentucky Wesleyan College, B
Lindsey Wilson College, B
Murray State University, B
Northern Kentucky University, B

Pikeville College, B

Louisiana

Centenary College of Louisiana, B
Louisiana State University in Shreveport, B
Louisiana Tech University, B
McNeese State University, B
Northwestern State University of Louisiana, BM
Southeastern Louisiana University, B
Southern University and Agricultural and Mechanical College, BD
University of Louisiana at Monroe, B
University of New Orleans, B

Maine

Saint Joseph's College of Maine, B
University of Maine, B
University of Maine at Farmington, B
University of Maine at Fort Kent, B
University of Maine at Machias, B

Maryland

Bowie State University, B
Columbia Union College, B
Frederick Community College, A
Hood College, O
Morgan State University, MD
Salisbury University, M
Towson University, M
University of Maryland, College Park, B

Massachusetts

Boston College, M
Boston University, BMDO
Bridgewater State College, M
Elms College, B
Fitchburg State College, B
Framingham State College, BM
Harvard University, M
Regis College, B
Salem State College, M
Smith College, M
University of Massachusetts Lowell, D
Western New England College, M

Michigan

Alma College, B
Central Michigan University, B
Concordia University, B
Cornerstone University, B
Eastern Michigan University, BM
Ferris State University, B
Hope College, B
Madonna University, B
Michigan State University, MD
Michigan Technological University, B
Northern Michigan University, BM
Oakland University, BO
Rochester College, B
University of Detroit Mercy, M
University of Michigan, MD
University of Michigan-Dearborn, B
Wayne State University, BMO
Western Michigan University, BMD

Minnesota

Bemidji State University, M
Bethel University, B
College of St. Catherine, B
Concordia College, B
Concordia University, St. Paul, B
Gustavus Adolphus College, B
Minnesota State University Mankato, M
Minnesota State University Moorhead, B
Northwestern College, B
Pillsbury Baptist Bible College, B
Saint Mary's University of Minnesota, B
Southwest Minnesota State University, B
University of Minnesota, Duluth, B
University of Minnesota, Twin Cities Campus, BMD
University of St. Thomas, B

Mississippi

Blue Mountain College, B
Delta State University, BM

Jackson State University, BM
Mississippi College, M
Mississippi Valley State University, B
Northwest Mississippi Community College, A
Rust College, B
University of Mississippi, B
University of Southern Mississippi, MD
William Carey College, B

Missouri

College of the Ozarks, B
Culver-Stockton College, B
Hannibal-LaGrange College, B
Lincoln University, B
Lindenwood University, B
Maryville University of Saint Louis, B
Missouri State University, B
Northwest Missouri State University, M
Southeast Missouri State University, B
Southwest Baptist University, B
University of Missouri-Columbia, BMDO
University of Missouri-Rolla, M
University of Missouri-St. Louis, B
Washington University in St. Louis, BM
Webster University, M
William Woods University, B

Montana

Carroll College, B
Montana State University-Billings, B
Rocky Mountain College, B
University of Great Falls, B
The University of Montana-Missoula, B
The University of Montana-Western, B

Nebraska

Chadron State College, B
Concordia University, B
Dana College, B
Hastings College, B
Union College, B
University of Nebraska-Lincoln, B
Wayne State College, BM
York College, B

Nevada

Nevada State College at Henderson, B
University of Nevada, Las Vegas, M
University of Nevada, Reno, BM

New Hampshire

Keene State College, B
Plymouth State University, M
Rivier College, B
University of New Hampshire, BMD

New Jersey

Bloomfield College, B
The College of New Jersey, B
Felician College, B
Kean University, M
Montclair State University, MD
New Jersey City University, M
Rider University, O
Rowan University, M
Rutgers, The State University of New Jersey, New Brunswick/Piscataway, MD

New York

Brooklyn College of the City University of New York, BM
Buffalo State College, State University of New York, BM
City College of the City University of New York, BMO
The College of Saint Rose, BM
Cornell University, BM
Daemen College, B
Dominican College, B
Dowling College, B
Elmira College, B
Hofstra University, BM
Hunter College of the City University of New York, BM
Iona College, BM

Ithaca College, B
Keuka College, B
Le Moyne College, B
Lehman College of the City University of New
    York, M
Long Island University, Brooklyn Campus, BM
Long Island University, C.W. Post Campus, BM
Manhattanville College, BM
Marist College, B
Mercy College, B
Molloy College, B
Nazareth College of Rochester, B
New York Institute of Technology, B
New York University, BMD
Niagara University, B
Pace University, B
Queens College of the City University of New
    York, MO
Roberts Wesleyan College, B
St. Bonaventure University, B
St. Francis College, B
St. John Fisher College, BM
St. John's University, B
State University of New York at Binghamton, M
State University of New York at Buffalo, MD
State University of New York College at
    Brockport, BM
State University of New York College at
    Cortland, BM
State University of New York College at Old
    Westbury, B
State University of New York College at Oneonta, B
State University of New York College at Potsdam, B
State University of New York, Fredonia, M
State University of New York at New Paltz, M
State University of New York at Plattsburgh, M
Syracuse University, BMD
University at Albany, State University of New
    York, BM
Utica College, B

North Carolina

Appalachian State University, BM
Campbell University, BM
Chowan University, B
East Carolina University, BM
Elizabeth City State University, B
Fayetteville State University, B
Gardner-Webb University, B
Greensboro College, B
Johnson C. Smith University, B
Louisburg College, A
North Carolina Agricultural and Technical State
    University, M
North Carolina Central University, B
North Carolina State University, BMD
Queens University of Charlotte, B
Saint Augustine's College, B
Shaw University, B
The University of North Carolina at Chapel Hill, M
The University of North Carolina at Charlotte, BM
The University of North Carolina at Greensboro, BM
The University of North Carolina at Pembroke, BM
The University of North Carolina Wilmington, B
Western Carolina University, BM
Winston-Salem State University, B

North Dakota

Jamestown College, B
Mayville State University, B
Minot State University, BM
North Dakota State University, BM
University of Mary, B
University of North Dakota, B
Valley City State University, B

Ohio

Bowling Green State University, BMO
Capital University, B
Cedarville University, B
Central State University, B
Miami University, M
Miami University Hamilton, B
Mount Vernon Nazarene University, B
Ohio Dominican University, B
Ohio Northern University, B

Ohio University, BMD
Ohio Wesleyan University, B
Shawnee State University, B
The University of Akron, B
University of Cincinnati, M
University of Rio Grande, B
The University of Toledo, BM
Ursuline College, B
Wright State University, BM
Youngstown State University, B

Oklahoma

East Central University, B
Oklahoma Baptist University, B
Oklahoma Christian University, B
Oral Roberts University, B
St. Gregory's University, B
Southeastern Oklahoma State University, B
Southern Nazarene University, B
Southwestern Oklahoma State University, M
University of Central Oklahoma, B
University of Oklahoma, B
University of Tulsa, M

Oregon

Concordia University, B
Corban College, B
Oregon State University, MD
Portland State University, D
Western Oregon University, M

Pennsylvania

Alvernia College, B
Arcadia University, MO
Cabrini College, B
California University of Pennsylvania, M
Chatham College, BM
Cheyney University of Pennsylvania, O
DeSales University, M
Duquesne University, B
Edinboro University of Pennsylvania, M
Geneva College, B
Gwynedd-Mercy College, B
Indiana University of Pennsylvania, BM
Juniata College, B
Keystone College, B
Kutztown University of Pennsylvania, M
La Roche College, B
Lebanon Valley College, B
Lincoln University, B
Mansfield University of Pennsylvania, B
Marywood University, B
Mercyhurst College, B
Messiah College, B
Millersville University of Pennsylvania, BM
Moravian College, B
Philadelphia Biblical University, B
Point Park University, B
Saint Francis University, B
Saint Joseph's University, M
Seton Hill University, B
Slippery Rock University of Pennsylvania, M
Temple University, BD
University of Pittsburgh, MD
University of Pittsburgh at Johnstown, B
Waynesburg College, B
West Chester University of Pennsylvania, B
Widener University, BM
Wilkes University, M
York College of Pennsylvania, B

Puerto Rico

Bayamon Central University, B
Caribbean University, B
Inter American University of Puerto Rico,
    Metropolitan Campus, B
Pontifical Catholic University of Puerto Rico, B
Universidad Adventista de las Antillas, B
University of Puerto Rico, Cayey University
    College, B
University of Puerto Rico, Río Piedras, M

Rhode Island

Providence College, M
Rhode Island College, B

Salve Regina University, B

South Carolina

Anderson University, B
Bob Jones University, B
Charleston Southern University, B
The Citadel, The Military College of South
    Carolina, BM
Claflin University, B
Clemson University, BM
Coker College, B
College of Charleston, M
Converse College, M
Limestone College, B
Morris College, B
South Carolina State University, M
Southern Wesleyan University, B
University of South Carolina, M

South Dakota

Black Hills State University, B
Dakota State University, B
Dakota Wesleyan University, B
Mount Marty College, B
The University of South Dakota, B

Tennessee

Belmont University, M
Christian Brothers University, B
Crichton College, B
Cumberland University, B
Freed-Hardeman University, B
King College, B
Lambuth University, B
Lincoln Memorial University, B
Maryville College, B
Middle Tennessee State University, M
Tennessee Temple University, B
Tennessee Wesleyan College, B
Trevecca Nazarene University, B
The University of Tennessee, MO
The University of Tennessee at Martin, B
Vanderbilt University, M

Texas

Abilene Christian University, B
Baylor University, B
East Texas Baptist University, B
Hardin-Simmons University, B
Houston Baptist University, B
Howard Payne University, B
Northeast Texas Community College, A
St. Edward's University, B
Sam Houston State University, B
Schreiner University, B
Stephen F. Austin State University, M
Texas A&M International University, B
Texas A&M University, MD
Texas Christian University, B
Texas Lutheran University, B
Texas State University-San Marcos, M
Texas Wesleyan University, B
Texas Woman's University, M
University of Houston, M
University of the Incarnate Word, D
University of Mary Hardin-Baylor, B
The University of Texas at Austin, MD
The University of Texas at Dallas, M
The University of Texas at San Antonio, M

Utah

Brigham Young University, BM
University of Utah, B
Utah State University, B
Utah Valley State College, B

Vermont

Bennington College, M
Castleton State College, B
College of St. Joseph, M
Johnson State College, B
Lyndon State College, B

University of Vermont, BM

Virginia

Averett University, BM
Bluefield College, B
Christopher Newport University, M
Eastern Mennonite University, B
Liberty University, B
Old Dominion University, B
Virginia State University, M

Washington

Central Washington University, B
Eastern Washington University, BM
Seattle Pacific University, B
Washington State University, BD

West Virginia

Davis & Elkins College, B
Glenville State College, B
Ohio Valley University, B
West Virginia University, M
West Virginia Wesleyan College, B
Wheeling Jesuit University, BM

Wisconsin

Alverno College, B
Carroll College, B
Marian College of Fond du Lac, B
Marquette University, BM
Mount Mary College, B
University of Wisconsin-Eau Claire, M
University of Wisconsin-Madison, M
University of Wisconsin-Oshkosh, M
University of Wisconsin-River Falls, BM
University of Wisconsin-Superior, B
Viterbo University, B

Wyoming

Eastern Wyoming College, A
University of Wyoming, M

Alberta

University of Lethbridge, B

British Columbia

The University of British Columbia, M
University of Victoria, M

Nova Scotia

Acadia University, M

Ontario

Brock University, B
University of Waterloo, B
The University of Western Ontario, B
University of Windsor, B
York University, B

Quebec

Bishop's University, B
Concordia University, M
McGill University, B
Université Laval, B
Université du Québec àTrois-Rivières, B

Saskatchewan

University of Regina, B

MECHANIC AND REPAIR TECHNOLOGIES/TECHNICIANS

Indiana

Ivy Tech Community College-Bloomington, A
Ivy Tech Community College-Columbus, A
Ivy Tech Community College-Kokomo, A
Ivy Tech Community College-Lafayette, A
Ivy Tech Community College-North Central, A
Ivy Tech Community College-Northwest, A

Ivy Tech Community College-Southwest, A

Michigan

Delta College, A
Hope College, B
Macomb Community College, A

Ohio

Cincinnati State Technical and Community College, A

Pennsylvania

Pennsylvania College of Technology, A

South Carolina

Bob Jones University, AB

Wisconsin

Northeast Wisconsin Technical College, A

MECHANICAL DRAFTING AND MECHANICAL DRAFTING CAD/CADD

California

Western Career College (San Jose), A
Western Career College (Walnut Creek), A

Colorado

IntelliTec College (Grand Junction), A

Florida

Florida Technical College (Orlando), A
North Florida Community College, A

Illinois

John Wood Community College, A
Morrison Institute of Technology, A
Oakton Community College, A

Indiana

Indiana University-Purdue University Indianapolis, A
Purdue University, AB

Kentucky

Louisville Technical Institute, A
Murray State University, B
Spencerian College-Lexington, A

Michigan

Baker College of Flint, A
Eastern Michigan University, B
Macomb Community College, A
Mott Community College, A
Oakland Community College, A

Minnesota

Alexandria Technical College, A
Anoka Technical College, A
Lake Superior College, A
Normandale Community College, A
Northwest Technical Institute, A
St. Cloud Technical College, A
South Central Technical College, A

Missouri

Ozarks Technical Community College, A

Montana

Montana Tech of The University of Montana, A

New Jersey

Brookdale Community College, A

New York

Adirondack Community College, A
Erie Community College, South Campus, A
Island Drafting and Technical Institute, A

Mohawk Valley Community College, A

North Carolina

Edgecombe Community College, A
Gaston College, A
Rowan-Cabarrus Community College, A
Stanly Community College, A
Wake Technical Community College, A

Oklahoma

Cameron University, A

Pennsylvania

Butler County Community College, A
Commonwealth Technical Institute, A
Community College of Allegheny County, A
Montgomery County Community College, A
Pennsylvania College of Technology, B
Triangle Tech, Inc.-Greensburg School, A

South Carolina

Central Carolina Technical College, A
Midlands Technical College, A
Piedmont Technical College, A
York Technical College, A

Utah

Dixie State College of Utah, A

Virginia

Piedmont Virginia Community College, A

Washington

North Seattle Community College, A

Wisconsin

Northeast Wisconsin Technical College, A
Waukesha County Technical College, A

British Columbia

British Columbia Institute of Technology, A

MECHANICAL ENGINEERING

Alabama

Alabama Agricultural and Mechanical University, B
Auburn University, BMD
Tuskegee University, BM
The University of Alabama, BMD
The University of Alabama at Birmingham, BMD
The University of Alabama in Huntsville, BMD
University of South Alabama, BM

Alaska

University of Alaska Fairbanks, BMD

Arizona

Arizona State University, BMD
Arizona State University at the Polytechnic Campus, M
Northern Arizona University, B
The University of Arizona, BMD

Arkansas

Arkansas Tech University, B
John Brown University, B
University of Arkansas, BMD

California

California Institute of Technology, BMDO
California Maritime Academy, B
California Polytechnic State University, San Luis Obispo, B
California State Polytechnic University, Pomona, BM
California State University, Chico, B
California State University, Fresno, BM
California State University, Fullerton, BM
California State University, Long Beach, BMD
California State University, Los Angeles, BM
California State University, Northridge, M
California State University, Sacramento, BM
Loyola Marymount University, BM

San Diego State University, BMD
San Francisco State University, B
San Jose State University, BM
Santa Clara University, BMDO
Stanford University, BMDO
University of California, Berkeley, BMD
University of California, Davis, BMDO
University of California, Irvine, BMD
University of California, Los Angeles, BMD
University of California, Riverside, BMD
University of California, San Diego, BMD
University of California, Santa Barbara, BDO
University of the Pacific, B
University of San Diego, B
University of Southern California, BMDO

Colorado

Colorado School of Mines, B
Colorado State University, BMD
United States Air Force Academy, B
University of Colorado at Boulder, BMD
University of Colorado at Colorado Springs, BM
University of Colorado at Denver and Health
  Sciences Center - Downtown Denver
  Campus, BM
University of Denver, BM

Connecticut

Central Connecticut State University, M
Fairfield University, A
Trinity College, B
United States Coast Guard Academy, B
University of Bridgeport, M
University of Connecticut, BMD
University of Hartford, B
University of New Haven, BM
Yale University, BMD

Delaware

Delaware State University, B
University of Delaware, BMD

District of Columbia

The Catholic University of America, BMD
Gallaudet University, B
The George Washington University, BMDO
Howard University, BMD
University of the District of Columbia, B

Florida

Embry-Riddle Aeronautical University, B
Florida Agricultural and Mechanical University, BMD
Florida Atlantic University, BMD
Florida Institute of Technology, BMD
Florida International University, BMD
Florida State University, BMD
Jacksonville University, B
University of Central Florida, BMDO
University of Florida, BMDO
University of Miami, BMD
University of North Florida, B
University of South Florida, BMD

Georgia

Georgia Institute of Technology, BMD
Macon State College, A
Mercer University, M

Hawaii

University of Hawaii at Manoa, BMD

Idaho

Boise State University, M
Idaho State University, BM
University of Idaho, BMD

Illinois

Bradley University, BM
Illinois Institute of Technology, BMD
Northern Illinois University, BM
Northwestern University, BMDO
Southern Illinois University Carbondale, BM
Southern Illinois University Edwardsville, BM
University of Illinois at Chicago, BMD

University of Illinois at Urbana-Champaign, BMD

Indiana

Indiana Tech, B
Indiana University-Purdue University Fort Wayne, B
Indiana University-Purdue University
  Indianapolis, BM
Purdue University, BMD
Purdue University Calumet, B
Rose-Hulman Institute of Technology, BM
Tri-State University, B
University of Evansville, B
University of Indianapolis, B
University of Notre Dame, BMD
Valparaiso University, B

Iowa

Dordt College, B
Iowa State University of Science and
  Technology, BMD
The University of Iowa, BMD
William Penn University, B

Kansas

Kansas State University, BMD
University of Kansas, BMD
Wichita State University, BMD

Kentucky

Murray State University, B
University of Kentucky, BMD
University of Louisville, BM
Western Kentucky University, B

Louisiana

Louisiana State University and Agricultural and
  Mechanical College, BMD
Louisiana Tech University, BMD
McNeese State University, M
Southern University and Agricultural and Mechanical
  College, B
Tulane University, BMD
University of Louisiana at Lafayette, BM
University of New Orleans, BM

Maine

University of Maine, BMD

Maryland

Frostburg State University, B
The Johns Hopkins University, BMD
United States Naval Academy, B
University of Maryland, Baltimore County, BMDO
University of Maryland, College Park, BMD

Massachusetts

Boston University, BMD
Eastern Nazarene College, B
Harvard University, B
Massachusetts Institute of Technology, BMDO
Northeastern University, BMD
Tufts University, BMD
University of Massachusetts Amherst, BMD
University of Massachusetts Dartmouth, BM
University of Massachusetts Lowell, BMDO
Western New England College, BM
Worcester Polytechnic Institute, BMDO

Michigan

Andrews University, B
Baker College of Flint, B
Calvin College, B
Grand Valley State University, BM
Kettering University, BM
Lake Superior State University, B
Lawrence Technological University, BM
Michigan State University, BMD
Michigan Technological University, BMD
Oakland University, BMD
Saginaw Valley State University, B
University of Detroit Mercy, BMD
University of Michigan, BMD
University of Michigan-Dearborn, BM
Wayne State University, BMD

Western Michigan University, BMD

Minnesota

Itasca Community College, A
Minnesota State University Mankato, B
St. Cloud State University, BM
University of Minnesota, Twin Cities Campus, BMD
University of St. Thomas, B
Walden University, M
Winona State University, B

Mississippi

Mississippi State University, BMD
University of Mississippi, B

Missouri

Saint Louis University, BM
University of Missouri-Columbia, BMD
University of Missouri-Kansas City, BM
University of Missouri-Rolla, BMD
University of Missouri-St. Louis, B
Washington University in St. Louis, BMD

Montana

Montana State University, BMD
Montana Tech of The University of Montana, B

Nebraska

University of Nebraska-Lincoln, BMD

Nevada

University of Nevada, Las Vegas, BMD
University of Nevada, Reno, BMD

New Hampshire

Dartmouth College, MD
University of New Hampshire, BMD

New Jersey

The College of New Jersey, B
New Jersey Institute of Technology, BMDO
Princeton University, BMD
Rowan University, B
Rutgers, The State University of New Jersey, New
  Brunswick/Piscataway, BMD
Stevens Institute of Technology, BMDO

New Mexico

New Mexico Institute of Mining and Technology, B
New Mexico State University, BMD
University of New Mexico, BMD

New York

Alfred University, BM
City College of the City University of New
  York, BMD
Clarkson University, BMD
Columbia University, The Fu Foundation School of
  Engineering and Applied Science, B
Cooper Union for the Advancement of Science and
  Art, B
Cornell University, BMD
Hofstra University, B
Manhattan College, BM
New York Institute of Technology, B
Polytechnic University, Brooklyn Campus, BMD
Rensselaer Polytechnic Institute, BMDO
Rochester Institute of Technology, BM
State University of New York at Binghamton, BMD
State University of New York at Buffalo, BMD
State University of New York Maritime College, B
Stony Brook University, State University of New
  York, BMDO
Syracuse University, BMD
Union College, B
United States Military Academy, B
University of Rochester, BMD

North Carolina

Duke University, BMDO
North Carolina Agricultural and Technical State
  University, BMD
North Carolina State University, BMD

The University of North Carolina at Charlotte, BMD

North Dakota

North Dakota State University, BMD
University of North Dakota, BM

Ohio

Case Western Reserve University, BMD
Cedarville University, B
Cleveland State University, BMD
Miami University, B
Northwest State Community College, A
Ohio Northern University, B
The Ohio State University, BMD
Ohio University, BMD
Ohio University-Eastern, B
The University of Akron, BMD
University of Cincinnati, BMD
University of Dayton, BMD
The University of Toledo, BMD
Wright State University, BM
Youngstown State University, BM

Oklahoma

Oklahoma Christian University, B
Oklahoma State University, BMD
Oral Roberts University, B
University of Oklahoma, BMD
University of Tulsa, BMD

Oregon

George Fox University, B
Oregon State University, BMD
Portland State University, BMD
University of Portland, B

Pennsylvania

Bucknell University, BM
Carnegie Mellon University, BMD
Drexel University, BMD
Gannon University, BM
Grove City College, B
Lafayette College, B
Lehigh Carbon Community College, A
Lehigh University, BMD
The Pennsylvania State University Abington College, B
The Pennsylvania State University Altoona College, B
The Pennsylvania State University Beaver Campus of the Commonwealth College, B
The Pennsylvania State University Berks Campus of the Berks-Lehigh Valley College, B
The Pennsylvania State University Delaware County Campus of the Commonwealth College, B
The Pennsylvania State University DuBois Campus of the Commonwealth College, B
The Pennsylvania State University at Erie, The Behrend College, B
The Pennsylvania State University Fayette Campus of the Commonwealth College, B
The Pennsylvania State University Harrisburg Campus, B
The Pennsylvania State University Hazleton Campus of the Commonwealth College, B
The Pennsylvania State University, Lehigh Valley Campus of the Berks-Lehigh Valley College, B
The Pennsylvania State University McKeesport Campus of the Commonwealth College, B
The Pennsylvania State University Mont Alto Campus of the Commonwealth College, B
The Pennsylvania State University New Kensington Campus of the Commonwealth College, B
The Pennsylvania State University Schuylkill Campus of the Capital College, B
The Pennsylvania State University Shenango Campus of the Commonwealth College, B
The Pennsylvania State University University Park Campus, BMD
The Pennsylvania State University Wilkes-Barre Campus of the Commonwealth College, B
The Pennsylvania State University Worthington Scranton Campus of the Commonwealth College, B

The Pennsylvania State University York Campus of the Commonwealth College, B
Temple University, BM
University of Pennsylvania, BMD
University of Pittsburgh, BMD
Ursinus College, B
Villanova University, BMO
Widener University, BM
Wilkes University, B
York College of Pennsylvania, B

Puerto Rico

Inter American University of Puerto Rico, Bayamón Campus, B
Polytechnic University of Puerto Rico, B
Universidad del Turabo, B
University of Puerto Rico, Mayagüez Campus, BM

Rhode Island

Brown University, BMD
University of Rhode Island, BMD

South Carolina

Clemson University, BMD
University of South Carolina, BMD

South Dakota

South Dakota School of Mines and Technology, BMD
South Dakota State University, BM

Tennessee

Christian Brothers University, B
Tennessee State University, B
Tennessee Technological University, BMD
University of Memphis, B
The University of Tennessee, BMDO
Vanderbilt University, BMD

Texas

Baylor University, BM
Lamar University, BMD
LeTourneau University, B
Prairie View A&M University, B
Rice University, BMD
Southern Methodist University, BMD
Texas A&M University, BMD
Texas A&M University-Kingsville, BM
Texas Tech University, BMD
University of Houston, BMD
The University of Texas at Arlington, BMD
The University of Texas at Austin, BMD
The University of Texas at El Paso, BM
The University of Texas-Pan American, B
The University of Texas at San Antonio, BM
The University of Texas at Tyler, B
West Texas A&M University, B

Utah

Brigham Young University, BMDO
University of Utah, BMD
Utah State University, BMD

Vermont

Norwich University, B
University of Vermont, BMD

Virginia

Old Dominion University, BMD
University of Virginia, BMD
Virginia Commonwealth University, B
Virginia Military Institute, B
Virginia Polytechnic Institute and State University, BMD

Washington

Gonzaga University, B
Henry Cogswell College, B
Saint Martin's University, B
Seattle University, B
University of Washington, BMD
Walla Walla College, B

Washington State University, BMD

West Virginia

West Virginia University, BMD
West Virginia University Institute of Technology, B

Wisconsin

Marquette University, BMD
Milwaukee School of Engineering, B
University of Wisconsin-Madison, BMD
University of Wisconsin-Milwaukee, B
University of Wisconsin-Platteville, B

Wyoming

University of Wyoming, BMD

Alberta

University of Alberta, BMDO
University of Calgary, BMD

British Columbia

The University of British Columbia, BMD
University of Victoria, BMD

Manitoba

University of Manitoba, BMD

New Brunswick

Université de Moncton, BM
University of New Brunswick Fredericton, BMD
University of New Brunswick Saint John, B

Newfoundland and Labrador

Memorial University of Newfoundland, BMD

Nova Scotia

Dalhousie University, BMD

Ontario

Carleton University, BMD
Lakehead University, B
McMaster University, BMD
Queen's University at Kingston, BMD
Royal Military College of Canada, BMD
Ryerson University, B
University of Ottawa, BMD
University of Toronto, BMD
University of Waterloo, BMD
The University of Western Ontario, B
University of Windsor, BMD

Quebec

Concordia University, BMDO
McGill University, BMD
Université Laval, BMD
Université du Québec en Abitibi-Témiscamingue, B
Universite du Quebec, Ecole de technologie superieure, B
Université du Québec àTrois-Rivières, B
Université de Sherbrooke, BMD

Saskatchewan

University of Saskatchewan, BMD

MECHANICAL ENGINEERING/MECHANICAL TECHNOLOGY/TECHNICIAN

Alabama

Alabama Agricultural and Mechanical University, B
Gadsden State Community College, A

Arizona

Arizona State University at the Polytechnic Campus, B

The Refrigeration School, A

Arkansas

University of Arkansas at Little Rock, AB

California

California Polytechnic State University, San Luis
Obispo, B
California State Polytechnic University, Pomona, B
California State University, Long Beach, B
California State University, Sacramento, B
Citrus College, A
City College of San Francisco, A
Compton Community College, A
Los Angeles Trade-Technical College, A
Los Angeles Valley College, A
Pasadena City College, A
San Joaquin Delta College, A

Colorado

Colorado State University-Pueblo, B
Metropolitan State College of Denver, B
Red Rocks Community College, A

Connecticut

Central Connecticut State University, B
Gateway Community College, A
Naugatuck Valley Community College, A
Three Rivers Community College, A

Delaware

Delaware State University, B
Delaware Technical & Community College,
Stanton/Wilmington Campus, A

District of Columbia

University of the District of Columbia, A

Florida

Broward Community College, A

Georgia

Augusta Technical College, A
Columbus Technical College, A
Georgia Southern University, B
Savannah State University, B
Southern Polytechnic State University, B

Hawaii

Hawaii Community College, A

Idaho

Boise State University, B
Brigham Young University -Idaho, A

Illinois

College of Lake County, A
Danville Area Community College, A
Highland Community College, A
Illinois Eastern Community Colleges, Lincoln Trail
College, A
Illinois Valley Community College, A
McHenry County College, A
Moraine Valley Community College, A
Sauk Valley Community College, A
William Rainey Harper College, A

Indiana

Indiana University-Purdue University Fort
Wayne, AB
Indiana University-Purdue University
Indianapolis, AB
Purdue University Calumet, AB
Purdue University North Central, AB
Vincennes University, A

Iowa

Hawkeye Community College, A
Iowa Western Community College, A
Kirkwood Community College, A

Southeastern Community College, North Campus, A

Kansas

Coffeyville Community College, A
Garden City Community College, A
Pittsburg State University, B
Wichita Area Technical College, A

Kentucky

Jefferson Community and Technical College, A
Louisville Technical Institute, A
Madisonville Community College, A
Murray State University, A

Louisiana

Nicholls State University, B
Southern University at Shreveport, A

Maine

University of Maine, B

Maryland

Anne Arundel Community College, A
Hagerstown Community College, A
Harford Community College, A

Massachusetts

Benjamin Franklin Institute of Technology, A
Massachusetts Bay Community College, A
Northeastern University, B
Springfield Technical Community College, A
University of Massachusetts Dartmouth, B
University of Massachusetts Lowell, AB
Wentworth Institute of Technology, AB

Michigan

Andrews University, AB
Baker College of Flint, A
Central Michigan University, B
Delta College, A
Eastern Michigan University, B
Ferris State University, A
Kalamazoo Valley Community College, A
Lake Superior State University, AB
Lansing Community College, A
Lawrence Technological University, A
Macomb Community College, A
Michigan Technological University, AB
Mott Community College, A
Northern Michigan University, B
Schoolcraft College, A
Washtenaw Community College, A
Wayne State University, B
Western Michigan University, B

Minnesota

Minnesota State Community and Technical
College-Fergus Falls, A
Normandale Community College, A
Rochester Community and Technical College, A

Mississippi

University of Southern Mississippi, B

Missouri

St. Louis Community College at Florissant Valley, A
St. Louis Community College at Forest Park, A

Montana

Montana State University, B

Nebraska

Southeast Community College, Milford Campus, A

Nevada

Community College of Southern Nevada, A

New Hampshire

New Hampshire Technical Institute, A
University of New Hampshire at Manchester, B

New Jersey

Camden County College, A
County College of Morris, A

Fairleigh Dickinson University, Metropolitan
Campus, B
Middlesex County College, A
Union County College, A

New York

Adirondack Community College, A
Broome Community College, A
Buffalo State College, State University of New
York, B
Corning Community College, A
Erie Community College, North Campus, A
Farmingdale State University of New York, AB
Finger Lakes Community College, A
Hudson Valley Community College, A
Jamestown Community College, A
Mohawk Valley Community College, A
Monroe Community College, A
New York City College of Technology of the City
University of New York, A
New York Institute of Technology, AB
Onondaga Community College, A
Queensborough Community College of the City
University of New York, A
Rochester Institute of Technology, AB
State University of New York College of Agriculture
and Technology at Morrisville, A
State University of New York College of Technology
at Alfred, AB
State University of New York College of Technology
at Canton, A
State University of New York Institute of
Technology, B
Suffolk County Community College, A
Westchester Community College, A

North Carolina

Alamance Community College, A
Asheville-Buncombe Technical Community
College, A
Blue Ridge Community College, A
Cape Fear Community College, A
Catawba Valley Community College, A
Central Piedmont Community College, A
Cleveland Community College, A
Craven Community College, A
Edgecombe Community College, A
Gaston College, A
Isothermal Community College, A
Richmond Community College, A
South Piedmont Community College, A
The University of North Carolina at Charlotte, B
Wake Technical Community College, A
Wayne Community College, A
Wilson Technical Community College, A

Ohio

Bowling Green State University, B
Central Ohio Technical College, A
Cincinnati State Technical and Community
College, A
Clark State Community College, A
Columbus State Community College, A
James A. Rhodes State College, A
Jefferson Community College, A
Kent State University, Ashtabula Campus, A
Kent State University, Trumbull Campus, A
Kent State University, Tuscarawas Campus, A
Lakeland Community College, A
Marion Technical College, A
Miami University Hamilton, AB
Miami University-Middletown Campus, A
North Central State College, A
Northwest State Community College, A
Ohio University, B
Owens Community College, A
Sinclair Community College, A
Stark State College of Technology, A
Terra State Community College, A
The University of Akron, AB
University of Cincinnati, AB
University of Dayton, B
University of Rio Grande, AB
The University of Toledo, AB
Washington State Community College, A
Wright State University, Lake Campus, A

Youngstown State University, AB

Oklahoma

Northeastern Oklahoma Agricultural and Mechanical College, A
Oklahoma State University, B
Tulsa Community College, A

Oregon

Mt. Hood Community College, A
Oregon Institute of Technology, B
Portland Community College, A

Pennsylvania

Delaware County Community College, A
Harrisburg Area Community College, A
Lehigh Carbon Community College, A
Montgomery County Community College, A
Penn Foster Career School, A
Pennsylvania College of Technology, B
Pennsylvania Institute of Technology, A
The Pennsylvania State University Altoona College, A
The Pennsylvania State University Berks Campus of the Berks-Lehigh Valley College, A
The Pennsylvania State University DuBois Campus of the Commonwealth College, A
The Pennsylvania State University at Erie, The Behrend College, AB
The Pennsylvania State University Hazleton Campus of the Commonwealth College, A
The Pennsylvania State University New Kensington Campus of the Commonwealth College, A
The Pennsylvania State University Shenango Campus of the Commonwealth College, A
The Pennsylvania State University York Campus of the Commonwealth College, A
Point Park University, AB
Reading Area Community College, A
University of Pittsburgh at Johnstown, B
Westmoreland County Community College, A

Puerto Rico

University of Puerto Rico at Bayamón, A
University of Puerto Rico at Carolina, A

South Carolina

Greenville Technical College, A
Midlands Technical College, A
Piedmont Technical College, A
South Carolina State University, B
Spartanburg Technical College, A
Trident Technical College, A
York Technical College, A

South Dakota

Southeast Technical Institute, A

Tennessee

Chattanooga State Technical Community College, A
Pellissippi State Technical Community College, A
Southwest Tennessee Community College, A

Texas

LeTourneau University, B
Midwestern State University, B
Richland College, A
San Antonio College, A
Tarrant County College District, A
Texas A&M University, B
Texas State Technical College Waco, A
University of Houston-Downtown, B
University of North Texas, B
The University of Texas at Brownsville, B

Utah

Weber State University, AB

Vermont

Vermont Technical College, A

Virginia

Central Virginia Community College, A
ECPI College of Technology (Newport News), A

ECPI College of Technology (Virginia Beach), A
ECPI Technical College (Richmond), A
ECPI Technical College (Roanoke), A
John Tyler Community College, A
Lord Fairfax Community College, A
Northern Virginia Community College, A
Thomas Nelson Community College, A
Virginia State University, B
Virginia Western Community College, A
Wytheville Community College, A

Washington

Bates Technical College, A
Central Washington University, B
Clover Park Technical College, A
Eastern Washington University, B
Green River Community College, A
Lower Columbia College, A
Shoreline Community College, A
Spokane Community College, A

West Virginia

Bluefield State College, AB
Community & Technical College at West Virginia University Institute of Technology, A
Fairmont State Community & Technical College, A
Fairmont State University, AB
Potomac State College of West Virginia University, A
West Virginia University at Parkersburg, A

Wisconsin

Fox Valley Technical College, A
Milwaukee Area Technical College, A
Northeast Wisconsin Technical College, A
Wisconsin Indianhead Technical College, A

British Columbia

British Columbia Institute of Technology, AB
The University of British Columbia, B

Ontario

Lakehead University, B

Quebec

Université du Québec en Abitibi-Témiscamingue, B

MECHANICAL ENGINEERING RELATED TECHNOLOGIES/TECHNICIANS

Connecticut

University of Hartford, B

Florida

University of Central Florida, B

Indiana

Indiana State University, B
Purdue University, AB

New York

New York Institute of Technology, B

North Carolina

Edgecombe Community College, A

Ohio

Cleveland State University, B

Pennsylvania

Delaware County Community College, A
Grove City College, B

Pennsylvania Institute of Technology, A

Virginia

Old Dominion University, B

MECHANICS

Alabama

The University of Alabama, MD

Arizona

The University of Arizona, MD

California

California Institute of Technology, MD
California State University, Fullerton, M
California State University, Northridge, M
San Diego State University, MD
University of California, Berkeley, MD
University of California, San Diego, MD
University of Southern California, M

Colorado

Colorado State University, MD

Connecticut

Yale University, MD

District of Columbia

The Catholic University of America, MD

Georgia

Georgia Institute of Technology, MD

Idaho

Idaho State University, M

Illinois

Southern Illinois University Carbondale, MD
University of Illinois at Urbana-Champaign, MD

Iowa

Iowa State University of Science and Technology, MD

Louisiana

Louisiana State University and Agricultural and Mechanical College, MD

Maryland

University of Maryland, College Park, MD

Massachusetts

Massachusetts Institute of Technology, D
University of Massachusetts Lowell, D

Michigan

Michigan State University, MD
Michigan Technological University, M

Minnesota

University of Minnesota, Twin Cities Campus, MD

Mississippi

Mississippi State University, M

Missouri

University of Missouri-Rolla, MD

Nebraska

University of Nebraska-Lincoln, MD

New Jersey

Rutgers, The State University of New Jersey, New Brunswick/Piscataway, MD

New Mexico

New Mexico Institute of Mining and Technology, M

New York

Cornell University, MD

Rensselaer Polytechnic Institute, MD

North Dakota

North Dakota State University, MD

Ohio

Case Western Reserve University, M
The Ohio State University, MD
University of Cincinnati, MD
University of Dayton, M

Pennsylvania

Drexel University, MD
Lehigh University, MD
The Pennsylvania State University University Park
  Campus, MD
University of Pennsylvania, MD

Rhode Island

Brown University, MD
University of Rhode Island, MD

Tennessee

The University of Tennessee, MD

Texas

The University of Texas at Austin, MD

Virginia

University of Virginia, M
Virginia Polytechnic Institute and State
  University, MD

Wisconsin

University of Wisconsin-Madison, MD

New Brunswick

University of New Brunswick Fredericton, MD

Quebec

McGill University, MD

MECHANICS AND REPAIRERS

California

Santa Rosa Junior College, A

Idaho

Idaho State University, A
Lewis-Clark State College, AB

Illinois

Black Hawk College, A

Indiana

Ivy Tech Community College-Bloomington, A
Ivy Tech Community College-Central Indiana, A
Ivy Tech Community College-Columbus, A
Ivy Tech Community College-Kokomo, A
Ivy Tech Community College-Lafayette, A
Ivy Tech Community College-North Central, A
Ivy Tech Community College-Northeast, A
Ivy Tech Community College-Northwest, A
Ivy Tech Community College-Southern Indiana, A
Ivy Tech Community College-Southwest, A
Ivy Tech Community College-Wabash Valley, A
Ivy Tech Community College-Whitewater, A

Oklahoma

Western Oklahoma State College, A

Wyoming

Western Wyoming Community College, A

MEDIA STUDIES

Alabama

The University of Alabama, M

Arizona

The University of Arizona, M

Arkansas

Arkansas State University, M

California

California State University, Fullerton, M
New College of California, M
San Diego State University, M
San Francisco State University, M
University of Southern California, MO

Colorado

University of Colorado at Boulder, D
University of Denver, M

District of Columbia

American University, M
Howard University, MD

Florida

Florida State University, M
Lynn University, M
University of Florida, MD

Georgia

Savannah College of Art and Design, M

Illinois

Governors State University, M
Northwestern University, MD
Southern Illinois University Edwardsville, O
University of Chicago, MD

Indiana

Indiana State University, M

Louisiana

Louisiana State University and Agricultural and
  Mechanical College, MD

Maryland

University of Maryland, College Park, D

Massachusetts

Boston University, MO
Emerson College, M
Lesley University, M
Massachusetts Institute of Technology, MD

Michigan

Central Michigan University, M
Michigan State University, MD
Saginaw Valley State University, M
University of Michigan, M
Wayne State University, MD

Missouri

Webster University, M

New Jersey

Monmouth University, O
William Paterson University of New Jersey, M

New York

City College of the City University of New York, M
College of Staten Island of the City University of
  New York, M
Fordham University, M
Hunter College of the City University of New
  York, M
Metropolitan College of New York, M
New York University, MDO
Rochester Institute of Technology, M
State University of New York at Buffalo, M

Syracuse University, M

Ohio

Ohio University, MD

Pennsylvania

Carnegie Mellon University, M
Kutztown University of Pennsylvania, M
Marywood University, M
The Pennsylvania State University University Park
  Campus, M
Temple University, MD

South Carolina

University of South Carolina, M

Tennessee

The University of Tennessee, MD

Texas

Texas Southern University, M
The University of Texas at Austin, MD

Virginia

Norfolk State University, M

Wisconsin

Marquette University, M

Ontario

The University of Western Ontario, MD

Quebec

Concordia University, M

MEDICAL ADMINISTRATIVE ASSISTANT/SECRETARY

Alabama

Enterprise-Ozark Community College, A
George C. Wallace Community College, A
Northeast Alabama Community College, A
Shelton State Community College, A
Wallace State Community College, A

Arizona

Central Arizona College, A
Cochise College (Sierra Vista), A
Mesa Community College, A
Phoenix College, A
Scottsdale Community College, A

Arkansas

National Park Community College, A
Ouachita Technical College, A
Phillips Community College of the University of
  Arkansas, A

California

American River College, A
Antelope Valley College, A
Berkeley City College, A
Butte College, A
Cabrillo College, A
Cerritos College, A
Chaffey College, A
College of Marin, A
College of San Mateo, A
Cosumnes River College (Sacramento), A
Crafton Hills College, A
Cypress College, A
East Los Angeles College, A
Fresno City College, A
Glendale Community College, A
Grossmont College, A
Heald College-Fresno, A
Heald College-Hayward, A
Heald College-Rancho Cordova, A
Heald College-Salinas, A
Heald College-San Francisco, A
Humphreys College, A
Lake Tahoe Community College, A

Lassen Community College District, A
Long Beach City College, A
Los Angeles City College, A
Los Angeles Harbor College, A
Merced College, A
Monterey Peninsula College, A
Mt. San Antonio College, A
Ohlone College, A
Orange Coast College, A
Pacific Union College, A
Palomar College, A
Sacramento City College, A
San Joaquin Valley College, A
Shasta College, A
Sierra College, A
West Los Angeles College, A
West Valley College, A
Western Career College (Walnut Creek), A

Colorado

Blair College, A
Institute of Business & Medical Careers, A
IntelliTec College (Grand Junction), A
IntelliTec Medical Institute, A
Lamar Community College, A
Mesa State College, A
Northeastern Junior College, A
Otero Junior College, A
Pueblo Community College, A

Connecticut

Briarwood College, A
Gateway Community College, A
Gibbs College, A
Goodwin College, A
Manchester Community College, A
Middlesex Community College, A
Naugatuck Valley Community College, A
Three Rivers Community College, A
Tunxis Community College, A

Delaware

Delaware Technical & Community College, Jack F.
 Owens Campus, A
Delaware Technical & Community College,
 Stanton/Wilmington Campus, A

Florida

ATI Career Training Center (Fort Lauderdale), A
Brevard Community College, A
Broward Community College, A
Daytona Beach Community College, A
Florida National College, A
Florida Technical College (DeLand), A
Florida Technical College (Orlando), A
Hillsborough Community College, A
Indian River Community College, A
Pensacola Junior College, A
Polk Community College, A
Santa Fe Community College, A
South Florida Community College, A
Valencia Community College, A
Webster College (Ocala), A

Georgia

Georgia Medical Institute-DeKalb, A

Hawaii

Heald College-Honolulu, A

Idaho

Boise State University, A
North Idaho College, A

Illinois

Career Colleges of Chicago, A
City Colleges of Chicago, Harry S. Truman
 College, A
City Colleges of Chicago, Richard J. Daley
 College, A
Danville Area Community College, A
Elgin Community College, A
Gem City College, A
Illinois Eastern Community Colleges, Olney Central
 College, A

John Wood Community College, A
Joliet Junior College, A
Lake Land College, A
Lewis and Clark Community College, A
Lincoln College-Normal, A
MacCormac College, A
Midstate College, A
Morton College, A
Rend Lake College, A
Richland Community College, A
Shawnee Community College, A
Southwestern Illinois College, A
Spoon River College, A
William Rainey Harper College, A

Indiana

Brown Mackie College-Michigan City, A
Vincennes University, A
Vincennes University Jasper Campus, A

Iowa

AIB College of Business, A
Des Moines Area Community College, A
Ellsworth Community College, A
Hawkeye Community College, A
Iowa Lakes Community College, A
Iowa Western Community College, A
Kirkwood Community College, A
Southeastern Community College, South
 Campus, A
Western Iowa Tech Community College, A

Kansas

Barton County Community College, A
Brown Mackie College-Kansas City, A
Butler Community College, A
Coffeyville Community College, A
Dodge City Community College, A
Fort Scott Community College, A
Highland Community College, A
Labette Community College, A
Tabor College, B

Kentucky

St. Catharine College, A
Southwestern College of Business, A
Sullivan University, A

Maine

Andover College, A
Beal College, A
Central Maine Community College, A
Northern Maine Community College, A

Maryland

Baltimore City Community College, A
Chesapeake College, A
Frederick Community College, A
Hagerstown Business College, A
Howard Community College, A

Massachusetts

Bay State College, A
Bristol Community College, A
Cape Cod Community College, A
Gibbs College, A
Marian Court College, A
North Shore Community College, A
Northern Essex Community College, A
Roxbury Community College, A
Springfield Technical Community College, A

Michigan

Baker College of Auburn Hills, AB
Baker College of Cadillac, A
Baker College of Clinton Township, A
Baker College of Flint, A
Baker College of Jackson, A
Baker College of Muskegon, A
Baker College of Owosso, A
Baker College of Port Huron, A
Bay de Noc Community College, A
Davenport University (Midland), A
Delta College, A
Gogebic Community College, A

Grand Rapids Community College, A
Henry Ford Community College, A
Kalamazoo Valley Community College, A
Kellogg Community College, A
Kirtland Community College, A
Lake Michigan College, A
Lewis College of Business, A
Mid Michigan Community College, A
Monroe County Community College, A
Montcalm Community College, A
Mott Community College, A
Muskegon Community College, A
St. Clair County Community College, A
Washtenaw Community College, A
Wayne County Community College District, A

Minnesota

Alexandria Technical College, A
Anoka Technical College, A
Central Lakes College, A
Century College, A
Globe College, A
Hennepin Technical College, A
Hibbing Community College, A
Inver Hills Community College, A
Lake Superior College, A
Minnesota School of Business, A
Minnesota School of Business-Brooklyn Center, A
Minnesota School of Business-Plymouth, A
Minnesota School of Business-St. Cloud, A
Minnesota State College-Southeast Technical, A
Minnesota State Community and Technical
 College-Fergus Falls, A
Minnesota West Community and Technical
 College, A
Normandale Community College, A
Northwest Technical College, A
Rasmussen College Eagan, A
Rasmussen College Eden Prairie, A
Rasmussen College Mankato, A
Rasmussen College St. Cloud, A
Ridgewater College, A
Riverland Community College, A
Rochester Community and Technical College, A
St. Cloud Technical College, A
Saint Paul College-A Community & Technical
 College, A
Vermilion Community College, A

Mississippi

Northeast Mississippi Community College, A
Northwest Mississippi Community College, A
Pearl River Community College, A

Missouri

Crowder College, A
East Central College, A
Hannibal-LaGrange College, A
Hickey College, A
Jefferson College, A
Longview Community College, A
Maple Woods Community College, A
Metro Business College (Cape Girardeau), A
Metro Business College (Jefferson City), A
Penn Valley Community College, A
State Fair Community College, A

Montana

Flathead Valley Community College, A
Miles Community College, A
Montana State University-Billings, A
Montana State University-Great Falls College of
 Technology, A
Montana Tech of The University of Montana, A
The University of Montana-Helena College of
 Technology, A
The University of Montana-Missoula, A

Nebraska

Central Community College-Hastings Campus, A
Hamilton College-Lincoln, A
Hamilton College-Omaha, A
Midland Lutheran College, A
Northeast Community College, A
Southeast Community College, Beatrice Campus, A

Vatterott College (Omaha), A

Nevada

Community College of Southern Nevada, A
Morrison University, A
Truckee Meadows Community College, A

New Hampshire

Hesser College, A
McIntosh College, A
New Hampshire Community Technical College,
  Manchester/Stratham, A

New Jersey

Bergen Community College, A
Essex County College, A
Gibbs College (Montclair), A
Gloucester County College, A

New Mexico

Clovis Community College, A
New Mexico Junior College, A

New York

Adirondack Community College, A
Bronx Community College of the City University of
  New York, A
Bryant and Stratton College (Albany), A
Bryant and Stratton College, Buffalo Campus, A
Bryant and Stratton College, Lackawanna
  Campus, A
Bryant and Stratton College (Rochester-Greece
  Campus), A
Bryant and Stratton College (Rochester-Henrietta
  Campus), A
Bryant and Stratton College (Syracuse), A
The College of Westchester, A
Elmira Business Institute, A
Eugenio María de Hostos Community College of the
  City University of New York, A
Fulton-Montgomery Community College, A
Interboro Institute, A
Jamestown Business College, A
Jefferson Community College, A
Katharine Gibbs School (New York), A
Monroe College (Bronx), A
Monroe College (New Rochelle), A
Nassau Community College, A
Olean Business Institute, A
State University of New York College of Agriculture
  and Technology at Morrisville, A
Trocaire College, A

North Carolina

Alamance Community College, A
Beaufort County Community College, A
Central Carolina Community College, A
Central Piedmont Community College, A
Cleveland Community College, A
Coastal Carolina Community College, A
College of The Albemarle, A
Craven Community College, A
Durham Technical Community College, A
Halifax Community College, A
Johnston Community College, A
Lenoir Community College, A
Martin Community College, A
Mayland Community College, A
Nash Community College, A
Piedmont Community College, A
Pitt Community College, A
Rockingham Community College, A
Sandhills Community College, A
South Piedmont Community College, A
Stanly Community College, A
Surry Community College, A
Vance-Granville Community College, A
Wake Technical Community College, A
Wayne Community College, A
Western Piedmont Community College, A

North Dakota

Bismarck State College, A
Dickinson State University, A
Lake Region State College, A

Minot State University-Bottineau Campus, A
United Tribes Technical College, A

Ohio

Brown Mackie College-Cincinnati, A
Bryant and Stratton College (Parma), A
Clark State Community College, A
Columbus State Community College, A
Davis College, A
Edison State Community College, A
Gallipolis Career College, A
Hocking College, A
James A. Rhodes State College, A
Jefferson Community College, A
Marion Technical College, A
Miami-Jacobs College, A
Miami University-Middletown Campus, A
Northwest State Community College, A
Ohio Business College (Lorain), A
Ohio Business College (Sandusky), A
Ohio University-Lancaster, A
Ohio Valley College of Technology, A
Sinclair Community College, A
Southwestern College of Business (Cincinnati), A
Southwestern College of Business (Franklin), A
Terra State Community College, A
Trumbull Business College, A
The University of Akron, A
The University of Akron-Wayne College, A
University of Cincinnati, A
University of Cincinnati Clermont College, A
University of Cincinnati Raymond Walters College, A
University of Northwestern Ohio, A
University of Rio Grande, A
Washington State Community College, A
Wright State University, A
Wright State University, Lake Campus, A

Oklahoma

Carl Albert State College, A
Northeastern Oklahoma Agricultural and Mechanical
  College, A
Oklahoma State University, Okmulgee, A
Tulsa Community College, A
Vatterott College (Tulsa), A

Oregon

Blue Mountain Community College, A
Chemeketa Community College, A
Clatsop Community College, A
Heald College-Portland, A
Linn-Benton Community College, A
Mt. Hood Community College, A
Portland Community College, A
Treasure Valley Community College, A
Umpqua Community College, A

Pennsylvania

Academy of Medical Arts and Business, A
Berean Institute, A
Business Institute of Pennsylvania (Meadville), A
Business Institute of Pennsylvania (Sharon), A
Butler County Community College, A
Cambria-Rowe Business College (Johnstown), A
Central Pennsylvania College, A
CHI Institute, A
Community College of Allegheny County, A
Community College of Beaver County, A
Community College of Philadelphia, A
Consolidated School of Business (Lancaster), A
Consolidated School of Business (York), A
Douglas Education Center, A
DuBois Business College, A
Duff's Business Institute, A
Erie Business Center, Main, A
Erie Business Center South, A
ICM School of Business & Medical Careers, A
Lackawanna College, A
Lansdale School of Business, A
Laurel Business Institute, A
Lehigh Valley College, A
Luzerne County Community College, A
Manor College, A
Median School of Allied Health Careers, A
Mercyhurst College, B
Newport Business Institute (Lower Burrell), A

Newport Business Institute (Williamsport), A
Northampton County Area Community College, A
Penn Commercial Business and Technical School, A
Pennsylvania College of Technology, A
Reading Area Community College, A
South Hills School of Business & Technology
  (Altoona), A
South Hills School of Business & Technology (State
  College), A
Westmoreland County Community College, A
Yorktowne Business Institute, A

Puerto Rico

Caribbean University, A
Universidad Adventista de las Antillas, A

Rhode Island

Community College of Rhode Island, A

South Carolina

Piedmont Technical College, A
Spartanburg Technical College, A
Trident Technical College, A
York Technical College, A

South Dakota

Mitchell Technical Institute, A

Tennessee

Chattanooga State Technical Community College, A
Martin Methodist College, A
Roane State Community College, A
South College, A
Walters State Community College, A

Texas

Alvin Community College, A
Amarillo College, A
Central Texas College, A
Del Mar College, A
El Centro College, A
Hallmark Institute of Technology, A
Houston Community College System, A
Lamar State College-Port Arthur, A
Lamar University, A
McLennan Community College, A
Northeast Texas Community College, A
St. Philip's College, A
South Plains College, A
Temple College, A
Tomball College, A
Tyler Junior College, A

Utah

LDS Business College, A
Stevens-Henager College, A

Virginia

Bryant and Stratton College, Richmond, A
Bryant and Stratton College, Virginia Beach, A
Dabney S. Lancaster Community College, A
ECPI College of Technology (Newport News), A
ECPI College of Technology (Virginia Beach), A
ECPI Technical College (Richmond), A
ECPI Technical College (Roanoke), A
New River Community College, A
Wytheville Community College, A

Washington

Centralia College, A
Clark College, A
Edmonds Community College, A
Everett Community College, A
Green River Community College, A
Lower Columbia College, A
Renton Technical College, A
Shoreline Community College, A
Skagit Valley College, A
South Puget Sound Community College, A
Spokane Community College, A
Tacoma Community College, A
Walla Walla Community College, A
Wenatchee Valley College, A
Whatcom Community College, A

Yakima Valley Community College, A

West Virginia

Community & Technical College at West Virginia
  University Institute of Technology, A
Huntington Junior College, A
Potomac State College of West Virginia
  University, A
West Virginia Junior College (Charleston), A

Wisconsin

Bryant and Stratton College, A
Lakeshore Technical College, A
Madison Area Technical College, A
Milwaukee Area Technical College, A
Nicolet Area Technical College, A
Northcentral Technical College, A
Northeast Wisconsin Technical College, A
Western Technical College, A
Wisconsin Indianhead Technical College, A

Wyoming

Western Wyoming Community College, A

British Columbia

British Columbia Institute of Technology, A

MEDICAL/CLINICAL ASSISTANT

Alabama

Faulkner University, A
George C. Wallace Community College, A
George Corley Wallace State Community College, A
H. Councill Trenholm State Technical College, A
Jefferson Davis Community College, A
South University, A
Virginia College at Birmingham, A
Virginia College at Huntsville, A
Wallace State Community College, A

Alaska

Charter College, A
University of Alaska Anchorage, A
University of Alaska Fairbanks, A
University of Alaska Southeast, Sitka Campus, A

Arizona

The Bryman School, A
Everest College, A
Phoenix College, A

Arkansas

Arkansas Tech University, A
Cossatot Community College of the University of
  Arkansas, A

California

Allan Hancock College, A
Argosy University/Orange County, A
Argosy University/San Diego, A
Argosy University/Santa Monica, A
Barstow College, A
California State University, Dominguez Hills, B
Cerritos College, A
Chabot College, A
College of the Desert, A
College of Marin, A
College of the Redwoods, A
College of San Mateo, A
Cosumnes River College (Sacramento), A
Cuesta College, A
De Anza College, A
East Los Angeles College, A
El Camino College, A
Empire College, A
Fresno City College, A
Glendale Community College, A
Grossmont College, A
Lake Tahoe Community College, A
Long Beach City College, A
Merced College, A
Modesto Junior College, A

Monterey Peninsula College, A
Ohlone College, A
Orange Coast College, A
Palomar College, A
Pasadena City College, A
Saddleback College, A
San Diego Mesa College, A
San Joaquin Valley College, A
Santa Ana College, A
Shasta College, A
Ventura College, A
West Valley College, A
Western Career College (San Jose), A

Colorado

Arapahoe Community College, A
Argosy University/Denver, A
Blair College, A
CollegeAmerica-Fort Collins, A
Institute of Business & Medical Careers, A
IntelliTec Medical Institute, A
National American University (Colorado Springs), A
National American University (Denver), A
Parks College (Denver), A

Connecticut

Briarwood College, A
Capital Community College, A
Goodwin College, A
Northwestern Connecticut Community College, A
Quinebaug Valley Community College, A
St. Vincent's College, A

Delaware

Delaware Technical & Community College, Jack F.
  Owens Campus, A

Florida

ATI Health Education Center, A
Brevard Community College, A
Broward Community College, A
Brown Mackie College-Miami, A
College of Business and Technology, A
Florida Metropolitan University-Brandon Campus, A
Florida Metropolitan University-Jacksonville
  Campus, AB
Florida Metropolitan University-Melbourne
  Campus, A
Florida Metropolitan University-North Orlando
  Campus, A
Florida Metropolitan University-South Orlando
  Campus, A
Florida Metropolitan University-Tampa Campus, A
Florida National College, A
Florida Technical College (DeLand), A
Gulf Coast College, A
International College, A
Jones College (Jacksonville), AB
Keiser College (Daytona Beach), A
Keiser College (Fort Lauderdale), A
Keiser College (Melbourne), A
Keiser College (Sarasota), A
Keiser College (Tallahassee), A
Miami Dade College, A
National School of Technology, Inc. (North Miami
  Beach), A
New England Institute of Technology at Palm
  Beach, A
South University (West Palm Beach), A
Southwest Florida College (Fort Myers), A
Webster College (Holiday), A
Webster College (Ocala), A

Georgia

Clayton State University, A
DeKalb Technical College, A
Georgia Southwestern State University, A
Gwinnett Technical College, A

South University, A

Guam

Guam Community College, A

Hawaii

Kapiolani Community College, A

Idaho

Eastern Idaho Technical College, A
Idaho State University, A

Illinois

City Colleges of Chicago, Malcolm X College, A
Gem City College, A
Midstate College, A
Northwestern Business College, A
Robert Morris College, A
Rockford Business College, A
Southwestern Illinois College, A
Waubonsee Community College, A
William Rainey Harper College, A

Indiana

Brown Mackie College-Fort Wayne, A
Brown Mackie College-Merrillville, A
Brown Mackie College-Michigan City, A
Brown Mackie College-South Bend, A
Indiana Business College (Anderson), A
Indiana Business College (Columbus), A
Indiana Business College (Evansville), A
Indiana Business College (Fort Wayne), A
Indiana Business College (Indianapolis), A
Indiana Business College (Indianapolis), A
Indiana Business College (Indianapolis-Northwest
  Campus), A
Indiana Business College (Lafayette), A
Indiana Business College (Marion), A
Indiana Business College-Medical, A
Indiana Business College (Terre Haute), A
International Business College (Fort Wayne), AB
International Business College (Indianapolis), A
Ivy Tech Community College-Central Indiana, A
Ivy Tech Community College-Columbus, A
Ivy Tech Community College-East Central, A
Ivy Tech Community College-Kokomo, A
Ivy Tech Community College-Lafayette, A
Ivy Tech Community College-North Central, A
Ivy Tech Community College-Northeast, A
Ivy Tech Community College-Northwest, A
Ivy Tech Community College-Southeast, A
Ivy Tech Community College-Southern Indiana, A
Ivy Tech Community College-Southwest, A
Ivy Tech Community College-Wabash Valley, A
Ivy Tech Community College-Whitewater, A
Vincennes University, A

Iowa

Des Moines Area Community College, A
Hamilton College (Cedar Falls), A
Hamilton College (Cedar Rapids), A
Iowa Central Community College, A
Iowa Lakes Community College, A
Iowa Western Community College, A
Kaplan University, A
Kirkwood Community College, A
North Iowa Area Community College, A
Palmer College of Chiropractic, A
Southeastern Community College, North Campus, A
Vatterott College, A

Kansas

Barton County Community College, A
Brown Mackie College-Kansas City, A

Kentucky

Brown Mackie College-Hopkinsville, A
Brown Mackie College-Louisville, A
Brown Mackie College-Northern Kentucky, A
Draughons Junior College, A
Eastern Kentucky University, A
National College of Business & Technology
  (Danville), A
National College of Business & Technology
  (Florence), A

National College of Business & Technology
  (Louisville), A
National College of Business & Technology
  (Pikeville), A
National College of Business & Technology
  (Richmond), A
Somerset Community College, A

Louisiana

Bossier Parish Community College, A
Remington College-Lafayette Campus, A

Maine

Andover College, A
Beal College, A
Kennebec Valley Community College, A
Southern Maine Community College, A

Maryland

Anne Arundel Community College, A
Hagerstown Business College, A
TESST College of Technology (Towson), A

Massachusetts

Bay State College, A
Massasoit Community College, A
Middlesex Community College, A
Mount Wachusett Community College, A
Springfield Technical Community College, A

Michigan

Baker College of Allen Park, A
Baker College of Auburn Hills, A
Baker College of Cadillac, A
Baker College of Clinton Township, A
Baker College of Flint, A
Baker College of Jackson, A
Baker College of Muskegon, A
Baker College of Owosso, A
Baker College of Port Huron, A
Davenport University (Dearborn), A
Davenport University (Midland), A
Delta College, A
Henry Ford Community College, A
Jackson Community College, A
Kalamazoo Valley Community College, A
Lansing Community College, A
Macomb Community College, A
Mid Michigan Community College, A
Northwestern Michigan College, A
Oakland Community College, A

Minnesota

Anoka Technical College, A
Century College, A
Duluth Business University, A
Globe College, A
Herzing College, A
Minnesota School of Business-Richfield, A
Minnesota West Community and Technical
  College, A
Northwest Technical College, A
Rasmussen College Mankato, A

Mississippi

Northeast Mississippi Community College, A
Virginia College at Jackson, A

Missouri

North Central Missouri College, A
Sanford-Brown College (North Kansas City), A
Sanford-Brown College (St. Charles), A
Springfield College, A
Vatterott College (St. Joseph), A
Vatterott College (Springfield), A

Montana

Flathead Valley Community College, A
Montana State University-Billings, A

Montana State University-Great Falls College of
  Technology, A

Nebraska

Central Community College-Hastings Campus, A
Hamilton College-Lincoln, A
Hamilton College-Omaha, A
Vatterott College (Omaha), A

Nevada

Career College of Northern Nevada, A
Community College of Southern Nevada, A
Las Vegas College, A

New Hampshire

Hesser College, A
McIntosh College, A

New Jersey

Bergen Community College, A
Hudson County Community College, A
Ocean County College, A
Union County College, A

New Mexico

New Mexico Junior College, A

New York

Broome Community College, A
Bryant and Stratton College (Albany), A
Bryant and Stratton College, Buffalo Campus, A
Bryant and Stratton College, Lackawanna
  Campus, A
Bryant and Stratton College (Rochester-Greece
  Campus), A
Bryant and Stratton College (Rochester-Henrietta
  Campus), A
Bryant and Stratton College (Syracuse), A
Dutchess Community College, A
Mildred Elley, A
Mohawk Valley Community College, A
Niagara County Community College, A
Suffolk County Community College, A
Trocaire College, A
Wood Tobe-Coburn School, A

North Carolina

Alamance Community College, A
Cabarrus College of Health Sciences, A
Carteret Community College, A
Central Carolina Community College, A
Central Piedmont Community College, A
Davidson County Community College, A
ECPI Technical College, A
Edgecombe Community College, A
Forsyth Technical Community College, A
Gaston College, A
Guilford Technical Community College, A
Haywood Community College, A
James Sprunt Community College, A
Johnston Community College, A
Lenoir Community College, A
Martin Community College, A
Mayland Community College, A
Mitchell Community College, A
Montgomery Community College, A
Pamlico Community College, A
Pitt Community College, A
Richmond Community College, A
Rockingham Community College, A
South College-Asheville, A
South Piedmont Community College, A
Stanly Community College, A
Tri-County Community College, A
Vance-Granville Community College, A
Wayne Community College, A
Western Piedmont Community College, A
Wilkes Community College, A

North Dakota

Minot State University-Bottineau Campus, A

Ohio

Belmont Technical College, A
Bradford School, A

Brown Mackie College-Akron, A
Brown Mackie College-Cincinnati, A
Brown Mackie College-Findlay, A
Brown Mackie College-North Canton, A
Bryant and Stratton College (Parma), A
Cincinnati State Technical and Community
  College, A
Davis College, A
ETI Technical College of Niles, A
Hocking College, A
Jefferson Community College, A
Miami-Jacobs College, A
Ohio University, A
Ohio Valley College of Technology, A
RETS Tech Center, A
Sinclair Community College, A
Southern State Community College, A
Southwestern College of Business (Cincinnati), A
Southwestern College of Business (Cincinnati), A
Southwestern College of Business (Dayton), A
Stark State College of Technology, A
Stautzenberger College, A
The University of Akron, A
University of Northwestern Ohio, A
The University of Toledo, A
Youngstown State University, A
Zane State College, A

Oklahoma

Community Care College, A
Eastern Oklahoma State College, A
Tulsa Community College, A

Oregon

Central Oregon Community College, A
Chemeketa Community College, A
Linn-Benton Community College, A
Mt. Hood Community College, A
Pioneer Pacific College, A
Portland Community College, A
Southwestern Oregon Community College, A

Pennsylvania

Academy of Medical Arts and Business, A
Berks Technical Institute, A
Bucks County Community College, A
Business Institute of Pennsylvania (Sharon), A
Butler County Community College, A
Career Training Academy (New Kensington), A
Central Pennsylvania College, A
CHI Institute, A
Community College of Allegheny County, A
Community College of Philadelphia, A
Delaware County Community College, A
Douglas Education Center, A
Duff's Business Institute, A
Erie Business Center, Main, A
ICM School of Business & Medical Careers, A
Lansdale School of Business, A
Laurel Business Institute, A
Lehigh Carbon Community College, A
Mount Aloysius College, A
Newport Business Institute (Lower Burrell), A
Pace Institute, A
Penn Commercial Business and Technical School, A
Thompson Institute, A
Western School of Health and Business Careers
  (Pittsburgh), A
Yorktowne Business Institute, A

Rhode Island

New England Institute of Technology, A

South Carolina

Midlands Technical College, A
South University, A
Tri-County Technical College, A
York Technical College, A

South Dakota

Colorado Technical University Sioux Falls
  Campus, A
Lake Area Technical Institute, A
Mitchell Technical Institute, A
National American University-Sioux Falls Branch, A

Presentation College, A

Tennessee

Draughons Junior College (Clarksville), A
Draughons Junior College (Nashville), A
National College of Business & Technology (Bristol), A
National College of Business & Technology (Nashville), A
Northeast State Technical Community College, A
South College, A
Southwest Tennessee Community College, A

Texas

Austin Community College, A
El Centro College, A
El Paso Community College, A
Kilgore College, A
Laredo Community College, A
San Antonio College, A

Utah

LDS Business College, A
Mountain West College, A
Salt Lake Community College, A
Utah Career College, A

Virginia

Bryant and Stratton College, Richmond, A
Bryant and Stratton College, Virginia Beach, A
ECPI Technical College (Roanoke), A
National College of Business & Technology (Bluefield), A
National College of Business & Technology (Charlottesville), A
National College of Business & Technology (Danville), A
National College of Business & Technology (Harrisonburg), A
National College of Business & Technology (Lynchburg), A
National College of Business & Technology (Salem), A

Washington

Clark College, A
Everett Community College, A
Highline Community College, A
Lake Washington Technical College, A
Lower Columbia College, A
North Seattle Community College, A
Olympic College, A
Renton Technical College, A
Skagit Valley College, A
South Puget Sound Community College, A
Wenatchee Valley College, A
Whatcom Community College, A

West Virginia

Bluefield State College, A
Huntington Junior College, A
Marshall Community and Technical College, A
Mountain State College, A
Mountain State University, A
National Institute of Technology, A
New River Community and Technical College, A
West Virginia Junior College (Charleston), A
West Virginia State University, A

Wisconsin

Bryant and Stratton College, A
Lac Courte Oreilles Ojibwa Community College, A
Moraine Park Technical College, A
Northeast Wisconsin Technical College, A

Southwest Wisconsin Technical College, A

Wyoming

Western Wyoming Community College, A

MEDICAL/HEALTH MANAGEMENT AND CLINICAL ASSISTANT/SPECIALIST

Colorado

National American University (Denver), A

Idaho

Lewis-Clark State College, AB

Oklahoma

Oklahoma State University, Oklahoma City, A

MEDICAL ILLUSTRATION AND INFORMATICS

Florida

Florida Agricultural and Mechanical University, B

Georgia

Medical College of Georgia, M

Illinois

University of Illinois at Chicago, M

Maryland

The Johns Hopkins University, M

Michigan

University of Michigan, M

New York

Rochester Institute of Technology, M

Texas

The University of Texas Southwestern Medical Center at Dallas, M

MEDICAL ILLUSTRATION/MEDICAL ILLUSTRATOR

Georgia

Clark Atlanta University, B
Clayton State University, A

Iowa

Iowa State University of Science and Technology, B

Michigan

Alma College, B
Olivet College, B

New York

Rochester Institute of Technology, B

Ohio

The Cleveland Institute of Art, B

Pennsylvania

Arcadia University, B

MEDICAL INFORMATICS

Arizona

DeVry University (Phoenix), B

California

DeVry University (Fremont), B
DeVry University (Long Beach), B
Stanford University, MD

University of California, Davis, M

Colorado

DeVry University (Westminster), B

Florida

DeVry University (Miramar), B
DeVry University (Orlando), B
University of Miami, B

Georgia

DeVry University (Alpharetta), B
DeVry University (Decatur), B
Emory University, M

Illinois

DeVry University (Addison), B
DeVry University (Chicago), B

Massachusetts

Harvard University, M
Massachusetts Institute of Technology, M

New Jersey

DeVry University, B
Montclair State University, B

Ohio

DeVry University (Columbus), B

Oregon

Oregon Health & Science University, MDO

Pennsylvania

DeVry University (Fort Washington), B

Texas

DeVry University (Irving), B

Utah

University of Utah, MD

Washington

DeVry University (Federal Way), B
University of Washington, M

Wisconsin

Milwaukee School of Engineering, M

Ontario

University of Waterloo, B

MEDICAL INSURANCE CODING SPECIALIST/CODER

Alabama

Virginia College at Birmingham, A

Connecticut

Goodwin College, A

Florida

National School of Technology, Inc. (North Miami Beach), A

Indiana

Indiana Business College (Evansville), A
Indiana Business College (Indianapolis), A
Indiana Business College (Indianapolis-Northwest Campus), A
Indiana Business College (Lafayette), A
Indiana Business College (Marion), A

Indiana Business College-Medical, A

Massachusetts

Springfield Technical Community College, A

Michigan

Baker College of Allen Park, A

Minnesota

Alexandria Technical College, A
Dakota County Technical College, A
Herzing College, A

Ohio

Columbus State Community College, A
Kent State University, Salem Campus, A

South Dakota

Kilian Community College, A

Texas

Paris Junior College, A

Utah

LDS Business College, A

MEDICAL INSURANCE SPECIALIST/MEDICAL BILLER

Alabama

Virginia College at Birmingham, A

California

San Joaquin Valley College, A

Connecticut

Goodwin College, A

Georgia

Georgia Medical Institute-DeKalb, A

Indiana

Indiana Business College (Anderson), A
Indiana Business College (Columbus), A
Indiana Business College (Evansville), A
Indiana Business College (Fort Wayne), A
Indiana Business College (Indianapolis), A
Indiana Business College (Indianapolis-Northwest Campus), A
Indiana Business College (Lafayette), A
Indiana Business College-Medical, A
Indiana Business College (Terre Haute), A

Michigan

Baker College of Allen Park, A
Jackson Community College, A

Ohio

Kent State University, Salem Campus, A

MEDICAL MICROBIOLOGY AND BACTERIOLOGY

Alabama

Auburn University, B
The University of Alabama, B

Arizona

Arizona State University, B
Northern Arizona University, B

California

California Polytechnic State University, San Luis Obispo, B
California State Polytechnic University, Pomona, B
California State University, Dominguez Hills, B
Humboldt State University, B
Pomona College, B
San Francisco State University, B
Sonoma State University, B

University of California, Los Angeles, B
University of California, San Diego, B
University of California, Santa Barbara, B

Colorado

Colorado State University, B

Connecticut

Quinnipiac University, B

Florida

University of Central Florida, B
University of Florida, B
University of Miami, B
University of South Florida, BD

Georgia

University of Georgia, B

Hawaii

University of Hawaii at Manoa, MD

Idaho

Idaho State University, B
University of Idaho, B

Indiana

Ball State University, B
Indiana University Bloomington, B

Kentucky

Eastern Kentucky University, B

Louisiana

University of Louisiana at Lafayette, B
Xavier University of Louisiana, B

Maine

University of Maine, B

Maryland

University of Maryland, College Park, B

Massachusetts

Harvard University, B
Worcester Polytechnic Institute, B

Michigan

Central Michigan University, B
Michigan Technological University, B
Northern Michigan University, B

Minnesota

Minnesota State University Mankato, B
St. Cloud State University, B
University of Minnesota, Duluth, MD
University of Minnesota, Twin Cities Campus, B

Mississippi

Mississippi State University, B
Mississippi University for Women, B

Missouri

Missouri Southern State University, B

Montana

Montana State University, B
The University of Montana-Missoula, B

Nebraska

Creighton University, MD

New Hampshire

University of New Hampshire, B

New Jersey

Rutgers, The State University of New Jersey, New Brunswick/Piscataway, B

New Mexico

New Mexico State University, B

New York

Wagner College, B

Ohio

Bowling Green State University, B
Miami University, B

The Ohio State University, B
Ohio University, B
Ohio University-Eastern, B
Ohio Wesleyan University, B
The University of Akron, B
University of Cincinnati, B

Oklahoma

Northeastern State University, B

Oregon

Oregon State University, B

Pennsylvania

The Pennsylvania State University Abington College, B
The Pennsylvania State University Altoona College, B
The Pennsylvania State University Beaver Campus of the Commonwealth College, B
The Pennsylvania State University Berks Campus of the Berks-Lehigh Valley College, B
The Pennsylvania State University Delaware County Campus of the Commonwealth College, B
The Pennsylvania State University DuBois Campus of the Commonwealth College, B
The Pennsylvania State University at Erie, The Behrend College, B
The Pennsylvania State University Fayette Campus of the Commonwealth College, B
The Pennsylvania State University Hazleton Campus of the Commonwealth College, B
The Pennsylvania State University, Lehigh Valley Campus of the Berks-Lehigh Valley College, B
The Pennsylvania State University McKeesport Campus of the Commonwealth College, B
The Pennsylvania State University Mont Alto Campus of the Commonwealth College, B
The Pennsylvania State University New Kensington Campus of the Commonwealth College, B
The Pennsylvania State University Schuylkill Campus of the Capital College, B
The Pennsylvania State University Shenango Campus of the Commonwealth College, B
The Pennsylvania State University University Park Campus, B
The Pennsylvania State University Wilkes-Barre Campus of the Commonwealth College, B
The Pennsylvania State University Worthington Scranton Campus of the Commonwealth College, B
The Pennsylvania State University York Campus of the Commonwealth College, B
University of Pittsburgh, B

Puerto Rico

Inter American University of Puerto Rico, Arecibo Campus, B
Inter American University of Puerto Rico, Bayamón Campus, B
Inter American University of Puerto Rico, San Germán Campus, B
University of Puerto Rico at Arecibo, B
University of Puerto Rico at Humacao, B
University of Puerto Rico, Mayagüez Campus, B

Rhode Island

University of Rhode Island, B

South Dakota

South Dakota State University, B

Tennessee

The University of Tennessee, B

Texas

Texas A&M University System Health Science Center, D
Texas Tech University, B
University of Houston-Downtown, B

The University of Texas at El Paso, B

Utah

Utah State University, B
Weber State University, B

Vermont

University of Vermont, B

Washington

University of Washington, B

Wisconsin

University of Wisconsin-Madison, BD
University of Wisconsin-Oshkosh, B

Alberta

University of Alberta, BMD

British Columbia

The University of British Columbia, B
University of Victoria, B

Manitoba

University of Manitoba, BMD

New Brunswick

University of New Brunswick Fredericton, B

Newfoundland and Labrador

Memorial University of Newfoundland, B

Nova Scotia

Dalhousie University, B
University of King's College, B

Ontario

University of Ottawa, B
University of Toronto, B
The University of Western Ontario, B
University of Windsor, B

Quebec

McGill University, B
Université Laval, B
Université de Montréal, B
Université de Sherbrooke, B

Saskatchewan

University of Saskatchewan, B

MEDICAL OFFICE ASSISTANT/SPECIALIST

Alabama

Virginia College at Birmingham, A

California

Western Career College (Walnut Creek), A

Connecticut

Asnuntuck Community College, A

Florida

Keiser College (Miami), A

Idaho

Lewis-Clark State College, AB

Illinois

Sauk Valley Community College, A

Indiana

Indiana Business College (Muncie), A
Sawyer College (Hammond), A

Iowa

Iowa Lakes Community College, A
Mercy College of Health Sciences, A

Kentucky

Daymar College (Louisville), A

Michigan

Alpena Community College, A
Lake Michigan College, A

Missouri

Vatterott College (St. Ann), A

New Mexico

Clovis Community College, A

Ohio

Stautzenberger College, A

Oklahoma

Vatterott College (Oklahoma City), A

Pennsylvania

Business Institute of Pennsylvania (Meadville), A
Commonwealth Technical Institute, A
Harrisburg Area Community College, A
Mount Aloysius College, B

Texas

MTI College of Business and Technology (Houston)
, A
MTI College of Business and Technology (Houston)
, A

Utah

LDS Business College, A

Wisconsin

Bryant and Stratton College, Wauwatosa Campus, A
Concordia University Wisconsin, B

Wyoming

Western Wyoming Community College, A

MEDICAL OFFICE COMPUTER SPECIALIST/ASSISTANT

Alabama

Virginia College at Birmingham, A

Iowa

Iowa Lakes Community College, A

Michigan

Baker College of Allen Park, A

Mississippi

Mississippi Delta Community College, A

Wyoming

Western Wyoming Community College, A

MEDICAL OFFICE MANAGEMENT/ADMINISTRATION

Arkansas

University of Arkansas Community College at
Batesville, A

California

MTI College of Business and Technology, A
San Joaquin Valley College, A

Colorado

Lamar Community College, A
National American University (Colorado Springs), A

Pikes Peak Community College, A

Connecticut

Briarwood College, A

Florida

Florida Community College at Jacksonville, A
Key College, A

Georgia

Columbus Technical College, A
Coosa Valley Technical College, A
Dalton State College, A

Idaho

Apollo College, A

Illinois

College of Lake County, A

Indiana

Brown Mackie College-Merrillville, A

Iowa

Vatterott College, A

Kansas

Brown Mackie College-Salina, A

Kentucky

Beckfield College, A
Daymar College (Owensboro), A
Eastern Kentucky University, B
Spencerian College, A

Maryland

Prince George's Community College, A

Minnesota

Minnesota School of Business-Richfield, A
St. Cloud Technical College, A

Mississippi

Virginia College at Jackson, A

Missouri

Patricia Stevens College, A

New Mexico

Eastern New Mexico University-Roswell, A

New York

Erie Community College, North Campus, A

North Carolina

Beaufort County Community College, A
Fayetteville Technical Community College, A
Gaston College, A
Wayne Community College, A

North Dakota

Minot State University-Bottineau Campus, A

Ohio

Brown Mackie College-Findlay, A
Ohio Institute of Photography and Technology, A
The University of Akron, A
The University of Akron-Wayne College, A

Pennsylvania

Academy of Medical Arts and Business, A
Douglas Education Center, A
McCann School of Business & Technology, A
Newport Business Institute (Lower Burrell), A
Pennsylvania Institute of Technology, A

Schuylkill Institute of Business and Technology, A

South Dakota

Kilian Community College, A

Wisconsin

Northeast Wisconsin Technical College, A

MEDICAL PHYSICS

Arkansas

University of Central Arkansas, M

California

University of California, Los Angeles, MD

Colorado

University of Colorado at Boulder, D

Georgia

Georgia Institute of Technology, M

Illinois

Rush University, MD
University of Chicago, D

Indiana

Purdue University, MD

Kentucky

University of Kentucky, M

Massachusetts

Harvard University, D
Massachusetts Institute of Technology, D

Michigan

Oakland University, D
Wayne State University, D

Minnesota

University of Minnesota, Twin Cities Campus, MD

New York

Stony Brook University, State University of New
   York, D

North Carolina

East Carolina University, M

Ohio

Cleveland State University, M
University of Cincinnati, M
Wright State University, M

Oklahoma

University of Oklahoma Health Sciences Center, MD

Pennsylvania

Drexel University, MD
University of Pennsylvania, M

Tennessee

Vanderbilt University, M

Texas

The University of Texas Health Science Center at
   Houston, MDO
The University of Texas Health Science Center at
   San Antonio, MD

Wisconsin

University of Wisconsin-Madison, MD

Alberta

University of Alberta, MD

British Columbia

University of Victoria, MD

Ontario

McMaster University, MD

Quebec

McGill University, MD

MEDICAL RADIOLOGIC TECHNOLOGY/SCIENCE - RADIATION THERAPIST

Alabama

Community College of the Air Force, A
Gadsden State Community College, A
Jefferson State Community College, A
The University of Alabama at Birmingham, B

Arizona

Apollo College-Westside, Inc., A
The Bryman School, A
GateWay Community College, A
Pima Community College, A

Arkansas

Arkansas State University, AB
North Arkansas College, A
South Arkansas Community College, A
University of Central Arkansas, B

California

California State University, Long Beach, B
Chaffey College, A
Charles R. Drew University of Medicine and
   Science, AB
Foothill College, A
Loma Linda University, AB
Santa Barbara City College, A

Colorado

Pueblo Community College, A

Connecticut

Capital Community College, A
St. Vincent's College, A
University of Hartford, B

Florida

Florida Community College at Jacksonville, A
Keiser College (Fort Lauderdale), A
Manatee Community College, A
University of Central Florida, B
Valencia Community College, A

Georgia

Albany Technical College, A
Athens Technical College, A
Augusta Technical College, A
Central Georgia Technical College, A
Chattahoochee Technical College, A
Coastal Georgia Community College, A
Columbus State University, B
Columbus Technical College, A
Georgia Southwestern State University, A
Griffin Technical College, A
Gwinnett Technical College, A
Heart of Georgia Technical College, A
Lanier Technical College, A
Middle Georgia Technical College, A
North Metro Technical College, A
Southeastern Technical College, A
Southwest Georgia Technical College, A
Valdosta Technical College, A
Waycross College, A
West Central Technical College, A
West Georgia Technical College, A

Idaho

College of Southern Idaho, A
Idaho State University, AB

Illinois

City Colleges of Chicago, Malcolm X College, A
City Colleges of Chicago, Wilbur Wright College, A

College of DuPage, A
College of Lake County, A
Illinois Eastern Community Colleges, Olney Central
   College, A
John Wood Community College, A
Kaskaskia College, A
Kishwaukee College, A
Lincoln Land Community College, A
Moraine Valley Community College, A
North Central College, B
Parkland College, A
Roosevelt University, B
Southern Illinois University Carbondale, B
Trinity College of Nursing and Health Sciences, A
University of St. Francis, B

Indiana

Indiana University Northwest, AB
Indiana University-Purdue University
   Indianapolis, AB
Indiana University South Bend, A
Ivy Tech Community College-Central Indiana, A
Ivy Tech Community College-Columbus, A
Ivy Tech Community College-East Central, A
Ivy Tech Community College-Wabash Valley, A
University of Saint Francis, A
University of Southern Indiana, A

Iowa

Mercy College of Health Sciences, A
Scott Community College, A

Kansas

Hutchinson Community College and Area Vocational
   School, A
Washburn University, B

Kentucky

Hazard Community and Technical College, A
Jefferson Community and Technical College, A
Lexington Community College, A
Morehead State University, AB
Northern Kentucky University, A
Owensboro Community and Technical College, A
Southeast Kentucky Community and Technical
   College, A

Louisiana

Delgado Community College, A
Louisiana State University at Alexandria, A
McNeese State University, B
Northwestern State University of Louisiana, B
Southern University at Shreveport, A
University of Louisiana at Monroe, B

Maryland

Allegany College of Maryland, A
Chesapeake College, A
Hagerstown Community College, A
Montgomery College, A
Wor-Wic Community College, A

Massachusetts

Bunker Hill Community College, A
Massachusetts Bay Community College, A
Massachusetts College of Pharmacy and Health
   Sciences, B
North Shore Community College, A
Quinsigamond Community College, A
Springfield Technical Community College, A

Michigan

Jackson Community College, A
Kellogg Community College, A
Lake Michigan College, A
Lansing Community College, A
Montcalm Community College, A
Mott Community College, A
Oakland Community College, A
University of Michigan-Flint, B

Minnesota

Century College, A
College of St. Catherine, A
College of St. Catherine-Minneapolis, A

Lake Superior College, A
Normandale Community College, A
Riverland Community College, A

Mississippi

Itawamba Community College, A
Meridian Community College, A
Mississippi Delta Community College, A

Missouri

Avila University, B
Mineral Area College, A
Missouri Southern State University, A
Missouri State University, B
University of Missouri-Columbia, B

Nebraska

Southeast Community College, Lincoln Campus, A
University of Nebraska Medical Center, B

Nevada

University of Nevada, Las Vegas, B

New Jersey

Burlington County College, A
Camden County College, A
Essex County College, A
Fairleigh Dickinson University, College at Florham, AB
Fairleigh Dickinson University, Metropolitan Campus, AB
Mercer County Community College, A
Passaic County Community College, A
Union County College, A

New Mexico

Clovis Community College, A
Northern New Mexico Community College, A
University of New Mexico, AB

New York

Broome Community College, A
Erie Community College, A
Eugenio María de Hostos Community College of the City University of New York, A
Long Island University, C.W. Post Campus, B
Mohawk Valley Community College, A
Nassau Community College, A
New York City College of Technology of the City University of New York, A
North Country Community College, A
St. Francis College, B
State University of New York Upstate Medical University, B

North Carolina

Asheville-Buncombe Technical Community College, A
Caldwell Community College and Technical Institute, A
Cape Fear Community College, A
Carolinas College of Health Sciences, A
Catawba Valley Community College, A
Cleveland Community College, A
Johnston Community College, A
Pitt Community College, A
Southwestern Community College, A
The University of North Carolina at Chapel Hill, B
Wake Technical Community College, A

North Dakota

Minot State University, B

Ohio

Central Ohio Technical College, A
Kent State University, Salem Campus, AB
Mercy College of Northwest Ohio, A
The Ohio State University, B
Shawnee State University, A
The University of Akron, A

Oklahoma

Bacone College, A
Rose State College, A

Southwestern Oklahoma State University at Sayre, A
Western Oklahoma State College, A

Oregon

Oregon Health & Science University, B

Pennsylvania

Bloomsburg University of Pennsylvania, B
College Misericordia, B
Community College of Allegheny County, A
Gannon University, AB
Harcum College, A
Harrisburg Area Community College, A
Holy Family University, A
Johnson College, A
Keystone College, A
La Roche College, AB
Montgomery County Community College, A
Pennsylvania College of Technology, A
The Pennsylvania State University New Kensington Campus of the Commonwealth College, A
The Pennsylvania State University Schuylkill Campus of the Capital College, A
Western School of Health and Business Careers (Pittsburgh), A

Puerto Rico

University of Puerto Rico, Medical Sciences Campus, A

Rhode Island

Community College of Rhode Island, A

South Carolina

Midlands Technical College, A
Orangeburg-Calhoun Technical College, A
Piedmont Technical College, A
Spartanburg Technical College, A
York Technical College, A

South Dakota

Mount Marty College, B
Presentation College, AB

Tennessee

Baptist College of Health Sciences, B
Jackson State Community College, A
Southwest Tennessee Community College, A
Volunteer State Community College, A

Texas

Central Texas College, A
Del Mar College, A
El Centro College, A
Galveston College, A
Houston Community College System, A
Kilgore College, A
Midland College, A
St. Philip's College, A
Texas State University-San Marcos, B

Utah

Weber State University, AB

Vermont

University of Vermont, B

West Virginia

Bluefield State College, A
Marshall Community and Technical College, A
Mountain State University, A

Wisconsin

Chippewa Valley Technical College, A
Marian College of Fond du Lac, B

Moraine Park Technical College, A

British Columbia

British Columbia Institute of Technology, AB

Prince Edward Island

University of Prince Edward Island, B

MEDICAL RECEPTION/RECEPTIONIST

Iowa

Iowa Lakes Community College, A

Minnesota

Alexandria Technical College, A

Washington

Edmonds Community College, A
Lower Columbia College, A

MEDICAL STAFF SERVICES TECHNOLOGY/TECHNICIAN

Colorado

Front Range Community College, A

Oklahoma

East Central University, B

MEDICAL/SURGICAL NURSING

Illinois

Rush University, MDO
Saint Francis Medical Center College of Nursing, MO
Southern Illinois University Edwardsville, MO

Maine

University of Southern Maine, M

New York

Daemen College, MO

Ohio

Case Western Reserve University, M

Pennsylvania

Gannon University, M
La Salle University, M
University of Pennsylvania, M

Puerto Rico

Pontifical Catholic University of Puerto Rico, M

South Carolina

University of South Carolina, M

Texas

Angelo State University, M

Virginia

George Mason University, M
Marymount University, MO

MEDICAL TECHNOLOGY

California

California State University, Long Beach, M

Georgia

Emory University, M
Medical College of Georgia, M

Illinois

Rush University, M

Massachusetts

Northeastern University, M

Michigan

Wayne State University, O

Mississippi

University of Southern Mississippi, M

Nebraska

University of Nebraska Medical Center, O

New Jersey

Fairleigh Dickinson University, Metropolitan
Campus, M

New York

St. John's University, M
State University of New York Upstate Medical
University, M

Ohio

Case Western Reserve University, M

Puerto Rico

Inter American University of Puerto Rico,
Metropolitan Campus, M
University of Puerto Rico, Medical Sciences
Campus, O
University of the Sacred Heart, O

South Carolina

Medical University of South Carolina, M

Utah

University of Utah, M

Ontario

University of Guelph, MD

MEDICAL TRANSCRIPTION/ TRANSCRIPTIONIST

Arizona

Central Arizona College, A
Northland Pioneer College, A

California

Ventura College, A

Colorado

Denver Academy of Court Reporting, A

Florida

Key College, A

Georgia

Dalton State College, A

Illinois

Black Hawk College, A
Elgin Community College, A
Rockford Business College, A

Iowa

Iowa Lakes Community College, A
Kaplan University, A

Kansas

Brown Mackie College-Salina, A

Massachusetts

Northern Essex Community College, A

Michigan

Baker College of Flint, A
Baker College of Jackson, A
Jackson Community College, A
Mid Michigan Community College, A

Oakland Community College, A

Minnesota

Alexandria Technical College, A
Dakota County Technical College, A

Missouri

Saint Charles Community College, A

Montana

Montana State University-Great Falls College of
Technology, A

North Dakota

Williston State College, A

Pennsylvania

Erie Business Center, Main, A
Laurel Business Institute, A
Lehigh Carbon Community College, A
Mercyhurst College, B

South Dakota

Kilian Community College, A
Presentation College, A
Southeast Technical Institute, A
Western Dakota Technical Institute, A

Texas

El Centro College, A

Utah

LDS Business College, A

Washington

Lower Columbia College, A

West Virginia

Marshall Community and Technical College, A
Mountain State College, A

Wisconsin

Moraine Park Technical College, A
Southwest Wisconsin Technical College, A

MEDICINAL AND PHARMACEUTICAL CHEMISTRY

California

University of California, San Diego, B

Connecticut

University of Connecticut, MD

Florida

Florida Agricultural and Mechanical University, MD
University of Florida, MDP

Georgia

University of Georgia, MD

Idaho

Idaho State University, M

Indiana

Butler University, B
Purdue University, MDO

Kansas

University of Kansas, MD

Massachusetts

Worcester Polytechnic Institute, B

Michigan

Michigan Technological University, B
University of Michigan, D

Wayne State University, MD

Minnesota

University of Minnesota, Twin Cities Campus, MD

Mississippi

University of Mississippi, MD

New Jersey

Rutgers, The State University of New Jersey, New
Brunswick/Piscataway, MD

New York

Long Island University, C.W. Post Campus, M
State University of New York at Buffalo, BMD

Ohio

Ohio Northern University, B
The Ohio State University, MD
The University of Toledo, MD

Pennsylvania

Duquesne University, MD
Temple University, MD
University of the Sciences in Philadelphia, BMD

Rhode Island

University of Rhode Island, MD

Utah

University of Utah, MD

Washington

University of Washington, D

West Virginia

West Virginia University, MD

MEDIEVAL AND RENAISSANCE STUDIES

California

University of California, Santa Barbara, B

Connecticut

Connecticut College, B
University of Connecticut, MD
Wesleyan University, B
Yale University, MD

District of Columbia

The Catholic University of America, BMDO
Georgetown University, B

Florida

New College of Florida, B

Georgia

Emory University, B

Illinois

University of Chicago, B

Indiana

Hanover College, B
Indiana University Bloomington, D
University of Notre Dame, BMD

Iowa

Cornell College, B
The University of Iowa, B

Louisiana

Tulane University, B

Massachusetts

College of the Holy Cross, B
Harvard University, BMD
Mount Holyoke College, B
Smith College, B

Wellesley College, B

Michigan
University of Michigan, B
Western Michigan University, M

Minnesota
University of Minnesota, Twin Cities Campus, MD

Missouri
Washington University in St. Louis, B

Nebraska
University of Nebraska-Lincoln, B

New Jersey
Rutgers, The State University of New Jersey, New Brunswick/Piscataway, BD

New York
Bard College, B
Barnard College, B
Columbia College, B
Cornell University, BMD
Fordham University, BM
Hamilton College, B
Hobart and William Smith Colleges, B
New York University, B
State University of New York at Binghamton, B
Syracuse University, B
University at Albany, State University of New York, B
Vassar College, B

North Carolina
Duke University, BO

Ohio
Ohio Wesleyan University, B
The University of Toledo, B

Pennsylvania
Dickinson College, B
The Pennsylvania State University Abington College, B
The Pennsylvania State University Altoona College, B
The Pennsylvania State University Beaver Campus of the Commonwealth College, B
The Pennsylvania State University Berks Campus of the Berks-Lehigh Valley College, B
The Pennsylvania State University Delaware County Campus of the Commonwealth College, B
The Pennsylvania State University DuBois Campus of the Commonwealth College, B
The Pennsylvania State University at Erie, The Behrend College, B
The Pennsylvania State University Fayette Campus of the Commonwealth College, B
The Pennsylvania State University Hazleton Campus of the Commonwealth College, B
The Pennsylvania State University, Lehigh Valley Campus of the Berks-Lehigh Valley College, B
The Pennsylvania State University McKeesport Campus of the Commonwealth College, B
The Pennsylvania State University Mont Alto Campus of the Commonwealth College, B
The Pennsylvania State University New Kensington Campus of the Commonwealth College, B
The Pennsylvania State University Schuylkill Campus of the Capital College, B
The Pennsylvania State University Shenango Campus of the Commonwealth College, B
The Pennsylvania State University University Park Campus, B
The Pennsylvania State University Wilkes-Barre Campus of the Commonwealth College, B
The Pennsylvania State University Worthington Scranton Campus of the Commonwealth College, B
The Pennsylvania State University York Campus of the Commonwealth College, B

Swarthmore College, B

Rhode Island
Brown University, B

Tennessee
Sewanee: The University of the South, B

Texas
Southern Methodist University, BM

Vermont
Marlboro College, B

Virginia
The College of William and Mary, B
Washington and Lee University, B

Wisconsin
Marquette University, M

Alberta
University of Calgary, B

British Columbia
University of Victoria, B

Manitoba
University of Manitoba, B

New Brunswick
Mount Allison University, B

Newfoundland and Labrador
Memorial University of Newfoundland, B

Ontario
Carleton University, B
University of Ottawa, B
University of Toronto, BMD
University of Waterloo, B

MEDIUM/HEAVY VEHICLE AND TRUCK TECHNOLOGY/TECHNICIAN

Minnesota
Dakota County Technical College, A

MENTAL AND SOCIAL HEALTH SERVICES AND ALLIED PROFESSIONS

Alaska
University of Alaska Fairbanks, A

Maine
The University of Maine at Augusta, AB

Michigan
Oakland Community College, A

New York
Broome Community College, A

North Carolina
Pitt Community College, A

Ohio
The University of Toledo, B
Wright State University, B

Pennsylvania
Pennsylvania College of Technology, B

Virginia
Marymount University, B
Old Dominion University, B

Washington
Edmonds Community College, A

Wisconsin
Waukesha County Technical College, A

MENTAL HEALTH COUNSELING/COUNSELOR

Florida
Florida Gulf Coast University, B

Kansas
Washburn University, AB

Pennsylvania
Marywood University, B

MENTAL HEALTH/REHABILITATION

Alabama
Community College of the Air Force, A
Wallace State Community College, A

Alaska
University of Alaska, Prince William Sound Community College, A

Arizona
Prescott College, B

California
Evergreen Valley College, A
Glendale Community College, A
Los Angeles City College, A
Mt. San Antonio College, A
Oxnard College, A
Porterville College, A
San Bernardino Valley College, A

Connecticut
Gateway Community College, A
Housatonic Community College, A
Middlesex Community College, A
Naugatuck Valley Community College, A

Illinois
City Colleges of Chicago, Harold Washington College, A
City Colleges of Chicago, Kennedy-King College, A
Elgin Community College, A
Governors State University, B
Prairie State College, A
St. Augustine College, A
South Suburban College, A

Iowa
Marshalltown Community College, A

Kansas
Kansas Wesleyan University, B
Newman University, B

Kentucky
Hopkinsville Community College, A
Northern Kentucky University, B

Louisiana
Southern University at Shreveport, A

Maine
University of Maine at Farmington, B

Maryland
Anne Arundel Community College, A
Morgan State University, B

Massachusetts
North Shore Community College, A
Northern Essex Community College, A

Springfield College, B
Tufts University, B

Michigan

Lake Superior State University, A
Macomb Community College, A
St. Clair County Community College, A

Minnesota

Ridgewater College, A
St. Cloud State University, B

Missouri

Evangel University, AB

Montana

Chief Dull Knife College, A
Fort Peck Community College, A

Nebraska

Metropolitan Community College, A

Nevada

Truckee Meadows Community College, A

New Hampshire

New Hampshire Technical Institute, A

New Jersey

Felician College, A

New York

Dutchess Community College, A
Elmira College, B
Fiorello H. LaGuardia Community College of the
    City University of New York, A
Kingsborough Community College of the City
    University of New York, A
Mohawk Valley Community College, A
North Country Community College, A
Orange County Community College, A

North Carolina

Lenoir Community College, A
Sandhills Community College, A
Southwestern Community College, A

Ohio

Belmont Technical College, A
Columbus State Community College, A
Sinclair Community College, A
The University of Toledo, A
Zane State College, A

Oregon

Mt. Hood Community College, A

Pennsylvania

Community College of Philadelphia, A
Lackawanna College, A
Reading Area Community College, A

Puerto Rico

University of Puerto Rico, Cayey University
    College, B

Texas

Alvin Community College, A
Blinn College, A
Del Mar College, A
El Paso Community College, A
Houston Community College System, A
McLennan Community College, A
South Plains College, A

Tarrant County College District, A

Virginia

Virginia Western Community College, A

Washington

Pierce College, A

Manitoba

Brandon University, B

MERCHANDISING AND BUYING OPERATIONS

Georgia

Clayton State University, A

Illinois

College of DuPage, A

Michigan

Delta College, A
Michigan State University, B

Ohio

Cuyahoga Community College, A
The University of Akron, A

Texas

North Central Texas College, A

METAL AND JEWELRY ARTS

Arizona

Mohave Community College, A

California

Academy of Art University, AB
California College of the Arts, B
California State University, Long Beach, B
Monterey Peninsula College, A
Palomar College, A
Pasadena City College, A

Colorado

Colorado State University, B
Pueblo Community College, A

Florida

Miami International University of Art & Design, A

Georgia

Savannah College of Art and Design, B
University of Georgia, B

Illinois

Gem City College, A
School of the Art Institute of Chicago, B

Indiana

Indiana University Bloomington, B

Iowa

The University of Iowa, B

Kansas

Garden City Community College, A
University of Kansas, B

Maine

Maine College of Art, B

Massachusetts

Massachusetts College of Art, B
School of the Museum of Fine Arts, Boston, B
Simon's Rock College of Bard, B

University of Massachusetts Dartmouth, B

Michigan

Ferris State University, B
Grand Valley State University, B
University of Michigan, B

Missouri

Northwest Missouri State University, B

Montana

Flathead Valley Community College, A

New Mexico

Institute of American Indian Arts, A
Mesalands Community College, A

New York

Fashion Institute of Technology, A
Hofstra University, B
Pratt Institute, B
Rochester Institute of Technology, AB
State University of New York College at
    Brockport, B
State University of New York at New Paltz, B
Syracuse University, B

North Carolina

College of The Albemarle, A
Haywood Community College, A

Ohio

The Cleveland Institute of Art, B
Kent State University, B
The University of Akron, B
Virginia Marti College of Art and Design, A

Oklahoma

Oklahoma State University, Okmulgee, A

Oregon

University of Oregon, B

Pennsylvania

Arcadia University, B
Seton Hill University, B
Temple University, B

Rhode Island

Rhode Island School of Design, B

Tennessee

Memphis College of Art, B

Texas

Paris Junior College, A
San Antonio College, A
University of North Texas, B

Washington

University of Washington, B

Wisconsin

University of Wisconsin-Milwaukee, B

Alberta

Alberta College of Art & Design, B

Nova Scotia

NSCAD University, B

METALLURGICAL ENGINEERING

Alabama

The University of Alabama, BMD

Colorado

Colorado School of Mines, BMD

Idaho

University of Idaho, BMD

Illinois

Illinois Institute of Technology, B

Massachusetts

Harvard University, B
Massachusetts Institute of Technology, O

Michigan

Michigan Technological University, BMD
University of Michigan, B
Wayne State University, MD

Missouri

University of Missouri-Rolla, BMD

Montana

Montana Tech of The University of Montana, BM

Nevada

University of Nevada, Reno, BMDO

Ohio

Cleveland State University, B
The Ohio State University, BMD
University of Cincinnati, BMD

Oregon

Oregon State University, B

Pennsylvania

The Pennsylvania State University University Park
   Campus, MD
University of Pittsburgh, BMD
Ursinus College, B

South Dakota

South Dakota School of Mines and
   Technology, BMD

Texas

The University of Texas at El Paso, BM

Utah

University of Utah, BMD

Washington

University of Washington, B

Wisconsin

University of Wisconsin-Madison, BMD

Alberta

University of Alberta, B

British Columbia

The University of British Columbia, BMD

Nova Scotia

Dalhousie University, BMD

Ontario

Laurentian University, B
University of Toronto, B

Quebec

McGill University, MD
Université Laval, BMD

METALLURGICAL TECHNOLOGY/TECHNICIAN

Alabama

Community College of the Air Force, A

Arkansas

Arkansas Northeastern College, A

California

Don Bosco Technical Institute, A
Sierra College, A

Idaho

Brigham Young University -Idaho, A

Illinois

Elgin Community College, A
Southwestern Illinois College, A

Indiana

Purdue University Calumet, A

Michigan

Macomb Community College, A
Schoolcraft College, A

Minnesota

Ridgewater College, A

Montana

Montana State University-Northern, A

Nebraska

Southeast Community College, Milford Campus, A

New York

Mohawk Valley Community College, A

Ohio

University of Cincinnati, B

Oklahoma

Murray State College, A

Oregon

Linn-Benton Community College, A

Pennsylvania

The Pennsylvania State University Altoona
   College, A
The Pennsylvania State University Berks Campus of
   the Berks-Lehigh Valley College, A
The Pennsylvania State University DuBois Campus
   of the Commonwealth College, A
The Pennsylvania State University at Erie; The
   Behrend College, A
The Pennsylvania State University Fayette Campus
   of the Commonwealth College, A
The Pennsylvania State University Hazleton
   Campus of the Commonwealth College, A
The Pennsylvania State University New Kensington
   Campus of the Commonwealth College, A
The Pennsylvania State University Schuylkill
   Campus of the Capital College, A
The Pennsylvania State University Shenango
   Campus of the Commonwealth College, A
The Pennsylvania State University Wilkes-Barre
   Campus of the Commonwealth College, A
The Pennsylvania State University York Campus of
   the Commonwealth College, A

Texas

Kilgore College, A

METALLURGY

California

California State University, Long Beach, M
University of California, Berkeley, MD
University of California, Los Angeles, MD

Connecticut

University of Connecticut, MD

Idaho

University of Idaho, MD

New York

Rensselaer Polytechnic Institute, MD

British Columbia

The University of British Columbia, MD

Ontario

Laurentian University, M

METEOROLOGY

California

San Jose State University, M

Connecticut

Yale University, D

Florida

Florida Institute of Technology, BM
Florida State University, BMD
University of Miami, BMD

Hawaii

University of Hawaii at Manoa, BMD

Illinois

Western Illinois University, B

Iowa

Iowa State University of Science and
   Technology, MD

Maryland

University of Maryland, College Park, MD

Missouri

Saint Louis University, BMD

New York

State University of New York College at
   Brockport, B

North Carolina

North Carolina State University, BMD
The University of North Carolina at Charlotte, B

Oklahoma

University of Oklahoma, MD

Pennsylvania

The Pennsylvania State University University Park
   Campus, MD

Texas

Texas A&M University, MD

Utah

University of Utah, BMD
Utah State University, MD

West Virginia

West Virginia State Community and Technical
   College, A

Nova Scotia

Dalhousie University, B

Quebec

McGill University, MD
Université du Québec àMontréal, MDO

MICROBIOLOGICAL SCIENCES AND IMMUNOLOGY

California

University of California, Los Angeles, B

Ohio

Wright State University, B

Nova Scotia

Dalhousie University, B

MICROBIOLOGY

Alabama

Auburn University, BMD
The University of Alabama at Birmingham, D
University of South Alabama, D

Arizona

Arizona State University, MD
The University of Arizona, MD

Arkansas

University of Arkansas for Medical Sciences, MDO

California

California State University, Chico, B
California State University, Fullerton, M
California State University, Long Beach, BM
California State University, Los Angeles, B
Loma Linda University, MD
San Diego State University, BM
San Francisco State University, M
San Jose State University, M
Stanford University, D
University of California, Berkeley, BD
University of California, Davis, BMD
University of California, Irvine, BMDO
University of California, Los Angeles, MD
University of California, Riverside, MD
University of California, San Diego, D
University of California, Santa Barbara, B
University of Southern California, MD

Colorado

Colorado State University, MD
University of Colorado at Boulder, MD

Connecticut

Quinnipiac University, M
University of Connecticut, MD
Yale University, DO

Delaware

University of Delaware, MD

District of Columbia

The Catholic University of America, MD
The George Washington University, M
Georgetown University, MD
Howard University, D

Florida

Florida State University, MD
University of Central Florida, M
University of Florida, MD
University of Miami, BDO
University of South Florida, M

Georgia

Emory University, D
Georgia State University, MD
University of Georgia, BMD

Hawaii

University of Hawaii at Manoa, BMD

Idaho

Idaho State University, BM
University of Idaho, MD

Illinois

Illinois Institute of Technology, M
Illinois State University, D
Loyola University Chicago, MDO
Northwestern University, D
Rush University, D
Southern Illinois University Carbondale, BMD
University of Chicago, D
University of Illinois at Chicago, DO

University of Illinois at Urbana-Champaign, BMDO

Indiana

Indiana State University, D
Indiana University Bloomington, MD
Indiana University-Purdue University
  Indianapolis, MDO
Purdue University, MD

Iowa

Iowa State University of Science and
  Technology, BMD
The University of Iowa, BMD
University of Northern Iowa, B

Kansas

Emporia State University, M
Kansas State University, MD
University of Kansas, BMDO

Kentucky

University of Kentucky, D
University of Louisville, MD

Louisiana

Louisiana State University and Agricultural and
  Mechanical College, B
Louisiana State University Health Sciences
  Center, MD
Tulane University, MDO

Maine

University of Maine, MD

Maryland

The Johns Hopkins University, MD
University of Maryland, College Park, MD

Massachusetts

Boston University, MDO
Brandeis University, D
Harvard University, D
Massachusetts Institute of Technology, D
Tufts University, D
University of Massachusetts Amherst, BMD

Michigan

Michigan State University, BMD
Michigan Technological University, B
Northern Michigan University, B
University of Michigan, D
University of Michigan-Dearborn, B
Wayne State University, MDO

Minnesota

University of Minnesota, Twin Cities Campus, D

Mississippi

University of Mississippi Medical Center, MDO
University of Southern Mississippi, MD

Missouri

Saint Louis University, D
University of Missouri-Columbia, BMD
Washington University in St. Louis, D

Montana

Montana State University, MD
The University of Montana-Missoula, MD

Nebraska

University of Nebraska Medical Center, MD

New Hampshire

Dartmouth College, D
University of New Hampshire, MD

New Jersey

Rutgers, The State University of New Jersey, New
  Brunswick/Piscataway, MD

Seton Hall University, M

New Mexico

New Mexico State University, B
University of New Mexico, MD

New York

Cornell University, BD
Long Island University, C.W. Post Campus, M
New York University, MDO
Rensselaer Polytechnic Institute, MD
State University of New York at Buffalo, MD
State University of New York Upstate Medical
  University, MDO
Stony Brook University, State University of New
  York, D
University of Rochester, MDO
Wagner College, M

North Carolina

Duke University, D
East Carolina University, D
North Carolina State University, BMD
The University of North Carolina at Chapel Hill, MD
Wake Forest University, D

North Dakota

North Dakota State University, BMD
University of North Dakota, MD

Ohio

Case Western Reserve University, DO
Miami University, MD
Miami University Hamilton, B
The Ohio State University, MD
Ohio University, MD
University of Cincinnati, MD
Wright State University, M

Oklahoma

Oklahoma State University, MD
University of Oklahoma, BMD
University of Oklahoma Health Sciences Center, MD

Oregon

Oregon Health & Science University, D
Oregon State University, BMD

Pennsylvania

Drexel University, MD
Juniata College, B
The Pennsylvania State University University Park
  Campus, MD
Temple University, MDO
Thomas Jefferson University, MD
University of Pennsylvania, DO
University of Pittsburgh, MD
University of the Sciences in Philadelphia, B

Puerto Rico

Inter American University of Puerto Rico, Aguadilla
  Campus, B
Inter American University of Puerto Rico,
  Barranquitas Campus, AB
University of Puerto Rico, Medical Sciences
  Campus, MD

Rhode Island

Brown University, MD
University of Rhode Island, MD

South Carolina

Clemson University, BMD
Medical University of South Carolina, MDO

South Dakota

South Dakota State University, M
The University of South Dakota, MD

Tennessee

East Tennessee State University, MD
University of Memphis, B
The University of Tennessee, MD

Vanderbilt University, MDO

Texas

Texas A&M University, BMD
Texas A&M University System Health Science
  Center, D
Texas State University-San Marcos, B
Texas Tech University, M
The University of Texas at Arlington, B
The University of Texas at Austin, BMD
The University of Texas Health Science Center at
  Houston, MDO
The University of Texas Health Science Center at
  San Antonio, MDO
The University of Texas Medical Branch, MD
The University of Texas Southwestern Medical
  Center at Dallas, D

Utah

Brigham Young University, BMD
Utah State University, M

Vermont

University of Vermont, MDO

Virginia

George Mason University, D
University of Virginia, DO
Virginia Commonwealth University, MDO
Virginia Polytechnic Institute and State
  University, MD

Washington

University of Washington, D
Washington State University, BMD

West Virginia

West Virginia University, MD

Wisconsin

Marquette University, MD
University of Wisconsin-La Crosse, BM
University of Wisconsin-Madison, D

Wyoming

University of Wyoming, B

Alberta

University of Alberta, MD
University of Calgary, MD

British Columbia

The University of British Columbia, MD
University of Victoria, MD

Manitoba

Canadian Mennonite University, A
University of Manitoba, MD

Nova Scotia

Dalhousie University, MDO

Ontario

Queen's University at Kingston, MD
University of Guelph, BMD
University of Ottawa, MD
University of Toronto, B
The University of Western Ontario, BMD

Quebec

McGill University, MD
Université Laval, MD
Université de Montréal, MDO

Université de Sherbrooke, MD

Saskatchewan

University of Saskatchewan, BMD

MIDDLE/NEAR EASTERN AND SEMITIC LANGUAGES, LITERATURES, AND LINGUISTICS

California

University of California, Los Angeles, B

Michigan

Wayne State University, B

New York

Sarah Lawrence College, B

Pennsylvania

Bryn Mawr College, B

MIDDLE SCHOOL EDUCATION

Alaska

Alaska Pacific University, M

Arkansas

Henderson State University, M
University of Arkansas, M
University of Arkansas at Little Rock, M

California

California State University, Fullerton, M

Connecticut

Quinnipiac University, M

Florida

University of South Florida, M
University of West Florida, M

Georgia

Albany State University, M
Armstrong Atlantic State University, M
Augusta State University, MO
Berry College, M
Brenau University, MO
Columbus State University, MO
Emory University, M
Fort Valley State University, M
Georgia College & State University, MO
Georgia Southern University, M
Georgia Southwestern State University, MO
Georgia State University, MDO
Kennesaw State University, M
Mercer University, MO
North Georgia College & State University, M
University of Georgia, MDO
University of West Georgia, MO
Valdosta State University, MO
Wesleyan College, M

Illinois

Eastern Illinois University, M

Indiana

Ball State University, M

Iowa

University of Northern Iowa, M

Kansas

Fort Hays State University, M
Newman University, M

Kentucky

Bellarmine University, M
Morehead State University, M
Murray State University, MO

Northern Kentucky University, M
Spalding University, M
Union College, M
University of the Cumberlands, M
University of Louisville, M
Western Kentucky University, M

Maine

University of Southern Maine, O

Maryland

Morgan State University, M

Massachusetts

Eastern Nazarene College, MO
Fitchburg State College, M
Hebrew College, O
Lesley University, M
Salem State College, M
Smith College, M
Tufts University, M
Westfield State College, M
Worcester State College, M

Michigan

Central Michigan University, M
Eastern Michigan University, M
Grand Valley State University, M
Saginaw Valley State University, M
Siena Heights University, M
Western Michigan University, M

Missouri

Drury University, M
Maryville University of Saint Louis, M
Missouri State University, M
Northwest Missouri State University, M
Park University, M
Southeast Missouri State University, M

Nevada

University of Nevada, Las Vegas, M

New Hampshire

Plymouth State University, M

New Jersey

Kean University, MO

New York

Brooklyn College of the City University of New
  York, M
City College of the City University of New York, M
College of Mount Saint Vincent, O
Daemen College, M
Hofstra University, O
Long Island University, C.W. Post Campus, M
Manhattanville College, M
Mount Saint Mary College, M
Nazareth College of Rochester, M
St. John Fisher College, MO
St. Thomas Aquinas College, M
State University of New York at Buffalo, O
State University of New York College at
  Brockport, M
State University of New York College at Oneonta, M
Wagner College, M

North Carolina

Campbell University, M
East Carolina University, M
Fayetteville State University, M
Gardner-Webb University, M
North Carolina Agricultural and Technical State
  University, M
North Carolina State University, M
The University of North Carolina at Charlotte, M
The University of North Carolina at Pembroke, M
The University of North Carolina Wilmington, M
Western Carolina University, M

Ohio

Ashland University, M
College of Mount St. Joseph, M

John Carroll University, M
Kent State University, M
The Ohio State University at Lima, M
The Ohio State University-Mansfield Campus, M
The Ohio State University at Marion, M
The Ohio State University-Newark Campus, M
Ohio University, MD
University of Dayton, M
Wright State University, M
Youngstown State University, M

Oregon

Pacific University, M

Pennsylvania

Rosemont College, M
Widener University, M

South Carolina

Clemson University, M
Winthrop University, M

Tennessee

Belmont University, M
Middle Tennessee State University, M

Texas

Austin College, M
Texas Christian University, M

Virginia

George Mason University, M
James Madison University, M
Mary Baldwin College, M
Old Dominion University, M
Shenandoah University, O
Virginia Commonwealth University, M

Washington

University of Puget Sound, M

Wisconsin

University of Wisconsin-Milwaukee, M
University of Wisconsin-Platteville, M

Nova Scotia

Mount Saint Vincent University, M

MILITARY AND DEFENSE STUDIES

California

California State University, San Bernardino, M

District of Columbia

The George Washington University, MO
Georgetown University, MO

Florida

Florida State University, D

Hawaii

Hawaii Pacific University, M

Missouri

Missouri State University, M

Pennsylvania

University of Pittsburgh, MO

Rhode Island

Salve Regina University, M

West Virginia

American Public University System, M

Alberta

University of Calgary, MD

Ontario

Royal Military College of Canada, M

MILITARY STUDIES

Colorado

United States Air Force Academy, B

Hawaii

Hawaii Pacific University, AB

Kansas

Barton County Community College, A

Nevada

Truckee Meadows Community College, A

Texas

Texas Christian University, B

MILITARY TECHNOLOGIES

Alabama

Calhoun Community College, A
Community College of the Air Force, A

Arizona

Cochise College (Douglas), A

Idaho

University of Idaho, B

Kentucky

Murray State University, A

Ohio

Wright State University, B

Ontario

Royal Military College of Canada, B

MINERAL ECONOMICS

Colorado

Colorado School of Mines, MD

Michigan

Michigan Technological University, M

Texas

The University of Texas at Austin, M

MINERAL/MINING ENGINEERING

Alaska

University of Alaska Fairbanks, MO

Arizona

The University of Arizona, MD

California

University of California, Berkeley, MD

Colorado

Colorado School of Mines, MD

Idaho

University of Idaho, MD

Illinois

Southern Illinois University Carbondale, M

Kentucky

University of Kentucky, MD

Michigan

Michigan Technological University, MD

Missouri

University of Missouri-Rolla, MD

Montana

Montana Tech of The University of Montana, M

Nevada

University of Nevada, Reno, MO

New Mexico

New Mexico Institute of Mining and Technology, M

Pennsylvania

The Pennsylvania State University University Park Campus, MD

Texas

The University of Texas at Austin, M

Utah

University of Utah, MD

Virginia

Virginia Polytechnic Institute and State University, MD

West Virginia

West Virginia University, MD

Alberta

University of Alberta, MD

British Columbia

The University of British Columbia, MD

Nova Scotia

Dalhousie University, MD

Ontario

Laurentian University, M
Queen's University at Kingston, MD

Quebec

McGill University, MDO
Université Laval, MD

MINERALOGY

Connecticut

Yale University, D

Illinois

University of Illinois at Chicago, MD

Indiana

Indiana University Bloomington, MD

Michigan

University of Michigan, MD

New York

Cornell University, MD

Quebec

Université du Québec àChicoutimi, D
Université du Québec àMontréal, D

MINING AND MINERAL ENGINEERING

Arizona

The University of Arizona, B

Colorado

Colorado School of Mines, B

Idaho

University of Idaho, B

Illinois

Southern Illinois University Carbondale, B

Kentucky

University of Kentucky, B

Missouri

University of Missouri-Rolla, B

Montana

Montana Tech of The University of Montana, B

Nevada

University of Nevada, Reno, B

New Mexico

New Mexico Institute of Mining and Technology, B

Oregon

Oregon State University, B

Pennsylvania

The Pennsylvania State University Abington
  College, B
The Pennsylvania State University Altoona
  College, B
The Pennsylvania State University Beaver Campus
  of the Commonwealth College, B
The Pennsylvania State University Berks Campus of
  the Berks-Lehigh Valley College, B
The Pennsylvania State University Delaware County
  Campus of the Commonwealth College, B
The Pennsylvania State University DuBois Campus
  of the Commonwealth College, B
The Pennsylvania State University at Erie, The
  Behrend College, B
The Pennsylvania State University Fayette Campus
  of the Commonwealth College, B
The Pennsylvania State University Hazleton
  Campus of the Commonwealth College, B
The Pennsylvania State University, Lehigh Valley
  Campus of the Berks-Lehigh Valley College, B
The Pennsylvania State University McKeesport
  Campus of the Commonwealth College, B
The Pennsylvania State University Mont Alto
  Campus of the Commonwealth College, B
The Pennsylvania State University New Kensington
  Campus of the Commonwealth College, B
The Pennsylvania State University Schuylkill
  Campus of the Capital College, B
The Pennsylvania State University Shenango
  Campus of the Commonwealth College, B
The Pennsylvania State University University Park
  Campus, B
The Pennsylvania State University Wilkes-Barre
  Campus of the Commonwealth College, B
The Pennsylvania State University Worthington
  Scranton Campus of the Commonwealth
  College, B
The Pennsylvania State University York Campus of
  the Commonwealth College, B

South Dakota

South Dakota School of Mines and Technology, B

Utah

University of Utah, B

Virginia

Virginia Polytechnic Institute and State University, B

West Virginia

West Virginia University, B

Wisconsin

University of Wisconsin-Madison, B

Alberta

University of Alberta, B

British Columbia

The University of British Columbia, B

Nova Scotia

Dalhousie University, B

Ontario

Laurentian University, B
Queen's University at Kingston, B
University of Toronto, B

Quebec

McGill University, B
Université Laval, B
Université du Québec en Abitibi-Témiscamingue, B

MINING AND PETROLEUM TECHNOLOGIES/TECHNICIANS

Alaska

University of Alaska Fairbanks, B

MINING TECHNOLOGY/TECHNICIAN

Arizona

Eastern Arizona College, A

California

Sierra College, A

Illinois

Illinois Eastern Community Colleges, Wabash Valley
  College, A
Southeastern Illinois College, A

Utah

College of Eastern Utah, A

Virginia

Mountain Empire Community College, A
Southwest Virginia Community College, A

West Virginia

Bluefield State College, B

Wyoming

Western Wyoming Community College, A

British Columbia

British Columbia Institute of Technology, A

MISSIONS/MISSIONARY STUDIES AND MISSIOLOGY

Arkansas

Harding University, B
John Brown University, B
Ouachita Baptist University, B

California

Bethesda Christian University, B
Biola University, BMD
Concordia University, M
Hope International University, AB
Simpson University, BM
Vanguard University of Southern California, B

Florida

Hobe Sound Bible College, AB
Southeastern University, B
Trinity Baptist College, B

Trinity College of Florida, B

Georgia

Luther Rice University, MP
Toccoa Falls College, B

Idaho

Northwest Nazarene University, B

Illinois

Moody Bible Institute, B
Trinity International University, MD
Wheaton College, MO

Indiana

Anderson University, M
Bethel College, B
Crossroads Bible College, B
Huntington University, B

Iowa

Dordt College, B
Emmaus Bible College, B
Faith Baptist Bible College and Theological
  Seminary, AB
Vennard College, B

Kansas

Central Christian College of Kansas, AB
Manhattan Christian College, AB
MidAmerica Nazarene University, B

Kentucky

Asbury College, B
Kentucky Mountain Bible College, B
Mid-Continent University, B
Southern Baptist Theological Seminary, MDP

Michigan

Grace Bible College, B
Kuyper College, B
Rochester College, B

Minnesota

Concordia University, St. Paul, B
Crossroads College, B
Crown College, B
North Central University, AB
Northwestern College, B
Pillsbury Baptist Bible College, B

Missouri

Calvary Bible College and Theological Seminary, B
Global University of the Assemblies of God, B
Messenger College, B

Nebraska

Grace University, B

New York

Nyack College, B

North Carolina

Gardner-Webb University, BP
Southeastern Baptist Theological Seminary, D

Ohio

Cedarville University, B
Circleville Bible College, AB
God's Bible School and College, AB

Oklahoma

Hillsdale Free Will Baptist College, AB
Oklahoma Baptist University, B
Oklahoma Christian University, B
Oral Roberts University, BMDP
Southern Nazarene University, B

Oregon

Corban College, B
Eugene Bible College, B
George Fox University, B

Multnomah Bible College and Biblical Seminary, B

Pennsylvania

Eastern University, B
Lancaster Bible College, B

South Carolina

Bob Jones University, AB
Columbia International University, MDPO
Southern Methodist College, AB

Tennessee

Freed-Hardeman University, B
Southern Adventist University, M
Tennessee Temple University, B

Texas

Abilene Christian University, BM
Dallas Baptist University, M
Hardin-Simmons University, B
LeTourneau University, B
Lubbock Christian University, B
Southwestern Assemblies of God University, B

Virginia

Regent University, MP

Washington

Northwest University, B

Wisconsin

Concordia University Wisconsin, B

Alberta

Alliance University College, BO
Prairie Bible Institute, AB
Rocky Mountain College, B
Taylor University College and Seminary, M

British Columbia

Columbia Bible College, B
Trinity Western University, B

Manitoba

Canadian Mennonite University, B
Providence College and Theological Seminary, BM

Ontario

Master's College and Seminary, B
Saint Paul University, MO
Tyndale University College & Seminary, PO

Saskatchewan

Briercrest College, B
Central Pentecostal College, B

MODERN GREEK LANGUAGE AND LITERATURE

California

Claremont McKenna College, B
Loyola Marymount University, B
Saint Mary's College of California, B
University of California, Los Angeles, B

District of Columbia

The Catholic University of America, B

Florida

Florida State University, B

Georgia

Emory University, B
University of Georgia, B

Idaho

Boise Bible College, B

Illinois

Monmouth College, B

Indiana

Ball State University, B
Butler University, B

Wabash College, B

Iowa

Cornell College, B
The University of Iowa, B

Louisiana

Tulane University, B

Massachusetts

Boston University, B
Harvard University, B
Mount Holyoke College, B
Tufts University, B

Michigan

Calvin College, B
Concordia University, B
University of Michigan, B

Minnesota

Macalester College, B
North Central University, A
University of Minnesota, Twin Cities Campus, B

Missouri

Saint Louis University, B
University of Missouri-Columbia, B

New Hampshire

University of New Hampshire, B

New York

Bard College, B
Barnard College, B
Brooklyn College of the City University of New
  York, B
Colgate University, B
Columbia College, B
Fordham University, B
Hamilton College, B
Lehman College of the City University of New
  York, B
New York University, B
Queens College of the City University of New
  York, B

Ohio

John Carroll University, B
Kenyon College, B
Miami University, B
Oberlin College, B
The Ohio State University, B
Wright State University, B

Oregon

University of Oregon, B

Pennsylvania

Haverford College, B

South Carolina

Furman University, B

Tennessee

Belmont University, B
Rhodes College, B
Sewanee: The University of the South, B
The University of Tennessee at Chattanooga, B

Utah

University of Utah, B

Vermont

Marlboro College, B

Virginia

The College of William and Mary, B
University of Richmond, B

Wisconsin

Concordia University Wisconsin, B
University of Wisconsin-Madison, B

University of Wisconsin-Milwaukee, B

Alberta

University of Alberta, B

Manitoba

University of Manitoba, B
The University of Winnipeg, B

New Brunswick

University of New Brunswick Fredericton, B

Newfoundland and Labrador

Memorial University of Newfoundland, B

Ontario

Carleton University, B
Trent University, B
University of Toronto, B
University of Windsor, B
Wilfrid Laurier University, B
York University, B

Saskatchewan

University of Saskatchewan, B

MODERN LANGUAGES

Alabama

Judson College, B

California

Citrus College, A
Claremont McKenna College, B
College of the Sequoias, A
Imperial Valley College, A
Pasadena City College, A
Pomona College, B
Saint Mary's College of California, B
San Diego City College, A
Santa Ana College, A
Santiago Canyon College, A
Scripps College, B
Westmont College, B

Colorado

Otero Junior College, A

Connecticut

Fairfield University, B
Sacred Heart University, A
Trinity College, B

Florida

Eckerd College, B
Florida Memorial College, B
Okaloosa-Walton College, A
University of South Florida, B

Georgia

Georgia Institute of Technology, B
Kennesaw State University, B
Macon State College, A

Illinois

City Colleges of Chicago, Harry S. Truman
  College, A
City Colleges of Chicago, Richard J. Daley
  College, A
City Colleges of Chicago, Wilbur Wright College, A
DePaul University, B
Greenville College, B
Monmouth College, B
North Park University, B
Olivet Nazarene University, B

University of Chicago, B

Indiana

Ball State University, B

Iowa

Cornell College, B

Kansas

Barton County Community College, A
Independence Community College, A

Louisiana

Dillard University, B
Louisiana College, B
University of Louisiana at Lafayette, B

Maine

University of Maine, B
University of Southern Maine, B

Maryland

College of Notre Dame of Maryland, B
University of Maryland, Baltimore County, B

Massachusetts

Atlantic Union College, B
Cape Cod Community College, A
Clark University, B
Harvard University, B
Northeastern University, B
Suffolk University, B

Michigan

Albion College, B
Alma College, B
Bay Mills Community College, A

Minnesota

Bemidji State University, B
Minnesota State University Mankato, B
North Central University, A

Mississippi

Itawamba Community College, A

Missouri

St. Louis Community College at Meramec, A
Stephens College, B
Washington University in St. Louis, B

Nebraska

Wayne State College, B

New Hampshire

Rivier College, B
University of New Hampshire, B

New Jersey

Brookdale Community College, A
Middlesex County College, A
Saint Peter's College, B

New York

Alfred University, B
Bard College, B
College of Mount Saint Vincent, B
Elmira College, B
Fordham University, B
Hamilton College, B
Hobart and William Smith Colleges, B
Long Island University, Brooklyn Campus, B
Nazareth College of Rochester, B
Purchase College, State University of New York, B
St. Bonaventure University, B
St. Lawrence University, B
St. Thomas Aquinas College, B
Sarah Lawrence College, B
Syracuse University, B

United States Military Academy, B

North Carolina

Lenoir-Rhyne College, B

Ohio

Kenyon College, B
Lake Erie College, B
Walsh University, B
Wilmington College, B
Wright State University, B

Oklahoma

Oklahoma City Community College, A
Rose State College, A

Oregon

Lewis & Clark College, B
Pacific University, B

Pennsylvania

Elizabethtown College, B
Gettysburg College, B
Grove City College, B
Immaculata University, B
La Salle University, B
Saint Francis University, B
Slippery Rock University of Pennsylvania, B
Westminster College, B
Widener University, B

South Carolina

Clemson University, B
Converse College, B
Presbyterian College, B
Winthrop University, B

Tennessee

King College, B
Lambuth University, B
Lee University, B

Texas

Amarillo College, A
Dallas Baptist University, B
Galveston College, A
Howard Payne University, B
Lon Morris College, A
Midland College, A
Odessa College, A
Palo Alto College, A
Tyler Junior College, A

Vermont

Marlboro College, B
Middlebury College, B
Saint Michael's College, B

Virginia

The College of William and Mary, B
Hampton University, B
Longwood University, B
University of Mary Washington, B
Virginia Military Institute, B

Washington

Everett Community College, A
Pacific Lutheran University, B
Walla Walla College, B

Wisconsin

Beloit College, B

Wyoming

Northwest College, A

Alberta

University of Alberta, B
University of Lethbridge, B

British Columbia

University of Victoria, B

New Brunswick

Mount Allison University, B
Université de Moncton, B

University of New Brunswick Fredericton, B

Nova Scotia

Mount Saint Vincent University, B
St. Francis Xavier University, B
Saint Mary's University, B

Ontario

Carleton University, B
Laurentian University, B
McMaster University, B
Trent University, B
University of Ottawa, B
University of Toronto, B
The University of Western Ontario, B
University of Windsor, B
York University, B

Quebec

Bishop's University, B
Concordia University, B
Université Laval, B
Université de Montréal, B
Université du Québec àChicoutimi, B

MOLECULAR BIOCHEMISTRY

California

University of California, Davis, B
University of California, Irvine, B
University of California, Los Angeles, B

Connecticut

Sacred Heart University, A

Michigan

Michigan Technological University, B

New York

Polytechnic University, Brooklyn Campus, B

British Columbia

Simon Fraser University, B

MOLECULAR BIOLOGY

Alabama

Auburn University, B
University of South Alabama, D

Arizona

Arizona State University, B
The University of Arizona, MD

Arkansas

University of Arkansas, MD
University of Arkansas for Medical Sciences, MDO

California

California Institute of Technology, D
California Lutheran University, B
California State University, Fresno, B
California State University, Sacramento, B
California State University, San Marcos, B
Chapman University, B
Humboldt State University, B
Pitzer College, B
Pomona College, B
San Diego State University, D
San Francisco State University, BM
San Jose State University, BM
Scripps College, B
University of California, Berkeley, D
University of California, Davis, MD
University of California, Irvine, MDO
University of California, Los Angeles, BMD
University of California, Riverside, MD
University of California, San Diego, BD
University of California, Santa Barbara, BMDO
University of California, Santa Cruz, BMD

University of Southern California, MD

Colorado

Colorado State University, MD
University of Colorado at Boulder, MD
University of Denver, B
Western State College of Colorado, B

Connecticut

Central Connecticut State University, BO
Quinnipiac University, M
University of Connecticut, MD
University of New Haven, M
Wesleyan University, BD
Yale University, BDO

Delaware

University of Delaware, MD

District of Columbia

The George Washington University, MD
Georgetown University, DO
Howard University, MD

Florida

Florida Agricultural and Mechanical University, B
Florida Institute of Technology, BD
Florida State University, MD
Stetson University, B
University of Central Florida, MD
University of Florida, MD
University of Miami, DO
University of South Florida, MD

Georgia

Emory University, D
Medical College of Georgia, D
University of Georgia, MD

Hawaii

University of Hawaii at Manoa, MD

Idaho

University of Idaho, BMD

Illinois

Benedictine University, B
Blackburn College, B
Bradley University, B
Chicago State University, B
Illinois Institute of Technology, MD
Loyola University Chicago, DO
Northwestern University, BD
Southern Illinois University Carbondale, MD
University of Chicago, DO
University of Illinois at Chicago, MD

Indiana

Ball State University, B
Indiana University Bloomington, MD
Indiana University-Purdue University
  Indianapolis, MDO
Purdue University, MD
University of Notre Dame, MD

Iowa

Coe College, B
Iowa State University of Science and
  Technology, MD
The University of Iowa, DO

Kansas

Baker University, B
Kansas State University, MD
University of Kansas, BMDO

Kentucky

Centre College, B
University of Louisville, MDO

Louisiana

Louisiana State University Health Sciences
  Center, MD

Tulane University, BMDO

Maine

Colby College, B
University of Maine, BMD
University of Southern Maine, M

Maryland

The Johns Hopkins University, MDO
University of Maryland, Baltimore County, BMD
University of Maryland, College Park, D

Massachusetts

Assumption College, B
Boston University, BMDO
Brandeis University, MD
Clark University, B
Elms College, B
Harvard University, BD
Massachusetts Institute of Technology, D
Tufts University, D
University of Massachusetts Amherst, D
University of Massachusetts Boston, D
Western New England College, B
Worcester Polytechnic Institute, B

Michigan

Michigan State University, MD
University of Michigan, BMD
Wayne State University, MD

Minnesota

Bethel University, B
University of Minnesota, Duluth, BMD
University of Minnesota, Twin Cities Campus, MD

Mississippi

Mississippi State University, MD
University of Southern Mississippi, MD

Missouri

Missouri State University, BM
Saint Louis University, D
University of Missouri-Columbia, MD
University of Missouri-Kansas City, MD
Washington University in St. Louis, D
William Jewell College, B

Montana

Montana State University, MD

Nebraska

University of Nebraska Medical Center, MD

Nevada

University of Nevada, Reno, MD

New Hampshire

Dartmouth College, B
University of New Hampshire, BMD

New Jersey

Montclair State University, BMO
Princeton University, BD
Rutgers, The State University of New Jersey, New
  Brunswick/Piscataway, BMD
Seton Hall University, MD
William Paterson University of New Jersey, M

New Mexico

New Mexico State University, MD
University of New Mexico, MD

New York

Bard College, B
Clarkson University, B
Colgate University, B
Cornell University, BD
Hamilton College, B
New York University, DO
Rensselaer Polytechnic Institute, MD
Sarah Lawrence College, B
State University of New York at Buffalo, D

State University of New York College at
  Brockport, B
State University of New York Downstate Medical
  Center, DO
State University of New York Upstate Medical
  University, MDO
Stony Brook University, State University of New
  York, MD
University at Albany, State University of New
  York, BMD
Wells College, B

North Carolina

Duke University, DO
East Carolina University, M
Meredith College, B
The University of North Carolina at Chapel Hill, MD
Wake Forest University, D
Winston-Salem State University, B

North Dakota

North Dakota State University, MD

Ohio

Case Western Reserve University, DO
The College of Wooster, B
Kent State University, MD
Kenyon College, B
Muskingum College, B
Ohio Northern University, B
The Ohio State University, MD
Ohio University, MD
Otterbein College, B
University of Cincinnati, MD
Wright State University, M

Oklahoma

Oklahoma State University, MD
University of Oklahoma Health Sciences Center, MD

Oregon

Oregon Health & Science University, DO
Oregon State University, MD
University of Oregon, D

Pennsylvania

Carnegie Mellon University, D
Cedar Crest College, B
Chestnut Hill College, B
Clarion University of Pennsylvania, B
Drexel University, MDO
Gettysburg College, B
Grove City College, B
Juniata College, B
Lehigh University, BD
The Pennsylvania State University University Park
  Campus, MD
Temple University, DO
Thomas Jefferson University, D
University of Pennsylvania, DO
University of Pittsburgh, BD
West Chester University of Pennsylvania, B
Westminster College, B

Rhode Island

Brown University, BMDO
University of Rhode Island, MD

South Carolina

Clemson University, MD
Medical University of South Carolina, DO
University of South Carolina, MD

South Dakota

The University of South Dakota, MD

Tennessee

University of Memphis, B
Vanderbilt University, BDO

Texas

Houston Baptist University, B
Texas A&M University, D

Texas A&M University System Health Science Center, D
Texas Lutheran University, B
Texas Tech University, B
Texas Woman's University, D
University of North Texas, MD
The University of Texas at Austin, BD
The University of Texas at Dallas, BMD
The University of Texas Health Science Center at Houston, MDO
The University of Texas Medical Branch, D
The University of Texas at San Antonio, D

Utah

Brigham Young University, BMD
Utah State University, MD

Vermont

Marlboro College, B
Middlebury College, B
University of Vermont, BMD

Virginia

George Mason University, MD
Hampton University, B
University of Richmond, B
Virginia Commonwealth University, D

Washington

University of Washington, BD
Washington State University, MD
Whitman College, B

West Virginia

Salem International University, BM
West Virginia University, MD

Wisconsin

Alverno College, B
Beloit College, B
Marquette University, BMD
University of Wisconsin-Eau Claire, B
University of Wisconsin-La Crosse, M
University of Wisconsin-Madison, BMD
University of Wisconsin-Parkside, BM

Wyoming

University of Wyoming, BMD

Alberta

University of Alberta, BMD
University of Calgary, BMD
University of Lethbridge, D

British Columbia

Simon Fraser University, BMD
Thompson Rivers University, B
The University of British Columbia, MD

Manitoba

The University of Winnipeg, B

New Brunswick

University of New Brunswick Fredericton, B

Ontario

Brock University, M
Lakehead University, B
McMaster University, BMD
University of Guelph, B
University of Ottawa, MD
University of Toronto, B
The University of Western Ontario, MD
York University, B

Quebec

Concordia University, B
McGill University, B
Université Laval, MD

Université de Montréal, MD

MOLECULAR BIOPHYSICS

California

California Institute of Technology, D

Connecticut

Yale University, DO

Florida

Florida State University, D

Illinois

Illinois Institute of Technology, MD

Missouri

Washington University in St. Louis, D

North Carolina

Duke University, O

Pennsylvania

University of Pennsylvania, DO
University of Pittsburgh, D

Texas

The University of Texas Medical Branch, MD
The University of Texas Southwestern Medical Center at Dallas, D

Virginia

Virginia Commonwealth University, MO

MOLECULAR GENETICS

California

Loma Linda University, MD
University of California, Irvine, MDO
University of California, Los Angeles, MD

Florida

University of Florida, MD

Georgia

Emory University, D
Georgia State University, MD

Illinois

University of Chicago, D
University of Illinois at Chicago, D

Indiana

Indiana University-Purdue University Indianapolis, MDO

Kansas

University of Kansas, DO

Maryland

University of Maryland, College Park, MD

Massachusetts

Harvard University, D

Michigan

Michigan State University, D

Missouri

Washington University in St. Louis, D

New Jersey

Rutgers, The State University of New Jersey, New Brunswick/Piscataway, MD

New York

Stony Brook University, State University of New York, D

North Carolina

Duke University, D
Wake Forest University, D

Ohio

The Ohio State University, MD
University of Cincinnati, MD

Oklahoma

Oklahoma State University, MD

Pennsylvania

University of Pittsburgh, MD

Texas

Texas A&M University, B
The University of Texas Health Science Center at Houston, MDO

Vermont

University of Vermont, BMDO

Virginia

University of Virginia, DO

Ontario

University of Guelph, B

MOLECULAR MEDICINE

Connecticut

Yale University, DO

Georgia

Medical College of Georgia, D

Maryland

The Johns Hopkins University, D

Massachusetts

Boston University, DO

New York

Cornell University, MD

North Carolina

Wake Forest University, MD

Ohio

University of Cincinnati, D

Texas

The University of Texas Health Science Center at San Antonio, MD

Washington

University of Washington, MD

MOLECULAR PATHOLOGY

California

University of California, San Diego, D

Connecticut

Yale University, DO

Massachusetts

Massachusetts Institute of Technology, D

North Dakota

North Dakota State University, D

Pennsylvania

University of Pittsburgh, MD

Texas

The University of Texas Health Science Center at Houston, MDO

MOLECULAR PHARMACOLOGY

California

Stanford University, D
University of California, Los Angeles, B

University of Southern California, MDO

Indiana

Purdue University, MDO

Massachusetts

Harvard University, D
Massachusetts Institute of Technology, D

Nevada

University of Nevada, Reno, MD

New Jersey

Rutgers, The State University of New Jersey, New
Brunswick/Piscataway, D

New York

College of Staten Island of the City University of
New York, D
State University of New York at Buffalo, BD

Pennsylvania

Thomas Jefferson University, D
University of Pittsburgh, D

Rhode Island

Brown University, MDO

South Carolina

Medical University of South Carolina, DO

MOLECULAR PHYSIOLOGY

California

University of California, Los Angeles, B

Connecticut

Yale University, D

Illinois

Loyola University Chicago, MD
University of Chicago, D

Massachusetts

Tufts University, D

New York

Stony Brook University, State University of New
York, D

North Carolina

The University of North Carolina at Chapel Hill, D

Pennsylvania

University of Pittsburgh, MD

Tennessee

Vanderbilt University, DO

Vermont

University of Vermont, MDO

Virginia

University of Virginia, MDO

MOLECULAR TOXICOLOGY

California

University of California, Berkeley, D
University of California, Los Angeles, BD

Massachusetts

Massachusetts Institute of Technology, D

North Carolina

North Carolina State University, MD

Ohio

University of Cincinnati, MD

Oregon

Oregon State University, MD

MONTESSORI TEACHER EDUCATION

Ohio

Xavier University, B

Oklahoma

Oklahoma City University, B

MORTUARY SCIENCE AND EMBALMING/EMBALMER

Michigan

Ferris State University, A

MOTORCYCLE MAINTENANCE AND REPAIR TECHNOLOGY/TECHNICIAN

Iowa

Iowa Lakes Community College, A

MOVEMENT THERAPY AND MOVEMENT EDUCATION

Texas

Texas Christian University, B

Vermont

University of Vermont, B

Ontario

Brock University, B

MULTI-/INTERDISCIPLINARY STUDIES

Alabama

Huntingdon College, B
Judson College, B
Northwest-Shoals Community College, A
Spring Hill College, B
University of South Alabama, B

Alaska

Sheldon Jackson College, B
University of Alaska Fairbanks, AB

Arizona

Arizona State University, B
Arizona State University at the Polytechnic
Campus, B
Arizona State University West, B
The University of Arizona, B

Arkansas

Arkansas Tech University, A
Mid-South Community College, A
University of Arkansas at Fort Smith, A

California

California Lutheran University, B
California State University, Chico, B
California State University, Long Beach, B
California State University, Los Angeles, B
California State University, Stanislaus, B
Saint Mary's College of California, B
San Diego Christian College, B
San Diego State University, B
San Francisco Art Institute, B
San Jose State University, B
Scripps College, B

Sonoma State University, B
Thomas Aquinas College, B
University of California, Berkeley, B
University of California, Davis, B
University of California, Irvine, B
University of California, Los Angeles, B
University of California, Santa Barbara, B

Colorado

The Colorado College, B
Naropa University, B
University of Colorado at Denver and Health
Sciences Center - Downtown Denver Campus, B
University of Denver, B
University of Northern Colorado, B

Connecticut

Central Connecticut State University, B
University of Connecticut, B
University of Hartford, B
Yale University, B

District of Columbia

Georgetown University, B

Florida

Florida Institute of Technology, B
International College, AB
Nova Southeastern University, B
University of Florida, B

Georgia

Berry College, B
Clayton State University, B
Georgia Institute of Technology, B
Georgia State University, B
Mercer University, B

Hawaii

Brigham Young University-Hawaii, B
Hawaii Pacific University, B

Idaho

Idaho State University, B
Lewis-Clark State College, B
University of Idaho, B

Illinois

Columbia College Chicago, B
Eastern Illinois University, B
Greenville College, B
Illinois Institute of Technology, B
Knox College, B
North Central College, B
Northwestern University, B
Southern Illinois University Carbondale, B
University of St. Francis, B
Wheaton College, B

Indiana

DePauw University, B
Purdue University, B
University of Evansville, B
Valparaiso University, B

Iowa

Ashford University, B
Buena Vista University, B
Cornell College, B
Hamilton College (Cedar Falls), A
Iowa State University of Science and Technology, B
Kaplan University, A
St. Ambrose University, B
Vennard College, B

Kansas

Emporia State University, B
University of Saint Mary, B

Kentucky

Georgetown College, B
Kentucky Wesleyan College, B
Mid-Continent University, B
University of Kentucky, B

Western Kentucky University, B

Louisiana

Tulane University, B

Maine

Bates College, B
Colby College, B

Maryland

Frostburg State University, B
Harford Community College, A
Hood College, B
McDaniel College, B
Mount St. Mary's University, B
St. Mary's College of Maryland, B
University of Maryland University College, B
Washington College, B

Massachusetts

Brandeis University, B
Cambridge College, B
Emmanuel College, B
Endicott College, B
Massachusetts College of Liberal Arts, B
Regis College, B
Stonehill College, B
University of Massachusetts Amherst, B

Michigan

Cornerstone University, B
Grace Bible College, B
Hope College, B
Rochester College, B
University of Michigan-Dearborn, B

Minnesota

Bethel University, B
St. Cloud State University, B
St. Olaf College, B
University of St. Thomas, B

Mississippi

Mississippi State University, B

Missouri

College of the Ozarks, B
Columbia College, B
Missouri Baptist University, B
Missouri Western State University, B
Park University, B
Southeast Missouri State University, B
Washington University in St. Louis, B

Montana

Montana State University-Billings, B
Rocky Mountain College, B

Nebraska

University of Nebraska at Omaha, B

Nevada

Nevada State College at Henderson, B

New Hampshire

Dartmouth College, B
Keene State College, B
Plymouth State University, B

New Jersey

Bloomfield College, B
Brookdale Community College, A
Caldwell College, B
College of Saint Elizabeth, B
Fairleigh Dickinson University, Metropolitan
    Campus, B
Princeton University, B
Ramapo College of New Jersey, B
Rutgers, The State University of New Jersey,
    Camden, B

Rutgers, The State University of New Jersey,
    Newark, B

New Mexico

College of Santa Fe, B
Eastern New Mexico University, B

New York

Adelphi University, B
Barnard College, B
Buffalo State College, State University of New
    York, B
The College of New Rochelle, B
Cornell University, B
Hofstra University, B
Ithaca College, B
Long Island University, Brooklyn Campus, B
Long Island University, Friends World Program, B
New York Institute of Technology, B
Queens College of the City University of New
    York, B
Sage College of Albany, B
St. John Fisher College, B
State University of New York at Buffalo, B
Stony Brook University, State University of New
    York, B
Vassar College, B

North Carolina

Brevard College, B
Davidson College, B
Meredith College, B

North Dakota

North Dakota State University, B
University of North Dakota, B
Williston State College, A

Ohio

Bluffton University, B
Bowling Green State University, B
Capital University, B
Cleveland State University, B
The College of Wooster, B
Kent State University, B
Kenyon College, B
Miami University, B
Miami University Hamilton, B
Notre Dame College, B
Ohio University, A
Ohio University-Southern Campus, B
Ohio Wesleyan University, B
Otterbein College, B
The University of Akron, A
The University of Toledo, AB
Ursuline College, B
Wright State University, B

Oklahoma

University of Oklahoma, B

Oregon

Linn-Benton Community College, A

Pennsylvania

Albright College, B
Allegheny College, B
Bloomsburg University of Pennsylvania, B
Bucknell University, B
Chestnut Hill College, B
Dickinson College, B
Franklin and Marshall College, B
Gannon University, B
Lebanon Valley College, B
Marywood University, B
Mercyhurst College, B
Pennsylvania College of Technology, A
The Pennsylvania State University at Erie, The
    Behrend College, B
Robert Morris University, B
Shippensburg University of Pennsylvania, B
Temple University, B
Ursinus College, B

Wilkes University, B

Rhode Island

Roger Williams University, B

South Carolina

Central Carolina Technical College, A
Columbia College, B
Midlands Technical College, A
North Greenville College, B
York Technical College, A

Tennessee

East Tennessee State University, B
Lambuth University, B
Lane College, B
Maryville College, B
Middle Tennessee State University, B
University of Memphis, B
The University of Tennessee, B

Texas

Abilene Christian University, B
Angelo State University, B
Austin College, B
Baylor University, B
Dallas Baptist University, B
Midwestern State University, B
Rice University, B
St. Edward's University, B
Sam Houston State University, B
Stephen F. Austin State University, B
Tarleton State University, B
Texas A&M University, B
Texas A&M University at Galveston, B
Texas A&M University-Texarkana, B
Texas Southern University, B
Texas State University-San Marcos, B
Texas Tech University, B
Texas Wesleyan University, B
University of Houston-Clear Lake, B
University of North Texas, B
The University of Texas at Arlington, B
The University of Texas at Austin, B
The University of Texas at Brownsville, B
The University of Texas-Pan American, B
The University of Texas at Tyler, B
West Texas A&M University, B

Utah

Utah State University, B

Vermont

Sterling College, AB

Virginia

The College of William and Mary, B
Eastern Mennonite University, B
Liberty University, B
Norfolk State University, B
Old Dominion University, B
University of Virginia, B
Washington and Lee University, B

Washington

The Evergreen State College, B
University of Washington, Bothell, B
University of Washington, Tacoma, B

West Virginia

Eastern West Virginia Community and Technical
    College, A
Glenville State College, B
Marshall Community and Technical College, A
Marshall University, B
West Virginia University Institute of Technology, B

Wisconsin

Marquette University, B
University of Wisconsin-Superior, B
Viterbo University, B
Waukesha County Technical College, A

Wisconsin Lutheran College, B

Wyoming

Laramie County Community College, A
University of Wyoming, B

British Columbia

University of Northern British Columbia, B

Nova Scotia

Dalhousie University, B
University of King's College, B

Ontario

Ryerson University, B
University of Waterloo, B

Quebec

Université Laval, B

MULTILINGUAL AND MULTICULTURAL EDUCATION

Alaska

University of Alaska Fairbanks, M

Arizona

Northern Arizona University, MO
Prescott College, M
The University of Arizona, MDO

California

Azusa Pacific University, M
California Baptist University, M
California State University, Bakersfield, M
California State University, Chico, M
California State University, Dominguez Hills, M
California State University, Fullerton, M
California State University, Sacramento, M
California State University, San Bernardino, M
California State University, Stanislaus, M
Fresno Pacific University, M
Loyola Marymount University, M
National University, M
San Diego State University, MD
University of California, Berkeley, MD
University of La Verne, O
University of San Francisco, MD

Colorado

University of Colorado at Boulder, MD

Connecticut

Fairfield University, MO
Southern Connecticut State University, M
University of Connecticut, MD

Delaware

University of Delaware, M

District of Columbia

Georgetown University, MO
Howard University, MD

Florida

Florida Atlantic University, M
Florida State University, BMDO

Illinois

Chicago State University, M
Columbia College Chicago, M
DePaul University, M

Northeastern Illinois University, M

Indiana

Indiana State University, O

Louisiana

McNeese State University, M

Maryland

University of Maryland, Baltimore County, MD

Massachusetts

Boston University, MO
Harvard University, D
Lesley University, M
Salem State College, M
University of Massachusetts Amherst, MDO
University of Massachusetts Boston, M

Michigan

Eastern Michigan University, M
University of Michigan, M
University of Michigan-Flint, M
Wayne State University, M

Minnesota

University of Minnesota, Twin Cities Campus, MD

Mississippi

Belhaven College, M

Missouri

Park University, M

New Jersey

Fairleigh Dickinson University, Metropolitan
  Campus, M
Kean University, MO
New Jersey City University, M
Rutgers, The State University of New Jersey, New
  Brunswick/Piscataway, MD
Seton Hall University, MO

New Mexico

College of Santa Fe, M
University of New Mexico, DO

New York

Adelphi University, M
Brooklyn College of the City University of New
  York, M
Buffalo State College, State University of New
  York, M
City College of the City University of New York, M
College of Mount Saint Vincent, MO
The College of New Rochelle, MO
The College of Saint Rose, O
Fordham University, M
Hofstra University, MO
Hunter College of the City University of New
  York, M
Iona College, M
Lehman College of the City University of New
  York, M
Long Island University, Brooklyn Campus, M
Long Island University, C.W. Post Campus, M
New York University, MDO
Queens College of the City University of New
  York, M
St. John's University, M
State University of New York at Buffalo, MO
State University of New York College at
  Brockport, M
State University of New York at New Paltz, M

Ohio

College of Mount St. Joseph, M
Ohio University, M
The University of Findlay, M

Xavier University, M

Oklahoma

Langston University, M

Oregon

Western Oregon University, M

Pennsylvania

DeSales University, O
Eastern University, M
Immaculata University, M
Mercyhurst College, M
The Pennsylvania State University University Park
  Campus, MD
University of Pennsylvania, MD

Puerto Rico

Universidad del Turabo, M

Rhode Island

Brown University, M
Rhode Island College, M

South Carolina

Columbia International University, M

Tennessee

The University of Tennessee, D

Texas

Southern Methodist University, M
Sul Ross State University, M
Texas A&M International University, M
Texas A&M University, MD
Texas A&M University-Kingsville, MD
Texas Southern University, M
Texas State University-San Marcos, M
Texas Tech University, M
University of Houston, M
University of Houston-Clear Lake, M
The University of Texas at Brownsville, M
The University of Texas-Pan American, M
The University of Texas at San Antonio, MD

Utah

Utah State University, M

Vermont

Bennington College, M

Virginia

George Mason University, M

Washington

Heritage University, M
Washington State University, M

Alberta

University of Alberta, M

MUSEOLOGY/MUSEUM STUDIES

Arizona

Northland Pioneer College, A

California

California College of the Arts, M
California State University, Chico, M
California State University, Fullerton, O
John F. Kennedy University, MO
San Francisco State University, M
University of California, Riverside, M

Colorado

Colorado State University, M
University of Colorado at Boulder, M

University of Denver, M

Connecticut

Connecticut College, B

Delaware

University of Delaware, O

District of Columbia

The George Washington University, MO

Florida

Florida State University, O
University of Florida, M

Illinois

Southern Illinois University Edwardsville, O

Iowa

The University of Iowa, B

Kansas

University of Kansas, M

Louisiana

Centenary College of Louisiana, B

Maine

College of the Atlantic, B

Massachusetts

Boston University, O
Harvard University, M
Regis College, B
Tufts University, O

Michigan

Wayne State University, O

Mississippi

University of Southern Mississippi, B

Missouri

University of Missouri-St. Louis, MO

Nebraska

University of Nebraska-Lincoln, M

New Hampshire

University of New Hampshire, M

New Jersey

Rutgers, The State University of New Jersey, New Brunswick/Piscataway, M
Seton Hall University, M

New Mexico

Institute of American Indian Arts, A

New York

Bard College, M
City College of the City University of New York, M
Fashion Institute of Technology, M
New York University, MO
State University of New York College at Oneonta, M
Syracuse University, M

North Carolina

The University of North Carolina at Greensboro, O

Ohio

Case Western Reserve University, MD

Oklahoma

Oklahoma Baptist University, B
University of Central Oklahoma, M

Pennsylvania

Duquesne University, M
Juniata College, B

The University of the Arts, M

South Carolina

University of South Carolina, MO

Tennessee

Tusculum College, B

Texas

Baylor University, BM
Texas A&M University, B
Texas Tech University, M

Virginia

Hampton University, M
Randolph-Macon Woman's College, B

Washington

Tacoma Community College, A
University of Washington, M

Wisconsin

Beloit College, B
University of Wisconsin-Milwaukee, O

Ontario

University of Toronto, M

Quebec

Université Laval, O
Université de Montréal, M
Université du Québec àMontréal, M

MUSEUM EDUCATION

District of Columbia

The George Washington University, M

New York

The College of New Rochelle, O

Pennsylvania

The University of the Arts, M

MUSIC

Alabama

Alabama Agricultural and Mechanical University, M
Alabama State University, BM
Auburn University, M
Birmingham-Southern College, B
Calhoun Community College, A
Chattahoochee Valley Community College, A
Huntingdon College, B
Jacksonville State University, BM
Jefferson Davis Community College, A
Judson College, B
Lawson State Community College, A
Oakwood College, B
Samford University, M
Southeastern Bible College, B
Stillman College, B
Talladega College, B
Troy University, M
The University of Alabama, BMD
The University of Alabama at Birmingham, B
The University of Alabama in Huntsville, B
University of Mobile, B
University of Montevallo, BM
University of North Alabama, B
University of South Alabama, B
Wallace State Community College, A

Alaska

University of Alaska Anchorage, B
University of Alaska Fairbanks, BM

Arizona

Arizona State University, BMD
Arizona Western College, A
Eastern Arizona College, A

Grand Canyon University, B
Mesa Community College, A
Mohave Community College, A
Northern Arizona University, BM
Pima Community College, A
South Mountain Community College, A
The University of Arizona, BMD

Arkansas

Arkansas State University, BMO
Arkansas Tech University, B
Central Baptist College, AB
Harding University, B
Henderson State University, B
Hendrix College, B
John Brown University, AB
Lyon College, B
Ouachita Baptist University, B
Philander Smith College, B
Phillips Community College of the University of Arkansas, A
University of Arkansas, BM
University of Arkansas at Fort Smith, B
University of Arkansas at Little Rock, B
University of Arkansas at Monticello, B
University of Arkansas at Pine Bluff, B
University of Central Arkansas, BM
University of the Ozarks, B
Williams Baptist College, AB

California

Allan Hancock College, A
American River College, A
Antelope Valley College, A
Azusa Pacific University, BM
Bakersfield College, A
Biola University, B
Butte College, A
California Baptist University, BM
California Institute of the Arts, BMO
California Lutheran University, B
California Polytechnic State University, San Luis Obispo, B
California State Polytechnic University, Pomona, B
California State University, Bakersfield, B
California State University, Chico, BM
California State University, Dominguez Hills, B
California State University, East Bay, BM
California State University, Fresno, BM
California State University, Fullerton, BM
California State University, Long Beach, BM
California State University, Los Angeles, BM
California State University, Northridge, BM
California State University, Sacramento, BM
California State University, San Bernardino, B
California State University, Stanislaus, B
Cañada College, A
Cerritos College, A
Chabot College, A
Chaffey College, A
Chapman University, B
Citrus College, A
City College of San Francisco, A
Claremont McKenna College, B
College of the Desert, A
College of Marin, A
College of San Mateo, A
College of the Sequoias, A
Columbia College, A
Compton Community College, A
Concordia University, B
Contra Costa College, A
Cosumnes River College (Sacramento), A
Crafton Hills College, A
Cypress College, A
De Anza College, A
Dominican University of California, B
East Los Angeles College, A
El Camino College, A
Foothill College, A
Fresno Pacific University, AB
Fullerton College, A
Gavilan College, A
Glendale Community College, A
Golden West College, A
Grossmont College, A

Holy Names University, BMO
Humboldt State University, B
Imperial Valley College, A
La Sierra University, B
Lake Tahoe Community College, A
Laney College, A
Long Beach City College, A
Los Angeles City College, A
Los Angeles Mission College, A
Los Angeles Pierce College, A
Los Angeles Southwest College, A
Los Angeles Valley College, A
Los Medanos College, A
Loyola Marymount University, B
The Master's College and Seminary, B
Mendocino College, A
Merced College, A
Mills College, BM
MiraCosta College, A
Modesto Junior College, A
Monterey Peninsula College, A
Moorpark College, A
Mount St. Mary's College, B
Mt. San Jacinto College, A
Musicians Institute, AB
Napa Valley College, A
Notre Dame de Namur University, BM
Occidental College, B
Orange Coast College, A
Pacific Union College, B
Palomar College, A
Pasadena City College, A
Pepperdine University, B
Pitzer College, B
Point Loma Nazarene University, B
Pomona College, B
Porterville College, A
Sacramento City College, A
Saddleback College, A
Saint Mary's College of California, B
San Bernardino Valley College, A
San Diego Christian College, B
San Diego City College, A
San Diego Mesa College, A
San Diego State University, BM
San Francisco Conservatory of Music, BM
San Francisco State University, BM
San Joaquin Delta College, A
San Jose State University, BM
Santa Ana College, A
Santa Barbara City College, A
Santa Clara University, B
Santa Monica College, A
Santa Rosa Junior College, A
Santiago Canyon College, A
Scripps College, B
Shasta College, A
Simpson University, B
Skyline College, A
Solano Community College, A
Sonoma State University, B
Southwestern College, A
Stanford University, BMD
University of California, Berkeley, BMD
University of California, Davis, BMD
University of California, Irvine, BM
University of California, Los Angeles, BMD
University of California, Riverside, BM
University of California, San Diego, BMD
University of California, Santa Barbara, BMD
University of California, Santa Cruz, BM
University of La Verne, B
University of the Pacific, BM
University of Redlands, BM
University of San Diego, B
University of Southern California, BMD
Vanguard University of Southern California, B
Ventura College, A
Victor Valley College, A
West Los Angeles College, A
West Valley College, A
Westmont College, B
Whittier College, B

Yuba College, A

Colorado

Adams State College, B
Colorado Christian University, B
The Colorado College, B
Colorado Northwestern Community College, A
Colorado State University, BM
Colorado State University-Pueblo, B
Fort Lewis College, B
Mesa State College, AB
Northeastern Junior College, A
Trinidad State Junior College, A
University of Colorado at Boulder, BMD
University of Colorado at Denver and Health
   Sciences Center - Downtown Denver
   Campus, BMD
University of Denver, BM
University of Northern Colorado, BMD
Western State College of Colorado, B

Connecticut

Central Connecticut State University, B
Connecticut College, BM
Manchester Community College, A
Naugatuck Valley Community College, A
Sacred Heart University, A
Southern Connecticut State University, B
Trinity College, B
University of Bridgeport, B
University of Connecticut, BMD
University of Hartford, BMDO
University of New Haven, B
Wesleyan University, BMD
Western Connecticut State University, B
Yale University, BMDO

Delaware

Delaware State University, B
University of Delaware, BM

District of Columbia

American University, B
The Catholic University of America, BMD
The George Washington University, B
Howard University, BMD
University of the District of Columbia, AB

Florida

Clearwater Christian College, B
Daytona Beach Community College, A
Eckerd College, B
Edison College, A
Florida Agricultural and Mechanical University, B
Florida Atlantic University, BM
Florida International University, BM
Florida Southern College, B
Florida State University, BMD
Gulf Coast Community College, A
Hillsborough Community College, A
Indian River Community College, A
Jacksonville University, B
Lynn University, B
Manatee Community College, A
Miami Dade College, A
New College of Florida, B
Okaloosa-Walton College, A
Palm Beach Atlantic University, B
Palm Beach Community College, A
Pensacola Junior College, A
Rollins College, B
Stetson University, B
University of Florida, BMD
University of Miami, BM
University of North Florida, B
University of South Florida, M
The University of Tampa, AB

Georgia

Abraham Baldwin Agricultural College, A
Agnes Scott College, B
Albany State University, B
Andrew College, A
Armstrong Atlantic State University, B
Atlanta Christian College, B

Atlanta Metropolitan College, A
Augusta State University, B
Berry College, B
Brenau University, B
Brewton-Parker College, B
Clark Atlanta University, B
Clayton State University, AB
Columbus State University, B
Covenant College, B
Darton College, A
Emmanuel College, B
Emory University, BM
Gainesville College, A
Georgia College & State University, B
Georgia Perimeter College, A
Georgia Southern University, BM
Georgia Southwestern State University, B
Georgia State University, M
Kennesaw State University, B
LaGrange College, B
Macon State College, A
Mercer University, B
Morehouse College, B
North Georgia College & State University, B
Piedmont College, B
Reinhardt College, B
Savannah College of Art and Design, M
Savannah State University, B
Shorter College, B
Spelman College, B
Toccoa Falls College, B
Truett-McConnell College, AB
University of Georgia, BMD
Valdosta State University, B
Wesleyan College, B
Young Harris College, A

Hawaii

Brigham Young University-Hawaii, AB
University of Hawaii at Hilo, B
University of Hawaii at Manoa, BMD

Idaho

Albertson College of Idaho, B
Boise State University, BM
Brigham Young University -Idaho, A
College of Southern Idaho, A
Idaho State University, B
North Idaho College, A
Northwest Nazarene University, B
University of Idaho, M

Illinois

Augustana College, B
Benedictine University, B
Blackburn College, B
Bradley University, B
Chicago State University, B
City Colleges of Chicago, Harold Washington
   College, A
City Colleges of Chicago, Malcolm X College, A
City Colleges of Chicago, Olive-Harvey College, A
City Colleges of Chicago, Richard J. Daley
   College, A
City Colleges of Chicago, Wilbur Wright College, A
College of Lake County, A
Columbia College Chicago, B
Concordia University, BM
DePaul University, BM
Eastern Illinois University, BM
Elmhurst College, B
Eureka College, B
Greenville College, B
Illinois College, B
Illinois Eastern Community Colleges, Lincoln Trail
   College, A
Illinois Eastern Community Colleges, Olney Central
   College, A
Illinois State University, BM
Illinois Wesleyan University, B
Judson College, B
Knox College, B
Lake Forest College, B
Lewis and Clark Community College, A
Lewis University, B
Lincoln College, A

Lincoln Land Community College, A
Loyola University Chicago, B
MacMurray College, B
McHenry County College, A
McKendree College, B
Millikin University, B
Monmouth College, B
Morton College, A
North Central College, B
North Park University, B
Northeastern Illinois University, BM
Northern Illinois University, BMO
Northwestern University, BMD
Oakton Community College, A
Olivet Nazarene University, B
Principia College, B
Quincy University, B
Rockford College, B
Roosevelt University, BMO
Saint Xavier University, B
Sauk Valley Community College, A
School of the Art Institute of Chicago, B
Southern Illinois University Carbondale, BM
Southern Illinois University Edwardsville, BM
Trinity Christian College, B
Trinity International University, B
Triton College, A
University of Chicago, BMD
University of Illinois at Chicago, B
University of Illinois at Urbana-Champaign, BMD
University of St. Francis, B
Waubonsee Community College, A
Western Illinois University, BM
Wheaton College, B
William Rainey Harper College, A

Indiana

Ball State University, B
Bethel College, AB
Butler University, BM
DePauw University, B
Earlham College, B
Goshen College, B
Hanover College, B
Huntington University, B
Indiana State University, BM
Indiana University Bloomington, BMD
Indiana University-Purdue University Fort Wayne, B
Indiana University-Purdue University Indianapolis, M
Indiana University South Bend, M
Indiana University Southeast, B
Indiana Wesleyan University, AB
Manchester College, B
Marian College, AB
Martin University, B
Oakland City University, B
Saint Mary-of-the-Woods College, B
Saint Mary's College, B
Taylor University, B
University of Evansville, B
University of Indianapolis, B
University of Notre Dame, BM
Valparaiso University, B
Vincennes University, A
Wabash College, B

Iowa

Ashford University, B
Briar Cliff University, B
Central College, B
Clarke College, B
Coe College, B
Cornell College, B
Dordt College, B
Drake University, B
Graceland University, B
Grand View College, B
Grinnell College, B
Iowa Lakes Community College, A
Iowa State University of Science and Technology, B
Iowa Wesleyan College, B
Kirkwood Community College, A
Loras College, B
Luther College, B
Morningside College, B
Mount Mercy College, B

Northwestern College, B
St. Ambrose University, B
Simpson College, B
Southwestern Community College, A
The University of Iowa, BMD
University of Northern Iowa, BM
Wartburg College, B

Kansas

Allen County Community College, A
Baker University, B
Barton County Community College, A
Benedictine College, B
Bethany College, B
Bethel College, B
Butler Community College, A
Central Christian College of Kansas, B
Cloud County Community College, A
Coffeyville Community College, A
Colby Community College, A
Cowley County Community College and Area
  Vocational-Technical School, A
Dodge City Community College, A
Emporia State University, BM
Fort Hays State University, B
Fort Scott Community College, A
Friends University, B
Garden City Community College, A
Highland Community College, A
Independence Community College, A
Kansas State University, BM
Labette Community College, A
McPherson College, B
Ottawa University, B
Pittsburg State University, BM
Pratt Community College, A
Seward County Community College, A
Southwestern College, B
Sterling College, B
Tabor College, B
University of Kansas, BMD
Washburn University, B
Wichita State University, BM

Kentucky

Asbury College, B
Bellarmine University, B
Berea College, B
Campbellsville University, BM
Centre College, B
Eastern Kentucky University, BM
Georgetown College, B
Kentucky Christian University, B
Morehead State University, B
Murray State University, BM
Northern Kentucky University, B
St. Catharine College, A
Thomas More College, A
Transylvania University, B
University of the Cumberlands, B
University of Kentucky, MD
University of Louisville, B
Western Kentucky University, B

Louisiana

Centenary College of Louisiana, B
Delgado Community College, A
Dillard University, B
Louisiana College, B
Louisiana State University and Agricultural and
  Mechanical College, BMD
Louisiana Tech University, B
Loyola University New Orleans, BM
McNeese State University, B
Nicholls State University, B
Northwestern State University of Louisiana, M
Southeastern Louisiana University, M
Tulane University, BM
University of Louisiana at Lafayette, BM
University of Louisiana at Monroe, M
University of New Orleans, BM
Xavier University of Louisiana, B

Maine

Bates College, B
Bowdoin College, B

Colby College, B
College of the Atlantic, B
University of Maine, BM
The University of Maine at Augusta, AB
University of Maine at Farmington, B
University of Maine at Machias, B
University of Southern Maine, B

Maryland

Anne Arundel Community College, A
Carroll Community College, A
Chesapeake College, A
College of Notre Dame of Maryland, B
College of Southern Maryland, A
Columbia Union College, B
Frostburg State University, B
Garrett College, A
Goucher College, B
Hood College, B
Howard Community College, A
The Johns Hopkins University, BMDO
McDaniel College, B
Morgan State University, BM
Peabody Conservatory of Music of The Johns
  Hopkins University, BMDO
St. Mary's College of Maryland, B
Salisbury University, B
Towson University, B
University of Maryland, Baltimore County, BO
University of Maryland, College Park, BMD
Washington Bible College, B
Washington College, B

Massachusetts

Amherst College, B
Anna Maria College, B
Atlantic Union College, B
Berklee College of Music, B
Berkshire Community College, A
Boston College, B
The Boston Conservatory, BMO
Boston University, MDO
Brandeis University, BMD
Bridgewater State College, B
Cape Cod Community College, A
Clark University, B
College of the Holy Cross, B
Eastern Nazarene College, B
Gordon College, B
Hampshire College, B
Harvard University, BMD
Hebrew College, BO
Holyoke Community College, A
Massachusetts College of Liberal Arts, B
Massachusetts Institute of Technology, B
Mount Holyoke College, B
New England Conservatory of Music, MDO
Northeastern University, B
Northern Essex Community College, A
Quincy College, A
Roxbury Community College, A
Simmons College, B
Simon's Rock College of Bard, B
Smith College, BM
Tufts University, BM
University of Massachusetts Amherst, BMD
University of Massachusetts Boston, B
University of Massachusetts Dartmouth, B
University of Massachusetts Lowell, BM
Wellesley College, B
Westfield State College, B
Wheaton College, B
Williams College, B
Worcester Polytechnic Institute, B

Michigan

Adrian College, B
Albion College, B
Alma College, B
Andrews University, BM
Aquinas College, B
Calvin College, B
Central Michigan University, BM
Concordia University, B
Cornerstone University, B
Eastern Michigan University, BM

Grace Bible College, B
Grand Rapids Community College, A
Grand Valley State University, B
Great Lakes Christian College, B
Hillsdale College, B
Hope College, B
Kalamazoo College, B
Kellogg Community College, A
Lansing Community College, A
Madonna University, B
Marygrove College, B
Michigan State University, BMD
Northern Michigan University, B
Northwestern Michigan College, A
Oakland University, BM
Rochester College, B
Saginaw Valley State University, B
Siena Heights University, B
Spring Arbor University, B
University of Michigan, BMDO
University of Michigan-Flint, B
Wayne State University, BMO
Western Michigan University, BM

Minnesota

Anoka-Ramsey Community College, A
Anoka-Ramsey Community College, Cambridge
    Campus, A
Augsburg College, B
Bemidji State University, B
Bethany Lutheran College, B
Bethel University, BMO
Carleton College, B
College of Saint Benedict, B
College of St. Catherine, B
Concordia College, B
Concordia University, St. Paul, B
Crown College, AB
Globe College, A
Gustavus Adolphus College, B
Hamline University, B
Macalester College, B
McNally Smith College of Music, A
Minnesota School of Business, A
Minnesota School of Business-Brooklyn Center, A
Minnesota School of Business-Plymouth, A
Minnesota School of Business-Richfield, A
Minnesota School of Business-St. Cloud, A
Minnesota School of Business-Shakopee, A
Minnesota State University Mankato, BM
Minnesota State University Moorhead, BM
North Central University, AB
Northwestern College, B
Pillsbury Baptist Bible College, B
Ridgewater College, A
St. Cloud State University, BM
Saint John's University, B
Saint Mary's University of Minnesota, B
St. Olaf College, B
Southwest Minnesota State University, B
University of Minnesota, Duluth, BM
University of Minnesota, Morris, B
University of Minnesota, Twin Cities Campus, BMD
University of St. Thomas, B
Vermilion Community College, A
Winona State University, B

Mississippi

Belhaven College, B
Blue Mountain College, B
Delta State University, B
East Central Community College, A
East Mississippi Community College, A
Hinds Community College, A
Itawamba Community College, A
Jones County Junior College, A
Millsaps College, B
Mississippi College, BM
Mississippi Delta Community College, A
Mississippi Valley State University, B
Northeast Mississippi Community College, A
Rust College, B
Southwest Mississippi Community College, A
Tougaloo College, B
University of Mississippi, BMD
University of Southern Mississippi, BMD

William Carey College, B

Missouri

Baptist Bible College, B
Calvary Bible College and Theological Seminary, B
Central Methodist University, B
Central Missouri State University, BM
College of the Ozarks, B
Crowder College, A
Culver-Stockton College, B
Drury University, B
Evangel University, B
Hannibal-LaGrange College, B
Jefferson College, A
Lindenwood University, B
Messenger College, B
Missouri Southern State University, B
Missouri State University, BM
Missouri Valley College, B
Missouri Western State University, B
Northwest Missouri State University, B
Park University, B
St. Louis Community College at Florissant Valley, A
St. Louis Community College at Forest Park, A
St. Louis Community College at Meramec, A
Saint Louis University, B
Southeast Missouri State University, B
Southwest Baptist University, B
Three Rivers Community College, A
Truman State University, BM
University of Missouri-Columbia, BM
University of Missouri-Kansas City, BMD
University of Missouri-St. Louis, B
Washington University in St. Louis, BMD
Webster University, BM
William Jewell College, B

Montana

Montana State University, B
Montana State University-Billings, B
The University of Montana-Missoula, BM

Nebraska

Chadron State College, B
Concordia University, B
Creighton University, B
Dana College, B
Doane College, B
Grace University, AB
Hastings College, B
Midland Lutheran College, B
Nebraska Wesleyan University, B
Northeast Community College, A
Peru State College, B
Union College, B
University of Nebraska at Kearney, B
University of Nebraska-Lincoln, BMD
University of Nebraska at Omaha, BM
Wayne State College, B
York College, B

Nevada

Community College of Southern Nevada, A
Sierra Nevada College, B
University of Nevada, Las Vegas, BMD
University of Nevada, Reno, BM

New Hampshire

Dartmouth College, BM
Franklin Pierce College, B
Keene State College, B
Plymouth State University, B
University of New Hampshire, BM

New Jersey

Bergen Community College, A
Brookdale Community College, A
Burlington County College, A
Caldwell College, B
The College of New Jersey, B
College of Saint Elizabeth, B
Drew University, B
Essex County College, A
Georgian Court University, B
Kean University, B

Mercer County Community College, A
Middlesex County College, A
Monmouth University, B
Montclair State University, BM
New Jersey City University, BM
Princeton University, BD
Ramapo College of New Jersey, B
Raritan Valley Community College, A
Rider University, BM
Rowan University, M
Rutgers, The State University of New Jersey,
    Camden, B
Rutgers, The State University of New Jersey, New
    Brunswick/Piscataway, BMDO
Rutgers, The State University of New Jersey,
    Newark, B
Seton Hall University, BM
Westminster Choir College of Rider University, B
William Paterson University of New Jersey, BM

New Mexico

College of Santa Fe, B
Eastern New Mexico University, B
New Mexico Highlands University, B
New Mexico Junior College, A
New Mexico State University, M
San Juan College, A
University of New Mexico, M
Western New Mexico University, B

New York

Adelphi University, B
Adirondack Community College, A
Bard College, B
Barnard College, B
Bernard M. Baruch College of the City University of
    New York, B
Bronx Community College of the City University of
    New York, A
Brooklyn College of the City University of New
    York, BMD
Buffalo State College, State University of New
    York, B
City College of the City University of New York, BM
Colgate University, B
The College of Saint Rose, BM
College of Staten Island of the City University of
    New York, B
Columbia College, B
Columbia University, School of General Studies, B
Concordia College, B
Cornell University, BMD
Dowling College, B
Elmira College, B
Excelsior College, B
Finger Lakes Community College, A
Five Towns College, ABMD
Fordham University, B
Hamilton College, B
Hartwick College, B
Hobart and William Smith Colleges, B
Hofstra University, B
Houghton College, B
Hunter College of the City University of New
    York, BM
Ithaca College, BM
The Jewish Theological Seminary, B
The Juilliard School, BMDO
Kingsborough Community College of the City
    University of New York, A
Lehman College of the City University of New
    York, B
Long Island University, Brooklyn Campus, B
Long Island University, C.W. Post Campus, BM
Manhattan School of Music, BMDO
Manhattanville College, B
Mannes College The New School for Music, BMO
Mercy College, B
Molloy College, B
Monroe Community College, A
Nazareth College of Rochester, B
New York University, BMDO
Niagara County Community College, A
Onondaga Community College, A
Purchase College, State University of New York, BM

Queens College of the City University of New
York, M
Roberts Wesleyan College, B
St. Lawrence University, B
Sarah Lawrence College, B
Schenectady County Community College, A
State University of New York at Binghamton, BM
State University of New York at Buffalo, BMD
State University of New York College at Geneseo, B
State University of New York College at Oneonta, B
State University of New York College at Potsdam, M
State University of New York, Fredonia, BM
State University of New York at New Paltz, B
State University of New York at Oswego, B
State University of New York at Plattsburgh, B
Stony Brook University, State University of New
York, BMD
Suffolk County Community College, A
Syracuse University, BM
University at Albany, State University of New York, B
University of Rochester, BMD
Vassar College, B
Villa Maria College of Buffalo, A
Wagner College, B
Wells College, B
Yeshiva University, B
York College of the City University of New York, B

North Carolina

Appalachian State University, M
Bennett College For Women, B
Brevard College, B
Caldwell Community College and Technical
Institute, A
Campbell University, B
Catawba College, B
Central Piedmont Community College, A
Chowan University, AB
College of The Albemarle, A
Davidson College, B
Duke University, BMD
East Carolina University, M
Elizabeth City State University, B
Elon University, B
Greensboro College, B
Guilford College, B
Isothermal Community College, A
Johnson C. Smith University, B
Lenoir-Rhyne College, B
Livingstone College, B
Mars Hill College, B
Meredith College, BM
Methodist College, AB
Mount Olive College, A
North Carolina Central University, B
North Carolina School of the Arts, M
Peace College, A
Pfeiffer University, B
Piedmont Baptist College, B
Queens University of Charlotte, B
Salem College, B
Sandhills Community College, A
Shaw University, B
Southeastern Community College, A
The University of North Carolina at Asheville, B
The University of North Carolina at Chapel
Hill, BMD
The University of North Carolina at Charlotte, B
The University of North Carolina at
Greensboro, BMD
The University of North Carolina at Pembroke, B
The University of North Carolina Wilmington, B
Wake Forest University, B
Western Carolina University, BM
Wingate University, B
Winston-Salem State University, B

North Dakota

Dickinson State University, B
Jamestown College, B
Minot State University, B
North Dakota State University, BMD
Trinity Bible College, A
University of North Dakota, BM

Valley City State University, B

Ohio

Antioch College, B
Ashland University, B
Bluffton University, B
Bowling Green State University, BM
Capital University, BM
Case Western Reserve University, BMD
Cedarville University, B
Central State University, B
Cleveland Institute of Music, B
Cleveland State University, BM
College of Mount St. Joseph, B
The College of Wooster, B
Denison University, B
Heidelberg College, B
Hiram College, B
Kent State University, BMD
Kenyon College, B
Lake Erie College, B
Lorain County Community College, A
Lourdes College, A
Malone College, B
Marietta College, B
Miami University, B
Miami University Hamilton, B
Mount Union College, B
Mount Vernon Nazarene University, AB
Muskingum College, B
Oberlin College, BM
Ohio Northern University, B
The Ohio State University, BMD
Ohio University, BMO
Ohio Wesleyan University, B
Otterbein College, B
Shawnee State University, A
Sinclair Community College, A
The University of Akron, BM
University of Cincinnati, BMDO
University of Dayton, B
University of Rio Grande, AB
The University of Toledo, BM
Wittenberg University, B
Wright State University, B
Xavier University, B
Youngstown State University, BM

Oklahoma

Cameron University, B
Carl Albert State College, A
East Central University, B
Eastern Oklahoma State College, A
Hillsdale Free Will Baptist College, A
Langston University, B
Mid-America Christian University, B
Northeastern Oklahoma Agricultural and Mechanical
College, A
Northeastern State University, B
Northwestern Oklahoma State University, B
Oklahoma Baptist University, B
Oklahoma Christian University, B
Oklahoma City Community College, A
Oklahoma City University, BM
Oklahoma State University, BM
Oklahoma Wesleyan University, B
Oral Roberts University, B
Rose State College, A
Southeastern Oklahoma State University, B
Southwestern Oklahoma State University, BM
Tulsa Community College, A
University of Central Oklahoma, BM
University of Oklahoma, BMD
University of Science and Arts of Oklahoma, B
University of Tulsa, B

Oregon

Corban College, B
Eastern Oregon University, B
George Fox University, B
Lewis & Clark College, B
Linfield College, B
Marylhurst University, B
Oregon State University, B
Pacific University, B
Portland State University, BM

Reed College, B
Southern Oregon University, BM
Treasure Valley Community College, A
Umpqua Community College, A
University of Oregon, BMD
University of Portland, BM
Warner Pacific College, B
Western Oregon University, B
Willamette University, B

Pennsylvania

Albright College, B
Allegheny College, B
Baptist Bible College of Pennsylvania, B
Bloomsburg University of Pennsylvania, B
Bryn Mawr College, B
Bucknell University, B
Bucks County Community College, A
Carnegie Mellon University, M
Cedar Crest College, B
Chatham College, B
Chestnut Hill College, B
Cheyney University of Pennsylvania, B
Community College of Allegheny County, A
Community College of Philadelphia, A
The Curtis Institute of Music, BM
Dickinson College, B
Drexel University, B
Duquesne University, BMO
Eastern University, B
Edinboro University of Pennsylvania, B
Elizabethtown College, B
Franklin and Marshall College, B
Geneva College, B
Gettysburg College, B
Gratz College, MO
Grove City College, B
Harrisburg Area Community College, A
Haverford College, B
Immaculata University, B
Indiana University of Pennsylvania, BM
Kutztown University of Pennsylvania, B
Lafayette College, B
Lebanon Valley College, B
Lehigh University, B
Lincoln University, B
Lock Haven University of Pennsylvania, B
Lycoming College, B
Mansfield University of Pennsylvania, BM
Marywood University, B
Mercyhurst College, B
Messiah College, B
Millersville University of Pennsylvania, B
Moravian College, B
Muhlenberg College, B
The Pennsylvania State University Altoona
College, B
The Pennsylvania State University Beaver Campus
of the Commonwealth College, B
The Pennsylvania State University Berks Campus of
the Berks-Lehigh Valley College, B
The Pennsylvania State University Delaware County
Campus of the Commonwealth College, B
The Pennsylvania State University DuBois Campus
of the Commonwealth College, B
The Pennsylvania State University at Erie, The
Behrend College, B
The Pennsylvania State University Hazleton
Campus of the Commonwealth College, B
The Pennsylvania State University McKeesport
Campus of the Commonwealth College, B
The Pennsylvania State University Mont Alto
Campus of the Commonwealth College, B
The Pennsylvania State University New Kensington
Campus of the Commonwealth College, B
The Pennsylvania State University Shenango
Campus of the Commonwealth College, B
The Pennsylvania State University University Park
Campus, BM
The Pennsylvania State University Wilkes-Barre
Campus of the Commonwealth College, B
The Pennsylvania State University Worthington
Scranton Campus of the Commonwealth
College, B
The Pennsylvania State University York Campus of
the Commonwealth College, B

Philadelphia Biblical University, B
Saint Vincent College, B
Seton Hill University, B
Slippery Rock University of Pennsylvania, B
Susquehanna University, B
Swarthmore College, B
Temple University, BMD
The University of the Arts, M
University of Pennsylvania, BMD
University of Pittsburgh, BMD
Washington & Jefferson College, B
West Chester University of Pennsylvania, BM
Westminster College, B
York College of Pennsylvania, AB

Puerto Rico

Conservatory of Music of Puerto Rico, B
Inter American University of Puerto Rico, Fajardo
  Campus, B
Inter American University of Puerto Rico,
  Metropolitan Campus, B
Inter American University of Puerto Rico, San
  Germán Campus, B
Pontifical Catholic University of Puerto Rico, B
Universidad Adventista de las Antillas, B
University of Puerto Rico, Río Piedras, B

Rhode Island

Brown University, BMD
Community College of Rhode Island, A
Providence College, B
Rhode Island College, B
Salve Regina University, B
University of Rhode Island, BM

South Carolina

Allen University, B
Anderson University, B
Benedict College, B
Bob Jones University, B
Charleston Southern University, B
Claflin University, B
Coastal Carolina University, B
Coker College, B
College of Charleston, B
Columbia College, B
Converse College, BM
Erskine College, B
Furman University, B
Lander University, B
Limestone College, B
Newberry College, B
North Greenville College, B
Presbyterian College, B
Southern Wesleyan University, B
University of South Carolina, BMDO
Winthrop University, BM

South Dakota

Augustana College, B
Black Hills State University, B
Dakota Wesleyan University, B
Mount Marty College, B
Northern State University, B
South Dakota State University, B
University of Sioux Falls, B
The University of South Dakota, BM

Tennessee

Austin Peay State University, BM
Belmont University, BM
Bryan College, B
Carson-Newman College, B
Columbia State Community College, A
Cumberland University, B
East Tennessee State University, B
Fisk University, B
Freed-Hardeman University, B
King College, B
Lambuth University, B
Lane College, B
Lee University, B
Lipscomb University, B
Martin Methodist College, A
Middle Tennessee State University, BM

Milligan College, B
Rhodes College, B
Sewanee: The University of the South, B
Southern Adventist University, B
Tennessee State University, B
Tennessee Technological University, B
Tennessee Wesleyan College, B
Trevecca Nazarene University, B
Union University, B
University of Memphis, BMD
The University of Tennessee, BM
The University of Tennessee at Chattanooga, BM
The University of Tennessee at Martin, B
Vanderbilt University, B

Texas

Abilene Christian University, B
Alvin Community College, A
Amarillo College, A
Angelina College, A
Angelo State University, B
Arlington Baptist College, B
Austin College, B
Austin Community College, A
Baylor University, BMO
Blinn College, A
Brazosport College, A
Cedar Valley College, A
Central Texas College, A
Clarendon College, A
Coastal Bend College, A
College of the Mainland, A
Dallas Baptist University, AB
Del Mar College, A
East Texas Baptist University, B
El Paso Community College, A
Frank Phillips College, A
Galveston College, A
Grayson County College, A
Hardin-Simmons University, BM
Hill College of the Hill Junior College District, A
Houston Baptist University, B
Howard Payne University, B
Huston-Tillotson University, B
Jarvis Christian College, B
KD Studio, A
Kilgore College, A
Lamar University, B
Lee College, A
Lon Morris College, A
Lubbock Christian University, B
McLennan Community College, A
Midland College, A
Midwestern State University, B
Navarro College, A
North Harris College, A
Odessa College, A
Palo Alto College, A
Prairie View A&M University, B
Rice University, BMD
St. Mary's University of San Antonio, B
St. Philip's College, A
Sam Houston State University, BM
Schreiner University, B
South Plains College, A
Southern Methodist University, BMO
Southwestern Adventist University, B
Southwestern Assemblies of God University, AB
Southwestern University, B
Stephen F. Austin State University, BM
Sul Ross State University, B
Tarleton State University, B
Texarkana College, A
Texas A&M University, B
Texas A&M University-Commerce, BM
Texas A&M University-Corpus Christi, B
Texas A&M University-Kingsville, B
Texas Christian University, BMO
Texas College, B
Texas Lutheran University, B
Texas Southern University, BM
Texas Southmost College, A
Texas State University-San Marcos, B
Texas Tech University, BMD
Texas Wesleyan University, B
Texas Woman's University, BM

Trinity University, B
Trinity Valley Community College, A
Tyler Junior College, A
University of Houston, BMD
University of the Incarnate Word, B
University of North Texas, BMD
University of St. Thomas, B
The University of Texas at Arlington, BM
The University of Texas at Austin, BMD
The University of Texas at Brownsville, B
The University of Texas at El Paso, BM
The University of Texas-Pan American, BM
The University of Texas at San Antonio, BM
The University of Texas at Tyler, BM
Wayland Baptist University, B
West Texas A&M University, BM
Wharton County Junior College, A
Wiley College, B

Utah

Brigham Young University, BM
Dixie State College of Utah, A
Salt Lake Community College, A
Snow College, A
Southern Utah University, B
University of Utah, BMD
Utah State University, B
Utah Valley State College, A
Weber State University, B

Vermont

Bennington College, BM
Castleton State College, B
Johnson State College, B
Marlboro College, B
Middlebury College, B
Saint Michael's College, B
University of Vermont, B

Virginia

Averett University, B
Bluefield College, B
Christopher Newport University, B
The College of William and Mary, B
Eastern Mennonite University, B
Emory & Henry College, B
George Mason University, M
Hampton University, B
Hollins University, B
J. Sargeant Reynolds Community College, A
James Madison University, M
Liberty University, B
Longwood University, B
Lynchburg College, B
Mary Baldwin College, B
Norfolk State University, BM
Northern Virginia Community College, A
Old Dominion University, B
Radford University, BM
Randolph-Macon College, B
Roanoke College, B
Shenandoah University, BMDO
Southern Virginia University, B
Southwest Virginia Community College, A
Sweet Briar College, B
Tidewater Community College, A
University of Mary Washington, B
University of Richmond, B
University of Virginia, BMD
Virginia Commonwealth University, M
Virginia Polytechnic Institute and State University, B
Virginia State University, B
Virginia Union University, B
Virginia Wesleyan College, B
Washington and Lee University, B

Washington

Central Washington University, BM
Centralia College, A
Cornish College of the Arts, B
Eastern Washington University, BM
Everett Community College, A
Gonzaga University, B
Highline Community College, A
Lower Columbia College, A
North Seattle Community College, A

Northwest University, B
Puget Sound Christian College, B
Seattle Pacific University, B
Shoreline Community College, A
Skagit Valley College, A
Spokane Falls Community College, A
Tacoma Community College, A
University of Puget Sound, B
University of Washington, BMD
Walla Walla College, B
Washington State University, BM
Wenatchee Valley College, A
Western Washington University, BM
Whitman College, B
Whitworth College, B

West Virginia

Alderson-Broaddus College, B
Bethany College, B
Davis & Elkins College, B
Marshall University, M
Potomac State College of West Virginia
    University, A
Shepherd University, B
West Virginia University, BMD
West Virginia Wesleyan College, B

Wisconsin

Alverno College, AB
Beloit College, B
Cardinal Stritch University, B
Carroll College, B
Carthage College, B
Concordia University Wisconsin, B
Edgewood College, B
Lakeland College, B
Lawrence University, B
Maranatha Baptist Bible College, B
Marian College of Fond du Lac, B
Milwaukee Area Technical College, A
Mount Mary College, B
Northland College, B
Ripon College, B
St. Norbert College, B
Silver Lake College, B
University of Wisconsin-Eau Claire, B
University of Wisconsin-Green Bay, B
University of Wisconsin-La Crosse, B
University of Wisconsin-Madison, BMD
University of Wisconsin-Milwaukee, BMO
University of Wisconsin-Oshkosh, B
University of Wisconsin-Parkside, B
University of Wisconsin-Platteville, B
University of Wisconsin-River Falls, B
University of Wisconsin-Stevens Point, B
University of Wisconsin-Superior, B
University of Wisconsin-Whitewater, B
Viterbo University, B
Wisconsin Lutheran College, B

Wyoming

Casper College, A
Central Wyoming College, A
Eastern Wyoming College, A
Laramie County Community College, A
Northwest College, A
Sheridan College-Sheridan and Gillette, A
University of Wyoming, BM
Western Wyoming Community College, A

Alberta

Concordia University College of Alberta, B
The King's University College, B
Prairie Bible Institute, B
Rocky Mountain College, B
Taylor University College and Seminary, B
University of Alberta, BMD
University of Calgary, BMD
University of Lethbridge, BM

British Columbia

Kwantlen University College, A
Simon Fraser University, B
Trinity Western University, B
The University of British Columbia, BMD

University of Victoria, BMD

Manitoba

Brandon University, BM
Canadian Mennonite University, B
Providence College and Theological Seminary, B
Steinbach Bible College, B
University of Manitoba, BM
The University of Winnipeg, B

New Brunswick

Bethany Bible College, B
Mount Allison University, B
Université de Moncton, B

Newfoundland and Labrador

Memorial University of Newfoundland, BO

Nova Scotia

Acadia University, B
Dalhousie University, B
St. Francis Xavier University, B
University of King's College, B

Ontario

Brock University, B
Carleton University, B
Lakehead University, B
Laurentian University, B
McMaster University, BM
Queen's University at Kingston, B
Redeemer University College, B
University of Guelph, B
University of Ottawa, BMO
University of Toronto, BMD
University of Waterloo, B
The University of Western Ontario, BMD
University of Windsor, B
Wilfrid Laurier University, B
York University, B

Prince Edward Island

University of Prince Edward Island, B

Quebec

Bishop's University, B
Concordia University, BO
McGill University, BMD
Université Laval, BMD
Université de Montréal, BMDO
Université du Québec àMontréal, B
Université de Sherbrooke, B

Saskatchewan

University of Regina, BMD
University of Saskatchewan, BM

MUSIC HISTORY, LITERATURE, AND THEORY

Alabama

Birmingham-Southern College, B

Alaska

University of Alaska Fairbanks, M

Arizona

Northern Arizona University, M

Arkansas

Ouachita Baptist University, B

California

California State University, Fresno, B
California State University, Fullerton, BM
California State University, Long Beach, B
Loyola Marymount University, B
San Francisco State University, M
Stanford University, M
University of California, Los Angeles, B
University of California, San Diego, B
University of the Pacific, B

University of Redlands, B
University of Southern California, M

Colorado

University of Denver, M

Connecticut

Fairfield University, B
University of Connecticut, D
University of Hartford, BM
Western Connecticut State University, B

District of Columbia

The Catholic University of America, B

Florida

Florida State University, B
New College of Florida, B

Idaho

University of Idaho, B

Illinois

Lincoln College, A
Northwestern University, B
Roosevelt University, B
Southern Illinois University Carbondale, M
Trinity International University, B
University of Chicago, B
University of Illinois at Urbana-Champaign, B
Wheaton College, B

Indiana

Butler University, BM
Indiana University Bloomington, B
Saint Joseph's College, B

Iowa

University of Northern Iowa, M

Kansas

Central Christian College of Kansas, A
Kansas State University, M
Pittsburg State University, M

Kentucky

University of Kentucky, B
University of Louisville, MD

Massachusetts

Boston University, BMD
Harvard University, B
New England Conservatory of Music, B
Northeastern University, B
Simmons College, B
Tufts University, M
Westfield State College, B

Michigan

Calvin College, B
Central Michigan University, B
University of Michigan, B
Western Michigan University, B

Minnesota

St. Cloud State University, B

Mississippi

University of Southern Mississippi, M

Missouri

University of Missouri-Kansas City, M
Washington University in St. Louis, B

Nebraska

Hastings College, B

New Hampshire

Keene State College, B
University of New Hampshire, BM

New Jersey

Rutgers, The State University of New Jersey, New
    Brunswick/Piscataway, MD

Rutgers, The State University of New Jersey, Newark, M

New York

Bard College, B
Eugene Lang College The New School for Liberal Arts, B
Fordham University, B
Hofstra University, B
Nazareth College of Rochester, B
Sarah Lawrence College, B
Skidmore College, B
State University of New York at Buffalo, MD
State University of New York College at Potsdam, M
State University of New York, Fredonia, B
State University of New York at New Paltz, B

North Carolina

The University of North Carolina at Greensboro, B

Ohio

Baldwin-Wallace College, B
Bowling Green State University, M
Cleveland State University, M
The College of Wooster, B
Oberlin College, B
The Ohio State University, B
Ohio University, BM
Otterbein College, B
The University of Akron, BM
University of Cincinnati, BMD
Wright State University, B
Youngstown State University, BM

Pennsylvania

Bucknell University, B
Indiana University of Pennsylvania, M
Lafayette College, B
The Pennsylvania State University University Park Campus, M
Temple University, BM
University of Pittsburgh, MD
West Chester University of Pennsylvania, B

South Carolina

Converse College, B
North Greenville College, B
University of South Carolina, M

Tennessee

Belmont University, B
Sewanee: The University of the South, B
University of Memphis, M

Texas

Baylor University, BM
Hardin-Simmons University, B
Hill College of the Hill Junior College District, A
Rice University, BM
Southern Methodist University, M
Texas Tech University, M
University of North Texas, B
The University of Texas at Austin, B

Utah

Brigham Young University, B
Snow College, A

Vermont

Bennington College, B
Marlboro College, B
University of Vermont, B

Virginia

Bridgewater College, B
Christopher Newport University, B
Randolph-Macon Woman's College, B
University of Richmond, B

Washington

Eastern Washington University, M
University of Washington, B

Western Washington University, B

West Virginia

West Virginia University, M

Wisconsin

University of Wisconsin-Milwaukee, B

Wyoming

University of Wyoming, M

Alberta

University of Alberta, B

British Columbia

The University of British Columbia, B
University of Victoria, B

Manitoba

Brandon University, B
Canadian Mennonite University, B

New Brunswick

Mount Allison University, B

Newfoundland and Labrador

Memorial University of Newfoundland, B

Nova Scotia

Dalhousie University, B

Ontario

McMaster University, B
University of Ottawa, B
University of Toronto, B
The University of Western Ontario, B
University of Windsor, B
York University, B

Quebec

McGill University, B
Université du Québec àMontréal, B

Saskatchewan

University of Regina, B

MUSIC MANAGEMENT AND MERCHANDISING

Arizona

Grand Canyon University, B

California

American River College, A
Bethesda Christian University, B
California State University, Sacramento, B
Los Medanos College, A
The Master's College and Seminary, B
Orange Coast College, A
University of the Pacific, B
University of Southern California, B

Colorado

Western State College of Colorado, B

Connecticut

University of Hartford, B
University of New Haven, B

Florida

Florida Southern College, B
Jacksonville University, B

University of Miami, B

Georgia

Berry College, B
Georgia State University, B

Idaho

Boise State University, B
University of Idaho, B

Illinois

Columbia College Chicago, B
DePaul University, B
Elmhurst College, B
Greenville College, B
Lewis University, B
Lincoln College, A
Millikin University, B
North Park University, B

Indiana

Anderson University, B
Butler University, B
DePauw University, B
Huntington University, B
Saint Joseph's College, B
Taylor University, B
University of Evansville, B
Valparaiso University, B

Iowa

Drake University, B
The University of Iowa, B
Waldorf College, B

Kansas

Friends University, AB
Independence Community College, A
Tabor College, B

Kentucky

Bellarmine University, B

Louisiana

Loyola University New Orleans, B

Massachusetts

Berklee College of Music, B
The New England Institute of Art, A
Northeastern University, B
Westfield State College, B

Michigan

Ferris State University, B
Madonna University, B

Minnesota

Century College, A
McNally Smith College of Music, AB
Minnesota State University Mankato, B
Minnesota State University Moorhead, B
Saint Mary's University of Minnesota, B
Winona State University, B

Mississippi

Mississippi University for Women, B

Missouri

College of the Ozarks, B
Northwest Missouri State University, B

Nebraska

Northeast Community College, A
Peru State College, B

New Jersey

Bloomfield College, B
William Paterson University of New Jersey, B

New York

Five Towns College, AB
Hofstra University, B
New York University, B

Schenectady County Community College, A
State University of New York College at Oneonta, B
State University of New York, Fredonia, B
Syracuse University, B
Villa Maria College of Buffalo, A

North Carolina

Appalachian State University, B
Chowan University, A
Elizabeth City State University, B
Methodist College, B
Montreat College, B

Ohio

Capital University, B
Heidelberg College, B
Ohio Northern University, B
Ohio University, B
Otterbein College, B

Oklahoma

Oklahoma City University, B
Southern Nazarene University, B
Southwestern Oklahoma State University, B

Oregon

Northwest Christian College, B
Southern Oregon University, B
Warner Pacific College, B

Pennsylvania

Clarion University of Pennsylvania, B
Geneva College, B
Grove City College, B
Lebanon Valley College, B
Mansfield University of Pennsylvania, B

South Carolina

South Carolina State University, B

South Dakota

South Dakota State University, B
University of Sioux Falls, B

Tennessee

Belmont University, B
Bryan College, B
Middle Tennessee State University, B
Trevecca Nazarene University, B
Union University, B
University of Memphis, B

Texas

Collin County Community College District, A
Dallas Baptist University, B
Hardin-Simmons University, B
Houston Community College System, A
University of the Incarnate Word, B
The University of Texas at San Antonio, B

Vermont

Johnson State College, B

Washington

Central Washington University, B
University of Puget Sound, B

Wisconsin

Marian College of Fond du Lac, B

MUSIC PEDAGOGY

California

California State University, Sacramento, B
Holy Names University, B

Florida

Florida State University, B

Georgia

Columbus State University, B

Illinois

Roosevelt University, B
Trinity International University, B

Louisiana

University of Louisiana at Lafayette, B

Michigan

Michigan State University, B

Minnesota

St. Cloud State University, B

Nebraska

Hastings College, B

New Jersey

Westminster Choir College of Rider University, B

North Carolina

Campbell University, B
Meredith College, B

Ohio

Cedarville University, B

Pennsylvania

Temple University, B

Tennessee

Bryan College, B
The University of Tennessee at Martin, B

Texas

Baylor University, B

Utah

Brigham Young University, B

Wisconsin

Lawrence University, B
Viterbo University, B

MUSIC PERFORMANCE

Alabama

Community College of the Air Force, A
Samford University, B
Talladega College, B

Alaska

University of Alaska Anchorage, B

Arizona

Arizona State University, B
Northern Arizona University, B
The University of Arizona, B

Arkansas

Arkansas State University, B
Henderson State University, B
Ouachita Baptist University, B
University of Central Arkansas, B

California

California Baptist University, B
California Institute of the Arts, B
California State University, Chico, B
California State University, Fullerton, B
California State University, Long Beach, B
California State University, Los Angeles, B
California State University, Stanislaus, B
Chapman University, B
The Colburn School Conservatory of Music, B
Dominican University of California, B
Fresno City College, A
Holy Names University, B
Notre Dame de Namur University, B
Point Loma Nazarene University, B
Reedley College, A
San Francisco Conservatory of Music, B

San Jose State University, B
University of California, Irvine, B
University of Redlands, B
University of Southern California, B

Colorado

Adams State College, B
Colorado Christian University, B
Colorado State University, B
Fort Lewis College, B
Metropolitan State College of Denver, B
Naropa University, B
University of Denver, B

Connecticut

University of Hartford, B

District of Columbia

The Catholic University of America, B

Florida

Bethune-Cookman College, B
Florida Agricultural and Mechanical University, B
Florida State University, B
Jacksonville University, B
Manatee Community College, A
Miami Dade College, A
New World School of the Arts, AB
Palm Beach Atlantic University, B
Southeastern University, B
Stetson University, B
University of Central Florida, B
University of Miami, B
University of North Florida, B
University of South Florida, B
University of West Florida, B

Georgia

Augusta State University, B
Berry College, B
Brewton-Parker College, B
Clayton State University, B
Georgia Southern University, B
Georgia State University, B
Mercer University, B
Piedmont College, B
Toccoa Falls College, B
University of Georgia, B
University of West Georgia, B
Valdosta State University, B

Hawaii

Brigham Young University-Hawaii, B

Idaho

Idaho State University, B
Northwest Nazarene University, B
University of Idaho, B

Illinois

Augustana College, B
Bradley University, B
Columbia College Chicago, B
DePaul University, B
Illinois State University, B
Millikin University, B
Northwestern University, B
Parkland College, A
Rockford College, B
Roosevelt University, B
Saint Xavier University, B
Trinity Christian College, B
University of Illinois at Urbana-Champaign, B
University of St. Francis, B
Wheaton College, B

Indiana

Anderson University, B
Bethel College, B
DePauw University, B
Indiana University South Bend, B
Oakland City University, B
Saint Mary-of-the-Woods College, B
Taylor University, B
University of Evansville, B

University of Indianapolis, B
Valparaiso University, B

Iowa

Buena Vista University, B
Coe College, B
Dordt College, B
Drake University, B
Simpson College, B
University of Northern Iowa, B
Waldorf College, B
Wartburg College, B

Kansas

Butler Community College, A
Central Christian College of Kansas, A
University of Kansas, B

Kentucky

Kentucky State University, B
Transylvania University, B
University of Kentucky, B

Louisiana

Centenary College of Louisiana, B
Dillard University, B
Grambling State University, B
Louisiana State University and Agricultural and
  Mechanical College, B
Louisiana Tech University, B
Loyola University New Orleans, B
McNeese State University, B
Northwestern State University of Louisiana, B
Southeastern Louisiana University, B
Southern University and Agricultural and Mechanical
  College, B
University of Louisiana at Lafayette, B
University of Louisiana at Monroe, B
Xavier University of Louisiana, B

Maine

University of Southern Maine, B

Maryland

Columbia Union College, B
Salisbury University, B
University of Maryland, College Park, B

Massachusetts

Berklee College of Music, B
Boston University, B
Eastern Nazarene College, B
Gordon College, B
New England Conservatory of Music, B
University of Massachusetts Amherst, B
University of Massachusetts Lowell, B

Michigan

Alma College, B
Aquinas College, B
Calvin College, B
Cornerstone University, B
Eastern Michigan University, B
Hope College, B
Macomb Community College, A
Marygrove College, B
Michigan State University, B
Oakland University, B
Western Michigan University, B

Minnesota

Bethel University, B
The College of St. Scholastica, B
Concordia College, B
McNally Smith College of Music, AB
North Central University, B
Northwestern College, AB
St. Cloud State University, B
Saint Mary's University of Minnesota, B
St. Olaf College, B

Mississippi

Alcorn State University, B
Jackson State University, B

Mississippi College, B
William Carey College, B

Missouri

Avila University, B
Central Methodist University, B
Drury University, B
Missouri Baptist University, B
Missouri State University, B
Truman State University, B
University of Missouri-Kansas City, B
University of Missouri-St. Louis, B
Webster University, B
William Jewell College, B

Montana

Rocky Mountain College, B
The University of Montana-Missoula, B

Nebraska

Hastings College, B
Nebraska Wesleyan University, B
Northeast Community College, A
Union College, B
University of Nebraska at Omaha, B

Nevada

University of Nevada, Reno, B

New Hampshire

University of New Hampshire, B

New Jersey

Rowan University, B
Seton Hall University, B

New Mexico

New Mexico State University, B
University of New Mexico, B

New York

Bard College, B
Brooklyn College of the City University of New
  York, B
City College of the City University of New York, B
Hofstra University, B
Houghton College, B
Ithaca College, B
The Juilliard School, B
Long Island University, Brooklyn Campus, B
Long Island University, C.W. Post Campus, B
Nassau Community College, A
New York University, B
Queens College of the City University of New
  York, B
Sarah Lawrence College, B
Schenectady County Community College, A
State University of New York at Binghamton, B
State University of New York at Buffalo, B
State University of New York College at Potsdam, B
Syracuse University, B

North Carolina

Appalachian State University, B
Campbell University, B
East Carolina University, B
Elon University, B
Gardner-Webb University, B
Greensboro College, B
Mars Hill College, B
Meredith College, B
Montreat College, B
North Carolina School of the Arts, B
Peace College, B
Saint Augustine's College, B
Salem College, B
The University of North Carolina at Chapel Hill, B
The University of North Carolina at Charlotte, B
The University of North Carolina at Greensboro, B
The University of North Carolina Wilmington, B

Western Carolina University, B

North Dakota

Jamestown College, B
University of Mary, B
University of North Dakota, B

Ohio

Baldwin-Wallace College, B
Bowling Green State University, B
Capital University, B
Cedarville University, B
The College of Wooster, B
Kent State University, B
Miami University, B
Mount Union College, B
Ohio Northern University, B
The Ohio State University, B
Ohio University, B
Ohio Wesleyan University, B
Otterbein College, B
The University of Akron, B
Wittenberg University, B
Wright State University, B
Youngstown State University, B

Oklahoma

Oklahoma Wesleyan University, B
Oral Roberts University, B
Southeastern Oklahoma State University, B
Southern Nazarene University, B
University of Oklahoma, B

Oregon

Corban College, B
George Fox University, B
Pacific University, B
University of Oregon, B
Willamette University, B

Pennsylvania

Allegheny College, B
Bucknell University, B
Carnegie Mellon University, B
Clarion University of Pennsylvania, B
Duquesne University, B
Geneva College, B
Grove City College, B
Immaculata University, B
Indiana University of Pennsylvania, B
Lebanon Valley College, B
Mansfield University of Pennsylvania, B
Marywood University, B
Mercyhurst College, B
Moravian College, B
The Pennsylvania State University University Park
  Campus, B
Saint Vincent College, B
Seton Hill University, B
Slippery Rock University of Pennsylvania, B
Temple University, B
The University of the Arts, B
West Chester University of Pennsylvania, B
Wilkes University, B

Rhode Island

Rhode Island College, B
University of Rhode Island, B

South Carolina

Anderson University, B
Bob Jones University, B
Charleston Southern University, B
Columbia College, B

South Dakota

Black Hills State University, B

Tennessee

Bryan College, B
Lambuth University, B
Maryville College, B
Southern Adventist University, B
Union University, B

The University of Tennessee at Martin, B

Texas

Baylor University, B
Hardin-Simmons University, B
Houston Baptist University, B
Howard Payne University, B
McMurry University, B
Midwestern State University, B
Rice University, B
Sam Houston State University, B
Stephen F. Austin State University, B
Texas Christian University, B
Texas State University-San Marcos, B
Texas Tech University, B
Trinity University, B
University of Houston, B
University of the Incarnate Word, B
University of Mary Hardin-Baylor, B
University of North Texas, B
The University of Texas at Austin, B
The University of Texas at San Antonio, B
West Texas A&M University, B

Utah

Brigham Young University, B
Weber State University, B

Vermont

Bennington College, B
Johnson State College, B
University of Vermont, B

Virginia

Averett University, B
George Mason University, B
James Madison University, B
Lynchburg College, B
Old Dominion University, B
Randolph-Macon Woman's College, B
Shenandoah University, B
Virginia Commonwealth University, B

Washington

Eastern Washington University, B
Northwest University, B
University of Puget Sound, B
University of Washington, B
Washington State University, B

Wisconsin

Lawrence University, B
University of Wisconsin-Superior, B
Viterbo University, B

Wyoming

University of Wyoming, B

British Columbia

Open Learning Agency, B

Manitoba

Brandon University, B
Canadian Mennonite University, B

New Brunswick

Mount Allison University, B

Nova Scotia

Dalhousie University, B

Ontario

The University of Western Ontario, B
University of Windsor, B

York University, B

Quebec

Concordia University, B
McGill University, B

Saskatchewan

University of Regina, B

MUSIC TEACHER EDUCATION

Alabama

Alabama Agricultural and Mechanical University, BM
Alabama State University, BM
Auburn University, BMDO
Birmingham-Southern College, B
Chattahoochee Valley Community College, A
Huntingdon College, B
Jacksonville State University, B
Judson College, B
Oakwood College, B
Samford University, BM
Talladega College, B
Troy University, B
The University of Alabama, BMDO
University of Montevallo, B
University of South Alabama, M

Alaska

University of Alaska Anchorage, B
University of Alaska Fairbanks, M

Arizona

Arizona State University, B
Grand Canyon University, B
Northern Arizona University, BM
Prescott College, B
Southwestern College, B
The University of Arizona, BMD

Arkansas

Arkansas State University, BMO
Arkansas Tech University, B
Harding University, B
Henderson State University, B
John Brown University, B
Ouachita Baptist University, B
Southern Arkansas University-Magnolia, B
University of Arkansas at Fort Smith, B
University of Arkansas at Monticello, B
University of Arkansas at Pine Bluff, B
University of Central Arkansas, M
Williams Baptist College, B

California

Azusa Pacific University, M
Bethany University, B
California Lutheran University, B
California State University, Chico, B
California State University, Dominguez Hills, B
California State University, Fresno, BM
California State University, Fullerton, BM
California State University, Los Angeles, M
California State University, Northridge, M
Chapman University, B
Fresno Pacific University, B
Holy Names University, MO
Hope International University, B
Humboldt State University, B
La Sierra University, B
The Master's College and Seminary, B
Mount St. Mary's College, B
Notre Dame de Namur University, M
Pacific Union College, B
Pepperdine University, B
Point Loma Nazarene University, B
San Diego Christian College, B
San Diego State University, BM
San Francisco State University, M
Simpson University, B
Sonoma State University, B
University of the Pacific, BM
University of Redlands, B

University of Southern California, BMD

Colorado

Colorado Christian University, B
The Colorado College, M
Colorado State University, BM
Colorado State University-Pueblo, B
Fort Lewis College, B
Mesa State College, B
Metropolitan State College of Denver, B
Northeastern Junior College, A
University of Colorado at Boulder, BMD
University of Denver, M
University of Northern Colorado, BMD
Western State College of Colorado, B

Connecticut

Central Connecticut State University, BM
Connecticut College, BM
University of Connecticut, BMD
University of Hartford, BMD
Western Connecticut State University, BM

Delaware

Delaware State University, B
University of Delaware, BM

District of Columbia

The Catholic University of America, BMD
Howard University, M
University of the District of Columbia, B

Florida

The Baptist College of Florida, B
Bethune-Cookman College, B
Clearwater Christian College, B
Florida Agricultural and Mechanical University, B
Florida Atlantic University, B
Florida International University, BM
Florida Memorial College, B
Florida Southern College, B
Florida State University, BMD
Hobe Sound Bible College, B
Jacksonville University, BM
Manatee Community College, A
Miami Dade College, A
Palm Beach Atlantic University, B
Pensacola Junior College, A
Southeastern University, B
Stetson University, B
University of Central Florida, BM
University of Florida, BMD
University of Miami, BMDO
University of North Florida, B
University of South Florida, BMD
University of West Florida, B
Warner Southern College, B

Georgia

Albany State University, M
Armstrong Atlantic State University, B
Augusta State University, B
Berry College, B
Brenau University, B
Brewton-Parker College, B
Clark Atlanta University, B
Columbus State University, BM
Emmanuel College, B
Georgia College & State University, B
Georgia Southern University, BM
Georgia State University, O
Kennesaw State University, B
LaGrange College, M
Mercer University, B
North Georgia College & State University, B
Shorter College, B
Toccoa Falls College, B
University of Georgia, BMDO
University of West Georgia, BM
Valdosta State University, BM

Young Harris College, A

Guam

University of Guam, B

Hawaii

Brigham Young University-Hawaii, B

Idaho

Boise State University, BM
Brigham Young University -Idaho, A
Idaho State University, B
North Idaho College, A
Northwest Nazarene University, B
University of Idaho, B

Illinois

Augustana College, B
Benedictine University, B
Bradley University, B
Chicago State University, B
College of Lake County, A
Concordia University, B
DePaul University, BM
Elmhurst College, B
Eureka College, B
Greenville College, B
Highland Community College, A
Illinois Eastern Community Colleges, Lincoln Trail College, A
Illinois Eastern Community Colleges, Olney Central College, A
Illinois State University, B
Illinois Wesleyan University, B
Judson College, B
MacMurray College, B
McKendree College, B
Millikin University, B
North Central College, B
North Park University, B
Northern Illinois University, B
Northwestern University, BMD
Olivet Nazarene University, B
Parkland College, A
Quincy University, B
Roosevelt University, BO
Saint Xavier University, B
Southern Illinois University Carbondale, M
Southern Illinois University Edwardsville, M
Trinity Christian College, B
Trinity International University, B
University of Illinois at Urbana-Champaign, B
University of St. Francis, B
VanderCook College of Music, BM
Waubonsee Community College, A
Wheaton College, B

Indiana

Anderson University, B
Ball State University, BMD
Bethel College, B
Butler University, BM
DePauw University, B
Goshen College, B
Grace College, B
Huntington University, B
Indiana University Bloomington, BMD
Indiana University-Purdue University Fort Wayne, B
Indiana University South Bend, B
Indiana Wesleyan University, B
Manchester College, B
Marian College, B
Oakland City University, B
Saint Mary-of-the-Woods College, B
Saint Mary's College, B
Taylor University, B
University of Evansville, B
University of Indianapolis, B
Valparaiso University, B
Vincennes University, A

Iowa

Ashford University, B
Buena Vista University, B
Central College, B

Clarke College, B
Coe College, B
Cornell College, B
Dordt College, B
Drake University, B
Faith Baptist Bible College and Theological Seminary, B
Graceland University, B
Iowa Lakes Community College, A
Iowa State University of Science and Technology, B
Iowa Wesleyan College, B
Morningside College, B
Mount Mercy College, B
Northwestern College, B
St. Ambrose University, B
Simpson College, B
The University of Iowa, BMD
University of Northern Iowa, BM
Waldorf College, B
Wartburg College, B

Kansas

Baker University, B
Benedictine College, B
Bethany College, B
Central Christian College of Kansas, A
Coffeyville Community College, A
Colby Community College, A
Dodge City Community College, A
Emporia State University, BM
Fort Hays State University, B
Friends University, B
Independence Community College, A
Kansas State University, BM
McPherson College, B
MidAmerica Nazarene University, B
Ottawa University, B
Pittsburg State University, BM
Southwestern College, B
Sterling College, B
Tabor College, B
University of Kansas, BMD
Washburn University, B
Wichita State University, BM

Kentucky

Asbury College, B
Berea College, B
Campbellsville University, BM
Eastern Kentucky University, BM
Georgetown College, B
Kentucky Christian University, B
Kentucky State University, B
Morehead State University, M
Murray State University, BM
Transylvania University, B
Union College, M
University of the Cumberlands, B
University of Kentucky, B
University of Louisville, BM
Western Kentucky University, BM

Louisiana

Centenary College of Louisiana, B
Dillard University, B
Grambling State University, B
Louisiana College, B
Louisiana State University and Agricultural and Mechanical College, BD
Louisiana Tech University, B
Loyola University New Orleans, B
McNeese State University, BM
Nicholls State University, B
Northwestern State University of Louisiana, B
Southeastern Louisiana University, B
Southern University and Agricultural and Mechanical College, B
University of Louisiana at Lafayette, BM
University of Louisiana at Monroe, B
University of New Orleans, B

Xavier University of Louisiana, B

Maine

University of Maine, B
University of Southern Maine, B

Maryland

Columbia Union College, B
Frederick Community College, A
Peabody Conservatory of Music of The Johns Hopkins University, B
Salisbury University, M
Towson University, BMO
University of Maryland, College Park, BMD
University of Maryland Eastern Shore, B
Washington Bible College, B

Massachusetts

Anna Maria College, B
Atlantic Union College, B
Berklee College of Music, B
The Boston Conservatory, BM
Boston University, BMD
Bridgewater State College, B
Eastern Nazarene College, B
Gordon College, BM
University of Massachusetts Lowell, M
Westfield State College, B

Michigan

Adrian College, B
Alma College, B
Andrews University, B
Aquinas College, B
Calvin College, B
Central Michigan University, BM
Concordia University, B
Cornerstone University, B
Eastern Michigan University, B
Grace Bible College, B
Grand Valley State University, B
Hope College, B
Madonna University, B
Michigan State University, BM
Northern Michigan University, B
Oakland University, B
Saginaw Valley State University, B
Schoolcraft College, A
Siena Heights University, B
Spring Arbor University, B
University of Michigan, BMDO
University of Michigan-Flint, B
Wayne State University, M
Western Michigan University, B

Minnesota

Augsburg College, B
Bemidji State University, B
Bethel University, B
College of St. Catherine, B
Concordia College, B
Concordia University, St. Paul, B
Crown College, B
Gustavus Adolphus College, B
Hamline University, B
Minnesota State University Mankato, B
Minnesota State University Moorhead, BM
Northwestern College, B
Pillsbury Baptist Bible College, B
St. Cloud State University, BM
Saint Mary's University of Minnesota, B
St. Olaf College, B
Southwest Minnesota State University, B
University of Minnesota, Duluth, BM
University of Minnesota, Twin Cities Campus, B
University of St. Thomas, BM
Winona State University, B

Mississippi

Alcorn State University, B
Blue Mountain College, B
Copiah-Lincoln Community College, A
Delta State University, BM
East Central Community College, A
Holmes Community College, A

Itawamba Community College, A
Jackson State University, BM
Jones County Junior College, A
Mississippi College, BM
Mississippi Delta Community College, A
Mississippi State University, B
Mississippi University for Women, B
Mississippi Valley State University, B
Northeast Mississippi Community College, A
Northwest Mississippi Community College, A
Southwest Mississippi Community College, A
University of Southern Mississippi, BMD
William Carey College, B

Missouri

Baptist Bible College, B
Calvary Bible College and Theological Seminary, B
Central Methodist University, B
Central Missouri State University, B
College of the Ozarks, B
Culver-Stockton College, B
Drury University, B
Evangel University, B
Hannibal-LaGrange College, B
Lincoln University, B
Lindenwood University, B
Missouri Baptist University, B
Missouri State University, B
Missouri Western State University, B
Northwest Missouri State University, BM
Southeast Missouri State University, BM
Southwest Baptist University, B
University of Missouri-Columbia, BMDO
University of Missouri-Kansas City, BMD
University of Missouri-St. Louis, BM
Webster University, BM
William Jewell College, B

Montana

Montana State University, B
Montana State University-Billings, B
Rocky Mountain College, B
The University of Montana-Missoula, B
The University of Montana-Western, B

Nebraska

Chadron State College, B
Concordia University, B
Dana College, B
Grace University, B
Hastings College, B
Midland Lutheran College, B
Nebraska Wesleyan University, B
Northeast Community College, A
Peru State College, B
Union College, AB
University of Nebraska at Kearney, M
University of Nebraska-Lincoln, B
University of Nebraska at Omaha, B
Wayne State College, BM
Western Nebraska Community College, A
York College, B

Nevada

University of Nevada, Las Vegas, M
University of Nevada, Reno, B

New Hampshire

Keene State College, B
Plymouth State University, B
University of New Hampshire, BM

New Jersey

The College of New Jersey, B
Kean University, B
Montclair State University, M
New Jersey City University, BM
Rider University, BM
Rowan University, M
Rutgers, The State University of New Jersey, New Brunswick/Piscataway, B
Westminster Choir College of Rider University, B

William Paterson University of New Jersey, B

New Mexico

Eastern New Mexico University, B
New Mexico Highlands University, B
New Mexico State University, B
University of New Mexico, B
Western New Mexico University, B

New York

Brooklyn College of the City University of New York, BMO
Buffalo State College, State University of New York, B
City College of the City University of New York, B
The College of Saint Rose, BMO
Concordia College, B
Dowling College, B
Five Towns College, BM
Hartwick College, B
Hofstra University, BM
Houghton College, B
Hunter College of the City University of New York, M
Ithaca College, BM
Lehman College of the City University of New York, M
Long Island University, Brooklyn Campus, B
Long Island University, C.W. Post Campus, BM
Manhattanville College, BM
Nazareth College of Rochester, BM
New York University, BMDO
Nyack College, B
Queens College of the City University of New York, BMO
Roberts Wesleyan College, B
State University of New York at Buffalo, MO
State University of New York College at Potsdam, BM
State University of New York, Fredonia, BM
Syracuse University, BM
University of Rochester, BMD

North Carolina

Appalachian State University, BM
Bennett College For Women, B
Campbell University, B
Catawba College, B
Chowan University, B
East Carolina University, BM
Elizabeth City State University, B
Elon University, B
Fayetteville State University, B
Gardner-Webb University, B
Greensboro College, B
Lenoir-Rhyne College, B
Livingstone College, B
Mars Hill College, B
Meredith College, B
Methodist College, B
North Carolina Agricultural and Technical State University, B
North Carolina Central University, B
Pfeiffer University, B
Piedmont Baptist College, B
Saint Augustine's College, B
Sandhills Community College, A
The University of North Carolina at Chapel Hill, M
The University of North Carolina at Charlotte, B
The University of North Carolina at Greensboro, BMD
The University of North Carolina at Pembroke, B
The University of North Carolina Wilmington, B
Western Carolina University, B
Wingate University, B
Winston-Salem State University, B

North Dakota

Dickinson State University, B
Jamestown College, B
Minot State University, BM
North Dakota State University, BM
University of Mary, B
University of North Dakota, BM

Valley City State University, B

Ohio

Ashland University, B
Baldwin-Wallace College, B
Bluffton University, B
Bowling Green State University, BM
Capital University, BM
Case Western Reserve University, BMD
Cedarville University, B
Central State University, B
Cleveland State University, M
The College of Wooster, B
God's Bible School and College, B
Heidelberg College, B
Kent State University, BMD
Malone College, B
Miami University, BM
Miami University Hamilton, B
Mount Union College, B
Mount Vernon Nazarene University, B
Muskingum College, B
Oberlin College, B
Ohio Northern University, B
The Ohio State University, B
Ohio University, BM
Ohio Wesleyan University, B
Otterbein College, B
The University of Akron, BM
University of Cincinnati, BM
University of Dayton, B
University of Rio Grande, B
The University of Toledo, BM
Wilmington College, B
Wittenberg University, B
Wright State University, BM
Xavier University, B
Youngstown State University, BM

Oklahoma

East Central University, B
Langston University, B
Mid-America Christian University, B
Northeastern State University, B
Northwestern Oklahoma State University, B
Oklahoma Baptist University, B
Oklahoma Christian University, B
Oklahoma City University, B
Oklahoma State University, B
Oral Roberts University, B
Southeastern Oklahoma State University, B
Southern Nazarene University, B
Southwestern Oklahoma State University, B
Tulsa Community College, A
University of Central Oklahoma, BM
University of Oklahoma, MD
University of Tulsa, B

Oregon

Corban College, B
George Fox University, B
Oregon State University, M
Pacific University, B
Portland State University, M
Treasure Valley Community College, A
Umpqua Community College, A
University of Oregon, BMD
University of Portland, B
Warner Pacific College, B

Pennsylvania

Arcadia University, M
Baptist Bible College of Pennsylvania, B
Bucknell University, B
Carnegie Mellon University, M
Chestnut Hill College, B
Clarion University of Pennsylvania, B
Duquesne University, BM
Elizabethtown College, B
Geneva College, B
Gettysburg College, B
Grove City College, B
Immaculata University, B
Indiana University of Pennsylvania, BM
Lancaster Bible College, B
Lebanon Valley College, BM

Lincoln University, B
Lycoming College, B
Mansfield University of Pennsylvania, B
Marywood University, BM
Mercyhurst College, B
Messiah College, B
Millersville University of Pennsylvania, B
Moravian College, B
The Pennsylvania State University University Park
    Campus, BMD
Saint Vincent College, B
Seton Hill University, B
Susquehanna University, B
Temple University, BMD
The University of the Arts, M
West Chester University of Pennsylvania, BM
Westminster College, B
Wilkes University, B
York College of Pennsylvania, B

Puerto Rico

Conservatory of Music of Puerto Rico, B
Inter American University of Puerto Rico, San
    Germán Campus, BM
Pontifical Catholic University of Puerto Rico, B
Universidad Adventista de las Antillas, B

Rhode Island

Rhode Island College, BM
Salve Regina University, B
University of Rhode Island, B

South Carolina

Anderson University, B
Bob Jones University, B
Charleston Southern University, B
Claflin University, B
Coker College, B
Columbia College, B
Converse College, BM
Erskine College, B
Furman University, B
Limestone College, B
Newberry College, B
North Greenville College, B
Presbyterian College, B
South Carolina State University, B
Southern Wesleyan University, B
University of South Carolina, BMD
University of South Carolina Aiken, B
Winthrop University, BM

South Dakota

Augustana College, B
Dakota Wesleyan University, B
Mount Marty College, B
Northern State University, B
South Dakota State University, B
University of Sioux Falls, B
The University of South Dakota, B

Tennessee

Austin Peay State University, M
Belmont University, BM
Bryan College, B
Carson-Newman College, B
Cumberland University, B
Fisk University, B
Free Will Baptist Bible College, B
Freed-Hardeman University, B
Lambuth University, B
Lee University, BM
Lipscomb University, B
Martin Methodist College, A
Maryville College, B
Milligan College, B
Roane State Community College, A
Southern Adventist University, B
Tennessee State University, M
Tennessee Technological University, B
Tennessee Wesleyan College, B
Trevecca Nazarene University, B
Union University, B
University of Memphis, MD
The University of Tennessee, BM

The University of Tennessee at Martin, B
Walters State Community College, A

Texas

Abilene Christian University, B
Amarillo College, A
Angelina College, A
Arlington Baptist College, B
Austin College, M
Baylor University, BM
Coastal Bend College, A
Dallas Baptist University, B
Del Mar College, A
East Texas Baptist University, B
Frank Phillips College, A
Hardin-Simmons University, BM
Hill College of the Hill Junior College District, A
Houston Baptist University, B
Howard College, A
Howard Payne University, B
Jarvis Christian College, B
Lamar University, BM
Lon Morris College, A
Lubbock Christian University, B
McMurry University, B
Midland College, A
Midwestern State University, B
Sam Houston State University, BM
Southern Methodist University, M
Stephen F. Austin State University, B
Tarleton State University, B
Texas A&M University-Commerce, BM
Texas A&M University-Kingsville, BM
Texas Christian University, BM
Texas Lutheran University, B
Texas Southern University, B
Texas State University-San Marcos, M
Texas Tech University, MD
Texas Wesleyan University, B
University of Houston, MD
University of the Incarnate Word, B
University of Mary Hardin-Baylor, B
University of North Texas, BMD
University of St. Thomas, B
The University of Texas at El Paso, M
The University of Texas-Pan American, M
Wayland Baptist University, B
Wiley College, B

United States Virgin Islands

University of the Virgin Islands, B

Utah

Brigham Young University, BM
Snow College, A
Southern Utah University, B
University of Utah, B
Utah State University, B
Weber State University, B

Vermont

Bennington College, M
Castleton State College, B
Johnson State College, B
University of Vermont, B

Virginia

Bluefield College, B
Christopher Newport University, M
Eastern Mennonite University, B
George Mason University, M
Hampton University, B
James Madison University, M
Liberty University, B
Longwood University, B
Norfolk State University, M
Old Dominion University, B
Shenandoah University, BMD
University of Mary Washington, B
Virginia Commonwealth University, M

Washington

Central Washington University, B
Eastern Washington University, BM
Gonzaga University, B

Northwest University, B
Pacific Lutheran University, B
Seattle Pacific University, B
University of Puget Sound, BM
University of Washington, BMD
Walla Walla College, B
Washington State University, B
Wenatchee Valley College, A
Western Washington University, B
Whitworth College, B

West Virginia

Alderson-Broaddus College, B
Concord University, B
Davis & Elkins College, B
Fairmont State University, B
Glenville State College, B
Potomac State College of West Virginia
    University, A
University of Charleston, B
West Liberty State College, B
West Virginia State University, B
West Virginia University, MD
West Virginia Wesleyan College, B

Wisconsin

Alverno College, B
Beloit College, B
Carroll College, B
Carthage College, B
Concordia University Wisconsin, B
Lakeland College, B
Lawrence University, B
Maranatha Baptist Bible College, B
Marian College of Fond du Lac, B
Mount Mary College, B
Northland College, B
Ripon College, B
St. Norbert College, B
Silver Lake College, BM
University of Wisconsin-Madison, BMD
University of Wisconsin-Milwaukee, B
University of Wisconsin-Oshkosh, B
University of Wisconsin-River Falls, B
University of Wisconsin-Stevens Point, BM
University of Wisconsin-Superior, B
University of Wisconsin-Whitewater, B
Viterbo University, B

Wyoming

Casper College, A
Eastern Wyoming College, A
Northwest College, A
University of Wyoming, BM

Alberta

University of Alberta, B
University of Lethbridge, B

British Columbia

The University of British Columbia, BM
University of Victoria, BM

Manitoba

Brandon University, BM

New Brunswick

Université de Moncton, B
University of New Brunswick Fredericton, B

Newfoundland and Labrador

Memorial University of Newfoundland, B

Nova Scotia

Acadia University, B

Ontario

Brock University, B
McMaster University, B
University of Ottawa, BO
University of Toronto, BMD
The University of Western Ontario, B
University of Windsor, B

York University, B

Prince Edward Island

University of Prince Edward Island, B

Quebec

Bishop's University, B
McGill University, BMD
Université Laval, BM
Université du Québec àMontréal, B

Saskatchewan

University of Regina, B
University of Saskatchewan, B

MUSIC THEORY AND COMPOSITION

Alabama

Samford University, B

Alaska

University of Alaska Fairbanks, M

Arizona

Arizona State University, B
Northern Arizona University, M
The University of Arizona, MD

Arkansas

Ouachita Baptist University, B
University of Central Arkansas, M

California

Bethesda Christian University, B
California Baptist University, B
California Institute of the Arts, B
California State University, Chico, B
California State University, Fullerton, M
California State University, Long Beach, B
California State University, Northridge, M
California State University, Sacramento, B
Chapman University, B
Loyola Marymount University, B
Point Loma Nazarene University, B
San Diego State University, M
San Francisco Conservatory of Music, B
Stanford University, MD
University of California, Santa Barbara, MD
University of the Pacific, B
University of Redlands, B
University of Southern California, B

Colorado

University of Denver, M

Connecticut

University of Connecticut, MD
University of Hartford, BM

Delaware

University of Delaware, B

District of Columbia

The Catholic University of America, B

Florida

Florida State University, BMD
Jacksonville University, B
Manatee Community College, A
New World School of the Arts, AB
Palm Beach Atlantic University, B
Stetson University, B
University of Miami, BMD
University of South Florida, M

Georgia

Clayton State University, B
Georgia Southern University, B
University of Georgia, B

University of West Georgia, B

Idaho

Northwest Nazarene University, B
University of Idaho, B

Illinois

Bradley University, B
DePaul University, B
Northwestern University, BMD
Roosevelt University, B
Southern Illinois University Carbondale, M
Trinity International University, B
University of Illinois at Urbana-Champaign, B
Wheaton College, B

Indiana

DePauw University, B
Huntington University, B
Indiana Wesleyan University, B
Valparaiso University, B

Iowa

Coe College, B
The University of Iowa, B
University of Northern Iowa, B
Wartburg College, B

Kansas

Kansas State University, M
Pittsburg State University, M
University of Kansas, BMD

Kentucky

Eastern Kentucky University, M
University of Louisville, M

Louisiana

Centenary College of Louisiana, B
Loyola University New Orleans, B
University of Louisiana at Lafayette, B

Massachusetts

Berklee College of Music, B
The Boston Conservatory, B
Boston University, BMD
Brandeis University, MD
Harvard University, MD
New England Conservatory of Music, B
Simon's Rock College of Bard, B
Tufts University, M

Michigan

Calvin College, B
Central Michigan University, B
Cornerstone University, B
Hope College, B
Michigan State University, BM
Oakland University, B
University of Michigan, B
Wayne State University, M
Western Michigan University, B

Minnesota

Concordia College, B
Minnesota State University Moorhead, B
North Central University, AB
Northwestern College, B
St. Cloud State University, B
St. Olaf College, B

Mississippi

Mississippi College, BM
University of Southern Mississippi, M

Missouri

Central Missouri State University, B
Drury University, B
Missouri State University, B
University of Missouri-Kansas City, BM
Washington University in St. Louis, B
Webster University, B

William Jewell College, B

Nebraska

Grace University, B
University of Nebraska at Omaha, B

Nevada

University of Nevada, Las Vegas, BM

New Jersey

Montclair State University, M
Rider University, B
Rowan University, B
Westminster Choir College of Rider University, B

New York

Bard College, B
Brooklyn College of the City University of New York, B
City College of the City University of New York, B
Cornell University, M
Hofstra University, B
Houghton College, B
Ithaca College, BM
Long Island University, Brooklyn Campus, B
Mannes College The New School for Music, BMO
New York University, BMD
Nyack College, B
Sarah Lawrence College, B
State University of New York at Buffalo, MD
State University of New York College at Potsdam, M
Syracuse University, B
University of Rochester, BMD

North Carolina

Campbell University, B
East Carolina University, BM
Meredith College, B
The University of North Carolina at Greensboro, B

Ohio

Baldwin-Wallace College, B
Bowling Green State University, BM
Capital University, B
Cedarville University, B
The College of Wooster, B
Kent State University, MD
Oberlin College, B
The Ohio State University, B
Ohio University, BM
The University of Akron, BM
University of Cincinnati, MD
Wilberforce University, B
Wittenberg University, B
Wright State University, B
Youngstown State University, BM

Oklahoma

Oklahoma Baptist University, B
Oklahoma City University, B
Oral Roberts University, B
University of Oklahoma, BM

Oregon

George Fox University, B
Willamette University, B

Pennsylvania

Bucknell University, B
Carnegie Mellon University, B
Duquesne University, M
Indiana University of Pennsylvania, M
Lehigh University, B
Moravian College, B
The Pennsylvania State University University Park Campus, M
Seton Hill University, B
Temple University, BM
The University of the Arts, B
University of Pittsburgh, MD

West Chester University of Pennsylvania, B

Rhode Island

University of Rhode Island, B

South Carolina

University of South Carolina, M

Tennessee

Carson-Newman College, B
Southern Adventist University, B
The University of Tennessee, M

Texas

Baylor University, BM
Dallas Baptist University, B
Hardin-Simmons University, BM
Hill College of the Hill Junior College District, A
Houston Baptist University, B
Houston Community College System, A
Rice University, BM
Southern Methodist University, BM
Texas A&M University-Commerce, M
Texas Christian University, BM
Texas Tech University, BM
Trinity University, B
University of Houston, BM
University of Mary Hardin-Baylor, B
University of North Texas, BMD
The University of Texas at Austin, B
The University of Texas at San Antonio, B
West Texas A&M University, B

Utah

Brigham Young University, B

Vermont

Bennington College, B

Virginia

Christopher Newport University, B
James Madison University, M
Lynchburg College, B
Norfolk State University, M
Randolph-Macon Woman's College, B
Shenandoah University, B

Washington

Central Washington University, B
Eastern Washington University, B
University of Washington, B
Washington State University, B

West Virginia

West Virginia University, M

Wisconsin

Lawrence University, B
University of Wisconsin-Madison, MD

Wyoming

University of Wyoming, B

British Columbia

Kwantlen University College, A
The University of British Columbia, B
University of Victoria, B

Manitoba

Brandon University, B
Canadian Mennonite University, B

Newfoundland and Labrador

Memorial University of Newfoundland, B

Nova Scotia

Dalhousie University, B

Ontario

The University of Western Ontario, B
University of Windsor, B

York University, B

Quebec

McGill University, BMD

Saskatchewan

University of Regina, BM

MUSIC THERAPY/THERAPIST

Arizona

Arizona State University, B

California

Chapman University, B
Pasadena City College, A
University of the Pacific, BM

Colorado

Colorado State University, BM
Naropa University, M

Florida

Florida State University, BM
University of Miami, BMDO

Georgia

Georgia College & State University, BM
University of Georgia, B

Indiana

Indiana University-Purdue University Fort Wayne, B
Saint Mary-of-the-Woods College, BM
University of Evansville, B

Iowa

The University of Iowa, B
Wartburg College, B

Kansas

University of Kansas, BM

Kentucky

University of Louisville, B

Louisiana

Dillard University, B

Massachusetts

Anna Maria College, B
Berklee College of Music, B

Michigan

Eastern Michigan University, B
Michigan State University, BM
Western Michigan University, B

Minnesota

Augsburg College, B
University of Minnesota, Twin Cities Campus, B

Mississippi

William Carey College, B

Missouri

Maryville University of Saint Louis, BM

New Jersey

Montclair State University, BM

New York

Molloy College, B
Nazareth College of Rochester, B
New York University, MD
State University of New York, Fredonia, B
State University of New York at New Paltz, B

North Carolina

Appalachian State University, B
East Carolina University, BM

Queens University of Charlotte, B

North Dakota

University of North Dakota, B

Ohio

Baldwin-Wallace College, B
The College of Wooster, B
Ohio University, M
University of Dayton, B

Oklahoma

Southwestern Oklahoma State University, B

Pennsylvania

Drexel University, M
Duquesne University, B
Elizabethtown College, B
Immaculata University, BM
Mansfield University of Pennsylvania, B
Marywood University, B
Slippery Rock University of Pennsylvania, B
Temple University, BMD

South Carolina

Charleston Southern University, B
Converse College, B

Texas

Sam Houston State University, B
Southern Methodist University, B
Texas Woman's University, B
University of the Incarnate Word, B
West Texas A&M University, B

Utah

Utah State University, B

Virginia

Radford University, M
Shenandoah University, BMO

Wisconsin

Alverno College, B
University of Wisconsin-Eau Claire, B
University of Wisconsin-Milwaukee, B
University of Wisconsin-Oshkosh, B

British Columbia

Open Learning Agency, B

Manitoba

Canadian Mennonite University, B

Ontario

University of Windsor, B
Wilfrid Laurier University, B

Quebec

Université du Québec àMontréal, B

MUSICAL INSTRUMENT FABRICATION AND REPAIR

California

Hartnell College, A
Orange Coast College, A

Delaware

Delaware State University, B

Indiana

Ball State University, B
Indiana University Bloomington, A

Kentucky

Bellarmine University, B

Minnesota

Minnesota State College-Southeast Technical, A

New York

Queensborough Community College of the City University of New York, A

North Carolina

Barton College, B

Tennessee

Bryan College, B

Washington

Renton Technical College, A
University of Washington, B

MUSICOLOGY AND ETHNOMUSICOLOGY

Arizona

The University of Arizona, M

California

California State University, Los Angeles, M
California State University, Northridge, M
Loyola Marymount University, B
San Diego State University, M
Stanford University, D
University of California, Davis, D
University of California, Los Angeles, BMD
University of California, Santa Barbara, MD
University of Southern California, D

Colorado

University of Colorado at Boulder, D
University of Denver, B

Connecticut

University of Connecticut, M

District of Columbia

The Catholic University of America, MDO

Florida

Florida State University, MD
University of Miami, BM

Illinois

Northwestern University, BMD

Kansas

University of Kansas, BMD

Kentucky

University of Louisville, D

Massachusetts

Brandeis University, MD
Harvard University, MD

Michigan

Michigan State University, M

New Jersey

Princeton University, D

New York

Brooklyn College of the City University of New York, M
Cornell University, D
State University of New York at Buffalo, D
University of Rochester, MD

North Carolina

Duke University, MD

Ohio

Bowling Green State University, B
Kent State University, MD
The University of Akron, B

University of Cincinnati, D

Oklahoma

University of Oklahoma, M

Pennsylvania

Marywood University, M
The Pennsylvania State University University Park Campus, M
University of Pittsburgh, MD

Rhode Island

Brown University, B

Tennessee

University of Memphis, D
The University of Tennessee, M

Texas

Texas Christian University, M
University of North Texas, MD

Utah

Brigham Young University, M

Vermont

Bennington College, B

Washington

University of Washington, B

Wisconsin

University of Wisconsin-Madison, MD

Alberta

Prairie Bible Institute, B

British Columbia

University of Victoria, MD

Manitoba

Canadian Mennonite University, B

Ontario

York University, BMD

Quebec

McGill University, MD
Université Laval, M
Université de Montréal, MD

Saskatchewan

University of Regina, BMD

NAIL TECHNICIAN/SPECIALIST AND MANICURIST

Colorado

Colorado Northwestern Community College, A

Kentucky

Somerset Community College, A

New Mexico

Clovis Community College, A

Washington

Olympic College, A

NATURAL RESOURCE ECONOMICS

Michigan

Michigan State University, B

New York

Cornell University, B

NATURAL RESOURCES AND CONSERVATION

Alaska

University of Alaska Fairbanks, B
University of Alaska Southeast, AB

Arizona

Prescott College, B
The University of Arizona, MD

Arkansas

University of Arkansas at Monticello, M

California

California State University, Sacramento, B
Humboldt State University, BM
Santa Rosa Junior College, A
University of California, Berkeley, B
University of California, Davis, B

Colorado

Colorado Northwestern Community College, A
Colorado State University, D

Connecticut

University of Connecticut, BMD

Florida

Pensacola Junior College, A
University of Florida, MDO
University of Miami, B

Georgia

Georgia Institute of Technology, MD
University of Georgia, MD

Hawaii

University of Hawaii at Manoa, MD

Illinois

University of Illinois at Urbana-Champaign, BMD

Indiana

Ball State University, M
Purdue University, BMD
Vincennes University, A

Iowa

Ellsworth Community College, A
Iowa Lakes Community College, A
Iowa State University of Science and Technology, MD
Kirkwood Community College, A
Muscatine Community College, A
Upper Iowa University, B

Kansas

Highland Community College, A

Kentucky

University of Kentucky, B

Louisiana

Louisiana State University and Agricultural and Mechanical College, MD
Louisiana Tech University, B
University of Louisiana at Lafayette, B

Maine

Unity College, B
University of Maine, D

Maryland

Frostburg State University, B
University of Maryland, College Park, BMD

Massachusetts

Harvard University, B

Michigan

Central Michigan University, B
Northern Michigan University, B

University of Michigan, MDO
University of Michigan-Flint, B

Minnesota

Itasca Community College, A
Rochester Community and Technical College, A
University of Minnesota, Crookston, A
University of Minnesota, Twin Cities Campus, MD
Vermilion Community College, A
Winona State University, B

Missouri

Northwest Missouri State University, B
University of Missouri-Columbia, B
Washington University in St. Louis, B

Montana

Montana State University, BMD
The University of Montana-Missoula, BM

Nebraska

Nebraska College of Technical Agriculture, A
Nebraska Indian Community College, A
Peru State College, B
University of Nebraska-Lincoln, BMD

Nevada

University of Nevada, Reno, B

New Hampshire

Keene State College, B
University of New Hampshire, BD

New Jersey

New Jersey Institute of Technology, B
Rutgers, The State University of New Jersey, New
  Brunswick/Piscataway, B

New Mexico

College of Santa Fe, B

New York

Cornell University, BMD
Finger Lakes Community College, A
Fulton-Montgomery Community College, A
Niagara County Community College, A
State University of New York College of Agriculture
  and Technology at Morrisville, A
State University of New York College of
  Environmental Science and Forestry, BMD

North Carolina

Duke University, MDO
North Carolina State University, BM

North Dakota

Minot State University-Bottineau Campus, A

Ohio

Hocking College, A
Kent State University, B
Mount Vernon Nazarene University, B
Muskingum College, B
The Ohio State University, MD

Oklahoma

Murray State College, A
Oklahoma State University, MD
St. Gregory's University, B
Southeastern Oklahoma State University, B
University of Oklahoma, M

Pennsylvania

The Pennsylvania State University Abington
  College, B
The Pennsylvania State University Altoona
  College, B
The Pennsylvania State University Beaver Campus
  of the Commonwealth College, B
The Pennsylvania State University Berks Campus of
  the Berks-Lehigh Valley College, B
The Pennsylvania State University Delaware County
  Campus of the Commonwealth College, B

The Pennsylvania State University DuBois Campus
  of the Commonwealth College, B
The Pennsylvania State University at Erie, The
  Behrend College, B
The Pennsylvania State University Fayette Campus
  of the Commonwealth College, B
The Pennsylvania State University Hazleton
  Campus of the Commonwealth College, B
The Pennsylvania State University, Lehigh Valley
  Campus of the Berks-Lehigh Valley College, B
The Pennsylvania State University McKeesport
  Campus of the Commonwealth College, B
The Pennsylvania State University Mont Alto
  Campus of the Commonwealth College, B
The Pennsylvania State University New Kensington
  Campus of the Commonwealth College, B
The Pennsylvania State University Schuylkill
  Campus of the Capital College, B
The Pennsylvania State University Shenango
  Campus of the Commonwealth College, B
The Pennsylvania State University University Park
  Campus, B
The Pennsylvania State University Wilkes-Barre
  Campus of the Commonwealth College, B
The Pennsylvania State University Worthington
  Scranton Campus of the Commonwealth
  College, B
The Pennsylvania State University York Campus of
  the Commonwealth College, B
Slippery Rock University of Pennsylvania, B

Rhode Island

University of Rhode Island, BMD

South Carolina

Clemson University, B

Texas

Stephen F. Austin State University, B
Texas A&M University, BM
Texas A&M University at Galveston, B
Texas Tech University, B

Utah

Dixie State College of Utah, A
Utah State University, BM

Vermont

Marlboro College, B
Sterling College, AB
University of Vermont, BMD

Virginia

Virginia Polytechnic Institute and State
  University, MD

Washington

Grays Harbor College, A
Washington State University, BMD

West Virginia

Mountain State University, B
West Virginia University, D

Wisconsin

Carroll College, B
College of Menominee Nation, A
Fox Valley Technical College, A
Northland College, B
University of Wisconsin-Milwaukee, B
University of Wisconsin-River Falls, B
University of Wisconsin-Stevens Point, BM

Wyoming

University of Wyoming, BMD

Alberta

University of Alberta, BMDO

British Columbia

Thompson Rivers University, B
The University of British Columbia, B

University of Northern British Columbia, MD

Newfoundland and Labrador

Memorial University of Newfoundland, M

Ontario

University of Guelph, MD

Quebec

McGill University, BMD
Université du Québec àMontréal, O

NATURAL RESOURCES CONSERVATION AND RESEARCH

Illinois

University of Illinois at Urbana-Champaign, B

Vermont

Sterling College, AB

NATURAL RESOURCES MANAGEMENT/DEVELOPMENT AND POLICY

Alabama

Tuskegee University, B

Alaska

Alaska Pacific University, B
University of Alaska Fairbanks, AM

Arizona

Prescott College, B

California

American River College, A
Butte College, A
California State University, Chico, B
Cerro Coso Community College, A
College of the Desert, A
Columbia College, A
Feather River College, A
Humboldt State University, B
Reedley College, A
Sacramento City College, A
San Joaquin Delta College, A
Santa Rosa Junior College, A
Shasta College, A
University of California, Berkeley, BMD
University of California, San Diego, B
University of La Verne, B
University of San Francisco, M
Ventura College, A

Colorado

Colorado State University, BM
Pikes Peak Community College, A
Trinidad State Junior College, A

Connecticut

University of Connecticut, MD

Delaware

University of Delaware, B

Florida

University of Miami, B

Hawaii

University of Hawaii at Manoa, B

Idaho

University of Idaho, BMD

Illinois

College of Lake County, A

Indiana

Ball State University, B
Huntington University, B

Vincennes University, A

Iowa

Hawkeye Community College, A
Iowa State University of Science and
Technology, BMD

Kansas

Fort Hays State University, B

Louisiana

Louisiana State University and Agricultural and
Mechanical College, B

Maine

Unity College, B
University of Maine, BM

Maryland

Garrett College, A

Massachusetts

Clark University, B
Greenfield Community College, A
University of Massachusetts Amherst, B

Michigan

Grand Valley State University, B
Lake Superior State University, A
Michigan State University, MD
University of Michigan, B
Wayne County Community College District, A

Minnesota

Itasca Community College, A
University of Minnesota, Crookston, AB
University of Minnesota, Twin Cities Campus, BMD
Vermilion Community College, A

Montana

Blackfeet Community College, A
Chief Dull Knife College, A
Fort Belknap College, A
Fort Peck Community College, A
Montana State University, M
Salish Kootenai College, A
The University of Montana-Missoula, BM

Nebraska

Nebraska College of Technical Agriculture, A
University of Nebraska-Lincoln, B

Nevada

University of Nevada, Reno, B

New Hampshire

University of New Hampshire, B

New Jersey

Rutgers, The State University of New Jersey, New
Brunswick/Piscataway, B

New Mexico

College of Santa Fe, B
New Mexico Highlands University, B
Santa Fe Community College, A
Southwestern Indian Polytechnic Institute, A

New York

Finger Lakes Community College, A
Paul Smith's College of Arts and Sciences, B
Rochester Institute of Technology, B
State University of New York College of Agriculture
and Technology at Morrisville, A

State University of New York College of
Environmental Science and Forestry, BMD

North Carolina

North Carolina State University, B
Western Carolina University, B

North Dakota

North Dakota State University, BMD
Turtle Mountain Community College, A

Ohio

Bowling Green State University, B
Hocking College, A
The Ohio State University, B
The Ohio State University Agricultural Technical
Institute, A
Zane State College, A

Oklahoma

Bacone College, A

Oregon

Eastern Oregon University, B
Oregon State University, B
Treasure Valley Community College, A

Pennsylvania

Albright College, B
Carnegie Mellon University, B
Keystone College, B
Moravian College, B

Puerto Rico

Universidad Metropolitana, M

Rhode Island

University of Rhode Island, B

South Carolina

Central Carolina Technical College, A
Charleston Southern University, B

South Dakota

Oglala Lakota College, A
Sinte Gleska University, A

Tennessee

Sewanee: The University of the South, B
The University of Tennessee at Martin, B

Texas

Frank Phillips College, A
The University of Texas at Austin, M

Utah

Dixie State College of Utah, A
Snow College, A

Vermont

Burlington College, B
Green Mountain College, B
Johnson State College, B
Sterling College, AB
University of Vermont, MD

Virginia

Lord Fairfax Community College, A

Washington

Central Washington University, BM
Heritage University, A
Spokane Community College, A
University of Washington, B

West Virginia

West Virginia University, BD

Wisconsin

Lac Courte Oreilles Ojibwa Community College, A
Northland College, B
University of Wisconsin-Madison, BMD

University of Wisconsin-Stevens Point, B

Wyoming

Northwest College, A

Alberta

University of Alberta, B

British Columbia

The University of British Columbia, BMD

Manitoba

University of Manitoba, MD

New Brunswick

University of New Brunswick Saint John, M

Ontario

University of Guelph, B
The University of Western Ontario, B
University of Windsor, B

Quebec

McGill University, B

NATURAL SCIENCES

Alabama

Oakwood College, B

Alaska

University of Alaska Anchorage, B

California

Azusa Pacific University, B
Cabrillo College, A
California State University, Fresno, B
California State University, Los Angeles, B
California State University, San Bernardino, B
Chabot College, A
Citrus College, A
College of the Canyons, A
College of Marin, A
Cypress College, A
Fresno Pacific University, AB
Gavilan College, A
Golden West College, A
Humboldt State University, B
Lake Tahoe Community College, A
Lassen Community College District, A
Loyola Marymount University, B
The Master's College and Seminary, B
Merced College, A
Moorpark College, A
Ohlone College, A
Orange Coast College, A
Pepperdine University, B
Porterville College, A
Sacramento City College, A
Saddleback College, A
San Joaquin Delta College, A
San Jose State University, B
Santiago Canyon College, A
University of La Verne, B
Victor Valley College, A

Colorado

Colorado Mountain College, A
Northeastern Junior College, A

Connecticut

Naugatuck Valley Community College, A
Saint Joseph College, B

Florida

Florida Southern College, B
Lynn University, B
Miami Dade College, A

New College of Florida, B

Georgia

Covenant College, B
Shorter College, B
Spelman College, B
Young Harris College, A

Hawaii

University of Hawaii at Hilo, B

Idaho

College of Southern Idaho, A
Lewis-Clark State College, B

Illinois

Concordia University, B
Eureka College, B
Monmouth College, B
North Park University, B
Olivet Nazarene University, B
Shimer College, B

Indiana

Goshen College, B
Taylor University, B

Iowa

Central College, B
Dordt College, B
Iowa Lakes Community College, A
Iowa Wesleyan College, B

Kansas

Benedictine College, B
Bethel College, B
Central Christian College of Kansas, B
Haskell Indian Nations University, A
Independence Community College, A
Seward County Community College, A
Tabor College, B
Washburn University, A

Kentucky

Eastern Kentucky University, B
Spalding University, B

Maine

College of the Atlantic, B
University of Maine, B

Maryland

Coppin State University, B
The Johns Hopkins University, B

Massachusetts

Atlantic Union College, B
Elms College, B
Lesley University, B
Quincy College, A
Simon's Rock College of Bard, B

Michigan

Calvin College, B
Grand Valley State University, B
Madonna University, AB
Siena Heights University, B

Minnesota

Augsburg College, B
Bemidji State University, B
College of Saint Benedict, B
The College of St. Scholastica, B
Concordia University, St. Paul, B
Minnesota State University Mankato, B
St. Cloud State University, B
Saint John's University, B

Winona State University, B

Mississippi

Blue Mountain College, B

Missouri

Avila University, B
Missouri Western State University, B
Park University, B
Stephens College, B
Washington University in St. Louis, B

Montana

Salish Kootenai College, A

Nebraska

College of Saint Mary, B
Concordia University, B
Doane College, B
Midland Lutheran College, B
Peru State College, B
University of Nebraska at Omaha, B
Wayne State College, B
York College, B

New Hampshire

University of New Hampshire, B

New Jersey

Felician College, AB
Georgian Court University, B
Passaic County Community College, A
Saint Peter's College, B

New York

Bard College, B
Bernard M. Baruch College of the City University of
   New York, B
Colgate University, B
Daemen College, B
Dowling College, B
Fordham University, B
Hofstra University, B
Houghton College, B
Jefferson Community College, A
Medgar Evers College of the City University of New
   York, A
Roberts Wesleyan College, A
St. Thomas Aquinas College, B
Sarah Lawrence College, B
State University of New York College at Geneseo, B

North Carolina

Lees-McRae College, B

Ohio

Antioch College, B
Case Western Reserve University, B
College of Mount St. Joseph, B
Defiance College, B
Kenyon College, B
Lourdes College, A
Ohio University-Eastern, B
Shawnee State University, AB
The University of Akron, B
University of Cincinnati, AB
The University of Toledo, AB
Xavier University, B

Oklahoma

Cameron University, B
Oklahoma Baptist University, B
Oklahoma Panhandle State University, B
Oklahoma Wesleyan University, B
St. Gregory's University, B
University of Science and Arts of Oklahoma, B

Oregon

Concordia University, B
Southwestern Oregon Community College, A
Umpqua Community College, A

Western Oregon University, B

Pennsylvania

Arcadia University, B
Cedar Crest College, B
Juniata College, B
Lock Haven University of Pennsylvania, B
Muhlenberg College, B
University of Pennsylvania, B
University of Pittsburgh at Greensburg, B
University of Pittsburgh at Johnstown, B
University of Pittsburgh at Titusville, A
Villanova University, AB

Puerto Rico

Inter American University of Puerto Rico, San
   Germán Campus, B
Universidad Metropolitana, AB
Universidad del Turabo, B
University of Puerto Rico at Arecibo, A
University of Puerto Rico at Bayamón, A
University of Puerto Rico at Carolina, A
University of Puerto Rico, Cayey University
   College, B
University of Puerto Rico at Ponce, A
University of Puerto Rico, Río Piedras, B
University of Puerto Rico at Utuado, A

South Carolina

Charleston Southern University, AB
Erskine College, B

South Dakota

Sisseton-Wahpeton Community College, A

Tennessee

Christian Brothers University, B
Lee University, B
LeMoyne-Owen College, B

Texas

Amarillo College, A
College of the Mainland, A
Dallas Baptist University, B
Galveston College, A
Lee College, A
LeTourneau University, B
Our Lady of the Lake University of San Antonio, B

Utah

Snow College, A
Utah Valley State College, A

Vermont

Castleton State College, B
Marlboro College, B
Sterling College, AB

Virginia

Longwood University, B
Virginia Wesleyan College, B

Washington

Centralia College, A
Eastern Washington University, B
The Evergreen State College, B
Highline Community College, A
Skagit Valley College, A
University of Puget Sound, B

West Virginia

Alderson-Broaddus College, AB
Davis & Elkins College, B

Wisconsin

Carthage College, B
Edgewood College, B
Northland College, B
University of Wisconsin-River Falls, B

University of Wisconsin-Stevens Point, B

Wyoming

Northwest College, A

British Columbia

Trinity Western University, B
University of Northern British Columbia, B

New Brunswick

Mount Allison University, B

Ontario

Lakehead University, B
Redeemer University College, B
Trent University, B
University of Ottawa, B
York University, B

Quebec

Bishop's University, B

NATUROPATHIC MEDICINE/NATUROPATHY

Connecticut

University of Bridgeport, D

Washington

Bastyr University, DO

NAVAL ARCHITECTURE AND MARINE ENGINEERING

Connecticut

United States Coast Guard Academy, B

Louisiana

University of New Orleans, B

Maine

Maine Maritime Academy, AB

Maryland

United States Naval Academy, B

Massachusetts

Massachusetts Maritime Academy, B

Michigan

University of Michigan, B

New York

State University of New York Maritime College, B
United States Merchant Marine Academy, B
Webb Institute, B

Texas

Texas A&M University at Galveston, B

British Columbia

British Columbia Institute of Technology, A

New Brunswick

University of New Brunswick Saint John, B

Newfoundland and Labrador

Memorial University of Newfoundland, B

NAVY/MARINE CORPS JROTC/ROTC

New York

Rensselaer Polytechnic Institute, B
State University of New York Maritime College, B

Virginia

Hampton University, B

Washington

University of Washington, B

NEAR AND MIDDLE EASTERN LANGUAGES

California

University of California, Los Angeles, MD

Connecticut

Yale University, MD

District of Columbia

The Catholic University of America, MD

Illinois

University of Chicago, MD

Indiana

Indiana University Bloomington, MD

Massachusetts

Harvard University, MD

Michigan

University of Michigan, MD

Ohio

The Ohio State University, M

Pennsylvania

University of Pennsylvania, MD

Texas

The University of Texas at Austin, MD

Utah

Brigham Young University, M
University of Utah, M

NEAR AND MIDDLE EASTERN STUDIES

Arizona

The University of Arizona, BMD

California

Claremont McKenna College, B
University of California, Berkeley, BMD
University of California, Los Angeles, BMDO
University of California, Santa Barbara, B

District of Columbia

The George Washington University, B
Georgetown University, MO

Illinois

University of Chicago, BMDO

Indiana

Indiana University Bloomington, B

Kansas

University of Kansas, MO

Maine

Bates College, B

Maryland

Baltimore Hebrew University, AB
The Johns Hopkins University, BD

Massachusetts

Brandeis University, BMDO
Harvard University, BMDO
Smith College, B

University of Massachusetts Amherst, B

Michigan

University of Michigan, BMDO
Wayne County Community College District, A
Wayne State University, BM

Minnesota

University of Minnesota, Twin Cities Campus, B

Missouri

Washington University in St. Louis, BM

New Hampshire

Dartmouth College, B

New Jersey

Drew University, MD
Princeton University, BMD
Rutgers, The State University of New Jersey, New
    Brunswick/Piscataway, B
Stevens Institute of Technology, B

New York

Barnard College, B
Columbia College, B
Columbia University, School of General Studies, B
Cornell University, BMD
Fordham University, B
New York University, BMD
Sarah Lawrence College, B
United States Military Academy, B

Ohio

Oberlin College, B
The Ohio State University, B
The University of Toledo, B

Oregon

Portland State University, B

Pennsylvania

Gratz College, O
University of Pennsylvania, MD

Rhode Island

Brown University, B

South Carolina

Columbia International University, B

Texas

Texas State University-San Marcos, B
The University of Texas at Austin, BMDO

Utah

University of Utah, BMD

Virginia

Emory & Henry College, B

Washington

University of Washington, BMD

Ontario

Carleton University, B
University of Toronto, BMD

Quebec

McGill University, BMDO

NEUROBIOLOGY AND NEUROPHYSIOLOGY

Alabama

The University of Alabama at Birmingham, D

Arkansas

University of Arkansas for Medical Sciences, MDO

California

California Institute of Technology, D
University of California, Davis, B

University of California, Irvine, MDO
University of California, Los Angeles, BD
University of California, San Diego, D
University of Southern California, MD

Colorado

University of Colorado at Boulder, MD

Connecticut

University of Connecticut, MD
Wesleyan University, D
Yale University, D

Florida

Florida State University, B
New College of Florida, B
University of Miami, B

Georgia

Georgia State University, MD

Illinois

Loyola University Chicago, MDO
Northwestern University, MD
University of Chicago, D
University of Illinois at Chicago, MDO

Indiana

Indiana University-Purdue University
    Indianapolis, MDO
Purdue University, MD

Iowa

The University of Iowa, D

Kentucky

University of Kentucky, D
University of Louisville, MD

Massachusetts

Boston University, MDO
Brandeis University, D
Harvard University, D
Massachusetts Institute of Technology, D

Michigan

Andrews University, B
Wayne State University, D

Missouri

University of Missouri-Columbia, MD

New Jersey

Rutgers, The State University of New Jersey, New
    Brunswick/Piscataway, D

New York

Cornell University, MD
St. Lawrence University, B
University at Albany, State University of New
    York, MD
University of Rochester, MD

North Carolina

Duke University, D
The University of North Carolina at Chapel Hill, D
Wake Forest University, D

Ohio

Case Western Reserve University, D

Pennsylvania

Carnegie Mellon University, D
University of Pennsylvania, D
University of Pittsburgh, MD

Texas

Texas A&M University System Health Science
    Center, D
The University of Texas at Austin, MDO

The University of Texas at San Antonio, D

Utah

University of Utah, MD

Vermont

University of Vermont, DO

Washington

University of Washington, D

West Virginia

West Virginia University, MD

Wisconsin

Marquette University, MD
University of Wisconsin-Madison, D

Nova Scotia

Dalhousie University, MD

Quebec

Université Laval, MD

NEUROSCIENCE

Alabama

The University of Alabama at Birmingham, D
University of South Alabama, D

Arizona

Arizona State University, MD
The University of Arizona, D

California

California Institute of Technology, MD
Pitzer College, B
Pomona College, B
Scripps College, B
Stanford University, D
University of California, Berkeley, D
University of California, Davis, D
University of California, Irvine, B
University of California, Los Angeles, BD
University of California, Riverside, BD
University of California, San Diego, D
University of Southern California, BD
Westmont College, B

Colorado

The Colorado College, B
Colorado State University, M
Regis University, B

Connecticut

Connecticut College, B
Trinity College, B
University of Connecticut, MD
University of Hartford, M
Wesleyan University, B
Yale University, DO

Delaware

University of Delaware, BD

District of Columbia

American University, D
The George Washington University, D
Georgetown University, DO

Florida

Florida Atlantic University, D
Florida State University, D
University of Florida, MD

University of Miami, BDO

Georgia

Emory University, BD

Hawaii

University of Hawaii at Manoa, MD

Illinois

Loyola University Chicago, MDO
Northwestern University, BD
Rush University, MD
University of Illinois at Urbana-Champaign, DO

Indiana

Indiana University Bloomington, D
Purdue University, D

Iowa

Drake University, B
Iowa State University of Science and
    Technology, MD
The University of Iowa, DO

Kansas

University of Kansas, MD

Louisiana

Centenary College of Louisiana, B
Louisiana State University Health Sciences
    Center, DO
Tulane University, BMDO

Maine

Bates College, B
Bowdoin College, B
Colby College, B

Maryland

The Johns Hopkins University, BD
University of Maryland, Baltimore County, D
University of Maryland, College Park, D

Massachusetts

Amherst College, B
Boston University, BMDO
Brandeis University, BMD
Clark University, B
Harvard University, BD
Massachusetts Institute of Technology, D
Smith College, B
Tufts University, D
University of Massachusetts Amherst, MD
Wellesley College, B

Michigan

Central Michigan University, B
Michigan State University, MD
University of Michigan, D

Minnesota

Macalester College, B
University of Minnesota, Twin Cities Campus, BMD

Missouri

Washington University in St. Louis, BD

Montana

Montana State University, BMD

New Hampshire

Dartmouth College, DO

New Jersey

Drew University, B
Princeton University, D
Rutgers, The State University of New Jersey, New
    Brunswick/Piscataway, D

Rutgers, The State University of New Jersey, Newark, D

New Mexico

University of New Mexico, MD

New York

Canisius College, B
Colgate University, B
College of Staten Island of the City University of New York, MD
Hamilton College, B
New York University, BDO
St. Lawrence University, B
Skidmore College, B
State University of New York at Buffalo, MD
State University of New York Downstate Medical Center, DO
State University of New York Upstate Medical University, D
Stony Brook University, State University of New York, D
Syracuse University, MD
Union College, B
University at Albany, State University of New York, MD
University of Rochester, MD

North Carolina

Duke University, DO
Pamlico Community College, A
Wake Forest University, D

Ohio

Baldwin-Wallace College, B
Bowling Green State University, B
Case Western Reserve University, DO
John Carroll University, B
Kent State University, MD
Kenyon College, B
Muskingum College, B
Oberlin College, B
The Ohio State University, D
Ohio University, MD
Ohio Wesleyan University, B
University of Cincinnati, D

Oklahoma

University of Oklahoma Health Sciences Center, MD

Oregon

Oregon Health & Science University, MDO
University of Oregon, D

Pennsylvania

Allegheny College, B
Cedar Crest College, B
Dickinson College, B
Drexel University, D
Franklin and Marshall College, B
Haverford College, B
King's College, B
Lehigh University, B
Muhlenberg College, B
Thomas Jefferson University, D
University of Pennsylvania, BDO
University of Pittsburgh, BD
The University of Scranton, B
Ursinus College, B

Rhode Island

Brown University, BD

South Carolina

Furman University, B
Medical University of South Carolina, MDO

Wofford College, B

South Dakota

The University of South Dakota, MD

Tennessee

Vanderbilt University, D

Texas

Baylor University, BMD
Rice University, B
Texas A&M University, MD
Texas A&M University System Health Science Center, D
Texas Christian University, B
The University of Texas at Austin, MDO
The University of Texas at Dallas, BMD
The University of Texas Health Science Center at Houston, MDO
The University of Texas Medical Branch, D
The University of Texas Southwestern Medical Center at Dallas, D

Utah

Brigham Young University, BMD
University of Utah, D

Vermont

Middlebury College, B
University of Vermont, DO

Virginia

George Mason University, D
University of Virginia, DO
Virginia Commonwealth University, MD
Washington and Lee University, B

Washington

University of Washington, D
Washington State University, BMD

Wisconsin

Carthage College, B
Lawrence University, B
University of Wisconsin-Madison, MD

Alberta

University of Alberta, MD
University of Calgary, MD
University of Lethbridge, BMD

British Columbia

The University of British Columbia, MD

Newfoundland and Labrador

Memorial University of Newfoundland, B

Nova Scotia

Dalhousie University, BMD
University of King's College, B

Ontario

Brock University, B
McMaster University, MD
University of Guelph, MD
University of Toronto, B
The University of Western Ontario, MD
University of Windsor, B

Quebec

Bishop's University, B
Concordia University, B
McGill University, MD
Université de Montréal, MD

NON-PROFIT/PUBLIC/ ORGANIZATIONAL MANAGEMENT

California

Azusa Pacific University, M
Fresno Pacific University, B
Hope International University, M

San Francisco State University, M
University of Judaism, M
University of San Diego, O
University of San Francisco, M
University of the West, M

Colorado

Regis University, MO

Delaware

University of Delaware, M

District of Columbia

The George Washington University, M

Florida

Carlos Albizu University, Miami Campus, M
Florida Atlantic University, M
Miami Dade College, A
University of Central Florida, O

Georgia

University of Georgia, M

Illinois

DePaul University, MO
North Central College, B
Saint Xavier University, M
Trinity International University, B

Indiana

Indiana University Northwest, O
Indiana University-Purdue University Indianapolis, M
Indiana University South Bend, O
Manchester College, B
Saint Mary-of-the-Woods College, B

Iowa

The University of Iowa, M

Kansas

Washburn University, B

Maine

University of Southern Maine, O

Maryland

College of Notre Dame of Maryland, M
University of Baltimore, B
University of Maryland, Baltimore County, O

Massachusetts

Boston University, M
Hebrew College, O
Suffolk University, M
Tufts University, O
Worcester State College, M

Michigan

University of Michigan-Dearborn, O

Minnesota

Hamline University, M
Metropolitan State University, M
St. Cloud State University, M
University of St. Thomas, M

Missouri

Park University, M
University of Missouri-St. Louis, MO

New Jersey

Fairleigh Dickinson University, Metropolitan Campus, O
Seton Hall University, M

New York

Clarkson University, B
The College of Saint Rose, O
Long Island University, C.W. Post Campus, MO
New York University, MO
Pace University, B

Utica School of Commerce, A

North Carolina

High Point University, M
The University of North Carolina at Greensboro, O
Warren Wilson College, B

Ohio

Case Western Reserve University, MO
Cleveland State University, O

Oklahoma

Oral Roberts University, M

Oregon

Willamette University, M

Pennsylvania

Carlow University, M
Duquesne University, B
Eastern University, M
Gettysburg College, B
Robert Morris University, M
Rosemont College, M
University of Pittsburgh, M

Puerto Rico

University of the Sacred Heart, M

Tennessee

Crichton College, B
Lipscomb University, M
Southern Adventist University, B
University of Memphis, M

Texas

University of Dallas, M

Washington

Seattle University, M

West Virginia

Mountain State University, B

Wisconsin

Lakeland College, B

Alberta

Concordia University College of Alberta, B

Nova Scotia

Dalhousie University, B

Ontario

University of Guelph, B

NORTHERN STUDIES

Alaska

University of Alaska Fairbanks, M

Manitoba

University of Manitoba, M

NORWEGIAN LANGUAGE AND LITERATURE

Utah

Brigham Young University, B

NUCLEAR ENGINEERING

Arizona

The University of Arizona, BMD

California

University of California, Berkeley, BMD

Florida

University of Florida, BMDO

Georgia

Georgia Institute of Technology, BMD

Idaho

Idaho State University, MDO
University of Idaho, MD

Illinois

University of Illinois at Urbana-Champaign, BMD

Indiana

Purdue University, BMD

Kansas

Kansas State University, BM

Maryland

University of Maryland, College Park, MD

Massachusetts

Massachusetts Institute of Technology, BMDO
Worcester Polytechnic Institute, B

Michigan

University of Michigan, BMDO

Minnesota

Itasca Community College, A

Missouri

University of Missouri-Columbia, MD
University of Missouri-Rolla, BMD

New Mexico

University of New Mexico, BMD

New York

Cornell University, MD
Rensselaer Polytechnic Institute, BMD
United States Military Academy, B

North Carolina

North Carolina State University, BMD

Ohio

The Ohio State University, MD
University of Cincinnati, BMD

Oregon

Oregon State University, BMD

Pennsylvania

The Pennsylvania State University Abington
    College, B
The Pennsylvania State University Altoona
    College, B
The Pennsylvania State University Beaver Campus
    of the Commonwealth College, B
The Pennsylvania State University Berks Campus of
    the Berks-Lehigh Valley College, B
The Pennsylvania State University Delaware County
    Campus of the Commonwealth College, B
The Pennsylvania State University DuBois Campus
    of the Commonwealth College, B
The Pennsylvania State University at Erie, The
    Behrend College, B
The Pennsylvania State University Fayette Campus
    of the Commonwealth College, B
The Pennsylvania State University Hazleton
    Campus of the Commonwealth College, B
The Pennsylvania State University, Lehigh Valley
    Campus of the Berks-Lehigh Valley College, B
The Pennsylvania State University McKeesport
    Campus of the Commonwealth College, B
The Pennsylvania State University Mont Alto
    Campus of the Commonwealth College, B
The Pennsylvania State University New Kensington
    Campus of the Commonwealth College, B
The Pennsylvania State University Schuylkill
    Campus of the Capital College, B

The Pennsylvania State University Shenango
    Campus of the Commonwealth College, B
The Pennsylvania State University University Park
    Campus, BMD
The Pennsylvania State University Wilkes-Barre
    Campus of the Commonwealth College, B
The Pennsylvania State University Worthington
    Scranton Campus of the Commonwealth
    College, B
The Pennsylvania State University York Campus of
    the Commonwealth College, B

South Carolina

South Carolina State University, B

Tennessee

The University of Tennessee, BMDO

Texas

Texas A&M University, BMD

Utah

University of Utah, MD

Virginia

University of Virginia, B

Wisconsin

University of Wisconsin-Madison, BMD

Ontario

McMaster University, D
Royal Military College of Canada, MD

NUCLEAR ENGINEERING TECHNOLOGY/TECHNICIAN

Arkansas

Arkansas Tech University, A

New York

Excelsior College, AB
United States Merchant Marine Academy, B

Virginia

Old Dominion University, B

NUCLEAR MEDICAL TECHNOLOGY/TECHNOLOGIST

Alabama

Community College of the Air Force, A
The University of Alabama at Birmingham, B

Arizona

GateWay Community College, A

Arkansas

University of Arkansas for Medical Sciences, B
University of Central Arkansas, B

California

California State University, Dominguez Hills, B
Charles R. Drew University of Medicine and
    Science, B
Compton Community College, A
Los Angeles City College, A
Orange Coast College, A

Connecticut

Gateway Community College, A

Delaware

Delaware Technical & Community College,
    Stanton/Wilmington Campus, A

District of Columbia

The George Washington University, A

Florida

Barry University, B
Broward Community College, A

Florida Hospital College of Health Sciences, A
Hillsborough Community College, A
Miami Dade College, A
Santa Fe Community College, A

Georgia

Dalton State College, A
Darton College, A
Medical College of Georgia, B

Illinois

Benedictine University, B
College of DuPage, A
North Central College, B
Roosevelt University, B
Triton College, A
University of St. Francis, B

Indiana

Ball State University, A
Indiana University-Purdue University Indianapolis, B
Vincennes University, A

Iowa

Loras College, B
The University of Iowa, B

Kentucky

Jefferson Community and Technical College, A
Lexington Community College, A

Maryland

Frederick Community College, A
Howard Community College, A
Prince George's Community College, A

Massachusetts

Massachusetts College of Pharmacy and Health
  Sciences, B
Salem State College, B
Springfield Technical Community College, A

Michigan

Ferris State University, AB
Oakland Community College, A

Minnesota

St. Cloud State University, B
Saint Mary's University of Minnesota, B

Missouri

Saint Louis University, B
University of Missouri-Columbia, B

Nebraska

Peru State College, B
University of Nebraska Medical Center, B

Nevada

University of Nevada, Las Vegas, B

New Jersey

Bloomfield College, B
Gloucester County College, A
Union County College, A

New York

Bronx Community College of the City University of
  New York, A
Long Island University, Brooklyn Campus, B
Long Island University, C.W. Post Campus, B
Manhattan College, B
Molloy College, A
State University of New York at Buffalo, B

North Carolina

Caldwell Community College and Technical
  Institute, A
Fayetteville Technical Community College, A
Forsyth Technical Community College, A

Pitt Community College, A

Ohio

Kettering College of Medical Arts, A
Lorain County Community College, A
University of Cincinnati, B
University of Cincinnati Raymond Walters College, A
The University of Findlay, AB

Oklahoma

University of Oklahoma Health Sciences Center, B

Pennsylvania

Cedar Crest College, B
Community College of Allegheny County, A
Harrisburg Area Community College, A
Indiana University of Pennsylvania, B
York College of Pennsylvania, B

Puerto Rico

University of Puerto Rico, Medical Sciences
  Campus, B

South Carolina

Midlands Technical College, A

South Dakota

Southeast Technical Institute, A

Tennessee

Baptist College of Health Sciences, B
Chattanooga State Technical Community College, A

Texas

Amarillo College, A
Galveston College, A
Houston Community College System, A
University of the Incarnate Word, B

Utah

Weber State University, B

Vermont

University of Vermont, B

Virginia

Old Dominion University, B

West Virginia

West Virginia State Community and Technical
  College, A
West Virginia State University, A
Wheeling Jesuit University, B

Wisconsin

Moraine Park Technical College, A
University of Wisconsin-La Crosse, B

British Columbia

British Columbia Institute of Technology, A

Nova Scotia

Dalhousie University, B

NUCLEAR/NUCLEAR POWER TECHNOLOGY/TECHNICIAN

Connecticut

Three Rivers Community College, A

Florida

Florida Community College at Jacksonville, A

Georgia

Georgia Military College, A

Illinois

Joliet Junior College, A

Kansas

Allen County Community College, A

Michigan

Lake Michigan College, A

Pennsylvania

Westmoreland County Community College, A

South Carolina

Aiken Technical College, A

Tennessee

Chattanooga State Technical Community College, A

Texas

Texas State Technical College Waco, A
University of North Texas, B

Washington

Columbia Basin College, A

Quebec

Université de Montréal, O

NUCLEAR PHYSICS

Massachusetts

Harvard University, B

NURSE ANESTHETIST

Alabama

The University of Alabama at Birmingham, M

Arizona

Midwestern University, Glendale Campus, M

Arkansas

Arkansas State University, M

California

California State University, Long Beach, M
Samuel Merritt College, MO

Florida

Barry University, M

Georgia

Emory University, M
Medical College of Georgia, M

Illinois

Bradley University, M
DePaul University, M
Rush University, M
Southern Illinois University Edwardsville, MO

Kansas

Newman University, M
University of Kansas, M

Maine

University of New England, M

Massachusetts

Boston College, M
Northeastern University, M

Michigan

Oakland University, MO
University of Detroit Mercy, M
University of Michigan-Flint, M

Wayne State University, MO

Minnesota

Saint Mary's University of Minnesota, M
University of Minnesota, Twin Cities Campus, M

Missouri

Missouri State University, M
Webster University, BM

New York

State University of New York at Buffalo, BM
State University of New York Downstate Medical
  Center, M

North Carolina

Duke University, MO
The University of North Carolina at Charlotte, M
The University of North Carolina at Greensboro, MO

Ohio

Case Western Reserve University, M
University of Cincinnati, M

Pennsylvania

Drexel University, M
Gannon University, MO
La Roche College, M
Saint Joseph's University, M
University of Pennsylvania, M
University of Pittsburgh, M
The University of Scranton, MO
Villanova University, MO

Puerto Rico

Inter American University of Puerto Rico, Arecibo
  Campus, M
University of Puerto Rico, Medical Sciences
  Campus, M

South Carolina

Medical University of South Carolina, M
University of South Carolina, M

South Dakota

Mount Marty College, M

Tennessee

The University of Tennessee at Chattanooga, M

Texas

Texas Christian University, M
Texas Wesleyan University, M

Virginia

Virginia Commonwealth University, M

Washington

Gonzaga University, M

West Virginia

Mountain State University, MO

Wisconsin

University of Wisconsin-La Crosse, M

Quebec

Université de Montréal, O

NURSE MIDWIFE/NURSING MIDWIFERY

Florida

The Florida School of Midwifery, A

Georgia

Emory University, M

Illinois

Illinois State University, O
University of Illinois at Chicago, M

Indiana

University of Indianapolis, M

Kansas

University of Kansas, O

Massachusetts

Boston University, O

Michigan

University of Michigan, M

Minnesota

University of Minnesota, Twin Cities Campus, M

New Mexico

National College of Midwifery, MD

New York

New York University, MO
Stony Brook University, State University of New
  York, MO

Ohio

Case Western Reserve University, M
University of Cincinnati, M

Oregon

Oregon Health & Science University, MO

Pennsylvania

Philadelphia University, MO
University of Pennsylvania, M

Puerto Rico

University of Puerto Rico, Medical Sciences
  Campus, MO

South Carolina

Medical University of South Carolina, M

Tennessee

Vanderbilt University, M

Texas

The University of Texas at El Paso, M

Virginia

Shenandoah University, O

Washington

Bastyr University, O

Wisconsin

Marquette University, O

Ontario

McMaster University, B
Ryerson University, B
University of Toronto, B

Quebec

Université du Québec àTrois-Rivières, B

NURSE/NURSING ASSISTANT/AIDE AND PATIENT CARE ASSISTANT

Arizona

Glendale Community College, A

California

Modesto Junior College, A

Colorado

Colorado Northwestern Community College, A
Front Range Community College, A

Trinidad State Junior College, A

Illinois

Waubonsee Community College, A

Iowa

North Iowa Area Community College, A
Western Iowa Tech Community College, A

Kansas

Allen County Community College, A
Central Christian College of Kansas, A
Johnson County Community College, A

Minnesota

Alexandria Technical College, A

Missouri

Jefferson College, A
Mineral Area College, A

Montana

Montana Tech of The University of Montana, A

North Carolina

Cabarrus College of Health Sciences, A
Sandhills Community College, A

North Dakota

Lake Region State College, A

Pennsylvania

Community College of Allegheny County, A

Texas

Lee College, A

Washington

Edmonds Community College, A
Lower Columbia College, A

Wisconsin

Moraine Park Technical College, A
Northeast Wisconsin Technical College, A
Southwest Wisconsin Technical College, A

Wyoming

Laramie County Community College, A
Western Wyoming Community College, A

NURSING

Alabama

Jacksonville State University, M
Samford University, MO
Troy University, M
The University of Alabama, M
The University of Alabama at Birmingham, MD
The University of Alabama in Huntsville, MO
University of Mobile, M
University of South Alabama, M

Alaska

University of Alaska Anchorage, M

Arizona

Arizona State University, MO
Northern Arizona University, MO
The University of Arizona, MD
University of Phoenix Online Campus, M
University of Phoenix-Phoenix Campus, MO
University of Phoenix-Southern Arizona
  Campus, MO

Arkansas

Arkansas State University, MO
University of Arkansas for Medical Sciences, MD
University of Central Arkansas, M

California

Azusa Pacific University, M
California State University, Bakersfield, M

California State University, Chico, M
California State University, Dominguez Hills, M
California State University, Fresno, M
California State University, Fullerton, BM
California State University, Long Beach, MO
California State University, Los Angeles, M
California State University, Sacramento, M
California State University, San Bernardino, M
Dominican University of California, M
Holy Names University, M
Loma Linda University, MO
Mount St. Mary's College, M
Point Loma Nazarene University, M
Samuel Merritt College, MO
San Diego State University, BM
San Francisco State University, M
San Jose State University, MO
University of California, Los Angeles, BMDO
University of Phoenix-Bay Area Campus, M
University of Phoenix-Sacramento Valley
    Campus, M
University of Phoenix-San Diego Campus, MO
University of Phoenix-Southern California
    Campus, MO
University of San Diego, MDO
University of San Francisco, MO

Colorado

Regis University, M
University of Colorado at Colorado Springs, M
University of Northern Colorado, M
University of Phoenix-Denver Campus, M
University of Phoenix-Southern Colorado
    Campus, M

Connecticut

Fairfield University, MO
Quinnipiac University, M
Sacred Heart University, MO
Saint Joseph College, MO
Southern Connecticut State University, M
University of Connecticut, MD
University of Hartford, M
Western Connecticut State University, M
Yale University, MDO

Delaware

University of Delaware, MO
Wesley College, M
Wilmington College, M

District of Columbia

The Catholic University of America, MD
Georgetown University, M
Howard University, MO

Florida

Barry University, MDO
Florida Agricultural and Mechanical University, M
Florida Atlantic University, MDO
Florida Gulf Coast University, M
Florida International University, MD
Florida Southern College, M
Florida State University, MO
Jacksonville University, M
Nova Southeastern University, M
University of Central Florida, MDO
University of Florida, MD
University of Miami, MD
University of North Florida, MO
University of Phoenix-Central Florida Campus, M
University of Phoenix-North Florida Campus, M
University of Phoenix-South Florida Campus, MO
University of Phoenix-West Florida Campus, M
University of South Florida, MD
The University of Tampa, MO

Georgia

Albany State University, M
Armstrong Atlantic State University, M
Emory University, MDO
Georgia College & State University, MO
Georgia Southern University, MO
Georgia State University, MDO
Kennesaw State University, M

Medical College of Georgia, MD
Mercer University, M
North Georgia College & State University, M
University of West Georgia, M
Valdosta State University, M

Hawaii

Hawaii Pacific University, M
University of Hawaii at Manoa, MDO
University of Phoenix-Hawaii Campus, M

Idaho

Idaho State University, MO

Illinois

Bradley University, M
DePaul University, M
Elmhurst College, M
Governors State University, M
Illinois State University, MO
Lewis University, MO
Loyola University Chicago, MDO
North Park University, MO
Northern Illinois University, M
Rush University, MDO
Saint Xavier University, MO
Southern Illinois University Edwardsville, MO
University of Illinois at Chicago, MDO
University of St. Francis, M

Indiana

Ball State University, M
Bethel College, M
Indiana State University, M
Indiana University-Purdue University Fort Wayne, M
Indiana University-Purdue University
    Indianapolis, MDO
Indiana Wesleyan University, MO
Purdue University Calumet, M
University of Evansville, M
University of Indianapolis, M
University of Saint Francis, BM
University of Southern Indiana, M
Valparaiso University, MO

Iowa

Allen College, M
Briar Cliff University, M
Clarke College, MO
Graceland University, MO
The University of Iowa, MDO

Kansas

Fort Hays State University, M
Pittsburg State University, M
University of Kansas, MDO
Wichita State University, MO

Kentucky

Bellarmine University, M
Big Sandy Community and Technical College, A
Eastern Kentucky University, BM
Murray State University, M
Northern Kentucky University, MO
Somerset Community College, A
Spalding University, M
Thomas More College, B
University of Kentucky, BMD
University of Louisville, M
Western Kentucky University, BM

Louisiana

Grambling State University, M
Louisiana State University Health Sciences
    Center, MD
Loyola University New Orleans, M
McNeese State University, M
Northwestern State University of Louisiana, M
Southeastern Louisiana University, M
Southern University and Agricultural and Mechanical
    College, MDO
University of Louisiana at Lafayette, M

University of Phoenix-Louisiana Campus, MO

Maine

Husson College, M
Saint Joseph's College of Maine, MO
University of Maine, MO
University of Southern Maine, MO

Maryland

Bowie State University, M
Coppin State University, MO
The Johns Hopkins University, MDO
Salisbury University, M
Towson University, MO

Massachusetts

American International College, M
Boston College, MDO
Northeastern University, BMO
Regis College, MO
Salem State College, MO
Simmons College, MO
University of Massachusetts Amherst, MDO
University of Massachusetts Boston, MDO
University of Massachusetts Dartmouth, B
University of Massachusetts Lowell, MD

Michigan

Andrews University, M
Ferris State University, M
Grand Valley State University, MO
Madonna University, ABMO
Michigan State University, MD
Northern Michigan University, M
Oakland University, MO
Saginaw Valley State University, M
University of Michigan, MDO
University of Michigan-Flint, M
University of Phoenix-Metro Detroit Campus, MO
University of Phoenix-West Michigan Campus, M
Wayne State University, D

Minnesota

Augsburg College, M
Bethel University, MO
College of St. Catherine, M
The College of St. Scholastica, M
Metropolitan State University, M
Minnesota State University Mankato, M
Minnesota State University Moorhead, M
University of Minnesota, Twin Cities Campus, MD
Winona State University, M

Mississippi

Alcorn State University, M
Delta State University, M
Mississippi University for Women, MO
University of Mississippi Medical Center, MD
University of Southern Mississippi, MD
William Carey College, M

Missouri

Avila University, B
Barnes-Jewish College of Nursing and Allied
    Health, M
Central Missouri State University, M
Maryville University of Saint Louis, M
Missouri State University, M
Research College of Nursing, M
Saint Louis University, MDO
Southeast Missouri State University, M
University of Missouri-Columbia, MD
University of Missouri-Kansas City, MD
University of Missouri-St. Louis, MD
Webster University, M

Montana

Montana State University, MO

Nebraska

Clarkson College, M
Creighton University, M
Nebraska Methodist College, M
Nebraska Wesleyan University, M

University of Nebraska Medical Center, MD

Nevada

University of Nevada, Las Vegas, MD
University of Nevada, Reno, M

New Hampshire

Rivier College, M
University of New Hampshire, M

New Jersey

The College of New Jersey, MO
Fairleigh Dickinson University, Metropolitan
 Campus, MO
Felician College, M
Kean University, MO
Monmouth University, MO
New Jersey City University, M
The Richard Stockton College of New Jersey, M
Rowan University, B
Rutgers, The State University of New Jersey,
 Newark, M
Saint Peter's College, M
Seton Hall University, MO
William Paterson University of New Jersey, M

New Mexico

New Mexico State University, M
University of New Mexico, MDO
University of Phoenix-New Mexico Campus, M

New York

Adelphi University, BMO
College of Mount Saint Vincent, MO
The College of New Rochelle, MO
College of Staten Island of the City University of
 New York, BMO
Daemen College, MO
Dominican College, M
D'Youville College, MO
Excelsior College, MO
Hunter College of the City University of New
 York, MO
Le Moyne College, B
Lehman College of the City University of New
 York, M
Long Island University, Brooklyn Campus, BMO
Long Island University, C.W. Post Campus, BMO
Mercy College, M
Molloy College, MO
Mount Saint Mary College, M
Nazareth College of Rochester, M
New York Institute of Technology, B
New York University, MDO
Pace University, MO
Roberts Wesleyan College, B
St. Francis College, B
State University of New York at Binghamton, MDO
State University of New York at Buffalo, BMDO
State University of New York Downstate Medical
 Center, MO
State University of New York Institute of
 Technology, MO
State University of New York at New Paltz, M
State University of New York Upstate Medical
 University, MO
Stony Brook University, State University of New
 York, MO
University of Rochester, MDO
Wagner College, M

North Carolina

Duke University, MO
East Carolina University, MD
Gardner-Webb University, MO
Queens University of Charlotte, M
The University of North Carolina at Chapel Hill, MD
The University of North Carolina at Charlotte, MO
The University of North Carolina at Greensboro, MO
The University of North Carolina Wilmington, M
Western Carolina University, M

North Dakota

Minot State University, B
North Dakota State University, MD

University of Mary, M
University of North Dakota, MD

Ohio

Capital University, BMO
Case Western Reserve University, MDO
Cincinnati State Technical and Community
 College, A
Cleveland State University, MO
College of Mount St. Joseph, M
Franciscan University of Steubenville, M
Kent State University, MD
Malone College, M
Mount Carmel College of Nursing, M
The Ohio State University, MD
The Ohio State University at Marion, MD
Otterbein College, MO
The University of Akron, BMD
University of Cincinnati, MDO
University of Phoenix-Cleveland Campus, M
The University of Toledo, B
Ursuline College, M
Wright State University, BMO
Xavier University, MO
Youngstown State University, M

Oklahoma

Rogers State University, A
Southern Nazarene University, M
University of Oklahoma Health Sciences
 Center, MO
University of Phoenix-Oklahoma City Campus, M

Oregon

Oregon Health & Science University, MDO
Tillamook Bay Community College, A
University of Portland, MO

Pennsylvania

Bloomsburg University of Pennsylvania, M
Carlow University, MO
Clarion University of Pennsylvania, M
College Misericordia, M
DeSales University, MO
Drexel University, MDO
Duquesne University, MDO
Edinboro University of Pennsylvania, M
Gannon University, MO
Gwynedd-Mercy College, M
Holy Family University, M
Immaculata University, M
Indiana University of Pennsylvania, M
La Roche College, M
La Salle University, MO
Mansfield University of Pennsylvania, M
Millersville University of Pennsylvania, M
Neumann College, M
The Pennsylvania State University University Park
 Campus, MD
Robert Morris University, M
Slippery Rock University of Pennsylvania, M
Temple University, M
Thomas Jefferson University, M
University of Pennsylvania, BMDO
University of Pittsburgh, MD
The University of Scranton, MO
Villanova University, MDO
West Chester University of Pennsylvania, M
Widener University, MDO
Wilkes University, M
York College of Pennsylvania, M

Puerto Rico

Caribbean University, B
Inter American University of Puerto Rico, Aguadilla
 Campus, AB
Pontifical Catholic University of Puerto Rico, M

University of Puerto Rico, Medical Sciences
 Campus, M

Rhode Island

Rhode Island College, B
University of Rhode Island, MD

South Carolina

Clemson University, M
Medical University of South Carolina, MDO
University of South Carolina, MDO

South Dakota

Augustana College, M
Mount Marty College, M
South Dakota State University, M
Southeast Technical Institute, A

Tennessee

Austin Peay State University, M
Belmont University, M
Carson-Newman College, M
East Tennessee State University, MDO
Middle Tennessee State University, M
Southern Adventist University, MO
Tennessee State University, MD
Tennessee Technological University, M
Union University, MO
The University of Tennessee, MD
The University of Tennessee at Chattanooga, M
Vanderbilt University, MDO

Texas

Abilene Christian University, M
Baylor University, M
East Texas Baptist University, B
Hardin-Simmons University, M
Lamar University, MO
Lubbock Christian University, B
Midwestern State University, M
Prairie View A&M University, M
Texas A&M University-Corpus Christi, M
Texas Christian University, M
Texas Woman's University, MD
University of the Incarnate Word, MO
The University of Texas at Arlington, MD
The University of Texas at Austin, MD
The University of Texas at El Paso, M
The University of Texas Health Science Center at
 Houston, MDO
The University of Texas Health Science Center at
 San Antonio, MD
The University of Texas Medical Branch, MD
The University of Texas-Pan American, M
The University of Texas at Tyler, MO
West Texas A&M University, M

Utah

Brigham Young University, M
University of Phoenix-Utah Campus, M
University of Utah, MD
Westminster College, M

Vermont

University of Vermont, M

Virginia

George Mason University, MD
Hampton University, M
James Madison University, M
Liberty University, MD
Marymount University, M
Old Dominion University, M
Radford University, M
Shenandoah University, MO
University of Virginia, MDO
Virginia Commonwealth University, MDO

Washington

Eastern Washington University, M
Gonzaga University, M
Pacific Lutheran University, M
Seattle Pacific University, MO
Seattle University, M
University of Washington, MDO

Washington State University, M
Whitworth College, M

West Virginia

Marshall University, M
Mountain State University, MO
West Virginia University, MDO
Wheeling Jesuit University, M

Wisconsin

Alverno College, B
Cardinal Stritch University, M
Concordia University Wisconsin, M
Edgewood College, M
Marian College of Fond du Lac, M
Marquette University, MDO
University of Wisconsin-Eau Claire, M
University of Wisconsin-Madison, MD
University of Wisconsin-Milwaukee, MDO
University of Wisconsin-Oshkosh, M
Viterbo University, M

Wyoming

University of Wyoming, M

Alberta

University of Alberta, MD
University of Calgary, MDO
University of Lethbridge, M

British Columbia

British Columbia Institute of Technology, AB
Malaspina University-College, B
The University of British Columbia, MD
University of Victoria, M

Manitoba

University of Manitoba, M

Newfoundland and Labrador

Memorial University of Newfoundland, M

Nova Scotia

Dalhousie University, MO

Ontario

McMaster University, MD
Queen's University at Kingston, M
University of Ottawa, MDO
University of Toronto, MDO
The University of Western Ontario, MD
University of Windsor, M
York University, M

Quebec

McGill University, MDO
Université Laval, MO
Université de Montréal, MDO
Université du Québec en Outaouais, MO
Université du Québec àTrois-Rivières, MO

Saskatchewan

University of Saskatchewan, M

NURSING ADMINISTRATION

Arizona

University of Phoenix-Phoenix Campus, M

California

Loma Linda University, MO
Samuel Merritt College, M
San Francisco State University, M
San Jose State University, M
University of Phoenix-Bay Area Campus, M
University of San Diego, M

University of San Francisco, BM

Colorado

University of Colorado at Colorado Springs, M

Connecticut

Sacred Heart University, M
Southern Connecticut State University, M

Delaware

University of Delaware, MO

Florida

Barry University, MDO
Florida Agricultural and Mechanical University, M
Florida Atlantic University, M
The University of Tampa, M

Georgia

Emory University, M
Valdosta State University, M

Hawaii

University of Hawaii at Manoa, M

Illinois

Bradley University, M
Lewis University, M
Loyola University Chicago, MO
Saint Xavier University, M
Southern Illinois University Edwardsville, MO
University of Illinois at Chicago, M

Indiana

Indiana University-Purdue University Fort Wayne, M
University of Phoenix-Indianapolis Campus, B

Iowa

Allen College, M
Clarke College, M
Graceland University, MO

Kansas

Wichita State University, M

Kentucky

Bellarmine University, M
Spalding University, M

Louisiana

Louisiana State University Health Sciences
    Center, MD
Southern University and Agricultural and Mechanical
    College, D

Maine

Saint Joseph's College of Maine, O

Maryland

Bowie State University, M
The Johns Hopkins University, M

Massachusetts

Emmanuel College, B
Northeastern University, MO
University of Massachusetts Lowell, D

Michigan

Ferris State University, M
Grand Valley State University, M
Madonna University, M
Saginaw Valley State University, M
University of Michigan, MO

University of Phoenix-Metro Detroit Campus, O

Minnesota

University of Minnesota, Twin Cities Campus, M
Winona State University, M

Mississippi

University of Southern Mississippi, MD

Missouri

Central Methodist University, B
University of Missouri-Kansas City, M

Nebraska

Clarkson College, BM
Nebraska Wesleyan University, B

New Hampshire

Rivier College, M

New Jersey

Kean University, M
Seton Hall University, M

New York

College of Mount Saint Vincent, M
The College of New Rochelle, M
Daemen College, M
Excelsior College, MO
Long Island University, Brooklyn Campus, M
Molloy College, O
State University of New York Institute of
    Technology, MO

North Carolina

Duke University, MO
Queens University of Charlotte, M
The University of North Carolina at Greensboro, M

North Dakota

University of Mary, M

Ohio

Capital University, M
Kent State University, M
Otterbein College, M
Wright State University, M
Xavier University, MO

Oregon

University of Portland, O

Pennsylvania

Carlow University, MO
Duquesne University, MO
Gannon University, M
La Roche College, M
La Salle University, M
Marywood University, M
University of Pennsylvania, MDO
University of Pittsburgh, M
Villanova University, MO

Puerto Rico

University of Puerto Rico, Medical Sciences
    Campus, M

Rhode Island

University of Rhode Island, M

South Carolina

Medical University of South Carolina, MO
University of South Carolina, M

Tennessee

Southern Adventist University, M
University of Phoenix-Nashville Campus, B
The University of Tennessee at Chattanooga, M
Vanderbilt University, M

Texas

Baylor University, M
Lamar University, MO

Texas A&M University-Corpus Christi, M
The University of Texas at Arlington, M
The University of Texas at El Paso, M
The University of Texas at Tyler, M

Virginia

George Mason University, M
Marymount University, MO
Virginia Commonwealth University, M

Washington

Pacific Lutheran University, M
Seattle Pacific University, M
Seattle University, M

West Virginia

Mountain State University, M
Wheeling Jesuit University, B

Alberta

Athabasca University, M

British Columbia

British Columbia Institute of Technology, A

Ontario

Ryerson University, B
The University of Western Ontario, B
University of Windsor, B

Saskatchewan

University of Saskatchewan, B

NURSING - ADULT

Alabama

University of South Alabama, M

California

University of San Diego, O

Colorado

University of Colorado at Colorado Springs, M

Connecticut

Quinnipiac University, M
Western Connecticut State University, M

Delaware

University of Delaware, MO

District of Columbia

The George Washington University, O

Florida

University of Central Florida, O
The University of Tampa, M

Georgia

Emory University, M
Georgia State University, M
Medical College of Georgia, M

Illinois

Loyola University Chicago, M
Saint Xavier University, M

Indiana

Indiana University-Purdue University Indianapolis, M

Kentucky

Spalding University, M

Louisiana

Louisiana State University Health Sciences
Center, MD

Maine

University of Southern Maine, MO

Michigan

Eastern Michigan University, M
Madonna University, M

Oakland University, M
University of Michigan, M

Minnesota

University of Minnesota, Twin Cities Campus, M
Winona State University, M

Mississippi

University of Southern Mississippi, M

Missouri

Barnes-Jewish College of Nursing and Allied
Health, M
University of Missouri-Kansas City, M

New Jersey

Seton Hall University, M

New York

College of Mount Saint Vincent, MO
College of Staten Island of the City University of
New York, MO
Hunter College of the City University of New
York, M
Lehman College of the City University of New
York, M
Molloy College, O
Mount Saint Mary College, M
New York University, MO
State University of New York at Buffalo, MO
State University of New York Institute of
Technology, MO
Stony Brook University, State University of New
York, MO

North Carolina

Duke University, O
The University of North Carolina at Charlotte, M

Ohio

Case Western Reserve University, M
Mount Carmel College of Nursing, M
Otterbein College, MO
Wright State University, M

Oregon

Oregon Health & Science University, MO

Pennsylvania

La Salle University, M
University of Pennsylvania, M
The University of Scranton, M
Villanova University, MO

South Carolina

Medical University of South Carolina, MO
University of South Carolina, M

Tennessee

Southern Adventist University, M
The University of Tennessee at Chattanooga, M
Vanderbilt University, M

Texas

Texas Christian University, M
The University of Texas-Pan American, M

Virginia

Virginia Commonwealth University, M

Wisconsin

Marian College of Fond du Lac, M
Marquette University, O

University of Wisconsin-Oshkosh, M

NURSING - ADVANCED PRACTICE

Arizona

University of Phoenix-Phoenix Campus, MO
University of Phoenix-Southern Arizona Campus, O

Arkansas

University of Central Arkansas, M

California

Holy Names University, M
Samuel Merritt College, MO
San Francisco State University, M
San Jose State University, M
Sonoma State University, M
University of Phoenix-Sacramento Valley
Campus, M
University of Phoenix-Southern California
Campus, MO
University of San Diego, MO
University of San Francisco, M

Colorado

University of Colorado at Colorado Springs, M
University of Northern Colorado, M

Connecticut

Fairfield University, MO
Quinnipiac University, M
Sacred Heart University, M
Saint Joseph College, M
Western Connecticut State University, M

Delaware

University of Delaware, MO
Wilmington College, M

District of Columbia

The Catholic University of America, M
The George Washington University, O
Howard University, O

Florida

Barry University, M
Florida State University, MO
University of North Florida, MO
The University of Tampa, M

Georgia

Brenau University, M
Emory University, M
Georgia Southern University, MO
Georgia State University, M
Kennesaw State University, M
Medical College of Georgia, M
North Georgia College & State University, M

Hawaii

Hawaii Pacific University, M
University of Hawaii at Manoa, M
University of Phoenix-Hawaii Campus, M

Illinois

DePaul University, M
Loyola University Chicago, M
Rush University, MDO
Saint Xavier University, MO
Southern Illinois University Edwardsville, MO

Indiana

Indiana University-Purdue University Indianapolis, M

Iowa

Allen College, M
Clarke College, MO

Graceland University, MO

Kentucky

Eastern Kentucky University, M
Spalding University, M

Louisiana

Grambling State University, M
Louisiana State University Health Sciences
  Center, M
Loyola University New Orleans, M
Southern University and Agricultural and Mechanical
  College, DO

Maine

Husson College, M
University of Southern Maine, M

Maryland

Bowie State University, M
Coppin State University, O
The Johns Hopkins University, MO

Massachusetts

Northeastern University, MO
Simmons College, MO

Michigan

Grand Valley State University, M
Madonna University, M
Oakland University, MO
Saginaw Valley State University, M
University of Detroit Mercy, MO
University of Michigan, M
Wayne State University, M

Minnesota

University of Minnesota, Twin Cities Campus, M
Winona State University, M

Mississippi

University of Southern Mississippi, M

Missouri

Barnes-Jewish College of Nursing and Allied
  Health, M
Research College of Nursing, M
University of Missouri-Kansas City, M

Montana

Montana State University, O

Nebraska

Clarkson College, M

Nevada

University of Nevada, Las Vegas, M

New Jersey

The College of New Jersey, MO
Felician College, M
Monmouth University, O
Seton Hall University, M

New York

College of Mount Saint Vincent, MO
Daemen College, MO
D'Youville College, MO
Hunter College of the City University of New
  York, MO
Long Island University, Brooklyn Campus, MO
Long Island University, C.W. Post Campus, MO
Mercy College, M
Molloy College, O
Mount Saint Mary College, M
New York University, MO
St. John Fisher College, MO
State University of New York at Buffalo, MO
State University of New York Downstate Medical
  Center, MO
State University of New York Institute of
  Technology, MO
State University of New York Upstate Medical
  University, O

Stony Brook University, State University of New
  York, MO
Wagner College, O

North Carolina

Duke University, M
The University of North Carolina at Charlotte, M

North Dakota

University of Mary, M

Ohio

Case Western Reserve University, M
Malone College, M
Otterbein College, O
University of Cincinnati, M
Wright State University, M

Oregon

Oregon Health & Science University, MO
University of Portland, O

Pennsylvania

Carlow University, MO
DeSales University, M
Duquesne University, MO
Edinboro University of Pennsylvania, M
Gannon University, MO
Gwynedd-Mercy College, M
La Roche College, M
La Salle University, M
University of Pennsylvania, MO
University of Pittsburgh, M
The University of Scranton, MO
Villanova University, MO

Puerto Rico

University of Puerto Rico, Medical Sciences
  Campus, M

South Carolina

Medical University of South Carolina, MO
University of South Carolina, MO

Tennessee

Carson-Newman College, M
East Tennessee State University, O
Southern Adventist University, M
The University of Tennessee at Chattanooga, M
Vanderbilt University, M

Texas

Baylor University, M
Hardin-Simmons University, M
Midwestern State University, M
Texas Woman's University, M
The University of Texas at Arlington, M
The University of Texas at El Paso, M
The University of Texas-Pan American, M
The University of Texas at Tyler, M

Virginia

George Mason University, M
Marymount University, MO
Shenandoah University, O
Virginia Commonwealth University, MO

Washington

Pacific Lutheran University, M
Seattle Pacific University, O
Seattle University, M

West Virginia

Mountain State University, M

Wisconsin

Concordia University Wisconsin, M
Marquette University, M

University of Wisconsin-Oshkosh, M

Alberta

Athabasca University, MO

Quebec

McGill University, O

NURSING EDUCATION

California

San Francisco State University, M
San Jose State University, M

Colorado

University of Northern Colorado, M

Connecticut

Southern Connecticut State University, M
University of Hartford, M

Florida

Barry University, M
Florida State University, MO
University of Central Florida, O
The University of Tampa, M

Illinois

Lewis University, M
Saint Francis Medical Center College of
  Nursing, M
Southern Illinois University Edwardsville, MO

Iowa

Clarke College, M
Graceland University, M

Kansas

University of Kansas, O
Wichita State University, M

Kentucky

Bellarmine University, M

Louisiana

Southern University and Agricultural and Mechanical
  College, D

Maine

Saint Joseph's College of Maine, O

Maryland

Bowie State University, M

Michigan

Eastern Michigan University, MO
Ferris State University, M
Grand Valley State University, M
Oakland University, M
Wayne State University, MO

Minnesota

Bethel University, MO
Minnesota State University Moorhead, M
University of Minnesota, Twin Cities Campus, M
Winona State University, M

Missouri

Barnes-Jewish College of Nursing and Allied
  Health, M
Research College of Nursing, M

University of Missouri-Kansas City, M

Nebraska

Clarkson College, M

New Hampshire

Rivier College, M

New Jersey

Seton Hall University, MO

New York

The College of New Rochelle, O
Molloy College, O
New York University, M

North Carolina

Duke University, M

North Dakota

University of Mary, M

Ohio

Kent State University, M
Mount Carmel College of Nursing, M

Oregon

University of Portland, O

Pennsylvania

DeSales University, M
Duquesne University, MO
La Salle University, O
University of Pittsburgh, M
Villanova University, MO
West Chester University of Pennsylvania, M

Puerto Rico

University of Puerto Rico, Medical Sciences
Campus, M

Rhode Island

University of Rhode Island, M

South Carolina

Medical University of South Carolina, M

Tennessee

Union University, MO
The University of Tennessee at Chattanooga, M

Texas

Lamar University, M
Midwestern State University, M
Texas Woman's University, M
The University of Texas at Arlington, M
The University of Texas at Tyler, M

Virginia

Marymount University, M

Washington

Eastern Washington University, M

West Virginia

Mountain State University, M

Wisconsin

Concordia University Wisconsin, M
Marian College of Fond du Lac, M

NURSING - REGISTERED NURSE TRAINING

Alabama

Alabama Southern Community College, A
Auburn University, B
Auburn University Montgomery, B
Bevill State Community College, A
Bishop State Community College, A
Calhoun Community College, A

Central Alabama Community College, A
Chattahoochee Valley Community College, A
Gadsden State Community College, A
George C. Wallace Community College, A
George Corley Wallace State Community College, A
Jacksonville State University, B
James H. Faulkner State Community College, A
Jefferson Davis Community College, A
Jefferson State Community College, A
Lawson State Community College, A
Northeast Alabama Community College, A
Northwest-Shoals Community College, A
Oakwood College, AB
Samford University, B
Shelton State Community College, A
Southern Union State Community College, A
Spring Hill College, B
Troy University, AB
Tuskegee University, B
The University of Alabama, B
The University of Alabama at Birmingham, B
The University of Alabama in Huntsville, B
University of Mobile, AB
University of North Alabama, B
University of South Alabama, B
The University of West Alabama, A
Wallace State Community College, A

Alaska

University of Alaska Anchorage, AB

Arizona

Arizona State University, B
Arizona Western College, A
Central Arizona College, A
Cochise College (Douglas), A
Cochise College (Sierra Vista), A
Eastern Arizona College, A
GateWay Community College, A
Glendale Community College, A
Grand Canyon University, B
International Institute of the Americas (Phoenix), A
Mesa Community College, A
Mohave Community College, A
Northern Arizona University, B
Northland Pioneer College, A
Phoenix College, A
Pima Community College, A
Scottsdale Community College, A
The University of Arizona, B
University of Phoenix-Southern Arizona Campus, B
Yavapai College, A

Arkansas

Arkansas Northeastern College, A
Arkansas State University, AB
Arkansas State University-Beebe, A
Arkansas Tech University, B
Black River Technical College, A
Harding University, B
Henderson State University, B
National Park Community College, A
North Arkansas College, A
NorthWest Arkansas Community College, A
Phillips Community College of the University of
Arkansas, A
Southern Arkansas University-Magnolia, A
University of Arkansas, B
University of Arkansas Community College at
Batesville, A
University of Arkansas at Fort Smith, AB
University of Arkansas at Little Rock, A
University of Arkansas for Medical Sciences, B
University of Arkansas at Monticello, B
University of Arkansas at Pine Bluff, B
University of Central Arkansas, B

California

Allan Hancock College, A
American River College, A
Antelope Valley College, A
Azusa Pacific University, B
Bakersfield College, A
Biola University, B
Butte College, A
Cabrillo College, A

California State University, Bakersfield, B
California State University, Chico, B
California State University, Dominguez Hills, B
California State University, East Bay, B
California State University, Fresno, B
California State University, Fullerton, B
California State University, Long Beach, B
California State University, Los Angeles, B
California State University, Northridge, B
California State University, Sacramento, B
California State University, San Bernardino, B
California State University, Stanislaus, B
Cerritos College, A
Chabot College, A
Chaffey College, A
City College of San Francisco, A
College of the Canyons, A
College of the Desert, A
College of Marin, A
College of the Redwoods, A
College of San Mateo, A
College of the Sequoias, A
Compton Community College, A
Contra Costa College, A
Cuesta College, A
Cypress College, A
De Anza College, A
Dominican University of California, B
East Los Angeles College, A
El Camino College, A
Evergreen Valley College, A
Fresno City College, A
Gavilan College, A
Glendale Community College, A
Golden West College, A
Grossmont College, A
Hartnell College, A
Holy Names University, B
Humboldt State University, B
Imperial Valley College, A
Lassen Community College District, A
Loma Linda University, AB
Long Beach City College, A
Los Angeles Harbor College, A
Los Angeles Pierce College, A
Los Angeles Southwest College, A
Los Angeles Trade-Technical College, A
Los Angeles Valley College, A
Los Medanos College, A
Maric College (San Diego), A
Merced College, A
Merritt College, A
Modesto Junior College, A
Monterey Peninsula College, A
Moorpark College, A
Mount St. Mary's College, AB
Mt. San Antonio College, A
Mt. San Jacinto College, A
Napa Valley College, A
Ohlone College, A
Pacific Union College, AB
Palomar College, A
Pasadena City College, A
Point Loma Nazarene University, B
Rio Hondo College, A
Riverside Community College District, A
Sacramento City College, A
Saddleback College, A
Saint Mary's College of California, B
Samuel Merritt College, B
San Bernardino Valley College, A
San Diego City College, A
San Diego State University, B
San Francisco State University, B
San Joaquin Delta College, A
San Joaquin Valley College, A
San Jose State University, B
Santa Ana College, A
Santa Barbara City College, A
Santa Monica College, A
Santa Rosa Junior College, A
Shasta College, A
Sierra College, A
Solano Community College, A
Sonoma State University, B
Southwestern College, A

University of California, Los Angeles, B
University of San Francisco, B
Ventura College, A
Victor Valley College, A
Yuba College, A

Colorado

Arapahoe Community College, A
Colorado Mountain College, A
Colorado Northwestern Community College, A
Colorado State University-Pueblo, B
Community College of Denver, A
Front Range Community College, A
Lamar Community College, A
Mesa State College, AB
Metropolitan State College of Denver, B
Northeastern Junior College, A
Otero Junior College, A
Pikes Peak Community College, A
Pueblo Community College, A
Regis University, B
Trinidad State Junior College, A
University of Colorado at Colorado Springs, B
University of Colorado at Denver and Health
    Sciences Center - Downtown Denver Campus, B
University of Northern Colorado, B

Connecticut

Capital Community College, A
Central Connecticut State University, B
Fairfield University, B
Goodwin College, A
Housatonic Community College, A
Naugatuck Valley Community College, A
Norwalk Community College, A
Quinnipiac University, B
Sacred Heart University, B
Saint Joseph College, B
St. Vincent's College, A
Southern Connecticut State University, B
Three Rivers Community College, A
University of Connecticut, B
University of Hartford, B
Western Connecticut State University, B

Delaware

Delaware State University, B
Delaware Technical & Community College, Jack F.
    Owens Campus, A
Delaware Technical & Community College,
    Stanton/Wilmington Campus, A
Delaware Technical & Community College, Terry
    Campus, A
University of Delaware, B
Wesley College, B
Wilmington College, B

District of Columbia

The Catholic University of America, B
Georgetown University, B
Howard University, B
University of the District of Columbia, AB

Florida

Barry University, B
Bethune-Cookman College, B
Brevard Community College, A
Broward Community College, A
Central Florida Community College, A
Chipola College, A
Daytona Beach Community College, A
Edison College, A
Florida Agricultural and Mechanical University, B
Florida Atlantic University, B
Florida Community College at Jacksonville, A
Florida Gulf Coast University, B
Florida Hospital College of Health Sciences, AB
Florida International University, B
Florida Keys Community College, A
Florida Southern College, B
Florida State University, B
Gulf Coast Community College, A
Hillsborough Community College, A
Indian River Community College, A
Jacksonville University, B

Keiser College (Miami), A
Lake City Community College, A
Lake-Sumter Community College, A
Lynn University, B
Manatee Community College, A
Miami Dade College, A
Nova Southeastern University, B
Okaloosa-Walton College, AB
Palm Beach Atlantic University, B
Palm Beach Community College, A
Pasco-Hernando Community College, A
Pensacola Junior College, A
Polk Community College, A
St. Johns River Community College, A
St. Petersburg College, A
Santa Fe Community College, A
Seminole Community College, A
South Florida Community College, A
South University (West Palm Beach), B
Tallahassee Community College, A
University of Central Florida, B
University of Florida, B
University of Miami, B
University of North Florida, B
University of Phoenix-West Florida Campus, B
University of South Florida, B
The University of Tampa, B
University of West Florida, B
Valencia Community College, A

Georgia

Abraham Baldwin Agricultural College, A
Albany State University, B
Armstrong Atlantic State University, B
Athens Technical College, A
Augusta State University, A
Bainbridge College, A
Berry College, B
Brenau University, B
Clayton State University, B
Coastal Georgia Community College, A
Columbus State University, B
Columbus Technical College, A
Covenant College, AB
Dalton State College, A
Darton College, A
East Georgia College, A
Emory University, B
Georgia College & State University, B
Georgia Highlands College, A
Georgia Perimeter College, A
Georgia Southern University, B
Georgia Southwestern State University, B
Georgia State University, B
Gordon College, A
Kennesaw State University, B
LaGrange College, B
Macon State College, AB
Medical College of Georgia, B
Mercer University, B
Middle Georgia College, A
North Georgia College & State University, AB
Northwestern Technical College, A
Piedmont College, B
Reinhardt College, A
South Georgia College, A
Southwest Georgia Technical College, A
Thomas University, AB
University of West Georgia, B
Valdosta State University, B
Waycross College, A
West Central Technical College, A
Young Harris College, A

Guam

University of Guam, B

Hawaii

Hawaii Community College, A
Hawaii Pacific University, B
Kapiolani Community College, A
Kauai Community College, A
Maui Community College, A
University of Hawaii at Hilo, B
University of Hawaii at Manoa, B

University of Phoenix-Hawaii Campus, B

Idaho

Boise State University, AB
Brigham Young University -Idaho, A
College of Southern Idaho, A
Idaho State University, B
Lewis-Clark State College, B
North Idaho College, A
Northwest Nazarene University, B

Illinois

Aurora University, B
Black Hawk College, A
Blessing-Rieman College of Nursing, B
Bradley University, B
Carl Sandburg College, A
Chicago State University, B
City Colleges of Chicago, Harry S. Truman
    College, A
City Colleges of Chicago, Kennedy-King College, A
City Colleges of Chicago, Malcolm X College, A
City Colleges of Chicago, Olive-Harvey College, A
City Colleges of Chicago, Richard J. Daley
    College, A
College of DuPage, A
College of Lake County, A
Concordia University, B
Danville Area Community College, A
DePaul University, B
Elgin Community College, A
Elmhurst College, B
Eureka College, B
Governors State University, B
Heartland Community College, A
Highland Community College, A
Illinois Central College, A
Illinois Eastern Community Colleges, Frontier
    Community College, A
Illinois Eastern Community Colleges, Olney Central
    College, A
Illinois State University, B
Illinois Valley Community College, A
Illinois Wesleyan University, B
John A. Logan College, A
John Wood Community College, A
Joliet Junior College, A
Judson College, B
Kankakee Community College, A
Kaskaskia College, A
Kishwaukee College, A
Lake Land College, A
Lakeview College of Nursing, B
Lewis and Clark Community College, A
Lewis University, B
Lincoln College, A
Lincoln College-Normal, A
Lincoln Land Community College, A
Loyola University Chicago, B
MacMurray College, B
McKendree College, B
Millikin University, B
Moraine Valley Community College, A
Morton College, A
North Park University, B
Northern Illinois University, B
Oakton Community College, A
Olivet Nazarene University, B
Parkland College, A
Prairie State College, A
Quincy University, B
Rend Lake College, A
Richland Community College, A
Rock Valley College, A
Rockford College, B
Rush University, B
Saint Anthony College of Nursing, B
Saint Francis Medical Center College of Nursing, B
St. John's College, B
Saint Xavier University, B
Sauk Valley Community College, A
Shawnee Community College, A
South Suburban College, A
Southeastern Illinois College, A
Southern Illinois University Edwardsville, B
Southwestern Illinois College, A

Spoon River College, A
Trinity Christian College, B
Trinity College of Nursing and Health Sciences, AB
Triton College, A
University of Illinois at Chicago, B
University of St. Francis, B
Waubonsee Community College, A
West Suburban College of Nursing, B
William Rainey Harper College, A

Indiana

Ancilla College, A
Anderson University, B
Ball State University, AB
Bethel College, AB
Goshen College, B
Indiana State University, B
Indiana University East, AB
Indiana University Kokomo, AB
Indiana University Northwest, AB
Indiana University-Purdue University Fort
   Wayne, AB
Indiana University-Purdue University
   Indianapolis, AB
Indiana University South Bend, AB
Indiana University Southeast, B
Indiana Wesleyan University, B
Ivy Tech Community College-Bloomington, A
Ivy Tech Community College-Central Indiana, A
Ivy Tech Community College-East Central, A
Ivy Tech Community College-Lafayette, A
Ivy Tech Community College-North Central, A
Ivy Tech Community College-Northwest, A
Ivy Tech Community College-Southeast, A
Ivy Tech Community College-Southern Indiana, A
Ivy Tech Community College-Southwest, A
Ivy Tech Community College-Wabash Valley, A
Ivy Tech Community College-Whitewater, A
Marian College, B
Purdue University, B
Purdue University Calumet, AB
Purdue University North Central, AB
Saint Joseph's College, B
Saint Mary's College, B
University of Evansville, B
University of Indianapolis, AB
University of Saint Francis, AB
University of Southern Indiana, AB
Valparaiso University, B
Vincennes University, A

Iowa

Allen College, B
Briar Cliff University, B
Clinton Community College, A
Coe College, B
Des Moines Area Community College, A
Dordt College, B
Ellsworth Community College, A
Graceland University, B
Grand View College, B
Hawkeye Community College, A
Indian Hills Community College, A
Iowa Central Community College, A
Iowa Lakes Community College, A
Iowa Wesleyan College, B
Iowa Western Community College, A
Kirkwood Community College, A
Luther College, B
Marshalltown Community College, A
Mercy College of Health Sciences, A
Morningside College, B
Mount Mercy College, B
North Iowa Area Community College, A
Northeast Iowa Community College, A
Northwest Iowa Community College, A
St. Ambrose University, B
St. Luke's College, A
Scott Community College, A
Southeastern Community College, North Campus, A
Southeastern Community College, South
   Campus, A
University of Dubuque, B
The University of Iowa, B

Western Iowa Tech Community College, A

Kansas

Baker University, B
Barton County Community College, A
Bethel College, B
Butler Community College, A
Central Christian College of Kansas, A
Cloud County Community College, A
Coffeyville Community College, A
Colby Community College, A
Dodge City Community College, A
Donnelly College, A
Emporia State University, B
Fort Hays State University, B
Fort Scott Community College, A
Garden City Community College, A
Hesston College, A
Highland Community College, A
Hutchinson Community College and Area Vocational
   School, A
Johnson County Community College, A
Kansas City Kansas Community College, A
Kansas Wesleyan University, AB
Labette Community College, A
Manhattan Area Technical College, A
MidAmerica Nazarene University, B
Neosho County Community College, A
Newman University, B
Pittsburg State University, B
Pratt Community College, A
Seward County Community College, A
Southwestern College, B
Washburn University, B

Kentucky

Ashland Community and Technical College, A
Beckfield College, B
Bellarmine University, B
Berea College, B
Big Sandy Community and Technical College, A
Eastern Kentucky University, AB
Elizabethtown Community and Technical College, A
Hazard Community and Technical College, A
Henderson Community College, A
Hopkinsville Community College, A
Jefferson Community and Technical College, A
Kentucky Christian University, B
Kentucky State University, AB
Lexington Community College, A
Madisonville Community College, A
Maysville Community and Technical College, A
Midway College, AB
Morehead State University, AB
Murray State University, B
Northern Kentucky University, AB
Owensboro Community and Technical College, A
Pikeville College, A
St. Catharine College, A
Somerset Community College, A
Southeast Kentucky Community and Technical
   College, A
Spalding University, B
Thomas More College, B
University of Kentucky, B
University of Louisville, B
West Kentucky Community and Technical College, A
Western Kentucky University, AB

Louisiana

Delgado Community College, A
Dillard University, B
Grambling State University, B
Louisiana College, B
Louisiana State University at Alexandria, A
Louisiana State University at Eunice, A
Louisiana State University Health Sciences
   Center, B
Louisiana Tech University, A
Loyola University New Orleans, B
McNeese State University, AB
Nicholls State University, AB
Northwestern State University of Louisiana, AB
Our Lady of Holy Cross College, B
Our Lady of the Lake College, AB
Southeastern Louisiana University, B

Southern University and Agricultural and Mechanical
   College, B
University of Louisiana at Lafayette, B
University of Louisiana at Monroe, B

Maine

Central Maine Community College, A
Central Maine Medical Center School of Nursing, A
Eastern Maine Community College, A
Husson College, B
Kennebec Valley Community College, A
Northern Maine Community College, A
Saint Joseph's College of Maine, B
Southern Maine Community College, A
University of Maine, B
The University of Maine at Augusta, A
University of Maine at Fort Kent, B
University of New England, AB
University of Southern Maine, B

Maryland

Allegany College of Maryland, A
Anne Arundel Community College, A
Baltimore City Community College, A
Bowie State University, B
Carroll Community College, A
Cecil Community College, A
College of Notre Dame of Maryland, B
College of Southern Maryland, A
Columbia Union College, B
Coppin State University, B
Frederick Community College, A
Hagerstown Community College, A
Harford Community College, A
Howard Community College, A
The Johns Hopkins University, B
Montgomery College, A
Prince George's Community College, A
Salisbury University, B
Towson University, B
Villa Julie College, B
Wor-Wic Community College, A

Massachusetts

American International College, B
Anna Maria College, B
Atlantic Union College, AB
Becker College, A
Berkshire Community College, A
Boston College, B
Bristol Community College, A
Bunker Hill Community College, A
Cape Cod Community College, A
Curry College, B
Elms College, B
Endicott College, B
Fitchburg State College, B
Framingham State College, B
Greenfield Community College, A
Holyoke Community College, A
Labouré College, A
Massachusetts Bay Community College, A
Massasoit Community College, A
Middlesex Community College, A
Mount Wachusett Community College, A
North Shore Community College, A
Northern Essex Community College, A
Quincy College, A
Quinsigamond Community College, A
Regis College, AB
Roxbury Community College, A
Salem State College, B
Simmons College, B
Springfield Technical Community College, A
University of Massachusetts Amherst, B
University of Massachusetts Boston, B
University of Massachusetts Dartmouth, B
University of Massachusetts Lowell, B
Worcester State College, B

Michigan

Alpena Community College, A
Andrews University, B
Baker College of Clinton Township, A
Baker College of Flint, A
Baker College of Muskegon, A

Baker College of Owosso, A
Bay de Noc Community College, A
Calvin College, B
Davenport University (Dearborn), AB
Davenport University (Midland), A
Delta College, A
Eastern Michigan University, B
Ferris State University, AB
Finlandia University, B
Glen Oaks Community College, A
Gogebic Community College, A
Grand Rapids Community College, A
Grand Valley State University, B
Henry Ford Community College, A
Hope College, B
Jackson Community College, A
Kalamazoo Valley Community College, A
Kellogg Community College, A
Kirtland Community College, A
Kuyper College, B
Lake Michigan College, A
Lake Superior State University, B
Lansing Community College, A
Macomb Community College, A
Madonna University, B
Michigan State University, B
Mid Michigan Community College, A
Monroe County Community College, A
Montcalm Community College, A
Mott Community College, A
Muskegon Community College, A
North Central Michigan College, A
Northern Michigan University, B
Northwestern Michigan College, A
Oakland Community College, A
Oakland University, B
Saginaw Valley State University, B
St. Clair County Community College, A
Schoolcraft College, A
Southwestern Michigan College, A
University of Detroit Mercy, B
University of Michigan, B
University of Michigan-Flint, B
University of Phoenix-West Michigan Campus, B
Washtenaw Community College, A
Wayne County Community College District, A
Wayne State University, B
West Shore Community College, A
Western Michigan University, B

Minnesota

Anoka-Ramsey Community College, A
Anoka-Ramsey Community College, Cambridge
  Campus, A
Augsburg College, B
Bemidji State University, B
Bethel University, B
Central Lakes College, A
Century College, A
College of Saint Benedict, B
College of St. Catherine, B
College of St. Catherine-Minneapolis, A
The College of St. Scholastica, B
Concordia College, B
Crown College, B
Globe College, B
Gustavus Adolphus College, B
Hibbing Community College, A
Inver Hills Community College, A
Lake Superior College, A
Metropolitan State University, B
Minneapolis Community and Technical College, A
Minnesota School of Business, B
Minnesota State College-Southeast Technical, A
Minnesota State Community and Technical
  College-Fergus Falls, A
Minnesota State University Mankato, B
Minnesota State University Moorhead, B
Normandale Community College, A
North Central University, B
North Hennepin Community College, A
Northland Community and Technical College-Thief
  River Falls, A
Ridgewater College, A
Riverland Community College, A
Rochester Community and Technical College, A

St. Cloud State University, B
Saint John's University, B
St. Olaf College, B
South Central Technical College, A
University of Minnesota, Twin Cities Campus, B
Winona State University, B

Mississippi

Alcorn State University, AB
Copiah-Lincoln Community College, A
Delta State University, B
East Central Community College, A
Hinds Community College, A
Holmes Community College, A
Itawamba Community College, A
Jones County Junior College, A
Meridian Community College, A
Mississippi College, B
Mississippi Delta Community College, A
Mississippi Gulf Coast Community College, A
Mississippi University for Women, AB
Northeast Mississippi Community College, A
Northwest Mississippi Community College, A
Pearl River Community College, A
Southwest Mississippi Community College, A
University of Mississippi Medical Center, B
University of Southern Mississippi, B
William Carey College, B

Missouri

Barnes-Jewish College of Nursing and Allied
  Health, AB
Central Methodist University, B
Central Missouri State University, B
Chamberlain College of Nursing, AB
Columbia College, A
Cox College of Nursing and Health Sciences, AB
Crowder College, A
Culver-Stockton College, B
East Central College, A
Hannibal-LaGrange College, AB
Jefferson College, A
Lincoln University, AB
Maryville University of Saint Louis, B
Mineral Area College, A
Missouri Southern State University, B
Missouri State University, B
Missouri State University-West Plains, A
Missouri Western State University, B
Moberly Area Community College, A
North Central Missouri College, A
Park University, A
Penn Valley Community College, A
Research College of Nursing, B
Rockhurst University, B
Saint Charles Community College, A
St. Louis Community College at Florissant Valley, A
St. Louis Community College at Forest Park, A
St. Louis Community College at Meramec, A
Saint Louis University, B
Saint Luke's College, B
Sanford-Brown College (St. Charles), A
Southeast Missouri State University, B
Southwest Baptist University, A
State Fair Community College, A
Three Rivers Community College, A
Truman State University, B
University of Missouri-Columbia, B
University of Missouri-Kansas City, B
University of Missouri-St. Louis, B
Webster University, B
William Jewell College, B

Montana

Carroll College, B
Miles Community College, A
Montana State University, B
Montana State University-Northern, AB
Montana Tech of The University of Montana, A
Salish Kootenai College, A

Nebraska

Central Community College-Grand Island
  Campus, A
Clarkson College, B
College of Saint Mary, AB

Creighton University, B
Grace University, B
Metropolitan Community College, A
Mid-Plains Community College, A
Midland Lutheran College, B
Nebraska Methodist College, AB
Northeast Community College, A
Southeast Community College, Lincoln Campus, A
Union College, B
University of Nebraska Medical Center, B
Western Nebraska Community College, A

Nevada

Community College of Southern Nevada, A
Great Basin College, AB
Nevada State College at Henderson, B
Truckee Meadows Community College, A
University of Nevada, Las Vegas, B
University of Nevada, Reno, B
Western Nevada Community College, A

New Hampshire

Colby-Sawyer College, B
New Hampshire Community Technical College,
  Berlin/Laconia, A
New Hampshire Community Technical College,
  Manchester/Stratham, A
New Hampshire Technical Institute, A
Rivier College, AB
University of New Hampshire, B

New Jersey

Atlantic Cape Community College, A
Bergen Community College, A
Bloomfield College, B
Brookdale Community College, A
Burlington County College, A
Camden County College, A
The College of New Jersey, B
County College of Morris, A
Cumberland County College, A
Essex County College, A
Fairleigh Dickinson University, Metropolitan
  Campus, B
Felician College, AB
Gloucester County College, A
Mercer County Community College, A
Middlesex County College, A
New Jersey Institute of Technology, B
Ocean County College, A
Passaic County Community College, A
Ramapo College of New Jersey, B
Raritan Valley Community College, A
The Richard Stockton College of New Jersey, B
Rutgers, The State University of New Jersey,
  Camden, B
Rutgers, The State University of New Jersey, New
  Brunswick/Piscataway, B
Rutgers, The State University of New Jersey,
  Newark, B
Seton Hall University, B
Union County College, A
William Paterson University of New Jersey, B

New Mexico

Central New Mexico Community College, A
Clovis Community College, A
Doña Ana Branch Community College, A
Eastern New Mexico University, B
Eastern New Mexico University-Roswell, A
New Mexico Junior College, A
New Mexico State University, B
New Mexico State University-Alamogordo, A
New Mexico State University-Carlsbad, A
San Juan College, A
Santa Fe Community College, A
University of New Mexico, B
University of New Mexico-Gallup, AB
University of Phoenix-New Mexico Campus, B
Western New Mexico University, A

New York

Adelphi University, B
Adirondack Community College, A

Borough of Manhattan Community College of the City University of New York, A
Bronx Community College of the City University of New York, A
Broome Community College, A
Cayuga County Community College, A
Clinton Community College, A
Cochran School of Nursing, A
College of Mount Saint Vincent, B
The College of New Rochelle, B
College of Staten Island of the City University of New York, A
Columbia-Greene Community College, A
Corning Community College, A
Crouse Hospital School of Nursing, A
Daemen College, B
Dominican College, B
Dutchess Community College, A
D'Youville College, B
Ellis Hospital School of Nursing, A
Elmira College, B
Erie Community College, A
Erie Community College, North Campus, A
Eugenio María de Hostos Community College of the City University of New York, A
Excelsior College, AB
Farmingdale State University of New York, A
Finger Lakes Community College, A
Fiorello H. LaGuardia Community College of the City University of New York, A
Fulton-Montgomery Community College, A
Genesee Community College, A
Hartwick College, B
Helene Fuld College of Nursing of North General Hospital, A
Hudson Valley Community College, A
Hunter College of the City University of New York, B
Jamestown Community College, A
Jefferson Community College, A
Keuka College, B
Kingsborough Community College of the City University of New York, A
Lehman College of the City University of New York, B
Long Island College Hospital School of Nursing, A
Long Island University, Brooklyn Campus, B
Long Island University, C.W. Post Campus, B
Maria College, A
Medgar Evers College of the City University of New York, B
Mercy College, B
Mohawk Valley Community College, A
Molloy College, B
Monroe Community College, A
Mount Saint Mary College, B
Nassau Community College, A
Nazareth College of Rochester, B
New York City College of Technology of the City University of New York, A
New York Institute of Technology, B
New York University, B
Niagara County Community College, A
North Country Community College, A
Onondaga Community College, A
Orange County Community College, A
Pace University, B
Phillips Beth Israel School of Nursing, A
Queensborough Community College of the City University of New York, A
Roberts Wesleyan College, B
Rockland Community College, A
Russell Sage College, B
St. John Fisher College, B
St. John's University, B
St. Joseph's College, New York, B
St. Joseph's College, Suffolk Campus, B
Saint Joseph's Hospital Health Center School of Nursing, A
Saint Vincent Catholic Medical Centers School of Nursing, A
Samaritan Hospital School of Nursing, A
State University of New York at Binghamton, B
State University of New York at Buffalo, B
State University of New York College of Agriculture and Technology at Morrisville, A

State University of New York College at Brockport, B
State University of New York College of Technology at Alfred, A
State University of New York College of Technology at Canton, A
State University of New York College of Technology at Delhi, A
State University of New York Downstate Medical Center, B
State University of New York Institute of Technology, B
State University of New York at New Paltz, B
State University of New York at Plattsburgh, B
Stony Brook University, State University of New York, B
Suffolk County Community College, A
Sullivan County Community College, A
Tompkins Cortland Community College, A
Trocaire College, A
Ulster County Community College, A
University of Rochester, B
Utica College, B
Wagner College, B
Westchester Community College, A
York College of the City University of New York, B

North Carolina

Alamance Community College, A
Asheville-Buncombe Technical Community College, A
Barton College, B
Beaufort County Community College, A
Bladen Community College, A
Blue Ridge Community College, A
Brunswick Community College, A
Cabarrus College of Health Sciences, AB
Caldwell Community College and Technical Institute, A
Cape Fear Community College, A
Carolinas College of Health Sciences, A
Catawba Valley Community College, A
Central Carolina Community College, A
Central Piedmont Community College, A
Cleveland Community College, A
Coastal Carolina Community College, A
College of The Albemarle, A
Craven Community College, A
Davidson County Community College, A
Durham Technical Community College, A
East Carolina University, B
Edgecombe Community College, A
Fayetteville State University, B
Fayetteville Technical Community College, A
Forsyth Technical Community College, A
Gardner-Webb University, AB
Gaston College, A
Guilford Technical Community College, A
Halifax Community College, A
Haywood Community College, A
James Sprunt Community College, A
Johnston Community College, A
Lenoir Community College, A
Lenoir-Rhyne College, B
Louisburg College, A
Mayland Community College, A
McDowell Technical Community College, A
Mitchell Community College, A
Nash Community College, A
North Carolina Agricultural and Technical State University, B
North Carolina Central University, B
Piedmont Community College, A
Pitt Community College, A
Randolph Community College, A
Richmond Community College, A
Roanoke-Chowan Community College, A
Robeson Community College, A
Rockingham Community College, A
Rowan-Cabarrus Community College, A
Sampson Community College, A
Sandhills Community College, A
Southeastern Community College, A
Southwestern Community College, A
Stanly Community College, A
Surry Community College, A

Tri-County Community College, A
The University of North Carolina at Chapel Hill, B
The University of North Carolina at Charlotte, B
The University of North Carolina at Greensboro, B
The University of North Carolina at Pembroke, B
The University of North Carolina Wilmington, B
Vance-Granville Community College, A
Wake Technical Community College, A
Wayne Community College, A
Western Carolina University, B
Western Piedmont Community College, A
Wilkes Community College, A
Wilson Technical Community College, A
Winston-Salem State University, B

North Dakota

Dickinson State University, B
Jamestown College, B
Medcenter One College of Nursing, B
Minot State University, B
North Dakota State University, B
Turtle Mountain Community College, A
University of Mary, B
University of North Dakota, B

Ohio

Belmont Technical College, A
Bowling Green State University, B
Bowling Green State University-Firelands College, A
Bryant and Stratton College (Parma), A
Capital University, B
Case Western Reserve University, B
Cedarville University, B
Central Ohio Technical College, A
Cincinnati State Technical and Community College, A
Clark State Community College, A
Cleveland State University, B
College of Mount St. Joseph, B
Columbus State Community College, A
Cuyahoga Community College, A
Edison State Community College, A
Franciscan University of Steubenville, B
Hocking College, A
James A. Rhodes State College, A
Kent State University, AB
Kent State University, Ashtabula Campus, A
Kent State University, East Liverpool Campus, A
Kent State University, Salem Campus, A
Kent State University, Tuscarawas Campus, AB
Kettering College of Medical Arts, A
Lakeland Community College, A
Lorain County Community College, A
Lourdes College, B
Malone College, B
Marion Technical College, A
MedCentral College of Nursing, B
Mercy College of Northwest Ohio, AB
Miami University, B
Miami University-Middletown Campus, AB
North Central State College, A
Northwest State Community College, A
The Ohio State University, B
Ohio University-Chillicothe, AB
Ohio University-Eastern, B
Ohio University-Southern Campus, AB
Ohio University-Zanesville, AB
Otterbein College, B
Owens Community College, A
Shawnee State University, AB
Sinclair Community College, A
Southern State Community College, A
Stark State College of Technology, A
The University of Akron, B
University of Cincinnati, AB
University of Cincinnati Raymond Walters College, A
University of Rio Grande, A
The University of Toledo, AB
Ursuline College, B
Walsh University, AB
Washington State Community College, A
Wright State University, B

Youngstown State University, B

Oklahoma

Bacone College, AB
Carl Albert State College, A
Connors State College, A
East Central University, B
Eastern Oklahoma State College, A
Hillsdale Free Will Baptist College, A
Langston University, B
Murray State College, A
Northeastern Oklahoma Agricultural and Mechanical
    College, A
Northeastern State University, B
Northern Oklahoma College, A
Northwestern Oklahoma State University, B
Oklahoma Baptist University, B
Oklahoma City Community College, A
Oklahoma City University, B
Oklahoma Panhandle State University, AB
Oklahoma State University, Oklahoma City, A
Oklahoma Wesleyan University, B
Oral Roberts University, B
Redlands Community College, A
Rogers State University, A
Rose State College, A
Seminole State College, A
Southern Nazarene University, B
Southwestern Oklahoma State University, B
Southwestern Oklahoma State University at
    Sayre, A
Tulsa Community College, A
University of Central Oklahoma, B
University of Oklahoma Health Sciences Center, B
University of Phoenix-Oklahoma City Campus, B
University of Phoenix-Tulsa Campus, B
University of Tulsa, B
Western Oklahoma State College, A

Oregon

Blue Mountain Community College, A
Central Oregon Community College, A
Chemeketa Community College, A
Clackamas Community College, A
Clatsop Community College, A
Concordia University, B
George Fox University, B
Lane Community College, A
Linn-Benton Community College, A
Mt. Hood Community College, A
Oregon Coast Community College, A
Oregon Health & Science University, B
Portland Community College, A
Rogue Community College, A
Southern Oregon University, B
Southwestern Oregon Community College, A
Treasure Valley Community College, A
Umpqua Community College, A
University of Portland, B
Warner Pacific College, A

Pennsylvania

Alvernia College, AB
Bloomsburg University of Pennsylvania, B
Bucks County Community College, A
Butler County Community College, A
California University of Pennsylvania, B
Carlow University, B
Clarion University of Pennsylvania, AB
College Misericordia, B
Community College of Allegheny County, A
Community College of Beaver County, A
Community College of Philadelphia, A
Delaware County Community College, A
DeSales University, B
Duquesne University, B
East Stroudsburg University of Pennsylvania, B
Eastern University, B
Edinboro University of Pennsylvania, B
Gannon University, B
Gwynedd-Mercy College, AB
Harcum College, A
Harrisburg Area Community College, A
Indiana University of Pennsylvania, B
Kutztown University of Pennsylvania, B
La Salle University, B

Lehigh Carbon Community College, A
Lock Haven University of Pennsylvania, A
Luzerne County Community College, A
Mansfield University of Pennsylvania, B
Marywood University, B
Mercyhurst College, AB
Messiah College, B
Millersville University of Pennsylvania, B
Montgomery County Community College, A
Moravian College, B
Mount Aloysius College, A
Neumann College, B
Northampton County Area Community College, A
Pennsylvania College of Technology, A
The Pennsylvania State University Abington
    College, B
The Pennsylvania State University Altoona
    College, AB
The Pennsylvania State University Beaver Campus
    of the Commonwealth College, B
The Pennsylvania State University Berks Campus of
    the Berks-Lehigh Valley College, B
The Pennsylvania State University Delaware County
    Campus of the Commonwealth College, B
The Pennsylvania State University DuBois Campus
    of the Commonwealth College, B
The Pennsylvania State University at Erie, The
    Behrend College, B
The Pennsylvania State University Fayette Campus
    of the Commonwealth College, AB
The Pennsylvania State University Harrisburg
    Campus, B
The Pennsylvania State University Hazleton
    Campus of the Commonwealth College, B
The Pennsylvania State University, Lehigh Valley
    Campus of the Berks-Lehigh Valley College, B
The Pennsylvania State University McKeesport
    Campus of the Commonwealth College, B
The Pennsylvania State University Mont Alto
    Campus of the Commonwealth College, AB
The Pennsylvania State University New Kensington
    Campus of the Commonwealth College, B
The Pennsylvania State University Schuylkill
    Campus of the Capital College, B
The Pennsylvania State University Shenango
    Campus of the Commonwealth College, B
The Pennsylvania State University University Park
    Campus, B
The Pennsylvania State University Wilkes-Barre
    Campus of the Commonwealth College, B
The Pennsylvania State University Worthington
    Scranton Campus of the Commonwealth
    College, AB
The Pennsylvania State University York Campus of
    the Commonwealth College, B
Reading Area Community College, A
Robert Morris University, B
Saint Francis University, B
Seton Hill University, B
Slippery Rock University of Pennsylvania, B
Temple University, B
Thomas Jefferson University, B
University of Pennsylvania, B
University of Pittsburgh, B
University of Pittsburgh at Bradford, AB
University of Pittsburgh at Titusville, A
The University of Scranton, B
Villanova University, B
Waynesburg College, B
West Chester University of Pennsylvania, B
Westmoreland County Community College, A
Widener University, B
Wilkes University, B
York College of Pennsylvania, B

Puerto Rico

Bayamon Central University, AB
Caribbean University, B
Columbia College (Caguas), A
Inter American University of Puerto Rico, Arecibo
    Campus, AB
Inter American University of Puerto Rico,
    Barranquitas Campus, A
Inter American University of Puerto Rico, Fajardo
    Campus, AB

Inter American University of Puerto Rico, Guayama
    Campus, AB
Inter American University of Puerto Rico,
    Metropolitan Campus, AB
Inter American University of Puerto Rico, Ponce
    Campus, A
Inter American University of Puerto Rico, San
    Germán Campus, B
Pontifical Catholic University of Puerto Rico, B
Technological College of San Juan, A
Universidad Adventista de las Antillas, AB
Universidad Metropolitana, AB
University of Puerto Rico at Humacao, AB
University of Puerto Rico, Mayagüez Campus, B
University of Puerto Rico, Medical Sciences
    Campus, B
University of the Sacred Heart, AB

Rhode Island

Community College of Rhode Island, A
Rhode Island College, B
Salve Regina University, B
University of Rhode Island, B

South Carolina

Bob Jones University, B
Central Carolina Technical College, A
Charleston Southern University, B
Clemson University, B
Columbia International University, B
Florence-Darlington Technical College, A
Francis Marion University, B
Greenville Technical College, A
Horry-Georgetown Technical College, A
Lander University, B
Medical University of South Carolina, B
Midlands Technical College, A
Orangeburg-Calhoun Technical College, A
Piedmont Technical College, A
South Carolina State University, B
Technical College of the Lowcountry, A
Tri-County Technical College, A
Trident Technical College, A
University of South Carolina, B
University of South Carolina Aiken, B
University of South Carolina Lancaster, A
University of South Carolina Upstate, AB
York Technical College, A

South Dakota

Augustana College, B
Dakota Wesleyan University, A
Mount Marty College, B
Oglala Lakota College, A
Presentation College, AB
Sisseton-Wahpeton Community College, A
South Dakota State University, B
The University of South Dakota, A

Tennessee

Aquinas College, AB
Austin Peay State University, B
Baptist College of Health Sciences, B
Belmont University, B
Carson-Newman College, B
Chattanooga State Technical Community College, A
Cleveland State Community College, A
Columbia State Community College, A
Cumberland University, B
Dyersburg State Community College, A
East Tennessee State University, B
Jackson State Community College, A
King College, B
Lincoln Memorial University, AB
Lipscomb University, B
Maryville College, B
Middle Tennessee State University, B
Milligan College, B
Motlow State Community College, A
Roane State Community College, A
South College, A
Southern Adventist University, A
Southwest Tennessee Community College, A
Tennessee State University, B
Tennessee Technological University, B
Tennessee Wesleyan College, B

Union University, B
University of Memphis, B
The University of Tennessee, B
The University of Tennessee at Chattanooga, B
The University of Tennessee at Martin, B
Walters State Community College, A

Texas

Abilene Christian University, B
Alvin Community College, A
Amarillo College, A
Angelina College, A
Angelo State University, AB
Austin Community College, A
Baylor University, B
Blinn College, A
Brazosport College, A
Brookhaven College, A
Central Texas College, A
Cisco Junior College, A
Clarendon College, A
Coastal Bend College, A
College of the Mainland, A
Collin County Community College District, A
Del Mar College, A
East Texas Baptist University, B
El Centro College, A
El Paso Community College, A
Frank Phillips College, A
Galveston College, A
Grayson County College, A
Hardin-Simmons University, B
Houston Baptist University, AB
Houston Community College System, A
Howard College, A
Kilgore College, A
Lamar State College-Orange, A
Lamar State College-Port Arthur, A
Lamar University, AB
Laredo Community College, A
McLennan Community College, A
McMurry University, B
Midland College, A
Midwestern State University, B
Navarro College, A
North Central Texas College, A
North Harris College, A
Northeast Texas Community College, A
Odessa College, A
Panola College, A
Paris Junior College, A
Prairie View A&M University, B
San Antonio College, A
South Plains College, A
South Texas College, A
Southwestern Adventist University, AB
Southwestern Christian College, B
Stephen F. Austin State University, B
Sul Ross State University, A
Tarleton State University, B
Tarrant County College District, A
Temple College, A
Texarkana College, A
Texas A&M International University, B
Texas A&M University-Corpus Christi, B
Texas A&M University-Texarkana, B
Texas Christian University, B
Texas Southern University, B
Texas Southmost College, A
Texas Woman's University, B
Tomball College, A
Trinity Valley Community College, A
Tyler Junior College, A
University of the Incarnate Word, B
University of Mary Hardin-Baylor, B
The University of Texas at Arlington, B
The University of Texas at Austin, B
The University of Texas at Brownsville, B
The University of Texas at El Paso, B
The University of Texas Health Science Center at Houston, B
The University of Texas Health Science Center at San Antonio, B
The University of Texas Medical Branch, B
The University of Texas-Pan American, B
The University of Texas at Tyler, B

Victoria College, A
Weatherford College, A
West Texas A&M University, B
Wharton County Junior College, A

United States Virgin Islands

University of the Virgin Islands, AB

Utah

Brigham Young University, B
College of Eastern Utah, A
Dixie State College of Utah, AB
Salt Lake Community College, A
University of Phoenix-Utah Campus, B
University of Utah, B
Utah Career College, A
Utah Valley State College, AB
Weber State University, AB
Westminster College, B

Vermont

Castleton State College, A
Norwich University, B
Southern Vermont College, AB
University of Vermont, B
Vermont Technical College, A

Virginia

Blue Ridge Community College, A
Dabney S. Lancaster Community College, A
Eastern Mennonite University, B
Eastern Shore Community College, A
George Mason University, B
Germanna Community College, A
Hampton University, B
J. Sargeant Reynolds Community College, A
James Madison University, B
Jefferson College of Health Sciences, AB
John Tyler Community College, A
Liberty University, B
Lord Fairfax Community College, A
Lynchburg College, B
Marymount University, B
Mountain Empire Community College, A
Norfolk State University, AB
Northern Virginia Community College, A
Old Dominion University, B
Patrick Henry Community College, A
Piedmont Virginia Community College, A
Radford University, B
Rappahannock Community College, A
Shenandoah University, B
Southside Virginia Community College, A
Southwest Virginia Community College, A
Thomas Nelson Community College, A
Tidewater Community College, A
University of Virginia, B
Virginia Commonwealth University, B
Virginia Highlands Community College, A
Virginia Western Community College, A
Wytheville Community College, A

Washington

Bellevue Community College, A
Big Bend Community College, A
Centralia College, A
Clark College, A
Columbia Basin College, A
Eastern Washington University, B
Everett Community College, A
Gonzaga University, B
Grays Harbor College, A
Heritage University, A
Highline Community College, A
Lower Columbia College, A
North Seattle Community College, A
Northwest University, B
Olympic College, A
Pacific Lutheran University, B
Peninsula College, A
Seattle Central Community College, A
Seattle Pacific University, B
Seattle University, B
Shoreline Community College, A
Skagit Valley College, A

South Puget Sound Community College, A
Spokane Community College, A
Tacoma Community College, A
University of Washington, B
University of Washington, Bothell, B
University of Washington, Tacoma, B
Walla Walla College, B
Walla Walla Community College, A
Washington State University, B
Wenatchee Valley College, A
Whatcom Community College, A
Whitworth College, B
Yakima Valley Community College, A

West Virginia

Alderson-Broaddus College, B
Bluefield State College, A
Davis & Elkins College, A
Fairmont State Community & Technical College, A
Fairmont State University, AB
Glenville State College, B
Marshall University, AB
Mountain State University, B
Southern West Virginia Community and Technical College, A
University of Charleston, AB
West Liberty State College, B
West Virginia Northern Community College, A
West Virginia University, B
West Virginia University Institute of Technology, B
West Virginia University at Parkersburg, A
West Virginia Wesleyan College, B
Wheeling Jesuit University, B

Wisconsin

Alverno College, B
Bellin College of Nursing, B
Blackhawk Technical College, A
Bryant and Stratton College, Wauwatosa Campus, A
Cardinal Stritch University, AB
Carroll College, B
Chippewa Valley Technical College, A
Columbia College of Nursing, B
Concordia University Wisconsin, B
Edgewood College, B
Fox Valley Technical College, A
Gateway Technical College, A
Lac Courte Oreilles Ojibwa Community College, A
Lakeshore Technical College, A
Madison Area Technical College, A
Maranatha Baptist Bible College, B
Marian College of Fond du Lac, B
Marquette University, B
Mid-State Technical College, A
Milwaukee Area Technical College, A
Milwaukee School of Engineering, B
Moraine Park Technical College, A
Mount Mary College, B
Nicolet Area Technical College, A
Northcentral Technical College, A
Northeast Wisconsin Technical College, A
Southwest Wisconsin Technical College, A
University of Wisconsin-Eau Claire, B
University of Wisconsin-Madison, B
University of Wisconsin-Milwaukee, B
University of Wisconsin-Oshkosh, B
University of Wisconsin-Parkside, B
Viterbo University, B
Waukesha County Technical College, A
Western Technical College, A

Wyoming

Casper College, A
Central Wyoming College, A
Laramie County Community College, A
Northwest College, A
Sheridan College-Sheridan and Gillette, A
University of Wyoming, B

Alberta

Athabasca University, B
University of Alberta, B
University of Calgary, B

University of Lethbridge, B

British Columbia

British Columbia Institute of Technology, AB
Kwantlen University College, B
Thompson Rivers University, B
Trinity Western University, B
The University of British Columbia, B
University College of the Fraser Valley, B
University of Northern British Columbia, B
University of Victoria, B

Manitoba

University of Manitoba, B

New Brunswick

University of New Brunswick Fredericton, B
University of New Brunswick Saint John, B

Newfoundland and Labrador

Memorial University of Newfoundland, B

Nova Scotia

Cape Breton University, B
Dalhousie University, B
St. Francis Xavier University, B

Ontario

Lakehead University, B
Laurentian University, B
McMaster University, B
Nipissing University, B
Queen's University at Kingston, B
Ryerson University, B
Trent University, B
University of Ottawa, B
University of Toronto, B
The University of Western Ontario, B
University of Windsor, B
York University, B

Prince Edward Island

University of Prince Edward Island, B

Quebec

McGill University, B
Université Laval, B
Université de Montréal, B
Université du Québec en Abitibi-Témiscamingue, B
Université du Québec àChicoutimi, B
Université du Québec en Outaouais, B
Université du Québec àRimouski, B
Université du Québec àTrois-Rivières, B
Université de Sherbrooke, B

Saskatchewan

University of Saskatchewan, B

NURSING SCIENCE

Arizona

University of Phoenix-Phoenix Campus, B
University of Phoenix-Southern Arizona Campus, B

California

Holy Names University, B
National University, AB
University of Phoenix-Bay Area Campus, B
University of Phoenix-Central Valley Campus, B
University of Phoenix-Sacramento Valley Campus, B
University of Phoenix-San Diego Campus, B

University of Phoenix-Southern California
Campus, B

Colorado

University of Phoenix-Denver Campus, B
University of Phoenix-Southern Colorado
Campus, B

Delaware

University of Delaware, B

Florida

University of Phoenix-Central Florida Campus, B
University of Phoenix-North Florida Campus, B
University of Phoenix-South Florida Campus, B

Georgia

University of Phoenix-Atlanta Campus, B
University of Phoenix-Columbus Georgia
Campus, B

Hawaii

University of Phoenix-Hawaii Campus, B

Illinois

Benedictine University, B
Trinity College of Nursing and Health Sciences, AB

Iowa

Clarke College, B
Mercy College of Health Sciences, B

Kansas

University of Kansas, B
Wichita State University, B

Louisiana

University of Phoenix-Louisiana Campus, B

Michigan

Davenport University (Dearborn), A
University of Phoenix-Metro Detroit Campus, B

Minnesota

Minnesota School of Business-Brooklyn Center, B
Minnesota School of Business-Plymouth, B
Minnesota School of Business-Richfield, B
Minnesota School of Business-St. Cloud, B
Minnesota School of Business-Shakopee, B

Missouri

Missouri Baptist University, B

Nebraska

Clarkson College, B

New Hampshire

University of New Hampshire at Manchester, B

New Jersey

College of Saint Elizabeth, B
Fairleigh Dickinson University, Metropolitan
Campus, B
Kean University, B
Monmouth University, B
New Jersey City University, B
New Jersey Institute of Technology, B
The Richard Stockton College of New Jersey, B
Saint Peter's College, B

New Mexico

University of Phoenix-New Mexico Campus, B

New York

Elmira College, B
State University of New York Upstate Medical
University, B

North Carolina

Queens University of Charlotte, B

Ohio

College of Mount St. Joseph, B
Kent State University, Geauga Campus, B

Kent State University, Trumbull Campus, B
The Ohio State University, B
The University of Akron, B
Xavier University, B

Pennsylvania

Cedar Crest College, B
Holy Family University, B
Immaculata University, B
Kutztown University of Pennsylvania, B
La Roche College, AB
Millersville University of Pennsylvania, B
Mount Aloysius College, B

Puerto Rico

Columbia College (Caguas), B

Tennessee

Southern Adventist University, B

Wisconsin

University of Wisconsin-Green Bay, B

British Columbia

Thompson Rivers University, B
University of Victoria, B

Manitoba

Brandon University, B

New Brunswick

Université de Moncton, B

Nova Scotia

St. Francis Xavier University, B

Ontario

Brock University, B
York University, B

NUTRITIONAL SCIENCES

Alabama

Auburn University, BMD
Tuskegee University, M
The University of Alabama, M
The University of Alabama at Birmingham, MDO

Arizona

Arizona State University at the Polytechnic
Campus, M
The University of Arizona, BMD

Arkansas

University of Arkansas for Medical Sciences, M

California

California State Polytechnic University, Pomona, M
California State University, Chico, M
California State University, Long Beach, M
California State University, Los Angeles, BM
Chapman University, BM
Loma Linda University, MD
San Diego State University, MO
San Jose State University, M
University of California, Berkeley, BMD
University of California, Davis, BMD
University of Southern California, M

Colorado

Colorado State University, MD

Connecticut

University of Bridgeport, M
University of Connecticut, BMD

University of New Haven, M

Delaware

University of Delaware, BM

District of Columbia

Howard University, MD
University of the District of Columbia, B

Florida

Florida International University, MD
Florida State University, BMD
University of Florida, MD
University of North Florida, M

Georgia

Emory University, MD
Georgia State University, M
University of Georgia, BMD

Hawaii

University of Hawaii at Manoa, M

Idaho

Idaho State University, O

Illinois

Benedictine University, BM
Eastern Illinois University, M
Elmhurst College, B
Northern Illinois University, M
Rush University, M
Southern Illinois University Carbondale, M
University of Chicago, D
University of Illinois at Chicago, MD
University of Illinois at Urbana-Champaign, MDO

Indiana

Indiana State University, M
Indiana University-Purdue University Indianapolis, M
Purdue University, MD

Iowa

Iowa State University of Science and
   Technology, MD

Kansas

Kansas State University, MD
University of Kansas, MO

Kentucky

Eastern Kentucky University, M
University of Kentucky, MD

Louisiana

Louisiana State University and Agricultural and
   Mechanical College, B
Louisiana Tech University, M
Tulane University, BM

Maine

University of Maine, MD

Maryland

The Johns Hopkins University, MD
University of Maryland, College Park, MD

Massachusetts

Boston University, BMD
Framingham State College, M
Hampshire College, B
Harvard University, D
Simmons College, MO
Tufts University, MD
University of Massachusetts Amherst, M

Michigan

Andrews University, M
Central Michigan University, M
Michigan State University, BMD
University of Michigan, M

Wayne State University, MD

Minnesota

University of Minnesota, Twin Cities Campus, MD

Mississippi

Mississippi State University, MD
University of Southern Mississippi, MD

Missouri

Barnes-Jewish College of Nursing and Allied
   Health, MO
Saint Louis University, M
Southeast Missouri State University, M
University of Missouri-Columbia, BMD

Nebraska

University of Nebraska-Lincoln, MD
University of Nebraska Medical Center, O

Nevada

University of Nevada, Las Vegas, B
University of Nevada, Reno, M

New Hampshire

University of New Hampshire, MD

New Jersey

College of Saint Elizabeth, O
Montclair State University, MO
Rutgers, The State University of New Jersey, New
   Brunswick/Piscataway, BMD

New Mexico

University of New Mexico, M

New York

Brooklyn College of the City University of New
   York, M
Cornell University, BMD
D'Youville College, M
Lehman College of the City University of New
   York, M
Long Island University, C.W. Post Campus, MO
Mohawk Valley Community College, A
New York Institute of Technology, BMO
New York University, MD
Russell Sage College, B
State University of New York at Buffalo, BMD
Syracuse University, BM

North Carolina

East Carolina University, M
Meredith College, M
North Carolina Agricultural and Technical State
   University, M
North Carolina State University, MD
The University of North Carolina at Chapel Hill, MD
The University of North Carolina at Greensboro, MD

North Dakota

North Dakota State University, M

Ohio

Bowling Green State University, M
Case Western Reserve University, BMD
Kent State University, M
The Ohio State University, MD
Ohio University, M
The University of Akron, M
University of Cincinnati, M

Oklahoma

Oklahoma State University, MD
University of Central Oklahoma, M
University of Oklahoma Health Sciences Center, M

Oregon

Oregon State University, MD

Pennsylvania

Drexel University, BMD
Edinboro University of Pennsylvania, B
Immaculata University, M

Indiana University of Pennsylvania, M
La Salle University, B
Marywood University, MD
The Pennsylvania State University University Park
   Campus, MD

Puerto Rico

University of Puerto Rico, Medical Sciences
   Campus, MDO
University of Puerto Rico, Río Piedras, M

Rhode Island

University of Rhode Island, MD

South Carolina

Clemson University, M
South Carolina State University, M
Winthrop University, M

South Dakota

Sisseton-Wahpeton Community College, A

Tennessee

East Tennessee State University, M
Middle Tennessee State University, M
University of Memphis, M
The University of Tennessee, MO
The University of Tennessee at Martin, M

Texas

Baylor University, D
Texas A&M University, MD
Texas Tech University, MD
Texas Woman's University, BMD
University of the Incarnate Word, BM
The University of Texas at Austin, MD

Utah

Brigham Young University, BM
University of Utah, M
Utah State University, MD

Vermont

Goddard College, B
University of Vermont, BM

Virginia

Virginia Polytechnic Institute and State
   University, MD

Washington

Bastyr University, M
Central Washington University, M
University of Washington, MD
Washington State University, MD

West Virginia

West Virginia University, M

Wisconsin

Mount Mary College, M
University of Wisconsin-Green Bay, B
University of Wisconsin-Madison, MD
University of Wisconsin-Stevens Point, M
University of Wisconsin-Stout, M

Wyoming

Casper College, A
University of Wyoming, M

British Columbia

The University of British Columbia, MD

Manitoba

University of Manitoba, MD

New Brunswick

Université de Moncton, M

Nova Scotia

Mount Saint Vincent University, BM

Ontario

University of Guelph, BMD
University of Toronto, MDO

Quebec

McGill University, BMD
Université Laval, BMD

Université de Montréal, MD

Saskatchewan

University of Saskatchewan, B

OCCUPATIONAL AND ENVIRONMENTAL HEALTH NURSING

British Columbia

British Columbia Institute of Technology, B

OCCUPATIONAL HEALTH AND INDUSTRIAL HYGIENE

California

California State University, Fresno, B

Montana

Montana Tech of The University of Montana, B

New Jersey

Rider University, B

New York

Clarkson University, B
Niagara County Community College, A

North Carolina

Saint Augustine's College, B

West Virginia

Mountain State University, B

British Columbia

British Columbia Institute of Technology, A

Ontario

Ryerson University, B

OCCUPATIONAL HEALTH NURSING

Massachusetts

University of Massachusetts Lowell, M

Michigan

University of Michigan, M

Minnesota

University of Minnesota, Twin Cities Campus, MDO

North Carolina

The University of North Carolina at Chapel Hill, M

Pennsylvania

University of Pennsylvania, M

Tennessee

Vanderbilt University, M

OCCUPATIONAL SAFETY AND HEALTH TECHNOLOGY/TECHNICIAN

Alabama

Columbia Southern University, B
Community College of the Air Force, A
Jacksonville State University, B

Wallace State Community College, A

Arizona

GateWay Community College, A
Paradise Valley Community College, A

Arkansas

Cossatot Community College of the University of
  Arkansas, A
NorthWest Arkansas Community College, A

California

California State University, Fresno, B
Cuyamaca College, A
Las Positas College, A
Mt. San Antonio College, A
National University, B
San Diego City College, A
San Diego Miramar College, A

Colorado

Trinidad State Junior College, A

Connecticut

University of New Haven, AB

Delaware

Delaware Technical & Community College,
  Stanton/Wilmington Campus, A

Florida

Embry-Riddle Aeronautical University, B

Georgia

Lanier Technical College, A
Okefenokee Technical College, A

Hawaii

Honolulu Community College, A

Indiana

Ball State University, B
Indiana State University, B
Indiana University Bloomington, A
Ivy Tech Community College-Central Indiana, A
Ivy Tech Community College-Northeast, A
Ivy Tech Community College-Northwest, A
Ivy Tech Community College-Wabash Valley, A

Iowa

Clinton Community College, A
Muscatine Community College, A
Scott Community College, A

Kentucky

Murray State University, B

Louisiana

Delgado Community College, A

Maine

Central Maine Community College, A

Michigan

Ferris State University, AB
Grand Valley State University, B
Oakland University, B

Missouri

Central Missouri State University, B
Mineral Area College, A

Southwest Baptist University, AB

Montana

Montana Tech of The University of Montana, AB

New Hampshire

Keene State College, B

New Jersey

Camden County College, A

New York

Rochester Institute of Technology, B

North Carolina

Durham Technical Community College, A
North Carolina Agricultural and Technical State
  University, B

North Dakota

University of North Dakota, B

Ohio

The University of Akron-Wayne College, A
University of Cincinnati, A
Wright State University, A

Oklahoma

Oklahoma State University, Oklahoma City, A
Southeastern Oklahoma State University, B
Tulsa Community College, A
University of Central Oklahoma, B

Oregon

Oregon State University, B

Pennsylvania

Indiana University of Pennsylvania, B
Millersville University of Pennsylvania, B
Slippery Rock University of Pennsylvania, B

Puerto Rico

Bayamon Central University, B

Texas

Brazosport College, A
Del Mar College, A
Houston Community College System, A
Kilgore College, A
Lamar State College-Port Arthur, A
Lamar University, A
Texas Southern University, B
Texas State Technical College Waco, A

Utah

Utah State University, B

Washington

Bates Technical College, A
Central Washington University, B

West Virginia

Fairmont State University, B
Marshall University, B

Wisconsin

University of Wisconsin-Whitewater, B

OCCUPATIONAL THERAPIST ASSISTANT

Arizona

Apollo College-Tucson, Inc., A
Apollo College-Westside, Inc., A

Arkansas

Pulaski Technical College, A

California

Loma Linda University, A
Mount St. Mary's College, A

Sonoma College (Petaluma), A

Colorado

Pueblo Community College, A

Connecticut

Briarwood College, A
Manchester Community College, A

Delaware

Delaware Technical & Community College,
Stanton/Wilmington Campus, A

Florida

Florida Hospital College of Health Sciences, A
Manatee Community College, A
Polk Community College, A

Georgia

Augusta Technical College, A
Darton College, A
Middle Georgia College, A
Northwestern Technical College, A

Idaho

Apollo College, A
Idaho State University, A

Illinois

College of DuPage, A
Lewis and Clark Community College, A
Lincoln Land Community College, A
Parkland College, A
Rend Lake College, A
South Suburban College, A

Indiana

Brown Mackie College-Fort Wayne, A
Brown Mackie College-South Bend, A
Ivy Tech Community College-Central Indiana, A
University of Saint Francis, A
University of Southern Indiana, A

Iowa

Scott Community College, A
Western Iowa Tech Community College, A

Kansas

Johnson County Community College, A

Kentucky

Madisonville Community College, A

Louisiana

Delgado Community College, A
Southeastern Louisiana University, B
University of Louisiana at Monroe, A

Maine

Kennebec Valley Community College, A

Maryland

Allegany College of Maryland, A

Massachusetts

Bristol Community College, A
Quinsigamond Community College, A
Springfield Technical Community College, A

Michigan

Baker College of Muskegon, A
Grand Valley State University, B
Macomb Community College, A
Mott Community College, A
Schoolcraft College, A

Minnesota

Anoka Technical College, A
College of St. Catherine, A
College of St. Catherine-Minneapolis, A
Lake Superior College, A

Northwest Technical College, A

Missouri

Ozarks Technical Community College, A

New Jersey

Union County College, A

New Mexico

Eastern New Mexico University-Roswell, A

New York

Adirondack Community College, A
Erie Community College, North Campus, A
Jamestown Community College, A
Maria College, A
Mercy College, A
State University of New York College of Technology
at Canton, A

North Carolina

Cabarrus College of Health Sciences, A
Guilford Technical Community College, A
Pitt Community College, A
Rockingham Community College, A
Stanly Community College, A

North Dakota

North Dakota State College of Science, A

Ohio

Cincinnati State Technical and Community
College, A
Hocking College, A
Owens Community College, A

Oklahoma

Southwestern Oklahoma State University at
Sayre, A
Tulsa Community College, A

Pennsylvania

California University of Pennsylvania, A
Clarion University of Pennsylvania, A
Community College of Allegheny County, A
Harcum College, A
Lehigh Carbon Community College, A
Mount Aloysius College, A
Pennsylvania College of Technology, A
The Pennsylvania State University Berks Campus of
the Berks-Lehigh Valley College, B
The Pennsylvania State University DuBois Campus
of the Commonwealth College, A
The Pennsylvania State University Mont Alto
Campus of the Commonwealth College, A

Puerto Rico

University of Puerto Rico at Humacao, AB

Rhode Island

Community College of Rhode Island, A
New England Institute of Technology, A

South Carolina

Midlands Technical College, A

South Dakota

Lake Area Technical Institute, A

Texas

Del Mar College, A
Houston Community College System, A

St. Philip's College, A

Utah

Salt Lake Community College, A

Virginia

J. Sargeant Reynolds Community College, A
Jefferson College of Health Sciences, A

Washington

Green River Community College, A

West Virginia

Mountain State University, A

OCCUPATIONAL THERAPY/THERAPIST

Alabama

Alabama Southern Community College, A
Alabama State University, B
Faulkner University, A
George Corley Wallace State Community College, A
Oakwood College, A
Tuskegee University, B
The University of Alabama at Birmingham, M
University of South Alabama, M
Wallace State Community College, A

Arizona

Apollo College-Phoenix, Inc., A
Midwestern University, Glendale Campus, M

Arkansas

University of Central Arkansas, BM

California

Dominican University of California, BM
Grossmont College, A
Loma Linda University, B
Monterey Peninsula College, A
Pasadena City College, A
Sacramento City College, A
Samuel Merritt College, M
San Jose State University, BM
Santa Ana College, A
University of Southern California, BMD

Colorado

Colorado State University, MD
Morgan Community College, A
Pueblo Community College, A

Connecticut

Quinnipiac University, BM
Sacred Heart University, BM
University of Hartford, B

District of Columbia

Howard University, B

Florida

Barry University, M
Daytona Beach Community College, A
Florida Agricultural and Mechanical University, B
Florida Gulf Coast University, B
Florida International University, BM
Hillsborough Community College, A
Keiser College (Fort Lauderdale), A
Manatee Community College, A
Nova Southeastern University, MD
Palm Beach Community College, A
University of Florida, M

Georgia

Andrew College, A
Brenau University, BM
Clayton State University, A
Coastal Georgia Community College, A
Dalton State College, A
Georgia Highlands College, A

Medical College of Georgia, BM

Hawaii

Kapiolani Community College, A

Idaho

Brigham Young University -Idaho, A
College of Southern Idaho, A
Idaho State University, M

Illinois

Augustana College, B
City Colleges of Chicago, Wilbur Wright College, A
College of DuPage, A
Danville Area Community College, A
Elmhurst College, B
Governors State University, M
Illinois Central College, A
Illinois College, B
John A. Logan College, A
McKendree College, B
Rush University, M
Sauk Valley Community College, A
Southeastern Illinois College, A
University of Illinois at Chicago, M

Indiana

Indiana University-Purdue University Indianapolis, B
University of Indianapolis, MD
University of Southern Indiana, BM
Vincennes University, A

Iowa

Iowa Central Community College, A
Kirkwood Community College, A
St. Ambrose University, M
Wartburg College, B

Kansas

Barton County Community College, A
Coffeyville Community College, A
Highland Community College, A
University of Kansas, BMD

Kentucky

Eastern Kentucky University, BM
Spalding University, BM

Louisiana

University of Louisiana at Monroe, B

Maine

Husson College, B
University of New England, BM
University of Southern Maine, M

Maryland

Allegany College of Maryland, A
Towson University, BM

Massachusetts

American International College, BM
Bay Path College, BM
Boston University, BMD
North Shore Community College, A
Quinsigamond Community College, A
Springfield College, BMO
Tufts University, MDO
Worcester State College, BM

Michigan

Baker College of Flint, B
Calvin College, B
Eastern Michigan University, BM
Grand Valley State University, M
Wayne County Community College District, A
Wayne State University, BM
Western Michigan University, BM

Minnesota

College of Saint Benedict, B
College of St. Catherine, BM
The College of St. Scholastica, M
Concordia College, B

Hamline University, B
Saint John's University, B
University of Minnesota, Twin Cities Campus, B

Mississippi

East Central Community College, A
Northeast Mississippi Community College, A
University of Mississippi Medical Center, M

Missouri

Drury University, B
Maryville University of Saint Louis, M
Ozarks Technical Community College, A
Penn Valley Community College, A
Rockhurst University, M
Saint Charles Community College, A
St. Louis Community College at Meramec, A
Saint Louis University, BM
Stephens College, B
University of Missouri-Columbia, B
Washington University in St. Louis, MD

Nebraska

Clarkson College, A
Creighton University, D

Nevada

Community College of Southern Nevada, A

New Hampshire

University of New Hampshire, BM

New Jersey

Kean University, BM
The Richard Stockton College of New Jersey, M
Seton Hall University, M

New Mexico

University of New Mexico, M
Western New Mexico University, A

New York

Dominican College, BM
D'Youville College, BM
Fiorello H. LaGuardia Community College of the
    City University of New York, A
Genesee Community College, A
Ithaca College, BM
Keuka College, BM
Long Island University, Brooklyn Campus, B
Mercy College, M
New York Institute of Technology, BM
New York University, MD
Orange County Community College, A
Rockland Community College, A
Russell Sage College, B
State University of New York at Buffalo, BM
State University of New York Downstate Medical
    Center, B
Stony Brook University, State University of New
    York, M
Touro College, AM
York College of the City University of New York, B

North Carolina

Durham Technical Community College, A
East Carolina University, BM
Lenoir-Rhyne College, B
Louisburg College, A
The University of North Carolina at Chapel Hill, MD
Winston-Salem State University, BM

North Dakota

University of Mary, M
University of North Dakota, M

Ohio

Cleveland State University, BM
Kent State University, East Liverpool Campus, A
The Ohio State University, BM
Ohio University-Eastern, B
Shawnee State University, AB
Sinclair Community College, A
Stark State College of Technology, A

The University of Findlay, BM
Xavier University, B
Zane State College, A

Oklahoma

Oklahoma City Community College, A
Tulsa Community College, A
University of Oklahoma Health Sciences Center, M

Oregon

Mt. Hood Community College, A
Pacific University, M

Pennsylvania

Alvernia College, BM
College Misericordia, M
Duquesne University, M
Elizabethtown College, B
Gannon University, MO
ICM School of Business & Medical Careers, A
Keystone College, A
Manor College, A
Mount Aloysius College, B
The Pennsylvania State University Mont Alto
    Campus of the Commonwealth College, B
Philadelphia University, M
Saint Francis University, BM
Saint Vincent College, B
Temple University, M
Thomas Jefferson University, BM
University of Pittsburgh, BM
The University of Scranton, M

Puerto Rico

University of Puerto Rico, Medical Sciences
    Campus, B
University of Puerto Rico at Ponce, A

South Carolina

Florence-Darlington Technical College, A
Medical University of South Carolina, M
Trident Technical College, A

South Dakota

The University of South Dakota, M

Tennessee

Belmont University, MD
Chattanooga State Technical Community College, A
Milligan College, M
Nashville State Technical Community College, A
Roane State Community College, A
Southern Adventist University, A

Texas

Amarillo College, A
Austin Community College, A
Kingwood College, A
Navarro College, A
North Central Texas College, A
South Texas College, A
Texas Woman's University, MD
Tomball College, A
The University of Texas Health Science Center at
    San Antonio, BM
The University of Texas Medical Branch, M
The University of Texas-Pan American, BM

Utah

University of Utah, BM

Virginia

James Madison University, M
Shenandoah University, M
Virginia Commonwealth University, M

Washington

Eastern Washington University, M
Everett Community College, A
Tacoma Community College, A
University of Puget Sound, M
University of Washington, BM

Yakima Valley Community College, A

West Virginia

West Virginia University, BM

Wisconsin

Carthage College, B
Concordia University Wisconsin, BM
Fox Valley Technical College, A
Madison Area Technical College, A
Milwaukee Area Technical College, A
Mount Mary College, BM
University of Wisconsin-Madison, B
University of Wisconsin-Milwaukee, BM
Western Technical College, A
Wisconsin Indianhead Technical College, A

Wyoming

Casper College, A

Alberta

University of Alberta, BM

British Columbia

The University of British Columbia, B

Manitoba

University of Manitoba, B

Nova Scotia

Dalhousie University, BM

Ontario

McMaster University, M
Queen's University at Kingston, B
University of Ottawa, B
The University of Western Ontario, BM

Quebec

McGill University, B
Université Laval, B
Université de Montréal, B

OCEAN ENGINEERING

California

California State University, Long Beach, B
University of California, Berkeley, MD
University of California, San Diego, MD
University of Southern California, M

Delaware

University of Delaware, MD

Florida

Florida Atlantic University, BMD
Florida Institute of Technology, BMD
University of Florida, MDO
University of Miami, M

Georgia

Georgia Institute of Technology, MD

Hawaii

University of Hawaii at Manoa, MD

Maryland

United States Naval Academy, B

Massachusetts

Massachusetts Institute of Technology, BMDO

Michigan

University of Michigan, MDO

New Hampshire

University of New Hampshire, BMD

New Jersey

Stevens Institute of Technology, MD

Oregon

Oregon State University, M

Rhode Island

University of Rhode Island, BMD

Texas

Texas A&M University, BMD
Texas A&M University at Galveston, B

Virginia

Virginia Polytechnic Institute and State
    University, BM

Newfoundland and Labrador

Memorial University of Newfoundland, BMD

OCEANOGRAPHY, CHEMICAL AND PHYSICAL

Alaska

University of Alaska Fairbanks, MD

California

Fullerton College, A
Humboldt State University, B
Santa Rosa Junior College, A
University of California, San Diego, MD
University of Southern California, D

Colorado

University of Colorado at Boulder, MD

Connecticut

United States Coast Guard Academy, B
University of Connecticut, MD
Yale University, D

Delaware

University of Delaware, MD

Florida

Florida Institute of Technology, BMD
Florida State University, MD
Nova Southeastern University, MD
University of Miami, BMD
University of South Florida, MD

Georgia

University of Georgia, MD

Hawaii

Hawaii Pacific University, B
University of Hawaii at Manoa, MD

Louisiana

Louisiana State University and Agricultural and
    Mechanical College, MD

Maine

College of the Atlantic, B
Maine Maritime Academy, B
Southern Maine Community College, A
University of Maine, MD

Maryland

The Johns Hopkins University, MD
United States Naval Academy, B

Massachusetts

Massachusetts Institute of Technology, MD

Michigan

Central Michigan University, B
University of Michigan, BMD

Mississippi

Northeast Mississippi Community College, A

New Hampshire

University of New Hampshire, BM

New Jersey

Princeton University, D
Rider University, B

Rutgers, The State University of New Jersey, New
    Brunswick/Piscataway, MD

New York

State University of New York Maritime College, B

North Carolina

Elizabeth City State University, B
North Carolina State University, BMD

Oklahoma

Tulsa Community College, A

Oregon

Oregon State University, MD

Pennsylvania

Kutztown University of Pennsylvania, B
Millersville University of Pennsylvania, B

Puerto Rico

University of Puerto Rico, Mayagüez Campus, MD

Rhode Island

University of Rhode Island, MD

South Carolina

University of South Carolina, B

Texas

Lamar University, B
Texas A&M University, MD
Texas A&M University at Galveston, B

Virginia

Old Dominion University, BMD

Washington

Everett Community College, A
Shoreline Community College, A
Tacoma Community College, A
University of Washington, BMD

Wisconsin

University of Wisconsin-Madison, MD

British Columbia

The University of British Columbia, BMD
University of Victoria, BMD

Newfoundland and Labrador

Memorial University of Newfoundland, BMD

Nova Scotia

Dalhousie University, BMD

Quebec

McGill University, MD
Université Laval, D
Université du Québec àRimouski, MD

OFFICE MANAGEMENT AND SUPERVISION

Alabama

Calhoun Community College, A
Community College of the Air Force, A
Gadsden State Community College-Ayers
    Campus, A
Virginia College at Birmingham, A

Arkansas

Southern Arkansas University Tech, A

California

Berkeley City College, A
Cuyamaca College, A
Modesto Junior College, A

Riverside Community College District, A

Colorado

Community College of Denver, A

Florida

Central Florida Community College, A
Florida Community College at Jacksonville, A
Lake-Sumter Community College, A
New England Institute of Technology at Palm
　　Beach, A
Valencia Community College, A

Georgia

Dalton State College, A
Emmanuel College, A
Georgia College & State University, B

Illinois

College of DuPage, A
Lake Land College, A

Indiana

Indiana State University, B
University of Southern Indiana, B

Iowa

Iowa Lakes Community College, A

Kansas

Washburn University, A

Kentucky

Eastern Kentucky University, B
Murray State University, B

Maryland

Howard Community College, A

Massachusetts

Babson College, B
Middlesex Community College, A

Michigan

Alpena Community College, A
Baker College of Flint, AB
Baker College of Jackson, A
Central Michigan University, B
Delta College, A
Eastern Michigan University, B
Gogebic Community College, A
Lake Superior State University, A
Mott Community College, A
Oakland Community College, A

Minnesota

Academy College, A
Alexandria Technical College, A
Metropolitan State University, B
St. Cloud Technical College, A

Mississippi

Delta State University, B
Jackson State University, B
Mississippi Valley State University, B
Northwest Mississippi Community College, A

Missouri

Central Missouri State University, B
Park University, A
Saint Charles Community College, A

Southeast Missouri State University, B

Montana

Chief Dull Knife College, A

Nebraska

University of Nebraska-Lincoln, B

Nevada

Great Basin College, A

New York

Berkeley College-New York City Campus, AB
Berkeley College-Westchester Campus, AB
Erie Community College, A
Erie Community College, North Campus, A
Erie Community College, South Campus, A
Globe Institute of Technology, A
Mohawk Valley Community College, A
State University of New York College of Technology
　　at Canton, A
Wood Tobe-Coburn School, A

North Carolina

Fayetteville Technical Community College, A
South College-Asheville, A

North Dakota

Lake Region State College, A
Mayville State University, B
Valley City State University, B

Ohio

Cincinnati State Technical and Community
　　College, A
God's Bible School and College, A
Miami University Hamilton, B
Miami University-Middletown Campus, A
Shawnee State University, A
Wright State University, B

Oklahoma

Southeastern Oklahoma State University, B

Oregon

Clackamas Community College, A
Southwestern Oregon Community College, A
Tillamook Bay Community College, A

Pennsylvania

Community College of Allegheny County, A
Consolidated School of Business (Lancaster), A
Consolidated School of Business (York), A
Delaware County Community College, A
Indiana University of Pennsylvania, B
Mercyhurst College, A
Peirce College, A
South Hills School of Business & Technology (State
　　College), A

Puerto Rico

University of Puerto Rico at Arecibo, AB
University of Puerto Rico, Cayey University
　　College, B
University of Puerto Rico at Utuado, B
University of the Sacred Heart, B

South Carolina

Bob Jones University, B
Piedmont Technical College, A
University of South Carolina, B

South Dakota

Dakota State University, A

Tennessee

Middle Tennessee State University, B
Tennessee Temple University, B

Texas

Central Texas College, A
Lee College, A
Stephen F. Austin State University, B
Tarleton State University, B

Texas Southern University, B
University of Houston-Downtown, B

Utah

Weber State University, B

Virginia

Lord Fairfax Community College, A
National College of Business & Technology (Salem)
　　, A
Norfolk State University, B

Washington

Big Bend Community College, A
Central Washington University, B
Clover Park Technical College, A
Edmonds Community College, A
Grays Harbor College, A
Green River Community College, A
Lower Columbia College, A
Olympic College, A
Peninsula College, A
Skagit Valley College, A
Walla Walla Community College, A

West Virginia

Mountain State University, A

Wisconsin

Western Technical College, A

Wyoming

Eastern Wyoming College, A

British Columbia

Thompson Rivers University, A

ONCOLOGY NURSING

Delaware

University of Delaware, MO

Illinois

Loyola University Chicago, M

Missouri

Barnes-Jewish College of Nursing and Allied
　　Health, M

North Carolina

Duke University, O

Pennsylvania

University of Pennsylvania, M

OPERATIONS MANAGEMENT AND SUPERVISION

Alabama

Auburn University, B
Remington College-Mobile Campus, AB

Arizona

DeVry University (Phoenix), B
The University of Arizona, B

California

California State University, Chico, B
California State University, Long Beach, B
California State University, Sacramento, B
DeVry University (Fremont), B
DeVry University (Long Beach), B
DeVry University (Pomona), B
DeVry University (West Hills), B
Golden Gate University, B
National University, B

San Diego State University, B

Colorado

Remington College-Colorado Springs Campus, B

Delaware

University of Delaware, B

Florida

Florida Southern College, B
Remington College-Tampa Campus, B

Georgia

Atlanta Metropolitan College, A
Dalton State College, B
DeKalb Technical College, A
DeVry University (Alpharetta), B
DeVry University (Decatur), B
Georgia Institute of Technology, B

Guam

Guam Community College, A

Idaho

Boise State University, B
University of Idaho, B

Illinois

Aurora University, B
DeVry University (Addison), B
DeVry University (Chicago), B
DeVry University (Tinley Park), B
Kishwaukee College, A
Loyola University Chicago, B
McHenry County College, A
Northern Illinois University, B
University of Illinois at Urbana-Champaign, B
Waubonsee Community College, A

Indiana

Indiana University-Purdue University Fort
   Wayne, AB
Indiana University-Purdue University
   Indianapolis, AB
Purdue University, AB
Tri-State University, B
University of Indianapolis, B
University of Phoenix-Indianapolis Campus, B

Iowa

Iowa State University of Science and Technology, B

Kansas

Pittsburg State University, B

Kentucky

Northern Kentucky University, A

Louisiana

Louisiana Tech University, B

Massachusetts

Babson College, B
Boston University, B
Bunker Hill Community College, A
Massasoit Community College, A

Michigan

Alpena Community College, A
Baker College of Flint, AB
Central Michigan University, B
Kettering University, B
Macomb Community College, A
Michigan State University, B
Michigan Technological University, B
Oakland Community College, A
Saginaw Valley State University, B
University of Michigan-Flint, B

Minnesota

Alexandria Technical College, A
Metropolitan State University, B

University of St. Thomas, B

Missouri

DeVry University (Kansas City), B
Mineral Area College, A
Missouri Baptist University, B
Washington University in St. Louis, B

Nebraska

University of Nebraska at Kearney, B

Nevada

Great Basin College, A

New York

Clarkson University, B
Excelsior College, B
Farmingdale State University of New York, B

North Carolina

Alamance Community College, A
Asheville-Buncombe Technical Community
   College, A
Catawba Valley Community College, A
Central Carolina Community College, A
Cleveland Community College, A
Durham Technical Community College, A
Fayetteville Technical Community College, A
Gaston College, A
Johnston Community College, A
Pitt Community College, A
South Piedmont Community College, A
The University of North Carolina at Asheville, B
The University of North Carolina at Charlotte, B

Ohio

Bowling Green State University, B
Bowling Green State University-Firelands College, A
DeVry University (Columbus), B
Franklin University, B
Kent State University, B
Miami University, B
North Central State College, A
The Ohio State University, B
Stark State College of Technology, A
The University of Toledo, B
Wright State University, B
Youngstown State University, B

Pennsylvania

Duquesne University, B
Edinboro University of Pennsylvania, B
Lehigh Carbon Community College, A
Robert Morris University, B
University of Pennsylvania, B
The University of Scranton, B
Widener University, B

South Carolina

Bob Jones University, B

South Dakota

National American University (Rapid City), B

Tennessee

Remington College-Memphis Campus, B
Tennessee Technological University, B
The University of Tennessee at Martin, B

Texas

Baylor University, B
DeVry University (Irving), B
Kilgore College, A
Lee College, A
Sam Houston State University, B
Texas Southern University, B
University of Houston, B
University of North Texas, B

The University of Texas at San Antonio, B

Utah

Utah State University, B
Utah Valley State College, B

Washington

Central Washington University, B
Seattle University, B
Washington State University, B
Western Washington University, B

Wisconsin

Gateway Technical College, A
University of Wisconsin-Stout, B
University of Wisconsin-Whitewater, B
Waukesha County Technical College, A

British Columbia

British Columbia Institute of Technology, A

New Brunswick

Université de Moncton, B

Saskatchewan

University of Saskatchewan, B

OPERATIONS RESEARCH

Alabama

The University of Alabama in Huntsville, M

Arkansas

University of Arkansas, M

California

California State University, East Bay, M
California State University, Fullerton, BM
University of California, Berkeley, BMD
University of California, Los Angeles, MD
University of Southern California, M

Colorado

United States Air Force Academy, B
University of Colorado at Boulder, M
University of Denver, B

Connecticut

United States Coast Guard Academy, B
University of New Haven, M

Delaware

University of Delaware, MD

Florida

Florida Institute of Technology, MD
University of Central Florida, MO

Georgia

Georgia Institute of Technology, M
Georgia State University, M

Idaho

Idaho State University, M

Illinois

DePaul University, B
Northwestern University, MD
University of Illinois at Chicago, D

Indiana

Indiana University-Purdue University Fort Wayne, M
Purdue University, MD

Iowa

Iowa State University of Science and Technology, M
The University of Iowa, MD

Kansas

Kansas State University, M

Louisiana

Louisiana Tech University, M

Maryland

The Johns Hopkins University, MD

Massachusetts

Babson College, B
Boston College, B
Massachusetts Institute of Technology, MD
Northeastern University, M
University of Massachusetts Amherst, MD

Michigan

Kettering University, M
University of Michigan, MDO
Wayne State University, MD
Western Michigan University, M

New Jersey

Princeton University, BMD
Rutgers, The State University of New Jersey, New Brunswick/Piscataway, D

New Mexico

New Mexico Institute of Mining and Technology, M

New York

Bernard M. Baruch College of the City University of New York, B
Columbia University, The Fu Foundation School of Engineering and Applied Science, B
Cornell University, BMD
Long Island University, Brooklyn Campus, B
New York University, B
Rensselaer Polytechnic Institute, MO
United States Military Academy, B

North Carolina

North Carolina State University, MD
The University of North Carolina at Chapel Hill, MD

North Dakota

North Dakota State University, M

Ohio

Case Western Reserve University, D
Miami University, BM
University of Cincinnati, B

Oklahoma

Oklahoma State University, D

Oregon

Oregon State University, M

Pennsylvania

Carnegie Mellon University, BD
Temple University, D

South Carolina

Bob Jones University, B
Clemson University, MD

Texas

St. Mary's University of San Antonio, M
Southern Methodist University, MD
The University of Texas at Austin, MD

Virginia

The College of William and Mary, M
George Mason University, M
Virginia Commonwealth University, M

Virginia Polytechnic Institute and State University, MD

British Columbia

The University of British Columbia, M

New Brunswick

University of New Brunswick Fredericton, B

Ontario

Carleton University, B
University of Toronto, B
University of Waterloo, BMD
York University, B

Quebec

Université de Montréal, B
Université du Québec àTrois-Rivières, B

OPHTHALMIC AND OPTOMETRIC SUPPORT SERVICES AND ALLIED PROFESSIONS

Michigan

Mid Michigan Community College, A

Minnesota

Concordia College, B

Tennessee

Tennessee Wesleyan College, B

OPHTHALMIC LABORATORY TECHNOLOGY/TECHNICIAN

Alabama

Community College of the Air Force, A

California

Los Angeles City College, A
Santa Rosa Junior College, A

Colorado

Pueblo Community College, A

Connecticut

Middlesex Community College, A

Florida

Hillsborough Community College, A

Georgia

DeKalb Technical College, A

Illinois

Triton College, A

Indiana

Indiana University Bloomington, A

Mississippi

East Mississippi Community College, A

New Hampshire

New Hampshire Community Technical College, Nashua/Claremont, A

New Jersey

Raritan Valley Community College, A

New York

Interboro Institute, A
New York City College of Technology of the City University of New York, A

Rochester Institute of Technology, A

North Carolina

Durham Technical Community College, A

Ohio

Hocking College, A
Lakeland Community College, A

Oregon

Portland Community College, A

Pennsylvania

Central Pennsylvania College, A
Westmoreland County Community College, A

Puerto Rico

University of Puerto Rico, Medical Sciences Campus, A

Texas

Abilene Christian University, B
El Paso Community College, A
Tyler Junior College, A

Virginia

Thomas Nelson Community College, A

Washington

Everett Community College, A
Seattle Central Community College, A
Spokane Community College, A

OPHTHALMIC/OPTOMETRIC SERVICES

Indiana

Indiana University Bloomington, B

Maryland

Howard Community College, A

New York

State University of New York College at Oneonta, B

Oklahoma

Northeastern State University, B

Pennsylvania

Gannon University, B
Luzerne County Community College, A

Ontario

University of Ottawa, B
University of Waterloo, B

Quebec

Université de Montréal, B

OPHTHALMIC TECHNICIAN/TECHNOLOGIST

Colorado

Pima Medical Institute, A

Florida

Miami Dade College, A

Illinois

Triton College, A

Louisiana

Louisiana State University Health Sciences Center, B

Tennessee

Volunteer State Community College, A

Virginia

Old Dominion University, B

OPTICAL TECHNOLOGIES

Florida

University of Central Florida, MDO

Ohio

Cleveland State University, M
University of Dayton, MD

Virginia

Norfolk State University, M

OPTICIANRY/OPHTHALMIC DISPENSING OPTICIAN

Arkansas

Arkansas State University-Mountain Home, A

Georgia

DeKalb Technical College, A
Ogeechee Technical College, A

Illinois

Triton College, A

Michigan

Ferris State University, A

New Jersey

Essex County College, A

New York

Erie Community College, North Campus, A
Suffolk County Community College, A

Ohio

Cuyahoga Community College, A
The University of Akron, A

Pennsylvania

Harrisburg Area Community College, A

Virginia

J. Sargeant Reynolds Community College, A

Wisconsin

Milwaukee Area Technical College, A

OPTICS/OPTICAL SCIENCES

Alabama

The University of Alabama in Huntsville, D

Arizona

The University of Arizona, BMD

Colorado

University of Colorado at Boulder, D

Florida

University of Central Florida, MDO

Indiana

Indiana University Bloomington, MD
Rose-Hulman Institute of Technology, M

Maryland

University of Maryland, Baltimore County, MD

Michigan

Saginaw Valley State University, B

New Mexico

University of New Mexico, MD

New York

Corning Community College, A
Rochester Institute of Technology, MD

University of Rochester, BMD

North Carolina

The University of North Carolina at Charlotte, MD

Ohio

The Ohio State University, MDO

OPTOMETRIC TECHNICIAN/ASSISTANT

Georgia

Darton College, A

Illinois

Sauk Valley Community College, A

Indiana

Indiana University Bloomington, A

Kansas

Barton County Community College, A

OPTOMETRY

Alabama

The University of Alabama at Birmingham, P

California

University of California, Berkeley, PO

Florida

Nova Southeastern University, MP

Indiana

Indiana University Bloomington, P

Michigan

Ferris State University, P

Missouri

University of Missouri-St. Louis, P

Ohio

The Ohio State University, P

Oklahoma

Northeastern State University, P

Oregon

Pacific University, P

Texas

University of Houston, P

Ontario

University of Waterloo, MDP

Quebec

Université de Montréal, P

ORAL AND DENTAL SCIENCES

Alabama

The University of Alabama at Birmingham, M

California

Loma Linda University, MO
University of Southern California, MD

Connecticut

University of Connecticut, M

Florida

University of Florida, MO

Idaho

Idaho State University, MO

Illinois

University of Illinois at Chicago, M

Iowa

The University of Iowa, MDO

Kentucky

University of Kentucky, M

Massachusetts

Boston University, MDPO
Harvard University, MDO
Tufts University, MO

Michigan

University of Detroit Mercy, MO
University of Michigan, MDO

Minnesota

University of Minnesota, Twin Cities Campus, MO

Mississippi

University of Mississippi Medical Center, MD

Missouri

Saint Louis University, M
University of Missouri-Kansas City, O

New York

New York University, MO
State University of New York at Buffalo, M
Stony Brook University, State University of New York, O
University of Rochester, M

North Carolina

The University of North Carolina at Chapel Hill, MD

Ohio

Case Western Reserve University, MO
The Ohio State University, MDO

Oregon

Oregon Health & Science University, MO

Pennsylvania

Temple University, MO
University of Pittsburgh, MO

Puerto Rico

University of Puerto Rico, Medical Sciences Campus, MO

Texas

Texas A&M University System Health Science Center, MDO
The University of Texas Health Science Center at Houston, M
The University of Texas Health Science Center at San Antonio, MO

Washington

University of Washington, MDO

West Virginia

West Virginia University, M

Wisconsin

Marquette University, M

Alberta

University of Alberta, MD

British Columbia

The University of British Columbia, MDO

Manitoba

University of Manitoba, M

Nova Scotia

Dalhousie University, MO

Ontario

University of Toronto, MD
The University of Western Ontario, M

Quebec

Université Laval, MO
Université de Montréal, MO

ORAL BIOLOGY

California

University of California, Los Angeles, MDO

District of Columbia

The George Washington University, M

Florida

Nova Southeastern University, M
University of Florida, D

Georgia

Medical College of Georgia, MD

Kentucky

University of Louisville, M

Massachusetts

Boston University, MD

Minnesota

University of Minnesota, Twin Cities Campus, MD

Missouri

University of Missouri-Kansas City, MD

New York

State University of New York at Buffalo, D
Stony Brook University, State University of New York, D

North Carolina

The University of North Carolina at Chapel Hill, D

Texas

Texas A&M University System Health Science Center, MD

Manitoba

University of Manitoba, MD

Quebec

Université de Montréal, M

ORAL PATHOLOGY

New York

Stony Brook University, State University of New York, D

Oregon

Oregon Health & Science University, O

Texas

Texas A&M University System Health Science Center, MDO

Ontario

University of Toronto, M

ORGANIC CHEMISTRY

California

California Institute of Technology, B
California State University, Fullerton, M

California State University, Los Angeles, M

Connecticut

Wesleyan University, MD
Yale University, D

District of Columbia

The George Washington University, MD
Georgetown University, MD
Howard University, MD

Florida

Florida State University, MD
University of Miami, D
University of South Florida, MD

Georgia

Clark Atlanta University, MD
University of Georgia, MD

Illinois

Illinois Institute of Technology, MD

Indiana

Purdue University, MD
University of Notre Dame, MD

Kansas

Kansas State University, M

Kentucky

University of Louisville, MD

Louisiana

Southern University and Agricultural and Mechanical College, M

Maryland

University of Maryland, College Park, MD

Massachusetts

Boston College, D
Brandeis University, MD
Harvard University, MD
Massachusetts Institute of Technology, D
Northeastern University, D
Tufts University, MD

Michigan

University of Michigan, D

Mississippi

University of Southern Mississippi, MD

Missouri

University of Missouri-Columbia, MD
University of Missouri-Kansas City, MD

Nebraska

University of Nebraska-Lincoln, D

New Jersey

Rutgers, The State University of New Jersey, New Brunswick/Piscataway, MD
Rutgers, The State University of New Jersey, Newark, MD
Seton Hall University, MD

New York

Clarkson University, MD
Cornell University, D
Rensselaer Polytechnic Institute, MD
Sarah Lawrence College, B
State University of New York at Binghamton, D
State University of New York College of Environmental Science and Forestry, MD

North Carolina

Wake Forest University, MD

Ohio

Case Western Reserve University, MD
Cleveland State University, M

Kent State University, MD
Miami University, MD
University of Cincinnati, MD
The University of Toledo, MD

Oregon

Oregon State University, MD

South Dakota

South Dakota State University, MD

Tennessee

The University of Tennessee, MD
Vanderbilt University, MD

Texas

Rice University, D
The University of Texas at Austin, MD

Utah

Brigham Young University, MD

Virginia

Old Dominion University, M

Washington

Washington State University, MD

West Virginia

West Virginia University, MD

Wisconsin

Marquette University, MD

Alberta

University of Calgary, MD

Ontario

McMaster University, MD

Saskatchewan

University of Regina, MD

ORGANIZATIONAL BEHAVIOR STUDIES

Alabama

Southern Christian University, M

Arkansas

Central Baptist College, B
Philander Smith College, B

California

California Lutheran University, M
Chapman University, B
National University, B
Pitzer College, B
Scripps College, B
Simpson University, B
University of California, Berkeley, D
University of San Francisco, B
Woodbury University, B

Connecticut

University of Hartford, M

District of Columbia

The George Washington University, M

Georgia

Georgia Institute of Technology, MD
Southern Polytechnic State University, B

Hawaii

University of Hawaii at Manoa, M

Illinois

Benedictine University, BMO
Greenville College, B
Loyola University Chicago, B

Northwestern University, BMD
University of Illinois at Urbana-Champaign, B
University of St. Francis, B

Indiana

Anderson University, B
Indiana University Bloomington, D
Oakland City University, B
Purdue University, MD

Iowa

St. Ambrose University, B

Kentucky

Mid-Continent University, B
Northern Kentucky University, B
University of the Cumberlands, B

Maryland

Towson University, O

Massachusetts

Boston College, D
Boston University, BD
Harvard University, D

Michigan

University of Michigan-Flint, B
Wayne State University, B

Minnesota

The College of St. Scholastica, B
Concordia University, St. Paul, B

Missouri

Calvary Bible College and Theological Seminary, B
Lindenwood University, M
Saint Louis University, B

New Jersey

Fairleigh Dickinson University, College at
   Florham, MO

New York

Bernard M. Baruch College of the City University of
   New York, M
Cornell University, MD
John Jay College of Criminal Justice of the City
   University of New York, D
Manhattan College, B
New York University, M
Polytechnic University, Brooklyn Campus, M
Syracuse University, D

North Carolina

Saint Augustine's College, B
The University of North Carolina at Chapel Hill, D

Ohio

Baldwin-Wallace College, B
Bluffton University, B
Case Western Reserve University, MD
Denison University, B
Miami University, B
The University of Toledo, B

Oklahoma

University of Oklahoma, M

Pennsylvania

Carnegie Mellon University, D
The Pennsylvania State University Abington
   College, B
The Pennsylvania State University Altoona
   College, B
The Pennsylvania State University Beaver Campus
   of the Commonwealth College, B
The Pennsylvania State University Berks Campus of
   the Berks-Lehigh Valley College, B
The Pennsylvania State University Delaware County
   Campus of the Commonwealth College, B
The Pennsylvania State University DuBois Campus
   of the Commonwealth College, B

The Pennsylvania State University at Erie, The
   Behrend College, B
The Pennsylvania State University Fayette Campus
   of the Commonwealth College, B
The Pennsylvania State University Harrisburg
   Campus, B
The Pennsylvania State University Hazleton
   Campus of the Commonwealth College, B
The Pennsylvania State University Lehigh Valley
   Campus of the Berks-Lehigh Valley College, B
The Pennsylvania State University McKeesport
   Campus of the Commonwealth College, B
The Pennsylvania State University Mont Alto
   Campus of the Commonwealth College, B
The Pennsylvania State University New Kensington
   Campus of the Commonwealth College, B
The Pennsylvania State University Schuylkill
   Campus of the Capital College, B
The Pennsylvania State University Shenango
   Campus of the Commonwealth College, B
The Pennsylvania State University University Park
   Campus, B
The Pennsylvania State University Wilkes-Barre
   Campus of the Commonwealth College, B
The Pennsylvania State University Worthington
   Scranton Campus of the Commonwealth
   College, B
The Pennsylvania State University York Campus of
   the Commonwealth College, B
Robert Morris University, B
Temple University, B
University of Pennsylvania, M

Rhode Island

Brown University, B

South Carolina

Claflin University, B
Columbia College, O

Texas

Southern Methodist University, B
University of Houston, B
University of the Incarnate Word, B
University of North Texas, B

Virginia

Regent University, B

West Virginia

Mountain State University, B

Wisconsin

Carroll College, B
Silver Lake College, M

Alberta

Athabasca University, B

British Columbia

The University of British Columbia, D

Newfoundland and Labrador

Memorial University of Newfoundland, B

Nova Scotia

Cape Breton University, B

Ontario

York University, B

Quebec

McGill University, B
Université de Sherbrooke, M

Saskatchewan

University of Saskatchewan, M

ORGANIZATIONAL COMMUNICATION

California

California State University, Chico, B
California State University, Sacramento, B

Colorado

Western State College of Colorado, B

Florida

Palm Beach Atlantic University, B

Georgia

Emmanuel College, B
Shorter College, B
Toccoa Falls College, B

Illinois

McKendree College, B
North Central College, B

Indiana

Indiana University-Purdue University Fort Wayne, B
Valparaiso University, B

Iowa

Buena Vista University, B
University of Northern Iowa, B

Massachusetts

Assumption College, B

Michigan

Aquinas College, B
University of Michigan-Flint, B
Western Michigan University, B

Nebraska

Creighton University, A
Dana College, B

New York

Iona College, B
Marist College, B
State University of New York College at
   Brockport, B

North Carolina

Pfeiffer University, B

Ohio

Capital University, B
Ohio Northern University, B
Ohio University-Southern Campus, B
Wright State University, B

Texas

University of Houston, B

Utah

Brigham Young University, B

Virginia

Lynchburg College, B

Washington

Eastern Washington University, B
Northwest University, B

Wisconsin

Carroll College, B

Ontario

University of Windsor, B

ORGANIZATIONAL MANAGEMENT

Alabama

Southern Christian University, M

Arizona

University of Phoenix Online Campus, MD
University of Phoenix-Phoenix Campus, M

University of Phoenix-Southern Arizona Campus, M

California

Antioch University Los Angeles, M
Antioch University Santa Barbara, M
Azusa Pacific University, M
Biola University, M
John F. Kennedy University, O
National University, M
University of La Verne, MDO
University of Phoenix-Bay Area Campus, M
University of Phoenix-Sacramento Valley
  Campus, M
University of Phoenix-San Diego Campus, M
University of Phoenix-Southern California
  Campus, M
University of San Francisco, M
Vanguard University of Southern California, M
Woodbury University, M

Colorado

Colorado Technical University, M
Jones International University, M
Regis University, M
University of Colorado at Boulder, MD
University of Denver, M
University of Phoenix-Denver Campus, M
University of Phoenix-Southern Colorado
  Campus, M

Connecticut

Eastern Connecticut State University, M

District of Columbia

American University, MO
The George Washington University, MO
Trinity (Washington) University, M

Florida

Carlos Albizu University, Miami Campus, M
Nova Southeastern University, D
Palm Beach Atlantic University, M
University of Phoenix-Central Florida Campus, M
University of Phoenix-North Florida Campus, M
University of Phoenix-South Florida Campus, M
University of Phoenix-West Florida Campus, M

Georgia

Brenau University, M
Emory University, D
University of Phoenix-Atlanta Campus, M

Hawaii

Hawaii Pacific University, M
University of Hawaii at Manoa, MD
University of Phoenix-Hawaii Campus, M

Illinois

Benedictine University, D
Dominican University, M
Lewis University, M
Northwestern University, MD
Roosevelt University, MD
University of Phoenix-Chicago Campus, M

Indiana

Indiana Wesleyan University, D

Iowa

St. Ambrose University, M
The University of Iowa, M

Upper Iowa University, M

Kansas

Newman University, M

Louisiana

University of Phoenix-Louisiana Campus, M

Maryland

University of Maryland Eastern Shore, D
University of Phoenix-Maryland Campus, M

Massachusetts

American International College, M
Boston College, D
Endicott College, M
Regis College, M
University of Phoenix-Central Massachusetts
  Campus, M
Worcester Polytechnic Institute, M
Worcester State College, M

Michigan

Eastern Michigan University, M
Michigan State University, MD
Spring Arbor University, M
University of Phoenix-Metro Detroit Campus, M
University of Phoenix-West Michigan Campus, M

Minnesota

Augsburg College, M
Bethel University, M
Capella University, MD
College of St. Catherine, M
Concordia University, St. Paul, M
Metropolitan State University, M
University of St. Thomas, MDO

Missouri

Evangel University, M
University of Phoenix-Kansas City Campus, M
University of Phoenix-St. Louis Campus, M

Nevada

University of Phoenix-Nevada Campus, M

New Hampshire

Southern New Hampshire University, M

New Jersey

Fairleigh Dickinson University, College at
  Florham, O
Rutgers, The State University of New Jersey,
  Newark, D

New Mexico

University of New Mexico, M
University of Phoenix-New Mexico Campus, M

New York

Bernard M. Baruch College of the City University of
  New York, D
Manhattanville College, M
Medaille College, M
Mercy College, M
New York University, O
University at Albany, State University of New
  York, D

North Carolina

Pfeiffer University, MO

Ohio

Bluffton University, M
Bowling Green State University, M
College of Mount St. Joseph, M
Defiance College, M
Lourdes College, M
University of Cincinnati, M
University of Phoenix-Cincinnati Campus, M

University of Phoenix-Cleveland Campus, M

Oklahoma

University of Phoenix-Oklahoma City Campus, M
University of Phoenix-Tulsa Campus, M

Oregon

George Fox University, M
University of Phoenix-Oregon Campus, M

Pennsylvania

Cabrini College, M
Carnegie Mellon University, D
College Misericordia, M
Geneva College, M
Immaculata University, M
Lehigh University, O
Mercyhurst College, MO
Philadelphia Biblical University, M
Saint Joseph's University, M
Shippensburg University of Pennsylvania, M
University of Pennsylvania, M
University of Phoenix-Pittsburgh Campus, M
The University of Scranton, M

Rhode Island

Johnson & Wales University, M

South Carolina

Charleston Southern University, M

South Dakota

Colorado Technical University Sioux Falls
  Campus, M

Tennessee

Cumberland University, M
Trevecca Nazarene University, M
Tusculum College, M
Vanderbilt University, MD

Texas

Dallas Baptist University, M
St. Edward's University, M
University of Dallas, M
University of the Incarnate Word, MD
University of North Texas, D
University of Phoenix-Dallas Campus, M
University of Phoenix-Houston Campus, M
The University of Texas at San Antonio, D

Utah

University of Phoenix-Utah Campus, M

Virginia

George Mason University, M
Marymount University, MO
Regent University, MDO

Washington

Antioch University Seattle, M
Gonzaga University, M
University of Phoenix-Washington Campus, M

Wisconsin

Marian College of Fond du Lac, M
University of Phoenix-Wisconsin Campus, M

Alberta

Athabasca University, M
University of Alberta, D

British Columbia

Royal Roads University, M
Trinity Western University, M

Quebec

Concordia University, M
Université Laval, M

ORNAMENTAL HORTICULTURE

Alabama

Auburn University, B

Arizona

Mesa Community College, A

Arkansas

University of Arkansas, B
University of Arkansas Community College at
  Morrilton, A

California

Antelope Valley College, A
Bakersfield College, A
Butte College, A
California Polytechnic State University, San Luis
  Obispo, B
California State Polytechnic University, Pomona, B
California State University, Fresno, B
Cerritos College, A
Chabot College, A
City College of San Francisco, A
College of the Desert, A
College of San Mateo, A
College of the Sequoias, A
Cuyamaca College, A
El Camino College, A
Foothill College, A
Fullerton College, A
Golden West College, A
Long Beach City College, A
Los Angeles Pierce College, A
Mendocino College, A
Merced College, A
MiraCosta College, A
Modesto Junior College, A
Monterey Peninsula College, A
Mt. San Antonio College, A
Orange Coast College, A
Saddleback College, A
San Joaquin Delta College, A
Santa Barbara City College, A
Shasta College, A
Sierra College, A
Solano Community College, A
Victor Valley College, A

Delaware

University of Delaware, B

District of Columbia

University of the District of Columbia, B

Florida

Florida Agricultural and Mechanical University, B
Florida Southern College, B
Hillsborough Community College, A
Miami Dade College, A
Pensacola Junior College, A
Santa Fe Community College, A
South Florida Community College, A
Valencia Community College, A

Georgia

Abraham Baldwin Agricultural College, A
Fort Valley State University, B
Gwinnett Technical College, A

Idaho

Brigham Young University -Idaho, A

Illinois

College of DuPage, A
College of Lake County, A
Danville Area Community College, A
Kishwaukee College, A
Triton College, A
University of Illinois at Urbana-Champaign, B

Iowa

Hawkeye Community College, A
Iowa State University of Science and Technology, B

Kirkwood Community College, A

Maine

University of Maine, B

Massachusetts

University of Massachusetts Amherst, A

Michigan

Ferris State University, A
Oakland Community College, A

Mississippi

Mississippi Gulf Coast Community College, A

Nebraska

Metropolitan Community College, A

Nevada

Community College of Southern Nevada, A

New Jersey

Bergen Community College, A
Cumberland County College, A
Mercer County Community College, A

New York

Bronx Community College of the City University of
  New York, A
Cornell University, B
Farmingdale State University of New York, A
Finger Lakes Community College, A
State University of New York College of Agriculture
  and Technology at Cobleskill, A

North Carolina

Forsyth Technical Community College, A
Lenoir Community College, A

North Dakota

Minot State University-Bottineau Campus, A

Ohio

Kent State University, Salem Campus, A

Oklahoma

Tulsa Community College, A

Oregon

Clackamas Community College, A
Mt. Hood Community College, A

Pennsylvania

Community College of Allegheny County, A
Delaware Valley College, B
Pennsylvania College of Technology, A

Tennessee

The University of Tennessee, B

Texas

Howard College, A
Richland College, A
Tarleton State University, B
Texas A&M University, B
Texas State Technical College Waco, A
Tyler Junior College, A
Wharton County Junior College, A

Utah

Utah State University, AB

Virginia

J. Sargeant Reynolds Community College, A

Washington

Spokane Community College, A

Wisconsin

University of Wisconsin-Platteville, B

ORTHODONTICS

California

Loma Linda University, MO
University of the Pacific, M

District of Columbia

Howard University, O

Florida

Jacksonville University, O
University of Florida, MO

Iowa

The University of Iowa, MO

Massachusetts

Boston University, MDO
Harvard University, O

Michigan

University of Detroit Mercy, MO

Minnesota

University of Minnesota, Twin Cities Campus, M

Missouri

University of Missouri-Kansas City, O

New York

New York University, O
State University of New York at Buffalo, MO
Stony Brook University, State University of New
  York, O

Ohio

Case Western Reserve University, MO

Oklahoma

University of Oklahoma Health Sciences Center, M

Pennsylvania

Temple University, O
University of Pittsburgh, MO

Puerto Rico

University of Puerto Rico, Medical Sciences
  Campus, M

Texas

Texas A&M University System Health Science
  Center, MO

West Virginia

West Virginia University, M

Wisconsin

Marquette University, M

Alberta

University of Alberta, MD

Manitoba

University of Manitoba, M

Ontario

University of Toronto, M

Quebec

Université de Montréal, MO

ORTHOPTICS/ORTHOPTIST

Oklahoma

Oklahoma City Community College, A

ORTHOTIST/PROSTHETIST

Florida

Florida International University, B
St. Petersburg College, B

Michigan

Baker College of Flint, A

Minnesota

Century College, A

Pennsylvania

Median School of Allied Health Careers, A

Texas

The University of Texas Southwestern Medical
Center at Dallas, B

Washington

Spokane Falls Community College, A
University of Washington, B

OSTEOPATHIC MEDICINE

Arizona

Midwestern University, Glendale Campus, P

Florida

Nova Southeastern University, MP

Kentucky

Pikeville College, P

Maine

University of New England, P

Michigan

Michigan State University, P

New York

New York Institute of Technology, PO

Ohio

Ohio University, PO

PACIFIC AREA/PACIFIC RIM STUDIES

California

Claremont McKenna College, B

Hawaii

Brigham Young University-Hawaii, B
University of Hawaii at Manoa, B

British Columbia

University of Victoria, B

PAINTING

Alabama

Birmingham-Southern College, B

Arkansas

Harding University, B
Henderson State University, B

California

Academy of Art University, ABM
Art Center College of Design, B
California College of the Arts, BM
California State University, East Bay, B
California State University, Fullerton, B
California State University, Long Beach, BM
Cuyamaca College, A
Laguna College of Art & Design, B
Mills College, M

Otis College of Art and Design, M
San Francisco Art Institute, BMO
University of San Francisco, B

Colorado

Colorado State University, BM
Rocky Mountain College of Art & Design, B
University of Colorado at Boulder, M

Connecticut

Lyme Academy College of Fine Arts, B
Paier College of Art, Inc., B
University of Hartford, B
Western Connecticut State University, M
Yale University, M

District of Columbia

American University, M
The Catholic University of America, B
The George Washington University, M
Howard University, M

Florida

Florida Atlantic University, M
New World School of the Arts, AB
University of Miami, BM

Georgia

Savannah College of Art and Design, BM
University of Georgia, B

Guam

University of Guam, M

Idaho

Northwest Nazarene University, B

Illinois

American Academy of Art, BM
Bradley University, M
Illinois State University, M
Lewis University, B
Lincoln College, A
School of the Art Institute of Chicago, BM
Southern Illinois University Carbondale, M
Trinity Christian College, B
University of Illinois at Urbana-Champaign, B

Indiana

Grace College, B
Indiana State University, M
Indiana University Bloomington, M
Indiana University-Purdue University Fort Wayne, B
Indiana Wesleyan University, B

Iowa

Coe College, B
Drake University, B
The University of Iowa, B

Kansas

Bethany College, B
University of Kansas, B

Kentucky

Bellarmine University, B

Louisiana

Louisiana State University and Agricultural and
Mechanical College, M

Maine

Maine College of Art, B

Maryland

Maryland Institute College of Art, BM

Massachusetts

Boston University, BM
Framingham State College, B
Massachusetts College of Art, BM
Montserrat College of Art, B
School of the Museum of Fine Arts, Boston, B

Simon's Rock College of Bard, B
University of Massachusetts Dartmouth, B

Michigan

Aquinas College, B
University of Michigan, B
University of Michigan-Flint, B

Minnesota

Minneapolis College of Art and Design, BM
Minnesota State University Moorhead, B
St. Cloud State University, B

Missouri

Columbia College, B
Kansas City Art Institute, B
University of Missouri-St. Louis, B
Washington University in St. Louis, BM

New Hampshire

Rivier College, B
University of New Hampshire, M

New Jersey

Rutgers, The State University of New Jersey, New
Brunswick/Piscataway, BM

New Mexico

College of Santa Fe, B

New York

Bard College, B
Brooklyn College of the City University of New
York, M
Buffalo State College, State University of New
York, B
City College of the City University of New York, M
Hofstra University, B
Pratt Institute, ABM
Rochester Institute of Technology, M
Sarah Lawrence College, B
State University of New York College at
Brockport, B
State University of New York at New Paltz, BM
Syracuse University, BM

Ohio

Art Academy of Cincinnati, B
The Cleveland Institute of Art, B
Ohio Northern University, B
The Ohio State University, B
Ohio University, BM
Shawnee State University, B
The University of Akron, B
Youngstown State University, B

Oklahoma

University of Oklahoma, M

Oregon

Pacific Northwest College of Art, B
Portland State University, M
University of Oregon, B

Pennsylvania

The Art Institute of Pittsburgh, AB
Keystone College, A
Luzerne County Community College, A
Marywood University, M
Seton Hill University, B
Temple University, BM
The University of the Arts, BM

Puerto Rico

Escuela de Artes Plasticas de Puerto Rico, B
Inter American University of Puerto Rico, San
Germán Campus, M

University of Puerto Rico, Río Piedras, B

Rhode Island

Rhode Island School of Design, BM
Salve Regina University, B

Tennessee

Memphis College of Art, BM
University of Memphis, M
The University of Tennessee, M

Texas

McMurry University, B
Sam Houston State University, B
Stephen F. Austin State University, M
Texas Christian University, B
University of Dallas, B
University of Houston, BM
University of North Texas, BM

Utah

Brigham Young University, B
Dixie State College of Utah, A
University of Utah, M

Vermont

Bennington College, B
Johnson State College, M

Virginia

James Madison University, M
Virginia Commonwealth University, BM

Washington

University of Washington, B
Washington State University, M
Western Washington University, B

West Virginia

West Virginia University, M
West Virginia Wesleyan College, B

Wisconsin

Milwaukee Institute of Art and Design, B

Alberta

Alberta College of Art & Design, B
University of Alberta, M

British Columbia

University of Victoria, M

Newfoundland and Labrador

Memorial University of Newfoundland, B

Nova Scotia

NSCAD University, B

Ontario

University of Windsor, B
York University, B

Quebec

Concordia University, B

Saskatchewan

University of Regina, B

PAINTING/PAINTER AND WALL COVERER

Indiana

Ivy Tech Community College-Central Indiana, A
Ivy Tech Community College-East Central, A
Ivy Tech Community College-Lafayette, A
Ivy Tech Community College-North Central, A
Ivy Tech Community College-Northeast, A
Ivy Tech Community College-Northwest, A
Ivy Tech Community College-Southwest, A

Ivy Tech Community College-Wabash Valley, A

PALEONTOLOGY

Delaware

University of Delaware, B

Illinois

University of Chicago, D
University of Illinois at Chicago, MD

Louisiana

Tulane University, D

New Mexico

Mesalands Community College, A

New York

Cornell University, MD

North Carolina

North Carolina State University, B

Pennsylvania

Mercyhurst College, B

South Dakota

South Dakota School of Mines and Technology, M

West Virginia

West Virginia University, MD

Alberta

University of Alberta, B

Ontario

University of Toronto, B

PAPER AND PULP ENGINEERING

Michigan

Western Michigan University, MD

New York

State University of New York College of
   Environmental Science and Forestry, MD

North Carolina

North Carolina State University, MD

Ohio

Miami University, M

Oregon

Oregon State University, MD

Washington

University of Washington, MD

Quebec

Université du Québec àTrois-Rivières, MD

PARASITOLOGY

Connecticut

Yale University, D

Georgia

University of Georgia, MD

Indiana

Purdue University, MD
University of Notre Dame, MD

Louisiana

Louisiana State University Health Sciences
   Center, MD

Tulane University, MDO

New York

New York University, MDO

Pennsylvania

University of Pennsylvania, DO

Texas

Texas A&M University, M

Washington

University of Washington, MD

West Virginia

West Virginia University, MD

Prince Edward Island

University of Prince Edward Island, MD

Quebec

McGill University, MDO

PARKS, RECREATION AND LEISURE FACILITIES MANAGEMENT

Alabama

James H. Faulkner State Community College, A
Stillman College, B

Arizona

Northland Pioneer College, A

Arkansas

Arkansas Tech University, B
Henderson State University, B
National Park Community College, A

California

Butte College, A
California State University, Chico, B
California State University, Fresno, B
California State University, Sacramento, B
Cerro Coso Community College, A
College of the Desert, A
Compton Community College, A
Cuesta College, A
Feather River College, A
Humboldt State University, B
Modesto Junior College, A
Monterey Peninsula College, A
Mt. San Antonio College, A
Palomar College, A
Southwestern College, A
West Valley College, A

Colorado

Colorado Mountain College, Alpine Campus, A
Colorado Mountain College, Timberline Campus, A
Colorado State University, B
Johnson & Wales University, B
University of Northern Colorado, B
Western State College of Colorado, B

Connecticut

Northwestern Connecticut Community College, A
University of Connecticut, B

Delaware

Delaware State University, B
University of Delaware, B

Florida

Florida Agricultural and Mechanical University, B
Florida International University, B
Florida State University, B
Johnson & Wales University, B
Lynn University, B
Santa Fe Community College, A
University of Florida, B

University of Miami, B

Georgia

Abraham Baldwin Agricultural College, A
Andrew College, A
Augusta Technical College, A
Chattahoochee Technical College, A
Coastal Georgia Community College, A
Georgia Southwestern State University, B
North Georgia Technical College, A
Savannah State University, B
South Georgia College, A
Thomas University, B
University of West Georgia, B

Illinois

Eastern Illinois University, B
Illinois State University, B
Moraine Valley Community College, A
University of St. Francis, B
Western Illinois University, B
William Rainey Harper College, A

Indiana

Ball State University, B
Indiana State University, B
Indiana Tech, AB
Indiana University Bloomington, B
Indiana University Southeast, B
Indiana Wesleyan University, B
Tri-State University, B

Iowa

Hawkeye Community College, A
Kirkwood Community College, A

Kansas

Allen County Community College, A
Kansas State University, B

Kentucky

Asbury College, B
Eastern Kentucky University, AB
Murray State University, B
Union College, B
Western Kentucky University, B

Maine

Unity College, B
University of Maine, B
University of Maine at Machias, B

Maryland

Garrett College, A

Massachusetts

Springfield College, B

Michigan

Central Michigan University, B
Eastern Michigan University, B
Grand Valley State University, B
Lake Superior State University, B
Michigan State University, B
Northern Michigan University, B

Minnesota

Minnesota State University Mankato, B
University of Minnesota, Twin Cities Campus, B
Vermilion Community College, A
Winona State University, B

Missouri

College of the Ozarks, B
Hannibal-LaGrange College, B
Missouri Valley College, B

Missouri Western State University, B

Nebraska

Hastings College, B

Nevada

Western Nevada Community College, A

New Hampshire

Franklin Pierce College, B
New England College, B

New Jersey

County College of Morris, A
Kean University, B

New Mexico

New Mexico State University, B

New York

Erie Community College, South Campus, A
Finger Lakes Community College, A
Mohawk Valley Community College, A
North Country Community College, A
Paul Smith's College of Arts and Sciences, A
State University of New York College of Agriculture
  and Technology at Cobleskill, A
State University of New York College of Agriculture
  and Technology at Morrisville, A
State University of New York College at Cortland, B
State University of New York College of Technology
  at Delhi, AB

North Carolina

Appalachian State University, B
East Carolina University, B
High Point University, B
Johnson & Wales University, AB
Methodist College, B
North Carolina Central University, B
North Carolina State University, BM
Southeastern Community College, A
The University of North Carolina at Chapel Hill, B
The University of North Carolina at Greensboro, B
The University of North Carolina at Pembroke, B
The University of North Carolina Wilmington, B
Wayne Community College, A
Western Carolina University, B

North Dakota

University of North Dakota, B

Ohio

Hocking College, A
Kent State University, B
Ohio University, B
Ohio University-Eastern, B
Zane State College, A

Oklahoma

Rose State College, A

Oregon

Oregon State University, B

Pennsylvania

Butler County Community College, A
California University of Pennsylvania, B
East Stroudsburg University of Pennsylvania, B
Keystone College, AB
The Pennsylvania State University Abington
  College, B
The Pennsylvania State University Altoona
  College, B
The Pennsylvania State University Beaver Campus
  of the Commonwealth College, B
The Pennsylvania State University Berks Campus of
  the Berks-Lehigh Valley College, B
The Pennsylvania State University Delaware County
  Campus of the Commonwealth College, B
The Pennsylvania State University DuBois Campus
  of the Commonwealth College, B
The Pennsylvania State University at Erie, The
  Behrend College, B

The Pennsylvania State University Fayette Campus
  of the Commonwealth College, B
The Pennsylvania State University Hazleton
  Campus of the Commonwealth College, B
The Pennsylvania State University, Lehigh Valley
  Campus of the Berks-Lehigh Valley College, B
The Pennsylvania State University McKeesport
  Campus of the Commonwealth College, B
The Pennsylvania State University Mont Alto
  Campus of the Commonwealth College, B
The Pennsylvania State University New Kensington
  Campus of the Commonwealth College, B
The Pennsylvania State University Schuylkill
  Campus of the Capital College, B
The Pennsylvania State University Shenango
  Campus of the Commonwealth College, B
The Pennsylvania State University University Park
  Campus, B
The Pennsylvania State University Wilkes-Barre
  Campus of the Commonwealth College, B
The Pennsylvania State University Worthington
  Scranton Campus of the Commonwealth
  College, B
The Pennsylvania State University York Campus of
  the Commonwealth College, B
Slippery Rock University of Pennsylvania, B

Puerto Rico

Inter American University of Puerto Rico, Aguadilla
  Campus, B

Rhode Island

Johnson & Wales University, AB

South Carolina

Clemson University, B
Horry-Georgetown Technical College, A

South Dakota

Mount Marty College, B
South Dakota State University, B

Tennessee

Martin Methodist College, A
Middle Tennessee State University, B
Union University, B
The University of Tennessee, B
The University of Tennessee at Martin, B

Texas

Texas A&M University, B
Texas State University-San Marcos, B
University of Houston-Clear Lake, B
University of North Texas, B
Western Texas College, A

Utah

University of Utah, B

Vermont

College of St. Joseph, B
Green Mountain College, B
Lyndon State College, B
Sterling College, B
University of Vermont, B

Virginia

Old Dominion University, B
Southern Virginia University, B
Virginia Commonwealth University, B

Washington

Eastern Washington University, B
Skagit Valley College, A
Spokane Community College, A

West Virginia

Concord University, B
Marshall University, B
Potomac State College of West Virginia
  University, A

West Virginia University, B

Wisconsin

Northland College, B
University of Wisconsin-La Crosse, B

Wyoming

Northwest College, A
University of Wyoming, B

Alberta

University of Alberta, B

British Columbia

The University of British Columbia, B
University of Northern British Columbia, B

Ontario

University of Waterloo, B

PARKS, RECREATION, LEISURE AND FITNESS STUDIES

Alabama

Alabama State University, B
Auburn University, B
Community College of the Air Force, A
Enterprise-Ozark Community College, A
Huntingdon College, B
Jacksonville State University, B
Jefferson Davis Community College, A
Lawson State Community College, A
Troy University, B
University of North Alabama, B
University of South Alabama, B

Alaska

Alaska Pacific University, B
Sheldon Jackson College, B

Arizona

Arizona State University, B
Arizona State University West, B
Northern Arizona University, B
Prescott College, B

Arkansas

National Park Community College, A
University of Arkansas at Pine Bluff, B

California

Allan Hancock College, A
American River College, A
Bakersfield College, A
Cabrillo College, A
California Polytechnic State University, San Luis Obispo, B
California State University, Chico, B
California State University, Dominguez Hills, B
California State University, East Bay, B
California State University, Fresno, B
California State University, Long Beach, B
California State University, Northridge, B
California State University, Sacramento, B
Cerritos College, A
Chabot College, A
City College of San Francisco, A
College of the Desert, A
Compton Community College, A
Feather River College, A
Fresno City College, A
Fullerton College, A
Glendale Community College, A
Hartnell College, A
Humboldt State University, B
Merritt College, A
Mt. San Antonio College, A
Pacific Union College, B
Palomar College, A
Pasadena City College, A
San Bernardino Valley College, A
San Diego City College, A

San Diego State University, B
San Francisco State University, B
San Jose State University, B
Santa Barbara City College, A
Santa Monica College, A
Skyline College, A
Taft College, A
Ventura College, A

Colorado

Colorado Mountain College, Timberline Campus, A
Colorado Northwestern Community College, A
Colorado State University-Pueblo, B
Metropolitan State College of Denver, B
Western State College of Colorado, B

Connecticut

Mitchell College, A
Northwestern Connecticut Community College, A
Norwalk Community College, A
Southern Connecticut State University, B

Delaware

Wesley College, B

District of Columbia

University of the District of Columbia, AB

Florida

Central Florida Community College, A
Florida Keys Community College, A
Miami Dade College, A
Tallahassee Community College, A

Georgia

Clayton State University, A
East Georgia College, A
Georgia College & State University, B
Georgia Southern University, B
Gordon College, A
Shorter College, B
South Georgia College, A
Young Harris College, A

Hawaii

Leeward Community College, A
University of Hawaii at Manoa, B

Idaho

Brigham Young University -Idaho, A
Northwest Nazarene University, B
University of Idaho, B

Illinois

Chicago State University, B
City Colleges of Chicago, Kennedy-King College, A
Greenville College, B
Rend Lake College, A
Southern Illinois University Carbondale, B
University of Illinois at Urbana-Champaign, B

Indiana

Franklin College, B
Huntington University, B
Indiana University Bloomington, B
Vincennes University, A

Iowa

Dordt College, B
Graceland University, B
Iowa Lakes Community College, A
Kirkwood Community College, A
University of Dubuque, B
The University of Iowa, B
University of Northern Iowa, B
Upper Iowa University, B
William Penn University, B

Kansas

Bethany College, B
Central Christian College of Kansas, AB
Cowley County Community College and Area Vocational-Technical School, A

Emporia State University, B

Kentucky

Campbellsville University, B
Lindsey Wilson College, B

Maine

University of Maine at Machias, B
University of Maine at Presque Isle, AB

Maryland

Chesapeake College, A
Frostburg State University, B
Garrett College, A
Morgan State University, B

Massachusetts

Boston University, B
Bridgewater State College, B
Cape Cod Community College, A
Gordon College, B
Greenfield Community College, A
Northern Essex Community College, A
Salem State College, B
Springfield College, B
Westfield State College, B

Michigan

Calvin College, B
Central Michigan University, B
Ferris State University, B
Lake Superior State University, B
Madonna University, B
Muskegon Community College, A
Western Michigan University, B

Minnesota

Bemidji State University, B
Minneapolis Community and Technical College, A
Minnesota State University Mankato, B
University of Minnesota, Duluth, B
Vermilion Community College, A
Winona State University, B

Mississippi

Alcorn State University, B
Mississippi University for Women, B
Northeast Mississippi Community College, A
University of Mississippi, B
University of Southern Mississippi, B

Missouri

Central Missouri State University, B
Culver-Stockton College, B
East Central College, A
Evangel University, B
Mineral Area College, A
Missouri State University, B
Missouri Valley College, B
Northwest Missouri State University, B
Southeast Missouri State University, B
Southwest Baptist University, B
University of Missouri-Columbia, B

Montana

The University of Montana-Missoula, B

Nebraska

Chadron State College, B
Midland Lutheran College, B
University of Nebraska at Kearney, B
University of Nebraska at Omaha, B

Nevada

Community College of Southern Nevada, A
University of Nevada, Las Vegas, B
University of Nevada, Reno, B

New Hampshire

New England College, B
Plymouth State University, B

University of New Hampshire, B

New Jersey

Bergen Community College, A
Camden County College, A
Montclair State University, B
William Paterson University of New Jersey, B

New Mexico

Central New Mexico Community College, A
New Mexico Junior College, A
San Juan College, A
Santa Fe Community College, A
University of New Mexico, B

New York

Dutchess Community College, A
Houghton College, B
Ithaca College, B
Kingsborough Community College of the City
   University of New York, A
Monroe Community College, A
Onondaga Community College, A
Orange County Community College, A
St. Joseph's College, Suffolk Campus, B
St. Thomas Aquinas College, B
State University of New York College at
   Brockport, B
State University of New York College at Cortland, B
State University of New York College of
   Environmental Science and Forestry, B
State University of New York College of Technology
   at Delhi, A
Suffolk County Community College, A
Tompkins Cortland Community College, A
Ulster County Community College, A

North Carolina

Brevard College, B
Catawba College, B
Elon University, B
High Point University, B
Johnson & Wales University, AB
Mars Hill College, B
Montreat College, B
Mount Olive College, AB
North Carolina Agricultural and Technical State
   University, B
North Carolina State University, B
Shaw University, B
Southeastern Community College, A
Southwestern Community College, A
The University of North Carolina at Greensboro, B
Vance-Granville Community College, A
Wingate University, B

North Dakota

Cankdeska Cikana Community College, A
North Dakota State University, B
University of North Dakota, B

Ohio

Ashland University, B
Bluffton University, B
Bowling Green State University, B
Central State University, B
Cincinnati State Technical and Community
   College, A
Malone College, B
Ohio University, B
The University of Toledo, B
Zane State College, A

Oklahoma

Oklahoma Baptist University, B
Oklahoma Panhandle State University, AB
Southeastern Oklahoma State University, B
Southwestern Oklahoma State University, B

Oregon

Oregon State University, B

Pennsylvania

Cheyney University of Pennsylvania, B
Lock Haven University of Pennsylvania, B

Marywood University, B
Messiah College, B
Temple University, B
York College of Pennsylvania, B

Puerto Rico

Universidad Metropolitana, B

Rhode Island

Johnson & Wales University, AB

South Carolina

Benedict College, B
Coker College, B
Morris College, B
Southern Wesleyan University, B

South Dakota

Black Hills State University, B
South Dakota State University, B
The University of South Dakota, B

Tennessee

Belmont University, B
Carson-Newman College, B
Cumberland University, B
Lambuth University, B
Maryville College, B
Tennessee State University, B
Tennessee Wesleyan College, B
The University of Tennessee at Chattanooga, B

Texas

Coastal Bend College, A
Del Mar College, A
Howard Payne University, B
St. Edward's University, B
Texas A&M University, B
Texas Tech University, B
Tyler Junior College, A
University of Mary Hardin-Baylor, B

Utah

Brigham Young University, B
University of Utah, B
Utah State University, B
Utah Valley State College, AB

Vermont

Green Mountain College, B
Johnson State College, B
Lyndon State College, B
Sterling College, B

Virginia

Ferrum College, B
Northern Virginia Community College, A
Radford University, B
Virginia Wesleyan College, B

Washington

Bellevue Community College, A
Central Washington University, B
Centralia College, A
Eastern Washington University, B
Skagit Valley College, A
Washington State University, B
Wenatchee Valley College, A
Western Washington University, B

West Virginia

Shepherd University, B
West Virginia State University, B
West Virginia University, B

Wisconsin

Madison Area Technical College, A
Northland College, B
University of Wisconsin-Madison, B

University of Wisconsin-Milwaukee, B

Wyoming

Northwest College, A

Alberta

University of Alberta, B
University of Calgary, B
University of Lethbridge, B

British Columbia

University of Northern British Columbia, B

Manitoba

Providence College and Theological Seminary, B

New Brunswick

Université de Moncton, B
University of New Brunswick Fredericton, B

Newfoundland and Labrador

Memorial University of Newfoundland, B

Nova Scotia

Cape Breton University, B
Dalhousie University, B

Ontario

Brock University, B
Lakehead University, B
Redeemer University College, B
Tyndale University College & Seminary, B
University of Ottawa, B
University of Waterloo, B
University of Windsor, B

Quebec

Concordia University, B
Université du Québec àMontréal, B
Université du Québec àTrois-Rivières, B

PARTS, WAREHOUSING, AND INVENTORY MANAGEMENT OPERATIONS

Wyoming

Central Wyoming College, A

PASTORAL COUNSELING AND SPECIALIZED MINISTRIES

Arkansas

Harding University, B
Ouachita Baptist University, B

Illinois

Greenville College, B
Trinity International University, B

Indiana

Crossroads Bible College, B

Iowa

Vennard College, B

Minnesota

Oak Hills Christian College, B

Missouri

Calvary Bible College and Theological Seminary, B

New York

St. John's University, B

Ohio

Cedarville University, B
College of Mount St. Joseph, B

Malone College, B

Oregon

Multnomah Bible College and Biblical Seminary, B

Pennsylvania

Lancaster Bible College, B

Alberta

Prairie Bible Institute, B

Saskatchewan

Central Pentecostal College, B

PASTORAL STUDIES/COUNSELING

Alabama

Faulkner University, B
Oakwood College, A
Southeastern Bible College, B
Southern Christian University, BMP

Arizona

American Indian College of the Assemblies of God, Inc., B
International Baptist College, MD

Arkansas

Harding University, BM
John Brown University, BM
Ouachita Baptist University, B
Williams Baptist College, B

California

Azusa Pacific University, MP
Bethany University, B
Bethesda Christian University, B
Biola University, B
Fresno Pacific University, B
Holy Names University, MO
Hope International University, M
Life Pacific College, B
Loma Linda University, MO
Loyola Marymount University, M
The Master's College and Seminary, BMD
Pacific Union College, B
Patten University, B
San Diego Christian College, B
Santa Clara University, M
Shasta Bible College, M
Simpson University, M
University of San Diego, MO
University of San Francisco, M
Vanguard University of Southern California, B

Colorado

Nazarene Bible College, B

Florida

Argosy University/Sarasota, D
Ave Maria University, M
The Baptist College of Florida, B
Barry University, M
Clearwater Christian College, B
Saint Leo University, M
St. Thomas University, BMDO
Southeastern University, B
Trinity Baptist College, B
Trinity College of Florida, B

Georgia

Emmanuel College, B
Luther Rice University, BDP

Hawaii

Chaminade University of Honolulu, M

Idaho

Boise Bible College, AB
Northwest Nazarene University, B

Illinois

Concordia University, B
Greenville College, BM

Hebrew Theological College, B
Lewis University, M
Loyola University Chicago, MO
Olivet Nazarene University, BM
Trinity International University, MDP

Indiana

Bethel College, BM
Grace College, B
Huntington University, M
Indiana Wesleyan University, AB
Martin University, M
Saint Joseph's College, B
Saint Mary-of-the-Woods College, B

Iowa

Dordt College, B
Faith Baptist Bible College and Theological Seminary, BMP
Graceland University, M
Loras College, M
St. Ambrose University, M
Vennard College, B

Kansas

Barclay College, B
Central Christian College of Kansas, B
Hesston College, A
Manhattan Christian College, B
Newman University, B
Southwestern College, B
Tabor College, B
University of Saint Mary, B

Kentucky

Bellarmine University, B
Campbellsville University, B
Kentucky Christian University, B
Southern Baptist Theological Seminary, D

Louisiana

New Orleans Baptist Theological Seminary, MDP
Xavier University of Louisiana, M

Maryland

The Johns Hopkins University, O
Loyola College in Maryland, MDO
Maple Springs Baptist Bible College and Seminary, M

Massachusetts

Anna Maria College, M
Boston College, MDO

Michigan

Andrews University, MDP
Cornerstone University, BMP
Grace Bible College, B
Kuyper College, B
Madonna University, BM
Marygrove College, M
Sacred Heart Major Seminary, M

Minnesota

Concordia University, St. Paul, M
Crown College, B
North Central University, AB
Oak Hills Christian College, B
Pillsbury Baptist Bible College, B
Saint John's University, M
Saint Mary's University of Minnesota, MO
University of St. Thomas, M

Mississippi

Southeastern Baptist College, B

Missouri

Baptist Bible College, BM
Calvary Bible College and Theological Seminary, BMP
Central Bible College, B
Global University of the Assemblies of God, B
Lindenwood University, B
Messenger College, B

Southwest Baptist University, B

Nebraska

Concordia University, BM
Grace University, BM
Nebraska Christian College, AB
Union College, B

New Jersey

Caldwell College, M
Seton Hall University, MP

New Mexico

College of Santa Fe, B

New York

Fordham University, MO
Houghton College, B
Iona College, MO
Nyack College, B
Roberts Wesleyan College, B
St. John's University, O

North Carolina

Campbell University, B
Gardner-Webb University, BDP
John Wesley College, B
Lenoir-Rhyne College, B
Piedmont Baptist College, M
Southeastern Baptist Theological Seminary, A
Wake Forest University, M

North Dakota

Trinity Bible College, B

Ohio

Cedarville University, B
Cincinnati Christian University, M
College of Mount St. Joseph, M
God's Bible School and College, B
Malone College, M
Notre Dame College, ABO
University of Dayton, M
Walsh University, BM

Oklahoma

Hillsdale Free Will Baptist College, M
Oklahoma Baptist University, B
Oklahoma Christian University, M
Oral Roberts University, BM
St. Gregory's University, B
Southwestern Christian University, BM

Oregon

Corban College, B
Eugene Bible College, B
George Fox University, BD
Marylhurst University, B
Multnomah Bible College and Biblical Seminary, BM
University of Portland, M
Warner Pacific College, B

Pennsylvania

Baptist Bible College of Pennsylvania, BMD
Chestnut Hill College, O
Gannon University, MO
La Salle University, M
Lancaster Bible College, BM
Neumann College, MO
Philadelphia Biblical University, M
Saint Francis University, B

Puerto Rico

Bayamon Central University, M
Colegio Biblico Pentecostal, B
Universidad Adventista de las Antillas, B

Rhode Island

Providence College, M

South Carolina

Charleston Southern University, B
Columbia International University, BMDPO
North Greenville College, B

Southern Wesleyan University, M

South Dakota

University of Sioux Falls, B

Tennessee

Belmont University, B
Freed-Hardeman University, M
Lee University, B
Milligan College, B
Tennessee Temple University, B

Texas

Abilene Christian University, BMD
The Criswell College, M
Dallas Baptist University, BM
East Texas Baptist University, B
Hardin-Simmons University, M
Houston Baptist University, M
St. Mary's University of San Antonio, M
Southwestern Assemblies of God University, B
Texas Christian University, D
University of Dallas, M
University of Mary Hardin-Baylor, B
University of St. Thomas, B
Wayland Baptist University, M

Virginia

Eastern Mennonite University, MO
Liberty University, D
Marymount University, MO

Washington

Gonzaga University, M
Northwest University, B
Puget Sound Christian College, B
Seattle University, M
Trinity Lutheran College, B
University of Puget Sound, M

Wisconsin

Concordia University Wisconsin, B

Alberta

Alliance University College, P
Prairie Bible Institute, B
Rocky Mountain College, B

British Columbia

Columbia Bible College, B
Summit Pacific College, B
Trinity Western University, M

Manitoba

Canadian Mennonite University, B
Providence College and Theological Seminary, BM
William and Catherine Booth College, B

Nova Scotia

Acadia University, M

Ontario

Collège Dominicain de Philosophie et de
   Théologie, BM
Saint Paul University, MDO
Tyndale University College & Seminary, BP
University of Ottawa, B
Wilfrid Laurier University, M

Saskatchewan

Briercrest College, B
Central Pentecostal College, B

PATHOBIOLOGY

Arizona

The University of Arizona, MD

California

University of Southern California, D

Connecticut

University of Connecticut, MD
Yale University, DO

Illinois

University of Illinois at Urbana-Champaign, MD

Indiana

Purdue University, MD

Kansas

Kansas State University, MD

Maryland

The Johns Hopkins University, D

Michigan

Michigan State University, MD

Missouri

University of Missouri-Columbia, MD

North Carolina

Wake Forest University, MD

Ohio

The Ohio State University, MD
University of Cincinnati, D

Pennsylvania

Drexel University, DO
The Pennsylvania State University University Park
   Campus, MD

Rhode Island

Brown University, MD

South Carolina

Medical University of South Carolina, DO

Texas

Texas A&M University, MD

Washington

University of Washington, MD

Wyoming

University of Wyoming, M

Ontario

University of Toronto, MDO

PATHOLOGY/EXPERIMENTAL PATHOLOGY

Alabama

The University of Alabama at Birmingham, D

Arkansas

University of Arkansas for Medical Sciences, M

California

University of California, Davis, MD
University of California, Los Angeles, BMD
University of Southern California, MD

Colorado

Colorado State University, MD

Connecticut

Quinnipiac University, M
University of Connecticut, B

Yale University, DO

District of Columbia

Georgetown University, MDO

Florida

University of Florida, D
University of South Florida, D

Georgia

University of Georgia, MD

Illinois

University of Chicago, D

Indiana

Indiana University-Purdue University
   Indianapolis, MDO
Purdue University, MD

Iowa

Iowa State University of Science and
   Technology, MD
The University of Iowa, M

Kansas

University of Kansas, MDO

Louisiana

Louisiana State University Health Sciences
   Center, MDO

Maryland

The Johns Hopkins University, D

Massachusetts

Boston University, DO
Harvard University, D

Michigan

Michigan State University, MD
University of Michigan, D
Wayne State University, MD

Mississippi

University of Mississippi Medical Center, MDO

Missouri

Saint Louis University, D

Nebraska

University of Nebraska Medical Center, MD

New Mexico

University of New Mexico, MD

New York

New York University, MDO
State University of New York at Buffalo, MD
Stony Brook University, State University of New
   York, D
University at Albany, State University of New
   York, MD
University of Rochester, MD

North Carolina

Duke University, MD
East Carolina University, D
North Carolina State University, MD
The University of North Carolina at Chapel Hill, BD

North Dakota

North Dakota State University, D

Ohio

Case Western Reserve University, MDO
The Ohio State University, M

University of Cincinnati, D

Oklahoma

University of Oklahoma Health Sciences Center, D

Oregon

Oregon State University, M

Pennsylvania

Temple University, D
Thomas Jefferson University, D
University of Pittsburgh, MD

Rhode Island

Brown University, D

South Carolina

Medical University of South Carolina, MDO

Tennessee

Vanderbilt University, DO

Texas

Texas A&M University, MD
Texas A&M University System Health Science
   Center, DO
The University of Texas Medical Branch, D

Utah

University of Utah, MD

Vermont

University of Vermont, MO

Virginia

Virginia Commonwealth University, MDO

Washington

University of Washington, MD
Washington State University, MD

Wisconsin

University of Wisconsin-Madison, D

Alberta

University of Alberta, MD

British Columbia

The University of British Columbia, MD

Manitoba

University of Manitoba, M

Nova Scotia

Dalhousie University, M

Ontario

Queen's University at Kingston, MD
University of Guelph, MDO
The University of Western Ontario, MD

Prince Edward Island

University of Prince Edward Island, MD

Quebec

McGill University, MD
Université Laval, O
Université de Montréal, MD

Saskatchewan

University of Saskatchewan, MD

PATHOLOGY/PATHOLOGIST ASSISTANT

Michigan

Wayne State University, B

New York

St. John's University, B

PEACE STUDIES AND CONFLICT RESOLUTION

California

Chapman University, B
University of California, Berkeley, B
University of California, Santa Cruz, B

District of Columbia

American University, B

Hawaii

University of Hawaii at Manoa, B

Indiana

DePauw University, B
Earlham College, B
Goshen College, B
Manchester College, B

Kansas

Bethel College, B

Maryland

Goucher College, B
Salisbury University, B

Massachusetts

Berkshire Community College, A
Clark University, B
Hampshire College, B
Wellesley College, B

Minnesota

College of Saint Benedict, B
Hamline University, B
Saint John's University, B
University of St. Thomas, B

Missouri

University of Missouri-Columbia, B

New Jersey

College of Saint Elizabeth, B

New York

Colgate University, B
Fordham University, B
Le Moyne College, B
Molloy College, B
Nazareth College of Rochester, B
Syracuse University, B

North Carolina

Guilford College, B
The University of North Carolina at Chapel Hill, B

Ohio

Antioch College, B
Kent State University, B
Ohio Dominican University, B
The Ohio State University, B

Pennsylvania

Elizabethtown College, B
Gettysburg College, B
Haverford College, B
Juniata College, B

Vermont

Bennington College, B
Norwich University, B

Woodbury College, A

Virginia

Eastern Mennonite University, B

Washington

Whitworth College, B

Wisconsin

Northland College, B
University of Wisconsin-Milwaukee, B
University of Wisconsin-Superior, B

Manitoba

Canadian Mennonite University, B
The University of Winnipeg, B

Nova Scotia

Mount Saint Vincent University, B

Ontario

University of Toronto, B
The University of Western Ontario, B

PEDIATRIC NURSE/NURSING

California

Loma Linda University, M
University of San Diego, MO

Delaware

University of Delaware, MO

Florida

University of Central Florida, O

Georgia

Emory University, M
Georgia State University, M

Illinois

Rush University, MDO
University of Illinois at Chicago, M

Indiana

Indiana University-Purdue University Indianapolis, M

Kentucky

Spalding University, M

Louisiana

Louisiana State University Health Sciences
   Center, M

Massachusetts

Northeastern University, MO

Michigan

University of Michigan, M
Wayne State University, MO

Minnesota

University of Minnesota, Twin Cities Campus, M

Missouri

University of Missouri-Kansas City, M

Nevada

University of Nevada, Las Vegas, M

New Jersey

Seton Hall University, M

New York

Hunter College of the City University of New
   York, MO
Lehman College of the City University of New
   York, M
Molloy College, O
New York University, MO
State University of New York at Buffalo, BM

Stony Brook University, State University of New York, MO

North Carolina

Duke University, MO

Ohio

Case Western Reserve University, M
Kent State University, M
University of Cincinnati, M
Wright State University, M
Youngstown State University, B

Oregon

Oregon Health & Science University, MO

Pennsylvania

University of Pennsylvania, M
University of Pittsburgh, M
Villanova University, MO

South Carolina

University of South Carolina, M

Tennessee

Vanderbilt University, M

Texas

Baylor University, M
The University of Texas-Pan American, M

Virginia

Virginia Commonwealth University, M

Wisconsin

Marquette University, O

British Columbia

British Columbia Institute of Technology, AB

PEDODONTICS

District of Columbia

Howard University, O

Iowa

The University of Iowa, O

Massachusetts

Boston University, MDO

Missouri

University of Missouri-Kansas City, O

New York

New York University, O

Ohio

Case Western Reserve University, O

Puerto Rico

University of Puerto Rico, Medical Sciences Campus, M

Texas

Texas A&M University System Health Science Center, MO

Quebec

Université de Montréal, MO

PERFORMANCE

Alabama

Troy University, M

Alaska

University of Alaska Fairbanks, M

Arizona

Northern Arizona University, M
The University of Arizona, MD

Arkansas

Arkansas State University, M
University of Central Arkansas, M

California

California Institute of the Arts, MO
California State University, Fresno, M
California State University, Fullerton, M
California State University, Los Angeles, M
California State University, Northridge, M
Holy Names University, M
Notre Dame de Namur University, M
San Diego State University, M
San Francisco Conservatory of Music, M
San Francisco State University, M
San Jose State University, M
University of California, Davis, MD
University of California, Santa Barbara, MD
University of Southern California, MD

Colorado

Colorado State University, M
University of Colorado at Boulder, MD
University of Denver, M

Connecticut

University of Connecticut, MD
University of Hartford, MDO

Delaware

University of Delaware, M

District of Columbia

The Catholic University of America, MD

Florida

Florida State University, MD
Lynn University, O
University of Miami, MD
University of South Florida, M

Georgia

University of West Georgia, M

Illinois

DePaul University, MO
Northwestern University, MDO
Southern Illinois University Carbondale, M

Indiana

Butler University, M

Iowa

University of Northern Iowa, M

Kansas

Emporia State University, M
Kansas State University, M
Pittsburg State University, M
University of Kansas, MD

Kentucky

Eastern Kentucky University, M
Morehead State University, M
University of Louisville, M

Louisiana

University of Louisiana at Lafayette, M

Maryland

Towson University, M

Massachusetts

The Boston Conservatory, MO
Boston University, MDO

Michigan

Michigan State University, MD
Wayne State University, M

Western Michigan University, M

Minnesota

University of Minnesota, Duluth, M

Mississippi

Mississippi College, M
University of Southern Mississippi, MD

Missouri

University of Missouri-Kansas City, MD
Webster University, M

Nevada

University of Nevada, Las Vegas, MD

New Jersey

Montclair State University, M
New Jersey City University, M
Rider University, M

New York

Brooklyn College of the City University of New York, MO
Cornell University, D
Hofstra University, M
Ithaca College, M
Manhattan School of Music, MD
Mannes College The New School for Music, MO
New York University, MDO
State University of New York at Buffalo, M
State University of New York College at Potsdam, M
Stony Brook University, State University of New York, MD
Syracuse University, M
University of Rochester, MD

North Carolina

Appalachian State University, M
Duke University, MD
East Carolina University, M
North Carolina School of the Arts, M
The University of North Carolina at Greensboro, MD

Ohio

Bowling Green State University, M
Cleveland Institute of Music, MDO
Cleveland State University, M
Kent State University, M
Miami University, M
Ohio University, MO
The University of Akron, M
University of Cincinnati, MDO
The University of Toledo, M
Wright State University, M
Youngstown State University, M

Oklahoma

Oklahoma City University, M
University of Central Oklahoma, M
University of Oklahoma, MD

Oregon

Portland State University, M
Southern Oregon University, M

Pennsylvania

Carnegie Mellon University, M
Duquesne University, MO
Indiana University of Pennsylvania, M
Mansfield University of Pennsylvania, M
The Pennsylvania State University University Park Campus, M
Point Park University, M
Temple University, MD
University of Pittsburgh, MD

South Carolina

Converse College, M
University of South Carolina, MDO

Winthrop University, M

Tennessee

Belmont University, M
University of Memphis, D
The University of Tennessee, M

Texas

Baylor University, M
Hardin-Simmons University, M
Lamar University, M
Rice University, MD
Sam Houston State University, M
Southern Methodist University, MO
Texas A&M University-Commerce, M
Texas Christian University, MO
Texas State University-San Marcos, M
Texas Tech University, MD
University of Houston, MD
University of North Texas, MD
The University of Texas-Pan American, M
West Texas A&M University, M

Utah

Brigham Young University, M
Southern Utah University, M

Virginia

Hollins University, M
James Madison University, M
Norfolk State University, M
Shenandoah University, MD
Virginia Commonwealth University, M

Washington

Eastern Washington University, M

West Virginia

West Virginia University, MD

Wisconsin

University of Wisconsin-Madison, MD

Wyoming

University of Wyoming, M

British Columbia

University of Victoria, M

Manitoba

Brandon University, M

Newfoundland and Labrador

Memorial University of Newfoundland, O

Quebec

Concordia University, O
McGill University, MD
Université de Montréal, O

PERFUSION TECHNOLOGY/PERFUSIONIST

Idaho

Boise State University, A

Illinois

Rush University, B

New York

State University of New York Upstate Medical University, B

South Carolina

Medical University of South Carolina, B

British Columbia

Thompson Rivers University, A

PERIODONTICS

California

Loma Linda University, M

Florida

University of Florida, MO

Iowa

The University of Iowa, MO

Massachusetts

Boston University, MDO
Harvard University, O

Minnesota

University of Minnesota, Twin Cities Campus, M

Missouri

University of Missouri-Kansas City, O

New York

New York University, O
Stony Brook University, State University of New York, O

Ohio

Case Western Reserve University, MO

Oklahoma

University of Oklahoma Health Sciences Center, M

Pennsylvania

Temple University, O
University of Pittsburgh, MO

South Carolina

Medical University of South Carolina, M

Texas

Texas A&M University System Health Science Center, MO

British Columbia

The University of British Columbia, O

Manitoba

University of Manitoba, M

Ontario

University of Toronto, M

PERIOPERATIVE/OPERATING ROOM AND SURGICAL NURSE/NURSING

Kentucky

Murray State University, B

Pennsylvania

Community College of Allegheny County, A

Texas

Texas A&M International University, B

British Columbia

British Columbia Institute of Technology, AB

PERSONAL AND CULINARY SERVICES

Illinois

Lexington College, AB

Pennsylvania

The Art Institute of Pittsburgh, AB

PETROLEUM ENGINEERING

Alaska

University of Alaska Fairbanks, BM

California

California State Polytechnic University, Pomona, B
Stanford University, BMDO
University of California, Berkeley, MD
University of Southern California, BMDO

Colorado

Colorado School of Mines, BMD

Kansas

University of Kansas, BMD

Louisiana

Louisiana State University and Agricultural and Mechanical College, BMD
University of Louisiana at Lafayette, BM

Missouri

University of Missouri-Rolla, BMD

Montana

Montana Tech of The University of Montana, BM

New Mexico

New Mexico Institute of Mining and Technology, BMD

Ohio

Marietta College, B

Oklahoma

University of Oklahoma, BMD
University of Tulsa, BMD

Pennsylvania

The Pennsylvania State University Abington College, B
The Pennsylvania State University Altoona College, B
The Pennsylvania State University Beaver Campus of the Commonwealth College, B
The Pennsylvania State University Berks Campus of the Berks-Lehigh Valley College, B
The Pennsylvania State University Delaware County Campus of the Commonwealth College, B
The Pennsylvania State University DuBois Campus of the Commonwealth College, B
The Pennsylvania State University at Erie, The Behrend College, B
The Pennsylvania State University Fayette Campus of the Commonwealth College, B
The Pennsylvania State University Hazleton Campus of the Commonwealth College, B
The Pennsylvania State University, Lehigh Valley Campus of the Berks-Lehigh Valley College, B
The Pennsylvania State University McKeesport Campus of the Commonwealth College, B
The Pennsylvania State University Mont Alto Campus of the Commonwealth College, B
The Pennsylvania State University New Kensington Campus of the Commonwealth College, B
The Pennsylvania State University Schuylkill Campus of the Capital College, B
The Pennsylvania State University Shenango Campus of the Commonwealth College, B
The Pennsylvania State University University Park Campus, BMD
The Pennsylvania State University Wilkes-Barre Campus of the Commonwealth College, B
The Pennsylvania State University Worthington Scranton Campus of the Commonwealth College, B
The Pennsylvania State University York Campus of the Commonwealth College, B
University of Pittsburgh, MDO

Texas

Texas A&M University, BMD
Texas A&M University-Kingsville, BM

Texas Tech University, BMD
University of Houston, M
The University of Texas at Austin, BMD

Utah
University of Utah, MD

West Virginia
West Virginia University, BMD

Wyoming
University of Wyoming, MD

Alberta
Southern Alberta Institute of Technology, B
University of Alberta, BMD
University of Calgary, MD

Ontario
University of Toronto, B

Saskatchewan
University of Regina, BMD

PETROLEUM TECHNOLOGY/TECHNICIAN

Alaska
University of Alaska Anchorage, A
University of Alaska Anchorage, Kenai Peninsula
  College, A

California
Bakersfield College, A

Louisiana
McNeese State University, A
Nicholls State University, AB

Montana
Montana State University-Billings, A
Montana Tech of The University of Montana, A

New Mexico
New Mexico Junior College, A

Oklahoma
Tulsa Community College, A

Pennsylvania
Mercyhurst College, B

Texas
Coastal Bend College, A
Frank Phillips College, A
Odessa College, A
South Plains College, A
Tyler Junior College, A

Wisconsin
Northeast Wisconsin Technical College, A

British Columbia
British Columbia Institute of Technology, A

Nova Scotia
Cape Breton University, B

PHARMACEUTICAL ADMINISTRATION

Arkansas
University of Arkansas for Medical Sciences, M

California
San Diego State University, M

Florida
Florida Agricultural and Mechanical University, M

University of Florida, MD

Georgia
University of Georgia, MD

Idaho
Idaho State University, MDP

Illinois
University of Illinois at Chicago, MD

Massachusetts
Massachusetts College of Pharmacy and Health
  Sciences, M

Michigan
University of Michigan, D
Wayne State University, MD

Minnesota
University of Minnesota, Twin Cities Campus, MD

Mississippi
University of Mississippi, MD

Missouri
St. Louis College of Pharmacy, M

New Jersey
Fairleigh Dickinson University, Metropolitan
  Campus, MO
Seton Hall University, M

New York
Long Island University, Brooklyn Campus, M
St. John's University, M

Ohio
The Ohio State University, MD
The University of Toledo, M

Pennsylvania
Duquesne University, M
University of the Sciences in Philadelphia, M

Rhode Island
University of Rhode Island, M

Texas
University of Houston, M

West Virginia
West Virginia University, MD

Wisconsin
University of Wisconsin-Madison, MD

PHARMACEUTICAL ENGINEERING

Michigan
University of Michigan, M

New Jersey
New Jersey Institute of Technology, M

PHARMACEUTICAL SCIENCES

Alabama
Auburn University, MD

Arizona
The University of Arizona, MD

Arkansas
University of Arkansas for Medical Sciences, M

California
Loma Linda University, MD
University of the Pacific, MD

University of Southern California, MDO

Connecticut
University of Connecticut, MD

Florida
Florida Agricultural and Mechanical University, MD
University of Florida, D

Georgia
Mercer University, DPO
University of Georgia, MD

Idaho
Idaho State University, MD

Illinois
Rush University, M
University of Illinois at Chicago, MD

Indiana
Butler University, MP
Purdue University, MD

Kansas
University of Kansas, M

Kentucky
University of Kentucky, MD

Louisiana
University of Louisiana at Monroe, M

Massachusetts
Boston University, MDO
Massachusetts College of Pharmacy and Health
  Sciences, MD
Northeastern University, P

Michigan
University of Michigan, D
Wayne State University, MDPO

Minnesota
University of Minnesota, Twin Cities Campus, MD

Mississippi
University of Mississippi, MD

Missouri
University of Missouri-Kansas City, MD

Montana
The University of Montana-Missoula, MD

Nebraska
Creighton University, MO
University of Nebraska Medical Center, MD

New Jersey
Rutgers, The State University of New Jersey, New
  Brunswick/Piscataway, MD

New Mexico
University of New Mexico, MD

New York
Long Island University, Brooklyn Campus, MD
St. John's University, MD
State University of New York at Buffalo, MD

North Carolina
Campbell University, M
The University of North Carolina at Chapel Hill, MD

North Dakota
North Dakota State University, MD

Ohio
The Ohio State University, MD
University of Cincinnati, MD

The University of Toledo, M

Oklahoma

University of Oklahoma Health Sciences
Center, MDO

Oregon

Oregon State University, MDP

Pennsylvania

Duquesne University, MDO
Temple University, MD
University of the Sciences in Philadelphia, MD

Puerto Rico

University of Puerto Rico, Medical Sciences
Campus, M

Rhode Island

University of Rhode Island, MD

South Carolina

Medical University of South Carolina, D
University of South Carolina, MD

South Dakota

South Dakota State University, M

Texas

University of Houston, MD
The University of Texas at Austin, MD

Virginia

Virginia Commonwealth University, MDP

Washington

University of Washington, MD

West Virginia

West Virginia University, MDO

Wisconsin

University of Wisconsin-Madison, MD

Alberta

University of Alberta, MD

British Columbia

The University of British Columbia, MDP

Manitoba

University of Manitoba, MD

Newfoundland and Labrador

Memorial University of Newfoundland, M

Nova Scotia

Dalhousie University, MD

Ontario

University of Toronto, MD

Quebec

Université Laval, MDO
Université de Montréal, MDO

Saskatchewan

University of Saskatchewan, MD

PHARMACEUTICS AND DRUG DESIGN

Montana

The University of Montana-Missoula, B

North Carolina

Campbell University, B

Pennsylvania

University of the Sciences in Philadelphia, B

PHARMACOGNOSY

Idaho

Idaho State University, M

Illinois

University of Illinois at Chicago, MD

Indiana

Purdue University, D

Mississippi

University of Mississippi, MD

Ohio

The Ohio State University, MD

Rhode Island

University of Rhode Island, MD

PHARMACOLOGY

Alabama

The University of Alabama at Birmingham, D
University of South Alabama, D

Arizona

The University of Arizona, MD

Arkansas

University of Arkansas for Medical Sciences, MDO

California

University of California, Davis, MD
University of California, Irvine, MDO
University of California, Los Angeles, D
University of California, San Diego, D
University of California, Santa Barbara, B

Connecticut

University of Connecticut, MD
Yale University, DO

District of Columbia

The George Washington University, D
Georgetown University, DO
Howard University, MDO

Florida

Florida Agricultural and Mechanical University, MD
Nova Southeastern University, M
University of Florida, MDO
University of Miami, DO
University of South Florida, D

Georgia

Emory University, D
Medical College of Georgia, D
University of Georgia, MD

Hawaii

Argosy University/Hawaii, O

Idaho

Idaho State University, MD

Illinois

Loyola University Chicago, MDO
Northwestern University, D
Rush University, MDO
Southern Illinois University Carbondale, MD
University of Chicago, D
University of Illinois at Chicago, DO

Indiana

Indiana University Bloomington, MD
Indiana University-Purdue University
Indianapolis, MDO

Purdue University, MD

Iowa

The University of Iowa, MD

Kansas

University of Kansas, MDO

Kentucky

University of Kentucky, DO
University of Louisville, MD

Louisiana

Louisiana State University Health Sciences
Center, MDO
Tulane University, MDO

Maryland

The Johns Hopkins University, D

Massachusetts

Boston University, MDO
Massachusetts College of Pharmacy and Health
Sciences, MD
Northeastern University, M
Tufts University, D

Michigan

Michigan State University, MD
University of Michigan, D
Wayne State University, MD

Minnesota

University of Minnesota, Duluth, MD
University of Minnesota, Twin Cities Campus, MD

Mississippi

University of Mississippi, MD
University of Mississippi Medical Center, MDO

Missouri

Saint Louis University, D
University of Missouri-Columbia, MD

Montana

The University of Montana-Missoula, D

Nebraska

Creighton University, MD
University of Nebraska Medical Center, MD

New Hampshire

Dartmouth College, DO

New Jersey

Fairleigh Dickinson University, College at
Florham, MO

New York

Cornell University, MD
Long Island University, Brooklyn Campus, M
New York University, MDO
State University of New York at Buffalo, BMDO
State University of New York Upstate Medical
University, MDO
Stony Brook University, State University of New
York, BD
University of Rochester, MD

North Carolina

Campbell University, B
Duke University, D
East Carolina University, DO
North Carolina State University, MD
The University of North Carolina at Chapel Hill, D
Wake Forest University, D

North Dakota

University of North Dakota, MD

Ohio

Case Western Reserve University, MDO
Kent State University, MD

The Ohio State University, MD
University of Cincinnati, BD
The University of Toledo, M
Wright State University, M

Oregon

Oregon Health & Science University, DO

Pennsylvania

Drexel University, MDO
Duquesne University, MD
Temple University, MDO
Thomas Jefferson University, M
University of Pennsylvania, DO
University of the Sciences in Philadelphia, MD

Puerto Rico

University of Puerto Rico, Medical Sciences
Campus, MD

Rhode Island

University of Rhode Island, MD

South Dakota

The University of South Dakota, MD

Tennessee

East Tennessee State University, MD
Vanderbilt University, DO

Texas

Texas A&M University System Health Science
Center, D
University of Houston, MD
The University of Texas Health Science Center at
San Antonio, D
The University of Texas Medical Branch, MD

Utah

University of Utah, MDO

Vermont

University of Vermont, MDO

Virginia

University of Virginia, DO
Virginia Commonwealth University, MDO

Washington

University of Washington, MD
Washington State University, MD

West Virginia

West Virginia University, MD

Wisconsin

University of Wisconsin-Madison, BMD

Alberta

University of Alberta, BMD

British Columbia

The University of British Columbia, BMD

Manitoba

University of Manitoba, MD

Nova Scotia

Dalhousie University, MDO

Ontario

McMaster University, BMD
Queen's University at Kingston, MD
University of Guelph, MD
University of Toronto, BMD
The University of Western Ontario, B

Prince Edward Island

University of Prince Edward Island, MD

Quebec

McGill University, MD
Université de Montréal, MD

Université de Sherbrooke, MD

Saskatchewan

University of Saskatchewan, MD

PHARMACOLOGY AND TOXICOLOGY

California

Western Career College (Walnut Creek), A

Ohio

Wright State University, B

Pennsylvania

University of the Sciences in Philadelphia, B

Washington

Washington State University, B

Ontario

The University of Western Ontario, B

PHARMACY

Alabama

Auburn University, P
Samford University, P

Arizona

Midwestern University, Glendale Campus, P
The University of Arizona, MDP

Arkansas

University of Arkansas for Medical Sciences, MP

California

Cerritos College, A
Pasadena City College, A
University of California, San Diego, P
University of the Pacific, BP
University of Southern California, PO

Connecticut

University of Connecticut, B

District of Columbia

Howard University, BP

Florida

Florida Agricultural and Mechanical University, BDP
Indian River Community College, A
Nova Southeastern University, P
Palm Beach Atlantic University, P
University of Florida, PO

Georgia

Clayton State University, A
Mercer University, DPO
South University, P
University of Georgia, P

Idaho

Idaho State University, MDP

Illinois

City Colleges of Chicago, Kennedy-King College, A
City Colleges of Chicago, Richard J. Daley
College, A
Southern Illinois University Edwardsville, P
University of Illinois at Chicago, MDP

Indiana

Butler University, BMP
Purdue University, BP
Vincennes University, A

Iowa

Drake University, BPO
Iowa Lakes Community College, A

The University of Iowa, BMDO

Kansas

Barton County Community College, A
Colby Community College, A
Highland Community College, A
University of Kansas, B

Kentucky

University of Kentucky, P

Louisiana

University of Louisiana at Monroe, BDP
Xavier University of Louisiana, P

Massachusetts

Eastern Nazarene College, B
Massachusetts College of Pharmacy and Health
Sciences, B
Northeastern University, B
Simmons College, B

Michigan

Ferris State University, P
Mid Michigan Community College, A
St. Clair County Community College, A
University of Michigan, BPO
Wayne State University, MDPO

Minnesota

University of Minnesota, Twin Cities Campus, P

Mississippi

East Central Community College, A
Holmes Community College, A
Northeast Mississippi Community College, A
University of Mississippi, BP

Missouri

St. Louis College of Pharmacy, BP
University of Missouri-Kansas City, BMDP

Montana

The University of Montana-Missoula, B

Nebraska

Creighton University, P
University of Nebraska Medical Center, P

Nevada

Community College of Southern Nevada, A

New Jersey

Rutgers, The State University of New Jersey, New
Brunswick/Piscataway, BP

New Mexico

University of New Mexico, BP

New York

Albany College of Pharmacy of Union University, BP
Long Island University, Brooklyn Campus, B
St. John's University, BP
State University of New York at Buffalo, PO

North Carolina

Campbell University, BMP
Durham Technical Community College, A
Isothermal Community College, A
Wingate University, P

North Dakota

North Dakota State University, B
Turtle Mountain Community College, A

Ohio

Lorain County Community College, A
Ohio Northern University, BP
The Ohio State University, BP
Ohio University-Eastern, B
University of Cincinnati, BP
University of Cincinnati Clermont College, A
University of Cincinnati Raymond Walters College, A

The University of Toledo, BP

Oklahoma

Southwestern Oklahoma State University, BP
University of Oklahoma Health Sciences Center, P

Oregon

Oregon State University, MDP

Pennsylvania

Duquesne University, P
Saint Vincent College, B
Temple University, P
University of Pittsburgh, BP
University of the Sciences in Philadelphia, P
Wilkes University, P

Puerto Rico

Huertas Junior College, A
Universidad del Este, A
University of Puerto Rico, Medical Sciences
    Campus, BMP

Rhode Island

University of Rhode Island, BP

South Carolina

Medical University of South Carolina, P
University of South Carolina, P

South Dakota

South Dakota State University, BP

Tennessee

Columbia State Community College, A
Martin Methodist College, A

Texas

Coastal Bend College, A
Navarro College, A
Texas Southern University, BMP
University of Houston, BMDP
The University of Texas at Austin, P

Utah

University of Utah, BMP

Virginia

Shenandoah University, P
Virginia Commonwealth University, PO

Washington

University of Washington, BP
Washington State University, P

West Virginia

West Virginia University, MDP

Wisconsin

University of Wisconsin-Madison, BP

Wyoming

University of Wyoming, P

Alberta

University of Alberta, BMD

British Columbia

The University of British Columbia, BMDP

Manitoba

University of Manitoba, B

Newfoundland and Labrador

Memorial University of Newfoundland, B

Nova Scotia

Dalhousie University, B

Ontario

University of Toronto, B

Quebec

Université Laval, B
Université de Montréal, B

Saskatchewan

University of Saskatchewan, B

PHARMACY ADMINISTRATION AND PHARMACY POLICY AND REGULATORY AFFAIRS

Iowa

Drake University, B

New York

State University of New York at Buffalo, B

Pennsylvania

DeSales University, B

PHARMACY, PHARMACEUTICAL SCIENCES, AND ADMINISTRATION

Connecticut

University of Connecticut, B

Massachusetts

Massachusetts College of Pharmacy and Health
    Sciences, B

Michigan

Ferris State University, B

New York

Albany College of Pharmacy of Union University, B
St. John's University, B
State University of New York at Buffalo, B

North Carolina

Campbell University, B

Ohio

Ohio Northern University, B
The University of Toledo, B

Pennsylvania

Duquesne University, B
University of the Sciences in Philadelphia, B
Wilkes University, B

Utah

University of Utah, B

Nova Scotia

Dalhousie University, B

Quebec

Université Laval, B

PHARMACY TECHNICIAN/ASSISTANT

Alabama

Community College of the Air Force, A

Arizona

Pima Community College, A

California

Charles R. Drew University of Medicine and
    Science, A
San Joaquin Valley College, A
Santa Ana College, A
Western Career College (San Jose), A

Western Career College (Walnut Creek), A

Colorado

Institute of Business & Medical Careers, A

Florida

Florida Metropolitan University-Brandon Campus, A
Hillsborough Community College, A

Georgia

Abraham Baldwin Agricultural College, A
Albany Technical College, A
Augusta Technical College, A
Columbus Technical College, A
Darton College, A
Griffin Technical College, A
Northwestern Technical College, A
West Georgia Technical College, A

Idaho

Idaho State University, A

Iowa

Clinton Community College, A
Muscatine Community College, A
Scott Community College, A

Kentucky

Brown Mackie College-Louisville, A
Brown Mackie College-Northern Kentucky, A

Maryland

TESST College of Technology (Towson), A

Michigan

Baker College of Flint, A
Baker College of Jackson, A
Baker College of Muskegon, A
Oakland Community College, A
Washtenaw Community College, A

Minnesota

Century College, A
Minnesota State Community and Technical
    College-Fergus Falls, A
Northwest Technical College, A

Missouri

Vatterott College (Springfield), A

Montana

The University of Montana-Missoula, B

North Carolina

Wake Technical Community College, A

North Dakota

North Dakota State College of Science, A

Ohio

Brown Mackie College-Akron, A
Brown Mackie College-Findlay, A
Brown Mackie College-North Canton, A
North Central State College, A
University of Northwestern Ohio, A

Oklahoma

Community Care College, A

Pennsylvania

Community College of Allegheny County, A
Harrisburg Area Community College, A
Mount Aloysius College, A

Western School of Health and Business Careers (Pittsburgh), A

Puerto Rico

Inter American University of Puerto Rico, Aguadilla Campus, A

South Carolina

Midlands Technical College, A

Tennessee

Draughons Junior College (Clarksville), A
Roane State Community College, A

Texas

Weatherford College, A

Utah

Utah Career College, A

Washington

Edmonds Community College, A
Everett Community College, A
North Seattle Community College, A
Tacoma Community College, A

Wyoming

Casper College, A

PHILANTHROPIC STUDIES

Indiana

Indiana University-Purdue University Indianapolis, MO

Minnesota

Saint Mary's University of Minnesota, M

PHILOSOPHY

Alabama

Auburn University, B
Birmingham-Southern College, B
Samford University, B
Spring Hill College, B
Stillman College, B
The University of Alabama, B
The University of Alabama at Birmingham, B
The University of Alabama in Huntsville, B
University of South Alabama, B

Alaska

University of Alaska Fairbanks, B

Arizona

Arizona State University, BMD
Northern Arizona University, B
Prescott College, B
The University of Arizona, BMDO

Arkansas

Arkansas State University, B
Hendrix College, B
Ouachita Baptist University, B
University of Arkansas, BMD
University of Arkansas at Little Rock, B
University of Central Arkansas, B

California

Azusa Pacific University, B
Bakersfield College, A
Biola University, B
California Baptist University, B
California Institute of Integral Studies, MD
California Lutheran University, B
California Polytechnic State University, San Luis Obispo, B
California State Polytechnic University, Pomona, B
California State University, Bakersfield, B
California State University, Chico, B
California State University, Dominguez Hills, B

California State University, East Bay, B
California State University, Fresno, B
California State University, Fullerton, B
California State University, Long Beach, BM
California State University, Los Angeles, BM
California State University, Northridge, B
California State University, Sacramento, B
California State University, San Bernardino, B
California State University, Stanislaus, B
Cañada College, A
Cerritos College, A
Chaffey College, A
Chapman University, B
Claremont McKenna College, B
College of Alameda, A
College of the Desert, A
College of Marin, A
College of the Siskiyous, A
Compton Community College, A
Contra Costa College, A
Crafton Hills College, A
Cypress College, A
De Anza College, A
Dominican School of Philosophy and Theology, BMO
East Los Angeles College, A
El Camino College, A
Foothill College, A
Fullerton College, A
Grossmont College, A
Holy Names University, B
Humboldt State University, B
Los Angeles Mission College, A
Loyola Marymount University, BM
Mills College, B
MiraCosta College, A
Monterey Peninsula College, A
Mount St. Mary's College, B
Notre Dame de Namur University, B
Occidental College, B
Orange Coast College, A
Oxnard College, A
Pasadena City College, A
Pepperdine University, B
Pitzer College, B
Point Loma Nazarene University, B
Pomona College, B
Saddleback College, A
Saint Mary's College of California, B
San Bernardino Valley College, A
San Diego Miramar College, A
San Diego State University, BM
San Francisco State University, BMO
San Joaquin Delta College, A
San Jose State University, BMO
Santa Ana College, A
Santa Barbara City College, A
Santa Clara University, B
Santa Monica College, A
Santa Rosa Junior College, A
Santiago Canyon College, A
Scripps College, B
Skyline College, A
Sonoma State University, B
Southwestern College, A
Stanford University, BMD
University of California, Berkeley, BD
University of California, Davis, BMD
University of California, Irvine, BMD
University of California, Los Angeles, BMD
University of California, Riverside, BMD
University of California, San Diego, BD
University of California, Santa Barbara, BMDO
University of California, Santa Cruz, BD
University of La Verne, B
University of the Pacific, B
University of Redlands, B
University of San Diego, B
University of San Francisco, B
University of Southern California, BMDO
University of the West, B
West Los Angeles College, A
Westmont College, B
Whittier College, B

Yuba College, A

Colorado

The Colorado College, B
Colorado State University, BM
Fort Lewis College, B
Metropolitan State College of Denver, B
Regis University, B
University of Colorado at Boulder, BMD
University of Colorado at Colorado Springs, B
University of Colorado at Denver and Health Sciences Center - Downtown Denver Campus, B
University of Denver, BM
University of Northern Colorado, B

Connecticut

Albertus Magnus College, B
Central Connecticut State University, B
Connecticut College, B
Fairfield University, B
Holy Apostles College and Seminary, B
Sacred Heart University, AB
Saint Joseph College, B
Southern Connecticut State University, B
Trinity College, B
University of Connecticut, BMD
University of Hartford, B
Wesleyan University, B
Yale University, BD

Delaware

University of Delaware, B

District of Columbia

American University, BM
The Catholic University of America, BMDO
Gallaudet University, B
The George Washington University, BM
Georgetown University, BMDO
Howard University, BM
University of the District of Columbia, AB

Florida

Ave Maria University, B
Barry University, B
Daytona Beach Community College, A
Eckerd College, B
Flagler College, B
Florida Agricultural and Mechanical University, B
Florida Atlantic University, B
Florida International University, B
Florida State University, BMD
Indian River Community College, A
Jacksonville University, B
Manatee Community College, A
Miami Dade College, A
New College of Florida, B
Palm Beach Atlantic University, B
Palm Beach Community College, A
Pensacola Junior College, A
Rollins College, B
St. John Vianney College Seminary, B
Stetson University, B
University of Central Florida, B
University of Florida, BMD
University of Miami, BMD
University of North Florida, BM
University of South Florida, BMD
The University of Tampa, A
University of West Florida, B

Georgia

Agnes Scott College, B
Clark Atlanta University, B
Clayton State University, A
Coastal Georgia Community College, A
Covenant College, B
Dalton State College, A
Darton College, A
Emory University, BD
Georgia Highlands College, A
Georgia Perimeter College, A
Georgia Southern University, B
Georgia State University, BMO
Mercer University, B

Morehouse College, B
Oglethorpe University, B
Paine College, B
Piedmont College, B
South Georgia College, A
Spelman College, B
Toccoa Falls College, B
University of Georgia, BMD
University of West Georgia, B
Valdosta State University, B
Wesleyan College, B

Hawaii

University of Hawaii at Hilo, B
University of Hawaii at Manoa, BMD
University of Hawaii-West Oahu, B

Idaho

Albertson College of Idaho, B
Boise State University, B
Idaho State University, B
Northwest Nazarene University, B
University of Idaho, B

Illinois

Augustana College, B
Aurora University, B
Benedictine University, B
Bradley University, B
City Colleges of Chicago, Harold Washington
     College, A
City Colleges of Chicago, Olive-Harvey College, A
Concordia University, B
Danville Area Community College, A
DePaul University, BMD
Dominican University, B
Eastern Illinois University, B
Elmhurst College, B
Eureka College, B
Greenville College, B
Illinois College, B
Illinois State University, B
Illinois Wesleyan University, B
Judson College, B
Knox College, B
Lake Forest College, B
Lewis University, B
Lincoln College, A
Lincoln College-Normal, A
Loyola University Chicago, BMD
MacMurray College, B
McKendree College, B
Millikin University, B
Monmouth College, B
North Central College, B
North Park University, B
Northeastern Illinois University, B
Northern Illinois University, BM
Northwestern University, BD
Olivet Nazarene University, B
Principia College, B
Quincy University, B
Rockford College, B
Roosevelt University, B
Saint Xavier University, B
Southern Illinois University Carbondale, BMD
Southern Illinois University Edwardsville, B
Trinity Christian College, B
Trinity International University, B
University of Chicago, BMD
University of Illinois at Chicago, BMD
University of Illinois at Springfield, B
University of Illinois at Urbana-Champaign, BMD
Western Illinois University, B
Wheaton College, B

Indiana

Anderson University, B
Ball State University, B
Bethel College, B
Butler University, B
DePauw University, B
Earlham College, B
Franklin College, B
Hanover College, B
Huntington University, B

Indiana State University, B
Indiana University Bloomington, BMD
Indiana University Northwest, B
Indiana University-Purdue University Fort Wayne, B
Indiana University-Purdue University Indianapolis, B
Indiana University South Bend, B
Indiana University Southeast, B
Indiana Wesleyan University, B
Manchester College, B
Marian College, B
Purdue University, BMD
Purdue University Calumet, BM
Saint Joseph's College, B
Saint Mary's College, B
Taylor University, B
University of Evansville, B
University of Indianapolis, B
University of Notre Dame, BD
University of Southern Indiana, B
Valparaiso University, B
Wabash College, B

Iowa

Central College, B
Clarke College, B
Coe College, B
Cornell College, B
Divine Word College, B
Dordt College, B
Drake University, B
Grinnell College, B
Iowa Lakes Community College, A
Iowa State University of Science and Technology, B
Loras College, B
Luther College, B
Morningside College, B
Northwestern College, B
St. Ambrose University, B
Simpson College, B
University of Dubuque, B
The University of Iowa, BMD
University of Northern Iowa, B
Wartburg College, B

Kansas

Allen County Community College, A
Baker University, B
Barton County Community College, A
Benedictine College, B
Bethany College, B
Donnelly College, A
Fort Hays State University, B
Friends University, B
Kansas State University, B
McPherson College, B
Tabor College, B
University of Kansas, BMDO
Washburn University, B
Wichita State University, B

Kentucky

Asbury College, B
Bellarmine University, B
Berea College, B
Centre College, B
Eastern Kentucky University, B
Georgetown College, B
Kentucky Wesleyan College, B
Morehead State University, B
Murray State University, B
Northern Kentucky University, B
Spalding University, B
Thomas More College, AB
Transylvania University, B
University of Kentucky, BMD
University of Louisville, BM
Western Kentucky University, B

Louisiana

Centenary College of Louisiana, B
Louisiana College, B
Louisiana State University and Agricultural and
     Mechanical College, BM
Loyola University New Orleans, B
Tulane University, BMD
University of Louisiana at Lafayette, B

University of New Orleans, B
Xavier University of Louisiana, B

Maine

Bates College, B
Bowdoin College, B
Colby College, B
College of the Atlantic, B
Saint Joseph's College of Maine, B
University of Maine, B
University of Maine at Farmington, B
University of Southern Maine, B

Maryland

Baltimore Hebrew University, AB
Coppin State University, B
Frostburg State University, B
Goucher College, B
Harford Community College, A
Hood College, B
The Johns Hopkins University, BMD
Loyola College in Maryland, B
McDaniel College, B
Morgan State University, B
Mount St. Mary's University, B
St. Mary's College of Maryland, B
Salisbury University, B
Towson University, B
University of Maryland, Baltimore County, B
University of Maryland, College Park, BMD
Washington College, B

Massachusetts

American International College, B
Amherst College, B
Anna Maria College, B
Assumption College, B
Bentley College, B
Boston College, BMD
Boston University, BMDO
Brandeis University, B
Bridgewater State College, B
Cape Cod Community College, A
Clark University, B
College of the Holy Cross, B
Curry College, B
Gordon College, B
Hampshire College, B
Harvard University, BMD
Massachusetts College of Liberal Arts, B
Massachusetts Institute of Technology, BD
Merrimack College, B
Mount Holyoke College, B
Northeastern University, B
Simmons College, B
Simon's Rock College of Bard, B
Smith College, B
Stonehill College, B
Suffolk University, B
Tufts University, BM
University of Massachusetts Amherst, BMD
University of Massachusetts Boston, B
University of Massachusetts Dartmouth, B
University of Massachusetts Lowell, B
Wellesley College, B
Western New England College, B
Wheaton College, B
Williams College, B
Worcester Polytechnic Institute, B

Michigan

Albion College, B
Alma College, B
Aquinas College, B
Ave Maria College, B
Calvin College, B
Central Michigan University, B
Concordia University, B
Cornerstone University, B
Eastern Michigan University, B
Grand Valley State University, B
Hillsdale College, B
Hope College, B
Kalamazoo College, B
Kellogg Community College, A
Lansing Community College, A

Madonna University, B
Michigan State University, BMD
Northern Michigan University, B
Oakland University, B
Sacred Heart Major Seminary, B
Siena Heights University, B
Spring Arbor University, B
University of Detroit Mercy, B
University of Michigan, BMD
University of Michigan-Dearborn, B
University of Michigan-Flint, B
Wayne State University, BMD
Western Michigan University, BM

Minnesota

Augsburg College, B
Bemidji State University, B
Bethel University, B
Carleton College, B
College of Saint Benedict, B
College of St. Catherine, B
Concordia College, B
Gustavus Adolphus College, B
Hamline University, B
Macalester College, B
Metropolitan State University, B
Minnesota State University Mankato, B
Minnesota State University Moorhead, B
St. Cloud State University, B
Saint John's University, B
Saint Mary's University of Minnesota, B
St. Olaf College, B
Southwest Minnesota State University, B
University of Minnesota, Duluth, B
University of Minnesota, Morris, B
University of Minnesota, Twin Cities Campus, BMD
University of St. Thomas, B

Mississippi

Belhaven College, B
Millsaps College, B
Mississippi State University, B
University of Mississippi, BM
University of Southern Mississippi, BM

Missouri

Central Methodist University, B
College of the Ozarks, B
Drury University, B
East Central College, A
Missouri State University, B
Missouri Valley College, B
Northwest Missouri State University, B
Rockhurst University, B
Saint Louis University, BMD
Southeast Missouri State University, B
Stephens College, B
Truman State University, B
University of Missouri-Columbia, BMD
University of Missouri-Kansas City, B
University of Missouri-Rolla, B
University of Missouri-St. Louis, BM
Washington University in St. Louis, BMD
Webster University, B
Westminster College, B
William Jewell College, B

Montana

Carroll College, B
Montana State University, B
Rocky Mountain College, B
The University of Montana-Missoula, BM

Nebraska

Creighton University, B
Doane College, B
Hastings College, B
Nebraska Wesleyan University, B
University of Nebraska-Lincoln, BMD

University of Nebraska at Omaha, B

Nevada

University of Nevada, Las Vegas, B
University of Nevada, Reno, BM

New Hampshire

Dartmouth College, B
New England College, B
Plymouth State University, B
Saint Anselm College, B
Thomas More College of Liberal Arts, B
University of New Hampshire, B

New Jersey

Bergen Community College, A
Bloomfield College, B
Burlington County College, A
The College of New Jersey, B
College of Saint Elizabeth, B
Drew University, B
Fairleigh Dickinson University, College at
    Florham, B
Fairleigh Dickinson University, Metropolitan
    Campus, B
Felician College, AB
Montclair State University, BMD
New Jersey City University, B
Princeton University, BD
The Richard Stockton College of New Jersey, B
Rider University, B
Rutgers, The State University of New Jersey,
    Camden, B
Rutgers, The State University of New Jersey, New
    Brunswick/Piscataway, BD
Rutgers, The State University of New Jersey,
    Newark, B
Saint Peter's College, B
Seton Hall University, B
Stevens Institute of Technology, B
William Paterson University of New Jersey, B

New Mexico

New Mexico State University, B
St. John's College, B
San Juan College, A
University of New Mexico, BMD

New York

Adelphi University, B
Alfred University, B
Bard College, B
Barnard College, B
Bernard M. Baruch College of the City University of
    New York, B
Brooklyn College of the City University of New
    York, B
Buffalo State College, State University of New
    York, B
Canisius College, B
City College of the City University of New York, B
Colgate University, B
College of Mount Saint Vincent, B
The College of New Rochelle, B
College of Staten Island of the City University of
    New York, B
Columbia College, B
Columbia University, School of General Studies, B
Cornell University, BD
Dowling College, B
D'Youville College, B
Elmira College, B
Eugene Lang College The New School for Liberal
    Arts, B
Excelsior College, B
Fordham University, BMD
Hamilton College, B
Hartwick College, B
Hobart and William Smith Colleges, B
Hofstra University, B
Houghton College, B
Hunter College of the City University of New York, B
Iona College, B
Ithaca College, B
The Jewish Theological Seminary, B

Le Moyne College, B
Lehman College of the City University of New
    York, B
Long Island University, Brooklyn Campus, B
Long Island University, C.W. Post Campus, B
Manhattan College, B
Manhattanville College, B
Marist College, B
Molloy College, B
Nazareth College of Rochester, B
New York University, BMDO
Niagara University, B
Nyack College, B
Purchase College, State University of New York, B
Queens College of the City University of New
    York, B
Rensselaer Polytechnic Institute, B
Roberts Wesleyan College, B
St. Bonaventure University, B
St. Francis College, B
St. John Fisher College, B
St. John's University, B
St. Lawrence University, B
St. Thomas Aquinas College, B
Sarah Lawrence College, B
Siena College, B
Skidmore College, B
State University of New York at Binghamton, BMD
State University of New York at Buffalo, BMD
State University of New York College at
    Brockport, B
State University of New York College at Cortland, B
State University of New York College at Geneseo, B
State University of New York College at Old
    Westbury, B
State University of New York College at Oneonta, B
State University of New York College at Potsdam, B
State University of New York, Fredonia, B
State University of New York at New Paltz, B
State University of New York at Oswego, B
State University of New York at Plattsburgh, B
Stony Brook University, State University of New
    York, BMD
Syracuse University, BMD
Touro College, B
Union College, B
United States Military Academy, B
University at Albany, State University of New
    York, BMD
University of Rochester, BMD
Utica College, B
Vassar College, B
Wells College, B
Yeshiva University, B
Yeshivat Mikdash Melech, B
York College of the City University of New York, B

North Carolina

Belmont Abbey College, B
Catawba College, B
Davidson College, B
Duke University, BMDO
East Carolina University, B
Elon University, B
Guilford College, B
High Point University, B
Lenoir-Rhyne College, B
Methodist College, A
North Carolina State University, B
North Carolina Wesleyan College, B
Queens University of Charlotte, B
St. Andrews Presbyterian College, B
Salem College, B
Shaw University, B
Southeastern Baptist Theological Seminary, D
The University of North Carolina at Asheville, B
The University of North Carolina at Chapel
    Hill, BMD
The University of North Carolina at Charlotte, B
The University of North Carolina at Greensboro, B
Wake Forest University, B
Warren Wilson College, B
Western Carolina University, B

Wingate University, B

North Dakota

Jamestown College, B
North Dakota State University, B
University of North Dakota, B

Ohio

Antioch College, B
Ashland University, B
Baldwin-Wallace College, B
Bowling Green State University, BMD
Capital University, B
Case Western Reserve University, B
Cedarville University, B
Cleveland State University, BMO
The College of Wooster, B
Denison University, B
Franciscan University of Steubenville, BM
Heidelberg College, B
Hiram College, B
John Carroll University, B
Kent State University, BM
Kenyon College, B
Marietta College, B
Miami University, BM
Miami University Hamilton, B
Miami University-Middletown Campus, A
Mount Union College, B
Mount Vernon Nazarene University, B
Muskingum College, B
Oberlin College, B
Ohio Dominican University, B
Ohio Northern University, B
The Ohio State University, BMD
Ohio University, BM
Ohio University-Eastern, B
Ohio Wesleyan University, B
Otterbein College, B
Pontifical College Josephinum, B
The University of Akron, B
University of Cincinnati, BMD
University of Dayton, B
The University of Findlay, B
The University of Toledo, BM
Urbana University, B
Ursuline College, B
Walsh University, B
Wilmington College, B
Wittenberg University, B
Wright State University, B
Xavier University, B
Youngstown State University, B

Oklahoma

Northeastern Oklahoma Agricultural and Mechanical
   College, A
Oklahoma Baptist University, B
Oklahoma City University, BM
Oklahoma State University, BM
Oral Roberts University, B
St. Gregory's University, B
Southern Nazarene University, B
Tulsa Community College, A
University of Central Oklahoma, B
University of Oklahoma, BMD
University of Tulsa, B

Oregon

George Fox University, B
Lewis & Clark College, B
Linfield College, B
Mount Angel Seminary, B
Oregon State University, B
Pacific University, B
Portland State University, B
Reed College, B
University of Oregon, BMD
University of Portland, B
Western Oregon University, B
Willamette University, B

Pennsylvania

Albright College, B
Allegheny College, B

Alvernia College, B
Arcadia University, B
Bloomsburg University of Pennsylvania, B
Bryn Mawr College, B
Bucknell University, B
Cabrini College, B
California University of Pennsylvania, B
Carlow University, B
Carnegie Mellon University, BMD
Clarion University of Pennsylvania, B
College Misericordia, B
DeSales University, B
Dickinson College, B
Duquesne University, BMD
East Stroudsburg University of Pennsylvania, B
Eastern University, B
Edinboro University of Pennsylvania, B
Elizabethtown College, B
Franklin and Marshall College, B
Gannon University, B
Geneva College, B
Gettysburg College, B
Grove City College, B
Haverford College, B
Indiana University of Pennsylvania, B
Juniata College, B
King's College, B
Kutztown University of Pennsylvania, B
La Salle University, B
Lafayette College, B
Lebanon Valley College, B
Lehigh University, B
Lincoln University, B
Lock Haven University of Pennsylvania, B
Lycoming College, B
Mansfield University of Pennsylvania, B
Mercyhurst College, B
Messiah College, B
Millersville University of Pennsylvania, B
Moravian College, B
Muhlenberg College, B
The Pennsylvania State University Abington
   College, B
The Pennsylvania State University Altoona
   College, B
The Pennsylvania State University Beaver Campus
   of the Commonwealth College, B
The Pennsylvania State University Berks Campus of
   the Berks-Lehigh Valley College, B
The Pennsylvania State University Delaware County
   Campus of the Commonwealth College, B
The Pennsylvania State University DuBois Campus
   of the Commonwealth College, B
The Pennsylvania State University at Erie, The
   Behrend College, B
The Pennsylvania State University Fayette Campus
   of the Commonwealth College, B
The Pennsylvania State University Hazleton
   Campus of the Commonwealth College, B
The Pennsylvania State University, Lehigh Valley
   Campus of the Berks-Lehigh Valley College, B
The Pennsylvania State University McKeesport
   Campus of the Commonwealth College, B
The Pennsylvania State University Mont Alto
   Campus of the Commonwealth College, B
The Pennsylvania State University New Kensington
   Campus of the Commonwealth College, B
The Pennsylvania State University Schuylkill
   Campus of the Capital College, B
The Pennsylvania State University Shenango
   Campus of the Commonwealth College, B
The Pennsylvania State University University Park
   Campus, BMD
The Pennsylvania State University Wilkes-Barre
   Campus of the Commonwealth College, B
The Pennsylvania State University Worthington
   Scranton Campus of the Commonwealth
   College, B
The Pennsylvania State University York Campus of
   the Commonwealth College, B
Rosemont College, B
St. Charles Borromeo Seminary, Overbrook, B
Saint Francis University, B
Saint Joseph's University, B
Saint Vincent College, B
Slippery Rock University of Pennsylvania, B

Susquehanna University, B
Swarthmore College, B
Temple University, BMD
Thiel College, B
University of Pennsylvania, BMDO
University of Pittsburgh, BMD
The University of Scranton, B
Ursinus College, B
Villanova University, BD
Washington & Jefferson College, B
West Chester University of Pennsylvania, BM
Westminster College, B
Wilkes University, B
York College of Pennsylvania, AB

Puerto Rico

Bayamon Central University, B
Pontifical Catholic University of Puerto Rico, B
University of Puerto Rico, Mayagüez Campus, B
University of Puerto Rico, Río Piedras, BM

Rhode Island

Brown University, BMD
Providence College, B
Rhode Island College, B
Roger Williams University, B
Salve Regina University, B
University of Rhode Island, BM

South Carolina

Benedict College, B
Clemson University, B
Coastal Carolina University, B
College of Charleston, B
Erskine College, B
Furman University, B
Newberry College, B
University of South Carolina, BMD
Winthrop University, B
Wofford College, B

South Dakota

Augustana College, B
Dakota Wesleyan University, B
University of Sioux Falls, B
The University of South Dakota, B

Tennessee

Austin Peay State University, B
Belmont University, B
Carson-Newman College, B
Christian Brothers University, B
East Tennessee State University, B
Fisk University, B
Freed-Hardeman University, B
Lipscomb University, B
Martin Methodist College, A
Middle Tennessee State University, B
Rhodes College, B
Sewanee: The University of the South, B
Union University, B
University of Memphis, BMD
The University of Tennessee, BMD
The University of Tennessee at Martin, B
Vanderbilt University, BMD

Texas

Austin College, B
Baylor University, BMD
Blinn College, A
Dallas Baptist University, B
Hardin-Simmons University, B
Howard Payne University, B
Lon Morris College, A
McMurry University, B
Our Lady of the Lake University of San Antonio, B
Palo Alto College, A
Rice University, BMD
St. Edward's University, B
St. Mary's University of San Antonio, B
St. Philip's College, A
Sam Houston State University, B
Southern Methodist University, B
Southwestern University, B
Texas A&M University, BMD

Texas Christian University, B
Texas Lutheran University, B
Texas State University-San Marcos, B
Texas Tech University, BM
Trinity University, B
University of Dallas, BMD
University of Houston, BM
University of the Incarnate Word, B
University of North Texas, BMD
University of St. Thomas, BMD
The University of Texas at Arlington, B
The University of Texas at Austin, BMD
The University of Texas at El Paso, B
The University of Texas-Pan American, B
The University of Texas at San Antonio, B
Wiley College, B

Utah

Brigham Young University, B
Dixie State College of Utah, A
Snow College, A
University of Utah, BMD
Utah State University, B
Utah Valley State College, AB
Westminster College, B

Vermont

Bennington College, B
Green Mountain College, B
Marlboro College, B
Middlebury College, B
Saint Michael's College, B
University of Vermont, B

Virginia

Bluefield College, B
Christendom College, B
Christopher Newport University, B
The College of William and Mary, B
Emory & Henry College, B
Ferrum College, B
George Mason University, B
Hampden-Sydney College, B
Hollins University, B
Liberty University, B
Lord Fairfax Community College, A
Lynchburg College, B
Mary Baldwin College, B
Marymount University, B
Old Dominion University, B
Randolph-Macon College, B
Randolph-Macon Woman's College, B
Roanoke College, B
Southern Virginia University, B
Sweet Briar College, B
University of Mary Washington, B
University of Richmond, B
University of Virginia, BMDO
Virginia Commonwealth University, B
Virginia Polytechnic Institute and State
  University, BM
Virginia Wesleyan College, B
Washington and Lee University, B

Washington

Central Washington University, B
Eastern Washington University, B
Everett Community College, A
Gonzaga University, BM
Lower Columbia College, A
Northwest University, B
Pacific Lutheran University, B
Seattle Pacific University, B
Seattle University, B
Skagit Valley College, A
Tacoma Community College, A
University of Puget Sound, B
University of Washington, BMD
Walla Walla College, B
Washington State University, B
Western Washington University, B
Whitman College, B

Whitworth College, B

West Virginia

American Public University System, B
West Virginia University, B
West Virginia Wesleyan College, B
Wheeling Jesuit University, B

Wisconsin

Alverno College, B
Beloit College, B
Carthage College, B
Lawrence University, B
Marquette University, BMD
Mount Mary College, B
Northland College, B
Ripon College, B
St. Norbert College, B
University of Wisconsin-Eau Claire, B
University of Wisconsin-Green Bay, AB
University of Wisconsin-La Crosse, B
University of Wisconsin-Madison, BMD
University of Wisconsin-Milwaukee, BM
University of Wisconsin-Oshkosh, B
University of Wisconsin-Parkside, B
University of Wisconsin-Platteville, B
University of Wisconsin-Stevens Point, B

Wyoming

Laramie County Community College, A
University of Wyoming, BM

Alberta

Concordia University College of Alberta, B
The King's University College, B
University of Alberta, BMD
University of Calgary, BMD
University of Lethbridge, BM

British Columbia

Kwantlen University College, A
Simon Fraser University, BMD
Trinity Western University, B
The University of British Columbia, BMD
University of Victoria, BM

Manitoba

Brandon University, B
Canadian Mennonite University, B
University of Manitoba, BM
The University of Winnipeg, B

New Brunswick

Mount Allison University, B
St. Thomas University, B
Université de Moncton, B
University of New Brunswick Fredericton, BM
University of New Brunswick Saint John, B

Newfoundland and Labrador

Memorial University of Newfoundland, BM

Nova Scotia

Acadia University, B
Cape Breton University, B
Dalhousie University, BMD
Mount Saint Vincent University, B
St. Francis Xavier University, B
Saint Mary's University, BM
University of King's College, B

Ontario

Brock University, BM
Carleton University, BM
Collège Dominicain de Philosophie et de
  Théologie, BMD
Lakehead University, BM
Laurentian University, B
McMaster University, BMD
Nipissing University, B
Queen's University at Kingston, BMD
Redeemer University College, B
Saint Paul University, B
Trent University, B

Tyndale University College & Seminary, B
University of Guelph, BMD
University of Ottawa, BMD
University of Toronto, BMD
University of Waterloo, BMD
The University of Western Ontario, BMD
University of Windsor, BM
Wilfrid Laurier University, BD
York University, BMD

Prince Edward Island

University of Prince Edward Island, B

Quebec

Bishop's University, B
Concordia University, BM
McGill University, BMD
Université Laval, ABMD
Université de Montréal, BMD
Université du Québec àMontréal, BMD
Université du Québec àTrois-Rivières, BMD
Université de Sherbrooke, BMD

Saskatchewan

University of Regina, BM
University of Saskatchewan, BM

PHILOSOPHY AND RELIGIOUS STUDIES

Alabama

Samford University, B

Arkansas

Lyon College, B
University of the Ozarks, B

California

California State University, Sacramento, B
Claremont McKenna College, B
Holy Names University, B
Point Loma Nazarene University, B

Florida

Bethune-Cookman College, B

Georgia

Berry College, B

Indiana

Saint Joseph's College, B
University of Notre Dame, B

Iowa

Buena Vista University, B
Graceland University, B
Iowa Wesleyan College, B

Kansas

Southwestern College, B
Sterling College, B

Kentucky

University of the Cumberlands, B

Mississippi

Millsaps College, B

Missouri

College of the Ozarks, B
Columbia College, B

Washington University in St. Louis, B

New Jersey

Kean University, B

New Mexico

St. John's College, B

New York

Pace University, B
Roberts Wesleyan College, B
St. John's University, B
Sarah Lawrence College, B
State University of New York at Oswego, B
Syracuse University, B

North Carolina

Appalachian State University, B
Barton College, B
The University of North Carolina at Pembroke, B
The University of North Carolina Wilmington, B

Ohio

Capital University, B

Pennsylvania

Juniata College, B
Ursinus College, B
Wilson College, B

South Carolina

Claflin University, B

Tennessee

Lambuth University, B
Union University, B
The University of Tennessee at Chattanooga, B

Virginia

Bridgewater College, B
Eastern Mennonite University, B
James Madison University, B
Radford University, B
Roanoke College, B

West Virginia

West Virginia Wesleyan College, B

Wisconsin

Viterbo University, B

Quebec

McGill University, B

PHLEBOTOMY/PHLEBOTOMIST

Minnesota

Alexandria Technical College, A

Ohio

Columbus State Community College, A

Washington

Edmonds Community College, A

PHOTOGRAPHIC AND FILM/VIDEO TECHNOLOGY/TECHNICIAN AND ASSISTANT

Alabama

Calhoun Community College, A

Florida

Miami Dade College, A

Maine

New England School of Communications, AB

Minnesota

Dakota County Technical College, A

New Jersey

County College of Morris, A

New York

Mohawk Valley Community College, A
Rochester Institute of Technology, B
St. John's University, B
Suffolk County Community College, A

North Carolina

Catawba Valley Community College, A
Randolph Community College, A

Ohio

Kent State University, B
Ohio University, B

Pennsylvania

The Art Institute of Philadelphia, A

Texas

Texas State Technical College Waco, A

Utah

Dixie State College of Utah, A
Salt Lake Community College, A

Vermont

Burlington College, A

Washington

Olympic College, A

PHOTOGRAPHY

Alabama

University of Montevallo, B

Arizona

The Art Center Design College, B
Northern Arizona University, B
Northland Pioneer College, A
Prescott College, B
Scottsdale Community College, A

California

Academy of Art University, ABM
Allan Hancock College, A
American InterContinental University, B
Antelope Valley College, A
Art Center College of Design, B
Bakersfield College, A
Brooks Institute of Photography, BM
Butte College, A
California College of the Arts, BM
California Institute of the Arts, BMO
California State University, East Bay, B
California State University, Fullerton, B
California State University, Long Beach, B
California State University, Sacramento, B
Cerritos College, A
Chabot College, A
Chaffey College, A
Citrus College, A
City College of San Francisco, A
College of San Mateo, A
Columbia College, A
Compton Community College, A
Cosumnes River College (Sacramento), A
Cypress College, A
De Anza College, A
East Los Angeles College, A
El Camino College, A
Foothill College, A
Fresno City College, A
Glendale Community College, A
Grossmont College, A
Hartnell College, A
Laney College, A

Lassen Community College District, A
Long Beach City College, A
Los Angeles City College, A
Los Angeles Pierce College, A
Los Angeles Trade-Technical College, A
Los Angeles Valley College, A
Mills College, M
Modesto Junior College, A
Monterey Peninsula College, A
Moorpark College, A
Mt. San Antonio College, A
Mt. San Jacinto College, A
Napa Valley College, A
Orange Coast College, A
Otis College of Art and Design, BM
Pacific Union College, A
Palomar College, A
Pasadena City College, A
Porterville College, A
Riverside Community College District, A
Saddleback College, A
San Bernardino Valley College, A
San Diego City College, A
San Francisco Art Institute, BMO
San Joaquin Delta College, A
San Jose State University, M
Santa Ana College, A
Santa Monica College, A
Sierra College, A
Solano Community College, A
Southwestern College, A
University of California, Santa Cruz, B
Yuba College, A

Colorado

The Art Institute of Colorado, A
Colorado Mountain College, A
Colorado State University, B
University of Colorado at Boulder, M

Connecticut

Albertus Magnus College, B
University of Hartford, B
Yale University, M

Delaware

Delaware College of Art and Design, A

District of Columbia

Corcoran College of Art and Design, AB
Gallaudet University, B
The George Washington University, M
Howard University, M

Florida

American InterContinental University, B
The Art Institute of Fort Lauderdale, A
Barry University, BMO
Daytona Beach Community College, A
Miami Dade College, A
New World School of the Arts, AB
Palm Beach Community College, A
Ringling School of Art and Design, B
University of Central Florida, B
University of Miami, BM

Georgia

Gwinnett Technical College, A
Savannah College of Art and Design, BM

Idaho

Brigham Young University -Idaho, A
College of Southern Idaho, A
University of Idaho, B

Illinois

Bradley University, M
City Colleges of Chicago, Olive-Harvey College, A
City Colleges of Chicago, Richard J. Daley College, A
College of DuPage, A
Columbia College Chicago, BM
Dominican University, B
Governors State University, B
Illinois State University, M

Lincoln College, A
Prairie State College, A
School of the Art Institute of Chicago, BM
Trinity Christian College, B
University of Illinois at Chicago, BM
University of Illinois at Urbana-Champaign, B

Indiana

Ball State University, B
Indiana State University, M
Indiana University Bloomington, BM
Indiana University-Purdue University Fort Wayne, B
Indiana Wesleyan University, B
Saint Mary-of-the-Woods College, B

Iowa

Coe College, B
Hawkeye Community College, A
Iowa Lakes Community College, A
Morningside College, B
The University of Iowa, B

Kansas

Central Christian College of Kansas, A
Fort Scott Community College, A

Louisiana

Louisiana State University and Agricultural and
   Mechanical College, M
Louisiana Tech University, BM
McNeese State University, B

Maine

Maine College of Art, B
The University of Maine at Augusta, A

Maryland

Anne Arundel Community College, A
Cecil Community College, A
Howard Community College, A
Maryland Institute College of Art, BM
University of Maryland, Baltimore County, B
Villa Julie College, A

Massachusetts

The Art Institute of Boston at Lesley University, B
Bridgewater State College, B
Fitchburg State College, B
Greenfield Community College, A
Holyoke Community College, A
Massachusetts College of Art, BM
Montserrat College of Art, B
Salem State College, B
School of the Museum of Fine Arts, Boston, B
Simon's Rock College of Bard, B
University of Massachusetts Dartmouth, B

Michigan

Andrews University, AB
Aquinas College, B
Grand Valley State University, B
Lansing Community College, A
Mott Community College, A
Oakland Community College, A
University of Michigan, B
University of Michigan-Flint, B
Washtenaw Community College, A

Minnesota

Brown College, B
College of Visual Arts, B
Dakota County Technical College, A
Hennepin Technical College, A
Minneapolis College of Art and Design, BM
Pillsbury Baptist Bible College, A
Ridgewater College, A

Mississippi

Northeast Mississippi Community College, A

Missouri

Central Missouri State University, B
Columbia College, B
Kansas City Art Institute, B

St. Louis Community College at Florissant Valley, A
St. Louis Community College at Forest Park, A
St. Louis Community College at Meramec, A
University of Missouri-St. Louis, B
Washington University in St. Louis, BM
Webster University, B

Nebraska

Metropolitan Community College, A

Nevada

Community College of Southern Nevada, A

New Hampshire

Chester College of New England, B
New England College, B
Rivier College, B

New Jersey

Bergen Community College, A
Brookdale Community College, A
Mercer County Community College, A
Middlesex County College, A
Rutgers, The State University of New Jersey, New
   Brunswick/Piscataway, B

New Mexico

College of Santa Fe, B
Institute of American Indian Arts, A

New York

Adirondack Community College, A
Bard College, B
Brooklyn College of the City University of New
   York, M
Buffalo State College, State University of New
   York, B
Cazenovia College, B
Fiorello H. LaGuardia Community College of the
   City University of New York, A
Fordham University, B
Herkimer County Community College, A
Hofstra University, B
Ithaca College, B
Long Island University, C.W. Post Campus, B
Nassau Community College, A
Nazareth College of Rochester, B
New York University, B
Onondaga Community College, A
Parsons The New School for Design, B
Pratt Institute, BM
Rochester Institute of Technology, ABM
Rockland Community College, A
Sage College of Albany, A
St. John's University, B
Sarah Lawrence College, B
School of Visual Arts, BM
State University of New York at New Paltz, B
Sullivan County Community College, A
Syracuse University, BM

North Carolina

Carteret Community College, A
Catawba Valley Community College, A
McDowell Technical Community College, A
Randolph Community College, A

Ohio

Antonelli College, A
Art Academy of Cincinnati, B
Bowling Green State University, B
The Cleveland Institute of Art, B
Columbus College of Art & Design, B
Cuyahoga Community College, A
Ohio Institute of Photography and Technology, A
Ohio University, M
Shawnee State University, B
The University of Akron, B
University of Dayton, B
Wright State University, B
Youngstown State University, B

Oklahoma

Northeastern Oklahoma Agricultural and Mechanical
   College, A

Oklahoma State University, Okmulgee, A
University of Central Oklahoma, B
University of Oklahoma, BM

Oregon

Linn-Benton Community College, A
Pacific Northwest College of Art, B
University of Oregon, B

Pennsylvania

Antonelli Institute, A
Arcadia University, B
The Art Institute of Philadelphia, AB
The Art Institute of Pittsburgh, AB
Community College of Philadelphia, A
Drexel University, B
Harrisburg Area Community College, A
Keystone College, A
Lehigh Valley College, A
Luzerne County Community College, A
Marywood University, BM
Moore College of Art & Design, B
Pennsylvania College of Art & Design, B
The Pennsylvania State University University Park
   Campus, M
Point Park University, B
Temple University, BM
The University of the Arts, B
Westmoreland County Community College, A

Puerto Rico

Inter American University of Puerto Rico, San
   Germán Campus, BM

Rhode Island

Rhode Island School of Design, BM
Salve Regina University, B

South Carolina

Coker College, B

Tennessee

Carson-Newman College, B
Memphis College of Art, BM
Nashville State Technical Community College, A
Nossi College of Art, A
Southern Adventist University, B
University of Memphis, M
The University of Tennessee, M
Watkins College of Art and Design, B

Texas

Amarillo College, A
Austin Community College, A
El Paso Community College, A
Hill College of the Hill Junior College District, A
Lamar University, M
Lee College, A
North Harris College, A
Odessa College, A
St. Edward's University, B
Sam Houston State University, B
Texas A&M University-Commerce, B
Texas Christian University, B
Texas Southern University, B
Tyler Junior College, A
University of Houston, BM
University of North Texas, BM

Utah

Brigham Young University, B
Dixie State College of Utah, A
University of Utah, M
Weber State University, B

Vermont

Bennington College, B
Marlboro College, B

Virginia

Hampton University, B
James Madison University, M
Northern Virginia Community College, A
Thomas Nelson Community College, A

Virginia Commonwealth University, BM
Virginia Intermont College, B

Washington

The Art Institute of Seattle, A
Everett Community College, A
Lower Columbia College, A
Seattle Central Community College, A
Seattle University, B
Shoreline Community College, A
University of Washington, B
Washington State University, M

Wisconsin

Carroll College, B
Madison Area Technical College, A
Milwaukee Area Technical College, A
Milwaukee Institute of Art and Design, B

Wyoming

Casper College, A
Northwest College, A
Western Wyoming Community College, A

Alberta

Alberta College of Art & Design, B

British Columbia

University of Victoria, M

New Brunswick

Mount Allison University, B

Newfoundland and Labrador

Memorial University of Newfoundland, B

Nova Scotia

NSCAD University, B

Ontario

Ryerson University, B
University of Ottawa, B
York University, B

Quebec

Concordia University, B

PHOTOJOURNALISM

District of Columbia

Corcoran College of Art and Design, B

Missouri

University of Missouri-Columbia, B

New York

Rochester Institute of Technology, B

Oklahoma

St. Gregory's University, B

Pennsylvania

Point Park University, B

Texas

Texas Tech University, B
University of North Texas, B

PHOTONICS

Arkansas

University of Arkansas, MD

California

University of California, San Diego, MD

Florida

University of Central Florida, MDO

Massachusetts

Boston University, M

New Jersey

Princeton University, D

Oklahoma

Oklahoma State University, MD

Pennsylvania

Lehigh University, M

PHYSICAL AND THEORETICAL CHEMISTRY

Michigan

Michigan State University, B

Pennsylvania

Lehigh University, B

Texas

Rice University, B

PHYSICAL ANTHROPOLOGY

Wyoming

Northwest College, A

PHYSICAL CHEMISTRY

California

California State University, Fullerton, M
California State University, Los Angeles, M
University of Southern California, D

Colorado

University of Colorado at Boulder, D

Connecticut

Wesleyan University, MD
Yale University, D

District of Columbia

The George Washington University, MD
Georgetown University, MD
Howard University, MD

Florida

Florida State University, MD
University of Miami, D
University of South Florida, MD

Georgia

Clark Atlanta University, MD
University of Georgia, MD

Illinois

Illinois Institute of Technology, MD

Indiana

Indiana University Bloomington, D
Purdue University, MD
University of Notre Dame, MD

Kansas

Kansas State University, M

Kentucky

University of Louisville, MD

Louisiana

Southern University and Agricultural and Mechanical College, M

Maryland

University of Maryland, College Park, MD

Massachusetts

Boston College, D
Brandeis University, MD

Harvard University, MD
Massachusetts Institute of Technology, D
Northeastern University, D
Tufts University, MD

Michigan

Michigan State University, D
University of Michigan, D

Mississippi

University of Southern Mississippi, MD

Missouri

University of Missouri-Columbia, MD
University of Missouri-Kansas City, MD

Nebraska

University of Nebraska-Lincoln, D

New Jersey

Princeton University, D
Rutgers, The State University of New Jersey, New Brunswick/Piscataway, MD
Rutgers, The State University of New Jersey, Newark, MD
Seton Hall University, MD

New York

Clarkson University, MD
Cornell University, D
Rensselaer Polytechnic Institute, MD
State University of New York at Binghamton, D

North Carolina

Wake Forest University, MD

Ohio

Case Western Reserve University, MD
Cleveland State University, M
Kent State University, MD
Miami University, M
University of Cincinnati, MD
The University of Toledo, MD

Oregon

Oregon State University, MD

South Dakota

South Dakota State University, MD

Tennessee

The University of Tennessee, MD
Vanderbilt University, MD

Texas

Rice University, D
The University of Texas at Austin, MD

Utah

Brigham Young University, MD
University of Utah, D

Virginia

Old Dominion University, M

Washington

Washington State University, M

West Virginia

West Virginia University, MD

Wisconsin

Marquette University, MD

Alberta

University of Calgary, MD

British Columbia

Simon Fraser University, MD

Ontario

McMaster University, MD

Saskatchewan

University of Regina, MD

PHYSICAL EDUCATION TEACHING AND COACHING

Alabama

Alabama Agricultural and Mechanical University, BM
Alabama Southern Community College, A
Alabama State University, BMO
Athens State University, B
Auburn University, BMDO
Auburn University Montgomery, MO
Chattahoochee Valley Community College, A
Faulkner University, B
Gadsden State Community College, A
Huntingdon College, B
Jacksonville State University, BM
Jefferson Davis Community College, A
Oakwood College, B
Samford University, B
Stillman College, B
Troy University, B
The University of Alabama, B
The University of Alabama at Birmingham, BM
University of South Alabama, BMO
The University of West Alabama, BM

Alaska

University of Alaska Anchorage, B

Arizona

Arizona Western College, A
Cochise College (Douglas), A
Cochise College (Sierra Vista), A
Grand Canyon University, B
Northern Arizona University, BM
Prescott College, B
South Mountain Community College, A
The University of Arizona, B

Arkansas

Arkansas State University, BMO
Arkansas Tech University, B
Harding University, B
Henderson State University, BM
Hendrix College, B
Ouachita Baptist University, B
Southern Arkansas University-Magnolia, B
University of Arkansas, M
University of Arkansas at Monticello, B
University of Arkansas at Pine Bluff, B
University of Central Arkansas, B
University of the Ozarks, B
Williams Baptist College, B

California

Allan Hancock College, A
Azusa Pacific University, BM
Bakersfield College, A
Barstow College, A
Biola University, B
Butte College, A
Cabrillo College, A
California Lutheran University, B
California Polytechnic State University, San Luis Obispo, BM
California State Polytechnic University, Pomona, B
California State University, Bakersfield, B
California State University, Chico, B
California State University, Dominguez Hills, BM
California State University, East Bay, BM
California State University, Fresno, B
California State University, Fullerton, BM
California State University, Long Beach, BM
California State University, Los Angeles, M
California State University, Sacramento, M
California State University, San Bernardino, B
California State University, Stanislaus, BM
Cañada College, A
Cerritos College, A
Chabot College, A
Chaffey College, A

Citrus College, A
College of the Canyons, A
College of the Desert, A
College of Marin, A
College of the Sequoias, A
Columbia College, A
Compton Community College, A
Crafton Hills College, A
Cuesta College, A
Cypress College, A
De Anza College, A
East Los Angeles College, A
El Camino College, A
Foothill College, A
Fresno Pacific University, AB
Fullerton College, A
Gavilan College, A
Hartnell College, A
Humboldt State University, BM
Imperial Valley College, A
Lake Tahoe Community College, A
Lassen Community College District, A
Long Beach City College, A
Los Angeles Mission College, A
Los Angeles Valley College, A
The Master's College and Seminary, B
Mendocino College, A
Merced College, A
Modesto Junior College, A
Monterey Peninsula College, A
Mt. San Jacinto College, A
Orange Coast College, A
Oxnard College, A
Pacific Union College, B
Palomar College, A
Pasadena City College, A
Pepperdine University, B
Porterville College, A
Sacramento City College, A
Saddleback College, A
San Bernardino Valley College, A
San Diego Christian College, B
San Diego City College, A
San Diego Golf Academy, A
San Diego Mesa College, A
San Diego Miramar College, A
San Diego State University, M
San Francisco State University, BM
San Joaquin Delta College, A
Santa Barbara City College, A
Santa Monica College, A
Santa Rosa Junior College, A
Skyline College, A
Solano Community College, A
Sonoma State University, B
Taft College, A
University of La Verne, B
University of San Francisco, B
Vanguard University of Southern California, B
West Hills Community College, A
West Los Angeles College, A
West Valley College, A
Westmont College, B
Whittier College, B
Yuba College, A

Colorado

Adams State College, M
Colorado State University-Pueblo, B
Fort Lewis College, B
Mesa State College, B
Northeastern Junior College, A
Trinidad State Junior College, A
University of Colorado at Boulder, M
Western State College of Colorado, B

Connecticut

Central Connecticut State University, BMO
Eastern Connecticut State University, B
Mitchell College, A
Southern Connecticut State University, M
University of Connecticut, B

Delaware

Delaware State University, B
University of Delaware, B

Wesley College, B

District of Columbia

Gallaudet University, B
Howard University, B
University of the District of Columbia, B

Florida

Barry University, B
Bethune-Cookman College, B
Clearwater Christian College, B
Daytona Beach Community College, A
Edward Waters College, B
Florida Agricultural and Mechanical University, BM
Florida International University, BM
Florida Memorial College, B
Florida Southern College, B
Florida State University, BMDO
Hillsborough Community College, A
Indian River Community College, A
Jacksonville University, B
Manatee Community College, A
Miami Dade College, A
Okaloosa-Walton College, A
Palm Beach Atlantic University, B
Palm Beach Community College, A
University of Central Florida, BM
University of Florida, M
University of North Florida, B
University of South Florida, BM
The University of Tampa, B
University of West Florida, M
Valencia Community College, A
Warner Southern College, B

Georgia

Abraham Baldwin Agricultural College, A
Albany State University, BM
Armstrong Atlantic State University, B
Augusta State University, B
Berry College, B
Brewton-Parker College, B
Clark Atlanta University, B
Clayton State University, A
Columbus State University, BM
East Georgia College, A
Fort Valley State University, B
Georgia College & State University, BMO
Georgia Perimeter College, A
Georgia Southern University, BM
Georgia Southwestern State University, BM
Georgia State University, M
Kennesaw State University, B
Macon State College, A
Morehouse College, B
North Georgia College & State University, B
Reinhardt College, B
South Georgia College, A
University of Georgia, BMDO
University of West Georgia, BMO
Valdosta State University, BM
Waycross College, A

Guam

University of Guam, B

Hawaii

Brigham Young University-Hawaii, B
University of Hawaii at Manoa, B

Idaho

Albertson College of Idaho, B
Boise State University, B
Brigham Young University -Idaho, A
College of Southern Idaho, A
Idaho State University, BM
Lewis-Clark State College, B
Northwest Nazarene University, B
University of Idaho, BMD

Illinois

Augustana College, B
Aurora University, B
Blackburn College, B
Chicago State University, BM

City Colleges of Chicago, Harry S. Truman
  College, A
City Colleges of Chicago, Malcolm X College, A
Concordia University, B
Danville Area Community College, A
DePaul University, BM
Eastern Illinois University, BM
Elmhurst College, B
Eureka College, B
Greenville College, B
Illinois College, B
Illinois State University, BM
John A. Logan College, A
Judson College, B
Lewis University, B
Lincoln College, A
Lincoln College-Normal, A
MacMurray College, B
McKendree College, B
Millikin University, B
Monmouth College, B
North Central College, B
North Park University, B
Northeastern Illinois University, B
Northern Illinois University, BM
Olivet Nazarene University, B
Quincy University, B
Rockford College, B
Sauk Valley Community College, A
Southern Illinois University Carbondale, BM
Southwestern Illinois College, A
Spoon River College, A
Trinity Christian College, B
Trinity International University, B
Western Illinois University, BM
William Rainey Harper College, A

Indiana

Anderson University, B
Ball State University, BMD
Bethel College, B
DePauw University, B
Franklin College, B
Goshen College, B
Grace College, B
Hanover College, B
Huntington University, B
Indiana State University, BM
Indiana University Bloomington, BMDO
Indiana University-Purdue University Indianapolis, B
Indiana Wesleyan University, B
Manchester College, B
Marian College, B
Oakland City University, B
Purdue University, BMD
Saint Joseph's College, B
Taylor University, B
Tri-State University, B
University of Evansville, B
University of Indianapolis, BM
University of Southern Indiana, B
Valparaiso University, B
Vincennes University, A

Iowa

Briar Cliff University, B
Buena Vista University, B
Clarke College, B
Coe College, B
Cornell College, B
Dordt College, B
Ellsworth Community College, A
Graceland University, B
Iowa Lakes Community College, A
Iowa State University of Science and
  Technology, MD
Iowa Wesleyan College, B
Kirkwood Community College, A
Loras College, B
Luther College, B
Northwestern College, B
St. Ambrose University, B
Simpson College, B
University of Dubuque, B
The University of Iowa, MD
University of Northern Iowa, BM

Upper Iowa University, B
Waldorf College, B
Wartburg College, B
William Penn University, B

Kansas

Barton County Community College, A
Benedictine College, B
Bethany College, B
Butler Community College, A
Central Christian College of Kansas, A
Cloud County Community College, A
Coffeyville Community College, A
Colby Community College, A
Cowley County Community College and Area
  Vocational-Technical School, A
Dodge City Community College, A
Emporia State University, M
Fort Hays State University, BM
Friends University, B
Garden City Community College, A
Highland Community College, A
Independence Community College, A
Kansas Wesleyan University, B
Labette Community College, A
McPherson College, B
MidAmerica Nazarene University, B
Ottawa University, B
Pittsburg State University, BM
Pratt Community College, A
Seward County Community College, A
Sterling College, B
Tabor College, B
University of Kansas, BMD
Washburn University, B
Wichita State University, BM

Kentucky

Alice Lloyd College, B
Asbury College, B
Berea College, B
Campbellsville University, B
Eastern Kentucky University, BM
Kentucky State University, B
Kentucky Wesleyan College, B
Lindsey Wilson College, B
Morehead State University, BM
Murray State University, BM
Northern Kentucky University, B
St. Catharine College, A
Transylvania University, B
Union College, BM
University of the Cumberlands, B
University of Kentucky, B
University of Louisville, M
Western Kentucky University, BM

Louisiana

Centenary College of Louisiana, B
Dillard University, B
Grambling State University, B
Louisiana College, B
Louisiana State University and Agricultural and
  Mechanical College, B
Louisiana State University in Shreveport, B
Louisiana Tech University, B
McNeese State University, BM
Nicholls State University, B
Northwestern State University of Louisiana, BM
Southeastern Louisiana University, B
Southern University and Agricultural and Mechanical
  College, B
Southern University at New Orleans, B
University of Louisiana at Lafayette, B
University of Louisiana at Monroe, B
University of New Orleans, BMO
Xavier University of Louisiana, B

Maine

Husson College, B
Saint Joseph's College of Maine, B
University of Maine, BM

University of Maine at Presque Isle, B

Maryland

Anne Arundel Community College, A
Chesapeake College, A
Coppin State University, B
Frederick Community College, A
Frostburg State University, BM
Garrett College, A
McDaniel College, BM
Morgan State University, B
Prince George's Community College, A
Salisbury University, B
Towson University, B
University of Maryland, College Park, B
University of Maryland Eastern Shore, B

Massachusetts

Atlantic Union College, B
Boston University, BMDO
Bridgewater State College, BM
Cape Cod Community College, A
Dean College, A
Eastern Nazarene College, B
Endicott College, B
Northern Essex Community College, A
Salem State College, B
Springfield College, BMDO
University of Massachusetts Amherst, MDO
University of Massachusetts Boston, B
Westfield State College, B

Michigan

Adrian College, AB
Albion College, B
Alma College, B
Aquinas College, B
Calvin College, B
Central Michigan University, BM
Concordia University, B
Cornerstone University, B
Eastern Michigan University, B
Grand Valley State University, B
Hillsdale College, B
Hope College, B
Kellogg Community College, A
Lansing Community College, A
Michigan State University, B
Northern Michigan University, B
Olivet College, B
Saginaw Valley State University, B
Spring Arbor University, B
University of Michigan, B
Wayne State University, BM
Western Michigan University, BM

Minnesota

Augsburg College, B
Bemidji State University, BM
Bethel University, B
College of St. Catherine, B
Concordia College, B
Concordia University, St. Paul, B
Crown College, B
Gustavus Adolphus College, B
Hamline University, B
Minnesota State University Mankato, BMO
Minnesota State University Moorhead, B
Northwestern College, B
Pillsbury Baptist Bible College, B
Ridgewater College, A
St. Cloud State University, BM
Southwest Minnesota State University, B
University of Minnesota, Duluth, B
University of Minnesota, Twin Cities Campus, BMD
University of St. Thomas, B
Vermilion Community College, A
Winona State University, B

Mississippi

Alcorn State University, B
Copiah-Lincoln Community College, A
Delta State University, BM
Itawamba Community College, A
Jackson State University, BM

Jones County Junior College, A
Mississippi Delta Community College, A
Mississippi State University, BM
Mississippi University for Women, B
Mississippi Valley State University, B
Northeast Mississippi Community College, A
Northwest Mississippi Community College, A
Southwest Mississippi Community College, A
University of Southern Mississippi, BMD
William Carey College, B

Missouri

Central Methodist University, B
Central Missouri State University, BM
College of the Ozarks, B
Crowder College, A
Culver-Stockton College, B
Drury University, M
East Central College, A
Evangel University, B
Hannibal-LaGrange College, B
Jefferson College, A
Lincoln University, B
Lindenwood University, B
Missouri Baptist University, B
Missouri State University, BM
Missouri Valley College, B
Northwest Missouri State University, BM
Southeast Missouri State University, B
Southwest Baptist University, B
University of Missouri-St. Louis, B
Westminster College, B
William Woods University, B

Montana

Carroll College, B
Montana State University-Billings, B
Montana State University-Northern, B
Rocky Mountain College, B
University of Great Falls, B
The University of Montana-Missoula, BM
The University of Montana-Western, B

Nebraska

Bellevue University, B
Chadron State College, B
Concordia University, B
Dana College, B
Doane College, B
Hastings College, B
Midland Lutheran College, B
Nebraska Wesleyan University, B
Northeast Community College, A
Peru State College, B
Union College, B
University of Nebraska at Kearney, BM
University of Nebraska-Lincoln, BM
University of Nebraska at Omaha, BM
Wayne State College, BM
York College, B

Nevada

University of Nevada, Las Vegas, BMD
University of Nevada, Reno, B

New Hampshire

Keene State College, B
New England College, B
University of New Hampshire, B

New Jersey

The College of New Jersey, BM
Essex County College, A
Kean University, B
Middlesex County College, A
Montclair State University, BM
Rowan University, B
William Paterson University of New Jersey, B

New Mexico

College of the Southwest, B
Eastern New Mexico University, BM
New Mexico Highlands University, B
New Mexico Junior College, A
New Mexico Military Institute, A

New Mexico State University, B
University of New Mexico, BMDO
University of New Mexico-Gallup, A
Western New Mexico University, B

New York

Adelphi University, BMO
Brooklyn College of the City University of New
    York, BM
Canisius College, BM
Clinton Community College, A
College of Mount Saint Vincent, B
Erie Community College, A
Erie Community College, North Campus, A
Erie Community College, South Campus, A
Finger Lakes Community College, A
Fulton-Montgomery Community College, A
Genesee Community College, A
Herkimer County Community College, A
Hofstra University, BMO
Houghton College, B
Hunter College of the City University of New York, B
Ithaca College, B
Long Island University, Brooklyn Campus, BM
Long Island University, C.W. Post Campus, B
Manhattan College, B
Mohawk Valley Community College, A
Monroe Community College, A
Niagara County Community College, A
Queens College of the City University of New
    York, B
St. Bonaventure University, B
St. Francis College, B
State University of New York College at
    Brockport, BM
State University of New York College at
    Cortland, BM
State University of New York College at Potsdam, B
Stony Brook University, State University of New
    York, O
Syracuse University, B
York College of the City University of New York, B

North Carolina

Appalachian State University, BM
Barton College, B
Campbell University, BM
Catawba College, B
Chowan University, B
East Carolina University, B
Elizabeth City State University, B
Elon University, B
Fayetteville State University, B
Gardner-Webb University, BM
Greensboro College, B
High Point University, B
Johnson C. Smith University, B
Lees-McRae College, B
Lenoir-Rhyne College, B
Livingstone College, B
Mars Hill College, B
Meredith College, B
Methodist College, AB
Mitchell Community College, A
North Carolina Agricultural and Technical State
    University, BM
North Carolina Central University, BM
North Carolina Wesleyan College, B
Pfeiffer University, B
Piedmont Baptist College, B
St. Andrews Presbyterian College, B
Saint Augustine's College, B
The University of North Carolina at Chapel Hill, M
The University of North Carolina at Greensboro, B
The University of North Carolina at Pembroke, BM
The University of North Carolina Wilmington, B
Western Carolina University, BM
Winston-Salem State University, B

North Dakota

Dickinson State University, B
Jamestown College, B
Mayville State University, B
Minot State University, B
North Dakota State University, BM
University of Mary, B

University of North Dakota, B
Valley City State University, B

Ohio

Ashland University, BM
Baldwin-Wallace College, B
Bowling Green State University, B
Capital University, B
Cedarville University, B
Central State University, B
Cleveland State University, BM
Defiance College, B
Denison University, B
Heidelberg College, B
John Carroll University, B
Kent State University, BMD
Lorain County Community College, A
Malone College, B
Miami University, B
Miami University Hamilton, B
Mount Union College, B
Mount Vernon Nazarene University, B
Muskingum College, B
Ohio Northern University, B
The Ohio State University, BMD
Ohio University, BM
Ohio University-Eastern, B
Ohio Wesleyan University, B
Otterbein College, B
Sinclair Community College, A
The University of Akron, BM
University of Cincinnati, B
University of Dayton, BM
The University of Findlay, B
University of Rio Grande, AB
The University of Toledo, BMD
Walsh University, B
Wilmington College, B
Wright State University, BM
Youngstown State University, B

Oklahoma

Bacone College, B
Carl Albert State College, A
East Central University, B
Eastern Oklahoma State College, A
Hillsdale Free Will Baptist College, A
Langston University, B
Murray State College, A
Northeastern Oklahoma Agricultural and Mechanical
    College, A
Northeastern State University, B
Northwestern Oklahoma State University, B
Oklahoma Baptist University, B
Oklahoma Christian University, B
Oklahoma City University, B
Oklahoma Panhandle State University, B
Oklahoma State University, BMD
Oklahoma Wesleyan University, B
Oral Roberts University, B
Redlands Community College, A
Rose State College, A
Seminole State College, A
Southeastern Oklahoma State University, B
Southern Nazarene University, B
Southwestern Oklahoma State University, B
Tulsa Community College, A
University of Central Oklahoma, B

Oregon

Chemeketa Community College, A
Concordia University, B
Corban College, B
Eastern Oregon University, B
George Fox University, B
Linn-Benton Community College, A
Oregon State University, BM
Southern Oregon University, B
Treasure Valley Community College, A
Umpqua Community College, A
Warner Pacific College, B

Pennsylvania

Bucks County Community College, A
Butler County Community College, A
East Stroudsburg University of Pennsylvania, BM

Edinboro University of Pennsylvania, B
Gettysburg College, B
Harrisburg Area Community College, A
Indiana University of Pennsylvania, BM
Lancaster Bible College, B
Lock Haven University of Pennsylvania, B
Luzerne County Community College, A
Messiah College, B
Montgomery County Community College, A
Philadelphia Biblical University, B
Temple University, BMD
University of Pittsburgh, B
West Chester University of Pennsylvania, BMO

Puerto Rico

American University of Puerto Rico, B
Bayamon Central University, B
Inter American University of Puerto Rico, Fajardo
    Campus, B
Inter American University of Puerto Rico, Guayama
    Campus, B
Inter American University of Puerto Rico,
    Metropolitan Campus, BM
Inter American University of Puerto Rico, San
    Germán Campus, BM
Pontifical Catholic University of Puerto Rico, B
Universidad Metropolitana, M
Universidad del Turabo, B
University of Puerto Rico at Bayamón, AB
University of Puerto Rico at Carolina, A
University of Puerto Rico, Cayey University
    College, B
University of Puerto Rico, Mayagüez Campus, B

Rhode Island

Rhode Island College, B
University of Rhode Island, BM

South Carolina

Anderson University, B
Charleston Southern University, B
The Citadel, The Military College of South
    Carolina, BM
Coastal Carolina University, B
Coker College, B
College of Charleston, B
Erskine College, B
Lander University, B
Limestone College, B
Newberry College, B
South Carolina State University, B
Southern Wesleyan University, B
University of South Carolina, BMD
University of South Carolina Upstate, B
Voorhees College, B
Winthrop University, BM

South Dakota

Augustana College, B
Dakota State University, B
Dakota Wesleyan University, B
Mount Marty College, B
Northern State University, BM
South Dakota State University, BM
University of Sioux Falls, B
The University of South Dakota, BM

Tennessee

Belmont University, B
Bethel College, BM
Bryan College, B
Carson-Newman College, B
Columbia State Community College, A
Cumberland University, B
East Tennessee State University, M
Free Will Baptist Bible College, B
Freed-Hardeman University, B
Lambuth University, B
Lane College, B
Lee University, B
LeMoyne-Owen College, B
Lincoln Memorial University, B
Lipscomb University, B
Martin Methodist College, A
Maryville College, B

Middle Tennessee State University, MD
Roane State Community College, A
Southern Adventist University, B
Tennessee State University, BM
Tennessee Technological University, BM
Tennessee Wesleyan College, B
Trevecca Nazarene University, B
Tusculum College, B
Union University, B
University of Memphis, BM
The University of Tennessee at Chattanooga, M
Walters State Community College, A

Texas

Abilene Christian University, B
Alvin Community College, A
Amarillo College, A
Angelina College, A
Austin College, BM
Baylor University, BMD
Blinn College, A
Brazosport College, A
Central Texas College, A
Cisco Junior College, A
Clarendon College, A
Coastal Bend College, A
Dallas Baptist University, B
Del Mar College, A
East Texas Baptist University, B
Frank Phillips College, A
Galveston College, A
Grayson County College, A
Hardin-Simmons University, BM
Hill College of the Hill Junior College District, A
Houston Baptist University, B
Howard College, A
Howard Payne University, B
Huston-Tillotson University, B
Jarvis Christian College, B
Kilgore College, A
Lamar University, B
Lee College, A
LeTourneau University, B
Lon Morris College, A
Lubbock Christian University, B
McLennan Community College, A
McMurry University, B
Midland College, A
Navarro College, A
North Harris College, A
Odessa College, A
Palo Alto College, A
Paul Quinn College, B
Prairie View A&M University, M
St. Edward's University, B
Sam Houston State University, B
Schreiner University, B
South Plains College, A
Sul Ross State University, BM
Tarleton State University, BMO
Texas A&M International University, B
Texas A&M University, MD
Texas A&M University-Commerce, BMD
Texas A&M University-Corpus Christi, B
Texas A&M University-Kingsville, B
Texas Christian University, B
Texas Lutheran University, B
Texas Southern University, BM
Texas State University-San Marcos, M
Texas Wesleyan University, B
Trinity Valley Community College, A
University of Houston, MD
University of the Incarnate Word, BMO
University of Mary Hardin-Baylor, B
The University of Texas at Arlington, M
The University of Texas at El Paso, M
Wayland Baptist University, B
Wharton County Junior College, A
Wiley College, B

Utah

Brigham Young University, BM
Dixie State College of Utah, A
Snow College, A
Southern Utah University, B
University of Utah, B

Utah State University, BM
Utah Valley State College, B
Weber State University, B

Vermont

Castleton State College, B
Johnson State College, B
Lyndon State College, B
Norwich University, B
University of Vermont, B

Virginia

Averett University, BM
Bluefield College, B
Bridgewater College, B
The College of William and Mary, B
Eastern Mennonite University, B
Ferrum College, B
George Mason University, B
Hampton University, B
Liberty University, B
Longwood University, B
Lynchburg College, B
Old Dominion University, BM
Radford University, B
Shenandoah University, B
University of Richmond, B
University of Virginia, BMD
Virginia Commonwealth University, M
Virginia Intermont College, B
Virginia Polytechnic Institute and State University, M

Washington

Central Washington University, BM
Eastern Washington University, BM
Everett Community College, A
Gonzaga University, B
Lower Columbia College, A
Northwest University, B
Pacific Lutheran University, B
Seattle Pacific University, B
Skagit Valley College, A
Tacoma Community College, A
Walla Walla College, B
Washington State University, B
Wenatchee Valley College, A
Western Washington University, BM
Whitworth College, B

West Virginia

Alderson-Broaddus College, B
Bethany College, B
Concord University, B
Davis & Elkins College, B
Fairmont State University, B
Glenville State College, B
Marshall University, BM
Ohio Valley University, B
Potomac State College of West Virginia
    University, A
Salem International University, B
West Liberty State College, B
West Virginia State University, B
West Virginia University, BMD
West Virginia University Institute of Technology, B
West Virginia Wesleyan College, B

Wisconsin

Carroll College, B
Carthage College, B
Concordia University Wisconsin, B
Maranatha Baptist Bible College, B
Ripon College, B
University of Wisconsin-La Crosse, M
University of Wisconsin-Madison, B
University of Wisconsin-Oshkosh, B
University of Wisconsin-River Falls, B
University of Wisconsin-Stevens Point, B
University of Wisconsin-Superior, B
University of Wisconsin-Whitewater, B

Wyoming

Casper College, A
Eastern Wyoming College, A
Laramie County Community College, A

Northwest College, A
University of Wyoming, BM

Alberta

University of Alberta, BMD
University of Lethbridge, B

British Columbia

Trinity Western University, B
The University of British Columbia, M
University College of the Fraser Valley, B
University of Victoria, BM

Manitoba

University of Manitoba, BM

New Brunswick

Université de Moncton, B
University of New Brunswick Fredericton, BM

Newfoundland and Labrador

Memorial University of Newfoundland, BM

Nova Scotia

St. Francis Xavier University, B

Ontario

Brock University, B
Lakehead University, BM
Laurentian University, B
Queen's University at Kingston, B
University of Ottawa, B
University of Toronto, MD
The University of Western Ontario, B
University of Windsor, B
Wilfrid Laurier University, B
York University, B

Quebec

McGill University, BMDO
Université Laval, B
Université de Montréal, BMDO
Université du Québec àChicoutimi, B
Université du Québec àMontréal, B
Université du Québec àTrois-Rivières, M
Université de Sherbrooke, BMO

Saskatchewan

University of Regina, B
University of Saskatchewan, B

PHYSICAL SCIENCE TECHNOLOGIES/TECHNICIANS

Kentucky

Western Kentucky University, A

Missouri

Missouri State University, B

Ohio

The University of Akron, A

West Virginia

Marshall Community and Technical College, A

PHYSICAL SCIENCES

Alabama

Auburn University Montgomery, B
Faulkner University, A
Lawson State Community College, A
Troy University, B

University of North Alabama, B

Arizona

Grand Canyon University, B
Northern Arizona University, B

Arkansas

Arkansas Tech University, B
National Park Community College, A
University of Arkansas at Monticello, B
University of Central Arkansas, B

California

American River College, A
Antelope Valley College, A
Biola University, B
Butte College, A
California Institute of Technology, B
California Polytechnic State University, San Luis
    Obispo, B
California State University, East Bay, B
California State University, Sacramento, B
California State University, Stanislaus, B
Cerritos College, A
Cerro Coso Community College, A
Chaffey College, A
Citrus College, A
College of the Canyons, A
College of San Mateo, A
College of the Siskiyous, A
Columbia College, A
Compton Community College, A
El Camino College, A
Feather River College, A
Folsom Lake College, A
Fresno City College, A
Golden West College, A
Humboldt State University, B
Imperial Valley College, A
La Sierra University, B
Long Beach City College, A
Los Angeles Mission College, A
The Master's College and Seminary, B
Mendocino College, A
Merced College, A
MiraCosta College, A
Mt. San Antonio College, A
Ohlone College, A
Pacific Union College, B
Pasadena City College, A
Reedley College, A
Sacramento City College, A
Saddleback College, A
San Bernardino Valley College, A
San Diego City College, A
San Diego Mesa College, A
San Diego Miramar College, A
San Diego State University, B
San Francisco State University, B
San Joaquin Delta College, A
Santa Rosa Junior College, A
Southwestern College, A
Taft College, A
University of California, Berkeley, B
University of California, Davis, B
University of the Pacific, B
University of Southern California, B
Ventura College, A
Victor Valley College, A

Colorado

Colorado Mountain College, Alpine Campus, A
Colorado Northwestern Community College, A
Colorado State University, B
Lamar Community College, A
Mesa State College, B
Northeastern Junior College, A

Connecticut

Central Connecticut State University, B
Mitchell College, A
Naugatuck Valley Community College, A

Northwestern Connecticut Community College, A

District of Columbia

University of the District of Columbia, A

Florida

Florida State University, B
Miami Dade College, A
Palm Beach Community College, A

Georgia

Abraham Baldwin Agricultural College, A
Augusta State University, B
Georgia Southwestern State University, B
Gordon College, A
South Georgia College, A
Wesleyan College, B

Guam

University of Guam, B

Hawaii

Brigham Young University-Hawaii, B

Idaho

Brigham Young University -Idaho, A
North Idaho College, A

Illinois

City Colleges of Chicago, Harold Washington
    College, A
City Colleges of Chicago, Wilbur Wright College, A
Concordia University, B
Eureka College, B
Highland Community College, A
Judson College, B
Lincoln College, A
Olivet Nazarene University, B
Spoon River College, A
William Rainey Harper College, A

Indiana

Goshen College, B
Taylor University, B
Tri-State University, B

Iowa

Coe College, B
Ellsworth Community College, A
Graceland University, B
Grand View College, B
Iowa Lakes Community College, A
Loras College, B

Kansas

Barton County Community College, A
Cloud County Community College, A
Dodge City Community College, A
Emporia State University, B
Fort Hays State University, B
Fort Scott Community College, A
Highland Community College, A
Hutchinson Community College and Area Vocational
    School, A
Independence Community College, A
Kansas State University, B
McPherson College, B
Neosho County Community College, A
Seward County Community College, A

Kentucky

Asbury College, B
Eastern Kentucky University, B

Louisiana

River Parishes Community College, A

Maryland

Cecil Community College, A
Chesapeake College, A
Frederick Community College, A
Frostburg State University, B
Howard Community College, A
United States Naval Academy, B

University of Maryland, College Park, B
Villa Julie College, A

Massachusetts

Framingham State College, B
Harvard University, B
Roxbury Community College, A
Westfield State College, B
Worcester Polytechnic Institute, B

Michigan

Calvin College, B
Central Michigan University, B
Eastern Michigan University, B
Grand Valley State University, B
Michigan State University, B
Michigan Technological University, B
Northwestern Michigan College, A
Schoolcraft College, A

Minnesota

Bemidji State University, B
The College of St. Scholastica, B
Minnesota State University Mankato, B
Ridgewater College, A
St. Cloud State University, B
Southwest Minnesota State University, B
Vermilion Community College, A
Winona State University, B

Mississippi

East Central Community College, A
Jones County Junior College, A
Mississippi University for Women, B
Southwest Mississippi Community College, A

Missouri

Crowder College, A
Jefferson College, A
Northwest Missouri State University, B
Ozarks Technical Community College, A

Nebraska

Concordia University, B
Doane College, B
Midland Lutheran College, B
Southeast Community College, Beatrice Campus, A
Southeast Community College, Milford Campus, A
Wayne State College, B

Nevada

Western Nevada Community College, A

New Jersey

Middlesex County College, A
Rowan University, B
Union County College, A
William Paterson University of New Jersey, B

New Mexico

Clovis Community College, A
New Mexico Institute of Mining and Technology, B
St. John's College, A
San Juan College, A
Santa Fe Community College, A
University of New Mexico-Gallup, A
Western New Mexico University, B

New York

Bard College, B
Colgate University, B
Fordham University, B
Fulton-Montgomery Community College, A
Long Island University, Brooklyn Campus, B
Roberts Wesleyan College, A
St. Bonaventure University, B
St. John's University, B
Stony Brook University, State University of New York, B
Ulster County Community College, A

North Carolina

Chowan University, B
Lenoir-Rhyne College, B

The University of North Carolina at Chapel Hill, B

North Dakota

Mayville State University, B
Minot State University, B

Ohio

Antioch College, B
Defiance College, B
Ohio University, B
Ohio University-Eastern, B
Otterbein College, B
Shawnee State University, B
University of Dayton, B
University of Rio Grande, B
The University of Toledo, B
Washington State Community College, A
Wittenberg University, B

Oklahoma

Bacone College, A
Carl Albert State College, A
Eastern Oklahoma State College, A
Northeastern Oklahoma Agricultural and Mechanical College, A
Oklahoma Baptist University, B
Redlands Community College, A
Rogers State University, A
Seminole State College, A
Tulsa Community College, A

Oregon

Central Oregon Community College, A
Concordia University, B
Linfield College, B
Linn-Benton Community College, A
Oregon State University, B
Portland Community College, A
Umpqua Community College, A
Warner Pacific College, B

Pennsylvania

Butler County Community College, A
East Stroudsburg University of Pennsylvania, B
Harrisburg Area Community College, A
Juniata College, B
Lehigh Carbon Community College, A
Lincoln University, B
Lock Haven University of Pennsylvania, B
Mansfield University of Pennsylvania, B
Montgomery County Community College, A
Muhlenberg College, B
Pennsylvania College of Technology, A
The Pennsylvania State University at Erie, The Behrend College, B
University of Pittsburgh, B
University of Pittsburgh at Bradford, B
York College of Pennsylvania, B

Puerto Rico

University of Puerto Rico, Mayagüez Campus, B

South Carolina

Charleston Southern University, B

South Dakota

Black Hills State University, B
Dakota State University, B

Tennessee

Freed-Hardeman University, B
Martin Methodist College, A
Roane State Community College, A

Texas

Alvin Community College, A
Amarillo College, A
Angelina College, A
Austin Community College, A
Coastal Bend College, A
Frank Phillips College, A
Hill College of the Hill Junior College District, A
Navarro College, A
Southwestern University, B

Texas A&M International University, B
Trinity Valley Community College, A
University of Houston-Clear Lake, B
Wayland Baptist University, B
Wiley College, B

Utah

Salt Lake Community College, A
Snow College, A
Southern Utah University, B
University of Utah, B
Utah Valley State College, A

Vermont

Bennington College, B
Lyndon State College, B
Saint Michael's College, B

Virginia

Hampton University, B
Radford University, B

Washington

Centralia College, A
Eastern Washington University, B
The Evergreen State College, B
Tacoma Community College, A
Washington State University, B

West Virginia

Mountain State University, B

Wisconsin

Ripon College, B
University of Wisconsin-River Falls, B
University of Wisconsin-Superior, B

Wyoming

Casper College, A
Central Wyoming College, A
Northwest College, A

Alberta

University of Alberta, B

Nova Scotia

St. Francis Xavier University, B

Ontario

Brock University, B
McMaster University, B
Trent University, B
University of Guelph, B
University of Ottawa, B
University of Toronto, B
York University, B

Quebec

Université du Québec àChicoutimi, B

PHYSICAL THERAPIST ASSISTANT

Alabama

Community College of the Air Force, A
George C. Wallace Community College, A
Jefferson State Community College, A
South University, A

Arizona

Apollo College-Westside, Inc., A
GateWay Community College, A
Pima Medical Institute (Tucson), A

Arkansas

Arkansas State University, A
South Arkansas Community College, A
University of Central Arkansas, A

California

Loma Linda University, A
Mount St. Mary's College, A

Ohlone College, A
Sacramento City College, A
San Diego Mesa College, A
Sonoma College (Petaluma), A

Colorado

Pima Medical Institute, A
Pueblo Community College, A

Connecticut

Capital Community College, A
Manchester Community College, A
Naugatuck Valley Community College, A

Delaware

Delaware Technical & Community College,
    Stanton/Wilmington Campus, A

Florida

Central Florida Community College, A
Florida Community College at Jacksonville, A
Gulf Coast Community College, A
Indian River Community College, A
Keiser College (Fort Lauderdale), A
Lake City Community College, A
Manatee Community College, A
Miami Dade College, A
Pasco-Hernando Community College, A
Pensacola Junior College, A
Polk Community College, A
St. Petersburg College, A
South University (West Palm Beach), A

Georgia

Darton College, A
Georgia Highlands College, A
Gwinnett Technical College, A
Middle Georgia College, A
South University, A

Idaho

Idaho State University, A

Illinois

Black Hawk College, A
College of DuPage, A
Kankakee Community College, A
Kaskaskia College, A
Lake Land College, A
Lincoln Land Community College, A
Oakton Community College, A
Southern Illinois University Carbondale, A
Southwestern Illinois College, A

Indiana

Brown Mackie College-South Bend, A
Ivy Tech Community College-East Central, A
University of Evansville, A
University of Indianapolis, A
University of Saint Francis, A

Iowa

North Iowa Area Community College, A
Western Iowa Tech Community College, A

Kansas

Barton County Community College, A
Colby Community College, A
Johnson County Community College, A
Kansas City Kansas Community College, A
Washburn University, A

Kentucky

Ashland Community and Technical College, A
Hazard Community and Technical College, A
Madisonville Community College, A
Southeast Kentucky Community and Technical
    College, A

Louisiana

Delgado Community College, A
Our Lady of the Lake College, A

Southern University at Shreveport, A

Maine

Kennebec Valley Community College, A

Maryland

Allegany College of Maryland, A
Carroll Community College, A
College of Southern Maryland, A
Montgomery College, A

Massachusetts

Becker College, A
Berkshire Community College, A
Cape Cod Community College, A
Massachusetts Bay Community College, A
North Shore Community College, A
Springfield Technical Community College, A

Michigan

Baker College of Flint, A
Baker College of Muskegon, A
Delta College, A
Finlandia University, A
Kellogg Community College, A
Macomb Community College, A
Mott Community College, A

Minnesota

Anoka-Ramsey Community College, A
College of St. Catherine, A
College of St. Catherine-Minneapolis, A
Lake Superior College, A
Northwest Technical College, A

Missouri

Linn State Technical College, A
Missouri Western State University, A
Ozarks Technical Community College, A

Montana

Montana State University-Great Falls College of
    Technology, A

Nebraska

Western Nebraska Community College, A

New Hampshire

Hesser College, A

New Jersey

Essex County College, A
Mercer County Community College, A
Union County College, A

New Mexico

San Juan College, A

New York

Adirondack Community College, A
Broome Community College, A
Dutchess Community College, A
Kingsborough Community College of the City
    University of New York, A
Maria College, A
Nassau Community College, A
New York University, A
Niagara County Community College, A
State University of New York College of Technology
    at Canton, A
Villa Maria College of Buffalo, A

North Carolina

Fayetteville Technical Community College, A
Guilford Technical Community College, A
Martin Community College, A
Rockingham Community College, A
Southwestern Community College, A

Stanly Community College, A

North Dakota

Williston State College, A

Ohio

Central Ohio Technical College, A
Hocking College, A
Lorain County Community College, A
Marion Technical College, A
North Central State College, A
Owens Community College, A
Professional Skills Institute, A
Zane State College, A

Oklahoma

Carl Albert State College, A
Southwestern Oklahoma State University at
    Sayre, A

Pennsylvania

Butler County Community College, A
Central Pennsylvania College, A
Community College of Allegheny County, A
Harcum College, A
Lehigh Carbon Community College, A
Mercyhurst College, B
Mount Aloysius College, A
The Pennsylvania State University DuBois Campus
    of the Commonwealth College, A
The Pennsylvania State University Hazleton
    Campus of the Commonwealth College, A
The Pennsylvania State University Mont Alto
    Campus of the Commonwealth College, A
The Pennsylvania State University Shenango
    Campus of the Commonwealth College, A
University of Pittsburgh at Titusville, A

Puerto Rico

University of Puerto Rico at Humacao, A

Rhode Island

Community College of Rhode Island, A

South Carolina

Midlands Technical College, A

South Dakota

Lake Area Technical Institute, A

Tennessee

Jackson State Community College, A
South College, A
Southwest Tennessee Community College, A
Volunteer State Community College, A

Texas

Angelina College, A
Blinn College, A
El Paso Community College, A
Houston Community College System, A
Kilgore College, A
St. Philip's College, A

Utah

Salt Lake Community College, A

Virginia

Jefferson College of Health Sciences, A

Washington

Everett Community College, A
Green River Community College, A
Spokane Falls Community College, A
Whatcom Community College, A

West Virginia

Marshall Community and Technical College, A
Mountain State University, A

Wisconsin

Gateway Technical College, A
Nicolet Area Technical College, A
Northeast Wisconsin Technical College, A

Western Technical College, A

PHYSICAL THERAPY/THERAPIST

Alabama

Alabama Southern Community College, A
Alabama State University, M
Faulkner University, A
George Corley Wallace State Community College, A
Huntingdon College, B
Lawson State Community College, A
Oakwood College, A
The University of Alabama at Birmingham, D
University of South Alabama, D
Wallace State Community College, A

Arizona

Northern Arizona University, D

Arkansas

Arkansas State University, M
NorthWest Arkansas Community College, A
University of Central Arkansas, ABMD

California

Allan Hancock College, A
Azusa Pacific University, D
California State University, Fresno, BM
California State University, Long Beach, M
California State University, Northridge, M
Cerritos College, A
Chapman University, D
City College of San Francisco, A
De Anza College, A
Hope International University, B
Humboldt State University, M
Loma Linda University, MD
Monterey Peninsula College, A
Mount St. Mary's College, D
Samuel Merritt College, M
San Francisco State University, MD
University of the Pacific, MD
University of Southern California, MD
Vanguard University of Southern California, B

Colorado

Arapahoe Community College, A
Morgan Community College, A
Pueblo Community College, A
Regis University, D

Connecticut

Housatonic Community College, A
Quinnipiac University, BM
Sacred Heart University, BMD
Tunxis Community College, A
University of Connecticut, BM
University of Hartford, BM

Delaware

University of Delaware, D

District of Columbia

The George Washington University, M
Howard University, B

Florida

Broward Community College, A
Daytona Beach Community College, A
Florida Agricultural and Mechanical University, BM
Florida Gulf Coast University, M
Florida International University, M
Hillsborough Community College, A
Indian River Community College, A
Lynn University, A
Manatee Community College, A
Nova Southeastern University, D
Palm Beach Community College, A
Pensacola Junior College, A
Seminole Community College, A
University of Central Florida, M
University of Florida, M

University of Miami, D
University of North Florida, M
University of South Florida, M

Georgia

Andrew College, A
Armstrong Atlantic State University, BM
Athens Technical College, A
Clayton State University, A
Coastal Georgia Community College, A
Dalton State College, A
Emory University, D
Georgia Highlands College, A
Georgia State University, M
Gwinnett Technical College, A
Macon State College, A
Medical College of Georgia, MD
North Georgia College & State University, M
Waycross College, A
Young Harris College, A

Hawaii

Kapiolani Community College, A

Idaho

Brigham Young University -Idaho, A
College of Southern Idaho, A
Idaho State University, D
Northwest Nazarene University, B

Illinois

Bradley University, BD
Danville Area Community College, A
Elmhurst College, B
Governors State University, M
Illinois Central College, A
Morton College, A
Northern Illinois University, BM
Northwestern University, D
Oakton Community College, A
Sauk Valley Community College, A
University of Illinois at Chicago, M

Indiana

Indiana University-Purdue University
    Indianapolis, BM
University of Indianapolis, MD
Vincennes University, A

Iowa

Clarke College, BM
Indian Hills Community College, A
Iowa Central Community College, A
St. Ambrose University, D
Scott Community College, A
Simpson College, B
The University of Iowa, MD

Kansas

Allen County Community College, A
Barton County Community College, A
Butler Community College, A
Colby Community College, A
Cowley County Community College and Area
    Vocational-Technical School, A
Dodge City Community College, A
Donnelly College, A
Highland Community College, A
University of Kansas, MD
Wichita State University, M

Kentucky

Jefferson Community and Technical College, A
Somerset Community College, A
University of Kentucky, BM

West Kentucky Community and Technical College, A

Louisiana

Bossier Parish Community College, A
Louisiana State University Health Sciences
    Center, M

Maine

Husson College, BM
University of New England, BD

Maryland

Baltimore City Community College, A
Coppin State University, B
University of Maryland Eastern Shore, BD

Massachusetts

American International College, BM
Bay State College, A
Boston University, BMD
Eastern Nazarene College, B
Merrimack College, B
Mount Wachusett Community College, A
Northeastern University, B
Simmons College, BD
Springfield College, BM
University of Massachusetts Lowell, M

Michigan

Andrews University, BD
Central Michigan University, D
Grand Valley State University, BMD
Mid Michigan Community College, A
Monroe County Community College, A
Oakland University, MDO
University of Michigan-Flint, D
Wayne State University, M

Minnesota

College of Saint Benedict, B
College of St. Catherine, MD
The College of St. Scholastica, D
Concordia College, B
Gustavus Adolphus College, B
Hamline University, B
St. Cloud State University, B
Saint John's University, B
Saint Mary's University of Minnesota, B
University of Minnesota, Morris, B
University of Minnesota, Twin Cities Campus, BMD
Winona State University, B

Mississippi

Alcorn State University, B
East Central Community College, A
Holmes Community College, A
Meridian Community College, A
Northeast Mississippi Community College, A
University of Mississippi Medical Center, M

Missouri

Maryville University of Saint Louis, M
Missouri State University, M
Penn Valley Community College, A
Rockhurst University, D
St. Louis Community College at Meramec, A
Saint Louis University, BMD
Sanford-Brown College (Hazelwood), A
Sanford-Brown College (North Kansas City), A
Southwest Baptist University, MD
University of Missouri-Columbia, M
Washington University in St. Louis, DO

Montana

The University of Montana-Missoula, BD

Nebraska

Clarkson College, A
Creighton University, D
Northeast Community College, A
University of Nebraska Medical Center, D

Western Nebraska Community College, A

Nevada

University of Nevada, Las Vegas, MD

New Hampshire

Franklin Pierce College, M
New Hampshire Community Technical College,
Manchester/Stratham, A

New Jersey

Essex County College, A
The Richard Stockton College of New Jersey, M
Rutgers, The State University of New Jersey,
Camden, M
Seton Hall University, D

New Mexico

Luna Community College, A
University of New Mexico, M

New York

Clarkson University, M
College of Staten Island of the City University of
New York, BM
Daemen College, D
Dominican College, MD
D'Youville College, BMDO
Fiorello H. LaGuardia Community College of the
City University of New York, A
Genesee Community College, A
Herkimer County Community College, A
Hunter College of the City University of New
York, M
Ithaca College, BD
Kingsborough Community College of the City
University of New York, A
Long Island University, Brooklyn Campus, BD
Mercy College, M
Mount Saint Mary College, B
Nazareth College of Rochester, B
New York Institute of Technology, BMD
New York University, MD
Onondaga Community College, A
Orange County Community College, A
Russell Sage College, B
State University of New York at Buffalo, D
State University of New York Downstate Medical
Center, B
State University of New York Upstate Medical
University, MD
Stony Brook University, State University of New
York, MD
Suffolk County Community College, A
Touro College, AM

North Carolina

Caldwell Community College and Technical
Institute, A
Central Piedmont Community College, A
Duke University, D
East Carolina University, M
Elon University, D
Louisburg College, A
Nash Community College, A
Southwestern Community College, A
The University of North Carolina at Chapel Hill, MD
Western Carolina University, M

North Dakota

Turtle Mountain Community College, A
University of Mary, MD
University of North Dakota, BMD

Ohio

Bowling Green State University, B
Clark State Community College, A
Cleveland State University, BM
College of Mount St. Joseph, MD
James A. Rhodes State College, A
Kent State University, Ashtabula Campus, A
Kent State University, East Liverpool Campus, A
Mount Vernon Nazarene University, B
The Ohio State University, BM
Ohio University, D

Shawnee State University, A
Sinclair Community College, A
Stark State College of Technology, A
University of Cincinnati, A
University of Cincinnati Raymond Walters College, A
The University of Findlay, BM
The University of Toledo, B
Walsh University, M
Youngstown State University, M

Oklahoma

Langston University, B
Murray State College, A
Northeastern Oklahoma Agricultural and Mechanical
College, A
Oklahoma City Community College, A
Oklahoma Wesleyan University, B
Rose State College, A
Tulsa Community College, A
University of Oklahoma Health Sciences Center, M

Oregon

Mt. Hood Community College, A
Pacific University, D

Pennsylvania

Alvernia College, A
Arcadia University, D
Chatham College, BD
College Misericordia, M
Drexel University, MDO
Duquesne University, D
Gannon University, MD
Keystone College, B
Manor College, A
Mercyhurst College, A
Mount Aloysius College, B
Neumann College, MD
Saint Francis University, BD
Saint Vincent College, B
Slippery Rock University of Pennsylvania, D
Temple University, MD
Thomas Jefferson University, BMD
University of Pittsburgh, D
University of the Sciences in Philadelphia, D
The University of Scranton, MD
Widener University, MD

Puerto Rico

University of Puerto Rico, Medical Sciences
Campus, BM
University of Puerto Rico at Ponce, A

Rhode Island

University of Rhode Island, M

South Carolina

Florence-Darlington Technical College, A
Greenville Technical College, A
Medical University of South Carolina, D
Trident Technical College, A

South Dakota

The University of South Dakota, M

Tennessee

Belmont University, D
Chattanooga State Technical Community College, A
Columbia State Community College, A
East Tennessee State University, D
Martin Methodist College, A
Roane State Community College, A
Southern Adventist University, A
Tennessee State University, B
The University of Tennessee at Chattanooga, BD

Texas

Amarillo College, A
Angelo State University, M
Baylor University, MD
Clarendon College, A
Hardin-Simmons University, D
Laredo Community College, A
McLennan Community College, A
Odessa College, A

South Plains College, A
Tarleton State University, B
Tarrant County College District, A
Texas Southern University, B
Texas State University-San Marcos, M
Texas Woman's University, MD
The University of Texas at El Paso, M
The University of Texas Health Science Center at
San Antonio, M
The University of Texas Medical Branch, M
The University of Texas Southwestern Medical
Center at Dallas, M
Wharton County Junior College, A

Utah

University of Utah, BMD

Vermont

University of Vermont, D

Virginia

Hampton University, BD
John Tyler Community College, A
Marymount University, MD
Northern Virginia Community College, A
Old Dominion University, D
Shenandoah University, D
Virginia Commonwealth University, D
Virginia Highlands Community College, A
Wytheville Community College, A

Washington

Eastern Washington University, BD
Tacoma Community College, A
University of Puget Sound, D
University of Washington, BD

West Virginia

Fairmont State University, A
West Virginia University, BM
Wheeling Jesuit University, BD

Wisconsin

Blackhawk Technical College, A
Carroll College, M
Concordia University Wisconsin, BMD
Gateway Technical College, A
Marquette University, BM
Milwaukee Area Technical College, A
Northeast Wisconsin Technical College, A
University of Wisconsin-La Crosse, BM
University of Wisconsin-Milwaukee, B

Alberta

University of Alberta, BM

British Columbia

The University of British Columbia, B

Manitoba

University of Manitoba, B

Nova Scotia

Dalhousie University, B

Ontario

McMaster University, M
Queen's University at Kingston, B
University of Ottawa, B
The University of Western Ontario, BM

Quebec

McGill University, B
Université Laval, B

Université de Montréal, B

Saskatchewan

University of Saskatchewan, B

PHYSICIAN ASSISTANT

Alabama

The University of Alabama at Birmingham, B
University of South Alabama, M

Arizona

Midwestern University, Glendale Campus, M

California

California State University, Dominguez Hills, BM
Charles R. Drew University of Medicine and
    Science, B
Foothill College, A
Hartnell College, A
Loma Linda University, M
Samuel Merritt College, M
Santa Rosa Junior College, A
University of Southern California, M

Colorado

Regis University, M

Connecticut

Quinnipiac University, BM
Yale University, M

District of Columbia

The George Washington University, BMO
Howard University, B

Florida

Barry University, M
Manatee Community College, A
Nova Southeastern University, BM
University of Florida, M

Georgia

Andrew College, A
Coastal Georgia Community College, A
Dalton State College, A
Darton College, A
Emory University, M
Georgia Highlands College, A
Medical College of Georgia, BM
South University, BM

Idaho

Boise State University, B
College of Southern Idaho, A
Idaho State University, M

Illinois

City Colleges of Chicago, Malcolm X College, A
Elmhurst College, B
Southern Illinois University Carbondale, B
University of St. Francis, M

Indiana

Butler University, B
University of Saint Francis, BM

Iowa

The University of Iowa, M

Kansas

Barton County Community College, A
Central Christian College of Kansas, A

Wichita State University, B

Kentucky

University of Kentucky, M

Maine

University of New England, BM

Maryland

Towson University, M

Massachusetts

Northeastern University, M
Springfield College, BM

Michigan

Central Michigan University, M
Delta College, A
Grand Valley State University, BM
University of Detroit Mercy, M
Wayne State University, M
Western Michigan University, M

Minnesota

Augsburg College, BM
Minnesota School of Business, A
Minnesota School of Business-Brooklyn Center, A
Minnesota School of Business-Plymouth, A
Minnesota School of Business-St. Cloud, A
Minnesota School of Business-Shakopee, A

Missouri

Missouri State University, M
Saint Louis University, BM

Montana

Rocky Mountain College, B

Nebraska

Peru State College, B
Union College, B
University of Nebraska Medical Center, M

New Jersey

Seton Hall University, M

New Mexico

University of New Mexico, B

New York

City College of the City University of New York, B
College of Staten Island of the City University of
    New York, B
Daemen College, BM
D'Youville College, B
Hofstra University, B
Le Moyne College, B
Long Island University, Brooklyn Campus, B
Mercy College, M
New York Institute of Technology, B
Pace University, B
Rochester Institute of Technology, B
St. Francis College, B
St. John's University, B
State University of New York Downstate Medical
    Center, B
Stony Brook University, State University of New
    York, B
Touro College, B
Wagner College, BM

North Carolina

Catawba College, B
Duke University, M
East Carolina University, BM
Gardner-Webb University, B
High Point University, B
Lenoir-Rhyne College, B
Methodist College, B
Salem College, B

Wake Forest University, B

North Dakota

University of North Dakota, M

Ohio

Cuyahoga Community College, A
Kettering College of Medical Arts, AB
Marietta College, M
The University of Findlay, B

Oklahoma

Tulsa Community College, A

Oregon

Pacific University, M

Pennsylvania

Chatham College, M
DeSales University, M
Drexel University, M
Duquesne University, B
Gannon University, BM
King's College, M
Lock Haven University of Pennsylvania, M
Marywood University, BM
Philadelphia University, BM
Saint Francis University, BM
Saint Vincent College, B
Seton Hill University, BM

South Carolina

Medical University of South Carolina, M

South Dakota

The University of South Dakota, M

Tennessee

Bethel College, B
Southern Adventist University, A
Trevecca Nazarene University, M

Texas

Sam Houston State University, B
The University of Texas Health Science Center at
    San Antonio, BM
The University of Texas Medical Branch, M
The University of Texas Southwestern Medical
    Center at Dallas, M

Utah

University of Utah, M

Virginia

James Madison University, M
Jefferson College of Health Sciences, B
Shenandoah University, M

Washington

University of Washington, B

West Virginia

Alderson-Broaddus College, B
Fairmont State Community & Technical College, A
Mountain State University, M

Wisconsin

Bryant and Stratton College, Wauwatosa Campus, A
Marquette University, BM
University of Wisconsin-La Crosse, BM
University of Wisconsin-Madison, B

PHYSICS

Alabama

Alabama Agricultural and Mechanical
    University, BMD
Athens State University, B
Auburn University, BMD
Birmingham-Southern College, B
Chattahoochee Valley Community College, A
Jacksonville State University, B

Miles College, B
Samford University, B
Stillman College, B
Talladega College, B
Tuskegee University, B
The University of Alabama, BMD
The University of Alabama at Birmingham, BMD
The University of Alabama in Huntsville, BMD
University of North Alabama, B
University of South Alabama, B

Alaska

University of Alaska Fairbanks, BMD

Arizona

Arizona State University, BMD
Arizona Western College, A
Eastern Arizona College, A
Embry-Riddle Aeronautical University, B
Northern Arizona University, B
South Mountain Community College, A
The University of Arizona, BMD

Arkansas

Arkansas State University, B
Harding University, B
Henderson State University, B
Hendrix College, B
Ouachita Baptist University, B
Phillips Community College of the University of
   Arkansas, A
University of Arkansas, BMD
University of Arkansas at Little Rock, B
University of Arkansas at Pine Bluff, B
University of Central Arkansas, B

California

Allan Hancock College, A
Azusa Pacific University, B
Bakersfield College, A
California Institute of Technology, BD
California Lutheran University, B
California Polytechnic State University, San Luis
   Obispo, B
California State Polytechnic University, Pomona, B
California State University, Bakersfield, B
California State University, Chico, B
California State University, Dominguez Hills, B
California State University, East Bay, B
California State University, Fresno, BM
California State University, Fullerton, BM
California State University, Long Beach, BM
California State University, Los Angeles, BM
California State University, Northridge, BM
California State University, Sacramento, B
California State University, San Bernardino, B
California State University, Stanislaus, B
Cerritos College, A
Chabot College, A
Chaffey College, A
Claremont McKenna College, B
College of the Desert, A
College of Marin, A
College of San Mateo, A
College of the Siskiyous, A
Columbia College, A
Compton Community College, A
Contra Costa College, A
Crafton Hills College, A
Cuesta College, A
Cuyamaca College, A
Cypress College, A
De Anza College, A
El Camino College, A
Folsom Lake College, A
Foothill College, A
Fullerton College, A
Grossmont College, A
Harvey Mudd College, B
Humboldt State University, B
Los Angeles City College, A
Los Angeles Harbor College, A
Loyola Marymount University, B
MiraCosta College, A
Monterey Peninsula College, A
Occidental College, B

Orange Coast College, A
Pacific Union College, B
Pasadena City College, A
Pitzer College, B
Point Loma Nazarene University, B
Pomona College, B
Saddleback College, A
Saint Mary's College of California, B
San Bernardino Valley College, A
San Diego Mesa College, A
San Diego Miramar College, A
San Diego State University, BM
San Francisco State University, BM
San Jose State University, BM
Santa Ana College, A
Santa Barbara City College, A
Santa Clara University, B
Santa Monica College, A
Santa Rosa Junior College, A
Santiago Canyon College, A
Scripps College, B
Skyline College, A
Solano Community College, A
Sonoma State University, B
Southwestern College, A
Stanford University, BD
University of California, Berkeley, BD
University of California, Davis, BMD
University of California, Irvine, BMDO
University of California, Los Angeles, BMD
University of California, Riverside, BMD
University of California, San Diego, BMD
University of California, Santa Barbara, BD
University of California, Santa Cruz, BMD
University of La Verne, B
University of the Pacific, B
University of Redlands, B
University of San Diego, B
University of San Francisco, B
University of Southern California, BMD
West Hills Community College, A
West Los Angeles College, A
West Valley College, A
Westmont College, B
Whittier College, B

Colorado

The Colorado College, B
Colorado School of Mines, MD
Colorado State University, BMD
Colorado State University-Pueblo, B
Fort Lewis College, B
Lamar Community College, A
Mesa State College, AB
Metropolitan State College of Denver, B
Red Rocks Community College, A
United States Air Force Academy, B
University of Colorado at Boulder, BMD
University of Colorado at Colorado Springs, B
University of Colorado at Denver and Health
   Sciences Center - Downtown Denver Campus, B
University of Denver, BMD
University of Northern Colorado, B
Western State College of Colorado, B

Connecticut

Central Connecticut State University, BM
Fairfield University, B
Southern Connecticut State University, B
Trinity College, B
University of Connecticut, BMD
University of Hartford, B
Wesleyan University, BMD
Yale University, BD

Delaware

Delaware State University, BM
University of Delaware, BMD

District of Columbia

American University, BM
The Catholic University of America, BMD
Gallaudet University, B
The George Washington University, BMD
Georgetown University, B
Howard University, BMD

University of the District of Columbia, B

Florida

Bethune-Cookman College, B
Daytona Beach Community College, A
Eckerd College, B
Embry-Riddle Aeronautical University, B
Florida Agricultural and Mechanical University, BMD
Florida Atlantic University, BMD
Florida Institute of Technology, BMD
Florida International University, BMD
Florida State University, BMD
Indian River Community College, A
Jacksonville University, B
Manatee Community College, A
Miami Dade College, A
New College of Florida, B
Okaloosa-Walton College, A
Pensacola Junior College, A
Rollins College, B
Stetson University, B
University of Central Florida, BMD
University of Florida, BMD
University of Miami, BMD
University of North Florida, B
University of South Florida, BMD
University of West Florida, B

Georgia

Agnes Scott College, B
Armstrong Atlantic State University, B
Atlanta Metropolitan College, A
Augusta State University, B
Berry College, B
Clark Atlanta University, BM
Clayton State University, A
Coastal Georgia Community College, A
Covenant College, B
Dalton State College, A
Darton College, A
Emory University, BD
Gainesville College, A
Georgia Institute of Technology, BMD
Georgia Perimeter College, A
Georgia Southern University, B
Georgia State University, BMD
Macon State College, A
Mercer University, B
Morehouse College, B
North Georgia College & State University, B
Oglethorpe University, B
Piedmont College, B
South Georgia College, A
Southern Polytechnic State University, B
Spelman College, B
University of Georgia, BMD
University of West Georgia, B
Valdosta State University, B
Wesleyan College, B
Young Harris College, A

Hawaii

University of Hawaii at Hilo, B
University of Hawaii at Manoa, BMD

Idaho

Albertson College of Idaho, B
Boise State University, B
Brigham Young University -Idaho, A
College of Southern Idaho, A
Idaho State University, ABM
North Idaho College, A
Northwest Nazarene University, B
University of Idaho, BMD

Illinois

Augustana College, B
Benedictine University, B
Bradley University, B
Chicago State University, B
City Colleges of Chicago, Harold Washington
   College, A
City Colleges of Chicago, Kennedy-King College, A
City Colleges of Chicago, Olive-Harvey College, A
DePaul University, BM

Eastern Illinois University, B
Elmhurst College, B
Greenville College, B
Highland Community College, A
Illinois College, B
Illinois Institute of Technology, BMD
Illinois State University, B
Illinois Wesleyan University, B
John A. Logan College, A
Knox College, B
Lake Forest College, B
Lewis University, B
Loyola University Chicago, B
MacMurray College, B
Millikin University, B
Monmouth College, B
North Central College, B
North Park University, B
Northeastern Illinois University, B
Northern Illinois University, BMD
Northwestern University, BMD
Principia College, B
Sauk Valley Community College, A
Southern Illinois University Carbondale, BMD
Southern Illinois University Edwardsville, BM
Spoon River College, A
University of Chicago, BMD
University of Illinois at Chicago, BMD
University of Illinois at Urbana-Champaign, BMD
Western Illinois University, BM
Wheaton College, B

Indiana

Anderson University, B
Ball State University, BM
Bethel College, B
Butler University, B
DePauw University, B
Earlham College, B
Goshen College, B
Hanover College, B
Indiana State University, B
Indiana University Bloomington, BMD
Indiana University-Purdue University Fort Wayne, B
Indiana University-Purdue University
  Indianapolis, BMD
Indiana University South Bend, B
Manchester College, B
Purdue University, BMD
Purdue University Calumet, B
Purdue University North Central, B
Rose-Hulman Institute of Technology, B
Taylor University, B
University of Evansville, B
University of Indianapolis, B
University of Notre Dame, BD
Valparaiso University, B
Vincennes University, A
Wabash College, B

Iowa

Buena Vista University, B
Central College, B
Coe College, B
Cornell College, B
Dordt College, B
Drake University, B
Grinnell College, B
Iowa State University of Science and
  Technology, BMD
Loras College, B
Luther College, B
Morningside College, B
St. Ambrose University, B
The University of Iowa, BMD
University of Northern Iowa, B
Wartburg College, B

Kansas

Allen County Community College, A
Baker University, B
Barton County Community College, A
Benedictine College, B
Bethel College, B
Butler Community College, A
Dodge City Community College, A

Emporia State University, BM
Fort Hays State University, B
Kansas State University, BMD
Kansas Wesleyan University, B
Pittsburg State University, BM
Southwestern College, B
University of Kansas, BMD
Washburn University, B
Wichita State University, BM

Kentucky

Berea College, B
Centre College, B
Eastern Kentucky University, B
Georgetown College, B
Kentucky Wesleyan College, B
Morehead State University, B
Murray State University, B
Northern Kentucky University, B
Thomas More College, AB
Transylvania University, B
University of the Cumberlands, B
University of Kentucky, BMD
University of Louisville, BMD
Western Kentucky University, B

Louisiana

Centenary College of Louisiana, B
Dillard University, B
Grambling State University, B
Louisiana College, B
Louisiana State University and Agricultural and
  Mechanical College, BMD
Louisiana State University in Shreveport, B
Louisiana Tech University, BMD
Loyola University New Orleans, B
McNeese State University, B
Northwestern State University of Louisiana, B
Southeastern Louisiana University, B
Southern University and Agricultural and Mechanical
  College, BM
Southern University at New Orleans, B
Tulane University, BMD
University of Louisiana at Lafayette, BM
University of New Orleans, BMD
Xavier University of Louisiana, B

Maine

Bates College, B
Bowdoin College, B
Colby College, B
University of Maine, BMD
University of Southern Maine, B

Maryland

Cecil Community College, A
College of Notre Dame of Maryland, B
Frostburg State University, B
Goucher College, B
The Johns Hopkins University, BD
Loyola College in Maryland, B
McDaniel College, B
Morgan State University, B
St. Mary's College of Maryland, B
Salisbury University, B
Towson University, B
United States Naval Academy, B
University of Maryland, Baltimore County, BMD
University of Maryland, College Park, BMD
Washington College, B

Massachusetts

Amherst College, B
Boston College, BMD
Boston University, BMD
Brandeis University, BMD
Bridgewater State College, B
Bunker Hill Community College, A
Clark University, BMD
College of the Holy Cross, B
Curry College, B
Eastern Nazarene College, B
Gordon College, B
Hampshire College, B
Harvard University, BMD

Holyoke Community College, A
Massachusetts College of Liberal Arts, B
Massachusetts Institute of Technology, BMD
Mount Holyoke College, B
Northeastern University, BMD
Simon's Rock College of Bard, B
Smith College, B
Suffolk University, B
Tufts University, BMD
University of Massachusetts Amherst, BMD
University of Massachusetts Boston, B
University of Massachusetts Dartmouth, BM
University of Massachusetts Lowell, BMD
Wellesley College, B
Wheaton College, B
Williams College, B
Worcester Polytechnic Institute, BMD

Michigan

Adrian College, AB
Albion College, B
Alma College, B
Andrews University, B
Aquinas College, B
Calvin College, B
Central Michigan University, BM
Concordia University, B
Eastern Michigan University, BM
Grand Valley State University, B
Hillsdale College, B
Hope College, B
Kalamazoo College, B
Kellogg Community College, A
Kettering University, B
Lawrence Technological University, B
Michigan State University, BMD
Michigan Technological University, BMD
Oakland University, BMD
Saginaw Valley State University, B
University of Michigan, MD
University of Michigan-Dearborn, B
University of Michigan-Flint, B
Wayne State University, BMD
Western Michigan University, BMD

Minnesota

Augsburg College, B
Bemidji State University, B
Bethel University, B
Carleton College, B
College of Saint Benedict, B
College of St. Catherine, B
Concordia College, B
Gustavus Adolphus College, B
Hamline University, B
Macalester College, B
Minnesota State University Mankato, BM
Minnesota State University Moorhead, B
St. Cloud State University, B
Saint John's University, B
St. Olaf College, B
University of Minnesota, Duluth, BM
University of Minnesota, Morris, B
University of Minnesota, Twin Cities Campus, BMD
University of St. Thomas, B
Vermilion Community College, A
Winona State University, B

Mississippi

Jackson State University, B
Millsaps College, B
Mississippi College, B
Mississippi State University, BMD
Tougaloo College, B
University of Mississippi, BMD
University of Southern Mississippi, BM

Missouri

Central Methodist University, B
Central Missouri State University, B
Drury University, B
East Central College, A
Lincoln University, B
Missouri Southern State University, B
Missouri State University, B
Northwest Missouri State University, B

Rockhurst University, B
Saint Louis University, B
Southeast Missouri State University, B
Truman State University, B
University of Missouri-Columbia, BMD
University of Missouri-Kansas City, BMD
University of Missouri-Rolla, BMD
University of Missouri-St. Louis, BMD
Washington University in St. Louis, BMD
Westminster College, B
William Jewell College, B

Montana

Montana State University, BMD
The University of Montana-Missoula, B

Nebraska

Chadron State College, B
Creighton University, BM
Doane College, B
Hastings College, B
Nebraska Wesleyan University, B
Northeast Community College, A
Union College, B
University of Nebraska at Kearney, B
University of Nebraska-Lincoln, BMD
University of Nebraska at Omaha, B
Western Nebraska Community College, A

Nevada

Great Basin College, A
University of Nevada, Las Vegas, BMD
University of Nevada, Reno, BMD

New Hampshire

Dartmouth College, BMD
University of New Hampshire, BMD

New Jersey

Bergen Community College, A
Brookdale Community College, A
Burlington County College, A
The College of New Jersey, B
Drew University, B
Georgian Court University, B
Mercer County Community College, A
Middlesex County College, A
Montclair State University, B
New Jersey City University, B
New Jersey Institute of Technology, B
Princeton University, BD
Ramapo College of New Jersey, B
The Richard Stockton College of New Jersey, B
Rider University, B
Rutgers, The State University of New Jersey,
   Camden, B
Rutgers, The State University of New Jersey, New
   Brunswick/Piscataway, BMD
Rutgers, The State University of New Jersey,
   Newark, B
Saint Peter's College, B
Salem Community College, A
Seton Hall University, B
Stevens Institute of Technology, BMDO

New Mexico

Eastern New Mexico University, B
New Mexico Institute of Mining and
   Technology, BMD
New Mexico Military Institute, A
New Mexico State University, BMD
St. John's College, B
San Juan College, A
University of New Mexico, BMD

New York

Adelphi University, B
Alfred University, B
Bard College, B
Barnard College, B
Brooklyn College of the City University of New
   York, BMD
Buffalo State College, State University of New
   York, B
Canisius College, B

City College of the City University of New
   York, BMD
Clarkson University, BMD
Colgate University, B
College of Mount Saint Vincent, B
The College of New Rochelle, B
College of Staten Island of the City University of
   New York, B
Columbia College, B
Columbia University, School of General Studies, B
Cornell University, BMD
Excelsior College, B
Finger Lakes Community College, A
Fordham University, B
Hamilton College, B
Hartwick College, B
Hobart and William Smith Colleges, B
Hofstra University, B
Houghton College, B
Hunter College of the City University of New
   York, BMD
Iona College, B
Ithaca College, B
Kingsborough Community College of the City
   University of New York, A
Le Moyne College, B
Lehman College of the City University of New
   York, B
Long Island University, Brooklyn Campus, B
Long Island University, C.W. Post Campus, B
Manhattan College, B
Manhattanville College, B
Monroe Community College, A
New York Institute of Technology, B
New York University, BMD
Pace University, B
Polytechnic University, Brooklyn Campus, BMD
Queens College of the City University of New
   York, BMD
Rensselaer Polytechnic Institute, MD
Roberts Wesleyan College, B
Rochester Institute of Technology, AB
St. Bonaventure University, B
St. John Fisher College, B
St. John's University, B
St. Lawrence University, B
Sarah Lawrence College, B
Siena College, B
Skidmore College, B
State University of New York at Binghamton, BM
State University of New York at Buffalo, BMD
State University of New York College of Agriculture
   and Technology at Morrisville, A
State University of New York College at
   Brockport, B
State University of New York College at Cortland, B
State University of New York College at Geneseo, B
State University of New York College at Oneonta, B
State University of New York College at Potsdam, B
State University of New York, Fredonia, B
State University of New York at New Paltz, B
State University of New York at Oswego, B
State University of New York at Plattsburgh, B
Stony Brook University, State University of New
   York, BMD
Syracuse University, BMD
Union College, B
United States Military Academy, B
University at Albany, State University of New
   York, BMD
University of Rochester, BMD
Utica College, B
Vassar College, B
Wagner College, B
Wells College, B
Yeshiva University, B
York College of the City University of New York, B

North Carolina

Appalachian State University, B
Davidson College, B
Duke University, BMD
East Carolina University, BMD
Elizabeth City State University, B
Elon University, B
Guilford College, B

Johnson C. Smith University, B
Lenoir-Rhyne College, B
Louisburg College, A
North Carolina Agricultural and Technical State
   University, B
North Carolina Central University, B
North Carolina State University, BMD
Shaw University, B
The University of North Carolina at Asheville, B
The University of North Carolina at Chapel
   Hill, BMD
The University of North Carolina at Charlotte, B
The University of North Carolina at Greensboro, B
The University of North Carolina at Pembroke, B
The University of North Carolina Wilmington, B
Wake Forest University, BMD

North Dakota

Minot State University, B
North Dakota State University, BMD
University of North Dakota, BMD

Ohio

Antioch College, B
Ashland University, B
Baldwin-Wallace College, B
Bluffton University, B
Bowling Green State University, BM
Case Western Reserve University, MD
Cedarville University, B
Cleveland State University, BM
The College of Wooster, B
Denison University, B
Heidelberg College, B
Hiram College, B
John Carroll University, BM
Kent State University, BMD
Kenyon College, B
Lorain County Community College, A
Marietta College, B
Miami University, BM
Miami University Hamilton, B
Miami University-Middletown Campus, A
Mount Union College, B
Muskingum College, B
Oberlin College, B
Ohio Northern University, B
The Ohio State University, BMD
Ohio University, BMD
Ohio Wesleyan University, B
Otterbein College, B
The University of Akron, BM
University of Cincinnati, BMD
University of Dayton, B
The University of Toledo, BMD
Wittenberg University, B
Wright State University, BM
Xavier University, B
Youngstown State University, B

Oklahoma

Cameron University, B
East Central University, B
Northeastern State University, B
Northwestern Oklahoma State University, B
Oklahoma Baptist University, B
Oklahoma City Community College, A
Oklahoma City University, B
Oklahoma State University, BMD
Oral Roberts University, B
Rose State College, A
Southern Nazarene University, B
Southwestern Oklahoma State University, B
Tulsa Community College, A
University of Central Oklahoma, B
University of Oklahoma, BMD
University of Science and Arts of Oklahoma, B
University of Tulsa, B

Oregon

Eastern Oregon University, B
Lewis & Clark College, B
Linfield College, B
Linn-Benton Community College, A
Oregon State University, BMD
Pacific University, B

Portland State University, BMD
Reed College, B
Southern Oregon University, B
University of Oregon, BMD
University of Portland, B
Willamette University, B

Pennsylvania

Albright College, B
Allegheny College, B
Bloomsburg University of Pennsylvania, B
Bryn Mawr College, BMD
Bucknell University, B
California University of Pennsylvania, B
Carnegie Mellon University, BD
Chatham College, B
Clarion University of Pennsylvania, B
Community College of Allegheny County, A
Dickinson College, B
Drexel University, BMD
Duquesne University, B
East Stroudsburg University of Pennsylvania, B
Edinboro University of Pennsylvania, B
Elizabethtown College, B
Franklin and Marshall College, B
Geneva College, B
Gettysburg College, B
Grove City College, B
Haverford College, B
Indiana University of Pennsylvania, BM
Juniata College, B
Kutztown University of Pennsylvania, B
Lafayette College, B
Lebanon Valley College, B
Lehigh University, BMD
Lincoln University, B
Lock Haven University of Pennsylvania, B
Lycoming College, B
Mansfield University of Pennsylvania, B
Mercyhurst College, B
Messiah College, B
Millersville University of Pennsylvania, B
Moravian College, B
Muhlenberg College, B
Northampton County Area Community College, A
The Pennsylvania State University Abington College, B
The Pennsylvania State University Altoona College, B
The Pennsylvania State University Beaver Campus of the Commonwealth College, B
The Pennsylvania State University Berks Campus of the Berks-Lehigh Valley College, B
The Pennsylvania State University Delaware County Campus of the Commonwealth College, B
The Pennsylvania State University DuBois Campus of the Commonwealth College, B
The Pennsylvania State University at Erie, The Behrend College, B
The Pennsylvania State University Fayette Campus of the Commonwealth College, B
The Pennsylvania State University Hazleton Campus of the Commonwealth College, B
The Pennsylvania State University, Lehigh Valley Campus of the Berks-Lehigh Valley College, B
The Pennsylvania State University McKeesport Campus of the Commonwealth College, B
The Pennsylvania State University Mont Alto Campus of the Commonwealth College, B
The Pennsylvania State University New Kensington Campus of the Commonwealth College, B
The Pennsylvania State University Schuylkill Campus of the Capital College, B
The Pennsylvania State University Shenango Campus of the Commonwealth College, B
The Pennsylvania State University University Park Campus, BMD
The Pennsylvania State University Wilkes-Barre Campus of the Commonwealth College, B
The Pennsylvania State University Worthington Scranton Campus of the Commonwealth College, B
The Pennsylvania State University York Campus of the Commonwealth College, B
Saint Joseph's University, B
Saint Vincent College, B

Seton Hill University, B
Shippensburg University of Pennsylvania, B
Slippery Rock University of Pennsylvania, B
Susquehanna University, B
Swarthmore College, B
Temple University, BMD
Thiel College, B
University of Pennsylvania, BMD
University of Pittsburgh, BMD
The University of Scranton, B
Ursinus College, B
Villanova University, B
Washington & Jefferson College, B
West Chester University of Pennsylvania, B
Westminster College, B
Widener University, B
York College of Pennsylvania, A

Puerto Rico

Inter American University of Puerto Rico, Metropolitan Campus, B
Pontifical Catholic University of Puerto Rico, B
University of Puerto Rico at Humacao, B
University of Puerto Rico, Mayagüez Campus, BM
University of Puerto Rico, Río Piedras, MD

Rhode Island

Brown University, BMD
Rhode Island College, B
University of Rhode Island, BMD

South Carolina

Benedict College, B
Bob Jones University, B
The Citadel, The Military College of South Carolina, B
Clemson University, BMD
Coastal Carolina University, B
College of Charleston, B
Erskine College, B
Francis Marion University, B
Furman University, B
Presbyterian College, B
South Carolina State University, B
University of South Carolina, BMD
Wofford College, B

South Dakota

Augustana College, B
South Dakota School of Mines and Technology, BMD
South Dakota State University, BM
The University of South Dakota, B

Tennessee

Austin Peay State University, B
Belmont University, B
Christian Brothers University, B
Columbia State Community College, A
East Tennessee State University, B
Fisk University, BM
King College, B
Lane College, B
Lipscomb University, B
Middle Tennessee State University, B
Rhodes College, B
Sewanee: The University of the South, B
Southern Adventist University, B
Tennessee State University, B
Tennessee Technological University, B
Trevecca Nazarene University, B
Union University, B
University of Memphis, BM
The University of Tennessee, BMD
The University of Tennessee at Chattanooga, B
Vanderbilt University, BMD

Texas

Abilene Christian University, B
Amarillo College, A
Angelo State University, B
Austin College, B
Austin Community College, A
Baylor University, BMD
Blinn College, A

Brazosport College, A
Coastal Bend College, A
Del Mar College, A
El Paso Community College, A
Grayson County College, A
Hardin-Simmons University, B
Hill College of the Hill Junior College District, A
Houston Baptist University, B
Jarvis Christian College, B
Kilgore College, A
Lamar University, B
Lee College, A
Lon Morris College, A
McMurry University, B
Midland College, A
Midwestern State University, B
Navarro College, A
Odessa College, A
Palo Alto College, A
Prairie View A&M University, B
Rice University, BMD
St. Mary's University of San Antonio, B
Sam Houston State University, B
Southern Methodist University, BMD
Southwestern Adventist University, B
Southwestern University, B
Stephen F. Austin State University, BM
Tarleton State University, B
Texarkana College, A
Texas A&M International University, M
Texas A&M University, BMD
Texas A&M University-Commerce, BM
Texas A&M University-Kingsville, B
Texas Christian University, BMD
Texas Lutheran University, B
Texas Southern University, B
Texas State University-San Marcos, BM
Texas Tech University, BMD
Trinity University, B
University of Dallas, B
University of Houston, BMD
University of Houston-Downtown, B
University of North Texas, BMD
The University of Texas at Arlington, BMD
The University of Texas at Austin, BMD
The University of Texas at Brownsville, M
The University of Texas at Dallas, BMD
The University of Texas at El Paso, BM
The University of Texas-Pan American, B
The University of Texas at San Antonio, B
West Texas A&M University, B
Wiley College, B

United States Virgin Islands

University of the Virgin Islands, A

Utah

Brigham Young University, BMD
Dixie State College of Utah, A
Salt Lake Community College, A
Snow College, A
University of Utah, BMD
Utah State University, BMD
Utah Valley State College, AB
Weber State University, B
Westminster College, B

Vermont

Bennington College, B
Marlboro College, B
Middlebury College, B
Norwich University, B
Saint Michael's College, B
University of Vermont, BM

Virginia

Bridgewater College, B
Christopher Newport University, BM
The College of William and Mary, BMD
Emory & Henry College, B
George Mason University, BM
Hampden-Sydney College, B
Hampton University, BMD
Hollins University, B
James Madison University, B
Longwood University, B

Lynchburg College, B
Mary Baldwin College, B
Norfolk State University, B
Old Dominion University, BMD
Randolph-Macon College, B
Randolph-Macon Woman's College, B
Roanoke College, B
Sweet Briar College, B
University of Mary Washington, B
University of Richmond, B
University of Virginia, BMD
Virginia Commonwealth University, BM
Virginia Military Institute, B
Virginia Polytechnic Institute and State
  University, BMD
Virginia State University, BM
Washington and Lee University, B

Washington

Central Washington University, B
Eastern Washington University, B
Everett Community College, A
Gonzaga University, B
Lower Columbia College, A
Seattle Pacific University, B
Seattle University, B
Tacoma Community College, A
University of Puget Sound, B
University of Washington, BMD
Walla Walla College, B
Washington State University, BMD
Western Washington University, B
Whitman College, B
Whitworth College, B

West Virginia

Bethany College, B
Marshall University, BM
West Virginia University, BMD
West Virginia Wesleyan College, B
Wheeling Jesuit University, B

Wisconsin

Beloit College, B
Carthage College, B
Lawrence University, B
Marquette University, B
St. Norbert College, B
University of Wisconsin-Eau Claire, B
University of Wisconsin-La Crosse, B
University of Wisconsin-Madison, MD
University of Wisconsin-Milwaukee, BMD
University of Wisconsin-Oshkosh, B
University of Wisconsin-Parkside, B
University of Wisconsin-River Falls, B
University of Wisconsin-Stevens Point, B
University of Wisconsin-Whitewater, B

Wyoming

Casper College, A
Northwest College, A
University of Wyoming, B

Alberta

University of Alberta, BMD
University of Calgary, BMD
University of Lethbridge, BM

British Columbia

Simon Fraser University, BMD
Thompson Rivers University, B
The University of British Columbia, BMD
University College of the Fraser Valley, B
University of Northern British Columbia, B
University of Victoria, BMD

Manitoba

Brandon University, B
University of Manitoba, BMD
The University of Winnipeg, B

New Brunswick

Mount Allison University, B
Université de Moncton, BM

University of New Brunswick Fredericton, BMD

Newfoundland and Labrador

Memorial University of Newfoundland, BMD

Nova Scotia

Acadia University, B
Dalhousie University, BMD
St. Francis Xavier University, BM
Saint Mary's University, B
Université Sainte-Anne, B
University of King's College, B

Ontario

Brock University, BM
Carleton University, BMD
Lakehead University, BM
Laurentian University, B
McMaster University, BD
Queen's University at Kingston, BMD
Royal Military College of Canada, BM
Trent University, BM
University of Guelph, BMD
University of Ottawa, BMD
University of Toronto, BMD
University of Waterloo, BMD
The University of Western Ontario, BMD
University of Windsor, BMD
Wilfrid Laurier University, B
York University, BMD

Prince Edward Island

University of Prince Edward Island, B

Quebec

Bishop's University, B
Concordia University, B
McGill University, BMD
Université Laval, BMD
Université de Montréal, BMD
Université du Québec àChicoutimi, B
Université du Québec àMontréal, B
Université du Québec àTrois-Rivières, B
Université de Sherbrooke, BMD

Saskatchewan

University of Regina, BMD
University of Saskatchewan, MD

PHYSICS TEACHER EDUCATION

Alabama

Auburn University, B

Arizona

Northern Arizona University, B
The University of Arizona, B

Arkansas

Arkansas State University, B
Southern Arkansas University-Magnolia, B

California

Collège of the Siskiyous, A
University of California, San Diego, B

Colorado

Colorado State University, B

Connecticut

Connecticut College, B

Delaware

Delaware State University, B
University of Delaware, B

Florida

Bethune-Cookman College, B
Florida Institute of Technology, B
Manatee Community College, A

Miami Dade College, B

Georgia

Georgia Southern University, B
University of West Georgia, B

Hawaii

Brigham Young University-Hawaii, B

Illinois

Chicago State University, B
Elmhurst College, B
Greenville College, B
Illinois Wesleyan University, B
University of Illinois at Chicago, B

Indiana

Indiana University Bloomington, B
Indiana University-Purdue University Fort Wayne, B
Indiana University South Bend, B
University of Evansville, B
Valparaiso University, B

Iowa

Buena Vista University, B
St. Ambrose University, B
The University of Iowa, B

Kansas

Pittsburg State University, B

Kentucky

Murray State University, B

Louisiana

Centenary College of Louisiana, B
Louisiana State University in Shreveport, B
Louisiana Tech University, B
Northwestern State University of Louisiana, B
Southern University and Agricultural and Mechanical
  College, B
University of Louisiana at Lafayette, B
University of Louisiana at Monroe, B

Michigan

Alma College, B
Central Michigan University, B
Eastern Michigan University, B
Hope College, B
University of Michigan-Flint, B
Western Michigan University, B

Minnesota

Bethel University, B
Concordia College, B
Gustavus Adolphus College, B
Minnesota State University Moorhead, B
Saint Mary's University of Minnesota, B
University of St. Thomas, B

Missouri

Central Methodist University, B
Central Missouri State University, B
Lincoln University, B
Missouri State University, B
University of Missouri-Columbia, B
University of Missouri-St. Louis, B
Washington University in St. Louis, B

Nebraska

Chadron State College, B
Concordia University, B
Hastings College, B
Union College, B
University of Nebraska-Lincoln, B

New Jersey

The College of New Jersey, B

New York

Brooklyn College of the City University of New
  York, B
City College of the City University of New York, B
Cornell University, B

Hofstra University, B
Ithaca College, B
Le Moyne College, B
New York Institute of Technology, B
New York University, B
Pace University, B
Roberts Wesleyan College, B
St. Bonaventure University, B
St. John's University, B
State University of New York College at
  Brockport, B
State University of New York College at Cortland, B
State University of New York College at Oneonta, B
State University of New York College at Potsdam, B
Syracuse University, B
Utica College, B

North Carolina

Appalachian State University, B
North Carolina Central University, B
North Carolina State University, B
The University of North Carolina Wilmington, B

North Dakota

Mayville State University, B
Minot State University, B
North Dakota State University, B

Ohio

Baldwin-Wallace College, B
Cedarville University, B
Miami University Hamilton, B
Ohio Dominican University, B
Ohio Northern University, B
Ohio Wesleyan University, B
Shawnee State University, B
The University of Akron, B
University of Rio Grande, B
Xavier University, B

Oklahoma

East Central University, B

Pennsylvania

Chatham College, B
Juniata College, B
Lebanon Valley College, B
Mansfield University of Pennsylvania, B
Moravian College, B
Saint Vincent College, B
West Chester University of Pennsylvania, B

Puerto Rico

Inter American University of Puerto Rico,
  Metropolitan Campus, B
Universidad Metropolitana, B
University of Puerto Rico, Cayey University
  College, B

Rhode Island

Rhode Island College, B

South Dakota

The University of South Dakota, B

Tennessee

Christian Brothers University, B
King College, B
Maryville College, B

Texas

Baylor University, B

Utah

Brigham Young University, B
University of Utah, B
Utah State University, B

Weber State University, B

Virginia

Old Dominion University, B

Washington

Eastern Washington University, B

West Virginia

Wheeling Jesuit University, B

Wisconsin

Carroll College, B
University of Wisconsin-River Falls, B

Ontario

University of Waterloo, B
University of Windsor, B
York University, B

Quebec

Bishop's University, B
McGill University, B

Saskatchewan

University of Regina, B

PHYSIOLOGICAL PSYCHOLOGY/PSYCHOBIOLOGY

California

Claremont McKenna College, B
Holy Names University, B
Hope International University, B
La Sierra University, B
Mills College, B
Occidental College, B
Saint Mary's College of California, B
Scripps College, B
University of California, Los Angeles, B
University of California, Riverside, B
University of California, Santa Cruz, B
University of Southern California, B

Connecticut

Quinnipiac University, B

Florida

Florida Atlantic University, B
University of Miami, B

Indiana

University of Evansville, B

Kentucky

Centre College, B

Maine

University of New England, B

Maryland

College of Notre Dame of Maryland, B
The Johns Hopkins University, B
Washington College, B

Massachusetts

Harvard University, B
Simmons College, B
Wheaton College, B

Michigan

Grand Valley State University, B

Nebraska

York College, B

New York

Hamilton College, B
Medaille College, B
State University of New York at Binghamton, B
State University of New York at New Paltz, B

Vassar College, B

Ohio

Hiram College, B
Oberlin College, B

Pennsylvania

Albright College, B
Arcadia University, B
Holy Family University, B
Lebanon Valley College, B
Lincoln University, B
Swarthmore College, B
Westminster College, B
Wilson College, B

Virginia

Averett University, B

Wisconsin

Ripon College, B

New Brunswick

Mount Allison University, B
University of New Brunswick Fredericton, B

Quebec

McGill University, B

PHYSIOLOGY

Alabama

Community College of the Air Force, A
The University of Alabama at Birmingham, MD
University of South Alabama, D

Arizona

Arizona State University, MD
The University of Arizona, D

Arkansas

University of Arkansas for Medical Sciences, MDO

California

California State University, Long Beach, B
Loma Linda University, MD
San Francisco State University, M
San Jose State University, BM
Stanford University, D
University of California, Berkeley, MD
University of California, Davis, MD
University of California, Irvine, DO
University of California, Los Angeles, BMD
University of California, San Diego, D
University of California, Santa Barbara, B
University of Southern California, MDO

Colorado

University of Colorado at Boulder, MD

Connecticut

University of Connecticut, MD
Wesleyan University, D
Yale University, DO

Delaware

University of Delaware, MD

District of Columbia

Georgetown University, MDO
Howard University, D

Florida

University of Florida, MD
University of Miami, DO
University of South Florida, D

Georgia

Georgia Institute of Technology, M
Georgia State University, MD
Medical College of Georgia, D

University of Georgia, MD

Illinois

Illinois State University, D
Northwestern University, M
Rush University, DO
Southern Illinois University Carbondale, BMD
University of Chicago, D
University of Illinois at Chicago, MD
University of Illinois at Urbana-Champaign, BMD

Indiana

Ball State University, M
Indiana State University, D
Indiana University Bloomington, MD
Indiana University-Purdue University
Indianapolis, MDO
Purdue University, MD
University of Notre Dame, MD

Iowa

Maharishi University of Management, MD
The University of Iowa, MD

Kansas

Kansas State University, MD
University of Kansas, MDO

Kentucky

University of Kentucky, D
University of Louisville, MD

Louisiana

Louisiana State University Health Sciences
Center, MDO
Tulane University, MDO

Maryland

The Johns Hopkins University, D
Salisbury University, M

Massachusetts

Boston University, MDO
Harvard University, D

Michigan

Michigan State University, BMD
University of Michigan, D
Wayne State University, MDO

Minnesota

University of Minnesota, Duluth, MD
University of Minnesota, Twin Cities Campus, MD

Mississippi

University of Mississippi Medical Center, MDO

Missouri

Saint Louis University, D
University of Missouri-Columbia, MD

Nebraska

University of Nebraska Medical Center, MD

Nevada

University of Nevada, Reno, MD

New Hampshire

Dartmouth College, DO

New Jersey

Rutgers, The State University of New Jersey, New
Brunswick/Piscataway, D
William Paterson University of New Jersey, M

New Mexico

University of New Mexico, MD

New York

Cornell University, MD
New York University, MDO
State University of New York at Buffalo, MD

State University of New York Upstate Medical
University, MDO
Stony Brook University, State University of New
York, D
University of Rochester, MD

North Carolina

East Carolina University, D
North Carolina State University, MD
Wake Forest University, D

North Dakota

University of North Dakota, MD

Ohio

Case Western Reserve University, MDO
Kent State University, MD
The Ohio State University, MD
Ohio University, MD
University of Cincinnati, D
Wright State University, M

Oklahoma

Oklahoma State University, B
University of Oklahoma Health Sciences Center, MD

Oregon

Oregon Health & Science University, DO
University of Oregon, BMD

Pennsylvania

The Pennsylvania State University University Park
Campus, MD
Temple University, MDO
Thomas Jefferson University, D
University of Pennsylvania, DO

Puerto Rico

University of Puerto Rico, Medical Sciences
Campus, MD

Rhode Island

Brown University, MDO

South Carolina

Medical University of South Carolina, MDO

South Dakota

The University of South Dakota, MD

Tennessee

East Tennessee State University, MD
The University of Tennessee, MD

Texas

Texas A&M University, MD
Texas A&M University System Health Science
Center, D
The University of Texas Health Science Center at
San Antonio, MD
The University of Texas Medical Branch, MD

Utah

Brigham Young University, BMD
University of Utah, D

Virginia

University of Virginia, DO
Virginia Commonwealth University, MDO

Washington

University of Washington, D

West Virginia

West Virginia University, MD

Wisconsin

Marquette University, MD
University of Wisconsin-La Crosse, M

University of Wisconsin-Madison, MD

Wyoming

University of Wyoming, MD

Alberta

University of Alberta, BMDO

British Columbia

The University of British Columbia, BMD
University of Victoria, MD

Manitoba

University of Manitoba, MDO

Nova Scotia

Dalhousie University, MDO

Ontario

McMaster University, MD
Queen's University at Kingston, MD
University of Guelph, MD
University of Ottawa, B
University of Toronto, MD
The University of Western Ontario, MDO

Prince Edward Island

University of Prince Edward Island, MD

Quebec

McGill University, MD
Université Laval, MD
Université de Montréal, MD
Université de Sherbrooke, MD

Saskatchewan

University of Saskatchewan, BMD

PIANO AND ORGAN

Alabama

Birmingham-Southern College, B
Huntingdon College, B
Samford University, B
University of Montevallo, B

Arizona

Grand Canyon University, B

Arkansas

Ouachita Baptist University, B

California

Bethesda Christian University, B
California Institute of the Arts, B
California State University, Chico, B
California State University, Fullerton, B
California State University, Sacramento, B
The Colburn School Conservatory of Music, B
Fresno City College, A
The Master's College and Seminary, B
Notre Dame de Namur University, B
Pacific Union College, B
San Francisco Conservatory of Music, B
University of the Pacific, B
University of Redlands, B

Delaware

University of Delaware, B

District of Columbia

The Catholic University of America, B

Florida

Barry University, B
Florida State University, B
New World School of the Arts, AB
Palm Beach Atlantic University, B
Stetson University, B

University of Miami, B

Georgia

Brenau University, B
Columbus State University, B
Shorter College, B

Hawaii

Brigham Young University-Hawaii, B

Idaho

Brigham Young University -Idaho, A

Illinois

Augustana College, B
Concordia University, B
DePaul University, B
Illinois Wesleyan University, B
Lincoln Christian College, B
Lincoln College, A
Millikin University, B
Northwestern University, B
Olivet Nazarene University, B
Roosevelt University, B
Trinity Christian College, B

Indiana

Ancilla College, A
Ball State University, B
Bethel College, B
Butler University, B
Grace College, B
Huntington University, B
Indiana University Bloomington, B
Indiana University-Purdue University Fort Wayne, B
Taylor University, B
Valparaiso University, B

Iowa

Dordt College, B
Drake University, B
Iowa Lakes Community College, A
The University of Iowa, B

Kansas

Friends University, B
Tabor College, B
University of Kansas, B

Kentucky

Campbellsville University, B
St. Catharine College, A

Louisiana

Centenary College of Louisiana, B
Dillard University, B
Louisiana College, B
Loyola University New Orleans, B
Xavier University of Louisiana, B

Maryland

Peabody Conservatory of Music of The Johns
   Hopkins University, B

Massachusetts

Anna Maria College, B
Berklee College of Music, B
The Boston Conservatory, B
Boston University, B
New England Conservatory of Music, B

Michigan

Andrews University, B
Calvin College, B
Grand Valley State University, B
Hope College, B
Spring Arbor University, B
University of Michigan, B

Minnesota

Concordia College, B
Minnesota State University Mankato, B
Minnesota State University Moorhead, B
Northwestern College, B

St. Cloud State University, B
University of Minnesota, Duluth, B

Mississippi

Itawamba Community College, A
Jackson State University, B
Mississippi College, B

Missouri

Calvary Bible College and Theological Seminary, B
Hannibal-LaGrange College, B
Northwest Missouri State University, B
Truman State University, B

Nebraska

Concordia University, B
Grace University, B
Hastings College, B

New Hampshire

University of New Hampshire, B

New Jersey

Rider University, B
Westminster Choir College of Rider University, B

New York

Houghton College, B
Ithaca College, B
Manhattan School of Music, B
Mannes College The New School for Music, B
New York University, B
Nyack College, B
Roberts Wesleyan College, B
Sarah Lawrence College, B
State University of New York, Fredonia, B
Syracuse University, B

North Carolina

Campbell University, B
Catawba College, B
Meredith College, B
North Carolina School of the Arts, B
Queens University of Charlotte, B

Ohio

Baldwin-Wallace College, B
Bowling Green State University, B
Capital University, B
Cedarville University, B
Cincinnati Christian University, B
Cleveland Institute of Music, B
Heidelberg College, B
Kent State University, B
Oberlin College, B
The Ohio State University, B
Ohio University, B
Otterbein College, B
The University of Akron, B
University of Cincinnati, B

Oklahoma

East Central University, B
Mid-America Christian University, B
Northeastern Oklahoma Agricultural and Mechanical
   College, A
Northeastern State University, B
Oklahoma Baptist University, B
Oklahoma City University, B
Southern Nazarene University, B
Southwestern Oklahoma State University, B
University of Central Oklahoma, B
University of Oklahoma, B
University of Tulsa, B

Oregon

Willamette University, B

Pennsylvania

Baptist Bible College of Pennsylvania, B
Carnegie Mellon University, B
The Curtis Institute of Music, B
Mansfield University of Pennsylvania, B
Seton Hill University, B

Susquehanna University, B
Temple University, B
West Chester University of Pennsylvania, B

Puerto Rico

Conservatory of Music of Puerto Rico, B
Inter American University of Puerto Rico, San
   Germán Campus, B

South Carolina

Bob Jones University, B
Coker College, B
Columbia College, B
Converse College, B
Furman University, B
Newberry College, B
North Greenville College, B

South Dakota

University of Sioux Falls, B

Tennessee

Belmont University, B
Bryan College, B
Carson-Newman College, B
Lee University, B
Maryville College, B
Union University, B
The University of Tennessee at Martin, B
Vanderbilt University, B

Texas

Abilene Christian University, B
Angelina College, A
Dallas Baptist University, B
East Texas Baptist University, B
Frank Phillips College, A
Hardin-Simmons University, B
Hill College of the Hill Junior College District, A
Howard Payne University, B
Lamar University, B
Lon Morris College, A
McMurry University, B
Prairie View A&M University, B
Southern Methodist University, B
Texas A&M University-Commerce, B
Texas Christian University, B
Texas Southern University, B
University of North Texas, B

Utah

Brigham Young University, B
Weber State University, B

Vermont

Bennington College, B

Virginia

Shenandoah University, B

Washington

Central Washington University, B
Cornish College of the Arts, B
Eastern Washington University, B
Pacific Lutheran University, B
University of Washington, B
Walla Walla College, B
Whitworth College, B

Wisconsin

Lawrence University, B

Alberta

University of Alberta, B

British Columbia

Kwantlen University College, A
The University of British Columbia, B

University of Victoria, B

Manitoba

Canadian Mennonite University, B

New Brunswick

Mount Allison University, B

Newfoundland and Labrador

Memorial University of Newfoundland, B

Nova Scotia

Acadia University, B

Ontario

The University of Western Ontario, B
York University, B

Quebec

McGill University, B

PIPEFITTING/PIPEFITTER AND SPRINKLER FITTER

Alabama

H. Councill Trenholm State Technical College, A

Arizona

GateWay Community College, A

California

Bakersfield College, A
College of San Mateo, A
Los Angeles Trade-Technical College, A
Palomar College, A

Indiana

Ivy Tech Community College-Bloomington, A
Ivy Tech Community College-Central Indiana, A
Ivy Tech Community College-Columbus, A
Ivy Tech Community College-East Central, A
Ivy Tech Community College-Kokomo, A
Ivy Tech Community College-Lafayette, A
Ivy Tech Community College-North Central, A
Ivy Tech Community College-Northeast, A
Ivy Tech Community College-Northwest, A
Ivy Tech Community College-Southern Indiana, A
Ivy Tech Community College-Southwest, A
Ivy Tech Community College-Wabash Valley, A
Ivy Tech Community College-Whitewater, A

Maine

Northern Maine Community College, A
Southern Maine Community College, A

Maryland

Cecil Community College, A

Michigan

Delta College, A
Kellogg Community College, A

Minnesota

St. Cloud Technical College, A

Missouri

Ranken Technical College, A
St. Louis Community College at Forest Park, A

Nebraska

Southeast Community College, Milford Campus, A

Nevada

Truckee Meadows Community College, A
Western Nevada Community College, A

New York

State University of New York College of Technology
at Alfred, A
State University of New York College of Technology
at Canton, A

State University of New York College of Technology
at Delhi, A

North Carolina

Forsyth Technical Community College, A

Oklahoma

Oklahoma State University, Okmulgee, A

Pennsylvania

Thaddeus Stevens College of Technology, A

Rhode Island

New England Institute of Technology, A

Texas

Brazosport College, A

British Columbia

British Columbia Institute of Technology, A
Thompson Rivers University, A

PLANETARY ASTRONOMY AND SCIENCE

Arizona

The University of Arizona, MD

California

California Institute of Technology, BMD
University of California, Los Angeles, MD

Connecticut

Western Connecticut State University, M

Florida

Embry-Riddle Aeronautical University, M
Florida Institute of Technology, MD

Hawaii

University of Hawaii at Manoa, MD

Illinois

University of Chicago, MD

Maryland

The Johns Hopkins University, MD

Massachusetts

Harvard University, MD
Massachusetts Institute of Technology, D

Michigan

University of Michigan, MD

Missouri

Washington University in St. Louis, MD

New Mexico

University of New Mexico, MD

New York

Cornell University, D
Stony Brook University, State University of New
York, MD

North Dakota

University of North Dakota, M

Pennsylvania

University of Pittsburgh, MD

Ontario

University of Waterloo, B
The University of Western Ontario, B

York University, MD

Quebec

McGill University, MD

PLANT BIOLOGY

California

University of California, Berkeley, D
University of California, Davis, MD
University of California, Riverside, MD
University of California, San Diego, D

Colorado

University of Colorado at Boulder, MD

Connecticut

Yale University, D

Florida

Florida State University, MD
University of Florida, MD

Georgia

University of Georgia, MD

Hawaii

University of Hawaii at Manoa, MD

Illinois

Southern Illinois University Carbondale, MD
University of Illinois at Chicago, MD
University of Illinois at Urbana-Champaign, MD

Indiana

Indiana University Bloomington, MD
Purdue University, D

Maine

University of Maine, D

Maryland

University of Maryland, College Park, MD

Massachusetts

University of Massachusetts Amherst, MD

Michigan

Michigan State University, MD

Minnesota

University of Minnesota, Twin Cities Campus, MD

Missouri

University of Missouri-Columbia, MD
Washington University in St. Louis, D

New Hampshire

University of New Hampshire, MD

New Jersey

Rutgers, The State University of New Jersey, New
Brunswick/Piscataway, MD

New York

Cornell University, MD

Ohio

The Ohio State University, MD
Ohio University, MD

Pennsylvania

University of Pennsylvania, D

South Carolina

Clemson University, MD

Texas

Texas A&M University, MD
The University of Texas at Austin, MD

Alberta

University of Alberta, MD

Ontario

The University of Western Ontario, MD

Quebec

Université Laval, MD

PLANT GENETICS

New York

Cornell University, B

Utah

Brigham Young University, B

PLANT MOLECULAR BIOLOGY

California

University of California, Los Angeles, D
University of California, San Diego, D

Florida

University of Florida, MD

Massachusetts

University of Massachusetts Amherst, MD

Michigan

Michigan Technological University, MD

New Jersey

Rutgers, The State University of New Jersey, New
Brunswick/Piscataway, MD

New York

Cornell University, MD

Washington

Washington State University, MD

PLANT NURSERY OPERATIONS AND MANAGEMENT

California

Cuyamaca College, A
Foothill College, A
Modesto Junior College, A

Florida

Miami Dade College, A

Illinois

Joliet Junior College, A

Minnesota

Dakota County Technical College, A

New York

State University of New York College of Agriculture
and Technology at Cobleskill, A

Ohio

The Ohio State University Agricultural Technical
Institute, A

Pennsylvania

Community College of Allegheny County, A
Pennsylvania College of Technology, A

Puerto Rico

Inter American University of Puerto Rico,
Barranquitas Campus, A

Washington

Edmonds Community College, A

PLANT PATHOLOGY/PHYTOPATHOLOGY

Alabama

Auburn University, BMD

Arizona

The University of Arizona, MD

Arkansas

University of Arkansas, M

California

University of California, Davis, MD
University of California, Riverside, MD

Colorado

Colorado State University, MD

Florida

University of Florida, BMD

Georgia

University of Georgia, MD

Hawaii

University of Hawaii at Manoa, MD

Indiana

Purdue University, MD

Iowa

Iowa State University of Science and
Technology, MD

Kansas

Kansas State University, MD

Kentucky

University of Kentucky, MD

Louisiana

Louisiana State University and Agricultural and
Mechanical College, MD

Maine

University of Maine, M

Michigan

Michigan State University, BMD

Minnesota

University of Minnesota, Twin Cities Campus, MD

Mississippi

Mississippi State University, MD

Missouri

University of Missouri-Columbia, MD

Montana

Montana State University, M

New Jersey

Rutgers, The State University of New Jersey, New
Brunswick/Piscataway, MD

New Mexico

New Mexico State University, BM

New York

Cornell University, BMD
State University of New York College of
Environmental Science and Forestry, BMD

North Carolina

North Carolina State University, MD

North Dakota

North Dakota State University, MD

Ohio

The Ohio State University, BMD

Oklahoma

Oklahoma State University, MD

Oregon

Oregon State University, MD

Pennsylvania

The Pennsylvania State University University Park
Campus, MD

Rhode Island

University of Rhode Island, MD

South Dakota

South Dakota State University, M

Tennessee

The University of Tennessee, MD

Texas

Texas A&M University, MD

Utah

Dixie State College of Utah, A

Virginia

Virginia Polytechnic Institute and State
University, MD

Washington

Washington State University, MD

West Virginia

West Virginia University, M

Wisconsin

University of Wisconsin-Madison, MD

Ontario

University of Guelph, MD

PLANT PHYSIOLOGY

Colorado

Colorado State University, MD
University of Colorado at Boulder, MD

Florida

Florida State University, B

Indiana

Purdue University, D

Iowa

Iowa State University of Science and
Technology, MD

Kentucky

University of Kentucky, D

Massachusetts

University of Massachusetts Amherst, MD

New Jersey

Rutgers, The State University of New Jersey, New
Brunswick/Piscataway, MD

New York

Cornell University, MD
State University of New York College of
Environmental Science and Forestry, B

Oregon

Oregon State University, MD

Pennsylvania

The Pennsylvania State University University Park Campus, MD

Tennessee

The University of Tennessee, MD

Virginia

Virginia Polytechnic Institute and State University, MD

PLANT PROTECTION AND INTEGRATED PEST MANAGEMENT

California

California State Polytechnic University, Pomona, B
Los Angeles Pierce College, A

Delaware

University of Delaware, B

Florida

Florida Agricultural and Mechanical University, B

Georgia

University of Georgia, B

Hawaii

University of Hawaii at Manoa, B

Iowa

Iowa State University of Science and Technology, B

Mississippi

Mississippi State University, B

Nebraska

University of Nebraska-Lincoln, B

New York

Cornell University, B
State University of New York College of Environmental Science and Forestry, B

North Carolina

North Carolina State University, A

North Dakota

North Dakota State University, B

Oklahoma

Tulsa Community College, A

Puerto Rico

University of Puerto Rico at Utuado, A

Tennessee

The University of Tennessee, B

Texas

Lubbock Christian University, B
Texas A&M University, B
Texas Tech University, B
West Texas A&M University, B

Utah

Dixie State College of Utah, A

Vermont

Sterling College, AB

Washington

Washington State University, B

PLANT SCIENCES

Alabama

Alabama Agricultural and Mechanical University, MD
Auburn University, B

Tuskegee University, BM

Arizona

The University of Arizona, BMD

Arkansas

Arkansas State University, B
University of Arkansas, D

California

California State University, Fresno, BM
Reedley College, A
University of California, Los Angeles, B
University of California, Riverside, MD
University of California, Santa Cruz, B
Ventura College, A

Colorado

Colorado State University, BMD

Connecticut

University of Connecticut, MD

Delaware

University of Delaware, MD

Florida

Florida Agricultural and Mechanical University, M
University of Florida, BD

Georgia

University of Georgia, B

Hawaii

University of Hawaii at Manoa, MD

Idaho

University of Idaho, BMD

Illinois

Rend Lake College, A
Southern Illinois University Carbondale, BM

Kentucky

University of Kentucky, M

Louisiana

Louisiana State University and Agricultural and Mechanical College, B
Louisiana Tech University, B
University of Louisiana at Lafayette, B

Maine

University of Maine, BMD

Maryland

University of Maryland, College Park, B

Massachusetts

University of Massachusetts Amherst, BMD

Michigan

Michigan State University, MD

Minnesota

University of Minnesota, Twin Cities Campus, BMD

Mississippi

Mississippi State University, MD
Northwest Mississippi Community College, A

Missouri

Missouri State University, M
University of Missouri-Columbia, B

Montana

Montana State University, BMD

New Jersey

Mercer County Community College, A
Rutgers, The State University of New Jersey, New Brunswick/Piscataway, BM

New Mexico

New Mexico State University, M

New York

Cornell University, BMD
Lehman College of the City University of New York, D

State University of New York College of Agriculture and Technology at Cobleskill, AB
State University of New York College of Environmental Science and Forestry, BMD

North Carolina

North Carolina Agricultural and Technical State University, M

North Dakota

North Dakota State University, MD

Ohio

The Ohio State University, B

Oklahoma

Oklahoma State University, BD

Rhode Island

University of Rhode Island, MD

South Carolina

Clemson University, MD

South Dakota

South Dakota State University, MD

Tennessee

Middle Tennessee State University, B
The University of Tennessee, BM

Texas

Lubbock Christian University, B
Texas A&M University, MD
Texas A&M University-Kingsville, MD
Texas Tech University, MD
West Texas A&M University, M

Utah

Brigham Young University, M
Utah State University, BMD

Vermont

Sterling College, AB
University of Vermont, BMD

Washington

Washington State University, B

West Virginia

West Virginia University, BMD

Wisconsin

University of Wisconsin-Madison, MD

British Columbia

The University of British Columbia, MD

Nova Scotia

Nova Scotia Agricultural College, B

Ontario

Lakehead University, B
The University of Western Ontario, BMD

Quebec

McGill University, BMDO

Saskatchewan

University of Saskatchewan, BMD

PLASMA AND HIGH-TEMPERATURE PHYSICS

Colorado

University of Colorado at Boulder, MD

Massachusetts

Massachusetts Institute of Technology, D

New Jersey

Princeton University, D

West Virginia

West Virginia University, MD

PLASTICS ENGINEERING TECHNOLOGY/TECHNICIAN

California

Cerritos College, A

Connecticut

Quinebaug Valley Community College, A

Florida

St. Petersburg College, A

Georgia

West Georgia Technical College, A

Idaho

Brigham Young University -Idaho, A

Illinois

College of DuPage, A

Indiana

Ball State University, B

Kansas

Pittsburg State University, B

Louisiana

Elaine P. Nunez Community College, A

Massachusetts

Mount Wachusett Community College, A

Michigan

Eastern Michigan University, B
Ferris State University, AB
Grand Rapids Community College, A
Kalamazoo Valley Community College, A
Kellogg Community College, A
Lake Michigan College, A
Macomb Community College, A
St. Clair County Community College, A
Western Michigan University, B

Minnesota

Hennepin Technical College, A

Nebraska

Southeast Community College, Milford Campus, A

New Jersey

Cumberland County College, A

New York

State University of New York College of Agriculture
  and Technology at Morrisville, A

North Carolina

Davidson County Community College, A
Edgecombe Community College, A
Isothermal Community College, A
Randolph Community College, A
Wake Technical Community College, A

Ohio

Cincinnati State Technical and Community
  College, A
Lorain County Community College, A
Northwest State Community College, A
Shawnee State University, AB
Sinclair Community College, A

Terra State Community College, A

Oklahoma

Northeastern Oklahoma Agricultural and Mechanical
  College, A

Pennsylvania

Pennsylvania College of Technology, AB
The Pennsylvania State University at Erie, The
  Behrend College, A

Texas

South Texas College, A
Tyler Junior College, A

Washington

Highline Community College, A
Western Washington University, B

British Columbia

British Columbia Institute of Technology, A

PLATEMAKER/IMAGER

Michigan

Western Michigan University, B

Pennsylvania

Pennsylvania College of Technology, A

PLAYWRITING AND SCREENWRITING

California

Loyola Marymount University, B
University of Southern California, B

Florida

Palm Beach Atlantic University, B

Illinois

Columbia College Chicago, B
DePaul University, B

Massachusetts

Emerson College, B
Hampshire College, B
Simon's Rock College of Bard, B

Minnesota

Metropolitan State University, B

New York

Bard College, B
Fordham University, B
New York University, B
Purchase College, State University of New York, B
Sarah Lawrence College, B

Ohio

Ohio University, B

Pennsylvania

Drexel University, B

Utah

Brigham Young University, B

Vermont

Bennington College, B

Ontario

York University, B

Quebec

Concordia University, B

PLUMBING TECHNOLOGY/PLUMBER

Michigan

Macomb Community College, A

Minnesota

Minnesota West Community and Technical
  College, A

Missouri

Vatterott College (St. Ann), A

North Carolina

Mayland Community College, A

Pennsylvania

Luzerne County Community College, A
Pennsylvania College of Technology, A

Virginia

Piedmont Virginia Community College, A

British Columbia

Thompson Rivers University, A

PODIATRIC MEDICINE

Arizona

Midwestern University, Glendale Campus, P

Florida

Barry University, PO

Pennsylvania

Temple University, PO

POLISH LANGUAGE AND LITERATURE

Illinois

University of Illinois at Chicago, B

Michigan

Madonna University, B

POLITICAL COMMUNICATION

Massachusetts

Emerson College, B

Nebraska

Nebraska Wesleyan University, B

Tennessee

Bryan College, B

POLITICAL SCIENCE AND GOVERNMENT

Alabama

Alabama Agricultural and Mechanical University, B
Alabama State University, B
Athens State University, B
Auburn University, BMDO
Auburn University Montgomery, BMD
Birmingham-Southern College, B
Faulkner University, B
Huntingdon College, B
Jacksonville State University, B
Jefferson Davis Community College, A
Lawson State Community College, A
Miles College, B
Samford University, B
Spring Hill College, B
Troy University, B

Tuskegee University, B
The University of Alabama, BMD
The University of Alabama at Birmingham, B
The University of Alabama in Huntsville, B
University of Mobile, B
University of Montevallo, B
University of North Alabama, B
University of South Alabama, B

Alaska

University of Alaska Anchorage, B
University of Alaska Fairbanks, B

Arizona

Arizona State University, BMD
Arizona State University West, B
Cochise College (Douglas), A
Cochise College (Sierra Vista), A
Eastern Arizona College, A
Grand Canyon University, B
Northern Arizona University, BMDO
Pima Community College, A
Prescott College, B
South Mountain Community College, A
The University of Arizona, BMD

Arkansas

Arkansas State University, BMO
Harding University, B
Henderson State University, B
Hendrix College, B
Lyon College, B
Ouachita Baptist University, B
Philander Smith College, B
Southern Arkansas University-Magnolia, B
University of Arkansas, BM
University of Arkansas at Little Rock, B
University of Arkansas at Monticello, B
University of Arkansas at Pine Bluff, B
University of Central Arkansas, B
University of the Ozarks, B

California

Azusa Pacific University, B
Bakersfield College, A
Butte College, A
California Baptist University, B
California Institute of Technology, D
California Lutheran University, B
California Polytechnic State University, San Luis
  Obispo, B
California State Polytechnic University, Pomona, B
California State University, Bakersfield, B
California State University Channel Islands, B
California State University, Chico, BM
California State University, Dominguez Hills, B
California State University, East Bay, B
California State University, Fresno, B
California State University, Fullerton, BM
California State University, Long Beach, BM
California State University, Los Angeles, BM
California State University, Northridge, BM
California State University, Sacramento, BM
California State University, San Bernardino, B
California State University, San Marcos, B
California State University, Stanislaus, BM
Cañada College, A
Cerritos College, A
Chabot College, A
Chaffey College, A
Chapman University, B
Claremont McKenna College, B
College of Alameda, A
College of the Canyons, A
College of the Desert, A
College of Marin, A
Concordia University, B
Contra Costa College, A
Crafton Hills College, A
Cypress College, A
De Anza College, A
Dominican University of California, B
East Los Angeles College, A
El Camino College, A
Foothill College, A
Fresno Pacific University, AB

Fullerton College, A
Gavilan College, A
Grossmont College, A
Humboldt State University, B
La Sierra University, B
Loyola Marymount University, B
The Master's College and Seminary, B
Merced College, A
Mills College, B
MiraCosta College, A
Monterey Peninsula College, A
Mount St. Mary's College, B
Notre Dame de Namur University, B
Occidental College, B
Orange Coast College, A
Pacific Union College, B
Palo Verde College, A
Pasadena City College, A
Pepperdine University, B
Pitzer College, B
Point Loma Nazarene University, B
Pomona College, B
Saddleback College, A
Saint Mary's College of California, B
San Bernardino Valley College, A
San Diego City College, A
San Diego State University, BM
San Francisco State University, BM
San Joaquin Delta College, A
San Jose State University, B
Santa Ana College, A
Santa Barbara City College, A
Santa Clara University, B
Santa Monica College, A
Santa Rosa Junior College, A
Santiago Canyon College, A
Scripps College, B
Skyline College, A
Solano Community College, A
Sonoma State University, BM
Southwestern College, A
Stanford University, BMD
University of California, Berkeley, BD
University of California, Davis, BMD
University of California, Irvine, BD
University of California, Los Angeles, BMD
University of California, Riverside, BMD
University of California, San Diego, BMD
University of California, Santa Barbara, BMD
University of California, Santa Cruz, BD
University of Judaism, B
University of La Verne, B
University of the Pacific, B
University of Redlands, B
University of San Diego, B
University of San Francisco, B
University of Southern California, BMD
Vanguard University of Southern California, B
West Los Angeles College, A
Westmont College, B
Whittier College, B
Woodbury University, B

Colorado

Adams State College, B
Colorado Christian University, B
The Colorado College, B
Colorado Northwestern Community College, A
Colorado State University, BMD
Colorado State University-Pueblo, B
Fort Lewis College, B
Mesa State College, B
Metropolitan State College of Denver, B
Otero Junior College, A
Red Rocks Community College, A
Regis University, B
United States Air Force Academy, B
University of Colorado at Boulder, BMD
University of Colorado at Colorado Springs, B
University of Colorado at Denver and Health
  Sciences Center - Downtown Denver
  Campus, BM
University of Denver, B
University of Northern Colorado, B

Western State College of Colorado, B

Connecticut

Albertus Magnus College, B
Central Connecticut State University, B
Connecticut College, B
Eastern Connecticut State University, B
Fairfield University, B
Quinnipiac University, B
Sacred Heart University, AB
Saint Joseph College, B
Southern Connecticut State University, BM
Trinity College, B
United States Coast Guard Academy, B
University of Connecticut, BMD
University of Hartford, B
University of New Haven, B
Wesleyan University, B
Western Connecticut State University, B
Yale University, BD

Delaware

Delaware State University, B
University of Delaware, BMD
Wesley College, B

District of Columbia

American University, BMDO
The Catholic University of America, BMDO
The George Washington University, BMDO
Georgetown University, BMDO
Howard University, BMD
Trinity (Washington) University, B
University of the District of Columbia, B

Florida

Barry University, B
Bethune-Cookman College, B
Eckerd College, B
Flagler College, B
Florida Agricultural and Mechanical University, BM
Florida Atlantic University, BM
Florida Gulf Coast University, B
Florida International University, BMD
Florida Memorial College, B
Florida Southern College, B
Florida State University, BMD
Gulf Coast Community College, A
Indian River Community College, A
Jacksonville University, B
Lynn University, B
Miami Dade College, A
New College of Florida, B
Palm Beach Atlantic University, B
Palm Beach Community College, A
Rollins College, B
Saint Leo University, B
St. Thomas University, B
Stetson University, B
University of Central Florida, BM
University of Florida, BMDO
University of Miami, BMO
University of North Florida, B
University of South Florida, BM
The University of Tampa, AB
University of West Florida, BM

Georgia

Abraham Baldwin Agricultural College, A
Agnes Scott College, B
Albany State University, B
Armstrong Atlantic State University, B
Atlanta Metropolitan College, A
Augusta State University, BM
Bainbridge College, A
Berry College, B
Brenau University, B
Brewton-Parker College, B
Clark Atlanta University, BMD
Clayton State University, A
Coastal Georgia Community College, A
Columbus State University, B
Dalton State College, A
Darton College, A
East Georgia College, A

Emory University, BD
Fort Valley State University, B
Gainesville College, A
Georgia College & State University, B
Georgia Highlands College, A
Georgia Perimeter College, A
Georgia Southern University, B
Georgia Southwestern State University, B
Georgia State University, BMD
Gordon College, A
Kennesaw State University, B
LaGrange College, B
Macon State College, A
Mercer University, B
Morehouse College, B
North Georgia College & State University, B
Oglethorpe University, B
Piedmont College, B
Savannah State University, B
South Georgia College, A
Spelman College, B
Thomas University, B
University of Georgia, BMD
University of West Georgia, B
Valdosta State University, B
Waycross College, A
Wesleyan College, B
Young Harris College, A

Guam

University of Guam, B

Hawaii

Brigham Young University-Hawaii, B
Hawaii Pacific University, BM
University of Hawaii at Hilo, B
University of Hawaii at Manoa, BMD
University of Hawaii-West Oahu, B

Idaho

Albertson College of Idaho, B
Boise State University, B
Brigham Young University -Idaho, A
College of Southern Idaho, A
Idaho State University, ABMD
North Idaho College, A
Northwest Nazarene University, B
University of Idaho, BMD

Illinois

Augustana College, B
Aurora University, B
Benedictine University, B
Blackburn College, B
Bradley University, B
Chicago State University, B
Concordia University, B
DePaul University, B
Dominican University, B
Eastern Illinois University, BM
Elmhurst College, B
Eureka College, B
Governors State University, M
Highland Community College, A
Illinois College, B
Illinois Institute of Technology, B
Illinois State University, BM
Illinois Wesleyan University, B
John A. Logan College, A
Knox College, B
Lake Forest College, B
Lewis University, B
Lincoln College, A
Loyola University Chicago, BMDO
MacMurray College, B
McKendree College, B
Millikin University, B
Monmouth College, B
North Central College, B
North Park University, B
Northeastern Illinois University, BM
Northern Illinois University, BMD
Northwestern University, BMDO
Principia College, B
Quincy University, B
Rend Lake College, A

Rockford College, B
Roosevelt University, BM
Saint Xavier University, B
Sauk Valley Community College, A
Southern Illinois University Carbondale, BMDO
Southern Illinois University Edwardsville, B
Spoon River College, A
University of Chicago, BD
University of Illinois at Chicago, BMD
University of Illinois at Springfield, BM
University of Illinois at Urbana-Champaign, BMD
University of St. Francis, B
Western Illinois University, BM
Wheaton College, B

Indiana

Anderson University, B
Ball State University, BM
Butler University, B
Calumet College of Saint Joseph, B
DePauw University, B
Earlham College, B
Franklin College, B
Hanover College, B
Huntington University, B
Indiana State University, BM
Indiana University Bloomington, BMD
Indiana University Northwest, B
Indiana University-Purdue University Fort
    Wayne, AB
Indiana University-Purdue University Indianapolis, B
Indiana University South Bend, B
Indiana University Southeast, B
Indiana Wesleyan University, AB
Manchester College, B
Martin University, B
Purdue University, BMD
Purdue University Calumet, BM
Saint Joseph's College, B
Saint Mary's College, B
Taylor University, B
University of Evansville, B
University of Indianapolis, B
University of Notre Dame, BD
University of Southern Indiana, B
Valparaiso University, B
Vincennes University, A
Wabash College, B

Iowa

Briar Cliff University, B
Buena Vista University, B
Central College, B
Coe College, B
Cornell College, B
Dordt College, B
Drake University, B
Ellsworth Community College, A
Grand View College, B
Grinnell College, B
Iowa Lakes Community College, A
Iowa State University of Science and
    Technology, BMO
Kirkwood Community College, A
Loras College, B
Luther College, B
Marshalltown Community College, A
Morningside College, B
Mount Mercy College, B
Northwestern College, B
St. Ambrose University, B
Simpson College, B
The University of Iowa, BMDO
University of Northern Iowa, B
Wartburg College, B
William Penn University, B

Kansas

Allen County Community College, A
Baker University, B
Barton County Community College, A
Benedictine College, B
Bethany College, B
Butler Community College, A
Coffeyville Community College, A
Colby Community College, A

Dodge City Community College, A
Donnelly College, A
Emporia State University, B
Fort Hays State University, B
Friends University, B
Highland Community College, A
Independence Community College, A
Kansas State University, BM
Ottawa University, B
Pittsburg State University, B
University of Kansas, BMD
University of Saint Mary, B
Washburn University, B
Wichita State University, BM

Kentucky

Bellarmine University, B
Berea College, B
Campbellsville University, B
Centre College, B
Eastern Kentucky University, BM
Georgetown College, B
Kentucky State University, B
Kentucky Wesleyan College, B
Morehead State University, B
Murray State University, B
Northern Kentucky University, B
Pikeville College, B
Thomas More College, A
Transylvania University, B
University of the Cumberlands, B
University of Kentucky, BMD
University of Louisville, BM
Western Kentucky University, B

Louisiana

Centenary College of Louisiana, B
Dillard University, B
Grambling State University, B
Louisiana State University and Agricultural and
    Mechanical College, BMD
Louisiana State University in Shreveport, B
Louisiana Tech University, B
Loyola University New Orleans, B
McNeese State University, B
Northwestern State University of Louisiana, B
Southeastern Louisiana University, B
Southern University and Agricultural and Mechanical
    College, BM
Tulane University, BMDO
University of Louisiana at Lafayette, B
University of Louisiana at Monroe, B
University of New Orleans, BMD
Xavier University of Louisiana, B

Maine

Bates College, B
Bowdoin College, B
Colby College, B
University of Maine, B
University of Maine at Farmington, B
University of Maine at Presque Isle, B
University of New England, B
University of Southern Maine, B

Maryland

Bowie State University, B
College of Notre Dame of Maryland, B
Columbia Union College, B
Frederick Community College, A
Frostburg State University, B
Goucher College, B
Harford Community College, A
Hood College, B
The Johns Hopkins University, BMD
Loyola College in Maryland, B
McDaniel College, B
Morgan State University, B
Mount St. Mary's University, B
St. Mary's College of Maryland, B
Salisbury University, B
Towson University, B
United States Naval Academy, B
University of Baltimore, B
University of Maryland, Baltimore County, B
University of Maryland, College Park, BD

Villa Julie College, A
Washington College, B

Massachusetts

American International College, B
Amherst College, B
Anna Maria College, B
Assumption College, B
Boston College, BMD
Boston University, BMD
Brandeis University, BMD
Bridgewater State College, B
Clark University, B
College of the Holy Cross, B
Curry College, B
Emmanuel College, B
Fitchburg State College, B
Framingham State College, B
Gordon College, B
Hampshire College, B
Harvard University, BMDO
Massachusetts Institute of Technology, BMD
Merrimack College, B
Mount Holyoke College, B
Northeastern University, BMD
Northern Essex Community College, A
Pine Manor College, B
Quincy College, A
Regis College, B
Salem State College, B
Simmons College, B
Simon's Rock College of Bard, B
Smith College, B
Stonehill College, B
Suffolk University, BM
Tufts University, B
University of Massachusetts Amherst, BMD
University of Massachusetts Boston, BO
University of Massachusetts Dartmouth, B
University of Massachusetts Lowell, B
Wellesley College, B
Western New England College, B
Westfield State College, B
Wheaton College, B
Williams College, B

Michigan

Adrian College, AB
Albion College, B
Alma College, B
Andrews University, B
Aquinas College, B
Ave Maria College, B
Calvin College, B
Central Michigan University, BM
Cornerstone University, B
Eastern Michigan University, B
Grand Valley State University, B
Hillsdale College, B
Hope College, B
Kalamazoo College, B
Kellogg Community College, A
Lake Superior State University, B
Marygrove College, B
Michigan State University, BMD
Northern Michigan University, B
Oakland University, B
Saginaw Valley State University, B
University of Detroit Mercy, B
University of Michigan, BMDO
University of Michigan-Dearborn, B
University of Michigan-Flint, B
Wayne State University, BMDO
Western Michigan University, BMD

Minnesota

Augsburg College, B
Bemidji State University, B
Bethel University, B
Carleton College, B
College of Saint Benedict, B
College of St. Catherine, B
Concordia College, B
Gustavus Adolphus College, B
Hamline University, B
Macalester College, B

Minnesota State University Mankato, BM
Minnesota State University Moorhead, B
St. Cloud State University, B
Saint John's University, B
Saint Mary's University of Minnesota, B
St. Olaf College, B
Southwest Minnesota State University, B
University of Minnesota, Duluth, B
University of Minnesota, Morris, B
University of Minnesota, Twin Cities Campus, BMD
University of St. Thomas, B
Vermilion Community College, A
Winona State University, B

Mississippi

Alcorn State University, B
Copiah-Lincoln Community College-Natchez
    Campus, A
Delta State University, B
East Central Community College, A
Hinds Community College, A
Itawamba Community College, A
Jackson State University, BM
Millsaps College, B
Mississippi College, BM
Mississippi Delta Community College, A
Mississippi State University, BMD
Mississippi University for Women, B
Mississippi Valley State University, B
Northeast Mississippi Community College, A
Rust College, B
Tougaloo College, B
University of Mississippi, BMD
University of Southern Mississippi, BM

Missouri

Avila University, B
Central Methodist University, B
Central Missouri State University, B
College of the Ozarks, B
Columbia College, B
Drury University, B
East Central College, A
Evangel University, B
Jefferson College, A
Lincoln University, B
Lindenwood University, B
Missouri Southern State University, B
Missouri State University, BM
Missouri Valley College, B
Missouri Western State University, B
Northwest Missouri State University, B
Park University, B
Rockhurst University, B
Saint Louis University, B
Southeast Missouri State University, B
Southwest Baptist University, B
Stephens College, B
Truman State University, B
University of Missouri-Columbia, BMD
University of Missouri-Kansas City, BMD
University of Missouri-St. Louis, BMD
Washington University in St. Louis, BMDO
Webster University, B
Westminster College, B
William Jewell College, B
William Woods University, B

Montana

Carroll College, B
Montana State University, B
Rocky Mountain College, B
University of Great Falls, B
The University of Montana-Missoula, M

Nebraska

Creighton University, B
Doane College, B
Hastings College, B
Nebraska Wesleyan University, B
University of Nebraska at Kearney, B
University of Nebraska-Lincoln, BMDO
University of Nebraska at Omaha, BM
Wayne State College, B

Western Nebraska Community College, A

Nevada

University of Nevada, Las Vegas, BM
University of Nevada, Reno, BMD

New Hampshire

Dartmouth College, B
Franklin Pierce College, B
New England College, B
Plymouth State University, B
Rivier College, B
Saint Anselm College, B
Southern New Hampshire University, B
Thomas More College of Liberal Arts, B
University of New Hampshire, BM

New Jersey

Bergen Community College, A
Bloomfield College, B
Brookdale Community College, A
Burlington County College, A
Caldwell College, B
Centenary College, B
The College of New Jersey, B
Drew University, B
Fairleigh Dickinson University, College at
    Florham, B
Fairleigh Dickinson University, Metropolitan
    Campus, BM
Felician College, B
Gloucester County College, A
Kean University, BM
Middlesex County College, A
Monmouth University, B
Montclair State University, B
New Jersey City University, B
Princeton University, BD
Ramapo College of New Jersey, B
The Richard Stockton College of New Jersey, B
Rider University, B
Rowan University, B
Rutgers, The State University of New Jersey,
    Camden, B
Rutgers, The State University of New Jersey, New
    Brunswick/Piscataway, BMDO
Rutgers, The State University of New Jersey,
    Newark, BMO
Saint Peter's College, B
Salem Community College, A
Seton Hall University, B
William Paterson University of New Jersey, B

New Mexico

College of Santa Fe, B
Eastern New Mexico University, B
New Mexico Highlands University, BM
New Mexico State University, BM
San Juan College, A
University of New Mexico, BMD

New York

Adelphi University, B
Alfred University, B
Bard College, B
Barnard College, B
Bernard M. Baruch College of the City University of
    New York, B
Brooklyn College of the City University of New
    York, BMDO
Buffalo State College, State University of New
    York, B
Canisius College, B
City College of the City University of New York, B
Clarkson University, B
Colgate University, B
The College of New Rochelle, B
The College of Saint Rose, BM
College of Staten Island of the City University of
    New York, B
Columbia College, B
Columbia University, School of General Studies, B
Cornell University, BD
Daemen College, B
Dowling College, B

Elmira College, B
Eugene Lang College The New School for Liberal Arts, B
Excelsior College, B
Finger Lakes Community College, A
Fordham University, BM
Hamilton College, B
Hartwick College, B
Hobart and William Smith Colleges, B
Hofstra University, B
Houghton College, B
Hunter College of the City University of New York, B
Iona College, B
Ithaca College, B
Le Moyne College, B
Lehman College of the City University of New York, B
Long Island University, Brooklyn Campus, BM
Long Island University, C.W. Post Campus, BM
Manhattan College, B
Manhattanville College, B
Marist College, B
Marymount Manhattan College, B
Molloy College, B
Monroe Community College, A
Mount Saint Mary College, B
Nazareth College of Rochester, B
New York Institute of Technology, B
New York University, BMDO
Niagara University, B
Pace University, B
Purchase College, State University of New York, B
Queens College of the City University of New York, B
Russell Sage College, B
St. Bonaventure University, B
St. Francis College, B
St. John Fisher College, B
St. John's University, BMO
St. Joseph's College, Suffolk Campus, B
St. Lawrence University, B
Sarah Lawrence College, B
Siena College, B
Skidmore College, B
State University of New York at Binghamton, BMD
State University of New York at Buffalo, BMD
State University of New York College at Brockport, B
State University of New York College at Cortland, B
State University of New York College at Geneseo, B
State University of New York College at Oneonta, B
State University of New York College at Potsdam, B
State University of New York, Fredonia, B
State University of New York at New Paltz, B
State University of New York at Oswego, B
State University of New York at Plattsburgh, B
Stony Brook University, State University of New York, BMD
Syracuse University, BMD
Touro College, B
Union College, B
United States Military Academy, B
University at Albany, State University of New York, BMD
University of Rochester, BMDO
Utica College, B
Vassar College, B
Wagner College, B
Wells College, B
Yeshiva University, B
York College of the City University of New York, B

North Carolina

Appalachian State University, BM
Barber-Scotia College, B
Barton College, B
Belmont Abbey College, B
Bennett College For Women, B
Campbell University, B
Catawba College, B
Davidson College, B
Duke University, BMDO
East Carolina University, BM
Elizabeth City State University, B
Elon University, B
Fayetteville State University, BM

Gardner-Webb University, B
Greensboro College, B
Guilford College, B
High Point University, B
Johnson C. Smith University, B
Lenoir-Rhyne College, B
Livingstone College, B
Louisburg College, A
Mars Hill College, B
Meredith College, B
Methodist College, AB
North Carolina Agricultural and Technical State University, B
North Carolina Central University, B
North Carolina State University, B
North Carolina Wesleyan College, B
Peace College, B
Pfeiffer University, B
Queens University of Charlotte, B
St. Andrews Presbyterian College, B
Saint Augustine's College, B
Shaw University, B
The University of North Carolina at Asheville, B
The University of North Carolina at Chapel Hill, BMD
The University of North Carolina at Charlotte, B
The University of North Carolina at Greensboro, BMO
The University of North Carolina at Pembroke, B
The University of North Carolina Wilmington, B
Wake Forest University, B
Western Carolina University, B
Winston-Salem State University, B

North Dakota

Dickinson State University, B
Jamestown College, B
North Dakota State University, BMD
University of North Dakota, B

Ohio

Antioch College, B
Ashland University, B
Baldwin-Wallace College, B
Bowling Green State University, BO
Capital University, B
Case Western Reserve University, BMD
Cedarville University, B
Central State University, B
Cleveland State University, B
The College of Wooster, B
Denison University, B
Franciscan University of Steubenville, B
Heidelberg College, B
Hiram College, B
John Carroll University, B
Kent State University, BMD
Kenyon College, B
Lorain County Community College, A
Malone College, B
Marietta College, B
Miami University, BMD
Miami University Hamilton, B
Miami University-Middletown Campus, A
Mount Union College, B
Muskingum College, B
Notre Dame College, B
Oberlin College, B
Ohio Dominican University, B
Ohio Northern University, B
The Ohio State University, BMD
Ohio University, BM
Ohio University-Eastern, B
Ohio Wesleyan University, B
Otterbein College, B
The University of Akron, BM
University of Cincinnati, BMD
University of Dayton, BM
The University of Findlay, B
University of Rio Grande, B
The University of Toledo, ABM
Walsh University, B
Wilberforce University, B
Wilmington College, B
Wittenberg University, B
Wright State University, B

Xavier University, AB
Youngstown State University, B

Oklahoma

Bacone College, A
Cameron University, B
East Central University, B
Eastern Oklahoma State College, A
Northeastern Oklahoma Agricultural and Mechanical College, A
Northeastern State University, B
Northwestern Oklahoma State University, B
Oklahoma Baptist University, B
Oklahoma City Community College, A
Oklahoma City University, B
Oklahoma State University, BM
Oklahoma Wesleyan University, B
Oral Roberts University, B
Rogers State University, A
Rose State College, A
St. Gregory's University, B
Southeastern Oklahoma State University, B
Southern Nazarene University, B
Southwestern Oklahoma State University, B
Tulsa Community College, A
University of Central Oklahoma, BM
University of Oklahoma, BMD
University of Science and Arts of Oklahoma, B
University of Tulsa, B

Oregon

Chemeketa Community College, A
Lewis & Clark College, B
Linfield College, B
Oregon State University, B
Pacific University, B
Portland State University, BMD
Reed College, B
Southern Oregon University, B
Treasure Valley Community College, A
Umpqua Community College, A
University of Oregon, BMD
University of Portland, B
Western Oregon University, B
Willamette University, B

Pennsylvania

Albright College, B
Allegheny College, B
Alvernia College, B
Arcadia University, B
Bloomsburg University of Pennsylvania, B
Bryn Mawr College, B
Bucknell University, B
Cabrini College, B
California University of Pennsylvania, B
Carlow University, B
Carnegie Mellon University, B
Cedar Crest College, B
Chatham College, B
Chestnut Hill College, B
Cheyney University of Pennsylvania, B
Clarion University of Pennsylvania, B
DeSales University, B
Dickinson College, B
Duquesne University, B
East Stroudsburg University of Pennsylvania, BM
Eastern University, B
Edinboro University of Pennsylvania, B
Elizabethtown College, B
Franklin and Marshall College, B
Gannon University, B
Geneva College, B
Gettysburg College, B
Grove City College, B
Haverford College, B
Indiana University of Pennsylvania, BM
Juniata College, B
King's College, B
Kutztown University of Pennsylvania, B
La Salle University, B
Lafayette College, B
Lebanon Valley College, B
Lehigh University, BM
Lincoln University, B
Lock Haven University of Pennsylvania, B

Lycoming College, B
Mansfield University of Pennsylvania, B
Mercyhurst College, B
Messiah College, B
Millersville University of Pennsylvania, B
Moravian College, B
Mount Aloysius College, B
Muhlenberg College, B
Neumann College, B
The Pennsylvania State University Abington
    College, B
The Pennsylvania State University Altoona
    College, B
The Pennsylvania State University Beaver Campus
    of the Commonwealth College, B
The Pennsylvania State University Berks Campus of
    the Berks-Lehigh Valley College, B
The Pennsylvania State University Delaware County
    Campus of the Commonwealth College, B
The Pennsylvania State University DuBois Campus
    of the Commonwealth College, B
The Pennsylvania State University at Erie, The
    Behrend College, B
The Pennsylvania State University Fayette Campus
    of the Commonwealth College, B
The Pennsylvania State University Hazleton
    Campus of the Commonwealth College, B
The Pennsylvania State University, Lehigh Valley
    Campus of the Berks-Lehigh Valley College, B
The Pennsylvania State University McKeesport
    Campus of the Commonwealth College, B
The Pennsylvania State University Mont Alto
    Campus of the Commonwealth College, B
The Pennsylvania State University New Kensington
    Campus of the Commonwealth College, B
The Pennsylvania State University Schuylkill
    Campus of the Capital College, B
The Pennsylvania State University Shenango
    Campus of the Commonwealth College, B
The Pennsylvania State University University Park
    Campus, BMD
The Pennsylvania State University Wilkes-Barre
    Campus of the Commonwealth College, B
The Pennsylvania State University Worthington
    Scranton Campus of the Commonwealth
    College, B
The Pennsylvania State University York Campus of
    the Commonwealth College, B
Point Park University, B
Reading Area Community College, A
Rosemont College, B
Saint Francis University, B
Saint Joseph's University, B
Saint Vincent College, B
Seton Hill University, B
Shippensburg University of Pennsylvania, B
Slippery Rock University of Pennsylvania, B
Susquehanna University, B
Swarthmore College, B
Temple University, BMD
Thiel College, B
University of Pennsylvania, BMDO
University of Pittsburgh, BMDO
University of Pittsburgh at Bradford, B
University of Pittsburgh at Greensburg, B
University of Pittsburgh at Johnstown, B
The University of Scranton, AB
Ursinus College, B
Villanova University, BM
Washington & Jefferson College, B
West Chester University of Pennsylvania, B
Westminster College, B
Widener University, B
Wilkes University, B
York College of Pennsylvania, AB

Puerto Rico

Inter American University of Puerto Rico,
    Metropolitan Campus, B
Inter American University of Puerto Rico, San
    Germán Campus, B
Pontifical Catholic University of Puerto Rico, B
University of Puerto Rico, Mayagüez Campus, B

University of Puerto Rico, Río Piedras, B

Rhode Island

Brown University, BMD
Providence College, B
Rhode Island College, B
Roger Williams University, B
Salve Regina University, B
University of Rhode Island, BMO

South Carolina

Benedict College, B
Bob Jones University, B
Charleston Southern University, B
The Citadel, The Military College of South
    Carolina, B
Clemson University, B
Coastal Carolina University, B
Coker College, B
College of Charleston, B
Columbia College, B
Converse College, BM
Francis Marion University, B
Furman University, B
Lander University, B
Morris College, B
Newberry College, B
Presbyterian College, B
South Carolina State University, B
University of South Carolina, BMD
University of South Carolina Aiken, B
University of South Carolina Upstate, B
Voorhees College, B
Winthrop University, B
Wofford College, B

South Dakota

Augustana College, B
Black Hills State University, B
Northern State University, B
South Dakota State University, B
University of Sioux Falls, B
The University of South Dakota, BMO

Tennessee

Austin Peay State University, B
Belmont University, B
Carson-Newman College, B
Columbia State Community College, A
Cumberland University, B
East Tennessee State University, B
Fisk University, B
King College, B
Lambuth University, B
LeMoyne-Owen College, B
Lipscomb University, B
Maryville College, B
Middle Tennessee State University, B
Rhodes College, B
Sewanee: The University of the South, B
Tennessee State University, B
Tennessee Technological University, B
Tennessee Temple University, B
Union University, B
University of Memphis, BM
The University of Tennessee, BMD
The University of Tennessee at Chattanooga, B
The University of Tennessee at Martin, B
Vanderbilt University, BMD

Texas

Abilene Christian University, B
Angelo State University, B
Austin College, B
Austin Community College, A
Baylor University, BMDO
Brazosport College, A
Coastal Bend College, A
Dallas Baptist University, B
Del Mar College, A
El Paso Community College, A
Frank Phillips College, A
Hardin-Simmons University, B
Hill College of the Hill Junior College District, A
Houston Baptist University, B

Howard Payne University, B
Huston-Tillotson University, B
Lamar University, BM
Lee College, A
Lon Morris College, A
McMurry University, B
Midland College, A
Midwestern State University, BM
North Harris College, A
Odessa College, A
Our Lady of the Lake University of San Antonio, B
Prairie View A&M University, B
Rice University, BMD
St. Edward's University, B
St. Mary's University of San Antonio, BMO
St. Philip's College, A
Sam Houston State University, BM
Schreiner University, B
Southern Methodist University, B
Southwestern University, B
Stephen F. Austin State University, B
Sul Ross State University, BM
Tarleton State University, BM
Texas A&M International University, BM
Texas A&M University, BMD
Texas A&M University-Commerce, B
Texas A&M University-Corpus Christi, B
Texas A&M University-Kingsville, BM
Texas Christian University, B
Texas College, B
Texas Lutheran University, B
Texas Southern University, B
Texas State University-San Marcos, BM
Texas Tech University, BMDO
Texas Wesleyan University, B
Texas Woman's University, BM
Trinity University, B
Trinity Valley Community College, A
University of Dallas, MD
University of Houston, BMD
University of Houston-Clear Lake, B
University of the Incarnate Word, B
University of Mary Hardin-Baylor, B
University of North Texas, BMD
University of St. Thomas, B
The University of Texas at Arlington, BM
The University of Texas at Austin, BMD
The University of Texas at Brownsville, BM
The University of Texas at Dallas, BD
The University of Texas at El Paso, BM
The University of Texas-Pan American, B
The University of Texas of the Permian Basin, B
The University of Texas at San Antonio, BM
The University of Texas at Tyler, BM
Wayland Baptist University, B
West Texas A&M University, BM

Utah

Brigham Young University, B
Dixie State College of Utah, A
Salt Lake Community College, A
Snow College, A
Southern Utah University, B
University of Utah, BMD
Utah State University, BM
Utah Valley State College, B
Weber State University, B
Westminster College, B

Vermont

Bennington College, B
College of St. Joseph, B
Johnson State College, B
Marlboro College, B
Middlebury College, B
Norwich University, B
Saint Michael's College, B
University of Vermont, B

Virginia

Averett University, B
Bridgewater College, B
Christendom College, B
Christopher Newport University, B
The College of William and Mary, B
Emory & Henry College, B

Ferrum College, B
George Mason University, B
Hampden-Sydney College, B
Hampton University, B
Hollins University, B
James Madison University, B
Liberty University, B
Longwood University, B
Lynchburg College, B
Mary Baldwin College, B
Marymount University, B
Norfolk State University, B
Old Dominion University, B
Patrick Henry College, B
Radford University, B
Randolph-Macon College, B
Randolph-Macon Woman's College, B
Regent University, B
Roanoke College, B
Saint Paul's College, B
Shenandoah University, B
Sweet Briar College, B
University of Mary Washington, B
University of Richmond, B
University of Virginia, BMDO
The University of Virginia's College at Wise, B
Virginia Commonwealth University, B
Virginia Intermont College, B
Virginia Polytechnic Institute and State
    University, BM
Virginia State University, B
Virginia Union University, B
Virginia Wesleyan College, B
Washington and Lee University, B

Washington

Central Washington University, B
Centralia College, A
Eastern Washington University, B
Everett Community College, A
The Evergreen State College, B
Gonzaga University, B
Heritage University, B
Lower Columbia College, A
Northwest University, B
Pacific Lutheran University, B
Saint Martin's University, B
Seattle Pacific University, B
Seattle University, B
Skagit Valley College, A
Tacoma Community College, A
University of Puget Sound, B
University of Washington, BMD
Washington State University, BMD
Western Washington University, BM
Whitman College, B
Whitworth College, B

West Virginia

Alderson-Broaddus College, B
American Public University System, M
Bethany College, B
Concord University, B
Davis & Elkins College, B
Fairmont State University, B
Marshall University, BM
Potomac State College of West Virginia
    University, A
Shepherd University, B
West Liberty State College, B
West Virginia State University, B
West Virginia University, BMD
West Virginia Wesleyan College, B
Wheeling Jesuit University, B

Wisconsin

Alverno College, B
Beloit College, B
Cardinal Stritch University, B
Carroll College, B
Carthage College, B
College of Menominee Nation, A
Edgewood College, B
Lawrence University, B
Marian College of Fond du Lac, B
Marquette University, BMO

Ripon College, B
St. Norbert College, B
University of Wisconsin-Eau Claire, B
University of Wisconsin-Green Bay, AB
University of Wisconsin-La Crosse, B
University of Wisconsin-Madison, BMD
University of Wisconsin-Milwaukee, BMD
University of Wisconsin-Oshkosh, BM
University of Wisconsin-Parkside, B
University of Wisconsin-Platteville, B
University of Wisconsin-River Falls, B
University of Wisconsin-Stevens Point, B
University of Wisconsin-Superior, B
University of Wisconsin-Whitewater, B
Wisconsin Lutheran College, B

Wyoming

Casper College, A
Eastern Wyoming College, A
Laramie County Community College, A
Northwest College, A
University of Wyoming, BM
Western Wyoming Community College, A

Alberta

Athabasca University, B
Concordia University College of Alberta, B
University of Alberta, BMD
University of Calgary, BMD
University of Lethbridge, BM

British Columbia

Kwantlen University College, A
Simon Fraser University, BMD
Thompson Rivers University, B
Trinity Western University, B
The University of British Columbia, BMD
University of Northern British Columbia, BM
University of Victoria, BM

Manitoba

Brandon University, B
Canadian Mennonite University, B
University of Manitoba, BM
The University of Winnipeg, B

New Brunswick

Mount Allison University, B
St. Thomas University, B
Université de Moncton, B
University of New Brunswick Fredericton, BM
University of New Brunswick Saint John, B

Newfoundland and Labrador

Memorial University of Newfoundland, BM

Nova Scotia

Acadia University, BM
Cape Breton University, B
Dalhousie University, BMD
Mount Saint Vincent University, B
St. Francis Xavier University, B
Saint Mary's University, B
University of King's College, B

Ontario

Brock University, BM
Carleton University, BMD
Lakehead University, B
Laurentian University, B
McMaster University, BMD
Queen's University at Kingston, BMD
Redeemer University College, B
Ryerson University, B
Trent University, B
University of Guelph, BM
University of Ottawa, BMD
University of Toronto, BMDO
University of Waterloo, BM
The University of Western Ontario, BMD
University of Windsor, BM
Wilfrid Laurier University, BM

York University, BMD

Prince Edward Island

University of Prince Edward Island, B

Quebec

Bishop's University, B
Concordia University, B
McGill University, BMD
Université Laval, ABMD
Université de Montréal, BMD
Université du Québec àChicoutimi, B
Université du Québec àMontréal, BMD

Saskatchewan

University of Regina, BM
University of Saskatchewan, BM

POLYMER CHEMISTRY

Georgia

Georgia Institute of Technology, B

Massachusetts

Harvard University, B

Minnesota

Winona State University, B

New York

Rochester Institute of Technology, B
State University of New York College of
    Environmental Science and Forestry, B

Ohio

The University of Akron, B

South Carolina

Clemson University, B

Wisconsin

University of Wisconsin-Stevens Point, B

POLYMER/PLASTICS ENGINEERING

California

University of Southern California, B

Connecticut

University of Connecticut, MD

Georgia

Georgia Institute of Technology, MD

Illinois

DePaul University, M

Indiana

Ball State University, B

Massachusetts

Massachusetts Institute of Technology, D
University of Massachusetts Amherst, MD
University of Massachusetts Lowell, BMD

Michigan

Eastern Michigan University, M
Ferris State University, B
Kettering University, B
University of Detroit Mercy, M

Wayne State University, O

Minnesota
Winona State University, B

Mississippi
University of Southern Mississippi, MD

Missouri
University of Missouri-Kansas City, MD

New Jersey
Princeton University, MD

New York
Cornell University, MD
Polytechnic University, Brooklyn Campus, M
Rensselaer Polytechnic Institute, MD

North Carolina
North Carolina State University, D

North Dakota
North Dakota State University, BMD

Ohio
Case Western Reserve University, BMDO
The University of Akron, BMD
University of Cincinnati, MD

Pennsylvania
Carnegie Mellon University, M
Lehigh University, MD
The Pennsylvania State University at Erie, The
  Behrend College, B
The Pennsylvania State University University Park
  Campus, MD

South Carolina
Clemson University, MD

Tennessee
The University of Tennessee, MD

Wisconsin
University of Wisconsin-Madison, M

POPULATION STUDIES

Massachusetts
Harvard University, MD

New York
Cornell University, MD

Pennsylvania
University of Pennsylvania, MD

Quebec
Université de Montréal, MD

PORTUGUESE LANGUAGE AND LITERATURE

California
Stanford University, B
University of California, Los Angeles, BM
University of California, Santa Barbara, BMD
University of Southern California, B

Connecticut
Yale University, BMD

District of Columbia
Georgetown University, B

Florida
Florida International University, B
Miami Dade College, A

University of Florida, B

Georgia
Emory University, DO

Illinois
University of Illinois at Urbana-Champaign, B

Indiana
Indiana University Bloomington, BMD

Iowa
The University of Iowa, B

Louisiana
Tulane University, BMD

Massachusetts
Harvard University, BMD
Smith College, B
University of Massachusetts Amherst, B
University of Massachusetts Dartmouth, BM

Michigan
Michigan State University, MD

Minnesota
University of Minnesota, Twin Cities Campus, BMD

New Jersey
Princeton University, D
Rutgers, The State University of New Jersey, New
  Brunswick/Piscataway, B

New Mexico
University of New Mexico, BMD

New York
Brooklyn College of the City University of New
  York, B
New York University, BMD
United States Military Academy, B

North Carolina
The University of North Carolina at Chapel Hill, MD

Ohio
The Ohio State University, BMD

Tennessee
The University of Tennessee, D
Vanderbilt University, BMD

Texas
The University of Texas at Austin, BMD

Utah
Brigham Young University, BM

Vermont
Marlboro College, B

Washington
University of Washington, M

Wisconsin
University of Wisconsin-Madison, BMD

Ontario
University of Toronto, BMD

POULTRY SCIENCE

Alabama
Auburn University, BMD
Tuskegee University, B

Wallace State Community College, A

Arkansas
University of Arkansas, BMD

California
Modesto Junior College, A

Delaware
Delaware State University, B

Florida
University of Florida, B

Georgia
Abraham Baldwin Agricultural College, A
University of Georgia, BMD

Maryland
University of Maryland, College Park, MD
University of Maryland Eastern Shore, B

Mississippi
Mississippi State University, BM
Northwest Mississippi Community College, A

Missouri
Crowder College, A

North Carolina
North Carolina State University, BM
Sampson Community College, A
Surry Community College, A
Wayne Community College, A

Texas
Northeast Texas Community College, A
Stephen F. Austin State University, B
Texas A&M University, BMD

Vermont
Sterling College, B

Virginia
Virginia Polytechnic Institute and State
  University, BMD

Wisconsin
University of Wisconsin-Madison, B

Ontario
University of Guelph, MD

PRE-DENTISTRY STUDIES

Alabama
Auburn University, B
Birmingham-Southern College, B
Calhoun Community College, A
Northwest-Shoals Community College, A
Spring Hill College, B
Troy University, B
University of Montevallo, B

Arizona
Grand Canyon University, B

Arkansas
Harding University, B
Ouachita Baptist University, B
University of Arkansas at Monticello, B
University of the Ozarks, B
Williams Baptist College, B

California
California State University, Chico, B
California State University, Dominguez Hills, B
California State University, East Bay, B
Claremont McKenna College, B
Humboldt State University, B
La Sierra University, B
Mount St. Mary's College, B

Notre Dame de Namur University, B
Pacific Union College, B
Pepperdine University, B
Sonoma State University, B
University of San Francisco, B
Westmont College, B

Colorado

Adams State College, B
Colorado State University-Pueblo, B
Regis University, B
University of Colorado at Colorado Springs, B
Western State College of Colorado, B

Connecticut

Albertus Magnus College, B
Quinnipiac University, B
Sacred Heart University, B
University of Bridgeport, B
University of Hartford, B
Western Connecticut State University, B

District of Columbia

The George Washington University, B

Florida

Barry University, B
Florida Agricultural and Mechanical University, B
Florida Southern College, B
Florida State University, B
Jacksonville University, B
Nova Southeastern University, B
Rollins College, B
St. Thomas University, B
Stetson University, B
The University of Tampa, B

Georgia

Andrew College, A
Coastal Georgia Community College, A
Columbus State University, B
Darton College, A
Georgia Perimeter College, A
Georgia Southwestern State University, B
LaGrange College, B
Mercer University, B
North Georgia College & State University, B
Oglethorpe University, B

Idaho

Boise State University, B

Illinois

Augustana College, B
Benedictine University, B
Blackburn College, B
Chicago State University, B
Concordia University, B
Dominican University, B
Elmhurst College, B
Eureka College, B
Illinois College, B
Lake Forest College, B
Lewis University, B
MacMurray College, B
McKendree College, B
Millikin University, B
North Central College, B
North Park University, B
Olivet Nazarene University, B
Quincy University, B
Rend Lake College, A
Rockford College, B
Roosevelt University, B
Sauk Valley Community College, A
Springfield College in Illinois, A
Trinity Christian College, B
University of Illinois at Chicago, B
University of St. Francis, B

Indiana

Anderson University, B
Ball State University, B
Goshen College, B
Huntington University, B

Indiana University Bloomington, B
Indiana University-Purdue University Fort Wayne, B
Indiana University-Purdue University Indianapolis, B
Indiana Wesleyan University, B
Manchester College, B
Marian College, B
Purdue University Calumet, B
Saint Mary-of-the-Woods College, B
Taylor University, B
University of Evansville, B
University of Indianapolis, B
University of Saint Francis, B

Iowa

Coe College, B
Dordt College, B
Drake University, B
Graceland University, B
Iowa Lakes Community College, A
Iowa State University of Science and Technology, B
Iowa Wesleyan College, B
Morningside College, B
Mount Mercy College, B
Simpson College, B
The University of Iowa, B
Upper Iowa University, B
William Penn University, B

Kansas

Allen County Community College, A
Barton County Community College, A
Central Christian College of Kansas, B
Friends University, B
Kansas State University, B
Kansas Wesleyan University, B
McPherson College, B
Newman University, B
Tabor College, B
Washburn University, B

Kentucky

Alice Lloyd College, B
Bellarmine University, B
Berea College, B
Campbellsville University, B
Kentucky Wesleyan College, B
Lindsey Wilson College, B
Northern Kentucky University, B

Louisiana

Centenary College of Louisiana, B
Dillard University, B
Nicholls State University, B
Xavier University of Louisiana, B

Maine

University of New England, B

Maryland

Columbia Union College, B
Coppin State University, B
Howard Community College, A
Morgan State University, B
University of Maryland, Baltimore County, B
University of Maryland Eastern Shore, B
Villa Julie College, B
Washington College, B

Massachusetts

American International College, B
Atlantic Union College, B
Boston University, B
Clark University, B
Elms College, B
Harvard University, B
Merrimack College, B
Salem State College, B
Simmons College, B
Springfield College, B
University of Massachusetts Amherst, B

Michigan

Alma College, B
Calvin College, B
Cornerstone University, B

Grand Valley State University, B
Hillsdale College, B
Lake Superior State University, B
Madonna University, B
Michigan Technological University, B
Northern Michigan University, B
Olivet College, B
University of Detroit Mercy, B
Western Michigan University, B

Minnesota

Augsburg College, B
College of Saint Benedict, B
College of St. Catherine, B
Concordia College, B
Gustavus Adolphus College, B
Hamline University, B
Minnesota State University Mankato, B
Minnesota State University Moorhead, B
St. Cloud State University, B
Saint John's University, B
Southwest Minnesota State University, B
University of Minnesota, Duluth, B
University of Minnesota, Morris, B
University of Minnesota, Twin Cities Campus, B
Winona State University, B

Mississippi

Blue Mountain College, B
Jackson State University, B
Mississippi College, B
Tougaloo College, B

Missouri

Central Missouri State University, B
Columbia College, B
Drury University, B
Evangel University, B
Lindenwood University, B
Missouri Southern State University, B
Missouri Valley College, B
Northwest Missouri State University, B
Truman State University, B
University of Missouri-Rolla, B
University of Missouri-St. Louis, B
Washington University in St. Louis, B
William Jewell College, B

Montana

Carroll College, B
The University of Montana-Western, B

Nebraska

College of Saint Mary, B
Concordia University, B
Hastings College, B
Midland Lutheran College, B
Peru State College, B
University of Nebraska-Lincoln, B
Western Nebraska Community College, A

New Hampshire

Franklin Pierce College, B
Rivier College, B
Saint Anselm College, B

New Jersey

Bloomfield College, B
Rutgers, The State University of New Jersey, New Brunswick/Piscataway, B
Stevens Institute of Technology, B
William Paterson University of New Jersey, B

New York

Bard College, B
Buffalo State College, State University of New York, B
City College of the City University of New York, B
Clarkson University, B
College of Mount Saint Vincent, B
D'Youville College, B
Elmira College, B
Fordham University, B
Hobart and William Smith Colleges, B
Hofstra University, B

Houghton College, B
Keuka College, B
Le Moyne College, B
Molloy College, B
Nazareth College of Rochester, B
New York University, B
Niagara University, B
Roberts Wesleyan College, B
Rochester Institute of Technology, B
St. Bonaventure University, B
St. Joseph's College, Suffolk Campus, B
Sarah Lawrence College, B
Siena College, B
State University of New York College at
   Brockport, B
State University of New York College at Cortland, B
State University of New York College of
   Environmental Science and Forestry, B
State University of New York College at Geneseo, B
State University of New York College at Oneonta, B
State University of New York at Oswego, B
Syracuse University, B
Touro College, B
Utica College, B
Wagner College, B
Wells College, B
Yeshiva University, B

North Carolina

Belmont Abbey College, B
Campbell University, B
Catawba College, B
Chowan University, B
Elon University, B
Gardner-Webb University, B
High Point University, B
Lenoir-Rhyne College, B
Meredith College, B
Methodist College, B

North Dakota

Dickinson State University, B
Mayville State University, B
Valley City State University, B

Ohio

Ashland University, B
Capital University, B
Cedarville University, B
Defiance College, B
Heidelberg College, B
Hiram College, B
John Carroll University, B
Kent State University, B
Kenyon College, B
Lake Erie College, B
Miami University, B
Mount Vernon Nazarene University, B
Muskingum College, B
Ohio Northern University, B
Ohio University-Eastern, B
Ohio Wesleyan University, B
Otterbein College, B
University of Dayton, B
University of Rio Grande, B
The University of Toledo, B
Urbana University, B
Walsh University, B
Wilmington College, B
Wright State University, B
Youngstown State University, B

Oklahoma

East Central University, B
Langston University, B
Northeastern State University, B
Northwestern Oklahoma State University, B
Oklahoma Baptist University, B
Oklahoma City University, B
Oklahoma Wesleyan University, B
Oral Roberts University, B
St. Gregory's University, B
Southern Nazarene University, B
Southwestern Oklahoma State University, B

Tulsa Community College, A

Oregon

Eastern Oregon University, B
Pacific University, B
University of Oregon, B
University of Portland, B

Pennsylvania

Allegheny College, B
Arcadia University, B
Cedar Crest College, B
DeSales University, B
Dickinson College, B
Elizabethtown College, B
Gannon University, B
Gettysburg College, B
Grove City College, B
Holy Family University, B
Immaculata University, B
Juniata College, B
King's College, B
La Salle University, B
Lehigh University, B
Lock Haven University of Pennsylvania, B
Lycoming College, B
Mercyhurst College, B
Saint Francis University, B
Seton Hill University, B
Susquehanna University, B
Thiel College, B
University of Pittsburgh at Johnstown, B
Waynesburg College, B
Westminster College, B
Widener University, B
York College of Pennsylvania, B

Rhode Island

Roger Williams University, B

South Carolina

Benedict College, B
Charleston Southern University, B
College of Charleston, B
Furman University, B
Limestone College, B
Newberry College, B
South Carolina State University, B
Wofford College, B

South Dakota

Augustana College, B
Northern State University, B
South Dakota State University, B
University of Sioux Falls, B

Tennessee

Bethel College, B
Cumberland University, B
Lambuth University, B
Lipscomb University, B
Tennessee Technological University, B
Tennessee Wesleyan College, B
Union University, B
The University of Tennessee at Martin, B

Texas

Abilene Christian University, B
Baylor University, B
Clarendon College, A
Hardin-Simmons University, B
Lamar University, B
LeTourneau University, B
Midwestern State University, B
St. Mary's University of San Antonio, B
St. Philip's College, A
Sam Houston State University, B
Schreiner University, B
Sul Ross State University, B
Tarleton State University, B
Texas A&M University-Kingsville, B
Texas Lutheran University, B
Texas Southern University, B
Texas Wesleyan University, B
Trinity University, B

University of Dallas, B
University of Houston, B
University of the Incarnate Word, B
University of St. Thomas, B
The University of Texas-Pan American, B
Wiley College, B

Utah

Utah State University, B

Vermont

Saint Michael's College, B

Virginia

Eastern Mennonite University, B
Emory & Henry College, B
Hampton University, B
Longwood University, B
Lynchburg College, B
University of Mary Washington, B
Virginia Wesleyan College, B

Washington

Centralia College, A
Eastern Washington University, B
Saint Martin's University, B
Seattle Pacific University, B
University of Puget Sound, B
Walla Walla College, B
Whitworth College, B

West Virginia

Alderson-Broaddus College, B
Bethany College, B
Davis & Elkins College, B
West Liberty State College, B
West Virginia State University, B
West Virginia Wesleyan College, B
Wheeling Jesuit University, B

Wisconsin

Beloit College, B
Cardinal Stritch University, B
Carroll College, B
Carthage College, B
Concordia University Wisconsin, A
Edgewood College, B
Lawrence University, B
Marian College of Fond du Lac, B
Marquette University, B
Mount Mary College, B
Northland College, B
Ripon College, B
University of Wisconsin-Green Bay, B
University of Wisconsin-Milwaukee, B
University of Wisconsin-Oshkosh, B
University of Wisconsin-Parkside, B
University of Wisconsin-River Falls, B

Wyoming

Eastern Wyoming College, A
Laramie County Community College, A
Western Wyoming Community College, A

Alberta

University of Alberta, B

British Columbia

Thompson Rivers University, B
Trinity Western University, B
The University of British Columbia, B
University of Victoria, B

Manitoba

Brandon University, B
University of Manitoba, B

The University of Winnipeg, B

New Brunswick

Mount Allison University, B
University of New Brunswick Fredericton, B

Nova Scotia

Acadia University, B
Cape Breton University, B
Dalhousie University, B
St. Francis Xavier University, B

Ontario

Redeemer University College, B
University of Windsor, B
York University, B

Prince Edward Island

University of Prince Edward Island, B

Quebec

Université Laval, B
Université de Montréal, B

Saskatchewan

University of Regina, B
University of Saskatchewan, B

PRE-ENGINEERING

Alabama

Alabama Southern Community College, A
Chattahoochee Valley Community College, A
Enterprise-Ozark Community College, A
Faulkner University, A
Lawson State Community College, A
Northeast Alabama Community College, A
Northwest-Shoals Community College, A

Arizona

Diné College, A
Mesa Community College, A
South Mountain Community College, A

Arkansas

Ouachita Baptist University, B

California

American River College, A
Azusa Pacific University, B
Cabrillo College, A
Cerritos College, A
Cerro Coso Community College, A
Chabot College, A
City College of San Francisco, A
College of the Canyons, A
College of the Desert, A
College of the Sequoias, A
Compton Community College, A
Cosumnes River College (Sacramento), A
Crafton Hills College, A
Cuesta College, A
De Anza College, A
East Los Angeles College, A
Evergreen Valley College, A
Gavilan College, A
Golden West College, A
Imperial Valley College, A
Lassen Community College District, A
Long Beach City College, A
Los Angeles Harbor College, A
Los Angeles Pierce College, A
Los Angeles Valley College, A
Merced College, A
Mission College, A
Mt. San Antonio College, A
Ohlone College, A
Palo Verde College, A
Porterville College, A
Saddleback College, A
San Bernardino Valley College, A
San Diego City College, A
Santa Monica College, A

Southwestern College, A
Taft College, A
West Hills Community College, A
Yuba College, A

Colorado

Adams State College, B
Colorado Mountain College, Alpine Campus, A
Lamar Community College, A
Mesa State College, A
Northeastern Junior College, A
Otero Junior College, A
Trinidad State Junior College, A

Connecticut

Housatonic Community College, A
Middlesex Community College, A
Naugatuck Valley Community College, A
Northwestern Connecticut Community College, A
Quinebaug Valley Community College, A
Three Rivers Community College, A

Delaware

Delaware State University, B

Florida

Broward Community College, A
Chipola College, A
Indian River Community College, A
Miami Dade College, A
Palm Beach Community College, A
Pensacola Junior College, A
Polk Community College, A
Valencia Community College, A

Georgia

Abraham Baldwin Agricultural College, A
Andrew College, A
Clayton State University, A
Coastal Georgia Community College, A
Columbus State University, A
Covenant College, A
Darton College, A
Fort Valley State University, A
Georgia Military College, A
Georgia Perimeter College, A
LaGrange College, A
Macon State College, A
South Georgia College, A
University of Georgia, B
Young Harris College, A

Idaho

Boise State University, A
Brigham Young University -Idaho, A

Illinois

City Colleges of Chicago, Harold Washington
  College, A
City Colleges of Chicago, Harry S. Truman
  College, A
City Colleges of Chicago, Kennedy-King College, A
City Colleges of Chicago, Richard J. Daley
  College, A
City Colleges of Chicago, Wilbur Wright College, A
Danville Area Community College, A
Elgin Community College, A
Highland Community College, A
Illinois Valley Community College, A
John A. Logan College, A
Lewis and Clark Community College, A
Lincoln Land Community College, A
Oakton Community College, A
Richland Community College, A
Rock Valley College, A
South Suburban College, A
Spoon River College, A
William Rainey Harper College, A

Indiana

Anderson University, A
Marian College, A
Purdue University North Central, A

Vincennes University, A

Iowa

Drake University, B
Ellsworth Community College, A
Iowa Lakes Community College, A
Kirkwood Community College, A
Marshalltown Community College, A

Kansas

Barton County Community College, A
Butler Community College, A
Cloud County Community College, A
Coffeyville Community College, A
Colby Community College, A
Cowley County Community College and Area
  Vocational-Technical School, A
Dodge City Community College, A
Friends University, A
Garden City Community College, A
Highland Community College, A
Independence Community College, A
Labette Community College, A
McPherson College, B
Neosho County Community College, A
Newman University, AB
Pratt Community College, A
Seward County Community College, A

Kentucky

Brescia University, A
Eastern Kentucky University, A

Massachusetts

Atlantic Union College, A
Bristol Community College, A
Cape Cod Community College, A
Greenfield Community College, A
Holyoke Community College, A
Middlesex Community College, A
North Shore Community College, A
Roxbury Community College, A

Michigan

Alpena Community College, A
Bay de Noc Community College, A
Ferris State University, A
Henry Ford Community College, A
Kalamazoo Valley Community College, A
Lansing Community College, A
Macomb Community College, A
Mid Michigan Community College, A
Monroe County Community College, A
North Central Michigan College, A
Oakland Community College, A
Siena Heights University, A
Washtenaw Community College, A

Minnesota

Anoka-Ramsey Community College, Cambridge
  Campus, A
Hibbing Community College, A
Itasca Community College, A
Mesabi Range Community and Technical College, A
Minnesota State Community and Technical
  College-Fergus Falls, A
Minnesota State University Mankato, A
Rainy River Community College, A
Ridgewater College, A
Rochester Community and Technical College, A
Vermilion Community College, A

Mississippi

East Central Community College, A
East Mississippi Community College, A
Hinds Community College, A
Itawamba Community College, A
Mississippi Gulf Coast Community College, A
Northeast Mississippi Community College, A

Missouri

Columbia College, B
Crowder College, A
East Central College, A
Hannibal-LaGrange College, A

Jefferson College, A
Lincoln University, A
Longview Community College, A
Maple Woods Community College, A
Missouri Southern State University, A
Moberly Area Community College, A
Saint Charles Community College, A
St. Louis Community College at Florissant Valley, A
St. Louis Community College at Forest Park, A

Montana

Fort Belknap College, A
Montana State University-Billings, A
The University of Montana-Missoula, B

Nebraska

Metropolitan Community College, A
Western Nebraska Community College, A

New Hampshire

Keene State College, A
University of New Hampshire, A

New Jersey

Cumberland County College, A
Essex County College, A
Passaic County Community College, A
Salem Community College, A

New Mexico

New Mexico Military Institute, A
University of New Mexico-Los Alamos Branch, A
University of New Mexico-Valencia Campus, A

New York

Adirondack Community College, A
Bronx Community College of the City University of
   New York, A
Corning Community College, A
Finger Lakes Community College, A
Jefferson Community College, A
Medgar Evers College of the City University of New
   York, A
Niagara University, A
Roberts Wesleyan College, B
State University of New York College of Agriculture
   and Technology at Morrisville, A
Vaughn College of Aeronautics and Technology, A
Wagner College, B

North Carolina

Caldwell Community College and Technical
   Institute, A
Campbell University, A
Davidson County Community College, A
Isothermal Community College, A
Lenoir Community College, A
Louisburg College, A
Methodist College, A
Sandhills Community College, A
Wake Technical Community College, A
Western Piedmont Community College, A

North Dakota

Turtle Mountain Community College, A
Valley City State University, B

Ohio

Baldwin-Wallace College, B
Bowling Green State University-Firelands College, A
Edison State Community College, A
Lorain County Community College, A
Miami University-Middletown Campus, A
Shawnee State University, A
University of Cincinnati Raymond Walters College, A
Wright State University, Lake Campus, A

Oklahoma

Carl Albert State College, A
Eastern Oklahoma State College, A
Murray State College, A
Northeastern Oklahoma Agricultural and Mechanical
   College, A
Oklahoma City Community College, A

Oral Roberts University, B
Rose State College, A
St. Gregory's University, A
Seminole State College, A
Tulsa Community College, A

Oregon

Central Oregon Community College, A
Lewis & Clark College, B
Linn-Benton Community College, A
Portland Community College, A
Umpqua Community College, A

Pennsylvania

Butler County Community College, A
Community College of Philadelphia, A
Reading Area Community College, A
Waynesburg College, B

Puerto Rico

University of Puerto Rico at Bayamón, A

South Carolina

Charleston Southern University, A
Greenville Technical College, A
Horry-Georgetown Technical College, A

South Dakota

Northern State University, A
University of Sioux Falls, A

Tennessee

Columbia State Community College, A
Roane State Community College, A
Walters State Community College, A

Texas

Amarillo College, A
Austin Community College, A
College of the Mainland, A
Del Mar College, A
El Paso Community College, A
Frank Phillips College, A
Grayson County College, A
Hill College of the Hill Junior College District, A
Lee College, A
Lon Morris College, A
Midland College, A
Midwestern State University, B
Navarro College, A
North Central Texas College, A
North Harris College, A
Northwest Vista College, A
Odessa College, A
St. Philip's College, A
Schreiner University, A
South Plains College, A
Southwestern Christian College, A
Trinity Valley Community College, A
Wharton County Junior College, A

Utah

College of Eastern Utah, A
Snow College, A
Southern Utah University, A
Utah Valley State College, A

Virginia

Mountain Empire Community College, A
Northern Virginia Community College, A
Virginia Western Community College, A

Washington

Centralia College, A
Everett Community College, A
Highline Community College, A
Lower Columbia College, A
Shoreline Community College, A
Skagit Valley College, A
Tacoma Community College, A
Wenatchee Valley College, A

Yakima Valley Community College, A

West Virginia

Potomac State College of West Virginia
   University, A
West Virginia State University, A
West Virginia University at Parkersburg, A

Wisconsin

Edgewood College, A
Milwaukee Area Technical College, A

Wyoming

Laramie County Community College, A
Northwest College, A
Western Wyoming Community College, A

PRE-LAW STUDIES

Alabama

Auburn University, B
Birmingham-Southern College, B
Calhoun Community College, A
Faulkner University, B
Lawson State Community College, A
Northwest-Shoals Community College, A
Talladega College, B
University of Montevallo, B

Arizona

Eastern Arizona College, A
Grand Canyon University, B
Northern Arizona University, B

Arkansas

Ouachita Baptist University, B
University of Arkansas at Monticello, B
Williams Baptist College, B

California

Azusa Pacific University, B
Biola University, B
California State Polytechnic University, Pomona, B
California State University, Dominguez Hills, B
California State University, Fresno, B
Claremont McKenna College, B
Fresno Pacific University, B
Humboldt State University, B
La Sierra University, B
The Master's College and Seminary, B
Mount St. Mary's College, B
National University, B
Notre Dame de Namur University, B
Pacific Union College, B
Pepperdine University, B
Sonoma State University, B
University of California, Riverside, B
University of California, Santa Barbara, B
University of La Verne, B
University of West Los Angeles, B
Vanguard University of Southern California, B
Westmont College, B

Colorado

Adams State College, B
Colorado State University-Pueblo, B
Regis University, B
University of Colorado at Colorado Springs, B
Western State College of Colorado, B

Connecticut

Albertus Magnus College, B
Quinnipiac University, B
Saint Joseph College, B
University of Bridgeport, B

District of Columbia

The George Washington University, B
Trinity (Washington) University, B

Florida

Barry University, B
Clearwater Christian College, B

Florida State University, B
Gulf Coast Community College, A
Jacksonville University, B
Lynn University, B
Nova Southeastern University, B
Palm Beach Atlantic University, B
Rollins College, B
St. Thomas University, B
Stetson University, B
The University of Tampa, B
Webber International University, B

Georgia

Andrew College, A
Brenau University, B
Brewton-Parker College, B
Columbus State University, B
Covenant College, B
Darton College, A
Emmanuel College, B
LaGrange College, B
Oglethorpe University, B
Toccoa Falls College, B
University of West Georgia, B

Idaho

Northwest Nazarene University, B

Illinois

Augustana College, B
Benedictine University, B
Blackburn College, B
Chicago State University, B
Concordia University, B
DePaul University, B
Dominican University, B
Elmhurst College, B
Eureka College, B
Illinois College, B
Judson College, B
Lake Forest College, B
Lewis University, B
MacMurray College, B
McKendree College, B
Millikin University, B
North Central College, B
North Park University, B
Olivet Nazarene University, B
Rend Lake College, A
Rockford College, B
Roosevelt University, B
Springfield College in Illinois, A
University of Illinois at Chicago, B
University of Illinois at Urbana-Champaign, B

Indiana

Anderson University, B
Ball State University, B
Bethel College, B
Calumet College of Saint Joseph, AB
Earlham College, B
Goshen College, B
Huntington University, B
Indiana University Bloomington, B
Indiana University-Purdue University Indianapolis, B
Indiana Wesleyan University, B
Manchester College, B
Marian College, B
Oakland City University, B
Purdue University Calumet, B
Saint Mary-of-the-Woods College, B
Taylor University, B
Taylor University Fort Wayne, B
Tri-State University, B
University of Indianapolis, B
University of Saint Francis, B
Wabash College, B

Iowa

Ashford University, B
Coe College, B
Dordt College, B
Drake University, B
Graceland University, B
Grand View College, B

Iowa Lakes Community College, A
Iowa State University of Science and Technology, B
Iowa Wesleyan College, B
Morningside College, B
Mount Mercy College, B
Simpson College, B
The University of Iowa, B
William Penn University, B

Kansas

Allen County Community College, A
Barton County Community College, A
Central Christian College of Kansas, B
Fort Hays State University, B
Kansas Wesleyan University, B
Newman University, B
Washburn University, B

Kentucky

Alice Lloyd College, B
Bellarmine University, B
Campbellsville University, B
Kentucky Wesleyan College, B
Lindsey Wilson College, B
Northern Kentucky University, B
Thomas More College, A

Louisiana

Centenary College of Louisiana, B
Dillard University, B
Grambling State University, B
Louisiana College, B
University of Louisiana at Lafayette, B
Xavier University of Louisiana, B

Maryland

College of Notre Dame of Maryland, B
Columbia Union College, B
Coppin State University, B
Morgan State University, B
University of Maryland, Baltimore County, B
University of Maryland Eastern Shore, B
Villa Julie College, B
Washington College, B

Massachusetts

American International College, B
Atlantic Union College, B
Babson College, B
Bay Path College, B
Clark University, B
Curry College, B
Eastern Nazarene College, B
Elms College, B
Harvard University, B
Lasell College, B
Massachusetts College of Liberal Arts, B
Merrimack College, B
Newbury College, B
Salem State College, B
Simmons College, B
Simon's Rock College of Bard, B
Smith College, B
Springfield College, B
Suffolk University, B
Westfield State College, B

Michigan

Albion College, B
Alma College, B
Andrews University, B
Aquinas College, B
Calvin College, B
Concordia University, B
Cornerstone University, B
Ferris State University, A
Grand Valley State University, B
Kellogg Community College, A
Lake Superior State University, B
Madonna University, B
Michigan State University, B
Michigan Technological University, B
Northern Michigan University, B
Olivet College, B
Siena Heights University, B

University of Detroit Mercy, B
Western Michigan University, B

Minnesota

Augsburg College, B
Bemidji State University, B
College of Saint Benedict, B
College of St. Catherine, B
Concordia College, B
Crown College, B
Gustavus Adolphus College, B
Hamline University, B
Minnesota State University Mankato, B
Minnesota State University Moorhead, B
St. Cloud State University, B
Saint John's University, B
Southwest Minnesota State University, B
University of Minnesota, Duluth, B
University of Minnesota, Morris, B
University of Minnesota, Twin Cities Campus, B
Winona State University, B

Mississippi

Blue Mountain College, B
Jackson State University, B
Mississippi College, B

Missouri

College of the Ozarks, B
Columbia College, B
Drury University, B
Evangel University, B
Fontbonne University, B
Hannibal-LaGrange College, B
Lindenwood University, B
Missouri Valley College, B
Northwest Missouri State University, B
Stephens College, B
Truman State University, B
University of Missouri-Rolla, B
University of Missouri-St. Louis, B
Westminster College, B
William Jewell College, B

Montana

Carroll College, B
Montana State University-Billings, B
The University of Montana-Missoula, B
The University of Montana-Western, B

Nebraska

College of Saint Mary, B
Concordia University, B
Creighton University, B
Hastings College, B
Midland Lutheran College, B
Northeast Community College, A
Peru State College, B
Western Nebraska Community College, A

New Hampshire

Franklin Pierce College, B
New England College, B
Rivier College, B
Saint Anselm College, B

New Jersey

The College of New Jersey, B
Felician College, B
Rutgers, The State University of New Jersey, New Brunswick/Piscataway, B
Stevens Institute of Technology, B
William Paterson University of New Jersey, B

New Mexico

New Mexico Highlands University, B
Western New Mexico University, B

New York

Bard College, B
Buffalo State College, State University of New York, B
City College of the City University of New York, B
Clarkson University, B
College of Mount Saint Vincent, B

The College of New Rochelle, B
Concordia College, B
Cornell University, B
Dominican College, B
D'Youville College, B
Elmira College, B
Fordham University, B
Hartwick College, B
Hobart and William Smith Colleges, B
Houghton College, B
Ithaca College, B
John Jay College of Criminal Justice of the City
  University of New York, B
Keuka College, B
Le Moyne College, B
Medaille College, B
Molloy College, B
Mount Saint Mary College, B
Nazareth College of Rochester, B
Niagara University, B
Rensselaer Polytechnic Institute, B
Roberts Wesleyan College, B
Rochester Institute of Technology, B
St. Bonaventure University, B
St. Joseph's College, New York, B
St. Joseph's College, Suffolk Campus, B
Sarah Lawrence College, B
Siena College, B
State University of New York at Binghamton, B
State University of New York College at
  Brockport, B
State University of New York College at Cortland, B
State University of New York College of
  Environmental Science and Forestry, B
State University of New York College at Geneseo, B
State University of New York College at Oneonta, B
State University of New York, Fredonia, B
State University of New York at Oswego, B
Syracuse University, B
Touro College, B
United States Military Academy, B
Utica College, B
Wagner College, B
Wells College, B
Yeshiva University, B

North Carolina

Barber-Scotia College, B
Belmont Abbey College, B
Campbell University, B
Catawba College, B
Chowan University, B
Elon University, B
Gardner-Webb University, B
High Point University, B
Lees-McRae College, B
Lenoir-Rhyne College, B
Louisburg College, A
Mars Hill College, B
Methodist College, B
Pfeiffer University, B
Queens University of Charlotte, B
St. Andrews Presbyterian College, B
Saint Augustine's College, B
Wingate University, B

North Dakota

Dickinson State University, B
Mayville State University, B
Valley City State University, B

Ohio

Antioch College, B
Ashland University, B
Bowling Green State University, B
Cedarville University, B
Defiance College, B
Heidelberg College, B
Hiram College, B
John Carroll University, B
Kenyon College, B
Lake Erie College, B
Miami University, B
Mount Vernon Nazarene University, B
Muskingum College, B
Notre Dame College, B

Ohio Northern University, B
Ohio University, B
Ohio University-Eastern, B
Ohio Wesleyan University, B
Otterbein College, B
Shawnee State University, B
Tiffin University, B
The University of Akron, B
University of Cincinnati, B
University of Dayton, B
The University of Findlay, B
University of Rio Grande, B
The University of Toledo, B
Urbana University, B
Wilmington College, B
Wright State University, B
Youngstown State University, B

Oklahoma

East Central University, B
Langston University, B
Northeastern State University, B
Northwestern Oklahoma State University, B
Oklahoma Baptist University, B
Oklahoma Christian University, B
Oklahoma City University, B
Oklahoma Wesleyan University, B
Oral Roberts University, B
St. Gregory's University, B
Southern Nazarene University, B
Southwestern Oklahoma State University, B

Oregon

Corban College, B
Eastern Oregon University, B
Southern Oregon University, B
University of Portland, B
Warner Pacific College, B

Pennsylvania

Albright College, B
Allegheny College, B
Alvernia College, B
Arcadia University, B
Cedar Crest College, B
Dickinson College, B
Elizabethtown College, B
Gannon University, B
Gettysburg College, B
Grove City College, B
Gwynedd-Mercy College, B
Haverford College, B
Holy Family University, B
Immaculata University, A
Juniata College, B
King's College, B
Lebanon Valley College, B
Lycoming College, B
Mansfield University of Pennsylvania, B
Marywood University, B
Mercyhurst College, B
Mount Aloysius College, B
Peirce College, A
Saint Francis University, B
Seton Hill University, B
Susquehanna University, B
Thiel College, B
University of Pittsburgh at Greensburg, B
University of Pittsburgh at Johnstown, B
Waynesburg College, B
Westminster College, B
York College of Pennsylvania, B

Puerto Rico

Caribbean University, B
Pontifical Catholic University of Puerto Rico, B

South Carolina

Benedict College, B
Bob Jones University, B
Charleston Southern University, B
Francis Marion University, B
Furman University, B
Limestone College, B
Newberry College, B

South Carolina State University, B
Wofford College, B

South Dakota

Augustana College, B
National American University (Rapid City), B
Northern State University, B
South Dakota State University, B
University of Sioux Falls, B

Tennessee

Cumberland University, B
King College, B
Lambuth University, B
Lincoln Memorial University, B
Lipscomb University, B
Tennessee Technological University, B
Tennessee Temple University, B
Tennessee Wesleyan College, B
Tusculum College, B
Union University, B

Texas

Abilene Christian University, B
Baylor University, B
Clarendon College, A
Hardin-Simmons University, B
Houston Baptist University, B
Howard Payne University, B
LeTourneau University, B
Lubbock Christian University, B
Midwestern State University, B
St. Philip's College, A
Sam Houston State University, B
Schreiner University, B
Sul Ross State University, B
Texas A&M University-Kingsville, B
Texas Lutheran University, B
Texas Wesleyan University, B
Trinity University, B
University of Dallas, B
University of Houston, B
University of the Incarnate Word, B
University of St. Thomas, B
West Texas A&M University, B
Wiley College, B

Utah

Dixie State College of Utah, A
Utah State University, B

Vermont

Bennington College, B
Champlain College, B
College of St. Joseph, B
Marlboro College, B
Saint Michael's College, B
Southern Vermont College, B

Virginia

Christopher Newport University, B
Emory & Henry College, B
Hampton University, B
Longwood University, B
Lynchburg College, B
University of Mary Washington, B
Virginia Intermont College, B
Virginia Wesleyan College, B

Washington

Centralia College, A
Eastern Washington University, B
Lower Columbia College, A
Saint Martin's University, B
Seattle Pacific University, B
University of Puget Sound, B
Walla Walla College, B
Washington State University, B
Whitworth College, B

West Virginia

Alderson-Broaddus College, B
Bethany College, B
Davis & Elkins College, B
West Liberty State College, B

West Virginia Wesleyan College, B
Wheeling Jesuit University, B

Wisconsin

Beloit College, B
Cardinal Stritch University, B
Carthage College, B
Concordia University Wisconsin, B
Edgewood College, B
Lawrence University, B
Marian College of Fond du Lac, B
Marquette University, B
Mount Mary College, B
Northland College, B
Ripon College, B
University of Wisconsin-Milwaukee, B
University of Wisconsin-Oshkosh, B
University of Wisconsin-Parkside, B
University of Wisconsin-River Falls, B
University of Wisconsin-Superior, B

Wyoming

Central Wyoming College, A
Laramie County Community College, A
Western Wyoming Community College, A

Alberta

University of Alberta, B

British Columbia

Trinity Western University, B
The University of British Columbia, B
University of Victoria, B

Manitoba

Brandon University, B
University of Manitoba, B
The University of Winnipeg, B

New Brunswick

Mount Allison University, B
University of New Brunswick Fredericton, B

Nova Scotia

Acadia University, B
Cape Breton University, B
Dalhousie University, B
St. Francis Xavier University, B

Ontario

Carleton University, B
Redeemer University College, B
University of Ottawa, B
University of Windsor, B
York University, B

Quebec

Université Laval, B

Saskatchewan

University of Regina, B
University of Saskatchewan, B

PRE-MEDICINE/PRE-MEDICAL STUDIES

Alabama

Alabama State University, B
Auburn University, B
Birmingham-Southern College, B
Calhoun Community College, A
Samford University, B
Spring Hill College, B
Troy University, B
University of Montevallo, B

Arizona

Eastern Arizona College, A
Grand Canyon University, B

Northern Arizona University, B

Arkansas

Harding University, B
Ouachita Baptist University, B
University of Arkansas at Monticello, B
University of Arkansas at Pine Bluff, B
University of the Ozarks, B
Williams Baptist College, B

California

California Polytechnic State University, San Luis
    Obispo, B
California State Polytechnic University, Pomona, B
California State University, Chico, B
California State University, Dominguez Hills, B
California State University, East Bay, B
Claremont McKenna College, B
Fresno Pacific University, B
Humboldt State University, B
La Sierra University, B
The Master's College and Seminary, B
Mount St. Mary's College, B
Notre Dame de Namur University, B
Pacific Union College, B
Pepperdine University, B
Pitzer College, B
Pomona College, B
Scripps College, B
Sonoma State University, B
University of Judaism, B
University of San Diego, B
University of San Francisco, B
Westmont College, B

Colorado

Adams State College, B
Colorado State University-Pueblo, B
Regis University, B
University of Colorado at Colorado Springs, B
Western State College of Colorado, B

Connecticut

Albertus Magnus College, B
Quinnipiac University, B
Sacred Heart University, B
Saint Joseph College, B
University of Bridgeport, B
University of Hartford, B
Western Connecticut State University, B

District of Columbia

The George Washington University, B
Trinity (Washington) University, B

Florida

Barry University, B
Clearwater Christian College, B
Florida Southern College, B
Florida State University, B
Jacksonville University, B
Lynn University, B
Nova Southeastern University, B
Rollins College, B
St. Thomas University, B
Southeastern University, B
Stetson University, B
The University of Tampa, B

Georgia

Andrew College, A
Coastal Georgia Community College, A
Columbus State University, B
Covenant College, B
Darton College, A
Gainesville College, A
Georgia Perimeter College, A
Georgia Southwestern State University, B
LaGrange College, B
Mercer University, B
North Georgia College & State University, B
Oglethorpe University, B
University of Georgia, B

University of West Georgia, B

Hawaii

Hawaii Pacific University, B

Idaho

Albertson College of Idaho, B
Boise State University, B
Northwest Nazarene University, B
University of Idaho, B

Illinois

Augustana College, B
Benedictine University, B
Blackburn College, B
Chicago State University, B
City Colleges of Chicago, Malcolm X College, A
Concordia University, B
Dominican University, B
Elmhurst College, B
Eureka College, B
Illinois College, B
Judson College, B
Lake Forest College, B
Lewis University, B
MacMurray College, B
McKendree College, B
Millikin University, B
North Central College, B
North Park University, B
Northwestern University, B
Olivet Nazarene University, B
Quincy University, B
Rend Lake College, A
Rockford College, B
Roosevelt University, B
Sauk Valley Community College, A
Springfield College in Illinois, A
Trinity Christian College, B
Trinity International University, B
University of St. Francis, B

Indiana

Anderson University, B
Ball State University, B
Bethel College, B
Earlham College, B
Goshen College, B
Huntington University, B
Indiana University Bloomington, B
Indiana University-Purdue University Fort Wayne, B
Indiana University-Purdue University Indianapolis, B
Indiana Wesleyan University, B
Manchester College, B
Marian College, B
Oakland City University, B
Purdue University Calumet, B
Saint Mary-of-the-Woods College, B
Taylor University, B
Tri-State University, B
University of Evansville, B
University of Indianapolis, B
University of Notre Dame, B
University of Saint Francis, B
Wabash College, B

Iowa

Ashford University, B
Coe College, B
Dordt University, B
Drake University, B
Graceland University, B
Iowa Lakes Community College, A
Iowa State University of Science and Technology, B
Iowa Wesleyan College, B
Morningside College, B
Mount Mercy College, B
Simpson College, B
The University of Iowa, B
Upper Iowa University, B
William Penn University, B

Kansas

Allen County Community College, A
Barton County Community College, A

Central Christian College of Kansas, B
Friends University, B
Kansas State University, B
Kansas Wesleyan University, B
McPherson College, B
Newman University, B
Tabor College, B
Washburn University, B

Kentucky

Alice Lloyd College, B
Bellarmine University, B
Berea College, B
Campbellsville University, B
Kentucky Wesleyan College, B
Lindsey Wilson College, B
Northern Kentucky University, B

Louisiana

Centenary College of Louisiana, B
Dillard University, B
Nicholls State University, B
Xavier University of Louisiana, B

Maine

Bowdoin College, B
University of Maine, B
University of Maine at Machias, B
University of New England, B

Maryland

College of Notre Dame of Maryland, B
Columbia Union College, B
Coppin State University, B
Howard Community College, A
Morgan State University, B
University of Maryland, Baltimore County, B
University of Maryland Eastern Shore, B
Villa Julie College, B
Washington College, B

Massachusetts

American International College, B
Atlantic Union College, B
Boston College, B
Clark University, B
College of the Holy Cross, B
Eastern Nazarene College, B
Elms College, B
Harvard University, B
Massachusetts College of Pharmacy and Health
    Sciences, B
Merrimack College, B
Salem State College, B
Simmons College, B
Simon's Rock College of Bard, B
Smith College, B
Springfield College, B
University of Massachusetts Amherst, B
Westfield State College, B
Wheaton College, B

Michigan

Adrian College, B
Albion College, B
Alma College, B
Andrews University, B
Calvin College, B
Concordia University, B
Cornerstone University, B
Grand Valley State University, B
Hillsdale College, B
Kellogg Community College, A
Madonna University, B
Michigan State University, B
Michigan Technological University, B
Northern Michigan University, B
Olivet College, B
University of Detroit Mercy, B
Western Michigan University, B

Minnesota

Augsburg College, B
Bemidji State University, B
College of Saint Benedict, B

College of St. Catherine, B
Concordia College, B
Gustavus Adolphus College, B
Hamline University, B
Minnesota State University Mankato, B
Minnesota State University Moorhead, B
St. Cloud State University, B
Saint John's University, B
Southwest Minnesota State University, B
University of Minnesota, Duluth, B
University of Minnesota, Morris, B
University of Minnesota, Twin Cities Campus, B
Winona State University, B

Mississippi

Blue Mountain College, B
Jackson State University, B
Mississippi College, B

Missouri

Central Missouri State University, B
College of the Ozarks, B
Columbia College, B
Drury University, B
Evangel University, B
Fontbonne University, B
Lindenwood University, B
Missouri Southern State University, B
Missouri Valley College, B
Northwest Missouri State University, B
Stephens College, B
Truman State University, B
University of Missouri-Rolla, B
University of Missouri-St. Louis, B
Washington University in St. Louis, B
William Jewell College, B

Montana

Carroll College, B
Montana State University-Billings, B
The University of Montana-Missoula, B
The University of Montana-Western, B

Nebraska

College of Saint Mary, B
Concordia University, B
Hastings College, B
Midland Lutheran College, B
Peru State College, B
University of Nebraska-Lincoln, B
Wayne State College, B
Western Nebraska Community College, A

Nevada

University of Nevada, Reno, B

New Hampshire

Franklin Pierce College, B
Rivier College, B
Saint Anselm College, B
University of New Hampshire, B

New Jersey

Bloomfield College, B
The College of New Jersey, B
Felician College, B
Rutgers, The State University of New Jersey, New
    Brunswick/Piscataway, B
Stevens Institute of Technology, B
William Paterson University of New Jersey, B

New Mexico

New Mexico Highlands University, B
St. John's College, B
San Juan College, A

New York

Bard College, B
Buffalo State College, State University of New
    York, B
City College of the City University of New York, B
Clarkson University, B
College of Mount Saint Vincent, B
The College of New Rochelle, B
D'Youville College, B

Elmira College, B
Fordham University, B
Hartwick College, B
Hobart and William Smith Colleges, B
Hofstra University, B
Houghton College, B
Ithaca College, B
Keuka College, B
Le Moyne College, B
Manhattanville College, B
Medgar Evers College of the City University of New
    York, B
Molloy College, B
Nazareth College of Rochester, B
New York Institute of Technology, B
New York University, B
Niagara University, B
Rensselaer Polytechnic Institute, B
Roberts Wesleyan College, B
Rochester Institute of Technology, B
St. Bonaventure University, B
St. Joseph's College, Suffolk Campus, B
St. Thomas Aquinas College, B
Sarah Lawrence College, B
Siena College, B
State University of New York at Binghamton, B
State University of New York College of Agriculture
    and Technology at Cobleskill, A
State University of New York College at
    Brockport, B
State University of New York College at Cortland, B
State University of New York College of
    Environmental Science and Forestry, B
State University of New York College at Geneseo, B
State University of New York College at Oneonta, B
State University of New York, Fredonia, B
State University of New York at Oswego, B
Syracuse University, B
Touro College, B
United States Military Academy, B
Utica College, B
Wagner College, B
Wells College, B
Yeshiva University, B

North Carolina

Belmont Abbey College, B
Campbell University, B
Catawba College, B
Chowan University, B
Elon University, B
Gardner-Webb University, B
High Point University, B
Johnson C. Smith University, B
Lees-McRae College, B
Lenoir-Rhyne College, B
Louisburg College, A
Mars Hill College, B
Meredith College, B
Methodist College, B
North Carolina Wesleyan College, B
Pfeiffer University, B
Queens University of Charlotte, B
St. Andrews Presbyterian College, B
Saint Augustine's College, B
Wingate University, B

North Dakota

Dickinson State University, B
Mayville State University, B
Valley City State University, B

Ohio

Antioch College, B
Ashland University, B
Bluffton University, B
Capital University, B
Cedarville University, B
Defiance College, B
Heidelberg College, B
Hiram College, B
John Carroll University, B
Kent State University, B
Kenyon College, B
Lake Erie College, B
Lourdes College, B

Miami University, B
Mount Vernon Nazarene University, B
Muskingum College, B
Notre Dame College, B
Ohio Northern University, B
Ohio University-Eastern, B
Ohio Wesleyan University, B
Otterbein College, B
Shawnee State University, B
University of Cincinnati, B
University of Dayton, B
The University of Findlay, B
University of Rio Grande, B
The University of Toledo, B
Urbana University, B
Walsh University, B
Wilmington College, B
Wright State University, B
Youngstown State University, B

Oklahoma

East Central University, B
Langston University, B
Northeastern State University, B
Northwestern Oklahoma State University, B
Oklahoma Baptist University, B
Oklahoma City University, B
Oklahoma Wesleyan University, B
Oral Roberts University, B
St. Gregory's University, B
Southern Nazarene University, B
Southwestern Oklahoma State University, B
Tulsa Community College, A

Oregon

Concordia University, B
Eastern Oregon University, B
Oregon Institute of Technology, B
Pacific University, B
Southern Oregon University, B
University of Oregon, B
University of Portland, B
Warner Pacific College, B

Pennsylvania

Allegheny College, B
Alvernia College, B
Arcadia University, B
Cedar Crest College, B
DeSales University, B
Dickinson College, B
Elizabethtown College, B
Gannon University, B
Gettysburg College, B
Grove City College, B
Haverford College, B
Holy Family University, B
Juniata College, B
King's College, B
La Salle University, B
Lebanon Valley College, B
Lehigh University, B
Lock Haven University of Pennsylvania, B
Lycoming College, B
Mansfield University of Pennsylvania, B
Mercyhurst College, B
The Pennsylvania State University Abington
   College, B
The Pennsylvania State University Altoona
   College, B
The Pennsylvania State University Beaver Campus
   of the Commonwealth College, B
The Pennsylvania State University Berks Campus of
   the Berks-Lehigh Valley College, B
The Pennsylvania State University Delaware County
   Campus of the Commonwealth College, B
The Pennsylvania State University DuBois Campus
   of the Commonwealth College, B
The Pennsylvania State University at Erie, The
   Behrend College, B
The Pennsylvania State University Fayette Campus
   of the Commonwealth College, B
The Pennsylvania State University Hazleton
   Campus of the Commonwealth College, B
The Pennsylvania State University, Lehigh Valley
   Campus of the Berks-Lehigh Valley College, B

The Pennsylvania State University McKeesport
   Campus of the Commonwealth College, B
The Pennsylvania State University Mont Alto
   Campus of the Commonwealth College, B
The Pennsylvania State University New Kensington
   Campus of the Commonwealth College, B
The Pennsylvania State University Schuylkill
   Campus of the Capital College, B
The Pennsylvania State University Shenango
   Campus of the Commonwealth College, B
The Pennsylvania State University University Park
   Campus, B
The Pennsylvania State University Wilkes-Barre
   Campus of the Commonwealth College, B
The Pennsylvania State University Worthington
   Scranton Campus of the Commonwealth
   College, B
The Pennsylvania State University York Campus of
   the Commonwealth College, B
Philadelphia University, B
Saint Francis University, B
Seton Hill University, B
Susquehanna University, B
Thiel College, B
University of Pittsburgh at Johnstown, B
Waynesburg College, B
West Chester University of Pennsylvania, B
Westminster College, B
Widener University, B
York College of Pennsylvania, B

Puerto Rico

Caribbean University, B
Inter American University of Puerto Rico, Bayamón
   Campus, B
Inter American University of Puerto Rico,
   Metropolitan Campus, B
Pontifical Catholic University of Puerto Rico, B
Universidad Metropolitana, B
University of Puerto Rico, Mayagüez Campus, B

Rhode Island

Roger Williams University, B

South Carolina

Benedict College, B
Bob Jones University, B
Charleston Southern University, B
College of Charleston, B
Furman University, B
Limestone College, B
Newberry College, B
South Carolina State University, B
Southern Wesleyan University, B
Wofford College, B

South Dakota

Augustana College, B
Northern State University, B
South Dakota State University, B
University of Sioux Falls, B

Tennessee

Bethel College, B
Bryan College, B
Cumberland University, B
King College, B
Lambuth University, B
Lincoln Memorial University, B
Lipscomb University, B
Tennessee Technological University, B
Tennessee Wesleyan College, B
Tusculum College, B
Union University, B
The University of Tennessee at Martin, B

Texas

Abilene Christian University, B
Baylor University, B
Brazosport College, A
Clarendon College, A
Hardin-Simmons University, B
Howard Payne University, B
Huston-Tillotson University, B
LeTourneau University, B

Midwestern State University, B
Paul Quinn College, B
St. Philip's College, A
Sam Houston State University, B
Schreiner University, B
Sul Ross State University, B
Tarleton State University, B
Texas A&M University-Kingsville, B
Texas Lutheran University, B
Texas Southern University, B
Texas Wesleyan University, B
Trinity University, B
University of Dallas, B
University of Houston, B
University of the Incarnate Word, B
University of St. Thomas, B
The University of Texas-Pan American, B
Wiley College, B

Utah

Utah State University, B

Vermont

Bennington College, B
Johnson State College, B
Marlboro College, B
Saint Michael's College, B

Virginia

Averett University, B
Eastern Mennonite University, B
Emory & Henry College, B
Hampton University, B
Longwood University, B
Lynchburg College, B
University of Mary Washington, B
Virginia Intermont College, B
Virginia Wesleyan College, B

Washington

Centralia College, A
Eastern Washington University, B
Saint Martin's University, B
Seattle Pacific University, B
University of Puget Sound, B
Walla Walla College, B
Washington State University, B
Whitworth College, B

West Virginia

Alderson-Broaddus College, B
Bethany College, B
Concord University, B
Davis & Elkins College, B
Mountain State University, B
West Liberty State College, B
West Virginia State University, B
West Virginia Wesleyan College, B
Wheeling Jesuit University, B

Wisconsin

Beloit College, B
Cardinal Stritch University, B
Carroll College, B
Carthage College, B
Concordia University Wisconsin, A
Edgewood College, B
Lawrence University, B
Marian College of Fond du Lac, B
Marquette University, B
Mount Mary College, B
Northland College, B
Ripon College, B
University of Wisconsin-Milwaukee, B
University of Wisconsin-Oshkosh, B
University of Wisconsin-Parkside, B
University of Wisconsin-River Falls, B

Wyoming

Eastern Wyoming College, A
Laramie County Community College, A

Western Wyoming Community College, A

Alberta

University of Alberta, B

British Columbia

Thompson Rivers University, B
Trinity Western University, B
The University of British Columbia, B
University of Victoria, B

Manitoba

Brandon University, B
University of Manitoba, B
The University of Winnipeg, B

New Brunswick

Mount Allison University, B
University of New Brunswick Fredericton, B

Newfoundland and Labrador

Memorial University of Newfoundland, B

Nova Scotia

Acadia University, B
Cape Breton University, B
Dalhousie University, B
St. Francis Xavier University, B

Ontario

Redeemer University College, B
University of Ottawa, A
University of Windsor, B
York University, B

Prince Edward Island

University of Prince Edward Island, B

Quebec

Université Laval, B
Université de Montréal, B
Université de Sherbrooke, B

Saskatchewan

University of Regina, B
University of Saskatchewan, B

PRE-NURSING STUDIES

Alabama

Northwest-Shoals Community College, A

Arizona

Cochise College (Douglas), A

Arkansas

Ouachita Baptist University, B

Colorado

Adams State College, B

Florida

South University (West Palm Beach), A

Georgia

Andrew College, A
Covenant College, B
Gainesville College, A

Illinois

Springfield College in Illinois, A
Trinity International University, A

Iowa

Dordt College, B
Iowa Lakes Community College, A

Missouri

Lindenwood University, B
Missouri Valley College, B

Montana

Montana State University-Billings, B

Nebraska

Concordia University, B

Nevada

Nevada State College at Henderson, B

Ohio

Cleveland State University, B

Oklahoma

Connors State College, A
Oklahoma City University, B
St. Gregory's University, B

Pennsylvania

Allegheny College, B
Gettysburg College, B
Juniata College, B
Keystone College, A
Marywood University, B

South Carolina

Limestone College, B

Tennessee

Lambuth University, B

Texas

Baylor University, B
St. Philip's College, A
Sam Houston State University, B

Utah

Brigham Young University, B

Wisconsin

Concordia University Wisconsin, A

Wyoming

Western Wyoming Community College, A

Manitoba

Canadian Mennonite University, B
The University of Winnipeg, B

PRE-PHARMACY STUDIES

Alabama

Auburn University, B
Calhoun Community College, A
Northwest-Shoals Community College, A

Arizona

Eastern Arizona College, A

Arkansas

Ouachita Baptist University, B

California

Santa Rosa Junior College, A
Westmont College, B

Colorado

Adams State College, B
Colorado State University-Pueblo, B

Connecticut

University of Connecticut, B

Florida

Barry University, B
Florida State University, B
Manatee Community College, A
University of Miami, B

Georgia

Andrew College, A
Coastal Georgia Community College, A

Columbus State University, B
Dalton State College, A
Darton College, A
Emmanuel College, A
Gainesville College, A
Georgia Perimeter College, A
Macon State College, A

Idaho

College of Southern Idaho, A

Illinois

City Colleges of Chicago, Malcolm X College, A
Elmhurst College, B
Rend Lake College, A
Roosevelt University, B
Sauk Valley Community College, A
Southwestern Illinois College, A
Springfield College in Illinois, A

Indiana

Saint Mary-of-the-Woods College, B
University of Evansville, B
University of Saint Francis, B

Iowa

Dordt College, B
Iowa Lakes Community College, A
Iowa Wesleyan College, B
The University of Iowa, B

Kansas

Allen County Community College, A
Central Christian College of Kansas, B
Dodge City Community College, A
McPherson College, B
Washburn University, B

Kentucky

Bellarmine University, B
Lindsey Wilson College, B

Maryland

Howard Community College, A

Michigan

Ferris State University, A
Kellogg Community College, A
Madonna University, B
Michigan Technological University, B

Minnesota

College of Saint Benedict, B
St. Cloud State University, B
Saint John's University, B
University of Minnesota, Duluth, B
University of Minnesota, Morris, B

Mississippi

Blue Mountain College, B
Mississippi College, B

Missouri

Central Missouri State University, B
College of the Ozarks, B
Drury University, B
Missouri Southern State University, B
Missouri Valley College, B
Truman State University, B
University of Missouri-St. Louis, B
Washington University in St. Louis, B

Montana

Carroll College, B
Montana State University-Billings, B
The University of Montana-Missoula, B

Nebraska

Concordia University, B
University of Nebraska-Lincoln, B

Western Nebraska Community College, A

New York

Fordham University, B
Le Moyne College, B
Long Island University, C.W. Post Campus, B
Monroe Community College, A
Roberts Wesleyan College, B

North Carolina

Belmont Abbey College, B
Campbell University, B
Gardner-Webb University, B
Louisburg College, A
Meredith College, B

North Dakota

Mayville State University, B
Valley City State University, B

Ohio

Ashland University, B
Mount Vernon Nazarene University, B
Muskingum College, B
Wright State University, B
Youngstown State University, B

Oklahoma

East Central University, B
Oklahoma Baptist University, B
Oklahoma City University, B
Rose State College, A
St. Gregory's University, B
Southern Nazarene University, B
Tulsa Community College, A

Oregon

Oregon State University, B

Pennsylvania

Allegheny College, B
Gettysburg College, B
Holy Family University, B
Juniata College, B
King's College, B
Luzerne County Community College, A
Reading Area Community College, A

South Carolina

Charleston Southern University, B
Limestone College, B

Tennessee

Cumberland University, B
King College, B
Lambuth University, B
Tennessee Wesleyan College, B
Union University, B
The University of Tennessee at Martin, B

Texas

Abilene Christian University, B
Amarillo College, A
Angelina College, A
Frank Phillips College, A
Hardin-Simmons University, B
Kilgore College, A
Midwestern State University, B
St. Philip's College, A
Sam Houston State University, B
Tarleton State University, B
Texas Southern University, B
University of the Incarnate Word, B
University of St. Thomas, B

The University of Texas-Pan American, B

Utah

University of Utah, B

Virginia

Longwood University, B

Washington

Centralia College, A
Saint Martin's University, B
Tacoma Community College, A

West Virginia

University of Charleston, B
West Virginia Wesleyan College, B

Wisconsin

Carroll College, B
University of Wisconsin-Parkside, B
University of Wisconsin-River Falls, B

Wyoming

Eastern Wyoming College, A
Laramie County Community College, A
Western Wyoming Community College, A

British Columbia

Thompson Rivers University, A

Manitoba

The University of Winnipeg, B

New Brunswick

Mount Allison University, B

Nova Scotia

Dalhousie University, B

Ontario

University of Windsor, B
York University, B

Quebec

Université Laval, B

Saskatchewan

University of Regina, B
University of Saskatchewan, B

PRE-THEOLOGY/
PRE-MINISTERIAL STUDIES

California

California Baptist University, B
California Christian College, B
Point Loma Nazarene University, B
Westmont College, B

Colorado

Nazarene Bible College, A

Florida

Ave Maria University, B

Georgia

Andrew College, A
Atlanta Christian College, B
Shorter College, B

Illinois

Concordia University, B
Loyola University Chicago, B
Moody Bible Institute, B
Trinity Christian College, B
Trinity International University, B

Indiana

Crossroads Bible College, B
Manchester College, A

University of Indianapolis, B

Iowa

Emmaus Bible College, B
Loras College, B

Kansas

Central Christian College of Kansas, B
Washburn University, B

Kentucky

Kentucky Mountain Bible College, B

Michigan

Alma College, B
Concordia University, B
Cornerstone University, B
Kellogg Community College, A
Kuyper College, B

Minnesota

College of Saint Benedict, B
Concordia College, B
Martin Luther College, B
Minnesota State University Mankato, B
Northwestern College, B
Saint John's University, B

Mississippi

Blue Mountain College, B

Nebraska

Concordia University, B
Grace University, B

New York

Roberts Wesleyan College, B
Wagner College, B

North Carolina

Campbell University, B

Ohio

Ashland University, B
Circleville Bible College, B
Ohio Northern University, B
Ohio Wesleyan University, B
University of Rio Grande, B

Oklahoma

St. Gregory's University, A

Oregon

Concordia University, B
Corban College, B

Pennsylvania

Geneva College, B
Juniata College, B
Waynesburg College, B

South Carolina

Columbia International University, B

Tennessee

Lambuth University, B
Tennessee Wesleyan College, B
Williamson Christian College, B

Texas

University of Dallas, B

Wisconsin

Viterbo University, B

Alberta

Concordia University College of Alberta, B
Prairie Bible Institute, B

British Columbia

Columbia Bible College, B

New Brunswick

Mount Allison University, B

Ontario

Redeemer University College, B

PRE-VETERINARY STUDIES

Alabama

Auburn University, B
Calhoun Community College, A
Northwest-Shoals Community College, A
Spring Hill College, B
Troy University, B
University of Montevallo, B

Arizona

Grand Canyon University, B
Northern Arizona University, B
The University of Arizona, B

Arkansas

Harding University, B
Ouachita Baptist University, B
University of Arkansas at Monticello, B
University of the Ozarks, B

California

California State Polytechnic University, Pomona, B
California State University, Chico, B
California State University, Dominguez Hills, B
California State University, East Bay, B
Humboldt State University, B
Pacific Union College, B
Sonoma State University, B
University of San Francisco, B
Westmont College, B

Colorado

Adams State College, B
Colorado State University, B
Colorado State University-Pueblo, B
Mesa State College, B
Regis University, B
University of Colorado at Colorado Springs, B
Western State College of Colorado, B

Connecticut

Albertus Magnus College, B
Quinnipiac University, B
Sacred Heart University, B
University of Bridgeport, B
University of Hartford, B

Delaware

Delaware State University, B
University of Delaware, B

Florida

Barry University, B
Florida Southern College, B
Florida State University, B
Jacksonville University, B
Stetson University, B
The University of Tampa, B

Georgia

Andrew College, A
Coastal Georgia Community College, A
Columbus State University, B
Darton College, A
Georgia Southwestern State University, B
LaGrange College, B
North Georgia College & State University, B
Oglethorpe University, B
University of Georgia, B

University of West Georgia, B

Idaho

Boise State University, B

Illinois

Augustana College, B
Benedictine University, B
Blackburn College, B
Chicago State University, B
Dominican University, B
Elmhurst College, B
Eureka College, B
Illinois College, B
Lake Forest College, B
Lewis University, B
MacMurray College, B
McKendree College, B
Millikin University, B
North Central College, B
North Park University, B
Olivet Nazarene University, B
Quincy University, B
Rend Lake College, A
Rockford College, B
Sauk Valley Community College, A
Springfield College in Illinois, A
Trinity Christian College, B
University of Illinois at Urbana-Champaign, B
University of St. Francis, B

Indiana

Anderson University, B
Goshen College, B
Huntington University, B
Indiana University-Purdue University Indianapolis, B
Indiana Wesleyan University, B
Manchester College, B
Marian College, B
Oakland City University, B
Purdue University Calumet, B
Saint Mary-of-the-Woods College, B
Taylor University, B
Tri-State University, B
University of Evansville, B
University of Indianapolis, B
University of Saint Francis, B
Wabash College, B

Iowa

Coe College, B
Dordt College, B
Drake University, B
Iowa Lakes Community College, A
Iowa State University of Science and Technology, B
Iowa Wesleyan College, B
Morningside College, B
Mount Mercy College, B
Simpson College, B
The University of Iowa, B
Upper Iowa University, B

Kansas

Allen County Community College, A
Barton County Community College, A
Central Christian College of Kansas, B
Friends University, B
Kansas State University, B
Kansas Wesleyan University, B
McPherson College, B
Newman University, B
Washburn University, B

Kentucky

Alice Lloyd College, B
Bellarmine University, B
Berea College, B
Campbellsville University, B
Kentucky Wesleyan College, B
Lindsey Wilson College, B
Northern Kentucky University, B

Louisiana

Centenary College of Louisiana, B
Dillard University, B

Xavier University of Louisiana, B

Maine

College of the Atlantic, B
University of Maine, B

Maryland

College of Notre Dame of Maryland, B
Columbia Union College, B
Howard Community College, A
University of Maryland, Baltimore County, B
Villa Julie College, B
Washington College, B

Massachusetts

American International College, B
Atlantic Union College, B
Becker College, B
Clark University, B
Elms College, B
Harvard University, B
Salem State College, B
University of Massachusetts Amherst, B

Michigan

Adrian College, B
Albion College, B
Alma College, B
Andrews University, B
Calvin College, B
Cornerstone University, B
Grand Valley State University, B
Hillsdale College, B
Kellogg Community College, A
Madonna University, B
Michigan State University, B
Michigan Technological University, B
Northern Michigan University, B
Olivet College, B

Minnesota

Augsburg College, B
Bemidji State University, B
College of Saint Benedict, B
College of St. Catherine, B
Concordia College, B
Gustavus Adolphus College, B
Hamline University, B
Minnesota State University Mankato, B
Minnesota State University Moorhead, B
St. Cloud State University, B
Saint John's University, B
Southwest Minnesota State University, B
University of Minnesota, Duluth, B
University of Minnesota, Morris, B
University of Minnesota, Twin Cities Campus, B
Winona State University, B

Mississippi

Blue Mountain College, B
Jackson State University, B
Mississippi College, B

Missouri

Central Missouri State University, B
College of the Ozarks, B
Columbia College, B
Drury University, B
Evangel University, B
Lindenwood University, B
Missouri Southern State University, B
Missouri Valley College, B
Northwest Missouri State University, B
Stephens College, B
Truman State University, B
University of Missouri-St. Louis, B
Washington University in St. Louis, B

William Jewell College, B

Montana

Carroll College, B
The University of Montana-Western, B

Nebraska

College of Saint Mary, B
Concordia University, B
Hastings College, B
Midland Lutheran College, B
Peru State College, B
University of Nebraska-Lincoln, B
Wayne State College, B
Western Nebraska Community College, A

Nevada

University of Nevada, Reno, B

New Hampshire

Franklin Pierce College, B
Rivier College, B
University of New Hampshire, B

New Jersey

Bloomfield College, B

New Mexico

Western New Mexico University, B

New York

Bard College, B
Buffalo State College, State University of New
    York, B
City College of the City University of New York, B
Clarkson University, B
D'Youville College, B
Elmira College, B
Fordham University, B
Hartwick College, B
Hobart and William Smith Colleges, B
Hofstra University, B
Houghton College, B
Keuka College, B
Le Moyne College, B
Molloy College, B
Nazareth College of Rochester, B
Niagara University, B
Roberts Wesleyan College, B
Rochester Institute of Technology, B
St. Bonaventure University, B
St. Joseph's College, Suffolk Campus, B
Sarah Lawrence College, B
State University of New York College at
    Brockport, B
State University of New York College of
    Environmental Science and Forestry, B
State University of New York College at Geneseo, B
State University of New York College at Oneonta, B
State University of New York, Fredonia, B
State University of New York at Oswego, B
Syracuse University, B
Utica College, B
Wells College, B

North Carolina

Belmont Abbey College, B
Campbell University, B
Catawba College, B
Chowan University, B
Elon University, B
Gardner-Webb University, B
High Point University, B
Lees-McRae College, B
Lenoir-Rhyne College, B
Louisburg College, A
Mars Hill College, B
Meredith College, B
Methodist College, B
Queens University of Charlotte, B
St. Andrews Presbyterian College, B

Wingate University, B

North Dakota

Dickinson State University, B
Mayville State University, B
Valley City State University, B

Ohio

Antioch College, B
Ashland University, B
Capital University, B
Cedarville University, B
Defiance College, B
Heidelberg College, B
Hiram College, B
John Carroll University, B
Kenyon College, B
Lake Erie College, B
Miami University, B
Mount Vernon Nazarene University, B
Muskingum College, B
Ohio Northern University, B
Ohio Wesleyan University, B
Otterbein College, B
Shawnee State University, A
University of Cincinnati, B
The University of Findlay, B
University of Rio Grande, B
The University of Toledo, B
Urbana University, B
Walsh University, B
Wilmington College, B
Wright State University, B
Youngstown State University, B

Oklahoma

East Central University, B
Langston University, B
Northeastern State University, B
Oklahoma Baptist University, B
Oklahoma City University, B
Oklahoma State University, B
Oklahoma Wesleyan University, B
Southwestern Oklahoma State University, B
Tulsa Community College, A

Oregon

Eastern Oregon University, B
Warner Pacific College, B

Pennsylvania

Allegheny College, B
Arcadia University, B
Cedar Crest College, B
DeSales University, B
Elizabethtown College, B
Gannon University, B
Gettysburg College, B
Grove City College, B
Haverford College, B
Holy Family University, B
Immaculata University, B
Juniata College, B
King's College, B
La Salle University, B
Lebanon Valley College, B
Lock Haven University of Pennsylvania, B
Lycoming College, B
Mercyhurst College, B
Saint Francis University, B
Seton Hill University, B
Susquehanna University, B
Thiel College, B
University of Pittsburgh at Johnstown, B
Waynesburg College, B
Westminster College, B
Widener University, B

York College of Pennsylvania, B

Puerto Rico

University of Puerto Rico, Mayagüez Campus, B

Rhode Island

Roger Williams University, B

South Carolina

Bob Jones University, B
Furman University, B
Limestone College, B
Newberry College, B
South Carolina State University, B
Wofford College, B

South Dakota

Augustana College, B
South Dakota State University, B
University of Sioux Falls, B

Tennessee

Cumberland University, B
King College, B
Lambuth University, B
Lincoln Memorial University, B
Lipscomb University, B
Tennessee Technological University, B
Tennessee Wesleyan College, B
Tusculum College, B
The University of Tennessee at Martin, B

Texas

Abilene Christian University, B
LeTourneau University, B
Midwestern State University, B
Sul Ross State University, B
Tarleton State University, B
Texas A&M University, B
Texas A&M University-Kingsville, B
Texas Lutheran University, B
Trinity University, B
University of Houston, B
University of St. Thomas, B

Utah

Utah State University, B

Vermont

Marlboro College, B
Saint Michael's College, B

Virginia

Eastern Mennonite University, B
Emory & Henry College, B
Hampton University, B
Longwood University, B
Lynchburg College, B
University of Mary Washington, B
Virginia Intermont College, B
Virginia Wesleyan College, B

Washington

Centralia College, A
Eastern Washington University, B
Saint Martin's University, B
University of Puget Sound, B
Walla Walla College, B
Whitworth College, B

West Virginia

Alderson-Broaddus College, B
Bethany College, B
Concord University, B
Davis & Elkins College, B
West Virginia State University, B
West Virginia Wesleyan College, B
Wheeling Jesuit University, B

Wisconsin

Cardinal Stritch University, B
Carroll College, B
Carthage College, B
Edgewood College, B

Lawrence University, B
Marian College of Fond du Lac, B
Mount Mary College, B
Northland College, B
Ripon College, B
University of Wisconsin-Oshkosh, B
University of Wisconsin-Parkside, B
University of Wisconsin-River Falls, B

Wyoming

Eastern Wyoming College, A
Laramie County Community College, A
Western Wyoming Community College, A

Alberta

University of Alberta, B

British Columbia

Thompson Rivers University, B
Trinity Western University, B
The University of British Columbia, B
University of Victoria, B

Manitoba

Brandon University, B
University of Manitoba, B
The University of Winnipeg, B

New Brunswick

Mount Allison University, B
University of New Brunswick Fredericton, B

Nova Scotia

Acadia University, B
Cape Breton University, B
Dalhousie University, B
Nova Scotia Agricultural College, B
St. Francis Xavier University, B
Université Sainte-Anne, B

Ontario

Redeemer University College, B
York University, B

Prince Edward Island

University of Prince Edward Island, B

Saskatchewan

University of Regina, B
University of Saskatchewan, B

PRECISION METAL WORKING

California

Reedley College, A

Michigan

Oakland Community College, A

Missouri

Jefferson College, A

Ohio

Northwest State Community College, A

Wisconsin

Northeast Wisconsin Technical College, A

PRECISION PRODUCTION

Michigan

Mott Community College, A
Southwestern Michigan College, A

Missouri

Jefferson College, A

South Carolina

Midlands Technical College, A

Wisconsin

Northeast Wisconsin Technical College, A
Western Technical College, A

PRECISION PRODUCTION TRADES

California

Santa Rosa Junior College, A

Illinois

College of DuPage, A

Michigan

Hope College, B
Lake Michigan College, A

Pennsylvania

Johnson College, A

PRECISION SYSTEMS MAINTENANCE AND REPAIR TECHNOLOGIES

Louisiana

Louisiana Technical College, A

Michigan

Southwestern Michigan College, A

Wisconsin

Northeast Wisconsin Technical College, A

British Columbia

British Columbia Institute of Technology, A

PREPRESS/DESKTOP PUBLISHING AND DIGITAL IMAGING DESIGN

California

Evergreen Valley College, A
Glendale Community College, A
Western Career College (Walnut Creek), AB

Idaho

Eastern Idaho Technical College, A

Illinois

College of DuPage, A
Lake Land College, A
Southwestern Illinois College, A

Iowa

Iowa Lakes Community College, A

Kentucky

Louisville Technical Institute, A

Louisiana

Louisiana Technical College, A

Massachusetts

Springfield Technical Community College, A

Michigan

Davenport University (Dearborn), A
Ferris State University, B

Minnesota

Dakota County Technical College, A
Hennepin Technical College, A

Minneapolis Business College, A

New Jersey

Brookdale Community College, A

New York

Touro College, A

Oklahoma

Tulsa Community College, A

Oregon

Linn-Benton Community College, A
Umpqua Community College, A

Pennsylvania

The Art Institute of Philadelphia, AB

Texas

Lee College, A
Texas State University-San Marcos, B

Washington

Edmonds Community College, A

Wyoming

Northwest College, A

British Columbia

Thompson Rivers University, A

PRINTING MANAGEMENT

Missouri

Central Missouri State University, B

New Jersey

Kean University, B

Wisconsin

Carroll College, B
University of Wisconsin-Stout, B

PRINTING PRESS OPERATOR

Illinois

Lake Land College, A

Iowa

Iowa Lakes Community College, A

Louisiana

Louisiana Technical College, A

PRINTMAKING

Alabama

Birmingham-Southern College, B
University of Montevallo, B

California

Academy of Art University, ABM
California College of the Arts, BM
California State University, East Bay, B
California State University, Fullerton, B
California State University, Long Beach, B
College of San Mateo, A
De Anza College, A
Laguna College of Art & Design, B
San Francisco Art Institute, BMO
Sonoma State University, B
University of California, Santa Cruz, B

University of San Francisco, B

Colorado

Colorado State University, BM
University of Colorado at Boulder, M

Connecticut

Yale University, M

District of Columbia

American University, M
Corcoran College of Art and Design, B
The George Washington University, M
Howard University, M

Florida

Florida Community College at Jacksonville, A
New World School of the Arts, AB
University of Miami, BM

Georgia

University of Georgia, B

Illinois

Bradley University, M
Illinois State University, M
School of the Art Institute of Chicago, BM
Southern Illinois University Carbondale, M
Trinity Christian College, B

Indiana

Ball State University, B
Indiana State University, M
Indiana University Bloomington, M
Indiana University-Purdue University Fort Wayne, B
Indiana Wesleyan University, B

Iowa

Drake University, B
The University of Iowa, B

Kansas

University of Kansas, B

Louisiana

Louisiana State University and Agricultural and
  Mechanical College, M
McNeese State University, B

Maine

Maine College of Art, B

Maryland

Maryland Institute College of Art, B

Massachusetts

Framingham State College, B
Massachusetts College of Art, BM
Montserrat College of Art, B
School of the Museum of Fine Arts, Boston, B
Simon's Rock College of Bard, B
University of Massachusetts Dartmouth, B

Michigan

Aquinas College, B
Grand Valley State University, B
University of Michigan, B
University of Michigan-Flint, B

Minnesota

College of Visual Arts, B
Minneapolis College of Art and Design, BM
Minnesota State University Moorhead, B
St. Cloud State University, B

Mississippi

Mississippi University for Women, B

Missouri

Columbia College, B
Kansas City Art Institute, B
University of Missouri-St. Louis, B

Washington University in St. Louis, BM

New Jersey

Rutgers, The State University of New Jersey, New
  Brunswick/Piscataway, B

New Mexico

College of Santa Fe, B
Institute of American Indian Arts, A

New York

Brooklyn College of the City University of New
  York, M
Buffalo State College, State University of New
  York, B
City College of the City University of New York, M
Pratt Institute, BM
Rochester Institute of Technology, M
Sarah Lawrence College, B
State University of New York at New Paltz, BM
Syracuse University, BM

Ohio

Art Academy of Cincinnati, B
The Cleveland Institute of Art, B
Kent State University, B
Ohio Northern University, B
The Ohio State University, B
Ohio University, BM
The University of Akron, B
Youngstown State University, B

Oklahoma

University of Oklahoma, M

Oregon

Pacific Northwest College of Art, B
Portland State University, M
University of Oregon, B

Pennsylvania

Keystone College, A
Marywood University, M
Seton Hill University, B
Temple University, BM
The University of the Arts, BM

Puerto Rico

Escuela de Artes Plasticas de Puerto Rico, B
Inter American University of Puerto Rico, San
  Germán Campus, M

Rhode Island

Rhode Island School of Design, BM

Tennessee

Memphis College of Art, BM
University of Memphis, M
The University of Tennessee, M

Texas

Texas Christian University, B
University of Dallas, B
University of Houston, B
University of North Texas, BM
The University of Texas at El Paso, B

Utah

Brigham Young University, B
Dixie State College of Utah, A
University of Utah, M

Vermont

Bennington College, B

Virginia

James Madison University, M
Longwood University, B
Virginia Commonwealth University, M

Washington

University of Washington, B
Washington State University, M

Western Washington University, B

West Virginia

West Virginia University, M

Wisconsin

Milwaukee Institute of Art and Design, B

Alberta

Alberta College of Art & Design, B
University of Alberta, BM

New Brunswick

Mount Allison University, B

Newfoundland and Labrador

Memorial University of Newfoundland, B

Nova Scotia

NSCAD University, B

Ontario

University of Windsor, B
York University, B

Quebec

Concordia University, B

Saskatchewan

University of Regina, B

PROFESSIONAL STUDIES

Hawaii

Windward Community College, A

Indiana

Saint Mary-of-the-Woods College, B

Iowa

Briar Cliff University, B
University of Dubuque, B

Kansas

Pratt Community College, A

Michigan

Western Michigan University, B

Minnesota

Bemidji State University, B

Missouri

Missouri Southern State University, B

Ohio

Kent State University, B

Oklahoma

University of Oklahoma, B

Pennsylvania

Mount Aloysius College, B

Tennessee

University of Memphis, B
The University of Tennessee at Martin, B

Vermont

Champlain College, B

West Virginia

Ohio Valley University, A

PROJECT MANAGEMENT

Colorado

Aspen University, MO
Colorado Technical University, M

Colorado Technical University Denver Campus, M
Regis University, MO

District of Columbia

The George Washington University, M

Illinois

American InterContinental University Online, M
DeVry University (Oakbrook Terrace), M
Northwestern University, M

Massachusetts

Lesley University, M

Minnesota

Saint Mary's University of Minnesota, M

Mississippi

Mississippi State University, M

Montana

Montana Tech of The University of Montana, M

New Jersey

Stevens Institute of Technology, MO
Thomas Edison State College, M

New York

New York Institute of Technology, M

North Carolina

Western Carolina University, M

Ohio

Wright State University, M

Pennsylvania

Cabrini College, O
Carnegie Mellon University, M
Lehigh University, O
The Pennsylvania State University at Erie, The
    Behrend College, M
Rosemont College, M

South Carolina

Winthrop University, MO

Texas

Texas A&M University, MD
University of Dallas, M

Virginia

University of Management and Technology, MO
University of Northern Virginia, M

Washington

City University, MO

Wisconsin

University of Wisconsin-Platteville, M

Alberta

Athabasca University, MO

Ontario

University of Ottawa, O

Quebec

Université du Québec en Abitibi-Témiscamingue, M
Université du Québec àChicoutimi, M
Université du Québec àMontréal, MO
Université du Québec en Outaouais, MO
Université du Québec àRimouski, M

Université du Québec àTrois-Rivières, MO

PSYCHIATRIC/MENTAL HEALTH NURSE/NURSING

Connecticut

Fairfield University, MO
Saint Joseph College, M

Delaware

University of Delaware, MO

Georgia

Georgia State University, M
Medical College of Georgia, M

Illinois

Rush University, MDO
Saint Xavier University, MO
Southern Illinois University Edwardsville, MO
University of Illinois at Chicago, M

Kansas

University of Kansas, O

Louisiana

Louisiana State University Health Sciences
    Center, MD

Maine

Husson College, M
University of Southern Maine, MO

Massachusetts

Boston College, M
Northeastern University, MO
University of Massachusetts Lowell, M

Michigan

University of Michigan, M
Wayne State University, MO

Minnesota

University of Minnesota, Twin Cities Campus, M

Mississippi

University of Southern Mississippi, M

New York

Hunter College of the City University of New
    York, M
Molloy College, O
New York University, MO
State University of New York at Buffalo, BMO
Stony Brook University, State University of New
    York, MO

Ohio

Case Western Reserve University, M

Oregon

Oregon Health & Science University, MO

Pennsylvania

Duquesne University, O
University of Pennsylvania, M
University of Pittsburgh, M

Puerto Rico

Pontifical Catholic University of Puerto Rico, M

South Carolina

Medical University of South Carolina, MO
University of South Carolina, MO

Tennessee

Vanderbilt University, M

Virginia

Virginia Commonwealth University, M

British Columbia

Open Learning Agency, B

Manitoba

Brandon University, B

PSYCHIATRIC/MENTAL HEALTH SERVICES TECHNICIAN

California

Cypress College, A
San Joaquin Delta College, A
Yuba College, A

Colorado

Pikes Peak Community College, A
Pueblo Community College, A

Georgia

Darton College, A

Indiana

Ivy Tech Community College-Bloomington, A
Ivy Tech Community College-Central Indiana, A
Ivy Tech Community College-Columbus, A
Ivy Tech Community College-East Central, A
Ivy Tech Community College-Kokomo, A
Ivy Tech Community College-Lafayette, A
Ivy Tech Community College-Northeast, A
Ivy Tech Community College-Northwest, A
Ivy Tech Community College-Southeast, A
Ivy Tech Community College-Southern Indiana, A
Ivy Tech Community College-Southwest, A
Ivy Tech Community College-Wabash Valley, A
Ivy Tech Community College-Whitewater, A

Kentucky

Northern Kentucky University, A

Maryland

Allegany College of Maryland, A
Hagerstown Community College, A

Michigan

Lake Superior State University, A

New York

Dutchess Community College, A
Kingsborough Community College of the City
    University of New York, A

North Carolina

Pitt Community College, A
South Piedmont Community College, A
Wayne Community College, A
Wilkes Community College, A

North Dakota

North Dakota State College of Science, A

Ohio

Franciscan University of Steubenville, B
The University of Toledo, A

Pennsylvania

Community College of Allegheny County, A
Montgomery County Community College, A
Pennsylvania College of Technology, AB

Rhode Island

Community College of Rhode Island, A

Texas

Eastfield College, A
Houston Community College System, A

PSYCHOANALYSIS AND PSYCHOTHERAPY

Colorado

Naropa University, M

Illinois

Argosy University/Chicago, D

New Hampshire

Rivier College, M

New York

New York University, O

PSYCHOLOGY

Alabama

Alabama Agricultural and Mechanical University, BMO
Alabama Southern Community College, A
Alabama State University, B
Athens State University, B
Auburn University, BMD
Auburn University Montgomery, BM
Birmingham-Southern College, B
Faulkner University, B
Jacksonville State University, BM
Judson College, B
Lawson State Community College, A
Oakwood College, B
Samford University, B
Spring Hill College, B
Talladega College, B
Troy University, B
Tuskegee University, B
The University of Alabama, BD
The University of Alabama at Birmingham, BMD
The University of Alabama in Huntsville, BM
University of Mobile, B
University of Montevallo, B
University of North Alabama, B
University of South Alabama, BM
The University of West Alabama, B

Alaska

Alaska Pacific University, B
University of Alaska Anchorage, BM
University of Alaska Fairbanks, BD

Arizona

Argosy University/Phoenix, BMDO
Arizona State University, BD
Arizona State University at the Polytechnic Campus, B
Arizona State University West, B
Cochise College (Douglas), A
Cochise College (Sierra Vista), A
Eastern Arizona College, A
GateWay Community College, A
Grand Canyon University, B
Mohave Community College, A
Northcentral University, B
Northern Arizona University, BM
Prescott College, B
South Mountain Community College, A
The University of Arizona, BDO

Arkansas

Arkansas State University, B
Arkansas Tech University, B
Harding University, B
Henderson State University, B
Hendrix College, B
John Brown University, B
Lyon College, B
Ouachita Baptist University, B
Philander Smith College, B
Southern Arkansas University-Magnolia, B
University of Arkansas, B
University of Arkansas at Fort Smith, B
University of Arkansas at Little Rock, BM
University of Arkansas at Monticello, B

University of Arkansas at Pine Bluff, B
University of Central Arkansas, BMD
University of the Ozarks, B
Williams Baptist College, B

California

Alliant International University, B
Antioch University Los Angeles, M
Antioch University Santa Barbara, M
Argosy University/Orange County, MD
Argosy University/San Francisco Bay Area, MD
Azusa Pacific University, BMD
Bakersfield College, A
Bethany University, B
Biola University, BMD
Butte College, A
California Baptist University, B
California Coast University, AB
California Institute of Integral Studies, BMD
California Lutheran University, BM
California Polytechnic State University, San Luis Obispo, BM
California State Polytechnic University, Pomona, BM
California State University, Bakersfield, BMO
California State University Channel Islands, B
California State University, Chico, BM
California State University, Dominguez Hills, BM
California State University, East Bay, B
California State University, Fresno, BM
California State University, Fullerton, BM
California State University, Long Beach, BM
California State University, Los Angeles, BM
California State University, Northridge, BM
California State University, Sacramento, BM
California State University, San Bernardino, BM
California State University, San Marcos, BM
California State University, Stanislaus, BM
Cañada College, A
Cerritos College, A
Chabot College, A
Chaffey College, A
Chapman University, B
City College of San Francisco, A
Claremont McKenna College, B
College of Alameda, A
College of the Canyons, A
College of the Desert, A
College of Marin, A
Columbia College, A
Compton Community College, A
Concordia University, B
Crafton Hills College, A
Cuesta College, A
Cypress College, A
De Anza College, A
Dominican University of California, B
East Los Angeles College, A
El Camino College, A
Folsom Lake College, A
Foothill College, A
Fresno Pacific University, AB
Fullerton College, A
Gavilan College, A
Golden Gate University, MO
Holy Names University, B
Hope International University, BM
Humboldt State University, BM
Imperial Valley College, A
John F. Kennedy University, BMDO
La Sierra University, B
Lake Tahoe Community College, A
Lassen Community College District, A
Los Angeles City College, A
Los Angeles Mission College, A
Los Angeles Valley College, A
Los Medanos College, A
Loyola Marymount University, B
Mendocino College, A
Mills College, B
MiraCosta College, A
Monterey Peninsula College, A
Mount St. Mary's College, B
National University, BM
New College of California, BM
Notre Dame de Namur University, BMO
Occidental College, B

Pacific Union College, B
Palo Verde College, A
Pasadena City College, A
Pepperdine University, B
Pitzer College, B
Point Loma Nazarene University, B
Pomona College, B
Sacramento City College, A
Saddleback College, A
Saint Mary's College of California, B
San Bernardino Valley College, A
San Diego Christian College, B
San Diego City College, A
San Diego Mesa College, A
San Diego Miramar College, A
San Diego State University, BMD
San Francisco State University, BM
San Joaquin Delta College, A
San Jose State University, BM
Santa Ana College, A
Santa Barbara City College, A
Santa Clara University, B
Santa Monica College, A
Santa Rosa Junior College, A
Santiago Canyon College, A
Scripps College, B
Simpson University, B
Skyline College, A
Solano Community College, A
Sonoma State University, B
Southwestern College, A
Stanford University, BD
University of California, Berkeley, BD
University of California, Davis, BD
University of California, Irvine, BD
University of California, Los Angeles, BMD
University of California, Riverside, BMD
University of California, San Diego, BD
University of California, Santa Barbara, BD
University of California, Santa Cruz, BD
University of Judaism, B
University of La Verne, BMD
University of the Pacific, BM
University of Redlands, B
University of San Diego, B
University of San Francisco, B
University of Southern California, BMD
University of the West, B
Vanguard University of Southern California, B
West Hills Community College, A
West Los Angeles College, A
West Valley College, A
Westmont College, B
Whittier College, B
William Jessup University, B
Woodbury University, B
Yuba College, A

Colorado

Adams State College, B
Colorado Christian University, B
The Colorado College, B
Colorado Mountain College, A
Colorado Northwestern Community College, A
Colorado State University, BMD
Colorado State University-Pueblo, B
Fort Lewis College, B
Mesa State College, B
Metropolitan State College of Denver, B
Naropa University, B
Northeastern Junior College, A
Otero Junior College, A
Parks College (Denver), A
Red Rocks Community College, A
Regis University, BM
University of Colorado at Boulder, BMD
University of Colorado at Colorado Springs, BMD
University of Colorado at Denver and Health Sciences Center - Downtown Denver Campus, BM
University of Denver, BMD
University of Northern Colorado, BM

Western State College of Colorado, B

Connecticut

Albertus Magnus College, B
Central Connecticut State University, BM
Connecticut College, BM
Eastern Connecticut State University, B
Fairfield University, BM
Mitchell College, A
Post University, B
Quinnipiac University, B
Sacred Heart University, AB
Saint Joseph College, B
Southern Connecticut State University, BM
Trinity College, B
University of Bridgeport, B
University of Connecticut, BMD
University of Hartford, BMD
University of New Haven, B
Wesleyan University, BM
Western Connecticut State University, B
Yale University, BD

Delaware

Delaware State University, B
University of Delaware, BD
Wesley College, B
Wilmington College, BM

District of Columbia

American University, BMD
The Catholic University of America, BMDO
Gallaudet University, BMDO
The George Washington University, BD
Georgetown University, BD
Howard University, BMD
Trinity (Washington) University, B
University of the District of Columbia, B

Florida

Argosy University/Sarasota, BMDO
Argosy University/Tampa, BMD
Barry University, BMO
Bethune-Cookman College, B
Carlos Albizu University, Miami Campus, BMD
Clearwater Christian College, B
Daytona Beach Community College, A
Eckerd College, B
Edward Waters College, B
Flagler College, B
Florida Agricultural and Mechanical University, BM
Florida Atlantic University, BMD
Florida Institute of Technology, BMD
Florida International University, BMD
Florida Memorial College, B
Florida Southern College, B
Florida State University, BMD
Gulf Coast Community College, A
Indian River Community College, A
Jacksonville University, B
Lynn University, B
Manatee Community College, A
Miami Dade College, A
New College of Florida, B
Nova Southeastern University, BMDO
Palm Beach Atlantic University, B
Palm Beach Community College, A
Pensacola Junior College, A
Rollins College, B
Saint Leo University, B
St. Thomas University, B
Southeastern University, B
Stetson University, B
University of Central Florida, BMD
University of Florida, BMDO
University of Miami, BMD
University of North Florida, BM
University of South Florida, BMD
The University of Tampa, AB
University of West Florida, BM
Warner Southern College, B

Georgia

Abraham Baldwin Agricultural College, A
Agnes Scott College, B

Albany State University, B
Andrew College, A
Argosy University/Atlanta, MD
Armstrong Atlantic State University, B
Atlanta Metropolitan College, A
Augusta State University, BM
Bainbridge College, A
Beacon University, B
Berry College, B
Brenau University, BM
Brewton-Parker College, B
Clark Atlanta University, B
Clayton State University, B
Coastal Georgia Community College, A
Columbus State University, B
Covenant College, B
Dalton State College, A
Darton College, A
East Georgia College, A
Emmanuel College, B
Emory University, BD
Fort Valley State University, B
Gainesville College, A
Georgia College & State University, B
Georgia Highlands College, A
Georgia Institute of Technology, MD
Georgia Perimeter College, A
Georgia Southern University, BM
Georgia Southwestern State University, B
Georgia State University, BMD
Gordon College, A
Kennesaw State University, B
LaGrange College, B
Macon State College, A
Mercer University, B
Morehouse College, B
North Georgia College & State University, B
Oglethorpe University, B
Paine College, B
Piedmont College, B
Reinhardt College, B
Shorter College, B
South Georgia College, A
Spelman College, B
Thomas University, B
University of Georgia, BMD
University of West Georgia, BM
Valdosta State University, BMO
Waycross College, A
Wesleyan College, B
Young Harris College, A

Guam

University of Guam, B

Hawaii

Argosy University/Hawaii, MDO
Brigham Young University-Hawaii, B
Chaminade University of Honolulu, B
Hawaii Pacific University, B
University of Hawaii at Hilo, B
University of Hawaii at Manoa, BMD
University of Hawaii-West Oahu, B

Idaho

Albertson College of Idaho, B
Boise State University, B
Brigham Young University -Idaho, A
College of Southern Idaho, A
Idaho State University, BMD
Lewis-Clark State College, B
North Idaho College, A
Northwest Nazarene University, B
University of Idaho, BM

Illinois

Argosy University/Chicago, BMDO
Argosy University/Schaumburg, BMD
Augustana College, B
Aurora University, B
Benedictine University, B
Blackburn College, B
Bradley University, B
Chicago State University, B
Concordia University, BM
Danville Area Community College, A

DePaul University, BMDO
Dominican University, B
Eastern Illinois University, BMO
Elmhurst College, B
Eureka College, B
Governors State University, BM
Greenville College, B
Highland Community College, A
Illinois College, B
Illinois Institute of Technology, BMD
Illinois State University, BMDO
Illinois Wesleyan University, B
John A. Logan College, A
John Wood Community College, A
Judson College, B
Kankakee Community College, A
Knox College, B
Lake Forest College, B
Lewis University, B
Lincoln College, A
Lincoln College-Normal, A
Loyola University Chicago, BMD
MacMurray College, B
McKendree College, B
Millikin University, B
Monmouth College, B
National-Louis University, BMO
North Central College, B
North Park University, B
Northeastern Illinois University, BM
Northern Illinois University, BMD
Northwestern University, BDO
Olivet Nazarene University, B
Quincy University, B
Rend Lake College, A
Rockford College, B
Roosevelt University, B
Saint Xavier University, BMO
Sauk Valley Community College, A
Southern Illinois University Carbondale, BMD
Southern Illinois University Edwardsville, BMO
Spoon River College, A
Trinity Christian College, B
Trinity International University, B
University of Chicago, BD
University of Illinois at Chicago, BD
University of Illinois at Springfield, B
University of Illinois at Urbana-Champaign, BMD
University of St. Francis, B
Western Illinois University, BMO
Wheaton College, BMD

Indiana

Anderson University, B
Ball State University, BM
Bethel College, B
Butler University, B
Calumet College of Saint Joseph, B
DePauw University, B
Earlham College, B
Franklin College, B
Goshen College, B
Grace College, B
Hanover College, B
Huntington University, B
Indiana State University, BMD
Indiana Tech, B
Indiana University Bloomington, BD
Indiana University East, B
Indiana University Kokomo, B
Indiana University Northwest, B
Indiana University-Purdue University Fort
    Wayne, AB
Indiana University-Purdue University
    Indianapolis, BMD
Indiana University South Bend, BM
Indiana University Southeast, B
Indiana Wesleyan University, B
Manchester College, B
Marian College, AB
Martin University, BM
Purdue University, BD
Purdue University Calumet, B
Saint Joseph's College, B
Saint Mary-of-the-Woods College, B
Saint Mary's College, B

Taylor University, B
Tri-State University, B
University of Evansville, B
University of Indianapolis, BMD
University of Notre Dame, BD
University of Saint Francis, BM
University of Southern Indiana, B
Valparaiso University, BMO
Vincennes University, A
Vincennes University Jasper Campus, A
Wabash College, B

Iowa

Ashford University, B
Briar Cliff University, B
Buena Vista University, B
Central College, B
Clarke College, B
Coe College, B
Cornell College, B
Dordt College, B
Drake University, B
Ellsworth Community College, A
Graceland University, B
Grand View College, B
Grinnell College, B
Iowa Lakes Community College, A
Iowa State University of Science and
   Technology, BMD
Iowa Wesleyan College, B
Kirkwood Community College, A
Loras College, BM
Luther College, B
Morningside College, B
Mount Mercy College, B
Northwestern College, B
St. Ambrose University, B
Simpson College, B
University of Dubuque, B
The University of Iowa, BMDO
University of Northern Iowa, BM
Upper Iowa University, B
Vennard College, B
Waldorf College, B
Wartburg College, B
William Penn University, B

Kansas

Allen County Community College, A
Baker University, B
Barclay College, B
Barton County Community College, A
Benedictine College, B
Bethany College, B
Bethel College, B
Butler Community College, A
Central Christian College of Kansas, B
Coffeyville Community College, A
Colby Community College, A
Dodge City Community College, A
Donnelly College, A
Emporia State University, BM
Fort Hays State University, BMO
Friends University, B
Highland Community College, A
Hutchinson Community College and Area Vocational
   School, A
Independence Community College, A
Kansas State University, BMD
Kansas Wesleyan University, B
McPherson College, B
MidAmerica Nazarene University, B
Newman University, B
Ottawa University, B
Pittsburg State University, BM
Pratt Community College, A
Seward County Community College, A
Southwestern College, B
Tabor College, B
University of Kansas, BMD
University of Saint Mary, BM
Washburn University, BM

Wichita State University, BMD

Kentucky

Asbury College, B
Bellarmine University, B
Berea College, B
Brescia University, B
Campbellsville University, B
Centre College, B
Eastern Kentucky University, BMO
Georgetown College, B
Kentucky Christian University, B
Kentucky State University, B
Kentucky Wesleyan College, B
Lindsey Wilson College, B
Mid-Continent University, B
Midway College, B
Morehead State University, BM
Murray State University, BM
Northern Kentucky University, B
Pikeville College, B
Spalding University, BMD
Thomas More College, AB
Transylvania University, B
Union College, B
University of the Cumberlands, B
University of Kentucky, BMD
University of Louisville, BMD
Western Kentucky University, BMO

Louisiana

Centenary College of Louisiana, B
Dillard University, B
Grambling State University, B
Louisiana College, B
Louisiana State University and Agricultural and
   Mechanical College, BMD
Louisiana State University at Alexandria, B
Louisiana State University in Shreveport, B
Louisiana Tech University, BMD
Loyola University New Orleans, B
McNeese State University, BM
Nicholls State University, B
Northwestern State University of Louisiana, BM
Southeastern Louisiana University, BM
Southern University and Agricultural and Mechanical
   College, BM
Tulane University, BMD
University of Louisiana at Lafayette, BM
University of Louisiana at Monroe, BMO
University of New Orleans, BMD
Xavier University of Louisiana, B

Maine

Bates College, B
Bowdoin College, B
Colby College, B
College of the Atlantic, B
Saint Joseph's College of Maine, B
Thomas College, B
University of Maine, BMD
University of Maine at Farmington, B
University of Maine at Machias, B
University of New England, B
University of Southern Maine, B

Maryland

Bowie State University, B
College of Notre Dame of Maryland, B
Columbia Union College, B
Coppin State University, B
Frederick Community College, A
Frostburg State University, BM
Garrett College, A
Goucher College, B
Harford Community College, A
Hood College, BMO
Howard Community College, A
The Johns Hopkins University, BD
Loyola College in Maryland, BMDO
McDaniel College, B
Morgan State University, B
Mount St. Mary's University, B
St. Mary's College of Maryland, B
Salisbury University, B
Sojourner-Douglass College, B

Towson University, B
University of Baltimore, BM
University of Maryland, Baltimore County, BMD
University of Maryland, College Park, BMD
University of Maryland University College, B
Villa Julie College, AB
Washington College, BM

Massachusetts

American International College, BMD
Amherst College, B
Anna Maria College, BM
Assumption College, B
Atlantic Union College, B
Bay Path College, B
Becker College, B
Boston College, BMD
Boston University, BMD
Brandeis University, BMD
Bridgewater State College, BM
Bunker Hill Community College, A
Cambridge College, B
Cape Cod Community College, A
Clark University, BD
College of the Holy Cross, B
Curry College, B
Eastern Nazarene College, B
Elms College, B
Emmanuel College, B
Endicott College, B
Fisher College, A
Fitchburg State College, B
Framingham State College, BM
Gordon College, B
Hampshire College, B
Harvard University, BMD
Lasell College, B
Lesley University, MDO
Massachusetts College of Liberal Arts, B
Merrimack College, B
Mount Holyoke College, B
Mount Ida College, B
Newbury College, AB
Nichols College, B
Northeastern University, BMDO
Pine Manor College, B
Quincy College, A
Regis College, B
Salem State College, BM
Simmons College, B
Simon's Rock College of Bard, B
Smith College, B
Springfield College, B
Stonehill College, B
Suffolk University, BD
Tufts University, BMD
University of Massachusetts Amherst, BMD
University of Massachusetts Boston, B
University of Massachusetts Dartmouth, BM
University of Massachusetts Lowell, BM
Wellesley College, B
Western New England College, B
Westfield State College, B
Wheaton College, B
Williams College, B
Worcester State College, B

Michigan

Adrian College, AB
Albion College, B
Alma College, B
Andrews University, BMDO
Aquinas College, B
Calvin College, B
Central Michigan University, BMDO
Concordia University, B
Cornerstone University, B
Delta College, A
Eastern Michigan University, BMD
Gogebic Community College, A
Grand Valley State University, B
Hillsdale College, B
Hope College, B
Kalamazoo College, B
Kellogg Community College, A
Lake Superior State University, B

Lawrence Technological University, B
Madonna University, BM
Marygrove College, B
Michigan State University, BMD
Michigan Technological University, B
Mid Michigan Community College, A
Monroe County Community College, A
Northern Michigan University, BM
Oakland University, B
Olivet College, B
Rochester College, B
Saginaw Valley State University, B
Siena Heights University, AB
Spring Arbor University, B
University of Detroit Mercy, BMDO
University of Michigan, BD
University of Michigan-Dearborn, B
University of Michigan-Flint, B
Wayne State University, BMD
Western Michigan University, BMDO

Minnesota

Augsburg College, B
Bemidji State University, B
Bethany Lutheran College, B
Bethel University, B
Capella University, MD
Carleton College, B
College of Saint Benedict, B
College of St. Catherine, B
The College of St. Scholastica, B
Concordia College, B
Concordia University, St. Paul, B
Crown College, AB
Gustavus Adolphus College, B
Hamline University, B
Itasca Community College, A
Macalester College, B
Metropolitan State University, B
Minnesota State University Mankato, BM
Minnesota State University Moorhead, B
North Central University, AB
Northwestern College, B
Ridgewater College, A
St. Cloud State University, BM
Saint John's University, B
Saint Mary's University of Minnesota, B
St. Olaf College, B
Southwest Minnesota State University, B
University of Minnesota, Duluth, B
University of Minnesota, Morris, B
University of Minnesota, Twin Cities Campus, BMD
University of St. Thomas, BMDO
Vermilion Community College, A
Walden University, MDO
Winona State University, B

Mississippi

Belhaven College, B
Blue Mountain College, B
Delta State University, B
East Central Community College, A
East Mississippi Community College, A
Hinds Community College, A
Itawamba Community College, A
Jackson State University, BD
Millsaps College, B
Mississippi College, BM
Mississippi State University, BMD
Mississippi University for Women, B
Northeast Mississippi Community College, A
Tougaloo College, B
University of Mississippi, BMD
University of Southern Mississippi, BMDO
William Carey College, BM

Missouri

Avila University, B
Central Methodist University, AB
Central Missouri State University, BM
College of the Ozarks, B
Columbia College, B
Crowder College, A
Culver-Stockton College, B
Drury University, B
East Central College, A

Evangel University, BM
Fontbonne University, B
Hannibal-LaGrange College, B
Jefferson College, A
Lincoln University, B
Lindenwood University, B
Maryville University of Saint Louis, B
Missouri Baptist University, B
Missouri Southern State University, B
Missouri State University, BM
Missouri Valley College, B
Missouri Western State University, B
Northwest Missouri State University, BM
Park University, B
Rockhurst University, B
Saint Louis University, BMD
Southeast Missouri State University, B
Southwest Baptist University, B
Stephens College, B
Truman State University, B
University of Missouri-Columbia, BMD
University of Missouri-Kansas City, B
University of Missouri-Rolla, B
University of Missouri-St. Louis, BMDO
Washington University in St. Louis, BMD
Webster University, B
Westminster College, B
William Jewell College, B
William Woods University, B

Montana

Carroll College, B
Montana State University, BM
Montana State University-Billings, ABM
Rocky Mountain College, B
University of Great Falls, B
The University of Montana-Missoula, BMDO

Nebraska

Chadron State College, B
College of Saint Mary, B
Concordia University, B
Creighton University, B
Dana College, B
Doane College, B
Grace University, B
Hastings College, B
Midland Lutheran College, B
Nebraska Wesleyan University, B
Peru State College, B
Union College, B
University of Nebraska at Kearney, B
University of Nebraska-Lincoln, BMDO
University of Nebraska at Omaha, BMDO
Wayne State College, B
Western Nebraska Community College, A
York College, B

Nevada

Great Basin College, A
Nevada State College at Henderson, B
University of Nevada, Las Vegas, BMD
University of Nevada, Reno, BMD

New Hampshire

Colby-Sawyer College, B
Dartmouth College, BD
Franklin Pierce College, B
Hesser College, A
Keene State College, B
New England College, B
Plymouth State University, B
Rivier College, B
Saint Anselm College, B
Southern New Hampshire University, BMO
University of New Hampshire, BD
University of New Hampshire at Manchester, B

New Jersey

Atlantic Cape Community College, A
Bergen Community College, A
Bloomfield College, B
Brookdale Community College, A
Burlington County College, A
Caldwell College, BM

Centenary College, B
The College of New Jersey, B
College of Saint Elizabeth, BM
Drew University, B
Fairleigh Dickinson University, College at
 Florham, BMO
Fairleigh Dickinson University, Metropolitan
 Campus, BMDO
Felician College, AB
Georgian Court University, B
Gloucester County College, A
Kean University, BMO
Middlesex County College, A
Monmouth University, BMO
Montclair State University, BM
New Jersey City University, BMO
Passaic County Community College, A
Princeton University, BD
Ramapo College of New Jersey, B
The Richard Stockton College of New Jersey, B
Rider University, B
Rowan University, BM
Rutgers, The State University of New Jersey,
 Camden, B
Rutgers, The State University of New Jersey, New
 Brunswick/Piscataway, BMD
Rutgers, The State University of New Jersey,
 Newark, BD
Saint Peter's College, B
Salem Community College, A
Seton Hall University, BMDO
William Paterson University of New Jersey, B

New Mexico

Clovis Community College, A
College of Santa Fe, B
College of the Southwest, B
Eastern New Mexico University, ABM
New Mexico Highlands University, BM
New Mexico Institute of Mining and Technology, B
New Mexico State University, BMD
San Juan College, A
University of New Mexico, BMD
Western New Mexico University, B

New York

Adelphi University, BMDO
Alfred University, B
Bard College, B
Barnard College, B
Bernard M. Baruch College of the City University of
 New York, B
Bronx Community College of the City University of
 New York, A
Brooklyn College of the City University of New
 York, BMD
Buffalo State College, State University of New
 York, B
Canisius College, B
Cazenovia College, B
City College of the City University of New
 York, BMD
Clarkson University, B
Colgate University, B
College of Mount Saint Vincent, B
The College of New Rochelle, B
The College of Saint Rose, B
College of Staten Island of the City University of
 New York, B
Columbia College, B
Columbia University, School of General Studies, B
Cornell University, BD
Daemen College, B
Dominican College, B
Dowling College, B
D'Youville College, B
Elmira College, B
Eugene Lang College The New School for Liberal
 Arts, B
Excelsior College, B
Finger Lakes Community College, A
Fordham University, BD
Fulton-Montgomery Community College, A
Genesee Community College, A
Hamilton College, B
Hartwick College, B

Hilbert College, B
Hobart and William Smith Colleges, B
Hofstra University, BMDO
Houghton College, B
Hunter College of the City University of New
York, BM
Iona College, BM
Ithaca College, B
Keuka College, B
Le Moyne College, B
Lehman College of the City University of New
York, B
Long Island University, Brooklyn Campus, BMD
Long Island University, C.W. Post Campus, BMDO
Manhattan College, B
Manhattanville College, B
Marist College, BMO
Marymount Manhattan College, B
Medaille College, BM
Medgar Evers College of the City University of New
York, B
Mercy College, BM
Molloy College, B
Mount Saint Mary College, B
Nazareth College of Rochester, B
New York Institute of Technology, B
New York University, BMDO
Niagara University, B
Nyack College, B
Pace University, BMD
Polytechnic University, Brooklyn Campus, M
Purchase College, State University of New York, B
Queens College of the City University of New
York, BM
Rensselaer Polytechnic Institute, B
Roberts Wesleyan College, B
Rochester Institute of Technology, B
Russell Sage College, B
Sage College of Albany, B
St. Bonaventure University, B
St. Francis College, B
St. John Fisher College, B
St. John's University, BMD
St. Joseph's College, New York, B
St. Joseph's College, Suffolk Campus, B
St. Lawrence University, B
St. Thomas Aquinas College, B
Sarah Lawrence College, B
Siena College, B
Skidmore College, B
State University of New York at Binghamton, BMD
State University of New York at Buffalo, BMD
State University of New York College at
Brockport, BM
State University of New York College at Cortland, B
State University of New York College at Geneseo, B
State University of New York College at Old
Westbury, B
State University of New York College at Oneonta, B
State University of New York College at Potsdam, B
State University of New York, Fredonia, B
State University of New York Institute of
Technology, B
State University of New York at New Paltz, BM
State University of New York at Oswego, B
State University of New York at Plattsburgh, BMO
Stony Brook University, State University of New
York, BMD
Syracuse University, BD
Touro College, B
Union College, B
United States Military Academy, B
University at Albany, State University of New
York, BMDO
University of Rochester, BMD
Utica College, B
Vassar College, B
Wagner College, B
Wells College, B
Yeshiva University, BMD
York College of the City University of New York, B

North Carolina

Appalachian State University, BMO
Barton College, B
Belmont Abbey College, B

Bennett College For Women, B
Brevard College, B
Campbell University, B
Catawba College, B
Chowan University, B
Davidson College, B
Duke University, BDO
East Carolina University, BM
Elizabeth City State University, B
Elon University, B
Fayetteville State University, BM
Gardner-Webb University, BM
Greensboro College, B
Guilford College, B
High Point University, B
John Wesley College, B
Johnson C. Smith University, B
Lees-McRae College, B
Lenoir-Rhyne College, B
Livingstone College, B
Louisburg College, A
Mars Hill College, B
Meredith College, B
Methodist College, AB
Mitchell Community College, A
Mount Olive College, AB
North Carolina Agricultural and Technical State
University, B
North Carolina Central University, BM
North Carolina State University, BD
North Carolina Wesleyan College, B
Peace College, B
Pfeiffer University, B
Queens University of Charlotte, B
St. Andrews Presbyterian College, B
Saint Augustine's College, B
Salem College, B
Shaw University, B
Southeastern Baptist Theological Seminary, M
The University of North Carolina at Asheville, B
The University of North Carolina at Chapel Hill, BD
The University of North Carolina at Charlotte, BM
The University of North Carolina at
Greensboro, BMD
The University of North Carolina at Pembroke, B
The University of North Carolina Wilmington, BM
Wake Forest University, BM
Warren Wilson College, B
Western Carolina University, BM
Wingate University, B
Winston-Salem State University, B

North Dakota

Dickinson State University, B
Jamestown College, B
Mayville State University, B
Minot State University, B
North Dakota State University, BMD
University of Mary, B
University of North Dakota, BMD
Valley City State University, B

Ohio

Antioch College, B
Ashland University, B
Baldwin-Wallace College, B
Bluffton University, B
Bowling Green State University, BMD
Capital University, B
Case Western Reserve University, BD
Cedarville University, B
Central State University, B
Cincinnati Christian University, B
Cleveland State University, BMO
College of Mount St. Joseph, B
The College of Wooster, B
Defiance College, B
Denison University, B
Franciscan University of Steubenville, B
Heidelberg College, B
Hiram College, B
John Carroll University, B
Kent State University, BMD
Kenyon College, B
Lake Erie College, B
Lorain County Community College, A

Lourdes College, AB
Malone College, B
Marietta College, BM
Miami University, BD
Miami University Hamilton, B
Miami University-Middletown Campus, A
Mount Union College, B
Mount Vernon Nazarene University, B
Muskingum College, B
Notre Dame College, B
Oberlin College, B
Ohio Dominican University, B
Ohio Northern University, B
The Ohio State University, BMD
The Ohio State University at Lima, B
The Ohio State University-Mansfield Campus, B
The Ohio State University at Marion, B
The Ohio State University-Newark Campus, B
Ohio University, BD
Ohio University-Eastern, B
Ohio Wesleyan University, B
Otterbein College, B
Shawnee State University, B
Terra State Community College, A
Tiffin University, B
Union Institute & University, BD
The University of Akron, BMD
University of Cincinnati, BD
University of Dayton, BM
The University of Findlay, B
University of Rio Grande, A
The University of Toledo, BMD
Urbana University, B
Ursuline College, B
Walsh University, B
Wilberforce University, B
Wilmington College, B
Wittenberg University, B
Wright State University, ABMD
Wright State University, Lake Campus, A
Xavier University, ABMD
Youngstown State University, B

Oklahoma

Cameron University, BM
Carl Albert State College, A
Connors State College, A
East Central University, BM
Eastern Oklahoma State College, A
Hillsdale Free Will Baptist College, A
Langston University, B
Northeastern Oklahoma Agricultural and Mechanical
College, A
Northeastern State University, BM
Northwestern Oklahoma State University, B
Oklahoma Baptist University, B
Oklahoma Christian University, B
Oklahoma City Community College, A
Oklahoma City University, B
Oklahoma Panhandle State University, B
Oklahoma State University, BMD
Oral Roberts University, B
Redlands Community College, A
Rose State College, A
St. Gregory's University, B
Southeastern Oklahoma State University, B
Southern Nazarene University, BM
Southwestern Oklahoma State University, B
Tulsa Community College, A
University of Central Oklahoma, BM
University of Oklahoma, BMD
University of Science and Arts of Oklahoma, B
University of Tulsa, BMDO

Oregon

Cascade College, B
Concordia University, B
Corban College, B
Eastern Oregon University, B
George Fox University, BMD
Lewis & Clark College, B
Linfield College, B
Marylhurst University, B
Northwest Christian College, B
Oregon State University, B
Pacific University, BMD

Portland State University, BMD
Reed College, B
Southern Oregon University, BM
Umpqua Community College, A
University of Oregon, BMD
University of Portland, B
Warner Pacific College, B
Western Oregon University, B
Willamette University, B

Pennsylvania

Albright College, B
Allegheny College, B
Alvernia College, B
Arcadia University, BM
Baptist Bible College of Pennsylvania, B
Bloomsburg University of Pennsylvania, B
Bryn Mawr College, BD
Bucknell University, BM
Bucks County Community College, A
Butler County Community College, A
Cabrini College, B
California University of Pennsylvania, B
Carlow University, B
Carnegie Mellon University, BD
Cedar Crest College, B
Chatham College, B
Chestnut Hill College, ABMDO
Cheyney University of Pennsylvania, B
Clarion University of Pennsylvania, B
College Misericordia, B
Community College of Allegheny County, A
Delaware County Community College, A
DeSales University, B
Dickinson College, B
Drexel University, BMDO
Duquesne University, BD
East Stroudsburg University of Pennsylvania, B
Eastern University, B
Edinboro University of Pennsylvania, BM
Elizabethtown College, B
Franklin and Marshall College, B
Gannon University, B
Geneva College, BM
Gettysburg College, B
Grove City College, B
Gwynedd-Mercy College, B
Harcum College, A
Harrisburg Area Community College, A
Haverford College, B
Holy Family University, B
Immaculata University, BMDO
Indiana University of Pennsylvania, BMD
Juniata College, B
King's College, B
Kutztown University of Pennsylvania, B
La Roche College, B
La Salle University, BD
Lafayette College, B
Lebanon Valley College, B
Lehigh University, BMD
Lincoln University, B
Lock Haven University of Pennsylvania, B
Lycoming College, B
Manor College, A
Mansfield University of Pennsylvania, B
Marywood University, BM
Mercyhurst College, B
Messiah College, B
Millersville University of Pennsylvania, BM
Moravian College, B
Mount Aloysius College, BM
Muhlenberg College, B
Neumann College, B
The Pennsylvania State University Abington College, B
The Pennsylvania State University Altoona College, B
The Pennsylvania State University Beaver Campus of the Commonwealth College, B
The Pennsylvania State University Berks Campus of the Berks-Lehigh Valley College, B
The Pennsylvania State University Delaware County Campus of the Commonwealth College, B
The Pennsylvania State University DuBois Campus of the Commonwealth College, B

The Pennsylvania State University at Erie, The Behrend College, B
The Pennsylvania State University Fayette Campus of the Commonwealth College, B
The Pennsylvania State University Harrisburg Campus, BM
The Pennsylvania State University Hazleton Campus of the Commonwealth College, B
The Pennsylvania State University, Lehigh Valley Campus of the Berks-Lehigh Valley College, B
The Pennsylvania State University McKeesport Campus of the Commonwealth College, B
The Pennsylvania State University Mont Alto Campus of the Commonwealth College, B
The Pennsylvania State University New Kensington Campus of the Commonwealth College, B
The Pennsylvania State University Schuylkill Campus of the Capital College, B
The Pennsylvania State University Shenango Campus of the Commonwealth College, B
The Pennsylvania State University University Park Campus, BMD
The Pennsylvania State University Wilkes-Barre Campus of the Commonwealth College, B
The Pennsylvania State University Worthington Scranton Campus of the Commonwealth College, B
The Pennsylvania State University York Campus of the Commonwealth College, B
Philadelphia University, B
Point Park University, B
Reading Area Community College, A
Robert Morris University, B
Rosemont College, B
Saint Francis University, B
Saint Joseph's University, BM
Saint Vincent College, B
Seton Hill University, B
Shippensburg University of Pennsylvania, BM
Slippery Rock University of Pennsylvania, B
Susquehanna University, B
Swarthmore College, B
Temple University, BD
Thiel College, B
University of Pennsylvania, BD
University of Pittsburgh, BMD
University of Pittsburgh at Bradford, B
University of Pittsburgh at Greensburg, B
University of Pittsburgh at Johnstown, B
University of the Sciences in Philadelphia, B
The University of Scranton, B
Ursinus College, B
Villanova University, BM
Washington & Jefferson College, B
Waynesburg College, B
West Chester University of Pennsylvania, BM
Westminster College, B
Widener University, BO
Wilkes University, B
York College of Pennsylvania, B

Puerto Rico

Bayamon Central University, BM
Carlos Albizu University, MD
Inter American University of Puerto Rico, Metropolitan Campus, BM
Inter American University of Puerto Rico, San Germán Campus, BMD
Pontifical Catholic University of Puerto Rico, BD
Universidad Metropolitana, B
Universidad del Turabo, B
University of Puerto Rico, Cayey University College, B
University of Puerto Rico, Mayagüez Campus, B
University of Puerto Rico, Río Piedras, BMD
University of the Sacred Heart, B

Rhode Island

Brown University, BMD
Bryant University, B
Providence College, B
Rhode Island College, BM
Roger Williams University, B
Salve Regina University, B

University of Rhode Island, BMD

South Carolina

Anderson University, B
Charleston Southern University, B
The Citadel, The Military College of South Carolina, BM
Clemson University, BM
Coastal Carolina University, B
Coker College, B
College of Charleston, B
Columbia College, B
Columbia International University, B
Converse College, B
Erskine College, B
Francis Marion University, BM
Furman University, B
Lander University, B
Limestone College, B
Newberry College, B
North Greenville College, B
Presbyterian College, B
South Carolina State University, B
Southern Wesleyan University, B
University of South Carolina, MD
University of South Carolina Aiken, B
University of South Carolina Beaufort, B
University of South Carolina Upstate, B
Winthrop University, BMO
Wofford College, B

South Dakota

Augustana College, B
Black Hills State University, B
Dakota Wesleyan University, B
Mount Marty College, B
Northern State University, B
South Dakota State University, B
University of Sioux Falls, B
The University of South Dakota, BMD

Tennessee

Austin Peay State University, BM
Belmont University, B
Bethel College, B
Bryan College, B
Carson-Newman College, B
Christian Brothers University, B
Columbia State Community College, A
Crichton College, B
Cumberland University, B
East Tennessee State University, BM
Fisk University, BM
Freed-Hardeman University, B
King College, B
Lambuth University, B
Lee University, B
Lincoln Memorial University, B
Lipscomb University, B
Martin Methodist College, A
Maryville College, B
Middle Tennessee State University, BM
Milligan College, B
Rhodes College, B
Sewanee: The University of the South, B
Southern Adventist University, BM
Tennessee State University, BMD
Tennessee Technological University, B
Tennessee Temple University, B
Tennessee Wesleyan College, B
Trevecca Nazarene University, B
Tusculum College, B
Union University, B
University of Memphis, BMD
The University of Tennessee, BMD
The University of Tennessee at Chattanooga, BM
The University of Tennessee at Martin, B
Vanderbilt University, BMD

Texas

Abilene Christian University, BM
Amarillo College, A
Angelo State University, BM
Argosy University/Dallas, BD
Austin College, B
Austin Community College, A

Baylor University, BMD
Blinn College, A
Brazosport College, A
Cisco Junior College, A
Clarendon College, A
Coastal Bend College, A
The Criswell College, B
Dallas Baptist University, B
Del Mar College, A
East Texas Baptist University, B
El Paso Community College, A
Frank Phillips College, A
Grayson County College, A
Hardin-Simmons University, BM
Hill College of the Hill Junior College District, A
Houston Baptist University, BM
Howard Payne University, B
Huston-Tillotson University, B
Kilgore College, A
Kingwood College, A
Lamar University, BM
Lee College, A
LeTourneau University, B
Lon Morris College, A
Lubbock Christian University, B
McMurry University, B
Midland College, A
Midwestern State University, BM
Navarro College, A
Odessa College, A
Our Lady of the Lake University of San
  Antonio, BMD
Palo Alto College, A
Prairie View A&M University, B
Rice University, BMD
St. Edward's University, B
St. Mary's University of San Antonio, BM
St. Philip's College, A
Sam Houston State University, BMD
San Antonio College, A
Schreiner University, B
Southern Methodist University, BMD
Southwestern Adventist University, B
Southwestern Assemblies of God University, A
Southwestern Christian College, A
Southwestern University, B
Stephen F. Austin State University, BM
Sul Ross State University, BM
Tarleton State University, B
Texas A&M International University, BM
Texas A&M University, BMD
Texas A&M University-Commerce, BMD
Texas A&M University-Corpus Christi, BM
Texas A&M University-Kingsville, BM
Texas A&M University-Texarkana, BM
Texas Christian University, BMD
Texas Lutheran University, B
Texas Southern University, BM
Texas State University-San Marcos, BM
Texas Tech University, BMD
Texas Wesleyan University, B
Texas Woman's University, BMD
Trinity University, B
Trinity Valley Community College, A
Tyler Junior College, A
University of Dallas, BM
University of Houston, BD
University of Houston-Clear Lake, BM
University of Houston-Downtown, B
University of Houston-Victoria, M
University of the Incarnate Word, B
University of Mary Hardin-Baylor, BM
University of North Texas, BMD
University of St. Thomas, B
The University of Texas at Arlington, BMD
The University of Texas at Austin, BD
The University of Texas at Brownsville, BM
The University of Texas at Dallas, B
The University of Texas at El Paso, BMD
The University of Texas-Pan American, BM
The University of Texas of the Permian Basin, BM
The University of Texas at San Antonio, BM
The University of Texas at Tyler, BM
Wayland Baptist University, B

West Texas A&M University, BM

United States Virgin Islands

University of the Virgin Islands, B

Utah

Brigham Young University, BMD
Dixie State College of Utah, A
Salt Lake Community College, A
Southern Utah University, B
University of Utah, BMD
Utah State University, BMD
Weber State University, B
Westminster College, B

Vermont

Bennington College, B
Burlington College, B
Castleton State College, BM
College of St. Joseph, BM
Green Mountain College, B
Johnson State College, B
Lyndon State College, B
Marlboro College, B
Middlebury College, B
Norwich University, B
Saint Michael's College, B
Southern Vermont College, B
University of Vermont, BD

Virginia

Argosy University/Washington D.C., BMD
Averett University, B
Bluefield College, B
Bridgewater College, B
The College of William and Mary, BMD
Eastern Mennonite University, B
Emory & Henry College, B
Ferrum College, B
George Mason University, BMD
Hampden-Sydney College, B
Hampton University, B
Hollins University, B
James Madison University, BMDO
Liberty University, B
Longwood University, B
Lynchburg College, B
Mary Baldwin College, B
Marymount University, B
Norfolk State University, BMD
Northern Virginia Community College, A
Old Dominion University, BMD
Radford University, BMO
Randolph-Macon College, B
Randolph-Macon Woman's College, B
Regent University, B
Roanoke College, B
Shenandoah University, B
Sweet Briar College, B
University of Mary Washington, B
University of Richmond, BM
University of Virginia, BMD
The University of Virginia's College at Wise, B
Virginia Commonwealth University, BD
Virginia Intermont College, B
Virginia Military Institute, B
Virginia Polytechnic Institute and State
  University, BMD
Virginia State University, BM
Virginia Union University, B
Virginia Wesleyan College, B
Washington and Lee University, B

Washington

Antioch University Seattle, M
Argosy University/Seattle, B
Bastyr University, B
Central Washington University, BM
Centralia College, A
City University, B
Eastern Washington University, BM
Everett Community College, A
Gonzaga University, B
Heritage University, AB
Highline Community College, A

Lower Columbia College, A
Northwest University, B
Pacific Lutheran University, B
Saint Martin's University, B
Seattle Pacific University, B
Seattle University, BM
Skagit Valley College, A
Tacoma Community College, A
University of Puget Sound, B
University of Washington, BD
Walla Walla College, B
Washington State University, BMD
Western Washington University, BM
Whitman College, B
Whitworth College, B

West Virginia

Alderson-Broaddus College, B
American Public University System, B
Bethany College, B
Bluefield State College, A
Concord University, B
Davis & Elkins College, B
Fairmont State University, B
Marshall University, BMD
Mountain State University, B
New River Community and Technical College, A
Ohio Valley University, B
Potomac State College of West Virginia
  University, A
Salem International University, A
Shepherd University, B
University of Charleston, B
West Liberty State College, B
West Virginia State University, B
West Virginia University, BMD
West Virginia Wesleyan College, B
Wheeling Jesuit University, B

Wisconsin

Alverno College, B
Beloit College, B
Cardinal Stritch University, BM
Carroll College, B
Carthage College, B
Concordia University Wisconsin, B
Edgewood College, B
Lakeland College, B
Lawrence University, B
Marian College of Fond du Lac, B
Marquette University, BMD
Mount Mary College, B
Northland College, B
Ripon College, B
St. Norbert College, B
Silver Lake College, B
University of Wisconsin-Eau Claire, BMO
University of Wisconsin-Green Bay, AB
University of Wisconsin-La Crosse, BMO
University of Wisconsin-Madison, BD
University of Wisconsin-Milwaukee, BMD
University of Wisconsin-Oshkosh, BM
University of Wisconsin-Parkside, B
University of Wisconsin-Platteville, B
University of Wisconsin-River Falls, B
University of Wisconsin-Stevens Point, B
University of Wisconsin-Stout, BM
University of Wisconsin-Superior, B
University of Wisconsin-Whitewater, BMO
Viterbo University, B
Wisconsin Lutheran College, B

Wyoming

Casper College, A
Central Wyoming College, A
Eastern Wyoming College, A
Laramie County Community College, A
Northwest College, A
University of Wyoming, BMD
Western Wyoming Community College, A

Alberta

Athabasca University, B
Concordia University College of Alberta, B
The King's University College, B
University of Alberta, BMD

University of Calgary, BMD
University of Lethbridge, BM

British Columbia

Kwantlen University College, A
Malaspina University-College, B
Simon Fraser University, BMD
Thompson Rivers University, B
Trinity Western University, B
The University of British Columbia, BMD
University College of the Fraser Valley, B
University of Northern British Columbia, BMD
University of Victoria, BMD

Manitoba

Brandon University, B
Canadian Mennonite University, B
University of Manitoba, BMD
The University of Winnipeg, B

New Brunswick

Atlantic Baptist University, B
Mount Allison University, B
St. Thomas University, B
Université de Moncton, BM
University of New Brunswick Fredericton, BD
University of New Brunswick Saint John, BM

Newfoundland and Labrador

Memorial University of Newfoundland, BMD

Nova Scotia

Acadia University, BM
Cape Breton University, B
Dalhousie University, BMD
Mount Saint Vincent University, B
St. Francis Xavier University, B
Saint Mary's University, BM
University of King's College, B

Ontario

Brock University, BM
Carleton University, BMD
Lakehead University, BMD
Laurentian University, B
McMaster University, BMD
Nipissing University, B
Queen's University at Kingston, BMD
Redeemer University College, B
Ryerson University, B
Trent University, B
Tyndale University College & Seminary, B
University of Guelph, BMD
University of Ottawa, BD
University of Toronto, BMD
University of Waterloo, BMD
The University of Western Ontario, BMD
University of Windsor, BMD
Wilfrid Laurier University, BM
York University, BMD

Prince Edward Island

University of Prince Edward Island, B

Quebec

Bishop's University, B
Concordia University, BMD
McGill University, BMD
Université Laval, BD
Université de Montréal, BMD
Université du Québec en Abitibi-Témiscamingue, B
Université du Québec àChicoutimi, B
Université du Québec àMontréal, BD
Université du Québec en Outaouais, B
Université du Québec àTrois-Rivières, BMD

Université de Sherbrooke, BM

Saskatchewan

University of Regina, BMD
University of Saskatchewan, BMD

PSYCHOLOGY TEACHER EDUCATION

California

California Lutheran University, B

Indiana

University of Evansville, B
Valparaiso University, B

Iowa

St. Ambrose University, B

Kansas

Central Christian College of Kansas, A
Pittsburg State University, B

Kentucky

Campbellsville University, B

Michigan

Alma College, B
University of Michigan-Flint, B

Missouri

University of Missouri-St. Louis, B

Nebraska

Wayne State College, B
York College, B

Ohio

Ohio Wesleyan University, B
Shawnee State University, B

Pennsylvania

Widener University, B

Tennessee

Cumberland University, B

Utah

Brigham Young University, B

Wisconsin

Carroll College, B

PSYCHOMETRICS AND QUANTITATIVE PSYCHOLOGY

North Dakota

North Dakota State University, B

PUBLIC ADMINISTRATION

Alabama

Andrew Jackson University, M
Auburn University, BMDO
Auburn University Montgomery, MD
Birmingham-Southern College, M
Huntingdon College, B
Jacksonville State University, M
Samford University, B
Talladega College, B
Troy University, BM
The University of Alabama, M
The University of Alabama at Birmingham, M

University of South Alabama, M

Alaska

University of Alaska Anchorage, M
University of Alaska Southeast, M

Arizona

Northern Arizona University, MO
Rio Salado College, A
Scottsdale Community College, A
The University of Arizona, BMD

Arkansas

Arkansas State University, M
Harding University, B
Henderson State University, B
National Park Community College, A
University of Arkansas, BM
University of Arkansas at Little Rock, M
University of Central Arkansas, B

California

California Lutheran University, M
California State Polytechnic University, Pomona, BM
California State University, Bakersfield, BM
California State University, Chico, BM
California State University, Dominguez Hills, BM
California State University, East Bay, BM
California State University, Fresno, BM
California State University, Fullerton, BM
California State University, Long Beach, MO
California State University, Los Angeles, M
California State University, Northridge, M
California State University, Sacramento, M
California State University, San Bernardino, BM
California State University, Stanislaus, M
Citrus College, A
City College of San Francisco, A
East Los Angeles College, A
Los Angeles City College, A
Mt. San Jacinto College, A
National University, M
Notre Dame de Namur University, M
Palomar College, A
San Diego State University, BM
San Francisco State University, M
San Joaquin Delta College, A
San Jose City College, A
San Jose State University, M
Santiago Canyon College, A
Solano Community College, A
Sonoma State University, M
Southwestern College, A
Touro University International, M
University of California, Los Angeles, B
University of California, Riverside, B
University of La Verne, BMD
University of San Francisco, BM
University of Southern California, BMDO

Colorado

Red Rocks Community College, A
University of Colorado at Colorado Springs, M
University of Colorado at Denver and Health
  Sciences Center - Downtown Denver Campus, M
University of Denver, B

Connecticut

Housatonic Community College, A
Three Rivers Community College, A
University of New Haven, BMO

Delaware

University of Delaware, M
Wilmington College, M

District of Columbia

American University, MDO
The George Washington University, MD
Howard University, M
Southeastern University, M

University of the District of Columbia, ABM

Florida

Argosy University/Sarasota, M
Edward Waters College, B
Flagler College, B
Florida Agricultural and Mechanical University, BM
Florida Atlantic University, BMD
Florida Gulf Coast University, M
Florida Institute of Technology, M
Florida International University, BMD
Florida Memorial College, B
Florida State University, MDO
Keiser College (Fort Lauderdale), A
Manatee Community College, A
Miami Dade College, A
Nova Southeastern University, MD
St. Thomas University, BMO
Tallahassee Community College, A
University of Central Florida, BMO
University of North Florida, M
University of South Florida, M
University of West Florida, M

Georgia

Albany State University, M
Clark Atlanta University, M
Columbus State University, M
Georgia College & State University, M
Georgia Southern University, M
Georgia State University, MO
Kennesaw State University, M
Macon State College, A
Middle Georgia College, A
North Georgia College & State University, BM
Savannah State University, M
University of Georgia, MD
University of Phoenix-Columbus Georgia
   Campus, B
University of West Georgia, M
Valdosta State University, M

Guam

University of Guam, BM

Hawaii

Hawaii Pacific University, B
University of Hawaii at Manoa, MO
University of Hawaii-West Oahu, B

Idaho

Boise State University, BM
Idaho State University, M
University of Idaho, M

Illinois

Augustana College, B
Blackburn College, B
DePaul University, MO
DeVry University (Oakbrook Terrace), M
Governors State University, BM
Illinois Institute of Technology, MO
Lewis University, B
Northern Illinois University, M
Roosevelt University, BM
Southern Illinois University Carbondale, MO
Southern Illinois University Edwardsville, M
University of Illinois at Chicago, MD
University of Illinois at Springfield, MDO

Indiana

Ball State University, M
Indiana State University, M
Indiana University Bloomington, AB
Indiana University Kokomo, O
Indiana University Northwest, ABM
Indiana University-Purdue University Fort
   Wayne, AB
Indiana University-Purdue University
   Indianapolis, ABMO
Indiana University South Bend, ABO
University of Evansville, M
University of Southern Indiana, M

Vincennes University, A

Iowa

Buena Vista University, B
Drake University, MO
Iowa State University of Science and
   Technology, BM
St. Ambrose University, B
University of Northern Iowa, B
Upper Iowa University, BM

Kansas

Barton County Community College, A
Kansas State University, M
University of Kansas, BMDO
Washburn University, B
Wichita State University, M

Kentucky

Eastern Kentucky University, M
Kentucky State University, BM
Murray State University, B
Northern Kentucky University, BMO
University of Kentucky, MDO
University of Louisville, MD

Louisiana

Grambling State University, BM
Louisiana College, B
Louisiana State University and Agricultural and
   Mechanical College, MDO
Southern University and Agricultural and Mechanical
   College, MD
Southern University at Shreveport, A
Tulane University, M
University of New Orleans, M

Maine

University of Maine, BMD
The University of Maine at Augusta, AB
University of Maine at Fort Kent, B
University of Maine at Machias, B

Maryland

Anne Arundel Community College, A
Bowie State University, M
Sojourner-Douglass College, B
University of Maryland, College Park, MO

Massachusetts

American International College, BM
Boston University, M
Brandeis University, M
Bridgewater State College, M
Clark University, MO
Framingham State College, M
Harvard University, M
Northeastern University, BM
Stonehill College, B
Suffolk University, BMO
Tufts University, M
University of Massachusetts Amherst, M

Michigan

Bay Mills Community College, A
Calvin College, B
Central Michigan University, MO
Eastern Michigan University, BM
Ferris State University, B
Grand Valley State University, BM
Lansing Community College, A
Michigan State University, B
Northern Michigan University, BM
Oakland University, BM
Saginaw Valley State University, BM
Siena Heights University, B
University of Michigan-Dearborn, MO
University of Michigan-Flint, BM
Wayne State University, BM
Western Michigan University, BMD

Minnesota

Hamline University, BM
Metropolitan State University, BM
Minnesota State University Mankato, BMO

Minnesota State University Moorhead, M
St. Cloud State University, B
Saint Mary's University of Minnesota, MO
Southwest Minnesota State University, B
University of St. Thomas, B
Walden University, MD
Winona State University, B

Mississippi

Hinds Community College, A
Itawamba Community College, A
Jackson State University, MD
Mississippi State University, MD
Mississippi Valley State University, B
Northeast Mississippi Community College, A
University of Mississippi, B

Missouri

Central Methodist University, AB
Evangel University, B
Harris-Stowe State University, B
Jefferson College, A
Lincoln University, B
Lindenwood University, BM
Missouri State University, BM
Missouri Valley College, B
Northwest Missouri State University, B
Park University, BM
Saint Louis University, M
Southeast Missouri State University, M
University of Missouri-Kansas City, MDO
University of Missouri-St. Louis, BMO
Webster University, M

Montana

Carroll College, B
Montana State University, M
The University of Montana-Missoula, MO

Nebraska

Doane College, B
Hastings College, B
University of Nebraska at Omaha, MD
Wayne State College, B

Nevada

Nevada State College at Henderson, B
University of Nevada, Las Vegas, MD
University of Nevada, Reno, M

New Hampshire

Plymouth State University, B
University of New Hampshire, M

New Jersey

Bloomfield College, B
County College of Morris, A
Fairleigh Dickinson University, College at
   Florham, M
Fairleigh Dickinson University, Metropolitan
   Campus, MO
Kean University, BMO
Passaic County Community College, A
Rutgers, The State University of New Jersey,
   Camden, MO
Rutgers, The State University of New Jersey,
   Newark, MD
Salem Community College, A
Seton Hall University, M

New Mexico

College of Santa Fe, B
Mesalands Community College, A
San Juan College, A
University of New Mexico, MO
Western New Mexico University, B

New York

Adelphi University, O
Alfred University, BM
Bernard M. Baruch College of the City University of
   New York, BM
Eugenio María de Hostos Community College of the
   City University of New York, A
Fordham University, B

Hudson Valley Community College, A
John Jay College of Criminal Justice of the City
  University of New York, BM
Long Island University, Brooklyn Campus, M
Long Island University, C.W. Post Campus, BMO
Marist College, MO
Medgar Evers College of the City University of New
  York, AB
Metropolitan College of New York, M
Mohawk Valley Community College, A
New York University, MDO
St. John's University, B
State University of New York at Binghamton, M
State University of New York College at
  Brockport, M
Syracuse University, BMDO
University at Albany, State University of New
  York, BMDO
Wagner College, B
Westchester Community College, A

North Carolina

Appalachian State University, M
Campbell University, B
East Carolina University, M
Elon University, B
Fayetteville Technical Community College, A
North Carolina Central University, M
North Carolina State University, MD
Shaw University, B
The University of North Carolina at Chapel Hill, MO
The University of North Carolina at Charlotte, M
The University of North Carolina at Pembroke, BM
The University of North Carolina Wilmington, M
Western Carolina University, B

North Dakota

University of North Dakota, M

Ohio

Bowling Green State University, BM
Capital University, B
Cedarville University, B
Cleveland State University, BMDO
David N. Myers University, AB
Heidelberg College, B
John Carroll University, B
Kent State University, M
Miami University, B
Miami University Hamilton, B
Notre Dame College, B
Ohio University, M
Ohio University-Eastern, B
Ohio Wesleyan University, B
Sinclair Community College, A
Union Institute & University, B
The University of Akron, MO
University of Dayton, M
The University of Findlay, M
The University of Toledo, M
Wright State University, BM

Oklahoma

Oklahoma City University, M
University of Oklahoma, BM

Oregon

Portland State University, MD
University of Oregon, B
Western Oregon University, B
Willamette University, MO

Pennsylvania

Carnegie Mellon University, M
Duquesne University, MO
Gannon University, MO
Juniata College, B
Kutztown University of Pennsylvania, BM
La Salle University, B
Lincoln University, B
Marywood University, BMO
The Pennsylvania State University Harrisburg
  Campus, BMD
Point Park University, AB
Reading Area Community College, A

Saint Francis University, B
Saint Joseph's University, B
Shippensburg University of Pennsylvania, BM
University of Pittsburgh, BMDO
Villanova University, M
Waynesburg College, B
West Chester University of Pennsylvania, M
Westmoreland County Community College, A
Widener University, MO
York College of Pennsylvania, B

Puerto Rico

Bayamon Central University, B
Inter American University of Puerto Rico, San
  Germán Campus, B
Pontifical Catholic University of Puerto Rico, BM
Universidad del Turabo, AB
University of Puerto Rico at Carolina, A
University of Puerto Rico, Río Piedras, M

Rhode Island

Rhode Island College, B
Roger Williams University, BM
University of Rhode Island, M

South Carolina

Clemson University, M
College of Charleston, M
University of South Carolina, MO

South Dakota

Northern State University, B
The University of South Dakota, M

Tennessee

Cumberland University, M
Fisk University, B
Lipscomb University, B
Tennessee State University, BMD
University of Memphis, M
The University of Tennessee, BMO
The University of Tennessee at Chattanooga, M
The University of Tennessee at Martin, B

Texas

Angelo State University, M
Baylor University, BM
Brazosport College, A
Del Mar College, A
Lamar University, M
Midwestern State University, M
St. Mary's University of San Antonio, MO
Sam Houston State University, M
San Antonio College, A
Stephen F. Austin State University, BM
Sul Ross State University, M
Texas A&M International University, M
Texas A&M University-Corpus Christi, M
Texas A&M University-Kingsville, B
Texas Southern University, BMO
Texas State University-San Marcos, BM
Texas Tech University, M
University of Houston-Clear Lake, BM
University of North Texas, BM
The University of Texas at Arlington, M
The University of Texas at Brownsville, M
The University of Texas at Dallas, B
The University of Texas-Pan American, M
The University of Texas at San Antonio, M
The University of Texas at Tyler, M

West Texas A&M University, B

United States Virgin Islands

University of the Virgin Islands, M

Utah

Brigham Young University, MO
University of Utah, MO

Vermont

University of Vermont, M

Virginia

George Mason University, B
James Madison University, BM
Mountain Empire Community College, A
Old Dominion University, M
Regent University, MO
Shenandoah University, BO
Thomas Nelson Community College, A
University of Management and Technology, M
University of Northern Virginia, M
Virginia Commonwealth University, MO
Virginia Intermont College, B
Virginia Polytechnic Institute and State
  University, MDO
Virginia State University, B

Washington

Crown College, B
Eastern Washington University, BMO
The Evergreen State College, M
Heritage University, B
Seattle University, BM
University of Washington, B

West Virginia

American Public University System, BM
West Virginia University, MO
West Virginia University Institute of Technology, B

Wisconsin

Concordia University Wisconsin, M
Edgewood College, B
University of Wisconsin-Milwaukee, MO
University of Wisconsin-Stevens Point, B
University of Wisconsin-Whitewater, BM

Wyoming

Laramie County Community College, A
University of Wyoming, M

Alberta

Athabasca University, B
University of Lethbridge, B

British Columbia

University of Victoria, BMO

Manitoba

University of Manitoba, BM
The University of Winnipeg, M

New Brunswick

Université de Moncton, MO
University of New Brunswick Fredericton, M

Nova Scotia

Dalhousie University, MO
Université Sainte-Anne, B

Ontario

Brock University, BM
Carleton University, BMD
McMaster University, M
Ryerson University, B
University of Ottawa, BO
University of Toronto, B
The University of Western Ontario, B
University of Windsor, B

York University, B

Quebec

Concordia University, BM
Université du Québec àMontréal, M
Université du Québec àRimouski, O

Saskatchewan

University of Regina, ABM
University of Saskatchewan, B

PUBLIC ADMINISTRATION AND SOCIAL SERVICE PROFESSIONS

Alabama

Southern Christian University, B

Arizona

University of Phoenix-Phoenix Campus, B
University of Phoenix-Southern Arizona Campus, B

California

University of Phoenix-Bay Area Campus, B
University of Phoenix-Central Valley Campus, B
University of Phoenix-Sacramento Valley Campus, B
University of Phoenix-San Diego Campus, B
University of Phoenix-Southern California
    Campus, B

Colorado

University of Phoenix-Denver Campus, B

Florida

University of Phoenix-West Florida Campus, B

Hawaii

University of Phoenix-Hawaii Campus, B

Illinois

Northeastern Illinois University, B
Quincy University, B
Roosevelt University, B
Sauk Valley Community College, A

Indiana

Indiana University-Purdue University Fort Wayne, A
Taylor University Fort Wayne, B
University of Saint Francis, AB

Kentucky

Kentucky Wesleyan College, B

Michigan

Eastern Michigan University, B
University of Phoenix-West Michigan Campus, B

Missouri

University of Phoenix-Kansas City Campus, B

Nevada

University of Phoenix-Nevada Campus, B

New Mexico

University of Phoenix-New Mexico Campus, B

New York

Cornell University, B
Erie Community College, A
Erie Community College, South Campus, A

Mercy College, B

Ohio

Ohio University, B
The University of Akron, A

Oregon

University of Phoenix-Oregon Campus, B

South Carolina

Columbia College, B

Tennessee

Cleveland State Community College, A
Milligan College, B

Texas

College of the Mainland, A
Texas Woman's University, B

Utah

University of Phoenix-Utah Campus, B

Washington

University of Phoenix-Washington Campus, B

PUBLIC AFFAIRS

Alabama

The University of Alabama in Huntsville, M

Arizona

Arizona State University, MD

Arkansas

University of Arkansas at Little Rock, M

Colorado

University of Colorado at Colorado Springs, M
University of Colorado at Denver and Health
    Sciences Center - Downtown Denver Campus, D

District of Columbia

American University, M
Howard University, M

Florida

University of Central Florida, D
University of Florida, M

Georgia

Georgia College & State University, M

Idaho

University of Idaho, MD

Illinois

DePaul University, O

Indiana

Indiana University Bloomington, MDO
Indiana University Northwest, MO
Indiana University-Purdue University Fort
    Wayne, MO
Indiana University South Bend, MO

Kentucky

Murray State University, M
University of Louisville, D
Western Kentucky University, M

Maryland

University of Baltimore, MDO

Massachusetts

University of Massachusetts Boston, MDO

Michigan

Western Michigan University, MD

Minnesota

University of Minnesota, Twin Cities Campus, M

Missouri

Park University, M
University of Missouri-Columbia, M

University of Missouri-Kansas City, MD

Nevada

University of Nevada, Las Vegas, D

New Jersey

Princeton University, MDO

New Mexico

New Mexico Highlands University, M

New York

Cornell University, M

North Carolina

The University of North Carolina at Greensboro, MO
Western Carolina University, M

Pennsylvania

Indiana University of Pennsylvania, M
University of Pennsylvania, M

Texas

Texas A&M University, M
The University of Texas at Arlington, D
The University of Texas at Austin, MDO
The University of Texas at Dallas, MD

Virginia

George Mason University, M

Washington

University of Washington, MO

Wisconsin

University of Wisconsin-Madison, M

Nova Scotia

Dalhousie University, M

Ontario

McMaster University, M

Quebec

Concordia University, O

PUBLIC/APPLIED HISTORY AND ARCHIVAL ADMINISTRATION

California

Chapman University, B
University of California, Santa Barbara, B

Georgia

Clayton State University, B

Maryland

Villa Julie College, B

North Carolina

East Carolina University, B
Meredith College, B

PUBLIC HEALTH

Alabama

The University of Alabama at Birmingham, MD

Arizona

Northern Arizona University, M
The University of Arizona, M

California

California State University, Fresno, M
California State University, Fullerton, M
California State University, Northridge, M
Loma Linda University, MD
San Diego State University, MDO

San Francisco State University, M
San Jose State University, M
Touro University International, MO
University of California, Berkeley, BMDO
University of California, Los Angeles, BMDO
University of California, San Diego, D
University of Southern California, M

Colorado

University of Northern Colorado, M

Connecticut

Southern Connecticut State University, M
University of Connecticut, MO
Yale University, MDO

District of Columbia

The George Washington University, MDO
Georgetown University, M

Florida

Florida Agricultural and Mechanical University, M
Florida International University, M
Florida State University, MO
Nova Southeastern University, M
University of Florida, M
University of Miami, MO
University of North Florida, MO
University of South Florida, MD

Georgia

Armstrong Atlantic State University, M
Emory University, MDO
Fort Valley State University, M
Georgia Southern University, M
Georgia State University, M

Hawaii

University of Hawaii at Manoa, MD

Idaho

Boise State University, M
Idaho State University, M

Illinois

Benedictine University, MO
Northern Illinois University, M
Northwestern University, MO
Saint Xavier University, M
University of Illinois at Chicago, MDO
University of Illinois at Springfield, M
University of Illinois at Urbana-Champaign, B

Indiana

Indiana University Bloomington, MDO
Purdue University, MD

Iowa

The University of Iowa, MDO

Kansas

Kansas State University, M
University of Kansas, MO
Wichita State University, M

Kentucky

University of Kentucky, MD
Western Kentucky University, M

Louisiana

Louisiana State University Health Sciences
    Center, M
Tulane University, MDO

Maine

University of New England, MO

Maryland

The Johns Hopkins University, MDO
Morgan State University, MD

University of Maryland, College Park, MD

Massachusetts

Boston University, MDO
Emerson College, M
Harvard University, MDO
Regis College, M
Tufts University, M
University of Massachusetts Amherst, MD

Michigan

Michigan State University, M
University of Michigan, MDO
Wayne State University, MO

Minnesota

College of St. Catherine, M
University of Minnesota, Twin Cities Campus, MDO
Walden University, MD

Mississippi

University of Southern Mississippi, M

Missouri

Missouri State University, M
Saint Louis University, MD

Nebraska

University of Nebraska Medical Center, M
University of Nebraska at Omaha, M

Nevada

University of Nevada, Reno, M

New Hampshire

Dartmouth College, M
University of New Hampshire, M

New Jersey

New Jersey Institute of Technology, M
Rutgers, The State University of New Jersey, New
    Brunswick/Piscataway, MDO

New Mexico

New Mexico State University, M
University of New Mexico, M

New York

Adelphi University, O
Brooklyn College of the City University of New
    York, M
Hunter College of the City University of New
    York, MO
New York University, MD
Sarah Lawrence College, M
State University of New York at Buffalo, M
State University of New York Downstate Medical
    Center, MO
Stony Brook University, State University of New
    York, M
University at Albany, State University of New
    York, MD
University of Rochester, MO

North Carolina

East Carolina University, M
The University of North Carolina at Chapel
    Hill, MDO

Ohio

Bowling Green State University, M
Case Western Reserve University, MO
Cleveland State University, M
Kent State University, M
Malone College, B
The Ohio State University, MDO
The University of Akron, M
The University of Toledo, M

Wright State University, M

Oklahoma

University of Oklahoma Health Sciences Center, MD

Oregon

Oregon State University, MD
Portland State University, MO

Pennsylvania

Drexel University, M
East Stroudsburg University of Pennsylvania, M
Marywood University, M
Temple University, MD
Thomas Jefferson University, M
University of Pittsburgh, MDO
West Chester University of Pennsylvania, BMO

Puerto Rico

University of Puerto Rico, Medical Sciences
    Campus, M

Rhode Island

Brown University, M

South Carolina

University of South Carolina, MO

Tennessee

East Tennessee State University, MO
The University of Tennessee, MO

Texas

Texas A&M University, MD
Texas A&M University System Health Science
    Center, M
Texas Chiropractic College, B
Texas Wesleyan University, M
The University of Texas Health Science Center at
    Houston, MDO

Utah

California College for Health Sciences, M
University of Utah, MD
Utah State University, B

Virginia

James Madison University, M
Old Dominion University, M
University of Virginia, M
Virginia Commonwealth University, MDO

Washington

University of Washington, MDO

West Virginia

American Public University System, M
West Virginia University, M

Wisconsin

University of Wisconsin-Eau Claire, M
University of Wisconsin-La Crosse, M
Western Technical College, A

Alberta

Concordia University College of Alberta, B
University of Alberta, MDO

Ontario

University of Ottawa, D
University of Toronto, MDO

PUBLIC HEALTH/COMMUNITY NURSE/NURSING

Illinois

Northern Illinois University, B

Ohio

Capital University, B
Wright State University, B

Washington
University of Washington, B

British Columbia
University of Northern British Columbia, B

Quebec
Université du Québec àTrois-Rivières, B

PUBLIC HEALTH EDUCATION AND PROMOTION

California
California State University, Long Beach, B
University of Southern California, B

Colorado
University of Northern Colorado, B

District of Columbia
American University, B

Georgia
Georgia Southern University, B

Idaho
College of Southern Idaho, A

Louisiana
Dillard University, B
Louisiana State University in Shreveport, B
Southeastern Louisiana University, B

Michigan
Delta College, A
Oakland University, B
University of Michigan-Flint, B

Minnesota
University of St. Thomas, B

New Hampshire
Plymouth State University, B

New Mexico
New Mexico State University, B

New York
Ithaca College, B

North Carolina
Appalachian State University, B
East Carolina University, B
North Carolina Central University, B
The University of North Carolina at Greensboro, B
The University of North Carolina at Pembroke, B

Ohio
Baldwin-Wallace College, B
Malone College, B
The University of Toledo, B

Pennsylvania
Temple University, B
West Chester University of Pennsylvania, B

South Carolina
Coastal Carolina University, B

Texas
University of North Texas, B

Virginia
Liberty University, B

Washington
Walla Walla College, B

West Virginia
Mountain State University, B

Nova Scotia
Dalhousie University, B

Ontario
Laurentian University, B

PUBLIC HEALTH (MPH, DPH)

Alabama
Athens State University, B
South University, A

Alaska
University of Alaska Anchorage, B
University of Alaska Fairbanks, A

Arizona
Arizona Western College, A
Diné College, A
Mohave Community College, A

Arkansas
National Park Community College, A
University of Arkansas, B
University of Arkansas at Little Rock, B

California
Azusa Pacific University, B
Butte College, A
Cabrillo College, A
California State University, Dominguez Hills, B
California State University, East Bay, B
California State University, Fresno, B
California State University, Long Beach, B
California State University, Los Angeles, B
California State University, Northridge, B
California State University, San Bernardino, B
Cañada College, A
City College of San Francisco, A
College of the Canyons, A
Compton Community College, A
Cypress College, A
Mendocino College, A
Merritt College, A
Mission College, A
National University, A
Ohlone College, A
Orange Coast College, A
Palo Verde College, A
San Francisco State University, B
San Joaquin Delta College, A
Sonoma State University, B
Touro University International, B
University of Southern California, B
West Hills Community College, A

Colorado
Northeastern Junior College, A
University of Colorado at Colorado Springs, B

Connecticut
Northwestern Connecticut Community College, A
Southern Connecticut State University, B
University of Hartford, AB

District of Columbia
American University, B
Georgetown University, B

Florida
Daytona Beach Community College, A
Florida Atlantic University, B
Florida International University, B
South University (Tampa), B
University of Central Florida, B

Georgia
Armstrong Atlantic State University, B
Columbus State University, B
Covenant College, A

Macon State College, A

Idaho
Boise State University, B
Brigham Young University -Idaho, A

Illinois
Benedictine University, B
Bradley University, B
Chicago State University, B
City Colleges of Chicago, Kennedy-King College, A
Northern Illinois University, B
Roosevelt University, B
Spoon River College, A

Indiana
Ball State University, B
Indiana University Bloomington, B
Indiana University-Purdue University Indianapolis, B
Manchester College, B
University of Saint Francis, B

Iowa
Graceland University, B
Waldorf College, B

Kansas
Kansas State University, B
Newman University, AB

Kentucky
Spalding University, B

Louisiana
Dillard University, B
Our Lady of Holy Cross College, B

Maine
University of New England, B
University of Southern Maine, B

Maryland
Carroll Community College, A
The Johns Hopkins University, B
University of Maryland, Baltimore County, B

Massachusetts
Boston University, B
Eastern Nazarene College, B
Fisher College, A
Hampshire College, B
Merrimack College, B
North Shore Community College, A
Northeastern University, B
Springfield College, B
Tufts University, B

Michigan
Alma College, B
Bay Mills Community College, A
Central Michigan University, B
Grand Valley State University, B
Kalamazoo College, B
Kalamazoo Valley Community College, A
Oakland University, B
Wayne State University, B

Minnesota
Minnesota State University Mankato, B
University of Minnesota, Twin Cities Campus, B
University of St. Thomas, B
Winona State University, B

Mississippi
Northeast Mississippi Community College, A
Southwest Mississippi Community College, A
University of Southern Mississippi, B

Missouri
College of the Ozarks, B
Drury University, B
Maryville University of Saint Louis, B
Northwest Missouri State University, B

Truman State University, B

Montana

Chief Dull Knife College, A
Montana Tech of The University of Montana, B

Nebraska

Union College, A

Nevada

University of Nevada, Las Vegas, B

New Jersey

Bergen Community College, A
Mercer County Community College, A
New Jersey City University, B
Ocean County College, A
The Richard Stockton College of New Jersey, B
Rutgers, The State University of New Jersey, New
Brunswick/Piscataway, B
Sussex County Community College, A
William Paterson University of New Jersey, B

New Mexico

New Mexico Junior College, A
New Mexico State University, B

New York

Borough of Manhattan Community College of the
City University of New York, A
Hunter College of the City University of New York, B
Long Island University, Brooklyn Campus, B
Nassau Community College, A
Queensborough Community College of the City
University of New York, A
St. Joseph's College, New York, B
State University of New York College at
Brockport, B
State University of New York College at Cortland, B
State University of New York College at Old
Westbury, B
Syracuse University, B
Touro College, B
Villa Maria College of Buffalo, A

North Carolina

Mount Olive College, B

Ohio

Hiram College, B
Kettering College of Medical Arts, B
Ohio University-Eastern, B
Union Institute & University, B
University of Cincinnati, B
Youngstown State University, B

Oklahoma

Murray State College, A
Oklahoma State University, B
Oral Roberts University, B
Tulsa Community College, A

Oregon

Corban College, B
Oregon State University, B
Pacific University, B
Warner Pacific College, B

Pennsylvania

Bucks County Community College, A
Carlow University, B
Cedar Crest College, B
College Misericordia, B
Gannon University, B
Gettysburg College, B
Gwynedd-Mercy College, B
Harcum College, A
Lock Haven University of Pennsylvania, B
Manor College, A
Slippery Rock University of Pennsylvania, B

West Chester University of Pennsylvania, B

Puerto Rico

Inter American University of Puerto Rico, San
Germán Campus, B
University of Puerto Rico, Medical Sciences
Campus, B

South Carolina

Clemson University, B
Greenville Technical College, A
Tri-County Technical College, A

Tennessee

East Tennessee State University, B
Martin Methodist College, A
Milligan College, B
Tennessee Wesleyan College, B
The University of Tennessee at Martin, B

Texas

El Paso Community College, A
Hill College of the Hill Junior College District, A
Howard Payne University, A
Lamar University, B
Palo Alto College, A
Texas A&M University-Corpus Christi, B
Texas Christian University, B
Texas Southern University, B
The University of Texas at El Paso, B

Utah

California College for Health Sciences, A
Salt Lake Community College, A

Vermont

Castleton State College, B
Johnson State College, B

Virginia

Jefferson College of Health Sciences, A
Longwood University, B

Washington

Bastyr University, B
Northwest University, A
University of Washington, B
Walla Walla College, B

West Virginia

Alderson-Broaddus College, B
Fairmont State University, B
Salem International University, B
West Liberty State College, B

Wisconsin

University of Wisconsin-Milwaukee, B

New Brunswick

University of New Brunswick Saint John, B

Nova Scotia

Dalhousie University, B

Ontario

Brock University, B
Ryerson University, B
University of Waterloo, B
The University of Western Ontario, B
York University, B

Quebec

Université du Québec àTrois-Rivières, B

PUBLIC HISTORY

Arizona

Arizona State University, M

Arkansas

University of Arkansas at Little Rock, M

California

California State University, Sacramento, M

Florida

Florida State University, M

Illinois

Eastern Illinois University, M
Loyola University Chicago, M
University of Illinois at Springfield, M

Indiana

Indiana University-Purdue University Indianapolis, M

Massachusetts

Northeastern University, M
Simmons College, MO
University of Massachusetts Amherst, M
University of Massachusetts Boston, M

New Jersey

Rutgers, The State University of New Jersey,
Camden, M

New York

New York University, O
University at Albany, State University of New
York, O

North Carolina

Appalachian State University, M
North Carolina State University, M

South Carolina

University of South Carolina, MO

Texas

University of Houston, M
The University of Texas at Austin, MD

British Columbia

The University of British Columbia, MDO

Ontario

University of Waterloo, M

PUBLIC POLICY ANALYSIS

Arizona

Northern Arizona University, BD
The University of Arizona, MD

Arkansas

University of Arkansas, D

California

California Lutheran University, M
California State University, Long Beach, MO
California State University, Monterey Bay, M
California State University, Sacramento, M
Mills College, B
Occidental College, B
Pepperdine University, M
Pomona College, B
San Francisco State University, M
Stanford University, B
University of California, Berkeley, MDO
University of California, Los Angeles, BM
University of the Pacific, M
University of Southern California, MD

Colorado

University of Colorado at Boulder, M
University of Denver, M

Western State College of Colorado, B

Connecticut

Trinity College, BM
University of Connecticut, MO

Delaware

University of Delaware, MD

District of Columbia

American University, M
The George Washington University, BMD
Georgetown University, MO

Florida

Florida State University, MDO
New College of Florida, B

Georgia

Albany State University, M
Georgia Institute of Technology, BMD
Georgia State University, D

Idaho

Boise State University, M

Illinois

DePaul University, B
Lewis University, M
Northwestern University, BD
University of Chicago, BMDO
University of Illinois at Chicago, D

Indiana

Indiana University Bloomington, AB
Indiana University-Purdue University Fort Wayne, B

Iowa

University of Northern Iowa, M

Kansas

Fort Scott Community College, A

Kentucky

University of Louisville, M

Louisiana

University of New Orleans, M

Maine

College of the Atlantic, B
University of Southern Maine, MDO

Maryland

Anne Arundel Community College, A
The Johns Hopkins University, M
St. Mary's College of Maryland, B
University of Maryland, Baltimore County, MD
University of Maryland, College Park, MDO

Massachusetts

Anna Maria College, MO
Bentley College, B
Brandeis University, D
Harvard University, BMDO
Northeastern University, MDO
Simmons College, B
Suffolk University, B
Tufts University, MO
University of Massachusetts Amherst, M
University of Massachusetts Boston, BMDO

Michigan

Albion College, B
Grand Valley State University, B
University of Michigan, MDO

University of Michigan-Dearborn, M

Minnesota

St. Cloud State University, B
University of Minnesota, Twin Cities Campus, MO

Mississippi

Jackson State University, MD
Mississippi State University, MD

Missouri

Saint Louis University, MD
University of Missouri-St. Louis, MO
Washington University in St. Louis, M

Nevada

University of Nevada, Las Vegas, M

New Hampshire

New England College, M

New Jersey

Bloomfield College, B
Princeton University, B
Rutgers, The State University of New Jersey, Camden, MO
Rutgers, The State University of New Jersey, New Brunswick/Piscataway, MO
Rutgers, The State University of New Jersey, Newark, M
Saint Peter's College, AB
William Paterson University of New Jersey, M

New York

Bernard M. Baruch College of the City University of New York, B
Brooklyn College of the City University of New York, M
Cornell University, BMD
Hamilton College, B
Hobart and William Smith Colleges, B
John Jay College of Criminal Justice of the City University of New York, D
Rochester Institute of Technology, BM
Sarah Lawrence College, B
State University of New York at Binghamton, MD
State University of New York Empire State College, M
Stony Brook University, State University of New York, M
United States Military Academy, B
University at Albany, State University of New York, BMDO
Wells College, B

North Carolina

Duke University, BMO
North Carolina State University, B
The University of North Carolina at Chapel Hill, BD
The University of North Carolina at Charlotte, D

Ohio

Kent State University, D
Kenyon College, B
Muskingum College, B
The Ohio State University, MD
University of Cincinnati, B
The University of Toledo, B

Oregon

University of Oregon, BM

Pennsylvania

Carlow University, B
Carnegie Mellon University, BMO
Chatham College, B
Dickinson College, B
Duquesne University, MO
Immaculata University, B
The Pennsylvania State University Harrisburg Campus, B
Saint Vincent College, B
University of Pennsylvania, BMD

University of Pittsburgh, MDO

Rhode Island

Brown University, M
University of Rhode Island, BM

South Carolina

Clemson University, DO

Tennessee

University of Memphis, M
Vanderbilt University, MD

Texas

Baylor University, M
Del Mar College, A
Hill College of the Hill Junior College District, A
Houston Baptist University, B
Rice University, B
Southern Methodist University, B
The University of Texas at Austin, D
The University of Texas at Brownsville, M

Utah

Brigham Young University, B

Virginia

The College of William and Mary, BMO
George Mason University, MD
Regent University, M
Virginia Commonwealth University, D
Virginia Polytechnic Institute and State University, BMDO
Washington and Lee University, B

Washington

Central Washington University, B

West Virginia

University of Charleston, B
West Virginia University, MD

Wisconsin

Edgewood College, B
University of Wisconsin-Whitewater, B

British Columbia

University of Victoria, M

Ontario

Carleton University, MD
McMaster University, MD
Queen's University at Kingston, MO
University of Ottawa, B
York University, B

Quebec

Concordia University, BM

Saskatchewan

University of Regina, M

PUBLIC RELATIONS, ADVERTISING, AND APPLIED COMMUNICATION

Arkansas

John Brown University, AB

California

California Lutheran University, B

Georgia

Shorter College, B

Iowa

Buena Vista University, B

Kentucky

Eastern Kentucky University, B
Murray State University, B

Massachusetts

Regis College, B

Michigan

Madonna University, AB
Western Michigan University, B

Minnesota

The College of St. Scholastica, B
Saint Mary's University of Minnesota, B

New York

Rochester Institute of Technology, B
State University of New York College at
  Brockport, B

North Carolina

Campbell University, B

Ohio

Marietta College, B
Notre Dame College, B
The University of Akron, B

Oklahoma

East Central University, B

Pennsylvania

Duquesne University, B
Keystone College, A

Tennessee

Belmont University, B
Lambuth University, B

Texas

Texas A&M University, B

Utah

Brigham Young University, B

Vermont

Champlain College, AB
University of Vermont, B

Wisconsin

Carroll College, B

British Columbia

Thompson Rivers University, B

PUBLIC RELATIONS/IMAGE MANAGEMENT

Alabama

Alabama State University, B
Auburn University, B
Community College of the Air Force, A
The University of Alabama, B

Arizona

Glendale Community College, A
Northern Arizona University, B

Arkansas

Harding University, B
John Brown University, AB

California

California Lutheran University, B
California State Polytechnic University, Pomona, B
California State University, Chico, B
California State University, Dominguez Hills, B
California State University, East Bay, B
California State University, Fresno, B
California State University, Fullerton, B
California State University, Long Beach, B
Cosumnes River College (Sacramento), A
Golden West College, A
Los Angeles City College, A
The Master's College and Seminary, B

Pacific Union College, B
Pepperdine University, B
San Diego State University, B
San Jose State University, B
University of Southern California, B

Colorado

Colorado State University, B
Colorado State University-Pueblo, B
Johnson & Wales University, B
Mesa State College, B
Metropolitan State College of Denver, B

Connecticut

Quinnipiac University, B

Delaware

Delaware State University, B
University of Delaware, B

District of Columbia

American University, B

Florida

Barry University, B
Florida Agricultural and Mechanical University, B
Florida Southern College, B
Florida State University, B
Johnson & Wales University, B
University of Florida, B
University of Miami, B

Georgia

Columbus State University, B
Georgia Southern University, B
Paine College, B
University of Georgia, B

Hawaii

Hawaii Pacific University, B

Idaho

Northwest Nazarene University, B
University of Idaho, B

Illinois

Bradley University, B
Columbia College Chicago, B
Greenville College, B
Illinois State University, B
Lewis University, B
McKendree College, B
Monmouth College, B
Quincy University, B
Roosevelt University, B
Trinity Christian College, B

Indiana

Ball State University, B
Butler University, B
Huntington University, B
Indiana University Northwest, B
Purdue University Calumet, B
Saint Mary-of-the-Woods College, B
University of Southern Indiana, B
Valparaiso University, B
Vincennes University, A

Iowa

Clarke College, B
Coe College, B
Drake University, B
Kirkwood Community College, A
Loras College, B
St. Ambrose University, B
University of Northern Iowa, B
Wartburg College, B
William Penn University, B

Kansas

Fort Hays State University, B
MidAmerica Nazarene University, B

Tabor College, B

Kentucky

Eastern Kentucky University, B
Murray State University, B
Western Kentucky University, B

Louisiana

University of Louisiana at Lafayette, B

Maine

New England School of Communications, AB
Saint Joseph's College of Maine, B

Maryland

Bowie State University, B

Massachusetts

Boston University, B
Curry College, B
Emerson College, B
Salem State College, B
Simmons College, B
Suffolk University, B

Michigan

Andrews University, B
Central Michigan University, B
Eastern Michigan University, B
Ferris State University, B
Grand Valley State University, B
Kellogg Community College, A
Lansing Community College, A
Madonna University, AB
Northern Michigan University, B
University of Detroit Mercy, B
Wayne State University, B

Minnesota

Concordia College, B
Minnesota State University Mankato, B
Minnesota State University Moorhead, B
Northwestern College, B
St. Cloud State University, B
Winona State University, B

Mississippi

Mississippi College, B
Northeast Mississippi Community College, A

Missouri

Central Missouri State University, B
College of the Ozarks, B
Crowder College, A
Drury University, B
Lindenwood University, B
Northwest Missouri State University, B
St. Louis Community College at Meramec, A
Stephens College, B
Webster University, B
William Woods University, B

Montana

Carroll College, B
Montana State University-Billings, B

Nebraska

Doane College, B
Hastings College, B
Union College, B

New Hampshire

New England College, B

New Jersey

Brookdale Community College, A
Rider University, B

New York

Buffalo State College, State University of New
  York, B
Hofstra University, B
Iona College, B
Ithaca College, B

Long Island University, C.W. Post Campus, B
Marist College, B
Mount Saint Mary College, B
Rochester Institute of Technology, B
State University of New York College at
   Brockport, B
State University of New York at Oswego, B
Syracuse University, B
Utica College, B

North Carolina

Appalachian State University, B
Campbell University, B
Johnson & Wales University, AB
North Carolina State University, B
Pfeiffer University, B

Ohio

Baldwin-Wallace College, B
Bowling Green State University, B
Capital University, B
Cleveland State University, B
Heidelberg College, B
Kent State University, B
Ohio Dominican University, B
Ohio Northern University, B
Ohio University, B
Ohio University-Eastern, B
Ohio University-Zanesville, B
Otterbein College, B
University of Dayton, B
The University of Findlay, B
University of Rio Grande, B
Ursuline College, B
Xavier University, AB

Oklahoma

East Central University, B
Oklahoma Baptist University, B
Oklahoma Christian University, B
Oklahoma City University, B
Oral Roberts University, B
University of Central Oklahoma, B
University of Oklahoma, B

Oregon

George Fox University, B
Marylhurst University, B
University of Oregon, B

Pennsylvania

The Art Institute of Pittsburgh, B
Community College of Beaver County, A
Duquesne University, B
Gwynedd-Mercy College, B
La Salle University, B
Mansfield University of Pennsylvania, B
Marywood University, B
Mercyhurst College, B
Point Park University, B
Saint Francis University, B
Susquehanna University, B
Temple University, B
University of Pittsburgh at Bradford, B
Westminster College, B
York College of Pennsylvania, B

Puerto Rico

Pontifical Catholic University of Puerto Rico, B

Rhode Island

Johnson & Wales University, B

South Carolina

Anderson University, B
Columbia College, B
University of South Carolina, B

South Dakota

University of Sioux Falls, B

Tennessee

Christian Brothers University, B
Freed-Hardeman University, B

Lipscomb University, B
Middle Tennessee State University, B
Southern Adventist University, B
Union University, B
The University of Tennessee at Martin, B

Texas

Amarillo College, A
Coastal Bend College, A
Howard Payne University, B
Sam Houston State University, B
Southern Methodist University, B
Texas State University-San Marcos, B
Texas Tech University, B
University of Houston, B
University of North Texas, B
The University of Texas at Arlington, B
The University of Texas at Austin, B

Utah

University of Utah, B
Weber State University, B

Vermont

Castleton State College, B
Champlain College, AB

Virginia

Bridgewater College, B
Hampton University, B

Washington

Central Washington University, B
Gonzaga University, B
Seattle University, B
Walla Walla College, B

West Virginia

West Virginia Wesleyan College, B
Wheeling Jesuit University, B

Wisconsin

Cardinal Stritch University, B
Marquette University, B
Mount Mary College, B
University of Wisconsin-Madison, B
University of Wisconsin-River Falls, B

Nova Scotia

Mount Saint Vincent University, B

Ontario

University of Toronto, B

PUBLISHING

Illinois

Benedictine University, B
Northwestern University, M

Iowa

Graceland University, B

Maryland

University of Baltimore, M

Massachusetts

Emerson College, BM

Minnesota

Hennepin Technical College, A
Saint Mary's University of Minnesota, B

Missouri

University of Missouri-Columbia, B

New York

New York University, M
Pace University, M

Rochester Institute of Technology, BM

Pennsylvania

Drexel University, M
Rosemont College, M
Westmoreland County Community College, A

Puerto Rico

Pontifical Catholic University of Puerto Rico, B

Wisconsin

Milwaukee Area Technical College, A

British Columbia

Simon Fraser University, M

PURCHASING, PROCUREMENT/ACQUISITIONS AND CONTRACTS MANAGEMENT

Alabama

Community College of the Air Force, A

Arizona

Arizona State University, B

California

California State University, East Bay, B
De Anza College, A
Fullerton College, A

District of Columbia

Potomac College, B
Strayer University, A
University of the District of Columbia, B

Florida

Okaloosa-Walton College, B

Georgia

North Georgia College & State University, B

Illinois

William Rainey Harper College, A

Kansas

Southwestern College, B
Washburn University, A

New Jersey

Bloomfield College, B

New York

St. John's University, B

Ohio

Cincinnati State Technical and Community
   College, A
Columbus State Community College, A
Miami University, B
Miami University Hamilton, A
Wright State University, B

Oklahoma

Tulsa Community College, A

Pennsylvania

Mercyhurst College, A
Saint Joseph's University, AB

Puerto Rico

American University of Puerto Rico, B

Texas

Brazosport College, A
University of Houston-Downtown, B

Virginia

Northern Virginia Community College, A

University of Management and Technology, AB

Washington

Shoreline Community College, A
South Puget Sound Community College, A

QUALITY CONTROL AND SAFETY TECHNOLOGIES/TECHNICIANS

Indiana

Ivy Tech Community College-Lafayette, A
Ivy Tech Community College-Wabash Valley, A

Michigan

Madonna University, AB

QUALITY CONTROL TECHNOLOGY/TECHNICIAN

Arizona

Mesa Community College, A

Arkansas

Arkansas State University-Beebe, A

California

California National University for Advanced
  Studies, B
California State University, Long Beach, B
Chaffey College, A
College of the Canyons, A
Contra Costa College, A
Los Angeles Pierce College, A
Los Angeles Southwest College, A
Mt. San Antonio College, A
San Jose State University, B
Santa Ana College, A

Colorado

Lamar Community College, A

Connecticut

Naugatuck Valley Community College, A

Florida

St. Petersburg College, A

Illinois

Heartland Community College, A
Illinois Eastern Community Colleges, Frontier
  Community College, A
Illinois Eastern Community Colleges, Lincoln Trail
  College, A
Kishwaukee College, A
Rock Valley College, A
Waubonsee Community College, A
William Rainey Harper College, A

Indiana

Ivy Tech Community College-Lafayette, A

Iowa

Des Moines Area Community College, A

Kansas

Fort Scott Community College, A

Kentucky

Eastern Kentucky University, A
Elizabethtown Community and Technical College, A

Massachusetts

Springfield Technical Community College, A

Michigan

Baker College of Cadillac, A
Baker College of Flint, A
Baker College of Muskegon, A
Ferris State University, B

Grand Rapids Community College, A
Henry Ford Community College, A
Lansing Community College, A
Macomb Community College, A
Mott Community College, A
St. Clair County Community College, A
Washtenaw Community College, A

Minnesota

Century College, A
Ridgewater College, A
Winona State University, B

Missouri

Metropolitan Community College-Business &
  Technology College, A

Nebraska

Central Community College-Columbus Campus, A
Southeast Community College, Milford Campus, A

New Hampshire

New Hampshire Community Technical College,
  Nashua/Claremont, A

New York

Broome Community College, A
Monroe Community College, A
Onondaga Community College, A

North Carolina

Central Carolina Community College, A

Ohio

Bowling Green State University, B
Columbus State Community College, A
Edison State Community College, A
James A. Rhodes State College, A
Lorain County Community College, A
North Central State College, A
Northwest State Community College, A
Sinclair Community College, A
Terra State Community College, A
University of Cincinnati, A

Oklahoma

Oklahoma State University, Oklahoma City, A
Spartan College of Aeronautics and Technology, A
Tulsa Community College, A

Pennsylvania

Butler County Community College, A
Community College of Allegheny County, A
Northampton County Area Community College, A
Pennsylvania College of Technology, A

Puerto Rico

University of Puerto Rico, Aguadilla University
  College, AB

South Carolina

Tri-County Technical College, A

Texas

Austin Community College, A
Brazosport College, A
Mountain View College, A
Tarrant County College District, A
Texas State Technical College Waco, A

Utah

Salt Lake Community College, A

Washington

Columbia Basin College, A
South Seattle Community College, A

Wisconsin

Chippewa Valley Technical College, A
Gateway Technical College, A
Lakeshore Technical College, A
Mid-State Technical College, A
Northeast Wisconsin Technical College, A

Wisconsin Indianhead Technical College, A

QUALITY MANAGEMENT

California

California State University, Dominguez Hills, M
San Jose State University, M
Touro University International, O

Florida

University of Central Florida, O

Georgia

Southern Polytechnic State University, M

Iowa

Upper Iowa University, M

Maine

Saint Joseph's College of Maine, M

Michigan

Eastern Michigan University, M
Ferris State University, M
Madonna University, M

New Jersey

Rutgers, The State University of New Jersey, New
  Brunswick/Piscataway, M

New York

Dowling College, MO

Ohio

The University of Akron, M

Pennsylvania

The Pennsylvania State University University Park
  Campus, M

Wisconsin

Marian College of Fond du Lac, M

QUANTITATIVE ANALYSIS

California

California State University, East Bay, M
University of California, Santa Barbara, D

Georgia

Clark Atlanta University, M

Indiana

Purdue University, MD

Maryland

Loyola College in Maryland, M

Missouri

University of Missouri-St. Louis, M

New York

Bernard M. Baruch College of the City University of
  New York, M
Hofstra University, MO
St. John's University, MO
Syracuse University, D

Ohio

University of Cincinnati, MD

Oregon

University of Oregon, M

Pennsylvania

Drexel University, M
Lehigh University, M

Rhode Island

University of Rhode Island, D

Texas

Texas Tech University, MD
The University of Texas at Arlington, MD

Virginia

Virginia Commonwealth University, M

RABBINICAL STUDIES

Colorado

Yeshiva Toras Chaim Talmudical Seminary, B

Florida

Talmudic College of Florida, B

Illinois

Telshe Yeshiva-Chicago, B

Maryland

Baltimore Hebrew University, AB
Ner Israel Rabbinical College, B

New Jersey

Beth Medrash Govoha, B

New York

Central Yeshiva Tomchei Tmimim-Lubavitch, B
Darkei Noam Rabbinical College, B
Kol Yaakov Torah Center, B
Mesivta of Eastern Parkway Rabbinical Seminary, B
Ohr Somayach/Joseph Tanenbaum Educational
    Center, B
Rabbinical Academy Mesivta Rabbi Chaim Berlin, B
Rabbinical Seminary of America, B
Sh'or Yoshuv Rabbinical College, B
Talmudical Institute of Upstate New York, B
Talmudical Seminary Oholei Torah, B
Yeshiva Karlin Stolin Rabbinical Institute, B
Yeshivat Mikdash Melech, B
Yeshivath Zichron Moshe, B

Pennsylvania

Talmudical Yeshiva of Philadelphia, B

Quebec

Université Laval, AB

RADIATION
BIOLOGY/RADIOBIOLOGY

Colorado

Colorado State University, MD

District of Columbia

Georgetown University, M

Iowa

The University of Iowa, MD

Michigan

Grand Valley State University, B

Oklahoma

University of Oklahoma Health Sciences Center, MD

Puerto Rico

Inter American University of Puerto Rico,
    Barranquitas Campus, AB

Texas

The University of Texas Southwestern Medical
    Center at Dallas, MD

Quebec

Université de Sherbrooke, MD

RADIATION
PROTECTION/HEALTH
PHYSICS TECHNICIAN

Oregon

Oregon State University, B

RADIO AND TELEVISION

Alabama

Alabama State University, B
Auburn University, B
Lawson State Community College, A
Spring Hill College, B
The University of Alabama, B
University of Montevallo, B

Arizona

Northern Arizona University, B
The University of Arizona, B

Arkansas

Arkansas State University, B
John Brown University, B
University of Arkansas at Little Rock, B

California

Academy of Art University, AB
Biola University, B
California State University, Chico, B
California State University, Fresno, B
California State University, Fullerton, B
California State University, Long Beach, B
California State University, Los Angeles, B
Chabot College, A
College of San Mateo, A
Columbia College Hollywood, B
Cosumnes River College (Sacramento), A
Cuesta College, A
De Anza College, A
Foothill College, A
Fullerton College, A
Golden West College, A
Grossmont College, A
Laney College, A
Lassen Community College District, A
Long Beach City College, A
Los Angeles City College, A
Los Angeles Southwest College, A
Los Angeles Valley College, A
The Master's College and Seminary, B
Modesto Junior College, A
Mt. San Antonio College, A
Napa Valley College, A
Ohlone College, A
Oxnard College, A
Palomar College, A
Pasadena City College, A
Saddleback College, A
San Bernardino Valley College, A
San Diego City College, A
San Diego State University, B
San Francisco State University, B
San Jose State University, B
Santa Monica College, A
University of Southern California, B
Vanguard University of Southern California, B

Colorado

Colorado State University, B
Colorado State University-Pueblo, B
Mesa State College, B
Northeastern Junior College, A
Western State College of Colorado, B

Connecticut

Asnuntuck Community College, A
Middlesex Community College, A

Sacred Heart University, B

Delaware

Delaware State University, B

District of Columbia

Gallaudet University, B
The George Washington University, B
Howard University, B

Florida

The Art Institute of Fort Lauderdale, A
Barry University, B
Brevard Community College, A
Daytona Beach Community College, A
Florida State University, B
Gulf Coast Community College, A
Hillsborough Community College, A
Manatee Community College, A
Miami Dade College, A
Palm Beach Atlantic University, B
University of Central Florida, B
University of Florida, B
University of Miami, B

Georgia

Georgia Southern University, B

Idaho

Brigham Young University -Idaho, A
University of Idaho, B

Illinois

Bradley University, B
City Colleges of Chicago, Kennedy-King College, A
Columbia College Chicago, B
Illinois Eastern Community Colleges, Wabash Valley
    College, A
Lake Land College, A
Lewis and Clark Community College, A
Lincoln College, A
North Central College, B
Northwestern University, B
Olivet Nazarene University, B
Parkland College, A
Quincy University, B
Roosevelt University, B
Southern Illinois University Carbondale, B
Western Illinois University, B

Indiana

Indiana State University, B
Indiana University Bloomington, B
Purdue University Calumet, B
University of Southern Indiana, B
Valparaiso University, B
Vincennes University, A

Iowa

Drake University, B
Grand View College, B
Iowa Central Community College, A
Iowa Lakes Community College, A
Kirkwood Community College, A
St. Ambrose University, B
University of Northern Iowa, B

Kansas

Coffeyville Community College, A
Colby Community College, A
Dodge City Community College, A
Fort Hays State University, B
Washburn University, B

Kentucky

Eastern Kentucky University, B
Murray State University, B
National College of Business & Technology
    (Lexington), A
Northern Kentucky University, B
University of Kentucky, B

Western Kentucky University, B

Maine

New England School of Communications, AB

Massachusetts

Boston University, B
Curry College, B
Eastern Nazarene College, B
Emerson College, B
Newbury College, A
Northeastern University, B
Westfield State College, B

Michigan

Central Michigan University, B
Grand Valley State University, B
Lansing Community College, A
Lawrence Technological University, A
Michigan State University, B
University of Detroit Mercy, B
Wayne State University, B
Western Michigan University, B

Minnesota

Bemidji State University, B
Concordia College, B
Northland Community and Technical College-Thief
   River Falls, A
Northwestern College, AB
St. Cloud State University, B
Southwest Minnesota State University, B
Winona State University, B

Mississippi

Coahoma Community College, A
Holmes Community College, A
Northeast Mississippi Community College, A
Northwest Mississippi Community College, A
University of Mississippi, B
University of Southern Mississippi, B

Missouri

Central Missouri State University, B
Evangel University, B
Lindenwood University, B
Northwest Missouri State University, B
St. Louis Community College at Florissant Valley, A
Stephens College, B
University of Missouri-Columbia, B
Webster University, B
William Woods University, B

Montana

The University of Montana-Missoula, B

Nebraska

Hastings College, B
Northeast Community College, A

Nevada

Community College of Southern Nevada, A

New Hampshire

Franklin Pierce College, B
Hesser College, A

New Jersey

Rider University, B

New York

Adirondack Community College, A
Brooklyn College of the City University of New
   York, B
Buffalo State College, State University of New
   York, B
Cayuga County Community College, A
Fordham University, B
Herkimer County Community College, A
Hofstra University, B
Iona College, B
Ithaca College, B
Marist College, B
New York Institute of Technology, B

New York University, B
Onondaga Community College, A
State University of New York College at
   Brockport, B
State University of New York, Fredonia, B
State University of New York at New Paltz, B
Sullivan County Community College, A
Syracuse University, B
Tompkins Cortland Community College, A

North Carolina

Appalachian State University, B
Campbell University, B
Central Carolina Community College, A
Isothermal Community College, A

North Dakota

Minot State University, B

Ohio

Ashland University, AB
Cedarville University, B
Central State University, B
International College of Broadcasting, A
Kent State University, B
Marietta College, B
Muskingum College, B
Ohio Northern University, B
Ohio University, AB
Ohio University-Zanesville, B
Otterbein College, B
University of Cincinnati, B
University of Dayton, B
Washington State Community College, A
Xavier University, AB
Youngstown State University, B

Oklahoma

East Central University, B
Langston University, B
Oklahoma Baptist University, B
Oklahoma Christian University, B
Oklahoma City University, B
Oral Roberts University, B
Rogers State University, A
Tulsa Community College, A
University of Central Oklahoma, B

Oregon

George Fox University, B
Lane Community College, A
Mt. Hood Community College, A
Pacific University, B
University of Oregon, B

Pennsylvania

The Art Institute of Pittsburgh, AB
Bucks County Community College, A
Gannon University, B
Geneva College, B
Keystone College, A
La Salle University, B
Mansfield University of Pennsylvania, B
Mercyhurst College, B
Messiah College, B
Point Park University, B
Susquehanna University, B
Temple University, B
Waynesburg College, B
Westminster College, B

York College of Pennsylvania, AB

Puerto Rico

Pontifical Catholic University of Puerto Rico, B

South Carolina

Bob Jones University, B
Tri-County Technical College, A

South Dakota

University of Sioux Falls, B

Tennessee

Belmont University, B
Chattanooga State Technical Community College, A
Draughons Junior College (Clarksville), A
Draughons Junior College (Nashville), A
Freed-Hardeman University, B
Union University, B
The University of Tennessee, B

Texas

Alvin Community College, A
Amarillo College, A
Austin Community College, A
Baylor University, B
Central Texas College, A
Del Mar College, A
Hardin-Simmons University, B
Lamar University, B
Lee College, A
Navarro College, A
Odessa College, A
Sam Houston State University, B
San Antonio College, A
Southern Methodist University, B
Stephen F. Austin State University, B
Texas A&M University-Commerce, B
Texas Christian University, B
Texas Southern University, B
Texas State University-San Marcos, B
Texas Tech University, B
Texas Wesleyan University, B
University of North Texas, B
The University of Texas at Arlington, B
The University of Texas at Austin, B

Utah

Dixie State College of Utah, A
University of Utah, B
Weber State University, B

Vermont

Castleton State College, B
Lyndon State College, B

Virginia

Virginia Western Community College, A

Washington

Central Washington University, B
Centralia College, A
Pacific Lutheran University, B
Walla Walla College, B

West Virginia

Salem International University, AB

Wisconsin

University of Wisconsin-Madison, B
University of Wisconsin-Oshkosh, B
University of Wisconsin-River Falls, B

University of Wisconsin-Superior, B

Ontario

Ryerson University, B
University of Windsor, B

RADIO AND TELEVISION BROADCASTING TECHNOLOGY/TECHNICIAN

Alabama

Alabama Agricultural and Mechanical University, B
Gadsden State Community College, A
Jefferson State Community College, A

Connecticut

Briarwood College, A

Florida

Hillsborough Community College, A
Manatee Community College, A
Miami Dade College, A

Idaho

Northwest Nazarene University, B

Illinois

Black Hawk College, A
Lewis University, B
Parkland College, A

Iowa

Iowa Lakes Community College, A
Scott Community College, A

Kentucky

Asbury College, B

Maine

New England School of Communications, AB

Massachusetts

Emerson College, B
Mount Wachusett Community College, A
The New England Institute of Art, A

Michigan

Delta College, A
Eastern Michigan University, B
Kellogg Community College, A
Oakland Community College, A
Schoolcraft College, A

Minnesota

Brown College, A

Mississippi

Northwest Mississippi Community College, A

Missouri

Mineral Area College, A
Ozarks Technical Community College, A

Nebraska

Central Community College-Hastings Campus, A

New Jersey

Brookdale Community College, A
County College of Morris, A
Mercer County Community College, A

New Mexico

Santa Fe Community College, A

New York

Cayuga County Community College, A
Hofstra University, B
Hudson Valley Community College, A
Iona College, B

New York Institute of Technology, A

North Carolina

Gardner-Webb University, B
Wilkes Community College, A

Ohio

Ohio University, B
Ohio University-Southern Campus, A

Pennsylvania

Geneva College, B
Luzerne County Community College, A
Northampton County Area Community College, A

Puerto Rico

University of Puerto Rico at Arecibo, AB

Rhode Island

New England Institute of Technology, AB

South Carolina

York Technical College, A

Tennessee

Southern Adventist University, A
Trevecca Nazarene University, B

Texas

Cedar Valley College, A
Houston Community College System, A

Utah

Salt Lake Community College, A

Vermont

Lyndon State College, A

Washington

Bates Technical College, A
Clover Park Technical College, A

Wisconsin

Gateway Technical College, A
Milwaukee Area Technical College, A

Wyoming

Central Wyoming College, A

British Columbia

British Columbia Institute of Technology, A

RADIO, TELEVISION, AND DIGITAL COMMUNICATION

Arkansas

John Brown University, B

California

California State Polytechnic University, Pomona, B
Santiago Canyon College, A

Connecticut

Sacred Heart University, B

Florida

Florida State University, B
Hillsborough Community College, A

Iowa

Drake University, B

Massachusetts

Emerson College, B

Michigan

Madonna University, B

New York

State University of New York College at
   Brockport, B

North Carolina

Campbell University, B

Ohio

Capital University, B

Pennsylvania

Keystone College, A

Texas

Texas Southern University, B

Utah

Brigham Young University, B
Dixie State College of Utah, B

RADIOLOGIC TECHNOLOGY/SCIENCE - RADIOGRAPHER

Alabama

George C. Wallace Community College, A
University of South Alabama, B

Arizona

Apollo College-Phoenix, Inc., A
Arizona Western College, A
Pima Medical Institute (Mesa), A
Pima Medical Institute (Tucson), A

Arkansas

National Park Community College, A
Southeast Arkansas College, A
University of Arkansas at Fort Smith, A

California

Foothill College, A
Los Angeles City College, A
Pima Medical Institute, A

Colorado

Community College of Denver, A
Mesa State College, A
Pima Medical Institute, A

Connecticut

Quinnipiac University, B

District of Columbia

The George Washington University, B

Florida

Brevard Community College, A
Edison College, A
Florida Hospital College of Health Sciences, AB
Florida National College, A
Hillsborough Community College, A
Keiser College (Miami), A
Manatee Community College, A
Miami Dade College, A
Pasco-Hernando Community College, A
Pensacola Junior College, A
Polk Community College, A
St. Petersburg College, A

Georgia

Andrew College, A
Clayton State University, A
Dalton State College, A
Georgia Highlands College, A
Medical College of Georgia, B
Waycross College, A

Idaho

Boise State University, AB
Brigham Young University -Idaho, A
Lewis-Clark State College, A

Illinois

Black Hawk College, A
Triton College, A

University of St. Francis, B

Indiana

Indiana University Northwest, AB
Indiana University-Purdue University Fort Wayne, A

Iowa

Allen College, A
St. Luke's College, A
The University of Iowa, B

Kansas

Barton County Community College, A
Newman University, A
Washburn University, A

Kentucky

Madisonville Community College, A
Somerset Community College, A

Louisiana

Louisiana State University at Alexandria, A
Louisiana State University at Eunice, A
MedVance Institute, A
Northwestern State University of Louisiana, B

Maine

Eastern Maine Community College, A
Southern Maine Community College, A

Maryland

Prince George's Community College, A

Massachusetts

Holyoke Community College, A
Massachusetts College of Pharmacy and Health
    Sciences, B
Massasoit Community College, A
Middlesex Community College, A
Northern Essex Community College, A
Suffolk University, B

Michigan

Baker College of Clinton Township, A
Baker College of Muskegon, A
Delta College, A
Henry Ford Community College, A
University of Michigan, B
Washtenaw Community College, A

Minnesota

Minnesota State Community and Technical
    College-Fergus Falls, A
Northwest Technical College, A

Missouri

East Central College, A
Missouri State University, B
Sanford-Brown College (Fenton), A
University of Missouri-Columbia, B

Montana

The University of Montana-Missoula, A

Nebraska

Clarkson College, AB
Nebraska Methodist College, A
University of Nebraska Medical Center, B
Western Nebraska Community College, A

Nevada

Community College of Southern Nevada, A
Pima Medical Institute, A

Truckee Meadows Community College, A

New Jersey

Brookdale Community College, A
Middlesex County College, A

New Mexico

Pima Medical Institute, A

New York

Hudson Valley Community College, A
Manhattan College, B
Niagara County Community College, A
State University of New York Upstate Medical
    University, B
Trocaire College, A

North Carolina

Carolinas College of Health Sciences, A
Edgecombe Community College, A
Fayetteville Technical Community College, A
Sandhills Community College, A

North Dakota

Jamestown College, B
North Dakota State University, B
University of Mary, B

Ohio

Columbus State Community College, A
Kent State University, B
Kettering College of Medical Arts, AB
Lakeland Community College, A
Marion Technical College, A
North Central State College, A
The Ohio State University, B
Sinclair Community College, A
University of Rio Grande, A

Oklahoma

Tulsa Community College, A
University of Oklahoma Health Sciences Center, B

Oregon

Oregon Institute of Technology, B

Pennsylvania

Clarion University of Pennsylvania, B
Holy Family University, B
Keystone College, A
Mansfield University of Pennsylvania, A
Montgomery County Community College, A
Mount Aloysius College, AB
Northampton County Area Community College, A
University of Pittsburgh at Bradford, B

South Dakota

Mitchell Technical Institute, A

Tennessee

Austin Peay State University, B
Baptist College of Health Sciences, B
South College, A

Texas

Amarillo College, A
Brookhaven College, A
El Centro College, A
Laredo Community College, A
Midland College, A
Midwestern State University, AB
Paris Junior College, A

Utah

Salt Lake Community College, A

Vermont

Champlain College, AB

Virginia

Averett University, B
Central Virginia Community College, A
Jefferson College of Health Sciences, B
Virginia Commonwealth University, B

Virginia Western Community College, A

Washington

Pima Medical Institute, A
Tacoma Community College, A

West Virginia

Alderson-Broaddus College, B
Mountain State University, A
University of Charleston, B

Wisconsin

Blackhawk Technical College, A
Lakeshore Technical College, A
Moraine Park Technical College, A
Northcentral Technical College, A
Western Technical College, A

Wyoming

Laramie County Community College, A

New Brunswick

Université de Moncton, B

Nova Scotia

Dalhousie University, B

Ontario

University of Toronto, B

RANGE SCIENCE AND MANAGEMENT

Arizona

The University of Arizona, MD

California

California State University, Chico, B
Humboldt State University, B
University of California, Berkeley, M

Colorado

Colorado State University, BMD
Lamar Community College, A

Idaho

Brigham Young University -Idaho, A
College of Southern Idaho, A
University of Idaho, BMD

Kansas

Colby Community College, A
Fort Hays State University, B
Kansas State University, MD

Kentucky

St. Catharine College, A

Minnesota

Vermilion Community College, A

Montana

Montana State University, BMD

Nebraska

Chadron State College, B
University of Nebraska-Lincoln, B

New Mexico

New Mexico State University, BMD

North Dakota

North Dakota State University, MD

Oklahoma

Eastern Oklahoma State College, A

Oregon

Oregon State University, BMD
Treasure Valley Community College, A

South Dakota

South Dakota State University, B

Texas

Northeast Texas Community College, A
Sul Ross State University, BM

Tarleton State University, B
Texas A&M University, BMD
Texas A&M University-Kingsville, BM
Texas Tech University, BMD
Trinity Valley Community College, A

Utah

Brigham Young University, B
Dixie State College of Utah, A
Snow College, A
Utah State University, BMD

Vermont

Sterling College, AB

Wyoming

Central Wyoming College, A
Eastern Wyoming College, A
Northwest College, A
University of Wyoming, BMD

Alberta

University of Alberta, B

Saskatchewan

University of Saskatchewan, B

READING TEACHER EDUCATION

Alabama

Auburn University, DO
Auburn University Montgomery, MO
Jacksonville State University, M
University of South Alabama, M

Arizona

Grand Canyon University, M
The University of Arizona, MDO

Arkansas

Arkansas State University, MO
Harding University, BM
Henderson State University, M
University of Arkansas at Little Rock, M
University of Central Arkansas, BM

California

California Baptist University, M
California Lutheran University, M
California Polytechnic State University, San Luis
   Obispo, M
California State University, Chico, M
California State University, Fresno, M
California State University, Fullerton, M
California State University, Los Angeles, M
California State University, Sacramento, M
California State University, San Bernardino, M
California State University, Stanislaus, M
Chapman University, M
Fresno Pacific University, M
Laney College, A
Loyola Marymount University, M
Merritt College, A
Notre Dame de Namur University, MO
Saint Mary's College of California, M
San Diego State University, M
San Francisco State University, MO
University of California, Berkeley, MD
University of La Verne, MO
University of Southern California, D

Colorado

University of Northern Colorado, MD

Connecticut

Central Connecticut State University, MO
Eastern Connecticut State University, M
Southern Connecticut State University, MO
University of Bridgeport, MO
University of Connecticut, MD

Western Connecticut State University, M

Delaware

Wilmington College, M

District of Columbia

Howard University, MO
Trinity (Washington) University, M

Florida

Barry University, MO
Florida Atlantic University, M
Florida Gulf Coast University, M
Florida International University, M
Florida State University, MDO
Jacksonville University, M
Nova Southeastern University, MO
St. Thomas University, M
Stetson University, M
University of Central Florida, M
University of Florida, MD
University of Miami, MDO
University of South Florida, MDO
University of West Florida, M

Georgia

Albany State University, M
Berry College, M
Georgia Southern University, M
Georgia Southwestern State University, M
Georgia State University, MO
Mercer University, M
North Georgia College & State University, B
University of Georgia, BMDO
University of West Georgia, MO
Valdosta State University, MO

Guam

University of Guam, M

Idaho

Boise State University, BM
Idaho State University, M
Northwest Nazarene University, M

Illinois

Benedictine University, M
Chicago State University, M
Concordia University, M
DePaul University, M
Governors State University, M
Illinois State University, M
National-Louis University, MDO
Northeastern Illinois University, M
Northern Illinois University, MD
Rockford College, M
Roosevelt University, M
Saint Xavier University, M
Southern Illinois University Edwardsville, M
Western Illinois University, M

Indiana

Butler University, M
Indiana State University, M
Indiana University Bloomington, MDO
Purdue University, MDO

Iowa

Clarke College, M
Dordt College, B
Morningside College, M
University of Northern Iowa, BM
Upper Iowa University, B
William Penn University, B

Kansas

Pittsburg State University, M
Washburn University, M

Kentucky

Eastern Kentucky University, M
Morehead State University, M
Murray State University, BM
Union College, M

University of the Cumberlands, M
University of Louisville, M
Western Kentucky University, M

Louisiana

Loyola University New Orleans, M
Northwestern State University of Louisiana, MO
Our Lady of Holy Cross College, B
University of Louisiana at Monroe, M

Maine

University of Maine, MDO
University of Southern Maine, MO

Maryland

Bowie State University, M
Coppin State University, M
Frostburg State University, M
Hood College, O
The Johns Hopkins University, MO
Loyola College in Maryland, MO
McDaniel College, M
Salisbury University, M
Towson University, MO
University of Maryland, College Park, MDO

Massachusetts

American International College, MO
Anna Maria College, M
Boston College, MO
Boston University, MDO
Bridgewater State College, MO
Curry College, MO
Eastern Nazarene College, MO
Elms College, M
Endicott College, M
Framingham State College, M
Harvard University, M
Lesley University, MO
Massachusetts College of Liberal Arts, M
Salem State College, M
University of Massachusetts Amherst, MDO
University of Massachusetts Lowell, MDO
Westfield State College, BM
Wheelock College, M
Worcester State College, M

Michigan

Andrews University, M
Aquinas College, B
Bay Mills Community College, A
Central Michigan University, M
Eastern Michigan University, BM
Grand Valley State University, BM
Madonna University, M
Marygrove College, M
Michigan State University, M
Oakland University, BMDO
Saginaw Valley State University, M
Siena Heights University, M
University of Detroit Mercy, B
University of Michigan, D
University of Michigan-Flint, M
Wayne State University, MDO
Western Michigan University, M

Minnesota

Bethel University, MO
Minnesota State University Moorhead, M
St. Cloud State University, B
University of Minnesota, Twin Cities Campus, MD
University of St. Thomas, O
Winona State University, B

Mississippi

East Mississippi Community College, A
University of Southern Mississippi, MO

Missouri

Central Missouri State University, BM
Evangel University, M
Maryville University of Saint Louis, M
Missouri State University, M
Northwest Missouri State University, BM
University of Missouri-Columbia, MDO

University of Missouri-Kansas City, MO
University of Missouri-St. Louis, M

Montana

Montana State University-Billings, M
University of Great Falls, B
The University of Montana-Missoula, B

Nebraska

Concordia University, M
University of Nebraska at Kearney, M
University of Nebraska-Lincoln, B
University of Nebraska at Omaha, M
York College, B

Nevada

University of Nevada, Reno, MD

New Hampshire

Plymouth State University, M
Rivier College, M
University of New Hampshire, MD

New Jersey

The College of New Jersey, MO
Fairleigh Dickinson University, College at
    Florham, O
Fairleigh Dickinson University, Metropolitan
    Campus, O
Kean University, MO
Monmouth University, MO
Montclair State University, M
New Jersey City University, M
Rider University, MO
Rowan University, M
Rutgers, The State University of New Jersey, New
    Brunswick/Piscataway, MD
Saint Peter's College, M
William Paterson University of New Jersey, M

New Mexico

New Mexico State University, O
Western New Mexico University, M

New York

Adelphi University, MO
Alfred University, M
Brooklyn College of the City University of New
    York, M
Buffalo State College, State University of New
    York, M
Canisius College, M
City College of the City University of New York, BM
The College of New Rochelle, M
The College of Saint Rose, MO
Dowling College, M
Fordham University, MO
Hofstra University, MDO
Hunter College of the City University of New
    York, M
Lehman College of the City University of New
    York, M
Long Island University, Brentwood Campus, M
Long Island University, Brooklyn Campus, M
Long Island University, C.W. Post Campus, M
Manhattanville College, M
Medaille College, M
Mercy College, M
Mount Saint Mary College, M
Nazareth College of Rochester, M
New York University, M
Niagara University, M
Queens College of the City University of New
    York, M
St. Bonaventure University, M
St. John Fisher College, M
St. John's University, BO
St. Thomas Aquinas College, MO
State University of New York at Binghamton, M
State University of New York at Buffalo, D
State University of New York College at
    Brockport, M
State University of New York College at
    Cortland, BM

State University of New York College at
    Geneseo, M
State University of New York College at
    Oneonta, BM
State University of New York College at Potsdam, M
State University of New York, Fredonia, M
State University of New York at New Paltz, M
State University of New York at Oswego, M
State University of New York at Plattsburgh, M
Syracuse University, MDO
University at Albany, State University of New
    York, MDO
Wagner College, M

North Carolina

Appalachian State University, M
Catawba College, B
East Carolina University, M
Fayetteville State University, M
Lenoir-Rhyne College, M
North Carolina Agricultural and Technical State
    University, M
Salem College, M
The University of North Carolina at Chapel Hill, MD
The University of North Carolina at Charlotte, M
The University of North Carolina at Pembroke, M
The University of North Carolina Wilmington, M
Western Carolina University, M
Wingate University, B

North Dakota

University of Mary, M
University of North Dakota, M

Ohio

Ashland University, M
Baldwin-Wallace College, M
Bowling Green State University, MO
Central State University, M
College of Mount St. Joseph, M
Kent State University, M
Lake Erie College, M
Malone College, M
Miami University, M
Notre Dame College, M
Ohio University, BMD
University of Cincinnati, MD
University of Dayton, M
Wilmington College, M
Wright State University, B
Xavier University, M
Youngstown State University, M

Oklahoma

Northeastern State University, BM
Northwestern Oklahoma State University, M
University of Central Oklahoma, BM

Oregon

Portland State University, M

Pennsylvania

Arcadia University, MO
Bloomsburg University of Pennsylvania, M
Bucknell University, M
California University of Pennsylvania, M
Clarion University of Pennsylvania, BM
Duquesne University, M
East Stroudsburg University of Pennsylvania, M
Edinboro University of Pennsylvania, MO
Gannon University, MO
Gwynedd-Mercy College, M
Holy Family University, M
Indiana University of Pennsylvania, M
King's College, M
Kutztown University of Pennsylvania, M
Marywood University, M
Millersville University of Pennsylvania, BM
The Pennsylvania State University University Park
    Campus, MD
Saint Joseph's University, M
Shippensburg University of Pennsylvania, M
Slippery Rock University of Pennsylvania, M
Temple University, MD
University of Pennsylvania, MD

University of Pittsburgh, MD
The University of Scranton, M
West Chester University of Pennsylvania, M
Westminster College, MO
Widener University, MD

Rhode Island

Providence College, M
Rhode Island College, M
Roger Williams University, M
University of Rhode Island, M

South Carolina

The Citadel, The Military College of South
    Carolina, M
Clemson University, M
Furman University, M
University of South Carolina, MD
Winthrop University, M

South Dakota

Northern State University, M
University of Sioux Falls, M

Tennessee

Austin Peay State University, M
East Tennessee State University, M
Middle Tennessee State University, M
Southern Adventist University, M
Tennessee State University, BM
Tennessee Technological University, MO
University of Memphis, MD
The University of Tennessee, MDO
Vanderbilt University, M

Texas

Abilene Christian University, BM
Angelo State University, M
Baylor University, B
Dallas Baptist University, M
Hardin-Simmons University, BM
Houston Baptist University, M
Jarvis Christian College, B
Midwestern State University, M
St. Mary's University of San Antonio, BM
Sam Houston State University, BM
Sul Ross State University, M
Tarleton State University, O
Texas A&M International University, BM
Texas A&M University, MD
Texas A&M University-Commerce, BM
Texas A&M University-Corpus Christi, M
Texas A&M University-Kingsville, M
Texas Southern University, BM
Texas State University-San Marcos, M
Texas Tech University, M
Texas Wesleyan University, B
Texas Woman's University, MD
University of Houston, M
University of Houston-Clear Lake, BM
University of the Incarnate Word, BM
University of Mary Hardin-Baylor, M
University of North Texas, MD
The University of Texas at Brownsville, M
The University of Texas-Pan American, M
The University of Texas of the Permian Basin, M
The University of Texas at San Antonio, M
The University of Texas at Tyler, M
West Texas A&M University, M

Vermont

Castleton State College, MO
College of St. Joseph, M
Johnson State College, M
Lyndon State College, BM
Saint Michael's College, M
University of Vermont, M

Virginia

Averett University, M
The College of William and Mary, M
George Mason University, M
James Madison University, M
Liberty University, M
Longwood University, BM

Old Dominion University, M
Radford University, M
Virginia Commonwealth University, M

Washington

Central Washington University, M
City University, M
Eastern Washington University, BM
Heritage University, M
Pacific Lutheran University, B
Seattle Pacific University, M
Seattle University, MO
Walla Walla College, M
Washington State University, BMD

West Virginia

Marshall University, MO
West Virginia University, M

Wisconsin

Alverno College, M
Cardinal Stritch University, M
Carthage College, MO
Concordia University Wisconsin, M
University of Wisconsin-Eau Claire, M
University of Wisconsin-La Crosse, M
University of Wisconsin-Milwaukee, M
University of Wisconsin-Oshkosh, M
University of Wisconsin-River Falls, M
University of Wisconsin-Stevens Point, M
University of Wisconsin-Superior, BM
University of Wisconsin-Whitewater, M

Alberta

University of Alberta, B

British Columbia

The University of British Columbia, BMD
University of Victoria, MD

Nova Scotia

Mount Saint Vincent University, BM

REAL ESTATE

Alabama

Calhoun Community College, A
Enterprise-Ozark Community College, A
Northeast Alabama Community College, A
Wallace State Community College, A

Arizona

Arizona State University, B
Arizona State University at the Polytechnic
  Campus, B
GateWay Community College, A
Glendale Community College, A
Mesa Community College, A
Phoenix College, A
Pima Community College, A
Scottsdale Community College, A

California

American River College, A
Antelope Valley College, A
Bakersfield College, A
Butte College, A
Cabrillo College, A
California State Polytechnic University, Pomona, B
California State University, Dominguez Hills, B
California State University, East Bay, B
California State University, Fresno, B
California State University, Sacramento, BM
Cerritos College, A
Chabot College, A
Chaffey College, A
Citrus College, A
City College of San Francisco, A
College of the Canyons, A
College of the Desert, A
College of Marin, A
College of the Redwoods, A
College of San Mateo, A

College of the Sequoias, A
Compton Community College, A
Contra Costa College, A
Cosumnes River College (Sacramento), A
Cuesta College, A
Cuyamaca College, A
De Anza College, A
East Los Angeles College, A
El Camino College, A
Folsom Lake College, A
Foothill College, A
Fresno City College, A
Fullerton College, A
Glendale Community College, A
Golden West College, A
Hartnell College, A
Lake Tahoe Community College, A
Las Positas College, A
Long Beach City College, A
Los Angeles City College, A
Los Angeles Harbor College, A
Los Angeles Mission College, A
Los Angeles Pierce College, A
Los Angeles Southwest College, A
Los Angeles Trade-Technical College, A
Los Angeles Valley College, A
Los Medanos College, A
Mendocino College, A
Merced College, A
Merritt College, A
MiraCosta College, A
Mission College, A
Modesto Junior College, A
Monterey Peninsula College, A
Mt. San Antonio College, A
Mt. San Jacinto College, A
Napa Valley College, A
Ohlone College, A
Oxnard College, A
Palomar College, A
Pasadena City College, A
Sacramento City College, A
Saddleback College, A
San Bernardino Valley College, A
San Diego City College, A
San Diego Mesa College, A
San Diego State University, B
San Francisco State University, B
San Jose City College, A
Santa Ana College, A
Santa Barbara City College, A
Santa Monica College, A
Santiago Canyon College, A
Shasta College, A
Sierra College, A
Southwestern College, A
University of California, Berkeley, D
University of Southern California, MO
Ventura College, A
Victor Valley College, A
West Los Angeles College, A

Colorado

Colorado State University, B
Red Rocks Community College, A
University of Colorado at Boulder, M
University of Denver, BM

Connecticut

University of Connecticut, B

District of Columbia

American University, M
The George Washington University, M

Florida

Florida Atlantic University, BM
Florida Community College at Jacksonville, A
Florida International University, B
Okaloosa-Walton College, A
University of Florida, BMDO

Georgia

Georgia State University, BMDO
University of Georgia, B

University of West Georgia, B

Hawaii

University of Hawaii at Manoa, M

Idaho

College of Southern Idaho, A

Illinois

Carl Sandburg College, A
College of DuPage, A
Danville Area Community College, A
Illinois Central College, A
Joliet Junior College, A
Kankakee Community College, A
McHenry County College, A
Morton College, A
Northwestern Business College, A
Oakton Community College, A
Southeastern Illinois College, A
Southwestern Illinois College, A
Triton College, A
University of Illinois at Urbana-Champaign, B
William Rainey Harper College, A

Indiana

Ball State University, B
Indiana University Bloomington, B

Iowa

Iowa Lakes Community College, A
University of Northern Iowa, B

Kansas

Dodge City Community College, A

Kentucky

Ashland Community and Technical College, A
Big Sandy Community and Technical College, A
Eastern Kentucky University, B
Elizabethtown Community and Technical College, A
Jefferson Community and Technical College, A
Madisonville Community College, A
Morehead State University, B

Louisiana

Southern University at New Orleans, A

Maryland

Anne Arundel Community College, A
The Johns Hopkins University, M

Massachusetts

Massachusetts Institute of Technology, M
Northern Essex Community College, A

Michigan

Ferris State University, A
Henry Ford Community College, A
Lansing Community College, A
University of Michigan, O

Minnesota

Fond du Lac Tribal and Community College, A
Minnesota State University Mankato, B
Rainy River Community College, A
Ridgewater College, A
St. Cloud State University, B
University of St. Thomas, BM

Mississippi

East Mississippi Community College, A
Hinds Community College, A
Mississippi State University, B
University of Mississippi, B

Missouri

St. Louis Community College at Florissant Valley, A
St. Louis Community College at Meramec, A
University of Missouri-Columbia, B

Webster University, M

Nebraska

Northeast Community College, A
University of Nebraska at Omaha, B

Nevada

Community College of Southern Nevada, A
Truckee Meadows Community College, A
University of Nevada, Las Vegas, B
Western Nevada Community College, A

New Hampshire

New Hampshire Technical Institute, A

New Jersey

Bergen Community College, A
Camden County College, A
Monmouth University, B
Ocean County College, A
Raritan Valley Community College, A

New Mexico

New Mexico Junior College, A
San Juan College, A
University of New Mexico-Valencia Campus, A

New York

Columbia-Greene Community College, A
Cornell University, M
Nassau Community College, A
New York University, BMO
Orange County Community College, A
St. John's University, B
Suffolk County Community College, A

North Carolina

Alamance Community College, A
Catawba Valley Community College, A
Central Piedmont Community College, A
Durham Technical Community College, A
Forsyth Technical Community College, A
Isothermal Community College, A
Saint Augustine's College, B

Ohio

Cincinnati State Technical and Community
  College, A
Cleveland State University, O
Columbus State Community College, A
Cuyahoga Community College, A
David N. Myers University, B
Edison State Community College, A
Hondros College, A
Jefferson Community College, A
Kent State University, Ashtabula Campus, A
Lorain County Community College, A
Miami University Hamilton, A
Miami University-Middletown Campus, A
The Ohio State University, B
Sinclair Community College, A
Southern State Community College, A
Southwestern College of Business (Cincinnati), A
University of Cincinnati, ABM
University of Cincinnati Raymond Walters College, A

Oklahoma

University of Central Oklahoma, B

Oregon

Chemeketa Community College, A
Lane Community College, A
Marylhurst University, B
Portland Community College, A

Pennsylvania

Clarion University of Pennsylvania, B
Community College of Allegheny County, A
Community College of Philadelphia, A
Harrisburg Area Community College, A
Lehigh Carbon Community College, A
Luzerne County Community College, A
Montgomery County Community College, A

The Pennsylvania State University University Park
  Campus, D
Saint Francis University, A
Temple University, B
University of Pennsylvania, BMD
Westmoreland County Community College, A

Puerto Rico

Caribbean University, A

South Carolina

Clemson University, M
University of South Carolina, B

Tennessee

University of Memphis, BM

Texas

Amarillo College, A
Angelina College, A
Angelo State University, B
Austin Community College, A
Baylor University, B
Blinn College, A
Cedar Valley College, A
Cisco Junior College, A
Collin County Community College District, A
Del Mar College, A
El Paso Community College, A
Grayson County College, A
Hill College of the Hill Junior College District, A
Houston Community College System, A
Lamar State College-Orange, A
Lamar University, A
Laredo Community College, A
McLennan Community College, A
Navarro College, A
North Central Texas College, A
North Lake College, A
San Antonio College, A
South Plains College, A
Southern Methodist University, B
Texarkana College, A
Texas A&M University, M
Texas A&M University-Kingsville, B
Texas Christian University, B
Trinity Valley Community College, A
Tyler Junior College, A
University of Houston-Downtown, B
University of North Texas, BMD
The University of Texas at Arlington, BM
The University of Texas at El Paso, B

Virginia

Tidewater Community College, A
Virginia Commonwealth University, MO
Wytheville Community College, A

Washington

Bellevue Community College, A
Columbia Basin College, A
North Seattle Community College, A
Spokane Falls Community College, A
Washington State University, B

West Virginia

Fairmont State University, A

Wisconsin

Chippewa Valley Technical College, A
Madison Area Technical College, A
Milwaukee Area Technical College, A
Nicolet Area Technical College, A
University of Wisconsin-Madison, BMD

University of Wisconsin-Milwaukee, B

British Columbia

British Columbia Institute of Technology, A
The University of British Columbia, B

Ontario

University of Guelph, B

RECEPTIONIST

Iowa

Iowa Lakes Community College, A

Michigan

Baker College of Allen Park, A

Minnesota

Alexandria Technical College, A

Montana

The University of Montana-Missoula, A

New York

Adirondack Community College, A

North Dakota

Minot State University-Bottineau Campus, A

Washington

Centralia College, A
Lower Columbia College, A

RECORDING ARTS TECHNOLOGY/TECHNICIAN

Florida

Full Sail Real World Education, A
Miami Dade College, A

Georgia

Savannah College of Art and Design, B

Illinois

Columbia College Chicago, B

Kansas

Kansas City Kansas Community College, A

Maine

New England School of Communications, AB

Massachusetts

Bay State College, A

Mississippi

Mississippi Valley State University, B

New York

Ithaca College, B

Ohio

Malone College, B

Pennsylvania

Lebanon Valley College, B

Texas

Northwest Vista College, A
Texas State University-San Marcos, B

Washington

Olympic College, A

RECREATION AND PARK MANAGEMENT

Arizona

Arizona State University, M

Arkansas

University of Arkansas, MD

California

California State University, Chico, M
California State University, Long Beach, M
California State University, Northridge, M
California State University, Sacramento, M
San Francisco State University, M
San Jose State University, M

Colorado

Colorado State University, MD

Connecticut

Southern Connecticut State University, M

District of Columbia

Howard University, M

Florida

Florida Agricultural and Mechanical University, M
Florida International University, M
Florida State University, MDO
University of Florida, MD

Georgia

Georgia Southern University, M
University of Georgia, MD

Idaho

University of Idaho, MD

Illinois

Southern Illinois University Carbondale, M
Western Illinois University, M

Indiana

Indiana University Bloomington, MDO

Kentucky

Eastern Kentucky University, M
Morehead State University, M
Murray State University, M
Western Kentucky University, M

Maryland

Frostburg State University, M

Massachusetts

Springfield College, M

Michigan

Central Michigan University, M
Michigan State University, MD
Wayne State University, M

Minnesota

University of Minnesota, Twin Cities Campus, MD

Mississippi

Delta State University, M
University of Mississippi, M
University of Southern Mississippi, MD

Missouri

Northwest Missouri State University, M
University of Missouri-Columbia, M

Montana

The University of Montana-Missoula, M

Nebraska

University of Nebraska-Lincoln, M
University of Nebraska at Omaha, M

New Hampshire

University of New Hampshire, M

New Mexico

University of New Mexico, MO

New York

Lehman College of the City University of New
 York, M
State University of New York College at
 Brockport, M
State University of New York College at Cortland, M
State University of New York College of
 Environmental Science and Forestry, MD

North Carolina

East Carolina University, M
North Carolina Central University, M
North Carolina State University, MD
The University of North Carolina at Chapel Hill, M
The University of North Carolina at Greensboro, M

Ohio

Bowling Green State University, M
Cleveland State University, M
Ohio University, M
The University of Toledo, M
Wright State University, M

Oklahoma

Southwestern Oklahoma State University, M

Pennsylvania

Temple University, M

Puerto Rico

Universidad Metropolitana, M

Rhode Island

University of Rhode Island, M

South Carolina

Clemson University, MD

South Dakota

South Dakota State University, M

Tennessee

Middle Tennessee State University, MD
The University of Tennessee, M

Texas

Hardin-Simmons University, M
Texas A&M University, MD
Texas State University-San Marcos, M
University of North Texas, MO

Utah

Brigham Young University, M
University of Utah, MD
Utah State University, MD

Virginia

Old Dominion University, M
Virginia Commonwealth University, M
Virginia Polytechnic Institute and State
 University, MD

Washington

Central Washington University, M

West Virginia

West Virginia University, M

Wisconsin

University of Wisconsin-La Crosse, M
University of Wisconsin-Madison, M

Alberta

University of Alberta, MD

Manitoba

University of Manitoba, M

New Brunswick

University of New Brunswick Fredericton, M

Nova Scotia

Acadia University, M

Ontario

University of Waterloo, MD

REGIONAL STUDIES (U.S., CANADIAN, FOREIGN)

California

Pitzer College, B

Georgia

Mercer University, B

New Mexico

College of Santa Fe, B

REHABILITATION AND THERAPEUTIC PROFESSIONS

Illinois

Southern Illinois University Carbondale, B

Louisiana

Southern University and Agricultural and Mechanical
 College, B

Massachusetts

Assumption College, B
Springfield Technical Community College, A

Michigan

Central Michigan University, B

Montana

Montana State University-Billings, B

New Jersey

Union County College, A

Pennsylvania

East Stroudsburg University of Pennsylvania, B
The Pennsylvania State University Abington
 College, B
The Pennsylvania State University Altoona
 College, B
The Pennsylvania State University Beaver Campus
 of the Commonwealth College, B
The Pennsylvania State University Berks Campus of
 the Berks-Lehigh Valley College, B
The Pennsylvania State University Delaware County
 Campus of the Commonwealth College, B
The Pennsylvania State University DuBois Campus
 of the Commonwealth College, B
The Pennsylvania State University at Erie, The
 Behrend College, B
The Pennsylvania State University Fayette Campus
 of the Commonwealth College, B
The Pennsylvania State University Hazleton
 Campus of the Commonwealth College, B
The Pennsylvania State University, Lehigh Valley
 Campus of the Berks-Lehigh Valley College, B
The Pennsylvania State University McKeesport
 Campus of the Commonwealth College, B
The Pennsylvania State University Mont Alto
 Campus of the Commonwealth College, B
The Pennsylvania State University New Kensington
 Campus of the Commonwealth College, B
The Pennsylvania State University Schuylkill
 Campus of the Capital College, B
The Pennsylvania State University Shenango
 Campus of the Commonwealth College, B

The Pennsylvania State University University Park Campus, B
The Pennsylvania State University Wilkes-Barre Campus of the Commonwealth College, B
The Pennsylvania State University Worthington Scranton Campus of the Commonwealth College, B
The Pennsylvania State University York Campus of the Commonwealth College, B
University of Pittsburgh, B
Wilson College, B

Rhode Island

Community College of Rhode Island, A

Texas

University of North Texas, B
The University of Texas-Pan American, B
The University of Texas Southwestern Medical Center at Dallas, B

Washington

Clover Park Technical College, A

Wisconsin

University of Wisconsin-La Crosse, B

Ontario

University of Waterloo, B

REHABILITATION COUNSELING

Alabama

Troy University, O
The University of Alabama at Birmingham, M

Arizona

The University of Arizona, MDO

Arkansas

Arkansas State University, M
University of Arkansas, MD

California

California State University, Fresno, M
California State University, Los Angeles, M
California State University, San Bernardino, M
San Diego State University, M
San Francisco State University, M

Colorado

University of Northern Colorado, MD

Connecticut

Central Connecticut State University, MO

District of Columbia

The George Washington University, M

Florida

Barry University, MO
Florida Atlantic University, M
University of Florida, M
University of North Florida, M
University of South Florida, M

Georgia

Fort Valley State University, M
Georgia State University, MO
Thomas University, M

Illinois

Illinois Institute of Technology, M
Southern Illinois University Carbondale, MD

University of Illinois at Urbana-Champaign, M

Indiana

Indiana University-Purdue University Indianapolis, MD

Iowa

Drake University, M
The University of Iowa, MD

Kansas

Emporia State University, M

Kentucky

University of Kentucky, M

Louisiana

Louisiana State University Health Sciences Center, M
Southern University and Agricultural and Mechanical College, M
University of Louisiana at Lafayette, M

Maryland

Coppin State University, M
University of Maryland, College Park, M
University of Maryland Eastern Shore, M

Massachusetts

Assumption College, MO
Boston University, MDO
Northeastern University, M
Springfield College, MO
University of Massachusetts Boston, MO

Michigan

Michigan State University, MD
Wayne State University, MO
Western Michigan University, M

Minnesota

Minnesota State University Mankato, M
St. Cloud State University, M

Mississippi

Jackson State University, M

Missouri

Maryville University of Saint Louis, M

Montana

Montana State University-Billings, M

Nevada

University of Nevada, Las Vegas, M

New York

Hofstra University, MO
Hunter College of the City University of New York, M
St. John's University, MO
State University of New York at Buffalo, M
Syracuse University, M
University at Albany, State University of New York, M

North Carolina

East Carolina University, M
The University of North Carolina at Chapel Hill, M

Ohio

Bowling Green State University, M
Kent State University, MO
Ohio University, M

Wright State University, M

Oklahoma

East Central University, M
Langston University, M

Oregon

Western Oregon University, M

Pennsylvania

La Salle University, D
The University of Scranton, M

Puerto Rico

University of Puerto Rico, Río Piedras, M

Rhode Island

Salve Regina University, MO

South Carolina

South Carolina State University, M
University of South Carolina, MO

Tennessee

The University of Tennessee, M

Texas

University of North Texas, M
The University of Texas-Pan American, M
The University of Texas Southwestern Medical Center at Dallas, M

Utah

Utah State University, M

Virginia

Virginia Commonwealth University, MO

Washington

Western Washington University, M

West Virginia

West Virginia University, M

Wisconsin

University of Wisconsin-Madison, MD
University of Wisconsin-Stout, M

REHABILITATION SCIENCES

Alabama

The University of Alabama at Birmingham, O

Florida

University of Florida, D

Illinois

University of Illinois at Urbana-Champaign, M

Indiana

Indiana University-Purdue University Indianapolis, M

Iowa

The University of Iowa, MD

Kansas

University of Kansas, D

Kentucky

University of Kentucky, D

Maryland

University of Maryland Eastern Shore, M

Massachusetts

Boston University, MD

Michigan

Central Michigan University, MD
Wayne State University, MO

Minnesota

University of Minnesota, Twin Cities Campus, D

New York

Canisius College, M
State University of New York at Buffalo, MDO

North Carolina

East Carolina University, M

Ohio

University of Cincinnati, M
The University of Toledo, M

Oklahoma

University of Oklahoma Health Sciences Center, M

Pennsylvania

Clarion University of Pennsylvania, M
Duquesne University, MD
East Stroudsburg University of Pennsylvania, M
Slippery Rock University of Pennsylvania, M
University of Pittsburgh, MDO

South Carolina

Medical University of South Carolina, MD
University of South Carolina, O

Texas

University of North Texas, M

Washington

University of Washington, M

Wisconsin

University of Wisconsin-La Crosse, M
University of Wisconsin-Madison, M

Alberta

University of Alberta, D

British Columbia

The University of British Columbia, MD

Manitoba

University of Manitoba, M

Ontario

McMaster University, M
Queen's University at Kingston, MD
University of Ottawa, M
University of Toronto, M

Quebec

McGill University, MD

REHABILITATION THERAPY

California

California State University, Los Angeles, B

Georgia

Thomas University, B

Illinois

William Rainey Harper College, A

Iowa

Iowa Lakes Community College, A

Louisiana

Southern University and Agricultural and Mechanical College, B

Maine

University of Maine at Farmington, B

Maryland

University of Maryland Eastern Shore, B

Massachusetts

Boston University, B
Northeastern University, B

Springfield College, B

Michigan

Baker College of Muskegon, B

Montana

Montana State University-Billings, B

New York

Ithaca College, B
Nassau Community College, A

North Carolina

Wayne Community College, A

Ohio

Wilberforce University, B

Pennsylvania

East Stroudsburg University of Pennsylvania, B

Texas

Stephen F. Austin State University, B
University of North Texas, B
The University of Texas-Pan American, B

British Columbia

The University of British Columbia, B

Manitoba

University of Manitoba, B

Ontario

University of Ottawa, B
York University, B

Quebec

Université de Montréal, B

RELIABILITY ENGINEERING

Arizona

The University of Arizona, M

Maryland

University of Maryland, College Park, MD

RELIGION/RELIGIOUS STUDIES

Alabama

Athens State University, B
Birmingham-Southern College, B
Faulkner University, B
Huntingdon College, B
Judson College, B
Miles College, B
Oakwood College, A
Samford University, B
Southeastern Bible College, B
Southern Christian University, D
Stillman College, B
The University of Alabama, B
University of Mobile, BM
Wallace State Community College, A

Arizona

Arizona State University, BMD
Grand Canyon University, B
Northern Arizona University, B
The University of Arizona, B

Arkansas

Arkansas Baptist College, B
Harding University, B
Hendrix College, B
John Brown University, B
Philander Smith College, B
University of Central Arkansas, B

Williams Baptist College, B

California

Azusa Pacific University, BM
Bethesda Christian University, M
Biola University, BM
California Institute of Integral Studies, MD
California Lutheran University, B
California State University, Bakersfield, B
California State University, Chico, B
California State University, Dominguez Hills, B
California State University, East Bay, B
California State University, Fresno, B
California State University, Fullerton, B
California State University, Long Beach, BM
California State University, Northridge, B
Chaffey College, A
Chapman University, B
Claremont McKenna College, B
Crafton Hills College, A
Dominican University of California, B
Fresno Pacific University, B
Fullerton College, A
Holy Names University, BMO
Humboldt State University, B
La Sierra University, BM
Loma Linda University, M
The Master's College and Seminary, B
Mount St. Mary's College, BM
Notre Dame de Namur University, B
Occidental College, B
Orange Coast College, A
Pacific Union College, B
Pasadena City College, A
Pepperdine University, BMP
Pitzer College, B
Point Loma Nazarene University, BM
Pomona College, B
Queen of the Holy Rosary College, A
Saint Mary's College of California, B
San Bernardino Valley College, A
San Diego State University, B
San Francisco State University, B
San Joaquin Delta College, A
San Jose State University, B
Santa Clara University, BM
Scripps College, B
Southern California Seminary, M
Stanford University, BMD
University of California, Berkeley, BD
University of California, Davis, B
University of California, Los Angeles, B
University of California, Riverside, B
University of California, San Diego, B
University of California, Santa Barbara, BMD
University of California, Santa Cruz, B
University of La Verne, B
University of the Pacific, B
University of Redlands, B
University of San Diego, B
University of San Francisco, B
University of Southern California, BMDO
University of the West, BMD
Vanguard University of Southern California, BM
Westmont College, B
Whittier College, B
Yeshiva Ohr Elchonon Chabad/West Coast Talmudical Seminary, B

Colorado

The Colorado College, B
Naropa University, BM
Regis University, B
University of Colorado at Boulder, BM
University of Denver, BM

Connecticut

Albertus Magnus College, B
Connecticut College, B
Fairfield University, B
Holy Apostles College and Seminary, AB
Sacred Heart University, ABM
Saint Joseph College, B
Trinity College, B
University of Bridgeport, B
Wesleyan University, B

Yale University, BD

District of Columbia

The Catholic University of America, BMDO
The George Washington University, BM

Florida

Eckerd College, B
Florida Agricultural and Mechanical University, B
Florida International University, BM
Florida Memorial College, B
Florida Southern College, B
Florida State University, BMD
Manatee Community College, A
New College of Florida, B
Palm Beach Atlantic University, B
Palm Beach Community College, A
Pensacola Junior College, A
Rollins College, B
St. Thomas University, B
Stetson University, B
University of Florida, BMD
University of Miami, B
University of South Florida, BM
University of West Florida, B

Georgia

Agnes Scott College, B
Brewton-Parker College, AB
Clark Atlanta University, B
Emory University, BD
Georgia State University, B
LaGrange College, B
Morehouse College, B
Paine College, B
Piedmont College, B
Reinhardt College, B
Shorter College, B
Spelman College, B
Toccoa Falls College, B
University of Georgia, BM
Wesleyan College, B
Young Harris College, A

Guam

Pacific Islands Bible College, AB

Hawaii

Chaminade University of Honolulu, B
Hawaii Theological Seminary, M
University of Hawaii at Manoa, BM

Idaho

Albertson College of Idaho, B
Boise Bible College, AB
Northwest Nazarene University, BM

Illinois

Augustana College, B
Bradley University, B
Concordia University, M
DePaul University, B
Dominican University, B
Eureka College, B
Greenville College, B
Hebrew Theological College, B
Illinois College, B
Illinois Wesleyan University, B
Judson College, B
Lewis University, B
Loyola University Chicago, M
MacMurray College, B
McKendree College, B
Monmouth College, B
North Central College, B
North Park University, B
Northwestern University, B
Olivet Nazarene University, BM
Principia College, B
Saint Xavier University, B
Trinity Christian College, B
Trinity International University, M
University of Chicago, BMDPO
University of Illinois at Urbana-Champaign, B

Wheaton College, BM

Indiana

Anderson University, B
Ball State University, B
Butler University, B
Calumet College of Saint Joseph, AB
DePauw University, B
Earlham College, B
Franklin College, B
Goshen College, B
Huntington University, B
Indiana University Bloomington, BMD
Indiana University-Purdue University Indianapolis, B
Manchester College, AB
Martin University, B
Oakland City University, B
Saint Mary-of-the-Woods College, B
Saint Mary's College, B
Taylor University, B
University of Evansville, B
University of Indianapolis, B
University of Notre Dame, M
University of Saint Francis, B
Wabash College, B

Iowa

Ashford University, B
Central College, B
Clarke College, B
Coe College, B
Cornell College, B
Dordt College, B
Drake University, B
Faith Baptist Bible College and Theological Seminary, M
Graceland University, BM
Grand View College, B
Grinnell College, B
Iowa State University of Science and Technology, B
Loras College, BM
Luther College, B
Morningside College, B
Mount Mercy College, B
Northwestern College, B
Simpson College, B
University of Dubuque, B
The University of Iowa, BMDO
University of Northern Iowa, B
Vennard College, AB
Wartburg College, B

Kansas

Allen County Community College, A
Baker University, B
Barton County Community College, A
Benedictine College, B
Bethany College, B
Bethel College, B
Central Christian College of Kansas, AB
Cowley County Community College and Area Vocational-Technical School, A
Friends University, B
Kansas Wesleyan University, B
Manhattan Christian College, B
McPherson College, B
MidAmerica Nazarene University, B
Ottawa University, B
Tabor College, AB
University of Kansas, BM
Washburn University, B

Kentucky

Berea College, B
Brescia University, AB
Campbellsville University, B
Centre College, B
Georgetown College, B
Kentucky Christian University, M
Kentucky Mountain Bible College, AB
Lindsey Wilson College, AB
Pikeville College, B
Spalding University, B
Thomas More College, AB
Transylvania University, B
Union College, B

Western Kentucky University, B

Louisiana

Centenary College of Louisiana, B
Dillard University, B
Louisiana College, B
Loyola University New Orleans, BMO
New Orleans Baptist Theological Seminary, AB
Tulane University, B

Maine

Bates College, B
Bowdoin College, B
Colby College, B
Saint Joseph's College of Maine, B
University of Maine at Farmington, B

Maryland

Baltimore Hebrew University, AB
College of Notre Dame of Maryland, B
Goucher College, B
Griggs University, AB
Hood College, B
Loyola College in Maryland, B
McDaniel College, B
Morgan State University, B
St. Mary's College of Maryland, B
Towson University, B
Washington Bible College, AB

Massachusetts

Amherst College, B
Anna Maria College, B
Atlantic Union College, AB
Boston University, BMD
College of the Holy Cross, B
Eastern Nazarene College, B
Elms College, BM
Emmanuel College, B
Hampshire College, B
Harvard University, BMD
Hellenic College, B
Merrimack College, B
Mount Holyoke College, B
Simon's Rock College of Bard, B
Smith College, BM
Stonehill College, B
Wellesley College, B
Wheaton College, B
Williams College, B

Michigan

Adrian College, AB
Albion College, B
Alma College, B
Andrews University, B
Aquinas College, B
Calvin College, B
Central Michigan University, B
Concordia University, B
Cornerstone University, B
Grace Bible College, A
Hillsdale College, B
Hope College, B
Kalamazoo College, B
Lansing Community College, A
Madonna University, AB
Marygrove College, B
Michigan State University, B
Siena Heights University, B
Spring Arbor University, BP
University of Detroit Mercy, BM
University of Michigan, B
Western Michigan University, BMD

Minnesota

Augsburg College, B
Bemidji State University, B
Carleton College, B
The College of St. Scholastica, B
Concordia College, B
Gustavus Adolphus College, B
Hamline University, B
Macalester College, B
North Central University, B

St. Olaf College, B
University of Minnesota, Twin Cities Campus, BM
University of St. Thomas, BM

Mississippi

Millsaps College, B
William Carey College, B

Missouri

Avila University, B
Central Bible College, B
Central Christian College of the Bible, B
Central Methodist University, B
Culver-Stockton College, B
Drury University, B
East Central College, A
Fontbonne University, B
Global University of the Assemblies of God, A
Lindenwood University, B
Messenger College, B
Missouri Baptist University, AB
Missouri State University, BM
Missouri Valley College, B
Southwest Baptist University, B
Truman State University, B
University of Missouri-Columbia, BM
Washington University in St. Louis, BM
Webster University, B
Westminster College, B
William Jewell College, B

Montana

Carroll College, B
Rocky Mountain College, B
University of Great Falls, B

Nebraska

Dana College, B
Doane College, B
Hastings College, B
Midland Lutheran College, B
Nebraska Christian College, B
Nebraska Wesleyan University, B
Union College, B
University of Nebraska at Omaha, B
York College, B

New Hampshire

Dartmouth College, B

New Jersey

Bloomfield College, B
Drew University, BMD
Felician College, AB
Georgian Court University, B
Montclair State University, B
Princeton University, BD
Rabbinical College of America, B
Rutgers, The State University of New Jersey, New
    Brunswick/Piscataway, B
Saint Peter's College, B
Seton Hall University, BM

New Mexico

College of Santa Fe, B
Eastern New Mexico University, B
St. John's College, B
University of New Mexico, B

New York

Bard College, B
Barnard College, B
Brooklyn College of the City University of New
    York, B
Canisius College, B
Colgate University, B
College of Mount Saint Vincent, B
The College of New Rochelle, B
The College of Saint Rose, B
Columbia College, B
Columbia University, School of General Studies, B
Concordia College, B
Cornell University, BD
Daemen College, B
Elmira College, B

Eugene Lang College The New School for Liberal
    Arts, B
Fordham University, BMDO
Hamilton College, B
Hartwick College, B
Hobart and William Smith Colleges, B
Houghton College, B
Hunter College of the City University of New York, B
Iona College, B
The Jewish Theological Seminary, BMD
Le Moyne College, B
Manhattan College, B
Manhattanville College, B
Mesivta of Eastern Parkway Rabbinical Seminary, B
Molloy College, B
Nazareth College of Rochester, B
New York University, BMO
Niagara University, B
Nyack College, B
Queens College of the City University of New
    York, B
St. Francis College, B
St. John Fisher College, B
St. Lawrence University, B
St. Thomas Aquinas College, B
Sarah Lawrence College, B
Siena College, B
Skidmore College, B
State University of New York College at Old
    Westbury, B
Stony Brook University, State University of New
    York, B
Syracuse University, BMD
University at Albany, State University of New York, B
University of Rochester, B
Vassar College, B
Wells College, B

North Carolina

Brevard College, B
Campbell University, B
Catawba College, B
Chowan University, B
Davidson College, B
Duke University, BMD
Elon University, B
Gardner-Webb University, B
Greensboro College, B
Guilford College, B
High Point University, B
John Wesley College, B
Lees-McRae College, B
Lenoir-Rhyne College, B
Mars Hill College, B
Meredith College, B
Methodist College, B
Mount Olive College, AB
North Carolina State University, B
North Carolina Wesleyan College, B
Pfeiffer University, B
Piedmont Baptist College, AB
Queens University of Charlotte, B
Roanoke Bible College, B
St. Andrews Presbyterian College, B
Salem College, B
Shaw University, AB
The University of North Carolina at Chapel
    Hill, BMD
The University of North Carolina at Charlotte, BM
The University of North Carolina at Greensboro, B
Wake Forest University, BM
Wingate University, B

North Dakota

Jamestown College, B
University of North Dakota, B

Ohio

Antioch College, B
Ashland University, B
Baldwin-Wallace College, B
Bluffton University, B
Capital University, B
Case Western Reserve University, B
Cedarville University, B
Cincinnati Christian University, M

Circleville Bible College, AB
Cleveland State University, B
College of Mount St. Joseph, B
The College of Wooster, B
Defiance College, B
Denison University, B
Heidelberg College, B
Hiram College, B
John Carroll University, BM
Kenyon College, B
Laura and Alvin Siegal College of Judaic Studies, B
Lourdes College, AB
Miami University, BM
Mount Union College, B
Muskingum College, B
Oberlin College, B
Ohio Northern University, B
The Ohio State University, B
Ohio Wesleyan University, B
Otterbein College, B
University of Dayton, B
The University of Findlay, AB
The University of Toledo, B
Urbana University, B
Ursuline College, B
Walsh University, B
Wilmington College, B
Wittenberg University, B
Wright State University, B
Youngstown State University, B

Oklahoma

Mid-America Christian University, B
Oklahoma Baptist University, B
Oklahoma Christian University, B
Oklahoma City University, BM
Oklahoma Wesleyan University, B
Oral Roberts University, B
Southern Nazarene University, M
Southwestern Christian University, B
Tulsa Community College, A
University of Oklahoma, B
University of Tulsa, B

Oregon

Concordia University, B
Corban College, B
George Fox University, BP
Lewis & Clark College, B
Linfield College, B
Marylhurst University, B
Reed College, B
University of Oregon, B
Warner Pacific College, BM
Willamette University, B

Pennsylvania

Albright College, B
Allegheny College, B
Alvernia College, B
Bryn Athyn College of the New Church, BM
Bryn Mawr College, B
Bucknell University, B
Cabrini College, B
Chestnut Hill College, MO
Dickinson College, B
Elizabethtown College, B
Franklin and Marshall College, B
Gettysburg College, B
Grove City College, B
Haverford College, B
Holy Family University, B
Indiana University of Pennsylvania, B
Juniata College, B
La Roche College, B
La Salle University, BM
Lafayette College, B
Lebanon Valley College, B
Lehigh University, B
Lincoln University, B
Lycoming College, B
Marywood University, B
Mercyhurst College, B
Messiah College, B
Moravian College, B
Muhlenberg College, B

The Pennsylvania State University Abington
  College, B
The Pennsylvania State University Altoona
  College, B
The Pennsylvania State University Beaver Campus
  of the Commonwealth College, B
The Pennsylvania State University Berks Campus of
  the Berks-Lehigh Valley College, B
The Pennsylvania State University Delaware County
  Campus of the Commonwealth College, B
The Pennsylvania State University DuBois Campus
  of the Commonwealth College, B
The Pennsylvania State University at Erie, The
  Behrend College, B
The Pennsylvania State University Fayette Campus
  of the Commonwealth College, B
The Pennsylvania State University Hazleton
  Campus of the Commonwealth College, B
The Pennsylvania State University, Lehigh Valley
  Campus of the Berks-Lehigh Valley College, B
The Pennsylvania State University McKeesport
  Campus of the Commonwealth College, B
The Pennsylvania State University Mont Alto
  Campus of the Commonwealth College, B
The Pennsylvania State University New Kensington
  Campus of the Commonwealth College, B
The Pennsylvania State University Schuylkill
  Campus of the Capital College, B
The Pennsylvania State University Shenango
  Campus of the Commonwealth College, B
The Pennsylvania State University University Park
  Campus, B
The Pennsylvania State University Wilkes-Barre
  Campus of the Commonwealth College, B
The Pennsylvania State University Worthington
  Scranton Campus of the Commonwealth
  College, B
The Pennsylvania State University York Campus of
  the Commonwealth College, B
Philadelphia Biblical University, B
Rosemont College, B
St. Charles Borromeo Seminary, Overbrook, M
Saint Francis University, B
Saint Joseph's University, B
Seton Hill University, B
Susquehanna University, B
Swarthmore College, B
Temple University, BMD
Thiel College, B
University of Pennsylvania, BD
University of Pittsburgh, BMD
The University of Scranton, B
Villanova University, B
Westminster College, B

Puerto Rico

Bayamon Central University, BM

Rhode Island

Brown University, BMD
Providence College, M
Salve Regina University, B

South Carolina

Allen University, B
Anderson University, B
Benedict College, B
Charleston Southern University, B
College of Charleston, B
Columbia College, B
Converse College, B
Erskine College, B
Furman University, B
Newberry College, B
North Greenville College, B
Presbyterian College, B
Southern Wesleyan University, B
University of South Carolina, BM
Winthrop University, B
Wofford College, B

South Dakota

Augustana College, B
Dakota Wesleyan University, B
Mount Marty College, AB
Presentation College, A

University of Sioux Falls, AB

Tennessee

Carson-Newman College, B
Christian Brothers University, B
Fisk University, B
King College, B
Lambuth University, B
Lane College, B
Lee University, M
Lipscomb University, M
Martin Methodist College, AB
Maryville College, B
Rhodes College, B
Sewanee: The University of the South, B
Southern Adventist University, BM
Tennessee Wesleyan College, B
Trevecca Nazarene University, BM
Union University, B
The University of Tennessee, BM
Vanderbilt University, BMD

Texas

Amarillo College, A
Arlington Baptist College, B
Austin College, B
Baylor University, BMD
Concordia University at Austin, B
The Criswell College, AB
East Texas Baptist University, B
Hardin-Simmons University, M
Houston Baptist University, B
Howard Payne University, AB
Jarvis Christian College, B
Kilgore College, A
LeTourneau University, B
Lon Morris College, A
McMurry University, B
Our Lady of the Lake University of San Antonio, B
Paul Quinn College, B
Rice University, BD
Schreiner University, B
Southern Methodist University, BMD
Southwestern Adventist University, B
Southwestern Assemblies of God University, B
Southwestern Christian College, AB
Southwestern University, B
Texas Christian University, B
Texas Wesleyan University, B
Trinity University, B
Trinity Valley Community College, A
University of the Incarnate Word, BM
University of Mary Hardin-Baylor, BM
University of North Texas, MD
The University of Texas at Austin, B
Wayland Baptist University, M
Wiley College, B

Vermont

Marlboro College, B
Middlebury College, B
Saint Michael's College, B
University of Vermont, B

Virginia

Averett University, B
Bluefield College, B
The College of William and Mary, B
Eastern Mennonite University, M
Emory & Henry College, B
Ferrum College, B
George Mason University, B
Hampden-Sydney College, B
Hampton University, B
Hollins University, B
Liberty University, ABMDP
Lynchburg College, B
Mary Baldwin College, B
Marymount University, B
Northern Virginia Community College, A
Randolph-Macon College, B
Randolph-Macon Woman's College, B
Roanoke College, B
Shenandoah University, B
Sweet Briar College, B
University of Mary Washington, B

University of Richmond, B
University of Virginia, BMD
Virginia Commonwealth University, B
Virginia Intermont College, B
Virginia University of Lynchburg, P
Virginia Wesleyan College, B
Washington and Lee University, B

Washington

Central Washington University, B
Gonzaga University, BMP
Northwest University, B
Pacific Lutheran University, B
Saint Martin's University, B
Seattle University, B
University of Puget Sound, B
University of Washington, BM
Walla Walla College, B
Washington State University, B
Whitman College, B
Whitworth College, B

West Virginia

Alderson-Broaddus College, B
Bethany College, B
Davis & Elkins College, B
Ohio Valley University, B
West Virginia Wesleyan College, B
Wheeling Jesuit University, B

Wisconsin

Alverno College, B
Beloit College, B
Cardinal Stritch University, BM
Carroll College, B
Carthage College, B
Concordia University Wisconsin, B
Edgewood College, BM
Lakeland College, B
Lawrence University, B
Maranatha Baptist Bible College, AB
Marquette University, B
Mount Mary College, B
Northland College, B
Ripon College, B
St. Norbert College, B
University of Wisconsin-Eau Claire, B
University of Wisconsin-Milwaukee, B
University of Wisconsin-Oshkosh, B
Viterbo University, B

Wyoming

Laramie County Community College, A

Alberta

Alliance University College, M
Concordia University College of Alberta, B
Taylor University College and Seminary, B
University of Alberta, B
University of Calgary, BMD
University of Lethbridge, BM

British Columbia

Columbia Bible College, B
Trinity Western University, B
The University of British Columbia, BMD

Manitoba

Brandon University, B
Canadian Mennonite University, B
Providence College and Theological Seminary, B
Steinbach Bible College, B
University of Manitoba, BMD
The University of Winnipeg, BM

New Brunswick

Atlantic Baptist University, B
Bethany Bible College, B
Mount Allison University, B

St. Thomas University, B

Newfoundland and Labrador

Memorial University of Newfoundland, BM

Nova Scotia

Cape Breton University, B
Dalhousie University, B
Mount Saint Vincent University, B
St. Francis Xavier University, B
Saint Mary's University, B
University of King's College, B

Ontario

Carleton University, B
Laurentian University, B
McMaster University, BMD
Queen's University at Kingston, BM
Redeemer University College, B
Saint Paul University, B
University of Ottawa, BMD
University of Toronto, BMD
University of Waterloo, B
The University of Western Ontario, B
Wilfrid Laurier University, BM
York University, B

Prince Edward Island

University of Prince Edward Island, B

Quebec

Bishop's University, B
Concordia University, BMD
McGill University, BMD
Université Laval, MD
Université de Montréal, B
Université du Québec àMontréal, BMD
Université du Québec àRimouski, B
Université de Sherbrooke, M

Saskatchewan

Briercrest College, B
University of Regina, BM
University of Saskatchewan, BM

RELIGIOUS EDUCATION

Alabama

Faulkner University, B
Huntingdon College, B
Oakwood College, B
Southeastern Bible College, B

Arkansas

Harding University, B
John Brown University, B
University of the Ozarks, B
Williams Baptist College, B

California

Azusa Pacific University, M
Bethesda Christian University, B
Biola University, BMD
Concordia University, B
La Sierra University, M
Loyola Marymount University, M
The Master's College and Seminary, B
Pepperdine University, B
Shasta Bible College, M
Simpson University, B
University of San Francisco, MD
Vanguard University of Southern California, B

Colorado

Nazarene Bible College, AB

District of Columbia

The Catholic University of America, BMD

Florida

The Baptist College of Florida, AB
Florida Southern College, B
Nova Southeastern University, O

Talmudic College of Florida, B

Georgia

LaGrange College, B
Luther Rice University, P
Toccoa Falls College, B

Idaho

Boise Bible College, AB
Northwest Nazarene University, B

Illinois

Concordia University, BM
Lincoln Christian College, B
Lincoln College, A
Loyola University Chicago, MO
Moody Bible Institute, B
Olivet Nazarene University, B
Trinity Christian College, B
Trinity International University, MD
Wheaton College, BM

Indiana

Crossroads Bible College, B
Indiana Wesleyan University, AB
Marian College, B
Oakland City University, B
Taylor University, B

Iowa

Faith Baptist Bible College and Theological
    Seminary, B
Northwestern College, B
Vennard College, B

Kansas

Barclay College, B
Kansas Wesleyan University, B
Manhattan Christian College, AB
MidAmerica Nazarene University, B
Sterling College, B

Kentucky

Asbury College, B
Campbellsville University, B
Kentucky Christian University, B
Kentucky Mountain Bible College, B
Mid-Continent University, B
Southern Baptist Theological Seminary, MDP
University of the Cumberlands, B

Louisiana

Louisiana College, B
Loyola University New Orleans, B
New Orleans Baptist Theological Seminary, MDP

Maryland

Baltimore Hebrew University, AB
Columbia Union College, B
Griggs University, B
Ner Israel Rabbinical College, B
Washington Bible College, AB

Massachusetts

Boston College, MDO
Brandeis University, M
Eastern Nazarene College, AB
Hebrew College, BMO

Michigan

Andrews University, BMDO
Aquinas College, B
Concordia University, B
Cornerstone University, ABMP
Great Lakes Christian College, A
Kuyper College, AB

Minnesota

College of Saint Benedict, B
Concordia University, St. Paul, B
Crossroads College, B
Crown College, B
Northwestern College, B
Oak Hills Christian College, B

Pillsbury Baptist Bible College, B
Saint John's University, B
Saint Mary's University of Minnesota, B
University of St. Thomas, M

Mississippi

Northeast Mississippi Community College, A
Wesley College, B

Missouri

Baptist Bible College, B
Calvary Bible College and Theological Seminary, AB
Central Bible College, AB
Central Christian College of the Bible, B
Global University of the Assemblies of God, B
Hannibal-LaGrange College, B
Messenger College, B
Missouri Baptist University, B
Ozark Christian College, B
St. Louis Christian College, B

Montana

Carroll College, B

Nebraska

Concordia University, BM
Grace University, B
Nebraska Christian College, AB
Union College, B
York College, B

New Jersey

Felician College, M
Seton Hall University, B

New York

Fordham University, MDO
Houghton College, AB
The Jewish Theological Seminary, BMD
Mesivta of Eastern Parkway Rabbinical Seminary, B
Nyack College, B
St. Bonaventure University, B
Yeshiva University, MDO
Yeshivat Mikdash Melech, B

North Carolina

Apex School of Theology, A
Campbell University, M
Gardner-Webb University, BP
John Wesley College, B
Lenoir-Rhyne College, B
Methodist College, A
Pfeiffer University, BM
Southeastern Baptist Theological Seminary, MP

Ohio

Ashland University, B
Capital University, B
Cedarville University, B
Cincinnati Christian University, AB
Circleville Bible College, AB
College of Mount St. Joseph, B
Defiance College, B
Franciscan University of Steubenville, B
John Carroll University, B
Laura and Alvin Siegal College of Judaic Studies, M
Malone College, B
Mount Vernon Nazarene University, B
University of Dayton, B

Oklahoma

Hillsdale Free Will Baptist College, AB
Oklahoma Baptist University, B
Oklahoma Christian University, B
Oklahoma City University, BM
Oral Roberts University, M
Southern Nazarene University, B
Southwestern Christian University, B

Oregon

Concordia University, B
Corban College, B
Eugene Bible College, B
George Fox University, BM

Multnomah Bible College and Biblical Seminary, B
University of Portland, M
Warner Pacific College, AB

Pennsylvania

Baptist Bible College of Pennsylvania, BM
Gratz College, MO
Holy Family University, B
La Roche College, B
La Salle University, B
Lancaster Bible College, B
Marywood University, B
Mercyhurst College, AB
Messiah College, B
Saint Vincent College, B
Thiel College, B
Valley Forge Christian College, B
Westminster College, B

Puerto Rico

Colegio Biblico Pentecostal, B
Pontifical Catholic University of Puerto Rico, M
Universidad Adventista de las Antillas, B

South Carolina

Bob Jones University, B
Columbia College, B
Columbia International University, BMPO
Erskine College, B
Morris College, B
North Greenville College, B

Tennessee

Bryan College, B
Free Will Baptist Bible College, B
Lee University, B
Southern Adventist University, BM
Tennessee Temple University, B

Texas

Concordia University at Austin, B
Dallas Baptist University, ABM
East Texas Baptist University, B
Howard Payne University, B
Lon Morris College, A
St. Edward's University, B
Southwestern Assemblies of God University, BM
Texas Wesleyan University, B
Wayland Baptist University, B

Utah

Brigham Young University, M

Virginia

Averett University, B

Washington

Northwest University, B
Puget Sound Christian College, B
Seattle Pacific University, B
Trinity Lutheran College, B

West Virginia

Davis & Elkins College, B
West Virginia Wesleyan College, B

Wisconsin

Cardinal Stritch University, B
Maranatha Baptist Bible College, B
Mount Mary College, B
Viterbo University, B

Alberta

Alliance University College, BMP
Concordia University College of Alberta, B
Newman Theological College, MO
Prairie Bible Institute, B

Rocky Mountain College, B

British Columbia

Summit Pacific College, B

Manitoba

Canadian Mennonite University, B
Providence College and Theological Seminary, BM
William and Catherine Booth College, B

New Brunswick

Bethany Bible College, B

Ontario

Emmanuel Bible College, B
Heritage Baptist College and Heritage Theological Seminary, B
Master's College and Seminary, B
McMaster University, B
Tyndale University College & Seminary, B

Quebec

McGill University, B
Université du Québec àChicoutimi, B
Université du Québec àMontréal, B
Université du Québec àRimouski, B

RELIGIOUS/SACRED MUSIC

Alabama

Samford University, B
Southeastern Bible College, B

Arizona

Grand Canyon University, B

Arkansas

Central Baptist College, B
Ouachita Baptist University, B
Williams Baptist College, B

California

Bethany University, B
Bethesda Christian University, B
Fresno Pacific University, B
Hope International University, B
The Master's College and Seminary, B
Patten University, B
Point Loma Nazarene University, B
San Diego Christian College, B

Colorado

Nazarene Bible College, AB

Florida

The Baptist College of Florida, AB
Clearwater Christian College, B
Florida Southern College, B
Palm Beach Atlantic University, B
Southeastern University, B
Warner Southern College, B

Georgia

Emmanuel College, B
Shorter College, B
Toccoa Falls College, B

Idaho

Boise Bible College, AB
Northwest Nazarene University, B

Illinois

Augustana College, B
Concordia University, B
Lincoln Christian College, B
Millikin University, B
Moody Bible Institute, B
North Park University, B
Olivet Nazarene University, B

Trinity International University, B

Indiana

Anderson University, B
Bethel College, B
Huntington University, B
Indiana Wesleyan University, AB
Taylor University, B
Valparaiso University, B

Iowa

Drake University, B
Faith Baptist Bible College and Theological Seminary, B
Vennard College, A
Wartburg College, B

Kansas

Barclay College, B
Friends University, B
Manhattan Christian College, AB
MidAmerica Nazarene University, AB

Kentucky

Campbellsville University, B

Louisiana

Centenary College of Louisiana, B
Louisiana College, B
Loyola University New Orleans, B

Massachusetts

Atlantic Union College, B
Eastern Nazarene College, B
Hebrew College, B

Michigan

Aquinas College, AB
Calvin College, B
Concordia University, B
Kuyper College, B

Minnesota

Bethany Lutheran College, B
Bethel University, B
Concordia University, St. Paul, B
Crossroads College, B
Gustavus Adolphus College, B
North Central University, AB
Pillsbury Baptist Bible College, B

Mississippi

Mississippi College, B
Southeastern Baptist College, A
William Carey College, B

Missouri

Calvary Bible College and Theological Seminary, B
Central Bible College, AB
Central Christian College of the Bible, B
College of the Ozarks, B
Evangel University, B
Hannibal-LaGrange College, B
Messenger College, B
Missouri Baptist University, B
Ozark Christian College, B
St. Louis Christian College, B
William Jewell College, B

Nebraska

Concordia University, B
Grace University, B

Nebraska Christian College, AB

New Jersey

Rider University, B
Westminster Choir College of Rider University, B

New York

Concordia College, B
Nyack College, B

North Carolina

Gardner-Webb University, B
Lenoir-Rhyne College, B
North Carolina Central University, B
Pfeiffer University, B

Ohio

Cedarville University, B
Cincinnati Christian University, AB
Circleville Bible College, AB
God's Bible School and College, B
Malone College, B
Mount Vernon Nazarene University, AB
Wittenberg University, B

Oklahoma

Hillsdale Free Will Baptist College, AB
Mid-America Christian University, B
Oklahoma Baptist University, B
Oklahoma City University, B
Oral Roberts University, B
Southwestern Christian University, B
Southwestern Oklahoma State University, B

Oregon

Corban College, B
Eugene Bible College, B
Multnomah Bible College and Biblical Seminary, B

Pennsylvania

Baptist Bible College of Pennsylvania, B
Immaculata University, A
Lancaster Bible College, B
Marywood University, B
Moravian College, B
Seton Hill University, B
Susquehanna University, B
Valley Forge Christian College, B
Westminster College, B

South Carolina

Anderson University, B
Charleston Southern University, B
Columbia International University, B
Erskine College, B
Furman University, B
Newberry College, B
North Greenville College, B
Southern Wesleyan University, B

Tennessee

Belmont University, B
Bryan College, B
Free Will Baptist Bible College, B
Johnson Bible College, B
Lambuth University, B
Trevecca Nazarene University, B
Union University, B

Texas

Baylor University, B
Concordia University at Austin, B
Dallas Baptist University, B
East Texas Baptist University, B
Hardin-Simmons University, B
Houston Baptist University, B
Howard Payne University, B
McMurry University, B
Southwestern Assemblies of God University, B
University of Mary Hardin-Baylor, B

Wayland Baptist University, B

Virginia

Averett University, B
Bluefield College, B

Washington

Northwest University, B
Pacific Lutheran University, B
Puget Sound Christian College, B

West Virginia

Alderson-Broaddus College, B

Wisconsin

Maranatha Baptist Bible College, B

Alberta

Alliance University College, B
Vanguard College, B

British Columbia

Summit Pacific College, B

Ontario

Emmanuel Bible College, B
Heritage Baptist College and Heritage Theological Seminary, B

Saskatchewan

Briercrest College, B
Central Pentecostal College, B

RENAL/DIALYSIS TECHNOLOGIST/TECHNICIAN

Georgia

Georgia Medical Institute-DeKalb, A

REPRODUCTIVE BIOLOGY

Hawaii

University of Hawaii at Manoa, MD

Illinois

Northwestern University, D

Maryland

The Johns Hopkins University, MD

New York

Cornell University, MD

Texas

Texas A&M University, D

West Virginia

West Virginia University, MD

Wyoming

University of Wyoming, MD

British Columbia

The University of British Columbia, MD

Saskatchewan

University of Saskatchewan, MD

RESORT MANAGEMENT

Colorado

Western State College of Colorado, B

Florida

Florida Gulf Coast University, B

New Hampshire

Southern New Hampshire University, B

New York

Rochester Institute of Technology, AB

Pennsylvania

The Art Institute of Pittsburgh, AB

South Carolina

Coastal Carolina University, B

Vermont

Green Mountain College, B

Wisconsin

Lakeland College, B

British Columbia

Thompson Rivers University, A

RESOURCE MANAGEMENT

Colorado

Colorado State University, MD

Indiana

Purdue University, MD

Missouri

Missouri State University, M

New Hampshire

University of New Hampshire, M

New York

State University of New York College of Environmental Science and Forestry, MD

North Carolina

East Carolina University, D

Washington

University of Washington, MD

RESPIRATORY CARE THERAPY/THERAPIST

Alabama

Alabama Southern Community College, A
Faulkner University, A
George C. Wallace Community College, A
George Corley Wallace State Community College, A
Shelton State Community College, A
The University of Alabama at Birmingham, B
University of South Alabama, B
Wallace State Community College, A

Arizona

Apollo College-Phoenix, Inc., A
Apollo College-Tri-City, Inc., A
GateWay Community College, A
Pima Community College, A

Arkansas

NorthWest Arkansas Community College, A
Pulaski Technical College, A
University of Arkansas Community College at Hope, A
University of Arkansas at Fort Smith, A
University of Arkansas for Medical Sciences, A

California

American River College, A
Butte College, A
City College of San Francisco, A
College of the Desert, A
Compton Community College, A
Crafton Hills College, A
East Los Angeles College, A
El Camino College, A
Foothill College, A
Fresno City College, A

Grossmont College, A
Loma Linda University, AB
Los Angeles Valley College, A
Modesto Junior College, A
Mt. San Antonio College, A
Napa Valley College, A
Ohlone College, A
Orange Coast College, A
San Joaquin Valley College, A
Santa Monica College, A
Skyline College, A
Victor Valley College, A

Colorado

Pueblo Community College, A

Connecticut

Goodwin College, A
Manchester Community College, A
Norwalk Community College, A
University of Hartford, B

Delaware

Delaware Technical & Community College,
Stanton/Wilmington Campus, A

District of Columbia

University of the District of Columbia, A

Florida

ATI Health Education Center, A
Broward Community College, A
Daytona Beach Community College, A
Edison College, A
Florida Agricultural and Mechanical University, B
Florida Community College at Jacksonville, A
Gulf Coast Community College, A
Hillsborough Community College, A
Indian River Community College, A
Manatee Community College, A
Miami Dade College, A
Pensacola Junior College, A
Polk Community College, A
St. Petersburg College, A
Santa Fe Community College, A
Seminole Community College, A
Tallahassee Community College, A
University of Central Florida, B
Valencia Community College, A

Georgia

Armstrong Atlantic State University, B
Athens Technical College, A
Augusta Technical College, A
Coastal Georgia Community College, A
Dalton State College, A
Darton College, A
Georgia Highlands College, A
Georgia State University, B
Gwinnett Technical College, A
Macon State College, A
Medical College of Georgia, B
Southwest Georgia Technical College, A
Waycross College, A

Hawaii

Kapiolani Community College, A

Idaho

Boise State University, B
College of Southern Idaho, A

Illinois

City Colleges of Chicago, Malcolm X College, A
College of DuPage, A
Danville Area Community College, A
Illinois Central College, A
Kankakee Community College, A
Kaskaskia College, A
Lincoln Land Community College, A
Moraine Valley Community College, A
National-Louis University, B
Parkland College, A
Rock Valley College, A
St. Augustine College, A

Southern Illinois University Carbondale, A
Triton College, A

Indiana

Ball State University, A
Indiana University Northwest, A
Indiana University-Purdue University
Indianapolis, AB
Ivy Tech Community College-Central Indiana, A
Ivy Tech Community College-Lafayette, A
Ivy Tech Community College-Northeast, A
Ivy Tech Community College-Northwest, A
Ivy Tech Community College-Southern Indiana, A
University of Indianapolis, B
University of Southern Indiana, A
Vincennes University, A

Iowa

Des Moines Area Community College, A
Hawkeye Community College, A
Kirkwood Community College, A
St. Luke's College, A
Scott Community College, A
Southeastern Community College, North Campus, A

Kansas

Barton County Community College, A
Dodge City Community College, A
Highland Community College, A
Johnson County Community College, A
Kansas City Kansas Community College, A
Labette Community College, A
Newman University, A
Seward County Community College, A
University of Kansas, B
Washburn University, A

Kentucky

Ashland Community and Technical College, A
Bellarmine University, B
Jefferson Community and Technical College, A
Lexington Community College, A
Madisonville Community College, A
Maysville Community and Technical College, A
Morehead State University, A
Northern Kentucky University, A
Somerset Community College, A
Southeast Kentucky Community and Technical
College, A
Western Kentucky University, A

Louisiana

Bossier Parish Community College, A
Delgado Community College, A
Louisiana State University at Eunice, A
Louisiana State University Health Sciences
Center, B
Our Lady of Holy Cross College, AB
Southern University at Shreveport, A

Maine

Kennebec Valley Community College, A
Southern Maine Community College, A

Maryland

Allegany College of Maryland, A
Baltimore City Community College, A
Columbia Union College, AB
Frederick Community College, A
Prince George's Community College, A
Salisbury University, B

Massachusetts

Berkshire Community College, A
Massachusetts Bay Community College, A
Massasoit Community College, A
North Shore Community College, A
Northern Essex Community College, A
Quinsigamond Community College, A
Springfield Technical Community College, A

Michigan

Delta College, A
Ferris State University, A
Henry Ford Community College, A

Kalamazoo Valley Community College, A
Lansing Community College, A
Macomb Community College, A
Monroe County Community College, A
Mott Community College, A
Oakland Community College, A
Washtenaw Community College, A

Minnesota

College of St. Catherine, B
Lake Superior College, A
Northwest Technical College, A
Rochester Community and Technical College, A
Saint Paul College-A Community & Technical
College, A

Mississippi

Copiah-Lincoln Community College-Natchez
Campus, A
Hinds Community College, A
Holmes Community College, A
Itawamba Community College, A
Meridian Community College, A
Mississippi Gulf Coast Community College, A
Northeast Mississippi Community College, A
Northwest Mississippi Community College, A
Pearl River Community College, A

Missouri

Missouri Southern State University, A
Missouri State University, B
Ozarks Technical Community College, A
Penn Valley Community College, A
St. Louis Community College at Forest Park, A
Sanford-Brown College (Fenton), A
University of Missouri-Columbia, B

Montana

Montana State University-Great Falls College of
Technology, A
The University of Montana-Missoula, A

Nebraska

Metropolitan Community College, A
Midland Lutheran College, AB
Nebraska Methodist College, AB
Southeast Community College, Lincoln Campus, A

Nevada

Community College of Southern Nevada, A

New Jersey

Atlantic Cape Community College, A
Bergen Community College, A
Brookdale Community College, A
Camden County College, A
County College of Morris, A
Essex County College, A
Gloucester County College, A
Mercer County Community College, A
Middlesex County College, A
Passaic County Community College, A
Raritan Valley Community College, A
Sussex County Community College, A
Union County College, A

New Mexico

Central New Mexico Community College, A
Doña Ana Branch Community College, A

New York

Borough of Manhattan Community College of the
City University of New York, A
Erie Community College, North Campus, A
Genesee Community College, A
Hudson Valley Community College, A
Long Island University, Brooklyn Campus, B
Mohawk Valley Community College, A
Molloy College, A
Nassau Community College, A
Onondaga Community College, A
Rockland Community College, A
State University of New York Upstate Medical
University, B

Stony Brook University, State University of New York, B
Westchester Community College, A

North Carolina

Carteret Community College, A
Catawba Valley Community College, A
Central Piedmont Community College, A
Durham Technical Community College, A
Edgecombe Community College, A
Fayetteville Technical Community College, A
Forsyth Technical Community College, A
Guilford Technical Community College, A
Pitt Community College, A
Robeson Community College, A
Rockingham Community College, A
Sandhills Community College, A
Southwestern Community College, A
Stanly Community College, A

North Dakota

North Dakota State University, B
University of Mary, B

Ohio

Bowling Green State University-Firelands College, A
Cincinnati State Technical and Community College, A
Columbus State Community College, A
Cuyahoga Community College, A
James A. Rhodes State College, A
Jefferson Community College, A
Kettering College of Medical Arts, AB
Lakeland Community College, A
North Central State College, A
The Ohio State University, B
Shawnee State University, A
Sinclair Community College, A
Stark State College of Technology, A
The University of Akron, A
The University of Toledo, A
Youngstown State University, B

Oklahoma

Cameron University, A
Oklahoma City Community College, A
Rose State College, A
Tulsa Community College, A

Oregon

Lane Community College, A
Mt. Hood Community College, A

Pennsylvania

Community College of Allegheny County, A
Community College of Philadelphia, A
Delaware County Community College, A
Gannon University, AB
Gwynedd-Mercy College, AB
Harrisburg Area Community College, A
Indiana University of Pennsylvania, B
La Roche College, B
Lehigh Carbon Community College, A
Luzerne County Community College, A
Mansfield University of Pennsylvania, A
Montgomery County Community College, A
Point Park University, A
Reading Area Community College, A
University of Pittsburgh at Johnstown, A
Western School of Health and Business Careers (Pittsburgh), A
York College of Pennsylvania, AB

Puerto Rico

Universidad Adventista de las Antillas, AB
Universidad Metropolitana, B

Rhode Island

Community College of Rhode Island, A

South Carolina

Florence-Darlington Technical College, A
Greenville Technical College, A
Midlands Technical College, A
Piedmont Technical College, A

Spartanburg Technical College, A
Trident Technical College, A

South Dakota

Dakota State University, AB

Tennessee

Baptist College of Health Sciences, B
Chattanooga State Technical Community College, A
Columbia State Community College, A
Jackson State Community College, A
Roane State Community College, A
Southern Adventist University, A
Tennessee State University, B
Volunteer State Community College, A

Texas

Alvin Community College, A
Amarillo College, A
Angelina College, A
Collin County Community College District, A
Del Mar College, A
El Centro College, A
El Paso Community College, A
Houston Community College System, A
Howard College, A
Lamar University, A
McLennan Community College, A
Midland College, A
Midwestern State University, B
North Harris College, A
Odessa College, A
St. Philip's College, A
Sam Houston State University, B
South Plains College, A
Tarrant County College District, A
Temple College, A
Texas Southern University, B
Texas Southmost College, A
Texas State University-San Marcos, B
Tyler Junior College, A
The University of Texas Health Science Center at San Antonio, B
The University of Texas Medical Branch, B
Weatherford College, A

Utah

California College for Health Sciences, AB
Weber State University, AB

Vermont

Vermont Technical College, A

Virginia

Central Virginia Community College, A
J. Sargeant Reynolds Community College, A
Jefferson College of Health Sciences, AB
Northern Virginia Community College, A
Piedmont Virginia Community College, A
Shenandoah University, AB
Southside Virginia Community College, A
Southwest Virginia Community College, A

Washington

Highline Community College, A
Seattle Central Community College, A
Spokane Community College, A
Tacoma Community College, A

West Virginia

Community & Technical College at West Virginia University Institute of Technology, A
Marshall Community and Technical College, A
Mountain State University, AB
Wheeling Jesuit University, B

Wisconsin

Madison Area Technical College, A
Mid-State Technical College, A
Milwaukee Area Technical College, A
Moraine Park Technical College, A
Northeast Wisconsin Technical College, A

Western Technical College, A

Wyoming

Casper College, A
Sheridan College-Sheridan and Gillette, A

British Columbia

Open Learning Agency, B
Thompson Rivers University, B

Nova Scotia

Dalhousie University, B

Ontario

University of Waterloo, B

RESPIRATORY THERAPY TECHNICIAN/ASSISTANT

Arizona

Pima Medical Institute (Mesa), A
Pima Medical Institute (Tucson), A

California

Pima Medical Institute, A

Colorado

Pima Medical Institute, A

Florida

Miami Dade College, A

Georgia

Augusta Technical College, A
Columbus Technical College, A
Coosa Valley Technical College, A
Georgia Medical Institute-DeKalb, A
Griffin Technical College, A
Heart of Georgia Technical College, A
Okefenokee Technical College, A
Southeastern Technical College, A

Illinois

City Colleges of Chicago, Olive-Harvey College, A

Kansas

Kansas City Kansas Community College, A

Louisiana

Louisiana Technical College, A

Massachusetts

Massasoit Community College, A
Northern Essex Community College, A

Mississippi

Coahoma Community College, A

Missouri

East Central College, A
Missouri State University-West Plains, A

Nevada

Pima Medical Institute, A

New Jersey

Bloomfield College, B

North Carolina

Edgecombe Community College, A

Ohio

Columbus State Community College, A

Pennsylvania

Harrisburg Area Community College, A

British Columbia

Thompson Rivers University, A

Nova Scotia

Dalhousie University, B

RESTAURANT, CULINARY, AND CATERING MANAGEMENT/MANAGER

Arizona

Northland Pioneer College, A
Pima Community College, A

California

The Art Institute of California-Orange County, B
The Art Institute of California-San Diego, B
California Culinary Academy, A
Orange Coast College, A

Florida

Central Florida Community College, A
Florida Culinary Institute, A
Hillsborough Community College, A
Johnson & Wales University, A

Georgia

The Art Institute of Atlanta, B

Illinois

City Colleges of Chicago, Malcolm X College, A
College of DuPage, A
College of Lake County, A
John Wood Community College, A
Kendall College, B
Lexington College, AB
Moraine Valley Community College, A
University of Illinois at Urbana-Champaign, B

Indiana

Vincennes University, A

Iowa

Iowa Lakes Community College, A

Maryland

Baltimore International College, B

Michigan

Ferris State University, A

Minnesota

The Art Institutes International Minnesota, B
Rasmussen College Mankato, A

Mississippi

Coahoma Community College, A

Missouri

Lindenwood University, B

Nevada

The Art Institute of Las Vegas, B

New Hampshire

University of New Hampshire, A

New York

The Art Institute of New York City, A
Erie Community College, North Campus, A
Mohawk Valley Community College, A
State University of New York College of Technology
  at Alfred, A
State University of New York College of Technology
  at Delhi, AB

North Carolina

Johnson & Wales University, A

Ohio

Cincinnati State Technical and Community
  College, A
Cuyahoga Community College, A

The University of Akron, A

Oregon

Linn-Benton Community College, A
Southwestern Oregon Community College, A

Pennsylvania

The Art Institute of Pittsburgh, B
Community College of Allegheny County, A
Keystone College, A

Rhode Island

Johnson & Wales University, AB

South Carolina

Bob Jones University, A

Texas

The Art Institute of Dallas, A
The Art Institute of Houston, A

Vermont

New England Culinary Institute, AB

Virginia

Virginia Intermont College, B

Wisconsin

Waukesha County Technical College, A

RESTAURANT/FOOD SERVICES MANAGEMENT

California

The Art Institute of California-San Diego, B
University of San Francisco, B

Colorado

Front Range Community College, A
Johnson & Wales University, AB

Illinois

Kendall College, B
Lexington College, AB

Iowa

Iowa Lakes Community College, A

Massachusetts

Massasoit Community College, A

Michigan

Ferris State University, A
Oakland Community College, A

Missouri

University of Missouri-Columbia, B

New Hampshire

University of New Hampshire, A

New York

Cornell University, B
Niagara University, B
Rochester Institute of Technology, AB
Syracuse University, B

Ohio

Columbus State Community College, A

Pennsylvania

The Art Institute of Pittsburgh, AB
Keystone College, A
Lehigh Carbon Community College, A

Northampton County Area Community College, A

Texas

St. Philip's College, A

RETAILING AND RETAIL OPERATIONS

California

Orange Coast College, A

Florida

Florida Community College at Jacksonville, A

Illinois

Black Hawk College, A
College of DuPage, A
Moraine Valley Community College, A
Waubonsee Community College, A

Iowa

Ellsworth Community College, A
Iowa Lakes Community College, A

Kansas

Garden City Community College, A
Hutchinson Community College and Area Vocational
  School, A
Johnson County Community College, A

Missouri

Patricia Stevens College, A

Nebraska

Northeast Community College, A

New Hampshire

Southern New Hampshire University, B

New York

Syracuse University, B

North Carolina

Catawba Valley Community College, A
Pitt Community College, A
Wayne Community College, A

Pennsylvania

Community College of Allegheny County, A

Rhode Island

Community College of Rhode Island, A
Johnson & Wales University, AB

Tennessee

Draughons Junior College (Clarksville), A

Texas

North Central Texas College, A

Utah

Brigham Young University, B

Washington

Bates Technical College, A
Centralia College, A
Clark College, A

Wisconsin

Waukesha County Technical College, A
Western Technical College, A

Wisconsin Indianhead Technical College, A

RHETORIC

Alabama
The University of Alabama, D

Arizona
Northern Arizona University, M
The University of Arizona, MD

Arkansas
University of Arkansas at Little Rock, M

California
California State University, Dominguez Hills, O
San Diego State University, M
University of California, Berkeley, D

Colorado
Colorado State University, M

District of Columbia
The Catholic University of America, MD

Georgia
Georgia State University, MD

Illinois
Southern Illinois University Carbondale, MD
University of Illinois at Chicago, D

Indiana
Ball State University, M

Iowa
Iowa State University of Science and Technology, D
The University of Iowa, MD

Kentucky
University of Louisville, D

Louisiana
University of Louisiana at Lafayette, D

Michigan
Michigan State University, MD
Michigan Technological University, MD

Minnesota
University of Minnesota, Twin Cities Campus, MD

New York
Rensselaer Polytechnic Institute, MD
Syracuse University, MD

Ohio
Kent State University, D
Miami University, MD
Wright State University, M

Pennsylvania
Carnegie Mellon University, MD
Duquesne University, MD
Indiana University of Pennsylvania, D

South Carolina
Clemson University, D

Texas
Abilene Christian University, M
Texas Tech University, D
Texas Woman's University, D
The University of Texas at Arlington, D

The University of Texas at El Paso, M

Virginia
Virginia Commonwealth University, M

ROBOTICS TECHNOLOGY/TECHNICIAN

Alabama
Jefferson State Community College, A

California
ITT Technical Institute (West Covina), B
Yuba College, A

Colorado
Pikes Peak Community College, A

Illinois
College of DuPage, A
Waubonsee Community College, A

Indiana
Indiana State University, B
Indiana University-Purdue University Indianapolis, AB
ITT Technical Institute (Fort Wayne), B
ITT Technical Institute (Indianapolis), B
ITT Technical Institute (Newburgh), B
Ivy Tech Community College-Columbus, A
Ivy Tech Community College-Lafayette, A
Ivy Tech Community College-North Central, A
Ivy Tech Community College-Northeast, A
Ivy Tech Community College-Southwest, A
Ivy Tech Community College-Wabash Valley, A
Ivy Tech Community College-Whitewater, A
Purdue University, AB

Kentucky
Louisville Technical Institute, A

Louisiana
Southern University at Shreveport, A

Michigan
Kellogg Community College, A
Lake Superior State University, B
Macomb Community College, A
Oakland Community College, A
Schoolcraft College, A

Missouri
Jefferson College, A

Ohio
Terra State Community College, A
University of Rio Grande, AB

Oregon
ITT Technical Institute, B

Pennsylvania
Community College of Allegheny County, A
Delaware County Community College, A

South Carolina
Spartanburg Technical College, A

Texas
Montgomery College, A
Texas State Technical College West Texas, A

Virginia
ITT Technical Institute (Norfolk), B

British Columbia
British Columbia Institute of Technology, A

ROMANCE LANGUAGES, LITERATURES, AND LINGUISTICS

Alabama
Judson College, B
The University of Alabama, MD

California
College of the Desert, A
Pitzer College, B
Point Loma Nazarene University, B
Pomona College, B
San Diego State University, M
University of California, Berkeley, D
University of California, Los Angeles, MD

Colorado
The Colorado College, B

Connecticut
Albertus Magnus College, B
Southern Connecticut State University, MO
Wesleyan University, B

District of Columbia
The Catholic University of America, BMD

Georgia
Clark Atlanta University, M
University of Georgia, BMD

Illinois
Northern Illinois University, M
Olivet Nazarene University, B
Rockford College, B
University of Chicago, BMD

Indiana
DePauw University, B
University of Notre Dame, M

Louisiana
University of New Orleans, M

Maine
Bowdoin College, B
University of Maine, B

Maryland
Hood College, B
The Johns Hopkins University, D

Massachusetts
Boston University, MD
Harvard University, B
Mount Holyoke College, B
Tufts University, B

Michigan
Michigan State University, MD
University of Michigan, BD
Wayne State University, MD

Minnesota
Carleton College, B

Missouri
Northwest Missouri State University, B
University of Missouri-Columbia, MD
University of Missouri-Kansas City, M

Washington University in St. Louis, BMD

Nevada

University of Nevada, Las Vegas, B

New Hampshire

Dartmouth College, B
University of New Hampshire, B

New York

Bard College, B
Bernard M. Baruch College of the City University of
    New York, B
City College of the City University of New York, B
Colgate University, B
Cornell University, BMD
Dowling College, B
Elmira College, B
Fordham University, B
Hunter College of the City University of New
    York, BM
Manhattanville College, B
New York University, BM
Queens College of the City University of New
    York, M
St. Thomas Aquinas College, B
Sarah Lawrence College, B
State University of New York at Buffalo, MD
Stony Brook University, State University of New
    York, M
University at Albany, State University of New York, B

North Carolina

Appalachian State University, M
The University of North Carolina at Chapel
    Hill, BMD

Ohio

Kenyon College, B
Oberlin College, B
University of Cincinnati, BMD

Oklahoma

Cameron University, B

Oregon

University of Oregon, BMD

Pennsylvania

Bryn Mawr College, B
Gettysburg College, B
Haverford College, B
University of Pennsylvania, BMD

Texas

Houston Baptist University, B
Lon Morris College, A
Texas Tech University, M
The University of Texas at Austin, MD

Vermont

Marlboro College, B

Virginia

University of Virginia, MD

Washington

Highline Community College, A
Tacoma Community College, A
University of Washington, BMD

Wisconsin

Beloit College, B
Ripon College, B

Alberta

University of Alberta, B

British Columbia

The University of British Columbia, B
University of Victoria, B

New Brunswick

Mount Allison University, B
University of New Brunswick Fredericton, B

Ontario

University of Toronto, B
University of Windsor, B

York University, B

RURAL PLANNING AND STUDIES

Alaska

University of Alaska Fairbanks, M

California

California State University, Chico, M

Georgia

University of West Georgia, M

Iowa

Iowa State University of Science and Technology, D

New York

Cornell University, M

Wyoming

University of Wyoming, M

Manitoba

Brandon University, MO

Nova Scotia

Dalhousie University, MO

Ontario

University of Guelph, MDO

Quebec

Concordia University, O
Université Laval, O

RURAL SOCIOLOGY

Alabama

Auburn University, MD

Idaho

University of Idaho, M

Iowa

Iowa State University of Science and
    Technology, MD

Missouri

University of Missouri-Columbia, MD

Montana

The University of Montana-Missoula, M

New York

Cornell University, MD

North Carolina

North Carolina State University, M

Ohio

The Ohio State University, MD

Pennsylvania

The Pennsylvania State University University Park
    Campus, MD

South Dakota

South Dakota State University, MD

Tennessee

The University of Tennessee, M

Wisconsin

University of Wisconsin-Madison, M

Alberta

University of Alberta, MDO

RUSSIAN LANGUAGE AND LITERATURE

Alabama

The University of Alabama, B

Arizona

Arizona State University, B
The University of Arizona, BM

Arkansas

Ouachita Baptist University, B

California

Claremont McKenna College, B
El Camino College, A
Pitzer College, B
Pomona College, B
San Diego State University, B
San Francisco State University, BM
Scripps College, B
Stanford University, M
University of California, Berkeley, MD
University of California, Davis, B
University of California, Irvine, B
University of California, Los Angeles, B
University of California, Riverside, B
University of California, San Diego, B
University of Southern California, B

Colorado

The Colorado College, B
University of Denver, B

Connecticut

Trinity College, B
Wesleyan University, B
Yale University, B

Delaware

University of Delaware, B

District of Columbia

American University, BO
The George Washington University, B
Georgetown University, B
Howard University, B

Florida

Florida State University, B
New College of Florida, B
University of Florida, B
University of South Florida, B

Georgia

Emory University, B
University of Georgia, B

Hawaii

University of Hawaii at Manoa, B

Idaho

Brigham Young University -Idaho, A

Illinois

DePaul University, M
Knox College, B
Northern Illinois University, B
Southern Illinois University Carbondale, B
University of Chicago, B
University of Illinois at Chicago, B
University of Illinois at Urbana-Champaign, BMD

Indiana

Indiana University Bloomington, B
University of Notre Dame, B

Iowa

Cornell College, B
Grinnell College, B
The University of Iowa, B

University of Northern Iowa, B

Kentucky

University of Kentucky, B

Louisiana

Loyola University New Orleans, B
Tulane University, B

Maine

Bates College, B
Bowdoin College, B

Maryland

Goucher College, B
University of Maryland, Baltimore County, BM
University of Maryland, College Park, BM

Massachusetts

Amherst College, B
Boston College, BMO
Boston University, B
Brandeis University, B
College of the Holy Cross, B
Harvard University, BMD
Northeastern University, B
Smith College, B
Tufts University, B
University of Massachusetts Boston, B
Wellesley College, B
Wheaton College, B
Williams College, B

Michigan

Michigan State University, B
University of Michigan, BMD
Wayne State University, M

Minnesota

Carleton College, B
Gustavus Adolphus College, B
Macalester College, B
St. Olaf College, B
University of Minnesota, Twin Cities Campus, B
University of St. Thomas, B

Missouri

Saint Louis University, B
Truman State University, B
University of Missouri-Columbia, B
Washington University in St. Louis, B

Montana

The University of Montana-Missoula, B

Nebraska

University of Nebraska-Lincoln, B

New Hampshire

Dartmouth College, B
University of New Hampshire, B

New Jersey

Drew University, B
Rider University, B
Rutgers, The State University of New Jersey, New
    Brunswick/Piscataway, B

New Mexico

University of New Mexico, B

New York

Bard College, B
Barnard College, B
Brooklyn College of the City University of New
    York, B
Colgate University, B
Columbia University, B
Columbia University, School of General Studies, B
Fordham University, B
Hobart and William Smith Colleges, B
Hofstra University, BM
Hunter College of the City University of New York, B

Lehman College of the City University of New
    York, B
New York University, BM
Queens College of the City University of New
    York, B
Sarah Lawrence College, B
Stony Brook University, State University of New
    York, BMD
Syracuse University, B
United States Military Academy, B
University at Albany, State University of New
    York, BMO
University of Rochester, B
Vassar College, B

North Carolina

Duke University, B
The University of North Carolina at Chapel Hill, MD
Wake Forest University, B

Ohio

Bowling Green State University, B
Kent State University, BM
Miami University, B
Miami University Hamilton, B
Oberlin College, B
The Ohio State University, B
Ohio University, B

Oklahoma

Oklahoma State University, B
Tulsa Community College, A
University of Oklahoma, B

Oregon

Portland State University, B
Reed College, B
University of Oregon, BM

Pennsylvania

Bryn Mawr College, BMD
Bucknell University, B
Dickinson College, B
Haverford College, B
Indiana University of Pennsylvania, B
Juniata College, B
Kutztown University of Pennsylvania, B
La Salle University, B
The Pennsylvania State University Abington
    College, B
The Pennsylvania State University Altoona
    College, B
The Pennsylvania State University Beaver Campus
    of the Commonwealth College, B
The Pennsylvania State University Berks Campus of
    the Berks-Lehigh Valley College, B
The Pennsylvania State University Delaware County
    Campus of the Commonwealth College, B
The Pennsylvania State University DuBois Campus
    of the Commonwealth College, B
The Pennsylvania State University at Erie, The
    Behrend College, B
The Pennsylvania State University Fayette Campus
    of the Commonwealth College, B
The Pennsylvania State University Hazleton
    Campus of the Commonwealth College, B
The Pennsylvania State University, Lehigh Valley
    Campus of the Berks-Lehigh Valley College, B
The Pennsylvania State University McKeesport
    Campus of the Commonwealth College, B
The Pennsylvania State University Mont Alto
    Campus of the Commonwealth College, B
The Pennsylvania State University New Kensington
    Campus of the Commonwealth College, B
The Pennsylvania State University Schuylkill
    Campus of the Capital College, B
The Pennsylvania State University Shenango
    Campus of the Commonwealth College, B
The Pennsylvania State University University Park
    Campus, BM
The Pennsylvania State University Wilkes-Barre
    Campus of the Commonwealth College, B
The Pennsylvania State University Worthington
    Scranton Campus of the Commonwealth
    College, B

The Pennsylvania State University York Campus of
    the Commonwealth College, B
Swarthmore College, B
Temple University, B
University of Pennsylvania, B
University of Pittsburgh, B
West Chester University of Pennsylvania, B

Rhode Island

Brown University, MD

Tennessee

Sewanee: The University of the South, B
The University of Tennessee, BD
Vanderbilt University, B

Texas

Austin Community College, A
Baylor University, B
Rice University, B
Southern Methodist University, B
Texas A&M University, B
Trinity University, B
The University of Texas at Arlington, B
The University of Texas at Austin, B

Utah

Brigham Young University, B
University of Utah, B

Vermont

Middlebury College, BMD
University of Vermont, B

Virginia

Ferrum College, B

Washington

Everett Community College, A
Seattle Pacific University, B
Tacoma Community College, A
University of Washington, BMD
Washington State University, B

Wisconsin

Beloit College, B
Lawrence University, B
University of Wisconsin-Madison, B
University of Wisconsin-Milwaukee, B

Wyoming

University of Wyoming, B

Alberta

University of Alberta, B
University of Calgary, B

British Columbia

The University of British Columbia, B
University of Victoria, B

Manitoba

University of Manitoba, B

New Brunswick

University of New Brunswick Fredericton, BM

Newfoundland and Labrador

Memorial University of Newfoundland, B

Nova Scotia

Dalhousie University, B
University of King's College, B

Ontario

Carleton University, B
McMaster University, B
University of Ottawa, B
University of Toronto, B
University of Waterloo, BM
The University of Western Ontario, B
University of Windsor, B

York University, B

Quebec

McGill University, BMD

Saskatchewan

University of Saskatchewan, B

RUSSIAN STUDIES

Alaska

University of Alaska Fairbanks, B

California

California State University, Fullerton, B
Claremont McKenna College, B
San Diego State University, B
University of California, Los Angeles, B
University of California, Riverside, B
University of California, San Diego, B
University of California, Santa Cruz, B

Colorado

The Colorado College, B
University of Colorado at Boulder, B

Connecticut

Wesleyan University, B
Yale University, B

District of Columbia

American University, B
The George Washington University, B

Florida

Florida State University, B
Manatee Community College, A
Stetson University, B

Illinois

Knox College, B
University of Chicago, B
University of Illinois at Urbana-Champaign, B

Indiana

DePauw University, B
Indiana University Bloomington, B

Iowa

Iowa State University of Science and Technology, B
The University of Iowa, B
University of Northern Iowa, B

Kansas

University of Kansas, B

Louisiana

Tulane University, B

Maine

Colby College, B
University of Southern Maine, B

Maryland

University of Maryland, College Park, B

Massachusetts

Boston College, B
Boston University, B
Brandeis University, B
College of the Holy Cross, B
Harvard University, B
Mount Holyoke College, B
Smith College, B
Tufts University, B
University of Massachusetts Amherst, B
Wellesley College, B
Wheaton College, B

Michigan

Grand Valley State University, B
University of Michigan, B

Western Michigan University, B

Minnesota

Carleton College, B
Concordia College, B
Gustavus Adolphus College, B
Hamline University, B
Macalester College, B
St. Olaf College, B
University of Minnesota, Twin Cities Campus, B
University of St. Thomas, B

Missouri

University of Missouri-Columbia, B
Washington University in St. Louis, B

Montana

The University of Montana-Missoula, B

New Hampshire

Dartmouth College, B

New Jersey

Rutgers, The State University of New Jersey, New
    Brunswick/Piscataway, B

New Mexico

University of New Mexico, B

New York

Bard College, B
Barnard College, B
Colgate University, B
Columbia College, B
Cornell University, B
Fordham University, B
Hamilton College, B
Hobart and William Smith Colleges, B
Syracuse University, B
University at Albany, State University of New York, B
University of Rochester, B

North Carolina

The University of North Carolina at Chapel Hill, B

Ohio

The College of Wooster, B
Kent State University, B
Oberlin College, B
The Ohio State University, B
Wittenberg University, B

Pennsylvania

Dickinson College, B
La Salle University, B
Lafayette College, B
Lehigh University, B
Muhlenberg College, B

Rhode Island

Brown University, B

Tennessee

Rhodes College, B
Sewanee: The University of the South, B

Texas

Rice University, B
Southern Methodist University, B
Texas State University-San Marcos, B
Texas Tech University, B
University of Houston, B
The University of Texas at Austin, B

Vermont

Marlboro College, B
Middlebury College, B
University of Vermont, B

Virginia

The College of William and Mary, B
George Mason University, B
Randolph-Macon Woman's College, B

Washington and Lee University, B

Washington

University of Washington, B

Wisconsin

Beloit College, B
Lawrence University, B
University of Wisconsin-Milwaukee, B

Alberta

University of Alberta, B

British Columbia

The University of British Columbia, B
University of Victoria, B

Manitoba

University of Manitoba, B

Nova Scotia

Dalhousie University, B

Ontario

Brock University, B
Carleton University, B
McMaster University, B
University of Toronto, B
University of Waterloo, B
York University, B

Quebec

McGill University, B

SACRED MUSIC

Alabama

Samford University, M

California

Hope International University, M
Santa Clara University, M
University of Southern California, MD

Colorado

University of Colorado at Boulder, M

District of Columbia

The Catholic University of America, MD

Illinois

Concordia University, M

Indiana

Saint Joseph's College, MO

Kansas

University of Kansas, MD

Kentucky

Campbellsville University, M
Southern Baptist Theological Seminary, MDP

Louisiana

New Orleans Baptist Theological Seminary, MD

Massachusetts

Hebrew College, O

Minnesota

Saint John's University, M

Mississippi

University of Southern Mississippi, M

Missouri

Webster University, M

New Jersey

Rider University, M

New York

The Jewish Theological Seminary, MD

North Carolina

Gardner-Webb University, P
Southeastern Baptist Theological Seminary, M

Pennsylvania

Duquesne University, M
Marywood University, M

Tennessee

Belmont University, M
Lee University, M
University of Memphis, MD

Texas

Baylor University, M
Hardin-Simmons University, M
Southern Methodist University, M

Virginia

Shenandoah University, MO

Wisconsin

Concordia University Wisconsin, M

SAFETY ENGINEERING

Arizona

Embry-Riddle Aeronautical University, M

California

National University, M

Kentucky

Murray State University, M

Minnesota

University of Minnesota, Duluth, M

New Jersey

New Jersey Institute of Technology, M

West Virginia

West Virginia University, M

Wisconsin

University of Wisconsin-Stout, M

SALES AND MARKETING OPERATIONS/MARKETING AND DISTRIBUTION TEACHER EDUCATION

Colorado

Colorado State University, B

Georgia

University of Georgia, B

Illinois

Parkland College, A

Kansas

Central Christian College of Kansas, A

Michigan

Central Michigan University, B
Eastern Michigan University, B

Mississippi

Northwest Mississippi Community College, A

Nebraska

University of Nebraska-Lincoln, B

New Hampshire

Southern New Hampshire University, B

New Mexico

Eastern New Mexico University, B

New York

New York Institute of Technology, B
State University of New York at Oswego, B

North Carolina

East Carolina University, B
Fayetteville State University, B
Louisburg College, A
North Carolina State University, B

North Dakota

University of North Dakota, B

Ohio

Bowling Green State University, B
Kent State University, B
Wright State University, B

Tennessee

Middle Tennessee State University, B

Utah

Utah State University, B

Virginia

Old Dominion University, B

Wisconsin

University of Wisconsin-Stout, B

SALES, DISTRIBUTION AND MARKETING OPERATIONS

Alabama

Tuskegee University, B

Arkansas

Harding University, B

California

Santa Ana College, A
Santa Barbara City College, A

Colorado

Western State College of Colorado, B

Connecticut

Norwalk Community College, A
Quinnipiac University, B

Georgia

Dalton State College, AB
University of Georgia, B

Illinois

College of DuPage, A
John Wood Community College, A
McKendree College, B
South Suburban College, A
Trinity Christian College, B
University of Illinois at Urbana-Champaign, B

Indiana

Purdue University North Central, AB
Vincennes University, A

Iowa

Iowa Lakes Community College, A
Iowa Western Community College, A

Kansas

Johnson County Community College, A
Newman University, B

Wichita State University, B

Louisiana

Our Lady of Holy Cross College, B

Maine

Husson College, B
Kennebec Valley Community College, A

Maryland

University of Baltimore, B

Massachusetts

Babson College, B
Mount Wachusett Community College, A

Michigan

Baker College of Flint, A
Baker College of Jackson, A
Central Michigan University, B

Minnesota

Academy College, A
Dakota County Technical College, A
Metropolitan State University, B
Ridgewater College, A
Saint Mary's University of Minnesota, B

Nevada

Sierra Nevada College, B

New Hampshire

Hesser College, A

New Jersey

Burlington County College, A
Fairleigh Dickinson University, College at
  Florham, B

New York

Dowling College, B
State University of New York College of Technology
  at Alfred, A
Syracuse University, B

North Carolina

Johnson & Wales University, AB
Lees-McRae College, B
Shaw University, B

North Dakota

Lake Region State College, A

Ohio

Cuyahoga Community College, A
The University of Findlay, AB

Oklahoma

Bacone College, B

Oregon

Pioneer Pacific College, A

Pennsylvania

Central Pennsylvania College, A
Johnson College, A
Montgomery County Community College, A
Seton Hill University, B
University of Pennsylvania, B
West Chester University of Pennsylvania, B

Puerto Rico

Caribbean University, B

Rhode Island

Johnson & Wales University, AB

South Carolina

Central Carolina Technical College, A
Midlands Technical College, A

South Dakota

Black Hills State University, B
Colorado Technical University Sioux Falls
  Campus, B

Tennessee

Belmont University, B
Middle Tennessee State University, B

University of Memphis, B

Texas

Baylor University, B
Collin County Community College District, A
North Central Texas College, A
St. Mary's University of San Antonio, B
Texas A&M University, B
University of Houston, B
University of North Texas, B

Utah

LDS Business College, A

Vermont

Champlain College, AB

Virginia

Hampton University, B

Washington

Centralia College, A

Wisconsin

University of Wisconsin-Stout, B
University of Wisconsin-Superior, B
Western Technical College, A

British Columbia

Thompson Rivers University, A

Nova Scotia

Cape Breton University, B

Ontario

Brock University, B
Ryerson University, B
York University, B

Quebec

HEC Montreal, B
McGill University, B

SALON/BEAUTY SALON MANAGEMENT/MANAGER

Michigan

Mott Community College, A
Oakland Community College, A

SANSKRIT AND CLASSICAL INDIAN LANGUAGES, LITERATURES, AND LINGUISTICS

Hawaii

University of Hawaii at Manoa, B

Illinois

University of Chicago, B

SCANDINAVIAN LANGUAGES, LITERATURES, AND LINGUISTICS

California

University of California, Berkeley, BMD
University of California, Los Angeles, BMD

Illinois

Augustana College, B
North Park University, B

Massachusetts

Harvard University, BMD

Minnesota

Augsburg College, B
Concordia College, B

Gustavus Adolphus College, B
St. Olaf College, B
University of Minnesota, Twin Cities Campus, BMD

New York

Cornell University, MD

North Dakota

University of North Dakota, B

Texas

The University of Texas at Austin, B

Washington

Pacific Lutheran University, B
University of Washington, BMD

Wisconsin

University of Wisconsin-Madison, BMD

Alberta

University of Alberta, B

SCANDINAVIAN STUDIES

Iowa

Luther College, B

Michigan

University of Michigan, B

Minnesota

Gustavus Adolphus College, B

Vermont

Sterling College, B

Washington

University of Washington, B

SCHOOL LIBRARIAN/SCHOOL LIBRARY MEDIA SPECIALIST

Minnesota

The College of St. Scholastica, B

Montana

University of Great Falls, B

Ohio

Ohio Dominican University, B

Washington

Eastern Washington University, B

SCHOOL NURSING

Minnesota

Bethel University, O

New Jersey

The College of New Jersey, O
Kean University, O
Monmouth University, O
Seton Hall University, M

Ohio

Capital University, M
Wright State University, M

Pennsylvania

Kutztown University of Pennsylvania, O
La Salle University, O

SCHOOL PSYCHOLOGY

Alabama

Auburn University, MDO
Troy University, M

The University of Alabama at Birmingham, M

Arizona

Argosy University/Phoenix, MD
Northern Arizona University, MD

Arkansas

Arkansas State University, M
University of Central Arkansas, MD

California

Azusa Pacific University, M
California State University, Dominguez Hills, O
California State University, Los Angeles, M
California State University, Sacramento, M
Chapman University, MO
Fresno Pacific University, M
La Sierra University, O
Loyola Marymount University, M
National University, M
San Diego State University, M
University of California, Berkeley, D
University of the Pacific, MDO

Colorado

University of Colorado at Denver and Health
  Sciences Center - Downtown Denver Campus, O
University of Northern Colorado, DO
University of Phoenix-Denver Campus, M
Western State College of Colorado, B

Connecticut

Central Connecticut State University, M
Fairfield University, MO
Southern Connecticut State University, MO
University of Connecticut, MD
University of Hartford, M

Delaware

University of Delaware, M
Wilmington College, M

District of Columbia

Gallaudet University, MO
Howard University, MDO

Florida

Argosy University/Sarasota, O
Barry University, MO
Carlos Albizu University, Miami Campus, M
Florida Agricultural and Mechanical University, M
Florida International University, O
Florida State University, MO
Nova Southeastern University, MDO
University of Central Florida, O
University of Florida, MDO
University of South Florida, DO

Georgia

Georgia Southern University, MO
Georgia State University, MDO
University of Georgia, O
Valdosta State University, BMO

Hawaii

Argosy University/Hawaii, MD

Idaho

Idaho State University, O
University of Idaho, DO

Illinois

Eastern Illinois University, O
Illinois State University, DO
Loyola University Chicago, MDO
National-Louis University, MDO
Southern Illinois University Edwardsville, O
Western Illinois University, O

Indiana

Ball State University, MDO
Indiana State University, MDO
Indiana University Bloomington, O

Valparaiso University, O

Iowa

The University of Iowa, DO
University of Northern Iowa, O

Kansas

Emporia State University, MO
Fort Hays State University, BO
Pittsburg State University, O
University of Kansas, DO
Wichita State University, O

Kentucky

Eastern Kentucky University, O
Western Kentucky University, O

Louisiana

Louisiana State University and Agricultural and
Mechanical College, MD
Louisiana State University in Shreveport, MO
McNeese State University, M
Nicholls State University, MO
University of Louisiana at Monroe, O

Maine

University of Southern Maine, MD

Maryland

Towson University, MO
University of Maryland, College Park, MD

Massachusetts

Assumption College, M
Lesley University, M
Northeastern University, MDO
Tufts University, MO
University of Massachusetts Amherst, D
University of Massachusetts Boston, MO

Michigan

Andrews University, MO
Central Michigan University, DO
Grand Valley State University, M
Michigan State University, MDO
University of Detroit Mercy, O
Wayne State University, MO
Western Michigan University, DO

Minnesota

Minnesota State University Moorhead, MO
University of Minnesota, Twin Cities Campus, MDO

Missouri

Evangel University, M
Maryville University of Saint Louis, M
Southeast Missouri State University, M
University of Missouri-Columbia, MDO
University of Missouri-St. Louis, O

Montana

University of Great Falls, M
The University of Montana-Missoula, MDO

Nebraska

University of Nebraska at Kearney, MO
University of Nebraska at Omaha, O

Nevada

University of Nevada, Las Vegas, O

New Jersey

Fairleigh Dickinson University, Metropolitan
Campus, MD
Kean University, MO
New Jersey City University, O
Rider University, BO
Rowan University, MO
Rutgers, The State University of New Jersey, New
Brunswick/Piscataway, MD

Seton Hall University, O

New York

Adelphi University, M
Alfred University, MDO
Brooklyn College of the City University of New
York, MO
The College of New Rochelle, M
The College of Saint Rose, MO
Fordham University, DO
Hofstra University, DO
Iona College, M
Long Island University, Brooklyn Campus, M
Marist College, MO
Mercy College, M
New York University, D
Niagara University, M
Pace University, MD
Queens College of the City University of New
York, MO
Rochester Institute of Technology, MO
St. John's University, BMD
State University of New York at Buffalo, M
State University of New York at Oswego, MO
State University of New York at Plattsburgh, MO
Syracuse University, D
University at Albany, State University of New
York, DO
Yeshiva University, D

North Carolina

Appalachian State University, MO
East Carolina University, O
Gardner-Webb University, M
Lenoir-Rhyne College, M
North Carolina State University, D
The University of North Carolina at Chapel Hill, MD
The University of North Carolina at Greensboro, O
Western Carolina University, M

North Dakota

Minot State University, O

Ohio

Bowling Green State University, MO
Cleveland State University, O
Kent State University, MDO
Miami University, MO
The University of Akron, M
University of Cincinnati, MD
University of Dayton, M
The University of Toledo, MO

Oklahoma

Southwestern Oklahoma State University, M
University of Oklahoma, M

Oregon

George Fox University, M
Lewis & Clark College, MO

Pennsylvania

Bucknell University, M
California University of Pennsylvania, M
Duquesne University, MDO
Edinboro University of Pennsylvania, O
Immaculata University, D
Indiana University of Pennsylvania, DO
Lehigh University, DO
Marywood University, M
Millersville University of Pennsylvania, M
The Pennsylvania State University University Park
Campus, MD
Temple University, MD
University of Pennsylvania, D

Puerto Rico

Inter American University of Puerto Rico, San
Germán Campus, MD

Pontifical Catholic University of Puerto Rico, M

Rhode Island

University of Rhode Island, MD

South Carolina

The Citadel, The Military College of South
Carolina, MO
Francis Marion University, M
University of South Carolina, D

Tennessee

Austin Peay State University, M
Middle Tennessee State University, O
Tennessee State University, MD
University of Memphis, MD
The University of Tennessee, DO
The University of Tennessee at Chattanooga, O

Texas

Abilene Christian University, M
Our Lady of the Lake University of San Antonio, M
St. Mary's University of San Antonio, M
Sam Houston State University, M
Stephen F. Austin State University, M
Tarleton State University, M
Texas A&M University, MD
Texas State University-San Marcos, M
Texas Wesleyan University, B
Texas Woman's University, MD
Trinity University, M
University of Houston-Clear Lake, BM
University of North Texas, MD
The University of Texas at Austin, D
The University of Texas-Pan American, M
The University of Texas at Tyler, M

United States Virgin Islands

University of the Virgin Islands, O

Utah

Brigham Young University, O
Utah State University, M

Vermont

College of St. Joseph, M

Virginia

The College of William and Mary, MO
George Mason University, M
James Madison University, MO
Radford University, O
University of Virginia, D

Washington

Central Washington University, M
City University, M
Eastern Washington University, M
Seattle University, O
University of Washington, MD

West Virginia

Marshall University, O

Wisconsin

University of Wisconsin-Eau Claire, MO
University of Wisconsin-La Crosse, MO
University of Wisconsin-River Falls, MO
University of Wisconsin-Stout, MO
University of Wisconsin-Whitewater, MO

Alberta

University of Alberta, MD
University of Calgary, MD

British Columbia

The University of British Columbia, MDO

Nova Scotia

Mount Saint Vincent University, M

Quebec

McGill University, MDO

SCIENCE TEACHER EDUCATION/GENERAL SCIENCE TEACHER EDUCATION

Alabama

Alabama State University, BMO
Athens State University, B
Auburn University, B
Judson College, B
Oakwood College, B
Samford University, B
Talladega College, B
Troy University, B
University of South Alabama, M
The University of West Alabama, M

Arizona

Arizona State University, MD
Grand Canyon University, B
Northern Arizona University, BM
Prescott College, B
The University of Arizona, B

Arkansas

Arkansas State University, MO
Arkansas Tech University, B
Harding University, B
Henderson State University, B
Ouachita Baptist University, B
Southern Arkansas University-Magnolia, B
University of Central Arkansas, B
University of the Ozarks, B

California

California Lutheran University, B
California State University, Chico, BM
California State University, Fullerton, M
California State University, San Bernardino, M
California State University, San Marcos, B
Fresno Pacific University, BM
The Master's College and Seminary, B
Occidental College, M
San Diego State University, D
Stanford University, MD
University of California, Berkeley, MD
University of California, Los Angeles, M
University of California, San Diego, D

Colorado

The Colorado College, M
Colorado State University, B
Colorado State University-Pueblo, B
Mesa State College, B
University of Northern Colorado, MD
Western State College of Colorado, B

Connecticut

Connecticut College, M
Eastern Connecticut State University, M
Quinnipiac University, M
Sacred Heart University, B
Southern Connecticut State University, MO
University of Connecticut, MD

Delaware

Delaware State University, BM
University of Delaware, B
Wilmington College, B

Florida

Chipola College, B
Florida Agricultural and Mechanical University, M
Florida Atlantic University, B
Florida Gulf Coast University, M
Florida Institute of Technology, BMDO
Florida International University, BMD
Florida State University, BMDO
Manatee Community College, A
Miami Dade College, A
Nova Southeastern University, MO
Southeastern University, B
University of Central Florida, BM

University of Florida, MD
University of Miami, MDO
University of North Florida, B
University of South Florida, BMDO
University of West Florida, BM
Warner Southern College, B

Georgia

Albany State University, BM
Brewton-Parker College, B
Clark Atlanta University, BD
Columbus State University, B
Georgia College & State University, MO
Georgia Southern University, M
Georgia State University, MDO
North Georgia College & State University, B
South Georgia College, A
University of Georgia, BMDO
University of West Georgia, MO
Wesleyan College, M

Hawaii

Brigham Young University-Hawaii, B

Idaho

Boise State University, BM
Lewis-Clark State College, B
University of Idaho, M

Illinois

Augustana College, B
Benedictine University, B
Chicago State University, B
Concordia University, B
Eureka College, B
Governors State University, B
Illinois Institute of Technology, MD
Judson College, B
National-Louis University, MO
Olivet Nazarene University, B
Southern Illinois University Edwardsville, BM
Trinity Christian College, B
University of Illinois at Chicago, B
University of Illinois at Urbana-Champaign, B
University of St. Francis, B
Wheaton College, B

Indiana

Anderson University, B
Ball State University, BMD
Bethel College, B
Calumet College of Saint Joseph, B
Goshen College, B
Grace College, B
Huntington University, B
Indiana State University, BM
Indiana University Bloomington, BMD
Indiana University-Purdue University Fort Wayne, B
Indiana University South Bend, B
Indiana University Southeast, B
Indiana Wesleyan University, B
Manchester College, B
Oakland City University, B
Purdue University, MDO
Purdue University Calumet, BM
Taylor University, B
Tri-State University, B
University of Evansville, B
University of Indianapolis, BM
University of Notre Dame, B
University of Saint Francis, B
Valparaiso University, B
Vincennes University, A

Iowa

Ashford University, B
Buena Vista University, B
Coe College, B
Dordt College, B
Drake University, M
Graceland University, B
Iowa Central Community College, A
Iowa Lakes Community College, A
Morningside College, B
Mount Mercy College, B

St. Ambrose University, B
The University of Iowa, BMD
University of Northern Iowa, BMO
Upper Iowa University, B
William Penn University, B

Kansas

Central Christian College of Kansas, A
Colby Community College, A
Fort Hays State University, B
Friends University, B
Independence Community College, A
Tabor College, B
Wichita State University, B

Kentucky

Alice Lloyd College, B
Asbury College, M
Campbellsville University, B
Eastern Kentucky University, BM
Murray State University, B
Northern Kentucky University, B
University of Kentucky, B
Western Kentucky University, BM

Louisiana

Dillard University, B
Grambling State University, BM
Louisiana College, B
Nicholls State University, B
Northwestern State University of Louisiana, M
Our Lady of Holy Cross College, B
Southeastern Louisiana University, B
Southern University and Agricultural and Mechanical College, BD
University of Louisiana at Lafayette, B
University of New Orleans, BM
Xavier University of Louisiana, B

Maine

College of the Atlantic, B
University of Maine, BMO
University of Maine at Farmington, B
University of Maine at Machias, B
University of Maine at Presque Isle, B

Maryland

Bowie State University, B
Coppin State University, B
The Johns Hopkins University, O
Morgan State University, MD
Salisbury University, M
Towson University, M
University of Maryland, College Park, B

Massachusetts

Boston College, M
Boston University, BMDO
Bridgewater State College, M
Elms College, B
Fitchburg State College, M
Harvard University, M
Lesley University, M
Salem State College, M
Smith College, M
Springfield College, B
University of Massachusetts Amherst, D
University of Massachusetts Lowell, D
Westfield State College, B

Michigan

Adrian College, B
Alma College, B
Andrews University, BM
Aquinas College, B
Calvin College, B
Central Michigan University, BM
Concordia University, B
Cornerstone University, B
Eastern Michigan University, BM
Ferris State University, B
Grand Valley State University, B
Hope College, B
Lawrence Technological University, M
Madonna University, B

Michigan State University, M
Michigan Technological University, BM
Northern Michigan University, BM
Oakland University, B
Rochester College, B
Saginaw Valley State University, BM
University of Detroit Mercy, B
University of Michigan, MD
University of Michigan-Dearborn, B
Wayne State University, BMO
Western Michigan University, BD

Minnesota

Bemidji State University, BM
Bethel University, B
Concordia College, B
Concordia University, St. Paul, B
Hamline University, B
Minnesota State University Mankato, B
Minnesota State University Moorhead, B
Pillsbury Baptist Bible College, B
St. Cloud State University, B
University of Minnesota, Duluth, B
University of Minnesota, Twin Cities Campus, BMD
University of St. Thomas, B
Vermilion Community College, A
Winona State University, B

Mississippi

Blue Mountain College, B
Delta State University, B
East Central Community College, A
Holmes Community College, A
Itawamba Community College, A
Jackson State University, M
Jones County Junior College, A
Mississippi College, BM
Mississippi Delta Community College, A
Mississippi University for Women, B
Mississippi Valley State University, B
Northeast Mississippi Community College, A
Northwest Mississippi Community College, A
University of Mississippi, B
University of Southern Mississippi, MD

Missouri

Central Methodist University, B
College of the Ozarks, B
Culver-Stockton College, B
Evangel University, B
Hannibal-LaGrange College, B
Lindenwood University, B
Missouri Baptist University, B
Missouri State University, BM
Missouri Valley College, B
Northwest Missouri State University, BM
Southeast Missouri State University, BM
Southwest Baptist University, B
University of Missouri-Columbia, BMDO
University of Missouri-Rolla, M
Washington University in St. Louis, B
Webster University, M
William Woods University, B

Montana

Montana State University-Billings, B
Montana State University-Northern, BM
University of Great Falls, B
The University of Montana-Missoula, BM
The University of Montana-Western, B

Nebraska

Chadron State College, B
College of Saint Mary, B
Concordia University, B
Dana College, B
Hastings College, B
Midland Lutheran College, B
Nebraska Wesleyan University, B
Peru State College, B
University of Nebraska at Kearney, M
University of Nebraska-Lincoln, B
Wayne State College, BM

York College, B

Nevada

Community College of Southern Nevada, A
Nevada State College at Henderson, B
University of Nevada, Reno, B

New Hampshire

Keene State College, B
University of New Hampshire, B

New Jersey

Bloomfield College, B
Fairleigh Dickinson University, Metropolitan
    Campus, M
Kean University, M
Montclair State University, M
Rider University, BO
Rowan University, M
Rutgers, The State University of New Jersey, New
    Brunswick/Piscataway, MD
Stevens Institute of Technology, O

New Mexico

College of the Southwest, B
New Mexico Highlands University, B
New Mexico Institute of Mining and Technology, M
Western New Mexico University, B

New York

Alfred University, B
Brooklyn College of the City University of New
    York, M
Buffalo State College, State University of New
    York, BM
Canisius College, B
City College of the City University of New York, BM
The College of Saint Rose, M
Concordia College, B
Cornell University, M
Dutchess Community College, A
D'Youville College, B
Elmira College, B
Hofstra University, BM
Hunter College of the City University of New
    York, BM
Iona College, BM
Ithaca College, B
Le Moyne College, B
Lehman College of the City University of New
    York, M
Long Island University, C.W. Post Campus, M
Manhattanville College, M
Nazareth College of Rochester, B
New York University, M
Niagara University, B
Pace University, B
Queens College of the City University of New
    York, MO
Roberts Wesleyan College, B
St. John Fisher College, BM
St. John's University, B
State University of New York at Binghamton, M
State University of New York at Buffalo, MD
State University of New York College at
    Brockport, BM
State University of New York College at
    Cortland, BM
State University of New York College of
    Environmental Science and Forestry, B
State University of New York College at Old
    Westbury, B
State University of New York College at Oneonta, B
State University of New York College at Potsdam, B
State University of New York, Fredonia, B
State University of New York at New Paltz, BM
State University of New York at Oswego, B
State University of New York at Plattsburgh, M
Stony Brook University, State University of New
    York, M
Syracuse University, MD

University at Albany, State University of New
    York, BM

North Carolina

Bennett College For Women, B
Campbell University, B
East Carolina University, BM
Elon University, B
Greensboro College, B
Johnson C. Smith University, B
Lenoir-Rhyne College, B
Mars Hill College, B
Methodist College, B
North Carolina Agricultural and Technical State
    University, M
North Carolina State University, BMD
Pfeiffer University, B
Sandhills Community College, A
The University of North Carolina at Chapel Hill, M
The University of North Carolina at Pembroke, BM
Western Carolina University, BM

North Dakota

Dickinson State University, B
Minot State University, BM
North Dakota State University, BM
University of North Dakota, B
Valley City State University, B

Ohio

Antioch College, B
Ashland University, B
Baldwin-Wallace College, B
Bowling Green State University, BM
Capital University, B
Cedarville University, B
Central State University, B
Defiance College, B
Heidelberg College, B
Kent State University, B
Malone College, B
Miami University, B
Miami University Hamilton, B
Mount Vernon Nazarene University, B
Muskingum College, B
Ohio Dominican University, B
Ohio Northern University, B
Ohio University, BM
Ohio University-Eastern, B
Otterbein College, B
Shawnee State University, B
The University of Akron, B
University of Cincinnati, A
University of Dayton, B
The University of Findlay, B
University of Rio Grande, B
The University of Toledo, BM
Urbana University, B
Ursuline College, B
Walsh University, B
Wilmington College, B
Wright State University, BM
Xavier University, B
Youngstown State University, B

Oklahoma

East Central University, B
Eastern Oklahoma State College, A
Northwestern Oklahoma State University, B
Oklahoma Baptist University, B
Oklahoma Christian University, B
Oklahoma City University, B
Oklahoma Panhandle State University, B
Oklahoma Wesleyan University, B
Oral Roberts University, B
Southeastern Oklahoma State University, B
Southern Nazarene University, B
Southwestern Oklahoma State University, BM
University of Central Oklahoma, B
University of Oklahoma, B
University of Tulsa, M

Oregon

Chemeketa Community College, A
Concordia University, B

Oregon State University, MD
Portland State University, M
Warner Pacific College, B
Western Oregon University, M

Pennsylvania

Alvernia College, B
Arcadia University, MO
Bloomsburg University of Pennsylvania, M
California University of Pennsylvania, M
Cedar Crest College, B
Chatham College, M
Clarion University of Pennsylvania, BM
DeSales University, M
Duquesne University, B
East Stroudsburg University of Pennsylvania, M
Edinboro University of Pennsylvania, M
Elizabethtown College, B
Gannon University, MO
Gettysburg College, B
Grove City College, B
Gwynedd-Mercy College, B
Harrisburg Area Community College, A
Indiana University of Pennsylvania, B
Juniata College, B
Kutztown University of Pennsylvania, M
La Salle University, B
Lebanon Valley College, BM
Mansfield University of Pennsylvania, B
Marywood University, B
Mercyhurst College, B
Millersville University of Pennsylvania, B
Moravian College, B
The Pennsylvania State University University Park Campus, MD
Saint Francis University, B
Slippery Rock University of Pennsylvania, M
Temple University, BD
University of Pittsburgh, MD
University of Pittsburgh at Johnstown, B
Waynesburg College, B
West Chester University of Pennsylvania, BM
Widener University, BM
York College of Pennsylvania, B

Puerto Rico

Bayamón Central University, B
Inter American University of Puerto Rico, Metropolitan Campus, M
Inter American University of Puerto Rico, San Germán Campus, BM
Pontifical Catholic University of Puerto Rico, B
Universidad Metropolitana, B
University of Puerto Rico, Cayey University College, B
University of Puerto Rico, Río Piedras, M

Rhode Island

Brown University, M
Rhode Island College, BM

South Carolina

Bob Jones University, B
Charleston Southern University, BM
The Citadel, The Military College of South Carolina, BM
Clemson University, BM
College of Charleston, M
Converse College, M
South Carolina State University, M
Southern Wesleyan University, B
University of South Carolina, M

South Dakota

Black Hills State University, B
Dakota Wesleyan University, B
University of Sioux Falls, B
The University of South Dakota, B

Tennessee

Belmont University, M
Bethel College, M
Bryan College, B
Freed-Hardeman University, B
Lincoln Memorial University, B

Martin Methodist College, A
Middle Tennessee State University, M
Tennessee Temple University, B
Union University, B
The University of Tennessee, MO
The University of Tennessee at Chattanooga, B
The University of Tennessee at Martin, B
Vanderbilt University, M

Texas

Abilene Christian University, B
Angelina College, A
Baylor University, B
Dallas Baptist University, B
East Texas Baptist University, B
Hardin-Simmons University, BD
Houston Baptist University, B
Howard Payne University, B
Ranger College, A
Southwestern University, B
Tarleton State University, B
Texas A&M International University, B
Texas A&M University, MD
Texas Christian University, B
Texas State University-San Marcos, M
Texas Wesleyan University, B
Texas Woman's University, M
University of Houston, M
University of Mary Hardin-Baylor, B
The University of Texas at Austin, MD
The University of Texas at Dallas, M
The University of Texas Health Science Center at San Antonio, M
The University of Texas-Pan American, B
The University of Texas at Tyler, M

Utah

Brigham Young University, BM
Snow College, A
University of Utah, BM
Utah State University, B
Utah Valley State College, B
Weber State University, B

Vermont

Bennington College, M
Castleton State College, B
Lyndon State College, BM
Sterling College, B
University of Vermont, BM

Virginia

Averett University, M
Bluefield College, B
Christopher Newport University, M
Longwood University, B
University of Virginia, M

Washington

Central Washington University, B
Eastern Washington University, BM
Heritage University, B
Pacific Lutheran University, B
Seattle Pacific University, B
University of Washington, BM
Washington State University, B
Western Washington University, BM

West Virginia

Alderson-Broaddus College, B
Fairmont State University, B
Glenville State College, B
Ohio Valley University, B
University of Charleston, B
West Virginia State University, B
Wheeling Jesuit University, BM

Wisconsin

Alverno College, BM
Beloit College, B
Cardinal Stritch University, B
Carroll College, B
Carthage College, M
Concordia University Wisconsin, B
Lakeland College, B

Maranatha Baptist Bible College, B
Marian College of Fond du Lac, B
Marquette University, B
Northland College, B
University of Wisconsin-Eau Claire, BM
University of Wisconsin-La Crosse, B
University of Wisconsin-Madison, BM
University of Wisconsin-Platteville, B
University of Wisconsin-River Falls, BM
University of Wisconsin-Stevens Point, M
University of Wisconsin-Superior, B
University of Wisconsin-Whitewater, B
Viterbo University, B

Wyoming

Northwest College, A
University of Wyoming, M

Alberta

University of Alberta, B
University of Lethbridge, B

British Columbia

The University of British Columbia, BM
University of Victoria, M

Manitoba

University of Manitoba, B

New Brunswick

University of New Brunswick Fredericton, B

Newfoundland and Labrador

Memorial University of Newfoundland, B

Nova Scotia

Acadia University, M

Ontario

Brock University, B
Lakehead University, B
Queen's University at Kingston, B
University of Toronto, B
University of Windsor, B
York University, B

Prince Edward Island

University of Prince Edward Island, M

Quebec

Bishop's University, B
McGill University, B
Université Laval, B
Université du Québec àChicoutimi, B
Université du Québec àMontréal, B
Université du Québec àRimouski, B

Saskatchewan

University of Regina, B

SCIENCE TECHNOLOGIES/TECHNICIANS

Alabama

Athens State University, B

Arizona

Arizona State University at the Polytechnic Campus, B
Northern Arizona University, B

The University of Arizona, B

California

Victor Valley College, A

Maryland

Harford Community College, A

Massachusetts

Bridgewater State College, B

Michigan

Hope College, B
Madonna University, AB

New Jersey

Kean University, B

New York

Maria College, A

Ohio

Cincinnati State Technical and Community
 College, A

Oregon

Willamette University, B

Pennsylvania

Community College of Allegheny County, A
Delaware County Community College, A
Lehigh University, B

South Carolina

Charleston Southern University, B
Clemson University, B

Washington

Cascadia Community College, A

West Virginia

Eastern West Virginia Community and Technical
 College, A
Marshall Community and Technical College, A
Ohio Valley University, A

Wisconsin

University of Wisconsin-Stout, B

British Columbia

British Columbia Institute of Technology, A

SCIENCE, TECHNOLOGY AND SOCIETY

Alabama

Samford University, AB

Alaska

University of Alaska Anchorage, B

Arizona

Embry-Riddle Aeronautical University, B

Arkansas

Southeast Arkansas College, A

California

California Institute of Technology, B
Pitzer College, B
Scripps College, B

Stanford University, B

Connecticut

Wesleyan University, B

District of Columbia

Georgetown University, B

Georgia

Georgia Institute of Technology, B

Illinois

Northwestern University, B

Indiana

Butler University, B

Maine

Colby College, B

Massachusetts

Massachusetts Institute of Technology, B
Worcester Polytechnic Institute, B

Michigan

Michigan State University, B

Missouri

College of the Ozarks, B
Washington University in St. Louis, B

Nevada

University of Nevada, Reno, B

New Jersey

New Jersey Institute of Technology, B
Rutgers, The State University of New Jersey,
 Newark, B

New York

Cornell University, B
Rensselaer Polytechnic Institute, B
Vassar College, B

North Carolina

North Carolina State University, B

Ohio

Cleveland State University, B

Pennsylvania

Carnegie Mellon University, B
Slippery Rock University of Pennsylvania, B

Texas

Texas Southern University, B

Virginia

James Madison University, B

Washington

University of Puget Sound, B

Nova Scotia

Dalhousie University, B
University of King's College, B

Ontario

University of Windsor, B
York University, B

Quebec

Université du Québec àMontréal, B

SCULPTURE

Alabama

Birmingham-Southern College, B
University of Montevallo, B

California

Academy of Art University, ABM
California College of the Arts, BM

California Institute of the Arts, B
California State University, East Bay, B
California State University, Fullerton, B
California State University, Long Beach, B
De Anza College, A
Grossmont College, A
Laguna College of Art & Design, B
Mills College, M
Monterey Peninsula College, A
Otis College of Art and Design, BM
San Francisco Art Institute, BMO
Sonoma State University, B
University of California, Santa Cruz, B

Colorado

Colorado State University, BM
Rocky Mountain College of Art & Design, B
University of Colorado at Boulder, M

Connecticut

Lyme Academy College of Fine Arts, B
University of Hartford, B
Yale University, M

District of Columbia

American University, M
The Catholic University of America, B
Corcoran College of Art and Design, B
The George Washington University, M
Howard University, M

Florida

New World School of the Arts, AB
University of Miami, BM

Georgia

University of Georgia, B

Idaho

Northwest Nazarene University, B

Illinois

Bradley University, M
DePaul University, B
Illinois State University, M
School of the Art Institute of Chicago, BM
Southern Illinois University Carbondale, M
Trinity Christian College, B
University of Illinois at Urbana-Champaign, B

Indiana

Ball State University, B
Indiana State University, M
Indiana University Bloomington, BM
Indiana University-Purdue University Fort Wayne, B

Iowa

Drake University, B
The University of Iowa, B

Kansas

Bethany College, B
University of Kansas, B

Kentucky

Bellarmine University, B

Louisiana

Louisiana State University and Agricultural and
 Mechanical College, M

Maine

Maine College of Art, B

Maryland

Maryland Institute College of Art, BM

Massachusetts

Boston University, BM
Framingham State College, B
Massachusetts College of Art, BM
Montserrat College of Art, B
School of the Museum of Fine Arts, Boston, B
Simon's Rock College of Bard, B

University of Massachusetts Dartmouth, B

Michigan

Aquinas College, B
Grand Valley State University, B
University of Michigan, B
University of Michigan-Flint, B
Western Michigan University, B

Minnesota

College of Visual Arts, B
Minneapolis College of Art and Design, BM
Minnesota State University Mankato, B
Minnesota State University Moorhead, B
St. Cloud State University, B

Missouri

Kansas City Art Institute, B
Northwest Missouri State University, B
Washington University in St. Louis, BM

New Jersey

Mercer County Community College, A
Rutgers, The State University of New Jersey, New
  Brunswick/Piscataway, BM

New Mexico

College of Santa Fe, B
Institute of American Indian Arts, A

New York

Alfred University, M
Bard College, B
Brooklyn College of the City University of New
  York, M
Buffalo State College, State University of New
  York, B
City College of the City University of New York, M
Parsons The New School for Design, B
Pratt Institute, BM
Rochester Institute of Technology, B
Sarah Lawrence College, B
State University of New York College at
  Brockport, B
State University of New York at New Paltz, BM
Syracuse University, BM

Ohio

Antioch College, B
Art Academy of Cincinnati, B
The Cleveland Institute of Art, B
Kent State University, B
Ohio Northern University, B
The Ohio State University, B
Ohio University, BM
The University of Akron, B

Oregon

Pacific Northwest College of Art, B
Portland State University, BM
University of Oregon, B

Pennsylvania

Keystone College, A
Marywood University, M
Mercyhurst College, B
Seton Hill University, B
Temple University, BM
The University of the Arts, BM

Puerto Rico

Escuela de Artes Plasticas de Puerto Rico, B
Inter American University of Puerto Rico, San
  Germán Campus, BM
University of Puerto Rico, Río Piedras, B

Rhode Island

Rhode Island School of Design, BM

Tennessee

Memphis College of Art, BM
University of Memphis, M

The University of Tennessee, M

Texas

Stephen F. Austin State University, M
Texas A&M University-Commerce, B
Texas Christian University, B
University of Dallas, B
University of Houston, BM
University of North Texas, BM
The University of Texas at El Paso, B

Utah

Brigham Young University, B
Dixie State College of Utah, A
University of Utah, M

Vermont

Bennington College, B
Johnson State College, M
Marlboro College, B

Virginia

James Madison University, M
Longwood University, B
Virginia Commonwealth University, BM

Washington

University of Washington, B
Washington State University, M
Western Washington University, B

West Virginia

West Virginia University, M

Wisconsin

Milwaukee Institute of Art and Design, B
University of Wisconsin-Milwaukee, B

Alberta

University of Alberta, BM

British Columbia

University of Victoria, M

New Brunswick

Mount Allison University, B

Newfoundland and Labrador

Memorial University of Newfoundland, B

Nova Scotia

NSCAD University, B

Ontario

University of Windsor, B
York University, B

Quebec

Concordia University, B

Saskatchewan

University of Regina, B

SECONDARY EDUCATION AND TEACHING

Alabama

Alabama Agricultural and Mechanical
  University, BMO
Alabama State University, BO
Athens State University, B
Auburn University, BMDO
Auburn University Montgomery, BMO
Birmingham-Southern College, B
Calhoun Community College, A
Faulkner University, B
Huntingdon College, B
Jacksonville State University, BM
Miles College, B
Northwest-Shoals Community College, A
Spring Hill College, BM
Troy University, BMO

The University of Alabama, BMDO
The University of Alabama at Birmingham, BM
University of Mobile, B
University of Montevallo, M
University of North Alabama, BM
University of South Alabama, BMO

Alaska

Sheldon Jackson College, B
University of Alaska Anchorage, B
University of Alaska Southeast, M

Arizona

Arizona State University, B
Arizona State University at the Polytechnic
  Campus, B
Arizona State University West, BMO
Eastern Arizona College, A
Grand Canyon University, BM
Northern Arizona University, M
Prescott College, B
Southwestern College, B
The University of Arizona, BMD
University of Phoenix Online Campus, M
University of Phoenix-Phoenix Campus, M
University of Phoenix-Southern Arizona Campus, M

Arkansas

Arkansas Baptist College, B
Arkansas Tech University, M
Harding University, BM
John Brown University, B
Ouachita Baptist University, B
University of Arkansas, MO
University of Arkansas at Little Rock, M
University of Arkansas at Pine Bluff, BM
University of the Ozarks, B

California

Biola University, B
California State University, Bakersfield, M
California State University, Fullerton, M
California State University, Long Beach, M
California State University, Los Angeles, M
California State University, Northridge, M
California State University, San Bernardino, M
California State University, Stanislaus, M
Chapman University, M
Fresno Pacific University, B
Humboldt State University, B
La Sierra University, B
Loyola Marymount University, M
The Master's College and Seminary, B
Mount St. Mary's College, BM
Notre Dame de Namur University, B
Occidental College, M
Pepperdine University, M
San Diego Christian College, B
San Diego State University, M
San Francisco State University, MO
San Jose State University, M
University of California, Irvine, M
University of Phoenix-San Diego Campus, M
University of Phoenix-Southern California
  Campus, M
University of Redlands, B
University of San Francisco, B
Vanguard University of Southern California, B
Westmont College, B
Whittier College, M

Colorado

Adams State College, B
The Colorado College, M
Colorado State University-Pueblo, B
Fort Lewis College, B
Mesa State College, B
Regis University, M
University of Phoenix-Denver Campus, M
University of Phoenix-Southern Colorado
  Campus, M

Western State College of Colorado, B

Connecticut

Albertus Magnus College, B
Central Connecticut State University, M
Connecticut College, BM
Eastern Connecticut State University, BM
Fairfield University, B
Quinnipiac University, M
Sacred Heart University, BM
Saint Joseph College, B
Southern Connecticut State University, B
University of Bridgeport, MO
University of Connecticut, MD
University of Hartford, B
Western Connecticut State University, B

Delaware

Delaware State University, B
University of Delaware, B

District of Columbia

American University, BMO
The Catholic University of America, B
Gallaudet University, BMO
The George Washington University, M
Howard University, MO
Trinity (Washington) University, BM

Florida

Chipola College, B
Edward Waters College, B
Flagler College, B
Florida Agricultural and Mechanical University, M
Florida Gulf Coast University, M
Florida Memorial College, B
Florida Southern College, B
Florida State University, B
Gulf Coast Community College, A
Hobe Sound Bible College, B
Jacksonville University, B
Lynn University, B
Palm Beach Atlantic University, B
Rollins College, M
St. Thomas University, B
Stetson University, B
Trinity Baptist College, B
University of North Florida, BM
University of South Florida, D
The University of Tampa, B
University of West Florida, M
Warner Southern College, B

Georgia

Armstrong Atlantic State University, M
Augusta State University, MO
Berry College, M
Brewton-Parker College, B
Clark Atlanta University, B
Columbus State University, BMO
Dalton State College, A
Emory University, M
Gainesville College, A
Georgia College & State University, MO
Georgia Highlands College, A
Georgia Southwestern State University, M
LaGrange College, M
Mercer University, M
Morehouse College, B
North Georgia College & State University, BM
Piedmont College, M
Thomas University, B
University of Georgia, MDO
University of West Georgia, BMO
Valdosta State University, BMO

Guam

University of Guam, BM

Hawaii

Brigham Young University-Hawaii, B
University of Hawaii at Hilo, B
University of Hawaii at Manoa, B

University of Phoenix-Hawaii Campus, O

Idaho

Boise State University, B
Idaho State University, B
Northwest Nazarene University, B
University of Idaho, BM

Illinois

Augustana College, B
Benedictine University, BM
Blackburn College, B
Chicago State University, BM
City Colleges of Chicago, Malcolm X College, A
Concordia University, B
DePaul University, BM
Elmhurst College, B
Eureka College, B
Greenville College, M
Illinois College, B
Illinois Wesleyan University, B
Judson College, B
Lake Forest College, B
Lewis University, B
Lincoln Christian College, B
MacMurray College, B
McKendree College, B
Monmouth College, B
National-Louis University, M
North Central College, B
North Park University, B
Northwestern University, BM
Olivet Nazarene University, BM
Parkland College, A
Rend Lake College, A
Rockford College, BM
Roosevelt University, BM
Saint Xavier University, M
Sauk Valley Community College, A
Southern Illinois University Edwardsville, M
Trinity Christian College, B
Trinity International University, B
University of Illinois at Chicago, B
University of Illinois at Urbana-Champaign, B
University of St. Francis, M
Western Illinois University, M
Wheaton College, M

Indiana

Ball State University, BM
Bethel College, B
Butler University, BM
Calumet College of Saint Joseph, B
Goshen College, B
Huntington University, B
Indiana University Bloomington, BMO
Indiana University East, B
Indiana University Kokomo, M
Indiana University Northwest, BM
Indiana University-Purdue University Fort
    Wayne, BM
Indiana University-Purdue University Indianapolis, B
Indiana University South Bend, BM
Indiana University Southeast, BM
Indiana Wesleyan University, B
Manchester College, B
Marian College, B
Martin University, B
Oakland City University, B
Purdue University Calumet, BM
Saint Joseph's College, B
Saint Mary-of-the-Woods College, B
Taylor University, B
Tri-State University, B
University of Indianapolis, BM
University of Saint Francis, B
University of Southern Indiana, M
Valparaiso University, B

Iowa

Ashford University, B
Briar Cliff University, B
Clarke College, B
Coe College, B
Cornell College, B
Dordt College, B

Drake University, BM
Graceland University, B
Iowa State University of Science and Technology, B
Iowa Wesleyan College, B
Loras College, B
Maharishi University of Management, BM
Morningside College, B
Mount Mercy College, B
Northwestern College, B
St. Ambrose University, B
Simpson College, B
University of Dubuque, B
The University of Iowa, BMD
Vennard College, AB
Wartburg College, B
William Penn University, B

Kansas

Allen County Community College, A
Baker University, B
Barton County Community College, A
Benedictine College, B
Central Christian College of Kansas, A
Emporia State University, B
Fort Hays State University, M
Friends University, BM
Kansas State University, BMD
McPherson College, B
MidAmerica Nazarene University, B
Newman University, B
Pittsburg State University, M
Tabor College, B
University of Kansas, B
Washburn University, B
Wichita State University, B

Kentucky

Alice Lloyd College, B
Bellarmine University, BM
Berea College, B
Brescia University, B
Campbellsville University, B
Centre College, B
Eastern Kentucky University, BM
Kentucky State University, B
Kentucky Wesleyan College, B
Lindsey Wilson College, B
Midway College, B
Morehead State University, M
Murray State University, BMO
Northern Kentucky University, M
Spalding University, M
Union College, BM
University of the Cumberlands, MO
University of Louisville, M
Western Kentucky University, MO

Louisiana

Centenary College of Louisiana, BM
Dillard University, B
Grambling State University, B
Louisiana College, B
Louisiana State University and Agricultural and
    Mechanical College, BM
Louisiana Tech University, M
Loyola University New Orleans, M
McNeese State University, BM
Nicholls State University, B
Northwestern State University of Louisiana, BMO
Our Lady of Holy Cross College, B
Southeastern Louisiana University, M
Southern University and Agricultural and Mechanical
    College, BM
Southern University at New Orleans, B
University of Louisiana at Lafayette, B
University of Louisiana at Monroe, M
Xavier University of Louisiana, BM

Maine

College of the Atlantic, B
University of Maine, BMO
University of Maine at Farmington, B

University of Maine at Presque Isle, B

Maryland

Bowie State University, BM
Coppin State University, B
Frostburg State University, BM
Howard Community College, A
The Johns Hopkins University, M
McDaniel College, M
Morgan State University, BM
Mount St. Mary's University, B
Salisbury University, BM
Towson University, M
University of Maryland, Baltimore County, M
University of Maryland, College Park, BMDO

Massachusetts

American International College, BMO
Assumption College, B
Atlantic Union College, B
Boston College, BM
Bridgewater State College, M
Clark University, B
Eastern Nazarene College, BMO
Elms College, BM
Emmanuel College, BM
Fitchburg State College, BM
Framingham State College, B
Lesley University, B
Massachusetts College of Liberal Arts, B
Merrimack College, B
Nichols College, B
Northeastern University, M
Salem State College, M
Simmons College, BMO
Smith College, M
Springfield College, BM
Suffolk University, BM
Tufts University, BM
University of Massachusetts Amherst, MDO
University of Massachusetts Boston, M
Western New England College, B
Westfield State College, BM
Worcester State College, M

Michigan

Adrian College, B
Albion College, B
Alma College, B
Alpena Community College, A
Andrews University, BM
Aquinas College, B
Calvin College, B
Central Michigan University, M
Concordia University, B
Cornerstone University, B
Eastern Michigan University, M
Ferris State University, B
Grace Bible College, B
Grand Valley State University, B
Hillsdale College, B
Hope College, B
Kellogg Community College, A
Kuyper College, B
Lake Superior State University, B
Madonna University, B
Marygrove College, M
Michigan Technological University, B
Mid Michigan Community College, A
Northern Michigan University, BM
Oakland University, M
Olivet College, B
Rochester College, B
Saginaw Valley State University, M
Siena Heights University, BM
Spring Arbor University, B
University of Detroit Mercy, B
University of Michigan, BO
University of Michigan-Dearborn, B
Wayne State University, MO
Western Michigan University, B

Minnesota

Augsburg College, B
Bemidji State University, B
Bethel University, M

College of Saint Benedict, B
College of St. Catherine, B
Concordia College, B
Concordia University, St. Paul, B
Gustavus Adolphus College, B
Hamline University, B
Minnesota State University Mankato, B
Minnesota State University Moorhead, B
North Central University, B
Pillsbury Baptist Bible College, B
St. Cloud State University, B
Saint John's University, B
Southwest Minnesota State University, B
University of Minnesota, Morris, B
Winona State University, B

Mississippi

Alcorn State University, BM
Belhaven College, M
Delta State University, B
Jackson State University, BMO
Mississippi College, BM
Mississippi State University, BMDO
Mississippi University for Women, B
Tougaloo College, B
University of Mississippi, BM
University of Southern Mississippi, MDO

Missouri

Calvary Bible College and Theological Seminary, B
Central Methodist University, B
Central Missouri State University, BM
College of the Ozarks, B
Drury University, BM
Evangel University, BM
Fontbonne University, B
Hannibal-LaGrange College, B
Harris-Stowe State University, B
Lincoln University, M
Lindenwood University, B
Maryville University of Saint Louis, BM
Missouri Southern State University, B
Missouri State University, MO
Missouri Valley College, B
Northwest Missouri State University, BMO
Park University, M
Rockhurst University, B
Southeast Missouri State University, M
University of Missouri-Columbia, B
University of Missouri-Kansas City, B
University of Missouri-Rolla, B
University of Missouri-St. Louis, BM
Washington University in St. Louis, B
Westminster College, B
William Jewell College, B
William Woods University, B

Montana

Carroll College, B
Montana State University, B
Montana State University-Billings, BM
Montana State University-Northern, B
Rocky Mountain College, B
University of Great Falls, BM
The University of Montana-Missoula, B
The University of Montana-Western, B

Nebraska

Chadron State College, BM
College of Saint Mary, B
Concordia University, B
Dana College, B
Doane College, B
Grace University, B
Hastings College, B
Midland Lutheran College, B
Nebraska Christian College, B
Peru State College, B
Union College, B
University of Nebraska at Omaha, BM
Western Nebraska Community College, A

York College, B

Nevada

Great Basin College, B
Sierra Nevada College, O
Truckee Meadows Community College, A
University of Nevada, Las Vegas, BM
University of Nevada, Reno, MO

New Hampshire

Franklin Pierce College, B
Keene State College, B
New England College, B
Plymouth State University, M
Rivier College, BM
Saint Anselm College, B
Southern New Hampshire University, BM
University of New Hampshire, BM

New Jersey

Centenary College, B
The College of New Jersey, BM
Essex County College, A
Kean University, MO
Monmouth University, B
New Jersey City University, M
Rider University, B
Rowan University, BM
Seton Hall University, BM
William Paterson University of New Jersey, B

New Mexico

College of Santa Fe, B
College of the Southwest, B
New Mexico Highlands University, B
New Mexico State University, B
University of New Mexico, B
Western New Mexico University, BM

New York

Adelphi University, M
Alfred University, B
Brooklyn College of the City University of New York, M
Buffalo State College, State University of New York, B
Canisius College, BM
City College of the City University of New York, BMO
Colgate University, M
The College of Saint Rose, MO
College of Staten Island of the City University of New York, M
Concordia College, B
Dominican College, B
Dowling College, BM
D'Youville College, BMO
Elmira College, B
Fordham University, BM
Hofstra University, BM
Houghton College, B
Hunter College of the City University of New York, BM
Iona College, BM
Ithaca College, B
Keuka College, B
Le Moyne College, B
Long Island University, Brooklyn Campus, B
Long Island University, C.W. Post Campus, BM
Manhattanville College, BM
Marist College, B
Mohawk Valley Community College, A
Molloy College, B
Mount Saint Mary College, BM
Nazareth College of Rochester, BM
New York University, B
Niagara University, BM
Nyack College, B
Queens College of the City University of New York, MO
Roberts Wesleyan College, B
Rochester Institute of Technology, M
St. Bonaventure University, B
St. John's University, BMO
St. Joseph's College, Suffolk Campus, B

St. Thomas Aquinas College, B
Siena College, B
State University of New York at Binghamton, M
State University of New York College at
 Brockport, B
State University of New York College at
 Cortland, BM
State University of New York College at
 Geneseo, M
State University of New York College at Old
 Westbury, B
State University of New York College at
 Oneonta, BM
State University of New York College at Potsdam, M
State University of New York, Fredonia, BM
State University of New York at New Paltz, BM
State University of New York at Oswego, BM
State University of New York at Plattsburgh, BM
Utica College, B
Wagner College, BM
Wells College, B

North Carolina

Appalachian State University, M
Belmont Abbey College, B
Brevard College, B
Campbell University, BM
Catawba College, B
Elizabeth City State University, B
Elon University, B
Fayetteville State University, M
Gardner-Webb University, B
Greensboro College, B
Guilford College, B
High Point University, B
Johnson C. Smith University, B
Lenoir-Rhyne College, B
Mars Hill College, B
Methodist College, B
North Carolina State University, B
North Carolina Wesleyan College, B
Piedmont Baptist College, B
Queens University of Charlotte, B
The University of North Carolina at Chapel Hill, M
The University of North Carolina at Charlotte, M
The University of North Carolina Wilmington, M
Wake Forest University, M
Warren Wilson College, B
Western Carolina University, M

North Dakota

Dickinson State University, B
Jamestown College, B
University of Mary, M
University of North Dakota, D
Valley City State University, B

Ohio

Antioch College, B
Ashland University, B
Capital University, B
Cedarville University, B
College of Mount St. Joseph, M
Defiance College, B
Heidelberg College, B
Hiram College, B
John Carroll University, BM
Kent State University, M
Marietta College, B
Miami University, BM
Mount Vernon Nazarene University, B
Muskingum College, B
Ohio Dominican University, B
Ohio Northern University, B
Ohio University, BM
Ohio Wesleyan University, B
Otterbein College, B
Shawnee State University, B
The University of Akron, BMD
University of Cincinnati, BMD
University of Dayton, BM
The University of Findlay, B
University of Rio Grande, B
The University of Toledo, BMDO
Urbana University, B
Walsh University, B

Wilmington College, B
Wright State University, BM
Xavier University, M
Youngstown State University, BM

Oklahoma

East Central University, B
Langston University, B
Mid-America Christian University, B
Northeastern State University, B
Northwestern Oklahoma State University, BM
Oklahoma Baptist University, B
Oklahoma Christian University, B
Oklahoma City University, B
Oklahoma Panhandle State University, B
Oklahoma State University, B
Oklahoma Wesleyan University, B
Rogers State University, A
Southeastern Oklahoma State University, BM
Southern Nazarene University, B
Southwestern Oklahoma State University, B
University of Central Oklahoma, BM

Oregon

Concordia University, BM
Corban College, B
Eastern Oregon University, M
Lewis & Clark College, M
Pacific University, BM
Portland State University, M
Southern Oregon University, M
University of Portland, BM
Warner Pacific College, B
Western Oregon University, BM

Pennsylvania

Albright College, B
Arcadia University, BMO
Baptist Bible College of Pennsylvania, B
Bucknell University, B
Cedar Crest College, B
Chatham College, M
Cheyney University of Pennsylvania, B
Delaware Valley College, B
Duquesne University, BM
East Stroudsburg University of Pennsylvania, BM
Eastern University, B
Edinboro University of Pennsylvania, M
Elizabethtown College, B
Gannon University, B
Geneva College, B
Gettysburg College, B
Grove City College, B
Gwynedd-Mercy College, B
Holy Family University, BM
Immaculata University, O
Indiana University of Pennsylvania, B
Juniata College, B
King's College, B
Kutztown University of Pennsylvania, BMO
La Salle University, B
Lebanon Valley College, B
Lehigh University, MO
Lincoln University, B
Lock Haven University of Pennsylvania, B
Lycoming College, B
Mansfield University of Pennsylvania, BM
Marywood University, B
Mercyhurst College, B
Montgomery County Community College, A
Moravian College, B
The Pennsylvania State University Abington
 College, B
The Pennsylvania State University Altoona
 College, B
The Pennsylvania State University Beaver Campus
 of the Commonwealth College, B
The Pennsylvania State University Berks Campus of
 the Berks-Lehigh Valley College, B
The Pennsylvania State University Delaware County
 Campus of the Commonwealth College, B
The Pennsylvania State University DuBois Campus
 of the Commonwealth College, B
The Pennsylvania State University at Erie, The
 Behrend College, B

The Pennsylvania State University Fayette Campus
 of the Commonwealth College, B
The Pennsylvania State University Hazleton
 Campus of the Commonwealth College, B
The Pennsylvania State University, Lehigh Valley
 Campus of the Berks-Lehigh Valley College, B
The Pennsylvania State University McKeesport
 Campus of the Commonwealth College, B
The Pennsylvania State University Mont Alto
 Campus of the Commonwealth College, B
The Pennsylvania State University New Kensington
 Campus of the Commonwealth College, B
The Pennsylvania State University Schuylkill
 Campus of the Capital College, B
The Pennsylvania State University Shenango
 Campus of the Commonwealth College, B
The Pennsylvania State University University Park
 Campus, B
The Pennsylvania State University Wilkes-Barre
 Campus of the Commonwealth College, B
The Pennsylvania State University Worthington
 Scranton Campus of the Commonwealth
 College, B
The Pennsylvania State University York Campus of
 the Commonwealth College, B
Point Park University, B
Saint Francis University, B
Saint Joseph's University, BM
Slippery Rock University of Pennsylvania, M
Susquehanna University, B
Temple University, M
Thiel College, B
University of Pennsylvania, M
University of Pittsburgh, MD
University of Pittsburgh at Johnstown, B
The University of Scranton, BM
Villanova University, BM
Waynesburg College, B
West Chester University of Pennsylvania, M
Wilkes University, M
York College of Pennsylvania, B

Puerto Rico

Caribbean University, B
Inter American University of Puerto Rico, Arecibo
 Campus, B
Inter American University of Puerto Rico,
 Barranquitas Campus, B
Inter American University of Puerto Rico, Ponce
 Campus, B
Inter American University of Puerto Rico, San
 Germán Campus, B
Pontifical Catholic University of Puerto Rico, B
Universidad Adventista de las Antillas, B
Universidad Metropolitana, B
University of Puerto Rico, Cayey University
 College, B
University of Puerto Rico, Río Piedras, BM
University of the Sacred Heart, B

Rhode Island

Brown University, M
Providence College, B
Rhode Island College, BM
Roger Williams University, B
Salve Regina University, B
University of Rhode Island, BM

South Carolina

Anderson University, B
Charleston Southern University, BM
The Citadel, The Military College of South
 Carolina, M
Clemson University, BM
Coastal Carolina University, BM
Converse College, BM
Francis Marion University, M
Furman University, B
Lander University, B
Newberry College, B
South Carolina State University, M
University of South Carolina, MD
University of South Carolina Aiken, B
University of South Carolina Upstate, B

Winthrop University, M

South Dakota

Augustana College, BM
Black Hills State University, B
Dakota Wesleyan University, B
Mount Marty College, B
Northern State University, BM
South Dakota State University, B
University of Sioux Falls, B
The University of South Dakota, BM

Tennessee

Austin Peay State University, O
Belmont University, M
Bryan College, B
Carson-Newman College, BM
Crichton College, B
Cumberland University, B
East Tennessee State University, M
Free Will Baptist Bible College, B
Freed-Hardeman University, B
King College, B
Lambuth University, B
Lee University, BM
LeMoyne-Owen College, B
Lincoln Memorial University, B
Lipscomb University, B
Tennessee State University, M
Tennessee Technological University, BMO
Tennessee Wesleyan College, B
Trevecca Nazarene University, BM
Tusculum College, B
Union University, B
University of Memphis, M
The University of Tennessee, M
The University of Tennessee at Chattanooga, BM
The University of Tennessee at Martin, M
Vanderbilt University, BM

Texas

Abilene Christian University, BM
Austin College, M
Baylor University, B
Brazosport College, A
Clarendon College, A
Concordia University at Austin, B
Dallas Baptist University, B
Houston Baptist University, B
Howard Payne University, B
Huston-Tillotson University, B
Jarvis Christian College, B
Lamar University, B
LeTourneau University, B
Lubbock Christian University, B
McMurry University, B
Midwestern State University, B
Northeast Texas Community College, A
Paul Quinn College, B
Sam Houston State University, M
Southwestern Assemblies of God University, B
Stephen F. Austin State University, MD
Sul Ross State University, M
Tarleton State University, BMO
Texas A&M University-Commerce, BMD
Texas A&M University-Corpus Christi, M
Texas A&M University-Kingsville, BM
Texas A&M University-Texarkana, M
Texas Christian University, BMO
Texas Southern University, BM
Texas State University-San Marcos, M
Texas Tech University, M
University of Dallas, B
University of Houston, M
University of the Incarnate Word, B
University of North Texas, M
University of St. Thomas, B
The University of Texas-Pan American, M
The University of Texas at Tyler, M

Utah

Dixie State College of Utah, A
Southern Utah University, B
University of Phoenix-Utah Campus, M
University of Utah, B
Utah State University, BM

Weber State University, B

Vermont

Bennington College, BM
Champlain College, B
College of St. Joseph, BM
Green Mountain College, B
Johnson State College, B
Saint Michael's College, B
University of Vermont, B

Virginia

Bluefield College, B
The College of William and Mary, M
Eastern Mennonite University, B
George Mason University, M
Hampton University, B
James Madison University, M
Liberty University, M
Longwood University, BM
Lynchburg College, B
Marymount University, M
Norfolk State University, M
Old Dominion University, M
Shenandoah University, O
University of Mary Washington, B
University of Richmond, B
Virginia Commonwealth University, MO
Virginia Intermont College, B
Virginia Polytechnic Institute and State University, B
Virginia Wesleyan College, B

Washington

Gonzaga University, B
Heritage University, B
Northwest University, B
Pacific Lutheran University, BM
Saint Martin's University, B
Seattle Pacific University, M
University of Puget Sound, M
University of Washington, B
Washington State University, BM
Western Washington University, BM
Whitworth College, BM

West Virginia

Alderson-Broaddus College, B
Concord University, B
Davis & Elkins College, B
Fairmont State University, B
Glenville State College, B
Marshall University, BM
Mountain State University, A
Ohio Valley University, B
Salem International University, BM
Shepherd University, B
West Liberty State College, B
West Virginia State University, B
West Virginia University, BM
West Virginia Wesleyan College, B
Wheeling Jesuit University, B

Wisconsin

Beloit College, B
Cardinal Stritch University, B
Carroll College, B
Carthage College, B
Concordia University Wisconsin, B
Lakeland College, B
Lawrence University, B
Maranatha Baptist Bible College, B
Marian College of Fond du Lac, B
Marquette University, B
Mount Mary College, B
Northland College, B
Ripon College, B
University of Wisconsin-Eau Claire, M
University of Wisconsin-La Crosse, M
University of Wisconsin-Madison, B
University of Wisconsin-Milwaukee, BM
University of Wisconsin-Oshkosh, B
University of Wisconsin-Platteville, BM
University of Wisconsin-River Falls, B
University of Wisconsin-Stevens Point, B

University of Wisconsin-Whitewater, BM

Wyoming

Central Wyoming College, A
Eastern Wyoming College, A
University of Wyoming, B
Western Wyoming Community College, A

Alberta

University of Alberta, BMD
University of Calgary, B

British Columbia

Trinity Western University, B
The University of British Columbia, B
University of Northern British Columbia, B
University of Victoria, B

Manitoba

University of Manitoba, B
The University of Winnipeg, B

New Brunswick

Université de Moncton, B
University of New Brunswick Fredericton, B

Newfoundland and Labrador

Memorial University of Newfoundland, B

Nova Scotia

Acadia University, B
Mount Saint Vincent University, B
St. Francis Xavier University, B
Université Sainte-Anne, B

Ontario

Brock University, B
Lakehead University, B
Trent University, B
University of Ottawa, B
The University of Western Ontario, B
University of Windsor, B
York University, B

Prince Edward Island

University of Prince Edward Island, B

Quebec

Bishop's University, B
McGill University, B
Université Laval, B
Université de Montréal, B
Université du Québec en Abitibi-Témiscamingue, B
Université du Québec àChicoutimi, B
Université du Québec àMontréal, B
Université du Québec en Outaouais, B
Université du Québec àRimouski, B
Université du Québec àTrois-Rivières, B
Université de Sherbrooke, B

Saskatchewan

University of Regina, B
University of Saskatchewan, B

SECONDARY SCHOOL ADMINISTRATION/PRINCIPALSHIP

Alabama

Auburn University, B

New York

Le Moyne College, B

South Carolina

Charleston Southern University, B

SECURITIES SERVICES ADMINISTRATION/MANAGEMENT

Alabama

Troy University, M
Virginia College at Birmingham, M

Colorado

Colorado Technical University Denver Campus, M

Connecticut

University of New Haven, M

District of Columbia

The George Washington University, MO

Florida

Lynn University, M

Georgia

Herzing College, AB

Kansas

Southwestern College, B

Kentucky

Eastern Kentucky University, M

Michigan

University of Detroit Mercy, M

Missouri

Central Missouri State University, M
Webster University, M

Nebraska

Bellevue University, M

New York

John Jay College of Criminal Justice of the City
    University of New York, M
Long Island University, C.W. Post Campus, M
Schenectady County Community College, A
State University of New York College at
    Brockport, B

Pennsylvania

Carnegie Mellon University, M
Mercyhurst College, MO
University of Pittsburgh, MD

West Virginia

American Public University System, M

SECURITY AND LOSS PREVENTION SERVICES

Alabama

Community College of the Air Force, A

California

San Joaquin Valley College, A

District of Columbia

Potomac College, A

Florida

St. Petersburg College, A

Kentucky

Eastern Kentucky University, B

Maryland

Harford Community College, A

Michigan

Delta College, A

New Hampshire

Hesser College, A

New York

Farmingdale State University of New York, B
John Jay College of Criminal Justice of the City
    University of New York, AB

Nassau Community College, A

Ohio

Cincinnati State Technical and Community
    College, A

SECURITY AND PROTECTIVE SERVICES

Arizona

Pima Community College, A

Connecticut

Goodwin College, A

Florida

St. Petersburg College, AB

Illinois

Black Hawk College, A
Lewis University, B

Indiana

Taylor University Fort Wayne, B

Iowa

St. Ambrose University, B

Kansas

Washburn University, B

Michigan

Eastern Michigan University, B

North Dakota

North Dakota State University, B

Ohio

Franklin University, B
Ohio University, A

Pennsylvania

Point Park University, B

Washington

Clover Park Technical College, A

SELLING SKILLS AND SALES OPERATIONS

California

Orange Coast College, A
Santa Barbara City College, A

Colorado

Jones International University, B

Illinois

College of DuPage, A
College of Lake County, A
Lincoln Land Community College, A
McHenry County College, A
Moraine Valley Community College, A

Iowa

Iowa Lakes Community College, A
Iowa Western Community College, A

Minnesota

Alexandria Technical College, A
Century College, A
Hibbing Community College, A

Lake Superior College, A

Ohio

Cuyahoga Community College, A
The University of Akron, A

Washington

Clark College, A

SEMITIC LANGUAGES, LITERATURES, AND LINGUISTICS

New York

Cornell University, B

Pennsylvania

University of Pennsylvania, B

Texas

The University of Texas at Austin, B

SHEET METAL TECHNOLOGY/SHEETWORKING

California

Santiago Canyon College, A

Illinois

Black Hawk College, A

Indiana

Ivy Tech Community College-Central Indiana, A
Ivy Tech Community College-Lafayette, A
Ivy Tech Community College-North Central, A
Ivy Tech Community College-Northeast, A
Ivy Tech Community College-Northwest, A
Ivy Tech Community College-Southern Indiana, A
Ivy Tech Community College-Southwest, A
Ivy Tech Community College-Wabash Valley, A

Michigan

Kellogg Community College, A
Macomb Community College, A

Montana

Montana State University-Billings, A

Nevada

Western Nevada Community College, A

Ohio

Northwest State Community College, A

Pennsylvania

Community College of Allegheny County, A

Texas

Brazosport College, A

British Columbia

British Columbia Institute of Technology, A

SIGN LANGUAGE INTERPRETATION AND TRANSLATION

Arizona

Pima Community College, A

Arkansas

University of Arkansas at Little Rock, AB

California

American River College, A
College of the Sequoias, A
Golden West College, A

Los Angeles Pierce College, A
Los Angeles Southwest College, A
Mt. San Antonio College, A
Ohlone College, A
Palomar College, A
Pasadena City College, A
Riverside Community College District, A

Colorado

Pikes Peak Community College, A

Connecticut

Northwestern Connecticut Community College, A

Delaware

Delaware Technical & Community College,
  Stanton/Wilmington Campus, A

District of Columbia

Gallaudet University, B

Florida

Florida Community College at Jacksonville, A
Hillsborough Community College, A
Miami Dade College, A
St. Petersburg College, A

Georgia

Georgia Perimeter College, A

Guam

Guam Community College, A

Idaho

Idaho State University, B

Illinois

Black Hawk College, A
Columbia College Chicago, B
John A. Logan College, A
MacMurray College, B
Southwestern Illinois College, A
Waubonsee Community College, A
William Rainey Harper College, A

Indiana

Bethel College, AB
Goshen College, B
Indiana University-Purdue University Indianapolis, B
Vincennes University, A

Iowa

Iowa Western Community College, A
Scott Community College, A

Kansas

Cowley County Community College and Area
  Vocational-Technical School, A
Johnson County Community College, A

Kentucky

Eastern Kentucky University, B
University of Louisville, AB

Louisiana

Delgado Community College, A

Massachusetts

Mount Wachusett Community College, A
Northeastern University, B
Northern Essex Community College, A

Michigan

Lansing Community College, A
Mott Community College, A

Minnesota

College of St. Catherine, A
North Central University, AB

Saint Paul College-A Community & Technical
  College, A

Missouri

Ozark Christian College, B
St. Louis Community College at Florissant Valley, A
William Woods University, B

Nebraska

Nebraska Christian College, A

Nevada

Community College of Southern Nevada, A

New Hampshire

University of New Hampshire at Manchester, B

New Jersey

Burlington County College, A
Union County College, A

New Mexico

Clovis Community College, A
Santa Fe Community College, A
University of New Mexico, B

New York

Rochester Institute of Technology, AB
Suffolk County Community College, A

North Carolina

Blue Ridge Community College, A
Central Piedmont Community College, A
Wilson Technical Community College, A

North Dakota

Lake Region State College, A

Ohio

Cincinnati Christian University, A
Cincinnati State Technical and Community
  College, A
Columbus State Community College, A
Sinclair Community College, A
Terra State Community College, A

Oklahoma

Oklahoma State University, Oklahoma City, A
Tulsa Community College, A

Oregon

Portland Community College, A
Western Oregon University, B

Pennsylvania

Bloomsburg University of Pennsylvania, B
Community College of Allegheny County, A
Community College of Philadelphia, A
Mount Aloysius College, AB

South Carolina

Converse College, B
Spartanburg Technical College, A

South Dakota

Southeast Technical Institute, A

Tennessee

Chattanooga State Technical Community College, A
Maryville College, B
Nashville State Technical Community College, A
Tennessee Temple University, A

Texas

Austin Community College, A
Collin County Community College District, A
Del Mar College, A
Eastfield College, A
El Paso Community College, A
Houston Community College System, A
McLennan Community College, A
Tarrant County College District, A

Tyler Junior College, A

Utah

Salt Lake Community College, A

Virginia

New River Community College, A

Washington

Seattle Central Community College, A
South Puget Sound Community College, A
Spokane Falls Community College, A

West Virginia

Fairmont State University, A

Wisconsin

Northcentral Technical College, A

Wyoming

Sheridan College-Sheridan and Gillette, A

Ontario

York University, B

SLAVIC, BALTIC, AND ALBANIAN LANGUAGES, LITERATURES, AND LINGUISTICS

New Jersey

Rutgers, The State University of New Jersey,
  Newark, B

North Carolina

The University of North Carolina at Chapel Hill, B

SLAVIC LANGUAGES, LITERATURES, AND LINGUISTICS

California

Stanford University, BMD
University of California, Berkeley, BMD
University of California, Los Angeles, BMD
University of California, Santa Barbara, B
University of Southern California, BMD

Connecticut

Yale University, D

Florida

Florida State University, M

Georgia

University of Georgia, B

Illinois

Northwestern University, BD
University of Chicago, BMD
University of Illinois at Chicago, BMD
University of Illinois at Urbana-Champaign, MD

Indiana

Indiana University Bloomington, BMD

Kansas

University of Kansas, BMD

Massachusetts

Boston College, BMO
Harvard University, BMD

Michigan

University of Michigan, MD
Wayne State University, B

New Jersey

Princeton University, BD

New York

Columbia College, B
Columbia University, School of General Studies, B

Cornell University, BMD
New York University, M
Stony Brook University, State University of New York, M
University at Albany, State University of New York, B

North Carolina

Duke University, BM
The University of North Carolina at Chapel Hill, MD

Ohio

The Ohio State University, MD

Pennsylvania

University of Pittsburgh, BMD

Rhode Island

Brown University, MD

Texas

The University of Texas at Austin, MD

Virginia

University of Virginia, BMD

Washington

University of Washington, BMD

Wisconsin

University of Wisconsin-Madison, BMD
University of Wisconsin-Milwaukee, BM

Alberta

University of Alberta, BMD

British Columbia

The University of British Columbia, B
University of Victoria, B

Manitoba

University of Manitoba, BM

Ontario

University of Ottawa, A
University of Toronto, BMD
University of Windsor, B

Saskatchewan

University of Saskatchewan, B

SLAVIC STUDIES

Connecticut

Connecticut College, B

Illinois

Northwestern University, B

Michigan

Oakland University, B

New York

Barnard College, B
Cornell University, B

Texas

Baylor University, B

Wisconsin

Lawrence University, B

Ontario

University of Ottawa, B
University of Waterloo, B

SMALL BUSINESS ADMINISTRATION/MANAGEMENT

Arizona

Northland Pioneer College, A

Idaho

Lewis-Clark State College, AB

Illinois

Black Hawk College, A
Kendall College, B
North Central College, B

Iowa

Iowa Lakes Community College, A

Kansas

Central Christian College of Kansas, AB

Maine

Husson College, B

Massachusetts

Babson College, B

Michigan

Northern Michigan University, B

Minnesota

Alexandria Technical College, A

North Carolina

Chowan University, B

North Dakota

Lake Region State College, A

Nova Scotia

Dalhousie University, B

SMALL ENGINE MECHANICS AND REPAIR TECHNOLOGY/TECHNICIAN

California

Los Medanos College, A
Southwestern College, A

Iowa

Iowa Lakes Community College, A

Kentucky

Louisville Technical Institute, A

Minnesota

Alexandria Technical College, A
Century College, A

Montana

The University of Montana-Missoula, A

North Dakota

North Dakota State College of Science, A

Washington

Bates Technical College, A

British Columbia

British Columbia Institute of Technology, A

SOCIAL AND PHILOSOPHICAL FOUNDATIONS OF EDUCATION

Illinois

Northwestern University, B

Missouri

Washington University in St. Louis, B

Texas

Texas Southern University, B

Vermont

Sterling College, B

SOCIAL PSYCHOLOGY

Arizona

Arizona State University, D
Prescott College, M

California

New College of California, M
University of California, Irvine, B
University of California, Santa Cruz, BD

Colorado

Colorado State University, M

Connecticut

University of Connecticut, MD

Delaware

University of Delaware, D

District of Columbia

American University, M
The George Washington University, D
Howard University, D

Florida

Florida Atlantic University, B
Florida State University, D
Manatee Community College, A

Georgia

Paine College, B

Illinois

Loyola University Chicago, MD
Northwestern University, D
University of Illinois at Urbana-Champaign, MD

Indiana

Ball State University, M
Indiana University Bloomington, D

Iowa

Iowa State University of Science and Technology, D

Kansas

Central Christian College of Kansas, A

Maine

University of Maine, M
University of New England, B

Maryland

University of Maryland, College Park, D

Massachusetts

Brandeis University, D
Clark University, D
Harvard University, MD
University of Massachusetts Lowell, M

Michigan

Macomb Community College, A
University of Michigan, D

Minnesota

University of Minnesota, Twin Cities Campus, D

Missouri

Maryville University of Saint Louis, B
Park University, AB

Washington University in St. Louis, MD

Nevada

University of Nevada, Reno, BD

New Jersey

Montclair State University, M
Rutgers, The State University of New Jersey, New Brunswick/Piscataway, D
Rutgers, The State University of New Jersey, Newark, D

New York

Cornell University, MD
Hunter College of the City University of New York, M
New York University, D
State University of New York at Buffalo, D
Stony Brook University, State University of New York, D
Syracuse University, D
University at Albany, State University of New York, D
University of Rochester, D

North Carolina

The University of North Carolina at Chapel Hill, D
The University of North Carolina at Greensboro, MD

Ohio

Bowling Green State University, MD
Miami University, D
The Ohio State University, D

Oregon

University of Oregon, MD

Pennsylvania

Carnegie Mellon University, D
Clarion University of Pennsylvania, B
Moravian College, B
The Pennsylvania State University Abington College, B
The Pennsylvania State University University Park Campus, MD
Temple University, D

Puerto Rico

Inter American University of Puerto Rico, Aguadilla Campus, B

Texas

Texas A&M University, MD
University of Houston, D

Utah

Brigham Young University, B

Wisconsin

Lawrence University, B
University of Wisconsin-Madison, D
University of Wisconsin-Superior, B

British Columbia

Kwantlen University College, AB
The University of British Columbia, MD
University of Northern British Columbia, B
University of Victoria, MD

Newfoundland and Labrador

Memorial University of Newfoundland, M

Ontario

Brock University, M
Queen's University at Kingston, MD
University of Guelph, MD

University of Windsor, MD

SOCIAL SCIENCE TEACHER EDUCATION

Alabama

Judson College, B
Samford University, B

Arizona

Northern Arizona University, B
Prescott College, B
The University of Arizona, B

Arkansas

Arkansas State University, B

California

California Lutheran University, B
California State University, Chico, B
Hope International University, B
Simpson University, B
Westmont College, B

Colorado

Western State College of Colorado, B

Connecticut

Sacred Heart University, B

Florida

Florida Atlantic University, B
Florida International University, B
Florida State University, B
Stetson University, B
University of Central Florida, B
University of South Florida, B
University of West Florida, B
Warner Southern College, B

Georgia

Columbus State University, B
Emmanuel College, B
Kennesaw State University, B
North Georgia College & State University, B
University of Georgia, B

Hawaii

Brigham Young University-Hawaii, B

Idaho

Lewis-Clark State College, B
Northwest Nazarene University, B

Illinois

Concordia University, B
Eastern Illinois University, B
McKendree College, B
Millikin University, B
University of Illinois at Chicago, B

Indiana

Oakland City University, B
Taylor University, B
University of Evansville, B
Valparaiso University, B

Iowa

Buena Vista University, B
Dordt College, B
St. Ambrose University, B
University of Northern Iowa, B
Upper Iowa University, B
Wartburg College, B

William Penn University, B

Kansas

Central Christian College of Kansas, A
Emporia State University, B

Kentucky

Campbellsville University, B
Lindsey Wilson College, B
Murray State University, B

Louisiana

Grambling State University, B

Maine

University of Maine at Farmington, B
University of Maine at Fort Kent, B
University of Maine at Machias, B

Michigan

Alma College, B
Central Michigan University, B
Cornerstone University, B
Eastern Michigan University, B
Michigan State University, B
Northern Michigan University, B
University of Detroit Mercy, B
Western Michigan University, B

Minnesota

Saint Mary's University of Minnesota, B
University of Minnesota, Twin Cities Campus, B

Mississippi

Blue Mountain College, B
Delta State University, B
Jackson State University, B
Mississippi College, B
Mississippi Valley State University, B
Northwest Mississippi Community College, A
Rust College, B

Missouri

Central Methodist University, B
Lindenwood University, B
Southwest Baptist University, B
Washington University in St. Louis, B

Montana

Carroll College, B
Montana State University-Billings, B
University of Great Falls, B
The University of Montana-Missoula, B
The University of Montana-Western, B

Nebraska

Chadron State College, B
Concordia University, B
Dana College, B
Grace University, B
Hastings College, B
Nebraska Wesleyan University, B
Union College, B
University of Nebraska-Lincoln, B
Wayne State College, B
York College, B

Nevada

Nevada State College at Henderson, B
University of Nevada, Reno, B

New Hampshire

Keene State College, B
Rivier College, B

New York

Dominican College, B
Elmira College, B
State University of New York College at Oneonta, B
University at Albany, State University of New York, B

Utica College, B

North Carolina

Elon University, B
Fayetteville State University, B
Louisburg College, A
The University of North Carolina at Greensboro, B

North Dakota

Mayville State University, B
Minot State University, B
North Dakota State University, B
University of Mary, B
Valley City State University, B

Ohio

The University of Akron, B
University of Rio Grande, B
Youngstown State University, B

Oklahoma

Oklahoma Baptist University, B
Southern Nazarene University, B
Southwestern Oklahoma State University, B

Oregon

Corban College, B

Pennsylvania

East Stroudsburg University of Pennsylvania, B
Mansfield University of Pennsylvania, B
Mercyhurst College, B
Point Park University, B
York College of Pennsylvania, B

Puerto Rico

University of Puerto Rico, Cayey University
College, B

Rhode Island

Rhode Island College, B

South Dakota

The University of South Dakota, B

Texas

Baylor University, B
Howard Payne University, B

Utah

Brigham Young University, B
University of Utah, B
Weber State University, B
Westminster College, B

Vermont

Johnson State College, B
Lyndon State College, B
University of Vermont, B

Virginia

Averett University, B
Eastern Mennonite University, B
Liberty University, B

Washington

Central Washington University, B
Seattle Pacific University, B

Wisconsin

Alverno College, B
Carroll College, B
Marquette University, B
University of Wisconsin-River Falls, B

University of Wisconsin-Superior, B

Ontario

York University, B

Quebec

McGill University, B

SOCIAL SCIENCES

Alabama

Alabama Southern Community College, A
Alabama State University, B
Enterprise-Ozark Community College, A
Faulkner University, AB
Lawson State Community College, A
Miles College, B
Oakwood College, B
Samford University, AB
Troy University, B
The University of Alabama at Birmingham, B
University of Mobile, B
University of Montevallo, B

Alaska

University of Alaska Southeast, B

Arizona

Arizona State University, MDO
Arizona State University West, B
Arizona Western College, A
Cochise College (Sierra Vista), A
Diné College, A
Grand Canyon University, B
Northern Arizona University, B

Arkansas

Harding University, B
John Brown University, B
Phillips Community College of the University of
  Arkansas, A
University of Arkansas at Pine Bluff, B
University of the Ozarks, B

California

Allan Hancock College, A
American River College, A
Azusa Pacific University, B
Barstow College, A
Bethany University, B
Biola University, B
Butte College, A
California Baptist University, B
California Institute of Technology, BMD
California Lutheran University, B
California Polytechnic State University, San Luis
  Obispo, B
California State Polytechnic University, Pomona, B
California State University, Chico, BM
California State University, Los Angeles, B
California State University, Sacramento, B
California State University, San Bernardino, BM
California State University, San Marcos, B
California State University, Stanislaus, B
Chabot College, A
Chaffey College, A
Citrus College, A
City College of San Francisco, A
College of Alameda, A
College of the Canyons, A
College of the Desert, A
College of San Mateo, A
College of the Sequoias, A
Compton Community College, A
Concordia University, B
Cosumnes River College (Sacramento), A
Cypress College, A
De Anza College, A
Feather River College, A
Folsom Lake College, A
Foothill College, A
Fresno City College, A
Fresno Pacific University, B
Gavilan College, A

Glendale Community College, A
Hope International University, B
Humboldt State University, BM
Imperial Valley College, A
Irvine Valley College, A
Lake Tahoe Community College, A
Laney College, A
Lassen Community College District, A
Long Beach City College, A
Los Angeles Mission College, A
Los Angeles Southwest College, A
Mendocino College, A
Merced College, A
Merritt College, A
MiraCosta College, A
Mission College, A
Modesto Junior College, A
Mount St. Mary's College, B
Mt. San Jacinto College, A
New College of California, B
Notre Dame de Namur University, B
Ohlone College, A
Orange Coast College, A
Pacific Union College, B
Pasadena City College, A
Point Loma Nazarene University, B
Porterville College, A
Reedley College, A
Sacramento City College, A
Saddleback College, A
Saint Mary's College of California, B
San Diego Christian College, B
San Diego City College, A
San Diego Mesa College, A
San Diego Miramar College, A
San Diego State University, B
San Francisco State University, BM
San Joaquin Delta College, A
San Jose State University, BM
Santa Ana College, A
Santa Rosa Junior College, A
Santiago Canyon College, A
Skyline College, A
Solano Community College, A
Taft College, A
University of California, Berkeley, B
University of California, Irvine, BMD
University of California, Riverside, B
University of California, Santa Cruz, D
University of La Verne, B
University of the Pacific, B
University of Southern California, B
Victor Valley College, A
West Hills Community College, A
West Valley College, A
Westmont College, B
Yuba College, A

Colorado

Adams State College, B
Colorado Christian University, B
The Colorado College, B
Colorado Mountain College, A
Colorado Mountain College, Alpine Campus, A
Colorado State University, B
Colorado State University-Pueblo, B
Lamar Community College, A
Mesa State College, AB
Northeastern Junior College, A
Otero Junior College, A
Regis University, M
University of Colorado at Denver and Health
  Sciences Center - Downtown Denver Campus, M
University of Denver, B
University of Northern Colorado, B
Western State College of Colorado, B

Connecticut

Albertus Magnus College, B
Central Connecticut State University, B
Holy Apostles College and Seminary, B
Housatonic Community College, A
Northwestern Connecticut Community College, A
Quinnipiac University, B
University of Bridgeport, B
Wesleyan University, B

Western Connecticut State University, B
Yale University, M

District of Columbia

Georgetown University, B

Florida

Daytona Beach Community College, A
Edison College, A
Edward Waters College, B
Florida Agricultural and Mechanical University, BM
Florida Atlantic University, B
Florida Southern College, B
Florida State University, BM
Indian River Community College, A
Lynn University, B
Manatee Community College, A
Miami Dade College, A
New College of Florida, B
Okaloosa-Walton College, A
Palm Beach Community College, A
Stetson University, B
University of Central Florida, B
University of Florida, M
University of South Florida, B
The University of Tampa, B
University of West Florida, B

Georgia

Abraham Baldwin Agricultural College, A
Andrew College, A
Berry College, B
Brewton-Parker College, B
Clark Atlanta University, B
Clayton State University, A
Fort Valley State University, B
North Georgia College & State University, B
Piedmont College, B
Shorter College, B
Thomas University, B
Wesleyan College, B

Hawaii

Chaminade University of Honolulu, B
Hawaii Pacific University, B
University of Hawaii-West Oahu, B

Idaho

Boise State University, B
Lewis-Clark State College, B
North Idaho College, A
Northwest Nazarene University, B
University of Idaho, MD

Illinois

Benedictine University, B
City Colleges of Chicago, Harold Washington College, A
City Colleges of Chicago, Olive-Harvey College, A
Danville Area Community College, A
DePaul University, B
Dominican University, B
East-West University, B
Eureka College, B
Governors State University, B
Greenville College, B
Judson College, B
Lincoln College-Normal, A
McKendree College, B
National-Louis University, B
North Central College, B
North Park University, B
Northwestern University, BMO
Olivet Nazarene University, B
Rockford College, B
Roosevelt University, B
Saint Xavier University, B
Shimer College, B
Southern Illinois University Carbondale, B
Spoon River College, A
Trinity International University, B
University of Chicago, BMD
University of Illinois at Springfield, M

William Rainey Harper College, A

Indiana

Ancilla College, A
Ball State University, BM
Bethel College, B
Indiana University Bloomington, D
Indiana Wesleyan University, AB
Oakland City University, B
Purdue University, B
Saint Mary-of-the-Woods College, B
Taylor University, B
Tri-State University, AB
University of Southern Indiana, AB
Valparaiso University, A
Vincennes University, A
Vincennes University Jasper Campus, A

Iowa

Ashford University, B
Buena Vista University, B
Central College, B
Divine Word College, AB
Dordt College, B
Graceland University, B
Iowa Lakes Community College, A
Kirkwood Community College, A
Simpson College, B
Upper Iowa University, B

Kansas

Benedictine College, B
Bethel College, B
Central Christian College of Kansas, B
Cloud County Community College, A
Coffeyville Community College, A
Dodge City Community College, A
Emporia State University, B
Friends University, B
Garden City Community College, A
Hutchinson Community College and Area Vocational School, A
Kansas State University, B
Kansas Wesleyan University, B
Labette Community College, A
McPherson College, B
Pittsburg State University, M
Pratt Community College, A
Tabor College, B
University of Kansas, MD

Kentucky

Asbury College, B
Brescia University, B
Campbellsville University, ABM
Lindsey Wilson College, AB
Mid-Continent University, B
Morehead State University, B
Northern Kentucky University, B
Pikeville College, B
St. Catharine College, A
Spalding University, B
Transylvania University, B
Union College, B
University of Kentucky, B
Western Kentucky University, B

Louisiana

Loyola University New Orleans, B
Northwestern State University of Louisiana, B
Our Lady of Holy Cross College, B

Maine

The University of Maine at Augusta, A
University of Maine at Fort Kent, B
University of New England, B
University of Southern Maine, B

Maryland

Anne Arundel Community College, A
Chesapeake College, A
College of Southern Maryland, A
Coppin State University, B
Frostburg State University, B
Garrett College, A

Howard Community College, A
The Johns Hopkins University, BMD
Mount St. Mary's University, B
Towson University, BM
University of Maryland Eastern Shore, B
University of Maryland University College, B
Villa Julie College, A

Massachusetts

American International College, B
Anna Maria College, B
Boston University, B
Framingham State College, B
Harvard University, B
Lesley University, B
Massachusetts Bay Community College, A
Massachusetts Institute of Technology, D
Newbury College, A
Quincy College, A
Roxbury Community College, A
Salem State College, B
Suffolk University, B
University of Massachusetts Amherst, B
Westfield State College, B
Worcester Polytechnic Institute, B

Michigan

Adrian College, AB
Alma College, B
Andrews University, B
Aquinas College, B
Bay Mills Community College, A
Calvin College, B
Central Michigan University, B
Concordia University, B
Eastern Michigan University, BM
Gogebic Community College, A
Grand Valley State University, B
Hope College, B
Lake Superior State University, B
Marygrove College, B
Michigan State University, BM
Michigan Technological University, B
Northern Michigan University, B
Northwestern Michigan College, A
Olivet College, B
Siena Heights University, B
Spring Arbor University, B
University of Michigan, BD
University of Michigan-Dearborn, B
University of Michigan-Flint, B
Western Michigan University, B

Minnesota

Augsburg College, B
Bemidji State University, B
Bethany Lutheran College, B
Bethel University, B
College of Saint Benedict, B
College of St. Catherine, B
The College of St. Scholastica, B
Crown College, B
Gustavus Adolphus College, B
Hamline University, B
Metropolitan State University, B
Minnesota State University Mankato, B
Northwestern College, B
St. Cloud State University, B
Saint John's University, B
Saint Mary's University of Minnesota, B
University of Minnesota, Morris, B
University of St. Thomas, B
Winona State University, B

Mississippi

Blue Mountain College, B
Delta State University, B
East Central Community College, A
East Mississippi Community College, A
Hinds Community College, A
Itawamba Community College, A
Jackson State University, B
Mississippi College, BM
Mississippi University for Women, B
Northeast Mississippi Community College, A
Southwest Mississippi Community College, A

William Carey College, B

Missouri

Evangel University, AB
Fontbonne University, B
Lincoln University, M
Missouri Baptist University, B
Northwest Missouri State University, B
Rockhurst University, B
Saint Louis University, B
Washington University in St. Louis, B
Webster University, B

Montana

Carroll College, B
Montana State University-Northern, AB
University of Great Falls, B
The University of Montana-Missoula, B
The University of Montana-Western, B

Nebraska

College of Saint Mary, B
Concordia University, B
Doane College, B
Midland Lutheran College, B
Northeast Community College, A
Peru State College, B
Union College, B
Wayne State College, B

Nevada

Community College of Southern Nevada, A
University of Nevada, Las Vegas, B

New Hampshire

Colby-Sawyer College, B
Daniel Webster College, B
Keene State College, B
Plymouth State University, B
Southern New Hampshire University, B

New Jersey

Atlantic Cape Community College, A
Brookdale Community College, A
Caldwell College, B
Essex County College, A
Felician College, AB
Gloucester County College, A
Kean University, O
Middlesex County College, A
Monmouth University, B
Montclair State University, M
Ramapo College of New Jersey, B
Raritan Valley Community College, A
Rutgers, The State University of New Jersey, New
    Brunswick/Piscataway, B
Saint Peter's College, AB
Salem Community College, A
Warren County Community College, A
William Paterson University of New Jersey, B

New Mexico

College of the Southwest, B
Eastern New Mexico University, B
New Mexico Military Institute, A
Western New Mexico University, B

New York

Adelphi University, B
Adirondack Community College, A
Bard College, B
Cazenovia College, B
Clarkson University, B
Clinton Community College, A
Colgate University, B
College of Mount Saint Vincent, B
Columbia-Greene Community College, A
Concordia College, B
Corning Community College, A
Dominican College, B
Dowling College, B
Dutchess Community College, A
Elmira College, B
Eugene Lang College The New School for Liberal
    Arts, B

Finger Lakes Community College, A
Fordham University, B
Fulton-Montgomery Community College, A
Herkimer County Community College, A
Hofstra University, B
Iona College, B
Ithaca College, B
Jamestown Community College, A
Keuka College, B
Long Island University, Brooklyn Campus, ABMO
Long Island University, C.W. Post Campus, M
Marymount Manhattan College, A
Medaille College, B
Mercy College, B
Monroe Community College, A
Mount Saint Mary College, B
Nazareth College of Rochester, B
New York Institute of Technology, B
New York University, B
Niagara County Community College, A
Niagara University, B
Nyack College, B
Pace University, B
Polytechnic University, Brooklyn Campus, M
Queens College of the City University of New
    York, BM
Rensselaer Polytechnic Institute, B
Sage College of Albany, A
St. Bonaventure University, B
St. John's University, B
St. Joseph's College, New York, B
St. Joseph's College, Suffolk Campus, B
St. Thomas Aquinas College, B
Sarah Lawrence College, B
Skidmore College, B
State University of New York at Binghamton, MO
State University of New York at Buffalo, M
State University of New York College of Agriculture
    and Technology at Morrisville, A
State University of New York College at Old
    Westbury, B
State University of New York College of Technology
    at Alfred, A
State University of New York College of Technology
    at Canton, A
State University of New York College of Technology
    at Delhi, A
State University of New York Empire State
    College, AB
State University of New York, Fredonia, M
Stony Brook University, State University of New
    York, BM
Suffolk County Community College, A
Syracuse University, MD
Tompkins Cortland Community College, A
Touro College, A
Ulster County Community College, A
Union College, B
University of Rochester, B
Utica College, B
Westchester Community College, A

North Carolina

Appalachian State University, M
Campbell University, B
Elizabeth City State University, B
Gardner-Webb University, B
Johnson C. Smith University, B
Lees-McRae College, B
Livingstone College, B
Mars Hill College, B
North Carolina Agricultural and Technical State
    University, B
Pfeiffer University, B
Piedmont Community College, A
Western Carolina University, B
Winston-Salem State University, B

North Dakota

Dickinson State University, B
Mayville State University, B
Minot State University, B
North Dakota State University, BMD
Turtle Mountain Community College, A
University of Mary, B
University of North Dakota, B

Valley City State University, B

Ohio

Antioch College, B
Ashland University, B
Bluffton University, B
Bowling Green State University-Firelands College, A
Cleveland State University, BM
David N. Myers University, B
Defiance College, B
Kent State University, B
Lake Erie College, B
Lorain County Community College, A
Miami University-Middletown Campus, A
Mount Vernon Nazarene University, B
Muskingum College, B
The Ohio State University, B
Ohio University, ABM
Ohio University-Eastern, B
Ohio University-Zanesville, A
Shawnee State University, AB
Union Institute & University, B
The University of Akron, B
University of Cincinnati, AB
The University of Findlay, AB
University of Rio Grande, B
The University of Toledo, A
Wilmington College, B
Youngstown State University, B

Oklahoma

Carl Albert State College, A
Northeastern Oklahoma Agricultural and Mechanical
    College, A
Northwestern Oklahoma State University, B
Oklahoma Baptist University, B
Oklahoma Panhandle State University, B
Oklahoma Wesleyan University, B
Redlands Community College, A
Rogers State University, AB
St. Gregory's University, B
Seminole State College, A
Tulsa Community College, A

Oregon

Central Oregon Community College, A
Chemeketa Community College, A
Concordia University, B
Corban College, B
Marylhurst University, B
Northwest Christian College, B
Portland State University, B
Rogue Community College, A
Southern Oregon University, BM
Treasure Valley Community College, A
Umpqua Community College, A
Warner Pacific College, AB
Western Oregon University, B

Pennsylvania

Alvernia College, B
Bloomsburg University of Pennsylvania, B
Bucks County Community College, A
California University of Pennsylvania, BM
Carnegie Mellon University, BD
Cheyney University of Pennsylvania, B
Clarion University of Pennsylvania, B
Community College of Allegheny County, A
Drexel University, B
East Stroudsburg University of Pennsylvania, B
Edinboro University of Pennsylvania, BM
Elizabethtown College, B
Gettysburg College, B
Harrisburg Area Community College, A
Holy Family University, B
Juniata College, B
Kutztown University of Pennsylvania, B
La Salle University, B
Lehigh Carbon Community College, A
Lehigh University, B
Lock Haven University of Pennsylvania, B
Luzerne County Community College, A
Mansfield University of Pennsylvania, B
Marywood University, B
Mercyhurst College, B
Millersville University of Pennsylvania, B

Montgomery County Community College, A
Moravian College, B
Mount Aloysius College, B
Muhlenberg College, B
Point Park University, B
Reading Area Community College, A
Robert Morris University, B
Rosemont College, B
Saint Joseph's University, B
Swarthmore College, B
University of Pittsburgh, B
University of Pittsburgh at Bradford, B
University of Pittsburgh at Greensburg, B
University of Pittsburgh at Johnstown, B
Ursinus College, B
Waynesburg College, B
Widener University, B
Wilson College, B

Puerto Rico

Inter American University of Puerto Rico, San
    Germán Campus, B
Universidad Metropolitana, B
Universidad del Turabo, B
University of Puerto Rico at Bayamón, A
University of Puerto Rico at Carolina, A
University of Puerto Rico, Cayey University
    College, B
University of Puerto Rico, Mayagüez Campus, B
University of Puerto Rico, Río Piedras, B
University of Puerto Rico at Utuado, A
University of the Sacred Heart, B

Rhode Island

Providence College, B
Roger Williams University, B

South Carolina

Allen University, B
Charleston Southern University, B
Columbia College, B
Southern Wesleyan University, B
University of South Carolina Beaufort, B

South Dakota

Black Hills State University, B
University of Sioux Falls, AB

Tennessee

Cumberland University, B
Freed-Hardeman University, B
LeMoyne-Owen College, B
Roane State Community College, A
Sewanee: The University of the South, B
Trevecca Nazarene University, B

Texas

Abilene Christian University, B
Amarillo College, A
Angelina College, A
Angelo State University, B
Brazosport College, A
Central Texas College, A
Clarendon College, A
Concordia University at Austin, AB
El Paso Community College, A
Galveston College, A
Hill College of the Hill Junior College District, A
Houston Community College System, A
Howard College, A
Howard Payne University, B
Kilgore College, A
Kingwood College, A
Lamar State College-Port Arthur, A
Laredo Community College, A
Lon Morris College, A
Midwestern State University, B
Navarro College, A
Odessa College, A
Our Lady of the Lake University of San Antonio, B
Southern Methodist University, B
Southwestern Adventist University, B
Southwestern Assemblies of God University, A
Southwestern University, B
Stephen F. Austin State University, B

Sul Ross State University, B
Texas A&M International University, BM
Texas A&M University-Commerce, BM
Texas Wesleyan University, B
Tyler Junior College, A
University of Houston-Downtown, B
University of Houston-Victoria, B
University of North Texas, B
The University of Texas-Pan American, B
The University of Texas at Tyler, M
Wayland Baptist University, AB
West Texas A&M University, B
Wiley College, B

United States Virgin Islands

University of the Virgin Islands, B

Utah

Southern Utah University, B
University of Utah, B
Westminster College, B

Vermont

Bennington College, B
Castleton State College, B
Community College of Vermont, A
Lyndon State College, B
Marlboro College, B

Virginia

Bluefield College, B
Eastern Mennonite University, B
George Mason University, D
Hampton University, B
Hollins University, M
J. Sargeant Reynolds Community College, A
James Madison University, B
Liberty University, B
Radford University, B
Saint Paul's College, B
Thomas Nelson Community College, A
Virginia Wesleyan College, B

Washington

Centralia College, A
The Evergreen State College, B
Heritage University, AB
Highline Community College, A
Lower Columbia College, A
Puget Sound Christian College, B
Skagit Valley College, A
Tacoma Community College, A
University of Washington, B
Washington State University, B

West Virginia

Bluefield State College, B
West Liberty State College, B

Wisconsin

Alverno College, B
Cardinal Stritch University, B
Carthage College, B
Edgewood College, B
Marian College of Fond du Lac, B
Northland College, B
Silver Lake College, B
University of Wisconsin-Madison, B
University of Wisconsin-Platteville, B
University of Wisconsin-River Falls, B
University of Wisconsin-Stevens Point, B
University of Wisconsin-Superior, B
University of Wisconsin-Whitewater, B
Viterbo University, B
Wisconsin Lutheran College, B

Wyoming

Casper College, A
Central Wyoming College, A
Laramie County Community College, A
Northwest College, A
Sheridan College-Sheridan and Gillette, A
University of Wyoming, B

Western Wyoming Community College, A

Alberta

Concordia University College of Alberta, B
The King's University College, B
Rocky Mountain College, B
University of Lethbridge, B

British Columbia

Kwantlen University College, A
Simon Fraser University, B
Thompson Rivers University, B
Trinity Western University, B
The University of British Columbia, B

Manitoba

Providence College and Theological Seminary, B

New Brunswick

Université de Moncton, B

Newfoundland and Labrador

Memorial University of Newfoundland, B

Nova Scotia

Mount Saint Vincent University, B

Ontario

Brock University, B
Royal Military College of Canada, B
Trent University, B
University of Ottawa, B
University of Waterloo, B
University of Windsor, B
York University, B

Quebec

Bishop's University, B
Concordia University, B
Université de Montréal, B
Université du Québec en Abitibi-Témiscamingue, B
Université du Québec àChicoutimi, B
Université du Québec en Outaouais, B

Saskatchewan

University of Regina, BM

SOCIAL STUDIES TEACHER EDUCATION

Alabama

Alabama State University, MO
The University of West Alabama, M

Arizona

The University of Arizona, B

Arkansas

Arkansas State University, M
Arkansas Tech University, B
Harding University, B
Henderson State University, M
John Brown University, B
Ouachita Baptist University, B
Southern Arkansas University-Magnolia, B
University of Central Arkansas, B
University of the Ozarks, B

California

California State University, Chico, M
California State University, San Bernardino, M
Occidental College, M
Stanford University, MD

Colorado

The Colorado College, M
Colorado State University, B

Colorado State University-Pueblo, B

Connecticut

Quinnipiac University, M
University of Connecticut, MD

Florida

Bethune-Cookman College, B
Clearwater Christian College, B
Florida Agricultural and Mechanical University, M
Florida Gulf Coast University, M
Florida International University, M
Florida State University, MDO
Manatee Community College, A
Nova Southeastern University, MO
Southeastern University, B
University of Central Florida, M
University of Florida, MD
University of South Florida, M

Georgia

Albany State University, M
Georgia College & State University, MO
Georgia Southern University, M
Georgia State University, MDO
University of Georgia, MD
University of West Georgia, MO

Hawaii

Chaminade University of Honolulu, M

Idaho

University of Idaho, M

Illinois

Illinois State University, B
Rockford College, M
Southern Illinois University Edwardsville, M
University of Illinois at Urbana-Champaign, B
University of St. Francis, B
Wheaton College, B

Indiana

Anderson University, B
Bethel College, B
Calumet College of Saint Joseph, B
Franklin College, B
Indiana State University, B
Indiana University Bloomington, BM
Indiana University Northwest, B
Indiana University-Purdue University Fort Wayne, B
Indiana University-Purdue University Indianapolis, B
Indiana University South Bend, B
Indiana University Southeast, B
Indiana Wesleyan University, B
Oakland City University, B
Purdue University, MDO
Tri-State University, B
University of Evansville, B
University of Indianapolis, BM
University of Saint Francis, B

Iowa

Dordt College, B
Drake University, M
The University of Iowa, BMD
University of Northern Iowa, B
Waldorf College, B

Kansas

Bethany College, B
Central Christian College of Kansas, A
Emporia State University, M
MidAmerica Nazarene University, B
Pittsburg State University, B

Kentucky

Brescia University, B
Campbellsville University, B
Eastern Kentucky University, M
Kentucky State University, B
Kentucky Wesleyan College, B
Murray State University, B
Pikeville College, B

Thomas More College, B
University of the Cumberlands, B

Louisiana

Centenary College of Louisiana, B
Grambling State University, M
Louisiana State University in Shreveport, B
Louisiana Tech University, B
McNeese State University, BM
Northwestern State University of Louisiana, BM
Southeastern Louisiana University, B
Southern University and Agricultural and Mechanical
    College, B
University of Louisiana at Lafayette, B
University of Louisiana at Monroe, B
University of New Orleans, B
Xavier University of Louisiana, B

Maine

University of Maine, BMO

Maryland

Salisbury University, M
University of Maryland, College Park, B

Massachusetts

Boston College, M
Boston University, BMDO
Bridgewater State College, M
Fitchburg State College, M
Framingham State College, M
Salem State College, M
Smith College, M
Worcester State College, M

Michigan

Alma College, B
Andrews University, M
Aquinas College, B
Central Michigan University, B
Concordia University, B
Cornerstone University, B
Eastern Michigan University, B
Grand Valley State University, B
Hope College, B
Madonna University, B
Michigan State University, M
Rochester College, B
University of Detroit Mercy, B
University of Michigan, M
University of Michigan-Dearborn, B
Wayne State University, BMDO

Minnesota

Bethel University, B
College of St. Catherine, B
Concordia College, B
Concordia University, St. Paul, B
Crown College, B
Gustavus Adolphus College, B
Minnesota State University Mankato, BM
Minnesota State University Moorhead, B
Northwestern College, B
Pillsbury Baptist Bible College, B
St. Olaf College, B
University of Minnesota, Duluth, B
University of Minnesota, Twin Cities Campus, MD
University of St. Thomas, B

Mississippi

Delta State University, M
Mississippi College, B
Northwest Mississippi Community College, A
University of Mississippi, B
University of Southern Mississippi, O
William Carey College, B

Missouri

Northwest Missouri State University, M
Southeast Missouri State University, BM
University of Missouri-Columbia, BMDO
University of Missouri-St. Louis, B
Washington University in St. Louis, B

Webster University, M

Montana

Rocky Mountain College, B
University of Great Falls, B

Nebraska

Chadron State College, M
Hastings College, B
Wayne State College, M
York College, B

Nevada

University of Nevada, Reno, B

New Hampshire

Colby-Sawyer College, B
Keene State College, B
Rivier College, M
Southern New Hampshire University, B

New Jersey

Bloomfield College, B
New Jersey Institute of Technology, M
Princeton University, D
Rider University, O
Rutgers, The State University of New Jersey, New
    Brunswick/Piscataway, MD

New York

Brooklyn College of the City University of New
    York, BM
Buffalo State College, State University of New
    York, B
City College of the City University of New York, BO
The College of Saint Rose, BM
Daemen College, B
Dowling College, B
Elmira College, B
Hofstra University, BM
Hunter College of the City University of New
    York, M
Iona College, BM
Ithaca College, B
Keuka College, B
Le Moyne College, B
Lehman College of the City University of New
    York, M
Long Island University, Brooklyn Campus, B
Long Island University, C.W. Post Campus, B
Manhattanville College, BM
Marist College, B
Mercy College, B
Molloy College, B
Nazareth College of Rochester, B
New York Institute of Technology, B
New York University, BMD
Niagara University, B
Pace University, B
Queens College of the City University of New
    York, BMO
Roberts Wesleyan College, B
St. Bonaventure University, B
St. Francis College, B
St. John Fisher College, M
St. John's University, B
State University of New York at Binghamton, M
State University of New York at Buffalo, M
State University of New York College at
    Brockport, BM
State University of New York College at
    Cortland, BM
State University of New York College at Old
    Westbury, B
State University of New York College at Potsdam, B
State University of New York at Plattsburgh, M
Stony Brook University, State University of New
    York, M
Syracuse University, BMO
Utica College, B

North Carolina

Appalachian State University, B
Campbell University, BM
East Carolina University, BM

Elon University, B
Fayetteville State University, M
Greensboro College, B
North Carolina Agricultural and Technical State
   University, M
North Carolina State University, B
Pfeiffer University, B
Saint Augustine's College, B
The University of North Carolina at Chapel Hill, M
The University of North Carolina at Greensboro, B
The University of North Carolina at Pembroke, BM
Western Carolina University, BM
Wingate University, B
Winston-Salem State University, B

North Dakota

North Dakota State University, M

Ohio

Bowling Green State University, B
Capital University, B
Cedarville University, B
Central State University, B
Kent State University, B
Malone College, B
Miami University, B
Miami University Hamilton, B
Mount Vernon Nazarene University, B
Ohio Dominican University, B
Ohio Northern University, B
Ohio University, BD
Ohio Wesleyan University, B
Shawnee State University, B
The University of Akron, B
University of Cincinnati, M
The University of Toledo, BM
Ursuline College, B
Wright State University, B
Youngstown State University, B

Oklahoma

Oklahoma Baptist University, B
Oklahoma Christian University, B
Oral Roberts University, B
St. Gregory's University, B
Southeastern Oklahoma State University, B
Southern Nazarene University, B
Southwestern Oklahoma State University, M
University of Central Oklahoma, B
University of Oklahoma, B

Oregon

Concordia University, B
Corban College, B
Portland State University, M
Western Oregon University, M

Pennsylvania

Arcadia University, M
Cabrini College, B
Carlow University, B
Chatham College, BM
Clarion University of Pennsylvania, B
Duquesne University, B
East Stroudsburg University of Pennsylvania, M
Edinboro University of Pennsylvania, BM
Gannon University, B
Holy Family University, B
Indiana University of Pennsylvania, B
Juniata College, B
Keystone College, B
Kutztown University of Pennsylvania, M
Lebanon Valley College, B
Mansfield University of Pennsylvania, B
Messiah College, B
Millersville University of Pennsylvania, B
Moravian College, B
The Pennsylvania State University Harrisburg
   Campus, B
The Pennsylvania State University University Park
   Campus, MD
Philadelphia Biblical University, B
Saint Francis University, B
Seton Hill University, B
Temple University, B

University of Pittsburgh, MD
University of Pittsburgh at Johnstown, B
Waynesburg College, B
West Chester University of Pennsylvania, B
Widener University, BM
York College of Pennsylvania, B

Puerto Rico

Inter American University of Puerto Rico,
   Metropolitan Campus, B
Pontifical Catholic University of Puerto Rico, B
Universidad Adventista de las Antillas, B
University of Puerto Rico, Cayey University
   College, B
University of Puerto Rico, Río Piedras, M

Rhode Island

Brown University, M

South Carolina

Bob Jones University, B
Charleston Southern University, BM
The Citadel, The Military College of South
   Carolina, BM
Clemson University, M
Converse College, M
Erskine College, B
Limestone College, B
Morris College, B
University of South Carolina, M

South Dakota

Augustana College, B
Dakota Wesleyan University, B

Tennessee

Belmont University, M
Bethel College, M
Maryville College, B
The University of Tennessee, MO

Texas

Abilene Christian University, B
Baylor University, B
East Texas Baptist University, B
Hardin-Simmons University, B
Houston Baptist University, B
Howard Payne University, B
Huston-Tillotson University, B
St. Edward's University, B
St. Mary's University of San Antonio, B
Southwestern University, B
Texas A&M International University, B
Texas A&M University, MD
Texas A&M University-Commerce, M
Texas Christian University, B
Texas Lutheran University, B
Texas State University-San Marcos, D
Texas Wesleyan University, B
University of Houston, M
University of Mary Hardin-Baylor, B
The University of Texas at Tyler, M

Utah

University of Utah, B
Utah State University, B
Weber State University, B

Vermont

Bennington College, M
Castleton State College, B
College of St. Joseph, M
Johnson State College, B

Virginia

Averett University, BM
Bluefield College, B
Virginia Commonwealth University, M
Virginia Intermont College, B

Virginia Wesleyan College, B

Washington

Eastern Washington University, BM
Washington State University, B

West Virginia

Glenville State College, B
Ohio Valley University, B
University of Charleston, B
Wheeling Jesuit University, B

Wisconsin

Alverno College, B
Carroll College, B
Carthage College, M
Marquette University, B
University of Wisconsin-Eau Claire, BM
University of Wisconsin-La Crosse, B
University of Wisconsin-Madison, M
University of Wisconsin-River Falls, BM
University of Wisconsin-Superior, B
Viterbo University, B

Alberta

University of Lethbridge, B

British Columbia

The University of British Columbia, M
University of Victoria, M

Nova Scotia

Acadia University, M

Ontario

York University, B

Quebec

McGill University, B

Saskatchewan

University of Regina, B

SOCIAL WORK

Alabama

Alabama Agricultural and Mechanical University, BM
Alabama State University, B
Auburn University, B
Community College of the Air Force, A
Jacksonville State University, B
Lawson State Community College, A
Miles College, B
Oakwood College, B
Talladega College, B
Troy University, B
Tuskegee University, B
The University of Alabama, BMD
The University of Alabama at Birmingham, B
University of Montevallo, B
University of North Alabama, B

Alaska

University of Alaska Anchorage, BM
University of Alaska Fairbanks, B

Arizona

Arizona State University, BMD
Arizona State University West, BM
Cochise College (Douglas), A
Cochise College (Sierra Vista), A
Diné College, A
GateWay Community College, A
Northern Arizona University, B

Arkansas

Arkansas Baptist College, B
Arkansas State University, B
Harding University, B
Henderson State University, B
Philander Smith College, B
Southern Arkansas University-Magnolia, B
University of Arkansas, BM

University of Arkansas at Little Rock, BM
University of Arkansas at Monticello, B
University of Arkansas at Pine Bluff, B

California

Azusa Pacific University, B
California State University, Bakersfield, M
California State University, Chico, BM
California State University, East Bay, BM
California State University, Fresno, BM
California State University, Long Beach, BM
California State University, Los Angeles, BM
California State University, Northridge, M
California State University, Sacramento, BM
California State University, San Bernardino, BM
California State University, Stanislaus, M
Chapman University, B
City College of San Francisco, A
Compton Community College, A
East Los Angeles College, A
El Camino College, A
Fresno Pacific University, B
Hope International University, B
Humboldt State University, B
La Sierra University, B
Loma Linda University, MD
Pacific Union College, B
Point Loma Nazarene University, B
Sacramento City College, A
San Diego City College, A
San Diego State University, BMDO
San Francisco State University, BM
San Jose State University, BMO
Southwestern College, A
University of California, Berkeley, BMDO
University of California, Los Angeles, BMDO
University of Judaism, M
University of Southern California, MDO
Whittier College, B

Colorado

Colorado State University, BM
Colorado State University-Pueblo, B
Lamar Community College, A
Metropolitan State College of Denver, B
Northeastern Junior College, A
University of Denver, MD

Connecticut

Albertus Magnus College, B
Capital Community College, A
Central Connecticut State University, B
Eastern Connecticut State University, B
Manchester Community College, A
Naugatuck Valley Community College, A
Sacred Heart University, B
Saint Joseph College, B
Southern Connecticut State University, BMO
University of Connecticut, MDO
Western Connecticut State University, B

Delaware

Delaware State University, BM

District of Columbia

The Catholic University of America, BMDO
Gallaudet University, BM
Howard University, BMD
University of the District of Columbia, B

Florida

Barry University, MD
Chipola College, A
Edward Waters College, B
Florida Agricultural and Mechanical University, BM
Florida Atlantic University, BM
Florida Gulf Coast University, BM
Florida International University, BMD
Florida State University, BMDO
Indian River Community College, A
Manatee Community College, A
Miami Dade College, A
Okaloosa-Walton College, A
Palm Beach Community College, A
Saint Leo University, B

Southeastern University, B
University of Central Florida, BMO
University of South Florida, BM
University of West Florida, B
Warner Southern College, B

Georgia

Abraham Baldwin Agricultural College, A
Albany State University, B
Andrew College, A
Atlanta Metropolitan College, A
Augusta State University, B
Clark Atlanta University, BMD
Dalton State College, AB
Darton College, A
Fort Valley State University, B
Gainesville College, A
Georgia State University, BM
Kennesaw State University, B
LaGrange College, B
Northwestern Technical College, A
Oglethorpe University, B
Savannah State University, BM
Thomas University, B
University of Georgia, BMD
Valdosta State University, M
West Georgia Technical College, A

Guam

University of Guam, B

Hawaii

Brigham Young University-Hawaii, B
Hawaii Pacific University, B
University of Hawaii at Manoa, BMD

Idaho

Boise State University, BM
Brigham Young University -Idaho, A
Idaho State University, B
Lewis-Clark State College, B
Northwest Nazarene University, BM

Illinois

Aurora University, BM
Bradley University, B
Chicago State University, M
City Colleges of Chicago, Harold Washington
    College, A
City Colleges of Chicago, Kennedy-King College, A
City Colleges of Chicago, Richard J. Daley
    College, A
College of Lake County, A
Concordia University, B
Danville Area Community College, A
Dominican University, M
Elgin Community College, A
Governors State University, BM
Greenville College, B
Illinois Eastern Community Colleges, Wabash Valley
    College, A
Illinois State University, BM
John A. Logan College, A
Lake Land College, A
Lewis University, B
Loyola University Chicago, BMDO
MacMurray College, B
McKendree College, B
Northeastern Illinois University, B
Quincy University, B
Rend Lake College, A
Rockford College, B
St. Augustine College, B
Sauk Valley Community College, A
Shawnee Community College, A
Southern Illinois University Carbondale, BMO
Southern Illinois University Edwardsville, BM
Trinity Christian College, B
University of Chicago, MDO
University of Illinois at Chicago, BMD
University of Illinois at Springfield, B
University of Illinois at Urbana-Champaign, MD
University of St. Francis, B
Waubonsee Community College, A

Western Illinois University, B

Indiana

Anderson University, B
Ball State University, B
Goshen College, B
Grace College, B
Huntington University, B
Indiana State University, B
Indiana University Bloomington, B
Indiana University East, AB
Indiana University Northwest, M
Indiana University-Purdue University
    Indianapolis, BMD
Indiana University South Bend, M
Indiana Wesleyan University, B
Manchester College, B
Saint Joseph's College, B
Saint Mary's College, B
Taylor University, B
Taylor University Fort Wayne, B
University of Indianapolis, B
University of Saint Francis, B
University of Southern Indiana, BM
Valparaiso University, B
Vincennes University, A
Vincennes University Jasper Campus, A

Iowa

Briar Cliff University, B
Buena Vista University, B
Clarke College, B
Des Moines Area Community College, A
Dordt College, B
Ellsworth Community College, A
Graceland University, B
Iowa Central Community College, A
Iowa Lakes Community College, A
Kirkwood Community College, A
Loras College, B
Luther College, B
Mount Mercy College, B
Northwestern College, B
St. Ambrose University, M
The University of Iowa, BMDO
University of Northern Iowa, BM
Wartburg College, B

Kansas

Allen County Community College, A
Barton County Community College, A
Bethany College, B
Bethel College, B
Central Christian College of Kansas, A
Coffeyville Community College, A
Colby Community College, A
Cowley County Community College and Area
    Vocational-Technical School, A
Dodge City Community College, A
Fort Hays State University, B
Haskell Indian Nations University, A
Highland Community College, A
Kansas State University, B
Newman University, M
Pittsburg State University, B
Pratt Community College, A
Seward County Community College, A
University of Kansas, B
Washburn University, BM
Wichita State University, BM

Kentucky

Asbury College, B
Brescia University, B
Campbellsville University, B
Eastern Kentucky University, B
Jefferson Community and Technical College, A
Kentucky Christian University, B
Kentucky State University, B
Morehead State University, B
Murray State University, B
Northern Kentucky University, B
Owensboro Community and Technical College, A
St. Catharine College, A
Spalding University, BM
University of the Cumberlands, B

University of Kentucky, BMD
University of Louisville, MD
Western Kentucky University, B

Louisiana

Dillard University, B
Grambling State University, BM
Louisiana College, B
Louisiana State University and Agricultural and
  Mechanical College, MD
Northwestern State University of Louisiana, B
Southeastern Louisiana University, B
Southern University and Agricultural and Mechanical
  College, B
Southern University at New Orleans, ABM
Tulane University, MDO
University of Louisiana at Monroe, B

Maine

Saint Joseph's College of Maine, B
University of Maine, BM
University of Maine at Presque Isle, B
University of New England, MO
University of Southern Maine, BM

Maryland

Bowie State University, B
Coppin State University, B
Frostburg State University, B
Hood College, B
McDaniel College, B
Morgan State University, BM
Salisbury University, BM
Sojourner-Douglass College, B
University of Maryland, Baltimore County, B
University of Maryland Eastern Shore, B

Massachusetts

Anna Maria College, B
Atlantic Union College, B
Berkshire Community College, A
Boston College, MDO
Boston University, MDO
Bridgewater State College, BM
Eastern Nazarene College, B
Elms College, B
Gordon College, B
Hebrew College, O
Massachusetts College of Liberal Arts, B
Mount Ida College, B
Quincy College, A
Regis College, B
Salem State College, BM
Simmons College, MDO
Smith College, MD
Springfield College, MO
Suffolk University, AB
Western New England College, B
Wheelock College, BM

Michigan

Adrian College, B
Andrews University, BM
Bay de Noc Community College, A
Calvin College, B
Central Michigan University, B
Cornerstone University, B
Eastern Michigan University, BMO
Ferris State University, B
Gogebic Community College, A
Grand Valley State University, BM
Hope College, B
Kellogg Community College, A
Kuyper College, B
Lansing Community College, A
Madonna University, B
Marygrove College, B
Michigan State University, BMD
Monroe County Community College, A
Northern Michigan University, B
Saginaw Valley State University, B
Siena Heights University, AB
Spring Arbor University, B
University of Detroit Mercy, B
University of Michigan, MDO

University of Michigan-Flint, B
Wayne State University, BMDO
Western Michigan University, BM

Minnesota

Augsburg College, BM
Bemidji State University, B
Bethel University, B
Century College, A
College of Saint Benedict, B
College of St. Catherine, BM
The College of St. Scholastica, B
Concordia College, B
Metropolitan State University, B
Minnesota State University Mankato, B
Minnesota State University Moorhead, B
Ridgewater College, A
St. Cloud State University, B
Saint John's University, B
St. Olaf College, B
Southwest Minnesota State University, B
University of Minnesota, Duluth, M
University of Minnesota, Twin Cities Campus, MDO
University of St. Thomas, BM
Winona State University, B

Mississippi

Belhaven College, B
Coahoma Community College, A
Delta State University, BM
Holmes Community College, A
Itawamba Community College, A
Jackson State University, BMD
Mississippi College, B
Mississippi Delta Community College, A
Mississippi State University, B
Mississippi Valley State University, B
Northeast Mississippi Community College, A
Rust College, B
University of Mississippi, B
University of Southern Mississippi, BM

Missouri

Avila University, B
Central Christian College of the Bible, B
Central Missouri State University, B
College of the Ozarks, B
Columbia College, B
Evangel University, B
Jefferson College, A
Lindenwood University, B
Missouri State University, BM
Missouri Western State University, B
Saint Louis University, BM
Southeast Missouri State University, B
University of Missouri-Columbia, BM
University of Missouri-Kansas City, M
University of Missouri-St. Louis, BMO
Washington University in St. Louis, MDO
William Woods University, B

Montana

Carroll College, B
The University of Montana-Missoula, B

Nebraska

Chadron State College, B
Creighton University, B
Dana College, B
Nebraska Indian Community College, A
Nebraska Wesleyan University, B
Northeast Community College, A
Union College, B
University of Nebraska at Kearney, B
University of Nebraska at Omaha, BM
Western Nebraska Community College, A

Nevada

Great Basin College, B
University of Nevada, Las Vegas, BM
University of Nevada, Reno, BM

New Hampshire

Franklin Pierce College, B
Hesser College, A

New Hampshire Community Technical College,
  Nashua/Claremont, A
Plymouth State University, B
University of New Hampshire, BM

New Jersey

Atlantic Cape Community College, A
Brookdale Community College, A
Cumberland County College, A
Essex County College, A
Georgian Court University, B
Kean University, BM
Monmouth University, BM
Ocean County College, A
Ramapo College of New Jersey, B
The Richard Stockton College of New Jersey, B
Rutgers, The State University of New Jersey,
  Camden, B
Rutgers, The State University of New Jersey, New
  Brunswick/Piscataway, BMDO
Rutgers, The State University of New Jersey,
  Newark, B
Seton Hall University, B

New Mexico

Eastern New Mexico University-Roswell, A
Mesalands Community College, A
New Mexico Highlands University, BM
New Mexico State University, BM
New Mexico State University-Alamogordo, A
New Mexico State University-Carlsbad, A
San Juan College, A
Santa Fe Community College, A
Western New Mexico University, B

New York

Adelphi University, BMD
Buffalo State College, State University of New
  York, B
The College of New Rochelle, B
The College of Saint Rose, B
College of Staten Island of the City University of
  New York, B
Concordia College, B
Cornell University, D
Daemen College, B
Dominican College, B
Elmira College, B
Fordham University, BMDO
Hunter College of the City University of New
  York, MD
Iona College, B
Keuka College, B
Lehman College of the City University of New
  York, B
Long Island University, Brooklyn Campus, B
Long Island University, C.W. Post Campus, B
Marist College, B
Mercy College, B
Molloy College, B
Mount Saint Mary College, B
Nazareth College of Rochester, BM
New York University, BMDO
Niagara University, B
Nyack College, B
Roberts Wesleyan College, BM
Siena College, B
Skidmore College, B
State University of New York at Buffalo, BMDO
State University of New York College at
  Brockport, BM
State University of New York College at Cortland, B
State University of New York, Fredonia, B
State University of New York at New Paltz, B
State University of New York at Plattsburgh, B
Stony Brook University, State University of New
  York, BMD
Syracuse University, BM
University at Albany, State University of New
  York, BMDO
Yeshiva University, MDO
York College of the City University of New York, B

North Carolina

Alamance Community College, A
Appalachian State University, B

Asheville-Buncombe Technical Community
  College, A
Barton College, B
Beaufort County Community College, A
Bennett College For Women, B
Campbell University, B
Central Carolina Community College, A
Central Piedmont Community College, A
East Carolina University, BM
Edgecombe Community College, A
Elizabeth City State University, B
Fayetteville State University, M
Johnson C. Smith University, B
Livingstone College, B
Louisburg College, A
Mars Hill College, B
Meredith College, B
Methodist College, AB
Mitchell Community College, A
North Carolina Agricultural and Technical State
  University, BM
North Carolina Central University, B
North Carolina State University, B
Shaw University, B
South Piedmont Community College, A
The University of North Carolina at Chapel
  Hill, MDO
The University of North Carolina at Charlotte, BM
The University of North Carolina at Greensboro, BM
The University of North Carolina at Pembroke, B
The University of North Carolina Wilmington, BM
Warren Wilson College, B
Western Carolina University, B

North Dakota

Dickinson State University, B
Minot State University, B
Sitting Bull College, A
Turtle Mountain Community College, A
University of Mary, B
University of North Dakota, BM

Ohio

Ashland University, B
Bluffton University, B
Bowling Green State University, B
Capital University, B
Case Western Reserve University, MDO
Cedarville University, B
Central State University, B
Clark State Community College, A
Cleveland State University, BM
College of Mount St. Joseph, B
Defiance College, B
Franciscan University of Steubenville, B
Kent State University, B
Lorain County Community College, A
Lourdes College, B
Malone College, B
Marion Technical College, A
Miami University, BM
Miami University Hamilton, B
Miami University-Middletown Campus, A
Mount Vernon Nazarene University, B
Northwest State Community College, A
Ohio Dominican University, B
The Ohio State University, BMD
The Ohio State University at Lima, M
The Ohio State University-Mansfield Campus, M
The Ohio State University-Newark Campus, M
Ohio University, BM
Ohio University-Eastern, B
Terra State Community College, A
Union Institute & University, B
The University of Akron, BM
The University of Akron-Wayne College, A
University of Cincinnati, ABM
University of Cincinnati Clermont College, A
University of Cincinnati Raymond Walters College, A
The University of Findlay, B
University of Rio Grande, AB
The University of Toledo, AB
Ursuline College, B
Washington State Community College, A
Wilmington College, B
Wright State University, AB

Wright State University, Lake Campus, A
Xavier University, B
Youngstown State University, B
Zane State College, A

Oklahoma

Connors State College, A
East Central University, B
Northeastern Oklahoma Agricultural and Mechanical
  College, A
Northeastern State University, B
Northwestern Oklahoma State University, B
Oklahoma Baptist University, B
Oral Roberts University, B
Southern Nazarene University, B
Southwestern Christian University, B
Southwestern Oklahoma State University, B
Tulsa Community College, A
University of Oklahoma, BM

Oregon

Blue Mountain Community College, A
Concordia University, B
George Fox University, B
Pacific University, B
Portland State University, MD
Southwestern Oregon Community College, A
Umpqua Community College, A
University of Portland, B
Warner Pacific College, B

Pennsylvania

Alvernia College, B
Bloomsburg University of Pennsylvania, B
Bryn Mawr College, MD
Bucks County Community College, A
Cabrini College, B
California University of Pennsylvania, BM
Carlow University, B
Cedar Crest College, B
Chatham College, B
College Misericordia, B
Community College of Allegheny County, A
Eastern University, B
Edinboro University of Pennsylvania, ABM
Elizabethtown College, B
Gannon University, B
Geneva College, B
Gratz College, MO
Gwynedd-Mercy College, B
Harrisburg Area Community College, A
Holy Family University, B
Immaculata University, B
Juniata College, B
Kutztown University of Pennsylvania, BM
La Salle University, B
Lancaster Bible College, B
Lehigh Carbon Community College, A
Lock Haven University of Pennsylvania, B
Mansfield University of Pennsylvania, B
Marywood University, BMDO
Mercyhurst College, B
Messiah College, B
Millersville University of Pennsylvania, B
Northampton County Area Community College, A
Philadelphia Biblical University, B
Reading Area Community College, A
Saint Francis University, B
Seton Hill University, B
Shippensburg University of Pennsylvania, B
Slippery Rock University of Pennsylvania, B
Temple University, BM
University of Pennsylvania, MDO
University of Pittsburgh, BMDO
West Chester University of Pennsylvania, BM
Widener University, BM

Puerto Rico

Bayamon Central University, B
Caribbean University, B
Inter American University of Puerto Rico, Arecibo
  Campus, A
Inter American University of Puerto Rico, Fajardo
  Campus, B
Inter American University of Puerto Rico,
  Metropolitan Campus, BM

Pontifical Catholic University of Puerto Rico, BM
Universidad del Este, A
Universidad del Turabo, B
University of Puerto Rico at Humacao, B
University of Puerto Rico, Río Piedras, BMD
University of the Sacred Heart, B

Rhode Island

Community College of Rhode Island, A
Providence College, B
Rhode Island College, BM
Salve Regina University, B

South Carolina

Benedict College, B
Coker College, B
Columbia College, B
Limestone College, B
Piedmont Technical College, A
South Carolina State University, B
University of South Carolina, MDO
Winthrop University, B

South Dakota

Augustana College, B
Kilian Community College, A
Northern State University, A
Oglala Lakota College, AB
Presentation College, B
University of Sioux Falls, B
The University of South Dakota, B

Tennessee

Austin Peay State University, B
Belmont University, B
East Tennessee State University, BM
Freed-Hardeman University, B
LeMoyne-Owen College, B
Lincoln Memorial University, B
Lipscomb University, B
Martin Methodist College, A
Middle Tennessee State University, B
Southern Adventist University, B
Tennessee State University, B
Tennessee Technological University, B
Union University, B
University of Memphis, B
The University of Tennessee, BMD
The University of Tennessee at Chattanooga, B
The University of Tennessee at Martin, B

Texas

Abilene Christian University, B
Amarillo College, A
Angelina College, A
Austin Community College, A
Baylor University, BMO
Clarendon College, A
College of the Mainland, A
Del Mar College, A
Eastfield College, A
Galveston College, A
Hardin-Simmons University, B
Hill College of the Hill Junior College District, A
Howard Payne University, B
Lamar University, B
Lubbock Christian University, B
Midwestern State University, B
Our Lady of the Lake University of San Antonio, BM
Paul Quinn College, B
Prairie View A&M University, B
St. Edward's University, B
St. Philip's College, A
South Plains College, A
Southwestern Adventist University, B
Stephen F. Austin State University, BM
Tarleton State University, B
Texas A&M University-Commerce, BM
Texas A&M University-Kingsville, B
Texas Christian University, B
Texas College, B
Texas Southern University, B
Texas Southmost College, A
Texas State University-San Marcos, BM
Texas Tech University, B

Texas Woman's University, B
University of Houston, MD
University of Houston-Clear Lake, B
University of Mary Hardin-Baylor, B
University of North Texas, B
The University of Texas at Arlington, BMD
The University of Texas at Austin, BMD
The University of Texas at El Paso, B
The University of Texas-Pan American, BM
West Texas A&M University, B
Wiley College, B

United States Virgin Islands

University of the Virgin Islands, B

Utah

Brigham Young University, BM
Dixie State College of Utah, A
Salt Lake Community College, A
University of Utah, BMDO
Utah State University, B
Weber State University, B

Vermont

Castleton State College, B
Champlain College, AB
University of Vermont, BM

Virginia

Christopher Newport University, B
Eastern Mennonite University, B
Ferrum College, B
George Mason University, BM
Hampton University, B
James Madison University, B
Longwood University, B
Mary Baldwin College, B
Norfolk State University, BMD
Radford University, BM
Virginia Commonwealth University, BMDO
Virginia Intermont College, B
Virginia State University, B
Virginia Union University, B

Washington

Eastern Washington University, BMO
Heritage University, B
Pacific Lutheran University, B
Seattle University, B
Spokane Falls Community College, A
University of Washington, BMDO
University of Washington, Tacoma, B
Walla Walla College, BM

West Virginia

Bethany College, B
Concord University, B
Marshall University, B
Mountain State University, B
Potomac State College of West Virginia
    University, A
Shepherd University, B
West Virginia Northern Community College, A
West Virginia State University, B
West Virginia University, BM
West Virginia University at Parkersburg, A

Wisconsin

Carthage College, B
College of Menominee Nation, A
Concordia University Wisconsin, B
Lac Courte Oreilles Ojibwa Community College, A
Marian College of Fond du Lac, B
Marquette University, B
Mount Mary College, B
University of Wisconsin-Eau Claire, B
University of Wisconsin-Green Bay, ABM
University of Wisconsin-Madison, BMD
University of Wisconsin-Milwaukee, BMO
University of Wisconsin-Oshkosh, BM
University of Wisconsin-River Falls, B
University of Wisconsin-Superior, B
University of Wisconsin-Whitewater, B

Viterbo University, B

Wyoming

Casper College, A
University of Wyoming, BM
Western Wyoming Community College, A

Alberta

University of Calgary, BMDO
University of Lethbridge, M

British Columbia

Thompson Rivers University, B
The University of British Columbia, BMD
University College of the Fraser Valley, B
University of Northern British Columbia, BM
University of Victoria, BM

Manitoba

University of Manitoba, BM
William and Catherine Booth College, B

New Brunswick

St. Thomas University, B
Université de Moncton, BM

Newfoundland and Labrador

Memorial University of Newfoundland, BMD

Nova Scotia

Dalhousie University, BM

Ontario

Carleton University, BM
Lakehead University, BM
Laurentian University, BM
McMaster University, BM
Redeemer University College, B
Ryerson University, B
University of Ottawa, M
University of Toronto, MD
University of Waterloo, B
The University of Western Ontario, B
University of Windsor, BM
Wilfrid Laurier University, MD
York University, BM

Quebec

McGill University, BMDO
Université Laval, BMD
Université de Montréal, BO
Université du Québec en Abitibi-Témiscamingue, B
Université du Québec àChicoutimi, B
Université du Québec àMontréal, BM
Université du Québec en Outaouais, BM
Université de Sherbrooke, BM

Saskatchewan

University of Regina, BMD

SOCIOBIOLOGY

California

University of California, Davis, D

Connecticut

Wesleyan University, D

SOCIOLOGY

Alabama

Alabama Agricultural and Mechanical University, B
Alabama State University, B
Athens State University, B
Auburn University, BM
Auburn University Montgomery, B
Birmingham-Southern College, B
Jacksonville State University, B
Lawson State Community College, A
Samford University, B
Stillman College, B

Talladega College, B
Troy University, B
Tuskegee University, B
The University of Alabama, B
The University of Alabama at Birmingham, BMD
The University of Alabama in Huntsville, B
University of Mobile, B
University of Montevallo, B
University of North Alabama, B
University of South Alabama, BM
The University of West Alabama, B

Alaska

University of Alaska Anchorage, B
University of Alaska Fairbanks, B

Arizona

Arizona State University, BMD
Arizona State University West, B
Cochise College (Douglas), A
Eastern Arizona College, A
Grand Canyon University, B
Mohave Community College, A
Northern Arizona University, BM
Pima Community College, A
Prescott College, B
South Mountain Community College, A
The University of Arizona, BMD

Arkansas

Arkansas State University, BMO
Arkansas Tech University, B
Henderson State University, B
Hendrix College, B
Ouachita Baptist University, B
Philander Smith College, B
Southern Arkansas University-Magnolia, B
University of Arkansas, BM
University of Arkansas at Little Rock, B
University of Arkansas at Pine Bluff, B
University of Central Arkansas, B
University of the Ozarks, B

California

Azusa Pacific University, B
Bakersfield College, A
Biola University, B
California Baptist University, B
California Lutheran University, B
California State Polytechnic University, Pomona, B
California State University, Bakersfield, BM
California State University Channel Islands, B
California State University, Chico, B
California State University, Dominguez Hills, BMO
California State University, East Bay, BM
California State University, Fresno, B
California State University, Fullerton, BM
California State University, Long Beach, B
California State University, Los Angeles, BM
California State University, Northridge, B
California State University, Sacramento, BM
California State University, San Bernardino, B
California State University, San Marcos, BM
California State University, Stanislaus, B
Cañada College, A
Cerritos College, A
Chabot College, A
Chaffey College, A
Chapman University, B
Claremont McKenna College, B
College of Alameda, A
College of the Desert, A
College of Marin, A
College of the Sequoias, A
Columbia College, A
Compton Community College, A
Contra Costa College, A
Crafton Hills College, A
Cypress College, A
De Anza College, A
East Los Angeles College, A
El Camino College, A
Foothill College, A
Fresno Pacific University, A
Fullerton College, A
Gavilan College, A

Holy Names University, B
Humboldt State University, BM
La Sierra University, B
Los Angeles City College, A
Los Angeles Mission College, A
Los Angeles Valley College, A
Los Medanos College, A
Loyola Marymount University, B
Mills College, B
MiraCosta College, A
Monterey Peninsula College, A
Mount St. Mary's College, B
National University, B
Notre Dame de Namur University, B
Occidental College, B
Orange Coast College, A
Oxnard College, A
Pacific Union College, B
Palo Verde College, A
Pasadena City College, A
Pepperdine University, B
Pitzer College, B
Point Loma Nazarene University, B
Pomona College, B
Saddleback College, A
Saint Mary's College of California, B
San Bernardino Valley College, A
San Diego City College, A
San Diego Mesa College, A
San Diego Miramar College, A
San Diego State University, BM
San Francisco State University, B
San Joaquin Delta College, A
San Jose State University, BM
Santa Ana College, A
Santa Barbara City College, A
Santa Clara University, B
Santa Monica College, A
Santa Rosa Junior College, A
Santiago Canyon College, A
Scripps College, B
Skyline College, A
Sonoma State University, B
Southwestern College, A
Stanford University, BD
University of California, Berkeley, BD
University of California, Davis, BMD
University of California, Irvine, BMD
University of California, Los Angeles, BMD
University of California, Riverside, BMD
University of California, San Diego, BD
University of California, Santa Barbara, BDO
University of California, Santa Cruz, BD
University of La Verne, B
University of the Pacific, B
University of Redlands, B
University of San Diego, B
University of San Francisco, B
University of Southern California, BMD
Vanguard University of Southern California, B
West Los Angeles College, A
West Valley College, A
Westmont College, B
Whittier College, B

Colorado

Adams State College, B
The Colorado College, B
Colorado State University, BMD
Colorado State University-Pueblo, B
Fort Lewis College, B
Mesa State College, B
Metropolitan State College of Denver, B
Red Rocks Community College, A
Regis University, B
University of Colorado at Boulder, BMD
University of Colorado at Colorado Springs, BM
University of Colorado at Denver and Health
   Sciences Center - Downtown Denver
   Campus, BM
University of Denver, BM
University of Northern Colorado, BM

Western State College of Colorado, B

Connecticut

Albertus Magnus College, B
Central Connecticut State University, B
Connecticut College, B
Eastern Connecticut State University, B
Fairfield University, B
Post University, B
Quinnipiac University, B
Sacred Heart University, AB
Saint Joseph College, B
Southern Connecticut State University, BM
Trinity College, B
University of Connecticut, BMD
University of Hartford, B
Wesleyan University, B
Western Connecticut State University, B
Yale University, BD

Delaware

Delaware State University, B
University of Delaware, BMD

District of Columbia

American University, BMO
The Catholic University of America, BMD
Gallaudet University, B
The George Washington University, BM
Georgetown University, B
Howard University, BMD
University of the District of Columbia, B

Florida

Barry University, B
Bethune-Cookman College, B
Daytona Beach Community College, A
Eckerd College, B
Edward Waters College, B
Flagler College, B
Florida Agricultural and Mechanical University, BM
Florida Atlantic University, BM
Florida International University, BMD
Florida Memorial College, B
Florida Southern College, B
Florida State University, BMD
Gulf Coast Community College, A
Indian River Community College, A
Jacksonville University, B
Miami Dade College, A
New College of Florida, B
Rollins College, B
Saint Leo University, B
St. Thomas University, B
Stetson University, B
University of Central Florida, BMDO
University of Florida, BMDO
University of Miami, BMD
University of North Florida, BM
University of South Florida, BM
The University of Tampa, AB
University of West Florida, B

Georgia

Abraham Baldwin Agricultural College, A
Agnes Scott College, B
Albany State University, B
Andrew College, A
Augusta State University, B
Bainbridge College, A
Berry College, B
Brewton-Parker College, B
Clark Atlanta University, BM
Clayton State University, A
Coastal Georgia Community College, A
Columbus State University, B
Covenant College, B
Dalton State College, A
Darton College, A
East Georgia College, A
Emory University, BMD
Fort Valley State University, B
Gainesville College, A
Georgia College & State University, B
Georgia Highlands College, A

Georgia Perimeter College, A
Georgia Southern University, BM
Georgia Southwestern State University, B
Georgia State University, BMD
Gordon College, A
Kennesaw State University, B
Macon State College, A
Mercer University, B
Morehouse College, B
North Georgia College & State University, B
Oglethorpe University, B
Paine College, B
Piedmont College, B
Reinhardt College, B
Savannah State University, B
Shorter College, B
South Georgia College, A
Spelman College, B
Thomas University, B
University of Georgia, BMD
University of West Georgia, BM
Valdosta State University, BM
Waycross College, A
Young Harris College, A

Guam

University of Guam, B

Hawaii

Hawaii Pacific University, B
University of Hawaii at Hilo, B
University of Hawaii at Manoa, BMD
University of Hawaii-West Oahu, B

Idaho

Albertson College of Idaho, B
Boise State University, B
Brigham Young University -Idaho, A
College of Southern Idaho, A
Idaho State University, BM
North Idaho College, A
University of Idaho, B

Illinois

Augustana College, B
Aurora University, B
Benedictine University, B
Bradley University, B
Chicago State University, B
Concordia University, B
DePaul University, BM
Dominican University, B
East-West University, B
Eastern Illinois University, B
Elmhurst College, B
Eureka College, B
Greenville College, B
Highland Community College, A
Illinois College, B
Illinois State University, BM
Illinois Wesleyan University, B
John Wood Community College, A
Judson College, B
Knox College, B
Lake Forest College, B
Lewis University, B
Lincoln College, A
Loyola University Chicago, BMD
McKendree College, B
Millikin University, B
Monmouth College, B
North Central College, B
North Park University, B
Northeastern Illinois University, B
Northern Illinois University, BM
Northwestern University, BDO
Principia College, B
Rend Lake College, A
Rockford College, B
Roosevelt University, BM
Saint Xavier University, B
Sauk Valley Community College, A
Southern Illinois University Carbondale, BMD
Southern Illinois University Edwardsville, BM
Spoon River College, A
Trinity Christian College, B

University of Chicago, BD
University of Illinois at Chicago, BMD
University of Illinois at Springfield, B
University of Illinois at Urbana-Champaign, BMD
Western Illinois University, BM
Wheaton College, B

Indiana

Anderson University, B
Ball State University, BM
Bethel College, B
Butler University, B
DePauw University, B
Earlham College, B
Franklin College, B
Goshen College, B
Grace College, B
Hanover College, B
Huntington University, B
Indiana State University, B
Indiana University Bloomington, BMD
Indiana University East, B
Indiana University Kokomo, B
Indiana University Northwest, B
Indiana University-Purdue University Fort
  Wayne, BM
Indiana University-Purdue University Indianapolis, B
Indiana University South Bend, B
Indiana University Southeast, B
Indiana Wesleyan University, B
Manchester College, B
Marian College, B
Martin University, B
Purdue University, BMD
Purdue University Calumet, B
Saint Joseph's College, B
Saint Mary's College, B
Taylor University, B
University of Evansville, B
University of Indianapolis, BM
University of Notre Dame, BD
University of Southern Indiana, B
Valparaiso University, B
Vincennes University, A
Vincennes University Jasper Campus, A

Iowa

Buena Vista University, B
Central College, B
Clarke College, B
Coe College, B
Cornell College, B
Dordt College, B
Drake University, BM
Ellsworth Community College, A
Graceland University, B
Grand View College, A
Grinnell College, B
Iowa Central Community College, A
Iowa Lakes Community College, A
Iowa State University of Science and
  Technology, BMD
Kirkwood Community College, A
Loras College, B
Luther College, B
Mount Mercy College, B
Northwestern College, B
St. Ambrose University, B
Simpson College, B
University of Dubuque, AB
The University of Iowa, BMDO
University of Northern Iowa, BM
Upper Iowa University, B
Wartburg College, B
William Penn University, B

Kansas

Allen County Community College, A
Baker University, B
Barton County Community College, A
Benedictine College, B
Bethany College, B
Butler Community College, A
Central Christian College of Kansas, A
Coffeyville Community College, A
Colby Community College, A

Emporia State University, B
Fort Hays State University, B
Friends University, AB
Garden City Community College, A
Highland Community College, A
Independence Community College, A
Kansas State University, BMD
Kansas Wesleyan University, B
McPherson College, B
MidAmerica Nazarene University, B
Newman University, B
Ottawa University, B
Pittsburg State University, B
Pratt Community College, A
Seward County Community College, A
Tabor College, B
University of Kansas, BMD
University of Saint Mary, B
Washburn University, B
Wichita State University, BM

Kentucky

Asbury College, B
Bellarmine University, B
Berea College, B
Campbellsville University, B
Centre College, B
Eastern Kentucky University, B
Georgetown College, B
Kentucky State University, B
Kentucky Wesleyan College, B
Morehead State University, BM
Murray State University, B
Northern Kentucky University, B
Pikeville College, B
St. Catharine College, A
Thomas More College, AB
Transylvania University, B
University of Kentucky, BMD
University of Louisville, BM
Western Kentucky University, BM

Louisiana

Centenary College of Louisiana, B
Dillard University, B
Grambling State University, B
Louisiana College, B
Louisiana State University and Agricultural and
  Mechanical College, BMD
Louisiana State University in Shreveport, B
Louisiana Tech University, B
Loyola University New Orleans, B
McNeese State University, B
Nicholls State University, B
Northwestern State University of Louisiana, B
Southeastern Louisiana University, BM
Southern University and Agricultural and Mechanical
  College, BM
Southern University at New Orleans, B
Southern University at Shreveport, A
Tulane University, BMD
University of Louisiana at Lafayette, B
University of Louisiana at Monroe, B
University of New Orleans, BM
Xavier University of Louisiana, B

Maine

Bates College, B
Bowdoin College, B
Colby College, B
Saint Joseph's College of Maine, B
University of Maine, B
University of Maine at Farmington, B
University of Maine at Presque Isle, B
University of New England, B
University of Southern Maine, B

Maryland

Bowie State University, B
Chesapeake College, A
Frostburg State University, B
Garrett College, A
Goucher College, B
Hood College, B
The Johns Hopkins University, BD
Loyola College in Maryland, B

McDaniel College, B
Morgan State University, BM
Mount St. Mary's University, B
St. Mary's College of Maryland, B
Salisbury University, B
Sojourner-Douglass College, B
University of Maryland, Baltimore County, BMO
University of Maryland, College Park, BMD
University of Maryland Eastern Shore, B
Villa Julie College, A
Washington College, B

Massachusetts

American International College, B
Amherst College, B
Assumption College, B
Atlantic Union College, B
Boston College, BMDO
Boston University, BMD
Brandeis University, BMD
Bridgewater State College, B
Bunker Hill Community College, A
Clark University, B
College of the Holy Cross, B
Curry College, B
Eastern Nazarene College, B
Elms College, B
Emmanuel College, B
Fitchburg State College, B
Framingham State College, B
Gordon College, B
Hampshire College, B
Harvard University, BMD
Lasell College, B
Massachusetts College of Liberal Arts, B
Merrimack College, B
Mount Holyoke College, B
Newbury College, A
Northeastern University, BMD
Quincy College, A
Regis College, B
Salem State College, B
Simmons College, B
Simon's Rock College of Bard, B
Smith College, B
Springfield College, B
Stonehill College, B
Suffolk University, B
Tufts University, B
University of Massachusetts Amherst, BMD
University of Massachusetts Boston, BM
University of Massachusetts Dartmouth, B
University of Massachusetts Lowell, BM
Wellesley College, B
Western New England College, B
Westfield State College, B
Wheaton College, B
Williams College, B
Worcester State College, B

Michigan

Adrian College, AB
Albion College, B
Alma College, B
Andrews University, B
Aquinas College, B
Calvin College, B
Central Michigan University, BM
Concordia University, B
Cornerstone University, B
Eastern Michigan University, BM
Gogebic Community College, A
Grand Valley State University, B
Hillsdale College, B
Hope College, B
Kalamazoo College, B
Kellogg Community College, A
Lake Superior State University, B
Madonna University, B
Michigan State University, BMD
Mid Michigan Community College, A
Northern Michigan University, B
Oakland University, B
Olivet College, B
Saginaw Valley State University, B
Spring Arbor University, B

University of Detroit Mercy, B
University of Michigan, BD
University of Michigan-Dearborn, B
University of Michigan-Flint, B
Wayne State University, BMD
Western Michigan University, BMD

Minnesota

Augsburg College, B
Bemidji State University, B
Carleton College, B
College of Saint Benedict, B
College of St. Catherine, B
Concordia College, B
Concordia University, St. Paul, B
Gustavus Adolphus College, B
Hamline University, B
Macalester College, B
Minnesota State University Mankato, BM
Minnesota State University Moorhead, B
Ridgewater College, A
St. Cloud State University, B
Saint John's University, B
St. Olaf College, B
Southwest Minnesota State University, B
University of Minnesota, Duluth, BM
University of Minnesota, Morris, B
University of Minnesota, Twin Cities Campus, BMD
University of St. Thomas, B
Vermilion Community College, A
Winona State University, B

Mississippi

Alcorn State University, B
East Mississippi Community College, A
Hinds Community College, A
Itawamba Community College, A
Jackson State University, BM
Millsaps College, B
Mississippi College, BM
Mississippi State University, BMD
Mississippi Valley State University, B
Rust College, B
Tougaloo College, B
University of Mississippi, BM

Missouri

Avila University, B
Central Methodist University, B
Central Missouri State University, BM
College of the Ozarks, B
Columbia College, B
Drury University, B
East Central College, A
Evangel University, B
Hannibal-LaGrange College, B
Jefferson College, A
Lincoln University, BM
Lindenwood University, B
Maryville University of Saint Louis, B
Missouri Southern State University, B
Missouri State University, B
Missouri Valley College, B
Northwest Missouri State University, B
Park University, B
Rockhurst University, B
Saint Louis University, BM
Southeast Missouri State University, B
Southwest Baptist University, B
Truman State University, B
University of Missouri-Columbia, BMD
University of Missouri-Kansas City, BMD
University of Missouri-St. Louis, BM
Westminster College, B

Montana

Carroll College, B
Montana State University, B
Montana State University-Billings, AB
Rocky Mountain College, B
University of Great Falls, B

The University of Montana-Missoula, BM

Nebraska

Chadron State College, B
Concordia University, B
Creighton University, B
Dana College, B
Doane College, B
Hastings College, B
Midland Lutheran College, B
Nebraska Wesleyan University, B
University of Nebraska at Kearney, B
University of Nebraska-Lincoln, BMD
University of Nebraska at Omaha, BM
Wayne State College, B
Western Nebraska Community College, A

Nevada

Community College of Southern Nevada, A
Great Basin College, A
University of Nevada, Las Vegas, BMD
University of Nevada, Reno, BM

New Hampshire

Dartmouth College, B
Franklin Pierce College, B
Keene State College, B
New England College, B
Rivier College, B
Saint Anselm College, B
University of New Hampshire, BMD

New Jersey

Atlantic Cape Community College, A
Bergen Community College, A
Bloomfield College, B
Brookdale Community College, A
Burlington County College, A
Caldwell College, B
Centenary College, B
The College of New Jersey, B
College of Saint Elizabeth, B
Drew University, B
Fairleigh Dickinson University, College at
  Florham, B
Fairleigh Dickinson University, Metropolitan
  Campus, B
Felician College, AB
Georgian Court University, B
Gloucester County College, A
Kean University, B
Middlesex County College, A
Montclair State University, BM
New Jersey City University, B
Princeton University, BD
Ramapo College of New Jersey, B
The Richard Stockton College of New Jersey, B
Rider University, B
Rowan University, B
Rutgers, The State University of New Jersey,
  Camden, B
Rutgers, The State University of New Jersey, New
  Brunswick/Piscataway, BMD
Rutgers, The State University of New Jersey,
  Newark, B
Saint Peter's College, B
Salem Community College, A
Seton Hall University, B
William Paterson University of New Jersey, BM

New Mexico

Eastern New Mexico University, B
New Mexico Highlands University, BM
New Mexico State University, BM
San Juan College, A
University of New Mexico, BMD
Western New Mexico University, B

New York

Adelphi University, B
Alfred University, B
Bard College, B
Barnard College, B
Bernard M. Baruch College of the City University of
  New York, B

Brooklyn College of the City University of New
  York, BMD
Buffalo State College, State University of New
  York, B
Canisius College, B
City College of the City University of New York, BM
Clarkson University, B
Colgate University, B
College of Mount Saint Vincent, B
The College of New Rochelle, B
The College of Saint Rose, B
College of Staten Island of the City University of
  New York, B
Columbia College, B
Columbia University, School of General Studies, B
Cornell University, BMD
Dowling College, B
D'Youville College, B
Elmira College, B
Eugene Lang College The New School for Liberal
  Arts, B
Excelsior College, B
Finger Lakes Community College, A
Fordham University, BMD
Hamilton College, B
Hartwick College, B
Hobart and William Smith Colleges, B
Hofstra University, B
Houghton College, B
Hunter College of the City University of New
  York, BM
Iona College, B
Ithaca College, B
Keuka College, B
Le Moyne College, B
Lehman College of the City University of New
  York, B
Long Island University, Brooklyn Campus, B
Long Island University, C.W. Post Campus, B
Manhattan College, B
Manhattanville College, B
Marymount Manhattan College, B
Mercy College, B
Molloy College, B
Mount Saint Mary College, B
Nazareth College of Rochester, B
New York Institute of Technology, B
New York University, BMDO
Niagara University, B
Purchase College, State University of New York, B
Queens College of the City University of New
  York, BM
Roberts Wesleyan College, B
Russell Sage College, B
St. Bonaventure University, B
St. Francis College, B
St. John Fisher College, B
St. John's University, BM
St. Joseph's College, Suffolk Campus, B
St. Lawrence University, B
Sarah Lawrence College, B
Siena College, B
Skidmore College, B
State University of New York at Binghamton, BMD
State University of New York at Buffalo, BMD
State University of New York College at
  Brockport, B
State University of New York College at Cortland, B
State University of New York College at Geneseo, B
State University of New York College at Old
  Westbury, B
State University of New York College at Oneonta, B
State University of New York College at Potsdam, B
State University of New York, Fredonia, B
State University of New York Institute of
  Technology, BM
State University of New York at New Paltz, BMO
State University of New York at Oswego, B
State University of New York at Plattsburgh, B
Stony Brook University, State University of New
  York, BMD
Syracuse University, BMD
Touro College, B
Union College, B
University at Albany, State University of New
  York, BMDO

Utica College, B
Vassar College, B
Wagner College, B
Wells College, B
Yeshiva University, B
York College of the City University of New York, B

North Carolina

Appalachian State University, B
Barber-Scotia College, B
Belmont Abbey College, B
Bennett College For Women, B
Catawba College, B
Davidson College, B
Duke University, BMD
East Carolina University, BM
Elizabeth City State University, B
Elon University, B
Fayetteville State University, BM
Gardner-Webb University, B
Greensboro College, B
Guilford College, B
High Point University, B
Johnson C. Smith University, B
Lees-McRae College, B
Lenoir-Rhyne College, B
Livingstone College, B
Louisburg College, A
Mars Hill College, B
Meredith College, B
Methodist College, AB
North Carolina Agricultural and Technical State
   University, B
North Carolina Central University, BM
North Carolina State University, BMD
North Carolina Wesleyan College, B
Pfeiffer University, B
Saint Augustine's College, B
Salem College, B
Shaw University, B
The University of North Carolina at Asheville, B
The University of North Carolina at Chapel
   Hill, BMD
The University of North Carolina at Charlotte, BM
The University of North Carolina at Greensboro, BM
The University of North Carolina at Pembroke, B
The University of North Carolina Wilmington, B
Wake Forest University, B
Warren Wilson College, B
Western Carolina University, B
Wingate University, B
Winston-Salem State University, B

North Dakota

Minot State University, B
North Dakota State University, BM
University of North Dakota, BM

Ohio

Antioch College, B
Ashland University, B
Baldwin-Wallace College, B
Bluffton University, B
Bowling Green State University, BMD
Capital University, B
Case Western Reserve University, BD
Cedarville University, B
Central State University, B
Cleveland State University, BM
College of Mount St. Joseph, B
The College of Wooster, B
Denison University, B
Franciscan University of Steubenville, B
Hiram College, B
John Carroll University, B
Kent State University, BMD
Kenyon College, B
Lake Erie College, B
Lorain County Community College, A
Lourdes College, AB
Miami University, B
Miami University Hamilton, B
Miami University-Middletown Campus, A
Mount Union College, B
Mount Vernon Nazarene University, B
Muskingum College, B

Oberlin College, B
Ohio Dominican University, B
Ohio Northern University, B
The Ohio State University, BMD
Ohio University, BM
Ohio University-Eastern, B
Ohio Wesleyan University, B
Otterbein College, B
Shawnee State University, B
The University of Akron, BMD
University of Cincinnati, BMD
University of Dayton, B
The University of Findlay, B
University of Rio Grande, AB
The University of Toledo, BM
Urbana University, B
Ursuline College, B
Walsh University, B
Wilberforce University, B
Wittenberg University, B
Wright State University, AB
Wright State University, Lake Campus, A
Xavier University, AB
Youngstown State University, B

Oklahoma

Bacone College, A
Cameron University, B
Connors State College, A
East Central University, B
Eastern Oklahoma State College, A
Langston University, B
Northeastern Oklahoma Agricultural and Mechanical
   College, A
Northeastern State University, B
Northwestern Oklahoma State University, B
Oklahoma Baptist University, B
Oklahoma City Community College, A
Oklahoma City University, B
Oklahoma State University, BMD
Rose State College, A
St. Gregory's University, B
Southeastern Oklahoma State University, B
Southern Nazarene University, B
Tulsa Community College, A
University of Central Oklahoma, B
University of Oklahoma, BMD
University of Science and Arts of Oklahoma, B
University of Tulsa, B

Oregon

Eastern Oregon University, B
George Fox University, B
Lewis & Clark College, B
Linfield College, B
Oregon State University, B
Pacific University, B
Portland State University, BMD
Reed College, B
Southern Oregon University, B
Treasure Valley Community College, A
Umpqua Community College, A
University of Oregon, BMD
University of Portland, B
Western Oregon University, B
Willamette University, B

Pennsylvania

Albright College, B
Arcadia University, B
Bloomsburg University of Pennsylvania, B
Bryn Mawr College, B
Bucknell University, B
Cabrini College, B
California University of Pennsylvania, B
Carlow University, B
Chestnut Hill College, B
Cheyney University of Pennsylvania, B
Clarion University of Pennsylvania, B
Community College of Allegheny County, A
Delaware County Community College, A
Dickinson College, B
Drexel University, B
Duquesne University, B
East Stroudsburg University of Pennsylvania, B
Eastern University, B

Edinboro University of Pennsylvania, B
Elizabethtown College, B
Franklin and Marshall College, B
Geneva College, B
Gettysburg College, B
Grove City College, B
Gwynedd-Mercy College, B
Haverford College, B
Holy Family University, B
Immaculata University, B
Indiana University of Pennsylvania, BM
Juniata College, B
King's College, B
Kutztown University of Pennsylvania, B
La Roche College, B
La Salle University, B
Lafayette College, B
Lebanon Valley College, B
Lehigh University, BM
Lincoln University, B
Lock Haven University of Pennsylvania, B
Lycoming College, B
Mansfield University of Pennsylvania, B
Mercyhurst College, B
Messiah College, B
Millersville University of Pennsylvania, B
Moravian College, B
Muhlenberg College, B
The Pennsylvania State University Abington
   College, B
The Pennsylvania State University Altoona
   College, B
The Pennsylvania State University Beaver Campus
   of the Commonwealth College, B
The Pennsylvania State University Berks Campus of
   the Berks-Lehigh Valley College, B
The Pennsylvania State University Delaware County
   Campus of the Commonwealth College, B
The Pennsylvania State University DuBois Campus
   of the Commonwealth College, B
The Pennsylvania State University at Erie, The
   Behrend College, B
The Pennsylvania State University Fayette Campus
   of the Commonwealth College, B
The Pennsylvania State University Harrisburg
   Campus, B
The Pennsylvania State University Hazleton
   Campus of the Commonwealth College, B
The Pennsylvania State University, Lehigh Valley
   Campus of the Berks-Lehigh Valley College, B
The Pennsylvania State University McKeesport
   Campus of the Commonwealth College, B
The Pennsylvania State University Mont Alto
   Campus of the Commonwealth College, B
The Pennsylvania State University New Kensington
   Campus of the Commonwealth College, B
The Pennsylvania State University Schuylkill
   Campus of the Capital College, B
The Pennsylvania State University Shenango
   Campus of the Commonwealth College, B
The Pennsylvania State University University Park
   Campus, ABMD
The Pennsylvania State University Wilkes-Barre
   Campus of the Commonwealth College, B
The Pennsylvania State University Worthington
   Scranton Campus of the Commonwealth
   College, B
The Pennsylvania State University York Campus of
   the Commonwealth College, B
Rosemont College, B
Saint Francis University, B
Saint Joseph's University, B
Saint Vincent College, B
Seton Hill University, B
Shippensburg University of Pennsylvania, BM
Slippery Rock University of Pennsylvania, B
Susquehanna University, B
Swarthmore College, B
Temple University, BMD
Thiel College, B
University of Pennsylvania, BMD
University of Pittsburgh, BMD
University of Pittsburgh at Bradford, B
University of Pittsburgh at Johnstown, B
The University of Scranton, AB
Ursinus College, B

Villanova University, B
Washington & Jefferson College, B
Waynesburg College, B
West Chester University of Pennsylvania, BMO
Westminster College, B
Widener University, B
Wilkes University, B
York College of Pennsylvania, B

Puerto Rico

Inter American University of Puerto Rico, Fajardo
    Campus, B
Inter American University of Puerto Rico,
    Metropolitan Campus, B
Inter American University of Puerto Rico, San
    Germán Campus, B
Pontifical Catholic University of Puerto Rico, B
University of Puerto Rico, Cayey University
    College, B
University of Puerto Rico, Mayagüez Campus, B
University of Puerto Rico, Río Piedras, BM

Rhode Island

Brown University, BMD
Providence College, B
Rhode Island College, B
Roger Williams University, B
Salve Regina University, B
University of Rhode Island, B

South Carolina

Benedict College, B
Charleston Southern University, B
Claflin University, B
Clemson University, BM
Coastal Carolina University, B
Coker College, B
College of Charleston, B
Converse College, B
Francis Marion University, B
Furman University, B
Lander University, B
Morris College, B
Newberry College, B
Presbyterian College, B
South Carolina State University, B
University of South Carolina, BMD
University of South Carolina Aiken, B
University of South Carolina Upstate, B
Voorhees College, B
Winthrop University, B
Wofford College, B

South Dakota

Augustana College, B
Black Hills State University, B
Dakota Wesleyan University, B
Northern State University, B
South Dakota State University, B
University of Sioux Falls, B
The University of South Dakota, BM

Tennessee

Austin Peay State University, B
Belmont University, B
Carson-Newman College, B
Columbia State Community College, A
Cumberland University, B
East Tennessee State University, BM
Fisk University, BM
Lambuth University, B
Lane College, B
Lee University, B
LeMoyne-Owen College, B
Martin Methodist College, A
Maryville College, B
Middle Tennessee State University, BMO
Milligan College, B
Rhodes College, B
Tennessee State University, B
Tennessee Technological University, B
Union University, B
University of Memphis, BM
The University of Tennessee, BMD
The University of Tennessee at Chattanooga, B

The University of Tennessee at Martin, B
Vanderbilt University, BMD

Texas

Abilene Christian University, B
Angelo State University, B
Austin College, B
Austin Community College, A
Baylor University, BMD
Brazosport College, A
Clarendon College, A
Coastal Bend College, A
College of the Mainland, A
Dallas Baptist University, B
Del Mar College, A
East Texas Baptist University, B
El Paso Community College, A
Frank Phillips College, A
Grayson County College, A
Hardin-Simmons University, B
Hill College of the Hill Junior College District, A
Houston Baptist University, B
Howard Payne University, B
Huston-Tillotson University, B
Jarvis Christian College, B
Lamar University, B
Lee College, A
Lon Morris College, A
McMurry University, B
Midland College, A
Midwestern State University, B
Navarro College, A
North Harris College, A
Odessa College, A
Our Lady of the Lake University of San Antonio, BM
Palo Alto College, A
Paul Quinn College, B
Prairie View A&M University, BM
Rice University, B
St. Edward's University, B
St. Mary's University of San Antonio, B
St. Philip's College, A
Sam Houston State University, BM
Southern Methodist University, B
Southwestern University, B
Stephen F. Austin State University, B
Tarleton State University, B
Texas A&M International University, BM
Texas A&M University, BMD
Texas A&M University-Commerce, BM
Texas A&M University-Corpus Christi, B
Texas A&M University-Kingsville, BM
Texas Christian University, B
Texas College, B
Texas Lutheran University, B
Texas Southern University, BM
Texas State University-San Marcos, BM
Texas Tech University, BM
Texas Wesleyan University, B
Texas Woman's University, BMD
Trinity University, B
Trinity Valley Community College, A
University of Houston, BM
University of Houston-Clear Lake, B
University of the Incarnate Word, B
University of Mary Hardin-Baylor, B
University of North Texas, BMD
The University of Texas at Arlington, BM
The University of Texas at Austin, BMD
The University of Texas at Brownsville, B
The University of Texas at Dallas, BM
The University of Texas at El Paso, BM
The University of Texas-Pan American, BM
The University of Texas of the Permian Basin, B
The University of Texas at San Antonio, BM
The University of Texas at Tyler, BM
West Texas A&M University, B
Wiley College, B

Utah

Brigham Young University, BMD
Dixie State College of Utah, A
Salt Lake Community College, A
Snow College, A
Southern Utah University, B
University of Utah, BMD

Utah State University, BMD
Weber State University, B
Westminster College, B

Vermont

Bennington College, B
Castleton State College, B
Green Mountain College, B
Johnson State College, B
Marlboro College, B
Middlebury College, B
Saint Michael's College, B
University of Vermont, B

Virginia

Averett University, B
Bridgewater College, B
Christopher Newport University, B
The College of William and Mary, B
Eastern Mennonite University, B
Emory & Henry College, B
Ferrum College, B
George Mason University, BM
Hampton University, B
Hollins University, B
James Madison University, B
Longwood University, B
Lynchburg College, B
Mary Baldwin College, B
Marymount University, B
Norfolk State University, BM
Old Dominion University, BM
Radford University, B
Randolph-Macon College, B
Randolph-Macon Woman's College, B
Roanoke College, B
Saint Paul's College, B
Shenandoah University, B
Sweet Briar College, B
University of Mary Washington, B
University of Richmond, B
University of Virginia, BMDO
The University of Virginia's College at Wise, B
Virginia Commonwealth University, BMO
Virginia Polytechnic Institute and State
    University, BMD
Virginia State University, B
Virginia Union University, B
Virginia Wesleyan College, B
Washington and Lee University, B

Washington

Central Washington University, B
Centralia College, A
Eastern Washington University, B
Everett Community College, A
Gonzaga University, B
Heritage University, B
Lower Columbia College, A
Pacific Lutheran University, B
Seattle Pacific University, B
Seattle University, B
Skagit Valley College, A
Tacoma Community College, A
University of Puget Sound, B
University of Washington, BMD
Walla Walla College, B
Washington State University, BMD
Wenatchee Valley College, A
Western Washington University, B
Whitman College, B
Whitworth College, B

West Virginia

Alderson-Broaddus College, B
Concord University, B
Davis & Elkins College, B
Fairmont State University, B
Marshall University, BM
Potomac State College of West Virginia
    University, A
Shepherd University, B
West Liberty State College, B
West Virginia State University, B
West Virginia University, BM

West Virginia Wesleyan College, B

Wisconsin

Beloit College, B
Cardinal Stritch University, B
Carroll College, B
Carthage College, B
Edgewood College, B
Lakeland College, B
Marian College of Fond du Lac, B
Marquette University, B
Northland College, B
Ripon College, B
St. Norbert College, B
University of Wisconsin-Eau Claire, B
University of Wisconsin-La Crosse, B
University of Wisconsin-Madison, BMD
University of Wisconsin-Milwaukee, BM
University of Wisconsin-Oshkosh, B
University of Wisconsin-Parkside, B
University of Wisconsin-River Falls, B
University of Wisconsin-Stevens Point, B
University of Wisconsin-Superior, B
University of Wisconsin-Whitewater, B
Viterbo University, B

Wyoming

Casper College, A
Eastern Wyoming College, A
Laramie County Community College, A
Northwest College, A
University of Wyoming, BM
Western Wyoming Community College, A

Alberta

Athabasca University, B
Concordia University College of Alberta, B
The King's University College, B
University of Alberta, BMD
University of Calgary, BMD
University of Lethbridge, BM

British Columbia

Kwantlen University College, A
Malaspina University-College, B
Simon Fraser University, BMD
Thompson Rivers University, B
The University of British Columbia, BMD
University College of the Fraser Valley, B
University of Victoria, BMD

Manitoba

Brandon University, B
University of Manitoba, BMD
The University of Winnipeg, B

New Brunswick

Atlantic Baptist University, B
Mount Allison University, B
St. Thomas University, B
Université de Moncton, B
University of New Brunswick Fredericton, BMD
University of New Brunswick Saint John, B

Newfoundland and Labrador

Memorial University of Newfoundland, BMD

Nova Scotia

Acadia University, BM
Cape Breton University, B
Dalhousie University, BMD
Mount Saint Vincent University, B
St. Francis Xavier University, B
Saint Mary's University, B
University of King's College, B

Ontario

Brock University, B
Carleton University, BMD
Lakehead University, BM
Laurentian University, BM
McMaster University, BMD
Nipissing University, B
Queen's University at Kingston, BMD
Redeemer University College, B

Ryerson University, B
Trent University, B
University of Guelph, BMD
University of Ottawa, BM
University of Toronto, BMD
University of Waterloo, BMD
The University of Western Ontario, BMD
University of Windsor, BMD
Wilfrid Laurier University, B
York University, BMD

Prince Edward Island

University of Prince Edward Island, B

Quebec

Bishop's University, B
Concordia University, BM
McGill University, BMD
Université Laval, BMD
Université de Montréal, BMD
Université du Québec àMontréal, BMD
Université du Québec en Outaouais, B
Université du Québec àRimouski, B

Saskatchewan

University of Regina, BM
University of Saskatchewan, BMD

SOFTWARE ENGINEERING

Alabama

Auburn University, MD
Jacksonville State University, M
The University of Alabama in Huntsville, MO

Alaska

University of Alaska Fairbanks, M

California

California State University, Fullerton, M
California State University, Sacramento, M
International Technological University, M
National University, M
Santa Clara University, MO
University of Southern California, M

Colorado

Colorado Technical University, M
Colorado Technical University Denver Campus, M
University of Colorado at Colorado Springs, M

Connecticut

Fairfield University, M
University of Connecticut, MD
University of New Haven, M

Florida

Embry-Riddle Aeronautical University, M
Florida Agricultural and Mechanical University, M
Florida Institute of Technology, M
Florida State University, M

Georgia

Mercer University, M
Southern Polytechnic State University, M

Illinois

DePaul University, M
Illinois Institute of Technology, M
Loyola University Chicago, M

Kansas

Kansas State University, M

Maryland

Towson University, O
University of Maryland, College Park, M
University of Maryland University College, MO

Michigan

Andrews University, M
Central Michigan University, MO

Grand Valley State University, M
Oakland University, M
University of Michigan-Dearborn, M

Minnesota

University of Minnesota, Twin Cities Campus, M
University of St. Thomas, MO
Walden University, M

New Jersey

Monmouth University, MO
Stevens Institute of Technology, O

New York

Marist College, M
Rochester Institute of Technology, M
Stony Brook University, State University of New York, O

North Dakota

North Dakota State University, MDO

Ohio

Miami University, O

Oregon

Portland State University, M

Pennsylvania

Carnegie Mellon University, MD
Drexel University, M
Gannon University, M
The University of Scranton, M
Widener University, M

South Carolina

University of South Carolina, M
Winthrop University, MO

Tennessee

East Tennessee State University, M

Texas

St. Mary's University of San Antonio, M
Southern Methodist University, M
Texas State University-San Marcos, M
Texas Tech University, M
University of Houston-Clear Lake, M
The University of Texas at Arlington, MD
The University of Texas at Dallas, MD

Virginia

George Mason University, M
Stratford University, M
University of Management and Technology, M

Washington

Seattle University, M

West Virginia

West Virginia University, M

Wisconsin

Carroll College, M
University of Wisconsin-La Crosse, M

Alberta

University of Calgary, M

British Columbia

Simon Fraser University, M
The University of British Columbia, M

Ontario

McMaster University, MD
Royal Military College of Canada, MD
University of Waterloo, M

Quebec

Concordia University, MDO
Université Laval, O

Université du Québec en Outaouais, O

SOIL SCIENCE AND AGRONOMY

Arizona

The University of Arizona, B

California

California State Polytechnic University, Pomona, B
University of California, Davis, B

Delaware

University of Delaware, B

Florida

University of Florida, B

Idaho

University of Idaho, B

Indiana

Ball State University, B

Iowa

Iowa Lakes Community College, A

Maine

University of Maine, B

Michigan

Michigan State University, B

Minnesota

University of Minnesota, Crookston, A
University of Minnesota, Twin Cities Campus, B
Vermilion Community College, A

Nebraska

Nebraska College of Technical Agriculture, A
Southeast Community College, Beatrice Campus, A
University of Nebraska-Lincoln, B

New Hampshire

University of New Hampshire, B

New Mexico

New Mexico State University, B

North Carolina

North Carolina State University, B

North Dakota

North Dakota State University, B

Ohio

The Ohio State University, B
The Ohio State University Agricultural Technical Institute, A

Oregon

Oregon State University, B

Pennsylvania

The Pennsylvania State University Abington College, B
The Pennsylvania State University Altoona College, B
The Pennsylvania State University Beaver Campus of the Commonwealth College, B
The Pennsylvania State University Berks Campus of the Berks-Lehigh Valley College, B
The Pennsylvania State University Delaware County Campus of the Commonwealth College, B
The Pennsylvania State University DuBois Campus of the Commonwealth College, B
The Pennsylvania State University at Erie, The Behrend College, B
The Pennsylvania State University Fayette Campus of the Commonwealth College, B

The Pennsylvania State University Hazleton Campus of the Commonwealth College, B
The Pennsylvania State University, Lehigh Valley Campus of the Berks-Lehigh Valley College, B
The Pennsylvania State University McKeesport Campus of the Commonwealth College, B
The Pennsylvania State University Mont Alto Campus of the Commonwealth College, B
The Pennsylvania State University New Kensington Campus of the Commonwealth College, B
The Pennsylvania State University Schuylkill Campus of the Capital College, B
The Pennsylvania State University Shenango Campus of the Commonwealth College, B
The Pennsylvania State University University Park Campus, B
The Pennsylvania State University Wilkes-Barre Campus of the Commonwealth College, B
The Pennsylvania State University Worthington Scranton Campus of the Commonwealth College, B
The Pennsylvania State University York Campus of the Commonwealth College, B

Tennessee

The University of Tennessee at Martin, B

Utah

Dixie State College of Utah, A
Snow College, A
Utah State University, B

Vermont

Sterling College, AB

Washington

Washington State University, B

Wisconsin

University of Wisconsin-River Falls, B
University of Wisconsin-Stevens Point, B

British Columbia

The University of British Columbia, B

Quebec

McGill University, B

Saskatchewan

University of Saskatchewan, B

SOIL SCIENCES

New York

Cornell University, B

Utah

Brigham Young University, B

Vermont

Sterling College, AB

SOLAR ENERGY TECHNOLOGY/TECHNICIAN

California

Cabrillo College, A
Chabot College, A
San Jose City College, A

Colorado

Red Rocks Community College, A

Nebraska

Southeast Community College, Milford Campus, A

Nevada

Truckee Meadows Community College, A

Pennsylvania

Community College of Allegheny County, A
Pennsylvania College of Technology, A

Vermont

Sterling College, B

SOLID STATE AND LOW-TEMPERATURE PHYSICS

Virginia

George Mason University, B

SOUTH AND SOUTHEAST ASIAN STUDIES

California

University of California, Berkeley, M

Illinois

University of Chicago, MD

Massachusetts

Harvard University, M

Michigan

University of Michigan, MO

New York

Cornell University, MD

Ohio

Ohio University, M

Pennsylvania

University of Pennsylvania, MD

Washington

University of Washington, M

Wisconsin

University of Wisconsin-Madison, M

Ontario

University of Toronto, MD

SOUTH ASIAN LANGUAGES, LITERATURES, AND LINGUISTICS

California

Claremont McKenna College, B

Connecticut

Yale University, B

Hawaii

University of Hawaii at Manoa, B

Illinois

Northwestern University, B
University of Chicago, B

Michigan

Oakland University, B

New York

Syracuse University, B

British Columbia

The University of British Columbia, B

SOUTH ASIAN STUDIES

California

University of California, Santa Cruz, B

Illinois

University of Chicago, B

Massachusetts

Harvard University, B

Michigan

University of Michigan, B

Minnesota

University of Minnesota, Twin Cities Campus, B

Missouri

University of Missouri-Columbia, B

New York

Sarah Lawrence College, B
Syracuse University, B

Pennsylvania

Gettysburg College, B
University of Pennsylvania, B

Rhode Island

Brown University, B

Washington

University of Washington, B

British Columbia

The University of British Columbia, B

Manitoba

University of Manitoba, B

Ontario

University of Toronto, B

Quebec

Concordia University, B

SOUTHEAST ASIAN STUDIES

California

University of California, Berkeley, B
University of California, Los Angeles, B
University of California, Santa Cruz, B

Illinois

University of Chicago, B

Massachusetts

Harvard University, B
Tufts University, B

Michigan

University of Michigan, B

Ohio

Ohio University, B

Washington

University of Washington, B

Wisconsin

University of Wisconsin-Madison, B

SPANISH AND IBERIAN STUDIES

Alabama

The University of Alabama, B

California

Santa Clara University, B

Iowa

Coe College, B

Massachusetts

Simon's Rock College of Bard, B

New York

Barnard College, B
Fordham University, B

Puerto Rico

University of Puerto Rico, Cayey University
College, B

Texas

Southern Methodist University, B
University of Houston, B

Manitoba

The University of Winnipeg, B

Ontario

York University, B

SPANISH LANGUAGE AND LITERATURE

Alabama

Alabama State University, B
Auburn University, BM
Birmingham-Southern College, B
Huntingdon College, B
Jacksonville State University, B
Oakwood College, B
Samford University, B
Spring Hill College, B
Talladega College, B
The University of Alabama, BMD
The University of Alabama at Birmingham, B
University of Montevallo, B

Arizona

Arizona State University, BMD
Arizona State University West, B
Arizona Western College, A
Northern Arizona University, B
Prescott College, B
The University of Arizona, BMD

Arkansas

Arkansas State University, B
Arkansas Tech University, M
Harding University, B
Henderson State University, B
Hendrix College, B
John Brown University, B
Lyon College, B
Ouachita Baptist University, B
Southern Arkansas University-Magnolia, B
University of Arkansas, BM
University of Arkansas at Little Rock, B
University of Central Arkansas, B

California

Allan Hancock College, A
Azusa Pacific University, B
Bakersfield College, A
Berkeley City College, A
Biola University, B
Cabrillo College, A
California Lutheran University, B
California State Polytechnic University, Pomona, B
California State University, Bakersfield, BM
California State University Channel Islands, B
California State University, Chico, B
California State University, Dominguez Hills, B
California State University, East Bay, B
California State University, Fresno, BM
California State University, Fullerton, BM

California State University, Long Beach, BM
California State University, Los Angeles, BM
California State University, Northridge, BM
California State University, Sacramento, BM
California State University, San Bernardino, BM
California State University, San Marcos, BM
California State University, Stanislaus, B
Cañada College, A
Cerritos College, A
Chabot College, A
Chaffey College, A
Chapman University, B
Citrus College, A
Claremont McKenna College, B
College of the Canyons, A
College of Marin, A
College of San Mateo, A
College of the Sequoias, A
Compton Community College, A
Contra Costa College, A
Crafton Hills College, A
De Anza College, A
East Los Angeles College, A
El Camino College, A
Foothill College, A
Fresno City College, A
Fresno Pacific University, AB
Gavilan College, A
Grossmont College, A
Holy Names University, B
Humboldt State University, B
Imperial Valley College, A
La Sierra University, B
Lake Tahoe Community College, A
Long Beach City College, A
Los Angeles City College, A
Los Angeles Mission College, A
Los Angeles Southwest College, A
Los Angeles Valley College, A
Loyola Marymount University, B
Mendocino College, A
Merritt College, A
Mills College, B
MiraCosta College, A
Monterey Peninsula College, A
Mount St. Mary's College, B
Occidental College, B
Orange Coast College, A
Oxnard College, A
Pacific Union College, B
Pasadena City College, A
Pepperdine University, B
Pitzer College, B
Point Loma Nazarene University, B
Pomona College, B
Saint Mary's College of California, B
San Bernardino Valley College, A
San Diego Mesa College, A
San Diego Miramar College, A
San Diego State University, BM
San Francisco State University, BM
San Joaquin Delta College, A
San Jose State University, BM
Santa Barbara City College, A
Santa Clara University, B
Scripps College, B
Skyline College, A
Solano Community College, A
Sonoma State University, B
Southwestern College, A
Stanford University, BMD
University of California, Berkeley, BMD
University of California, Davis, BMD
University of California, Irvine, BMD
University of California, Los Angeles, BM
University of California, Riverside, BMD
University of California, San Diego, BM
University of California, Santa Barbara, BMD
University of California, Santa Cruz, B
University of La Verne, B
University of the Pacific, B
University of Redlands, B
University of San Diego, B
University of San Francisco, B
University of Southern California, B
Vanguard University of Southern California, B

West Los Angeles College, A
West Valley College, A
Westmont College, B

Colorado

Adams State College, B
The Colorado College, B
Colorado State University, BM
Colorado State University-Pueblo, B
Fort Lewis College, B
Metropolitan State College of Denver, B
Red Rocks Community College, A
Regis University, B
University of Colorado at Boulder, BMD
University of Colorado at Colorado Springs, B
University of Colorado at Denver and Health
  Sciences Center - Downtown Denver Campus, B
University of Denver, BM
University of Northern Colorado, BM
Western State College of Colorado, B

Connecticut

Albertus Magnus College, B
Central Connecticut State University, BM
Connecticut College, B
Eastern Connecticut State University, B
Fairfield University, B
Quinnipiac University, B
Sacred Heart University, AB
Saint Joseph College, B
Southern Connecticut State University, BMO
Trinity College, B
University of Connecticut, BMD
Wesleyan University, B
Western Connecticut State University, B
Yale University, BMD

Delaware

Delaware State University, B
University of Delaware, B

District of Columbia

American University, BMO
The Catholic University of America, BMD
Gallaudet University, B
The George Washington University, B
Georgetown University, BMDO
Howard University, BM
Trinity (Washington) University, B
University of the District of Columbia, B

Florida

Barry University, B
Eckerd College, B
Flagler College, B
Florida Agricultural and Mechanical University, B
Florida Atlantic University, BM
Florida International University, BMD
Florida Southern College, B
Florida State University, BMD
Indian River Community College, A
Jacksonville University, B
Manatee Community College, A
Miami Dade College, A
New College of Florida, B
Nova Southeastern University, M
Rollins College, B
Stetson University, B
University of Central Florida, BM
University of Florida, BMD
University of Miami, BMD
University of North Florida, B
University of South Florida, BM
The University of Tampa, AB

Georgia

Agnes Scott College, B
Albany State University, B
Armstrong Atlantic State University, B
Augusta State University, B
Berry College, B
Clark Atlanta University, B
Clayton State University, A
Emory University, BDO
Georgia College & State University, B

Georgia Southern University, B
Georgia State University, BM
Gordon College, A
Kennesaw State University, B
LaGrange College, B
Mercer University, B
Morehouse College, B
North Georgia College & State University, B
Oglethorpe University, B
Piedmont College, B
Shorter College, B
South Georgia College, A
Spelman College, B
University of Georgia, BM
University of West Georgia, B
Valdosta State University, B
Wesleyan College, B
Young Harris College, A

Hawaii

University of Hawaii at Manoa, BM

Idaho

Albertson College of Idaho, B
Boise State University, B
Brigham Young University -Idaho, A
Idaho State University, AB
North Idaho College, A
Northwest Nazarene University, B
University of Idaho, BM

Illinois

Augustana College, B
Benedictine University, B
Blackburn College, B
Bradley University, B
Chicago State University, B
City Colleges of Chicago, Harold Washington
  College, A
DePaul University, B
Dominican University, B
Elmhurst College, B
Greenville College, B
Illinois College, B
Illinois State University, BM
Illinois Wesleyan University, B
Knox College, B
Lake Forest College, B
Lincoln College, A
Loyola University Chicago, BM
MacMurray College, B
Millikin University, B
Monmouth College, B
North Central College, B
North Park University, B
Northeastern Illinois University, B
Northern Illinois University, BM
Northwestern University, B
Olivet Nazarene University, B
Principia College, B
Rockford College, B
Roosevelt University, BM
Saint Xavier University, B
Sauk Valley Community College, A
Southern Illinois University Carbondale, B
Trinity Christian College, B
University of Chicago, BMD
University of Illinois at Chicago, B
University of Illinois at Urbana-Champaign, BMD
Western Illinois University, B
Wheaton College, B

Indiana

Anderson University, B
Ball State University, B
Butler University, B
DePauw University, B
Earlham College, B
Franklin College, B
Goshen College, B
Grace College, B
Hanover College, B
Indiana State University, BM
Indiana University Bloomington, BMD
Indiana University Northwest, B

Indiana University-Purdue University Fort
  Wayne, AB
Indiana University-Purdue University Indianapolis, B
Indiana University South Bend, B
Indiana University Southeast, B
Indiana Wesleyan University, B
Manchester College, B
Marian College, B
Purdue University, MD
Purdue University Calumet, B
Saint Mary-of-the-Woods College, B
Saint Mary's College, B
Taylor University, B
University of Evansville, B
University of Indianapolis, B
University of Notre Dame, BM
University of Southern Indiana, B
Valparaiso University, B
Vincennes University, A
Wabash College, B

Iowa

Briar Cliff University, B
Buena Vista University, B
Central College, B
Clarke College, B
Coe College, B
Cornell College, B
Dordt College, B
Graceland University, B
Grinnell College, B
Iowa Lakes Community College, A
Iowa State University of Science and Technology, B
Kirkwood Community College, A
Loras College, B
Luther College, B
Morningside College, B
Northwestern College, B
St. Ambrose University, B
Simpson College, B
The University of Iowa, BMDO
University of Northern Iowa, BM
Wartburg College, B

Kansas

Baker University, B
Benedictine College, B
Bethel College, B
Fort Hays State University, B
Friends University, AB
Independence Community College, A
Kansas State University, M
Kansas Wesleyan University, B
McPherson College, B
MidAmerica Nazarene University, B
Pittsburg State University, B
University of Kansas, BMD
Washburn University, B
Wichita State University, BM

Kentucky

Asbury College, B
Bellarmine University, B
Berea College, B
Brescia University, B
Centre College, B
Eastern Kentucky University, B
Georgetown College, B
Kentucky Wesleyan College, B
Morehead State University, B
Murray State University, B
Northern Kentucky University, B
St. Catharine College, A
Thomas More College, A
University of Kentucky, BMD
University of Louisville, BM
Western Kentucky University, B

Louisiana

Centenary College of Louisiana, B
Dillard University, B
Grambling State University, B
Louisiana College, B
Louisiana State University and Agricultural and
  Mechanical College, BM
Louisiana State University in Shreveport, B

Louisiana Tech University, B
Loyola University New Orleans, B
McNeese State University, B
Southeastern Louisiana University, B
Southern University and Agricultural and Mechanical
  College, B
Southern University at New Orleans, B
Tulane University, BMD
University of Louisiana at Lafayette, B
University of Louisiana at Monroe, B
University of New Orleans, B
Xavier University of Louisiana, B

Maine

Bates College, B
Bowdoin College, B
Colby College, B
University of Maine, B

Maryland

Goucher College, B
Hood College, B
The Johns Hopkins University, BD
Loyola College in Maryland, B
McDaniel College, B
Mount St. Mary's University, B
Salisbury University, B
Towson University, B
University of Maryland, Baltimore County, BM
University of Maryland, College Park, BMD
Washington College, B

Massachusetts

American International College, B
Amherst College, B
Assumption College, B
Atlantic Union College, B
Boston College, MD
Boston University, BMD
Brandeis University, B
Bridgewater State College, B
Clark University, B
College of the Holy Cross, B
Elms College, B
Emmanuel College, B
Endicott College, B
Framingham State College, BM
Gordon College, B
Harvard University, BMD
Merrimack College, B
Mount Holyoke College, B
Northeastern University, B
Regis College, B
Simmons College, BMO
Simon's Rock College of Bard, B
Smith College, B
Suffolk University, B
Tufts University, B
University of Massachusetts Amherst, BMD
University of Massachusetts Boston, B
University of Massachusetts Dartmouth, B
Wellesley College, B
Williams College, B
Worcester State College, B

Michigan

Adrian College, AB
Albion College, B
Alma College, B
Andrews University, B
Aquinas College, B
Calvin College, B
Central Michigan University, BM
Concordia University, B
Cornerstone University, B
Eastern Michigan University, BM
Grand Valley State University, B
Hillsdale College, B
Hope College, B
Kalamazoo College, B
Madonna University, B
Michigan State University, BMD
Northern Michigan University, B
Oakland University, B
Saginaw Valley State University, B
Siena Heights University, B

Spring Arbor University, B
University of Michigan, BD
University of Michigan-Dearborn, B
University of Michigan-Flint, B
Wayne State University, M
Western Michigan University, BM

Minnesota

Augsburg College, B
Bemidji State University, B
Bethel University, B
Carleton College, B
College of Saint Benedict, B
College of St. Catherine, B
Concordia College, B
Gustavus Adolphus College, B
Hamline University, B
Macalester College, B
Minnesota State University Mankato, BM
Minnesota State University Moorhead, B
St. Cloud State University, B
Saint John's University, B
Saint Mary's University of Minnesota, B
St. Olaf College, B
Southwest Minnesota State University, B
University of Minnesota, Duluth, B
University of Minnesota, Morris, B
University of Minnesota, Twin Cities Campus, BMD
University of St. Thomas, B
Winona State University, B

Mississippi

Blue Mountain College, B
Millsaps College, B
Mississippi College, B
Mississippi State University, M
Mississippi University for Women, B
University of Mississippi, BM

Missouri

Central Methodist University, B
Central Missouri State University, B
College of the Ozarks, B
Drury University, B
Evangel University, B
Jefferson College, A
Lincoln University, B
Lindenwood University, B
Missouri Southern State University, B
Missouri State University, B
Missouri Western State University, B
Northwest Missouri State University, B
Park University, B
Rockhurst University, B
Saint Louis University, BM
Southeast Missouri State University, B
Southwest Baptist University, B
Truman State University, B
University of Missouri-Columbia, BMD
University of Missouri-Kansas City, B
University of Missouri-St. Louis, B
Washington University in St. Louis, BMD
Webster University, B
Westminster College, B
William Jewell College, B
William Woods University, B

Montana

Carroll College, B
Montana State University-Billings, B
The University of Montana-Missoula, BM

Nebraska

Chadron State College, B
Concordia University, B
Creighton University, B
Dana College, B
Doane College, B
Hastings College, B
Nebraska Wesleyan University, B
Union College, B
University of Nebraska at Kearney, B
University of Nebraska-Lincoln, BMD
University of Nebraska at Omaha, B
Wayne State College, B

Western Nebraska Community College, A

Nevada

University of Nevada, Las Vegas, BM
University of Nevada, Reno, BM

New Hampshire

Dartmouth College, B
Keene State College, B
Plymouth State University, B
Rivier College, B
Saint Anselm College, B
University of New Hampshire, BM

New Jersey

Caldwell College, B
The College of New Jersey, BM
College of Saint Elizabeth, B
Drew University, B
Fairleigh Dickinson University, College at
  Florham, B
Fairleigh Dickinson University, Metropolitan
  Campus, B
Georgian Court University, B
Kean University, B
Montclair State University, BM
New Jersey City University, B
Princeton University, BD
Ramapo College of New Jersey, B
Rider University, B
Rowan University, B
Rutgers, The State University of New Jersey,
  Camden, B
Rutgers, The State University of New Jersey, New
  Brunswick/Piscataway, BMD
Rutgers, The State University of New Jersey,
  Newark, B
Saint Peter's College, B
Seton Hall University, B
William Paterson University of New Jersey, B

New Mexico

Eastern New Mexico University, B
New Mexico Highlands University, BM
New Mexico Military Institute, A
New Mexico State University, M
Santa Fe Community College, A
University of New Mexico, BMD
Western New Mexico University, B

New York

Adelphi University, B
Alfred University, B
Bard College, B
Barnard College, B
Bernard M. Baruch College of the City University of
  New York, B
Brooklyn College of the City University of New
  York, BMD
Buffalo State College, State University of New
  York, B
Canisius College, B
City College of the City University of New York, BM
Colgate University, B
College of Mount Saint Vincent, B
The College of New Rochelle, B
The College of Saint Rose, B
College of Staten Island of the City University of
  New York, B
Columbia College, B
Columbia University, School of General Studies, B
Cornell University, BD
Daemen College, B
Dominican College, B
Elmira College, B
Fordham University, B
Hamilton College, B
Hartwick College, B
Hobart and William Smith Colleges, B
Hofstra University, BM
Houghton College, B
Hunter College of the City University of New
  York, BM
Iona College, BM
Ithaca College, B

Le Moyne College, B
Lehman College of the City University of New
York, BM
Long Island University, C.W. Post Campus, BM
Manhattan College, B
Manhattanville College, B
Marist College, B
Mercy College, B
Molloy College, B
Nazareth College of Rochester, B
New York University, BMD
Niagara University, B
Pace University, B
Purchase College, State University of New York, B
Queens College of the City University of New
York, BM
Russell Sage College, B
St. Bonaventure University, B
St. Francis College, B
St. John Fisher College, B
St. John's University, BM
St. Joseph's College, New York, B
St. Joseph's College, Suffolk Campus, B
St. Lawrence University, B
St. Thomas Aquinas College, B
Sarah Lawrence College, B
Siena College, B
Skidmore College, B
State University of New York at Binghamton, BMO
State University of New York at Buffalo, BMD
State University of New York College at
Brockport, B
State University of New York College at Cortland, B
State University of New York College at Geneseo, B
State University of New York College at Old
Westbury, B
State University of New York College at Oneonta, B
State University of New York College at Potsdam, B
State University of New York, Fredonia, B
State University of New York at New Paltz, B
State University of New York at Oswego, B
State University of New York at Plattsburgh, B
Stony Brook University, State University of New
York, B
Syracuse University, BM
United States Military Academy, B
University at Albany, State University of New
York, BMD
University of Rochester, B
Vassar College, B
Wagner College, B
Wells College, B
York College of the City University of New York, B

North Carolina

Appalachian State University, B
Barton College, B
Campbell University, B
Catawba College, B
Cleveland Community College, A
Davidson College, B
Duke University, BDO
East Carolina University, B
Elon University, B
Fayetteville State University, B
Gardner-Webb University, B
Greensboro College, B
Guilford College, B
High Point University, B
Johnson C. Smith University, B
Lenoir-Rhyne College, B
Mars Hill College, B
Meredith College, B
Methodist College, AB
North Carolina Central University, B
North Carolina State University, BM
Peace College, B
Salem College, B
Shaw University, B
The University of North Carolina at Asheville, B
The University of North Carolina at Chapel Hill, MD
The University of North Carolina at Charlotte, BM
The University of North Carolina at Greensboro, BM
The University of North Carolina at Pembroke, B
The University of North Carolina Wilmington, B
Wake Forest University, B

Warren Wilson College, B
Western Carolina University, B
Wingate University, B
Winston-Salem State University, B

North Dakota

Dickinson State University, B
Minot State University, B
North Dakota State University, B
University of North Dakota, B
Valley City State University, B

Ohio

Antioch College, B
Ashland University, B
Baldwin-Wallace College, B
Bluffton University, B
Bowling Green State University, BM
Capital University, B
Case Western Reserve University, B
Cedarville University, B
Cleveland State University, BM
The College of Wooster, B
Denison University, B
Franciscan University of Steubenville, B
Heidelberg College, B
Hiram College, B
John Carroll University, B
Kent State University, BM
Kenyon College, B
Lake Erie College, B
Malone College, B
Marietta College, B
Miami University, BM
Miami University Hamilton, B
Miami University-Middletown Campus, A
Mount Union College, B
Mount Vernon Nazarene University, B
Muskingum College, B
Oberlin College, B
Ohio Northern University, B
The Ohio State University, BMD
Ohio University, BM
Ohio Wesleyan University, B
Otterbein College, B
The University of Akron, BM
University of Cincinnati, BMD
University of Dayton, B
The University of Findlay, B
The University of Toledo, BM
Walsh University, B
Wilmington College, B
Wittenberg University, B
Wright State University, B
Xavier University, AB
Youngstown State University, B

Oklahoma

Northeastern State University, B
Northwestern Oklahoma State University, B
Oklahoma Baptist University, B
Oklahoma Christian University, B
Oklahoma City University, B
Oklahoma State University, B
Oral Roberts University, B
Southeastern Oklahoma State University, B
Southern Nazarene University, B
Tulsa Community College, A
University of Central Oklahoma, B
University of Oklahoma, BMDO
University of Tulsa, B

Oregon

George Fox University, B
Lewis & Clark College, B
Linfield College, B
Oregon State University, B
Pacific University, B
Portland State University, BM
Reed College, B
Southern Oregon University, B
University of Oregon, BM
University of Portland, B
Western Oregon University, B

Willamette University, B

Pennsylvania

Albright College, B
Allegheny College, B
Arcadia University, B
Bloomsburg University of Pennsylvania, B
Bryn Mawr College, B
Bucknell University, B
Cabrini College, B
California University of Pennsylvania, B
Carlow University, B
Carnegie Mellon University, B
Cedar Crest College, B
Chatham College, BM
Chestnut Hill College, AB
Cheyney University of Pennsylvania, B
Clarion University of Pennsylvania, B
DeSales University, B
Dickinson College, B
Duquesne University, B
East Stroudsburg University of Pennsylvania, B
Eastern University, B
Edinboro University of Pennsylvania, B
Elizabethtown College, B
Franklin and Marshall College, B
Geneva College, B
Gettysburg College, B
Grove City College, B
Haverford College, B
Holy Family University, B
Immaculata University, B
Indiana University of Pennsylvania, B
Juniata College, B
King's College, B
Kutztown University of Pennsylvania, B
La Salle University, B
Lafayette College, B
Lebanon Valley College, B
Lehigh University, B
Lincoln University, B
Lock Haven University of Pennsylvania, B
Lycoming College, B
Mansfield University of Pennsylvania, B
Marywood University, B
Mercyhurst College, B
Messiah College, B
Millersville University of Pennsylvania, BM
Moravian College, B
Muhlenberg College, B
The Pennsylvania State University Abington
College, B
The Pennsylvania State University Altoona
College, B
The Pennsylvania State University Beaver Campus
of the Commonwealth College, B
The Pennsylvania State University Berks Campus of
the Berks-Lehigh Valley College, B
The Pennsylvania State University Delaware County
Campus of the Commonwealth College, B
The Pennsylvania State University DuBois Campus
of the Commonwealth College, B
The Pennsylvania State University at Erie, The
Behrend College, B
The Pennsylvania State University Fayette Campus
of the Commonwealth College, B
The Pennsylvania State University Hazleton
Campus of the Commonwealth College, B
The Pennsylvania State University, Lehigh Valley
Campus of the Berks-Lehigh Valley College, B
The Pennsylvania State University McKeesport
Campus of the Commonwealth College, B
The Pennsylvania State University Mont Alto
Campus of the Commonwealth College, B
The Pennsylvania State University New Kensington
Campus of the Commonwealth College, B
The Pennsylvania State University Schuylkill
Campus of the Capital College, B
The Pennsylvania State University Shenango
Campus of the Commonwealth College, B
The Pennsylvania State University University Park
Campus, BMD
The Pennsylvania State University Wilkes-Barre
Campus of the Commonwealth College, B

The Pennsylvania State University Worthington
  Scranton Campus of the Commonwealth
  College, B
The Pennsylvania State University York Campus of
  the Commonwealth College, B
Rosemont College, B
Saint Francis University, B
Saint Joseph's University, B
Saint Vincent College, B
Seton Hill University, B
Shippensburg University of Pennsylvania, B
Slippery Rock University of Pennsylvania, B
Susquehanna University, B
Swarthmore College, B
Temple University, BMD
Thiel College, B
University of Pennsylvania, BMD
University of Pittsburgh, BMD
The University of Scranton, B
Ursinus College, B
Villanova University, B
Washington & Jefferson College, B
West Chester University of Pennsylvania, BM
Westminster College, B
Widener University, B
Wilkes University, B
Wilson College, B
York College of Pennsylvania, B

Puerto Rico

Inter American University of Puerto Rico,
  Metropolitan Campus, BM
Inter American University of Puerto Rico, San
  Germán Campus, B
Pontifical Catholic University of Puerto Rico, B
Universidad Adventista de las Antillas, B
Universidad del Turabo, B
University of Puerto Rico, Cayey University
  College, B
University of Puerto Rico, Río Piedras, B

Rhode Island

Brown University, B
Providence College, B
Rhode Island College, B
Salve Regina University, B
University of Rhode Island, BM

South Carolina

Anderson University, B
Bob Jones University, B
Charleston Southern University, B
The Citadel, The Military College of South
  Carolina, B
Coastal Carolina University, B
College of Charleston, B
Columbia College, B
Converse College, B
Erskine College, B
Francis Marion University, B
Furman University, B
Lander University, B
Newberry College, B
Presbyterian College, B
South Carolina State University, B
University of South Carolina, BM
University of South Carolina Upstate, B
Winthrop University, M
Wofford College, B

South Dakota

Augustana College, B
Black Hills State University, B
Dakota Wesleyan University, B
Northern State University, B
South Dakota State University, B
The University of South Dakota, B

Tennessee

Austin Peay State University, B
Belmont University, B
Bryan College, B
Carson-Newman College, B
Fisk University, B
King College, B

Lambuth University, B
Lipscomb University, B
Maryville College, B
Rhodes College, B
Sewanee: The University of the South, B
Southern Adventist University, B
Tennessee State University, B
Tennessee Technological University, B
Union University, B
University of Memphis, M
The University of Tennessee, BMD
The University of Tennessee at Chattanooga, B
The University of Tennessee at Martin, B
Vanderbilt University, BMD

Texas

Abilene Christian University, B
Angelo State University, B
Austin College, B
Austin Community College, A
Baylor University, BM
Blinn College, A
East Texas Baptist University, B
Hardin-Simmons University, B
Hill College of the Hill Junior College District, A
Houston Baptist University, B
Howard Payne University, B
Lamar University, B
Lee College, A
Lon Morris College, A
McMurry University, B
Midland College, A
Midwestern State University, B
Our Lady of the Lake University of San Antonio, B
Prairie View A&M University, B
Rice University, BM
St. Edward's University, B
St. Mary's University of San Antonio, B
St. Philip's College, A
Sam Houston State University, B
Southern Methodist University, B
Southwestern University, B
Stephen F. Austin State University, B
Sul Ross State University, B
Tarleton State University, B
Texas A&M International University, BM
Texas A&M University, BM
Texas A&M University-Commerce, BMD
Texas A&M University-Corpus Christi, B
Texas A&M University-Kingsville, BM
Texas Christian University, B
Texas Lutheran University, B
Texas Southern University, B
Texas State University-San Marcos, BM
Texas Tech University, BMD
Texas Wesleyan University, B
Trinity University, B
Trinity Valley Community College, A
University of Dallas, B
University of Houston, BMDO
University of the Incarnate Word, B
University of Mary Hardin-Baylor, B
University of North Texas, BM
University of St. Thomas, B
The University of Texas at Arlington, BM
The University of Texas at Austin, BMD
The University of Texas at Brownsville, BM
The University of Texas at El Paso, BM
The University of Texas-Pan American, BM
The University of Texas of the Permian Basin, B
The University of Texas at San Antonio, BM
The University of Texas at Tyler, B
Wayland Baptist University, B
West Texas A&M University, B
Wharton County Junior College, A

Utah

Brigham Young University, BM
Snow College, A
Southern Utah University, B
University of Utah, BMD
Utah State University, B
Utah Valley State College, B

Weber State University, B

Vermont

Bennington College, BM
Castleton State College, B
Marlboro College, B
Middlebury College, BMD
Saint Michael's College, B
University of Vermont, B

Virginia

Bridgewater College, B
Christopher Newport University, BM
The College of William and Mary, B
Eastern Mennonite University, B
Emory & Henry College, B
Ferrum College, B
Hampden-Sydney College, B
Hollins University, B
Liberty University, B
Longwood University, B
Lynchburg College, B
Mary Baldwin College, B
Old Dominion University, B
Randolph-Macon College, B
Randolph-Macon Woman's College, B
Roanoke College, B
Shenandoah University, B
Southern Virginia University, B
Sweet Briar College, B
University of Mary Washington, B
University of Richmond, B
University of Virginia, BMD
The University of Virginia's College at Wise, B
Virginia Polytechnic Institute and State University, B
Virginia Wesleyan College, B
Washington and Lee University, B

Washington

Centralia College, A
Eastern Washington University, B
Everett Community College, A
Gonzaga University, B
Heritage University, B
Pacific Lutheran University, B
Seattle Pacific University, B
Seattle University, B
Skagit Valley College, A
Tacoma Community College, A
University of Puget Sound, B
University of Washington, BM
Walla Walla College, B
Washington State University, BM
Western Washington University, B
Whitman College, B
Whitworth College, B

West Virginia

Bethany College, B
Davis & Elkins College, B
West Virginia University, M
Wheeling Jesuit University, B

Wisconsin

Beloit College, B
Cardinal Stritch University, B
Carroll College, B
Carthage College, B
Concordia University Wisconsin, B
Edgewood College, B
Lakeland College, B
Lawrence University, B
Marian College of Fond du Lac, B
Marquette University, BM
Mount Mary College, B
Ripon College, B
St. Norbert College, B
University of Wisconsin-Eau Claire, B
University of Wisconsin-Green Bay, AB
University of Wisconsin-La Crosse, B
University of Wisconsin-Madison, BMD
University of Wisconsin-Milwaukee, BM
University of Wisconsin-Oshkosh, B
University of Wisconsin-Parkside, B
University of Wisconsin-Platteville, B

University of Wisconsin-River Falls, B
University of Wisconsin-Stevens Point, B
University of Wisconsin-Whitewater, B
Viterbo University, B
Wisconsin Lutheran College, B

Wyoming

Casper College, A
Laramie County Community College, A
University of Wyoming, BM
Western Wyoming Community College, A

Alberta

University of Alberta, B
University of Calgary, BMD
University of Lethbridge, M

British Columbia

The University of British Columbia, B
University of Victoria, B

Manitoba

University of Manitoba, BMD

New Brunswick

Mount Allison University, B
St. Thomas University, B
University of New Brunswick Fredericton, BM

Newfoundland and Labrador

Memorial University of Newfoundland, B

Nova Scotia

Dalhousie University, B
Mount Saint Vincent University, B
University of King's College, B

Ontario

Brock University, B
Carleton University, B
Laurentian University, B
Queen's University at Kingston, BM
Trent University, B
University of Guelph, B
University of Ottawa, BMD
University of Toronto, BMD
University of Waterloo, B
The University of Western Ontario, BMD
University of Windsor, B
Wilfrid Laurier University, B
York University, B

Prince Edward Island

University of Prince Edward Island, B

Quebec

Bishop's University, B
Concordia University, B
McGill University, B
Université Laval, BMD
Université de Montréal, BMD

Saskatchewan

University of Regina, B
University of Saskatchewan, B

SPANISH LANGUAGE TEACHER EDUCATION

Alabama

Auburn University, B

Arizona

Northern Arizona University, B
The University of Arizona, B

Arkansas

Arkansas State University, B
Southern Arkansas University-Magnolia, B

California

California Lutheran University, B

California State University, Chico, B

Colorado

Colorado State University, B
Colorado State University-Pueblo, B

Delaware

Delaware State University, B

District of Columbia

The Catholic University of America, B

Georgia

Columbus State University, B
Georgia Southern University, B

Idaho

Northwest Nazarene University, B

Illinois

Chicago State University, B
Elmhurst College, B
Greenville College, B
Illinois Wesleyan University, B
Saint Xavier University, B
University of Illinois at Chicago, B
University of Illinois at Urbana-Champaign, B

Indiana

Anderson University, B
Franklin College, B
Grace College, B
Indiana University Bloomington, B
Indiana University Northwest, B
Indiana University-Purdue University Fort Wayne, B
Indiana University-Purdue University Indianapolis, B
Indiana University South Bend, B
Taylor University, B
University of Evansville, B
University of Indianapolis, B
Valparaiso University, B

Iowa

Buena Vista University, B
Dordt College, B
St. Ambrose University, B
The University of Iowa, B

Kansas

MidAmerica Nazarene University, B
Pittsburg State University, B

Kentucky

Berea College, B
Kentucky Wesleyan College, B
Murray State University, B

Louisiana

Centenary College of Louisiana, B
Southeastern Louisiana University, B
Southern University and Agricultural and Mechanical College, B
University of Louisiana at Lafayette, B
University of Louisiana at Monroe, B
Xavier University of Louisiana, B

Maine

University of Maine, B

Maryland

Frederick Community College, A

Michigan

Alma College, B
Central Michigan University, B
Eastern Michigan University, B
Hope College, B
Northern Michigan University, B
University of Michigan-Flint, B
Western Michigan University, B

Minnesota

Bethel University, B
College of St. Catherine, B

Concordia College, B
Minnesota State University Moorhead, B
Saint Mary's University of Minnesota, B
University of Minnesota, Duluth, B

Mississippi

Blue Mountain College, B

Missouri

Evangel University, B
Lindenwood University, B
Missouri State University, B
Missouri Western State University, B
University of Missouri-St. Louis, B
Washington University in St. Louis, B

Montana

Carroll College, B
Montana State University-Billings, B

Nebraska

Chadron State College, B
Concordia University, B
Hastings College, B
University of Nebraska-Lincoln, B

New Hampshire

Keene State College, B

New Jersey

The College of New Jersey, B

New York

Brooklyn College of the City University of New York, B
The College of Saint Rose, B
Daemen College, B
Dowling College, B
Elmira College, B
Hofstra University, B
Iona College, B
Ithaca College, B
Le Moyne College, B
Long Island University, Brooklyn Campus, B
Long Island University, C.W. Post Campus, B
Manhattanville College, B
Marist College, B
Mercy College, B
Molloy College, B
Niagara University, B
Pace University, B
St. Bonaventure University, B
St. John's University, B
St. Joseph's College, Suffolk Campus, B
State University of New York College at Brockport, B
State University of New York College at Cortland, B
State University of New York College at Old Westbury, B
State University of New York College at Oneonta, B
State University of New York College at Potsdam, B
University at Albany, State University of New York, B

North Carolina

Appalachian State University, B
Campbell University, B
East Carolina University, B
Fayetteville State University, B
Greensboro College, B
North Carolina Central University, B
North Carolina State University, B
The University of North Carolina at Charlotte, B
The University of North Carolina at Greensboro, B
The University of North Carolina Wilmington, B
Western Carolina University, B
Winston-Salem State University, B

North Dakota

Minot State University, B
North Dakota State University, B

Valley City State University, B

Ohio

Cedarville University, B
Kent State University, B
Malone College, B
Miami University Hamilton, B
Mount Vernon Nazarene University, B
Notre Dame College, B
Ohio Northern University, B
Ohio University, B
Ohio Wesleyan University, B
The University of Akron, B
The University of Toledo, B
Youngstown State University, B

Oklahoma

Oklahoma Baptist University, B
Oral Roberts University, B
Southeastern Oklahoma State University, B
Southern Nazarene University, B

Pennsylvania

Duquesne University, B
Juniata College, B
La Roche College, B
Lebanon Valley College, B
Mansfield University of Pennsylvania, B
Marywood University, B
Messiah College, B
Moravian College, B
Seton Hill University, B
West Chester University of Pennsylvania, B
Widener University, B

Puerto Rico

Bayamon Central University, B
Inter American University of Puerto Rico, Aguadilla
    Campus, B
Inter American University of Puerto Rico,
    Metropolitan Campus, B
Universidad Adventista de las Antillas, B
University of Puerto Rico, Cayey University
    College, B

Rhode Island

Rhode Island College, B
Salve Regina University, B

South Carolina

Anderson University, B
Bob Jones University, B
Charleston Southern University, B

South Dakota

The University of South Dakota, B

Tennessee

King College, B
Maryville College, B
The University of Tennessee at Martin, B

Texas

Abilene Christian University, B
Baylor University, B
East Texas Baptist University, B
Hardin-Simmons University, B
Howard Payne University, B
St. Edward's University, B
Texas A&M International University, B
University of the Incarnate Word, B

Utah

Brigham Young University, B
University of Utah, B
Utah Valley State College, B
Weber State University, B

Virginia

Eastern Mennonite University, B
Liberty University, B

Old Dominion University, B

Washington

Central Washington University, B
Eastern Washington University, B
Washington State University, B

West Virginia

Wheeling Jesuit University, B

Wisconsin

Carroll College, B
Concordia University Wisconsin, B
Marian College of Fond du Lac, B
Mount Mary College, B
University of Wisconsin-River Falls, B
Viterbo University, B

Quebec

Bishop's University, B

SPECIAL EDUCATION AND TEACHING

Alabama

Alabama Agricultural and Mechanical University, BM
Alabama State University, BM
Athens State University, B
Auburn University, BMDO
Auburn University Montgomery, MO
Jacksonville State University, BM
Troy University, B
The University of Alabama, B
The University of Alabama at Birmingham, BM
University of North Alabama, BM
University of South Alabama, BMO
The University of West Alabama, BM

Alaska

University of Alaska Anchorage, M

Arizona

Arizona State University, BM
Arizona State University West, BM
Grand Canyon University, B
Northern Arizona University, BM
Prescott College, B
The University of Arizona, BMDO
University of Phoenix Online Campus, MO
University of Phoenix-Phoenix Campus, MO
University of Phoenix-Southern Arizona Campus, O

Arkansas

Arkansas State University, BMDO
Harding University, BM
Henderson State University, MO
John Brown University, B
University of Arkansas, M
University of Arkansas at Little Rock, M
University of Arkansas at Monticello, B
University of Arkansas at Pine Bluff, B
University of Central Arkansas, BM
University of the Ozarks, B

California

Argosy University/San Francisco Bay Area, M
Azusa Pacific University, M
California Baptist University, M
California Lutheran University, M
California Polytechnic State University, San Luis
    Obispo, M
California State University, Chico, M
California State University, East Bay, M
California State University, Fresno, M
California State University, Fullerton, M
California State University, Long Beach, M
California State University, Northridge, M
California State University, Sacramento, M
California State University, San Bernardino, M
California State University, Stanislaus, M
Chapman University, M
Dominican University of California, O
Fresno Pacific University, M

Holy Names University, M
La Sierra University, BM
Loyola Marymount University, M
Mount St. Mary's College, M
National University, M
Notre Dame de Namur University, MO
Pacific Oaks College, B
Saint Mary's College of California, M
San Diego State University, M
San Francisco State University, MDO
San Jose State University, MO
Santa Clara University, MO
Sonoma State University, M
University of California, Berkeley, D
University of California, Los Angeles, BD
University of La Verne, M
University of the Pacific, BM
University of Phoenix-Southern California
    Campus, M
University of Southern California, M

Colorado

Adams State College, M
Regis University, M
University of Colorado at Colorado Springs, M
University of Northern Colorado, BMD
Western State College of Colorado, B

Connecticut

Central Connecticut State University, M
Fairfield University, MO
Southern Connecticut State University, BMO
University of Connecticut, BMD
University of Hartford, B
Western Connecticut State University, M

Delaware

Delaware State University, BM
University of Delaware, BM
Wilmington College, M

District of Columbia

American University, M
Gallaudet University, MDO
The George Washington University, MDO
Howard University, MO
Trinity (Washington) University, BM
University of the District of Columbia, BM

Florida

Barry University, BMDO
Carlos Albizu University, Miami Campus, M
Florida Atlantic University, BMD
Florida Gulf Coast University, BM
Florida International University, MD
Jacksonville University, B
Lynn University, M
Miami Dade College, B
Nova Southeastern University, B
St. Petersburg College, B
St. Thomas University, M
Stetson University, M
University of Central Florida, BMD
University of Florida, BMDO
University of Miami, BMDO
University of North Florida, BM
University of South Florida, BM
University of West Florida, BM
Warner Southern College, B

Georgia

Albany State University, BM
Armstrong Atlantic State University, BM
Augusta State University, BMO
Brenau University, BM
Columbus State University, BO
Georgia College & State University, BM
Georgia Southern University, BM
Georgia Southwestern State University, BM
Georgia State University, MDO
Kennesaw State University, M
North Georgia College & State University, BM
Piedmont College, B
University of Georgia, MDO
University of West Georgia, MO

Valdosta State University, BMO

Guam

University of Guam, BM

Hawaii

Brigham Young University-Hawaii, B
University of Hawaii at Manoa, BMD
University of Phoenix-Hawaii Campus, MO

Idaho

Boise State University, BM
Idaho State University, BMO
Northwest Nazarene University, M
University of Idaho, BM

Illinois

Benedictine University, BM
Chicago State University, BM
DePaul University, M
Dominican University, M
Eastern Illinois University, BM
Elmhurst College, BM
Governors State University, M
Greenville College, B
Illinois State University, BMD
Lewis University, BM
Loyola University Chicago, BM
MacMurray College, B
National-Louis University, MO
Northeastern Illinois University, BM
Northern Illinois University, BM
Northwestern University, MD
Quincy University, B
Rend Lake College, A
Rockford College, BM
Roosevelt University, BM
St. Augustine College, A
Saint Xavier University, M
Sauk Valley Community College, A
Southern Illinois University Carbondale, BM
Southern Illinois University Edwardsville, BM
Trinity Christian College, B
University of Illinois at Chicago, MD
University of Illinois at Urbana-Champaign, BMDO
University of St. Francis, BM
Western Illinois University, BM

Indiana

Ball State University, BMDO
Butler University, M
Grace College, B
Huntington University, B
Indiana State University, B
Indiana University Bloomington, BMDO
Indiana University South Bend, BM
Indiana University Southeast, B
Indiana Wesleyan University, B
Manchester College, B
Marian College, B
Purdue University, MD
Saint Mary-of-the-Woods College, B
University of Evansville, B
University of Saint Francis, BM
University of Southern Indiana, B
Valparaiso University, M

Iowa

Buena Vista University, B
Clarke College, BM
Drake University, M
Iowa State University of Science and Technology, M
Iowa Wesleyan College, B
Loras College, M
Morningside College, BM
St. Ambrose University, M
The University of Iowa, MD
University of Northern Iowa, BMD
William Penn University, B

Kansas

Benedictine College, B
Emporia State University, M
Fort Hays State University, M
Kansas State University, MD

Kansas Wesleyan University, B
McPherson College, B
MidAmerica Nazarene University, M
Pittsburg State University, M
Southwestern College, M
Tabor College, B
University of Kansas, MD
University of Saint Mary, M
Washburn University, M
Wichita State University, M

Kentucky

Asbury College, M
Bellarmine University, BM
Brescia University, B
Campbellsville University, M
Eastern Kentucky University, BM
Midway College, B
Morehead State University, BM
Murray State University, BM
Northern Kentucky University, BO
Spalding University, BM
Union College, BM
University of the Cumberlands, BM
University of Kentucky, BMDO
University of Louisville, MD
Western Kentucky University, BM

Louisiana

Dillard University, B
Grambling State University, B
Louisiana College, B
Louisiana State University in Shreveport, B
Louisiana Tech University, BM
McNeese State University, B
Nicholls State University, B
Northwestern State University of Louisiana, BMO
Southeastern Louisiana University, BM
Southern University and Agricultural and Mechanical
   College, BMD
University of Louisiana at Lafayette, B
University of Louisiana at Monroe, BM
University of New Orleans, MDO
Xavier University of Louisiana, BM

Maine

University of Maine, MO
University of Maine at Farmington, B
University of Southern Maine, M

Maryland

Bowie State University, BM
College of Notre Dame of Maryland, B
Columbia Union College, B
Coppin State University, BM
Frostburg State University, M
Goucher College, B
The Johns Hopkins University, MDO
Loyola College in Maryland, BMO
McDaniel College, M
Towson University, BM
University of Maryland, College Park, BMDO
University of Maryland Eastern Shore, BM

Massachusetts

American International College, BMO
Assumption College, M
Boston College, BMO
Boston University, BMDO
Bridgewater State College, BM
Curry College, BMO
Eastern Nazarene College, BMO
Elms College, BM
Endicott College, M
Fitchburg State College, BM
Framingham State College, M
Gordon College, B
Hebrew College, O
Lesley University, BMO
Massachusetts College of Liberal Arts, M
Northeastern University, M
Salem State College, M
Simmons College, BMO
Smith College, M
Tufts University, B

University of Massachusetts Amherst, MDO
University of Massachusetts Boston, M
Westfield State College, BM
Wheelock College, BM
Worcester State College, M

Michigan

Andrews University, M
Calvin College, BM
Central Michigan University, M
Eastern Michigan University, BMO
Grand Valley State University, BM
Kellogg Community College, A
Madonna University, BM
Michigan State University, BMD
Northern Michigan University, BM
Oakland University, BMO
Saginaw Valley State University, BM
University of Detroit Mercy, BM
University of Michigan, D
University of Michigan-Dearborn, M
University of Phoenix-Metro Detroit Campus, M
Wayne State University, BMDO
Western Michigan University, MD

Minnesota

Bemidji State University, M
Minnesota State University Mankato, M
Minnesota State University Moorhead, BM
St. Cloud State University, BM
Saint Mary's University of Minnesota, M
Southwest Minnesota State University, M
University of Minnesota, Duluth, B
University of Minnesota, Twin Cities Campus, MDO
University of St. Thomas, MO
Winona State University, BM

Mississippi

Alcorn State University, BM
Delta State University, BM
Jackson State University, BMO
Mississippi College, B
Mississippi State University, BMDO
Mississippi University for Women, B
University of Mississippi, B
University of Southern Mississippi, BMDO
William Carey College, M

Missouri

Avila University, B
Central Missouri State University, BMO
Culver-Stockton College, B
Evangel University, B
Fontbonne University, BM
Lincoln University, BM
Lindenwood University, B
Missouri Southern State University, B
Missouri State University, BMO
Missouri Valley College, B
Northwest Missouri State University, BM
Saint Louis University, M
Southeast Missouri State University, BM
University of Missouri-Columbia, BMD
University of Missouri-Kansas City, M
University of Missouri-St. Louis, BM
Washington University in St. Louis, M
Webster University, M
William Woods University, B

Montana

Montana State University-Billings, ABM
University of Great Falls, B

Nebraska

Chadron State College, B
College of Saint Mary, B
Concordia University, B
Dana College, B
Doane College, B
Hastings College, B
Nebraska Wesleyan University, B
Peru State College, B
University of Nebraska at Kearney, BM
University of Nebraska-Lincoln, BM
University of Nebraska at Omaha, M

Wayne State College, BM
York College, B

Nevada

Nevada State College at Henderson, B
University of Nevada, Las Vegas, BMDO
University of Nevada, Reno, BMD

New Hampshire

Keene State College, BMO
New England College, BM
Plymouth State University, M
Rivier College, BM
Southern New Hampshire University, O
University of New Hampshire, M

New Jersey

Bloomfield College, B
Caldwell College, M
Centenary College, BM
The College of New Jersey, BM
College of Saint Elizabeth, B
Fairleigh Dickinson University, Metropolitan
  Campus, MO
Felician College, B
Georgian Court University, BMO
Kean University, BM
Monmouth University, BMO
Montclair State University, M
New Jersey City University, BM
Rider University, M
Rowan University, BM
Rutgers, The State University of New Jersey, New
  Brunswick/Piscataway, MD
Seton Hall University, B
William Paterson University of New Jersey, BM

New Mexico

College of Santa Fe, M
College of the Southwest, B
Eastern New Mexico University, BM
New Mexico Highlands University, BM
New Mexico State University, BM
University of New Mexico, BMDO
Western New Mexico University, BM

New York

Adelphi University, MO
Brooklyn College of the City University of New
  York, M
Buffalo State College, State University of New
  York, BM
Canisius College, M
City College of the City University of New York, M
The College of New Rochelle, BM
The College of Saint Rose, BM
College of Staten Island of the City University of
  New York, M
Daemen College, BM
Dominican College, BM
Dowling College, BM
D'Youville College, BM
Fordham University, MO
Hofstra University, MO
Houghton College, B
Hunter College of the City University of New
  York, M
Keuka College, B
Lehman College of the City University of New
  York, M
Long Island University, Brentwood Campus, M
Long Island University, Brooklyn Campus, M
Long Island University, C.W. Post Campus, M
Manhattan College, BMO
Manhattanville College, M
Marist College, B
Medgar Evers College of the City University of New
  York, B
Mercy College, B
Molloy College, B
Mount Saint Mary College, BM
Nazareth College of Rochester, B
New York University, BMO
Niagara University, BM
Pratt Institute, M

Queens College of the City University of New
  York, M
Roberts Wesleyan College, B
Rochester Institute of Technology, MO
St. Bonaventure University, B
St. John Fisher College, BMO
St. John's University, BM
St. Joseph's College, Suffolk Campus, BM
St. Thomas Aquinas College, BMO
State University of New York at Binghamton, M
State University of New York at Buffalo, D
State University of New York College at
  Brockport, M
State University of New York College at Cortland, M
State University of New York College at
  Geneseo, BM
State University of New York College at Old
  Westbury, B
State University of New York College at Potsdam, M
State University of New York at New Paltz, BM
State University of New York at Oswego, M
State University of New York at Plattsburgh, BM
Syracuse University, BMD
Touro College, B
University at Albany, State University of New
  York, M

North Carolina

Appalachian State University, M
Barton College, B
Bennett College For Women, B
Cleveland Community College, A
East Carolina University, M
Elizabeth City State University, B
Elon University, BM
Fayetteville Technical Community College, A
Greensboro College, B
High Point University, B
Louisburg College, A
Mars Hill College, B
Methodist College, B
North Carolina Agricultural and Technical State
  University, B
North Carolina Central University, M
North Carolina State University, M
Pfeiffer University, B
Saint Augustine's College, B
Salem College, M
The University of North Carolina at Charlotte, MD
The University of North Carolina at Greensboro, BM
The University of North Carolina Wilmington, M
Western Carolina University, BM
Winston-Salem State University, B

North Dakota

Minot State University, ABM
University of Mary, M
University of North Dakota, MD

Ohio

Ashland University, BM
Baldwin-Wallace College, M
Bowling Green State University, BM
Capital University, B
Cedarville University, B
Central State University, B
Cleveland State University, B
College of Mount St. Joseph, B
Heidelberg College, B
John Carroll University, B
Kent State University, BMDO
Malone College, M
Miami University, BM
Miami University Hamilton, B
Mount Vernon Nazarene University, B
Muskingum College, B
Notre Dame College, M
Ohio Dominican University, B
The Ohio State University, B
Ohio University, BMD
Shawnee State University, B
The University of Akron, BM
University of Cincinnati, BMD
University of Dayton, BM
The University of Findlay, BM
The University of Toledo, BMDO

Ursuline College, B
Walsh University, B
Wilmington College, M
Wright State University, BM
Xavier University, BM
Youngstown State University, BM

Oklahoma

East Central University, B
Langston University, B
Northeastern State University, BM
Northwestern Oklahoma State University, B
Oklahoma Baptist University, B
Oral Roberts University, B
Southeastern Oklahoma State University, B
Southwestern Oklahoma State University, BM
University of Central Oklahoma, BM
University of Oklahoma, BMD
University of Oklahoma Health Sciences Center, M

Oregon

Eastern Oregon University, B
Lewis & Clark College, M
Pacific University, M
Portland State University, MD
University of Portland, M

Pennsylvania

Albright College, BM
Arcadia University, MDO
Bloomsburg University of Pennsylvania, BM
Cabrini College, B
California University of Pennsylvania, BM
Carlow University, B
Chatham College, BM
Cheyney University of Pennsylvania, BM
Clarion University of Pennsylvania, BM
College Misericordia, B
DeSales University, MO
Duquesne University, BM
East Stroudsburg University of Pennsylvania, BM
Edinboro University of Pennsylvania, ABM
Gannon University, B
Geneva College, BM
Gwynedd-Mercy College, BM
Holy Family University, B
Immaculata University, O
Indiana University of Pennsylvania, BM
Juniata College, B
King's College, B
Kutztown University of Pennsylvania, BO
La Salle University, B
Lehigh Carbon Community College, A
Lehigh University, MDO
Lincoln University, B
Lock Haven University of Pennsylvania, B
Lycoming College, B
Mansfield University of Pennsylvania, B
Marywood University, BM
Mercyhurst College, BMO
Millersville University of Pennsylvania, BM
The Pennsylvania State University Abington
  College, B
The Pennsylvania State University Altoona
  College, B
The Pennsylvania State University Beaver Campus
  of the Commonwealth College, B
The Pennsylvania State University Berks Campus of
  the Berks-Lehigh Valley College, B
The Pennsylvania State University Delaware County
  Campus of the Commonwealth College, B
The Pennsylvania State University DuBois Campus
  of the Commonwealth College, B
The Pennsylvania State University at Erie, The
  Behrend College, B
The Pennsylvania State University Fayette Campus
  of the Commonwealth College, B
The Pennsylvania State University Hazleton
  Campus of the Commonwealth College, B
The Pennsylvania State University, Lehigh Valley
  Campus of the Berks-Lehigh Valley College, B
The Pennsylvania State University McKeesport
  Campus of the Commonwealth College, B
The Pennsylvania State University Mont Alto
  Campus of the Commonwealth College, B

The Pennsylvania State University New Kensington
Campus of the Commonwealth College, B
The Pennsylvania State University Schuylkill
Campus of the Capital College, B
The Pennsylvania State University Shenango
Campus of the Commonwealth College, B
The Pennsylvania State University University Park
Campus, BMD
The Pennsylvania State University Wilkes-Barre
Campus of the Commonwealth College, B
The Pennsylvania State University Worthington
Scranton Campus of the Commonwealth
College, B
The Pennsylvania State University York Campus of
the Commonwealth College, B
Saint Joseph's University, BM
Saint Vincent College, M
Seton Hill University, BMO
Shippensburg University of Pennsylvania, M
Slippery Rock University of Pennsylvania, BM
Temple University, M
University of Pittsburgh, MD
The University of Scranton, BM
Waynesburg College, B
West Chester University of Pennsylvania, BM
Widener University, BM
Wilkes University, M
York College of Pennsylvania, B

Puerto Rico

American University of Puerto Rico, B
Bayamon Central University, BM
Caribbean University, B
Inter American University of Puerto Rico, Arecibo
Campus, B
Inter American University of Puerto Rico, Fajardo
Campus, B
Inter American University of Puerto Rico, Guayama
Campus, B
Inter American University of Puerto Rico,
Metropolitan Campus, BM
Inter American University of Puerto Rico, Ponce
Campus, B
Inter American University of Puerto Rico, San
Germán Campus, M
Pontifical Catholic University of Puerto Rico, B
Universidad Metropolitana, BM
Universidad del Turabo, BM
University of Puerto Rico at Bayamón, B
University of Puerto Rico, Medical Sciences
Campus, O
University of Puerto Rico, Río Piedras, M

Rhode Island

Community College of Rhode Island, A
Providence College, BM
Rhode Island College, BMO
Salve Regina University, B

South Carolina

Anderson University, B
Bob Jones University, B
Clemson University, BM
Coastal Carolina University, B
College of Charleston, BM
Columbia College, B
Converse College, BM
Erskine College, B
Francis Marion University, M
Furman University, BM
Lander University, B
Newberry College, B
South Carolina State University, BM
Southern Wesleyan University, B
University of South Carolina, MD
University of South Carolina Aiken, B
University of South Carolina Upstate, M
Winthrop University, BM

South Dakota

Augustana College, B
Black Hills State University, B
Dakota State University, B
Dakota Wesleyan University, B
Mount Marty College, B
Northern State University, BM

Oglala Lakota College, B
The University of South Dakota, BM

Tennessee

Austin Peay State University, B
Belmont University, B
Bethel College, BM
Carson-Newman College, B
Cumberland University, B
East Tennessee State University, BM
Freed-Hardeman University, B
Lambuth University, B
Lee University, BM
Middle Tennessee State University, BMO
Tennessee State University, BMD
Tennessee Technological University, BMO
Tusculum College, B
Union University, B
University of Memphis, BMD
The University of Tennessee, BMO
The University of Tennessee at Chattanooga, BM
The University of Tennessee at Martin, B
Vanderbilt University, BMD

Texas

Abilene Christian University, B
Baylor University, B
Houston Baptist University, B
Jarvis Christian College, B
Lamar University, BMD
Lubbock Christian University, B
Midwestern State University, M
Our Lady of the Lake University of San Antonio, BM
Prairie View A&M University, M
Sam Houston State University, M
Stephen F. Austin State University, M
Tarleton State University, O
Texas A&M International University, BM
Texas A&M University, MD
Texas A&M University-Commerce, BMD
Texas A&M University-Corpus Christi, M
Texas A&M University-Kingsville, M
Texas A&M University-Texarkana, M
Texas Christian University, BM
Texas Southern University, BM
Texas State University-San Marcos, M
Texas Tech University, MDO
Texas Woman's University, MD
University of Houston, MD
University of the Incarnate Word, BM
University of Mary Hardin-Baylor, B
University of North Texas, MD
The University of Texas at Austin, MD
The University of Texas at Brownsville, BM
The University of Texas-Pan American, M
The University of Texas of the Permian Basin, M
The University of Texas at San Antonio, M
The University of Texas at Tyler, M
West Texas A&M University, M
Wiley College, B

Utah

Brigham Young University, BMDO
Southern Utah University, B
University of Utah, BMD
Utah State University, BMDO
Westminster College, B

Vermont

Castleton State College, MO
College of St. Joseph, BM
Green Mountain College, B
Johnson State College, M
Lyndon State College, BM
Saint Michael's College, MO
University of Vermont, M

Virginia

Averett University, M
The College of William and Mary, M
George Mason University, M
Hampton University, BM
James Madison University, M
Liberty University, BM
Longwood University, B

Lynchburg College, BM
Marymount University, M
Norfolk State University, M
Old Dominion University, MD
University of Virginia, MDO
Virginia Commonwealth University, M
Virginia Polytechnic Institute and State
University, DO
Virginia Union University, B

Washington

Central Washington University, BM
City University, B
Eastern Washington University, BM
Gonzaga University, BM
Heritage University, M
Pacific Lutheran University, B
Saint Martin's University, BM
Seattle Pacific University, B
Seattle University, MO
University of Washington, MD
Walla Walla College, M
Washington State University, B
Western Washington University, BM
Whitworth College, BM

West Virginia

Concord University, B
Fairmont State University, B
Glenville State College, B
Marshall University, M
West Virginia University, MD
West Virginia Wesleyan College, B

Wisconsin

Cardinal Stritch University, BM
Carthage College, B
Edgewood College, MO
University of Wisconsin-Eau Claire, BM
University of Wisconsin-La Crosse, B
University of Wisconsin-Madison, BMD
University of Wisconsin-Milwaukee, BM
University of Wisconsin-Oshkosh, BM
University of Wisconsin-Stevens Point, M
University of Wisconsin-Superior, BM
University of Wisconsin-Whitewater, BM

Wyoming

University of Wyoming, BMO
Western Wyoming Community College, A

Alberta

University of Alberta, BMD
University of Calgary, MD
University of Lethbridge, B

British Columbia

The University of British Columbia, BMDO
University of Victoria, B

Manitoba

Brandon University, MO
University of Manitoba, M

New Brunswick

University of New Brunswick Fredericton, BM

Newfoundland and Labrador

Memorial University of Newfoundland, B

Nova Scotia

Acadia University, M
Mount Saint Vincent University, M

Ontario

University of Ottawa, B
The University of Western Ontario, BM
University of Windsor, B
York University, B

Quebec

Université de Montréal, BO
Université du Québec en Abitibi-Témiscamingue, B
Université du Québec àChicoutimi, B

Université du Québec àMontréal, B
Université du Québec en Outaouais, B
Université du Québec àRimouski, B
Université de Sherbrooke, BMO

Saskatchewan

University of Saskatchewan, MDO

SPECIAL PRODUCTS MARKETING OPERATIONS

Alabama

Enterprise-Ozark Community College, A
Wallace State Community College, A

Arizona

Phoenix College, A
Scottsdale Community College, A

California

American River College, A
Cabrillo College, A
Chaffey College, A
Columbia College, A
Cosumnes River College (Sacramento), A
Cuyamaca College, A
Cypress College, A
El Camino College, A
Long Beach City College, A
Los Angeles City College, A
Merced College, A
Mission College, A
Modesto Junior College, A
Orange Coast College, A
Palomar College, A
Saddleback College, A
San Diego City College, A
San Francisco State University, B
San Joaquin Delta College, A

Colorado

Pueblo Community College, A

Connecticut

Asnuntuck Community College, A
Gateway Community College, A
Naugatuck Valley Community College, A
Three Rivers Community College, A

Florida

Broward Community College, A
Daytona Beach Community College, A
Indian River Community College, A
Johnson & Wales University, A
Lynn University, B
Palm Beach Community College, A

Hawaii

Kapiolani Community College, A

Idaho

Brigham Young University -Idaho, A

Illinois

City Colleges of Chicago, Kennedy-King College, A
Dominican University, B
Joliet Junior College, A
Oakton Community College, A

Indiana

Ball State University, AB

Iowa

Des Moines Area Community College, A
Iowa State University of Science and Technology, B
Iowa Western Community College, A

Kirkwood Community College, A

Maine

Southern Maine Community College, A

Maryland

University of Maryland Eastern Shore, B

Massachusetts

Newbury College, A

Michigan

Ferris State University, A
Henry Ford Community College, A
Lansing Community College, A
Madonna University, B
Muskegon Community College, A

Minnesota

University of Minnesota, Crookston, A
Vermilion Community College, A

Mississippi

Copiah-Lincoln Community College, A
Hinds Community College, A
Northeast Mississippi Community College, A

Missouri

East Central College, A
Lindenwood University, B
St. Louis Community College at Florissant Valley, A
State Fair Community College, A

Nebraska

Wayne State College, B

Nevada

Community College of Southern Nevada, A

New Jersey

Bergen Community College, A
Brookdale Community College, A
Burlington County College, A
Camden County College, A

New Mexico

Western New Mexico University, B

New York

Buffalo State College, State University of New York, B
Dutchess Community College, A
Fashion Institute of Technology, B
Fiorello H. LaGuardia Community College of the City University of New York, A
Monroe Community College, A
Onondaga Community College, A
Rochester Institute of Technology, B
State University of New York College of Agriculture and Technology at Morrisville, A
Westchester Community College, A

North Carolina

Central Piedmont Community College, A
North Carolina Wesleyan College, B

Ohio

Hocking College, A
Jefferson Community College, A
Sinclair Community College, A

Oklahoma

Oklahoma State University, Oklahoma City, A
Oklahoma State University, Okmulgee, A

Oregon

Lane Community College, A
Oregon State University, B

Pennsylvania

Carlow University, B
Community College of Philadelphia, A

Westmoreland County Community College, A

Rhode Island

Johnson & Wales University, AB

South Carolina

Greenville Technical College, A

Texas

Del Mar College, A
El Centro College, A
Lamar University, A
South Plains College, A

Virginia

Northern Virginia Community College, A

Washington

South Puget Sound Community College, A
South Seattle Community College, A
Yakima Valley Community College, A

West Virginia

Concord University, B

Wisconsin

Fox Valley Technical College, A

Alberta

University of Alberta, B

Nova Scotia

Mount Saint Vincent University, B

SPECIALIZED MERCHANDISING, SALES, AND MARKETING OPERATIONS

Georgia

Clayton State University, A

Michigan

Eastern Michigan University, B

Ohio

The University of Akron, B

Pennsylvania

Gannon University, B

Texas

Baylor University, B

SPEECH AND INTERPERSONAL COMMUNICATION

Alabama

The University of Alabama, M

Arizona

Arizona State University, M

Arkansas

Arkansas State University, MO
University of Arkansas at Little Rock, M

California

California State University, Fullerton, M
California State University, Los Angeles, M

San Jose State University, M

Colorado

Colorado State University, M
University of Denver, MD

Georgia

University of Georgia, MD

Idaho

Idaho State University, M

Illinois

Eastern Illinois University, M
Northwestern University, MD
Southern Illinois University Carbondale, MD
Southern Illinois University Edwardsville, M

Indiana

Ball State University, M
Indiana University Bloomington, MD

Iowa

Drake University, M

Maryland

University of Maryland, College Park, MD

Massachusetts

Northeastern University, D

Michigan

Central Michigan University, M
Wayne State University, MD

Mississippi

University of Southern Mississippi, MD

Missouri

Washington University in St. Louis, D

New Jersey

Montclair State University, M

New York

Brooklyn College of the City University of New
  York, MD
Hofstra University, M
Rensselaer Polytechnic Institute, MD

North Carolina

Wake Forest University, M

North Dakota

North Dakota State University, M

Ohio

Bowling Green State University, MD
Ohio University, MD

Oregon

Portland State University, MO

South Dakota

The University of South Dakota, M

Tennessee

The University of Tennessee, MD

Texas

Abilene Christian University, M
Texas Christian University, M
Texas Southern University, M
University of Houston, M

Wisconsin

Marquette University, M
University of Wisconsin-Stevens Point, M

University of Wisconsin-Superior, M

SPEECH AND RHETORICAL STUDIES

Alabama

Alabama State University, B
Auburn University, B
Huntingdon College, B
Samford University, B
Troy University, B
The University of Alabama, B
The University of Alabama in Huntsville, B
University of Montevallo, B
University of North Alabama, B

Alaska

University of Alaska Fairbanks, B

Arizona

Grand Canyon University, B
Northern Arizona University, B

Arkansas

Arkansas State University, B
University of Arkansas at Little Rock, B
University of Arkansas at Monticello, B
University of Arkansas at Pine Bluff, B
University of Central Arkansas, B

California

Bakersfield College, A
California Polytechnic State University, San Luis
  Obispo, B
California State University, Chico, B
California State University, East Bay, B
California State University, Fresno, B
California State University, Fullerton, B
California State University, Long Beach, B
California State University, Los Angeles, B
California State University, Northridge, M
Cañada College, A
Cerritos College, A
Chaffey College, A
College of the Desert, A
College of Marin, A
College of San Mateo, A
College of the Sequoias, A
Compton Community College, A
Crafton Hills College, A
Cuyamaca College, A
Cypress College, A
De Anza College, A
East Los Angeles College, A
El Camino College, A
Foothill College, A
Fresno City College, A
Fullerton College, A
Glendale Community College, A
Grossmont College, A
Humboldt State University, B
Irvine Valley College, A
Long Beach City College, A
Los Angeles City College, A
Los Angeles Mission College, A
Los Angeles Valley College, A
The Master's College and Seminary, B
Mendocino College, A
MiraCosta College, A
Modesto Junior College, A
Palomar College, A
Pasadena City College, A
Pepperdine University, B
Sacramento City College, A
Saddleback College, A
San Diego City College, A
San Diego Mesa College, A
San Diego State University, B
San Francisco State University, BM
San Joaquin Delta College, A
San Jose State University, BM
Shasta College, A
Skyline College, A
University of California, Berkeley, B

Vanguard University of Southern California, B
West Los Angeles College, A
West Valley College, A

Colorado

Adams State College, B
Metropolitan State College of Denver, B

District of Columbia

The George Washington University, B

Florida

Bethune-Cookman College, B
Florida Atlantic University, B
Florida State University, D
Indian River Community College, A
Manatee Community College, A
University of Central Florida, B
University of South Florida, B

Georgia

Abraham Baldwin Agricultural College, A
Albany State University, B
Atlanta Metropolitan College, A
Bainbridge College, A
Clark Atlanta University, B
Clayton State University, A
Dalton State College, A
Darton College, A
Georgia College & State University, B
Georgia Southern University, B
Georgia State University, B
Macon State College, A
South Georgia College, A
University of Georgia, B

Hawaii

University of Hawaii at Manoa, BM

Illinois

Augustana College, B
Blackburn College, B
Bradley University, B
Chicago State University, B
City Colleges of Chicago, Harold Washington
  College, A
City Colleges of Chicago, Harry S. Truman
  College, A
City Colleges of Chicago, Richard J. Daley
  College, A
City Colleges of Chicago, Wilbur Wright College, A
Governors State University, B
Greenville College, B
Illinois College, B
Illinois State University, B
Judson College, B
Lewis University, B
McKendree College, B
Monmouth College, B
North Central College, B
North Park University, B
Northeastern Illinois University, BM
Northwestern University, B
Olivet Nazarene University, B
Rend Lake College, A
Sauk Valley Community College, A
Southern Illinois University Carbondale, B
Southern Illinois University Edwardsville, BMO
Spoon River College, A
University of Illinois at Chicago, B
University of Illinois at Urbana-Champaign, BMD

Indiana

Ball State University, B
Butler University, B
Indiana University Bloomington, B
Indiana University South Bend, B
Manchester College, B
Wabash College, B

Iowa

Coe College, B
Cornell College, B
Drake University, BM
Graceland University, B

Iowa Lakes Community College, A
Iowa State University of Science and Technology, B
Mount Mercy College, B
Northwestern College, B
Simpson College, B
University of Dubuque, B
The University of Iowa, B
University of Northern Iowa, B

Kansas

Allen County Community College, A
Dodge City Community College, A
Friends University, B
Garden City Community College, A
Kansas State University, M
Kansas Wesleyan University, B
Pratt Community College, A
Seward County Community College, A
University of Kansas, B

Kentucky

Asbury College, B
Eastern Kentucky University, B
Morehead State University, BM
Murray State University, B
Northern Kentucky University, B
Thomas More College, B
University of the Cumberlands, B
Western Kentucky University, B

Louisiana

Dillard University, B
Louisiana College, B
Louisiana State University and Agricultural and
    Mechanical College, B
Louisiana State University in Shreveport, B
Louisiana Tech University, BM
McNeese State University, B
Southern University and Agricultural and Mechanical
    College, B
University of Louisiana at Monroe, B

Maine

Bates College, B

Maryland

Frostburg State University, B
Morgan State University, B

Massachusetts

Emerson College, B
Stonehill College, B

Michigan

Calvin College, B
Central Michigan University, BM
Cornerstone University, B
Eastern Michigan University, M
Ferris State University, A
Hillsdale College, B
Lansing Community College, A
Madonna University, AB
Mid Michigan Community College, A
Monroe County Community College, A
Northern Michigan University, B
University of Michigan, B

Minnesota

Augsburg College, B
Bemidji State University, B
College of Saint Benedict, B
College of St. Catherine, B
Concordia College, B
Gustavus Adolphus College, B
Minnesota State University Mankato, BM
Minnesota State University Moorhead, B
Ridgewater College, A
St. Cloud State University, B
Saint John's University, B
University of Minnesota, Morris, B
Vermilion Community College, A

Winona State University, B

Mississippi

Itawamba Community College, A
Jackson State University, B
Mississippi Valley State University, B

Missouri

Central Missouri State University, BM
College of the Ozarks, B
East Central College, A
Evangel University, B
Hannibal-LaGrange College, B
Jefferson College, A
Missouri Valley College, B
Northwest Missouri State University, B
St. Louis Community College at Meramec, A
Southeast Missouri State University, B
Truman State University, B
William Jewell College, B

Montana

The University of Montana-Missoula, B

Nebraska

Chadron State College, B
Concordia University, B
Creighton University, B
Doane College, B
Hastings College, B
Nebraska Wesleyan University, B
Northeast Community College, A
University of Nebraska at Kearney, B
University of Nebraska at Omaha, B
Wayne State College, B

Nevada

University of Nevada, Reno, M

New Jersey

Brookdale Community College, A
The College of New Jersey, B
Kean University, M
Rider University, B

New Mexico

University of New Mexico, B

New York

Brooklyn College of the City University of New
    York, MD
Dowling College, B
Hofstra University, B
Ithaca College, B
Lehman College of the City University of New
    York, B
Long Island University, Brooklyn Campus, B
New York University, MO
Pace University, B
St. John's University, B
St. Joseph's College, New York, B
St. Joseph's College, Suffolk Campus, B
State University of New York College at
    Brockport, B
State University of New York College at Cortland, B
State University of New York College at Oneonta, B
State University of New York College at Potsdam, B
Syracuse University, B
University at Albany, State University of New York, B
Yeshiva University, B
York College of the City University of New York, B

North Carolina

Appalachian State University, B
Louisburg College, A
North Carolina Agricultural and Technical State
    University, B
The University of North Carolina at Greensboro, B
The University of North Carolina Wilmington, B

North Dakota

Dickinson State University, B
Minot State University, B

North Dakota State University, B

Ohio

Ashland University, B
Bowling Green State University, B
Capital University, B
Cedarville University, B
Denison University, B
Kent State University, B
Marietta College, B
Miami University, BM
Ohio University, B
Ohio University-Eastern, B
The University of Akron, B
Youngstown State University, B

Oklahoma

Carl Albert State College, A
East Central University, B
Eastern Oklahoma State College, A
Northwestern Oklahoma State University, B
Oklahoma Baptist University, B
Oklahoma Christian University, B
Oklahoma City University, B
Oklahoma State University, B
Oral Roberts University, B
Rose State College, A
Southern Nazarene University, B
Tulsa Community College, A

Oregon

Linn-Benton Community College, A
Oregon State University, B
Portland State University, B
Willamette University, B

Pennsylvania

Clarion University of Pennsylvania, B
Geneva College, B
Kutztown University of Pennsylvania, B
Lock Haven University of Pennsylvania, B
Mansfield University of Pennsylvania, B
Shippensburg University of Pennsylvania, B
Susquehanna University, B
Temple University, B
University of Pittsburgh, B
West Chester University of Pennsylvania, B
York College of Pennsylvania, B

South Carolina

Anderson University, B
Bob Jones University, B
Charleston Southern University, B
Clemson University, B
Newberry College, B
University of South Carolina, M

South Dakota

Black Hills State University, B
Northern State University, B
South Dakota State University, B
University of Sioux Falls, B

Tennessee

Belmont University, B
Carson-Newman College, B
Columbia State Community College, A
East Tennessee State University, B
Fisk University, B
Lipscomb University, B
Union University, B
The University of Tennessee, B

Texas

Abilene Christian University, B
Amarillo College, A
Austin Community College, A
Blinn College, A
Brazosport College, A
Clarendon College, A
Coastal Bend College, A
Del Mar College, A
East Texas Baptist University, B
El Paso Community College, A
Grayson County College, A

Hardin-Simmons University, B
Hill College of the Hill Junior College District, A
Houston Baptist University, B
Howard College, A
Howard Payne University, B
Kilgore College, A
Lee College, A
Lon Morris College, A
McMurry University, B
Midland College, A
Navarro College, A
North Harris College, A
Odessa College, A
Palo Alto College, A
St. Mary's University of San Antonio, B
St. Philip's College, A
Sam Houston State University, B
Stephen F. Austin State University, B
Tarleton State University, B
Texas A&M University, B
Texas A&M University-Commerce, M
Texas A&M University-Kingsville, B
Texas Southern University, B
Texas State University-San Marcos, B
Texas Tech University, B
Texas Wesleyan University, B
Trinity University, B
Trinity Valley Community College, A
Tyler Junior College, A
University of Houston, B
University of the Incarnate Word, B
The University of Texas at Arlington, B
The University of Texas at El Paso, B
The University of Texas-Pan American, B
The University of Texas of the Permian Basin, B
The University of Texas at Tyler, B
West Texas A&M University, B
Wharton County Junior College, A

United States Virgin Islands

University of the Virgin Islands, B

Utah

Brigham Young University, B
Southern Utah University, B
University of Utah, B
Utah State University, B

Virginia

George Mason University, B
Lynchburg College, B
Northern Virginia Community College, A
Old Dominion University, B
University of Richmond, B
University of Virginia, B

Washington

Everett Community College, A
Gonzaga University, B
Lower Columbia College, A
Skagit Valley College, A
Tacoma Community College, A
University of Washington, B
Walla Walla College, B
Whitworth College, B

West Virginia

Fairmont State University, B
Marshall University, B
West Virginia Wesleyan College, B

Wisconsin

Carthage College, B
Maranatha Baptist Bible College, B
Marquette University, B
University of Wisconsin-Platteville, B
University of Wisconsin-River Falls, B
University of Wisconsin-Superior, B

University of Wisconsin-Whitewater, B

Wyoming

Casper College, A
Northwest College, A

Nova Scotia

Cape Breton University, B

Ontario

University of Waterloo, B

SPEECH-LANGUAGE PATHOLOGY/PATHOLOGIST

Arkansas

Harding University, B

California

Crafton Hills College, A
Santa Rosa Junior College, A

Colorado

University of Northern Colorado, B

Georgia

University of West Georgia, B
Valdosta State University, B

Illinois

Augustana College, B
College of DuPage, A
Northwestern University, B
Parkland College, A
Saint Xavier University, B

Iowa

University of Northern Iowa, B

Louisiana

Grambling State University, B
Xavier University of Louisiana, B

Maryland

Loyola College in Maryland, B
Towson University, B
University of Maryland, College Park, B

Massachusetts

Elms College, A
Emerson College, B

Michigan

Baker College of Muskegon, A
Eastern Michigan University, B
Northern Michigan University, B

Minnesota

St. Cloud State University, B

Missouri

Central Missouri State University, B
Rockhurst University, B

Nebraska

University of Nebraska-Lincoln, B

Nevada

Nevada State College at Henderson, B
University of Nevada, Reno, B

New York

Brooklyn College of the City University of New
  York, B
Lehman College of the City University of New
  York, B
Mount Saint Mary College, B
Pace University, B

Yeshiva University, B

North Carolina

Catawba Valley Community College, A
Fayetteville Technical Community College, A
Guilford Technical Community College, A
Randolph Community College, A
Wilkes Community College, A

Ohio

Miami University, B
Miami University Hamilton, B
The University of Akron, B
The University of Toledo, B

Oklahoma

University of Oklahoma Health Sciences Center, B
University of Science and Arts of Oklahoma, B

Pennsylvania

Duquesne University, B

South Carolina

Bob Jones University, B
Columbia College, B

Tennessee

Southern Adventist University, A
The University of Tennessee, B

Texas

Abilene Christian University, B
Southern Methodist University, B
Southwestern University, B
Texas Christian University, B

Virginia

James Madison University, B

West Virginia

Marshall University, B

Wisconsin

University of Wisconsin-Whitewater, B

SPEECH TEACHER EDUCATION

Alabama

Samford University, B

Arizona

The University of Arizona, B

Arkansas

Arkansas State University, B
Harding University, B

Georgia

Columbus State University, B

Illinois

Concordia University, B
Highland Community College, A
Lewis University, B
McKendree College, B

Indiana

Anderson University, B
Indiana University Bloomington, B
Indiana University-Purdue University Fort Wayne, B
Indiana University-Purdue University Indianapolis, B
Taylor University, B
University of Indianapolis, B
Vincennes University, A

Iowa

Buena Vista University, B
Dordt College, B
Graceland University, B
Iowa Western Community College, A

Northwestern College, B
St. Ambrose University, B
The University of Iowa, B
University of Northern Iowa, B
Wartburg College, B

Kansas

Central Christian College of Kansas, A
McPherson College, B
Pittsburg State University, B
Pratt Community College, A

Kentucky

Murray State University, B

Louisiana

Grambling State University, B
Louisiana Tech University, B
McNeese State University, B
Northwestern State University of Louisiana, B
Southeastern Louisiana University, B
University of Louisiana at Lafayette, B
University of Louisiana at Monroe, B

Massachusetts

Boston University, B

Michigan

Central Michigan University, B
Concordia University, B
Mid Michigan Community College, A
Saginaw Valley State University, B
University of Michigan-Flint, B

Minnesota

Bemidji State University, B
College of St. Catherine, B
Hamline University, B
Minnesota State University Moorhead, B
Pillsbury Baptist Bible College, B
Southwest Minnesota State University, B
University of Minnesota, Morris, B
University of St. Thomas, B

Mississippi

Northwest Mississippi Community College, A
William Carey College, B

Missouri

Culver-Stockton College, B
Missouri Western State University, B
Southeast Missouri State University, B
Southwest Baptist University, B
William Jewell College, B
William Woods University, B

Nebraska

Chadron State College, B
Concordia University, B
Dana College, B
Hastings College, B
Midland Lutheran College, B
Wayne State College, B
York College, B

New Jersey

Kean University, B

New York

Brooklyn College of the City University of New
  York, B
Elmira College, B

North Carolina

The University of North Carolina at Greensboro, B

North Dakota

Dickinson State University, B
North Dakota State University, B

Ohio

Capital University, B
The University of Akron, B

University of Rio Grande, B

Oklahoma

East Central University, B
Northwestern Oklahoma State University, B
Oklahoma Baptist University, B
Oklahoma City University, B
Southern Nazarene University, B

Pennsylvania

Baptist Bible College of Pennsylvania, B

South Dakota

Augustana College, B
The University of South Dakota, B

Tennessee

King College, B

Texas

Angelina College, A
Baylor University, B
East Texas Baptist University, B
Hardin-Simmons University, B
Howard Payne University, B
San Antonio College, A
Texas Wesleyan University, B

Utah

Brigham Young University, B

Wisconsin

Viterbo University, B

Ontario

University of Windsor, B
York University, B

SPORT AND FITNESS ADMINISTRATION/MANAGEMENT

Alabama

Columbia Southern University, B
Faulkner University, B
Huntingdon College, B
Troy University, BM

Arkansas

Arkansas State University, B
Harding University, B
Henderson State University, BM

California

Fresno Pacific University, B
National University, B
Saint Mary's College of California, B
San Diego Golf Academy, A
University of San Francisco, M

Colorado

Fort Lewis College, B
Western State College of Colorado, B

Connecticut

Eastern Connecticut State University, B
Mitchell College, A
Sacred Heart University, B
University of New Haven, M

Delaware

Delaware State University, B
University of Delaware, B
Wilmington College, B

District of Columbia

The George Washington University, M

Florida

Barry University, BMO
Flagler College, B
Florida Atlantic University, M
Florida State University, BMDO

Lake-Sumter Community College, A
Lynn University, BM
Northwood University, Florida Campus, AB
Nova Southeastern University, B
Saint Leo University, B
St. Thomas University, B
Stetson University, B
University of Central Florida, M
University of Miami, M
Webber International University, ABM

Georgia

Andrew College, A
Emmanuel College, B
Gainesville College, A
Georgia Southern University, BM
Georgia State University, M
Kennesaw State University, B
Reinhardt College, B
South Georgia College, A
University of Georgia, B

Idaho

Albertson College of Idaho, B
Boise State University, M

Illinois

Elmhurst College, B
Greenville College, B
Judson College, B
MacMurray College, B
North Central College, B
Northern Illinois University, M
Olivet Nazarene University, B
Principia College, B
Quincy University, B
Western Illinois University, M

Indiana

Ball State University, B
Bethel College, B
Indiana State University, M
Indiana University Bloomington, BM
Indiana Wesleyan University, B
Taylor University, B
Tri-State University, B
University of Indianapolis, B
Valparaiso University, BM
Vincennes University, A

Iowa

Buena Vista University, B
Graceland University, B
Iowa Lakes Community College, A
Iowa Wesleyan College, B
Loras College, B
Luther College, B
North Iowa Area Community College, A
St. Ambrose University, B
Simpson College, B
The University of Iowa, BM
University of Northern Iowa, M
Wartburg College, B
William Penn University, B

Kansas

Barton County Community College, A
Bethany College, B
Central Christian College of Kansas, B
MidAmerica Nazarene University, B
Southwestern College, B
University of Saint Mary, B
Wichita State University, M

Kentucky

Asbury College, B
Eastern Kentucky University, M
Kentucky Wesleyan College, B
Midway College, B
Morehead State University, BM
Union College, B

University of Louisville, BM

Louisiana

Grambling State University, M
Northwestern State University of Louisiana, M
Tulane University, B
University of New Orleans, M

Maine

Husson College, B
Saint Joseph's College of Maine, B
Thomas College, B
University of New England, B
University of Southern Maine, O

Maryland

Frostburg State University, B
Howard Community College, A
Morgan State University, B
Mount St. Mary's University, B
Towson University, B

Massachusetts

Becker College, B
Bridgewater State College, B
Dean College, A
Endicott College, B
Fitchburg State College, B
Holyoke Community College, A
Nichols College, B
Salem State College, B
Springfield College, BM
University of Massachusetts Amherst, BMD
Western New England College, B

Michigan

Calvin College, B
Central Michigan University, BM
Cornerstone University, B
Lake Superior State University, A
Northern Michigan University, B
Northwood University, AB
Oakland Community College, A
Olivet College, B
Rochester College, B
Spring Arbor University, B
University of Michigan, BM
Wayne State University, M
Western Michigan University, M

Minnesota

Bemidji State University, B
Crown College, B
Minnesota State University Mankato, B
Minnesota State University Moorhead, B
St. Cloud State University, M
University of Minnesota, Crookston, B
University of Minnesota, Twin Cities Campus, MD
University of St. Thomas, M
Winona State University, B

Mississippi

Belhaven College, B
Coahoma Community College, A
Mississippi College, B
Mississippi State University, M
Mississippi University for Women, B
University of Southern Mississippi, M

Missouri

Central Methodist University, B
Drury University, B
Lindenwood University, BM
Missouri Baptist University, B
Missouri Valley College, B
Northwest Missouri State University, B
Southeast Missouri State University, B
Southwest Baptist University, B

Montana

Carroll College, B
Montana State University, B

Montana State University-Billings, BM

Nebraska

Concordia University, B
Hastings College, B
Nebraska Wesleyan University, B
Union College, B
University of Nebraska at Kearney, B
Wayne State College, BM

Nevada

University of Nevada, Las Vegas, BMD

New Hampshire

Colby-Sawyer College, B
Daniel Webster College, B
Franklin Pierce College, B
Hesser College, A
Keene State College, B
New England College, B
New Hampshire Technical Institute, A
Southern New Hampshire University, BM

New Jersey

Centenary College, B
Montclair State University, M
Seton Hall University, BMO

New Mexico

New Mexico Military Institute, A

New York

Canisius College, M
Cazenovia College, B
Globe Institute of Technology, B
Ithaca College, B
Kingsborough Community College of the City
   University of New York, A
Medaille College, B
Metropolitan College of New York, M
New York University, BMO
St. John's University, B
State University of New York College at
   Brockport, B
State University of New York College of Technology
   at Alfred, A
State University of New York at Oswego, B
Sullivan County Community College, A
Syracuse University, B
Tompkins Cortland Community College, A

North Carolina

Appalachian State University, M
Barton College, B
Campbell University, B
Chowan University, B
Elon University, B
Gardner-Webb University, B
Greensboro College, B
Guilford College, B
High Point University, B
Livingstone College, B
Louisburg College, A
Mars Hill College, B
Methodist College, B
North Carolina State University, BM
Pfeiffer University, B
The University of North Carolina at Chapel Hill, M
Western Carolina University, B
Wingate University, B
Winston-Salem State University, B

North Dakota

Minot State University, B
North Dakota State University, BM

Ohio

Baldwin-Wallace College, B
Bluffton University, B
Bowling Green State University, BM
Cedarville University, B
Cleveland State University, BM
Columbus State Community College, A
Defiance College, B
Lorain County Community College, A

Malone College, B
Miami University, B
Mount Union College, B
Mount Vernon Nazarene University, B
Notre Dame College, B
Ohio Dominican University, B
Ohio Northern University, B
Ohio University, BM
Otterbein College, B
Shawnee State University, B
University of Dayton, B
Wilmington College, B
Xavier University, BM

Oklahoma

Southern Nazarene University, B
University of Tulsa, B

Oregon

Central Oregon Community College, A
Concordia University, B
Corban College, B
George Fox University, B

Pennsylvania

Alvernia College, B
Bucks County Community College, A
Butler County Community College, A
College Misericordia, B
DeSales University, B
East Stroudsburg University of Pennsylvania, M
Edinboro University of Pennsylvania, B
Harcum College, A
Holy Family University, B
Indiana University of Pennsylvania, M
Keystone College, AB
Lehigh Carbon Community College, A
Mercyhurst College, B
Millersville University of Pennsylvania, M
Neumann College, BM
Northampton County Area Community College, A
Robert Morris University, BM
Slippery Rock University of Pennsylvania, M
Temple University, M
University of Pittsburgh at Bradford, B
West Chester University of Pennsylvania, M
Widener University, B
York College of Pennsylvania, B

Rhode Island

University of Rhode Island, M

South Carolina

Coker College, B
Erskine College, B
Limestone College, B
North Greenville College, B
Southern Wesleyan University, B
University of South Carolina, BM
Winthrop University, B

South Dakota

Augustana College, B
Black Hills State University, B

Tennessee

Belmont University, M
East Tennessee State University, M
Lambuth University, B
Southern Adventist University, B
Tennessee Wesleyan College, B
Tusculum College, B
Union University, B
University of Memphis, B
The University of Tennessee, BM
The University of Tennessee at Martin, B

Texas

Abilene Christian University, B
Baylor University, B
Hardin-Simmons University, M
Howard Payne University, B
LeTourneau University, B
Lubbock Christian University, B
Midwestern State University, B

Northwood University, Texas Campus, AB
St. Edward's University, O
Texas Lutheran University, B
Texas State University-San Marcos, B
Texas Wesleyan University, B
University of Dallas, M
University of the Incarnate Word, BMO
University of Mary Hardin-Baylor, B
The University of Texas at Austin, B

Vermont

Johnson State College, B
Lyndon State College, B

Virginia

Averett University, B
Eastern Mennonite University, B
Ferrum College, B
Hampton University, B
Liberty University, B
Longwood University, B
Lynchburg College, B
Marymount University, B
Old Dominion University, BM
Virginia Intermont College, B

Washington

Central Washington University, B
Clark College, A
Gonzaga University, BM
Seattle Pacific University, M
Spokane Falls Community College, A
Washington State University, B

West Virginia

American Public University System, B
Bethany College, B
Davis & Elkins College, B
Salem International University, B
West Virginia University, BM
West Virginia Wesleyan College, B

Wisconsin

Carthage College, B
Concordia University Wisconsin, B
Marian College of Fond du Lac, B
University of Wisconsin-La Crosse, M
University of Wisconsin-Parkside, B

Alberta

University of Alberta, BM

British Columbia

Thompson Rivers University, A
University of Victoria, B

New Brunswick

Université de Moncton, B
University of New Brunswick Fredericton, M

Nova Scotia

Cape Breton University, B

Ontario

Brock University, B
Laurentian University, B
University of Windsor, B
York University, B

Quebec

Concordia University, O
Université de Montréal, M

Saskatchewan

University of Regina, B
University of Saskatchewan, B

SPORT PSYCHOLOGY

Arizona

Argosy University/Phoenix, MDO

California

California State University, Fresno, M
John F. Kennedy University, M

Connecticut

Southern Connecticut State University, M

Florida

Florida State University, MD
University of Florida, MD

Indiana

Purdue University, D

Iowa

The University of Iowa, MD

Massachusetts

Springfield College, MDO

Ohio

Cleveland State University, M

West Virginia

West Virginia University, MD

Ontario

Queen's University at Kingston, M

SPORTS MEDICINE

Florida

University of Florida, MD
University of Miami, M

Georgia

Armstrong Atlantic State University, M
Georgia State University, M

Indiana

Indiana State University, D

Tennessee

The University of Tennessee, MD

STATISTICS

Alabama

The University of Alabama, MD

Alaska

University of Alaska Fairbanks, M

Arizona

Arizona State University, MD
Northern Arizona University, M

Arkansas

University of Arkansas, M

California

California Polytechnic State University, San Luis
  Obispo, B
California State Polytechnic University, Pomona, B
California State University, Chico, B
California State University, East Bay, BM
California State University, Fullerton, BM
California State University, Long Beach, B
California State University, Sacramento, M
Chabot College, A
Pasadena City College, A
San Diego State University, BM
San Francisco State University, B
Sonoma State University, B
Stanford University, BMD
University of California, Berkeley, BMD
University of California, Davis, BMD
University of California, Los Angeles, BMD
University of California, Riverside, BMD
University of California, San Diego, M

University of California, Santa Barbara, BMD
University of Southern California, M

Colorado

Colorado State University, MD
Mesa State College, B
University of Denver, B

Connecticut

University of Connecticut, BMD
Yale University, MD

Delaware

University of Delaware, M

District of Columbia

American University, BMO
The George Washington University, BMD

Florida

Daytona Beach Community College, A
Florida International University, BM
Florida State University, BMD
Manatee Community College, A
University of Central Florida, BMO
University of Florida, BMD
University of North Florida, BM
University of West Florida, M

Georgia

Georgia Institute of Technology, M
University of Georgia, BMD

Idaho

University of Idaho, M

Illinois

DePaul University, BM
Lincoln College, A
Loyola University Chicago, B
Northern Illinois University, M
Northwestern University, BMD
Roosevelt University, B
Southern Illinois University Carbondale, M
University of Chicago, BMD
University of Illinois at Chicago, BMD
University of Illinois at Urbana-Champaign, BMD

Indiana

Ball State University, M
Indiana University Bloomington, MD
Indiana University-Purdue University Fort Wayne, B
Indiana University-Purdue University Indianapolis, M
Purdue University, BMD
Purdue University North Central, B

Iowa

Iowa State University of Science and
  Technology, BMDO
Luther College, B
The University of Iowa, BMD

Kansas

Kansas State University, BMD
University of Kansas, MD
Wichita State University, MD

Kentucky

Eastern Kentucky University, B
University of Kentucky, MD

Louisiana

Louisiana State University and Agricultural and
  Mechanical College, M
Louisiana Tech University, M
McNeese State University, M
Tulane University, BM

Xavier University of Louisiana, B

Maine

University of Southern Maine, M

Maryland

The Johns Hopkins University, MD
University of Maryland, Baltimore County, BMD
University of Maryland, College Park, MD

Massachusetts

Harvard University, BMD
Mount Holyoke College, B
University of Massachusetts Amherst, MD
Worcester Polytechnic Institute, M

Michigan

Central Michigan University, B
Eastern Michigan University, BM
Ferris State University, B
Grand Valley State University, B
Kettering University, B
Michigan State University, BMD
Michigan Technological University, B
Oakland University, BMO
University of Michigan, BMD
Wayne State University, MD
Western Michigan University, BMD

Minnesota

Minnesota State University Mankato, M
St. Cloud State University, BM
University of Minnesota, Duluth, B
University of Minnesota, Morris, B
University of Minnesota, Twin Cities Campus, MD
Winona State University, B

Mississippi

Mississippi State University, MD

Missouri

University of Missouri-Columbia, BMD
University of Missouri-Kansas City, BMD
Washington University in St. Louis, BMD

Montana

Montana State University, MD
The University of Montana-Missoula, B

Nebraska

University of Nebraska at Kearney, B
University of Nebraska-Lincoln, MD

Nevada

University of Nevada, Las Vegas, BM

New Hampshire

University of New Hampshire, BM

New Jersey

The College of New Jersey, B
Kean University, M
Montclair State University, M
New Jersey Institute of Technology, M
Princeton University, MD
Rutgers, The State University of New Jersey, New
    Brunswick/Piscataway, BMD
Stevens Institute of Technology, MO

New Mexico

Eastern New Mexico University, B
New Mexico State University, M
University of New Mexico, BMD

New York

Barnard College, B
Bernard M. Baruch College of the City University of
    New York, BM
Clarkson University, B
Columbia College, B
Columbia University, School of General Studies, B
Cornell University, BMD
Hofstra University, B
Hunter College of the City University of New York, B

New York University, BD
Rensselaer Polytechnic Institute, MO
Rochester Institute of Technology, BMO
St. John's University, M
State University of New York at Binghamton, MD
State University of New York College at Oneonta, B
Stony Brook University, State University of New
    York, MD
Syracuse University, M
University at Albany, State University of New
    York, MD
University of Rochester, BMD

North Carolina

Appalachian State University, B
Duke University, D
North Carolina State University, BMD
The University of North Carolina at Chapel Hill, MD
The University of North Carolina at Greensboro, B
The University of North Carolina Wilmington, B

North Dakota

North Dakota State University, BMDO

Ohio

Bowling Green State University, BMDO
Case Western Reserve University, BMD
Kenyon College, B
Miami University, BM
Miami University Hamilton, B
Ohio Northern University, B
The Ohio State University, MD
Ohio Wesleyan University, B
The University of Akron, BM
University of Cincinnati, MD
The University of Toledo, M
Wright State University, BM

Oklahoma

Oklahoma State University, BMD
University of Central Oklahoma, M

Oregon

Oregon State University, MD
Portland State University, M

Pennsylvania

Carnegie Mellon University, BMD
Lehigh University, BM
Mercyhurst College, B
The Pennsylvania State University Abington
    College, B
The Pennsylvania State University Altoona
    College, B
The Pennsylvania State University Beaver Campus
    of the Commonwealth College, B
The Pennsylvania State University Berks Campus of
    the Berks-Lehigh Valley College, B
The Pennsylvania State University Delaware County
    Campus of the Commonwealth College, B
The Pennsylvania State University DuBois Campus
    of the Commonwealth College, B
The Pennsylvania State University at Erie, The
    Behrend College, B
The Pennsylvania State University Fayette Campus
    of the Commonwealth College, B
The Pennsylvania State University Hazleton
    Campus of the Commonwealth College, B
The Pennsylvania State University, Lehigh Valley
    Campus of the Berks-Lehigh Valley College, B
The Pennsylvania State University McKeesport
    Campus of the Commonwealth College, B
The Pennsylvania State University Mont Alto
    Campus of the Commonwealth College, B
The Pennsylvania State University New Kensington
    Campus of the Commonwealth College, B
The Pennsylvania State University Schuylkill
    Campus of the Capital College, B
The Pennsylvania State University Shenango
    Campus of the Commonwealth College, B
The Pennsylvania State University University Park
    Campus, BMD
The Pennsylvania State University Wilkes-Barre
    Campus of the Commonwealth College, B

The Pennsylvania State University Worthington
    Scranton Campus of the Commonwealth
    College, B
The Pennsylvania State University York Campus of
    the Commonwealth College, B
Temple University, MD
University of Pennsylvania, BMD
University of Pittsburgh, BMD
Villanova University, M

Puerto Rico

University of Puerto Rico, Mayagüez Campus, M

Rhode Island

University of Rhode Island, MD

South Carolina

Clemson University, MD
University of South Carolina, BMDO

Tennessee

University of Memphis, MD
The University of Tennessee, BMD
The University of Tennessee at Martin, B

Texas

Baylor University, BMD
Rice University, BMD
St. Mary's University of San Antonio, B
Sam Houston State University, BM
Southern Methodist University, BMD
Stephen F. Austin State University, M
Texas A&M University, MD
University of Houston, B
University of Houston-Clear Lake, BM
The University of Texas at Austin, M
The University of Texas at Dallas, BMD
The University of Texas at El Paso, BM
The University of Texas at San Antonio, BM

Utah

Brigham Young University, BM
University of Utah, M
Utah State University, BM

Vermont

University of Vermont, BM

Virginia

George Mason University, M
James Madison University, BM
University of Virginia, MD
Virginia Commonwealth University, MO
Virginia Polytechnic Institute and State
    University, BMD

Washington

University of Washington, BMD
Washington State University, M

West Virginia

West Virginia University, M

Wisconsin

Marquette University, BM
University of Wisconsin-Madison, BMD
University of Wisconsin-Milwaukee, B

Wyoming

Eastern Wyoming College, A
University of Wyoming, BMD

Alberta

University of Alberta, BMDO
University of Calgary, BMD

British Columbia

Simon Fraser University, BMD
The University of British Columbia, BMD
University College of the Fraser Valley, B

University of Victoria, BMD

Manitoba

University of Manitoba, BMD
The University of Winnipeg, B

New Brunswick

University of New Brunswick Fredericton, BMD
University of New Brunswick Saint John, B

Newfoundland and Labrador

Memorial University of Newfoundland, BMD

Nova Scotia

Acadia University, M
Dalhousie University, BMD
Mount Saint Vincent University, B
University of King's College, B

Ontario

Brock University, B
Carleton University, B
Lakehead University, M
McMaster University, BM
Queen's University at Kingston, BMD
University of Guelph, BMD
University of Ottawa, BMD
University of Toronto, BMD
University of Waterloo, BMD
The University of Western Ontario, BMD
University of Windsor, BMD
Wilfrid Laurier University, B
York University, BMD

Quebec

Concordia University, B
McGill University, BMD
Université Laval, BM
Université de Montréal, BMD

Saskatchewan

University of Regina, BMD
University of Saskatchewan, BMD

STRUCTURAL BIOLOGY

California

Stanford University, D
University of California, San Diego, D

Connecticut

University of Connecticut, BMD
Yale University, DO

Florida

Florida State University, D

Illinois

Northwestern University, D
University of Illinois at Urbana-Champaign, D

Iowa

Iowa State University of Science and
Technology, MD

Louisiana

Tulane University, MDO

Massachusetts

Brandeis University, MD
Harvard University, D

New York

Cornell University, MD
New York University, D
State University of New York at Buffalo, MD
Stony Brook University, State University of New
York, D
Syracuse University, D

University at Albany, State University of New
York, MD

North Carolina

Duke University, O

Pennsylvania

Thomas Jefferson University, D
University of Pennsylvania, DO

Texas

The University of Texas Health Science Center at
San Antonio, D
The University of Texas Medical Branch, D

Washington

University of Washington, D

STRUCTURAL ENGINEERING

Alabama

Auburn University, MD

California

California State Polytechnic University, Pomona, M
California State University, Northridge, M
University of California, Berkeley, MD
University of California, Los Angeles, MD
University of California, San Diego, BMD
University of Southern California, BM

Colorado

Colorado State University, MD
University of Colorado at Boulder, MD

Delaware

University of Delaware, MD

District of Columbia

The Catholic University of America, M

Florida

University of Central Florida, O

Illinois

Illinois Institute of Technology, M
Northwestern University, MD
University of Illinois at Urbana-Champaign, B

Louisiana

Louisiana State University and Agricultural and
Mechanical College, MD

Massachusetts

Massachusetts Institute of Technology, D

Michigan

Western Michigan University, B

Missouri

University of Missouri-Columbia, MD
University of Missouri-Rolla, MD
Washington University in St. Louis, MD

New Jersey

Princeton University, MD

New York

Clarkson University, B
Cornell University, MD
Rensselaer Polytechnic Institute, MD
State University of New York at Buffalo, BMD

Ohio

Ohio University, M
University of Dayton, M

The University of Toledo, B

Oklahoma

University of Oklahoma, M

Pennsylvania

Lehigh University, B
The Pennsylvania State University Harrisburg
Campus, B
The Pennsylvania State University University Park
Campus, MD

Rhode Island

University of Rhode Island, MD

Tennessee

University of Memphis, M

Texas

Texas A&M University, MD

Washington

University of Washington, MD

Wisconsin

Marquette University, MD
Milwaukee School of Engineering, M

Alberta

University of Alberta, MD

New Brunswick

University of New Brunswick Fredericton, MD

Quebec

McGill University, MD

STUDENT PERSONNEL SERVICES

Arkansas

Arkansas State University, M
Arkansas Tech University, M
University of Central Arkansas, M

California

Azusa Pacific University, M
Fresno Pacific University, M
San Jose State University, M
University of Southern California, M

Colorado

University of Northern Colorado, D

Florida

Nova Southeastern University, M
University of Florida, M
University of South Florida, M

Georgia

University of Georgia, MD

Illinois

Eastern Illinois University, M
Lewis University, M
Western Illinois University, M

Iowa

The University of Iowa, D
University of Northern Iowa, M

Kansas

Emporia State University, M
Kansas State University, MD

Kentucky

University of Louisville, M

Louisiana

Northwestern State University of Louisiana, M

Maryland

University of Maryland, College Park, MDO

Massachusetts

Northeastern University, M
Springfield College, MO

Minnesota

Minnesota State University Mankato, M
University of Minnesota, Twin Cities Campus, MDO

Mississippi

University of Mississippi, M

Missouri

Saint Louis University, M

New Jersey

Rowan University, M

New York

Buffalo State College, State University of New
   York, M
Canisius College, M
The College of Saint Rose, M
New York University, M

Ohio

Ashland University, M
Bowling Green State University, M
Kent State University, MDO
Miami University, M
Ohio University, M
University of Dayton, M

Oklahoma

Oklahoma State University, MD

Oregon

Oregon State University, M

Pennsylvania

The Pennsylvania State University University Park
   Campus, M
Slippery Rock University of Pennsylvania, M

South Carolina

University of South Carolina, M

Tennessee

Tennessee Technological University, MO
The University of Tennessee, M

Virginia

Hampton University, M

Washington

Western Washington University, M

Wisconsin

Concordia University Wisconsin, M
University of Wisconsin-La Crosse, M

SUBSTANCE ABUSE/ADDICTION COUNSELING

Alabama

Gadsden State Community College, A

Alaska

University of Alaska Anchorage, O

Arizona

Rio Salado College, A

California

Bethany University, B
Charles R. Drew University of Medicine and
   Science, A

College of San Mateo, A
Fresno City College, A
Hartnell College, A
Mendocino College, A
Mt. San Jacinto College, A
Notre Dame de Namur University, M
Saddleback College, A
Yuba College, A

Connecticut

Gateway Community College, A
Housatonic Community College, A
Middlesex Community College, A
Naugatuck Valley Community College, A
Northwestern Connecticut Community College, A
Norwalk Community College, A
Quinebaug Valley Community College, A
Three Rivers Community College, A
Tunxis Community College, A

Delaware

Delaware Technical & Community College,
   Stanton/Wilmington Campus, A

Florida

Florida Community College at Jacksonville, A
Miami Dade College, A
St. Petersburg College, A

Illinois

City Colleges of Chicago, Harold Washington
   College, A
College of DuPage, A
College of Lake County, A
Danville Area Community College, A
Elgin Community College, A
Governors State University, M
National-Louis University, BMO
Prairie State College, A
Triton College, A
University of Illinois at Springfield, M

Indiana

Calumet College of Saint Joseph, B
Indiana University-Purdue University Fort Wayne, B
Indiana Wesleyan University, AB
Martin University, B
Vincennes University, A

Iowa

Graceland University, B
Iowa Western Community College, A
Southeastern Community College, North Campus, A
Southeastern Community College, South
   Campus, A

Kansas

Butler Community College, A
Kansas City Kansas Community College, A
Kansas Wesleyan University, B
Newman University, AB
Washburn University, AB

Kentucky

Eastern Kentucky University, M

Louisiana

Northwestern State University of Louisiana, B
Southern University at Shreveport, A
University of Louisiana at Monroe, M

Maine

University of New England, O

Maryland

Coppin State University, M
Howard Community College, A
The Johns Hopkins University, O
Loyola College in Maryland, O
Wor-Wic Community College, A

Massachusetts

Fitchburg State College, O
North Shore Community College, A

Springfield College, MO

Michigan

University of Detroit Mercy, BMO
Washtenaw Community College, A
Wayne State University, O

Minnesota

Century College, A
College of St. Catherine, B
Mesabi Range Community and Technical College, A
Metropolitan State University, B
Minneapolis Community and Technical College, A
Ridgewater College, A
St. Cloud State University, B

Montana

Dawson Community College, A
University of Great Falls, ABM

Nevada

Truckee Meadows Community College, A

New Hampshire

Keene State College, A
New Hampshire Technical Institute, A
Southern New Hampshire University, O

New Jersey

The College of New Jersey, MO
Georgian Court University, O
Kean University, M
Monmouth University, O
Thomas Edison State College, M

New York

Broome Community College, A
Corning Community College, A
D'Youville College, O
Erie Community College, A
Finger Lakes Community College, A
Genesee Community College, A
Hofstra University, O
Hudson Valley Community College, A
Mercy College, O
Mohawk Valley Community College, A
State University of New York College at
   Brockport, B
Stony Brook University, State University of New
   York, M
Suffolk County Community College, A
Sullivan County Community College, A
Tompkins Cortland Community College, A
Westchester Community College, A

North Carolina

East Carolina University, M
Sandhills Community College, A
Southwestern Community College, A

North Dakota

Minot State University, B
University of Mary, B

Ohio

Columbus State Community College, A
The University of Akron, A
The University of Toledo, A

Oklahoma

Bacone College, A
Oklahoma State University, Oklahoma City, A
Rogers State University, A

Oregon

Lane Community College, A
Lewis & Clark College, M
Rogue Community College, A
Southwestern Oregon Community College, A
Tillamook Bay Community College, A

Pennsylvania

Alvernia College, B
Community College of Allegheny County, A

Marywood University, M

Rhode Island

Community College of Rhode Island, A

South Dakota

Sisseton-Wahpeton Community College, A
The University of South Dakota, B

Texas

Alvin Community College, A
Amarillo College, A
Central Texas College, A
Eastfield College, A
Howard College, A
Lee College, A
Midland College, A
Odessa College, A
St. Mary's University of San Antonio, MO
Texarkana College, A
Texas Southmost College, A

Virginia

The College of William and Mary, M
Northern Virginia Community College, A

Washington

Clark College, A
Edmonds Community College, A
Lower Columbia College, A
Northwest Indian College, A
Peninsula College, A
Pierce College, A
Seattle Central Community College, A
Spokane Falls Community College, A
Tacoma Community College, A
Wenatchee Valley College, A
Yakima Valley Community College, A

Wisconsin

Chippewa Valley Technical College, A
Lac Courte Oreilles Ojibwa Community College, A
Milwaukee Area Technical College, A
Moraine Park Technical College, A

Alberta

University of Lethbridge, B

SUPERINTENDENCY AND EDUCATIONAL SYSTEM ADMINISTRATION

Iowa

Dordt College, B

New York

Le Moyne College, B

SURGICAL NURSING

Illinois

University of Illinois at Chicago, M

Michigan

University of Michigan, M
Wayne State University, M

New York

Hunter College of the City University of New York, M

Ohio

Case Western Reserve University, M

SURGICAL TECHNOLOGY/TECHNOLOGIST

Alabama

Community College of the Air Force, A
James H. Faulkner State Community College, A

Virginia College at Birmingham, A

Arizona

The Bryman School, A
GateWay Community College, A

Arkansas

North Arkansas College, A
Southeast Arkansas College, A
University of Arkansas at Fort Smith, A
University of Arkansas for Medical Sciences, A

California

Loma Linda University, A
San Joaquin Valley College, A
Skyline College, A
Southwestern College, A

Colorado

Pueblo Community College, A

Connecticut

Manchester Community College, A

Florida

Brevard Community College, A
Florida Metropolitan University-Brandon Campus, A
National School of Technology, Inc. (North Miami Beach), A

Georgia

Athens Technical College, A
Augusta Technical College, A
Columbus Technical College, A
Coosa Valley Technical College, A
DeKalb Technical College, A
Georgia Southwestern State University, A
Griffin Technical College, A
Lanier Technical College, A
Northwestern Technical College, A
Okefenokee Technical College, A
Savannah Technical College, A
Southwest Georgia Technical College, A
Waycross College, A

Idaho

Boise State University, A
College of Southern Idaho, A
Eastern Idaho Technical College, A

Illinois

City Colleges of Chicago, Malcolm X College, A
College of DuPage, A
Parkland College, A
Robert Morris College, A
Southeastern Illinois College, A
Trinity College of Nursing and Health Sciences, A

Indiana

Brown Mackie College-Merrillville, A
Indiana Business College (Fort Wayne), A
Indiana Business College (Indianapolis), A
Indiana Business College (Indianapolis-Northwest Campus), A
Indiana Business College-Medical, A
Ivy Tech Community College-Central Indiana, A
Ivy Tech Community College-Columbus, A
Ivy Tech Community College-East Central, A
Ivy Tech Community College-Kokomo, A
Ivy Tech Community College-Lafayette, A
Ivy Tech Community College-Northwest, A
Ivy Tech Community College-Southwest, A
Ivy Tech Community College-Wabash Valley, A

University of Saint Francis, A

Iowa

Iowa Lakes Community College, A
Mercy College of Health Sciences, A

Kansas

Seward County Community College, A

Kentucky

Somerset Community College, A

Louisiana

Louisiana Technical College, A
Our Lady of the Lake College, A
Southern University at Shreveport, A

Maine

Southern Maine Community College, A

Maryland

Baltimore City Community College, A
Frederick Community College, A

Massachusetts

Berkshire Community College, A
Springfield Technical Community College, A

Michigan

Baker College of Clinton Township, A
Baker College of Flint, A
Baker College of Jackson, A
Baker College of Muskegon, A
Delta College, A
Lansing Community College, A
Macomb Community College, A
Oakland Community College, A
Washtenaw Community College, A

Minnesota

Northwest Technical College, A
Rochester Community and Technical College, A
St. Cloud Technical College, A

Mississippi

Hinds Community College, A

Missouri

East Central College, A
St. Louis Community College at Forest Park, A

Montana

Montana State University-Billings, A
The University of Montana-Missoula, A

Nebraska

Metropolitan Community College, A
Northeast Community College, A

New York

Mohawk Valley Community College, A
Nassau Community College, A
Niagara County Community College, A
Trocaire College, A

North Carolina

Blue Ridge Community College, A
Cabarrus College of Health Sciences, A
Coastal Carolina Community College, A
Durham Technical Community College, A
Edgecombe Community College, A
Fayetteville Technical Community College, A
Guilford Technical Community College, A
Sandhills Community College, A

North Dakota

Bismarck State College, A

Ohio

Cincinnati State Technical and Community College, A
Columbus State Community College, A
Cuyahoga Community College, A

Lorain County Community College, A
Sinclair Community College, A
The University of Akron, A

Oklahoma

Community Care College, A
Oklahoma City Community College, A
Tulsa Community College, A

Oregon

Mt. Hood Community College, A

Pennsylvania

Community College of Allegheny County, A
Delaware County Community College, A
Luzerne County Community College, A
Montgomery County Community College, A
Mount Aloysius College, A
Northampton County Area Community College, A
University of Pittsburgh at Johnstown, A
Western School of Health and Business Careers
(Pittsburgh), A

Rhode Island

New England Institute of Technology, A

South Carolina

Central Carolina Technical College, A
Midlands Technical College, A
York Technical College, A

South Dakota

Presentation College, A
Southeast Technical Institute, A

Tennessee

Northeast State Technical Community College, A

Texas

Austin Community College, A
El Centro College, A
Lamar State College-Port Arthur, A
Odessa College, A
Paris Junior College, A
South Plains College, A
Tarrant County College District, A
Texas State Technical College Harlingen, A
Trinity Valley Community College, A

Washington

Renton Technical College, A
Spokane Community College, A

West Virginia

Community & Technical College at West Virginia
University Institute of Technology, A

Wisconsin

Gateway Technical College, A
Moraine Park Technical College, A
Northeast Wisconsin Technical College, A
Waukesha County Technical College, A
Western Technical College, A

Wyoming

Central Wyoming College, A

SURVEY METHODOLOGY

Maryland

University of Maryland, College Park, MD

Michigan

University of Michigan, MDO

Nebraska

University of Nebraska-Lincoln, M

New York

Hunter College of the City University of New
York, M

SURVEY
TECHNOLOGY/SURVEYING

Alabama

Troy University, B

Alaska

University of Alaska Anchorage, AB

Arkansas

University of Arkansas Community College at
Morrilton, A
University of Arkansas at Little Rock, B

California

Bakersfield College, A
California State Polytechnic University, Pomona, B
California State University, Fresno, B
Chabot College, A
Cuyamaca College, A
Mt. San Antonio College, A
Palomar College, A
Sacramento City College, A
Santiago Canyon College, A
Sierra College, A

Colorado

Metropolitan State College of Denver, B
Red Rocks Community College, A
Westwood College-Denver North, A

Delaware

Delaware Technical & Community College, Terry
Campus, A

Florida

Indian River Community College, A
Palm Beach Community College, A
University of Florida, B
Valencia Community College, A

Georgia

Middle Georgia College, A
Southern Polytechnic State University, B

Idaho

Idaho State University, B

Illinois

Morrison Institute of Technology, A
Rend Lake College, A

Indiana

Purdue University, B
Vincennes University, A

Iowa

Hawkeye Community College, A

Louisiana

Louisiana Technical College, A
Nicholls State University, B

Maine

University of Maine, B

Michigan

Ferris State University, AB
Lansing Community College, A
Macomb Community College, A
Michigan Technological University, B

Mott Community College, A

Montana

Flathead Valley Community College, A

Nebraska

Southeast Community College, Milford Campus, A

Nevada

Community College of Southern Nevada, A

New Hampshire

New Hampshire Community Technical College,
Berlin/Laconia, A
University of New Hampshire, A

New Jersey

Burlington County College, A
Middlesex County College, A

New Mexico

New Mexico State University, B
Santa Fe Community College, A

New York

Mohawk Valley Community College, A
Paul Smith's College of Arts and Sciences, A
State University of New York College of
Environmental Science & Forestry, Ranger
School, A
State University of New York College of Technology
at Alfred, A
Sullivan County Community College, A

North Carolina

Asheville-Buncombe Technical Community
College, A
Central Piedmont Community College, A
Fayetteville Technical Community College, A
Guilford Technical Community College, A
Sandhills Community College, A
Wake Technical Community College, A

Ohio

Cincinnati State Technical and Community
College, A
The Ohio State University, B
Owens Community College, A
Sinclair Community College, A
Stark State College of Technology, A
The University of Akron, AB

Oklahoma

Eastern Oklahoma State College, A
Oklahoma State University, Oklahoma City, A
Tulsa Community College, A

Oregon

Oregon Institute of Technology, B
Treasure Valley Community College, A

Pennsylvania

Pennsylvania College of Technology, A
The Pennsylvania State University Wilkes-Barre
Campus of the Commonwealth College, AB

Puerto Rico

Caribbean University, A
Polytechnic University of Puerto Rico, B
University of Puerto Rico at Bayamón, A
University of Puerto Rico, Mayagüez Campus, B

South Dakota

Southeast Technical Institute, A

Tennessee

Chattanooga State Technical Community College, A
East Tennessee State University, B

Texas

Austin Community College, A
Frank Phillips College, A
Texas A&M University-Corpus Christi, B

Tyler Junior College, A

Utah

Salt Lake Community College, A

Washington

Bates Technical College, A
Centralia College, A
Renton Technical College, A

Wisconsin

Milwaukee Area Technical College, A
Nicolet Area Technical College, A
University of Wisconsin-Madison, B

British Columbia

British Columbia Institute of Technology, AB

New Brunswick

University of New Brunswick Fredericton, B
University of New Brunswick Saint John, B

Quebec

Université Laval, B

SURVEYING ENGINEERING

California

Santa Rosa Junior College, A

Maine

University of Maine, B

North Dakota

Minot State University-Bottineau Campus, A

Ohio

The Ohio State University, MD

New Brunswick

University of New Brunswick Fredericton, MD

SUSTAINABLE DEVELOPMENT

Arizona

Prescott College, M

California

New College of California, M

Connecticut

University of Connecticut, M

Georgia

University of Georgia, M

Illinois

Illinois Institute of Technology, M
Western Illinois University, O

Maryland

University of Maryland, College Park, M

Massachusetts

Brandeis University, M
Clark University, M

Pennsylvania

Carnegie Mellon University, M
Slippery Rock University of Pennsylvania, M

Washington

University of Washington, M

Wisconsin

University of Wisconsin-Madison, M

SWEDISH LANGUAGE AND LITERATURE

Illinois

Augustana College, B

Utah

Brigham Young University, B

SYSTEM ADMINISTRATION/ ADMINISTRATOR

Alabama

American College of Computer & Information Sciences, B
Gadsden State Community College-Ayers Campus, A

Arizona

GateWay Community College, A
ITT Technical Institute (Phoenix), A
Rio Salado College, A

Arkansas

University of Arkansas Community College at Batesville, A

California

American River College, A
Coleman College (La Mesa), AB
Cuesta College, A
Cypress College, A
Los Angeles City College, A
Mt. Sierra College, B
Santa Barbara City College, A
Western Career College (San Jose), A
Western Career College (Walnut Creek), A

Colorado

IntelliTec College (Grand Junction), A
National American University (Denver), AB

Connecticut

Naugatuck Valley Community College, A
Quinebaug Valley Community College, A

Florida

Brevard Community College, A
Edison College, A
Florida Community College at Jacksonville, A
Florida National College, A
Gulf Coast College, A
Keiser College (Fort Lauderdale), A
Palm Beach Community College, A
Seminole Community College, A
Tallahassee Community College, A

Illinois

Heartland Community College, A
Parkland College, A
Triton College, A
University of St. Francis, B

Indiana

Vincennes University, A

Iowa

AIB College of Business, A
Dordt College, B
Hawkeye Community College, A
Iowa Lakes Community College, A

Kansas

Brown Mackie College-Kansas City, A

Kentucky

Daymar College (Owensboro), A
Louisville Technical Institute, A

Owensboro Community and Technical College, A

Louisiana

Louisiana Technical College, A
Remington College-New Orleans Campus, A

Maine

Andover College, A

Maryland

Anne Arundel Community College, A

Massachusetts

Cape Cod Community College, A

Michigan

Gogebic Community College, A
Michigan Technological University, B
Washtenaw Community College, A

Minnesota

Academy College, A
Dakota County Technical College, A
Inver Hills Community College, A
Northland Community and Technical College-Thief River Falls, A
Rasmussen College Mankato, A
Ridgewater College, A
University of Minnesota, Crookston, B

Mississippi

Hinds Community College, A
Holmes Community College, A
Southwest Mississippi Community College, A

Missouri

Metropolitan Community College-Business & Technology College, A
Mineral Area College, A

Montana

University of Great Falls, B

Nebraska

Central Community College-Columbus Campus, A
Central Community College-Grand Island Campus, A
Central Community College-Hastings Campus, A

New Jersey

Berkeley College, A
Camden County College, A
Cumberland County College, A

New York

Adirondack Community College, A
The College of Westchester, A
Fiorello H. LaGuardia Community College of the City University of New York, A
Genesee Community College, A
Island Drafting and Technical Institute, A
Onondaga Community College, A
Rochester Institute of Technology, B
Rockland Community College, A
Sage College of Albany, AB
State University of New York College of Technology at Alfred, B
Tompkins Cortland Community College, A

North Carolina

Blue Ridge Community College, A
Cleveland Community College, A
Durham Technical Community College, A
Edgecombe Community College, A
Randolph Community College, A
Sampson Community College, A
Sandhills Community College, A
Stanly Community College, A

Wake Technical Community College, A

North Dakota
Minot State University-Bottineau Campus, A

Ohio
Davis College, A
Lakeland Community College, A
Sinclair Community College, A

Oklahoma
Tulsa Community College, A

Oregon
Linn-Benton Community College, A

Pennsylvania
Berks Technical Institute, A
CHI Institute, A
Laurel Business Institute, A
McCann School of Business & Technology, A
Pennsylvania Highland Community College, A
Thaddeus Stevens College of Technology, A
York Technical Institute, A

South Dakota
Lake Area Technical Institute, A
Southeast Technical Institute, A

Texas
Angelina College, A
Austin Community College, A
Coastal Bend College, A
Del Mar College, A
Eastfield College, A
El Paso Community College, A
Midland College, A
MTI College of Business and Technology (Houston)
, A
San Antonio College, A
Texas State Technical College Harlingen, A

Utah
Western Governors University, A

Vermont
Champlain College, B

Washington
Bellingham Technical College, A
Centralia College, A
Edmonds Community College, A
Olympic College, A
Tacoma Community College, A

West Virginia
Potomac State College of West Virginia
University, A

Wisconsin
Milwaukee Area Technical College, A
Western Technical College, A

Wyoming
Sheridan College-Sheridan and Gillette, A

British Columbia
Thompson Rivers University, A

SYSTEM MANAGEMENT

Colorado
Colorado Technical University Denver Campus, M

Florida
Florida Institute of Technology, M

Massachusetts
University of Phoenix-Boston Campus, M

Minnesota
Metropolitan State University, M

Mississippi
Jackson State University, M
University of Mississippi, M

Nebraska
University of Nebraska-Lincoln, M

New York
Fordham University, M

Ohio
Kent State University, D

Washington
City University, M

SYSTEM, NETWORKING, AND LAN/WAN MANAGEMENT/MANAGER

Arizona
ITT Technical Institute (Tempe), A
ITT Technical Institute (Tucson), A

Arkansas
ITT Technical Institute, A

California
DeVry University (Fremont), B
ITT Technical Institute (Anaheim), A
ITT Technical Institute (Lathrop), A
ITT Technical Institute (Oxnard), A
ITT Technical Institute (Rancho Cordova), A
ITT Technical Institute (San Bernardino), A
ITT Technical Institute (San Diego), A
ITT Technical Institute (Sylmar), A
ITT Technical Institute (Torrance), A
ITT Technical Institute (West Covina), A
Mt. Sierra College, B
Western Career College (Walnut Creek), A
Westwood College-Inland Empire, B

Colorado
ITT Technical Institute, A
National American University (Denver), AB
Pikes Peak Community College, A
Westwood College-Denver South, B

Florida
Brevard Community College, A
College of Business and Technology, A
ITT Technical Institute (Fort Lauderdale), A
ITT Technical Institute (Jacksonville), A
ITT Technical Institute (Lake Mary), A
ITT Technical Institute (Miami), A
ITT Technical Institute (Tampa), A

Georgia
Herzing College, AB
ITT Technical Institute (Duluth), A
ITT Technical Institute (Kennesaw), A

Idaho
ITT Technical Institute, A

Illinois
American InterContinental University Online, B
ITT Technical Institute (Burr Ridge), A
ITT Technical Institute (Matteson), A
ITT Technical Institute (Mount Prospect), A
Westwood College-Chicago Du Page, B
Westwood College-Chicago O'Hare Airport, B
Westwood College-Chicago River Oaks, B

Indiana
International Business College (Indianapolis), A
ITT Technical Institute (Fort Wayne), A
ITT Technical Institute (Indianapolis), A
ITT Technical Institute (Newburgh), A

Sawyer College (Hammond), A

Iowa
Iowa Lakes Community College, A
University of Northern Iowa, B

Kentucky
Brown Mackie College-Northern Kentucky, A
ITT Technical Institute (Lexington), A
ITT Technical Institute (Louisville), A

Louisiana
ITT Technical Institute, A

Maryland
ITT Technical Institute, A

Massachusetts
Berkshire Community College, A
ITT Technical Institute (Norwood), A
ITT Technical Institute (Woburn), A

Michigan
Baker College of Auburn Hills, A
Davenport University (Dearborn), B
ITT Technical Institute (Canton), A
ITT Technical Institute (Grand Rapids), A
ITT Technical Institute (Troy), A

Minnesota
Academy College, A
DeVry University, A
ITT Technical Institute, A
Minneapolis Business College, A
University of Minnesota, Crookston, B

Missouri
DeVry University (Kansas City), A
Hickey College, A
ITT Technical Institute (Arnold), A
ITT Technical Institute (Earth City), A
ITT Technical Institute (Kansas City), A
Metropolitan Community College-Business &
Technology College, A
Vatterott College (Springfield), A

Montana
University of Great Falls, B

Nebraska
ITT Technical Institute, A

Nevada
ITT Technical Institute, A

New Mexico
ITT Technical Institute, A

New York
Hudson Valley Community College, A
ITT Technical Institute (Albany), A
ITT Technical Institute (Getzville), A
ITT Technical Institute (Liverpool), A
Rochester Institute of Technology, B
Wood Tobe-Coburn School, A

North Carolina
Fayetteville Technical Community College, A
Southwestern Community College, A

Ohio
ITT Technical Institute (Dayton), A
ITT Technical Institute (Hilliard), A
ITT Technical Institute (Norwood), A
ITT Technical Institute (Strongsville), A
ITT Technical Institute (Warrensville Heights), A

ITT Technical Institute (Youngstown), A

Oklahoma

ITT Technical Institute, A

Oregon

ITT Technical Institute, A

Pennsylvania

DeVry University (Fort Washington), A
Peirce College, A

South Carolina

ITT Technical Institute, A

South Dakota

Mitchell Technical Institute, A
National American University (Rapid City), B

Tennessee

ITT Technical Institute (Knoxville), A
ITT Technical Institute (Memphis), A
ITT Technical Institute (Nashville), A

Texas

ITT Technical Institute (Arlington), A
ITT Technical Institute (Austin), A
ITT Technical Institute (Houston), A
ITT Technical Institute (Houston), A
ITT Technical Institute (Houston), A
ITT Technical Institute (Richardson), A
ITT Technical Institute (San Antonio), A
Midland College, A
Montgomery College, A
MTI College of Business and Technology (Houston)
, A
St. Philip's College, A

Utah

ITT Technical Institute, A
LDS Business College, A

Vermont

Champlain College, AB

Virginia

ITT Technical Institute (Norfolk), A
ITT Technical Institute (Richmond), A
ITT Technical Institute (Springfield), A

Washington

DeVry University (Federal Way), B
ITT Technical Institute (Bothell), A
ITT Technical Institute (Seattle), A
ITT Technical Institute (Spokane), A
Olympic College, A

Wisconsin

Carroll College, B
ITT Technical Institute (Green Bay), A
ITT Technical Institute (Greenfield), A

British Columbia

Thompson Rivers University, A

SYSTEMATIC BIOLOGY/BIOLOGICAL SYSTEMATICS

California

University of California, San Diego, D

Massachusetts

Harvard University, D
Massachusetts Institute of Technology, D

SYSTEMS ENGINEERING

Alabama

Auburn University, MD

Arizona

The University of Arizona, BMD

California

California Institute of Technology, MD
California State University, Fullerton, M
Loyola Marymount University, MO
San Jose State University, M
University of California, San Diego, B
University of Southern California, BMDO

Colorado

Colorado School of Mines, MD
Colorado State University-Pueblo, M

Connecticut

University of Connecticut, MD

Delaware

Delaware State University, B

District of Columbia

The George Washington University, BMDO

Florida

Embry-Riddle Aeronautical University, M
Florida Institute of Technology, M
Florida International University, B
University of Central Florida, O
University of Florida, BMDO
University of West Florida, M

Georgia

Georgia Institute of Technology, MD
Southern Polytechnic State University, M

Idaho

University of Idaho, M

Illinois

University of Illinois at Urbana-Champaign, MO

Indiana

Purdue University, MD
Rose-Hulman Institute of Technology, B

Iowa

Iowa State University of Science and Technology, M

Louisiana

Louisiana State University in Shreveport, M

Maine

Maine Maritime Academy, B
University of Maine, B

Maryland

The Johns Hopkins University, M
United States Naval Academy, B
University of Maryland, Baltimore County, O
University of Maryland, College Park, M

Massachusetts

Boston University, MD
Eastern Nazarene College, B
Harvard University, B
Massachusetts Institute of Technology, MDO
Northeastern University, M

Michigan

Oakland University, BMD
University of Detroit Mercy, B
University of Michigan, MD
University of Michigan-Dearborn, MO

Minnesota

University of Minnesota, Twin Cities Campus, M
University of St. Thomas, M

Walden University, M

Missouri

Missouri Tech, AB
University of Missouri-Rolla, BM
Washington University in St. Louis, BD

Montana

Montana Tech of The University of Montana, B

New Jersey

Rutgers, The State University of New Jersey, New
   Brunswick/Piscataway, MD
Stevens Institute of Technology, B

New York

Cornell University, M
Polytechnic University, Brooklyn Campus, M
Rensselaer Polytechnic Institute, BMDO
Rochester Institute of Technology, BMD
Stony Brook University, State University of New
   York, M
United States Military Academy, B

North Carolina

North Carolina Agricultural and Technical State
   University, MD
The University of North Carolina at Charlotte, D

Ohio

Case Western Reserve University, BMD
The Ohio State University, BMD
Ohio University, BM
Wright State University, B

Oklahoma

Oklahoma State University, M

Oregon

Portland State University, MO

Pennsylvania

Lehigh University, MDO
University of Pennsylvania, BMD

Rhode Island

University of Rhode Island, MD

Tennessee

University of Memphis, B

Texas

Southern Methodist University, M
Texas Tech University, M
University of Houston, MD
University of Houston-Clear Lake, BM
The University of Texas at Arlington, MD

Virginia

George Mason University, BM
Old Dominion University, M
University of Virginia, BMDO

Washington

Washington State University, MD

Wisconsin

University of Wisconsin-Madison, MD

Alberta

University of Alberta, MD

Ontario

Carleton University, BM
University of Waterloo, BMD

Quebec

Concordia University, MO

Saskatchewan

University of Regina, BMD

SYSTEMS SCIENCE AND THEORY

Arkansas

Arkansas Tech University, M

California

Stanford University, B

Colorado

Colorado Technical University, M
Colorado Technical University Denver Campus, M

Connecticut

Yale University, B

Florida

Florida Institute of Technology, M

Illinois

American InterContinental University Online, M
Eastern Illinois University, O

Indiana

Indiana University Bloomington, B

Kentucky

Northern Kentucky University, M

Louisiana

Louisiana State University and Agricultural and
    Mechanical College, M
Louisiana State University in Shreveport, M

Maryland

Hood College, M

Michigan

Oakland University, M
University of Michigan-Dearborn, M

Missouri

Washington University in St. Louis, BMD

New Jersey

Fairleigh Dickinson University, Metropolitan
    Campus, M

New York

State University of New York at Binghamton, MD
Syracuse University, M

North Carolina

The University of North Carolina at Charlotte, MD
The University of North Carolina Wilmington, M

Ohio

Miami University, BM
Miami University-Middletown Campus, A
Wright State University, B

Oregon

Portland State University, MDO

Pennsylvania

Carnegie Mellon University, B

Rhode Island

Providence College, B

Texas

Southern Methodist University, MD

Vermont

Sterling College, B

Virginia

George Mason University, M

West Virginia

Marshall University, B

Wisconsin

Northeast Wisconsin Technical College, A

Ontario

Carleton University, MD
University of Ottawa, BMO

TALMUDIC STUDIES

Florida

Talmudic College of Florida, B

New York

The Jewish Theological Seminary, B

TAMIL LANGUAGE AND LITERATURE

Illinois

University of Chicago, B

TAXATION

Alabama

The University of Alabama, M

California

California State University, East Bay, M
California State University, Fullerton, BM
Chapman University, M
Golden Gate University, MO
Loyola Marymount University, M
National University, M
San Jose State University, M
University of San Diego, MO
University of Southern California, MO

Colorado

University of Colorado at Boulder, M
University of Denver, M

Connecticut

University of Hartford, MO
University of New Haven, M

District of Columbia

American University, M
Georgetown University, M

Florida

Florida Atlantic University, M
Florida International University, M
Nova Southeastern University, M
St. Thomas University, M
University of Central Florida, M
University of Florida, MD
University of Miami, M

Georgia

Georgia State University, M

Hawaii

University of Hawaii at Manoa, M

Illinois

DePaul University, M
Illinois Institute of Technology, M
Northern Illinois University, M

Louisiana

University of New Orleans, M

Maryland

University of Baltimore, M

Massachusetts

Bentley College, MO
Boston University, M

Northeastern University, MO
Suffolk University, M

Michigan

Grand Valley State University, M
Walsh College of Accountancy and Business
    Administration, M
Wayne State University, M

Minnesota

Globe College, A
Minnesota School of Business, A
Minnesota School of Business-Brooklyn Center, A
Minnesota School of Business-Plymouth, A
Minnesota School of Business-Richfield, A
Minnesota School of Business-St. Cloud, A
University of Minnesota, Twin Cities Campus, M

Mississippi

Mississippi State University, M
University of Mississippi, M

Missouri

Fontbonne University, M
University of Missouri-St. Louis, MO

New Jersey

Fairleigh Dickinson University, College at
    Florham, MO
Rutgers, The State University of New Jersey,
    Newark, M
Seton Hall University, MO

New Mexico

University of New Mexico, M

New York

Bernard M. Baruch College of the City University of
    New York, M
Fordham University, M
Hofstra University, MO
Long Island University, Brooklyn Campus, M
Long Island University, C.W. Post Campus, MO
New York University, O
Pace University, M
St. John's University, BMO
University at Albany, State University of New
    York, M

Ohio

Capital University, BMO
Cleveland State University, M
The University of Akron, M
University of Cincinnati, M

Oklahoma

University of Tulsa, M

Pennsylvania

Drexel University, BM
Duquesne University, M
Philadelphia University, M
Robert Morris University, M
Temple University, M
Villanova University, MO
Widener University, M

Puerto Rico

University of the Sacred Heart, M

Rhode Island

Bryant University, MO

Tennessee

University of Memphis, M

Texas

St. Mary's University of San Antonio, M
Southern Methodist University, M
Texas Tech University, M
The University of Texas at Arlington, M

The University of Texas at San Antonio, M

Virginia

Virginia Commonwealth University, M

Washington

University of Washington, M
Washington State University, M

British Columbia

British Columbia Institute of Technology, A

Ontario

University of Waterloo, M

Quebec

HEC Montreal, MO
Université de Sherbrooke, MO

TEACHER ASSISTANT/AIDE

Alabama

Alabama State University, A

Arizona

Cochise College (Sierra Vista), A
Mesa Community College, A
Northland Pioneer College, A

California

Antelope Valley College, A
Chabot College, A
College of the Desert, A
Compton Community College, A
Fresno City College, A
Los Angeles City College, A
Los Angeles Mission College, A
Los Angeles Southwest College, A
Merced College, A
MiraCosta College, A
Moorpark College, A
Pasadena City College, A
Saddleback College, A
San Diego City College, A
San Jose City College, A
Sierra College, A
Victor Valley College, A

Colorado

Colorado Northwestern Community College, A
Community College of Denver, A
Lamar Community College, A

Connecticut

Goodwin College, A

Florida

Indian River Community College, A
Miami Dade College, A

Idaho

Boise State University, A

Illinois

Black Hawk College, A
City Colleges of Chicago, Harold Washington
   College, A
City Colleges of Chicago, Harry S. Truman
   College, A
City Colleges of Chicago, Kennedy-King College, A
City Colleges of Chicago, Malcolm X College, A
City Colleges of Chicago, Richard J. Daley
   College, A
Danville Area Community College, A
Illinois Eastern Community Colleges, Lincoln Trail
   College, A
John A. Logan College, A
Joliet Junior College, A
Lewis and Clark Community College, A
Prairie State College, A

South Suburban College, A

Iowa

Des Moines Area Community College, A
Dordt College, A
Ellsworth Community College, A
Kirkwood Community College, A

Kansas

Fort Scott Community College, A
Garden City Community College, A
Neosho County Community College, A

Louisiana

Our Lady of Holy Cross College, A
Southern University at Shreveport, A

Massachusetts

Mount Ida College, A

Michigan

Lansing Community College, A
Mott Community College, A

Minnesota

Ridgewater College, A
St. Cloud Technical College, A

Mississippi

Northeast Mississippi Community College, A

Missouri

East Central College, A

Nevada

Community College of Southern Nevada, A

New Hampshire

New Hampshire Technical Institute, A

New Jersey

Mercer County Community College, A
Middlesex County College, A
Ocean County College, A

New Mexico

Clovis Community College, A
New Mexico Highlands University, A
New Mexico State University, A
University of New Mexico, A

New York

Fulton-Montgomery Community College, A
Kingsborough Community College of the City
   University of New York, A

North Carolina

Alamance Community College, A
Brunswick Community College, A
Carteret Community College, A
Catawba Valley Community College, A
Cleveland Community College, A
College of The Albemarle, A
Durham Technical Community College, A
Isothermal Community College, A
McDowell Technical Community College, A
Rockingham Community College, A
Sandhills Community College, A
Southeastern Community College, A
Vance-Granville Community College, A

North Dakota

Sitting Bull College, A

Ohio

The University of Akron, A

Oregon

Chemeketa Community College, A
Linn-Benton Community College, A

Pennsylvania

Bucks County Community College, A
Delaware County Community College, A

Montgomery County Community College, A
Northampton County Area Community College, A

Tennessee

Johnson Bible College, A
Martin Methodist College, A

Texas

Angelina College, A
El Centro College, A
Lamar University, A
Odessa College, A
St. Philip's College, A
Southwest Texas Junior College, A

Utah

Salt Lake Community College, A

Vermont

Community College of Vermont, A

Washington

Big Bend Community College, A
Centralia College, A
Clover Park Technical College, A
Lower Columbia College, A
Renton Technical College, A
Shoreline Community College, A
Walla Walla Community College, A

Wisconsin

Alverno College, A
Waukesha County Technical College, A

TEACHER EDUCATION AND PROFESSIONAL DEVELOPMENT, SPECIFIC LEVELS AND METHODS

Alaska

Sheldon Jackson College, A

Illinois

Columbia College Chicago, B
Kendall College, B

Massachusetts

Boston University, B

Minnesota

St. Cloud State University, B

Missouri

Washington University in St. Louis, B

New Jersey

Rowan University, B

Ohio

The University of Akron, B
The University of Toledo, B
Wright State University, B
Xavier University, B

Pennsylvania

Community College of Allegheny County, A

Rhode Island

Rhode Island College, B

Utah

Brigham Young University, B

Wyoming

Laramie County Community College, A

TEACHER EDUCATION AND PROFESSIONAL DEVELOPMENT, SPECIFIC SUBJECT AREAS

Arizona

Northern Arizona University, B
The University of Arizona, B

Arkansas

Henderson State University, B

Florida

Miami Dade College, B

Illinois

Bradley University, B
Columbia College Chicago, B

Kansas

Baker University, B

Kentucky

Eastern Kentucky University, B
Thomas More College, B
University of Kentucky, B

Louisiana

Louisiana State University and Agricultural and
    Mechanical College, B
Louisiana Tech University, B
University of Louisiana at Lafayette, B
University of Louisiana at Monroe, B

Michigan

Central Michigan University, B
Hope College, B
Madonna University, B
University of Michigan-Flint, B

Minnesota

University of St. Thomas, B

Missouri

Avila University, B
Missouri State University, B

Nebraska

Chadron State College, B
University of Nebraska-Lincoln, B

Nevada

University of Nevada, Reno, B

New Hampshire

Keene State College, B
Plymouth State University, B

New York

Hofstra University, B
Syracuse University, B

North Carolina

Appalachian State University, B
The University of North Carolina Wilmington, B

Ohio

Bowling Green State University, B
Ohio University, B
The University of Akron, B
The University of Toledo, B
Wright State University, B

Oklahoma

Cameron University, B
University of Central Oklahoma, B
University of Oklahoma, B

Pennsylvania

Community College of Allegheny County, A
Drexel University, B
Marywood University, B

Pennsylvania College of Technology, A
The Pennsylvania State University Harrisburg
    Campus, B
Point Park University, B

Texas

Baylor University, B
St. Edward's University, B
Schreiner University, B

Utah

Brigham Young University, B
Utah State University, B

Virginia

Averett University, B

Washington

Eastern Washington University, B

Wisconsin

Marquette University, B
University of Wisconsin-Eau Claire, B

TEACHER EDUCATION, MULTIPLE LEVELS

Alabama

University of North Alabama, B

Arizona

International Baptist College, B

Arkansas

Harding University, B
University of the Ozarks, B

California

Biola University, B
Pacific Union College, B
San Diego Christian College, B

Colorado

Metropolitan State College of Denver, B

Connecticut

Connecticut College, B

Florida

The University of Tampa, B

Georgia

Coastal Georgia Community College, A
Columbus State University, B
Georgia Perimeter College, A

Illinois

Dominican University, B
Illinois College, B
Lewis University, B
McKendree College, B
Trinity International University, B

Indiana

Indiana Wesleyan University, B
Saint Mary-of-the-Woods College, B
Vincennes University, A
Vincennes University Jasper Campus, A

Iowa

Dordt College, B
Graceland University, B
Northwestern College, B
St. Ambrose University, B

Kansas

McPherson College, B
Pratt Community College, A

Tabor College, B

Kentucky

Pikeville College, B

Louisiana

Centenary College of Louisiana, B
Our Lady of Holy Cross College, B

Maine

University of Maine at Fort Kent, B

Maryland

Carroll Community College, A
Cecil Community College, A

Michigan

Adrian College, B
Finlandia University, B
Hillsdale College, B
Lake Superior State University, B
Mid Michigan Community College, A

Minnesota

The College of St. Scholastica, B
Hamline University, B
Itasca Community College, A
Martin Luther College, B
University of Minnesota, Morris, B
University of St. Thomas, B

Missouri

Lindenwood University, B
Saint Louis University, B
Washington University in St. Louis, B

Montana

University of Great Falls, B
The University of Montana-Western, B

Nebraska

College of Saint Mary, B
Grace University, B
Midland Lutheran College, B
University of Nebraska-Lincoln, B
York College, B

Nevada

Truckee Meadows Community College, A

New Hampshire

New England College, B

New Jersey

College of Saint Elizabeth, B
Felician College, B
The Richard Stockton College of New Jersey, B

New York

Columbia College, B
D'Youville College, B
Hofstra University, B
Iona College, B
Ithaca College, B
Manhattan College, B
Mount Saint Mary College, B
Syracuse University, B

North Carolina

Campbell University, B
Louisburg College, A
Methodist College, B
Saint Augustine's College, B
Wake Forest University, B

North Dakota

Dickinson State University, B
Jamestown College, B

Ohio

John Carroll University, B
Lake Erie College, B
Miami University Hamilton, B

Ohio Dominican University, B
Ohio Northern University, B
Ohio Wesleyan University, B
Shawnee State University, B
The University of Akron, B
University of Rio Grande, B
Wright State University, B

Oklahoma

Oral Roberts University, B

Oregon

Northwest Christian College, B

Pennsylvania

Chestnut Hill College, B
Delaware County Community College, A
Gannon University, B
Gwynedd-Mercy College, B
Juniata College, B
Keystone College, AB

Puerto Rico

Caribbean University, B

Rhode Island

Rhode Island College, B

South Carolina

Charleston Southern University, B
Columbia International University, B

South Dakota

Augustana College, B
Dakota Wesleyan University, B

Tennessee

Bethel College, B
Lambuth University, B
LeMoyne-Owen College, B
Tennessee Wesleyan College, B
Trevecca Nazarene University, B
University of Memphis, B
The University of Tennessee at Martin, B

Texas

Angelina College, A
Howard Payne University, B
Tarleton State University, B
Texas Lutheran University, B

Utah

Utah State University, B

Virginia

Averett University, B
Liberty University, B

Washington

University of Washington, B
Walla Walla College, B
Western Washington University, B

West Virginia

Ohio Valley University, B
Salem International University, B
West Virginia Wesleyan College, B

Wisconsin

Concordia University Wisconsin, B

Wyoming

Western Wyoming Community College, A

Alberta

University of Lethbridge, B

New Brunswick

Atlantic Baptist University, B

Ontario

Queen's University at Kingston, B
Redeemer University College, B

University of Windsor, B
York University, B

TEACHING ASSISTANTS/AIDES

Arizona

Northland Pioneer College, A

Arkansas

Southern Arkansas University Tech, A

TEACHING ENGLISH AS A SECOND OR FOREIGN LANGUAGE/ESL LANGUAGE INSTRUCTOR

Alabama

Auburn University, B

Arizona

Northern Arizona University, B
The University of Arizona, B

Arkansas

John Brown University, B

California

University of California, Los Angeles, B

Delaware

University of Delaware, B

Florida

Hobe Sound Bible College, B

Hawaii

Brigham Young University-Hawaii, B
Hawaii Pacific University, B
University of Hawaii at Manoa, B

Illinois

Moody Bible Institute, B

Indiana

Goshen College, B

Iowa

The University of Iowa, B
University of Northern Iowa, B
William Penn University, B

Kentucky

Murray State University, B

Massachusetts

Simmons College, B

Michigan

Aquinas College, B
Calvin College, B

Minnesota

Bethel University, B
Concordia University, St. Paul, B
Northwestern College, B

Montana

Carroll College, B
The University of Montana-Missoula, B

Nebraska

Concordia University, B
Doane College, B
University of Nebraska-Lincoln, B

New York

Mercy College, B
Nyack College, B

Queens College of the City University of New
York, B
St. John's University, B

Ohio

Ohio Dominican University, B
Ohio University, B
The University of Findlay, B
Wright State University, B

Oklahoma

Langston University, B
Oklahoma Christian University, B
Oklahoma Wesleyan University, B
Oral Roberts University, B

Pennsylvania

Carnegie Mellon University, B

Puerto Rico

Inter American University of Puerto Rico, Aguadilla
Campus, B
Inter American University of Puerto Rico, Arecibo
Campus, B
Inter American University of Puerto Rico, Fajardo
Campus, B
Inter American University of Puerto Rico, Guayama
Campus, B
Inter American University of Puerto Rico,
Metropolitan Campus, B
Inter American University of Puerto Rico, San
Germán Campus, B
University of Puerto Rico, Cayey University
College, B
University of Puerto Rico at Humacao, B

Tennessee

Maryville College, B
Union University, B

Texas

Howard Payne University, B
Tarleton State University, B
Texas Wesleyan University, B

Utah

Brigham Young University, B

Virginia

Liberty University, B

Washington

Eastern Washington University, B
Northwest University, B
University of Washington, B
Washington State University, B

Wisconsin

Concordia University Wisconsin, B
University of Wisconsin-Oshkosh, B
University of Wisconsin-River Falls, B

Alberta

University of Alberta, B

British Columbia

The University of British Columbia, B
University of Victoria, B

Manitoba

Providence College and Theological Seminary, B

New Brunswick

University of New Brunswick Fredericton, B

Ontario

Brock University, B
Carleton University, B
University of Ottawa, B

York University, B

Quebec

Concordia University, B
McGill University, B
Université Laval, B
Université du Québec àChicoutimi, B
Université du Québec àMontréal, B

Saskatchewan

University of Saskatchewan, B

TEACHING ENGLISH OR FRENCH AS A SECOND OR FOREIGN LANGUAGE

Michigan

Western Michigan University, B

Ontario

University of Ottawa, B

TEACHING FRENCH AS A SECOND OR FOREIGN LANGUAGE

Michigan

Western Michigan University, B

North Carolina

Campbell University, B

Ontario

University of Toronto, B
University of Windsor, B

Quebec

Bishop's University, B
Université Laval, B

TECHNICAL AND BUSINESS WRITING

Alabama

The University of Alabama in Huntsville, O

Arkansas

University of Arkansas at Fort Smith, B
University of Arkansas at Little Rock, BM

California

De Anza College, A
El Camino College, A
Golden West College, A
San Francisco State University, B

Colorado

Colorado State University, M
Regis University, O

Connecticut

Three Rivers Community College, A
University of Hartford, B

Delaware

University of Delaware, B

Florida

Florida National College, A
University of Central Florida, M

Warner Southern College, B

Georgia

Georgia State University, MD
Southern Polytechnic State University, B

Idaho

Boise State University, B

Illinois

Chicago State University, B
College of Lake County, A
Illinois Institute of Technology, BMD

Iowa

Iowa State University of Science and Technology, B

Kentucky

Murray State University, A

Maryland

The Johns Hopkins University, M
University of Baltimore, B

Massachusetts

Fitchburg State College, BM
Massachusetts Institute of Technology, M

Michigan

Eastern Michigan University, B
Ferris State University, AB
Grand Valley State University, B
Madonna University, B
Michigan State University, B
Michigan Technological University, B
Northern Michigan University, B
University of Michigan-Flint, B
Washtenaw Community College, A

Minnesota

Metropolitan State University, BM
Northwestern College, B

Missouri

Missouri State University, B
Webster University, B

Montana

Carroll College, B
Montana Tech of The University of Montana, B
The University of Montana-Missoula, B

New Jersey

New Jersey Institute of Technology, B

New Mexico

Clovis Community College, A
College of Santa Fe, B
New Mexico Institute of Mining and Technology, B

New York

Clarkson University, B
Medaille College, B
New York Institute of Technology, B
State University of New York College of Agriculture
    and Technology at Morrisville, A

North Carolina

The University of North Carolina at Greensboro, O

Ohio

Bowling Green State University, B
Cedarville University, B
Cincinnati State Technical and Community
    College, A
Columbus State Community College, A
Miami University, BM
Miami University Hamilton, B
Ohio Northern University, B
Terra State Community College, A

Youngstown State University, B

Oklahoma

Oklahoma State University, MD

Oregon

Linn-Benton Community College, A

Pennsylvania

Allegheny College, B
Carlow University, B
Carnegie Mellon University, BM
Drexel University, BM
La Roche College, B
Pennsylvania College of Technology, B
The Pennsylvania State University Berks Campus of
    the Berks-Lehigh Valley College, B
The Pennsylvania State University, Lehigh Valley
    Campus of the Berks-Lehigh Valley College, B
University of the Sciences in Philadelphia, M

South Carolina

Bob Jones University, B
Winthrop University, B

Tennessee

King College, B
Maryville College, B
Tennessee Technological University, B

Texas

Austin Community College, A
Houston Community College System, A
Tarleton State University, B
Texas Tech University, MD
University of Houston-Downtown, B

Utah

Weber State University, B

Vermont

Champlain College, B

Virginia

James Madison University, BM

Washington

University of Washington, B

Wisconsin

Gateway Technical College, A
Mount Mary College, B
University of Wisconsin-Stout, B

British Columbia

University of Victoria, B

Ontario

University of Waterloo, M
York University, B

TECHNICAL COMMUNICATION

Colorado

Colorado State University, M
University of Colorado at Denver and Health
    Sciences Center - Downtown Denver Campus, M

Georgia

Southern Polytechnic State University, M

Idaho

Boise State University, M

Massachusetts

Harvard University, M

Michigan

Michigan Technological University, MD

Minnesota

University of Minnesota, Twin Cities Campus, MD

Montana

Montana Tech of The University of Montana, M

Nebraska

University of Nebraska at Omaha, O

New Jersey

New Jersey Institute of Technology, M

New York

Rensselaer Polytechnic Institute, M
Rochester Institute of Technology, O

North Carolina

North Carolina State University, M

Texas

Texas State University-San Marcos, M

Washington

University of Washington, MD

TECHNICAL TEACHER EDUCATION

Idaho

University of Idaho, B

Illinois

Eastern Illinois University, B

Kentucky

Eastern Kentucky University, AB
Northern Kentucky University, A
Western Kentucky University, A

Louisiana

Louisiana Technical College, A

Michigan

Wayne State University, B

Mississippi

Mississippi State University, B

Missouri

University of Missouri-Columbia, B

Nebraska

University of Nebraska at Kearney, B

New York

New York City College of Technology of the City
    University of New York, B
New York Institute of Technology, AB

North Dakota

Lake Region State College, A
North Dakota State College of Science, A
Valley City State University, B

Ohio

Bowling Green State University, B
The Ohio State University, B
The University of Akron, B
Wright State University, B

Rhode Island

Rhode Island College, B

Tennessee

The University of Tennessee, B

Texas

Texas Christian University, B

Utah

Utah State University, B

Wisconsin

University of Wisconsin-Stout, B

Ontario

Queen's University at Kingston, B

Quebec

Université Laval, B

Saskatchewan

University of Saskatchewan, B

TECHNICAL THEATRE/THEATRE DESIGN AND TECHNOLOGY

Alaska

University of Alaska Fairbanks, B

Arizona

The University of Arizona, B

California

California Institute of the Arts, B
Fresno City College, A
Santa Barbara City College, A
University of California, Santa Cruz, B
University of Southern California, B

Connecticut

University of Connecticut, B

Delaware

University of Delaware, B

Florida

Florida Community College at Jacksonville, A
Florida State University, B
Lake-Sumter Community College, A

Illinois

Columbia College Chicago, B
DePaul University, B

Indiana

Huntington University, B
Indiana University Bloomington, A

Iowa

Coe College, B
University of Northern Iowa, B

Kansas

University of Kansas, B

Maryland

Howard Community College, A

Massachusetts

Boston University, B
Emerson College, B
Fitchburg State College, B
Simon's Rock College of Bard, B

Michigan

Michigan Technological University, B
University of Michigan, B

Western Michigan University, B

Missouri

Webster University, B
William Woods University, B

Montana

Carroll College, B
Rocky Mountain College, B

New Hampshire

Keene State College, B

New Jersey

Centenary College, B

New Mexico

College of Santa Fe, B
University of New Mexico, B

New York

Five Towns College, B
Ithaca College, B
Nassau Community College, A
New York City College of Technology of the City
    University of New York, B
Purchase College, State University of New York, B
Syracuse University, B

North Carolina

Greensboro College, B
North Carolina School of the Arts, B

Ohio

Bowling Green State University, B
Ohio University, B
The University of Akron, B
University of Rio Grande, A
Wright State University, B

Oklahoma

Oklahoma City University, B

Oregon

George Fox University, B

Pennsylvania

Elizabethtown College, B
The Pennsylvania State University Abington
    College, B
The Pennsylvania State University Altoona
    College, B
The Pennsylvania State University Beaver Campus
    of the Commonwealth College, B
The Pennsylvania State University Berks Campus of
    the Berks-Lehigh Valley College, B
The Pennsylvania State University Delaware County
    Campus of the Commonwealth College, B
The Pennsylvania State University DuBois Campus
    of the Commonwealth College, B
The Pennsylvania State University at Erie, The
    Behrend College, B
The Pennsylvania State University Fayette Campus
    of the Commonwealth College, B
The Pennsylvania State University Hazleton
    Campus of the Commonwealth College, B
The Pennsylvania State University, Lehigh Valley
    Campus of the Berks-Lehigh Valley College, B
The Pennsylvania State University McKeesport
    Campus of the Commonwealth College, B
The Pennsylvania State University Mont Alto
    Campus of the Commonwealth College, B
The Pennsylvania State University New Kensington
    Campus of the Commonwealth College, B
The Pennsylvania State University Schuylkill
    Campus of the Capital College, B
The Pennsylvania State University Shenango
    Campus of the Commonwealth College, B
The Pennsylvania State University University Park
    Campus, B
The Pennsylvania State University Wilkes-Barre
    Campus of the Commonwealth College, B

The Pennsylvania State University Worthington
  Scranton Campus of the Commonwealth
  College, B
The Pennsylvania State University York Campus of
  the Commonwealth College, B
Seton Hill University, B
The University of the Arts, B

Rhode Island

Community College of Rhode Island, A

South Carolina

Coker College, B

Texas

Baylor University, B
Texas Tech University, B
Trinity University, B

Utah

Brigham Young University, B

Vermont

Bennington College, B
Johnson State College, A

Virginia

Shenandoah University, B

Washington

Cornish College of the Arts, B

West Virginia

Davis & Elkins College, B

Wyoming

Central Wyoming College, A
Western Wyoming Community College, A

Alberta

University of Alberta, B
University of Lethbridge, B

Newfoundland and Labrador

Memorial University of Newfoundland, B

Ontario

Ryerson University, B

Quebec

Concordia University, B

Saskatchewan

University of Regina, B

TECHNOLOGY AND PUBLIC POLICY

California

California State University, Los Angeles, M

District of Columbia

The George Washington University, MO

Illinois

Western Illinois University, M

Massachusetts

Massachusetts Institute of Technology, MDO

Michigan

Eastern Michigan University, M

Minnesota

St. Cloud State University, M
University of Minnesota, Twin Cities Campus, MO

New York

Rensselaer Polytechnic Institute, MD
Rochester Institute of Technology, M

Ohio

Ohio University, M

Pennsylvania

Carnegie Mellon University, D

Texas

The University of Texas at Austin, M

TECHNOLOGY EDUCATION/INDUSTRIAL ARTS

Arkansas

Phillips Community College of the University of
  Arkansas, A
University of Arkansas at Pine Bluff, B

California

American River College, A
Bakersfield College, A
California State University, Fresno, B
Cerritos College, A
Chabot College, A
College of the Sequoias, A
Contra Costa College, A
El Camino College, A
Fresno City College, A
Fullerton College, A
Humboldt State University, B
Long Beach City College, A
Los Angeles Pierce College, A
Merced College, A
Modesto Junior College, A
Mt. San Antonio College, A
Porterville College, A
Saddleback College, A
San Diego City College, A
San Francisco State University, B
Santa Monica College, A
Sierra College, A
Taft College, A

Colorado

Colorado State University-Pueblo, B
Western State College of Colorado, B

District of Columbia

University of the District of Columbia, B

Florida

Florida Agricultural and Mechanical University, B

Georgia

Dalton State College, A

Hawaii

Honolulu Community College, A

Idaho

Brigham Young University -Idaho, A

Illinois

Chicago State University, B

Indiana

Ball State University, B

Iowa

William Penn University, B

Kansas

Allen County Community College, A
Cowley County Community College and Area
  Vocational-Technical School, A
Dodge City Community College, A
Fort Hays State University, B
Fort Scott Community College, A
Garden City Community College, A
Highland Community College, A
McPherson College, B
Pittsburg State University, B

Pratt Community College, A

Kentucky

Berea College, B
Eastern Kentucky University, AB

Maine

Northern Maine Community College, A
University of Southern Maine, B

Maryland

University of Maryland Eastern Shore, B

Massachusetts

Fitchburg State College, B

Michigan

Andrews University, B
Delta College, A
Muskegon Community College, A
Washtenaw Community College, A

Minnesota

Bemidji State University, B
Minnesota State University Mankato, B
St. Cloud State University, B
Vermilion Community College, A

Mississippi

Hinds Community College, A
Itawamba Community College, A
Jackson State University, B

Missouri

College of the Ozarks, B

Montana

The University of Montana-Missoula, A
The University of Montana-Western, B

Nebraska

Southeast Community College, Milford Campus, A

New Hampshire

Keene State College, B

New Mexico

Luna Community College, A
New Mexico Highlands University, B
New Mexico Junior College, A

New York

Buffalo State College, State University of New
  York, B

North Carolina

Elizabeth City State University, B
Guilford Technical Community College, A
Haywood Community College, A
North Carolina Agricultural and Technical State
  University, B
Rockingham Community College, A
Western Piedmont Community College, A

Ohio

Ohio Northern University, B
University of Cincinnati, A

Oklahoma

Carl Albert State College, A
Eastern Oklahoma State College, A
Langston University, B
Northeastern Oklahoma Agricultural and Mechanical
  College, A
Northeastern State University, B
Oklahoma Panhandle State University, B

Southwestern Oklahoma State University, B

Pennsylvania

Community College of Beaver County, A
Thaddeus Stevens College of Technology, A

South Carolina

South Carolina State University, B

South Dakota

Northern State University, B

Tennessee

Austin Peay State University, A
Cleveland State Community College, A
Pellissippi State Technical Community College, A
Tennessee State University, B
Volunteer State Community College, A

Texas

El Paso Community College, A
Sul Ross State University, B
Tarleton State University, B
Texas A&M University-Commerce, B

Utah

Southern Utah University, B
Weber State University, A

Virginia

Virginia State University, B

Washington

Everett Community College, A
Walla Walla College, B

West Virginia

Fairmont State University, B

Wisconsin

University of Wisconsin-Platteville, B

Wyoming

Casper College, A

Alberta

University of Alberta, B

New Brunswick

Université de Moncton, B

TECHNOLOGY TEACHER EDUCATION/INDUSTRIAL ARTS TEACHER EDUCATION

Arizona

Eastern Arizona College, A
Northern Arizona University, B

Arkansas

Arkansas State University, A

Connecticut

Central Connecticut State University, B

Florida

Manatee Community College, A
St. Petersburg College, B

Georgia

Georgia Southern University, B
University of Georgia, B

Idaho

University of Idaho, B

Illinois

Chicago State University, B
Illinois State University, B

Indiana

Purdue University, B

Iowa

Iowa Lakes Community College, A
University of Northern Iowa, B

Kansas

Allen County Community College, A
Cowley County Community College and Area
   Vocational-Technical School, A
Pittsburg State University, B

Kentucky

Eastern Kentucky University, B
Murray State University, B

Louisiana

Grambling State University, B

Massachusetts

Fitchburg State College, B

Michigan

Central Michigan University, B
Eastern Michigan University, B
Kellogg Community College, A
Michigan Technological University, B
Northern Michigan University, B
Western Michigan University, B

Minnesota

Bemidji State University, B
St. Cloud State University, B

Mississippi

Alcorn State University, B
Jackson State University, B
Mississippi State University, B
University of Southern Mississippi, B

Missouri

College of the Ozarks, B
Lindenwood University, B
Missouri Southern State University, B
Southeast Missouri State University, B

Montana

Montana State University, B
The University of Montana-Western, B

Nebraska

Chadron State College, B
Concordia University, B
University of Nebraska-Lincoln, B

Nevada

University of Nevada, Reno, B

New Hampshire

Keene State College, B

New Jersey

The College of New Jersey, B
Kean University, B

New Mexico

University of New Mexico, B

New York

Buffalo State College, State University of New
  York, B
New York Institute of Technology, B
St. John Fisher College, B
State University of New York at Oswego, B

North Carolina

Appalachian State University, B
Elizabeth City State University, B

North Carolina State University, B

North Dakota

Valley City State University, B

Ohio

Kent State University, B
The Ohio State University, B

Oklahoma

Oklahoma Panhandle State University, B
Southwestern Oklahoma State University, B

Rhode Island

Rhode Island College, B

Tennessee

Middle Tennessee State University, B
Roane State Community College, A

Texas

Sam Houston State University, B
Texas Southern University, B
Texas Wesleyan University, B

Utah

Brigham Young University, B
Utah State University, B

Washington

Central Washington University, B

Wisconsin

University of Wisconsin-Stout, B
Viterbo University, B

Wyoming

University of Wyoming, B

Alberta

University of Lethbridge, B

Saskatchewan

University of Regina, B

TELECOMMUNICATIONS

Arkansas

University of Arkansas, M

California

Azusa Pacific University, O
National University, M
University of California, San Diego, MD

Colorado

University of Colorado at Boulder, MO
University of Denver, M

Florida

Florida International University, M

Illinois

DePaul University, M
Illinois Institute of Technology, M
Roosevelt University, M
Western Illinois University, MO

Indiana

Ball State University, M

Louisiana

University of Louisiana at Lafayette, M

Maryland

University of Maryland, College Park, M

Massachusetts

Boston University, M

Michigan

Michigan State University, M

Minnesota

Saint Mary's University of Minnesota, MO

Missouri

University of Missouri-Kansas City, D

New Jersey

New Jersey Institute of Technology, M

New York

Iona College, MO
Pace University, MO
Polytechnic University, Brooklyn Campus, M
Rochester Institute of Technology, M
State University of New York Institute of
Technology, M
Syracuse University, MO

Oklahoma

University of Oklahoma, M

Pennsylvania

Drexel University, M
The Pennsylvania State University University Park
Campus, M
University of Pennsylvania, M
University of Pittsburgh, MDO
Widener University, M

Texas

Southern Methodist University, M
Texas Tech University, M
The University of Texas at Dallas, MD

Virginia

George Mason University, M

Alberta

University of Alberta, MD

TELECOMMUNICATIONS MANAGEMENT

Alaska

Alaska Pacific University, M

California

San Diego State University, M
Santa Clara University, O
University of San Francisco, M

Colorado

Regis University, M
University of Colorado at Boulder, MO

Illinois

DeVry University (Oakbrook Terrace), M

Kentucky

Murray State University, M

Maryland

Capitol College, M
Morgan State University, M
University of Maryland University College, MO

Massachusetts

Northeastern University, M

Missouri

University of Missouri-St. Louis, O
Webster University, M

New Jersey

Stevens Institute of Technology, MDO

New York

Polytechnic University, Brooklyn Campus, M

Syracuse University, MO

Oklahoma

Oklahoma State University, MD

Pennsylvania

University of Pennsylvania, M

Virginia

University of Management and Technology, M

Ontario

Carleton University, M

TELECOMMUNICATIONS TECHNOLOGY/TECHNICIAN

Alabama

Gadsden State Community College, A

California

Brooks College (Long Beach), A
Butte College, A
California State Polytechnic University, Pomona, B
California State University, East Bay, B
California State University, Monterey Bay, B
Chaffey College, A
Columbia College Hollywood, AB
Compton Community College, A
Cuesta College, A
Golden West College, A
Grossmont College, A
Heald College-San Jose, A
Los Angeles City College, A
Moorpark College, A
Napa Valley College, A
National University, B
Oxnard College, A
Palomar College, A
Pasadena City College, A
Pepperdine University, B
San Bernardino Valley College, A
San Diego City College, A
Santa Ana College, A
Skyline College, A
Solano Community College, A
Southwestern College, A

Colorado

Colorado State University-Pueblo, B
Colorado Technical University, B

Florida

Daytona Beach Community College, A
Miami Dade College, A
St. Petersburg College, A
Seminole Community College, A

Georgia

Clayton State University, A
DeKalb Technical College, A
Southern Polytechnic State University, B
University of Georgia, B

Illinois

City Colleges of Chicago, Richard J. Daley
College, A
Illinois Eastern Community Colleges, Lincoln Trail
College, A
Lake Land College, A
Roosevelt University, B

Indiana

Ball State University, B
Butler University, B
Indiana University Bloomington, B
Ivy Tech Community College-North Central, A
Ivy Tech Community College-Northwest, A

Iowa

Des Moines Area Community College, A
Iowa Central Community College, A

Kirkwood Community College, A

Kansas

Coffeyville Community College, A
Highland Community College, A

Kentucky

Murray State University, B

Louisiana

Bossier Parish Community College, A

Maine

Central Maine Community College, A

Maryland

Anne Arundel Community College, A
Capitol College, AB
Howard Community College, A
Morgan State University, B
TESST College of Technology (Towson), A

Massachusetts

Middlesex Community College, A
Mount Wachusett Community College, A
Northern Essex Community College, A

Michigan

Grand Valley State University, B
Lansing Community College, A
Michigan State University, B
Western Michigan University, B

Minnesota

Minnesota State Community and Technical
College-Fergus Falls, A
Northwest Technical College, A
Winona State University, B

Mississippi

Hinds Community College, A
Meridian Community College, A
Northwest Mississippi Community College, A

Missouri

Jefferson College, A
St. Louis Community College at Florissant Valley, A

Montana

Miles Community College, A

New Hampshire

McIntosh College, A
New Hampshire Community Technical College,
Nashua/Claremont, A

New Jersey

Brookdale Community College, A

New York

Briarcliffe College, A
Cayuga County Community College, A
Dutchess Community College, A
Herkimer County Community College, A
Hudson Valley Community College, A
Ithaca College, B
Monroe Community College, A
New York City College of Technology of the City
University of New York, AB
New York Institute of Technology, B
Onondaga Community College, A
Queensborough Community College of the City
University of New York, A
Rochester Institute of Technology, B
St. John's University, B
Schenectady County Community College, A
State University of New York College of Agriculture
and Technology at Cobleskill, A
Suffolk County Community College, A

Syracuse University, B

North Carolina

Central Carolina Community College, A
Wake Technical Community College, A

Ohio

Bowling Green State University, B
Cincinnati State Technical and Community
College, A
Marion Technical College, A
Ohio University, B
Ohio University-Eastern, B
Owens Community College, A

Oklahoma

Oklahoma Baptist University, B
Tulsa Community College, A

Oregon

Pacific University, B

Pennsylvania

Community College of Beaver County, A
Kutztown University of Pennsylvania, B
The Pennsylvania State University Altoona
College, A
The Pennsylvania State University Berks Campus of
the Berks-Lehigh Valley College, A
The Pennsylvania State University DuBois Campus
of the Commonwealth College, A
The Pennsylvania State University at Erie, The
Behrend College, A
The Pennsylvania State University Fayette Campus
of the Commonwealth College, A
The Pennsylvania State University Hazleton
Campus of the Commonwealth College, A
The Pennsylvania State University New Kensington
Campus of the Commonwealth College, A
The Pennsylvania State University Schuylkill
Campus of the Capital College, A
The Pennsylvania State University Shenango
Campus of the Commonwealth College, A
The Pennsylvania State University Wilkes-Barre
Campus of the Commonwealth College, A
The Pennsylvania State University York Campus of
the Commonwealth College, A
Reading Area Community College, A
Westminster College, B

Puerto Rico

Inter American University of Puerto Rico, Bayamón
Campus, AB
University of the Sacred Heart, B

South Carolina

Trident Technical College, A

South Dakota

Mitchell Technical Institute, A

Tennessee

Tusculum College, B

Texas

Amarillo College, A
Collin County Community College District, A
Howard Payne University, B
Lee College, A
South Plains College, A
Southern Methodist University, B
Texas Southern University, B

Utah

Salt Lake Community College, A

Vermont

Champlain College, AB

Virginia

ECPI College of Technology (Newport News), A
ECPI College of Technology (Virginia Beach), A
ECPI Technical College (Glen Allen), A
ECPI Technical College (Richmond), A

ECPI Technical College (Roanoke), A

Washington

Clark College, A
North Seattle Community College, A
Skagit Valley College, A
South Puget Sound Community College, A

West Virginia

Salem International University, AB

Wisconsin

Northeast Wisconsin Technical College, A
University of Wisconsin-Platteville, B
Waukesha County Technical College, A

TEXTILE DESIGN

California

Academy of Art University, M
California College of the Arts, M
University of California, Davis, M

Colorado

Colorado State University, M

Florida

Florida State University, MD

Georgia

Savannah College of Art and Design, M

Illinois

Illinois State University, M

Indiana

Indiana University Bloomington, M

Massachusetts

Massachusetts College of Art, M

Michigan

Western Michigan University, M

Minnesota

University of Minnesota, Twin Cities Campus, MDO

New York

Cornell University, MD
Syracuse University, M

North Carolina

The University of North Carolina at Greensboro, MD

Ohio

University of Cincinnati, M

Pennsylvania

Drexel University, M
Marywood University, M
Philadelphia University, M
Temple University, M

Rhode Island

Rhode Island School of Design, M

Tennessee

Memphis College of Art, M

Texas

University of North Texas, M

Virginia

James Madison University, M

Washington

Central Washington University, M

TEXTILE SCIENCE

Florida

Florida State University, B

New York

Cornell University, B

North Carolina

North Carolina State University, B

TEXTILE SCIENCES AND ENGINEERING

Alabama

Auburn University, BMD

Georgia

Georgia Institute of Technology, BMD

Massachusetts

University of Massachusetts Dartmouth, BM

New York

Cornell University, MD

North Carolina

North Carolina State University, BMD

Pennsylvania

Philadelphia University, BMD

South Carolina

Clemson University, BMD

Texas

Texas Tech University, B

THANATOLOGY

Maryland

Hood College, MO

New York

Brooklyn College of the City University of New
York, M
The College of New Rochelle, O

THEATER

Alabama

The University of Alabama, M

Arizona

Arizona State University, MD
The University of Arizona, M

Arkansas

Arkansas State University, MO
University of Arkansas, M

California

California Institute of the Arts, MO
California State University, Fullerton, M
California State University, Long Beach, M
California State University, Los Angeles, M
California State University, Northridge, M
California State University, Sacramento, M
Humboldt State University, M
San Diego State University, M
San Francisco State University, M
San Jose State University, M
Stanford University, D
University of California, Berkeley, D
University of California, Davis, M
University of California, Irvine, MD
University of California, Los Angeles, MD
University of California, San Diego, MD

University of California, Santa Barbara, MDO
University of California, Santa Cruz, O
University of San Diego, M
University of Southern California, M

Colorado

Naropa University, M
University of Colorado at Boulder, MD
University of Colorado at Denver and Health
  Sciences Center - Downtown Denver Campus, M

Connecticut

University of Connecticut, M
Yale University, MDO

Delaware

University of Delaware, M

District of Columbia

The Catholic University of America, M
The George Washington University, M

Florida

Florida Atlantic University, M
Florida State University, MD
University of Central Florida, M
University of Florida, M

Georgia

University of Georgia, MD

Hawaii

University of Hawaii at Manoa, MD

Idaho

Idaho State University, M
University of Idaho, M

Illinois

DePaul University, MO
Illinois State University, M
Northern Illinois University, M
Northwestern University, MD
Roosevelt University, M
Southern Illinois University Carbondale, MD
University of Illinois at Urbana-Champaign, MD
Western Illinois University, M

Indiana

Indiana State University, M
Indiana University Bloomington, MD
Purdue University, M

Iowa

Drake University, M
The University of Iowa, M

Kansas

Pittsburg State University, M
University of Kansas, MD

Kentucky

Eastern Kentucky University, M
Morehead State University, M
University of Kentucky, M
University of Louisville, M

Louisiana

Louisiana State University and Agricultural and
  Mechanical College, MD
Tulane University, M
University of New Orleans, M

Maryland

Towson University, M
University of Maryland, College Park, MD

Massachusetts

The Boston Conservatory, M
Boston University, MO
Brandeis University, M
Emerson College, M
Massachusetts College of Art, M

Smith College, M
Tufts University, MD
University of Massachusetts Amherst, M

Michigan

Central Michigan University, M
Eastern Michigan University, M
Michigan State University, M
University of Michigan, MD
Wayne State University, MD

Minnesota

Minnesota State University Mankato, M
University of Minnesota, Twin Cities Campus, MD

Mississippi

University of Mississippi, M
University of Southern Mississippi, M

Missouri

Central Missouri State University, M
Fontbonne University, M
Lindenwood University, M
Missouri State University, M
University of Missouri-Columbia, MD
University of Missouri-Kansas City, M
Washington University in St. Louis, M

Montana

The University of Montana-Missoula, M

Nebraska

University of Nebraska-Lincoln, MD
University of Nebraska at Omaha, M

Nevada

University of Nevada, Las Vegas, M

New Jersey

Montclair State University, M
Rowan University, M
Rutgers, The State University of New Jersey, New
  Brunswick/Piscataway, M

New Mexico

University of New Mexico, M

New York

Brooklyn College of the City University of New
  York, MD
Cornell University, D
Hunter College of the City University of New
  York, M
Long Island University, C.W. Post Campus, M
New York University, MDO
Purchase College, State University of New York, M
Sarah Lawrence College, M
State University of New York at Binghamton, M
Stony Brook University, State University of New
  York, M
University at Albany, State University of New
  York, M

North Carolina

North Carolina School of the Arts, M
The University of North Carolina at Chapel Hill, M
The University of North Carolina at Greensboro, M

North Dakota

University of North Dakota, M

Ohio

Bowling Green State University, MD
Case Western Reserve University, M
Kent State University, M
Miami University, M
The Ohio State University, MD
Ohio University, M
The University of Akron, M
University of Cincinnati, MO

Oklahoma

Oklahoma City University, M
Oklahoma State University, M

University of Oklahoma, M

Oregon

Portland State University, MO
University of Oregon, MD
University of Portland, M

Pennsylvania

Arcadia University, M
Carnegie Mellon University, M
The Pennsylvania State University University Park
  Campus, M
Point Park University, M
Temple University, M
University of Pittsburgh, MD
Villanova University, M

Rhode Island

Brown University, M
Rhode Island College, M

South Carolina

University of South Carolina, M

South Dakota

South Dakota State University, M
The University of South Dakota, M

Tennessee

Austin Peay State University, M
University of Memphis, M
The University of Tennessee, M

Texas

Baylor University, M
Lamar University, M
Southern Methodist University, M
Texas A&M University-Commerce, M
Texas State University-San Marcos, M
Texas Tech University, MD
Texas Woman's University, M
University of Houston, M
University of North Texas, M
The University of Texas at Austin, MD
The University of Texas at El Paso, M
The University of Texas-Pan American, M

Utah

Brigham Young University, MD
Utah State University, M

Vermont

Bennington College, M

Virginia

Averett University, M
Christopher Newport University, M
University of Virginia, M
Virginia Commonwealth University, M
Virginia Polytechnic Institute and State University, M

Washington

Central Washington University, M
University of Washington, MD
Western Washington University, M

West Virginia

West Virginia University, M

Wisconsin

University of Wisconsin-Madison, MD
University of Wisconsin-Milwaukee, M

University of Wisconsin-Superior, M

Alberta

University of Alberta, M
University of Calgary, M

British Columbia

The University of British Columbia, MD
University of Victoria, MD

Ontario

University of Guelph, MD
University of Ottawa, M
University of Toronto, MD
York University, M

Quebec

Université Laval, MD
Université du Québec àMontréal, M
Université de Sherbrooke, M

Saskatchewan

University of Saskatchewan, M

THEATRE LITERATURE, HISTORY AND CRITICISM

California

Saint Mary's College of California, B

Connecticut

University of Connecticut, B

Illinois

DePaul University, B
Northwestern University, B

Iowa

Buena Vista University, B
University of Northern Iowa, B

Massachusetts

Boston University, B
Simon's Rock College of Bard, B

Missouri

Washington University in St. Louis, B

New Jersey

Montclair State University, B

New York

Bard College, B
Marymount Manhattan College, B
New York University, B

Ohio

Ohio University, B

Pennsylvania

Moravian College, B
Washington & Jefferson College, B

Texas

Texas Christian University, B

Vermont

Bennington College, B

Virginia

Averett University, B

Newfoundland and Labrador

Memorial University of Newfoundland, B

Nova Scotia

Dalhousie University, B

THEATRE/THEATRE ARTS MANAGEMENT

California

California Institute of the Arts, B
University of Southern California, B

Florida

Gulf Coast Community College, A

Georgia

Berry College, B
Oglethorpe University, B

Illinois

Parkland College, A

Indiana

University of Evansville, B

Iowa

The University of Iowa, B

Kansas

Haskell Indian Nations University, A

Louisiana

Louisiana State University at Alexandria, B

Michigan

Eastern Michigan University, B
Western Michigan University, B

Minnesota

St. Cloud State University, B

New Jersey

Ramapo College of New Jersey, B

New Mexico

College of Santa Fe, B

New York

Brooklyn College of the City University of New York, B

North Carolina

Campbell University, B

Ohio

Miami University Hamilton, B
Ohio Northern University, B
Ohio University, B

Oklahoma

East Central University, B

Pennsylvania

Elizabethtown College, B
Juniata College, B
Seton Hill University, B

South Carolina

North Greenville College, B

British Columbia

The University of British Columbia, B

THEOLOGICAL AND MINISTERIAL STUDIES

California

California Baptist University, B
Point Loma Nazarene University, B

Florida

Palm Beach Atlantic University, B
Southeastern University, B

Trinity College of Florida, B

Illinois

Quincy University, B

Indiana

Huntington University, B
University of Saint Francis, AB

Kentucky

Brescia University, AB

Minnesota

Pillsbury Baptist Bible College, A

Missouri

Messenger College, B

Ohio

God's Bible School and College, B

Oregon

Northwest Christian College, B

South Carolina

Bob Jones University, AB

Tennessee

Tennessee Temple University, B
Williamson Christian College, B

Texas

Hardin-Simmons University, B

Alberta

Prairie Bible Institute, B

Saskatchewan

Central Pentecostal College, B

THEOLOGY AND RELIGIOUS VOCATIONS

Alabama

Samford University, MDPO
Southern Christian University, MDP
Spring Hill College, M
University of Mobile, M

Arizona

International Baptist College, M

Arkansas

Central Baptist College, B
Harding University, M

California

Azusa Pacific University, MD
Bethesda Christian University, MP
Biola University, MDP
California Institute of Integral Studies, M
Concordia University, M
Dominican School of Philosophy and Theology, MPO
Loyola Marymount University, M
The Master's College and Seminary, MDP
Simpson University, B
Southern California Seminary, MP
University of Judaism, M
University of San Diego, M
University of San Francisco, M

Vanguard University of Southern California, M

Colorado

Naropa University, MP

Connecticut

Holy Apostles College and Seminary, MPO
Yale University, MPO

District of Columbia

The Catholic University of America, MDPO
Howard University, MDP

Florida

Ave Maria University, MD
Barry University, MD
Palm Beach Atlantic University, M
St. Thomas University, D
Talmudic College of Florida, MD

Georgia

Emory University, MDPO
Luther Rice University, MDP
Mercer University, DP

Hawaii

Chaminade University of Honolulu, M
Hawaii Theological Seminary, MP

Illinois

Hebrew Theological College, O
Loyola University Chicago, MDPO
Moody Bible Institute, MPO
Olivet Nazarene University, M
Trinity International University, MDPO
University of Chicago, MDPO

Indiana

Anderson University, MDP
Bethel College, M
Indiana Wesleyan University, M
Oakland City University, DP
Saint Mary-of-the-Woods College, M
Taylor University Fort Wayne, B
University of Notre Dame, MDP
Valparaiso University, MO

Iowa

Faith Baptist Bible College and Theological
   Seminary, MP
Loras College, M
University of Dubuque, MDP

Kansas

Friends University, M

Kentucky

Campbellsville University, M
Kentucky Christian University, M
Southern Baptist Theological Seminary, MDP

Louisiana

Loyola University New Orleans, MO
New Orleans Baptist Theological Seminary, DP
Xavier University of Louisiana, M

Maryland

Maple Springs Baptist Bible College and
   Seminary, MDPO
Mount St. Mary's University, MP
Ner Israel Rabbinical College, MD

Massachusetts

Boston College, MD
Boston University, MDPO
Harvard University, MDP

Michigan

Andrews University, MDPO
Cornerstone University, MP
Hope College, B
Madonna University, M

Sacred Heart Major Seminary, MP

Minnesota

College of St. Catherine, M
Concordia University, St. Paul, M
Crossroads College, B
Crown College, M
Saint John's University, MPQ
University of St. Thomas, MP

Missouri

Baptist Bible College, MP
Calvary Bible College and Theological
   Seminary, MP
Global University of the Assemblies of God, MP
Missouri Baptist University, B
Saint Louis University, MD

Nebraska

Creighton University, M
Grace University, M

New Jersey

College of Saint Elizabeth, M
Drew University, MDPO
Georgian Court University, MO
Seton Hall University, MPO

New York

Fordham University, MD
The Jewish Theological Seminary, MDO
Kol Yaakov Torah Center, O
Machzikei Hadath Rabbinical College, O
Rabbinical Academy Mesivta Rabbi Chaim Berlin, O
St. Bonaventure University, MO
St. John's University, MPO
Yeshiva Karlin Stolin Rabbinical Institute, O
Yeshivath Zichron Moshe, O

North Carolina

Apex School of Theology, MP
Campbell University, MDP
Duke University, MPO
Gardner-Webb University, DPO
Piedmont Baptist College, M
Shaw University, MP
Southeastern Baptist Theological Seminary, MDP

Ohio

Cincinnati Christian University, MP
College of Mount St. Joseph, M
Franciscan University of Steubenville, M
Malone College, M
Mount Vernon Nazarene University, M
Pontifical College Josephinum, MP
University of Dayton, MD
Ursuline College, M
Xavier University, M

Oklahoma

Oklahoma Christian University, MP
Oral Roberts University, MDP
Southern Nazarene University, M

Oregon

George Fox University, MDP
Marylhurst University, MP
Mount Angel Seminary, MP
Multnomah Bible College and Biblical
   Seminary, MPO

Pennsylvania

Bryn Athyn College of the New Church, MP
Duquesne University, MD
La Salle University, M
Lancaster Bible College, M
Philadelphia Biblical University, MP
St. Charles Borromeo Seminary, Overbrook, MP
The University of Scranton, M
Villanova University, M

Yeshiva Beth Moshe, O

Puerto Rico

Bayamon Central University, MP
Colegio Pentecostal Mizpa, M
Inter American University of Puerto Rico,
   Metropolitan Campus, D
Pontifical Catholic University of Puerto Rico, M

Rhode Island

Providence College, M

South Carolina

Columbia International University, MDPO

Tennessee

Freed-Hardeman University, MP
Johnson Bible College, M
Lee University, M
Lipscomb University, MP
Mid-America Baptist Theological Seminary, MDP
Sewanee: The University of the South, MDP
Union University, B
Vanderbilt University, MPO
Williamson Christian College, B

Texas

Abilene Christian University, BMP
Arlington Baptist College, B
Austin Graduate School of Theology, M
Baptist Missionary Association Theological
   Seminary, MP
Baylor University, MDPO
The Criswell College, MP
Hardin-Simmons University, P
Houston Baptist University, M
Lubbock Christian University, BM
St. Mary's University of San Antonio, MO
Southern Methodist University, MDP
Southwestern Assemblies of God University, MO
Texas Christian University, MDPO
University of Dallas, M
University of St. Thomas, BMP
Wayland Baptist University, B

Vermont

Saint Michael's College, MO

Virginia

Christendom College, M
Eastern Mennonite University, MPO
Liberty University, MDP
Regent University, MDPO
Virginia Union University, DP

Washington

Gonzaga University, P
Seattle University, MPO

West Virginia

Wheeling Jesuit University, M

Wisconsin

Lakeland College, M
Maranatha Baptist Bible College, M
Marquette University, MD
St. Norbert College, M

Alberta

Alliance University College, MPO
Concordia University College of Alberta, B
Newman Theological College, MP
Prairie Bible Institute, B
Taylor University College and Seminary, MP

British Columbia

Trinity Western University, MP

Manitoba

Providence College and Theological
   Seminary, MDPO
University of Manitoba, P

The University of Winnipeg, MPO

Nova Scotia

Acadia University, MDP

Ontario

Collège Dominicain de Philosophie et de Théologie, MDO
Heritage Baptist College and Heritage Theological Seminary, MO
Master's College and Seminary, B
McMaster University, MPO
Queen's University at Kingston, MP
Saint Paul University, MDO
Tyndale University College & Seminary, MPO
Wilfrid Laurier University, MDPO

Quebec

Concordia University, M
McGill University, MD
Université Laval, MD
Université de Montréal, MDO
Université du Québec àChicoutimi, MD
Université de Sherbrooke, MDO

Saskatchewan

Central Pentecostal College, B
College of Emmanuel and St. Chad, MP

THEOLOGY/THEOLOGICAL STUDIES

Alabama

Faulkner University, B
Oakwood College, B
Southeastern Bible College, B
Spring Hill College, B

Arizona

Grand Canyon University, B

Arkansas

Harding University, B
John Brown University, B
Ouachita Baptist University, B
Williams Baptist College, AB

California

Azusa Pacific University, B
Bethany University, B
California Baptist University, B
Concordia University, B
Life Pacific College, B
Loyola Marymount University, B
The Master's College and Seminary, B
Pacific Union College, B
Saint Mary's College of California, B
San Diego Christian College, B
University of San Francisco, B
William Jessup University, AB
Yeshiva Ohr Elchonon Chabad/West Coast Talmudical Seminary, B

Connecticut

Holy Apostles College and Seminary, B

District of Columbia

Georgetown University, B

Florida

Ave Maria University, B
The Baptist College of Florida, AB
Barry University, B
Florida Christian College, B
Hobe Sound Bible College, B
St. John Vianney College Seminary, B

Saint Leo University, B

Georgia

Atlanta Christian College, B

Hawaii

Hawaii Theological Seminary, B

Idaho

Northwest Nazarene University, B

Illinois

Concordia University, B
Elmhurst College, B
Hebrew Theological College, B
Lincoln Christian College, B
Loyola University Chicago, B
North Park University, B
Olivet Nazarene University, B
Quincy University, B
Trinity Christian College, B
University of St. Francis, B

Indiana

Calumet College of Saint Joseph, B
Hanover College, B
Huntington University, B
Indiana Wesleyan University, B
Marian College, AB
Oakland City University, B
Saint Mary-of-the-Woods College, B
Taylor University, B
University of Notre Dame, B
Valparaiso University, B

Iowa

Briar Cliff University, AB
Dordt College, B
St. Ambrose University, B
University of Dubuque, B
Vennard College, B

Kansas

Central Christian College of Kansas, A
Friends University, B
Highland Community College, A
Manhattan Christian College, B
MidAmerica Nazarene University, B
Newman University, B
University of Saint Mary, B

Kentucky

Bellarmine University, B

Louisiana

Louisiana College, B
Xavier University of Louisiana, B

Maryland

Columbia Union College, B
Griggs University, AB
Washington Bible College, AB

Massachusetts

Assumption College, B
Atlantic Union College, B
Boston College, B
Hellenic College, B

Michigan

Andrews University, B
Ave Maria College, B
Calvin College, B
Grace Bible College, B
Great Lakes Christian College, B
Kuyper College, B
Sacred Heart Major Seminary, A

Minnesota

Augsburg College, B
College of Saint Benedict, B
College of St. Catherine, B
Concordia University, St. Paul, B
Crossroads College, B

Martin Luther College, B
Saint John's University, B
Saint Mary's University of Minnesota, B

Mississippi

Northeast Mississippi Community College, A

Missouri

Central Bible College, B
Central Christian College of the Bible, B
Global University of the Assemblies of God, B
Ozark Christian College, AB
Rockhurst University, B
St. Louis Christian College, B
Saint Louis University, B

Montana

Carroll College, B
University of Great Falls, B

Nebraska

Concordia University, B
Creighton University, AB
Nebraska Christian College, B
Union College, B

New Hampshire

Saint Anselm College, B

New Jersey

Assumption College for Sisters, A
Caldwell College, B
College of Saint Elizabeth, B
Saint Peter's College, B

New York

Fordham University, B
Holy Trinity Orthodox Seminary, B
Houghton College, B
Nyack College, B
Rabbinical Academy Mesivta Rabbi Chaim Berlin, B
Rabbinical College Bobover Yeshiva B'nei Zion, B
Rabbinical Seminary of America, B
St. John's University, B
Yeshiva Karlin Stolin Rabbinical Institute, B

North Carolina

Apex School of Theology, B
Belmont Abbey College, B
Heritage Bible College, AB
John Wesley College, B
Lenoir-Rhyne College, B
Roanoke Bible College, B
Southeastern Baptist Theological Seminary, A

North Dakota

University of Mary, B

Ohio

Cedarville University, B
Circleville Bible College, AB
Franciscan University of Steubenville, AB
Laura and Alvin Siegal College of Judaic Studies, B
Mount Vernon Nazarene University, B
Notre Dame College, B
Ohio Dominican University, AB
Walsh University, B
Xavier University, AB

Oklahoma

Hillsdale Free Will Baptist College, B
Mid-America Christian University, B
Oklahoma Baptist University, B
Oklahoma Wesleyan University, B
Oral Roberts University, B
St. Gregory's University, B
Southern Nazarene University, B
Southwestern Christian University, B

Oregon

Concordia University, B
Corban College, B
Multnomah Bible College and Biblical Seminary, B
University of Portland, B

Warner Pacific College, B

Pennsylvania

Alvernia College, B
Carlow University, B
DeSales University, B
Duquesne University, B
Eastern University, B
Gannon University, B
Immaculata University, B
King's College, B
Saint Joseph's University, B
Saint Vincent College, B
Talmudical Yeshiva of Philadelphia, B
Valley Forge Christian College, B

Puerto Rico

Pontifical Catholic University of Puerto Rico, B
Universidad Adventista de las Antillas, B

Rhode Island

Providence College, B

South Carolina

Morris College, B
North Greenville College, B
Southern Wesleyan University, B

South Dakota

Dakota Wesleyan University, B

Tennessee

American Baptist College of American Baptist
   Theological Seminary, B
Aquinas College, B
Lee University, B
Lipscomb University, B
Martin Methodist College, A
Mid-America Baptist Theological Seminary, A
Southern Adventist University, B
Union University, B

Texas

Baptist Missionary Association Theological
   Seminary, AB
Brazosport College, A
The Criswell College, AB
Hardin-Simmons University, B
Howard Payne University, B
Lon Morris College, A
St. Mary's University of San Antonio, B
Texas Lutheran University, B
University of Dallas, B
University of Mary Hardin-Baylor, B
University of St. Thomas, B

Virginia

Bluefield College, B
Christendom College, B
Eastern Mennonite University, B

Washington

Puget Sound Christian College, B
Seattle Pacific University, B
Walla Walla College, B

West Virginia

Appalachian Bible College, AB
Wheeling Jesuit University, B

Wisconsin

Concordia University Wisconsin, B
Silver Lake College, B
Wisconsin Lutheran College, B

Alberta

Alliance University College, B
The King's University College, B
Prairie Bible Institute, B
Rocky Mountain College, B

Vanguard College, B

British Columbia

Summit Pacific College, B

Manitoba

Canadian Mennonite University, B
Providence College and Theological Seminary, B
The University of Winnipeg, B
William and Catherine Booth College, B

Ontario

Collège Dominicain de Philosophie et de
   Théologie, B
Emmanuel Bible College, B
Heritage Baptist College and Heritage Theological
   Seminary, B
Master's College and Seminary, B
Ner Israel Yéshiva College of Toronto, B
Queen's University at Kingston, B
Redeemer University College, B
Saint Paul University, B
University of Ottawa, B
University of Toronto, B
The University of Western Ontario, B

Quebec

Concordia University, B
Université Laval, AB
Université de Montréal, B
Université du Québec àChicoutimi, B
Université du Québec àRimouski, B
Université du Québec àTrois-Rivières, B
Université de Sherbrooke, B

Saskatchewan

Briercrest College, B
Central Pentecostal College, B
College of Emmanuel and St. Chad, B

THEORETICAL AND MATHEMATICAL PHYSICS

California

San Diego State University, B

New York

State University of New York at Buffalo, B

Virginia

Sweet Briar College, B

Ontario

University of Guelph, B

Saskatchewan

University of Saskatchewan, B

THEORETICAL CHEMISTRY

Connecticut

Wesleyan University, MD

District of Columbia

Georgetown University, MD

New York

Cornell University, D

Tennessee

The University of Tennessee, D
Vanderbilt University, M

West Virginia

West Virginia University, MD

Alberta

University of Calgary, MD

THEORETICAL PHYSICS

Massachusetts

Harvard University, MD

New Jersey

Rutgers, The State University of New Jersey, New
   Brunswick/Piscataway, MD

New York

Cornell University, MD
St. John's University, O

West Virginia

West Virginia University, MD

British Columbia

University of Victoria, MD

THERAPEUTIC RECREATION

Alabama

University of South Alabama, M

Colorado

Naropa University, M

Illinois

Aurora University, M

Indiana

Indiana University Bloomington, M

Iowa

The University of Iowa, M

Louisiana

Southern University and Agricultural and Mechanical
   College, M

Massachusetts

Springfield College, M

Minnesota

University of Minnesota, Twin Cities Campus, MD

New Hampshire

University of New Hampshire, M

North Carolina

East Carolina University, M
North Carolina Central University, M

Pennsylvania

Temple University, M

Tennessee

The University of Tennessee, M

Wisconsin

University of Wisconsin-La Crosse, M

THERAPEUTIC RECREATION/RECREATIONAL THERAPY

California

California State University, Chico, B
California State University, East Bay, B
Cuesta College, A
Santa Barbara City College, A

Colorado

Colorado Mountain College, A

Connecticut

Mitchell College, A
Northwestern Connecticut Community College, A

Norwalk Community College, A

District of Columbia

Gallaudet University, B

Georgia

Shorter College, B

Illinois

Moraine Valley Community College, A

Indiana

Indiana Tech, AB
Indiana University Bloomington, B
Indiana University-Purdue University Fort Wayne, B
Vincennes University, A

Iowa

The University of Iowa, B

Louisiana

Southern University and Agricultural and Mechanical
   College, B

Maine

University of Southern Maine, AB

Massachusetts

Northeastern University, B
Springfield College, B

Michigan

Calvin College, B
Central Michigan University, B
Eastern Michigan University, B
Grand Valley State University, B

Minnesota

Minnesota State University Mankato, B
St. Cloud State University, B
Winona State University, B

Mississippi

Jackson State University, B

Missouri

Northwest Missouri State University, B

Nebraska

University of Nebraska at Kearney, B

New Hampshire

University of New Hampshire, B

New York

Ithaca College, B
Mercy College, B
St. Joseph's College, Suffolk Campus, B
State University of New York College at
   Brockport, B
State University of New York College at Cortland, B
Suffolk County Community College, A
Utica College, B

North Carolina

Belmont Abbey College, B
Carteret Community College, A
Catawba College, B
East Carolina University, B
St. Andrews Presbyterian College, B
Shaw University, B
The University of North Carolina Wilmington, B
Western Carolina University, B
Western Piedmont Community College, A
Winston-Salem State University, B

Ohio

Ashland University, B
College of Mount St. Joseph, B

North Central State College, A

Oklahoma

Southwestern Oklahoma State University, B
Tulsa Community College, A

Pennsylvania

Butler County Community College, A
Community College of Allegheny County, A
Keystone College, A
Messiah College, B
Temple University, B

South Carolina

Coker College, B

Utah

Brigham Young University, B

Virginia

Hampton University, B
Longwood University, B

Washington

Eastern Washington University, B
Pacific Lutheran University, B

West Virginia

Alderson-Broaddus College, B
West Virginia State University, B

Wisconsin

Northland College, B
University of Wisconsin-La Crosse, B
University of Wisconsin-Milwaukee, B

Nova Scotia

Dalhousie University, B

Ontario

University of Waterloo, B

Quebec

Concordia University, B

THERAPIES--DANCE, DRAMA, AND MUSIC

Massachusetts

Lesley University, MD

TIBETAN LANGUAGE AND LITERATURE

Illinois

University of Chicago, B

TOOL AND DIE TECHNOLOGY/TECHNICIAN

Alabama

Bevill State Community College, A
Gadsden State Community College, A
H. Councill Trenholm State Technical College, A

California

Ventura College, A

Illinois

Black Hawk College, A
Kishwaukee College, A
Prairie State College, A

Indiana

Ivy Tech Community College-Bloomington, A
Ivy Tech Community College-Central Indiana, A
Ivy Tech Community College-Columbus, A
Ivy Tech Community College-East Central, A

Ivy Tech Community College-Lafayette, A
Ivy Tech Community College-North Central, A
Ivy Tech Community College-Northeast, A
Ivy Tech Community College-Northwest, A
Ivy Tech Community College-Southern Indiana, A
Ivy Tech Community College-Southwest, A
Ivy Tech Community College-Wabash Valley, A
Ivy Tech Community College-Whitewater, A

Iowa

Hawkeye Community College, A
North Iowa Area Community College, A
Northwest Iowa Community College, A
Western Iowa Tech Community College, A

Michigan

Delta College, A
Macomb Community College, A
Oakland Community College, A

Minnesota

Dunwoody College of Technology, A

New York

Mohawk Valley Community College, A

North Carolina

Asheville-Buncombe Technical Community
   College, A
Craven Community College, A
Wake Technical Community College, A
Wilson Technical Community College, A

Ohio

Northwest State Community College, A
Terra State Community College, A

Pennsylvania

Pennsylvania College of Technology, A

Tennessee

Jackson State Community College, A

Utah

Utah State University, B

Wisconsin

Milwaukee Area Technical College, A
Moraine Park Technical College, A

TOURISM AND TRAVEL SERVICES MANAGEMENT

Alaska

University of Alaska Southeast, Ketchikan
   Campus, A

Arizona

Phoenix College, A

California

Alliant International University, B
Butte College, A
Cañada College, A
Chabot College, A
Cypress College, A
Foothill College, A
Fullerton College, A
Long Beach City College, A
Los Angeles City College, A
Los Medanos College, A
MiraCosta College, A
Palomar College, A
Pasadena City College, A
Saddleback College, A
San Diego City College, A
San Diego Mesa College, A
San Diego State University, B
Santa Ana College, A
Santiago Canyon College, A
Southwestern College, A

West Los Angeles College, A

Colorado

Arapahoe Community College, A
Blair College, A
Fort Lewis College, B
Mesa State College, A
National American University (Colorado Springs), A
Pueblo Community College, A

Connecticut

Briarwood College, A
Three Rivers Community College, A

Delaware

Delaware State University, B

Florida

Broward Community College, A
Daytona Beach Community College, A
Florida International University, B
Florida Metropolitan University-Melbourne
   Campus, A
Florida National College, A
Lynn University, B
Miami Dade College, A
St. Petersburg College, A
Schiller International University, AB
Valencia Community College, A
Webber International University, AB
Webster College (Holiday), A

Georgia

Albany Technical College, A
Athens Technical College, A
Atlanta Technical College, A
Central Georgia Technical College, A
Gwinnett Technical College, A
Ogeechee Technical College, A

Guam

Guam Community College, A

Hawaii

Brigham Young University-Hawaii, AB
Hawaii Business College, A
Hawaii Pacific University, B
Heald College-Honolulu, A
Kapiolani Community College, A
University of Hawaii at Manoa, B

Illinois

City Colleges of Chicago, Harold Washington
   College, A
College of DuPage, A
Danville Area Community College, A
Elgin Community College, A
John A. Logan College, A
Lincoln College, A
Lincoln College-Normal, A
MacCormac College, A
Midstate College, A
Robert Morris College, A

Indiana

Ball State University, B
International Business College (Fort Wayne), AB

Iowa

AIB College of Business, A
Hamilton College (Cedar Rapids), A
Iowa Lakes Community College, A

Kaplan University, A

Kansas

Cloud County Community College, A
Johnson County Community College, A

Louisiana

Our Lady of Holy Cross College, B
Southern University at Shreveport, A

Maine

Beal College, A
University of Maine at Machias, B

Massachusetts

Bay State College, A
Becker College, B
Bunker Hill Community College, A
Fisher College, A
Holyoke Community College, A
Marian Court College, A
Massasoit Community College, A
Newbury College, A
North Shore Community College, A
Northern Essex Community College, A
Quinsigamond Community College, A

Michigan

Baker College of Flint, A
Baker College of Muskegon, A
Grand Valley State University, B
Lansing Community College, A
Western Michigan University, B

Minnesota

Dakota County Technical College, A
Minneapolis Business College, A
Rasmussen College Eagan, A
Rasmussen College Mankato, A
Rasmussen College St. Cloud, A
Ridgewater College, A
St. Cloud State University, B

Missouri

East Central College, A
Mineral Area College, A
Patricia Stevens College, A
St. Louis Community College at Forest Park, A

Montana

The University of Montana-Western, A

Nebraska

Hamilton College-Lincoln, A
Midland Lutheran College, A

Nevada

Morrison University, A
University of Nevada, Las Vegas, B

New Hampshire

New Hampshire Technical Institute, A
Southern New Hampshire University, B
University of New Hampshire, B

New Jersey

Bergen Community College, A
Raritan Valley Community College, A

New York

Adirondack Community College, A
Bryant and Stratton College (Syracuse), A
Corning Community College, A
Dowling College, B
Dutchess Community College, A
Elmira Business Institute, A
Finger Lakes Community College, A
Fiorello H. LaGuardia Community College of the
   City University of New York, A
Genesee Community College, A
Herkimer County Community College, A
Jefferson Community College, A
Kingsborough Community College of the City
   University of New York, A

Monroe Community College, A
New York University, B
Niagara University, B
Paul Smith's College of Arts and Sciences, A
Rochester Institute of Technology, AB
Rockland Community College, A
Schenectady County Community College, A
State University of New York College of Agriculture
   and Technology at Morrisville, A
State University of New York College of Technology
   at Delhi, AB
Sullivan County Community College, A
Taylor Business Institute, A
Tompkins Cortland Community College, A
Westchester Community College, A

North Carolina

Blue Ridge Community College, A
Central Piedmont Community College, A
Johnson & Wales University, B
North Carolina State University, B
Rockingham Community College, A

Ohio

Bradford School, A
Columbus State Community College, A
Hocking College, A
Lakeland Community College, A
Lorain County Community College, A
Ohio University, A
Sinclair Community College, A
The University of Akron, A
Zane State College, A

Oklahoma

Northeastern State University, B
Tulsa Community College, A

Oregon

Mt. Hood Community College, A

Pennsylvania

Butler County Community College, A
Central Pennsylvania College, A
Consolidated School of Business (Lancaster), A
Consolidated School of Business (York), A
Erie Business Center, Main, A
Erie Business Center South, A
Harrisburg Area Community College, A
ICM School of Business & Medical Careers, A
Lehigh Valley College, A
Luzerne County Community College, A
Mansfield University of Pennsylvania, B
Newport Business Institute (Lower Burrell), A
Pace Institute, A
Pennsylvania College of Technology, A
Reading Area Community College, A
Westmoreland County Community College, A

Puerto Rico

Inter American University of Puerto Rico, Fajardo
   Campus, B
Inter American University of Puerto Rico, Ponce
   Campus, A
Pontifical Catholic University of Puerto Rico, B
University of the Sacred Heart, B

Rhode Island

Johnson & Wales University, AB

South Dakota

Black Hills State University, AB

Tennessee

The University of Tennessee at Martin, B

Texas

Amarillo College, A
El Paso Community College, A
Houston Community College System, A
North Harris College, A
St. Philip's College, A
Texas A&M University, B

The University of Texas at San Antonio, B

Utah

Mountain West College, A

Vermont

Champlain College, AB
Johnson State College, B

Virginia

Bryant and Stratton College, Virginia Beach, A
Ferrum College, B
Northern Virginia Community College, A

Washington

Highline Community College, A
Yakima Valley Community College, A

West Virginia

Concord University, B
Davis & Elkins College, B
Mountain State University, A

Wisconsin

Madison Area Technical College, A
Northeast Wisconsin Technical College, A

Wyoming

Northwest College, A

Alberta

University of Calgary, B

British Columbia

British Columbia Institute of Technology, A
Malaspina University-College, B

Nova Scotia

Cape Breton University, B
Mount Saint Vincent University, B

Ontario

Brock University, B
University of Guelph, B

TOURISM AND TRAVEL SERVICES MARKETING OPERATIONS

California

San Diego Mesa College, A

Colorado

Western State College of Colorado, B

Connecticut

Central Connecticut State University, B

Florida

Florida Community College at Jacksonville, A

Guam

Guam Community College, A

Illinois

College of DuPage, A
Moraine Valley Community College, A
Waubonsee Community College, A

Indiana

International Business College (Indianapolis), A

Iowa

AIB College of Business, A
Hamilton College (Cedar Falls), A

Iowa Lakes Community College, A

Michigan

Western Michigan University, B

Minnesota

Dakota County Technical College, A
Rasmussen College Mankato, A

Missouri

Central Missouri State University, B
University of Missouri-Columbia, B

Montana

The University of Montana-Western, AB

New York

Herkimer County Community College, A
Rochester Institute of Technology, B
State University of New York College of Agriculture
  and Technology at Cobleskill, A
Tompkins Cortland Community College, A
Wood Tobe-Coburn School, A

Ohio

Ohio University, A
Ohio University-Southern Campus, A

Pennsylvania

Harrisburg Area Community College, A
Lehigh Carbon Community College, A
Luzerne County Community College, A

Puerto Rico

Pontifical Catholic University of Puerto Rico, A
University of the Sacred Heart, B

Rhode Island

Johnson & Wales University, AB

Utah

Dixie State College of Utah, A

Vermont

Champlain College, AB

Virginia

National College of Business & Technology (Salem)
  , A

Washington

Edmonds Community College, A

West Virginia

Mountain State University, A

Wisconsin

Milwaukee Area Technical College, A

British Columbia

Thompson Rivers University, B

Nova Scotia

Mount Saint Vincent University, B

TOURISM PROMOTION OPERATIONS

Florida

Florida National College, A

Guam

Guam Community College, A

Illinois

College of DuPage, A

Iowa

AIB College of Business, A
Iowa Lakes Community College, A

Louisiana

Our Lady of Holy Cross College, B

Minnesota

Rasmussen College Mankato, A

New Mexico

New Mexico State University, B

New York

Herkimer County Community College, A
Westchester Community College, A

Ohio

Bowling Green State University, B

Oregon

Central Oregon Community College, A

Pennsylvania

Community College of Allegheny County, A
Lehigh Carbon Community College, A

Vermont

Champlain College, AB

British Columbia

Open Learning Agency, B
Thompson Rivers University, A

Nova Scotia

Cape Breton University, B

TOXICOLOGY

Alabama

The University of Alabama at Birmingham, D
University of South Alabama, M

Arizona

The University of Arizona, D

Arkansas

University of Arkansas for Medical Sciences, MDO

California

Humboldt State University, B
San Diego State University, M
University of California, Berkeley, B
University of California, Davis, MD
University of California, Irvine, MDO
University of California, Riverside, MD
University of California, Santa Cruz, MD
University of Southern California, MDO

Connecticut

University of Connecticut, MD

District of Columbia

American University, MO

Florida

Florida Agricultural and Mechanical University, MD
University of Florida, O

Georgia

Medical College of Georgia, D
University of Georgia, MD

Illinois

Northwestern University, D

Indiana

Indiana University-Purdue University
  Indianapolis, MDO

Purdue University, MD

Iowa

Iowa State University of Science and
  Technology, MD

Kansas

University of Kansas, MDO

Kentucky

University of Kentucky, MD
University of Louisville, MD

Louisiana

Louisiana State University and Agricultural and
  Mechanical College, M
University of Louisiana at Monroe, B

Maryland

The Johns Hopkins University, D
University of Maryland, College Park, MD
University of Maryland Eastern Shore, MD

Massachusetts

Massachusetts Institute of Technology, MD
Northeastern University, M

Michigan

Eastern Michigan University, B
Michigan State University, MD
University of Michigan, MD
Wayne State University, MDO

Minnesota

Minnesota State University Mankato, B
University of Minnesota, Duluth, MD
University of Minnesota, Twin Cities Campus, MD

Mississippi

University of Mississippi, D
University of Mississippi Medical Center, MDO

Montana

The University of Montana-Missoula, MD

Nebraska

University of Nebraska-Lincoln, MD
University of Nebraska Medical Center, MD

New Hampshire

Dartmouth College, DO

New Jersey

Bloomfield College, B
Felician College, B
Rutgers, The State University of New Jersey, New
  Brunswick/Piscataway, MD

New Mexico

University of New Mexico, MD

New York

Clarkson University, B
Cornell University, MD
Long Island University, Brooklyn Campus, M
St. John's University, BM
State University of New York at Buffalo, MDO
University at Albany, State University of New
  York, MD
University of Rochester, MD

North Carolina

Duke University, DO
North Carolina State University, MD
The University of North Carolina at Chapel Hill, MD

Ohio

Ashland University, B
Case Western Reserve University, MDO
The Ohio State University, MD
University of Cincinnati, MD

Wright State University, M

Oregon

Oregon State University, MD

Pennsylvania

Duquesne University, MD
The Pennsylvania State University Abington
  College, B
The Pennsylvania State University Altoona
  College, B
The Pennsylvania State University Beaver Campus
  of the Commonwealth College, B
The Pennsylvania State University Berks Campus of
  the Berks-Lehigh Valley College, B
The Pennsylvania State University DuBois Campus
  of the Commonwealth College, B
The Pennsylvania State University at Erie, The
  Behrend College, B
The Pennsylvania State University Fayette Campus
  of the Commonwealth College, B
The Pennsylvania State University Hazleton
  Campus of the Commonwealth College, B
The Pennsylvania State University McKeesport
  Campus of the Commonwealth College, B
The Pennsylvania State University Mont Alto
  Campus of the Commonwealth College, B
The Pennsylvania State University New Kensington
  Campus of the Commonwealth College, B
The Pennsylvania State University Shenango
  Campus of the Commonwealth College, B
The Pennsylvania State University University Park
  Campus, B
The Pennsylvania State University Wilkes-Barre
  Campus of the Commonwealth College, B
The Pennsylvania State University York Campus of
  the Commonwealth College, B
University of the Sciences in Philadelphia, MD

Puerto Rico

University of Puerto Rico, Medical Sciences
  Campus, MD

Rhode Island

Brown University, D
University of Rhode Island, MD

Texas

Texas A&M University, MD
Texas A&M University System Health Science
  Center, D
Texas Southern University, MD
Texas Tech University, MD
The University of Texas Health Science Center at
  Houston, MDO
The University of Texas Medical Branch, D

Utah

University of Utah, MDO
Utah State University, MD

Virginia

Virginia Commonwealth University, M

Washington

University of Washington, MD
Washington State University, MD

West Virginia

West Virginia University, MD

Wisconsin

University of Wisconsin-Madison, BMD

British Columbia

Simon Fraser University, O

Ontario

Queen's University at Kingston, MD
University of Guelph, MD
University of Toronto, B

The University of Western Ontario, B

Prince Edward Island

University of Prince Edward Island, MD

Quebec

Université de Montréal, O

Saskatchewan

University of Saskatchewan, BMDO

TRADE AND INDUSTRIAL TEACHER EDUCATION

Alabama

Athens State University, B
Auburn University, B

Arkansas

University of Arkansas Community College at
  Hope, A
University of Arkansas at Pine Bluff, B

California

California Polytechnic State University, San Luis
  Obispo, B
California State University, Fresno, B
California State University, Long Beach, B
California State University, San Bernardino, B
Compton Community College, A
East Los Angeles College, A
San Diego State University, B
San Francisco State University, B
Victor Valley College, A

Colorado

Northeastern Junior College, A

Delaware

Delaware State University, B

District of Columbia

University of the District of Columbia, B

Florida

Florida Agricultural and Mechanical University, B
Florida International University, B
Manatee Community College, A
University of Central Florida, B
University of North Florida, B
University of South Florida, B
University of West Florida, B

Georgia

Valdosta State University, B

Idaho

Brigham Young University -Idaho, A
University of Idaho, B

Illinois

Southern Illinois University Carbondale, B
Western Illinois University, B

Indiana

Ball State University, B
Indiana State University, AB
Purdue University, A

Iowa

Ellsworth Community College, A
Iowa Lakes Community College, A
Iowa State University of Science and Technology, B
Northeast Iowa Community College, A
Southeastern Community College, North Campus, A
Upper Iowa University, B

Kansas

Garden City Community College, A
Neosho County Community College, A
Pittsburg State University, B

Pratt Community College, A

Kentucky

Eastern Kentucky University, B
Murray State University, AB
Northern Kentucky University, B
University of Louisville, B
Western Kentucky University, B

Maine

University of Southern Maine, B

Michigan

Madonna University, B

Minnesota

Bemidji State University, B

Mississippi

Copiah-Lincoln Community College, A
Itawamba Community College, A
Northeast Mississippi Community College, A

Nebraska

Concordia University, B
University of Nebraska-Lincoln, B
Wayne State College, B

Nevada

University of Nevada, Reno, B

New Hampshire

Keene State College, B
University of New Hampshire, B

New Mexico

New Mexico Junior College, A
Western New Mexico University, B

New York

Buffalo State College, State University of New
York, B
The College of Saint Rose, B
New York City College of Technology of the City
University of New York, B
New York Institute of Technology, B
State University of New York at Oswego, B

North Carolina

Isothermal Community College, A
Lenoir Community College, A
North Carolina Agricultural and Technical State
University, B
Southwestern Community College, A

North Dakota

Cankdeska Cikana Community College, A
Turtle Mountain Community College, A

Ohio

Cincinnati Christian University, A
Kent State University, B
The University of Toledo, B
Wright State University, B

Oklahoma

Northeastern Oklahoma Agricultural and Mechanical
College, A
Northeastern State University, B
University of Central Oklahoma, B

Oregon

Portland Community College, A

Pennsylvania

Indiana University of Pennsylvania, B
Temple University, B

South Carolina

Florence-Darlington Technical College, A
South Carolina State University, B

Spartanburg Technical College, A

South Dakota

Sinte Gleska University, A

Texas

Del Mar College, A
Kilgore College, A
Palo Alto College, A
Prairie View A&M University, B
Texas A&M University-Commerce, B
Texas A&M University-Corpus Christi, B
Wayland Baptist University, B

United States Virgin Islands

University of the Virgin Islands, B

Utah

Snow College, A

Virginia

ECPI Technical College (Richmond), A
Norfolk State University, B

Washington

Central Washington University, B
South Seattle Community College, A
Wenatchee Valley College, A

Wyoming

Northwest College, A
University of Wyoming, B

Alberta

University of Alberta, B

British Columbia

British Columbia Institute of Technology, A

Newfoundland and Labrador

Memorial University of Newfoundland, B

Quebec

Université du Québec àChicoutimi, B
Université du Québec àMontréal, B
Université du Québec àRimouski, B

Saskatchewan

University of Regina, B
University of Saskatchewan, B

TRANSCULTURAL NURSING

Minnesota

Augsburg College, M

New Jersey

New Jersey City University, M

TRANSLATION AND INTERPRETATION

Arkansas

University of Arkansas, M

District of Columbia

American University, O
Gallaudet University, M

Georgia

Georgia State University, O

Iowa

The University of Iowa, M

Michigan

Marygrove College, M

New Jersey

Rutgers, The State University of New Jersey, New
Brunswick/Piscataway, M

New York

State University of New York at Binghamton, O
University at Albany, State University of New
York, O

Ohio

Kent State University, M

Puerto Rico

University of Puerto Rico, Río Piedras, MO

Ontario

University of Ottawa, MD
York University, M

Quebec

Concordia University, O
Université Laval, MO

TRANSPERSONAL AND HUMANISTIC PSYCHOLOGY

Colorado

Naropa University, M

Washington

Seattle University, M

Ontario

Brock University, M

TRANSPORTATION AND HIGHWAY ENGINEERING

Alabama

Auburn University, MD

Arkansas

University of Arkansas, BM

California

University of California, Berkeley, MD
University of California, Davis, MD
University of California, Irvine, MD
University of Southern California, M

Delaware

University of Delaware, MD

Florida

University of Central Florida, O

Illinois

Illinois Institute of Technology, M
Northwestern University, MD

Louisiana

Louisiana State University and Agricultural and
Mechanical College, MD

Maryland

Morgan State University, M

Massachusetts

Massachusetts Institute of Technology, D

Missouri

University of Missouri-Columbia, M
Washington University in St. Louis, D

Nevada

University of Nevada, Las Vegas, M

New Jersey

New Jersey Institute of Technology, MD
Princeton University, MD

New York

Cornell University, MD
Polytechnic University, Brooklyn Campus, M

Rensselaer Polytechnic Institute, MD

Ohio

Ohio University, M
University of Dayton, M

Pennsylvania

The Pennsylvania State University University Park
    Campus, MD
Villanova University, M

Rhode Island

University of Rhode Island, MD

Tennessee

University of Memphis, M

Texas

Texas A&M University, MD
Texas Southern University, M

Washington

University of Washington, MD

Wisconsin

Marquette University, MD

British Columbia

British Columbia Institute of Technology, A

New Brunswick

University of New Brunswick Fredericton, MD

Ontario

University of Toronto, B

TRANSPORTATION AND MATERIALS MOVING

California

City College of San Francisco, A
Los Angeles Trade-Technical College, A
Mt. San Antonio College, A
Oxnard College, A
Palo Verde College, A
Sacramento City College, A
San Diego City College, A
San Diego Miramar College, A
San Francisco State University, B
West Hills Community College, A

Delaware

Delaware Technical & Community College,
    Stanton/Wilmington Campus, A

Illinois

City Colleges of Chicago, Richard J. Daley
    College, A
College of DuPage, A
Triton College, A

Kansas

Fort Scott Community College, A

Kentucky

Eastern Kentucky University, B

Maine

Maine Maritime Academy, AB

Maryland

Cecil Community College, A

Michigan

Baker College of Flint, A
Henry Ford Community College, A
Hope College, B

Muskegon Community College, A

Nebraska

Mid-Plains Community College, A
Southeast Community College, Milford Campus, A

New York

Dowling College, B
Nassau Community College, A
Niagara University, B
St. John's University, B
Syracuse University, B
United States Merchant Marine Academy, B

North Carolina

Central Piedmont Community College, A
North Carolina Agricultural and Technical State
    University, B

Ohio

Sinclair Community College, A
University of Cincinnati, AB
The University of Toledo, A

Tennessee

Chattanooga State Technical Community College, A
Tennessee State University, B

Texas

Houston Community College System, A
Texas A&M University at Galveston, B

Washington

Highline Community College, A

Wisconsin

Milwaukee Area Technical College, A
Northeast Wisconsin Technical College, A

British Columbia

The University of British Columbia, B

TRANSPORTATION/ TRANSPORTATION MANAGEMENT

Alabama

Calhoun Community College, A

Arizona

Arizona State University, O
Arizona State University at the Polytechnic
    Campus, M

Arkansas

Arkansas State University, B
University of Arkansas, M

California

San Jose State University, M
University of California, Davis, MD

Colorado

University of Denver, M

Florida

Florida Institute of Technology, M
University of North Florida, B

Iowa

Iowa State University of Science and Technology, M

Maine

Maine Maritime Academy, MO

Maryland

Morgan State University, M

Massachusetts

Bridgewater State College, B

Missouri

Central Missouri State University, M

New Jersey

New Jersey Institute of Technology, MD

New York

Polytechnic University, Brooklyn Campus, M
State University of New York at Buffalo, O
State University of New York Maritime College, M

North Dakota

North Dakota State University, D

Ohio

Northwest State Community College, A

Pennsylvania

University of Pennsylvania, B

Tennessee

Middle Tennessee State University, M
The University of Tennessee, MD

Texas

Del Mar College, A

Virginia

George Mason University, M

Washington

University of Washington, O

Wisconsin

Milwaukee Area Technical College, A
University of Wisconsin-Superior, B

British Columbia

The University of British Columbia, D

Quebec

McGill University, M

TRAVEL AND TOURISM

Colorado

University of Denver, M

Connecticut

University of New Haven, M

District of Columbia

The George Washington University, MO

Florida

Schiller International University, M
University of Central Florida, M

Hawaii

University of Hawaii at Manoa, MO

Illinois

Saint Xavier University, M
Western Illinois University, M

Indiana

Purdue University, MD

Louisiana

University of New Orleans, M

Massachusetts

Boston University, M
University of Massachusetts Amherst, M

Michigan

Central Michigan University, MO

New York

New York University, MO

Rochester Institute of Technology, M

North Carolina

North Carolina State University, MD

Pennsylvania

East Stroudsburg University of Pennsylvania, M
Temple University, MD

South Carolina

Clemson University, MD
University of South Carolina, M

Tennessee

The University of Tennessee, M

Virginia

Old Dominion University, M
Virginia Polytechnic Institute and State
University, MD

Wisconsin

University of Wisconsin-Stout, M

Ontario

University of Waterloo, M

Quebec

Université du Québec àTrois-Rivières, MO

TRUCK AND BUS DRIVER/COMMERCIAL VEHICLE OPERATION

Illinois

Black Hawk College, A

Minnesota

Alexandria Technical College, A
Dakota County Technical College, A

TURF AND TURFGRASS MANAGEMENT

Arizona

Northland Pioneer College, A

California

Cuyamaca College, A

Colorado

Colorado State University, B

Florida

Lake City Community College, A

Georgia

North Georgia Technical College, A
University of Georgia, B

Illinois

College of Lake County, A
Joliet Junior College, A
Kishwaukee College, A

Iowa

Iowa Lakes Community College, A
Western Iowa Tech Community College, A

Massachusetts

University of Massachusetts Amherst, A

Michigan

Northwestern Michigan College, A

Minnesota

Anoka Technical College, A
Rochester Community and Technical College, A

University of Minnesota, Crookston, B

Missouri

Ozarks Technical Community College, A

New Jersey

Rutgers, The State University of New Jersey, New
Brunswick/Piscataway, B

New York

State University of New York College of Agriculture
and Technology at Cobleskill, AB

North Carolina

Brunswick Community College, A
Guilford Technical Community College, A
North Carolina State University, AB
Sandhills Community College, A
Wayne Community College, A

North Dakota

Minot State University-Bottineau Campus, A
North Dakota State University, B

Ohio

Cincinnati State Technical and Community
College, A
Kent State University, Salem Campus, A
The Ohio State University, B
The Ohio State University Agricultural Technical
Institute, A

Oklahoma

Oklahoma State University, Oklahoma City, A

Oregon

Southwestern Oregon Community College, A

Pennsylvania

Community College of Allegheny County, A
Delaware Valley College, B
Pennsylvania College of Technology, A
The Pennsylvania State University Abington
College, B
The Pennsylvania State University Altoona
College, B
The Pennsylvania State University Beaver Campus
of the Commonwealth College, B
The Pennsylvania State University Berks Campus of
the Berks-Lehigh Valley College, B
The Pennsylvania State University Delaware County
Campus of the Commonwealth College, B
The Pennsylvania State University DuBois Campus
of the Commonwealth College, B
The Pennsylvania State University at Erie, The
Behrend College, B
The Pennsylvania State University Fayette Campus
of the Commonwealth College, B
The Pennsylvania State University Hazleton
Campus of the Commonwealth College, B
The Pennsylvania State University, Lehigh Valley
Campus of the Berks-Lehigh Valley College, B
The Pennsylvania State University McKeesport
Campus of the Commonwealth College, B
The Pennsylvania State University Mont Alto
Campus of the Commonwealth College, B
The Pennsylvania State University New Kensington
Campus of the Commonwealth College, B
The Pennsylvania State University Schuylkill
Campus of the Capital College, B
The Pennsylvania State University Shenango
Campus of the Commonwealth College, B
The Pennsylvania State University University Park
Campus, B
The Pennsylvania State University Wilkes-Barre
Campus of the Commonwealth College, B
The Pennsylvania State University Worthington
Scranton Campus of the Commonwealth
College, B
The Pennsylvania State University York Campus of
the Commonwealth College, B

The Williamson Free School of Mechanical
Trades, A

Rhode Island

University of Rhode Island, B

South Carolina

Clemson University, B

South Dakota

Southeast Technical Institute, A

Tennessee

Tennessee Technological University, B

Texas

Texas State Technical College Waco, A

Washington

Walla Walla Community College, A

TURKISH LANGUAGE AND LITERATURE

Illinois

University of Chicago, B

Texas

The University of Texas at Austin, B

UKRAINE STUDIES

Massachusetts

Simon's Rock College of Bard, B

UKRAINIAN LANGUAGE AND LITERATURE

Saskatchewan

University of Saskatchewan, B

URBAN AND REGIONAL PLANNING

Alabama

Alabama Agricultural and Mechanical University, M
Auburn University, MO

Arizona

Arizona State University, M
The University of Arizona, M

California

California Polytechnic State University, San Luis
Obispo, MO
California State Polytechnic University, Pomona, M
California State University, Chico, M
San Diego State University, M
San Jose State University, MO
University of California, Berkeley, MDO
University of California, Davis, M
University of California, Irvine, MD
University of Southern California, MDO

Colorado

University of Colorado at Denver and Health
Sciences Center - Downtown Denver Campus, M

District of Columbia

The Catholic University of America, M

Florida

Florida Atlantic University, M
Florida State University, MDO

University of Florida, MDO

Georgia

Georgia Institute of Technology, MDO
Valdosta State University, M

Hawaii

University of Hawaii at Manoa, MO

Illinois

DePaul University, O
North Park University, M
University of Illinois at Chicago, MD
University of Illinois at Urbana-Champaign, MDO

Indiana

Indiana University-Purdue University
   Indianapolis, MO

Iowa

Iowa State University of Science and
   Technology, MO
The University of Iowa, MO

Kansas

Kansas State University, M
University of Kansas, MO

Kentucky

Eastern Kentucky University, M
University of Louisville, M

Louisiana

University of New Orleans, M

Maine

University of Southern Maine, MO

Maryland

Morgan State University, M
University of Maryland, College Park, MDO

Massachusetts

Boston University, M
Clark University, M
Harvard University, M
Massachusetts Institute of Technology, MD
Tufts University, M
University of Massachusetts Amherst, MDO

Michigan

Michigan State University, M
University of Michigan, MDO
Wayne State University, M

Minnesota

University of Minnesota, Twin Cities Campus, MO

Mississippi

Delta State University, M
Jackson State University, M

Missouri

Missouri State University, M

Nebraska

University of Nebraska-Lincoln, MO

New Jersey

Rutgers, The State University of New Jersey, New
   Brunswick/Piscataway, MDO

New Mexico

University of New Mexico, MO

New York

Cornell University, MD
Pratt Institute, M
State University of New York at Buffalo, MO
State University of New York College of
   Environmental Science and Forestry, MD

University at Albany, State University of New
   York, M

North Carolina

The University of North Carolina at Chapel
   Hill, MDO

Ohio

The Ohio State University, MD
University of Cincinnati, MO
The University of Toledo, M

Oklahoma

University of Oklahoma, MO

Oregon

Portland State University, M
University of Oregon, M

Pennsylvania

The Pennsylvania State University University Park
   Campus, M
Temple University, M
University of Pennsylvania, MDO
University of Pittsburgh, MO
West Chester University of Pennsylvania, M

Puerto Rico

University of Puerto Rico, Río Piedras, M

Rhode Island

University of Rhode Island, M

South Carolina

Clemson University, MD

Tennessee

East Tennessee State University, M
University of Memphis, M

Texas

Texas A&M University, MD
Texas Southern University, MO
The University of Texas at Arlington, MO
The University of Texas at Austin, MDO

Utah

Utah State University, M

Virginia

Old Dominion University, M
University of Virginia, M
Virginia Commonwealth University, MO
Virginia Polytechnic Institute and State University, M

Washington

Eastern Washington University, MO
University of Washington, MD
Washington State University, M

West Virginia

West Virginia University, MD

Wisconsin

University of Wisconsin-Madison, MD

Alberta

University of Calgary, M

British Columbia

The University of British Columbia, MD

Manitoba

University of Manitoba, M

Nova Scotia

Dalhousie University, MO

Ontario

Queen's University at Kingston, M
University of Toronto, M

University of Waterloo, MD

Quebec

Concordia University, O
McGill University, MD
Université Laval, MD
Université du Québec en Outaouais, M

URBAN DESIGN

California

University of California, Berkeley, MD
University of California, Los Angeles, MD

Colorado

University of Colorado at Denver and Health
   Sciences Center - Downtown Denver Campus, M

Florida

University of Miami, M

Georgia

Georgia Institute of Technology, M

Massachusetts

Harvard University, M

Michigan

University of Michigan, M

Missouri

Washington University in St. Louis, MO

New York

City College of the City University of New York, M
Cornell University, M
New York Institute of Technology, M
Pratt Institute, M
State University of New York at Buffalo, MO
State University of New York College of
   Environmental Science and Forestry, M

Ohio

Cleveland State University, M

Texas

Prairie View A&M University, M
Rice University, M

Washington

University of Washington, MDO

Alberta

University of Calgary, M

URBAN EDUCATION AND LEADERSHIP

California

Holy Names University, M

Florida

Florida International University, M

Georgia

Georgia State University, M

Illinois

Columbia College Chicago, M
Concordia University, M
DePaul University, M
Northeastern Illinois University, M
University of Illinois at Chicago, D

Massachusetts

Harvard University, D
Simmons College, MO

University of Massachusetts Boston, D

Michigan

Marygrove College, M
University of Michigan-Flint, M

Missouri

Harris-Stowe State University, B
University of Missouri-Kansas City, B

Nebraska

University of Nebraska at Omaha, O

New Jersey

New Jersey City University, M
Saint Peter's College, M

New York

College of Mount Saint Vincent, M
Mercy College, M

Ohio

Cleveland State University, D

Oklahoma

Langston University, M

Pennsylvania

Temple University, MD

Texas

Texas A&M University, MD
Texas Southern University, D

Virginia

George Mason University, M
Norfolk State University, M
Old Dominion University, D
Virginia Commonwealth University, D

Wisconsin

University of Wisconsin-Milwaukee, MD

URBAN FORESTRY

California

University of California, Davis, B

Louisiana

Southern University and Agricultural and Mechanical College, B

Texas

Texas A&M University, B

Quebec

Université Laval, B

URBAN PLANNING

California

University of California, Los Angeles, MDO

Indiana

Ball State University, M

Kentucky

University of Louisville, M

Massachusetts

Harvard University, MD

New York

Hunter College of the City University of New York, MO
New York University, MO

Pratt Institute, M

Ohio

Cleveland State University, MO
The University of Akron, M

Texas

Texas A&M University, M

Virginia

Virginia Commonwealth University, M

West Virginia

West Virginia University, M

Wisconsin

University of Wisconsin-Milwaukee, MO

URBAN STUDIES/AFFAIRS

Alabama

Lawson State Community College, A

Arizona

Arizona State University, B

California

California State Polytechnic University, Pomona, B
California State University, Northridge, B
Loyola Marymount University, B
Mount St. Mary's College, A
San Diego State University, B
San Francisco State University, B
Santa Monica College, A
Stanford University, B
University of California, Berkeley, B
University of California, Irvine, MD
University of California, San Diego, B
University of San Diego, B
University of Southern California, B

Colorado

Metropolitan State College of Denver, B

Connecticut

Albertus Magnus College, B
Connecticut College, B
Southern Connecticut State University, MO
University of Connecticut, B

Delaware

University of Delaware, MD

District of Columbia

University of the District of Columbia, AB

Florida

Florida International University, B
Florida Memorial College, B
New College of Florida, B
The University of Tampa, B

Georgia

Beulah Heights Bible College, AB
Georgia State University, BM
Morehouse College, B
Oglethorpe University, B
Savannah State University, M

Illinois

DePaul University, B
Elmhurst College, B
North Park University, B
Northeastern Illinois University, B
Northwestern University, B

Roosevelt University, B

Indiana

Crossroads Bible College, B
Indiana University Bloomington, B

Iowa

Mount Mercy College, B

Kansas

MidAmerica Nazarene University, B

Kentucky

University of Louisville, D

Louisiana

Dillard University, B
University of New Orleans, BMD

Maryland

Sojourner-Douglass College, B

Massachusetts

Boston University, BM
Hampshire College, B
Harvard University, B
Massachusetts Institute of Technology, MD
Tufts University, BMO
Worcester State College, B

Michigan

Aquinas College, B

Minnesota

Augsburg College, B
Hamline University, B
Macalester College, B
Minnesota State University Mankato, BMO
St. Cloud State University, B
University of Minnesota, Duluth, B
University of Minnesota, Twin Cities Campus, B

Mississippi

Jackson State University, B

Missouri

Calvary Bible College and Theological Seminary, B
Harris-Stowe State University, B
Saint Louis University, BM
University of Missouri-Kansas City, B
Washington University in St. Louis, B

New Jersey

New Jersey City University, BM
Rutgers, The State University of New Jersey, New Brunswick/Piscataway, B
Rutgers, The State University of New Jersey, Newark, MD
Saint Peter's College, AB

New York

Barnard College, B
Brooklyn College of the City University of New York, M
Buffalo State College, State University of New York, B
Canisius College, B
College of Mount Saint Vincent, B
Columbia College, B
Columbia University, School of General Studies, B
Cornell University, B
Eugene Lang College The New School for Liberal Arts, B
Fordham University, B
Hobart and William Smith Colleges, B
Hunter College of the City University of New York, BM
Long Island University, Brooklyn Campus, M
Manhattan College, B
Metropolitan College of New York, B
New York University, B
Queens College of the City University of New York, BM
Sarah Lawrence College, B

University at Albany, State University of New York, BO
Vassar College, B

Ohio

Cleveland State University, BMD
The College of Wooster, B
Lorain County Community College, A
Ohio Wesleyan University, B
The University of Akron, MD
University of Cincinnati, B
University of Cincinnati Raymond Walters College, A
The University of Toledo, B
Wittenberg University, B
Wright State University, BM

Oklahoma

Langston University, B
Southern Nazarene University, B
University of Central Oklahoma, M

Oregon

Portland State University, BMD

Pennsylvania

Bryn Mawr College, B
Haverford College, B
Lehigh University, B
Temple University, M
University of Pennsylvania, B
University of Pittsburgh, B

Rhode Island

Brown University, B
Community College of Rhode Island, A

South Carolina

College of Charleston, B
Furman University, B

Tennessee

East Tennessee State University, M
Lipscomb University, B
Rhodes College, B
Vanderbilt University, B

Texas

Baylor University, B
The Criswell College, B
St. Philip's College, A
Trinity University, B
University of the Incarnate Word, M
The University of Texas at Austin, B

Utah

University of Utah, B

Virginia

Norfolk State University, M
Old Dominion University, MD
University of Richmond, B
Virginia Commonwealth University, B

Washington

University of Washington, Tacoma, B

Wisconsin

University of Wisconsin-Green Bay, AB
University of Wisconsin-Madison, B
University of Wisconsin-Milwaukee, BMDO
University of Wisconsin-Oshkosh, B

Alberta

University of Alberta, B
University of Calgary, B

University of Lethbridge, BM

British Columbia

The University of British Columbia, B

Manitoba

The University of Winnipeg, B

Ontario

Carleton University, B
Ryerson University, B
University of Toronto, B
The University of Western Ontario, B
York University, B

Quebec

Concordia University, B
McGill University, B
Université de Montréal, B
Université du Québec àMontréal, BMD

Saskatchewan

University of Saskatchewan, B

URDU LANGUAGE AND LITERATURE

Illinois

University of Chicago, B

VEHICLE AND VEHICLE PARTS AND ACCESSORIES MARKETING OPERATIONS

Florida

Northwood University, Florida Campus, AB

Guam

Guam Community College, A

Michigan

Northwood University, AB

Minnesota

Dakota County Technical College, A

Pennsylvania

Pennsylvania College of Technology, A

Texas

Northwood University, Texas Campus, AB

Wisconsin

Northeast Wisconsin Technical College, A

VEHICLE MAINTENANCE AND REPAIR TECHNOLOGIES

Alaska

University of Alaska Fairbanks, A

Arkansas

Arkansas State University-Beebe, A

California

Victor Valley College, A

Illinois

Black Hawk College, A

Massachusetts

Massasoit Community College, A

New Mexico

Central New Mexico Community College, A

North Dakota

North Dakota State College of Science, A

Pennsylvania

Pennsylvania College of Technology, A

British Columbia

British Columbia Institute of Technology, A

VETERINARY/ANIMAL HEALTH TECHNOLOGY/TECHNICIAN AND VETERINARY ASSISTANT

Alabama

Jefferson State Community College, A

Arizona

Pima Community College, A

California

Cosumnes River College (Sacramento), A
Foothill College, A
Hartnell College, A
Los Angeles Pierce College, A
San Diego Mesa College, A
San Joaquin Valley College, A
Yuba College, A

Colorado

Bel-Rea Institute of Animal Technology, A
Colorado Mountain College, A
Community College of Denver, A
Front Range Community College, A

Connecticut

Northwestern Connecticut Community College, A
Quinnipiac University, B

Delaware

Delaware Technical & Community College, Jack F. Owens Campus, A

Florida

Brevard Community College, A
Central Florida Community College, A
St. Petersburg College, AB

Georgia

Athens Technical College, A
Central Georgia Technical College, A
Fort Valley State University, A
Gwinnett Technical College, A
Ogeechee Technical College, A

Idaho

College of Southern Idaho, A

Illinois

Joliet Junior College, A
Parkland College, A

Indiana

Purdue University, AB

Iowa

Kirkwood Community College, A

Kansas

Colby Community College, A
Johnson County Community College, A

Kentucky

Morehead State University, A
Murray State University, B

Louisiana

Northwestern State University of Louisiana, A

Maine

The University of Maine at Augusta, A

Massachusetts

Becker College, A
Holyoke Community College, A

Mount Ida College, AB
North Shore Community College, A

Michigan

Baker College of Cadillac, A
Baker College of Jackson, A
Baker College of Muskegon, A
Lansing Community College, A
Macomb Community College, A
Michigan State University, B
Wayne County Community College District, A

Minnesota

Duluth Business University, A
Globe College, A
Minnesota School of Business, A
Minnesota School of Business-Brooklyn Center, A
Minnesota School of Business-Plymouth, A
Minnesota School of Business-Richfield, A
Minnesota School of Business-St. Cloud, A
Minnesota School of Business-Shakopee, A
Ridgewater College, A

Mississippi

Hinds Community College, A

Missouri

Jefferson College, A
Maple Woods Community College, A

Nebraska

Nebraska College of Technical Agriculture, A
Northeast Community College, A
University of Nebraska-Lincoln, B
Vatterott College (Omaha), A

Nevada

Community College of Southern Nevada, A

New Jersey

Bergen Community College, A
County College of Morris, A
Sussex County Community College, A

New York

Fiorello H. LaGuardia Community College of the
    City University of New York, A
Medaille College, AB
State University of New York College of Technology
    at Canton, A
State University of New York College of Technology
    at Delhi, AB

North Carolina

Central Carolina Community College, A
Gaston College, A

North Dakota

North Dakota State University, B
Turtle Mountain Community College, A

Ohio

Columbus State Community College, A
Stautzenberger College, A
University of Cincinnati Raymond Walters College, A

Oklahoma

Community Care College, A
Murray State College, A
Oklahoma State University, Oklahoma City, A
Tulsa Community College, A

Pennsylvania

Harcum College, A
Johnson College, A
Lehigh Carbon Community College, A
Manor College, A
Northampton County Area Community College, A
Penn Foster Career School, A
Western School of Health and Business Careers
    (Pittsburgh), A

Wilson College, B

Puerto Rico

University of Puerto Rico, Medical Sciences
    Campus, B

South Carolina

Newberry College, B
Tri-County Technical College, A
Trident Technical College, A

South Dakota

National American University (Rapid City), A

Tennessee

Columbia State Community College, A
Lincoln Memorial University, A

Texas

Midland College, A
Sul Ross State University, A
Tomball College, A

Utah

Brigham Young University, B
Utah Career College, A

Vermont

Vermont Technical College, A

Virginia

Blue Ridge Community College, A
Northern Virginia Community College, A

Washington

Pierce College, A
Yakima Valley Community College, A

West Virginia

Fairmont State University, A

Wisconsin

Madison Area Technical College, A

Wyoming

Eastern Wyoming College, A

British Columbia

Thompson Rivers University, A

VETERINARY MEDICINE

Alabama

Auburn University, PO
Tuskegee University, P

California

University of California, Davis, PO

Colorado

Colorado State University, P

Florida

University of Florida, P

Georgia

University of Georgia, P

Illinois

University of Illinois at Urbana-Champaign, P

Indiana

Purdue University, PO

Iowa

Iowa State University of Science and
    Technology, MP

Kansas

Kansas State University, P

Louisiana

Louisiana State University and Agricultural and
    Mechanical College, P

Maryland

University of Maryland, College Park, P

Massachusetts

Tufts University, PO

Michigan

Michigan State University, P

Minnesota

University of Minnesota, Twin Cities Campus, PO

Mississippi

Mississippi State University, P

Missouri

University of Missouri-Columbia, P

New York

Cornell University, MDP

North Carolina

North Carolina State University, MPO

Ohio

The Ohio State University, PO

Oklahoma

Oklahoma State University, P

Oregon

Oregon State University, P

Pennsylvania

University of Pennsylvania, PO

Tennessee

The University of Tennessee, P

Texas

Texas A&M University, MPO

Virginia

Virginia Polytechnic Institute and State University, P

Washington

Washington State University, PO

Wisconsin

University of Wisconsin-Madison, P

Ontario

University of Guelph, MD

Prince Edward Island

University of Prince Edward Island, P

Quebec

Université de Montréal, P

Saskatchewan

University of Saskatchewan, MDP

VETERINARY SCIENCES

Alabama

Auburn University, MD
Tuskegee University, M

California

University of California, Davis, MO

Colorado

Colorado State University, MD

Florida

University of Florida, MDO

Georgia

University of Georgia, MD

Idaho

University of Idaho, MD

Illinois

University of Illinois at Urbana-Champaign, MD

Indiana

Purdue University, MD

Iowa

Iowa State University of Science and
   Technology, MD

Kansas

Kansas State University, M

Kentucky

University of Kentucky, MD

Louisiana

Louisiana State University and Agricultural and
   Mechanical College, MD

Maryland

University of Maryland, College Park, MD

Massachusetts

Tufts University, MDO

Michigan

Michigan State University, MD

Minnesota

University of Minnesota, Twin Cities Campus, MDO

Mississippi

Mississippi State University, MD

Missouri

University of Missouri-Columbia, MD

Montana

Montana State University, MD

Nebraska

University of Nebraska-Lincoln, MD

North Carolina

North Carolina State University, MD

North Dakota

North Dakota State University, MD

Ohio

The Ohio State University, MD

Oklahoma

Oklahoma State University, MD

Oregon

Oregon State University, MD

Pennsylvania

Drexel University, M
The Pennsylvania State University University Park
   Campus, MD

South Carolina

Clemson University, MD

Texas

Texas A&M University, MDO

Utah

Utah State University, MD

Virginia

Virginia Polytechnic Institute and State
   University, MD

Washington

University of Washington, M
Washington State University, MD

West Virginia

West Virginia University, M

Wisconsin

University of Wisconsin-Madison, MD

Ontario

University of Guelph, MDO

Prince Edward Island

University of Prince Edward Island, MD

Quebec

Université de Montréal, MDO

Saskatchewan

University of Saskatchewan, MD

VIOLIN, VIOLA, GUITAR AND OTHER STRINGED INSTRUMENTS

California

Bethesda Christian University, B
California Institute of the Arts, B
California State University, Fullerton, B
The Colburn School Conservatory of Music, B
Notre Dame de Namur University, B
San Francisco Conservatory of Music, B
University of Southern California, B

Florida

Florida State University, B
New World School of the Arts, AB
Stetson University, B

Georgia

Columbus State University, B

Illinois

Augustana College, B
DePaul University, B
Illinois Wesleyan University, B
Northwestern University, B
Olivet Nazarene University, B
Roosevelt University, B

Indiana

Ball State University, B
Butler University, B

Iowa

The University of Iowa, B

Kansas

Friends University, B
University of Kansas, B

Louisiana

Xavier University of Louisiana, B

Maryland

Peabody Conservatory of Music of The Johns
   Hopkins University, B

Massachusetts

Berklee College of Music, B
The Boston Conservatory, B

New England Conservatory of Music, B

Michigan

Grand Valley State University, B
Hope College, B
University of Michigan, B

Minnesota

Minnesota State College-Southeast Technical, A
St. Cloud State University, B

Missouri

Northwest Missouri State University, B

Nebraska

Hastings College, B

New Hampshire

University of New Hampshire, B

New York

Five Towns College, AB
Houghton College, B
Manhattan School of Music, B
Mannes College The New School for Music, B
Sarah Lawrence College, B
State University of New York, Fredonia, B
Syracuse University, B

North Carolina

Meredith College, B

Ohio

Capital University, B
Cleveland Institute of Music, B
Heidelberg College, B
Oberlin College, B
Otterbein College, B
The University of Akron, B
University of Cincinnati, B

Oklahoma

Oklahoma City University, B
University of Central Oklahoma, B
University of Oklahoma, B

Oregon

Willamette University, B

Pennsylvania

Carnegie Mellon University, B
The Curtis Institute of Music, B
Seton Hill University, B
Susquehanna University, B
Temple University, B

Puerto Rico

Conservatory of Music of Puerto Rico, B
Inter American University of Puerto Rico, San
   Germán Campus, B

South Carolina

Converse College, B

Tennessee

Vanderbilt University, B

Texas

Hardin-Simmons University, B
Howard Payne University, B
Lamar University, B

University of North Texas, B

Utah

Brigham Young University, B

Vermont

Bennington College, B

Washington

Cornish College of the Arts, B
University of Washington, B

Wisconsin

Lawrence University, B
University of Wisconsin-Milwaukee, B

Alberta

University of Alberta, B

British Columbia

Kwantlen University College, A
The University of British Columbia, B

New Brunswick

Mount Allison University, B

Newfoundland and Labrador

Memorial University of Newfoundland, B

Nova Scotia

Acadia University, B

Ontario

The University of Western Ontario, B

VIROLOGY

California

University of California, San Diego, D

Connecticut

Yale University, DO

Illinois

Loyola University Chicago, MD

Indiana

Purdue University, MD

Iowa

The University of Iowa, MD

Kansas

Kansas State University, MD

Massachusetts

Harvard University, D

New Jersey

Rutgers, The State University of New Jersey, New
  Brunswick/Piscataway, MD

Ohio

The Ohio State University, MD

Pennsylvania

University of Pennsylvania, DO
University of Pittsburgh, MD

Texas

Texas A&M University System Health Science
  Center, D
The University of Texas Health Science Center at
  Houston, MDO

The University of Texas Medical Branch, DO

West Virginia

West Virginia University, MD

Ontario

McMaster University, MD

Prince Edward Island

University of Prince Edward Island, MD

Quebec

Université de Montréal, D

VISION SCIENCE/PHYSIOLOGICAL OPTICS

Alabama

The University of Alabama at Birmingham, MD
The University of Alabama in Huntsville, D

California

University of California, Berkeley, MD

Florida

Nova Southeastern University, M

Georgia

Emory University, M

Illinois

University of Chicago, D

Indiana

Indiana University Bloomington, MD

Missouri

University of Missouri-St. Louis, MD

Oregon

Pacific University, M

Texas

University of Houston, MD

Alberta

University of Alberta, MD

Ontario

University of Guelph, MD
University of Waterloo, MDP

Quebec

Université de Montréal, MO

VISUAL AND PERFORMING ARTS

Alabama

Huntingdon College, B
Samford University, B
The University of Alabama at Birmingham, B

Arizona

Arizona State University West, B
The University of Arizona, B

Arkansas

University of Arkansas at Fort Smith, A

California

Art Center College of Design, B
California Baptist University, B
California State University Channel Islands, B
California State University, San Marcos, B
Citrus College, A
Claremont McKenna College, B
Dominican University of California, B

Mt. San Jacinto College, A
Saint Mary's College of California, B
San Francisco Art Institute, B
San Jose State University, B
Scripps College, B
University of California, Davis, B
University of California, Los Angeles, B
University of San Diego, B
University of San Francisco, B
William Jessup University, B

Colorado

Naropa University, B
Regis University, B

Connecticut

Eastern Connecticut State University, B
University of New Haven, B

Florida

Eckerd College, B
Florida Community College at Jacksonville, A
Jacksonville University, B
Miami International University of Art & Design, AB
Stetson University, B
University of Miami, B
The University of Tampa, B

Georgia

Andrew College, A
Armstrong Atlantic State University, B
LaGrange College, B
Valdosta State University, B

Illinois

American Academy of Art, B
Illinois State University, B
Illinois Wesleyan University, B
Moraine Valley Community College, A
Northwestern University, B
Quincy University, B
School of the Art Institute of Chicago, B
University of St. Francis, B

Indiana

Indiana University East, A

Iowa

Ashford University, B
Iowa State University of Science and Technology, B
Loras College, B

Kansas

Bethel College, B
Hutchinson Community College and Area Vocational
  School, A
Wichita State University, B

Kentucky

Thomas More College, A
Western Kentucky University, B

Louisiana

Centenary College of Louisiana, B
University of Louisiana at Lafayette, B

Maine

Maine College of Art, B
University of Maine at Machias, B

Maryland

Frostburg State University, B
Maryland Institute College of Art, B
University of Maryland, Baltimore County, B
University of Maryland, College Park, B

Massachusetts

Assumption College, B
Berkshire Community College, A
Emerson College, B
Holyoke Community College, A
Massachusetts College of Liberal Arts, B
Quincy College, A
Roxbury Community College, A

School of the Museum of Fine Arts, Boston, B
Simon's Rock College of Bard, B

Michigan

University of Michigan, B
University of Michigan-Flint, B

Minnesota

College of Visual Arts, B
St. Cloud State University, B
St. Olaf College, B

Mississippi

Jackson State University, B
Mississippi State University, B
University of Southern Mississippi, B

Missouri

Missouri State University, B
Southeast Missouri State University, B

Montana

Carroll College, B

New Hampshire

New Hampshire Technical Institute, A

New Jersey

Atlantic Cape Community College, A
Brookdale Community College, A
Fairleigh Dickinson University, College at
  Florham, B
Fairleigh Dickinson University, Metropolitan
  Campus, B
Ramapo College of New Jersey, B
The Richard Stockton College of New Jersey, B
Rutgers, The State University of New Jersey, New
  Brunswick/Piscataway, B
Saint Peter's College, B
Seton Hall University, B

New Mexico

New Mexico State University, B
Santa Fe Community College, A

New York

Adelphi University, B
Bard College, B
Barnard College, B
Briarcliffe College, A
Cazenovia College, B
Columbia College, B
Columbia University, School of General Studies, B
Cooper Union for the Advancement of Science and
  Art, B
Ithaca College, B
Long Island University, C.W. Post Campus, B
Nassau Community College, A
Queensborough Community College of the City
  University of New York, A
Rensselaer Polytechnic Institute, B
St. Bonaventure University, B
Sarah Lawrence College, B
State University of New York College at Geneseo, B
State University of New York College at Old
  Westbury, B
Vassar College, B

North Carolina

Meredith College, B
North Carolina School of the Arts, B
Saint Augustine's College, B

Ohio

Antioch College, B
Ohio Northern University, B
Ohio University, B
The University of Akron, B
University of Rio Grande, B

Oklahoma

Cameron University, B
St. Gregory's University, B

University of Oklahoma, B

Pennsylvania

Bucks County Community College, A
Community College of Allegheny County, A
East Stroudsburg University of Pennsylvania, B
Gannon University, B
Gettysburg College, B
Kutztown University of Pennsylvania, B
Marywood University, B
The Pennsylvania State University Abington
  College, B
The Pennsylvania State University Altoona
  College, B
The Pennsylvania State University Beaver Campus
  of the Commonwealth College, B
The Pennsylvania State University Berks Campus of
  the Berks-Lehigh Valley College, B
The Pennsylvania State University Delaware County
  Campus of the Commonwealth College, B
The Pennsylvania State University DuBois Campus
  of the Commonwealth College, B
The Pennsylvania State University at Erie, The
  Behrend College, B
The Pennsylvania State University Fayette Campus
  of the Commonwealth College, B
The Pennsylvania State University Hazleton
  Campus of the Commonwealth College, B
The Pennsylvania State University, Lehigh Valley
  Campus of the Berks-Lehigh Valley College, B
The Pennsylvania State University McKeesport
  Campus of the Commonwealth College, B
The Pennsylvania State University Mont Alto
  Campus of the Commonwealth College, B
The Pennsylvania State University New Kensington
  Campus of the Commonwealth College, B
The Pennsylvania State University Schuylkill
  Campus of the Capital College, B
The Pennsylvania State University Shenango
  Campus of the Commonwealth College, B
The Pennsylvania State University University Park
  Campus, B
The Pennsylvania State University Wilkes-Barre
  Campus of the Commonwealth College, B
The Pennsylvania State University Worthington
  Scranton Campus of the Commonwealth
  College, B
The Pennsylvania State University York Campus of
  the Commonwealth College, B
Saint Joseph's University, B
Swarthmore College, B
The University of the Arts, B
University of Pennsylvania, B

Puerto Rico

University of the Sacred Heart, B

Rhode Island

Brown University, B
Providence College, B
Roger Williams University, B

South Carolina

Clemson University, B

South Dakota

South Dakota State University, B

Tennessee

Cumberland University, B
Lambuth University, B
The University of Tennessee at Martin, B

Texas

Amarillo College, A
Angelo State University, B
Kingwood College, A
Lee College, A
Rice University, B
Texas Southern University, B
Texas Wesleyan University, B
The University of Texas at Austin, B

The University of Texas at Dallas, B

Utah

Brigham Young University, B
University of Utah, B

Vermont

Bennington College, B
Green Mountain College, B
Johnson State College, B

Virginia

George Mason University, B
Piedmont Virginia Community College, A
Shenandoah University, B
Virginia State University, B

Washington

The Evergreen State College, B
Western Washington University, B

West Virginia

Alderson-Broaddus College, B
West Virginia University, B

Wisconsin

University of Wisconsin-Superior, B
Viterbo University, B

Wyoming

Laramie County Community College, A
Western Wyoming Community College, A

Alberta

Concordia University College of Alberta, B

British Columbia

Simon Fraser University, B
Thompson Rivers University, B
Trinity Western University, B
The University of British Columbia, B

Ontario

University of Toronto, B
University of Windsor, B
York University, B

Saskatchewan

University of Regina, B

VOCATIONAL AND TECHNICAL EDUCATION

Alaska

University of Alaska Anchorage, M

Arizona

Northern Arizona University, M

Arkansas

University of Arkansas, MDO

California

California Baptist University, M
California State University, Long Beach, M
California State University, Sacramento, M
California State University, San Bernardino, M

Colorado

Colorado State University, MD

Connecticut

Central Connecticut State University, MO

Delaware

Wilmington College, M

Florida

Florida Agricultural and Mechanical University, M
Florida International University, M
Nova Southeastern University, D

University of Central Florida, M
University of South Florida, MDO

Georgia

Georgia Southern University, M
Georgia State University, M
University of Georgia, MDO
Valdosta State University, MDO

Idaho

Idaho State University, M
University of Idaho, MDO

Illinois

Chicago State University, M
Southern Illinois University Carbondale, MD
University of Illinois at Urbana-Champaign, MDO

Indiana

Ball State University, M
Indiana State University, M
Purdue University, MDO

Iowa

Drake University, M
Iowa State University of Science and
  Technology, MD

Kansas

Pittsburg State University, MO

Kentucky

Morehead State University, M
Murray State University, M
University of Kentucky, MDO

Louisiana

Louisiana State University and Agricultural and
  Mechanical College, MD

Maryland

University of Maryland Eastern Shore, M

Massachusetts

Fitchburg State College, M
Westfield State College, M

Michigan

Wayne State University, MDO
Western Michigan University, M

Minnesota

University of Minnesota, Twin Cities Campus, MO

Mississippi

Mississippi State University, MDO
University of Southern Mississippi, M

Missouri

University of Missouri-Columbia, MDO

Nebraska

Wayne State College, M

Nevada

University of Nevada, Las Vegas, M

New Hampshire

University of New Hampshire, M

New York

Buffalo State College, State University of New
  York, M

State University of New York at Oswego, M

North Carolina

East Carolina University, M
North Carolina Agricultural and Technical State
  University, M

North Dakota

University of North Dakota, M

Ohio

Bowling Green State University, M
Kent State University, MO
The Ohio State University, D
The University of Akron, M
The University of Toledo, MO
Wright State University, M

Oklahoma

Oklahoma State University, MD
Southwestern Oklahoma State University, M

Oregon

Oregon State University, M

Pennsylvania

California University of Pennsylvania, M
The Pennsylvania State University University Park
  Campus, MD
Temple University, M

Puerto Rico

Inter American University of Puerto Rico,
  Metropolitan Campus, M

Rhode Island

Rhode Island College, M

South Carolina

Clemson University, MD
University of South Carolina, M

Tennessee

East Tennessee State University, M
Tennessee State University, M

Texas

Texas A&M University-Corpus Christi, M
Texas State University-San Marcos, M
University of North Texas, MD
The University of Texas at Tyler, M

Virginia

James Madison University, M
Old Dominion University, M
Virginia Polytechnic Institute and State
  University, MD
Virginia State University, MO

West Virginia

Marshall University, M
West Virginia University, MD

Wisconsin

University of Wisconsin-Madison, MD
University of Wisconsin-Platteville, M
University of Wisconsin-Stout, MO

Alberta

University of Calgary, MDO

New Brunswick

University of New Brunswick Fredericton, M

VOCATIONAL REHABILITATION COUNSELING/COUNSELOR

Colorado

University of Northern Colorado, B

Florida

Florida State University, B
Manatee Community College, A

Illinois

University of Illinois at Urbana-Champaign, B

Kansas

Emporia State University, B

Missouri

Maryville University of Saint Louis, B

North Carolina

East Carolina University, B
Winston-Salem State University, B

Ohio

Wright State University, B

Washington

Edmonds Community College, A
Spokane Falls Community College, A

Wisconsin

University of Wisconsin-Stout, B

VOICE AND OPERA

Alabama

Birmingham-Southern College, B
Huntingdon College, B
Samford University, B
Talladega College, B
University of Montevallo, B

Arizona

Grand Canyon University, B

Arkansas

Ouachita Baptist University, B

California

California Institute of the Arts, B
California State University, Fullerton, B
California State University, Long Beach, B
Chapman University, B
Fresno City College, A
Loyola Marymount University, B
The Master's College and Seminary, B
Notre Dame de Namur University, B
Reedley College, A
San Diego Christian College, B
San Francisco Conservatory of Music, B
University of the Pacific, B
University of Redlands, B

Delaware

Delaware State University, B
University of Delaware, B

District of Columbia

The Catholic University of America, B

Florida

Barry University, B
Florida State University, B
Jacksonville University, B
New World School of the Arts, AB
Palm Beach Atlantic University, B
Stetson University, B
University of Miami, B

Georgia

Brenau University, B
Columbus State University, B

Shorter College, B

Hawaii

Brigham Young University-Hawaii, B

Idaho

University of Idaho, B

Illinois

Augustana College, B
Concordia University, B
DePaul University, B
Eureka College, B
Illinois Wesleyan University, B
Judson College, B
Lincoln Christian College, B
Lincoln College, A
Millikin University, B
North Park University, B
Northwestern University, B
Olivet Nazarene University, B
Roosevelt University, B
University of Illinois at Urbana-Champaign, B

Indiana

Ball State University, B
Bethel College, B
Butler University, B
Huntington University, B
Indiana University Bloomington, B
Indiana University-Purdue University Fort Wayne, B
Taylor University, B
Valparaiso University, B

Iowa

Clarke College, B
Dordt College, B
Drake University, B
Iowa Lakes Community College, A
Kirkwood Community College, A
Mount Mercy College, B
The University of Iowa, B

Kansas

Coffeyville Community College, A
Friends University, B
Tabor College, B
University of Kansas, B

Kentucky

Campbellsville University, B

Louisiana

Centenary College of Louisiana, B
Louisiana College, B

Maryland

Peabody Conservatory of Music of The Johns
  Hopkins University, B

Massachusetts

Anna Maria College, B
Berklee College of Music, B
The Boston Conservatory, B
Boston University, B
New England Conservatory of Music, B
Westfield State College, B

Michigan

Andrews University, B
Calvin College, B
Grand Valley State University, B
Hope College, B
Lansing Community College, A
University of Michigan, B

Minnesota

Concordia College, B
Minnesota State University Mankato, B
Minnesota State University Moorhead, B
Northwestern College, B
St. Cloud State University, B

Winona State University, B

Mississippi

Mississippi College, B

Missouri

Calvary Bible College and Theological Seminary, B
Hannibal-LaGrange College, B
Lindenwood University, B
Northwest Missouri State University, B
Truman State University, B
Washington University in St. Louis, B

Nebraska

Grace University, B
Hastings College, B
Peru State College, B
University of Nebraska at Omaha, B

New Hampshire

University of New Hampshire, B

New Jersey

Rider University, B
Westminster Choir College of Rider University, B
William Paterson University of New Jersey, B

New York

Bard College, B
Five Towns College, AB
Houghton College, B
Ithaca College, B
Long Island University, C.W. Post Campus, B
Manhattan School of Music, B
Mannes College The New School for Music, B
New York University, B
Nyack College, B
Roberts Wesleyan College, B
Sarah Lawrence College, B
State University of New York, Fredonia, B
Syracuse University, B

North Carolina

Catawba College, B
Meredith College, B
North Carolina School of the Arts, B
Queens University of Charlotte, B

Ohio

Bowling Green State University, B
Capital University, B
Cedarville University, B
Cincinnati Christian University, B
Cleveland Institute of Music, B
Heidelberg College, B
Oberlin College, B
The Ohio State University, B
Ohio University, B
Otterbein College, B
The University of Akron, B
University of Cincinnati, B
Wilberforce University, B

Oklahoma

East Central University, B
Langston University, B
Mid-America Christian University, B
Northeastern State University, B
Oklahoma Baptist University, B
Oklahoma Christian University, B
Oklahoma City University, B
Southern Nazarene University, B
Southwestern Oklahoma State University, B
University of Central Oklahoma, B
University of Oklahoma, B
University of Tulsa, B

Oregon

Corban College, B
Willamette University, B

Pennsylvania

Carnegie Mellon University, B
The Curtis Institute of Music, B

Mansfield University of Pennsylvania, B
Mercyhurst College, B
Seton Hill University, B
Susquehanna University, B
Temple University, B
West Chester University of Pennsylvania, B
Westminster College, B

Puerto Rico

Conservatory of Music of Puerto Rico, B
Inter American University of Puerto Rico, San
  Germán Campus, B

South Carolina

Charleston Southern University, B
Coker College, B
Columbia College, B
Converse College, B
Furman University, B
Newberry College, B
North Greenville College, B

South Dakota

Black Hills State University, B
Northern State University, B
University of Sioux Falls, B

Tennessee

Belmont University, B
Bryan College, B
Carson-Newman College, B
Lee University, B
Maryville College, B
Union University, B
The University of Tennessee at Martin, B
Vanderbilt University, B

Texas

Abilene Christian University, B
Alvin Community College, A
Angelina College, A
Coastal Bend College, A
Del Mar College, A
East Texas Baptist University, B
Hardin-Simmons University, B
Hill College of the Hill Junior College District, A
Howard Payne University, B
Lamar University, B
Lon Morris College, A
Navarro College, A
Prairie View A&M University, B
Texas A&M University-Commerce, B
Texas Southern University, B
Texas Wesleyan University, B
Trinity University, B
University of North Texas, B

Utah

Brigham Young University, B
Snow College, A

Vermont

Bennington College, B

Washington

Central Washington University, B
Eastern Washington University, B
Pacific Lutheran University, B
University of Washington, B
Walla Walla College, B
Whitworth College, B

Wisconsin

Lawrence University, B
University of Wisconsin-Milwaukee, B

Alberta

University of Alberta, B

British Columbia

Kwantlen University College, A
The University of British Columbia, B

University of Victoria, B

Manitoba

Brandon University, B
Canadian Mennonite University, B

New Brunswick

Mount Allison University, B

Newfoundland and Labrador

Memorial University of Newfoundland, B

Nova Scotia

Acadia University, B

Ontario

University of Ottawa, B
The University of Western Ontario, B
York University, B

Quebec

McGill University, B

WALDORF/STEINER TEACHER EDUCATION

Vermont

Sterling College, B

WATCHMAKING AND JEWELRYMAKING

Washington

North Seattle Community College, A

Wisconsin

Northeast Wisconsin Technical College, A

WATER QUALITY AND WASTEWATER TREATMENT MANAGEMENT AND RECYCLING TECHNOLOGY/TECHNICIAN

Alabama

Northwest-Shoals Community College, A

Alaska

University of Alaska Southeast, Sitka Campus, A

Arizona

Arizona Western College, A

California

Santiago Canyon College, A

District of Columbia

University of the District of Columbia, A

Florida

Florida Community College at Jacksonville, A

Georgia

Ogeechee Technical College, A

Kentucky

Murray State University, AB

Michigan

Bay de Noc Community College, A
Delta College, A

Lake Superior State University, A

Minnesota

St. Cloud Technical College, A
Vermilion Community College, A

Mississippi

Mississippi Valley State University, B

New Hampshire

New Hampshire Community Technical College, Berlin/Laconia, A

New Mexico

San Juan College, A

North Dakota

Minot State University-Bottineau Campus, A

Ohio

Wright State University, A

Oregon

Clackamas Community College, A
Linn-Benton Community College, A

Texas

Angelina College, A
Collin County Community College District, A
Northwest Vista College, A

Washington

Green River Community College, A

WATER RESOURCES

Arizona

The University of Arizona, MD

California

University of California, Riverside, MD

Colorado

Colorado State University, MD

Florida

University of Florida, MD

Georgia

Albany State University, M

Illinois

University of Illinois at Chicago, MD

Iowa

Iowa State University of Science and Technology, MD

Kansas

University of Kansas, M

Maryland

The Johns Hopkins University, MD

Minnesota

University of Minnesota, Twin Cities Campus, MD

Missouri

University of Missouri-Rolla, MD

Nevada

University of Nevada, Las Vegas, M

New Hampshire

University of New Hampshire, M

New Jersey

Montclair State University, O
Rutgers, The State University of New Jersey, New Brunswick/Piscataway, MD

New Mexico

University of New Mexico, M

New York

State University of New York College of Environmental Science and Forestry, MD

North Carolina

Duke University, MO

Oklahoma

University of Oklahoma, M

South Dakota

South Dakota School of Mines and Technology, D
South Dakota State University, D

Wisconsin

University of Wisconsin-Madison, M

Wyoming

University of Wyoming, MD

New Brunswick

University of New Brunswick Fredericton, MD

WATER RESOURCES ENGINEERING

Arizona

The University of Arizona, BM

California

California Polytechnic State University, San Luis Obispo, M
Santa Ana College, A
University of California, Berkeley, MD
University of California, Los Angeles, MD
University of Southern California, BM

Colorado

University of Colorado at Boulder, MD

Delaware

University of Delaware, MD

Florida

University of Central Florida, O

Louisiana

Louisiana State University and Agricultural and Mechanical College, MD

Maryland

University of Maryland, College Park, MD

Missouri

University of Missouri-Columbia, MD

Nevada

University of Nevada, Reno, B

New Jersey

Princeton University, D

New York

Cornell University, MD
State University of New York College of Environmental Science and Forestry, B

Ohio

Central State University, B
Ohio University, M

Oregon

Oregon State University, MD

Pennsylvania

The Pennsylvania State University University Park Campus, MD

Villanova University, M

Tennessee

University of Memphis, M

Texas

Texas A&M University, MD
The University of Texas at Austin, M

Utah

Dixie State College of Utah, A
Utah State University, MD

Wisconsin

Marquette University, MD

Alberta

University of Alberta, MD

Ontario

University of Guelph, BMD

Quebec

McGill University, MD

WATER, WETLANDS, AND MARINE RESOURCES MANAGEMENT

Georgia

University of Georgia, B

Iowa

Iowa Lakes Community College, A

Minnesota

University of Minnesota, Crookston, B

Pennsylvania

Keystone College, A

Texas

Texas State University-San Marcos, B

Vermont

Sterling College, B

WEB/MULTIMEDIA MANAGEMENT AND WEBMASTER

Alabama

Remington College-Mobile Campus, A

Arizona

ITT Technical Institute (Tempe), A
ITT Technical Institute (Tucson), A
Rio Salado College, A

Arkansas

ITT Technical Institute, A
Mid-South Community College, A
Southern Arkansas University Tech, A

California

Academy of Art University, AB
American River College, A
College of the Siskiyous, A
ITT Technical Institute (Rancho Cordova), A
Los Angeles City College, A
Mt. Sierra College, B
Platt College San Diego, A
Southwestern College, A
Westwood College-Inland Empire, B

Westwood College-Los Angeles, B

Colorado

ITT Technical Institute, A
Westwood College-Denver South, B

Florida

Florida Career College, A
Florida Community College at Jacksonville, A
ITT Technical Institute (Fort Lauderdale), A
ITT Technical Institute (Jacksonville), A
ITT Technical Institute (Lake Mary), A
ITT Technical Institute (Miami), A
ITT Technical Institute (Tampa), A
St. Petersburg College, A
Seminole Community College, A

Georgia

Westwood College-Atlanta Midtown, B

Idaho

ITT Technical Institute, A
Lewis-Clark State College, AB

Illinois

Black Hawk College, A
ITT Technical Institute (Burr Ridge), A
ITT Technical Institute (Matteson), A
Triton College, A
University of St. Francis, B
Westwood College-Chicago Du Page, B
Westwood College-Chicago Loop Campus, B
Westwood College-Chicago O'Hare Airport, B
Westwood College-Chicago River Oaks, B

Indiana

ITT Technical Institute (Indianapolis), A
ITT Technical Institute (Newburgh), A
Sawyer College (Hammond), A
Vincennes University, A

Iowa

Hawkeye Community College, A
University of Dubuque, B

Kentucky

Daymar College (Owensboro), A
ITT Technical Institute (Louisville), B

Louisiana

ITT Technical Institute, A

Maine

Andover College, A
Kennebec Valley Community College, A
New England School of Communications, AB

Maryland

ITT Technical Institute, A

Massachusetts

Bristol Community College, A
Cape Cod Community College, A
ITT Technical Institute (Norwood), A
ITT Technical Institute (Woburn), A
The New England Institute of Art, B
Northern Essex Community College, A
Springfield Technical Community College, A

Michigan

Delta College, A
ITT Technical Institute (Canton), A
ITT Technical Institute (Grand Rapids), A
ITT Technical Institute (Troy), A
Monroe County Community College, A
Washtenaw Community College, A

Minnesota

Academy College, A
Dakota County Technical College, A
Minneapolis Community and Technical College, A
Northland Community and Technical College-Thief
   River Falls, A
Ridgewater College, A

Riverland Community College, A

Missouri

ITT Technical Institute (Arnold), A
ITT Technical Institute (Earth City), A
Metropolitan Community College-Business &
   Technology College, A
Saint Charles Community College, A

Montana

Flathead Valley Community College, A
University of Great Falls, B

Nebraska

Central Community College-Columbus Campus, A
Central Community College-Grand Island
   Campus, A
Central Community College-Hastings Campus, A
Dana College, B
Grace University, B
ITT Technical Institute, A

Nevada

ITT Technical Institute, A

New Jersey

Camden County College, A
Salem Community College, A

New Mexico

Clovis Community College, A
ITT Technical Institute, A

New York

The College of Westchester, A
Columbia-Greene Community College, A
ITT Technical Institute (Albany), A
ITT Technical Institute (Liverpool), A
Onondaga Community College, A
Rochester Institute of Technology, B

North Carolina

Mars Hill College, B
Sandhills Community College, A
Stanly Community College, A
Wake Technical Community College, A

North Dakota

Minot State University-Bottineau Campus, A

Ohio

Antonelli College, A
ITT Technical Institute (Dayton), A
ITT Technical Institute (Norwood), A
ITT Technical Institute (Strongsville), A
ITT Technical Institute (Youngstown), A
Lakeland Community College, A
Sinclair Community College, A
Stark State College of Technology, A

Oklahoma

Tulsa Community College, A

Oregon

ITT Technical Institute, A
Pioneer Pacific College, A

Pennsylvania

The Art Institute of Pittsburgh, AB
Bradley Academy for the Visual Arts, A
Central Pennsylvania College, A
Duquesne University, B
Harrisburg Area Community College, A
Pennsylvania Highland Community College, A

South Carolina

Horry-Georgetown Technical College, A
ITT Technical Institute, A
Limestone College, AB

Trident Technical College, A

South Dakota

Lake Area Technical Institute, A
Southeast Technical Institute, A

Tennessee

ITT Technical Institute (Knoxville), A
ITT Technical Institute (Nashville), A

Texas

Del Mar College, A
El Paso Community College, A
ITT Technical Institute (Arlington), A
ITT Technical Institute (Austin), A
ITT Technical Institute (Houston), A
ITT Technical Institute (Houston), A
ITT Technical Institute (Houston), A
ITT Technical Institute (Richardson), A
ITT Technical Institute (San Antonio), A
Montgomery College, A
St. Philip's College, A
Texas State Technical College Harlingen, A

Utah

ITT Technical Institute, A

Vermont

Champlain College, AB

Virginia

ITT Technical Institute (Chantilly), A
ITT Technical Institute (Norfolk), A
ITT Technical Institute (Richmond), A
Piedmont Virginia Community College, A

Washington

Bates Technical College, A
Bellingham Technical College, A
Clark College, A
Edmonds Community College, A
ITT Technical Institute (Bothell), A
ITT Technical Institute (Seattle), A
ITT Technical Institute (Spokane), A
Olympic College, A

Wisconsin

ITT Technical Institute (Green Bay), A
ITT Technical Institute (Greenfield), A
Milwaukee Area Technical College, A

Wyoming

Laramie County Community College, A
Sheridan College-Sheridan and Gillette, A
Western Wyoming Community College, A

WEB PAGE, DIGITAL/MULTIMEDIA AND INFORMATION RESOURCES DESIGN

Arizona

The Art Institute of Phoenix, B
ITT Technical Institute (Phoenix), A
ITT Technical Institute (Tempe), A
ITT Technical Institute (Tucson), A
Rio Salado College, A

Arkansas

ITT Technical Institute, A
Southern Arkansas University Tech, A
University of Arkansas Community College at
    Batesville, A

California

American River College, A
The Art Institute of California-Inland Empire, B
The Art Institute of California-Los Angeles, AB
The Art Institute of California-San Francisco, B
Azusa Pacific University, B
Berkeley City College, A
Cerro Coso Community College, A

College of the Redwoods, A
College of the Sequoias, A
College of the Siskiyous, A
Cuesta College, A
Cypress College, A
ITT Technical Institute (Anaheim), A
ITT Technical Institute (Lathrop), A
ITT Technical Institute (Oxnard), A
ITT Technical Institute (Rancho Cordova), A
ITT Technical Institute (San Bernardino), A
ITT Technical Institute (San Diego), A
ITT Technical Institute (Sylmar), A
ITT Technical Institute (Torrance), A
ITT Technical Institute (West Covina), A
Los Angeles City College, A
Platt College San Diego, AB
Southwestern College, A
Westwood College-Inland Empire, B
Westwood College-Long Beach, A

Colorado

CollegeAmerica-Fort Collins, A
Community College of Aurora, A
ITT Technical Institute, A
National American University (Denver), AB
Platt College, AB
Westwood College-Denver North, B

Connecticut

Capital Community College, A
Quinnipiac University, B

District of Columbia

Strayer University, AB

Florida

Brevard Community College, A
Florida Community College at Jacksonville, A
Florida Metropolitan University-North Orlando
    Campus, B
Florida National College, A
Florida Technical College (DeLand), A
ITT Technical Institute (Fort Lauderdale), A
ITT Technical Institute (Jacksonville), A
ITT Technical Institute (Lake Mary), A
ITT Technical Institute (Miami), A
ITT Technical Institute (Tampa), A
Lake City Community College, A
Palm Beach Community College, A
Pasco-Hernando Community College, A
St. Petersburg College, A
Seminole Community College, A
Stetson University, B

Georgia

The Art Institute of Atlanta, AB
Central Georgia Technical College, A
Chattahoochee Technical College, A
Columbus Technical College, A
Coosa Valley Technical College, A
Flint River Technical College, A
Griffin Technical College, A
ITT Technical Institute (Duluth), A
ITT Technical Institute (Kennesaw), A
Lanier Technical College, A
Middle Georgia Technical College, A
Moultrie Technical College, A
North Georgia Technical College, A
North Metro Technical College, A
Northwestern Technical College, A
Southeastern Technical College, A
West Central Technical College, A
West Georgia Technical College, A

Hawaii

Hawaii Business College, A

Idaho

ITT Technical Institute, A

Illinois

Columbia College Chicago, B
DePaul University, B
Heartland Community College, A
Highland Community College, A

The Illinois Institute of Art-Chicago, B
The Illinois Institute of Art-Schaumburg, B
ITT Technical Institute (Burr Ridge), A
ITT Technical Institute (Matteson), A
ITT Technical Institute (Mount Prospect), A
Joliet Junior College, A
Parkland College, A
Robert Morris College, A
School of the Art Institute of Chicago, B
Triton College, A
Westwood College-Chicago Loop Campus, B

Indiana

Indiana Tech, A
ITT Technical Institute (Fort Wayne), A
ITT Technical Institute (Indianapolis), A
ITT Technical Institute (Newburgh), A
Vincennes University, A

Iowa

Hawkeye Community College, A
University of Dubuque, B

Kansas

Kansas City Kansas Community College, A

Kentucky

Daymar College (Owensboro), A
ITT Technical Institute (Lexington), A
ITT Technical Institute (Louisville), A
Louisville Technical Institute, A
Thomas More College, A

Louisiana

ITT Technical Institute, A
Remington College-Lafayette Campus, A

Maine

Kennebec Valley Community College, A
New England School of Communications, AB
York County Community College, A

Maryland

Hagerstown Community College, A
ITT Technical Institute, A

Massachusetts

Bunker Hill Community College, A
Cape Cod Community College, A
ITT Technical Institute (Norwood), A
ITT Technical Institute (Woburn), A
Mount Wachusett Community College, A
The New England Institute of Art, B
Northern Essex Community College, A

Michigan

Baker College of Allen Park, A
Delta College, A
ITT Technical Institute (Canton), A
ITT Technical Institute (Grand Rapids), A
ITT Technical Institute (Troy), A
Monroe County Community College, A
Washtenaw Community College, A

Minnesota

Academy College, A
Alexandria Technical College, A
The Art Institutes International Minnesota, AB
Dakota County Technical College, A
Duluth Business University, A
Hibbing Community College, A
ITT Technical Institute, A
Minneapolis Community and Technical College, A
Minnesota School of Business-Plymouth, A
Minnesota School of Business-Richfield, A
Minnesota School of Business-St. Cloud, A
Minnesota School of Business-Shakopee, A
Minnesota State Community and Technical
    College-Fergus Falls, A
Northland Community and Technical College-Thief
    River Falls, A
Rasmussen College Mankato, A
Ridgewater College, A

Riverland Community College, A

Missouri

ITT Technical Institute (Arnold), A
ITT Technical Institute (Earth City), A
Metropolitan Community College-Business &
   Technology College, A

Montana

Montana State University-Great Falls College of
   Technology, A
University of Great Falls, B

Nebraska

Bellevue University, B
Dana College, B
ITT Technical Institute, A

Nevada

ITT Technical Institute, A

New Jersey

Berkeley College, A
Bloomfield College, B
Camden County College, A

New Mexico

Clovis Community College, A
ITT Technical Institute, A

New York

Adirondack Community College, A
The College of Westchester, A
Hudson Valley Community College, A
Iona College, B
ITT Technical Institute (Albany), A
ITT Technical Institute (Getzville), A
ITT Technical Institute (Liverpool), A
Medaille College, B
Niagara County Community College, A
Onondaga Community College, A
Rochester Institute of Technology, B
State University of New York College of Technology
   at Delhi, B
Tompkins Cortland Community College, A

North Carolina

Guilford Technical Community College, A
Stanly Community College, A
Wake Technical Community College, A

North Dakota

Minot State University-Bottineau Campus, A

Ohio

Baldwin-Wallace College, B
The Cleveland Institute of Art, B
Davis College, A
Franklin University, B
ITT Technical Institute (Dayton), A
ITT Technical Institute (Hilliard), A
ITT Technical Institute (Norwood), A
ITT Technical Institute (Strongsville), A
ITT Technical Institute (Warrensville Heights), A
ITT Technical Institute (Youngstown), A
Lakeland Community College, A
Stark State College of Technology, A
Stautzenberger College, A
Zane State College, A

Oklahoma

ITT Technical Institute, A
Tulsa Community College, A

Oregon

The Art Institute of Portland, AB
ITT Technical Institute, A

Pennsylvania

The Art Institute of Pittsburgh, AB
Bradley Academy for the Visual Arts, A
Delaware County Community College, A
Drexel University, B
Duquesne University, B

Erie Business Center, Main, A
Laurel Business Institute, A
Northampton County Area Community College, A
Pennsylvania College of Technology, A
Pennsylvania Institute of Technology, A
Thaddeus Stevens College of Technology, A
Thiel College, B
York Technical Institute, A

South Carolina

Horry-Georgetown Technical College, A
ITT Technical Institute, A
Trident Technical College, A

South Dakota

Dakota State University, B
National American University-Sioux Falls Branch, B
Southeast Technical Institute, A

Tennessee

ITT Technical Institute (Knoxville), A
ITT Technical Institute (Memphis), A
ITT Technical Institute (Nashville), A
Tennessee Technological University, B

Texas

The Art Institute of Dallas, AB
The Art Institute of Houston, A
College of the Mainland, A
Del Mar College, A
El Paso Community College, A
Galveston College, A
ITT Technical Institute (Arlington), A
ITT Technical Institute (Austin), A
ITT Technical Institute (Houston), A
ITT Technical Institute (Houston), A
ITT Technical Institute (Houston), A
ITT Technical Institute (Richardson), A
ITT Technical Institute (San Antonio), A
Montgomery College, A
San Antonio College, A
Texas State Technical College Harlingen, A

Utah

Dixie State College of Utah, A
ITT Technical Institute, A
LDS Business College, A
Neumont University, B

Vermont

Champlain College, AB

Virginia

The Art Institute of Washington, B
ECPI Technical College (Glen Allen), A
ECPI Technical College (Richmond), A
ITT Technical Institute (Chantilly), A
ITT Technical Institute (Norfolk), A
ITT Technical Institute (Richmond), A
ITT Technical Institute (Springfield), A
Southern Virginia University, B

Washington

Bellingham Technical College, A
Clover Park Technical College, A
Columbia Basin College, A
Edmonds Community College, A
Highline Community College, A
ITT Technical Institute (Bothell), A
ITT Technical Institute (Seattle), A
ITT Technical Institute (Spokane), A
North Seattle Community College, A
Peninsula College, A
Tacoma Community College, A

West Virginia

Mountain State University, A

Wisconsin

ITT Technical Institute (Green Bay), A
ITT Technical Institute (Greenfield), A
Moraine Park Technical College, A
Silver Lake College, B
University of Wisconsin-Stevens Point, B

Viterbo University, B

Wyoming

Central Wyoming College, A
Laramie County Community College, A
Sheridan College-Sheridan and Gillette, A
Western Wyoming Community College, A

British Columbia

Thompson Rivers University, A

Quebec

Bishop's University, B

WELDING TECHNOLOGY/WELDER

Alabama

Bevill State Community College, A
George C. Wallace Community College, A
George Corley Wallace State Community College, A
Northwest-Shoals Community College, A
Shelton State Community College, A
Wallace State Community College, A

Alaska

University of Alaska Anchorage, A

Arizona

Arizona Western College, A
Cochise College (Douglas), A
Cochise College (Sierra Vista), A
Eastern Arizona College, A
Northland Pioneer College, A
Pima Community College, A

Arkansas

Cossatot Community College of the University of
   Arkansas, A
University of Arkansas Community College at
   Morrilton, A

California

Allan Hancock College, A
American River College, A
Antelope Valley College, A
Bakersfield College, A
Butte College, A
Cabrillo College, A
Cerritos College, A
Cerro Coso Community College, A
Chabot College, A
College of the Desert, A
College of the Redwoods, A
College of San Mateo, A
College of the Sequoias, A
Cuesta College, A
El Camino College, A
Glendale Community College, A
Hartnell College, A
Imperial Valley College, A
Laney College, A
Las Positas College, A
Lassen Community College District, A
Long Beach City College, A
Los Angeles Pierce College, A
Los Angeles Trade-Technical College, A
Los Medanos College, A
Mendocino College, A
Modesto Junior College, A
Mt. San Antonio College, A
Napa Valley College, A
National Polytechnic College of Engineering and
   Oceaneering, A
Orange Coast College, A
Oxnard College, A
Palomar College, A
Pasadena City College, A
Porterville College, A
Reedley College, A
Riverside Community College District, A
San Bernardino Valley College, A
San Diego City College, A

Santa Ana College, A
Santa Monica College, A
Shasta College, A
Sierra College, A
Solano Community College, A
Ventura College, A
Victor Valley College, A
West Hills Community College, A
Yuba College, A

Colorado

Aims Community College, A
Community College of Aurora, A
Community College of Denver, A
Front Range Community College, A
Mesa State College, A
Pikes Peak Community College, A
Pueblo Community College, A
Red Rocks Community College, A

Delaware

Delaware Technical & Community College, Jack F.
    Owens Campus, A

Florida

Okaloosa-Walton College, A

Georgia

Bainbridge College, A
Georgia Southwestern State University, A
Waycross College, A

Hawaii

Hawaii Community College, A
Honolulu Community College, A
Maui Community College, A

Idaho

Boise State University, A
Brigham Young University -Idaho, A
College of Southern Idaho, A
Eastern Idaho Technical College, A
Idaho State University, A
Lewis-Clark State College, AB
North Idaho College, A

Illinois

Black Hawk College, A
College of DuPage, A
Danville Area Community College, A
Elgin Community College, A
Heartland Community College, A
Illinois Central College, A
John A. Logan College, A
Joliet Junior College, A
Kankakee Community College, A
Rend Lake College, A
Rock Valley College, A
Shawnee Community College, A
Southeastern Illinois College, A
Southwestern Illinois College, A
Triton College, A

Indiana

Oakland City University, A
Vincennes University, A

Iowa

Des Moines Area Community College, A
Iowa Central Community College, A
Iowa Lakes Community College, A
Kirkwood Community College, A
North Iowa Area Community College, A
Northwest Iowa Community College, A
Southeastern Community College, North Campus, A

Kansas

Butler Community College, A
Coffeyville Community College, A
Cowley County Community College and Area
    Vocational-Technical School, A
Dodge City Community College, A
Fort Scott Community College, A
Garden City Community College, A

Hutchinson Community College and Area Vocational
    School, A
Manhattan Area Technical College, A
Neosho County Community College, A
Pratt Community College, A

Kentucky

Jefferson Community and Technical College, A
Somerset Community College, A

Maine

Eastern Maine Community College, A

Maryland

Cecil Community College, A

Michigan

Delta College, A
Ferris State University, AB
Grand Rapids Community College, A
Kalamazoo Valley Community College, A
Kellogg Community College, A
Kirtland Community College, A
Lansing Community College, A
Macomb Community College, A
Monroe County Community College, A
Muskegon Community College, A
Oakland Community College, A
St. Clair County Community College, A
Schoolcraft College, A
Southwestern Michigan College, A
Washtenaw Community College, A
Wayne County Community College District, A
West Shore Community College, A

Minnesota

Alexandria Technical College, A
Anoka Technical College, A
Dunwoody College of Technology, A
Minnesota State College-Southeast Technical, A
Northland Community and Technical College-Thief
    River Falls, A
St. Cloud Technical College, A

Mississippi

Coahoma Community College, A
Hinds Community College, A
Mississippi Gulf Coast Community College, A
Southwest Mississippi Community College, A

Missouri

East Central College, A
Jefferson College, A
Moberly Area Community College, A
Ozarks Technical Community College, A
Vatterott College (St. Ann), A

Montana

Montana State University-Northern, A
Montana Tech of The University of Montana, B
The University of Montana-Helena College of
    Technology, A
The University of Montana-Missoula, A

Nebraska

Central Community College-Columbus Campus, A
Central Community College-Grand Island
    Campus, A
Central Community College-Hastings Campus, A
Metropolitan Community College, A
Mid-Plains Community College, A
Southeast Community College, Lincoln Campus, A
Southeast Community College, Milford Campus, A

Nevada

Community College of Southern Nevada, A
Great Basin College, A
Truckee Meadows Community College, A

Western Nevada Community College, A

New Hampshire

New Hampshire Community Technical College,
    Manchester/Stratham, A

New Mexico

Doña Ana Branch Community College, A
Eastern New Mexico University-Roswell, A
New Mexico Junior College, A
New Mexico State University-Carlsbad, A
San Juan College, A
University of New Mexico-Gallup, A
Western New Mexico University, A

New York

State University of New York College of Technology
    at Alfred, A
State University of New York College of Technology
    at Delhi, A

North Carolina

Alamance Community College, A
Beaufort County Community College, A
Bladen Community College, A
Central Piedmont Community College, A
Forsyth Technical Community College, A
Isothermal Community College, A
Lenoir Community College, A
McDowell Technical Community College, A
Randolph Community College, A
Southeastern Community College, A
Tri-County Community College, A
Vance-Granville Community College, A

North Dakota

Bismarck State College, A

Ohio

Belmont Technical College, A
North Central State College, A
Terra State Community College, A
The University of Toledo, A

Oklahoma

Northeastern Oklahoma Agricultural and Mechanical
    College, A
Tulsa Welding School, A

Oregon

Central Oregon Community College, A
Chemeketa Community College, A
Lane Community College, A
Portland Community College, A
Rogue Community College, A
Southwestern Oregon Community College, A
Treasure Valley Community College, A

Pennsylvania

Community College of Allegheny County, A
Pennsylvania College of Technology, A
Triangle Tech, Inc.-DuBois School, A
Westmoreland County Community College, A

South Carolina

York Technical College, A

South Dakota

Lake Area Technical Institute, A

Tennessee

Chattanooga State Technical Community College, A
Northeast State Technical Community College, A

Texas

Angelina College, A
Austin Community College, A
Brazosport College, A
Central Texas College, A
Cisco Junior College, A
Coastal Bend College, A
Del Mar College, A
Frank Phillips College, A
Grayson County College, A

Hill College of the Hill Junior College District, A
Lamar University, A
Lee College, A
LeTourneau University, B
Midland College, A
North Central Texas College, A
North Harris College, A
Odessa College, A
Paris Junior College, A
Ranger College, A
St. Philip's College, A
South Plains College, A
Tarrant County College District, A
Texarkana College, A
Texas State Technical College Harlingen, A
Texas State Technical College Waco, A
Trinity Valley Community College, A
Tyler Junior College, A
Western Texas College, A

Utah

College of Eastern Utah, A
Salt Lake Community College, A

Virginia

New River Community College, A

Washington

Big Bend Community College, A
Centralia College, A
Clark College, A
Columbia Basin College, A
Everett Community College, A
Grays Harbor College, A
Green River Community College, A
Lower Columbia College, A
Skagit Valley College, A
South Puget Sound Community College, A
South Seattle Community College, A
Spokane Community College, A
Walla Walla Community College, A

West Virginia

West Virginia University at Parkersburg, A

Wisconsin

Chippewa Valley Technical College, A
Fox Valley Technical College, A
Madison Area Technical College, A
Milwaukee Area Technical College, A
Moraine Park Technical College, A
Nicolet Area Technical College, A
Northeast Wisconsin Technical College, A
Southwest Wisconsin Technical College, A

Wyoming

Casper College, A
Central Wyoming College, A
Eastern Wyoming College, A
Northwest College, A
Sheridan College-Sheridan and Gillette, A
Western Wyoming Community College, A

British Columbia

British Columbia Institute of Technology, A

WESTERN EUROPEAN STUDIES

California

Claremont McKenna College, B
San Diego State University, M
University of California, Santa Barbara, M

Connecticut

University of Connecticut, M

District of Columbia

The Catholic University of America, M
The George Washington University, MO

Georgetown University, MO

Illinois

Illinois Wesleyan University, B

Indiana

Indiana University Bloomington, MDO

Massachusetts

Boston College, M

Nebraska

University of Nebraska-Lincoln, B

Nevada

University of Nevada, Reno, D

New York

Cornell University, MD
New York University, M

North Carolina

East Carolina University, M

Ohio

The Ohio State University, B

Rhode Island

Brown University, MD

Texas

University of Houston, B

Washington

Seattle University, B

WILDLIFE AND WILDLANDS SCIENCE AND MANAGEMENT

Alabama

Auburn University, B

Alaska

University of Alaska Fairbanks, B

Arizona

Northern Arizona University, B
Prescott College, B
The University of Arizona, B

Arkansas

Arkansas State University, B
University of Arkansas at Monticello, B

California

Cabrillo College, A
Cerritos College, A
City College of San Francisco, A
Fullerton College, A
Humboldt State University, B
Monterey Peninsula College, A
Moorpark College, A
Mt. San Antonio College, A
Santa Rosa Junior College, A

Colorado

Colorado State University, B

Delaware

Delaware State University, B
University of Delaware, B

Florida

University of Miami, B

Georgia

Abraham Baldwin Agricultural College, A
Ogeechee Technical College, A

University of Georgia, B

Idaho

Brigham Young University -Idaho, A
North Idaho College, A
University of Idaho, B

Illinois

Shawnee Community College, A
Southeastern Illinois College, A
University of Illinois at Urbana-Champaign, B

Indiana

Purdue University, B

Iowa

Iowa Lakes Community College, A
Kirkwood Community College, A

Kansas

Barton County Community College, A
Fort Hays State University, B
Pratt Community College, A
Seward County Community College, A

Kentucky

Eastern Kentucky University, B

Louisiana

McNeese State University, B

Maine

University of Maine, B

Maryland

Garrett College, A

Massachusetts

Framingham State College, B
University of Massachusetts Amherst, B

Michigan

Grand Valley State University, B
Lake Superior State University, B
Michigan Technological University, B

Minnesota

Itasca Community College, A
University of Minnesota, Crookston, AB
Vermilion Community College, A
Winona State University, AB

Mississippi

Mississippi State University, B
Northeast Mississippi Community College, A

Missouri

East Central College, A
Missouri State University, B
Northwest Missouri State University, B

Montana

Flathead Valley Community College, A
The University of Montana-Missoula, B

Nebraska

Peru State College, B

Nevada

Community College of Southern Nevada, A
University of Nevada, Reno, B

New Hampshire

University of New Hampshire, B

New Mexico

Eastern New Mexico University, B
New Mexico State University, B
Western New Mexico University, B

New York

State University of New York College of Agriculture
   and Technology at Cobleskill, AB

State University of New York College of Agriculture
and Technology at Morrisville, A
State University of New York College of
Environmental Science and Forestry, B

North Carolina

Haywood Community College, A
North Carolina State University, B

North Dakota

Turtle Mountain Community College, A

Ohio

Hocking College, A
The Ohio State University, B

Oklahoma

Eastern Oklahoma State College, A
Northeastern Oklahoma Agricultural and Mechanical
College, A
Southeastern Oklahoma State University, B

Oregon

Oregon State University, B
Treasure Valley Community College, A

Pennsylvania

Delaware Valley College, B
Keystone College, A
The Pennsylvania State University DuBois Campus
of the Commonwealth College, A

Puerto Rico

University of Puerto Rico at Humacao, B

Rhode Island

University of Rhode Island, B

South Dakota

Dakota Wesleyan University, B
South Dakota State University, B

Tennessee

Chattanooga State Technical Community College, A
Martin Methodist College, A
Tennessee Technological University, B
The University of Tennessee, B
The University of Tennessee at Martin, B

Texas

Stephen F. Austin State University, B
Sul Ross State University, B
Tarleton State University, B
Texas A&M University, B
Texas A&M University-Kingsville, B
Texas Tech University, B
West Texas A&M University, B

Utah

Brigham Young University, B
Dixie State College of Utah, A
Snow College, A
Utah State University, B

Vermont

Sterling College, AB

Washington

Spokane Community College, A
Tacoma Community College, A
University of Washington, B
Washington State University, B

West Virginia

Potomac State College of West Virginia
University, A
West Virginia University, B

Wisconsin

Northland College, B
University of Wisconsin-Madison, B

University of Wisconsin-Stevens Point, B

Wyoming

Casper College, A
Eastern Wyoming College, A
Laramie County Community College, A
Northwest College, A
Western Wyoming Community College, A

Alberta

University of Alberta, B

British Columbia

British Columbia Institute of Technology, A
The University of British Columbia, B
University of Northern British Columbia, B

New Brunswick

University of New Brunswick Fredericton, B

Quebec

McGill University, B

WILDLIFE BIOLOGY

Arizona

Eastern Arizona College, A
Grand Canyon University, B

Colorado

Colorado Northwestern Community College, A
Western State College of Colorado, B

Idaho

North Idaho College, A

Indiana

Ball State University, B

Iowa

Ellsworth Community College, A
Iowa Lakes Community College, A
Kirkwood Community College, A

Kansas

Baker University, B
Central Christian College of Kansas, A
Colby Community College, A
Dodge City Community College, A
Kansas State University, B
Pratt Community College, A

Maine

College of the Atlantic, B
Unity College, B

Maryland

Garrett College, A

Massachusetts

Framingham State College, B

Michigan

Grand Valley State University, B
University of Michigan, B
University of Michigan-Flint, B

Minnesota

St. Cloud State University, B
Vermilion Community College, A

Winona State University, B

Mississippi

Holmes Community College, A
Northeast Mississippi Community College, A

Missouri

Northwest Missouri State University, B

New Hampshire

University of New Hampshire, B

New Mexico

New Mexico State University, B

New York

State University of New York College of
Environmental Science and Forestry, B

North Carolina

Lees-McRae College, B

North Dakota

University of North Dakota, B

Ohio

Ohio University, B

Oklahoma

Northeastern Oklahoma Agricultural and Mechanical
College, A
Northeastern State University, B

Pennsylvania

Keystone College, A

South Carolina

Clemson University, B

Tennessee

Martin Methodist College, A

Texas

Texas State University-San Marcos, B

Vermont

Sterling College, B
University of Vermont, B

Washington

Everett Community College, A
Tacoma Community College, A

Wisconsin

Northland College, B

British Columbia

University of Northern British Columbia, B

New Brunswick

University of New Brunswick Fredericton, B

Ontario

University of Guelph, B

Quebec

McGill University, B

WIND AND PERCUSSION INSTRUMENTS

Arizona

Grand Canyon University, B

California

California State University, Fullerton, B
Chapman University, B
San Francisco Conservatory of Music, B

University of Southern California, B

Florida

Florida State University, B
New World School of the Arts, AB
Palm Beach Atlantic University, B

Illinois

Augustana College, B
Concordia University, B
DePaul University, B
Illinois Wesleyan University, B
Northwestern University, B
Olivet Nazarene University, B
Roosevelt University, B

Indiana

Ball State University, B
Butler University, B
Indiana University Bloomington, B

Iowa

Iowa Lakes Community College, A
Kirkwood Community College, A
The University of Iowa, B

Kansas

Coffeyville Community College, A
University of Kansas, B

Louisiana

Xavier University of Louisiana, B

Maryland

Peabody Conservatory of Music of The Johns
  Hopkins University, B

Massachusetts

Berklee College of Music, B
The Boston Conservatory, B
New England Conservatory of Music, B

Michigan

Grand Valley State University, B
University of Michigan, B

Minnesota

Minnesota State University Mankato, B
Minnesota State University Moorhead, B

Mississippi

Itawamba Community College, A

Missouri

Northwest Missouri State University, B

Nebraska

Peru State College, B

New Hampshire

University of New Hampshire, B

New York

Five Towns College, AB
Houghton College, B
Manhattan School of Music, B
Mannes College The New School for Music, B
Sarah Lawrence College, B
State University of New York, Fredonia, B
Syracuse University, B

North Carolina

Meredith College, B

Ohio

Capital University, B
Cleveland Institute of Music, B
Oberlin College, B
Otterbein College, B
The University of Akron, B

University of Cincinnati, B

Oklahoma

Oklahoma Baptist University, B
Oklahoma Christian University, B
Oklahoma City University, B
Southwestern Oklahoma State University, B
University of Central Oklahoma, B
University of Oklahoma, B

Pennsylvania

The Curtis Institute of Music, B
Mercyhurst College, B
Seton Hill University, B
Susquehanna University, B
Temple University, B

Puerto Rico

Conservatory of Music of Puerto Rico, B
Inter American University of Puerto Rico, San
  Germán Campus, B

Tennessee

Bryan College, B
Maryville College, B
Vanderbilt University, B

Texas

Prairie View A&M University, B
Texas Southern University, B
Texas Wesleyan University, B
University of North Texas, B

Wisconsin

Lawrence University, B
University of Wisconsin-Milwaukee, B

Alberta

University of Alberta, B

New Brunswick

Mount Allison University, B

Newfoundland and Labrador

Memorial University of Newfoundland, B

Nova Scotia

Acadia University, B

Ontario

The University of Western Ontario, B

WOMEN'S HEALTH NURSING

Colorado

University of Colorado at Colorado Springs, M

Delaware

University of Delaware, MO

Georgia

Emory University, M
Georgia Southern University, MO
Georgia State University, M

Illinois

Loyola University Chicago, M

Indiana

Indiana University-Purdue University Indianapolis, M

Michigan

University of Michigan, O

Minnesota

University of Minnesota, Twin Cities Campus, M

New Jersey

Seton Hall University, M

New York

State University of New York at Buffalo, MO
Stony Brook University, State University of New
  York, MO

Ohio

Case Western Reserve University, M

Pennsylvania

University of Pennsylvania, M

South Carolina

University of South Carolina, MO

Tennessee

Vanderbilt University, M

Texas

The University of Texas at El Paso, M

Virginia

Virginia Commonwealth University, M

WOMEN'S STUDIES

Alabama

The University of Alabama, M

Arizona

Arizona State University, B
Arizona State University West, B
Northern Arizona University, B
The University of Arizona, BM

California

Cabrillo College, A
California State University, Chico, B
California State University, Fresno, B
California State University, Fullerton, B
California State University, Long Beach, B
California State University, Northridge, B
California State University, Sacramento, B
California State University, San Marcos, B
Chabot College, A
City College of San Francisco, A
Cosumnes River College (Sacramento), A
Dominican University of California, B
Foothill College, A
Fresno City College, A
Mills College, B
Monterey Peninsula College, A
New College of California, M
Occidental College, B
Palomar College, A
Pitzer College, B
Pomona College, B
Sacramento City College, A
Saddleback College, A
Saint Mary's College of California, B
San Diego State University, BM
San Francisco State University, BM
Santa Ana College, A
Santa Rosa Junior College, A
Santiago Canyon College, A
Scripps College, B
Sonoma State University, B
Southwestern College, A
Stanford University, B
University of California, Berkeley, B
University of California, Davis, B
University of California, Irvine, B
University of California, Los Angeles, BMD
University of California, Riverside, B
University of California, San Diego, B
University of California, Santa Barbara, BD
University of California, Santa Cruz, B
West Valley College, A
Yuba College, A

Colorado

The Colorado College, B
Fort Lewis College, B
Nazarene Bible College, A

University of Colorado at Boulder, B
University of Denver, B

Connecticut

Connecticut College, B
Southern Connecticut State University, M
Trinity College, B
University of Connecticut, B
Wesleyan University, B
Yale University, B

District of Columbia

American University, B
The George Washington University, MO
Georgetown University, B

Florida

Eckerd College, B
Florida Atlantic University, MO
Florida International University, B
Florida State University, B
Manatee Community College, A
University of Florida, MDO
University of Miami, B
University of South Florida, BM

Georgia

Agnes Scott College, B
Clark Atlanta University, MD
Emory University, BDO
Georgia State University, BM
Spelman College, B
University of Georgia, B

Hawaii

University of Hawaii at Manoa, B

Illinois

Augustana College, B
DePaul University, BO
Illinois Wesleyan University, B
Knox College, B
Loyola University Chicago, B
Northeastern Illinois University, B
Northwestern University, B
Roosevelt University, BM
University of Illinois at Urbana-Champaign, B
Western Illinois University, B

Indiana

DePauw University, B
Earlham College, B
Indiana University Bloomington, B
Indiana University-Purdue University Fort
    Wayne, AB
Indiana University South Bend, B

Iowa

Iowa State University of Science and Technology, B
The University of Iowa, BD
University of Northern Iowa, M

Kansas

Kansas State University, B
University of Kansas, B
Wichita State University, B

Kentucky

Berea College, B
University of Louisville, BMO

Louisiana

Louisiana State University and Agricultural and
    Mechanical College, B
Tulane University, B
University of New Orleans, B

Maine

Bates College, B
Bowdoin College, B
Colby College, B
University of Maine, B
University of Maine at Farmington, B

University of Southern Maine, B

Maryland

Goucher College, B
Towson University, BM
University of Maryland, Baltimore County, O
University of Maryland, College Park, BMD

Massachusetts

Amherst College, B
Brandeis University, BM
Clark University, BD
Curry College, B
Harvard University, B
Mount Holyoke College, B
Northeastern University, B
Northern Essex Community College, A
Simmons College, B
Simon's Rock College of Bard, B
Smith College, B
Suffolk University, B
Tufts University, B
University of Massachusetts Amherst, B
University of Massachusetts Boston, BO
Wellesley College, B
Wheaton College, B
Williams College, B

Michigan

Albion College, B
Central Michigan University, B
Eastern Michigan University, BM
Grand Valley State University, B
Oakland University, B
University of Michigan, BDO
University of Michigan-Dearborn, B
Western Michigan University, B

Minnesota

Augsburg College, B
Carleton College, B
College of St. Catherine, B
Hamline University, B
Macalester College, B
Metropolitan State University, B
Minnesota State University Mankato, BM
St. Olaf College, B
University of Minnesota, Duluth, B
University of Minnesota, Morris, B
University of Minnesota, Twin Cities Campus, B
University of St. Thomas, B

Missouri

Saint Louis University, B
Washington University in St. Louis, B

Montana

The University of Montana-Missoula, B

Nebraska

Nebraska Wesleyan University, B
University of Nebraska-Lincoln, B
University of Nebraska at Omaha, B

Nevada

University of Nevada, Las Vegas, B
University of Nevada, Reno, B

New Hampshire

Dartmouth College, B
University of New Hampshire, B

New Jersey

Bergen Community College, A
The College of New Jersey, B
Drew University, BM
Montclair State University, B
Rutgers, The State University of New Jersey, New
    Brunswick/Piscataway, BMD

Rutgers, The State University of New Jersey,
    Newark, B

New Mexico

University of New Mexico, B

New York

Barnard College, B
Brooklyn College of the City University of New
    York, B
Canisius College, B
City College of the City University of New York, B
Colgate University, B
The College of New Rochelle, B
College of Staten Island of the City University of
    New York, B
Columbia College, B
Columbia University, School of General Studies, B
Cornell University, BD
Eugene Lang College The New School for Liberal
    Arts, B
Fordham University, B
Hamilton College, B
Hobart and William Smith Colleges, B
Hunter College of the City University of New York, B
The Jewish Theological Seminary, B
Nazareth College of Rochester, B
Pace University, B
Purchase College, State University of New York, B
Queens College of the City University of New
    York, B
St. Bonaventure University, B
Sarah Lawrence College, BM
Skidmore College, B
State University of New York at Buffalo, B
State University of New York College at
    Brockport, B
State University of New York, Fredonia, B
State University of New York at New Paltz, B
State University of New York at Oswego, B
Stony Brook University, State University of New
    York, BO
Suffolk County Community College, A
Syracuse University, B
Tompkins Cortland Community College, A
University at Albany, State University of New
    York, BMD
University of Rochester, B
Vassar College, B
Wells College, B

North Carolina

Duke University, BO
East Carolina University, B
Guilford College, B
Mars Hill College, B
Meredith College, B
Southeastern Baptist Theological Seminary, P
The University of North Carolina at Asheville, B
The University of North Carolina at Chapel Hill, B
The University of North Carolina at Greensboro, BO
Warren Wilson College, B

Ohio

Antioch College, B
Bowling Green State University, B
Case Western Reserve University, B
The College of Wooster, B
Denison University, B
Kenyon College, B
Miami University, B
Oberlin College, B
The Ohio State University, BM
Ohio University-Eastern, B
Ohio Wesleyan University, B
University of Cincinnati, MO
The University of Toledo, B
Wright State University, B

Oklahoma

University of Oklahoma, B

Oregon

Portland State University, B
University of Oregon, B

Willamette University, B

Pennsylvania

Albright College, B
Allegheny College, B
Bucknell University, B
Chatham College, B
Dickinson College, B
Edinboro University of Pennsylvania, B
Gettysburg College, B
Haverford College, B
The Pennsylvania State University Abington
  College, B
The Pennsylvania State University Beaver Campus
  of the Commonwealth College, B
The Pennsylvania State University Berks Campus of
  the Berks-Lehigh Valley College, B
The Pennsylvania State University Delaware County
  Campus of the Commonwealth College, B
The Pennsylvania State University DuBois Campus
  of the Commonwealth College, B
The Pennsylvania State University at Erie, The
  Behrend College, B
The Pennsylvania State University Fayette Campus
  of the Commonwealth College, B
The Pennsylvania State University Hazleton
  Campus of the Commonwealth College, B
The Pennsylvania State University, Lehigh Valley
  Campus of the Berks-Lehigh Valley College, B
The Pennsylvania State University McKeesport
  Campus of the Commonwealth College, B
The Pennsylvania State University Mont Alto
  Campus of the Commonwealth College, B
The Pennsylvania State University New Kensington
  Campus of the Commonwealth College, B
The Pennsylvania State University Schuylkill
  Campus of the Capital College, B
The Pennsylvania State University Shenango
  Campus of the Commonwealth College, B
The Pennsylvania State University University Park
  Campus, B
The Pennsylvania State University Wilkes-Barre
  Campus of the Commonwealth College, B
The Pennsylvania State University Worthington
  Scranton Campus of the Commonwealth
  College, B
The Pennsylvania State University York Campus of
  the Commonwealth College, B
Rosemont College, B
Temple University, B
University of Pennsylvania, B
University of Pittsburgh, MDO
West Chester University of Pennsylvania, B

Rhode Island

Brown University, B
Rhode Island College, B
University of Rhode Island, B

South Carolina

University of South Carolina, BO

Texas

Rice University, B
Southwestern University, B
Texas Woman's University, M

Utah

University of Utah, B

Vermont

Bennington College, B
Burlington College, B
Marlboro College, B
Middlebury College, B
University of Vermont, B

Virginia

The College of William and Mary, B
Hollins University, B
Old Dominion University, B
Randolph-Macon College, B
Shenandoah University, O
University of Richmond, B

Virginia Wesleyan College, B

Washington

Pacific Lutheran University, B
University of Washington, BMD
Washington State University, B
Western Washington University, B

Wisconsin

Beloit College, B
Marquette University, B
University of Wisconsin-Madison, B
University of Wisconsin-Milwaukee, B
University of Wisconsin-Whitewater, B

Wyoming

Casper College, A
University of Wyoming, B

Alberta

Athabasca University, B
University of Alberta, B
University of Calgary, B

British Columbia

Simon Fraser University, BM
The University of British Columbia, B
University of Northern British Columbia, B
University of Victoria, B

Manitoba

University of Manitoba, B
The University of Winnipeg, B

Newfoundland and Labrador

Memorial University of Newfoundland, BM

Nova Scotia

Dalhousie University, BM
Mount Saint Vincent University, BM
St. Francis Xavier University, B
Saint Mary's University, BM
University of King's College, B

Ontario

Brock University, B
Lakehead University, BM
Laurentian University, B
McMaster University, B
Nipissing University, B
Queen's University at Kingston, B
Trent University, B
University of Guelph, B
University of Ottawa, BM
University of Toronto, B
University of Waterloo, B
The University of Western Ontario, B
University of Windsor, B
Wilfrid Laurier University, B
York University, BMD

Quebec

Bishop's University, B
Concordia University, B
McGill University, B
Université Laval, O

Saskatchewan

University of Regina, B
University of Saskatchewan, BMD

WOOD SCIENCE AND WOOD PRODUCTS/PULP AND PAPER TECHNOLOGY

Arkansas

Cossatot Community College of the University of
  Arkansas, A

University of Arkansas at Monticello, A

California

Bakersfield College, A
Laney College, A

Georgia

Ogeechee Technical College, A

Idaho

University of Idaho, B

Kansas

Allen County Community College, A

Maine

Kennebec Valley Community College, A
University of Maine, B

Massachusetts

University of Massachusetts Amherst, B

Michigan

Bay de Noc Community College, A
Western Michigan University, B

Minnesota

University of Minnesota, Twin Cities Campus, B

Mississippi

Copiah-Lincoln Community College, A

New York

State University of New York College of Agriculture
  and Technology at Morrisville, A
State University of New York College of
  Environmental Science and Forestry, B

North Carolina

Haywood Community College, A
North Carolina State University, B

Ohio

Miami University, B

Oregon

Oregon State University, B

Texas

Texarkana College, A

Vermont

Sterling College, B

Virginia

Dabney S. Lancaster Community College, A

Washington

Lower Columbia College, A
Tacoma Community College, A
University of Washington, B

West Virginia

Potomac State College of West Virginia
  University, A
West Virginia University, B

Wisconsin

Fox Valley Technical College, A
University of Wisconsin-Stevens Point, B

British Columbia

The University of British Columbia, B

Ontario

University of Toronto, B

WOODWORKING

Idaho

College of Southern Idaho, A

Michigan

Oakland Community College, A

New York

State University of New York College of Technology at Delhi, A

Pennsylvania

Bucks County Community College, A
Pennsylvania College of Technology, A

WORD PROCESSING

Arizona

Mohave Community College, A

California

College of the Desert, A
College of the Sequoias, A
Cypress College, A
Los Angeles City College, A
Los Angeles Valley College, A
Modesto Junior College, A
Orange Coast College, A
Santa Ana College, A
Yuba College, A

Connecticut

Gateway Community College, A
Naugatuck Valley Community College, A
Quinebaug Valley Community College, A

Florida

Florida Community College at Jacksonville, A
Florida National College, A
Okaloosa-Walton College, A
Palm Beach Community College, A
Seminole Community College, A
Tallahassee Community College, A
Valencia Community College, A

Georgia

West Central Technical College, A

Illinois

Kishwaukee College, A
Richland Community College, A

Indiana

Vincennes University, A
Vincennes University Jasper Campus, A

Iowa

Hawkeye Community College, A
Iowa Lakes Community College, A
Iowa Western Community College, A

Kentucky

Daymar College (Owensboro), A
Henderson Community College, A
Owensboro Community and Technical College, A

Maryland

Baltimore City Community College, A

Massachusetts

Northern Essex Community College, A

Michigan

Baker College of Allen Park, A
Gogebic Community College, A
Kellogg Community College, A
Monroe County Community College, A
Washtenaw Community College, A

Minnesota

Dakota County Technical College, A
Northland Community and Technical College-Thief River Falls, A

Riverland Community College, A

Mississippi

Mississippi Gulf Coast Community College, A

Missouri

Metropolitan Community College-Business & Technology College, A
St. Louis Community College at Forest Park, A
Three Rivers Community College, A

Montana

Flathead Valley Community College, A

Nebraska

Hamilton College-Lincoln, A

New Jersey

Camden County College, A

New York

Adirondack Community College, A
The College of Westchester, A
Corning Community College, A
Orange County Community College, A

North Carolina

Edgecombe Community College, A
Sampson Community College, A
Wake Technical Community College, A

Ohio

ETI Technical College of Niles, A
Lorain County Community College, A
Sinclair Community College, A
Stark State College of Technology, A
Trumbull Business College, A

Oklahoma

Tulsa Community College, A

Pennsylvania

Academy of Medical Arts and Business, A
Laurel Business Institute, A
Newport Business Institute (Lower Burrell), A
Thaddeus Stevens College of Technology, A

South Carolina

Horry-Georgetown Technical College, A

Texas

Coastal Bend College, A
Del Mar College, A
Eastfield College, A
El Paso Community College, A
Galveston College, A
North Central Texas College, A
San Antonio College, A
Texas State Technical College Harlingen, A

Washington

Lower Columbia College, A
Tacoma Community College, A

West Virginia

West Virginia Northern Community College, A

Wisconsin

Milwaukee Area Technical College, A

Wyoming

Western Wyoming Community College, A

WORK AND FAMILY STUDIES

California

Antelope Valley College, A

North Carolina

The University of North Carolina at Charlotte, B

Ohio

Miami University Hamilton, B
Ursuline College, B

Texas

Texas Tech University, B
University of North Texas, B

Utah

Brigham Young University, B

Washington

Centralia College, A

West Virginia

American Public University System, B

WRITING

Alabama

The University of Alabama, M

Alaska

University of Alaska Anchorage, M
University of Alaska Fairbanks, M

Arizona

Arizona State University, M
Northern Arizona University, M
The University of Arizona, M

Arkansas

University of Arkansas, M
University of Arkansas at Little Rock, M

California

Antioch University Los Angeles, MO
California College of the Arts, M
California Institute of the Arts, MO
California State University, Fresno, M
California State University, Long Beach, M
California State University, Sacramento, M
California State University, San Marcos, M
Chapman University, M
Loyola Marymount University, M
Mills College, M
National University, M
Otis College of Art and Design, M
Saint Mary's College of California, M
San Diego State University, M
San Francisco State University, M
San Jose State University, M
Sonoma State University, M
University of California, Davis, M
University of California, Irvine, M
University of California, Riverside, M
University of San Francisco, M
University of Southern California, M

Colorado

Colorado State University, M
Naropa University, M

District of Columbia

American University, M

Florida

Florida International University, M
Florida State University, MD
University of Central Florida, MO
University of Florida, M
University of North Florida, M

Georgia

Georgia College & State University, M
Georgia State University, MD

Kennesaw State University, M

Idaho

University of Idaho, M

Illinois

Columbia College Chicago, MO
DePaul University, M
Illinois State University, M
National-Louis University, M
Northeastern Illinois University, M
Northwestern University, M
Roosevelt University, M
Saint Xavier University, MO
School of the Art Institute of Chicago, M
Southern Illinois University Carbondale, M
Southern Illinois University Edwardsville, M
University of Illinois at Chicago, D
Western Illinois University, M

Indiana

Indiana University Bloomington, M
Purdue University, M
University of Notre Dame, M

Iowa

The University of Iowa, M

Kansas

Wichita State University, M

Kentucky

Eastern Kentucky University, M
Spalding University, M
Western Kentucky University, M

Louisiana

Louisiana State University and Agricultural and
　Mechanical College, M
McNeese State University, M
University of Louisiana at Lafayette, D

Maine

University of Southern Maine, M

Maryland

Goucher College, M
The Johns Hopkins University, M
Salisbury University, M
Towson University, M
University of Baltimore, M
University of Maryland, College Park, MD

Massachusetts

Boston University, MD
Emerson College, M
Massachusetts Institute of Technology, M
Northeastern University, M
University of Massachusetts Amherst, M
University of Massachusetts Dartmouth, M

Michigan

Central Michigan University, M
Eastern Michigan University, M
Michigan State University, MD
Northern Michigan University, M
University of Michigan, M
Wayne State University, MD
Western Michigan University, M

Minnesota

Minnesota State University Mankato, M
Minnesota State University Moorhead, M

Mississippi

University of Mississippi, M

Missouri

Lindenwood University, M
University of Missouri-St. Louis, M

Washington University in St. Louis, M

Montana

The University of Montana-Missoula, M

Nebraska

University of Nebraska at Kearney, M
University of Nebraska at Omaha, O

Nevada

University of Nevada, Las Vegas, M

New Hampshire

New England College, M
Rivier College, M
University of New Hampshire, M

New Jersey

Fairleigh Dickinson University, College at
　Florham, M
Rowan University, M
Rutgers, The State University of New Jersey, New
　Brunswick/Piscataway, M

New Mexico

New Mexico State University, M
University of New Mexico, M

New York

City College of the City University of New York, M
Cornell University, M
Hofstra University, M
Long Island University, Brooklyn Campus, M
Manhattanville College, M
New York University, M
Queens College of the City University of New
　York, M
Sarah Lawrence College, M
Syracuse University, MD

North Carolina

North Carolina State University, M
Queens University of Charlotte, M
The University of North Carolina at Greensboro, M
The University of North Carolina Wilmington, M
Warren Wilson College, M

Ohio

Bowling Green State University, M
Kent State University, M
Miami University, M
Union Institute & University, M
The University of Akron, M
Wright State University, M

Oklahoma

Oklahoma City University, M
Oklahoma State University, MD
University of Central Oklahoma, M
University of Oklahoma, M

Oregon

University of Oregon, M

Pennsylvania

Carnegie Mellon University, M
Chatham College, M
Indiana University of Pennsylvania, MD
The Pennsylvania State University University Park
　Campus, MD
Saint Joseph's University, M
Seton Hill University, M
Temple University, M
University of Pennsylvania, MD
University of Pittsburgh, M

Wilkes University, M

Rhode Island

Brown University, M

South Carolina

Clemson University, M
University of South Carolina, M

Tennessee

Belmont University, M
University of Memphis, MD

Texas

Abilene Christian University, M
Texas State University-San Marcos, M
University of Houston, MD
The University of Texas at Austin, M
The University of Texas at El Paso, M

Utah

University of Utah, M
Westminster College, M

Vermont

Bennington College, M
Goddard College, M

Virginia

George Mason University, M
Hollins University, M
Longwood University, M
Old Dominion University, M
University of Virginia, M
Virginia Commonwealth University, M

Washington

Eastern Washington University, M
Pacific Lutheran University, M

West Virginia

West Virginia University, M

British Columbia

The University of British Columbia, MO

Ontario

University of Windsor, M

Quebec

Concordia University, M

YOUTH MINISTRY

Arizona

Southwestern College, B

Arkansas

Harding University, B
Ouachita Baptist University, B

California

California Baptist University, B
Point Loma Nazarene University, B
Vanguard University of Southern California, B

Colorado

Colorado Christian University, B

Florida

Trinity College of Florida, B

Georgia

Emmanuel College, B
Toccoa Falls College, B

Illinois

Greenville College, B
Trinity International University, B

Indiana

Bethel College, B
Crossroads Bible College, B

University of Indianapolis, B

Iowa

Dordt College, B
Vennard College, B

Kansas

Benedictine College, B
Central Christian College of Kansas, B

Massachusetts

Gordon College, B

Michigan

Andrews University, B
Grace Bible College, B
Kuyper College, B
Rochester College, B
Spring Arbor University, B

Minnesota

Bethel University, B
Crossroads College, B
Northwestern College, B
Oak Hills Christian College, B
Pillsbury Baptist Bible College, B
Saint Mary's University of Minnesota, B

Missouri

Calvary Bible College and Theological Seminary, B
Lindenwood University, B
Messenger College, B

Nebraska

Grace University, B

North Carolina

Campbell University, B
Gardner-Webb University, B
Pfeiffer University, B

Ohio

Bluffton University, B
Cedarville University, B
Malone College, B
Mount Vernon Nazarene University, B

Oklahoma

Southern Nazarene University, B

Oregon

Eugene Bible College, B
George Fox University, B
Multnomah Bible College and Biblical Seminary, B

Pennsylvania

Lancaster Bible College, B

South Carolina

Charleston Southern University, B
Columbia International University, B

Tennessee

Crichton College, B
Tennessee Temple University, B

Texas

East Texas Baptist University, B
Lubbock Christian University, B

Washington

Northwest University, B

Wisconsin

Concordia University Wisconsin, B

Alberta

Rocky Mountain College, B

Manitoba

Canadian Mennonite University, B
Providence College and Theological Seminary, B

Ontario

Master's College and Seminary, B

Saskatchewan

Central Pentecostal College, B

YOUTH SERVICES/ADMINISTRATION

Indiana

Indiana University-Purdue University Fort Wayne, B

New York

Medaille College, B

South Carolina

Midlands Technical College, A

British Columbia

University of Northern British Columbia, B

ZOOLOGY/ANIMAL BIOLOGY

Alabama

Auburn University, BMD

Arizona

Northern Arizona University, B

California

California State Polytechnic University, Pomona, B
California State University, Long Beach, B
Cerritos College, A
Chabot College, A
El Camino College, A
Fullerton College, A
Humboldt State University, B
Palomar College, A
San Bernardino Valley College, A
San Francisco State University, B
Sonoma State University, B
University of California, Davis, BM
University of California, Santa Barbara, B

Colorado

Colorado State University, BMD
Northeastern Junior College, A

Connecticut

Connecticut College, M

Florida

Daytona Beach Community College, A
Florida State University, B
Palm Beach Community College, A
Pensacola Junior College, A
University of Florida, BMD
University of South Florida, M

Georgia

Fort Valley State University, B

Hawaii

University of Hawaii at Manoa, BMD

Idaho

Brigham Young University -Idaho, A
College of Southern Idaho, A
Idaho State University, B
North Idaho College, A
University of Idaho, B

Illinois

Illinois State University, D
Lincoln College, A
Olivet Nazarene University, B
Southern Illinois University Carbondale, BMD
Spoon River College, A
University of Chicago, D
University of Illinois at Urbana-Champaign, D

Western Illinois University, O

Indiana

Ball State University, B
Indiana University Bloomington, MD

Kansas

Central Christian College of Kansas, A
Colby Community College, A
Emporia State University, M

Maine

College of the Atlantic, B
University of Maine, BMD

Michigan

Andrews University, B
Michigan State University, BMD
Northern Michigan University, B
University of Michigan, B

Minnesota

Winona State University, B

Mississippi

Northeast Mississippi Community College, A

Missouri

East Central College, A
Northwest Missouri State University, B

Montana

Montana State University, D
The University of Montana-Missoula, BMD

New Hampshire

University of New Hampshire, BMD

New Jersey

Rutgers, The State University of New Jersey, Newark, B

New Mexico

Western New Mexico University, B

New York

Cornell University, MD
State University of New York College of Environmental Science and Forestry, B
State University of New York at Oswego, B

North Carolina

North Carolina State University, BMD

North Dakota

North Dakota State University, BMD

Ohio

Kent State University, B
Malone College, B
Miami University, BMD
Miami University Hamilton, B
Miami University-Middletown Campus, A
The Ohio State University, B
Ohio University, B
Ohio Wesleyan University, B
The University of Akron, B

Oklahoma

Carl Albert State College, A
Northeastern State University, B
Oklahoma State University, BMD
Southeastern Oklahoma State University, B
Tulsa Community College, A

University of Oklahoma, BMD

Oregon

Oregon State University, BMD

Pennsylvania

Delaware Valley College, B
Juniata College, B

Puerto Rico

University of Puerto Rico, Medical Sciences
  Campus, MD

Rhode Island

University of Rhode Island, B

South Carolina

Clemson University, MD

Texas

Frank Phillips College, A
Hill College of the Hill Junior College District, A
Texas A&M University, BMD
Texas State University-San Marcos, B
Texas Tech University, BMD
The University of Texas at Austin, B

The University of Texas at El Paso, B

Utah

Brigham Young University, B
Dixie State College of Utah, A
Snow College, A
Southern Utah University, B
Utah State University, B
Weber State University, B

Vermont

Bennington College, B
University of Vermont, B

Virginia

Virginia Polytechnic Institute and State
  University, MD

Washington

Centralia College, A
Everett Community College, A
Tacoma Community College, A
University of Washington, BD
Washington State University, BMD

Wisconsin

Northland College, B
University of Wisconsin-Madison, BMD

University of Wisconsin-Milwaukee, B

Wyoming

University of Wyoming, BMD

Alberta

University of Alberta, B
University of Calgary, B

British Columbia

Thompson Rivers University, B
The University of British Columbia, BMD
University of Victoria, B

Manitoba

Brandon University, B
University of Manitoba, BMD

New Brunswick

University of New Brunswick Fredericton, B

Newfoundland and Labrador

Memorial University of Newfoundland, B

Ontario

University of Guelph, B
University of Toronto, BMD
The University of Western Ontario, BMD

Quebec

McGill University, B